2009
STANDARD POSTAGE
STAMP CATALOGUE

ONE HUNDRED AND SIXTY-FIFTH EDITION IN SIX VOLUMES

VOLUME 6
COUNTRIES OF THE WORLD
So-Z

EDITOR	James E. Kloetzel
ASSOCIATE EDITOR	William A. Jones
ASSISTANT EDITOR /NEW ISSUES & VALUING	Martin J. Frankevicz
ASSISTANT EDITOR	Charles Snee
VALUING ANALYST	Steven R. Myers
ADMINISTRATIVE ASSISTANT/IMAGE COORDINATOR	Beth L. Brown
DESIGN MANAGER	Teresa M. Wenrick
ADVERTISING	Phyllis Stegemoller
CIRCULATION / PRODUCT PROMOTION MANAGER	Tim Wagner
VICE PRESIDENT/EDITORIAL AND PRODUCTION	Steve Collins
PRESIDENT	William Fay

Released September 2008

Includes New Stamp Listings through the September 2008 *Scott Stamp Monthly* Catalogue Update

Copyright© 2008 by

Scott Publishing Co.

911 Vandemark Road, Sidney, OH 45365-0828

A division of AMOS PRESS, INC., publishers of *Scott Stamp Monthly, Linn's Stamp News, Coin World* and *Coin World's Coin Values.*

Table of Contents

See Volume 1 for United States, United Nations and Countries of the World A-B
See Volume 2, 3, 4, 5 for Countries of the World, C-Sl.

Volume 2: C-F
Volume 3: G-I
Volume 4: J-O
Volume 5: P-Sl

Scott Publishing Co.

911 VANDEMARK ROAD, SIDNEY, OHIO 45365   937-498-0802

Dear Scott Catalogue User:

A new record for value changes is set.

The 2009 edition of the *Scott Standard Postage Stamp Catalogue* has set a record for the total number of value changes made in one catalogue season. The previous record for all six Standard volumes was 199,578 value changes made in the 2006 catalogues. The 36,172 changes made in this Volume 6 for 2009 bring the total this year to 274,129. For the sake of the health of the editors, let us hope this record stands for many years to come!

If you have purchased Volume 1, 2, 3, 4 and/or 5 for 2009, please bear with us while we repeat one last time some important information for those whose first contact with the 2009 Scott Standard catalogue is this Volume 6. (We are well aware that not all collectors buy all six Scott volumes each year, though they should, of course.) It is important for collectors as well as dealers to understand the reasons for these huge numbers of value changes.

One of the main reasons for the enormous quantity of upward value changes this year is the same phenomenon that we witnessed when we prepared the 2006 catalogues: worldwide currency fluctuations that have seen the U.S. dollar drop against other strong currencies. We suspect that almost all Scott catalogue users have read reports concerning the significant devaluation of the U.S. dollar in relation to virtually every other major currency in the world during the past year. The euro, British pound, Australian dollar, New Zealand dollar, Canadian dollar, Swiss franc and Japanese yen all have gained significant strength in relation to the U.S. dollar.

The market for stamps denominated in euros, British pounds, Canadian dollars and other various foreign currencies are largely made in the home countries, and anyone who wants to compete for those stamps must compete with those home-country buyers who are using their own strong currencies. This means that it will take more U.S. dollars to buy those stamps, and it will take more U.S. dollars for U.S. dealers to replenish their stocks.

Being a retail value catalogue, Scott must react to this situation. Catalogue values for a great many better stamps (not to mention the values for many recent issues that are generally valued at about double face value) must rise to the correct retail level in U.S. dollars in order to reflect the actual market and to ensure that the U.S. and international stamp markets mesh properly for the benefit of all concerned.

Of course, there are many value changes made throughout the catalogue based on the basic laws of supply and demand rather than currency fluctuations. Each year, thousands of value changes are made that are not tied in any way to currency questions. These additional changes in stamp values help to swell the total number of value changes in this year's catalogues.

Where are the value changes in Volume 6?

As has been true for all 2009 Standard volumes, value changes in large numbers have been made in countries from all parts of the globe. The value-change leader in Volume 6 is Yugoslavia, with 3,201. Other countries with large numbers of value changes are South Africa (3,026 changes), Tanzania (2,322), Somalia (1,877), Wallis & Futuna Islands (1,683), Thailand (1,654), Turks & Caicos Islands (1,517), Sri Lanka (1,498), Virgin Islands (1,333), Solomon Islands (1,083) and Sudan (1,064). Other countries with significant numbers of value changes include Somali Coast, Trinidad & Tobago, Tristan da Cunha, Turkey, Uganda, Ukraine, United Arab Emirates, Uzbekistan, Vanuatu, South Vietnam, People's Democratic Republic of Yemen, Zambia and Zimbabwe.

In Yugoslavia, the value changes start with the general issues in 1921. The 1923 1d-30d King Alexander set of five, Scott 22-26, shows a big jump to $101.03 unused from $68.65 unused in the 2008 Volume 6. An even larger increase in value is seen in the 1928 1d-30d set of 10 overprinted semi-postals of 1926, Scott 53-62, which leaps to $246.50 unused and $14.85 used, from just $124 unused and $10.20 used last year. Value changes continue right through to the last issues of Yugoslavia in 2003. The back-of-the-book issues of Yugoslavia also see value increases, including the stamps of Ljubljana, Istria and Trieste.

Value changes in South Africa begin in the mid-1930s, and they are scattered but numerous from that point forward, with most changes being fairly modest increases of 10 to 15 percent. The 1954 1/2p-10sh Animal set, Scott 200-213, is a good example of what South African stamps with a good topic have done over the past year. It rises to $40.00 mint never hinged and $8.90 used, from $35.45 mint never hinged and $8.05 used last year. Value changes in the self-governing Tribal Homelands issues also are numerous, with occasional value decreases but generally value advances.

Some final comments on editorial changes and catalogue illustrations.

Volume 6 sees a new major number for Solomon Islands. Solomon Islands Scott 884A is the 1991 7c Sweet Potato Weevil which was overprinted "China '99" in red in 1999 for the International Stamp Exhibition in Beijing. This stamp, valued at $1.75 both mint never hinged and used, was widely available from the Solomon Islands as well as at the exhibition, and as such merits a major Scott listing. We will leave it to others to explain why the 7c Sweet Potato Weevil was the stamp picked for overprinting. Perhaps there was a large unsold surplus on the post office shelves. Philately works in mysterious ways.

In South Africa, a new illustration has been added to the setenant English-Afrikaans pictorials of 1933-54, thus correcting a long-standing illustration error in the catalogue. This should end the confusion felt by many concerning the 2p denominations of these popular stamps.

Many lettered minors have been added to Somali Coast, mostly for surcharge errors. Lettered minors also have been added to the listings of Sudan, Tokelau, Trinidad & Tobago, Vietnam, Western Ukraine and Yugoslavia.

We wish to express our deep appreciation to George Holschauer of Colonial Stamp Co. for his generous support of our color image project. He has responded with great stamps before, and recently he came through again with more than 120 valuable stamps which were needed for color representation in the catalogues. Some of these items replace old black and white images, some are unused stamps replacing current used examples, while still others are new images of items not previously pictured in the catalogues. These stamps have now been scanned, and many have made it into the catalogues this year while the rest will appear for the first time in next year's edition.

As usual, there are new footnotes and notes modified for clarity and accuracy throughout this catalogue to aid collectors. See the Volume 6 Number Additions, Deletions & Changes listing on page 1192 for listing changes.

A hobby is a great gift. Enjoy.

James E. Kloetzel/Catalogue Editor

Acknowledgments

Our appreciation and gratitude go to the following individuals who have assisted us in preparing information included in this year's Scott Catalogues. Some helpers prefer anonymity. These individuals have generously shared their stamp knowledge with others through the medium of the Scott Catalogue.

Those who follow provided information that is in addition to the hundreds of dealer price lists and advertisements and scores of auction catalogues and realizations that were used in producing the catalogue values. It is from those noted here that we have been able to obtain information on items not normally seen in published lists and advertisements. Support from these people goes beyond data leading to catalogue values, for they also are key to editorial changes.

> A special acknowledgment to Liane and Sergio Sismondo of The Classic Collector for their extraordinary assistance and knowledge sharing that has aided in the preparation of this year's Standard and Classic Specialized Catalogues.

A. R. Allison Ryukyu Philatelic Specialist Society
AMEXFIL (Asociacion Mexicana de Filatelia)
Roland Austin
Robert Ausubel (Great Britain Collectors Club)
Jack Hagop Barsoumian (International Stamp Co.)
William Batty-Smith
Jules K. Beck (Latin American Philatelic Society)
Vladimir Berrio-Lemm
George G. Birdsall (Northland Auctions)
John Birkinbine II
Keith & Margie Brown
Bernard Bujnak
Alan C. Campbell
Tina & John Carlson (JET Stamps)
Richard A. Champagne (Richard A. Champagne, Inc.)
Henry Chlanda (Liberian Philatelic Society)
Bob Coale
Leroy P. Collins III (United Postal Stationery Society)
Laurie Conrad
Frank D. Correl
Andrew Cronin (Canadian Society of Russian Philately)
Tony L. Crumbley (Carolina Coin & Stamp, Inc.)
Stephen R. Datz
Tony Davis
Kenneth E. Diehl
Bob Dumaine
Mark Eastzer (Markest Stamp Co.)
Esi Ebrani (Iran Philatelic Study Circle)
Paul G. Eckman
Marty Farber
Leon Finik (Loral Stamps)
Henry Fisher
Jeffrey M. Forster
Robert S. Freeman
Ernest E. Fricks (France & Colonies Philatelic Society)
Bob Genisol (Sultan Stamp Center)
Michael A. Goldman (Regency Superior, Ltd.)
Daniel E. Grau
Jan E. Gronwall
Joe Hahn (Associated Collectors of El Salvador)
Jerone Hart
John B. Head
Bruce Hecht (Bruce L. Hecht Co.)
Clifford O. Herrick (Fidelity Trading Co.)

George W. Holschauer
Philip J. Hughes (Croatian Philatelic Society)
Doug Iams
Eric Jackson
N. M. Janoowalla
Peter C. Jeannopoulos
Richard Juzwin (Richard Juzwin PTY LTD)
John Kardos (The Stamp Gallery)
Allan Katz (Ventura Stamp Co.)
Stanford M. Katz
Patricia A. Kaufmann
William V. Kriebel
Dr. Ingert (Ihor) Kuzych-Berlzovsky
Roberto Liera
William A. Litle
Gary B. Little (Luxembourg Collectors Club)
Pedro Llach (Filatelia Llach S.L.)
George Luzitano
Dennis Lynch
Leo Malz
Robert L. Markovits (Quality Investors, Ltd.)
Marilyn R. Mattke
William K. McDaniel
Gary N. McLean
Mark S. Miller (India Study Circle)
Allen Mintz (United Postal Stationery Society)
William E. Mooz
Brian Moorhouse
David Mordant
Gary M. Morris (Pacific Midwest Co.)
Peter Mosiondz, Jr.
Bruce M. Moyer (Moyer Stamps & Collectibles)
Richard H. Muller (Richard's Stamps)
James Natale
Robert Odenweller (AIEP)
Albert Olejnik
Mark Parren
John E. Pearson (Pittwater Philatelic Service)
John Pedneault
Donald J. Peterson (International Philippine Philatelic Society)
Stanley M. Piller (Stanley M. Piller & Associates)
Todor Drumev Popov
Peter W. W. Powell
Stephen Radin (Albany Stamp Co.)
Dr. Reuben a. Ramkissoon
Ghassan D. Riachi
Omar Rodriquez
Michael Rogers (Michael Rogers, Inc.)
Michael Ruggiero
Mehrdad Sadri (Persiphila)

Richard H. Salz
Alex Schauss (Schauss Philatelics)
Jacques C. Schiff, Jr. (Jacques C. Schiff, Jr., Inc.)
Bernard Seckler (Fine Arts Philatelists)
Guy Shaw
Charles F. Shreve (Spink Shreves Galleries)
Jeff Siddiqui
Sergio & Liane Sismondo (The Classic Collector)
Christopher Smith
Jay Smith
Jerry Summers
Scott R. Trepel (Siegel Auction Galleries)
Steve Unkrich
Philip T. Wall
Daniel C. Warren
Richard A. Washburn
Ed Wener (Indigo)
Hans A. Westphal
Don White (Dunedin Stamp Centre)
Robert F. Yacano (K-Line Philippines)
Ralph Yorio
Val Zabijaka
Michal Zika
John P. Zuckerman (Siegel Auction Galleries)
Alfonsa G. Zulueta, Jr.

Addresses, Telephone Numbers, Web Sites, E-Mail Addresses of General & Specialized Philatelic Societies

Collectors can contact the following groups for information about the philately of the areas within the scope of these societies, or inquire about membership in these groups. Aside from the general societies, we limit this list to groups that specialize in particular fields of philately, particular areas covered by the Scott Standard Postage Stamp Catalogue, and topical groups. Many more specialized philatelic society exist than those listed below. These addresses are updated yearly, and they are, to the best of our knowledge, correct and current. Groups should inform the editors of address changes whenever they occur. The editors also want to hear from other such specialized groups not listed.

Unless otherwise noted all website addresses begin with http://

American Philatelic Society
100 Match Factory Place
Bellefonte PA 16823-1367
Ph: (814) 933-3803
www.stamps.org
E-mail: apsinfo@stamps.org

American Stamp Dealers Association
Matthew Hansen
3 School St. Suite #205
Glen Cove NY 11542
Ph: (516) 759-7000
www.asdaonline.com
E-mail: asda@erols.com

International Society of Worldwide
Stamp Collectors
Terry Myers, MD
9463 Benbrook Blvd. #114
Benbrook TX 76126
www.iswsc.org
E-mail: executivedirector@iswsc.org

Royal Philatelic Society
41 Devonshire Place
London, United Kingdom W1G 6JY
www.rpsl.org.uk
E-mail: secretary@rpsl.org.uk

Royal Philatelic Society of Canada
PO Box 929, Station Q
Toronto, ON, Canada M4T 2P1
Ph: (888) 285-4143
www.rpsc.org
E-mail: info@rpsc.org

Young Stamp Collectors of America
Janet Houser
100 Match Factory Place
Bellefonte PA 16823-1367
Ph: (814) 933-3820
www.stamps.org/ysca/intro.htm
E-mail: ysca@stamps.org

Groups focusing on fields or aspects found in worldwide philately (some may cover U.S. area only)

American Air Mail Society
Stephen Reinhard
PO Box 110
Mineola NY 11501
www.americanairmailsociety.org
E-mail: sreinhard1@optonline.net

American First Day Cover Society
Douglas Kelsey
PO Box 16277
Tucson AZ 85732-6277
Ph: (520) 321-0880
www.afdcs.org
E-mail: afdcs@aol.com

American Revenue Association
Eric Jackson
PO Box 728
Leesport PA 19533-0728
Ph: (610) 926-6200
www.revenuer.org
E-mail: eric@revenuer.com

American Topical Association
Ray E. Cartier
PO Box 57
Arlington TX 76004-0057
Ph: (817) 274-1181
americantopicalassn.org
E-mail: americantopical@msn.com

Errors, Freaks and Oddities
Collectors Club
Stan Raugh
4217 8th Avenue
Temple PA 19560
Ph: (610) 921-5717
www.efocc.org
E-mail: trex@bigplanet.com

First Issues Collectors Club
Clark Buchi
P.O. Box 453
Brentwood TN 37024-0453
www.firstissues.org
E-mail: orders@firstissues.org

The Joint Stamp Issues Society
Pascal LeBlond
60-600 Rue Cormier
Gatineau, QC, Canada J9H 6B4
jointissues.ovh.org
E-mail: jointissues@yahoo.com

National Duck Stamp Collectors
Society
Anthony J. Monico
PO Box 43
Harleysville PA 19438-0043
www.ndscs.org
E-mail: ndscs@hwcn.org

No Value Identified Club
Albert Sauvanet
Le Clos Royal B, Boulevard des Pas
Enchantes
St. Sebastien-sur Loire, France 44230
E-mail: alain.vailly@irin.univ nantes.fr

The Perfins Club
Kurt Ottenheimer
462 West Walnut St.
Long Beach NY 11561
Ph: (516) 431-3412
E-mail: oak462@optonline.net

Postage Due Mail Study Group
John Rawlins
13, Longacre
Chelmsford
United Kingdom, CM1 3BJ
E-mail: john.rawlins2@ukonline.co.uk.

Post Mark Collectors Club
David Proulx
7629 Homestead Drive
Baldwinsville NY 13027
E-mail: stampdance@baldcom.net

Postal History Society
Kalman V. Illyefalvi
8207 Daren Court
Pikesville MD 21208-2211
Ph: (410) 653-0665
E-mail: kalphyl@juno.com

Precancel Stamp Society
Arthur Damm
176 Bent Pine Hill
North Wales PA 19454
Ph: (215) 368-6082
E-mail: shirldamm@comcast.net

United Postal Stationery Society
Stuart Leven
1445 Foxworthy Ave. #187
San Jose, CA 95118-1119
www.upss.org
E-mail: poststat@gmail.com

United States Possessions Philatelic
Society
Geoffrey Brewster
6453 E. Stallion Rd.
Paradise Valley AZ 85253
Ph: (480) 607-7184

Groups focusing on U.S. area philately as covered in the Standard Catalogue

Canal Zone Study Group
Richard H. Salz
60 27th Ave.
San Francisco CA 94121-1026

Carriers and Locals Society
John D. Bowman
PO Box 74
Grosse Ile MI 48138
Ph: (205) 222-7314
www.pennypost.org
E-mail: jbowman@stx.rr.net

Confederate Stamp Alliance
Gen. Francis J. Crown
PO Box 278
Capshaw AL 35742-0278
Ph: (302) 422-2656
www.csalliance.org
E-mail: csaas@knology.net

Hawaiian Philatelic Society
Kay H. Hoke
PO Box 10115
Honolulu HI 96816-0115
Ph: (808) 521-5721

Plate Number Coil Collectors Club
Ronald E. Maifeld
PO Box 54622
Cincinnati OH 45254-0622
Ph: (513) 231-4208
www.pnc3.org
E-mail: president@pnc3.org

Ryukyu Philatelic Specialist Society
Laura Edmonds, Secy.
PO Box 240177
Charlotte NC 28224-0177
Ph: (704) 519-5157
www.ryukyustamps.org
E-mail: secretary@ryukyustamps.org

United Nations Philatelists
Blanton Clement, Jr.
P.O. Box 146
Morrisville PA 19067-0146
www.unpi.com
E-mail: bclemjr@yahoo.com

United States Stamp Society
Executive Secretary
PO Box 6634
Katy TX 77491-6631
www.usstamps.org
E-mail: webmaster@usstamps.org

U.S. Cancellation Club
Roger Rhoads
6160 Brownstone Ct.
Mentor OH 44060
www.geocities.com/athens/2088/
uscchome.htm
E-mail: rrrhoads@aol.com

U.S. Philatelic Classics Society
Rob Lund
2913 Fulton
Everett WA 98201-3733
www.uspcs.org
E-mail: membershipchairman@uspcs.org

Groups focusing on philately of foreign countries or regions

Aden & Somaliland Study Group
Gary Brown
PO Box 106
Briar Hill, Victoria, Australia 3088
E-mail: garyjohn951@optushome.com.au

American Society of Polar
Philatelists (Antarctic areas)
Alan Warren
PO Box 39
Exton PA 19341-0039
Ph: (847) 421-7655
www.polarphilatelists.org
E-mail: cjenner00@yahoo.com

Andorran Philatelic Study Circle
D. Hope
17 Hawthorn Dr.
Stalybridge, Cheshire, United Kingdom
SK15 1UE
http://apsc.free.fr
E-mail: apsc@free.fr

Australian States Study Circle of
The Royal Sydney Philatelic Club
Ben Palmer
GPO 1751
Sydney, N.S.W., Australia 2001

Austria Philatelic Society
Ralph Schneider
PO Box 23049
Belleville IL 62223
Ph: (618) 277-6152
www.austriaphilatelicsociety.com
E-mail: rsstamps@aol.com

American Belgian Philatelic Society
Edward de Bary
11 Wakefield Dr. Apt. 2105
Asheville NC 28803
groups.hamptonroads.com/ABPS
E-mail: belgam@charter.net

Bechuanalands and Botswana Society
Neville Midwood
69 Porlock Lane
Furzton, Milton Keynes, United
Kingdom MK4 1JY
www.nevsoft.com
E-mail: bbsoc@nevsoft.com

Bermuda Collectors Society
Thomas J. McMahon
PO Box 1949
Stuart FL 34995
www.bermudacollectorssociety.org

Brazil Philatelic Association
William V. Kriebel
1923 ManningSt.
Philadelphia PA 19103-5728
Ph: (215) 735-3697
E-mail: kriebewv@drexel.edu

British Caribbean Philatelic Study Group
Dr. Reuben A. Ramkissoon
3011 White Oak Lane
Oak Brook IL 60523-2513
Ph: (630) 963-1439
www.bcpsg.org
E-mail: rramkissoon@juno.com

The King George VI Collectors Society (British Commonwealth)
John Shaw
17 Balcaskie Road, Eltham
London, United Kingdom, SE9 1HQ

British North America Philatelic Society (Canada & Provinces)
H. P. Jacobi
6-2168 150A St.
Surrey, B.C., Canada V4A 9W4
www.bnaps.org
E-mail: pjacobi@shaw.ca

British West Indies Study Circle
W. Clary Holt
PO Drawer 59
Burlington NC 27216
Ph: (336) 227-7461

Burma Philatelic Study Circle
Michael Whittaker
1, Ecton Leys, Hillside
Rugby, Warwickshire, United Kingdom,
CV22 5SL
E-mail: whittaker2004@ntlworld.com

Ceylon Study Group
R. W. P. Frost
42 Lonsdale Road, Cannington
Bridgewater, Somerset, United
Kingdom TA5 2JS
E-mail: rodney.frost@tiscali.co.uk

Channel Islands Specialists Society
Moira Edwards
86, Hall Lane, Sandon,
Chelmsford, United Kingdom, CM2
7RQ
E-mail: am012e5360@blueyonder.co.uk

China Stamp Society
Paul H. Gault
PO Box 20711
Columbus OH 43220
www.chinastampsociety.org
E-mail: secretary@chinastampsociety.org

Colombia/Panama Philatelic Study Group (COPAPHIL)
Thomas P. Myers
7411 Old Post Road #1
Lincoln NE 68506
www.copaphil.org
E-mail: tpmphil@hotmail.com

Association Filatelic de Costa Rica
Giana Wayman
c/o Interlink 102, PO Box 52-6770
Miami, FL 33152
E-mail: scotland@racsa.co.cr

Society for Costa Rica Collectors
Dr. Hector R. Mena
PO Box 14831
Baton Rouge LA 70808
www.socorico.org
E-mail: hrmena@aol.com

Croatian Philatelic Society (Croatia & other Balkan areas)
Ekrem Spahich
502 Romero, PO Box 696
Fritch TX 79036-0696
Ph: (806) 273-5609
www.croatianstamps.com
E-mail: eckSpahich@cableone.net

Cuban Philatelic Society of America
Ernesto Cuesta
PO Box 34434
Bethesda MD 20827
www.philat.com/cpsa
E-mail: ecuesta@philat.com

Cyprus Study Circle
Jim Wigmore
20 Gilpin Close, Dawlish
Devon, United Kingdom EX7 9SZ
www.cyprusstudycircle.org/index.htm
E-mail: jameswigmore@aol.com

Society for Czechoslovak Philately
Phil Rhoade
28168 Cedar Trail
Cleveland MN 56017
www.csphilately.org
E-mail: philip.rhoade@mnsu.edu

Danish West Indies Study Unit of the Scandinavian Collectors Club
Arnold Sorensen
7666 Edgedale Drive
Newburgh IN 47630
Ph: (812) 853-2653
dwistudygroup.com
E-mail: valbydwi@hotmail.com

East Africa Study Circle
Jonathan Smalley
1 Lincoln Close
Tweeksbury, United Kingdom B91 1AE
easc.org.uk
E-mail: jpasmalley@tiscali.co.uk

Egypt Study Circle
Mike Murphy
109 Chadwick Road
London, United Kingdom SE15 4PY
Dick Wilson: North American Agent
egyptstudycircle.org.uk
E-mail: egyptstudycircle@hotmail.com

Estonian Philatelic Society
Juri Kirsimagi
29 Clifford Ave.
Pelham NY 10803
Ph: (914) 738-3713

Ethiopian Philatelic Society
Ulf Lindahl
21 Westview Place
Riverside CT 06878
Ph: (203) 866-3540
home.comcast.net/~fbheiser/ethiopia5.htm
E-mail: ulindahl@optonline.net

Falkland Islands Philatelic Study Group
Carl J. Faulkner
Williams Inn, On-the-Green
Williamstown MA 01267-2620
www.fipsg.org.uk
Ph: (413) 458-9371

Faroe Islands Study Circle
Norman Hudson
28 Enfield Road
Ellesmere Port, Cheshire, United
Kingdom CH65 8BY
www.faroeislandssc.org.
E-mail: jntropics@hotmail.com

Former French Colonies Specialist Society
BP 628
75367 Paris Cedex 08, France
www.colfra.com
E-mail: clubcolfra@aol.com

France & Colonies Philatelic Society
Edward Grabowski
741 Marcellus Drive
Westfield NJ 07090-2012
www.drunkenboat.net/frandcol/
E-mail: edjjg@alum.mit.edu

Germany Philatelic Society
PO Box 6547
Chesterfield MO 63006
www.gps.nu

German Democratic Republic Study Group of the German Philatelic Society
Ken Lawrence
PO Box 98
Bellefonte PA 16823-0098
Ph: (814) 422-0625
E-mail: apsken@aol.com

Gibraltar Study Circle
David R. Stirrups
34 Glamis Drive
Dundee, United Kingdom DD2 1QP
E-mail: drstirrups@dundee.ac.uk

Great Britain Collectors Club
Timothy Bryan Burgess
3547 Windmill Way
Concord CA 94518
www.gbstamps.com/gbcc
E-mail: Pennyred@earthlink.net

Hellenic Philatelic Society of America (Greece and related areas)
Dr. Nicholas Asimakopulos
541 Cedar Hill Ave.
Wyckoff NJ 07481
Ph: (201) 447-6262
E-mail: nick1821@aol.com

Haiti Philatelic Society
Ubaldo Del Toro
5709 Marble Archway
Alexandria VA 22315
www.haitiphilately.org
E-mail: u007ubi@aol.com

Hong Kong Stamp Society
Dr. An-Min Chung
3300 Darby Rd. Cottage 503
Haverford PA 19041-1064

Society for Hungarian Philately
Robert Morgan
2201 Roscomare Rd.
Los Angeles CA 90077-2222
www.hungarianphilately.org
E-mail: h.alan.hoover@hungarianphilately.org

India Study Circle
John Warren
PO Box 7326
Washington DC 20044
Ph: (202) 564-6876
www.indiastudycircle.org
E-mail: warren.john@epa.gov

Indian Ocean Study Circle
Mrs. S. Hopson
Field Acre, Hoe Benham
Newbury, Berkshire, United Kingdom
RG20 8PD

Society of Indo-China Philatelists
Ron Bentley
2600 North 24th Street
Arlington VA 22207
www.sicp-online.org
E-mail: ron.bentley@verizon.net

Iran Philatelic Study Circle
Mehdi Esmaili
PO Box 750096
Forest Hills NY 11375
www.iranphilatelic.org
E-mail: m.esmaili@earthlink.net

Eire Philatelic Association (Ireland)
David J. Brennan
PO Box 704
Bernardsville NJ 07924
eirephilatelicassoc.org
E-mail: brennan704@aol.com

Society of Israel Philatelists
Paul S. Aufrichtig
300 East 42nd St.
New York NY 10017

Italy and Colonies Study Circle
Andrew D'Anneo
1085 Dunweal Lane
Calistoga CA 94515
www.icsc.pwp.blueyonder.co.uk
E-mail: audanneo@napanet.net

International Society for Japanese Philately
Kenneth Kamholz
PO Box 1283
Haddonfield NJ 08033
www.isjp.org
E-mail: isjp@isjp.org

Korea Stamp Society
John E. Talmage
PO Box 6889
Oak Ridge TN 37831
www.pennfamily.org/KSS-USA
E-mail: jtalmage@usit.net

Latin American Philatelic Society
Jules K. Beck
30 1/2 Street #209
St. Louis Park MN 55426-3551

Latvian Philatelic Society
Aris Birze
569 Rougemount Dr.
Pickering, ON, Canada L1W 2C1

Liberian Philatelic Society
William Thomas Lockard
PO Box 106
Wellston OH 45692
Ph: (740) 384-2020
E-mail: tlockard@zoomnet.net

Liechtenstudy USA (Liechtenstein)
Paul Tremaine
PO Box 601
Dundee OR 97115
Ph: (503) 538-4500
www.liechtenstudy.org
E-mail: editor@liechtenstudy.org

Lithuania Philatelic Society
John Variakojis
3715 W. 68th St.
Chicago IL 60629
Ph: (773) 585-8649
www.filatelija.lt/lps/and
www.withgusto.org/lps/index.htm
E-mail: variakojis@earthlink.net

Luxembourg Collectors Club
Gary B. Little
7319 Beau Road
Sechelt, BC, Canada V0N 3A8
http://lcc.luxcentral.com
E-mail: gary@luxcentral.com

Malaya Study Group
David Tett
PO Box 34
Wheathampstead, Herts, United
Kingdom AL4 8JY
www.m-s-g/org/uk
E-mail: davidtett@aol.com

Malta Study Circle
Alec Webster
50 Worcester Road
Sutton, Surrey,
United Kingdom SM2 6QB
E-mail: alecwebster50@hotmail.com

Mexico-Elmhurst Philatelic Society
International
David Pietsch
PO Box 50997
Irvine CA 92619-0997
E-mail: mepsi@msn.com

Society for Moroccan and Tunisian
Philately
206, bld. Pereire
75017 Paris, France
members.aol.com/Jhaik5814
E-mail: splm206@aol.com

Natal and Zululand Study Circle
Dr. Guy Dillaway
PO Box 181
Weston MA 02493
www.nzsc.demon.co.uk

Nepal & Tibet Philatelic Study
Group
Roger D. Skinner
1020 Covington Road
Los Altos CA 94024-5003
Ph: (650) 968-4163
fuchs-online.com/ntpsc/
E-mail: colinhepper@hotmail.co.uk

American Society of Netherlands
Philately
Hans Kremer
50 Rockport Ct.
Danville CA 94526
Ph: (925) 820-5841
www.angelfire.com/ca2/asnp
E-mail: hkremer@usa.net

New Zealand Society of Great Britain
Keith C. Collins
13 Briton Crescent
Sanderstead, Surrey, United Kingdom
CR2 0JN
www.cs.stir.ac.uk/~rgc/nzsgb
E-mail: rgc@cs.stir.ac.uk

Nicaragua Study Group
Erick Rodriguez
11817 S.W. 11th St.
Miami FL 33184-2501
clubs.yahoo.com/clubs/nicara-
guastudygroup
E-mail: nsgsec@yahoo.com

Society of Australasian Specialists/
Oceania
Henry Bateman
PO Box 4862
Monroe LA 71211-4862
Ph: (800) 571-0293 members.aol.
com/stampsho/saso.html
E-mail: hbateman@jam.rr.com

Orange Free State Study Circle
J. R. Stroud
28 Oxford St.
Burnham-on-sea, Somerset, United
Kingdom TA8 1LQ
E-mail: richardstroudph@gofast.co.uk

Pacific Islands Study Circle
John Ray
24 Woodvale Avenue
London, United Kingdom SE25 4AE
www.pisc.org.uk
E-mail: info@pisc.org.uk

Pakistan Philatelic Study Circle
Jeff Siddiqui
PO Box 7002
Lynnwood WA 98046
E-mail: jeffsiddiqui@msn.com

Centro de Filatelistas
Independientes de Panama
Vladimir Berrio-Lemm
Apartado 0823-02748
Plaza Concordia Panama, Panama
E-mail: panahistoria@gmail.com

Papuan Philatelic Society
Steven Zirinsky
PO Box 49, Ansonia Station
New York NY 10023
Ph: (718) 706-0616
www.communigate.co.uk/york/pps
E-mail: szirinsky@cs.com

International Philippine Philatelic
Society
Robert F. Yacano
PO Box 100
Toast NC 27049
Ph: (336) 783-0768
www.theipps.info
E-mail: ryacano@triad.rr.com

Pitcairn Islands Study Group
Nelson A. L. Weller
619 Flick Circle
Thomasville NC 27360
Ph: (336) 475-4558
www.pisg.net
E-mail: nalweller@aol.com

Plebiscite-Memel-Saar Study Group
of the German Philatelic Society
Clay Wallace
100 Lark Court
Alamo CA 94507
E-mail: clayw1@sbcglobal.net

Polonus Philatelic Society (Poland)
Chris Kulpinski
9350 E. Palm Tree Dr.
Scottsdale AZ 85255
Ph: (480) 585-7114
www.polonus.org
E-mail: ctk@kulpinski.net

International Society for
Portuguese Philately
Clyde Homen
1491 Bonnie View Rd.
Hollister CA 95023-5117
www.portugalstamps.com
E-mail: cjh1491@sbcglobal.net

Rhodesian Study Circle
William R. Wallace
PO Box 16381
San Francisco CA 94116
www.rhodesianstudycircle.org.uk
E-mail: bwall8rscr@earthlink.net

Rossica Society of Russian Philately
Edward J. Laveroni
P.O. Box 320997
Los Gatos CA 95032-0116
www.rossica.org
E-mail: ed.laveroni@rossica.org

St. Helena, Ascension & Tristan Da
Cunha Philatelic Society
Dr. Everett L. Parker
719 Moosehead Lake Rd.
Greenville ME 04441-9727
Ph: (207) 695-3163
ourworld.compuserve.com/homep-
ages/ ST_HELENA_ASCEN_TDC
E-mail: eparker@midmaine.net

St. Pierre & Miquelon Philatelic
Society
David Allen
2159 W. 47 Avenue
Vancouver, BC, V6M 2M6, Canada
Ph: (604) 263-0029
E-mail: dallen@axion.net

Associated Collectors of El Salvador
Joseph D. Hahn
1015 Old Boalsburg Rd. Apt G-5
State College PA 16801-6149
www.elsalvadorphilately.org
E-mail: joehahn2@yahoo.com

Fellowship of Samoa Specialists
Jack R. Hughes
PO Box 1260
Boston MA 02117-1260
members.aol.com/tongaJan/foss.html

Sarawak Specialists' Society
Stu Leven
PO Box 24764
San Jose CA 95154-4764
Ph: (408) 978-0193
www.britborneostamps.org.uk
E-mail: stulev@ix.netcom.com

Scandinavian Collectors Club
Donald B. Brent
PO Box 13196
El Cajon CA 92020
www.scc-online.org
E-mail: dbrent47@sprynet.com

Slovakia Stamp Society
Jack Benchik
PO Box 555
Notre Dame IN 46556

Philatelic Society for Greater
Southern Africa
Alan Hanks
34 Seaton Drive
Aurora, ON, L4G 2KI, Canada
Ph: (905) 727-6993
www.psgsa.thestampweb.com
Email: alan.hanks@sympatico.ca

Spanish Philatelic Society
Robert H. Penn
1108 Walnut Drive
Danielsville PA 18038
Ph: (610) 767-6793

Sudan Study Group
c/o North American Agent
Richard S. Wilson
53 Middle Patent Road
Bedford NY 10506
www.sudanphilately.co.uk
E-mail: dadu1@verizon.net

American Helvetia Philatelic
Society (Switzerland,
Liechtenstein)
Richard T. Hall
PO Box 15053
Asheville NC 28813-0053
www.swiss-stamps.org
E-mail: secretary2@swiss-stamps.org

Tannu Tuva Collectors Society
Ken Simon
513 Sixth Ave. So.
Lake Worth FL 33460-4507
Ph: (561) 588-5954
www.tuva.tk
E-mail: fpo09501@yahoo.com

Society for Thai Philately
H. R. Blakeney
PO Box 25644
Oklahoma City OK 73125
E-mail: HRBlakeney@aol.com

Transvaal Study Circle
J. Woolgar
PO Box 379
Gravesend, DA11 9EW, United
Kingdom
www.transvaal.org.uk

Ottoman and Near East Philatelic
Society (Turkey and related areas)
Bob Stuchell
193 Valley Stream Lane
Wayne PA 19087
www.oneps.org
E-mail: rstuchell@msn.com

Ukrainian Philatelic & Numismatic
Society
George Slusarczuk
PO Box 303
Southfields NY 10975-0303
www.upns.org
E-mail: Yurko@warwick.net

Vatican Philatelic Society
Sal Quinonez
1 Aldersgate, Apt. 1002
Riverhead NY 11901-1830
Ph: (516) 727-6426
www.vaticanphilately.org

British Virgin Islands Philatelic
Society
Giorgio Migliavacca
PO Box 7007
St. Thomas VI 00801-0007
www.islandsun.com/FEATURES/
bviphil9198.html
E-mail: issun@candwbvi.net

West Africa Study Circle
Dr. Peter Newroth
Suite 603
5332 Sayward Hill Crescent
Victoria, BC, Canada V8Y 3H8
www.wasc.org.uk/

Western Australia Study Group
Brian Pope
PO Box 423
Claremont, Western Australia,
Australia 6910

Yugoslavia Study Group of the
Croatian Philatelic Society
Michael Lenard
1514 North 3rd Ave.
Wausau WI 54401
Ph: (715) 675-2833
E-mail: mjlenard@aol.com

Topical Groups

Americana Unit
Dennis Dengel
17 Peckham Rd.
Poughkeepsie NY 12603-2018
www.americanaunit.org
E-mail: info@americanaunit.org

Astronomy Study Unit
John Budd
29203 Coharie Loop
San Antonio FL 33576-4643
Ph: (978) 851-8283
www.fandm.edu/departments/
astronomy/miscell/astunit.html
E-mail: jwgbudd@earthlink.net

Bicycle Stamp Club
Norman Batho
358 Iverson Place
East Windsor NJ 08520
Ph: (609) 448-9547
members.tripod.com/~bicyclestamps
E-mail: normbatho@worldnet.att.net

Biology Unit
Alan Hanks
34 Seaton Dr.
Aurora, ON, Canada L4G 2K1
Ph: (905) 727-6993

Bird Stamp Society
Mrs. Rosie Bradley
31 Park View,
Chepsow, Gwent, United Kingdom
NP16 5NA
www.bird-stamps.org/bss
E-mail: bradley666@lycos.co.uk

Canadiana Study Unit
John Peebles
PO Box 3262, Station "A"
London, ON, Canada N6A 4K3
E-mail: john.peebles@sympatico.ca

Captain Cook Study Unit
Brian P. Sandford
173 Minuteman Dr.
Concord MA 01742-1923
www.captaincooksociety.com
E-mail: US@captaincooksociety.com/

Casey Jones Railroad Unit
Donald Kesler
709 NW 35th Place
Lawton OK 73505-5121
www.uqp.de/cjr/index.htm
E-mail: normaned@rochester.rr.com

Cats on Stamps Study Unit
Mary Ann Brown
3006 Wade Rd.
Durham NC 27705
www.catsonstamps.org
E-mail: mabrown@nc.rr.com

Chemistry & Physics on Stamps Study Unit
Dr. Roland Hirsch
20458 Water Point Lane
Germantown MD 20874
www.cpossu.org
E-mail: rfhirsch@cpossu.org

Chess on Stamps Study Unit
Anne Kasonic
7625 County Road #153
Interlaken NY 14847
E-mail: akasonic@capital.net

Christmas Philatelic Club
Linda Lawrence
312 Northwood Drive
Lexington KY 40505
www.hwcn.org/link/cpc
E-mail: stamplinda@aol.com

Christopher Columbus Philatelic Society
Donald R. Ager
PO Box 71
Hillsboro NH 03244-0071
http://ccps.maphist.nl/
Ph: (603) 464-5379
E-mail: meganddon@tds.net

Collectors of Religion on Stamps
Verna Shackleton
425 North Linwood Avenue #110
Appleton WI 54914
www://my.vbe.com/~cmfourl/
coros1.htm
E-mail: corosec@sbcglobal.net

Dogs on Stamps Study Unit
Morris Raskin
202A Newport Rd.
Monroe Township NJ 08831
Ph: (609) 655-7411
www.dossu.org
E-mail: mraskin@cellurian.com

Earth's Physical Features Study Group
Fred Klein
515 Magdalena Ave.
Los Altos CA 94024
epfsu.jeffhayward.com

Ebony Society of Philatelic Events and Reflections (African-American topicals)
Manuel Gilyard
800 Riverside Drive, Ste 4H
New York NY 10032-7412
www.esperstamps.org
E-mail: gilyardmani@aol.com

Embroidery, Stitchery, Textile Unit
http://www.caratexstamps.com/

Europa Study Unit
Donald W. Smith
PO Box 576
Johnstown PA 15907-0576
www.europanews.emperors.net
E-mail: eunity@aol.com or
donsmith65@msn.com

Fine & Performing Arts
Deborah L. Washington
6922 So. Jeffery Boulevard
#7 - North
Chicago IL 60649
E-mail: brasslady@comcast.net

Fire Service in Philately
Brian R. Engler, Sr.
726 1/2 W. Tilghman St.
Allentown PA 18102-2324
Ph: (610) 433-2782
www.firestamps.com

Gay & Lesbian History on Stamps Club
Joe Petronie
PO Box 190842
Dallas TX 75219-0842
www.glhsc.org
E-mail: glhsc@aol.com

Gems, Minerals & Jewelry Study Unit
George Young
PO Box 632
Tewksbury MA 01876-0632
Ph: (978) 851-8283
www.rockhounds.com/rockshop/
gmjsuapp.txt
E-mail: george-young@msn.com

Graphics Philately Association
Mark H Winnegrad
PO Box 380
Bronx NY 10462-0380
www.graphics-stamps.org
E-mail: indybruce1@yahoo.com

Journalists, Authors & Poets on Stamps
Ms. Lee Straayer
P.O. Box 6808
Champaign IL 61826
E-mail: lstraayer@dcbnet.com

Lighthouse Stamp Society
Dalene Thomas
8612 West Warren Lane
Lakewood CO 80227-2352
Ph: (303) 986-6620
www.lighthousestampsociety.org
E-mail: dalene@lighthousestampsociety.org

Lions International Stamp Club
John Bargus
304-2777 Barry Rd. RR 2
Mill Bay, BC, Canada V0R 2P0
Ph: (250) 743-5782

Mahatma Gandhi On Stamps Study Circle
Pramod Shivagunde
Pratik Clinic, Akluj
Solapur, Maharashtra, India 413101
E-mail: drnanda@bom6.vsnl.net.in

Mask Study Unit
Carolyn Weber
1220 Johnson Drive, Villa 104
Ventura CA 93003-0540
E-mail: cweber@venturalink.net

Masonic Study Unit
Stanley R. Longenecker
930 Wood St.
Mount Joy PA 17552-1926
Ph: (717) 653-1155
E-mail: natsco@usa.net

Mathematical Study Unit
Estelle Buccino
5615 Glenwood Rd.
Bethesda MD 20817-6727
Ph: (301) 718-8898
www.math.ttu.edu/msu/
E-mail: m.strauss@ttu.edu

Medical Subjects Unit
Dr. Frederick C. Skvara
PO Box 6228
Bridgewater NJ 08807
E-mail: fcskvara@verizon.net

Mourning Stamps and Covers Club
John Hotchner
PO Box 1125
Falls Church VA 22041-0125
E-mail: jmhstamp@ix.netcom.com

Napoleonic Age Philatelists
Ken Berry
7513 Clayton Dr.
Oklahoma City OK 73132-5636
Ph: (405) 721-0044
www.nap-stamps.org
E-mail: krb2@earthlink.net

Old World Archeological Study Unit
Caroline Scannel
11 Dawn Drive
Smithtown NY 11787-1761
www.owasu.org
E-mail: editor@owasu.org

Petroleum Philatelic Society International
Dr. Chris Coggins
174 Old Bedford Road
Luton, England, LU2 7HW, United Kingdom
E-mail: WAMTECH@Luton174.fsnet.co.uk

Philatelic Computing Study Group
Robert de Violini
PO Box 5025
Oxnard CA 93031-5025
www.pcsg.org
E-mail: dviolini@adelphia.net

Philatelic Lepidopterists' Association
Alan Hanks
34 Seaton Dr.
Aurora, ON, Canada L4G 2K1
Ph: (905) 727-6933
E-mail: alan.hanks@sympatico.ca

Rotary on Stamps Unit
Gerald L. Fitzsimmons
105 Calla Ricardo
Victoria TX 77904
rotaryonstamps.org
E-mail: glfitz@suddenlink.net

Scouts on Stamps Society International
Lawrence Clay
PO Box 6228
Kennewick WA 99336
Ph: (509) 735-3731
www.sossi.org
E-mail: rfrank@sossi.org

Ships on Stamps Unit
Les Smith
302 Conklin Avenue
Penticton, BC, Canada, V2A 2T4
Ph: (250) 493-7486
www.shipsonstamps.org
E-mail: lessmith440@shaw.ca

Space Unit
Carmine Torrisi
PO Box 780241
Maspeth NY 11378
Ph: (718) 386-7882
stargate.1usa.com/stamps/
E-mail: ctorrisi1@nyc.rr.com

Sports Philatelists International
Margaret Jones
5310 Lindenwood Ave.
St. Louis MO 63109-1758
www.sportstamps.org

Stamps on Stamps Collectors Club
Alf Jordan
156 West Elm Street
Yarmouth ME 04096
www.stampsonstamps.org
E-mail: ajordan1@maine.rr.com

Windmill Study Unit
Walter J. Hollien
PO Box 346
Long Valley NJ 07853-0346
Ph: (862) 812-0030
E-mail: whollien@earthlink.net

Wine On Stamps Study Unit
Bruce L. Johnson
115 Raintree Drive
Zionsville IN 46077
E-mail: indybruce@yahoo.com

Women on Stamps Study Unit
Hugh Gottfried
2232 26th St.
Santa Monica CA 90405-1902
E-mail: hgottfried@adelphia.net

Zeppelin Collectors Club
Cheryl Ganz
PO Box 77196
Washington DC 20013
www.americanairmailsociety.org

Expertizing Services

The following organizations will, for a fee, provide expert opinions about stamps submitted to them. Collectors should contact these organizations to find out about their fees and requirements before submitting philatelic material to them. The listing of these groups here is not intended as an endorsement by Scott Publishing Co.

General Expertizing Services

American Philatelic Expertizing
  Service (a service of the
  American Philatelic Society)
100 Match Factory Place
Bellefonte PA 16823-1367
Ph: (814) 237-3803
Fax: (814) 237-6128
www.stamps.org
E-mail: ambristo@stamps.org
Areas of Expertise: Worldwide

B. P. A. Expertising, Ltd.
PO Box 137
Leatherhead, Surrey, United Kingdom
KT22 0RG
E-mail: sec.bpa@tcom.co.uk
Areas of Expertise: British
Commonwealth, Great Britain,
Classics of Europe, South America and
the Far East

Philatelic Foundation
70 West 40th St., 15th Floor
New York NY 10018
Ph: (212) 221-6555
Fax: (212) 221-6208
www.philatelicfoundation.org
E-mail:philatelicfoundation@verizon.net
Areas of Expertise: U.S. & Worldwide

Professional Stamp Experts
PO Box 6170
Newport Beach CA 92658
Ph: (877) STAMP-88
Fax: (949) 833-7955
www.collectors.com/pse
E-mail: pseinfo@collectors.com
Areas of Expertise: Stamps and
covers of U.S., U.S. Possessions,
British Commonwealth

Royal Philatelic Society Expert
  Committee
41 Devonshire Place
London, United Kingdom W1N 1PE
www.rpsl.org.uk/experts.html
E-mail: experts@rpsl.org.uk
Areas of Expertise: All

Expertizing Services Covering Specific Fields Or Countries

China Stamp Society Expertizing
  Service
1050 West Blue Ridge Blvd
Kansas City MO 64145
Ph: (816) 942-6300
E-mail: hjmesq@aol.com
Areas of Expertise: China

Confederate Stamp Alliance
  Authentication Service
Gen. Frank Crown, Jr.
PO Box 278
Capshaw AL 35742-0396
Ph: (302) 422-2656
Fax: (302) 424-1990
www.csalliance.org
E-mail: csaas@knology.net
Areas of Expertise: Confederate stamps
and postal history

Croatian Philatelic Society
  Expertizing Service
PO Box 696
Fritch TX 79036-0696
Ph: (806) 857-0129
E-mail: ou812@arn.net
Areas of Expertise: Croatia and other
Balkan areas

Errors, Freaks and Oddities
  Collectors Club
  Expertizing Service
138 East Lakemont Dr.
Kingsland GA 31548
Ph: (912) 729-1573
Areas of Expertise: U.S. errors, freaks
and oddities

Estonian Philatelic Society
  Expertizing Service
39 Clafford Lane
Melville NY 11747
Ph: (516) 421-2078
E-mail: esto4@aol.com
Areas of Expertise: Estonia

Hawaiian Philatelic Society
  Expertizing Service
PO Box 10115
Honolulu HI 96816-0115
Areas of Expertise: Hawaii

Hong Kong Stamp Society
  Expertizing Service
PO Box 206
Glenside PA 19038
Fax: (215) 576-6850
Areas of Expertise: Hong Kong

International Association of
  Philatelic Experts
United States Associate members:

Paul Buchsbayew
119 W. 57th St.
New York NY 10019
Ph: (212) 977-7734
Fax: (212) 977-8653
Areas of Expertise: Russia, Soviet
Union

William T. Crowe
(see Professional Stamp Experts)
Areas of Expertise: United States

John Lievsay
(see American Philatelic Expertizing
Service and Philatelic Foundation)
Areas of Expertise: France

Robert W. Lyman
P.O. Box 348
Irvington on Hudson NY 10533
Ph and Fax: (914) 591-6937
Areas of Expertise: British North
America, New Zealand

Robert Odenweller
P.O. Box 401
Bernardsville, NJ 07924-0401
Ph and Fax: (908) 766-5460
Areas of Expertise: New Zealand,
Samoa to 1900

Alex Rendon
P.O. Box 323
Massapequa NY 11762
Ph and Fax: (516) 795-0464
Areas of Expertise: Bolivia,
Colombia, Colombian States

Sergio Sismondo
10035 Carousel Center Dr.
Syracuse NY 13290-0001
Ph: (315) 422-2331
Fax: (315) 422-2956
Areas of Expertise: British East
Africa, Camerouns,
Cape of Good Hope, Canada, British
North America

International Society for Japanese
  Philately Expertizing Committee
32 King James Court
Staten Island NY 10308-2910
Ph: (718) 227-5229
Areas of Expertise: Japan and
related areas, except WWII Japanese
Occupation issues

International Society for
  Portuguese Philately Expertizing
  Service
PO Box 43146
Philadelphia PA 19129-3146
Ph: (215) 843-2106
Fax: (215) 843-2106
E-mail: s.s.washburne@worldnet.att.
net
Areas of Expertise: Portugal and
Colonies

Mexico-Elmhurst Philatelic Society
  International Expert Committee
PO Box 1133
West Covina CA 91793
Areas of Expertise: Mexico

Ukrainian Philatelic & Numismatic
  Society Expertizing Service
30552 Dell Lane
Warren MI 48092-1862
Ph: (810) 751-5754
Areas of Expertise: Ukraine, Western
Ukraine

V. G. Greene Philatelic Research
  Foundation
P.O. Box 204, Station Q
Toronto, ON, Canada M4T 2M1
Ph: (416) 921-2073
Fax: (416) 921-1282
E-mail: vggfoundation@on.aibn.com
www.greenefoundation.ca
Areas of Expertise: British North
America

Information on Catalogue Values, Grade and Condition

Catalogue Value

The Scott Catalogue value is a retail value; that is, an amount you could expect to pay for a stamp in the grade of Very Fine with no faults. Any exceptions to the grade valued will be noted in the text. The general introduction on the following pages and the individual section introductions further explain the type of material that is valued. The value listed for any given stamp is a reference that reflects recent actual dealer selling prices for that item.

Dealer retail price lists, public auction results, published prices in advertising and individual solicitation of retail prices from dealers, collectors and specialty organizations have been used in establishing the values found in this catalogue. Scott Publishing Co. values stamps, but Scott is not a company engaged in the business of buying and selling stamps as a dealer.

Use this catalogue as a guide for buying and selling. The actual price you pay for a stamp may be higher or lower than the catalogue value because of many different factors, including the amount of personal service a dealer offers, or increased or decreased interest in the country or topic represented by a stamp or set. An item may occasionally be offered at a lower price as a "loss leader," or as part of a special sale. You also may obtain an item inexpensively at public auction because of little interest at that time or as part of a large lot.

Stamps that are of a lesser grade than Very Fine, or those with condition problems, generally trade at lower prices than the values shown in this catalogue. Stamps of exceptional quality in both grade and condition often command higher prices than the values listed.

Values for pre-1900 unused issues are for stamps with approximately half or more of their original gum. Stamps with most or all of their original gum may be expected to sell for more, and stamps with less than half of their original gum may be expected to sell for somewhat less than the values listed. On rarer stamps, it may be expected that the original gum will be somewhat more disturbed than it will be on more common issues. Post-1900 unused issues are assumed to have full original gum. From breakpoints in most countries' listings, stamps are valued as never hinged, due to the wide availability of stamps in that condition. These notations are prominently placed in the listings and in the country information preceding the listings. Some countries also feature listings with dual values for hinged and never-hinged stamps.

Grade

A stamp's grade and condition are crucial to its value. The accompanying illustrations show examples of Very Fine stamps from different time periods, along with examples of stamps in Fine to Very Fine and Extremely Fine grades as points of reference. When a stamp seller offers a stamp in any grade from fine to superb without further qualifying statements, that stamp should not only have the centering grade as defined, but it also should be free of faults or other condition problems.

FINE stamps (illustrations not shown) have designs that are quite off center, with the perforations on one or two sides very close to the design but not quite touching it. There is white space between the perforations and the design that is minimal but evident to the unaided eye. Imperforate stamps may have small margins, and earlier issues may show the design just touching one edge of the stamp design. Very early perforated issues normally will have the perforations slightly cutting into the design. Used stamps may have heavier than usual cancellations.

FINE-VERY FINE stamps will be somewhat off center on one side, or slightly off center on two sides. Imperforate stamps will have two margins of at least normal size, and the design will not touch any edge. For perforated stamps, the perfs are well clear of the design, but are still noticeably off center. *However, early issues of a country may be printed in such a way that the design naturally is very close to the edges. In these cases, the perforations may cut*

into the design very slightly. Used stamps will not have a cancellation that detracts from the design.

VERY FINE stamps will be just slightly off center on one or two sides, but the design will be well clear of the edge. The stamp will present a nice, balanced appearance. Imperforate stamps will be well centered within normal-sized margins. *However, early issues of many countries may be printed in such a way that the perforations may touch the design on one or more sides. Where this is the case, a boxed note will be found defining the centering and margins of the stamps being valued.* Used stamps will have light or otherwise neat cancellations. This is the grade used to establish Scott Catalogue values.

EXTREMELY FINE stamps are close to being perfectly centered. Imperforate stamps will have even margins that are slightly larger than normal. Even the earliest perforated issues will have perforations clear of the design on all sides.

Scott Publishing Co. recognizes that there is no formally enforced grading scheme for postage stamps, and that the final price you pay or obtain for a stamp will be determined by individual agreement at the time of transaction.

Condition

Grade addresses only centering and (for used stamps) cancellation. *Condition* refers to factors other than grade that affect a stamp's desirability.

Factors that can increase the value of a stamp include exceptionally wide margins, particularly fresh color, the presence of selvage, and plate or die varieties. Unusual cancels on used stamps (particularly those of the 19th century) can greatly enhance their value as well.

Factors other than faults that decrease the value of a stamp include loss of original gum, regumming, a hinge remnant or foreign object adhering to the gum, natural inclusions, straight edges, and markings or notations applied by collectors or dealers.

Faults include missing pieces, tears, pin or other holes, surface scuffs, thin spots, creases, toning, short or pulled perforations, clipped perforations, oxidation or other forms of color changelings, soiling, stains, and such man-made changes as reperforations or the chemical removal or lightening of a cancellation.

Grading Illustrations

On the following two pages are illustrations of various stamps from countries appearing in this volume. These stamps are arranged by country, and they represent early or important issues that are often found in widely different grades in the marketplace. The editors believe the illustrations will prove useful in showing the margin size and centering that will be seen on the various issues.

In addition to the matters of margin size and centering, collectors are reminded that the very fine stamps valued in the Scott catalogues also will possess fresh color and intact perforations, and they will be free from defects.

Examples shown are computer-manipulated images made from single digitized master illustrations.

Stamp Illustrations Used in the Catalogue

It is important to note that the stamp images used for identification purposes in this catlaogue may not be indicative of the grade of stamp being valued. Refer to the written discussion of grades on this page and to the grading illustrations on the following two pages for grading information.

Fine-Very Fine →

SCOTT
CATALOGUES
VALUE
STAMPS IN
THIS GRADE

Very Fine →

Extremely Fine →

Fine-Very Fine →

SCOTT
CATALOGUES
VALUE
STAMPS IN
THIS GRADE

Very Fine →

Extremely Fine →

Fine-Very Fine →

SCOTT
CATALOGUES
VALUE
STAMPS IN
THIS GRADE

Very Fine →

Extremely Fine →

Fine-Very Fine →

SCOTT
CATALOGUES
VALUE
STAMPS IN
THIS GRADE

Very Fine →

Extremely Fine →

For purposes of helping to determine the gum condition and value of an unused stamp, Scott Publishing Co. presents the following chart which details different gum conditions and indicates how the conditions correlate with the Scott values for unused stamps. Used together, the Illustrated Grading Chart on the previous pages and this Illustrated Gum Chart should allow catalogue users to better understand the grade and gum condition of stamps valued in the Scott catalogues.

Gum Categories:	MINT N.H.	ORIGINAL GUM (O.G.)				NO GUM
	Mint Never Hinged *Free from any disturbance*	Lightly Hinged *Faint impression of a removed hinge over a small area*	Hinge Mark or Remnant *Prominent hinged spot with part or all of the hinge remaining*	Large part o.g. *Approximately half or more of the gum intact*	Small part o.g. *Approximately less than half of the gum intact*	No gum *Only if issued with gum*
Commonly Used Symbol:	★★	★	★	★	★	(★)
Pre-1900 Issues (Pre-1881 for U.S.)	*Very fine pre-1900 stamps in these categories trade at a premium over Scott value*			Scott Value for "Unused"		Scott "No Gum" listings for selected unused classic stamps
From 1900 to break-points for listings of never-hinged stamps	Scott "Never Hinged" listings for selected unused stamps	Scott Value for "Unused" (Actual value will be affected by the degree of hinging of the full o.g.)				
From breakpoints noted for many countries	Scott Value for "Unused"					

Never Hinged (NH; ★★): A never-hinged stamp will have full original gum that will have no hinge mark or disturbance. The presence of an expertizer's mark does not disqualify a stamp from this designation.

Original Gum (OG; ★): Pre-1900 stamps should have approximately half or more of their original gum. On rarer stamps, it may be expected that the original gum will be somewhat more disturbed than it will be on more common issues. Post-1900 stamps should have full original gum. Original gum will show some disturbance caused by a previous hinge(s) which may be present or entirely removed. The actual value of a post-1900 stamp will be affected by the degree of hinging of the full original gum.

Disturbed Original Gum: Gum showing noticeable effects of humidity, climate or hinging over more than half of the gum. The significance of gum disturbance in valuing a stamp in any of the Original Gum categories depends on the degree of disturbance, the rarity and normal gum condition of the issue and other variables affecting quality.

Regummed (RG; (★)): A regummed stamp is a stamp without gum that has had some type of gum privately applied at a time after it was issued. This normally is done to deceive collectors and/or dealers into thinking that the stamp has original gum and therefore has a higher value. A regummed stamp is considered the same as a stamp with none of its original gum for purposes of grading.

Understanding the Listings

On the opposite page is an enlarged "typical" listing from this catalogue. Below are detailed explanations of each of the highlighted parts of the listing.

1 **Scott number** — Scott catalogue numbers are used to identify specific items when buying, selling or trading stamps. Each listed postage stamp from every country has a unique Scott catalogue number. Therefore, Germany Scott 99, for example, can only refer to a single stamp. Although the Scott catalogue usually lists stamps in chronological order by date of issue, there are exceptions. When a country has issued a set of stamps over a period of time, those stamps within the set are kept together without regard to date of issue. This follows the normal collecting approach of keeping stamps in their natural sets.

When a country issues a set of stamps over a period of time, a group of consecutive catalogue numbers is reserved for the stamps in that set, as issued. If that group of numbers proves to be too few, capital-letter suffixes, such as "A" or "B," may be added to existing numbers to create enough catalogue numbers to cover all items in the set. A capital-letter suffix indicates a major Scott catalogue number listing. Scott uses a suffix letter only once. Therefore, a catalogue number listing with a capital-letter suffix will not also be found with the same letter (lower case) used as a minor-letter listing. If there is a Scott 16A in a set, for example, there will not also be a Scott 16a. However, a minor-letter "a" listing may be added to a major number containing an "A" suffix (Scott 16Aa, for example).

Suffix letters are cumulative. A minor "b" variety of Scott 16A would be Scott 16Ab, not Scott 16b.

There are times when a reserved block of Scott catalogue numbers is too large for a set, leaving some numbers unused. Such gaps in the numbering sequence also occur when the catalogue editors move an item's listing elsewhere or have removed it entirely from the catalogue. Scott does not attempt to account for every possible number, but rather attempts to assure that each stamp is assigned its own number.

Scott numbers designating regular postage normally are only numerals. Scott numbers for other types of stamps, such as air post, semipostal, postal tax, postage due, occupation and others have a prefix consisting of one or more capital letters or a combination of numerals and capital letters.

2 **Illustration number** — Illustration or design-type numbers are used to identify each catalogue illustration. For most sets, the lowest face-value stamp is shown. It then serves as an example of the basic design approach for other stamps not illustrated. Where more than one stamp use the same illustration number, but have differences in design, the design paragraph or the description line clearly indicates the design on each stamp not illustrated. Where there are both vertical and horizontal designs in a set, a single illustration may be used, with the exceptions noted in the design paragraph or description line.

When an illustration is followed by a lower-case letter in parentheses, such as "A2(b)," the trailing letter indicates which overprint or surcharge illustration applies.

Illustrations normally are 70 percent of the original size of the stamp. An effort has been made to note all illustrations not illustrated at that percentage. Virtually all souvenir sheet illustrations are reduced even more. Overprints and surcharges are shown at 100 percent of their original size if shown alone, but are 70 percent of original size if shown on stamps. In some cases, the illustration will be placed above the set, between listings or omitted completely. Overprint and surcharge illustrations are not placed in this catalogue for purposes of expertizing stamps.

3 **Paper color** — The color of a stamp's paper is noted in italic type when the paper used is not white.

4 **Listing styles** — There are two principal types of catalogue listings: major and minor.

Major listings are in a larger type style than minor listings. The catalogue number is a numeral that can be found with or without a capital-letter suffix, and with or without a prefix.

Minor listings are in a smaller type style and have a small-letter suffix or (if the listing immediately follows that of the major number) may show only the letter. These listings identify a variety of the major item.

Examples include perforation, color, watermark or printing method differences, multiples (some souvenir sheets, booklet panes and se-tenant combinations), and singles of multiples.

Examples of major number listings include 16, 28A, B97, C13A, 10N5, and 10N6A. Examples of minor numbers are 16a and C13Ab.

5 **Basic information about a stamp or set** — Introducing each stamp issue is a small section (usually a line listing) of basic information about a stamp or set. This section normally includes the date of issue, method of printing, perforation, watermark and, sometimes, some additional information of note. *Printing method, perforation and watermark apply to the following sets until a change is noted.* Stamps created by overprinting or surcharging previous issues are assumed to have the same perforation, watermark and printing method as the original. Dates of issue are as precise as Scott is able to confirm and often reflect the dates on first-day covers, rather than the actual date of release.

6 **Denomination** — This normally refers to the face value of the stamp; that is, the cost of the unused stamp at the post office at the time of issue. When a denomination is shown in parentheses, it does not appear on the stamp. This includes the non-denominated stamps of the United States, Brazil and Great Britain, for example.

7 **Color or other description** — This area provides information to solidify identification of a stamp. In many recent cases, a description of the stamp design appears in this space, rather than a listing of colors.

8 **Year of issue** — In stamp sets that have been released in a period that spans more than a year, the number shown in parentheses is the year that stamp first appeared. Stamps without a date appeared during the first year of the issue. Dates are not always given for minor varieties.

9 **Value unused and Value used** — The Scott catalogue values are based on stamps that are in a grade of Very Fine unless stated otherwise. Unused values refer to items that have not seen postal, revenue or any other duty for which they were intended. Pre-1900 unused stamps that were issued with gum must have at least most of their original gum. Later issues are assumed to have full original gum. From breakpoints specified in most countries' listings, stamps are valued as never hinged. Stamps issued without gum are noted. Modern issues with PVA or other synthetic adhesives may appear ungummed. Unused self-adhesive stamps are valued as appearing undisturbed on their original backing paper. Values for used self-adhesive stamps are for examples either on piece or off piece. For a more detailed explanation of these values, please see the "Catalogue Value," "Condition" and "Understanding Valuing Notations" sections elsewhere in this introduction.

In some cases, where used stamps are more valuable than unused stamps, the value is for an example with a contemporaneous cancel, rather than a modern cancel or a smudge or other unclear marking. For those stamps that were released for postal and fiscal purposes, the used value represents a postally used stamp. Stamps with revenue cancels generally sell for less.

Stamps separated from a complete se-tenant multiple usually will be worth less than a pro-rated portion of the se-tenant multiple, and stamps lacking the attached labels that are noted in the listings will be worth less than the values shown.

10 **Changes in basic set information** — Bold type is used to show any changes in the basic data given for a set of stamps. This includes perforation differences from one stamp to the next or a different paper, printing method or watermark.

11 **Total value of a set** — The total value of sets of three or more stamps issued after 1900 are shown. The set line also notes the range of Scott numbers and total number of stamps included in the grouping. The actual value of a set consisting predominantly of stamps having the minimum value of twenty cents may be less than the total value shown. Similary, the actual value or catalogue value of se-tenant pairs or of blocks consisting of stamps having the minimum value of twenty cents may be less than the catalogue values of the component parts.

A6

King George VI
A7

BASIC INFORMATION ON STAMP OR SET — 5

DENOMINATION — 6

SCOTT NUMBER — 1

ILLUS. NUMBER — 2

PAPER COLOR — 3

LISTING STYLES — 4

MAJORS

MINORS

COLOR OR OTHER DESCRIPTION — 7

YEAR OF ISSUE — 8

CATALOGUE VALUES — 9
UNUSED
USED

CHANGES IN BASIC SET INFORMATION — 10

TOTAL VALUE OF SET — 11

				Unused	Used
1938-44		**Engr.**		**Perf. 12½**	
54	A6	½p	green	.20	1.50
54A	A6	½p	dk brown ('42)	.20	2.00
55	A6	1p	dark brown	1.75	.35
55A	A6	1p	green ('42)	.20	.90
56	A6	1½p	dark carmine	3.00	4.50
56A	A6	1½p	gray ('42)	.20	5.75
57	A6	2p	gray	4.00	1.25
57A	A6	2p	dark car ('42)	.20	2.00
58	A6	3p	blue	.50	.50
59	A6	4p	rose lilac	1.50	1.25
60	A6	6p	dark violet	2.00	1.25
61	A6	9p	olive bister	2.00	3.25
62	A6	1sh	orange & blk	1.75	2.00

Typo.
Perf. 14
Chalky Paper

63	A7	2sh	ultra & dl vio, *bl*	7.00	11.00
64	A7	2sh6p	red & blk, *bl*	8.00	13.00
65	A7	5sh	red & grn, *yel*	25.00	22.50
a.		5sh dk red & dp grn, *yel* ('44)		55.00	80.00
66	A7	10sh	red & grn, *grn*	35.00	45.00

Wmk. 3

67	A7	£1	blk & vio, *red*	22.50	32.50
		Nos. 54-67 (18)		115.00	150.50
		Set, never hinged		200.00	

National Album Series

The National series offers a panoramic view of our country's heritage through postage stamps. It is the most complete and comprehensive U.S. album series you can buy. There are spaces for every major U.S. stamp listed in the Scott Catalogue, including Special Printings, Newspaper stamps and much more.

- Pages printed on one side.

- All spaces identified by Scott numbers.

- All major variety of stamps are either illustrated or described.

- Chemically neutral paper protects stamps.

- Sold as page units only. Binders, slipcases and labels sold separately.

Item			Retail
100NTL1	1845-1934	108 pgs	$39.95
100NTL2	1935-1976	108 pgs	$39.95
100NTL3	1977-1993	114 pgs	$39.95
100NTL4	1994-1999	100 pgs	$39.95
100NTL5	2000-2004	108 pgs	$39.95

Supplemented in March.

U.S. National Kit

The most complete and comprehensive U.S. stamp album is now available in a money-saving complete kit package! This kit contains all five National album parts, 4 large National Series 3-ring binders, slipcases, protector sheets and National album labels, pre-cut value pack of black ScottMounts and the *U.S. Specialized Catalogue*.

Item	Retail
NATLKIT	$519.99

What ever your collecting specialty Scott Publishing has an album for you. For more information on the entire line of Scott albums and products visit your local stamp dealer or online at:
www.amosadvantage.com

SCOTT.

1-800-572-6885
P.O. BOX 828
Sidney OH 45365
www.amosadvantage.com

AMOS
PUBLISHING

Catalogue Listing Policy

It is the intent of Scott Publishing Co. to list all postage stamps of the world in the *Scott Standard Postage Stamp Catalogue*. The only strict criteria for listing is that stamps be decreed legal for postage by the issuing country and that the issuing country actually have an operating postal system. Whether the primary intent of issuing a given stamp or set was for sale to postal patrons or to stamp collectors is not part of our listing criteria. Scott's role is to provide basic comprehensive postage stamp information. It is up to each stamp collector to choose which items to include in a collection.

It is Scott's objective to seek reasons why a stamp should be listed, rather than why it should not. Nevertheless, there are certain types of items that will not be listed. These include the following:

1. Unissued items that are not officially distributed or released by the issuing postal authority. If such items are officially issued at a later date by the country, they will be listed. Unissued items consist of those that have been printed and then held from sale for reasons such as change in government, errors found on stamps or something deemed objectionable about a stamp subject or design.

2. Stamps "issued" by non-existent postal entities or fantasy countries, such as Nagaland, Occusi-Ambeno, Staffa, Sedang, Torres Straits and others. Also, stamps "issued" in the names of legitimate, stamp-issuing countries that are not authorized by those countries.

3. Semi-official or unofficial items not required for postage. Examples include items issued by private agencies for their own express services. When such items are required for delivery, or are valid as prepayment of postage, they are listed.

4. Local stamps issued for local use only. Postage stamps issued by governments specifically for "domestic" use, such as Haiti Scott 219-228, or the United States non-denominated stamps, are not considered to be locals, since they are valid for postage throughout the country of origin.

5. Items not valid for postal use. For example, a few countries have issued souvenir sheets that are not valid for postage. This area also includes a number of worldwide charity labels (some denominated) that do not pay postage.

6. Intentional varieties, such as imperforate stamps that look like their perforated counterparts and are usually issued in very small quantities. Also, other egregiously exploitative issues such as stamps sold for far more than face value, stamps purposefully issued in artificially small quantities or only against advance orders, stamps awarded only to a selected audience such as a philatelic bureau's standing order customers, or stamps sold only in conjunction with other products. All of these kinds of items are usually controlled issues and/or are intended for speculation. These items normally will be included in a footnote.

7. Items distributed by the issuing government only to a limited group, club, philatelic exhibition or a single stamp dealer or other private company. These items normally will be included in a footnote.

The fact that a stamp has been used successfully as postage, even on international mail, is not in itself sufficient proof that it was legitimately issued. Numerous examples of so-called stamps from non-existent countries are known to have been used to post letters that have successfully passed through the international mail system.

There are certain items that are subject to interpretation. When a stamp falls outside our specifications, it may be listed along with a cautionary footnote.

A number of factors are considered in our approach to analyzing how a stamp is listed. The following list of factors is presented to share with you, the catalogue user, the complexity of the listing process.

Additional printings — "Additional printings" of a previously issued stamp may range from an item that is totally different to cases where it is impossible to differentiate from the original. At least a minor number (a small-letter suffix) is assigned if there is a distinct change in stamp shade, noticeably redrawn design, or a significantly different perforation measurement. A major number (numeral or capital-letter combination) is assigned if the editors feel the "additional printing" is sufficiently different from the original that it constitutes a different issue.

Commemoratives — Where practical, commemoratives with the same theme are placed in a set. For example, the U.S. Civil War Centennial set of 1961-65 and the Constitution Bicentennial series of 1989-90 appear as sets. Countries such as Japan and Korea issue such material on a regular basis, with an announced, or at least predictable, number of stamps known in advance. Occasionally, however, stamp sets that were released over a period of years have been separated. Appropriately placed footnotes will guide you to each set's continuation.

Definitive sets — Blocks of numbers generally have been reserved for definitive sets, based on previous experience with any given country. If a few more stamps were issued in a set than originally expected, they often have been inserted into the original set with a capital-letter suffix, such as U.S. Scott 1059A. If it appears that many more stamps than the originally allotted block will be released before the set is completed, a new block of numbers will be reserved, with the original one being closed off. In some cases, such as the U.S. Transportation and Great Americans series, several blocks of numbers exist. Appropriately placed footnotes will guide you to each set's continuation.

New country — Membership in the Universal Postal Union is not a consideration for listing status or order of placement within the catalogue. The index will tell you in what volume or page number the listings begin.

"No release date" items — The amount of information available for any given stamp issue varies greatly from country to country and even from time to time. Extremely comprehensive information about new stamps is available from some countries well before the stamps are released. By contrast some countries do not provide information about stamps or release dates. Most countries, however, fall between these extremes. A country may provide denominations or subjects of stamps from upcoming issues that are not issued as planned. Sometimes, philatelic agencies, those private firms hired to represent countries, add these later-issued items to sets well after the formal release date. This time period can range from weeks to years. If these items were officially released by the country, they will be added to the appropriate spot in the set. In many cases, the specific release date of a stamp or set of stamps may never be known.

Overprints — The color of an overprint is always noted if it is other than black. Where more than one color of ink has been used on overprints of a single set, the color used is noted. Early overprint and surcharge illustrations were altered to prevent their use by forgers.

Se-tenants — Connected stamps of differing features (se-tenants) will be listed in the format most commonly collected. This includes pairs, blocks or larger multiples. Se-tenant units are not always symmetrical. An example is Australia Scott 508, which is a block of seven stamps. If the stamps are primarily collected as a unit, the major number may be assigned to the multiple, with minors going to each component stamp. In cases where continuous-design or other unit se-tenants will receive significant postal use, each stamp is given a major Scott number listing. This includes issues from the United States, Canada, Germany and Great Britain, for example.

Special Notices

Classification of stamps

The *Scott Standard Postage Stamp Catalogue* lists stamps by country of issue. The next level of organization is a listing by section on the basis of the function of the stamps. The principal sections cover regular postage, semi-postal, air post, special delivery, registration, postage due and other categories. Except for regular postage, catalogue numbers for all sections include a prefix letter (or number-letter combination) denoting the class to which a given stamp belongs. When some countries issue sets containing stamps from more than one category, the catalogue will at times list all of the stamps in one category (such as air post stamps listed as part of a postage set).

The following is a listing of the most commonly used catalogue prefixes.

Prefix	Category
C	Air Post
M	Military
P	Newspaper
N	Occupation - Regular Issues
O	Official
Q	Parcel Post
J	Postage Due
RA	Postal Tax
B	Semi-Postal
E	Special Delivery
MR	War Tax

Other prefixes used by more than one country include the following:

H	Acknowledgment of Receipt
I	Late Fee
CO	Air Post Official
CQ	Air Post Parcel Post
RAC	Air Post Postal Tax
CF	Air Post Registration
CB	Air Post Semi-Postal
CBO	Air Post Semi-Postal Official
CE	Air Post Special Delivery
EY	Authorized Delivery
S	Franchise
G	Insured Letter
GY	Marine Insurance
MC	Military Air Post
MQ	Military Parcel Post
NC	Occupation - Air Post
NO	Occupation - Official
NJ	Occupation - Postage Due
NRA	Occupation - Postal Tax
NB	Occupation - Semi-Postal
NE	Occupation - Special Delivery
QY	Parcel Post Authorized Delivery
AR	Postal-fiscal
RAJ	Postal Tax Due
RAB	Postal Tax Semi-Postal
F	Registration
EB	Semi-Postal Special Delivery
EO	Special Delivery Official
QE	Special Handling

New issue listings

Updates to this catalogue appear each month in the *Scott Stamp Monthly* magazine. Included in this update are additions to the listings of countries found in the *Scott Standard Postage Stamp Catalogue* and the *Specialized Catalogue of United States Stamps*, as well as corrections and updates to current editions of this catalogue.

From time to time there will be changes in the final listings of stamps from the *Scott Stamp Monthly* to the next edition of the catalogue. This occurs as more information about certain stamps or sets becomes available.

The catalogue update section of the *Scott Stamp Monthly* is the most timely presentation of this material available. Annual subscriptions to the *Scott Stamp Monthly* are available from Scott Publishing Co., Box 828, Sidney, OH 45365-0828.

Number additions, deletions & changes

A listing of catalogue number additions, deletions and changes from the previous edition of the catalogue appears in each volume. See Catalogue Number Additions, Deletions & Changes in the table of contents for the location of this list.

Understanding valuing notations

The *minimum catalogue value* of an individual stamp or set is 20 cents. This represents a portion of the cost incurred by a dealer when he prepares an individual stamp for resale. As a point of philatelic-economic fact, the lower the value shown for an item in this catalogue, the greater the percentage of that value is attributed to dealer mark up and profit margin. In many cases, such as the 20-cent minimum value, that price does not cover the labor or other costs involved with stocking it as an individual stamp. The sum of minimum values in a set does not properly represent the value of a complete set primarily composed of a number of minimum-value stamps, nor does the sum represent the actual value of a packet made up of minimum-value stamps. Thus a packet of 1,000 different common stamps — each of which has a catalogue value of 20-cents — normally sells for considerably less than 200 dollars!

The *absence of a retail value* for a stamp does not necessarily suggest that a stamp is scarce or rare. A dash in the value column means that the stamp is known in a stated form or variety, but information is either lacking or insufficient for purposes of establishing a usable catalogue value.

Stamp values in *italics* generally refer to items that are difficult to value accurately. For expensive items, such as those priced at $1,000 or higher, a value in italics indicates that the affected item trades very seldom. For inexpensive items, a value in italics represents a warning. One example is a "blocked" issue where the issuing postal administration may have controlled one stamp in a set in an attempt to make the whole set more valuable. Another example is an item that sold at an extreme multiple of face value in the marketplace at the time of its issue.

One type of warning to collectors that appears in the catalogue is illustrated by a stamp that is valued considerably higher in used condition than it is as unused. In this case, collectors are cautioned to be certain the used version has a genuine and contemporaneous cancellation. The type of cancellation on a stamp can be an important factor in determining its sale price. Catalogue values do not apply to fiscal, telegraph or non-contemporaneous postal cancels, unless otherwise noted.

Some countries have released back issues of stamps in canceled-to-order form, sometimes covering as much as a 10-year period. The Scott Catalogue values for used stamps reflect canceled-to-order material when such stamps are found to predominate in the marketplace for the issue involved. Notes frequently appear in the stamp listings to specify which items are valued as canceled-to-order, or if there is a premium for postally used examples.

Many countries sell canceled-to-order stamps at a marked reduction of face value. Countries that sell or have sold canceled-to-order stamps at *full* face value include United Nations, Australia, Netherlands, France and Switzerland. It may be almost impossible to identify such stamps if the gum has been removed, because official government canceling devices are used. Postally used copies of these items on cover, however, are usually worth more than the canceled-to-order stamps with original gum.

Abbreviations

Scott Publishing Co. uses a consistent set of abbreviations throughout this catalogue to conserve space, while still providing necessary information.

COLOR ABBREVIATIONS

amb .amber	crim .crimson	ol .....olive
anil ..aniline	cr .....cream	olvn .olivine
ap ....apple	dk .....dark	org ...orange
aqua.aquamarine	dl .....dull	pck...peacock
az.....azure	dp .....deep	pnksh pinkish
bis....bister	db ....drab	Prus .Prussian
bl .....blue	emer emerald	pur...purple
bld ...blood	gldn .golden	redsh reddish
blk ....black	grysh grayish	res....reseda
bril ...brilliant	grn ...green	ros ...rosine
brn...brown	grnsh greenish	ryl ....royal
brnsh brownish	hel ....heliotrope	sal ....salmon
brnz .bronze	hn ....henna	saph .sapphire
brt....bright	ind ...indigo	scar ..scarlet
brnt..burnt	int....intense	sep ...sepia
car ...carmine	lav....lavender	sien ..sienna
cer ...cerise	lem ...lemon	sil .....silver
chlky chalky	lil .....lilac	sl ......slate
cham chamois	lt ......light	stl .....steel
chnt .chestnut	mag..magenta	turq..turquoise
choc.chocolate	man ..manila	ultra..ultramarine
chr...chrome	mar ...maroon	Ven ..Venetian
cit ....citron	mv ...mauve	ver ...vermilion
cl .....claret	multi multicolored	vio ...violet
cob...cobalt	mlky milky	yel....yellow
cop...copper	myr ..myrtle	yelsh yellowish

When no color is given for an overprint or surcharge, black is the color used. Abbreviations for colors used for overprints and surcharges include: "(B)" or "(Blk)," black; "(Bl)," blue; "(R)," red; and "(G)," green.

Additional abbreviations in this catalogue are shown below:

Adm.............	Administration
AFL.............	American Federation of Labor
Anniv.	Anniversary
APS.............	American Philatelic Society
Assoc.	Association
ASSR...........	Autonomous Soviet Socialist Republic
b.	Born
BEP.............	Bureau of Engraving and Printing
Bicent.	Bicentennial
Bklt.............	Booklet
Brit.	British
btwn............	Between
Bur.	Bureau
c. or ca.........	Circa
Cat.............	Catalogue
Cent............	Centennial, century, centenary
CIO.............	Congress of Industrial Organizations
Conf............	Conference
Cong...........	Congress
Cpl..............	Corporal
CTO............	Canceled to order
d.	Died
Dbl..............	Double
EKU	Earliest known use
Engr.	Engraved
Exhib.	Exhibition
Expo.	Exposition
Fed.	Federation
GB	Great Britain
Gen.............	General
GPO............	General post office
Horiz...........	Horizontal
Imperf..........	Imperforate
Impt............	Imprint

Intl..............	International
Invtd............	Inverted
L	Left
Lieut., lt.	Lieutenant
Litho.	Lithographed
LL	Lower left
LR	Lower right
mm	Millimeter
Ms.	Manuscript
Natl.............	National
No.	Number
NY	New York
NYC............	New York City
Ovpt.	Overprint
Ovptd..........	Overprinted
P	Plate number
Perf.............	Perforated, perforation
Phil.	Philatelic
Photo.	Photogravure
PO	Post office
Pr.................	Pair
P.R.	Puerto Rico
Prec.	Precancel, precanceled
Pres.............	President
PTT.............	Post, Telephone and Telegraph
Rio	Rio de Janeiro
Sgt.	Sergeant
Soc..............	Society
Souv.	Souvenir
SSR	Soviet Socialist Republic, see ASSR
St.	Saint, street
Surch.	Surcharge
Typo............	Typographed
UL	Upper left
Unwmkd......	Unwatermarked
UPU............	Universal Postal Union
UR	Upper Right
US...............	United States
USPOD	United States Post Office Department
USSR...........	Union of Soviet Socialist Republics
Vert.............	Vertical
VP	Vice president
Wmk............	Watermark
Wmkd..........	Watermarked
WWI	World War I
WWII..........	World War II

Examination

Scott Publishing Co. will not comment upon the genuineness, grade or condition of stamps, because of the time and responsibility involved. Rather, there are several expertizing groups that undertake this work for both collectors and dealers. Neither will Scott Publishing Co. appraise or identify philatelic material. The company cannot take responsibility for unsolicited stamps or covers sent by individuals.

All letters, E-mails, etc. are read attentively, but they are not always answered due to time considerations.

How to order from your dealer

When ordering stamps from a dealer, it is not necessary to write the full description of a stamp as listed in this catalogue. All you need is the name of the country, the Scott catalogue number and whether the desired item is unused or used. For example, "Japan Scott 422 unused" is sufficient to identify the unused stamp of Japan listed as "422 A206 5y brown."

Basic Stamp Information

A stamp collector's knowledge of the combined elements that make a given stamp issue unique determines his or her ability to identify stamps. These elements include paper, watermark, method of separation, printing, design and gum. On the following pages each of these important areas is briefly described.

Paper

Paper is an organic material composed of a compacted weave of cellulose fibers and generally formed into sheets. Paper used to print stamps may be manufactured in sheets, or it may have been part of a large roll (called a web) before being cut to size. The fibers most often used to create paper on which stamps are printed include bark, wood, straw and certain grasses. In many cases, linen or cotton rags have been added for greater strength and durability. Grinding, bleaching, cooking and rinsing these raw fibers reduces them to a slushy pulp, referred to by paper makers as "stuff." Sizing and, sometimes, coloring matter is added to the pulp to make different types of finished paper.

After the stuff is prepared, it is poured onto sieve-like frames that allow the water to run off, while retaining the matted pulp. As fibers fall onto the screen and are held by gravity, they form a natural weave that will later hold the paper together. If the screen has metal bits that are formed into letters or images attached, it leaves slightly thinned areas on the paper. These are called watermarks.

When the stuff is almost dry, it is passed under pressure through smooth or engraved rollers - dandy rolls - or placed between cloth in a press to be flattened and dried.

Stamp paper falls broadly into two types: wove and laid. The nature of the surface of the frame onto which the pulp is first deposited causes the differences in appearance between the two. If the surface is smooth and even, the paper will be of fairly uniform texture throughout. This is known as *wove paper*. Early papermaking machines poured the pulp onto a continuously circulating web of felt, but modern machines feed the pulp onto a cloth-like screen made of closely interwoven fine wires. This paper, when held to a light, will show little dots or points very close together. The proper name for this is "wire wove," but the type is still considered wove. Any U.S. or British stamp printed after 1880 will serve as an example of wire wove paper.

Closely spaced parallel wires, with cross wires at wider intervals, make up the frames used for what is known as *laid paper*. A greater thickness of the pulp will settle between the wires. The paper, when held to a light, will show alternate light and dark lines. The spacing and the thickness of the lines may vary, but on any one sheet of paper they are all alike. See Russia Scott 31-38 for examples of laid paper.

Batonne, from the French word meaning "a staff," is a term used if the lines in the paper are spaced quite far apart, like the printed ruling on a writing tablet. Batonne paper may be either wove or laid. If laid, fine laid lines can be seen between the batons.

Quadrille is the term used when the lines in the paper form little squares. *Oblong quadrille* is the term used when rectangles, rather than squares, are formed. See Mexico-Guadalajara Scott 35-37 for examples of oblong quadrille paper.

Paper also is classified as thick or thin, hard or soft, and by color if dye is added during manufacture. Such colors may include yellowish, greenish, bluish and reddish.

Brief explanations of other types of paper used for printing stamps, as well as examples, follow.

Pelure — Pelure paper is a very thin, hard and often brittle paper that is sometimes bluish or grayish in appearance. See Serbia Scott 169-170.

Native — This is a term applied to handmade papers used to produce some of the early stamps of the Indian states. Stamps printed on native paper may be expected to display various natural inclusions that are normal and do not negatively affect value. Japanese paper, originally made of mulberry fibers and rice flour, is part of this group. See Japan Scott 1-18.

Manila — This type of paper is often used to make stamped envelopes and wrappers. It is a coarse-textured stock, usually smooth on one side and rough on the other. A variety of colors of manila paper exist, but the most common range is yellowish-brown.

Silk — Introduced by the British in 1847 as a safeguard against counterfeiting, silk paper contains bits of colored silk thread scattered throughout. The density of these fibers varies greatly and can include as few as one fiber per stamp or hundreds. U.S. revenue Scott R152 is a good example of an easy-to-identify silk paper stamp.

Silk-thread paper has uninterrupted threads of colored silk arranged so that one or more threads run through the stamp or postal stationery. See Great Britain Scott 5-6 and Switzerland Scott 14-19.

Granite — Filled with minute cloth or colored paper fibers of various colors and lengths, granite paper should not be confused with either type of silk paper. Austria Scott 172-175 and a number of Swiss stamps are examples of granite paper.

Chalky — A chalk-like substance coats the surface of chalky paper to discourage the cleaning and reuse of canceled stamps, as well as to provide a smoother, more acceptable printing surface. Because the designs of stamps printed on chalky paper are imprinted on what is often a water-soluble coating, any attempt to remove a cancellation will destroy the stamp. *Do not soak these stamps in any fluid.* To remove a stamp printed on chalky paper from an envelope, wet the paper from underneath the stamp until the gum dissolves enough to release the stamp from the paper. See St. Kitts-Nevis Scott 89-90 for examples of stamps printed on this type of chalky paper.

India — Another name for this paper, originally introduced from China about 1750, is "China Paper." It is a thin, opaque paper often used for plate and die proofs by many countries.

Double — In philately, the term double paper has two distinct meanings. The first is a two-ply paper, usually a combination of a thick and a thin sheet, joined during manufacture. This type was used experimentally as a means to discourage the reuse of stamps.

The design is printed on the thin paper. Any attempt to remove a cancellation would destroy the design. U.S. Scott 158 and other Banknote-era stamps exist on this form of double paper.

The second type of double paper occurs on a rotary press, when the end of one paper roll, or web, is affixed to the next roll to save time feeding the paper through the press. Stamp designs are printed over the joined paper and, if overlooked by inspectors, may get into post office stocks.

Goldbeater's Skin — This type of paper was used for the 1866 issue of Prussia, and was a tough, translucent paper. The design was printed in reverse on the back of the stamp, and the gum applied over the printing. It is impossible to remove stamps printed on this type of paper from the paper to which they are affixed without destroying the design.

Ribbed — Ribbed paper has an uneven, corrugated surface made by passing the paper through ridged rollers. This type exists on some copies of U.S. Scott 156-165.

Various other substances, or substrates, have been used for stamp manufacture, including wood, aluminum, copper, silver and gold foil, plastic, and silk and cotton fabrics.

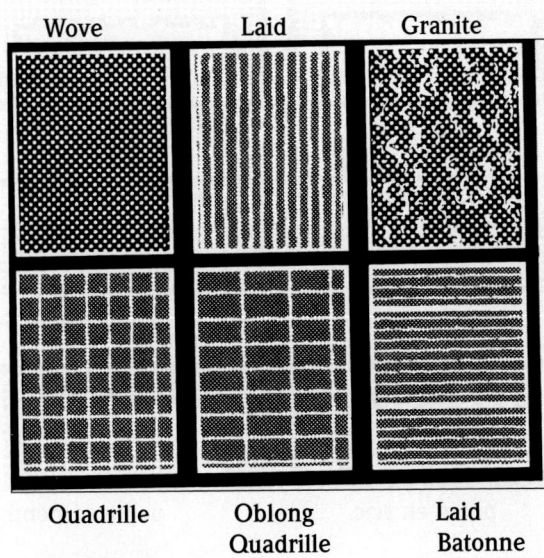

Wove   Laid   Granite

Quadrille   Oblong Quadrille   Laid Batonne

Watermarks

Watermarks are an integral part of some papers. They are formed in the process of paper manufacture. Watermarks consist of small designs, formed of wire or cut from metal and soldered to the surface of the mold or, sometimes, on the dandy roll. The designs may be in the form of crowns, stars, anchors, letters or other characters or symbols. These pieces of metal - known in the paper-making industry as "bits" - impress a design into the paper. The design sometimes may be seen by holding the stamp to the light. Some are more easily seen with a watermark detector. This important tool is a small black tray into which a stamp is placed face down and dampened with a fast-evaporating watermark detection fluid that brings up the watermark image in the form of dark lines against a lighter background. These dark lines are the thinner areas of the paper known as the watermark. Some watermarks are extremely difficult to locate, due to either a faint impression, watermark location or the color of the stamp. There also are electric watermark detectors that come with plastic filter disks of various colors. The disks neutralize the color of the stamp, permitting the watermark to be seen more easily.

Multiple watermarks of Crown Agents and Burma

Watermarks of Uruguay, Vatican City and Jamaica

WARNING: Some inks used in the photogravure process dissolve in watermark fluids (Please see the section on Soluble Printing Inks). Also, see "chalky paper."
Watermarks may be found normal, reversed, inverted, reversed and inverted, sideways or diagonal, as seen from the back of the stamp. The relationship of watermark to stamp design depends on the position of the printing plates or how paper is fed through the press. On machine-made paper, watermarks normally are read from right to left. The design is repeated closely throughout the sheet in a "multiple-watermark design." In a "sheet watermark," the design appears only once on the sheet, but extends over many stamps. Individual stamps may carry only a small fraction or none of the watermark.

"Marginal watermarks" occur in the margins of sheets or panes of stamps. They occur on the outside border of paper (ostensibly outside the area where stamps are to be printed). A large row of letters may spell the name of the country or the manufacturer of the paper, or a border of lines may appear. Careless press feeding may cause parts of these letters and/or lines to show on stamps of the outer row of a pane.

Soluble Printing Inks

WARNING: Most stamp colors are permanent; that is, they are not seriously affected by short-term exposure to light or water. Many colors, especially of modern inks, fade from excessive exposure to light. There are stamps printed with inks that dissolve easily in water or in fluids used to detect watermarks. Use of these inks was intentional to prevent the removal of cancellations. Water affects all aniline inks, those on so-called safety paper and some photogravure printings - all such inks are known as *fugitive colors. Removal from paper of such stamps requires care and alternatives to traditional soaking.*

Separation

"Separation" is the general term used to describe methods used to separate stamps. The three standard forms currently in use are perforating, rouletting and die-cutting. These methods are done during the stamp production process, after printing. Sometimes these methods are done on-press or sometimes as a separate step. The earliest issues, such as the 1840 Penny Black of Great Britain (Scott 1), did not have any means provided for separation. It was expected the stamps would be cut apart with scissors or folded and torn. These are examples of imperforate stamps. Many stamps were first issued in imperforate formats and were later issued with perforations. Therefore, care must be observed in buying single imperforate stamps to be certain they were issued imperforate and are not perforated copies that have been altered by having the perforations trimmed away. Stamps issued imperforate usually are valued as singles. However, imperforate varieties of normally perforated stamps should be collected in pairs or larger pieces as indisputable evidence of their imperforate character.

PERFORATION

The chief style of separation of stamps, and the one that is in almost universal use today, is perforating. By this process, paper between the stamps is cut away in a line of holes, usually round, leaving little bridges of paper between the stamps to hold them together. Some types of perforation, such as hyphen-hole perfs, can be confused with roulettes, but a close visual inspection reveals that paper has been removed. The little perforation bridges, which project from the stamp when it is torn from the pane, are called the teeth of the perforation.

As the size of the perforation is sometimes the only way to differentiate between two otherwise identical stamps, it is necessary to be able to accurately measure and describe them. This is done with a perforation gauge, usually a ruler-like device that has dots or graduated lines to show how many perforations may be counted in the space of two centimeters. Two centimeters is the space universally adopted in which to measure perforations.

Perforation gauge

perce en arc   perce en lignes

perce en points   oblique roulette

perce en scie   perce serpentin

To measure a stamp, run it along the gauge until the dots on it fit exactly into the perforations of the stamp. If you are using a graduated-line perforation gauge, simply slide the stamp along the surface until the lines on the gauge perfectly project from the center of the bridges or holes. The number to the side of the line of dots or lines that fit the stamp's perforation is the measurement. For example, an "11" means that 11 perforations fit between two centimeters. The description of the stamp therefore is "perf. 11." If the gauge of the perforations on the top and bottom of a stamp differs from that on the sides, the result is what is known as *compound perforations*. In measuring compound perforations, the gauge at top and bottom is always given first, then the sides. Thus, a stamp that measures 11 at top and bottom and 10 1/2 at the sides is "perf. 11 x 10 1/2." See U.S. Scott 632-642 for examples of compound perforations.

Stamps also are known with perforations different on three or all four sides. Descriptions of such items are clockwise, beginning with the top of the stamp.

A perforation with small holes and teeth close together is a "fine perforation." One with large holes and teeth far apart is a "coarse perforation." Holes that are jagged, rather than clean-cut, are "rough perforations." *Blind perforations* are the slight impressions left by the perforating pins if they fail to puncture the paper. Multiples of stamps showing blind perforations may command a slight premium over normally perforated stamps.

The term *syncopated perfs* describes intentional irregularities in the perforations. The earliest form was used by the Netherlands from 1925-33, where holes were omitted to create distinctive patterns. Beginning in 1992, Great Britain has used an oval perforation to help prevent counterfeiting. Several other countries have started using the oval perfs or other syncopated perf patterns.

A new type of perforation, still primarily used for postal stationery, is known as microperfs. Microperfs are tiny perforations (in some cases hundreds of holes per two centimeters) that allows items to be intentionally separated very easily, while not accidentally breaking apart as easily as standard perforations. These are not currently measured or differentiated by size, as are standard perforations.

ROULETTING

In rouletting, the stamp paper is cut partly or wholly through, with no paper removed. In perforating, some paper is removed. Rouletting derives its name from the French roulette, a spur-like wheel. As the wheel is rolled over the paper, each point makes a small cut. The number of cuts made in a two-centimeter space determines the gauge of the roulette, just as the number of perforations in two centimeters determines the gauge of the perforation.

The shape and arrangement of the teeth on the wheels varies. Various roulette types generally carry French names:

Perce en lignes - rouletted in lines. The paper receives short, straight cuts in lines. This is the most common type of rouletting. See Mexico Scott 500.

Perce en points - pin-rouletted or pin-perfed. This differs from a small perforation because no paper is removed, although round, equidistant holes are pricked through the paper. See Mexico Scott 242-256.

Perce en arc and *perce en scie* - pierced in an arc or saw-toothed designs, forming half circles or small triangles. See Hanover (German States) Scott 25-29.

Perce en serpentin - serpentine roulettes. The cuts form a serpentine or wavy line. See Brunswick (German States) Scott 13-18.

Once again, no paper is removed by these processes, leaving the stamps easily separated, but closely attached.

DIE-CUTTING

The third major form of stamp separation is die-cutting. This is a method where a die in the pattern of separation is created that later cuts the stamp paper in a stroke motion. Although some standard stamps bear die-cut perforations, this process is primarily used for self-adhesive postage stamps. Die-cutting can appear in straight lines, such as U.S. Scott 2522, shapes, such as U.S. Scott 1551, or imitating the appearance of perforations, such as New Zealand Scott 935A and 935B.

Printing Processes

ENGRAVING (Intaglio, Line-engraving, Etching)

Master die — The initial operation in the process of line engraving is making the master die. The die is a small, flat block of softened steel upon which the stamp design is recess engraved in reverse.

Master die

Photographic reduction of the original art is made to the appropriate size. It then serves as a tracing guide for the initial outline of the design. The engraver lightly traces the design on the steel with his graver, then slowly works the design until it is completed. At various points during the engraving process, the engraver hand-inks the die and makes an impression to check his progress. These are known as progressive die proofs. After completion of the engraving, the die is hardened to withstand the stress and pressures of later transfer operations.

Transfer roll

Transfer roll — Next is production of the transfer roll that, as the name implies, is the medium used to transfer the subject from the master die to the printing plate. A blank roll of soft steel, mounted on a mandrel, is placed under the bearers of the transfer press to allow it to roll freely on its axis. The hardened die is placed on the bed of the press and the face of the transfer roll is applied to the die, under pressure. The bed or the roll is then rocked back and forth under increasing pressure, until the soft steel of the roll is forced into every engraved line of the die. The resulting impression on the roll is known as a "relief" or a "relief transfer." The engraved image is now positive in appearance and stands out from the steel. After the required number of reliefs are "rocked in," the soft steel transfer roll is hardened.

Different flaws may occur during the relief process. A defective relief may occur during the rocking in process because of a minute piece of foreign material lodging on the die, or some other cause. Imperfections in the steel of the transfer roll may result in a breaking away of parts of the design. This is known as a relief break, which will show up on finished stamps as small, unprinted areas. If a damaged relief remains in use, it will transfer a repeating defect to the plate. Deliberate alterations of reliefs sometimes occur. "Altered reliefs" designate these changed conditions.

Plate — The final step in pre-printing production is the making of the printing plate. A flat piece of soft steel replaces the die on the bed of the transfer press. One of the reliefs on the transfer roll is positioned over this soft steel. Position, or layout, dots determine the correct position on the plate. The dots have been lightly marked on

the plate in advance. After the correct position of the relief is determined, the design is rocked in by following the same method used in making the transfer roll. The difference is that this time the image is being transferred from the transfer roll, rather than to it. Once the design is entered on the plate, it appears in reverse and is recessed. There are as many transfers entered on the plate as there are subjects printed on the sheet of stamps. It is during this process that double and shifted transfers occur, as well as re-entries. These are the result of improperly entered images that have not been properly burnished out prior to rocking in a new image.

Modern siderography processes, such as those used by the U.S. Bureau of Engraving and Printing, involve an automated form of rocking designs in on preformed cylindrical printing sleeves. The same process also allows for easier removal and re-entry of worn images right on the sleeve.

Transferring the design to the plate

Following the entering of the required transfers on the plate, the position dots, layout dots and lines, scratches and other markings generally are burnished out. Added at this time by the siderographer are any required *guide lines, plate numbers* or other *marginal markings.* The plate is then hand-inked and a proof impression is taken. This is known as a plate proof. If the impression is approved, the plate is machined for fitting onto the press, is hardened and sent to the plate vault ready for use.

On press, the plate is inked and the surface is automatically wiped clean, leaving ink only in the recessed lines. Paper is then forced under pressure into the engraved recessed lines, thereby receiving the ink. Thus, the ink lines on engraved stamps are slightly raised, and slight depressions (debossing) occur on the back of the stamp. Prior to the advent of modern high-speed presses and more advanced ink formulations, paper had to be dampened before receiving the ink. This sometimes led to uneven shrinkage by the time the stamps were perforated, resulting in improperly perforated stamps, or misperfs. Newer presses use drier paper, thus both *wet* and *dry printings* exist on some stamps.

Rotary Press — Until 1914, only flat plates were used to print engraved stamps. Rotary press printing was introduced in 1914, and slowly spread. Some countries still use flat-plate printing.

After approval of the plate proof, older *rotary press plates* require additional machining. They are curved to fit the press cylinder. "Gripper slots" are cut into the back of each plate to receive the "grippers," which hold the plate securely on the press. The plate is then hardened. Stamps printed from these bent rotary press plates are longer or wider than the same stamps printed from flat-plate presses. The stretching of the plate during the curving process is what causes this distortion.

Re-entry — To execute a re-entry on a flat plate, the transfer roll is re-applied to the plate, often at some time after its first use on the press. Worn-out designs can be resharpened by carefully burnishing out the original image and re-entering it from the transfer roll. If the original impression has not been sufficiently removed and the transfer roll is not precisely in line with the remaining impression, the resulting double transfer will make the re-entry obvious. If the registration is true, a re-entry may be difficult or impossible to distinguish. Sometimes a stamp printed from a successful re-entry is identified by having a much sharper and clearer impression than its neighbors. With the advent of rotary presses, post-press re-entries were not possible. After a plate was curved for the rotary press, it was impossible to make a re-entry. This is because the plate had already been bent once (with the design distorted).

However, with the introduction of the previously mentioned modern-style siderography machines, entries are made to the pre-formed cylindrical printing sleeve. Such sleeves are dechromed and softened. This allows individual images to be burnished out and re-entered on the curved sleeve. The sleeve is then rechromed, resulting in longer press life.

Double Transfer — This is a description of the condition of a transfer on a plate that shows evidence of a duplication of all, or a portion of the design. It usually is the result of the changing of the registration between the transfer roll and the plate during the rocking in of the original entry. Double transfers also occur when only a portion of the design has been rocked in and improper positioning is noted. If the worker elected not to burnish out the partial or completed design, a strong double transfer will occur for part or all of the design.

It sometimes is necessary to remove the original transfer from a plate and repeat the process a second time. If the finished re-worked image shows traces of the original impression, attributable to incomplete burnishing, the result is a partial double transfer.

With the modern automatic machines mentioned previously, double transfers are all but impossible to create. Those partially doubled images on stamps printed from such sleeves are more than likely re-entries, rather than true double transfers.

Re-engraved — Alterations to a stamp design are sometimes necessary after some stamps have been printed. In some cases, either the original die or the actual printing plate may have its "temper" drawn (softened), and the design will be re-cut. The resulting impressions from such a re-engraved die or plate may differ slightly from the original issue, and are known as "re-engraved." If the alteration was made to the master die, all future printings will be consistently different from the original. If alterations were made to the printing plate, each altered stamp on the plate will be slightly different from each other, allowing specialists to reconstruct a complete printing plate.

Dropped Transfers — If an impression from the transfer roll has not been properly placed, a dropped transfer may occur. The final stamp image will appear obviously out of line with its neighbors.

Short Transfer — Sometimes a transfer roll is not rocked its entire length when entering a transfer onto a plate. As a result, the finished transfer on the plate fails to show the complete design, and the finished stamp will have an incomplete design printed. This is known as a "short transfer." U.S. Scott No. 8 is a good example of a short transfer.

TYPOGRAPHY (Letterpress, Surface Printing, Flexography, Dry Offset, High Etch)

Although the word "Typography" is obsolete as a term describing a printing method, it was the accepted term throughout the first century of postage stamps. Therefore, appropriate Scott listings in this catalogue refer to typographed stamps. The current term for this form of printing, however, is "letterpress."

As it relates to the production of postage stamps, letterpress printing is the reverse of engraving. Rather than having recessed areas trap the ink and deposit it on paper, only the raised areas of the design are inked. This is comparable to the type of printing seen by inking and using an ordinary rubber stamp. Letterpress includes all printing where the design is above the surface area, whether it is wood, metal or, in some instances, hardened rubber or polymer plastic.

For most letterpress-printed stamps, the engraved master is made in much the same manner as for engraved stamps. In this instance, however, an additional step is needed. The design is transferred to another surface before being transferred to the transfer roll. In this way, the transfer roll has a recessed stamp design, rather than one done in relief. This makes the printing areas on the final plate raised, or relief areas.

For less-detailed stamps of the 19th century, the area on the die not used as a printing surface was cut away, leaving the surface area raised. The original die was then reproduced by stereotyping or electrotyping. The resulting electrotypes were assembled in the required number and format of the desired sheet of stamps. The plate used in printing the stamps was an electroplate of these assembled electrotypes.

Once the final letterpress plates are created, ink is applied to the raised surface and the pressure of the press transfers the ink impression to the paper. In contrast to engraving, the fine lines of letterpress are impressed on the surface of the stamp, leaving a debossed surface. When viewed from the back (as on a typewritten page), the corresponding line work on the stamp will be raised slightly (embossed) above the surface.

PHOTOGRAVURE (Gravure, Rotogravure, Heliogravure)

In this process, the basic principles of photography are applied to a chemically sensitized metal plate, rather than photographic paper. The design is transferred photographically to the plate through a halftone, or dot-matrix screen, breaking the reproduction into tiny dots. The plate is treated chemically and the dots form depressions, called cells, of varying depths and diameters, depending on the degrees of shade in the design. Then, like engraving, ink is applied to the plate and the surface is wiped clean. This leaves ink in the tiny cells that is lifted out and deposited on the paper when it is pressed against the plate.

Gravure is most often used for multicolored stamps, generally using the three primary colors (red, yellow and blue) and black. By varying the dot matrix pattern and density of these colors, virtually any color can be reproduced. A typical full-color gravure stamp will be created from four printing cylinders (one for each color). The original multicolored image will have been photographically separated into its component colors.

Modern gravure printing may use computer-generated dot-matrix screens, and modern plates may be of various types including metal-coated plastic. The catalogue designation of Photogravure (or "Photo") covers any of these older and more modern gravure methods of printing.

For examples of the first photogravure stamps printed (1914), see Bavaria Scott 94-114.

LITHOGRAPHY (Offset Lithography, Stone Lithography, Dilitho, Planography, Collotype)

The principle that oil and water do not mix is the basis for lithography. The stamp design is drawn by hand or transferred from engraving to the surface of a lithographic stone or metal plate in a greasy (oily) substance. This oily substance holds the ink, which will later be transferred to the paper. The stone (or plate) is wet with an acid fluid, causing it to repel the printing ink in all areas not covered by the greasy substance.

Transfer paper is used to transfer the design from the original stone or plate. A series of duplicate transfers are grouped and, in turn, transferred to the final printing plate.

Photolithography — The application of photographic processes to lithography. This process allows greater flexibility of design, related to use of halftone screens combined with line work. Unlike photogravure or engraving, this process can allow large, solid areas to be printed.

Offset — A refinement of the lithographic process. A rubber-covered blanket cylinder takes the impression from the inked lithographic plate. From the "blanket" the impression is *offset* or transferred to the paper. Greater flexibility and speed are the principal reasons offset printing has largely displaced lithography. The term "lithography" covers both processes, and results are almost identical.

EMBOSSED (Relief) Printing

Embossing, not considered one of the four main printing types, is a method in which the design first is sunk into the metal of the die. Printing is done against a yielding platen, such as leather or linoleum. The platen is forced into the depression of the die, thus forming the design on the paper in relief. This process is often used for metallic inks.

Embossing may be done without color (see Sardinia Scott 4-6); with color printed around the embossed area (see Great Britain Scott 5 and most U.S. envelopes); and with color in exact registration with the embossed subject (see Canada Scott 656-657).

HOLOGRAMS

For objects to appear as holograms on stamps, a model exactly the same size as it is to appear on the hologram must be created. Rather than using photographic film to capture the image, holography records an image on a photoresist material. In processing, chemicals eat away at certain exposed areas, leaving a pattern of constructive and destructive interference. When the phororesist is developed, the result is a pattern of uneven ridges that acts as a mold. This mold is then coated with metal, and the resulting form is used to press copies in much the same way phonograph records are produced.

A typical reflective hologram used for stamps consists of a reproduction of the uneven patterns on a plastic film that is applied to a reflective background, usually a silver or gold foil. Light is reflected off the background through the film, making the pattern present on the film visible. Because of the uneven pattern of the film, the viewer will perceive the objects in their proper three-dimensional relationships with appropriate brightness.

The first hologram on a stamp was produced by Austria in 1988 (Scott 1441).

FOIL APPLICATION

A modern tecnique of applying color to stamps involves the application of metallic foil to the stamp paper. A pattern of foil is applied to the stamp paper by use of a stamping die. The foil usually is flat, but it may be textured. Canada Scott 1735 has three different foil applications in pearl, bronze and gold. The gold foil was textured using a chemical-etch copper embossing die. The printing of this stamp also involved two-color offset lithography plus embossing.

COMBINATION PRINTINGS

Sometimes two or even three printing methods are combined in producing stamps. In these cases, such as Austria Scott 933 or Canada 1735 (described in the preceding paragraph), the multiple-printing technique can be determined by studying the individual characteristics of each printing type. A few stamps, such as Singapore Scott 684-684A, combine as many as three of the four major printing types (lithography, engraving and typography). When this is done it often indicates the incorporation of security devices against counterfeiting.

INK COLORS

Inks or colored papers used in stamp printing often are of mineral origin, although there are numerous examples of organic-based pigments. As a general rule, organic-based pigments are far more subject to varieties and change than those of mineral-based origin.

The appearance of any given color on a stamp may be affected by many aspects, including printing variations, light, color of paper, aging and chemical alterations.

Numerous printing variations may be observed. Heavier pressure or inking will cause a more intense color, while slight interruptions in the ink feed or lighter impressions will cause a lighter appearance. Stamps printed in the same color by water-based and solvent-based inks can differ significantly in appearance. This affects several stamps in the U.S. Prominent Americans series. Hand-mixed ink formulas (primarily from the 19th century) produced under different conditions (humidity and temperature) account for notable color variations in early printings of the same stamp (see U.S. Scott 248-250, 279B, for example). Different sources of pigment can also result in significant differences in color.

Light exposure and aging are closely related in the way they affect stamp color. Both eventually break down the ink and fade colors, so that a carefully kept stamp may differ significantly in color from an identical copy that has been exposed to light. If stamps are exposed to light either intentionally or accidentally, their colors can be faded or completely changed in some cases.

Papers of different quality and consistency used for the same stamp printing may affect color appearance. Most pelure papers, for example, show a richer color when compared with wove or laid papers. See Russia Scott 181a, for an example of this effect.

The very nature of the printing processes can cause a variety of differences in shades or hues of the same stamp. Some of these shades are scarcer than others, and are of particular interest to the advanced collector.

Luminescence

All forms of tagged stamps fall under the general category of luminescence. Within this broad category is fluorescence, dealing with forms of tagging visible under longwave ultraviolet light, and phosphorescence, which deals with tagging visible only under shortwave light. Phosphorescence leaves an afterglow and fluorescence does not. These treated stamps show up in a range of different colors when exposed to UV light. The differing wavelengths of the light activates the tagging material, making it glow in various colors that usually serve different mail processing purposes.

Intentional tagging is a post-World War II phenomenon, brought about by the increased literacy rate and rapidly growing mail volume. It was one of several answers to the problem of the need for more automated mail processes. Early tagged stamps served the purpose of triggering machines to separate different types of mail. A natural outgrowth was to also use the signal to trigger machines that faced all envelopes the same way and canceled them.

Tagged stamps come in many different forms. Some tagged stamps have luminescent shapes or images imprinted on them as a form of security device. Others have blocks (United States), stripes, frames (South Africa and Canada), overall coatings (United States), bars (Great Britain and Canada) and many other types. Some types of tagging are even mixed in with the pigmented printing ink (Australia Scott 366, Netherlands Scott 478 and U.S. Scott 1359 and 2443).

The means of applying taggant to stamps differs as much as the intended purposes for the stamps. The most common form of tagging is a coating applied to the surface of the printed stamp. Since the taggant ink is frequently invisible except under UV light, it does not interfere with the appearance of the stamp. Another common application is the use of phosphored papers. In this case the paper itself either has a coating of taggant applied before the stamp is printed, has taggant applied during the papermaking process (incorporating it into the fibers), or has the taggant mixed into the coating of the paper. The latter method, among others, is currently in use in the United States.

Many countries now use tagging in various forms to either expedite mail handling or to serve as a printing security device against counterfeiting. Following the introduction of tagged stamps for public use in 1959 by Great Britain, other countries have steadily joined the parade. Among those are Germany (1961); Canada and Denmark (1962); United States, Australia, France and Switzerland (1963); Belgium and Japan (1966); Sweden and Norway (1967); Italy (1968); and Russia (1969). Since then, many other countries have begun using forms of tagging, including Brazil, China, Czechoslovakia, Hong Kong, Guatemala, Indonesia, Israel, Lithuania, Luxembourg, Netherlands, Penrhyn Islands, Portugal, St. Vincent, Singapore, South Africa, Spain and Sweden to name a few.

In some cases, including United States, Canada, Great Britain and Switzerland, stamps were released both with and without tagging. Many of these were released during each country's experimental period. Tagged and untagged versions are listed for the aforementioned countries and are noted in some other countries' listings. For at least a few stamps, the experimentally tagged version is worth far more than its untagged counterpart, such as the 1963 experimental tagged version of France Scott 1024.

In some cases, luminescent varieties of stamps were inadvertently created. Several Russian stamps, for example, sport highly fluorescent ink that was not intended as a form of tagging. Older stamps, such as early U.S. postage dues, can be positively identified by the use of UV light, since the organic ink used has become slightly fluorescent over time. Other stamps, such as Austria Scott 70a-82a (varnish bars) and Obock Scott 46-64 (printed quadrille lines), have become fluorescent over time.

Various fluorescent substances have been added to paper to make it appear brighter. These optical brightners, as they are known, greatly affect the appearance of the stamp under UV light. The brightest of these is known as Hi-Brite paper. These paper varieties are beyond the scope of the Scott Catalogue.

Shortwave UV light also is used extensively in expertizing, since each form of paper has its own fluorescent characteristics that are impossible to perfectly match. It is therefore a simple matter to detect filled thins, added perforation teeth and other alterations that involve the addition of paper. UV light also is used to examine stamps that have had cancels chemically removed and for other purposes as well.

Gum

The Illustrated Gum Chart in the first part of this introduction shows and defines various types of gum condition. Because gum condition has an important impact on the value of unused stamps, we recommend studying this chart and the accompanying text carefully.

The gum on the back of a stamp may be shiny, dull, smooth, rough, dark, white, colored or tinted. Most stamp gumming adhesives use gum arabic or dextrine as a base. Certain polymers such as polyvinyl alcohol (PVA) have been used extensively since World War II.

The *Scott Standard Postage Stamp Catalogue* does not list items by types of gum. The *Scott Specialized Catalogue of United States Stamps* does differentiate among some types of gum for certain issues.

Reprints of stamps may have gum differing from the original issues. In addition, some countries have used different gum formulas for different seasons. These adhesives have different properties that may become more apparent over time.

Many stamps have been issued without gum, and the catalogue will note this fact. See, for example, United States Scott 40-47. Sometimes, gum may have been removed to preserve the stamp. Germany Scott B68, for example, has a highly acidic gum that eventually destroys the stamps. This item is valued in the catalogue with gum removed.

Reprints and Reissues

These are impressions of stamps (usually obsolete) made from the original plates or stones. If they are valid for postage and reproduce obsolete issues (such as U.S. Scott 102-111), the stamps are *reissues*. If they are from current issues, they are designated as *second, third,* etc., *printing*. If designated for a particular purpose, they are called *special printings*.

When special printings are not valid for postage, but are made from original dies and plates by authorized persons, they are *official reprints*. Private reprints are made from the original plates and dies by private hands. An example of a private reprint is that of the 1871-1932 reprints made from the original die of the 1845 New Haven, Conn., postmaster's provisional. *Official reproductions* or imitations are made from new dies and plates by government authorization. Scott will list those reissues that are valid for postage if they differ significantly from the original printing.

The U.S. government made special printings of its first postage stamps in 1875. Produced were official imitations of the first two stamps (listed as Scott 3-4), reprints of the demonetized pre-1861 issues (Scott 40-47) and reissues of the 1861 stamps, the 1869 stamps and the then-current 1875 denominations. Even though the official imitations and the reprints were not valid for postage, Scott lists all of these U.S. special printings.

Most reprints or reissues differ slightly from the original stamp in some characteristic, such as gum, paper, perforation, color or watermark. Sometimes the details are followed so meticulously that only a student of that specific stamp is able to distinguish the reprint or reissue from the original.

Remainders and Canceled to Order

Some countries sell their stock of old stamps when a new issue replaces them. To avoid postal use, the *remainders* usually are canceled with a punch hole, a heavy line or bar, or a more-or-less regular-looking cancellation. The most famous merchant of remainders was Nicholas F. Seebeck. In the 1880s and 1890s, he arranged printing contracts between the Hamilton Bank Note Co., of which he was a director, and several Central and South American countries. The contracts provided that the plates and all remainders of the yearly issues became the property of Hamilton. Seebeck saw to it that ample stock remained. The "Seebecks," both remainders and reprints, were standard packet fillers for decades.

Some countries also issue stamps *canceled-to-order (CTO)*, either in sheets with original gum or stuck onto pieces of paper or envelopes and canceled. Such CTO items generally are worth less than postally used stamps. In cases where the CTO material is far more prevalent in the marketplace than postally used examples, the catalogue value relates to the CTO examples, with postally used examples noted as premium items. Most CTOs can be detected by the presence of gum. However, as the CTO practice goes back at least to 1885, the gum inevitably has been soaked off some stamps so they could pass as postally used. The normally applied postmarks usually differ slightly from standard postmarks, and specialists are able to tell the difference. When applied individually to envelopes by philatelically minded persons, CTO material is known as *favor canceled* and generally sells at large discounts.

Cinderellas and Facsimiles

Cinderella is a catch-all term used by stamp collectors to describe phantoms, fantasies, bogus items, municipal issues, exhibition seals, local revenues, transportation stamps, labels, poster stamps and many other types of items. Some cinderella collectors include in their collections local postage issues, telegraph stamps, essays and proofs, forgeries and counterfeits.

A *fantasy* is an adhesive created for a nonexistent stamp-issuing authority. Fantasy items range from imaginary countries (Occusi-Ambeno, Kingdom of Sedang, Principality of Trinidad or Torres Straits), to non-existent locals (Winans City Post), or nonexistent transportation lines (McRobish & Co.'s Acapulco-San Francisco Line).

On the other hand, if the entity exists and could have issued stamps (but did not) or was known to have issued other stamps, the items are considered *bogus* stamps. These would include the Mormon postage stamps of Utah, S. Allan Taylor's Guatemala and Paraguay inventions, the propaganda issues for the South Moluccas and the adhesives of the Page & Keyes local post of Boston.

Phantoms is another term for both fantasy and bogus issues.

Facsimiles are copies or imitations made to represent original stamps, but which do not pretend to be originals. A catalogue illustration is such a facsimile. Illustrations from the Moens catalogue of the last century were occasionally colored and passed off as stamps. Since the beginning of stamp collecting, facsimiles have been made for collectors as space fillers or for reference. They often carry the word "facsimile," "falsch" (German), "sanko" or "mozo" (Japanese), or "faux" (French) overprinted on the face or stamped on the back. Unfortunately, over the years a number of these items have had fake cancels applied over the facsimile notation and have been passed off as genuine.

Forgeries and Counterfeits

Forgeries and counterfeits have been with philately virtually from the beginning of stamp production. Over time, the terminology for the two has been used interchangeably. Although both forgeries and counterfeits are reproductions of stamps, the purposes behind their creation differ considerably.

Among specialists there is an increasing movement to more specifically define such items. Although there is no universally accepted terminology, we feel the following definitions most closely mirror the items and their purposes as they are currently defined.

Forgeries (also often referred to as *Counterfeits*) are reproductions of genuine stamps that have been created to defraud collectors. Such spurious items first appeared on the market around 1860, and most old-time collections contain one or more. Many are crude and easily spotted, but some can deceive experts.

An important supplier of these early philatelic forgeries was the Hamburg printer Gebruder Spiro. Many others with reputations in this craft included S. Allan Taylor, George Hussey, James Chute, George Forune, Benjamin & Sarpy, Julius Goldner, E. Oneglia and L.H. Mercier. Among the noted 20th-century forgers were Francois Fournier, Jean Sperati and the prolific Raoul DeThuin.

Forgeries may be complete replications, or they may be genuine stamps altered to resemble a scarcer (and more valuable) type. Most forgeries, particularly those of rare stamps, are worth only a small fraction of the value of a genuine example, but a few types, created by some of the most notable forgers, such as Sperati, can be worth as much or more than the genuine. Fraudulently produced copies are known of most classic rarities and many medium-priced stamps.

In addition to rare stamps, large numbers of common 19th- and early 20th-century stamps were forged to supply stamps to the early packet trade. Many can still be easily found. Few new philatelic forgeries have appeared in recent decades. Successful imitation of well-engraved work is virtually impossible. It has proven far easier to produce a fake by altering a genuine stamp than to duplicate a stamp completely.

Counterfeit (also often referred to as *Postal Counterfeit* or *Postal Forgery*) is the term generally applied to reproductions of stamps that have been created to defraud the government of revenue. Such items usually are created at the time a stamp is current and, in some cases, are hard to detect. Because most counterfeits are seized when the perpetrator is captured, postal counterfeits, particularly used on cover, are usually worth much more than a genuine example to spe-cialists. The first postal counterfeit was of Spain's 4-cuarto carmine of 1854 (the real one is Scott 25). Apparently, the counterfeiters were not satisfied with their first version, which is now very scarce, and they soon created an engraved counterfeit, which is common. Postal counterfeits quickly followed in Austria, Naples, Sardinia and the Roman States. They have since been created in many other countries as well, including the United States.

An infamous counterfeit to defraud the government is the 1-shilling Great Britain "Stock Exchange" forgery of 1872, used on telegraph forms at the exchange that year. The stamp escaped detection until a stamp dealer noticed it in 1898.

Fakes

Fakes are genuine stamps altered in some way to make them more desirable. One student of this part of stamp collecting has estimated that by the 1950s more than 30,000 varieties of fakes were known. That number has grown greatly since then. The widespread existence of fakes makes it important for stamp collectors to study their philatelic holdings and use relevant literature. Likewise, collectors should buy from reputable dealers who guarantee their stamps and make full and prompt refunds should a purchased item be declared faked or altered by some mutually agreed-upon authority. Because fakes always have some genuine characteristics, it is not always possible to obtain unanimous agreement among experts regarding specific items. These students may change their opinions as philatelic knowledge increases. More than 80 percent of all fakes on the philatelic market today are regummed, reperforated (or perforated for the first time), or bear forged overprints, surcharges or cancellations.

Stamps can be chemically treated to alter or eliminate colors. For example, a pale rose stamp can be re-colored to resemble a blue shade of high market value. In other cases, treated stamps can be made to resemble missing color varieties. Designs may be changed by painting, or a stroke or a dot added or bleached out to turn an ordinary variety into a seemingly scarcer stamp. Part of a stamp can be bleached and reprinted in a different version, achieving an inverted center or frame. Margins can be added or repairs done so deceptively that the stamps move from the "repaired" into the "fake" category.

Fakers have not left the backs of the stamps untouched either. They may create false watermarks, add fake grills or press out genuine grills. A thin India paper proof may be glued onto a thicker backing to create the appearance an issued stamp, or a proof printed on cardboard may be shaved down and perforated to resemble a stamp. Silk threads are impressed into paper and stamps have been split so that a rare paper variety is added to an otherwise inexpensive stamp. The most common treatment to the back of a stamp, however, is regumming.

Some in the business of faking stamps have openly advertised foolproof application of "original gum" to stamps that lack it, although most publications now ban such ads from their pages. It is believed that very few early stamps have survived without being hinged. The large number of never-hinged examples of such earlier material offered for sale thus suggests the widespread extent of regumming activity. Regumming also may be used to hide repairs or thin spots. Dipping the stamp into watermark fluid, or examining it under long-wave ultraviolet light often will reveal these flaws.

Fakers also tamper with separations. Ingenious ways to add margins are known. Perforated wide-margin stamps may be falsely represented as imperforate when trimmed. Reperforating is commonly done to create scarce coil or perforation varieties, and to eliminate the naturally occurring straight-edge stamps found in sheet margin positions of many earlier issues. Custom has made straight-edged stamps less desirable. Fakers have obliged by perforating straight-edged stamps so that many are now uncommon, if not rare.

Another fertile field for the faker is that of overprints, surcharges and cancellations. The forging of rare surcharges or overprints began in the 1880s or 1890s. These forgeries are sometimes difficult to detect, but experts have identified almost all. Occasionally, overprints or cancellations are removed to create non-overprinted stamps or seemingly unused items. This is most commonly done by removing a manuscript cancel to make a stamp resemble an unused example. "SPECIMEN" overprints may be removed by scraping and repainting to create non-overprinted varieties. Fakers use inexpensive revenues or pen-canceled stamps to generate unused stamps for further faking by adding other markings. The quartz lamp or UV lamp and a high-powered magnifying glass help to easily detect removed cancellations.

The bigger problem, however, is the addition of overprints, surcharges or cancellations - many with such precision that they are very difficult to ascertain. Plating of the stamps or the overprint can be an important method of detection.

Fake postmarks may range from many spurious fancy cancellations to a host of markings applied to transatlantic covers, to adding normally appearing postmarks to definitives of some countries with stamps that are valued far higher used than unused. With the increased popularity of cover collecting, and the widespread interest in postal history, a fertile new field for fakers has come about. Some have tried to create entire covers. Others specialize in adding stamps, tied by fake cancellations, to genuine stampless covers, or replacing less expensive or damaged stamps with more valuable ones. Detailed study of postal rates in effect at the time a cover in question was mailed, including the analysis of each handstamp used during the period, ink analysis and similar techniques, usually will unmask the fraud.

Restoration and Repairs

Scott Publishing Co. bases its catalogue values on stamps that are free of defects and otherwise meet the standards set forth earlier in this introduction. Most stamp collectors desire to have the finest copy of an item possible. Even within given grading categories there are variances. This leads to a controversial practice that is not defined in any universal manner: stamp *restoration*.

There are broad differences of opinion about what is permissible when it comes to restoration. Carefully applying a soft eraser to a stamp or cover to remove light soiling is one form of restoration, as is washing a stamp in mild soap and water to clean it. These are fairly accepted forms of restoration. More severe forms of restoration include pressing out creases or removing stains caused by tape. To what degree each of these is acceptable is dependent upon the individual situation. Further along the spectrum is the freshening of a stamp's color by removing oxide build-up or the effects of wax paper left next to stamps shipped to the tropics.

At some point in this spectrum the concept of *repair* replaces that of restoration. Repairs include filling thin spots, mending tears by reweaving or adding a missing perforation tooth. Regumming stamps may have been acceptable as a restoration or repair technique many decades ago, but today it is considered a form of fakery.

Restored stamps may or may not sell at a discount, and it is possible that the value of individual restored items may be enhanced over that of their pre-restoration state. Specific situations dictate the resultant value of such an item. Repaired stamps sell at substantial discounts from the value of sound stamps.

Terminology

Booklets — Many countries have issued stamps in small booklets for the convenience of users. This idea continues to become increasingly popular in many countries. Booklets have been issued in many sizes and forms, often with advertising on the covers, the panes of stamps or on the interleaving.

The panes used in booklets may be printed from special plates or made from regular sheets. All panes from booklets issued by the United States and many from those of other countries contain stamps that are straight edged on the sides, but perforated between. Others are distinguished by orientation of watermark or other identifying features. Any stamp-like unit in the pane, either printed or blank, that is not a postage stamp, is considered to be a *label* in the catalogue listings.

Scott lists and values booklet panes. Modern complete booklets also are listed and valued. Individual booklet panes are listed only when they are not fashioned from existing sheet stamps and, therefore, are identifiable from their sheet stamp counterparts.

Panes usually do not have a used value assigned to them because there is little market activity for used booklet panes, even though many exist used and there is some demand for them.

Cancellations — The marks or obliterations put on stamps by postal authorities to show that they have performed service and to prevent their reuse are known as cancellations. If the marking is made with a pen, it is considered a "pen cancel." When the location of the post office appears in the marking, it is a "town cancellation." A "postmark" is technically any postal marking, but in practice the term generally is applied to a town cancellation with a date. When calling attention to a cause or celebration, the marking is known as a "slogan cancellation." Many other types and styles of cancellations exist, such as duplex, numerals, targets, fancy and others. See also "precancels," below.

Coil Stamps — These are stamps that are issued in rolls for use in dispensers, affixing and vending machines. Those coils of the United States, Canada, Sweden and some other countries are perforated horizontally or vertically only, with the outer edges imperforate. Coil stamps of some countries, such as Great Britain and Germany, are perforated on all four sides and may in some cases be distinguished from their sheet stamp counterparts by watermarks, counting numbers on the reverse or other means.

Covers — Entire envelopes, with or without adhesive postage stamps, that have passed through the mail and bear postal or other markings of philatelic interest are known as covers. Before the introduction of envelopes in about 1840, people folded letters and wrote the address on the outside. Some people covered their letters with an extra sheet of paper on the outside for the address, producing the term "cover." Used airletter sheets, stamped envelopes and other items of postal stationery also are considered covers.

Errors — Stamps that have some major, consistent, unintentional deviation from the normal are considered errors. Errors include, but are not limited to, missing or wrong colors, wrong paper, wrong watermarks, inverted centers or frames on multicolor printing, inverted or missing surcharges or overprints, double impressions, missing perforations, unintentionally omitted tagging and others. Factually wrong or misspelled information, if it appears on all examples of a stamp, are not considered errors in the true sense of the word. They are errors of design. Inconsistent or randomly appearing items, such as misperfs or color shifts, are classified as freaks.

Color-Omitted Errors — This term refers to stamps where a missing color is caused by the complete failure of the printing plate to deliver ink to the stamp paper or any other paper. Generally, this is caused by the printing plate not being engaged on the press or the ink station running dry of ink during printing.

Color-Missing Errors — This term refers to stamps where a color or colors were printed somewhere but do not appear on the finished stamp. There are four different classes of color-missing errors, and the catalog indicates with a two-letter code appended to each such listing what caused the color to be missing. These codes are used only for the United States' color-missing error listings.

FO = A *foldover* of the stamp sheet during printing may block ink from appearing on a stamp. Instead, the color will appear on the back of the foldover (where it might fall on the back of the selvage or perhaps on the back of the stamp or another stamp). FO also will be used in the case of foldunders, where the paper may fold underneath the other stamp paper and the color will print on the platen.

EP = A piece of *extraneous paper* falling across the plate or stamp paper will receive the printed ink. When the extraneous paper is removed, an unprinted portion of stamp paper remains and shows partially or totally missing colors.

CM = A misregistration of the printing plates during printing will result in a *color misregistration*, and such a misregistraion may result in a color not appearing on the finished stamp.

PS = A *perforation shift* after printing may remove a color from the finished stamp. Normally, this will occur on a row of stamps at the edge of the stamp pane.

Overprints and Surcharges
— Overprinting involves applying wording or design elements over an already existing stamp. Overprints can be used to alter the place of use (such as "Canal Zone" on U.S. stamps), to adapt them for a special purpose ("Porto" on Denmark's 1913-20 regular issues for use as postage due stamps, Scott J1-J7) or to commemorate a special occasion (United States Scott 647-648).

A *surcharge* is a form of overprint that changes or restates the face value of a stamp or piece of postal stationery.

Surcharges and overprints may be handstamped, typeset or, occasionally, lithographed or engraved. A few hand-written overprints and surcharges are known.

Personalized Stamps
— In 1999, Australia issued stamps with se-tenant labels that could be personalized with pictures of the customer's choice. Other countries quickly followed suit, with some offering to print the selected picture on the stamp itself within a frame that was used exclusively for personalized issues. As the picture used on these stamps or labels vary, listings for such stamps are for *any* picture within the common frame (or any picture on a se-tenant label), be it a "generic" image or one produced especially for a customer, almost invariably at a premium price.

Precancels
— Stamps that are canceled before they are placed in the mail are known as precancels. Precanceling usually is done to expedite the handling of large mailings and generally allow the affected mail pieces to skip certain phases of mail handling.

In the United States, precancellations generally identified the point of origin; that is, the city and state. This information appeared across the face of the stamp, usually centered between parallel lines. More recently, bureau precancels retained the parallel lines, but the city and state designations were dropped. Recent coils have a service inscription that is present on the original printing plate. These show the mail service paid for by the stamp. Since these stamps are not intended to receive further cancellations when used as intended, they are considered precancels. Such items often do not have parallel lines as part of the precancellation.

In France, the abbreviation *Affranchts* in a semicircle together with the word *Postes* is the general form of precancel in use. Belgian precancellations usually appear in a box in which the name of the city appears. Netherlands precancels have the name of the city enclosed between concentric circles, sometimes called a "lifesaver." Precancellations of other countries usually follow these patterns, but may be any arrangement of bars, boxes and city names.

Precancels are listed in the Scott catalogues only if the precancel changes the denomination (Belgium Scott 477-478); if the precanceled stamp is different from the non-precanceled version (such as untagged U.S. precancels); or if the stamp exists only precanceled (France Scott 1096-1099, U.S. Scott 2265).

Proofs and Essays
— Proofs are impressions taken from an approved die, plate or stone in which the design and color are the same as the stamp issued to the public. Trial color proofs are impressions taken from approved dies, plates or stones in colors that vary from the final version. An essay is the impression of a design that differs in some way from the issued stamp. "Progressive die proofs" generally are considered to be essays.

Provisionals
— These are stamps that are issued on short notice and intended for temporary use pending the arrival of regular issues. They usually are issued to meet such contingencies as changes in government or currency, shortage of necessary postage values or military occupation.

During the 1840s, postmasters in certain American cities issued stamps that were valid only at specific post offices. In 1861, postmasters of the Confederate States also issued stamps with limited validity. Both of these examples are known as "postmaster's provisionals."

Se-tenant
— This term refers to an unsevered pair, strip or block of stamps that differ in design, denomination or overprint.

Unless the se-tenant item has a continuous design (see U.S. Scott 1451a, 1694a) the stamps do not have to be in the same order as shown in the catalogue (see U.S. Scott 2158a).

Specimens
— The Universal Postal Union required member nations to send samples of all stamps they released into service to the International Bureau in Switzerland. Member nations of the UPU received these specimens as samples of what stamps were valid for postage. Many are overprinted, handstamped or initial-perforated "Specimen," "Canceled" or "Muestra." Some are marked with bars across the denominations (China-Taiwan), punched holes (Czechoslovakia) or back inscriptions (Mongolia).

Stamps distributed to government officials or for publicity purposes, and stamps submitted by private security printers for official approval, also may receive such defacements.

The previously described defacement markings prevent postal use, and all such items generally are known as "specimens."

Tete Beche
— This term describes a pair of stamps in which one is upside down in relation to the other. Some of these are the result of intentional sheet arrangements, such as Morocco Scott B10-B11. Others occurred when one or more electrotypes accidentally were placed upside down on the plate, such as Colombia Scott 57a. Separation of the tete-beche stamps, of course, destroys the tete beche variety.

Currency Conversion

Country	Dollar	Pound	S Franc	Yen	HK $	Euro	Cdn $	Aus $
Australia	1.0601	2.0697	1.0182	0.0103	0.1360	1.6413	1.0543	—
Canada	1.0055	1.9631	0.9657	0.0098	0.1290	1.5567	—	0.9485
European Union	0.6459	1.2611	0.6203	0.0063	0.0829	—	0.6424	0.6093
Hong Kong	7.7956	15.220	7.4871	0.0757	—	12.069	7.7530	7.3536
Japan	102.97	201.03	98.891	—	13.208	159.41	102.40	97.128
Switzerland	1.0412	2.0328	—	0.0101	0.1336	1.6120	1.0355	0.9822
United Kingdom	0.5122	—	0.4919	0.0050	0.0657	0.7930	0.5094	0.4832
United States	—	1.9524	0.9604	0.0097	0.1283	1.5482	0.9945	0.9433

Country	Currency	U.S. $ Equiv.
Solomon Islands	dollar	.1300
Somalia	shilling	.0007
South Africa	rand	.1293
S. Georgia & S. Sandwich Isls	British pound	1.9524
Spain	euro	1.5482
Sri Lanka	rupee	.0093
Sudan	pound	.4869
Surinam	dollar	.3636
Swaziland	emalangeni	.1294
Sweden	krona	.1670
Switzerland	franc	.9604
Syria	pound	.0196
Tajikistan	somoni	.2913
Tanzania	shilling	.0008
Thailand	baht	.0313
Timor	U.S. dollar	1.00
Togo	Community of French Africa (CFA) franc	.0024
Tokelau	New Zealand dollar	.7688
Tonga	pa'anga	.5497
Niuafo'ou	pa'anga	.5497
Trinidad & Tobago	dollar	.1592
Tristan da Cunha	British pound	1.9524
Tunisia	dinar	.8503
Turkey	lira	.7899
Turk. Rep. of Northern Cyprus	lira	.7899
Turkmenistan	manat	.0002
Turks & Caicos Islands	U.S. dollar	1.00
Tuvalu	Australian dollar	.9433
Uganda	shilling	.0006
Ukraine	hryvnia	.2089
United Arab Emirates	dirham	.2723
Uruguay	peso	.0501
Uzbekistan	sum	.0008
Vanuatu	vatu	.0105
Vatican City	euro	1.5482
Venezuela	bolivar	.4662
Viet Nam	dong	.00006
Virgin Islands	U.S. dollar	1.00
Wallis & Futuna Islands	Community of French Pacific (CFP) franc	.0130
Yemen	rial	.0050
Zambia	kwacha	.0003
Zaire (Congo Dem. Rep.)	franc	.0018
Zimbabwe	dollar	.000000005

*Source: **Wall Street Journal** May 12, 2008. Figures reflect values as of May 9, 2008.*

COMMON DESIGN TYPES

Pictured in this section are issues where one illustration has been used for a number of countries in the Catalogue. Not included in this section are overprinted stamps or those issues which are illustrated in each country.

EUROPA
Europa, 1956

The design symbolizing the cooperation among the six countries comprising the Coal and Steel Community is illustrated in each country.

Belgium	496-497
France	805-806
Germany	748-749
Italy	715-716
Luxembourg	318-320
Netherlands	368-369

Europa, 1958

"E" and Dove — CD1

European Postal Union at the service of European integration.

1958, Sept. 13

Belgium	527-528
France	889-890
Germany	790-791
Italy	750-751
Luxembourg	341-343
Netherlands	375-376
Saar	317-318

Europa, 1959

6-Link Enless Chain — CD2

1959, Sept. 19

Belgium	536-537
France	929-930
Germany	805-806
Italy	791-792
Luxembourg	354-355
Netherlands	379-380

Europa, 1960

19-Spoke Wheel CD3

First anniverary of the establishment of C.E.P.T. (Conference Europeenne des Administrations des Postes et des Telecommunications.) The spokes symbolize the 19 founding members of the Conference.

1960, Sept.

Belgium	553-554
Denmark	379
Finland	376-377
France	970-971
Germany	818-820
Great Britain	377-378
Greece	688
Iceland	327-328

Ireland	175-176
Italy	809-810
Luxembourg	374-375
Netherlands	385-386
Norway	387
Portugal	866-867
Spain	941-942
Sweden	562-563
Switzerland	400-401
Turkey	1493-1494

Europa, 1961

19 Doves Flying as One — CD4

The 19 doves represent the 19 members of the Conference of European Postal and Telecommunications Administrations C.E.P.T.

1961-62

Belgium	572-573
Cyprus	201-203
France	1005-1006
Germany	844-845
Great Britain	383-384
Greece	718-719
Iceland	340-341
Italy	845-846
Luxembourg	382-383
Netherlands	387-388
Spain	1010-1011
Switzerland	410-411
Turkey	1518-1520

Europa, 1962

Young Tree with 19 Leaves CD5

The 19 leaves represent the 19 original members of C.E.P.T.

1962-63

Belgium	582-583
Cyprus	219-221
France	1045-1046
Germany	852-853
Greece	739-740
Iceland	348-349
Ireland	184-185
Italy	860-861
Luxembourg	386-387
Netherlands	394-395
Norway	414-415
Switzerland	416-417
Turkey	1553-1555

Europa, 1963

Stylized Links, Symbolizing Unity — CD6

1963, Sept.

Belgium	598-599
Cyprus	229-231
Finland	419
France	1074-1075
Germany	867-868
Greece	768-769
Iceland	357-358
Ireland	188-189
Italy	880-881
Luxembourg	403-404
Netherlands	416-417
Norway	441-442
Switzerland	429
Turkey	1602-1603

Europa, 1964

Symbolic Daisy — CD7

5th anniversary of the establishment of C.E.P.T. The 22 petals of the flower symbolize the 22 members of the Conference.

1964, Sept.

Austria	738
Belgium	614-615
Cyprus	244-246
France	1109-1110
Germany	897-898
Greece	801-802
Iceland	367-368
Ireland	196-197
Italy	894-895
Luxembourg	411-412
Monaco	590-591
Netherlands	428-429
Norway	458
Portugal	931-933
Spain	1262-1263
Switzerland	438-439
Turkey	1628-1629

Europa, 1965

Leaves and "Fruit" CD8

1965

Belgium	636-637
Cyprus	262-264
Finland	437
France	1131-1132
Germany	934-935
Greece	833-834
Iceland	375-376
Ireland	204-205
Italy	915-916
Luxembourg	432-433
Monaco	616-617
Netherlands	438-439
Norway	475-476
Portugal	958-960
Switzerland	469
Turkey	1665-1666

Europa, 1966

Symbolic Sailboat — CD9

1966, Sept.

Andorra, French	172
Belgium	675-676
Cyprus	275-277
France	1163-1164
Germany	963-964
Greece	862-863
Iceland	384-385
Ireland	216-217
Italy	942-943
Liechtenstein	415
Luxembourg	440-441
Monaco	639-640
Netherlands	441-442
Norway	496-497
Portugal	980-982
Switzerland	477-478
Turkey	1718-1719

Europa, 1967

Cogwheels CD10

1967

Andorra, French	174-175
Belgium	688-689
Cyprus	297-299
France	1178-1179
Germany	969-970
Greece	891-892
Iceland	389-390
Ireland	232-233
Italy	951-952
Liechtenstein	420
Luxembourg	449-450
Monaco	669-670
Netherlands	444-447
Norway	504-505
Portugal	994-996
Spain	1465-1466
Switzerland	482
Turkey	B120-B121

Europa, 1968

Golden Key with C.E.P.T. Emblem CD11

1968

Andorra, French	182-183
Belgium	705-706
Cyprus	314-316
France	1209-1210
Germany	983-984
Greece	916-917
Iceland	395-396
Ireland	242-243
Italy	979-980
Liechtenstein	442
Luxembourg	466-467
Monaco	689-691
Netherlands	452-453
Portugal	1019-1021
San Marino	687
Spain	1526
Turkey	1775-1776

Europa, 1969

"EUROPA" and "CEPT" CD12

Tenth anniversary of C.E.P.T.

1969

Andorra, French	188-189
Austria	837
Belgium	718-719
Cyprus	326-328
Denmark	458
Finland	483
France	1245-1246
Germany	996-997
Great Britain	585
Greece	947-948
Iceland	406-407
Ireland	270-271
Italy	1000-1001
Liechtenstein	453
Luxembourg	474-475
Monaco	722-724
Netherlands	475-476
Norway	533-534
Portugal	1038-1040
San Marino	701-702
Spain	1567
Sweden	814-816

Switzerland 500-501
Turkey 1799-1800
Vatican..................................470-472
Yugoslavia 1003-1004

Europa, 1970

Interwoven Threads CD13

1970

Andorra, French 196-197
Belgium..................................741-742
Cyprus 340-342
France...................................1271-1272
Germany...............................1018-1019
Greece 985, 987
Iceland 420-421
Ireland...................................279-281
Italy 1013-1014
Liechtenstein 470
Luxembourg 489-490
Monaco..................................768-770
Netherlands 483-484
Portugal 1060-1062
San Marino.............................729-730
Spain 1607
Switzerland 515-516
Turkey 1848-1849
Yugoslavia 1024-1025

Europa, 1971

"Fraternity, Cooperation, Common Effort" CD14

1971

Andorra, French 205-206
Belgium..................................803-804
Cyprus 365-367
Finland..504
France...1304
Germany...............................1064-1065
Greece 1029-1030
Iceland 429-430
Ireland...................................305-306
Italy 1038-1039
Liechtenstein 485
Luxembourg 500-501
Malta.....................................425-427
Monaco..................................797-799
Netherlands 488-489
Portugal 1094-1096
San Marino.............................749-750
Spain 1675-1676
Switzerland 531-532
Turkey 1876-1877
Yugoslavia 1052-1053

Europa, 1972

Sparkles, Symbolic of Communications CD15

1972

Andorra, French 210-211
Andorra, Spanish 62
Belgium..................................825-826
Cyprus 380-382
Finland...................................512-513
France...1341
Germany...............................1089-1090
Greece 1049-1050
Iceland 439-440
Ireland...................................316-317
Italy 1065-1066
Liechtenstein 504
Luxembourg 512-513
Malta.....................................450-453
Monaco..................................831-832

Netherlands 494-495
Portugal 1141-1143
San Marino.............................771-772
Spain 1718
Switzerland 544-545
Turkey 1907-1908
Yugoslavia 1100-1101

Europa, 1973

Post Horn and Arrows CD16

1973

Andorra, French 219-220
Andorra, Spanish 76
Belgium..................................839-840
Cyprus 396-398
Finland..526
France...1367
Germany...............................1114-1115
Greece 1090-1092
Iceland 447-448
Ireland...................................329-330
Italy 1108-1109
Liechtenstein 528-529
Luxembourg 523-524
Malta.....................................469-471
Monaco..................................866-867
Netherlands 504-505
Norway...................................604-605
Portugal 1170-1172
San Marino.............................802-803
Spain 1753
Switzerland 580-581
Turkey 1935-1936
Yugoslavia 1138-1139

Europa, 2000

CD17

2000

Albania...................................2621-2622
Andorra, French 522
Andorra, Spanish 262
Armenia..................................610-611
Austria 1814
Azerbaijan...............................698-699
Belarus..350
Belgium..1818
Bosnia & Herzegovina (Moslem) ...358
Bosnia & Herzegovina (Serb) ...111-112
Croatia 428-429
Cyprus 959
Czech Republic 3120
Denmark..1189
Estonia 394
Faroe Islands..................................376
Finland..1129
Aland Islands..................................166
France...2771
Georgia 228-229
Germany...............................2086-2087
Gibraltar.................................837-840
Great Britain (Guernsey)..........805-809
Great Britain (Jersey)...............935-936
Great Britain (Isle of Man) 883
Greece 1959
Greenland.......................................363
Hungary 3699-3700
Iceland 910
Ireland...................................1230-1231
Italy 2349
Latvia 504
Liechtenstein 1178
Lithuania 668
Luxembourg 1035
Macedonia.......................................187
Malta.....................................1011-1012
Moldova..355
Monaco..................................2161-2162
Poland 3519
Portugal 2358
Portugal (Azores)...........................455
Portugal (Madeira).........................208

Romania 4370
Russia 6589
San Marino.....................................1480
Slovakia 355
Slovenia 424
Spain 3036
Sweden 2394
Switzerland 1074
Turkey 2762
Turkish Rep. of Northern Cyprus....500
Ukraine 379
Vatican City 1152

The Gibraltar stamps are similar to the stamp illustrated, but none have the design shown above. All other sets listed above include at least one stamp with the design shown, but some include stamps with entirely different designs. Bulgaria Nos. 4131-4132 and Yugoslavia Nos. 2485-2486 are Europa stamps with completely different designs.

PORTUGAL & COLONIES
Vasco da Gama

Fleet Departing CD20

Fleet Arriving at Calicut — CD21

Embarking at Rastello CD22

Muse of History CD23

San Gabriel, da Gama and Camoens CD24

Archangel Gabriel, the Patron Saint CD25

Flagship San Gabriel — CD26

Vasco da Gama — CD27

Fourth centenary of Vasco da Gama's discovery of the route to India.

1898

Azores 93-100
Macao.....................................67-74
Madeira...................................37-44
Portugal 147-154
Port. Africa 1-8
Port. Congo 75-98
Port. India 189-196
St. Thomas & Prince Islands ...170-193
Timor 45-52

Pombal
POSTAL TAX
POSTAL TAX DUES

Marquis de Pombal — CD28

Planning Reconstruction of Lisbon, 1755 — CD29

Pombal Monument, Lisbon — CD30

Sebastiao Jose de Carvalho e Mello, Marquis de Pombal (1699-1782), statesman, rebuilt Lisbon after earthquake of 1755. Tax was for the erection of Pombal monument. Obligatory on all mail on certain days throughout the year. Postal Tax Dues are inscribed "Multa."

1925

Angola RA1-RA3, RAJ1-RAJ3
Azores RA9-RA11, RAJ2-RAJ4
Cape Verde RA1-RA3, RAJ1-RAJ3
Macao RA1-RA3, RAJ1-RAJ3
Madeira............. RA1-RA3, RAJ1-RAJ3
Mozambique RA1-RA3, RAJ1-RAJ3
Nyassa RA1-RA3, RAJ1-RAJ3
Portugal RA11-RA13, RAJ2-RAJ4
Port. Guinea RA1-RA3, RAJ1-RAJ3
Port. India RA1-RA3, RAJ1-RAJ3
St. Thomas & Prince
Islands RA1-RA3, RAJ1-RAJ3
Timor RA1-RA3, RAJ1-RAJ3

Vasco da Gama CD34

Mousinho de Albuquerque CD35

Dam CD36

Prince Henry the Navigator CD37

Affonso de Albuquerque CD38

Plane over Globe CD39

1938-39

Angola 274-291, C1-C9
Cape Verde 234-251, C1-C9
Macao.......................289-305, C7-C15
Mozambique 270-287, C1-C9
Port. Guinea 233-250, C1-C9
Port. India 439-453, C1-C8
St. Thomas & Prince
Islands ... 302-319, 323-340, C1-C18
Timor 223-239, C1-C9

Lady of Fatima

Our Lady of the Rosary, Fatima, Portugal — CD40

948-49

Angola	315-318
Cape Verde	266
Macao	336
Mozambique	325-328
Port. Guinea	271
St. Thomas & Prince Islands	351
Timor	254

A souvenir sheet of 9 stamps was issued in 951 to mark the extension of the 1950 Holy ear. The sheet contains: Angola No. 316, ape Verde No. 266, Macao No. 336, lozambique No. 325, Portuguese Guinea No. 71, Portuguese India Nos. 480, 485, St. homas & Prince Islands No. 351, Timor No. 54. The sheet also contains a portrait of Pope ius XII and is inscribed "Encerramento do no Santo, Fatima 1951." It was sold for 11 scudos.

Holy Year

Church Bells and Dove CD41 — Angel Holding Candelabra CD42

Holy Year, 1950.

950-51

Angola	331-332
Cape Verde	268-269
Macao	339-340
Mozambique	330-331
Port. Guinea	273-274
Port. India	490-491, 496-503
St. Thomas & Prince Islands	353-354
Timor	258-259

A souvenir sheet of 8 stamps was issued in 951 to mark the extension of the Holy Year. he sheet contains: Angola No. 331, Cape erde No. 269, Macao No. 340, Mozambique o. 331, Portuguese Guinea No. 275, Portu-ese India No. 490, St. Thomas & Prince ands No. 354, Timor No. 258, some with lors changed. The sheet contains doves and inscribed "Encerramento do Ano Santo, Fat-a 1951.' It was sold for 17 escudos.

Holy Year Conclusion

Our Lady of Fatima — CD43

Conclusion of Holy Year. Sheets contain ernate vertical rows of stamps and labels aring quotation from Pope Pius XII, different each colony.

951

ngola	357
ape Verde	270
acao	352
ozambique	356
ort. Guinea	275
ort. India	506
Thomas & Prince Islands	355
mor	270

Medical Congress

CD44

First National Congress of Tropical Medicine, Lisbon, 1952. Each stamp has a different design.

1952

Angola	358
Cape Verde	287
Macao	364
Mozambique	359
Port. Guinea	276
Port. India	516
St. Thomas & Prince Islands	356
Timor	271

Postage Due Stamps

CD45

1952

Angola	J37-J42
Cape Verde	J31-J36
Macao	J53-J58
Mozambique	J51-J56
Port. Guinea	J40-J45
Port. India	J47-J52
St. Thomas & Prince Islands	J52-J57
Timor	J31-J36

Sao Paulo

Father Manuel da Nobrega and View of Sao Paulo — CD46

Founding of Sao Paulo, Brazil, 400th anniv.

1954

Angola	385
Cape Verde	297
Macao	382
Mozambique	395
Port. Guinea	291
Port. India	530
St. Thomas & Prince Islands	369
Timor	279

Tropical Medicine Congress

CD47

Sixth International Congress for Tropical Medicine and Malaria, Lisbon, Sept. 1958. Each stamp shows a different plant.

1958

Angola	409
Cape Verde	303
Macao	392
Mozambique	404
Port. Guinea	295
Port. India	569
St. Thomas & Prince Islands	371
Timor	289

Sports

CD48

Each stamp shows a different sport.

1962

Angola	433-438
Cape Verde	320-325
Macao	394-399
Mozambique	424-429
Port. Guinea	299-304
St. Thomas & Prince Islands	374-379
Timor	313-318

Anti-Malaria

Anopheles Funestus and Malaria Eradication Symbol — CD49

World Health Organization drive to eradicate malaria.

1962

Angola	439
Cape Verde	326
Macao	400
Mozambique	430
Port. Guinea	305
St. Thomas & Prince Islands	380
Timor	319

Airline Anniversary

Map of Africa, Super Constellation and Jet Liner — CD50

Tenth anniversary of Transportes Aereos Portugueses (TAP).

1963

Angola	490
Cape Verde	327
Mozambique	434
Port. Guinea	318
St. Thomas & Prince Islands	381

National Overseas Bank

Antonio Teixeira de Sousa — CD51

Centenary of the National Overseas Bank of Portugal.

1964, May 16

Angola	509
Cape Verde	328
Port. Guinea	319
St. Thomas & Prince Islands	382
Timor	320

ITU

ITU Emblem and the Archangel Gabriel — CD52

International Communications Union, Cent.

1965, May 17

Angola	511
Cape Verde	329
Macao	402
Mozambique	464
Port. Guinea	320
St. Thomas & Prince Islands	383
Timor	321

National Revolution

CD53

40th anniv. of the National Revolution. Different buildings on each stamp.

1966, May 28

Angola	525
Cape Verde	338
Macao	403
Mozambique	465
Port. Guinea	329
St. Thomas & Prince Islands	392
Timor	322

Navy Club

CD54

Centenary of Portugal's Navy Club. Each stamp has a different design.

1967, Jan. 31

Angola	527-528
Cape Verde	339-340
Macao	412-413
Mozambique	478-479
Port. Guinea	330-331
St. Thomas & Prince Islands	393-394
Timor	323-324

Admiral Coutinho

CD55

Centenary of the birth of Admiral Carlos Viegas Gago Coutinho (1869-1959), explorer and aviation pioneer. Each stamp has a different design.

1969, Feb. 17

Angola	547
Cape Verde	355
Macao	417
Mozambique	484
Port. Guinea	335
St. Thomas & Prince Islands	397
Timor	335

Administration Reform

Luiz Augusto Rebello da Silva — CD56

Centenary of the administration reforms of the overseas territories.

1969, Sept. 25

Angola	549
Cape Verde	357
Macao	419
Mozambique	491
Port. Guinea	337
St. Thomas & Prince Islands	399
Timor	338

Marshal Carmona

CD57

Birth centenary of Marshal Antonio Oscar Carmona de Fragoso (1869-1951), President of Portugal. Each stamp has a different design.

1970, Nov. 15

Angola	563
Cape Verde	359
Macao	422
Mozambique	493
Port. Guinea	340
St. Thomas & Prince Islands	403
Timor	341

Olympic Games

CD59

20th Olympic Games, Munich, Aug. 26-Sept. 11. Each stamp shows a different sport.

1972, June 20

Angola	569
Cape Verde	361
Macao	426
Mozambique	504
Port. Guinea	342
St. Thomas & Prince Islands	408
Timor	343

Lisbon-Rio de Janeiro Flight

CD60

50th anniversary of the Lisbon to Rio de Janeiro flight by Arturo de Sacadura and Coutinho, March 30-June 5, 1922. Each stamp shows a different stage of the flight.

1972, Sept. 20

Angola	570
Cape Verde	362
Macao	427
Mozambique	505
Port. Guinea	343
St. Thomas & Prince Islands	409
Timor	344

WMO Centenary

WMO Emblem — CD61

Centenary of international meterological cooperation.

1973, Dec. 15

Angola	571
Cape Verde	363
Macao	429
Mozambique	509
Port. Guinea	344
St. Thomas & Prince Islands	410
Timor	345

FRENCH COMMUNITY
Upper Volta can be found under Burkina Faso in Vol. 1
Madagascar can be found under Malagasy in Vol. 3
Colonial Exposition

People of French Empire CD70

Women's Heads CD71

France Showing Way to Civilization CD72

"Colonial Commerce" CD73

International Colonial Exposition, Paris.

1931

Cameroun	213-216
Chad	60-63
Dahomey	97-100
Fr. Guiana	152-155
Fr. Guinea	116-119
Fr. India	100-103
Fr. Polynesia	76-79
Fr. Sudan	102-105
Gabon	120-123
Guadeloupe	138-141
Indo-China	140-142
Ivory Coast	92-95
Madagascar	169-172
Martinique	129-132
Mauritania	65-68
Middle Congo	61-64
New Caledonia	176-179
Niger	73-76
Reunion	122-125
St. Pierre & Miquelon	132-135
Senegal	138-141
Somali Coast	135-138
Togo	254-257
Ubangi-Shari	82-85
Upper Volta	66-69
Wallis & Futuna Isls.	85-88

Paris International Exposition
Colonial Arts Exposition

"Colonial Resources"
CD74   CD77

Overseas Commerce CD75

Exposition Building and Women CD76

"France and the Empire" CD78

Cultural Treasures of the Colonies CD79

Souvenir sheets contain one imperf. stamp.

1937

Cameroun	217-222A
Dahomey	101-107
Fr. Equatorial Africa	27-32, 73
Fr. Guiana	162-168
Fr. Guinea	120-126
Fr. India	104-110
Fr. Polynesia	117-123
Fr. Sudan	106-112
Guadeloupe	148-154
Indo-China	193-199
Inini	41
Ivory Coast	152-158
Kwangchowan	132
Madagascar	191-197
Martinique	179-185
Mauritania	69-75
New Caledonia	208-214
Niger	72-83
Reunion	167-173
St. Pierre & Miquelon	165-171
Senegal	172-178
Somali Coast	139-145
Togo	258-264
Wallis & Futuna Isls.	89

Curie

Pierre and Marie Curie CD80

40th anniversary of the discovery of radium. The surtax was for the benefit of the Intl. Union for the Control of Cancer.

1938

Cameroun	B1
Cuba	B1-B2
Dahomey	B2
France	B76
Fr. Equatorial Africa	B1
Fr. Guiana	B3
Fr. Guinea	B2
Fr. India	B6
Fr. Polynesia	B5
Fr. Sudan	B1
Guadeloupe	B3

Indo-China	B14
Ivory Coast	B2
Madagascar	B2
Martinique	B2
Mauritania	B3
New Caledonia	B4
Niger	B1
Reunion	B4
St. Pierre & Miquelon	B3
Senegal	B3
Somali Coast	B2
Togo	B1

Caillie

Rene Caillie and Map of Northwestern Africa — CD81

Death centenary of Rene Caillie (1799-1838), French explorer. All three denominations exist with colony name omitted.

1939

Dahomey	108-110
Fr. Guinea	161-163
Fr. Sudan	113-115
Ivory Coast	160-162
Mauritania	109-111
Niger	84-86
Senegal	188-190
Togo	265-267

New York World's Fair

Natives and New York Skyline CD82

1939

Cameroun	223-224
Dahomey	111-112
Fr. Equatorial Africa	78-79
Fr. Guiana	169-170
Fr. Guinea	164-165
Fr. India	111-112
Fr. Polynesia	124-125
Fr. Sudan	116-117
Guadeloupe	155-156
Indo-China	203-204
Inini	42-43
Ivory Coast	163-164
Kwangchowan	121-122
Madagascar	209-210
Martinique	186-187
Mauritania	112-113
New Caledonia	215-216
Niger	87-88
Reunion	174-175
St. Pierre & Miquelon	205-206
Senegal	191-192
Somali Coast	179-180
Togo	268-269
Wallis & Futuna Isls.	90-91

French Revolution

Storming of the Bastille CD83

French Revolution, 150th anniv. The surtax was for the defense of the colonies.

1939

Cameroun	B2-B6
Dahomey	B3-B7
Fr. Equatorial Africa	B4-B8, CB1
Fr. Guiana	B4-B8, CB1
Fr. Guinea	B3-B7
Fr. India	B7-B11
Fr. Polynesia	B6-B10, CB1
Fr. Sudan	B2-B6
Guadeloupe	B4-B8
Indo-China	B15-B19, CB1
Inini	B1-B5
Ivory Coast	B3-B7

Kwangchowan B1-B5
Madagascar.......................B3-B7, CB1
Martinique...............................B3-B7
Mauritania..............................B4-B8
New Caledonia B5-B9, CB1
Niger.......................................B2-B6
Reunion B5-B9, CB1
St. Pierre & Miquelon..............B4-B8
Senegal B4-B8, CB1
Somali Coast B3-B7
Togo.......................................B2-B6
Wallis & Futuna Isls. B1-B5

Plane over Coastal Area CD85

All five denominations exist with colony name omitted.

1940

Dahomey C1-C5
Fr. Guinea C1-C5
Fr. Sudan C1-C5
Ivory Coast C1-C5
Mauritania C1-C5
Niger C1-C5
Senegal C12-C16
Togo C1-C5

Defense of the Empire

Colonial Infantryman — CD86

1941

Cameroun B13B
Dahomey B13
Fr. Equatorial Africa B8B
Fr. Guiana B10
Fr. Guinea B13
Fr. India B13
Fr. Polynesia B12
Fr. Sudan B12
Guadeloupe B10
Indo-China B19B
Inini B7
Ivory Coast B13
Kwangchowan B7
Madagascar B9
Martinique B9
Mauritania B14
New Caledonia B11
Niger B12
Reunion B11
St. Pierre & Miquelon B8B
Senegal B14
Somali Coast B9
Togo B10B
Wallis & Futuna Isls. B7

Colonial Education Fund

CD86a

1942

Cameroun CB3
Dahomey CB4
Fr. Equatorial Africa CB5
Fr. Guiana CB4
Fr. Guinea CB4

Fr. India CB3
Fr. Polynesia CB4
Fr. Sudan CB4
Guadeloupe CB3
Indo-China CB5
Inini CB4
Ivory Coast CB4
Kwangchowan CB4
Malagasy CB5
Martinique CB3
Mauritania CB4
New Caledonia CB4
Niger CB4
Reunion CB4
St. Pierre & Miquelon CB3
Senegal CB5
Somali Coast CB3
Togo CB3
Wallis & Futuna CB3

Cross of Lorraine & Four-motor Plane CD87

1941-5

Cameroun C1-C7
Fr. Equatorial Africa C17-C23
Fr. Guiana C9-C10
Fr. India C1-C6
Fr. Polynesia C3-C9
Fr. West Africa C1-C3
Guadeloupe C1-C2
Madagascar......................... C37-C43
Martinique............................ C1-C2
New Caledonia C7-C13
Reunion C18-C24
St. Pierre & Miquelon C1-C7
Somali Coast C1-C7

Transport Plane CD88

Caravan and Plane CD89

1942

Dahomey C6-C13
Fr. Guinea C6-C13
Fr. Sudan C6-C13
Ivory Coast C6-C13
Mauritania C6-C13
Niger C6-C13
Senegal C17-C25
Togo C6-C13

Red Cross

Marianne CD90

The surtax was for the French Red Cross and national relief.

1944

Cameroun B28
Fr. Equatorial Africa B38
Fr. Guiana B12
Fr. India B14
Fr. Polynesia B13
Fr. West Africa B1
Guadeloupe B12
Madagascar................................. B15
Martinique................................. B11
New Caledonia B13
Reunion B15
St. Pierre & Miquelon B13
Somali Coast B13

Wallis & Futuna Isls. B9

Eboue

CD91

Felix Eboue, first French colonial administrator to proclaim resistance to Germany after French surrender in World War II.

1945

Cameroun................................296-297
Fr. Equatorial Africa 156-157
Fr. Guiana 171-172
Fr. India 210-211
Fr. Polynesia 150-151
Fr. West Africa 15-16
Guadeloupe 187-188
Madagascar.........................259-260
Martinique..........................196-197
New Caledonia 274-275
Reunion 238-239
St. Pierre & Miquelon 322-323
Somali Coast 238-239

Victory

Victory — CD92

European victory of the Allied Nations in World War II.

1946, May 8

Cameroun................................... C8
Fr. Equatorial Africa C24
Fr. Guiana C11
Fr. India C7
Fr. Polynesia C10
Fr. West Africa C4
Guadeloupe C3
Indo-China C19
Madagascar.............................. C44
Martinique............................... C3
New Caledonia C14
Reunion C25
St. Pierre & Miquelon C8
Somali Coast C8
Wallis & Futuna Isls. C1

Chad to Rhine

Leclerc's Departure from Chad — CD93

Battle at Cufra Oasis — CD94

Tanks in Action, Mareth — CD95

Normandy Invasion — CD96

Entering Paris — CD97

Liberation of Strasbourg — CD98

"Chad to the Rhine" march, 1942-44, by Gen. Jacques Leclerc's column, later French 2nd Armored Division.

1946, June 6

Cameroun C9-C14
Fr. Equatorial Africa C25-C30
Fr. Guiana C12-C17
Fr. India C8-C13
Fr. Polynesia C11-C16
Fr. West Africa C5-C10
Guadeloupe C4-C9
Indo-China C20-C25
Madagascar.......................... C45-C50
Martinique............................ C4-C9
New Caledonia C15-C20
Reunion C26-C31
St. Pierre & Miquelon C9-C14
Somali Coast C9-C14
Wallis & Futuna Isls. C2-C7

UPU

French Colonials, Globe and Plane — CD99

Universal Postal Union, 75th anniv.

1949, July 4

Cameroun................................... C29
Fr. Equatorial Africa C34
Fr. India C17
Fr. Polynesia C20
Fr. West Africa C15
Indo-China C26
Madagascar............................... C55
New Caledonia C24
St. Pierre & Miquelon C18
Somali Coast C18
Togo....................................... C18
Wallis & Futuna Isls. C10

Tropical Medicine

Doctor Treating Infant CD100

The surtax was for charitable work.

1950

Cameroun	B29
Fr. Equatorial Africa	B39
Fr. India	B15
Fr. Polynesia	B14
Fr. West Africa	B3
Madagascar	B17
New Caledonia	B14
St. Pierre & Miquelon	B14
Somali Coast	B14
Togo	B11

Military Medal

Medal, Early Marine and Colonial Soldier — CD101

Centenary of the creation of the French Military Medal.

1952

Cameroun	332
Comoro Isls.	39
Fr. Equatorial Africa	186
Fr. India	233
Fr. Polynesia	179
Fr. West Africa	57
Madagascar	286
New Caledonia	295
St. Pierre & Miquelon	345
Somali Coast	267
Togo	327
Wallis & Futuna Isls.	149

Liberation

Allied Landing, Victory Sign and Cross of Lorraine — CD102

Liberation of France, 10th anniv.

1954, June 6

Cameroun	C32
Comoro Isls.	C4
Fr. Equatorial Africa	C38
Fr. India	C18
Fr. Polynesia	C22
Fr. West Africa	C17
Madagascar	C57
New Caledonia	C25
St. Pierre & Miquelon	C19
Somali Coast	C19
Togo	C19
Wallis & Futuna Isls.	C11

FIDES

Plowmen CD103

Efforts of FIDES, the Economic and Social Development Fund for Overseas Possessions

---

(Fonds d' Investissement pour le Developpement Economique et Social). Each stamp has a different design.

1956

Cameroun	326-329
Comoro Isls.	43
Fr. Polynesia	181
Fr. West Africa	65-72
Madagascar	292-295
New Caledonia	303
Somali Coast	268
Togo	331

Flower

CD104

Each stamp shows a different flower.

1958-9

Cameroun	333
Comoro Isls.	45
Fr. Equatorial Africa	200-201
Fr. Polynesia	192
Fr. So. & Antarctic Terr.	11
Fr. West Africa	79-83
Madagascar	301-302
New Caledonia	304-305
St. Pierre & Miquelon	357
Somali Coast	270
Togo	348-349
Wallis & Futuna Isls.	152

Human Rights

Sun, Dove and U.N. Emblem CD105

10th anniversary of the signing of the Universal Declaration of Human Rights.

1958

Comoro Isls.	44
Fr. Equatorial Africa	202
Fr. Polynesia	191
Fr. West Africa	85
Madagascar	300
New Caledonia	306
St. Pierre & Miquelon	356
Somali Coast	274
Wallis & Futuna Isls.	153

C.C.T.A.

CD106

Commission for Technical Cooperation in Africa south of the Sahara, 10th anniv.

1960

Cameroun	335
Cent. Africa	3
Chad	66
Congo, P.R.	90
Dahomey	138
Gabon	150
Ivory Coast	180
Madagascar	317
Mali	9
Mauritania	117
Niger	104
Upper Volta	89

Air Afrique, 1961

Modern and Ancient Africa, Map and Planes — CD107

Founding of Air Afrique (African Airlines).

1961-62

Cameroun	C37
Cent. Africa	C5
Chad	C7
Congo, P.R.	C5
Dahomey	C17
Gabon	C5
Ivory Coast	C18
Mauritania	C17
Niger	C22
Senegal	C31
Upper Volta	C4

Anti-Malaria

CD108

World Health Organization drive to eradicate malaria.

1962, Apr. 7

Cameroun	B36
Cent. Africa	B1
Chad	B1
Comoro Isls.	B1
Congo, P.R.	B3
Dahomey	B15
Gabon	B4
Ivory Coast	B15
Madagascar	B19
Mali	B1
Mauritania	B16
Niger	B14
Senegal	B16
Somali Coast	B15
Upper Volta	B1

Abidjan Games

CD109

Abidjan Games, Ivory Coast, Dec. 24-31, 1961. Each stamp shows a different sport.

1962

Chad	83-84
Cent. Africa	19-20
Congo, P.R.	103-104
Gabon	163-164, C6
Niger	109-111
Upper Volta	103-105

African and Malagasy Union

Flag of Union CD110

First anniversary of the Union.

1962, Sept. 8

Cameroun	373
Cent. Africa	21

Chad	85
Congo, P.R.	105
Dahomey	155
Gabon	165
Ivory Coast	198
Madagascar	332
Mauritania	170
Niger	112
Senegal	211
Upper Volta	106

Telstar

Telstar and Globe Showing Andover and Pleumeur-Bodou — CD111

First television connection of the United States and Europe through the Telstar satellite, July 11-12, 1962.

1962-63

Andorra, French	154
Comoro Isls.	C7
Fr. Polynesia	C29
Fr. So. & Antarctic Terr.	C5
New Caledonia	C33
Somali Coast	C31
St. Pierre & Miquelon	C26
Wallis & Futuna Isls.	C17

Freedom From Hunger

World Map and Wheat Emblem CD112

U.N. Food and Agriculture Organization's "Freedom from Hunger" campaign.

1963, Mar. 21

Cameroun	B37-B38
Cent. Africa	B2
Chad	B2
Congo, P.R.	B4
Dahomey	B16
Gabon	B5
Ivory Coast	B16
Madagascar	B21
Mauritania	B17
Niger	B15
Senegal	B17
Upper Volta	B2

Red Cross Centenary

CD113

Centenary of the International Red Cross.

1963, Sept. 2

Comoro Isls.	55
Fr. Polynesia	205
New Caledonia	328
St. Pierre & Miquelon	367
Somali Coast	297
Wallis & Futuna Isls.	165

African Postal Union, 1963

UAMPT Emblem, Radio Masts, Plane and Mail CD114

Establishment of the African and Malagasy Posts and Telecommunications Union.

1963, Sept. 8

Cameroun	C47
Cent. Africa	C10
Chad	C9
Congo, P.R.	C13
Dahomey	C19
Gabon	C13
Ivory Coast	C25
Madagascar	C75
Mauritania	C22
Niger	C27
Rwanda	36
Senegal	C32
Upper Volta	C9

Air Afrique, 1963

Symbols of Flight — CD115

First anniversary of Air Afrique and inauguration of DC-8 service.

1963, Nov. 19

Cameroun	C48
Chad	C10
Congo, P.R.	C14
Gabon	C18
Ivory Coast	C26
Mauritania	C26
Niger	C35
Senegal	C33

Europafrica

Europe and Africa Linked — CD116

Signing of an economic agreement between the European Economic Community and the African and Malagasy Union, Yaounde, Cameroun, July 20, 1963.

1963-64

Cameroun	402
Chad	C11
Cent. Africa	C12
Congo, P.R.	C16
Gabon	C19
Ivory Coast	217
Niger	C43
Upper Volta	C11

Human Rights

Scales of Justice and Globe CD117

15th anniversary of the Universal Declaration of Human Rights.

1963, Dec. 10

Comoro Isls.	58
Fr. Polynesia	206
New Caledonia	329
St. Pierre & Miquelon	368
Somali Coast	300
Wallis & Futuna Isls.	166

PHILATEC

Stamp Album, Champs Elysees Palace and Horses of Marly CD118

Intl. Philatelic and Postal Techniques Exhibition, Paris, June 5-21, 1964.

1963-64

Comoro Isls.	60
France	1078
Fr. Polynesia	207
New Caledonia	341
St. Pierre & Miquelon	369
Somali Coast	301
Wallis & Futuna Isls.	167

Cooperation

CD119

Cooperation between France and the French-speaking countries of Africa and Madagascar.

1964

Cameroun	409-410
Cent. Africa	39
Chad	103
Congo, P.R.	121
Dahomey	193
France	1111
Gabon	175
Ivory Coast	221
Madagascar	360
Mauritania	181
Niger	143
Senegal	236
Togo	495

ITU

Telegraph, Syncom Satellite and ITU Emblem CD120

Intl. Telecommunication Union, Cent.

1965, May 17

Comoro Isls.	C14
Fr. Polynesia	C33
Fr. So. & Antarctic Terr.	C8
New Caledonia	C40
New Hebrides	124-125
St. Pierre & Miquelon	C29
Somali Coast	C36
Wallis & Futuna Isls.	C20

French Satellite A-1

Diamant Rocket and Launching Installation — CD121

Launching of France's first satellite, Nov. 26, 1965.

1965-66

Comoro Isls.	C15-C16
France	1137-1138
Fr. Polynesia	C40-C41
Fr. So. & Antarctic Terr.	C9-C10
New Caledonia	C44-C45
St. Pierre & Miquelon	C30-C31
Somali Coast	C39-C40
Wallis & Futuna Isls.	C22-C23

French Satellite D-1

D-1 Satellite in Orbit — CD122

Launching of the D-1 satellite at Hammaguir, Algeria, Feb. 17, 1966.

1966

Comoro Isls.	C17
France	1148
Fr. Polynesia	C42
Fr. So. & Antarctic Terr.	C11
New Caledonia	C46
St. Pierre & Miquelon	C32
Somali Coast	C49
Wallis & Futuna Isls.	C24

Air Afrique, 1966

Planes and Air Afrique Emblem — CD123

Introduction of DC-8F planes by Air Afrique.

1966

Cameroun	C79
Cent. Africa	C35
Chad	C26
Congo, P.R.	C42
Dahomey	C42
Gabon	C47
Ivory Coast	C32
Mauritania	C57
Niger	C63
Senegal	C47
Togo	C54
Upper Volta	C31

African Postal Union, 1967

Telecommunications Symbols and Map of Africa — CD124

Fifth anniversary of the establishment of the African and Malagasy Union of Posts and Telecommunications, UAMPT.

1967

Cameroun	C90
Cent. Africa	C46
Chad	C37
Congo, P.R.	C57
Dahomey	C61
Gabon	C58
Ivory Coast	C34
Madagascar	C85
Mauritania	C65
Niger	C75
Rwanda	C1-C3
Senegal	C60
Togo	C81
Upper Volta	C50

Monetary Union

Gold Token of the Ashantis, 17-18th Centuries — CD125

West African Monetary Union, 5th anniv.

1967, Nov. 4

Dahomey	244
Ivory Coast	259
Mauritania	238
Niger	204
Senegal	294
Togo	623
Upper Volta	181

WHO Anniversary

Sun, Flowers and WHO Emblem CD126

World Health Organization, 20th anniv.

1968, May 4

Afars & Issas	317
Comoro Isls.	73
Fr. Polynesia	241-242
Fr. So. & Antarctic Terr.	31
New Caledonia	367
St. Pierre & Miquelon	377
Wallis & Futuna Isls.	169

Human Rights Year

Human Rights Flame — CD127

1968, Aug. 10

Afars & Issas	322-323

Comoro Isls. 76
Fr. Polynesia...........................243-244
Fr. So. & Antarctic Terr. 32
New Caledonia..............................369
St. Pierre & Miquelon....................382
Wallis & Futuna Isls. 170

2nd PHILEXAFRIQUE

CD128

Opening of PHILEXAFRIQUE, Abidjan, Feb. 14. Each stamp shows a local scene and stamp.

1969, Feb. 14

Cameroun....................................C118
Cent. Africa C65
Chad C48
Congo, P.R..................................C77
Dahomey C94
Gabon C82
Ivory Coast C38-C40
Madagascar C92
Mali C65
Mauritania C80
Niger C104
Senegal C68
Togo C104
Upper Volta..................................C62

Concorde

Concorde in Flight
CD129

First flight of the prototype Concorde supersonic plane at Toulouse, Mar. 1, 1969.

1969

Afars & Issas C56
Comoro Isls. C29
France.. C42
Fr. Polynesia............................... C50
Fr. So. & Antarctic Terr. C18
New Caledonia C63
St. Pierre & Miquelon C40
Wallis & Futuna Isls. C30

Development Bank

Bank Emblem — CD130

African Development Bank, fifth anniv.

1969

Cameroun 499
Chad... 217
Congo, P.R..........................181-182
Ivory Coast 281
Mali 127-128
Mauritania 267
Niger 220
Senegal 317-318
Upper Volta................................ 201

ILO

ILO Headquarters, Geneva, and Emblem — CD131

Intl. Labor Organization, 50th anniv.

1969-70

Afars & Issas 337
Comoro Isls. 83
Fr. Polynesia.............................251-252
Fr. So. & Antarctic Terr. 35
New Caledonia 379
St. Pierre & Miquelon 396
Wallis & Futuna Isls. 172

ASECNA

Map of Africa, Plane and Airport CD132

10th anniversary of the Agency for the Security of Aerial Navigation in Africa and Madagascar (ASECNA, Agence pour la Securite de la Navigation Aerienne en Afrique et a Madagascar).

1969-70

Cameroun.......................................500
Cent. Africa 119
Chad 222
Congo, P.R.....................................197
Dahomey 269
Gabon 260
Ivory Coast 287
Mali 130
Niger 221
Senegal 321
Upper Volta....................................204

U.P.U. Headquarters

CD133

New Universal Postal Union headquarters, Bern, Switzerland.

1970

Afars & Issas 342
Algeria 443
Cameroun.................................503-504
Cent. Africa 125
Chad 225
Comoro Isls. 84
Congo, P.R.....................................216
Fr. Polynesia.............................261-262
Fr. So. & Antarctic Terr. 36
Gabon 258
Ivory Coast 295
Madagascar....................................444
Mali 134-135
Mauritania 283
New Caledonia 382
Niger 231-232
St. Pierre & Miquelon 397-398
Senegal 328-329
Tunisia 535
Wallis & Futuna Isls. 173

De Gaulle

CD134

First anniversay of the death of Charles de Gaulle, (1890-1970), President of France.

1971-72

Afars & Issas 356-357
Comoro Isls. 104-105
France....................................1322-1325
Fr. Polynesia............................270-271
Fr. So. & Antarctic Terr. 52-53
New Caledonia 393-394
Reunion 377, 380
St. Pierre & Miquelon...............417-418
Wallis & Futuna Isls. 177-178

African Postal Union, 1971

UAMPT Building, Brazzaville, Congo — CD135

10th anniversary of the establishment of the African and Malagasy Posts and Telecommunications Union, UAMPT. Each stamp has a different native design.

1971, Nov. 13

Cameroun C177
Cent. Africa C89
Chad C94
Congo, P.R. C136
Dahomey C146
Gabon C120
Ivory Coast C47
Mauritania C113
Niger C164
Rwanda C8
Senegal C105
Togo C166
Upper Volta................................. C97

West African Monetary Union

African Couple, City, Village and Commemorative Coin — CD136

West African Monetary Union, 10th anniv.

1972, Nov. 2

Dahomey 300
Ivory Coast 331
Mauritania 299
Niger 258
Senegal 374
Togo 825
Upper Volta................................. 280

African Postal Union, 1973

Telecommunications Symbols and Map of Africa — CD137

11th anniversary of the African and Malagasy Posts and Telecommunications Union (UAMPT).

1973, Sept. 12

Cameroun 574
Cent. Africa 194
Chad 294
Congo, P.R. 289
Dahomey 311
Gabon 320
Ivory Coast 361
Madagascar.................................. 500
Mauritania 304
Niger 287

Rwanda 540
Senegal 393
Togo 849
Upper Volta................................297

Philexafrique II — Essen

CD138

CD139

Designs: Indigenous fauna, local and German stamps. Types CD138-CD139 printed horizontally and vertically se-tenant in sheets of 10 (2x5). Label between horizontal pairs alternately commemorates Philexafrique II, Libreville, Gabon, June 1978, and 2nd International Stamp Fair, Essen, Germany, Nov. 1-5.

1978-1979

Benin C285-C286
Central Africa C200-C201
Chad......................................C238-C239
Congo Republic...................C245-C246
Djibouti................................C121-C122
Gabon...................................C215-C216
Ivory Coast C64-C65
Mali C356-C357
Mauritania C185-C186
Niger C291-C292
Rwanda C12-C13
Senegal C146-C147

BRITISH COMMONWEALTH OF NATIONS

The listings follow established trade practices when these issues are offered as units by dealers. The Peace issue, for example, includes only one stamp from the Indian state of Hyderabad. The U.P.U. issue includes the Egypt set. Pairs are included for those varieties issues with bilingual designs se-tenant.

Silver Jubilee

Windsor Castle and King George V CD301

Reign of King George V, 25th anniv.

1935

Antigua 77-80
Ascension 33-36
Bahamas 92-95
Barbados 186-189
Basutoland 11-14
Bechuanaland Protectorate 117-120
Bermuda 100-103
British Guiana 223-226
British Honduras......................108-111
Cayman Islands 81-84
Ceylon 260-263
Cyprus 136-139
Dominica 90-93
Falkland Islands 77-80
Fiji 110-113
Gambia 125-128
Gibraltar 100-103
Gilbert & Ellice Islands 33-36

Coronation

Queen
Elizabeth
and King
George VI
CD302

1937

Peace

King
George VI
and
Parliament
Buildings,
London
CD303

Return to peace at the close of World War II.

1945-46

Silver Wedding

King George VI and Queen
Elizabeth

CD304   CD305

1948-49

Sarawak 176-179
Seychelles 153-156
Sierra Leone 190-193
Singapore 23-26
Solomon Islands 84-87
Somaliland Protectorate 112-115
Southern Rhodesia 71-72
Swaziland 50-53
Tonga 87-90
Trinidad & Tobago 66-69
Turks & Caicos Islands 101-104
Virgin Islands 92-95
Zanzibar 226-229

The following have different designs but are
included in the omnibus set:

Great Britain 276-279
  Offices in Morocco 546-549
Australia 223
Bahrain 68-71
Burma 116-121
Ceylon 304-306
Egypt 281-283
India 223-226
Kuwait 89-92
Oman 31-34
Pakistan-Bahawalpur 26-29, O25-O28
South Africa 109-111
South-West Africa 160-162

319 stamps

University

Arms of   Alice, Princess
University   of Athlone
College   CD311
CD310

1948 opening of University College of the
West Indies at Jamaica.

1951

Antigua 104-105
Barbados 228-229
British Guiana 250-251
British Honduras 141-142
Dominica 120-121
Grenada 164-165
Jamaica 146-147
Leeward Islands 130-131
Montserrat 112-113
St. Kitts-Nevis 105-106
St. Lucia 149-150
St. Vincent 174-175
Trinidad & Tobago 70-71
Virgin Islands 96-97

28 stamps

Coronation

Queen Elizabeth
II — CD312

1953

Aden 47
  Kathiri State of Seiyun 28
  Qu'aiti State of Shihr and Mukalla .....
 28
Antigua 106
Ascension 61
Bahamas 157
Barbados 234
Basutoland 45
Bechuanaland Protectorate 153
Bermuda 142
British Guiana 252
British Honduras 143
Cayman Islands 150

Cyprus 167
Dominica 141
Falkland Islands 121
Falkland Islands Dependencies 1L18
Fiji 145
Gambia 152
Gibraltar 131
Gilbert & Ellice Islands 60
Gold Coast 160
Grenada 170
Hong Kong 184
Jamaica 153
Kenya, Uganda, Tanganyika 101
Leeward Islands 132
Malaya
  Johore 155
  Kedah 82
  Kelantan 71
  Malacca 27
  Negri Sembilan 63
  Pahang 71
  Penang 27
  Perak 126
  Perlis 28
  Selangor 101
  Trengganu 74
Malta 241
Mauritius 250
Montserrat 127
New Hebrides, British 77
Nigeria 79
North Borneo 260
Northern Rhodesia 60
Nyasaland Protectorate 96
Pitcairn 19
St. Helena 139
St. Kitts-Nevis 119
St. Lucia 156
St. Vincent 185
Sarawak 196
Seychelles 172
Sierra Leone 194
Singapore 27
Solomon Islands 88
Somaliland Protectorate 127
Swaziland 54
Trinidad & Tobago 84
Tristan da Cunha 13
Turks & Caicos Islands 118
Virgin Islands 114

The following have different designs but are
included in the omnibus set:

Great Britain 313-316
  Offices in Morocco 579-582
Australia 259-261
Bahrain 92-95
Canada 330
Ceylon 317
Cook Islands 145-146
Kuwait 113-116
New Zealand 280-284
Niue 104-105
Oman 52-55
Samoa 214-215
South Africa 192
Southern Rhodesia 80
South-West Africa 244-248
Tokelau Islands 4

106 stamps

Royal Visit 1953

Separate designs for each country for the
visit of Queen Elizabeth II and the Duke of
Edinburgh.

1953

Aden 62
Australia 267-269
Bermuda 163
Ceylon 318
Fiji 146
Gibraltar 146
Jamaica 154
Kenya, Uganda, Tanganyika 102
Malta 242
New Zealand 286-287

13 stamps

West Indies Federation

Map of the
Caribbean
CD313

Federation of the West Indies, April 22,
1958.

1958

Antigua 122-124
Barbados 248-250
Dominica 161-163
Grenada 184-186
Jamaica 175-177
Montserrat 143-145
St. Kitts-Nevis 136-138
St. Lucia 170-172
St. Vincent 198-200
Trinidad & Tobago 86-88

30 stamps

Freedom from Hunger

Protein Food
CD314

U.N. Food and Agricultural Organization's
"Freedom from Hunger" campaign.

1963

Aden 65
Antigua 133
Ascension 89
Bahamas 180
Basutoland 83
Bechuanaland Protectorate 194
Bermuda 192
British Guiana 271
British Honduras 179
Brunei 100
Cayman Islands 168
Dominica 181
Falkland Islands 146
Fiji 198
Gambia 172
Gibraltar 161
Gilbert & Ellice Islands 76
Grenada 190
Hong Kong 218
Malta 291
Mauritius 270
Montserrat 150
New Hebrides, British 93
North Borneo 296
Pitcairn 35
St. Helena 173
St. Lucia 179
St. Vincent 201
Sarawak 212
Seychelles 213
Solomon Islands 109
Swaziland 108
Tonga 127
Tristan da Cunha 68
Turks & Caicos Islands 138
Virgin Islands 140
Zanzibar 280

37 stamps

Red Cross Centenary

Red Cross
and
Elizabeth
II
CD315

1963

Antigua 134-135
Ascension 90-91
Bahamas 183-184
Basutoland 84-85
Bechuanaland Protectorate 195-196
Bermuda 193-194
British Guiana 272-273
British Honduras 180-181
Cayman Islands 169-170
Dominica 182-183
Falkland Islands 147-148
Fiji 203-204
Gambia 173-174
Gibraltar 162-163
Gilbert & Ellice Islands 77-78
Grenada 191-192
Hong Kong 219-220
Jamaica 203-204

Malta 292-293
Mauritius 271-272
Montserrat 151-152
New Hebrides, British 94-95
Pitcairn Islands 36-37
St. Helena 174-175
St. Kitts-Nevis 143-144
St. Lucia 180-181
St. Vincent 202-203
Seychelles 214-215
Solomon Islands 110-111
South Arabia 1-2
Swaziland 109-110
Tonga 134-135
Tristan da Cunha 69-70
Turks & Caicos Islands 139-140
Virgin Islands 141-142

70 stamps

Shakespeare

Shakespeare Memorial Theatre,
Stratford-on-Avon — CD316

400th anniversary of the birth of William
Shakespeare.

1964

Antigua 151
Bahamas 201
Bechuanaland Protectorate 197
Cayman Islands 171
Dominica 184
Falkland Islands 149
Gambia 192
Gibraltar 164
Montserrat 153
St. Lucia 196
Turks & Caicos Islands 141
Virgin Islands 143

12 stamps

ITU

ITU
Emblem
CD317

Intl. Telecommunication Union, cent.

1965

Antigua 153-154
Ascension 92-93
Bahamas 219-220
Barbados 265-266
Basutoland 101-102
Bechuanaland Protectorate 202-203
Bermuda 196-197
British Guiana 293-294
British Honduras 187-188
Brunei 116-117
Cayman Islands 172-173
Dominica 185-186
Falkland Islands 154-155
Fiji 211-212
Gibraltar 167-168
Gilbert & Ellice Islands 87-88
Grenada 205-206
Hong Kong 221-222
Mauritius 291-292
Montserrat 157-158
New Hebrides, British 108-109
Pitcairn Islands 52-53
St. Helena 180-181
St. Kitts-Nevis 163-164
St. Lucia 197-198
St. Vincent 224-225
Seychelles 218-219
Solomon Islands 126-127
Swaziland 115-116
Tristan da Cunha 85-86
Turks & Caicos Islands 142-143
Virgin Islands 159-160

64 stamps

Intl. Cooperation Year

ICY Emblem CD318

1965

Antigua	155-156
Ascension	94-95
Bahamas	222-223
Basutoland	103-104
Bechuanaland Protectorate	204-205
Bermuda	199-200
British Guiana	295-296
British Honduras	189-190
Brunei	118-119
Cayman Islands	174-175
Dominica	187-188
Falkland Islands	156-157
Fiji	213-214
Gibraltar	169-170
Gilbert & Ellice Islands	104-105
Grenada	207-208
Hong Kong	223-224
Mauritius	293-294
Montserrat	176-177
New Hebrides, British	110-111
New Hebrides, French	126-127
Pitcairn Islands	54-55
St. Helena	182-183
St. Kitts-Nevis	165-166
St. Lucia	199-200
Seychelles	220-221
Solomon Islands	143-144
South Arabia	17-18
Swaziland	117-118
Tristan da Cunha	87-88
Turks & Caicos Islands	144-145
Virgin Islands	161-162

64 stamps

Churchill Memorial

Winston Churchill and St. Paul's, London, During Air Attack CD319

1966

Antigua	157-160
Ascension	96-99
Bahamas	224-227
Barbados	281-284
Basutoland	105-108
Bechuanaland Protectorate	206-209
Bermuda	201-204
British Antarctic Territory	16-19
British Honduras	191-194
Brunei	120-123
Cayman Islands	176-179
Dominica	189-192
Falkland Islands	158-161
Fiji	215-218
Gibraltar	171-174
Gilbert & Ellice Islands	106-109
Grenada	209-212
Hong Kong	225-228
Mauritius	295-298
Montserrat	178-181
New Hebrides, British	112-115
New Hebrides, French	128-131
Pitcairn Islands	56-59
St. Helena	184-187
St. Kitts-Nevis	167-170
St. Lucia	201-204
St. Vincent	241-244
Seychelles	222-225
Solomon Islands	145-148
South Arabia	19-22
Swaziland	119-122
Tristan da Cunha	89-92
Turks & Caicos Islands	146-149
Virgin Islands	163-166

136 stamps

Royal Visit, 1966

Queen Elizabeth II and Prince Philip CD320

Caribbean visit, Feb. 4 - Mar. 6, 1966.

1966

Antigua	161-162
Bahamas	228-229
Barbados	285-286
British Guiana	299-300
Cayman Islands	180-181
Dominica	193-194
Grenada	213-214
Montserrat	182-183
St. Kitts-Nevis	171-172
St. Lucia	205-206
St. Vincent	245-246
Turks & Caicos Islands	150-151
Virgin Islands	167-168

26 stamps

World Cup Soccer

Soccer Player and Jules Rimet Cup CD321

World Cup Soccer Championship, Wembley, England, July 11-30.

1966

Antigua	163-164
Ascension	100-101
Bahamas	245-246
Bermuda	205-206
Brunei	124-125
Cayman Islands	182-183
Dominica	195-196
Fiji	219-220
Gibraltar	175-176
Gilbert & Ellice Islands	125-126
Grenada	230-231
New Hebrides, British	116-117
New Hebrides, French	132-133
Pitcairn Islands	60-61
St. Helena	188-189
St. Kitts-Nevis	173-174
St. Lucia	207-208
Seychelles	226-227
Solomon Islands	167-168
South Arabia	23-24
Tristan da Cunha	93-94

42 stamps

WHO Headquarters

World Health Organization Headquarters, Geneva — CD322

1966

Antigua	165-166
Ascension	102-103
Bahamas	247-248
Brunei	126-127
Cayman Islands	184-185
Dominica	197-198
Fiji	224-225
Gibraltar	180-181
Gilbert & Ellice Islands	127-128
Grenada	232-233
Hong Kong	229-230
Montserrat	184-185
New Hebrides, British	118-119
New Hebrides, French	134-135
Pitcairn Islands	62-63
St. Helena	190-191
St. Kitts-Nevis	177-178
St. Lucia	209-210

St. Vincent	247-248
Seychelles	228-229
Solomon Islands	169-170
South Arabia	25-26
Tristan da Cunha	99-100

46 stamps

UNESCO Anniversary

"Education" — CD323

"Science" (Wheat ears & flask enclosing globe). "Culture" (lyre & columns). 20th anniversary of the UNESCO.

1966-67

Antigua	183-185
Ascension	108-110
Bahamas	249-251
Barbados	287-289
Bermuda	207-209
Brunei	128-130
Cayman Islands	186-188
Dominica	199-201
Gibraltar	183-185
Gilbert & Ellice Islands	129-131
Grenada	234-236
Hong Kong	231-233
Mauritius	299-301
Montserrat	186-188
New Hebrides, British	120-122
New Hebrides, French	136-138
Pitcairn Islands	64-66
St. Helena	192-194
St. Kitts-Nevis	179-181
St. Lucia	211-213
St. Vincent	249-251
Seychelles	230-232
Solomon Islands	171-173
South Arabia	27-29
Swaziland	123-125
Tristan da Cunha	101-103
Turks & Caicos Islands	155-157
Virgin Islands	176-178

84 stamps

Silver Wedding, 1972

Queen Elizabeth II and Prince Philip — CD324

Designs: borders differ for each country.

1972

Anguilla	161-162
Antigua	295-296
Ascension	164-165
Bahamas	344-345
Bermuda	296-297
British Antarctic Territory	43-44
British Honduras	306-307
British Indian Ocean Territory	48-49
Brunei	186-187
Cayman Islands	304-305
Dominica	352-353
Falkland Islands	223-224
Fiji	328-329
Gibraltar	292-293
Gilbert & Ellice Islands	206-207
Grenada	466-467
Hong Kong	271-272
Montserrat	286-287
New Hebrides, British	169-170
Pitcairn Islands	127-128
St. Helena	271-272
St. Kitts-Nevis	257-258
St. Lucia	328-329
St.Vincent	344-345
Seychelles	309-310
Solomon Islands	248-249
South Georgia	35-36

Tristan da Cunha	178-179
Turks & Caicos Islands	257-258
Virgin Islands	241-242

60 stamps

Princess Anne's Wedding

Princess Anne and Mark Phillips — CD325

Wedding of Princess Anne and Mark Phillips, Nov. 14, 1973.

1973

Anguilla	179-180
Ascension	177-178
Belize	325-326
Bermuda	302-303
British Antarctic Territory	60-61
Cayman Islands	320-321
Falkland Islands	225-226
Gibraltar	305-306
Gilbert & Ellice Islands	216-217
Hong Kong	289-290
Montserrat	300-301
Pitcairn Island	135-136
St. Helena	277-278
St. Kitts-Nevis	274-275
St. Lucia	349-350
St. Vincent	358-359
St. Vincent Grenadines	1-2
Seychelles	311-312
Solomon Islands	259-260
South Georgia	37-38
Tristan da Cunha	189-190
Turks & Caicos Islands	286-287
Virgin Islands	260-261

44 stamps

Elizabeth II Coronation Anniv.

CD326   CD327

CD328

Designs: Royal and local beasts in heraldic form and simulated stonework. Portrait of Elizabeth II by Peter Grugeon. 25th anniversary of coronation of Queen Elizabeth II.

1978

Ascension	229
Barbados	474
Belize	397
British Antarctic Territory	71
Cayman Islands	404
Christmas Island	87
Falkland Islands	275
Fiji	384
Gambia	380
Gilbert Islands	312
Mauritius	464
New Hebrides, British	258
St. Helena	317
St. Kitts-Nevis	354
Samoa	472

Solomon Islands	368
South Georgia	51
Swaziland	302
Tristan da Cunha	238
Virgin Islands	337

20 sheets

Queen Mother Elizabeth's 80th Birthday

CD330

Designs: Photographs of Queen Mother Elizabeth. Falkland Islands issued in sheets of 50; others in sheets of 9.

1980

Ascension	261
Bermuda	401
Cayman Islands	443
Falkland Islands	305
Gambia	412
Gibraltar	393
Hong Kong	364
Pitcairn Islands	193
St. Helena	341
Samoa	532
Solomon Islands	426
Tristan da Cunha	277

12 stamps

Royal Wedding, 1981

Prince Charles and Lady Diana — CD331   CD331a

Wedding of Charles, Prince of Wales, and Lady Diana Spencer, St. Paul's Cathedral, London, July 29, 1981.

1981

Antigua	623-625
Ascension	294-296
Barbados	547-549
Barbuda	497-499
Bermuda	412-414
Brunei	268-270
Cayman Islands	471-473
Dominica	701-703
Falkland Islands	324-326
Falkland Islands Dep.	1L59-1L61
Fiji	442-444
Gambia	426-428
Ghana	759-761
Grenada	1051-1053
Grenada Grenadines	440-443
Hong Kong	373-375
Jamaica	500-503
Lesotho	335-337
Maldive Islands	906-908
Mauritius	520-522
Norfolk Island	280-282
Pitcairn Islands	206-208
St. Helena	353-355
St. Lucia	543-545
Samoa	558-560
Sierra Leone	509-517
Solomon Islands	450-452
Swaziland	382-384
Tristan da Cunha	294-296
Turks & Caicos Islands	486-488
Caicos Island	8-10
Uganda	314-316
Vanuatu	308-310
Virgin Islands	406-408

Princess Diana

CD332

CD333

Designs: Photographs and portrait of Princess Diana, wedding or honeymoon photographs, royal residences, arms of issuing country. Portrait photograph by Clive Friend. Souvenir sheet margins show family tree, various people related to the princess. 21st birthday of Princess Diana of Wales, July 1.

1982

Antigua	663-666
Ascension	313-316
Bahamas	510-513
Barbados	585-588
Barbuda	544-546
British Antarctic Territory	92-95
Cayman Islands	486-489
Dominica	773-776
Falkland Islands	348-351
Falkland Islands Dep.	1L72-1L75
Fiji	470-473
Gambia	447-450
Grenada	1101A-1105
Grenada Grenadines	485-491
Lesotho	372-375
Maldive Islands	952-955
Mauritius	548-551
Pitcairn Islands	213-216
St. Helena	372-375
St. Lucia	591-594
Sierra Leone	531-534
Solomon Islands	471-474
Swaziland	406-409
Tristan da Cunha	310-313
Turks and Caicos Islands	530A-534
Virgin Islands	430-433

250th anniv. of first edition of Lloyd's List (shipping news publication) & of Lloyd's marine insurance.

CD335

Designs: First page of early edition of the list; historical ships, modern transportation or harbor scenes.

1984

Ascension	351-354
Bahamas	555-558
Barbados	627-630
Cayes of Belize	10-13
Cayman Islands	522-525
Falkland Islands	404-407
Fiji	509-512
Gambia	519-522
Mauritius	587-590
Nauru	280-283
St. Helena	412-415
Samoa	624-627
Seychelles	538-541
Solomon Islands	521-524
Vanuatu	368-371
Virgin Islands	466-469

Queen Mother 85th Birthday

CD336

Designs: Photographs tracing the life of the Queen Mother, Elizabeth. The high value in each set pictures the same photograph taken of the Queen Mother holding the infant Prince Henry.

1985

Ascension	372-376
Bahamas	580-584
Barbados	660-664
Bermuda	469-473
Falkland Islands	420-424
Falkland Islands Dep.	1L92-1L96
Fiji	531-535
Hong Kong	447-450
Jamaica	599-603
Mauritius	604-608
Norfolk Island	364-368
Pitcairn Islands	253-257
St. Helena	428-432
Samoa	649-653
Seychelles	567-571
Solomon Islands	543-547
Swaziland	476-480
Tristan da Cunha	372-376
Vanuatu	392-396
Zil Elwannyen Sesel	101-105

Queen Elizabeth II, 60th Birthday

CD337

1986, April 21

Ascension	389-393
Bahamas	592-596
Barbados	675-679
Bermuda	499-503
Cayman Islands	555-559
Falkland Islands	441-445
Fiji	544-548
Hong Kong	465-469
Jamaica	620-624
Kiribati	470-474
Mauritius	629-633
Papua New Guinea	640-644
Pitcairn Islands	270-274
St. Helena	451-455
Samoa	670-674
Seychelles	592-596
Solomon Islands	562-566
South Georgia	101-105
Swaziland	490-494
Tristan da Cunha	388-392
Vanuatu	414-418
Zambia	343-347
Zil Elwannyen Sesel	114-118

Royal Wedding

Marriage of Prince Andrew and Sarah Ferguson CD338

1986, July 23

Ascension	399-400
Bahamas	602-603
Barbados	687-688
Cayman Islands	560-561
Jamaica	629-630
Pitcairn Islands	275-276
St. Helena	460-461
St. Kitts	181-182

Seychelles	602-603
Solomon Islands	567-568
Tristan da Cunha	397-398
Zambia	348-349
Zil Elwannyen Sesel	119-120

Queen Elizabeth II, 60th Birthday

Queen Elizabeth II & Prince Philip, 1947 Wedding Portrait — CD339

Designs: Photographs tracing the life of Queen Elizabeth II.

1986

Anguilla	674-677
Antigua	925-928
Barbuda	783-786
Dominica	950-953
Gambia	611-614
Grenada	1371-1374
Grenada Grenadines	749-752
Lesotho	531-534
Maldive Islands	1172-1175
Sierra Leone	760-763
Uganda	495-498

Royal Wedding, 1986

CD340

Designs: Photographs of Prince Andrew and Sarah Ferguson during courtship, engagement and marriage.

1986

Antigua	939-942
Barbuda	809-812
Dominica	970-973
Gambia	635-638
Grenada	1385-1388
Grenada Grenadines	758-761
Lesotho	545-548
Maldive Islands	1181-1184
Sierra Leone	769-772
Uganda	510-513

Lloyds of London, 300th Anniv.

CD341

Designs: 17th century aspects of Lloyds, representations of each country's individual connections with Lloyds and publicized disasters insured by the organization.

1986

Ascension	454-457
Bahamas	655-658
Barbados	731-734
Bermuda	541-544
Falkland Islands	481-484
Liberia	1101-1104
Malawi	534-537
Nevis	571-574
St. Helena	501-504
St. Lucia	923-926
Seychelles	649-652
Solomon Islands	627-630

South Georgia 131-134
Trinidad & Tobago 484-487
Tristan da Cunha 439-442
Vanuatu 485-488
Zil Elwannyen Sesel 146-149

Moon Landing, 20th Anniv.

CD342

Designs: Equipment, crew photographs, spacecraft, official emblems and report profiles created for the Apollo Missions. Two stamps in each set are square in format rather than like the stamp shown; see individual country listings for more information.

1989

Ascension Is. 468-472
Bahamas 674-678
Belize 916-920
Kiribati 517-521
Liberia 1125-1129
Nevis 586-590
St. Kitts 248-252
Samoa 760-764
Seychelles 676-680
Solomon Islands 643-647
Vanuatu 507-511
Zil Elwannyen Sesel 154-158

Queen Mother, 90th Birthday

CD343   CD344

Designs: Portraits of Queen Elizabeth, the Queen Mother. See individual country listings for more information.

1990

Ascension Is. 491-492
Bahamas 698-699
Barbados 782-783
British Antarctic Territory 170-171
British Indian Ocean Territory 106-107
Cayman Islands........................622-623
Falkland Islands 524-525
Kenya 527-528
Kiribati 555-556
Liberia 1145-1146
Pitcairn Islands 336-337
St. Helena 532-533
St. Lucia 969-970
Seychelles 710-711
Solomon Islands 671-672
South Georgia 143-144
Swaziland 565-566
Tristan da Cunha 480-481
Zil Elwannyen Sesel 171-172

Queen Elizabeth II, 65th Birthday, and Prince Philip, 70th Birthday

CD345

CD346

Designs: Portraits of Queen Elizabeth II and Prince Philip differ for each country. Printed in sheets of 10 + 5 labels (3 different) between. Stamps alternate, producing 5 different triptychs.

1991

Ascension Is. 505-506
Bahamas 730-731
Belize 969-970
Bermuda 617-618
Kiribati 571-572
Mauritius 733-734
Pitcairn Islands 348-349
St. Helena 554-555
St. Kitts 318-319
Samoa 790-791
Seychelles 723-724
Solomon Islands 688-689
South Georgia 149-150
Swaziland 586-587
Vanuatu 540-541
Zil Elwannyen Sesel 177-178

Royal Family Birthday, Anniversary

CD347

Queen Elizabeth II, 65th birthday, Charles and Diana, 10th wedding anniversary: Various photographs of Queen Elizabeth II, Prince Philip, Prince Charles, Princess Diana and their sons William and Henry.

1991

Antigua 1446-1455
Barbuda 1229-1238
Dominica................................1328-1337
Gambia 1080-1089
Grenada 2006-2015
Grenada Grenadines............1331-1340
Guyana 2440-2451
Lesotho 871-875
Maldive Islands....................1533-1542
Nevis 666-675
St. Vincent 1485-1494
St. Vincent Grenadines 769-778
Sierra Leone...........................1387-1396
Turks & Caicos Islands 913-922
Uganda 918-927

Queen Elizabeth II's Accession to the Throne, 40th Anniv.

CD348

CD349

Various photographs of Queen Elizabeth II with local Scenes.

1992 - CD348

Antigua 1513-1518
Barbuda 1306-1309
Dominica................................1414-1419
Gambia 1172-1177
Grenada 2047-2052
Grenada Grenadines............1368-1373

Lesotho 881-885
Maldive Islands....................1637-1642
Nevis 702-707
St. Vincent 1582-1587
St. Vincent Grenadines 829-834
Sierra Leone...........................1482-1487
Turks and Caicos Islands........978-987
Uganda 990-995
Virgin Islands...........................742-746

1992 - CD349

Ascension Islands 531-535
Bahamas 744-748
Bermuda 623-627
British Indian Ocean Territory 119-123
Cayman Islands........................648-652
Falkland Islands 549-553
Gibraltar.................................605-609
Hong Kong 619-623
Kenya 563-567
Kiribati 582-586
Pitcairn Islands 362-366
St. Helena 570-574
St. Kitts 332-336
Samoa 805-809
Seychelles 734-738
Solomon Islands 708-712
South Georgia 157-161
Tristan da Cunha 508-512
Vanuatu 555-559
Zambia 561-565
Zil Elwannyen Sesel 183-187

Royal Air Force, 75th Anniversary

CD350

1993

Ascension 557-561
Bahamas 771-775
Barbados 842-846
Belize 1003-1008
Bermuda 648-651
British Indian Ocean Territory 136-140
Falkland Is. 573-577
Fiji 687-691
Montserrat 830-834
St. Kitts 351-355

Royal Air Force, 80th Anniv.

Design CD350 Re-inscribed

1998

Ascension 697-701
Bahamas 907-911
British Indian Ocean Terr 198-202
Cayman Islands........................754-758
Fiji 814-818
Gibraltar.................................755-759
Samoa 957-961
Turks & Caicos Islands 1258-1265
Tuvalu 763-767
Virgin Islands...........................879-883

End of World War II, 50th Anniv.

CD351

CD352

1995

Ascension 613-617
Bahamas 824-828
Barbados 891-895
Belize 1047-1050
British Indian Ocean Territory 163-167
Cayman Islands........................704-708
Falkland Islands 634-638
Fiji 720-724
Kiribati 662-668
Liberia 1175-1179
Mauritius 803-805
St. Helena 646-654
St. Kitts 389-393
St. Lucia 1018-1022
Samoa 890-894
Solomon Islands 799-803
South Georgia & S. Sandwich Is.
....198-200
Tristan da Cunha 562-566

UN, 50th Anniv.

CD353

1995

Bahamas 839-842
Barbados 901-904
Belize 1055-1058
Jamaica 847-851
Liberia 1187-1190
Mauritius 813-816
Pitcairn Islands 436-439
St. Kitts 398-401
St. Lucia 1023-1026
Samoa 900-903
Tristan da Cunha 568-571
Virgin Islands...........................807-810

Queen Elizabeth, 70th Birthday

CD354

1996

Ascension 632-635
British Antarctic Territory 240-243
British Indian Ocean Territory 176-180
Falkland Islands 653-657
Pitcairn Islands 446-449
St. Helena 672-676
Samoa 912-916
Tokelau 223-227
Tristan da Cunha 576-579
Virgin Islands...........................824-828

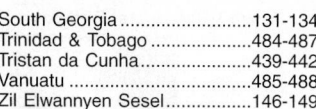

Diana, Princess of Wales (1961-97)

CD355

1998

Ascension	696
Bahamas	901A-902
Barbados	950
Belize	1091
Bermuda	753
Botswana	659-663
British Antarctic Territory	258
British Indian Ocean Terr.	197
Cayman Islands	752A-753
Falkland Islands	694
Fiji	819-820
Gibraltar	754
Kiribati	719A-720
Namibia	909
Niue	706
Norfolk Island	644-645
Papua New Guinea	937
Pitcairn Islands	487
St. Helena	711
St. Kitts	437A-438
Samoa	955A-956
Seycelles	802
Solomon Islands	866-867
South Georgia & S. Sandwich Islands	220
Tokelau	252B-253
Tonga	980
Niuafo'ou	201
Tristan da Cunha	618
Tuvalu	762
Vanuatu	719
Virgin Islands	878

Wedding of Prince Edward and Sophie Rhys-Jones

CD356

1999

Ascension	729-730
Cayman Islands	775-776
Falkland Islands	729-730
Pitcairn Islands	505-506
St. Helena	733-734
Samoa	971-972
Tristan da Cunha	636-637
Virgin Islands	908-909

1st Manned Moon Landing, 30th Anniv.

CD357

1999

Ascension	731-735
Bahamas	942-946
Barbados	967-971
Bermuda	778
Cayman Islands	777-781

Fiji	853-857
Jamaica	889-893
Kirbati	746-750
Nauru	465-469
St. Kitts	460-464
Samoa	973-977
Solomon Islands	875-879
Tuvalu	800-804
Virgin Islands	910-914

Queen Mother's Century

CD358

1999

Ascension	736-740
Bahamas	951-955
Cayman Islands	782-786
Falkland Islands	734-738
Fiji	858-862
Norfolk Island	688-692
St. Helena	740-744
Samoa	978-982
Solomon Islands	880-884
South Georgia & South Sandwich Islands	231-235
Tristan da Cunha	638-642
Tuvalu	805-809

Prince William, 18th Birthday

CD359

2000

Ascension	755-759
Cayman Islands	797-801
Falkland Islands	762-766
Fiji	889-893
South Georgia and South Sandwich Islands	257-261
Tristan da Cunha	664-668
Virgin Islands	925-929

Reign of Queen Elizabeth II, 50th Anniv.

CD360

2002

Ascension	790-794
Bahamas	1033-1037
Barbados	1019-1023
Belize	1152-1156
Bermuda	822-826
British Antarctic Territory	307-311
British Indian Ocean Territory	239-243
Cayman Islands	844-848
Falkland Islands	804-808
Gibraltar	896-900
Jamaica	952-956
Nauru	491-495
Norfolk Island	758-762
Papua New Guinea	1019-1023
Pitcairn Islands	552
St. Helena	788-792
St. Lucia	1146-1150
Solomon Islands	931-935
South Georgia & So. Sandwich Is.	274-278
Swaziland	706-710
Tokelau	302-306
Tonga	1059

Niuafo'ou	239
Tristan da Cunha	706-710
Virgin Islands	967-971

Queen Mother Elizabeth (1900-2002)

CD361

2002

Ascension	799-801
Bahamas	1044-1046
Bermuda	834-836
British Antarctic Territory	312-314
British Indian Ocean Territory	245-247
Cayman Islands	857-861
Falkland Islands	812-816
Nauru	499-501
Pitcairn Islands	561-565
St. Helena	808-812
St. Lucia	1155-1159
Seychelles	830
Solomon Islands	945-947
South Georgia & So. Sandwich Isls.	281-285
Tokelau	312-314
Tristan da Cunha	715-717
Virgin Islands	979-983

Head of Queen Elizabeth II

CD362

2003

Ascension	822
Bermuda	865
British Antarctic Territory	322
British Indian Ocean Territory	261
Cayman Islands	878
Falkland Islands	828
St. Helena	820
South Georgia & South Sandwich Islands	294
Tristan da Cunha	731
Virgin Islands	1003

Coronation of Queen Elizabeth II, 50th Anniv.

CD363

2003

Ascension	823-825
Bahamas	1073-1075
Bermuda	866-868
British Antarctic Territory	323-325
British Indian Ocean Territory	262-264
Cayman Islands	879-881
Jamaica	970-972
Kiribati	825-827
Pitcairn Islands	577-581
St. Helena	821-823
St. Lucia	1171-1173
Tokelau	320-322
Tristan da Cunha	732-734
Virgin Islands	1004-1006

Prince William, 21st Birthday

CD364

2003

Ascension	826
British Indian Ocean Territory	265
Cayman Islands	882-884
Falkland Islands	829
South Georgia & South Sandwich Islands	295
Tokelau	323
Tristan da Cunha	735
Virgin Islands	1007-1009

British Commonwealth of Nations

Dominions, Colonies, Territories, Offices and Independent Members

Comprising stamps of the British Commonwealth and associated nations.

A strict observance of technicalities would bar some or all of the stamps listed under Burma, Ireland, Kuwait, Nepal, New Republic, Orange Free State, Samoa, South Africa, South-West Africa, Stellaland, Sudan, Swaziland, the two Transvaal Republics and others but these are included for the convenience of collectors.

1. Great Britain

Great Britain: Including England, Scotland, Wales and Northern Ireland.

2. The Dominions, Present and Past

AUSTRALIA

The Commonwealth of Australia was proclaimed on January 1, 1901. It consists of six former colonies as follows:

New South Wales	Victoria
Queensland	Tasmania
South Australia	Western Australia

The following islands and territories are, or have been, administered by Australia: Australian Antarctic Territory, Christmas Island, Cocos (Keeling) Islands, Nauru, New Guinea, Norfolk Island, Papua.

CANADA

The Dominion of Canada was created by the British North America Act in 1867. The following provinces were former separate colonies and issued postage stamps:

British Columbia and Vancouver Island	Newfoundland
	Nova Scotia
New Brunswick	Prince Edward Island

FIJI

The colony of Fiji became an independent nation with dominion status on Oct. 10, 1970.

GHANA

This state came into existence Mar. 6, 1957, with dominion status. It consists of the former colony of the Gold Coast and the Trusteeship Territory of Togoland. Ghana became a republic July 1, 1960.

INDIA

The Republic of India was inaugurated on January 26, 1950. It succeeded the Dominion of India which was proclaimed August 15, 1947, when the former Empire of India was divided into Pakistan and the Union of India. The Republic is composed of about 40 predominantly Hindu states of three classes: governor's provinces, chief commissioner's provinces and princely states. India also has various territories, such as the Andaman and Nicobar Islands.

The old Empire of India was a federation of British India and the native states. The more important princely states were autonomous. Of the more than 700 Indian states, these 43 are familiar names to philatelists because of their postage stamps.

CONVENTION STATES

Chamba	Jhind
Faridkot	Nabha
Gwalior	Patiala

NATIVE FEUDATORY STATES

Alwar	Jammu
Bahawalpur	Jammu and Kashmir
Bamra	Jasdan
Barwani	Jhalawar
Bhopal	Jhind (1875-76)
Bhor	Kashmir
Bijawar	Kishangarh
Bundi	Las Bela
Bussahir	Morvi
Charkhari	Nandgaon
Cochin	Nowanuggur
Dhar	Orchha
Dungarpur	Poonch
Duttia	Rajpeepla
Faridkot (1879-85)	Sirmur
Hyderabad	Soruth
Idar	Travancore
Indore	Wadhwan
Jaipur	

NEW ZEALAND

Became a dominion on September 26, 1907. The following islands and territories are, or have been, administered by New Zealand:

Aitutaki	Ross Dependency
Cook Islands (Rarotonga)	Samoa (Western Samoa)
Niue	Tokelau Islands
Penrhyn	

PAKISTAN

The Republic of Pakistan was proclaimed March 23, 1956. It succeeded the Dominion which was proclaimed August 15, 1947. It is made up of all or part of several Moslem provinces and various districts of the former Empire of India, including Bahawalpur and Las Bela. Pakistan withdrew from the Commonwealth in 1972.

SOUTH AFRICA

Under the terms of the South African Act (1909) the self-governing colonies of Cape of Good Hope, Natal, Orange River Colony and Transvaal united on May 31, 1910, to form the Union of South Africa. It became an independent republic May 3, 1961.

Under the terms of the Treaty of Versailles, South-West Africa, formerly German South-West Africa, was mandated to the Union of South Africa.

SRI LANKA (CEYLON)

The Dominion of Ceylon was proclaimed February 4, 1948. The island had been a Crown Colony from 1802 until then. On May 22, 1972, Ceylon became the Republic of Sri Lanka.

3. Colonies, Past and Present; ControlledTerritory and Independent Members of the Commonwealth

Aden	Bechuanaland
Aitutaki	Bechuanaland Prot.
Antigua	Belize
Ascension	Bermuda
Bahamas	Botswana
Bahrain	British Antarctic Territory
Bangladesh	British Central Africa
Barbados	British Columbia and
Barbuda	Vancouver Island
Basutoland	British East Africa
Batum	British Guiana

British Honduras
British Indian Ocean Territory
British New Guinea
British Solomon Islands
British Somaliland
Brunei
Burma
Bushire
Cameroons
Cape of Good Hope
Cayman Islands
Christmas Island
Cocos (Keeling) Islands
Cook Islands
Crete,
  British Administration
Cyprus
Dominica
East Africa & Uganda
  Protectorates
Egypt
Falkland Islands
Fiji
Gambia
German East Africa
Gibraltar
Gilbert Islands
Gilbert & Ellice Islands
Gold Coast
Grenada
Griqualand West
Guernsey
Guyana
Heligoland
Hong Kong
Indian Native States
  (see India)
Ionian Islands
Jamaica
Jersey

Kenya
Kenya, Uganda & Tanzania
Kuwait
Labuan
Lagos
Leeward Islands
Lesotho
Madagascar
Malawi
Malaya
  Federated Malay States
  Johore
  Kedah
  Kelantan
  Malacca
  Negri Sembilan
  Pahang
  Penang
  Perak
  Perlis
  Selangor
  Singapore
  Sungei Ujong
  Trengganu
Malaysia
Maldive Islands
Malta
Man, Isle of
Mauritius
Mesopotamia
Montserrat
Muscat
Namibia
Natal
Nauru
Nevis
New Britain
New Brunswick
Newfoundland
New Guinea

New Hebrides
New Republic
New South Wales
Niger Coast Protectorate
Nigeria
Niue
Norfolk Island
North Borneo
Northern Nigeria
Northern Rhodesia
North West Pacific Islands
Nova Scotia
Nyasaland Protectorate
Oman
Orange River Colony
Palestine
Papua New Guinea
Penrhyn Island
Pitcairn Islands
Prince Edward Island
Queensland
Rhodesia
Rhodesia & Nyasaland
Ross Dependency
Sabah
St. Christopher
St. Helena
St. Kitts
St. Kitts-Nevis-Anguilla
St. Lucia
St. Vincent
Samoa
Sarawak
Seychelles
Sierra Leone
Solomon Islands
Somaliland Protectorate
South Arabia
South Australia
South Georgia

Southern Nigeria
Southern Rhodesia
South-West Africa
Stellaland
Straits Settlements
Sudan
Swaziland
Tanganyika
Tanzania
Tasmania
Tobago
Togo
Tokelau Islands
Tonga
Transvaal
Trinidad
Trinidad and Tobago
Tristan da Cunha
Trucial States
Turks and Caicos
Turks Islands
Tuvalu
Uganda
United Arab Emirates
Victoria
Virgin Islands
Western Australia
Zambia
Zanzibar
Zululand

POST OFFICES IN FOREIGN COUNTRIES
Africa
  East Africa Forces
  Middle East Forces
Bangkok
China
Morocco
Turkish Empire

Colonies, Former Colonies, Offices, Territories Controlled by Parent States

Belgium
Belgian Congo
Ruanda-Urundi

Denmark
Danish West Indies
Faroe Islands
Greenland
Iceland

Finland
Aland Islands

France

COLONIES PAST AND PRESENT, CONTROLLED TERRITORIES
Afars & Issas, Territory of
Alaouites
Alexandretta
Algeria
Alsace & Lorraine
Anjouan
Annam & Tonkin
Benin
Cambodia (Khmer)
Cameroun
Castellorizo
Chad
Cilicia
Cochin China
Comoro Islands
Dahomey
Diego Suarez
Djibouti (Somali Coast)
Fezzan
French Congo
French Equatorial Africa
French Guiana
French Guinea
French India
French Morocco
French Polynesia (Oceania)
French Southern & Antarctic Territories
French Sudan
French West Africa
Gabon
Germany
Ghadames
Grand Comoro
Guadeloupe
Indo-China
Inini
Ivory Coast
Laos
Latakia
Lebanon
Madagascar
Martinique
Mauritania
Mayotte
Memel
Middle Congo
Moheli
New Caledonia
New Hebrides
Niger Territory
Nossi-Be

Obock
Reunion
Rouad, Ile
Ste.-Marie de Madagascar
St. Pierre & Miquelon
Senegal
Senegambia & Niger
Somali Coast
Syria
Tahiti
Togo
Tunisia
Ubangi-Shari
Upper Senegal & Niger
Upper Volta
Viet Nam
Wallis & Futuna Islands

POST OFFICES IN FOREIGN COUNTRIES
China
Crete
Egypt
Turkish Empire
Zanzibar

Germany

EARLY STATES
Baden
Bavaria
Bergedorf
Bremen
Brunswick
Hamburg
Hanover
Lubeck
Mecklenburg-Schwerin
Mecklenburg-Strelitz
Oldenburg
Prussia
Saxony
Schleswig-Holstein
Wurttemberg

FORMER COLONIES
Cameroun (Kamerun)
Caroline Islands
German East Africa
German New Guinea
German South-West Africa
Kiauchau
Mariana Islands
Marshall Islands
Samoa
Togo

Italy

EARLY STATES
Modena
Parma
Romagna
Roman States
Sardinia
Tuscany
Two Sicilies
  Naples
  Neapolitan Provinces
  Sicily

FORMER COLONIES, CONTROLLED TERRITORIES, OCCUPATION AREAS
Aegean Islands
  Calimno (Calino)
  Caso
  Cos (Coo)
  Karki (Carchi)
  Leros (Lero)
  Lipso
  Nisiros (Nisiro)
  Patmos (Patmo)
  Piscopi
  Rodi (Rhodes)
  Scarpanto
  Simi
  Stampalia
Castellorizo
Corfu
Cyrenaica
Eritrea
Ethiopia (Abyssinia)
Fiume
Ionian Islands
  Cephalonia
  Ithaca
  Paxos
Italian East Africa
Libya
Oltre Giuba
Saseno
Somalia (Italian Somaliland)
Tripolitania

POST OFFICES IN FOREIGN COUNTRIES
"ESTERO"*
Austria
China
  Peking
  Tientsin
Crete
Tripoli
Turkish Empire
  Constantinople
  Durazzo
  Janina
Jerusalem
Salonika
Scutari
Smyrna
Valona

*Stamps overprinted "ESTERO" were used in various parts of the world.

Netherlands
Aruba
Netherlands Antilles (Curacao)
Netherlands Indies
Netherlands New Guinea
Surinam (Dutch Guiana)

Portugal

COLONIES PAST AND PRESENT, CONTROLLED TERRITORIES
Angola
Angra
Azores
Cape Verde
Funchal
Horta
Inhambane
Kionga
Lourenco Marques
Macao
Madeira
Mozambique
Mozambique Co.
Nyassa
Ponta Delgada
Portuguese Africa
Portuguese Congo
Portuguese Guinea
Portuguese India
Quelimane
St. Thomas & Prince Islands
Tete
Timor
Zambezia

Russia

ALLIED TERRITORIES AND REPUBLICS, OCCUPATION AREAS
Armenia
Aunus (Olonets)
Azerbaijan
Batum
Estonia
Far Eastern Republic
Georgia
Karelia
Latvia
Lithuania
North Ingermanland
Ostland
Russian Turkestan
Siberia
South Russia
Tannu Tuva
Transcaucasian Fed. Republics
Ukraine
Wenden (Livonia)
Western Ukraine

Spain

COLONIES PAST AND PRESENT, CONTROLLED TERRITORIES
Aguera, La
Cape Juby
Cuba
Elobey, Annobon & Corisco
Fernando Po
Ifni
Mariana Islands
Philippines
Puerto Rico
Rio de Oro
Rio Muni
Spanish Guinea
Spanish Morocco
Spanish Sahara
Spanish West Africa

POST OFFICES IN FOREIGN COUNTRIES
Morocco
Tangier
Tetuan

Dies of British Colonial Stamps

DIE A	DIE B	DIE I	DIE II

DIE A:
1. The lines in the groundwork vary in thickness and are not uniformly straight.
2. The seventh and eighth lines from the top, in the groundwork, converge where they meet the head.
3. There is a small dash in the upper part of the second jewel in the band of the crown.
4. The vertical color line in front of the throat stops at the sixth line of shading on the neck.

DIE B:
1. The lines in the groundwork are all thin and straight.
2. All the lines of the background are parallel.
3. There is no dash in the upper part of the second jewel in the band of the crown.
4. The vertical color line in front of the throat stops at the eighth line of shading on the neck.

DIE I:
1. The base of the crown is well below the level of the inner white line around the vignette.
2. The labels inscribed "POSTAGE" and "REVENUE" are cut square at the top.
3. There is a white "bud" on the outer side of the main stem of the curved ornaments in each lower corner.
4. The second (thick) line below the country name has the ends next to the crown cut diagonally.

DIE Ia.	DIE Ib.
1 as die II.	1 and 3 as die II.
2 and 3 as die I.	2 as die I.

DIE II:
1. The base of the crown is aligned with the underside of the white line around the vignette.
2. The labels curve inward at the top inner corners.
3. The "bud" has been removed from the outer curve of the ornaments in each corner.
4. The second line below the country name has the ends next to the crown cut vertically.

Wmk. 1	Wmk. 2	Wmk. 3	Wmk. 4
Crown and C C	Crown and C A	Multiple Crown and C A	Multiple Crown and Script C A

Wmk. 4a	Wmk. 314
	St. Edward's Crown and C A Multiple

Wmk. 373	Wmk. 384

British Colonial and Crown Agents Watermarks

Watermarks 1 to 4, 314, 373, and 384, common to many British territories, are illustrated here to avoid duplication.

The letters "CC" of Wmk. 1 identify the paper as having been made for the use of the Crown Colonies, while the letters "CA" of the others stand for "Crown Agents." Both Wmks. 1 and 2 were used on stamps printed by De La Rue & Co.

Wmk. 3 was adopted in 1904; Wmk. 4 in 1921; Wmk. 314 in 1957; Wmk. 373 in 1974; and Wmk. 384 in 1985.

In Wmk. 4a, a non-matching crown of the general St. Edwards type (bulging on both sides at top) was substituted for one of the Wmk. 4 crowns which fell off the dandy roll. The non-matching crown occurs in 1950-52 printings in a horizontal row of crowns on certain regular stamps of Johore and Seychelles, and on various postage due stamps of Barbados, Basutoland, British Guiana, Gold Coast, Grenada, Northern Rhodesia, St. Lucia, Swaziland and Trinidad and Tobago. A variation of Wmk. 4a, with the non-matching crown in a horizontal row of crown-CA-crown, occurs on regular stamps of Bahamas, St. Kitts-Nevis and Singapore.

Wmk. 314 was intentionally used sideways, starting in 1966. When a stamp was issued with Wmk. 314 both upright and sideways, the sideways varieties usually are listed also – with minor numbers. In many of the later issues, Wmk. 314 is slightly visible.

Wmk. 373 is usually only faintly visible.

SOLOMON ISLANDS

ˈsä-lə-mən ˈī-ləndz

British Solomon Islands

LOCATION — West Pacific Ocean, east of Papua
GOVT. — Independent state in British Commonwealth
AREA — 10,954 sq. mi.
POP. — 455,429 (1999 est.)
CAPITAL — Honiara

The Solomons include 10 large islands and four groups of small islands extending over an area of 375,000 square miles.

The British protectorate of British Solomon Islands changed its name to Solomon Islands in 1975 and achieved independence July 7, 1978.

12 Pence = 1 Shilling
20 Shillings = 1 Pound
100 Cents = 1 Dollar (1966)

Catalogue values for unused stamps in this country are for Never Hinged items, beginning with Scott 80 in the regular postage section and Scott B1 in the semi-postal section.

War Canoe — A1

Unwmk.

1907, Feb. 14		**Litho.**	**Perf. 11**	
1	A1	½p ultra	11.00	16.00
2	A1	1p red	27.50	30.00
3	A1	2p dull blue	36.00	36.00
a.		Horiz. pair, imperf. btwn.	15,000.	
4	A1	2½p orange	38.50	50.00
a.		Vert. pair, imperf. btwn.	7,000.	
b.		Horiz. pair, imperf. btwn.	9,250.	7,000.
5	A1	5p yellow green	67.50	80.00
6	A1	6p chocolate	75.00	77.50
a.		Vertical pair, imperf. btwn.	6,250.	
7	A1	1sh violet	97.50	110.00
		Nos. 1-7 (7)	353.00	399.50

Imperf. between varieties should be accompanied by certificates of authenticity issued by competent authorities. Excellent counterfeits are plentiful.

War Canoe
A2

George V
A3

Wmk. Multiple Crown and CA (3)

1908-11		**Engr.**	**Perf. 14**	
8	A2	½p green	1.75	1.25
9	A2	1p carmine	1.50	1.25
10	A2	2p gray	1.50	1.25
11	A2	2½p ultra	4.25	13.50
12	A2	4p red, yel ('11)	3.75	13.50
13	A2	5p olive green	10.50	8.75
14	A2	6p claret	11.50	8.25
15	A2	1sh black, green	9.75	9.25
16	A2	2sh vio, bl ('10)	47.50	70.00
17	A2	2sh6p red, bl ('10)	62.50	95.00
18	A2	5sh bl, yel ('10)	115.00	140.00
		Nos. 8-18 (11)	269.50	351.00

Inscribed "POSTAGE — POSTAGE"

1913-24			**Typo.**	
19	A3	½p green	.95	4.00
20	A3	1p carmine	1.75	16.50
21	A3	3p violet, yel	1.00	4.75
a.		3p violet, orange buff	5.00	27.50
22	A3	11p dull violet & red	5.75	14.00

Wmk. 4

23	A3	1½p scarlet ('24)	2.50	.80
		Nos. 19-23 (5)	11.95	40.05

Inscribed "POSTAGE — REVENUE"

1914-23			**Wmk. 3**	
28	A3	½p green	1.10	13.50
a.		½p yellow green ('17)	5.25	21.00
29	A3	1p carmine	1.75	1.50
a.		1p scarlet ('17)	5.50	7.50
30	A3	2p gray	3.50	10.50
31	A3	2½p ultra	2.50	5.75

Chalky Paper

32	A3	3p violet, yel ('23)	22.50	97.50
33	A3	4p blk & red, yel	2.25	3.00
34	A3	5p dull vio & ol grn	22.50	35.00
a.		5p brown purple & olive green	22.50	35.00
35	A3	6p dull vio & red vio	7.00	16.00
36	A3	1sh blk, green	5.50	8.00
a.		1sh blk, bl grn, ol back	8.50	27.50
37	A3	2sh dull vio & ultra, bl	8.00	11.50
38	A3	2sh6p blk & red, bl	11.00	22.50
39	A3	5sh grn & red, yel	37.50	55.00
a.		5sh green & red, orange buff	52.50	80.00
40	A3	10sh grn & red, grn	97.50	100.00
41	A3	£1 vio & blk, red	350.00	150.00
		Nos. 28-41 (14)	572.60	529.75

Inscribed "POSTAGE - REVENUE"

1922-31			**Wmk. 4**	
43	A3	½p green	.40	4.00
44	A3	1p carmine ('23)	12.50	12.50
45	A3	1p violet ('27)	1.10	8.50
46	A3	2p gray ('23)	5.25	17.00
47	A3	3p ultra ('23)	.85	5.25

Chalky Paper

48	A3	4p blk & red, yel ('27)	4.25	26.00
49	A3	4½p red brn ('31)	3.75	22.50
50	A3	5p dull vio & ol grn	3.75	32.50
51	A3	6p dull vio & red vio	4.50	32.50
52	A3	1sh black, emer	9.50	15.00
53	A3	2sh dull vio & ultra, bl ('27)	11.00	45.00
54	A3	2sh6p blk & red, bl	8.75	52.50
55	A3	5sh grn & red, yel	32.50	65.00
56	A3	10sh grn & red, emer ('25)	120.00	130.00
		Nos. 43-56 (14)	218.10	468.25

No. 49 is on ordinary paper.

Common Design Types
pictured following the introduction.

Silver Jubilee Issue
Common Design Type

1935, May 6		**Engr.**	**Perf. 13½x14**	
60	CD301	1½p car & dk bl	1.50	1.50
61	CD301	3p blue & brown	4.25	7.75
62	CD301	6p ol grn & lt bl	12.00	14.00
63	CD301	1sh brt vio & ind	9.25	14.50
		Nos. 60-63 (4)	27.00	37.75
		Set, never hinged	47.50	

Coronation Issue
Common Design Type

1937, May 13			**Perf. 11x11½**	
64	CD302	1p dark purple	.25	.60
65	CD302	1½p dark carmine	.25	.50
66	CD302	3p deep ultra	.40	.40
		Nos. 64-66 (3)	.90	1.50
		Set, never hinged	1.40	

Spears and Shield — A4

Policeman and Chief — A5

Artificial Island, Malaita — A6

Canoe House, New Georgia A7

Roviana War Canoe — A8

View of Munda Point — A9

Meeting House, Reef Islands A10

Coconut Plantation A11

Breadfruit A12

Tinakula Volcano, Santa Cruz Islands A13

Scrub Fowl — A14

Malaita Canoe — A15

Perf. 12½, 13½ (A7, A13, A14)				
1939-51			**Wmk. 4**	
67	A4	½p deep grn & ultra	.20	1.10
68	A5	1p dk pur & choc	.20	1.75
69	A6	1½p car & sl grn	.30	1.50
70	A7	2p blk & org brn	.35	1.60
a.		2p black & red brown ('43)	.35	1.75
		Never hinged	.70	
b.		Perf. 12 ('51)	.20	1.60
		Never hinged	.35	
71	A8	2½p ol grn & rose vio	1.25	2.75
a.		Vert. pair, imperf. horiz.	12,000.	
72	A9	3p ultra & blk, perf. 13½	.60	2.00
a.		Perf. 12 ('51)	.85	3.00
		Never hinged	2.00	
73	A10	4½p dk brn & yel grn	3.25	14.50
74	A11	6p rose lil & dk pur	.40	1.25
75	A12	1sh blk & grn	.80	1.25

76	A13	2sh dp org & blk	4.75	6.00
a.		2sh dp org & vio blk ('43)	4.75	6.50
		Never hinged	12.00	
77	A14	2sh6p dull vio & blk	18.50	6.00
78	A15	5sh red & brt bl	22.50	13.00
79	A10	10sh red lil & ol ('42)	6.75	10.00
		Nos. 67-79 (13)	59.85	62.70
		Set, never hinged	110.00	

Catalogue values for unused stamps in this section, from this point to the end of the section, are for Never Hinged items.

Peace Issue
Common Design Type

			Perf. 13½x14	
1946, Oct. 15		**Wmk. 4**	**Engr.**	
80	CD303	1½p carmine	.20	.70
81	CD303	3p deep blue	.20	.30

Silver Wedding Issue
Common Design Types

1949, Mar. 14		**Photo.**	**Perf. 14x14½**	
82	CD304	2p black	.40	.40
			Perf. 11½x11	
		Engr.; Name Typo.		
83	CD305	10sh red violet	17.50	13.50

UPU Issue
Common Design Types
Engr.; Name Typo. on 3p and 5p
Perf. 13½, 11x11½

1949, Oct. 10			**Wmk. 4**	
84	CD306	2p red brown	1.00	.85
85	CD307	3p indigo	2.40	.85
86	CD308	5p green	1.00	1.25
87	CD309	1sh slate	1.00	.85
		Nos. 84-87 (4)	5.40	3.80

Coronation Issue
Common Design Type

1953, June 2		**Engr.**	**Perf. 13½x13**	
88	CD312	2p gray & black	1.10	.90

Ysabel Canoe A16

Prow of Roviana Canoe — A17

Designs: 1p, Roviana canoe. 1½p, Artificial Island, Malaita. 2p, Canoe house. 3p, Malaita canoe. 5p, 1sh3p, Map. 6p, Trading schooner. 8p, 9p, Henderson Field, Guadalcanal. 1sh, Chart of Solomons and H.M.S. Swallow, recalling Capt. Philip Carteret's voyage of 1767. 2sh, Tinakula Volcano. 2sh6p, Meeting house, Reef Islands. 5sh, Alvaro de Mendana de Neyra and Caravel. 10sh, Constable and Chief. £1, Coat of Arms.

		Perf. 11½x11, 11x11½, 12, 13		
1956-60		**Engr.**	**Wmk. 4**	
89	A16	½p lilac & orange	.20	.55
90	A16	1p red brn & ol grn	.20	.20
91	A16	1½p dk car & sl bl	.20	1.10
92	A16	2p grey grn & choc	.35	.30
93	A17	2½p gray bl & blk	.90	.90
94	A16	3p dull red & grn	.80	.20
95	A16	5p blue & black	.30	.65
96	A16	6p bluish grn & blk	.65	.30
97	A16	8p black & ultra	.45	.20
98	A16	9p black & brt grn	4.00	1.00
99	A16	1sh brn org & sl	1.75	.75
100	A16	1sh3p blue & black	7.00	2.00
101	A16	2sh car rose & blk	14.50	3.00
102	A17	2sh6p rose lil & emer	9.25	.55
103	A16	5sh red brown	18.00	6.25

104	A17	10sh black brown	25.00	7.25
105	A16	£1 lt blue & blk	37.50	40.00
		Nos. 89-105 (17)	121.05	65.20

Issued: £1, 11/5/58; 9p, 1sh3p, 1/28/60; others, 3/1/56.

See Nos. 113-125.

Great
Frigate
Bird — A18

Perf. 13x12½

1961, Jan. 19   Litho.   Wmk. 314

106	A18	2p blue green & black	.20	.25
107	A18	3p rose red & black	.25	.20
108	A18	9p lilac & black	.35	.40
		Nos. 106-108 (3)	.80	.85

New constitution, brought into operation Oct. 18, 1960. The watermark is sideways and may be found facing both left and right.

Freedom from Hunger Issue
Common Design Type

1963, June 4   Photo.   Perf. 14x14½

109	CD314	1sh3p ultra	3.50	1.50

Red Cross Centenary Issue
Common Design Type

1963, Sept. 2   Litho.   Perf. 13

110	CD315	2p black & red	.40	.25
111	CD315	9p ultra & red	2.00	1.75

Types of 1956-60

Perf. 12, 13, 11½x11

1963-64   Engr.   Wmk. 314

113	A16	1p red brn & ol grn	.40	.45
114	A16	1½p dk car & sl bl	1.00	.80
115	A16	2p gray grn & choc	.30	.25
117	A16	3p dull red & grn	.80	.20
119	A16	6p bluish grn & blk	1.00	.65
121	A16	9p black & brt grn	1.10	.55
123	A16	1sh3p blue & blk	1.25	1.75
124	A16	2sh car rose & blk	3.00	7.50
125	A17	2sh6p rose lil & emer	19.00	17.50
		Nos. 113-125 (9)	27.85	29.65

Issued: 3p, 11/16; 6p, 9p, 1sh3p, 7/7/64; 1p, 1½p, 2p, 2sh, 2sh6p, 7/9/64.

ITU Issue
Common Design Type

Perf. 11x11½

1965, June 28   Litho.   Wmk. 314

126	CD317	2p ver & grnsh blue	.35	.25
127	CD317	3p grnsh bl & ol bis	.55	.40

Makira Food
Bowl — A19

Designs: 1p, 1sh, 1sh3p, Various orchids. 1½p, Scorpion shell. 2p, Papuan hornbill. 2½p, Ysabel shield. 3p, Rennellese club. 6p, Moorish idol (fish). 9p, Great frigate bird. 2sh, Sanford's sea eagle. 2sh6p, Malaita belt. 5sh, Ornithoptera Victoreae (butterfly). 10sh, White cockatoo. £1, Figurehead, western canoe.

Perf. 13x12½

1965, May 24   Litho.   Wmk. 314
Design Subject in Black

128	A19	½p sl blue & lt bl	.20	1.50
129	A19	1p orange & yel	.45	.60
130	A19	1½p blue & yel grn	.25	1.25
131	A19	2p vio bl & lt bl	.35	1.60
132	A19	2½p red brn & buff	.20	1.25
133	A19	3p grn & lt grn	.20	.20
134	A19	6p brt car rose & org	.25	.85
135	A19	9p slate grn & buff	.50	.20
136	A19	1sh dp cl & rose	1.10	.20
137	A19	1sh3p ver & buff	4.75	2.50
138	A19	2sh dp mag & lil	9.00	3.00
139	A19	2sh6p ol brn & buff	1.10	.75
140	A19	5sh dk vio bl & lil	13.50	4.75
141	A19	10sh ol grn & yel	16.50	3.75
142	A19	£1 purple & red	10.00	4.75
		Nos. 128-142 (15)	58.35	27.15

For surcharges see Nos. 149-166.

Intl. Cooperation Year Issue
Common Design Type

1965, Oct. 25   Litho.   Perf. 14½

143	CD318	1p bl grn & cl	.20	.20
144	CD318	2sh6p lt violet & grn	1.10	.90

Churchill Memorial Issue
Common Design Type

1966, Jan. 24   Photo.   Perf. 14

145	CD319	2p multicolored	.25	.30
146	CD319	9p multicolored	.45	.30
147	CD319	1sh3p multicolored	.60	.30
148	CD319	2sh6p multicolored	.70	.85
		Nos. 145-148 (4)	2.00	1.75

Nos. 128-142 Surcharged with New Value and Three Bars in Black or Red

Perf. 13x12½

1966-67   Litho.   Wmk. 314

149	A19	1c on ½p multi	.20	.20
150	A19	2c on 1p multi	.20	.20
151	A19	3c on 1½p multi	.20	.20
152	A19	4c on 2p multi	.20	.20
153	A19	5c on 6p multi	.20	.20
154	A19	6c on 2½p multi	.20	.20
155	A19	7c on 3p multi	.30	.30
156	A19	8c on 9p multi	.35	.35
b.		"8" inverted	40.00	22.50
157	A19	10c on 1sh	.45	.45
158	A19	12c on 1sh3p multi	.80	.45
159	A19	13c on 1sh3p multi	4.00	.50
160	A19	14c on 3p multi	.65	.50
161	A19	20c on 2sh multi	4.00	.85
162	A19	25c on 2sh6p multi	3.00	1.10
163	A19	35c on 2p multi	2.75	1.60
164	A19	50c on 5sh multi (R)	10.00	2.25
165	A19	$1 on 10sh multi	8.50	2.00
166	A19	$2 on £1 multi	7.50	2.25
		Nos. 149-166 (18)	44.75	15.30

The 12c, 14c, 35c have watermark sideways.
Issued: 12c, 14c, 35c, 3/1/67; others, 2/14/66.

1966   Wmk. 314 Sideways

149a	A19	1c on ½p	.20	.20
150a	A19	2c on 1p	.20	.20
151a	A19	3c on 1½p	.20	.20
152a	A19	4c on 2p	.25	.25
153a	A19	5c on 6p	.35	.30
154a	A19	6c on 2½p	.35	.35
155a	A19	7c on 3p	.40	.40
156a	A19	8c on 9p	.45	.45
157a	A19	10c on 1sh	.60	.60
159a	A19	13c on 1sh3p	.75	2.75
161a	A19	20c on 2sh	1.25	1.25
162a	A19	25c on 2sh6p	1.50	1.50
164a	A19	50c on 5sh (R)	10.00	4.75
165a	A19	$1 on 10sh	7.50	2.00
166a	A19	$2 on £1	6.50	3.00
		Nos. 149a-166a (15)	30.45	18.20

World Cup Soccer Issue
Common Design Type

1966, July 1   Litho.   Perf. 14

167	CD321	8c multicolored	.30	.30
168	CD321	35c multicolored	1.10	1.10

WHO Headquarters Issue
Common Design Type

1966, Sept. 20   Litho.   Perf. 14

169	CD322	3c multicolored	.20	.20
170	CD322	50c multicolored	1.60	1.60

UNESCO Anniversary Issue
Common Design Type

1966, Dec. 1   Litho.   Perf. 14

171	CD323	3c "Education"	.40	.20
172	CD323	25c "Science"	.95	.40
173	CD323	$1 "Culture"	2.40	1.90
		Nos. 171-173 (3)	3.75	2.50

Henderson Field, Guadalcanal — A20

Design: 35c, US Marines landing, Red Beach, Guadalcanal, 1942.

Perf. 14x14½

1967, Aug. 28   Photo.   Wmk. 314

174	A20	8c multi & silver	.20	.20
175	A20	35c multi & gold	.75	.75

Guadalcanal campaign in WW II, 25th anniv.

Mendana's Ship Off Puerta de la Cruz (Honiara), Guadalcanal, 1568 — A21

Designs: 8c, Arrival of Missionaries. 35c, Naval battle during World War II. $1, Honor guard raising Union Jack during proclamation of Protectorate.

1968, Feb. 2   Photo.   Perf. 14½

176	A21	3c pink & multi	.40	.20
177	A21	8c emerald & multi	.40	.20
178	A21	35c multicolored	.85	.20
179	A21	$1 blue & multi	1.10	2.25
		Nos. 176-179 (4)	2.75	2.85

400th anniv. of the discovery of the British Solomon Islands by the Spanish navigator Alvaro de Mendana de Neyra.

Vine Fishing A22

Designs: 2c, Kite fishing. 3c, Platform fishing. 4c, Net fishing. 6c, Gold lip shell diving. 8c, Night fishing. 12c, Boat building. 14c, Cocoa harvest. 15c, Road building. 20c, Geological survey by plane. 24c, Hauling timber. 35c, Copra. 45c, Harvesting rice. $1, Honiara Port. $2, Map of the Islands, plane and route of Internal Air Service.

Wmk. 314

1968, May 20   Photo.   Perf. 14½

180	A22	1c aqua, brn & blk	.20	.20
181	A22	2c lt yel grn, brn & blk	.20	.20
182	A22	3c brt grn, dk grn & blk	.20	.20
183	A22	4c brt rose lil, brn & blk	.20	.20
184	A22	6c multicolored	.30	.20
185	A22	8c dp ultra, org & blk	.20	.30
186	A22	12c bister, red & blk	.85	.35
187	A22	14c red org, brn & blk	4.00	2.25
188	A22	15c multicolored	.90	.70
189	A22	20c ultra, red & blk	4.75	3.25
190	A22	24c scarlet, yel & blk	2.50	3.75
191	A22	35c multicolored	2.50	.45
192	A22	45c yellow, red & blk	2.00	.85
193	A22	$1 vio bl, emer & blk	3.00	1.75
194	A22	$2 multicolored	7.50	4.00
		Nos. 180-194 (15)	29.30	18.25

Map of South Pacific and University Degrees — A23

Perf. 12½x12

1969, Feb. 10   Litho.   Unwmk.

195	A23	3c multicolored	.20	.20
196	A23	12c multicolored	.25	.20
197	A23	35c multicolored	.55	.50
		Nos. 195-197 (3)	1.00	.90

Inauguration of the University of the South Pacific in 1969, at the Royal New Zealand Air Force Seaplane Station, Laucala Bay, Fiji.

Field Ball and
Games'
Emblem — A24

Stained Glass Window with Melanesian Peace Symbol — A25

Perf. 14½x14

1969, Aug. 13   Photo.   Wmk. 314

198	A24	3c shown	.20	.20
199	A24	8c Soccer	.20	.20
200	A24	14c Running	.35	.30
201	A24	45c Rugby	1.10	.95
a.		Souvenir sheet of 4, #198-201	6.50	6.50
		Nos. 198-201 (4)	1.85	1.65

3rd S. Pacific Games, Port Moresby, Aug. 13-23.
In No. 201a, shading was added below athlete's foot on 14c, and strengthened on 8c and 45c.

1969, Nov. 21   Photo.   Wmk. 314

Christmas: 8c, South Sea Islands scene with palms and Star of Bethlehem.

202	A25	8c vio, grnsh bl & blk	.20	.20
203	A25	35c black & multi	.60	.60

C. M. Woodford and Stamp of 1907 — A26

Designs: 7c, British Solomon Islands 1906 handstamp and cancellation, and New South Wales No. 99. 18c, British Solomon Islands No. 18 and 1913 Tulagi cancellation. 23c, New General Post Office, Honiara.

1970, Apr. 15   Litho.   Perf. 13

204	A26	7c lilac rose & black	.20	.20
205	A26	14c lt olive & black	.35	.35
206	A26	18c orange, yel & blk	.45	.45
207	A26	23c multicolored	.65	.65
		Nos. 204-207 (4)	1.65	1.65

Issued to publicize the opening of the new General Post Office in Honiara.

Map of
Solomon
Islands
A27

18c, British Solomon Islands coat of arms, vert.

Perf. 14½x14, 14x14½

1970, June 15   Litho.   Wmk. 314

208	A27	18c multicolored	.55	.55
209	A27	35c multicolored	1.00	1.00

Adoption of the new 1970 Constitution.

Red Cross Headquarters, Honiara — A28

35c, Map of British Solomon Islands showing Red Cross stations, wheelchair.

1970, Aug. 17   Perf. 14½x14

210	A28	3c multicolored	.20	.20
211	A28	35c multicolored	.95	.85

Centenary of British Red Cross Society.

Carved Angel and Southern Cross — A29

Reredos: Symbols of Trinity and Light at St. Luke's Church, Kia — A30

Perf. 14x13½, 13½x14

1970, Oct. 19   Litho.   Wmk. 314
212	A29	8c violet & bister brn	.25	.25
213	A30	45c multicolored	1.00	1.00

Christmas 1970.

Count de La Pérouse and "La Boussole" — A31

4c, Astrolabe, Polynesian reed map. 12c, Abel Tasman, sailing ship Heemskerk, 1643. 35c, Te Puki canoe, Santa Cruz.

1971, Jan. 28   Perf. 14½x14
214	A31	3c multicolored	1.00	.50
215	A31	4c multicolored	1.00	.50
216	A31	12c multicolored	1.25	.75
217	A31	35c multicolored	1.50	1.25
		Nos. 214-217 (4)	4.75	3.00

In honor of famous explorers and ships. See Nos. 228-231, 250-253.

Bishop Patteson, J. Atkin and S. Taroniara — A32

Designs: 4c, Last landing of the "Southern Cross" at Nukapu. 14c, Memorial for Bishop Patteson and map of Nukapu, vert. 45c, Ceremonial leaf tag (had been attached to Bishop's body), vert.

Perf. 14½x14, 14x14½

1971, Apr. 5   Litho.   Wmk. 314
218	A32	2c lt green & multi	.25	.25
219	A32	4c blue green & multi	.25	.25
220	A32	14c brt pink & multi	.25	.25
221	A32	45c brown & multi	.50	.50
		Nos. 218-221 (4)	1.25	1.25

Bishop John Coleridge Patteson (1827-71), head of the Melanesian mission.

Boxing, Games Emblem A33

8c, Soccer. 12c, Running. 35c, Spear fishing.

1971, Aug. 9   Perf. 14½x14
222	A33	3c orange & multi	.30	.30
223	A33	8c emerald & multi	.30	.30
224	A33	12c yellow & multi	.30	.30
225	A33	35c blue & multi	.50	.50
		Nos. 222-225 (4)	1.40	1.40

4th South Pacific Games, Papeete, French Polynesia, Sept. 8-19.

Melanesian Lectern (wood carving) — A34

Christmas: 45c, Stylized birds, painted by school girl Margarita Bara.

1971, Nov. 15   Litho.   Wmk. 314
226	A34	9c orange & multi	.20	.20
227	A34	45c blue & multi	1.10	1.10

Explorer Type of 1971

4c, Louis Antoine de Bougainville, La Boudeuse, 1776. 9c, Horizontal planisphere, 1574, ivory backstaff, 1695. 15c, Philip Carteret, H.M.S. Swallow, 1707. 45c, Small canoe of Malaita.

1972, Feb. 1   Perf. 14½
228	A31	4c brown & multi	.45	.45
229	A31	9c green & multi	.65	.25
230	A31	15c lt blue & multi	1.10	.90
231	A31	45c blue & multi	2.40	2.50
		Nos. 228-231 (4)	4.60	3.50

Cupha Woodfordi A35

Designs: 1c, 2c, 3c, 4c, $2, Butterflies. 5c, 8c, 9c, 15c, $1, Fishes. 12c, 20c, 25c, 35c, 45c, Orchids. $5, Birds.

1972-73   Perf. 14
232	A35	1c shown	.20	.20
233	A35	2c Ornithoptera priamus	.30	.30
234	A35	3c Vindula sapor	.30	.30
235	A35	4c Papilio orssippus	.30	.30
236	A35	5c Great trevally	.40	.40
237	A35	8c Little bonito	.50	.50
238	A35	9c Sapphire demoiselle	.60	.70
239	A35	12c Costus speciosus	1.50	.80
240	A35	15c Orange anemone	1.50	1.00
241	A35	20c Spathoglottis plicata	3.50	1.25
242	A35	25c Ephemerantha comata	3.50	1.50
243	A35	35c Dendrobium cuthbertsonii	3.75	2.00
244	A35	45c Heliconia salomonica	3.00	3.00
245	A35	$1 Blue-finned triggerfish	3.75	5.00
246	A35	$2 Ornithoptera allotti	11.00	17.50
247	A35	$5 Great frigate bird	16.50	18.00
		Nos. 232-247 (16)	50.60	52.75

Issued: $5, 7/2/73; others, 7/2/72. For overprints see Nos. 300-311.

Silver Wedding Issue, 1972
Common Design Type

Design: Queen Elizabeth II, Prince Philip, scroll and message drum on woven mat.

1972, Nov. 20   Photo.   Perf. 14x14½
248	CD324	8c car rose & multi	.20	.20
249	CD324	45c olive & multi	.50	.50

Explorer Type of 1971

Designs: 4c, Antoine R. J. d'Entrecasteaux and "The Recherche," 1791. 9c, Ship's hourglass, 17th century, and chronometer, 1761. 15c, Lieutenant Shortland and "The Alexander," 1788. 35c, Tomoko (war canoe).

Wmk. 314

1973, Mar. 9   Litho.   Perf. 14½
250	A31	4c blue & multi	.20	.20
251	A31	9c blue & multi	.55	.55
252	A31	15c blue & multi	1.00	1.00
253	A31	35c blue & multi	3.25	3.25
		Nos. 250-253 (4)	5.00	5.00

Pan Pipes A36

Musical Instruments: 9c, Castanets. 15c, Bamboo flute. 35c, Bauro gongs. 45c, Bamboo band.

1973, Oct. 1   Perf. 13½x14
254	A36	4c brick red & multi	.20	.20
255	A36	9c yellow bis & multi	.25	.25
256	A36	15c pink & multi	.40	.40
257	A36	35c blue green & multi	.90	.90
258	A36	45c multicolored	1.25	1.25
		Nos. 254-258 (5)	3.00	3.00

Princess Anne's Wedding Issue
Common Design Type

1973, Nov. 14   Perf. 14
259	CD325	4c slate & multi	.30	.30
260	CD325	35c multicolored	.70	.70

Adoration of the Kings, by Jan Brueghel A37

Adoration of the Kings by: 22c, Peter Brueghel, vert. 45c, Botticelli.

1973, Nov. 26   Litho.   Perf. 14
Size: 39x25mm, 25x39mm
261	A37	8c pink & multi	.25	.25
262	A37	22c lilac & multi	.50	.50

Perf. 13½
Size: 47x35mm
263	A37	45c gray & multi	1.25	1.25
		Nos. 261-263 (3)	2.00	2.00

Christmas 1973.

Map of Solomon Islands — A38

1974, Feb. 18   Litho.   Perf. 13½
264	A38	4c blue & multi	.20	.20
265	A38	9c citron & multi	.25	.25
266	A38	15c violet gray & multi	.45	.45
267	A38	35c emerald & multi	1.50	1.50
		Nos. 264-267 (4)	2.40	2.40

Visit of British Royal Family.

First Resident Commissioner Landing at Tulagi — A39

Designs: 9c, Marine radar and scanner unit, map of Islands. 15c, Islanders taken to "Blackbirder" ship. 45c, John F. Kennedy's P.T. 109 off Lumbari Island, 1943.

1974, May 15   Litho.   Perf. 14½
268	A39	4c multicolored	.20	.20
269	A39	9c multicolored	.45	.45
270	A39	9c multicolored	.60	.60
271	A39	45c multicolored	2.75	2.75
		Nos. 268-271 (4)	4.00	4.00

Ships and navigators.

Mailman, Map of Islands — A40

9c, Carrier pigeon, horiz. 15c, Angel Gabriel. 45c, Pegasus, horiz. Designs based on origami (folded paper) figures.

1974, Aug. 29   Wmk. 314   Perf. 14
272	A40	4c brt green & multi	.20	.20
273	A40	9c lemon & multi	.30	.20
274	A40	15c multicolored	.45	.35
275	A40	45c blue & multi	1.25	1.10
		Nos. 272-275 (4)	2.20	1.85

Centenary of Universal Postal Union.

Solomon Islands No. 208 A41

1974, Dec. 16   Litho.   Perf. 14½
276	A41	4c shown	.20	.20
277	A41	9c No. 107	.30	.30
278	A41	15c same	.50	.50
279	A41	35c like 4c	1.10	1.10
a.		Souvenir sheet of 4, #276-279	5.00	5.00
		Nos. 276-279 (4)	2.10	2.10

New Constitution, inaugurated Oct. 18, 1960.

Golden Whistler A42

Birds: 2c, River kingfisher. 3c, Red-throated fruit dove. 4c, Button quail. $2, Duchess lorikeet.

1975, Apr. 7   Wmk. 314   Perf. 14
280	A42	1c yellow grn & multi	.50	.75
281	A42	2c lt blue & multi	.60	1.00
282	A42	3c brt pink & multi	.70	1.00
283	A42	4c orange & multi	.80	.80
284	A42	$2 dp orange & multi	13.50	13.50
		Nos. 280-284 (5)	16.10	17.05

See Nos. 316-320, 323, 330-331. For overprints see Nos. 296-299.

Motor Vessel Walande A43

1975, May 29   Perf. 13½
285	A43	4c shown	.60	.20
286	A43	9c M. V. Melanesian	.80	.20
287	A43	15c Ship Marsina, house flag	1.10	.25
288	A43	45c S. S. Himalaya	2.00	1.50
		Nos. 285-288 (4)	4.50	2.15

Runner, 800-meters — A44

1975, Aug. 4   Litho.   Perf. 13½
289 A44   4c shown   .20   .20
290 A44   9c Long jump   .20   .20
291 A44 15c Javelin   .35   .35
292 A44 45c Soccer   1.00   1.00
  a. Souvenir sheet of 4, #289-292 5.25   5.25
      Nos. 289-292 (4)   1.75   1.75

5th South Pacific Games, Guam, Aug. 1-10.

Nativity and Candles A45

Christmas: 35c, Angels, shepherds and candles. 45c, Three Kings approaching Bethlehem, and candles.

1975, Oct. 13   Wmk. 373   Perf. 14
293 A45 15c multicolored   .35   .35
294 A45 35c multicolored   .80   .80
295 A45 45c multicolored   1.10   1.10
  a. Souvenir sheet of 3, #293-295 6.00   6.00
      Nos. 293-295 (3)   2.25   2.25

Nos. 236-245, 247, 280-284
Overprinted with Bar Obliterating
"British" in Black or Silver

1975, Nov. 12   Litho.   Wmk. 314
296 A42   1c multicolored   .70   .60
297 A42   2c multicolored   1.10   .60
298 A42   3c multicolored   .80   .60
299 A42   4c multicolored   1.25   .60
300 A35   5c multicolored   .60   .60
301 A35   8c multicolored   .60   .60
302 A35   9c multicolored   .60   .60
303 A35 12c multicolored   2.00   1.10
304 A35 15c multicolored   2.00   1.50
305 A35 20c multicolored   2.50   2.00
306 A35 25c multicolored   2.50   2.00
307 A35 35c multicolored   2.75   1.60
308 A35 45c multicolored   2.50   2.25
309 A35 $1 multicolored   2.00   3.50
310 A42 $2 multicolored   7.00   8.00
311 A35 $5 multicolored (S)   6.75 18.00
      Nos. 296-311 (16)   35.65 44.15

Ceremonial Food Bowl — A46

Artifacts: 15c, Barava, chief's money. 35c, Nguzu-nguzu, canoe protector spirit, vert. 45c, Nguzu-nguzu on canoe prow.

**   Wmk. 314**
1976, Jan. 12   Litho.   Perf. 14
312 A46   4c scarlet & black   .20   .20
313 A46 15c lt violet & multi   .25   .25
314 A46 35c multicolored   .75   .75
315 A46 45c multicolored   .90   .90
      Nos. 312-315 (4)   2.10   2.10

Type of 1975 Inscribed "Solomon Islands" and

Golden Cowries A47

1c, Golden whistler. 2c, River kingfisher. 3c, Red-throated fruit dove. 4c, Button quail. 5c, Willie wagtail. 10c, Glory-of-the-sea cones. 12c, Rainbow lory. 15c, Pearly nautilus. 20c, Venus comb murex. 25c, Commercial trochus. 35c, Melon or baler shell. 45c, Orange spider conch. $1, Pacific triton. $2, Duchess lorikeet. $5, Great frigate bird.

1976   Wmk. 373   Perf. 14
316 A42   1c yel grn & multi   .40   .35
317 A42   2c lt blue & multi   .80   .70
318 A42   3c pink & multi   .45   .35
319 A42   4c orange & multi   .45   .40
320 A42   5c red brown & multi   .80   .70
321 A47   6c rose & multi   .55   .50
322 A47 10c multicolored   .55   .50
323 A42 12c yel grn & multi   .90   .80
324 A47 15c lilac & multi   .40   .35
325 A47 20c ultra & multi   .90   .75
326 A47 25c dull grn & multi   .70   .65
327 A47 35c bister & multi   .95   .95
328 A47 45c fawn & multi   1.10   1.10
329 A47 $1 olive & multi   2.50   2.50
330 A42 $2 multicolored   5.00   5.00
331 A42 $5 multicolored   9.75   9.75
      Nos. 316-331 (16)   26.20 25.35

Issue dates: $5, Dec. 6; others Mar. 8.

Coast Watchers, World War II A48

American Bicentennial: 20c, "Amagiri" ramming "P.T.109" and Lt. John F. Kennedy. 35c, Plane on Henderson Airfield. 45c, Map showing landing of US forces on Guadalcanal.

1976, May 24   Perf. 14
333 A48   6c black & multi   .40   .20
334 A48 20c black & multi   1.10   .55
335 A48 35c black & multi   1.50   .90
336 A48 45c black & multi   1.50   1.10
  a. Souvenir sheet of 4, #333-336 8.25   8.25
      Nos. 333-336 (4)   4.50   2.75

Alexander Graham Bell — A49

Designs: 20c, Radio-telephone and satellite. 35c, Ericsson's magneto telephone. 45c, Telephone, 1876, and stick telephone.

1976, July 26   Litho.   Perf. 14½x14
337 A49   6c lt ultra & multi   .20   .20
338 A49 20c multicolored   .45   .45
339 A49 35c orange & multi   .70   .70
340 A49 45c bister & multi   1.00   1.00
      Nos. 337-340 (4)   2.35   2.35

Centenary of first telephone call by Alexander Graham Bell, Mar. 10, 1876.

One-Eleven BAC — A50

Planes: 20c, Solair Britten Norman Islander. 35c, DC-3 Dakota. 45c, De Havilland DH50A.

1976, Sept. 13   Wmk. 373   Perf. 14
341 A50   6c black & multi   .20   .20
342 A50 20c black & multi   .65   .65
343 A50 35c black & multi   1.10   1.10
344 A50 45c black & multi   1.40   1.40
      Nos. 341-344 (4)   3.35   3.35

1st flight to Solomon Islands, 50th anniv.

Queen Receiving Lei, 1974 Visit — A51

Carved Wooden Figure — A52

35c, Communion plate, cup. 45c, Communion.

1977, Feb. 7   Litho.   Perf. 14x13½
345 A51   6c multicolored   .20   .20
346 A51 35c multicolored   .50   .50
347 A51 45c multicolored   .65   .65
      Nos. 345-347 (3)   1.35   1.35

25th anniv. of the reign of Elizabeth II.

1977, May 9   Perf. 14

Artifacts: 20c, Sea adaro or spirit. 35c, Shark-headed man. 45c, Seated man.

348 A52   6c yellow & multi   .25   .25
349 A52 20c blue & multi   .25   .25
350 A52 35c rose & multi   .55   .55
351 A52 45c multicolored   .70   .70
      Nos. 348-351 (4)   1.75   1.75

Man Spraying House, Anopheles Mosquito — A53

Designs: 20c, Taking blood samples. 35c, Microscope, map of Solomon Islands, Malaria Eradication Program emblem. 45c, Messenger delivering medicine to malaria patient.

1977, July 27   Litho.   Wmk. 373
352 A53   6c multicolored   .25   .25
353 A53 20c multicolored   .40   .40
354 A53 35c multicolored   .55   .55
355 A53 45c multicolored   .80   .80
      Nos. 352-355 (4)   2.00   2.00

Malaria eradication.

Adoration of the Shepherds — A54

Christmas: 20c, Nativity. 35c, Adoration of the Kings. 45c, Flight into Egypt.

**   Wmk. 373**
1977, Sept. 12   Litho.   Perf. 14
356 A54   6c multicolored   .25   .25
357 A54 20c multicolored   .40   .40
358 A54 35c multicolored   .55   .55
359 A54 45c multicolored   .80   .80
      Nos. 356-359 (4)   2.00   2.00

Traditional Feather Money — A55

Designs: No. 361, New coins. No. 362, Banknotes. No. 363, Traditional shell money.

1977, Oct. 24   Litho.   Perf. 14x14½
360 A55   6c brt green & multi   .20   .20
361 A55   6c brt green & multi   .20   .20
  a. A55 Pair, #360-361   .30   .30
362 A55 45c buff & multi   1.00   1.00
363 A55 45c buff & multi   1.00   1.00
  a. A55 Pair, #362-363   2.00   2.00
      Nos. 360-363 (4)   2.40   2.40

New coinage.

Shortland Islands Figure — A56

Artifacts: 20c, Ceremonial shield. 35c, Santa Cruz ritual figure. 45c, Decorative combs.

1978, Jan. 11   Perf. 14
364 A56   6c multicolored   .20   .20
365 A56 20c multicolored   .45   .45
366 A56 35c multicolored   .80   .80
367 A56 45c multicolored   1.00   1.00
      Nos. 364-367 (4)   2.45   2.45

Elizabeth II Coronation Anniversary Issue
Common Design Types
Souvenir Sheet
Unwmk.
1978, Apr. 21   Litho.   Perf. 15
368   Sheet of 6   3.50   3.50
  a. CD326 45c King's dragon   .50   .50
  b. CD327 45c Elizabeth II   .50   .50
  c. CD328 45c Sandford eagle   .50   .50

No. 368 contains 2 se-tenant strips of Nos. 368a-368c, separated by horizontal gutter with commemorative and descriptive inscriptions and showing central part of coronation procession with coach.

National Flag — A57

Apostles by Dürer — A58

Independence: 15c, Governor General's flag. 35c, Cenotaph, Honiara, flags of U.S., Great Britain, New Zealand and Australia. 45c, Coat of Arms.

**   Wmk. 373**
1978, July 7   Litho.   Perf. 14
369 A57   6c multicolored   .20   .20
370 A57 15c multicolored   .30   .30
371 A57 35c multicolored   .70   .70
372 A57 45c multicolored   .95   .95
      Nos. 369-372 (4)   2.15   2.15

1978, Oct. 4   Litho.   Perf. 14
373 A58   6c John   .20   .20
374 A58 20c Peter   .40   .40
375 A58 35c Paul   .70   .70
376 A58 45c Mark   .90   .90
      Nos. 373-376 (4)   2.20   2.20

Albrecht Dürer (1471-1528), German painter, 450th death anniversary.

Scouts Making Fire — A59

Designs: 20c, Camping. 35c, Solomon Islands Scouts. 45c, Canoeing.

1978, Nov. 15   Litho.   Perf. 14
377 A59 6c multicolored   .20 .20
378 A59 20c multicolored   .30 .30
379 A59 35c multicolored   .55 .55
380 A59 45c multicolored   .70 .70
    Nos. 377-380 (4)   1.75 1.75

50 years of Scouting in Solomon Islands.

Discovery A60

Designs: 18c, Capt. Cook, 1776, painting by Nathaniel Dance. 35c, Sextant. 45c, Capt. Cook after Flaxman / Wedgwood medallion.

Wmk. 373
1979, Jan. 16   Litho.   Perf. 11
381 A60 8c multicolored   .20 .20
382 A60 18c multicolored   .40 .40
383 A60 35c multicolored   .80 .80

Litho.; Embossed
384 A60 45c multicolored   1.00 1.00
    Nos. 381-384 (4)   2.40 2.40

Capt. Cook's voyages.

Fish Net Float A61

Artifacts: 20c, Armband made of shell money, vert. 35c, Ceremonial food bowl. 45c, Forehead ornament, vert.

1979, Mar. 21   Litho.   Perf. 14
385 A61 8c multicolored   .30 .30
386 A61 20c multicolored   .30 .30
387 A61 35c multicolored   .45 .45
388 A61 45c multicolored   .60 .60
    Nos. 385-388 (4)   1.65 1.65

6th South Pacific Games A62

1979, June 4   Litho.   Wmk. 373
389 A62 8c Running   .20 .20
390 A62 20c Hurdles   .25 .25
391 A62 35c Soccer   .30 .30
392 A62 45c Swimming   .50 .50
    Nos. 389-392 (4)   1.25 1.25

Solomon Islands No. 14 — A63   Sea Snake — A64

Designs (Rowland Hill and): 20c, Great Britain No. 27. 35c, Solomon Islands No. 372. 45c, Solomon Islands No. 40.

1979, Aug. 16   Litho.   Perf. 14
393 A63 8c multicolored   .20 .20
394 A63 20c multicolored   .40 .40
395 A63 35c multicolored   .65 .65
    Nos. 393-395 (3)   1.25 1.25

Souvenir Sheet
396 A63 45c multicolored   1.25 1.25

Sir Rowland Hill (1795-1879), originator of penny postage.

Perf. 13½x13
1979-83   Litho.   Wmk. 373
397 A64 1c Sea snake   .20 .50
398 A64 3c Red-banded tree snake   .20 .75
399 A64 4c Whip snake   .20 .75
400 A64 6c Pacific boa   .20 .75
401 A64 8c Skink   .20 .45
402 A64 10c Gecko   .20 .50
403 A64 12c Monitor   .30 .50
404 A64 15c Angelhead   .30 .75
405 A64 20c Giant toad   .40 .35
406 A64 25c Marsh frog   .45 .60
407 A64 30c Horned frog   1.50 .60
408 A64 35c Tree frog   .50 .60
408A A64 40c Burrowing snake   .55 1.40
409 A64 45c Guppy's snake   .65 .85
409A A64 50c Tree gecko   .60 .85
410 A64 $1 Large skink   2.00 1.25
411 A64 $2 Guppy's frog   2.50 2.50
412 A64 $5 Estuarine crocodile   6.50 6.50
412A A64 $10 Hawksbill turtle   11.50 13.00
    Nos. 397-412A (19)   28.95 33.45

Issued: $10, 9/20/82; 40c, 50c, 1/24/83; others, 9/1979 (undated).
Nos. 403, 406, 410, 412 reissued inscribed "1982." No. 407, "1983."

Madonna and Child, by Morando — A65

IYC Emblem and Madonna and Child: 20c, Bernardino Luini. 35c, Bellini. 50c, Raphael.

1979, Nov. 15   Perf. 14½
413 A65 4c multicolored   .20 .20
414 A65 20c multicolored   .25 .25
415 A65 35c multicolored   .40 .40
416 A65 50c multicolored   .65 .65
    a. Souvenir sheet of 4, #413-416   2.00 2.00
    Nos. 413-416 (4)   1.50 1.50

Christmas 1979, Intl. Year of the Child.

Curacoa and Crest A66

Ships and Crests: 20c, Herald, 1854. 35c, Royalist, 1889. 45c, Beagle, 1878.

Wmk. 373
1980, Jan. 23   Litho.   Perf. 14
417 A66 8c multicolored   .20 .20
418 A66 20c multicolored   .45 .45
419 A66 35c multicolored   .70 .70
420 A66 45c multicolored   .95 .95
    Nos. 417-420 (4)   2.30 2.30

See Nos. 435-438.

Steel Fishery Training Ship — A67

1980, Mar. 27   Litho.   Perf. 13½
421 A67 8c shown   .20 .20
422 A67 20c Fishery training ship   .25 .25
423 A67 45c Refrigerated carrier   .45 .40
424 A67 80c Research ship   .85 1.75
    Nos. 421-424 (4)   1.75 2.60

"Comliebank," Tulag Cancel — A68

1980, May 6   Litho.   Perf. 14½
425   Sheet of 4   2.00 2.00
    a. A68 45c shown   .50 .50
    b. A68 45c Douglas C-47   .50 .50
    c. A68 45c BAC 1-11, Honiara cancel   .50 .50
    d. A68 45c "Corabank," Auki cancel   .50 .50

London 1980 Intl. Stamp Exhib., May 6-14.

Queen Mother Elizabeth Birthday Issue
Common Design Type
Wmk. 373
1980, Aug. 4   Litho.   Perf. 14
426 CD330 45c multicolored   .50 .50

Angel with Trumpet — A69

Christmas: 20c, Angel with violin. 45c, Angel with trumpet. 80c, Angel with lute.

Wmk. 373
1980, Sept. 2   Litho.   Perf. 14½
427 A69 8c multicolored   .20 .20
428 A69 20c multicolored   .20 .20
429 A69 45c multicolored   .40 .40
430 A69 80c multicolored   .70 .70
    Nos. 427-430 (4)   1.50 1.50

Parthenos Sylvia — A70

Wmk. 373
1980, Nov. 12   Litho.   Perf. 13½
431 A70 8c shown   .75 .45
432 A70 20c Delias schoenbergi   1.00 .65
433 A70 45c Jamides cephion   1.75 1.25
434 A70 80c Ornithoptera victoriae   3.00 3.00
    Nos. 431-434 (4)   6.50 5.35

See Nos. 461-464.

Ship & Crest Type of 1980

8c, Mounts Bay, 1959. 20c, Charybdis, 1970. 45c, Hydra, 1972-73. $1, Britannia, 1974.

1981, Jan. 14
435 A66 8c multicolored   .20 .20
436 A66 20c multicolored   .20 .20
437 A66 45c multicolored   .45 .45
438 A66 $1 multicolored   1.25 1.25
    Nos. 435-438 (4)   2.10 2.10

Maurelle's Map, 1742 — A71

Wmk. 373
1981, Mar. 23   Litho.   Perf. 14
439 A71 8c Francisco Maurelle, vert.   .20 .20
440 A71 10c shown   .20 .20
441 A71 45c La Princesa   .60 .60
442 A71 $1 Compass cards, vert.   1.00 1.00
    Nos. 439-442 (4)   2.00 2.00

Souvenir Sheet
443   Sheet of 4   1.60 1.60
    a. A71 25c any single   .35 .35

Bicent. of arrival of Francisco Antonio Maurelle and of charts of mapmaker Jean Nicholas Buache (1741-1825). No. 443 contains 4 44x28mm stamps, perf. 14½.

Women's Basketball — A72

Wmk. 373
1981, July 7   Litho.   Perf. 12
444 A72 8c shown   .20 .20
445 A72 10c Tennis   .20 .20
446 A72 25c Women's running   .35 .35
447 A72 30c Soccer   .35 .35
448 A72 45c Boxing   .50 .50
    Nos. 444-448 (5)   1.60 1.60

Souvenir Sheet
449 A72 $1 Emblem   1.25 1.25

Mini South Pacific Games, July.

Royal Wedding Issue
Common Design Type
1981, July 22   Perf. 13½x13
450 CD331 8c Bouquet   .20 .20
451 CD331 45c Charles   .30 .30
452 CD331 $1 Couple   1.00 1.00
    Nos. 450-452 (3)   1.50 1.50

For surcharge see No. B1.

Duke of Edinburgh's Awards, 25th Anniv. — A73

Wmk. 373
1981, Sept. 28   Litho.   Perf. 14
453 A73 8c Music   .25 .25
454 A73 25c Handicrafts   .25 .25
455 A73 45c Canoeing   .35 .35
456 A73 $1 Duke of Edinburgh   .90 .90
    Nos. 453-456 (4)   1.75 1.75

Holy Cross Cathedral, Honiara — A74

Christmas: 8c, 25c, Old churches, diff. 10c, St. Barnabas Anglican Cathedral, Honiara.

1981, Oct. 12
457 A74 8c multicolored   .30 .30
458 A74 10c multicolored   .30 .30
459 A74 25c multicolored   .40 .40
460 A74 $2 multicolored   1.50 1.50
    Nos. 457-460 (4)   2.50 2.50

Butterfly Type of 1980
Wmk. 373
1982, Jan. 5   Litho.   Perf. 13½
461 A70 10c Doleschallia bisaltide   .75 .40
462 A70 25c Papilio bridgei hecataeus   1.00 .75

463	A70	35c Taenaris phorcas	1.50	1.25
464	A70	$1 Graphium sarpedon	3.75	3.75
		Nos. 461-464 (4)	7.00	6.15

Sanford's Eagle — A75

1982, May 15   Litho.   Perf. 14

465	A75	12c Pair facing left	.60	.60
466	A75	12c Chick	.60	.60
467	A75	12c Mother feeding chicks	.60	.60
468	A75	12c Pair facing right	.60	.60
469	A75	12c Male flying	.60	.60
470	A75	12c Pair flying	.60	.60
		Nos. 465-470 (6)	3.60	3.60

Se-tenant in sheets of 24. The center horiz. row consists of 4 No. 470 + label. No block of 6 contains all 6 designs.

Princess Diana Issue
Common Design Type
Perf. 14½x14

1982, July 1   Litho.   Wmk. 373

471	CD333	12c Arms	.20	.20
472	CD333	40c Diana	.65	.65
473	CD333	50c Wedding	.90	.90
474	CD333	$1 Portrait	1.75	1.75
		Nos. 471-474 (4)	3.50	3.50

A76

1982, Oct. 11   Litho.   Perf. 14

475	A76	25c Running	.40	.40
476	A76	25c Boxing	.40	.40

Souvenir Sheet

477		Sheet of 3, #475-476, 477a	3.00	3.00
a.		A76 $1 Britannia facing left	2.25	2.25

12th Commonwealth Games, Brisbane, Australia, Sept. 30-Oct. 9.

1982, Oct. 11

478	A76	12c Royal couple	.25	.25
479	A76	12c Flags	.25	.25

Souvenir Sheet

480		Sheet of 3, #478-479, 480a	3.00	3.00
a.		A76 $1 Britannia facing right	2.25	2.25

Visit of Queen Elizabeth II and Prince Philip.

Scouting Year A78

Designs: Nos. 481, 485, Scout patroller. Nos. 482, 486, Brigade bugler. Nos. 483, 487, Baden-Powell. Nos. 484, 488, William Smith.

1982, Nov. 30

481	A78	12c dark blue & multi	.25	.25
482	A78	12c brown & multi	.25	.25
483	A78	25c dark blue & multi	.30	.30
484	A78	25c brown & multi	.30	.30
485	A78	35c green & multi	.30	.30
486	A78	35c red & multi	.30	.30
487	A78	50c green & multi	.50	.50
488	A78	50c red & multi	.50	.50
		Nos. 481-488 (8)	2.70	2.70

Turtles A79

1983, Jan. 5   Perf. 14

489	A79	18c Leatherback	.50	.50
490	A79	35c Loggerhead	.65	.65
491	A79	45c Pacific Ridley	.90	.90
492	A79	50c Green	.90	.90
		Nos. 489-492 (4)	2.95	2.95

Commonwealth Day — A80

1983, Mar. 14

493	A80	12c Oliva vidum, conus generalis, murex tribulus	.20	.20
494	A80	35c Romu, kurila, kakadu, money belt	.55	.55
495	A80	45c Shells, bride neck-laces	.70	.70
496	A80	50c Trochus niloticus, natural, polished	.75	.75
		Nos. 493-496 (4)	2.20	2.20

Manned Flight Bicentenary — A81

Wmk. 373

1983, June 30   Litho.   Perf. 14

497	A81	30c Montgolfliere, 1783	.45	.45
498	A81	35c Lockheed Hercules	.50	.50
499	A81	40c Wright Brothers' Flyer III, 1905	.55	.55
500	A81	45c Columbia space shuttle	.60	.60
501	A81	50c Beechcraft Baron-Solair	.75	.75
		Nos. 497-501 (5)	2.85	2.85

Christmas 1983 — A82

1983, Aug. 25

502	A82	12c Weto dance	.20	.20
503	A82	15c Custom wrestling	.20	.20
504	A82	18c Girl dancers	.25	.25
505	A82	20c Devil dancers	.30	.30
506	A82	25c Bamboo band	.35	.35
507	A82	35c Gilbertese dancers	.50	.50
508	A82	40c Pan pipers	.60	.60
509	A82	45c Afufu girl dancers	.65	.65
510	A82	50c Cross, flowers	.75	.75
a.		Souvenir sheet of 9, #502-510	3.80	3.80
		Nos. 502-510 (9)	3.80	3.80

Stamps in #510a do not have "Christmas 1983."
For overprints see Nos. 519-520.

World Communications Year — A83

Wmk. 373

1983, Dec. 19   Litho.   Perf. 14

511	A83	12c Telephone Ex-change building	.20	.20
512	A83	18c Ham radio operator	.20	.20
513	A83	25c No. 11	.35	.35
514	A83	$1 No. 14	1.25	1.25
a.		Souvenir sheet of 1	2.00	2.00
		Nos. 511-514 (4)	2.00	2.00

No. 514a is inscribed "1908-1983." See No. 525 for sheet inscribed "1907-1984."

Local Fungi — A84

1984, Jan. 30   Perf. 13½

515	A84	6c Calvatia gardneri	.30	.30
516	A84	18c Marasmiellus in-oderma	.50	.50
517	A84	35c Pycnoporus sanguineus	.75	.75
518	A84	$2 Filoboletus manipu-laris	3.00	3.00
		Nos. 515-518 (4)	4.55	4.55

Type of No. 510 overprinted "VISIT OF POPE JOHN PAUL II May 9th, 1984"

1984, Apr. 16   Wmk. 373

519	A82	12c multicolored	.20	.20
520	A82	50c multicolored	.70	.70

Lloyd's List Issue
Common Design Type

1984, Apr. 21   Litho.   Perf. 14½x14

521	CD335	12c Olivebank, 1892	.75	.75
522	CD335	15c Tinhow, 1906	1.00	.75
523	CD335	18c Oriana, Point Cruz	1.10	1.00
524	CD335	$1 Point Cruz view	2.75	2.75
		Nos. 521-524 (4)	5.60	4.75

WCY Type of 1983
Souvenir Sheet
Wmk. 373

1984, June 18   Litho.   Perf. 14

525	A83	$1 multicolored	2.25	2.25

UPU Congress. No. 514a is inscribed "1908-1983," No. 525 inscribed "1907-1984."

Asia-Pacific Broadcasting Union, 20th Anniv. — A86

1984, July 2   Perf. 13½

526	A86	12c Village drums	.20	.20
527	A86	45c Radio City Guadal-canal	.60	.60
528	A86	60c Broadcasting studio	.80	.80
529	A86	$1 Broadcasting station	1.40	1.40
		Nos. 526-529 (4)	3.00	3.00

1984 Summer Olympics — A87

Perf. 13½x14

1984, Aug. 4   Litho.   Wmk. 373

530	A87	12c Flag, vert.	.20	.20
531	A87	25c Lawson Tama Stadi-um, Honiara	.45	.45

532	A87	50c Honiara Community Center	.85	.85
a.		Booklet pane, 2 ea #531-532	2.75	
533	A87	$1 Olympic Stadium	1.75	1.75
		Nos. 530-533 (4)	3.25	3.25

Souvenir Sheet

534	A87	95c Bronte Baths	8.50	8.50

Solomon Islds. first olympic participation. No. 534 available in booklet only. Margin shows swimmer A. Wickham (1886-1976).

Little Pied Cormorant (Ausipex '84) A88

Wmk. 373

1984, Sept. 21   Litho.   Perf. 14½

535	A88	12c shown	.65	.65
536	A88	18c Australian grey duck	.85	.85
537	A88	35c Nankeen night-her-on	1.10	1.00
538	A88	$1 Dollarbird	2.00	2.00
a.		Souvenir sheet of 4, #535-538	5.00	5.00
		Nos. 535-538 (4)	4.60	4.50

EXPO '85, Tsukuba, Japan A89

Designs: 12c, Japanese Memorial Shrine, Mt. Austen, Guadalcanal. 25c, Digital tele-phone exchange equipment. 45c, Soltai No. 7 fishing vessel. 85c, Coastal village.

Wmk. 373

1985, June 28   Litho.   Perf. 14

539	A89	12c multicolored	.20	.20
540	A89	25c multicolored	.35	.35
541	A89	45c multicolored	.60	.60
542	A89	85c multicolored	1.25	1.25
		Nos. 539-542 (4)	2.40	2.40

Queen Mother 85th Birthday
Common Design Type
Perf. 14½x14

1985, June 7   Litho.   Wmk. 384

543	CD336	12c VE Day, 1945	.20	.20
544	CD336	25c With Margaret	.30	.30
545	CD336	35c St. Patrick's Day celebra-tion	.40	.40
546	CD336	$1 Holding Prince Henry	1.25	1.25
		Nos. 543-546 (4)	2.15	2.15

Souvenir Sheet

547	CD336	$1.50 In a gondola, Venice	2.25	2.25

For surcharge see No. B2.

Christmas — A90

1985, Aug. 30   Wmk. 373   Perf. 14½

548	A90	12c Titiana Village	.20	.20
549	A90	25c Sigana, Santa Isa-bel	.35	.35
550	A90	35c Artificial Island, Lan-ga Lagoon	.45	.45
		Nos. 548-550 (3)	1.00	1.00

Intl. Youth Year — A91

12c, Girl Guide activities. 15c, Stop Polio Campaign. 25c, Relay runners, views of the islands. 35c, Relay runners, views of Australia. 45c, Saluting natl. flag, badges.

1985, Sept. 30   **Perf. 14**

551	A91	12c multicolored	.90	.25
552	A91	15c multicolored	1.00	.60
553	A91	25c multicolored	1.25	.90
554	A91	35c multicolored	1.40	1.00
a.		Souvenir sheet of 2, #553-554	2.25	2.25
555	A91	45c multicolored	2.50	1.50
		Nos. 551-555 (5)	7.05	4.25

Girl Guides 75th anniv., 12c, 45c; IYY, others.

Souvenir Sheet

Audubon Birth Bicent. — A92

Bird illustration by Audubon.

1985, Nov. 25   **Wmk. 384**

556	A92	Sheet of 3, 45c, 2 50c	6.50	6.50
a.		Portrait	1.75	1.75
b.		Osprey	2.25	2.25

Souvenir Sheet

Mini Hydro-Electric Project, Iriri Village — A93

Designs: 30c, Water-driven generator. 60c, Illuminated village house.

1986, Jan. 24   **Perf. 14**

557	A93	Sheet of 2	3.00	3.00
a.		30c multicolored	1.00	1.00
b.		60c multicolored	1.75	1.75

Halley's Comet A94

Operation Raleigh, 1986: 18c, Construction of Red Cross Center, Gizo. 30c, Exploring rain forest. 60c, Observing Halley's Comet. $1, Ships Sir Walter Raleigh and Zebu.

1986, Mar. 27   **Wmk. 373**

558	A94	18c multicolored	1.00	.20
559	A94	30c multicolored	1.75	.50
560	A94	60c multicolored	3.00	1.50
561	A94	$1 multicolored	3.50	2.25
		Nos. 558-561 (4)	9.25	4.45

Queen Elizabeth II 60th Birthday
Common Design Type

Designs: 5c, Visiting Clydebank Town Hall with Prince Philip, 1947. 18c, At Queen Mother's 80th birthday, St. Paul's Cathedral, 1980. 22c, Walking among children of the islands, Pacific tour, 1982. 55c, 50th birthday, Windsor Castle, 1976. $2, Visiting Crown Agents' offices, 1983.

1986, Apr. 21   **Wmk. 384**   **Perf. 14½**

562	CD337	5c scarlet, blk & sil	.20	.20
563	CD337	18c ultra & multi	.20	.20
564	CD337	22c green & multi	.20	.20
565	CD337	55c violet & multi	.50	.50
566	CD337	$2 rose vio & multi	1.90	1.90
		Nos. 562-566 (5)	3.00	3.00

Royal Wedding Issue, 1986
Common Design Type

Designs: 55c, Informal portrait. 60c, Andrew aboard royal navy vessel.

Wmk. 384

1986, July 23   **Litho.**   **Perf. 14**

567	CD338	55c multicolored	.50	.50
568	CD338	60c multicolored	.60	.60

Souvenir Sheet

AMERIPEX '86 — A95

55c, U.S. Memorial, Henderson Field, Guadalcanal. $1.65, Peace Corps emblem, Statue of Liberty, Pres. John F. Kennedy.

1986, May 22   **Litho.**   **Perf. 13½**

569	A95	Sheet of 2	2.50	2.50
a.		55c multicolored	.60	.60
b.		$1.65 multicolored	1.75	1.75

Intl. Peace Year, Peace Corps 25th anniv. For surcharge see No. B3.

1987 America's Cup — A96

Previous winners, challengers, maps and club emblems: No. 570a, America, US, 1851. b, Magic, US, 1870. c, Madeleine, US, 1876. d, Mischief, US, 1881. e, Columbia, US, 1871. f, British Cup course, 1851. g, America II, US, 1987. h, America's Cup. i, Heart of America, US, 1987. j, French Kiss, France, 1987.
No. 571a, Puritan, US, 1885. b, Mayflower, US, 1886. c, Defender, US, 1895. d, Vigilant, US, 1893. e, Volunteer, US, 1887. f, America Cup course, Newport, 1930-1962. g, South Australia, Australia, 1987. h, KA14, Australia, 1987. i, New Zealand II, New Zealand, 1987. j, St. Francis IX, US, 1987.
No. 572a, Columbia, US, 1899. b, Columbia, US, 1901. c, Enterprise, US, 1930. d, Resolute, US, 1920. e, Reliance, US, 1903. f, America Cup course, 1964-1983. g, Kookaburra, Australia, 1987. h, Eagle, US, 1987. i, True North, Canada, 1987. j, Italia, Italy, 1987.
No. 573a, Rainbow, US, 1934. b, Ranger, US, 1937. c, Constellation, US, 1964. d, Weatherly, US, 1962. e, Columbia, US, 1958. f, Western Australia Cup course, 1987. g, Secret Cove, syndicate, 1987. h, Courageous III, US, 1987. i, France, France, 1987. j, Azzurra, Italy, 1987.

No. 574a, Intrepid, US, 1967. b, Intrepid, US, 1970. c, Freedom, US, 1980. d, Courageous, US, 1977. e, Courageous, US, 1974. f, Australia II, Australia, 1983. g, Crusader, Great Britain, 1987. h, Sail America, US, 1987. i, Australia III, Australia, 1987. j, Royal Perth Yacht Club/America's Cup '87 emblem, 1987.

1986, Aug. 22   **Litho.**   **Perf. 14½**

570		Strip of 10 + label	6.50	6.50
a.-d.	A96	18c any single	.25	.25
e.-f.	A96	30c any single	.35	.35
g.-j.	A96	$1 any single	1.00	1.00
571		Strip of 10 + label	6.50	6.50
a.-d.	A96	18c any single	.25	.25
e.-f.	A96	30c any single	.35	.35
g.-j.	A96	$1 any single	1.00	1.00
572		Strip of 10 + label	6.50	6.50
a.-d.	A96	18c any single	.25	.25
e.-f.	A96	30c any single	.35	.35
g.-j.	A96	$1 any single	1.00	1.00
573		Strip of 10 + label	6.50	6.50
a.-d.	A96	18c any single	.25	.25
e.-f.	A96	30c any single	.35	.35
g.-j.	A96	$1 any single	1.00	1.00
574		Strip of 10 + label	6.50	6.50
a.-d.	A96	18c any single	.25	.25
e.-f.	A96	30c any single	.35	.35
g.-j.	A96	$1 any single	1.00	1.00
		Nos. 570-574 (5)	32.50	32.50

Nos. 570-574 printed se-tenant with center labels picturing natl. arms, 1987 America's Cup emblem and trophy in sheets of 50.

Souvenir Sheet

1987, Feb. 4   **Litho.**   **Perf. 14½**

575	A96	$5 Stars and Stripes, U.S., victor	5.50	5.50

Coral — A97

1987, Feb. 11   **Litho.**   **Wmk. 384**

576	A97	18c Dendrophyllia gracilis	.50	.20
577	A97	45c Dendronephthya	.95	.50
578	A97	60c Clavularia	1.25	1.25
579	A97	$1.50 Melithaea squa- mata	2.75	2.75
		Nos. 576-579 (4)	5.45	4.70

Flowering Plants — A98

1987-88

580	A98	1c Cassia fistula	.20	.20
581	A98	5c Allamanda cathartica	.20	.20
582	A98	10c Catharanthus roseus	.20	.20
583	A98	18c Mimosa pudica	.40	.20
584	A98	20c Hibiscus rosa- sinensis	.40	.20
585	A98	22c Clerodendrum thomsonae	.45	.25
586	A98	25c Bauhinia varie- gata	.50	.30
587	A98	28c Gloriosa roth- schildiana	.55	.30
588	A98	30c Heliconia solomonensis	.60	.35
589	A98	40c Episcia hybrid	.70	.45
590	A98	45c Bougainvillea hybrid	.75	.50
591	A98	50c Alpinia purpurata	.80	.60
592	A98	55c Plumeria rubra	.90	.60
593	A98	60c Acacia farne- siana	1.00	.70
594	A98	$1 Ipomea purpurea	2.50	1.10
595	A98	$2 Dianella en- sifolia	3.50	3.50
596	A98	$5 Passiflora foe- tida	5.75	5.75
596A	A98	$10 Hemigraphis specie ('88)	9.00	9.00
		Nos. 580-596A (18)	28.40	24.40

Issue dates: $10, Mar. 1; others, May 12.

Mangrove Kingfisher — A99   Orchids — A100

Designs: a, Perched on root. b, Diving. c, Landing in water. d, Emerging with fish.

Perf. 14x14½

1987, July 15   **Wmk. 373**

597		Strip of 4	18.00	18.00
a.-d.	A99	60c any single	4.00	4.00

No. 597 has a continuous design.

Perf. 13½x13

1987, Sept. 23   **Wmk. 384**

598	A100	18c Dendrobium conanthum	1.50	.35
599	A100	30c Spathoglottis plicata	3.00	.40
600	A100	55c Dendrobium gouldii	3.50	1.00
601	A100	$1.50 Dendrobium goldfinchii	6.50	6.50
		Nos. 598-601 (4)	14.50	8.25

Christmas 1987

Transportation and Communications Decade — A101

Designs: 18c, Telecommunications link. 30c, Express mail service. 60c, Guadalcanal Road Improvement Project. $2, Beechcraft Queen Air, Henderson Airfield control tower.

Perf. 14x13½

1987, Oct. 31   **Litho.**   **Unwmk.**

602	A101	18c multicolored	.35	.25
603	A101	30c multicolored	.65	.35
604	A101	60c multicolored	.85	.85
605	A101	$2 multicolored	3.50	3.50
		Nos. 602-605 (4)	5.35	4.95

Queen Victoria's Birdwing Butterfly — A102

Designs: No. 606a, Male. No. 606b, Larva. No. 606c, Pupa. No. 606d, Female.

1987, Nov. 25   **Wmk. 384**   **Perf. 14½**

606		Strip of 4	23.50	23.50
a.-d.	A102	45c any single	5.00	5.00

Intl. Fund for Agricultural Development (IFAD), 10th Anniv. — A103

Natl. colors and: No. 607, Student, Natl. Agricultural Training Institute (NATI) farm and emblem (left stamp). No. 608, Students in working in NATI field and emblem (right stamp). No. 609, Flatbed truck transporting produce and emblem (left stamp). No. 610, Canoes, seagulls and emblem (right stamp).

Wmk. 384

1988, Feb. 12   Litho.   Perf. 14½
607		50c multicolored	.80	.80
608	120	61 multicolored	.80	.80
a.	A103	Pair, #607-608	1.75	1.75
609		$1 multicolored	1.00	1.00
610		$1 multicolored	1.00	1.00
a.	A103	Pair, #609-610	2.25	2.25
		Nos. 607-610 (4)	3.60	3.60

EXPO '88, Brisbane, Apr. 30-Oct. 30 — A104

Designs: 22c, Yacht in dry dock. 80c, Canoe. $1.50, Huts.

Perf. 13½x14
1988, Apr. 30   Unwmk.
611	A104	22c multicolored	.25	.25
612	A104	80c multicolored	.85	.85
613	A104	$1.50 multicolored	1.75	1.75
a.		Souv. sheet of 3, #611-613	3.00	3.00
b.		As "a," surcharged $3.50 in margin ('90)	12.00	12.00
		Nos. 611-613 (3)	2.85	2.85

National Independence, 10th Anniv. — A105

Perf. 13x13½
1988, July 7   Litho.   Wmk. 373
614	A105	22c *Capitana* in Estrella Bay	1.25	.25
615	A105	55c Flag raising, 1893	2.00	.60
616	A105	80c Supreme Court	1.75	1.50
617	A105	$1 Traditional celebration	2.00	2.00
		Nos. 614-617 (4)	7.00	4.35

Australia Bicentennial — A106

Ships: 35c, M.V. *Papuan Chief.* 60c, M.V. *Nimos.* 70c, S.S. *Malaita.* $1.30, S.S. *Makambo.*

1988, July 30   Wmk. 384   Perf. 14
618	A106	35c multicolored	1.25	.35
619	A106	60c multicolored	1.60	.55
620	A106	70c multicolored	1.60	.85
621	A106	$1.30 multicolored	2.10	2.10
a.		Souvenir sheet of 4, #618-621	5.00	5.00
		Nos. 618-621 (4)	6.55	3.85

A107   Orchids — A108

Wmk. 384
1988, Aug. 5   Litho.   Perf. 14½
622	A107	22c Archery	1.00	.25
623	A107	55c Weight lifting	1.25	.65
624	A107	70c Running	1.50	1.25
625	A107	80c Boxing	1.75	1.50
		Nos. 622-625 (4)	5.50	3.65

Souvenir Sheet
Wmk. 373
626	A107	$2 Olympic Stadium, horiz.	3.50	3.50

1988 Summer Olympics, Seoul.

Lloyds of London, 300th Anniv.
Common Design Type
Designs: 22c, King George V and Queen Mary at Lloyd's ground-breaking ceremony, 1925. 50c, *Forthbank,* horiz. 65c, Soltel Satellite Ground Station, horiz. $2, *Empress of China.*

1988, Oct. 31   Perf. 14
627	CD341	22c multicolored	.75	.75
628	CD341	50c multicolored	2.25	.45
629	CD341	65c multicolored	2.50	.75
630	CD341	$2 multicolored	4.50	3.00
		Nos. 627-630 (4)	10.00	4.45

Perf. 13½x13
1989, Jan. 20   Litho.   Wmk. 373
631	A108	22c *Bulbophyllum dennisii*	1.25	.30
632	A108	35c *Calanthe langei*	1.50	.55
633	A108	55c *Bulbophyllum blumei*	2.00	1.25
634	A108	$2 *Grammatophyllum speciosum*	3.75	3.75
		Nos. 631-634 (4)	8.50	5.85

Intl. Red Cross, 125th Anniv. — A109

Perf. 14x14½
1989, May 16   Wmk. 384
635		35c Disabled children	.75	.75
636		35c Children's Center minibus	.75	.75
a.	A109	Pair, #635-636	1.75	1.75
637		$1.50 Patient abed	3.00	3.00
638		$1.50 Physical therapy	3.00	3.00
a.	A109	Pair, #637-638	6.50	6.50
		Nos. 635-638 (4)	7.50	7.50

Sea Slugs A110

1989, June 30   Wmk. 373   Perf. 14½
639	A110	22c *Phyllidia varicosa*	1.50	.30
640	A110	70c *Chromodoris bullocki*	3.25	1.75
641	A110	80c *Chromodoris leopardus*	3.50	2.50
642	A110	$1.50 *Phidiana indica*	5.00	5.00
		Nos. 639-642 (4)	13.25	9.55

Moon Landing, 20th Anniv.
Common Design Type
Apollo 16: 22c, Splashdown. 35c, Launch. 70c, Mission emblem. 80c, Ultraviolet color enhancement of Earth. $4, The Moon, as photographed during the *Apollo 11* mission.

1989, July 20   Wmk. 384   Perf. 14
Size of Nos. 644-645: 29x29mm
643	CD342	22c multicolored	.75	.30
644	CD342	35c multicolored	1.25	.55
645	CD342	70c multicolored	2.00	2.00
646	CD342	80c multicolored	2.25	2.25
		Nos. 643-646 (4)	6.25	5.10

Souvenir Sheet
647	CD342	$4 multicolored	6.50	6.50

Blowing Soap Bubbles A111

Children's games.

1989, Nov. 17   Wmk. 384
648	A111	5c Five stones catch, vert.	.30	.55
649	A111	67c shown	2.00	2.00
650	A111	73c Coconut shell empire	2.00	2.00
651	A111	$1 Seed wind sound, vert.	3.00	3.00
		Nos. 648-651 (4)	7.30	7.55

Souvenir Sheet
Wmk. 373
652	A111	$3 Baseball, softball, vert.	10.50	10.50

World Stamp Expo '89.

Christmas — A112

1989, Nov. 30   Wmk. 384
653	A112	18c Butterfly, fishermen	.75	.30
654	A112	25c Nativity	1.00	.35
655	A112	45c Hospital ward	1.75	.50
656	A112	$1.50 Tug of war	4.00	4.00
		Nos. 653-656 (4)	7.50	5.15

Personal Ornaments A113

1990, Feb. 14   Litho.   Wmk. 373
657	A113	5c shown	.50	1.00
658	A113	12c Necklace	.90	.45
659	A113	18c Islander, diff.	1.00	.60
660	A113	$2 Head ornament	9.00	9.00
		Nos. 657-660 (4)	11.40	11.05

Cowrie Shells A114

1990, July 23
666	A114	4c Spindle cowrie	.50	1.00
667	A114	20c Map cowrie	1.50	.40
668	A114	35c Sieve cowrie	1.75	.50
669	A114	50c Egg cowrie	2.75	2.75
670	A114	$1 Prince cowrie	5.00	5.00
		Nos. 666-670 (5)	11.50	9.65

Queen Mother, 90th Birthday
Common Design Types
25c, Queen Mother, 1987. $5, Inspecting damage to Buckingham Palace, 1940.

1990, Aug. 4   Wmk. 384   Perf. 14x15
671	CD343	25c multicolored	1.25	.40

Perf. 14½
672	CD344	$5 brown & blk	5.25	6.00

First Postage Stamp, 150th Anniv. A115

Designs: 35c, Postman, mail van. 45c, Solomon Islands Post Office. 50c, Solomon Islands No. 1. 55c, Young philatelist. 60c, Solomon Islands No. 20, Penny Black.

1990, Oct. 15   Wmk. 373   Perf. 14
673	A115	35c multicolored	2.00	.50
674	A115	45c multicolored	2.00	.55
675	A115	50c multicolored	2.25	1.75
676	A115	55c multicolored	2.25	2.25
677	A115	60c multicolored	3.00	3.00
		Nos. 673-677 (5)	11.50	8.05

Birds A116

1990, Dec. 5
678	A116	10c Purple swamphen	1.25	1.00
679	A116	25c Rufous brown pheasant dove	2.00	.70
680	A116	30c Superb fruit dove	2.50	.75
681	A116	45c Cardinal honeyeater	2.75	.90
682	A116	$2 Pigmy parrot	7.00	7.00
		Nos. 678-682 (5)	15.50	10.35

Birdpex '90, 20th Intl. Ornithological Congress, New Zealand.

Crop Pests — A117

Perf. 14x13½
1991, Jan. 16   Litho.   Wmk. 373
683	A117	7c Sweet potato weevil	1.00	.50
684	A117	25c Melon fly	1.50	.35
685	A117	40c Taro beetle	2.00	.65
686	A117	90c Cocoa weevil borer	3.00	3.00
687	A117	$1.50 Rhinoceros beetle	4.50	4.50
		Nos. 683-687 (5)	12.00	9.00

For No. 683 overprinted, see No. 884A.

Elizabeth & Philip, Birthdays
Common Design Types
Wmk. 384
1991, June 17   Litho.   Perf. 14½
688	CD346	90c multicolored	1.40	1.40
689	CD345	$2 multicolored	3.00	3.00
a.		Pair, #688-689 + label	4.50	4.50

No. 689a exists with two different labels.

Nutritional Foods — A118

1991, June 24   Wmk. 373   Perf. 14
690	A118	5c Coconut water	.35	.50
691	A118	75c Feed your child	2.00	2.00
692	A118	80c Mother's milk	2.25	2.25
693	A118	90c Local food	3.00	3.00
		Nos. 690-693 (4)	7.60	7.75

A 65c value, depicting healthy and unhealthy foods, was prepared but not issued. Value $300.

9th South Pacific Games — A119

Wmk. 384
1991, Aug. 8   Litho.   Perf. 14
694	A119	25c Volleyball	1.50	.35
695	A119	40c Judo	2.00	.75
696	A119	65c Squash	2.75	2.75
697	A119	90c Lawn bowling	3.00	3.00
		Nos. 694-697 (4)	9.25	6.85

Souvenir Sheet
698	A119	$2 Games emblem	8.75	8.75

Christmas — A120

Wmk. 373

1991, Oct. 28		**Litho.**	**Perf. 14**	
699	A120	10c Food prepara-tion	.55	.20
700	A120	25c Church service	1.00	.25
701	A120	65c Feast	2.75	1.00
702	A120	$2 Cricket match	5.75	5.75
a.		Souvenir sheet of 4, #699-702	10.50	10.50
		Nos. 699-702 (4)	10.05	7.20

Phila Nippon '91 — A121

Tuna fishing: 5c, Yellowfin tuna. 30c, Boat for pole and line tuna fishing. 80c, Pole and line tuna fishing. $2, Arabushi processing. No. 707a, Food made from tuna, tori nanban. b, Aka miso soup.

Wmk. 384

1991, Nov. 16		**Litho.**	**Perf. 14**	
703	A121	5c multicolored	.40	.25
704	A121	30c multicolored	1.25	.50
705	A121	80c multicolored	3.00	3.00
706	A121	$2 multicolored	5.50	5.50
		Nos. 703-706 (4)	10.15	9.25

Souvenir Sheet

707	A121	80c Sheet of 2, #a.-b.	4.00	4.00

No. 707 contains two 28x45mm stamps.

Queen Elizabeth II's Accession to the Throne, 40th Anniv.
Common Design Type
Wmk. 384 (5c, 60c), 373

1992, Feb. 6		**Litho.**	**Perf. 14**	
708	CD349	5c multicolored	.35	.60
709	CD349	20c multicolored	.65	.25
710	CD349	40c multicolored	.95	.45
711	CD349	60c multicolored	1.00	1.00
712	CD349	$5 multicolored	5.00	5.00
		Nos. 708-712 (5)	7.95	7.30

Alvaro Mendana de Niera (1541-1595), Discoveries in the Solomon Islands — A122

Granada '92: 10c, Thousand Ships Bay. 65c, Route to the Solomon Islands. 80c, Alvaro Mendana de Niera. $1, Graciosa Bay settlement. $5, Sailing ships.

Perf. 15x14½

1992, Apr. 24		**Litho.**	**Wmk. 373**	
713	A122	10c multicolored	1.00	.45
714	A122	65c multicolored	1.75	.70
715	A122	80c multicolored	1.90	1.90
716	A122	$1 multicolored	2.50	2.50
717	A122	$5 multicolored	5.50	5.50
		Nos. 713-717 (5)	12.65	11.05

A123

A124

Perf. 14x13½

1992, May 3		**Litho.**	**Wmk. 373**	
718	A123	25c Early portrait	.75	.40
719	A123	70c Wearing USMC fatigues	1.50	1.50
720	A123	90c Wearing uniform, cap	1.50	1.50
a.		Booklet pane, 2 ea #718, 720	4.50	
721	A123	$2 Statue	2.25	2.25
a.		Booklet pane, 2 ea #719, 721	7.50	
		Nos. 718-721 (4)	6.00	5.65

Souvenir Sheet

722	A123	$4 In dress uniform	9.50	9.50
a.		Booklet pane of 1	7.50	
		Complete booklet, one each #720a, 721a, and 722a	17.00	

Sergeant Major Jacob Vouza (1891-1984). One margin of Nos. 720a, 721a, and 722a is rouletted 8.

1992, May 22

World Columbian Stamp Expo '92, Chicago: 25c, Solomon Airlines domestic routes. 80c, Boeing 737-400 airplanes. $1.50, Solomon Airlines international routes. $5, Columbus and Santa Maria.

723	A124	25c multicolored	1.00	.25
724	A124	80c multicolored	2.75	2.00
725	A124	$1.50 multicolored	3.75	3.75
726	A124	$5 multicolored	7.50	7.50
a.		Souvenir sheet of 4, #723-726	15.00	15.00
b.		As "a," ovptd. with Taipei '93 emblem in sheet margin	8.00	8.00
		Nos. 723-726 (4)	15.00	13.50

No. 726b issued Aug. 14, 1993.

Miniature Sheets

Battle of Guadalcanal, 50th Anniv. A125

Scenes from battle of Guadalcanal: No. 727a, Japanese landing at Esperance. b, US landings. c, Australian Navy cruiser. d, US Navy post office. e, Royal New Zealand Air Force PBY Catalina.
No. 728a, US Marine Wildcat fighters. b, Henderson Field under construction and attack. c, Heavy cruiser USS Quincy. d, Australian Navy heavy cruiser Canberra. e, US Marines land on Guadalcanal. f, Japanese aircraft carrier Ryujo. g, Japanese Zeke fighters attack US positions. h, Japanese bombers attack American beachhead. i, Japanese destroyers of Tokyo Express. j, Japanese heavy cruiser Chokai.

Wmk. 384

1992, Aug. 7		**Litho.**	**Perf. 14**	
727	A125	30c Sheet of 5, #a.-e.	9.00	9.00
728	A125	80c Sheet of 10, #a.-j.	20.00	20.00

See No. 889.

Orchids A126

Perf. 14½x14

1992, Dec. 14		**Litho.**	**Wmk. 373**	
729	A126	15c Dendrobium hybrid	1.00	.30
730	A126	70c Vanda "Amy Laycock"	2.00	1.25
731	A126	95c Dendrobium mirbelianum	2.50	2.50
732	A126	$2.50 Dendrobium macrophyllum	4.00	4.00
		Nos. 729-732 (4)	9.50	8.05

See Nos. 752-755.

Crabs A127

Wmk. 373

1993, Jan. 15		**Litho.**	**Perf. 13**	
733	A127	5c Stalk-eyed ghost	.20	.55
734	A127	10c Red-spotted	.20	.55
735	A127	25c Flat	.20	.55
736	A127	30c Land hermit	.20	.20
737	A127	40c Grapsid	.25	.30
738	A127	45c Red & white painted	.25	.30
739	A127	55c Swift-footed	.30	.35
740	A127	60c Spanner	.35	.35
741	A127	70c Red hermit	.45	.45
742	A127	80c Red-eyed	.50	.50
743	A127	90c Rathbun red	.55	.55
744	A127	$1 Coconut	.60	.60
745	A127	$1.10 Red-spotted white	.65	.65
746	A127	$4 Ghost	2.25	2.75
a.		Souvenir sheet of 1, perf. 14	4.00	4.00
747	A127	$10 Mangrove fiddler	6.25	6.25
		Nos. 733-747 (15)	13.20	14.90

No. 746a for Hong Kong '97. Issued: #733-747, 1/15/93; #746a, 2/3/97.

World War II, 50th Anniv. A128

Designs: 30c, US War Memorial, Skyline Ridge. 80c, Country flags, Guadalcanal. 95c, Major General Alexander A. Vandegrift, map. $4, WWII Scouts, Gizo Islands.

Wmk. 373

1993, Apr. 19		**Litho.**	**Perf. 14**	
748	A128	30c multicolored	.55	.35
749	A128	80c multicolored	1.75	1.40
750	A128	95c multicolored	2.00	1.75
751	A128	$4 multicolored	6.25	6.25
		Nos. 748-751 (4)	10.55	9.75

Orchid Type of 1992
Perf. 14½x14

1993		**Litho.**	**Wmk. 373**	
752	A126	20c like #729	1.00	.40
753	A126	85c like #730	2.50	2.25
754	A126	$1.15 like #731	3.00	2.75
755	A126	$3 like #732	5.00	5.00
		Nos. 752-755 (4)	11.50	10.40

Nos. 752, 755 are inscribed "World Orchid Conference." Nos. 753-754 are inscribed "Indopex '93 Exhibition." Issued: #752, 755, 4/24; #753-754, 4/29.

Sinking of PT 109, 50th Anniv. A129

Designs: 30c, PT 109 about to be rammed. 50c, Native, Lt. John F. Kennedy. 95c, Message for help written on coconut, natives in canoe. $1.10, Kennedy, Navy and Marine Corps Medal. $5, PT 109.

Wmk. 373

1993, July 30		**Litho.**	**Perf. 13**	
756	A129	30c multicolored	.75	.50
757	A129	50c multicolored	1.00	.70
758	A129	95c multicolored	1.25	1.25
759	A129	$1.10 multicolored	2.50	2.50
		Nos. 756-759 (4)	5.50	4.95

Souvenir Sheet
Perf. 13x13½

760	A129	$5 multicolored	8.50	8.50

Nicobar Pigeon — A130

Wmk. 373

1993, Sept. 21		**Litho.**	**Perf. 14**	
761	A130	30c shown	1.50	1.00
762	A130	50c One on ground	2.00	1.25
763	A130	65c Two on branches	2.50	1.75
764	A130	70c One on branch	3.50	2.50
765	A130	$1.10 One on berry branch	1.50	1.50
766	A130	$3 Two in flight	2.75	2.75
		Nos. 761-766 (6)	13.75	10.75

World Wildlife Fund.

Dogs A131

Wmk. 373

1994, Feb. 18		**Litho.**	**Perf. 14½**	
767	A131	30c Dachshund	1.00	.35
768	A131	80c German shepherd	1.50	1.50
769	A131	95c Dobermann pinscher	1.75	1.75
770	A131	$1.10 Australian cattle dog	2.00	2.00
		Nos. 767-770 (4)	6.25	5.60

Souvenir Sheet

771	A131	$4 Boxer	10.00	10.00

Hong Kong '94. No. 771 overprinted "19-25 Aug. Jakarta '95 Surcharge $2-00." was available only at the exhibition.

Dolphins A132

Wmk. 373

1994, May 9		**Litho.**	**Perf. 14**	
772	A132	75c Striped	1.25	.90
773	A132	85c Risso's	1.40	1.25
774	A132	$1.15 Common	2.00	2.00
775	A132	$2.50 Spinner	4.25	4.25
776	A132	$3 Bottlenose	4.75	4.75
		Nos. 772-776 (5)	13.65	13.15

Miniature Sheet

Butterflies A133

Designs: a, Vindula sapor. b, Papilio aegeus. c, Graphium hicetaon. d, Graphium mendana. e, PHILAKOREA '94 emblem. f, Graphium meeki. g, Danaus schenkii. h, Papilio ptolychus. i, Phaedyma fissizonata.

Wmk. 373

1994, Aug. 16		**Litho.**	**Perf. 13½**	
777	A133	70c Sheet of 9, #a.-i.	8.50	8.50

For overprint see No. 842.

Intl. Year of the
Family — A134

Designs: a, Girl writing letter in Brisbane,
Australia, family reading letter on Santa Isabel,
Solomon Islands. b, Boeing 737-400, Brisbane
Intl. Airport, Australia. c, Boeing 737-400,
Henderson Airfield, Guadalcanal, DHC 6-Twin
Otter. d, Fera Airfield, Buala, Santa Isabel. e,
Family.

1994, Aug. 18   Perf. 13
778 A134 $1.10 Strip of 5, #a.-e.   6.75 6.75
  f.   Sheet of 1, #778   7.25 7.25

Volcanoes of
the Solomon
Islands
A135

Designs: 30c, Cook Island Volcano erupting
under sea, 1967. 70c, Kavachi Volcano erupting from sea, 1977. 80c, Kavachi Volcano
forming temporary island, 1978. 90c, Tinakulu
Volcano, permanent island.
No. 783: a, Map of Solomon Island volcanoes. b, Diagram illustrating formation of volcanic island archipelago.

Wmk. 373
1994, Oct. 24   Litho.   Perf. 14
779 A135 30c multicolored   1.00   .50
780 A135 70c multicolored   1.25 1.25
781 A135 80c multicolored   1.50 1.50
782 A135 90c multicolored   2.25 2.00
    Nos. 779-782 (4)   6.00 5.25
Souvenir Sheet
783 A135 $2 Sheet of 2, #a.-b.   6.00 6.00

La Perouse
Expedition,
210th Anniv.
A136

Designs: 30c, La Perouse, King Louis XVI.
80c, Map of Ile de La Perouse. 95c,
L'Astrolabe. $1.10, La Boussole. $3,
L'Astrolabe foundering on reef.

Wmk. 384
1994, Dec. 16   Litho.   Perf. 14
784 A136 30c multicolored   .75   .35
785 A136 80c multicolored   1.50 1.50
786 A136 95c multicolored   2.00 2.00
787 A136 $1.10 multicolored 2.25 2.25
788 A136 $3 multicolored   3.50 3.50
    Nos. 784-788 (5)   10.00 9.60

Visit
South
Pacific
Year
A137

30c, Tourists watching traditional dance,
land hermit crab. 50c, Dendrobium rennellii,
milkweed butterfly. 95c, Diver, moorish idol,
fish. $1.15, Boats at shore, grapsid crab.
$4, Flower, yellow-bibbed lorry.

Perf. 15x14½
1995, Feb. 17   Litho.   Wmk. 373
789 A137 30c multicolored   .30   .30
790 A137 70c multicolored   .70   .70
791 A137 95c multicolored   .85   .85
792 A137 $1.15 multicolored .95   .95
    Nos. 789-792 (4)   2.80 2.80
Souvenir Sheet
793 A137 $4 multicolored   8.50 8.50

FAO, 50th
Anniv.
A138

1995, Apr. 5   Perf. 12
794 A138 70c Banana   1.10   .90
795 A138 75c Paw paw   1.10   .90
796 A138 95c Pomelo   1.50 1.40
797 A138 $2 Star fruit   2.75 2.75
    Nos. 794-797 (4)   6.45 5.95
Souvenir Sheet
798 A138 $3 Mango   4.00 4.00

End of World War II, 50th Anniv.
Common Design Types
Admirals, aircraft carriers: 95c, Vice Adm.
Chuichi Nagumo, Akagi. $1, Rear Adm. Frank
J. Fletcher, USS Yorktown. $2, Vice Adm.
Robert L. Ghormley, USS Wasp. $3, Vice
Adm. William F. Halsey, USS Enterprise.
$5, Reverse of War Medal 1939-45.

1995, May 8   Perf. 13½
799 CD351 95c multicolored   1.75   1.75
800 CD351 $1 multicolored   1.75   1.75
801 CD351 $2 multicolored   3.25   3.25
802 CD351 $3 multicolored   4.25   4.25
    Nos. 799-802 (4)   11.00 11.00
Souvenir Sheet
Perf. 14
803 CD352 $5 multicolored   5.50   5.50

Orchids — A139

Designs: 45c, Calanthe triplicata. 75c, Dendrobium mohlianum. 85c, Flickingeria comata.
$1.15, Dendrobium spectabile.
$4, Coelogyne asperata.

Wmk. 373
1995, Sept. 1   Litho.   Perf. 14
804 A139 45c multicolored   1.50   .35
805 A139 75c multicolored   1.75 1.10
806 A139 85c multicolored   1.75 1.50
807 A139 $1.15 multicolored 2.25 2.25
    Nos. 804-807 (4)   7.25 5.20
Souvenir Sheet
808 A139 $4 multicolored   6.00 6.00
Singapore '95 (#808).

Christmas — A140

Designs: 90c, Start of canoe race. $1.05,
Pan pipers, Christmas tree. $1.25, Picnic on
beach. $1.45, Local church, nativity.

1995, Nov. 6   Perf. 13x13½
810 A140 90c multicolored   1.00   .80
811 A140 $1.05 multicolored 1.00   .85
812 A140 $1.25 multicolored 1.25 1.10
813 A140 $1.45 multicolored 1.75 1.50
    Nos. 810-813 (4)   5.00 4.25

Guglielmo
Marconi (1847-
1937), Radio,
Cent. — A141

Designs: $1.05, Demonstration, Salisbury
Plain, 1896. $1.20, Birth of maritime radio,

1900. $1.35, First ground air transmitter, Croy-
don, 1920. $1.45, Marconi visiting Japan on
world tour, 1933-34.

Perf. 14½x14
1996, Feb. 28   Litho.   Wmk. 373
814 A141 $1.05 multicolored 1.00 1.00
815 A141 $1.20 multicolored 1.25 1.25
816 A141 $1.35 multicolored 1.50 1.50
817 A141 $1.45 multicolored 1.75 1.75
    Nos. 814-817 (4)   5.50 5.50

Lories
A142

1996, Apr. 10   Litho.   Perf. 14
818 A142 75c Palm lorikeet   1.50   .60
819 A142 $1.05 Duchess lori-
           keet   1.60   .80
820 A142 $1.20 Yellow-bibbed
           lory   1.75 1.50
821 A142 $1.35 Cardinal lory   2.50 2.50
822 A142 $1.45 Meek's lori-
           keet   2.50 2.50
    Nos. 818-822 (5)   9.85 7.90
Souvenir Sheet
823 A142 $3 Rainbow lori-
           keet   5.50 5.50

CAPEX
'96 — A143

Island scenes: 40c, Dug-out canoe. 90c,
Man, bicycle. $1.20, Mobile Post Office bus.
$1.45, "Tulagi Express."
$4, "Tepuke," traditional canoe from Temotu
Province.

Wmk. 384
1996, June 8   Litho.   Perf. 13
824 A143 40c multicolored   .60   .45
825 A143 90c multicolored   1.50 1.00
826 A143 $1.20 multicolored 1.60 1.60
827 A143 $1.45 multicolored 2.75 2.75
    Nos. 824-827 (4)   6.45 5.80
Souvenir Sheet
828 A143 $4 multicolored   4.50 4.50

1996 Summer
Olympic Games,
Atlanta — A144

Olympic posters: 90c, Tokyo, 1964. $1.20,
Los Angeles, 1932. $1.35, Paris, 1924. $2.50,
London, 1908.

Wmk. 384
1996, June 30   Litho.   Perf. 14
829 A144 90c multicolored   .75   .60
830 A144 $1.20 multicolored .95   .95
831 A144 $1.35 multicolored 1.10 1.10
832 A144 $2.50 multicolored 1.75 1.75
    Nos. 829-832 (4)   4.55 4.40

First Christian Mission, 150th
Anniv. — A145

Designs: 40c, Suiesi, Makira Bay, 1846-47.
65c, Original sketches by Rev. L. Verguet,

1846, Surimahe. $1.35, Bishop Epalle's grave,
Isabel, 1845. $1.45, Makira Mission, Jean
Claude Colin, Marist founder.

Wmk. 373
1996, Sept. 12   Litho.   Perf. 14
833 A145 40c multicolored   .45   .25
834 A145 65c multicolored   .55   .55
835 A145 $1.35 multicolored .90   .85
836 A145 $1.45 multicolored 1.10 1.10
    Nos. 833-836 (4)   3.00 2.75
Souvenir Sheet

Taipei '96 — A146

Illustration reduced.

1996, Oct. 21
837 A146 $1.50 Sandford's eagle 2.00 2.00

UNICEF,
50th
Anniv.
A147

Wmk. 373
1996, Nov. 21   Litho.   Perf. 14½
838 A147 40c Food   .40   .30
839 A147 $1.05 Recreation   .80   .80
840 A147 $1.35 Medicine   1.10 1.10
841 A147 $2.50 Education   1.75 1.75
    Nos. 838-841 (4)   4.05 3.95

No. 777 Ovptd. in Red with SINGPEX
'97 Emblem
Wmk. 373
1997, Feb. 21   Litho.   Perf. 13½
842 A133 70c Sheet of 9, #a.-i.   7.00 7.00

Overprint is centered over entire sheet with
each stamp containing portion of SINGPEX
'97 emblem.
Overprint exists in black from a limited
printing.

Northern
Common
Cuscus
A148

15c, In tree. 60c, Eating berries. $2.50, In
tree, climbing right. $3, Two in branches.

Wmk. 373
1997, Apr. 21   Litho.   Perf. 12
843 A148 15c multicolored   .25   .25
844 A148 60c multicolored   .35   .35
845 A148 $2.50 multicolored 1.25 1.25
846 A148 $3 multicolored   1.50 1.50
    Nos. 843-846 (4)   3.35 3.35

Whales — A149

a, Whale, calf, vert. b, Whale breaching.

Wmk. 373
1997, May 29   Litho.   Perf. 14½
847 A149 $2 Sheet of 2, #a.-b.   3.50 3.50
PACIFIC 97.

Queen Elizabeth II & Prince Philip,
50th Wedding Anniv. — A150

#848, Queen with two horses. #849, Prince.
#850, Prince on polo pony. #851, Queen.
#852, Queen, Prince at Royal Ascot.

1997, July 10   Perf. 13
848    $3 multicolored   3.25 3.25
849    $3 multicolored   3.25 3.25
  a.   A150 Pair, #848-849   7.00 7.00
850    $3 multicolored   3.25 3.25
851    $3 multicolored   3.25 3.25
  a.   A150 Pair, #850-851   7.00 7.00
  Nos. 848-851 (4)   13.00 13.00

Souvenir Sheet
852 A150 $3 multicolored   4.50 4.50

South Pacific Commission, 50th
Anniv. — A151

Chelonia mydas: 50c, Laying eggs. 90c,
Young turtles entering water. $1.50, Group
swimming under water. $2, Two adults under
water.

Wmk. 384
1997, Sept. 29   Litho.   Perf. 14
853 A151 50c multicolored   .65 .40
854 A151 90c multicolored   .95 .85
855 A151 $1.50 multicolored   1.40 1.40
856 A151 $2 multicolored   1.60 1.60
  Nos. 853-856 (4)   4.60 4.25

Christmas
A152

Designs: $1.10, Oni mako. $1.40, Ysabel
dancing women with bamboo sticks. $1.50,
Pan pipers from Small Malaita. $1.70, Western
bamboo band.
No. 861, vert.: a, Pachycephala pectoralis.
b, Papilio aegeus, graphium meeki.

Wmk. 373
1997, Nov. 24   Litho.   Perf. 13½
857 A152 $1.10 multicolored   .85 .85
858 A152 $1.40 multicolored   1.00 1.00
859 A152 $1.50 multicolored   1.10 1.10
860 A152 $1.70 multicolored   1.50 1.50
  Nos. 857-860 (4)   4.45 4.45

Souvenir Sheet of 2
Perf. 14
861 A152 $1.50 #a.-b.   4.50 4.50

China Stamp Exhibition, Bangkok '97 (#861).
Issued: #857-860, 11/24; #861, 12/5.

Game
Fish — A153

50c, Black marlin. $1.20, Shortbill swordfish.
$1.40, Swordfish. $2, Indo-Pacific sailfish.

Perf. 14½
1998, Feb. 27   Litho.   Unwmk.
862 A153 50c multicolored   .85 .45
863 A153 $1.20 multicolored   1.40 1.10
864 A153 $1.40 multicolored   1.75 1.75
865 A153 $2 multicolored   2.00 2.00
  a.   Souv. sheet of 1, wmk. triangles   2.50 2.50
  Nos. 862-865 (4)   6.00 5.30

Singpex '98 (#865a). No. 865a issued 7/23
and sold for $3.

Diana, Princess of Wales (1961-97)
Common Design Type

$2, Wearing white dress (without hat).
#867: a, Up close. b, Wearing white hat,
dress. c, Wearing evening dress, black background. d, Taking flowers from children.

Perf. 14½x14
1998, Mar. 31   Wmk. 373
866 CD355 $2 multicolored   1.10 1.10
  Complete booklet, 10 #866   11.00

Sheet of 4
867 CD355 $2.50 #a.-d.   6.00 6.00

No. 867 sold for $10 + 50c, with surtax from
international sales being donated to the Princess Diana Memorial Fund and surtax from
national sales being donated to designated
local charity.

Technical
Cooperation
Between
Solomon
Islands and
Republic of
China
A154

Designs: 50c, Harvesting watermelons.
$1.50, Harvesting rice.
No. 870: a, 80c, Growing cucumbers. b,
$1.20, Growing tomatoes.

Wmk. 373
1998, May 29   Litho.   Perf. 13
868 A154 50c multicolored   .40 .40
869 A154 $1.50 multicolored   1.10 1.10

Souvenir Sheet
870 A154 Sheet of 2, #a.-b.   2.00 2.00

Melanesian Trade and Culture
Show — A155

a, Group raising arms during traditional
dance. b, Men with bows and arrow. c, Man
smiling in front of water. d, Four men with
poles in traditional dance. e, Masked man
kneeling down with bow and arrow. f, Man in
traditional garb, flowers. g, Group carrying
poles. h, Man with spear and shield. i, Man in
traditional garb, sun over water.

1998, July 3   Perf. 13½
871   Sheet of 9   7.50 7.50
  a.-c.   A155 50c any single   .45 .45
  d.-f.   A155 $1.20 any single   .55 .55
  g.-i.   A155 $1.50 any single   .75 .75

Souvenir Sheet

New Natl. Parliament Building — A156

Illustration reduced.

1998, July 7
872 A156 $4 multicolored   3.50 3.50

Independence, 20th anniv.

Souvenir Sheet

Australia '99 World Stamp
Expo — A157

Designs: a, HMS Endeavour, 1770. b, Los
Reyes being careened at Guadalcanal, 1568.

1999, Mar. 19   Perf. 13¼x13¾
873 A157 $10 Sheet of 2, #a.-
  b.   11.00 11.00

PhilexFrance
'99, World
Philatelic
Exhibition.
A158

Marine Life: a, Beach. b, Great frigate bird.
c, Coconut crab. d, Green turtle. e, Royal
Spanish dancer nudibranch. f, Sun moon and
stars butterflyfish. g, Striped Sweetlips. h,
Saddle-back butterflyfish. i, Cuttlefish. j, Giant
clam. k, Lionfish. l, Spiny lobster.

1999, July 2   Perf. 13¼
874 A158 $1 Sheet of 12, #a.-l.   7.50 7.50

1st Manned Moon Landing, 30th
Anniv.
Common Design Type

Designs: 50c, Lift-off. $1.50, Lunar module
above moon's surface. $2.50, Aldrin beside
US flag. $3.40, Splashdown.
$4, Earth as seen from moon.

Perf. 14x13¾
1999, July 20   Litho.   Wmk. 384
875 CD357 50c multicolored   .50 .35
876 CD357 $1.50 multicolored   1.00 1.00
877 CD357 $2.50 multicolored   2.00 2.00
878 CD357 $3.40 multicolored   2.50 2.50
  Nos. 875-878 (4)   6.00 5.85

Souvenir Sheet
Perf. 14
879 CD357 $4 multicolored   4.00 4.00
  a   Ovptd. in margin in red   4.50 4.50

No. 879 contains one circular stamp 40mm
in diameter.
Issued 7/7/2000, overprint on No. 879a
reads "WORLD STAMP EXPO - USA VALUE
$5.00." Sold for $5.

Queen Mother's Century
Common Design Type

Queen Mother: $1, Inspecting bomb dam-
age at Portsmouth, 1941. $1.50, At the Derby,
1983. $2.30, Receiving birthday wishes.
$4.90, As colonel-in-chief of Royal Army Medi-
cal Corps.
$3, With King George VI, Winston Churchill,
V-E Day, 1945.

1999, Aug. 16   Perf. 13½
880 CD358 $1 multicolored   .90 .50
881 CD358 $1.50 multicolored   1.10 .95
882 CD358 $2.30 multicolored   1.50 1.50
883 CD358 $4.90 multicolored   2.50 2.50
  Nos. 880-883 (4)   6.00 5.45

Souvenir Sheet
884 CD358 $5 black   4.00 4.00

No. 683 overprinted "China '99" in red
for international stamp exhibition,
Beijing.

1999, Aug. 21
884A A117 7c Sweet potato
  weevil   1.75 1.75

Ferrari
Racing
Cars
A159

1999, Sept. 27   Wmk. 373   Perf. 14
885 A159 $1 212E   .85 .55
886 A159 $1.50 250TR   1.00 .75
887 A159 $3.30 250LM   1.75 1.75
888 A159 $4.20 612 Can-Am   3.00 3.00
  Nos. 885-888 (4)   6.60 6.05

Guadalcanal Type of 1992

Designs: a, Flags at half staff. b, Cenotaph,
Honiara. c, Solomon Peace Memorial Park. d,
US War Memorial, Skyline Ridge. e, Reunion
ship Ocean Pearl.

1999, Aug. 16   Wmk. 384
889 A125 30c Strip of 5, #a.-e., +
  label   2.75 2.75

Melanesian
Mission, 150th
Anniv. — A160

Christmas: a, $1, Bishop George Augustus
Selwynd. b, $1, Bishop John Coleridge Patte-
son. c, $3.30, Text. d, $1.50, Stained glass. e,
$1.50, Southern Cross.

1999, Nov. 12   Unwmk.
890 A160 Strip of 5, #a.-e.   4.50 4.50

See Norfolk Islands #693.

Millennium
A161

Designs: Nos. 891, 893a, $1 Munda light-
house, war canoe. Nos. 892, 893b, $4, Tulagi
lighthouse, security boat.

2000, Apr. 27   Perf. 13½x13¼
891 A161 $1 multi   1.50 1.00
892 A161 $4 multi   5.00 5.00

Souvenir Sheet
893 A161 Sheet of 2, #a.-b.   7.50 7.50

Nos. 893a, 893b have red violet margins.

Souvenir Sheet

Commonwealth Youth Minister's
Meeting — A162

Illustration reduced.

2000, May 22 Litho. Perf. 13½x13¼
894 A162 $6 multi   9.50 9.50

Year of the
Dragon
A163

Dragon head facing: $1, Front. $3.90, Left.

Perf. 11¾x11½
2000, Nov. 13   Litho.   Unwmk.
895-896 A163 Set of 2   2.75 2.75
896a   Souvenir sheet, #895-896 2.75 2.75

East
Rennell
Island
World
Heritage
Site
A164

Map and: 50c, Rennell Island. $3.40, Lake
Tegano. $4, Rennell shrikebill. $4.90, Endemic
orchid.

Perf. 11¾x11½
2000, Nov. 30   Litho.
897-900 A164 Set of 4   8.50 8.50

2000 Summer
Olympics and
Olymphilex,
Sydney — A165

Runners in: $1, 100-meter race. $4.50,
1500-meter race.

2000, Dec. 11   Perf. 14
901-902 A165 Set of 2   4.75 4.75
  a.   Souvenir sheet, #901-902 4.25 4.25

Birds
A166

Designs: 5c, Yellow-throated white eye. 20c,
Purple swamphen. 50c, Blyth's hornbill. 80c,
Yellow-faced myna. 90c, Blue-faced parrotfinch. $1, Crested tern. $2, Rainbow lorikeet. $3, Eclectus parrot. $4, Dwarf kingfisher.
$10, Beach thick-knee. $20, Brahminy kite.
$50, Superb fruit dove.

2001   Wmk. 373   Perf. 14¼x14½
903   A166   5c multi   .20   .20
904   A166   20c multi   .20   .20
905   A166   50c multi   .25   .25
906   A166   80c multi   .35   .35
907   A166   90c multi   .40   .40
908   A166 $1 multi   .50   .50
909   A166 $2 multi   .90   .90
910   A166 $3 multi   1.25   1.25
911   A166 $4 multi   1.75   1.75

912   A166 $10 multi   3.75   3.75
Size: 48x38mm
Perf. 13¾x13½
913   A166 $20 multi   8.25   8.25
913A A166 $50 multi   22.50 22.50
  Nos. 903-913 (11)   17.80 17.80
Issued: Nos. 5c-$20, 2/1/01; $50, 6/1/01.

East Rennell Island Type of 2000 and

Hong
Kong 2001
Stamp
Exhibition
A167

Snake color: $1.70, Yellow and brown.
$2.30, Green and yellow.

2001, Feb. 1   Litho.   Perf. 11¾x11½
914-915 A167 Set of 2   3.00 3.00
Souvenir Sheet
916 A164 $5 Like #900   5.00 5.00

UN High
Commissioner for
Refugees, 50th
Anniv. — A168

Designs: 50c, Refugees. $1, Food and med-
ical supplies. $1.90, Shelter. $2.30, Education.

Perf. 14¼
2001, July 28   Litho.   Unwmk.
917-920 A168 Set of 4   3.75 3.75

Souvenir Sheet

New Year 2001 (Year of the
Snake) — A168a

No. 920A: b, Red-banded tree snake. c,
Whip snake. d, Pacific boa. e, Guppy's snake.
920A A168a $1 Sheet of 4, #b-e 4.50 4.50

Reef Fish
A169

Designs: 70c, Amphiprion chrysopterus.
90c, Amphiprion perideraion. $1, Premnas
biaculeatus. $1.50, Amphiprion melanopus.
$2.10, Amphiprion clarkii. $4.50, Dascyllus
trimaculatus.

Wmk. 373
2001, Dec. 27   Litho.   Perf. 14
921-926 A169 Set of 6   6.50 6.50
926a   Souvenir sheet, #921-926 7.50 7.50

Worldwide
Fund for
Nature
(WWF)
A170

Various depictions of gray cuscus: $1,
$1.70, $2.30, $5.

2002, Jan. 31
927-930 A170 Set of 4   5.00 5.00
  a.   Horiz. strip of 4   5.25 5.25

Reign Of Queen Elizabeth II, 50th Anniv. Issue
Common Design Type

Designs: Nos. 931, 935a, $1, Princess Eliz-
abeth with baby carriage, 1933. Nos. 932,
935b, $1.90, Wearing sunglasses. Nos. 933,
935c, $2.10, In 1955. Nos. 934, 935d, $2.30,
Wearing hat. No. 935e, $10, 1955 portrait by
Annigoni (38x50mm).

Perf. 14¼x14½, 13¾ (#935e)
2002, Feb. 6   Litho.   Wmk. 373
With Gold Frames
931-934 CD360 Set of 4   6.00 6.00
Souvenir Sheet
Without Gold Frames
935 CD360 Sheet of 5, #a-e   8.00 8.00

Methodist
Mission,
Cent.
A172

Designs: $1, Typical old school building,
Western Solomons. $1.70, Mrs. J. F. Goldie
and companions. $2.10, Tandanya, first mis-
sion schooner. $2.30, Rev. J. F. Goldie and
Solomon Islands chiefs.
$5, Rev. Goldie and Sam Aqarao, vert.

2002, May 23   Unwmk.   Perf. 14¼
937-940 A172 Set of 4   7.50 7.50
Souvenir Sheet
941 A172 $5 multi   3.00 3.00

United We Stand
— A173

Perf. 13½x13¼
2002, June 17   Unwmk.
942   A173 $2.10 multi   3.50 3.50
Souvenir Sheet

New Year 2002 (Year of the
Horse) — A173a

No. 942A: b, Horse. c, Horse, horiz.

Perf. 13½x13¾, 13¾x13½
2002, July 7   Litho.
942A A173a $4 Sheet of 2,
             #a-b   7.50 7.50
No. 942 was printed in sheets of 4.

Cowrie Shells — A174

No. 943: a, $1, Sieve cowrie. b, $1, Kitten
cowrie. c, $1, Stolid cowrie, eroded cowrie. d,
$1.90, Tapering cowrie. e, $1.90, Tiger cowrie.
f, $1.90, Lynx cowrie. g, $2.30, Map cowrie. h,
$2.30, Pacific deer cowrie. i, $2.30, Tortoise
cowrie.
$10, Golden cowrie.

Perf. 14¼x14½
2002, Aug. 2   Wmk. 373
943   A174   Sheet of 9, #a-i   14.00 14.00
Souvenir Sheet
944   A174 $10 multi   12.00 12.00

Phila Korea 2002 World Stamp Exhibition,
Seoul.

Queen Mother Elizabeth (1900-2002)
Common Design Type

Designs: No. 945, $1, Without hat (sepia
photograph). No. 946, $2.30, Wearing blue
hat.
No. 947: a, $5, Wearing tiara (black and
white photograph). b, $5, Wearing green blue
hat.

Wmk. 373
2002, Aug. 5   Litho.   Perf. 14¼
With Purple Frames
945-946 CD361 Set of 2   4.00 4.00
Souvenir Sheet
Without Purple Frames
Perf. 14½x14¼
947 CD361 Sheet of 2, #a-b   7.00 7.00

Battle of
Guadalcanal, 60th
Anniv. — A175

US servicemen: $1, No. 952d, Coast Guard
signalman First Class Douglas Munro. $1.90,
No. 952b, Marine Corps Capt. Joe Foss.
$2.10, No. 952c, Marine Corps Platoon Ser-
geant Mitchell Paige. $2.30, No. 952a, Navy
Rear Admiral Norman Scott.

2002, Aug. 7   Unwmk.   Perf. 14
948-951 A175 Set of 4   7.00 7.00
Souvenir Sheet
952 A175 $5 Sheet of 4, #a-d 11.00 11.00

Christmas — A176

Paintings: $1, Christmas Night, by Lucas
Cranach, the Elder. $2.10, Madonna and
Child, by Giovanni Bellini. $2.30, Nativity, by
Perugino, horiz. $5, Madonna and Child, by
Simone Martini.

2002, Nov. 25   Litho.   Perf. 14
953-956 A176 Set of 4   7.50 7.50

New Year
2003 (Year
of the
Ram)
A177

Perf. 14¼x14½
2003, Apr. 15   Litho.   Unwmk.
957   A177 $3 multi   3.00 3.00
Issued in sheets of 4.

U. S. Medals of Honor — A178

Designs: $1, Air Force Medal of Honor. $1.90 Navy Medal of Honor. $2.10, Army Medal of Honor. $2.30, Medal of Honor ribbon.

2003, June 6   *Perf. 14*
958-961 A178   Set of 4   8.00 8.00

Prince William, 21st Birthday — A179

No. 962: a, In gray suit. b, In red shirt. c, In black suit.
$15, In blue shirt.

2003, June 21
962 A179 $9 Sheet of 3, #a-c   14.00 14.00
Souvenir Sheet
963 A179 $15 multi   12.00 12.00

Solomon Islands — Republic of China Diplomatic Relations, 20th Anniv. A180

Designs: $1.50, Rice farmers. $2.10, Hospital.

2003, July 8   *Perf. 14¼*
964-965 A180   Set of 2   4.00 4.00

Coronation of Queen Elizabeth II, 50th Anniv. — A181

No. 966: a, Wearing tiara. b, Wearing green hat. c, Wearing blue hat.
$15, Wearing tiara, diff.

2003, June 2   *Litho.*   *Perf. 14*
966 A181 $9 Sheet of 3, #a-c   15.00 15.00
Souvenir Sheet
967 A181 $15 multi   14.00 14.00

Powered Flight, Cent. — A182

No. 968: a, Boeing 747. b, Boeing 707. c, Lockheed Model 649. d, Boeing Model 247D. e, Fokker F.VII. f, Orville and Wilbur Wright. $15, Concorde.

2003, Dec. 17
968 A182 $4 Sheet of 6, #a-f   14.00 14.00
Souvenir Sheet
969 A182 $15 multi   10.00 10.00

Souvenir Sheet

Visit of Pope John Paul II, 20th Anniv. — A183

No. 970: a, $5, Pope waving. b, $10, Pope with crucifix.

2004, Aug. 6   *Litho.*   *Perf. 14*
970 A183   Sheet of 2, #a-b   7.00 7.00
For No. 970 overprinted, see No. 1025.

2004 Summer Olympics, Athens — A184

Designs: $1.50, Runner at starting blocks. $2, Runner in full stride. $2.20, Runner at finish line. $10, Solomon Islands flag, Olympic rings.

2004, Aug. 13   *Perf. 14*
971-974 A184   Set of 4   7.00 7.00

Orchids A185

No. 975: a, Calanthe triplicata. b, Dendrobium johnsoniae. c, Dendrobium capituliflorum. d, Spathoglottis plicata. e, Dendrobium mirbelianum. f, Dendrobium polysema. g, Paphiopedilum bougainvilleanum. h, Coelogyne asperata. i, Dendrobium macrophyllum. j, Dendrobium spectabile.

2004, Aug. 28   *Perf. 13½*
975   Block of 10   15.00 15.00
   a.-e.   A185 $2.60 Any single   .90 .90
   f.-j.   A185 $5 Any single   1.75 1.75

Pres. Ronald Reagan (1911-2004) — A186

2004, Sept. 30   *Litho.*   *Perf. 14*
976 A186 $5 multi   9.00 9.00
Printed in sheets of 4.

Merchant Ships A187

Designs: $1.50, MV Bilikiki. $2.20, MV Spirit of Solomons. $3, SS Oceana. $20, RMS Queen Elizabeth 2.

2004, Oct. 11   *Perf. 13¼*
977-980 A187   Set of 4   12.00 12.00

FIFA (Fédération Internationale de Football Association), Cent. — A188

No. 981, $2.10: a, Player and ball. b, Players.
No. 982, $10: a, Players. b, Player and ball. Illustration reduced.

2004, Nov. 1   *Perf. 14*
Horiz. Pairs, #a-b
981-982 A188   Set of 2   10.00 10.00

Bird Life International — A189

No. 983, $2.10: a, Rufous-tailed waterhen. b, Buff-banded rail. c, Purple swamphen. d, Woodford's rail e, Roviana rail. f, Makira moorhen.
No. 984, $5: a, Solomon Islands hawk-owl (denomination at LR). b, White-throated eared nightjar (denomination at LR). c, Solomon Islands hawk-owl (denomination at LL). d, White-throated eared nightjar (denomination at UR). e, Marbled frogmouth. f, Fearful owl.
No. 985, $7.50: a, Beach kingfisher. b, Collared kingfisher. c, Ultramarine kingfisher. d, Moustached kingfisher. e, Little kingfisher. f, Variable kingfisher.

2004, Nov. 15   *Perf. 13¾*
Sheets of 6, #a-f
983-985 A189   Set of 3   36.00 36.00

Christmas — A190

Paintings: 10c, Adoration of the Magi, by Peter Paul Rubens. 50c, Madonna della Tenda, by Raphael, vert. $1.50, Madonna and Child, by Titian, vert. $2.60, Madonna by the Arch, by Albrecht Dürer, vert. $3, Holy Family,

by Frans Floris. $10, Madonna and Child, by unknown artist.

2004, Dec. 8   *Perf. 14*
986-991 A190   Set of 6   7.00 7.00

Battle of Trafalgar, Bicent. — A191

No. 992, $1.90: a, Vice-Admiral Horatio Lord Nelson. b, HMS Victory. c, Sir Thomas Masterman Hardy. d, The first engagement. e, Breaking the line. f, The death of Nelson.
No. 993, $2.60: a, Lord Cuthbert Collingwood. b, Napoleon Bonaparte. c, Destruction of the Bucentaure. d, Race and chase, 1805. e, The Nelson Touch — Band of Brothers. f, The Nelson Touch.
No. 994, $5: a, Nelson and Hardy on deck. b, Nelson sends the signal "England expects." c, Attempted siege of HMS Victory. d, Neptune tows Victory to Gibraltar. e, Funeral procession on Thames. f, Nelson's Column.
No. 995, $10: a, Nelson's early years. b, The letters of Nelson. c, Siege of Calvi — Nelson loses the sight of his eye. d, Santa Cruz de Tenerife — Nelson loses his arm. e, The Battle of Cape St. Vincent. f, The Battle of the Nile.

2005, Jan. 3   *Perf. 13¼*
Sheets of 6, #a-f
992-995 A191   Set of 4   50.00 50.00

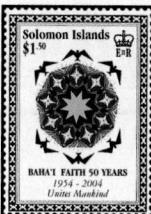

Baha'is in Solomon Islands, 50th Anniv. — A192

Designs: $1.50, Geometric design. $3, Globe, hands, laurel branches. $5, Alvin and Gertrude Blum, horiz.

2005, Mar. 21   *Litho.*   *Perf. 14¼*
996-998 A192   Set of 3   4.00 4.00

End of World War II, 60th Anniv. — A193

No. 999: a, $2.50, Japanese forces land at Tulagi. b, $2.50, USS Lexington under air attack during Battle of the Coral Sea. c, $2.50, Coastwatcher and Solomon Island scouts. d, $2.50, US forces land at Tulagi and Guadalcanal virtually unopposed. e, $2.50, HMAS Canberra sinking at Iron Bottom Sound. f, $5, Cactus Air Force in action over Henderson Airfield. g, $5, "Tokyo Express" nightly bombardments by Japanese warships. h, $5, P-38 Lightnings shoot down Admiral Yamamoto. i, $5, Lt. John F. Kennedy's PT-109 sank after collision with Japanese warship Amagiri. j, $5, Sgt. Maj. Vouza and medals.
No. 1000, RAN coastwatchers sending enemy intelligence reports by teleradio.

2005, Apr. 21   *Perf. 13¾*
999 A193   Sheet of 10, #a-j   16.00 16.00
Souvenir Sheet
1000 A193 $5 multi   3.50 3.50
Pacific Explorer 2005 World Stamp Expo, Sydney (#1000).

Europa Stamps, 50th Anniv. (in 2006) A194

No. 1001: a, Spain #1262. b, Netherlands #417.
No. 1002: a, Andorra (French) #174. b, Belgium #573.
No. 1003: a, Belgium #496. b, Spain #1567.
No. 1004: a, Austria #657. b, San Marino #701.
No. 1005: a, Netherlands #494. b, Norway #842.
No. 1006: a, Germany #749. b, Italy #750.

2005, May 16   *Perf. 13½x13¾*

1001	Horiz. pair	1.25	1.25
a.-b.	A194 $1 Either single	.55	.55
c.	Souvenir sheet, #1001	1.25	1.25
1002	Horiz. pair	2.50	2.50
a.-b.	A194 $2.10 Either single	1.10	1.10
c.	Souvenir sheet, #1002	2.50	2.50
1003	Horiz. pair	2.75	2.75
a.-b.	A194 $2.50 Either single	1.25	1.25
c.	Souvenir sheet, #1003	2.75	2.75
1004	Horiz. pair	4.75	4.75
a.-b.	A194 $5 Either single	2.00	2.00
c.	Souvenir sheet, #1004	4.75	4.75
1005	Horiz. pair	9.00	9.00
a.-b.	A194 $10 Either single	4.25	4.25
c.	Souvenir sheet, #1005	9.00	9.00
1006	Horiz. pair	16.00	16.00
a.-b.	A194 $15 Either single	7.50	7.50
c.	Souvenir sheet, #1006	16.00	16.00
	Nos. 1001-1006 (6)	36.25	36.25

Queen Elizabeth II's Royal Year — A195

No. 1007, $1: a, Order of the Garter. b, Trooping the Color.
No. 1008, $2.10: a, Royal Ascot. b, Garden party.
No. 1009, $2.50: a, Royal visits. b, State visits.
No. 1010, $5: a, State Opening of Parliament. b, Remembrance Day.
No. 1011, $10: a, Investitures. b, Christmas broadcast.
No. 1012, $15: a, Maundy service. b, Chelsea Flower Show.
Illustration reduced.

2005, June 3   *Perf. 14½*
Horiz. Pairs, #a-b
1007-1012   A195   Set of 6   36.00   36.00

A196

A197

Pope John Paul II (1920-2005) A199

Embossed on Metal
2005, July   *Die Cut Perf. 12½*
Self-Adhesive

1013	A196	$1.20 shown	.70	.70
1014	A196	$1.20 Pope, diff.	.70	.70
1015	A197	$2.60 shown	1.40	1.40
1016	A197	$2.60 Pope, diff.	1.40	1.40
1017	A198	$5 shown	2.75	2.75
1018	A198	$5 Pope, diff.	2.75	2.75
1019	A199	$10 shown	5.75	5.75
1020	A199	$10 Pope, diff.	5.75	5.75
		Nos. 1013-1020 (8)	21.20	21.20

BirdLife International — A200

No. 1021, $2.10: a, Finsch's pygmy parrot. b, Cardinal lory. c, Solomon's cockatoo. d, Eclectus parrot. e, Rainbow lory. f, Song parrot.
No. 1022, $5: a, Red-knobbed imperial pigeon. b, Yellow-bibbed fruit dove. c, Claret-breasted fruit dove. d, Nicobar pigeon. e, Stephan's ground dove. f, Crested cuckoo dove.
No. 1023, $7.50: a, Pied goshawk. b, Imitator sparrowhawk. c, Buff-headed coucal. d, Black-faced pitta. e, Melanesian megapode. f, Blyth's hornbill.

2005, Sept. 1   Litho.   *Perf. 14½x14¾*
Sheets of 6, #a-f
1021-1023   A200   Set of 3   36.00   36.00

Rotary International, Cent. — A201

2005, Sept. 12   *Perf. 14½*
1024   A201 $2.50 multi   1.50   1.50

No. 970 Overprinted

No. 1025: a, $5. b, $10.
2005, Oct. 3   *Perf. 14*
1025   A183   Sheet of 2, #a-b   7.00   7.00

Christmas — A202

Stories by Hans Christian Andersen (1805-75): $1, The Little Fir Tree. $2.10, The Nightingale. $2.50, The Emperor's New Clothes. $5, The Phoenix. $10, The Tinderbox. $15, The Red Shoes.

2005, Oct. 10
1026-1031   A202   Set of 6   17.00   17.00

Battle of Trafalgar, Bicent. — A203

Designs: $5, HMS Victory. $10, Ship in battle, horiz. $20, Admiral Horatio Nelson.

2005, Oct. 18   *Perf. 13¼*
1032-1034   A203   Set of 3   17.00   17.00

Worldwide Fund for Nature (WWF) — A204

Various views of prehensile-tailed skink: $1.50, $2.60, $3, $10.

2005, Dec. 7   *Perf. 14½*

1035-1038	A204	Set of 4	5.25	5.25
1038a		Sheet, 2 each # 1035-1038	11.50	11.50

Queen Elizabeth II, 80th Birthday A205

Queen Elizabeth II: $2.10, As young girl. $2.50, As woman. $5, Holding camera. $20, Wearing red hat.
No. 1043: a, $10, Like $2.50. b, $15, Like $5.

2006, Apr. 21   Litho.   *Perf. 14*
Stamps With White Frames
1039-1042   A205   Set of 4   11.00   11.00
Souvenir Sheet
Stamps Without Frames
1043   A205   Sheet of 2, #a-b   9.00   9.00

Anniversaries — A206

No. 1044, $2.20: a, Great Eastern. b, Isambard Kingdom Brunel (1806-59), engineer.
No. 1045, $2.50: a, Charles Darwin. b, Green turtle.
No. 1046, $5: a, Diving bell. b, Edmond Halley (1656-1742), astronomer.
No. 1047, $10: a, Locomotive "Rocket." b, George Stephenson (1781-1848), inventor.

2006, Apr. 30   *Perf. 14¾x14½*
Horiz. Pairs, #a-b
1044-1047   A206   Set of 4   14.00   14.00
Darwin's voyage on the Beagle, 175th anniv. (#1045).

Christopher Columbus (1451-1506), Explorer — A207

Designs: $1.90, Niña. $2.20, Pinta. $2.60, Santa Maria. $10, Arms of Columbus. $20, Columbus.

2006, May 22   *Perf. 13¼x13*
1048-1051   A207   Set of 4   6.50   6.50
Souvenir Sheet
1051A   A207 $20 multi   5.50   5.50
Washington 2006 World Philatelic Exhibition.

2006 World Cup Soccer Championships, Germany — A208

Match scenes from: $4, 1954 West Germany finals victory. $5, 1966 England finals victory. $10, 1998 France finals victory. $20, 2006 Solomon Islands vs. Australia playoff.

2006, June 9   *Perf. 14*
1052-1055   A208   Set of 4   13.00   13.00

Victoria Cross, 150th Anniv. A209

Victoria Cross and: $1, Captured Russian gun used to cast the Victoria Cross. $2.20, Midshipman Charles Lucas, first recipient of Victoria Cross. $2.50, Queen Victoria awarding first Victoria Crosses. $5, Corporal Sukanaivalu, Fijian infantryman at Bougainville, 1944. $10, Corporal Rattey, Australian infantryman at Bougainville, 1945. $15, Private Partridge, Australian infantryman at Bougainville, 1945.

2006, June 26   *Perf. 14x14½*
1056-1061   A209   Set of 6   13.00   13.00

Prehistoric Animals — A210

Designs: 5c, Baryonyx. 10c, Diplodocus. $1.50, Pteranodon. $2.15, Argentinosaurus. $2.40, Centrosaurus. $3, Allosaurus. $10, Ankylosaurus. $20, Iguanodon.

2006, Aug. 14   *Perf. 13¼x13¾*
1062-1069   A210   Set of 8   15.00   15.00

Cone Shells — A211

Designs: 5c, Conus marmoreus. 10c, Conus auratinus. 20c, Conus ferruginus. 50c, Conus consors. 80c, Conus magdalenae. 90c, Conus sulcatus brettinghami. $1, Conus tmetus. $1.50, Conus aureus. $2, Conus corallinus.

$3, Conus floccatus. $4, Conus punniculus. $10, Conus pohlianus. $20, Conus proximus. $50, Conus canonicus.

2006, Oct. 31 — Perf. 13x12½
1070	A211	5c multi	.20	.20
1071	A211	10c multi	.20	.20
1072	A211	20c multi	.20	.20
1073	A211	50c multi	.20	.20
1074	A211	80c multi	.20	.20
1075	A211	90c multi	.25	.25
1076	A211	$1 multi	.30	.30
1077	A211	$1.50 multi	.40	.40
1078	A211	$2 multi	.55	.55
1079	A211	$3 multi	.80	.80
1080	A211	$4 multi	1.10	1.10
1081	A211	$10 multi	2.75	2.75
1082	A211	$20 multi	5.75	5.75
1083	A211	$50 multi	14.00	14.00
Nos. 1070-1083 (14)			26.90	26.90

Tales of Beatrix Potter — A212

Designs: $1.50, The Tale of Peter Rabbit. $1.90, The Tale of Squirrel Nutkin. $2.15, The Tailor of Gloucester. $2.40, The Tale of Benjamin Bunny. $2.65, The Tale of Two Bad Mice. $5, The Tale of Mrs. Tiggy-Winkle.

2006, Dec. 4 — Perf. 13x13½
1084-1089	A212	Set of 6	6.00	6.00
1089a	Miniature sheet, #1084-1089		6.00	6.00

Wedding of Queen Elizabeth II and Prince Philip, 60th Anniv. — A213

Designs: $2.10, Couple looking straight ahead. $2.50, Couple looking at each other. $5, Wedding ceremony. No. 1093, $20, Elizabeth with flowers. No. 1094, $20, Wedding party.

2007, Jan. 31 — Perf. 13¾
1090-1093 A213 Set of 4 11.00 11.00
Souvenir Sheet Perf. 14
1094 A213 $20 multi 7.00 7.00
No. 1094 contains one 42x56mm stamp.

SEMI-POSTAL STAMPS

Catalogue values for unused stamps in this section are for Never Hinged items.

No. 452 Overprinted in Red: "+ 50c SURCHARGE / CYCLONE RELIEF FUND / 1982"
Perf. 13½x13
1982, May 3 Litho. Wmk. 373
B1 CD331 $1 + 50c multi 2.25 2.25

Nos. 546 and 569 Surcharged "Cyclone Relief Fund 1986" and New Value in Scarlet
Perf. 14½x14
1986, Sept. 23 Litho. Wmk. 384
B2 CD336 $1 + 50c multi 1.75 1.75

Souvenir Sheet Perf. 13½
B3 Sheet of 2 4.75 4.75
a. A95 55c + 25c multi 1.25 1.25
b. A95 $1.65 + 75c multi 3.00 3.00

No. 840 Surcharged in Red

Wmk. 373
2003, Feb. 8 Litho. Perf. 14½
B4 A147 $1.35 +$3 multi 6.00 6.00
World AIDS Day.

No. 866 Surcharged in Red

Perf. 14½x14
2003, Mar. 17 Wmk. 373
B5 CD355 $2 +$5 multi 6.50 6.50
Surtax for Cyclones Zoe and Beni Relief Fund.

POSTAGE DUE STAMPS

D1
Perf. 12
1940, Sept. 1 Typo. Wmk. 4
J1	D1	1p emerald	4.50	8.00
J2	D1	2p dark red	4.75	8.00
J3	D1	3p chocolate	4.75	13.00
J4	D1	4p dark blue	7.25	13.00
J5	D1	5p deep green	8.00	27.50
J6	D1	6p brt red vio	8.00	20.00
J7	D1	1sh dull violet	10.00	32.50
J8	D1	1sh6p turq green	17.50	60.00
Nos. J1-J8 (8)			64.75	182.00
Set, never hinged			120.00	

SOMALIA
sō-'mä-lē-ə
(Somali Democratic Republic)
(Italian Somaliland)
(Benadir)

LOCATION — Eastern Africa, bordering on the Indian Ocean and the Gulf of Aden
GOVT. — Probably none
AREA — 246,201 sq. mi.
POP. — 7,140,643 (1999 est.)
CAPITAL — Mogadishu

The former Italian colony which included the territory west of the Juba River became known as Oltre Giuba (Trans-Juba), was absorbed into Italian East Africa in 1936. Somalia stamps continued in use in Italian East Africa for several years. It was under British military administration from 1941-49. Italian trusteeship took effect in 1950, with a UN Advisory Council helping the

---

administrator. On July 1, 1960, the former Italian colony merged with Somaliland Protectorate (British) to form the independent Republic of Somalia.

4 Besas = 1 Anna
16 Annas = 1 Rupee
100 Besas = 1 Rupee (1922)
100 Centesimi = 1 Lira (1905, 1925)
100 Centesimi = 1 Somalo (1950)
100 Centesimi = 1 Somali Shilling (1961)

Catalogue values for unused stamps in this country are for Never Hinged items, beginning with Scott 170 in the regular postage section, Scott B52 in the semi-postal section, Scott C17 in the airpost section, Scott CB11 in the airpost semi-postal section, Scott CE1 in the airpost special delivery section, Scott E8 in the special delivery section, Scott J55 in the postage due section, and Scott Q56 in the parcel post section.

Used values in italics are for postally used Italian Somalia stamps. CTO's or stamps with fake cancels sell for about the same as unused, hinged stamps.

Watermark

Wmk. 140 — Crown

Italian Somaliland

Elephant — A1   Lion — A2

Wmk. 140
1903, Oct. 12 Typo. Perf. 14
1	A1	1b brown	80.00	16.00
2	A1	2b blue green	1.60	9.50
3	A2	1a claret	1.60	11.00
4	A2	2a orange brown	2.00	20.00
5	A2	2½a blue	1.60	20.00
6	A2	5a orange	2.00	47.50
7	A2	10a lilac	2.00	47.50
Nos. 1-7 (7)			90.80	171.50

For surcharges see Nos. 8-27, 40-50, 70-77.

Surcharged
1905, Dec. 29
8 A2 15c on 5a orange 3,250. 950.00
9 A2 40c on 10a lilac 800.00 325.00

Surcharged

1906-07
10 A1 2c on 1b brown 6.50 16.00
11 A1 5c on 2b blue grn 6.50 11.00

Surcharged

12	A2	10c on 1a claret	6.50	11.00
13	A2	15c on 2a brn org ('06)	6.50	11.00
14	A2	25c on 2½a blue	16.00	11.00
15	A2	50c on 5a yellow	24.00	27.50

Surcharged

16 A2 1 l on 10a lilac 24.00 35.00
Nos. 10-16 (7) 90.00 122.50

Nos. 15 and 16 with bars over former Surcharge and

1916, Apr.
18 A2 5c on 50c on 5a yel 35.00 40.00
19 A2 20c on 1 l on 10a dl lil 9.50 32.50

No. 4 Surcharged

20 A2 20c on 2a org brn 20.00 12.00
Nos. 18-20 (3) 64.50 84.50

Nos. 11-16 Surcharged:

a   b

1922, Feb. 1
22	A1(a)	3b on 5c on 2b	11.00	21.00
23	A2(b)	6c on 10c on 1a	20.00	16.00
24	A2(b)	9b on 15c on 2a	20.00	21.00
25	A2(b)	15b on 25c on 2½a	20.00	16.00
26	A2(b)	30b on 50c on 5a	22.50	40.00
27	A2(b)	60b on 1 l on 10a	22.50	72.50
Nos. 22-27 (6)		116.00	186.50

Victory Issue

Italy Nos. 136-139 Surcharged

1922, Apr.
28	A64	3b on 5c olive grn	2.00	7.25
29	A64	6b on 10c red	2.00	7.25
30	A64	9b on 15c slate grn	2.00	11.00
31	A64	15b on 25c ultra	2.00	11.00
Nos. 28-31 (4)		8.00	36.50

Nos. 10-16 Surcharged with Bars and

c   d

1923, July 1

40	A1	1b brown	9.50	30.00
41	A1(c)	2b on 2c on 1b	9.50	30.00
42	A1(c)	3b on 2c on 1b	9.50	17.50
43	A2(d)	5b on 50c on 5a	9.50	16.00
44	A1(c)	6b on 5c on 2b	14.50	16.00
45	A2(d)	18b on 10c on 1a	14.50	16.00
46	A2(d)	20b on 15c on 2a	17.50	16.00
47	A2(d)	25b on 15c on 2a	17.50	16.00
48	A2(d)	30b on 25c on 2½a	19.00	21.00
49	A2(d)	60b on 1l on 10a	19.00	45.00
50	A2(d)	1r on 1l on 10a	47.50	55.00
		Nos. 40-50 (11)	187.50	278.50

No. 40 is No. 10 with bars over the 1907 surcharge.

Propagation of the Faith Issue
Italy Nos. 143-146 Surcharged

1923, Oct. 24   Wmk. 140

51	A68	6b on 20c ol grn & brn org	8.00	40.00
52	A68	13b on 30c cl & brn org	8.00	40.00
53	A68	20b on 50c vio & brn org	4.75	47.50
54	A68	30b on 1l bl & brn org	4.75	60.00
		Nos. 51-54 (4)	25.50	187.50

Fascisti Issue

Italy Nos. 159-164
Surcharged in Red or Black

1923, Oct. 29   Unwmk.   Perf. 14

55	A69	3b on 10c dk grn (R)	9.50	14.50
56	A69	13b on 30c dk vio (R)	9.50	14.50
57	A69	20b on 50c brn car	9.50	16.00
		Wmk. 140		
58	A70	30b on 1l blue	9.50	40.00
59	A70	1r on 2l brown	9.50	47.50
60	A71	3r on 5l blk & bl (R)	9.50	65.00
		Nos. 55-60 (6)	57.00	197.50

Manzoni Issue
Italy Nos. 165-170 Surcharged in Red

1924, Apr. 1

61	A72	6b on 10c brn red & blk	12.50	40.00
62	A72	9b on 15c bl grn & blk	12.50	40.00
63	A72	13b on 30c blk & sl	12.50	40.00
64	A72	20b on 50c org brn & blk	12.50	40.00

Surcharged

65	A72	30b on 1l bl & blk	80.00	275.00
66	A72	3r on 5l vio & blk	525.00	2,100.
		Nos. 61-66 (6)	655.00	2,535.

Victor Emmanuel Issue

Italy Nos. 175-177
Overprinted

1925-26   Unwmk.   Perf. 13½, 11

67	A78	60c brown car	1.60	8.00
a.		Perf. 11	110.00	200.00
68	A78	1l dk bl, perf 11	2.40	12.00
a.		Perf. 13½	8.00	40.00
69	A78	1.25l dk blue ('26)	1.60	20.00
a.		Perf. 11	725.00	1,000.
		Nos. 67-69 (3)	5.60	40.00

Stamps of 1907-16 with Bars over
Original Values

1926, Mar. 1   Wmk. 140   Perf. 14

70	A1	2c on 1b brown	22.50	47.50
71	A1	5c on 2b blue grn	16.00	24.00
72	A2	10c on 1a rose red	9.50	8.00
73	A2	15c on 2a org brn	9.50	11.00
74	A2	20c on 2a org brn	11.00	11.00
75	A2	25c on 2½a blue	11.00	16.00
76	A2	50c on 5a yellow	16.00	27.50
77	A2	1l on 10a dull lil	22.50	40.00
		Nos. 70-77 (8)	118.00	185.00

Saint Francis of Assisi Issue

Italy Nos.
178-180
Overprinted

1926, Apr. 12   Perf. 14

78	A79	20c gray green	2.40	11.00
79	A80	40c dark violet	2.40	11.00
80	A81	60c red brown	2.40	20.00

Italy Nos. 182 and Type of 1926
Overprinted in Red

		Unwmk.		**Perf. 11**
81	A82	1.25l dark blue	2.40	27.50
		Perf. 14		
82	A83	5l + 2.50l ol grn	6.50	55.00
		Nos. 78-82 (5)	16.10	124.50

Italian Stamps of 1901-
26 Overprinted

1926-30   Wmk. 140

83	A43	2c orange brown	4.00	6.50
84	A48	5c green	4.00	6.50
85	A48	10c claret	3.25	.40
86	A49	20c violet brown	3.25	2.40
87	A46	25c grn & pale grn	3.25	1.60
88	A49	30c gray ('30)	16.00	35.00
89	A49	60c brown orange	4.75	12.00
90	A46	75c dk red & rose	110.00	35.00
91	A46	1l brown & grn	4.75	.80
92	A46	1.25l blue & ultra	11.00	2.40
93	A46	2l dk grn & org	27.50	16.00

94	A46	2.50l dk grn & org	27.50	22.50
95	A46	5l blue & rose	72.50	45.00
96	A51	10l gray grn & red	72.50	72.50
		Nos. 83-96 (14)	364.25	258.60

Volta Issue

Type of Italy, 1927,
Overprinted

1927, Oct. 10

97	A84	20c purple	4.75	32.50
98	A84	50c deep orange	8.00	20.00
a.		Double overprint	175.00	
99	A84	1.25l brt blue	11.00	52.50
		Nos. 97-99 (3)	23.75	105.00

Italian Stamps of
1927-28 Overprinted
in Black or Red

1928-30

100	A86	7½c lt brown	19.00	55.00
a.		Double overprint	475.00	
101	A85	50c brn & sl (R)	19.00	6.50
102	A86	50c brt violet ('30)	40.00	65.00
		Perf. 11		
		Unwmk.		
103	A85	1.75l deep brown	75.00	20.00
		Nos. 100-103 (4)	153.00	146.50

Monte Cassino Issue

Types of Monte Cassino Issue of Italy
Overprinted in Red or Blue

1929, Oct. 14   Wmk. 140   Perf. 14

104	A96	20c dk green (R)	4.75	17.50
105	A96	25c red org (Bl)	4.75	17.50
106	A98	50c + 10c crim (Bl)	4.75	20.00
107	A98	75c + 15c ol brn (R)	4.75	20.00
108	A96	1.25l + 25c dk vio (R)	11.00	35.00
109	A98	5l + 1l saph (R)	11.00	40.00

Overprinted in Red

		Unwmk.		
110	A100	10l + 2l gray brn	11.00	55.00
		Nos. 104-110 (7)	52.00	205.00

Royal Wedding Issue

Type of Italian Royal Wedding Stamps
of 1930 Overprinted

1930, Mar. 17   Wmk. 140

111	A101	20c yellow green	1.60	4.75
112	A101	50c + 10c dp org	1.20	8.00
113	A101	1.25l + 25c rose red	1.20	16.00
		Nos. 111-113 (3)	4.00	28.75

Ferrucci Issue

Types of Italian Stamps of 1930
Overprinted in Red or Blue

1930, July 26

114	A102	20c violet (R)	4.75	4.75
115	A103	25c dark green (R)	4.75	4.75
116	A103	50c black (R)	4.75	9.50
117	A103	1.25l deep blue (R)	4.75	17.50
118	A104	5l + 2l dp car (bl)	9.50	32.50
		Nos. 114-118 (5)	28.50	69.00

Virgil Issue
Types of Italian Stamps of 1930
Overprinted in Red or Blue

1930, Dec. 4   Photo.   Wmk. 140

119	A106	15c violet blue	1.20	8.00
120	A106	20c orange brown	1.20	3.25
121	A106	25c dark green	1.20	3.25
122	A106	30c lt brown	1.20	3.25
123	A106	50c dull violet	1.20	3.25
124	A106	75c rose red	1.20	6.50
125	A106	1.25l gray blue	1.20	8.00
		Engr.		
		Unwmk.		
126	A106	5l + 1.50l dk vio	3.50	40.00
127	A106	10l + 2.50l ol brn	3.50	60.00
		Nos. 119-127 (9)	15.40	135.50

Saint Anthony of Padua Issue
Types of Italian Stamps of 1931
Overprinted in Blue or Red

1931, May 7   Photo.   Wmk. 140

129	A116	20c brown (Bl)	1.60	17.50
130	A116	25c green (R)	1.60	6.50
131	A118	30c gray brn (Bl)	1.60	6.50
132	A118	50c dull vio (Bl)	1.60	6.50
133	A120	1.25l slate bl (R)	1.60	32.50

Overprinted in Red or Black

		Engr.		**Unwmk.**
134	A121	75c black (R)	1.60	17.50
135	A122	5l + 2.50l dk brn (Bk)	6.50	67.50
		Nos. 129-135 (7)	16.10	154.50

Italy Nos. 218, 221
Overprinted in Red

1931   Wmk. 140

136	A94	25c dk green (R)	12.00	20.00
137	A95	50c purple (R)	12.00	4.50

Lighthouse at Cape Guardafui — A3

Tower at Mnara Ciromo — A4

Governor's Palace at Mogadishu — A5

Termite Nest — A6

Ostrich — A7

Hippopotamus — A8

Greater Kudu — A9

Lion — A10

1932		Wmk. 140	Photo.	Perf. 12	
138	A3	5c deep brown		8.00	9.50
139	A3	7½c violet		12.00	24.00
140	A3	10c gray black		16.00	.40
141	A3	15c olive green		6.50	1.20
142	A4	20c carmine		275.00	.40
143	A4	25c deep green		6.50	.40
144	A4	30c dark brown		47.50	1.20
145	A5	35c dark blue		8.00	16.00
146	A5	50c violet		350.00	.40
147	A5	75c carmine		8.00	.80
148	A6	1.25 l dark blue		24.00	.80
149	A6	1.75 l red orange		16.00	.80
150	A6	2 l carmine		8.00	.40
151	A7	2.55 l indigo		40.00	80.00
152	A7	5 l carmine		24.00	9.50
153	A8	10 l violet		32.50	24.00
154	A9	20 l dark green		87.50	100.00
155	A10	25 l dark blue		87.50	175.00
		Nos. 138-155 (18)		1,057.	444.80
		Set, never hinged		2,075.	

1934-37				Perf. 14	
138a	A3	5c deep brown		2.40	.80
139a	A3	7½c violet		2.40	27.50
140a	A3	10c gray black		2.40	.40
141a	A3	15c olive green		2.40	2.40
142a	A4	20c carmine		2.40	.20
143a	A4	25c deep green		2.40	.40
144a	A4	30c dark brown		4.00	.40
145a	A5	35c dark blue		9.50	40.00
146a	A5	50c violet		27.50	.40
147a	A5	75c carmine		47.50	.40
148a	A6	1.25 l dark blue		80.00	1.20
149a	A6	1.75 l red orange		200.00	24.00
150a	A6	2 l carmine		55.00	.80
151a	A7	2.55 l indigo		240.00	550.00
152a	A7	5 l carmine		20.00	3.25
153a	A8	10 l violet		200.00	35.00
154a	A9	20 l dark green		14,500.	1,600.
		Never hinged		18,000.	
155a	A10	25 l dark blue		800.00	475.00
		Nos. 138a-153a,155a (17)		1,697.	1,162.
		Set, never hinged		4,250.	

Eleven denominations in the foregoing series exist perf. 12x14 or 14x12.

Types of 1932 Issue Overprinted in Black or Red

1934, May				Perf. 14	
156	A3	10c brown (Bk)		11.00	24.00
157	A4	25c green		11.00	24.00
158	A5	50c dull vio (Bk)		9.50	24.00
159	A6	1.25 l blue		9.50	24.00
160	A7	5 l brown black		11.00	24.00
161	A8	10 l car rose (Bk)		11.00	45.00
162	A9	20 l dull blue		11.00	45.00
163	A10	25 l dark green		11.00	45.00
		Nos. 156-163 (8)		85.00	255.00
		Set, never hinged		210.00	

Duke of the Abruzzi (Luigi Amadeo, 1873-1933).

Mother and Child A11

1934, Oct.					
164	A11	5c ol grn & brn		4.00	20.00
165	A11	10c yel brn & blk		4.00	20.00
166	A11	20c scarlet & blk		4.00	16.00
167	A11	50c dk violet & brn		4.00	16.00
168	A11	60c org brn & blk		4.00	24.00
169	A11	1.25 l dk blue & grn		4.00	40.00
		Nos. 164-169,C1-C6 (12)		48.00	272.00
		Set, never hinged		75.00	

Second Colonial Arts Exhibition, Naples.

> **Catalogue values for unused stamps in this section, from this point to the end of the section, are for Never Hinged items.**

Somalia

Tower at Mnara Ciromo — A12

Governor's Palace, Mogadishu — A13

Design: 5c, 20c, 60c, Ostrich.

1950, Mar. 24		Wmk. 277 Photo.		Perf. 14	
170	A12	1c gray black		4.00	8.00
171	A12	5c carmine rose		.20	.20
172	A13	6c violet		2.40	4.00
173	A12	8c Prus green		2.40	4.00
174	A13	10c dark green		.20	.20
175	A12	20c blue green		.20	.20
176	A12	35c red		6.50	8.00
177	A13	55c brt blue		4.00	.80
178	A12	60c purple		4.00	.80
179	A12	65c brown		8.00	4.00
180	A13	1s deep orange		12.00	4.00
		Nos. 170-180,E8-E9 (13)		71.90	58.20

Council in Session A14

1951, Oct. 4

181	A14	20c dk green & brn	3.25	2.00
182	A14	55c brown & violet	8.75	10.00
		Nos. 181-182,C27A-C27B (4)	24.00	22.00

Meeting of First Territorial Council.

Fair Emblem, Palm Tree and Minaret — A16

Mother and Child — A17

1952, Sept. 14 Wmk. 277 Perf. 14

185	A16	25c red & dk brown	2.40	2.60
186	A16	55c blue & dk brown	2.40	3.25
		Nos. 185-186,C28 (3)	8.05	9.85

1st Somali Fair, Mogadishu, Sept. 14-28.

1953, May 27
Center in Dark Brown

187	A17	5c rose violet	.60	1.60
188	A17	5c rose	.60	1.60
189	A17	50c blue	.80	1.60
		Nos. 187-189,C29 (4)	4.00	8.05

Anti-tuberculosis campaign.

Laborer at Fair Entrance A18

1953, Sept. 28 Unwmk. Perf. 11½

190	A18	25c dk green & gray	.40	.60
191	A18	60c blue & gray	1.00	1.40
		Nos. 190-191,C30-C31 (4)	2.80	4.00

2nd Somali Fair, Mogadishu, 9/28-10/12.

Map and Stamps of 1903 A19

Perf. 13x13½
1953, Dec. 16 Engr. Wmk. 277
"Stamps" in Brown and Rose Carmine

192	A19	25c deep magenta	.40	1.00
193	A19	35c dark green	.40	1.00
194	A19	60c orange	.40	2.00
		Nos. 192-194,C32-C33 (5)	2.40	8.00

50th anniv. of the 1st Somali postage stamps.

Somalia Brushwood A20

Perf. 12½x13½
1954, June 1 Photo. Unwmk.

195	A20	25c dp blue & dk gray	.80	1.60
196	A20	60c orange brn & brown	.80	1.60
		Nos. 195-196,C37-C38 (4)	4.00	6.40

Convention of Nov. 11, 1953, with the Sovereign Military Order of Malta, providing for the care of lepers.

Somali Flag A21

Adenium Somalense A22

Perf. 13½x13
1954, Oct. 12 Litho. Wmk. 277

197	A21	25c blk, grn, bl, red & yel	.30	.30

Adoption of a Somali flag. See No. C39.

1955, Feb. Photo. Perf. 13

Flowers: 5c, Haemanthus multiflorus martyn. 10c, Grinum scabrum. 25c, Poinciana elata. 60c, Calatropis procera. 1s, Pancratium. 1.20s, Sesamothamnus bussernus.

198	A22	1c bl, dp rose & dk ol brn	.20	.20
199	A22	5c bl, rose lil & grn	.20	.20
200	A22	10c lilac & green	.60	.20
201	A22	25c vio brn, yel & grn	1.40	.80
202	A22	60c blk, car & grn	.20	.20
203	A22	1s red brn & grn	.20	.80
204	A22	1.20s dk brn, yel & grn	.35	1.60
		Nos. 198-204,E10-E11 (9)	4.50	6.50

See #216-220. For overprint see #242.

Weaver at Loom A23

Design: 30c, Cattle fording stream.

Perf. 13½x14
1955, Sept. 24 Wmk. 303

205	A23	25c dark brown	.60	.80
206	A23	30c dark green	.60	.20
		Nos. 205-206,C46-C47 (4)	2.20	3.20

3rd Somali Fair, Mogadishu, Sept. 1955.

Casting Ballots — A24

Arms of Somalia — A25

1956, Apr. 30 Perf. 14

207	A24	5c brown & gray grn	.20	.20
208	A24	10c brown & ol bis	.20	.20
209	A24	25c brown & brn red	.20	.40
		Nos. 207-209,C48-C49 (5)	1.40	2.00

Opening of the territory's first democratically elected Legislative Assembly.

1957, May 6 Wmk. 303 Perf. 13½
Coat of Arms in Dull Yellow, Blue and Black

210	A25	5c lt red brown	.20	.40
211	A25	25c carmine	.20	.40
212	A25	60c bluish violet	.20	.80
		Nos. 210-212,C50-C51 (5)	1.40	2.80

Issued in honor of the new coat of arms.

Dam at Falcheiro A26

10c, Juba River Bridge. 25c, Silos at Margherita.

1957, Sept. 28 Photo. Perf. 14

213	A26	5c brown & purple	.20	.20
214	A26	10c bister & bl grn	.20	.20
215	A26	25c carmine & blue	.20	.80
		Nos. 213-215,C52-C53 (5)	2.20	2.80

Fourth Somali Fair and Film Festival.

Flower Type of 1955

Flowers: 1c, Adenium Somalense. 10c, Grinum scabrum. 15c, Adansonia digitata. 25c, Poinciana elata. 50c, Gloriosa virescens.

1956-59   Wmk. 303   Photo.   Perf. 13
216	A22	1c bl, dp rose & dk ol brn	.25	.25
217	A22	10c lil, grn & yel ('59)	.20	.20
218	A22	15c red, grn & yel ('58)	.40	.30
219	A22	25c dull lil, grn & yel ('59)	.20	.40
220	A22	50c bl, grn, red & yel ('58)	.40	.60

Nos. 216-220 (5)   1.45   1.75

Fencer — A27

Soccer Player A28

Designs: 5c, Discus thrower. 6c, Motorcyclist. 8c, Fencer. 10c, Archer. 25c, Boxers.

1958, Apr. 28   Wmk. 303   Perf. 14
221	A27	2c violet	.20	.20
222	A28	4c green	.20	.20
223	A27	5c vermilion	.20	.20
224	A28	6c gray	.20	.20
225	A27	8c violet blue	.20	.20
226	A28	10c orange	.20	.20
227	A28	25c dark green	.20	.20

Nos. 221-227,C54-C56 (10)   2.00   2.40

Book and Assembly Palace — A29

White Stork — A30

1959, June 19
228	A29	5c green & ultra	.20	.20
229	A29	25c ocher & ultra	.20	.20

Nos. 228-229,C59-C60 (4)   .90   1.20

Opening of Somalia's Constituent Assembly. See No. C60a.

1959, Sept. 4   Photo.   Perf. 14

Birds: 10c, Saddle-billed stork. 15c, Sacred ibis. 25c, Pink-backed pelican.

230	A30	5c yellow, blk & red	.30	.20
231	A30	10c brown, red & yel	.30	.40
232	A30	15c orange & black	.30	.20
233	A30	25c dk car, blk & org	.30	.20

Nos. 230-233,C61-C62 (6)   3.20   1.80

Incense Bush — A31

Arms of University Institute — A32

Design: 60c, Girl burning incense.

1959, Sept. 28   Wmk. 303
234	A31	20c orange & black	.20	.25
235	A31	60c blk, org & dk red	.20	.25

Nos. 234-235,C63-C64 (4)   1.35   1.50

5th Somali Fair, Mogadishu.

1960, Jan. 14   Photo.   Perf. 14

Designs: 50c, Map of Africa and arms, horiz. 80c, Arms of University Institute.

236	A32	5c brown & salmon	.20	.20
237	A32	50c lt vio bl, brn & blk	.20	.20
238	A32	80c brt red & blk	.25	.25

Nos. 236-238,C65-C66 (5)   1.30   1.40

Opening of the University Institute of Somalia.

Globe and Uprooted Oak Emblem A33

Palm — A34

Design: 60c, Like 10c but with inscription and emblem rearranged.

1960, Apr. 7   Perf. 14
239	A33	10c yel brn, grn & blk	.20	.20
240	A33	60c dp bister & blk	.20	.20
241	A34	80c pink, grn & blk	.20	.20

Nos. 239-241,C67 (4)   1.00   1.20

World Refugee Year, 7/1/59-6/30/60.

Republic

No. 217 Overprinted

Wmk. 303
1960, June 26   Photo.   Perf. 13
242	A22	10c lilac, grn & yel	19.00	24.00

Nos. 242,C68-C69 (3)   88.00   96.50

Independence of British Somaliland, which became part of the Republic of Somalia.

Gazelle and Map of Africa — A36

25c, NYC skyline, UN Building and UN flag.

1960, July 1   Perf. 14
243	A36	5c lilac & brown	.40	.40
244	A36	25c blue	.45	.45

Nos. 243-244,C70-C71 (4)   4.90   4.90

Somalia independence.

Boy Drawing Giraffe A37

1960, Nov. 24
245	A37	10c shown	.30	.30
246	A37	15c Zebra	.40	.40
247	A37	25c Black rhinoceros	.45	.45

Nos. 245-247,C72 (4)   5.65   5.65

Olympic Torch, Somalia Flag — A38

Girl Harvesting Papaya — A39

10c, Runners, flag and Olympic rings.

1960   Wmk. 303   Perf. 14
248	A38	5c green & blue	.25	.20
249	A38	10c yellow & blue	.25	.20

Nos. 248-249,C73-C74 (4)   3.10   3.00

17th Olympic Games, Rome, 8/25-9/11.

1961, July 5   Photo.

Girl harvesting: 10c, Durrah (sorghum). 20c, Cotton. 25c, Sesame. 40c, Sugar cane. 50c, Bananas. 75c, Peanuts, horiz. 80c, Grapefruit, horiz.

250	A39	5c multicolored	.20	.20
251	A39	10c multicolored	.20	.20
252	A39	20c multicolored	.20	.20
253	A39	25c multicolored	.20	.20
254	A39	40c multicolored	.30	.25
255	A39	50c multicolored	.50	.40
256	A39	75c multicolored	.75	.75
257	A39	80c multicolored	2.75	2.75

Nos. 250-257 (8)   5.10   4.95

Shield, Bow and Quiver — A40

Pomacanthus Semicirculatus A41

Design: 45c, Pottery and incense jug.

1961, Sept. 28
258	A40	25c blk, car & ocher	.20	.20
259	A40	45c blk, bl grn & ocher	.25	.25

Nos. 258-259,C82-C83 (4)   3.10   3.10

6th Somali Fair, Mogadishu.

1962, Apr. 26   Photo.

Fish: 15c, Girl embroidering fish on cloth. 40c, Novaculichthys taeniourus.

260	A41	15c brown, blk & pink	.40	.40
261	A41	25c orange, blk & ultra	.40	.40
262	A41	40c green, blk & rose	.80	.80

Nos. 260-262,C84 (4)   5.10   5.10

Mosquito Trapped by Sprays A42

Design: 25c, Man with spray gun and malaria eradication emblem, vert.

1962, Oct. 25   Wmk. 303   Perf. 14
263	A42	10c orange red & grn	.45	.45
264	A42	25c rose lilac, brn & blk	.45	.45

Nos. 263-264,C85-C86 (4)   4.50   4.50

WHO drive to eradicate malaria.

Police Auxiliary Woman A43

10c, Army auxiliary woman. 25c, Radio police car. 75c, First aid army auxiliary, vert.

1963, May 15   Wmk. 303   Perf. 14
265	A43	5c multicolored	.25	.25
266	A43	10c black & orange	.25	.25
267	A43	25c multicolored	.25	.25
268	A43	75c multicolored	.55	.55

Nos. 265-268,C87-C88 (6)   4.90   4.90

Women's auxiliary forces.

Carved Fork and Spoon and Wheat Emblem A44

1963, June 25   Photo.
269	A44	75c green & red brown	.65	.65

FAO "Freedom from Hunger" campaign. See No. C89.

Pres. Aden Abdulla Osman — A45

1963, Sept. 15   Wmk. 303   Perf. 14
270	A45	25c bl, dk brn, org & lt bl	.45	.45

Nos. 270,C90-C91 (3)   3.05   3.05

3rd anniv. of independence.

Dunes Theater A46

55c, African Merchants' and Artisans' Exhibit.

1963, Sept. 28   **Photo.**
271 A46 25c blue green   .45   .45
272 A46 55c carmine rose   1.00   1.00
    Nos. 271-272,C92 (3)   4.20   4.20

7th Somali Fair, Mogadishu.

Somali
Credit
Bank
Building
A47

1964, May 16   **Wmk. 303**   **Perf. 14**
273 A47 60c indigo, red lil & yel   .85   .85
    Nos. 273,C93-C94 (3)   5.35   5.35

10th anniv. of the Somali Credit Bank.

Running — A48   ITU Emblem and
                    Map of
                    Africa — A50

DC-3
A49

1964, Oct. 10   **Wmk. 303**   **Perf. 14**
274 A48 10c shown   .25   .25
275 A48 25c High jump   .25   .25
    Nos. 274-275,C95-C96 (4)   4.10   4.10

18th Olympic Games, Tokyo, Oct. 10-25.

1964, Nov. 8   **Photo.**   **Perf. 14**

Design: 20c, Passengers leaving DC-3.

276 A49   5c dk blue & lil rose   .45   .45
277 A49 20c blue & orange   .95   .95
    Nos. 276-277,C97-C98 (4)   9.55   9.55

Establishment of Somali Air Lines.

1965, May 17   **Wmk. 303**   **Perf. 14**
278 A50 25c dp blue & dp org   .55   .30
    Nos. 278,C99-C100 (3)   3.50   2.35

ITU centenary.

Tanning
Industry
A51

   25c, Meat industry; cannery; cattle. 35c,
Fishing industry; cannery, fishing boats.

1965, Sept. 28   **Photo.**   **Perf. 14**
279 A51 10c sepia & buff   .20   .20
280 A51 25c sepia & pink   .25   .25
281 A51 35c sepia & lt blue   .25   .20
    Nos. 279-281,C101-C102 (5)   4.40   3.25

8th Somali Fair, Mogadishu.

Hottentot
Fig and
Gazelle
A52

Designs: 60c, African tulip and giraffes. 1sh,
Ninfea and flamingos. 1.30sh, Pervincia and
ostriches. 1.80sh, Bignonia and zebras.

1965, Nov. 1   **Wmk. 303**   **Perf. 14**
Flowers in Natural Colors
282 A52   20c blk & brt bl   .25   .25
283 A52   60c blk & dk gray   .25   .25
284 A52   1sh blk, sl grn & ol
             grn   .70   .55
285 A52 1.30sh blk & dp grn   1.60   1.40
286 A52 1.80sh blk & brt bl   4.50   4.00
    Nos. 282-286 (5)   7.30   6.45

Narina's
Trogon
A53

   Birds: 35c, Bateleur eagle, vert. 50c, Vulture. 1.30sh, European roller. 2sh, Vulturine
guinea fowl, vert.

1966, June 1   **Photo.**   **Wmk. 303**
287 A53   25c multicolored   .25   .25
288 A53   35c brt blue & multi   .25   .25
289 A53   50c multicolored   .40   .40
290 A53 1.30sh multicolored   1.90   1.90
291 A53   2sh multicolored   3.25   3.25
    Nos. 287-291 (5)   6.05   6.05

Globe and UN
Emblem
A54

   UN emblem and: 1sh, Map of Africa. 1.50sh,
Map of Somalia.

1966, Oct. 24   **Litho.**   **Perf. 13x12½**
292 A54   35c bl, pur & brt bl   .60   .25
293 A54   1sh brn, yel & brick
            red   .60   .60
294 A54 1.50sh grn, blk, bl & yel   1.20   .55
    Nos. 292-294 (3)   2.40   1.05

21st anniversary of United Nations.

Woman
Sitting on
Crocodile
A55

   Paintings: 1sh, Woman and warrior. 1.50sh,
Boy leading camel. 2sh, Women pounding
grain.

Wmk. 303
1966, Dec. 1   **Photo.**   **Perf. 14**
295 A55   25c multicolored   .20   .20
296 A55   1sh multicolored   .25   .20
297 A55 1.50sh multicolored   .55   .25
298 A55   2sh multicolored   1.50   .95
    Nos. 295-298 (4)   2.50   1.60

Somali art, exhibited in the Garesa
Museum, Mogadishu.

UNESCO
Emblem
A56

1966, Dec. 20   **Wmk. 303**   **Perf. 14**
299 A56   35c blk, dk red &
            gray   .25   .25
300 A56   1sh blk, emer & yel   .25   .25
301 A56 1.80sh blk, ultra & red   1.75   1.75
    Nos. 299-301 (3)   2.25   2.25

UNESCO, 20th anniv.

Haggard's   Dancers — A58
Oribi — A57

   Gazelles: 60c, Long-snouted dik-dik. 1sh,
Gerenuk. 1.80sh, Soemmering's gazelle.

1967, Feb. 20   **Photo.**   **Perf. 14**
302 A57   35c blk, ultra & bis   .20   .20
303 A57   60c blk, org & brn   .20   .20
304 A57   1sh blk, red & brn   .40   .40
305 A57 1.80sh blk, yel grn & brn   2.75   2.75
    Nos. 302-305 (4)   3.55   3.55

Unwmk.
1967, July 15   **Litho.**   **Perf. 13**

Designs: Various Folk Dances.

306 A58   25c multicolored   .25   .25
307 A58   50c multicolored   .25   .25
308 A58 1.30sh multicolored   .25   .25
309 A58   2sh multicolored   2.10   2.10
    Nos. 306-309 (4)   2.85   2.85

Boy Scout
Giving Scout
Sign — A59

   Designs: 50c, Boy Scouts with flags. 1sh,
Boy Scout cooking and tent. 1.80sh, Jamboree emblem.

1967, Aug. 15
310 A59   35c multicolored   .20   .20
311 A59   50c multicolored   .20   .20
312 A59   1sh multicolored   .55   .95
313 A59 1.80sh multicolored   2.10   2.10
    Nos. 310-313 (4)   3.05   3.05

12th Boy Scout World Jamboree, Farragut
State Park, Idaho, Aug. 1-9.

Pres. Abdirascid Ali Scermarche and
King Faisal — A60

   Designs: 1sh, Clasped hands, flags of
Somalia and Saudi Arabia.

Wmk. 303
1967, Sept. 21   **Photo.**   **Perf. 14**
314 A60 50c black & lt blue   .25   .25
315 A60 1sh multicolored   .55   .55
    Nos. 314-315,C103 (3)   2.90   2.90

Visit of King Faisal of Saudi Arabia.

Gaterin
Gaterinus
A61

   Tropical Fish: 50c, Chaetodon semilar-
vatus. 1sh, Priacanthus hamrur. 1.80sh,
Epinephelus summana.

1967, Nov. 15   **Litho.**   **Perf. 14**
316 A61   35c dk bl, yel & blk   .40   .40
317 A61   50c brt bl, ocher &
            blk   .40   .40
318 A61   1sh emer, org, brn &
            blk   1.25   1.25
319 A61 1.80sh pur, yel & blk   2.40   2.40
    Nos. 316-319 (4)   4.45   4.45

Physician Treating   Waterbuck
Infant   A64
A62

Woman and
Basket with
Lemons
A63

   WHO, 20th anniv.: 1sh, Physician examining boy, and nurse. 1.80sh, Physician and
nurse treating patient.

Wmk. 303
1968, Mar. 20   **Photo.**   **Perf. 14**
320 A62   35c blk, scar, bl &
            brn   .30   .30
321 A62   1sh blk, grn & brn   .30   .30
322 A62 1.80sh blk, org & brn   1.75   1.75
    Nos. 320-322 (3)   2.35   2.35

1968   **Litho.**   **Perf. 11½**

Designs: 10c, Oranges. 25c, Coconuts. 35c,
Papayas. 40c, Limes. 50c, Grapefruit. 1sh,
Bananas. 1.30sh, Cotton bolls. 1.80sh,
Speke's gazelle. 2sh, Lesser kudu. 5sh,
Hunter's hartebeest. 10sh, Clark's gazelle
(dibatag).

323 A63   5c lt blue & multi   .25   .25
324 A63   10c yellow & multi   .25   .25
325 A63   25c lt lilac & multi   .25   .25
326 A63   35c salmon & multi   .25   .25
327 A63   40c buff & multi   .25   .25
328 A63   50c multicolored   .25   .25
329 A63   1sh lt blue & multi   .85   .85
330 A63 1.30sh gray & multi   2.50   2.50
331 A64 1.80sh lt blue & multi   .45   .45
332 A64 1.80sh multicolored   .45   .45
333 A64   2sh pink & multi   1.40   1.40
334 A64   5sh multicolored   2.75   2.75
335 A64   10sh multicolored   10.00   10.00
    Nos. 323-335 (13)   19.90   19.90

Issued: #323-330, 4/25; #331-335, 5/10.

Javelin — A65   Statuette — A66

Wmk. 303
1968, Oct. 12   **Photo.**   **Perf. 14**
336 A65   35c shown   .20   .20
337 A65   50c Running   .20   .20
338 A65   80c High jump   .25   .25
339 A65 1.50sh Basketball   1.90   1.20
   a.   Souvenir sheet of 4, #336-339   6.75   6.75
    Nos. 336-339 (4)   2.55   1.85

19th Olympic Games, Mexico City, Oct. 12-
27. No. 339a sold for 3.65sh.

Perf. 11½x12
1968, Dec. 1   **Litho.**   **Unwmk.**

Statuettes: 25c, Woman grinding grain. 35c,
Woman potter. 2.80sh, Woman mat maker.

340 A66   25c rose lil, blk & brn   .25   .20
341 A66   35c brick red, blk &
            brn   .25   .20
342 A66 2.80sh green, blk & brn   1.90   1.20
    Nos. 340-342 (3)   2.40   1.60

Cornflower and Rhinoceros A67

80c, Sunflower & elephant. 1sh, Oleander & antelopes. 1.80sh, Chrysanthemums & storks.

Perf. 13x12½
1969, Mar. 25   Litho.   Unwmk.

343	A67	40c red & multi	.20	.20
344	A67	80c violet & multi	.20	.20
345	A67	1sh blue & multi	.55	.55
346	A67	1.80sh yellow & multi	2.90	2.90
		Nos. 343-346 (4)	3.85	3.85

ILO Emblem and Blacksmiths — A68

Designs: 1sh, Oxdrawn plow. 1.80sh, Drawing water from well.

Wmk. 303
1969, May 10   Photo.   Perf. 14

347	A68	25c dk rose, dp bis & blk	.25	.25
348	A68	1sh car rose, brn & blk	.25	.25
349	A68	1.80sh multicolored	1.75	1.75
		Nos. 347-349 (3)	2.25	2.25

ILO, 50th anniversary.

Mahatma Gandhi — A69

Designs: 1.50sh, Gandhi, globe and hands releasing dove, horiz. 1.80sh, Gandhi seated.

Unwmk.
1969, Oct. 2   Photo.   Perf. 13
Size: 25x35½mm

350	A69	35c brown violet	.40	.40

Perf. 14½x14
Size: 37½x20mm

351	A69	1.50sh bister brn	.55	.55

Perf. 13
Size: 25x35½mm

352	A69	1.80sh olive gray	3.75	3.75
		Nos. 350-352 (3)	4.70	4.70

Mohandas K. Gandhi (1869-1948), leader in India's fight for independence.

1970
US Space Explorations. Set of seven. 60, 80c, 1, 1.50, 1.80, 2, 2.80sh. Souv. sheet, 14sh, issued Feb. 14. Nos. 7001-7008. Values: set, $6; souvenir sheet, $30.

Nivprale Vevanes A70

Butterflies: 50c, Leschenault. 1.50sh, Papilio (ornytoptera) aeacus. 2sh, Urania riphaeus.

Perf. 12½x13
1970, Mar. 25   Litho.   Unwmk.

353	A70	25c multicolored	.25	.25
354	A70	50c multicolored	.25	.25
355	A70	1.50sh orange & multi	.65	.65
356	A70	2sh yellow & multi	2.40	2.40
		Nos. 353-356 (4)	3.55	3.55

Somali Democratic Republic

Lenin Addressing Crowd — A71

Designs: 25c, Lenin walking with children. 1.80sh, Lenin in his study, horiz.

Perf. 12x12½, 12½x12
1970, Apr. 22   Litho.   Unwmk.

357	A71	25c multicolored	.25	.25
358	A71	1sh multicolored	.45	.45
359	A71	1.80sh multicolored	2.10	2.10
		Nos. 357-359 (3)	2.80	2.80

Lenin (1870-1924), Russian communist leader.

Bird Feeding Young A72

35c, Monument & Battle of Dagahtur. 1sh, Arms of Somalia, UN emblem, vert. 2.80sh, Boy milking camel, & star, vert.

Perf. 14x13½, 13½x14
1970, July 28   Photo.   Wmk. 303

360	A72	25c blue & multi	.20	.20
361	A72	35c slate & multi	.20	.20
362	A72	1sh violet & multi	.55	.55
363	A72	2.80sh blue & multi	2.00	2.00
		Nos. 360-363 (4)	2.95	2.95

10th anniversary of independence.

"Agriculture" — A73

40c, Soldier and flag. 1sh, Hand on open book. 1.80sh, Grain, scales of justice and dove.

Perf. 14x13½
1970, Oct. 21   Photo.   Wmk. 303

364	A73	35c green & multi	.20	.20
365	A73	40c ultra & blk	.40	.40
366	A73	1sh red brown & blk	.45	.45
367	A73	1.80sh multicolored	1.25	1.25
		Nos. 364-367 (4)	2.30	2.30

First anniversary of Oct. 21st Revolution.

Snake Strangling Black Man, Map of South Africa A74

Design: 1.80sh, Concentration camp and symbols of justice holding scales.

Perf. 14x13½
1971, June 20   Photo.   Wmk. 303

368	A74	1.30sh multicolored	.55	.55
369	A74	1.80sh gray, red & blk	2.10	2.10

Against racial discrimination in South Africa.

Waves A75

Design: 2.80sh, Waves and globe.

1971, June 30

370	A75	25c black & blue	.40	.40
371	A75	2.80sh blk, grn & bl	2.10	2.10

3rd World Telecommunications Day, May 17.

Map of Africa and Telecommunications System — A76

Design: 1.50sh, Map of Africa and telecommunications system, diff.

1971, July 25

372	A76	1sh blk, lt bl & grn	.55	.55
373	A76	1.50sh black & yellow	1.75	1.75

Pan-African Telecommunications system.

White Rhinoceros A77

Wild Animals: 1sh, Cheetahs. 1.30sh, Zebras. 1.80sh, Lion attacking camel.

1971, Aug. 25

374	A77	35c ocher & multi	.40	.40
375	A77	1sh violet & multi	.95	.95
376	A77	1.30sh violet & multi	2.25	2.25
377	A77	1.80sh multicolored	4.50	4.50
		Nos. 374-377 (4)	8.10	8.10

Headquarters, Mogadishu, Flag, Map of Africa — A78

Design: 1.30sh, Desert Fort.

1971, Oct. 18

378	A78	1.30sh blk & red org	.85	.85
379	A78	1.50sh blk, blue & yel	1.75	1.75

East and Central African Summit Conf.

Revolution Monument A79

1sh, Field workers. 1.35sh, Building workers.

1971, Oct. 21

380	A79	10c black & blue	.25	.25
381	A79	1sh blk, yel brn & grn	.55	.55
382	A79	1.35sh blk, dp brn & yel	1.75	1.75
		Nos. 380-382 (3)	2.55	2.55

2nd anniversary of 1969 revolution.

Vaccination of Cow — A80

1.80sh, Veterinarian vaccinating cow.

Perf. 14x13½
1971, Nov. 28   Photo.   Wmk. 303

383	A80	40c blk, red & bl	.40	.20
384	A80	1.80sh lt green & multi	1.75	1.75

Rinderpest campaign.

Postal Union Emblem, Dove and Letter A81

1972, Jan. 25   Unwmk.

385	A81	1.50sh multicolored	1.75	1.75

10th anniv. of APU. See No. C108.

Children and UNICEF Emblem A82

Design: 50c, Mother and child, vert.

1972, Mar. 30   Perf. 13x14, 14x13

386	A82	50c blk, bis brn & dk brn	.25	.25
387	A82	2.80sh lt blue & multi	2.10	2.10

UNICEF, 25th anniv. (in 1971).

Camel A83

Designs: 10c, Cattle and cargo ship. 20c, Bull. 40c, Sheep. 1.70sh, Goat.

1972, Apr. 10   Perf. 14x13

388	A83	5c green & multi	.25	.25
389	A83	10c multicolored	.30	.30
390	A83	20c multicolored	.30	.30
391	A83	40c orange red & blk	.30	.30
392	A83	1.70sh dull grn & blk	3.50	3.50
		Nos. 388-392 (5)	4.65	4.65

Hands Holding Infant A84

1sh, Youth Corps emblem, marchers with flags. 1.50sh, Woman, man, tent, tractor.

1972, Oct. 21   Photo.   Perf. 14x13½

393	A84	70c yellow & multi	.20	.20
394	A84	1sh red & multi	.40	.40
395	A84	1.50sh lt blue & multi	1.60	1.60
		Nos. 393-395 (3)	2.20	2.20

3rd anniversary of October 21 Revolution.

Folk Dance
A85

Folk Dances: 40c, Man and woman, vert. 1sh, Group dance, vert. 2sh, Two men and a woman.

1973 Photo. Perf. 14x13½, 13½x14
396	A85	5c dull blue & multi	.20	.20
397	A85	40c brown & multi	.20	.20
398	A85	1sh yellow & multi	.55	.55
399	A85	2sh brick red & multi	1.90	1.90
		Nos. 396-399 (4)	2.85	2.85

Hand Writing Somali Script
A86

40c, Flame and "FAR SOMALI" inscription, vert. 1sh, Woman and sunburst with Somali script.

Perf. 13½x14, 14x13½
1973, Oct. 21 Photo.
400	A86	40c red & multi	.20	.20
401	A86	1sh blue & multi	.35	.35
402	A86	2sh yellow & multi	1.90	1.90
		Nos. 400-402 (3)	2.45	2.45

Publicity for use of Somali script.

Map of Africa and Emblem — A87

Map of Africa with Target on Somalia — A88

1974, June 12 Perf. 13½x14
403	A87	40c multicolored	.40	.40
404	A88	2sh multicolored	2.00	2.00

OAU Meeting, Mogadishu.

Hurdler
A89

1sh, Runners. 1.40sh, Netball, vert.

1974, Aug. 1 Perf. 14x13, 13x14
405	A89	50c black & orange	.20	.20
406	A89	1sh black & green	.40	.40
407	A89	1.40sh black & olive	2.00	2.00
		Nos. 405-407 (3)	2.60	2.60

Victory Pioneers — A90

Pioneers Helping Woman — A91

1974, Aug. 25 Photo. Perf. 13x14
408	A90	40c multicolored	.20	.20
409	A91	2sh multicolored	1.90	1.90

Victory Pioneers, founded Aug. 24, 1972, to defend Socialist Revolution.

Map of Arab Countries
A92

Flags of Arab Countries
A93

1974, Sept. 1 Perf. 14x13
410	A92	1.50sh multicolored	.95	.95
411	A93	1.70sh multicolored	3.00	3.00

Somalia's admission to the Arab League, Feb. 14, 1974.

Tank Tracks in Desert
A94

Somalis Reading Books — A95

Perf. 14x13½, 13½x14
1974, Oct. 21 Litho.
412	A94	40c multicolored	.25	.25
413	A95	2sh multicolored	1.75	1.75

5th anniversary of the Oct. 21st Revolution.

Carrier Pigeons
A96

Design: 3sh, Postrider.

1975, Feb. 15 Litho. Perf. 14x13½
414	A96	50c blue & multi	.25	.25
415	A96	3sh multicolored	1.75	1.75

UPU centenary (in 1974).

Africa
A97

Design: 1.50sh, Carrier pigeons.

1975, Apr. 10
416	A97	1sh multicolored	.30	.30
417	A97	1.50sh multicolored	1.60	1.60

African Postal Union.

Somali Warrior — A98

Designs: Traditional costumes of Somali men (1sh, 10sh) and women (40c, 50c, 5sh).

1975, Oct. 27 Photo. Perf. 13½
418	A98	10c yellow & multi	.20	.20
419	A98	40c lt blue & multi	.20	.20
420	A98	50c multicolored	.25	.25
421	A98	1sh green & multi	.25	.25
422	A98	5sh claret & multi	2.40	.80
423	A98	10sh rose & multi	6.50	2.40
		Nos. 418-423 (6)	9.80	4.10

Monument — A99

IWY Emblem
A100

1975, Dec. 10 Litho. Perf. 13½x14
424	A99	50c blk & red org	.25	.25
425	A100	2.30sh blk, pink & mag	2.40	2.40

International Women's Year.

Abdulla Hassan Monument
A101

Abdulla Hassan with Warriors — A102

1.50sh, Abdulla Hassan speaking to his men. 2.30sh, Attacking horsemen, horiz.

Perf. 14x13½, 13½x14
1976, Nov. 30 Photo.
426	A101	50c multicolored	.25	.25
427	A102	60c multicolored	.25	.25
428	A102	1.50sh multicolored	.85	.85
429	A102	2.30sh multicolored	2.50	2.50
		Nos. 426-429 (4)	3.85	3.85

Sayid Mohammed Abdulla Hassan (1864-1920), poet and military leader.

Cypraea Gracilis
A103

Sea Shells: 75c, Charonia bardayi. 1sh, Chlamys townsendi. 2sh, Cymatium ranzanii. 2.75sh, Conus argillaceus. 2.90sh, Strombus oldi.

1976, Dec. 15 Photo. Perf. 14x13½
430	A103	50c blue & multi	.25	.25
431	A103	75c blue & multi	.25	.25
432	A103	1sh blue & multi	.55	.55
433	A103	2sh blue & multi	2.25	2.25
434	A103	2.75sh blue & multi	6.00	6.00
435	A103	2.90sh blue & multi	8.75	8.75
a.		Souvenir sheet of 6, #430-435	30.00	30.00
		Nos. 430-435 (6)	18.05	18.05

No. 435a sold for 11sh.

Benin Head and Hunters — A104

Benin Head and: 75c, Handicrafts. 2sh, Dancers. 2.90sh, Musicians.

1977, Aug. 30 Photo. Perf. 14x13½
436	A104	50c multicolored	.20	.20
437	A104	75c multicolored	.25	.25
438	A104	2sh multicolored	.95	.95
439	A104	2.90sh multicolored	3.00	3.00
		Nos. 436-439 (4)	4.40	4.40

2nd World Black and African Festival, FESTAC '77, Lagos, Nigeria, Jan. 15-Feb. 12.

Arms of Somalia
A105

Designs: 75c, Somali flags, vert. 1.50sh, Pres. Mohammed Siad Barre and globe. 2sh, Arms over rising sun and flags, vert.

Perf. 13½x14, 14x13½
1977, Sept. 30 Photo.
440	A105	75c multicolored	.25	.25
441	A105	1sh multicolored	.95	.95
442	A105	1.50sh multicolored	1.20	1.20
443	A105	2sh multicolored	2.40	2.40
		Nos. 440-443 (4)	4.80	4.80

Somali Socialist Revolutionary Party, established July 1, 1976.

Licaon Pictus
A106

Protected Animals: 75c, Bush baby. 1sh, Somali ass. 1.50sh, Aardwolf. 2sh, Greater kudu. 3sh, Giraffe.

1977, Nov. 25 Photo. Perf. 14x13½
444	A106	50c multicolored	.30	.30
445	A106	75c multicolored	.30	.30
446	A106	1sh multicolored	1.00	1.00

447	A106	1.50sh multicolored	1.60	1.60
448	A106	2sh multicolored	2.40	2.40
449	A106	3sh multicolored	6.50	6.50
a.		Souvenir sheet of 6, #444-449	24.00	24.00
		Nos. 444-449 (6)	12.10	12.10

Leonardo da Vinci's Flying Machine A107

ICAO Emblem and: 1.50sh, Montgolfier's balloon. 2sh, Wright brothers' plane. 2.90sh, Somali Airlines turbojet.

1977, Dec. 23   Photo.   Perf. 14x13½

450	A107	1sh multicolored	.25	.25
451	A107	1.50sh multicolored	.55	.55
452	A107	2sh multicolored	1.20	1.20
453	A107	2.90sh multicolored	2.40	2.40
a.		Souvenir sheet of 4, #450-453	16.00	16.00
		Nos. 450-453 (4)	4.40	4.40

ICAO, 30th anniv. No. 453a sold for 10sh.

Dome of the Rock — A108

Lithographed and Engraved
1978, Apr. 30   Perf. 13x14

454	A108	75c multicolored	.25	.25
455	A108	2sh multicolored	1.75	1.75

Palestinian fighters and their families.

Stadium and Soccer Player — A109

Designs: 4.90sh, Stadium and goalkeeper. 5.50sh, Stadium and player.

1978, Aug. 5   Litho.   Perf. 14x13½

456	A109	1.50sh multicolored	.80	.80
457	A109	4.90sh multicolored	2.40	2.40
458	A109	5.50sh multicolored	4.00	4.00
a.		Souvenir sheet of 3, #456-458	16.00	16.00
		Nos. 456-458 (3)	7.20	7.20

11th World Cup Soccer Championship, Argentina, June 1-25. No. 458a sold for 14sh.

Acacia Tortilis — A110

Trees: 50c, Ficus sycomorus, vert. 75c, Terminalia catapa, vert. 2.90sh, Baobab.

1978, Sept. 5   Photo.   Perf. 14

459	A110	40c multicolored	.20	.20
460	A110	50c multicolored	.20	.20
461	A110	75c multicolored	.25	.25
462	A110	2.90sh multicolored	3.25	3.25
		Nos. 459-462 (4)	3.90	3.90

Forest conservation.

Hibiscus — A111

Flowers of Somalia: 1sh, Cassia baccarinii. 1.50sh, Kigelia somalensis. 2.30sh, Dichrostachys glomerata.

1978, Dec. 15   Photo.   Perf. 13½x14

463	A111	50c multicolored	.25	.25
464	A111	1sh multicolored	.55	.55
465	A111	1.50sh multicolored	1.60	1.60
466	A111	2.30sh multicolored	2.40	2.40
a.		Souv. sheet, #463-466, perf. 14	12.00	12.00
		Nos. 463-466 (4)	4.80	4.80

Huri and Siganus Rivulatus A112

Fishery Development: 80c, Sail huri, gaterin gaterinus. 2.30sh, Fishing boats, hypacanthus amia. 2.50sh, Motorized fishing boat, mackerel.

1979, Sept. 1   Photo.   Perf. 14x13½

467	A112	75c multicolored	.55	.55
468	A112	80c multicolored	.55	.55
469	A112	2.30sh multicolored	1.60	1.60
470	A112	2.50sh multicolored	3.75	3.75
		Nos. 467-470 (4)	6.45	6.45

Sailing, IYC Emblem — A113

IYC Emblem, Children's Drawings: 50c, 90c, Schoolboy. 1.50sh, 2.50sh, Houses. 3sh, 4sh, Bird and flower. 1sh, as 75c.

1979, Sept. 10   Photo.   Perf. 13½x14

471	A113	50c multicolored	.30	.30
472	A113	75c multicolored	.30	.30
473	A113	1.50sh multicolored	.80	.80
474	A113	3sh multicolored	2.50	2.50
		Nos. 471-474 (4)	3.90	3.90

Souvenir Sheet of 4

474A		#b.-e.	14.00	14.00

Intl. Year of the Child. No. 474A contains 90c, 1sh, 2.50sh, 4sh stamps and sold for 10sh.

University Students, Outdoor Classrooms — A114

Flower and: 50c, Housing construction. 75c, Children's recreation. 1sh, Doctor examining child, woman and man carrying grain and fish. 2.40sh, Woman and children carrying produce over dam. 3sh, Dish antenna.

1979, Nov. 30   Litho.   Perf. 14x13½

475	A114	20c multicolored	.30	.30
476	A114	50c multicolored	.30	.30
477	A114	75c multicolored	.65	.65
478	A114	1sh multicolored	.65	.65
479	A114	2.40sh multicolored	1.90	1.90
480	A114	3sh multicolored	2.40	2.40
		Nos. 475-480 (6)	6.20	6.20

Oct. 21 revolution, 10th anniversary.

Barbopsis Devecchii A115

Freshwater Fish: 90c, Phreatichthys andruzzii. 1sh, Uegitglanis zammaranoi. 2.50sh, Pardi's catfish.

1979, Dec. 12

481	A115	50c multicolored	.65	.65
482	A115	90c multicolored	.65	.65
483	A115	1sh multicolored	1.75	1.75
484	A115	2.50sh multicolored	1.75	1.75
a.		Souvenir sheet of 4, #481-484	11.00	11.00
		Nos. 481-484 (4)	4.80	4.80

No. 484a sold for 10sh.

Taleh Fortress, Congress Emblem — A116

1980, June 1   Photo.   Perf. 14x13½

485	A116	2.25sh multicolored	1.20	1.20
486	A116	3.50sh multicolored	2.40	2.40

1st International Congress of Somalian Studies, Mogadishu, July 6-13.

View of Marka — A117

1980, July 1   Litho.   Perf. 14

487	A117	75c shown	.25	.25
488	A117	1sh Gandershe + label	.80	.80
489	A117	2.30sh Afgooye + label	.80	.80
490	A117	3.50sh Muqdisho + label	3.25	3.25
		Nos. 487-490 (4)	5.10	5.10

See Nos. 502-505, 527-530.

A118

1980, July 30   Photo.   Perf. 13½x14

491	A118	1sh Batis perkeo	.55	.55
492	A118	2.25sh Rynchostruthus socotranus louisae	1.40	1.40
493	A118	5sh Laniarius ruficeps	3.25	3.25
a.		Souvenir sheet of 3, #491-493	12.00	12.00
		Nos. 491-493 (3)	5.20	5.20

A119

Perf. 13½x14, 14x13½
1981, Oct. 16   Litho.

494	A119	75c Globe, grain	.30	.30
495	A119	3.25sh Emblem, horiz.	1.50	1.50
496	A119	5.50sh like No. 494	3.00	3.00
		Nos. 494-496 (3)	4.80	4.80

World Food Day.

13th World Telecommunications Day — A120

1981, Oct. 10   Perf. 13½x14

497	A120	1sh Shepherdess, sheep, dish antenna	.80	.80
498	A120	3sh Emblems	1.60	1.60
499	A120	4.60sh like No. 498	3.25	3.25
		Nos. 497-499 (3)	5.65	5.65

Hegira, 1500th Anniv. — A121

1982 World Cup — A122

1981, Oct.   Photo.   Perf. 13½x14

500	A121	1.50sh multicolored	.55	.55
501	A121	3.80sh multicolored	1.90	1.90

View Type of 1980

1982, May 31   Litho.   Perf. 13½x14

502	A117	2.25sh Balcad	1.20	1.20
503	A117	4sh Jowhar	1.60	1.60
504	A117	5.50sh Golaleey	2.40	2.40
505	A117	8.30sh Muqdisho	2.75	2.75
		Nos. 502-505 (4)	7.95	7.95

Nos. 502-505 were each printed in sheets of 10 stamps and 5 labels showing regional map. Value for stamps with attached label: +50%.

1982, June 13

Designs: Various soccer players.

506	A122	1sh multicolored	.55	.55
507	A122	1.50sh multicolored	1.25	1.25
508	A122	3.25sh multicolored	3.00	3.00
a.		Souvenir sheet of 3, #506-508	12.00	12.00
		Nos. 506-508 (3)	4.80	4.80

ITU Plenipotentiaries Conference, Nairobi, Sept. — A123

1982, Oct. 15   Photo.   Perf. 14x13½

509	A123	75c green & multi	.25	.25
510	A123	3.25sh orange & multi	1.40	1.40
511	A123	5.50sh blue & multi	3.50	3.50
		Nos. 509-511 (3)	5.15	5.15

Local Snakes — A124

2.80sh, Bitis arietans. 3.20sh, Psammophis
punctulatus.   4.60sh,   Rhamphiophis
oxyrhynchus.   8.60sh,   Sphalerosophis
josephscorteccii.

1982, Dec. 20   Photo.   Perf. 14
512 A124 2.80sh multicolored   1.60   1.60
513 A124 3.20sh multicolored   3.25   3.25
514 A124 4.60sh multicolored   4.75   4.75
    Nos. 512-514 (3)   9.60   9.60

Souvenir Sheet

515 A124 8.60sh multicolored   21.00 21.00

Somali
Woman — A125   A126

1982, Dec. 30   Perf. 14x13½
516 A125   1sh yel & multi   .30   .30
517 A125 5.20sh lilac & multi 1.75   1.75
518 A125 5.80sh org & multi   1.90   1.90
519 A125 6.40sh blue & multi   2.10   2.10
520 A125 9.40sh lt brn & multi 3.25   3.25
521 A125 25sh green & multi   8.00   8.00
    Nos. 516-521 (6)   17.30 17.30

1983, July 20   Perf. 13½x14
522 A126 5.20sh multicolored   1.40   1.40
523 A126 6.40sh multicolored   2.40   2.40

World Communications Year.

2nd Intl. Congress of Somali Studies,
Hamburg — A127

Various views of Hamburg.

1983, Aug. 1   Perf. 14
524 A127 5.20sh multicolored   .85   .85
525 A127 6.40sh multicolored   3.25   3.25

Military
Uniforms — A128

Designs: a, Air Force. b, Women's Auxiliary
Corps. c, Border Police. d, People's Militia. e,
Army Infantry. f, Custodial Corps. g, Police. h,
Navy.

1983, Oct. 21   Litho.   Perf. 13½x14
526   Strip of 8   9.50   9.50
a.-h. A128 3.20sh, any single 1.20   1.20

View Type of 1980
1983
527 A117 2.80sh Barawe   .80   .80
528 A117 3.20sh Bur Hakaba   .80   .80
529 A117 5.50sh Baydhabo   1.60   1.60
530 A117 8.60sh Dooy Nuunaay   4.00   4.00
    Nos. 527-530 (4)   7.20   7.20

Nos. 527-530 were each printed in sheets of
10 stamps and 5 decorative labels. Value for
stamps with attached label: +25%.

Sea Shells
A129

1984, Feb. 15   Litho.   Perf. 14x13½
531 A129 2.80sh Volutocorbis
                rosavittoriae   .65   .65
532 A129 3.20sh Phalium bi-
                tuberculosum   1.90   1.90
533 A129 5.50sh Conus
                milneed-
                warsi   4.75   4.75
    Nos. 531-533 (3)   7.30   7.30

Souvenir Sheet
Perf. 14
534 A129 15sh Cypraea
                broderipi   12.00 12.00

Olympics
1984 — A130

Riccione
Fair — A131

1984, Sept.   Litho.   Perf. 13½x14
535 A130 1.50sh Runners   .55   .55
536 A130   3sh Discus   1.20   1.20
537 A130   8sh Pole vaulting   3.50   3.50
a.   Souvenir sheet of 3, #535-537 8.00 8.00
    Nos. 535-537 (3)   5.25   5.25

No. 537a sold for 15sh.

1984, Sept.   Litho.   Perf. 13½x14
538 A131 5.20sh multicolored   1.75   1.75
539 A131 6.40sh multicolored   4.50   4.50

Animals
A132

1984, Sept.   Litho.   Perf. 14x13½
540 A132   1sh Hystrix cris-
                tata   .30   .30
541 A132 1.50sh Ichneumia al-
                bicauda   .30   .30
542 A132   2sh Mungos
                mungo   1.60   1.60
543 A132   4sh Mellivora
                capensis   2.50   2.50
a.   Souvenir sheet of 4, #540-
543   10.00 10.00
    Nos. 540-543 (4)   4.70   4.70

No. 543a sold for 10sh.

Intl. Civil Aviation Org., 40th
Anniv. — A133

1984, Nov. 20   Litho.   Perf. 14
544 A133   3sh multicolored   1.20   1.20
545 A133 6.40sh multicolored   2.40   2.40

Souvenir Sheet
546   Sheet of 2   8.00   8.00
a.   A133 3sh like No. 544   1.20   1.20
b.   A133 6.40sh like No. 545 2.40 2.40

No. 546 contains 2 49½x46mm stamps.
Sold for 10sh.

Dove — A134

Constellations from the Book of Fixed Stars,
by Abd al-Rahman al-Sufi.

1985, Aug. 10   Litho.   Perf. 13½x14
547 A134 4.30sh shown   1.20   1.20
548 A134 11sh Bull   2.40   2.40
549 A134 12.50sh Rams   2.40   2.40
550 A134 13.80sh Archer   2.90   2.90
    Nos. 547-550 (4)   8.90   8.90

Architecture — A135

1985, Sept.   Litho.   Perf. 13½x14
551 A135   2sh Ras Kiambone   .25   .25
552 A135 6.60sh Hannassa   .40   .40
553 A135 10sh Mnarani   1.20   1.20
554 A135 18.60sh as #551, diff. 4.75 4.75
    Nos. 551-554 (4)   6.60   6.60

Nos. 551-554 were each printed in sheets of
10 stamps and 5 decorative labels. Value for
stamps with attached label: +10%.
See Nos. 572-575.

Lady
Somalia
Seated in
Posthorn
A136

1985, Oct.   Perf. 14x14½
555 A136   2sh multicolored   .95   .95
556 A136 20sh multicolored   4.00   4.00
a.   Souvenir sheet of 2, #555-556,
       perf. 13½   9.50   9.50

ITALIA '85, Rome. No. 556a sold for 30sh.

Bats
A137

1985, Dec. 25   Litho.   Perf. 14x13½
557 A137 2.50sh Triaenops
                persicus   1.00   1.00
558 A137 4.50sh Cardioderma
                cor   1.40   1.40
559 A137 16sh Tadarida con-
                dylura   4.00   4.00
560 A137 18sh Coleura afra   5.25   5.25
    Nos. 557-560 (4)   11.65 11.65

Souvenir Sheet
561   Sheet of 4   16.00 16.00
a.   A137 2.50sh like #552   1.00   1.00
b.   A137 4.50sh like #553   1.40   1.40
c.   A137 16sh like #554   4.00   4.00
d.   A137 18sh like #555   5.25   5.25

Nos. 561a-561d printed in continuous
design. No. 561 sold for 50sh.

Economic Trade Agreement with
Kenya — A138

Design: Presidents Arap Moi and Barre, satellite communications.

1986, Feb. 15   Perf. 14
562 A138   9sh multi   1.75   1.75
563 A138 14.50sh multi   2.75   2.75

EUROFLORA
Flower Exhibition,
Genoa — A139

3rd Intl. Congress
on Somali
Studies — A140

1986, Apr. 25   Perf. 13½x14
564 A139 10sh Flower arrange-
                ment   .80   .80
565 A139 15sh Arrangement, diff. 2.40 2.40
a.   Souvenir sheet of 2, #564-565 5.25 5.25

No. 565a sold for 30sh.

1986, May 26
566 A140 11.35sh multi   .80   .80
567 A140 20sh multi   2.40   2.40

1986 World Cup Soccer
Championships, Mexico — A141

Various soccer plays.

1986, June   Perf. 14x13½

568	A141	3.60sh multi	.55	.55
569	A141	4.80sh multi	.55	.55
570	A141	6.80sh multi	1.75	1.75
571	A141	22.60sh multi	2.40	2.40
a.		Souvenir sheet of 4, #568-571	10.00	10.00
		Nos. 568-571 (4)	5.25	5.25

No. 571a sold for 50sh.

Architecture Type of 1985

1986   Litho.   Perf. 13½x14

572	A135	10sh Bulaxaar	.40	.40
573	A135	15sh Saylac	.40	.40
574	A135	20sh Saylac, diff.	.80	.80
575	A135	31sh Jasiiradaha Jawaay	4.75	4.75
		Nos. 572-575 (4)	6.35	6.35

Nos. 572-575 were each printed in sheets of 10 stamps and 5 decorative labels. Value for stamps with attached label: +10%.

Red Crescent — Red Cross Rehabilitation Center, Mogadishu — A143

1987, May 8   Litho.   Perf. 13½x13

576	A143	56sh multi	6.75	6.75

Souvenir Sheet

577	A143	56sh multi, diff.	18.75	8.75

No. 577 sold for 60sh. See Norway No. 908.

A144

A145

1987, Sept. 27   Litho.   Perf. 13½x14

578	A144	20sh Running	2.10	2.10
579	A144	48sh Javelin	4.75	4.75
a.		Souvenir sheet of 2, #578-579	10.00	10.00

OLYMPHILEX '87, Rome. No. 579a sold for 75sh.

1987, Oct. 5   Photo.   Perf. 13½x14½

580	A145	53sh multicolored	2.40	2.40
581	A145	72sh multicolored	4.00	4.00

Intl. Year of Shelter for the Homeless.

GEOSOM '87 — A146

A147

Maps: 10sh, 160,000,000 years ago. 20sh, 60,000,000 years ago. 40sh, 15,000,000 years nest. 50sh, Today.

1987, Nov. 24   Litho.   Perf. 13½x14

582	A146	10sh multi	1.25	1.25
583	A146	20sh multi, diff.	2.40	2.40
584	A146	40sh multi, diff.	4.75	4.75
585	A146	50sh multi, diff.	6.50	6.50
a.		Souv. sheet of 2, #583, 585	35.00	35.00
		Nos. 582-585 (4)	14.90	14.90

Symposium on the Geology of Somalia, Mogadishu, 11/24-12/1. #585a sold for 130sh.

1988, Dec. 31   Litho.   Perf. 13½x14

586	A147	50sh multicolored	.80	.80
587	A147	168sh multicolored	4.00	4.00

World Health Organization, 40th anniv.

Wildlife A148

Perf. 13½x14, 14x13½

1989, Oct. 20   Litho.

588	A148	75sh Lepus somaliensis	.55	.55
589	A148	198sh Syncerus caffer	1.90	1.90
590	A148	200sh Papio hamadryas	3.25	3.25
591	A148	216sh Hippopotamus amphibius	4.00	4.00
a.		Souvenir sheet of 2, #590-591	12.00	12.00
		Nos. 588-591 (4)	9.70	9.70

No. 591a contains 2 labels like #588-589. Sold for 700sh.

Somali Revolution, 20th Anniv. A149

Flowers, children's games: 70sh, Kick ball. 100sh, Swinging. 150sh, Teeter-totter. 300sh, Jumping rope, stick and hoop.

1989, Dec. 12   Litho.   Perf. 14x13½

592	A149	70sh multicolored	1.40	1.40
593	A149	100sh multicolored	2.00	2.00
594	A149	150sh multicolored	3.00	3.00
595	A149	300sh multicolored	6.00	6.00
		Nos. 592-595 (4)	12.40	12.40

A150

A151

Liberation: Nos. 599-600, Dove breaking chains, horiz.

1991   Litho.   Perf. 13½x14, 14x13½

596	A150	70sh lilac & multi	.65	.65
597	A150	100sh grn bl & multi	.90	.90
598	A150	150sh brt blue & multi	1.40	1.40
599	A150	150sh yellow & multi	1.40	1.40
600	A150	300sh yel grn & multi	2.75	2.75
601	A150	300sh yel grn & multi	2.75	2.00
		Nos. 596-601 (6)	9.85	9.10

Issued: Nos. 599-600, July 2; others, July 4.

No. 599 Ovptd. in Blue

1991   Litho.   Perf. 14x13½

602	A150	150sh yellow & multi	4.00	4.00

1991   Litho.   Perf. 14

Various minarets.

603	A151	30sh multicolored	.30	.30
604	A151	40sh multicolored	.45	.45
605	A151	50sh multicolored	.55	.55
606	A151	150sh multicolored	1.75	1.75
		Nos. 603-606 (4)	3.05	3.05

Relief efforts have demonstrated the breakdown of government services in Somalia. It is unclear which faction has control of the Postal Service, if any is operating. The status of Scott Nos. 607-638 will be reviewed once more information is available.

Gazelles A152

1992   Perf. 14x13½

Inscribed in Black

607	A152	500sh Two Speke's	3.25
608	A152	700sh One Speke's	4.50
609	A152	800sh One Soemmering's	6.00
610	A152	1000sh Two Soemmering's	7.25
		Nos. 607-610 (4)	21.00

World Wildlife Fund.

Without WWF Emblem
Inscribed in red lilac

611	A152	100sh like #607	.85
612	A152	200sh like #608	1.75
613	A152	300sh like #609	2.40
614	A152	400sh like #610	3.50

Inscribed in black

615	A152	1500sh Baboons	13.00
616	A152	2500sh Hippopotamus	20.00
617	A152	3000sh Giraffes	25.00
618	A152	5000sh Leopard	40.00
		Nos. 607-618 (12)	127.50

Nos. 607-618 are part of an expanding set. Numbers may change.
For overprints see No. 629-632.

Nos. 607-610 Ovptd. "PARTICIPANT / RIO 1992" in Orange

1992   Litho.   Perf. 14x13½

629	A152	500sh on #607	5.00
630	A152	700sh on #608	7.50
631	A152	800sh on #609	10.00
632	A152	1000sh on #610	12.50
		Nos. 629-632 (4)	35.00

Discovery of America, 500th Anniv. A153

Designs: 100sh, Sighting land from crow's nest. 200sh, Three men pointing from ship. 300sh, Columbus in his cabin. 400sh, Claiming land. 2000sh, Building fort in New World.
No. 638: a, 800sh, like #634. b, 900sh, like #635. c, 1300sh, like #633.

1992

633	A153	100sh multicolored	.55
634	A153	200sh multicolored	1.10
635	A153	300sh multicolored	1.60
636	A153	400sh multicolored	2.25
637	A153	2000sh multicolored	11.00
		Nos. 633-637 (5)	16.50

Souvenir Sheet

638	A153	Sheet of 3, #a.-c.	16.50

Nos. 638a-638c do not have white border. No. 638 exists imperf.

SEMI-POSTAL STAMPS

Italy Nos. B1-B4 Overprinted

1916   Wmk. 140   Perf. 14

B1	SP1	10c + 5c rose	16.00	35.00
B2	SP2	15c + 5c slate	40.00	47.50
B3	SP2	20c + 5c orange	16.00	45.00
B4	SP2	20c on 15c + 5c slate	40.00	80.00
		Nos. B1-B4 (4)	112.00	207.50

Holy Year Issue
Italy Nos. B20-B25 Surcharged in Black or Red

1925, June 1   Perf. 12

B5	SP4	6b + 3b on 20c + 10c	3.25	20.00
B6	SP4	13b + 6b on 30c + 15c	3.25	22.50
B7	SP4	15b + 8b on 50c + 25c	3.25	20.00
B8	SP4	18b + 9b on 60c + 30c	3.25	25.00
B9	SP8	30b + 15b on 1 l +50c (R)	3.25	32.50
B10	SP8	1r + 50b on 5 l +2.50 l (R)	3.25	47.50
		Nos. B5-B10 (6)	19.50	167.50

Colonial Institute Issue

"Peace" Substituting Spade for Sword — SP10

1926, June 1   Typo.   Perf. 14

B11	SP10	5c + 5c brown	.95	8.00
B12	SP10	10c + 5c olive grn	.95	8.00
B13	SP10	20c + 5c blue grn	.95	8.00
B14	SP10	40c + 5c brown red	.95	8.00
B15	SP10	60c + 5c orange	.95	8.00
B16	SP10	1 l + 5c blue	.95	17.50
		Nos. B11-B16 (6)	5.70	57.50

The surtax was for the Italian Colonial Institute.

Types of Italian Semi-Postal Stamps of 1926 Overprinted

1927, Apr. 21   Unwmk.   Perf. 11½

B17	SP10	40c + 20c dk brn & blk	2.40	32.50
B18	SP10	60c + 30c brn red & ol brn	2.40	32.50
B19	SP10	1.25 l + 60c dp bl & blk	2.40	52.50
B20	SP10	5 l + 2.50 l dk grn & blk	4.00	72.50
		Nos. B17-B20 (4)	11.20	190.00

The surtax was for the charitable work of the Voluntary Militia for Italian National Defense.

Allegory of Fascism and Victory — SP11

1928, Oct. 15   Wmk. 140   Perf. 14

B21	SP11	20c + 5c blue grn	2.40	12.00
B22	SP11	30c + 5c red	2.40	12.00
B23	SP11	50c + 10c purple	2.40	20.00
B24	SP11	1.25 l + 20c dk blue	3.25	24.00
		Nos. B21-B24 (4)	10.45	68.00

46th anniv. of the Societa Africana d'Italia. The surtax aided that society.

Types of Italian Semi-Postal Stamps of 1928 Overprinted

1929, Mar. 4   Unwmk.   Perf. 11

B25	SP10	30c + 10c red & blk	4.00	20.00
B26	SP10	50c + 20c vio & blk	4.00	22.50
B27	SP10	1.25 l + 50c brn & bl	4.75	40.00
B28	SP10	5 l + 2 l ol grn & blk	4.75	72.50
		Nos. B25-B28 (4)	17.50	155.00

The surtax was for the charitable work of the Voluntary Militia for Italian National Defense.

Types of Italian Semi-Postal Stamps of 1926 Overprinted in Black or Red

1930, Oct. 20   Perf. 14

B29	SP10	30c + 10c dk grn & bl grn (Bk)	21.00	32.50
B30	SP10	50c + 10c dk grn & vio (R)	21.00	45.00
B31	SP10	1.25 l + 30c ol brn & red brn (R)	21.00	55.00
B32	SP10	5 l + 1.50 l ind & grn (R)	65.00	160.00
		Nos. B29-B32 (4)	128.00	292.50

The surtax was for the charitable work of the Voluntary Militia for Italian National Defense.

Irrigation Canal SP14

1930, Nov. 27   Photo.   Wmk. 140

B33	SP14	50c + 20c olive brn	4.00	20.00
B34	SP14	1.25 l + 20c dp blue	4.00	20.00
B35	SP14	1.75 l + 20c green	6.50	22.50
B36	SP14	2.55 l + 50c purple	6.50	35.00
B37	SP14	5 l + 1 l dp car	6.50	52.50
		Nos. B33-B37 (5)	25.00	150.00

25th anniv. of the Italian Colonial Agricultural Institute. The surtax was for the aid of that institution.

SP15

King Victor Emmanuel III — SP16

1935, Jan. 1

B38	SP15	5c + 5c blk brn	4.75	24.00
B39	SP15	7½c + 7½c vio	4.75	24.00
B40	SP15	15c + 10c ol blk	4.75	24.00
B41	SP15	20c + 10c rose red	4.75	24.00
B42	SP15	25c + 10c dp grn	4.75	24.00
B43	SP15	30c + 10c brn	4.75	24.00
B44	SP15	50c + 10c pur	4.75	24.00
B45	SP15	75c + 15c rose car	4.75	24.00
B46	SP15	1.25 l + 15c dp bl	4.75	24.00
B47	SP15	1.75 l + 25c red org	4.75	24.00
B48	SP15	2.75 l + 25c gray	24.00	95.00
B49	SP15	5 l + 1 l dp cl	24.00	95.00
B50	SP15	10 l + 1.80 l red brn	24.00	95.00
B51	SP16	25 l + 2.75 l brn & red	175.00	400.00
		Nos. B38-B51 (14)	294.50	925.00
		Set, never hinged	750.00	

Visit of King Victor Emmanuel III.

> **Catalogue values for unused stamps in this section, from this point to the end of the section, are for Never Hinged items.**

Somalia

Nurse Holding Infant — SP17

1957, Nov. 30   Wmk. 303   Perf. 14

B52	SP17	10c + 10c red & brn	.40	.40
B53	SP17	25c + 10c grn & brn	.40	.40
		Nos. B52-B53,CB11-CB12 (4)	1.60	2.00

The surtax was for the fight against tuberculosis.

Republic

Refugees SP18

1964, Dec. 12   Photo.   Perf. 14

B54	SP18	25c + 10c vio bl & red	.55	.30
		Nos. B54,CB13-CB14 (3)	3.90	2.35

The surtax was to help refugees.

Red Cross Nurse Feeding Child — SP19

Refugees SP20

Famine Relief: 80c+20c, Nomad in parched land, horiz. 2.40sh+10c, Family with fish and produce. 2.90sh+10c, Physician and Aid Society emblem, horiz.

1976, Dec. 10   Perf. 13x14, 14x13

B55	SP19	75c + 25c multi	.55	.55
B56	SP19	80c + 20c multi	.55	.55
B57	SP19	2.40sh + 10c multi	1.75	1.75
B58	SP19	2.90sh + 10c multi	2.40	2.40
		Nos. B55-B58 (4)	5.25	5.25

1981, Dec. 15   Photo.   Perf. 13½x14

B59	SP20	2sh + 50c multi	.85	.85
B60	SP20	6.80sh + 50c multi	4.00	4.00
a.		Souvenir sheet of 2, #B59-B60	8.00	8.00

TB Bacillus Centenary — SP31

1982, Dec. 30   Photo.   Perf. 14

B61	SP31	4.60sh + 60c multi	2.00	2.00
B62	SP31	5.80sh + 60c multi	2.50	2.50

AIR POST STAMPS

View of Coast AP1

Cheetahs AP2

Wmk. 140
1934, Oct.   Photo.   Perf. 14

C1	AP1	25c sl bl & red org	4.00	20.00
C2	AP1	50c dk grn & blk	4.00	16.00
C3	AP1	75c brn & red org	4.00	16.00
a.		Imperf.	2,000.	
C4	AP2	80c org brn & blk	4.00	20.00
C5	AP2	1 l scar & blk	4.00	24.00
C6	AP2	2 l dk bl & brn	4.00	40.00
		Nos. C1-C6 (6)	24.00	136.00
		Set, never hinged	60.00	

2nd Colonial Arts Exhibition, Naples. For overprint see No. CO1.

Banana Tree and Airplane AP3

25c, 1.50 l, Banana tree, plane. 50c, 2 l, Plane over cotton field. 60c, 5 l, Plane over orchard. 75c, 10 l, Plane over field workers. 1 l, 3 l, Small girl watching plane.

1936			Photo.	
C7	AP3	25c slate green	1.60	8.00
C8	AP3	50c brown	.80	.20
C9	AP3	60c red orange	2.40	12.00
C10	AP3	75c orange brn	1.60	2.40
C11	AP3	1 l deep blue	.80	.20
C12	AP3	1.50 l purple	1.60	.80
C13	AP3	2 l slate blue	4.75	1.20
C14	AP3	3 l copper red	17.50	12.00
C15	AP3	5 l yellow green	20.00	16.00
C16	AP3	10 l dp rose red	24.00	27.50
		Nos. C7-C16 (10)	75.05	80.30
		Set, never hinged	190.00	

> **Catalogue values for unused stamps in this section, from this point to the end of the section, are for Never Hinged items.**

Somalia

AP8

1950-51			Wmk. 277	
C17	AP8	30c yellow brn	6.50	3.25
C18	AP8	45c dk carmine	6.50	3.25
C19	AP8	65c dk blue vio	6.50	3.25
C20	AP8	70c dull blue	6.50	3.25
C21	AP8	90c olive brn	6.50	3.25
C22	AP8	1s lilac rose	8.00	3.25
C23	AP8	1.35s violet	9.50	8.00
C24	AP8	1.50s blue green	9.50	9.50
C25	AP8	3s blue	55.00	32.50
C26	AP8	5s chocolate	55.00	32.50
C27	AP8	10s red org ('51)	95.00	20.00
		Nos. C17-C27 (11)	264.50	122.00

Scene in Mogadishu AP8a

1951, Oct. 4

C27A	AP8a	1s vio & Prus bl	3.25	1.25
C27B	AP8a	1.50s ol grn & chnt brn	8.75	8.75

First Territorial Council meeting.

Plane, Palm Tree and Minaret — AP9

Mother and Child — AP10

1952, Sept. 14
C28 AP9 1.20s ol bis & dp bl   3.25   4.00

1st Somali Fair, Mogadishu, Sept. 14-28.

1953, May 27
C29 AP10 1.20s dk grn & dk brn   2.00   3.25

Somali anti-tuberculosis campaign.

Fair Entrance AP11

1953, Sept. 28   Unwmk.   Perf. 11½
C30 AP11 1.20s brn car & pink   .60   .80
C31 AP11 1.50s yel brn & buff   .80   1.20

2nd Somali Fair, Mogadishu, Sept. 28-Oct. 12, 1953.

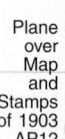

Plane over Map and Stamps of 1903 AP12

Perf. 13x13½
1953, Dec. 16   Engr.   Wmk. 277
Early Stamps in Brn and Rose Car
C32 AP12 60c orange brown   .60   1.60
C33 AP12 1s greenish black   .60   2.40

1st Somali postage stamps, 50th anniv.

"UPU" among Constellations — AP13

Perf. 11½
1953, Dec. 16   Photo.   Unwmk.
C34 AP13 1.20s red & cream   .45   1.20
C35 AP13 1.50s brown & cream   .80   2.40
C36 AP13 2s green & lt blue   .80   2.40
    Nos. C34-C36 (3)   2.05   6.00

UPU, 75th anniv. (in 1949).

Alexander Island Juba River — AP14

Somali Flag — AP15

1954, June 1   Perf. 13½x12½
C37 AP14 1.20s dk grn & brn   1.00   1.20
C38 AP14 2s dk carmine & pur   1.40   2.00

See note after No. 196.

Perf. 13½x13
1954, Oct. 12   Litho.   Wmk. 277
C39 AP15 1.20s multicolored   .35   .45

Adoption of Somali flag.

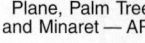

Haggard's Oribi — AP16

Designs: 45c, Phillip's dik-dik. 50c, Speke's gazelle. 75c, Gerenuk. 1.20s, Soemmering's gazelle. 1.50s, Waterbuck.

Wmk. 277
1955, Apr. 12   Photo.   Perf. 13½
Antelopes in Natural Colors
Size: 22x33mm
C40 AP16 35c gray grn & blk   .35   .80
C41 AP16 45c lilac & blk   4.75   1.60
C42 AP16 50c rose lil & blk   .40   .80
C43 AP16 75c red   3.25   .80
C44 AP16 1.20s dk gray grn   3.25   4.00
C45 AP16 1.50s bright blue   4.75   8.00
    Nos. C40-C45 (6)   16.75   16.00

See Nos. C57-C58.

Caravan at Water Hole AP17

Design: 1.20s, Village well.

Perf. 13½x14
1955, Sept. 24   Wmk. 303
C46 AP17 45c brown & orange   .40   .80
C47 AP17 1.20s sapphire & pink   .60   .80

3rd Somali Fair, Mogadishu, Sept. 1955.

Ballot Type of Regular Issue
1956, Apr. 30   Photo.   Perf. 14
C48 A24 60c brown & ultra   .40   .60
C49 A24 1.20s brown & org   .40   .60

Opening of the territory's first democratically elected Legislative Assembly.

Arms Type of Regular Issue
1957, May 6   Wmk. 303   Perf. 13½
Coat of Arms in Dull Yellow, Blue and Black
C50 A25 45c blue   .40   .60
C51 A25 1.20s bluish green   .40   .60

Issued in honor of the new coat of arms.

Type of Regular Issue, 1957 and

Oil Well — AP18

Design: 60c, Irrigation canal construction.

1957, Sept. 28   Perf. 14
C52 A26 60c blue & brown   .80   .80
C53 AP18 1.20s black & ver   .80   .80

Fourth Somali Fair and Film Festival.

Sport Type of Regular Issue
60c, Runner. 1.20s, Bicyclist. 1.50s, Basketball player.

1958, Apr. 28   Wmk. 303   Perf. 14
C54 A27 60c brown   .20   .20
C55 A27 1.20s blue   .20   .40
C56 A27 1.50s rose carmine   .20   .40
    Nos. C54-C56 (3)   .60   1.00

Animal Type of 1955
3s, Lesser kudu. 5s, Hunter's hartebeest.

1958-59   Photo.
Size: 20½x36½mm
C57 AP16 3s ocher & sepia   .60   .85
C58 AP16 5s gray, blk & yel ('59)   .60   .85

See No. CE1.

Police Bugler AP19

1959, June 19   Photo.
C59 AP19 1.20s ocher & ultra   .25   .40
C60 AP19 1.50s olive grn & ultra   .25   .40
a.   Souv. sheet of 4, #228-229, C59-C60   2.00   2.75

Opening of the Constituent Assembly of Somalia.

Marabou AP20

1959, Sept. 4   Wmk. 303
C61 AP20 1.20s shown   1.00   .50
C62 AP20 2s Great egret   1.00   .50

Incense Shipment, 15th Century B.C. AP21

Design: 2s, Incense burner and view of Mogadishu harbor.

1959, Sept. 28   Perf. 14
C63 AP21 1.20s red & blk   .35   .40
C64 AP21 2s blue, blk & org   .60   .60

5th Somali Fair, Mogadishu.

University Institute and Arms AP22

Design: 1.20s, Front view of Institute.

1960, Jan. 14
C65 AP22 45c grn, blk & org brn   .25   .25
C66 AP22 1.20s blue, ultra & blk   .40   .50

Opening of the University Institute of Somalia.

Stork and Uprooted Oak Emblem — AP23

1960, Apr. 7   Wmk. 303   Perf. 14
C67 AP23 1.50s lt grn, bl & red   .40   .60

World Refugee Year, 7/1/59-6/30/60.

Republic
#C42, C44 Overprinted Like #242
Wmk. 277
1960, June 26   Photo.   Perf. 13½
Antelopes in Natural Colors
C68 AP16 50c rose lil & blk   40.00   40.00
C69 AP16 1.20s dk gray grn   29.00   32.50

See note after No. 242.

Parliament and Italian Flag AP25

1.80s, Somali flag and assembly building.

1960, July 1   Wmk. 303   Perf. 14
C70 AP25 1s org red, grn & red   .80   .80
C71 AP25 1.80s red org, ultra & blk   3.25   3.25

Somalia's independence.

Animal Type of Regular Issue
1960, Nov. 24
C72 A37 3s Leopard   4.50   4.50

Olympic Games Type
45c, Runner, flag, Olympic rings. 1.80s, Long distance runner, flag, Olympic rings.

1960, Nov. 24
C73 A38 45c lilac & blue   .85   .85
C74 A38 1.80s org ver & bl   1.75   1.75

17th Olympic Games, Rome, 8/25-9/11.

Amauris Fenestrata and Jet Plane AP26

Various Butterflies.

1961, Sept. 9
C75 AP26 60c blue, brn & yel   .40   .40
C76 AP26 90c yel, blk & grn   .50   .50
C77 AP26 1s multicolored   2.40   .35
C78 AP26 1.80s org, blk & red   1.10   1.10
C79 AP26 3s multicolored   2.40   2.40
C80 AP26 5s ver, blk & brt bl   8.00   3.50
C81 AP26 10s multicolored   12.50   6.50
    Nos. C75-C81 (7)   27.30   14.75

Wooden Headrest, Comb and Cap AP27

Design: 1.80sh, Camel, metal sculpture.

1961, Sept. 28   Wmk. 303   Perf. 14
C82 AP27 1sh blk, ultra & ocher   .40   .40
C83 AP27 1.80sh blk, yel & brn   2.25   2.25

6th Somali Fair, Mogadishu.

Fish Type
Fish: 2.70sh, Lutianus sebae.

1962, Apr. 26
C84 A41 2.70sh ultra, brn & rose brn   3.50   3.50

Mosquitoes and
Malaria
Eradication
Emblem — AP28

Police Auxiliary
Women — AP29

Wmk. 303
1962, Oct. 25   Photo.   Perf. 14

C85	AP28	1sh bis brn & blk	.85	.85
C86	AP28	1.80sh lt green & blk	2.75	2.75

WHO drive to eradicate malaria.

1963, May 15   Wmk. 303   Perf. 14

Women's Auxiliary Forces: 1.80sh, Army
auxiliary women with flag.

C87	AP29	1sh dk bl, yel & org	.85	.85
C88	AP29	1.80sh multicolored	2.75	2.75

Freedom from Hunger Type
Design: 1sh, Sower and wheat.

1963, June 25

C89	A44	1sh dk brn, yel & bl	2.75	2.75

President Osman Type
1963, Sept. 15   Wmk. 303   Perf. 14

C90	A45	1sh multicolored	.85	.85
C91	A45	1.80sh multicolored	1.75	1.75

Somali Fair Type
Design: 1.80sh, Government Pavilion.

1963, Sept. 28   Photo.

C92	A46	1.80sh blue	2.75	2.75

Map of
Somalia,
Animals
and Globe
AP30

1.80sh, Somali Credit Bank emblem.

1964, May 16   Wmk. 303   Perf. 14

C93	AP30	1sh multicolored	1.75	1.75
C94	AP30	1.80sh blk, bl & yel	2.75	2.75

10th anniversary of Somali Credit Bank.

Olympic Type
1964, Oct. 10   Photo.

C95	A48	90c Diving	.85	.85
C96	A48	1.80sh Soccer	2.75	2.75
a.		Souvenir sheet, #274-275, C95-C96	40.00	

No. C96a sold for 3.55sh.

Elephants
and DC-3
AP31

Design: 1.80sh, Plane over Mogadishu.

1964, Nov. 8   Photo.   Perf. 14

C97	AP31	1sh brown & green	2.90	2.90
C98	AP31	1.80sh black & blue	5.25	5.25

Establishment of Somali Air Lines.

ITU Type
1965, May 17   Wmk. 303   Perf. 14

C99	A50	1sh dp grn & blk	.85	.65
C100	A50	1.80sh rose lil & brn	2.10	1.40

Somali Fair Type
Designs: 1.50sh, Sugar industry; harvesting
sugar cane and refinery. 2sh, Dairy industry;
bottling plant and milk cow.

1965, Sept. 28   Photo.   Perf. 14

C101	A51	1.50sh sepia & pale bl	1.20	.55
C102	A51	2sh sepia & rose	2.50	2.10

Faisal Type
Design: 1.80sh, Ka'aba, Mecca, Pres.
Abdirascid Ali Scermarche and King Faisal.

1967, Sept. 21   Wmk. 303   Perf. 14

C103	A60	1.80sh blk, dp rose & org	2.10	2.10

Egret — AP32

Birds: 1sh, Southern carmine bee-eater.
1.30sh, Bruce's green pigeon. 1.80sh, Broad-
tailed paradise whydah.

Perf. 11½

1968, Nov. 1		**Unwmk.**	**Litho.**	
C104	AP32	35c blue & multi	.25	.25
C105	AP32	1sh green & multi	.25	.25
C106	AP32	1.30sh vio bl & multi	.95	.95
C107	AP32	1.80sh yellow & multi	2.50	2.50
Nos. C104-C107 (4)			3.95	3.95

Somali Democratic Republic
Postal Union Type
1.30sh, Postal Union emblem and letter.

Perf. 14x13½

1972, Jan. 25		**Photo.**	**Unwmk.**	
C108	A81	1.30sh multicolored	1.75	1.75

AIR POST SEMI-POSTAL STAMPS

King Victor
Emmanuel
III
SPAP1

Wmk. 140
1934, Nov. 5   Photo.   Perf. 14

CB1	SPAP1	25c + 10c gray grn	6.50	14.50
CB2	SPAP1	50c + 10c brn	6.50	14.50
CB3	SPAP1	75c + 15c rose red	6.50	14.50
CB4	SPAP1	80c + 15c blk brn	6.50	14.50
CB5	SPAP1	1 l + 20c red brn	6.50	14.50
CB6	SPAP1	2 l + 20c brt bl	6.50	14.50
CB7	SPAP1	3 l + 25c pur	22.50	72.50
CB8	SPAP1	5 l + 25c org	22.50	72.50
CB9	SPAP1	10 l + 30c rose vio	22.50	72.50
CB10	SPAP1	25 l + 2 l dp grn	22.50	72.50
Nos. CB1-CB10 (10)			129.00	377.00
Set, never hinged			370.00	

65th birthday of King Victor Emmanuel III;
non-stop flight from Rome to Mogadishu.
For overprint see No. CBO1.

> **Catalogue values for unused
> stamps in this section, from this
> point to the end of the section, are
> for Never Hinged items.**

Somalia
Type of Semi-Postal Stamps, 1957
1957, Nov. 30   Wmk. 303   Perf. 14

CB11	SP17	55c + 20c dk bl & brn	.40	.60
CB12	SP17	1.20s + 20c vio & brn	.40	.60

The surtax was for the fight against
tuberculosis.

Type of Semi-Postal Issue, 1964
Designs: 75c+20c, Destroyed Somali village. 1.80sh+50c, Soldier aiding children, and
map of Somalia, vert.

1964, Dec. 12   Photo.   Perf. 14

CB13	SP18	75c + 20c blk, org red & brn	.85	.65
CB14	SP18	1.80sh + 50c blk, ol bis & slate	2.50	1.40

AIR POST SPECIAL DELIVERY STAMP

> **Catalogue value for the stamp in
> this section is for a Never Hinged
> item.**

Antelopes
APSD1

Wmk. 303
1958, Oct. 4   Photo.   Perf. 14

CE1	APSD1	1.70s org ver & blk	2.00	1.60

AIR POST OFFICIAL STAMP

No. C1 Overprinted

Wmk. 140
1934, Nov. 11   Photo.   Perf. 14

CO1	AP1	25c sl bl & red org	2,750.	4,000.
		Never hinged	4,250.	

Forgeries of this overprint exist.

AIR POST SEMI-POSTAL OFFICIAL STAMP

Type of Air Post Semi-Postal Stamps,
1934 Overprinted Crown and
"SERVIZIO DI STATO" in Black

1934, Nov. 5   Wmk. 140   Perf. 14

CBO1	SPAP1	25 l + 2 l cop red	2,750.	4,400.
		Never hinged	4,250.	

SPECIAL DELIVERY STAMPS

Italy No. E3 Surcharged

1923, July 16   Wmk. 140   Perf. 14

E1	SD1	30b on 60c dl red	25.00	22.50

Italy, Type of 1908 Special Delivery
Stamp Surcharged

E2	SD2	60b on 1.20 l bl & red	37.50	45.00

"Italia"
SD3

1924, June   Engr.   Unwmk.

E3	SD3	30b dk red & brn	9.50	16.00
E4	SD3	60b dk blue & red	16.00	24.00

Nos. E3-E4 Surcharged in Black or
Red with Bars and

1926, Oct.

E5	SD3	70c on 30b (Bk)	11.00	18.00
E6	SD3	2.50 l on 60b (R)	14.00	22.00
a.		Imperf., pair	950.00	

Same Surcharge on No. E3

1927   Perf. 11

E7	SD3	1.25 l on 30b	14.50	14.50
a.		Perf. 14	225.00	550.00
b.		Imperf., pair	875.00	

> **Catalogue values for unused
> stamps in this section, from this
> point to the end of the section, are
> for Never Hinged items.**

Somalia

Bananas,
Grant's
Gazelles
SD4

Wmk. 277
1950, Apr. 24   Photo.   Perf. 14

E8	SD4	40c blue green	12.00	9.50
E9	SD4	80c violet	16.00	14.50

Gardenias
SD5

Design: 1s, Eryrhina melanocantha.

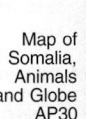

1955, Feb.   *Perf. 13*

E10	SD5	50c lilac & green	.50	1.00
E11	SD5	1s bl, rose brn & grn	.85	1.50

AUTHORIZED DELIVERY STAMP

Italy No. EY2
Overprinted in Black

1939   **Wmk. 140**   *Perf. 14*

EY1 AD2 10c brown   72.50 —

No. EY1 has yellowish gum. A 1941 printing in grayish brown, with white gum, was not issued. Value, 65 cents.

POSTAGE DUE STAMPS

Postage Due Stamps
of Italy Overprinted

1906-08   **Wmk. 140**   *Perf. 14*

J1	D3	5c buff & magenta	20.00	45.00
J2	D3	10c buff & magenta	65.00	55.00
J3	D3	20c org & magenta	47.50	67.50
J4	D3	30c buff & magenta	40.00	72.50
J5	D3	40c buff & magenta	275.00	72.50
J6	D3	50c buff & magenta	72.50	87.50
J7	D3	60c buff & mag ('08)	65.00	87.50
J8	D3	1 l blue & magenta	1,200.	400.00
J9	D3	2 l blue & magenta	1,200.	400.00
J10	D3	5 l blue & magenta	1,200.	400.00
J11	D3	10 l blue & magenta	225.00	350.00
	Nos. J1-J11 (11)		4,410.	2,037.

Postage Due Stamps
of Italy Overprinted at
Top of Stamps

1909-19

J12	D3	5c buff & magenta	9.50	22.50
J13	D3	10c buff & magenta	9.50	22.50
J14	D3	20c buff & magenta	20.00	45.00
J15	D3	30c buff & magenta	45.00	45.00
J16	D3	40c buff & magenta	45.00	47.50
J17	D3	50c buff & magenta	45.00	72.50
J18	D3	60c buff & mag ('19)	55.00	65.00
J19	D3	1 l blue & magenta	145.00	150.00
J20	D3	2 l blue & magenta	200.00	190.00
J21	D3	5 l blue & magenta	225.00	225.00
J22	D3	10 l blue & magenta	55.00	72.50
	Nos. J12-J22 (11)		854.00	880.00

Same with Overprint at Bottom of Stamps

1920

J12a	D3	5c buff & magenta	110.00	160.00
J13a	D3	10c buff & magenta	110.00	160.00
J14a	D3	20c buff & magenta	160.00	105.00
J15a	D3	30c buff & magenta	175.00	105.00
J16a	D3	40c buff & magenta	175.00	160.00
J17a	D3	50c buff & magenta	160.00	145.00
J18a	D3	60c buff & magenta	175.00	145.00
J19a	D3	1 l blue & magenta	175.00	210.00
J20a	D3	2 l blue & magenta	175.00	210.00
J21a	D3	5 l blue & magenta	175.00	250.00
	Nos. J12a-J21a (10)		1,590.	1,650.

D4   D5

1923, July 1

J23	D4	1b buff & black	1.60	8.00
J24	D4	2b buff & black	1.60	8.00
a.	Inverted numeral and ovpt.		525.00	
J25	D4	3b buff & black	1.60	8.00
J26	D4	5b buff & black	3.25	8.00
J27	D4	10b buff & black	3.25	8.00
J28	D4	20b buff & black	3.25	8.00
J29	D4	40b buff & black	3.25	8.00
J30	D4	1r blue & black	4.00	47.50
	Nos. J23-J30 (8)		21.80	103.50

Type of Postage Due
Stamps of Italy
Overprinted

1926, Mar. 1

J31	D3	5c buff & black	22.50	32.50
J32	D3	10c buff & black	22.50	24.00
J33	D3	20c buff & black	22.50	35.00
J34	D3	30c buff & black	22.50	24.00
J35	D3	40c buff & black	22.50	24.00
J36	D3	50c buff & black	35.00	24.00
J37	D3	60c buff & black	35.00	24.00
J38	D3	1 l blue & black	52.50	35.00
J39	D3	2 l blue & black	80.00	35.00
J40	D3	5 l blue & black	87.50	47.50
J41	D3	10 l blue & black	105.00	67.50
	Nos. J31-J41 (11)		507.50	372.50

Numerals and Ovpt. Invtd.

J32a	D3	10c	210.00
J33a	D3	20c	650.00
J34a	D3	30c	210.00
J35a	D3	40c	210.00
J36a	D3	50c	210.00
J37a	D3	60c	210.00

Postage Due Stamps
of Italy, 1934,
Overprinted in Black

1934, May 12

J42	D6	5c brown	.80	4.75
J43	D6	10c blue	.80	4.75
J44	D6	20c rose red	3.25	9.50
J45	D6	25c green	3.25	9.50
J46	D6	30c red orange	8.00	14.50
J47	D6	40c black brown	8.00	20.00
J48	D6	50c violet	14.50	6.50
J49	D6	60c black	17.50	35.00
J50	D7	1 l red orange	22.50	16.00
J51	D7	2 l green	40.00	35.00
J52	D7	5 l violet	45.00	72.50
J53	D7	10 l blue	45.00	80.00
J54	D7	20 l carmine	47.50	105.00
	Nos. J42-J54 (13)		256.10	413.00

> **Catalogue values for unused stamps in this section, from this point to the end of the section, are for Never Hinged items.**

Somalia

1950   **Wmk. 277**   **Photo.**   *Perf. 14*

J55	D5	1c dark gray violet	4.00	4.00
J56	D5	2c deep blue	4.00	4.00
J57	D5	5c blue green	4.00	4.00
J58	D5	10c rose lilac	4.00	4.00
J59	D5	40c violet	12.00	12.00
J60	D5	1s dark brown	17.50	17.50
	Nos. J55-J60 (6)		45.50	45.50

PARCEL POST STAMPS

These stamps were used by affixing them to the way bill so that one half remained on it following the parcel, the other half staying on the receipt given the sender. Most used halves are right halves. Complete stamps were and are obtainable canceled, probably to order. Both unused and used values are for complete stamps.

Parcel Post Stamps
of Italy, 1914-17,
Overprinted

1917-19   **Wmk. 140**   *Perf. 13½*

Q1	PP2	5c brown	6.50	47.50
a.	Double overprint		450.00	
Q2	PP2	10c blue	8.00	32.50
Q3	PP2	20c black ('19)	325.00	145.00
Q4	PP2	25c red	14.50	55.00
a.	Double overprint			
Q5	PP2	50c orange	145.00	72.50
Q6	PP2	1 l lilac	47.50	72.50
Q7	PP2	2 l green	65.00	72.50
Q8	PP2	3 l bister	72.50	120.00
Q9	PP2	4 l slate	80.00	120.00
	Nos. Q1-Q9 (9)		764.00	737.50

Halves Used

Q1		1.60
Q2		1.60
Q3		7.25
Q4		3.50
Q5		6.00
Q6		4.75
Q7		4.75
Q8		4.75
Q9		4.75

Nos. Q5-Q9 were overprinted in 1922 with a slightly different type in which the final "A" of SOMALIA is directly over the final "A" of ITALIANA. They were not regularly issued. Value for set, unused $1,400; never hinged $2,100.

Parcel Post Stamps
of Italy, 1914-17,
Overprinted

1923

Q10	PP2	25c red	65.00	120.00
Q11	PP2	50c orange	95.00	120.00
Q12	PP2	1 l violet	110.00	175.00
Q13	PP2	2 l green	110.00	175.00
Q14	PP2	3 l bister	175.00	175.00
Q15	PP2	4 l slate	175.00	175.00
	Nos. Q10-Q15 (6)		730.00	940.00

Halves Used

Q10		4.75
Q11		4.75
Q12		3.00
Q13		3.00
Q14		4.75
Q15		5.50

Parcel Post Stamps of Italy, 1914-17, Surcharged

1923

Q16	PP2	3b on 5c brown	27.50	27.50
Q17	PP2	5b on 5c brown	27.50	27.50
Q18	PP2	10b on 10c blue	27.50	24.00
Q19	PP2	25b on 25c red	27.50	45.00
Q20	PP2	50b on 50c org	35.00	60.00
Q21	PP2	1r on 1 l lilac	47.50	60.00
Q22	PP2	2r on 2 l green	72.50	87.50
Q23	PP2	3r on 3 l bister	72.50	87.50
Q24	PP2	4r on 4 l slate	87.50	87.50
	Nos. Q16-Q24 (9)		425.00	506.50

Halves Used

Q16		1.60
Q17		1.60
Q18		1.60
Q19		3.25
Q20		3.25
Q21		3.25
Q22		3.25
Q23		3.25
Q24		3.25

No. Q16 has the numeral "3" at the left also.

Parcel Post Stamps
of Italy, 1914-22
Overprinted

1926-31

Red Overprint

Q25	PP2	5c brown	27.50	55.00
Q26	PP2	10c blue	27.50	55.00
Q27	PP2	20c black	65.00	55.00
Q28	PP2	25c red	65.00	55.00
Q29	PP2	50c orange	65.00	55.00
Q30	PP2	1 l violet	80.00	55.00
Q31	PP2	2 l green	145.00	55.00
Q32	PP2	3 l yellow	24.00	55.00
Q33	PP2	4 l slate	24.00	55.00
Q34	PP2	10 l vio brn ('30)	47.50	72.50
Q35	PP2	12 l red brn '31)	47.50	125.00
Q36	PP2	15 l olive ('31)	47.50	125.00
Q37	PP2	20 l dull vio ('31)	47.50	125.00
	Nos. Q25-Q37 (13)		713.00	890.00

Halves Used

Q25		2.00
Q26		2.00
Q27		3.25
Q28		3.25
Q29		3.25
Q30		3.25

Q31		3.25
Q32		3.25
Q33		4.00
Q34		4.00
Q35		4.00
Q36		4.00
Q37		4.00

Nos. Q25-Q31 come with two types of overprint: I — The first "I" and last "A" of ITALIANA extend slightly at both sides of SOMALIA. II — Only the "I" extends. These seven stamps with type I overprint were not regularly issued, and Nos. Q27-Q31 (type I) sell for less than with type II overprint.

Black Overprint

Q38	PP2	10 l violet brown	80.00	72.50
Q39	PP2	12 l red brown	55.00	72.50
Q40	PP2	15 l olive	55.00	72.50
Q41	PP2	20 l dull violet	55.00	72.50
	Nos. Q38-Q41 (4)		245.00	290.00

Halves Used

Q38		4.00
Q39		4.00
Q40		4.00
Q41		4.00

Same Overprint on Parcel Post Stamps of Italy, 1927-38

1928-39

Black Overprint

Q42	PP3	25c red ('31)	47.50	40.00
Q43	PP3	30c ultra	3.25	4.75
Q43A	PP3	50c orange	12,750.	
Q44	PP3	60c red	3.25	8.00
Q45	PP3	1 l lilac ('31)	800.00	1,800.
Q46	PP3	2 l green ('31)	800.00	2,600.
Q47	PP3	3 l bister	6.50	20.00
Q48	PP3	4 l gray black	6.50	20.00
Q49	PP3	10 l rose lil ('34)	475.00	525.00
Q50	PP3	20 l lil brn ('34)	475.00	550.00
	Nos. Q42-Q43, Q44-Q50 (9)		2,617.	5,567.

Halves Used

Q42		8.75
Q43		.45
Q43A		160.00
Q44		.45
Q45		2.75
Q46		2.75
Q47		.80
Q48		.80
Q49		20.00
Q50		20.00

The 25c, 1 l and 2 l come with both types of overprint (see note below No. Q37). Both types were regularly issued. Values are for type I on 25c, type II on 1 l and 2 l.

Red Overprint

Q51	PP3	5c brown ('39)	16.00	
Q52	PP3	3 l bister ('30)	32.50	60.00
	Half stamp			2.00
Q53	PP3	4 l gray black ('30)	32.50	60.00
	Half stamp			2.00
	Nos. Q51-Q53 (3)		81.00	

Same Overprint in Black on Italy Nos. Q24-Q25

1940   *Perf. 13*

Q54	PP3	5c brown	3.25	9.50
	Half stamp			.45
Q55	PP3	10c deep blue	4.00	9.50
	Half stamp			.45

> **Catalogue values for unused stamps in this section, from this point to the end of the section, are for Never Hinged items.**

Somalia

PP1

1950   **Wmk. 277**   **Photo.**   *Perf. 14*

Q56	PP1	1c cerise	8.00	8.00
Q57	PP1	3c dark gray violet	8.00	8.00
Q58	PP1	5c rose lilac	8.00	8.00
Q59	PP1	10c red orange	8.00	8.00
Q60	PP1	20c dark brown	8.00	8.00
Q61	PP1	50c blue green	20.00	20.00
Q62	PP1	1s violet	47.50	47.50
Q63	PP1	2s brown	65.00	65.00
Q64	PP1	3s blue	95.00	95.00
	Nos. Q56-Q64 (9)		267.50	267.50

Halves Used

Q56		.20
Q57		.20
Q58		.20
Q59		.20
Q60		.20

Q61		.25
Q62		1.60
Q63		2.00
Q64		3.25

SOMALI COAST

sō-'mä-lē 'kōst

(Djibouti)

LOCATION — Eastern Africa, bordering on the Gulf of Aden
GOVT. — French Overseas Territory
AREA — 8,500 sq. mi.
POP. — 86,000 (est. 1963)
CAPITAL — Djibouti (Jibuti)

The port of Obock, which issued postage stamps in 1892-1894, was included in the territory and began to use stamps of Somali Coast in 1902. See Obock in Vol. 4.

On Mar. 19, 1967, the territory changed its name to the French Territory of the Afars and Issas. The Republic of Djibouti was proclaimed June 27, 1977.

100 Centimes = 1 Franc

> Catalogue values for unused stamps in this country are for Never Hinged items, beginning with Scott 224 in the regular postage section, Scott B13 in the semi-postal section, Scott C1 in the air-post section, Scott CB1 in the air-post semi-postal section, and Scott J39 in the postage due section.

Navigation and Commerce
A1   A2

A3

Camel and Rider
A4

Obock Nos. 32-33, 35, 45 with Overprint or Surcharge Handstamped in Black, Blue or Red

1894		Unwmk.	Perf. 14x13½	
1	A1	5c grn & red, *grnsh*		
		(with bar)	160.00	150.00
a.		Without bar	1,400.	900.00
2	A2	25c on 2c brn & bl, *buff* (Bl & Bk)	375.00	240.00
a.		"25" omitted	1,100.	925.00
b.		"DJIBOUTI" omitted	1,100.	925.00
c.		"DJIBOUTI" inverted	1,200.	1,050.
3	A3	50c on 1c blk & red, *bl* (R & Bl)	400.00	275.00
a.		"5" instead of "50"	1,700.	1,200.
b.		"0" instead of "50"	1,700.	1,200.
c.		"DJIBOUTI" omitted	1,750.	1,350.

Imperf

4	A4	1fr on 5fr car	700.00	550.00
5	A4	5fr carmine	2,200.	1,500.

The overprint on No. 1 includes a bar to obliterate "OBOCK."

"DJIBOUTI" is in blue on No. 2, in red on No. 3.

Counterfeits exist of Nos. 4-5.

View of Djibouti, Somali Warriors — A5

French Gunboat A7

Crossing Desert (Size: 66mm wide, including simulated perfs.) — A8

Designs: 15c, 25c, 30c, 40c, 50c, 75c, Different views of Djibouti. 1fr, 2fr, Djibouti quay.

Imperf. (Simulated Perforations in Frame Color)

1894-1902				Typo.
Quadrille Lines Printed on Paper				
6	A5	1c blk & claret	4.00	3.25
7	A5	2c claret & blk	4.00	3.25
8	A5	4c vio brn & bl	14.50	8.75
9	A5	5c bl grn & red	14.50	7.25
10	A5	5c grn & yel grn ('02)	10.50	8.75
11	A5	10c brown & grn	19.00	8.75
a.		Half used as 5c on cover ('01)		150.00
12	A5	15c violet & grn	20.00	8.75
13	A5	25c rose & blue	27.50	11.00
14	A5	30c gray brn & rose	20.00	11.00
a.		Half used as 15c on cover ('01)		500.00
15	A5	40c org & bl ('00)	60.00	40.00
16	A5	50c blue & rose	27.50	17.50
a.		Half used as 25c on cover ('01)		1,600.
17	A5	75c violet & org	52.50	45.00
18	A5	1fr ol grn & blk	24.00	20.00
19	A5	2fr gray brn & rose	105.00	80.00
20	A7	5fr rose & blue	210.00	150.00
21	A8	25fr rose & blue	1,050.	1,100.
22	A8	50fr blue & rose	650.00	700.00
		Nos. 6-20 (15)	613.00	423.25

High values are found with the overprint "S" (Specimen) erased and, usually, a cancellation added.

For surcharges see Nos. 24-27B.

A9

1899				
Black Surcharge				
23	A9	40c on 4c brn & bl	*3,400.*	32.50
a.		Double surcharge	*6,250.*	1,500.

Nos. 17-20 Surcharged

1902			**Blue Surcharge**	
24	A5	0.05c on 75c	72.50	45.00
a.		Inverted surcharge	625.00	550.00
b.		Double surcharge	625.00	550.00
25	A5	0.10c on 1fr	92.50	60.00
a.		Inverted surcharge	500.00	450.00
b.		Double surcharge	575.00	450.00
26	A5	0.40c on 2fr	625.00	450.00
a.		Double surcharge	2,250.	2,100.
Black Surcharge				
27	A7	0.75c on 5fr	600.00	450.00
a.		Inverted surcharge	2,900.	2,300.
c.		Double surcharge	2,900.	2,300.
Obock No. 57 Surcharged in Blue				
27B	A7	0.05c on 75c gray lil & org	1,650.	1,200.

A10

Nos. 15-16 Surcharged in Black

28	A10	5c on 40c	8.75	5.50
a.		Double surcharge	140.00	140.00
29	A10	10c on 50c	27.50	27.50
a.		Inverted surcharge	575.00	550.00
b.		Double surcharge	650.00	

Surcharged on Stamps of Obock

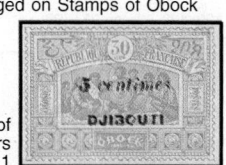

Group of Warriors A11

Black Surcharge

30	A11	5c on 30c bis & yel grn	16.00	12.00
a.		Inverted surcharge	300.00	300.00
b.		Double surcharge	350.00	300.00
c.		Triple surcharge		1,600.

A12

Red Surcharge

31	A12	10c on 25c blk & bl	16.00	13.50
a.		Inverted surcharge	300.00	300.00
b.		Double surcharge	350.00	350.00
c.		Triple surcharge	1,800.	1,800.

A13

Black Surcharge

32	A13	10c on 10fr org & red vio	40.00	35.00
a.		Double surcharge	275.00	225.00
b.		Double surch., one invtd.	2,400.	2,300.
c.		Triple surcharge	1,600.	1,600.
d.		"Djibouti" omitted	120.00	80.00

A14

Black Surcharge

33	A14	10c on 2fr dl vio & org	67.50	55.00
a.		"DJIBOUTI" inverted	275.00	250.00
b.		Large "0" in "10"	160.00	130.00
c.		Double surcharge	500.00	475.00

Same Surcharge on Obock No. 53 in Red

33D	A7	10c on 25c blk & bl	*35,000.*	*25,000.*

A14a

Black Surcharge on Obock Nos. 63-64

33E	A14a	5c on 25fr brn & bl	67.50	60.00
33F	A14a	10c on 50fr red vio & grn	87.50	65.00
g.		"01" instead of "10"	240.00	225.00
h.		"CENTIMES" inverted	2,900.	2,900.
i.		Double surcharge	2,700.	2,250.

Tadjoura Mosque
A15   Somalis on Camel A16

Warriors — A17

1902		**Engr.**	*Perf. 11½*	
34	A15	1c brn vio & org	1.00	1.00
35	A15	2c yel brn & yel grn	1.40	1.00
36	A15	4c bl & carmine	2.75	2.10
37	A15	5c bl grn & yel grn	2.75	1.90
38	A15	10c car & red org	7.25	4.50
39	A15	15c brn org & bl	7.25	4.50
40	A16	20c vio & green	17.00	8.75
41	A16	25c blue	25.00	14.50
a.		25c indigo & blue ('03)	25.00	14.50
42	A16	30c red & black	7.75	5.50
43	A16	40c orange & blue	17.50	10.50
44	A16	50c grn & red org	52.50	45.00
45	A16	75c orange & vio	10.50	6.50
46	A17	1fr red org & vio	27.50	19.00
47	A17	2fr yel grn & car	45.00	35.00
a.		Without names of designer and engraver at bottom	160.00	160.00
48	A17	5fr orange & blue	27.50	24.00
		Nos. 34-48 (15)	252.15	183.75

1903				
49	A15	1c brn vio & blk	1.20	.95
50	A15	2c yel brn & blk	1.60	1.10
51	A15	4c lake & blk	2.00	1.75
		4c red & black	3.25	2.75
52	A15	5c bl grn & blk	4.75	3.25
53	A15	10c carmine & blk	9.50	4.50
54	A15	15c org brn & blk	21.00	11.00
a.		15c brown & black	21.00	11.00
55	A16	20c dl vio & blk	27.50	20.00
56	A16	25c ultra & blk	16.00	11.00
58	A16	40c orange & blk	12.00	12.00
a.		40c bister & black	25.00	25.00
59	A16	50c green & blk	27.50	17.00
60	A16	75c buff & blk	13.50	12.00
		75c brown orange & black	87.50	87.50
61	A17	1fr orange & blk	22.50	21.00
62	A17	2fr yel grn & blk	12.00	9.50
a.		Without names of designer and engraver at bottom	52.50	52.50
63	A17	5fr red org & blk	27.50	23.00
		5fr ocher & black	40.00	35.00
		Nos. 49-63 (14)	198.55	148.05

Imperforates, transposed colors and inverted centers exist in the 1902 and 1903 issues. Most of these were issued from Paris and some are said to have been fraudulently printed.

Tadjoura
Mosque
A18

Somalis on
Camel — A19

Warriors — A20

1909		Typo.		Perf. 14x13½	
64	A18	1c maroon & brn	1.00	.95
65	A18	2c vio & ol gray	1.00	.95
66	A18	4c ol gray & bl	1.30	1.20
67	A18	5c grn & gray grn	1.80	1.10
68	A18	10c car & ver	4.75	1.75
69	A18	20c blk & red brn	7.50	6.00
70	A19	25c bl & pale bl	5.50	4.00
71	A19	30c brn & scar	8.75	6.50
72	A19	35c vio & grn	10.50	7.25
73	A19	40c rose & vio	9.50	6.50
74	A19	45c brn & bl grn	9.50	6.50
75	A19	50c maroon & brn	9.50	8.00
76	A19	75c scarlet & grn	22.50	14.50
77	A20	1fr vio & brn	26.00	23.00
78	A20	2fr brn & rose	40.00	32.50
79	A20	5fr vio brn & bl grn	65.00	47.50
		Nos. 64-79 (16)	224.10	168.20

Drummer
A21

Somali Girl
A22

Djibouti-Addis Ababa Railroad
Bridge — A23

1915-33			Perf. 13½x14	
		Chalky Paper		
80	A21	1c brt vio & red brn	.25	.25
81	A21	2c ocher & ind	.25	.25
82	A21	4c dk brn & red	.30	.30
83	A21	5c yel grn & grn	1.20	1.20
84	A21	5c org & dl red ('22)	.70	.70
85	A22	10c car & dk red	2.10	1.10
86	A22	10c ap grn & grn ('22)	1.00	1.00
87	A22	10c ver & grn ('25)	.40	.40
88	A22	15c brn vio & car	1.00	.65
89	A22	20c org & blk brn	.30	.30
90	A22	20c dp grn & bl grn ('25)	.40	.40
91	A22	20c dk grn & red ('27)	.55	.55
92	A22	25c ultra & dl bl	1.10	.80
93	A22	25c blk & bl grn ('22)	1.10	1.10
94	A22	30c blk & bl grn	2.40	2.10
95	A22	30c rose & red brn ('22)	1.40	1.40
96	A22	30c vio & ol grn ('25)	.40	.40
97	A22	30c grn & dl grn ('27)	.55	.55
98	A22	35c lt grn & dl rose	.80	.65
99	A22	40c bl & brn vio	.95	.80
100	A22	45c red brn & dk bl	1.00	.80
101	A22	50c car rose & blk	12.00	8.00
102	A22	50c ultra & ind ('24)	1.25	1.25
103	A22	50c dk brn & red vio ('25)	.80	.55
104	A22	60c ol grn & red vio ('25)	.55	.45
105	A22	65c car rose & ol grn ('25)	.80	.65
106	A22	75c dl vio & choc	.80	.80
107	A22	75c ind & ultra ('25)	.65	.65
108	A22	75c brt vio & ol brn ('27)	2.10	1.75

109	A22	85c vio brn & bl grn ('25)	1.20	1.10
110	A22	90c brn red & brt red ('30)	8.75	6.50
111	A23	1fr bis brn & red	2.10	1.25
112	A23	1.10fr lt brn & ultra ('28)	4.75	6.00
113	A23	1.25fr dk bl & blk brn ('33)	10.50	8.00
114	A23	1.50fr lt bl & dk bl ('30)	1.60	1.20
115	A23	1.75fr gray grn & lt red ('33)	8.75	5.50
116	A23	2fr bl vio & blk	3.50	2.75
117	A23	3fr red vio ('30)	11.50	9.25
118	A23	5fr rose red & blk	6.00	3.25
		Nos. 80-118 (39)	95.75	74.60

No. 99 is on ordinary paper.
For surcharges and overprints see Nos. 119-134, 183-193.

Nos. 83, 92
Surcharged in Green
or Blue

1922

119	A21	10c on 5c (G)	.80	.80
a.		Double surcharge	110.00	
120	A22	50c on 25c (Bl)	.80	.80

Type of 1915
Surcharged in
Various Colors

1922

121	A22	0,01c on 15c vio & rose (Bk)	.30	.30
122	A22	0,02c on 15c vio & rose (Bl)	.45	.45
123	A22	0,04c on 15c vio & rose (G)	.70	.70
124	A22	0,05c on 15c vio & rose (R)	.70	.70
		Nos. 121-124 (4)	2.15	2.15

Nos. 88, 99 and Type of 1915
Surcharged

1923-27

125	A22	60c on 75c ol grn & vio	.55	.55
126	A22	65c on 15c ('25)	2.10	2.10
127	A22	85c on 40c ('25)	1.80	1.80
128	A22	90c on 75c brn red & red ('27)	5.25	5.50
		Nos. 125-128 (4)	9.70	9.95

No. 118 and Type of 1915-17
Surcharged with New Value and Bars
in Black or Red

1924-27

129	A23	25c on 5fr	1.20	1.20
130	A23	1.25fr on 1fr dk bl & ultra (R) ('26)	1.20	1.20
131	A23	1.50fr on 1fr lt bl & dk bl ('27)	1.20	1.20
132	A23	3fr on 5fr ver & red vio ('27)	5.25	5.50
133	A23	10fr on 5fr brn red & ol brn ('27)	8.75	9.50
134	A23	20fr on 5fr gray grn & lil rose ('27)	14.50	16.00
		Nos. 129-134 (6)	32.10	34.60

Common Design Types
pictured following the introduction.

Colonial Exposition Issue
Common Design Types
Engr., Name of Country Typo. in
Black

1931			Perf. 12½	
135	CD70	40c deep green	5.50	5.50
136	CD71	50c violet	5.50	5.50
137	CD72	90c red orange	6.00	6.00
138	CD73	1.50fr dull blue	6.00	6.00
		Nos. 135-138 (4)	23.00	23.00

Paris International Exposition Issue
Common Design Types

1937		Engr.	Perf. 13	
139	CD74	20c deep violet	1.80	1.80
140	CD75	30c dark green	1.90	1.90
141	CD76	40c carmine rose	1.90	1.90
142	CD77	50c dk brn & bl	1.80	1.80
143	CD78	90c red	1.75	1.75
144	CD79	1.50fr ultra	1.90	1.90
		Nos. 139-144 (6)	11.05	11.05

Colonial Arts Exhibition Issue
Souvenir Sheet
Common Design Type

1937			Imperf.	
145	CD75	3fr dull violet	12.00	13.50

Mosque of
Djibouti — A24

Somali
Warriors — A25

Governor Léonce
Lagarde — A26

View of Djibouti — A27

1938-40			Perf. 12x12½, 12½	
146	A24	2c dull red vio	.20	.20
147	A24	3c slate grn	.20	.20
148	A24	4c dull red brn	.20	.20
149	A24	5c carmine	.20	.20
150	A24	10c blue gray	.20	.20
151	A24	15c slate black	.30	.30
152	A24	20c dark orange	.30	.30
153	A24	25c dark brown	.80	.70
154	A25	30c dark blue	.40	.40
155	A25	35c olive grn	.95	.80
156	A24	40c org brn ('40)	.95	.80
157	A24	45c dull grn ('40)	.35	.35
158	A25	50c red	.70	.55
159	A25	55c dull red vio	.95	.80
160	A25	60c black ('40)	.70	.70
161	A25	65c orange brown	1.00	.95
162	A25	70c lt violet ('40)	1.40	1.40
163	A25	80c gray blk	2.25	1.90
164	A25	90c rose vio ('39)	1.60	1.60
165	A26	1fr carmine	3.25	2.10
166	A26	1fr black ('40)	.55	.55
167	A26	1.25fr magenta ('39)	1.25	1.25
168	A26	1.40fr pck bl ('40)	1.20	1.20
169	A26	1.50fr dull green	.95	.95
170	A26	1.60fr brn car ('40)	1.20	1.20
171	A26	1.75fr ultra	1.40	1.20
172	A26	2fr dk orange	1.00	.90
173	A26	2.25fr ultra ('39)	1.90	1.90
174	A26	2.50fr org brn ('40)	2.10	2.10
175	A26	3fr dull violet	1.00	.90
176	A27	5fr brn & pale cl	2.25	2.25

177	A27	10fr ind & pale bl	2.75	2.75
178	A27	20fr car lake & gray	2.75	2.75
		Nos. 146-178 (33)	36.45	33.95

For types A24-A26 without "RF," see Nos. 237A-237C.
For overprints and surcharge see Nos. 194-223.

New York World's Fair Issue
Common Design Type

1939		Engr.	Perf. 12½x12	
179	CD82	1.25fr car lake	1.25	1.25
180	CD82	2.25fr ultra	1.25	1.25

Mosque of Djibouti
and Marshal
Pétain — A28

1941, Nov. 10   Engr.   Perf. 12x12½

181	A28	1fr yellow brown	.80	
182	A28	2.50fr blue	.80	

For types A24-A26 without "RF," see Nos. 237A-237C. Nos. 181-182 were issued by the Vichy government in France, but were not placed on sale in Somali Coast.
For surcharges, see Nos. B11-B12.

Nos. 80-82, 84, 88,
91, 97, 103, 105,
114-115 Overprinted
in Black or Red

1943			Perf. 13½x14, 14x13½	
			Unwmk.	
183	A21	1c	2.75	2.75
184	A21	2c	2.75	2.75
185	A21	4c	30.00	30.00
186	A21	5c	2.75	2.75
187	A22	15c	10.50	10.50
188	A22	20c	2.75	2.75
189	A22	30c	2.75	2.75
190	A22	50c	2.75	2.75
191	A22	65c	2.75	2.75
192	A23	1.50fr (R)	2.75	2.75
193	A23	1.75fr	13.50	13.50
		Nos. 183-193 (11)	76.00	76.00

Stamps of 1938-40 Overprinted in
Black or Red

On A24

On A25

On A26

On
A27

1943 Perf. 12x12½, 12½

194	A24	2c dl red vio	3.50	3.50
195	A24	3c sl grn (R)	3.50	3.50
196	A24	4c dl red brn	3.50	3.50
197	A24	5c carmine	3.50	3.50
198	A24	10c bl gray (R)	1.20	1.20
199	A24	15c sl blk (R)	3.50	3.50
200	A24	20c dk org	3.50	3.50
201	A25	25c dk brn (R)	4.00	4.00
202	A25	30c dk bl (R)	1.20	1.20
203	A25	35c olive (R)	4.75	4.75
204	A24	40c brn org	1.20	1.20
205	A24	45c dl grn	4.75	4.75
206	A25	55c dl red vio (R)	3.50	3.50
207	A25	60c blk (R)	1.20	1.20
208	A25	70c lt vio (R)	1.20	1.20
a.		Inverted overprint	275.00	275.00
b.		Double overprint	300.00	300.00
209	A26	80c gray blk (R)	1.60	1.60
210	A26	90c rose vio (R)	1.20	1.20
211	A26	1.25fr magenta	2.40	2.40
212	A26	1.40fr pck bl (R)	1.20	1.20
213	A26	1.50fr dl grn	2.40	2.40
214	A26	1.60fr brn car	2.40	2.40
215	A26	1.75fr ultra	12.00	12.00
216	A26	2fr dk org	1.60	1.60
217	A26	2.25fr ultra (R)	2.40	2.40
218	A26	2.50fr chestnut	2.00	2.00
219	A26	3fr dl vio (R)	2.40	2.40
220	A27	5fr brn & pale cl	14.00	14.00
221	A27	10fr ind & pale bl	175.00	175.00
222	A27	20fr car lake & gray	12.00	12.00

The space between overprint on Nos. 206 and 208 measures 10½mm.

No. 161 Surcharged in Black

223	A25	50c on 65c org brn	1.60	1.60
		Nos. 194-223 (30)	278.20	278.20

> **Catalogue values for unused stamps in this section, from this point to the end of the section, are for Never Hinged items.**

Locomotive and Palms — A29

1943 Unwmk. Photo. Perf. 14½x14

224	A29	5c royal blue	.20	.20
225	A29	10c pink	.20	.20
226	A29	25c emerald	.55	.55
227	A29	30c gray blk	.55	.55
228	A29	40c violet	.55	.55
229	A29	80c red brn	.55	.55
230	A29	1fr aqua	.55	.55
231	A29	1.50fr scarlet	.55	.55
232	A29	2fr brown	.55	.55
233	A29	2.50fr ultra	.85	.85
234	A29	4fr brt org	1.10	1.10
235	A29	5fr dp rose lil	1.10	1.10
236	A29	10fr lt ultra	1.25	1.25
237	A29	20fr green	1.60	1.60
		Nos. 224-237 (14)	10.15	10.15

For surcharges see Nos. 240-247.

Types of 1938-40 Without "RF"

1944, Apr. 3 Engr. Perf. 12½

237A	A24	40c org brn	.95	
237B	A25	50c red	1.20	
237C	A26	1.50fr dull green	1.75	
		Nos. 237A-237C (3)	3.90	

Nos. 237A-237C were issued by the Vichy government in France, but were not placed on sale in Somali Coast.

Eboue Issue
Common Design Type

1945 Engr. Perf. 13

238	CD91	2fr black	.70	.70
239	CD91	25fr Prus grn	1.40	1.40

Nos. 238 and 239 exist imperforate.

Nos. 224, 226 and 233 Surcharged with New Values and Bars in Carmine or Black

1945 Perf. 14½x14

240	A29	50c on 5c (C)	.65	.65
a.		Inverted surcharge	250.00	
b.		Double surcharge	210.00	
241	A29	60c on 5c (C)	.65	.65
a.		Inverted surcharge	190.00	
b.		Double surcharge	150.00	
242	A29	70c on 5c (C)	.65	.65
a.		Inverted surcharge	175.00	
b.		Double surcharge, one inverted	275.00	
243	A29	1.20fr on 5c (C)	.70	.70
a.		Double surcharge, one inverted	275.00	
244	A29	2.40fr on 25c	.95	.95
a.		Inverted surcharge	190.00	
b.		Double surcharge	175.00	
c.		Bars doubly surcharged	87.50	
245	A29	3fr on 25c	.95	.95
a.		Inverted surcharge	250.00	
b.		Double surcharge, one inverted	325.00	
246	A29	4.50fr on 25c	1.00	1.00
a.		Inverted surcharge	175.00	
247	A29	15fr on 2.50fr (C)	1.60	1.60
a.		Surcharge bars omitted	140.00	
b.		Value doubly surcharged	210.00	
		Nos. 240-247 (8)	7.15	7.15

Danakil Tent — A30

Khor-Angar Outpost A31

Obock-Tadjouran Road — A32

Somali Woman A33

Somali Village A34

Djibouti Mosque A35

1947 Unwmk. Photo. Perf. 13

248	A30	10c vio bl & org	.20	.20
249	A30	30c ol brn & org	.20	.20
250	A30	40c dp plum & org	.20	.20
251	A31	50c bl grn & org	.30	.30
252	A31	60c choc & dp yel	.30	.30
253	A31	80c vio bl & org	.30	.30
254	A32	1fr bl & choc	.30	.30
255	A32	1.20fr bl grn & ol grn	1.10	.85
256	A32	1.50fr org & vio bl	.45	.30
257	A33	2fr red lil & bl gray	.80	.65
258	A33	3fr dp bl & brn org	1.20	.85
259	A33	3.60fr car rose & cop red	2.10	1.75
260	A33	4fr choc & bl gray	1.60	1.10
261	A34	5fr org & choc	.95	.70
262	A34	6fr gray bl & int bl	1.60	.85
263	A34	10fr gray bl & red lil	1.60	.95
264	A35	15fr choc, gray bl & pink	1.90	1.20
265	A35	20fr dk bl, gray bl & org	2.50	1.50
266	A35	25fr vio brn, lil rose & gray bl	5.25	3.50
		Nos. 248-266 (19)	22.85	16.00

Military Medal Issue
Common Design Type

1952 Engraved and Typographed

267	CD101	15fr blk, grn, yel & dk pur	8.00	8.00

> **Imperforates**
> Most stamps of Somali Coast from 1956 onward exist imperforate in issued and trial colors, and also in small presentation sheets in issued colors.

FIDES Issue
Common Design Type and

Lighthouse, Ras-Bir — A36

15fr, Loading ship and map, Djibouti.

1956 Unwmk. Engr. Perf. 13

268	CD103	15fr purple	2.40	1.00
269	A36	40fr dp ultra & gray	3.25	1.75

Flower Issue
Common Design Type

Design: 10fr, Haemanthus, horiz.

1958 Photo. Perf. 12½x12

270	CD104	10fr grn, red & yel	3.25	1.10

Wart Hog — A37

40c, Cheetah. 50c, Gerenuk, vert.

1958 Engr. Perf. 13

271	A37	30c red brn & sepia	.70	.20
272	A37	40c brn & olive	.70	.30
273	A37	50c brn, grn & gray	.85	.45
		Nos. 271-273,C21 (4)	13.25	6.45

Human Rights Issue
Common Design Type

1958, Dec. 10 Unwmk.

274	CD105	20fr brt pur & dk bl	2.50	2.10

Universal Declaration of Human Rights, 10th anniv.

Parrotfish A38

Designs: Various Tropical Fish.

1959 Engr. Perf. 13

275	A38	1fr brt bl, brn & red org	.85	.55
276	A38	2fr blk, lt bl, yel & grn	.85	.55
277	A38	3fr vio & blk brn	.85	.55
278	A38	4fr brt grnsh bl, org & lt brn	1.10	.70
279	A38	5fr brt grnsh bl & blk	1.75	1.00
280	A38	20fr brt bl, dl red brn & rose	3.25	2.10
281	A38	25fr red, grn & bl	5.50	2.75
282	A38	60fr bl & dk grn	12.50	5.50
		Nos. 275-282 (8)	26.65	13.70

No. 276 is vertical.

Flamingo — A39

Birds: 15fr, Bee-eater, horiz. 30fr, Sacred ibis, horiz. 75fr, Pink-backed pelican.

1960 Unwmk. Perf. 13

283	A39	10fr bluish grn, bis & cl	2.75	1.40
284	A39	15fr rose lil, grn & yel	4.00	1.40
285	A39	30fr bl, blk, org & brn	8.75	4.50
286	A39	75fr grn, sl grn & yel	13.50	8.00
		Nos. 283-286 (4)	29.00	15.30

Dragon Tree — A40

Klipspringer A41 / Meleagrina Margaritifera A42

Designs: 4fr, Cony. 6fr, Large flatfish. 25fr, Fennecs. 40fr, Griffon vulture.

1962, Mar. 24 Engr. Perf. 13

287	A40	2fr grn, yel, org & brn	2.00	1.25
288	A40	4fr ocher & choc	2.25	1.40
289	A40	6fr brn, mar, grn & yel	4.50	2.75
290	A40	25fr red brn, ocher & grn	9.50	5.50
291	A40	40fr dk bl, brn & gray	12.50	8.00
292	A41	50fr bis, bl & lil	12.50	9.50
		Nos. 287-292 (6)	43.25	28.40

1962, Nov. 24 Photo.

Sea Shells: 10fr, Tridacna squamosa, horiz. 25fr, Strombus tricornis, horiz. 30fr, Trochus dentatus.

Shells in Natural Colors

293	A42	8fr red & blk	2.00	1.00
294	A42	10fr car rose & blk	2.00	1.25
295	A42	25fr dp bl & brn	4.50	1.75
296	A42	30fr rose lil & brn	4.50	2.25
		Nos. 293-296 (4)	13.00	6.25

See Nos. C28-C29.

Red Cross Centenary Issue
Common Design Type

1963, Sept. 2 Engr. Perf. 13

297	CD113	50fr org brn, gray & car	7.25	7.25

Astraea Coral — A43

Design: 6fr, Organ-pipe coral.

1963, Nov. 30 Photo. Perf. 13x13½

298	A43	5fr multi	2.00	1.40
299	A43	6fr multi	2.00	1.40

See Nos. C26-C27, C30.

Human Rights Issue
Common Design Type
1963, Dec. 20   **Engr.**   *Perf. 13*
300 CD117 70fr dk brn & ultra   9.00 9.00

Philatec Issue
Common Design Type
1964, Apr. 7   **Engr.**   *Perf. 13*
301 CD118 80fr dp lil rose, grn &
brn   8.75 8.75

Houri
(Somali
Sailboats)
A44

Design: 25fr, Sambouk (Somali sailboats).

1964, June 9   **Engr.**
302 A44 15fr multi   1.75 1.10
303 A44 25fr multi   2.50 1.60

View of
Dadwayya
and Map of
Somali
Coast
A45

Design: 20fr, View of Tadjourah and map of
Somali Coast.

1965, Oct. 20   **Engr.**   *Perf. 13*
304 A45 6fr ultra, sl grn & red
brn   1.00 .70
305 A45 20fr ultra, org brn & brt
grn   1.20 .95

Senna — A46

1966   **Engr.**   *Perf. 13*
306 A46 5fr shown   1.40 .95
307 A46 8fr Poinciana   1.40 .95
308 A46 25fr Aloe   1.90 1.60
Nos. 306-308,C41 (4)   9.70 6.75

Desert
Monitor
A47

1967, May 8   **Engr.**   *Perf. 13*
309 A47 20fr red brn, ocher &
sepia   5.50 4.75

Stamps of Somali Coast were replaced in
1967 by those of the French Territory of the
Afars and Issas.

SEMI-POSTAL STAMPS

Somali Girl — SP1

1915   **Unwmk.**   *Perf. 13½x14*
Chalky Paper
B1 SP1 10c + 5c car & dk red   9.50 8.75

Curie Issue
Common Design Type
1938   **Engr.**   *Perf. 13*
B2 CD80 1.75fr + 50c brt ultra   8.75 8.75

French Revolution Issue
Common Design Type
Photo., Name and Value Typo. in Black
1939
B3 CD83 45c + 25c green   10.00 10.00
B4 CD83 70c + 30c brown   10.00 10.00
B5 CD83 90c + 35c red org   10.00 10.00
B6 CD83 1.25fr + 1fr rose
pink   10.00 10.00
B7 CD83 2.25fr + 2fr blue   10.00 10.00
Nos. B3-B7 (5)   50.00 50.00

Common Design Type and

Somali
Guard
SP2

Local Police — SP3

1941   **Photo.**   *Perf. 13½*
B8 SP2 1fr + 1fr red   1.40
B9 CD86 1.50fr + 3fr maroon   1.40
B10 SP3 2.50fr + 1fr blue   1.40
Nos. B8-B10 (3)   4.20

Nos. B8-B10 were issued by the Vichy government in France, but were not placed on
sale in Somali Coast.

Nos. 181-182
Surcharged in Black or Red

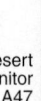

1944   **Engr.**   *Perf. 12x12½*
B11 50c + 1.50fr on 2.50fr deep
blue (R)   .80
B12 + 2.50fr on 1fr yellow brown   .80
Colonial Development Fund.
Nos. B11-B12 were issued by the Vichy
government in France, but were not placed on
sale in Somali Coast.

> **Catalogue values for unused
> stamps in this section, from this
> point to the end of the section, are
> for Never Hinged items.**

Red Cross Issue
Common Design Type
Inscribed "Djibouti"
1944   *Perf. 14½x14*
B13 CD90 5fr + 20fr emerald   1.75 1.75

The surtax was for the French Red Cross
and national relief.

Tropical Medicine Issue
Common Design Type
1950   **Engr.**   *Perf. 13*
B14 CD100 10fr + 2fr red brn &
red   6.50 6.50

The surtax was for charitable work.

Anti-Malaria Issue
Common Design Type
1962, Apr. 7   **Unwmk.**   *Perf. 13*
B15 CD108 25fr + 5fr aqua   7.00 7.00

Infant, Sun,
Chest and
Skulls
SP4

1965, Dec. 10   **Engr.**   *Perf. 13*
B16 SP4 25fr + 5fr ocher, sl & brt
grn   2.50 2.50

Campaign against tuberculosis.

AIR POST STAMPS

> **Catalogue values for unused
> stamps in this section are for
> Never Hinged items.**

Common Design Type
Inscribed "Djibouti"
1941 Unwmk. Photo. *Perf. 14½x14*
C1 CD87 1fr dk orange   1.10 .85
C2 CD87 1.50fr brt red   1.20 .95
C3 CD87 5fr brown red   1.50 1.20
C4 CD87 10fr black   1.75 1.40
C5 CD87 25fr ultra   2.90 2.25
C6 CD87 50fr dark green   2.75 2.10
C7 CD87 100fr plum   3.00 3.00
Nos. C1-C7 (7)   14.20 11.75

Obock & Djibouti

1943, June 21   **Engr.**   *Perf. 13*
C7A 1.50fr red brown   1.00
C7B 4fr ultramarine   1.00
50th Ann. of transfer of capital from Obock
to Djibouti.
Nos. C7A-C7B were issued by the Vichy
government in France, but were not placed on
sale in Somali Coast.

Victory Issue
Common Design Type
1946   *Perf. 12½*
C8 CD92 8fr deep blue   2.00 1.40

Chad to Rhine Issue
Common Design Types
1946
C9 CD93 5fr gray black   2.40 1.75
C10 CD94 10fr dp orange   2.40 1.75
C11 CD95 15fr violet brn   2.40 1.75
C12 CD96 20fr brt violet   2.40 1.75
C13 CD97 25fr blue green   4.50 3.50
C14 CD98 50fr lt ultra   5.00 3.50
Nos. C9-C14 (6)   19.10 14.00

Somali Gazing
Skyward — AP1

Frontier Post, Loyada — AP2

Governor's Mansion, Djibouti — AP3

Perf. 12½x13, 13x12½
1947   **Photo.**   **Unwmk.**
C15 AP1 50fr gray bl & choc   6.75 1.40
C16 AP2 100fr multicolored   8.00 3.00
C17 AP3 200fr multicolored   11.50 4.50
Nos. C15-C17 (3)   26.25 8.90

UPU Issue
Common Design Type
1949   **Engr.**   *Perf. 13*
C18 CD99 30fr bl, dp bl, brn
red & grn   12.50 10.50

Liberation Issue
Common Design Type
1954, June 6
C19 CD102 15fr indigo & purple   8.75 8.75

Somali Woman and Map of
Djibouti — AP4

1956, Feb. 20   **Unwmk.**
C20 AP4 500fr dk vio & rose
vio   67.50 55.00

Mountain Reedbucks — AP5

1958, July 7   **Engr.**   *Perf. 13*
C21 AP5 100fr ultra, lt grn & dk
red brn   11.00 5.50

Albert Bernard, Flag and
Troops — AP6

1960, Jan. 18
C22 AP6 55fr ultra, sepia & car   2.50 1.60
25th death anniv. of Administrator Albert
Bernard at Moraito.

Great Bustard — AP7

1960, Oct. 24   Unwmk.   Perf. 13
C23 AP7 200fr brn, org & slate 25.00 17.50

Salt Dealers' Caravan at Assal
Lake — AP8

1962, Jan. 6   Engr.   Perf. 13
C24 AP8 500fr dk bl, red brn,
pink & blk 27.50 17.50

Obock — AP9

1962, Mar. 11   Unwmk.   Perf. 13
C25 AP9 100fr blue & org brn 5.50 3.50
Centenary of the founding of Obock.

Rostellaria Magna — AP10

40fr, Millepore coral. 55fr, Brain coral. 100fr,
Lambis bryonia (seashell). 200fr, Branch
coral.

1962-63   Photo.   Perf. 13½x12½
C26 AP10 40fr multi ('63) 3.75 1.40
C27 AP10 55fr multi ('63) 5.50 3.25
C28 AP10 60fr multi 6.75 2.75
C29 AP10 100fr multi 10.50 5.25
C30 AP10 200fr multi ('63) 13.50 8.00
Nos. C26-C30 (5) 40.00 20.65

Telstar Issue
Common Design Type
1963, Feb. 9   Engr.   Perf. 13
C31 CD111 20fr dp claret & dk
grn 1.00 1.00

Zaroug (Somali Sailboats) — AP11

Designs: 50fr, Sambouk (boat) building.
300fr, Zeima sailboat.

1964-65   Engr.   Perf. 13
C32 AP11 50fr blue, ocher &
choc 4.00 2.00
C33 AP11 85fr dk Prus grn,
dk brn &
mag 5.50 2.50
C34 AP11 300fr ultra, lt brn &
bl grn ('65) 16.00 8.00
Nos. C32-C34 (3) 25.50 12.50

Discus
Thrower — AP12

1964, Oct. 10   Engr.
C35 AP12 90fr rose lil, red brn
& blk 11.00 8.75
18th Olympic Games, Tokyo, Oct. 10-25.

ITU Issue
Common Design Type
1965, May 17
C36 CD120 95fr lil rose, brt bl
& lt brn 17.50 10.00

Camels in Ghoubet Kharab and Map
of Somali Coast — AP13

1965   Engr.   Perf. 13
C37 AP13 45fr Abbe Lake 3.25 1.75
C38 AP13 65fr shown 4.25 1.75
Issue dates: 45fr, Oct. 20; 65fr, July 16.

French Satellite A-1 Issue
Common Design Type
Designs: 25fr, Diamant rocket and launch-
ing installations. 30fr, A-1 satellite.

1966, Jan. 28   Engr.   Perf. 13
C39 CD121 25fr redsh brn, ol brn
& dl red 3.25 3.25
C40 CD121 30fr ol brn, dl red &
redsh brn 3.25 3.25
a.   Strip of 2, #C39-C40 + label 9.00 9.00
Each sheet contains 16 triptychs (2x8).

Stapelia — AP14

1966   Engr.   Perf. 13
C41 AP14 55fr sl grn, dl mag &
emer 5.00 3.25

Feather Starfish
and
Coral — AP15

Fish: 25fr, Regal angelfish. 40fr, Pomo-
canthops filamentosus. 50fr, Amphiprion
ephippium. 70fr, Squirrelfish. 80fr, Surgeonfish. 100fr, Pterois lunulatus.

1966   Photo.   Perf. 13
C42 AP15 8fr multicolored 2.00 2.00
C43 AP15 25fr multicolored 4.25 4.25
C44 AP15 40fr multicolored 6.00 6.00
C45 AP15 50fr multicolored 8.00 8.00
C46 AP15 70fr multicolored 13.50 13.50

C47 AP15 80fr multicolored 16.00 16.00
C48 AP15 100fr multicolored 21.00 21.00
Nos. C42-C48 (7) 70.75 70.75

French Satellite D-1 Issue
Common Design Type
1966, June 10   Engr.   Perf. 13
C49 CD122 48fr dk brn, brt bl &
grn 4.75 2.75

AIR POST SEMI-POSTAL STAMPS

Catalogue values for unused
stamps in this section are for
Never Hinged items.

SPAP1

Unwmk.
1942, June 22   Engr.   Perf. 13
CB1 SPAP1 1.50f+ 3.50fr green 1.75
CB2 SPAP1 2fr + 6fr brown 1.75
Native children's welfare fund.
Nos. CB1-CB2 were issued by the Vichy
government in France, but were not placed on
sale in Somali Coast

Colonial Education Fund
Common Design Type
1942, June 22
CB3 CD86a 1.20fr + 1.80fr blue
& red 1.75
No. CB3 was issued by the Vichy govern-
ment in France, but was not placed on sale in
Somali Coast.

Pharaoh Sacrificing before Horus and
Hathor — SPAP2

Unwmk.
1964, Aug. 28   Engr.   Perf. 13
CB4 SPAP2 25fr + 5fr multi 9.50 8.75
UNESCO world campaign to save historic
monuments in Nubia.

POSTAGE DUE STAMPS

D1

1915   Unwmk.   Typo.   Perf. 14x13½
Chalky Paper
J1 D1 5c deep ultra .30 .40
J2 D1 10c brown red .55 .65
J3 D1 15c black .80 1.00
J4 D1 20c purple 1.60 1.75
J5 D1 30c orange 1.60 1.75
J6 D1 50c maroon 3.00 3.25
J7 D1 60c green 4.50 4.75
J8 D1 1fr dark blue 5.25 5.50
Nos. J1-J8 (8) 17.60 19.05
See Nos. J11-J20.

Type of 1915 Issue
Surcharged

1927
J9 D1 2fr on 1fr light red 8.75 8.75
J10 D1 3fr on 1fr lilac rose 8.75 8.75

Type of 1915
1938   Engr.   Perf. 12½x13
J11 D1 5c light ultra .20 .20
J12 D1 10c dark carmine .20 .20
J13 D1 15c brown black .30 .30
J14 D1 20c violet .30 .30
J15 D1 30c orange yellow 1.10 1.10
J16 D1 50c brown .70 .70
J17 D1 60c emerald 1.10 1.10
J18 D1 1fr indigo 2.25 2.25
J19 D1 2fr red 1.00 1.00
J20 D1 3fr dark brown 1.40 1.40
Nos. J11-J20 (10) 8.55 8.55
Set, never hinged 12.50
Inscribed "Inst de Grav" below design.

Postage Due Stamps of
1915 Overprinted in
Red or Black

1943   Unwmk.   Perf. 14x13½
J21 D1 5c ultra (R) 2.00 2.00
J22 D1 10c brown red 2.00 2.00
J23 D1 15c black (R) 2.00 2.00
J24 D1 20c purple 2.00 2.00
J25 D1 30c orange 2.00 2.00
J26 D1 50c maroon 2.00 2.00
J27 D1 60c green 2.00 2.00
J28 D1 1fr dark blue (R) 8.00 8.00
Nos. J21-J28 (8) 22.00 22.00
Set, never hinged 32.50

Postage Due Stamps
of 1938 Overprinted in
Red or Black

1943   Perf. 12½x13
J29 D1 5c lt ultra (R) 2.00 2.00
J30 D1 10c dark car 2.00 2.00
J31 D1 15c brn blk (R) 2.00 2.00
J32 D1 20c violet 2.00 2.00
J33 D1 30c org yel 2.00 2.00
J34 D1 50c brown 2.00 2.00
J35 D1 60c emerald 2.00 2.00
J36 D1 1fr indigo (R) 2.40 2.40
J37 D1 2fr red 9.25 9.25
J38 D1 3fr dk brn (R) 10.00 10.00
Nos. J29-J38 (10) 35.65 35.65
Set, never hinged 55.00
For type D1 without "RF," see Nos. J38A-
J38E.

Type D1 Without "RF"
Engraved, Values Typo
1944, Apr. 3
J38A D1 30c org yel & lilac .30
J38B D1 50c yel brn & blk brn .30
J38C D1 60c grn & dk grn .65
J38D D1 2fr red & rose .70
J38E D1 3fr sepia & blk 120.00
Nos. J38A-J38E (5) 121.95
Nos. J38A-J38E were issued by the Vichy
government in France, but were not placed on
sale in Somali Coast.

Catalogue values for unused
stamps in this section, from this
point to the end of the section, are
for Never Hinged items.

D2

1947		Photo.		Perf. 13½x13	
J39	D2	10c	purple	.40	.20
J40	D2	30c	brown	.40	.20
J41	D2	50c	green	.65	.45
J42	D2	1fr	deep orange	.65	.45
J43	D2	2fr	lilac rose	.95	.80
J44	D2	3fr	dk org brn	.95	.80
J45	D2	4fr	blue	1.10	.95
J46	D2	5fr	orange red	1.10	.95
J47	D2	10fr	olive green	1.10	.95
J48	D2	20fr	blue violet	2.60	2.10
		Nos. J39-J48 (10)		9.90	7.85

SOMALILAND PROTECTORATE

sō-ʹmä-lē-ˌland

prə-ʹtek-tˌə-ˌrət

LOCATION — Eastern Africa, bordering on the Gulf of Aden
GOVT. — British Protectorate
AREA — 68,000 sq. mi.
POP. — 640,000 (estimated)
CAPITAL — Hargeisa

Formerly administered by the Indian Government, the territory was taken over by the British Foreign Office in 1898 and transferred to the Colonial Office in 1905.

Somaliland Protectorate became part of independent Somalia in 1960.

16 Annas = 1 Rupee
100 Cents = 1 Shilling (1951)

Catalogue values for unused stamps in this country are for Never Hinged items, beginning with Scott 108.

Stamps of India, 1882-1900, Overprinted at Top of Stamp

1903		Wmk. 39		Perf. 14	
1	A17	½a light green		3.00	4.50
2	A19	1a carmine rose		3.00	4.00
3	A21	2a violet		2.50	1.60
a.		Double overprint		725.00	
4	A28	2½a ultra		2.25	1.90
5	A22	3a brown orange		3.50	3.50
6	A23	4a olive green		4.00	3.00
7	A25	8a red violet		4.25	5.50
8	A26	12a brown, red		3.50	8.00
a.		Inverted overprint			1,200.
9	A29	1r car rose & grn		7.50	11.00
10	A30	2r yel brn & car rose		38.00	52.50
11	A30	3r green & brown		36.00	62.50
12	A30	5r violet & blue		59.00	72.50
Wmk. Elephant's Head (38)					
13	A14	6a bister		5.50	5.25
		Nos. 1-13 (13)		172.00	235.75

Nos. 1-5 exist without the 2nd "I" of "BRITISH."

Same, but Overprinted at Bottom of Stamp

1903		Wmk. 39			
14	A28	2½a ultra		3.50	7.25
15	A26	12a violet, red		13.00	14.00
16	A29	1r car rose & grn		4.00	17.50
17	A30	2r yel brn & car rose		110.00	175.00
18	A30	3r green & brn		105.00	175.00
a.		Inverted overprint		750.00	
19	A30	5r violet & blue		100.00	140.00
Wmk. 38					
20	A14	6a bister		8.50	8.00
		Nos. 14-20 (7)		344.00	536.75

Stamps of India, 1902-03, Ovptd.

1903		Wmk. 39			
21	A33	½a light green		2.50	.60
22	A34	1a car rose		1.40	.35
23	A35	2a violet		1.90	2.75
24	A37	3a brown orange		2.75	2.75
25	A38	4a olive green		1.60	4.50
26	A40	8a red violet		1.90	2.50
		Nos. 21-26 (6)		12.05	13.45

The above overprints vary in length, also in the relative positions of the letters. Nos. 21-23 exist without the second "I" of "British."

A1

King Edward VII — A2

1904		Wmk. 2		Typo.	
27	A1	½a dl grn & grn		2.10	4.50
28	A1	1a carmine & blk		13.00	3.50
29	A1	2a red vio & dull vio		2.25	2.40
30	A1	2½a ultramarine		4.50	4.00
31	A1	3a gray grn & vio brn		2.40	2.75
32	A1	4a black & gray grn		2.50	5.00
33	A1	6a vio & gray grn		5.75	18.00
34	A1	8a pale blue & blk		4.50	5.75
35	A1	12a ocher & blk		7.50	11.50
Wmk. Crown and C C (1)					
36	A2	1r gray grn		14.00	47.50
37	A2	2r red vio & dull vio		50.00	85.00
38	A2	3r blk & gray grn		52.50	120.00
39	A2	5r carmine & blk		52.50	120.00
		Nos. 27-39 (13)		213.50	429.90

1905				Wmk. 3	
40	A1	½a dl grn & grn		2.00	8.00
41	A1	1a carmine & blk		13.00	1.75
42	A1	2a red vio & dull vio		8.25	10.00
43	A1	2½a ultramarine		4.50	11.00
44	A1	3a gray grn & vio brn		2.50	16.00
45	A1	4a black & gray		5.00	16.00
46	A1	6a violet & gray grn		6.00	27.50
47	A1	8a pale blue & blk		6.75	10.00
48	A1	12a ocher & black		7.25	11.00
		Nos. 40-48 (9)		55.25	111.25

Nos. 41, 42, 44-48 are on both ordinary and chalky paper.

1909					
49	A1	½a bluish green		30.00	32.50
50	A1	1a carmine		3.00	2.25

For overprints see Nos. O11-O16.

King George V
A3   A4

The ½, 1 and 2½a of type A3 are on ordinary paper, the other values of types A3 and A4 are on chalky paper.

1912-19					
51	A3	½a green		.90	9.25
52	A3	1a carmine		3.00	.60
53	A3	2a red vio & dull vio		4.25	16.00
54	A3	2½a ultramarine		1.25	9.75
55	A3	3a gray grn & vio brn		2.75	7.50
56	A3	4a blk & grn ('13)		3.00	11.50
57	A3	6a violet & green		3.00	5.75
58	A3	8a lt blue & blk		4.25	17.50
59	A3	12a ocher & blk		4.00	24.00
60	A4	1r dull grn & blk		15.00	18.00
61	A4	2r red vio & dull vio ('19)		25.00	80.00
62	A4	3r blk & gray grn ('19)		75.00	150.00
63	A4	5r car & blk ('19)		72.50	190.00
		Nos. 51-63 (13)		213.90	539.85

1921				Wmk. 4	
64	A3	½a blue green		3.25	11.50
65	A3	1a scarlet		4.25	.80
66	A3	2a vio & dull vio		5.00	1.10
67	A3	2½a ultramarine		1.25	5.25
68	A3	3a gray grn & vio brown		3.00	8.50
69	A3	4a black & grn		3.00	8.50
70	A3	6a violet & grn		2.00	15.00

71	A3	8a lt blue & blk	2.50	6.25
72	A3	12a ocher & blk	11.00	17.50
73	A4	1r dull grn & grn	10.00	55.00
74	A4	2r vio & dull vio	30.00	62.50
75	A4	3r blk & gray grn	42.50	125.00
76	A4	5r scarlet & blk	82.50	200.00
		Nos. 64-76 (13)	200.25	516.90

Common Design Types
pictured following the introduction.

Silver Jubilee Issue
Common Design Type

1935, May 6		Engr.		Perf. 11x12	
77	CD301	1a car & dk blue		2.75	3.75
78	CD301	2a black & ultra		3.25	3.75
79	CD301	3a ultra & brown		2.75	16.00
80	CD301	1r brown vio & ind		8.00	18.00
		Nos. 77-80 (4)		16.75	41.50
		Set, never hinged		30.00	

Coronation Issue
Common Design Type

1937, May 13				Perf. 13½x14	
81	CD302	1a carmine		.20	.25
82	CD302	2a black		.35	1.75
83	CD302	3a bright ultra		.40	.90
		Nos. 81-83 (3)		.95	2.90
		Set, never hinged		2.25	

Blackhead Sheep — A5

Greater Kudu — A6

Map of Somaliland Protectorate
A7

1938, May 10		Wmk. 4		Perf. 12½	
84	A5	½a green		.30	5.50
85	A5	1a carmine		.30	1.60
86	A5	2a deep claret		1.75	1.90
87	A5	3a ultra		7.00	15.00
88	A6	4a dark brown		4.00	8.75
89	A6	6a purple		6.00	13.00
90	A6	8a gray black		1.50	13.50
91	A6	12a orange		6.50	25.00
92	A7	1r green		7.50	65.00
93	A7	2r rose violet		14.00	65.00
94	A7	3r ultramarine		16.00	42.50
95	A7	5r black		17.50	42.50
a.		Horiz. pair, imperf. btwn.		13,000.	
		Nos. 84-95 (12)		82.35	299.25
		Set, never hinged		130.00	

A10

1942, Apr. 22					
96	A8	½a green		.25	.50
97	A8	1a carmine		.25	.20
98	A8	2a deep claret		.50	.25
99	A8	3a ultramarine		1.50	.25
100	A9	4a dark brown		2.25	.25
101	A9	6a purple		2.25	.25
102	A9	8a gray		2.50	.25
103	A9	12a orange		2.50	.65
104	A10	1r green		1.50	1.75
105	A10	2r rose violet		1.50	7.00

106	A10	3r ultra	2.75	13.00
107	A10	5r black	7.00	10.00
		Nos. 96-107 (12)	24.75	34.35
		Set, never hinged	42.50	

For surcharges see Nos. 116-126.

Catalogue values for unused stamps in this section, from this point to the end of the section, are for Never Hinged items.

Peace Issue
Common Design Type

		Perf. 13½x14			
1946, Oct. 15		Engr.		Wmk. 4	
108	CD303	1a carmine		.20	.20
a.		Perf. 13½		20.00	70.00
109	CD303	3a deep blue		.20	.20

Silver Wedding Issue
Common Design Types

1949, Jan. 28		Photo.		Perf. 14x14½	
110	CD304	1a scarlet		.25	.20

Engraved; Name Typographed
Perf. 11½x11

111	CD305	5r gray black		7.00	9.25

UPU Issue
Common Design Types
Surcharged in Black or Carmine with New Values in Annas

1949, Oct. 10		Engr.; Name Typo. on 3a, 6a		Perf. 13½, 11x11½	
112	CD306	1a on 10c rose car		.25	.20
113	CD307	3a on 30c ind (C)		1.40	.25
114	CD308	6a on 50c rose vio		.50	1.10
115	CD309	12a on 1sh red org		.50	.60
		Nos. 112-115 (4)		2.65	2.75

Nos. 96 and 98 to 107 Surcharged with New Value in Black or Carmine

1951, Apr. 2		Wmk. 4		Perf. 12½	
116	A8	5c on ½a green		.40	2.00
117	A8	10c on 2a deep claret		.40	.50
118	A8	15c on 3a ultramarine		1.40	2.00
119	A9	20c on 4a dark brown		2.40	.25
120	A9	30c on 6a purple		2.25	.60
121	A9	50c on 8a gray		2.75	.25
122	A9	70c on 12a red		4.75	6.25
123	A10	1sh on 1r green		2.50	.65
124	A10	2sh on 2r rose violet		6.50	19.00
125	A10	3sh on 3r ultra		9.00	7.00
126	A10	5sh on 5r black (C)		13.00	12.00
		Nos. 116-126 (11)		45.35	50.50

Coronation Issue
Common Design Type

1953, June 2		Engr.		Perf. 13½x13	
127	CD312	15c dark green & blk		.35	.20

Camel Carrying Somali House
A11

Askari Militiaman
A12

Designs: 35c, 2sh, Rock Pigeon. 50c, 5sh, Martial eagle. 1sh, Blackhead sheep. 1sh30c, Tomb of Sheik Isaaq, Mait. 10sh, Taleh Fort.

1953-58		Engr.		Perf. 12½	
128	A11	5c gray		.20	.50
129	A12	10c red orange		2.50	.60
130	A11	15c blue green		.70	.40
131	A11	20c rose red		.70	.40
132	A12	30c lt chocolate		2.50	.40
133	A11	35c blue		5.75	2.00
134	A11	50c lil rose & brn		5.75	.55
135	A11	1sh grnsh blue		.70	.40
136	A11	1sh30c dark gray & ultra ('58)		12.50	3.75
137	A11	2sh violet & brn		30.00	7.00
138	A11	5sh emer & brn		32.50	7.50
139	A11	10sh rose lilac & brn		20.00	24.50
		Nos. 128-139 (12)		113.80	48.10

Nos. 131 and 135 Overprinted: "Opening of the Legislative Council 1957"

1957, May 21					
140	A11	20c rose red		.20	.20
141	A11	1sh greenish blue		.35	.40

Nos. 131 and 136 Overprinted:
"Legislative Council Unofficial
Majority, 1960"

1960, Apr. 5
142	A11	20c rose red	.20	.20
143	A11	1sh30c dk gray & ultra	.90	.30

Changes in the Legislative Council.

Three stamps of Somalia were overprinted "Somaliland Independence 26 June 1960" and issued in Hargeisa on that day. Somaliland Protectorate became part of Somalia on July 1, 1960. These three stamps are listed in Vol. 5 as Somalia Nos. 242, C68-C69.

Stamps of Somaliland Protectorate were replaced by those of Somalia in 1960.

OFFICIAL STAMPS

Official Stamps of India,
1883-1900, Overprinted

1903, June 1   Wmk. 39   Perf. 14
O1	A17	½a light green	7.50	55.00
O2	A19	1a carmine rose	17.50	9.25
O3	A21	2a violet	9.25	55.00
O4	A25	8a red violet	11.50	425.00
O5	A29	1r car rose & grn	11.50	625.00
		Nos. O1-O5 (5)	57.25	1,169.

India Nos. 61-63, 68, 49
Overprinted

1903
O6	A33	½a green	.50
O7	A34	1a carmine rose	.50
O8	A35	2a violet	.80
O9	A40	8a red violet	5.00
O10	A29	1r car rose & grn	20.00
		Nos. O6-O10 (5)	26.80

Nos. O6-O10 were not regularly issued.

Regular Issue of 1904
Overprinted

1904   Wmk. Crown and C A (2)
O11	A1	½a gray green	4.75	55.00
O12	A1	1a carmine & blk	3.75	8.00
O13	A1	2a red vio & dull vio	200.00	70.00
O14	A1	8a pale blue & blk	70.00	150.00
		Nos. O11-O14 (4)	278.50	283.00

Wmk. Crown and C C (1)
O15	A2	1r gray green	190.00	675.00

Same Overprint on No. 42

1905   Wmk. 3
O16	A1	2a red vio & dull vio	90.00	900.00

The period after "M" may be found missing on Nos. O11-O14 and O16.

SOUTH AFRICA

sauth 'a-fri-kə

LOCATION — Southern Africa
GOVT. — Republic
AREA — 472,730 sq. mi.
POP. — 43,426,386 (1999 est.)
CAPITAL — Pretoria (administrative); Cape Town (legislative); Bloemfontein (Judicial)

The union was formed on May 31, 1910, comprising the former British colonies of Cape of Good Hope, Natal, Transvaal and the Orange Free State, which became provinces. The union became a republic in 1961.

For previous listings, see individual headings.

12 Pence = 1 Shilling
20 Shillings = 1 Pound
100 Cents = 1 Rand (1961)

Catalogue values for unused stamps in this country are for Never Hinged items, beginning with Scott 74 in the regular postage section, Scott B1 in the semipostal section, Scott J30 in the postage due section, and Scott O21 in the officials section.

Watermarks

Wmk. 47 —
Multiple Rosette

Wmk. 177 —
Springbok's Head

Wmk. 201 — Multiple Springbok's Head

Wmk. 330 —
Coat of Arms,
Multiple

Wmk. 348 — RSA in Triangle, Multiple

Wmk. 359 — RSA in Triangle, Tete Beche

George V
A1   A2

1910   Engr.   Wmk. 47   Perf. 14
1	A1	2½p blue	3.00	1.75

Union Parliament opening, Nov. 4, 1910.

Type A2 stamps have very small margins at top and bottom. Values are for copies with perfs close to, or touching the frame.

1913-24   Typo.   Wmk. 177
2	A2	½p green	1.50	.20
a.		Double impression	15,000.	
3	A2	1p scarlet	1.50	.20
4	A2	1½p org brn ('20)	.75	.20
a.		Tête bêche pair	4.50	15.00
5	A2	2p dull violet	2.25	.20
6	A2	2½p ultra	5.50	1.60
7	A2	3p brn org & blk	13.00	.55
8	A2	3p ultra ('22)	4.75	1.60
9	A2	4p ol grn & org	11.00	.55
10	A2	6p violet & blk	9.50	.70
11	A2	1sh orange	20.00	.70
12	A2	1sh3p violet ('20)	17.50	11.00
13	A2	2sh6p green & cl	70.00	5.50
14	A2	5sh blue & claret	140.00	9.00
15	A2	10sh ol grn & blue	225.00	14.50
16	A2	£1 red & dp grn ('16)	850.00	450.00
a.		£1 lt red & gray green ('24)	1,100.	1,600.
		Nos. 2-16 (15)	1,372.	496.50

The ½p, 1p and 1½p have the words "Revenue" and "Inkomst" on the stamps. On other stamps of this type these words are replaced by short vertical lines.

All values exist in many shades. No. 4a exists with and without gutter between.

Unwatermarked copies of the 1p are the result of misplaced watermarks.

All values except the 2sh6p and £1 exist with watermark inverted.

For overprint see No. O1.

Coil Stamps
Perf. 14 Horizontally
17	A2	½p green	9.25	1.90
18	A2	1p scarlet ('14)	11.50	6.25
19	A2	1½p org brown ('20)	17.00	27.50
20	A2	2p dull violet ('21)	18.00	9.00
		Nos. 17-20 (4)	55.75	44.65

"Hope" — A3

Design: No. 22, inscribed SUIDAFRIKA.

1926   Engr.   Wmk. 201   Imperf.
21	A3	4p blue gray	2.00	1.40
22	A3	4p blue gray	2.00	1.40

Nos. 21 and 22 were privately rouletted and perforated, but such varieties were not officially made.

No. 21 (English inscription) was printed in a separate sheet from No. 22 (Afrikaans inscription).

English-Afrikaans Se-Tenant

Stamps with English inscriptions and with Afrikaans inscriptions were printed alternately in the same sheets, starting with No. 23. Major-number listings and values are for horizontal pairs (vertical pairs sell for about one-third less) of such stamps consisting of one English and one Afrikaans-inscribed stamp, unless otherwise described.

Values are for pairs with no fold marks between stamps and no perf separations.

Beware of pairs that have been rejoined.

Springbok
A5

Jan van Riebeek's Ship,
Drommedaris — A6

Orange
Tree — A7

1926   Typo.   Perf. 14½x14
23	A5	½p dk grn & blk, pair	3.00	3.50
a.		Single, English	.25	.20
b.		Single, Afrikaans	.25	.20
c.		Tete beche pair	1,500.	
d.		Center omitted	1,400.	
e.		Booklet pane of 6	190.00	
f.		As "e," perf. 14	300.00	
24	A6	1p car & blk, pair	3.00	3.00
a.		Single, English	.25	.20
b.		Single, Afrikaans	.25	.20
c.		Imperf., pair	1,350.	
d.		Tete beche pair	1,750.	
e.		Center omitted	275.00	
f.		Booklet pane of 6	160.00	
g.		As "f," perf. 14	250.00	
25	A7	6p org & grn, pair	42.50	47.50
a.		Single, English	3.00	2.25
b.		Single, Afrikaans	3.00	2.25
		Nos. 23-25 (3)	48.50	54.00

Nos. 23c and 24d are from uncut sheets printed for the perf. 14 booklet panes of 1928, Nos. 23f and 24g.

See Nos. 33-35, 42, 45-50, 59-61, 98-99. For overprints see Nos. O2-O4, O6-O9, O12-O15, O18, O21-O25, O30-O32, O42-O45, O48.

Government Buildings, Pretoria — A8

"Groote Schuur," Rhodes's Home — A9

Native Kraal — A10

Gnu — A11

Trekking — A12

Ox Wagon — A13

Cape Town and Table Mountain — A14

Perf. 14, 14x13½

				Engr.	Wmk. 201
1927-28					
26	A8	2p vio brn & gray, pair		13.50	26.00
a.		Single, English		2.10	1.40
b.		Single, Afrikaans		2.10	1.40
27	A9	3p red & blk, pair		24.00	37.50
a.		Single, English		2.10	1.40
b.		Single, Afrikaans		2.10	1.40
c.		Perf. 14x13½, pair		67.50	82.50
d.		As "c", single, English		3.25	2.75
e.		As "c", single, Afrikaans		3.25	2.75
28	A10	4p brown, pair ('28)		32.50	67.50
a.		Single, English		3.25	1.90
b.		Single, Afrikaans		3.25	1.90
29	A11	1sh dp bl & bis brn, pair		47.50	87.50
a.		Single, English		6.75	2.75
b.		Single, Afrikaans		6.75	2.75
30	A12	2sh6p brn & bl grn, pair		140.00	400.00
a.		Single, English		20.00	24.00
b.		Single, Afrikaans		20.00	24.00
c.		Perf. 14x13½, pair		475.00	675.00
d.		As "c", single, English		32.50	37.50
e.		As "c", single, Afrikaans		32.50	37.50
31	A13	5sh dp grn & blk, pair		275.00	650.00
a.		Single, English		30.00	40.00
b.		Single, Afrikaans		30.00	40.00
c.		Perf. 14x13½, pair		525.00	750.00
d.		As "c", single, English		47.50	52.50
e.		As "c", single, Afrikaans		47.50	52.50
32	A14	10sh ol brn & bl, pair		200.00	200.00
a.		Single, English		20.00	16.00
b.		Single, Afrikaans		20.00	16.00
c.		Perf. 14x13½, pair		275.00	375.00
d.		As "c", single, English		24.00	20.00
e.		As "c", single, Afrikaans		24.00	20.00
		Nos. 26-32 (7)		732.50	1,468.

See Nos. 36-41, 43-44, 53-54, 58, 62-66. For overprints see Nos. O5, O10-O111, O16-O17, O19-O20, O28, O33-O35, O39, O41, O49-O53.

Types of 1926-28 Redrawn "SUIDAFRIKA" (No Hyphen) on Afrikaans Stamps

The photogravure, unhyphenated stamps of 1930-45 are distinguished from the 1926-28 typographed or engraved stamps (also unhyphenated) by the following characteristics:

½p, 1p, 6p. Leg of "R" in AFRICA or AFRIKA ends in a straight line in the photogravure set; in a curved line in the typographed set. No. 35 differs from No. 34, having 2mm space between POSSEEL—INKOMSTE instead of 1mm.

2p. A memorial statue has been added just above and leftward of the "2" in value tablet on Nos. 36-37 (photogravure).

3p. Top frame on No. 38 consists of 3 heavy lines. On No. 27 it has 3 heavy and 2 very thin lines.

4p. On Nos. 40-41 the background in upper corners is solid. On No. 28 it consists of horizontal and vertical lines. No. 41 has pretzel-shaped scroll endings at bottom. On No. 40 these scroll endings enclose a solid mass of color.

1sh. No. 43 has no fine shading lines projecting from the curved top of the left inner frame, as No. 29 has. On No. 43 the shading of the last "A" of the country name partly covers the flower below it.

2sh6p. On No. 44 the shading below the country name is solid or shows signs of wear. On No. 30 it is composed of fine lines.

The engraved pictorials are much more finely executed and show details more clearly than the photogravure.

Perf. 15x14 (½p, 1p, 6p), 14

				Photo.	Wmk. 201
1930-45					
33	A5	½p bl grn & blk, pair		3.50	3.50
a.		Single, English		.20	.20
b.		Single, Afrikaans		.20	.20
c.		Tete-beche pair		1,250.	
d.		As "c", gutter between		1,750.	
e.		Booklet pane of 6		40.00	40.00
f.		Vert. pair, monolingual		5.00	5.00
34	A6	1p car & blk, pair		4.00	3.50
a.		Single, English		.20	.20
b.		Single, Afrikaans		.20	.20
c.		Center omitted		2,500.	
d.		Frame omitted		2,500.	
e.		Tete-beche pair		1,800.	
f.		As "e", gutter between		1,500.	
g.		Booklet pane of 6		16.00	16.00
35	A6	1p rose & blk, pair ('32)		35.00	4.50
a.		Single, English		1.00	.20
b.		Single, Afrikaans		1.00	.20
c.		Center omitted		750.00	
36	A8	2p vio & gray, pair ('31)		24.00	16.00
a.		Single, English		1.10	.40
b.		Single, Afrikaans		1.10	.40
c.		Frame omitted		1,000.	
d.		Tete-beche pair		6,500.	
e.		Booklet pane of 4		200.00	200.00
37	A8	2p vio & ind, pair ('38)		250.00	100.00
a.		Single, English		12.50	7.25
b.		Single, Afrikaans		12.50	7.25
38	A9	3p red & blk, pair ('31)		72.50	95.00
a.		Single, English		6.75	6.75
b.		Single, Afrikaans		6.75	6.75
39	A9	3p ultra & bl, pair ('33)		22.50	10.00
a.		Single, English		1.10	.80
b.		Single, Afrikaans		1.10	.80
c.		Center omitted		1,000.	
40	A10	4p redsh brn, pair ('32)		250.00	210.00
a.		Single, English		25.00	11.00
b.		Single, Afrikaans		25.00	11.00
41	A10	4p brn, pair ('36)		6.50	5.00
a.		Single, English		1.10	.45
b.		Single, Afrikaans		1.10	.45
42	A7	6p org & grn, pair ('31)		29.00	6.50
a.		Single, English		1.10	.45
b.		Single, Afrikaans		1.10	.45
43	A11	1sh dl bl & yel brn, pair		140.00	57.50
a.		Single, English		7.25	1.10
b.		Single, Afrikaans		7.25	1.10
c.		1sh dp bl & brn, pair ('32)		72.50	32.50
d.		As "c", single, English		5.25	.40
e.		As "c", single, Afrikaans		5.25	.40
44	A12	2sh 6p brn & bl, pair ('45)		29.00	19.00
a.		Single, English		1.75	.70
b.		Single, Afrikaans		1.75	.70
c.		2sh6p brn & sl grn ('36), pair		85.00	50.00
d.		As "c", single, English		10.00	4.00
e.		As "c", single, Afrikaans		10.00	4.00
f.		2sh6p choc & dp grn ('37), pair		75.00	40.00
g.		As "f", single, English		9.00	4.00
h.		As "f", single, Afrikaans		9.00	4.00
i.		2sh6p red brn & grn, pair ('32)		210.00	200.00
j.		As "i", single, English		17.00	6.50
k.		As "i", single, Afrikaans		17.00	6.50
		Nos. 33-44 (12)		866.00	530.50

No. 34 unwatermarked, or watermarked multiple clover leaf, is a proof.

Types of 1926-28 with "SUID-AFRIKA" Hyphenated on Afrikaans Stamps, and

Gold Mine — A15

Government Buildings, Pretoria — A16

Government Buildings, Pretoria — A16a

Groote Schuur — A17

Groot Constantia — A18

½p. No. 45 shading in leaves and ornaments strengthened; 40 lines in center background. Size: 18½x22½mm.

No. 46 has 28 heavy horizontal shading lines in center background and similar thicker lines in frame. Top and bottom green bars are scored by a white horizontal line. Size: 18½x22½mm.

No. 47 is smaller, 18x22mm.
1p. No. 48, size 18½x22½mm.
No. 49, size 18x22mm.
No. 50. Size: 17½x21½mm.
2p. On Nos. 53-54, S's in SOUTH and POSTAGE are narrower than on Nos. 36-37.
6p. Die I, "SUID-AFRIKA" 16½mm. Shading in leaves framing oval very faint and broken. Size: 18½x22½mm.

Die II, "SUID-AFRIKA" 17mm. Leaves strongly shaded in background of tree. Size: 18½x22½mm.

Die III, "question mark" scrolls below top panel are cleanly defined without intrusion of background shading. Size: 18x22mm.

Nos. 45-67 were printed in many shades. Some denominations in some printings were partly or wholly screened. Except for No. 47, the screened stamps were issued after 1947.
5sh. No. 65. Type I, letters "U" and "A" in SOUTH AFRICA have projections. Size: 27x21½mm.

No. 66. Type II, letters "U" and "A" redrawn to eliminate projections. Size: 26½x21½mm.

Perf. 15x14 (½p, 1p, 6p), 14

				Photo.	Wmk. 201
1933-54					
45	A5	½p grn & gray, pair ('36)		4.00	.80
a.		Single, English		.25	.20
b.		Single, Afrikaans		.25	.20
c.		Bklt. pane of 6, marginal ads		25.00	25.00
d.		Perf. 13½x14 (coil), pair		30.00	47.50
e.		As "d", single, English		1.75	1.25
f.		As "d", single, Afrikaans		1.75	1.25
46	A5	½p grn & gray, redrawn, pair ('37)		4.00	.40
a.		Single, English		.20	.20
b.		Single, Afrikaans		.20	.20
c.		Booklet pane of 6		37.50	30.00
d.		Booklet pane of 2		8.00	1.00
e.		As "c", 4 blank margins		35.00	35.00
f.		Perf. 14½x14 (coil), pair		12.50	7.25
g.		As "f", single, English		2.25	.80
h.		As "f", single, Afrikaans		2.25	.80
47	A5	½p grn & gray, pair ('47)		1.25	.40
a.		Single, English		.20	.20
b.		Single, Afrikaans		.20	.20
c.		Bklt. pane of 6, marginal ads		4.00	3.50
d.		As "c", no horiz. margins		5.00	3.50
48	A6	1p car & gray, pair ('34)		1.10	.65
a.		Single, English		.20	.20
b.		Single, Afrikaans		.20	.20
c.		Booklet pane of 6		37.50	37.50
d.		Booklet pane of 2		3.00	1.25
e.		Perf. 13½x14 (coil), pair		30.00	52.50
f.		As "e", single, English		1.40	1.00
g.		As "e", single, Afrikaans		1.40	1.00
h.		Center omitted, pair		325.00	
j.		Bklt. pane of 6, marginal ads		27.50	27.50
k.		As "j", 4 blank margins		30.00	30.00
m.		Perf. 14½x14 (coil), pair		11.00	11.00
n.		As "m", single, English		1.40	1.40
p.		As "m", single, Afrikaans		1.40	1.40
49	A6	1p rose car & gray blk, pair ('40)		1.50	.30
a.		Single, English		.20	.20
b.		Single, Afrikaans		.20	.20
c.		Unwmkd., pair		325.00	325.00
d.		Booklet pane of 6		3.75	2.75
e.		Perf. 14½x14 (coil), pair		4.00	6.00
f.		As "e", single, English		1.40	.90
g.		As "e", single, Afrikaans		1.40	.90
h.		As "d", marginal ads		5.00	4.25
50	A6	1p car & blk, pair ('51)		.75	.20
a.		Single, English		.20	.20
b.		Single, Afrikaans		.20	.20
51	A15	1½p dk grn & gold, 27x21½mm, pair ('36)		2.00	1.40
a.		Single, English		.25	.20
b.		Single, Afrikaans		.25	.20
c.		Booklet pane of 4		9.00	8.00
d.		Center omitted, pair		1,000.	
52	A15	1½p sl grn & och, 22x18mm, pair ('41)		1.25	.25
a.		Single, English		.20	.20
b.		Single, Afrikaans		.20	.20
c.		Center omitted, pair		900.00	
d.		Booklet pane of 6		5.75	4.50
53	A16	2p bl vio & dl bl, pair ('38)		40.00	32.50
a.		Single, English		3.00	1.25
b.		Single, Afrikaans		3.00	1.25
54	A16	2p dl vio & gray, pair ('41)		24.00	45.00
a.		Single, English		.90	.50
b.		Single, Afrikaans		.90	.50
55	A16a	2p dp reddish vio & sl, 27x21½mm, pair ('45)		1.50	4.00
a.		Single, English		.20	.20
b.		Single, Afrikaans		.20	.20
56	A16a	2p purple & sl bl, 21½ x 17¼mm, pair ('50)		1.00	4.50
a.		Single, English		.20	.20
b.		Single, Afrikaans		.20	.20
c.		Booklet pane of 6 ('51)		3.75	2.75
57	A17	3p ultra, pair ('40)		5.00	1.75
a.		Single, English		.20	.20
b.		Single, Afrikaans		.20	.20
c.		3p bl, pair ('49)		2.00	4.00
d.		As "c", single, English		.20	.20
e.		As "c", single, Afrikaans		.20	.20
58	A10	4p choc brn, pair ('52)		1.25	5.50
a.		Single, English		.20	.20
b.		Single, Afrikaans		.20	.20
59	A7	6p org & bl grn, I, pair ('37)		50.00	22.50
a.		Single, English		3.75	1.10
b.		Single, Afrikaans		3.75	1.10
60	A7	6p org & grn, II, pair ('38)		22.50	3.00
a.		Single, English		1.50	.25
b.		Single, Afrikaans		1.50	.25
61	A7	6p red org & bl grn, III ('50), pair		1.75	1.00
a.		Single, English		.20	.20
b.		Single, Afrikaans		.20	.20
c.		6p org & grn, III, pair ('46)		13.50	1.90
d.		As "c", single, English		1.00	.20
e.		As "c", single, Afrikaans		1.00	.20
62	A11	1sh chlky bl & lt brn ('50), pair		9.00	6.00
a.		As "f", single, English		.55	.20
b.		As "f", single, Afrikaans		.55	.20
c.		1sh lt bl & ol brn, pair ('39)		35.00	7.50
d.		As "c", single, English		1.00	.20
e.		As "c", single, Afrikaans		1.00	.20
f.		1sh vio bl & brnsh blk, pair		16.00	10.00
g.		Single, English		.50	.30
h.		Single, Afrikaans		.50	.30
63	A12	2sh6p brn & brt grn, pair ('49)		7.50	24.00
a.		Single, English		1.25	.75
b.		Single, Afrikaans		1.25	.75
64	A13	5sh grn & blk, I, pair		55.00	55.00
a.		Single, English		2.50	2.00
b.		Single, Afrikaans		2.50	2.00
65	A13	5sh bl grn & blk, I, pair ('49)		42.50	62.50
a.		Single, English		4.00	3.50
b.		Single, Afrikaans		4.00	3.50
66	A13	5sh grn & blk, II, pair ('54)		55.00	75.00
a.		Single, English		4.00	3.50
b.		Single, Afrikaans		4.00	3.50
67	A18	10sh ol blk & bl, pair ('39)		50.00	17.50
a.		Single, English		3.00	1.00
b.		Single, Afrikaans		3.00	1.00
		Nos. 45-67 (23)		381.85	364.15

See Nos. 98-99. For overprints see Nos. O26-O27, O29, O36-O38, O40, O46-O47, O54.

George V and Springboks — A19

1935, May 1　　Wmk. 201　　Perf. 15x14

68	A19	½p Prus grn & blk, pair		5.00	10.00
a.		Single, English top		.25	.25
b.		Single, Afrikaans top		.25	.25
69	A19	1p car rose & blk, pair		5.00	10.00
a.		Single, English top		.25	.25
b.		Single, Afrikaans top		.25	.25
70	A19	3p bl & dk bl, pair		17.50	55.00
a.		Single, English top		1.40	2.75
b.		Single, Afrikaans top		1.40	2.75
71	A19	6p org & grn, pair		35.00	90.00
a.		Single, English top		2.10	3.00
b.		Single, Afrikaans top		2.10	3.00
		Nos. 68-71 (4)		62.50	165.00
		Set, never hinged		100.00	

25th anniv. of the reign of George V.

English and Afrikaans inscriptions are transposed on alternate stamps. On the ½p, 3p and 6p with "SOUTH AFRICA" at top, "SILWER JUBILEUM" is at left of medallion, but on 1p with English at top, it is at the right.

Johannesburg International Philatelic Exhibition Issue
Souvenir Sheets

A20

A21

Black Overprint, "JIPEX 1936"

1936, Nov. 2			**Perf. 15x14**	
72	A20	Sheet of 6 (½p)	6.00	9.50
73	A21	Sheet of 6 (1p)	5.75	6.50
		Set, never hinged	25.00	

Sheets made by overprinting booklet panes Nos. 45c and 48j. Sheets exist with and without horizontal perforations through right margin. Sheet size: 81x72½mm.

> **Catalogue values for unused stamps in this section, from this point to the end of the section, are for Never Hinged items.**

George VI — A22

"KRONING SUID-AFRIKA" on alternate stamps.

1937, May 12			**Perf. 14**	
74	A22	½p grn & ol blk, pair	.55	.40
a.		Single, English	.20	.20
b.		Single, Afrikaans	.20	.20
75	A22	1p car & ol blk, pair	.85	.40
a.		Single, English	.20	.20
b.		Single, Afrikaans	.20	.20
76	A22	1½p Prus grn & org, pair	.85	.70
a.		Single, English	.20	.20
b.		Single, Afrikaans	.20	.20
77	A22	3p bl & ultra, pair	1.75	2.00
a.		Single, English	.20	.20
b.		Single, Afrikaans	.20	.20
78	A22	1sh Prus bl & org brn, pair	5.00	3.50
a.		Single, English	.50	.25
b.		Single, Afrikaans	.50	.25
		Nos. 74-78 (5)	9.00	7.00

Coronation of George VI and Queen Elizabeth.

Wagon Wheel A23

Voortrekker Family A24

Alternate stamps inscribed "SOUTH AFRICA," "SUID-AFRIKA."

1938, Dec. 14			**Perf. 15x14**	
79	A23	1p rose & slate, pair	7.00	5.50
a.		Single, English	.30	.30
b.		Single, Afrikaans	.30	.30
80	A24	1½p red brn & Prus bl, pair	8.00	6.50
a.		Single, English	.30	.35
b.		Single, Afrikaans	.30	.35

Issued to commemorate the Voortrekkers.

Infantry A25

Nurse and Ambulance A26

Airman and Spitfires (Flight Lt. Robert Kershaw) A27

Sailor A28

Women's Services A29

Artillery — A30

Welder — A31

Tank Corps A32

POSSEËL POSTAGE

Signal Corps — A33

Bilingual inscriptions on 2p and 1sh.

Perf. 14 (2p, 4p, 6p), 15x14				
1941-43		**Photo.**	**Wmk. 201**	
81	A25	½p dp bl grn, pair	.90	.40
a.		Single, English	.20	.20
b.		Single, Afrikaans	.20	.20
82	A26	1p brt rose, pair	1.75	.70
a.		Single, English	.20	.20
b.		Single, Afrikaans	.20	.20
83	A27	1½p Prus grn, pair ('42)	1.10	.40
a.		Single, English	.20	.20
b.		Single, Afrikaans	.20	.20
84	A28	2p dk violet	.50	.20
85	A29	3p dp blue, pair	14.00	11.50
a.		Single, English	.50	.50
b.		Single, Afrikaans	.50	.50
86	A30	4p org brn, pair	12.25	8.75
a.		Single, English	.75	.20
b.		Single, Afrikaans	.75	.20
c.		4p red brown, pair	32.50	32.50
d.		As "c," single, English	1.50	1.00
e.		As "c," single, Afrikaans	1.50	1.00
87	A31	6p brt red org, pair	11.75	6.75
a.		Single, English	.50	.20
b.		Single, Afrikaans	.50	.20
88	A32	1sh dark brown	2.25	.50
89	A33	1sh3p dk ol brn, pair ('43)	10.00	6.00
a.		Single, English	.50	.30
b.		Single, Afrikaans	.50	.30
c.		1sh3p dark brown, pair	6.00	6.50
d.		As "c," single, English	.50	.30
e.		As "c," single, Afrikaans	.50	.30
		Nos. 81-89 (9)	54.50	35.20

Infantry-Nurse A34   A35

Airman-Sailor A36   A37

Women's Services — A38

Artillery — A39

Welder — A40

Tank Corps — A41

Bilingual inscriptions on 4p and 1sh.

Pairs: Perf. 14, Roul. 6½ btwn.				
Strips of 3: Perf. 15x14, Roul. 6½ btwn.				
1942-43		**Photo.**	**Wmk. 201**	
90	A34	½p Horiz. strip of 3	.70	.55
a.		Single, English	.20	.20
b.		Single, Afrikaans	.20	.20
c.		As #90, imperf. between	350.00	
91	A35	1p Horiz. strip of 3 ('43)	.90	.60
a.		Single, English	.20	.20
b.		Single, Afrikaans	.20	.20
c.		As #91, imperf. between	350.00	
92	A36	1½p Horiz. pair	.70	.60
a.		Single, English	.20	.20
b.		Single, Afrikaans	.20	.20
c.		As #92, roul. 13	4.50	4.50
d.		As #92, imperf. btwn.	350.00	375.00
93	A37	2p Horiz. pair ('43)	.70	.50
a.		Single, English	.20	.20
b.		Single, Afrikaans	.20	.20
c.		As #93, imperf. btwn.	350.00	
94	A38	3p Vert strip of 3	5.50	8.50
a.		Single, English	.20	.20
b.		Single, Afrikaans	.20	.20
95	A39	4p Vert. strip of 3	16.00	9.00
a.		Single	.20	.20
96	A40	6p Horiz. pair	3.00	2.75
a.		Single, English	.20	.20
b.		Single, Afrikaans	.20	.20
97	A41	1sh Vert. pair	12.50	3.50
a.		Single	.20	.20
		Nos. 90-97 (8)	40.00	26.00

Because of the rouletting these are collected as pairs or strips of three, even on the bilingual stamps.

Types of 1926, Redrawn "SUID-AFRIKA" Hyphenated Coil Stamps

1943		**Photo.**	**Perf. 15x14**	
98	A5	½p myrtle grn, vert. pair	1.25	3.00
a.		Single, English	.20	.20
b.		Single, Afrikaans	.20	.20
99	A6	1p rose pink, vert. pair	2.00	3.00
a.		Single, English	.20	.20
b.		Single, Afrikaans	.20	.20

"Victory" — A42

"Peace" — A43

Design: 3p, Profiles of couple ("Hope").

1945, Dec. 3		**Photo.**	**Perf. 14**	
100	A42	1p rose pink & choc, pair	.35	.30
a.		Single, English	.20	.20
b.		Single, Afrikaans	.20	.20
101	A43	2p vio & sl bl, pair	.35	.30
a.		Single, English	.20	.20
b.		Single, Afrikaans	.20	.20
102	A43	3p ultra & dp ultra, pair	.50	.40
a.		Single, English	.20	.20
b.		Single, Afrikaans	.20	.20
		Nos. 100-102 (3)	1.20	1.00

World War II victory of the Allies.

George VI — A44

King George VI and Queen Elizabeth A45

Princesses Margaret Rose and Elizabeth A46

Perf. 15x14

1947, Feb. 17			**Wmk. 201**	
103	A44	1p cer & gray, pair	.30	.30
a.		Single, English	.20	.20
b.		Single, Afrikaans	.20	.20
104	A45	2p purple, pair	.30	.30
a.		Single, English	.20	.20
b.		Single, Afrikaans	.20	.20
105	A46	3p dk blue, pair	.40	.40
a.		Single, English	.20	.20
b.		Single, Afrikaans	.20	.20
		Nos. 103-105 (3)	1.00	1.00

Visit of the British Royal Family, Mar.-Apr., 1947.

George VI, Elizabeth — A47   Gold Mine — A48

1948, Apr. 26		**Photo.**	**Perf. 14**	
106	A47	3p dp chlky bl & sil, pair	.70	.70
a.		Single, English	.20	.20
b.		Single, Afrikaans	.20	.20

25th anniv. of the marriage of George VI and Queen Elizabeth.

Vertical Pairs Perf. 14 all around, Rouletted 6½ between

1948, Apr.				
107	A48	1½p sl & och, vert. pair	1.25	2.00
a.		Single, English	.20	.20
b.		Single, Afrikaans	.20	.20

"Wanderer" in Port Natal A49

1949, May 2		**Photo.**	**Perf. 15x14**	
108	A49	1½p red brown, pair	.60	.60
a.		Single, English	.20	.20
b.		Single, Afrikaans	.20	.20

Mercury and Globe — A50

1949, Oct. 1			**Perf. 14x15**	
109	A50	½p dk green, pair	.60	.60
a.		Single, English	.20	.20
b.		Single, Afrikaans	.20	.20
110	A50	1½p dk red, pair	.90	.90
a.		Single, English	.20	.20
b.		Single, Afrikaans	.20	.20
111	A50	3p ultra, pair	1.50	1.50
a.		Single, English	.20	.20
b.		Single, Afrikaans	.20	.20
		Nos. 109-111 (3)	3.00	3.00

75th anniv. of the UPU.

Except for Nos. 216, 310-313, 518a, 669a this is the end of bi-lingual multiples in the postage section.

Voortrekkers en Route to Natal — A51

Voortrekker Monument, Pretoria A52

Voortrekkers Looking Toward Natal, and Open Bible — A53

1949, Dec. 1   **Perf. 15x14**
112	A51	1p magenta	.20	.20
113	A52	1½p dull green	.20	.20
114	A53	3p dark blue	.20	.20
		Nos. 112-114 (3)	.60	.60

Inauguration of the Voortrekker Monument at Pretoria.

Riebeeck's Seal and Dutch East India Company Monogram A54

Maria de la Quellerie — A55

2p, van Riebeeck's Ships. 4½p, Jan van Riebeeck. 1sh, Landing of van Riebeeck.

Perf. 15x14, 14x15
1952, Mar. 14   **Wmk. 201**
115	A54	½p dk brn & red vio	.20	.20
116	A55	1p dark green	.20	.20
117	A54	2p dark purple	.20	.20
118	A55	4½p dark blue	.20	.20
119	A54	1sh brown	.55	.50
		Nos. 115-119 (5)	1.35	1.30

300th anniv. of the landing of Jan van Riebeeck at the Cape of Good Hope.

Nos. 116-117 Overprinted "SATISE" (1p) and "SADIPU" (2p)
1952, Mar. 26
120	A55	1p dark green	.30	.55
121	A54	2p dark purple	.35	.70

South African Tercentenary Intl. Stamp Exhib., Cape Town, Mar. 26-Apr. 5, 1952.

Coronation Issue

Queen Elizabeth II — A97

1953, June 3   **Perf. 14x15**
192	A97	2p violet blue	.30	.20

Cape Triangle of 1853 A98

1953, Sept. 1   **Perf. 15x14**
193	A98	1p red & dk brown	.20	.20
194	A98	4p blue & indigo	.25	.20

Cent. of the introduction of postage stamps in South Africa.

Merino Ram and Sheep — A99

1953, Oct. 1   **Perf. 14**
195	A99	4½p shown	.50	.20
196	A99	1sh3p Springbok	1.25	.20
197	A99	1sh6p Aloes	1.25	.40
		Nos. 195-197 (3)	3.00	.80

Arms of Orange Free State, Pen and Scroll A100

1954, Feb. 23   **Perf. 15x14**
198	A100	2p red org & dk brown	.20	.20
199	A100	4½p gray & rose violet	.25	.25

Orange Free State centenary.

Wart Hog A101

White Rhinoceros A102

Lion — A103

1954, Oct. 14   **Perf. 15x14**
200	A101	½p shown	.20	.20
201	A101	1p Gnu	.20	.20
202	A101	1½p Leopard	.20	.20
203	A101	2p Zebra	.20	.20

Perf. 14
204	A102	3p shown	.20	.20
205	A102	4p Elephant	.45	.20
206	A102	4½p Hippopotamus	.55	.80
207	A103	6p shown	.50	.20
208	A102	1sh Kudu	3.00	.20
209	A103	1sh3p Springbok	2.00	.35
210	A102	1sh6p Gemsbok	1.75	.50
211	A102	2sh6p Nyala	4.25	.30
212	A102	5sh Giraffe	10.50	1.60
213	A102	10sh Sable antelope	16.00	3.75
		Nos. 200-213 (14)	40.00	8.90

See Nos. 221-228, 241-244, 247, 250-253.

Paul Kruger — A104

Portrait: 6p, Martinus Wessels Pretorius.

Perf. 14x15
1955, Oct. 21   **Photo.**   **Wmk. 201**
214	A104	3p slate green	.30	.20
215	A104	6p brown violet	.60	.30

Centenary of Pretoria.

Andries Pretorius, Church of the Vow and Flag of Natalia — A105

German Wagon and House — A106

1955, Dec. 1   **Perf. 14**

Inscribed alternately in English and Afrikaans.

216	A105	2p ultra & cer, pair	.80	4.00
a.		Single, English	.20	.20
b.		Single, Afrikaans	.20	.20

Union Covenant Celebrations, Pietermaritzburg, Dec. 13-18, 1955.

1958, July 1   **Perf. 14**
218	A106	2p pale lilac & brown	.20	.20

Cent. of the arrival of German settlers.

Seal of Academy A107

Perf. 15x14
1959, May 1   **Photo.**   **Wmk. 201**
219	A107	3p brt blue & dk blue	.20	.20
a.		Dark blue omitted		2,250.

50th anniv. of the South African Academy of Science and Art, Pretoria.

Globe Showing Antarctica and South Africa — A108

Perf. 14x15
1959, Nov. 16   **Wmk. 330**
220	A108	3p blue grn, brn & org	.25	.20

South African Natl. Antarctic Expedition.

Animal Types of 1954

1959-60   **Wmk. 330**   **Perf. 15x14**
221	A101	½p Wart hog ('60)	.35	2.00
222	A101	1p Gnu	.20	.20
a.		Redrawn	.40	.20

Perf. 14
223	A102	3p White rhino	.40	.20
224	A102	4p Elephant	1.10	.30
225	A103	6p Lion	2.10	.30
226	A102	1sh Kudu	3.25	.30

227	A102	2sh6p Nyala	9.75	.70
228	A102	5sh Giraffe ('60)	20.00	29.00
		Nos. 221-228 (8)	37.15	33.00

On No. 222a, the numeral "1" is centered above "S." On No. 222, "1" is slightly to right of "S."

Prime Ministers Botha, Smuts, Hertzog, Malan, Strydom and Verwoerd A109

Flag and Notes from National Anthem — A110

Pushing Wheel Uphill A111

6p, Arms of the Union and of four provinces. 1sh6p, Official Union festival emblem.

Perf. 14x15, 15x14
1960   **Photo.**   **Wmk. 330**
235	A109	3p chocolate	.20	.20
236	A110	4p lt blue & red org	.30	.20
237	A110	6p yel grn, red & brn	.45	.20
238	A111	1sh yel, dk bl & blk	.90	.20
239	A111	1sh6p lt blue & blk	3.00	2.00
		Nos. 235-239 (5)	4.85	2.80

50th anniv. of the founding of the Union. See Nos. 245-246, 248-249.

Map, Old and New Locomotives — A112

1960, May 2   **Perf. 15x14**
240	A112	1sh3p dark blue	3.25	1.25

Centenary of railways in South Africa.

Types of 1954 and 1960.

Designs: ½c, Wart hog. 1c, Gnu. 1½c, Leopard. 2c, Zebra. 2½c, Prime Ministers. 3½c, Flag and music notes. 5c, Lion. 7½c, Arms of Union and four provinces. 10c, Pushing wheel uphill. 12½c, Springbok. 20c, Gemsbok. 50c, Giraffe. 1r, Sable antelope.

Perf. 15x14, 14x15, 14 (A102, A103)
1961, Feb. 14   **Photo.**   **Wmk. 330**
241	A101	½c dk bluish grn	.20	.20
242	A101	1c rose brown	.20	.20
243	A101	1½c sepia	.20	.20
244	A101	2c purple	.20	.20
245	A109	2½c chocolate	.25	.20
246	A110	3½c lt bl & red org	.40	.25
247	A103	5c org & dk brn	.50	.20
248	A110	7½c yel grn, red & brn	.60	.25
249	A111	10c yel, dk bl & blk	.70	.20
250	A103	12½c dull grn & dk brn	1.25	.60
251	A102	20c pink & dk brn	2.10	1.25
252	A102	50c org yel & blk brn	8.25	8.25
253	A102	1r blue & black	19.00	16.00
		Nos. 241-253 (13)	33.85	28.00

Republic

Natal Pigmy
Kingfisher
A112a

Coral Tree
Flower
A112b

Pouring Gold
A113

Groot
Constantia
A114

Designs: 1½c, Afrikander bull. 3c, Crimson-breasted shrike. 5c, Baobab tree. 7½c, Corn. 10c, Castle entrance, Cape Town. 12½c, Protea flower. 20c, Secretary bird. 50c, Cape Town, harbor. 1r, Bird of Paradise flower.

Two types of 2½c:
Type I — Lines of building faint.
Type II — Lines of building very strong; strong line between bottom of building and top of name panel.

Perf. 14x15, 15x14

1961, May 31   Photo.   Wmk. 330

254	A112a	½c blue, mag & brn	.20	.20
a.		Perf. 14x13½ ('63)	.20	.20
255	A112b	1c gray & red	.20	.20
256	A112a	1½c brown carmine	.20	.20

Perf. 14

257	A113	2c ultra & orange	.20	.20
258	A114	2½c violet & grn (I)	.30	.20
a.		Type II	.40	.20
259	A113	3c pink, dk bl & red	.30	.20
260	A114	5c grnsh bl & yel	.35	.20
261	A114	7½c emerald & brn	.50	.20
a.		Brown omitted		
262	A114	10c emer & dk brn	.75	.20
263	A114	12½c dk grn, red & yel	1.50	.20
a.		Yellow omitted	600.00	
264	A114	20c sal, sl bl & pink	4.00	.30
265	A113	50c ultra & blk	30.00	2.10
266	A113	1r blue, org & grn	22.50	2.10
		Nos. 254-266 (13)	61.00	6.50

1961-63   Unwmk.   Perf. 15x14

269	A112b	1c gray & red	.25	.20

Perf. 14

270	A113	2c ultra & org ('63)	7.25	.35
271	A114	2½c violet & grn (II)	.30	.20
272	A113	3c pink, dk bl & red	.60	.20
273	A114	5c grnsh blue & yel	.75	.20
274	A114	7½c emer & brn ('62)	1.10	.20
275	A114	10c green & dk brn ('63)	1.25	.50
276	A114	20c sal, sl bl & pink ('63)	17.50	4.75
277	A113	50c ultra & blk ('62)	26.00	5.25
		Nos. 269-277 (9)	55.00	12.00

See Nos. 289-298, 317-322, 324, 326-338, 340-342, 376-377, 379-382, 383-385 and designs A135-A136.

Boeing 707 and
Bleriot
Monoplane
A115

Folk Dancers
A116

Perf. 14x15

1961, Dec. 1   Photo.   Wmk. 330

280	A115	3c blue & red	.60	.20

50th anniv. of South Africa's 1st air mail.

1962, Mar. 1

281	A116	2½c lt brn, choc & red org	.35	.20

50th anniv. of folk dancing in South Africa.

"Chapman"
Arriving in
1820
A117

Perf. 15x14

1962, Aug. 20   Photo.   Wmk. 330

282	A117	2½c dp plum & bl grn	.40	.20
283	A117	2½c choc & blue	3.00	1.60

Unveiling of the precinct stone of the British Settlers Monument at Grahamstown.

Red Disa Orchid, Castle Rock,
Kirstenbosch Botanic Gardens — A118

1963, Mar. 14   Perf. 14

284	A118	2½c multicolored	.40	.20

50th anniv. of the Kirstenbosch Botanic Gardens, Cape Town.

Centenary Emblem
and Nurse — A119

12½c, Centenary emblem and globe, horiz.

1963, Aug. 30   Wmk. 348   Perf. 14

285	A119	2½c rose claret, blk & red	.35	.20

Perf. 15x14

286	A119	12½c dk bl gray & red	3.50	1.60
a.		Red Cross omitted	1,600.	

Centenary of the International Red Cross.

Assembly
Seat,
Bunga
Building,
Umtata
A120

Perf. 14½x14

1963, Dec. 11   Wmk. 348

287	A120	2½c dk brn & lt grn	.30	.20
a.		Light green omitted	1,600.	

Transkei Legislative Assembly, 1st meeting.

Types of 1961
Perf. 15x14, 14x15

1963-67   Photo.   Wmk. 348
Colors as Before

289	A112b	1c	.20	.20
290	A112a	1½c ('67)	2.50	1.00

Perf. 14

291	A113	2c ('64)	.20	.20
292	A114	2½c (II) ('64)	.60	.20
293	A114	5c ('66)	2.50	.20
294	A114	7½c ('66)	13.00	2.50
295	A114	10c ('64)	1.25	.20
296	A114	20c ('64)	5.25	.45
297	A113	50c ('66)	42.50	7.50
298	A113	1r ('64)	80.00	37.50
		Nos. 289-298 (10)	148.00	49.95

Rugby Board
Emblem,
Springbok and
Ball — A121

John
Calvin — A122

Design: 12½c, Rugby player diving over goal line, horiz.

Perf. 14x15, 15x14

1964, May 8   Photo.   Wmk. 348

301	A121	2½c dk green & brn	.50	.20
302	A121	12½c yellow grn & blk	4.50	3.00

South African Rugby Board, 75th anniv.

1964, July 10   Perf. 14

303	A122	2½c choc, brt car & vio	.35	.20

John Calvin (1509-64), French theologian and leader of the Reformation.

Nurse's
Lamp — A123

Design: 12½c, Nurse holding lamp, horiz.

Perf. 14x15, 15x14

1964, Oct. 12   Photo.   Wmk. 348

304	A123	2½c gold & ultra	.50	.20
305	A123	12½c ultra & gold	3.50	3.50
a.		Gold omitted	1,500.	

South African Nursing Assoc., 50th anniv.

ITU
Emblem
and
Satellites
A124

Design: 12½c, ITU emblem, old and new communication equipment.

1965, May 17   Perf. 15x14

306	A124	2½c brt blue & org	.50	.20
307	A124	12½c green & claret	3.50	3.00

Cent. of the ITU.

Pulpit, Groote Kerk,
Cape Town — A125

Design: 12½c, Emblem of Dutch Reformed Church of South Africa, horiz.

Perf. 14x15, 15x14

1965, Oct. 21   Photo.   Wmk. 348

308	A125	2½c dp brown & yel	.25	.20
309	A125	12½c lt ultra, ocher & blk	3.00	2.75

Tercentenary of the Dutch Reformed Church in South Africa.

Diamond — A126

1966, May 31   Perf. 14

2½c, Flying bird, symbol of freedom & the future, horiz. 3c, Corn. 7½c, Table Mountain, horiz. Inscribed alternately in English & Afrikaans.

310	A126	1c blk, yel, dk & lt grn, pair	.60	.60
a.		Single, English	.20	.20
b.		Single, Afrikaans	.20	.20
311	A126	2½c dk bl, ultra & yel grn, pair	1.50	1.50
a.		Single, English	.20	.20
b.		Single, Afrikaans	.20	.20

Perf. 14x15, 15x14

312	A126	3c red brn, red & yel, pair	3.00	3.00
a.		Single, English	.20	.20
b.		Single, Afrikaans	.20	.20
313	A126	7½c ultra, vio bl, och & blk, pair	8.75	8.75
a.		Single, English	.60	.50
b.		Single, Afrikaans	.60	.50
		Nos. 310-313 (4)	13.85	13.85

5th anniversary of the Republic.
Nos. 310-313 with watermark 359 are reprints made for U.P.U. presentation booklets.

Hendrik F.
Verwoerd
and Union
Buildings,
Pretoria
A127

Designs: 3c, Verwoerd's portrait, vert. 12½c, Verwoerd and map of South Africa.

Perf. 15x14, 14x15

1966, Dec. 6   Photo.   Wmk. 348

314	A127	2½c grnsh blue & blk	.20	.20
315	A127	3c yellow grn & blk	.20	.20
316	A127	12½c dull blue & blk	1.60	1.40
		Nos. 314-316 (3)	2.00	1.80

Dr. Verwoerd (1901-1966), Prime Minister.

Types of 1961 Redrawn and

Industry — A128

(Inscriptions in larger, bolder type)

½c, 1½c and 1r

On the 1r, the "N" of "VAN" is over the final "A" of "AFRIKA." On Nos. 266 and 298, the "N" is over "KA."

1c, 7½c and
12½c

2½c, 5c, 10c
and 20c

2c, 3c and 50c
(similar)

Perf. 14x15, 15x14

1964-68   Photo.   Wmk. 348
Colors as Before

317	A112a	½c	.20	.20
a.		Imperf., pair	400.00	
318	A112b	1c	.40	.20

Perf. 14

319	A113	2c ('68)	.40	.20
320	A114	2½c	.45	.20
321	A113	3c	.75	.20
322	A113	12½c	2.75	.20

323	A128	15c ('67)	6.00	.20
324	A113	1r	19.00	3.00
		Nos. 317-324 (8)	29.95	4.40

See No. 339.

Redrawn Types of 1964-68

4c, Groot Constantia (like 2½c). 6c, Corn (like 7½c). 9c, Protea flower (like 12½c).

1967-71   Photo.   Wmk. 359

326	A112a	½c	.20	.20
327	A112b	1c	.20	.20
328	A112c	1½c	.20	.20
329	A113	2c ('68)	2.00	.20
330	A114	2½c	.20	.20
331	A113	3c	.20	.20
332	A114	4c ('71)	.40	.20
333	A114	5c ('68)	.20	.20
334	A114	6c ('71)	1.10	.20
335	A114	7½c	1.90	.20
336	A114	9c ('68)	1.40	.20
337	A114	10c ('68)	4.25	.30
338	A114	12½c ('70)	3.50	.65
339	A114	15c ('69)	6.50	.50
340	A114	20c ('68)	8.00	.65
341	A113	50c ('68)	8.75	1.00
342	A113	1r ('68)	12.00	2.10
		Nos. 326-342 (17)	51.00	7.40

Luminescence

Starting in 1969, South Africa began to add phosphorescent "frames" to its definitive stamps.

In 1971, stamps began to appear with the phosphorescent element through-out the paper.

Phosphorescent commemoratives include Nos. 357, 359 et cetera.

Martin Luther — A129   Door of Wittenberg Church — A130

1967, Oct. 31   Litho.   Wmk. 348

343	A129	2½c pink & black	.20	.20

Wmk. 359

344	A130	12½c black & orange	2.75	2.50

450th anniversary of the Reformation.

Pres. J. J. Fouché — A133   James B. M. Hertzog Statue — A134

Design: 12½c, Full-face portrait.

Perf. 14x15
1968, Apr. 10   Photo.   Wmk. 348

345	A133	2½c lt rose brn & dk brn	.30	.20
346	A133	12½c grysh bl & vio bl	2.50	2.25

Wmk. 359

347	A133	12½c grysh bl & vio bl	2.75	2.25
		Nos. 345-347 (3)	5.55	4.70

Pres. Jacobus Johannes Fouché, inauguration.

Perf. 13½x14, 14x13½
1968, Sept. 21   Photo.   Wmk. 359

Designs: 2½c, Hertzog in 1902, with hat, horiz. 3c, Hertzog in 1924, horiz.

348	A134	2½c dk brn, lem & blk	.20	.20

Wmk. 348

349	A134	3c multicolored	.30	.20
350	A134	12½c org brn, org & blk	2.00	1.75
		Nos. 348-350 (3)	2.50	2.15

Unveiling of a monument in Bloemfontein honoring James Barry Munnik Hertzog (1866-1942), Boer general, prime minister of South Africa (1924-39).

Natal Pigmy Kingfisher A135   Kaffir Boom Flower A136

1969   Wmk. 359   Photo.   Perf. 14

351	A135	½c blue & multi	.20	.20
a.		Perf. 14x14½ (coil)	1.50	1.50
352	A136	1c grysh brown & multi	.20	.20

See Nos. 374-375.

Springbok, Torch and Rings — A137

1969, Mar. 15   Perf. 14x13½

353	A137	2½c olive, ind & red	.20	.20
354	A137	12½c bister, ind & red	1.60	1.40

South African Natl. Games, Bloemfontein, Mar. 15-Apr. 19.

Groote Schuur Hospital and Dr. Barnard A138

Hands Holding Heart A139

Perf. 13½x14
1969, July 7   Photo.   Wmk. 348

355	A138	2½c dp rose, pink & plum	.20	.20

Perf. 15x14
Wmk. 359

356	A139	12½c dp bl & dp car	2.25	1.75

1st heart transplant operation (by Dr. Christiaan Barnard) and opening of the 47th South African Medical Cong., Pretoria.

Stagecoach of 1869 — A140

Transvaal No. 1 — A141   Water Drop and Flower — A142

Perf. 13½x14, 14x13½
1969, Oct. 6   Photo.   Wmk. 359

357	A140	2½c ocher, Prus bl & yel	.35	.20
358	A141	12½c sal, grn & gold	3.25	2.25

Centenary of South African postage stamps.

1970, Feb. 14   Perf. 14

Design: 3c, Waves, horiz.

359	A142	2½c brn, brt bl & grn	.20	.20
360	A142	3c pale gray, bl & ind	.50	.20

Issued to publicize the Water 70 campaign of the Department of Water Affairs.

Sower — A143

"BIBLIA" A144

1970, Aug. 24   Photo.   Perf. 14

361	A143	2½c multicolored	.40	.20

Photo; Gold Impressed

362	A144	12½c ultra, blk & gold	3.25	2.75

150th anniv. of the South African Bible Soc.

Strijdom Tower, Johannes G. Strijdom — A145

Map of Antarctica A146

Perf. 14x13½, 13½x14
1971, May 22   Photo.   Wmk. 359

363	A145	5c blue, yel & blk	.50	.20
364	A146	12½c grnsh bl, vio bl & red	4.50	4.50

Wmk. 330

365	A145	5c blue, yel & blk	2.25	1.00
		Nos. 363-365 (3)	7.25	5.70

Intl. Stamp Exhib. (INTERSTEX), Cape Town, May 22-31. No. 364 also for the 10th anniv. of the Antarctic Treaty pledging peaceful uses of and scientific cooperation in Antarctica.

Landing of British Settlers, 1820, by Thomas Baines A147

Martinus Steyn, Paul Kruger, Unification Monument — A148

1971, May 31   Wmk. 359

366	A147	2c magenta & rose red	.20	.20
367	A148	4c blue green & blk	.30	.20

10th anniv. of the Republic of South Africa.

Hendrik Verwoerd Dam A149

1972, Mar. 4   Photo.   Perf. 14
Size: 37x22mm

368	A149	4c shown	.25	.20
369	A149	5c Aerial view of dam	.45	.20

Size: 57x22mm

370	A149	10c Dam, reservoir and Verwoerd	1.50	.90
		Nos. 368-370 (3)	2.20	1.30

Inauguration of the Hendrik F. Verwoerd Dam of the Orange River Project.

Ram's Head and Wool Mark — A150

Lamb and Wool Mark — A151

1972, May 15   Wmk. 359   Perf. 14

371	A150	4c blue & multi	.20	.20
372	A151	15c dull bl & dk bl	1.75	.40

South African wool industry. Issued in sheets of 100 with advertisements in margin. See Nos. 378-378A, 382A.

Cats — A152   Pylon — A153

1972, Sept. 19   Wmk. 359

373	A152	5c multicolored	1.00	.25

Centenary of the SPCA.

Redrawn Types of 1964-69 and Types of 1972

Perf. 14x15 (½c), 14 (1c, #382A), 12½

1972-74   Photo.   Unwmk.

374	A135	½c blue & multi	8.00	8.75
375	A136	1c grysh brn & red	.20	.20
376	A113	2c brt blue & org	.55	.20
377	A113	3c rose red & bluish black	.60	.70
378	A150	4c blue & multi	1.00	.20
378A	A150	4c brown & multi	.45	.20
379	A114	5c grnsh bl & yel	1.25	.30
380	A114	6c emerald & brn	2.75	4.25
381	A114	9c dk grn, red & yel	2.50	.85
382	A114	10c emer & dk brn	2.75	.50
382A	A151	15c dull bl & dk bl	3.00	4.00
383	A114	20c sal, sl bl & pink	3.00	.65
384	A113	50c ultra & black	7.75	2.00
385	A113	1r bl, org & grn	21.00	4.00
		Nos. 374-385 (14)	54.80	26.80

Issued: 2c, 1972; 6c, 15c, 1974: others, 1973.

1973, Feb. 1   Photo.   Perf. 12x12½

Designs: 4c, Electrical usage, pylon, power plant, horiz. 15c, Smokestacks.

Size: 37½x20mm

386	A153	4c blue & multi	.25	.20

Size: 20x27mm
Perf. 12½

387 A153 5c blue & black .35 .20
388 A153 15c ocher & multi 3.75 1.50
Nos. 386-388 (3) 4.35 1.90

Electricity Supply Commission, 50th anniv.

Arms of University A154

Old University, Cape Town A156

New University, Pretoria A155

1973, Apr. 2   Unwmk.   Perf. 12½
389 A154 4c blue & multi .25 .20

Perf. 12x12½
Wmk. 359
390 A155 5c gold & multi .35 .20

Unwmk.   Perf. 12½
391 A156 15c gold & blk 3.25 1.65

Cent. of the Univ. of South Africa (UNISA).

Woltemade, Sailor and Horse — A157

Designs: 5c, Sinking ship in storm. 15c, "De Jonge Thomas" sinking.

1973, June 2   Photo.   Perf. 12x12½
392 A157 4c brown red, ol & blk .25 .20
393 A157 5c olive, blk & citron .45 .20
394 A157 15c brown, blk & ocher 5.50 4.50
Nos. 392-394 (3) 6.20 4.90

Bicentenary of Wolraad Woltemade's heroism in saving 14 people from the ship "De Jonge Thomas" in Table Bay.

C. J. Langenhoven and Anthem — A158

4c, 5c, vert., Portrait and signature.

1973, Aug. 1   Perf. 12½
395 A158 4c orange, blk & ultra .75 .20

Perf. 12½x12, 12x12½
Size: 21x38mm, 37x21mm
396 A158 5c orange, blk & ultra .90 .20
397 A158 15c orange, blk & ultra 4.50 1.50
Nos. 395-397 (3) 6.15 1.90

Cornelis Jacob Langenhoven (1873-1932), lawyer, writer, who worked for recognition of Afrikaans language.

World Map and Communications Network — A159

1973, Oct. 1   Photo.   Unwmk.
398 A159 15c ultra & multi 1.75 1.65
a. Wmk. 359 2.50 2.25

International Telecommunications Day.

Restored Houses, Tulbagh — A160

Design: 5c, Church Street, Tulbagh.

1974, Mar. 14   Unwmk.   Perf. 12½
Size: 27x21mm
400 A160 4c Prus green & multi .25 .20
Size: 57x20mm
401 A160 5c ocher & multi .45 .20

Restoration of historic Church Street in Tulbagh after 1969 earthquake.

Burgerspond A161

Prime Minister D. F. Malan A162

1974, Apr. 7   Photo.   Perf. 12½x12
402 A161 9c multicolored .90 .55

Centenary of the first official coin struck in South Africa, 1874. The £1 gold coin shows portrait of Pres. Thomas Francois Burger.

1974, May 22   Photo.   Unwmk.
403 A162 4c lt ultra & dk blue .30 .20

Centenary of the birth of Daniel F. Malan (1874-1959), prime minister of South Africa.

Congress Emblem A163

1974, June 13   Perf. 12x12½
404 A163 15c silver & dk blue 1.25 .50

15th World Sugar Cong., Durban, 6/13-30.

"50" A164

1974, July 13   Photo.   Unwmk.
405 A164 4c red & black .40 .20

50th anniversary of radio in South Africa.

Cultural Center, Grahamstown — A165

1974, July 13   Perf. 12x12½
406 A165 5c red & black .35 .20

Natl. Monument to British settlers of 1820.

Natal No. 78, Transvaal No. 145, Cape of Good Hope No. 28 and Orange River Colony No. 4 — A166

1974, Oct. 9   Photo.   Perf. 12½
407 A166 15c multicolored 1.25 .90

Centenary of Universal Postal Union.

Wild Iris — A167

Cape Gannet — A168

Galjoen — A169

Bokmakierie (Shrike) — A170

Designs: 2c, Heather. 3c, Geranium. 4c, Calla lily. 7c, Zebrafish. 9c, Angelfish. 10c, Moorish idol. 14c, Roman fish. 15c, Greater double-collared sunbird. 20c, Yellow-billed hornbill. 25c, Barberton daisy. 50c, Blue cranes. 1r, Bateleur eagles.

Photo. and Engr.
1974, Nov. 11   Unwmk.   Perf. 12½
408 A167 1c pink & multi .20 .20
409 A167 2c yellow & multi .20 .20
410 A167 3c multicolored .20 .20
411 A167 4c multicolored .20 .20
412 A168 5c dull blue & multi .20 .20
413 A167 6c multicolored .25 .20
414 A169 7c lilac & multi .30 .20
415 A169 9c buff & multi .35 .20
416 A169 10c lt blue & multi .40 .20
417 A169 14c salmon & multi .60 .20
418 A168 15c gray & multi .60 .20
419 A168 20c yellow & multi .80 .30
420 A167 25c dk brown & multi 1.10 .35

Perf. 12x12½
421 A170 30c gray & multi 4.50 .75
422 A170 50c citron & multi 4.00 1.00
423 A170 1r multicolored 7.50 2.00
Nos. 408-423 (16) 21.40 6.60

The coils that follow are two colors while the above sheet stamps are multicolored.

1974   Photo.   Perf. 12½
Coil Stamps
430 A167 1c pink & violet .45 .30
431 A167 2c yellow & grn .65 .25
432 A168 5c dull blue & blk 1.40 .70
433 A169 10c lt blue & indigo 9.50 5.75
Nos. 430-433 (4) 12.00 7.00

See note on color that follows No. 423.

1975-76   Perf. 14
Same Designs
430a A167 1c .55 .25
431a A167 2c ('76) .45 .25
433a A169 10c ('76) 5.00 5.00
Nos. 430a-433a (3) 6.00 6.00

No. 430a has black control number on back of every fifth stamp.

Voortrekker Monument and Encampment — A171

1974, Dec. 6   Unwmk.   Perf. 12½
438 A171 4c multicolored .35 .20

Voortrekker Monument, 25th anniversary.

Sasolburg Refinery A172

Perf. 12x12½, 12½
1975, Feb. 26   Litho.
439 A172 15c red & multi 1.25 .90

25th anniversary of South Africa Coal, Oil and Gas Corp., Ltd. (SASOL).

Pres. Nicolaes Diederichs A173

Jan C. Smuts A174

Litho. and Engr.
1975, Apr. 19   Perf. 12½x12
440 A173 4c brown & gold .20 .20

Litho.
441 A173 15c ultra & gold .85 .85

Installation of Dr. Nicolaes Diederichs as third State President.

Litho. and Engraved
1975, May 24
442 A174 4c black .30 .20

Smuts (1870-1950), lawyer, gen., statesman.

Dutch East Indiaman, by Baines A175

Designs: Paintings by John Thomas Baines.

1975, June 18   Photo.   Perf. 12x12½
443 A175 5c gold & multi .20 .20
444 A175 9c gold & multi .30 .25
445 A175 15c gold & multi .55 .45
446 A175 30c gold & multi 1.00 1.00
a. Souvenir sheet of 4 4.00 4.00
Nos. 443-446 (4) 2.05 1.90

John Thomas Baines (1820-75), painter. #446a contains 4 litho. stamps similar to #443-446.

Gideon Malherbe House, Paarl — A176

Photo. and Engr.
1975, Aug. 14   Perf. 12½
447 A176 4c multicolored .30 .20

Society of Real Afrikanders (Genootskap of Regte Afrikaaners), cent.

Automatic Letter Sorting — A177

1975, Sept. 11   Photo.   Perf. 12½x12
448 A177 4c brt blue & multi   .30   .20
Postal automation.

Title Page, First Afrikaans Paper — A178

Afrikaans Monument, Paarl — A179

1975, Oct. 10   Litho.   Perf. 12½x12
449 A178 4c black & orange   .20   .20
450 A179 5c multicolored   .25   .20
Inauguration of Afrikaans Language Monument.

Table Mountain — A180

1975, Nov. 13   Litho.   Perf. 12½
451 A180 15c shown   2.75 1.75
452 A180 15c Johannesburg   2.75 1.75
453 A180 15c Cape vineyards   2.75 1.75
454 A180 15c Lions, Kruger
                Natl. Park   2.75 1.75
  a.   Block of 4, #451-454   11.00 11.00
Tourist publicity.

Satellites, Radar and Africa on Globe — A181

1975, Dec. 3   Litho.   Perf. 12½
455 A181 15c dk vio blue & multi   .60   .50
Satellite communications.

Lawn Bowler — A182

#457, Cricket batsman. #458, Polo player. #459, Golfer (Gary Player).

1976   Photo.   Perf. 12½x12
456 A182 15c green & blk   .60   .35
457 A182 15c yellow grn & blk   .60   .35
458 A182 15c olive & blk   .60   .35
459 A182 15c brt green & blk   .60   .35
  a.   Miniature sheet of 4, #456-459 3.75 2.75
        Nos. 456-459 (4)   2.40 1.40

3rd World Bowling Championships, Zoo Lake Club, Johannesburg, Feb. 1976 (No. 456); cent. of cricket in South Africa (No. 457);

intl. polo (No. 458); Gary Player, South African golf champion (No. 459).
    Issue dates: #456, Feb. 18. #457, Mar. 12. #458, Aug. 16. #459, 459a, Dec. 2.

No. 456 Overprinted in Gold

1976, Apr. 6   Photo.   Perf. 12½x12
460 A182 15c green & black   .45   .45
Victory of South Africa in 3rd World Bowling championships.

Picnic under Baobab Tree A183

Paintings by Erich Mayer: 10c, Wagons at Foot of Blauberg, Transvaal. 15c, Hartbeesspport Dam, near Pretorial. 20c, Street in Doornfontein.

1976, Apr. 20   Photo.   Perf. 12x12½
461 A183 4c ocher & multi   .25   .20
462 A183 10c dk green & multi   .50   .45
463 A183 15c multicolored   .70   .60
464 A183 20c multicolored   1.10 1.00
  a.   Souvenir sheet of 4, #461-464 3.50 3.50
        Nos. 461-464 (4)   2.55 2.25

Erich Mayer (1876-1960), painter. Artist's signature in horizontal gutter between 2 setenant pairs.

Wildlife Protection A184

1976, June 5   Litho.   Perf. 12x12½
465 A184 3c Cheetah   .25   .20
466 A184 10c Black rhinoceros   .55   .35
467 A184 15c Blesbok   1.10 .70
468 A184 20c Zebra   1.40 .95
        Nos. 465-468 (4)   3.30 2.20

All values exist on yellow toned paper. Value, twice that of stamps on white paper.

Emily Hobhouse, by Johan Hoekstra — A185

1976, June 8   Photo.   Perf. 12½x12
469 A185 4c multicolored   .30   .20
Emily Hobhouse (1860-1926), the "Angel of Mercy" during Anglo-Boer War.

S.S. Dunrobin Castle, 1876 A186

1976, Oct. 5   Litho.   Perf. 12x12½
470 A186 10c multicolored   .75   .30
Ocean Mail Service contract, centenary.

Family with Globe — A187

1976, Nov. 6   Photo.   Perf. 12½x12
471 A187 4c salmon & dull red   .30   .20
Family planning.

Wine Glasses A188

Jacob Daniel du Toit A189

1977, Feb. 14   Litho.   Perf. 12½x12
472 A188 15c multicolored   .50   .25
  a.   Word "Die" omitted from left
          inscription   16.00 20.00
Quality of the Vintage Symposium, Cape Town, Feb. 14-21.

1977, Feb. 21   Photo.
473 A189 4c multicolored   .30   .20
Dr. Jacob Daniel du Toit (Totius; 1877-1953), theologian, educator, poet.

Transvaal Supreme Court A190

1977, May 18   Photo.   Perf. 12x12½
474 A190 4c red brown   .30   .20
Transvaal Supreme Court, centenary.

Sugarbush (Protea Repens) — A191

Photo. (1-5, 8, 10, 15, 20c); Litho. (others)

1977, May 27   Perf. 12½
475 A191 1c shown   .20   .20
476 A191 2c P. punctata   .20   .20
477 A191 3c P. neriifolia   .20   .20
478 A191 4c P. longifolia   .20   .20
479 A191 5c P. cynaroides   .20   .20
480 A191 6c P. canaliculata   .20   .20
481 A191 7c P. lorea   .20   .20
482 A191 8c P. mundii   .20   .20
483 A191 9c P. roupelliae   .20   .20
484 A191 10c P. aristata   .25   .20
485 A191 15c P. eximia   .25   .20
486 A191 20c P. magnifica   .25   .20
487 A191 25c P. grandiceps   .30   .20
488 A191 30c P. amplexicaulis   .45   .20
489 A191 50c Leucospermum
                cordifolium   .60   .30
490 A191 1r Paranomus
                reflexus   1.60   .90
491 A191 2r Orothamnus
                zeyheri   3.50 1.75
        Nos. 475-491 (17)   9.00 5.75

Perf. 14
477a A191 3c litho.   .20   .20
479a A191 5c   .20   .20
480a A191 6c   .20   .20
481a A191 7c   .20   .20
482a A191 8c   .20   .20
483a A191 9c   .20   .20
484a A191 10c   .25   .20
486a A191 20c litho.   .85   .35
487a A191 25c   .65   .30
488a A191 30c   .80   .30

489a A191 50c   1.50   .50
490a A191 1r   3.00   .95
491a A191 2r   5.75 1.75
        Nos. 477a-491a (13)   14.00 5.45

Perf. 14 Vertically
                   Photo.   Coil Stamps
492 A191 1c Silver tree   .30   .20
493 A191 2c Bottle brush   .30   .20
494 A191 5c Blushing bride   .30   .20
495 A191 10c Leucadendrom
                sessile   .30   .20
        Nos. 492-495 (4)   1.20   .80

Some printings have control number on back of every fifth stamp.

Gymnastics — A192

1977, Aug. 15   Litho.   Perf. 12½x12
496 A192 15c multicolored   .40   .30
8th Intl. Cong. of Physical Education and Sports for Girls and Women, Cape Town, Aug. 14-20.

World Map and "M" A193

1977, Sept. 15   Litho.   Perf. 12x12½
497 A193 15c multicolored   .40   .30
Introduction of international metric system.

Nuclear Power Plant and Uranium Atom A194

1977, Oct. 8
498 A194 15c multicolored   .40   .30
Uranium development.

Flag of South Africa A195

1977, Nov. 11
499 A195 5c multicolored   .25   .20
50th anniversary of national flag.

Walvis Bay, 1878 — A196

1978, Mar. 10   Litho.   Perf. 12½
500 A196 15c multicolored   .55   .40
Centenary of Walvis Bay annexation.

Dr. Andrew
Murray — A197

1978, May 9   **Perf. 12½x12**
501 A197 4c multicolored .... .25 .20
Dr. Andrew Murray, pioneer theologian,
150th birth anniversary.

Railroad Rail and ISCOR
Emblem — A198

1978, June 5   **Litho.**   **Perf. 12**
502 A198 15c multicolored ...... .45 .40
50th anniversary of ISCOR (Iron and Steel
Industrial Corporation).

Saldanha Bay — A199

Design: No. 504, Richard's Bay.

1978, July 21   **Litho.**   **Perf. 12½**
503 A199 15c multicolored ...... .55 .55
504 A199 15c multicolored ...... .55 .55
a.   Pair, #503-504 .... 1.10 1.10
Opening of new harbors on east and west
coasts of South Africa.

Landscape by Volschenk — A200

Designs: Landscapes by J. E. A. Volschenk.

1978, Aug. 21
505 A200 10c multicolored ...... .35 .35
506 A200 15c multicolored ...... .50 .50
507 A200 20c multicolored ...... .70 .70
508 A200 25c multicolored ...... .90 .90
a.   Souvenir sheet of 4, #505-508 3.00 3.00
     Nos. 505-508 (4) 2.45 2.45
Jan Ernst Abraham Volschenk (1853-1936),
first South African professional artist.

B. J. Vorster — A201

1978, Oct. 10   **Litho.**   **Perf. 12½x12**
509 A201 4c maroon & gold ...... .20 .20
a.   Perf. 14½x14 .... .75 .30

Perf. 14½x14
510 A201 15c violet & gold ...... .40 .30
Inauguration of Balthazar John Vorster as
president of South Africa.

Golden Gate Highlands National
Park — A202

Designs: 15c, Blyde River Canyon, Transvaal. 20c, Amphitheater, Natal National Park.
25c, Cango Caves, Cape Province.

1978, Nov. 13   **Perf. 12½**
511 A202 10c multicolored ...... .30 .30
512 A202 15c multicolored ...... .40 .40
513 A202 20c multicolored ...... .60 .60
514 A202 25c multicolored ...... .95 .95
     Nos. 511-514 (4) 2.25 2.25
Tourist publicity.

Tellurometer and Dr. I. R.
Wadley — A203

1979, Feb. 12   **Litho.**   **Perf. 12½**
515 A203 15c multicolored ...... .30 .25
15th anniversary of the invention of the tellurometer (to measure radio distances).

South
Africa
No.
C5
A204

1979, Mar. 30   **Litho.**   **Perf. 14½x14**
516 A204 15c multicolored ...... .35 .30
First stamp printed by South African Government Printer, 50th anniversary.

"Save Fuel"
A205

Fuel Economy: No. 518, Language inscriptions reversed.

1979, Apr. 2   **Photo.**   **Perf. 12x12½**
517 A205 4c red & black .... .20 .20
518 A205 4c red & black .... .20 .20
a.   Pair, #517-518 .... .30 .30

Battle of Isandlwana, by Melton
Prior — A206

15c, Battle of Ulundi, by Louis Creswicke.
20c, Battle of Rorke's Drift, by Lt. Col.
Crealock.

1979, May 25   **Litho.**   **Perf. 14x13½**
519 A206 4c red & black .... .20 .20
520 A206 15c red & black .... .40 .35
521 A206 20c red & black .... .50 .40
a.   Souv. sheet, #519-521 + label 3.00 3.00
     Nos. 519-521 (3) .... 1.10 .95
Centenary of Zulu War.

"Health Care and
Service" — A207

1979, June 19   **Litho.**   **Perf. 12½x12**
522 A207 4c multicolored .... .25 .20
a.   Perf. 14¼x14 .... .30 .30
Health Year.

Boy and Girl Watching Candle — A208

1979, Sept. 13   **Litho.**   **Perf. 14½x14**
523 A208 4c multicolored .... .25 .20
South African Christmas Stamp Fund, 50th
anniversary.

Cape Town University, 150th
Anniversary — A209

1979, Oct. 1   **Litho.**   **Perf. 14x14½**
524 A209 4c multicolored .... .25 .20
a.   Perf. 12x12½ .... .30 .30

Southern Sun
Rose — A210

Designs: Roses.

1979, Oct. 4   **Litho.**   **Perf. 14½x14**
525 A210 4c multicolored .... .20 .20
526 A210 15c multicolored ...... .35 .30
527 A210 20c multicolored ...... .45 .40
528 A210 25c multicolored ...... .65 .55
a.   Souvenir sheet of 4, #525-528 2.25 2.25
     Nos. 525-528 (4) 1.65 1.45
Rosafari 1979, 4th World Rose Convention,
Pretoria, October.

Stellenbosch University — A211

1979, Nov. 8
529 A211 4c shown .... .20 .20
530 A211 15c Rhenish Church ... .30 .25
Stellenbosch (oldest town in South Africa),
300th anniversary.

A212   A213

1979, Dec. 18   **Photo.**   **Perf. 12½x12**
531 A212 4c multicolored .... .25 .20
Federation of Afrikaans Cultural Societies,
50th anniv.

1980, May 6   **Litho.**   **Perf. 14½x14**
Paintings by Pieter Wenning (1873-1921):
5c, Still Life with Sweet Peas. 25c, House in
the Suburbs, Cape Town.
532 A213 5c multicolored .... .25 .20

          Size: 45x37mm
533 A213 25c multicolored ...... .50 .35
a.   Souvenir sheet of 2, #532-533 1.75 1.00

Great Star of
Africa
Diamond — A214

1980, May 12   **Litho.**   **Perf. 14x14½**
534 A214 15c shown .... .65 .50
535 A214 20c Cullinan II diamond .75 .65
World Diamond Congress.

A215   A216

1980, Sept. 3   **Litho.**   **Perf. 14½x14**
536 A215 5c multicolored .... .25 .20
Christian Louis Leipoldt (1880-1947), writer
and physician.

1980, Oct. 9   **Litho.**
537 A216 5c multicolored .... .25 .20
University of Pretoria, 50th anniv.

Marine With Ships, by Willem van de
Velde — A217

Paintings: 10c, Firetail and Trainer, by
George Stubbs. 15c, Lavinia, by Thomas
Gainsborough, vert. 20c, Landscape, by Pieter
Post.

1980, Nov. 3   **Perf. 14½x14**
538 A217 5c multicolored .... .20 .20
539 A217 10c multicolored ...... .20 .20
540 A217 15c multicolored ...... .30 .25
541 A217 20c multicolored ...... .35 .30
a.   Souvenir sheet of 4, #538-541 1.50 1.25
     Nos. 538-541 (4) .... 1.05 .95
Natl. Gallery, 50th anniv.

P.J. Joubert, Paul Kruger, M.W. Pretorius (First Leaders of Triumvirate Government) — A218

Design: 10c, Monument, flag of South African Republic, 1880, vert.

1980, Dec. 15   Perf. 14x14½ 14½x14
542 A218 5c multicolored .20 .20
543 A218 10c multicolored .20 .20

Paardekraal Monument (built on site of founding of triumverate government) centennial.

British Troops in Battle of Amajuba — A219

1981, Feb. 27   Litho.   Perf. 14x14½
544 A219 5c Boer snipers, vert. .20 .20
545 A219 15c shown .35 .30

Battle of Amajuba centenary (led to independence of Orange Free State).

Scene from Verdi's Aida A220

1981, May 23   Litho.   Perf. 14½x14
546 A220 20c Raka ballet scene .35 .30
547 A220 25c shown .45 .35
a.   Souvenir sheet of 2, #546-547 1.25 1.00

Opening of State Theater, Pretoria.

Pres. Marais Viljoen — A221

Deaf Girl Learning to Speak — A222

1981, May 30   Perf. 14x14½
Size: 57x21mm
548 A221 5c Former presidents .20 .20
549 A221 15c shown .30 .25

1981, June 12   Perf. 14½x14
550 A222 5c shown .20 .20
551 A222 15c Man reading braille .30 .25

Institute for the Deaf and Blind, Worcester, centenary.

Natl. Cancer Assn. 50th Anniv. — A223

1981, July 10
552 A223 5c multicolored .25 .20

Calanthe Natalensis A224

Voortrekker Movement, 50th Anniv. A225

1981, Sept. 11   Litho.
553 A224 5c shown .20 .20
554 A224 15c Eulophia speciosa .45 .30
555 A224 20c Disperis fanniniae .60 .40
556 A224 25c Disa uniflora .75 .50
a.   Souvenir sheet of 4, #553-556 3.00 2.75
      Nos. 553-556 (4) 2.00 1.40

10th World Orchid Conf., Durban, 9/11-17.

1981, Sept. 30   Perf. 14x14½
557 A225 5c multicolored .25 .20

Scouting Year A226

TB Bacillus Centenary A227

1982, Feb. 22   Litho.   Perf. 14½x14
558 A226 15c Baden-Powell .40 .25

1982, Mar. 24   Litho.
559 A227 20c multicolored .40 .25

Return of Simonstown Naval Base, 25th Anniv. — A228

1982, Apr. 2   Perf. 14½x14
560 A228 8c Submarine .20 .20
561 A228 15c Strike craft .25 .20
562 A228 20c Mine sweeper .35 .30
563 A228 25c Harbor patrol
              boats .45 .35
a.   Souvenir sheet of 4, #560-563 2.75 2.25
      Nos. 560-563 (4) 1.25 1.05

Old Provost, Grahamstown A229

Design: 2c, Tuynhuys, Kaapstad (Cape Town). 3c, Appelhof, Bloemfontein. 4c, Raadsaal, Pretoria. 5c, Die Kasteel, Kaapstad. 6c, Goewermentsgebou, Bloemfontein. 7c, Drostdy, Graaf-Reinet. 8c, Leeuwenhof, Cape Town. 9c, Libertas, Pretoria. 10c, City Hall, Pietermaritzburg. 11c, City Hall, Kimberley. 12c, City Hall, Port Elizabeth. 14c, Johannesburg City Hall. 15c, Hotel Milner, Matjesfontein. 16c, Durban City Hall. 20c, Post Office, Durban. 25c, Melrose House, Pretoria. 30c, Old Legislative Assembly Building, Pietermaritzburg. 50c, Raadsaal, Bloemfontein. 1r, Houses of Parliament, Cape Town. 2r, Uniegebou, Pretoria.
Coils have different designs.

1982-87   Litho.   Perf. 14x14½
564 A229 1c brown ('84) .20 .20
565 A229 2c apple green .20 .20
566 A229 2c green .75 .20
567 A229 2c slate grn ('85) .20 .20
568 A229 3c purple ('85) 1.25 .20
569 A229 4c olive grn ('85) .20 .20
570 A229 5c carmine .20 .20
571 A229 6c brt green .20 .20
572 A229 7c gray green .20 .20
573 A229 8c blue .20 .20
574 A229 8c intense bl ('83) .20 .20
575 A229 9c brt rose lilac .20 .20
576 A229 10c lt red brown .20 .20
577 A229 10c violet brn ('83) .30 .20
578 A229 11c cerise ('84) .25 .20
579 A229 12c dp ultra ('85) .35 .20
580 A229 14c rose brn ('86) .50 .20
581 A229 16c red ('87) .60 .20
582 A229 20c vermilion .25 .20
583 A229 20c black ('85) .60 .20
584 A229 25c bister .25 .20

Size: 45x27mm
Perf. 14½x14
586 A229 30c brown ('86) 1.50 .20
587 A229 50c Prus blue ('86) 2.25 .20
588 A229 1r violet blue ('86) 2.50 .20
589 A229 2r cerise ('85) 5.00 .20
      Nos. 564-589 (25) 18.55 5.00

For surcharge see No. B12.

Engr.
590 A229 1c dark brown .20 .20
591 A229 2c slate grn ('83) .20 .20
592 A229 3c violet .20 .20
593 A229 4c olive green .20 .20
594 A229 5c dark lake ('83) .20 .20
595 A229 6c green blk ('84) .20 .35
596 A229 15c blue .20 .20
597 A229 20c black ('83) .50 .20
598 A229 30c violet brown .45 .20
599 A229 50c Prus blue .70 .25
600 A229 1r violet blue 1.50 .20
601 A229 2r rose carmine 3.00 .30
      Nos. 590-601 (12) 7.55 2.75

In some cases there are slight design differences from litho. stamp.

Perf. 14 Horiz.
Photo.   Coil Stamps
602 A229 1c Residence,
              Swellendam .20 .20
603 A229 2c City Hall, East
              London .40 .20
604 A229 5c Rissik St. PO,
              Johannesburg .45 .20
605 A229 10c Morgenster,
              Somerset West .70 .20
      Nos. 602-605 (4) 1.75 .80

Bradysaurus A230

Prehistoric Animals (Karoo Fossils).

1982, Dec. 1   Litho.   Perf. 14x14½
606 A230 8c shown .30 .20
607 A230 15c Lystrosaurus .60 .20
608 A230 20c Euparkeria .85 .25
609 A230 25c Thrinaxodon 1.25 .45
a.   Souvenir sheet of 4, #606-609 3.25 3.25
      Nos. 606-609 (4) 3.00 1.10

Weather Station, Gough Island A231

1983, Jan. 19   Litho.
610 A231 8c shown .20 .20
611 A231 20c Marion Isld. station .40 .30
612 A231 25c Reading instru-
              ments .55 .35
613 A231 40c Weather balloon,
              Antarctica .85 .55
      Nos. 610-613 (4) 2.00 1.40

Steam Locomotives — A232

1983, Apr. 27   Litho.
614 A232 10c Class 82, 1952 .35 .20
615 A232 20c Class 16E, 1935 .65 .50
616 A232 25c Class 6H, 1901 .80 .65
617 A232 40c Class 15F, 1939 1.40 1.00
      Nos. 614-617 (4) 3.20 2.35

Soccer — A233

Perf. 14½x14 (10c, 25c), 14x14½ (20c, 40c)
1983, July 20   Litho.
618 A233 10c Rugby, vert. .20 .20
619 A233 20c shown .40 .25
620 A233 25c Sailing, vert. .60 .35
621 A233 40c Equestrian .80 .55
      Nos. 618-621 (4) 2.00 1.35

Plettenberg Bay — A234

1983, Oct. 12   Litho.   Perf. 14½x14
622 A234 10c shown .20 .20
623 A234 20c Durban Beach .30 .20
624 A234 25c West Coast beach .40 .25
625 A234 40c Clifton beach
              scene .65 .45
a.   Souvenir sheet of 4, #622-625 2.50 2.00
      Nos. 622-625 (4) 1.55 1.10

English Writers of South Africa — A235

Designs: 10c, Thomas Pringle (1789-1834). 20c, Pauline Smith (1882-1959). 25c, Olive Schreiner (1855-1920). 40c, Percy FitzPatrick (1862-1931).

1984, Feb. 24   Litho.   Perf. 14½x14
626 A235 10c multicolored .20 .20
627 A235 20c multicolored .25 .20
628 A235 25c multicolored .35 .25
629 A235 40c multicolored .60 .35
      Nos. 626-629 (4) 1.40 1.00

Manganese — A236

1984, June 8   Litho.   Perf. 14½x14
630 A236 11c shown .50 .20
631 A236 20c Chromium .90 .35
632 A236 25c Vanadium 1.25 .40
633 A236 30c Titanium 1.40 .45
      Nos. 630-633 (4) 4.05 1.40

Bloukrans River Bridge A237

1984, Aug. 24
634 A237 11c shown .20 .20
635 A237 25c Durban 4-level
              Bridge In-
              terchange .80 .35
636 A237 30c Mfolozi Railroad
              Bridge .95 .40
637 A237 45c Gouritz River
              Bridge 1.40 .60
      Nos. 634-637 (4) 3.35 1.55

New Constitution
A238

Military Medals
A239

1984, Sept. 3   Litho.   Perf. 14x14½
638 A238 11c Preamble (English) .50 .20
639 A238 11c Preamble (Afri-
            caans)   .50 .20
  a. Pair, #638-639   1.00 .50
640 A238 25c Symbolic pillars,
            anthem   1.10 .60
641 A238 30c Arms   1.25 .65
      Nos. 638-641 (4)   3.35 1.65

1984, Nov. 9   Perf. 14½x14
642 A239 11c Pro Patria   .20 .20
643 A239 25c De Wet   .40 .25
644 A239 30c John Chard Deco-
            ration   .60 .30
645 A239 45c Honoris Crux   .80 .45
  a. Miniature sheet of 4, #642-645 2.50 1.75
      Nos. 642-645 (4)   2.00 1.20

Pres. Pieter
Willem Botha (b.
1916) — A240

1984, Nov. 2   Litho.   Perf. 14x14½
646 A240 11c multicolored   .30 .20
647 A240 25c multicolored   .60 .30

Frans David
Oerder,
Painter
(1867-1944)
A241

1985, Feb. 22   Litho.   Perf. 14½x14
648 A241 11c Reflections   .25 .20
649 A241 25c Ladies in a Garden .55 .30
650 A241 30c Still-Life with Lob-
            ster   .70 .35
651 A241 50c Still-Life with Mari-
            golds   1.10 .50
  a. Souvenir sheet of 4, #648-651 3.00 3.00
      Nos. 648-651 (4)   2.60 1.35

Cape
Parliament
Cent.
A242

1985, May 15   Litho.
652 A242 12c Parliament   .25 .20
653 A242 25c Speaker's chair .50 .30
654 A242 30c The National Con-
            vention, by Ed-
            ward Roworth   .55 .35
655 A242 50c South African
            arms   1.00 .45
      Nos. 652-655 (4)   2.30 1.30

Indigenous
Flowers
A243

Cape Silver
A244

1985, Aug. 23   Litho.   Perf. 14½x14
656 A243 12c Freesia   .20 .20
657 A243 25c Nerine   .65 .45
658 A243 30c Ixia   .75 .55
659 A243 50c Gladiolus   1.40 .90
      Nos. 656-659 (4)   3.00 2.05

1985, Nov. 5   Perf. 14½x14, 14x14½
660 A244 12c Sugar bowl, horiz. .20 .20
661 A244 25c Tea pot, horiz. .65 .20
662 A244 30c Goblet   .75 .30
663 A244 50c Coffee pot   1.40 .50
      Nos. 660-663 (4)   3.00 1.20

Blood
Transfusion
Services
A245

1986, Feb. 20   Perf. 14½x14
664 A245 12c Blood donation   .30 .20
665 A245 20c Transfusion   .70 .20
666 A245 25c Surgery   .90 .20
667 A245 30c Emergency aid   1.10 .35
      Nos. 664-667 (4)   3.00 .95

Republic of
South
Africa, 25th
Anniv.
A246

1986, May 30   Litho.   Perf. 14x14½
668 A246 14c Text in Afrikaans .75 .20
669 A246 14c Text in English .75 .20
  a. Pair, #668-669   2.00 2.00

Cultural Heritage — A247

Restoration projects: 14c, Drostdyhof, Free
Street, Graaff-Reinet, 19th cent. 20c, Pilgrim's
Rest, Eastern Transvaal, 1873. 25c, J.T.
Strapp and Son importers, c. 1893, Bethle-
hem. 30c, Palmdene, c. 1897,
Pietermaritzburg.

1986, Aug. 14   Perf. 14½x14
670 A247 14c multicolored   .40 .20
671 A247 20c multicolored   .60 .20
672 A247 25c multicolored   .70 .35
673 A247 30c multicolored   .85 .40
      Nos. 670-673 (4)   2.55 1.25

Johannesburg, Cent. — A248

Discovery of Gold
in Roodepoort,
Cent. — A249

1986, Sept. 25   Perf. 14x14½
674 A248 14c Johannesburg,
            1886   .65 .20
675 A249 20c Gold mine   .95 .35
676 A248 25c Johannesburg,
            1986   1.10 .40
677 A249 30c Gold   1.40 .50
  a. Souvenir sheet of 1   3.00 3.00
      Nos. 674-677 (4)   4.10 1.45

No. 677a for Johannesburg stamp exhibition. Sold for 50c.

Pearl
Mountain — A250

Beetles — A251

1986, Nov. 20   Litho.   Perf. 14x14½
678 A250 14c shown   .70 .70
679 A250 20c The Column,
            Drakensburg   1.00 1.00
680 A250 25c Maltese Cross,
            Cedarberg   1.25 1.25
681 A250 30c Bourke's Luck
            Potholes   1.50 1.50
      Nos. 678-681 (4)   4.45 4.45

1987, Mar. 6   Litho.   Perf. 14x14½
690 A251 14c Chaetodera regalis .70 .70
691 A251 20c Trichostetha fas-
            cicularis   1.00 1.00
692 A251 25c Julodis viridipes 1.25 1.25
693 A251 30c Ceroplesis militaris 1.50 1.50
      Nos. 690-693 (4)   4.45 4.45

Petroglyphs
A252

1987, June 4   Perf. 14½x14
694 A252 16c Eland, Sebaaieni
            Cave   .65 .65
695 A252 20c Leaping lion,
            Clocolan   .90 .90
696 A252 25c Black wildebeest,
            uMhlwazini Valley 1.10 1.10
697 A252 30c San dance,
            Floukraal   1.40 1.40
      Nos. 694-697 (4)   4.05 4.05

Paarl,
300th
Anniv.
A253

1987, Sept. 3
698 A253 16c Oude Pastorie   .40 .40
699 A253 20c Winegrowing   .55 .55
700 A253 25c Wagon-building   .65 .65
701 A253 30c KWV Cathedral
            Cellar   .80 .80
      Nos. 698-701 (4)   2.40 2.40

A souvenir sheet of one, No. 701, has decorative margin picturing emblem of the natl.
philatelic exhibition at Paarl, Sept. 16-19. Sold
for 50c.

Map, "The Bible" in 76
Languages — A254

Religious
Paintings by
Rembrandt
A255

Designs: 30c, Belshazzar's Feast. 50c, St.
Matthew and the Angel, vert.

Perf. 14x14½, 14½x14 (30c)
1987, Nov. 19
702 A254 16c shown   .40 .40
703 A255 30c shown   .80 .80
704 A255 50c multicolored   1.40 1.40
      Nos. 702-704 (3)   2.60 2.60

Bible Society of South Africa.
A 40c stamp was prepared and sent to post
offices, but was not issued. Some were sold
contrary to the withdrawal order, and used
examples are known.
For surcharge see No. B13.

Discovery of
the Cape of
Good Hope
by
Bartolomeu
Dias — A256

Designs: 16c, Dias, astrolabe, Cape of
Good Hope. 30c, Kwaaihoek Memorial. 40c,
Caravels, 1488. 50c, Martellus Map, c. 1489.

1988, Feb. 3   Perf. 14½x14
706 A256 16c multicolored   .55 .55
707 A256 30c multicolored   1.00 1.00
708 A256 40c multicolored   1.25 1.25
709 A256 50c multicolored   1.60 1.60
      Nos. 706-709 (4)   4.40 4.40

A souvenir sheet of one, No. 709, has decorative margin picturing emblem of the natl.
philatelic exhibition held at Pietermaritzburg,
Nov. 22-27. Sold for 70c.
For surcharge see No. B14.

French Huguenot
Settlement of the
Cape, 300th
Anniv. — A257

1988, Apr. 13   Perf. 14x14½
710 A257 16c Memorial, Frans-
            chhoek   .40 .40
711 A257 30c Map of France   .75 .75
712 A257 40c French-Dutch Bi-
            ble, 1672   1.10 1.10
713 A257 50c St. Bartholomew's
            Day Massacre,
            1572   1.50 1.50
      Nos. 710-713 (4)   3.75 3.75

For surcharges see Nos. B15-B18.

Lighthouses
A258

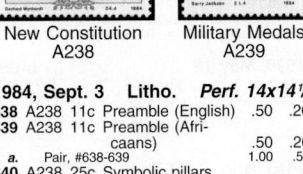

1988, June 9 — Perf. 14½x14

714	A258	16c	Pelican Point, 1932	.65	.65
715	A258	30c	Groenpunt, 1824	1.25	1.25
716	A258	40c	Agulhas, 1849	1.60	1.60
717	A258	50c	Umhlanga Rocks, 1954	2.00	2.00
a.			Souvenir sheet of 4, #714-717	7.00	7.00
			Nos. 714-717 (4)	5.50	5.50

"Standardised Mail"
"STANDARD POSTAGE"
Stamps inscribed thus were sold for the amount shown in ( ) on date of issue.

Succulents
A259

1988-93 — Litho. — Perf. 14x14½

735	A259	1c	Huernia zebrina	.20	.20
736	A259	2c	Euphorbia symmetrica	.20	.20
737	A259	5c	Lithops dorotheae	.20	.20
738	A259	7c	Gibbaeum newbrownii	.20	.20
739	A259	10c	Didymaotus lapidiformis	.20	.20
740	A259	16c	Vanheerdea divergens	.20	.20
741	A259	18c	Faucaria tigrina	.20	.20
742	A259	20c	Conophytum mundum	.20	.20
743	A259	21c	Gasteria armstrongii	.20	.20
744	A259	25c	Cheiridopsis pecularis	.20	.20
745	A259	30c	Tavaresia barklyi	.20	.20
a.			Strip, 2 ea 1c, 2c, 5c, 7c, 30c	6.00	
746	A259	35c	Dinteranthus wilmotianus	.35	.20
747	A259	40c	Frithia pulchra	.40	.20
748	A259	(45c)	Stapelia grandiflora	.40	.20
749	A259	50c	Lapidaria margaretae	.50	.50
750	A259	90c	Dioscorea elephantipes	.80	.50
751	A259	1r	Trichocaulon cactiforme	1.00	.70
752	A259	2r	Crassula columnaris	2.00	1.00
753	A259	5r	Anacampseros albissima	7.50	3.00
			Nos. 735-753 (19)	15.15	8.50

Coil Stamps
Photo.
Perf. 14 Horiz.

754	A259	1c	Adromischus marianiae	1.75	1.75
755	A259	2c	Titanopsis calcarea	.45	.45
756	A259	5c	Dactylopsis digitata	.45	.45
757	A259	10c	Pleiospilos bolusii	.85	.85
			Nos. 754-757 (4)	3.50	3.50

Issued: 18c, 4/1/89; 5r, 3/1/90; 21c, 4/2/90; #748, 4/1/93; others, 9/1/88.

Map and Settlers — A260

Exodus, Tapestry by W.H. Coetzer Studio — A261

Crossing the Drakensburg, Tapestry by Coetzer Studio (illustration reduced) — A262

Church of the Vow, Pietermaritzburg — A263

Perf. 14x14½, 14½x14 (50c)
1988, Nov. 21 — Litho.

758	A260	16c multicolored	.65	.40
759	A261	30c multicolored	1.10	.70
760	A262	40c multicolored	1.50	.95
761	A263	50c multicolored	1.75	1.25
		Nos. 758-761 (4)	5.00	3.30

The Great Trek, 150th anniv.

Discovery of a Living Specimen of the Coelacanth, 50th Anniv. A264

Designs: 16c, *Latimeria chalumnae*. 30c, J. L. B. Smith, Margaret Courtenay-Latimer. 40c, Smith Institute of Ichthyology, Grahamstown. 50c, Fish, GEO two-man research submarine.

1989, Feb. 9 — Perf. 14½x14

762	A264	16c multicolored	.80	.80
763	A264	30c multicolored	1.40	1.40
764	A264	40c multicolored	2.00	2.00
765	A264	50c multicolored	2.50	2.50
a.		Souvenir sheet of 1	7.00	7.00
b.		Souvenir sheet of 2	1.25	1.25
		Nos. 762-765 (4)	6.70	6.70

No. 765a has decorative margin picturing emblem of the natl. philatelic exhibition WANDERERS 101, held Sept. 6-9. Sold for 1.50r.
No. 765b was issued 6/97, sold for 1r and is inscribed for Old Mutual Environmental Education Center in sheet margin.

Soil Conservation Campaign of the Natl. Grazing Strategy — A265

1989, May 3 — Perf. 14x14½

766	A265	18c Desertification	.50	.50
767	A265	30c Eroded gullies	.80	.80
768	A265	40c Barrage	1.10	1.10
769	A265	50c Verdant plain	1.40	1.40
		Nos. 766-769 (4)	3.80	3.80

Natl. Rugby Board, Cent. A266

Springboks, foreign team emblems, match scenes.

1989, June 22

770	A266	18c France, 1980	.60	.45
771	A266	30c Australia, 1963	1.10	.80
772	A266	40c New Zealand, 1937	1.50	1.10
773	A266	50c British Isles, 1896	1.90	1.40
		Nos. 770-773 (4)	5.10	3.75

Paintings by Jacob Hendrik Pierneef (1886-1957) A267

1989, Aug. 3 — Perf. 14½x14

774	A267	18c *Composition in Blue*, 1928	.40	.20
775	A267	30c *Zanzibar*, 1926	.75	.30
776	A267	40c *The Bushveld*, 1949	1.10	.40
777	A267	50c *Cape Homestead*, 1942	1.25	1.00
a.		Souvenir sheet of 4, #774-777	3.50	3.50
		Nos. 774-777 (4)	3.50	1.40

Election of Pres. Frederik Willem de Klerk, Aug. 15 — A268

1989, Sept. 20 — Perf. 14x14½

778	A268	18c shown	.40	.20
779	A268	45c Portrait, diff.	1.00	.55

Fossil Fuels, Nuclear and Thermal Power A269

18c, SOEKOR gas project, Mossel Bay. 30c, SASOL coal conversion plant. 40c, Koeberg nuclear power plant. 50c, ESKOM thermal power station.

1989, Oct. 19

780	A269	18c multicolored	.45	.20
781	A269	30c multicolored	.80	.45
782	A269	40c multicolored	.95	.50
783	A269	50c multicolored	1.25	.60
		Nos. 780-783 (4)	3.45	1.75

Cooperation in Southern Africa — A270

Maps and: 18c, Cahora Bassa hydroelectric power project. 30c, Railway network. 40c, Lesotho Highlands water project. 50c, Veterinary care.

1990, Feb. 15 — Perf. 14½x14
Size of 18c, 40c: 68x26mm

784	A270	18c multicolored	.65	.35
785	A270	30c multicolored	1.10	.60
786	A270	40c multicolored	1.25	.75
787	A270	50c multicolored	1.75	.85
a.		Miniature sheet of 4, #784-787	4.75	4.75
		Nos. 784-787 (4)	4.75	2.55

Stamp Day — A271

Birds — A272

Stamps on stamps: a, Great Britain #1. b, Cape of Good Hope #2. c, Natal #4. d, Orange River Colony #10. e, Transvaal #3.

1990, May 12 — Litho.

788		Strip of 5	2.75	2.75
a.-e.	A271	21c any single	.50	.50

Penny Black, 150th anniv.

1990, Aug. 2 — Litho. — Perf. 14x14½

Designs: 21c, *Tauraco corythaix*. 35c, *Cossypha natalensis*. 40c, *Mirafra africana*. 50c, *Telophorus zeylonus*.

789	A272	21c multicolored	.65	.40
790	A272	35c multicolored	1.00	.70
791	A272	40c multicolored	1.25	.90
792	A272	50c multicolored	1.50	.95
		Nos. 789-792 (4)	4.40	2.95

A souvenir sheet of 1 #792 was sold by the Philatelic Foundation of South Africa. Value $5.

Karoo Landscape, Near Britstown A273

Tourism: #794, Camps Bay, Cape Peninsula. #795, Giraffes, Kruger Natl. Park. #796, Boschendal homestead, Drakenstein.

1990, Nov. 1 — Litho. — Perf. 14½x14

793	A273	50c multicolored	1.00	1.00
794	A273	50c multicolored	1.00	1.00
795	A273	50c multicolored	1.00	1.00
796	A273	50c multicolored	1.00	1.00
a.		Block of 4, #793-796	4.25	4.25

A274

A275

National Decorations: No. 797, Woltemade Cross for Bravery. No. 798, Order of the Southern Cross. No. 799, Order of the Star of South Africa. No. 800, Order for Meritorious Service. No. 801, Order of Good Hope.

1990, Dec. 6

797	A274	21c multicolored	.40	.30
798	A274	21c multicolored	.40	.30
799	A274	21c multicolored	.40	.30
800	A274	21c multicolored	.40	.30
801	A274	21c multicolored	.40	.30
a.		Souv. sheet of 5, #797-801	2.50	2.50
b.		Strip of 5, #797-801	2.00	2.00

1991, Feb. 21 — Litho.

Animal Breeding: a, Boer horse. b, Bonsmara cattle. c, Dorper sheep. d, Ridgeback dog. e, Putterie racing pigeon.

802	A275	21c Strip of 5, #a.-e.	3.75	3.00

Achievements — A276

Designs: 25c, First heart transplant, vert. 40c, Matimba power plant. 50c, Dolos breakwater blocks. 60c, Western Deep Levels Gold Mine, world's deepest mine, vert.

Perf. 14½x14 (25c, 60c), 14x14½ (40c, 50c, #806a)

1991, May 30   **Litho.**
803	A276	25c multicolored	.40	.20
804	A276	40c multicolored	.60	.30
805	A276	50c multicolored	.70	.35
806	A276	60c multicolored	.55	.40
a.		Souvenir sheet of 1	3.75	3.75
		Nos. 803-806 (4)	2.25	1.25

30th anniv. of Republic of South Africa.

1st Registration of Nurses & Midwives, Cent. — A277

1991, Aug. 15   Litho.   Perf. 14x14½
807	A277	60c multicolored	.85	.85

Creation of South African Post Office Ltd. — A278

1991, Oct. 1   **Litho.**
808	27c Post office	.40	.20
809	27c Telkom SA Ltd.	.40	.20
a.	A278 Pair, #808-809	.80	.80

South African Scientists A279

Designs: 27c, Sir Arnold Theiler (1867-1936), veterinarian. 45c, Sir Basil Schonland (1896-1972), physicist. 65c, Dr. Robert Broom (1866-1951), paleontologist. 85c, Dr. Alexander L. du Toit (1878-1948), geologist.

1991, Oct. 9   **Perf. 14½x14**
810	A279	27c multicolored	.50	.20
811	A279	45c multicolored	.80	.50
812	A279	65c multicolored	1.25	.65
813	A279	85c multicolored	1.50	.80
		Nos. 810-813 (4)	4.05	2.15

Antarctic Treaty, 30th Anniv. A280

1991, Dec. 5   **Litho.**
814	A280	27c SA Agulhas, penguins	.85	.20
815	A280	65c Meteorological chart	2.10	.95

Conservation — A281

1992, Feb. 6   Litho.   Perf. 14x14½
816	A281	27c Prevent erosion	.55	.20
817	A281	65c Water pollution	1.50	.90
818	A281	85c Air pollution	1.90	1.10
		Nos. 816-818 (3)	3.95	2.20

A souvenir sheet of 1 #817 was sold by Intersapa. Value $5.

A282

A283

Designs depicting history of postal stones: No. 819, Sailing ships at Table Bay. No. 820, Sailors going ashore at Aguada de Saldanha. No. 821, Sailors discovering postal stone near Versse River. No. 822, Finding letters under postal stones. No. 823, Reading news from other mariners.

1992, May 9   Litho.   Perf. 14x14½
819	A282	35c multicolored	.60	.50
820	A282	35c multicolored	.60	.50
821	A282	35c multicolored	.60	.50
822	A282	35c multicolored	.60	.50
823	A282	35c multicolored	.60	.50
a.		Strip of 5, #819-823	3.25	3.25

Stamp Day.

Perf. 14½x14, 14x14½
1992, July 9   **Litho.**

Antique Cape Furniture: No. 824, Queen Anne settee, c. 1750-70. No. 825, Stinkwood settee, c. 1800. No. 826, Canopy bed, c. 1800, vert. No. 827, Rocking cradle, 19th cent. No. 828, Waterbutt, c. 1800, vert. No. 829, Flemish style cabinet, c. 1700, vert. No. 830, Armoire, c. 1780-1790, vert. No. 831, Church chair, late 17th cent, vert. No. 832, Tub chair, c. 1770-1790, vert. No. 833, Bible desk, c. 1770, vert.

824	A283	35c multicolored	.65	.55
825	A283	35c multicolored	.65	.55
826	A283	35c multicolored	.65	.55
827	A283	35c multicolored	.65	.55
828	A283	35c multicolored	.65	.55
829	A283	35c multicolored	.65	.55
830	A283	35c multicolored	.65	.55
831	A283	35c multicolored	.65	.55
832	A283	35c multicolored	.65	.55
833	A283	35c multicolored	.65	.55
a.		Miniature sheet of 10, #824-833	6.50	6.50

Sports A284

1992, July 24   **Perf. 14x14½**
834	A284	35c Formula 1 Grand Prix	.40	.30
835	A284	35c Soccer	.40	.30
836	A284	55c Paris-le Cap Rally	.65	.50
837	A284	70c Track	.80	.65
838	A284	90c Rugby	1.00	.85
839	A284	1.05r Cricket	1.50	1.25
a.		Souvenir sheet of 6, #834-839	4.75	4.75
		Nos. 834-839 (6)	4.75	3.85

A285

A286

1992, Oct. 8   Litho.   Perf. 14½x14
840	A285	35c Women's Monument	.35	.35
841	A285	70c Sekupu Player	.90	.75
842	A285	90c The Hunter	1.25	.95
843	A285	1.05r Postman Lehman	1.50	.85
a.		Souvenir sheet of 4, #840-843	4.00	4.00
		Nos. 840-843 (4)	4.00	2.90

Sculptures by Anton van Wouw (1862-1945). No. 843a sold for 3.30r.

1993, Jan. 28   **Litho.**

South African Harbors.

844	A286	35c Walvis Bay	.35	.30
845	A286	55c East London	.65	.45
846	A286	70c Port Elizabeth	.85	.60
847	A286	90c Cape Town	1.00	.80
848	A286	1.05r Durban	1.25	.90
a.		Souv. sheet of 5, #844-848 + label	4.25	4.25
		Nos. 844-848 (5)	4.10	3.05

No. 848a sold for 3.90r.

A287

A288

Aircraft: a, Bristol Boxkite, 1907. b, Voisin, 1909. c, Bleriot XI, 1911. d, Paterson No. 2 biplane, 1913. e, Henri Farman F.27, 1915. f, BE2e, 1918. g, Vickers Vimy Silver Queen, 1920. h, SE-5a, 1921. i, Avro 504K, 1921. j, Armstrong-Whitworth Atalanta, 1930. k, DH66 Hercules, 1931. l, Westland Wapiti, 1931. m, Junkers F.13, 1932. n, Handley Page HP-42, 1933. o, Junkers Ju52/3m, 1934. p, Junkers Ju86, 1936. q, Hawker Hartbees, 1936. r, Short Empire flying boat Canopus, 1937. s, Miles Master II and Airspeed AS-10 Oxford, 1940. t, Harvard Mk IIa, 1942. u, Short Sunderland, 1945. v, Avro York, 1946. w, Douglas DC-7B, 1955. x, Sikorsky S-55C, 1956. y, Boeing 707-344, 1959.

1993, May 7   Litho.   Perf. 14x14½
Miniature Sheet of 25
849	A287	45c #a.-y.	18.00	18.00

A souvenir sheet containing #849a, 849y was sold by the Philatelic Foundation of South Africa.

1993-95   Litho.   Perf. 14x14½,

Endangered Fauna: 1c, Heleophryne rosei. 2c, Bradypodion taeniabronchum. 5c, Cordylus giganteus. 10c, Psammobates geometricus. 20c, Atelerix frontalis. 40c, Bunolagus monticularis. #856, Diceros bicornis. #856A, "Black Rhinocerous." 50c, Cercopithecus mitis. 55c, Proteles cristatus. 60c, Lycaon pictus. 70c, Hippotragus equinus. 75c, Poecilogale albinucha. 80c, Otis kori. 85c, Serinus citrinipectus. 90c, Spheniscus demersus. 1r, Grus carunculatus. 2r, Hirundo atrocaerulea. 5r, Polemaetus bellicosus. 10r, Terathopius ecaudatus.

Inscriptions in Latin
850	A288	1c multicolored	.20	.20
851	A288	2c multicolored	.20	.20
852	A288	5c multicolored	.20	.20
853	A288	10c multicolored	.20	.20

854	A288	20c multicolored	.20	.20
a.		Strip, 1c, 2 ea 2c, 20c	1.00	
b.		Strip, 20c, 2 ea 5c, 10c	1.00	
c.		Strip, 20c, 2 each 5c, 10c, perf. 14½ vert.	1.00	
855	A288	40c multicolored	.30	.20
856	A288	(45c) multicolored	.35	.20
857	A288	50c multicolored	.35	.20
a.		Strip, #850, 852, 857, 2 #851, Perf. 14½ Vert.	1.10	
858	A288	55c multicolored	.35	.20
859	A288	60c multicolored	.40	.20
860	A288	70c multicolored	.45	.20
861	A288	75c multicolored	.50	.20
862	A288	80c multicolored	.60	.20
862A	A288	85c multicolored	.60	.30
863	A288	90c multicolored	.65	.20
a.		Booklet pane of 10 Complete booklet, #863a	—	
864	A288	1r multicolored	.75	.20
865	A288	2r multicolored	1.75	.20
866	A288	5r multicolored	4.00	.50
867	A288	10r multicolored	7.50	1.50
		Nos. 850-867 (19)	19.55	5.50

#857a exists with tab showing Reader's Digest emblem in either red or black; also in different order with emblem in blue.

Issued: #854b, 8/24/94; #854c, 10/94; #857a, 9/1/95; 85c, 10/2/95; #863a, 1995; others, 9/3/93.

See designs A336 and A343 (no frames).

Wildlife Type with English Inscriptions

Designs: 1c, Table Mountain ghost frog. 2c, Smith's dwarf chameleon. 10c, Geometric tortoise. 20c, Southern African hedgehog. 40c, Riverine rabbit. (45c), Black rhinoceros. 50c, Samango monkey. 60c, Cape hunting dog. 70c, Roan antelope. 90c, Jackass penguin. 1r, Wattled crane. 2r, Blue swallow. 5r, Martial eagle. 20r, Fish Eagle.

Perf. 14x14¼, 14 Vert. on 1 or 2 sides (1c, 2c, 10c, 55c), 13x14½ (#867F)

1996-98   **Litho.**
867A	A288	1c multicolored	.20	.20
867B	A288	2c multicolored	.20	.20
867C	A288	10c multicolored	.20	.20
867D	A288	20c multicolored	.20	.20
867E	A288	40c multicolored	.20	.20
867F	A288	(45c) multicolored	.40	.25
n.		Booklet pane of 10	3.00	
		Complete booklet, #867Fn	3.00	
o.		Souvenir sheet of 1	.55	.55
867G	A288	50c multicolored	.50	.50
867H	A288	60c multicolored	.60	.60
p.		Strip of 5, 1c, 10c, 55c, 2 2c, perf 14 vert.	1.10	
867I	A288	70c multicolored	.25	.20
867J	A288	90c multicolored	.45	.20
867K	A288	1r multicolored	.45	.20
867L	A288	2r multicolored	1.00	.20
867M	A288	5r multicolored	2.00	.90

Perf. 14x14¼ Syncopated
867Q	A288	20c multicolored	.20	.20
867R	A288	(45c) multicolored	.60	.45
867S	A288	50c multicolored	.50	.25
867T	A288	60c multicolored	.25	.20
867U	A288	1r multicolored	3.50	.40

Size: 34x25mm
Perf. 14¾ Syncopated
867V	A288	20r multiticolored	9.50	4.75

No. 867Fn is inscribed in sheet margin for ExpoScience Internationale '97, and sold for 1r.

No. 867Hp has tab showing Reader's Digest emblem and release date in either green or orange.

Issued: #867Hp, 8/1; #867F, 7/7/97.

First Postal Services in South Africa, 190th Anniv. A289

Designs: 45c, Dragoons, Cape Town-False Bay Route. 65c, Ox train, Cape Town-Stellenbosch. 85c, Khoi-Khoin runners. 1.05r, Post riders, Cape Town-eastern districts.

1993, Oct. 8   **Perf. 14x14½**
868	A289	45c multicolored	.55	.55
869	A289	65c multicolored	.85	.75
870	A289	85c multicolored	1.00	.95
871	A289	1.05r multicolored	1.25	1.25
		Nos. 868-871 (4)	3.65	3.50

Tourism
A290

a, Namaqualand. b, North Beach, Durban.
c, Lion. d, Apple Express. e, Oryx gazella.

1993, Nov. 12   Litho.   Perf. 14½x14
872 A290 85c Strip of 5, #a.-e.   5.50 5.50

Export
Fruits
A291

1994, Jan. 28   Litho.   Perf. 14½x14
873 A291 85c Grapes   .80 .65
874 A291 90c Apples   .85 .70
875 A291 1.05r Plums   1.00 .80
876 A291 1.25r Oranges   1.25 1.00
877 A291 1.40r Avocados   1.40 1.10
    Nos. 873-877 (5)   5.30 4.25

A souvenir sheet of 1 #873 was sold for 3r
by the Philatelic Foundation of South Africa.
Value $3.50.

Peace and Goodwill — A292

Childrens' drawings: 45c, Smiling faces, by
Nicole Davies. 70c, Dove flying toward olive
tree, by Robynne Lawrie. 95c, Three girls,
dove, scattered cartridge cases, by Batami
Nothmann. 1.15r, Faces surrounding "peace,"
by Karen Uys.

1994, Apr. 8   Litho.   Perf. 14½x14
878 A292 45c multicolored   .50 .50
879 A292 70c multicolored   .75 .70
880 A292 95c multicolored   1.00 .95
881 A292 1.15r multicolored   1.25 1.10
   a.   Souvenir sheet of 1   3.50 3.50
    Nos. 878-881 (4)   3.50 3.20

No. 881a was issued 8/97, sold for 1.15r
and is inscribed "Chernobyl's Children, a decade later 1986-1996" in margin.

Inauguration of
Pres. Nelson
Mandela — A293

Perf. 14x14½, 14½x14
1994, May 10   Litho.
882 A293 45c shown   .70 .60
883 A293 70c Anthems, horiz.   1.10 .90
884 A293 95c Flag, horiz.   1.60 1.25
885 A293 1.15r Union Bldgs.,
      horiz.   2.00 1.50
    Nos. 882-885 (4)   5.40 4.25

Tugboats — A294

1994, May 13   Perf. 14½x14
886 A294 45c TS McEwen   .50 .40
887 A294 70c Sir William Hoy   .70 .65
888 A294 95c Sir Charles Elliott   .95 .90
889 A294 1.15r Eland   1.25 1.00
890 A294 1.35r Pioneer   1.40 1.25
   a.   Souvenir sheet of 5, #886-890   5.50 5.50
    Nos. 886-890 (5)   4.80 4.20

Our Family — A295

Children's paintings: a, Mother Hands Out
Work (C1.5). b, My Friends and I at Play
(C2.5). c, Family Life (C3.5). d, Sunday in
Church (C4.5). e, I Visit My Brother in the Hos-
pital (C5.5).

1994, July 10   Litho.   Perf. 14x14½
891 A295 45c Strip of 5, #a.-e.   2.50 2.50

Stamp Day — A296

1994, Sept. 30   Litho.   Perf. 14
892 A296 50c Bulk mail   .50 .50
893 A296 70c Proof of delivery   .70 .70
894 A296 95c Registered mail   .95 .95
895 A296 1.15r Express delivery   1.10 1.10
    Nos. 892-895 (4)   3.25 3.25

Heather — A297

Designs: a, Erica tenuifolia. b, Erica urna-
viridis. c, Erica decora. d, Erica aristata. e,
Erica dichrus.

1994, Nov. 18   Litho.   Perf. 14
896 A297 95c Strip of 5, #a.-e.   4.50 4.50

Tourism — A298

#897, Phacochoerus aethiopicus, Eastern,
Transvaal Province. #898, Lost City, Sun City,
North West Province. #899, Ceratotherium
simum, KwaZulu/Natal Province. #900, Water-
front, Cape Town, Western Cape Province.
#901, Adansonia digitata, Northern Transvaal
Province. #902, Highland Route, Free State.
#903, Augrabies Falls, Northern Cape Prov-
ince. #904, Addo Elephant Natl. Park, Eastern
Cape Province. #905, Union Buildings, Preto-
ria, Gauteng.
Illustration reduced.

1995-97   Litho.   Perf. 14
897 A298 50c multicolored   .60 .60
898 A298 50c multicolored   .60 .60
899 A298 (60c) multicolored   .70 .70
900 A298 (60c) multicolored   .70 .70
901 A298 (60c) multicolored   .70 .70
   a.   #901 + label, perf. 14 on one
      side   1.25 1.25
   b.   Souvenir sheet of 1   3.50 3.50

---

902 A298 (60c) multicolored   .70 .70
903 A298 (60c) multicolored   .70 .70
904 A298 (60c) multicolored   .70 .70
905 A298 (60c) multicolored   .70 .70
   a.   Strip of 5, #901-905   3.75 3.75
    Nos. 897-905 (9)   6.10 6.10

#901a sold for 70c; #901b for 1.10r on date
of issue.
Issued: #897, 1/18; #898, 2/15; #899, 4/28;
#900, 5/12; #901-905, 6/30; #901a, 2/97;
#901b 8/97.

South African Airforce, 75th
Anniv. — A299

DeHavilland DH-9 biplane, Cheetah D
fighter.

1995, Feb. 1   Litho.   Perf. 14
906 A299 50c multicolored   1.75 1.75

First Trans-Africa Flight, 75th
Anniv. — A300

Vickers Vimy bomber Silver Queen, map of
route.

1995, Feb. 1
907 A300 95c multicolored   .55 .55

South
Africa,
1995
Rugby
World
Cup
Champions
A301

Designs: No. 908, Shown. No. 909, Player
running with ball, vert. No. 910, Player holding
trophy, vert. No. 911, Like #908, World Champions. No. 912, Scrum, two players.

1995   Litho.   Perf. 14
908 A301 (60c) multicolored   .30 .30
   a.   Perf. 14 horiz.   .30 .30
909 A301 (60c) multicolored   .30 .30
   a.   Souvenir sheet of 1   1.25 1.25
   b.   Perf. 14 vert.   .30 .30
   c.   Booklet pane, 5 each #908a,
      909b   5.25
      Complete booklet, #909c   5.25
   d.   Booklet pane, 10 #909b   5.25
      Complete booklet #909d   5.25
910 A301 (60c) multicolored   .30 .30
911 A301 (60c) multicolored   .30 .30
Size: 68x26mm
912 A301 1.15r multicolored   .55 .55
    Nos. 908-912 (5)   1.75 1.75

Issued: #910-911, 6/28; others 5/25.

CSIR
(Council for
Scientific
and
Industrial
Research),
50th Anniv.
A302

1995, June 15
913 A302 (60c) Purifying water   .60 .60

Marine
Science in
South
Africa, Cent.
A303

1995, Aug. 25   Litho.   Perf. 14
914 A303 (60c) Dr. JDF Gilchrist   .60 .60

Souvenir Sheet

Singapore '95 — A304

Illustration reduced.

1995, Sept. 1
915 A304 (60c) multicolored   1.00 1.00

Masakhane
Campaign
A305

1995   Perf. 14x14¼
916 A305 (60c) multicolored   .60 .60
   a.   Booklet pane of 10   6.00
      Complete booklet, No. 916a   6.00
Booklet Stamp
Size: 29x20mm
916B A305 (60c) multicolored   .60 .60
   c.   Booklet pane of 10   6.00
      Complete booklet, #916c   6.00
    Issued: #916, 9/16; #916B, 12/1.

Visit of Pope John   Mahatma
Paul II — A306   Gandhi — A307

1995, Sept. 16   Perf. 14
917 A306 (60c) multicolored   .90 .90

1995, Oct. 2
Designs: (60c), 1906 Photograph. 1.40r,
Ghandhi in later years.
918 A307 (60c) blue   .50 .50
   a.   Souvenir sheet of 1   .70 .70
919 A307 1.40r brown   1.10 1.10
   a.   Souvenir sheet of 1   1.40 1.40

No. 918a is inscribed in sheet margin for
50th anniv. of Congress Alliance for Democratic South Africa. Issued July 1997.
Design on stamp in No. 919a extends to
perforations.
See India Nos. 1534-1535.

World Post
Day — A308

1995
920 A308 (60c) multicolored   .70 .70
Size: 65x60mm
Imperf
921 A308   5r multicolored   4.00 4.00
Stampex '95.
Issued: (60c), 10/9; 5r, 10/19.

UN, 50th
Anniv.
A309

1995, Oct. 24   **Litho.**   *Perf. 14*
922 A309 (60c) multicolored   .50 .50

Souvenir Sheet

UNESCO, 50th Anniv. — A310

Illustration reduced.

1995, Oct. 24
923 A310 (60c) multicolored   .50 .50

Shells — A311   A312

1995, Nov. 24
924 A311 (60c) Afrivoluta priglei   .55 .55
925 A311 (60c) Lyria africana   .55 .55
926 A311 (60c) Marginella mosai-
      ca   .55 .55
927 A311 (60c) Conus pictus   .55 .55
928 A311 (60c) Gypreaea fultoni   .55 .55
   a.   Strip of 5, #924-928   2.75 2.75

1996, Jan. 8   **Litho.**   *Perf. 14*
1996 African Cup of Nations Soccer Championships: Nos. 929-933, Various soccer
plays, map of Africa. No. 934, Player in traditional uniform.

Color of "RSA"
929 A312 (60c) blue   .60 .60
930 A312 (60c) yellow   .60 .60
931 A312 (60c) red   .60 .60
932 A312 (60c) gray   .60 .60
933 A312 (60c) green   .60 .60
   a.   Strip of 5, Nos. 929-933   3.00 3.00
Souvenir Sheet
934 A312 (1.15r) multicolored   .70 .70

South African Victory
in African Nations
Soccer
Championship
A312a

1996, Feb. 8   **Litho.**   *Perf. 14½x14*
934A A312a (60c) multicolored   .70 .70

City of Bloemfontein, 150th
Anniv. — A313

1996, Mar. 28   **Litho.**   *Perf. 14*
935 A313 (60c) multicolored   .80 .80

Souvenir Sheet

New Year 1996 (Year of the Rat) —
A313a

Illustration reduced.

1996, May 18   **Litho.**   *Perf. 14*
940D   A313a 60c multicolored   1.00 1.00
CHINA '96.

Man in a Donkey Cart, by Gerard
Sekoto (1913-93) — A314

Paintings: #942, 2r, Song of the Pick. #943,
2r, Yellow Houses, Sophiatown, 1940, vert.

1996, June 1   **Litho.**   *Perf. 14*
941 A314 1r multicolored   .60 .60
942 A314 2r multicolored   1.25 1.25
Souvenir Sheet
943 A314 2r multicolored   1.50 1.50

Youth
Day — A315

1996, June 8
944 A315 (60c) multicolored   .50 .50

Comrades Marathon, 75th
Anniv. — A316

1996, June 8   **Litho.**   *Perf. 14*
945 A316 (60c) multicolored   .50 .50

Souvenir Sheet

Parliament Building, Toronto — A316a

Illustration reduced.

1996, June 8   **Litho.**   *Perf. 14*
945A   A316a 2r multicolored   1.50 1.50
CAPEX '96.

A317   A318

1996 Summer Olympic Games, Atlanta: No.
946: a, Cycling. b, Swimming. c, Boxing. d,
Running. e, Pole vault.
1.40r, South African Olympic emblem.

1996, July 5   **Litho.**   *Perf. 14½x14*
946 A317 (70c) Strip of 5, #a.-e.   2.40 2.40
              Perf. 14
947 A317 1.40r multicolored   .85 .85
No. 946 was issued in sheets of 10 stamps.

1996, Aug. 1   **Litho.**   *Perf. 14*
Background color: a, Vermilion & multi. b,
Deep blue & multi. c, Deep yellow & multi. d,
Bright blue & multi. e, Red & multi.
948   Strip of 5   2.50 2.50
   a.-e.   A318 (70c) any single   .50 .50
New Democratic Constitution.

South African Merchant Marine, 50th
Anniv. — A319

Paintings of ships, by Peter Bilas: No. 949:
a, Sea Pioneer. b, SA Winterberg.
No. 950: a, Langloof. b, SA Vaal.
2r, Constantia.

1996, Aug. 5   **Litho.**   *Perf. 14*
949   Pair   1.25 1.25
   a.-b.   A319 (70c) any single   .60 .60
950   Pair   2.75 2.75
   a.-b.   A319 1.40r any single   1.25 1.25
Souvenir Sheet
950C A319 2r multicolored   1.50 1.50
No. 950C contains one 72x30mm stamp.

A320

A321

1996, Aug. 9   **Litho.**   *Perf. 14*
951 A320 70c multicolored   .50 .50
Natl. Women's Day.

1996, Oct. 9
952 A321 70c multicolored   .50 .50
World Post Day.

Christmas — A322

1996, Oct. 9
953 A322 70c multicolored   .50 .50
No. 953 exists in a privately produced souvenir, sold at 2r for charitable purposes.

Souvenir Sheet

Bloemfontein, 150th Natl. Stamp
Show — A323

Illustration reduced.

1996, Oct. 9   **Litho.**   *Perf. 14½x14*
954 A323 2r multicolored   1.00 1.00

South African Nobel
Laureates, Death
Cent. of Alfred
Nobel — A324

a, Max Theiler, medicine, 1951. b, Albert
Luthuli, peace, 1960. c, Alfred Nobel (1833-
96). d, Allan Cormack, medicine, 1979. e,
Aaron Klug, chemistry, 1982. f, Desmond
Tutu, peace, 1984. g, Nadine Gordimer, literature, 1991. h, Symbol for Nobel Prizes 1901-
96. i, Nelson R. Mandela, peace, 1993. j, F.W.
de Klerk, peace, 1993.

1996, Nov. 4
955 A324 (70c) Sheet of 10, #a.-
      k.   4.75 4.75
   k.   Souvenir sheet, #955c   .60 .60

First
Motor
Car in
South
Africa,
Cent.
A325

1997, Jan. 4   **Litho.**   *Perf. 14*
956 A325 (70c) multicolored   1.00 1.00

Souvenir Sheet

Hong Kong '97 — A326

Perf. 14 Syncopated
1997, Feb. 12   Litho.
957 A326 3r multicolored   2.50 2.50

Natl. Water Week and Water Day — A328

Save water for: No. 959, Farming. No. 960, Gardening. No. 961, Health. No. 962, Housing. No. 963, For all.

Perf. 14 Syncopated on 2 or 3 Sides
1997, Mar. 22   Litho.
Booklet Stamps
959	A328	(70c) multicolored	.60	.60
960	A328	(70c) multicolored	.60	.60
961	A328	(70c) multicolored	.60	.60
962	A328	(70c) multicolored	.60	.60
963	A328	(70c) multicolored	.60	.60
a.		Booklet pane, 2 each #959-963	6.00	6.00
		Complete booklet	6.00	6.00

Perf. 14x14¼ on 2 or 3 Sides
1997, Mar.   Litho.
Booklet Stamps
963B	A328	(70c) Like #959	.60	.60
963C	A328	(70c) Like #960	.60	.60
963D	A328	(70c) Like #961	.60	.60
963E	A328	(70c) Like #962	.60	.60
963F	A328	(70c) Like #963	.60	.60
g.		Bklt. pane, 2 ea #963B-963F	6.00	6.00
		Complete booklet, #963Fg	6.00	6.00

South African Navy, 75th Anniv. — A329

Warships: No. 964, Strike craft SAS Kobie Coetsee. No. 965, Survey ship SAS Protea. No. 966, Mine counter-measures ship SAS Umkomaas. No. 967, Submarine Emily Hobhouse, anti-submarine frigate SAS President Pretorius.

1997, Apr. 1   **Perf. 14 Syncopated**
964	A329	(70c) multicolored	.60	.60
965	A329	(70c) multicolored	.60	.60
966	A329	(70c) multicolored	.60	.60
967	A329	(70c) multicolored	.60	.60
a.		Block of 4, #964-967	2.40	2.40

First Democratic Elections, 5th Anniv. — A330

People voting, signs saying: No. 968, "Election Day, 27, April, 1994." No. 969, "Polling Station." No. 970, "Register Here." No. 971, "Vote Here." No. 972, "Ballot Box."

Perf. 14 Syncopated
1997, Apr. 26   Litho.
968	A330	(70c) black & red	.50	.50
969	A330	(70c) black & red	.50	.50
970	A330	(70c) black & red	.50	.50
971	A330	(70c) black & red	.50	.50
972	A330	(70c) black & red	.50	.50
b.		Strip of 5, #968-972	2.50	2.50

Souvenir Sheet

New Year 1997 (Year of the Ox) — A330a

Illustration reduced.

1997, May 2   Litho.   **Perf. 14**
972A   A330a 4.50r multicolored   2.25 2.25
SAPDA '97.

A331   A332

Cultural Artifacts.

1997, May 18   **Perf. 14**
973	A331	(70c) Zulu baskets	.50	.50
974	A331	(70c) S. Sotho figure	.50	.50
975	A331	(70c) S. Ndebele figure	.50	.50
976	A331	(70c) Venda door	.50	.50
977	A331	(70c) Tsonga medicine gourd	.50	.50
978	A331	(70c) Wooden pot, N. cape	.50	.50
979	A331	(70c) Khoi walking stick	.50	.50
980	A331	(70c) Tswana knife handle	.50	.50
981	A331	(70c) Xhosa pipe	.50	.50
982	A331	(70c) Swazi vessel	.50	.50
a.		Sheet of 10, #973-982	5.00	5.00

1997, Dec.   **Perf. 14x15**
973a		Zulu baskets	.60	.60
974a		S. Sotho figure	.60	.60
975a		S. Ndebele figure	.60	.60
976a		Venda door	.60	.60
977a		Tsonga medicine gourd	.60	.60
978a		Wooden pot, N. cape	.60	.60
979a		Khoi walking stick	.60	.60
980a		Tswana knife handle	.60	.60
981a		Xhosa pipe	.60	.60
982b		Swazi vessel	.60	.60
982c		Bklt. pane, #973a-981a, 982b	6.00	
		Complete booklet, 2 #982c	12.00	

1997, June 5   **Perf. 14**
Birds.
983	A332	(70c) White-breasted cormorant	.50	.50
984	A332	(70c) Hammerkop	.50	.50
985	A332	(70c) Pied kingfisher	.50	.50
986	A332	(70c) Purple heron	.50	.50
987	A332	(70c) Black-headed heron	.50	.50
988	A332	(70c) Darter	.50	.50
989	A332	(70c) Green-backed heron	.50	.50
990	A332	(70c) White-faced duck	.50	.50
a.		Souvenir sheet of 1	1.25	1.25
991	A332	(70c) Saddle-billed stork	.50	.50
992	A332	(70c) Water dikkop	.50	.50
a.		Sheet of 10, #983-992	5.00	5.00
b.		Booklet pane of 10, #983-992, perf. 14x14¾	5.00	5.00
		Complete booklet, 2 #992b	10.00	

Birds look bluer and browner on some stamps from No. 992b. No. 992a has Ilsapex 98 emblem in margin, which is not found on No. 992b.
No. 990a, issued 7/11/97, is inscribed in sheet margin for JUNASS '97, and sold for 2r.

Grocott's, Muirhead & Gowie Buildings, Grahamstown — A333

Illustration reduced.

1997, May 29   Litho.   **Perf. 14**
993 A333 5r multicolored   3.00 3.00
PACIFIC 97.

Indigenous Cattle A335

Perf. 14½ Syncopated
1997, Aug. 10
999	A335	(70c) Nguni	.60	.60
1000	A335	(70c) Bonsmara	.60	.60
1001	A335	(70c) Afrikander	.60	.60
1002	A335	(70c) Drakensberger	.60	.60
a.		Block of 4, #999-1002	2.40	2.40

Antarctic Wildlife A336

1997, Aug. 27   Litho.   **Perf. 14**
1003	A336	(70c) Leopard seal	.60	.60
1004	A336	1.20r Antarctic skua	1.00	1.00
1005	A336	1.70r King penguin	1.40	1.40
		Nos. 1003-1005 (3)	3.00	3.00

Enoch Sontonga (1873-1905), Author of Africa's Natl. Anthem — A337

Perf. 14 Syncopated
1997, Sept. 24   Litho.
1006	A337	(70c) shown	.50	.50
1007	A337	(70c) "Nkosi Sikelel iAfrika"	.50	.50
a.		Pair, #1006-1007	1.00	1.00

Heritage Day.

Souvenir Sheet

Cape Town '97 Natl. Stamp Show — A338

1997, Oct. 8   **Perf. 14**
1008 A338 4.50r multicolored   2.25 2.25

Souvenir Sheet

World Post Day — A339

1997, Oct. 9   **Perf. 14 Syncopated**
1009 A339 (70c) multicolored   .70 .70
No. 1009 sold for 1r on day of issue.

SANTA (South African Natl. Tuberculosis Assoc., 50th Anniv. — A340

Designs featuring former Christmas seals: No. 1010, Bethlehem. No. 1011, Candles on each side of Cross of Lorraine. No. 1012, Candles, angels, Cross. No. 1013, Cross, angel kneeling. No. 1014, Santa carrying Cross. No. 1015, Madonna and Child, Cross. No. 1016, Christmas trees. No. 1017, Magi. No. 1018, Bell, stained glass window. No. 1019, Native African kneeling, flag.

1997, Nov. 3   **Perf. 14 Syncopated**
1010	A340	(70c) multicolored	.50	.50
1011	A340	(70c) multicolored	.50	.50
1012	A340	(70c) multicolored	.50	.50
1013	A340	(70c) multicolored	.50	.50
1014	A340	(70c) multicolored	.50	.50
1015	A340	(70c) multicolored	.50	.50
1016	A340	(70c) multicolored	.50	.50
1017	A340	(70c) multicolored	.50	.50
1018	A340	(70c) multicolored	.50	.50
1019	A340	(70c) multicolored	.50	.50
a.		Sheet of 10, #1010-1019	5.00	5.00

Souvenir Sheet

New Year 1998 (Year of the Tiger) — A341

Illustration reduced.

1998, Jan. 28   Litho.   **Perf. 14x14½**
1020 A341 5r multicolored   2.50 2.50

Natl. Sea Rescue Institute A342

1998, Feb. 11   **Perf. 14 Syncopated**
1021 A342 (70c) multicolored   .90 .90

South Africa Standard Postage

Fauna (no frame) — A343

5c, Giant girdle-tailed lizard. 10c, Geometric tortoise. 20c, Southern African hedgehog. 30c, Spotted hyena. 40c, Riverine rabbit. 50c, Samango monkey. 60c, Cape hunting dog. 70c, Roan antelope. 80c, Kori bustard. 90c, Jackass penguin. 1r, Wattled crane. #1032, Impala. #1033, Waterbuck. #1034, Blue wildebeest. #1035, Eland. #1036, Kudu. #1037, Black rhinoceros. #1038, White rhinoceros. #1039, Buffalo. #1040, Lion. #1041, Leopard. #1042, African elephant. #1044, Giraffe. 1.50r, Tawny eagle, vert. 2r, Blue swallow. 2.30r, Cape vulture, vert.   5r, Martial eagle. 10r, Bateluer. 20r, Fish eagle.

Perf. 14x14¼, 14x14¼, 14¼x14
Syncopated (#1043), 14x14¼
Syncopated on 2 or 3 Sides
(#1036B-1036F, 1042B-1042F)

1998-2000			Litho.	
1021A	A343	5c multi	.20	.20
1022	A343	10c multi	.20	.20
1023	A343	20c multi	.20	.20
1024	A343	30c multi	.20	.20
1025	A343	40c multi	.20	.20
1026	A343	50c multi	.20	.20
1027	A343	60c multi	.20	.20
1028	A343	70c multi	.20	.20
1029	A343	80c multi	.35	.35
1030	A343	90c multi	.35	.35
1031	A343	1r multi	.35	.35
1032	A343	(1.10r) multi, vert.	.65	.65
1033	A343	(1.10r) multi, vert.	.65	.65
1034	A343	(1.10r) multi, vert.	.65	.65
1035	A343	(1.10r) multi, vert.	.65	.65
1036	A343	(1.10r) multi, vert.	.65	.65
a.		Strip of 5, #1032-1036	3.25	3.25
h.		Booklet pane, 2 each #1032-1036, "Standard" 5mm long	6.50	
		Booklet, #1036h	6.50	
1036B	A343	(1.10r) Like #1034	.40	.40
1036C	A343	(1.10r) Like #1035	.40	.40
1036D	A343	(1.10r) Like #1036	.40	.40
1036E	A343	(1.10r) Like #1032	.40	.40
1036F	A343	(1.10r) Like #1033	.40	.40
g.		Booklet pane, 2 each #1036B-1036F	4.00	
		Booklet, #1036Fg	4.00	
1037	A343	(1.10r) multi	.40	.40
a.		Booklet pane of 10	4.00	
		Complete bklt., #1037a	4.00	
1038	A343	(1.30r) multi	.50	.50
1039	A343	(1.30r) multi	.50	.50
1040	A343	(1.30r) multi	.50	.50
1041	A343	(1.30r) multi	.50	.50
1042	A343	(1.30r) multi	.50	.50
a.		Booklet pane, 2 ea #1038-1042	5.00	
		Complete bklt., #1042a	5.00	
1042B	A343	(1.30r) Like #1038	.50	.50
1042C	A343	(1.30r) Like #1039	.50	.50
1042D	A343	(1.30r) Like #1040	.50	.50
1042E	A343	(1.30r) Like #1041	.50	.50
1042F	A343	(1.30r) Like #1042	.50	.50
g.		Booklet pane, 2 each #1042B-1042F	5.00	
		Complete bklt., #1042Fg	5.00	
1043	A343	2r multi	.80	.80
1043A	A343	2r multi	.80	.80
1044	A343	3r multi	1.25	1.25
1045	A343	5r multi	2.25	2.25

Size: 20x38mm
Perf. 14¼x13¾

| 1045A | A343 | 1.50r multi | .60 | .60 |
| 1045B | A343 | 2.30r multi | .90 | .90 |

Size: 35x25mm
Perf. 14¼x14

| 1046 | A343 | 10r multi | 4.00 | 4.00 |
| a. | | Perf. 14¾ | 4.00 | 4.00 |

Perf. 14¾ Syncopated

| 1047 | A343 | 20r multi | 7.75 | 7.75 |
| | Nos. 1021A-1047 (40) | | 31.65 | 31.65 |

Self-adhesive
Litho.
Die Cut Perf. 13x12¾

1048	A343	(1.10r) like #1033	.65	.65
1049	A343	(1.10r) like #1032	.65	.65
1050	A343	(1.10r) like #1036	.65	.65
1051	A343	(1.10r) like #1035	.65	.65
1052	A343	(1.10r) like #1034	.65	.65
a.		Strip of 5, #1048-1052	3.25	
h.		Booklet, 2 each #1048-1052	6.50	

Booklet Stamps
Self-Adhesive
Serpentine Die Cut 11x11¼

1052B	A343	(1.30r) Like #1035	.45	.45
1052C	A343	(1.30r) Like #1036	.45	.45
1052D	A343	(1.30r) Like #1032	.45	.45
1052E	A343	(1.30r) Like #1034	.45	.45

| 1052F | A343 | (1.30r) Like #1033 | .45 | .45 |
| g. | | Booklet pane, 2 each #1052B-1052F | 4.50 | |

Nos. 1038-1042F are inscribed "Airmail Postcard."

"Standard" on Nos. 1032-1036, 1036a is 5½mm long.

Nos. 1042B-1042F are booklet stamps. No. 1052Fg is a complete booklet. Nos. 1036B-1036F were issued in a booklet.

Issued: #1037, 1/98; 10c, 40c, 50c, 70c, 90c, 1r, 1/16/98; #1038-1042, 4/98; #1036B-1036F, 5/18/98; 3r, 6/24/98; 20c, 6/25/98; #1032-1036, 1048-1052, 5/18/98; 10r, 20r, 9/21/98; #1046a, 10/28/98; #1043A, 1/9/99; #1052B-1052F, 12/99; 1.50r, 2.30r, 6/5/00; 5c, 7/4/00.

Leopard — A344

Illustration reduced.

1998, May 1   Perf. 14
1053 A344 5r multicolored   2.50 2.50
SAPDA '98 Stamp Show, Johannesburg.

A345   A346

1998, June 8
1054 A345 (1.10r) multicolored   .80 .80
1998 World Cup Soccer Championships, France. No. 1054 was issued in sheets of 10.

1998, June 28   Perf. 14x14½

Early South African History: #1055, Early stone age hand axe. #1056, Musuku. #1057, San rock engravings. #1058, Early iron age pots. #1059, Khoekhoe pot. #1060, Florisbad skull. #1061, San rock art. #1062, Mapungubwe gold. #1063, Lydenburg head. #1064, Taung child.

1055	A346	(1.10r) multicolored	.55	.55
1056	A346	(1.10r) multicolored	.55	.55
1057	A346	(1.10r) multicolored	.55	.55
1058	A346	(1.10r) multicolored	.55	.55
1059	A346	(1.10r) multicolored	.55	.55
1060	A346	(1.10r) multicolored	.55	.55
1061	A346	(1.10r) multicolored	.55	.55
1062	A346	(1.10r) multicolored	.55	.55
1063	A346	(1.10r) multicolored	.55	.55
1064	A346	(1.10r) multicolored	.55	.55
a.		Sheet of 10, #1055-1064	5.50	5.50
		Booklet, 2 #1064a	11.00	

Raptors — A347

Designs: No. 1065, Pale chanting goshawk. No. 1066, Jackal buzzard. No. 1067, Lanner falcon. No. 1068, Bearded vulture. No. 1069, Black harrier. No. 1070, Cape vulture. No. 1071, Bateleur. No. 1072, Spotted eagle owl. No. 1073, White-headed vulture. No. 1074, African fish eagle.

1998, Aug. 16   Perf. 14x15

1065	A347	(1.10r) multicolored	.65	.65
1066	A347	(1.10r) multicolored	.65	.65
1067	A347	(1.10r) multicolored	.65	.65
1068	A347	(1.10r) multicolored	.65	.65
1069	A347	(1.10r) multicolored	.65	.65
1070	A347	(1.10r) multicolored	.65	.65
1071	A347	(1.10r) multicolored	.65	.65
1072	A347	(1.10r) multicolored	.65	.65
1073	A347	(1.10r) multicolored	.65	.65
1074	A347	(1.10r) multicolored	.65	.65
a.		Sheet of 10, #1065-1074	6.50	6.50
b.		Booklet pane, #1065-1074 + 2 prepaid postcards	6.50	
		Complete booklet, 2 #1074b	14.00	

Vert. and horiz. perforations extend to top, bottom and right edges of sheet on No. 1074a, but do not on No. 1074b.

Natl. Arbor Week A348

Trees: No. 1075, Baobab. No. 1076, Umbrella thorn. No. 1077, Shepherd's tree. No. 1078, Karee.

1998, Sept. 4   Litho.   Perf. 13¾x14
1075	A348	(1.10r) multi	.75	.75
1076	A348	(1.10r) multi	.75	.75
1077	A348	(1.10r) multi	.75	.75
1078	A348	(1.10r) multi	.75	.75
a.		Block of 4, #1075-1078	3.00	3.00

Christmas — A349

1998, Oct. 9   Litho.   Perf. 14x15
1079	A349	(1.10r) Angel	.80	.80
1080	A349	(1.10r) Bell	.80	.80
1081	A349	(1.10r) Package	.80	.80
1082	A349	(1.10r) Christmas tree	.80	.80
1083	A349	(1.10r) Star	.80	.80
a.		Strip of 5, #1079-1083	4.00	4.00

World Post Day — A351

Illustration reduced.

1998, Oct. 9   Litho.   Perf. 14x14½
1089 A351 5r multicolored   2.50 2.50

ILSAPEX 1998, Midrand, South Africa — A352

Designs of unissued stamps created for 1927 definitive series in colors of: a, Red and green. b, Green and black.

1998, Oct. 20 Litho.   Perf. 14½x14¼
1090 A352 5r Sheet of 2, #a.-b.   4.00 4.00

Whales — A354

Illustration reduced.

1998, Oct. 23 Litho.   Perf. 13½x14
1095 A354 5r multicolored   4.25 4.25
See Namibia #919, Norfolk Island #665.

Clover SA Limited, 100th Anniv. — A354a

Illustration reduced.

1998, Nov. 15 Litho.   Perf. 14¼x14
1095A A354a (1.10r) multicolored 1.50 1.50

Universal Declaration of Human Rights, 50th Anniv. — A355

1998, Dec. 9   Perf. 14¼
1096 A355 (1.10r) multicolored   1.00 1.00

UPU, 125th Anniv. A356

Designs: No. 1097, Dennis Royal Mail vehicle, 1913. No. 1098, Ford V8 Mail van, 1935. No. 1099, Mobile post office, 1937. No. 1100, Trojan post office van, 1927.

1999, Feb. 15 Litho.   Perf. 13¾x14
1097	A356	(1.10r) multi	.75	.75
1098	A356	(1.10r) multi	.75	.75
1099	A356	(1.10r) multi	.75	.75
1100	A356	(1.10r) multi	.75	.75
a.		Block of 4, #1097-1100	3.00	3.00

New Year 1999 (Year of the Rabbit) — A357

Illustration reduced.

1999, Feb. 16   Litho.   Perf. 14x13½
1101 A357 5r multicolored   2.50 2.50

Ships of the Southern Oceans — A358

1999, Mar. 19   Litho.   Perf. 13¾x14
1102 A358 (1.10r) Endeavour   .75 .75
1103 A358 (1.10r) HMS Beagle   .75 .75
1104 A358 (1.10r) Discovery   .75 .75
1105 A358 (1.10r) Heemskerck   .75 .75
   a. Block of 4, #1102-1105   3.00 3.00

Souvenir Sheet
Perf. 13¾
1106 A358   5r Lawhill, vert.   2.25 2.25
Australia 99 World Stamp Expo (No. 1106).

AIDS Awareness — A359

Perf. 14¼x14 on 3 sides
1999, Apr. 1
1107 A359 (1.20r) purple & multi   .60 .60
1108 A359 (1.20r) green & multi   .60 .60
   a. Booklet pane, 5 each #1107-
     1108   6.00
     Complete booklet, #1108a   6.00

Souvenir Sheets

IBRA '99, Nuremberg, Germany — A360

Illustration reduced.

1999, Apr. 27   Perf. 14¼x14
1109 A360 5r multi   3.00 3.00

SAPDA '99, Johannesburg — A361

Illustration reduced.

1999, Apr. 30   Perf. 13¾
1110 A361 5r multi   2.75 2.75

A362   A363

1999, May 1   Perf. 14x14¾
1111 A362 (1.20r) Nurse   .70 .70
1112 A362 (1.20r) Washerwoman   .70 .70
1113 A362 (1.20r) Lumberjack   .70 .70
1114 A362 (1.20r) Tree planter   .70 .70
1115 A362 (1.20r) Cook   .70 .70
1116 A362 (1.20r) Fisherman   .70 .70
1117 A362 (1.20r) Construction
               worker   .70 .70
1118 A362 (1.20r) Miner   .70 .70
1119 A362 (1.20r) Mailman   .70 .70
1120 A362 (1.20r) Jackhammerer   .70 .70
   a. Sheet of 10, #1111-1120   7.00 7.00

Labor Day.

1999, June 16   Perf. 14x14¼
1121 A363 (1.20r) multi   1.00 1.00
Inauguration of Pres. Thabo Mbeki.

Souvenir Sheet

Order of St. John, 900th Anniv. — A364

Illustration reduced.

1999, June 23   Perf. 14x14¾
1122 A364 2r multi   1.10 1.10

Standard Bank Arts Festival, 25th Anniv. — A365

1999, June 29   Perf. 14x14¼
1123 A365 (1.20r) shown   .90 .90
1124 A365 (1.20r) Film   .90 .90
1125 A365 (1.20r) Music   .90 .90
1126 A365 (1.20r) Mask, diff.   .90 .90
1127 A365 (1.20r) Painter   .90 .90
   a. Strip of 5, #1123-1127   4.50 4.50

Traditional Wall Art — A366

1999, Aug. 8   Perf. 13¼x13¾
1128 A366 (1.20r) North Ndebele .80 .80
1129 A366 (1.20r) South Ndebele .80 .80
1130 A366 (1.20r) Swazi   .80 .80
1131 A366 (1.20r) Venda   .80 .80
1132 A366 (1.20r) South Sotho   .80 .80
1133 A366 (1.20r) Xhosa   .80 .80
1134 A366 (1.20r) North Sotho   .80 .80
1135 A366 (1.20r) Tsonga   .80 .80
1136 A366 (1.20r) Zulu   .80 .80
1137 A366 (1.20r) Tswana   .80 .80
   a. Sheet of 10, #1128-1137   8.00 8.00

Souvenir Sheet

China 1999 World Philatelic Exhibition — A367

1999, Aug. 21   Perf. 14x13¼
1138 A367 5r multi   3.00 3.00

Souvenir Sheet

JOPEX '99 — A368

1999, Sept. 8   Litho.   Perf. 14¼x14½
1139 A368 5r Strelitzia flower   3.25 3.25

Migratory Animals — A369

1999, Oct. 4   Litho.   Perf. 14x14¾
1140 A369 (1.20r) Barn swallow   .80 .80
1141 A369 (1.20r) Great white
             shark   .80 .80
1142 A369 (1.20r) Lesser kes-
             trel   .80 .80
1143 A369 (1.20r) Common
             dolphin   .80 .80
1144 A369 (1.20r) European
             bee-eater   .80 .80
1145 A369 (1.20r) Loggerhead
             turtle   .80 .80
1146 A369 (1.20r) Curlew sand-
             piper   .80 .80
1147 A369 (1.20r) Wandering
             albatross   .80 .80
1148 A369 (1.20r) Springbok   .80 .80
1149 A369 (1.20r) Lesser fla-
             mingo   .80 .80
   a. Sheet of 10, #1140-1149   8.00 8.00
     Complete booklet, 2 #1149a
     (stitched in) + 2 postal
     cards   20.00

Complete booklet sold for 29r.

Boer War, Cent. A370

1999, Oct. 11   Litho.   Perf. 13¾
1150 A370 (1.20r) Boer men, wo-
             man   1.25 1.25
1151 A370 (1.20r) Soldiers, ship 1.25 1.25
   a. Pair, #1150-1151   2.50 2.50
   b. Booklet pane, #1150-1151,
     perf. 13¼x13¾ ('02)   2.75 —

Issued: No. 1151b, 5/31/02. See note after No. 1282.

Millennium — A371

2000, Jan. 1   Litho.   Perf. 13¼x13¾
1152 A371 (1.20r) multi   1.10 1.10

Start of National Lottery A372

2000, Mar. 2   Litho.   Perf. 13¼x13¾
1153 A372 (1.20r) multi   1.00 1.00

Family Day — A373

2000, Apr. 5   Litho.   Perf. 13¼
1154 A373 (1.30r) multi   1.00 1.00

Souvenir Sheet

The Stamp Show 2000, London — A374

Illustration reduced.

2000, May 20   Litho.   Perf. 13¼
1155 A374 4.60r multi   2.75 2.75

Frogs and Toads — A375

No. 1156: a, Banded stream frog. b, Yellow-striped reed frog. c, Natal leaf-folding frog. d, Paradise toad. e, Table Mountain ghost frog. f, Banded rubber frog. g, Dwarf grass frog. h, Long-toed tree frog. i, Namaqua rain frog. j, Bubbling kassina.
    4.60r, Forest tree frog.

Perf. 13¼x13¾

2000, June 23   **Litho.**
1156		Sheet of 10	7.00	7.00
a.-j.		A375 1.30r Any single	.70	.70

Souvenir Sheet
Perf. 13¼
1157	A375	4.60r multi	2.75	2.75

Junass 2000, Boksburg (No. 1157). No. 1157 contains one 48x30mm stamp.

Medicinal Plants — A376

No. 1158: a, Stalked bulbine. b, Wild dagga. c, Wild garlic. d, Pig's ear. e, Wild ginger. No. 1159: a, Red paintbrush. b, Cancer bush. c, Yellow star flower. d, Bitter aloe. e, Sour fig.

2000, Aug. 1   **Perf. 13¾x13¼**
1158		Horiz. strip of 5	2.50	2.50
a.-e.		A376 1.30r Any single	.50	.50
1159		Horiz. strip of 5	4.00	4.00
a.-e.		A376 2.30r Any single	.80	.80

2000 Summer Olympics, Sydney — A377

Olympic rings and: 1.30r, Flagbearer. 1.50r, Elena Meyer of South Africa and Derartu Tulu of Ethiopia. 2.20r, Joshua Thugwane. 2.30r, South African flag. 6.30r, Penny Heyns.

2000, Sept. 1   **Perf. 13¼x13¾**
1160-1164	A377	Set of 5	5.00	5.00

Intl. Year for the Culture of Peace A378

2000, Sept. 19   **Litho.**   **Perf. 13¼**
1165	A378	1.30r multi	.70	.70

World Heritage Sites — A379

Designs: No. 1166, 1.30r, Robben Island. No. 1167, 1.30r, Greater St. Lucia Wetland Park. No. 1168, 1.30r, Sterkfontein Fossil Hominid Complex.

2000, Sept. 22   **Perf. 13¼x13¾**
1166-1168	A379	Set of 3	2.00	2.00

World Post Day — A380

2000   **Litho.**   **Perf. 13¼x13**
1169	A380	1.30r multi	.70	.70
a.		Perf. 13¾x13 + label	.75	.75

Issued: No. 1169, 10/9; No. 1169a, 11/8. No. 1169a was issued in sheets of 20 stamps + 20 different labels depicting characters on the MTN Gladiators 3 television show that sold for 35r.

Souvenir Sheet

Year of the Dragon — A381

2000, Oct. 9   **Litho.**   **Perf. 13½x13**
1170	A381	4.60r multi	2.10	2.10

Writers of the Boer War Era — A382

Medals and: 1.30r, Sol Plaatje, Johanna Brandt. 4.40r, Sir Arthur Conan Doyle, Sir Winston Churchill.

2000, Oct. 25   **Litho.**   **Perf. 13¼x13¾**
1171-1172	A382	Set of 2	2.75	2.75
a.		Booklet pane, #1171-1172	3.25	—

Issued: No. 1172a, 5/31/02. See note after No. 1282.

A383

Fish, Flowers, Butterflies and Birds — A384

Designs: 5c, Palette surgeonfish. 10c, Blue-banded surgeonfish. 20c, Royal angelfish. 30c, Emperor angelfish. 40c, Blackbar trigger-fish. 50c, Coral rockcod. 60c, Powder-blue surgeonfish. 70c, Threadfin butterflyfish. 80c, Longhorn cowfish. 90c, Longnose butterflyfish. 1r, Coral beauty. Nos. 1184, 1200, 1205, 1210, 1215, 1219A, 1220, 1225, Botterblom, vert. Nos. 1185, 1201, 1206, 1211, 1216, 1219B, 1221, 1226, Blue marguerite, vert. Nos. 1186, 1202, 1207, 1212, 1217, 1219C, 1222, 1227, Karoo violet, vert. Nos. 1187, 1203, 1208, 1213, 1218, 1219D, 1223, 1228, Tree pelargonium, vert. Nos. 1188, 1204, 1209, 1214, 1219, 1219E, 1224, 1229, Black-eyed susy, vert. 1.40r, Gold-banded forester. 1.50r, Brenton blue. 1.60r, Yellow pansy butterfly. No. 1191, Silver-barred charaxes. No. 1231, Large-spotted acraea butterfly. 2r, Lilac-breasted roller, vert. 2.10r, Koppie charaxes butterfly. 2.30r, Citrus swallowtail. 2.50r, Common grass-yellow butterfly. 3r, Woodland king-fisher, vert. 5r, White-fronted bee-eater, vert. 6.30r, Green-banded swallowtail. 7r, Southern milkweed butterfly. 10r, African green pigeon, vert. 12.60r, False dotted-border. 14r, Lilac tip butterfly. 20r, Purple-crested lourie, vert.

Non-English country name inscriptions at top: Nos. 1200, 1204, 1207, 1217, 1219A, 1219E, 1220, 1224, 1227, Afrika Borwa. Nos. 1201, 1208, 1218, 1219B, 1221, 1226, Ningizimu Afrika. Nos. 1202, 1219C, 1222, Suid-Afrika. Nos. 1203, 1219D, 1223, Afrika Tshipembe. Nos. 1205, 1215, 1225, Afrika Dzonga. Nos. 1206, 1216, 1226, Afrika Sewula. Nos. 1209, 1219, 1229, Mzantsi Afrika.

Perf. 14½x14¾, 14¾x14½
2000, Nov. 15   **Litho.**
1173	A383	5c multi	.20	.20
a.		Perf. 13	.20	.20
1174	A383	10c multi	.20	.20
a.		Perf. 13	.20	.20
1175	A383	20c multi	.20	.20
a.		Perf. 13	.20	.20
1176	A383	30c multi	.20	.20
a.		Perf. 13	.20	.20
1177	A383	40c multi	.20	.20
a.		Perf. 13	.20	.20
1178	A383	50c multi	.20	.20
a.		Perf. 13	.20	.20
1179	A383	60c multi	.20	.20
a.		Perf. 13	.20	.20
1180	A383	70c multi	.20	.20
a.		Perf. 13	.20	.20
1181	A383	80c multi	.30	.30
a.		Perf. 13	.30	.30
1182	A383	90c multi	.35	.35
a.		Perf. 13	.30	.30
1183	A383	1r multi	.35	.35
a.		Perf. 13	.35	.35
1184	A383	1.30r multi	.50	.50
1185	A383	1.30r multi	.50	.50
1186	A383	1.30r multi	.50	.50
1187	A383	1.30r multi	.50	.50
1188	A383	1.30r multi	.50	.50
a.		Horiz. strip of 5, #1184-1188	2.50	2.50
1189	A383	1.40r multi	.55	.55
1190	A383	1.50r multi	.60	.60
1191	A383	1.90r multi	.70	.70
1192	A383	2r multi	.80	.80
a.		Perf. 13	.80	.80
1193	A383	2.30r multi	.85	.85
1194	A383	3r multi	1.10	1.10
a.		Perf. 13	1.10	1.10
1195	A383	5r multi	2.10	2.10
a.		Perf. 13	2.10	2.10
1196	A383	6.30r multi	2.75	2.75
1197	A383	10r multi	4.00	4.00
a.		Perf. 13 ('01)	4.00	4.00
1198	A383	12.60r multi	5.50	5.50
a.		Perf. 13 ('01)	6.00	6.00
1199	A383	20r multi	8.00	8.00
a.		Perf. 13	6.50	6.50

Issued: Nos. 1197a, 1199a, 10/1/01. No. 1179a, 10/1/01. Nos. 1178a, 1192a, 1194a, 1195a, 2002. No. 1173a, 4/2/03; No. 1174a, 5/22/03; Nos. 1175a, 1181a, 9/22/03; Nos. 1176a, 1182a, 1199a, 2/27/03; Nos. 1177a, 1180a, 1183a, 9/23/03.

Types of 2000
Die Cut Perf. 13x12½ on 2 or 3 Sides
2000, Nov. 15   **Litho.**
Booklet Stamps
Self-Adhesive
1200	A384	1.30r multi	.50	.50
1201	A384	1.30r multi	.50	.50
1202	A384	1.30r multi	.50	.50
1203	A384	1.30r multi	.50	.50
1204	A384	1.30r multi	.50	.50
1205	A384	1.30r multi	.50	.50
1206	A384	1.30r multi	.50	.50
1207	A384	1.30r multi	.50	.50
1208	A384	1.30r multi	.50	.50
1209	A384	1.30r multi	.50	.50
a.		Booklet, #1200-1209	5.00	

2001, May 16   **Litho.**   **Perf. 13**
1210	A383	1.40r multi	.55	.55
1211	A383	1.40r multi	.55	.55
1212	A383	1.40r multi	.55	.55
1213	A383	1.40r multi	.55	.55
1214	A383	1.40r multi	.55	.55
a.		Horiz. strip of 5, #1210-1214	2.75	2.75

Coil Stamps
Self-Adhesive
Serpentine Die Cut 13½
1215	A384	(1.40r) multi	.55	.55
1216	A384	(1.40r) multi	.55	.55
1217	A384	(1.40r) multi	.55	.55
1218	A384	(1.40r) multi	.55	.55
1219	A384	(1.40r) multi	.55	.55
1219A	A384	(1.40r) multi	.55	.55
1219B	A384	(1.40r) multi	.55	.55
1219C	A384	(1.40r) multi	.55	.55
1219D	A384	(1.40r) multi	.55	.55
1219E	A384	(1.40r) multi	.55	.55
f.		Strip of 10, #1215-1219E	5.50	

Booklet Stamps
Die Cut Perf. 13x12½ on 2 or 3 Sides
1220	A384	(1.40r) multi	.55	.55
1221	A384	(1.40r) multi	.55	.55
1222	A384	(1.40r) multi	.55	.55
1223	A384	(1.40r) multi	.55	.55
1224	A384	(1.40r) multi	.55	.55
1225	A384	(1.40r) multi	.55	.55
1226	A384	(1.40r) multi	.55	.55
1227	A384	(1.40r) multi	.55	.55
1228	A384	(1.40r) multi	.55	.55
1229	A384	(1.40r) multi	.55	.55
a.		Booklet, #1220-1229	5.50	
		Nos. 1173-1229 (62)	50.80	50.80

Type of 2000
			Perf. 13	
1230	A383	1.60r multi	.60	.60
1231	A383	1.90r multi	.75	.75
1232	A383	2.10r multi	.80	.80
1233	A383	2.50r multi	1.00	1.00
1234	A383	7r multi	2.75	2.75
1235	A383	14r multi	6.00	6.00
		Nos. 1230-1235 (6)	11.90	11.90

Myths and Legends — A385

Designs: 1.30r, The Rain Bull. 1.50r, The Treasure of the Grosvenor. 2.20r, Seven Magic Birds. 2.30r, The Hole in the Wall. 6.30r, Van Hunks and the Devil.

2001, Jan. 24   **Litho.**   **Perf. 13¾**
1236-1240	A385	Set of 5	4.50	4.50

Souvenir Sheet

Hong Kong 2001 Stamp Exhibition — A386

2001, Feb. 1   **Perf. 14½x14**
1241	A386	4.60r Tree snake	2.75	2.75

Sports Stars A387

Designs: No. 1242, 1.40r, Ernie Els, golfer. No. 1243, 1.40r, Terence Parkin, swimmer. No. 1244, 1.40r, Hezekiel Sepeng, runner. No. 1245, 1.40r, Rosina Magola, netball player. No. 1246, 1.40r, Francois Pienaar, rugby player. No. 1247, 1.40r, Zanele Situ, javelin thrower. No. 1248, 1.40r, Hestrie Cloete, high jumper. No. 1249, 1.40r, Lucas Radebe, soccer player. No. 1250, 1.40r, Vuyani Bungu, boxer. No. 1251, 1.40r, Jonty Rhodes, cricket player.

2001, Feb. 28   **Perf. 13¾x14**
1242-1251	A387	Set of 10	5.00	5.00
1251a		Sheet of 15 #1251 +15 labels, perf. 14½x14	7.00	

Labels on No. 1251a depict players from the 2000-01 South African World Cup Cricket team.

Kgalagadi Transfrontier Park — A388

Designs: 1.40r, Gemsboks, flags of South Africa and Botswana. 2.50r, Cheetahs. 2.90r, Sociable weaver birds. 3.60r, Meerkats.

2001, May 12   Litho.   Perf. 13x13¼
1252-1255 A388   Set of 4   4.50 4.50
1254a   Souvenir sheet, #1253-
            1254   3.00 3.00

See Botswana Nos. 714-717.

Campaign Against Child Abuse — A389

2001, May 16   Perf. 13¾
1256 A389 1.40r multi   .50 .50

Soweto Uprising, 25th Anniv. — A390

2001, June 16   Litho.   Perf. 13¾
1257 A390 1.40r multi   .50 .50

Bats — A391

No. 1258: a, Cape horseshoe bat. b, Welwitsch's hairy bat. c, Schreiber's long-fingered bat. d, Wahlberg's epauletted fruit bat. e, Short-eared trident bat. f, Common slit-faced bat. g, Egyptian fruit bat. h, Egyptian free-tailed bat, vert. i, De Winton's long-eared bat. j, Large-eared free-tailed bat.

Serpentine Die Cut 11¼
2001, June 22
Self-Adhesive
1258 A391   Sheet of 10, #a-j   4.50 4.50
a.-j.   1.40r Any single   .45 .45

Boer War, Cent. — A392

Designs: 1.40r, Rev. J. D. Kestell. 3r, Capt. Thomas Crean.

2001, Aug. 1   Perf. 13¼
1259-1260 A392   Set of 2   2.00 2.00
a.   Booklet pane, #1259-
      1260, perf. 13¼x13¾ 2.25   —

Issued: No. 1260a, 5/31/02. See note after No. 1282.

World Conference Against Racism, Durban — A393

No. 1262: a, Kgotlelelo le pharologantsho. b, Kubeketelelana kanye nekwehlukana. c, Verdraagsaamheid en diversiteit. d, U kondelelana na u fhambana. e, Kutlwisiso ka mefutafuta. f, Ku va ni mbilu yo leha ni kuhambana-hambana. g, Ibekezelelwano nehlukahlukano. h, Kgothlelelo le pharologano. i, Ukubekezelelana nokungafani. j, Ukunyamezelana nokungafani.

2001, Aug. 1   Perf. 13¾x13½
1261 A393 2.10r shown   .75 .75
1262   Sheet of 10   6.00 6.00
a.-j. A393 1.40r Any single   .60 .60

See Brazil No. 2809.

Musical Instruments — A394

Designs: 1.40r, Concertina. 1.90r, Trumpet. 2.50r, Electric guitar. 3r, African drum. 7r, Cello.

Litho. with Foil Application
2001, Aug. 23   Perf. 13¼x14
1263-1267 A394   Set of 5   5.25 5.25

Christmas A395

Designs: 2r, Tree. 3r, Angel.

2001, Oct. 1   Litho.   Perf. 13¼
1268-1269 A395   Set of 2   1.90 1.90

Frame — A396

2001, Oct. 1   Serpentine Die Cut
Self-Adhesive
1270 A396 (1.40r) multi   .60 .60
a.   Double-sided pane of 10 + 40
     labels   6.00

Volvo Round-the-World Yacht Race — A397

Designs: 1.40r, Yacht. 6r, Yacht, horiz.

2001, Oct. 23   Perf. 13
1271 A397 1.40r multi   .60 .60
Souvenir Sheet
Perf. 14x13¼
1272 A397   6r multi   2.25 2.25
No. 1272 contains one 40x30mm stamp.

2003 ICC Cricket World Cup, South Africa — A398

2001, Nov. 1   Perf. 14x13¾
1273 A398 (1.40r) multi   .60 .60

Souvenir Sheet

New Year 2002 (Year of the Horse) — A399

2001, Nov. 2   Perf. 14x13¼
1274 A399 6r multi   2.25 2.25

Marine Life — A400

No. 1275: a, Hammerhead shark. b, Loggerhead turtle, vert. c, Clown triggerfish, vert. d, Cape fur seal, vert. e, Bottlenosed dolphins. f, Crowned seahorse, vert. g, Blue-spotted ribbontail ray, vert. h, Moorish idol. i, Common octopus. j, Coral rock cod.

Serpentine Die Cut 12¾
2001, Nov. 2
Self-Adhesive
1275 A400   Sheet of 10   4.50 4.50
a.-j.   (1.40r) Any single   .45 .45

Johannesburg World Summit on Sustainable Development — A401

Designs: Nos. 1276a, 1281c, Prosperity, vert. Nos. 1276b, 1281a, People, vert. Nos. 1276c, 1281b, Planet, vert. (1.50r), Water, sanitation and energy for all. No. 1278, Buildings, globe. No. 1279, Clean environment for health. (3.30r), Food security for all.
Sizes: Nos. 1276a-1276c, 22x32mm, Nos. 1281a-1281c, 21x26mm.

Perf. 13¾x13¼, 13¼x13 (#1277, 1279, 1280), 13¼x13¾ (#1278)
2002   Litho.
1276 A401 (1.40r) Strip of 3,
     #a-c   1.40 1.40
1277 A401 (1.50r) multi   .50   .50
1278 A401   (3r) multi   .95   .95
1279 A401   (3r) multi   .95   .95
1280 A401 (3.30r) multi 1.00 1.00

Booklet Stamps
Self-Adhesive
Serpentine Die Cut on 2 or 3 Sides
1281 A401 (1.40r) Strip of 3,
     #a-c   1.40 1.40
d.   Booklet pane, 4 #1281a, 3
     #1281b-1281c   4.50 4.50
     Nos. 1276-1281 (6) 6.20 6.20

Issued: Nos. 1276, 1278, 1281, 4/17. Nos. 1277, 1279, 1280, 8/25. No. 1279 is airmail.

Souvenir Sheet

End of Boer War, Cent. — A402

No. 1282: a, 1.50r, Army officer. b, 3.30r, Government official.

2002, May 31   Perf. 13¼x13¾
1282 A402   Sheet of 2, #a-b   1.50 1.50
c.   Booklet pane, #1282   1.90
     Complete booklet, #1151b,
     1172a, 1260a, 1282c + 2
     postal cards   10.50
No. 1282c has rouletting between margin of No. 1282 and the booklet pane margin. Complete booklet sold for 45r.

African Union Summit A403

2002, June 25   Perf. 13½
1283 A403 1.50r multi   .75 .75
Values are for stamps with surrounding selvage.

Type of 2000
Designs: 1.80r, Emperor moth. 2.20r, Peach moth. 2.80r, Snouted tiger moth. 9r, False tiger moth. 16r, Moon moth.

2002, Sept. 20 Litho.   Perf. 13
1284 A383 1.80r multi   .55   .55
1285 A383 2.20r multi   .70   .70
1286 A383 2.80r multi   .85   .85
1287 A383   9r multi   2.75 2.75
1288 A383 16r multi   5.00 5.00
     Nos. 1284-1288 (5) 9.85 9.85

A404   A405

A406 A407

A408 A409

ICC Cricket World Cup

2002 *Perf. 12½x12¾*
1289 A404 (1.50r) multi .50 .50
1290 A405 (1.50r) multi .50 .50
1291 A407 (1.50r) multi .50 .50
1292 A409 (1.50r) multi .50 .50
1293 A406 (1.50r) multi .50 .50
1294 A408 (1.50r) multi .50 .50
Nos. 1289-1294 (6) 3.00 3.00

Issued: Nos. 1289, 1290, 9/23; 1292, 1294, 11/1; Nos. 1291, 1293, 12/21.

Souvenir Sheet

Steve Biko (1946-77), Anti-apartheid Leader — A410

2002, Oct. 9 *Perf. 14¾x14½*
1295 A410 4.75r multi 1.50 1.50
See note under No. 1321.

Souvenir Sheet

World Post Day — A411

2002, Oct. 9 *Perf. 13¼x13½*
1296 A411 4.75r multi 1.50 1.50

Christmas — A412

Stained glass patterns: 1.50r, 3r.

2002, Oct. 23 *Perf. 14x14¾*
1297-1298 A412 Set of 2 1.40 1.40

Souvenir Sheets

Sawfish — A413

Designs: No. 1299, 7r, Pristis pectinata. No. 1300, 7r, Pristis microdon.

2002, Oct. 23 *Perf. 13¾*
1299-1300 A413 Set of 2 4.50 4.50
JUNASS Philatelic Exhibition (#1299); Algoapex Philatelic Exhibition (#1300).

Souvenir Sheet

New Year 2003 (Year of the Ram) — A414

2002, Nov. 1 *Perf. 14½*
1301 A414 7r multi 2.25 2.25

AIDS Prevention — A415

No. 1302 — AIDS prevention ribbon and: a, Man with sunglasses, male symbol. b, Woman with open mouth. c, Woman with sunglasses, female symbol. d, Hand holding candle, "Stop." e, Woman, candle. f, Hand holding candle, "Be safe." g, Candle, hand pointing at ribbon. h, Open hand. i, Face in droplet. j, Open hand, pills.

Serpentine Die Cut 11¾
2002, Nov. 29
Self-Adhesive
1302 Booklet of 10 5.25 5.25
a.-j. A415 (1.50r) Any single .50 .50

Souvenir Sheet

Solar Eclipse of Dec. 4, 2002 — A416

2002, Dec. 4 *Perf. 14½*
1303 A416 4.75r multi 1.50 1.50

ICC Cricket World Cup — A417

No. 1304: a, Huts with windmill blades. b, Horseman. c, Cricket players with bats. d, Bus with people on roof. e, Mother and child. f, Double-decker bus.

2003, Feb. 28 *Perf. 14¼x13¾*
1304 A417 (1.50r) Sheet of 6, #a-
f 2.75 2.75

Souvenir Sheet

Tembisile (Chris) Hani (1942-93), African National Congress Leader — A418

2003, Apr. 27 Litho. *Perf. 14¾*
1305 A418 (1.65r) multi .60 .60
See note after No. 1321.

Life in Informal Settlements — A419

No. 1306: a, Women carrying water jugs on head. b, Man with guitar. c, Man with rake. d, Woman using sewing machine. e, Two children. f, Drink vendor. g, Shoemakers. h, Woman with green cap. i, Young woman with cap and tire. j, Woman with child.

2003, May 16 *Perf. 14x13¾*
1306 A419 (1.65r) Sheet of 10,
#a-j 5.25 5.25

Souvenir Sheet

Africa Day — A420

2003, May 25 *Perf. 14¾*
1307 A420 11.70r multi 3.75 3.75

Souvenir Sheet

Oliver Reginald Tambo (1917-93), African National Congress President — A421

2003, May 29
1308 A421 (1.65r) multi 1.25 1.25
See note after No. 1321.

Ballroom Dancing — A422

Designs: 1.65r, Salsa. 2.20r, Rumba. 2.80r, Waltz. 3.30r, Foxtrot. 3.80r, Tango.

2003, July 23 *Perf. 13¼x13¾*
1309-1313 A422 Set of 5 4.75 4.75

Dogs — A423

No. 1314: a, Africanis. b, Rhodesian Ridgeback. c, Boerboel. d, Basenji.

2003, Aug. 1 *Perf. 14½*
1314 A423 (1.65r) Sheet of 4, #a-
d 2.75 2.75

Type of 2000

Designs: No. 1315, Botterblom, vert. No. 1316, Blue marguerite, vert. No. 1317, Karoo violet, vert. No. 1318, Tree pelargonium, vert. No. 1319, Black-eyed susy, vert.

2003, Sept. 15 Litho. *Perf. 13*
1315 A383 (1.65r) multi .60 .60
1316 A383 (1.65r) multi .60 .60
1317 A383 (1.65r) multi .60 .60
1318 A383 (1.65r) multi .60 .60
1319 A383 (1.65r) multi .60 .60
a. Horiz. strip of 5, #1315-1319 3.00 3.00

Souvenir Sheet

Walter Max Ulyate Sisulu (1912-2003), African National Congress Deputy President — A424

2003, Sept. 24 *Perf. 14¾*
1320 A424 11.70r multi 4.75 4.75
See note after No. 1321.

Souvenir Sheet

Robert Mangaliso Sobukwe (1924-1978), Pan Africanist Congress President — A425

2003, Sept. 24 *Perf. 14¾*
1321 A425 11.70r multi 4.75 4.75

Nos. 1295, 1305, 1308, 1320 and 1321 were sold in, but unattached to, a commemorative booklet that sold for 60r.

Stamp of Fortune Television Show — A426

2003, Sept. 29   **Perf. 14¼x14**
1322 A426 (1.65r) multi   .60   .60

Engineering and Postal Communication — A427

No. 1323: a, Shongweni Dam (60x23mm). b, Kimberley Microwave Tower (30x47mm). c, Northern Cape Legislature Building (30x23mm). d, Durban Westville highway interchange (30x47mm). e, Postal truck on Community Bridge, Limpopo (30x23mm). f, Nelson Mandela Bridge, Johannesburg (60x23mm).

2003, Oct. 9   **Perf. 14x14¼**
1323 A427 (3.30r) Sheet of 6, #a-
   f   8.00 8.00
  g.   Like No. 1323, with PIARC
     World Road Congress in-
     scription in margin   8.00 8.00

Souvenir Sheet

South Africa - India Diplomatic Relations, 10th Anniv. — A428

2003, Oct. 16   **Perf. 14¾**
1324 A428 3.35r multi   1.40 1.40

Bid for Hosting 2010 World Cup Soccer Championships — A429

Emblem, soccer fan with painted face and: No. 1325, (3.80r), Map of Africa. No. 1326, (4.25r), Soccer players.

2003, Oct. 23
1325-1326 A429   Set of 2   2.40 2.40
     No. 1325 is airmail.

Cape of Good Hope Triangle Stamps, 150th Anniv. A430

2003, Oct. 23 Litho.   **Perf. 12½x12¾**
1327 A430 (1.65r) blue   .60   .60
     Printed in sheets of 4.

A431

Christmas — A432

No. 1328: a, Joseph, Mary on donkey. b, Angels. c, Magi. d, Madonna and Child. e, Dove.

2003, Nov. 3 Litho.   **Perf. 14x14¼**
1328   Horiz. strip of 5   3.00 3.00
  a.-e.   A431 (1.65r) Any single   .55 .55
        Perf. 14¾
1329 A432 3.80r shown   1.50 1.50

Elephants — A433

No. 1330: a, African elephants. b, Asian elephant.
Illustration reduced.

2003, Dec. 9   **Perf. 14¼x14**
1330 A433 3.35r Horiz. pair, #a-b 3.25 3.25
     South Africa — Thailand diplomatic relations, 10th anniv. See Thailand No. 2105.

Powered Flight, Cent. — A434

No. 1331: a, Paterson Biplane. b, "Silver Queen" Vickers Vimy. c, Wapiti. d, De Havilland DH-9. e, Junkers Ju52/53. f, Sikorsky S-55 helicopter. g, Boeing 707. h, Rooivalk helicopter. i, SUNSAT Microsatellite. j, Mark Shuttleworth, first African in space, and Space Station.

2003, Dec. 17   **Perf. 14¼x14**
1331 A434 (1.65r) Sheet of 10,
    #a-j   7.00 7.00

Souvenir Sheet

New Year 2004 (Year of the Monkey) — A435

2004, Jan. 22   **Perf. 13¾**
1332 A435 11.70r multi   4.50 4.50

Road Safety — A436

No. 1333 — Inscriptions: a, Be visible. b, Don't drink and drive. c, Maintain your vehicle. d, Slow down. e, Don't drive when tired.

     Perf. 13¼x13¾
2004, Mar. 24   **Litho.**
1333   Vert. strip of 5   3.00 3.00
  a.-e.   A436 (1.70r) Any single   .60 .60

End of Apartheid, 10th Anniv. — A437

No. 1334: a, Dove, map of Africa. b, People voting. c, Women and child. d, Sports fans holding flag and trophies. e, Woman with handicrafts.

2004, Apr. 27 Litho.   **Perf. 13¼**
1334   Vert. strip of 5   3.00 3.00
  a.-e.   A437 (1.70r) Any single   .60 .60

Miniature Sheet

Legacy of Slaves — A438

No. 1335: a, Slave bell, Vergelegen, and slave lodge, Cape Town. b, Hidayat al-Islam, first book in Arabic-Afrikaans. c, Chair and cupboard. d, Traditional foods. e, Indian workers in sugar cane fields. f, Chinese mine workers.

2005, May 1
1335 A438 (1.70r) Sheet of 6, #a-
    f   4.25 4.25

Souvenir Sheet

FIFA (Fédération Internationale de Football Association), Cent. — A439

2004, Apr. 30 Litho.   **Perf. 14¾**
1336 A439 4.35r multi   2.00 2.00

Spiders — A440

No. 1337: a, Hedgehog spider. b, Golden orb-web spider, vert. c, Lynx spider, vert. d, Black button spider, vert. e, Ladybird spider. f, Flower crab spider. g, Rain spider, vert. h, Horn baboon spider. i, Trap door spider. j, Spotted crab spider.

Serpentine Die Cut 9½x9, 9x9½
2004, July 30
      Self-Adhesive
1337 A440   Sheet of 10, #a-j   7.50 7.50
  a.-j.   (1.70r) Any single   .75 .75

Volunteers — A441

No. 1338: a, Environmental helpers. b, Caring for the elderly. c, Education. d, Medical and ambulance services. e, Surf life saving. f, Helping abandoned pets. g, Caring for orphans. h, Fire fighters. i, Community gardens. j, Tape aids for the blind.

2004, Aug. 9   **Perf. 13½x13¾**
1338 A441 (1.70r) Sheet of 10,
    #a-j   7.00 7.00

Sports — A442

No. 1339: a, Archery. b, Track. c, Equestrian. d, Cycling. e, Rhythmic gymnastics. f, Canoeing. g, Soccer. h, Swimming. i, Boxing. j, Tennis.

2004, Aug. 13   **Perf. 13¾x13½**
1339 A442 (1.70r) Sheet of 10,
    #a-j   7.00 7.00

Christmas
A443

Icons: (1.70r), Madonna and Child. (4r), Jesus Christ, Pantocrator.

2004, Oct. 1
1340-1341 A443 Set of 2 2.00 2.00
No. 1341 is inscribed "International Airmail Letter."

Birds — A444

No. 1342: a, African fish eagles, national bird of Namibia. b, African fish eagles, national bird of Zimbabwe. c, Peregrine falcons, national bird of Angola. d, Cattle egrets, national bird of Botswana. e, Purple-crested louries, national bird of Swaziland. f, Blue cranes, national bird of South Africa. g, Bar-tailed trogons, national bird of Zambia. h, African fish eagles, national bird of Zambia.

2004, Oct. 9 **Perf. 14**
1342 A444 12.05r Sheet of 8,
#a-h 32.50 32.50
See Angola No. , Botswana Nos. 792-793, Malawi No., Namibia No. 1052, Swaziland Nos. 727-735, Zambia No. 1033, and Zimbabwe No. 975.

Souvenir Sheet

Regular Air Mail Service in South Africa, 75th Anniv. — A445

Litho. with Hologram
2004, Oct. 9 **Perf. 13¾**
1343 A445 12.05r multi 4.25 4.25

South African Police Service, 10th Anniv. — A446

No. 1344: a, South African Police Service badge, South African flag. b, Fighting drugs. c, Police air wing. d, Fingerprint and forensic science. e, Special task force. f, Protecting women and children. g, Sector policing. h, The Dignified Blue. i, SAPS mounted unit. j, Dog unit.

Serpentine Die Cut 13½x13
2004, Nov. 23 **Litho.**
Self-Adhesive
1344 A446 Sheet of 10 7.00 7.00
a.-j. (1.70r) Any single .70 .70

South African Large Telescope A447

No. 1345: a, Exterior of building. b, Cut-away view of building. c, Building aperture, top of telescope, Southern Cross constellation. d, Telescope. e, Building aperture, entire telescope.

2004, Dec. 1 **Perf. 13¾x13½**
1345 Horiz. strip of 5 8.00 8.00
a.-e. A447 4r Any single 1.60 1.60

Souvenir Sheet

New Year 2005 (Year of the Rooster) — A448

2005, Feb. 9 **Perf. 14¾x14½**
1346 A448 12.05r multi 4.50 4.50

Souvenir Sheet

Freedom Charter, 50th Anniv. — A449

No. 1347: a, "Freedom Charter" in mirror image. b, "Freedom Charter" and "50."

Perf. 14¼x14¾
2005, June 24 **Litho.**
1347 A449 (1.77r) Sheet of 2, #a-b 1.40 1.40

Miniature Sheet

Legends — A450

No. 1348: a, Honeyguide's Revenge. b, How Ostrich Got His Long Neck. c, How Serval Got His Spots. d, How Zebra Got His Stripes. e, Jackal, the Tiger Eater. f, Jackal and Wolf. g, King Lion and King Eagle. h, Mantis and the Moon. i, Words as Sweet as Honey from Sankhambi. j, When Lion Could Fly.

2005, July 1
1348 A450 B5 Sheet of 10, #a-j 12.00 12.00
Nos. 1348a-11348j each sold for 3.75r on day of issue.

Miniature Sheet

Small Mammals — A451

No. 1349: a, Lesser bushbaby (24x60mm). b, Riverine rabbit (24x30mm). c, African wildcat (48x30mm). d, Yellow mongoose (24x60mm). e, Steenbok (48x30mm). f, Cape fox (24x30mm).

2005, July 15 **Perf. 14**
1349 A451 (1.77r) Sheet of 6, #a-f 4.25 4.25

Energy Sources — A452

2005, Sept. 26 **Perf. 14x14¼**
1350 A452 (1.77r) Wave .70 .70
1351 A452 (3.65r) Wind 1.40 1.40
1352 A452 (4.25r) Sun 1.75 1.75
Nos. 1350-1352 (3) 3.85 3.85
Inscription on No. 1350, Standard Postage; No. 1351, International Airmail Postcard; No. 1352, International Airmail Letter.

Christmas A453

Wire and bead sculptures: (1.77r), Candle, Christmas tree, heart. (4.25r), Angel and dove.

2005, Oct. 3
1353 A453 (1.77r) multi .70 .70
1354 A453 (4.25r) multi 1.60 1.60
Inscription on No. 1353, Standard Postage; No. 1354, International Airmail Letter.

Prevention of Blindness — A454

Litho. & Embossed
2005, Oct. 13 **Perf. 14¼x14**
1355 A454 (1.77r) org brn & gray .70 .70

Souvenir Sheet

New Year 2006 (Year of the Dog) — A455

No. 1356: a, Seeing-eye dog. b, Drug-sniffing dog and luggage. c, Bird-chasing dog at airport.

2006, Jan. 26 **Perf. 13¼x13**
1356 A455 B5 Sheet of 3, #a-c 4.25 4.25
Nos. 1356a-1356c each sold for 3.75r on day of issue.

Rock Art — A456

No. 1357: a, Detail of Linton Panel, Iziko South African Museum. b, Reedbuck, South African Museum of Rock Art (inscription at LR). c, San ritual specialist, South African Museum of Rock Art (inscription at LL). d, Rhinoceros, Wildebeest Kuil rock art site. e, Eland, Game Pass rock art site.

2006, Feb. 15
1357 Horiz. strip of 5 3.50 3.50
a.-e. A456 (1.77r) Any single .70 .70

Miniature Sheet

Rural Medical Outreach — A457

No. 1358: a, Helicopter and rescuer (24x60mm). b, Doctors clasping hands (24x30mm). c, Airplane, paramedics tending to man on stretcher, horiz. (48x30mm). d, Motorcycle ambulance, paramedic assisting man (24x30mm). e, Phelophepa Health Train, doctor examining woman, horiz. (72x30mm). f, Ambulance, attendants moving patient on gurney (24x30mm).

2006, May 2 **Litho.** **Perf. 13¼**
1358 A457 (1.85r) Sheet of 6, #a-f 4.25 4.25

Chief Bhambatha Zondi, Leader of 1906 Rebellion — A458

Illustration reduced.

2006, June 9 **Perf. 14x13½**
1359 A458 (1.85r) multi .65 .65

Red Cross War Memorial Children's Hospital, 50th Anniv. — A459

Designs: (1.85r), Nurse and ill child. (4.40r), Hospital building, horiz.

Perf. 13¾x13½, 13½x13¾
2006, June 18
1360-1361 A459 Set of 2 2.25 2.25
Inscription on No. 1360 reads "Standard Postage;" on No. 1361, "International Letter."

Souvenir Sheet

Women's Anti-Apartheid March to the Union Building, Pretoria, 50th Anniv. — A460

2006, Aug. 9   **Perf. 14¾x14**
1362 A460 B5 multi   1.40   1.40
No. 1362 sold for 3.75r on day of issue.

Miniature Sheet

Clivia Flowers — A461

No. 1363: a, Clivia nobilis. b, Clivia miniata. c, Clivia gardenii. d, Clivia caulescens. e, Clivia mirabilis. f, Clivia robusta.

2006, Sept. 6   **Perf. 13x13¼**
1363 A461 (1.85r) Sheet of 6, #a-f   3.25   3.25

Animal, Text and Tracks A462

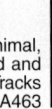

Animal, Herd and Tracks A463

No. 1364: a, Buffalo. b, Elephant. c, Blue wildebeest. d, Hippopotamus. e, Black rhinoceros. f, Giraffe. g, Spotted hyena. h, Leopard. i, Warthog. j, Zebra.

Litho. & Embossed
2006, Sept. 15   **Perf. 13¾x13¼**
1364   Sheet of 10   6.00 6.00
a.-e. A462 (1.85r) Any single   .60 .60
f.-j. A463 (1.85r) Any single   .60 .60

Christmas — A464

No. 1365: a, Antelope. b, Warthog. c, Zebra. d, Hippopotamus. e, Lion, as Santa, in sleigh. (4.40r), Lion as Santa.

2006, Oct. 2   **Litho.**   **Perf. 13½x13**
1365   Horiz. strip of 5   2.50 2.50
a.-e. A464 (1.85r) Any single   .50 .50
1366 A464 (4.40r) multi   1.40 1.40
Inscriptions on Nos. 1365a-1365e read "Standard Postage;" on No. 1366, "International Airmail Letter."

World Post Day — A465

No. 1367 — Boy and slogan: a, "Start an Adventure." b, "Be Cool." c, "Learn More." d, "Have Fun." e, "Travel the World."

2006, Oct. 9   **Perf. 13x13¼**
1367   Horiz. strip of 5   2.50 2.50
a.-e. A465 (1.85r) Any single   .50 .50

Owls — A466

No. 1368: a, Barn owl. b, Cape eagle owl. c, African barred owlet. d, Verreaux's eagle owl. e, Pel's fishing owl.

2007, Aug. 3   **Litho.**   **Perf. 14½**
1368   Horiz. strip of 5   6.50 6.50
a.-e. A466 (4.64r) Any single   1.25 1.25

Souvenir Sheet

Scouting, Cent. — A467

No. 1369: a, Scout saluting. b, Scouting fleur-de-lis.

2007, Aug. 22
1369 A467 (3.90r) Sheet of 2, #a-b   2.25 2.25

Souvenir Sheet

New Year 2007 (Year of the Pig) — A468

Litho. & Embossed With Foil Application
2007, Sept. 7
1370 A468 (4.89r) green & gold   2.75 2.75

World Post Day — A469

2007, Oct. 9   **Litho.**   **Perf. 14x14¼**
1371 A469 (3.90r) multi   1.25 1.25
First telephone exchange in South Africa, 125th anniv.

Cheetah A470

Ostrich A471

2007, Oct. 19   **Perf. 14**
1372 A470 (3.90r) multi   1.25 1.25
1373 A471 (4.89r) multi   1.50 1.50

Miniature Sheet

Intl. Polar and Heliophysical Year — A472

No. 1374: a, King penguins (24x30mm). b, Scientists at SANAE IV Base, Antarctica (72x30mm). c, Wandering albatross (24x60mm). d, Adélie penguins (24x30mm). e, Killer whale (48x30mm). f, Weddell seal (24x30mm).

2007, Oct. 31
1374 A472 (1.93r) Sheet of 6, #a-f   3.50 3.50

Mills — A473

No. 1375: a, Mostert's Mill, Cape Town. b, La Cotte Watermill, Franschhoek. c, Witpoort Watermill, Stoffberg. d, Dwars Rivier Watermill, Cederberg. e, Colesberg Horse and Mill, Colesberg.

2007, Nov. 9   **Perf. 14½**
1375   Vert. strip of 5   7.00 7.00
a.-e. A473 (4.64r) Any single   1.40 1.40

Union Castle Line Ships A474

No. 1376: a, Dane. b, Kildonan Castle. c, SA Vaal. d, Edinburgh Castle. e, Windsor Castle.

2007, Dec. 5
1376   Vert. strip of 5   6.25 6.25
a.-e. A474 (4.01r) Any single   1.25 1.25

SEMI-POSTAL STAMPS

Catalogue values for unused stamps in this section are for Never Hinged items.

English-Afrikaans Se-Tenant Stamps with English inscriptions and with Afrikaans inscriptions of Nos. B1-B11 were printed alternately in the same sheets. Major-number listings and values are for pairs consisting of one English and one Afrikaans-inscribed stamp.

Church of the Vow — SP1

Cradock's Pass — SP2

Voortrekker — SP3

Voortrekker Woman — SP4

1933-36 Photo. Wmk. 201 Perf. 14
B1 SP1 ½p + ½p grn & blk, pair ('36)   11.00 4.75
  a. Single, English   .55 .55
  b. Single, Afrikaans   .55 .55
B2 SP2 1p + ½p rose & blk, pair   7.25 3.75
  a. Single, English   .45 .35
  b. Single, Afrikaans   .45 .35
B3 SP3 2p + 1p dull vio & gray, pair   12.00 6.00
  a. Single, English   .55 .55
  b. Single, Afrikaans   .55 .55
B4 SP4 3p + 1½p dp blue & gray, pair   18.00 9.50
  a. Single, English   1.50 1.10
  b. Single, Afrikaans   1.50 1.10
  Nos. B1-B4 (4)   48.25 24.00
Issued to commemorate the Voortrekkers. Surtax went to the National Memorial Fund for a national Voortrekker monument.

Voortrekker Plowing — SP5

Crossing the Drakensberg — SP6

Signing Dingaan-Retief Treaty — SP7

Proposed Monument — SP8

1938, Dec. 14   Perf. 14

B5	SP5 ½p + ½p dl grn &	
	ind, pair	7.00 6.75
a.	Single, English	.70 .60
b.	Single, Afrikaans	.70 .60
B6	SP6 1p + 1p rose & sl,	
	pair	9.50 7.75
a.	Single, English	.85 .70
b.	Single, Afrikaans	.85 .70

Perf. 15x14

B7	SP7 1½p + 1½p Prus grn	
	& choc, pair	22.50 13.50
a.	Single, English	1.40 1.40
b.	Single, Afrikaans	1.40 1.40
B8	SP8 3p + 3p chlky bl,	
	pair	26.00 16.00
a.	Single, English	1.75 2.00
b.	Single, Afrikaans	1.75 2.00
	Nos. B5-B8 (4)	65.00 44.00

Voortrekker centenary. Surtax went to the Natl. Memorial Fund for a Voortrekker monument.

"The Old Vicarage," Huguenot Museum — SP9

Rising Sun and Cross — SP10

Huguenot Dwelling, Drakenstein Mountain Valley — SP11

1939, July 17   Photo.   Perf. 14

B9	SP9 ½p + ½p Prus grn	
	& gray brn, pair	11.00 8.00
a.	Single, English	.85 .85
b.	Single, Afrikaans	.85 .85
B10	SP10 1p + 1p rose car &	
	Prus grn, pair	10.50 10.00
a.	Single, English	1.00 1.00
b.	Single, Afrikaans	1.00 1.00

Perf. 15x14

B11	SP11 1½p + 1½p, pair	27.50 15.00
a.	Single, English	1.60 1.60
b.	Single, Afrikaans	1.60 1.60
	Nos. B9-B11 (3)	49.00 33.00

250th anniv. of the landing of the Huguenots in South Africa. Surtax went to a fund to build a Huguenot memorial at Paarl.

No. 581 Surcharged in English or Afrikaans

a

b

---

c

d

1987, Nov. 16   Litho.   Perf. 14x14½

B12	Pair	1.00 1.00
a.	A229(a) 16c +10c red	.50 .50
b.	A229(b) 16c +10c red	.50 .50

Surcharge for flood relief.

No. 702 Surcharged in English or Afrikaans

1987, Dec. 1

B13	Pair	1.00 1.00
a.	A254(a) 16c +10c multicolored	.50 .50
b.	A254(b) 16c +10c multicolored	.50 .50

"+10c" is overprinted below text on Nos. B13a-B13b. Surcharge for flood relief.

No. 706 Surcharged in English or Afrikaans

1988, Mar. 1   Perf. 14½x14

B14	Pair	1.00 1.00
a.	A256(a) 16c +10c multicolored	.50 .50
b.	A256(b) 16c +10c multicolored	.50 .50

Surcharge for flood relief.

Nos. 710-713 Surcharged in English or Afrikaans

1988, Apr. 13   Perf. 14x14½

B15	Pair	.85 .85
a.	A257(c) 16c +10c multicolored	.40 .40
b.	A257(d) 16c +10c multicolored	.40 .40
B16	Pair	1.60 1.60
a.	A257(c) 30c +10c multicolored	.80 .80
b.	A257(d) 30c +10c multicolored	.80 .80
B17	Pair	2.25 2.25
a.	A257(c) 40c +10c multicolored	1.10 1.10
b.	A257(d) 40c +10c multicolored	1.10 1.10
B18	Pair	2.75 2.75
a.	A257(c) 50c +10c multicolored	1.25 1.25
b.	A257(d) 50c +10c multicolored	1.25 1.25
	Nos. B12-B18 (7)	10.45 10.45

Surcharge for flood relief.
On Nos. B16a, B16b, the "+ 10" is in upper left corner.

AIR POST STAMPS

Mail Plane — AP1

Biplane in Flight — AP2

Unwmk.

1925, Feb. 26   Litho.   Perf. 12

C1	AP1	1p red	3.00 4.75
C2	AP1	3p ultramarine	10.00 13.00
C3	AP1	6p violet	17.50 24.00
C4	AP1	9p gray green	29.00 32.50
		Nos. C1-C4 (4)	59.50 74.25
		Set, never hinged	150.00

Forgeries exist.

National Flood Disaster +10c

Nasionale Vloedramp +10c

1929, Aug. 16   Typo.   Perf. 14x13½

C5	AP2	4p blue green	8.50 2.75
C6	AP2	1sh orange	27.50 21.00
		Set, never hinged	75.00

> **Catalogue values for unused stamps in this section, from this point to the end of the section, are for Never Hinged items.**

"AIRMAIL POSTCARD" "AIRMAIL POSTCARD RATE"

Stamps inscribed thus were sold for the amount shown in ( ) on date of issue.

See Nos. 1038-1042F for stamps included with postage sets.

Endangered Fauna Type of 1993

1996, May 8   Litho.   Perf. 14x14½

C6A	A288	(1r) White rhinoceros	.70 .70
C6B	A288	(1r) Buffalo	.70 .70
C6C	A288	(1r) Lion	.70 .70
f.		Souvenir sheet of 1 + label	.80 .80
C6D	A288	(1r) Leopard	.70 .70
C6E	A288	(1r) African elephant	.70 .70
g.		Strip of 5, #936-940	3.50
h.		Sheet of 10, 2 each #936-940	7.00
i.		Booklet pane of 5, #936-940 + 5 labels	4.00
		Complete booklet, #940c	4.00

No. C6Cf is inscribed in sheet margin for Coach House, and sold for 1r.
Issued: #C6Cf, 2/97; #C6Ei, 7/27/97.

Inauguaration of Blue Train — AP3

Designs: No. C7, Double-headed Class 6E 1, electric lovomotives, Cape Town to Beaufort West. No. C8, Double-headed Class 6E 1 electric lovomotives, Hex River Valley. No. C9, 1960's Steam powered locomotives between Three Sisters and Huchinson. No. C10, Diesel locomotives, Modder River Bridge near Kimberly. No. C11, Diesel locomotives, Northern Transvaal.

1997, Aug. 1   Perf. 14 Syncopated

C7	AP3	(1r) multicolored	.70 .70
a.		Souv. sheet of 1, perf. 14	.70 .70
C8	AP3	(1r) multicolored	.70 .70
C9	AP3	(1r) multicolored	.70 .70
a.		Souvenir sheet of 1, perf. 14	.70 .70
C10	AP3	(1r) multicolored	.70 .70
C11	AP3	(1r) multicolored	.70 .70
a.		Strip of 5, #C7-C11	3.50 3.50

No. C7a is inscribed in sheet margin for The Cape Stamp Show and Harmers of London stamp auctioneers.
No. C9a was issued 11/97, sold for 1.30r and is inscribed for Eastgate Universal Stamps & Coins in sheet margin.

1998, Nov.   Litho.   Perf. 14¾x14
Booklet Stamps

C12	AP3	(1r) Like #C7	.70 .70
C13	AP3	(1r) Like #C8	.70 .70
C14	AP3	(1r) Like #C9	.70 .70
C15	AP3	(1r) Like #C10	.70 .70
C16	AP3	(1r) Like #C11	.70 .70
a.		Bklt. pane, 2 ea #C12-C16	7.00
		Complete booklet, #C16a	7.00
		Nos. C12-C16 (5)	3.50 3.50

Tourism AP4

Western Cape of South Africa: No. C7, Sandstone Cliffs. No. C8, Robben Island. No. C9, Pinehurst Homestead. No. C10, Waterfront, Capetown. No. C11, Boschendal Wine Estate.

1998, Sept. 28   Litho.   Perf. 14½x14
Booklet Stamps

C17	AP4	(1.30r) multicolored	.60 .60
C18	AP4	(1.30r) multicolored	.60 .60
C19	AP4	(1.30r) multicolored	.60 .60
C20	AP4	(1.30r) multicolored	.60 .60
C21	AP4	(1.30r) multicolored	.60 .60
a.		Bklt. pane, 2 ea #C17-C21 + label	6.00
		Complete booklet, #C21a	6.00
		Nos. C17-C21 (5)	3.00 3.00

Perf. 14¾x14 on 3 sides
1998, Sept. 28   Litho.

KwaZulu-Natal: No. C22, Drakensberge. No. C23, Zulu women and huts. No. C24, Rhinoceros and pelicans. No. C25, Rickshaw driver. No. C26, Indian dancers.

C22	AP4	(1.30r) multicolored	.60 .60
C23	AP4	(1.30r) multicolored	.60 .60
C24	AP4	(1.30r) multicolored	.60 .60
C25	AP4	(1.30r) multicolored	.60 .60
C26	AP4	(1.30r) multicolored	.60 .60
a.		Booklet pane, 2 ea #C22-C26	6.00
		Complete booklet, #C26a	6.00

Worldwide Fund for Nature AP5

1998, Oct. 23   Litho.   Perf. 14¾x14

C27	AP5	(1.30r) Cuvier's beaked whale	1.00 1.00
C28	AP5	(1.30r) Minke whale	1.00 1.00
C29	AP5	(1.30r) Bryde's whale	1.00 1.00
C30	AP5	(1.30r) Pygmy right whale	1.00 1.00
a.		Block of 4, #C27-C30	4.00 4.00
b.		Booklet pane, 3 each #C27-C28, 2 each #C29-C30	10.00
		Complete booklet	10.00
		Complete booklet, 2 #C30b + 2 postal cards	30.00

No. C30b exists with and without perfs running through side and bottom pane margins.

Tourism Type of 1998

Mpumalanga and Northern Province: No. C31, Blyde River Canyon. No. C32, Lone Creek Falls. No. C33, Ndebele women. No. C34, Pilgrim's Rest historical town. No. C35, Elephants, Thulamela, Kruger National Park.

1999, Aug.   Litho.   Perf. 14¾x14

C31	AP4	(1.30r) multi	.50 .50
C32	AP4	(1.30r) multi	.50 .50
C33	AP4	(1.30r) multi	.50 .50
C34	AP4	(1.30r) multi	.50 .50
C35	AP4	(1.30r) multi	.50 .50
a.		Booklet pane, 2 each #C31-C35	5.00
		Complete booklet, #C35a	5.00

Big Game Animals — AP6

Designs: Nos. C36, C45, Elephant. Nos. C37, C44, Lion. Nos. C38, C43, Rhinoceros. Nos. C39, C42, Leopard. Nos. C40, C41, Buffalo.

Perf. 14¾x14½ on 3 or 4 Sides
2001, Apr. 25   Litho.
Booklet Stamps

C36	AP6	(1.90r) multi	.70 .70
C37	AP6	(1.90r) multi	.70 .70
C38	AP6	(1.90r) multi	.70 .70
C39	AP6	(1.90r) multi	.70 .70
C40	AP6	(1.90r) multi	.70 .70
a.		Booklet pane, 2 each #C36-C40	7.00
		Booklet, 2 #C40a + 2 postal cards	14.00

Self-Adhesive
Size: 30x24mm
Serpentine Die Cut 12x11½ on 2 or 3 Sides

C41	AP6	(1.90r) multi	.70 .70
C42	AP6	(1.90r) multi	.70 .70
C43	AP6	(1.90r) multi	.70 .70
C44	AP6	(1.90r) multi	.70 .70
C45	AP6	(1.90r) multi	.70 .70
a.		Booklet, 2 each #C41-C45	7.00

Tourism — AP7

Designs: No. C46, (2.10r), Cango Caves. No. C47, (2.10r), Table Mountain. No. C48, (2.10r), West Coast. No. C49, (2.10r), Snow-covered mountains near Elliot. No. C50, (2.10r), Augrabies Waterfall. No. C51, (2.10r),

Stellenbosch vineyard country. No. C52, (2.10r), Flowers, Namaqualand. No. C53, (2.10r), Tsitsikamma Forest. No. C54, (2.10r), Cape Mountain zebras. No. C55, (2.10r), Richtersveld Desert.

2001, Sept. 6 Litho. Perf. 13¼x13¾
C46-C55 AP7   Set of 10   7.00 7.00

Pres. Nelson
Mandela — AP8

Various photographs. Color of country name and size of stamps: a, Lilac, 31x48mm. b, Red and lilac, 50x38mm. c, Orange, 31x48mm. d, Orange, 31x31mm. e, Orange, 38x50mm. f, White, 38x50mm. g, White, 50x38mm. h, White, 31x48mm. i, Lilac, 38x50mm. j, Red, 31x31mm.

2001, Nov. 26   Perf. 14¾x14, 13¾
C56   Booklet   9.00
a.-j. AP8 (2.10r) Any booklet pane .90   .90
No. C56 sold for 45r and included two postal cards.

Shaka (1785-1828), Zulu King — AP9

2003, Sept. 24 Litho. Perf. 13x13¼
C57 AP9 (3.30r) multi   1.10 1.10

Miniature Sheet

Flora and Fauna of Table
Mountain — AP10

No. C58: a, Cape sugarbird, vert. b, Dark opal butterflies. c, King protea. d, Cape rock hyrax. e, Cuckoo wasp. f, Table Mountain ghost frog. g, Table Mountain cockroaches. h, Staavia dodii, vert. i, Spotted skaapsteker. j, Duvalia immaculata.

Serpentine Die Cut 9x9½, 9½x9
2004, Sept. 1   Litho.
Self-Adhesive
C58   AP10   Sheet of 10   17.50 17.50
a.-j.   (10r) Any single   1.75 1.75

World Post Day — AP11

2004, Sept. 23   Perf. 14
C59 AP11 (3.45r) multi   1.25 1.25

Rotary International, Cent. — AP12

No. C60: a, Doctor listening to boy's heart-beat, infant receiving oral vaccination. b, Child at computer, welder.

2005, Feb. 23   Perf. 14¼x14
C60   Horiz. pair   3.25 3.25
a.-b.   AP12 (4r) Either single 1.50 1.50

Miniature Sheet

National Orders — AP13

No. C61: a, Order of Mapungubwe. b, Order of Merit for Bravery. c, Order of the Baobab. d, Order of Luthuli. e, Order of Ikhamanga. f, Order of the Companions of O. R. Tambo.

**Litho. & Embossed with Foil
Application**
2005, Nov. 26   Perf. 14¾x14¼
C61 AP13 (4.25r) Sheet of 6, #a-f 9.00 9.00

Miniature Sheet

Art — AP14

No. C62: a, Boland Winter, by Eric Laubscher. b, Table Mountain, by Maggie Laubser. c, Fishermen Drawing Nets, by Walter Battis. d, Oh, South Africa, You've Turned My World Completely Upside Down, by Lallitha Jawahirlal. e, Untitled, by Lucky Sibiya. f, Untitled, by Sophie Masiza. g, Azibuye Emasisweni, by Trevor Makhoba. h, Kontantwinkel Riebeck-Wes, by John Kramer. i, Houses in the Hills, by Gladys Mgudlandlu. j, Sequence City, by Usha Seejarim.

2005, May 6   Litho. Perf. 14¼x14¾
C62 AP14 (3.65r) Sheet of 10,
           #a-j   13.50 13.50

Intl. Year of
Physics — AP15

2005, July 7   Perf. 14½
C63 AP15 (3.65r) multi   1.40 1.40

Miniature Sheet

"Hello" in Various Languages and
Flag — AP16

No. C64: a, Hallo! b, Hi! c, Sawubona. d, Ndi Masiari! e, Lotjha!. f, Avuxeni. g, Dumela. h, Molo!

2005, Oct. 9
C64 AP16 (3.65r) Sheet of 8, #a-
              h   9.50 9.50

Big Game Animals Type of 2001
**Serpentine Die Cut 12¼x12¾ on 2
or 3 Sides**
2005, Oct. 10
Self-Adhesive
Booklet Stamps
Size: 30x24mm
C65 AP6 (3.65r) Buffalo   1.25 1.25
C66 AP6 (3.65r) Leopard   1.25 1.25
C67 AP6 (3.65r) Rhinoceros   1.25 1.25
C68 AP6 (3.65r) Lion   1.25 1.25
C69 AP6 (3.65r) Elephant   1.25 1.25
a.   Booklet, 2 each # C65-C69   12.50

Big Game
Animals — AP17

Serpentine Die Cut 12½x13½
2006, Feb. 24
Self-Adhesive
Booklet Stamps
C70 AP17 (3.65r) Lion   1.25 1.25
C71 AP17 (3.65r) Buffalo   1.25 1.25
C72 AP17 (3.65r) Elephant   1.25 1.25
C73 AP17 (3.65r) Rhinoceros 1.25 1.25
C74 AP17 (3.65r) Leopard   1.25 1.25
a.   Booklet, 2 each #C70-C74   12.50

Cyclists — AP18

2006, Mar. 6   Perf. 13¼x13¾
C75 AP18 (4.25r) multi   1.50 1.50

Souvenir Sheet

2010 World Cup Soccer
Championships, South Africa — AP19

2006, July 7 Litho. Perf. 14¾x14½
C76 AP19 (4.40r) multi   1.40 1.40

Miniature Sheet

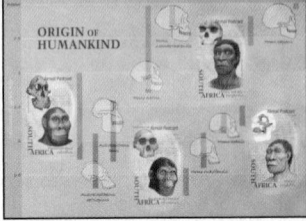

Origins of Humans — AP20

No. C77: a, Paranthropus robustus. b, Australopithecus africanus. c, Homo heidelbergensis. d, Homo ergaster.

Serpentine Die Cut 11½x11¾
2006, Nov. 10
Self-Adhesive
C77 AP20 (3.80r) Sheet of 4, #a-
              d   4.75 4.75

Big Game
Animals — AP21

**Serpentine Die Cut 13½x13¾ on 2
or 3 Sides**
2007, Aug. 17   Litho.
Booklet Stamps
Self-Adhesive
C78 AP21 (4.01r) Elephant   1.10 1.10
C79 AP21 (4.01r) Leopard   1.10 1.10
C80 AP21 (4.01r) Buffalo   1.10 1.10
C81 AP21 (4.01r) Lion   1.10 1.10
C82 AP21 (4.01r) Rhinoceros 1.10 1.10
a.   Booklet pane, 2 each #C78-
       C82   11.00
       Nos. C78-C82 (5)   5.50 5.50

Souvenir Sheet

24th UPU Congress, Nairobi — AP22

2007, Oct. 9   Perf. 13¾
C83 AP22 (4.64r) multi   1.40 1.40

Souvenir Sheet

2010 World Cup Soccer
Championships, South Africa — AP23

2007, Nov. 23   *Perf. 13¼x13½*
C84 AP23 (4.64r) multi   1.40 1.40

POSTAGE DUE STAMPS

D1   D2

Wmk. Springbok's Head (177)
1914-15   Typo.   Perf. 14
J1	D1	½p green & blk	1.10 4.25
J2	D1	1p red & blk	1.10 .20
J3	D1	2p vio & blk ('14)	5.50 .80
J4	D1	3p ultra & blk	.85 .80
J5	D1	5p brown & blk	2.25 19.00
J6	D1	6p gray & blk	11.00 19.00
J7	D1	1sh black & red	77.50 160.00

Nos. J1-J7 (7)   99.30 204.05

1922 Unwmk. Litho. Rouletted 7-8
J8	D1	½p blue grn & blk	1.60 12.50
J9	D1	1p dull red & blk	1.75 1.25
J10	D1	1½p yellow brn & blk	2.00 2.40

Nos. J8-J10 (3)   5.35 16.15

1922-26   Perf. 14
J11	D1	½p blue grn & blk	.20 .20
J12	D1	1p rose & blk ('23)	.55 .20
J13	D1	1½p yel brn & blk ('24)	1.60 1.25
J14	D1	2p vio & blk ('23)	1.40 .60
a.		Imperf. pair	300.00
J15	D1	3p blue & blk ('26)	8.00 8.00
J16	D1	6p gray & blue ('23)	16.00 8.00

Nos. J11-J16 (6)   27.75 18.30

1927-28   Typo.
J17	D2	½p blue green & blk	.80 1.00
J18	D2	1p rose & black	.80 .80
J19	D2	2p violet & black	1.40 1.25
J20	D2	3p ultra & black	13.00 13.00
J21	D2	6p gray & black	24.00 20.00

Nos. J17-J21 (5)   40.00 36.05

Type of 1927-28 Redrawn
1932-40 Photo. Perf. 15x14 Wmk. 201
J22	D2	½p blue grn & blk ('34)	1.00 1.25
J23	D2	1p rose car & blk ('34)	.95 .95
J24	D2	2p blk violet & blk	4.00 .30
a.		2p dark purple & black ('40)	11.00 .20
J25	D2	3p dp blue & blk	18.00 12.00
J26	D2	3p ultra & dk bl ('35)	3.50 .40
J27	D2	3p blue & dk bl ('40)	21.00 2.00
J28	D2	6p brn org & grn ('33)	18.00 6.00
J29	D2	6p red org & grn ('38)	8.50 2.00

Nos. J22-J29 (8)   74.95 24.90

The ½p No. J22 photogravure has larger but thinner and the "d" is taller and thinner than on No. J17.

The 1p No. J23 photogravure has numeral with parallel sides. The "d" is taller and thicker than on No. J18.

On Nos. J25 and J27 the numeral is followed by a large "d" with thick lines and a large round period below it.

Nos. J22, J24 and J25 have frame in photogravure, value typographed.

Catalogue values for unused stamps in this section, from this point to the end of the section, are for Never Hinged items.

See "English-Afrikaans Se-tenant" note preceding No. 23.

D3

Horiz. strips of Three, Perf. 15x14
All Around, Rouletted 6½ Between
1943-44   Photo.   Wmk. 201
J30	D3	½p Prus green ('44)	8.50 22.50
a.		Single	.20 .20
J31	D3	1p brt carmine	9.50 5.25
a.		Single	.20 .20
J32	D3	2p dark purple	9.00 9.00
a.		Single	.20 .20
J33	D3	3p dark blue	55.00 62.50
a.		Single	.20 .20

Nos. J30-J33 (4)   82.00 99.25

Catalogued as strips of 3 because of the perforations.

Type of 1932-38, Redrawn
Thick Numerals, Capital "D"
1948-49   Perf. 15x14
J34	D2	½p blue green & blk	9.00 6.00
J35	D2	1p deep rose & blk	10.50 2.50
J36	D2	2p dk pur & blk ('49)	14.00 2.00
J37	D2	3p ultra & dk blue	12.00 9.00
J38	D2	6p dp org & grn ('49)	37.50 7.00

Nos. J34-J38 (5)   83.00 27.00

Redrawn Type of 1948-49
Hyphen between Suid-Afrika
1950-58   Perf. 15x14
J40	D2	1p car rose & blk	1.25 .45
J41	D2	2p dk pur & blk ('51)	.85 .30
J42	D2	3p ultra & dk blue	6.25 2.50
J43	D2	4p emer & dk grn ('58)	14.50 11.00
J44	D2	6p dp org & grn ('52)	11.50 11.00
J45	D2	1sh brn red & dk brn ('58)	17.50 14.50

Nos. J40-J45 (6)   51.85 40.25

D4   D5

Perf. 15x14
1961, Feb. 14 Photo. Wmk. 330
J46	D4	1c cerise & blk	.20 2.50
J47	D4	2c purple & blk	.20 2.50
J48	D4	4c brt & dk green	1.00 6.00
J49	D4	5c chalky bl & slate	2.00 6.50
J50	D4	6c vermilion & blk	8.00 7.00
J51	D4	10c maroon & dk brn	8.50 10.00

Nos. J46-J51 (6)   20.90 34.50

Republic
1961-69   Perf. 15x14
Afrikaans Inscription on Top and Left Side
J52	D5	1c cerise & blk	.50 .50
J53	D5	4c brt & dk green	4.25 3.00
J54	D5	6c vermilion & dk grn	8.50 7.25

English Inscription on Top and Left Side
J55	D5	1c cerise & blk ('62)	.30 3.50
J56	D5	2c purple & blk	.40 .40
J57	D5	4c brt & dk grn ('69)	12.00 17.00
J58	D5	5c chlky bl & dk bl	2.40 3.00
J59	D5	5c chlky bl & blk ('62)	2.75 11.00
J60	D5	10c maroon & dk brn	4.50 6.50

Nos. J52-J60 (9)   35.85 48.65

1967-70   Photo.   Wmk. 359
Afrikaans Inscription on Top and Left Side
J61	D5	1c carmine rose & blk	.20 .20
J62	D5	2c brt purple & blk	.20 .20
a.		Perf. 14 ('71)	25.00 25.00
J63	D5	4c lt grn & blk ('71)	27.50 25.00
a.		4c bright & dark green ('70)	110.00 110.00
J64	D5	5c dk blue & blk	.85 .85
J65	D5	6c orange & dk grn	4.25 9.75
J66	D5	10c dk rose brown & blk	3.50 2.10

English Inscription on Top and Left Side
J67	D5	1c car rose & blk	.20 .20
J68	D5	2c brt purple & blk	.40 .40
a.		Perf. 14 ('71)	25.00 25.00
J69	D5	4c lt green & blk ('71)	27.50 25.00
a.		4c bright & dark green ('70)	35.00 35.00
b.		As "a," perf. 14 ('71)	6.00 6.00
J70	D5	5c dk blue & blk	.85 .85
J71	D5	6c orange & dk grn	4.25 9.75

J72	D5	10c dk rose brown & blk	3.50 2.10

Nos. J61-J72 (12)   73.20 76.40

D6

1972, Mar. 22   Perf. 14x13½
J73	D6	1c brt yellow green	.55 1.75
J74	D6	2c orange	.80 3.00
J75	D6	4c dull purple	2.00 3.00
J76	D6	6c yellow	2.00 5.50
J77	D6	8c bright blue	3.50 5.50
J78	D6	10c rose red	6.00 8.50

Nos. J73-J78 (6)   14.85 27.25

On the 2c, 6c and 10c "TO PAY" in first row at left.

OFFICIAL STAMPS

Type A2 stamps have very small margins at top and bottom. Values are for examples with perfs close to, or touching the frame.

Regular Issues Overprinted in Black

Periods in Overprint
On No. 5
1926   Wmk. 177   Perf. 14
O1 A2 2p dull violet   18.00 2.00

See "English-Afrikaans Se-tenant" note preceding No. 23.

On Nos. 23-25
Perf. 14½x14
Wmk. 201
O2	A5	½p dk grn & blk, pair	6.00 12.00
a.		Single, English	.75 1.25
b.		Single, Afrikaans	.75 1.25
O3	A6	1p car & blk, pair	4.00 7.00
a.		Single, English	.25 .50
b.		Single, Afrikaans	.25 .50
O4	A7	6p org & grn, pair	550.00 75.00
a.		Single, English	25.00 9.00
b.		Single, Afrikaans	25.00 9.00

Nos. 26 and 25 Overprinted
(Reading Up)

b

No Periods in Overprint
1928-29   Perf. 14, 14½x14
Space between words 19mm
O5	A8	2p vio brn & gray, pair ('29)	3.50 10.00
a.		Single, English	.50 1.50
b.		Single, Afrikaans	.50 1.50
c.		Space 17½mm, pair	4.00 12.50
d.		As "c," single, English	.50 2.00
e.		As "c," single, Afrikaans	.50 2.00

Space between words 11½mm
O6	A7	6p org & grn, pair	18.00 25.00
a.		Single, English	2.00 2.75
b.		Single, Afrikaans	2.00 2.75

#23-25 Ovptd. type "b" Reading Down
Space between words 13½-14mm
1929   Perf. 14½x14
O7	A5	½p grn & blk, pair	2.00 2.75
a.		Single, English	.25 .30
b.		Single, Afrikaans	.25 .30
c.		Period after "OFFISIEEL" on English stamp	3.25 3.25
d.		Pair, "c" + normal ½p	30.00 30.00
e.		Period after "OFFISIEEL" on Afrikaans stamp	3.25 3.25
f.		Pair, "e" + normal ½p	35.00 35.00

O8	A6	1p car & blk, pair	2.50 3.50
a.		Single, English	.30 .40
b.		Single, Afrikaans	.30 .40
O9	A7	6p org & grn, pair	7.75 26.00
a.		Single, English	1.25 3.00
b.		Single, Afrikaans	1.25 3.00
c.		Period after "OFFISIEEL." on English stamp	8.00 10.00
d.		Pair, "c" + normal 6p	60.00 100.00
e.		Period after "OFFISIEEL." on Afrikaans stamp	9.00 12.00
f.		Pair, "e" + normal 6p	70.00 110.00

Nos. O7-O9 (3)   12.25 32.25

#29-30 Ovptd. type "b" Reading Down
Space between words 17½-19mm
1931   Engr.   Perf. 14, 14x13½
O10	A11	1sh dp bl & bis brn, pair	30.00 85.00
a.		Single, English	3.00 9.00
b.		Single, Afrikaans	3.00 9.00
c.		Period after "OFFICIAL." on Afrikaans stamp	50.00 50.00
d.		Pair, "c" + normal 1sh	100.00 225.00
O11	A12	2sh6p brn & bl grn, pair	60.00 150.00
a.		Single, English	7.50 17.50
b.		Single, Afrikaans	7.50 17.50
c.		Period after "OFFICIAL." on Afrikaans stamp	72.50 72.50
d.		Pair, "c" + normal 2sh6p	275.00 475.00

Regular Issues of 1930-45 Overprinted type "b" Reading Down
("SUIDAFRIKA" on Afrikaans stamps)
Perf. 15x14 (½p, 1p, 6p), 14
1930-47   Photo.   Wmk. 201
Space between words 9½-12mm
(Various spacings occur in same setting)
O12	A5	½p bl grn & blk (#33), pair ('31)	2.00 3.50
a.		Single, English	.20 .40
b.		Single, Afrikaans	.20 .40
c.		Period after "OFFISIEEL." on English stamp	3.50 4.00
d.		Pair, "c" + normal ½p	25.00 42.50
e.		Period after "OFFISIEEL." on Afrikaans stamp	3.25 3.50
f.		Pair, "e" + normal ½p	25.00 42.50

Space between words 12½-13½mm
O13	A5	½p bl grn & blk, pair (#33)	3.00 4.00
a.		Single, English	.25 .50
b.		Single, Afrikaans	.25 .50
O14	A6	1p car & blk, pair (#34)	3.50 3.50
a.		Single, English	.40 .50
b.		Single, Afrikaans	.40 .50
c.		Period after "OFFISIEEL." on Afrikaans stamp	3.75 4.00
d.		Pair, "c" + normal 1p	25.00 32.50
e.		Period after "OFFISIEEL." on Afrikaans stamp	3.00 3.50
f.		Pair, "e" + normal 1p	25.00 32.50
O15	A6	1p rose & blk, pair (#35) ('33)	7.50 9.00
a.		Single, English	.75 1.00
b.		Single, Afrikaans	.75 1.00
c.		Double ovpt. pair	275.00 300.00
d.		As "c," English	45.00
e.		As "c," Afrikaans	45.00

Space between words 20½-22mm
O16	A8	2p vio & gray, pair (#36) ('31)	4.50 10.00
a.		Single, English	.60 1.25
b.		Single, Afrikaans	.60 1.25
O17	A8	2p vio & ind, pair (#37)	75.00 85.00
a.		Single, English	6.00 9.00
b.		Single, Afrikaans	6.00 9.00

Space between words 12½-13½mm
O18	A7	6p org & grn, pair (#42)	7.00 8.50
a.		Single, English	.75 .90
b.		Single, Afrikaans	.75 .90
c.		Period after "OFFISIEEL." on English stamp	6.50 6.50
d.		Pair, "c" + normal 6p	50.00 60.00
e.		Period after "OFFISIEEL." on Afrikaans stamp	5.50 5.50
f.		Pair, "e" + normal 6p	40.00 40.00

Space between words 21mm
O19	A11	1sh dp bl & brn, pair (#43c) ('32)	42.50 75.00
a.		Single, English	4.00 7.50
b.		Single, Afrikaans	4.00 7.50
c.		1sh dk bl & yel brn (#43), 19mm, pair	42.50 75.00
d.		As "c," single, English	3.00 7.50
e.		As "c," single, Afrikaans	3.00 7.50
f.		As "c," spaced 21mm, pair	42.50 65.00
g.		As "f," single, English	6.00 7.50
h.		As "f," single, Afrikaans	6.00 7.50

Space between words 17½-18½mm
O20	A12	2sh6p brn & sl grn (#44c) ('37), pair	65.00 100.00
a.		Single, English	10.00 12.50
b.		Single, Afrikaans	10.00 12.50
c.		Spaced 21mm, pair	45.00 70.00
d.		As "c," single, English	4.50 8.00
e.		As "c," single, Afrikaans	4.50 8.00
f.		2sh6p red brn & grn, pair (#44i) ('33)	50.00 90.00
g.		As "f," single, English	5.00 8.50
h.		As "f," single, Afrikaans	5.00 8.50
j.		2sh6p brn & bl, 19-20mm (#44) ('47), pair	30.00 60.00

k.	As "j," single, English		3.00	5.00
m.	As "j," single, Afrikaans		3.00	5.00
	Nos. O12-O20 (9)		*210.00*	*298.50*

Catalogue values for unused stamps in this section, from this point to the end of the section, are for Never Hinged items.

Regular Issue of 1933-54 Overprinted type "b" Reading Down ("SUID-AFRIKA" Hyphenated)

1935-50 Photo. Perf. 15x14, 14
Space between words given with each listing

O21	A5	½p grn & gray (#45), 12½-13mm, pair ('36)	3.25	15.00
a.	Single, English		.25	1.25
b.	Single, Afrikaans		.25	1.25
O22	A5	½p grn & gray, (#46), 11½-13mm, pair ('38)	12.00	12.50
a.	Single, English		.50	1.00
b.	Single, Afrikaans		.50	1.00
O23	A5	½p grn & gray (#47), 11½mm, pair ('48)	1.25	5.00
a.	Single, English		.20	.70
b.	Single, Afrikaans		.20	.70
O24	A6	1p car & gray (#48), 11-13mm, pair	1.00	1.00
a.	Single, English		.20	.20
b.	Single, Afrikaans		.20	.20
O25	A6	1p rose car & gray blk (#49), 11½-12mm, pair ('41)	1.00	.50
a.	Single, English		.20	.20
b.	Single, Afrikaans		.20	.20
O26	A15	1½p dk grn & gold (#51), 19-21mm, pair ('37)	30.00	22.50
a.	Single, English		2.25	1.75
b.	Single, Afrikaans		2.25	1.75
O27	A15	1½p sl grn & och (#52), 16mm, pair ('44)	3.00	8.00
a.	Single, English		.30	.45
b.	Single, Afrikaans		.30	.45
c.	Ovpt. spaced 14-14½mm, pair		3.00	5.00
d.	As "c," single, English		.25	.80
e.	As "c," single, Afrikaans		.25	.80
O28	A8	2p bl vio & dl bl (#53), 20-21mm, pair ('39)	80.00	30.00
a.	Single, English		7.50	2.50
b.	Single, Afrikaans		7.50	2.50
O29	A16	2p pur & sl (#55), 19-21mm, pair ('48)	4.50	16.00
a.	Single, English		.25	1.50
b.	Single, Afrikaans		.25	1.50
O30	A7	6p org & bl grn, I (#59), 12-13mm, pair ('38)	80.00	40.00
a.	Single, English		6.50	3.75
b.	Single, Afrikaans		6.50	3.75
O31	A7	6p org & grn, II (#60), 12-13mm, pair ('39)	12.00	10.00
a.	Single, English		1.25	1.25
b.	Single, Afrikaans		1.25	1.25
O32	A7	6p org & grn III (#61), 11½-12mm, pair ('47)	5.50	8.00
a.	Single, English		.50	.90
b.	Single, Afrikaans		.50	.90
O33	A11	1sh lt bl & ol brn (#62c), 19-21mm, pair ('40)	65.00	27.50
a.	Single, English		4.50	2.00
b.	Single, Afrikaans		4.50	2.00
c.	"OFFICIAL" on both sides		500.00	
d.	"OFFISIEEL" on both sides		500.00	
e.	1sh chlky bl & lt brn (#62) ('50), pair		10.00	25.00
f.	As "e," single, English		.90	2.50
g.	As "e," single, Afrikaans		.90	2.50
h.	1sh vio bl & brnsh blk (#62f), 18-19mm, pair		65.00	27.50
j.	As "h," single, English		4.50	2.00
k.	As "h," single, Afrikaans		4.50	2.00
O34	A13	5sh grn & blk (#64) 19-20mm, pair	55.00	110.00
a.	Single, English		3.50	12.50
b.	Single, Afrikaans		3.50	12.50
O35	A13	5sh grn & blk (#65), 20mm, pair	40.00	110.00
a.	Single, English		3.50	12.50
b.	Single, Afrikaans		3.50	12.50
O36	A18	10sh ol blk & bl (#67), 19½-20mm, pair ('48)	85.00	175.00
a.	Single, English		7.50	22.50
b.	Single, Afrikaans		7.50	22.50
	Nos. O21-O36 (16)		*478.50*	*591.00*

Nos. 52 and 56 Overprinted type "b" Reading Up
Space between words 16mm

1949-50 Size: 22x18mm Perf. 14

O37	A15	1½p sl grn & ocher, pair	35.00	40.00
a.	Single, English		2.25	3.50
b.	Single, Afrikaans		2.25	3.50
	Size: 21½x17½mm			
O38	A16	2p pur & sl bl, pair ('50)	1,500.	1,750.
a.	Single, English		125.	175.
b.	Single, Afrikaans		125.	175.

Nos. 64, 67 Overprinted

c

Space between words 18-19mm

1940 Perf. 14

O39	A13	5sh grn & blk, pair	85.00	100.00
a.	Single, English		3.00	10.00
b.	Single, Afrikaans		3.00	10.00
O40	A18	10sh ol brn & bl, pair	375.00	350.00
a.	Single, English		25.00	35.00
b.	Single, Afrikaans		25.00	35.00

No. 54 Overprinted type "c" Reading Up
Space between words 19mm

1945 Perf. 14

O41	A8	2p dl vio & gray, pair	8.00	22.50
a.	Single, English		.50	2.25
b.	Single, Afrikaans		.50	2.25

No. 47 Overprinted

1947 Perf. 15x14

O42	A5	½p grn & gray, pair	22.50	20.00
a.	Single, English		1.00	2.00
b.	Single, Afrikaans		1.00	2.00

Stamps of 1937-54 Overprinted

1950-54 Perf. 15x14, 14
Space between words 10mm

O43	A5	½p grn & gray, pair (#47)	.90	1.50
a.	Single, English		.20	.20
b.	Single, Afrikaans		.20	.20
O44	A6	1p rose car & gray blk, pair (#49)	1.00	2.00
a.	Single, English		.20	.20
b.	Single, Afrikaans		.20	.20
O45	A6	1p car & blk, pair (#50)	1.00	1.50
a.	Single, English		.20	.20
b.	Single, Afrikaans		.20	.20
	Space between words 14½mm			
O46	A15	1½p sl grn & ocher, pair (#52)	1.50	3.00
a.	Single, English		.20	.35
b.	Single, Afrikaans		.20	.35
O47	A16	2p pur & sl bl, pair (#56)	1.00	2.00
a.	Single, English		.20	.20
b.	Single, Afrikaans		.20	.20
c.	Ovpt. reading up, pair			
	Space between words 10mm			
O48	A7	6p red org & bl grn, III, pair (#61c)	2.00	3.00
a.	Single, English		.35	.35
b.	Single, Afrikaans		.35	.35
	Space between words 19mm			
O49	A11	1sh chlky bl & lt brn, pair (#62)	6.75	15.00
a.	Single, English		.50	1.75
b.	Single, Afrikaans		.50	1.75
c.	1sh vio bl & brnsh blk (#62f), pair		140.00	150.00
d.	As "c," single, English		12.50	17.50
e.	As "c," single, Afrikaans		12.50	17.50

O50	A12	2sh6p brn & brt grn, pair (#63)	10.00	32.50
a.	Single, English		1.00	3.25
b.	Single, Afrikaans		1.00	3.25
O51	A13	5sh grn & blk, pair (#64)	175.00	90.00
a.	Single, English		2.00	9.00
b.	Single, Afrikaans		2.00	9.00
O52	A13	5sh bl grn & blk, I, pair (#65)	65.00	75.00
a.	Single, English		3.00	6.50
b.	Single, Afrikaans		3.00	6.50
O53	A13	5sh grn & blk, II, pair (#66)	80.00	80.00
a.	Single, English		4.00	9.00
b.	Single, Afrikaans		4.00	9.00
O54	A18	10sh ol blk & bl, pair (#67)	80.00	200.00
a.	Single, English		5.00	21.00
b.	Single, Afrikaans		5.00	21.00
	Nos. O43-O54 (12)		*424.15*	*505.50*

BOPHUTHATSWANA

ˌbō-ˌdⁱpü-tät-ˈswä-nə

LOCATION — Noncontiguous enclaves, Republic of South Africa
GOVT. — Self-governing tribal homeland
AREA — 27,340 sq. mi.
POP. — 1,660,000 (1985)
CAPITAL — Mmabatho

Catalogue values for all unused stamps in this country are for Never Hinged items.

Independence from South Africa — A1

Perf. 12½

1977, Dec. 6 Litho. Unwmk.

1	A1	4c Hands, dove released	.75	.75
2	A1	10c Leopard (state emblem)	1.50	1.10
3	A1	15c Coat of arms	3.00	2.25
4	A1	20c Flag	4.00	3.00
	Nos. 1-4 (4)		*9.25*	*7.10*

An imperf. souvenir sheet exists containing Nos. 1-4 printed in one color (blue). Not valid for postage.

Tribal Totems — A2

Designs: 1c, African buffalo (Malete, Hwaduba). 2c, Bush pig (Kolobeng). 3c, Chacma baboon (Hurutshe, Thlaro). 4c, Leopard (state emblem). 5c, Crocodile (Kwena-Fokeng). 6c, Savanna monkey (Kgatla). 7c, Lion (Taung). 8c, Spotted hyena (Phiring). 9c, Cape porcupine (Rokologadi). 10c, Aardvark (Tlokwa). 15c, Fish (Tlhaping). 20c, Hunting dog (Tlhalerwa). 25c, Common duiker (Mfatlha). 30c, African elephant (Tlhako, Tloung). 50c, Python (Nogeng). 1r, Hippopotamus (Kubung). 2r, Greater kudu (Rolong).

1977, Dec. 6

5	A2	1c multicolored	.20	.20
6	A2	2c multicolored	.20	.20
7	A2	3c multicolored	.20	.20
8	A2	4c multicolored	5.00	2.40
9	A2	5c on 4c multi	1.40	.80
10	A2	6c multicolored	.25	.25
11	A2	7c multicolored	1.25	1.25
12	A2	8c multicolored	.35	.25
13	A2	9c multicolored	.45	.25
14	A2	10c multicolored	.35	.25
15	A2	15c multicolored	.45	.25
16	A2	20c multicolored	.45	.35
17	A2	25c multicolored	.50	.35
18	A2	30c multicolored	.60	.35
19	A2	50c multicolored	.85	.50

20	A2	1r multicolored	1.75	1.40
21	A2	2r multicolored	3.25	3.25
	Nos. 5-21 (17)		*17.50*	*12.50*

No. 9 was printed as a 4c stamp. Grass was printed over the 4c at upper right and 5c printed at upper left. Copies exist without the surcharge. No. 9A does not have the 4c.

Perf. 14

5a	A2	1c	.20	.20
6a	A2	2c	.20	.20
7a	A2	3c	.20	.20
8a	A2	4c	.20	.20
9A	A2	5c multicolored	.20	.20
11a	A2	7c	.25	.25
12a	A2	8c	.25	.25
14a	A2	10c	.25	.25
	Nos. 5a-14a (8)		*1.70*	*1.70*

World Hypertension Month — A3

1978, Apr. 7 Perf. 12x12½

22	A3	4c Avoid kidney infections	.70	.70
23	A3	10c Lower salt intake	1.25	1.25
24	A3	15c Overeating is dangerous	1.75	1.75
	Nos. 22-24 (3)		*3.70*	*3.70*

Road Safety A4

1978, July 12

25	A4	4c Don't drink and drive	.75	.45
26	A4	10c Keep children off roads	1.10	.65
27	A4	15c Pedestrians observe crossing signals	1.40	.80
28	A4	20c Observe stop signs	2.25	1.10
	Nos. 25-28 (4)		*5.50*	*3.00*

Cutting and Polishing Semi-precious Stones — A5

1978, Oct. 3

29	A5	4c Cutting slabs of travertine	.65	.20
30	A5	10c Polishing travertine	1.25	.90
31	A5	15c Sorting stones	2.00	1.25
32	A5	20c Factory at Taung	2.50	1.60
	Nos. 29-32 (4)		*6.40*	*3.95*

1st Airplane Flight, 75th Anniv. — A6

Illustration reduced.

1978, Dec. 1 Perf. 12½

33	A6	10c Wright Flyer	1.50	1.50
34	A6	15c Orville and Wilbur Wright	2.00	2.00

Pres. Lucas M. Mangope — A7

1978, Dec. 6

35	A7	4c Profile	.40	.40
36	A7	15c Portrait	.85	.85

Sorghum
Beer
Production
A8

1979, Feb. 28   *Perf. 14x14½*
37	A8	4c	Drying germinated wheat	.30 .30
38	A8	15c	Cooking ground grain	.80 .80
39	A8	20c	Straining the liquid	1.00 1.00
40	A8	25c	Drinking beer	1.40 1.40
			Nos. 37-40 (4)	3.50 3.50

Tate-Knoetze
Boxing
Match — A9

1979, June 2
41	A9	15c	John Tate	.90 .90
42	A9	15c	Kallie Knoetze	.90 .90
a.			Pair, #41-42	2.00 2.00

Intl. Children's Year — A10

Illustrations by local youths: 4c, Boy dazzled by sun, from a folk tale, by Hendrick Sebapo. 15c, Africans and animal silhouettes, by Daisy Morapedi. 20c, Man in profile and landscape, by Peter Tladi. 25c, Old man, boy and mule, by Sebapo.

1979, June 7   *Perf. 14½x14*
43	A10	4c	multicolored	.20 .20
44	A10	15c	multicolored	.40 .40
45	A10	20c	multicolored	.60 .60
46	A10	25c	multicolored	.80 .80
			Nos. 43-46 (4)	2.00 2.00

Platinum
Industry
A11

Designs: 4c, Pouring molten metal. 15c, Platinum in industrial use. 20c, Telecommunications satellite in orbit. 25c, Jewelry.

1979, Aug. 15   *Perf. 14x14½*
47	A11	4c	multicolored	.20 .20
48	A11	15c	multicolored	.40 .40
49	A11	20c	multicolored	.55 .55
50	A11	25c	multicolored	.85 .85
			Nos. 47-50 (4)	2.00 2.00

Agriculture
A12

1979, Oct. 25
51	A12	5c	Cattle	.20 .20
52	A12	15c	Picking cotton	.30 .30
53	A12	20c	Researcher in corn field	.45 .45
54	A12	25c	Fish in net	.55 .55
			Nos. 51-54 (4)	1.50 1.50

Stop Smoking
Campaign
A13

1980, Mar. 5   *Perf. 14½x14*
55	A13	5c	multicolored	.65 .65

Edible Wild
Fruit
A14

1980, June 4
56	A14	5c	*Landolphia capensis*	.20 .20
57	A14	10c	*Vangueria infausta*	.40 .40
58	A14	15c	*Bequaertiodendron magalismontanum*	.60 .60
59	A14	20c	*Sclerocarya caffra*	.80 .80
			Nos. 56-59 (4)	2.00 2.00

Birds — A15

1980, Sept. 10
60	A15	5c	Pied babbler	.20 .20
61	A15	10c	Carmine bee-eater	.50 .50
62	A15	15c	Shaft-tailed whydah	.80 .80
63	A15	20c	Meyer's parrot	1.00 1.00
			Nos. 60-63 (4)	2.50 2.50

Sun City
Tourist
Attractions
A16

1980, Dec. 5   *Perf. 14x14½*
64	A16	5c	Hotel, casino, country club	.20 .20
65	A16	10c	Golfer at Gary Player Country Club	.40 .40
66	A16	15c	Casino interior	.60 .60
67	A16	20c	Night club dancers	.80 .80
			Nos. 64-67 (4)	2.00 2.00

Intl. Year for the
Disabled — A17

1981, Jan. 30   *Perf. 14½x14*
68	A17	5c	shown	.20 .20
69	A17	15c	Blind boy	.30 .30
70	A17	20c	Archer in wheelchair	.45 .45
71	A17	25c	X-ray (tuberculosis)	.55 .55
			Nos. 68-71 (4)	1.50 1.50

Easter
A18

Bible quotes and: 5c, Lamb, sunset. 15c, Bread. 20c, Man holding lamb. 25c, Wheat field.

1981, Apr. 1   *Perf. 14x14½*
72	A18	5c	multicolored	.20 .20
73	A18	15c	multicolored	.30 .30
74	A18	20c	multicolored	.45 .45
75	A18	25c	multicolored	.55 .55
			Nos. 72-75 (4)	1.50 1.50

Telephones
A19

Grasses
A20

5c, Siemens & Halske wall telephone, 1885. 15c, Ericsson table model, 1895. 20c, Hasler table model, 1900. 25c, Mix & Genest wall model, 1904.

1981, July 31   *Perf. 14½x14*
76	A19	5c	multicolored	.20 .20
77	A19	15c	multicolored	.30 .30
78	A19	20c	multicolored	.35 .35
79	A19	25c	multicolored	.45 .45
			Nos. 76-79 (4)	1.30 1.30

1981, Nov. 25
80	A20	5c	*Themeda triandra*	.20 .20
81	A20	15c	*Rhynchelytrum repens*	.30 .30
82	A20	20c	*Eragrostis capensis*	.35 .35
83	A20	25c	*Monocymbium ceresiiforme*	.45 .45
			Nos. 80-83 (4)	1.30 1.30

Boy Scouts,
75th
Anniv. — A21

Easter — A22

1982, Jan. 29
84	A21	5c	Scout, 1982	.20 .20
85	A21	15c	Mafeking Siege stamps	.35 .35
86	A21	20c	Scout cadet, 1907	.45 .45
87	A21	25c	Lord Baden-Powell	.55 .55
			Nos. 84-87 (4)	1.55 1.55

1982, Apr. 1
88	A22	15c	John 12:1	.20 .20
89	A22	20c	Matthew 21:1-2	.20 .20
90	A22	25c	Mark 11:5-6	.50 .50
91	A22	30c	Matthew 21:7	.60 .60
			Nos. 88-91 (4)	1.50 1.50

Table
Telephones — A23

1982, Sept. 3
92	A23	8c	Ericsson, 1878	.20 .20
93	A23	15c	Ericsson, 1885	.30 .30
94	A23	20c	Ericsson, 1893	.35 .35
95	A23	25c	Siemens & Halske, 1898	.45 .45
			Nos. 92-95 (4)	1.30 1.30

Independence, 5th Anniv. — A24

8c, Old parliament building. 15c, New government offices. 20c, University, Mmabatho. 25c, Civic Center, Mmabatho.

1982, Dec. 6   *Perf. 14x14½*
96	A24	8c	multicolored	.20 .20
97	A24	15c	multicolored	.30 .30
98	A24	20c	multicolored	.35 .35
99	A24	25c	multicolored	.45 .45
			Nos. 96-99 (4)	1.30 1.30

Pilanesberg Nature Reserve — A25

1983, Jan. 5
100	A25	8c	*Ceratotherium simum*	.25 .25
101	A25	20c	*Equus burchelli*	.60 .60
102	A25	25c	*Hippotragus niger*	.75 .75
103	A25	40c	*Alcelaphus caama*	1.10 1.10
			Nos. 100-103 (4)	2.70 2.70

Easter
A26

1983, Mar. 30   *Perf. 14½x14*
104	A26	8c	Matthew 21:7	.20 .20
105	A26	20c	Mark 11:7	.40 .40
106	A26	25c	Matthew 21:8	.45 .45
107	A26	40c	Mark 11:9	.75 .75
			Nos. 104-107 (4)	1.80 1.80

Telephones
A27

Birds of the
Veld
A28

10c, ATM table model, c. 1920. 20c, A/S Elektrisk wall model, c. 1900. 25c, Ericsson wall model, c. 1900. 40c, Ericsson wall model, c. 1900, diff.

1983, June 22
108	A27	10c	multicolored	.20 .20
109	A27	20c	multicolored	.35 .35
110	A27	25c	multicolored	.45 .45
111	A27	40c	multicolored	.70 .70
			Nos. 108-111 (4)	1.70 1.70

1983, Sept. 14
112	A28	10c	Kori bustard	.25 .25
113	A28	20c	Black korhaan	.55 .55
114	A28	25c	Red-crested korhaan	.70 .70
115	A28	40c	Stanley bustard	1.25 1.25
			Nos. 112-115 (4)	2.75 2.75

Grasses — A29

1984, Jan. 20
116	A29	10c	*Panicum maximum*	.20 .20
117	A29	20c	*Hyparrhenia dregeana*	.35 .35
118	A29	25c	*Cenchrus ciliaris*	.40 .40
119	A29	40c	*Urochloa brachyura*	.65 .65
			Nos. 116-119 (4)	1.60 1.60

Easter
A30

1984, Mar. 23   Perf. 14½x14
120 A30 10c Mark 11:11 .20 .20
121 A30 20c Mark 11:15 .30 .30
122 A30 25c Matthew 21:19 .40 .40
123 A30 40c Matthew 21:19, diff. .65 .65
    Nos. 120-123 (4) 1.55 1.55
    See Nos. 165-168, 173-176.

Mining
Industry
A31

1984, Apr. 2   Perf. 14½x14
124 A31 11c multicolored .70 .70

Telephones — A32

11c, Shuchhardt table model, c. 1905. 20c, Siemens wall model, c. 1925. 25c, Ericsson table model, c. 1900. 30c, Oki table model, c. 1930.

1984, July 20
125 A32 11c multicolored .20 .20
126 A32 20c multicolored .35 .35
127 A32 25c multicolored .45 .45
128 A32 30c multicolored .50 .50
    Nos. 125-128 (4) 1.50 1.50

Lizards
A33

Designs: 11c, Yellow-throated plated lizard. 25c, Transvaal girdled lizard. 30c, Ocellated sand lizard. 45c, Bibron's thick-toed gecko.

1984, Sept. 25   Perf. 14x14½
129 A33 11c multicolored .20 .20
130 A33 25c multicolored .40 .40
131 A33 30c multicolored .50 .50
132 A33 45c multicolored .75 .75
    Nos. 129-132 (4) 1.85 1.85

Child Health
Care — A34

Mafeking,
Cent. — A35

1985, Jan. 25
133 A34 11c Stop Polio .20 .20
134 A34 25c Stop Measles .50 .50
135 A34 30c Stop Diphtheria .65 .65
136 A34 50c Stop Whooping
       Cough 1.10 1.10
    Nos. 133-136 (4) 2.45 2.45

1985, Mar. 11

Portraits: 11c, Montshiwa (1814-1896), chief of the Barolong booRatshidi. 25c, Sir Charles Warren (1840-1927), army commander who established the Crown Colony and laid out the town of Mafeking.

137 A35 11c multicolored .20 .20
138 A35 25c multicolored .60 .60

Industries
A36

Designs: 1c, Textile mill, Bophuthatswana. 2c, Sewing cloth sacks, Selosesha. 3c, Ceramic tile production line. 4c, Processing sheepskin. 5c, Manufacture of crossbows. 6c, Automobile parts. 7c, Hosiery factory, Babelegi. 8c, Specialized bicycle factory. 9c, Lawn mower assembly line. 10c, Dress factory, Thaba Nchu. 12c, Automobile upholstery factory. 14c, Milling industry, Mafeking. 15c, Manufacturing of plastic bags. 16c, Brickworks, Mmabatho. 18c, Manufacturing of cutlery. 20c, Men's clothing factory. 25c, Chromium plating baby carriage parts. 30c, Spray-painting metal beds. 50c, Milk processing plant. 1r, Printing works. 2r, Industrial complex, Babelegi.

1985-89   Perf. 14½x14
139 A36 1c multicolored .20 .20
140 A36 2c multicolored .20 .20
141 A36 3c multicolored .20 .20
142 A36 4c multicolored .20 .20
143 A36 5c multicolored .20 .20
144 A36 6c multicolored .20 .20
145 A36 7c multicolored .20 .20
146 A36 8c multicolored .20 .20
147 A36 9c multicolored .20 .20
148 A36 10c multicolored .20 .20
149 A36 12c multicolored .25 .25
150 A36 14c multicolored .30 .30
151 A36 15c multicolored .35 .35
152 A36 16c multicolored .35 .35
153 A36 18c multicolored .40 .40
154 A36 20c multicolored .45 .45
155 A36 25c multicolored .60 .60
156 A36 30c multicolored .70 .70
157 A36 50c multicolored 1.10 1.10
158 A36 1r multicolored 2.25 2.25
159 A36 2r multicolored 4.75 4.75
    Nos. 139-159 (21) 13.50 13.50

Issued: 1c-10c, 15c, 20c, 25c, 30c-2r, 10/25/85; 12c, 4/1/85; 14c, 4/1/86; 16c, 4/1/87; 18c, 7/3/89.

Easter Type of 1984

1985, Apr. 2
165 A30 12c Matthew 21:14 .20 .20
166 A30 25c Matthew 21:14, diff. .35 .35
167 A30 30c Matthew 21:15 .40 .40
168 A30 50c Matthew 21:15-16 .70 .70
    Nos. 165-168 (4) 1.65 1.65

Tree Conservation
A37

1985, July 4   Perf. 14x14½
169 A37 12c *Fourea saligna* .20 .20
170 A37 25c *Boscia albitrunca* .45 .45
171 A37 30c *Erythrina lysistemon* .55 .55
172 A37 50c *Bequaertiodendron*
       magalismontanum .90 .90
    Nos. 169-172 (4) 2.10 2.10

Easter Type of 1984

1986, Mar. 6   Perf. 14½x14
173 A30 12c John 12:2 .20 .20
174 A30 20c John 12:3 .35 .35
175 A30 25c John 12:3, diff. .45 .45
176 A30 30c Matthew 26:7 .60 .60
    Nos. 173-176 (4) 1.60 1.60

Paintings of Thaba Nchu in the
Africana Museum,
Johannesburg — A38

14c, *Wesleyan Mission Station and Residence of Moroka, Chief of the Barolong, 1834,* by Charles Davidson Bell. 20c, *James Archbell's Congregation, 1834,* by Bell. 25c, *Mission Station at Thaba Nchu, 1850,* by Thomas Baines (1822-75).

1986, May 15   Perf. 14x14½
177 A38 14c multicolored .35 .35
178 A38 20c multicolored .45 .45
179 A38 30c multicolored .70 .70
    Nos. 177-179 (3) 1.50 1.50

Incorporation of Thaba Nchu and Bophuthatswana, Oct. 1, 1983.
A souvenir sheet of one No. 179 has decorative margin continuing the painting and picturing the emblem of the philatelic exhibition held at Johannesburg, Oct. 6-11. Sold for 50c.

Temisano
Development
Projects
A39

1986, Aug. 6   Perf. 14½x14
180 A39 14c Agricultural produc-
       tion .20 .20
181 A39 20c Community develop-
       ment .35 .35
182 A39 25c Vocational training .45 .45
183 A39 30c Secondary indus-
       tries .55 .55
    Nos. 180-183 (4) 1.55 1.55

BOP
Airways,
5th Anniv.
A40

1986, Oct. 16   Perf. 14x14½
184 A40 14c Airline personnel,
       aircraft .30 .30
185 A40 20c Passengers .45 .45
186 A40 25c Mmabatho Intl. Air-
       port .60 .60
187 A40 30c Cessna Citation .65 .65
    Nos. 184-187 (4) 2.00 2.00

Sports — A41

Wildflowers — A42

1987, Jan. 22
188 A41 14c Netball .30 .30
189 A41 20c Tennis .45 .45
190 A41 25c Soccer .55 .55
191 A41 30c Running .70 .70
    Nos. 188-191 (4) 2.00 2.00

1987, Apr. 23
192 A42 16c *Berkheya zeyheri* .40 .40
193 A42 20c *Plumbago auriculata* .50 .50
194 A42 25c *Pterodiscus speci-*
       osus .65 .65
195 A42 30c *Gazania krebsiana* .75 .75
    Nos. 192-195 (4) 2.30 2.30

A souvenir sheet of one No. 194 has decorative black and white inscribed margin picturing the emblem of the natl. philatelic exhibition held at Paarl, Sept. 16-19. Sold for 70c. Value $3.

Education — A43

Designs: 16c, E.M. Mokgoko Farmer Training Center, Ramatlabama. 20c, Main lecture block, University of Bophuthatswana, Mmabatho. 25c, Manpower Center. 30c, Hotel training school, Odi.

1987, Aug. 6   Perf. 14½x14
196 A43 16c multicolored .35 .35
197 A43 20c multicolored .45 .45
198 A43 25c multicolored .60 .60
199 A43 30c multicolored .75 .75
    Nos. 196-199 (4) 2.15 2.15

Independence, 10th Anniv. — A44

Communications.

1987, Dec. 4
200 A44 16c Postal service .25 .25
201 A44 30c Telephone .45 .45
202 A44 40c Radio .65 .65
203 A44 50c Television .80 .80
    Nos. 200-203 (4) 2.15 2.15

Easter
A45

1988, Mar. 31
204 A45 16c John 12:12-14 .25 .25
205 A45 30c Mark 14:10-11 .50 .50
206 A45 40c John 13:5 .70 .70
207 A45 50c John 13:26 .85 .85
    Nos. 204-207 (4) 2.30 2.30

Natl. Parks Board Activities — A46

1988, June 23   Perf. 14½x14
208 A46 16c Environmental edu-
       cation .40 .40
209 A46 30c Conservation .80 .80
210 A46 40c Catering 1.10 1.10
211 A46 50c Tourism 1.40 1.40
    Nos. 208-211 (4) 3.70 3.70

A souvenir sheet of one No. 211 has black and white decorative margin picturing the emblem of the natl. philatelic exhibition held at Pietermaritzburg, Nov. 22-27. Sold for 70c. Value $4.25.

Crops
A47

1988, Sept. 15   Perf. 14½x14
212 A47 16c Sunflowers .35 .35
213 A47 30c Peanuts .70 .70
214 A47 40c Cotton 1.00 1.00
215 A47 50c Cabbages 1.25 1.25
    Nos. 212-215 (4) 3.30 3.30

Dams — A48

1988, Nov. 17
216 A48 16c Ngotwane .35 .35
217 A48 30c Groothoek .65 .65
218 A48 40c Sehujwane 1.00 1.00
219 A48 50c Molatedi 1.10 1.10
Nos. 216-219 (4) 3.10 3.10

Easter A49

1989, Mar. 9
220 A49 16c Mark 26:26 .35 .35
221 A49 30c Matthew 26:39 .65 .65
222 A49 40c Mark 14:45 1.00 1.00
223 A49 50c John 18:10 1.25 1.25
Nos. 220-223 (4) 3.25 3.25

Children's Art — A50

Designs: 18c, "Rooster," by Thembi Atong. 30c, "Thatched Hut in Rural Setting," by Muhammad Mahri. 40c, "Modern World," by Tshepo Mashokwe. 50c, "Cityscape," by Miles Brown.

1989, May 11
224 A50 18c multicolored .45 .45
225 A50 30c multicolored .70 .70
226 A50 40c multicolored .95 .95
227 A50 50c multicolored 1.25 1.25
Nos. 224-227 (4) 3.35 3.35

Birds of Prey — A51

1989, Sept. 1 *Perf. 14x14½*
228 A51 18c Elanus caeruleus 1.00 1.00
229 A51 30c Melierax canorus 1.60 1.60
230 A51 40c Falco naumanni 2.10 2.10
231 A51 50c Circaetus gallicus 2.75 2.75
a. Souvenir sheet of 1 7.00 7.00
Nos. 228-231 (4) 7.45 7.45

No. 231a has multicolored decorative margin picturing emblem of the WANDERERS 101 natl. philatelic exhibition held Sept. 6-9. Sold for 1.50r.

Traditional Thatched Dwellings A52

1989, Nov. 28 *Perf. 14½x14*
232 A52 18c shown .40 .40
233 A52 30c multi, diff. .75 .75
234 A52 40c multi, diff. .90 .90
235 A52 50c multi, diff. 1.10 1.10
Nos. 232-235 (4) 3.15 3.15

Community Services A53

1990, Jan. 11
236 A53 18c Playground .40 .40
237 A53 30c Immunization clinic .65 .65
238 A53 40c Library .95 .95
239 A53 50c Hospital 1.25 1.25
Nos. 236-239 (4) 3.25 3.25

Wildlife (Small Mammals) A54

1990, Apr. 11 Litho. *Perf. 14½x14*
240 A54 21c Dendromus mystacalis .55 .55
241 A54 30c Ictonyx striatus .80 .80
242 A54 40c Elephantulus myurus 1.00 1.00
243 A54 50c Procavia capensis 1.25 1.25
a. Souvenir sheet of 1 4.00 4.00
Nos. 240-243 (4) 3.60 3.60

No. 243a has multicolored inscribed margin; text publicizes the natl. philatelic exhibition. Sold for 1.50r.

Sandgrouses — A55

1990, July 12 Litho. *Perf. 14x14½*
244 A55 21c Pterocles burchelli .75 .75
245 A55 35c Pterocles bicinctus 1.40 1.40
246 A55 40c Pterocles namaqua 1.50 1.50
247 A55 50c Pterocles gutturalis 1.90 1.90
Nos. 244-247 (4) 5.55 5.55

Bus Manufacturing — A56

a, Chassis welding. b, Mounting the engine. c, Body construction. d, Spray painting. e, Completed models and bare chassis.

1990, Aug. 3 *Perf. 14½x14*
248 Strip of 5 4.00 4.00
a.-e. A56 21c any single .80 .80

Traditional Activities — A57

1990, Oct. 4 *Perf. 14x14½*
249 A57 21c Basketry .45 .45
250 A57 35c Tanning .75 .75
251 A57 40c Beer making .85 .85
252 A57 50c Pottery making 1.25 1.25
Nos. 249-252 (4) 3.30 3.30

Bophuthatswana Air Force, 10th Anniv. — A58

Helicopters: a, Alouette III. b, BK117. Airplanes: c, Pilatus Trainer PC-7. d, Pilatus Porter PC-6. e, Casa 212.

1990, Dec. 12 *Perf. 14½x14*
253 Strip of 5 9.00 9.00
a.-e. A58 21c any single 1.60 1.60

Edible Wild Fruit — A59

1991, Jan. 24 Litho. *Perf. 14x14½*
254 A59 21c Annona senegalensis .45 .45
255 A59 35c Strychnos pungens .75 .75
256 A59 40c Ficus sycomorus 1.00 1.00
257 A59 50c Dovyalis caffra 1.25 1.25
Nos. 254-257 (4) 3.45 3.45

Easter A60

1991, Mar. 21 Litho. *Perf. 14½x14*
258 A60 21c Mark 14:46 .55 .55
259 A60 35c Mark 14:53 .85 .85
260 A60 40c Mark 14:65 1.10 1.10
261 A60 50c Mark 14:67 1.25 1.25
Nos. 258-261 (4) 3.75 3.75

Locomotives A61

1991, July 4 Litho.
Size: 72x25mm (25c, 50c)
262 A61 25c Class 6A .85 .85
263 A61 40c Class 7A 1.40 1.40
264 A61 50c Class 6Z 1.75 1.75
265 A61 60c Class 8 2.40 2.40
Nos. 262-265 (4) 6.40 6.40

A souvenir sheet of 1 #265 was sold by the Philatelic Foundation of South Africa. Value $6.
See Nos. 291-294.

Maps of Africa — A62

1991, Sept. 12 Litho. *Perf. 14x14½*
266 A62 25c Caneiro chart, 1502 .90 .90
267 A62 40c Cantino chart, 1502 1.50 1.50
268 A62 50c Contarini map, 1506 1.90 1.90
269 A62 60c Waldseemuller map, 1507 2.50 2.50
Nos. 266-269 (4) 6.80 6.80

Maps of Africa A63

1992, Jan. 9 Litho. *Perf. 14½x14*
270 A63 27c Fracanzano, 1508 .90 .90
271 A63 45c Waldseemuller, 1513 1.50 1.50
272 A63 65c Waldseemuller, 1516 1.90 1.90
273 A63 85c Laurent Fries, 1522 2.50 2.50
Nos. 270-273 (4) 6.80 6.80

Easter A64

1992, Apr. 1 Litho.
274 A64 27c Mark 15:1 .45 .45
275 A64 45c Mark 15:15 .80 .80
276 A64 65c Mark 15:17-18 1.10 1.10
277 A64 85c Mark 15:19 1.40 1.40
Nos. 274-277 (4) 3.75 3.75

Acacia Trees — A65

1992, Sept. 17 Litho.
278 A65 35c Karroo .45 .45
279 A65 70c Erioloba .90 .90
280 A65 90c Tortilis 1.10 1.10
281 A65 1.05r Mellifera 1.25 1.25
Nos. 278-281 (4) 3.70 3.70

A souvenir sheet of 1 #279 exists. Sold for 2.50r. Value $3.75.

Lost City Hotel Complex, Sun City — A66

a, View from lake. b, Palace. c, Porte cochere. d, Lobby of Palace. e, Tusk bar.

1992, Nov. 19 Litho. *Perf. 14x14½*
282 Strip of 5 3.25 3.25
a.-e. A66 35c any single .65 .65

Chickens A67

1993, Feb. 12 Litho. *Perf. 14½x14*
283 A67 35c Light Sussex .45 .45
284 A67 70c Rhode Island red .90 .90
285 A67 90c Brown leghorn 1.25 1.25
286 A67 1.05r White leghorn 1.40 1.40
Nos. 283-286 (4) 4.00 4.00

A souvenir sheet of 1 #284 exists. Sold for 3r. Value $5.

Easter A68

1993, Mar. 5
287 A68 35c Luke 23:25 .60 .60
288 A68 70c John 19:17 1.25 1.25
289 A68 90c Mark 15:21 1.60 1.60
290 A68 1.05r Mark 15:23 1.90 1.90
Nos. 287-290 (4) 5.35 5.35

Trains Type of 1991

Designs: 45c, Mafeking locomotive shed, c. 1933, RR classes 10, 8, & 12. 65c, Locomotive No. 5. 85c, 1934 Royal visit, White Train, SAR Class 16B. 1.05r, SAR class 19D.

1993, June 18 Litho.
Size: 72x25mm (45c, 85c)
291 A61 45c multicolored .75 .75
292 A61 65c multicolored 1.10 1.10
293 A61 85c multicolored 1.40 1.40
294 A61 1.05r multicolored 1.75 1.75
a. Souvenir sheet of 4, #291-294 5.00 5.00
Nos. 291-294 (4) 5.00 5.00

Maps of
Africa
A69

Name of cartographer, year published: 45c, Sebastian Munster, 1540. 65c, Jacopo Gastaldi, 1564. 85c, Gerardus Mercator the Younger, 1595. 1.05r, Abraham Ortelius, 1570.

1993, Aug. 20   **Litho.**
295	A69	45c multicolored	.60	.60
296	A69	65c multicolored	.90	.90
297	A69	85c multicolored	1.25	1.25
298	A69	1.05r multicolored	1.50	1.50
		Nos. 295-298 (4)	4.25	4.25

Easter
A70

1994, Mar. 25　Litho.　Perf. 14½x14
299	A70	35c Luke 22:33	.65	.65
300	A70	65c Luke 23:35-36	1.25	1.25
301	A70	85c Luke 23:36	1.60	1.60
302	A70	1.05r Luke 23:38	1.90	1.90
		Nos. 299-302 (4)	5.40	5.40

Bophuthatswana ceased to exist 4/27/94.

CISKEI

'sis-ˌkī

LOCATION — Enclave, Republic of South Africa
GOVT. — Self-governing tribal homeland
AREA — 5,592 sq. mi.
POP. — 1,000,000
CAPITAL — Bisho

> **Catalogue values for all unused stamps in this country are for Never Hinged Items.**

Independence
from South
Africa — A1

Perf. 14x14½
1981, Dec. 4　Litho.　Unwmk.
1	A1	5c Pres. Sebe	.20	.20
2	A1	15c Coat of arms	.25	.25
3	A1	20c Flag	.30	.30
4	A1	25c Mace	.35	.35
		Nos. 1-4 (4)	1.10	1.10

An imperf. souvenir sheet exists containing Nos. 1-4 printed in one color (black). Not valid for postage.

Birds
A2　　　　A3

1981-90   **Perf. 14½x14**
5	A2	1c *Tauraco corythaix*	.20	.20
6	A2	2c *Motacilla capensis*	.20	.20
7	A2	3c *Centropus superciliosus*	.20	.20
8	A2	4c *Nectarinia famosa*	.20	.20
9	A2	5c *Anthropoides paradisea*	.20	.20
10	A2	6c *Onychognathus morio*	.20	.20
11	A2	7c *Ceryle maxima*	.20	.20
12	A2	8c *Bostrychia hagedash*	.25	.25
13	A2	9c *Cuculus clamosus*	.25	.20
14	A2	10c *Lybius torquatus*	.25	.20
15	A2	11c *Oriolus larvatus*	.55	.20
16	A2	12c *Alcedo cristata*	.55	.20
17	A2	14c *Upupa epops*	.65	.20
18	A2	15c *Haliaeetus vocifer*	.25	.20
19	A2	16c *Batis capensis*	.65	.20
20	A3	18c *Euplectes progne*	1.00	.20
21	A2	20c *Macronyx capensis*	.35	.25
22	A2	21c *Aplopelia larvata*	3.25	.20
23	A2	25c *Burhinus capensis*	.40	.25
24	A2	30c *Treron calva*	.55	.35
25	A2	50c *Poicephalus robustus*	.90	.60
26	A2	1r *Apaloderma narina*	1.50	1.10
27	A2	2r *Bubo capensis*	3.25	2.25
		Nos. 5-27 (23)	16.00	8.20

Issued: 11c, 4/4/82; 12c, 4/1/85; 14c, 4/1/86; 16c, 4/1/87; 18c, 7/3/89; 21c, 7/3/90; others, 12/4/81.

Nursing
A4

1982, Apr. 30　Perf. 14½x14, 14x14½
34	A4	8c Cecilia Makiwane, vert.	.20	.20
35	A4	15c Surgery, vert.	.30	.30
36	A4	20c Nurses pledge to serve	.45	.45
37	A4	25c Hospital care	.55	.55
		Nos. 34-37 (4)	1.50	1.50

Pineapple
Industry
A5

1982, Aug. 20   **Perf. 14x14½**
38	A5	8c Spraying	.20	.20
39	A5	15c Harvesting	.20	.20
40	A5	20c Transporting fruit to cannery	.20	.20
41	A5	30c Packing	.40	.40
		Nos. 38-41 (4)	1.00	1.00

Small
Mammals
A6

1982, Oct. 29
42	A6	8c *Lepus capensis*	.20	.20
43	A6	15c *Vulpes chama*	.35	.35
44	A6	20c *Xerus inaurus*	.40	.40
45	A6	25c *Felis caracal*	.45	.45
		Nos. 42-45 (4)	1.40	1.40

Trees — A7

1983, Feb. 2   **Perf. 14½x14**
46	A7	8c *Cussonia spicata*	.20	.20
47	A7	20c *Curtisia dentata*	.30	.30
48	A7	25c *Calodendrum capense*	.35	.35
49	A7	40c *Podocarpus falcatus*	.60	.60
		Nos. 46-49 (4)	1.45	1.45

1984, Jan. 6
50	A7	10c *Rhus chirindensis*	.20	.20
51	A7	20c *Phoenix reclinata*	.30	.30
52	A7	25c *Ptaeroxylon obliquum*	.35	.35
53	A7	40c *Apodytes dimidiata*	.60	.60
		Nos. 50-53 (4)	1.45	1.45

Sharks — A8

1983, Apr. 13   **Perf. 14x14½**
54	A8	8c Dusky	.20	.20
55	A8	20c Ragged-tooth	.50	.50

Size: 57x21mm
56	A8	25c Tiger	.60	.60
57	A8	30c Scalloped hammer-head	.75	.75
58	A8	40c Great white	.95	.95
		Nos. 54-58 (5)	3.00	3.00

Educational Institutions — A9

1983, July 6
59	A9	10c Lovedale	.20	.20
60	A9	20c Fort Hare	.20	.20
61	A9	25c Healdtown	.30	.30
62	A9	40c Lennox Sebe	.40	.40
		Nos. 59-62 (4)	1.10	1.10

Military
Uniforms — A10

6th Foot, 1st Warwickshire Regiment, 1821-27 (No. 63): a, White drill uniform (D1.5). b, Light Company privates (D2.5). c, Grenadier Company sergeants (D3.5). d, Light Co. Officers (D4.5). e, Officer and field officer (D5.5).
Cape Mounted Rifles, 1827-35 (No. 64): a, Trooper and sergeant, 1830 (D1.5). b, Trooper and sergeant in full dress, 1835 (D2.5). c, Officers, 1830 (D3.5). d, Officers in full dress, 1827-34 (D4.5). e, Officers in full dress, 1834 (D5.5).

1983, Sept. 28   **Perf. 14½x14**
63		Strip of 5	2.25	2.25
a.-e.		A10 20c any single	.45	.45

1984, Oct. 26
64		Strip of 5	2.50	2.25
a.-e.		A10 25c any single	.50	.40

Sheets of 10 containing two strips of five.

Coastal
Angling
A11

Bait.

1984, Apr. 12   **Perf. 14x14½**
65	A11	11c Sand prawn	.20	.20
66	A11	20c Coral worm	.20	.20
67	A11	25c Bloodworm	.45	.45
68	A11	30c Red-bait	.55	.55
		Nos. 65-68 (4)	1.40	1.40

1985, Mar. 7

Game fish.
69	A11	11c *Lithognathus lithognathus*	.20	.20
70	A11	25c *Pachymetopon grande*	.55	.40
71	A11	30c *Argyrosomus hololepidotus*	.65	.45

72	A11	50c *Pomadasys commersonni*	1.00	.70
		Nos. 69-72 (4)	2.40	1.75

Migratory Birds and Maps — A12

1984, Aug. 17   **Perf. 14½x14**
73	A12	11c Banded sand martin	.25	.25
74	A12	25c House martin	.80	.80
75	A12	30c Greater striped swallow	.90	.90
76	A12	45c European swallow	1.25	1.25
		Nos. 73-76 (4)	3.20	3.20

Brownies
A13

1985, May 3
77	A13	12c shown	.20	.20
78	A13	25c Rangers planting saplings	.35	.35
79	A13	30c Guide color guard	.40	.40
80	A13	50c Camping	.70	.70
		Nos. 77-80 (4)	1.65	1.65

Intl. Year of the Child, 75th anniv. of the Girl Guide movement.

Small
Businesses
A14

1985, Aug. 8   **Perf. 14x14½**
81	A14	12c Furniture	.20	.20
82	A14	25c Dress making	.30	.30
83	A14	30c Welding	.40	.40
84	A14	50c Basketry	.70	.70
		Nos. 81-84 (4)	1.60	1.60

Troop
Ships — A15

1985, Nov. 15   **Perf. 14½x14**
85	A15	12c Antelope	.25	.25
86	A15	25c Pilot	.55	.55
87	A15	30c Salisbury	.60	.60
88	A15	50c Olive Branch	1.10	1.10
		Nos. 85-88 (4)	2.50	2.50

Miniature Sheet

Halley's Comet — A16

Comet streaking through the solar system: a, A1.10. b, A2.10. c, A3.10. d, A4.10. e, A5.10. f, A6.10. g, A7.10. h, A8.10. i, A9.10. j, A10.10.
Illustration reduced.

1986, Mar. 20
89	A16	Sheet of 10	14.00	14.00
a.-j.		12c any single	1.40	1.40

Military Uniforms — A17

98th Foot Regiment: 14c, Fifer in winter. 20c, Private in summer. 25c, Grenadier Company sergeant in summer. 30c, Sergeant-major in winter.

1986, June 12
90	A17	14c multicolored	.25	.25
91	A17	20c multicolored	.35	.35
92	A17	25c multicolored	.45	.45
93	A17	30c multicolored	.50	.50
a.		Souvenir sheet of 1	3.50	3.50
		Nos. 90-93 (4)	1.55	1.55

No. 93a for the natl. philatelic exhibition held at Johannesberg, Oct. 6-11. Sold for 50c.

Bicycle Factory, Dimbaza A18

1986, Sept. 18
94	A18	14c Welding frames	.25	.25
95	A18	20c Painting	.35	.35
96	A18	25c Spoke installation	.40	.40
97	A18	30c Assembly	.50	.50
		Nos. 94-97 (4)	1.50	1.50

Independence, 5th Anniv. — A19

14c, Pres. Sebe. 20c, Natl. shrine, Ntaba kaNdoda. 25c, Legislative Assembly, Bisho. 30c, Automatic telephone exchange, Bisho.

1986, Dec. 4   **Perf. 14x14½**
98	A19	14c multicolored	.25	.25
99	A19	20c multicolored	.35	.35
100	A19	25c multicolored	.40	.40
101	A19	30c multicolored	.50	.50
		Nos. 98-101 (4)	1.50	1.50

Edible Mushrooms A20

1987, Mar. 19
102	A20	14c *Boletus edulis*	.40	.40
103	A20	20c *Macrolepiota zeyheri*	.55	.55
a.		Souvenir sheet of 1	4.75	4.75
104	A20	25c *Termitomyces*	.65	.65
105	A20	30c *Russula capensis*	.80	.80
		Nos. 102-105 (4)	2.40	2.40

No. 103a has fawn and black decorative margin picturing emblem of the natl. philatelic exhibition held at Paarl, Sept. 16-19. Sold for 50c.

Nkone Cattle A21

1987, June 18   **Perf. 14½x14**
106	A21	16c Cow and calf	.25	.25
107	A21	20c Cow	.35	.35
108	A21	25c Bull	.40	.40
109	A21	30c Herd	.50	.50
		Nos. 106-109 (4)	1.50	1.50

Toys — A22

Perf. 14x14½, 14½x14
1987, Sept. 17
110	A22	16c Windmill, vert.	.25	.25
111	A22	20c Rag doll, vert.	.35	.35
112	A22	25c Clay horse	.40	.40
113	A22	30c Wire vehicle	.50	.50
		Nos. 110-113 (4)	1.50	1.50

Folklore A23

Legend of Sikulume: 16c, Seven birds. 20c, Sikulume escapes cannibals. 25c, Fights sea monster. 30c, Elopes and is pursued by bride's father.

1987, Nov. 6   **Perf. 14½x14**
114	A23	16c multicolored	.25	.25
115	A23	20c multicolored	.35	.35
116	A23	25c multicolored	.45	.45
117	A23	30c multicolored	.55	.55
		Nos. 114-117 (4)	1.60	1.60

See Nos. 122, 139-142, 147-150.

Endangered and Protected Plant Species — A24

1988, Mar. 17   **Perf. 14x14½**
118	A24	16c *Clivia nobilis*	.30	.30
119	A24	30c *Dierama pulcherrimum*	.60	.60
120	A24	40c *Moraea reticulata*	.75	.75
121	A24	50c *Crinum campanulatum*	.95	.95
a.		Souvenir sheet of 1	3.50	3.50
		Nos. 118-121 (4)	2.60	2.60

No. 121a margin pictures the emblem of the natl. philatelic exhibition held at Pietermaritzburg, Nov. 22-27. Sold for 1r.

Folklore Type of 1987
Miniature Sheet

Legend of Mbulukazi: a, Two wives (B1.10). b, Two doves appear to Numbakatali (B2.10). c, Birth of Mbulukazi and brother (B3.10). d, Mbulukazi and brother at river (B4.10). e, Chief's son announces marriage (B5.10). f, Chief's son presents wives Mbulukazi and Mahlunguluza with huts (B6.10). g, Mahlunguluza drowns Mbulukazi (B7.10). h, Ox tears down Mahlunguluza's hut (B8.10). i, Mbulukazi revived (B9.10). j, Chief's son embraces Mbulukazi, banishes Mahlunguluza (B10.10).

1988, Aug. 26
Size of Nos. 122a-122j: 36x20mm
122		Sheet of 10	4.25	4.25
a.-j.		A23 16c any single	.40	.40

Citrus Farming A25

1988, Sept. 29
123	A25	16c Nursery	.30	.30
124	A25	30c Grafting	.60	.60
125	A25	40c Picking fruit	.70	.70
126	A25	50c Grading	.95	.95
		Nos. 123-126 (4)	2.55	2.55

Poisonous Mushrooms A26

1988, Dec. 1
127	A26	16c *Amanita phalloides*	.75	.75
128	A26	30c *Chlorophyllum molybdites*	1.50	1.50
129	A26	40c *Amanita muscaria*	1.90	1.90
130	A26	50c *Amanita pantherina*	2.40	2.40
		Nos. 127-130 (4)	6.55	6.55

Dams — A27

1989, Mar. 2   **Perf. 14½x14**
131	A27	16c Kat River	.25	.25
132	A27	30c Cata	.50	.50
133	A27	40c Binfield Park	.60	.60
134	A27	50c Sandile	.70	.70
		Nos. 131-134 (4)	2.05	2.05

Trout Hatcheries A28

Artificial fertilization: 18c, Obtaining eggs from trout. 30c, Fertilized ova, alevins. 40c, Rainbow trout at 5 weeks. 40c, Adult male rainbow trout.

1989, June 8
135	A28	18c multicolored	.40	.40
136	A28	30c multicolored	.60	.60
137	A28	40c multicolored	.85	.85
138	A28	50c multicolored	.95	.95
a.		Souvenir sheet of 1	4.00	4.00
		Nos. 135-138 (4)	2.80	2.80

No. 138a margin pictures emblem of the natl. philatelic exhibition WANDERERS 101, held Sept. 6-9. Sold for 1.50r.

Folklore Type of 1987

Legend of the Little Jackal and the Lion: 18c, Lion and Jackal hunt large eland. 30c, Jackal and offspring climbing to lair. 40c, Lion roaring, jackal under rock. 50c, Lion falling.

1989, Sept. 21
139	A23	18c multicolored	.25	.25
140	A23	30c multicolored	.50	.50
141	A23	40c multicolored	.65	.65
142	A23	50c multicolored	.85	.85
		Nos. 139-142 (4)	2.25	2.25

Early Transportation A29

1989, Dec. 7   **Perf. 14x14½**
143	A29	18c Cape cart	.25	.25
144	A29	30c Jubilee Spider	.50	.50
145	A29	40c Transport wagon	.65	.65
146	A29	50c Voortrekker wagon	.85	.85
		Nos. 143-146 (4)	2.25	2.25

Folklore Type of 1987

The Legend of Five Heads: 18c, Mpunzikazi presenting offering to Makanda Mahlanu, the 5-headed snake chief. 30c, Snake chief kills

Mpunzikazi. 40c, Mpunzanyan presents offering to snake chief. 50c, Snake chief transformed into a man and marries Mpunzanyan.

1990, Mar. 15   **Perf. 14½x14**
147	A23	18c multicolored	.25	.25
148	A23	30c multicolored	.50	.50
149	A23	40c multicolored	.65	.65
150	A23	50c multicolored	.85	.85
		Nos. 147-150 (4)	2.25	2.25

Handmade Carpets — A30

1990, June 14 Litho. Perf. 14x14½
151	A30	21c Hand weaving	.40	.40
152	A30	35c Spinning	.60	.60
153	A30	40c Dyeing yarn	.70	.70
154	A30	50c Hand weaving, diff.	.85	.85
a.		Souvenir sheet of 1	3.50	3.50
		Nos. 151-154 (4)	2.55	2.55

No. 154a for the 150th anniv. of the Penny Black. Sold for 1.50r.

Plows — A31

1990, Sept. 6 Litho. Perf. 14½x14
155	A31	21c Wooden beam, c. 1855	.35	.35
156	A31	35c Triple disc, c. 1895	.60	.60
157	A31	40c Reversible disc, c. 1895	.70	.70
158	A31	50c "Het Volk", c. 1910	.85	.85
		Nos. 155-158 (4)	2.50	2.50

Prickly Pear — A32

1990, Nov. 29   **Litho.**
159	A32	21c Vendor	.45	.45
160	A32	35c Prickly pear bush	.70	.70
161	A32	40c not shown	.80	.80
162	A32	50c Flowering prickly pear	1.00	1.00
		Nos. 159-162 (4)	2.95	2.95

Owls — A33

1991, Feb. 2 Litho. Perf. 14x14½
163	A33	21c Marsh owl	.95	.95
164	A33	35c Scops owl	1.50	1.50
165	A33	40c Barn owl	1.90	1.90
166	A33	50c Wood owl	2.10	2.10
a.		Miniature sheet of 1	7.00	7.00
		Nos. 163-166 (4)	6.45	6.45

First Letter From South Africa — A34

Designs: a, Map showing location of Sao Bras (Mossel Bay), 1500. b, Storm-damaged ship off Cabo Tormentoso, 1500. c, Pedro d'Ataide lands at Sao Bras, 1501. d, D'Ataide leaves letter in boot, 1501. e, Joao da Nova finds letter, 1501.

1991, May 11   Litho.
167 A34 25c Strip of 5, #a.-e.   4.50 4.50
Inscriptions on #167a & 167b are reversed.

Solar System A35

1991, Aug. 1   Litho.   Perf. 14½x14
168 A35 1c Comet nucleus   .20   .20
169 A35 2c Trojan asteroids   .20   .20
170 A35 5c Meteoroid   .20   .20
171 A35 7c Pluto   .20   .20
172 A35 10c Neptune   .20   .20
173 A35 20c Uranus   .20   .20
174 A35 25c Saturn   .30   .30
175 A35 30c Jupiter   .35   .35
176 A35 35c Asteroid belt   .40   .40
177 A35 40c Mars   .50   .50
178 A35 50c Earth's moon   .60   .60
179 A35 60c Earth   .70   .70
180 A35 1r Venus   1.25 1.25
181 A35 2r Mercury   2.75 2.75
182 A35 5r Sun   6.50 6.50
  a. Min. sheet of 15, #168-182 17.50 17.50
     Nos. 168-182 (15)   14.55 14.55

Frontier Forts A36

Designs: 27c, Xhosa warrior, Fort Armstrong. 45c, Sir George Grey, Keiskamma Hoek Post. 65c, Chief Sandile, Fort Hare. 85c, Cavalryman, Cavalry Barracks, Peddie.

1991, Nov. 7   Litho.   Perf. 14x14½
183 A36 27c multicolored   .40   .40
184 A36 45c multicolored   .75   .75
185 A36 65c multicolored   .95   .95
186 A36 85c multicolored   1.50 1.50
     Nos. 183-186 (4)   3.60 3.60

Cloud Formations — A37

1992, Mar. 19   Litho.
187 A37 27c Cumulonimbus   .40   .40
188 A37 45c Altocumulus   .75   .75
189 A37 65c Cirrus   .95   .95
190 A37 85c Cumulus   1.40 1.40
     Nos. 187-190 (4)   3.50 3.50

Satellites A38

1992, June 4   Litho.   Perf. 14½x14
191 A38 35c Intelsat VI   .60   .60
192 A38 70c GPS Navstar   1.10 1.10
193 A38 90c Meteosat   1.40 1.40
194 A38 1.05r Landsat VI   1.60 1.60
     Nos. 191-194 (4)   4.70 4.70

A souvenir sheet of one No. 192 exists. Sold for 2.50r.

Farm Implements A39

35c, John Deere universal disc-harrow, c. 1914. 70c, John Deere clod crusher & pulverizer, c. 1914. 90c, Self-dump hay rake, c. 1910. 1.05r, McCormick hay tedder, c. 1900.

1992, Aug. 20   Litho.
195 A39 35c multicolored   .60   .60
196 A39 70c multicolored   1.10 1.10
197 A39 90c multicolored   1.40 1.40
198 A39 1.05r multicolored   1.60 1.60
     Nos. 195-198 (4)   4.70 4.70

Hotels A40

Designs: 35c, Mpekweni Sun Marine Resort. 70c, Katberg Protea Hotel. 90c, Fish River Sun Hotel. 1.05r, Amatola Sun Hotel.

1992, Nov. 5   Litho.
199 A40 35c multicolored   .60   .60
200 A40 70c multicolored   1.10 1.10
201 A40 90c multicolored   1.40 1.40
202 A40 1.05r multicolored   1.60 1.60
     Nos. 199-202 (4)   4.70 4.70

Famous Explorers A41

Map of voyage, sailing ship, and explorer: 45c, San Gabriel, 1497-98, Vasco da Gama. 65c, Endeavour, 1768-71, James Cook. 85c, Victoria, 1519, Ferdinand Magellan. 90c, Golden Hinde, 1577-80, Sir Francis Drake. 1.05r, Heemskerck, 1642, Abel Tasman.

1993, May 19   Litho.
203 A41 45c multicolored   .70   .70
204 A41 65c multicolored   1.25 1.25
205 A41 85c multicolored   1.80 1.40
206 A41 90c multicolored   1.50 1.50
207 A41 1.05r multicolored   1.75 1.75
     Nos. 203-207 (5)   7.00 6.60

Small Cage Birds — A42

Designs: 45c, Serinus canarius domesticus. 65c, Melopsittacus undulatus. 85c, Agapornis roseicollis. 90c, Nymphicus hollandicus. 1.05r, Chloebia gouldiae.

1993, July 16   Litho.
208 A42 45c multicolored   .60   .60
209 A42 65c multicolored   1.10 1.10
210 A42 85c multicolored   1.25 1.25
211 A42 90c multicolored   1.40 1.40
212 A42 1.05r multicolored   1.50 1.50
     Nos. 208-212 (5)   5.85 5.85

A souvenir sheet of one No. 210 has inscription for National Philatelic Exhibition. Sold for 3r. Value $5.75.

Churches A43

45c, Goshen Mission Church. 65c, Kamastone Mission Church. 85c, Richie Thompson Memorial Church. 1.05r, Bryce Ross Memorial Church.

1993, Sept. 17   Litho.
213 A43 45c black, buff & red   .50   .50
214 A43 65c black, blue & red   .70   .70
215 A43 85c black, tan & red   .95   .95
216 A43 1.05r blk, lt yel & red 1.25 1.25
     Nos. 213-216 (4)   3.40 3.40

Invader Plants — A44

1993, Nov. 5   Litho.   Perf. 14x14½
217 A44 45c Opuntia aurantiaca   .70   .70
218 A44 65c Datura stramonium   .95   .95
219 A44 85c Sesbania punicea   1.25 1.25
220 A44 1.05r Nicotiana glauca 1.60 1.60
  a. Souvenir sheet, #217-220   4.50 4.50
     Nos. 217-220 (4)   4.50 4.50

Shipwrecks A45

1994, Feb. 18   Litho.   Perf. 14½x14
221 A45 45c SS Losna, 1921   .85   .85
222 A45 65c Catherine, 1846   1.25 1.25
223 A45 85c Bennebroek, 1713   1.50 1.50
224 A45 1.05r Sao Joao Bapista,
                1622   2.10 2.10
     Nos. 221-224 (4)   5.70 5.70

Roses A46

1994, Apr. 15   Litho.   Perf. 14½x14
225 A46 45c Herman Steyn   .65   .65
226 A46 70c Esther
              Geldenhuys   1.00 1.00
227 A46 95c Margaret Was-
              serfall   1.25 1.25
228 A46 1.15r Prof. Fred Ziady 1.60 1.60
  a. Souvenir sheet of 4, #225-228 5.00 5.00
     Nos. 225-228 (4)   4.50 4.50

Ciskei ceased to exist April 27, 1994.

TRANSKEI

ₜₐtranˌtsˈki

LOCATION — Enclave, East Cape Province, Republic of South Africa
GOVT. — Self-governing tribal homeland
AREA — 16,910 sq. mi.
POP. — 2,876,122 (1985)
CAPITAL — Umtata

Catalogue values for all unused stamps in this country are for Never Hinged items.

Independence from South Africa — A1

Perf. 12½
1976, Oct. 26   Litho.   Unwmk.
1 A1 4c Paramount Chief
          K.D. Matanzima   .50   .50
2 A1 10c Mace, flag   1.10 1.10
3 A1 15c Matanzima, diff.   1.90 1.90
4 A1 20c Coat of arms   2.50 2.50
     Nos. 1-4 (4)   6.00 6.00

An imperf. souvenir sheet exists containing Nos. 1-4 printed in one color (black). Not valid for postage.

Lubisi Dam — A2

1976, Oct. 26   Perf. 12x12½
5   A2 1c shown   .20   .20
6   A2 2c Soil cultivation   .20   .20
7   A2 3c Threshing sor-
            ghum   .20   .20
8   A2 4c Transkei matron   3.50   .40
9   A2 5c Grinding corn   3.50   .40
10 A2 6c Cutting *Phormium*
            tenax   .25   .20
11 A2 7c Shepherd boy   .25   .20
12 A2 8c Felling timber   .25   .20
13 A2 9c Agricultural school .30   .25
14 A2 10c Picking tea   .30   .25
15 A2 15c Wood gathering   .35   .35
16 A2 20c Weaving industry   .35   .20
17 A2 25c Improving cattle
            breeds   .45   .25
18 A2 30c Sledge transporta-
            tion   .75   .60
19 A2 50c Map, coat of arms .65   .60
20 A2 1r Administrative
            Building, Umtata 1.50 1.50
21 A2 2r The Bunga, flag   2.50 2.40
     Nos. 5-21 (17)   15.50 8.25

Perf. 14
5a   A2 1c   .20   .20
6a   A2 2c   .20   .20
7a   A2 3c   .20   .20
8a   A2 4c   .20   .20
9a   A2 5c   .20   .20
10a A2 6c   .20   .20
12a A2 8c   .20   .20
13a A2 9c   .20   .20
14a A2 10c   .40   .40
15a A2 15c   .50   .50
16a A2 20c   .70   .70
17a A2 25c   1.00 1.00
18a A2 30c   1.25 1.25
19a A2 50c   2.00 2.00
     Nos. 5a-19a (14)   7.45 7.45

Transkei Airways Inaugural Flight, Umtata-Johannesburg — A3

1977, Feb. 11
22 A3 4c Aircraft   .75   .75
23 A3 15c Aircraft, terminal 3.00 3.00

Artemesia affra — A4

Medicinal plants.

1977, May 16   Perf. 12½x12
24 A4 4c shown   .50   .50
25 A4 10c *Bulbine natalensis* 2.00 2.00
26 A4 15c *Melianthus major* 3.00 3.00
27 A4 20c *Cotyledon orbiculata* 4.25 4.25
     Nos. 24-27 (4)   9.75 9.75

1978, Sept. 25
Edible fruit.
28 A4 4c *Carissa bispinosa* .20   .20
29 A4 10c *Dovyalis caffra*   .45   .45
30 A4 15c *Harpephyllum caffrum* .65   .65
31 A4 20c *Syzygium cordatum* .90   .90
     Nos. 28-31 (4)   2.20 2.20

1981, Apr. 15
Medicinal plants.
32 A4 5c *Leonotis leonurus* .20   .20
33 A4 15c *Euphorbia bupleurifolia* .35 .35
34 A4 20c *Pelargonium reniforme* .45 .45
35 A4 25c *Hibiscus trionum* .60   .60
     Nos. 32-35 (4)   1.60 1.60

Transkei
Radio, 1st
Anniv.
A5

1977, Oct. 26 *Perf. 12x12½*
36 A5 4c Disc jockey .50 .50
37 A5 15c Announcer 1.25 1.25

"Help the Blind" — A6

1977, Nov. 18 *Perf. 12½x12*
38 A6 4c Basket weaver .20 .20
39 A6 15c Reading Braille .80 .80
40 A6 20c Spinning wool 1.00 1.00
Nos. 38-40 (3) 2.00 2.00

1978, Nov. 30
"Care for Cripples."
41 A6 4c Leg brace on boy .20 .20
42 A6 10c Man in wheelchair .60 .60
43 A6 15c Nurse examining boy .85 .85
Nos. 41-43 (3) 1.65 1.65

Men's
Pipes
A7

1978, Mar. 1 *Perf. 12x12½*
44 A7 4c shown .50 .50
45 A7 10c multi, diff. .75 .75
46 A7 15c multi, diff. 1.25 1.25
47 A7 20c Woman's and witch
 doctor's pipes 1.50 1.50
Nos. 44-47 (4) 4.00 4.00

Weaving
Industry
A8

1978, June 9
48 A8 4c Angora goat .35 .35
49 A8 10c Spinning mohair .80 .80
50 A8 15c Dyeing mohair 1.25 1.25
51 A8 20c Weaving mohair rug 1.60 1.60
Nos. 48-51 (4) 4.00 4.00

Initiation Ceremony of Xhosa
Men — A9

1979, Jan. 30 *Perf. 12½*
52 A9 4c Chi Cha youth .50 .50
53 A9 10c Youths in seclusion .75 .75
54 A9 15c Umtshilo dance 1.25 1.25
55 A9 20c Leaving the Sutu 1.50 1.50
Nos. 52-55 (4) 4.00 4.00

Chief   Water
Matanzima   Resources
A10   A11

1979, Feb. 20 *Perf. 14½x14*
56 A10 4c brn car & gold .30 .30
57 A10 15c olive grn & gold .70 .70
Inauguration of Matanzima, second state president.

1979, Mar. 13 *Perf. 14½x14, 14x14½*
58 A11 4c Windmill .20 .20
59 A11 10c Woman filling water
 jar .40 .40
60 A11 15c Irrigation, Indwe River, horiz. .60 .60
61 A11 20c Ncora dam, horiz. .75 .75
Nos. 58-61 (4) 1.95 1.95

Waterfalls   Child Healh
A12   Care
              A13

1979, Sept. 4
62 A12 4c Magwa Falls .20 .20
63 A12 10c Bawa Falls .30 .30
64 A12 15c Waterfall Bluff, horiz. .45 .45
65 A12 20c Tsitsa Falls, horiz. .60 .60
Nos. 62-65 (4) 1.55 1.55

1979, Dec. 3 *Perf. 14½x14*
66 A13 5c Pre-natal nourish-
 ment .20 .20
67 A13 15c Primary feeding .60 .60
68 A13 20c Immunization .80 .80
Nos. 66-68 (3) 1.60 1.60

Fishing
Flies — A14

a, Durham ranger. b, Colonel Bates. c, Black gnat. d, Zug bug. e, March brown.

1980, Jan. 15 *Perf. 14x14½*
69 Strip of 5 2.50 2.50
a.-e. A14 5c any single .50 .50

1981, Jan. 15
Designs: a, Kent's lightning. b, Wickham's fancy. c, Jock Scott. d, Green highlander. e, Tan nymph.
70 Strip of 5 1.50 1.50
a.-e. A14 10c any single .30 .30

1982, Jan. 6
a, Royal coachman. b, Light spruce. c, Montana nymph. d, Butcher. e, Blue charm.
71 Strip of 5 2.00 2.00
a.-e. A14 10c any single .40 .40

1983, Mar. 2
Designs: a, Alexandra. b, Kent's marbled sedge. c, White marabou. d, Mayfly nymph. e, Silver Wilkinson.
72 Strip of 5 2.00 2.00
a.-e. A14 20c any single .40 .40

1984, Feb. 10
Designs: a, Silver gray. b, Ginger quill. c, Hardy's favorite. d, March brown nymph. e, Kent's spectrum Mohawk.
73 Strip of 5 2.50 2.50
a.-e. A14 20c any single .50 .50

Rotary Intl.,   Cycads — A16
75th
Anniv. — A15

1980, Feb. 22 *Perf. 14½x14*
74 A15 15c blk, ultra & gold .50 .50

1980, Apr. 30
75 A16 5c *Encephalartos alten-
 steinii* .20 .20
76 A16 10c *Encephalartos
 princeps* .30 .30
77 A16 15c *Encephalartos
 vilosus* .40 .40
78 A16 20c *Encephalartos frider-
 ici-guilielmi* .60 .60
Nos. 75-78 (4) 1.50 1.50

Birds — A17

1980, July 30
79 A17 5c *Cuculus solitarius* .25 .25
80 A17 10c *Batis capensis* .55 .55
81 A17 15c *Balearica pavonina* .85 .85
82 A17 20c *Ploceus ocularius* 1.10 1.10
Nos. 79-82 (4) 2.75 2.75

Tourism — A18

1980, Oct. 26
83 A18 5c Hole in the Wall .20 .20
84 A18 10c Port St. Johns .30 .30
85 A18 15c The Citadel .45 .45
86 A18 20c The Archway .55 .55
Nos. 83-86 (4) 1.50 1.50

Xhosa Women's Headdresses — A19

1981, Aug. 28
87 A19 5c Eyamakhwenkwe .20 .20
88 A19 15c Eyabafana .35 .35
89 A19 20c Umfazana .40 .40
90 A19 25c Ixhegokazi .55 .55
a. Souvenir sheet of 4, #87-90 1.90 1.90
Nos. 87-90 (4) 1.50 1.50

Independence, 5th Anniv. — A20

Boy Scout   Great Medical
Movement,   Pioneers
75th Anniv.   A22
A21

1981, Oct. 26 *Perf. 14x14½*
91 A20 5c State House .30 .30
92 A20 15c University .50 .50

1982, May 14 *Perf. 14½x14*
93 A21 8c Salute .20 .20
94 A21 10c Planting tree .20 .20
95 A21 20c Rafting .40 .40
96 A21 25c Nature hike with dog .50 .50
Nos. 93-96 (4) 1.30 1.30

1982, Oct. 5
97 A22 15c Hippocrates .35 .35
98 A22 20c Anton van
 Leeuwenhoek .45 .45
99 A22 25c William Harvey .55 .55
100 A22 30c Joseph Lister .65 .65
Nos. 97-100 (4) 2.00 2.00

1983, Aug. 17
101 A22 10c Edward Jenner .30 .30
102 A22 20c Gregor Mendel .45 .45
103 A22 25c Louis Pasteur .55 .55
104 A22 40c Florence Nightingale .70 .70
Nos. 101-104 (4) 2.00 2.00

1984, Oct. 12
105 A22 11c Nicholas of Cusa .30 .30
106 A22 25c William Morton .55 .55
107 A22 30c Wilhelm Roentgen .65 .65
108 A22 45c Karl Landsteiner 1.00 1.00
Nos. 105-108 (4) 2.50 2.50

1985, Sept. 20
109 A22 12c Andreas Vesalius .30 .30
110 A22 25c Marcello Malpighi .55 .55
111 A22 30c Francois
 Magendie .65 .65
112 A22 50c William Stewart
 Halsted 1.00 1.00
Nos. 109-112 (4) 2.50 2.50
Nos. 97-112 (16) 9.00 9.00

Umtata,
Cent.
A23

Architecture: 8c, City Hall. 15c, The Bunga. 20c, Botha Sigcau Building. 25c, Palace of Justice, Matanzima Building.

1982, Nov. 10 *Perf. 14x14½*
113 A23 8c multicolored .20 .20
114 A23 15c multicolored .20 .20
115 A23 20c multicolored .30 .30
116 A23 25c multicolored .40 .40
Nos. 113-116 (4) 1.10 1.10

Wildcoast
Holiday
Resort,
Mzamba
A24

1983, May 25
117 A24 10c Hotel complex .20 .20
118 A24 20c Beach scene .35 .35
119 A24 25c Casino .45 .45
120 A24 40c Carousel .65 .65
Nos. 117-120 (4) 1.65 1.65

Post
Offices
A25

1983, Nov. 9   Perf. 14½x14
121	A25	10c Lady Frere	.20	.20
122	A25	20c Idutywa	.30	.30
123	A25	25c Lusikisiki	.40	.40
124	A25	40c Cala	.60	.60
		Nos. 121-124 (4)	1.50	1.50

1984, May 11
125	A25	11c Umzimkulu	.20	.20
126	A25	20c Mount Fletcher	.30	.30
127	A25	25c Qumbu	.40	.40
128	A25	30c Umtata	.60	.60
		Nos. 125-128 (4)	1.50	1.50

Xhosa Lifestyle A26

1984-90
129	A26	1c Amagqira	.20	.20
130	A26	2c Horsemen	.20	.20
131	A26	3c Mat maker	.20	.20
132	A26	4c Xhosa dancers	.20	.20
133	A26	5c Man, donkeys	.20	.20
134	A26	6c Musicians	.20	.20
135	A26	7c Fingo brides	.20	.20
136	A26	8c Tasting beer	.20	.20
137	A26	9c Thinning corn	.20	.20
138	A26	10c Dance demonstration	.20	.20
139	A26	11c Carrying water from the river	.20	.20
140	A26	12c Meal preparation	.25	.25
141	A26	14c Weeding	.25	.25
142	A26	15c Stick fighting	.30	.30
143	A26	16c Morning pasture	.30	.30
144	A26	20c Abakhwetha dancers	.40	.40
145	A26	21c Building initiation hut	.40	.40
146	A26	25c Tribesmen singing	.45	.45
147	A26	30c Matrons	.50	.50
148	A26	50c Pipe maker	.95	.95
149	A26	1r Intonjane women	1.90	1.90
150	A26	2r Abakhwetha	4.00	4.00
		Nos. 129-150 (22)	11.90	11.90

Issued: 11c, 4/2/84; 12c, 4/1/85; 14c, 4/1/86; 16c, 4/1/87; 21c, 7/3/90; others, 7/6/84.

Soil Conservation A27

Designs: 11c, Erosion from over-grazing. 25c, Wall construction to collect sediment. 30c, Regeneration of vegetation. 50c, Cattle grazing on verdant plain.

1985, Feb. 7
155	A27	11c shown	.20	.20
156	A27	25c multicolored	.45	.45
157	A27	30c multicolored	.50	.50
158	A27	50c multicolored	.85	.85
		Nos. 155-158 (4)	2.00	2.00

Bridges A28

1985, Apr. 18
159	A28	12c Tsitsa	.20	.20
160	A28	25c White Kei	.45	.45
161	A28	30c Mitchell	.50	.50
162	A28	50c Umzimvubu	.85	.85
		Nos. 159-162 (4)	2.00	2.00

Match Industry — A29

1985, July 25   Perf. 14½x14
163	A29	12c Peeling logs	.20	.20
164	A29	25c Splint chopping	.45	.45
165	A29	30c VPO machine	.50	.50
166	A29	50c Filling boxes	.85	.85
		Nos. 163-166 (4)	2.00	2.00

Port St. Johns A30

Designs: 12c, Early street scene. 20c, Coaster *Umzimvubu* at the Old Jetty. 25c, Unloading corn from wagons at the Jetty. 30c, View of the town, 1890's.

1986, Feb. 6
167	A30	12c multicolored	.20	.20
168	A30	20c multicolored	.50	.50
169	A30	25c multicolored	.60	.60
170	A30	30c multicolored	.70	.70
a.		Souvenir sheet of 4, #167-170	2.50	2.50
		Nos. 167-170 (4)	2.00	2.00

Aloes — A31

1986, May 1
171	A31	14c *Aloe ferox*	.20	.20
172	A31	20c *Aloe arborescens*	.30	.30
173	A31	25c *Aloe maculata*	.40	.40
174	A31	30c *Aloe ecklonis*	.50	.50
a.		Souvenir sheet of 1	4.00	4.00
		Nos. 171-174 (4)	1.40	1.40

No. 174a margin pictures emblem of the natl. philatelic exhibition held at Johannesburg, Oct. 6-11. Sold for 50c.

Hydroelectric Power Stations A32

14c, First Falls, Umtata River. 20c, Second Falls, Umtata River. 25c, Ncora, Qumanco River. 30c, Collywobbles, Mbashe River.

1986, July 24
175	A32	14c shown	.25	.25
176	A32	20c multicolored	.35	.35
177	A32	25c multicolored	.40	.40
178	A32	30c multicolored	.50	.50
		Nos. 175-178 (4)	1.50	1.50

Independence, 10th Anniv. — A33

Designs: 14c, Prime Minister G. M. Matanzima. 20c, Technical College, Umtata. 25c, University of Transkei, Umtata. 30c, Palace of Justice, Umtata.

1986, Oct. 26
179	A33	14c multicolored	.20	.20
180	A33	20c multicolored	.35	.35
181	A33	25c multicolored	.40	.40
182	A33	30c multicolored	.45	.45
		Nos. 179-182 (4)	1.40	1.40

Transkei Airways, 10th Anniv. — A34

1987, Feb. 5
183	A34	14c shown	.25	.25
184	A34	20c Aircraft tail	.40	.40
185	A34	25c Nose, propellers	.50	.50
186	A34	30c Plane, control tower	.60	.60
		Nos. 183-186 (4)	1.75	1.75

Beadwork — A35

Spiders — A36

1987, May 22   Perf. 14x14½
187	A35	16c Pondo girl	.30	.30
188	A35	20c Bomvana woman	.40	.40
189	A35	25c Xessibe woman	.50	.50
a.		Souvenir sheet of 1	3.50	3.50
190	A35	30c Xhosa man	.65	.65
		Nos. 187-190 (4)	1.85	1.85

No. 189a has blue and black decorative margin picturing the emblem of the natl. philatelic exhibition held at Paarl, Sept. 16-19. Sold for 50c.

1987, Aug. 24
191	A36	16c *Latrodectus indistinctus*	.35	.35
192	A36	20c *Nephila pilipes fenestrata*	.45	.45
193	A36	25c *Lycosidae*	.55	.55
194	A36	30c *Argiope nigrovittata*	.65	.65
		Nos. 191-194 (4)	2.00	2.00

Domestic Animals A37

1987, Oct. 22
195	A37	16c Black pigs	.25	.25
196	A37	30c Goats	.50	.50
197	A37	40c Merino sheep	.65	.65
198	A37	50c Cattle	.85	.85
		Nos. 195-198 (4)	2.25	2.25

Seaweed — A38

1988, Feb. 18
199	A38	16c *Plocamium corallorhiza*	.25	.25
200	A38	30c *Gelidium amanzil*	.50	.50
201	A38	40c *Ecklonia biruncinata*	.65	.65
202	A38	50c *Halimeda cuneata*	.85	.85
		Nos. 199-202 (4)	2.25	2.25

Blanket Factory, Butterworth A39

1988, May 5   Perf. 14½x14
203	A39	16c Spinning machines	.25	.25
204	A39	30c Warping machine	.50	.50
205	A39	40c Weaving machine	.65	.65
206	A39	50c Raising the nap	.85	.85
		Nos. 203-206 (4)	2.25	2.25

Wreck of the *Grosvenor*, 1782 — A40

Designs: 16c, Ship, map. 30c, *The Wreck of the Grosvenor*, by R. Smirke. 40c, Dirk hilt, compass and coins salvaged. 50c, *African Hospitality*, by G. Morland.

1988, Aug. 4
207	A40	16c multicolored	.40	.40
208	A40	30c multicolored	.75	.75
209	A40	40c multicolored	1.00	1.00
210	A40	50c multicolored	1.25	1.25
a.		Souvenir sheet of 1	4.00	4.00
		Nos. 207-210 (4)	3.40	3.40

No. 210a margin pictures emblem of the natl. philatelic exhibition at Pietermaritzburg, Nov. 22-27. Sold for 1r.

Endangered Species A41

1988, Oct. 20
211	A41	16c *Felis nigripes*	.50	.50
212	A41	30c *Philantomba monticola*	.95	.95
213	A41	40c *Ourebia ourebi*	1.25	1.25
214	A41	50c *Lycaon pictus*	1.50	1.50
		Nos. 211-214 (4)	4.20	4.20

Locomotive, Trains and Bridges — A42

Designs: 16c, Class 14 CRB locomotive. 30c, CRB pulling train over Toleni-Halt Bridge. 40c, Train on the Great Kei River Bridge, vert. 50c, Train in the Kei Valley.

1989, Jan. 19   Perf. 14x14½, 14½x14
215	A42	16c multi	.45	.45
216	A42	30c multi	.85	.85
217	A42	40c multi	1.25	1.25
218	A42	50c multi, vert.	1.40	1.40
		Nos. 215-218 (4)	3.95	3.95

A souvenir sheet of one No. 218 has margin picturing the emblem of the natl. philatelic exhibition WANDERERS 101, held Sept. 6-9. Sold for 1.50r. Value $5.

Basketry A43

1989, Apr. 20   Perf. 14½x14
219	A43	18c shown	.35	.35
220	A43	30c multi, diff.	.60	.60
221	A43	40c multi, diff.	.75	.75
222	A43	50c multi, diff.	1.00	1.00
		Nos. 219-222 (4)	2.70	2.70

Mackerel
A44

1989, July 20
223	A44	18c shown	.55	.55
224	A44	30c Squid	.90	.90
225	A44	40c Brown mussel	1.10	1.10
226	A44	50c Rock lobster	1.50	1.50
		Nos. 223-226 (4)	4.05	4.05

Trees
A45

1989, Oct. 5   *Perf. 14x14½*
227	A45	18c Broom cluster fig	.50	.50
228	A45	30c Natal fig	.90	.90
229	A45	40c Broad-leaved coral	1.10	1.10
230	A45	50c Cabbage tree	1.50	1.50
		Nos. 227-230 (4)	4.00	4.00

Fossils
A46

1990, Jan. 18
231	A46	18c *Ginkgo koningensis*	.65	.65
232	A46	30c *Pseudoctenis spatulata*	1.25	1.25
233	A46	40c *Rissikia media*	1.60	1.60
234	A46	50c *Taeniopteris anavolans*	2.25	2.25
		Nos. 231-234 (4)	5.75	5.75

Great Medical
Pioneers — A47

Diviners — A48

1990, Mar. 29   *Perf. 14x14½*
235	A47	18c Aretaeus	.65	.65
236	A47	30c Claude Bernard	1.10	1.10
237	A47	40c Oscar Minkowski	1.50	1.50
238	A47	50c Frederick Banting	2.00	2.00
		Nos. 235-238 (4)	5.25	5.25

1990, June 28   **Litho.**   *Perf. 14x14½*
239	A48	21c Dancing to the Drum	.65	.65
240	A48	35c Lecturing Imichetywa	1.10	1.10
241	A48	40c Initiation ceremony	1.25	1.25
242	A48	50c Induction ceremony	1.50	1.50
a.		Souvenir sheet of 1	5.00	5.00
		Nos. 239-242 (4)	4.50	4.50

No. 242a for the 150th anniv. of the Penny Black. Sold for 1.50r.

Flowers — A49

Parasitic
Plants — A50

1990, Sept. 20 Litho.   *Perf. 14x14½*
243	A49	21c Cyrtanthus obliquus	.70	.70
244	A49	35c Disa crassicornis	1.10	1.10
245	A49	40c Sandersonia aurantiaca	1.40	1.40
246	A49	50c Podranea ricasoliana	1.50	1.50
		Nos. 243-246 (4)	4.70	4.70

1991, Jan. 10   **Litho.**
247	A50	21c Harveya pulchra	.65	.65
248	A50	35c Harveya speciosa	1.10	1.10
249	A50	40c Alectra sessiliflora	1.25	1.25
250	A50	50c Hydnora africana	1.60	1.60
		Nos. 247-250 (4)	4.60	4.60

Dolphins
A51

1991, Apr. 4   **Litho.**   *Perf. 14½x14*
251	A51	25c Delphinus delphis	.95	.95
252	A51	40c Tursiops truncatus	1.50	1.50
253	A51	50c Sousa plumbea	1.90	1.90
254	A51	60c Grampus griseus	2.25	2.25
		Nos. 251-254 (4)	6.60	6.60

Birds — A52

Medical
Pioneers — A53

1991, June 20   **Litho.**
255	A52	25c Balearica regulorum	.80	.80
256	A52	40c Gyps coprotheres	1.25	1.25
257	A52	50c Grus carunculata	1.50	1.50
258	A52	60c Neophron percnopterus	1.75	1.75
a.		Souvenir sheet of 1	5.50	5.50
		Nos. 255-258 (4)	5.30	5.30

1991, Sept. 26 Litho.   *Perf. 14x14½*

Developers of vaccines: 25c, Emil von Behring (1854-1917) and Shibasaburo Kitasato (1852-1931), diphtheria. 40c, Leon Albert Calmette (1863-1933) and Camille Guerin (1872-1961), tuberculosis. 50c, Jonas Salk (b. 1914), polio. 60c, John Franklin Enders (1897-1985), measles.

259	A53	25c multicolored	.85	.85
260	A53	40c multicolored	1.50	1.50
261	A53	50c multicolored	1.75	1.75
262	A53	60c multicolored	2.40	2.40
		Nos. 259-262 (4)	6.50	6.50

Orchids — A54

1992, Feb. 20   **Litho.**
263	A54	27c Eulophia speciosa	.40	.40
264	A54	45c Satyrium sphaerocarpum	.65	.65
265	A54	65c Disa scullyi	1.00	1.00
266	A54	85c Disa tysonii	1.25	1.25
		Nos. 263-266 (4)	3.30	3.30

Medical
Pioneers
A55

27c, Thomas Huckle Weller (b. 1915), developer of rubella vaccine. 45c, Ignaz Philipp Semmelweis (1818-65), diagnosed septicaemia. 65c, Sir James Young Simpson (1811-70), 1st to use chloroform in obstetrics. 85c, Rene Theophile Hyacinthe Laennec (1781-1826), inventor of stethoscope.

1992, Apr. 1   **Litho.**   *Perf. 14½x14*
267	A55	27c multicolored	.70	.70
268	A55	45c multicolored	1.25	1.25
269	A55	65c multicolored	1.75	1.75
270	A55	85c multicolored	2.25	2.25
		Nos. 267-270 (4)	5.95	5.95

Waterfowl — A56

1992, July 16 Litho.   *Perf. 14x14½*
271	A56	35c Anas erythrorhyncha	.60	.60
272	A56	35c Anas hottentota	.60	.60
a.		Pair, #271-272	1.25	1.25
273	A56	70c Oxyura punctata	1.25	1.25
274	A56	70c Thalassornis leuconotus	1.25	1.25
a.		Pair, #273-274	2.50	2.50
275	A56	90c Anas sparsa	1.60	1.60
276	A56	90c Alopochen aegyptiacus	1.60	1.60
a.		Pair, #275-276	3.25	3.25
277	A56	1.05r Anas smithi	1.60	1.60
278	A56	1.05r Anas capensis	1.60	1.60
a.		Pair, #277-278	3.25	3.25
		Nos. 271-278 (8)	10.10	10.10

A souvenir sheet of 1 #273 was sold by the Philatelic Foundation of South Africa. Value $8.

Fossils
A57

Designs: 35c, Pseudomelania sutherlandi. 70c, Gaudryceras denseplicatum. 90c, Neithea quinquecostata. 1.05r, Pugilina (Mayeria) acuticarinatus.

1992, Sept. 17 Litho.   *Perf. 14½x14*
279	A57	35c multicolored	.75	.75
280	A57	70c multicolored	1.50	1.50
281	A57	90c multicolored	2.00	2.00
282	A57	1.05r multicolored	2.25	2.25
		Nos. 279-282 (4)	6.50	6.50

Dogs — A58

1993, Feb. 12   **Litho.**
283	A58	35c Papillon	.55	.55
284	A58	70c Pekingese	1.10	1.10
285	A58	90c Chihuahua	1.50	1.50
286	A58	1.05r Dachshund	1.75	1.75
		Nos. 283-286 (4)	4.90	4.90

A souvenir sheet of one No. 284 exists. Sold for 3r. Value $5.

Prehistoric
Animals
A59

1993, June 18   **Litho.**
287	A59	45c Fabrosaurus	1.00	1.00
288	A59	65c Diictodon	1.40	1.40
289	A59	85c Chasmatosaurus	1.75	1.75
290	A59	1.05r Rubidgea	2.25	2.25
		Nos. 287-290 (4)	6.40	6.40

Medical
Pioneers
A60

Designs: 45c, Sir Alexander Fleming (1881-1955), discovered penicillin and Lord Howard Walter Florey (1898-1968), purified penicillin for general use. 65c, Alexis Carrel (1873-1944), developed Carrel-Dakin fluid and method to suture blood vessels. 85c, James Lind (1716-1794), recommended citrus fruit to combat scurvy. 1.05r, Santiago Ramon y Cajal (1852-1934), established neuron as basic unit of nervous structure.

1993, Aug. 20   **Litho.**
291	A60	45c multicolored	1.00	1.00
292	A60	65c multicolored	1.25	1.25
293	A60	85c multicolored	1.60	1.60
294	A60	1.05r multicolored	2.00	2.00
		Nos. 291-294 (4)	5.85	5.85

Doves — A61

Designs: 45c, Streptopelia senegalensis. 65c, Turtur tympanistria. 85c, Turtur chalcospilos. 1.05r, Oena capensis.

1993, Oct. 15 Litho.   *Perf. 14x14½*
295	A61	45c multicolored	.90	.90
296	A61	65c multicolored	1.25	1.25
297	A61	85c multicolored	1.60	1.60
298	A61	1.05r multicolored	1.90	1.90
a.		Souvenir sheet of 4, #295-298	5.50	5.50
		Nos. 295-298 (4)	5.65	5.65

No. 298a sold for 3.50r.

Modern
Shipwrecks
A62

1994, Mar. 18 Litho.   *Perf. 14½x14*
299	A62	45c Clan Lindsay, 1898	1.10	1.10
300	A62	65c Horizon, 1967	1.75	1.75
301	A62	85c Oceanos, 1991	2.40	2.40
302	A62	1.05r Forresbank, 1958	2.75	2.75
		Nos. 299-302 (4)	8.00	8.00

A souvenir sheet of 1 #301 exists. Sold for 3r. Value $8.

Transkei ceased to exist April 27, 1994.

VENDA

'ven-də

LOCATION — Enclave, Republic of South Africa

GOVT. — Self-governing tribal
  homeland
AREA — 4,040 sq. mi.
POP. — 343,480 (1980)
CAPITAL — Thohoyandou

Catalogue values for all unused
stamps in this country are for
Never Hinged items.

Independence from South Africa — A1

Designs: 4c, Mace, flag. 15c, Administrative
buildings. 20c, P.R. Mphephu, paramount
chief and president. 25c, Coat of arms.

Perf. 14½x14

1979, Sept. 13   Litho.   Unwmk.
1	A1	4c multicolored	.40	.40
2	A1	15c multicolored	1.10	1.10
3	A1	20c multicolored	1.50	1.50
4	A1	25c multicolored	2.00	2.00
		Nos. 1-4 (4)	5.00	5.00

Flowers — A2

Wood Carvings — A3

1979-85   **Perf. 12½, 14 (11c, 12c)**
5	A2	1c Tecomaria capensis	.20	.20
6	A2	2c Catophractes alexandri	.20	.20
7	A2	3c Tricliceras longipedunculatum	.20	.20
8	A2	4c Dissotis princeps	.20	.20
9	A2	5c Gerbera jamesonii	2.00	.65
10	A2	6c Hibiscus mastersianus	.20	.20
11	A2	7c Nymphaea caerulaea	.20	.20
12	A2	8c Crinum lugardiae	.35	.20
13	A2	9c Xerophyta retinervis	.20	.20
14	A2	10c Hypoxis angustifolia	.30	.20
15	A2	11c Combretum microphyllum	.30	.20
16	A2	12c Clivia caulescens	.40	.20
17	A2	15c Pycnostachys urticifolia	.20	.20
18	A2	20c Zantedeschia jucunda	.20	.20
19	A2	25c Leonotis mollis	2.50	.90
20	A2	30c Littonia modesta	.40	.25
21	A2	50c Protea caffra	.70	.25
22	A2	1r Adenium multiflorum	1.00	.50
23	A2	2r Strelitzia caudata	2.25	1.25
		Nos. 5-23 (19)	12.00	6.40

Issue dates: 11c, Apr. 2, 1984; 12c, Apr. 1,
1985; others, Sept. 13, 1979.

Perf. 14
5a	A2	1c	.20	.20
6a	A2	2c	.20	.20
7a	A2	3c	.20	.20
9a	A2	5c	.20	.20
12a	A2	8c	.20	.20
14a	A2	10c	.40	.20
19a	A2	25c	1.25	.90
21a	A2	50c	2.75	1.25
		Nos. 5a-21a (8)	5.40	3.05

1980, Feb. 13   **Perf. 14½x14, 14x14½**

Designs: 5c, Man with cup. 10c, Woman
with corn, bowl and spoon. 15c, King Nebu-
chadnezzar, horiz. 20c, Python killing woman,
horiz.
24	A3	5c multicolored	.20	.20
25	A3	10c multicolored	.40	.40
26	A3	15c multicolored	.60	.60
27	A3	20c multicolored	.80	.80
		Nos. 24-27 (4)	2.00	2.00

Tea Cultivation A4

1980, May 14   **Perf. 14x14½**
28	A4	5c Plants in nursery	.20	.20
29	A4	10c Harvest	.20	.20
30	A4	15c Withering	.40	.40
31	A4	20c Cut, twist, curl unit	.60	.60
		Nos. 28-31 (4)	1.40	1.40

Banana Industry A5

1980, Aug. 13
32	A5	5c Plants	.20	.20
33	A5	10c Cutting "hands"	.20	.20
34	A5	15c Sorting	.40	.40
35	A5	20c Packing	.60	.60
		Nos. 32-35 (4)	1.40	1.40

Butterflies A6

Sunbirds A7

1980, Nov. 13   **Perf. 14½x14**
36	A6	5c Precis tugela	.20	.20
37	A6	10c Charaxes bohemani	.35	.35
38	A6	15c Catacroptera cloanthe	.65	.65
39	A6	20c Papilio dardanus	.80	.80
		Nos. 36-39 (4)	2.00	2.00

1981, Feb. 16
40	A7	5c Anthreptes collaris	.20	.20
41	A7	15c Nectarinia mariquensis	.45	.45
42	A7	20c Nectarinia talatala	.60	.60
43	A7	25c Nectarinia senegalensis	.75	.75
		Nos. 40-43 (4)	2.00	2.00

Nwanedi Dam — A8

1981, May 6
44	A8	5c shown	.20	.20
45	A8	15c Mahovhohovho Falls	.35	.35
46	A8	20c Phiphidi Falls	.40	.40
47	A8	25c Lake Fundudzi	.55	.55
		Nos. 44-47 (4)	1.50	1.50

Orchids — A9

Musical Instruments — A10

1981, Sept. 11
48	A9	5c Cynorkis kassnerana	.20	.20
49	A9	15c Eulophia fridericii	.35	.35
50	A9	20c Bonatea densiflora	.65	.65
51	A9	25c Mystacidium brayboniae	.80	.80
a.		Souvenir sheet of 4, #48-51	2.25	2.25
		Nos. 48-51 (4)	2.00	2.00

1981, Nov. 13   **Perf. 14x14½**
52	A10	5c Mbila	.20	.20
53	A10	15c Phalaphala	.25	.25
54	A10	20c Tshizambi	.35	.35
55	A10	25c Ngoma	.50	.50
		Nos. 52-55 (4)	1.30	1.30

Sisal Cultivation A11

1982, Feb. 26
56	A11	5c Harvesting	.20	.20
57	A11	10c Drying	.25	.25
58	A11	20c Grading	.40	.40
59	A11	25c Baling	.55	.55
		Nos. 56-59 (4)	1.40	1.40

History of Writing — A12

Designs: 8c, Bison, petroglyph, Altamira,
Spain. 15c, Animal, petroglyph, eastern California. 20c, Pictographic script on a Sumerian
tablet. 25c, Bushman burial stone, Humans-
dorp, South Africa.

1982, June 15   **Perf. 14½x14**
60	A12	8c multicolored	.20	.20
61	A12	15c multicolored	.25	.25
62	A12	20c multicolored	.35	.35
63	A12	25c multicolored	.45	.45
		Nos. 60-63 (4)	1.25	1.25

1983, May 11   **Size: 21x37mm**

10c, Indus Valley script, 3000 B.C. 20c,
Sumerian cuneiform, 2000 B.C. 25c, Egyptian
hieroglyphics, 1300 B.C. 40c, Chinese hand-
scroll, A.D. 1100.
64	A12	10c multicolored	.20	.20
65	A12	20c multicolored	.30	.30
66	A12	25c multicolored	.35	.35
67	A12	40c multicolored	.40	.40
		Nos. 64-67 (4)	1.25	1.25

1984, Feb. 17   **Perf. 14x14½**
     Size: 37½x20½mm

Designs: 10c, Evolution of the cuneiform
sign. 20c, Evolution of the Chinese character.
25c, Development of Cretan hieroglyphics.
40c, Development of Egyptian hieroglyphics.
68	A12	10c multicolored	.20	.20
69	A12	20c multicolored	.45	.45
70	A12	25c multicolored	.50	.50
71	A12	40c multicolored	.85	.85
		Nos. 68-71 (4)	2.00	2.00

1985, Mar. 21   **Perf. 14½x14**
     Size: 34x24½mm

Designs: 11c, Southern Arabic characters.
25c, Phoenician characters. 30c, Aramaic
characters. 50c, Canaanite characters.
72	A12	11c multicolored	.20	.20
73	A12	25c multicolored	.50	.50
74	A12	30c multicolored	.60	.60
75	A12	50c multicolored	1.00	1.00
		Nos. 72-75 (4)	2.30	2.30

1986, Apr. 10   **Perf. 14x14½**
     Size: 24½x34mm
76	A12	14c Etruscan	.30	.30
77	A12	20c Greek	.45	.45
78	A12	25c Roman	.55	.55
79	A12	30c Cyrillic	.65	.65
		Nos. 76-79 (4)	1.95	1.95

1988, Apr. 28   **Perf. 14½x14**
     Size: 34x26mm
80	A12	16c Chinese	.40	.40
81	A12	30c Hindi	.65	.65
82	A12	40c Russian	.90	.90
83	A12	50c Arabic	1.10	1.10
		Nos. 80-83 (4)	3.05	3.05
		Nos. 60-83 (24)	11.80	11.80

See Nos. 209-212.

Trees A13

1982, Sept. 17
84	A13	8c Euphorbia ingens	.20	.20
85	A13	15c Pterocarpus angolensis	.25	.25
86	A13	20c Ficus ingens	.35	.35
87	A13	25c Adansonia digitata	.45	.45
		Nos. 84-87 (4)	1.25	1.25

1983, Aug. 3
88	A13	10c Gardenia spatulifolia	.20	.20
89	A13	20c Hyphaene natalensis	.35	.35
90	A13	25c Albizia adianthifolia	.40	.40
91	A13	40c Sesamothamnus lugardii	.70	.70
		Nos. 88-91 (4)	1.65	1.65

1984, June 21
92	A13	11c Afzelia quanzensis	.20	.20
93	A13	20c Peltophorum africanum	.35	.35
94	A13	25c Gyrocarpus americanus	.45	.45
95	A13	30c Acacia sieberana	.55	.55
		Nos. 92-95 (4)	1.55	1.55
		Nos. 84-95 (12)	4.45	4.45

Frogs — A14

1982, Nov. 26   **Perf. 14x14½**
96	A14	8c Rana angolensis	.20	.20
97	A14	15c Chiromantis xerampelina	.40	.40
98	A14	20c Leptopelis	.50	.50
99	A14	25c Ptychadena anchietae	.65	.65
		Nos. 96-99 (4)	1.75	1.75

Migratory Birds and Maps — A15

1983, Feb. 16   **Perf. 14½x14**
100	A15	8c European bee-eater	.30	.30
101	A15	20c Steppe eagle	.75	.75
102	A15	25c Plum-colored starling	.90	.90
103	A15	40c White-bellied stork	1.50	1.50
		Nos. 100-103 (4)	3.45	3.45

Subtropical Fruit A16

1983, Oct. 26   **Perf. 14x14½**
104	A16	10c Avocado	.20	.20
105	A16	20c Mango	.30	.30
106	A16	25c Papaya	.35	.35
107	A16	40c Litchi	.60	.60
		Nos. 104-107 (4)	1.45	1.45

Migratory Birds — A17

1984, Apr. 26   **Perf. 14½x14**
108 A17 11c White stork   .35   .35
109 A17 20c Paradise flycatcher   .70   .70
110 A17 25c Yellow-billed kite   .85   .85
111 A17 30c Wood sandpiper   1.10 1.10
     Nos. 108-111 (4)   3.00 3.00

Independence, 5th Anniv. — A18

1984, Sept. 13   **Perf. 14½x14**
112 A18 11c Dzata Ruins   .20   .20
113 A18 25c Traditional hut   .40   .40
114 A18 30c Low-income housing   .45   .45
115 A18 45c Modern home   .70   .70
     Nos. 112-115 (4)   1.75 1.75

Songbirds A19   Food of the Veld A20

1985, Jan. 10
116 A19 11c Heuglin's robin   .30   .30
117 A19 25c Black-collared bar-
            bet   .70   .70
118 A19 30c Black-headed oriole   .85   .85
119 A19 50c Kurrichane thrush   1.40 1.40
     Nos. 116-119 (4)   3.25 3.25

1985, June 21   **Perf. 14x14½**
120 A20 12c Mimusops zeyheri   .25   .25
121 A20 25c Ziziphus mucronata   .55   .55
122 A20 30c Citrullus lanatus   .60   .60
123 A20 50c Berchemia discolor   1.10 1.10
     Nos. 120-123 (4)   2.50 2.50

See Nos. 173-176.

Ferns — A21

1985, Sept. 5   **Perf. 14½x14**
124 A21 12c Pellaea dura   .25   .25
125 A21 25c Actiniopteris radiata   .55   .55
126 A21 30c Adiantum his-
            pidulum   .60   .60
127 A21 50c Polypodium poly-
            podioides   1.10 1.10
     Nos. 124-127 (4)   2.50 2.50

Reptiles A22

1986-90   **Perf. 14x14½**
128 A22 1c Psammophylax
            tritaeniatus   .20   .20
129 A22 2c Pseudaspis cana   .20   .20
130 A22 3c Nucras taeniolata
            ornata   .20   .20
131 A22 4c Bitis arietans   .20   .20
132 A22 5c Mabuya capensis   .20   .20
133 A22 6c Naja haje annu-
            lifera   .20   .20
134 A22 7c Mabuya quin-
            quetaeniata
            margaritifer   .20   .20
135 A22 8c Philothamnus
            semivariegatus   .20   .20
136 A22 9c Gerrhosaurus
            flavigularis   .20   .20
137 A22 10c Prosymna sun-
            devallii lineata   .20   .20

138 A22 14c Platysaurus in-
            termedius   .30   .30
139 A22 15c Lacerta rupicola   .30   .30
140 A22 16c Varanus niloticus   .35   .35
141 A22 18c Dendroaspis
            polylepis   .40   .40
142 A22 20c Afroedura trans-
            vaalica   .45   .45
143 A22 21c Chamaeleo dilep-
            sis   .45   .45
144 A22 25c Elapsoidea sun-
            devallii longi-
            cauda   .55   .55
145 A22 30c Pachydactylus
            tigrinus   .65   .65
146 A22 50c Mehelya capensis   1.10 1.10
147 A22 1r Cordylus warreni
            depressus   2.25 2.25
148 A22 2r Python sebae
            natalensis   4.50 4.50
     Nos. 128-148 (21)   13.30 13.30

Issued: 14c, 4/1/86; 16c, 4/1/87; 18c, 7/3/89; 21c, 8/3/90; others, 1/16/86.

Forestry A23

Designs: 14c, Planting pine seedlings. 20c, Felling and extracting saw timber. 25c, Unloading timber at sawmill. 30c, Construction workers using pre-cut lumber.

1986, June 26   **Perf. 14x14½**
153 A23 14c multicolored   .20   .20
154 A23 20c multicolored   .40   .40
155 A23 25c multicolored   .45   .45
156 A23 30c multicolored   .55   .55
     Nos. 153-156 (4)   1.60 1.60

FIVA World Classic Car Rally — A24

1986, Sept. 4   **Perf. 14½x14**
157 A24 14c 1910 Maxwell   .45   .45
158 A24 20c 1929 Bentley 4½ l   .65   .65
159 A24 25c 1933 Plymouth
            Coupe   .85   .85
160 A24 30c 1958 Mercedes
            Cabriolet   1.00 1.00
  a. Souvenir sheet of 1   5.00 5.00
     Nos. 157-160 (4)   2.95 2.95

No. 160a for the natl. philatelic exhibition held at Johannesburg, Oct. 6-11. Sold for 50c.

Waterfowl A25   Wood Carvings A26

1987, Jan. 8   **Perf. 14x14½, 14½x14**
161 A25 14c Sarkidiornis mela-
            notos   .90   .90
162 A25 20c Dendrocygna vidu-
            ata   1.40 1.40
163 A25 25c Plectropterus
            gambensis   1.60 1.60
  a. Souvenir sheet of 1   6.50 6.50
164 A25 30c Alopochen aegyp-
            tiacus   2.10 2.10
     Nos. 161-164 (4)   6.00 6.00

Nos. 163-164 are horiz. No. 163a margin pictures emblem of the natl. philatelic exhibition held at Paarl, Sept. 16-19. Sold for 50c.

1987, Apr. 9   **Perf. 14½x14**
165 A26 16c Iron Master   .35   .35
166 A26 20c Distant Drums   .40   .40
167 A26 25c Sunrise   .55   .55
168 A26 30c Obedience   .70   .70
     Nos. 165-168 (4)   2.00 2.00

Freshwater Fish — A27

1987, July 2   **Perf. 14x14½**
169 A27 16c Hydrocynus vittatus   .50   .50
170 A27 20c Opsardium
            zambezense   .60   .60
171 A27 25c Oreochromis mos-
            sambicus   .70   .70
172 A27 25c Clarias gariepinus   .90   .90
     Nos. 169-172 (4)   2.70 2.70

Food of the Veld Type
1987, Oct. 2
173 A20 16c Grewia occidentalis   .25   .25
174 A20 30c Phoenix reclinata   .50   .50
175 A20 40c Halleria lucida   .70   .70
176 A20 50c Cucumis africanus   .90   .90
     Nos. 173-176 (4)   2.35 2.35

Coffee Industry A28

1988, Jan. 21   **Perf. 14½x14**
177 A28 16c Harvesting   .30   .30
178 A28 30c Weighing   .55   .55
179 A28 40c Sun drying   .70   .70
180 A28 50c Roasting   .90   .90
     Nos. 177-180 (4)   2.45 2.45

Nurse's Training College, Shayandima A29

1988, Aug. 18
181 A29 16c shown   .30   .30
182 A29 30c Microscopy   .50   .50
183 A29 40c Anatomy lecture   .70   .70
184 A29 50c Clinical training   .90   .90
     Nos. 181-184 (4)   2.40 2.40

Watercolors by Kenneth Thabo A30

1988, Oct. 6
185 A30 16c Fetching Water   .30   .30
186 A30 30c Grinding Maize   .50   .50
187 A30 40c Offering Food   .70   .70
188 A30 50c Kindling the Fire   .90   .90
  a. Souvenir sheet of 1   4.00 4.00
     Nos. 185-188 (4)   2.40 2.40

No. 188a for the natl. philatelic exhibition held at Pietermaritzburg, Nov. 22-27. Sold for 1.50r.
See Nos. 193-196.

Traditional Kitchenware A31

1989, Jan. 5
189 A31 16c Ndongwana   .25   .25
190 A31 30c Ndilo   .45   .45
191 A31 40c Mufaro   .60   .60
192 A31 50c Muthatha   .80   .80
     Nos. 189-192 (4)   2.10 2.10

Art Type of 1988
Traditional dances: watercolors by Kenneth Thabo.

1989, Apr. 5
193 A30 18c Domba   .25   .25
194 A30 30c Tshinzerere   .45   .45
195 A30 40c Malende   .60   .60
196 A30 50c Malombo   .80   .80
     Nos. 193-196 (4)   2.10 2.10

Endangered Bird Species — A32

1989, June 27
197 A32 18c Bucorvus
            leadbeateri   .90   .90
198 A32 30c Torgos tracheliotus   1.25 1.25
199 A32 40c Terathopius
            ecaudatus   1.60 1.60
200 A32 50c Polemaetus bel-
            licosus   2.25 2.25
  a. Souvenir sheet of 1   5.75 5.75
     Nos. 197-200 (4)   6.00 6.00

No. 200a for the natl. philatelic exhibition WANDERERS 101, held Sept. 6-9. Sold for 1.50r.

Independence, 10th Anniv. — A33

1989, Sept. 13
201 A33 18c Pres. Ravele   .35   .35
202 A33 30c Presidential office   .65   .65
203 A33 40c Presidential resi-
            dence   .80   .80
204 A33 50c Thohoyandou Stadi-
            um   1.00 1.00
     Nos. 201-204 (4)   2.80 2.80

Wildlife Conservation, Nwanedi Natl. Park — A34

1990, Mar. 1
205 A34 18c Panthera leo   .55   .55
206 A34 30c Equus burchelli   1.00 1.00
207 A34 40c Acinonyx jubatus   1.25 1.25
208 A34 50c Ceratotherium
            simum   1.50 1.50
  a. Souvenir sheet of 1   4.75 4.75
     Nos. 205-208 (4)   4.30 4.30

No. 208a for the natl. philatelic exhibition. Sold for 1.50r.

History of Writing Type
Designs: 21c, Calligraphy. 30c, Musical notation, Beethoven's Moonlight Sonata. 40c, Computer characters. 50c, Black-and-white television picture transmitted across interstellar distances by the Arecibo radio telescope.

1990, May 23   **Litho.** **Perf. 14½x14**
209 A12 21c multicolored   .40   .40
210 A12 30c multicolored   .55   .55
211 A12 40c multicolored   .70   .70
212 A12 50c multicolored   1.00 1.00
     Nos. 209-212 (4)   2.65 2.65

Aloe
Plants — A35   Butterflies — A36

1990, Aug. 23   Litho.   Perf. 14½x14
213 A35 21c Aloe globuligemma   .45   .45
214 A35 35c Aloe aculeata   .70   .70
215 A35 40c Aloe lutescens   .85   .85
216 A35 50c Aloe angelica   1.00 1.00
     Nos. 213-216 (4)   3.00 3.00

1990, Nov. 15   Perf. 14x14½
217 A36 21c Pseudacraea bois-
             duvalii   .75   .75
218 A36 35c Papilio nireus   1.40 1.40
219 A36 40c Charaxes jasius   1.50 1.50
220 A36 50c Aeropetes tulbaghia   1.75 1.75
     Nos. 217-220 (4)   5.40 5.40

Birds
A37

A38

1991, Mar. 7   Litho.   Perf. 14½x14
221 A37 21c Batis capensis   .65   .65
222 A37 35c Cossypha natalen-
             sis   1.00 1.00
223 A37 40c Anthreptes collaris   1.25 1.25
224 A37 50c Phyllastrephus
             flavostriatus   1.50 1.50
     Nos. 221-224 (4)   4.40 4.40

1991, June 6   Litho.   Perf. 14½x14
Chinese inventions.
225 A38 25c Paper made from
             pulp   .90   .90
226 A38 40c Magnetic compass   1.40 1.40
227 A38 50c Abacus   1.75 1.75
228 A38 60c Gunpowder   2.00 2.00
  a.   Souvenir sheet of 1   5.75 5.75
     Nos. 225-228 (4)   6.05 6.05

Hotels
A39

1991, Aug. 29   Litho.
229 A39 25c Venda Sun   .50   .50
230 A39 40c Mphephu Resort   .90   .90
231 A39 50c Sagole Spa   1.10 1.10
232 A39 60c Luphephe-Nwanedi
             Resort   1.50 1.50
     Nos. 229-232 (4)   4.00 4.00

Trees
A40

1991, Nov. 21   Litho.
233 A40 27c Acacia
             xanthophloea   .55   .55
234 A40 45c Faurea saligna   1.00 1.00

---

235 A40 65c Strelitzia caudata   1.40 1.40
236 A40 85c Kigelia africana   1.75 1.75
     Nos. 233-236 (4)   4.70 4.70

Clothing
Factory
A41

1992, Mar. 5   Litho.
237 A41 27c Setting the web   .35   .35
238 A41 45c Knitting a pattern   .80   .80
239 A41 65c Using sewing ma-
             chine   1.10 1.10
240 A41 85c Testing for flaws   1.40 1.40
     Nos. 237-240 (4)   3.65 3.65

Bees
A42

1992, May 21   Litho.
241 A42 35c Honey bee   .80   .80
242 A42 70c Carder bee   1.60 1.60
243 A42 90c Leafcutter bee   1.75 1.75
244 A42 1.05r Carpenter bee   2.25 2.25
     Nos. 241-244 (4)   6.40 6.40

A souvenir sheet of 1 #242 was sold by the
Philatelic Foundation of South Africa. Value
$6.

Inventions
A43

Designs: 35c, Plow, Egypt 1259 B.C. 70c,
Wheel, Mesopotamia, 3200 B.C. 90c,
Brickmaking, Egypt, 3000 B.C. 1.05r, Sailing
ship, Egypt, 1600 B.C.

1992, Aug. 13
245 A43 35c multicolored   .70   .70
246 A43 70c multicolored   1.40 1.40
247 A43 90c multicolored   1.50 1.50
248 A43 1.05r multicolored   2.00 2.00
     Nos. 245-248 (4)   5.60 5.60

Crocodile
Farming
A44

1992, Oct. 15   Litho.
249 A44 35c Emerging from
             water   .70   .70
250 A44 70c Egg laying   1.40 1.40
251 A44 90c Hatchlings   1.50 1.50
252 A44 1.05r Maternal care   2.00 2.00
     Nos. 249-252 (4)   5.60 5.60

Domestic
Cats — A45

1993, Mar. 19   Litho.
253 A45 45c Burmese   .90   .90
254 A45 65c Tabby   1.75 1.75
255 A45 85c Siamese   1.90 1.90
256 A45 1.05r Persian   2.50 2.50
     Nos. 253-256 (4)   7.05 7.05

A souvenir sheet of one No. 254 has inscription for National Philatelic Exhibition. Sold for
3r. Value $6.50.

Herons
A46

Designs: 45c, Butorides striatus. 65c, Nycticorax nycticorax. 85c, Ardea purpurea. 1.05r,
Ardea melanocephala.

1993, July 16   Litho.   Perf. 14½x14
257 A46 45c multicolored   1.00 1.00
258 A46 65c multicolored   1.50 1.50
259 A46 85c multicolored   1.75 1.75
260 A46 1.05r multicolored   2.25 2.25
  a.   Souvenir sheet of 4, #257-260   6.50 6.50
     Nos. 257-260 (4)   6.50 6.50

Shoe
Factory — A47

1993, Sept. 17   Litho.   Perf. 14x14½
261 A47 45c Punching out sole
             lining   .60   .60
262 A47 65c Shaping heel   .90   .90
263 A47 85c Joining upper to
             inner sole   1.10 1.10
264 A47 1.05r Forming sole   1.40 1.40
     Nos. 261-264 (4)   4.00 4.00

Inventions
A48

1993, Nov. 5   Litho.   Perf. 14½x14
265 A48 45c Axe   .60   .60
266 A48 65c Armor   .90   .90
267 A48 85c Arch   1.10 1.10
268 A48 1.05r Aqueduct   1.40 1.40
     Nos. 265-268 (4)   4.00 4.00

Dogs
A49

1994, Jan. 14   Litho.   Perf. 14½x14
269 A49 45c Cocker spaniel   1.00 1.00
270 A49 65c Maltese   1.60 1.60
271 A49 85c Scottish terrier   1.90 1.90
272 A49 1.05r Miniature schnau-
             zer   2.50 2.50
     Nos. 269-272 (4)   7.00 7.00

A souvenir sheet of 1 #271 was sold for 3r
by the Philatelic Foundation of Southern Africa
and sold for 1.50r. Value $7.

Monkeys
A50

Designs: 45c, Cercopithecus aethiops. 65c,
Galago moholi. 85c, Cercopithecus mitis.
1.05r, Otolemur crassicaudatus.

1994, Mar. 4   Litho.   Perf. 14½x14
273 A50 45c multicolored   .90   .90
274 A50 65c multicolored   1.40 1.40
275 A50 85c multicolored   1.60 1.60
276 A50 1.05r multicolored   2.10 2.10
  a.   Souvenir sheet of 4, #273-276   6.00 6.00
     Nos. 273-276 (4)   6.00 6.00

Starlings
A51

45c, Lamprotornis nitens. 70c, Cinnyricinclus leucogaster. 95c, Onychognathus morio.
1.15r, Creatophora cinerea.

1994, Apr. 29   Litho.   Perf. 14½x14
277 A51 45c multicolored   1.10 1.10
278 A51 70c multicolored   1.75 1.75
279 A51 95c multicolored   2.25 2.25
280 A51 1.15r multicolored   2.75 2.75
     Nos. 277-280 (4)   7.85 7.85

Venda ceased to exist April 27, 1994.
The Venda postal service continued to oper-
ate until 1996.

SOUTH ARABIA

sauth ə-'rā-bē-ə

LOCATION — Southern Arabia
GOVT. — Federation; British dependency
AREA — 61,890 sq. mi.
POP. — 771,000 (est. 1966)
CAPITAL — Al Ittihad

The Federation of South Arabia was established in 1959 and consists of 14 states including Aden colony and part of Aden protectorate. When the Federation became independent, Nov. 30, 1967, it became the People's Republic of Southern Yemen. See People's Democratic Republic of Yemen, Vol. 6.

100 Cents = 1 Shilling
1000 Fils = 1 Dinar (1965)

> Catalogue values for all unused stamps in this country are for Never Hinged items.

Common Design Types pictured following the introduction.

Red Cross Centenary Issue
Common Design Type
Wmk. 314

1963, Nov. 25		**Litho.**		**Perf. 13**
1	CD315	15c black & red	.50	.45
2	CD315	1sh25c ultra & red	1.00	.90

Arms of Federation of South Arabia — A1

Flag of Federation — A2

Perf. 14½x14

1965, Apr. 1		**Photo.**	**Unwmk.**	
3	A1	5f blue	.20	.20
4	A1	10f light violet blue	.20	.20
5	A1	15f blue green	.20	.20
6	A1	20f green	.20	.20
7	A1	25f orange brown	.20	.20
8	A1	30f lemon	.30	.20
9	A1	35f red brown	.30	.20
10	A1	50f rose red	.30	.20
11	A1	65f light yellow green	.35	.20
12	A1	75f rose carmine	.40	.20

Perf. 14½

Flag in Black, Yellow, Green and Blue

13	A2	100f reddish brown	.55	.25
14	A2	250f dark blue	6.50	2.00
15	A2	500f dark red	11.50	2.25
16	A2	1d violet	21.00	10.00
		Nos. 3-16 (14)	42.20	16.50

Intl. Cooperation Year Issue
Common Design Type with Coat of Arms Replacing Queen's Portrait
Wmk. 314

1965, Oct. 24		**Litho.**		**Perf. 14½**
17	CD318	5f blue grn & claret	.30	.20
18	CD318	65f it violet & green	.90	.25

Churchill Memorial Issue
Common Design Type with Coat of Arms Replacing Queen's Portrait
Unwmk.

1966, Jan. 24		**Photo.**		**Perf. 14**

Design in Black, Gold and Carmine Rose

19	CD319	5f bright blue	.20	.20
20	CD319	10f green	.55	.20
21	CD319	65f brown	1.25	.50
22	CD319	125f violet	1.75	1.25
		Nos. 19-22 (4)	3.75	2.15

World Cup Soccer Issue
Common Design Type with Coat of Arms Replacing Queen's Portrait

1966, July 1		**Litho.**		**Perf. 14**
23	CD321	10f multicolored	.60	.20
24	CD321	50f multicolored	1.40	.30

WHO Headquarters Issue
Common Design Type with Coat of Arms Replacing Queen's Portrait

1966, Sept. 20		**Litho.**		**Unwmk.**
25	CD322	10f multicolored	.80	.20
26	CD322	75f multicolored	1.60	.50

UNESCO Anniversary Issue
Common Design Type with Coat of Arms Replacing Queen's Portrait

1966, Dec. 15		**Litho.**		**Perf. 14**
27	CD323	10f "Education"	.50	.30
28	CD323	65f "Science"	1.75	1.40
29	CD323	125f "Culture"	4.00	5.25
		Nos. 27-29 (3)	6.25	6.95

SOUTHERN NIGERIA

'sə-<u>th</u>ərn nī-'jir-ē-ə

LOCATION — In western Africa bordering on the Gulf of Guinea
GOVT. — British Crown Colony and Protectorate
AREA — 90,896 sq. mi.
POP. — 8,590,545
CAPITAL — Lagos

The Protectorate of Southern Nigeria, formed in 1900, absorbed in that year the Niger Coast Protectorate. In 1906 it united with Lagos and became the Colony and Protectorate of Southern Nigeria. An amalgamation was effected in 1914 between Northern and Southern Nigeria to form the Colony and Protectorate of Nigeria. See Nigeria, Northern Nigeria, Niger Coast Protectorate and Lagos.

12 Pence = 1 Shilling
20 Shillings = 1 Pound

Victoria A1	Edward VII A2

Wmk. Crown and C A (2)

1901, Mar.		**Typo.**		**Perf. 14**
1	A1	½p yel grn & blk	2.00	2.50
a.		½p yel grn & sepia ('02)	2.50	3.00
2	A1	1p car rose & blk	1.75	1.75
a.		1p carmine rose & sepia ('02)	2.50	2.00
3	A1	2p org brn & blk	3.75	4.25
4	A1	4p ol grn & blk	3.25	22.50
5	A1	6p red vio & blk	3.25	7.50
6	A1	1sh blk & gray grn	9.75	30.00
7	A1	2sh6p brn & blk	57.50	92.50
8	A1	5sh yellow & blk	60.00	120.00
9	A1	10sh vio & blk, *yel*	120.00	220.00
		Nos. 1-9 (9)	261.25	501.00

1903-04

10	A2	½p yel grn & blk	1.10	.35
11	A2	1p car rose & blk	1.50	.80
12	A2	2p org brn & blk	8.75	1.75
13	A2	2½p ultra & blk ('04)	2.25	.85
14	A2	4p ol grn & blk	3.25	6.25
15	A2	6p red vio & blk	5.00	9.25
16	A2	1sh blk & gray grn	40.00	22.50
17	A2	2sh6p brown & blk	37.50	70.00
18	A2	5sh yellow & blk	82.50	175.00
19	A2	10sh vio & blk, *yel*	40.00	110.00
20	A2	£1 pur & gray grn	400.00	800.00
		Nos. 10-20 (11)	621.85	1,196.

1904-07   **Wmk. 3**

Chalky Paper

21	A2	½p yel grn & blk	.75	.20
22	A2	1p carmine & blk	14.00	.25
23	A2	2p org brn & blk	3.00	.50
24	A2	2½p ultra & blk	1.25	1.10

24A	A2	3p vio & org brn ('07)	11.00	1.50
25	A2	4p ol grn & blk ('05)	16.00	29.00
26	A2	6p red vio & blk	14.50	4.00
27	A2	1sh blk & gray grn	3.75	4.00
28	A2	2sh6p brn & blk ('05)	27.50	21.00
29	A2	5sh yellow & blk	47.50	85.00
30	A2	10sh vio & blk, *yel* ('08)	120.00	210.00
31	A2	£1 pur & gray grn ('05)	240.00	300.00
		Nos. 21-31 (12)	499.25	656.55

#23 and 24 are on ordinary paper, #24A and 25 on chalky, and the other values on both papers.

1907-10

Ordinary Paper

32	A2	½p green ('08)	2.00	.25
33	A2	1p carmine	4.00	.70
34	A2	2p gray	3.00	.80
35	A2	2½p ultra	2.25	4.25

Chalky Paper

36	A2	3p violet, *yel*	2.25	.35
37	A2	4p scar & blk, *yel*	2.50	.90
38	A2	6p red vio & dl vio	29.00	3.75
39	A2	1sh black, *green*	8.00	.50
40	A2	2sh6p car & blk, *bl*	5.75	1.10
41	A2	5sh scar & grn, *yel*	45.00	55.00
42	A2	10sh red & grn, *grn*	75.00	110.00
43	A2	£1 blk & vio, *red*	225.00	260.00
		Nos. 32-43 (12)	403.75	437.60

1910   **Ordinary Paper**   **Redrawn**

44	A2	1p carmine	1.10	.20

In the redrawn stamp the "1" of "1d" is not as thick as in No. 33 but the "d" is taller and broader.

King George V — A3

1912

45	A3	½p green	3.00	.20
46	A3	1p carmine	3.00	.20
47	A3	2p gray	1.00	.95
48	A3	2½p ultra	3.50	3.25
49	A3	3p violet, *yel*	1.25	.35
50	A3	4p scar & blk, *yel*	1.60	2.40
51	A3	6p red vio & dl vio	1.60	1.50
52	A3	1sh black, *green*	3.50	1.00
53	A3	2sh6p red & blk, *bl*	10.00	42.50
54	A3	5sh red & grn, *yel*	26.00	87.50
55	A3	10sh red & grn, *grn*	60.00	110.00
56	A3	£1 blk & vio, *red*	225.00	275.00
		Nos. 45-56 (12)	339.45	524.85

Stamps of Southern Nigeria were replaced in 1914 by those of Nigeria.

SOUTHERN RHODESIA

'sə-<u>th</u>ərn rō-'dē-zh‾ē-,ə

LOCATION — Southeastern Africa between Northern Rhodesia and Mozambique
GOVT. — British Colony
AREA — 150,333 sq. mi.
POP. — 4,010,000 (est. 1963)
CAPITAL — Salisbury

Prior to 1923 this territory was administered by the British South Africa Company. The colony was created in that year by the British Government at the request of the inhabitants. In 1953, Southern Rhodesia joined Northern Rhodesia and Nyasaland to form the Federation of Rhodesia and Nyasaland. When the Federation dissolved at the end of 1963, Southern Rhodesia again became an internally self-governing colony. See Rhodesia and Northern Rhodesia.

12 Pence = 1 Shilling
20 Shillings = 1 Pound

> Catalogue values for unused stamps in this country are for Never Hinged items, beginning with Scott 56 in the regular postage section and Scott J1 in the postage due section.

King George V — A1

1924-30	**Unwmk.**	**Engr.**		**Perf. 14**
1	A1	½p dark green	2.50	.20
a.		Vert. pair, imperf. btwn.	950.00	1,050.
b.		Horiz. pair, imperf. btwn.	950.00	1,050.
c.		Horiz. pair, imperf. vert.	1,100.	
2	A1	1p scarlet	2.00	.20
a.		Horiz. pair, imperf. btwn.	850.00	950.00
b.		Perf. 12½ (coil) ('30)	3.25	92.50
c.		Vert. pair, imperf. btwn.	1,500.	
d.		Vert. pair, imperf. horiz.	950.00	
3	A1	1½p bister brown	2.50	.90
a.		Horiz. pair, imperf. btwn.	10,000.	
b.		Vert. pair, imperf. btwn.	6,250.	
4	A1	2p vio blk & blk	3.75	.80
a.		Horiz. pair, imperf. btwn.	12,500.	
5	A1	3p deep blue	3.25	3.50
6	A1	4p org red & blk	3.00	3.25
7	A1	6p lilac & blk	2.50	4.75
a.		Horiz. pair, imperf. btwn.	40,000.	
8	A1	8p gray grn & vio	12.50	50.00
9	A1	10p rose red & bl	14.50	57.50
10	A1	1sh turq bl & blk	5.75	7.50
11	A1	1sh6p yellow & blk	22.50	37.50
12	A1	2sh brown & blk	20.00	20.00
13	A1	2sh6p blk brn & blk	37.50	70.00
14	A1	5sh bl grn & bl	72.50	175.00
		Nos. 1-14 (14)	204.75	431.10

Values for imperf between pairs are for stamps from the same pane. Stamps separated by wide margins are cross-gutter pairs and sell for much lower prices.

George V A2	Victoria Falls A3

1931-37			**Perf. 11½, 14 (1p)**	
16	A2	½p dp green ('33)	.75	.20
a.		Bklt. pane of 6 ('32)	150.00	
b.		Perf. 12	.95	1.10
c.		Perf. 14 ('35)	1.90	.35
17	A2	1p scarlet ('35)	.60	.20
a.		Bklt. pane of 6 ('32)	150.00	
b.		Perf. 11½ ('33)	2.00	.20
c.		Perf. 12	1.10	.80
18	A2	1½p dp brown ('32)	3.00	.90
a.		Bklt. pane of 6 ('32)	600.00	
b.		Perf. 12 ('33)	62.50	47.50

		Typo.	**Perf. 14½x14**	
19	A3	2p blk brn & blk	4.75	1.75
20	A3	3p dark blue	11.50	12.50

Perf. 12, 11½ (2sh6p)
Engr.

21	A2	4p org red & blk	1.50	1.75
a.		Perf. 14 ('37)	37.50	55.00
b.		Perf. 11½ ('35)	20.00	5.75
22	A2	6p rose lilac & blk	2.50	3.50
a.		Perf. 14 ('36)	8.00	1.00
b.		Perf. 11½ ('33)	17.50	1.75
23	A2	8p green & violet	2.00	3.75
a.		Perf. 11½ ('34)	20.00	37.50
24	A2	9p gray grn & ver ('34)	7.25	10.50

25	A2	10p car & ultra	8.50	2.75
a.		Perf. 11½ ('33)	7.50	15.00
26	A2	1sh turq bl & blk	2.25	3.00
a.		Perf. 11½ ('36)	125.00	70.00
b.		Perf. 14 ('37)	225.00	160.00
27	A2	1sh6p ocher & blk	12.00	17.50
a.		Perf. 11½ ('36)	57.50	125.00
28	A2	2sh dk brn & blk	25.00	7.50
a.		Perf. 11½ ('33)	42.50	35.00
29	A2	2sh6p ol brn & ultra ('33)	35.00	35.00
a.		Perf. 12	40.00	42.50
30	A2	5sh bl grn & ultra	60.00	55.00
		Nos. 16-30 (15)	176.60	155.80

Victoria Falls — A4

1932, May   **Perf. 12½**

31	A4	2p dark brn & grn	5.50	1.10
32	A4	3p dark blue	5.50	2.10
a.		Vert. pair, imperf. horiz.	10,000.	12,000.
b.		Vert. pair, imperf. btwn.	25,000.	
		Set, never hinged	20.00	

See Nos. 37-37A.

Silver Jubilee Issue

Victoria Falls and George V A5

1935, May 6   **Perf. 11x12**

33	A5	1p car rose & olive	3.50	2.75
34	A5	2p blk brn & lt grn	5.75	6.75
35	A5	3p blue & violet	6.25	11.00
36	A5	6p dp violet & blk	9.00	18.50
		Nos. 33-36 (4)	24.50	39.00
		Set, never hinged	37.50	

25th anniv. of the reign of George V.

"Postage and Revenue" A6

1935-41   **Perf. 14**

37	A6	2p dk brn & grn ('41)	1.10	.25
b.		Perf. 12½	1.75	10.00
		Never hinged	5.00	
37A	A6	3p deep blue ('38)	2.00	.25
		Set, never hinged	7.50	

Queen Elizabeth, George VI — A7

1937, May 12   **Perf. 12½**

38	A7	1p carmine & gray grn	.60	.70
39	A7	2p brown & green	.65	1.75
40	A7	3p lt blue & violet	3.00	8.00
41	A7	6p red violet & blk	1.75	3.75
		Nos. 38-41 (4)	6.00	14.20
		Set, never hinged	9.00	

Coronation of George VI & Elizabeth.

King George VI — A8

1937, Nov. 25   **Perf. 14**

42	A8	½p yellow green	.40	.20
43	A8	1p red	.40	.20
44	A8	1½p red brown	.75	.35
45	A8	4p orange red	1.00	.20
46	A8	6p dark gray	1.00	.60
47	A8	8p blue green	1.50	3.50
48	A8	9p blue	1.25	1.10
49	A8	10p violet	1.75	3.25
50	A8	1sh green & blk	1.50	.20
51	A8	1sh6p ocher & blk	8.00	3.00
52	A8	2sh brown & blk	12.50	.70
53	A8	2sh6p violet & blue	9.00	7.00
54	A8	5sh green & blue	20.00	3.00
		Nos. 42-54 (13)	59.05	23.30
		Set, never hinged	85.00	

Catalogue values for unused stamps in this section, from this point to the end of the section, are for Never Hinged items.

Seal of British South Africa Co. — A9

Fort Salisbury, 1890 — A10

Cecil John Rhodes — A11

Pioneer Fort and Mail Coach A12

Rhodes Makes Peace, 1896 — A13

Victoria Falls Bridge — A14

Sir Charles Coghlan — A15

Queen Victoria, George VI, Lobengula's Kraal and Government House A16

Pioneer — A17

Unwmk.

1940, June 3   **Engr.**   **Perf. 14**

56	A9	½p dp grn & dull vio	.20	.40
57	A10	1p red & vio blue	.20	.20
58	A11	1½p cop brn & blk	.20	.50
59	A12	2p pur & brt grn	.50	.40
60	A13	3p dk blue & blk	.80	1.00
61	A14	4p brn & bl grn	2.00	1.50
62	A15	6p sepia & dull grn	1.50	1.40
63	A16	1sh dk bl & brt grn	1.50	1.40
		Nos. 56-63 (8)	6.90	6.80

50th anniv. of the founding of Southern Rhodesia by Cecil John Rhodes.

1943, Nov. 1   **Photo.**   **Wmk. 201**

64	A17	2p Prus grn & choc	.35	.50

50th anniv. of Matabeleland under British control.

Princess Elizabeth and Princess Margaret Rose A18

King George VI and Queen Elizabeth A19

Unwmk.

1947, Apr. 1   **Engr.**   **Perf. 14**

65	A18	½p dk green & blk	.30	.60
66	A19	1p carmine & blk	.30	.60

Visit of the British Royal Family, Apr., 1947.

Victory Issue

Queen Elizabeth A20

George VI A21

Princess Elizabeth A22

Princess Margaret Rose A23

1947, May 8

67	A20	1p deep carmine	.20	.20
68	A21	2p slate black	.20	.20
69	A22	3p deep blue	.60	.50
70	A23	6p red orange	.40	.75
		Nos. 67-70 (4)	1.40	1.65

Victory of the Allied Nations in WW II.

Common Design Types pictured following the introduction.

UPU Issue

Common Design Types

Engr.; Name Typo.

1949, Oct. 10   **Wmk. 4**   **Perf. 11x11½**

71	CD307	2p slate black	.70	.50
72	CD308	3p slate blue	1.25	1.75

75th anniv. of the UPU.

Queen Victoria and King George VI A24

Unwmk.

1950, Sept. 12   **Engr.**   **Perf. 14**

73	A24	2p choc & blue grn	.75	1.10

60th anniversary of Rhodesia.

Hospital, Doctor and Natives A25

Designs: 1p, African Scene. 2p, Native Houses, Modern City and Cecil Rhodes. 4½p, Dam and Natives. 1sh, Transportation.

1953, Apr. 15

74	A25	½p dk brown & blue	.20	.40
75	A25	1p blue grn & fawn	.20	.20
76	A25	2p vio & dk bl grn	.35	.20
77	A25	4½p dk bl & bl grn	1.50	2.25
78	A25	1sh chestnut & blk	3.25	1.50
		Nos. 74-78 (5)	5.50	4.55

#77 is inscribed Matabeleland Diamond Jubilee.

Type of Nyasaland Prot., 1953

1953, May 30   **Perf. 14x13½**

79	A17	6p purple	.35	.35

Nos. 74-79 were issued to commemorate the Central African Cecil Rhodes Centenary Exhibition.

Coronation Issue

Elizabeth II — A26

1953, June 1   **Perf. 12x12½**

80	A26	2sh6p cerise	6.50	9.00

Sable Antelope A27

Rhodes' Grave A28

Flame Lily — A29

Designs: 1p, Tobacco planter. 3p, Farm Worker. 4½p, Victoria Falls. 6p, Baobab tree. 9p, Lion. 1sh, Zimbabwe ruins. 2sh, Birchenough Bridge. 2sh6p, Kariba Gorge. 5sh, Basket maker. 10sh, Balancing rocks. £1, Arms.

Perf. 14x13½, 13½x14

1953, Aug. 31
Portrait in Various Positions

81	A27	½p rose lake & dk ol grn	.35	.35
82	A27	1p choc & grn	.35	.20
83	A28	2p rose vio & org brn	.35	.20

Size: 28x22½mm

84	A29	3p car & sep	.70	1.50
85	A29	4p gray, brn, car & grn	3.50	.40

86	A29	4½p ultra & blk	3.00	4.50
87	A28	6p aqua & olive	3.75	.20
88	A29	9p org brn & dp bl	3.75	4.00
89	A29	1sh grnsh bl & rose vio	1.75	.20
90	A29	2sh red & rose vio	14.00	5.00
91	A29	2sh6p org brn & ol grn	7.00	6.00
92	A28	5s dk grn & org brn	13.00	8.00

Size: 37x27mm

93	A29	10sh ol grn & red brn	19.00	32.50
94	A29	£1 dk gray & car	29.00	32.50
		Nos. 81-94 (14)	99.50	95.55

Ansellia
Orchid — A30

1964, Feb. 19   Photo.   Perf. 14½
Size: 23x19mm

95	A30	½p Corn	.20	1.00
96	A30	1p Cape buffalo	.20	.20
a.		Purple omitted	2,500.	
97	A30	2p Tobacco	.60	.20
98	A30	3p Kudu	.20	.20
99	A30	4p Oranges	.20	.20

Perf. 13½x13
Size: 27x23mm

100	A30	6p Flame lily	.50	.20
101	A30	9p shown	2.00	.80
102	A30	1sh Emeralds	2.00	.20
a.		Green omitted	3,250.	
103	A30	1sh3p Aloe	3.00	.20
104	A30	2sh Lake Kyle	2.50	1.00
105	A30	2sh6p Tiger fish	4.00	.80
a.		Red omitted	4,000.	
b.		Ultra omitted	8,500.	

Perf. 14½x14
Size: 32x27mm

106	A30	5sh Cattle	4.00	2.75
107	A30	10sh Guinea fowl	13.50	8.00
108	A30	£1 Arms	20.00	18.00
		Nos. 95-108 (14)	52.90	33.75

#95-108 with overprint "Independence 11th November 1965" are listed as Rhodesia #208-221.

Stamps of Southern Rhodesia were replaced in 1965 by those of Rhodesia (formerly Southern Rhodesia).

POSTAGE DUE STAMPS

Catalogue values for unused stamps in this section are for Never Hinged items.

Great Britain Postage Due Stamps of 1938-51 Overprinted in Black

1951   Wmk. 251   Perf. 14x14½

J1	D1	½p emerald	3.75	17.50
J2	D1	1p violet blue	3.50	2.75
J3	D1	2p black brown	3.00	2.25
J4	D1	3p violet	3.25	3.00
J5	D1	4p brt blue	2.25	4.00
a.		4p slate green	275.00	600.00
J6	D1	1sh blue	3.00	4.50
		Nos. J1-J6 (6)	18.75	34.00

SOUTH GEORGIA

'sauth 'jor-jə

LOCATION — Island in South Atlantic Ocean, 1,100 mi. east of Tierra del Fuego
GOVT. — Dependency of Falkland Islands
AREA — 1,450 sq. mi.
POP. — Military and biological staff only.
CAPITAL — Grytviken Harbor (military garrison)

South Georgia remained a dependency of the Falkland Islands in 1962 when three other dependencies became Antarctic Territory, a separate colony. In 1985 South Georgia and the South Sandwich Islands became a separate colony. See Falkland Islands Dependencies Nos. 3L1-3L8.

12 Pence = 1 Shilling
20 Shillings = 1 Pound
100 Pence = 1 Pound (1971)

Catalogue values for all unused stamps in this country are for Never Hinged items.

Reindeer A1

Sperm Whale — A2

Designs: 1p, South Sandwich Islands map. 2½p, Penguins. 3p, Fur seals. 4p, Finback whale and ship. 5½p, Elephant seals. 6p, Sooty albatross. 9p, Whaling 1sh, Leopard seal. 2sh, Shackleton's cross. 2sh6p, Wandering albatross. 5sh, Elephant and fur seals. 10sh, Plankton and krill (shrimp). No. 15, Blue whale. No. 16, King penguins.

Wmk. 314 Upright

1963-69   Engr.   Perf. 15

1	A1	½p dull red	.55	1.00
a.		Perf. 14x15 ('67)	1.25	1.50
b.		Watermark sideways ('70)	1.50	3.75
2	A2	1p violet blue	1.00	1.00
3	A2	2p blue green	1.40	1.00
4	A1	2½p black	5.75	2.25
5	A2	3p olive	3.00	.35
6	A1	4p green	5.50	.75
7	A1	5½p dull violet	2.75	.40
8	A1	6p orange	.80	.45
9	A1	9p blue	6.25	1.75
10	A1	1sh lilac	.90	.30
11	A1	2sh cit & lt blue	26.00	6.00
12	A1	2sh6p blue	25.00	4.50
13	A1	5sh ocher	23.00	4.50
14	A2	10sh rose claret	40.00	12.50
15	A1	£1 ultra	100.00	62.50
16	A2	£1 slate green	12.00	17.50
		Nos. 1-16 (16)	253.90	116.75
		Set, hinged	145.00	

Issued: No. 16, 12/1/69; others 7/10/63.

Stamps and Type of 1963 Surcharged with New Value (Decimal Currency) and 3 Bars

Wmk. 314 Upright; Sideways on ½p

1971-72   Perf. 15

17	A1	½p on ½p dull red	1.25	.75
a.		Wmk. upright ('73)	3.00	2.75
18	A2	1p on 1p vio blue	1.60	.90
a.		Wmk. sideways ('76)	2.75	3.25
19	A1	1½p on 5½p dull vio	1.00	.70
20	A2	2p on 2p blue grn	.90	.50
21	A1	2½p on 2½p black	2.50	.70
22	A2	3p on 3p olive	1.25	.75
23	A1	4p on 4p green	1.25	.90
24	A2	5p on 6p orange	2.25	1.25
25	A1	6p on 9p blue	1.75	.55
26	A1	7½p on 1sh lilac	2.50	.70
27	A1	10p on 2sh cit & lt bl	22.50	7.50
28	A1	15p on 2sh6p blue	20.00	9.00
29	A1	25p on 5sh ocher	15.00	7.50
30	A2	50p on 10sh rose claret, glazed paper ('72)	25.00	20.00
a.		Wmk. sideways ('76)	30.00	30.00
c.		Ordinary paper	47.50	25.00
		Nos. 17-30 (14)	98.75	53.00

Two types of surcharge are found on ½p, 1p, 1½p and 50p.
Issued: Nos. 17-29, 30b, 2/15/71. No. 30, 12/1/72. No. 30a, 3/9/76.

Wmk. 373 Sideways; Upright on 3p, 50p; Inverted on 1p, 5p

1977

17b	A1	½p on ½p dull red	1.75	2.00
18b	A2	1p on 1p vio blue	1.00	2.00
19b	A1	1½p on 5½p dl vio	1.25	2.00
21b	A1	2½p on 2½p black	14.00	3.25
22b	A2	3p on 3p olive	7.75	3.25
23b	A1	4p on 4p green	20.00	15.00
24b	A2	5p on 6p orange	4.00	2.75
26b	A1	7½p on 1sh lilac	2.00	9.50
27b	A1	10p on 2sh cit & lt bl	2.00	8.25
28b	A1	15p on 2sh6p blue	2.75	11.00
29b	A1	25p on 5sh ocher	2.00	11.00
30b	A2	50p on 10sh lil rose ('79)	2.00	11.00
		Nos. 17b-30b (12)	60.50	81.00

Ernest Shackleton and "Quest" — A3

1½p, "Endurance" in ice of Weddell Sea. 5p, Launching of sailboat "James Caird." 10p, Route of "James Caird" to South Georgia.

1972, Jan. 5   Litho.   Perf. 13½

31	A3	1½p vio bl, blk & yel	1.25	1.75
32	A3	5p bl grn, blk & yel	1.50	2.25
33	A3	10p lt blue & blk	2.25	2.50
34	A3	20p multicolored	2.50	3.00
		Nos. 31-34 (4)	7.50	9.50

Sir Ernest Shackleton (1874-1922), explorer of Antarctica.

Common Design Types pictured following the introduction.

Silver Wedding Issue, 1972
Common Design Type

Design: Queen Elizabeth II, Prince Philip, elephant seal and king penguins.

1972, Nov. 20   Photo.   Perf. 14x14½

35	CD324	5p slate grn & multi	.50	.50
36	CD324	10p violet & multi	1.00	1.00

Princess Anne's Wedding Issue
Common Design Type

1973, Dec. 1   Litho.   Perf. 14

37	CD325	5p citron & multi	.20	.20
38	CD325	15p slate & multi	.60	.60

Churchill, Parliament and Big Ben — A4

Design: 25p, Churchill and battleship.

1974, Dec. 14   Litho.   Perf. 14½

39	A4	15p vio blue & multi	1.40	1.40
40	A4	25p orange & multi	2.25	2.25
a.		Souvenir sheet of 2, #39-40	7.50	7.50

Sir Winston Churchill (1874-1965).

Capt. James Cook — A5

Cook's "Possession" — A6

Design: 16p, Possession Bay.

"Discovery" and Biological Laboratory — A7

1975, Apr. 26   Wmk. 314

41	A5	2p multicolored	2.50	1.25
42	A6	8p multicolored	3.75	1.75
43	A6	16p multicolored	4.25	2.50
		Nos. 41-43 (3)	10.50	5.50

Bicentenary of Capt. Cook's discovery of South Georgia.

Designs: 8p, "William Scoresby" and Nansen-Pettersson water sampling bottles. 11p, "Discovery II" and plankton net. 25p, Biological station and krill (shrimp).

Wmk. 373

1976, Dec. 21   Litho.   Perf. 14

44	A7	2p multicolored	1.75	.75
45	A7	8p multicolored	2.00	1.25
46	A7	11p multicolored	2.25	1.40
47	A7	25p multicolored	3.75	2.50
		Nos. 44-47 (4)	9.75	5.90

25th anniversary of the biological investigations of the "Discovery."

Queen with Regalia and Westminster Abbey — A8

6p, Prince Philip visiting Shackleton Memorial, 1957. 33p, Queen in procession after coronation.

1977, Feb. 7   Perf. 13½x14

48	A8	6p multicolored	.30	.25
49	A8	11p multicolored	.55	.40
50	A8	33p multicolored	1.25	1.25
		Nos. 48-50 (3)	2.10	1.90

25th anniv. of the reign of Elizabeth II.

Elizabeth II Coronation Anniversary Issue
Common Design Types
Souvenir Sheet
Unwmk.

1978, June 2   Litho.   Perf. 15

51		Sheet of 6	4.75	4.75
a.	CD326	25p Panther of Henry VI	1.25	1.00
b.	CD327	25p Elizabeth II	1.25	1.00
c.	CD328	25p Fur seal	1.25	1.00

No. 51 contains 2 se-tenant strips of Nos. 51a-51c, separated by horizontal gutter with commemorative and descriptive inscriptions and showing central part of coronation procession with coach.

Resolution A9

Cook's voyages: 6p, Map of South Georgia and South Sandwich Islands with Cook's route. 11p, King penguin, drawing by Forster. 25p, Cook after Flaxman/Wedgwood medallion.

1979, Feb. 14   Litho.   Perf. 11
52	A9	3p multicolored	1.75	1.10
53	A9	6p multicolored	1.75	1.00
54	A9	11p multicolored	2.25	2.00

Lithographed; Embossed
55	A9	25p multicolored	2.75	2.25
		Nos. 52-55 (4)	8.50	6.35

Capt. Cook's voyages.

SOUTH GEORGIA and SOUTH SANDWICH ISLANDS
Queen Elizabeth II 60th Birthday
Common Design Type

Designs: 10p, With King George and Queen Mary at christening of Prince Charles, 1948. 24p, Engagement of Prince Charles and Lady Diana, Buckingham Palace Music Room, 1981. 29p, Order of the British Empire, service at St. Paul's Cathedral, London, 1974. 45p, Banquet for Canadian Prime Minister Trudeau during the 1976 Olympics. 58p, Visiting Crown Agents' offices, 1983.

1986, Apr. 21   Wmk. 384   Perf. 14½
101	CD337	10p multicolored	.40	.40
102	CD337	24p multicolored	.60	.60
103	CD337	29p multicolored	.75	.75
104	CD337	45p multicolored	1.10	1.10
105	CD337	58p multicolored	1.50	1.50
		Nos. 101-105 (5)	4.35	4.35

Wedding of Prince Andrew and Sarah Ferguson — A12

1986, Nov. 10   Litho.   Perf. 14½
106	A12	17p Couple at Ascot	.85	1.10
107	A12	22p Wedding	.95	1.40
108	A12	29p Andrew, helicopter	1.90	1.75
		Nos. 106-108 (3)	3.70	4.25

Birds A13

1987, Apr. 24   Litho.   Wmk. 384
109	A13	1p Dominican gull	1.75	2.25
110	A13	2p Blue-eyed cormorant	2.00	2.50
111	A13	3p Wattled sheathbill	2.50	2.50
112	A13	4p Brown skua	2.25	2.25
113	A13	5p Cape pigeon	2.25	2.25
114	A13	6p South Georgia diving petrel	2.25	2.25
115	A13	7p South Georgia pipit	2.50	2.75
116	A13	8p South Georgia pintail	2.50	2.75
117	A13	9p Fairy prion	2.50	2.75
118	A13	10p Chinstrap penguin	2.75	3.00
119	A13	20p Macaroni penguin	3.00	3.50
120	A13	25p Light-mantled sooty albatross	3.00	3.50
121	A13	50p Southern giant petrel	3.75	4.00
122	A13	£1 Wandering albatross	4.25	6.00
123	A13	£3 King penguin	10.00	11.50
		Nos. 109-123 (15)	47.25	53.75

3, 4, 7, 8, 20, 25, 50p and £3 vert.

Intl. Geophysical Year, 30th Anniv. — A14

1987, Dec. 5   Litho.   Perf. 14½
124	A14	24p shown	1.00	.85
125	A14	29p Grytviken Whaling Station	1.10	.95
126	A14	58p Glaciologist	2.00	1.90
		Nos. 124-126 (3)	4.10	3.70

Sea Shells A15

1988, Feb. 26   Wmk. 384   Perf. 14½
127	A15	10p Gaimardia trapesina	.80	.65
128	A15	24p Margarella tropidophoroides	1.50	1.40
129	A15	29p Trophon scotianus	1.75	1.60
130	A15	58p Chlanidota densesculpta	3.25	3.25
		Nos. 127-130 (4)	7.30	6.90

Lloyds of London, 300th Anniv.
Common Design Type

10p, Queen Mother at the official opening of the Lloyds Building, Lime Street, 1957. 24p, Lindblad Explorer, horiz. 29p, Leith Harbor whaling station, horiz. 58p, Whale oil tanker Horatio on fire.

1988, Sept. 17   Perf. 14
131	CD341	10p multicolored	.70	.40
132	CD341	24p multicolored	1.10	.90
133	CD341	29p multicolored	1.10	1.10
134	CD341	58p multicolored	2.50	2.50
		Nos. 131-134 (4)	5.40	4.90

Glacier Formations — A16

1989, July 31
135	A16	10p Glacier headwall	.70	.55
136	A16	24p Accumulation area	1.25	1.10
137	A16	29p Ablation area	1.50	1.50
138	A16	58p Calving front	2.75	2.50
		Nos. 135-138 (4)	6.20	5.40

Combined Services Expedition, 1964-65 A17

1989, Nov. 28   Perf. 14x14½
139	A17	10p "Last ordeal" of the trek	.70	.55
140	A17	24p Survey of Royal Bay	1.25	1.10
141	A17	29p HMS Protector	1.50	1.25
142	A17	58p 1st Ascent of Mt. Paget	2.50	2.40
		Nos. 139-142 (4)	5.95	5.30

Queen Mother, 90th Birthday
Common Design Types

Designs: 26p, Queen Mother. £1, King, Queen & Air Raid Wardens, 1940.

Perf. 14x15

1990, Sept. 15   Wmk. 384
143	CD343	26p multicolored	1.50	1.50

Perf. 14½
144	CD344	£1 blue & black	4.75	4.75

Shipwrecks A18

1990, Dec. 22   Litho.   Perf. 14
145	A18	12p Brutus	.65	.55
146	A18	26p Bayard	1.40	1.10
147	A18	31p Karrakatta	1.60	1.40
148	A18	62p Louise	3.00	2.50
		Nos. 145-148 (4)	6.65	5.55

Elizabeth & Philip, Birthdays
Common Design Types

1991, July 2   Perf. 14½
149	CD345	31p multicolored	2.75	2.75
150	CD346	31p multicolored	2.75	2.75
a.		Pair, #149-150 + label	7.00	7.00

No. 150a exists with two different labels.

Elephant Seals A19

1991, Nov. 2   Wmk. 373   Perf. 14
151	A19	12p Two bulls	.85	.85
152	A19	26p One bull	1.75	1.75
153	A19	29p Using sand as sunscreen	2.00	2.00
154	A19	31p Bull, close up	2.00	2.00
155	A19	34p Harem on beach	2.25	2.25
156	A19	62p Cow and pup	3.50	2.50
		Nos. 151-156 (6)	12.35	11.35

Queen Elizabeth II's Accession to the Throne, 40th Anniv.
Common Design Type

1992, Feb. 6
157	CD349	7p multicolored	.50	.45
158	CD349	14p multicolored	.75	.70
159	CD349	29p multicolored	1.25	1.10
160	CD349	34p multicolored	1.40	1.25
161	CD349	68p multicolored	2.50	2.50
		Nos. 157-161 (5)	6.40	6.00

South Georgia Teal A20

1992, Mar. 22   Wmk. 384
162	A20	2p Adult, young	.75	.40
163	A20	6p Adult, nest of eggs	1.10	.75
164	A20	12p Four swimming	1.75	1.75
165	A20	20p Adult, two chicks	2.25	2.25
		Nos. 162-165 (4)	5.85	5.15

World Wildlife Fund.

South Georgia Whaling Museum A21

Designs: 15p, Abandoned factory, Grytviken. 31p, Whaler's lighter, bones. 36p, King Edward Cove. 72p, Museum Building.

Wmk. 373

1993, June 29   Litho.   Perf. 13½
166-169	A21	Set of 4	8.25	8.25

Macaroni Penguins A22

16p, Swimming underwater. 34p, Part of rookery. 39p, Two juveniles. 78p, Two adults.

Perf. 14x14½

1993, Dec. 10   Litho.   Wmk. 373
170-173	A22	Set of 4	8.75	8.75

Ovptd. with Hong Kong '94 Emblem

1994, Feb. 18
174-177	A22	Set of 4	10.00	10.00

Whales and Dolphins A23

Designs: 1p, Hourglass dolphin. 2p, Southern right whale dolphin. 5p, Long-finned pilot whale. 8p, Southern bottlenose whale. 9p, Killer whale. 10p, Minke whale. 20p, Sei whale. 25p, Humpback whale. 50p, Southern right whale. £1, Sperm whale. £3, Fin whale. £5, Blue whale.

Wmk. 373

1994, Jan. 24   Litho.   Perf. 14
178	A23	1p multicolored	1.50	1.10
179	A23	2p multicolored	2.00	1.75
180	A23	5p multicolored	2.50	2.00
181	A23	8p multicolored	2.75	2.00
182	A23	9p multicolored	2.75	2.00
183	A23	10p multicolored	2.75	2.00
184	A23	20p multicolored	4.00	3.00
185	A23	25p multicolored	4.00	3.00
186	A23	50p multicolored	5.00	3.25
187	A23	£1 multicolored	6.25	4.50
188	A23	£3 multicolored	11.50	11.00
189	A23	£5 multicolored	18.50	18.00
		Nos. 178-189 (12)	63.50	53.60

Native Wildlife A24

Wmk. 384

1994, Sept. 28   Litho.   Perf. 14
190	A24	17p Bull elephant seals	1.00	1.00
191	A24	35p Fur seal, vert.	2.00	2.00
192	A24	40p Gray-headed albatrosses	2.25	2.25
193	A24	65p King penguins, vert.	3.25	3.25
		Nos. 190-193 (4)	8.50	8.50

Capt. C. A. Larsen's First Voyage to South Georgia A25

1994, Dec. 1
194	A25	17p Map of Jason Harbor	.75	.75
195	A25	35p Castor, 1886	2.00	2.00
196	A25	40p Hertha, 1884	2.25	2.25
197	A25	65p Jason, 1881	3.50	3.50
		Nos. 194-197 (4)	8.50	8.50

End of World War II, 50th Anniv.
Common Design Types

#198, HMS Queen of Bermuda moored at Leith Harbor. #199, 4-inch gun, Hansen Point, four men of Norwegian Defense Force. £1, Reverse of War Medal 1939-45.

Wmk. 384

1995, May 8   Litho.   Perf. 14
198	CD351	50p multicolored	3.50	3.50
199	CD351	50p multicolored	3.50	3.50
a.		Pair, #198-199	7.75	7.75

Souvenir Sheet
Wmk. 373
200	CD352	£1 multicolored	7.00	7.00

No. 199a is a continuous design.

Yachts — A26

Wmk. 373

1995, Nov. 16 Litho. Perf. 14½
201	A26	35p Damien II	2.00 2.00
202	A26	40p Curlew	2.50 2.50
203	A26	76p Mischief	4.00 4.00
		Nos. 201-203 (3)	8.50 8.50

Sir Ernest Shackleton's King Haakon Bay-Stromness Trek, 80th Anniv. — A27

Designs: 15p, Shackleton, Ridge 2493 Point of No Return. 20p, Frank Worsley, King Haakon Bay from Shackleton Gap. 30p, Map of Shackleton's route. 65p, Tom Crean, Manager's Villa, Stromness Whaling Station.

Wmk. 384

1996, May 20 Litho. Perf. 14
204	A27	15p multicolored	.85 .85
205	A27	20p multicolored	1.50 1.50
206	A27	30p multicolored	2.00 2.00
207	A27	65p multicolored	3.75 3.75
		Nos. 204-207 (4)	8.10 8.10

Chinstrap Penguins — A28

Perf. 14½x14

1996, Nov. 8 Litho. Wmk. 373
208	A28	17p Swimming	1.25 1.25
209	A28	35p Male, female	1.75 1.75
210	A28	40p Feeding chicks	2.25 2.25
211	A28	76p Feeding on krill	4.25 4.25
a.		Souvenir sheet of 1, perf. 14x14½	5.00 5.00
		Nos. 208-211 (4)	9.50 9.50

Return of Hong Kong to China (#211a).

Queen Elizabeth and Prince Philip, 50th Wedding Anniv. — A29

#212, Queen. #213, Prince driving team of horses. #214, Queen looking at horses. #215, Prince. #216, Princess Anne on horseback, Queen. #217, Prince, child on horseback. £1.50, Queen, Prince in open carriage, horiz.

Perf. 14½x14

1997, July 10 Litho. Wmk. 384
212		15p multicolored	1.00 1.00
213		15p multicolored	1.00 1.00
a.	A29	Pair, #212-213	2.25 2.25
214		17p multicolored	1.25 1.25
215		17p multicolored	1.25 1.25
a.	A29	Pair, #214-215	2.75 2.75
216		40p multicolored	2.50 2.50
217		40p multicolored	5.50 5.50
a.	A29	Pair, #216-217	8.25 8.25
		Nos. 212-217 (6)	12.50 12.50

Souvenir Sheet

218	A29	£1.50 multicolored	9.00 9.00

Flora and Fauna A30

---

a, Reindeer. b, Antarctic tern. c, Gray-headed albatross. d, King penguin. e, Prickly burr. f, Fur seal.

Perf. 14½x14

1998, Mar. 16 Litho. Wmk. 373
219	A30	35p Sheet of 6, #a.-f.	10.00 10.00

Diana, Princess of Wales (1961-97)
Common Design Type

Designs: a, Looking left. b, In white evening dress. c, In red dress. d, In white.

1998, Mar. 31
220	CD355	35p Sheet of 4, #a.-d.	6.00 6.00

No. 220 sold for £1.40 + 20p, with surtax and 50% of the profits from the issue being donated to the Princess Diana Memorial Fund.

Tourism A31

Designs: 30p, MS Explorer. 35p, Wandering albatross. 40p, Elephant seal. 65p, Post Office, King Edward Point.

Wmk. 373

1998, Sept. 28 Litho. Perf. 14½
221	A31	30p multicolored	2.75 1.75
222	A31	35p multicolored	3.00 2.00
223	A31	40p multicolored	3.25 2.25
224	A31	65p multicolored	4.00 3.50
		Nos. 221-224 (4)	13.00 9.50

Island Views A32

Designs: 9p, Grytviken and Sugartop Mountain. 17p, Old sealing ships, Grytviken. 35p, King Edward Point. 40p, Arrival at South Georgia. 65p, Church, Grytviken.

Wmk. 384

1999, Jan. 4 Litho. Perf. 14
225	A32	9p multicolored	1.75 1.25
226	A32	17p multicolored	2.25 1.50
227	A32	35p multicolored	3.25 2.25
228	A32	40p multicolored	3.50 2.75
229	A32	65p multicolored	4.25 3.50
		Nos. 225-229 (5)	15.00 11.25

Souvenir Sheet

Capt. James Cook's Ship HMS Resolution, 1773 — A33

Illustration reduced.

1999, Mar. 5 Perf. 13½
230	A33	£1.50 multicolored	14.00 14.00

Australia '99, World Stamp Expo.

Queen Mother's Century
Common Design Type

Queen Mother: 25p, At air raid shelter, 1940. 30p, With Prince Edward, Lady Sarah Armstrong-Jones, Viscount Linley, 70th birthday. 35p, With Prince William, 94th birthday. 40p, As colonel-in-chief of Royal Anglian Regiment. £1, Funeral procession for Queen Victoria, portrait of Victoria.

Perf. 13¾x14¼, 14¼x13¾

2000, June 21 Litho. Wmk. 373
Stamps With White Border
257	CD359	25p multi	2.00 1.75
258	CD359	30p multi	2.25 2.00
259	CD359	35p multi	2.50 2.25
260	CD359	40p multi	3.25 2.75
		Nos. 257-260 (4)	10.00 8.75

Wmk. 384

1999, Aug. 18 Litho. Perf. 13½
231	CD358	25p multicolored	2.50 2.50
232	CD358	30p black	3.25 3.25
233	CD358	35p multicolored	3.75 3.75
234	CD358	40p multicolored	4.25 4.25
		Nos. 231-234 (4)	13.75 13.75

Souvenir Sheet
235	CD358	£1 black	14.00 14.00

Birds — A34

Designs: 1p, Chinstrap penguin, vert. 2p, White chinned petrel. 5p, Gray backed storm petrel, vert. 10p, South Georgia pipit, vert. 11p, Gray headed albatross. 35p, Black browed albatross. 40p, South Georgia diving petrel. 50p, Macaroni penguin, vert. £1, Light mantled sooty albatross. £3, South Georgia pintail. £5, King penguin, vert.

Wmk. 384

1999, Nov. 15 Litho. Perf. 14
236	A34	1p multicolored	.75 1.25
237	A34	2p multicolored	.85 1.25
238	A34	5p multicolored	.95 1.25
239	A34	10p multicolored	1.00 1.25
240	A34	11p multicolored	1.25 1.25
241	A34	30p multicolored	2.25 2.50
242	A34	35p multicolored	2.50 2.50
243	A34	40p multicolored	2.50 2.50
244	A34	50p multicolored	2.75 3.00
245	A34	£1 multicolored	4.75 5.00
246	A34	£3 multicolored	11.00 12.50
247	A34	£5 multicolored	16.00 17.50
		Nos. 236-247 (12)	46.55 51.75

Millennium — A35

Perf. 14½x14¼

1999, Dec. 18 Litho. Wmk. 384
248	A35	11p Sunrise	2.00 2.00
249	A35	11p Church	2.00 2.00
250	A35	11p Albatrosses	2.00 2.00
251	A35	35p Penguins	3.00 3.00
252	A35	35p Reindeer	3.00 3.00
253	A35	35p Sunset	3.00 3.00
		Nos. 248-253 (6)	15.00 15.00

Sir Ernest Shackleton (1874-1922), Polar Explorer — A36

Designs: 35p, Voyage across Scotia Sea, 1916. 40p, Shackleton, Thomas Crean and Frank Worsley crossing South Georgia. 65p, Shackleton's grave.

2000, Feb. 20 Wmk. 373 Perf. 14
254	A36	35p multi	4.50 4.50
255	A36	40p multi	4.75 4.75
256	A36	65p multi	5.75 5.75
		Nos. 254-256 (3)	15.00 15.00

See British Antarctic Territory Nos. 285-287, Falkland Islands Nos. 758-760.

Prince William, 18th Birthday
Common Design Type

William: 25p, In suit, carrying bag, vert. 30p, With ski equipment, vert. 35p, Wearing suit and wearing sweater. 40p, In suit, waving. 50p, In beret, saluting.

Souvenir Sheet
Stamps Without White Border
Perf. 14¼

261		Sheet of 5	11.00 11.00
a.	CD359	25p multi	1.50 1.50
b.	CD359	30p multi	1.75 1.75
c.	CD359	35p multi	2.00 2.00
d.	CD359	40p multi	2.25 2.25
e.	CD359	50p multi	2.50 2.50

King Penguins — A37

#262, 37p, Penguins at sea. #263, 37p, Adult & creche. #264, 43p, Advertisement walk & courtship. #265, 43p, Nesting.

Perf. 14¾x14

2000, Oct. 16 Litho. Wmk. 373
262-265	A37	Set of 4	15.00 15.00

Royal Fleet Auxiliary Vessels A38

Designs: No. 266, 37p, RFA Sir Percivale. No. 267, 37p, RFA Tidespring. No. 268, 43p, RFA Diligence. No. 269, 43p, RFA Gold Rover.

Wmk. 373

2001, May 28 Litho. Perf. 14
266-269	A38	Set of 4	14.50 14.50

Marine Life — A39

Designs: 33p, Icefish. No. 271, 37p, Spiny back crab. No. 272, 37p, Krill, vert. 43p, Toothfish, vert.

Wmk. 373

2001, Oct. 22 Litho. Perf. 13¾
270-273	A39	Set of 4	11.00 11.00

Reign Of Queen Elizabeth II, 50th Anniv. Issue
Common Design Type

Designs: Nos. 274, 278a, 20p, With dog, 1952. Nos. 275, 278b, 37p, With Prince Philip, 1997. Nos. 276, 278c, 43p, Examining royal stamp collection, 1946. No. 277, 278d, 50p, Wearing blue hat, 1966. No. 278e, 50p, 1955 portrait by Annigoni (38x50mm).

Perf. 14¼x14½, 13¾ (#278e)

2002, Feb. 6 Litho. Wmk. 373
With Gold Frames
274-277	CD360	Set of 4	9.00 9.00

Souvenir Sheet
Without Gold Frames
278	CD360	Sheet of 5, #a-e	11.00 11.00

World Record Animals — A40

No. 279: a, 10p, Fin whale. b, 10p, Blue whale. c, 20p, Sperm whale. d, 37p, Leopard seal with mouth open. e, 37p, Leopard seal on ice. f, 43p, Elephant seal. £1.50, Elephant seal, diff.

2002, Mar. 2   Litho.   Perf. 13¾
279 A40   Sheet of 6, #a-f   11.00 11.00

Souvenir Sheet
280 A40   £1.50 multi   10.00 10.00

Queen Mother Elizabeth (1900-2002)
Common Design Type

Designs: 22p, Wearing hat (black and white photograph). 40p, Wearing tiara. Nos. 283, 285a, 45p, Holding dog (black and white photograph). Nos. 284, 285b, 95p, Wearing white stole.

Perf. 14¼, 13¾x14¼ (#283-284)
2002, Aug. 5   Litho.   Wmk. 373
With Purple Frames
281-284 CD361   Set of 4   11.00 11.00

Souvenir Sheet
Without Purple Frames
Perf. 14½x14¼
285 CD361   Sheet of 2, #a-b   8.00 8.00

Antarctic Fur Seals — A41

Designs: No. 286, 40p, Seal in water. No. 287, 40p, Two seals on ice. No. 288, 45p, Six seals. No. 289, 45p, One seal.

Wmk. 373
2002, Oct. 25   Litho.   Perf. 13¾
286-289 A41   Set of 4   13.00 13.00

Worldwide Fund for Nature (WWF) — A42

Gray-headed albatross: 40p, Adults at nesting ground. No. 291, 45p, Adult and chick (WWF emblem at LL). No. 292, 45p, Two adults (WWF emblem at UL). 70p, Bird's head.

Wmk. 373
2003, Jan. 6   Litho.   Perf. 14
290-293 A42   Set of 4   11.00 11.00
293a   Strip of 4   12.00 12.00

Head of Queen Elizabeth II
Common Design Type
Wmk. 373
2003, June 2   Litho.   Perf. 13¾
294 CD362   £2 multi   9.00 9.00

Prince William, 21st Birthday
Common Design Type

No. 295: a, Color photograph at right. b, Color photograph at left.

Wmk. 373
2003, June 21   Litho.   Perf. 14¼
295   Horiz. pair   7.00 7.00
a.-b.   CD364 70p Either single   3.00 3.00

History of South Georgia — A43

No. 296: a, HMS Sappho visits Grytviken, 1906. b, Norwegian reindeer introduced, 1911. c, Largest blue whale landed, 1912. d, Shackleton's island crossing, 1916. e, Shackleton Memorial Cross, 1922. f, Discovery investigations, 1925. g, First powered flight over South Georgia, 1938. h, Operation Tabarin, 1943. i, Duke of Edinburgh visits, 1957. j, Bird Island Research Station, 1958. k, Mt. Paget climbed, 1964. l, Liberation of the island, 1982. m, Royal charter and crest, 1985. n, Museum inaugurated, 1992. o, Applied fishery research, 2001. p, Grytviken remedial work, 2003.

Wmk. 373
2004, Feb. 6   Litho.   Perf. 13¼
296 A43 40p Sheet of 16, #a-p 35.00 35.00

Royal Navy Ships A44

Designs: 10p, HMS Ajax. 25p, HMS Amazon. 45p, HMS Dartmouth. 50p, HMS Penelope. 70p, HMS St. Austell Bay. £1, HMS Plymouth.

Wmk. 373
2004, Apr. 26   Litho.   Perf. 14
297-302 A44   Set of 6   13.00 13.00

Merchant Ships A45

Designs: No. 303, 42p, RMS Queen Elizabeth 2. No. 304, 42p, MS Endeavour. 50p, MS Lindblad Explorer. 75p, SS Canberra.

Perf. 13¼x13½
2004, Nov. 10   Litho.
303-306 A45   Set of 4   9.00 9.00

Animal Juveniles — A46

Designs: 1p, Skua. 2p, Reindeer. 3p, Antarctic prion, horiz. 5p, Humpback whale, horiz. 10p, Gentoo penguins. 25p, Antarctic fur seal. 50p, South Georgia pintail, horiz. 75p, Light-mantled sooty albatross. £1, Weddell seal, horiz. £2, King penguin, horiz. £3, Southern right whale, horiz. £5, Wandering albatross.

(42p), Elephant seal, horiz.

Perf. 13½x13¼, 13¼x13½
2004, Nov. 15   Wmk. 373
307 A46   1p multi   .20   .20
308 A46   2p multi   .40   .40
309 A46   3p multi   .50   .50

---

310 A46   5p multi   .65   .65
311 A46   10p multi   .80   .80
312 A46   25p multi   1.10 1.10
313 A46   50p multi   2.40 2.40
314 A46   75p multi   3.50 3.50
315 A46   £1 multi   4.75 4.75
316 A46   £2 multi   9.00 9.00
317 A46   £3 multi   13.00 13.00
318 A46   £5 multi   20.00 20.00
    Nos. 307-318 (12)   56.30 56.30

Booklet Stamp
Self-Adhesive
Unwmk.
Serpentine Die Cut 12½
319 A46 (42p) multi   1.90 1.90
a.   Booklet pane of 4   7.75
    Complete booklet, 2 #319a   15.50

No. 319 is inscribed "Airmail Postcard."

Grytviken, Cent. — A47

Designs: 24p, Capt. Carl Anton Larsen, founder of Grytviken. 42p, Grytviken from Mount Hodges. 50p, Whale catcher Fortuna. £1, Ski jumper.

2004, Dec. 10   Wmk. 373   Perf. 13¾
320-323 A47   Set of 4   8.75 8.75

Duncan Carse (1913-2004), Survey Expedition Leader — A48

Designs: No. 324, 50p, Carse. No. 325, 50p, Map of South Georgia, surveyors. 75p, Carse as radio broadcaster. £1, AMOW, Carse's hut, Undine South.

Wmk. 373
2005, Sept. 26   Litho.   Perf. 13¾
324-327 A48   Set of 4   11.00 11.00

A49

A50

A51

A52

A53

Penguins A54

2005, Nov. 1   Perf. 14
328 A49   45p multi   1.90 1.90
329 A50   45p multi   1.90 1.90
330 A51   45p multi   1.90 1.90
331 A52   45p multi   1.90 1.90
332 A53   45p multi   1.90 1.90
333 A54   45p multi   1.90 1.90
    Nos. 328-333 (6)   11.40 11.40

Queen Elizabeth II, 80th Birthday A55

Queen: No. 334, 50p, As child, with dog. Nos. 335, 338a, 50p, As young woman. Nos. 336, 338b, 75p, As older woman. £1, Wearing hat.

2006, Apr. 21   Litho.   Perf. 14
With White Frames
334-337 A55   Set of 4   11.00 11.00

Souvenir Sheet
Without White Frames
338 A55   Sheet of 2, #a-b   5.00 5.00

BirdLife International A56

Birds: 24p, Black-browed albatross. 45p, Southern giant petrel. 50p, White-chinned petrel. 75p, Wandering albatross.
No. 343: a, Black-browed albatross, diff. b, White-chinned petrel, diff.

Wmk. 373
2006, Oct. 18   Litho.   Perf. 13¾
339-342 A56   Set of 4   7.75 7.75

Souvenir Sheet
343 A56   £1 Sheet of 2, #a-b   8.00 8.00

Communications — A57

Designs: 25p, Mail drop from Royal Air Force Hercules plane. 50p, Radio/wireless room. 60p, MV Sigma. £1.05, SS Fleurus.

Perf. 14¼x14
2006, Nov. 30   Litho.   Wmk. 373
344-347 A57   Set of 4   10.00 10.00

Mapping — A58

No. 348, 50p: a, Map of Neumayer Glacier, 1958. b, Map of Neumayer Glacier, 2003.

No. 349, 60p: a, Kern DKM1 theodolite and map. b, Landsat 7 satellite. Illustration reduced.

2007, Jan. 5   **Perf. 13¾**
Horiz. Pairs, #a-b
348-349 A58   Set of 2   9.00 9.00

Falkland Islands War, 25th Anniv. — A59

Designs: 25p, Ellerbeck Peak, Wasp helicopter. 50p, Stanley Peak, Wessex 3 helicopter. 60p, Sheridan Peak, Royal Marines Commandos. £1.05, Mills Peak, Royal Marines.

Perf. 12½x13
2007, Apr. 25   Litho.   **Wmk. 373**
350-353 A59   Set of 4   9.75 9.75
353a   Souvenir sheet, #350-353   9.75 9.75
On No. 353a, the bottom perforations of Nos. 352-353 measure 13¼.

Scouting, Cent. — A60

Designs: 25p, Cover of Oct. 8, 1921 *Young Britain* magazine. 50p, Scouts James Marr and Norman Mooney raising flag on the Quest. 60p, Marr and Mooney with Sir Ernest Shackleton. 85p, Autographed postcard depicting Marr. £1.05, The Quest locked in ice.

Perf. 14¼
2007, Oct. 15   Litho.   **Unwmk.**
354-358 A60   Set of 5   13.50 13.50

Intl. Polar Year A61

Designs: 50p, Zoological Building, Moltke Base. 60p, Meteorological Station, King Edward Point. 85p, Zooplankton. £1.05, Leopard seals.

2008, Jan. 25   Litho.   **Perf. 14¼x14**
359-362 A61   Set of 4   12.00 12.00

Marine Stewardship Council — A62

Ships and marine life: 50p, Longliner, Patagonian toothfish. 60p, Trawler, Mackerel icefish. 85p, Krill trawler and refrigerator ship, Krill. £1.05, Fishery Patrol Vessel Pharos SG.

Perf. 14¼
2008, May 1   Litho.   **Unwmk.**
363-366 A62   Set of 4   12.00 12.00

SEMI-POSTAL STAMPS

Liberation of South Georgia, 10th Anniv. — SP1

Designs: 14p+6p, King Edward Point, Winter 1982. 29p+11p, Queen Elizabeth 2 in Cumberland Bay. 34p+16p, Royal Marines on South Sandwich Islands. 68p+32p, HMS Endurance and Wasp Helicopter.

Wmk. 384
1992, June 20   Litho.   **Perf. 14**
B1 SP1 14p +6p multicolored   1.25 1.25
B2 SP1 29p +11p multicolored   1.75 1.75
B3 SP1 34p +16p multicolored   2.00 2.00
B4 SP1 68p +32p multicolored   4.25 4.25
   a.   Souvenir sheet of 4, #B1-B4   11.00 11.00
    Nos. B1-B4 (4)   9.25 9.25
Surtax for Soldiers', Sailors' and Airmen's Families Association.

SOUTH KASAI

This part of a Congo province declared itself an autonomous state and in 1961 issued several series of stamps, some of which were overprints on Congo (ex-Belgian) stamps. Established nations did not recognize South Kasai as an independent state.

SOUTH MOLUCCAS
(Republik Maluku Selatan)

It appears that stamps of the so-called republic of South Moluccas were privately issued and had no postal use. Accordingly, they are not recognized as postage stamps.

SOUTH RUSSIA

sauth ˈrəsh-ə

LOCATION — An area in southern Russia bordering on the Caspian and Black Seas.

A provisional government set up and maintained by General Denikin in opposition to the Bolshevik forces in Russia following the downfall of the Empire. The stamps were used in the field postal service established for carrying on communication between the various armies united in the revolt. These armies included the Don Cossacks, the Kuban Cossacks, and also the neighboring southern Russian people in favor of the counter-revolution against the Bolsheviks.

100 Kopecks = 1 Ruble

Values for used stamps are for CTO copies. Postally used specimens sell for considerably more.

Watermark

Wmk. 171 — Diamonds

Don Government (Novocherkassk) Rostov Issue

Russian Stamps of 1909-17 Surcharged

1918   Unwmk.   **Perf. 14x14½**
1	A14	25k on 1k dl org yel	2.00	1.90
a.		Inverted surcharge	100.00	100.00
2	A14	25k on 2k dl grn	.50	.60
a.		Inverted surcharge	100.00	75.00
3	A14	25k on 3k car	.75	.75
a.		Double surcharge	50.00	75.00
4	A15	25k on 4k car	2.50	3.50
a.		Inverted surcharge	100.00	100.00
5	A14	50k on 7k blue	5.00	6.50

Imperf
6	A14	25k on 1k orange	.60	1.25
a.		Inverted surcharge	75.00	100.00
7	A14	25k on 2k gray grn	7.50	12.50
8	A14	25k on 3k red	4.50	3.00
		Nos. 1-8 (8)	23.35	30.00

Counterfeits exist of Nos. 1-8.

Ermak, Cossack Leader — A1

Inscription on Back

1919   **Perf. 11½**
10   A1   20k green   50.00 85.00
This stamp was available for both postage and currency.

Novocherkassk Issue

25   **1P.**   **1 P.**

Russian stamps with these surcharges are bogus.

Kuban Government Ekaterinodar Issues
Russian Stamps of 1909-17 Surcharged:

d

e

f

g

h

i

1918-20   Unwmk.   **Perf. 14x14½**
20	A14(d)	25k on 1k dl org yel	.50	.65
a.		Inverted surcharge	75.00	27.50
b.		Dbl. surch., one inverted	75.00	25.00
21	A14(d)	50k on 2k dl grn	6.00	6.00
a.		Inverted surcharge	50.00	27.50
b.		Double surcharge	100.00	20.00
c.		Dbl. surcharge inverted	75.00	20.00
22	A14(e)	70k on 5k dk cl	2.40	6.00
23	A14(f)	1r on 3k car	2.50	4.75
a.		Inverted surcharge	50.00	20.00
b.		Double surcharge	50.00	15.00
c.		Pair, one without surch.	50.00	15.00

24	A14(g)	1r on 3k car	.65	1.00
a.		Inverted surcharge	50.00	20.00
b.		Double surcharge	100.00	20.00
c.		Pair, one without surcharge	100.00	12.00
25	A15(h)	3r on 4k rose	12.00	18.00
b.		Inverted surcharge	100.00	50.00
c.		Double surcharge	100.00	60.00
d.		Dbl. surcharge inverted	100.00	60.00
26	A15(i)	10r on 4k rose	4.00	5.00
a.		10r on 4k carmine	8.00	13.00
b.		Inverted surcharge	75.00	55.00
27	A11(i)	10r on 15k red brn & dp bl	1.25	2.00
a.		Surchd. on face & back	40.00	15.00
b.		Dbl. surch., one inverted	75.00	60.00
28	A14(i)	25r on 3k car	2.25	2.00
a.		Inverted surcharge	100.00	20.00
29	A14(i)	25r on 7k bl	30.00	27.50
a.		Inverted surcharge	100.00	60.00
30	A11(i)	25r on 14k bl & car	75.00	65.00
a.		Inverted surcharge	100.00	80.00
31	A11(i)	25r on 25k dl grn & dk vio	30.00	60.00
a.		Inverted surcharge	100.00	70.00
		Nos. 20-31 (12)	166.55	197.90

Imperf
35	A14(d)	25d on 1k org	1.25	2.00
36	A14(d)	50k on 2k gray grn	.30	.35
a.		Inverted surcharge	50.00	25.00
b.		Double surcharge	50.00	25.00
c.		Pair, one without surch.	50.00	30.00
37	A14(e)	70k on 5k claret	2.50	3.25
38	A14(f)	1r on 3k red	1.40	2.00
a.		Inverted surcharge	40.00	20.00
b.		Double surcharge	30.00	15.00
c.		Pair, one without surch.	30.00	15.00
39	A14(g)	1r on 3k red	.50	.65
a.		Double surcharge	20.00	20.00
b.		Pair, one without surch.	20.00	20.00
c.		As "a," inverted	40.00	45.00
40	A11(i)	10r on 15k red brn & dp bl	4.75	6.00
41	A14(i)	25r on 3k red	6.00	9.50
a.		Inverted surcharge	100.00	
		Nos. 35-41 (7)	16.70	23.75

Russian Stamps of 1909-17 Surcharged

1919   **Perf. 14, 14½x15**
45   A14   70k on 1k dl org yel   1.25 1.00

Imperf
46	A14	70k on 1k orange	1.25	2.40
a.		Inverted surcharge	100.00	20.00
b.		Double surch., one inverted	100.00	25.00

The 1k postal savings stamp with this surcharge inverted is a proof.
Counterfeits exist of Nos. 20-46.

Postal Savings Stamps Surcharged for Postal Use

A2

1919   Wmk. 171   **Perf. 14½x15**
47	A2	10r on 1k red, buff	18.00	24.00
a.		Inverted surcharge	75.00	
48	A2	10r on 5k grn, buff	40.00	45.00
a.		Double surcharge	250.00	
49	A2	10r on 10k brn, buff	120.00	150.00
		Nos. 47-49 (3)	178.00	219.00

Counterfeits exist of Nos. 47-49.

Crimea
Russian Stamp of 1917 Surcharged   **35 коп.**

1919   Unwmk.   **Imperf.**
51	A14	35k on 1k orange	.30	1.00
a.		Comma, instead of period in surcharge		1.00

A3

Paper with Buff Network Inscription on Back

1919			Imperf.
52	A3 50k brown	50.00	100.00

Available for both postage and currency.

Russia Nos. 77, 82, 123, 73, 119 Surcharged

Nos. 53-57   Nos. 58-59

1920			Perf. 14x14½
53	A14 5r on 5k dk claret	1.25	2.40
a.	Inverted surcharge	100.00	
b.	Double surcharge	100.00	
54	A8 5r on 20k dl bl & dk car	1.25	2.40
a.	Inverted surcharge	100.00	
b.	Double surcharge	100.00	
c.	"5" omitted	75.00	

			Imperf
55	A14 5r on 5k claret	1.25	2.40
a.	Double surcharge	25.00	

Same Surcharge on Stamp of Denikin Issue, No. 64

57	A5 5r on 35k lt bl	12.00	14.00
a.	Double surcharge	80.00	
	Nos. 53-57 (4)	15.75	21.20

1920			Perf. 14x14½
58	A14 100r on 1k dl org yel	3.75	
a.	"10" in place of "100"	100.00	
b.	Inverted surcharge	150.00	
c.	Double surcharge	150.00	

			Imperf
59	A14 100r on 1k orange	2.75	

Nos. 53-57 were issued at Sevastopol during the occupation by General Wrangel's army. Nos. 58-59 were prepared but not used.

Denikin Issue

A5   St. George — A6

1919		Unwmk.	Imperf.
61	A5 5k orange	.20	.25
62	A5 10k green	.20	.25
63	A5 15k red	.20	.35
64	A5 35k light blue	.20	.25
65	A5 70k dark blue	.20	.35
a.	Tête bêche pair	90.00	
66	1r brown & red	.65	.75
67	A6 2r gray vio & yellow	1.25	1.40
68	A6 3r dl rose & green	1.00	1.25
69	A6 5r slate & violet	1.25	1.40
70	A6 7r gray grn & rose	2.25	3.25
71	A6 10r red & gray	2.00	2.50
	Nos. 61-71 (11)	9.40	12.00

			Perf. 11½
68a	A6 3r dull rose & green	1.50	1.50
69a	A6 5r slate & violet	2.50	2.50
71a	A6 10r red & gray	1.60	1.60
	Nos. 68a-71a (3)	5.60	5.60

Nos. 61-71 were issued at Ekaterinodar and used in all parts of South Russia that were occupied by the People's Volunteer Army under Gen. Anton Ivanovich Denikin. The inscription on the stamps reads "United Russia."

Stamps of type A6 with rosettes instead of numerals in the small circles at the sides may be essays. Perforated copies of Nos. 61-67 and 70 are of private origin.

For surcharges see Russia, Offices in Turkish Empire Nos. 303-319.

SOUTH WEST AFRICA

sauth 'west 'a-fri-kə

(Namibia)

LOCATION — Southwestern Africa between Angola, Botswana and South Africa, bordering on the Atlantic Ocean
GOVT. — Administered by the Republic of South Africa under a mandate of the League of Nations
AREA — 318,261 sq. mi.
POP. — 1,039,800 (1982)
CAPITAL — Windhoek

Formerly a German possession, South West Africa was occupied by South African forces in 1915 and by the Treaty of Versailles was mandated to the Union of South Africa. On March 20, 1990 it became Namibia.

12 Pence = 1 Shilling
20 Shillings = 1 Pound
100 Cents = 1 Rand (1961)

> **Catalogue values for unused stamps in this country are for Never Hinged items, beginning with Scott 125 in the regular postage section, Scott B1 in the semipostal section, Scott J86 in the postage due section, and Scott O13 in the officials section.**

Watermarks

Watermarks 177, 201, 330, 348 and 359 can be found at the beginning of South Africa.

Stamps of South Africa, Nos. 2-3, 5 and 9-16, Overprinted in English or Afrikaans alternately throughout the sheets.

Major-number listings and values of Nos. 1-40 and 85-93 are for pairs with both overprints.

Setting I

"South West" 14½mm wide
"Zuid-West" 13mm wide
Overprint Spaced 14mm

1923, Jan. 2		Wmk. 177		Perf. 14
1	A2 ½p green, pair		3.00	10.50
a.	Single, Dutch		1.10	1.10
2	A2 1p red, pair		3.75	10.50
a.	Single, Dutch		1.10	1.10
b.	Inverted overprint, pair		550.00	
c.	As "b," single, English		125.00	
d.	As "b," single, Dutch		125.00	
e.	"Af.rica"		175.00	210.00
f.	Double overprint, pair		1,000.	
g.	As "f," single, English		500.00	
h.	As "f," single, Dutch		500.00	
3	A2 2p dull vio, pair		4.75	14.00
a.	Single, Dutch		1.75	1.75
b.	Inverted overprint, pair		625.00	700.00
c.	As "b," single, English		110.00	
d.	As "b," single, Dutch		110.00	
4	A2 3p ultra, pair		8.50	19.00
a.	Single, Dutch		3.25	3.25
5	A2 4p ol grn & org, pair		15.00	52.50
a.	Single, Dutch		4.50	4.50
6	A2 6p vio & blk, pair		9.25	50.00
a.	Single, Dutch		4.75	4.75
7	A2 1sh orange, pair		27.50	55.00
a.	Single, Dutch		5.75	5.25

8	A2 1sh3p violet, pair	35.00	62.50
a.	Single, Dutch	6.50	6.50
b.	Inverted overprint, pair	375.00	
c.	As "b," single, English	45.00	
d.	As "b," single, Dutch	45.00	
9	A2 2sh6p grn & cl, pair	70.00	150.00
a.	Single, Dutch	22.50	22.50
10	A2 5sh blue & cl, pair	175.00	375.00
a.	Single, Dutch	57.50	57.50
11	A2 10sh ol grn & bl, pair	1,500.	2,900.
a.	Single, Dutch	475.00	500.00
12	A2 £1 red & dp grn, pair	800.00	2,000.
a.	Single, Dutch	300.00	300.00
	Nos. 1-12 (12)	2,651.	5,699.

Most values exist with "t" of "West" partly or totally missing. Vertical displacement in overprinting accounts for the copies with only one line of overprint.

For English from setting I "a," see note after No. 27.

Setting II

Words Same Width as Setting I
Overprint Spaced 9½-10mm

1923, Apr.			
13	A2 5sh blue & cl, pair	160.00	300.00
a.	Single, English	52.50	52.50
b.	Single, Dutch	52.50	52.50
c.	As #13, without period after "Afrika"	1,200.	1,300.
14	A2 10sh ol grn & bl, pair	575.00	1,000.
a.	Single, English	160.00	160.00
b.	Single, Dutch	160.00	160.00
c.	As #14, without period after "Afrika"	2,600.	3,250.
15	A2 £1 red & green, pair	1,150.	1,700.
a.	Single, English	225.00	225.00
b.	Single, Dutch	225.00	225.00
c.	As #15, without period after "Afrika"	6,000.	5,750.

Setting III

English as in Setting I
"Zuidwest" 11mm wide, No Hyphen
Overprint Spaced 14mm

1923-24			
16	A2 ½p grn, pair ('24)	7.00	40.00
a.	Single, English	.30	4.25
b.	Single, Dutch	.30	4.25
17	A2 1p red, pair	6.25	10.50
a.	Single, English	.30	1.60
b.	Single, Dutch	.30	1.60
18	A2 2p dull vio, pair	6.25	10.50
a.	Single, English	.30	1.50
b.	Single, Dutch	.30	1.50
c.	Dbl. ovpt., pair	1,200.	
d.	As "c," single, English	90.00	
e.	As "c," single, Dutch	90.00	
19	A2 3p ultra, pair	5.75	11.50
a.	Single, English	.50	1.50
b.	Single, Dutch	.50	1.50
20	A2 4p ol grn & org, pair	7.00	24.00
a.	Single, English	.50	3.25
b.	Single, Dutch	.50	3.25
21	A2 6p vio & blk, pair	16.00	52.50
a.	Single, English	1.00	5.75
b.	Single, Dutch	1.00	5.75
22	A2 1sh orange, pair	16.00	52.50
a.	Single, English	1.00	5.75
b.	Single, Dutch	1.00	5.75
23	A2 1sh3p violet, pair	32.50	52.50
a.	Single, English	1.75	6.25
b.	Single, Dutch	1.75	6.25
24	A2 2sh6p grn & cl, pair	52.50	92.50
a.	Single, English	4.00	11.50
b.	Single, Dutch	4.00	11.50
25	A2 5sh blue & cl, pair	70.00	150.00
a.	Single, English	7.50	21.00
b.	Single, Dutch	7.50	21.00
26	A2 10sh ol grn & bl, pair	190.00	300.00
a.	Single, English	30.00	47.50
b.	Single, Dutch	30.00	47.50

27	A2 £1 red & green, pair	350.00	450.00
a.	Single, English	40.00	70.00
b.	Single, Dutch	40.00	70.00
	Nos. 16-27 (12)	759.25	1,246.

The English overprint of Setting III is the same as that of Setting I.

Setting IV

g   h

"South West" 16mm wide
"Zuidwest" 12mm wide
Overprint Spaced 14mm

1924, July			
28	A2 2sh6p grn & cl, pair	92.50	175.00
a.	Single, English	13.00	32.50
b.	Single, Dutch	13.00	32.50

Setting VI

"South West" 16, 16½mm wide
"Zuidwest" 12½mm wide
Overprint Spaced 9½mm

1924, Dec.			
29	A2 ½p green, pair	8.00	45.00
a.	Single, English	.35	5.75
b.	Single, Dutch	.35	5.75
30	A2 1p red, pair	3.75	11.50
a.	Single, English	.25	1.60
b.	Single, Dutch	.25	1.60
31	A2 2p dull vio, pair	5.75	25.00
a.	Single, English	.30	2.00
b.	Single, Dutch	.30	2.00
32	A2 3p ultra, pair	5.25	32.50
a.	Single, English	.45	3.25
b.	Single, Dutch	.45	3.25
33	A2 4p ol grn & org, pair	7.50	52.50
a.	Single, English	.50	4.50
b.	Single, Dutch	.50	4.50
34	A2 6p vio & blk, pair	10.50	55.00
a.	Single, English	.75	5.75
b.	Single, Dutch	.75	5.75
35	A2 1sh orange, pair	12.50	55.00
a.	Single, English	.75	5.75
b.	Single, Dutch	.75	5.75
36	A2 1sh3p violet, pair	17.50	55.00
a.	Single, English	.75	5.75
b.	Single, Dutch	.75	5.75
37	A2 2sh6p grn & cl, pair	32.50	80.00
a.	Single, English	3.00	11.50
b.	Single, Dutch	3.00	11.50
38	A2 5sh blue & cl, pair	52.50	140.00
a.	Single, English	6.00	16.00
b.	Single, Dutch	6.00	16.00
39	A2 10sh ol grn & bl, pair	92.50	180.00
a.	Single, English	10.00	22.50
b.	Single, Dutch	10.00	22.50
40	A2 £1 red & grn, pair	290.00	475.00
a.	Single, English	40.00	75.00
b.	Single, Dutch	40.00	75.00
	Nos. 29-40 (12)	538.25	1,206.

Setting VII

South Africa Nos. 21-22 Overprinted:

m

n

o

1926-27   Wmk. 201   Imperf.

81	A3 (m)	4p blue gray	.85	3.50
82	A3 (n)	4p blue gray	.85	3.50
83	A3 (o)	4p blue gray ('27)	7.00	22.50
		Nos. 81-83 (3)	8.70	29.50

Nos. 81-83 were not officially perforated, but firms and individuals applied various forms of perforation and rouletting for their own convenience. Perf. 11 examples of Nos. 81-82 were made by John Meinert, Ltd., Windhoek, same values.

Setting VIII
South Africa Nos. 23-25 Overprinted Alternately with type "p" on English-inscribed Stamps and type "q" on Afrikaans-inscribed Stamps

"South West" 16½mm wide
"Suidwes" 11mm wide
Overprint Spaced 11½mm

1926   Typo.   Perf. 14½x14

85	A5	½p dk grn & blk, pair	2.25	8.00
a.		Single, English	.35	1.00
b.		Single, Afrikaans	.35	1.00
c.		Afrikaans ovpt. on English stamp	.35	1.00
d.		English ovpt. on Afrikaans stamp	.35	1.00
e.		Pair, "c" + "d"	1.75	6.00
f.		As "e," without period after "Africa"	175.00	
86	A6	1p car & blk, pair	3.00	3.00
a.		Single, English	.35	.60
b.		Single, Afrikaans	.35	.60
c.		Afrikaans ovpt. on English stamp	.35	.60
d.		English ovpt. on Afrikaans stamp	.35	.60
e.		Pair, "c" + "d"	6.00	8.00
f.		As "e," without period after "Africa"	350.00	
87	A7	6p org & grn, pair	27.50	35.00
a.		Single, English	2.50	5.00
b.		Single, Afrikaans	2.50	5.00
c.		Afrikaans ovpt. on English stamp	2.00	3.50
d.		English ovpt. on Afrikaans stamp	2.00	3.50
e.		Pair, "c" + "d"	30.00	50.00
f.		As "e," without period after "Africa"	210.00	
		Nos. 85-87 (3)	32.75	46.00

For overprints see Nos. O1-O3.

Setting IX
South Africa Nos. 26-27, 29-32 Overprinted in Blue with types "p" and "q" Spaced 16mm

1927   Engr.   Perf. 14

88	A8	2p vio brn & gray, pair	5.50	17.50
a.		Single, English	.25	2.00
b.		Single, Afrikaans	.25	2.00
89	A9	3p red & blk, pair	5.50	32.50
a.		Single, English	.50	3.00
b.		Single, Afrikaans	.50	3.00
90	A11	1sh dp bl & bis brn, pair	17.50	37.50
a.		Single, English	1.25	4.50
b.		Single, Afrikaans	1.25	4.50
91	A12	2sh6p brn & bl grn, pair	40.00	110.00
a.		Single, English	5.50	15.00
b.		Single, Afrikaans	5.50	15.00
92	A13	5sh dp grn & blk, pair	85.00	225.00
a.		Single, English	10.00	22.50
b.		Single, Afrikaans	10.00	22.50
93	A14	10sh ol brn & bl, pair	75.00	180.00
a.		Single, English	9.00	22.50
b.		Single, Afrikaans	9.00	22.50
		Nos. 88-93 (6)	228.50	602.50

South Africa Nos. 12 and 16a Overprinted at Foot

1927   Typo.   Wmk. 177

94	A2	1sh3p violet	1.50	7.50
a.		Without period after "A"	110.00	
95	A2	£1 lt red & gray grn	110.00	190.00
a.		Without period after "A"	1,750.	2,600.

South Africa Nos. 23-25 Overprinted type "r" at Foot

1927   Wmk. 201   Perf. 14½x14

96	A5	½p green & blk, pair	2.75	8.00
a.		Single, English	.20	.90
b.		Single, Afrikaans	.20	.90
c.		As #96, without period after "A" on one stamp	47.50	85.00
97	A6	1p car & blk, pair	1.50	3.75
a.		Single, English	.20	.65
b.		Single, Afrikaans	.20	.65
c.		As #97, without period after "A" on one stamp	47.50	85.00
d.		Ovpt. at top, pair ('30)	2.00	16.00
e.		As "d," single, English	.35	1.90
f.		As "d," single, Afrikaans	.35	1.90
98	A7	6p org & grn, pair	13.00	26.00
a.		Single, English	1.25	3.25
b.		Single, Afrikaans	1.25	3.25
c.		As #98, without period after "A" on one stamp	125.00	
		Nos. 96-98 (3)	17.25	37.75

For overprints see Nos. O5-O7.

South Africa Nos. 26-32 Overprinted type "r" at Top

1927-28   Engr.   Perf. 14

99	A8	2p vio brn & gray, pair	10.50	32.50
a.		Single, English	1.00	1.75
b.		Single, Afrikaans	1.00	1.75
c.		As #99, without period after "A" on one stamp	85.00	125.00
d.		Double ovpt., one inverted	800.00	1,050.
100	A9	3p red & blk, pair	7.00	26.00
a.		Single, English	.50	3.75
b.		Single, Afrikaans	.50	3.75
c.		As #100, without period after "A" on one stamp	92.50	150.00
101	A10	4p brn, pair ('28)	17.50	45.00
a.		Single, English	1.25	8.00
b.		Single, Afrikaans	1.25	8.00
c.		As #101, without period after "A" on one stamp	97.50	150.00
102	A11	1sh dp bl & bis brn, pair	22.50	55.00
a.		Single, English	1.50	5.75
b.		Single, Afrikaans	1.50	5.75
c.		As #102, without period after "A" on one stamp	1,500.	
103	A12	2sh6p brn & bl grn, pair	47.50	97.50
a.		Single, English	6.00	14.00
b.		Single, Afrikaans	6.00	14.00
c.		As #103, without period after "A" on one stamp	250.00	400.00
104	A13	5sh dp grn & blk, pair	70.00	140.00
a.		Single, English	8.00	21.00
b.		Single, Afrikaans	8.00	21.00
c.		As #104, without period after "A" on one stamp	325.00	475.00
105	A14	10sh ol brn & bl, pair	110.00	225.00
a.		Single, English	20.00	32.50
b.		Single, Afrikaans	20.00	32.50
c.		As #105, without period after "A" on one stamp	425.00	675.00
		Nos. 99-105 (7)	285.00	621.00

For overprint see No. O8.

South Africa Nos. 33-34 Overprinted type "r" at Foot

1930   Photo.   Perf. 15x14

106	A5	½p bl grn & blk, pair	12.50	34.50
a.		Single, English	.50	3.25
b.		Single, Afrikaans	.50	3.25
107	A6	1p car rose & blk, pair	9.75	30.00
a.		Single, English	.50	3.25
b.		Single, Afrikaans	.50	3.25

Kori Bustard — A15

Cape Cross — A16

Mail Transport — A17

Bogenfels — A18

Windhoek — A19

Waterberg — A20

Lüderitz Bay — A21

Bush Scene — A22

Elands — A23

Zebras and Brindled Gnus — A24

Herero Houses — A25

Welwitschia Plant — A26

Okuwahakan Falls — A27

Perf. 14x13½

1931-37   Wmk. 201   Engr.

108	A15	½p grn & blk, pair	3.25	3.00
a.		Single, English	.20	.20
b.		Single, Afrikaans	.20	.20
109	A16	1p red & ind, pair	2.75	3.00
a.		Single, English	.20	.20
b.		Single, Afrikaans	.20	.20
110	A17	1½p vio brn & bl, pair ('37)	25.00	3.50
a.		Single, English	.20	.30
b.		Single, Afrikaans	.20	.30
111	A18	2p dk brn & dk bl, pair	.80	5.25
a.		Single, English	.20	.25
b.		Single, Afrikaans	.20	.25
112	A19	3p dp bl & gray blk, pair	.80	5.00
a.		Single, English	.20	.25
b.		Single, Afrikaans	.20	.25
113	A20	4p brn vio & grn, pair	2.10	8.00
a.		Single, English	.20	.25
b.		Single, Afrikaans	.20	.25
114	A21	6p ol brn & bl, pair	1.75	10.50
a.		Single, English	.20	.25
b.		Single, Afrikaans	.20	.25
115	A22	1sh bl & vio brn, pair	2.60	13.00
a.		Single, English	.20	.30
b.		Single, Afrikaans	.20	.30
116	A23	1sh3p ocher & pur, pair	8.75	12.50
a.		Single, English	.45	.60
b.		Single, Afrikaans	.45	.60
117	A24	2sh6p dk gray & rose, pair	22.50	27.50
a.		Single, English	1.25	2.00
b.		Single, Afrikaans	1.25	2.00
118	A25	5sh vio brn & ol grn, pair	19.00	45.00
a.		Single, English	1.25	3.25
b.		Single, Afrikaans	1.25	3.25
119	A26	10sh grn & brn, pair	52.50	57.50
a.		Single, English	4.50	7.00
b.		Single, Afrikaans	4.50	7.00
120	A27	20sh bl grn & mar, pair	85.00	95.00
a.		Single, English	12.50	12.50
b.		Single, Afrikaans	12.50	12.50
		Nos. 108-120 (13)	226.80	288.75

For overprints see Nos. O13-O27.

George V — A28

1935, May 6   Perf. 14x13½

121	A28	1p carmine & blk	1.25	.30
122	A28	2p dk brown & blk	1.25	.30
123	A28	3p blue & blk	10.00	21.00
124	A28	6p violet & blk	4.50	11.50
		Nos. 121-124 (4)	17.00	33.10
		Set, never hinged	30.00	

25th anniv. of the reign of George V.

> Catalogue values for unused stamps in this section, from this point to the end of the section, are for Never Hinged items.

Coronation Issue
Inscribed alternately in English and Afrikaans

George VI — A29

1937, May 12   Engr.   Perf. 13½x14

125	A29	½p emer & blk, pair	.45	.25
a.		Single, English	.20	.20
b.		Single, Afrikaans	.20	.20
126	A29	1p car & blk, pair	.45	.25
a.		Single, English	.20	.20
b.		Single, Afrikaans	.20	.20
127	A29	1½p org & blk, pair	.45	.25
a.		Single, English	.20	.20
b.		Single, Afrikaans	.20	.20
128	A29	2p dk brn & blk, pair	.45	.30
a.		Single, English	.20	.20
b.		Single, Afrikaans	.20	.20
129	A29	3p brt bl & blk, pair	.55	.30
a.		Single, English	.20	.20
b.		Single, Afrikaans	.20	.20
130	A29	4p dk vio & blk, pair	.55	.35
a.		Single, English	.20	.20
b.		Single, Afrikaans	.20	.20

131 A29	6p yel & blk, pair	.55	2.75
a.	Single, English	.20	.30
b.	Single, Afrikaans	.20	.30
132 A29	1sh gray & blk, pair	2.00	3.25
a.	Single, English	.20	.75
b.	Single, Afrikaans	.20	.75
	Nos. 125-132 (8)	5.45	7.70

George VI & Queen Elizabeth coronation.

Voortrekker Issue

South Africa Nos. 79-80 Overprinted type "r"

1938, Dec. 14	**Photo.**	**Perf. 15x14**	
133 A23	1p rose & sl, pair	14.00	20.00
a.	Single, English	1.00	1.25
b.	Single, Afrikaans	1.00	1.25
134 A24	1½p red brn & Prus bl, pair	21.00	25.00
a.	Single, English	1.50	1.50
b.	Single, Afrikaans	1.50	1.50

Issued to commemorate the Voortrekkers.

South Africa Nos. 81-89 Overprinted

136ovpt

Perf. 14 (2p, 4p, 6p); 15x14

1941-43		**Wmk. 201**	
135 A25	½p dp blue grn, pair	1.75	2.75
a.	Single, English	.20	.20
b.	Single, Afrikaans	.20	.20
136 A26	1p brt rose, pair	2.00	3.75
a.	Single, English	.20	.20
b.	Single, Afrikaans	.20	.20
137 A27	1½p Prus grn, pair ('42)	3.00	4.00
a.	Single, English	.20	.20
b.	Single, Afrikaans	.20	.20
138 A28	2p dk violet	.60	1.50
139 A29	3p dp blue, pair	24.50	24.50
a.	Single, English	.75	1.00
b.	Single, Afrikaans	.75	1.00
140 A30	4p brown, pair	7.50	18.50
a.	Single, English	.30	.75
b.	Single, Afrikaans	.30	.75
141 A31	6p brt red org, pair	7.00	8.00
a.	Single, English	.30	1.00
b.	Single, Afrikaans	.30	1.00
142 A32	1sh dk brown	1.60	2.00
143 A33	1sh3p dk ol brn, pair ('43)	15.00	24.50
a.	Single, English	1.00	1.25
b.	Single, Afrikaans	1.00	1.25
	Nos. 135-143 (9)	62.95	89.50

South Africa Nos. 90-97 Overprinted

t   u

Pairs or Strips of 3 Perf. 14 or 15x14 all around, Rouletted 6½ or 13 btwn.

1942-45		**Wmk. 201**	
144 A34(t)	½p dp grn, horiz. strip of 3	.75	4.50
a.	Single, English	.20	.20
b.	Single, Afrikaans	.20	.20
c.	½p dp bl grn, horiz. strip of 3	3.00	7.00
d.	As "c," single, English	.20	.20
e.	As "c," single, Afrikaans	.20	.20
145 A35(t)	1p brt car, horiz. strip of 3	3.25	5.50
a.	Single, English	.20	.20
b.	Single, Afrikaans	.20	.20
c.	1p rose car, horiz. strip of 3	3.25	5.50
d.	As "c," single, English	.20	.20
e.	As "c," single, Afrikaans	.20	.20
146 A36(u)	1½p cop brn, horiz. pair	.75	1.50
a.	Single, English	.20	.20
b.	Single, Afrikaans	.20	.20
147 A37(t)	2p dk vio, horiz. pair	7.00	5.50
a.	Single, English	.20	.20
b.	Single, Afrikaans	.20	.20
148 A38(t)	3p dp bl, vert. strip of 3	4.00	19.00
a.	Single, English	.20	.40
b.	Single, Afrikaans	.20	.40
149 A39(t)	4p sl grn, vert. strip of 3	5.00	22.50
a.	Single	.20	.30
b.	As "c," single	50.00	
c.	Invtd. ovpt., strip of 3	800.00	500.00
150 A40(t)	6p brt red org, horiz. pair	7.00	3.00
a.	Single, English	.20	.30
b.	Single, Afrikaans	.20	.30

c.	Inverted overprint, pair	575.00	
d.	As "c," single, English	50.00	50.00
e.	As "c," single, Afrikaans	50.00	50.00
151 A41(u)	1sh dk brn, vert. pair	13.00	27.50
a.	Single	.75	1.50
b.	As "c," single	70.00	
c.	Inverted overprint, pair	575.00	375.00
152 A41(t)	1sh dk brn, vert. pair	5.00	6.50
a.	Single	.20	.30
b.	As "c," single	45.00	40.00
c.	Invtd. ovpt., vert. pair	550.00	350.00
	Nos. 144-152 (9)	45.75	95.50

Issue years: #144-145, 147-151, 1943; #152, 1944; #144c, 145c, 149c, 1945.

Peace Issue

South Africa Nos. 100-102 Overprinted Type "w"

1945, Dec. 3	**Wmk. 201**	**Perf. 14**	
153 A42	1p rose pink & choc, pair	.40	.40
a.	Single, English	.20	.20
b.	Single, Afrikaans	.20	.20
c.	Inverted overprint, pair	350.00	375.00
d.	As "c," single, English	37.50	
e.	As "c," single, Afrikaans	37.50	
154 A43	2p vio & sl bl, pair	.40	.40
a.	Single, English	.20	.20
b.	Single, Afrikaans	.20	.20
155 A43	3p ultra & dp ultra, pair	1.75	2.00
a.	Single, English	.20	.20
b.	Single, Afrikaans	.20	.20
	Nos. 153-155 (3)	2.55	2.80

WW II victory of the Allies.

Royal Visit Issue

South Africa Nos. 103-105 Overprinted

1947, Feb. 17		**Perf. 15x14**	
156 A44	1p cerise & gray, pair	.30	.20
a.	Single, English	.20	.20
b.	Single, Afrikaans	.20	.20
157 A45	2p purple, pair	.30	.25
a.	Single, English	.20	.20
b.	Single, Afrikaans	.20	.20
158 A46	3p dk blue, pair	.35	.30
a.	Single, English	.20	.20
b.	Single, Afrikaans	.20	.20
	Nos. 156-158 (3)	.95	.75

Visit of the British Royal Family, Mar.-Apr., 1947.

South Africa No. 106 Overprinted

1948, Apr. 26		**Perf. 14**	
159 A47	3p dp chalky bl & sil, pair	1.25	.30
a.	Single, English	.20	.20
b.	Single, Afrikaans	.20	.20

25th anniv. of the marriage of George VI and Queen Elizabeth.

UPU Issue

South Africa Nos. 109-111 Overprinted type "w" 13mm wide

1949, Oct. 1		**Perf. 14x15**	
160 A50	½p dk green, pair	1.10	1.50
a.	Single, English	.20	.25
b.	Single, Afrikaans	.20	.25
161 A50	1½p dk red, pair	1.10	1.50
a.	Single, English	.20	.20
b.	Single, Afrikaans	.20	.20
162 A50	3p ultra, pair	1.75	2.00
a.	Single, English	.20	.25
b.	Single, Afrikaans	.20	.25
	Nos. 160-162 (3)	3.95	5.00

75th anniv. of the UPU.

Except for Nos. 312-313, 423-428, this ends the bi-lingual multiples in the postage section.

Voortrekker Monument Issue

South Africa Nos. 112-114 Overprinted

1949, Dec. 1		**Perf. 15x14**	
163 A51	1p magenta	.20	.20
164 A52	1½p dull green	.20	.20
165 A53	3p dark blue	.30	.30
	Nos. 163-165 (3)	.70	.70

Inauguration of the Voortrekker Monument at Pretoria.

South Africa Nos. 115-119 Overprinted

w

x

1952, Mar. 14		**Perf. 15x14, 14x15**	
166 A54(w)	½p dk brown & red vio	.40	.40
167 A55(x)	1p dark green	.40	.40
168 A54(w)	2p dark purple	.85	.40
169 A55(x)	4½p dark blue	1.00	1.00
170 A54(w)	1sh brown	2.00	2.00
	Nos. 166-170 (5)	4.65	4.20

300th anniv. of the landing of Jan van Riebeeck at the Cape of Good Hope.

Coronation Issue

Queen Elizabeth II and Flowers — A54

Various flowers.

1953, June 2	**Photo.**	**Perf. 14**	
244 A54	1p carmine rose	.55	.30
245 A54	2p dark green	.55	.30
246 A54	4p deep magenta	1.10	.65
247 A54	6p deep blue	1.10	1.00
248 A54	1sh chestnut brown	1.60	1.25
	Nos. 244-248 (5)	4.90	3.50

Rock Painting of Two Bucks — A55   Rhinoceros Hunt — A56

Designs: 2p, "White Lady" (rock painting). 4p, Elephant and giraffe (rock painting). 4½p, Karakul lamb. 6p, Owambo blowing Kudu horn. 1sh, Ukuanjama woman. 1sh3p, Herero woman. 1sh6p, Ukuanjama girl. 2sh6p, Lioness. 5sh, Cape Oryx. 10sh, Elephant.

1954, Nov. 15	**Wmk. 201**	**Perf. 14**	
249 A55	1p rose brown	.55	.20
250 A55	2p dk brown	.55	.20
251 A56	3p brown vio	1.40	.20
252 A56	4p olive gray	1.75	.20
253 A55	4½p blue vio	1.10	.20
254 A55	6p gray green	1.50	.40
255 A55	1sh magenta	2.10	.50
256 A55	1sh3p rose brown	4.00	1.25
257 A55	1sh6p dull purple	4.50	1.10
258 A55	2sh6p yel brown	8.50	2.50

259 A55	5sh blue	19.00	6.00
260 A55	10sh dk green	37.50	16.00
	Nos. 249-260 (12)	82.45	28.75

1960	**Wmk. 330**	**Perf. 14**	
261 A55	1p rose brown	1.50	.60
262 A55	2p dark brown	1.75	.80
263 A56	3p brown vio	2.40	1.50
264 A56	4p olive gray	5.50	6.25
265 A55	1sh6p dull purple	26.00	21.00
	Nos. 261-265 (5)	37.15	30.15

General Post Office, Windhoek — A57   Fishing Industry — A58

Designs: 1c, Finger Rock, Asab. 1½c, Monument, Mounted Soldier. 2c, Quivertree (aloe dichotoma Masson). 2½c, Administrator's residence. 3c, Swakopmund Lighthouse and flamingoes. 5c, Flamingo. 7½c, Christchurch. 10c, Diamonds. 12½c, Fort Namutoni. 15c, Hardap Dam. 20c, Topaz. 50c, Tourmaline. 1r, Heliodor.

1961-63	**Wmk. 330**	**Photo.**	**Perf. 14**	
266 A57	½c blue & brown		.70	.35
267 A58	1c pale lil & brn		.35	.30
268 A58	1½c sal & dk pur		.35	.30
269 A58	2c yel & green		1.00	1.00
270 A57	2½c lt bl & red brn		.75	.35
271 A58	3c dp rose & vio bl		5.00	1.25
272 A58	3½c blue grn & ind		1.00	.40
273 A58	5c bluish gray & red		7.25	2.10
274 A58	7½c yellow & brn		.90	.90
275 A58	10c brt blue & yel		1.60	.55
276 A57	12½c yellow & ind		2.75	2.75
277 A57	15c dp brn & blue		16.00	5.00
278 A58	20c sal, brn & blk		5.50	2.10
279 A58	50c org yel & Prus grn		9.75	5.50
280 A58	1r brt blue, mar & yel		14.50	11.00
	Nos. 266-280 (15)		67.40	34.60

Issued: 3c, 10/1/62; 15c, 3/16/63; others, 2/14/61.

1962-73		**Unwmk.**	
281 A57	½c blue & brn	.60	2.25
282 A58	1½c sal & dk pur ('63)	6.75	.55
283 A58	2c yellow & grn	5.25	5.00
284 A57	2½c lt bl & red brn ('64)	7.50	7.00
285 A58	3c dp rose & vio bl ('73)	1.50	1.50
286 A58	3½c bl grn & ind ('66)	15.00	5.50
287 A58	5c bluish gray & red	7.75	3.25
	Nos. 281-287 (7)	44.35	25.05

See Nos. 304-308, 314-328.

Hardap Dam and Development A59   Centenary Emblem and S.W.A. Map A60

1963, Mar. 16		**Wmk. 330**	
294 A59	3c sepia green	.90	.90

Opening of Hardap Dam near Mariental.

1963, Aug. 30	**Unwmk.**	**Perf. 14**	

Design: 15c, Emblem and globe.

295 A60	7½c blue, blk & red	5.75	3.50
296 A60	15c brn org, blk & red	12.00	7.00

Centenary of the International Red Cross.

Assembly Hall — A61   John Calvin — A62

1964, May 14   Photo.   Wmk. 330
297 A61 3c salmon pink & vio bl   .90 .75

Issued to commemorate the opening of the new hall of the Legislative Assembly.

1964, Oct. 1   Unwmk.   Perf. 14
298 A62 2½c magenta & gold   .85 .55
299 A62 15c green & gold   4.50 3.50

John Calvin (1509-64), French theologian and leader of the Reformation.

Mail Runner, 1890 — A63   Kurt von François — A64

Wmk. 348
1965, Oct. 18   Photo.   Perf. 14
300 A63 3c red & deep brown   .55 .30
301 A64 15c green & deep brn   2.75 1.75

75th anniversary of Windhoek.

Dr. H. H. Vedder, Missionary, Educator and Senator, 90th Birthday — A65

1966, July 4   Perf. 14
302 A65 3c black & salmon   .40 .30
303 A65 15c black & light blue   2.50 2.25

Types of 1961-62
1966-67   Wmk. 348   Photo.   Perf. 14
Chalky Paper
304 A57 ½c lt blue & brn   .2.00 .50
304A A58 1c pale lil & brn   .75 .20
305 A58 2c brt yel & dp grn   .75 .20
306 A57 2½c gray blue & red brn   1.00 .20
307 A58 3½c pale grn & vio bl   4.25 2.00
308 A58 7½c brt yel & brn   4.00 .80
   Nos. 304-308 (6)   12.75 3.90

The watermark on Nos. 304, 305-308 is very faint, and these stamps can be distinguished by the shades and by the thick chalky paper. The watermark on No. 304A is clear. Issued: 2c, 2½c, 1966; others, 1967.

Camelthorn Tree — A66

Verwoerd A67   Swart A68

Design: 3c, Waves breaking against rock.

Perf. 14, 14x15 (15c)
1967, Jan. 6   Litho.   Wmk. 348
309 A66 2½c green & black   .30 .20
310 A67 3c brt blue & brown   .40 .20
311 A67 15c rose lilac & black   2.75 2.50
   Nos. 309-311 (3)   3.45 2.90

Dr. Hendrik F. Verwoerd (1901-1966), Prime Minister of South Africa.

Perf. 14x15
1968, Jan. 2   Photo.   Wmk. 359

15c, President and Mrs. C. R. Swart.

312   Strip of 3   5.00 5.00
  a. A68 3c Single, English   .60 .30
  b. A68 3c Single, Afrikaans   .60 .30
  c. A68 3c Single, German   .60 .30
313   Strip of 3   12.50 12.50
  a. A68 15c Single, English   3.25 2.50
  b. A68 15c Single, Afrikaans   3.25 2.50
  c. A68 15c Single, German   3.25 2.50

Charles Robberts Swart, 1st president of South Africa, (1961-67).

Types of 1961-62
Designs: 4c, like 2½c. 6c, Christchurch. 9c, Fort Namutoni.

1968-72   Wmk. 359   Photo.   Perf. 14
314 A57 ½c blue & brown   1.00 .25
315 A57 ½c blue & brn, redrawn ('70)   2.50 1.00
316 A58 1c pale lilac & brn ('70)   1.00 .25
317 A58 1½c salmon & dk pur   1.25 .35
318 A58 1½c sal & dk pur, redrawn ('71)   14.00 6.50
319 A58 2c yel & grn, redrawn ('70)   1.40 .35
320 A57 2½c lt bl & red brn ('70)   1.25 .25
321 A58 3c dp rose & vio bl   6.00 .30
322 A57 4c lt bl & red brn ('71)   2.00 .85
323 A58 5c bluish gray & red   4.25 .45
324 A58 6c yel & brn ('71)   8.75 3.50
325 A57 9c yel & brn ('71)   9.00 4.50
326 A58 10c brt bl & yel   20.00 1.65
327 A57 15c dp brn & bl ('72)   24.50 3.50
328 A58 20c org, brn & blk   19.00 2.00
   Nos. 314-328 (15)   115.90 25.70

Nos. 315, 318-319 are without inscription "Posgeld Incomste Postage Revenue" and the numerals have been enlarged. The ½c (#315), 2c and 10c were also issued as coils.

Water Type of South Africa, 1970
2½c, Water drop and flower. 3c, Waves, horiz.

1970, Feb. 14   Perf. 14
329 A142 2½c brown, brt bl & grn   .90 .65
330 A142 3c pale gray, bl & indigo   1.10 .80

Water '70 campaign of the South African Department of Water Affairs.

Bible Society Types of South Africa
Designs: 2½c, Sower, stained glass window. 12½c, "BIBLIA" and open book.

1970, Aug. 24   Photo.   Perf. 14
331 A143 2½c multicolored   1.10 .55
Photo.; Gold Impressed
332 A144 12½c ultra, blk & gold   11.00 8.00

South African Bible Soc., 150th anniv.

Stamp Exhibition Types of South Africa
Perf. 14x13½, 13½x14
1971, May 31   Photo.   Wmk. 359
333 A145 5c blue, yel & blk   4.00 3.25
334 A146 12½c grnsh bl, vio bl & red   47.50 27.50

Intl. Stamp Exhib. (INTERSTEX), Cape Town, May 22-31. No. 334 also for the 10th anniv. of the Antarctic Treaty pledging peaceful uses of and scientific cooperation in Antarctica.

Republic Anniversary Types of South Africa
1971, May 31   Perf. 14
335 A147 2c mag, rose red & buff   2.25 1.40
336 A148 4c blue green & black   4.50 2.00

10th anniv. of the Republic of South Africa.

Cat Type of South Africa
1972, Sept. 19   Perf. 14
337 A152 5c multicolored   4.25 3.25

Cent. of the SPCA.

Landscape, by Adolph Jentsch — A69

Designs: Various landscapes by Adolph Jentsch (1888-1977). 10c, 15c, vert.

1973, Apr. 28   Litho.   Perf. 11½x12½
338 A69 2c multicolored   .85 .85
339 A69 4c multicolored   1.40 1.40
340 A69 5c multicolored   1.75 1.75
341 A69 10c multicolored   3.75 3.75
342 A69 15c multicolored   5.50 5.50
   Nos. 338-342 (5)   13.25 13.25

Sarcocaulon Rigidum A70   Pachypodium Namaqua-num A71

Designs: 1c-50c, Various succulent plants. 1r, Welwitschia. 30c, 1r, horiz.

1973, Sept. 1   Litho.   Perf. 12½
Plants in Natural Colors
343 A70 1c light blue   .25 .25
344 A70 2c yellow   .25 .25
345 A70 3c salmon pink   .25 .25
346 A70 4c gray   .30 .25
347 A70 5c blue   .60 .25
348 A70 6c greenish gray   2.75 2.75
349 A70 7c bright yellow   1.75 1.75
350 A70 9c dull yellow   1.25 1.25
351 A70 10c blue green   .60 .25
352 A70 14c yellow green   2.25 2.25
353 A70 15c light brown   1.50 .50
354 A70 20c light olive   5.75 3.50
355 A70 25c orange   5.75 5.00
Perf. 12x12½, 12½x12
356 A71 30c dull yellow   1.50 1.00
357 A71 50c light green   2.00 1.60
358 A71 1r blue green   3.00 5.00
   Nos. 343-358 (16)   29.75 26.10

1979   Same Designs   Perf. 14
344a A70 2c   .70 .35
345a A70 3c   .70 .35
347a A70 5c   1.00 .50
351a A70 10c   1.00 .50
356a A70 30c   1.75 .75
357a A70 50c   3.00 .90
   Nos. 344a-357a (6)   8.15 3.35

Coil Stamps
1973, Sept. 1   Photo.   Perf. 14
359 A70 1c brt pink & black   1.25 .70
360 A70 2c yellow & black   .75 .60
361 A70 5c red & black   2.25 .80

1978   Perf. 14 Vertically
361A A70 1c brt pink & black   5.00 4.00
362 A70 2c yellow & black   1.50 .50
362A A70 5c red & black   1.50 .65
   Nos. 359-362A (6)   12.25 7.25

For overprints, see Nos. 423-428.

NOTE: coil stamps, Nos. 359-362A, are printed in two colors, sheet stamps are multicolored.

Chat-shrike — A72

Designs: Rare birds.

Perf. 12½x11½
1974, Feb. 13   Litho.
363 A72 4c shown   3.50 3.00
364 A72 5c Rosy-faced love-birds   5.25 3.50
365 A72 10c Damara rockjumper   12.00 11.00
366 A72 15c Ruppell's parrot   21.00 17.00
   Nos. 363-366 (4)   41.75 34.50

Rock Carvings, Twyfelfontein A73   Mining A74

1974, Apr. 10   Litho.   Perf. 12½
367 A73 4c Giraffe & horse   1.60 .90
368 A73 5c Elephant   2.50 1.25
Perf. 12x12½
Size: 37x21½mm
369 A73 15c Deer, horiz.   10.00 5.50
   Nos. 367-369 (3)   14.10 7.65

1974, Sept. 30   Perf. 12½x11½
370 A74 10c Diamonds   5.75 4.00
371 A74 15c Diamond open pit mining   7.00 5.00

Map Showing Route, Covered Wagons A75

Perf. 11½x12
1974, Nov. 13   Unwmk.
372 A75 4c yellow & multi   1.25 .85

Centenary of "Thirstland Trek" from Transvaal through Kalahari Desert to Angola.

Peregrine Falcon — A76

Designs: Protected Birds of Prey.

1975, Mar. 19   Perf. 12½x11½
373 A76 4c shown   3.00 1.75
374 A76 5c Black eagle   3.50 2.00
375 A76 10c Martial eagle   7.25 4.75
376 A76 15c Egyptian vulture   9.75 7.75
   Nos. 373-376 (4)   23.50 16.25

Kolmanskop, Ghost Diamond Mining Town — A77

Designs: 9c, German steam traction engine, 1896. 15c, Old Fort, Windhoek and statue of Colonial German trooper on horseback.

1975, July 23　Litho.　Perf. 12x12½
377	A77	5c violet & multi	.35	.30
378	A77	9c ocher & multi	.75	.75
379	A77	15c yellow & multi	1.25	1.25
		Nos. 377-379 (3)	2.35	2.30

Historic monuments.

Paintings by Otto Schröder (1913-75) A78

1975, Oct. 15　Litho.　Perf. 12x12½
380	A78	15c Luderitz	1.25	1.25
381	A78	15c Swakopmund	1.25	1.25
382	A78	15c Unloading freighters	1.25	1.25
383	A78	15c Ships at anchor, Walvis Bay	1.25	1.25
a.		Souvenir sheet of 4, #380-383	6.00	6.00
b.		Block of 4, #380-383	5.00	5.00

No. 383a has a horizontal gutter with black inscription on silver panel.

Elephants A79

Pre-historic Rock Paintings: 10c, Rhinoceros. 15c, Antelope and hunter. 20c, Hunter with bow and arrow.

1976, Mar. 12　Litho.　Perf. 12x12½
384	A79	4c red brown & multi	.25	.20
385	A79	10c red brown & multi	.60	.60
386	A79	15c red brown & multi	.90	.90
387	A79	20c red brown & multi	1.50	1.50
a.		Souvenir sheet of 4, #384-387	4.25	4.25
		Nos. 384-387 (4)	3.25	3.20

Schloss Duwisib A80

Castles Built by German Settlers: 10c, Schwerinsburg. 20c, Heynitzburg.

1976, May 14　Litho.　Perf. 12x12½
388	A80	10c multicolored	.60	.60
389	A80	15c multicolored	.90	.90
390	A80	20c multicolored	1.25	1.25
		Nos. 388-390 (3)	2.75	2.75

Nature Protection A81

1976, July 16　Litho.　Perf. 11½x12½
391	A81	4c Daman	.45	.25
392	A81	10c Dik-diks	1.10	.65
393	A81	15c Tree squirrel	1.75	1.10
		Nos. 391-393 (3)	3.30	2.00

Augustineum Training Institute, Windhoek — A82

20c, Katutura State Hospital, Windhoek.

1976, Sept. 17　Litho.　Perf. 12x12½
394	A82	15c ocher & black	.60	.60
395	A82	20c citron & black	.80	.80

Owambo Canal System A83

20c, Ruacana Dam and hydroelectric station.

1976, Nov. 19　Litho.　Perf. 12x12½
396	A83	15c multicolored	.60	.60
397	A83	20c multicolored	.80	.80

Water and electricity supply.

Sinking Ship off Namib Shore — A84

Designs: Namib Desert, various views.

1977, Mar. 29　Litho.　Perf. 12½
398	A84	4c multicolored	.20	.20
399	A84	10c multicolored	.50	.45
400	A84	15c multicolored	.75	.65
401	A84	20c multicolored	1.10	.95
		Nos. 398-401 (4)	2.55	2.25

Owambo Kraal A85

Designs: 10c, Giant grain baskets. 15c, Women pounding corn. 20c, Body painting.

1977, July 15　Litho.　Perf. 12x12½
402	A85	4c multicolored	.20	.20
403	A85	10c multicolored	.40	.40
404	A85	15c multicolored	.55	.55
405	A85	20c multicolored	.85	.85
		Nos. 402-405 (4)	2.00	2.00

Traditions of the Wambo people.

J. G. Strijdom Airport, Windhoek — A86

1977, Aug. 22　　　　Perf. 12½
406	A86	20c multicolored	.60	.50

Drostdy, Lüderitz, 1910 A87

Historic Houses: 10c, Woermannhaus, Swakopmund, 1895. 15c, Neu-Heusis, Windhoek. 20c, Schmelenhaus, Bethanie, 1814.

1977, Nov. 4　Litho.　Perf. 12x12½
407	A87	5c multicolored	.20	.20
408	A87	10c multicolored	.40	.40
409	A87	15c multicolored	.60	.60
410A	A87	20c multicolored	.80	.80
a.		Souvenir sheet of 4, #407-410	2.40	2.40
		Nos. 407-410 (4)	2.00	2.00

Side-winding Adder — A88

Small Animals of the Namib Desert: 10c, Golden sand mole. 15c, Palmato gecko. 20c, Namaqua chameleon.

1978, Feb. 6　Litho.　Perf. 12½
411	A88	4c multicolored	.20	.20
412	A88	10c multicolored	.45	.45
413	A88	15c multicolored	.65	.65
414	A88	20c multicolored	.90	.90
		Nos. 411-414 (4)	2.20	2.20

Bushman Hunter Disguised as Ostrich A89

Bushmen: 10c, Woman carrying ostrich eggs on back. 15c, Making fire. 20c, Family sitting in front of hut.

1978, Apr. 14　Litho.　Perf. 12x12½
415	A89	4c brown, buff & blk	.20	.20
416	A89	10c brown, buff & blk	.35	.35
417	A89	15c brown, buff & blk	.55	.55
418	A89	20c brown, buff & blk	.70	.70
		Nos. 415-418 (4)	1.80	1.80

Lutheran Church, Windhoek — A90

Designs: 10c, Lutheran Church, Swakopmund. 15c, Rhenish Mission Church, Otjimbingwe. 20c, Rhenish Mission Church, Keetmanshoop.

1978, June 16　Litho.　Perf. 12½
419	A90	4c ol bister & blk	.20	.20
420	A90	10c bister & blk	.35	.35
421	A90	15c pale red brn & blk	.55	.55
422	A90	20c blue gray & blk	.70	.70
a.		Souvenir sheet of 4, #419-422	1.90	1.90
		Nos. 419-422 (4)	1.80	1.80

Type of 1973 Inscribed in English, German or Afrikaans:

a, UNIVERSAL / SUFFRAGE
b, ALLGEMEINES / WAHLRECHT
c, ALGEMENE / STEMREG

1978, Nov. 1　Litho.　Perf. 12½
423		Strip of 3	.25	.25
a.-c.	A70 4c any single		.20	.20
424		Strip of 3	.30	.30
a.-c.	A70 5c any single		.20	.20
425		Strip of 3	.60	.60
a.-c.	A70 10c any single		.20	.20
426		Strip of 3	.95	.95
a.-c.	A70 15c any single		.30	.30
427		Strip of 3	1.25	1.25
a.-c.	A70 20c any single		.40	.40
428		Strip of 3	1.60	1.60
a.-c.	A70 25c any single		.55	.55
		Nos. 423-428 (6)	4.95	4.95

General suffrage. Printed se-tenant with inscriptions alternating horizontally and vertically in sheets of 30 (3x10).

Greater Flamingoes A91

Water Birds: 15c, White-breasted cormorants. 20c, Chestnut-banded plovers. 25c, White pelicans.

1979, Apr. 5　Litho.　Perf. 14x14½
429	A91	4c multicolored	.20	.20
430	A91	15c multicolored	.45	.45
431	A91	20c multicolored	.60	.60
432	A91	25c multicolored	.75	.75
		Nos. 429-432 (4)	2.00	2.00

Silver Topaz A92

1979, Nov. 26　Litho.　Perf. 14x14½
433	A92	4c shown	.35	.35
434	A92	15c Aquamarine	.55	.55
435	A92	20c Malachite	.85	.85
436	A92	25c Amethyst	1.00	1.00
		Nos. 433-436 (4)	2.75	2.75

Killer Whale — A93

1980, Mar. 25　Litho.　Perf. 14x14½
437	A93	4c shown	.35	.30

Size: 37½x21mm
438	A93	5c Humpback whale	.40	.30
439	A93	10c Southern right whale	.80	.60

Size: 57½x21mm
440	A93	15c Sperm whale, giant squid	1.40	.90
441	A93	20c Fin whale	1.90	1.25

Size: 87½x21mm
442	A93	25c Blue whale, diver	2.00	1.50
a.		Souvenir sheet of 6, #437-442	7.50	7.50
		Nos. 437-442 (6)	6.85	4.85

Impala A94

1980, June 25　Litho.　Perf. 14½x14
443	A94	5c shown	.20	.20
444	A94	10c Tsessebe	.30	.30
445	A94	15c Roan antelope	.45	.45
446	A94	20c Sable antelope	.60	.60
		Nos. 443-446 (4)	1.55	1.55

Cape Hunting Dog — A95

1980-85　　Litho.　Perf. 14½x14
447	A95	1c Black backed jackal	.25	.25
448	A95	2c shown	.25	.25
449	A95	3c Hyena	.25	.25
450	A95	4c Dorcas antelope	.25	.25
451	A95	5c Oryx	.25	.25
452	A95	6c Greater kudu	.25	.25

Perf. 14x1414½
453	A95	7c Zebra, horiz.	.25	.25
454	A95	8c Porcupine, horiz.	.25	.25
455	A95	9c Honey badger, horiz.	.25	.25
456	A95	10c Cheetah, horiz.	.25	.25
456A	A95	11c Blue wildebeest ('84)	.90	.35
456B	A95	12c Syncerus caffer, horiz. ('85)	.55	.30
c.		Booklet pane of 10	4.50	
457	A95	15c Hippopotamus, horiz.	.30	.30
458	A95	20c Taurotragus oryx, horiz.	.45	.45
459	A95	25c Rhinoceros, horiz.	.55	.55
460	A95	30c Lion, horiz.	.65	.65

Perf. 14½x14
461	A95	50c Giraffe	1.25	1.25
462	A95	1r Leopard	2.10	2.10
463	A95	2r Elephant	4.25	4.25
		Nos. 447-463 (19)	13.50	12.70

Coil Stamps

1980, Oct. 1   Litho.   Perf. 14 Vert.
464 A95 1c Suricate suricate   .45   .45
465 A95 2c Guenon   .45   .45
466 A95 5c South African chac-
                ma   .45   .45
        Nos. 464-466 (3)   1.35 1.35
        See Nos. 556-557.

Von Bach Dam, Swakop River — A96

1980, Nov. 25   Litho.   Perf. 14x14½
467 A96 5c shown   .20   .20
468 A96 10c Swakoppoort Dam   .20   .20
469 A96 15c Naute Dam   .25   .25
470 A96 20c Hardap Dam   .35   .35
        Nos. 467-470 (4)   1.00 1.00
        Water conservation in the desert.

Fish River Canyon — A97

Designs: Views of Fish River Canyon.

1981, Mar. 20   Litho.   Perf. 14½x14
471 A97 5c multicolored   .20   .20
472 A97 15c multicolored   .20   .20
473 A97 20c multicolored   .25   .25
474 A97 25c multicolored   .35   .35
        Nos. 471-474 (4)   1.00 1.00

Aloe Erinacea — A98

1981, Aug. 14
475 A98 5c shown   .20   .20
476 A98 15c Aloe viridiflora   .20   .20
477 A98 20c Aloe pearsonii   .30   .30
478 A98 25c Aloe littoralis   .35   .35
        Nos. 475-478 (4)   1.05 1.05

Paul Weiss-Haus Building, 1909,
Luderitz — A99

Designs: Historic buildings in Luderitz.

1981, Oct. 16
479 A99 5c shown   .20   .20
480 A99 15c Deutsche Afrika
                Bank, 1906   .25   .25
481 A99 20c Schroederhaus,
                1911   .35   .35
482 A99 25c Imperial P.O., 1908   .45   .45
 a.   Souvenir sheet of 4, #479-482 1.40 1.40
        Nos. 479-482 (4)   1.25 1.25

Salt
Making
A100

1981, Dec. 4   Litho.   Perf. 14x14½
483 A100 5c Salt pan   .20   .20
484 A100 15c Dumping and
                 washing   .20   .20
485 A100 20c Stockpiling   .25   .25
486 A100 25c Loading   .35   .35
        Nos. 483-486 (4)   1.00 1.00

Kalahari
Starred
Tortoise
A101

1982, Mar. 12
487 A101 5c shown   .20   .20
488 A101 15c Leopard tortoise   .25   .25
489 A101 20c Angulated tortoise   .45   .45
490 A101 25c Speckled padloper   .55   .55
        Nos. 487-490 (4)   1.45 1.45

Discoverers of South-West
Africa — A102

1982, May 28   Litho.   Perf. 14½x14
491 A102 15c Archbishop Olaus
                 Magnus, sea
                 monster   .25   .25
492 A102 20c Bartolomeu Dias,
                 ships, map   .45   .35
493 A102 25c Caravel   .70   .45
494 A102 30c Dias erecting
                 cross, Angra das
                 Voltas   .75   .55
        Nos. 491-494 (4)   2.15 1.60

The
Needle,
Upper
Brandberg
A103

Designs: Mountain peaks.

1982, Aug. 3   Litho.   Perf. 14x14½
495 A103 6c Brandberg   .20   .20
496 A103 15c Omatako twin
                 peaks   .20   .20
497 A103 20c shown   .30   .30
498 A103 25c Spitzkuppe, Kara-
                 kul sheep   .40   .40
        Nos. 495-498 (4)   1.10 1.10

Traditional
Headdress,
Herero
Tribe — A104

1982, Oct. 15   Litho.   Perf. 14x14½
499 A104 6c shown   .20   .20
500 A104 15c Himba   .25   .25
501 A104 20c Ngandjera   .35   .35
502 A104 25c Kwanyama   .45   .45
        Nos. 499-502 (4)   1.25 1.25
        See Nos. 524-527.

Fort
Vogelsang
A105

Bethany Chief Joseph
Fredericks — A106

Perf. 14x14½ (6c, 25c), 14½x14 (20c, 30-40c)
1983, Mar. 16
503 A105 6c shown   .20   .20
504 A106 20c shown   .30   .30
505 A105 25c Angra Pequena
                 Bay   .40   .40
506 A106 30c Explorer Heinrich
                 Vogelsang   .45   .45
507 A106 40c Adolf Luderitz
                 (1834-1886)   .65   .65
        Nos. 503-507 (5)   2.00 2.00
        City of Luderitz centenary (1982).

Diamond
Field, 1908
A107

Ernest Oppenheimer
(1880-1957),
Diamond Industry
Leader — A108

Perf. 14x14½ (10-20c), 14½x14 (25-40c)
1983, June 8   Litho.
508 A107 10c shown   .20   .20
509 A107 20c Field, diff.   .40   .40
510 A108 25c shown   .50   .50
511 A108 40c August Stauch,
                 prospector   .80   .80
        Nos. 508-511 (4)   1.90 1.90
        75th anniv. of discovery of diamonds at
Luderitz.

Zebras Drinking, by J.J. van
Ellinckhuijzen (b. 1940) — A109

Paintings: 20c, Rossing Mountain, by Herman H.-J. Henckert (b. 1906). 25c, Stamped-
ing Buffalo, by Fritz Krampe (1913-1966). 40c,
Erongo Mountains, by Johann Blatt (1905-
1973).

1983, Sept. 1   Perf. 14x14½
512 A109 10c multicolored   .20   .20
513 A109 20c multicolored   .35   .35
514 A109 25c multicolored   .45   .45
515 A109 40c multicolored   .70   .70
        Nos. 512-515 (4)   1.70 1.70

Lobster
Industry
A110

1983, Nov. 23   Perf. 13½x14
516 A110 10c Lobsters   .20   .20
517 A110 20c Dinghies   .35   .35
518 A110 25c Raising trap   .45   .45
519 A110 40c Packaging   .70   .70
        Nos. 516-519 (4)   1.70 1.70

Historic Buildings,
Swakopmund — A111

1984, Mar. 8   Litho.   Perf. 14x13½
520 A111 10c Hohenzollern
                 House   .20   .20
521 A111 20c Railway Station   .40   .40
522 A111 25c Imperial District
                 Bureau   .50   .50
523 A111 30c Ritterburg   .60   .60
        Nos. 520-523 (4)   1.70 1.70

Headdress Type of 1982

1984, May 25   Litho.
524 A104 11c Kwambi   .20   .20
525 A104 20c Bushman   .40   .40
526 A104 25c Kwaluudhi   .50   .50
527 A104 30c Mbukushu   .60   .60
        Nos. 524-527 (4)   1.70 1.70

German Colonization
Centenary — A112

1984, Aug. 7   Litho.   Perf. 13½x14
528 A112 11c Map, flag   .40   .40
529 A112 25c Flag raising   .70   .70
530 A112 30c Land marker   .75   .75
531 A112 45c Corvettes Elisa-
                 beth & Leipzig   1.75 1.75
        Nos. 528-531 (4)   3.60 3.60

Spring
Flowers — A113

1984, Nov. 22   Litho.   Perf. 14½x14
532 A113 11c Sweet thorn   .20   .20
533 A113 25c Camel thorn   .50   .50
534 A113 30c Hook thorn   .60   .60
535 A113 45c Candle-pod acacia   .90   .90
        Nos. 532-535 (4)   2.20 2.20

Ostrich
A114

1985, Mar. 15
536 A114 11c Head of bird   .25   .25
537 A114 25c Female nesting   .70   .70
538 A114 30c Chick, eggs   .80   .80
539 A114 50c Male mating dance   1.40 1.40
        Nos. 536-539 (4)   3.15 3.15

Historic Buildings, 1900-1912,
Windhoek — A115

1985, June 6
540 A115 12c Erkrath,
                 Gathemann Build-
                 ings, Kaiser
                 Street   .20   .20
541 A115 25c Gymnasium   .35   .35

542 A115 30c Supreme Court   .45   .45
543 A115 50c Railway Station   .80   .80
Nos. 540-543 (4)   1.80   1.80

600mm Narrow-gauge
Locomotives — A116

1985, Aug. 2
544 A116 12c Zwilling Schmal-
     spur, 1898   .35   .35
545 A116 25c Feldspur Side-Tank .70   .70
546 A116 30c Okambulum
     1904   .80   .80
547 A116 50c Henschel hd Smal-
     spoor, 1912   1.50   1.50
Nos. 544-547 (4)   3.35   3.35

Swakopmund-Tsumeb Railway line, 79th
anniv.

Endemic
Musical
Instruments
A117

1985, Oct. 17
548 A117 12c Lidumu-dumu   .20   .20
549 A117 25c Ngoma   .30   .30
550 A117 30c Okambulum
     bumbwa   .35   .35
551 A117 50c Gwashi   .60   .60
Nos. 548-551 (4)   1.45   1.45

Diogo Cao,
Portuguese
Explorer,
1486 Visit to
SWA
A118

1986, Jan. 24   *Perf. 14½x14*
552 A118 12c Erecting padroes
     on shore   .40   .40
553 A118 20c Cao coat of arms   .60   .60
554 A118 25c Caravel   .80   .80
555 A118 30c Portrait   1.00   1.00
Nos. 552-555 (4)   2.80   2.80

Wildlife Type of 1980

1986-87   **Litho.**   *Perf. 14x14½*
556 A95 14c Caracal, horiz.   4.25   4.25
557 A95 16c Warthog, horiz.   2.50   2.50

Issue dates: 14c, Apr. 1; 16c, Apr. 1, 1987.

Rock
Formations
A119

Designs: 14c, Granite bornhardt, Erongo.
20c, Vingerklip, Outjo. 25c, Aeolian sandstone, Kuiseb River. 30c, Columnar dolerite,
Twyfelfontein.

1986, Apr. 24   *Perf. 14½x14*
566 A119 14c multicolored   .35   .35
567 A119 20c multicolored   .55   .55
568 A119 25c multicolored   .70   .70
569 A119 30c multicolored   1.00   1.00
Nos. 566-569 (4)   2.60   2.60

Karakul Wool
(Swakara)
Industry — A120

1986, July 10   *Perf. 14x14½*
570 A120 14c Model   .35   .35
571 A120 20c Hand loom   .50   .50
572 A120 25c Sheep   .70   .70
573 A120 30c Rams   .80   .80
    a.   Souvenir sheet of 1   3.00   3.00
Nos. 570-573 (4)   2.35   2.35

No. 573a margin pictures design of No. 570
and Johannesburg stamp exhib. emblem. Sold
for 50c to benefit stamp exhib.

Caprivi
Strip — A121

1986, Nov. 6   **Litho.**   *Perf. 14½x14*
574 A121 14c Lake Liambezi   .40   .40
575 A121 20c Stock and crop
     farming   .65   .65
576 A121 25c Settlement   .80   .80
577 A121 30c Map   1.25   1.25
Nos. 574-577 (4)   3.10   3.10

Paintings by
Thomas
Baines
(1820-1875)
A122

Designs: 14c, *Rhenish Mission Church at
Gababis,* 1863. 20c, *Outspan in October,*
1861. 25c, *Outspan Under Oomahaama Tree,*
1862. 30c, *Swa-Kop River S.W. Africa,* 1861.

1987, Feb. 19   **Litho.**   *Perf. 14½x14*
578 A122 14c multicolored   .50   .50
579 A122 20c multicolored   .75   .75
580 A122 25c multicolored   .90   .90
    a.   Souvenir sheet of 1   3.25   3.25
581 A122 30c multicolored   1.10   1.10
Nos. 578-581 (4)   3.25   3.25

No. 580a for the natl. philatelic exhibition at
Paarl, Sept. 16-19. Sold for 50c.

Insects
A123

1987, May 7
582 A123 16c *Garreta nitens*   .75   .75
583 A123 20c *Alcimus stenurus*   .95   .95
584 A123 25c *Anthophora
     caerulea*   1.25   1.25
585 A123 30c *Hemiempusa
     capensis*   1.40   1.40
Nos. 582-585 (4)   4.35   4.35

Resorts — A124

1987, July 23
586 A124 16c Okaukuejo, Etosha
     Natl. Park   .45   .45
587 A124 20c Daan Viljoen
     Game Park   .60   .60
588 A124 25c Ai-Ais Hot Springs   .70   .70
589 A124 30c Hardap, Mariental   .85   .85
Nos. 586-589 (4)   2.60   2.60

Shipwrecks
A125

1987, Oct. 15
590 A125 16c *Hope,* 1804   .75   .75
591 A125 30c *Tilly,* 1885   1.25   1.25
592 A125 40c *Eduard Bohlen,*
     1909   1.75   1.75
593 A125 50c *Dunedin Star,*
     1942   2.25   2.25
Nos. 590-593 (4)   6.00   6.00

Discovery of the
Cape of Good
Hope by
Bartolomeu Dias,
500th
Anniv. — A126

1988, Jan. 7   *Perf. 14x14½*
594 A126 16c shown   .45   .45
595 A126 30c Caravel   .75   .75
596 A126 40c The Cantino Map,
     1502   1.10   1.10
597 A126 50c King John II   1.40   1.40
Nos. 594-597 (4)   3.70   3.70

Historic
Sites
A127

1988, Mar. 3   *Perf. 14½x14*
598 A127 16c Sossusvlei Clay
     Pans   .40   .40
599 A127 30c Sesriem Canyon   .65   .65
600 A127 40c Hoaruseb clay
     castles   .90   .90
601 A127 50c Hoba meteorite   1.50   1.50
Nos. 598-601 (4)   3.45   3.45

Postal
Service,
Cent.
A128

1988, July 7   *Perf. 14x14½*
602 A128 16c Otyimbingue P.O.,
     1888   .45   .45
603 A128 30c Windhoek P.O.,
     1904   .90   .90
604 A128 40c Mail runner, 1888   1.25   1.25
605 A128 50c Camel post, 1904   1.50   1.50
    a.   Souvenir sheet of 1   4.00   4.00
Nos. 602-605 (4)   4.10   4.10

No. 605a for the natl. philatelic exhibition
held at Windhoek, July 7-9. Sold for 1r.

Birds — A129

1988, Nov. 3
606 A129 16c *Namibornis hereo* 1.25   1.25
607 A129 30c *Ammomanes grayi* 1.75   1.75
608 A129 40c *Eupodotis rueppel-
     lii*   2.00   2.00
609 A129 50c *Tockus monteiri*   2.25   2.25
Nos. 606-609 (4)   7.25   7.25

Missionaries and Mission
Stations — A130

16c, Carl Hahn (1818-95) & Gross-Barmen
Mission. 30c, Johann Kronlein (1826-92) &
Berseba Mission. 40c, Franz Kleinschmidt
(1812-64) & Rehoboth Mission. 50c, Johann
Schmelen (1777-1848) & Bethanien Mission.

1989, Feb. 16
610 A130 16c multicolored   .45   .45
611 A130 30c multicolored   .80   .80
612 A130 40c multicolored   1.25   1.25
613 A130 50c multicolored   1.50   1.50
Nos. 610-613 (4)   4.00   4.00

Aviation
Industry,
75th Anniv.
A131

Maps and aircraft.

1989, May 18   *Perf. 14½x14*
614 A131 18c Beechcraft 1900   .90   .90
615 A131 30c Ryan Navion, 1948 1.25   1.25
616 A131 40c Junkers F13, 1930 1.75   1.75
617 A131 50c Pfalz Otto biplane,
     1914   2.25   2.25
    a.   Souvenir sheet of 1   4.75   4.75
Nos. 614-617 (4)   6.15   6.15

No. 617a has decorative bright blue and
black inscribed margin picturing emblem of
natl. philatelic exhibition WANDERERS 101,
held Sept. 6-9. Sold for 1.50r.

Namib Desert Sand Dunes — A132

1989, Aug. 14   *Perf. 14x14½*
   Size of 30c, 50c: 31x21½mm
618 A132 18c Barchan dunes   .30   .30
619 A132 30c Star dunes   .55   .55
620 A132 40c Transverse dunes   .80   .80
621 A132 50c Crescent dunes   1.00   1.00
Nos. 618-621 (4)   2.65   2.65

Suffrage, UN
Resolution
435 — A133

1989, Aug. 24
622 A133 18c dull org & gray vio   .30   .30
623 A133 35c green & blue   .60   .60
624 A133 45c yellow & purple   .85   .85
625 A133 60c golden brn & gray
     grn   1.25   1.25
Nos. 622-625 (4)   3.00   3.00

Minerals — A134

Mines
A135

1989-90   *Perf. 14½x14*
626 A134 1c Gypsum   .20   .20
627 A134 2c Fluorite   .20   .20
628 A134 5c Mimetite   .20   .20
629 A134 7c Cuprite   .20   .20
630 A134 10c Azurite   .20   .20
631 A134 18c Boltwoodite   .30   .30
631A A134 18c see footnote   14.00   8.00
632 A134 20c Dioptase   .30   .30
633 A135 25c Alluvial dia-
     mond field,
     Oranjemund   .35   .35
634 A135 30c Lead, copper
     & zinc mine,
     Tsumeb   .40   .40

635	A135	35c Zinc mine, Rosh Pinah	.50	.50
636	A134	40c Diamonds	.55	.55
637	A134	45c Wulfenite	.65	.65
638	A135	50c Tin mine, Uis	.70	.70
639	A135	1r Uranium mine, Rossing	1.50	1.50
640	A134	2r Gold	3.00	3.00
		Nos. 626-640 (16)	23.25	17.25

#631 has formula, K(H3O)(UO2)(SiO4);
#631A K2(UO2)2(SiO3)2(OH)2.5HO2O.
Issued: #631A, 10/25/90; others, 11/16/89.
This set remained in use until Namibia issued a definitive set Jan. 2, 1991.

Flora — A136

1990, Feb. 1 **Perf. 14½x14**

641	A136	18c Adenium boehmianum	.45	.45
642	A136	35c Adansonia digitata	.85	.85
643	A136	45c Kigelia africana	1.10	1.10
644	A136	60c Harpagophytum procumbens	1.40	1.40
a.		Souvenir sheet of 1	6.00	6.00
		Nos. 641-644 (4)	3.80	3.80

No. 644a margin publicizes the natl. phil. exhib. Sold for 1.50r.

SEMI-POSTAL STAMPS

Catalogue values for unused stamps in this section are for Never Hinged items.

Voortrekker Monument Issue

South Africa Nos. B1-B4 Overprinted

1935-36 **Wmk. 201** **Perf. 14**

B1	SP1	½p + ½p grn & blk, pair	4.00	7.00
a.		Single, English	.25	.85
b.		Single, Afrikaans	.25	.85
B2	SP2	1p + ½p rose & blk, pair	5.00	4.00
a.		Single, English	.30	.45
b.		Single, Afrikaans	.30	.45
B3	SP3	2p + 1p dl vio & gray, pair	17.50	10.00
a.		Single, English	.75	.90
b.		Single, Afrikaans	.75	.90
B4	SP4	3p + 1½p dp bl & gray, pair	30.00	40.00
a.		Single, English	1.50	4.50
b.		Single, Afrikaans	1.50	4.50
		Nos. B1-B4 (4)	56.50	61.00

Voortrekker Centenary Issue

South Africa Nos. B5-B8 Overprinted

1938, Dec. 14 **Perf. 14**

B5	SP5	½p + ½p dl grn & indigo, pair	10.00	12.00
a.		Single, English	.75	1.25
b.		Single, Afrikaans	.75	1.25

Perf. 15x14

B6	SP6	1p + 1p rose & sl, pair	27.50	17.00
a.		Single, English	.50	1.00
b.		Single, Afrikaans	.50	1.00
B7	SP7	1½p + 1½p Prus grn & choc, pair	29.00	32.50
a.		Single, English	1.25	2.50
b.		Single, Afrikaans	1.25	2.50
B8	SP8	3p + 3p chlky bl, pair	60.00	55.00
a.		Single, English	2.75	5.00
b.		Single, Afrikaans	2.75	5.00
		Nos. B5-B8 (4)	126.50	116.50

Same Overprint on South Africa Nos. B9-B11

1939, July 17 **Perf. 14**

B9	SP9	½p + ½p Prus grn & gray brn, pair	15.00	13.00
a.		Single, English	.85	.85
b.		Single, Afrikaans	.85	.85
B10	SP10	1p + 1p rose car & Prus grn, pair	22.50	14.00
a.		Single, English	1.00	1.00
b.		Single, Afrikaans	1.00	1.00

Perf. 15x14

B11	SP11	1½p + 1½p rose vio, dk vio & Prus grn, pair	32.50	20.00
a.		Single, English	1.25	1.25
b.		Single, Afrikaans	1.25	1.25
		Nos. B9-B11 (3)	70.00	47.00

250th anniv. of the landing of the Huguenots in South Africa. Surtax went to a fund to build a Huguenot memorial at Paarl.

AIR POST STAMPS

South Africa Nos. C5-C6 Overprinted

1930 **Unwmk.** **Perf. 14x13½**

C1	AP2	4p blue green	10.00	32.50
a.		Without period after "A"	80.00	150.00
C2	AP2	1sh orange	16.00	57.50
a.		Without period after "A"	500.00	750.00

Overprinted

C3	AP2	4p blue green	1.50	7.00
a.		Double overprint	200.00	
b.		Inverted overprint	200.00	
c.		Small "I" in "AIR"	6.00	
C4	AP2	1sh orange	4.25	17.50
a.		Double overprint	575.00	

Monoplane over Windhoek — AP3

Biplane over Windhoek — AP4

Wmk. 201

1931, Mar. 5 **Engr.** **Perf. 14**

C5	AP3	3p blue & dk brn, pair	55.00	45.00
a.		Single, English	2.00	3.00
b.		Single, Afrikaans	2.00	3.00
C6	AP4	10p brn vio & blk, pair	85.00	85.00
a.		Single, English	3.00	6.00
b.		Single, Afrikaans	3.00	6.00

POSTAGE DUE STAMPS

Postage Due Stamps of South Africa and Transvaal Overprinted like Regular Issues.
Setting I
On South Africa Nos. J11, J14

1923 **Unwmk.** **Perf. 14**

J1	D1	½p blue grn & blk, pair	6.75	30.00
a.		Single, English	.35	4.00
b.		Single, Dutch	.35	4.00
c.		As #J1, without period after "Afrika"	125.00	
d.		Inverted ovpt., pair	575.00	

J2	D1	2p vio & blk, pair	4.00	27.50
a.		Single, English	.20	4.00
b.		Single, Dutch	.20	4.00
c.		As #J2, without period after "Afrika"	150.00	150.00

On South Africa Nos. J9-J10
Rouletted 7-8

J3	D1	1p dull red & blk, pair	8.00	30.00
a.		Single, English	.20	3.00
b.		Single, Dutch	.20	3.00
c.		As #J3, without period after "Afrika"	125.00	125.00
d.		Pair, imperf. between	1,500.	
J4	D1	1½p yel brn & blk, pair	1.50	16.00
a.		Single, English	.20	1.75
b.		Single, Dutch	.20	1.75
c.		As #J4, without period after "Afrika"	110.00	110.00

On South Africa Nos. J3-J4, J6
Perf. 14
Wmk. 177

J5	D1	2p vio & blk, pair	35.00	55.00
a.		Single, English	1.75	7.50
b.		Single, Dutch	1.75	7.50
c.		As #J5, without period after "Afrika"	260.00	
J6	D1	3p ultra & blk, pair	20.00	55.00
a.		Single, English	.85	7.50
b.		Single, Dutch	.85	7.50
J7	D1	6p gray & blk, pair	32.50	60.00
a.		Single, English	2.50	12.50
b.		Single, Dutch	2.50	12.50
		Nos. J5-J7 (3)	87.50	170.00

On Transvaal Nos. J5-J6
Wmk. Multiple Crown and C A (3)

J8	D1	5p vio & blk, pair	4.50	55.00
a.		Single, English	.50	7.50
b.		Single, Dutch	.50	7.50
c.		As #J8, without period after "Afrika"	125.00	125.00
J9	D1	6p red brn & blk, pair	19.00	55.00
a.		Single, Dutch	1.75	7.50
b.		As #J9, without period after "Afrika"	225.00	

For No. J9 single in English see No. J17a and note after No. 27.
The "t" of "West" may be found partly or entirely missing on Nos. J1, J3-J6, J8-J9.

Setting II
On South Africa No. J9
Rouletted
Unwmk.

J10	D1	1p dull red & blk, pair	14,000.	
a.		Single, English	800.00	—
b.		Single, Dutch	800.00	

On South Africa Nos. J3-J4
Perf. 14
Wmk. 177

J11	D1	2p vio & blk, pair	19.00	47.50
a.		Single, English	1.25	7.00
b.		Single, Dutch	1.25	7.00
c.		As #J11, without period after "Afrika"	225.00	200.00
J12	D1	3p ultra & blk, pair	8.50	32.50
a.		Single, English	.75	5.00
b.		Single, Dutch	.75	5.00
c.		As #J12, without period after "Afrika"	110.00	125.00

On Transvaal No. J5
Wmk. Multiple Crown and C A (3)

J13	D1	5p vio & blk, pair	75.00	200.00
a.		Single, English	15.00	
b.		Single, Dutch	15.00	

Setting III
On South Africa Nos. J11, J12, J9
Unwmk.

J14	D1	½p blue grn & blk, pair	15.00	37.50
a.		Single, Dutch	.75	4.50
J15	D1	1p rose & blk, pair	23.50	37.50
a.		Single, English	.75	4.50
b.		Single, Dutch	.75	4.50

Rouletted 7

J16	D1	1p dull red & blk, pair	7.50	37.50
a.		Single, English	.20	4.00

For Nos. J14 and J16 singles in English see Nos. J1a and J3a and note after No. 27.

On Transvaal No. J6
Perf. 14
Wmk. 3

J17	D1	6p red brown & blk, pair	23.50	100.00
a.		Single, English	1.75	17.50
b.		Single, Dutch	1.75	17.50

See note below No. 27.

Setting IV
On South Africa Nos. J11-J12, J16
1924 **Unwmk.**

J18	D1	½p blue grn & blk, pair	8.50	32.50
a.		Single, English	.45	5.00
b.		Single, Dutch	.45	5.00
J19	D1	1p rose & blk, pair	8.50	32.50
a.		Single, English	.60	5.00
b.		Single, Dutch	.60	5.00
J20	D1	6p gray & blk, pair	3.00	45.00
a.		Single, English	.30	8.00
b.		Single, Dutch	.30	8.00

On Transvaal No. J5
Wmk. Multiple Crown and C A (3)

J21	D1	5p violet & blk, pair	575.00	1,100.
a.		Single, English	100.00	
b.		Single, Dutch	100.00	

Setting V

i j

"South West" 16mm wide
"Zuidwest" 12mm wide
Overprint Spaced 12mm
On South Africa Nos. J4, J11, J13

1924 **Unwmk.**

J22	D1	½p green & blk, pair	3.50	32.50
a.		Single, English	.25	6.50
b.		Single, Dutch	.25	6.50
J23	D1	1½p yel brown & blk	5.75	45.00
a.		Single, English	.50	6.50
b.		Single, Dutch	.50	6.50

Wmk. Springbok's Head (177)

J24	D1	3p ultra & black, pair	12.50	60.00
a.		Single, English	1.40	10.00
b.		Single, Dutch	1.40	10.00

On Transvaal No. J5
Wmk. Multiple Crown and C A (3)

J25	D1	5p violet & blk, pair	3.00	25.00
a.		Single, English	.40	7.50
b.		Single, Dutch	.40	7.50

Setting VI
On South Africa Nos. J4, J11-J16

1924, Dec. **Unwmk.**

J26	D1	½p blue grn & blk, pair	12.00	40.00
a.		Single, English	.60	6.00
b.		Single, Dutch	.60	6.00
J27	D1	1p rose & blk, pair	2.25	14.00
a.		Single, English	.20	1.75
b.		Single, Dutch	.20	1.75
c.		As #J27, without period after "Africa"	100.00	
J28	D1	1½p yel brown & blk, pair	5.00	35.00
a.		Single, English	.30	5.50
b.		Single, Dutch	.30	5.50
c.		As #J28, without period after "Africa"	110.00	
J29	D1	2p vio & blk, pair	3.00	19.00
a.		Single, English	.30	3.00
b.		Single, Dutch	.30	3.00
c.		As #J29, without period after "Africa"	85.00	
J30	D1	3p bl & blk, pair	5.25	20.00
a.		Single, English	.75	3.50
b.		Single, Dutch	.75	3.50
c.		As #J30, without period after "Africa"	92.50	
J31	D1	6p gray & blk, pair	13.00	57.50
a.		Single, English	1.00	12.50
b.		Single, Dutch	1.00	12.50
c.		As #J31, without period after "Africa"	170.00	
		Nos. J26-J31 (6)	40.50	185.50

Wmk. Springbok's Head (177)

J32	D1	3p ultra & black, pair	9.25	62.50
a.		Single, English	.75	9.00
b.		Single, Dutch	.75	9.00

On Transvaal No. J5
Wmk. 3

J33	D1	5p violet & blk, pair	3.25	22.50
a.		Single, English	.25	3.00
b.		Single, Dutch	.25	3.00
c.		As #J33, without period after "Africa"	92.50	75.00

Setting VIII
On South Africa Nos. J18, J13-J16

1927 **Unwmk.**

J34	D2	1p rose & blk, pair	1.25	13.00
a.		Single, English	.20	2.00
b.		Single, Afrikaans	.20	2.00
c.		As #J34, without period after "Africa"	10.50	17.50
J35	D1	1½p yel brown & blk, pair	1.25	22.50
a.		Single, English	.20	2.50
b.		Single, Afrikaans	.20	2.50

c. As #J35, without period after "Africa" 50.00 60.00
J36 D1 2p vio & blk, pair 6.00 18.00
a. Single, English .30 3.25
b. Single, Afrikaans .30 3.25
c. As #J36, without period after "Africa" 50.00 60.00
J37 D1 3p bl & blk, pair 15.00 50.00
a. Single, English 1.25 10.00
b. Single, Afrikaans 1.25 10.00
c. As #J37, without period after "Africa" 70.00 70.00
J38 D1 6p gray & blk, pair 9.00 40.00
a. Single, English 1.00 8.00
b. Single, Afrikaans 1.00 8.00
c. As #J38, without period after "Africa" 100.00 115.00
Nos. J34-J38 (5) 32.50 143.50

On Transvaal No. J5
Wmk. Multiple Crown and C A (3)
J39 D1 5p violet & blk, pair 22.50 97.50
a. Single, English 1.75 20.00
b. Single, Afrikaans 1.75 20.00

South Africa Nos. J15-J16 Overprinted

1928 Unwmk.
J79 D1 3p blue & black 1.65 12.00
a. Without period after "A" 40.00 45.00
J80 D1 6p gray & black 7.50 32.50
a. Without period after "A" 125.00

Same Overprint on South Africa Nos. J17-J21
J81 D2 ½p blue grn & blk .65 9.00
J82 D2 1p rose & black .65 4.00
a. Without period after "A" 45.00 50.00
J83 D2 2p violet & black .65 3.75
a. Without period after "A" 62.50 5.00
J84 D2 3p ultra & black 2.75 30.00
J85 D2 6p gray & black 1.75 22.50
a. Without period after "A" 62.50 225.00
Nos. J81-J85 (5) 6.45 69.25

> **Catalogue values for unused stamps in this section, from this point to the end of the section, are for Never Hinged items.**

D3   D4

Wmk. 201
1931, Feb. 23 Litho. *Perf. 12*
Size: 19x22mm
J86 D3 ½p yel green & blk 3.00 8.50
J87 D3 1p rose & black 3.00 1.65
J88 D3 2p violet & black 3.00 3.25
J89 D3 3p blue & black 8.00 18.00
J90 D3 6p gray & black 29.00 35.00
Nos. J86-J90 (5) 46.00 66.40

Photo. (Frame) & Typo. (Center)
1959 *Perf. 14½x14*
Size: 17x21mm
J91 D3 1p rose & black 2.75 15.00
J92 D3 2p violet & black 2.75 15.00
J93 D3 3p blue & black 2.75 15.00
Nos. J91-J93 (3) 8.25 45.00

1960 Wmk. 330
Size: 17x21mm
J94 D3 1p rose & black 4.00 4.50
J95 D3 3p blue & black 4.00 6.00

1961, Feb. Photo. *Perf. 14½x14*
J96 D4 1c green & black 1.00 4.25
J97 D4 2c red & black 1.00 4.25
J98 D4 4c lilac & black 1.00 4.25
J99 D4 5c blue & black 1.75 5.25
J100 D4 6c emerald & black 2.00 7.50
J101 D4 10c yellow & black 4.50 11.00
Nos. J96-J101 (6) 11.25 36.50

Type of South Africa, 1972
1972 Wmk. 359 *Perf. 14x13½*
J102 D6 1c bright green 1.25 3.75
J103 D6 8c violet blue 4.00 7.25

OFFICIAL STAMPS

Nos. 85-87 (Setting VIII) Overprinted at top with type "c" on English-inscribed Stamps and type "d" on Afrikaans-inscribed Stamps

c   d

Without Periods after Words
1927 Wmk. 201 *Perf. 14½x14*
O1 A5 ½p dk green & blk, pair 87.50 200.00
a. Single, English 9.00 25.00
b. Single, Afrikaans 9.00 25.00
O2 A6 1p car & blk, pair 87.50 200.00
a. Single, English 9.00 25.00
b. Single, Afrikaans 9.00 25.00
O3 A7 6p org & grn, pair 110.00 200.00
a. Single, English 9.50 25.00
b. Single, Afrikaans 9.50 25.00

South Africa No. 5 Overprinted As Nos. 85-87 plus "c" and "d"
Perf. 14
Wmk. 177
O4 A2 2p dull violet 190.00 275.00
a. Single, English 22.50 40.00
b. Single, Afrikaans 22.50 40.00

Nos. 96-98 Overprinted like Nos. J79-J85 at foot, Overprinted Types "c" and "d" at Top
1929 Wmk. 201 *Perf. 14½x14*
O5 A5 ½p green & blk, pair 1.25 16.50
a. Single, English .20 2.50
b. Single, Afrikaans .20 2.50
O6 A6 1p car & blk, pair 2.00 23.00
a. Single, English .20 2.50
b. Single, Afrikaans .20 2.50
O7 A7 6p org & grn, pair 4.50 23.00
a. Single, English .75 3.50
b. Single, Afrikaans .75 3.50
Nos. O5-O7 (3) 7.75 62.50

No. 99 Overprinted like Nos. J79-J85 at foot,
Overprinted at top
OFFICIAL.   OFFISIEEL.

With Periods after Words
Perf. 14
O8 A8 2p vio brn & gray, pair 2.50 17.00
a. Single, English .30 3.75
b. Single, Afrikaans .30 3.75
c. Without period after "OFFICIAL" 7.00 40.00
d. Pair, "c" + normal 2p 16.00 90.00
e. Without period after "OFFISIEEL" 7.00 40.00
f. Pair, "e" + normal 2p 16.00 90.00
g. Pair, "c" + "e" 20.00 100.00
In each sheet of 120 stamps there were 12 No. O8c and 10 No. O8e.

South Africa Nos. 23-25 Overprinted

Without Periods after Words
1929 Wmk. 201 *Perf. 14½x14*
O9 A5 ½p green & blk, pair .85 16.00
a. Single, English .20 2.50
b. Single, Afrikaans .20 2.50
O10 A6 1p car & blk, pair 1.25 16.00
a. Single, English .20 2.50
b. Single, Afrikaans .20 2.50
O11 A7 6p org & grn, pair 3.00 22.00
a. Single, English .30 6.00
b. Single, Afrikaans .30 6.00
Nos. O9-O11 (3) 5.10 54.00

South Africa No. 26 Overprinted

With Periods after Words
Perf. 14
O12 A8 2p vio brn & gray, pair 1.25 16.00
a. Single, English .20 3.50
b. Single, Afrikaans .20 3.50
c. Without period after "OFFICIAL" 3.50 35.00
d. Pair, "c" + normal 2p 12.50 70.00
e. Without period after "OFFISIEEL" 3.50 35.00
f. Pair, "e" + normal 2p 12.50 70.00
g. Pair, "c" + "e" 17.50 80.00

> **Catalogue values for unused stamps in this section, from this point to the end of the section, are for Never Hinged items.**

Nos. 108-109, 111 and 114 Overprinted in Red

1931
O13 A15 ½p green & blk, pair 15.00 22.00
a. Single, English 1.00 3.50
b. Single, Afrikaans 1.00 3.50
O14 A16 1p red & indigo, pair 1.50 19.00
a. Single, English .20 3.50
b. Single, Afrikaans .20 3.50
O15 A18 2p dk brn & dk bl, pair 3.75 11.00
a. Single, English .20 2.00
b. Single, Afrikaans .20 2.00
O16 A21 6p ol brn & bl, pair 5.75 15.00
a. Single, English .25 3.00
b. Single, Afrikaans .25 3.00
Nos. O13-O16 (4) 26.00 67.00

No. 110 Overprinted in Red

1938, July 1 Wmk. 201
O17 A17 1½p violet brn, pair 36.50 47.50
a. Single, English 2.75 6.00
b. Single, Afrikaans 2.75 6.00

Nos. 108-111, 114 Ovptd. in Red

1945-50 Wmk. 201 *Perf. 14x13½*
O18 A15 ½p grn & blk, pair 14.00 30.00
a. Single, English 1.00 4.25
b. Single, Afrikaans 1.00 4.25
O19 A16 1p red & ind, pair ('50) 9.00 17.50
a. Single, English .25 3.00
b. Single, Afrikaans .25 3.00
O20 A17 1½p vio brn, pair 40.00 50.00
a. Single, English 5.00 5.00
b. Single, Afrikaans 5.00 5.00
O21 A18 2p dk brn & dk bl, pair ('47) 675.00 875.00
a. Single, English 75.00 100.00
b. Single, Afrikaans 75.00 100.00
O22 A21 6p ol brn & bl, pair 30.00 60.00
a. Single, English .80 5.00
b. Single, Afrikaans .80 5.00
Nos. O18-O20,O22 (4) 93.00 157.50

Nos. 108-111, 114 Ovptd. in Red

1951-52
O23 A15 ½p grn & blk, pair ('52) 19.00 25.00
a. Single, English 1.25 4.00
b. Single, Afrikaans 1.25 4.00
O24 A16 1p red & ind, pair 6.00 18.00
a. Single, English .30 1.75
b. Single, Afrikaans .30 1.75
c. Ovpt. transposed, pair 110.00 82.50
d. As "c," single, English ovpt. 10.00
e. As "c," single, Afrikaans ovpt. 10.00
O25 A17 1½p violet brn, pair 30.00 30.00
a. Single, English 3.00 5.00
b. Single, Afrikaans 3.00 5.00
c. Ovpt. transposed, pair 80.00 75.00
d. As "c," single, English ovpt. 7.50
e. As "c," single, Afrikaans ovpt. 7.50
O26 A18 2p dk brn & dk bl, pair 3.00 21.00
a. Single, English .20 3.50
b. Single, Afrikaans .20 3.50
c. Ovpt. transposed, pair 70.00 90.00
d. As "c," single, English ovpt. 4.50
e. As "c," single, Afrikaans ovpt. 4.50
O27 A21 6p ol brn & blue, pair 4.00 50.00
a. Single, English .35 7.00
b. Single, Afrikaans .35 7.00
c. Ovpt. transposed, pair 27.50 110.00
d. As "c," single, English ovpt. 4.00
Nos. O23-O27 (5) 62.00 144.00

"Overprint transposed" means English inscription on Afrikaans stamp, or vice versa.
Use of official stamps ceased in Jan. 1955.

SPAIN

'spän

LOCATION — Southwestern Europe,
Iberian Peninsula
GOVT. — Monarchy
AREA — 194,884 sq. mi.
POP. — 39,167,744 (1999 est.)
CAPITAL — Madrid

Spain was a monarchy until about 1931, when a republic was established. After the Civil War (1936-39), the Spanish State of Gen. Francisco Franco was recognized. The monarchy was restored in 1975.

32 Maravedis = 8 Cuartos = 1 Real

1000 Milesimas = 100 Centimos = 1 Escudo (1866)

100 Milesimas = 1 Real

4 Reales = 1 Peseta

100 Centimos = 1 Peseta (1872)

100 Cents = 1 Euro (2002)

Catalogue values for unused stamps in this country are for Never Hinged items, beginning with Scott 909 in the regular postage section, Scott B139 in the semi-postal section, Scott C159 in the airpost section, and Scott E21 in the special delivery section.

Watermarks

Wmk. 104 — Loops

Wmk. 105 — Crossed Lines

Wmk. 116 — Crosses and Circles

Wmk. 178 — Castle

Stamps punched with a small round hole have done telegraph service. In this condition most of them sell for 20 cents to $20.

Stamps of 1854 to 1882 canceled with three parallel horizontal bars or two thin lines are remainders. Most of these are valued through No. 101.

For additional shades see the *Scott Classic Catalogue.*

Kingdom

Queen Isabella II
A1   A2

6 CUARTOS:
Type I — "T" and "O" of CUARTOS separated.
Type II — "T" and "O" joined.

Unwmk.

1850, Jan. 1   Litho.   *Imperf.*

1	A1	6c blk, thin paper (II)	675.00	16.00
a.		Thick paper (II)	675.00	25.00
b.		Thick paper (I)	800.00	20.00
c.		Thin paper (I)	800.00	32.50
2	A2	12c lilac	2,500.	300.00
a.		Thin paper	3,400.	325.00
3	A2	5r red	2,600.	300.00
4	A2	6r blue	3,350.	850.00
5	A2	10r green	4,650.	2,400.

Stamps of types A2, A3, A4, A6, A7a and A8 are inscribed "FRANCO" on the cuarto values and "CERTIFICADO," "CERTIFO" or "CERT DO" on the reales values.

A3   A4

1851, Jan. 1   Typo.

Thin Paper

6	A3	6c black	275.00	3.50
a.		Thick paper	575.00	20.00
7	A3	12c lilac	4,600.	190.00
8	A3	2r red	20,000.	11,500.
9	A3	5r rose	2,625.	275.00
a.		5r red brown (error)	22,000.	
10	A3	6r blue	4,100.	1,100.
a.		Cliche of 2r in plate of 6r	150,000.	125,000.
11	A3	10r green	2,950.	550.00

1852, Jan. 1

Thick Paper

12	A4	6c rose	400.00	3.00
a.		Thin paper	525.00	5.50
13	A4	12c lilac	2,050.	150.00
14	A4	2r pale red	16,750.	5,500.
15	A4	5r yellowish green	2,350.	125.00
16	A4	6r grnsh blue	3,600.	525.00

Arms of Madrid — A5

Isabella II — A6

1853, Jan. 1

Thin Paper

17	A5	1c bronze	2,600.	550.00
18	A5	3c bronze	15,000.	8,000.
19	A6	6c carmine rose	450.00	2.25
a.		Thick paper	675.00	16.00
b.		Thick bluish paper	900.00	22.50

20	A6	12c red violet	2,200.	125.00
21	A6	2r vermilion	11,500.	3,500.
22	A6	5r lt green	2,400.	125.00
23	A6	6r deep blue	3,250.	450.00

Nos. 17-18 were issued for use on Madrid city mail only. *They were reprinted on this white paper in duller colors.*

A7   A7a

Coat of Arms of Spain — A8

1854

Thin White Paper

24	A7	2c green	2,650.	525.00
c.		Thick paper	3,350.	850.00
25	A7a	4c carmine	400.00	2.25
a.		Thick paper	625.00	17.50
26	A8	6c carmine	325.00	1.60
27	A7a	1r indigo	3,500.	350.00
		Bar cancellation		21.00
28	A8	2r scarlet	1,675.	110.00
		Bar cancellation		10.00
c.		Thick paper	—	250.00
29	A8	5r green	1,575.	110.00
		Bar cancellation		16.00
30	A8	6r blue	2,700.	325.00
		Bar cancellation		25.00

See boxed note on bar cancellation before #1.

Thick Bluish Paper

31	A7	2c green	13,750.	2,100.
b.		Thin paper	16,000.	2,400.
32	A7a	4c carmine	425.00	6.00
c.		Thin paper	525.00	17.50
32A	A8	6c carmine	950.00	19.00
d.		Thin paper	—	100.00
33	A7a	1r pale blue		8,250.
		Bar cancellation		150.00
a.		Thin paper		9,500.
34	A8	2r dull red	7,500.	825.00
a.		Thin paper	7,500.	825.00

The 2c with watermark 104 is a proof.

Isabella II — A9

1855, Apr. 1   Wmk. 104

Blue Paper

36	A9	2c green	2,875.	140.00
a.		2c yellow green	3,475.	175.00
		Bar cancellation, #36 or 36a		10.00
37	A9	4c brown red	275.00	.80
a.		4c carmine	325.00	2.50
b.		4c lake	275.00	.90
		Bar cancellation, #37, 37a or 37b		2.50
38	A9	1r green blue	1,225.	15.00
a.		1r blue	1,350.	20.00
		Bar cancellation, #38 or 38a		5.00
b.		Cliché of 2r in plate of 1r	20,000.	3,250.
		Bar cancellation		850.00
39	A9	2r reddish violet	825.00	15.00
a.		2r deep violet	1,225.	20.00
		Bar cancellation		13.50

1856, Jan. 1   Wmk. 105

Rough Yellowish Paper

40	A9	2c green	3,500.	250.00
		Bar cancellation		15.00

41	A9	4c rose	10.50	2.25
		Bar cancellation		2.50
42	A9	1r grnsh blue	3,575.	200.00
a.		1r dull blue	4,750.	275.00
		Bar cancellation, #42 or 42a		8.50
43	A9	2r brown violet	500.00	15.00
a.		2r dark reddish violet	650.00	45.00
		Bar cancellation, #43 or 43a		7.50

1856, Apr. 11   Unwmk.

White Smooth Paper

44	A9	2c blue green	550.00	42.50
a.		2c yellow green	700.00	50.00
		Bar cancellation, #44 or 44a		7.50
45	A9	4c rose	4.50	.35
a.		4c carmine	25.00	20.00
46	A9	1r blue	21.00	25.00
a.		1r pale greenish blue	32.50	32.50
		Bar cancellation, #46 or 46a		3.75
47	A9	2r brown lilac	70.00	25.00
a.		2r dull lilac	100.00	35.00
		Bar cancellation, #47 or 47a		8.75

Three types of No. 45.

1859

48	A9	12c dark orange	150.00	
		Bar cancellation		50.00

No. 48 was never put in use. *Reprints exist.*

A10   A11

1860-61

Tinted Paper

49	A10	2c green, *grn*	350.00	21.00
		Bar cancellation		2.50
50	A10	4c orange, *grn*	42.50	.80
51	A10	12c car, *buff*	350.00	14.00
		Bar cancellation		8.75
52	A10	19c brn, buff ('61)	2,800.	1,500.
53	A10	1r blue, *grn*	275.00	12.50
		Bar cancellation		4.50
54	A10	2r lilac, *lil*	375.00	11.00
		Bar cancellation		4.50

1862, July 16

55	A11	2c dp bl, *yel*	37.50	11.00
56	A11	4c dk brn, redsh buff	2.40	.70
a.		4c brown, *white*	24.00	7.00
57	A11	12c blue, *pnksh*	45.00	9.25
		Bar cancellation		3.25
58	A11	19c car, *lil*	190.00	250.00
a.		19c carmine, *white*	300.00	275.00
59	A11	1r brown, *yel*	62.50	21.00
		Bar cancellation		3.50
60	A11	2r green, *pnksh*	37.50	14.00
		Bar cancellation		3.25
		Nos. 55-60 (6)	374.90	305.95

A12   A13

1864, Jan. 1

61	A12	2c dk bl, *lil*	55.00	20.00
62	A12	4c rose, redsh buff	2.50	.75
a.		4c carmine, *reddish buff*	22.50	7.50
63	A12	12c green, *pnksh*	47.50	14.50
64	A12	19c violet, *pnksh*	200.00	210.00
65	A12	1r brown, *grn*	200.00	90.00
		Bar cancellation		5.00
66	A12	2r bl, *pnksh*	47.50	14.50
		Bar cancellation		5.00
		Nos. 61-66 (6)	552.50	349.75

1865, Jan. 1   Litho.   _Imperf._

67	A13	2c rose	300.00	35.00
68	A13	4c blue	2,750.	
69	A13	12c blue & rose	425.00	21.00
		Bar cancellation		5.25
_a._		Frame inverted	_13,500._	1,175.
70	A13	19c brown & rose	1,500.	800.00
				100.00
71	A13	1r yellow grn	425.00	65.00
		Bar cancellation		17.50
72	A13	2r red lilac	425.00	35.00
		Bar cancellation		16.00
73	A13	2r rose	550.00	65.00
		Bar cancellation		17.50
_a._		2r salmon	475.00	70.00
		Bar cancellation		12.50

No. 68 is without gum and was never put into use.

A majority of the perforated stamps from 1865 to about 1950 are rather poorly centered. The very fine examples that are valued will be fairly well centered. Poorly centered stamps sell for less. Stamps of some issues are almost always badly centered, and our values will be for examples with fine centering. Such issues will be noted.

1865, Jan. 1   _Perf. 14_

74	A13	2c rose red	475.00	125.00
		Bar cancellation		13.50
75	A13	4c blue	37.50	.80
76	A13	12c blue & rose	575.00	60.00
		Bar cancellation		10.50
_a._		Frame inverted	_20,000._	2,050.
		As "a," bar cancel		50.00
77	A13	19c brown & rose	_3,750._	2,500.
78	A13	1r yellow grn	1,800.	525.00
		Bar cancellation		26.50
79	A13	2r violet	1,225.	250.00
		Bar cancellation		24.00
80	A13	2r rose	1,400.	350.00
_a._		2r salmon	1,400.	350.00
_b._		2r dull orange	1,400.	350.00
		Bar cancellation		35.00

Values for Nos. 74-80 are for stamps with perforations touching the frame on at least one side.

A14   A14a

1866, Jan. 1

81	A14	2c rose	250.00	32.50
		Bar cancellation		5.50
82	A14	4c blue	42.50	.80
		Bar cancellation		3.50
83	A14	12c orange	250.00	12.75
_a._		12c orange yellow	350.00	25.00
84	A14	19c brown	1,125.	525.00
				50.00
		Nos. 81-84 (4)	1,667.	571.05

1866

85	A14	10c green	300.00	27.50
		Bar cancellation		4.00
86	A14	20c lilac	200.00	21.00
		Bar cancellation		4.00
87	A14a	20c dull lilac	1,125.	75.00
		Bar cancellation		3.00
		Nos. 85-87 (3)	1,625.	123.50

For the Type A14a 20c in green, see Cuba No. 25.

A15   A15a

A15b   A15c

1867-68

88	A15	2c yellow brown	450.00	47.50
89	A15a	4c blue	27.50	1.00
90	A15b	12c orange yellow	210.00	8.00
_a._		12c dark orange	300.00	12.00
_b._		12c red orange ('68)	925.00	40.00
91	A15c	19c rose	1,450.	425.00
				22.50

See Nos. 100-102. For overprints see Nos. 114a-115a, 124-128, 124a-128a, 124c-124c, 124e-126e.

A15d   A15e

92	A15d	10c blue green	275.00	24.50
		Bar cancellation		2.50
93	A15e	20c lilac	130.00	10.50
		Bar cancellation		2.50

For overprints see Nos. 116-117, 116a-117a, 116c-117c, 117d, 117e, 117f.

A16   A17

A18   A19

94	A16	5m green	45.00	17.50
		Bar cancellation		2.50
95	A17	10m brown	45.00	17.50
_a._		Tête bêche pair	_20,000._	
96	A18	25m blue & rose	225.00	24.00
_a._		Frame inverted		50,000.
		Bar cancellation		5.00
97	A18	50m bister brown	21.00	.80
		Nos. 94-97 (4)	336.00	59.80

See No. 98. For overprints see Nos. 118-122, 118a-122a, 120c-122c, 122d, 120e, 122e, 119f, 122f.

1868-69

98	A18	25m blue	275.00	17.00
		Bar cancellation		3.50
99	A19	50m violet	25.00	.60
100	A15b	100m brown	550.00	75.00
		Bar cancellation		2.50
101	A15c	200m green	190.00	14.00
		Bar cancellation		2.50
102	A15c	19c brown	2,350.	525.00

For overprints see Nos. 123, 123a, 123c, 123e.

Provisional Government

Excellent counterfeits exist of the provisional and provincial overprints.

For Madrid

Regular Issues Handstamped in Black

1868-69

116	A15d	10c green	24.00	14.50
117	A15e	20c lilac	19.00	11.00
118	A16	5m green	14.50	5.00
119	A17	10m brown	11.00	5.00
120	A18	25m blue & rose	32.50	13.00
121	A18	25m blue	32.50	11.00
122	A18	50m bister brown	6.50	4.50
123	A19	50m violet	6.50	4.50
124	A15b	100m brown	75.00	26.00
125	A15c	200m green	24.00	8.25
126	A15c	12c orange	45.00	15.00
127	A15c	19c rose	300.00	125.00
128	A15c	19c brown	650.00	150.00
		Nos. 116-128 (13)	1,240.	392.75

Nos. 116-128 exist with handstamp in blue, a few in red. These sell for more.

For Andalusian Provinces

Regular Issues Handstamped Vertically in Blue

114a	A15	2c brown	67.50	32.50
115a	A15a	4c blue	32.50	22.50
116a	A15d	10c green	32.50	13.50
117a	A15e	20c lilac	25.00	14.00
118a	A16	5m green	17.00	7.50
119a	A17	10m brown	12.00	5.50
120a	A18	25m blue & rose	37.50	13.50
_b._		Frame inverted	_22,000._	
121a	A18	25m blue	37.50	14.00
122a	A18	50m bister brown	8.50	5.00
123a	A19	50m violet	8.50	5.00
124a	A15b	100m brown	82.50	30.00
125a	A15c	200m green	27.50	11.00
126a	A15b	12c orange yel	30.00	12.50
127a	A15c	19c rose	375.00	190.00
128a	A15c	19c brown	700.00	250.00
		Nos. 114a-128a (15)	1,493.	626.50

For Valladolid Province

Regular Issues Handstamped in Black

(Two types of overprint)

116c	A15d	10c green	35.00	15.00
117c	A15e	20c lilac	32.50	17.50
120c	A18	25m blue & rose	50.00	13.50
121c	A18	25m blue	50.00	19.00
122c	A18	50m bister brown	13.50	8.50
123c	A19	50m violet	13.50	7.00
124c	A15b	100m brown	100.00	35.00
125c	A15c	200m green	35.00	13.50
126c	A15b	12c orange	35.00	11.50
127c	A15c	19c rose	325.00	160.00
128c	A15c	19c brown	875.00	210.00
		Nos. 116c-126c (9)	364.50	140.50

For Asturias Province

Regular Issues Handstamped in Black

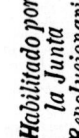

117d	A15e	20c lilac	160.00	110.00
122d	A18	50m bister brown	175.00	110.00

For Teruel Province

Regular Issues Handstamped in Black

117e	A15e	20c lilac	67.50	50.00
120e	A18	25m blue & rose	82.50	50.00
122e	A18	50m bister brown	62.50	30.00
123e	A19	50m violet	62.50	30.00
124e	A15b	100m brown	140.00	67.50
125e	A15c	200m green	100.00	40.00
126e	A15b	12c orange	85.00	55.00
		Nos. 117e-126e (7)	600.00	322.50

For Salamanca Province

Regular Issues Handstamped in Blue

117f	A15e	20c lilac	67.50	50.00
119f	A17	10m brown	60.00	37.50
122f	A18	50m bister brown	67.50	45.00
		Nos. 117f-122f (3)	195.00	132.50

Duke de la Torre Regency

"España" — A20

1870, Jan. 1   Typo.

159	A20	1m brn lil, _buff_	6.50	6.50
		Bar cancellation		2.00
_b._		1m brown lilac, _pinkish buff_	7.00	7.75
161	A20	2m blk, _pinkish_	7.75	8.00
_a._		2m black, _buff_	8.75	9.00

163	A20	4m bister brn	15.00	13.50
164	A20	10m rose	17.00	6.00
_a._		10m carmine	21.00	7.50
165	A20	25m lilac	52.50	6.50
				2.00
_a._		25m gray lilac	55.00	6.50
_b._		25m aniline violet	85.00	8.25
166	A20	50m ultra	10.00	.35
_a._		50m dull blue	125.00	5.00
167	A20	100m red brown	31.00	5.25
				2.00
_a._		100m claret	30.00	6.25
_b._		100m orange brown	30.00	5.50
168	A20	200m pale brn	27.50	5.25
				2.00
169	A20	400m green	260.00	23.50
				3.00
170	A20	1e600m dull lilac	1,350.	850.00
		Bar cancellation		22.50
171	A20	2e blue	1,100.	525.00
		Bar cancellation		27.50
172	A20	12c red brown	240.00	6.50
173	A20	19c yel grn	325.00	175.00

The 12c carmine rose and 12c blue on pink paper were never put into use. Value, $1,350.

Kingdom

A21   A22

King Amadeo
A23   A24

1872, Oct. 1   _Imperf._

174	A21	¼c ultra	2.25	2.25
_a._		Complete 1c (block of 4 ¼c)	100.00	82.50
_b._		As "a," one cliche inverted	1,800.	1,750.

See No. 221A.

1872-73   _Perf. 14_

176	A22	2c gray lilac	18.50	8.00
_a._		2c violet	29.00	18.00
_b._		_imperf._		75.00
177	A22	5c green	130.00	62.50
_a._		_imperf._	170.00	
178	A23	5c rose ('73)	21.00	5.75
179	A23	6c blue	125.00	39.00
180	A23	10c brown lilac	375.00	240.00
181	A23	10c ultra ('73)	8.00	.55
182	A23	12c gray lilac	18.50	2.25
		Bar cancellation		2.10
183	A23	20c gray vio ('73)	140.00	87.50
		Bar cancellation		5.25
184	A23	25c brown	75.00	12.00
		Bar cancellation		2.10
185	A23	40c pale red brn	65.00	10.50
		Bar cancellation		2.10
186	A23	50c deep green	105.00	11.00
		Bar cancellation		2.10
187	A24	1p lilac	105.00	55.00
		Bar cancellation		3.50
188	A24	4p red brown	650.00	625.00
		Bar cancellation		8.00
189	A24	10p deep green	2,300.	2,400.
		Bar cancellation		260.00

First Republic

Mural   "España"
Crown   A26
A25

1873, July 1   _Imperf._

190	A25	¼c green	1.00	1.00
_a._		Complete 1c (block of 4 ¼c)	37.50	19.00
		As "a," bar cancellation		2.50
_d._		As "a," ultra (error)	210.00	160.00

1873, July 1   _Perf. 14_

191	A26	2c orange	13.50	6.00
192	A26	5c claret	30.00	6.00
		Bar cancellation		2.00
193	A26	10c green	6.75	.35
		Bar cancellation		2.00
_a._		Tête bêche pair		32,500.
194	A26	20c black	85.00	22.50
		Bar cancellation		3.75
195	A26	25c deep brown	31.50	6.00
		Bar cancellation		2.00
196	A26	40c brown vio	34.00	6.00

197	A26	50c ultra	17.50	6.75
		Bar cancellation		2.00
198	A26	1p lilac	55.00	30.00
		Bar cancellation		2.00
199	A26	4p red brown	600.00	475.00
		Bar cancellation		12.50
200	A26	10p violet brn	1,850.	1,750.
		Bar cancellation		13.50

Only one example of No. 193a is known, and it is in a block of six stamps.

"Justice"
A27

Coat of Arms
A28

1874, July 1

201	A27	2c yellow	19.00	8.50
		Bar cancellation		2.10
202	A27	5c violet	36.00	10.00
		Bar cancellation		2.10
a.		5c red violet	32.50	10.00
203	A27	10c ultra	11.00	.40
a.		Imperf.	13.00	
204	A27	20c dark green	155.00	45.00
		Bar cancellation		4.00
205	A27	25c red brown	32.50	6.75
		Bar cancellation		2.10
a.		25c lilac (error)	325.00	
		Bar cancellation		30.00
b.		Imperf.		57.50
206	A27	40c violet	325.00	8.00
		Bar cancellation		2.10
a.		40c brown (error)	250.00	
b.		Imperf.	190.00	
207	A27	50c yellow	105.00	8.25
		Bar cancellation		2.10
a.		Imperf.	120.00	
208	A27	1p yellow green	90.00	34.00
		Bar cancellation		2.10
a.		1p emerald	92.50	47.50
b.		Imperf.	175.00	
209	A27	4p rose	700.00	410.00
		Bar cancellation		8.00
a.		4p carmine	800.00	600.00
210	A27	10p black	3,000.	1,900.
		Bar cancellation		10.50

1874, Oct. 1

211	A28	10c red brown	25.00	.70
		Bar cancellation		1.60
a.		10c brown	42.50	3.50
b.		Imperf.	90.00	

Kingdom

Nos. 212-221 are almost always badly centered and are often irregularly perforated. Values are for stamps with complete perforations and fine centering. Sound stamps with average centering are worth about 50% of these values. Stamps with very fine centering sell for more.

King Alfonso XII — A29

1875, Aug. 1
Blue Framed Numbers on Back, 1-100 on Each Sheet

212	A29	2c orange brown	22.50	11.00
a.		2c chocolate brown	30.00	15.00
b.		Imperf.	45.00	45.00
213	A29	5c lilac	85.00	13.00
a.		Imperf.	95.00	87.50
214	A29	10c blue	9.25	.40
		Bar cancellation		1.90
- a.		Imperf.	22.50	22.50
215	A29	20c brown orange	275.00	125.00
216	A29	25c rose	72.50	8.00
		Bar cancellation		1.90
217	A29	40c deep brown	125.00	37.50
		Bar cancellation		4.50
a.		Imperf.	140.00	140.00
218	A29	50c gray lilac	175.00	42.50
		Bar cancellation		5.25
219	A29	1p black	190.00	80.00
		Bar cancellation		3.00
220	A29	4p dark green	475.00	525.00
221	A29	10p ultra	1,650.	1,750.

1876, June 1 — Imperf.

221A	A21	¼c green	.25	.20
b.		Complete 1c (block 4 ¼c)	1.10	.30
c.		As "b," two ¼c sideways, one invtd.	110.00	110.00
d.		As "b," both upper ¼c invtd.	140.00	140.00

e.		As "b," upper left ¼c invtd.	1,000.	500.00
f.		As "b," both lower ¼c invtd.	140.00	140.00

No. 221Ac has one stamp upright, one inverted, one facing right and one facing left.

Nos. 222-230 are almost always badly centered. Values are for stamps with fine centering, fresh color and, in the case of mint stamps, full original gum. Sound stamps with average centering are worth about 50% of these values. Stamps with very fine centering sell for more.

King Alfonso XII
A30   A31

ONE PESETA:
Type I — Thin figures of value and "PESETA" in thick letters.
Type II — Thick figures of value and "PESETA" in thin letters.

Wmk. 178

1876, June 1			Engr.	Perf. 14
222	A30	5c yellow brown	14.00	3.75
223	A30	10c blue	3.75	.45
224	A30	20c bronze green	17.50	13.00
225	A30	25c brown	7.75	5.50
226	A30	40c black brown	75.00	100.00
227	A30	50c green	15.00	6.75
228	A30	1p dp blue, I	20.00	9.00
a.		1p ultra, II	27.50	13.00
229	A30	4p brown violet	47.50	55.00
230	A30	10p vermilion	125.00	125.00
		Nos. 222-230 (9)	325.50	318.45

Imperf

222a	A30	5c		11.00
223a	A30	10c		5.50
225a	A30	25c		12.00
227a	A30	50c		17.00
228b	A30	1p		25.00
229a	A30	4p		87.50
230a	A30	10p		190.00

Two plates each were used for the 5c, 10c, 25c, 50c, 1p and 10p. The 1p plates are most easily distinguished.
The 20c value also exists imperf. Value $500.

Unwmk.

1878, July 1			Typo.	Perf. 14
232	A31	2c mauve	32.50	11.00
a.		Imperf.	60.00	
233	A31	5c orange	40.00	14.00
234	A31	10c brown	7.75	.50
		Bar cancellation		.50
235	A31	20c black	160.00	125.00
a.		Imperf.	275.00	
236	A31	25c olive bister	22.50	2.75
		Bar cancellation		6.25
237	A31	40c red brown	150.00	140.00
238	A31	50c blue green	87.50	11.00
		Bar cancellation		2.00
239	A31	1p gray	72.50	21.00
		Bar cancellation		2.00
240	A31	4p violet	190.00	125.00
241	A31	10p blue	375.00	350.00
a.		Imperf.	450.00	
		Nos. 232-241 (10)	1,137.	800.25

A32   A33

1879, May 1

242	A32	2c black	8.25	4.50
		Bar cancellation		3.00
243	A32	5c gray green	14.00	1.10
		Bar cancellation		3.00
244	A32	10c rose	13.50	.45
		Bar cancellation		2.00
245	A32	20c red brown	125.00	15.00
		Bar cancellation		2.00
246	A32	25c bluish gray	14.00	.45
		Bar cancellation		2.00
247	A32	40c brown	26.00	5.50
		Bar cancellation		2.00
248	A32	50c dull buff	100.00	1.00
		Bar cancellation		2.00
a.		50c yellow	170.00	7.00
249	A32	1p brt rose	125.00	2.25
		Bar cancellation		2.00
250	A32	4p lilac gray	575.00	32.50
		Bar cancellation		3.00
251	A32	10p olive bister	1,650.	175.00
		Bar cancellation		6.25

1882, Jan. 1

252	A33	15c salmon	7.75	.20
		Bar cancellation		2.00
a.		15c reddish orange	27.50	.45
253	A33	30c red lilac	310.00	5.25
		Bar cancellation		2.00
254	A33	75c gray lilac	210.00	4.75
		Bar cancellation		2.00
a.		Imperf.	300.00	

Nos. 255-270 are usually poorly centered and often exhibit defective perforations. Values are for fine to very fine examples, well centered but not very fine, fresh and without perforation faults. Average stamps sell for about half these values.

King Alfonso XIII
A34   A35

1889-99

255	A34	2c blue green	6.00	.45
256	A34	2c black ('99)	35.00	7.25
257	A34	5c blue	11.00	.20
258	A34	5c blue grn ('99)	125.00	1.40
259	A34	10c yellow brown	13.00	.20
260	A34	10c red ('99)	225.00	4.50
261	A34	15c violet brown	4.75	.20
262	A34	20c yellow green	45.00	4.75
263	A34	25c blue	17.50	.20
264	A34	30c olive gray	72.50	5.25
265	A34	40c brown	72.50	3.00
266	A34	50c rose	70.00	2.10
267	A34	75c orange	210.00	4.25
268	A34	1p dark violet	55.00	.45
a.		1p carmine rose (error)		350.00
269	A34	4p carmine rose	650.00	47.50
270	A34	10p carmine rose	1,050.	110.00

The 15c yellow, type A34 is an official stamp listed as No. O9.
Several values exist imperf.

Nos. 272-286 are almost always badly centered. Values are for stamps with fine centering, fresh color and, if unused, full original gum. Sound stamps with average centering sell for about half these values. Very fine copies sell for more.

Control Number on Back

1900-05			Engr.	Unwmk.
272	A35	2c bister brown	3.25	.20
273	A35	5c dark green	5.75	.20
274	A35	10c rose red	9.50	.20
275	A35	15c blue black	15.50	.20
276	A35	15c dull lilac ('02)	11.50	.20
277	A35	15c purple ('05)	6.25	.20
278	A35	20c grnsh black	32.50	2.75
279	A35	25c blue	5.25	.40
280	A35	30c deep green	42.50	.35
281	A35	40c olive bister	125.00	5.00
282	A35	40c rose ('05)	300.00	4.50
283	A35	50c slate blue	32.50	.55
284	A35	1p lake	30.00	.80
285	A35	4p dk violet	250.00	22.50
286	A35	10p brown orange	225.00	72.50
		Nos. 272-286 (15)	1,094.	110.55
		Set, never hinged	1,650.	

There are numerous shades and unissued colors for this issue.

Imperf

272a	A35	2c		57.50
273a	A35	5c		25.00
274a	A35	10c		25.00
275a	A35	15c		110.00
276a	A35	15c		22.50
277a	A35	15c		17.00
278a	A35	20c		90.00
279a	A35	25c		17.00
280b	A35	30c		110.00
282a	A35	40c		300.00
283a	A35	50c		125.00
284a	A35	1p		57.50
285a	A35	4p		200.00
286a	A35	10p		190.00

The 15c in red brown (value $700), 30c blue ($900), 40c olive ($800), 1p blue green ($750) and 1p dark violet ($750) were prepared but not issued.

Nos. 287-296 are almost always badly centered. Values are for stamps with fine centering, fresh color and, if unused, full original gum. Sound stamps with average centering sell for about half these values. Very fine copies sell for more.

Don Quixote Starts Forth
A36

10c, Don Quixote attacks windmill. 15c, Meets country girls. 25c, Sancho Panza tossed in blanket. 30c, Don Quixote knighted. 40c, Tilting at sheep. 50c, On Wooden horse. 1p, Adventure with lions. 4p, In bullock cart, 10p, The Enchanted Lady.

Control Number on Back

1905, May 1				Typo.
287	A36	5c dark green	1.25	1.10
a.		Imperf.	55.00	
288	A36	10c orange red	2.50	1.75
289	A36	15c violet	2.50	1.75
a.		Imperf.	82.50	
290	A36	25c dark blue	6.75	3.25
291	A36	30c dk blue green	55.00	9.25
292	A36	40c bright rose	85.00	30.00
293	A36	50c slate	23.00	6.25
294	A36	1p rose red	260.00	80.00
295	A36	4p dk violet	125.00	80.00
296	A36	10p brown orange	190.00	125.00
		Nos. 287-296 (10)	751.00	338.35
		Set, never hinged	1,500.	

300th anniversary of the publication of Cervantes' "Don Quixote."
Counterfeits exist of Nos. 287-296.
For surcharges see Nos. 586-588, C91.

Six stamps picturing King Alfonso XIII and Queen Victoria Eugenia were put on sale Oct. 1, 1907, at the Madrid Industrial Exhibition. They were not valid for postage. Value, unused $40, mint never hinged $60.

The original labels were engraved and perf 11½. Examples printed by other methods or with other perfs are reprints. Value $2.

Alfonso
XIII — A46   A47

Blue Control Number on Back
Perf. 13x12½, 13, 13½x13, 14
1909-22   **Engr.**
297	A46	2c dark brown	.55	.55
a.	No control number		.55	.20
	Never hinged		1.00	
298	A46	5c green	1.25	.20
299	A46	10c carmine	2.10	.20
300	A46	15c violet	9.50	.20
301	A46	20c olive green	50.00	.90
302	A46	25c deep blue	4.75	.20
303	A46	30c blue green	8.50	.20
304	A46	40c rose	15.50	.65
305	A46	50c blue ('22)	11.50	.40
a.	50c slate blue		12.50	.40
	Never hinged		18.50	
306	A46	1p lake	30.00	.40
307	A46	4p deep violet	80.00	12.00
309	A46	10p orange	100.00	26.00
	Nos. 297-309 (12)		313.65	41.90
	Set, never hinged		725.00	

Nos. 297-309 exist imperforate. Value, unused $500.

The 5c exists in carmine; the 10c in yellow orange (value $400); the 15c in blue (value $400); the 4p in lake (value $1,000). The 5c and 15c are unissued trial colors, privately perforated and back-numbered. The 4p lake is known only with perfin "B.H.A." (Banco Hispano-Americano). 100 copies of the 4p exist, most poorly centered.

See Nos. 310, 315-317. For overprints see Nos. C1-C5, C58-C61.

Counterfeits exist.

Control Number on Back in Red or Orange
1917
310	A46	15c yellow ocher	3.50	.35
	Never hinged		6.00	
a.	Control number in blue		14.50	1.10

Control Number on Back in Blue
1918
313	A46	40c light red	82.50	5.75
	Never hinged		150.00	

1920   **Typo.**   **Imperf.**
314	A47	1c blue green	.20	.20

Perf. 13x12½
Litho.
315	A46	2c bister	5.00	.20
316	A46	20c violet	42.50	.20
	Nos. 314-316 (3)		47.70	.60
	Set, never hinged		145.00	

Nos. 314-315 have no control number on back.

For overprints and surcharge see Nos. 358, 449, 457, 468, 10L1, 11LB1.

1921   **Engr.**
317	A46	20c violet	30.00	.20
	Never hinged		52.50	

Madrid Post
Office — A48

1920, Oct. 1   **Typo.**   ***Perf. 13½***
Center and Portrait in Black
318	A48	1c blue green	.20	.25
319	A48	2c olive bister	.20	.25

Control Number on Back
320	A48	5c green	.90	.95
321	A48	10c red	.90	.95
322	A48	15c yellow	1.50	1.25
323	A48	20c violet	1.75	1.60
324	A48	25c gray blue	2.75	2.75
325	A48	30c dark green	6.50	5.00
326	A48	40c rose	26.50	6.75
327	A48	50c brt blue	29.00	18.50
328	A48	1p brown red	29.00	15.00
329	A48	4p brown violet	90.00	62.50
330	A48	10p orange	185.00	130.00
	Nos. 318-330 (13)		374.20	245.75
	Set, never hinged		1,100.	

Universal Postal Union Congress, Madrid, Oct. 10-Nov. 30.

Nos. 318, 320, 322-326, 330 exist perf 14. See *Scott Classic Specialized Catalogue* for listings. Nos. 318-330 exist imperforate. Value, $2,500. stamps.

King Alfonso XIII
A49   A49a

FIFTEEN CENTIMOS:
Die I — Narrow "5."
Die II — Wide "5."

TWENTY FIVE CENTIMOS:
Die I — "25" is 2¾mm high. Vertical stroke of "5" is 1mm long.
Die II — "25" is 3mm high. Vertical stroke of "5" is 1½mm long.

Perf. 11 to 14, Compound
1922-26   **Engr.**   **Unwmk.**
331	A49	2c olive green	.75	.20
a.	2c deep orange (error)		87.50	210.00
	Never hinged		110.00	

Control Number on Back
332	A49	5c red violet	3.50	.20
333	A49	5c claret	1.50	.20
334	A49	10c carmine	1.50	1.00
335	A49	10c yellow green	1.40	.20
a.	10c blue green ('23)		2.25	.20
	Never hinged		5.50	
336	A49	15c slate bl (I)	7.25	.20
a.	15c black green (II)		27.50	2.25
	Never hinged		47.50	
337	A49	20c violet	3.25	.20
338	A49	25c carmine (I)	3.25	.20
a.	25c rose red (II)		5.50	1.00
	Never hinged		11.00	
b.	25c lilac rose (error)		100.00	160.00
	Never hinged		175.00	
339	A49	30c black brn ('26)	13.50	.20
340	A49	40c deep rose	3.75	.20
341	A49	50c orange	17.50	.20
a.	50c orange red		77.50	1.90
	Never hinged		110.00	
342	A49a	1p blue black	16.50	.20
343	A49a	4p lake	77.50	3.50
344	A49a	10p brown	35.00	12.00
	Nos. 331-344 (14)		186.15	18.70
	Set, never hinged		450.00	

Nos. 331, 334, 336-344 exist imperf.
The 5c exists in vermilion (value $110); the 25c in dark blue (value $200). The 50c exists in red brown, the 4p in brown and 10p in lake; value, each $90. These five were not regularly issued.

For overprints see Nos. 359-370, 467.

"Santa
Maria" and
View of
Seville
A50

Herald of
Barcelona — A51

Exposition
Buildings — A52

King Alfonso
XIII and
View of
Barcelona
A53

1929, Feb. 15   ***Perf. 11***
345	A50	1c grnsh blue	2.25	2.25
346	A51	2c pale yel grn	.25	.25
347	A52	5c rose lake	.45	.45

Control Number on Back
348	A53	10c green	.45	.45
349	A53	15c Prus blue	.75	.75
350	A51	20c purple	.50	.50
351	A52	25c brt rose	.50	.50
352	A52	30c black brn	3.75	4.25
353	A53	40c dark blue	7.00	7.25
354	A51	50c deep orange	3.75	4.25
355	A52	1p blue black	10.50	11.00
356	A53	4p deep rose	22.50	22.50
357	A53	10p brown	60.00	62.50
	Nos. 345-357,E2 (14)		130.15	136.90
	Set, never hinged		290.00	

Perf. 14
345a	A50	1c greenish blue	.70	.70
348a	A53	10c green	20.00	37.50
349a	A53	15c Prus blue	22.50	22.50
350a	A51	20c purple	26.00	37.50
351a	A50	25c bright rose	32.50	37.50
352a	A52	30c black brown	32.50	37.50
353a	A53	40c dark blue	70.00	90.00
354a	A51	50c deep orange	32.50	37.50
355a	A52	1p blue black	32.50	37.50
356a	A53	4p deep rose	25.00	25.00
357a	A53	10p brown	110.00	140.00
	Nos. 345a-357a,E2a (12)		433.20	535.70
	Set, never hinged		700.00	

Seville and Barcelona Exhibitions.
Nos. 345-357 exist imperf. Value, $85 each.
See note after No. 432.

Sociedad
de las Naciones
LV reunión
del Consejo
Madrid

Nos. 314, 331, 333,
335-344 Overprinted in
Red or Blue

1929, June 10   **Imperf.**
358	A47	1c blue green	.50	.80

Perf. 13½x12½
359	A49	2c olive green	.50	.90
360	A49	5c claret (Bl)	.50	.90
361	A49	10c yellow green	.50	.90
362	A49	15c slate blue	.50	.90
363	A49	20c violet	.50	.90
364	A49	25c carmine (Bl)	.50	.90
365	A49	30c black brown	2.10	3.50
366	A49	40c deep blue	2.10	3.50
367	A49	50c orange (Bl)	2.10	3.50
368	A49a	1p blue black	10.00	17.50
369	A49a	4p lake (Bl)	10.00	19.00
370	A49a	10p brown (Bl)	35.00	65.00
	Nos. 358-370,E4 (14)		76.80	143.20
	Set, never hinged		150.00	

55th assembly of League of Nations at Madrid June 10-16. The stamps were available for postal use only on those days.
Nos. 359-370 values are for off-center copies. Well-centered stamps sell for about 4 times these values.

Exposition
Building — A54

1930   **Litho.**   ***Perf. 11***
371	A54	5c dk blue & salmon	5.50	5.00
372	A54	5c dk violet & blue	5.50	5.00
	Set, never hinged		19.00	

Barcelona Philatelic Congress and Exhibition. "C. F. y E. F." are the initials of "Congreso Filatelico y Exposicion Filatelica." For each admission ticket, costing 2.75 pesetas, the holder was allowed to buy one of each of these stamps.

A55

Locomotives
A56

1930, May 10   ***Perf. 14***
373	A55	1c light blue	.50	.60
374	A55	2c apple green	.50	.60

Control Number on Back
375	A55	5c lake	.50	.60
376	A55	10c yellow green	.50	.60
377	A55	15c bluish gray	.50	.60
378	A55	20c purple	.50	.60
379	A55	25c brt rose	.50	.60
380	A55	30c olive gray	1.60	1.40
381	A55	40c dark blue	1.60	1.50
382	A55	50c dk orange	3.50	4.50
383	A56	1p dark gray	4.25	5.00
384	A56	4p deep rose	77.50	60.00
385	A56	10p bister brn	300.00	300.00
	Nos. 373-385,C12-C17,E6 (20)		526.20	510.85
	Set, never hinged		1,100.	

11th Intl. Railway Congress, Madrid, 1930. These stamps were on sale May 10-21, 1930, exclusively at the Palace of the Senate in Madrid and at the Barcelona and Seville expositions.

Francisco de Goya at Age 80
("1746 1828") ("1828 1928")
A57   A59

"La Maja Desnuda" — A58

1930, June 15   **Litho.**   ***Perf. 12½***
Inscribed "Correos Espana"
386	A57	1c yellow	.20	.20
387	A57	2c bister brn	.20	.20
388	A57	5c lilac rose	.20	.20
389	A57	10c green	.20	.20

Engr.
390	A57	15c lt blue	.20	.20
391	A57	20c brown violet	.20	.20
392	A57	25c red	.20	.20
393	A57	30c brown	4.25	4.25
394	A57	40c dark blue	4.25	4.25
395	A57	50c vermilion	4.25	4.25
396	A57	1p black	5.25	5.25
397	A58	1p dark violet	.75	.65
398	A58	4p slate gray	.55	.50
399	A58	10p red brown	10.50	8.00

Inscribed "1828 Goya 1928"
Litho.
400	A59	2c olive green	.20	.20
401	A59	5c gray violet	.20	.20

Engr.
402	A59	25c rose carmine	.25	.25
	Nos. 386-402,C18-C30,CE1,E7 (32)		46.60	44.05
	Set, never hinged		60.00	

To commemorate the death of Francisco de Goya y Lucientes, painter and engraver.
Nos. 386-399 were issued in connection with the Spanish-American Exposition at Seville.
Nos. 386-402 exist imperf. Value, set $300.
See note after No. 432.

King
Alfonso XIII — A61

Two types of the 40c:

Type I   Type II

1930   *Perf. 11½, 12x11½*
406 A61 2c red brown   .20   .20

Control Number on Back
407 A61 5c black brown   .65   .20
408 A61 10c green   3.00 .20
409 A61 15c slate green   10.00 .20
410 A61 20c dark violet   5.50 .65
411 A61 25c carmine   .65   .20
412 A61 30c brown lake   14.00 1.60
413 A61 40c dk blue (I)   19.00 1.00
  a. Type II   25.00 1.00
    Never hinged   45.00
414 A61 50c orange   17.50 1.75
   Nos. 406-414 (9)   70.50 6.00
   Set, never hinged   210.00

#406-414 exist imperf. Value for set, $350.
For overprints see #450-455, 458-466, 469-487.

Bow of "Santa
Maria" — A63

Stern of "Santa
Maria" — A64

"Santa Maria," "Niña," "Pinta" — A65

Columbus Leaving Palos — A66

Columbus Arriving in America — A67

1930, Sept. 29   **Litho.**   *Perf. 12½*
418 A63 1c olive gray   .20   .20
419 A64 2c olive green   .20   .20
420 A63 2c olive green   .20   .20
421 A64 5c red brown   .20   .20
422 A63 5c red brown   .20   .20
423 A64 10c blue green   .85   .70
424 A63 15c ultra   .85   .90
425 A64 20c violet   1.25 1.10

Engr.
426 A65 25c dark red   1.25 1.10
427 A66 30c bis brn, bl & blk
      brn   6.00 5.25
428 A65 40c ultra   5.50 5.75
429 A66 50c dk vio, bl & vio
      brn   7.75 5.75
430 A65 1p black   7.75 5.75
431 A67 4p blk & dk blue   8.75 6.50
432 A67 10p red brn & dk
      brn   35.00 32.50
   Nos. 418-432,E8 (16) 77.70 68.05
   Set, never hinged   140.00

Christopher Columbus tribute.
Nos. 418 to 432 were privately produced.
Their promoters presented a certain quantity
of these labels to the Spanish Postal Authorities, who placed them on sale and allowed
them to be used for three days, retaining the
money obtained from the sale.
This note will also apply to Nos. 345-357,
386-402, 433-448, 557-571, B1-B105, C18-C57, C73-C87, CB1-CB5, CE1, E2, E7-E9,
E15 and EB1.
Many so-called "errors" of color and perforation are known.
Nos. 418-432 exist imperf. Value, set $450.
stamps.
See Nos. 2671, B194.

Arms of
Spain,
Bolivia,
Paraguay
A68

Pavilion and Map
of Central
America — A69

Exhibition
Pavilion of
Ecuador — A70

Colombia
Pavilion — A71

Dominican
Republic
Pavilion
A72

Uruguay
Pavilion
A73

Argentina
Pavilion
A74

Chile
Pavilion
A75

Brazil
Pavilion
A76

Mexico
Pavilion
A77

Cuba
Pavilion
A78

Peru
Pavilion
A79

U.S.
Pavilion
A80

Exhibition
Pavilion of
Portugal — A81

King Alfonso XIII
and Queen
Victoria — A82

Unwmk.
1930, Oct. 10   **Photo.**   *Perf. 14*
433 A68 1c blue green   .20   .20
434 A69 2c bister brown   .20   .20
435 A70 5c olive brown   .20   .20
436 A71 10c dark green   .30   .30
437 A72 15c indigo   .30   .30
438 A73 20c violet   .30   .30
439 A74 25c car rose   .30   .30
440 A75 25c car rose   .30   .30
441 A76 30c rose lilac   1.50 1.50
442 A77 40c slate blue   .90   .90
443 A78 40c slate blue   .90   .90
444 A79 50c brown org   1.50 1.50
445 A80 1p ultra   2.25 2.25
446 A81 4p brown violet   30.00 27.50
447 A82 10p brown   2.10 2.10

Perf. 11, 14
Engr.
448 A82 10p orange brown   42.50 42.50
   Nos. 433-448,C50-C57,E9 (25) 104.30 96.00
   Set, never hinged   265.00

Spanish-American Union Exhibition, Seville.
The note after No. 432 will also apply to
Nos. 433-448. All values exist imperforate.
Value, set: hinged $250; never hinged $325.
*Reprints of Nos. 433-448 have blurred colors, yellowish paper and an inferior, almost
invisible gum. They sell for about $1 per set.*

Revolutionary Issues
Madrid Issue

Regular Issues of 1920-30 Overprinted in Black,
Green or Red

On No. 314
1931   *Imperf.*
449 A47 1c blue green   .20   .20

On Nos. 406-411
Perf. 11½
450 A61 2c red brown (G)   .30   .25
451 A61 5c black brn (R)   .40   .40
452 A61 10c green   .70   .70
453 A61 15c slate grn (R)   1.40 1.50
454 A61 20c dk violet (R)   1.40 1.50
455 A61 25c carmine (G)   1.90 2.25
   Nos. 449-455,E10 (8) 10.80 11.30
   Set, never hinged   22.50

The status of Nos. 449-455, E10 has been
questioned.

First Barcelona Issue

Regular Issues of 1920-30 Overprinted in Black
or Red

On No. 314
1931   *Imperf.*
457 A47 1c blue green   .20   .20
On Nos. 406-414
Perf. 11½
458 A61 2c red brown   .20   .20
459 A61 5c black brown   .20   .20
460 A61 10c green   .55   .55
461 A61 15c slate grn (R)   .60   .60
462 A61 20c dk violet (R)   .60   .60
463 A61 25c carmine   .60   .60
464 A61 30c brown lake   4.50 4.50
465 A61 40c dk blue (R)   1.25 1.25
466 A61 50c orange   1.25 1.25
On Stamp of 1922-26
467 A49a 1p blue blk (R)   7.50 6.25
   Nos. 457-467,E11 (12) 22.45 21.20
   Set, never hinged   45.00

Nos. 457-467 are known both with and without accent over "U."
The status of Nos. 457-467, E11 has been
questioned.

Second Barcelona Issue

Regular Issues of 1920-30 Overprinted in Black or Red

On No. 314
Imperf

468	A47	1c blue green	.20	.20

On Nos. 406-414
Perf. 11½

469	A61	2c red brown	.20	.20
470	A61	5c black brown (R)	.20	.20
471	A61	10c green	.20	.20
472	A61	15c slate grn (R)	1.40	1.25
473	A61	20c dark violet (R)	.40	.45
474	A61	25c carmine	.40	.45
475	A61	30c brown lake	5.75	5.75
476	A61	40c dark blue (R)	1.25	1.25
477	A61	50c orange	4.50	3.50
		Nos. 468-477 (10)	14.50	13.45
		Set, never hinged	27.50	

The status of Nos. 469-477, C58-C61 has been questioned.

General Issue of the Republic
Nos. 406-414, 342 Overprinted in Blue or Red

1931, May 27

478	A61	2c red brown	.20	.20
479	A61	5c black brn (R)	.20	.20
480	A61	10c green (R)	.25	.20
481	A61	15c slate grn (R)	3.00	.20
482	A61	20c dk violet (R)	1.25	.75
483	A61	25c carmine	.40	.20
484	A61	30c brown lake	3.75	.75
485	A61	40c dk blue (R)	3.75	.45
486	A61	50c orange	6.50	.45
487	A49a	1p blue blk (R)	47.50	.75
		Nos. 478-487,E12 (11)	72.30	5.15
		Set, never hinged	175.00	

The setting contained 18 repetitions of "Republica Espanola" for each vertical row of 10 stamps. According to its sheet position, a stamp received different parts of the overprinted words.

Overprint position varieties include: reading down on 25c, 30c, 40c and 50c; double on 1p; double, both reading down, on 25c, 40c and 50c.

"Republica Espanola"
Stamps of various Spanish colonies overprinted "Republica Espanola" are listed with the colonies.

Fountain of Lions, The Alhambra, Granada A84

Interior of Mosque, Córdoba — A85

Alcántara Bridge and Alcazar, Toledo A86

Francisco García y Santos A87

Puerta del Sol, Madrid, on April 14, 1931 as Republic Was Proclaimed A88

Perf. 12½

1931, Oct. 10　　Unwmk.　　Engr.

491	A84	5c violet brown	.20	.25
492	A85	10c blue green	.30	.30
493	A86	15c dark violet	.30	.30
494	A85	25c deep red	.30	.30
495	A87	30c olive green	.30	.30
496	A84	40c indigo	.90	.90
497	A85	50c orange red	.90	.90
498	A86	1p black	1.75	1.75
499	A88	4p red violet	8.50	8.50
500	A88	10p red brown	27.50	30.00
		Nos. 491-500,C62-C67,CO1-		
		CO6,O20-O29 (32)	93.20	97.15
		Set, never hinged	125.00	

3rd Pan-American Postal Union Cong., Madrid.
Nos. 491-500 exist imperforate. Value, set: hinged $150; never hinged $250.

Symbolical of Montserrat Cut With a Saw — A89

Abbott Oliva and Monastery Workman — A90

"Black Virgin"
A91　　　　A92

Montserrat Monastery — A93

1931, Dec. 9　　　*Perf. 11, 14*

501	A89	1c myrtle green	1.10	1.40
a.		Perf. 14	19.00	19.00
		Never hinged	37.50	
502	A89	2c red brown	.65	1.00
a.		Perf. 14	14.00	15.00
		Never hinged	27.50	

Control Number on Back

503	A89	5c black brown	.75	1.25
a.		Perf. 14	14.00	15.00
		Never hinged	27.50	
504	A89	10c yellow green	.85	1.25
a.		Perf. 14	14.00	17.00
		Never hinged	27.50	
505	A90	15c myrtle green	1.10	1.60
a.		Perf. 14	19.00	22.50
		Never hinged	37.50	
506	A91	20c dark violet	2.25	2.25
a.		Perf. 11	100.00	140.00
		Never hinged	190.00	
507	A92	25c lake	3.25	3.25
a.		Perf. 14	5.75	6.50
		Never hinged	11.50	
508	A91	30c deep red	35.00	32.50
a.		Perf. 14	37.50	37.50
		Never hinged	77.50	
509	A93	40c dull blue	20.00	17.50
a.		Perf. 11	140.00	160.00
		Never hinged	275.00	
510	A90	50c dark orange	45.00	42.50
a.		Perf. 14	62.50	72.50
		Never hinged	125.00	
511	A92	1p gray black	45.00	42.50
a.		Perf. 11	80.00	100.00
		Never hinged	160.00	
512	A93	4p lilac rose	450.00	450.00
a.		Perf. 14	475.00	825.00
		Never hinged	875.00	
513	A92	10p deep brown	350.00	300.00
a.		Perf. 14	725.00	875.00
		Never hinged	1,400.	
		Nos. 501-511,C68-C72,E13		
		(17)	244.20	236.25
		Set, never hinged	375.00	
		Nos. 501-513,C68-C72,E13		
		(19)	1,044.	986.25
		Set, never hinged	2,100.	

Commemorative of the building of the old Monastery at Montserrat, started in 1031, and of the image of the Black Virgin (said to have been carved by St. Luke) which was crowned by Pope Leo XIII in 1881.
Nos. 501-513 exist imperforate. Value, set $4,000.
For surcharges see Nos. 589, C92-C96.

Francisco Pi y Margall — A95

Joaquín Costa — A96

Nicolás Salmerón A97

Pablo Iglesias A99

Emilio Castelar — A100

1931-32　　　*Perf. 11½*
Control Number on Back

516	A95	5c brnsh black	3.00	.30
517	A96	10c yellow green	7.25	.30
518	A97	15c slate green	4.75	.20
520	A99	25c lake	22.50	.70
b.		Imperf.	175.00	
		Never hinged	225.00	
521	A99	30c carmine rose	7.25	.20
c.		Imperf.	82.50	
		Never hinged	125.00	
522	A100	40c dark blue	42.50	4.50
523	A97	50c orange	52.50	7.75
		Nos. 516-523 (7)	139.75	13.95
		Set, never hinged	400.00	

Without Control Number

516a	A95	5c brownish blk ('32)	4.50	.20
517a	A96	10c yel grn ('32)	4.00	.20
518a	A97	15c slate green ('32)	.60	.20
520a	A99	25c lake	32.50	.20
521a	A99	30c carmine rose	1.90	.20
522a	A100	40c dark blue ('32)	.20	.20
523a	A97	50c orange ('32)	26.00	.20
		Nos. 516a-523a (7)	69.70	1.70
		Set, never hinged	150.00	

Without Control Number, Imperf.

516b	A95	5c	6.50
517b	A96	10c	11.00
518b	A97	15c	6.25
520c	A99	25c	110.00
521b	A99	30c	5.50
522b	A100	40c	14.00
523b	A97	50c	125.00
		Nos. 516b-523b (7)	278.25
		Set, never hinged	550.00

See Nos. 532, 538, 550, 579, 579a.
For overprints and surcharges see Nos. 7LC12-7LC13, 7LC15-7LC16, 7LC18, 7LE4, 8LB6, 8LB9-8LB10, 9LC17-9LC18, 10L7, 10L10-10L12, 10L16-10L18, 10L22-10L23, 11L7, 11L10-11L12, 11LB8, 12L4, 12L8, 12L11-12L12, 13L8, 14L6, 14L10-14L12, 14L18, 14L22-14L24.

Blasco Ibáñez A103

Manuel Ruiz-Zorrilla A104

Without Control Number

1931-34　　　*Perf. 11½*

526	A103	2c red brown ('32)	.20	.20
528	A103	5c chocolate ('34)	.20	.20
532	A95	20c dark violet	.25	.20
534	A104	25c lake ('34)	.45	.20
538	A100	60c apple green ('32)	.20	.20
		Nos. 526-538 (5)	1.30	1.00
		Set, never hinged	2.50	

Imperf

526a	A103	2c	14.00
528a	A103	5c	2.75
532a	A95	20c	6.25
534a	A104	25c	5.25
538a	A100	60c	6.25
		Nos. 526a-538a (5)	34.50
		Set, never hinged	70.00

For overprints and surcharges see Nos. 8LB3, 8LB7, 9LC3, 9LC8-9LC9, 9LC14, 10L6, 10L13, 11L4, 11L8, 11LB5, 11LB9, 12L5, 12L9, 13L5, 13L7, 14L3, 14L7, 14L15, 14L19.

Cliff Houses, Cuenca — A105

Alcázar of Segovia — A106

Gate of the Sun at Toledo — A107

1932-38　　　*Perf. 10*

539	A105	1p gray black ('38)	.20	.20
540	A106	4p magenta ('38)	.30	.40
541	A107	10p deep brn ('38)	.65	.70
		Nos. 539-541 (3)	1.15	1.30
		Set, never hinged	2.75	

Imperf

539a	A105	1p	5.25	2.75
540a	A106	4p	9.00	6.50
541a	A107	10p	6.50	6.00
		Nos. 539a-541a (3)	20.75	15.25
		Set, never hinged	45.00	

Perf. 11½

539b	A105	1p	.20	.20
540b	A106	4p	.70	.85
541b	A107	10p	1.90	3.00
		Nos. 539b-541b (3)	2.80	4.05
		Set, never hinged	5.00	

For overprints and surcharge see Nos. 9LC19, 10L19, 13L9, 14L25, 14L27-14L28.

Numeral
A108

Santiago
Ramón y
Cajal
A109

1933   Unwmk.   Typo.   Imperf.
542 A108 1c blue green   .20   .20

Perf. 11½
543 A108 2c buff   .20   .20
 a. Perf. 13½x13   .65   .20
   Never hinged   1.40
   Set, never hinged   .65

See Nos. 592-597. For surcharges and overprints see Nos. 590-590A, 634A-634D, 8LB1-8LB2, 9LC1-9LC2, 9LC4-9LC7, 9LC11-9LC12, 9LC20, 9LC26, 10L2-10L4, 11L1-11L2, 11LB2-11LB3, 12L1-12L2, 13L1-13L3, 14L1, 14L13.

1934   Engr.   Perf. 11½x11
545 A109 30c black brown   6.00   1.10
   Never hinged   15.00
 a. Perf. 14   22.50 30.00
   Never hinged   42.50
 b. Imperf.   32.50
   Never hinged   55.00

Type of 1931 and

Mariana
Pineda
A110

Concepción
Arenal
A111

Gumersindo
de Azcarate
A112

Gaspar
Melchor de
Jovellanos
A113

1935-36
546 A110 10c light green   .20   .20
 b. 10c blue green ('36)   .20   .20
547 A111 15c dark green   .20   .20
 b. 15c yellow green ('36)   .20   .20
548 A112 30c carmine rose   7.25
549 A113 30c rose red   .20   .20
550 A97 50c dark blue   1.00   .30
   Nos. 546-550 (5)   8.85   1.10
   Set, never hinged   20.00

Imperf.
546a A110 10c   1.60
547a A111 15c   5.25
548a A112 30c   26.00
549a A113 30c   1.90
550a A97 50c   225.00
   Nos. 546a-550a (5)   259.75
   Set, never hinged   500.00

Shades exist.
For overprints and surcharges see Nos. 7LE3, 8LB4-8LB5, 8LB8, 10L8-10L9, 10L14, 10L20-10L21, 11L5-11L6, 11L9, 11LB6-11LB7, 11LB10, 12L6-12L7, 12L10, 13L6, 14L4-14L5, 14L8, 14L16-14L17, 14L20.

Lope's
Bookplate
A116

Lope de
Vega
A117

Alcántara
and Alcázar,
Toledo
A118

1935, Oct. 12   Perf. 11½x11, 11x11½
552 A116 15c myrtle green   6.25   .30
553 A117 30c rose red   2.75   .30
554 A117 50c dark blue   12.00 3.00
555 A118 1p blue black   23.00 2.00
   Nos. 552-555 (4)   44.00 5.60
   Set, never hinged   110.00

Imperf
552a A116 15c   400.00
553a A117 30c   11.00
554a A117 50c   65.00
555a A118 1p   60.00
   Nos. 552a-555a (4)   536.00
   Set, never hinged   925.00

Perf. 14
553b A117 30c   6.50 14.50
554b A117 50c   29.00 45.00
555b A118 1p   32.50 50.00
   Nos. 553b-555b (3)   68.00 109.50
   Set, never hinged   150.00

Lope Felix de Vega Carpio (1562-1635), Spanish dramatist and poet.
For surcharge see No. 11LB11.

Map of Amazon
by Bartolomeo
Oliva, 16th
Century
A119

1935, Oct. 12   Perf. 11½
556 A119 30c rose red   2.10   .95
   Never hinged   4.50
 a. Perf. 14   26.00
   Never hinged   54.00
 b. Imperf.   37.50
   Never hinged   72.50

Proposed Iglesias Amazon Expedition.

Miguel
Moya — A120

Torcuato Luca
de Tena — A121

José Francos
Rodríguez
A122

Alejandro
Lerroux
A123

Nazareth School and Rotary
Press — A124

1936, Feb. 14   Photo.   Perf. 12½
Size: 22x26mm
557 A120 1c crimson   .20   .20
558 A121 2c orange brown   .20   .20
559 A122 5c black brown   .20   .20
560 A123 10c emerald   .20   .20

Size: 24x28½mm
561 A120 15c blue green   .20   .20
562 A121 20c violet   .20   .20
563 A122 25c red violet   .20   .20
564 A123 30c crimson   .20   .20

Size: 25½x30½mm
565 A120 40c orange   .50   .35
566 A121 50c ultra   .20   .20
567 A122 60c olive green   .50   .35
568 A123 1p gray black   .50   .35
569 A124 2p lt blue   6.50 3.00

---

570 A124 4p lilac rose   6.50   6.00
571 A124 10p red brown   17.00 14.00
   Nos. 557-571,E15 (16)   33.55 26.15
   Set, never hinged   55.00
   Nos. 557-571,C73-C87,E15 (31) 61.25 45.00
   Set, never hinged   110.00

Madrid Press Association, 40th anniversary.
   Nos. 557-571 exist imperf. Values about 7 times those of perf. stamps.
   See note after No. 432. See Nos. C73-C87.

Arms of
Madrid — A125

1936, Apr. 2   Engr.   Imperf.
572 A125 10c brown black   47.50 47.50
573 A125 30c dark green   47.50 47.50
   Set, never hinged   135.00

1st National Philatelic Exhibition which opened in Madrid, Apr. 2, 1936.
   For overprints see Nos. C88-C89.

"Republica
Espanola"
A126

Gregorio
Fernández
A127

1936   Litho.   Perf. 11½, 13½x13
574 A126 2c orange brown   .20   .20
   Never hinged   .35

For surcharges & overprints see #591, 9LC24, 10L5, 11L3, 11LB4, 12L3, 13L4, 14L2, 14L14.

1936, Mar. 10   Engr.   Perf. 11½
576 A127 30c carmine   1.10   .85
   Never hinged   2.00
 a. Perf. 14   9.00   8.25
   Never hinged   17.50
 b. Imperf.   15.00
   Never hinged   22.50

Tercentenary of the death of Gregorio Fernandez, sculptor.
For overprints see Nos. 7LC20-7LC21.

Type of 1931 and

Pablo Iglesias
A128   A129

Velázquez
A130

Fermín
Salvoechea
A131

1936-38   Perf. 11, 11½, 11½x11
577 A128 30c rose red   .20   .20
578 A129 30c car rose   1.10   .50
579 A100 40c car rose ('37) 1.10   .50
580 A129 45c carmine ('37)   .20   .20
581 A130 50c dark blue   .20   .20
582 A131 60c indigo ('37)   .75   .90
583 A131 60c dp orange ('38) 6.00 5.00
   Nos. 577-583 (7)   9.55 7.50
   Set, never hinged   26.00

Perf. 14
577a A128 30c rose red   6.50
578a A129 30c carmine rose   6.75
579a A100 40c carmine rose   6.50
580a A129 45c carmine   6.00

582a A131 60c indigo   6.00
583a A131 60c deep orange   9.50
   Nos. 577a-583a (6)   41.25
   Set, never hinged   90.00

Nos. 577-583 exist imperf. Value, set $70.
   Set, never hinged, $150.
   For overprints see Nos. C90, 7LC17, 7LC22-7LC23, 10L15, 14L21.

Statue of Liberty, Spanish and US
Flags — A132

1938, June 1   Photo.   Perf. 11½
585 A132 1p multicolored   15.00 16.00
   Never hinged   26.00
 a. Imperf., pair   75.00 50.00
   Never hinged   100.00
 b. Horiz. pair, imperf. vert. 57.50 75.00
   Never hinged   85.00
 c. Souvenir sheet of 1   25.00 30.00
   Never hinged   40.00
 d. As "c," imperf.   275.00 225.00
   Never hinged   475.00

150th anniv. of the U.S. Constitution.
For surcharge see No. C97.

No. 289 Surcharged in Black

1938   Perf. 14
586 A36 45c on 15c violet   14.00 14.00
   Never hinged   17.50

7th anniversary of the Republic.
Values are for examples with perforations nearly touching the design on one or two sides.

No. 289 Surcharged in Black:

a

b

1938, May 1
587 A36 45c on 15c violet   3.00   3.00
588 A36 1p on 15c violet   5.25   5.25
   Set, never hinged   12.00

Issued to commemorate Labor Day.
Values are for examples with perforations nearly touching the design on one or two sides.

No. 507 Surcharged in Black

1938, Nov. 10   *Perf. 11½*
589 A92 2.50p on 25c lake   .20   .20
   Never hinged   .20
b.   Perf. 14   3.50   6.00
   Never hinged   6.00

Types of 1933-36
Surcharged in Blue or
Red

1938   *Perf. 10, 11, 13½x13, 13x14*
590 A108 45c on 1c grn (R)   .40   .25
b.   Imperf.   6.00   5.00
   Never hinged   10.00
590A A108 45c on 2c buff (Bl)   17.00   14.00
591 A126 45c on 2c org brn
     (Bl)   .20   .20
   Nos. 590-591 (3)   17.60   14.45
   Set, never hinged   29.00

   Many overprint varieties exist.

Numeral Type of 1933
1938-39   Litho.   *Perf. 11½, 13*
White or Gray Paper
592 A108 5c gray brown   .20   .20
593 A108 10c yellow green   .20   .20
594 A108 15c slate gray   .20   .20
595 A108 20c vio, gray paper   .20   .20
596 A108 25c red violet   .20   .20
597 A108 30c scarlet   .20   .20
   Nos. 592-597 (6)   1.20   1.20
   Set, never hinged   1.40

"Republic" — A133

1938   *Perf. 11½*
598 A133 40c rose red   .20   .20
599 A133 45c car rose   .20   .20
a.   Printed on both sides   11.00   11.00
   Never hinged   27.50
600 A133 50c ultra   .20   .20
601 A133 60c dp ultra   .50   .30
   Nos. 598-601 (4)   1.10   .90
   Set, never hinged   1.10

   Nos. 598-601 exist imperf. Value for set
$22.50.

Machine
Gunners
A134

Infantry — A135

Perf. 11½x11, 11x11½, Imperf.
1938, Sept. 1   **Photo.**
602 A134 25c dark green   9.25   9.25
603 A135 45c red brown   9.25   9.25
   Set, never hinged   50.00

   43rd Division of the Republican Army. Sold
only at the Philatelic Agency and for foreign
exchange.

Blast Furnace   Steel Mill and
A136   Sculpture,
             "Defenders of
             Numantia"
             A137

1938, Aug. 9   *Perf. 16*
604 A136 45c black   .20   .20
605 A137 1.25p dark blue   .20   .20
   Set, never hinged   .30

   Issued in honor of the workers of Sagunto.

Submarine — A137a

   Designs: 1p, 15p, U-Boat D1. 2p, 6p, U-
Boat A1. 4p, 10p, U-Boat B2.

1938, Aug. 11   *Perf. 16*
605A A137a 1p blue   5.50   5.50
605B A137a 2p red brown   10.00   10.00
605C A137a 4p red orange   12.00   12.00
605D A137a 6p deep blue   27.50   27.50
605E A137a 10p magenta   45.00   45.00
605F A137a 15p dp gray
       green   500.00   500.00
   Nos. 605A-605F (6)   600.00   600.00
   Set, never hinged   725.00

Souvenir Sheet
Perf. 10½
605G A137a Sheet of 3   550.00   550.00
   Never hinged   700.00
a.   4p carmine & gray
     black   125.00   125.00
b.   6p dull blue & gray
     black   125.00   125.00
c.   15p green & gray black   125.00   125.00

   Nos. 605A-605G were issued for use on a
proposed submarine mail service between
Barcelona and Mahon, Minorca. One voyage
was made on this mail route, carrying 300
agency-prepared covers. The stamps were
also valid for ordinary mail.
   Nos. 605A-605G were sold only at the Philatelic Agency in Barcelona, for double their
face value.
   Nos. 605A-605G exist imperf. Value: set of 6
stamps, $775 unused, $1,000 never hinged;
souvenir sheet, $2,250 unused, $2,900 never
hinged.

Riflemen
A138

Machine
Gunners
A139

Bomb
Throwing — A140

1938, Nov. 25   Engr.   *Perf. 10*
606 A138 5c sepia   3.50   3.50
607 A138 10c dp violet   3.50   3.50
608 A138 25c blue green   3.50   3.50
609 A139 45c rose red   3.50   3.50
610 A139 60c dark blue   6.25   6.25
611 A139 1.20p black   125.00   125.00
612 A140 2p orange   37.50   37.50
613 A140 5p dark brown   220.00   220.00
614 A140 10p dk blue grn   40.00   40.00
   Nos. 606-614 (9)   442.75   442.75
   Set, never hinged   725.00

   Honoring the Militia. Sold only at the Philatelic Agency and for foreign exchange. Exist
imperf. Value, set $1,200. Set, never hinged,
$1,800.

Spanish State

Arms of Spain — A141

1936   Litho.   *Imperf.*
Thin Transparent Paper
615 A141 30c blue   190.00
616 A141 30c pale green   190.00
Perf. 11
Thick Wove Paper
617 A141 30c dark blue   550.00   110.00
   Set, never hinged   1,200.

   Issued in Granada during siege. After the
city was liberated, these stamps were used
throughout the province of Granada.
   Well-centered copies of No. 617 are worth
twice as much as the values above.
   Many forgeries exist.

A143   Cathedral of
             Burgos — A145

University of
Salamanca
A146

Cathedral del Pilar,   "La Giralda,"
Zaragoza — A147   Seville — A148

Xavier Castle,
Navarre — A149

Court of Lions,
Alhambra at
Granada
A150

Mosque,
Córdoba
A151

Alcántara Bridge   Soldier Carrying
and Alcázar,   Flag — A153
Toledo — A152

Troops Landing
at Algeciras
A154

   Two types of 30c:
   Type I — Imprint 12mm long; "3" does not
touch frame.
   Type II — Imprint 8mm long; "3" touches
frame.

1936   Unwmk.   Litho.   *Imperf.*
623 A143 1c green   6.00   4.50
Perf. 11½
624 A143 2c orange brown   .60   .45
625 A145 5c gray brown   .60   .55
626 A146 10c green   .60   .45
627 A147 15c dull green   .60   .45
628 A148 25c rose lake   .85   .45
629 A149 30c carmine (I)   .60   .45
a.   Type II   .70   .55
   Never hinged   1.40
630 A150 50c deep blue   14.00   8.75
631 A151 60c yellow green   .95   .70
632 A152 1p black   5.25   3.75
633 A153 4p rose vio, red &
       yel   52.50   29.00
634 A154 10p light brown   52.50   29.00
   Nos. 623-634 (12)   135.05   78.50
   Set, never hinged   240.00

   Nos. 624-634 exist imperf. Value, set $275.
   Nos. 625-631, 633-634 were privately overprinted "VIA AEREA" and plane, supposedly
for use in Ifni.
   For surcharges see Nos. 9LC21, 9LC23.

   Nos. 542-543 Surcharged "Habilitado
0'05 ptas." in Two Lines
1936   *Imperf., Perf. 11½*
634A A108 5c on 1c bl grn   2.25   3.00
634B A108 5c on 2c buff   2.25   3.00
634C A108 10c on 1c bl grn   2.25   3.00
634D A108 15c on 2c buff   2.25   3.00
   Nos. 634A-634D (4)   9.00   12.00
   Set, never hinged   15.00

   Issued in the Balearic Islands to meet a
shortage of these values. Nos. 634A and
634C are imperf., Nos. 634B and 634D are
perf. 11½.

St. James of
Compostela — A155

St. James
Cathedral
A156

Pórtico de
la Gloria
A157

   Two types of 30c:
   I — No dots in "1937."
   II — Dot before and after "1937."

1937   *Perf. 11½, 11x11½*
635 A155 15c violet brown   .95   1.25
636 A156 30c rose red (I)   5.00   .55
a.   Type II   17.50   14.00
   Never hinged   35.00

637	A157	1p blue & org	14.50	3.25
a.		Center inverted	275.00	250.00
		Never hinged	425.00	
		Nos. 635-637 (3)	20.45	5.05
		Set, never hinged	50.00	

Holy Year of Compostela. Nos. 635-637 exist imperf. Value for set $150.

"Estado Espanol"
A159   A160

"El Cid" — A161   Isabella I — A162

Two types of 5c, 30c and 10p:
5 Centimos: Type I Imprint 9½mm long. Type II Imprint 14mm long.
30 Centimos: Type I Imprint, "Hija De B. Fournier Burgos." Type II Imprint, "Fournier Burgos".
10 Pesetas: Type I "10" 2½mm high. Type II "10" 3mm high.

With Imprint

1936-40 Imperf.

638	A159	1c green	.20	.20

Perf. 11

640	A160	2c brown	.20	.20

Perf. 11, 11½, 11½x11, 11½x10½

641	A161	5c brown (I)	.45	.20
642	A161	5c brown (II)	.20	.20
643	A161	10c green	.20	.20

Perf. 11, 11x11½

644	A162	15c gray black	.20	.20
645	A162	20c dark violet	.40	.20
646	A162	25c brown lake	.20	.20
647	A162	30c rose (I)	.50	.20
648	A162	30c rose (II)	17.50	2.10
649	A162	40c orange	1.60	.20
650	A162	50c dark blue	1.60	.20
651	A162	60c yellow	.30	.20
652	A162	1p blue	16.50	.50
653	A162	4p magenta	21.00	5.25
654	A161	10p dk bl (I) ('37)	75.00	40.00
655	A161	10p dp bl (II) ('40)	32.50	15.00
		Nos. 638-655 (17)	168.55	65.25
		Set, never hinged	375.00	

No. 638 was privately perforated. See Nos. 662-667. For overprint and surcharges see Nos. E18, 9LC10, 9LC13, 9LC15-9LC16, 9LC22, 9LC25, 9LC27-9LC30, 9LC34-9LC53.

Ferdinand the Catholic A163   Emblem of the Falange A164

1938 Perf. 10½, 11½x11
Imprint: "Lit Fournier Vitoria"

656	A163	15c deep green	1.25	.20
657	A163	30c deep red	3.75	.20

Imprint: "Fournier Vitoria"
Perf. 10

658	A163	15c deep green	1.25	.20
659	A163	20c purple	8.25	1.25
660	A163	25c brown car	.60	.20
661	A163	30c deep red	3.75	.20
		Nos. 656-661 (6)	18.85	2.25
		Set, never hinged	65.00	

Nos. 656-661 exist imperf.; value for set, $150 hinged, $225 never hinged. Part-perf. varieties exist.
For overprints see Nos. C98-C99.

Without Imprint
1938-50 Perf. 11, 13½x13¼

Two types of the 15 Centimos:

Type I — Medieval style numerals with diagonal line through "5."
Type II — Modern numerals. Narrower "5" without diagonal line.

662	A159	1c green, imperf.	.20	.20
663	A160	2c brn (18½x22mm; '40)	.20	.20
a.		2c bis brn (17½x21mm; '48)	.20	.20
		Never hinged	.30	
664	A161	5c gray brn ('39)	.20	.20
a.		Perf 13½x13¼ ('49)	.20	.20
665	A161	10c dk carmine	.25	.20
		10c rose	.35	.20
		Never hinged	.75	
b.		Perf 13½x13¼ ('49)	.20	.20
666	A161	15c dk green (I)	.90	.20
666A	A161	15c dk green (II)	.60	.20
b.		Perf 13½x13¼ ('50)	.65	.20
		Never hinged	1.25	
667	A162	70c dk blue ('39)	.75	.20
		Nos. 662-667 (7)	3.10	1.40
		Set, never hinged	4.25	

1938, July 17 Perf. 10

668	A164	15c bl grn & lt grn	4.25	3.75
669	A164	25c rose red & rose	4.25	3.75
670	A164	30c bl & lt bl	2.25	2.50
671	A164	1p brown & yellow	90.00	80.00
		Nos. 668-671 (4)	100.75	90.00
		Set, never hinged	190.00	

Second anniversary of the Civil War.
Nos. 678-681 exist imperforate, Value, set $725 hinged, $950 never hinged.

Isabella I A165   Gen. Francisco Franco A166

1938-39 Litho. Perf. 10

672	A165	20c brt violet ('39)	.60	.20
673	A165	25c brown carmine	6.00	.60
674	A165	30c rose red	.25	.20
675	A165	40c dull violet	.30	.20
676	A165	50c indigo ('39)	27.50	2.50
677	A165	1p deep blue	9.00	.90
		Nos. 672-677 (6)	43.65	4.60
		Set, never hinged	90.00	

Nos. 672-677 exist imperforate. Value set, $225 hinged, $350 never hinged.

Imprint: "Sanchez Toda"
1939-40 Perf. 10

678	A166	20c brt violet	.30	.20
679	A166	25c rose lake	.30	.20
680	A166	30c rose carmine	.25	.20
681	A166	40c slate green	.20	.20
682	A166	45c vermilion ('40)	2.00	1.60
683	A166	50c indigo	.25	.20
684	A166	60c orange	3.00	2.50
685	A166	70c blue	.35	.20
686	A166	1p black	12.00	.20
687	A166	2p dark brown	18.00	1.10
688	A166	4p dark violet	95.00	16.00
689	A166	10p light brown	50.00	40.00
		Nos. 678-689 (12)	181.65	62.60
		Set, never hinged	325.00	

#686-689 have value & "Pta." on 1 line while #702-705 have value & "Pta." on 2 lines.
Nos. 678-689 exist imperforate. Value set, $525 hinged, $700 never hinged.

Without Imprint
Perf. 9½x10¼
1939-47 Litho. Unwmk.

690	A166	5c dull brn vio	.45	.20
691	A166	10c brown orange	2.00	.60
692	A166	15c lt green	.50	.20
693	A166	20c brt violet ('40)	.45	.20
694	A166	25c dp claret ('40)	.45	.20
695	A166	30c blue ('40)	.45	.20
697	A166	40c Prus grn ('40)	.45	.20
a.		40c greenish black	.60	.20
		Never hinged	.70	
698	A166	45c ultra ('41)	.50	.20
699	A166	50c indigo ('40)	.45	.20
a.		Perf. 11½ ('47)	32.50	3.00
		Never hinged	55.00	
700	A166	60c dull org ('40)	.65	.20
701	A166	70c blue ('40)	.75	.20
702	A166	1p gray blk ('40)	7.25	.20
703	A166	2p dull brn ('41)	8.50	.20
704	A166	4p dull rose ('40)	32.50	.20
705	A166	10p lt brown ('40)	155.00	.20
		Nos. 690-705 (15)	210.35	5.70
		Set, never hinged	375.00	

Perf. 13x13¼
1949-53 Litho. Unwmk.

693a	A166	20c brt violet	.20	.20
694a	A166	25c dp claret	.20	.20
695a	A166	30c blue	.20	.20

696	A166	35c aqua ('51)	.20	.20
697b	A166	40c Prus grn ('50)	.20	.20
698a	A166	45c ultra ('52)	.20	.20
698b	A166	50c indigo	.20	.20
700a	A166	60c dull org	.20	.20
701a	A166	70c blue ('53)	16.00	
702a	A166	1p gray blk ('51)	8.25	
703a	A166	2p dull brn ('50)	3.00	
704a	A166	4p dull rose	5.00	
705a	A166	10p lt brown ('53)	1.10	.30
		Nos. 693a-705a (13)	34.95	2.70
		Set, never hinged	80.00	

The 40c exists in three types, with variations in the value tablet: I. "CTS" does not touch bottom line. II. Light background in tablet. "CTS" touches bottom line. III. As type I, but with well defined lines of white and color around rectangle.
The 60c exists in two types: I. Top and left side of value tablet touch rest of design. II. Tablet separated from rest of design by white lines.
Five values exist with perf. 10: 5c, 10c, 45c, 4p and 10p.
The imperforate 10c dull claret, type A166, without imprint, is a postal tax stamp, RA14.

1944 Redrawn

706	A166	1p gray	50.00	.65
		Never hinged	110.00	

"PTS" instead of "PTA" as No. 702.
Nos. 690-704 and 706 exist imperforate. Value, set $925.

The value reads "PTAS" instead of "PTS"

1944 Unwmk. Perf. 9½x10½, 13

709	A166	10p brown	14.00	.30
		Never hinged	20.00	

General Franco — A167   St. John of the Cross — A168

1942-48 Engr. Perf. 12½x13

712	A167	40c chestnut	.40	.20
713	A167	75c dk bl, perf. 9½x10½ ('46)	3.50	.40
714	A167	90c dk green ('48)	.30	.20
a.		Perf 9½x10½ ('47)	1.40	.20
715	A167	1.35p purple ('48)	.90	.20
a.		Perf. 9½x10½ ('46)	2.00	.40
		Nos. 712-715 (4)	5.10	1.00
		Set, never hinged	8.00	

1942 Litho. Perf. 9½x10½

721	A168	20c violet	.55	.20
722	A168	40c salmon	1.25	.60
723	A168	75c ultra	1.50	1.75
		Nos. 721-723 (3)	3.30	2.55
		Set, never hinged	4.75	

St. John of the Cross (1542-1591).
Nos. 721-723 exist imperforate. Value, $65 hinged, $80 never hinged.

Holy Year Issues

Statue in St. James Cathedral A169   St. James of Compostela A170

Incense Burner — A171

Carvings in St. James Cathedral
A172   A174

St. James — A173   St. James' Casket — A175

East Portal of Cathedral A176   St. James Cathedral A177

Perf. 9½x10½
1943, Oct. Litho. Unwmk.

724	A169	20c deep blue	.20	.20
725	A170	40c dk red brown	.45	.20
726	A171	75c deep blue	1.90	1.90

Nos. 725 and 727 exist imperforate. Value, $550.

1943-44 Perf. 9½x10½, 10½x9½

727	A172	20c rose red ('44)	.20	.20
728	A173	40c dull green	.45	.20
729	A174	75c dk blue ('44)	2.50	2.00

1944

730	A175	20c red violet	.20	.20
731	A176	40c dull brown	.65	.20
732	A177	75c bright blue	27.50	29.00
		Nos. 724-732 (9)	34.05	34.10
		Set, never hinged	72.50	

Millenium of Castile Issues

Arms of Soria — A178   Arms of Castile — A179

Arms of Avila A180   Fortress A181

Arms of Segovia A182   Arms of Fernan Gonzalez A183

Arms of Burgos
A185

Arms of
Santander
A186

1944　　Litho.　　Perf. 9½x10½

733	A178	20c violet	.25	.20
734	A179	40c dull brown	2.75	.45
735	A180	75c blue	2.75	2.75

1944

736	A181	20c rose violet	.20	.20
737	A182	40c dull brown	2.50	.45
738	A183	75c dull blue	2.40	2.50

1944

739	A180	20c red violet	.20	.20
740	A185	40c dull brown	1.90	.45
741	A186	75c blue	2.75	3.00
		Nos. 733-741 (9)	15.70	10.20
		Set, never hinged	26.00	

Nos. 733, 738 and 741 exist imperforate. Value, $650. Value never hinged, $900.
No. 739 exists imperforate on grayish paper.

Francisco Gomez de
Quevedo y Villegas
(1580-1645),
Writer — A187

1945, Sept. 8　Engr.　　Perf. 10

742	A187	40c dark brown	.65	.55
		Never hinged	1.10	

Exists imperf. Value $80.

Type of Semi-Postal Stamp, 1940,
Without Imprint at Lower Left and
Right

1946, Jan. 1　Litho.　　Perf. 11

743	SP20	50c (40c + 10c) sl grn & rose vio	1.40	.25
		Never hinged	2.40	

No. 743 was used as an ordinary postage stamp of 50c denomination.
Exists imperf. Value $80.

Elio Antonio de
Nebrija — A188

University of
Salamanca and
Signature of
Francisco de
Vitoria — A189

1946, Oct. 12　Engr.　　Perf. 9½x10

744	A188	50c deep plum	.40	.30
745	A189	75c deep blue	.50	.45
		Nos. 744-745,C121 (3)	2.80	3.25
		Set, never hinged	4.75	

Stamp Day and the Day of the Race, Oct. 12, 1946.
Nos. 744-745 and C121 exist imperforate. Value set, $160 inged, $240 never hinged.

Francisco de
Goya
A190

Benito Jeronimo
Feijoo y
Montenegro
A191

1946, Oct 26

746	A190	25c deep plum	.20	.20
747	A190	50c green	.20	.20
748	A190	75c dark blue	.60	.75
		Nos. 746-748 (3)	1.15	
		Set, never hinged	1.00	

Francisco de Goya, birth bicentenary.
Nos. 746-748 exist imperforate. Value set, $25 hinged, $32.50 never hinged.

1947, June 1　　　　　　Unwmk.

749	A191	50c deep green	.45	.35
		Never hinged	.65	

No. 749 exists imperforate. Value, $35.

Don Quixote
Reading
A192

"Don Quixote"
by Zuloaga
A193

1947, Oct. 9　Engr.　　Perf. 9½x10½

750	A192	50c sepia	.25	.25
751	A193	75c dark blue	.40	.45
		Nos. 750-751,C122 (3)	5.15	5.20
		Set, never hinged	7.75	

Stamp Day and the 400th anniv. of the birth of Miguel de Cervantes Saavedra.
Nos. 750-751 and C122 exist imperforate. Value set, $550 hinged, $650 never hinged.

General Franco

A194　　　　　A195

1948　　Litho.　　Perf. 12½x13

752	A194	15c green	.20	.20
753	A195	50c violet	.80	.20
		Set, never hinged	1.25	

Nos. 752 and 753 exist imperforate. Value set, $400 hinged, $550 never hinged.
See Nos. 760-768, 780, 801-803. For surcharges see Nos. B137-B138.

Hernando
Cortez — A196

Mateo
Aleman — A197

1948, June 15　Engr.　Perf. 12½x13

754	A196	35c black	.20	.20

Perf. 9½x10½

755	A197	70c dk violet brn	1.40	2.00
a.		Perf. 12½x13	25.00	25.00
		Set, never hinged	2.25	

No. 754 exists imperforate. Value set, $100 hinged, $125 never hinged.

Ferdinand III
(The
Saint) — A198

Grandson of
Adm. Ramon de
Bonifaz — A199

1948, Sept. 20　Litho.　Perf. 12½x13

756	A198	25c rose violet	.20	.20
757	A199	30c scarlet	.20	.20
		Set, never hinged	.50	

700th anniversary of the Spanish navy and of the capture of Seville by Ferdinand the Saint.

José de
Salamanca y
Mayol — A200

Train Crossing
Pancorbo
Viaduct — A201

Perf. 12½x13, 13x12½

1948, Oct. 9　　　　　Unwmk.

758	A200	50c brown	.50	.20
759	A201	5p deep green	1.40	.20
		Nos. 758-759,C125 (3)	3.40	1.90
		Set, never hinged	5.50	

Centenary of Spanish railroads.

Franco Types of 1948

1948-49　　Litho.　　Perf. 12½x13

760	A194	5c brown	.25	.20
761	A195	25c vermilion	.25	.20
762	A195	35c blue green	.25	.20
763	A195	40c red brown	.60	.20
764	A195	45c car rose ('49)	.35	.20
765	A194	50c bister	1.00	.20
766	A195	70c purple ('49)	1.75	.25
767	A195	75c dk vio blue	1.50	.25
768	A195	1p rose pink	4.50	.20
		Nos. 760-768 (9)	10.45	1.90
		Set, never hinged	16.00	

Imperforates exist of Nos. 761 ($100), 762 ($300), 764 ($300) and 768 ($500)

Symbols of
UPU
A202

1949, Oct. 9

769	A202	50c red brown	.35	.20
770	A202	75c violet blue	.35	.55
		Nos. 769-770,C126 (3)	.90	1.20
		Set, never hinged	1.90	

75th anniv. of the UPU.

St. John of
God — A203

Pedro Calderon
de la
Barca — A204

1950, Mar. 8　Engr.　　Unwmk.

771	A203	1p dark violet	6.25	4.00
		Never hinged	11.50	

400th anniversary of the death of St. John of God, humanitarian.

1950-53　　Photo.　　Perf. 12½

Designs: 10c Lope de Vega. 15c, Tirso de Molina. 20c, Juan Ruiz de Alarcon, dramatist. 50c, St. Antonio Maria Claret y Clara.

772	A204	5c brown ('51)	.20	.20
773	A204	10c dp rose brn ('51)	.20	.20
773A	A204	15c dk sl grn ('53)	.20	.20
774	A204	20c violet	.20	.20

Perf. 12½x13

Engr.

775	A204	50c dk blue ('51)	2.50	1.50
		Nos. 772-775 (5)	3.30	2.30
		Set, never hinged	4.35	

No. 774 exists imperforate. Value, $250.

Stamp of
1850 — A205

Queen Isabella
I — A206

1950, Oct. 12　Engr.　　Imperf.

776	A205	50c purple	4.75	6.50
777	A205	75c ultra	4.75	6.50
778	A205	10p dk slate grn	85.00	87.50
779	A205	15p red	85.00	87.50
		Nos. 776-779,C127-C130 (8)	348.50	376.00
		Set, never hinged	575.00	

Centenary of Spain's stamps.

Franco Type of 1948

1950　　Litho.　　Perf. 12½x13

780	A195	45c red	.60	.20
		Never hinged	.90	

1951, Apr. 22　Photo.　Perf. 12½

781	A206	50c brown	.50	.35
782	A206	75c blue	.60	.35
783	A206	90c rose brown	.35	.25
784	A206	1.50p orange	7.50	7.50
785	A206	2.80p olive grn	18.00	20.00
		Nos. 781-785 (5)	26.95	28.45
		Set, never hinged	47.50	

500th anniversary of the birth of Queen Isabella I. See Nos. C132-C136.

Ferdinand, the
Catholic
A210

Maria Michaela
Dermaisiéres
A211

1952, May 10　Photo.　　Perf. 13

787	A210	50c green	.45	.35
788	A210	75c indigo	2.50	1.40
789	A210	90c rose brown	.40	.35
790	A210	1.50p orange	7.00	8.00
791	A210	2.80p brown	12.50	16.00
		Nos. 787-791 (5)	22.85	26.05
		Set, never hinged	45.00	

500th anniversary of the birth of Ferdinand the Catholic of Spain. See Nos. C139-C143.

1952, May 26　　　　Perf. 12½x13

792	A211	90c claret	.20	.20
		Never hinged	.45	

35th International Eucharistic Congress, Barcelona, 1952. See No. C137.

Dr. Santiago Ramon
y Cajal — A212

Portrait: 4.50p, Dr. Jaime Ferran y Clua.

1952, July 8　　　　　Photo.

793	A212	2p bright blue	11.00	.50
794	A212	4.50p red brown	.50	.80
		Set, never hinged	20.00	

Centenary of the births of Dr. Santiago Ramon y Cajal and Dr. Jaime Ferran y Clua.

University Seal — A213

Luis de Leon — A214

Cathedral of Salamanca A215

1953, Oct. 12   Perf. 12½x13, 13x12½
795 A213 50c deep magenta   .50 .35
796 A214 90c dark olive gray 1.75 2.25
797 A215 2p brown 12.00 3.50
  Nos. 795-797 (3) 14.25 6.10
  Set, never hinged 19.00

Stamp Day, 10/12/53, and 700th anniv. of the founding of the University of Salamanca.

The Magdalene — A216

1954, Jan. 10   Perf. 12½x13
798 A216 1.25p deep magenta .20 .20
  Never hinged .20

José de Ribera, painter, 300th death anniv.

St. James of Compostela A217

St. James Cathedral A218

1954, Mar. 1
799 A217 50c dark brown .20 .20
800 A218 3p blue 27.50 3.00
  Set, never hinged 47.50

Holy year of Compostela, 1954.

Franco Types of 1948
1954   Litho.   Perf. 12½x13
801 A194 5c olive gray .20 .20
802 A195 30c deep green .20 .20
803 A194 80c dull car rose 1.65 .60
  Nos. 801-803 (3) 2.05 .60
  Set, never hinged 5.00

Virgin by Alonso Cano — A219

Marcelino Menendez y Pelayo — A220

Virgins: 15c, Begoña. 25c, Of the Abandoned. 30c, Black. 50c, Of the Pillar. 60c, Covadonga. 80c, Kings'. 1p, Almudena. 2p, Africa. 3p, Guadalupe.

1954, July 18   Photo.   Perf. 12½x13
804 A219 10c dk car rose .20 .20
805 A219 15c olive green .20 .20
806 A219 25c purple .20 .20
807 A219 30c brown .25 .20
808 A219 50c brown olive .55 .20
809 A219 60c gray .25 .20
810 A219 80c grnsh gray 2.50 .20
811 A219 1p lilac gray 2.50 .20

812 A219 2p red brown .75 .20
813 A219 3p bright blue .65 .65
  Nos. 804-813 (10) 8.05 2.45
  Set, never hinged 11.00

Issued to publicize the Marian Year.

1954, Oct. 12
814 A220 80c dk gray grn 5.75 .40
  Never hinged 10.00

Stamp Day, October 12, 1954.

Gen. Franco — A221

Imprint: "F.N.M.T."

1954-56   Perf. 12½x13
815 A221 10c dk car lake .20 .20
816 A221 15c bister .20 .20
817 A221 20c dk ol grn ('55) .20 .20
818 A221 25c blue violet .20 .20
819 A221 30c brown .20 .20
820 A221 40c rose vio ('55) .20 .20
821 A221 50c dk brn olive .20 .20
822 A221 60c dk vio brown .20 .20
823 A221 70c dk green .20 .20
824 A221 80c dk blue grn .20 .20
825 A221 1p dp orange .20 .20
826 A221 1.40p lil rose ('56) .20 .20
827 A221 1.50p lt bl grn ('56) .20 .20
828 A221 1.80p emerald ('56) .20 .20
829 A221 2p red 13.00 1.25
830 A221 2p red lilac ('56) .20 .20
831 A221 3p Prus blue .20 .20
832 A221 5p dk red brn .20 .20
833 A221 6p dk gray ('55) .20 .20
834 A221 8p brt vio ('56) .20 .20
835 A221 10p yel grn ('55) .25 .20
  Nos. 815-835 (21) 17.05 5.25
  Set, never hinged 20.00

Coils: The 1.50p, No. 830, the 3p and the 6p were issued in coils in brighter tones (the 3p in 1974, others in 1973). Every fifth stamp has a black control number on the back.
  See Nos. 937-938, 1852-1855.

St. Ignatius of Loyola — A222

St. Ignatius and Loyola Palace A223

Perf. 13x12½, 12½x13
1955, Oct. 12   Photo.   Unwmk.
836 A222 25c dull purple .20 .20
837 A223 60c bister .40 .30
838 A222 80c Prus green 1.65 .25
  Nos. 836-838 (3) 2.25 .75
  Set, never hinged 4.25

4th cent. of the death of St. Ignatius of Loyola, founder of the Jesuit Order, and Day of the Stamp.

Symbols of Telegraph and Radio Communication A224

St. Vincent Ferrer A225

1955, Dec. 8   Perf. 13x12½
839 A224 15c dk olive bis .30 .20
840 A224 80c Prus green 4.50 .25
841 A224 3p bright blue 8.50 1.25
  Nos. 839-841 (3) 13.30 1.70
  Set, never hinged 27.50

Spanish telegraph system centenary.

1955, Dec. 20   Perf. 13
842 A225 15c olive bister .40 .25
  Never hinged .85

Canonization of St. Vincent Ferrer, 5th cent.

"Holy Family" by El Greco — A226

Marching Soldiers and Dove — A227

1955, Dec. 24   Perf. 13x12½
843 A226 80c dark green 3.75 .95
  Never hinged 6.00

1956, July 17   Unwmk.
844 A227 15c olive bis & brn .20 .20
845 A227 50c lt ol grn & ol .50 .30
846 A227 80c mag & grnsh blk 4.25 .25
847 A227 3p ultra & dp blue 4.25 1.40
  Nos. 844-847 (4) 9.20 2.15
  Set, never hinged 19.00

20th anniversary of Civil War.

Ciudad de Toledo A228

1956, Aug. 3   Perf. 12½x13
848 A228 3p blue 3.50 2.00
  Never hinged 5.75

Issued to publicize the voyage of the S. S. Ciudad de Toledo to Central and South America carrying the First Floating (Industrial) Exposition.

Black Virgin of Montserrat A229

Archangel Gabriel by Fra Angelico A230

Design: 60c, Monastery of Montserrat, mountains and crucifix.

1956, Sept. 11   Perf. 13x12½
849 A229 15c bister .20 .20
850 A229 60c violet black .20 .20
851 A229 80c blue green .35 .45
  Nos. 849-851 (3) .75 .85
  Set, never hinged .85

75th anniv. of the coronation of the Black Virgin of Montserrat.

1956, Oct. 12   Engr.
852 A230 80c dull green .90 .45
  Never hinged 1.25

Stamp Day, Oct. 12.

Statistical Chart A231

1956, Nov. 3   Perf. 12½x13
853 A231 15c dk olive bis .35 .35
854 A231 80c green 3.50 .90
855 A231 1p red orange 3.50 .90
  Nos. 853-855 (3) 7.35 2.15
  Set, never hinged 10.00

Centenary of Spanish Statistics.

Hermitage and Monument A232

1956, Dec. 4
856 A232 80c dull blue grn 2.00 .25
  5.50

20th anniversary of the nomination of Gen. Franco as chief of state and commander in chief of the army.

Hungarian Children A233

St. Marguerite Alacoque's Vision of Jesus A234

1956, Dec. 17   Perf. 13x12½
857 A233 10c brown lake .20 .20
858 A233 15c dk bister .20 .20
859 A233 50c olive gray .30 .20
860 A233 80c dk blue grn 2.25 .20
861 A233 1p red orange 2.50 .20
862 A233 3p brt blue 6.50 2.50
  Nos. 857-862 (6) 11.95 3.50
  Set, never hinged 20.00

Issued in sympathy to the children of Hungary.

1957, Oct. 12   Photo.   Unwmk.
863 A234 15c dk olive bis .20 .20
864 A234 60c violet blk .25 .20
865 A234 80c dk blue grn .35 .20
  Nos. 863-865 (3) .80 .60
  Set, never hinged 1.00

Centenary of the feast of the Sacred Heart of Jesus and for Stamp Day 1957.

Gonzalo de Cordoba — A235

1958, Feb. 28   Engr.   Perf. 13x12½
866 A235 1.80p yellow green .25 .20
  Never hinged .35

Issued in honor of El Gran Capitan, 15th century military leader.

"The Parasol," by Goya — A236

"Wife of the Bookseller of Carretas Street" — A237

Goya Paintings: 50c, Duke of Fernan-Nunez. 60c, The Crockery Seller. 70c, Isabel Cobos de Porcel. 80c, Goya by Vicente Lopez. 1p, "El Pelele" (Carnival Doll). 1.80p, Goya's grandson Marianito. 2p, The Vintage. 3p, The Drinker.

1958, Mar. 24   Photo.   Perf. 13
Gold Frame

867	A236	15c bister	.20	.20
868	A237	40c plum	.20	.20
869	A237	50c olive gray	.20	.20
870	A237	60c violet gray	.20	.20
871	A237	70c dp yellow grn	.20	.20
872	A237	80c dk slate grn	.20	.20
873	A237	1p orange red	.20	.20
874	A237	1.80p brt green	.20	.20
875	A237	2p red lilac	.40	.45
876	A237	3p brt blue	.65	.85
		Nos. 867-876 (10)		2.90
		Set, never hinged	2.40	

Issued to honor Francisco Jose de Goya and for the "Day of the Stamp," Mar. 24.
See Nos. 1111-1114. For other art types see A240a, A246a, A257, A272, A285a, A300, A310, A324, A340-A341, A360, A371 and footnote following No. 1606.

Exhibition Emblem and Globe — A238

1958, June 7   Perf. 13x12½

877	A238	80c car, dk brn & gray	.45	.20
a.		Souvenir sheet, imperf.	20.00	20.00
878	A238	3p car, vio blk & bl	1.75	.90
a.		Souvenir sheet, imperf.	20.00	20.00
		Set, never hinged	3.00	
		#877a-878a never hinged	55.00	

No. 877a sold for 2p, No. 878a for 5p.
Universal and Intl. Exposition at Brussels.

Charles V — A239

Various Portraits of Charles V: 50c, 1.80p, with helmet. 70c, 2p, facing left. 80c, 3p, with beret.

1958, July 30   Photo.   Perf. 13

879	A239	15c buff & brown	.20	.20
880	A239	50c lt grn & ol brn	.20	.20
881	A239	70c gray, grn & blk	.20	.20
882	A239	80c pale brn & Prus grn	.20	.20
883	A239	1p bis & brick red	.20	.20
884	A239	1.80p pale grn & brt grn	.20	.20
885	A239	2p gray & lilac	.30	.30
886	A239	3p pale brn & brt bl	.85	.65
		Nos. 879-886 (8)	2.35	2.15
		Set, never hinged	3.25	

400th anniv. of the death of Charles V (Carlos I of Spain.)

Escorial and Streamlined Train — A240

Designs: 60c, 2p, Railroad bridge at Despeñaperros, vert. 80c, 3p, Train and Castle de La Mota.

1958, Sept. 29   Perf. 12½x13

887	A240	15c dk olive bis	.20	.20
888	A240	60c dk purple	.20	.20
889	A240	80c dk blue grn	.20	.20
890	A240	1p red orange	.20	.20
891	A240	2p red lilac	.20	.20
892	A240	3p blue	.70	.40
		Nos. 887-892 (6)	1.70	1.40
		Set, never hinged	3.00	

Intl. Railroad Cong., Madrid, Sept. 28-Oct. 7.

Velazquez Self-portrait A240a

Velazquez Paintings: 15c, The Drinkers, horiz. 40c, The Spinners. 50c, Surrender of Breda. 60c, The Little Princesses. 70c, Prince Balthazar. 1p, The Coronation of Our Lady. 1.80p, Aesop. 2p, Vulcan's Forge. 3p, Menippus.

1959, Mar. 24   Photo.   Perf. 13
Gold Frame

893	A240a	15c dk brown	.20	.20
894	A240a	40c rose violet	.20	.20
895	A240a	50c olive	.20	.20
896	A240a	60c black brown	.20	.20
897	A240a	70c dp yellow grn	.20	.20
898	A240a	80c dk slate grn	.20	.20
899	A240a	1p orange red	.20	.20
900	A240a	1.80p emerald	.20	.20
901	A240a	2p red lilac	.20	.20
902	A240a	3p brt blue	.35	.45
		Nos. 893-902 (10)		2.25
		Set, never hinged	2.00	

Issued to honor Diego de Silva Velazquez (1599-1660) and for Stamp Day, Mar. 24.
For other art types see A236-A237, A246a, A257, A272, A285a, A300, A310, A324, A340-A341, A360, A371 and footnote following No. 1606.

Civil War Memorial — A241

1959, Apr. 1.   Litho.   Unwmk.

903	A241	80c yel grn & dk sl grn	.20	.20
		Never hinged		.30

Inauguration of the war memorial at the monastery of the Holy Cross in the Valley of the Fallen.

Louis XIV and Philip IV — A242

1959, Oct. 24   Photo.   Perf. 13x12½

904	A242	1p gold & rose brn	.20	.20
		Never hinged		.30

300th anniv. of the signing of the Treaty of the Pyrenees. Design shows the French-Spanish meeting at Isle des Faisans in 1659, as pictured in the Lebrun Tapestry, Versailles.

Monastery of Guadalupe A243

80c, Monastery, different view. 1p, Portals.

1959, Nov. 16   Engr.   Perf. 12½x13

905	A243	15c lt red brown	.20	.20
906	A243	80c slate	.20	.20
907	A243	1p rose red	.20	.20
		Nos. 905-907 (3)		.60
		Set, never hinged	.60	

Entrance of the Franciscan Brothers into Guadalupe monastery, 50th anniv.

Holy Family, by Goya — A244

1959, Dec. 10   Photo.   Perf. 13x12½

908	A244	1p orange brown	.20	.20
		Never hinged		.40

Catalogue values for unused stamps in this section, from this point to the end of the section, are for Never Hinged items.

Lidian Bull A245

Bullfighter, 19th Century — A246

Designs: 20c, Rounding up bulls. 25c, Running with the bulls, Pamplona. 30c, Bull entering arena. 50c, Bullfighting with cape. 70c, Bullfighting with banderillas. 80c, 1p, 1.40p, 1.50p, Fighting with muleta, various poses. 1.80p, Mounted bullfighter placing banderillas.

Perf. 12½x13, 13x12½
1960, Feb. 29   Engr.   Unwmk.

909	A245	15c sepia & bis	.20	.20
910	A245	20c vio & bl vio	.20	.20
911	A246	25c gray	.20	.20
912	A246	30c sepia & bister	.20	.20
913	A246	50c dull vio & sep	.20	.20
914	A246	70c sepia & sl grn	.20	.20
915	A246	80c blue grn & grn	.20	.20
916	A246	1p red & brn	.20	.20
917	A246	1.40p brown & lake	.20	.20
918	A246	1.50p grnsh bl & grn	.20	.20
919	A245	1.80p grn & dk grn	.20	.20
920	A246	5p brn & brn car	.55	.45
		Nos. 909-920,C159-C162 (16)	3.90	3.65

Murillo Self-portrait A246a

Christ of Lepanto A247

Murillo Paintings: 25c, The Good Shepherd. 40c, Rebecca and Eliezer. 50c, Virgin of the Rosary. 70c, Immaculate Conception. 80c, Children with Shell. 1.50p, Holy Family with Bird, horiz. 2.50p, Children Playing Dice. 3p, Children Eating. 5p, Children counting Money.

1960, Mar. 24   Photo.   Perf. 13
Gold Frame

921	A246a	25c dull violet	.20	.20
922	A246a	40c plum	.20	.20
923	A246a	50c olive gray	.20	.20
924	A246a	70c dp yel grn	.20	.20
925	A246a	80c deep green	.20	.20
926	A246a	1p violet brown	.20	.20
927	A246a	1.50p blue green	.20	.20
928	A246a	2.50p rose car	.20	.20
929	A246a	3p brt blue	1.25	.60
930	A246a	5p deep red brn	.35	.25
		Nos. 921-930 (10)	3.20	2.45

Issued to honor Bartolome Esteban Murillo (1617-1682) and for Stamp Day, Mar. 24.
For other art types see A236-A237, A240a, A257, A272, A285a, A300, A310, A324, A340-A341, A360, A371 and footnote following No. 1606.

1960, Mar. 27   Perf. 13x12½

80c, 2.50p, 10p, Holy Family Church, Barcelona.

931	A247	70c brn car & grn	1.60	1.25
932	A247	80c blk & ol grn	1.60	1.25
933	A247	1p cl & brt red	1.60	1.25
934	A247	2.50p brt vio & gray vio	1.60	1.25
935	A247	5p sepia & bister	1.60	1.25
936	A247	10p sepia & bister	1.60	1.25
		Nos. 931-936,C163-C166 (10)	28.60	20.50

First International Congress of Philately, Barcelona, March 26-Apr. 5. Nos. 931-936 could be bought at the exhibition upon presentation of 5p entrance ticket.

Franco Type of 1954-56
Imprint: "F.N.M.T.-B"

1960, Mar. 31   Photo.   Perf. 13

937	A221	1p deep orange	1.40	.60
938	A221	5p dark red brown	1.40	.60

Printed and issued at the International Congress of Philately in Barcelona.

St. Juan de Ribera — A248

St. Vincent de Paul — A249

1960, Aug. 16   Photo.   Perf. 13

939	A248	1p orange red	.20	.20
940	A248	2.50p lilac rose	.20	.20

Canonization of St. Juan de Ribera.

Common Design Types
pictured following the introduction.

Europa Issue, 1960
Common Design Type

1960, Sept. 19   Perf. 12½x13
Size: 38½x21½mm

941	CD3	1p sl grn & ol bis	.75	.20
942	CD3	5p choc & salmon	.75	.50

1960, Sept. 27   Unwmk.   Perf. 13

943	A249	25c violet	.20	.20
944	A249	1p orange red	.40	.20

3rd centenary of the death of St. Vincent de Paul.

Pedro
Menendez de
Aviles — A250

Runner — A251

70c, 2.50p, Hernando de Soto. 80c, 3p, Ponce de Leon. 1p, 5p, Alvar Nunez Cabeza de Vaca.

1960, Oct. 12   **Perf. 13x12½**
945	A250	25c vio bl, *bl*	.20 .20
946	A250	70c slate grn, *pink*	.20 .20
947	A250	80c dk grn, *pale brn*	.20 .20
948	A250	1p org brn, *yel*	.20 .20
949	A250	2p dk car rose, *pink*	.30 .20
950	A250	2.50p lil rose, *buff*	.60 .20
951	A250	3p dk blue, *grnsh*	2.75 .50
952	A250	5p dk brown, *cit*	2.25 .85
	Nos. 945-952 (8)		6.70 2.55

Florida's discovery & colonization, 4th cent.

Perf. 13x12½, 12½x13
1960, Oct. 31   **Photo.**

Sports: 40c, 2p, Bicycling, horiz. 70c, 2.50p, Soccer, horiz. 80c, 3p, Athlete with rings. 1p, 5p, Hockey on roller skates, horiz.

953	A251	25c dk vio, brn & blk	.20 .20
954	A251	40c purple, org & blk	.20 .20
955	A251	70c brt green & red	.30 .20
956	A251	80c dp grn, car & blk	.25 .20
957	A251	1p red org, brt grn & blk	.55 .20
958	A251	1.50p Prus grn, brn & blk	.40 .20
959	A251	2p red lil, emer & blk	1.10 .20
960	A251	2.50p lil rose & green	.40 .20
961	A251	3p ultra, red & blk	.75 .20
962	A251	5p red brn, bl & blk	.75 .35
	Nos. 953-962,C167-C170 (14)		7.70 3.65

Isaac
Albeniz — A252

1960, Nov. 7   **Perf. 13**
963	A252	25c dark gray	.20 .20
964	A252	1p orange red	.20 .20

Isaac Albeniz, composer, birth centenary.

Courtyard
of Samos
Monastery
A253

1p, Fountain, vert. 5p, Facade, vert.

Perf. 12½x13, 13x12½
1960, Nov. 21   **Engr.**
965	A253	80c bl grn & Prus grn	.20 .20
966	A253	1p org brn & car rose	1.10 .20
967	A253	5p sepia & ocher	1.10 .45
	Nos. 965-967 (3)		2.40 .85

Issued in honor of the reconstructed Benedictine monastery at Samos, Lugo.

Adoration, by
Velazquez — A254

1960, Dec. 1   **Photo.**   **Perf. 13x12½**
968	A254	1p orange red	.30 .20

Flight into
Egypt by
Francisco
Bayeu
A255

1961, Jan. 23   **Perf. 12½x13**
969	A255	1p copper red	.25 .20
970	A255	5p dull red brown	.45 .30

World Refugee Year.

Leandro F. de
Moratin, by
Goya — A256

St. Peter by El
Greco — A257

1961, Feb. 13   **Perf. 13**
971	A256	1p henna brown	.20 .20
972	A256	1.50p dk blue green	.20 .20

Leandro Fernandez de Moratin (1760-1828), poet and dramatist, 200th birth anniv.

1961, Mar. 24   **Perf. 13**

El Greco Paintings: 40c, Virgin Mary. 70c, Head of Christ. 80c, Knight with Hand on Chest. 1p, Self-portrait. 1.50p, Baptism of Christ. 2.50p, Holy Trinity. 3p, Burial of Count Orgaz. 5p, Christ Stripped of His Garments. 10p, St. Mauritius and the Theban Legion.

Gold Frame
973	A257	25c violet black	.20 .20
974	A257	40c lilac	.20 .20
975	A257	70c green	.30 .20
976	A257	80c Prus green	.30 .20
977	A257	1p chocolate	2.50 .20
978	A257	1.50p grnsh blue	.30 .20
979	A257	2.50p dk car rose	.50 .20
980	A257	3p bright blue	1.25 .45
981	A257	5p black brown	3.50 1.40
982	A257	10p purple	.60 .30
	Nos. 973-982 (10)		9.65 3.55

El Greco and Stamp Day, March 24.
For other art types see A236-A237, A240a, A246a, A272, A285a, A300, A310, A324, A340-A341, A360, A371 and footnote following No. 1606.

Diego
Velazquez — A258

Canceled
Stamp — A259

Velazquez Paintings: 1p, Duke de Olivares. 2.50p, Infanta Margarita. 10p, Detail from The Spinners, horiz.

Unwmk.
1961, Apr. 17   **Engr.**   **Perf. 13**
983	A258	80c dk blue & sl grn	2.00 .75
a.		Souvenir sheet	8.00 8.50
984	A258	1p brn red & choc	6.00 .75
a.		Souvenir sheet	8.50 8.50
985	A258	2.50p vio bl & bl	1.50 1.00
a.		Souvenir sheet	8.50 8.50
986	A258	10p grn & yel grn	7.00 2.50
a.		Souvenir sheet	8.50 8.50
	Nos. 983-986 (4)		16.50 5.00

300th anniversary (in 1960) of the death of Velazquez, painter.
Each souvenir sheet contains one imperf. stamp. The colors of the stamps have been changed: 80c, red brown & slate; 1p, blue & violet; 2.50p, green & blue; 10p, slate blue & greenish blue. The sheets were sold at a premium.

1961, May 6   **Photo.**   **Perf. 13x12½**
987	A259	25c gray & red	.20 .20
988	A259	1p orange & blk	1.10 .20
989	A259	10p olive grn & brn	1.10 .60
	Nos. 987-989 (3)		2.40 1.00

Issued for International Stamp Day.

Juan Vazquez
de
Mella — A260

Flag, Angel and
Peace
Doves — A261

1961, June 8   **Unwmk.**   **Perf. 13**
990	A260	1p henna brown	.45 .20
991	A260	2.30p red lilac	.50 .20

Birth centenary of Juan Vazquez de Mella y Fanjul, politician and writer.

1961, July 10

Designs: 80c, Ships and Strait of Gibraltar. 1p, Alcazar and horseman. 1.50p, Ruins and triumphal arch. 2p, Horseman over Ebro. 2.30p, Victory parade. 2.50p, Ship building. 3p, Steel industry. 5p, Map of Spanish irrigation dams and statue, horiz. 6p, Dama de Elche statue and power station. 8p, Mining development. 10p, General Franco.

992	A261	70c multicolored	.20 .20
993	A261	80c multicolored	.20 .20
994	A261	1p multicolored	.20 .20
995	A261	1.50p gold, pink & brn	.20 .20
996	A261	2p gold, gray & bl	.20 .20
997	A261	2.30p multicolored	.20 .20
998	A261	2.50p multicolored	.20 .20
999	A261	3p gold, red & dk gray	.35 .25
1000	A261	5p bl grn, ol gray & pink	2.25 1.10
1001	A261	6p multicolored	1.10 .75
1002	A261	8p gold, ol & sep	.70 .55
1003	A261	10p gold, gray & grn	.70 .55
	Nos. 992-1003 (12)		6.50 4.60

25th anniversary of national uprising.

Christ, San
Clemente, Tahull
A262

Luis de Argote
y Gongora
A263

Designs: 25c, Bas-relief, Compostela Cathedral. 1p, Cloister of Silos. 2p, Virgin of Irache.

1961, July 24   **Unwmk.**   **Perf. 13**
Gold Frame
1004	A262	25c blue violet	.40 .20
1005	A262	1p orange brown	.50 .20
1006	A262	2p deep plum	.70 .20
1007	A262	3p grnsh bl, sal & blk	.90 .40
	Nos. 1004-1007 (4)		2.50 1.00

Seventh Exposition of the Council of Europe dedicated to Romanesque art, Barcelona-Santiago de Compostela, July 10-Oct. 10.

1961, Aug. 10   **Photo.**   **Perf. 13**
1008	A263	25c violet black	.20 .20
1009	A263	1p henna brown	.50 .20

400th anniversary of the birth of Luis de Argote y Gongora, poet.

Europa Issue, 1961
Common Design Type
1961, Sept. 18   **Perf. 12½x13**
Size: 37½x21½mm
1010	CD4	1p brt vermilion	.20 .20
1011	CD4	5p brown	.45 .30

Cathedral at
Burgos
A264

Sebastian de
Belalcazar
A265

1961, Oct. 1   **Perf. 13**
1012	A264	1p gold & olive green	.20 .20

25th anniversary of the nomination of Gen. Francisco Franco as Head of State.

Builders of the New World

Portraits: 70c, 2.50p, Blas de Lezo. 80c, 3p, Rodrigo de Bastidas. 1p, 5p, Nuflo de Chaves.

1961, Oct. 12   **Photo.**   **Perf. 13x12½**
1013	A265	25c indigo, *grn*	.20 .20
1014	A265	70c grn, *cream*	.20 .20
1015	A265	80c sl grn, *pnksh*	.20 .20
1016	A265	1p dk blue, *sal*	.60 .20
1017	A265	2p dk car, *bluish*	3.75 .20
1018	A265	2.50p lil, *pale lil*	.90 .45
1019	A265	3p blue, *grysh*	1.90 .80
1020	A265	5p brown, *yel*	2.00 .90
	Nos. 1013-1020 (8)		9.75 3.15

Issued to honor the discoverers and conquerors of Colombia and Bolivia.
See Nos. 1131-1138, 1187-1194, 1271-1278, 1316-1323, 1377-1384, 1489-1496, 1548, 1550, 1587-1588, 1632-1633.

Patio of the Kings,
Escorial — A266

Views of Escorial: 80c, Patio. 1p, Garden of the Monks and Escorial, horiz. 2.50p, Staircase. 5p, General view of Escorial, horiz. 6p, Main altar.

Perf. 13x12½, 12½x13
1961, Oct. 31   **Engr.**   **Unwmk.**
1021	A266	70c bl grn & ol grn	.20 .20
1022	A266	80c Prus grn & ind	.20 .20
1023	A266	1p ocher & dk red	.55 .20
1024	A266	2.50p cl & dull vio	.55 .20
1025	A266	5p bister & dk brn	1.60 .70
1026	A266	6p sl bl & dull pur	2.25 1.50
	Nos. 1021-1026 (6)		5.35 3.00

Alfonso XII
Monument, Retiro
Park — A267

Church of St.
Mary,
Naranco — A268

Designs: 1p, King Philip II. 2p, Town hall, horiz. 2.50p, Cibeles fountain, horiz. 3p, Alcala gate, horiz. 5p, Cervantes memorial, Plaza de Espagna.

Photogravure (25c, 2p, 5p)
Engraved (1p, 2.50p, 3p)
1961, Nov. 13   **Unwmk.**   **Perf. 13**
1027	A267	25c gray & dull pur	.20 .20
1028	A267	1p bis brn & gray	.30 .20
1029	A267	2p claret & gray	.30 .20
1030	A267	2.50p black & lilac	.25 .20
1031	A267	3p slate & ind	.60 .35

1032 A267   5p Prus grn &
                    beige   1.10   .55
                Nos. 1027-1032 (6)   2.75   1.70

400th anniv. of Madrid as capital of Spain.

1961, Nov. 27

Designs: 1p, King Fruela I, founder of Oviedo. 2p, Cross of the Angels. 2.50p, King Alfonso II. 3p, King Alfonso III. 5p, Apostles from Oviedo Cathedral (sculpture).

1033 A268   25c pur & gray grn   .20   .20
1034 A268   1p bis brn & brn   .30   .20
1035 A268   2p dk brn & pale
                    pur   .65   .20
1036 A268   2.50p claret & ind   .30   .20
1037 A268   3p slate & indigo   .65   .45
1038 A268   5p ol & ol grn   1.25   .55
                Nos. 1033-1038 (6)   3.35   1.80

1200th anniversary of the founding of Oviedo, capital of Asturia.

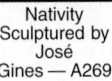

Nativity
Sculptured by
José
Gines — A269

"La Cierva"
Autogiro — A270

1961, Dec. 1   Photo.   *Perf. 13x12½*
1039 A269   1p dull purple   .30   .20

1961, Dec. 11   Unwmk.   *Perf. 13*

2p, Hydroplane "Plus Ultra.," horiz. 3p, "Jesus del Gran Poder," plane of Madrid-Manila flight, horiz. 5p, Bustard hunt by plane. 10p, Madonna of Loretto, patron saint of Spanish airmen.

1040 A270   1p indigo & blue   .20   .20
1041 A270   2p grn, dl pur & blk   .20   .20
1042 A270   3p blk & ol grn   1.25   .35
1043 A270   5p dl pur, gray bl &
                    blk   2.50   .90
1044 A270   10p blk, lt bl & ol gray   1.25   .60
                Nos. 1040-1044 (5)   5.40   2.25

50th anniversary of Spanish aviation.

Provincial Arms Issue

Alava — A271

Arms of
Spain — A271a

1962   Photo.   *Perf. 13*
1045 A271   5p Alava   .20   .20
1046 A271   5p Albacete   .20   .20
1047 A271   5p Alicante   .25   .20
1048 A271   5p Almeria   .25   .20
1049 A271   5p Avila   .25   .20
1050 A271   5p Badajoz   .20   .20
1051 A271   5p Baleares   .20   .20
1052 A271   5p Barcelona   .20   .20
1053 A271   5p Burgos   .65   .40
1054 A271   5p Caceres   .35   .25
1055 A271   5p Cadiz   .45   .35
1056 A271   5p Castellon de la
                    Plana   3.50   1.50
                Nos. 1045-1056 (12)   6.70   4.10

1963
1057 A271   5p Ciudad Real   .45   .35
1058 A271   5p Cordoba   3.50   1.25
1059 A271   5p Coruña   .55   .35
1060 A271   5p Cuenca   .55   .35
1061 A271   5p Fernando Po   .80   .75
1062 A271   5p Gerona   .20   .20
1063 A271   5p Gran Canaria   .20   .20
1064 A271   5p Granada   .25   .20
1065 A271   5p Guadalajara   .55   .35
1066 A271   5p Guipuzcoa   .20   .20
1067 A271   5p Huelva   .20   .20
1068 A271   5p Huesca   .20   .20
                Nos. 1057-1068 (12)   7.65   4.65

1964
1069 A271   5p Ifni   .20   .20
1070 A271   5p Jaen   .20   .20
1071 A271   5p Leon   .20   .20
1072 A271   5p Lerida   .20   .20
1073 A271   5p Logrono   .20   .20
1074 A271   5p Lugo   .20   .20
1075 A271   5p Madrid   .20   .20
1076 A271   5p Malaga   .20   .20
1077 A271   5p Murcia   .20   .20
1078 A271   5p Navarra   .20   .20
1079 A271   5p Orense   .20   .20
1080 A271   5p Oviedo   .20   .20
                Nos. 1069-1080 (12)   2.40   2.40

1965
1081 A271   5p Palencia   .20   .20
1082 A271   5p Pontevedra   .20   .20
1083 A271   5p Rio Muni   .20   .20
1084 A271   5p Sahara   .20   .20
1085 A271   5p Salamanca   .20   .20
1086 A271   5p Santander   .20   .20
1087 A271   5p Segovia   .20   .20
1088 A271   5p Seville   .20   .20
1089 A271   5p Soria   .20   .20
1090 A271   5p Tarragona   .20   .20
1091 A271   5p Tenerife   .20   .20
1092 A271   5p Teruel   .20   .20
                Nos. 1081-1092 (12)   2.40   2.40

1966
1093 A271   5p Toledo   .20   .20
1094 A271   5p Valencia   .20   .20
1094A A271   5p Valladolid   .20   .20
1094B A271   5p Vizcaya   .20   .20
1094C A271   5p Zamora   .20   .20
1094D A271   5p Zaragoza   .20   .20
1094E A271   5p Ceuta   .20   .20
1094F A271   5p Melilla   .20   .20
1094G A271a   10p black   .20   .20
                Nos. 1093-1094G (9)   1.80   1.80
                Nos. 1045-1094G (57)   20.95 15.35

Zurbaran Self-
portrait
A272

Zurbaran Paintings: 25c, Martyr, horiz. 40c, Burial of St. Catherine. 70c, St. Casilda. 80c, Jesus crowning St. Joseph. 1.50p, St. Jerome. 2.50p, Virgin of Grace. 3p, The Apotheosis of St. Thomas Aquinas. 5p, The Virgin as a child. 10p, The Immaculate Virgin.

Unwmk.
1962, Mar. 24   Photo.   *Perf. 13*
Gold Frame
1095 A272   25c olive gray   .40   .20
1096 A272   40c purple   .40   .20
1097 A272   70c green   .50   .20
1098 A272   80c Prus green   .40   .20
1099 A272   1p chocolate   7.50   .20
1100 A272   1.50p brt blue grn   .90   .20
1101 A272   2.50p dk car rose   .90   .20
1102 A272   3p bright blue   1.00   .35
1103 A272   5p deep brown   2.50   .75
1104 A272   10p olive green   2.50   .75
                Nos. 1095-1104 (10)   17.00   3.25

Issued to honor Francisco de Zurbaran (1598-1664) and for Stamp Day, March 24.

For other art types see A236-A237, A240a, A246a, A257, A285a, A300, A310, A324, A340-A341, A360, A371 and footnote following No. 1606.

San Jose
Convent, Avila
A272a

St. Theresa (by
Velázquez?)
A273

Design: 1p, St. Theresa by Bernini.

1962, Apr. 10   *Perf. 13*
1105 A272a   25c bluish blk   .20   .20
1106 A272a   1p brown   .20   .20

Perf. 13x12½
1107 A273   3p bright blue   1.25   .40
                Nos. 1105-1107 (3)   1.65   .80

4th centenary of St. Theresa's reform of the Carmelite order.

Mercury — A274

1962, May 7
1108 A274   25c vio, rose & mag   .20   .20
1109 A274   1p brn, org & lt brn   .20   .20
1110 A274   10p dp grn, ol grn &
                    brt grn   1.75   .80
                Nos. 1108-1110 (3)   2.15   1.20

International Stamp Day, May 7.

Painting Type of 1958

Rubens Paintings: 25c, Ferdinand of Austria. 1p, Self-portrait. 3p, Philip II. 10p, Duke of Lerma on horseback.

1962, May 28   *Perf. 13*
Gold Frame
Size: 25x30mm
1111 A237   25c violet black   .65   .30
1112 A237   1p chocolate   5.75   .30
1113 A237   3p blue   5.25   2.00
Perf. 13x12½
Size: 26x38mm
1114 A237   10p slate green   4.00   2.75
                Nos. 1111-1114 (4)   15.65   5.35

St. Benedict
A275

El Cid, Statue
by Cristobal
A276

Berruguete Sculptures: 80c, Apostle. 1p, St. Peter. 2p, St. Christopher carrying Christ Child. 3p, Ecce Homo (Christ). 10p, St. Sebastian.

1962, July 9   *Perf. 13x12½*
1115 A275   25c lt blue & plum   .20   .20
1116 A275   80c sal & ol gray   .35   .20
1117 A275   1p gray & red   .45   .20
1118 A275   2p gray & magenta   3.50   .20
1119 A275   3p brn pink & dk bl   1.50   .85
1120 A275   10p rose & brown   1.50   .50
                Nos. 1115-1120 (6)   7.50   2.15

Alonso Berruguete (1486-1561), architect, sculptor and painter.

Perf. 13x12½, 12½x13
1962, July 30   Engr.

2p, Equestrian statue by Anna Huntington. 3p, El Cid's treasure chest, horiz. 10p, Oath-taking ceremony at Santa Gadea, horiz.

1121 A276   1p lt green & gray   .25   .20
1122 A276   2p brown & choc   1.40   .20
1123 A276   3p blue & sl grn   4.25   1.10
1124 A276   10p lt grn & sl grn   2.75   .60
                Nos. 1121-1124 (4)   8.65   2.10

El Cid Campeador (Rodrigo Diaz de Vivar, 1040-99), Spain's national hero.

Europa Issue, 1962

Bee and Honeycomb — A277

1962, Sept. 13   Photo.   *Perf. 12½x13*
1125 A277   1p deep rose   .20   .20
1126 A277   5p dull green   1.00   .40

Discus Thrower
A278

UPAE Emblem
A279

80c, Runner. 1p, Hurdler. 3p, Sprinter at start.

1962, Oct. 7   *Perf. 13x12½*
1127 A278   25c pale pink & vio
                    blk   .20   .20
1128 A278   80c pale yel & dk grn   .25   .20
1129 A278   1p pale rose & brn   .20   .20
1130 A278   3p pale bl & dk bl   .25   .30
                Nos. 1127-1130 (4)   .90   .90

Second Spanish-American Games, Madrid, Oct. 7-12.

Builders of the New World
Portrait Type of 1961

Portraits: 25c, 2p, Alonso de Mendoza. 70c, 2.50p, Jiménez de Quesada. 80c, 3p, Juan de Garay. 1p, 5p, Pedro de la Gasca.

1962, Oct. 12   Unwmk.
1131 A265   25c rose lil, gray   .20   .20
1132 A265   70c grn, *pale pink*   1.00   .20
1133 A265   80c dk grn, *pale
                    yel*   .70   .20
1134 A265   1p red brn, *gray*   1.40   .20
1135 A265   2p car, *lt bl*   3.25   .20
1136 A265   2.50p dk vio,*pnksh*   .70   .25
1137 A265   3p dp bl, *pale
                    pink*   7.00   1.25
1138 A265   5p brn, *pale yel*   3.50   1.50
                Nos. 1131-1138 (8)   17.75   4.00

1962, Oct. 20   Engr.   *Perf. 13*
1139 A279   1p sepia & green   .20   .20

50th anniv. of the founding of the Postal Union of the Americas and Spain, UPAE.

The Annunciation,
by Murillo — A280

Holy Family by
Pedro de
Mena — A281

Mysteries of the Rosary: 70c, The Visitation, Correa. 80c, Nativity, Murillo. 1p, The Presentation, Pedro de Campaña. 1.50p, The Finding in the Temple, (unknown painter). 2p, The Agony in the Garden, Gianquinto. 2.50p, The Scourging at the Pillar, Alonso Cano. 3p, The Crowning with Thorns, Tiepolo. 5p, Carrying of the Cross, El Greco. 8p, The Crucifixion, Murillo. 10p, The Resurrection, Murillo.

1962, Oct. 26
1140 A280   25c lilac & brown   .20   .20
1141 A280   70c grn & dk bl
                    grn   .20   .20
1142 A280   80c ol & dk bl grn   .20   .20
1143 A280   1p green & gray   4.00   .70
1144 A280   1.50p green & dk bl   .20   .20
1145 A280   2p brown & violet   1.10   .50
1146 A280   2.50p dk brn & rose
                    claret   .40   .20
1147 A280   3p lilac & gray   .40   .20
1148 A280   5p brn & dk car   .60   .35
1149 A280   8p vio brn & blk   .60   .25
1150 A280   10p grn & yel grn   .95   .25
                Nos. 1140-1150,C171-C174 (15) 11.45 4.40

1962, Dec. 6   Photo.   *Perf. 13x12½*
1151 A281   1p olive gray   .35   .20

Malaria Eradication Emblem A282

1962, Dec. 21   **Perf. 12½x13**
1152 A282 1p blk, yel grn & yel   .20 .20
WHO drive to eradicate malaria.

Pope John XXIII and St. Peter's, Rome A283

1962, Dec. 29   **Engr.**
1153 A283 1p dp plum & blk   .25 .20
Vatican II, the 21st Ecumenical Council of the Roman Catholic Church. See No. 1199.

St. Paul, by El Greco A284

Courtyard, Poblet Monastery A285

1963, Jan. 25   **Perf. 13**
1154 A284 1p brn, blk & olive   .30 .20
St. Paul's visit to Spain, 1,900th anniv.

Perf. 12½x13, 13x12½
1963, Feb. 25   **Unwmk.**
Designs: 1p, Royal sepulcher. 3p, View of monastery, horiz. 5p, Gothic arch.

1155 A285 25c choc & slate grn   .20 .20
1156 A285 1p org ver & rose car   .35 .20
1157 A285 3p vio bl & dk bl   1.10 .20
1158 A285 5p brown & ocher   2.40 .90
    Nos. 1155-1158 (4)   4.05 1.50

Issued in honor of the Cistercian monastery of Santa Maria de Poblet.

José de Ribera, Self-portrait A285a

Coach A286

Ribera Paintings: 25c, Archimedes. 40c, Jacob's Flock. 70c, Triumph of Bacchus. 80c, St. Christopher. 1.50p, St. Andrew. 2.50p, St. John the Baptist. 3p, St. Onofre. 5p, St. Peter. 10p, The Immaculate Virgin.

Unwmk.
1963, Mar. 24   **Photo.**   **Perf. 13**
Gold Frame
1159 A285a 25c violet   .35 .20
1160 A285a 40c red lilac   .40 .20
1161 A285a 70c green   1.00 .20
1162 A285a 80c dark green   1.00 .20
1163 A285a 1p brown   1.00 .20
1164 A285a 1.50p blue green   1.00 .20
1165 A285a 2.50p car rose   2.75 .20
1166 A285a 3p dark blue   3.00 .50
1167 A285a 5p olive   10.50 2.25
1168 A285a 10p dull red brn   4.00 1.40
    Nos. 1159-1168 (10)   25.00 5.55

Issued to honor José de Ribera (1588-1652) and for Stamp Day, Mar. 24.

For other art types see A236-A237, A240a, A246a, A257, A272, A300, A310, A324, A340-A341, A360, A371 and footnote following No. 1606.

1963, May 3   **Perf. 13x12½**
1169 A286 1p multicolored   .20 .20
First Intl. Postal Conference, Paris, 1863.

Globe A287

1963, May 8   **Perf. 12½x13**
1170 A287 25c multicolored   .20 .20
1171 A287 1p multicolored   .20 .20
1172 A287 10p multicolored   1.10 .65
    Nos. 1170-1172 (3)   1.50 1.05
Issued for International Stamp Day, 1963.

"Give us this Day our Daily Bread..." A288

1963, June 1   **Unwmk.**
1173 A288 1p multicolored   .20 .20
FAO "Freedom from Hunger" campaign.

"Pillars of Hercules" and Globes — A289

Seal of Council of San Sebastian A290

Designs: 80c, Fleet of Columbus. 1p, Columbus and compass rose.

1963, June 4   **Perf. 13**
1174 A289 25c multicolored   .20 .20
1175 A289 80c brn, lt grn & gold   .20 .20
1176 A289 1p sl grn, sepia & gold   .25 .20
    Nos. 1174-1176 (3)   .65 .60
Cong. of Institutions of Spanish Culture, June 5-15.

1963, June 27   **Photo.**
80c, Burning of city, 1813. 1p, View, 1836.
1177 A290 25c vio, grn & blk   .20 .20
1178 A290 80c dk brn, gray & red   .20 .20
1179 A290 1p dk grn, grn & ol   .30 .20
    Nos. 1177-1179 (3)   .70 .60
Rebuilding of San Sebastian, 150th anniv.

Europa Issue, 1963

Our Lady of Europe — A291

1963, Sept. 16   **Engr.**   **Perf. 13x12½**
1180 A291 1p bis brn & choc   .20 .20
1181 A291 5p bluish grn & blk   .55 .40

Arms of Order of Mercy — A292

King James I — A293

Designs: 1p, Our Lady of Mercy. 1.50p, St. Pedro Nolasco. 3p, St. Raimundo de Penafort.

1963, Sept. 24   **Photo.**   **Perf. 13**
1182 A292 25c blk, car rose & gold   .20 .20

Engr.
1183 A293 80c sepia & green   .20 .20
1184 A293 1p gray vio & brn vio   .20 .20
1185 A293 1.50p dull bl & blk   .20 .20
1186 A293 3p gray & black   .20 .20
    Nos. 1182-1186 (5)   1.00 1.00
Coronation of Our Lady of Mercy, 75th anniv.

Builders of the New World
Portrait Type of 1961

25c, 2p, Father Junipero Serra. 70c, 2.50p, Vasco Nuñez de Balboa. 80c, 3p, José de Galvez. 1p, 5p, Diego Garcia de Paredes.

1963, Oct. 12   **Perf. 13x12½**
1187 A265 25c vio bl, bl   .20 .20
1188 A265 70c grn, pale rose   .20 .20
1189 A265 80c dk grn, yel   .50 .20
1190 A265 1p dk bl, pale rose   .60 .20
1191 A265 2p magenta, lt bl   1.75 .20
1192 A265 2.50p vio blk, dl rose   1.10 .20
1193 A265 3p brt bl, pink   2.40 1.00
1194 A265 5p brown, yel   3.00 2.25
    Nos. 1187-1194 (8)   9.75 4.45

The Good Samaritan — A294

1963, Oct. 28   **Unwmk.**
1195 A294 1p gold, pur & brt car   .20 .20
Centenary of International Red Cross.

Holy Family by Alonso Berruguete (1486-1561) A295

Father Raymond Lully A296

1963, Dec. 2   **Photo.**   **Perf. 13x12½**
1196 A295 1p dark green   .20 .20
Christmas 1963. See No. 1279.

1963, Dec. 5   **Engr.**
Portrait: 1.50p, Cardinal Luis Antonio de Belluga (1662-1743).
1197 A296 1p dk violet & blk   .20 .20
1198 A296 1.50p sepia & dull vio   .20 .20
    Nos. 1197-1198,C175-C176 (4)   3.40 1.35

Papal Type of 1962
Design: 1p, Pope Paul VI and St. Peter's, Rome.

1963, Dec. 30   **Perf. 12½x13**
1199 A283 1p dk green & blk   .20 .20
Second session of Vatican II, the 21st Ecumenical Council of the Roman Catholic Church.

Alcazar, Segovia A297

Dragon Caves, Majorca — A298

Tourism: 40c, Potes, Santander. 50c, Leon Cathedral. No. 1202, Crypt of San Isidro at Leon. No. 1203, Costa Brava. 80c, Christ of the Lanterns, Cordova. No. 1206, Court of Lions, Alhambra, Granada. No. 1208, Interior of La Mezquita, Cordova. 1.50p, View of Gerona.

1964   **Engr.**   **Perf. 13**
1200 A297 40c sepia & blue   .20 .20
1201 A298 50c gray & sepia   .20 .20
1202 A297 70c ind & dk bl grn   .20 .20
1203 A298 70c violet & brown   .20 .20
1204 A298 80c dp ultra & blk   .20 .20
1205 A297 1p vio bl & pur   .20 .20
1206 A297 1p rose red & dl pur   .20 .20
1207 A298 1p dk green & blk   .20 .20
1208 A298 1p brn vio & rose   .20 .20
1209 A297 1.50p gray grn, brn & blk   .20 .20
    Nos. 1200-1209 (10)   2.00 2.00
See Nos. 1280-1289.

Santa Maria de Huerta Monastery A299

Joaquin Sorolla, Self-portrait A300

Designs: 1p, Great Hall. 5p, View of monastery with apse, horiz.

1964, Feb. 24   **Perf. 13x12½, 12½x13**
1212 A299 1p gray grn & grn   .20 .20
1213 A299 2p grnsh blue & sepia   .25 .20
1214 A299 5p dark blue   1.50 .75
    Nos. 1212-1214 (3)   1.95 1.15
Santa Maria Monastery, Huerta, 8th cent.

1964, Mar. 24   **Photo.**   **Perf. 13**
Sorolla Paintings: 25c, The Jug (woman and child). 40c, Oxen and Driver, horiz. 70c, Man and Woman from La Mancha. 80c, Fisher Woman of Valencia. 1p, Self-portrait. 1.50p, Round up, horiz. 2.50p, Fishermen, horiz. 3p, Children at the Beach, horiz. 5p, Unloading the Boat. 10p, Man and Woman on Horseback, Valencia.

Gold Frame
1215 A300 25c violet   .20 .20
1216 A300 40c purple   .20 .20
1217 A300 70c dp yellow grn   .20 .20
1218 A300 80c bluish grn   .20 .20
1219 A300 1p brown   .20 .20
1220 A300 1.50p Prus blue   .20 .20
1221 A300 2.50p dk car rose   .20 .20
1222 A300 3p violet brn   .45 .45

1223 A300 5p chocolate   1.40 1.00
1224 A300 10p deep green   .65 .35
Nos. 1215-1224 (10)   3.90 3.20

Issued to honor Joaquin Sorolla y Bastida (1863-1923) and for Stamp Day, March 24.

For other art types see A236-A237, A240a, A246a, A257, A272, A285a, A310, A324, A340-A341, A360, A371 and footnote following No. 1606.

"Peace"
A301

"Sport" — A302

Designs: 40c, Radio and television. 50c, New apartments. 70c, Agriculture. 80c, Reforestation. 1p, Economic development. 1.50p, Modern architecture. 2p, Transportation. 2.50p, Hydroelectric development. 3p, Electrification. 5p, Scientific achievements. 6p, Buildings, tourism. 10p, Generalissimo Franco.

1964, Apr. 1
1225 A301 25c blk, emer &
                gold   .20 .20
1226 A302 30c blk, bl & sal
                pink   .20 .20
1227 A301 40c gold & blk   .20 .20
1228 A302 50c multicolored   .20 .20
1229 A301 70c multicolored   .20 .20
1230 A301 80c multicolored   .20 .20
1231 A301 1p multicolored   .25 .20
1232 A302 1.50p multicolored .20 .20
1233 A301 2p multicolored   .20 .20
1234 A302 2.50p multicolored .20 .20
1235 A301 3p gold, blk & red .90 .90
1236 A302 5p gold, grn & red .30 .30
1237 A301 6p multicolored   .45 .45
1238 A302 10p multicolored   .55 .55
Nos. 1225-1238 (14)   4.25 4.20

Issued to commemorate 25 years of peace.

Bullfight and   Stamp of 1850
Unisphere   and Modern
A303   Stamps
                       A304

Designs: 1p, Spanish pavilion, horiz. 2.50p, La Mota castle, Medina de Campo. 5p, Spanish dancer. 50p, Jai alai.

Perf. 12½x13, 13x12½
1964, Apr. 23   **Engr.**
1239 A303 1p bl grn & yel grn .20 .20
1240 A303 1.50p carmine & brn .20 .20
1241 A303 2.50p dk bl & sl grn .20 .20
1242 A303 5p car & dk car
                rose   .30 .30
1243 A303 50p vio bl & dk bl   .85 .40
Nos. 1239-1243 (5)   1.75 1.30

New York World's Fair, 1964-65.

1964, May 6   *Perf. 13x12½*
1244 A304 25c dk car rose & dl
                pur   .20 .20
1245 A304 1p yel grn & dk bl   .20 .20
1246 A304 10p orange & rose
                red   .40 .35
Nos. 1244-1246 (3)   .80 .75

Issued for International Stamp Day, 1964.

Virgin of
Hope — A305

Santa
Maria — A306

1964, May 31 Photo. Perf. 13x12½
1247 A305 1p dark green   .20 .20

Canonical coronation of the Virgin of Hope (La Macarena) in St. Gil's Church, Seville, May 31.

1964, July 16   *Perf. 13*

Designs (ships): 15c, 13th cent. ship of King Alfonso X, from medieval manuscript, vert. 25c, Carrack, from 15th cent. engraving, vert. 50c, Galley. 70c, Galleon. 80c, Xebec. 1p, Warship, Santisima Trinidad, vert. 1.50p, 18th cent. corvette, Atrevida, vert. 2p, Steamer, Isabel II. 2.50p, Frigate, Numancia, Spain's 1st armored ship. 3p, Destroyer. 5p, Submarine of Isaac Peral. 6p, Cruiser, Baleares. 10p, Training ship, Juan Sebastian Elcano.

1248 A306 15c dp rose & vio
                blk   .20 .20
1249 A306 25c org yel & gray
                grn   .20 .20
1250 A306 40c ultra & dk bl   .20 .20
1251 A306 50c slate grn & dk
                bl   .20 .20
1252 A306 70c vio & dk bl   .20 .20
1253 A306 80c dl bl grn & ultra .20 .20
1254 A306 1p org & vio brn   .20 .20
1255 A306 1.50p car & sepia   .20 .20
1256 A306 2p blk & slate grn   .75 .20
1257 A306 2.50p rose car & dl
                vio   .20 .20
1258 A306 3p sepia & indigo   .20 .20
1259 A306 5p dk bl, lt grn &
                vio   .90 .90
1260 A306 6p lt green & vio   .80 .80
1261 A306 10p org yel & rose
                red   .35 .20
Nos. 1248-1261 (14)   4.80 4.10

Issued to honor the Spanish Navy.

Europa Issue, 1964
Common Design Type
1964, Sept. 14 Photo. Perf. 12½x13
Size: 21½x39mm
1262 CD7 1p bis, red & grn   .30 .20
1263 CD7 5p brt bl, mag & grn 1.00 .55

Madonna of   Shot Put — A308
Alcazar — A307

1964, Oct. 9   Photo.   Perf. 13
1264 A307 25c bister & brn   .20 .20
1265 A307 1p gray & indigo   .20 .20

Reconquest of Jerez de la Frontera, 700th anniv.

1964, Oct. 10
Gold Olympic Rings
1266 A308 25c shown   .20 .20
1267 A308 80c Broad jump   .20 .20
1268 A308 1p Slalom   .20 .20
1269 A308 3p Judo   .20 .20
1270 A308 5p Discus   .20 .20
Nos. 1266-1270 (5)   1.00 1.00

1964 Olympic Games.

Builders of the New World
Portrait Type of 1961

25c, 2p, Diego de Almagro. 70c, 2.50p, Francisco de Toledo. 80c, 3p, Archbishop Toribio de Mogrovejo. 1p, 5p, Francisco Pizarro.

1964, Oct. 12   *Perf. 13x12½*
1271 A265 25c pale grn & vio   .20 .20
1272 A265 70c pink & ol gray   .20 .20
1273 A265 80c buff & Prus grn .30 .20
1274 A265 1p buff & gray vio   .20 .20
1275 A265 2p pale bl & ol
                gray   .30 .20
1276 A265 2.50p pale grn & cl .25 .20
1277 A265 3p gray & dk bl   3.00 1.00
1278 A265 5p yellow & brown 1.75 1.25
Nos. 1271-1278 (8)   6.30 3.45

Christmas Type of 1963

Nativity by Francisco de Zurbaran (1598-1664).

1964, Dec. 4   **Photo.**
1279 A295 1p olive black   .20 .20

Tourism Types of 1964

Designs: 25c, Columbus monument, Barcelona. 30s, Facade of Santa Maria, Burgos. 50c, Santa Maria la Blanca (medieval synagogue), Toledo. 70c, Bridge, Zamora. 80c, La Giralda (tower) and Cathedral of Seville. 1p, Boat and nets in Cudillero harbor. No. 1286, Cathedral of Burgos, interior. No. 1287, View of Mogrovejo, Santander. 3p, Bridge, Cambados, Pontevedra. 6p, Silk merchants' hall (Lonja), Valencia, interior.

1965   **Engr.**   *Perf. 13*
1280 A298 25c dk blue & blk   .20 .20
1281 A298 30c dull grn & sep   .20 .20
1282 A298 50c cl & rose car   .20 .20
1283 A297 70c vio bl & ind   .20 .20
1284 A298 80c rose cl & dk
                pur   .20 .20
1285 A298 1p dp cl, car & blk .20 .20
1286 A298 2.50p brn vio & bis .20 .20
1287 A297 2.50p dull bl & gray .20 .20
1288 A298 3p rose car & dk
                brn   .20 .20
1289 A298 6p slate & black   .20 .20
Nos. 1280-1289 (10)   2.00 2.00

Alfonso X, the   Julio Romero de
Wise (1232-84)   Torres, Self-
A309   portrait
                        A310

25c, Juan Donoso-Cortes (1809-53). 2.50p, Gaspar M. Jovellanos (1744-1810). 5p, St. Dominic de Guzman (1170-1221).

1965, Feb. 25 Engr. Perf. 13x12½
1292 A309 25c slate bl & blk   .20 .20
1293 A309 70c blue & indigo   .20 .20
1294 A309 2.50p slate grn & sep .20 .20
1295 A309 5p dull grn & sl
                grn   .25 .25
Nos. 1292-1295 (4)   .85 .85

1965, Mar. 24   Photo.   Perf. 13

De Torres Paintings: 25c, Girl with Jar. 40c, "The Song" (girl with guitar). 70c, Madonna of the Lanterns. 80c, Girl with guitar. 1.50p, "The Poem of Cordova" (pensive woman). 2.50p, Martha and Mary. 3p, "The Poem of Cordova" (two women holding statue of angel). 5p, Girl with the Charcoal. 10p, Back of woman's head.

Gold Frame
1296 A310 25c dull purple   .20 .20
1297 A310 40c purple   .20 .20
1298 A310 70c olive green   .20 .20
1299 A310 80c slate green   .20 .20
1300 A310 1p dk red brn   .20 .20
1301 A310 1.50p blue green   .20 .20
1302 A310 2.50p lilac rose   .20 .20
1303 A310 3p dark blue   .35 .25
1304 A310 5p brown   .35 .25
1305 A310 10p slate green   .50 .30
Nos. 1296-1305 (10)   2.60 2.20

Issued to honor Julio Romero de Torres (1880-1930) and for Stamp Day, March 24.

For other art types see A236-A237, A240a, A246a, A257, A272, A285a, A300, A324, A340-A341, A360, A371 and footnote following No. 1606.

Bull and Symbolic
Stamps — A311

1965, May 6   *Perf. 13x12½*
1306 A311 25c multicolored   .20 .20
1307 A311 1p orange & multi   .20 .20
1308 A311 10p multicolored   .50 .30
Nos. 1306-1308 (3)   .90 .70

Issued for International Stamp Day, 1965.

ITU Emblem, Old and New
Communication Equipment — A312

1965, May 17   *Perf. 12½x13*
1309 A312 1p salmon, blk & red .20 .20

International Telecommunication Union, cent.

Pilgrim — A313   Explorer, Royal
                        Flag of Spain
                        and
                        Ships — A314

Design: 2p, Pilgrim (profile).

1965, July 25   Photo.   Perf. 13
1310 A313 1p multicolored   .20 .20
1311 A313 2p multicolored   .20 .20

Issued to commemorate the Holy Year of St. James of Compostela, patron saint of Spain.

1965, Aug. 28   *Perf. 13x12½*
1312 A314 3p red, blk & yel   .20 .20

400th anniv. of the settlement of Florida, and the 1st permanent European settlement in the continental US, St. Augustine, Fla. See US No. 1271.

St. Benedict — A315

Sports Palace,
Madrid — A316

Europa Issue, 1965
1965, Sept. 27 Engr. Perf. 13x12½
1313 A315 1p yel grn & sl grn .20 .20
1314 A315 5p lilac & violet   .40 .25

1965, Oct. 9　Photo.　Perf. 13
1315 A316 1p gray, gold & dk
　　　　 brn　　　　　　.20　.20
　Issued to commemorate the meeting of the International Olympic Committee in Madrid.

Builders of the New World
Portrait Type of 1961

　25c, 2p, Don Fadrique de Toledo. 70c, 2.50p, Father José de Anchieta. 80c, 3p, Francisco de Orellana. 1p, 5p, St. Luis Beltran.

1965, Oct. 12　Photo.　Perf. 13x12½
1316 A265　25c pale grn & dp
　　　　　　　pur　　　　　.20　.20
1317 A265　70c pink & brown　.20　.20
1318 A265　80c cream & Prus
　　　　　　　grn　　　　　　.20　.20
1319 A265　1p buff & dk vio　.20　.20
1320 A265　2p lt bl & dk ol grn　.20　.20
1321 A265　2.50p lt blue & pur　.20　.20
1322 A265　3p gray & dk bl　1.00　.35
1323 A265　5p yellow & brn　1.00　.30
　　Nos. 1316-1323 (8)　3.20　1.85

Chamber of　　　Stamp of 1865
Charles V,　　　(No. 78)
Yuste　　　　　　A318
Monastery
A317

　Yuste Monastery: 1p, Courtyard, horiz. 5p, View of monastery, horiz.

Perf. 12½x13, 13x12½
1965, Nov. 15　　　　　Engr.
1324 A317　1p bl gray & blk　.20　.20
1325 A317　2p red brn & brn blk　.20　.20
1326 A317　5p grayish bl & grn　.25　.25
　　Nos. 1324-1326 (3)　.65　.65
　Monastery of Yuste, Estremadura.

1965, Nov. 22　　　Perf. 13x12½
　Designs: 1p, Stamp of 1865 (No. 77). 5p, Stamp of 1865 (No. 80).
1327 A318　80c blk & yel grn　.20　.20
1328 A318　1p plum, brn & rose　.20　.20
1329 A318　5p sepia & org brn　.20　.20
　　Nos. 1327-1329 (3)　.60　.60
　Cent. of the 1st Spanish perforated postage stamps.

Nativity
A319

1965, Dec. 1　Photo.　Perf. 12½x13
1330 A319　1p bright green　.20　.20

Virgin of Peace,　　Globe and Four
Antipolo　　　　　Beasts of
A320　　　　　　　Apocalypse
　　　　　　　　　　A321

　Design: 3p, Father Andres de Urdaneta.

1965, Dec. 3　　　Perf. 13x12½
1331 A320　1p pale sal & ol brn　.20　.20
1332 A320　3p gray & dp blue　.20　.20
　Christianization of the Philippines, 400th anniv.

1965, Dec. 29　Photo.　Perf. 13x12½
1333 A321　1p grnsh bl, yel & brn　.20　.20
　Vatican II, the 21st Ecumenical Council of the Roman Catholic Church, 10/11/62-12/8/65.

Adm. Alvaro de　　Exhibition
Bazan (1526-　　Emblem; Type
88)　　　　　　　Block "P"
A322　　　　　　A323

　2p, Daza de Valdes, scientist, 17th cent.

1966, Feb. 26　Engr.　Perf. 13x12½
1334 A322　25c dull blue & gray　.20　.20
1335 A322　2p magenta & violet　.20　.20
　See Nos. C177-C178.

1966, Mar. 4　Photo.　Perf. 13
1336 A323　1p red, grn & vio bl　.20　.20
　Graphic Arts and Advertising Packaging Exhibition "Graphispack," Barcelona, 3/4-13.

José Maria Sert,
Self-portrait
A324

Santa Maria
Church,
Guernica — A325

　Sert Paintings: 25c, The Magic Ball. 40c, Evocation of Toledo, horiz. 70c, Christ on the Cross. 80c, Parachutists. 1.50p, "Audacity." 2.50p, "Justice." 3p, Jacob Wrestling with the Angel. 5p, "The Five Continents." 10p, Sts. Peter and Paul.

1966, Mar. 24
Gold Frame
1337 A324　25c dk purple　.20　.20
1338 A324　40c dp magenta　.20　.20
1339 A324　70c green　.20　.20
1340 A324　80c dk ol grn　.20　.20
1341 A324　1p claret brn　.20　.20
1342 A324　1.50p dull blue　.20　.20
1343 A324　2.50p dk red　.20　.20
1344 A324　3p deep blue　.20　.20
1345 A324　5p sepia　.20　.20
1346 A324　10p grnsh blk　.20　.20
　　Nos. 1337-1346 (10)　2.00　2.00
　Issued to honor José Maria Sert (1876-1945) and for Stamp Day, Mar. 24.
　For other art types see A236-A237, A240a, A246a, A257, A272, A285a, A300, A310, A340-A341, A360, A371 and footnote following No. 1606.

1966, Apr. 28　Photo.　Perf. 13
　Designs: 1p, Arms of Guernica and Luno. 3p, Tree of Guernica.
1347 A325　80c bl, sepia & grn　.20　.20
1348 A325　1p yel grn & multi　.20　.20
1349 A325　3p bl, grn & vio brn　.20　.20
　　Nos. 1347-1349 (3)　.60　.60
　Founding of Guernica and Luno, 6th cent.

Cover with
Stamp of
1850 (#1)
A326

　Designs (covers): 1p, 5r (#3). 10p, 10r (#5).

1966, May 6　　　Perf. 12½x13
1350 A326　25c rose vio, blk &
　　　　　　　red　　　　　.20　.20
1351 A326　1p red brn, org & blk　.20　.20
1352 A326　10p ol grn, grn & org　.25　.20
　　Nos. 1350-1352 (3)　.65　.60
　Issued for International Stamp Day, 1966.

Bohi
Valley — A327

Torla, Huesca
A328

　Tourism: 40c, Portal of Sigena Monastery, Huesca. 50c, Santo Domingo Church, Soria. 80c, Torre del Oro, Seville. 1p, Palm and view, Pico de Teyde, Santa Cruz de Tenerife. 1.50p, Monastery of Guadalupe, Caceres. 2p, Alcala de Henares University. 3p, Seo Cathedral, Lerida. 10p, Courtyard of St. Gregorio, Valladolid.

1966　　　　　　Engr.
1353 A327　10c gray grn & bl
　　　　　　　grn　　　　　.20　.20
1354 A328　15c gray grn & brn　.20　.20
1355 A327　40c bis brn & brn　.20　.20
1356 A327　50c car rose & dp
　　　　　　　cl　　　　　　.20　.20
1357 A327　80c lilac & rose vio　.20　.20
1358 A327　1p vio bl & bl grn　.20　.20
1359 A328　1.50p dk bl & blk　.20　.20
1360 A328　2p sl bl & sepia　.20　.20
1361 A328　3p ultra & blk　.20　.20
1362 A327　10p brt bl & grnsh
　　　　　　　bl　　　　　　.20　.20
　　Nos. 1353-1362 (10)　2.00　2.00

Tree and
Globe
A329

1966, June 6　Photo.　Perf. 12½x13
1363 A329　1p brn & dk grn　.20　.20
　6th Intl. Forestry Cong., Madrid, June 6-18.

Navy
Emblem — A330

1966, July 1　Photo.　Perf. 13
1364 A330　1p gray & dk bl　.20　.20
　Naval Week, Barcelona, July 1-8.

Guadamur
Castle — A331

　Castles: 25c, Alcazar, Segovia. 40c, La Mota. 50c, Olite. 70c, Monteagudo. 80c, Butron, vert. 1p, Manzanares. 3p, Almansa, vert.

1966, Aug. 13　Engr.　Perf. 13
1365 A331　10c grysh bl & sep　.20　.20
1366 A331　25c violet & purple　.20　.20
1367 A331　40c grnsh bl & bl grn　.20　.20
1368 A331　50c grnsh bl & ultra　.20　.20
1369 A331　70c vio bl & ind　.20　.20
1370 A331　80c vio & sl grn　.20　.20
1371 A331　1p ol bis & gray　.20　.20
1372 A331　3p rose & red lil　.20　.20
　　Nos. 1365-1372 (8)　1.60　1.60

Don Quixote, Dulcinea and Aldonza
Lorenzo — A332

1966, Sept. 5　Photo.　Perf. 13
1373 A332　1.50p sal, lt grn & blk　.20　.20
　4th World Congress of Psychiatry, Madrid.

Europa Issue, 1966

The Rape
of Europa
A333

1966, Sept. 28　Photo.　Perf. 12½x13
1374 A333　1p multicolored　.20　.20
1375 A333　5p multicolored　.25　.20

Don Quixote　　　Title Page of
and Sancho　　　"Dotrina
Panza on　　　　Christiana"
Clavileno　　　　A335
A334

1966, Oct. 9　　　Perf. 13x12½
1376 A334　1.50p sl bl, red brn &
　　　　　　　dk brn　　　.20　.20
　17th Cong. of the Intl. Astronautical Federation.

Builders of the New World
Types of 1961 and A335

　30c, Antonio de Mendoza. 1p, José A. Manso de Velasco. 1.20p, Coins of Lima, 1699. 1.50p, Manuel de Castro y Padilla. 3p, Portal of Oruro Convent, Bolivia. 3.50p, Manuel de Amat. 6p, Inca courier, El Chasqui.

1966, Oct. 12
1377 A265　30c pale pink & brn　.20　.20
1378 A335　50c pale bis & brn　.20　.20
1379 A265　1p gray & vio　.20　.20
1380 A335　1.20p gray & slate　.20　.20
1381 A265　1.50p pale grn & dp
　　　　　　　grn　　　　　.20　.20
1382 A335　3p pale gray & dp
　　　　　　　bl　　　　　　.20　.20
1383 A265　3.50p pale lil & pur　.25　.25
1384 A265　6p buff & sepia　.20　.20
　　Nos. 1377-1384 (8)　1.65　1.65

Ramon del Valle Inclan — A336

Portraits: 3p, Carlos Arniches. 6p, Jacinto Benavente y Martinez.

1966, Nov. 7   Photo.   Perf. 13

1385	A336	1.50p blk & green	.20	.20
1386	A336	3p blk & gray vio	.20	.20
1387	A336	6p blk & slate	.20	.20
		Nos. 1385-1387 (3)	.60	.60

Issued to honor Spanish writers.
See design A355.

Carthusian Monastery, Jerez A337

St. Mary Carthusian Monastery: 1p, Portal, vert. 5p, Entrance gate.

Perf. 13x12½, 12½x13

1966, Nov. 24   Engr.

1388	A337	1p grnsh bl & sl bl	.20	.20
1389	A337	2p green & yel grn	.20	.20
1390	A337	5p lilac & claret	.20	.20
		Nos. 1388-1390 (3)	.60	.60

Nativity, Sculpture by Pedro Duque Cornejo A338

1966, Dec. 5   Photo.   Perf. 12½x13

| 1391 | A338 | 1.50p multicolored | .20 | .20 |

Regional Costumes Issue

Woman from Alava — A339

1967   Photo.   Perf. 13

1392	A339	6p shown	.20	.20
1393	A339	6p Albacete	.20	.20
1394	A339	6p Alicante	.20	.20
1395	A339	6p Almeria	.20	.20
1396	A339	6p Avila	.20	.20
1397	A339	6p Badajoz	.20	.20
1398	A339	6p Baleares	.20	.20
1399	A339	6p Barcelona	.20	.20
1400	A339	6p Burgos	.20	.20
1401	A339	6p Caceres	.20	.20
1402	A339	6p Cadiz	.20	.20
1403	A339	6p Castellon de la Plana	.20	.20
		Nos. 1392-1403 (12)	2.40	2.40

1968

1404	A339	6p Ciudad Real	.20	.20
1405	A339	6p Cordoba	.20	.20
1406	A339	6p Coruna	.20	.20
1407	A339	6p Cuenca	.20	.20
1408	A339	6p Fernando Po	.20	.20
1409	A339	6p Gerona	.20	.20
1410	A339	6p Gran Canaria, Las Palmas	.20	.20
1411	A339	6p Granada	.20	.20
1412	A339	6p Guadalajara	.20	.20
1413	A339	6p Guipuzcoa	.20	.20
1414	A339	6p Huelva	.20	.20
1415	A339	6p Huesca	.20	.20
		Nos. 1404-1415 (12)	2.40	2.40

1969

1416	A339	6p Ifni	.20	.20
1417	A339	6p Jaen	.20	.20
1418	A339	6p Leon	.20	.20
1419	A339	6p Lerida	.20	.20
1420	A339	6p Logroño	.20	.20
1421	A339	6p Lugo	.20	.20
1422	A339	6p Madrid	.20	.20
1423	A339	6p Malaga	.20	.20
1424	A339	6p Murcia	.20	.20
1425	A339	6p Navarra	.20	.20
1426	A339	6p Orense	.20	.20
1427	A339	6p Oviedo	.20	.20
		Nos. 1416-1427 (12)	2.40	2.40

1970

1428	A339	6p Palencia	.20	.20
1429	A339	6p Pontevedra	.20	.20
1430	A339	6p Sahara	.20	.20
1431	A339	6p Salamanca	.20	.20
1432	A339	6p Santa Cruz de Tenerife	.20	.20
1433	A339	6p Santander	.20	.20
1434	A339	6p Segovia	.20	.20
1435	A339	6p Seville	.20	.20
1436	A339	6p Soria	.20	.20
1437	A339	6p Tarragona	.20	.20
1438	A339	6p Teruel	.20	.20
1439	A339	6p Toledo	.20	.20
		Nos. 1428-1439 (12)	2.40	2.40

1971

1440	A339	6p Valencia	.20	.20
1441	A339	6p Valladolid	.20	.20
1442	A339	8p Vizcaya	.20	.20
1443	A339	8p Zamora	.20	.20
1444	A339	8p Zaragoza	.20	.20
		Nos. 1440-1444 (5)	1.00	1.00
		Nos. 1392-1444 (53)	10.60	10.60

Archers A340

Ornament — A341

50c, Boar hunt. 1.20p, Bison. 1.50p, Hands. 2p, Warrior. 2.50p, Deer. 3.50p, Archers. 4p, Hunters & gazelle. 6p, Hunters & deer herd.

1967, Mar. 27   Photo.   Perf. 13
Gold Frame

1449	A340	40c ocher & car rose	.20	.20
1450	A340	50c gray & dk red	.20	.20
1451	A341	1p ocher & org ver	.20	.20
1452	A340	1.20p gray & rose brn	.20	.20
1453	A340	1.50p gray & red	.20	.20
1454	A341	2p lt brn & dk car rose	.20	.20
1455	A341	2.50p sky bl & rose brn	.20	.20
1456	A340	3.50p yellow & blk	.20	.20
1457	A341	4p citron & red	.20	.20
1458	A341	6p olive & red	.20	.20
		Nos. 1449-1458 (10)	2.00	2.00

Issued for Stamp Day, 1967. The designs are from paleolithic and mesolithic wall paintings found in Spanish caves.
For other art types see A236-A237, A240a, A246a, A257, A272, A285a, A300, A310, A324, A360, A371 and footnote following No. 1606.

Palma Cathedral and Conference Emblem — A342

1967, Mar. 28

| 1459 | A342 | 1.50p brt blue grn | .20 | .20 |

Issued to publicize the Congress of the Interparliamentary Union, Palma de Mallorca.

W. K. Röntgen, X-ray Tube and Atom — A343

1967, Apr. 3   Photo.   Perf. 13

| 1460 | A343 | 1.50p green | .20 | .20 |

7th Cong. of Latin Radiologists and 1st Cong. of European Radiologists, Barcelona, Apr. 2-8.

Averroes (1120-1198), Physician and Philosopher — A344

Portraits: 3.50p, José de Acosta (1539-1600), Jesuit, historian, poet. 4p, Moses ben Maimonides (1135-1204), Jewish philosopher and physician. 25p, Andres Laguna, 16th century physician.

1967, Apr. 6   Engr.   Perf. 13x12½

1461	A344	1.20p lil & dl vio	.20	.20
1462	A344	3.50p mag & dl pur	.20	.20
1463	A344	4p brn & sep	.20	.20
1464	A344	25p dl bl & blk	.25	.20
		Nos. 1461-1464 (4)	.85	.80

Europa Issue, 1967
Common Design Type

1967, May 2   Photo.   Perf. 13
Size: 25x31mm

| 1465 | CD10 | 1.50p sl grn, red brn & dl red | .20 | .20 |
| 1466 | CD10 | 6p vio, brt bl & brn | .20 | .20 |

Exhibition Building and Fountain, Valencia — A345

1967, May 3

| 1467 | A345 | 1.50p gray grn | .20 | .20 |

International Fair at Valencia, 50th anniv.

Numeral Postmark No. 3 of 1850 — A346

Designs: 1.50p, No. 2, 12c stamp of 1850 with crowned M postmark of Madrid. 6p, No. 4, 6r stamp of 1850 with 1r postmark.

1967, May 6

1468	A346	40c brn org, dl bl & blk	.20	.20
1469	A346	1.50p brn, grn & blk	.20	.20
1470	A346	6p bl, red & blk	.20	.20
		Nos. 1468-1470 (3)	.60	.60

Intl. Stamp Day, 1967. See #1527-1528.

Guardian Angel Over Indigent Sleeper — A347

1967, May 16   Perf. 13

| 1471 | A347 | 1.50p bl, blk, brn & red | .20 | .20 |

Issued for National Caritas Day to honor Caritas, Catholic welfare organization.

Betanzos Church, Coruña — A348

International Tourist Year Emblem A349

Tourism: 1p, Tower of St. Miguel Church, Palencia. 1.50p, Human pyramid (Castellers). 2.50p, Columbus monument, Huelva. 5p, The Enchanted City, Cuenca. 6p, Church of Our Lady, Sanlucar, Cadiz.

1967, July 26   Engr.   Perf. 13

1472	A348	10c ultra & blk	.20	.20
1473	A348	1p dl bl & blk	.20	.20
1474	A348	1.50p lt brn & blk	.20	.20
1475	A348	2.50p grnsh bl & dk bl	.20	.20
1476	A348	3.50p dl pur & dk bl	.20	.20
1477	A348	5p yel grn & dk grn	.20	.20
1478	A348	6p red lil & dl lil	.20	.20
		Nos. 1472-1478 (7)	1.40	1.40

Balsareny Castle — A350

Castles: 1p, Jarandilla. 1.50p, Almodovar. 2p, Ponferrada, vert. 2.50p, Peniscola. 5p, Coca. 6p, Loarre. 10p, Belmonte.

1967, Aug. 11   Engr.

1479	A350	50c gray & lt brn	.20	.20
1480	A350	1p bl gray & dl pur	.20	.20
1481	A350	1.50p bl gray & sage grn	.20	.20
1482	A350	2p brick red & bis brn	.20	.20
1483	A350	2.50p grnsh bl & sep	.20	.20
1484	A350	5p rose vio & vio	.20	.20
1485	A350	6p bis brn & gray	.20	.20
1486	A350	10p aqua & slate	.20	.20
		Nos. 1479-1486 (8)	1.60	1.60

Globe, Snowflake and Thermometer A351

Galleon, Map of Americas, Spain and Philippines A352

1967, Aug. 30   **Photo.**
1487 A351 1.50p bright blue   .20 .20

12th Intl. Refrigeration Cong., Madrid, Sept. 4-8.

1967, Oct. 10   **Photo.**   *Perf. 13*
1488 A352 1.50p red lilac   .20 .20

4th Congress of Spanish, Portuguese, American & Philippine Municipalities, Barcelona, Oct. 6-12.

Builders of the New World
Type of 1961 and

Nootka Settlement A353

Designs: 40c, Francisco de la Bodega. 50c, Old map of Nootka coast, vert. 1p, Francisco Antonio Mourelle. 1.50p, Esteban José Martinez. 3p, Old maps of coast of Northern California. 3.50p, Cayetano Valdes. 6p, Ships, San Elias, Alaska.

1967, Oct. 12
1489 A265   40c pink & grnsh
    gray   .20 .20
1490 A353   50c dk brn   .20 .20
1491 A265   1p pale bl & red lil   .20 .20
1492 A353   1.20p dk ol grn   .20 .20
1493 A265   1.50p pale pink & bl
    grn   .20 .20
1494 A353   3p buff & vio blk   .20 .20
1495 A265   3.50p pale pink & bl   .25 .25
1496 A353   6p red brn, *bluish*   .20 .20
    Nos. 1489-1496 (8)   1.65 1.65

Issued to honor the explorers of the Northwest coast of North America.

Roman Statue and Gate A354   José Bethencourt A355

Designs: 3.50p, Ancient plower with ox team, horiz. 6p, Roman coins of Caceres.

1967, Oct. 31   **Photo.**   *Perf. 13*
1497 A354 1.50p multi   .20 .20
1498 A354 3.50p multi   .20 .20
1499 A354 6p multi   .20 .20
    Nos. 1497-1499 (3)   .60 .60

Founding of Caceres by the Romans, 2000th anniv.

1967, Nov. 15

1.50p, Enrique Granados (composer). 3.50p, Ruben Dario (poet). 6p, St. Ildefonso.

1500 A355 1.20p gray & red brn   .20 .20
1501 A355 1.50p blk & grn   .20 .20
1502 A355 3.50p brn & pur   .20 .20
1503 A355 6p blk & slate   .20 .20
    Nos. 1500-1503 (4)   .80 .80

Issued to honor famous Spanish men. See design A336.

Santa Maria de Veruela Monastery A356   St. José Receiving Last Unction, by Goya A357

Designs: 3.50p, Aerial view of monastery, horiz. 6p, Inside view, horiz.

1967, Nov. 24   **Engr.**   *Perf. 13*
1504 A356 1.50p ultra & ind   .20 .20
1505 A356 3.50p grn & blk   .20 .20
1506 A356 6p rose vio & bis
    brn   .20 .20
    Nos. 1504-1506 (3)   .60 .60

1967, Nov. 27   **Photo.**
1507 A357 1.50p multi   .20 .20

200th anniversary of the canonization of St. José de Calasanz (1556-1648), founder of the first Christian Schools in Rome.

Nativity, by Francisco Salzillo — A358

1967, Dec. 5
1508 A358 1.50p multi   .20 .20

Christmas, 1967.

Slalom A359

3.50p, Bobsled, vert. 6p, Ice hockey.

1968, Feb. 6   **Photo.**   *Perf. 13*
1509 A359 1.50p multi   .20 .20
1510 A359 3.50p multi   .20 .20
1511 A359 6p multi   .20 .20
    Nos. 1509-1511 (3)   .60 .60

Issued to commemorate the 10th Winter Olympic Games, Grenoble, France, Feb. 6-18.

Mariano Fortuny, Self-portrait A360

Fortuny Paintings: 40c, The Vicariate, horiz. 50c, "Fantasy" (pianist). 1p, "Idyll" (piper and sheep). 1.20p, The Print Collector, horiz. 2p, Old Man in the Sun. 2.50p, Calabrian Man. 3.50p, Lady with Fan. 4p, Battle of Tetuan, 1860. 6p, Queen Christina in Carriage, horiz.

1968, Mar. 25   **Photo.**   *Perf. 13*
Gold Frame

1512 A360 40c dp red lil   .20 .20
1513 A360 50c dk bl grn   .20 .20
1514 A360 1p brown   .20 .20
1515 A360 1.20p dp vio   .20 .20
1516 A360 1.50p dp grn   .20 .20
1517 A360 2p org brn   .20 .20
1518 A360 2.50p car rose   .20 .20
1519 A360 3.50p dk red brn   .20 .20
1520 A360 4p dk ol   .20 .20
1521 A360 6p brt bl   .20 .20
    Nos. 1512-1521 (10)   2.00 2.00

Issued to honor Mariano Fortuny y Carbo (1838-74), and for Stamp Day.
For other art types see A236-A237, A240a, A246a, A257, A272, A285a, A300, A310,

A324, A340-A341, A371 and footnote following No. 1606.

Beatriz Galindo A361

Famous Women: 1.50p, Agustina de Aragon. 3.50p, Maria Pacheco. 6p, Rosalia de Castro.

1968, Apr. 8   **Engr.**   *Perf. 12½x13*
1522 A361 1.20p yel brn & blk
    brn   .20 .20
1523 A361 1.50p bl grn & dk bl   .20 .20
1524 A361 3.50p lt vio & dk vio   .20 .20
1525 A361 6p gray bl & blk   .20 .20
    Nos. 1522-1525 (4)   .80 .80

Europa Issue, 1968
Common Design Type

1968, Apr. 29   **Photo.**   *Perf. 13*
Size: 38x22mm
1526 CD11 3.50p brt bl, gold &
    brn   .20 .20

Spain No. 1 with Galicia Puebla Postmark — A362

Map of León and Seal — A363

Stamp Day: 3.50p, Spain No. 4 with Serena postmark.

1968, May 6   **Photo.**   *Perf. 13*
1527 A362 1.50p blk, bl & ocher   .20 .20
1528 A362 3.50p bl, dk grn & blk   .20 .20

See Nos. 1568-1569, 1608, 1677, 1754.

Perf. 13x12½, 12½x13
1968, June 15   **Photo.**

Designs: 1.50p, Roman legionary. 3.50p, Emperor Galba coin, horiz.

Size: 25x38½mm
1529 A363 1p lil, red brn & yel   .20 .20
Size: 25x47½mm
1530 A363 1.50p brn, dk brn &
    buff   .20 .20
Size: 37½x26mm
1531 A363 3.50p ocher & sl grn   .25 .25
    Nos. 1529-1531 (3)   .65 .65

1900th anniversary of the founding of León by the Roman Legion VII Gemina.

Human Rights Emblem A364   Benavente Palace, Baeza A365

1968, June 25   **Photo.**   *Perf. 13x12½*
1532 A364 3.50p bl, red & grn   .20 .20

International Human Rights Year, 1968.

1968, July 15   **Engr.**   *Perf. 13*

Tourism: 1.20p, View of Salamanca with Tormes River Bridge, horiz. 1.50p, Statuary group from St. Vincent's Church, Avila (The Adoration of the Magi). 2p, Tomb of Martin Vazquez de Arce, Cathedral of Sigüenza, horiz. 3.50p, Portal of St. Mary's Church, Sangüesa, Navarre.

1533 A365 50c dp rose & brn   .20 .20
1534 A365 1.20p emer & sl grn   .20 .20
1535 A365 1.50p dp grn & ind   .20 .20
1536 A365 2p lil rose & blk   .20 .20
1537 A365 3.50p brt lil & rose lil   .20 .20
    Nos. 1533-1537 (5)   1.00 1.00

Escalona Castle, Toledo — A366

Castles: 1.20p, Fuensaldaña, Valladolid. 1.50p, Peñafiel, Valladolid. 2.50p, Villasobroso, Pontevedra. 6p, Frias, Burgos, vert.

1968, July 29   **Engr.**   *Perf. 13*
1538 A366 40c dk bl & sepia   .20 .20
1539 A366 1.20p vio brn & vio
    blk   .20 .20
1540 A366 1.50p ol & blk   .20 .20
1541 A366 2.50p ol grn & blk   .20 .20
1542 A366 6p vio bl & bl grn   .20 .20
    Nos. 1538-1542 (5)   1.00 1.00

Rifle Shooting A367

Designs: 1.50p, Horse jumping. 3.50p, Bicycling. 6p, Sailing, vert.

Perf. 12½x13, 13x12½
1968, Sept. 24   **Photo.**
1543 A367 1p multi   .20 .20
1544 A367 1.50p multi   .20 .20
1545 A367 3.50p multi   .20 .20
1546 A367 6p multi   .20 .20
    Nos. 1543-1546 (4)   .80 .80

19th Olympic Games, Mexico City, 10/12-27.

Builders of the New World
Type of 1961 and

Map of Capuchin Missions along Orinoco River, 1732 — A368

1p, Diego de Losada. 1.50p, Losada family coat of arms. 3.50p, Diego de Henares. 6p, Map of Caracas, drawn by Diego de Henares, 1578, horiz.

1968, Oct. 12   **Photo.**   *Perf. 13*
1547 A368 40c grnsh bl, *bluish*   .20 .20
1548 A265 1p red lil, *gray*   .20 .20
1549 A368 1.50p sl, *pale rose*   .20 .20
1550 A265 3.50p dk bl, *pnksh*   .20 .20
1551 A368 6p dk ol bis   .20 .20
    Nos. 1547-1551 (5)   1.00 1.00

Christianization of Venezuela and the founding of Caracas.

St. Maria del Parral Monastery, Segovia — A369

3.50p, Monastery, inside view. 6p, Madonna & Child, statue from main altar.

1968, Nov. 25   **Engr.**   *Perf. 13*

1552	A369	1.50p	gray bl & rose vio	.20 .20
1553	A369	3.50p	brn & red brn	.20 .20
1554	A369	6p	rose claret & brn	.20 .20
		Nos. 1552-1554 (3)		.60 .60

Nativity, by Federico Fiori da Urbino — A370

Alonso Cano by Velázquez A371

1968, Dec. 2   **Photo.**   *Perf. 13x12½*

1555 A370 1.50p gold & multi   .20 .20

Christmas, 1968.

1969, Mar. 24   **Photo.**   *Perf. 13*

Cano Paintings: 40c, St. Agnes. 50c, St. John. 1p, Jesus and Angel. 2p, Holy Family. 2.50p, Circumcision of Jesus. 3p, Jesus and the Samaritan Woman. 3.50p, Madonna and Child. 4p, Sts. John Capistrano and Bernardino, horiz. 6p, Vision of St. John the Baptist.

Gold Frame

1556	A371	40c	deep plum	.20 .20
1557	A371	50c	green	.20 .20
1558	A371	1p	sepia	.20 .20
1559	A371	1.50p	slate grn	.20 .20
1560	A371	2p	red brown	.20 .20
1561	A371	2.50p	dp red lil	.20 .20
1562	A371	3p	ultra	.20 .20
1563	A371	3.50p	dk rose brn	.20 .20
1564	A371	4p	dull lilac	.20 .20
1565	A371	6p	slate blue	.20 .20
		Nos. 1556-1565 (10)		2.00 2.00

Alonso Cano (1601-1667), and Stamp Day. For other art types see A236-A237, A240a, A246a, A257, A272, A285a, A300, A310, A324, A340-A341, A360 and footnote following No. 1606.

DNA (Genetic Code) Molecule and Chart A372

1969, Apr. 7   **Photo.**   *Perf. 13*

1566 A372 1.50p gray & multi   .20 .20

Issued to publicize the 6th European Congress of Biochemistry, Madrid, Apr. 7-11.

Europa Issue, 1969
Common Design Type

1969, Apr. 28
Size: 38x22mm

1567 CD12 3.50p multi   .20 .20

Stamp Day Type of 1968

1.50p, Spain #6 with crowned M postmark. 3.50p, Spain #11 with Corvera postmark.

1969, May 6   **Photo.**   *Perf. 13*

1568	A362	1.50p	blk, red & grn	.20 .20
1569	A362	3.50p	grn, bl & red	.20 .20

Issued for Stamp Day, 1969.

Spectrum A373

1969, May 26

1570 A373 1.50p blk & multi   .20 .20

Issued to publicize the 15th International Spectroscopy Colloquium, Madrid, May 26-30.

World Map, Red Crescent, Cross, Lion and Sun Emblems A374

1969, May 30

1571 A374 1.50p multi   .20 .20

League of Red Cross Societies, 50th anniv.

Last Supper, Finial from Lugo Cathedral — A375

1969, June 4

1572 A375 1.50p grn, brn & blk   .20 .20

300th anniversary of the dedication of Galicia Province to the reign of Jesus.

Turegano Castle, Segovia A376

Father Junipero Serra — A377

Castles: 1.50p, Villalonso, Zamora. 2.50p, Velez Blanco, Almeria. 3.50p, Castilnovo, Segovia. 6p, Torrelobaton, Valladolid.

1969, June 24   **Engr.**   *Perf. 13*

1573	A376	1p	dl grn & sl	.20 .20
1574	A376	1.50p	bluish lil & dk bl	.20 .20
1575	A376	2.50p	bl vio & bluish lil	.20 .20
1576	A376	3.50p	red brn & ol grn	.20 .20
1577	A376	6p	gray grn & dl brn	.20 .20
		Nos. 1573-1577 (5)		1.00 1.00

1969, July 16   **Photo.**   *Perf. 13*

1578 A377 1.50p multi   .20 .20

Bicentenary of San Diego, Calif.

Rock of Gibraltar — A378

Dama de Elche — A379

2p, View of Gibraltar across the Bay of Algeciras.

1969, July 18

1579	A378	1.50p	bl grn	.20 .20
1580	A378	2p	brt rose lil	.20 .20

1969, July 23   **Engr.**   *Perf. 13*

Tourism: 1.50p, Alcañiz Castle, Teruel, horiz. 3p, Murcia Cathedral. 6p, St. Maria de la Redonda, Logrono.

1581	A379	1.50p	dl grn & blk	.20 .20
1582	A379	3p	yel grn & bl grn	.20 .20
1583	A379	3.50p	gray bl & dk bl	.20 .20
1584	A379	6p	yel grn & vio blk	.20 .20
		Nos. 1581-1584 (4)		.80 .80

Builders of the New World
Type of 1961 and

Santo Domingo Church, Santiago, Chile — A380

1.50p, Casa de Moneda de Chile, horiz. 2p, Ambrosio O'Higgins. 3.50p, Pedro de Valdivia. 6p, First large bridge over Mapocho River, horiz.

1969, Oct. 12   **Photo.**   *Perf. 13*

1585	A380	40c	lt bl & dk red brn	.20 .20
1586	A380	1.50p	pale rose & dk vio	.20 .20
1587	A265	2p	pale pink & ol	.20 .20
1588	A265	3.50p	pale yel & dk Prus grn	.35 .30
1589	A380	6p	pale yel & blk brn	.25 .20
		Nos. 1585-1589 (5)		1.20 1.10

Exploration and development of Chile. See Nos. 1630-1631, 1634.

Adoration of the Magi, by Juan Bautista Mayno — A381

Christmas: 2p, Nativity, bas-relief from altar of Cathedral of Gerona.

1969, Nov. 3

1590	A381	1.50p	multi	.20 .20
1591	A381	2p	multi	.20 .20

Tomb of Alfonso VIII and Wife, Las Huelgas Monastery, Burgos — A382

Designs: 1.50p, Las Huelgas Monastery. 6p, Inside view, vert.

1969, Nov. 22   **Engr.**

1592	A382	1.50p	lt bl grn & indigo	.25 .20
1593	A382	3.50p	ultra & vio bl	.40 .35
1594	A382	6p	olive & yel grn	.20 .20
		Nos. 1592-1594 (3)		.85 .75

See Nos. 1639-1641.

St. Juan de Avila, by El Greco — A383

St. Stephen, by Luis de Morales — A384

Design: 50p, Bishop Rodrigo Ximenez de Rada, Juan de Borgona mural.

1970, Feb. 25   **Engr.**   *Perf. 13*

1595	A383	25p	pale pur & ind	4.00 .20
1596	A383	50p	brn org & brn	1.60 .20

1970, Mar. 24   **Photo.**   *Perf. 13*

Morales Paintings: 1p, Annunciation. 1.50p, Madonna and Child with St. John. 2p, Madonna and Child. 3p, Presentation at the Temple. 3.50p, St. Jerome. 4p, St. John de Ribera. 5p, Ecce Homo. 6p, Pieta. 10p, St. Francis of Assisi.

1597	A384	50c	gold & multi	.20 .20
1598	A384	1p	gold & multi	.20 .20
1599	A384	1.50p	gold & multi	.20 .20
1600	A384	2p	gold & multi	.20 .20
1601	A384	3p	gold & multi	.20 .20
1602	A384	3.50p	gold & multi	.20 .20
1603	A384	4p	gold & multi	.20 .20
1604	A384	5p	gold & multi	.20 .20
1605	A384	6p	gold & multi	.20 .20
1606	A384	10p	gold & multi	.20 .20
		Nos. 1597-1606 (10)		2.00 2.00

Issued to honor Luis de Morales, "El Divino" (1509-1586), and for Stamp Day.

For other art types see A397, A410, A431, A448, A473, A501, A522, A538, A558 and footnote following No. 876.

Europa Issue, 1970
Common Design Type

1970, May 4   **Photo.**   *Perf. 13x12½*
Size: 37½x22mm

1607 CD13 3.50p brt bl & gold   .20 .20

Stamp Day Type of 1968

Stamp Day: 2p, Spain No. 51 with "Ferro Carril de Langreo" postmark.

1970, May 4   *Perf. 13x12½*

1608 A362 2p dl red, grn & blk   .20 .20

Barcelona Fair Building A385

1970, May 27   *Perf. 13*

1609 A385 15p multi   .25 .20

Barcelona Trade Fair, 50th anniversary.

Miguel Primo de Rivera — A386

1970, June 6   **Photo.**   *Perf. 13*

1610 A386 2p buff, brn & ol grn   .20 .20

Gen. Miguel Primo de Rivera (1870-1930), Spanish dictator, 1923-1930.

Valencia de Don Juan Castle — A387

Castles: 1.20p, Monterrey. 3.50p, Mombeltran. 6p, Sadaba. 10p, Bellver.

1970, June 24   **Engr.**
1611 A387   1p blk & dl bl   .35   .20
1612 A387   1.20p lt grnsh bl & vio   .20   .20
1613 A387   3.50p pale grn & brn   .20   .20
1614 A387   6p sep & dl pur   .20   .20
1615 A387   10p fawn & sepia   .80   .20
    Nos. 1611-1615 (5)   1.75 1.00

Alcazaba Castle, Almeria A388

Tourism: 1p, Malaga Cathedral. 1.50p, St. Mary of the Assumption, Lequemo, vert. 2p, Cloister of St. Francis of Orense. 3.50p, Market (Lonja), Zaragoza, vert. 5p, The Gate of Vitoria, vert.

1970, July 23   **Engr.**   **Perf. 13**
1616 A388   50c bluish gray & dl pur   .20   .20
1617 A388   1p red brn & ocher   .20   .20
1618 A388   1.50p bluish gray & sl grn   .20   .20
1619 A388   2p sl & dk bl   .40   .20
1620 A388   3.50p pur & vio bl   .20   .20
1621 A388   5p gray grn & red brn   .80   .20
    Nos. 1616-1621 (6)   2.00 1.20

Tailor, from Book Published in Madrid, 1589 A389

1970, Aug. 18   **Photo.**   **Perf. 13**
1622 A389   2p mag, brn & dl vio   .20   .20

14th Intl. Tailoring Congress, Madrid.

Diver and Map of Europe A390

1970, Aug. 25
1623 A390   2p grn & brt bl   .20   .20

12th European Championships in Swimming, Diving and Water Polo, Barcelona.

Concha Espina — A391

1p, Guillen de Castro. 1.50p, Juan Ramon Jimenez. 2p, Gustavo Adolfo Becquer. 2.50p, Miguel de Unamuno. 3.50p, José M. Gabriel y Galan.

1970, Sept. 21   Photo.   Perf. 13x12½
1624 A391   50c brn, vio bl & pale rose   .20   .20
1625 A391   1p sl grn, dp rose lil & gray   .20   .20
1626 A391   1.50p dk bl, brt grn & gray   .20   .20
1627 A391   2p grn, dk ol & buff   .20   .20
1628 A391   2.50p pur, rose lake & buff   .20   .20

1629 A391   3.50p brn, dk red & gray   .20   .20
    Nos. 1624-1629 (6)   1.20 1.20

Issued to honor Spanish writers.

Builders of the New World
Portrait Type of 1961 and Building Type of 1969

40c, Ecala House, Queretaro, Mexico. 1.50p, Mexico Cathedral, horiz. 2p, Vasco de Quiroga. 3.50p, Brother Juan de Zumarraga. 6p, Cathedral Towers, Morelia, Mexico.

1970, Oct. 12   Photo.
1630 A380   40c lt bl & ol gray   .20   .20
1631 A380   1.50p lt bl & brn   .20   .20
1632 A265   2p buff & dk vio   .50   .20
1633 A265   3.50p pale grn & dk grn   .20   .20
1634 A380   6p pale pink & Prus bl   .25   .20
    Nos. 1630-1634 (5)   1.35 1.00

Exploration and development of Mexico.

Map of Western Mediterranean — A392

1970, Oct. 20   Photo.   Perf. 13
1635 A392   2p multi   .20   .20

Geographical and Statistical Institute, cent.

Adoration of the Shepherds, by El Greco — A393

Christmas: 2p, Adoration of the Shepherds, by Murillo.

1970, Oct. 30
1636 A393   1.50p multi   .20   .20
1637 A393   2p multi   .20   .20

UN Emblem and Headquarters — A394

1970, Nov. 3
1638 A394   8p multi   .20   .20

25th anniversary of the United Nations.

Monastery Type of 1969
Ripoll Monastery: 2p, Portal. 3.50p, View of monastery. 5p, Inside court.

1970, Nov. 12   Engr.
1639 A382   2p vio & pur   .45   .20
1640 A382   3.50p org & mar   .20   .20
1641 A382   5p Prus grn & yel grn   .90   .20
    Nos. 1639-1641 (3)   1.55   .60

Map with Main European Pilgrimage Routes — A395

Cathedral of St. David, Wales A396

#1643, Map of main pilgrimage routes. #1644, St. Bridget statue, Vadstena, Sweden. #1645, Santiago Cathedral. #1646, Tower of St. Jacques, Paris. #1647, Pilgrim before entering Santiago de Compostela. #1648, St. James statue, Pistoia, Italy. #1649, Lugo Cathedral. 2.50p, Villafranca del Bierzo church. #1652, Astorga Cathedral. 3.50p, San Marcos de León. #1654, Charlemagne, bas-relief, Aachen Cathedral, Germany. #1655, San Tirso de Sahagun. 5p, San Martín de Fromista. 6p, Bas-relief, King's Hospital, Burgos. 7p, Portal of Santo Domingo de la Calzada. 7.50p, Cloister, Najera. 8p, Puente de la Reina (Christ on the Cross and portal). 9p, Santa Maria de Eunate. 10p, Cross of Roncesvalles.

1971   Engr.   Perf. 13
1642 A395   50c grnsh bl & sep   .20   .20
1643 A396   50c bl & dl vio   .20   .20
1644 A395   1p brn & sl grn   .20   .20
1645 A395   1p grn & sl grn   .20   .20
1646 A395   1.50p dl grn & dp plum   .25   .20
1647 A396   1.50p vio bl & lil   .20   .20
1648 A395   2p dk pur & blk   .25   .20
1649 A395   2p sl grn & dk bl   .80   .20
1650 A396   2.50p vio brn & dl vio   .20   .20
1651 A395   3p ultra & dk bl   .25   .20
1652 A395   3p dl red & rose lil   .40   .20
1653 A396   3.50p dp org & gray grn   .20   .20
1654 A396   4p ol grn   .35   .20
1655 A395   4p grnsh bl & brn   .20   .20
1656 A395   5p lt grn & blk   .35   .20
1657 A395   6p lt ultra   .20   .20
1658 A396   7p lil & dl vio   .45   .20
1659 A396   7.50p car lake & dl vio   .20   .20
1660 A395   8p grn & vio blk   .25   .25
1661 A396   9p grn & vio   .25   .25
1662 A395   10p grn & brn   .40   .20
    Nos. 1642-1662 (21)   6.00 4.30

Holy Year of Compostela, 1971.

Ignacio Zuloaga, Self-portrait A397

Amadeo Vives, Composer A398

Zuloaga Paintings: 50c, "My Uncle Daniel." 1p, View of Segovia, horiz. 1.50p, Countess of Alba. 3p, Juan Belmonte. 4p, Countess of Noailles. 5p, Pablo Uranga. 8p, Cobblers' Houses at Lerma, horiz.

1971, Mar. 24   Photo.   Perf. 13
1663 A397   50c gold & multi   .20   .20
1664 A397   1p gold & multi   .20   .20
1665 A397   1.50p gold & multi   .20   .20
1666 A397   3p gold & multi   .20   .20
1667 A397   3p gold & multi   .20   .20
1668 A397   4p gold & multi   .20   .20
1669 A397   5p gold & multi   .20   .20
1670 A397   8p gold & multi   .20   .20
    Nos. 1663-1670 (8)   1.60 1.60

Ignacio Zuloaga (1870-1945). Stamp Day. For other art types see A384, A410, A431, A448, A473, A501, A522, A538, A558 and footnote following No. 876.

1971, Apr. 20
2p, St. Teresa of Avila. 8p, Benito Perez Galdos, writer. 15p, Ramon Menendez Pidal, writer.

1671 A398   1p multicolored   .20   .20
1672 A398   2p multicolored   .20   .20
1673 A398   8p multicolored   .20   .20
1674 A398   15p multicolored   .20   .20
    Nos. 1671-1674 (4)   .80   .80

Europa Issue, 1971
Common Design Type

1971, Apr. 29   Photo.   Perf. 13
Size: 37x26mm
1675 CD14   2p lt bl, brn & vio bl   .45   .20
1676 CD14   8p lt grn, dk brn & dk grn   .30   .30

Stamp Day Type of 1968
Spain No. 1 with blue "A" cancellation.

1971, May 6
1677 A362   2p black, bl & olive   .20   .20

Gymnast — A399

Design: 2p, Gymnast on bar.

1971, May 14
1678 A399   1p ocher & multi   .20   .20
1679 A399   2p lt blue & multi   .20   .20

9th European Gymnastic Championships for Men, Madrid, May 14-15.

Great Bustard A400

Designs: 2p, Pardine lynx. 3p, Brown bear. 5p, Red-legged partridge, vert. 8p. Spanish ibex, vert.

1971, May 24
1680 A400   1p multicolored   .20   .20
1681 A400   2p multicolored   .20   .20
1682 A400   3p multicolored   .20   .20
1683 A400   5p multicolored   .35   .25
1684 A400   8p multicolored   .35   .35
    Nos. 1680-1684 (5)   1.30 1.20

Legionnaires — A401

2p, Legionnaires on dress parade. 5p, Memorial service. 8p, Desert fighter and tank column.

1971, June 21   Photo.   Perf. 13
1685 A401   1p multicolored   .20   .20
1686 A401   2p multicolored   .20   .20
1687 A401   2p multicolored   .20   .20
1688 A401   8p multicolored   .30   .30
    Nos. 1685-1688 (4)   .90   .90

50th anniversary of the Legion, a voluntary military organization.

UNICEF Emblem, Children of Various Races — A402

1971, Sept. 10
1689 A402 8p multicolored   .20 .20
25th anniv. of UNICEF.

Don Juan of Austria, Fleet Commander A403

Hockey Players, Hockey League and Games Emblems — A404

Designs: 5p, Battle of Lepanto, horiz. 8p, Holy League banner in Cathedral.

1971, Oct. 7   Engr.   Perf. 13
1690 A403 2p sepia & slate grn   .40 .20
1691 A403 5p chocolate   .75 .20
1692 A403 8p rose car & vio bl   .60 .60
    Nos. 1690-1692 (3)   1.75 1.00
400th anniversary of the Battle of Lepanto against the Turks.

1971, Oct. 15   Photo.
1693 A404 5p multicolored   .50 .20
First World Hockey Cup, Barcelona, Oct. 15-24.

De Havilland DH-9 over Seville A405

Design: 15p, Boeing 747 over Plaza de la Cibeles, Madrid.

1971, Oct. 25
1694 A405 2p multicolored   .25 .20
1695 A405 15p multicolored   .25 .20
50th anniversary of Spanish air mail service.

Nativity, Avia Altarpiece A406

Emilia Pardo Bazan — A407

Christmas: 8p, Nativity, Sagas altarpiece.

1971, Nov. 4   Perf. 12½x13
1696 A406 2p multicolored   .20 .20
1697 A406 8p multicolored   .20 .20

1972, Jan. 27   Engr.   Perf. 13
Portraits: 25p, José de Espronceda. 50p, King Fernan Gonzalez.
1698 A407 15p brown & slate grn   .20 .20
1699 A407 25p lt grn & slate grn   .25 .20
1700 A407 50p claret & dp brn   .55 .20
    Nos. 1698-1700 (3)   1.00 .60
Honoring Emilia Pardo Bazan (1852-1921), novelist (15p); José de Espronceda (1808-1842), poet (25p); Fernan Gonzalez (910-970), first King of Castile (50p).

Figure Skating — A408

Don Quixote Title Page, 1605 — A409

Design: 2p, Ski jump and Sapporo Olympic emblem, horiz.

1972, Feb. 10   Photo.
1701 A408 2p gray & multi   .35 .20
1702 A408 15p blue & multi   .20 .20
11th Winter Olympic Games, Sapporo, Japan, Feb. 3-13.

1972, Feb. 24   Engr.   Perf. 13x12½
1703 A409 2p brown & claret   .20 .20
International Book Year 1972.

A410

A411

Gutierrez Solana Paintings: 1p, Clowns, horiz. 2p, José Gutierrez Solana with wife and child. 3p, Balladier. 4p, Fisherman. 5p, Mask makers. 7p, The book collector. 10p, Merchant marine captain. 15p, Afterdinner speaker, horiz.

1972, Mar. 24   Photo.   Perf. 13
1704 A410 1p gold & multi   .20 .20
1705 A410 2p gold & multi   .35 .20
1706 A410 3p gold & multi   .40 .20
1707 A410 4p gold & multi   .20 .20
1708 A410 5p gold & multi   1.25 .35
1709 A410 7p gold & multi   .55 .20
1710 A410 10p gold & multi   .55 .20
1711 A410 15p gold & multi   .55 .25
    Nos. 1704-1711 (8)   4.05 1.80
José Gutierrez Solana (1886-1945). Stamp Day 1972.
For other art types see A384, A397, A431, A448, A473, A501, A522, A538, A558 and footnote following No. 876.

1972, Apr. 21
1712 A411 1p Fir   .20 .20
1713 A411 2p Strawberry tree   .35 .20
1714 A411 3p Cluster pine   .40 .20

1715 A411 5p Evergreen oak   .55 .20
1716 A411 8p Juniper   .35 .30
    Nos. 1712-1716 (5)   1.85 1.10

Europeans Interlocking A412

Pre-stamp Cordoba Postmark (1824-42) A413

Europa, 1972
Common Design Type and Type A412

1972, May 2
1717 A412 2p dull grn & ocher   1.40 .20
    Size: 25x38mm
1718 CD15 8p multicolored   .50 .40

1972, May 6   Perf. 12½x13
1719 A413 2p dull yel, blk & car   .20 .20
Stamp Day 1972.

Santa Catalina Castle, Jaen — A414

Castles: 1p, Sajazarra, Rioja, vert. 3p, Biar, Alicante. 5p, San Servando, Toledo. 10p, Pedraza, Segovia.

1972, June 22   Engr.   Perf. 13
1720 A414 1p dull bl grn & brn   .45 .35
1721 A414 2p gray olive & grn   .85 .20
1722 A414 3p rose car & red brn   .85 .20
1723 A414 5p vio bl & dull grn   .85 .20
1724 A414 10p slate & lilac   2.50 .20
    Nos. 1720-1724 (5)   5.50 1.15

Weight Lifting, Olympic Emblems — A415

1972, Aug. 26   Photo.   Perf. 13
1725 A415 1p Olympic emblems, fencing, horiz.   .20 .20
1726 A415 2p shown   .25 .20
1727 A415 5p Sculling   .20 .20
1728 A415 8p Pole vaulting   .25 .25
    Nos. 1725-1728 (4)   .90 .85
20th Olympic Games, Munich, 8/26-9/11.

Egyptian Mongoose A416

1972, Sept. 14
1729 A416 1p Aquatic mole, vert.   .20 .20
1730 A416 2p Chamois   .20 .20
1731 A416 3p Wolf   .25 .20
1732 A416 5p shown   .50 .20
1733 A416 7p Spotted genet   .40 .20
    Nos. 1729-1733 (5)   1.55 1.00

Brigadier M.A. de Ustariz — A417

San Juan, 1870 A418

1972, Oct. 12   Photo.   Perf. 13
1734 A417 1p shown   .20 .25
1735 A418 2p shown   .25 .20
1736 A418 5p San Juan, 1625   .40 .20
1737 A418 8p Map of Plaza and Bay, 1792   .40 .30
    Nos. 1734-1737 (4)   1.25 .95
450th anniversary of San Juan.

St. Tomas Monastery, Avila — A419

8p, Inside view. 15p, Cloister, horiz.

1972, Oct. 26   Engr.
1738 A419 2p Prus bl & gray grn   .80 .20
1739 A419 8p gray & claret   .65 .30
1740 A419 15p violet & red lil   .50 .20
    Nos. 1738-1740 (3)   1.95 .70

Teatro del Liceo, Barcelona A420

1972, Nov. 7   Perf. 12½x13
1741 A420 8p ultra & sepia   .25 .20
125th anniversary of the Gran Teatro del Liceo in Barcelona.

Annunciation — A421

Christmas: 8p, Angel and shepherds. Designs are from Romanesque murals in the Collegiate Basilica of San Isidro, Leon.

1972, Nov. 14   Photo.   Perf. 13
1742 A421 2p gold & multi   .20 .20
1743 A421 8p gold & multi   .20 .20

Juan de Herrera and Escorial A422

Great Spanish Architects: 10p, Juan de Villanueva and Prado. 15p, Ventura Rodriguez and Apollo Fountain.

1973, Jan. 29   Engr.   Perf. 12½x13
1744 A422 8p sepia & slate grn   .50 .20
1745 A422 10p blk brn & bluish
              blk   1.60 .20
1746 A422 15p brt green & indigo   .40 .20
       Nos. 1744-1746 (3)   2.50 .60

Myrica
Faya — A423

Europa, Roman
Mosaic — A424

Designs: Flora of Canary Islands.

1973, Mar. 21   Photo.   Perf. 13
1747 A423 1p Apollonias
              canariensis,
              horiz.   .20 .20
1748 A423 2p shown   .55 .20
1749 A423 4p Palms   .20 .20
1750 A423 5p Holly   .55 .20
1751 A423 15p Dracaena draco   .30 .20
       Nos. 1747-1751 (5)   1.80 1.00

Europa Issue
Common Design Type and A424

1973, Apr. 30   Photo.   Perf. 13
1752 A424 2p multicolored   .40 .20

Size: 37x26mm
1753 CD16 8p lt blue, blk & red   .35 .25

Stamp Day Type of 1968
Stamp Day: 2p, Spain No. 23 with red
Madrid, 1853, cancellation.

1973, May 5
1754 A362 2p black, blue & red   .20 .20

Iznajar Dam on
Genil
River — A425

1973, June 9   Photo.   Perf. 12½x13
1755 A425 8p multicolored   .20 .20

11th Congress of the International Commission on High Dams, Madrid, June 11-15.

Oñate
University,
Guipuzcoa
A426

Designs: 2p, Plaza del Campo and fountain,
Lugo. 3p, Plaza de Llerena and fountain,
Badajoz, vert. 5p, House of Columbus, Las
Palmas. 8p, Windmills, La Mancha.

1973, June 11   Engr.   Perf. 13
1756 A426 1p gray & sepia   .20 .20
1757 A426 2p brt grn & sl grn   .55 .20
1758 A426 3p dk brn & org brn   .55 .20
1759 A426 5p dk gray & vio blk   1.40 .20
1760 A426 8p dk gray & car   .60 .20
       Nos. 1756-1760 (5)   3.30 1.00

Azure-winged
Magpie — A427

Knight, Holy
Fraternity of
Castile,
1488 — A428

Birds: 1p, Black-bellied sand grouse, horiz.
2p, Black stork, horiz. 7p, Imperial eagle,
horiz. 15p, Red-crested pochard.

1973, July 3   Photo.   Perf. 13
1761 A427 1p multicolored   .20 .20
1762 A427 2p multicolored   .35 .20
1763 A427 5p multicolored   .50 .40
1764 A427 7p multicolored   .60 .20
1765 A427 15p multicolored   .25 .25
       Nos. 1761-1765 (5)   1.90 1.25

1973, July 17
Uniforms: 2p, Knight, Castile, 1493, horiz.
3p, Harquebusier, 1534. 7p, Mounted rifleman, 1560. 8p, Infantry sergeants, 1567.
1766 A428 1p multicolored   .20 .20
1767 A428 2p multicolored   .50 .20
1768 A428 3p multicolored   .50 .20
1769 A428 7p multicolored   .40 .20
1770 A428 8p multicolored   .40 .25
       Nos. 1766-1770 (5)   2.00 1.05

See Nos. 1794-1798, 1824-1828, 1869-
1873, 1902-1906, 1989-1993, 2020-2024,
2051-2055, 2078-2082.

Fish in Net
A429

1973, Sept. 12   Photo.   Perf. 13
1771 A429 2p multicolored   .20 .20

6th Intl. Fishing Exhibition, Vigo, Sept. 12-19.

Conference Hall — A430

1973, Sept. 14
1772 A430 8p multicolored   .20 .20

Plenipotentiary Conf. of the Intl. Telecommunications Union, Torremolinos, Sept. 1973.

Vicente López,
Self-portrait
A431

Stamp Day (Paintings by Vicente López y
Portana (1772-1850)): 1p, King Ferdinand VII.
3p, Señora de Carvallo. 4p, Marshal Cas-
telldosrrius. 5p, Queen Isabella II. 7p, Francisco Goya. 10p, Maria Amalia de Sajonia.
15p, The organist Felix López.

1973, Sept. 29   Photo.   Perf. 13
1773 A431 1p gold & multi   .20 .20
1774 A431 2p gold & multi   .25 .20
1775 A431 3p gold & multi   .25 .20
1776 A431 4p gold & multi   .20 .20
1777 A431 5p gold & multi   .20 .20
1778 A431 7p gold & multi   .25 .20
1779 A431 10p gold & multi   .25 .20
1780 A431 15p gold & multi   .25 .20
       Nos. 1773-1780 (8)   1.80 1.60

For other art types see A384, A397, A410,
A448, A473, A501, A522, A538, A558 and
footnote following No. 876.

Leon
Cathedral,
Nicaragua
A432

Designs: 2p, Subtiava Church. 5p, Portal of
Governor's House, vert. 8p, Rio San Juan
Castle.

1973, Oct. 12
1781 A432 1p multicolored   .20 .20
1782 A432 2p multicolored   .30 .20
1783 A432 5p multicolored   .50 .25
1784 A432 8p multicolored   .50 .20
       Nos. 1781-1784 (4)   1.50 .85

Hispanic-American buildings in Nicaragua.

Pope Gregory XI
and Pedro
Fernandez
Pecha — A433

1973, Oct. 26
1785 A433 2p multicolored   .20 .20

600th anniversary of the founding of the
Order of the Hermites of St. Jerome by Pedro
Fernandez Pecha.

St. Domingo de
Silos Monastery
A434

Nativity, Column
Capital, Silos
Church
A435

Designs: 8p, Cloister walk, horiz. 15p, Three
saints, sculpture.

Perf. 13x12½, 12½x13
1973, Oct. 26   Engr.
1786 A434 2p brn & rose mag   .45 .20
1787 A434 8p dk blue & purple   .20 .20
1788 A434 15p Prus grn & indigo   .25 .20
       Nos. 1786-1788 (3)   .90 .60

St. Domingo de Silos Monastery, Burgos.

1973, Nov. 6   Photo.   Perf. 13
Christmas: 8p, Adoration of the Kings,
Butrera Church, horiz.
1789 A435 2p multicolored   .20 .20
1790 A435 8p multicolored   .20 .20

Map of
Spain and
Americas
with Dates
of First
Printings
A436

500 years of Spanish Printing: 7p, Teacher
and Pupils, woodcut from "Libros de los Sue-
nos," Valencia, 1474, vert. 15p, Title page
from "Los Sinodales," Segovia, 1472.

1973, Dec. 11   Engr.   Perf. 13
1791 A436 1p ind & slate grn   .30 .20
1792 A436 7p violet bl & purple   .20 .20
1793 A436 15p purple & black   .25 .20
       Nos. 1791-1793 (3)   .75 .60

Uniform Type of 1973
Uniforms: 1p, Harquebusier on horseback,
1603. 2p, Harquebusiers, 1632. 3p, Cuiras-
sier, 1635. 5p, Mounted drummer of the
Dragoons, 1677. 9p, Two Musketeers, 1694.

1974, Jan. 5   Photo.   Perf. 13
1794 A428 1p multicolored   .20 .20
1795 A428 2p multicolored   .50 .20
1796 A428 3p multicolored   .70 .20
1797 A428 5p multicolored   .90 .25
1798 A428 9p multicolored   .25 .20
       Nos. 1794-1798 (5)   2.55 1.10

Nautical Chart of
Western Europe
and North
Africa — A437

1974, Jan. 26
1799 A437 2p multicolored   .20 .20

50th anniv. of the Superior Geographical
Council of Spain. The chart is from a 14th
cent. Catalan atlas.

M. Biada
and Steam
Engine
A438

1974, Apr. 2   Photo.   Perf. 13
1800 A438 2p multicolored   .20 .20

Barcelona-Mataro Railroad, 125th anniv.

Young
Collector,
Album,
Magnifier
A439

Exhibition Emblem — A440

Design: 8p, Emblem, globe and arrows.

1974, Apr. 4   Perf. 13
1801 A439 2p lilac rose & multi   .20 .20
Perf. 12½
1802 A440 5p buff, blk & dull bl   .35 .30
1803 A440 8p dull green & multi   .30 .25
       Nos. 1801-1803 (3)   .85 .75

Espana 75, International Philatelic Exhibition, Madrid, Apr. 4-13, 1975.

Woman with
Offering — A441

Europa: 8p, Woman from Baza, painted
sculpture.

1974, Apr. 29   Photo.   Perf. 13
1804 A441 2p multicolored   .45 .20
1805 A441 8p multicolored   .25 .25

No. 28 and 1854 Seville Cancel A442

1974, May 6
1806 A442 2p black, blue & red .20 .20
World Stamp Day.

Father Jaime Balmes A443

Designs: 10p, Father Pedro Poveda. 15p, Jorge Juan y Santacilla.

1974, May 28   Engr.   Perf. 13
1807 A443 8p blue gray & sepia .20 .20
1808 A443 10p red brn & dk brn .60 .20
1809 A443 15p brown & slate .20 .20
    Nos. 1807-1809 (3) 1.00 .60

Famous Spaniards: Jaime Balmes (1810-1848), mathematician; death centenary of Pedro Poveda, pedagogue; Don Jorge Juan (1712-1773), explorer and writer.

Templeto, by Bramante, Rome — A444

1974, June 4   Photo.
1810 A444 5p multicolored .20 .20
Cent. of the Spanish Academy of Fine Arts, Rome.

Aqueduct, Segovia A445

Designs: 2p, Tajo Bridge, Alcantara. 3p, Marcus Valerius Martial lecturing. 4p, Triumphal Arch, Tarragona, vert. 5p, Theater, Merida. 7p, Bishop Ossius of Cordoba preaching. 8p, Tribunal Arch, Talavera Forum, vert. 9p, Emperor Trajan, vert.

1974, June 25   Engr.
1811 A445 1p brown & black .20 .20
1812 A445 2p gray grn & sepia .30 .20
1813 A445 3p lt & dk brown .20 .20
1814 A445 4p green & indigo .20 .20
1815 A445 5p gray bl & choc .20 .20
1816 A445 7p gray grn & lilac .20 .20
1817 A445 8p dk brown & green .20 .20
1818 A445 9p brt red lil & cl .20 .20
    Nos. 1811-1818 (8) 1.70 1.60
Roman architecture and history in Spain.

Greek Tortoise A446

Reptiles: 2p, Common chameleon. 5p, Wall gecko. 7p, Emerald lizard. 15p, Blunt-nosed viper.

1974, July 3   Photo.
1819 A446 1p multicolored .20 .20
1820 A446 2p multicolored .30 .20
1821 A446 5p multicolored .60 .10
1822 A446 7p multicolored .40 .25
1823 A446 15p multicolored .20 .20
    Nos. 1819-1823 (5) 1.70 1.35

Uniform Type of 1973
Uniforms: 1p, Hussar and horse, 1705. 2p, Artillery officers, 1710. 3p, Piper and drummer, Granada Regiment, 1734. 7p, Mounted standard-bearer, Numancia Dragoons, 1737. 8p, Standard-bearer and soldier, Zamora Regiment, 1739.

1974, July 17
1824 A428 1p multicolored .20 .20
1825 A428 2p multicolored .40 .20
1826 A428 3p multicolored .40 .20
1827 A428 7p multicolored .30 .20
1828 A428 8p multicolored .20 .20
    Nos. 1824-1828 (5) 1.50 1.00

Life Saving A447

1974, Sept. 5   Photo.   Perf. 13
1829 A447 2p multicolored .20 .20
18th World Life Saving Championships, Barcelona, Sept. 1974.

Eduardo Rosales, by Federico Madrazo — A448

Stamp Day (Eduardo Rosales, 1836-73, Paintings): 1p, Tobias and the Angel. 3p, The Last Will of Isabella the Catholic. 4p, Nena (little girl). 5p, Presentation of John of Austria to Charles I. 7p, The First Step. 10p, St. John the Evangelist. 15p, St. Matthew.

1974, Sept. 29   Photo.   Perf. 13
1830 A448 1p gold & multi .20 .20
1831 A448 2p gold & multi .20 .20
1832 A448 3p gold & multi, horiz. .20 .20
1833 A448 4p gold & multi .20 .20
1834 A448 5p gold & multi, horiz. .20 .20
1835 A448 7p gold & multi, horiz. .20 .20
1836 A448 10p gold & multi .30 .20
1837 A448 15p gold & multi .20 .20
    Nos. 1830-1837 (8) 1.70 1.60
For other art types see A384, A397, A410, A431, A473, A501, A522, A538, A558 and footnote following No. 876.

"International Mail" — A449

UPU Monument, Bern — A450

1974, Oct. 9
1838 A449 2p dark blue & multi .20 .20
1839 A450 8p red & multi .20 .20
Centenary of Universal Postal Union.

Sobremonte House, Cordoba, Argentina — A451

Ruins of San Ignacio de Mini, 18th Century — A452

The Gaucho Martin Fierro — A453

Design: 2p, Municipal Council Building, Buenos Aires, 1829.

1974, Oct. 12
1840 A451 1p multicolored .20 .20
1841 A451 2p multicolored .40 .20
1842 A452 5p multicolored .30 .20
1843 A453 10p multicolored .25 .20
    Nos. 1840-1843 (4) 1.15 .80
Cultural ties with Latin America.

Nativity, Valdavia Church A454

Adoration of the Kings, Valcobero Church — A455

1974   Photo.   Perf. 13
1844 A454 2p multicolored .20 .20
1845 A455 3p lt blue & multi .20 .20
1846 A455 8p olive & multi .20 .20
    Nos. 1844-1846 (3) .60 .60
Christmas 1974.
Issue dates: 2p, 8p, Nov. 4; 3p, Dec. 2.

Teucriun Lanigerum A456

Flowers: 2p, Hypericum ericoides. 4p, Thymus longiflorus. 5p, Anthyllis onobrychioides. 8p, Helianthemun paniculatum.

1974, Nov. 8
1847 A456 1p multicolored .20 .20
1848 A456 2p multicolored .20 .20
1849 A456 4p multicolored .20 .20

1850 A456 5p multicolored .25 .20
1851 A456 8p multicolored .20 .20
    Nos. 1847-1851 (5) 1.05 1.00

Franco Type of 1954-56
Imprint: "F.N.M.T."
1974-75   Photo.   Perf. 12½x13
1852 A221 4p rose car ('75) .20 .20
1853 A221 7p brt ultra .20 .20
1854 A221 12p blue green .20 .20
1855 A221 20p rose carmine .25 .20
    Nos. 1852-1855 (4) .85 .80

Leyre Monastery A457

8p, Column and bas-relief, vert. 15p, Crypt.

1974, Dec. 10   Engr.   Perf. 12½x13
1862 A457 2p slate grn & bl gray .45 .20
1863 A457 8p carmine .20 .20
1864 A457 15p grnsh black .35 .20
    Nos. 1862-1864 (3) 1.00 .60
Leyre Monastery, Navarre.

Spain Nos. 1 and 1802 — A458

Mail Coach, 1850 A459

Designs: 8p, Mail ship of Indian Service. 10p, Chapel of St. Mark.

Perf. 12½x13, 13x12½
1975, Jan. 2   Engr.
1865 A458 2p slate blue .35 .30
1866 A459 3p olive & brown .45 .40
1867 A459 8p lilac & slate bl 1.00 .50
1868 A458 10p brn & slate grn .50 .40
    Nos. 1865-1868 (4) 2.30 1.60
125th anniversary of Spanish postage stamps.

Uniform Type of 1973
1p, Sergeant and grenadier, Toledo Regiment, 1750. 2p, Royal Artillery, 1762. 3p, Queen's Regiment, 1763. 5p, Fusiliers, Vitoria Regiment, 1766. 10p, Dragoon, Sagunto Regiment, 1775.

1975, Jan. 7   Photo.   Perf. 13
1869 A428 1p multicolored .20 .20
1870 A428 2p multicolored .20 .20
1871 A428 3p multicolored 1.60 .25
1872 A428 5p multicolored .50 .20
1873 A428 10p multicolored 1.40 .25
    Nos. 1869-1873 (5) 3.90 1.10

Antonio Gaudi A460

Designs: 10p, Antonio Palacios and Casa Guell, Barcelona. 15p, Secundino Zuazo.

1975, Feb. 25   Engr.   Perf. 13
1874 A460 8p green & black .20 .20
1875 A460 10p carmine & dp claret .40 .20
1876 A460 15p brown & black .20 .20
    Nos. 1874-1876 (3) .80 .60
Contemporary Spanish architects.

Souvenir Sheets

Spanish Goldsmiths' Works — A461

Designs: 2p, Agate box, 9th cent. 3p, Votive crown of Recesvinto. 8p, Cover of Evangelistary, Roncesvalles Collegiate Church, 12th cent. 10p, Chalice of Infanta Donna Urraca, 11th cent. 12p, Processional monstrance, St. Domingo de Silos, 16th cent. 15p, Sword of Boabdil, 15th cent. 25p, Sword and head of Charles V (Carlos I of Spain). 50p, Earring and bracelet from Aliseda, 6th-4th centuries B.C. 3p, 10p, 12p, 25p vertical (No. 1878).

1975, Apr. 4   Engr.   Perf. 13
1877	A461	Sheet of 4	8.00	8.00
a.		2p gray & Prussian blue	2.00	2.00
b.		8p brown & Prus blue	2.00	2.00
c.		15p gray & dark carmine	2.00	2.00
d.		50p dark carmine & gray	2.00	2.00
1878	A461	Sheet of 4	8.00	8.00
a.		3p slate green & gray	2.00	2.00
b.		10p sepia & slate	2.00	2.00
c.		12p gray & bluish black	2.00	2.00
d.		25p sepia & bluish black	2.00	2.00

Espana 75 Intl. Phil. Exhib., Madrid, 4/4-13.

Pomegranates A462

Woman Gathering Honey, Arana Cave — A463

1975, Apr. 21   Photo.
1879	A462	1p Almonds, nuts and blossoms, horiz.	.20	.20
1880	A462	2p shown	.25	.20
1881	A462	3p Oranges	.25	.20
1882	A462	4p Chestnuts	.20	.20
1883	A462	5p Apples	.20	.20
		Nos. 1879-1883 (5)	1.10	1.00

1975, Apr. 28   Photo.   Perf. 13
Europa: 12p, Horse, wall painting from Tito Bustillo Cave, horiz.
1884	A463	3p brown & multi	.25	.20
1885	A463	12p brown & multi	.35	.20

Pre-stamp León Cancellation A464

1975, May 6   Perf. 12½x13
1886	A464	3p multicolored	.20	.20

World Stamp Day.

World Tourism Organization Emblem — A465

1975, May 12   Photo.   Perf. 13
1887	A465	3p dark blue	.20	.20

First General Assembly of the World Tourism Organization, Madrid, May 1975.

Fair Emblem, Agricultural Symbols — A466

1975, May 14
1888	A466	3p multicolored	.20	.20

25th Agricultural Fair.

Equality Between Men and Women A467

1975, June 3
1889	A467	3p multicolored	.20	.20

International Women's Year.

Virgin of Cabeza Sanctuary A468

1975, June 18   Photo.   Perf. 13
1890	A468	3p multicolored	.20	.20

Virgin of Cabeza Sanctuary, site of siege during Civil War, 1937.

Cervantes' Prison Cell, Argamasilla de Alba — A469

Tourism: 2p, Bridge of St. Martin, Toledo. 3p, Church of St. Peter, Tarrasa. 4p, Arch, Alhambra, Granada, vert. 5p, Street, Mijas, Malaga, vert. 7p, Church of St. Mary, Tarrasa, vert.

1975, June 25   Engr.   Perf. 13
1891	A469	1p purple & black	.20	.20
1892	A469	2p red brn & brn	.20	.20
1893	A469	3p slate & sepia	.20	.20
1894	A469	4p orange & claret	.20	.20
1895	A469	5p slate grn & indigo	.20	.20
1896	A469	7p violet bl & indigo	.40	.20
		Nos. 1891-1896 (6)	1.40	1.20

Salamander — A470

1975, July 9   Photo.   Perf. 13
1897	A470	1p shown	.20	.20
1898	A470	2p Newt	.25	.20
1899	A470	3p Tree toad	.25	.20
1900	A470	6p Midwife toad	.20	.20
1901	A470	7p Leaf frog	.20	.20
		Nos. 1897-1901 (5)	1.10	1.00

Uniform Type of 1973

1p, Cavalry officer, 1788. 2p, Fusilier, Asturias Regiment, 1789. 3p, Infantry Colonel, 1802. 4p, Artillery standard-bearer, 1803. 7p, Sapper, 1809.

1975, July 17
1902	A428	1p multicolored	.20	.20
1903	A428	2p multicolored	.50	.20
1904	A428	3p multicolored	.20	.20
1905	A428	4p multicolored	.20	.20
1906	A428	7p multicolored	.20	.20
		Nos. 1902-1906 (5)	1.30	1.00

Infant and Children Playing A471

1975, Sept. 9   Photo.   Perf. 13
1907	A471	3p multicolored	.20	.20

"Defend Life."

Scroll and Emblem A472

1975, Sept. 25
1908	A472	3p multicolored	.20	.20

13th International Congress of Latin Notaries, Barcelona, Sept. 26-Oct. 4.

Blessing of the Birds A473

Scenes from Apocalypse: 2p, Angel at River of Life. 3p, Angel Guarding Gate of Paradise. 4p, Fox carrying cock. 6p, Daniel with wild bulls. 7p, The Last Judgment. 10p, Four horsemen of the Apocalypse. 12p, Bird holding snake.

1975, Sept. 29
1909	A473	1p gold & multi	.20	.20
1910	A473	2p gold & multi, vert.	.20	.20
1911	A473	3p gold & multi, vert.	.20	.20
1912	A473	4p gold & multi	.20	.20
1913	A473	6p gold & multi	.20	.20
1914	A473	7p gold & multi, vert.	.25	.25
1915	A473	10p gold & multi, vert.	.20	.20
1916	A473	12p gold & multi, vert.	.20	.20
		Nos. 1909-1916 (8)	1.65	1.65

Millenium Gerona Cathedral.
For other art types see A384, A397, A410, A431, A448, A501, A522, A538, A558 and footnote following No. 876.

Symbols of Industry A474

1975, Oct. 7   Engr.   Perf. 13
1917	A474	3p violet & lilac	.20	.20

Spanish industrialization.

Pioneers' Covered Wagon A475

Designs: 1p, El Cabildo, meeting house of 1st Uruguayan Government. 3p, Fort St. Theresa over River Plate. 8p, Montevideo Cathedral, vert.

1975, Oct. 12   Photo.
1918	A475	1p multicolored	.20	.20
1919	A475	2p multicolored	.20	.20
1920	A475	3p multicolored	.25	.20
1921	A475	8p multicolored	.20	.20
		Nos. 1918-1921 (4)	.85	.80

Cultural ties with Latin America; sesquicentennial of Uruguay's independence.

Ruined Columns, San Juan de la Peña — A476

Madonna, Mosaic, Navarra Cathedral — A477

3p, Monastery, horiz. 8p, Cloister, horiz.

Perf. 13x12½, 12½x13
1975, Oct. 28   Engr.
1922	A476	3p slate grn & brn	.30	.20
1923	A476	8p violet & brt lil	.20	.20
1924	A476	10p dp magenta & car	.25	.20
		Nos. 1922-1924 (3)	.75	.60

San Juan de la Pena Monastery.

1975, Nov. 4   Photo.   Perf. 13
Christmas: 12p, Flight into Egypt, carved capital, Navarra Cathedral, horiz.
1925	A477	3p multicolored	.20	.20
1926	A477	12p multicolored	.20	.20

King Juan Carlos I — A478

Queen Sofia and King — A479

Designs: No. 1928, Queen Sofia.

1975, Dec. 29   Photo.   Perf. 13x12½
1927	A478	3p multicolored	.20	.20
1928	A478	3p multicolored	.20	.20

Perf. 12½
1929	A479	3p multicolored	.20	.20
1930	A479	12p multicolored	.20	.20
		Nos. 1927-1930 (4)	.80	.80

King Juan Carlos I, accession to the throne.

Pilgrim Virgin,
Pontevedra
A480

Mountains and
Center Emblem
A481

1976, Jan. 2   Engr.   Perf. 13
1931 A480 3p rose & brown   .20 .20

Holy Year of St. James of Compostela,
patron saint of Spain.

1976, Feb. 10   Photo.
1932 A481 6p multicolored   .20 .20

Catalunya Excursion Center, centenary.

Cosme Damian
Churruca — A482

Navigators: 12p, Luis de Requesens. 50p,
Juan Sebastian Elcano, horiz.

1976, Mar. 1   Engr.   Perf. 13
1933 A482 7p vio brn & grnsh blk 1.50 .25
1934 A482 12p lt blue & violet   .20 .20
1935 A482 50p dp brn & gray ol   .55 .20
    Nos. 1933-1935 (3)   2.25 .65

A. G. Bell,
Radar and
Telephone
A483

1976, Mar. 10   Photo.
1936 A483 3p multicolored   .20 .20

Centenary of first telephone call by Alexander Graham Bell, March 10, 1876.

"Watch at
Street
Crossings"
A484

Road Safety: 3p, "Don't pass when in
doubt," vert. 5p, "Wear seat belts."

1976, Apr. 6   Photo.   Perf. 13
1937 A484 1p orange & multi   .20 .20
1938 A484 3p gray & multi   .35 .20
1939 A484 5p lilac & multi   .20 .20
    Nos. 1937-1939 (3)   .75 .60

St.
George,
Alcoy
Cathedral
A485

1976, Apr. 23
1940 A485 3p multicolored   .20 .20

7th centenary of the apparition of St.
George in Alcoy.

Talavera
Pottery
A486

Europa: 12p, Lace making.

1976, May 3   Photo.   Perf. 13
1941 A486 3p multicolored   .65 .20
1942 A486 12p multicolored   .80 .30

17th Conference of European Postal and
Telecommunications Administrations.

6r Stamp of 1851
with Coruna
Cancel — A487

1976, May 6
1943 A487 3p blue, org & blk   .20 .20

World Stamp Day.

Coin of
Caesar
Augustus
A488

7p, Map of Roman camp on banks of Ebro,
and coin. 25p, Orpheus, mosaic from Roman
era, vert.

1976, May 26   Engr.   Perf. 13
1944 A488 3p dk brn & mar   1.90 .20
1945 A488 7p dk brown & blue   1.00 .30
1946 A488 25p brown & black   .50 .20
    Nos. 1944-1946 (3)   3.40 .70

Founding of Saragossa, 2000th anniv.

Spanish-made Rifle, 1757 — A489

Designs (Bicentennial Emblem and): 3p,
Bernardo de Galvez, Spanish governor. 5p,
Dollar bank note, Richmond, 1861. 12p, Span-
ish capture of Pensacola from English.

1976, May 29
1947 A489 1p dk brn & vio bl   .20 .20
1948 A489 3p sl grn & dk brn   .90 .20
1949 A489 5p dk brn & sl grn   .40 .20
1950 A489 12p sl grn & dk brn   .40 .30
    Nos. 1947-1950 (4)   1.90 .90

American Bicentennial.

Old
Customs
House,
Cadiz
A490

Customs Houses: 3p, Madrid. 7p,
Barcelona.

1976, June 9
1951 A490 1p black & maroon   .20 .20
1952 A490 3p sepia & green   .55 .20
1953 A490 7p red brn & vio brn   1.10 .35
    Nos. 1951-1953 (3)   1.85 .75

Postal Savings
Box with
Symbols — A491

Railroad Post
Office — A492

Rural
Mailman in
Winter
A493

Postal Service: 10p, Automatic letter sorting
machine.

1976, June 16   Photo.
1954 A491 1p multicolored   .20 .20
1955 A492 3p multicolored   .35 .20
1956 A493 6p multicolored   .20 .20
1957 A493 10p multicolored   .25 .20
    Nos. 1954-1957 (4)   1.00 .80

King and
Queen,
Map of
Americas
A494

1976, June 25
1958 A494 12p multicolored   .25 .20

Visit of King Juan Carlos I and Queen Sofia
to the Americas, June 1976.

San Marcos,
León — A495

Greco-Roman
Wrestling — A496

Tourism (Famous Hotels): 2p, Las Cañadas,
Tenerife. 3p, Portal of R. R. Catolicos, Santi-
ago, vert. 4p, Cruz de Tejeda, Las Palmas. 7p,
Gredos, Avila. 12p, La Arruzafa, Cordoba.

1976, June 30   Engr.   Perf. 13
1959 A495 1p slate & sepia   .20 .20
1960 A495 2p green & indigo   .65 .20
1961 A495 3p brn & red brn   .45 .20
1962 A495 4p sepia & slate   .25 .20
1963 A495 7p slate & sepia   .85 .35
1964 A495 12p rose brn & pur   1.00 .20
    Nos. 1959-1964 (6)   3.40 1.40

1976, July 9   Photo.

Montreal Olympic Emblem and: 1p, Men's
rowing, horiz. 2p, Boxing, horiz. 12p,
Basketball.

1965 A496 1p multicolored   .20 .20
1966 A496 2p lilac & multi   .35 .20
1967 A496 3p multicolored   .25 .20
1968 A496 12p multicolored   .25 .20
    Nos. 1965-1968 (4)   1.05 .80

21st Olympic Games, Montreal, Canada,
July 17-Aug. 1.

King Juan Carlos
I — A497

1976-77   Photo.   Perf. 13
1969 A497 10c orange ('77)   .20 .20
1970 A497 25c apple grn ('77)   .20 .20
1971 A497 30c dp blue ('77)   .20 .20
1972 A497 50c purple ('77)   .20 .20
1973 A497 1p emerald ('77)   .20 .20
1974 A497 1.50p scarlet   .20 .20
1975 A497 2p dp blue   .20 .20
1976 A497 3p dp green   .20 .20
1977 A497 4p blue grn ('77)   .20 .20
1978 A497 5p dp car rose   .20 .20
1979 A497 6p brt green ('77)   .20 .20
1980 A497 7p olive   .20 .20
1982 A497 8p brt blue ('77)   .20 .20
1983 A497 10p lilac rose ('77)   .20 .20
1984 A497 12p golden brown   .25 .20
1985 A497 15p vio blue ('77)   .30 .20
1986 A497 20p brt red lil ('77)   .35 .20
    Nos. 1969-1986 (17)   3.70 3.40

Nos. 1976, 1978-1980, 1982-1983 also
issued as coils with number on back of every
fifth stamp.
See Nos. 2185-2194, 2268-2270.
Nos. 1969-1970, 1972-1973, 1975-1983,
1985-1986, 2185-2194 and 2268-2270 also
printed on prephosphored paper. Value, mint
set of 27 values, $40.

Uniform Type of 1973

Uniforms: 1p, Trumpeter, Alcantara Regiment, 1815. 2p, Sapper, 1821. 3p, Engineer in
dress uniform, 1825. 7p, Artillery infantry,
1828. 25p, Infantry riflemen, 1830.

1976, July 17
1989 A428 1p multicolored   .20 .20
1990 A428 2p multicolored   .80 .20
1991 A428 3p multicolored   .30 .20
1992 A428 7p multicolored   .25 .25
1993 A428 25p multicolored   .30 .20
    Nos. 1989-1993 (5)   1.85 1.05

Blood Donors
A498

Mosaic,
Batitales
A499

1976, Sept. 7   Engr.   Perf. 13
1994 A498 3p carmine & black   .20 .20

Give blood, save a life!

1976, Sept. 22

Designs: 3p, Lugo city wall. 7p, Obverse
and reverse of Roman 1st Legion coin.

1995 A499 1p black & purple   .20 .20
1996 A499 3p black & dp brn   .25 .20
1997 A499 7p green & magenta   .45 .20
    Nos. 1995-1997 (3)   .90 .60

2000th anniversary of Lugo City.

Parliament, Madrid
A500

1976, Sept. 23
1998 A500 12p green & sepia   .20 .20
63rd Conference of Inter-parliamentary Union, Madrid.

Still Life, by L. E. Menendez — A501

St. Christopher Carrying Christ Child — A502

Luis Eugenio Menendez Paintings: 2p, Peaches and jar. 3p, Pears, melon and barrel. 4p, Brace of pigeons and basket. 6p, Sea bream and oranges, horiz. 7p, Water melon and bread, horiz. 10p, Figs, bread and jug, horiz. 12p, Various fruits, horiz.

1976, Sept. 29   Photo.   Perf. 13
1999 A501 1p gold & multi   .20 .20
2000 A501 2p gold & multi   .20 .20
2001 A501 3p gold & multi   .20 .20
2002 A501 4p gold & multi   .20 .20
2003 A501 6p gold & multi   .20 .20
2004 A501 7p gold & multi   .30 .25
2005 A501 10p gold & multi   .25 .20
2006 A501 12p gold & multi   .30 .25
     Nos. 1999-2006 (8)   1.85 1.70
Luis Eugenio Menendez (1716-1780). Stamp Day 1976.
For other art types see A384, A397, A410, A431, A448, A473, A522, A538, A558 and footnote following No. 876.

1976, Oct. 8
Christmas: 3p, Nativity, horiz. Both designs after painted wood carvings.
2007 A502 3p multicolored   .75 .20
2008 A502 12p multicolored   1.50 .50

Nicoya Church, Costa Rica — A503

Juan Vazquez de Coronado — A504

Designs: 3p, Orosi Mission, Costa Rica, horiz. 12p, Tomas de Acosta.

1976, Oct. 12
2009 A503 1p multicolored   .20 .20
2010 A504 2p multicolored   .25 .20
2011 A503 3p multicolored   .20 .20
2012 A504 12p multicolored   .25 .20
     Nos. 2009-2012 (4)   .90 .80
Spain's link with Costa Rica.

Map of South and Central America, Santa Maria, King and Queen
A505

1976, Oct. 12
2013 A505 12p multicolored   .20 .20
Visit of King Juan Carlos I and Queen Sofia to Latin America.

St. Peter of Alcantara Monastery
A506

Tomb of Peter of Alcantara
A507

St. Peter of Alcantara
A508

1976, Oct. 29   Engr.   Perf. 13
2014 A506 3p dp brown & sepia   .30 .20
2015 A507 7p dk purple & blk   .20 .20
2016 A508 20p brown & dk brown   .30 .20
     Nos. 2014-2016 (3)   .80 .60
St. Peter of Alcantara (1499-1562), Franciscan reformer.

Hand Releasing Doves
A509

1976, Nov. 23   Litho.   Perf. 13
2017 A509 3p multicolored   .20 .20
11th Philatelic Exhibition of the National Association of the Handicapped.

Casals and Cello
A510

Design: 5p, Manuel de Falla and Fire Dance from El Amor Brujo.

1976, Dec. 29   Engr.   Perf. 13
2018 A510 3p black & vio bl   .20 .20
2019 A510 5p slate grn & car   .20 .20
Birth centenaries of Pablo Casals (1876-1973), cellist and composer, and of Manuel de Falla (1876-1946), composer.

Uniform Type of 1973

Uniforms: 1p, Outrider, Calatrava Lancers, 1844. 2p, Sapper, 1850. 3p, Corporal, Light Infantry, 1861. 4p, Drum Major, 1861. 20p, Artillery Captain, Mounted, 1862.

1977, Jan. 5   Photo.   Perf. 13
2020 A428 1p multicolored   .20 .20
2021 A428 2p multicolored   .35 .20
2022 A428 3p multicolored   .20 .20
2023 A428 4p multicolored   .20 .20
2024 A428 20p multicolored   .25 .20
     Nos. 2020-2024 (5)   1.20 1.00

King James I
A511

1977, Feb. 10   Engr.   Perf. 13
2025 A511 4p purple & ocher   .20 .20
James I, El Conquistador (1208-1276), King of Aragon, 700th death anniversary.

Jacinto Verdaguer — A512

Portraits: 7p, Miguel Servet. 12p, Pablo Sarasate. 50p, Francisco Tarrega.

1977, Feb. 22
2026 A512 5p purple & dk red   .25 .20
2027 A512 7p olive & slate grn   .20 .20
2028 A512 12p dk blue & bl grn   .20 .20
2029 A512 50p lt green & brown   .55 .20
     Nos. 2026-2029 (4)   1.20 .80
Honoring Jacinto Verdaguer (1845-1902), Catalan poet; Miguel Servet (1511-1553), physician and theologian; Pablo Sarasate (1844-1908), violinist and composer; Francisco Tarrega (1854-1909), creator of modern Spanish guitar music.

Marquis de Penaflorida — A513

1977, Feb. 24   Engr.   Perf. 13
2030 A513 4p dull green & brn   .20 .20
Bicentenary of the Economic Society of the Friends of the Land (agricultural improvements).

Trout
A514

1977, Mar. 8   Photo.
2031 A514 1p Salmon, vert.   .20 .20
2032 A514 2p shown   .20 .20
2033 A514 3p Eel   .20 .20
2034 A514 4p Carp   .20 .20
2035 A514 6p Barbel   .20 .20
     Nos. 2031-2035 (5)   1.00 1.00

Slalom
A515

1977, Mar. 24   Engr.   Perf. 13
2036 A515 5p multicolored   .20 .20
World Ski Championships, Granada, Sierra Nevada, Mar. 24-27.

La Cuadra, 1900
A516

Spanish Pioneer Automobiles: 4p, Hispano Suiza, 1916. 5p, Elizalde, 1915. 7p, Abadal, 1914.

1977, Apr. 23   Photo.   Perf. 13
2037 A516 2p multicolored   .20 .20
2038 A516 4p multicolored   .20 .20
2039 A516 5p multicolored   .20 .20
2040 A516 7p multicolored   .20 .20
     Nos. 2037-2040 (4)   .80 .80

Ordesa National Park
A517

Europa: 3p, Tree in Doñana National Park.

1977, May 2   Litho.
2041 A517 3p multicolored   .20 .20
2042 A517 12p multicolored   .25 .20

Plaza Mayor, Spanish Stamps, Tongs
A518

1977, May 7   Engr.   Perf. 13
2043 A518 3p multicolored   .20 .20
50th anniversary of Philatelic Market on Plaza Mayor, Madrid.

Enrique de Osso, St. Theresa and Book
A519

1977, June 7   Photo.   Perf. 13
2044 A519 8p multicolored   .20 .20
Centenary of the founding by Enrique de Osso of the Society of St. Theresa of Jesus.

Toledo Gate, Ciudad Real — A520

Tourism: 2p, Roman aqueduct, Almuñecar. 3p, Cathedral, Jaen, vert. 4p, Ronda Gorge,

Malaga, vert. 7p, Ampudia Castle, Palencia. 12p, Bisagra Gate, Toledo.

1977, June 24　Engr.　Perf. 13
2045	A520	1p orange & brown	.20	.20
2046	A520	2p sepia & slate	.20	.20
2047	A520	3p violet & purple	.20	.20
2048	A520	4p brt & dk green	.20	.20
2049	A520	7p brown & black	.20	.20
2050	A520	12p vio & org brn	.20	.20
		Nos. 2045-2050 (6)	1.20	1.20

Uniform Type of 1973

Uniforms: 1p, Military Administration official, 1875. 2p, Cavalry lancers, 1883. 3p, General Staff Commander, 1884. 7p, Trumpeter, Divisional Artillery, 1887. 25p, Medical Corps official, 1895.

1977, July 16　　　　　　　Photo.
2051	A428	1p multicolored	.20	.20
2052	A428	2p multicolored	.20	.20
2053	A428	3p multicolored	.20	.20
2054	A428	7p multicolored	.20	.20
2055	A428	25p multicolored	.30	.20
		Nos. 2051-2055 (5)	1.10	1.00

A521

A522

St. Emilian Cuculatus and earliest known Catalan manuscript.

1977, Sept. 9　Engr.　Perf. 13
2056	A521	5p violet, grn & brn	.20	.20

Millennium of Catalan language.

1977, Sept. 29　Photo.　Perf. 13

Federico Madrazo (1815-94) Portraits: 1p, The Boy Florez. 2p, Duke of San Miguel. 3p, Senora Coronado. 4p, Campoamor. 6p, Marquesa de Montelo. 7p, Rivadeneyra. 10p, Countess de Vilches. 15p, Senora Gomez de Avellaneda.

2057	A522	1p gold & multi	.20	.20
2058	A522	2p gold & multi	.20	.20
2059	A522	3p gold & multi	.20	.20
2060	A522	4p gold & multi	.20	.20
2061	A522	6p gold & multi	.20	.20
2062	A522	7p gold & multi	.20	.20
2063	A522	10p gold & multi	.20	.20
2064	A522	15p gold & multi	.20	.20
		Nos. 2057-2064 (8)	1.60	1.60

For other art types see A384, A397, A410, A431, A448, A473, A501, A538, A558 and footnote following No. 876.

Sailing Ship and Mail Routes, 18th Century — A523

1977, Oct. 7　　　　　　　Engr.
2065	A523	15p black, brn & grn	.30	.30

ESPAMER '77 Philatelic Exhibition, Barcelona, Oct. 7-13, and for the Bicentenary of regular mail routes to the Indies (Central and South America). No. 2065 issued in sheets of 8 stamps and 8 labels showing exhibition emblem.

Church of St. Francis, Guatemala City A524

Designs (Guatemala City): 3p, Modern buildings. 7p, Government Palace. 12p, Columbus Square and monument.

1977, Oct. 12　Photo.　Perf. 13
2066	A524	1p multicolored	.20	.20
2067	A524	3p multicolored	.20	.20
2068	A524	7p multicolored	.20	.20
2069	A524	12p multicolored	.20	.20
		Nos. 2066-2069 (4)	.80	.80

Spain's link with Guatemala.

San Pedro Monastery, Cardeña A525

Designs: 7p, Cloister. 20p, Tomb of El Cid and Dona Gimena.

1977, Oct. 28　　　　　　　Engr.
2070	A525	3p vio blue & slate	.20	.20
2071	A525	7p brown & maroon	.20	.20
2072	A525	20p green & slate	.25	.20
		Nos. 2070-2072 (3)	.65	.60

San Pedro Monastery, Cardena, Burgos.

Adoration of the Kings A526

Christmas: 12p, Flight into Egypt, vert. Designs from Romanesque paintings in Jaca Cathedral Museum.

1977, Nov. 3　　　　　　　Photo.
2073	A526	5p multicolored	.20	.20
2074	A526	12p multicolored	.20	.20

Old and New Iberia Planes A527

1977, Nov. 3
2075	A527	12p multicolored	.20	.20

IBERIA, Spanish Airlines, 50th anniversary.

Felipe de Borbon, Prince of Asturias — A528

Judo, Games Emblem — A529

1977, Dec. 22　Photo.　Perf. 13
2076	A528	5p multicolored	.20	.20

Felipe de Borbon, Spanish crown prince.

1977, Dec. 29
2077	A529	3p	.20	.20

10th World Judo Championships, Taiwan.

Uniform Type of 1973

Uniforms: 1p, Flag bearer, 1908. 2p, Lieutenant Colonel, Hussar, 1909. 3p, Mounted artillery lieutenant, 1912. 5p, Engineers' captain, 1921. 12p, Captain General, 1925.

1978, Jan. 5
2078	A428	1p multicolored	.20	.20
2079	A428	2p multicolored	.20	.20
2080	A428	3p multicolored	.20	.20
2081	A428	5p multicolored	.20	.20
2082	A428	12p multicolored	.20	.20
		Nos. 2078-2082 (5)	1.00	1.00

Hilarión Eslava and Score A530

8p, José Clara and sculpture. 25p, Pio Baroja and farm. 50p, Antonio Machado Ruiz and castle.

1978, Feb. 20　Engr.　Perf. 13
2083	A530	5p black & dk pur	.20	.20
2084	A530	8p blue grn & blk	.20	.20
2085	A530	25p yel grn & blk	.30	.20
2086	A530	50p dk pur & dk brn	.55	.20
		Nos. 2083-2086 (4)	1.25	.80

Miguel Hilarión Eslava (1807-1878), composer; José Clara, sculptor; Pio Baroja (1872-1956), author and physician; Antonio Machado Ruiz (1875-1939), poet and playwright.

Burial of Christ, by de Juni — A531

Detail from Burial of Christ — A532

Designs: No. 2089, Juan de Juni. No. 2090, Rape of Sabine Women, by Rubens. No. 2091, Rape (detail) and Rubens portrait. No. 2092, Rubens signature and palette. No. 2093, Judgment of Paris, by Titian. No. 2094, Judgment and Titian portrait. No. 2095, Initial "TF" and palette.

1978, Mar. 28　Engr.　Perf. 12½x13
2087	A532	3p multicolored	.20	.20
2088	A531	3p multicolored	.20	.20
2089	A532	3p multicolored	.20	.20
	a.	Strip of 3, #2087-2089	.25	.25
2090	A532	5p multicolored	.20	.20
2091	A531	5p multicolored	.20	.20
2092	A532	5p multicolored	.20	.20
	a.	Strip of 3, #2090-2092	.25	.25
2093	A532	8p multicolored	.20	.20
2094	A531	8p multicolored	.20	.20
2095	A532	8p multicolored	.20	.20
	a.	Strip of 3, #2093-2095	.25	.25

Juan de Juni (1507-77), sculptor, (3p); Peter Paul Rubens (1577-1640), painter, (5p); Titian (1477-1576), painter, (8p).

Edelweiss in Pyrenees — A533

Designs: 5p, Fish and duck, wetlands. 7p, Forest, and forest destroyed by fire. 12p, Waves, oil rig, tanker and city. 20p, Sea gulls and seals, vert.

1978, Apr. 4　Photo.　Perf. 13
2096	A533	3p multicolored	.20	.20
2097	A533	5p multicolored	.20	.20
2098	A533	7p multicolored	.20	.20
2099	A533	12p multicolored	.20	.20
2100	A533	20p multicolored	.25	.20
		Nos. 2096-2100 (5)	1.05	1.00

Protection of the environment.

Palace of Charles V, Granada A534

Europa: 12p, The Lonja, Seville.

1978, May 2　Engr.　Perf. 13
2101	A534	5p dull grn & sl grn	.20	.20
2102	A534	12p dull grn & car rose	.20	.20

"España" — A535

1978, May 5　Photo.　Perf. 12½
2103	A535	12p multicolored	.20	.20

Spain's admission to the Council of Europe.

Symbols and Emblems of Postal Service A536

1978, June 27　Engr.　Perf. 13
2104	A536	5p slate green	.20	.20

Stamp Day.

Map of Las Palmas, 16th Century A537

5p, Hermitage of Columbus Church, vert. 12p, View of Las Palmas, 16th century.

1978, June 23　　　　　　　Photo.
2105	A537	3p multicolored	.20	.20
2106	A537	5p multicolored	.20	.20
2107	A537	12p multicolored	.20	.20
		Nos. 2105-2107 (3)	.60	.60

Founding of Las Palmas, 500th anniv.

Pablo Picasso, Self-portrait A538

Picasso Paintings: 3p, Señora Canals. 8p, Jaime Sabartes. 10p, End of the Act (actress). 12p, Science and Charity (woman patient, doctor, nurse and child), horiz. 15p, "Las Mennas" (blue period), horiz. 20p, The Sparrows. 25p, The Painter and his Model, horiz.

1978, Sept. 29   Photo.   Perf. 13

2108	A538	3p gold & multi	.20	.20
2109	A538	5p gold & multi	.20	.20
2110	A538	8p gold & multi	.20	.20
2111	A538	10p gold & multi	.20	.20
2112	A538	12p gold & multi	.20	.20
2113	A538	15p gold & multi	.20	.20
2114	A538	20p gold & multi	.25	.20
2115	A538	25p gold & multi	.30	.20
		Nos. 2108-2115 (8)	1.75	1.60

Pablo Picasso (1881-1973). Stamp Day 1978.
A 7p stamp like No. 2111 was not issued.
For other art types see A384, A397, A410, A431, A448, A473, A501, A522, A558 and footnote following No. 876.

José de San Martín A539

Design: 12p, Simon Bolivar.

1978, Oct. 12   Engr.   Perf. 13

2116	A539	7p sepia & car	.20	.20
2117	A539	12p violet & car	.20	.20

José de San Martín (1778-1850) and Simon Bolivar (1783-1830), South American liberators.

Flight into Egypt, Capital from St. Mary de Nieva A540

Christmas: 12p, Annunciation, capital from St. Mary de Nieva.

1978, Nov. 3   Photo.   Perf. 13

2118	A540	5p multicolored	.20	.20
2119	A540	12p multicolored	.20	.20

Mexican Calendar Stone A541

Designs (King Juan Carlos I, Queen Sofia and): No. 2121, Machu Picchu. No. 2122, Calchaqui jars from Tucuman and Angalala.

1978

2120	A541	5p multicolored	.20	.20
2121	A541	5p multicolored	.20	.20
2122	A541	5p multicolored	.20	.20
		Nos. 2120-2122 (3)	.60	.60

Royal visits to Mexico, Peru and Argentina. Issued: #2120 (Mexico), Nov. 17; #2121 (Peru), Nov. 22; #2122 (Argentina), Nov. 26.

King Philip V — A542

Rulers of Spain: No. 2124, Louis I. 8p, Ferdinand VI. 10p, Carlos III. 12p, Carlos IV. 15p, Ferdinand VII. 20p, Isabella II. 25p, Alfonso XII. 50p, Alfonso XIII. 100p, Juan Carlos I.

1978, Nov. 22   Engr.   Perf. 13

2123	A542	5p dk blue & rose red	.20	.20
2124	A542	5p olive & dull grn	.20	.20
2125	A542	8p vio bl & red brn	.20	.20
2126	A542	10p blue grn & blk	.20	.20
2127	A542	12p brown & mar	.20	.20
2128	A542	15p black & indigo	.20	.20
2129	A542	20p olive & indigo	.25	.20
2130	A542	25p ultra & vio brn	.30	.20
2131	A542	50p vermilion & brn	.55	.25
2132	A542	100p ultra & vio blk	1.10	.35
		Nos. 2123-2132 (10)	3.40	2.20

Spanish Flag, Preamble to Constitution, Parliament — A543

1978, Dec.   Photo.   Perf. 13

2133	A543	5p multicolored	.20	.20

Proclamation of New Constitution.

Illuminated Pages from Bible and Codex — A544

1978, Dec. 27

2134	A544	5p multicolored	.20	.20

Millennium of the consecration of the Basilica of Santa Maria de Ripoll.

Car and Drop of Oil — A545

Designs: 8p, Insulated house and thermometer. 10p, Hand pulling plug.

1979, Jan. 24   Photo.   Perf. 13

2135	A545	5p multicolored	.20	.20
2136	A545	8p multicolored	.20	.20
2137	A545	10p multicolored	.20	.20
		Nos. 2135-2137 (3)	.60	.60

Energy conservation.

De La Salle, Students A546

1979, Feb. 14   Photo.   Perf. 13

2138	A546	5p multicolored	.20	.20

Institute of Christian Brothers, founded by Jean-Baptiste de la Salle, centenary.

Jorge Manrique — A547

Portraits: 8p, Fernan Caballero (pen name of Cecilia Böhl de Faber). 10p, Francisco Villaespesa. 20p, Gregorio Marañon.

1979, Feb. 28   Engr.

2139	A547	5p green & brown	.20	.20
2140	A547	8p dark red & blue	.20	.20
2141	A547	10p brown & purple	.20	.20
2142	A547	20p green & olive	.25	.20
		Nos. 2139-2142 (4)	.85	.80

Jorge Manrique, poet, 500th death anniversary; Fernan Caballero, Francisco Villaespesa, and Gregorio Marañon, writers, birth centenaries.

Running and Jumping A548

Sport for All: 8p, Children kicking ball and skipping rope, jogging and bicycling. 10p, Family jogging, and dog.

1979, Mar. 14   Photo.   Perf. 13

2143	A548	5p multicolored	.20	.20
2144	A548	8p multicolored	.20	.20
2145	A548	10p multicolored	.20	.20
		Nos. 2143-2145 (3)	.60	.60

Children in Library A549

1979, Apr. 27   Photo.   Perf. 13

2146	A549	5p multicolored	.20	.20

International Year of the Child.

Manuel Ysasi (1810-1855) Postal Reformer — A550

Europa: 5p, Mounted messenger and postilion, 1761 engraving, vert.

1979, Apr. 30   Engr.

2147	A550	5p brown & sepia	.20	.20
2148	A550	12p red brn & sl grn	.20	.20

Radar and Satellite A551

5p, Symbolic people and cables, vert.

1979, May 17   Photo.   Perf. 13

2149	A551	5p multicolored	.20	.20
2150	A551	8p multicolored	.20	.20

World Telecommunications Day, May 17.

Bulgaria No. 1, Sofia Opera House, Housing Development — A552

1979, May 18

2151	A552	12p multicolored	.20	.20

Philaserdica '79, International Philatelic Exhibition, Sofia, Bulgaria, May 18-27.

Tank, Jet and Destroyer A553

1979, May 25

2152	A553	5p multicolored	.20	.20

Armed Forces Day.

Messenger Handing Letter to King — A554

1979, June 15   Litho. & Engr.

2153	A554	5p multicolored	.20	.20

Stamp Day 1979.

Daroca Gate, Zaragoza — A555

Architecture: 8p, Gerona Cathedral. 10p, Interior, Carthusian Monastery Church, Granada. 20p, Portal, Palace of the Marques de Dos Aguas, Valencia.

1979, June 27   Engr.

2154	A555	5p vio bl & lilac brn	.20	.20
2155	A555	8p dk blue & sepia	.20	.20
2156	A555	10p black & green	.20	.20
2157	A555	20p brown & sepia	.25	.20
		Nos. 2154-2157 (4)	.85	.80

Turkey Sponge A556

Fauna: 7p, Crayfish. 8p, Scorpion. 20p, Starfish. 25p, Sea anemone.

1979, July 11   Photo.   Perf. 13

2158	A556	5p multicolored	.20	.20
2159	A556	7p multicolored	.20	.20
2160	A556	8p multicolored	.20	.20
2161	A556	20p multicolored	.25	.20
2162	A556	25p multicolored	.30	.20
		Nos. 2158-2162 (5)	1.15	1.00

Gen. Antonio Gutierrez and Battle
A557

1979, Aug.   **Engr.**
2163 A557 5p multicolored   .20 .20

Naval defense of Tenerife, 18th century.

A558

A559

Juan de Juanes Paintings: 8p, Immaculate Conception. 10p, Holy Family. 15p, Ecce Homo. 20p, St. Stephen in the Synagogue. 25p, The Last Supper, horiz. 50p, Adoration of the Mystic Lamb, horiz.

1979, Sept. 28 Photo. Perf. 13x13½
2164 A558 8p multicolored   .20 .20
2165 A558 10p multicolored   .20 .20
2166 A558 15p multicolored   .20 .20
2167 A558 20p multicolored   .25 .20
2168 A558 25p multicolored   .30 .20
2169 A558 50p multicolored   .55 .20
     Nos. 2164-2169 (6)   1.70 1.20

For other art types see A384, A397, A410, A431, A448, A473, A501, A522, A538 and footnote following No. 876.

1979, Oct. 3 Photo. Perf. 13x13½

Zaragoza Cathedral, Mother and Child statue.

2170 A559 5p multicolored   .20 .20

8th Mariology and 15th International Marianist Congresses, Zaragoza, Oct. 3-12.

Felipe de Borbon, Hospital
A560

1979, Oct.   **Perf. 13½x13**
2171 A560 5p multicolored   .20 .20

Hospital of the Child Jesus, centenary.

St. Bartholomew College, Bogota — A561

Hispanidad 79: 12p, University of St. Mark, Lima, coat of arms.

1979, Oct. 12 Engr. Perf. 13
2172 A561 7p multicolored   .20 .20
2173 A561 12p multicolored   .20 .20

Clasped Hands, Badge, Governor's Palace
A562

Design: No. 2175, Statute book, vert.

Lithographed and Engraved
1979, Oct. 27   **Perf. 13**
2174 A562 8p multicolored   .20 .20
2175 A562 8p multicolored   .20 .20

Catalonian and Basque autonomy statute.

Type A54, Barcelona Coat of Arms
A563

Photogravure and Engraved
1979, Nov. 6   **Perf. 13½x13**
2176 A563 5p multicolored   .20 .20

Barcelona Philatelic Congress and Exhibition, 50th anniversary.

Nativity, Capital from St. Peter the Elder
A564

Christmas 1979: 19p, Flight into Egypt, column from St. Peter the Elder, Huesca.

1979, Nov. 14   **Photo.**
2177 A564 8p multicolored   .20 .20
2178 A564 19p multicolored   .25 .20

Carlos I, Coat of Arms
A565

Kings of the House of Austria (Hapsburg Dynasty): 20p, Philip II. 25p, Philip III. 50c, Philip IV. 100p, Carlos II.

1979, Nov. 22 Engr. Perf. 13
2179 A565 15p sl grn & dk bl   .20 .20
2180 A565 20p dk blue & mag   .25 .20
2181 A565 25p violet & yel bis .30 .20
2182 A565 50p brown & sl grn   .55 .20
2183 A565 100p magenta & brn   1.10 .30
     Nos. 2179-2183 (5)   2.40 1.10

2nd International Olive Oil Year — A566

1979, Dec. 4 Photo. Perf. 13½x13
2184 A566 8p multicolored   .20 .20

King Juan Carlos I Type of 1976
1980-84   Photo.   Perf. 13
2185 A497 13p dk red brn ('81)   .25 .20
2186 A497 14p red orange ('82)   .25 .20
2187 A497 16p sepia   .30 .20
2188 A497 17p bluish gray ('84) .25 .20
2189 A497 19p orange   .35 .20
2190 A497 30p dk green ('81)   .40 .20
2191 A497 50p org ver ('81)   .90 .20
2192 A497 60p blue ('81)   .80 .20
2193 A497 75p brt yel grn ('81) 1.00 .30
2194 A497 85p gray ('81)   1.25 .45
     Nos. 2185-2194 (10)   5.75 2.35

No. 2186 and 2187 also issued as coil with number on back of every fifth stamp.

Train and People
A567

1980, Feb. 20   Engr.   Perf. 13½
2200 A567 3p shown   .20 .20
2201 A567 4p Bus   .20 .20
2202 A567 5p Subway   .20 .20
     Nos. 2200-2202 (3) .60 .60

Public transportation.

Steel Export
A568

1980, Mar. 15   Photo.   Perf. 13½x13
2203 A568 5p shown   .20 .20
2204 A568 8p Ships   .20 .20
2205 A568 13p Shoes   .20 .20
2206 A568 19p Machinery .25 .20
2207 A568 25p Technology .30 .20
     Nos. 2203-2207 (5) 1.15 1.00

Federico Garcia Lorca (1899-1936) — A569

Europa: 19p, José Ortega y Gasset (1883-1955), philosopher and statesman.

1980, Apr. 28   Perf. 13½
2208 A569 8p violet & ol grn   .20 .20
2209 A569 19p brown & dk grn   .25 .20

Armed Forces Day
A570

1980, May 24 Photo. Perf. 13½x13
2210 A570 8p multicolored   .20 .20

Soccer Players
A571

1980, May 23
2211 A571 8p shown   .20 .20
2212 A571 19p Soccer ball, flags .25 .20

World Soccer Cup 1982.

Bourbon Arms, Ministry of Finance
A572

1980, June 9   Engr.   Perf. 13½
2213 A572 8p dark brown   .20 .20

Public Finances in Bourbon Spain Exhibition.

Helen Keller, Sign Language
A573

1980, June 27
2214 A573 19p dk yel grn & rose lake   .25 .20

Helen Keller (1880-1968), deaf mute writer and lecturer.

Mounted Postman, 12th Century Panel, Barcelona — A574

Lithographed and Engraved
1980, June 28   Perf. 13x12½
2215 A574 8p multicolored   .20 .20

Stamp Day.

King Alfonso and Count of Maceda at 1930 National Exhibition
A575

1980, July 1   Photo.   Perf. 13½
2216 A575 8p multicolored   .20 .20

1st Natl. Stamp Exhibition, Barcelona, 50th anniv.

A576

Altar of the Virgin, La Palma Cathedral.

1980, July 12   Engr.   Perf. 13
2217 A576 8p black & brown   .20 .20

Appearance of the Virgin of the Snow at La Palma, 300th anniversary.

A577

1980, Aug. 9   Engr.   Perf. 13
2218 A577 100p slate & sepia   1.10 .20

Ramon Perez de Ayala (1881-1962), novelist and diplomat.

Souvenir Sheet

La Atlantida Ruins, Mexican
Bonampak Musicians — A578

Designs: b, Sun Gate, Tiahuanaco; Roman
arch, Medinaceli. c, Alonso de Ercilla, Garcilaso de la Vega; title pages from La Arauca
and Commentario Reales. d, Virgin of Quito,
Virgin of Seafarers.

1980, Oct. 3   Engr.   Perf. 13
2219 A578 Sheet of 4 + 2 labels   2.25 2.25
  a. 25p multicolored   .30   .30
  b. 25p multicolored   .30   .30
  c. 50p multicolored   .55   .45
  d. 100p multicolored   1.10   .85
ESPAMER '80 Stamp Exhib., Madrid, Oct.
3-12.

400th Anniversary of Buenos
Aires — A579

1980, Oct. 24
2220 A579 19p multicolored   .25 .20

Miniature Sheet

The Creation, Tapestry, Gerona
Cathedral — A580

1980, Nov.   Litho.   Perf. 13½x13
2221 A580 Sheet of 6   2.50 2.00
  a.-c. 25p, any single   .25   .20
  d.-f. 50p, any single   .55   .25

Conference
Building, Flags of
Participants
A581

Holy Family
Church of Santa
Maria,
Cuina — A582

1980, Nov. 11   Photo.   Perf. 13½
2222 A581 22p multicolored   .25 .20

1980, Nov. 12

Christmas 1980, 22p, Adoration of the
Kings, portal, Church of Santa Maria, Cuina,
horiz.
2223 A582 10p multicolored   .20 .20
2224 A582 22p multicolored   .25 .20

Pedro
Vives and
His
Airplane
A583

Designs: Aviation pioneers.

1980, Dec. 10
2225 A583 5p shown   .20 .20
2226 A583 10p Benito Loygorri   .20 .20
2227 A583 15p Alfonso De Orle-
        ans   .20 .20
2228 A583 22p Alfredo Kindelan   .25 .20
    Nos. 2225-2228 (4)   .85 .80

Winter
University
Games
A584

1981, Mar. 4   Perf. 13½x13
2229 A584 30p multicolored   .35 .20

Picasso's Birth Centenary Emblem, by
Joan Miro — A585

1981, Mar. 27   Perf. 13
2230 A585 100p multicolored   1.00 .25
    Pablo Picasso (1881-1973).

Galician
Autonomy — A586

1981, Mar. 27   Photo.   Perf. 13
2231 A586 12p multicolored   .20 .20

Homage to
the Press
A587

1981, Apr. 8   Photo.   Perf. 13½x13
2232 A587 12p multicolored   .20 .20

International Year
of the
Disabled — A588

1981, Apr. 29   Litho.
2233 A588 30p multicolored   .35 .20

Soccer
Players
A589

1981, May 2   Photo.
2234 A589 12p Soccer players, diff.,
        vert.   .20 .20
2235 A589 30p shown   .35 .20
    1982 World Cup Soccer.

Europa Issue 1981

La Jota
Folkdance
A590

1981, May 4   Engr.
2236 A590 12p shown   .20 .20
2237 A590 30p Virgin of Rocio pro-
        cession   .35 .20

Armed Forces
Day — A591

1981, May 29   Photo.   Perf. 13x13½
2238 A591 12p multicolored   .20 .20

1981, June 17   Engr.

Famous Men: 12p, Francisco de Quevedo
(1580-1645), writer. 30p, St. Benedict (480-
543), patron saint of Europe.

2239 A592 6p purple & dk grn   .20 .20
2240 A592 12p brown & purple   .20 .20
2241 A592 30p dk green & brown   .35 .20
    Nos. 2239-2241 (3)   .75 .60

Gabriel Miro
(1879-1930),
Writer — A592

Mail
Messenger,
14th Cent.,
Woodcut
A593

Photogravure and Engraved
1981, June 19   Perf. 12½x13
2242 A593 12p multicolored   .20 .20
    Stamp Day.

Map of Balearic Islands, Diego
Homem's Atlas, 1563 — A594

1981, July 8   Photo.   Perf. 13x12½
2243 A594 7p shown   .20 .20
2244 A594 12p Canary Islds.,
        Prunes map, 1563   .20 .20

Kings
Alfonso XII
and Juan
Carlos,
Advocates
Arms
A595

1981, July 27   Engr.   Perf. 13½x13
2245 A595 50p multicolored   .55 .20
    Chamber of Advocates of State (Public
Prosecutor) centenary.

King Sancius VI
of Navarre with
City Charter,
12th Cent.
Miniature
A596

1981, Aug. 5   Photo.   Perf. 12½x13
2246 A596 12p multicolored   .20 .20
    Vitoria, 800th anniv.

Exports
A597

1981, Sept. 30   Photo.   Perf. 13½x13
2247 A597 6p Fruit   .20 .20
2248 A597 12p Wine   .20 .20
2249 A597 30p Vehicles   .35 .20
    Nos. 2247-2249 (3)   .75 .60

Congress Palace, Buenos Aires A598

1981, Oct. 12   Engr.   Perf. 13½x13
2250 A598 12p dk bl & car rose   .20 .20
ESPAMER '81 Intl. Stamp Exhibition, Buenos Aires, Nov. 13-22.

World Food Day A599

1981, Oct. 16
2251 A599 30p multicolored   .35 .20

Souvenir Sheet

Guernica, by Pablo Picasso (1881-1973) — A600

1981, Oct. 25   Photo.
2252 A600 200p multicolored   2.25 2.25
Control number comes in two types.

A601

Christmas 1981: 12p, Adoration of the Kings, Cervera de Pisuerga, Palencia. 30p, Nativity, Paredes de Nava.

1981, Nov. 18   Litho.   Perf. 13
2253 A601 12p shown   .20 .20
2254 A601 30p multicolored   .35 .20

A602

1981, Oct. 21   Engr.   Perf. 13x12½
King Juan Carlos I.
2268 A602 100p brown   1.25 .20
2269 A602 200p dark green   2.60 .20
2270 A602 500p dark blue   6.25 .55
   Nos. 2268-2270 (3)   10.10 .95

Postal Museum, Madrid A603

1981, Nov. 30   Engr.   Perf. 13
2273 A603 7p Telegrapher   .20 .20
2274 A603 12p Coach   .20 .20

Souvenir Sheet
2275   Sheet of 4   1.90 1.90
 c.   A603 50p Emblem   .55 .50
 d.   A603 100p Cap, posthorn,
          pouch   1.10 1.00
No. 2275 also contains Nos. 2273, 2274.

Royal Mint Building, Seville A604

1981, Dec. 4   Engr.   Perf. 13
2276 A604 12p black & brown   .20 .20
Spanish Administration of the Bourbons in the Indies.

A605

12p, Iparraguirre (1820-81). 30p, Juan Ramon Jimenez (1881-1958), writer. 50p, Pedro Calderon (1600-81), playwright.

1981-82
2277 A605 12p black & dk bl   .20 .20
2278 A605 30p dk bl & dk grn   .35 .20
2279 A605 50p black & violet   .55 .20
   Nos. 2277-2279 (3)   1.10 .60
Issued: 12p, 12/16; 30p, 50p, 3/10/82.

A606

1982, Feb. 24   Photo.
2280 A606 14p Poster by Joan Miro .20 .20
2281 A606 33p Cup, emblem   .40 .20
Espana '82 World Cup Soccer.

A607   A608

1982, Mar. 10   Engr.
2282 A607 30p grn & dk grn   .35 .20
Andres Bello (1782-1865), writer.

1982, Mar. 31   Photo.   Perf. 13
2283 A608 14p St. John of Com-
          postelo   .20 .20
Holy Year of Compostelo.

A609-A610

Operetta composers and scenes from their works: #2284, Manuel Fernandez Caballero (1835-1906). #2285, Gigantes and Cabezudos. #2286, Amadeo Vives Roig (1871-1932). #2287, Dona Francisquita. #2288, Tomas Breton Hernandez (1850-1923). #2289, Verbena of Paloma.

Lithographed and Engraved
1982, Apr. 28   Perf. 13
2284 A609 3p multicolored   .20 .20
2285 A610 3p multicolored   .20 .20
 a.   Pair, #2284-2285   .20 .20
2286 A609 6p multicolored   .20 .20
2287 A610 6p multicolored   .20 .20
 a.   Pair, #2284-2285   .20 .20
2288 A609 8p multicolored   .20 .20
2289 A610 8p multicolored   .20 .20
 a.   Pair, #2284-2285   .25 .20
See Nos. 2319-2324, 2378-2383.

Europa 1982 — A611

1982, May 3   Engr.   Perf. 12½
2290 A611 14p Unification, 1512 .20 .20
2291 A611 33p Discovery of New
             World, 1492   .40 .20

Armed Forces Day — A612

1982, May 28   Photo.   Perf. 13
2292 A612 14p multicolored   .20 .20

1982 World Cup A613

Designs: Soccer players.

1982, June 13   Perf. 13
2293 A613 14p multicolored   .20 .20
2294 A613 33p multicolored   .40 .20

Souvenir Sheets
2295   Sheets of 4, #2293-2294,
           9p, 100p, each   1.75 1.75
 a.   A613 9p Captains' handshake .20 .20
 b.   A613 100p Player holding cup 1.10 1.10
#2295 has two types of margin, each showing 7 arms of the 14 host cities. One sheet has 3 blue coats of arms, the other has 2.

Stamp Day — A614

1982, July 16   Litho.   Perf. 12½
2296 A614 14p Map, postal code   .20 .20

Organ Transplants A615

1982, July 28   Photo.   Perf. 13
2297 A615 14p Symbolic organs   .20 .20

Storks and Express Train — A616

Locomotive, 1850 — A617

Perf. 12½, 13 (A617)
1982, Sept. 27   Photo.
2298 A616 9p shown   .20 .20
2299 A617 14p shown   .20 .20
2300 A617 33p Santa Fe locomo-
             tive   .40 .40
   Nos. 2298-2300 (3)   .80 .60
23rd Intl. Railways Congress, Malaga.

ESPAMER '82 Intl. Stamp Exhibition, San Juan, Oct. 12-17 — A618

1982, Oct. 12   Engr.   Perf. 13½x13
2301 A618 33p dk blue & pur   .40 .20

St. Teresa of Avila (1515-1582) — A619

1982, Oct. 15
2302 A619 33p Statue by Gregorio
             Hernandez   .40 .20

Visit of Pope John Paul II, Oct. 31-Nov. 9 — A620

1982, Oct. 31   Engr.   Perf. 12½
2303 A620 14p multicolored   .20 .20

Water Wheel,
Alcantarilla
A621

Landscapes and Monuments: 6p, Bank of Spain, 19th cent., horiz. 9p, Crucifixion. 14p, St. Martin's Tower, Teruel. 33p, St. Andrew's Gate, Zamora.

1982, Nov. 5   *Perf. 13x12½, 12½x13*
2304	A621	4p gray & dk blue	.20	.20
2305	A621	6p dk blue & gray	.20	.20
2306	A621	9p brt blue & vio	.20	.20
2307	A621	14p brt blue & vio	.20	.20
2308	A621	33p claret & brown	.40	.20
	Nos. 2304-2308 (5)		1.20	1.00

Christmas
1982
A622

1982, Nov. 17   **Photo.**   *Perf. 13½*
2309	A622	14p Nativity, wood carving, by Gil de Siloe	.20	.20
2310	A622	33p Flight into Egypt	.40	.20

Pablo Gargallo,
Sculptor, Birth
Centenary
A623

Salesian
Fathers in
Spain,
Centenary
A624

1982, Dec. 9   **Engr.**   *Perf. 13*
2311	A623	14p blue & dk grn	.20	.20

1982, Dec. 16   **Photo.**   *Perf. 12½x13*
2312	A624	14p multicolored	.20	.20

Arms
of King
Juan
Carlos
I
A625

1983, Feb. 9   **Photo.**   *Perf. 12½*
2313	A625	14p multicolored	.20	.20

Andalusia
Autonomy
Statute
A626

1983   **Litho.**   *Perf. 13½*
2314	A626	14p shown	.25	.20
2315	A626	14p Cantabria	.25	.20

Issued: #2314, Feb. 28; #2315, Mar. 15.

State
Security
Forces
A627

1983, Mar. 23   **Photo.**
2316	A627	9p Natl. Police Force	.20	.20
2317	A627	14p Civil Guard	.20	.20
2318	A627	33p Superior Police Corps	.40	.20

Operetta Type of 1982

Designs: #2319, Scene from La Parranda. Francisco Alonso Lopez (1887-1948). #2320, Francisco Alonso Lopez (1887-1948). #2321, Jacinto Guerrero y Torres (1895-1951). #2322, Scene from La Rosa del Azafran. #2323, Jesus de Guridi Bidaola (1886-1961). #2324, Scene from El Caserio.

Lithographed and Engraved
1983, Apr. 22   *Perf. 13*
2319	A610	4p multicolored	.20	.20
2320	A609	4p multicolored	.20	.20
a.		Pair, #2319-2320	.20	.20
2321	A609	6p multicolored	.20	.20
2322	A610	6p multicolored	.20	.20
a.		Pair, #2321-2322	.25	.25
2323	A609	9p multicolored	.20	.20
2324	A610	9p multicolored	.20	.20
a.		Pair, #2323-2324	.35	.35

Europa 1983 — A628

Designs: 16p, Scene from Don Quixote, by Miguel Cervantes. 38p, L. Torres Quevaedo's Niagara Spanish aerocar.

1983, May 5   **Engr.**   *Perf. 13x12½*
Granite Paper
2325	A628	16p dk grn & brn red	.20	.20
2326	A628	38p brown	.45	.20

Francisco Salzillo
Alvarez (1707-83),
Painter — A629

World
Communications
Year — A630

Designs: 38p, Antonio Soler Ramos (1729-1783), composer. 50p, Joaquin Turina Perez (1882-1949), composer. 100p, St. Isidro Labrador (1082-1170), patron saint of Madrid.

1983, May 14   *Perf. 13*
2327	A629	16p purple & dk grn	.20	.20
2328	A629	38p blue & brown	.45	.20
2329	A629	50p bl grn & dk brn	.55	.20
2330	A629	100p red brn & pur	1.10	.25
	Nos. 2327-2330 (4)		2.30	.85

1983, May 17   **Photo.**   *Perf. 13*
2331	A630	38p multicolored	.45	.20

Rioja Autonomous Region — A631

Lithographed and Engraved
1983, May 25   *Perf. 13*
2332	A631	16p multicolored	.25	.20

Armed Forces
Day — A632

1983, May 26   **Photo.**
2333	A632	16p multicolored	.20	.20

Intl.
Canine
Exhibition,
Madrid,
June 1984
A633

Lithographed and Engraved
1983, June 8   *Perf. 13½*
2334	A633	10p Pointer	.20	.20
2335	A633	16p Mastiff	.20	.20
2336	A633	26p Iberian hound	.35	.25
2337	A633	38p Navarro pointer	.50	.20
	Nos. 2334-2337 (4)		1.25	.85

Discovery of Tungsten
Bicentenary — A634

Scouting
Year
A635

400th
Anniv. of
University
of
Zaragoza
A636

1983, June 22   **Photo.**   *Perf. 13*
2338	A634	16p Elhuyar brothers	.20	.20
2339	A635	38p multicolored	.45	.20
2340	A636	50p multicolored	.60	.20
	Nos. 2338-2340 (3)		1.25	.60

Murcia Autonomous Region — A637

Photogravure and Engraved
1983, July 8   *Perf. 13½*
2341	A637	16p Arms	.25	.20

Asturias Autonomous Region — A638

Lithographed and Engraved
1983, Sept. 8   *Perf. 13*
2342	A638	14p Victory Cross, Covadonga Basilica	.25	.20

Intl. Institute of Statistics, 44th
Congress, Madrid, Sept. 12-22
A639

1983, Sept. 12   **Photo.**   *Perf. 13*
2343	A639	38p Institute building	.45	.20

Stamp Day — A640

Lithographed and Engraved
1983, Oct. 8   *Perf. 13x12½*
2344	A640	16p Roman mail cart	.35	.30

No. 2344 se-tenant with label publicizing ESPANA '84 Philatelic Exhibition, April 27-May 6, 1984.

Valencia
Autonomy
Statute,
1st Anniv.
A641

1983, Oct. 10   *Perf. 13*
2345	A641	16p multicolored	.25	.20

View of Seville, 16th cent. — A642

1983, Oct. 12   **Engr.**   *Perf. 12½x13*
2346	A642	38p multicolored	.45	.20

Spanish-American trade in 17th century.

Stained-glass
Windows
A643

Designs: 10p King, Leon Cathedral. 16p, Epiphany, Gerona Cathedral. 38p, Apostle Santiago, Royal Hospital Chapel, Santiago.

Lithographed and Engraved

1983, Oct. 28   Perf. 12½x13
2347 A643 10p multicolored .20 .20
2348 A643 16p multicolored .25 .20
2349 A643 38p multicolored .45 .20
Nos. 2347-2349 (3) .90 .60

Church at Llivia, Gerona — A644

Designs: 6p, Temple, Santa Maria del Mar, Barcelona. 16p, Cathedral, Ceuta. 38p, Gate of the Santiago Bridge, Melilla. 50p, Charity Hospital, Seville.

1983, Nov. 9   Engr.   Perf. 13x12½
2350 A644 3p dk bl gray & grn .20 .20
2351 A644 6p dark blue gray .20 .20
2352 A644 16p red brn & dull vio .20 .20
2353 A644 38p bis brn & rose car .45 .25
2354 A644 50p brown & org red .55 .20
Nos. 2350-2354 (5) 1.60 1.05

Christmas 1983 — A645

Indalecio Prieto (1883-1962), Patriot — A646

1983, Nov. 23   Photo.   Perf. 13x13½
2355 A645 16p The Nativity, Tortosa .20 .20
2356 A645 38p The Adoration, Vich .45 .20

1983, Dec. 14   Engr.   Perf. 13
2357 A646 16p red brn & blk .20 .20

Industrial Accident Prevention A647

1984, Jan. 25   Photo.   Perf. 13½
2358 A647 7p Construction worker .20 .20
2359 A647 10p Fire .20 .20
2360 A647 16p Electrical plug, pliers .20 .20
Nos. 2358-2360 (3) .60 .60

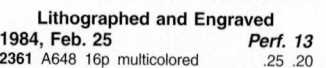

Extremadura Statute of Autonomy, First Anniv. — A648

Lithographed and Engraved
1984, Feb. 25   Perf. 13
2361 A648 16p multicolored .25 .20

1500th Anniv. of City of Burgos A649

1984, Mar. 1   Engr.
2362 A649 16p multicolored .20 .20

Carnivals A650

1984   Photo.   Perf. 13½x13
2363 A650 16p Santa Cruz de Tenerife .25 .20
2364 A650 16p Valencia Fallas .25 .20
Issued: #2363, Mar. 5; #2364, Mar. 16.

Man and the Biosphere A651

1984, Apr. 11
2365 A651 38p da Vinci's Study of Man .45 .25

Aragon Statute of Autonomy, 2nd Anniv. A652

Lithographed and Engraved
1984, Apr. 23   Perf. 13x13½
2366 A652 16p Map .25 .20

Juan Carlos — A653

Souvenir Sheet

Espana '84 (Spanish Royal Family): b, Sofia of Greece. c, Cristina de Borbon. d, Prince of Asturias Felipe de Borbon. e, Elene de Borbon.

1984, Apr. 27   Perf. 12½x13
2367 A653 Sheet of 5 3.25 3.25
a.-e. 38p, any single .65 .65

Congress Emblem — A654

1984, May 3   Engr.   Perf. 13x13½
2368 A654 38p purple & red .45 .20
World Philatelic Federation, 53rd Congress, Madrid, May 7-9.

Europa (1959-84) A655

1984, May 5
2369 A655 16p orange .20 .20
2370 A655 38p dark blue .45 .25

Armed Forces Day A656

Design: 17p, Monument to Hunters Regiment of Caceres, by Mariano Benlliure.

1984, May 19   Photo.   Perf. 13½x13
2371 A656 17p multicolored .25 .20

Canary Islds. Statute of Autonomy — A657

Castilla-La Mancha Statute of Autonomy — A658

Lithographed and Engraved
1984, May 29   Perf. 13
2372 A657 16p Arms, map .25 .20

1984, May 31   Perf. 13
2373 A658 17p Arms .25 .20

King Alfonso X (1252-84) A659

Design: 38p, Ignacio Barroquer (1884-1965), ophthalmologist

1984, June 20   Engr.   Perf. 13
2374 A659 16p multicolored .25 .20
2375 A659 38p multicolored .45 .20

Balearic Islands Statute of Autonomy — A660

1984, June 29   Litho. & Engr.
2376 A660 17p multicolored .25 .20

Feast of San Fermin of Pamplona A661

1984, July 5   Photo.
2377 A661 17p Bull runners .25 .20

Operetta Type of 1982

#2378, El Nino Judio. #2379, Pablo Luna (1880-1942). #2380, Ruperto Chapi (1851-1909). #2381, La Revoltosa. #2382, La Reina Mora. #2383, Jose Serrano (1873-1941).

Lithographed and Engraved
1984, July 20   Perf. 13
2378 A610 6p multicolored .20 .20
2379 A609 6p multicolored .20 .20
a. Pair, #2378-2379 .20 .20
2380 A609 7p multicolored .20 .20
2381 A610 7p multicolored .20 .20
a. Pair, #2380-2381 .20 .20
2382 A610 10p multicolored .20 .20
2383 A609 10p multicolored .20 .20
a. Pair, #2382-2383 .30 .30

1984 Summer Olympics A662

Greek or Roman sculptures.

1984, July 27   Photo.
2384 A662 1p Chariot race .20 .20
2385 A662 2p Diving, vert. .20 .20
2386 A662 5p Wrestling .20 .20
2387 A662 8p Discus, vert. .20 .20
Nos. 2384-2387 (4) .80 .80

Navarra Statute of Autonomy A663

Lithographed and Engraved
1984, Aug. 16   Perf. 13
2388 A663 17p multicolored .25 .20

Intl. Bicycling Championship, Barcelona, Aug. 27-Sept. 2 — A664

1984, Aug. 27   Photo.
2389 A664 17p multicolored .20 .20

Castilla and Leon Statute of Autonomy A665

1984, Sept. 5   Litho. & Engr.
2390 A665 17p multicolored .25 .20

Jerez Vintage Feast — A666

1984, Sept. 20   Photo.   Perf. 13
2391 A666 17p Women picking grapes   .25 .20

Journey to the Holy Land by Sister Egeria, 1600th Anniv. — A667

1984, Sept. 26
2392 A667 40p Map, Sister Egeria   .45 .25

Stamp Day — A668

1984, Oct. 5   Litho. & Engr.
2393 A668 17p Arab postrider   .20 .20

Father Junipero Serra (1713-84), Mission Founder in California A669

1984, Oct. 12   Engr.   Perf. 13
2394 A669 40p Map, Serra, mission   .45 .20

Christmas 1984 A670

1984, Nov. 21   Photo.
2395 A670 17p Nativity   .20 .20
2396 A670 40p Adoration of the Kings, vert.   .45 .20

Madrid Autonomy Statue A671

1984, Nov. 28   Litho. & Engr.
2397 A671 17p Arms, buildings   .25 .20

Andean Pact, 15th Anniv. A672

Condor, Flags of Bolivia, Colombia, Ecuador, Peru and Venezuela.

1985, Jan. 16   Photo.   Perf. 13
2398 A672 17p multicolored   .20 .20

The Virgin of Louvain, by Jan Gossaert (c. 1478-1536) A673

Santa Cruz College, Valladolid University, 500th Anniv. — A674

1985, Jan. 21   Perf. 13½
2399 A673 40p multicolored   .45 .20
EUROPALIA '85. See Belgium No. 1185.

1985, Feb. 20   Litho. & Engr.
2400 A674 17p Main gateway   .20 .20

OLYMPHILEX '85, Lausanne, Switz. — A675

1985, Mar. 18   Photo.
2401 A675 40p multicolored   .45 .20

ESPAMER '85, Cuba A676

1985, Mar. 20   Engr.
2402 A676 40p Cathedral, Havana   .45 .25

Fairs A677

Perf. 13½, 13½x14 (#2405)
1985   Photo.
2403 A677 17p Seville   .25 .20
2404 A677 17p Alcoy   .25 .20
2405 A677 17p Arriondas-Ribadesella   .25 .20
2406 A677 18p Toledo, vert.   .25 .20
   Nos. 2403-2406 (4)   1.00 .80

Issued: #2403, Apr. 16; #2404, Apr. 22; #2405, Aug. 2; #2406, June 6.

Intl. Youth Year — A678

1985, Apr. 17   Engr.   Perf. 13½
2407 A678 17p blk, hn brn & dk grn .20 .20

Europa '85 A680

Designs: 18p, Antonio de Cabezon (1510-1566), organist and composer, court Musician to Felipe II. 45p, Natl. Youth Orchestra.

1985, May 3   Engr.
2408 A680 18p dk bl, dk red & blk, *buff*   .25 .20
2409 A680 45p ol grn, dk red & blk, *buff*   .45 .25

Armed Forces Day A681

1985, May 24   Photo.
2410 A681 18p multicolored   .25 .20

Natl. Flag Bicent. — A682

#2411, Arms of King Carlos III, text of 1785 Decree, sailing ship Santisima Trinidad. #2412, Natl. arms, Article No. 4 from 1978 Constitution, lion ornament from Chamber of Deputies Building.

Lithographed and Engraved
1985, May 28   Perf. 13x13½
2411   18p multicolored   .25 .20
2412   18p multicolored   .25 .20
   a. A682 Pair, #2411-2412   .45 .45

Intl. Environment Day — A683

1985, June 5   Photo.
2413 A683 17p multicolored   .20 .20

Juan Carlos — A684

1985-92   Photo.   Perf. 14
2414 A684 10c indigo   .20 .20
2415 A684 50c lt blue green   .20 .20
2416 A684 1p brt blue   .20 .20
2417 A684 2p dark green   .20 .20
2418 A684 3p chestnut brn   .20 .20
2419 A684 4p olive green   .20 .20
2420 A684 5p brt rose lilac   .20 .20
2421 A684 6p brown black   .20 .20
2422 A684 7p brt violet   .20 .20
2423 A684 7p apple grn   .20 .20
2424 A684 8p gray black   .20 .20
2425 A684 10p lake   .20 .20
2426 A684 12p red   .20 .20
2427 A684 13p Prus blue   .20 .20
2428 A684 15p emerald   .20 .20
2429 A684 17p yellow bis   .20 .20
2430 A684 18p brt grnsh bl   .25 .20
2431 A684 19p violet brn   .25 .20
   a.   Booklet pane of 6   1.50
2432 A684 20p brt pink   .25 .20
2433 A684 25p olive green   .30 .20
2434 A684 27p deep rose lil   .35 .20
2435 A684 30p ultra   .35 .20
2436 A684 45p brt green   .50 .20
2437 A684 50p violet blue   .55 .20
2438 A684 55p black brown   .60 .20
2439 A684 60p dark orange   .65 .25
2440 A684 75p deep rose lil   .80 .30
   Nos. 2414-2440 (27)   8.05 5.55

Issued: 1p, 5p, 8p, 12p, 18p, 45p, 6/12; #2422, 17p, 7/16; #2423, 1/86; 2p, 3p, 4p, 10p, 4/3/86; 19p, 9/27/86; 6p, 20p, 30p, 1/26/87; 50p, 60p, 75p, 4/24/89; 10c, 50c, 13p, 15p, 5/16/89; 25p, 55p, 12/14/90; 27p, 2/92.

Astrophysical Observatory Opening, La Palma, Canary Islands — A685

1985, June 25   Photo.   Perf. 14
2441 A685 45p multicolored   .50 .20

European Music Year — A686

Designs: 12p, Ataulfo Argenta, conductor. 17p, Tomas Luis de Victoria, composer. 45p, Fernando Sor, composer.

Litho. & Engr.
1985, June 26   Perf. 13
2442 A686 12p multicolored   .20 .20
2443 A686 17p multicolored   .25 .20
2444 A686 45p multicolored   .50 .20
   Nos. 2442-2444 (3)   .95 .60

Bernal Diaz del Castillo (1492-1585), Historian — A687

Famous men: 12p, Esteban Terradas (1883-1950), mathematician. 17p, Vicente Aleixandre (1898-1984), 1977 Nobel laureate in literature. 45p, Leon Felipe Camino (1884-1968), poet.

1985, July 24   Engr.   Perf. 13½
2445 A687 7p dk red, blk & dk grn, *buff*   .20 .20
2446 A687 12p brt ver, dk bl & blk, *buff*   .20 .20
2447 A687 17p blk, dk grn & dk red, *buff*   .25 .20
2448 A687 45p bis, blk & dk grn, *buff*   .55 .20
   Nos. 2445-2448 (4)   1.20 .80

Monastic Mail
Delivery,
1122 — A688

Lithographed and Engraved
1985, Sept. 27   **Perf. 13**
2449 A688 17p multicolored   .25 .20
Stamp Day 1985.

12th Rhythmic
Gymnastics World
Championships,
Valladolid — A689

1985, Oct. 9   Photo.   Perf. 13x13½
2450 A689 17p Ribbon exercise   .20 .20
2451 A689 45p Hoop exercise   .50 .25

Souvenir Sheet

Prado Museum, La Alcachofa
Fountain — A690

Lithographed and Engraved
1985, Oct. 18   **Perf. 13**
2452 A690 17p multicolored   .50 .50
EXFILNA '85, Madrid, Oct. 18-27.

Virgin and
Child, Seville
Cathedral
A691

Stained glass windows: 12p, Monk, by Peter
Boniface, Toledo Cathedral. 17p, King Henry II
of Castile, Alcazar of Segovia.

1985, Oct. 24   **Perf. 12½x13**
2453 A691 7p multicolored   .20 .20
2454 A691 12p multicolored   .20 .20
2455 A691 17p multicolored   .20 .20
     Nos. 2453-2455 (3)   .60 .60

Christmas
1985
A692

14th-15th century paintings in the Episcopal
Museum, Vich: 17p, Nativity, Guimera Altarpiece retable, 14th cent., by Ramon de Mur.
45p, Epiphany, from an embroidered frontal,
15th cent.

1985, Nov. 27   Photo.   Perf. 13½
2456 A692 17p multicolored   .20 .20
2457 A692 45p multicolored   .50 .20

Birds — A693

1985, Dec. 4   **Litho. & Engr.**
2458 A693 6p Sylvia cantillans   .20 .20
2459 A693 7p Monticola saxa-
               tilis   .20 .20
2460 A693 12p Sturnus unicolor   .25 .20
2461 A693 17p Panurus
               biarmicus   .35 .20
     Nos. 2458-2461 (4)   1.00 .80
     Wildlife conservation.

Count of Penaflorida (1729-
1785) — A694

1985, Dec. 11   Engr.   Perf. 13½
2462 A694 17p dark blue   .20 .20
Francisco Javier de Munibe e Idiaquez,
founded Natl. Economic Society of Friends in
1765.

Government Palace, Madrid, and
Accession Agreement Text — A695

17p, Map and flags of EEC countries. 30p,
Hall of Columns, Royal Palace. 45p, Member
flags.

1986, Jan. 7.   Litho.   Perf. 13½x13
2463 A695 7p multicolored   .20 .20
2464 A695 17p multicolored   .20 .20
2465 A695 30p multicolored   .35 .20
2466 A695 45p multicolored   .60 .20
   a.   Bklt. pane of 4, #2463-2466   3.25
     Nos. 2463-2466 (4)   1.35 .80
Admission of Spain and Portugal to European Economic Community. See Portugal
Nos. 1661-1662.

Tourism — A696

Historic sites: 12p, Inner courtyard, La Lupi-
ana Monastery, Guadalajara. 35p, Balcony of
Europe, Nerja.

1986, Jan. 20   Engr.   Perf. 13x12½
2467 A696 12p dk rose, brn & gray
               brn   .20 .20
2468 A696 35p brt blue & sep   .45 .20

2nd World Conference on Merino
Sheep — A697

1986, Jan. 27   Photo.   Perf. 13½
2469 A697 45p multicolored   .50 .25

Masquerade, 19th Cent., by F.
Hohenleiter — A698

1986, Feb. 5
2470 A698 17p multicolored   .25 .20
Cadiz Carnival.

Intl. Peace Year — A699

Lithographed and Engraved
1986, Feb. 12   **Perf. 13x13½**
2471 A699 45p multicolored   .50 .25

Festival of
Religious
Music,
Cuenca
A700

1986, Mar. 26   Photo.   Perf. 13½
2472 A700 17p multicolored   .25 .20

Chamber of Commerce, Cent. — A701

Painting detail: Swearing in of the Regent,
Queen Maria Christina, Before the Spanish
Parliament, 1886, by Francisco Jover and Joa-
quin Sorolla y Bastida, Senate Palace, Madrid.

1986, Apr. 9   Engr.   Perf. 13½
2473 A701 17p sage grn & grnsh
               blk   .20 .20

Emigration of
Spaniards — A702

1986, Apr. 22   **Photo.**
2474 A702 45p multicolored   .50 .25

Europa 1986 — A703

Lithographed and Engraved
1986, May 5   **Perf. 13x13½**
2475 A703 17p Youth feeding birds   .25 .20
2476 A703 45p Girl watering tree   .55 .25

Our Lady
of the Dew
Festival,
Almonte
A704

1986, May 14   Photo.   Perf. 13½x13
2477 A704 17p multicolored   .25 .20

Army Day
A705

Captains-General Building, Canary Islands.

1986, May 16   Engr.   Perf. 13½
2478 A705 17p pale yel brn, sep &
               red   .20 .20

Rodrigo City
Cathedral
A706

Design: 35p, Calella Lighthouse.

1986, June 16   **Perf. 12½x13½**
2479 A706 12p blue & black   .20 .20
2480 A706 35p multicolored   .55 .20

10th World Basketball Championships,
July 5-20 — A707

1986, July 4   Photo.   Perf. 12½
2481 A707 45p multicolored   .50 .20

Famous
Men — A708

Mystery of the Virgin's Death Festival Elche — A709

Designs: 7p, Francisco Loscos Bernal (1823-1886), botanist. 11p, Salvador Espriu (1913-1985), author. 17p, Jose Martinez Ruiz (Azorin, 1873-1967), writer. 45p, Jose Vitoriano Gonzalez (Juan Gris, 1887-1927), painter.

1986, July 16   **Engr.**   *Perf. 13*
2482 A708 7p olive grn & bl .20 .20
2483 A708 11p brt rose & blk .20 .20
2484 A708 17p dk brn vio & blk .20 .20
2485 A708 45p org, red vio & blk .50 .25
  Nos. 2482-2485 (4) 1.10 .85

1986, Aug. 11   **Photo.**   *Perf. 13x13½*
2486 A709 17p Angels carrying soul .25 .20

5th World Swimming, Water Polo, Diving and Synchronized Swimming Championships — A710

1986, Aug. 13   **Engr.**   *Perf. 13½*
2487 A710 45p multicolored .50 .25

10th World Pelota Championships — A711

1986, Sept. 12
2488 A711 17p multicolored .25 .20

Stamp Day — A712

Messenger, The Husband's Return, Song 63, TI1 Codex, 1979 edition, Spanish Royal Academy.

1986, Sept. 27   **Litho.**   *Perf. 13x12½*
2489 A712 17p multicolored .20 .20

Souvenir Sheet

EXFILNA '86, Cordova, Oct. 9-18 — A713

1986, Oct. 7   **Litho. & Engr.**
2490 A713 17p Man, Cordova "Mosque" .25 .25

Discovery of America, 500th Anniv. (in 1992) — A714

Men and text: 7p, Aristotle, text from De Cielo et Mundo. 12p, Seneca, text from Medea. 17p, San Isidoro, text from Etimologias. 30p, Pedro de Ailly, text from Imago Mundi. 35p, Mayan, prophesy from Libros de Chilam Balam. 45p, European, prophesy from Libros de Chilam Balam.

Lithographed and Engraved
1986, Oct. 15   *Perf. 13x13½*
2491 A714 7p multicolored .20 .20
2492 A714 12p multicolored .20 .20
2493 A714 17p multicolored .20 .20
2494 A714 30p multicolored .35 .20
2495 A714 35p multicolored .40 .20
2496 A714 45p multicolored .50 .20
  a. Bklt. pane of 6, #2491-2496 1.90
  Nos. 2491-2496 (6) 1.85 1.20

Caspar de Portola y Rovira (1717-1786), Pioneer of California — A715

1986, Nov. 6   *Perf. 13½*
2497 A715 22p multicolored .25 .20

Christmas A716

Wood carving details: 19p, The Holy Family, by Diego de Siloe (c. 1495-1563), Natl. Sculpture Museum, Valladolid, vert. 48p, Nativity, Toledo Cathedral altarpiece, by Felipe de Borgona (c. 1475-1543).

1986, Nov. 19   **Photo.**   *Perf. 13½*
2498 A716 19p multicolored .25 .20
2499 A716 48p multicolored .55 .20

Spanish-Islamic Cultural Heritage — A717

Famous men: 7p, Abd Al Rahman II (792-852), 4th independent emir of Cordoba. 12p, Ibn Hazm (994-1064), scholar. 17p, Al-Zarqali (1061-1100), astronomer. 45p, Alfonso VII, scholar, Toledo School of Translators.

1986, Dec. 3   **Engr.**
2500 A717 7p org red & dk red brn .20 .20
2501 A717 12p brn blk & red org .20 .20
2502 A717 17p black & dk blue .25 .20
2503 A717 45p green & black .50 .20
  Nos. 2500-2503 (4) 1.15 .80

Alfonso R. Castelao (1886-1950), Artist, Writer — A718

Lithographed and Engraved
1986, Dec. 11   *Perf. 13x13½*
2504 A718 32p El Buen Cura, 1917 .40 .20

Globe, Chateau de la Muette A719

1987, Jan. 14   *Perf. 14*
2505 A719 48p multicolored .55 .20
Organization for Economic Cooperation and Development, OECD, 25th anniv.

EXPO '92, Seville A720

1987, Jan. 21   **Photo.**
2506 A720 19p Geometric shapes .35 .20
2507 A720 48p Earth, Moon's surface .95 .20
See Nos. 2540-2541, 2550-2551.

Portrait of Vitoria, by Vera Fajardo A721

1987, Feb. 11   **Engr.**
2508 A721 48p dark rose brown .55 .20
Francisco de Vitoria (c. 1486-1546), theologian, teacher and a founder of intl. law.

Marine Corps, 450th Anniv. A722

Design: 18th Cent. 74-gun man-of-war, period standard bearer, corps insignia.

1987, Feb. 25
2509 A722 19p multicolored .25 .20

Deusto University, Cent. — A723

1987, Feb. 26   **Engr.**   *Perf. 14x13½*
2510 A723 19p blk, hn brn & dk grn .25 .20

UN Child Survival Campaign A724

1987, Mar. 4   *Perf. 13½x14*
2511 A724 19p red brown & blk .25 .20

Constitution of Cadiz, 175th Anniv. — A725

Nos. 2512a-2512c in a continuous design: The Promulgation of 1812, by Salvador Viniegra. No. 2512d, Anniv. emblem.

1987, Mar. 18   **Litho.**   *Perf. 13½*
2512 Strip of 4 1.25 1.25
  a.-d. A725 25p, any single .30 .20

Ceramicware A726

Designs: 7p, Pharmaceutical jar, 15th cent., Manises of Valencia. 14p, Abstract figurine, 20th cent., Sargadelos of Galicia. 19p, Neoclassical lidded urn, 18th cent., Buen Retiro of Madrid. 32p, Water jar, 20th cent., Salvatierra of Extremadura. 40p, Pitcher, 18th cent., Talavera of Toledo. 48p, Pitcher, 18th-19th cent., Granada of Andalucia.

Lithographed and Engraved
1987, Mar. 20   *Perf. 12½x13*
2513 Block of 6 + 3 labels 2.25 2.25
  a. A726 7p multicolored .20 .20
  b. A726 14p multicolored .20 .20
  c. A726 19p multicolored .30 .20
  d. A726 32p multicolored .45 .30
  e. A726 40p multicolored .50 .30
  f. A726 48p multicolored .60 .30
See No. 2552.

Passion Week in Zamora and Seville A727

Paintings: 19p, The Amanecer Procession, by Gallego Marquina, vert. 48p, Jesus Carrying the Cross, by Martinez Montanes, and the Gate of Forgiveness, Seville Cathedral.

1987, Apr. 13   **Photo.**   *Perf. 14x13½*
2514 A727 19p multicolored .25 .20
2515 A727 48p multicolored .55 .20

Tourism A728

14p, Rock of Ifach, Calpe. 19p, Nave of Santa Marina d'Ozo Church, Pontevedra, before restoration. 40p, Sonanes Palace, Villacarriedo. 48p, Monastery of St. Joan de les Abadesses, Gerona, vert.

1987   **Engr.**   *Perf. 12½x13*
2515A A728 14p dp bl & sage grn .25 .20
2516 A728 19p dp grn & grnsh blk .30 .20
2516A A728 40p dp claret .50 .20
2517 A728 48p black .60 .20
  Nos. 2515A-2517 (4) 1.65 .80

Issued: 19p, 48p, 4/21; 14p, 40p, 6/10.

Europa 1987 A729

Modern architecture: 19p, Bilbao Bank, Madrid, designed by Saenz de Oiza, vert. 48p, Natl. Museum of Roman Art, Merida, designed by Rafael Moneo.

Lithographed and Engraved
1987, May 4   **Perf. 14x13½**
2518 A729 19p multicolored   .25 .20
2519 A729 48p multicolored   .55 .20

Horse Fair, Jerez de La Frontera A730

1987, May 6   Photo.   Perf. 13½x14
2520 A730 19p multicolored   .25 .20

Ramon Carande (1887-1986), Historian — A731

1987, May 29   Engr.
2521 A731 40p blk & dk vio brn   .45 .20

Postal Code Inauguration — A732

1987, June 1   Litho.   Perf. 14
2522 A732 19p multicolored   .25 .20

Eibar Weaponry School, 75th Anniv. A733

1987, July 2   Litho.   Perf. 14
2523 A733 20p multicolored   .25 .20

1992 Summer Olympics, Barcelona A734

1987, July 15   Photo.
2524 A734 32p Casa de Battlo
          masonry   .50 .20
2525 A734 65p Athletes   1.00 .20

25th Folk Festival of the Pyrenees, Jaca — A735

1987, July 22
2526 A735 50p multicolored   .55 .20

Monturiol and Submarine Designs A736

1987, Sept. 9   Engr.   Perf. 13½x14
2527 A736 20p black brown   .25 .20
Narcis Monturiol (d. 1887), builder of the submarine Ictineos.

Stamp Day — A737

Illuminated codex from *Constitutiones Jacobi II Regis Majoricum,* 14th cent., King Albert I Royal Library, Brussels.

Litho & Engr.
1987, Sept. 16   Perf. 13
2528 A737 20p multicolored   .25 .20
Postal service of Mallorca under James II.

ESPAMER '87 — A738

Designs: 8p, Handstamped letter that traveled from La Coruna to Havana, Cuba, 18th cent. 12p, La Coruna Harbor, 19th cent., engraving. 20p, Illustration of Havana harbor from *Viaje Alrededor da La Isla de Cuba,* by Francisco Mialche, 18th cent. 50p, West Indies packets.

1987, Oct. 2   Litho. & Engr.   Perf. 13
2529 A738 Sheet of 4   3.25 3.25
  a.   8p blk, brt blue & red   .30 .30
  b.   12p brt blue, red & blk   .45 .45
  c.   20p brt blue & red   .75 .75
  d.   50p blk, brt blue & red 1.75 1.75
No. 2529 printed se-tenant (rouletted between) with ESPAMER entrance ticket. Sold for 180p. Size: 150x83mm (including ticket).

Souvenir Sheet

EXFILNA '87, Gerona, Oct. 24-Nov. 1 — A739

Greek statue, Emporion, Olympic torch-bearer.

1987, Oct. 24   Photo.   Perf. 13x12½
2530 A739 20p multicolored   .25 .25

Discovery of America, 500th Anniv. (in 1992) — A740

Ships and: 14p, Amerigo Vespucci (1454-1512), Italian navigator. 20p, Ferdinand and Isabella. 32p, Friar Juan Perez, Queen's confessor. 40p, Juan de la Cosa (c. 1460-1510), master of the Santa Maria, cartographer who made first map of the New World. 50p, Christopher Columbus. 65p, Vicente Yanez Pinzon (c. 1460-1523), brothers, navigators and ship owners, accompanied Columbus on voyage.

Litho. & Engr.
1987, Oct. 30   Perf. 13
2531 A740 14p multicolored   .20 .20
2532 A740 20p multicolored   .25 .20
2533 A740 32p multicolored   .40 .20
2534 A740 40p multicolored   .45 .20
2535 A740 50p multicolored   .55 .20
2536 A740 65p multicolored   .75 .30
  a.   Bklt. pane of 6, #2531-2536   3.00
       Nos. 2531-2536 (6)   2.60 1.30

Christmas — A741

Self-portrait, Sculpture by Victorio Macho (1887-1966) A742

1987, Nov. 17   Photo.   Perf. 14x13½
2537 A741 20p Ornaments   .30 .20
2538 A741 50p Zambomba, tambourine   .60 .20

1987, Dec. 23   Engr.
2539 A742 50p brown black   .55 .20

EXPO '92 Type of 1987
1987, Dec. 29   Photo.   Perf. 13½x14
2540 A720 20p like No. 2506   .30 .20
2541 A720 50p like No. 2507   .55 .20

HRH Sofia and Juan Carlos, 50th Birth Annivs. — A743

1988, Jan. 5   Perf. 13x13½
2542 A743 20p Sofia   .30 .20
2543 A743 20p Juan Carlos   .30 .20
  a.   Pair, #2542-2543 + label   .60 .50

Clara Campoamor (b. 1888), Suffragette — A744

1988, Feb. 12   Photo.   Perf. 14
2544 A744 20p multicolored   .25 .20

1988 Winter Olympics, Calgary — A745

Passion Week in Valladolid and Malaga — A746

1988, Feb. 15   Perf. 14
2545 A745 45p Speed skater   .60 .20

1988, Mar. 30   Photo.   Perf. 14
Designs: 20p, Valladolid Cathedral and 17th cent. statue of Christ at the column by Gregorio Fernandez. 50p, Christ carrying the cross along Malaga procession route.
2546 A746 20p multicolored   .30 .20
2547 A746 50p multicolored   .60 .20

Tourism A747

1988, Apr. 7
2548 A747 18p Paella pan, ingredients   .25 .20
2549 A747 45p Covadonga Natl. Park   .50 .20

EXPO '92 Type of 1987
Era of Discoveries: 8p, Road to globe, rays of light, vert. 45p, Compass rose, globe.

1988, Apr. 12
2550 A720 8p multicolored   .20 .20
2551 A720 45p multicolored   .50 .20

Art Type of 1987
Glassware: a, Chalice, Valencia, 18th cent. b, Cadalso de los Vidrios, Madrid, 18th cent. c, Candy dish, La Granja de San Ildefonso, 18th cent. d, Castril double-handled jar, Andalucia, 18th cent. e, Jug, Catalina, 17th cent. f, Bottle, Baleares, 20th cent.

Litho. & Engr.
1988, Apr. 13   Perf. 12½x13
2552 Block of 6 + 6 labels   1.75 1.75
  a.-f. A726 20p any single   .25 .20

Stamp Day
1988 — A748

Francis of Taxis, postmaster by royal appointment (1505) in charge of establishing communications between Spain, France, Germany, Rome, Naples.

1988, Apr. 29 Engr. Perf. 12½x13
2553 A748 20p dk violet & dk brn .25 .20

General Workers' Union (UGT), Cent. A749

Emblem and Pablo Iglesias, union pioneer.

1988, May 1 Photo. Perf. 14
2554 A749 20p multicolored .25 .20

Europa 1988 — A750

Transport and communication: 20p, Locomotive made in Spain and operated in Cuba, 1837. 50p, Spanish telegraph in the Philippines linking Plaza de Manila and Bagumbayan Camp, 1818.

1988, May 5 Engr. Perf. 13
2555 A750 20p black & dk red .25 .20
2556 A750 50p black & dk grn .50 .20

Jean Monnet (1888-1979), Economist A751

1988, May 9 Perf. 14x13½
2557 A751 45p blue black .50 .20

Universal Exposition, Barcelona, Cent. A752

1988, May 31 Photo. Perf. 13½x14
2558 A752 50p multicolored .55 .20

Intl. Music and Dance Festival, Granada — A753

1988, June 1 Perf. 14x13½
2559 A753 50p multicolored .55 .20

World Expo '88, Brisbane, Australia A754

1988, June 14 Perf. 13½x14
2560 A754 50p Bull .55 .20

Coronation of the Virgin of Hope — A755

1988, June 18 Perf. 14x13½
2561 A755 20p multicolored .25 .20
Holy Week in Malaga.

Souvenir Sheet

EXFILNA '88, June 25-July 3, Madrid — A756

1988, June 25 Perf. 13x12½
2562 A756 20p Ciudadela Fortress floor plan .25 .25

Tourism A757

1988, July 11 Engr. Perf. 13½x14
2563 A757 18p Cantabrian Coast storehouse .30 .20
2564 A757 45p Dulzaina (wind instrument) .60 .20

28th World Roller Hockey Championships, La Coruna — A758

1988, Sept. 7 Photo. Perf. 13½x14
2565 A758 20p multicolored .25 .20

1st World Cong. of Spanish Regional Shelters — A759

1988, Sept. 9 Perf. 14
2566 A759 20p multicolored .25 .20

1988 Summer Olympics, Seoul — A760

1988, Sept. 10 Litho.
2567 A760 50p Yachting .55 .20

Catalonia Millennium — A761

1988, Sept. 21 Photo. Perf. 12½
2568 A761 20p multicolored .25 .20

1st Call to Session of the Leon Court, 800th Anniv. — A762

Illumination & seal of Alfonso IX, King of Leon.

1988, Sept. 26 Photo. Perf. 12½x13
2569 A762 20p multicolored .25 .20

Federation of Spanish Philatelic Societies, 25th Anniv. A763

1988, Sept. 27 Perf. 14x13½
2570 A763 20p multicolored .25 .20

1992 Summer Olympics, Barcelona A764

1988, Oct. 3 Photo. Perf. 14
2571 A764 8p multicolored .20 .20
See Nos. B139-B141.

A765

A766

Design: Castle in Valencia and royal seal of James I, 13th cent.

1988, Oct. 7 Perf. 14x13½
2572 A765 20p multicolored .25 .20
Reconquest of Valencia by King James I, 750th anniv.

1988, Oct. 10 Perf. 13x13½
2573 A766 20p multicolored .25 .20
Civil Law, cent.

Discovery of America (in 1992), 500th Anniv. — A767

Conquerors, explorers and symbols: No. 2574, Hernando Cortez, conqueror of Mexico, and serpent Quetzalcoatl. No. 2575, Vasco Nunez de Balboa, discoverer of the Pacific Ocean, and sun setting over sea. No. 2576, Francisco Pizarro, conqueror of Peru, and llama. No. 2577, Portuguese navigator Ferdinand Magellan, Juan de Elcano (c. 1476-1526) and globe symbolizing circumnavigation of the world. No. 2578, Alvar Nunez Cabeza de Vaca (c. 1490-1560), explorer, and sunrise. No. 2579, Andres de Urdaneta (1498-1568), and symbol of the west-to-east route between the Philippines and America that he discovered.

1988, Oct. 13 Engr. Perf. 13x13½
2574 A767 10p multicolored .20 .20
2575 A767 10p multicolored .20 .20
2576 A767 20p multicolored .25 .20
2577 A767 20p multicolored .25 .20
2578 A767 50p multicolored .55 .20
2579 A767 50p multicolored .55 .20
a. Bklt. pane of 6, #2574-2579 2.25
Nos. 2574-2579 (6) 2.00 1.20

Henry III of Castile, 1st Prince of Asturias — A768

1988, Oct. 26 Photo. Perf. 13
2580 A768 20p multicolored .25 .20

1st Bestowal of the title Prince of Asturias, 600th anniv., guaranteeing that the throne would continue to be inherited according to primogeniture.

Christmas — A769

1988, Nov. 24 Photo. *Perf. 14*
2581 A769 20p Snowflakes .25 .20
2582 A769 50p Shepherd, horiz. .55 .20

Sites and Cities Appearing on the
UNESCO World Heritage List — A770

1988, Dec. 1 Engr. *Perf. 12½x13*
2583 A770 18p Mosque de Cor-
doba, vert. .25 .20
2584 A770 20p Burgos Cathedral, vert. .30 .20
2585 A770 45p El Escorial
Monastery .55 .20
2586 A770 50p The Alhambra,
Granada .65 .20
Nos. 2583-2586 (4) 1.75 .80

Natl. Constitution, 10th Anniv. — A771

1988, Dec. 7 Photo. *Perf. 14*
2587 A771 20p multicolored .25 .20

Souvenir Sheet

Charles III (1759-1788) and the
Enlightenment — A772

1988, Dec. 14 Engr. *Perf. 13x12½*
2588 A772 45p black & dk grn .55 .55

Natl. Organization for the Blind, 50th
Anniv. — A773

1988, Dec. 27 Photo. *Perf. 14*
2589 A773 20p multicolored .25 .20

Fr. Luis de
Granada (1504-
1588)
A774

1988, Dec. 31
2590 A774 20p multicolored .25 .20

1992
Summer
Olympics,
Barcelona
A775

1989, Jan. 3
2591 A775 20p multicolored .25 .20

Stamp
Collecting — A776

1989, Jan. 3
2592 A776 20p multicolored .25 .20

French
Revolution,
Bicent. — A777

1989, Jan. 24 Photo. *Perf. 13*
2593 A777 45p multicolored .50 .20

Maria de
Maeztu (b.
1882),
Educator
A778

1989, Feb. 7 Photo. *Perf. 14x13½*
2594 A778 20p multicolored .25 .20

Postal
Service,
Cent.
A779

Litho. & Engr.
1989, Mar. 11 *Perf. 13½x14*
2595 A779 20p Uniform, 1889 .25 .20

Stamp
Day — A780

Design: Intl. postal treaty negotiated with
France and Italy by Franz von Taxis, 1601.

1989, Apr. 4 Engr. *Perf. 13*
2596 A780 20p black .25 .20

A781

1989, Apr. 22 *Perf. 14x13½*
2597 A781 20p black .25 .20
Casa del Cordon, Burgos.

A782

1989, May 5 Photo. *Perf. 13x13½*
Europa: Children's toys.
2598 A782 40p shown .40 .20
2599 A782 50p Top .50 .20

Spain's
Presidency
of the
European
Economic
Community
A783

1989, May 9 *Perf. 13½x14*
2600 A783 45p multicolored .50 .20

Souvenir Sheet

Holy Family with St. Anne, by El
Greco — A784

1989, May 20 Litho. *Perf. 14x13½*
2601 A784 20p multicolored .25 .25
EXFILNA '89. Exists imperf in different
colors.

Gabriela Mistral
(1889-1957),
Chilean Poet
Awarded 1945
Nobel Prize for
Literature — A785

Litho. & Engr.
1989, June 1 *Perf. 14x13½*
2602 A785 50p multicolored .60 .20

European Parliament 3rd
Elections — A786

1989, June 12 Photo. *Perf. 13x13½*
2603 A786 45p multicolored .50 .20

Lace
A787

Lace produced in: a, Catalonia. b, Andalusia. c, Extremadura. d, Canary Isls. e, Castile-
La Mancha. f, Galicia.

Litho. & Engr.
1989, June 20 *Perf. 13x12½*
2604 Block of 6 + 3 labels 1.40 1.40
a.-f. A787 20p any single .25 .20
Three center labels printed in a continuous
design and picture lace-making.

Pope John Paul II at the Intl. Catholic
Youth Forum, Santiago — A788

1989, Aug. 19 Engr. *Perf. 13x12½*
2605 A788 50p myrtle grn, dk red
brn & blk .55 .20

Athletics
World Cup,
Barcelona
A789

1989, Sept. 1 Photo. *Perf. 13½x14*
2606 A789 50p multicolored .55 .20

A790

Type A34 — A791

Litho. & Engr.
1989, Sept. 19   **Perf. 14x13½**
2607 A790 50p multicolored   .55 .20
Charlie Chaplin (1889-1977), English comedian and actor.

1989, Oct. 2   Photo.   Perf. 14x13½
2608 A791 50p gray, ver & blk   .55 .20
Cent. of the 1st Alfonso XIII issue.

A792

A793

Fr. Andres Manjon (d. 1923), teacher.

1989, Oct. 13
2609 A792 20p multicolored   .25 .20
Founding of the Ave Maria Schools by Fr. Manjon, cent.

1989, Nov. 7   Litho. & Engr.
UPAE emblem and "Irrigating Corn Field in November, 17th Cent.," an illustration from the *New Chronicle and Good Government,* by Guaman Poma de Ayala.
2610 A793 50p multicolored   .55 .20
America issue.

Christmas A794

Perf. 14x13½, 13½x14
1989, Nov. 29   Photo.
2611 A794 20p Star, "NAVIdAd 89," vert.   .25 .20
2612 A794 45p shown   .50 .20

Sites on the UNESCO World Heritage List — A795

Litho. & Engr.
1989, Dec. 5   Perf. 13x12½
2613 A795 20p Altamira Caverns   .25 .20
2614 A795 20p Santiago de Compostela   .25 .20

2615 A795 20p Roman aqueduct, Segovia   .25 .20
2616 A795 20p Guell Park and palace, Mila House   .25 .20
Nos. 2613-2616 (4)   1.00 .80

Souvenir Sheet

Sites on the World Heritage List — A796

Royal palaces: a, El Escorial. b, Aranjuez. c, Summer palace, La Granja, San Ildefonso. e, Madrid.

1989, Dec. 20   Engr.   Perf. 13x13½
2617   Sheet of 4   2.00 2.00
a.-d. A796 45p any single   .30 .30

Illustration by Daniel Garcia Perez, Winner of the 2nd Youth Stamp Design Contest — A797

1990, Jan. 29   Photo.   Perf. 14x13½
2618 A797 20p multicolored   .25 .20
1992 Summer Olympics, Barcelona.

A798

A799

1990, Feb. 2
2619 A798 20p multicolored   .25 .20
World Cycle Cross Championship, Getzu.

1990, Feb. 12   Engr.
2620 A799 20p dark purple   .25 .20
Victoria Kent (1897-1987), prisons directer, reformer.

Honorary Postman Rafael Alvarez Sereix and Cancel — A800

Litho. & Engr.
1990, Apr. 18   Perf. 13
2621 A800 20p sepia, buff & dull grn   .25 .20
Stamp Day.

Europa 1990 A801

Post offices.

Perf. 13½x14, 14x13½
1990, May 4   Photo.
2622 A801 20p Vitoria   .25 .20
2623 A801 50p Malaga, vert.   .50 .20

Intl. Telecommunications Union, 125th Anniv. — A802

1990, May 17   Perf. 13½x14
2624 A802 8p multicolored   .20 .20

Wrought Iron — A803

Designs: a, 15th Cent. door knocker. b, 16th cent. lyre-shaped door knocker. c, 17th Cent. pistol. d, 17th-18th Cent. door knocker. e, 19th Cent. lock. f, Fire iron.

Litho. & Engr.
1990, May 18   Perf. 12½
2625   Block of 6 + 3 labels   1.75 1.75
a.-f. A803 20p any single   .25 .20
Nos. 2625a-2625f printed se-tenant in a continuous design. Three labels continue the design and contain text or picture a forge.

Souvenir Sheet

Patio de La Infanta, Zaporta Palace, Zaragoza — A804

Illustration reduced.

1990, May 25   Engr.   Perf. 14x13½
2626 A804 20p red brown   .25 .25
EXFILNA '90.

Charity, by Lopez Alonso — A805

1990, June 19   Litho.   Perf. 13½x13
2627 A805 8p multicolored   .20 .20
Daughters of Charity in Spain, bicentennial.

Jose Padilla, Composer, Birth Centenary — A806

1990, June 19   Photo.   Perf. 13x12½
2628 A806 20p multicolored   .30 .20

Town of Estella, 900th Anniv. — A807

1990, June 19   Litho. & Engr.
2629 A807 45p multicolored   .60 .20

Novel, "Tirant lo Blanch," 500th Anniv. — A808

1990, June 19   Perf. 12½x13
2630 A808 50p multicolored   .65 .20

Souvenir Sheet

Crypt, Palencia Cathedral — A809

Illustration reduced.

1990, June 22   Engr.   Perf. 13½x14
2631 A809 20p red brown   .25 .25
Topical philatelic exposition.

A810

A811

1990, Aug. 27 Photo. Perf. 14x13½
2632 A810 50p multicolored   .55 .20
17th Intl. Congress of Historical Sciences.

Litho. & Engr.
1990, Nov. 14   Perf. 14
America Issue: UPAE emblem and Car-
ribean fauna.
2633 A811 50p multicolored   .55 .20

A812

A813

Christmas: Scenes from the film "Cosmic
Poem" by Jose Antonio Sistiaga.

1990, Nov. 22   Photo.
2634 A812 25p multicolored   .30 .20
2635 A812 45p multi, horiz.   .50 .20

Litho. & Engr.
1990, Nov. 28   Perf. 13
Tapestries in Monastery of San Lorenzo: a,
The Crucifixion by Jan van Roome and Bernard van Orley. b, Flamenco Soldiers by Philip
Wouvermans. c, Shipwreck of the Telemac by
Miguel Angel Houasse. d, Flowers by Francisco Goya.
2636   Sheet of 4   1.00 1.00
  a.-d. A813 20p any single   .25 .20

European Tourism
Year — A814

1990, Dec. 1   Photo.   Perf. 14
2637 A814 45p multicolored   .50 .20

World Heritage List — A815

Designs: No. 2638, Church of San Vicente,
Avila. No. 2639, Tower of San Pedro, Teruel,
vert. No. 2640, Church of San Miguel de Lillo,
Oviedo, vert. No. 2641, Tower of Bujaco,
Caceres.

Litho. & Engr.
1990, Dec. 10   Perf. 13
2638 A815 20p multicolored   .30 .20
2639 A815 20p multicolored   .30 .20
2640 A815 20p multicolored   .30 .20
2641 A815 20p multicolored   .30 .20
  Nos. 2638-2641 (4)   1.20 .80

Natl.
Orchestra
of Spain
A816

1990, Dec. 20 Photo. Perf. 13½x14
2642 A816 25p grn, yel grn & blk   .30 .20

Maria Moliner
(1900-1981),
Spanish
Linguist — A817

1991, Jan. 21 Photo. Perf. 14x13½
2643 A817 25p multicolored   .35 .20

Souvenir Sheet

Santa Fe, 500th Anniv. — A818

Illustration reduced.

Litho. & Engr.
1991, Apr. 19   Perf. 13½x14
2644 A818 25p brown & purple   .35 .35
World Philatelic Exhibition, Granada '92.

Child's
Drawing — A819

1991, Apr. 12 Photo. Perf. 14x13½
2645 A819 25p Olympic rings,
           sailboats   .35 .20

Juan de Tassis
y Peralta (1582-
1622), Postal
Reformer
A820

1991, Apr. 26   Engr.   Perf. 12½
2646 A820 25p black   .35 .20
Stamp Day.

Souvenir Sheet

Porcelain and Ceramics — A821

a, Apothecary jar, 17th cent. b, Figurine,
18th cent. c, Vase, 19th cent. d, Plate, 19th
cent.

1991, May 3 Litho. & Engr. Perf. 13
2647 A821 25p Sheet of 4, #a.-d. 1.50 1.50
  a.-d. Any single   .30 .25
          See No. 2692.

Europa
A822

1991, May 28 Litho. Perf. 13½x14
2648 A822 25p INTA-NASA
              ground station   .35 .20
2649 A822 45p Olympus I satel-
              lite   .55 .20

St. John of the Cross (1651-1695),
Mystic — A823

Anniversaries: No. 2651, Fr. Luis de Leon
(1527-1591), Augustinian writer, vert. No.
2652, Abd Al Rahman III (891-961), Moslem
caliph, vert. No. 2653, St. Ignatius of Loyola
(1451-1556), founder of Society of Jesus, vert.

Perf. 13½x14, 14x13½
1991, June 6   Litho.
2650 A823 15p multicolored   .20 .20
2651 A823 15p multicolored   .20 .20
2652 A823 25p multicolored   .35 .20
2653 A823 25p multicolored   .35 .20
  Nos. 2650-2653 (4)   1.10 .80

Antique
Furniture
A824

Designs: a, Wedge top armoire, 18th cent.
b, Hutch cabinet, c. 19th cent. c, Ladder-back
cane chair, c. 19th cent. d, Baby cradle, 19th
cent. e, Round-top trunk, c. 19th cent. f,
Ornate chest, c. 18th cent.

Litho. & Engr.
1991, Sept. 9   Perf. 12½x13
2654   Block of 6 + 3 labels   1.90 1.90
  a.-f. A824 25p any single   .30 .20

Orfeo Catala
(Catalan Choral
Society),
Cent. — A825

Intl. Fishing
Exposition,
Vigo — A826

1991, Sept. 6 Litho. Perf. 14x13½
2655 A825 25p multicolored   .35 .20

1991, Sept. 10
2656 A826 55p multicolored   .65 .20

America
Issue — A827

Christmas — A828

Litho. & Engr.
1991, Nov. 4   Perf. 14x13½
2657 A827 55p Nocturlabe   .65 .20

1991, Nov. 22 Photo. Perf. 14x13½
25p, The Nativity, illustration from 17th cent.
book. 45p, The Birth of Christ, 16th cent. icon.
2658 A828 25p multicolored   .35 .20
2659 A828 45p multicolored   .55 .20

Souvenir Sheet

The Meadowlands of St. Isidro by Goya — A829

Litho. & Engr.
1991, Dec. 12   **Perf. 13½x14**
2660 A829 25p multicolored   .35 .35
EXFILNA '91, Madrid.

Sites on UNESCO World Heritage List — A830

#2661, Giralda bell tower, Seville Cathedral. #2662, Alcantara Gate, Toledo, vert. #2663, Casa de las Conchas, Salamanca, vert. #2664, Garajonay Natl. Park, Gomera, Canary Islands.

		Perf. 12½x13, 13x12½	
1991, Dec. 16			**Engr.**
2661 A830 25p brown & blue		.40	.20
2662 A830 25p red brn & brn		.40	.20
2663 A830 25p red brn & blk		.40	.20
2664 A830 25p violet & dk grn		.40	.20
Nos. 2661-2664 (4)		1.60	.80

See Nos. 2756, 2830.

Carlos Ibanez de Ibero (1825-1891), Cartographer A831

Antarctic Treaty, Research Ship A52 — A832

1991, Dec. 27 Litho.   Perf. 14x13½
2665 A831 25p multicolored   .35 .20
2666 A832 55p multicolored   .65 .20

Margarita Xirgu (1889-1969), Actress — A833

1992, Jan. 20   Perf. 14
2667 A833 25p lake & gold   .35 .20

Child's Drawing A834

1992, Feb. 14   Perf. 13½x14
2668 A834 25p multicolored   .35 .20
EXPO 92.

Pedro Rodriguez Campomanes (1723-1802), Historian, Postal Administrator — A835

1992, Feb. 21   Perf. 13x12½
2669 A835 27p multicolored   .45 .20

Expo '92, Seville A836

1992, Feb. 28   Perf. 13½x14
2670 A836 27p gray, blk & brn   .40 .20

Columbus Types of 1930
Souvenir Sheet

1992, Apr. 24   Engr.   Perf. 14
2671 Sheet of 2   10.00 10.00
  a. A65 250p black   4.50 2.50
  b. A67 250p brown   4.50 2.50

Intl. Philatelic Exhibition, Granada '92.

Miniature Sheets

Expo '92, Seville A837

#2672: a, Expo '92 World Trade Center. b, Aerial tram. c, Avenue 4. d, Barqueta Gate. e, Nature pavilion. f, Biosphere. g, Alamillo Bridge. h, Press center. i, 15th Century pavilion. j, Expo harbor. k, Tourist train. l, One day entrance ticket.
#2673: a, Cartuja Monastery. b, Arena. c, Monorail train. d, Europe Avenue. e, Discovery pavilion. f, Auditorium. g, Avenue 1. h, Plaza of the Future. i, Gate to Italy's exhibit. j, Terminal. k, Expo theater. l, Expo Mascot, Curro.

1992, Apr. 21 Litho.   Perf. 13½x14
2672 A837 Sheet of 12 + 4 labels   5.00 5.00
  a.-l. 17p any single   .40 .25
2673 A837 Sheet of 12 + 4 labels   8.50 8.50
  a.-l. 27p any single   .60 .30
  See No. B195.

1992 Paralympics, Barcelona — A838

1992, Apr. 22   Photo.   Perf. 14
2674 A838 27p multicolored   .60 .20

Discovery of America, 500th Anniv. A839

Europa: 17p, Preparation Before Departing from Palos, by R. Espejo. 45p, Globe, ships, and buildings at La Rabida.

1992, May 5   Photo.   Perf. 14
2675 A839 17p multicolored   .75 .20
2676 A839 45p multicolored   1.50 .20

Souvenir Sheets

Voyages of Columbus — A840

#2677, Columbus in sight of land. #2678, Landing of Columbus. #2679, Columbus soliciting aid from Isabella. #2680, Columbus welcomed at Barcelona. #2681, Columbus presenting natives. #2682, Columbus.
Borders on Nos. 2677-2682 are lithographed. Nos. 2677-2682 are similar in design to US Nos. 230-231, 234-235, 237, 245.

Litho. & Engr.
1992, May 22   Perf. 14
2677 A840 60p blue   1.25 1.10
2678 A840 60p brown violet   1.25 1.10
2679 A840 60p chocolate   1.25 1.10
2680 A840 60p purple   1.25 1.10
2681 A840 60p black brown   1.25 1.10
2682 A840 60p black   1.25 1.10
  Nos. 2677-2682 (6)   7.50 6.60

See US Nos. 2624-2629, Italy Nos. 1883-1888 and Portugal Nos. 1918-1923.

1992 Winter & Summer Olympics, Albertville & Barcelona A841

1992, June 19   Photo.   Perf. 14
2683 A841 45p multicolored   .60 .20

A842

A843

1992, June 5   Photo.   Perf. 14x13½
2684 A842 27p blue & yellow   .40 .20
World Environment Day.

1992, Oct. 29   Litho.   Perf. 14x13½
2685 A843 17p multicolored   .25 .20
Juan Luis Vives (1492-1540), Philosopher.

Pamplona Choir, Cent. A844

1992, Oct. 29   Perf. 13½x14
2686 A844 27p multicolored   .35 .20

Unified Europe — A845

1992, Nov. 4 Photo. Perf. 14x13½
2687 A845 45p multicolored   .60 .20

Christmas A846

1992, Nov. 5   Perf. 13½x14
2688 A846 27p multicolored   .40 .20

1992 Special Olympics, Madrid A847

1992, Sept. 7 Photo. Perf. 13½x14
2689 A847 27p brown & blue   .35 .20

Souvenir Sheet

St. Paul's Church, Valladolid — A848

Litho. & Engr.
1992, Oct. 9   Perf. 14x13½
2690 A848 27p multicolored   .35 .35
Exfilna '92, Natl. Philatelic Exhibition, Valladolid.

Discovery of America, 500th Anniv. A849

1992, Oct. 15   Perf. 13½x140
2691 A849 60p dk brn, lt brn & bis   .75 .20

Natl. Heritage Type of 1991
Miniature Sheet

Codices: a, Veitia, 18th cent. b, Trujillo of Peru, 18th cent. c, The Chess Book, 13th cent. d, General History of New Spain, 16th cent.

Litho. & Engr.
1992, Dec. 10   Perf. 13
2692 A821 27p Sheet of 4, #a.-d. 1.75 1.40

Road Safety
A850

Environmental
Protection
A851

Health and
Sanitation — A852

1993   Photo.   Perf. 14x13½
2693 A850 17p green & red   .35 .20
2694 A851 28p green & blue   .40 .20
2695 A852 65p blue & green   .90 .20
      Nos. 2693-2695 (3)   1.65 .60

Issued: 17p, 4/20; 28p, 1/4; 65p, 2/12.

Maria Zambrano (1904-1991),
Writer — A854

1993, Jan. 18   Photo.   Perf. 14
2697 A854 45p buff, lil rose & brn   .65 .25

Andres Segovia
(1893-1987),
Guitarist — A855

1993, Feb. 19   Engr.   Perf. 14x13½
2698 A855 65p black & brown   .90 .25

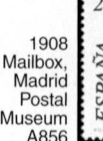
1908
Mailbox,
Madrid
Postal
Museum
A856

Litho. & Engr.
1993, Mar. 12   Perf. 13½x14
2699 A856 28p multicolored   .45 .20
Stamp Day.

Mushrooms — A857

1993, Mar. 18   Photo.   Perf. 14
2700 A857 17p Amanita caesa-
              rea   .35 .20
2701 A857 17p Lepiota procera   .35 .20
2702 A857 28p Lactarius
              sanguifluus   .40 .20
2703 A857 28p Russula cyanox-
              antha   .40 .20
      Nos. 2700-2703 (4)   1.50 .80
      See Nos. 2759-2762.

Souvenir Sheet

Holy Week Celebration — A858

1993, Apr. 2   Litho.   Perf. 14x13½
2704 A858 100p multicolored   1.40 1.40
Exfilna '93, Alcaniz. Margin of No. 2704 is
Litho. & Engr.

Fusees, by
Joan Miro
A859

Europa: 65p, La Bague d'Aurore, by Miro,
vert.

Perf. 13½x14, 14x13½
1993, May 5   Litho.
2705 A859 45p blue & black   .90 .20
Litho. & Engr.
2706 A859 65p multicolored   1.40 .20

Year of St.
James
A860

Designs: 17p, Transfer of St. James' body
by boat. 28p, Discovery of tomb of St. James.
45p, St. James on horseback.

1993, May 13   Photo.   Perf. 13½x14
2707 A860 17p multicolored   .35 .20
2708 A860 28p multicolored   .40 .20
2709 A860 45p multicolored   .60 .25
      Nos. 2707-2709 (3)   1.35 .65

World Telecommunications
Day — A861

1993, May 17
2710 A861 28p multicolored   .40 .20

Compostela '93 — A862

Stylized designs: 28p, Pilgrims paying homage to Saint James. 100p, Pilgrim under star
tree while on way to Santiago de Compostela,
vert.

1993, May 18   Photo.   Perf. 13½x14
2711 A862 28p multicolored   .45 .20
Souvenir Sheet
Perf. 14x13½
2712 A862 100p multicolored   3.00 1.75

World
Environment
Day — A863

1993, June 4   Litho.   Perf. 14x13½
2713 A863 28p multicolored   .40 .20

King Juan Carlos — A864a
   A864   2738

1993-98   Photo.   Perf. 14x13½
A864 Gold and:
2714 A864   1p prussian bl   .20 .20
2715 A864   2p green   .20 .20
2716 A864   10p magenta   .20 .20
2717 A864   15p green   .20 .20
2718 A864   16p brn lake   .20 .20
2719 A864   17p yel org   .25 .20
2720 A864   18p grn bl   .25 .20
2721 A864   19p brown   .25 .20
2722 A864   20p lil rose   .25 .20
2723 A864   21p dark grn   .25 .20
2724 A864   28p vio brn   .35 .20
2725 A864   29p olive   .40 .20
2726 A864   30p ultramarine   .40 .20
2727 A864   32p green   .45 .20
2728 A864   35p red   .40 .25
2729 A864   45p bluish grn   .55 .20
2730 A864   55p sepia   3.00 .50
  a. Block of 4, #2714, 2720,
       2725, 2730 + 2 labels   3.00 .50
2731 A864   60p org brn   1.00 .50
  a. Block of 4, #2716, 2721,
       2726, 2731 + 2 labels   2.50 1.25
2732 A864   65p red org   .70 .20
  a. Block of 4, #2719, 2724,
       2729, 2732 + 2 labels   2.50 2.00
2733 A864   70p vermilion   .90 .45
Engr.
2734 A864a 100p brown   2.50 .30
2735 A864a 200p green   6.25 .60
2736 A864a 300p maroon   11.00 .90
2737 A864a 500p blue   17.50 1.50
2738 A864a 1000p vio blk   35.00 4.00
      Nos. 2714-2738 (25)   82.60 12.20

Issued: 17p, 28p, 45p, 65p, 5/21/93; 1p,
18p, 29p, 1/31/94; 19p, 30p, 1994; 19p, 30p,
1/3/95; 10p, 60p, 6/5/95; 1000p, 11/24/95;
100p, 200p, 300p, 500p, 12/12/96; 21p, 32p,
1/27/97; 2p, 16p, 5/19/97; 15p, 3/6/98; 35p,
2/13/98; 70p, 1/30/98. 20p, 11/20/00.

Don Juan de
Borbon (1913-
1993), Count of
Barcelona — A865

1993, June 20   Photo.   Perf. 14x13½
2744 A865 28p multicolored   .35 .20

Igualada-Martorell Railway,
Cent. — A866

1993, July 4   Engr.   Perf. 13½x14
2745 A866 45p black & green   .60 .20

Natl. Mint
(F.N.M.T.),
Cent.
A867

1993, Sept. 13
2746 A867 65p dark blue   .90 .20

Explorers
A868

Designs: 45p, Alejandro Malaspina (1754-
1809), Italian explorer of South America. 65p,
Jose Celestino Mutis (1732-1808), Spanish
naturalist in the Americas, vert.

Perf. 13½x14, 14x13½
1993, Sept 20   Litho.
2747 A868 45p multicolored   .60 .20
2748 A868 65p multicolored   .90 .20

Ciconia
Nigra
A869

Endangered birds: No. 2750, Gypaetus
barbatus (Quebrantahuesos).

Litho. & Engr.
1993, Oct. 11   Perf. 13½x14
2749 A869 65p pink & black   .90 .20
2750 A869 65p orange & black   .90 .20

Child's
Painting — A870

1993, Oct. 2   Litho.   Perf. 14x13½
2751 A870 45p multicolored   .60 .20

European
Year of the
Elderly
A871

1993, Oct. 29   Photo.   Perf. 14
2752 A871 45p multicolored   .60 .20

A872

Christmas — A873

Perf. 13½x14, 14x13½
1993, Nov. 23   Photo.
2753 A872 17p multicolored   .25 .20
Litho., Photo. & Engr.
2754 A873 28p multicolored   .40 .20

Jorge Guillen (1893-1984), Poet — A874

1993, Nov. 29   Engr.   Perf. 14x13½
2755 A874 28p green   .40 .20

UNESCO World Heritage Type of 1991

Design: 50p, Monastery of Santa Maria of Poblet, Tarragona.

1993, Dec. 3   Engr.   Perf. 13x12½
2756 A830 50p multicolored   .65 .20

Spanish Film Industry A875

29p, Luis Bunuel (1900-83), director. 55p, Segundo de Chomon (1871-1929), film pioneer.

1994, Jan. 28   Photo.   Perf. 14
2757 A875 29p multicolored   .40 .20
2758 A875 55p multicolored   .75 .20

Mushroom Type of 1993

1994, Feb. 18   Photo.   Perf. 14
2759 A857 18p Boletus satanas   .20 .20
2760 A857 18p Boletus edulis   .20 .20
2761 A857 29p Amanita phalloides   .35 .20
2762 A857 29p Lactarius deliciosus   .35 .20
  Nos. 2759-2762 (4)   1.10 .80

Minerals A876

a, Cinnabar. b, Sphalerite. c, Pyrite. d, Galena.

1994, Feb. 25
2763 A876 29p Block of 4, #a.-d., + 2 labels   2.75 2.00

Barrister's Mailbox A877

Litho. & Engr.
1994, Mar. 9   Perf. 13½x14
2764 A877 29p light & dark brn   .40 .20
Stamp Day.

ILO, 75th Anniv. A878

1994, Apr. 7   Photo.   Perf. 13½x14
2765 A878 65p multicolored   .85 .20

Art of Salvador Dali (1904-89) A879

Paintings: #2766, Retrato de Gala. #2767, Poesia de America. #2768, El Gran Masturbador. #2769, Port Alguer. #2770, Self portrait. #2771, Cesta del Pan. #2772, El Enigma Sin Fin. #2173, Galatea de las Esferas.

1994, Apr. 22   Perf. 13½x14, 14x13½
2766 A879 18p multi   .25 .20
2767 A879 18p multi, vert.   .25 .20
2768 A879 29p multi   .40 .20
2769 A879 29p multi, vert.   .40 .20
2770 A879 55p multi, vert.   .80 .20
2771 A879 55p multi, vert.   .80 .20
2772 A879 65p multi   1.00 .20
2773 A879 65p multi, vert.   1.00 .20
  Nos. 2766-2773 (8)   4.90 1.60

Josep Pla (1897-1981), Writer — A880

1994, Apr. 23   Engr.   Perf. 13½x14
2774 A880 65p dark grn & lake   .85 .20

A881

A882

A883

Painting: Martyrdom of St. Andrew, by Rubens.

1994, Apr. 29   Photo.   Perf. 14
2775 A881 55p multicolored   .70 .20
Carlos de Amberes Foundation, 400th anniv.

1994, May 3   Photo.
2776 A882 18p multicolored   .25 .20
Litho., Photo. & Engr.
2777 A883 29p multicolored   .40 .20
Santa Cruz de Tenerife, 400th anniv. (#2776). Complutense University of Madrid, 700th Anniv. (#2777).

Europa A884

Designs: 55p, Severo Ochoa (1905-93), 1959 Nobel Laureate in Medicine. 65p, Miguel Angel Catalan (1894-1957), physicist.

1994, May 5   Litho. & Engr.
2778 A884 55p multicolored   .65 .20
2779 A884 65p multicolored   .80 .20

Spanish Literature A885

Novels by Camilo Jose Cela: 18p, The Family of Pascual Duarte. 29p, Journey to Alcarria.

1994, May 11   Photo.
2780 A885 18p multicolored   .25 .20
2781 A885 29p multicolored   .55 .20

King Sancho Ramirez, 900th Death Anniv. — A886

Treaty of Tordesillas, 500th Anniv. — A887

Design: 55p, Natl. Archives, Simancas.

Litho. & Engr.
1994, June 7   Perf. 14
2782 A886 18p multicolored   .20 .20
2783 A887 29p multicolored   .35 .20
2784 A887 55p multicolored   .70 .20
  Nos. 2782-2784 (3)   1.25 .60

Souvenir Sheet

Cathedral of St. Anne, Las Palmas, Grand Canary Island — A888

Illustration reduced.

1994, July 1   Perf. 13½x14
2785 A888 100p multicolored   2.00 1.50
Exfilna '94, Natl. Philatelic Exhibition, Grand Canary Island.

Yachts — A889

1994, July 15   Photo.   Perf. 14x13½
2786 A889 16p Giralda   .20 .20
2787 A889 29p Saltillo   .35 .20

Roman City of Augusta Emerita (Merida), Badajoz — A890

Litho. & Engr.
1994, Sept. 8   Perf. 13
2788 A890 55p lake, brn & buff   .80 .20
UNESCO World Heritage list.

Museum of Cards, Alava — A891

Antique cards: 18p, Horse of Spades. 29p, Jack of Diamonds. 55p, King of Hearts. 65p, War god, Mars, of Diamonds.

1994, Sept. 20   Photo.   Perf. 14x13½
2789 A891 18p multicolored   .20 .20
2790 A891 29p multicolored   .35 .20
2791 A891 55p multicolored   .70 .20
2792 A891 65p multicolored   .90 .20
  Nos. 2789-2792 (4)   2.15 .80

Postal Transportation — A892

1994, Oct. 11   Litho.   Perf. 13½
2793 A892 65p DC-8   .90 .20

Public Transit — A893

Civil Guard A894

1994, Oct. 17   Photo.   Perf. 14x13½
2794 A893 18p multicolored   .20 .20
    Perf. 13½x14
2795 A894 29p multicolored   .40 .20

Western European Union
A895

1994, Oct. 21   *Perf. 13½x14*
2796 A895 55p multicolored   .75   .20

Olympic Venues
A896

Designs: a, Track. b, Skiing. c, Equestrian. d, Wrestling. e, Archery. f, Cycling. g, Soccer. h, Field hockey. i, Swimming. j, Sailing.

1994, Oct. 27
2797   Block of 10 + 10 labels   6.00 5.00
a.-j. A896 29p any single   .50   .40
Labels inscribed with names of Spanish gold medalists and Intl. Olympic Committee cent.
See Nos. 2822, 2850.

Christmas — A897

1994, Nov. 18   *Perf. 14x13½*
2798 A897 29p multicolored   .40   .20

Spanish Motion Pictures
A898

Designs: 30p, Belle Epoque, by Fernando Trueba. 60p Volver A Empezar (Begin the Beguine), by Jose Luis Garci.

1995, Jan. 20   **Photo.**   *Perf. 14*
2799 A898 30p multicolored   .40   .20
2800 A898 60p multicolored   .85   .20

City of Logrono, 900th Anniv.
A899

1995, Jan. 25
2801 A899 30p multicolored   .40   .20

Souvenir Sheet

SIERRA NEVADA '95, Granada — A900

Illustration reduced.

1995, Jan. 30
2802 A900 130p White star flow-
            er   1.75 1.75
World Alpine Skiing Championships.

Mushrooms — A901

1995, Feb. 9   Photo.   *Perf. 13½x14*
2803 A901 19p Coprinus co-
            matus   .25   .20
2804 A901 30p Dermocybe cin-
            namomea   .40   .20

Minerals A902

Designs: a, Dolomite. b, Technical School for Mining Engineers, Madrid. c, Aragonite.

1995, Feb. 24
2805   Strip of 3   1.25 1.25
a.-c. A902 30p any single   .40   .20

Stamp Day A903

1995, Mar. 9   **Engr.**
2806 A903 30p Bronze lion's
            head   .40   .20

Alejandro Goicoechea Omar, TALGO Train — A904

Design: 60p, Young Omar, early train.

1995, Mar. 17   Photo.   *Perf. 14*
2807 A904 30p multicolored   .40   .20
2808 A904 60p multicolored   .85   .20

A905   A906

1995, Apr. 6
2809 A905 60p multicolored   .85   .20
Nature conservation in Europe.

Litho. & Engr.
1995, Apr. 7   *Perf. 14*
18th Century Sailing Ships: 19p, San Juan Nepomuceno. 30p, San Telmo.
2810 A906 19p multicolored   .30   .20
a.   Miniature sheet of 4   1.00 1.00
2811 A906 30p multicolored   .70   .20
a.   Miniature sheet of 4   1.60 1.60

Lebaniego Celebration Year — A907

60p, Mountains, St. Toribio Monastery.

1995, Apr. 21   Photo.   *Perf. 12½*
2812 A907 30p multicolored   .40   .20
2813 A907 60p multicolored   .85   .20

Spanish Literature A908

Designs: 19p, El Nino Yuntero, by Miguel Hernandez (1910-42). 30p, Juanita la Larga, by Juan Valera (1824-1905), vert.

Litho. & Engr.
1995, Apr. 27   *Perf. 14*
2814 A908 19p multicolored   .25   .20
Engr.
2815 A908 30p green & blue   .40   .20

Jose Marti (1853-95), Cuban Writer
A909

1995, Apr. 28   **Photo.**
2816 A909 60p multicolored   .85   .20

Spanish Cartoon Characters
A910

1995, May 4   Photo.   *Perf. 14*
2817 A910 30p Captain Trueno   .45   .20
2818 A910 60p Carpanta, vert.   .90   .20
See Nos. 2854-2855.

Europa A911

1995, May 5
2819 A911 60p multicolored   .90   .20

Motion Pictures, Cent.
A912

19p, Auguste and Louis Lumiere, early camera.

1995, May 12   Engr.   *Perf. 14*
2820 A912 19p brownish black   .25   .20

Press Assoc. of Madrid, Cent.
A913

1995, May 12   **Litho.**
2821 A913 30p multicolored   .45   .20

Olympic Venue Type of 1994

Designs: a, Track. b, Basketball. c, Boxing. d, Soccer. e, Gymnastics. f, Equestrian. g, Field hockey. h, Canoeing. i, Polo. j, Two-man rowing. k, Tennis. l, Shooting. m, Sailing. n, Water polo.

1995, June 2   Photo.   *Perf. 14*
2822   Block of 14 + 6 labels   6.25 6.25
a.-n. A896 30p any single   .45   .20
Labels are inscribed with names of Spanish silver medallists.

UN, 50th Anniv.
A914

FAO, 50th Anniv. — A915

World Tourism Organization, 20th Anniv. — A916

1995, June 26
2823 A914 60p multicolored   .90   .20
2824 A915 60p multicolored   .90   .20
2825 A916 60p multicolored   .90   .20
        Nos. 2823-2825 (3)   2.70   .60

A917

A918

1995, July 1
2826 A917 60p multicolored   .90   .20
Spanish Presidentcy of the European Community Council of Ministers.

1995, Sept. 4   Photo.   *Perf. 14*
2827 A918 60p multicolored   .90   .20
4th World Conference on Women, Beijing.

Souvenir Sheet

17th Intl. Conference of Cartography, Barcelona — A919

Illustration reduced.

1995, Sept. 5
2828 A919 130p multicolored   2.75 2.25

Santiago de Compostela University, 500th Anniv. — A920

1995, Sept. 15
2829 A920 30p multicolored   .45 .20

UNESCO World Heritage Type of 1991 and

A921

#2830, Royal Monastery of Santa Maria de Guadalupe, vert. #2831, Map of Santiago de Compostela's 9th cent. route through northern Spain.

1995, Sept. 29   Engr.   Perf. 12½
2830 A830 60p dark brown   1.00 .20
    Photo. & Engr.
2831 A921 60p multicolored   1.00 .20

Ecological Protection System, Lagunas Manchegas — A922

Ducks: 60p, Anade real, pato colorado.

1995, Oct. 11   Photo.   Perf. 14
2832 A922 60p multicolored   .90 .20
    America Issue.

Souvenir Sheet

EXFILNA '95, Nat. Philatelic Exhibition, Malaga — A923

Illustration reduced.

Litho. & Engr.
1995, Oct. 6   Perf. 14x13½
2833 A923 130p dark green   2.00 2.00

Archaeology — A924

#2834, Cave of Menga, Antequera, Malaga. #2835, Ruins of Torralba, Minorca.

1995, Oct. 20   Photo.
2834 A924 30p multicolored   .50 .20
2835 A924 30p multicolored   .50 .20

Souvenir Sheet

The Contemporary Poets, by Antonio Maria Esquivel (1806-57) — A925

Group of poets: a, Seated at left. b, One reading from paper. c, Four standing. d, Standing, seated at right.
Illustration reduced.

1995, Oct. 27
2836 A925 Sheet of 4   3.25 3.25
  a.   19p multicolored   .30 .25
  b.   30p multicolored   .55 .45
  c.-d.   60p any single   1.25 .90

Christmas A926

Design: 30p, Capital sculpture of "Adoration of the Magi," Collegiate Church of San Martin de Elines, Cantabria.

1995, Nov. 17   Photo.   Perf. 14
2837 A926 30p multicolored   .45 .20

Espamer '96, Aviation & Space Philatelic Exhibitions, Seville — A927

#2838, Sevilla-Plaza de Armas Railway Station. #2839, Lorenzo Galindez de Carvajal, Master Courier, King Fernando's Court, vert.

1995, Dec. 20   Photo.   Perf. 13
2838 A927 60p multicolored   .90 .20
2839 A927 60p multicolored   .90 .20

Spanish Motion Pictures, Cent. A928

Designs: 30p, Scene from first Spanish motion picture, "Salida de los Fieles del Pilar de Zaragoza." 60p, Poster for 1952 motion picture, "Bienvenido, Mister Marshall."

1996, Jan. 30   Photo.   Perf. 14
2840 A928 30p multicolored   .45 .20
2841 A928 60p multicolored   .90 .20

Spanish Mining — A929

Designs: 30p, Miner's lamp from Museum of Mining and Industry, mine shaft. 60p, Fluorite.

1996, Feb. 7
2842 A929 30p multicolored   .45 .20
2843 A929 60p multicolored   .90 .20

Madrid-Irun Visual Telegraph Line, 150th Anniv. — A930

1996, Mar. 8   Engr.   Perf. 14
2844 A930 60p lake & gray grn   .90 .20
    Stamp Day.

Barcelona, 10th Anniv. of Urban Transformation — A931

1996, Mar. 22
2845 A931 30p multicolored   .45 .20

Endangered Wildlife — A932

1996, Mar. 27   Photo.
2846 A932 30p Ursus arctos   .45 .20

18th Cent. Sailing Ship Type of 1995

Designs: 30p, King Phillip. 60p, Catalán.

Litho. & Engr.
1996, Apr. 19   Perf. 14x13½
2847 A906 30p multicolored   .50 .20
  a.   Miniature sheet of 4   2.50 2.50
2848 A906 60p multicolored   1.00 .20
  a.   Miniature sheet of 4   4.50 4.50

Nos. 2847-2848 printed in miniature sheets of 4.

Madrid Bar Assoc., 400th Anniv. A933

1996, Apr. 23   Photo.   Perf. 14
2849 A933 19p multicolored   .30 .20

Olympic Venue Type of 1994

Symbols of Olympic venues, bronze ribbon: a, like #2797a. b, like #2822c. c, like #2797b. d, like 2797h. e, like #2797i. f, like 2822h. g, like #2822k. h, like #2822 l. i, like #2797j.

1996, Apr. 26   Photo.   Perf. 14
2850   Block of 9 + la-
     bels   5.00 4.50
  a.-i.   A896 30p Any single   .50 .20

Labels are inscribed with names of Spanish bronze medalists.

Souvenir Sheets

A934

Royal Family — A935

Espamer '96 Philatelic Exhibition, World Aviation and Space Exposition: No. 2851a, Map of Seville-Larache Air Route, 1921. b, Zeppelin cover, Seville, 1930. c, Rocket launch. d, Hispano HA 200 SAETA aircraft.
Illustration reduced (A935).

1996, May 4
2851   Sheet of 4   7.00 6.50
  a.-d.   A934 100p any single   1.60 1.40
2852 A935 400p multicolored   7.00 6.50

Carmen Amaya, Flamenco Dancer — A936

1996, May 6   Perf. 14x13½
2853 A936 60p multicolored   .90 .20
    Europa.

Cartoon Characters Type of 1995

1996, May 10   Perf. 14x13½, 13½x14
2854 A910 19p El Jabato, vert.   .35 .20
2855 A910 30p El Reporter
     Tribulete   .65 .20

Paintings by Francisco de Goya Y Lucientes (1746-1828) — A937

19p, Gen. Don Antonio Ricardos, vert. 30p, Dairymaid of Bordeaux, vert. 60p, Boys with a Mastiff. 130p, The 3rd of May, 1808.

1996, May 31   Photo.   Perf. 14x13½
2856 A937 19p multicolored   .35 .20
2857 A937 30p multicolored   .60 .20
     Perf. 13½x14
2858 A937 60p multicolored   1.10 .20
2859 A937 130p multicolored   2.00 .40
    Nos. 2856-2859 (4)   4.05 1.00

Philatelic Service, 50th Anniv. A938

1996, June 4   Perf. 13½x14
2860 A938 30p multicolored   .65 .20

Popular Personalities — A939

Designs: 19p, José Monge Cruz, singer, vert. 30p, Lola Flores, movie star.

Perf. 14x13½, 13½x14
1996, June 14
2861 A939 19p multicolored   .25   .20
2862 A939 30p multicolored   .45   .20

Lanuza Central Market, Zaragoza A940

1996, July 5   Photo.   Perf. 13½x14
2863 A940 30p multicolored   .65   .20
19th Intl. Congress of Architects, Barcelona.

Gerardo Diego (1896-1987), Poet — A941

Joaquín Costa (1846-1911), Lawyer, Teacher — A942

1996, Sept. 13   Engr.
2864 A941 19p red, black & vio   .30   .20
Litho. & Engr.
2865 A942 30p multicolored   .60   .20

UNICEF, 50th Anniv. — A943

1996, Sept. 13   Photo.
2866 A943 60p blue, black & red   1.00   .20

Archaeological Finds — A944

Designs: No. 2867, Naveta Des Tudons, tomb, 2000-1500BC. No. 2868, Cabezo de Alcala, reamains of Roman temple, 54-49BC.

1996, Sept. 27   Photo.
2867 A944 30p multicolored   .50   .20
2868 A944 30p multicolored   .50   .20

Souvenir Sheet

Exfilna '96, Natl. Philatelic Exhibition, Vitoria-Gasteiz — A945

Painting of Vitoria-Gasteiz, capital of Alava Province, by Ignacio Diaz Ruiz de Olano (1860-1937). Illustration reduced.

1996, Oct. 11   Engr.   Perf. 14x13½
2869 A945 130p rose carmine   2.25 2.00
Sheet margin is litho.

America Issue — A946

Traditional costume of Charro Region, Salamanca.

1996, Oct. 15   Photo.   Perf. 14
2870 A946 60p multicolored   .85   .20

Sites on UNESCO World Heritage List — A947

Designs: 19p, Albaicin, old Muslim quarter, Granada, vert. 30p, Gateway to Tiberiades Square, statue of Maimonides. 60p, Deer, De Donana Natl. Park, Huelva province, vert.

Perf. 12½x13, 13x12½
1996, Oct. 25   Engr.
2871 A947 19p dark blue violet   .35   .20
2872 A947 30p deep claret   .55   .20
2873 A947 60p dark blue   1.10   .20
Nos. 2871-2873 (3)   2.00   .60

Spanish Literature A948

Designs: 30p, "La Regenta," by Leopoldo Garcia-Alas Ureña (1852-1901), vert. 60p, Don Juan Tenorio, by José Zorrilla Moral (1817-93).

Perf. 14x13½, 13½x14
1996, Nov. 13   Engr.
2874 A948 30p bl, dep mag & dp
          vio   .40   .20
2875 A948 60p dp blue & dp brn   .80   .20

Christmas — A949

Birth of Christ, by Fernando Gallego.

1996, Nov. 22   Photo.   Perf. 14
2876 A949 30p multicolored   .40   .20

Souvenir Sheet

Official Map of Spain and Its Provinces — A950

Illustration reduced.

1996, Dec. 5
2877 A950 130p multicolored   2.25 2.00

A951

A952

Endangered species.

1997, Jan. 30   Photo.   Perf. 14x13½
2878 A951 32p Genetta genetta   .45   .20
See Nos. 2928, 2978-2980.

1997, Feb. 28   Photo.   Perf. 14x13½
2879 A952 32p multicolored   .40   .20
Juvenia '97, Natl. Juvenile Philatelic Exhibition.

Stamp Day A953

1997, Mar. 7   Engr.   Perf. 14
2880 A953 65p Antique letter box   1.00   .20

Spanish Motion Pictures — A954

1997, Mar. 12   Photo.
2881 A954 21p "Trip to Nowhere"   .25   .20
2882 A954 32p "The South"   .40   .20

World Day of Water — A955

19th Cent. Sailing Ships — A956

1997, Mar. 22   Perf. 14x13½
2883 A955 65p multicolored   .80   .20

1997, Apr. 16   Litho. & Engr.
2884 A956 21p Frigate Asturias   .40   .20
  a.   Miniature sheet of 4   1.50 1.50
2885 A956 32p Spanish Brigan-
          tine   .60   .20
  a.   Miniature sheet of 4   3.00 3.00

Bilbao School of Engineering, Cent., — A957

194p, Atocha Station, High-Speed Spanish Train (AVE), 5th Anniv.

1997, Apr. 22   Photo.   Perf. 14x13½
2886 A957 32p multicolored   .75   .20
2887 A957 194p multicolored   3.00   .70

Dr. Josep Trueta (1897-1977), Orthopedic Surgeon — A958

1997, Apr. 30   Perf. 14
2888 A958 32p multicolored   .40   .20

Stories and Legends — A959

Europa: Princess, Prince, gnome, castle.

1997, May 5   Photo.   Perf. 14x13½
2889 A959 65p multicolored   1.25   .20

Fictional Characters A960

Designs: 21p, "El Lazarillo de Tormes," vert. 32p, "El Séneca," by José María Pemán.

1997, May 8   Engr.   Perf. 14
2890 A960 21p green & black   .30   .20
2891 A960 32p black & blue   .60   .20

Anxel Fole (1903-86), Poet, Writer A961

1997, May 17   Photo.
2892 A961 65p multicolored   1.00   .20

Comics A962

1997, May 30
2893 A962 21p The Ulysses Family   .30   .20
2894 A962 32p The Masked Warrior   .65   .20

Popular Personalities — A963

32p, Manuel Rodríguez Sánchez (Manolete) (1917-47), bullfighter. 65p, Charlie Rivel (Josep Andreu i Lasserre) (1896-1983), circus clown.

1997, June 5   Photo.   Perf. 14
2895 A963 32p multicolored   .50   .20
2896 A963 65p multicolored   1.25   .20

A964

A965

"The Age of Man" Cultural Exhibition: a, 21p, Painting, "The Annunciation," from Church of Nuestra Señora de la Peña, Agreda. b, 32p, Cathedral of El Burgo de Osma. c, 65p, Miniature from Codex titled "Commentary on the Apocalypse," by Beatus of Liebana, 786AD. d, 140p, Statue of Santo Domingo de Silos.

1997, June 13   Perf. 13
2897 A964   Sheet of 4, #a.-d.   4.50 4.00

1997, June 24   Perf. 14
2898 A965 65p multicolored   .80   .20

30th European Men's Basketball Championships.

NATO Summit, Madrid — A966

1997, July 8   Perf. 13
2899 A966 65p multicolored   1.25   .20

A967

A968

Design: Natl. monument to honor grape harvesting, Requena.

1997, July 11   Litho.   Perf. 14
2900 A967 32p multicolored   .40   .20

1997, July 24   Photo.
Anniversaries: 21p, Don Antonio Canovas del Castillo (1828-97), politician. 32p, Roman colony of Elche, 2000th anniv. 65p, Naval defense of Tenerife, bicent.
2901 A968 21p multicolored   .25   .20
2902 A968 32p multicolored   .40   .20
2903 A968 65p multicolored   .80   .25
   Nos. 2901-2903 (3)   1.45   .65

Peace in Basque Region — A969

Spanish Artists — A970

1997, July 30   Photo.   Perf. 14
2904 A969 32p multicolored   .35   .20

1997, Sept. 12
Designs: 32p, Mariano Benlliure Gil (1862-1947), sculptor. 65p, Photograph of Remero Vasco, by José Ortiz Echagüe (1886-1980).
2905 A970 32p multicolored   .50   .20
2906 A970 65p black & beige   1.00   .20

VIGO '97, World Exposition on Fisheries A971

1997, Sept. 17   Litho.
2907 A971 32p multicolored   .35   .20

Anniversaries — A972

21p, City of Melilla, 500th anniv., vert. 32p, Declaration of St. Pascual Baylon as patron saint of World Eucharistic Congress, cent., vert. 65p, Ausias March (1397-1459), writer.

1997, Sept. 24   Photo.
2908 A972 21p multicolored   .25   .20
2909 A972 32p multicolored   .50   .20
      Engr.
2910 A972 65p multicolored   1.00   .20
   Nos. 2908-2910 (3)   1.75   .60

Sites on UNESCO World Heritage List — A973

Churches in Oviedo: 21p, San Julian de los Prados. 32p, Santa Cristina de Lena.

1997, Sept. 26   Engr.   Perf. 13
2911 A973 21p multicolored   .50   .20
2912 A973 32p multicolored   .75   .20

29th Intl. Congress of Transport and Communications Museums, Madrid — A974

1997, Oct. 1   Litho.   Perf. 14x13½
2913 A974 140p multicolored   2.00   .65

Souvenir Sheet

Monument to Don Pelayo, Revillagigedo Palace, Gijón — A975

Illustration reduced.

1997, Oct. 4 Litho. & Engr.   Perf. 14
2914 A975 140p multicolored   2.50 2.00

Exfilna '97, Natl. Stamp Exhibition, Gijón, Asturias

Opening of Royal Theater, Madrid — A976

Designs: 21p, Miguel Fleta (1897-1938), opera singer. 32p, Outside view of theater.

1997, Oct. 11   Engr.   Perf. 14x13½
2915 A976 21p violet brown   .25   .20
2916 A976 32p gray brown   .40   .20

America Issue — A977

Foundation of St. Cristobal de La Laguna, 500th Anniv. — A978

1997, Oct. 10   Photo.
2917 A977 65p Postman   .80   .30

1997, Oct. 17   Litho. & Engr.
2918 A978 32p multicolored   .40   .20

6th World Conference on Down Syndrome, Madrid — A979

1997, Oct. 23   Photo.   Perf. 13½x14
2919 A979 65p blue & yellow   .80   .30

Veterinary College, Cordoba, 150th Anniv. A980

1997, Nov. 14   Engr.   Perf. 14
2920 A980 21p green & blue   .25   .20

Christmas — A981

Painting, Adoration of the Kings, by Pedro Berruguete.

1997, Nov. 20   Photo.
2921 A981 32p multicolored   .40   .20

Jewish Heritage in Spain
A982

Designs: 21p, Porta Nova, Ourense. No. 2923, Women's Gallery, Cordoba Synagogue. No. 2924, Jewish quarter, Caceres, 15th cent. 65p, Jewish Museum, Girona.

1997, Nov. 28 Engr. Perf. 13½x14
2922	A982	21p black & brown	.30	.20
2923	A982	32p black & violet	.50	.20
2924	A982	32p black & brown	.50	.20
2925	A982	65p black & violet	1.00	.30
a.		Strip of 4, #2922-2925	3.00	1.25

See Nos. 2969-2972.

Spanish Sports Accomplishments — A983

1997, Dec. 5 Photo.
2926	A983	32p multicolored	1.25	.20

XACOBEO 99 — A984

1998, Jan. 12 Photo. Perf. 14x13½
2927	A984	35p blk, org & gray	.60	.25

Endangered Fauna — A985

1998, Feb. 5
2928	A985	35p Lynx pardina	.90	.25

Bilbao Athletic Club, Cent. A986

1998, Feb. 10 Perf. 13½x14
2929	A986	35p multicolored	.45	.25

Comic Book Characters A987

Designs: 35p, Mortadelo and Filemón, by Ibáñez, vert. 70p, Zipi & Zape, by Escobar.

Perf. 14x13½, 13½x14
1998, Feb. 26 Photo.
2930	A987	35p multicolored	.50	.25
2931	A987	70p multicolored	1.10	.45

See Nos. 2998-2999.

Gredos State Hotel A988

1998, Mar. 12 Photo. Perf. 13½x14
2932	A988	35p multicolored	.45	.25

Self-Government Statutes for Melilla and Ceuta — A989

1998, Mar. 16 Perf. 13½x14, 14x13½
2933	A989	150p Melilla	1.90	1.00
2934	A989	150p Ceuta, vert.	1.90	1.00

"Generation of '98" Authors — A990

Design: Azorín (José Martinez Ruiz) (1873-1967), Pío Baroja (1872-1956), Miguel de Unamuno (1864-1936), Ramiro de Maetzu (1874-1936), Antonio Machado (1875-1939), Ramon Valle Inclán (1866-1936).

1998, Apr. 3 Photo. Perf. 14
2935	A990	70p multicolored	1.10	.45

A991

Design: Pedro Abarca de Bolea, Count of Aranda (1719-98), soldier, politician.

1998, Apr. 17
2936	A991	35p multicolored	.45	.25

1998, Apr. 29 Engr. Perf. 14x13½
Literary characters from: 35p, Fernando de Rojas' "Le Celestina." 70p, Benito Perez Galdos' "Fortunata and Jacinta."

2937	A992	35p multicolored	.55	.25
2938	A992	70p multicolored	1.10	.45

A992

Ships A993

1998, Apr. 30 Litho. Perf. 14
2939	A993	35p Embarcación real	.45	.25
2940	A993	70p Jabeque tajo	.90	.45

Popular Festivals — A994

1998, May 5 Photo.
2941	A994	70p Bonfire of St. John	.90	.45

Europa.

College of Medicine, Madrid, Cent. A995

Dr. D. Carlos Jiménez Díaz (1898-1967).

1998, May 18 Perf. 13½x14
2942	A995	35p multicolored	.45	.25

Popular Personalities — A996

35p, Félix Rodríguez de la Fuente (b. 1928), wildlife activist. 70p, Alfonso Aragón Bermúdez ("Fofó") (1923-76), circus comic, vert.

1998, May 28 Perf. 13½x14, 14x13½
2943	A996	35p multicolored	.55	.25
2944	A996	70p multicolored	1.10	.45

A997

Design: King Philip II (1527-98).

1998, June 1 Photo. Perf. 14x13½
2945	A997	35p multicolored	.45	.25

1998, June 2 Litho. & Engr.
Fedrico Garcia Lorca (1898-1936), poet, dramatist.

2946	A998	35p multicolored	.85	.25

A998

Spanish Stamp Engravers A999

35p, Antonio Manso (1934-93), Spain #2129. 70p, J.L.L. Sánchez Toda (1901-), Spain #546.

1998, June 5 Perf. 14
2947	A999	35p multicolored	.45	.25
2948	A999	70p multicolored	.90	.45

Philippine Independence, Cent. — A1000

Design: Spanish flag, Basilica of Cebu, Holy Child of Cebu, Philippine flag.

1998, June 12 Photo. Perf. 13½x14
2949	A1000	70p multicolored	.95	.50

See Philippines No. 2539.

Sculpture, "Foster Brothers," by Aniceto Marinas (1866-1953) A1000a

1998, July 10 Photo. Perf. 14
2949A	A1000a	35p multi	.50	.25

Expo '98, Lisbon A1001

1998, Sept. 4
2950	A1001	70p multicolored	1.00	.50

Letter Writing — A1002

Scenes from "Don Quixote" — #2951: a, "En un lugas de la Mancha." b, "Llenósele la fantasía." c, "Armado caballero." d, "La del alba sería." e, "Le molió como cibera." f, "El donoso escrutinio." g, "Has de saber, amigo Sancho." h, "Los gigantes." i, "Viole bajar y subir con tanta gracia." j, "El escuadrón de ovejas." k, "Los galeotes." l, "Los cueros."
No. 2952: a, "El encantamiento." b, "Oh princesa del toboso." c, "El caballero de los espejos." d, "El leon." e, "La cueva de montesinos." f, "Clavileño." g, "Sancho gobernador." h, "Doña Rodríguez." i, "Compañero mío." j, "Parecioles espaciosísimo." k, "El caballero de la blanca luna." l, "La vuelta a casa."

1998, Sept. 25 Perf. 13
2951		Sheet of 12	4.50	4.50
a.-l.		A1002 20p any single	.30	.20
2952		Sheet of 12	4.50	4.50
a.-l.		A1002 20p any single	.30	.20

See #3016, 3053-3954, 3121, 3175.

20th Intl. Conference on Data Protection, Santiago de Compostela — A1003

1998, Sept. 16 Litho. Perf. 14
2953	A1003	70p multicolored	.90	.45

Souvenir Sheet

EXFILNA '98 Natl. Philatelic
Exhibition — A1004

Litho. & Engr.

1998, Sept. 18   *Perf. 14*
2954 A1004 150p Cathedral of
Barcelona   2.75 2.25

UNESCO World Heritage
Sites — A1005

Designs: 35p, Walled city of Cuenca. 70p,
Silk Exchange, Valencia.

1998, Sept. 19   Engr.   Perf. 13
2955 A1005 35p blue & brown   .60   .25
2956 A1005 70p red & brown   1.40   .45

Angel
Ganivet
(1865-98),
Writer
A1006

1998, Oct. 6   Engr.   Perf. 14
2957 A1006 35p brown & purple   .50   .25

A1007

A1008

1998, Oct. 6
2958 A1007 70p multicolored   1.00   .50
The Giralda of Seville, 800th Anniv.

1998, Oct. 8   Engr.   Perf. 14
2959 A1008 35p brn & yel grn   .50   .25
Aga Khan Architecture Award, Alhambra of
Granada.

Stamp Day
A1009

1998, Oct. 9   Photo.
2960 A1009 70p multicolored   1.00   .50

María Guerrero (1867-1928), Theater
Actress — A1010

1998, Oct. 13
2961 A1010 70p multicolored   1.00   .50
America Issue.

Spanish
Railroads,
150th
Anniv.
A1011

1998, Oct. 28   Engr.
2962 A1011 35p multicolored   .50   .25

Juan
Carlos I
Antarctic
Base
A1012

1998, Nov. 6   Photo.
2963 A1012 35p multicolored   .50   .25

A1013

Christmas (Works of art): 35p, Chestnut
Seller, by Rafael Seco. 70p, Marriage of the
Virgin and St. Joseph, Cathedral of Oviedo.

1998, Nov. 13
2964 A1013 35p multicolored   .50   .25
2965 A1013 70p multicolored   1.00   .50

Souvenir Sheet

A1014

1998, Nov. 11   Photo.   Perf. 14
The Cathedral of San Salvador, Zaragoza
(Details from Altarpiece: a, Holding cross,
angel. b, Holy family.
2966 A1014 35p Sheet of 2, a.-b. 1.50 1.25

Founding
of New
Mexico,
400th
Anniv.
A1015

Designs: 35p, Expedition of Juan de Oñate.
70p, Early map of Nueva Espana (Mexico) and
Nuevo Mexico.

1998, Nov. 20
2967 A1015 35p multicolored   .50   .25
2968 A1015 70p multicolored   1.00   .50

Jewish Heritage in Spain Type of 1997

Designs: No. 2969, Bust of Benjamin de
Tudela, Tudela Commune, Navarre. No. 2970,
Residence, Hervás Community, Cáceres. No.
2971, Courtyard, Corpus Christi Church,
Segovia. No. 2972, Santa Maria la Blanca
Synagogue, Toledo.

1998, Nov. 23   Engr.
2969 A982 35p dp blue & dp ol   .60   .25
2970 A982 35p dp blue & dp cl   .60   .25
2971 A982 70p dp blue & dp cl   1.10   .50
2972 A982 70p dp blue & dp ol   1.10   .50
  a.   Strip of 4, #2969-2972   4.00 4.00

Nos. 2969, 2971 have Star of David. Nos.
2970, 2972 have menorah.

UNESCO
Biosphere
Reserve,
Minorca
A1016

1998, Dec. 2   Photo.
2973 A1016 35p multicolored   .50   .25

Spanish
Olympic
Academy,
30th Anniv.
A1017

1998, Dec. 9
2974 A1017 70p Bust of Plato,
amphora   1.00   .50

Universal Declaration of Human
Rights, 50th Anniv.
A1018   A1019
Designs: 35p, Angel Sanz Briz (1910-80),
Spanish ambassador. 70p, Fingerprints.

1998, Dec. 10
2975 A1018 35p multicolored   .50   .25
2976 A1019 70p multicolored   1.00   .50

Carthusian Horses — A1020

Designs: a, 100p, Mare standing with colt. b,
185p, Two with heads together. c, 35p, Adult
standing in grass. d, 150p, Adult standing in
flowers. e, 20p, Colt lying down, mare eating
grass. f, 70p, Head of adult, silhouette.

1998, Dec. 29
2977 A1020 Block of 6, #a.-f. 25.00 25.00
España 2000, Intl. Philatelic Exhibition.
Issued in sheets of two blocks, the lower
one in a different order. Two of the devices
shown on the coat of arms appear on each
block at the intersection of the perfs. On the
top block the crown is on a.-b., d.-e., while the
"H" is on b.-c., e.-f. On the bottom block the
location of these devices is reversed, giving all
the stamps in the sheet a slightly different
design.
See #3019, 3052.

Endangered Fauna Type of 1997

Gallotia
simonyi
machadoi
A1020a

Pandion haliaetus

Puffinus
puffinus

1999, Jan. 28   Photo.   Perf. 14
2978 A1020a 35p multicolored   .50   .25
2979 A1020b 70p multicolored   1.00   .50
2980 A1020c 100p multicolored   1.40   .70
  Nos. 2978-2980 (3)   2.90 1.45

Xacobeo
'99
A1021

Designs: 35p, Stone cross of Paradela, vert.
70p, Sculpture of St. James, door on Church
of St. James, Sangüesa. 100p, Stone cross,
Cizur Bridge, Pamplona, vert. 185p, Jurisdic-
tional stone pillar, Boadilla del Camino, vert.

Litho. & Engr.

1999, Feb. 22   Perf. 13¾
2981 A1021 35p multicolored   .60   .25
2982 A1021 70p multicolored   1.25   .45
2983 A1021 100p multicolored   1.50   .65
2984 A1021 185p multicolored   2.75 1.10
  Nos. 2981-2984 (4)   6.10 2.45

Barcelona Soccer
Club,
Cent. — A1022

1999, Mar. 11   Photo.   Perf. 14
2985 A1022 35p multicolored   .45   .25

Juvenia '99, Natl. Junior Philatelic Exhibition A1023

1999, Mar. 12   Litho.   Perf. 14
2986 A1023 35p multicolored   .50 .25

Spanish Police Force, 175th Anniv. A1024

1999, Mar. 26
2987 A1024 35p multicolored   .50 .25

Souvenir Sheet

Palace of Alfonso I el Batallador, Zaragoza — A1025

Illustration reduced.

Litho. & Engr.
1999, Apr. 9   Perf. 14x13½
2988 A1025 185p multicolored   3.00 2.75
Exfilna '99, Zaragoza.

Spanish Amateur Radio Union, 50th Anniv. A1026

1999, Apr. 16   Photo.   Perf. 14
2989 A1026 70p multicolored   .95 .50

7th World Track & Field Championships, Seville — A1027

1999, Apr. 30   Photo.   Perf. 14x13½
2990 A1027 70p multicolored   .90 .45

Monfragüe Nature Park A1028

Litho. & Engr.
1999, May 5   Perf. 13½x14
2991 A1028 70p multicolored   .90 .45
Europa.

Barcelona Subway System, 75th Anniv. A1029

1999, May 7   Photo.   Perf. 14
2992 A1029 70p multicolored   .90 .45

Spanish Art — A1030

Designs: 35p, Portrait of King Solomon. 70p, Artifact from cathedral, Palencia.

1999, May 14
2993 A1030 35p multicolored   .50 .25
2994 A1030 70p multicolored   1.00 .45

Introduction of the Euro — A1031

Design: a, European Union flag.
Maps: b, Germany. c, Austria. d, Belgium e, Spain. f, Finland. g, France. h, Netherlands. i, Ireland. j, Italy. k, Luxembourg. l, Portugal.

1999, May 28   Perf. 13½x14
2995 A1031 166p Sheet of 12,
              #a.-l.   35.00 30.00

Denomination is shown in both pesetas and euros. Each stamp shows the equivilent of 1 euro in the currency of the represented country.

Royal Recreation Club of Huelva A1032

1999, June 7
2996 A1032 35p multicolored   .45 .25

Souvenir Sheet

Palma '99, Natl. Topical Philatelic Exhibition — A1033

Illustration reduced.

1999, June 18   Perf. 14x13½
2997 A1033 185p multicolored   3.00 3.00

Comic Book Character Type
35p, Dona Urraca, by Jorge, vert. 70p, El Coyote, by José Mallorquí Figuerola, vert.

1999, June 11   Photo.   Perf. 13¾
2998 A987 35p multicolored   .50 .25
2999 A987 70p multicolored   1.00 .45

Defense of Las Palmas de Gran Canaria, 400th Anniv. A1034

1999, June 25   Litho. & Engr.
3000 A1034 70p multicolored   .90 .45

A1035

A1036

1999, July 2   Photo.   Perf. 13¾
3001 A1035 35p multicolored   .45 .25
San Pedro de Villanueva Benedictine Monastery.

1999, July 12
3002 A1036 35p multicolored   .45 .25
Village of Balmaseda, 800th anniv.

Carlos Buigas (b. 1898), Graphic Designer A1037

1999, July 12
3003 A1037 70p multicolored   .90 .45

General Society of Authors and Editors, Cent. — A1038

1999, July 12
3004 A1038 70p multicolored   .90 .45

Spanish Mining Institute, 150th Anniv. A1039

1999, July 12
3005 A1039 150p multicolored   1.90 .95

El Cid (Rodrigo Diaz de Vivar) (1040-99) A1040

1999, July 16   Photo.   Perf. 13¾
3006 A1040 35p multicolored   .45 .25

Paintings by Jose Vela Zanetti (1913-99) A1041

70p, "Winter." 150p, "The Harvest."

1999, Sept. 10   Photo.   Perf. 13¾
3007 A1041 70p multi   1.25 .45
3008 A1041 150p multi, vert.   2.25 .95

Diego Velazquez (1599-1660), Painter — A1042

Paintings: 35p, Sebastián de Morra. 70p, Sibyl.

1999, Sept. 24
3009 A1042 35p multicolored   .45 .25
3010 A1042 70p multicolored   .90 .45

Intl. Year of Older Persons A1043

1999, Sept. 30
3011 A1043 35p multicolored   .45 .25

Oix Castle, Lower Pyrenees A1044

1999, Oct. 1   Engr.   Perf. 13½x14
3012 A1044 70p blue & vio brn   .90 .45

World Heritage Sites — A1045

Designs: 35p, San Millán de Yuso Monastery. 70p, San Millán de Suso Monastery.

1999, Oct. 8   Perf. 13x12½
3013 A1045 35p multicolored   .75 .25
3014 A1045 70p multicolored   1.50 .45

UPU, 125th Anniv. A1046

1999, Oct. 9   Photo.   Perf. 13¾
3015 A1046 70p multicolored   .90 .45

Letter Writing Type of 1998

Designs: a, "Cumplimos 150 años." b, "Recorremos el mundo." c, "Llegamos juntos." d, "Escríbeme." e, "Ama la lectura." f, "Vive la naturaleza." g, "Te mostramos el patrimonio." h, "Te acercamos a la pintura." i, "Jugamos contigo." j, "Sentimos la musica." k, "Y además nos coleccionan." l, "Os esperamos."

1999, Oct. 13   Photo.   Perf. 13x12½
3016   Sheet of 12   4.50 4.50
a.-l. A1002 20p any single   .30 .20

America Issue, A new Millennium Without Arms — A1047

1999, Oct. 15   Perf. 13¾
3017 A1047 70p multicolored   .90 .45

Intl. Congress of Money Museums, Madrid — A1048

1999, Oct. 18   Engr.   Perf. 13x12½
3018 A1048 70p blue & brown   .90 .45

Carthusian Horse Type of 1998

Designs: a, 185p, White horse, six men. b, 70p, Espana Intl. Philatelic Exhibition emblem. c, 100p, Two white horses. d, 150p, Two white horses, one with leg raised. e, 35p, Emblem, exhibition dates. f, 20p, Horse, handler.

1999, Nov. 3   Photo.   Perf. 13¾
3019 A1020 Block of 6, #a.-f.   14.00 14.00
See footnote following No. 2977.

Christmas A1049

35p, Adoration of the Magi, Toledo Cathedral retable. 70p, Child, statue, candles.

1999, Nov. 5
3020 A1049 35p multi, vert.   .60 .25
3021 A1049 70p multi   1.25 .45

Spanish Postage Stamps, 150th Anniv. A1050

a, King Juan Carlos, altered 12c design A2. b, King, altered 6c design A1. c, King, altered 5r design A2. d, King, altered 6r design A2. e, 150th anniv. emblem, altered 6c design A1. f, King, altered 10r design A2. g, King, coat of arms.

Litho. & Engr.
2000, Jan. 3   Perf. 13¾x14
3022   Sheet of 12   7.00 6.50
a.-g. A1050 35p any single   .60 .25
#3022 contains 2 ea #3022a-3022d, 3022f, 1 ea #3022e, 3022g.

Endangered Butterflies — A1051

Designs: 35p, Parnassius apollo. 70p, Agriades zullichi.

2000, Jan. 31   Photo.   Perf. 13¾
3023 A1051 35p multi   .60 .25
3024 A1051 70p multi   1.25 .45

First Printing at Montserrat Monastery, 500th Anniv. — A1052

2000, Feb. 4   Photo.   Perf. 13¾
3025 A1052 35p multi   .45 .25

Holy Roman Emperor Charles V (1500-58) A1053

2000, Feb. 24   Perf. 12¾x13
3026 A1053 35p shown   .60 .25
3027 A1053 70p At age 40   1.25 .45

Souvenir Sheet
Perf. 13¼x12¾
3028 A1053 150p In armor   2.75 1.75
No. 3028 contains one 40x49mm stamp. See Belgium Nos. 1791-1793.

"Age of Man" Exhibition, Astorga — A1054

Designs: 70p, Carving of the Virgin Mary. 100p, Cross, Arab perfume bottle.

2000, Mar. 24   Photo.   Perf. 14x13¾
3029 A1054 70p multi   .75 .40
3030 A1054 100p multi   1.10 .55

Ferdinand of Aragon Inn, Sos A1055

2000, Apr. 7   Perf. 13¾x14
3031 A1055 35p multi   .60 .20

University Anniversaries — A1056

35p, Lleida, 700th anniv. 70p, Valencia, 500th anniv. (in 1999).

2000, Apr. 12   Engr.   Perf. 13¾x14
3032 A1056 35p red lil & brown   .50 .20
3033 A1056 70p blue & choc   1.00 .40

A1057

A1058

2000, Apr. 28   Photo.   Perf. 14x13¾
3034 A1057 35p multi   .60 .20
Royal Barcelona Sports Club, soccer team, cent.

2000, May 4
3035 A1058 35p multi   .60 .20
María de las Mercedes de Borbón y Orleáns (1910-2000), mother of King Juan Carlos.

Europa Issue
Common Design Type
2000, May 9
3036 CD17 70p multi   .75 .40

Royal Academy of Medicine, Seville, 300th Anniv. A1060

Julio Rey Pastor (1888-1962), Mathematician — A1061

Pharmacy College of Granada, 150th Anniv. — A1062

Valencia, City of Arts and Sciences A1063

2000, May 25   Perf. 13¾x14, 14x13¾
3037 A1060 35p multi   .60 .20
3038 A1061 70p multi   1.00 .40
3039 A1062 100p multi   1.50 .55
3040 A1063 185p multi   3.00 1.00
    Nos. 3037-3040 (4)   6.10 2.15
Intl. Mathematics Year (No. 3038).

Comic Strips A1064

Designs: 35p, Las Hermanas Gilda, by Manuel Vázquez. 70p, Roberto Alcázar y Pedrín, by Eduardo Vañó, vert.

2000, May 26   Perf. 13¾x14, 14x13¾
3041 A1064 35p multi   .60 .20
3042 A1064 70p multi   1.25 .40

Guggenheim Museum, Bilbao — A1065

2000, June 2   Photo.   Perf. 13¾x14
3043 A1065 70p multi   1.00 .40
Bilbao, 700th anniv.

Angel From Prayer in the Garden, Sculpture by Francisco Salzillo (1707-73) A1066

2000, June 9   Photo.   Perf. 14x13¼
3044 A1066 70p multi   1.10 .40

Souvenir Sheet

Fountains of San Francisco, Aviles — A1067

Illustration reduced.

Litho. & Engr.
2000, June 16   Perf. 14x13¾
3045 A1067 185p multi   3.50 2.50
Exfilna 2000 Philatelic Exhibition, Aviles.

Trees
A1068

Designs: 70p, Pinus sylvestris. 150p, Quercus ilex (encina).

Perf. 12¾x12½
2000, June 19 **Photo.**
3046-3047 A1068 Set of 2 3.50 1.10

Local Festivals
A1069

Designs: 35p, Fire Walking Festival, San Pedro Manrique. 70p, Chivalry Festival of San Juan, Ciudadela.

2000, June 23 **Perf. 13¾x14**
3048-3049 A1069 Set of 2 1.60 .55

Josemaria Escrivá de Balaguer (1902-75), Founder of Opus Dei. A1070

Litho. & Engr.
2000, June 26 **Perf. 13¾x14**
3050 A1070 70p black & orange 1.10 .40

Souvenir Sheet

World Map of Juan de la Cosa, 500th Anniv. — A1071

2000, July 14 Photo. Perf. 13¾x14
3051 A1071 150p multi 2.50 1.50

Carthusian Horses Type of 1998

No. 3052: a, 20p, Head of horse, five horses. b, 35p, White horse, sun partially obscured by clouds. c, 70p, Horse's head, two horses galloping. d, 100p, Heads of two horses. e, 150p, Horse's head, horse in lilac. f, 185p, Horse with bridle.

2000, July 28
3052 A1020 Block of 6, #a-f 13.00 13.00
See note following No. 2977.

Letter Writing Type of 1998

No. 3053: a, Atapuerca Man, 800,000 B.C. b, Cave paintings of Altamira, 12,000 B.C. c, Phoenecians, 1100 B.C. d, Tartessians, 800 B.C. e, Iberians and Celts, 500 B.C. f, Lady of Elche, Iberian statue, 480 B.C. g, Carthaginians, 237 B.C. h, Roman Spain, 197 B.C. i, Viriathus, Lusitanian war leader against Romans, 147 B.C. j, Siege of Numantia, 133 B.C. k, Segovia aqueduct, A.D. 50. l, Vandals, Suebis, and Alanis, 409.
No. 3054: a, Visigoths, 415. b, Conversion of Recared to Catholicism, 589. c, Arabs, 711. d, Victory over Arabs by Asturian King, Pelayo, 722. e, Discovery of alleged tomb of St. James, 813. f, Collapse of the caliphate, 1031. g, Death of El Cid, 1099. h, Alfonso VIII's victory at Las Navas de Tolosa, 1212. i, Alfonso X (the Wise) becomes King, 1252. j, Trastámara Dynasty, 1369. k, Spanish Inquisition, 1478. l, Union of Aragon and Castile, 1479.

2000, Sept. 22 **Perf. 13x12¾**
3053 Sheet of 12 2.50 2.50
a.-l. A1002 20p Any single .20 .20
3054 Sheet of 12 2.50 2.50
a.-l. A1002 20p Any single .20 .20

World Heritage Sites — A1072

Designs: 35p, Las Médulas. 70p, Pyrénées — Mt. Perdido, vert. 150p, Catalan Music Palace, Barcelona.

Perf. 13x12¾(35p), 12¾
2000, Sept. 21 **Litho. (35p), Engr.**
3055-3057 A1072 Set of 3 2.75 1.40

Souvenir Sheets

España 2000 Intl. Philatelic Exhibition — A1073

Designs: No. 3058, Hand of Julio Iglesias, singer. No. 3059, Signature of Alejandro Sanz, singer. No. 3060, Signature of Antonio Banderas, movie star. No. 3061, Mannequin, signature of Jesús del Pozo, fashion designer. No. 3062, Signature of Miguel Induráin, cyclist. No. 3063, Soccer ball, signature of Raúl González, soccer player. No. 3064, Hands of Joaquín Cortés, dancer. No. 3065, Feet of Sara Baras, dancer. No. 3066, Emblem of TVE 1 television network. No. 3067, Radio and antenna. No. 3068, Newspaper mastheads.
Illustration reduced.

Perf. 13 (round stamps), 13¾x14
2000 **Photo.**
3058-3068 A1073 200p Set of 11 35.00 35.00

150th anniv. of Spanish stamps, #3066.
Nos. 3060-3061, 3064-3068 each contain one 41x28mm rectangular stamp.
Exist imperf. Value $65.
Issued: #3058-3059, 10/6; #3060, 10/7; #3061, 10/8; #3062-3063, 10/9; #3064-3065, 10/10; #3066, 10/11; #3067, 10/12; #3068, 10/13.

Alfredo Kraus (1927-99), Operatic Tenor — A1074

2000, Oct. 27 **Perf. 14x13¾**
3069 A1074 70p multi 1.00 .40

America Issue, Fight Against AIDS — A1075

2000, Oct. 19 Photo. Perf. 14x13¾
3070 A1075 70p multi 1.00 .40

Christmas
A1076

Designs: 35p, Nativity scene. 70p, Birth of Christ, by Conrad von Soest.

2000, Nov. 9 **Perf. 12¾**
3071-3072 A1076 Set of 2 1.50 .55
See Germany No. B878-B879.

Santa María la Real Church, Aranda de Duero — A1077

2000, Nov. 10 **Engr.** **Perf. 14x13¾**
3073 A1077 35p brown .50 .25

Spanish Literature
A1078

Designs: 35p, Entre Naranjos, by Vicente Blasco Ibáñez. 70p, La Venganza de Don Mendo, by Pedro Muñoz Seca. 100p, El Alcalde Zalamea, by Pedro Calderón de la Barca.

Photo., Engr. (100p)
2000, Nov. 17 **Perf. 13¾x14**
3074-3076 A1078 Set of 3 3.25 1.50

Commercial Agents College, 75th Anniv. — A1079

2001, Jan. 8 **Photo.** **Perf. 14x13¾**
3077 A1079 40p multi .60 .25

Fire Fighters — A1080

2001, Jan. 19
3078 A1080 75p multi 1.10 .45

Infantry College, Toledo, 150th Anniv. A1081

2001, Feb. 16 **Perf. 13¾x14**
3079 A1081 120p multi 2.00 .65

Intl. Campaign Against Domestic Violence — A1082

2001, Feb. 22 **Perf. 14x13¾**
3080 A1082 155p multi 2.25 .85

First Spanish Mail Box, Mayorga A1083

2001, Mar. 2 **Engr.** **Perf. 13¾x14**
3081 A1083 155p black 2.25 .85
Stamp Day.

Juvenia 2001, Natl. Youth Philatelic Exhibition A1084

2001, Mar. 9 **Photo.**
3082 A1084 120p multi 1.75 .70

Placencia Inn — A1084a

2001, Mar. 16 **Perf. 14x13¾**
3083 A1084a 40p multicolored .60 .20

Famous People A1085

Designs: 40p, Joaquín Rodrigo (1901-99), musician. 75p, Rafael Alberti (1902-99), writer.

2001, Mar. 22 **Engr.** **Perf. 13¾x14**
3084-3085 A1085 Set of 2 1.75 .60

Castles A1086

Designs: 40p, Zuda, Tortosa, vert. 75p, Cid, Jadraque. 155p, San Fernando, Figueres. 260p, Montesquiu, Montesquiu.

2001, Apr. 20 Perf. 14x13¾, 13¾x14
3086-3089 A1086 Set of 4 8.00 3.00

Book Day — A1087

2001, Apr. 23   Photo.   Perf. 14x13¾
3090 A1087 40p multi   .60   .20

Souvenir Sheet

First Flights, 75th Anniv. — A1088

No. 3091: a, 40p, Spain-Argentina. b, 75p, Spain-Philippines. c, 155p, Spain-Equatorial Guinea. d, 260p, Commemorative flight.

2001, Apr. 26   Perf. 13¾x14
3091 A1088   Sheet of 4, #a-d   8.00 3.00

Grand Theater, Liceu — A1089

2001, Apr. 27   Perf. 14x13¾
3092 A1089 120p multi   1.75   .65

King Juan Carlos — A1091

2001   Photo.   Perf. 12¾x13¼
3093 A1091   5p sil & lil rose   .20   .20
3094 A1091   40p sil & yel grn   .60   .25
3095 A1091   75p sil & bl vio   1.10   .40
3096 A1091 100psil & lt red brn   1.50   .55
          Nos. 3093-3096 (4)   3.40 1.40

Issued: 40p, 5/4; 5p, 75p, 6/28; 100p, 7/15.

Europa — A1092

2001, May 9   Photo.   Perf. 14x13¾
3097 A1092 75p multi   .80   .40

Architecture A1093

Designs: 40p, San Martiño Church, Noia. 75p, Santa Maria Cathedral, Tui. 155p, Villaconcha dovecote, Frechilla.

Engr., Photo. (75p)
2001, May 17   Perf. 14x13¾
3098-3100 A1093 Set of 3   4.00 1.50

Luarca Harbor A1094

2001, May 26   Photo.   Perf. 13¾x14
3101 A1094 40p multi   .60   .25

Cardinal Rodrigo de Castro (1523-1600) — A1095

2001, June 1
3102 A1095 40p multi   .60   .25

Leopoldo Alas, "Clarín," (1852-1901), Writer — A1096

2001, June 13
3103 A1096 75p multi   1.10   .40

Trees A1097

Designs: 40p, Olive. 75p, Beech.

2001, June 22   Perf. 12¾
3104-3105 A1097   Set of 2   1.75   .60

King's Soccer Cup, 25th Anniv. A1098

2001, July 6   Litho.   Perf. 13¾x14
3106 A1098 40p multi   .60   .25

Issued in sheets of 8 + 4 labels.

Local Festivals A1099

Designs: 40p, Cipotegato, Tarazona. 120p, Giants of Pí, Barcelona, vert.

Perf. 13¾x14, 14x13¾
2001, July 10   Photo.
3107-3108 A1099   Set of 2   2.40   .80

Baltasar Gracian (1601-58), Writer A1100

2001, July 13   Perf. 13¾x14
3109 A1100 120p multi   1.75   .60

"Age of Man" Exhibition — A1101

Designs: 120p, Our Lady of La Calva. 155p, Cathedral dome, Zamora.

2001, July 20   Engr.   Perf. 14x13¾
3110-3111 A1101   Set of 2   4.00 1.50

Grandparent's Day — A1102

Siervas de Jesús de la Caridad A1103

Perf. 14x13¾, 13¾x14
2001, July 26   Photo.
3112 A1102 40p multi   .60   .25
3113 A1103 75p multi   1.10   .40

Salamanca, European City of Culture — A1104

Illustration reduced.

2001, Sept. 5   Photo.   Perf. 13x13¼
3114 A1104 75p multi   1.10   .40

Covadonga Basilica, Cent. of Consecration — A1105

2001, Sept. 7   Perf. 13¾x14
3115 A1105 40p multi   .60   .25

Emblem of Privatized Postal System A1106

2001, Sept. 15
3116 A1106 40p multi   .60   .25

Souvenir Sheet

Exfilna 2001 Natl. Philatelic Exhibition, Vigo — A1107

Engr. (Litho. Margin)
2001, Sept. 21
3117 A1107 260p multi   4.00 4.00

St. Dominic of Silos (c. 1000-73) — A1108

Litho. & Engr.
2001, Oct. 4   Perf. 14x13¾
3118 A1108 40p multi   .60   .25
  a.   Souvenir sheet of 1 with margin like stamp design   .60   .60
  b.   Souvenir sheet of 1 with margin differing   .60   .60

Year of Dialogue Among Civilizations A1109

2001, Oct. 9   Photo.
3119 A1109 120p multi   1.75   .70

Stamp Day.

Posidonia Oceanica, Ses Salines Nature Reserve A1110

2001, Oct. 15   Perf. 13¾x14
3120 A1110 155p multi   2.25   .85

America issue — UNESCO World Heritage Sites.

Letter Writing Type of 1998

No. 3121: a, Christopher Columbus, 1492. b, Treaty of Tordesillas, 1494. c, Election of King Charles I as Holy Roman Emperor Charles V, 1519. d, Conquest of Mexico by Hernán Cortés, 1519. e, Circumnavigation by Juan Sebastián Elcano, 1522. f, Campaign against Incas by Francisco Pizarro, 1532. g, Ascension to throne of King Philip II, 1556. h, Start of construction of El Escoríal Monastery, 1563. i, Battle of Lepanto, 1571. j, Saints John of the Cross, Teresa of Jesus and painter El Greco, 1580. k, First play by Lope de Vega, 1593. l, Ascension to throne of King Philip III, 1598.

2001, Oct. 19   Perf. 13x12½
3121   Sheet of 12   5.25 5.25
  a.-l. A1002 25p Any single   .40   .20

Souvenir Sheet

Bullfighter Curro Romero — A1111

2001, Oct. 25   **Perf. 14x13¾**
3122 A1111 260p multi   4.00 4.00

Christmas
A1112

Designs: 40p, Virgin With Child, by Alfredo Roldan. 75p, Adoration of the Shepherds, by José Ribera.

2001, Nov. 8   **Perf. 12¾**
3123-3124 A1112   Set of 2   1.75   .60
a.   Souvenir sheet, # 3123-
          3124, Germany
          #B895-B896, litho.,
          perf. 13¼   6.00 5.50

See Germany No. B896a.

Score of "El Sombrero de Tres Picos," by Manuel de Falla (1876-1946) — A1113

2001, Nov. 14 Photo.   Perf. 13¾x14
3125 A1113 75p multi   1.10   .40

Comic Strips
A1114

Designs: 40p, Cartoon by Josep Coll i Coll. 75p, Rompetechos, by Francisco Ibañez.

2001, Nov. 20
3126-3127 A1114   Set of 2   1.75   .60

Carlos Cano
(1946-2000),
Singer — A1115

2001, Nov. 23   **Perf. 14x13¾**
3128 A1115 40p black   .60   .25

Intl. Volunteer Day for Economic and Social Development
A1116

2001, Nov. 27
3129 A1116 120p multi   1.75   .70

World Heritage Sites — A1117

No. 3130: a, Catalan Romanesque Churches of the Vall de Boí. b, The Mystery of Elx (Elche). c, Hospital de Sant Pau, Barcelona. d, San Cristóbal de La Laguna. e, Archaeological Site of Atapuerca. f, Palmeral de Elche. g, Monuments of Oviedo. h, Roman Walls of Lugo. i, Rock Art of the Mediterranean Basin. j, Ibiza, Biodiversity and Culture. k, Archaeological Ensemble of Tarraco. l, University and Historic Precinct of Alcalá de Henares.

2001, Nov. 30   **Perf. 12¾**
3130   Sheet of 12   7.00 7.00
a.-l. A1117 40p Any single   .60   .25

Souvenir Sheet

Ministry of Development, 150th Anniv. — A1118

No. 3131 — Maps showing: a, 40p, Automated postal centers. b, 75p, Ports. c, 120p, High-speed train lines. d, 155p, Airports. e, 260p, Highways.

2001, Dec. 11
3131 A1118   Sheet of 5, #a-
              e, + label   11.00 10.00

Souvenir Sheet

King Juan Carlos, 25th Anniv. of Reign — A1119

No. 3132: a, 40p, Crown Prince Felipe. b, 40p, Princess Elena (patterned dress). c, 40p, Royal arms. d, 40p, Princess Cristina (black dress). e, 75p, King Juan Carlos. f, 75p, Queen Sofía. g, 260p, Royal palace, Madrid (49x28mm).

2001, Dec. 14   **Perf. 12¾x13¼**
3132 A1119   Sheet of 7, #a-g 10.00 10.00

100 Cents = 1 Euro (€)
King Juan Carlos Type of 2001 With Euro Denominations Only

2002, Jan. 2   Photo.   Perf. 13¾x14
3133 A1091   1c sil & black   .20   .20
3134 A1091   5c sil & brt blue   .20   .20
3135 A1091 10c sil & gray blue .20   .20
3136 A1091 25c sil & claret   .60   .20
3137 A1091 50c sil & gray   1.25   .35

3138 A1091 75c sil & red lil   1.90   .55
      Perf. 12¾x13¼
3139 A1091 €1 sil & green   2.50   .75
3140 A1091 €2 sil & ver   5.00 1.50
      Nos. 3133-3140 (8)   11.85 3.95

Spain's Presidency of European Union
A1120

Color of star at UR: 25c, Orange. 50c, White.

2002, Jan. 2   Photo.   Perf. 13¾x14
3141-3142 A1120   Set of 2   1.90   .65

Trees
A1121

Designs: 50c, Savin (sabina). 75c, Elm (olmo).

2002, Jan. 25   **Perf. 12¾**
3143-3144 A1121   Set of 2   3.00 1.10

Souvenir Sheet

A1122   A1123

A1124   A1125

A1126   A1127

Flowers
A1128   A1129

Die Cut Perf. 13
2002, Feb. 20   **Litho.**
Self-Adhesive
3145   Booklet of 8   5.50
a. A1122 25c multi   .60   .25
b. A1123 25c multi   .60   .25
c. A1124 25c multi   .60   .25
d. A1125 25c multi   .60   .25
e. A1126 25c multi   .60   .25
f. A1127 25c multi   .60   .25
g. A1128 25c multi   .60   .25
h. A1129 25c multi   .60   .25

España 2002 Youth Philatelic Exhibition, Salamanca
A1130

Designs: 50c, Exhibition emblem. €1.80, Emblem and New Cathedral, vert.

2002, Feb. 22   Photo.   Perf. 13¾x14
3146 A1130 50c multi   1.25   .45
          Souvenir Sheet
          Perf. 14x13¾
3147 A1130 €1.80 multi   5.00 4.50
          See No. 3183.

Father Francisco Piquer, Founder of Pawn Brokerage
A1131

2002, Feb. 25   Litho.   Perf. 14x13¾
3148 A1131 25c multi   .60   .25

Caja Madrid Savings Bank, 300th anniv.

Real Madrid Soccer Team, Cent.
A1132

2002, Feb. 25   **Perf. 13¾x14**
3149 A1132 75c yel & gray   1.90   .65

Souvenir Sheet

Tarazona Town Hall Portico — A1133

2002, Feb. 26
3150 A1133 €2.10 multi   5.25 5.25

Philaiberia '02, Tarazona.

Alejandro Mon
(1801-82),
Politician — A1134

2002, Feb. 27   **Perf. 14x13¾**
3151 A1134 25c multi   .60   .25

Retirement of
Peseta
Currency — A1135

2002, Feb. 28   **Litho.**
3152 A1135 25c multi   .60 .25

Sil Canyons,
Ribiera
Sacra — A1136

Cabo de
Gata Natl.
Park
A1137

2002, Mar. 8   Perf. 14x13¾, 13¾x14
3153 A1136   75c multi   2.00 .65
3154 A1137   €2.10 multi   5.50 2.75

Zaragoza Military
Academy, 75th
Anniv. — A1138

2002, Mar. 15   Perf. 14x13¾
3155 A1138 25c multi   .60 .25

Real Unión Soccer
Team,
Cent. — A1139

2002, Mar. 22
3156 A1139 50c multi   1.25 .45

Stamp Day
A1140

2002, Mar. 25   Perf. 13¾x14
3157 A1140 25c multi   .60 .25

Castle Type of 2001

Designs: 25c, Banyeres de Mariola. 50c,
Soutomaior. 75c, Catalorao.

2002, Apr. 8   Engr.   Perf. 13¾x14
3158-3160 A1086   Set of 3   3.75 1.40

Tudela,
1200th
Anniv.
A1141

2002, Apr. 12   **Photo.**
3161 A1141 75c multi   1.90 .70

Monastery
of Sant
Cugat,
1000th
Anniv.
A1142

2002, Apr. 12
3162 A1142 €1.80 multi   4.50 2.25

Luis
Cernuda
(1902-63),
Poet
A1143

2002, May 8
3163 A1143 50c multi   .90 .45

Dr. Federico Rubio (1827-
1902) — A1144

2002, May 8
3164 A1144 50c multi   1.25 .45

Europa
A1145

2002, May 9
3165 A1145 50c multi   1.25 .45

Reincorporation of Menorca to
Spanish Crown, Bicent. — A1146

2002, May 10
3166 A1146 50c multi   1.25 .45

World Equestrian Games — A1147

No. 3167: a, Carriage driving. b, Endurance
(Raid). c, Dressage (Doma). d, Reining. e,
Vaulting (Volteo). f, Jumping (Saltos). g,
Three-day event (Completo).
Illustration reduced.

2002, May 11   Perf. 12¾x13¼
3167   Sheet of 7 + 2 labels   9.50 9.50
  a.-e. A1147 25c Any single   .60 .25
  f. A1147 75c multi   1.90 .70
  g. A1147 €1.80 multi   4.50 2.25

Dolores
Peinado
(1819-94),
Character
From Folk
Song "La
Dolores"
A1148

2002, May 31   Perf. 13¾x14
3168 A1148 50c multi   1.25 .50

Souvenir Sheet

Exfilna 2002 Natl. Philatelic Exhibition,
Salamanca — A1149

No. 3169 — Plaza Mayor, Salamanca: a,
25c, West facade. b, 25c, City Hall. c, 25c,
Royal Pavilion. d, €1.80, Aerial view.

Engr. (#a-c), Litho. (#d, margin)
2002, July 7   Perf. 13¾x14
3169 A1149   Sheet of 4, #a-d   6.25 6.25

Iberian
Airlines,
75th Anniv.
A1150

Airplanes: 25c, Rohrbach R-VIII Roland.
50c, Boeing 747.

2002, June 10 Photo. Perf. 13¾x14
3170-3171 A1150   Set of 2   1.90 .75

Wine Producing
Regions — A1151

Grapes and map of: 25c, Rias Baixas
region. 50c, Rioja region. 75c, Manzanilla —
Sanlúcar de Barrameda region.

2002   **Perf. 14x13¼**
3172-3174 A1151   Set of 3   3.75 1.50
  Issued: 25c, 7/27; 50c, 75c, 9/20.

Letter Writing Type of 1998

No. 3175: a, Publication of *Don Quixote*, by
Miguel de Cervantes, 1605. b, Accession to
throne of King Philip IV and rise in power of
Conde-Duque de Olivares, 1621. c, Rivalry of
poets Francisco de Quevedo and Luis de
Góngora, 1620. d, Painting of "Las Meninas"
by Diego Velázquez, 1656. e, Accession to
throne of King Charles II, 1665. f, Accession to
throne of King Philip V, 1701. g, Accesstion to
throne of Kign Ferdinand VI, 1746. h, Accession to throne of King Charles III, 1759. i,
Squillaci Riots, 1766. j, Gaspar Melchor de
Jovellanos, 1787. k, Accession to throne of
King Charles IV, 1788. l, Appointment of
Manuel de Godoy as prime minister, 1792.

2002, Sept. 27   Perf. 12¾
3175   Sheet of 12   4.50 4.50
  a.-l. A1002 10c Any single   .30 .20

Expiatory Temple of
the Holy Family, by
Architect Antonio
Gaudí (1852-1926)
A1152

2002, Sept. 27 Litho. Perf. 14x13¾
3176 A1152 50c blue & black   1.25 .50

A1153

A1154

A1155

A1156

A1157

A1158

A1159

Paintings With
Musical
Instruments by
Goyo
Domínguez
A1160

2002, Sept. 30   Die Cut Perf. 13
Self-Adhesive
3177   Booklet pane of 8   5.00
  a. A1153 25c multi   .60 .25
  b. A1154 25c multi   .60 .25
  c. A1155 25c multi   .60 .25
  d. A1156 25c multi   .60 .25
  e. A1157 25c multi   .60 .25
  f. A1158 25c multi   .60 .25
  g. A1159 25c multi   .60 .25
  h. A1160 25c multi   .60 .25

America
Issue —
Youth,
Education
and
Literacy
A1161

2002, Oct. 14 Photo. Perf. 13¾x14
3178 A1161 75c multi 1.90 .75

Almanzor (Muhammad ibn Abu Amir
al-Mansur, c. 938-1002), Caliph of
Córdoba — A1162

2002, Oct. 25
3179 A1162 75c multi 1.90 .75

Dijous Bó Fair,
Mallorca — A1163

2002, Nov. 4 Perf. 14x13¾
3180 A1163 75c multi 1.90 .75

UNESCO World Heritage
Sites — A1164

No. 3181 — Architectural details of: a,
Aranjuez. b, Santa Maria Church, Calatayud.
c, San Martin Church, Teruel. d, Santa Maria
Church, Tobed. e, Santa Tecla Church,
Cervera de la Cañada. f, San Pablo Church,
Zaragoza.

2002, Nov. 8
3181 A1164 Sheet of 7, #a-
d, f, 2 #e, + 5
labels 19.00 19.00
a.-b. 25c Either single .60 .25
c. 50c multi 1.25 .50
d. 75c multi 1.90 .75
e. €1.80 multi 4.50 2.25
f. €2.10 multi 5.25 2.75

The two examples of No. 3181e are tete-
beche in the sheet.

Alcañiz Inn
— A1164a

2002, Nov. 15 Perf. 13¾x14
3182 A1164a 25c multicolored .60 .25

España 2002 Youth Philatelic
Exhibition, Salamanca — A1165

Designs: No. 3183a, 50c, Like #3146. Nos.
3183b, 3190, 75c, Character from comic Strip
"El Capitan Alatriste," by Arturo Pérez-
Reverte. Nos. 3183c, 3185, 75c, Television
and names of television shows. Nos. 3183d,
3189, 75c, Hand and compact disc. Nos.
3183e, 3187, 75c, Radio, musical notes and
logos of Spanish radio stations. Nos. 3183f,
3188, 75c, Skier, race car, soccer ball, bicyclist and names of Spanish sports stars. Nos.
3183g, 3186, 75c, Photojournalist. Nos.
3183h, 3184, 75c, Clapboard and names of
Spanish film personalities. No. 3183i, €1.80,
Like #3147, vert.

2002 Litho. Die Cut Perf. 13
Self-Adhesive (#3183)
3183 A1165 Sheet of 9 19.00 19.00
a. 50c multi 1.25 .50
b.-h. 75c Any single 1.90 .75
i. €1.80 multi 4.50 2.25

Souvenir Sheets
Perf. 13¾x14
3184-3190 A1165 Set of 7 11.50 11.50

Issued: No. 3183, 11/17; No. 3184, 11/18;
No. 3185, 11/19; No. 3186, 11/20; No. 3187,
11/21; No. 3188, 11/22; No. 3189, 11/23; No.
3190, 11/24.

No. 3183 exists with at least three different
pictures on backing paper.

San Jorge Church,
Alcoy — A1166

Litho. & Engr.
2002, Nov. 25 Perf. 14x13¾
3191 A1166 75c multi 1.90 .75

Compludo
Forge,
León
A1167

2002, Nov. 27 Perf. 13¾x14
3192 A1167 50c multi 1.25 .50

Souvenir Sheet

Stained Glass Window, Santa Maria
Cathedral, Vitoria-Gasteiz — A1168

2002, Nov. 27 Perf. 14x13¾
3193 A1168 50c multi 1.50 1.00

Crucifix, Hío Christmas
A1169 A1170

2002, Nov. 29
3194 A1169 25c multi .60 .25

2002, Nov. 29 Photo.

Designs: 25c, Adoration of the Magi, from
church altarpiece, Calzadilla de los Barros.
50c, Maternity, by Goyo Dominguez.
3195-3196 A1170 Set of 2 1.90 .75

Opening of
Somport
Tunnel
A1171

2003, Jan. 17 Photo. Perf. 13¾x14
3197 A1171 51c multi 1.10 .55

Traditional Dress
from Ansó
Valley — A1172

2003, Jan. 20 Perf. 14x13¾
3198 A1172 76c multi 1.75 .85

World Leprosy
Day, 50th
Anniv. — A1173

2003, Jan. 21
3199 A1173 26c multi .55 .30

Pedro Rodríguez
de Campomanes
(1723-1802),
Jurist — A1174

2003, Feb. 14
3200 A1174 26c multi .55 .30

Juvenia
2003 Natl.
Youth
Philatelic
Exhibition,
Benissa
A1175

2003, Feb. 21 Perf. 13¾x14
3201 A1175 51c multi 1.10 .55

Práxedes Mateo Sagasta (1825-1903),
Politician — A1176

2003, Mar. 11
3202 A1176 26c multi .55 .30

ABC
Newspaper,
Cent.
A1177

2003, Mar. 17
3203 A1177 €2.15 multi 4.50 2.25

Nobel Prize Winners For Physiology or
Medicine From Spain — A1178

No. 3204: a, Santiago Ramón y Cajal, 1906.
b, Severo Ochoa, 1959.
Illustration reduced.

Litho. & Engr.
2003, Mar. 20 Perf. 13x12¾
3204 A1178 Horiz. pair 3.25 3.25
a. 51c multi 1.25 .55
b. 76c multi 1.90 .80

See Sweden No. 2460.

School of Civil Engineering, Madrid,
Bicent. — A1179

Designs: 26c, Tui Bridge.
No. 3206: a, Estrecho de Puentes Dam. b,
El Musel Port.

2003, Mar. 21 Photo. Perf. 13¾x14
3205 A1179 26c multi .55 .30
Souvenir Sheet
3206 Sheet of 3, #3205,
3206a, 3206b 4.00 2.00
a. A1179 51c multi 1.25 .55
b. A1179 76c multi 1.75 .80

La Verdad Newspaper, Cent. A1180

2003, Mar. 26
3207 A1180 26c multi .55 .30

Paintings by Chico Montilla A1181

No. 3208: a, La Hoz de Priego. b, Fields of Gold. c, Desfiladero de los Tornos. d, Campos de Pastrana. e, Campos de Armilla. f, Nenúfar. g, De qué Color es el Vento? h, Flores Tempranas.

Die Cut Perf. 13
2003, Mar. 28 **Litho.**
Self-Adhesive
3208 Booklet pane of 8 4.50
a.-h. A1181 26c Any single .55 .30

Ramón José Sender (1901-82), Writer A1182

Litho. & Engr.
2003, Mar. 31 ***Perf. 13½x14***
3209 A1182 €2.15 multi 4.75 2.40

Rural Schools A1183

2003, Apr. 3 **Photo.** ***Perf. 13¾x14***
3210 A1183 26c multi .55 .30

Souvenir Sheet

EXFILNA 2003 Natl. Philatelic Exhibition, Granada — A1184

Litho. (margin) & Engr. (stamp)
2003, Apr. 7
3211 A1184 €2.15 multi 4.75 2.40

Aviles, 1000th Anniv. A1185

2003, Apr. 11 **Photo.**
3212 A1185 51c multi 1.10 .55

Stamp Day A1186

2003, Apr. 11
3213 A1186 €1.85 multi 4.00 2.00

Europa A1187

2003, Apr. 24
3214 A1187 76c multi 1.75 .85

Atlético de Madrid Soccer Team, Cent. — A1188

2003, Apr. 25 ***Perf. 14x13¾***
3215 A1188 26c red & blue .60 .30

Roman Theater, Zaragoza A1189

2003, May 5 ***Perf. 13¾x14***
3216 A1189 €1.85 multi 4.25 2.10

European Year of the Disabled A1190

2003, May 8 **Photo. & Embossed**
3217 A1190 76c multi 1.75 .85

Castles A1191

Designs: 26c, San Felipe Castle, Ferrol. 51c, Cuellar Castle, Segovia. 76c, Montilla Castle, Córdoba.

2003, May 17 **Engr.** ***Perf. 13¾x14***
3218-3220 A1191 Set of 3 3.75 1.90
Battles of Ceriñola and Garellano, 500th anniv. (No. 3220).

World Swimming Championships, Barcelona — A1192

2003, May 23 **Photo.** ***Perf. 14x13¾***
3221 A1192 Sheet of 5 + label 13.00 6.50
a. 26c Breaststroke .60 .30
b. 51c Diving 1.25 .60
c. 76c Synchronized swimming 1.75 .85
d. €1.85 Freestyle 4.25 2.10
e. €2.15 Water polo 5.00 2.50

Max Aub (1903-72), Writer — A1193

2003, June 2 **Engr.**
3222 A1193 76c black & red 1.75 .85

Sabadell Soccer Team, Cent. — A1194

2003, June 4 **Photo.**
3223 A1194 76c multi 1.75 .85

Juan Bravo Murillo (1803-73), Prime Minister — A1195

2003, June 9
3224 A1195 51c multi 1.25 .60

Diario de Cadiz Newspaper, 136th Anniv. — A1196

2003, June 16
3225 A1196 26c multi .60 .30

Souvenir Sheet

Royal Automobile Club of Spain, Cent. — A1197

2003, June 27 ***Perf. 13¾x14***
3226 A1197 Sheet of 4 7.75 4.00
a. 26c 1967 Dodge Dart Barreiros .60 .30
b. 51c 1957-73 Seat 600 1.10 .55
c. 76c 1907 Hispano-Suiza 20/30 HP 1.75 .85
d. €1.85 1953 Pegaso Z-102 Berlinetta 4.25 2.10

Chilean Postage Stamps, 150th Anniv. — A1198

2003, July 1 **Photo.** ***Perf. 14x13¾***
3227 A1198 76c Chile Type A1 1.75 .85

El Diario Montañés Newspaper, Cent. — A1199

2003, July 4
3228 A1199 26c multi .60 .30

Santa Catalina Inn, Jaén — A1200

Illustration reduced.

2003, July 9 ***Perf. 13x13¼***
3229 A1200 76c multi + label 1.75 .85

Diario de Navarra Newspaper, Cent. — A1201

2003, July 11 ***Perf. 13¾x14***
3230 A1201 26c multi .60 .30

Seu Vella, Lleida, 800th Anniv. A1202

2003, July 22 **Engr.** ***Perf. 13¾x14***
3231 A1202 €1.85 pur & brn blk 4.25 2.10

El Adelanto de Salamanca Newspaper, 120th Anniv. — A1203

2003, July 24   Photo.   Perf. 14x13¾
3232 A1203 26c multi   .60   .30

A1204   A1205

A1206   A1207

A1208   A1209

A1210   A1211

Paintings by Alfredo Roldán
A1210   A1211

Die Cut Perf. 13
2003, July 28   Litho.
Self-Adhesive
3233   Booklet pane of 8   5.00
  a. A1204 A multi   .60   .30
  b. A1205 A multi   .60   .30
  c. A1206 A multi   .60   .30
  d. A1207 A multi   .60   .30
  e. A1208 A multi   .60   .30
  f. A1209 A multi   .60   .30
  g. A1210 A multi   .60   .30
  h. A1211 A multi   .60   .30
  Nos. 3233a-3233g each sold for 26c on day of issue.

El Correo Gallego Newspaper, 125th Anniv. — A1212

2003, Aug. 1   Photo.   Perf. 13¾x14
3234 A1212 26c multi   .60   .30

El Comercio de Gijón Newspaper, 125th Anniv. — A1213

2003, Sept. 2
3235 A1213 26c multi   .60   .30

Holy Cross of Caravaca
A1214

2003, Sept. 4   Perf. 14x13¾
3236 A1214 76c multi   1.75   .85
Holy Year 2003.

World Sailing Championships, Gulf of Cádiz — A1215

2003, Sept. 9   Perf. 13¾x14
3237 A1215 76c multi   1.75   .85

Wine of Penedés Region — A1216

Wine of Montilla-Moriles Region — A1217

Wine of Valdepeñas Region — A1218

Wine of Bierzo Region — A1219

2003   Perf. 14x13¾
3238 A1216 26c multi   .60   .30
3239 A1217 51c multi   1.25   .60
3240 A1218 76c multi   1.75   .90
3241 A1219 €1.85 multi   4.50 2.25
  Nos. 3238-3241 (4)   8.10 4.05
  Issued: 26c, 10/30; others, 9/22.

Academy of Military Engineering, Bicent. — A1220

2003, Sept. 24   Perf. 13¾x14
3242 A1220 51c multi   1.25   .60

Souvenir Sheet

Santa María Cathedral, León, 700th Anniv — A1221

2003, Sept. 26   Litho. & Engr.
3243 A1221 76c multi   2.00 1.00

Souvenir Sheet

Royal Geographical Society, Cent. — A1222

2003, Oct. 1
3244 A1222 €1.85 multi   4.75 2.50

Trees — A1223

Designs: 26c, Ficus macrophylla. 51c, Quercus rober.

2003, Oct. 3   Photo.   Perf. 14x13¾
3245-3246 A1223 Set of 2   1.90   .95

School of Aeronautical Engineering, Madrid, 75th Anniv. — A1224

2003, Oct. 6   Perf. 13¾x14
3247 A1224 51c multi   1.25   .60

America Issue - Rail Transport A1225

2003, Oct. 14
3248 A1225 76c multi   1.75   .90

El Viejo y el Pájaro, by Luis Seoane (1910-79) A1226

2003, Oct. 17   Perf. 14x13¾
3249 A1226 €1.85 multi   4.50 2.25

El Correo de Andalucia Newspaper, Cent. — A1227

Faro de Vigo Newspaper, 150th Anniv. — A1228

La Voz de Galicia Newspaper, 121st Anniv. — A1229

2003, Nov. 3   Perf. 13¾x14
3250 A1227 26c multi   .60   .30
3251 A1228 26c multi   .60   .30
3252 A1229 26c multi   .60   .30
  Nos. 3250-3252 (3)   1.80   .90

Camilo José Cela (1916-2002), 1989 Nobel Laureate in Literature A1230

2003, Nov. 10   Perf. 14x13¾
3253 A1230 26c multi   .65   .30

Parade of the Magi — A1231

Nativity, by
Raquel
Fariñas — A1232

2003, Nov. 10
3254 A1231 26c multi .65 .30
3255 A1232 51c multi 1.25 .60

Christmas.

España
2004 Intl.
Philatelic
Exhibition
A1233

Designs: 76c, Exhibition emblem. €1.85,
Exhibition venue, Valencia.

2003, Nov. 14 *Perf. 13¾x14*
3256 A1233 76c multi 1.90 .95

Souvenir Sheet
3257 A1233 €1.85 multi 4.50 2.25

Organos
de
Montoro
A1234

2003, Nov. 17
3258 A1234 51c multi 1.25 .60

Souvenir Sheet

Completion of National Geological
Map — A1235

2003, Nov. 24
3259 A1235 26c multi .65 .30

Souvenir Sheets

Constitution, 25th Anniv. — A1236

Various photos or paintings with inscriptions
in lower left corner of: No. 3260, 26c; RCM-
FNMT. No. 3261, 26c, Miguel Torner. No.
3262, 26c, R. Seco. No. 3263, 26c, Araceli

Alarcón. No. 3264, 26c, Galicia. No. 3265,
26c, Fesanpe. No. 3266, 26c, J. Carrero. No.
3267, 26c, J. Carrero, vert. No. 3268, 26c,
Goyo Domínguez, vert. No. 3269, 26c, Juan
Bautista Nieto, vert.

2003, Dec. 5 *Perf. 13¾x14, 14x13¾*
3260-3269 A1236 Set of 10 6.50 3.25

Powered
Flight,
Cent.
A1237

2003, Dec. 17 Engr. *Perf. 13¾x14*
3270 A1237 76c blue & brown 1.90 .95

**King Juan Carlos Type of 2001 With
Euro Denominations Only**

2004, Jan. 2 Photo. *Perf. 12¾x13¼*
3271 A1091 2c sil & brt pink .20 .20
3272 A1091 27c sil & blue .70 .35
a. Sheet of 4 + label 2.80 2.80
3273 A1091 52c sil & bister brn 1.25 .65
3274 A1091 77c sil & dull grn 1.90 .95
Nos. 3271-3274 (4) 4.05 2.15

No. 3272a issued 5/25.

Roman Art of
Jaca — A1238

No. 3275: a, Grate. b, Huesca Cathedral
Bible page. c, Painting of two apostles. d,
Cloister, Monastery of San Juan de la Peña. e,
Coins. f, Capital, Church of Santiago de Jaca.
g, Detail of sarcophagus of Doña Sancha. h,
Wooden carved crucifix.

Serpentine Die Cut 13
2004, Jan. 16 Litho.
Self-Adhesive
3275 Booklet pane of 8 5.75
a.-h. A1238 A Any single .70 .35

Nos. 3275a-3275h each sold for 27c on day
of issue.

Souvenir Sheets

Paintings of Women Reading by Fabio
Hurtado (1960-) — A1239

No. 3276: a, 27c, Woman reading book in
rowboat. b, 52c, Woman with head on hand
reading book. c, 77c, Woman reading
newspaper.
No. 3277: a, 27c, Woman with legs crossed
reading book. b, 52c, Woman on back reading
book. c, 77c, Woman with black hat reading
book.

2004, Jan. 23 Photo. *Perf. 13¾x14*
Sheets of 3, #a-c, + label
3276-3277 A1239 Set of 2 8.00 4.50

Campaign
Against
Cancer
A1240

2004, Feb. 2
3278 A1240 27c multi .70 .35

"La Terrona" Oak
Tree, Zarza de
Montánchez
A1241

2004, Feb. 6 *Perf. 14x13¾*
3279 A1241 52c multi 1.40 .70

World Rowing Championships,
Banyoles — A1242

2004, Feb. 9 *Perf. 13¾x14*
3280 A1242 77c multi 1.90 .95

School Letter Writing
Campaign — A1243

No. 3281 — Scenes from comic strip Trazo
de Tiza, by Miguelanxo Prado: a, Woman on
cliff. b, Sailboat. c, Woman near injured gull. d,
Aerial view of lighthouse.

2004, Feb. 10
3281 A1243 27c Sheet of 4, #a-
d, + 12 labels 2.75 1.40

Souvenir Sheet

Santa María de Carracedo Monastery,
Bierzo — A1244

2004, Mar. 8 *Perf. 14x13¾*
3282 A1244 €1.90 multi 4.75 2.40

36th
Chess
Olympiad
A1245

2004, Mar. 18 *Perf. 13¾x14*
3283 A1245 77c multi 1.90 .95

Clocks — A1246

No. 3284: a, 27c, Clock with Muse Calliope,
19th cent. b, 52c, Clock with Cupid, 18th cent.
c, 77c, Clock with Empress María Luisa, child
and harp, 19th cent. d, €1.90, Clock with
Venus and Cupid, 18th cent.

Perf. 13¼x12¾
2004, Mar. 31 Litho. & Engr.
3284 A1246 Sheet of 4, #a-d 8.50 4.25

Diario de Burgos
Newspaper, 113th
Anniv. — A1247

2004, Apr. 1 Photo. *Perf. 14x13¾*
3285 A1247 27c multi .65 .35

March 11, 2004
Terrorist
Attacks — A1248

2004, Apr. 2 Litho. *Perf. 14x13¾*
3286 A1248 27c black & gray .65 .35
Booklet Stamp
Self-Adhesive
Size: 22x33mm
Serpentine Die Cut 13
3287 A1248 A black & gray .65 .35
a. Booklet pane of 8 5.25

No. 3287 sold for 27c on day of issue.

Egg
Painting
Festival,
Pola de
Siero
A1249

2004, Apr. 5 Photo. *Perf. 13¾*
3288 A1249 27c multi .65 .35

Miniature Sheet

Paintings of Shawls, by Soledad Fernández — A1250

2004, Apr. 7   **Perf. 14x13¾**

3289	A1250	Sheet of 4	8.50 8.50
a.		27c Shawl, shell	.65 .35
b.		52c Shawl, hands	1.25 .65
c.		77c Shawl, flowers	1.90 .95
d.		€1.90 Shawl on chair	4.50 2.25

Department of Technical Engineering of Public Works, 150th Anniv. — A1251

2004, Apr. 15   **Perf. 13¾x14**
3290 A1251 52c multi   1.25 .60

Cable Inglés Loading Pier, Almadrabillas, Cent. — A1252

2004, Apr. 27
3291 A1252 52c multi   1.25 .60

Europa — A1253

2004, Apr. 29   **Perf. 14x13¾**
3292 A1253 77c multi   1.90 .95

Expansion of the European Union A1254

2004, May 3   **Perf. 13¾x14**
3293 A1254 52c multi   1.25 .60

Self-Portrait with the Neck of Rafael, by Salvador Dali (1904-89) — A1255

2004, May 11   **Photo.**
3294 A1255 77c multi   1.90 .95

FIFA (Fédération Internationale de Football Association), Cent. — A1256

2004, May 21
3295 A1256 77c multi   1.90 .95

Wedding of Prince Felipe and Letizia Ortiz Rocasolano — A1257

2004, May 22
3296 A1257 27c multi   .65 .30

España 2004 Intl. Philatelic Exhibition — A1258

No. 3297 — Music: a, Vicente Martín y Soler (1754-1806), opera composer. b, Band instruments.
Illustration reduced.

2004, May 23   **Photo.**   **Perf. 13¾x14**

3297	A1258	Horiz. pair + central label	1.90 1.90
a.		27c multi	.65 .30
b.		52c multi	1.25 .60

Miniature Sheet

España 2004 Intl. Philatelic Exhibition — A1259

No. 3298 — Royalty: a, Prince Felipe and Letizia Ortiz Rocasolano. b, Prince Felipe. c, King Juan Carlos and Queen Sofia.

Litho., Litho. & Engr. (#3298c)
2004, May 24   **Perf. 13¾x14**

3298	A1259	Sheet of 3 + 3 labels	17.00 17.00
a.		27c multi	.65 .30
b.		77c multi	1.90 .95
c.		€6 multi	14.00 7.00

España 2004 Intl. Philatelic Exhibition — A1260

No. 3299 — Festival of the Bulls, Valencia: a, Running of the bulls. b, Bullfighter.
Illustration reduced.

2004, May 26   **Photo.**   **Perf. 13¾x14**

3299	A1260	Horiz. pair + central label	2.50 2.50
a.		27c multi	.60 .30
b.		77c multi	1.90 .95

Miniature Sheet

España 2004 Intl. Philatelic Exhibition — A1261

No. 3300 — Sports: a, Tennis. b, Motorcycle racing. c, Golf.

2004, May 27   **Perf. 12¾x13**

3300	A1261	Sheet of 3 + 3 labels	7.00 7.00
a.		35c multi	.85 .40
b.		52c multi	1.25 .65
c.		€1.90 multi	4.50 2.25

España 2004 Intl. Philatelic Exhibition — A1262

No. 3301 — The Sea: a, Yacht Bravo España. b, Valencia skyline.
Illustration reduced.

2004, May 28   **Photo.**   **Perf. 13¾x14**

3301	A1262	Horiz. pair + central label	3.25 3.25
a.		52c multi	1.25 .65
b.		77c multi	1.90 .95

Diario de Valencia Newspaper, 214th Anniv. — A1263

2004, May 29
3302 A1263 27c multi   .65 .30

Jacobean Holy Year — A1264

2004, June 11   **Perf. 14x13¾**
3303 A1264 52c multi   1.25 .65

Lerma Inn A1265

2004, July 18   **Perf. 13¾x14**
3304 A1265 52c multi   1.25 .65

Castles A1266

Designs: 27c, Granadilla Fortress, Granadilla. 52c, Aguas Mansas Castle, Agoncillo.

77c, Mota Fortress, Alcalá la Real. €1.90, Villafuerte de Esgueva Castle, Villafuerte de Esgueva, vert.

2004   **Engr.**   **Perf. 13¾x14, 14x13¾**
3305-3308 A1266   Set of 4   8.50 4.25

Issued: 27c, 77c, 7/1; 52c, €1.90, 7/19.

Anchor Museum, Salinas — A1267

2004, July 16   **Photo.**   **Perf. 14x13¾**
3309 A1267 €1.90 multi   4.75 2.40

Ceramics in Paintings by Antonio Miguel González — A1268

No. 3310: a, Jar with two handles and lid, oranges. b, Goblet, amphora and jar. c, Pitcher with handle at top, bread, garlic. d, Decorated pitcher with side handle. e, Pitcher with handle at top, pentagonal dodecahedron, bread, tomatoes. f, Vase. g, Pitcher with side handle, plate of pears, grapes. h, Jar with flower design and lid.

Serpentine Die Cut 13
2004, July 22   **Litho.**
Self-Adhesive

3310		Booklet pane of 8	5.25
a.-h.	A1268	A Any single	.65 .35

Nos. 3310a-3310h sold for 27c on day of issue.

Círculo Oscense Building, Huesca, Cent. A1269

2004, July 23   **Photo.**   **Perf. 13¾x14**
3311 A1269 52c multi   1.25 .65

Our Lady of the Snows Festival, Vitoria-Gasteiz, 50th Anniv. — A1270

2004, July 30   **Perf. 14x13¾**
3312 A1270 27c multi   .65 .30

Ribeiro Wine Grapes — A1271

Wine of
Malaga — A1272

2004, Sept. 1   **Perf. 14x13¾**
3313 A1271 27c multi   .70 .35
3314 A1272 52c multi   1.25 .65

First Philippines Stamp, 150th
Anniv. — A1273

2004, Sept. 6   **Perf. 13¾x14**
3315 A1273 77c Philippines #1   1.90 .95

Heraldo de
Aragón
Newspaper, 109th
Anniv. — A1274

2004, Sept. 20   **Perf. 14x13¾**
3316 A1274 27c multi   .70 .35

Nautical Astronomy, 250th
Anniv. — A1275

2004, Sept. 24   **Perf. 13¾x14**
3317 A1275 €1.90 multi   4.75 2.40

Souvenir Sheet

EXFILNA 2004 National Philatelic
Exhibition, Valladolid — A1276

Litho. & Engr.
2004, Oct. 1   **Perf. 14x13¾**
3318 A1276 €1.90 multi   4.75 4.75

Buildings in China
and
Spain — A1277

Designs: 52c, Park Guell, Barcelona. 77c, Jinmao Tower, Shanghai.

2004, Oct. 8   **Photo.**
3319-3320 A1277 Set of 2   3.25 1.60
See People's Republic of China Nos. 3406-3407.

America Issue — Environmental
Protection — A1278

2004, Oct. 14   **Perf. 13¾x14**
3321 A1278 77c multi   2.00 1.00

CERN (European Organization for
Nuclear Research), 50th
Anniv. — A1279

2004, Oct. 19
3322 A1279 €1.90 multi   5.00 2.50

Nature — A1280

Designs: 27c, Cíes Islands. 52c, Ebro Delta Natural Park, horiz. 77c, Taburiente Caldera National Park, horiz.

2004, Oct. 21   **Perf. 14x13¾, 13¾x14**
3323-3325 A1280 Set of 3   4.25 2.10
Taburiente Caldera National Park, 50th anniv. (#3325).

First Registered Letter, 400th
Anniv. — A1281

2004, Oct. 22   **Perf. 13¾x14**
3326 A1281 77c multi   2.00 1.00
Stamp Day.

Ebre Observatory, Cent. — A1282

2004, Nov. 5
3327 A1282 €1.90 multi   5.00 2.50

Start of Reign of
Alfonso I, King of
Aragon, 900th
Anniv. — A1283

Litho. & Engr.
2004, Nov. 12   **Perf. 14x13¾**
3328 A1283 €1.90 multi   5.00 2.50

Christmas
A1284

Designs: 27c, Birth of Christ, 18th cent. Neapolitan nativity scene. 52c, Nativity, by Juan Manuel Cossío.

2004, Nov. 17   **Photo.**
3329-3330 A1284 Set of 2   2.25 1.10

Queen Isabella I
(1451-1504)
A1285

2004, Nov. 26
3331 A1285 €2.19 multi   6.00 3.00

Royal Expedition for Smallpox
Vaccination in Latin America and
Philippines, Bicent. — A1286

2004, Nov. 30   **Engr.**   **Perf. 13¾x14**
3332 A1286 77c brown   2.10 1.10

Souvenir Sheet

Stained Glass, Toledo
Cathedral — A1287

Litho. & Engr.
2004, Dec. 3   **Perf. 14x13¾**
3333 A1287 €1.90 multi   5.25 5.25

Arms of
the Prince
of
Asturias
A1288

2004, Dec. 23 Photo.   **Perf. 13¾x14**
3334 A1288 27c multi   .75 .40

Best wishes for Prince Felipe's marriage to Letizia Ortiz Rocasolano on May 22, 2004.

A1289   A1290

A1291   A1292

A1293   A1294

A1295   A1296

Paintings of Circus Performers by
Manolo Elices
A1295   A1296

2005, Jan. 3 Litho.   **Die Cut Perf. 13**
Self-Adhesive
3335   Booklet pane of 8   6.00
a.   A1289 A multi   .75 .35
b.   A1290 A multi   .75 .35
c.   A1291 A multi   .75 .35
d.   A1292 A multi   .75 .35
e.   A1293 A multi   .75 .35
f.   A1294 A multi   .75 .35
g.   A1295 A multi   .75 .35
h.   A1296 A multi   .75 .35

Nos. 3335a-3335h each sold for 28c on day of issue.

Signing of European Union
Constitutional Treaty — A1297

2005, Jan. 12 Photo. Perf. 13¾x14
3336 A1297 28c multi .75 .35

**King Juan Carlos Type of 2001 With
Euro Denominations Only**

2005, Jan. 14 Photo. Perf. 13
3337 A1091 28c sil & ol grn .75 .35
3338 A1091 35c sil & orange .90 .45
3339 A1091 40c sil & blue
gray 1.00 .50
3340 A1091 53c sil & dull
pur 1.40 .70
3341 A1091 78c sil & red 2.00 1.00
3342 A1091 €1.95 sil & yel brn 5.00 2.50
3343 A1091 €2.21 sil & ol brn 5.75 2.75
Nos. 3337-3343 (7) 16.80 8.25

Ahuehuete Tree,
Retiro Park,
Madrid — A1298

2005, Jan. 17 Photo. Perf. 14x13¾
3344 A1298 78c multi 2.00 1.00

Road
Safety
A1299

Blood
Donation
A1300

2005, Jan. 26 Perf. 13¾x14
3345 A1299 28c multi .75 .35
3346 A1300 53c multi 1.40 .70

University of
Seville, 500th
Anniv. — A1301

2005, Feb. 3 Engr. Perf. 14x13¾
3347 A1301 28c brn & claret .75 .35

First Royal
Spanish
Pharmacopoeia,
500th
Anniv. — A1302

2005, Feb. 3 Litho. & Engr.
3348 A1302 28c multi .75 .35

Miniature Sheet

Children's Songs and Stories — A1303

No. 3349: a, Al Levantar una Lancha. b,
Aquí te Espero. c, Estaba la Pájara Pinta. d,
Cuatro Esquinitas. e, El Patio de mi Casa. f,
Pero Mira Cómo Beben. g, Los Pollitos
Cantan. h, Para Entrar en Clase.

2005, Feb. 14 Photo.
3349 A1303 Sheet of 8 11.00 11.00
a.-c. 28c Any single .75 .40
d.-f. 53c Any single 1.40 .70
g.-h. 78c Either single 2.10 1.10

Juvenia 2005
Youth Stamp
Exhibition,
Tordera — A1304

2005, Feb. 25 Perf. 14x13¾
3350 A1304 28c multi .75 .35

Sevilla FC
(Seville
Soccer
Team),
Cent.
A1305

Real Sporting de
Gijón Soccer
Team,
Cent. — A1306

15th Mediterranean
Games,
Almería — A1307

2005, Mar. 1 Perf. 13¾x14
3351 A1305 35c red .95 .45

Perf. 14x13¾
3352 A1306 40c multi 1.10 .55
3353 A1307 78c multi 2.10 1.10
Nos. 3351-3353 (3) 4.15 2.10

Europa
A1308

2005, Apr. 15 Perf. 13¾x14
3354 A1308 53c multi 1.40 .70

Juan Valera
(1824-1905),
Writer and
Diplomat
A1309

2005, Apr. 18 Engr. Perf. 14x13¾
3355 A1309 €2.21 vio brn &
blue 5.75 2.75

Souvenir Sheet

Publication of Don Quixote, 400th
Anniv. — A1310

Various scenes from book.

2005, Apr. 22
3356 A1310 Sheet of 4 10.00 10.00
a. 28c black .75 .35
b. 53c black 1.40 .70
c. 78c black 2.00 1.00
d. €2.21 black 5.75 2.75

Telegraphy in Spain, 150th
Anniv. — A1311

2005, Apr. 26 Photo. Perf. 13¾x14
3357 A1311 28c multi .75 .35

Intl. Year of
Physics — A1312

Die Cut Perf. 13¼
2005, Apr. 28 Litho.
Self-Adhesive
3358 A1312 28c multi .75 .35

Souvenir Sheet

Fans — A1313

No. 3359 — Fan depicting: a, Flowers. b,
Madrid street scene. c, Nymphs.

2005, May 9 Photo. Perf. 13¾
3359 A1313 Sheet of 3 + label 4.00 4.00
a. 28c multi .70 .35
b. 53c multi 1.40 .70
c. 78c multi 1.90 .95

Diario Palentino
Newspaper, 124th
Anniv. — A1314

Ultima Hora Newspaper, 112th
Anniv. — A1315

Diario de Ibiza Newspaper, 112th
Anniv. — A1316

2005, May 16 Perf. 14x13¾
3360 A1314 78c multi 1.90 .95

Perf. 13¾x14
3361 A1315 €1.95 multi 4.75 2.40
3362 A1316 €2.21 multi 5.50 2.75
Nos. 3360-3362 (3) 12.15 6.10

Inn,
Oropesa
A1317

2005, June 13 Engr. Perf. 13¾x14
3363 A1317 €1.95 brown 4.75 2.40

Souvenir Sheet

EXFILNA 2005, Alicante — A1318

Litho. & Engr.
2005, June 20 Perf. 14x13¾
3364 A1318 €2.21 multi 5.50 2.75

Castles
A1319

Designs: 78c, Alcaudete Castle. €1.95, Valderrobres Castle. €2.21, Molina de Aragón Castle.

2005, July 4 Engr. Perf. 13¾x14
3365-3367 A1319 Set of 3 12.00 6.00

Fingerprint Registration for Newborns — A1320

2005, July 11 Photo.
3368 A1320 28c multi .70 .35

Stamp Day — A1321

Die Cut Perf. 13
2005, Sept. 1 Litho.
Self-Adhesive
3369 A1321 28c multi .70 .35

Nuestra Señora de la Asuncion Church, Pont de Suert A1322

2005, Sept. 7 Photo. Perf. 13¾x14
3370 A1322 28c multi .70 .35

Lunnispark Building A1323

Lucho A1324

Lupita in Bed — A1325

Die Cut Perf. 13
2005, Sept. 16 Litho.
Self-Adhesive
3371 Booklet pane of 8 5.75
  a. A1323 28c shown .70 .35
  b. A1324 28c shown .70 .35
  c. A1323 28c Green building .70 .35
  d. A1324 28c Lulila .70 .35
  e. A1324 28c Lupita .70 .35

---

  f. A1325 28c shown .70 .35
  g. A1324 28c Lublú .70 .35
  h. A1323 28c Orange building .70 .35
Los Lunnis children's television show.

World Cycling Championships, Madrid — A1326

2005, Sept. 20 Photo. Perf. 13¾x14
3372 A1326 78c multi 1.90 .95

España 2006 World Philatelic Exhibition, Malaga A1327

2005 Photo. Perf. 13¾x14
3373 A1327 53c multi 1.40 .70

Gardens A1328

No. 3374: a, Gardens of La Granja de San Ildefonso, Segovia. b, Bagh-e-Shahzadeh Garden, Kerman, Iran.

2005, Oct. 10
3374 Horiz. pair + central label 7.25 3.75
  a. A1328 78c multi 1.90 .95
  b. A1328 €2.21 multi 5.25 2.60
See Iran No. 2912.

15th Iberoamerican Summit, Salamanca — A1329

2005, Oct. 13
3375 A1329 78c multi 1.90 .95

America Issue, Fight Against Poverty A1330

2005, Oct. 14 Perf. 12¾
3376 A1330 78c multi 1.90 .95

La Orotava, 500th Anniv. — A1331

2005, Oct. 20 Perf. 14x13¾
3377 A1331 €2.21 multi 5.50 2.75

Colonial Postage Stamps for Cuba and Philippines, 150th Anniv. — A1332

2005, Oct. 20 Perf. 13¾x14
3378 A1332 €2.21 multi 5.50 2.75

Prince of Asturias Awards, 25th Anniv. — A1333

Illustration reduced.

2005, Oct. 20 Perf. 13¼x13
3379 A1333 28c multi + label .70 .35
Printed in sheets of 8 stamps + 8 different labels.

Miniature Sheet

Scenes from Television Show "Al Filo de lo Imposible" — A1334

No. 3380: a, Underwater cave explorers. b, Hot-air balloon with man on rope outside of gondola. c, Man pulling sled. d, Kayaker. e, Climber on snowy mountain. f, Rock climber.

2005, Oct. 24 Perf. 14x13¾
3380 A1334 Sheet of 6 + 6 labels 4.25 2.10
  a.-f. 28c Any single .70 .35
See No. 3398.

A1335

Christmas A1336

2005, Oct. 31
3381 A1335 28c multi .70 .35
3382 A1336 53c multi 1.25 .65

Souvenir Sheet

Stained Glass Window, Avila Cathedral — A1337

2005, Nov. 2 Litho. & Engr.
3383 A1337 €2.21 multi 5.25 2.60

Euromediterranean Summit, Barcelona — A1338

2005, Nov. 3 Photo. Perf. 13¾x14
3384 A1338 53c multi 1.25 .65

Queen Juana of Castile (1479-1555) A1339

2005, Nov. 4 Perf. 14x13¾
3385 A1339 28c multi .70 .35
Parliament of Toro, 500th anniv.

Toys — A1340

No. 3386: a, Marionettes. b, Tops. c, Toy car. d, Toy truck. e, Doll. f, Container of marbles. g, Toy horse and cart. h, Toy motorcycle.

2006, Jan. 2 Litho. Die Cut Perf. 13
Self-Adhesive
3386 Booklet pane of 8 5.50
  a.-h. A1340 A Any single .65 .35
Nos. 3386a-3386h each sold for 28c on day of issue.

King Juan Carlos Type of 2001 With Euro Denominations Only

2006   **Photo.**   *Perf. 12¾x13¼*

3387	A1091	29c sil & brown	.70	.35
3388	A1091	57c sil & org	1.40	.70
3389	A1091	€2.26 sil & pur	5.50	2.75
3390	A1091	€2.33 sil & claret	5.50	2.75
3391	A1091	€2.39 sil & dull grn	5.75	2.75
		Nos. 3387-3391 (5)	18.85	9.30

Issued: 29c, 57c, 2/1; €2.26, 1/5; €2.33, €2.39, 2/13.

Carnation — A1341

Die Cut Perf. 13

2006, Jan. 20   **Litho.**
Self-Adhesive

3392   A1341   28c multi   .70   .35

No. 3392 was printed in sheets of 10, which were bound in booklets of 10 sheets.

Bank of Spain, 150th Anniv. — A1342

2006, Jan. 27   **Engr.**   *Perf. 14x13¾*
3393   A1342   78c brown & black   1.90   .95

Cypress Tree, La Anunciada Convent, Villafranca del Bierzo — A1343

2006, Jan. 30   **Photo.**
3394   A1343   53c multi   1.40   .70

Sparrow — A1344

Die Cut Perf. 13

2006, Feb. 1   **Litho.**
Self-Adhesive

3395   A1344   A multi   .70   .35

No. 3395 sold for 29p on day of issue, and was printed in sheets of 10 which were bound in booklets of 10 sheets.

Intl. Year of Deserts and Desertification — A1345

2006, Feb. 6   **Photo.**   *Perf. 13¾x14*
3396   A1345   29c multi   .70   .35

Woman Suffrage, 75th Anniv. — A1346

2006, Mar. 8
3397   A1346   29c blue & sepia   .70   .35

"Al Filo de lo Imposible" Type of 2005

No. 3398: a, Cyclists. b, Man in desert. c, Parachutist. d, Kayakers. e, Rafters. f, Waterfall rock climbers.

2006, Mar. 22   *Perf. 14x13¾*

3398	A1334	Sheet of 6 + 6 labels	12.00	6.00
a.		29c multi	.70	.35
b.		38c multi	.95	.45
c.		41c multi	1.00	.50
d.		57c multi	1.40	.70
e.		78c multi	1.90	.95
f.		€2.39 multi	6.00	3.00

Goldfinch   Strelitzia Flower
A1347   A1348

2006, Apr. 1   **Litho.**   *Die Cut Perf. 13*
3399   A1347   29c multi   .70   .35
3400   A1348   38c multi   .95   .45

Nos. 3399-3400 were each printed in sheets of 10, which were bound in booklets of 10 sheets.

Civic Values — A1349

Designs: No. 3401, 29c, Water conservation. No. 3402, 29c, Man with "No Drugs" balloons. 38c, Social Security and Labor inspectors, cent., horiz. 57c, Fight against human trafficking, horiz.

Perf. 14x13¾, 13¾x14

2006, Apr. 4   **Photo.**
3401-3404   A1349   Set of 4   3.75   1.90

Diario de Pontevedra Newspaper, 117th Anniv. — A1350

Diario de Léon Newspaper, Cent. — A1351

Diario de Avila Newspaper, 108th Anniv. — A1352

El Norte de Castilla Newspaper, 150th Anniv. — A1353

Levante-El Mercantil Valenciano Newspaper, 134th Anniv. — A1354

2006, Apr. 20   *Perf. 13¾x14, 14x13¾*

3405	A1350	41c multi	1.10	.55
3406	A1351	41c multi	1.10	.55
3407	A1352	41c multi	1.10	.55
3408	A1353	41c red & blk	1.10	.55
3409	A1354	41c multi	1.10	.55
		Nos. 3405-3409 (5)	5.50	2.75

Souvenir Sheet

Christopher Columbus (1451-1506), Explorer — A1355

2006, Apr. 24   *Perf. 14x13¾*
3410   A1355   €2.39 multi   6.25   3.00

Coronation of Santa Maria de Los Remedios Icon, Cent. — A1356

2006, Apr. 27
3411   A1356   €2.33 multi   6.00   3.00

Souvenir Sheet

Exfilna 2006 Philatelic Exhibition, Algeciras — A1357

Litho. & Engr.

2006, May 5   *Perf. 13¾x14*
3412   A1357   €2.39 multi   6.25   3.00

Inauguration of Taxis Family Postal System in Spain, 500th Anniv. — A1358

2006, May 9   **Photo.**
3413   A1358   29c multi   .75   .35

Internet Day A1359

25th Intl. Mathematics Conference, Madrid — A1360

Die Cut Perf. 13

2006, May 17   **Litho.**
3414   A1359   29c multi   .75   .35
3515   A1360   57c multi   1.50   .75

Socialist Youth In Spain, Cent. A1361

2006, May 23   **Photo.**   *Perf. 13¾x14*
3416   A1361   78c multi   2.00   1.00

Souvenir Sheet

España 06 Intl. Philatelic Exhibition, Málaga — A1362

2006, May 29
3417   A1362   78c multi   2.00   1.00

San Pedro and San Marcial Festivals, Irún — A1363

2006, June 5 **Perf. 14x13¾**
3418 A1363 29c multi   .75 .35

Architecture A1364

Designs: 29c, Casa Battló, Barcelona. 38c, Vapor Aymerich, Amt y Jover, Terrassa. 41c, Depósitos del Sol Library, Albacete. 57c, Campos Eliseos Theater, Bilbao. 78c, Alfredo Kraus Auditorium, Las Palmas, horiz. €2.33, Bus station, Casar de Cáceres, horiz.

Engr., Photo. (41c, 78c, €2.33)
2006, June 8 Perf. 14x13¾, 13¾x14
3419-3424 A1364 Set of 6   12.00 6.00

Al-Idrisi (c. 1100-65), Geographer A1365

2006, June 15 Photo. Perf. 14x13¾
3425 A1365 78c multi   2.00 1.00

Greenfinch A1366   Iris A1367

2006, July 5 Litho. Die Cut Perf. 13
Self-Adhesive
3426 A1366 29c multi   .75 .35
3427 A1367 41c multi   1.10 .55

Nos. 3426-3427 were each printed in sheets of 10 which were bound in booklets of 10 sheets.

Sanlúcar de Barrameda Horse Race A1368

2006, July 6 Photo. Perf. 13¾x14
3428 A1368 €2.33 multi   6.00 3.00

Archaeology A1369

Designs: 29c, Los Millares archaeological site. 57c, Art on vase from L'Alcudia archaeological site, horiz. 78c Moixent Warrior, bronze sculpture.

2006, July 6 Perf. 14x13¾, 13¾x14
3429-3431 A1369 Set of 3   4.25 2.10

Earth Sciences A1370

Designs: No. 3432, 29c, Derived cartography. No. 3433, 29c, Vulcanology and seismology.

2006, July 13 Perf. 13¾x14
3432-3433 A1370 Set of 2   1.50 .75

Benavides Thursday Market, Orbigo, 700th Anniv. A1371

Aragon-Cataluña Canal, Cent. — A1372

2006, July 20
3434 A1371 38c multi   1.00 .50
3435 A1372 38c multi   1.00 .50

Diplomatic Relations Between Spain and Israel, 20th Anniv. A1373

2006, Sept. 1
3436 A1373 78c multi   2.00 1.00

Castles A1374

Designs: 29c, Baños de la Encina Castle. €2.39, Torroella de Montgri.

2006, Sept. 8 Engr.
3437-3438 A1374 Set of 2   6.75 3.50

A1375

Europa — A1376

2006, Sept. 12 Photo. Perf. 14x13¾
3439 A1375 29c multi   .75 .35
3440 A1376 57c multi   1.50 .75

Bridges Between Spain and Portugal — A1377

No. 3441: a, Ayamonte International Bridge (Vila Real de Santo António). b, Alcántara Bridge.
Illustration reduced.

2006, Sept. 14 Perf. 13x13¼
3441   Horiz. pair   2.25 1.10
 a. A1377 29c multi   .75 .35
 b. A1377 57c multi   1.50 .75

See Portugal Nos. 2855-2856.

Rioja Grape Harvest Festival A1378

2006, Sept. 21 Perf. 13¾x14
3442 A1378 29c multi   .75 .35

Real Club Deportivo La Coruna Soccer Team, Cent. A1379

2006, Sept. 25
3443 A1379 57c multi   1.50 .75

Souvenir Sheet

Victory of Spanish Team at 2006 World Basketball Championships — A1380

2006, Oct. 2 Photo. Perf. 13¾x14
3444 A1380 29c multi   .75 .35

Swallow A1381   Poinsettia A1382

2006, Oct. 4 Litho. Die Cut Perf. 13
Self-Adhesive
3445 A1381 29c multi   .75 .35
3446 A1382 29c multi   .75 .35

Souvenir Sheets

España 06 World Philatelic Exhibition, Malaga — A1383

Exhibition emblem and: No. 3447, €2.33, Emblem of Vitorio & Lucchino, fashion designers. No. 3448, €2.33, Silhouette of hat and hand (cinema), vert. No. 3449, €2.33, Musical notes and staff. No. 3450, €2.33, Guitarist, vert. No. 3451, €2.33, Hand (flamenco dancing). No. 3452, €2.33, Tennis racquet and basketball, vert. No. 3453, €2.33, Pablo Picasso (1881-1973), artist.

2006 Photo. Perf. 13¾x14, 14x13¾
3447-3453 A1383 Set of 7   42.00 21.00

Issued: No. 3447, 10/8; No. 3448, 10/9; Nos. 3449-3450, 10/10; No. 3451, 10/11; No. 3452, 10/12; No. 3453, 10/13.

America Issue, Energy Conservation — A1384

2006, Oct. 14 Perf. 13¾
3454 A1384 78c multi   2.00 1.00

Appointment of First Spanish Postmen, 250th Anniv. — A1385

Die Cut Perf. 13
2006, Oct. 25 Litho.
Self-Adhesive
3455 A1385 29c multi   .75 .35
    Stamp Day.

Ramón Rubial
(1906-99),
Politician
A1386

2006, Oct. 27 Engr. Perf. 14x13¾
3456 A1386 57c multi   1.50 .75

A1387

Christmas
A1388

Die Cut Perf. 13
2006, Nov. 2   Litho.
Self-Adhesive
3457 A1387 29c multi   .75 .35
3458 A1388 57c multi   1.50 .75

Souvenir Sheet

Stained Glass Window, School of
Architecture, Polytechnic University of
Madrid — A1389

Litho. & Engr.
2006, Nov. 3   Perf. 14x13¾
3459 A1389 €2.39 multi   6.25 3.25

St.
Francis
Xavier
(1506-52)
A1390

2006, Nov. 7   Perf. 13¾x14
3460 A1390 29c multi   .80 .40

Television Broadcasting in Spain, 50th
Anniv. — A1391

2006, Nov. 8   Photo.
3461 A1391 29c multi   .80 .40

La Vanguardia
Newspaper, 125th
Anniv. — A1392

2006, Nov. 9   Perf. 14x13¾
3462 A1392 29c multi   .80 .40

Pío Baroja (1872-
1956),
Writer — A1393

2006, Nov. 23
3463 A1393 29c multi   .80 .40

Revision of
Spanish Coat of
Arms, 25th
Anniv. — A1394

2006, Nov. 23
3464 A1394 29c multi   .80 .40

A1395

Historical
Memory
Year
A1396

2006, Nov. 30   Perf. 13¾x14
3465 A1395 29c multi   .80 .40
3466 A1396 29c multi   .80 .40

Toys — A1397

No. 3467: a, Tricycle. b, Bus. c, Train. d,
Bowling game. e, Baby carriage. f, Seaplane.
g, Printing kit. h, Firetruck.

2007, Jan. 2 Litho. Die Cut Perf. 13
Self-Adhesive
3467   Booklet pane of 8   6.50
a.-h. A1397 A Any single   .80 .40
Nos. 3467a-3467h each sold for 30c on day
of issue.

King Juan
Carlos — A1398

2007, Jan. 13   Photo.   Perf. 13
Color of Portrait
3468 A1398   30c blue   .80   .40
3469 A1398   58c olive grn   1.50   .75
3470 A1398   €2.43 org brn   6.25 3.25
3471 A1398   €2.49 rose pink   6.50 3.25
   Nos. 3468-3471 (4)   15.05 7.65
      See Nos. 3532-3539.

Hoopoe   Red Rose
A1399   A1400

Die Cut Perf. 13
2007, Jan. 20   Litho.
Self-Adhesive
3472 A1399 30c multi   .80 .40
3473 A1400 39c multi   1.00 .50
   Nos. 3472-3473 each were printed in sheets
of 10, which were bound in booklets of 10
sheets.

Teacher
and Pupils
A1401

2007, Jan. 23
Self-Adhesive
3474 A1401 58c multi   1.50 .75

Las Provincias Newspaper, 140th
Anniv. (in 2006) — A1402

2007, Jan. 31 Photo. Perf. 13¾x14
3475 A1402 42c multi   1.10 .55

Stylized
Periodic
Table of
Elements
A1403

Gregorian
Calendar, 425th
Anniv. — A1404

Die Cut Perf. 13
2007, Feb. 2   Litho.
Self-Adhesive
3476 A1403 30c multi   .80   .40
3477 A1404 42c multi   1.10   .55

Institute of
Catalan
Studies,
Cent.
A1405

2007, Feb. 5 Photo. Perf. 13¾x14
3478 A1405 30c multi   .80 .40

2007 America's Cup Challenger
Races — A1406

2007, Feb. 8
3479 A1406 30c multi   .80 .40

Earth and
Space
Sciences
A1407

Designs: 30c, Map (cartography). 78c,
Yebes Astronomical Center radio telescope.

Die Cut Perf. 13
2007, Feb. 16   Litho.
Self-Adhesive
3480-3481 A1407 Set of 2   3.00 1.50

Fuentepiña Pine Tree — A1408

2007, Mar. 5 Photo. Perf. 13¾x14
3482 A1408 78c multi   2.10 1.10

Mosaic
from
Roman
Villa,
Pedrosa
de la
Vega
A1409

Roman
Baths,
Campo
Valdés
A1410

2007, Mar. 8
3483 A1409 30c multi   .80 .40
3484 A1410 30c multi   .80 .40

European
Economic
Community, 50th
Anniv. — A1411

2007, Mar. 23   Perf. 14x13¾
3485 A1411 58c multi   1.60 .80

Canary
A1412

Violet
A1413

2007, Apr. 2 Litho. *Die Cut Perf. 13*
Self-Adhesive
3486 A1412 30c multi .80 .40
3487 A1413 42c multi 1.25 .60

Souvenir Sheet

Madrid Movement, 25th
Anniv. — A1414

2007, Apr. 13 Photo. *Perf. 13¾x14*
3488 A1414 30c multi .85 .40

Souvenir Sheet

Mallorca Cathedral — A1415

Engr., Litho. Margin
2007, Apr. 16
3489 A1415 €2.43 blue 6.75 3.25
Exfilna 2007 National Philatelic Exhibition,
Palma de Mallorca.

Europa — A1416

2007, Apr. 23 Photo. *Perf. 14x13¾*
3490 A1416 58c multi 1.60 .80
Scouting, cent.

Architecture
A1417

Designs: 30c, Valleacerón Chapel,
Almadenejos. 39c, El Capricho, Comillas. 42c,
Santa Caterina Market, Barcelona. 58c, Viz-
caya Bridge, Las Arenas, horiz. 78c, Barajas
Airport, Madrid. €2.49, Casa Lis, Salamanca,
horiz.

Photo., Engr. (39c, 58c)
2007, Apr. 26 *Perf. 14x13¾, 13¾x14*
3491-3496 A1417 Set of 6 13.50 6.75

Juvenia
2007 Natl.
Youth
Philatelic
Exhibition,
Calahorra
A1418

2007, Apr. 28 Photo. *Perf. 13¾x14*
3497 A1418 30c multi .85 .40

Stamp
Day — A1419

2007, May 7 Litho. *Die Cut Perf. 13*
Self-Adhesive
3498 A1419 30c multi .80 .40

Song of
the Cid,
800th
Anniv.
A1420

2007, May 9 *Die Cut Perf. 13*
Self-Adhesive
3499 A1420 30c multi .80 .40

Law of the Court
of Auditors, 25th
Anniv. — A1421

2007, May 12 Photo. *Perf. 14x13¾*
3500 A1421 30c multi .80 .40

Civic
Values — A1422

Designs: 30c, Racial integration. 39c, No
school violence. 58c, Organ donation. 78c,
Equality of the sexes.

2007, May 16
3501-3504 A1422 Set of 4 5.50 2.75

Mushrooms
A1423

Designs: 30c, Tricholoma equestre. 78c,
Amanita muscaria.

2007, June 1
3505-3506 A1423 Set of 2 3.00 1.50

Carmen
Conde
(1907-96),
Writer
A1424

Rosa Chacel (1898-1994),
Writer — A1425

2007, June 4 Engr. *Perf. 13¾x14*
3507 A1424 €2.49 red & blk 6.75 3.50
3508 A1425 €2.49 org & blk 6.75 3.50

Real Betis
Balompié
Soccer
Team,
Cent.
A1426

2007, June 14 Photo. *Perf. 13¾x14*
3509 A1426 78c multi 2.10 1.10

Canonical
Coronation of
Blessed Mary of
the O — A1427

2007, June 16 *Perf. 14x13¾*
3510 A1427 30c multi .85 .40

Nightingale
A1428

Hyacinth
A1429

2007, July 2 Litho. *Die Cut Perf. 13*
Self-Adhesive
3511 A1428 30c multi .85 .40
3512 A1429 30c multi .85 .40

Spanish Armed Forces Peace
Missions — A1430

Illustration reduced.

2007, July 4 Photo. *Perf. 13x13¼*
3513 A1430 30c multi .85 .40

Expo
Zaragoza
2008
A1431

2007, July 5 Litho. *Die Cut Perf. 13*
Self-Adhesive
3514 A1431 58c multi 1.60 .80

Miniature Sheet

Scenes From Television Show "Al Filo
de lo Imposible" — A1432

No. 3515: a, Diver under ice shelf. b, Skier.
c, People pulling sleds. d, Sailboat in Antarctic
waters. e, Kayaker in fjord. f, Iditarod dog sled
team.

2007, July 12 Photo. *Perf. 14x13¾*
3515 A1432 Sheet of 6 + 6
labels 13.50 13.50
a. 30c multi .85 .40
b. 39c multi 1.00 .50
c. 42c multi 1.10 .55
d. 58c multi 1.60 .80
e. 78c multi 2.10 1.10
f. €2.43 multi 6.75 3.25

Nature
Parks
A1433

Designs: No. 3516, 30c, Albufera Nature
Park. No. 3517, 30c, Lagunas de Ruidera
Nature Park.

2007, July 19 *Perf. 13¾x14*
3516-3517 A1433 Set of 2 1.75 .85

Miniature Sheet

Lighthouses — A1434

No. 3518: a, Punta del Hidalgo Lighthouse, Tenerife. b, Cabo Mayor Lighthouse, Cantabria. c, Punta Almina Lighthouse, Ceuta. d, Melilla Lighthouse, Melilla. e, Cabo de Palos Lighthouse, Murcia. f, Gorliz Lighthouse, Vizcaya.

2007, Sept. 6

3518	A1434	Sheet of 6 + 6 labels	13.50	13.50
a.		30c multi	.85	.40
b.		39c multi	1.00	.50
c.		42c multi	1.10	.55
d.		58c multi	1.60	.80
e.		78c multi	2.10	1.10
f.		€2.43 multi	6.75	3.25

Castles
A1435

Designs: No. 3519, €2.49, Almenar Castle. No. 3520, €2.49, Villena Castle.

2007, Sept. 10   Engr.   Perf. 13¾x14

3519-3520	A1435	Set of 2	14.00	7.00

Souvenir Sheet

Statues of Asclepius, Greek God of Medicine — A1436

No. 3521: a, Statue from Museum of Ampurias, Spain. b, Statue from National Archaeological Museum, Athens.

2007, Sept. 13   Photo.   Perf. 12¾x13

3521	A1436	Sheet of 2	2.50	2.50
a.		30c multi	.85	.40
b.		58c multi	1.60	.80

See Greece No. 2319.

Dupont Lark — A1437   Daisy — A1438

2007, Oct. 1   Litho.   Die Cut Perf. 13
Self-Adhesive

3522	A1437	30c multi	.85	.40
3523	A1438	30c multi	.85	.40

El Adelantado de Segovia Newspaper, 106th Anniv. — A1439

2007, Oct. 4   Photo.   Perf. 13¾x14

3524	A1439	78c multi	2.25	1.10

America Issue, Education For All A1440

2007, Oct. 11

3525	A1440	78c multi	2.25	1.10

Miniature Sheet

Women's Clothing by Balenciaga In Costume Museum, Madrid — A1441

No. 3526: a, Ivory chantily lace and taffeta dress, 1948-50. b, Red silk satin two-piece party dress, 1960. c, Red morning coat and dress, 1960s. d, Yellow linen dress.

2007, Oct. 18   Photo.   Perf. 13¼x13

3526	A1441	Sheet of 4	6.25	6.25
a.		39c multi	1.10	.55
b.		42c multi	1.25	.60
c.		58c multi	1.60	.80
d.		78c multi	2.25	1.10

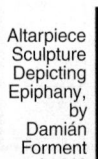

Altarpiece Sculpture Depicting Epiphany, by Damián Forment A1442

Children in Envelope A1443

Die Cut Perf. 13
2007, Oct. 31   Litho.
Self-Adhesive

3527	A1442	30c multi	.90	.45
3528	A1443	58c multi	1.75	.85

Christmas.

Self-Portraits A1444

Self-portraits of: 39c, Pedro Berruguete. 42c, Mariano Salvador Maella.

2007, Nov. 5   Photo.   Perf. 14x13¾

3529-3530	A1444	Set of 2	2.40	1.25

Souvenir Sheet

Stained-Glass Window by Alberto Martorell — A1445

Litho. & Engr.
2007, Nov. 9   Perf. 13¾x14

3531	A1445	€2.43 multi	7.25	3.75

King Juan Carlos Type of 2007
2008, Jan. 2   Photo.   Perf. 13
Color of Portrait

3532	A1398	1c black	.20	.20
3533	A1398	2c lilac rose	.20	.20
3534	A1398	5c blue	.20	.20
3535	A1398	10c greenish blue	.30	.20
3536	A1398	31c brown	.90	.45
3537	A1398	60c violet blue	1.75	.90
3538	A1398	78c rose	2.40	1.25
3539	A1398	€2.60 slate green	7.75	3.50
		Nos. 3532-3539 (8)	13.70	6.90

Toys — A1446

No. 3540: a, Steamship with wheels. b, Bean bag target with clown's face. c, Three sand pails. d, Stagecoach. e, Wafer container. f, Diabolo. g, Building blocks. h, Submarine.

2008, Jan. 2   Litho.   Die Cut Perf. 13
Self-Adhesive

3540		Booklet pane of 8	7.50	
a.-h.		A1446 A Any single	.90	.45

Nos. 3540a-3540h each sold for 31c on day of issue.

Green Woodpecker A1447   Camellia A1448

2008, Jan. 10   Die Cut Perf. 13
Self-Adhesive

3541	A1447	31c multi	.90	.45
3542	A1448	60c multi	1.75	.90

Sciences A1449

Designs: 39c, Medicine. 43c, Meteorology.

2008, Jan. 17   Litho.
Self-Adhesive

3543-3544	A1449	Set of 2	2.40	1.25

La Voz de Avilés Newspaper, Cent. — A1450

2008, Jan. 30   Photo.   Perf. 13¾x14

3545	A1450	31c multi	.95	.45

International Years — A1451

Designs: 78c, Intl. Polar Year. €2.60, Intl. Year of Planet Earth.

Die Cut Perf. 13
2008, Feb. 4   Litho.
Self-Adhesive

3546-3547	A1451	Set of 2	10.50	5.25

Hand and Phone Number for Abused Women's Hotline A1452

2008, Feb. 11   Die Cut Perf. 13
Self-Adhesive

3548	A1452	31c multi	.95	.45

Black Poplar of Horcajuelo A1453

2008, Feb. 18   Photo.   Perf. 14x13¾

3549	A1453	€2.44 multi	7.50	3.75

Expo Zaragoza 2008 A1454

Die Cut Perf. 13
2008, Feb. 22   Litho.
Self-Adhesive

3550	A1454	31c multi	.95	.45

Civic Values A1455

Designs: 31c, Fight against child exploitation. 39c, Intergenerational solidarity. 43c, Cultural diversity.

2008, Feb. 29   Photo.   Perf. 13¾x14

3551-3553	A1455	Set of 3	3.50	1.75

Archaeology — A1456

Designs: No. 3554, 31c, Bicha de Balazote. No. 3555, 31c, Funerary urn of Apophis I.

2008, Mar. 3
3554-3555 A1456 Set of 2   1.90   .95

Landscapes — A1457

Designs: No. 3556, 31c, Hoces del Rio Duratón Nature Park. No. 3557, 31c, Montes de Toledo.

2008, Mar. 10
3556-3557 A1457 Set of 2   2.00 1.00

Maritime Rescue Craft A1458

Die Cut Perf. 13
2008, Mar. 12   Self-Adhesive   Litho.
3558 A1458 31c multi   1.00   .50

University of Oviedo, 400th Anniv. A1459

2008, Mar. 14   Photo.   Perf. 13¾x14
3559 A1459 31c multi   1.00   .50

European Parliament, 50th Anniv. — A1460

2008, Mar. 19
3560 A1460 60c multi   1.90   .95

SEMI-POSTAL STAMPS

Red Cross Issue

Princesses María Cristina and Beatrice SP1

Queen as a Nurse — SP2   Queen Victoria Eugénia — SP3

Prince of Asturias — SP4   King Alfonso XIII — SP5

Perf. 12½

1926, Sept. 15   Unwmk.   Engr.
B1	SP1	1c black	2.00	1.90
B2	SP2	2c ultra	2.00	1.90
B3	SP3	5c violet brn	4.50	3.25
B4	SP4	10c green	3.75	3.25
B5	SP1	15c indigo	1.50	1.25
B6	SP4	20c dull violet	1.50	1.25
a.		20c violet brown (error)	500.00	375.00
B7	SP5	25c rose red	.25	.25
B8	SP1	30c blue green	35.00	32.50
B9	SP3	40c dark blue	20.00	17.50
B10	SP2	50c red orange	20.00	17.00
B11	SP4	1p slate	1.50	.90
B12	SP3	4p magenta	1.10	.65
B13	SP5	10p brown	1.10	.90
		Nos. B1-B13,EB1 (14)	102.95	91.25
		Set, never hinged	210.00	

The 20c was printed in violet brown for use in the colonies (Cape Juby, Spanish Guinea, Spanish Morocco and Spanish Sahara). No. B6a, the missing overprint error, is listed here because it is not known to which colony it belongs.
For overprints see Nos. B19-B46.

Airplane and Map of Madrid-Manila Flight — SP6

1926, Sept. 15
B14	SP6	15c dp ultra & org	.30	.30
B15	SP6	20c car & yel grn	.30	.30
B16	SP6	30c dk brn & ultra	.30	.30
B17	SP6	40c dk grn & brn org	.30	.30
B18	SP6	4p magenta & yel	82.50	82.50
		Nos. B14-B18,CB1-CB5 (10)	91.20	91.20
		Set, never hinged	160.00	

Madrid to Manila flight of Captains Eduardo G. Gallarza and Joaquim Loriga y Taboada.
Nos. B1-B18, CB1-CB5 and EB1 were used for regular postage on Sept. 15, 16, 17, 1926. Subsequently the unsold stamps were given to the Spanish Red Cross Society, by which they were sold uncanceled but they then had no franking power.
For overprints see Nos. B47-B53.

Coronation Silver Jubilee Issue
Red Cross Stamps of 1926 Overprinted "ALFONSO XIII," Dates and Ornaments in Various Colors

1927, May 27
B19	SP1	1c black (R)	4.50	4.00
B20	SP2	2c ultra (Bl)	7.75	7.75
B21	SP3	5c vio brn (R)	1.90	1.90
a.		Double overprint	37.50	
B22	SP4	10c green (Bl)	55.00	55.00
B23	SP1	15c indigo (R)	1.60	1.60
B24	SP2	20c dull vio (Bl)	3.00	3.00
B25	SP5	25c rose red (Bl)	.45	.45
B26	SP1	30c blue grn (Bl)	.85	.85
B27	SP3	40c dk blue (R)	.85	.85
B28	SP2	50c red org (Bl)	.85	.85
B29	SP4	1p slate (R)	1.60	1.60
B30	SP3	4p magenta (Bl)	8.25	8.25
B31	SP5	10p brown (G)	32.50	32.50
		Nos. B19-B31 (13)	119.10	118.60
		Set, never hinged	275.00	

Same with Additional Surcharges of New Values
B32	SP2	3c on 2c (G)	9.50	9.50
B33	SP2	4c on 2c (Bk)	9.50	9.50
B34	SP5	10c on 25c (Bk)	.55	.55
B35	SP5	25c on 25c (Bl)	.55	.55
B36	SP2	55c on 2c (R)	1.00	1.00
B37	SP4	55c on 10c (Bk)	55.00	55.00
B38	SP4	55c on 20c (Bk)	55.00	55.00
B39	SP1	75c on 15c (R)	.70	.70
B40	SP1	75c on 30c (R)	140.00	140.00
B41	SP3	80c on 5c (R)	52.50	50.00
B42	SP2	2p on 40c (R)	1.00	1.00
B43	SP4	2p on 1p (R)	1.00	1.00
B44	SP2	5p on 50c (G)	1.90	1.90
B45	SP3	5p on 4p (Bk)	3.25	3.25
B46	SP5	10p on 10p (G)	27.50	27.50
		Nos. B32-B46 (15)	358.95	356.45
		Set, never hinged	675.00	

Nos. B14-B18 Overprinted

B47	SP6	15c (Br)	.40	.40
a.		Double overprint	30.00	
B48	SP6	20c (Bl)	.40	.40
a.		Brown overprint (error)	65.00	
b.		Inverted overprint	30.00	
B50	SP6	30c (R)	.40	.40
a.		Blue overprint (error)	65.00	
b.		Double overprint	30.00	
B52	SP6	40c (Br)	.40	.40
a.		Inverted overprint	30.00	
b.		Double ovpt. (Bl + Br)	95.00	
B53	SP6	4p (Bl)	95.00	95.00
a.		Inverted overprint	160.00	

Semi-Postal Special Delivery Stamp
Overprinted "ALFONSO XIII," Dates and Ornaments in Violet
B54	SPSD1	20c	5.50	5.50
		Nos. B47-B54 (6)	102.10	102.10

Nos. CB1-CB5 Overprinted in Various Colors

B55	SPAP1	5c (R)	1.90	1.60
a.		Inverted overprint	30.00	
B56	SPAP1	10c (R)	2.25	2.25
a.		Inverted overprint	30.00	
B57	SPAP1	25c (Bl)	.40	.40
B58	SPAP1	50c (Bl)	.40	.40
a.		Double ovpt., one invtd.	72.50	
B59	SPAP1	1p (R)	2.50	2.50
a.		Inverted overprint	95.00	

Same with Additional Surcharges of New Values
B60	SPAP1	75c on 5c (R)	4.50	3.25
a.		Inverted surcharge	30.00	
B61	SPAP1	75c on 10c (R)	17.00	13.00
a.		Inverted surcharge	30.00	
B62	SPAP1	75c on 25c (Bl)	32.50	27.50
a.		Double surcharge	55.00	
B63	SPAP1	75c on 50c (Bl)	15.00	13.00
		Nos. B55-B63 (9)	76.45	63.90
		Set, never hinged	225.00	

Nos. B54-B63 were available for ordinary postage.

Stamps of Spanish Offices in Morocco and Spanish Colonies, 1926 (Spain Types SP3, SP5) Surcharged in Various Colors with New Values and

On Spanish Morocco
B64	SP3	55c on 4p bis (Bl)	21.00	17.50
B65	SP5	80c on 10p vio (Br)	21.00	17.50

On Spanish Tangier
B66	SP5	1p on 10p vio (Br)	110.00	90.00
B67	SP3	4p bis (G)	37.50	32.50

On Cape Juby
B68	SP3	5p on 4p bis (R)	70.00	57.50
B69	SP5	10p on 10p vio (R)	37.50	32.50

On Spanish Guinea
B70	SP5	1p on 10p vio (Bl)	21.00	17.50
B71	SP3	2p on 4p bis (G)	21.00	17.50

On Spanish Sahara
B72	SP5	80c on 10p vio (R)	32.50	27.50
B73	SP3	2p on 4p bis (R)	21.00	17.50
		Nos. B64-B73 (10)	392.50	327.50
		Set, never hinged	800.00	

Nos. B64-B73 were available for postage in Spain only.
Nos. B19-B73 were for the 25th year of the reign of King Alfonso XIII.
Counterfeits of Nos. B64-B73 abound.

Catacombs Restoration Issues

Pope Pius XI and King Alfonso XIII SP7

1928, Dec. 23   Engr.   Perf. 12½
Santiago Issue
B74	SP7	2c violet & blk	.25	.25
B75	SP7	2c lake & blk	.30	.30
B76	SP7	3c bl blk & vio	.25	.25
B77	SP7	3c dl bl & vio	.30	.30
B78	SP7	5c ol grn & vio	.65	.65
B79	SP7	10c yel grn & blk	1.10	1.10
B80	SP7	15c bl grn & vio	3.75	3.75
B81	SP7	25c dp rose & vio	3.75	3.75
B82	SP7	40c ultra & blk	.25	.25
B83	SP7	55c ol brn & vio	.25	.25
B84	SP7	80c red & blk	.25	.25
B85	SP7	1p gray blk & vio	.25	.25
B86	SP7	2p red brn & blk	5.25	5.25
B87	SP7	3p pale rose & vio	5.25	5.25
B88	SP7	4p vio brn & blk	5.25	5.25
B89	SP7	5p grnsh blk & vio	5.25	5.25

Toledo Issue
B90	SP7	2c bl blk & car	.25	.25
B91	SP7	2c ultra & car	.30	.30
B92	SP7	3c bis brn & ultra	.25	.25
B93	SP7	3c ol grn & ultra	.30	.30
B94	SP7	5c red vio & car	.65	.65
B95	SP7	10c yel grn & ultra	1.10	1.10
B96	SP7	15c slate bl & car	3.75	3.75
B97	SP7	25c red brn & ultra	3.75	3.75
B98	SP7	40c ultra & car	.25	.25
B99	SP7	55c dk brn & ultra	.25	.25
B100	SP7	80c black & car	.25	.25
B101	SP7	1p yellow & car	.25	.25
B102	SP7	2p dk gray & ultra	5.25	5.25
B103	SP7	3p violet & car	5.25	5.25
B104	SP7	4p vio brn & car	5.25	5.25
B105	SP7	5p bister & ultra	5.25	5.25
		Nos. B74-B105 (32)	64.70	64.70
		Set, never hinged	105.00	

Nos. B74-B105 replaced regular stamps from Dec. 23, 1928 to Jan. 6, 1929. The proceeds from their sale were given to a fund to restore the catacombs of Saint Damasus and Saint Praetextatus at Rome.
Nos. B74-B105 exist imperforate. Value set, $325 hinged, $375 never hinged.

Issues of the Republic

SP13

1938, Apr. 15   Perf. 11½
B106	SP13	45c + 2p bl & grnsh bl	.75	.65
a.		Imperf., pair	15.00	12.50
b.		Souv. sheet of 1	22.50	22.50
c.		Souv. sheet of 1, imperf.	625.00	575.00
		Never hinged	900.00	

Surtax for the defenders of Madrid.
For overprint and surcharge see Nos. B108, CB6.

Nurse and Orderly
Carrying Wounded
Soldier — SP14

1938, June 1   Engr.   Perf. 10
B107 SP14 45c + 5p cop red   .55   .55
a.   Imperf., pair   220.00

For surcharge see No. CB7.

No. B106 Overprinted in Black

1938, Nov. 7   Perf. 11½
B108 SP13 45c + 2p   3.25 3.25
     Never hinged   5.00

Defense of Madrid, 2nd anniversary.
A similar but larger overprint was applied to
cover blocks of four. Value never hinged, $30.

Values for souvenir sheets of 1937-38
are for examples with some faults.
Undamaged sheets are very hard to
find.

Spanish State
Souvenir Sheets

Alcazar,
Toledo
SP15

Design: No. B108C, A patio of Alcazar after
Civil War fighting.

1937 Unwmk. Photo. Perf. 11½
Control Numbers on Back
B108A SP15 2p org brn   19.00 19.00
b.   Imperf.   450.00 400.00
B108C SP15 2p dark green   19.00 19.00
d.   Imperf.   450.00 400.00
Set, never hinged   110.00
Set, B108Ab, B108Cd,
    never hinged   1,100.

Nos. B108A-B108C sold for 4p each.

SP16

Designs: 20c, Covadonga Cathedral. 30c,
Palma Cathedral, Majorca. 50c, Alcazar of
Segovia. 1p, Leon Cathedral.

1938 Unwmk. Photo. Perf. 12½
Control Numbers on Back
B108E SP16   Sheet of 4   42.50 42.50
f.   20c dull violet   5.00   5.00
g.   30c rose red   5.00   5.00
h.   50c bright blue   5.00   5.00
i.   1p greenish gray   5.00   5.00
j.   Imperf. sheet   72.50 65.00
      Never hinged   125.00

Each sheet sold for 4p.

SP17

Designs, alternating in sheet: Flag bearer.
Battleship "Admiral Cervera." Soldiers in
trenches. Moorish guard.

1938, July 1   Unwmk.   Perf. 13
Control Numbers on Back
B108K SP17   Sheet of 20 35.00 35.00
      Never hinged   45.00
l.   Imperf. sheet   160.00 160.00
      Never hinged   210.00

Sheet measures 175x132mm. Consists of
five vertical rows of four 2c violet, 3c deep
blue, 5c olive gray, 10c deep green and 30c
red orange, with each denomination appearing
in two different designs. Marginal inscription:
"Homenaje al Ejercito y a la Marina" (Honoring
the Army and Navy). Sold for 4p, or double
face value.

Souvenir Sheets

Don Juan of
Austria — SP18

Battle of
Lepanto
SP19

Perf. 12½
1938, Dec. 15   Unwmk.   Engr.
Control Numbers on Back
B108M SP18 30c dk car   22.50 22.50
B108N SP19 50c blue black 22.50 22.50
   Nos. B108M-B108N (2)   45.00 45.00
   Set, never hinged   77.50

Imperf
B108O SP18 30c black vio 550.00 550.00
B108P SP19 50c dk sl grn 550.00 550.00
   Nos. B108O-B108P (2)   1,100. 1,100.
   Set, never hinged   1,300.

Victory over the Turks in the Battle of
Lepanto, 1571.
Nos. B108M-B108P contain one stamp. The
dates "1571-1938" appear in the lower sheet
margin. Size: 89x74mm. Sold for 10p a pair.

LOCAL CHARITY STAMPS
Hundreds of different charity stamps
were issued by local organizations and
cities during the Civil War, 1936-39.
Some had limited franking value, but
most were simply charity labels. They
are of three kinds: 1. Local semipostals.
2. Obligatory surtax stamps. 3. Propaganda or charity labels.

Ruins of
Belchite
SP20

Miracle of Calanda — SP21

Designs: 10c+5c, 70c+20c, Ruins of
Belchite. 15c+10c, 80c+20c, The Rosary.
20c+10c, 1.50p+50c, El Pilar Cathedral.
25c+10c, 1p+30c, Mother Raffols praying.
40c+10c, 2.50p+50c, The Little Chamber.
45c+15c, 1.40p+40c, Oath of the Besieged.
10p+4p, The Apparition.

Perf. 10½, 11½x10½, 11½
1940, Jan. 29   Litho.   Unwmk.
Design SP20
B109 10c + 5c dp bl & vio
              brn   .20   .20
B110 15c + 10c rose vio &
              dk grn   .25   .25
B111 20c + 10c vio & dp bl .25 .25
B112 25c + 10c dp rose &
              vio brn   .25   .25
B113 40c + 10c sl grn &
              rose vio   .20   .20
B114 45c + 15c vio & dp
              rose   .30   .30
B115 70c + 20c multi   .30   .30
B116 80c + 20c dp rose &
              vio   .40   .40
B117 1p + 30c dk sl grn &
              pur   .40   .40
B118 1.40p + 40c pur &
              gray blk   32.50 32.50
B119 1.50p + 50c lt bl &
              brn vio   .50   .50
B120 2.50p + 50c choc & bl .50 .50
Design SP21
B121 4p + 1p rose lil &
              sl grn   11.00 11.00
B122 10p + 4p ultra &
              chnt   160.00 160.00
   Nos. B109-B122,CB8-
       CB17,EB2 (25)   444.35 444.25
   Set, never hinged   850.00

19th centenary of the Virgin of the Pillar.
The surtax was used to help restore the
Cathedral at Zaragoza, damaged during the
Civil War.
No. B121 exists in violet & slate green, No.
B122 in ultramarine & brown violet. Value,
$42.50 each.
Nos. B109-B122 exist imperf. Value, $750.
See No. 743, CB8-CB17.

General
Franco — SP23

Knight and
Lorraine
Cross — SP24

1940, Dec. 23   Unwmk.   Perf. 10
B123 SP23 20c + 5c dk grn &
              red   .65   .65
B124 SP23 40c + 10c dk bl & red .90 .40
   Set, never hinged   3.25

The surtax was for the tuberculosis fund.
See Nos. RA15, RAC1.

Stamps of 10c denomination, types
SP23 to SP28, are postal tax issues.

1941, Dec. 23
B125 SP24 20c + 5c bl vio & red .50 .30
B126 SP24 40c + 10c sl grn &
              red   .50   .25
   Set, never hinged   1.25

The surtax was used to fight tuberculosis.
See Nos. RA16, RAC2.

Cross of Lorraine
SP25   SP26

1942, Dec. 23   Litho.
B127 SP25 20c + 5c pale brn &
              rose red   1.40 1.25
B128 SP25 40c + 10c lt bluish
              grn & rose red .80   .45
   Set, never hinged   3.50

The surtax was used to fight tuberculosis.
See Nos. RA17, RAC3.

1943, Dec. 23   Photo.   Perf. 11½
B129 SP26 20c + 5c dl sl grn
              & dl red   3.25 1.40
B130 SP26 40c + 10c brt bl &
              dl red   2.00 1.10
   Set, never hinged   11.00

The surtax was used to fight tuberculosis.
See Nos. RA18, RAC4.

Dragon   St. George
Slaying — SP27   Slaying the
                  Dragon — SP28

Perf. 9½x10
1944, Dec. 23   Litho.   Unwmk.
B131 SP27 20c + 5c sl grn &
              red   .25   .25
B132 SP27 40c + 10c dl vio &
              red   .50   .50
B133 SP27 80c + 10c ultra &
              rose   7.75 7.75
   Nos. B131-B133 (3)   8.50 8.50
   Set, never hinged   14.50

The surtax was used to fight tuberculosis.
See Nos. RA19, RAC5.

1945, Dec. 23
Lorraine Cross in Red
B134 SP28 20c + 5c dl gray
              grn   .25   .20
B135 SP28 40c + 10c vio   .30   .20
B136 SP28 80c + 10c ultra 8.00 7.50
   Nos. B134-B136 (3)   8.55 7.90
   Set, never hinged   14.00

The surtax was used to fight tuberculosis.
See Nos. RA20, RAC6.

Nos. 753 and 768
Surcharged in Blue

1950, Oct. 23
B137 A195 50c + 10c   32.50 32.50
a.   "Caudillo" 14¾mm wide 95.00 97.50
B138 A195 1p + 10c   32.50 32.50
a.   "Caudillo" 14¾mm wide 95.00 97.50
   Set, never hinged   100.00
a   #B137a-B138a, never
        hinged   225.00

Visit of General Franco to Canary Islands.
First printing, brighter colors and pale blue
surcharge, was issued in Canary Islands.
Value, $200 hinged, $300 never hinged, $200
used. Second printing was issued in Madrid
Feb. 22, 1951. See No. CB18.

**Catalogue values for unused
stamps in this section, from this
point to the end of the section, are
for Never Hinged items.**

1992 Summer Olympics, Barcelona SP29

1988, Oct. 3 Photo. Perf. 14
B139 SP29 20p +5p Track and
field .35 .35
B140 SP29 45p +5p Badminton .60 .60
B141 SP29 50p +5p Basketball .70 .70
Nos. B139-B141 (3) 1.65 1.65

See Nos. B146-B152, B163-B168, B177-B179, B184-B186, B191-B193.

EXPO '92, Seville — SP30

Globes and sites of previous exhibitions: No. B142, Crystal Palace, London, 1851. No. B143, Eiffel Tower, Paris, 1889. No. B144, "The Atom," Brussels, 1958. No. B145, Monument, Osaka, 1970.

1989, Feb. 9 Photo. Perf. 14x13½
B142 SP30 8p +5p multi .20 .20
B143 SP30 8p +5p multi .20 .20
B144 SP30 20p +5p multi .30 .30
B145 SP30 20p +5p multi .30 .30
Nos. B142-B145 (4) 1.00 1.00

1992 Summer Olympics Type of 1988

1989, Mar. 7 Photo. Perf. 14
B146 SP29 8p +5p Handball .25 .25
B147 SP29 18p +5p Boxing .35 .35
B148 SP29 20p +5p Cycling .35 .35
B149 SP29 45p +5p Equestrian .60 .60
Nos. B146-B149 (4) 1.55 1.55

1989, Oct. 3 Photo. Perf. 13½x14
B150 SP29 18p +5p Fencing .65 .65
B151 SP29 20p +5p Soccer .65 .65
B152 SP29 45p +5p Pommel
horse 1.25 1.25
Nos. B150-B152 (3) 2.55 2.55

500th Anniv. Emblem and Produce or Fauna Indigenous to the Americas — SP31

1989, Oct. 16 Litho. Perf. 13x13½
B153 SP31 8p +5p Cocoa .20 .20
B154 SP31 8p +5p Corn .20 .20
B155 SP31 20p +5p Tomato .30 .30
B156 SP31 20p +5p Horse .30 .30
B157 SP31 45p +5p Potato .60 .60
B158 SP31 50p +5p Turkey .60 .60
a. Bklt. pane of 6, #B153-B158 2.25
Nos. B153-B158 (6) 2.20 2.20

Discovery of America, 500th anniv.

EXPO '92, Seville SP32

Curro, the character trademark, and symbols of development in Spain.

1990, Feb. 22 Photo. Perf. 14
B159 SP32 8p +5p multi .20 .20
B160 SP32 20p +5p multi, diff. .30 .30
B161 SP32 45p +5p multi, diff. .60 .60
B162 SP32 50p +5p multi, diff. .70 .70
Nos. B159-B162 (4) 1.80 1.80

1992 Summer Olympics Type of 1988
1990, Mar. 7 Photo. Perf. 13½x14
B163 SP29 18p +5p Weight lifting .30 .30
B164 SP29 20p +5p Field hockey .30 .30
B165 SP29 45p +5p Judo .55 .55
Nos. B163-B165 (3) 1.15 1.15

1990, Oct. 3 Photo. Perf. 13½x14
B166 SP29 8p +5p Wrestling .20 .20
B167 SP29 18p +5p Swimming .40 .40
B168 SP29 20p +5p Baseball .50 .50
Nos. B166-B168 (3) 1.10 1.10

Discovery of America, 500th Anniv. (in 1992) — SP33

Drawings of sailing ships.

1990, Oct. 15 Litho. Perf. 13
B169 SP33 8p +5p "Viajes-A" .20 .20
B170 SP33 8p +5p "Viajes-B" .20 .20
B171 SP33 20p +5p "Viajes-C" .30 .30
B172 SP33 20p +5p "Viajes-D" .30 .30
a. Bklt. pane of 4, #B169-B172 1.00
Nos. B169-B172 (4) 1.00 1.00

Expo '92, Seville SP34

Designs: 15p+5p, La Cartuja, Monastery of Santa Maria de las Cuevas. 25p+5p, Amphitheater. 45p+5p, La Cartuja Bridge. 55p+5p, La Bargueta Bridge.

Litho. & Engr.
1991, Feb. 12 Perf. 14
B173 SP34 15p +5p multi .30 .30
B174 SP34 25p +5p multi .40 .40
B175 SP34 45p +5p multi .65 .65
B176 SP34 55p +5p multi .80 .80
Nos. B173-B176 (4) 2.15 2.15

Summer Olympics Type of 1988
1991, Mar. 7 Litho. Perf. 13½x14
B177 SP29 15p + 5p Five athletes .30 .30
B178 SP29 25p + 5p Kayaking .40 .40
B179 SP29 45p + 5p Rowing .65 .65
Nos. B177-B179 (3) 1.35 1.35

Madrid, European City of Culture, 1992 SP35

Designs: 15p+5p, Fountain of Apollo. 25p+5p, Statue of Alvaro de Bazan. 45p+5p, Bank of Spain. 55p+5p, St. Isidore's Institute.

1991, July 29 Photo. Perf. 13½x14
B180 SP35 15p + 5p multi .30 .30
B181 SP35 25p + 5p multi .40 .40
B182 SP35 45p + 5p multi .60 .60
B183 SP35 55p + 5p multi .75 .75
Nos. B180-B183 (4) 2.05 2.05

1992 Summer Olympics Type of 1988
1991, Oct. 3 Litho. Perf. 14
B184 SP29 15p +5p Tennis .45 .45
B185 SP29 25p +5p Table tennis .60 .60
B186 SP29 55p +5p Shooting 1.25 1.25
Nos. B184-B186 (3) 2.30 2.30

Discovery of America, 500th Anniv., 1992 — SP36

15p+5p, Garcilaso Gomez Suarez de Figueroa, the Inca, poet. 25p+5p, Pope Alexander VI. 45p+5p, Luis de Santangel, banker. 55p+5p, Friar Toribio de Paredes, monk.

1991, Oct. 15 Photo. Perf. 13x13½
B187 SP36 15p +5p multi .30 .30
B188 SP36 25p +5p multi .40 .40
B189 SP36 45p +5p multi .60 .60
B190 SP36 55p +5p multi .75 .75
a. Bklt. pane of 4, #B187-B190 2.00
Nos. B187-B190 (4) 2.05 2.05

1992 Summer Olympics Type of 1988
1992, Mar. 6 Photo. Perf. 13½x14
B191 SP29 15p +5p Archery .40 .40
B192 SP29 25p +5p Sailing .55 .55
B193 SP29 55p +5p Volleyball 1.10 1.10
Nos. B191-B193 (3) 2.05 2.05

Columbus Type of 1930 Souvenir Sheet
1992, Mar. 31 Engr. Perf. 14
B194 Sheet of 3 1.00 1.00
a. A65 17p +5p dark red .30 .30
b. A65 17p +5p ultramarine .30 .30
c. A65 17p +5p black .30 .30

Discovery of America, 500th anniv.

Expo '92 Type
Design: No. B195, Seville, 16th cent.
1992, Apr. 21 Litho. Perf. 13½x14
Souvenir Sheet
B195 A837 17p +5p multi .35 .35

1992 Summer Olympics, Barcelona — SP37

Perf. 14x13½, 13½x14
1992, July 16 Photo.
B196 SP37 17p +5p Mascot
COBI .40 .40
B197 SP37 17p +5p Hand holding torch, horiz. .40 .40
B198 SP37 17p +5p "25 Jul" .40 .40
Nos. B196-B198 (3) 1.20 1.20

1992 Summer Olympics, Barcelona SP38

Designs: a, Olympic Stadium. b, San Jordi Sports Palace. c, INEF Sports University.

1992, July 25 Perf. 13½x14
B199 SP38 27p +5p Triptych,
#a.-c. 1.40 1.40

1992 Summer Olympics, Barcelona SP39 SP40

#B200, Olympic mascot as stamp collector. #B201, Sagrada Family Church, Barcelona.

1992, July 29 Photo. Perf. 14x13½
B200 SP39 17p +5p multi .35 .35
B201 SP40 17p +5p multi .35 .35

Olymphilex '92 (#B201).

Madrid, European City of Culture — SP41

#B202, Municipal Museum. #B203, Royal Theater. #B204, The Prado Museum. #B205, Queen Sofia Natl. Center for the Arts.

1992, Nov. 24 Photo. Perf. 14x13½
B202 SP41 17p +5p multi .35 .30
B203 SP41 17p +5p multi .35 .30
B204 SP41 17p +5p multi .35 .30
B205 SP41 17p +5p multi .35 .30
Nos. B202-B205 (4) 1.40 1.20

AIR POST STAMPS

Regular Issue of 1909-10 Overprinted in Red or Black

Perf. 13x12½, 14
1920, Apr. 4 Unwmk.
C1 A46 5c green (R) 1.25 .80
a. Imperf., pair 105.00 105.00
b. Double overprint 35.00 35.00
c. Inverted overprint 90.00 90.00
d. Double ovpt., one invtd. 35.00 35.00
e. Triple overprint 35.00 35.00
C2 A46 10c car (Bk) 1.50 1.00
a. Imperf., pair 105.00 105.00
b. Double overprint 35.00 35.00
d. Double ovpt., one invtd. 35.00 35.00
C3 A46 25c dp blue (R) 2.75 1.40
a. Inverted overprint 90.00 90.00
b. Double overprint 35.00 35.00
C4 A46 50c sl blue (R) 11.00 5.00
a. Imperf., pair 105.00 105.00
C5 A46 1p lake (Bk) 35.00 19.00
a. Imperf., pair 385.00 385.00
Nos. C1-C5 (5) 51.50 27.20
Set, never hinged 125.00

Dangerous counterfeits are plentiful.
A 30c green was authorized, but not issued.
Value: hinged $550; never hinged $750.
For overprints see Nos. C58-C61.

"Spirit of St. Louis" over Coast of Europe — AP1

Plane and Congress Seal — AP2

Seville-Barcelona Exposition Issue
Control Numbers on Back
1929, Feb. 15 Engr. Perf. 11
C6 AP1 5c brown 5.00 5.00
C7 AP1 10c rose 5.00 5.00
C8 AP1 25c dark blue 5.50 5.50
C9 AP1 50c purple 5.75 5.75
C10 AP1 1p green 30.00 25.00
C11 AP1 4p black 21.00 20.00
Nos. C6-C11 (6) 72.25 66.25
Set, never hinged 210.00

Nos. C6 to C11 exist imperforate. Value, $575.

The so-called errors of color of Nos. C10, C18-C21, C23-C24, C28-C31, C37, C40, C42, C44, C46, C48, C50, C52, C55, C62-C67 are believed to have been irregularly produced.

Railway Congress Issue
Control Numbers on Back
1930, May 10 Litho. Perf. 14
C12 AP2 5c bister brn 5.25 5.25
C13 AP2 10c rose 5.25 5.25
C14 AP2 25c dark blue 5.25 5.25

C15 AP2 50c purple   13.50   13.50
  a.   Vert. pair, imperf. between   300.00
        Never hinged   600.00
C16 AP2 1p yellow green   27.50   27.50
C17 AP2 4p black   27.50   27.50
     Nos. C12-C17 (6)   84.25   84.25
     Set, never hinged   175.00

The note after No. 385 will apply here also.
Dangerous counterfeits exist.

Goya Issue

Fantasy of Flight AP3

Asmodeus and Cleofas — AP4

Fantasy of Flight AP5

Fantasy of Flight — AP6

1930, June 15   **Engr.**   **Perf. 12½**

C18	AP3	5c brn red & yel	.20	.20
C19	AP3	15c blk & red org	.20	.20
C20	AP3	25c brn car & dp red	.20	.20
C21	AP4	5c ol grn & grnsh bl	.20	.20
C22	AP4	10c sl grn & yel grn	.20	.20
C23	AP4	20c ultra & rose red	.20	.20
C24	AP4	40c vio bl & lt bl	.30	.30
C25	AP5	30c brown & vio	.30	.30
C26	AP5	50c ver & grn	.30	.30
C27	AP5	4p brn car & blk	2.10	2.10
C28	AP6	1p vio brn & vio	.30	.30
C29	AP6	4p bl blk & sl grn	2.10	2.10
C30	AP6	10p blk brn & bis brn	7.75	7.75
		Nos. C18-C30,CE1 (14)	14.55	14.55
		Set, never hinged	25.00	

Exist imperf. Value, set $150.

Christopher Columbus Issue

La Rábida Monastery — AP7

Martín Alonso Pinzón — AP8   Vicente Yanez Pinzón — AP9

Columbus in His Cabin — AP10

1930, Sept. 29   **Litho.**

C31	AP7	5c lt red brn	.25	.20
C32	AP7	5c olive bister	.25	.20
C33	AP7	10c blue green	.25	.20
C34	AP7	15c dark violet	.25	.20
C35	AP7	20c ultra	.25	.20

Engr.

C36	AP8	25c carmine rose	.25	.20
C37	AP9	30c dp red brn	1.75	1.75
C38	AP8	40c indigo	1.75	1.75
C39	AP9	50c orange	1.75	1.75
C40	AP8	1p dull violet	1.75	1.75
C41	AP10	4p olive brown	1.75	1.75
C42	AP10	10p light brown	10.00	11.00
		Nos. C31-C42 (12)	20.25	20.95
		Set, never hinged	30.00	

Exist imperf. Value, set $190.

Spanish-American Issue

AP11

Columbus AP12

Columbus and Pinzón Brothers AP13

1930, Sept. 29   **Litho.**

C43	AP11	5c lt red	.20	.20
C44	AP11	10c dull green	.20	.20

Engr.

C45	AP12	25c scarlet	.20	.20
C46	AP12	50c slate gray	2.25	1.90
C47	AP12	1p fawn	2.25	1.90
C48	AP13	4p slate blue	2.25	1.90
C49	AP13	10p brown violet	10.00	9.25
		Nos. C43-C49 (7)	17.35	15.55
		Set, never hinged	30.00	

Exist imperf. Value, set $175.

Spanish-American Exhibition Issue

Santos-Dumont and First Flight of His Airplane — AP14

Teodoro Fels and His Airplane AP15

Dagoberto Godoy and Pass over Andes — AP16

Sacadura Cabral and Gago Coutinho and Their Airplane AP17

Sidar of Mexico and Map of South America — AP18

Ignacio Jiménez and Francisco Iglesias — AP19

Charles A. Lindbergh, Statue of Liberty, Spirit of St. Louis and Cat AP20

Santa Maria, Plane and Torre del Oro, Seville AP21

1930, Oct. 10   **Photo.**   **Perf. 14**

C50	AP14	5c gray black	.80	.50
C51	AP15	10c dk olive grn	.80	.50
C52	AP16	25c ultra	.80	.50
C53	AP17	50c blue gray	1.75	1.25
C54	AP18	50c black	1.75	1.25
C55	AP19	1p car lake	3.75	2.75
a.		1p brown violet	65.00	65.00
		Never hinged	140.00	
C56	AP20	1p deep green	3.75	2.75
C57	AP21	4p slate blue	6.75	5.00
		Nos. C50-C57 (8)	20.15	14.50
		Set, never hinged	75.00	

Exist imperf. Value, set $110.
Note after No. 432 also applies to Nos. C31-C57.

Reprints of Nos. C50-C57 have blurred impressions, yellowish paper. Value: one-tenth of originals.

Nos. C1-C4 Overprinted in Red or Black

1931   **Perf. 13x12½**

C58	A46	5c green (R)	11.00	10.00
C59	A46	10c carmine (Bk)	11.00	10.00
C60	A46	25c deep blue (R)	15.00	14.50
C61	A46	50c slate blue (R)	30.00	22.50
		Nos. C58-C61 (4)	67.00	57.00
		Set, never hinged	140.00	

Counterfeits of overprint exist.
The status of Nos. C58-C61 has been questioned.

Plane and Royal Palace, Madrid AP22

Madrid Post Office and Cibeles Fountain AP23

Plane over Calle de Alcalá, Madrid AP24

1931, Oct. 10   **Engr.**   **Perf. 12**

C62	AP22	5c brown violet	.20	.30
C63	AP22	10c deep green	.20	.30
C64	AP22	25c dull red	.20	.30
C65	AP23	50c deep blue	.40	.45
C66	AP23	1p deep violet	.60	.55
C67	AP24	4p black	7.75	10.00
		Nos. C62-C67 (6)	9.35	11.90
		Set, never hinged	13.00	

3rd Pan-American Postal Union Congress, Madrid.
Exist imperf. Value, set $45.
For overprints see Nos. CO1-CO6.

Montserrat Issue

Plane over Montserrat Pass — AP25

1931, Dec. 9   **Perf. 11½**
Control Number on Back

C68	AP25	5c black brown	.50	.50
C69	AP25	10c yellow green	2.25	2.25
C70	AP25	25c deep rose	9.00	9.00
C71	AP25	50c orange	32.50	32.50
C72	AP25	1p gray black	22.50	22.50
		Nos. C68-C72 (5)	66.75	66.75
		Set, never hinged	85.00	

Perf. 14

C68a	AP25	5c	6.75	13.00
C69a	AP25	10c	37.50	40.00
C70a	AP25	25c	67.50	67.50
C71a	AP25	50c	67.50	67.50
C72f	AP25	1p	67.50	67.50
		Nos. C68a-C72f (5)	246.75	255.50
		Set, never hinged	275.00	

900th anniv. of Montserrat Monastery.
Nos. C68-C72 exist imperf. Value, $525.

Autogiro over
Seville — AP26

1935-39   **Perf. 11½**
C72A AP26 2p gray blue   20.00   4.50
   g.   Imperf., pair   300.00

Re-engraved
C72B AP26 2p dk blue ('38)   .65   .25
   c.   Imperf., pair   20.00
   d.   Perf. 10 ('39)   1.50   1.10
   Set, #C72A-C72B, never
   hinged   42.50

The sky has heavy horizontal lines of shading. Entire design is more heavily shaded than No. C72A.
No. C72B exists privately perforated 14. Value, $9 unused, $9 used.
For overprints see Nos. 7LC14, 7LC19, 14L26.

Eagle and Newspapers — AP27

Press Building,
Madrid — AP28

Don Quixote and Sancho Panza Flying
on the Wooden Horse — AP29

Design: 15c, 30c, 50c, 1p, Autogiro over House of Nazareth.

1936, Mar. 11   **Photo.**   **Perf. 12½**
C73 AP27   1c rose car   .20   .20
C74 AP27   2c dark brown   .20   .20
C75 AP27   5c black brown   .20   .20
C76 AP28 10c dk yellow grn   .20   .20
C77 AP27 15c Prus blue   .20   .20
C78 AP27 20c violet   .20   .20
C79 AP27 25c magenta   .20   .20
C80 AP28 30c red orange   .20   .20
C81 AP27 40c orange   .50   .20
C82 AP28 50c light blue   .30   .20
C83 AP28 60c olive green   .65   .40
C84 AP28   1p brnsh black   .65   .45
C85 AP29   2p brt ultra   5.00   2.25
C86 AP29   4p lilac rose   5.00   2.25
C87 AP29 10p violet brown   14.00   11.00
   Nos. C73-C87 (15)   27.70   18.85
   Set, never hinged   37.50

Madrid Press Association, 40th anniv.
Exist imperf. Value, set $250 hinged and $325 never hinged.
See note after No. 432.

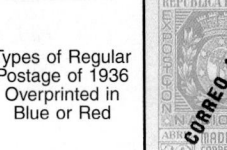

Types of Regular
Postage of 1936
Overprinted in
Blue or Red

1936   **Imperf.**
C88 A125 10c dk red (Bl)   150.00 150.00
C89 A125 15c dk blue (R)   150.00 150.00
   Set, never hinged   500.00

1st National Philatelic Exhibition which opened in Madrid, Apr. 2, 1936.

No. 577 Overprinted in
Black

1936, Aug. 1   **Perf. 11½**
C90 A128 30c rose red   3.00   3.75
   Never hinged   6.00
   b.   Imperf., pair   140.00

Issued in commemoration of the flight of aviators Antonio Arnaiz and Juan Calvo from Manila to Spain.
Counterfeit overprints exist.
Exists privately perforated 14. Value, $50 unused, $50 used.

No. 288 Surcharged in Black

1938, Apr. 13   **Perf. 14**
C91 A36 2.50p on 10c   80.00   72.50
   Never hinged   150.00

7th anniversary of the Republic.
Values are for examples with perforations nearly touching the design on one or two sides.

No. 507 Surcharged in Various Colors

1938, Aug.   **Perf. 11½**
C92 A92   50c on 25c (Bk)   25.00 25.00
C93 A92   1p on 25c (G)   1.90   1.40
C94 A92 1.25p on 25c (R)   1.90   1.40
C95 A92 1.50p on 25c (Bl)   1.90   1.40
C96 A92   2p on 25c (Bk &
           R)   35.00 30.00
   Nos. C92-C96 (5)   65.70 59.20
   Set, never hinged   110.00

No. 585 Surcharged

1938, June 1   **Perf. 11**
C97 A132 5p on 1p multi   250.00 250.00
   Never hinged   375.00
   a.   Imperf., pair   550.00 550.00
   b.   Inverted surcharge   350.00 350.00
   c.   Souvenir sheet   3,000. 3,000.
     Never hinged   6,000.
   d.   As "c," imperf.   6,500. 6,500.
   e.   As "c," inverted
     surcharge   6,000.

Counterfeit overprints exist.

Type of 1938-39
Overprinted in Red or
Carmine

1938, May   **Perf. 10, 10½**
C98 A163 50c indigo (R)   .70   .55
C99 A163   1p dk blue (C)   3.00   .70
   Set, never hinged   4.50

Exist imperf. Value, each $100.
Copies without overprint are proofs.

Juan de
la Cierva
and his
Autogiro
over
Madrid
AP30

1939, Jan. Unwmk. Litho. Perf. 11
C100 AP30 20c red orange   .60   .40
C101 AP30 25c dk carmine   .45   .20
C102 AP30 35c brt violet   .65   .40
C103 AP30 50c dk brown   .65   .25
C105 AP30   1p blue   .65   .25
C107 AP30   2p green   3.25   1.75
C108 AP30   4p dull blue   5.00   2.75
   Nos. C100-C108 (7)   11.25   6.00
   Set, never hinged   19.00

Exist imperf. Value, set $325.

1941-47   **Perf. 10**
C109 AP30 20c dk red orange   .20   .20
C110 AP30 25c redsh brown   .20   .20
C111 AP30 35c lilac rose   1.60   .50
C112 AP30 50c brown   .45   .20
C113 AP30   1p chalky blue   1.40   .20
C114 AP30   2p lt gray grn   1.60   .20
C115 AP30   4p gray blue   5.00   .30
C116 AP30 10p brt purple ('47)   3.75   .65
   Nos. C109-C116 (8)   14.20   2.45
   Set, never hinged   26.00

Issued in honor of Juan de la Cierva (1895-1936), inventor of the autogiro.
Nos. C109-C115 exist imperf. Value, set $300.
The overprint "EXPOSICION NACIONAL DE FILATELIA 1948 SAN SEBASTIAN" multiple, in parallel horizontal lines, on Nos. C109 to C113 and other airmail stamps, was privately applied.

Correo Aéreo   **Correo Aéreo**

Nos. 625-634, 660, 676 and 677 with either of these overprints have not been established as issues of the Spanish government.

Mariano
Pardo de
Figueroa
(Dr.
Thebussem)
AP31

1944, Oct. 12   **Engr.**   **Perf. 10**
C117 AP31 5p brt ultra   15.00 13.00
   Never hinged   23.00

"Stamp Day" and "Day of the Race," Oct. 12, 1944. Valid for franking air mail correspondence one day only.

Mail
Coach,
Plane and
Count of
St. Louis
AP32

1945, Oct. 12   **Unwmk.**
C118 AP32 10p yellow green   17.50 *19.00*
   Never hinged   25.00

"Stamp Day" and "Day of the Race," Oct. 12, 1945, and to honor Luis José Sartorius, Count of St. Louis, who issued the decree for Spain's 1st postage stamps. No. C118 was valid for franking air mail correspondence one day only.
C118 exists imperf. Value, $800.

Maj.
Joaquin
Garcia
Morato
AP33

1945, Nov. 27
C119 AP33 10p deep claret   13.50   5.50
   Never hinged   32.50

C119 exists imperf. Value, $275 hinged, $425 never hinged.

Capt. Carlos   Bartolomé de las
Haya Gonzalez   Casas
AP34   AP35

1945, Dec. 14
C120 AP34 4p red   5.50   4.50
   Never hinged   12.50

C120 exists imperf. Value, $375 hinged and $500 never hinged.

1946, Oct. 12   **Perf. 11½x11**
C121 AP35 5.50p green   1.90   2.50
                    3.00

Stamp Day and Day of the Race. Exists imperf. Value $16.

Don Quixote
and Sancho
Panza Astride
Claviieno
AP36

1947, Oct. 9   **Perf. 10**
C122 AP36 5.50p purple   4.50   4.50
   Never hinged   6.75

Stamp Day and the 400th anniversary of the birth of Miguel de Cervantes Saavedra.
C122 exists imperf. Value, $500.

Manuel de   Ignacio
Falla — AP37   Zuloaga — AP38

1947, Dec. 1   **Perf. 9½x10½**
     Control Number on Back
C123 AP37 25p dk vio brn   27.50 15.00
C124 AP38 50p dk carmine   110.00 40.00
   Set, never hinged   250.00

For overprint see No. CB18.
C124 exists imperf. Value, $925.

Train and
Plane — AP39

1948, Oct. 9   **Litho.**   **Perf. 13x12½**
C125 AP39 2p scarlet   1.50   1.50
   Never hinged   2.25

Cent. of Spanish railroads and Stamp Day.

UPU Type of Regular Issue with Pedestal and Propeller Added

1949, Oct. 9   *Perf. 12½x13*
C126 A202 4p dk olive green   .20   .45
   Never hinged   .40

Stamp Day and the 75th anniv. of the UPU.

Stamp of 1850
AP40

Map of Western
Hemisphere
AP41

1950, Oct. 12   **Engr.**   *Imperf.*
C127 AP40 1p rose brn   4.50   6.50
C128 AP40 2.50p brown org   4.50   6.50
C129 AP40 20p dark blue   80.00   87.50
C130 AP40 25p green   80.00   87.50
   Nos. C127-C130 (4)   169.00   188.00
   Set, never hinged   290.00

Centenary of Spanish postage stamps.

1951, Apr. 16   **Photo.**   *Perf. 12½*
C131 AP41 1p blue   4.50   2.25
   Never hinged   6.25

6th Congress of the Postal Union of the Americas and Spain.

Isabella I
AP42

1951, Oct. 12   **Engr.**   *Perf. 13*
C132 AP42 60c dk gray grn   6.50   .40
C133 AP42 90c orange   .80   .55
C134 AP42 1.30p plum   5.00   4.00
C135 AP42 1.90p sepia   4.50   4.00
C136 AP42 2.30p dk blue   2.75   2.75
   Nos. C132-C136 (5)   19.55   11.70
   Set, never hinged   27.50

Stamp Day and 500th anniv. of the birth of Queen Isabella I.

"The Eucharist"
by
Tiepolo — AP43

St. Francis
Xavier — AP44

1952, May 26   **Photo.**   *Perf. 12½x13*
C137 AP43 1p gray green   3.00   .60
   Never hinged   3.50

35th International Encharistic Congress, Barcelona, 1952.

1952, July 3   **Engr.**
C138 AP44 2p deep blue   30.00   14.00
   Never hinged   60.00

400th anniv. of the death of St. Francis Xavier.

Ferdinand the Catholic and Columbus
Presenting Natives
AP45

1952, Oct. 12
C139 AP45 60c dull green   .25   .20
C140 AP45 90c orange   .25   .20
C141 AP45 1.30p plum   .45   .30

C142 AP45 1.90p sepia   2.00   2.00
C143 AP45 2.30p deep blue   10.00   9.50
   Nos. C139-C143 (5)   12.95   12.20
   Set, never hinged   17.50

500th anniversary of the birth of Ferdinand the Catholic and to publicize Stamp Day.

Joaquin Sorolla
y Bastida
AP46

Miguel Lopez
de Legazpi
AP47

1953, Oct. 9   *Perf. 13x12½*
C144 AP46 50p dark violet   300.00   22.50
   Never hinged   675.00

Issued to honor Joaquin Sorolla y Bastida (1863-1923), impressionist painter.

1953, Nov. 5
C145 AP47 25p gray black   57.50   27.50
   Never hinged   125.00

Spanish-Philippine Postal Convention of 1951.

Leonardo Torres
Quevedo (1852-
1939),
Mathematician and
Inventor — AP48

Perf. 13x12½
1955, Sept. 6   **Engr.**   **Unwmk.**
C146 AP48 50p bluish gray & blk   5.00   .90
   Never hinged   11.00

Plane and
Caravel
AP49

1955-56   **Photo.**   *Perf. 12½x13*
C147 AP49 20c gray grn ('56)   .20   .20
C148 AP49 25c gray violet   .20   .20
C149 AP49 50c ol gray ('56)   .20   .20
C150 AP49 1p red orange   .20   .20
C151 AP49 1.10p emer ('56)   .20   .20
C152 AP49 1.40p rose car   .20   .20
C153 AP49 3p brt blue ('56)   .20   .20
C154 AP49 4.80p yellow   .20   .20
C155 AP49 5p redsh brown   1.50   .20
C156 AP49 7p lilac ('56)   .45   .20
C157 AP49 10p lt ol grn ('56)   .50   .25
   Nos. C147-C157 (11)   2.25
   Set, never hinged   4.00

Mariano Fortuny y
Carbo (1838-1874),
Painter — AP50

1956, Jan. 10   **Engr.**   *Perf. 13x12½*
C158 AP50 25p grnsh black   14.00   .90
   Never hinged   30.00

> **Catalogue values for unused stamps in this section, from this point to the end of the section, are for Never Hinged items.**

Bullfight Type of Regular Issue

25c, Small town arena. 50c, Fighting with cape. 1p, Dedication of the bull. 5p, Bull ring.

Perf. 13x12½, 12½x13
1960, Feb. 29   **Engr.**   **Unwmk.**
C159 A246 25c brn car & dl lil   .20   .20
C160 A245 50c blue   .20   .20
C161 A246 1p red & dull red   .20   .20
C162 A245 5p red lilac & vio   .55   .40
   Nos. C159-C162 (4)   1.15   1.00

Jai Alai
AP51

1960, Mar. 27   **Photo.**   *Perf. 12½x13*
C163 AP51 1p brt red & dk
      brn   4.75   3.25
C164 AP51 5p dull brn &
      mag   4.75   3.25
C165 AP51 6p vio blk & mag   4.75   3.25
C166 AP51 10p grn, mag & dk
      brn   4.75   3.25
   Nos. C163-C166 (4)   19.00   13.00

1st Intl. Cong. of Philately, Barcelona, Mar. 26-Apr. 5. Nos. C163-C166 could be bought at the exhibition upon presentation of 5p entrance ticket.

Sport Type of Regular Issue

Sports: 1.25p, 6p, Steeplechase, horiz. 1.50p, 10p, Basque ball game.

Perf. 12½x13, 13x12½
1960, Oct. 31   **Unwmk.**
C167 A251 1.25p choc & car   .30   .20
C168 A251 1.50p pur, brn & blk   .30   .20
C169 A251 6p vio blk & car   .95   .55
C170 A251 10p ol grn, red &
      blk   1.25   .55
   Nos. C167-C170 (4)   2.80   1.55

Rosary Type of Regular Issue

Mysteries of the Rosary: 25c, The Ascension, Bayeu. 1p, The Descent of the Holy Ghost, El Greco. 5p, The Assumption, Mateo Cerezo. 10p, The Coronation of the Virgin Mary, El Greco.

1962, Oct. 26   **Engr.**   *Perf. 13*
C171 A280 25c vio & dl gray vio   .25   .20
C172 A280 1p olive & brown   .35   .20
C173 A280 5p brn & rose cl   .60   .25
C174 A280 10p bluish grn & yel
      grn   1.40   .50
   Nos. C171-C174 (4)   2.60   1.15

Recaredo I,
Visigothic King, 586-
601 — AP52

Portrait: 50p, Francisco Cardinal Jimenez de Cisneros (1436-1517).

1963, Dec. 5   **Engr.**   *Perf. 13x12½*
C175 AP52 25p dull purple   1.10   .40
C176 AP52 50p green & black   1.90   .55

1966, Feb. 26

Portraits: 25p, Seneca (4 B.C.-65 A.D.). 50p, Pope St. Damasus I (304?-384).

C177 AP52 25p yel grn & dk grn   1.75   .20
C178 AP52 50p sky bl & gray bl   2.75   .55

Plaza de
Espana,
Seville
AP53

1981, Nov. 26   **Engr.**   *Perf. 13*
C179 AP53 13p shown   .20   .20
C180 AP53 20p Rande River
      Bridge,
      Pontevedra   .25   .20

St. Thomas, by El
Greco — AP54

1982, July 7   **Photo.**   *Perf. 13*
C181 AP54 13p Sts. Andrew and
      Francis   .20   .20
C182 AP54 20p shown   .20   .20

Bowling
AP55

1983, Apr. 13   **Photo.**   *Perf. 13*
C183 AP55 13p Bicycling, vert.   .20   .20
C184 AP55 20p shown   .20   .20

AIR POST SEMI-POSTAL STAMPS

Red Cross Issue

Ramon
Franco's
Plane Plus
Ultra
SPAP1

Perf. 12½, 13
1926, Sept. 15   **Engr.**   **Unwmk.**
CB1 SPAP1 5c black & vio   1.40   1.40
CB2 SPAP1 10c ultra & blk   3.00   3.00
CB3 SPAP1 25c carmine & blk   .30   .30
CB4 SPAP1 50c red org & blk   .30   .30
CB5 SPAP1 1p black & green   2.50   2.50
   Nos. CB1-CB5 (5)   7.50   7.50
   Set, never hinged   10.00

For overprints and surcharges see Nos. B55-B63.

No. B106 Surcharged in Black

1938, Apr. 15   *Perf. 11½*
CB6 SP13 45c + 2p + 5p   250.00   225.00
   Never hinged   450.00
   a.   Imperf., pair   1,150.   900.00
   b.   Souvenir sheet of 1   4,500.   4,500.
   c.   Souvenir sheet, imperf.   6,000.   6,000.
   d.   Souv. sheet, surch. invtd.   6,500.   5,750.

The surtax was used to benefit the defenders of Madrid.
This issue has been extensively counterfeited.

No. B107 Surcharged

1938, June 1   *Perf. 10*
CB7 SP14 45c + 5p + 3p   10.00   9.75
   Never hinged   17.50

Monument
SPAP2

Dome Fresco by Goya, Cathedral of Zaragoza SPAP3

#CB8, CB11, Monument. #CB9, CB14, Caravel Santa Maria. #CB10, CB12, The Ascension. #CB13, CB15, The Coronation. #CB17, Bombardment of Cathedral of Zaragoza.

Perf. 10½, 11½x10½, 11½

1940, Jan. 29   Litho.   Unwmk.
Bicolored

CB8	SPAP2	25c + 5c	.25 .25
CB9	SPAP2	50c + 5c	.25 .25
CB10	SPAP2	65c + 15c	.25 .25
CB11	SPAP2	70c + 15c	.25 .25
CB12	SPAP2	90c + 20c	.25 .25
CB13	SPAP2	1.20p + 30c	.25 .25
CB14	SPAP2	1.40p + 40c	.25 .25
CB15	SPAP2	2p + 50c	.40 .40
CB16	SPAP3	4p + 1p sl grn & rose lil	9.75 9.75
CB17	SPAP3	10p + 4p chnt & ultra	225.00 225.00
	Nos. CB8-CB17 (10)		236.90 236.90
	Set, never hinged		350.00

19th centenary of the Pillar Virgin. The surtax was used to help restore the Cathedral at Zaragoza, damaged during the Civil War.
No. CB16 exists in slate green & violet, No. CB17 in red violet & ultramarine. Value, $32.50 each.
Exist imperf. Value, set $350.

No. C123 Surcharged in Black

1950-51   Perf. 9½x10½
Control Number on Back

CB18	AP37	25p + 10c	275.00 225.00
	Never hinged		550.00
a.	Without control number		3,250. 1,250.
	Without control number, never hinged		5,000.

Visit of Gen. Franco to the Canary Islands, Oct., 1950.
The control number was printed on the gum, and regummed copies of No. CB18 are frequently offered as No. CB18a.
Counterfeit surcharges exist.
Issued: #CB18a, 10/23/50; #CB18 2/22/51.

AIR POST SPECIAL DELIVERY STAMP

Goya Commemorative Issue

Type of Air Post Stamp of 1930 Overprinted

1930   Unwmk.   Perf. 12½

CE1	AP4	20c bl blk & lt brn (Bk)	.20 .20
	Never hinged		.25
a.	Blue overprint		15.00 7.75
	Never hinged		21.00
b.	Overprint omitted		15.00 22.50
	Never hinged		25.00

See note after No. 432.

AIR POST OFFICIAL STAMPS

Pan-American Postal Union Congress Issue
Types of Air Post Stamps of 1931 Overprinted in Red or Blue

1931   Unwmk.   Perf. 12

CO1	AP22	5c red brown (R)	.20 .20
CO2	AP22	10c blue grn (Bl)	.20 .20
CO3	AP22	25c rose (Bl)	.20 .20
CO4	AP23	50c lt blue (R)	.20 .20
CO5	AP23	1p violet (R)	.20 .20
CO6	AP24	4p gray blk (R)	3.25 3.25
	Nos. CO1-CO6 (6)		4.25 4.25
	Set, never hinged		5.75

Shades exist.
Exist imperf. Value, set $22.50.

SPECIAL DELIVERY STAMPS

Pegasus and Coat of Arms — SD1

1905-25   Unwmk.   Typo.   Perf. 14
Control Number on Back

E1	SD1	20c deep red	40.00 .30
	Never hinged		75.00
a.	20c rose red, litho. ('25)		35.00 .30
b.	Imperf., pair		275.00
c.	As "a," imperf., pair		275.00

Gazelle SD2

Pegasus — SD3

1929   Engr.   Perf. 11
Control Number on Back

E2	SD2	20c dull red	17.50 20.00
	Never hinged		32.50
a.	Perf. 14		29.00 32.50
	Never hinged		55.00

Seville and Barcelona Exhibitions. See note after No. 432.

1929-32   Perf. 13½x12½, 11½
Control Number on Back

E3	SD3	20c red	19.00 3.75
	Never hinged		37.50
a.	Imperf., pair		375.00
b.	Without control number, perf. 11½ ('32)		55.00 1.40
	Never hinged		87.50
c.	As "b," imperf., pair		875.00

No. E3 Overprinted like Nos. 358-370

E4	SD3	20c red (Bl)	12.00 25.00
	Never hinged		25.00

League of Nations 55th assembly.
For overprints see Nos. E5, E10-E12.

No. E3 Overprinted in Blue

1930   Perf. 13½x12½, 11½

E5	SD3	20c red	12.00 .65
	Never hinged		32.50

Railway Congress Issue

Electric Locomotive — SD4

1930, May 10   Litho.   Perf. 14
Control Number on Back

E6	SD4	20c brown orange	50.00 50.00
	Never hinged		95.00

See note after No. 385.

Goya Issue

Type of Regular Issue of 1930 Overprinted

1930   Perf. 12½

E7	A57	20c lilac rose	.20 .30
	Never hinged		.40

Christopher Columbus Issue
Type of Regular Issue of 1930 Overprinted

1930 Sept. 29

E8	A64	20c brown violet	1.75 1.75
	Never hinged		2.75

See note after No. 432.

Spanish-American Exhibition Issue

View of Seville Exhibition — SD5

1930, Oct. 10   Photo.   Perf. 14

E9	SD5	20c orange	.40 .25
	Never hinged		.55

See note after No. 432.

Madrid Issue

No. E5 Overprinted in Green

1931   Perf. 11½

E10	SD3	20c red	4.50 4.50
	Never hinged		7.25

The status of No. E10 has been questioned.

Barcelona Issue

No. E3 Overprinted

E11	SD3	20c red	5.00 5.00
	Never hinged		11.00

No. E11 also exists with accent over "U."
The status of No. E11 has been questioned.

No. E3 Overprinted in Blue

E12	SD3	20c red	5.50 1.00
	Never hinged		19.00

Montserrat Issue

Pegasus — SD6

1931   Engr.   Perf. 11
Control Number on Back

E13	SD6	20c vermilion	22.50 22.50
	Never hinged		35.00
a.	Perf. 14		55.00 60.00

SD7

1934   Perf. 10

E14	SD7	20c vermilion	.20 .20
	Never hinged		.20
a.	Imperf., pair		32.50

For overprints see #10LE1, 11LE1-11LE4, 14LE1.

Newsboy — SD8

Pegasus SD9

1936   Photo.   Perf. 12½
E15 SD8 20c rose carmine   .25 .30
   Never hinged   .40
Madrid Press Association, 40th anniv.
See note after No. 432.

Spanish State
1937-38   Unwmk.   Litho.   Perf. 11
With imprint "Hija. de B Fournier-Burgos"
E16 SD9 20c violet brn   7.75 4.50
   Never hinged   11.00
  a. Imperf., pair   77.50
Without Imprint
E17 SD9 20c dk vio brn ('38)   1.50   .30
   Never hinged   2.75
  a. Imperf., pair   50.00

No. 645 Overprinted in
Black

1937
E18 A162 20c dark violet   11.00 11.00
   Never hinged   14.50

Pegasus
SD10

1939-42   Perf. 10½
Imprint: "SANCHEZ TODA"
E19 SD10 25c carmine   4.50   .70
   Never hinged   6.25
  a. Imperf., pair   50.00
Without Imprint
Perf. 10
E20 SD10 25c carmine ('42)   .20   .20
   Never hinged   .30

> Catalogue values for unused stamps in this section, from this point to the end of the section, are for Never Hinged items.

"Flight"
SD11

Centaur — SD12

Perf. 12½x13, 13x12½
1956, Feb. 12   Photo.   Unwmk.
E21 SD11 2p scarlet   .20 .20
E22 SD12 4p black & magenta   .20 .20

1965-66
E23 SD11   3p dp car   .20   .20
E24 SD11   5p dp org ('66)   .20   .20
E25 SD12 6.50p dk vio & rose
      brn ('66)   .20   .20
  Nos. E21-E25 (5)   1.00 1.00

Chariot
SD13

Mail Circling
Globe — SD14

1971, June 1   Photo.   Perf. 13
E26 SD13 10p red & yel grn   .20   .20
E27 SD14 15p red, bl & blk   .20   .20

Communications — SD15

1993, Apr. 20 Photo. Perf. 14x13½
E28 SD15 180p red & yellow   2.50   .35

SEMI-POSTAL SPECIAL DELIVERY STAMPS

Red Cross Issue

Royal Family
Group
SPSD1

1926   Unwmk.   Engr.   Perf. 12½, 13
EB1 SPSD1 20c red vio & vio
      brn   8.75   8.75
   Never hinged   17.00
See notes after Nos. 432 and B18.
For overprint see No. B54.

Motorcyclist
and
Zaragoza
Cathedral
SPSD2

1940   Litho.   Perf. 11½
EB2 SPSD2 25c + 5c rose red &
      buff   .40 .30
19th cent. of the Pillar Virgin. The surtax was used to help restore the Cathedral at Zaragoza, damaged during the Civil War.

DELIVERY TAX STAMPS

D1

1931   Unwmk.   Litho.   Perf. 11½
ER1 D1 5c black   7.25   .20
   Never hinged   12.00
For overprints see Nos. ER2-ER3, 7LE5-7LE6.

No. ER1 Overprinted in
Red

1931
ER2 D1 5c black   1.25 1.40
   Never hinged   2.25
No. ER2 also exists with accent over "U."

No. ER1 Overprinted in
Red

ER3 D1 5c black   3.00 3.00
                         5.50
These stamps were originally issued for Postage Due purpose but were later used as regular postage stamps.

WAR TAX STAMPS

These stamps did not pay postage but represented a fiscal tax on mail matter in addition to the postal fees. Their use was obligatory.

Coat of Arms
WT1   WT2
Unwmk.
1874, Jan. 1   Typo.   Perf. 14
MR1 WT1 5c black   9.50   .95
  a. Imperf. pair   14.00
MR2 WT1 10c pale blue   10.50 1.60
  a. Imperf., pair   62.50

1875, Jan. 1
MR3 WT2 5c green   5.25   .60
  a. Imperf., pair   27.50
MR4 WT2 10c lilac   11.00 2.75
  a. Imperf., pair   55.00

King Alfonso XII
WT3   WT4
1876, June 1
MR5 WT3 5c pale green   6.25 1.00
MR6 WT3 10c blue   6.25 1.00
  a. Cliche of 5c in plate of
     10c   125.00
MR7 WT3 25c black   50.00 17.00
MR8 WT3 1p lilac   475.00 110.00
MR9 WT3 5p rose   775.00 300.00
Nos. MR5-MR9 exist imperforate. Value, $1,100.

1877, Sept. 1
MR10 WT4 15c claret   27.50 1.00
  a. Imperf., pair   100.00
MR11 WT4 50c yellow   775.00 110.00

WT5   WT6
1879
MR12 WT5 5c blue   42.00
MR13 WT5 10c rose   25.00
MR14 WT5 15c violet   15.50
MR15 WT5 25c brown   25.00
MR16 WT5 50c olive green   15.50
MR17 WT5 1p bister   25.00
MR18 WT5 5p gray   90.00
  Nos. MR12-MR18 (7)   238.00
Nos. MR12-MR18 were never placed in use.
Nos. MR17 and MR18 exist imperf. Value, $225.

Inscribed "1897 A 1898"
1897   Perf. 14
MR19 WT6 5c green   3.00 1.90
MR20 WT6 10c green   3.00 1.90
MR21 WT6 15c green   450.00 190.00
MR22 WT6 20c green   7.50 3.00
Nos. MR19-MR22 exist imperf. Value for set $825.

Inscribed "1898-99"
1898
MR23 WT6 5c black   2.25 1.75
MR24 WT6 10c black   2.25 1.75
MR25 WT6 15c black   50.00 9.50
MR26 WT6 20c black   3.50 3.50
  Nos. MR23-MR26 (4)   58.00 16.00
Nos. MR23-MR26 exist imperf. Value about $275 a pair.

King Alfonso
XIII — WT7

1898
MR27 WT7 5c black   7.50   .60
  a. Imperf., pair   85.00

OFFICIAL STAMPS

Coat of Arms
O1   O2
Unwmk.
1854, July 1   Typo.   Imperf.
O1 O1 ½o blk, yellow   2.10 2.75
O2 O1 1o blk, rose   2.75 3.25
  a. 1o black, blue   29.00
O3 O1 4o blk, green   7.50 9.25
O4 O1 1 l blk, blue   52.50 60.00
  Nos. O1-O4 (4)   64.85 75.25

1855-63
O5 O2 ½o blk, yellow   1.50 1.75
  a. ½o black, straw ('63)   1.75 1.90
O6 O2 1o blk, rose   1.50 1.75
  a. 1o black, salmon rose   3.25 1.90
O7 O2 4o blk, green   3.25 1.90
  a. 4o black, yellow green   8.75 1.90
O8 O2 1 l blk, gray blue   14.50 17.50
  Nos. O5-O8 (4)   20.75 22.90
The "value indication" on Nos. O1-O8 actually is the weight of the mail in onzas (ounces, "o") and libras (pounds, "l") for which they were valid.

Type of Regular Issue of 1889
1895   Perf. 14
O9 A34 15c yellow   10.00 6.00
  a. Imperf., pair   250.00

Coat of Arms — O5

1896-98
O10 O5   rose   5.25 1.75
  a. Imperf., pair   87.50
O11 O5 dk blue ('98)   17.50 6.00

Cervantes Issue

Chamber of
Deputies
O6

Statue of
Cervantes — O7

Cervantes — O9

National
Library
O8

1916, Apr. 22   Engr.   Perf. 12
For the Senate

O12	O6	green & blk	1.10	.90
O13	O7	brown & blk	1.10	.90
O14	O8	carmine & blk	1.10	.90
O15	O9	brown & blk	1.10	.90

For the Chamber of Deputies

O16	O6	violet & blk	1.10	.90
O17	O7	carmine & blk	1.10	.90
O18	O8	green & blk	1.10	.90
O19	O9	violet & blk	1.10	.90
	Nos. O12-O19 (8)		8.80	7.20

Exist imperf. Value set of pairs, $110.
Exist with centers inverted. Value for set,
$87.50.

Pan-American Postal Union Congress Issue

Types of
Regular Issue
of 1931
Overprinted in
Red or Blue

1931   Perf. 12½

O20	A84	5c dk brown (R)	.40	.20
O21	A85	10c brt green (Bl)	.40	.20
O22	A86	15c dull violet (R)	.40	.20
O23	A85	25c deep rose (Bl)	.40	.20
O24	A87	30c olive green (Bl)	.40	.20
O25	A84	40c ultra (R)	.55	.50
O26	A85	50c deep orange (Bl)	.55	.50
O27	A86	1p blue black (R)	.55	.50
O28	A88	4p magenta (Bl)	12.50	12.50
O29	A88	10p lt brown (R)	22.50	22.50
	Nos. O20-O29 (10)		38.65	37.50
	Set, never hinged		55.00	

Nos. O22-O29 exist imperf. Values about 3
times those quoted.

Mail
Coach
O30

Decorative
Mailbox
Opening
O10

Mail
Pouch
O11

Bicycle for
Mail
Delivery
O12

1999   Photo.   Perf. 13¾x14

O30	O9	multi	—
O31	O10	multi	—
O32	O11	multi	—
O33	O12	multi	—
a.	Horiz. strip, #O30-O33		—

For use by the Philatelic Service to any
address. Not normally available unused.

POSTAL TAX STAMPS

PT5

PT6

Perf. 10½x11½
1937, Dec. 23   Litho.

RA11	PT5	10c blk, pale bl & red	7.25	4.50
	Never hinged		19.00	
a.	Imperf. pair		72.50	
	Never hinged		110.00	

The tax was for the tuberculosis fund.

1938, Dec. 23   Perf. 11½

RA12	PT6	10c multicolored	4.50	1.75
	Never hinged		10.00	
a.	Imperf. pair		45.00	
	Never hinged		55.00	

The tax was for the tuberculosis fund.

"Spain"
Holding
Wreath of
Peace
over
Marching
Soldiers
PT7

1939, July 18   Perf. 11

RA13	PT7	10c blue	.20	.20
	Never hinged		.25	
a.	Imperf. pair		65.00	
	Never hinged		82.50	

Type of Regular Issue, 1939
Without Imprint
Unwmk.

1939, Dec. 23   Litho.   Imperf.

RA14	A166	10c dull claret	.20	.20
	Never hinged		.25	

Tuberculosis Fund Issues
Types of Corresponding Semi-Postal
Stamps

1940, Dec. 23   Perf. 10

RA15	SP23	10c violet & red	.20	.20
	Never hinged		.25	

1941, Dec. 23

RA16	SP24	10c black & red	.20	.20
	Never hinged		.25	

1942, Dec. 23

RA17	SP25	10c dl sal & rose red	.20	.20
	Never hinged		.25	

1943, Dec. 23   Photo.   Perf. 11

RA18	SP26	10c purple & dl red	.30	.25
	Never hinged		.50	

Perf. 9½x10
1944, Dec. 23   Litho.   Unwmk.

RA19	SP27	10c salmon & rose	.20	.20
	Never hinged		.25	

1945, Dec. 23

RA20	SP28	10c salmon & car	.20	.20
	Never hinged		.25	

Mother and
Child — PT8

1946, Dec. 22   Litho.   Perf. 9½x10½

RA21	PT8	5c violet & red	.20	.20
A22	PT8	10c green & red	.20	.20
	Set, never hinged		.40	

See No. RAC7.

Lorraine
Cross
PT9

Tuberculosis
Sanatorium
PT10

Perf. 9½x10½
1947, Dec. 22   Unwmk.

RA23	PT9	5c dk brown & red	.20	.20
RA24	PT10	10c vio bl & red	.20	.20
	Set, never hinged		.40	

See No. RAC8.

Aesculapius
PT11

"El Cid"
PT11a

Photogravure; Cross Engraved
1948, Dec. 22   Unwmk.   Perf. 12½

RA25	PT11	5c brown & car	.20	.20
RA26	PT11	10c dp green & car	.20	.20
	Set, never hinged		.40	

The tax on Nos. RA15-RA26 was used to
fight tuberculosis. See Nos. RAB1, RAC9.

1949, Feb. 1   Litho.   Perf. 10½x9½

RA27	PT11a	5c violet	.20	.20
	Never hinged		.25	

The tax aided displaced children. Valid for
ordinary postage after Dec. 24, 1949.

Tuberculosis Fund Issues

Galleon and
Lorraine
Cross — PT12

Pine Branch and
Candle — PT13

Photogravure; Cross Engraved
1949, Dec. 22   Perf. 12½

RA28	PT12	5c violet & red	.20	.20
RA29	PT12	10c yel grn & red	.20	.20
	Set, never hinged		.40	

See Nos. RAB2, RAC10.

1950, Dec. 22
Cross in Carmine

RA30	PT13	5c rose violet	.20	.20
RA31	PT13	10c deep green	.20	.20
	Set, never hinged		.35	

See Nos. RAB3, RAC11.

Children at
Seashore
PT14

Nurse and Baby
PT15

1951, Oct. 1
Cross in Carmine

RA32	PT14	5c rose brown	.20	.20
RA33	PT14	10c dull green	.35	.20
	Set, never hinged		.75	

See No. RAC12.

1953, Oct. 1
Cross in Carmine

RA34	PT15	5c carmine lake	.30	.20
RA35	PT15	10c gray blue	.80	.20
	Set, never hinged		2.25	

The tax on RA28-RA35 was used to fight
tuberculosis. See No. RAC13.

POSTAL TAX SEMI-POSTAL STAMPS

Types of Corresponding Postal Tax
Stamps

Photogravure; Cross Engraved
1948   Unwmk.   Perf. 12½

RAB1	PT11	50c + 10c red brn & car	.80	.75
	Never hinged		1.25	

1949

RAB2	PT12	50c + 10c dk ol bis & red	.50	.25
	Never hinged		.80	

1950

RAB3	PT13	50c + 10c brn & car	1.25	1.25
	Never hinged		2.25	

The surtax on Nos. RAB1-RAB3 was used
to fight tuberculosis. Combines domestic letter rate and tax obligatory Dec. 22-Jan. 3.

POSTAL TAX AIR POST STAMPS

Tuberculosis Fund Issues
Franco Type of Semi-Postal Stamps
Unwmk.

1940, Dec. 23   Litho.   Perf. 10

RAC1	SP23	10c bright pink & red	.90	.90
	Never hinged		2.50	

Knight and
Lorraine
Cross — PTAP2

1941, Dec. 23

RAC2	PTAP2	10c blue & red	.25	.25
	Never hinged		.50	

Lorraine
Cross and
Doves
PTAP3

1942, Dec. 23

RAC3	PTAP3	10c dl sal & rose	.80	.50
	Never hinged		1.25	

Cross of
Lorraine — PTAP4

Tuberculosis
Sanatorium
PTAP5

1943, Dec. 23   Photo.   *Perf. 11*
RAC4 PTAP4 10c vio & dl red   .90 1.00
   Never hinged   1.60

1944, Dec. 23   Litho.   *Perf. 10x9½*
RAC5 PTAP5 25c salmon & rose   3.75 3.75
   Never hinged   5.50

Lorraine Cross
and
Eagle — PTAP6

1945, Dec. 23   *Perf. 10*
RAC6 PTAP6 25c red & car   1.40 1.25
   Never hinged   1.75

Eagle — PTAP7

1946, Dec. 22
RAC7 PTAP7 25c red & car   .20 .20
   Never hinged   .40

Tuberculosis
Sanatorium
PTAP8

Plane over
Sanatorium
PTAP9

1947, Dec. 22   *Perf. 11½*
RAC8 PTAP8 25c red vio   .20 .20
   Never hinged   .40

Photogravure; Cross Engraved
1948, Dec. 22   *Perf. 12½*
RAC9 PTAP9 25c ultra & car   .30 .25
   Never hinged   .60

Bell and Lorraine   Dove and
Cross   Flowers
PTAP10   PTAP11

1949, Dec. 22
RAC10 PTAP10 25c maroon & red   .20 .20
   Never hinged   .25

1950, Dec. 22
RAC11 PTAP11 25c dk bl & car   .30 .30
   Never hinged   .60

Mother and   Tobias and
Child   Archangel
PTAP12   PTAP13

1951, Oct. 1
RAC12 PTAP12 25c brn & car   .50 .20
   Never hinged   .80

1953, Oct. 1
RAC13 PTAP13 25c brn & car   3.50 5.50
   Never hinged   6.50

FRANCHISE STAMPS

F1   F2

1869   Unwmk.   Litho.   *Imperf.*
S1   F1   blue   47.50 35.00
   a. Tête bêche pair   125.00 110.00
The franchise of No. S1 was granted to
Diego Castell to use in distributing his publica-
tions on Spanish postal history.

1881
S2   F2   black, *buff*   32.50 14.00
The franchise of No. S2 was granted to
Antonio Fernandez Duro for his book, "Resena
histórico-descriptiva de los sellos correos de
Espana."
*Reprints of No. S2 have been made on car-
mine, blue, gray, fawn and yellow paper.*

CARLIST STAMPS

From the beginning of the Civil War
(April 21, 1872) until separate stamps
were issued on July 1, 1873, stamps of
France were used on all mail from the
provinces under Carlist rule.

King Carlos   Tilde on N —
VII — A1   A1a

Unwmk.
1873, July 1   Litho.   *Imperf.*
X1   A1   1r blue   550.00
X2   A1a   1r blue   450.00 300.00
*These stamps were reprinted three times in
1881 and once in 1887. The originals have 23
white lines and dots in the lower right spandrel. They are thin and of even width and
spacing. The first reprint has 17 to 20 lines in
the spandrel, most of them thick and of irregu-
lar width and length. The second and third
reprints have 21 very thin lines, the second
from the bottom being almost invisible. In the
fourth reprint the lower right spandrel is an
almost solid spot of color.*
*Originals of type A1 have the curved line
above "ESPANA" broken at the left of the "E."
All reprints of this type have the curved line
continuous.*
*The reprints exist in various shades of blue,
rose, red, violet and black.*

King Carlos VII
A2   A3

A4   A5

1874
X3   A2   1r violet   240.00 240.00
X4   A3   16m rose   4.75 72.50
X5   A4   ½r rose   100.00 100.00
Nos. X3 and X6-X7 were for use in the
Basque Provinces and Navarra; No. X4 in Cat-
alonia, and No. X5 in Valencia.
Two types of No. X5, alternating in each
sheet.
No. X4 with favor cancellation (lozenge of
dots) sells for same price as unused.

1875   White Paper
X6   A5   50c green   8.00 82.50
   a.   50c blue green 25.00 100.00
   b.   Bluish paper   50.00
X7   A5   1r brown   8.00 82.50
   a.   Bluish paper   50.00
   Set, #X6-X7, never hinged 24.00
Fake cancellations exist on Nos. X1-X7.

REVOLUTIONARY OVERPRINTS

**Issued by the Nationalist
(Revolutionary) Forces**

Many districts or cities made use of
the stamps of the Republic overprinted
in various forms. Most such overprinting
was authorized by military or postal officials but some were without official
sanction. These overprints were applied
in patriotic celebration and partly as a
protection from the use of unoverprinted stamps seized or stolen by
soldiers.

BURGOS AIR POST STAMPS

RAP1

Revenue Stamps Overprinted in Red,
Blue or Black
1936, Dec. 1   Unwmk.   *Perf. 11½*
Control Number on Face of Stamp
7LC1 RAP1 25c gray grn &
             blk (R)   42.50 42.50
   a.   Blue overprint 42.50 42.50
7LC2 RAP1 1.50p bl & blk (R) 5.50 5.50
7LC3 RAP1 3p rose & blk
             (Bl)   5.50   5.50
   Nos. 7LC1-7LC3 (3)   53.50 53.50
   Set, never hinged   95.00

RAP2   RAP4

Perf. 13½
Blue Control Number on Back
7LC4 RAP2 15c green (R)   3.75   3.75
7LC5 RAP2 25c blue (R)   27.50 27.50
   Set, never hinged   45.00

Perf. 11½
**Without Control Number
Overprint in Black**
7LC6 RAP4 1.50p dk blue   6.50   6.50
7LC7 RAP4 3p carmine   6.50   6.50
   Set, never hinged   21.00

RAP5   RAP6

Overprint in Black
Perf. 13½, 11½
7LC8 RAP5 1.20p green   25.00 25.00
   Never hinged   37.50

Perf. 14
Control Number on Back
7LC9 RAP6 1.20p green   25.00 25.00
7LC10 RAP6 2.40p green   25.00 25.00
   Set #7LC9-7LC10, never hinged 70.00
No. 7LC9 is inscribed "CLASE 8a."

RAP7

1937   Unwmk.   *Perf. 11½*
Control Number on Back
7LC11 RAP7 25c ultra (R) 225.00 225.00

Stamps of Spain, 1931-
36, Overprinted in Red
or Black (10p)

Perf. 11, 11½, 11x11½
1937   Unwmk.
Overprint 13mm high
7LC12 A100 40c blue   1.10   1.10
   a.   Ovpt. 15mm high   1.10   1.10
7LC13 A97   50c dark blue   1.40   1.40
   a.   Ovpt. 15mm high   1.40   1.40
7LC14 A130 50c dark blue   1.75   1.75
   a.   Ovpt. 15mm high   1.75   1.75
7LC15 A100 60c apple
             green   2.50   2.50
   a.   Ovpt. 15mm high   2.50   2.50
7LC16 AP26 2p gray blue   32.50 32.50
   a.   Ovpt. 15mm high   32.50 32.50
7LC17 A49a 10p brown   82.50 82.50
   a.   Ovpt. 15mm high   82.50 82.50
   Nos. 7LC12-7LC17 (6)   121.75 121.75
Issue dates: Nos. 7LC12-7LC17, 4/1. Nos.
7LC12a-7LC17a, 5/1.

Spain Nos. 576, 578 and 541b
overprinted in Blue or Black

Nos. 7LC18,   Nos. 7LC20,
7LC19   7LC21

Perfs as on Basic Stamps
1937, May
7LC18 A127 30c carmine (Bk) 1.40 1.40
7LC19 A127 30c carmine (Bl)   .70   .70
7LC20 A129 30c car rose (Bk) 1.40 1.40

7LC21 A129 30c car rose (Bl) .70 .70
7LC22 A107 10p dp brn (Bk) 11.00 11.00
Nos. 7LC18-7LC22 (5) 15.20 15.20

Spain Nos. 539b and 540b, the 1p and 4p values, were prepared with this overprint in January, 1938, but were not issued. Value, each $4.50.

BURGOS ISSUE SPECIAL DELIVERY STAMPS

Pair of Spain No. 546 Overprinted in Black

1936 Unwmk. Perf. 11½x11
7LE3 A110 20c (10c+10c) emer 4.50 4.50
Never hinged 9.00
a. Overprint inverted 14.00

Type of Regular Stamp of 1931 Overprinted in Red

7LE4 A95 20c dark violet 10.00 10.00

Type of Delivery Tax Stamp of 1931 Overprinted in Red on four 5c stamps

Perf. 11½
7LE5 D1 20c black 8.75 8.00
Never hinged 13.50

Same Overprinted in Red on four 5c stamps

7LE6 D1 20c black 30.00 25.00
Never hinged 50.00

SD1

1936 Unwmk. Perf. 11½
7LE7 SD1 20c green & blk 7.25 5.50
7LE8 SD1 20c green & red 7.25 5.50
Set, never hinged 25.00

Nos. 7LE7-7LE8 exist with control number on back. Value $42.50 each.

CADIZ ISSUE SEMI-POSTAL STAMPS

Stamps of Spain, 1931-36, Surcharged in Black or Red

1936 Unwmk. Imperf.
8LB1 A108 1c + 5c blue grn .20 .20
Perf. 11½x11, 11½
8LB2 A108 2c + 5c orange
brn .20 .20
8LB3 A103 5c + 5c choc (R) .45 .45
8LB4 A110 10c + 5c green .45 .45
8LB5 A111 15c + 5c Prus grn
(R) 2.75 2.75
8LB6 A95 20c + 5c dk vio
(R) 3.25 3.25
8LB7 A104 25c + 5c lake 2.50 2.50
8LB8 A113 30c + 5c rose red 1.40 1.40
8LB9 A100 40c + 5c dk blue
(R) 3.25 3.25
8LB10 A97 50c + 5c dk blue
(R) 6.50 6.50
Nos. 8LB1-8LB10 (10) 20.95 20.95

CANARY ISLANDS AIR POST STAMPS

Issued for Use via the Lufthansa Service

Stamps of Spain, 1932-34, Surcharged in Blue

1936, Oct. 27 Unwmk. Imperf.
9LC1 A108 50c on 1c bl grn 27.50 17.50
Perf. 11½x11
9LC2 A108 80c on 2c buff 14.50 6.50
9LC3 A103 1.25p on 5c choc 30.00 17.50
Nos. 9LC1-9LC3 (3) 72.00 41.50
Set, never hinged 82.50

The date July 18, 1936, in the overprints of Nos. 9LC1-9LC22 marks the beginning of the Franco insurrection.

Spain Nos. 542, 543, 528 and 641 Surcharged in Black, Red or Green

The surcharge on Nos. 9LC4 and 9LC6 exists in two types: Type I, 2½-3mm space between numerals and "Cts.". Type II, 1½-2mm space between numerals and "Cts."

1936-37 Imperf.
9LC4 A108 50c on 1c bl
grn (I) 4.50 2.75
a. Overprint type II 11.00 7.75
9LC5 A108 50c on 1c bl
grn (R)
('37) 4.50 2.75
Perf. 11, 11½x11
9LC6 A108 80c on 2c buff
(I) 2.25 1.60
a. Overprint type II 5.50 3.25
9LC7 A108 80c on 2c buff
(G) ('37) 3.25 1.60
9LC8 A103 1.25 Pts on 5c
choc (R) 6.25 4.50
9LC9 A103 Pts 1.25 on 5c
choc (R)
('37) 17.00 11.00
9LC10 A161 1.25p on 5c brn
(G) ('37) 3.25 1.40
Nos. 9LC4-9LC10 (7) 41.00 25.60
Set, never hinged 65.00

Issued: Nos. 9LC4, 9LC6, 11/28/36; No. 9LC8, 1/7/37; Nos. 9LC4a, 9LC6a, 9LC9, 2/12/37; Nos. 9LC5, 9LC7, 9LC10, 3/2/37.

Spain Nos. 542, 543 and 641 Surcharged in Blue

1937, Mar. 31 Imperf.
The surcharge on Nos. 9LC11-9LC13 exists in two types: Type I, 18mm tall. Type II, 20mm tall.

9LC11 A108 50c on 1c bl
grn (I) 11.00 5.50
a. Overprint type II 4.50 2.25
Perf. 11
9LC12 A108 80c on 2c buff
(I) 11.00 4.50
a. Overprint type II 2.75 1.10
9LC13 A161 1.25p on 5c
brown (I) 3.25 1.10
Nos. 9LC11-9LC13 (3) 25.25 11.10
Set, never hinged 40.00

Type II overprints issued 4/17/37.

Stamps of Spain, 1931-1936, Surcharged in Blue or Red (#9LC17, 9LC19)

The surcharge on Nos. 9LC15 and 9LC18 exists in two types: Type I, 2mm space between "+" and denomination. Type II, "+" abuts surcharged denomination. Other values are Type I.

1937
9LC14 A104 25c + 50c lake 50.00 10.00
9LC15 A162 30c + 80c rose 17.50 7.75
a. Overprint type II 17.50 7.75
9LC16 A162 30c + 1.25p
rose 22.50 8.25
9LC17 A97 50c + 1.25p dp
bl 29.00 11.00
9LC18 A100 60c + 80c ap
grn 22.50 8.75
a. Overprint type II 25.00 10.00
9LC19 A105 1p + 1.25p bl
blk 72.50 22.50
Nos. 9LC14-9LC19 (6) 214.00 68.25
Set, never hinged 300.00

The surcharge represents the airmail rate and the basic stamp the postage rate.
Issued: 9LC15a, 9LC18a, 4/15. 9LC14-9LC19, 5/5.

Spain Nos. 542, 624 and 641 Surcharged in Black

1937, May 25 Unwmk. Imperf.
9LC20 A108 50c on 1c bl
grn 7.75 4.50
Perf. 11½, 11½x11
9LC21 A143 80c on 2c org
brn 6.50 2.25
9LC22 A161 1.25p on 5c gray
brn 6.50 2.25
Nos. 9LC20-9LC22 (3) 20.75 9.00
Set, never hinged 30.00

Stamps and Type of Spain, 1933-36, Surcharged in Black

1937, July Perf. 13½x13, 11, 11½
9LC23 A143 50c on 2c
org brn 3.25 2.25
9LC24 A126 80c on 2c
org brn 325.00 180.00
9LC25 A161 80c on 5c
gray brn 3.25 2.25
9LC26 A108 1.25p on 1c bl
grn 3.75 2.25
9LC27 A161 2.50p on 10c
grn 14.50 8.75

Spain Nos. 647, 650 and 652 Surcharged in Black or Red

Perf. 11
9LC28 A162 30c + 80c rose 2.75 1.40
9LC29 A162 50c + 1.25p dk
bl (R) 9.50 5.00

9LC30 A162 1p + 1.25p bl
(R) 14.50 8.75
Nos. 9LC23-9LC30 (8) 376.50 210.65
Set, never hinged 375.00
See note after No. 9LC19.

AP1

Perf. 14x13½
1937, July 16 Wmk. 116
Surcharge in Various Colors
9LC31 AP1 50c on 5c ultra
(Br) 2.75 2.50
9LC32 AP1 80c on 5c ultra
(G) 1.90 1.75
9LC33 AP1 1.25p on 5c ultra
(V) 2.25 2.25
Nos. 9LC31-9LC33 (3) 6.90 6.50
Set, never hinged 10.00

Spain Nos. 641, 643 and 640 Surcharged in Green or Orange

1937, Oct. 29 Unwmk. Perf. 11
9LC34 A161 50c on 5c (G) 8.50 3.75
9LC35 A161 80c on 10c (O) 5.25 2.75
9LC36 A160 1.25p on 2c (G) 9.50 7.25
Nos. 9LC34-9LC36 (3) 23.25 13.75
Set, never hinged 35.00

Spain Nos. 638, 640 and 643 Surcharged in Red, Blue or Violet

1937, Dec. 23 Imperf.
9LC37 A159 50c on 1c (R) 9.50 4.50
Perf. 11, 11x11½
9LC38 A160 80c on 2c (Bl) 3.75 2.75
9LC39 A161 1.25p on 10c (V) 8.50 3.50
Nos. 9LC37-9LC39 (3) 21.75 10.75
Set, never hinged 32.50

Spain Nos. 647, 650 to 652 Surcharged in Black, Green or Brown

1937, Dec. 29
9LC40 A162 30c + 30c rose 4.50 3.75
9LC41 A162 50c + 2.50p dk
bl (G) 29.00 21.00
9LC42 A162 60c + 2.30p yel
(G) 29.00 21.00
9LC43 A162 1p + 5p bl (Br) 35.00 21.00
Nos. 9LC40-9LC43 (4) 97.50 66.75
Set, never hinged 110.00

See note after No. 9LC19.

Stamps of Spain, 1936, Surcharged in Black, Green, Blue or Red

1938, Feb. 2 Perf. 11, 11½, 11x11½
9LC44 A160 50c on 2c brn 5.00 3.75
9LC45 A161 80c on 5c brn
(G) 3.75 3.25
9LC46 A162 80c on 30c rose
(Bl) 4.50 2.50
9LC47 A161 1.25p on 10c grn
(Bl) 4.50 3.25
9LC48 A162 1.25p on 50c dk
bl (R) 4.50 2.75
Nos. 9LC44-9LC48 (5) 22.25 15.50
Set, never hinged 27.50

Spain Nos. 645, 646 and 649 Surcharged in Brown, Green or Violet

1938, Feb. 14

9LC51	A162	2.50p on 20c (Br)	
			50.00 25.00
9LC52	A162	5p on 25c (G)	50.00 25.00
9LC53	A162	10p on 40c (V)	50.00 25.00
		Nos. 9LC51-9LC53 (3)	150.00 75.00
		Set, never hinged	175.00

MALAGA ISSUE

Stamps of 1920-36 Overprinted in Black or Red

1937 — **Unwmk.** — **Imperf.**

10L1	A47	1c blue green	.20 .20
10L2	A108	1c blue green	.20 .20
10L3	A108	1c lt green (R)	.20 .20

Perf. 13½, 13½x13, 11, 11½x11

10L4	A108	2c orange brn	14.50 14.50
10L5	A126	2c orange brn	.20 .20
10L6	A103	5c chocolate (R)	.20 .20
10L7	A96	10c yellow green	12.00 12.00
10L8	A110	10c emerald	.30 .30
10L9	A111	15c Prus grn (R)	.55 .55
10L10	A97	15c blue grn (R)	.55 .55
10L11	A95	20c dk violet (R)	.50 .50
10L12	A99	25c lake	1.50 1.50
10L13	A104	25c lake	.50 .50
10L14	A113	30c carmine	.50 .50
10L15	A129	30c carmine rose	2.50 2.50
10L16	A100	40c blue (R)	.45 .45
10L17	A97	50c dk blue (R)	2.50 2.50
10L18	A100	60c apple green	1.40 1.40
10L19	A105	1p black (R)	2.75 2.75
		Nos. 10L1-10L19 (19)	41.50 41.50

Stamps of 1932-35 Overprinted in Red or Black in panes of 25, reading down. "8.2.37" and "!Arriba Espana!" form the lower half of all overprints. The upper half varies.

Overprint a (1st and 2nd rows): "MALAGA AGRADECIDA A TRANQUILLO-BIANCHI"
Overprint b (3rd row): "MALAGA A SU SALVADOR QUEIPO DE LLANO"
Overprint c (4th and 5th rows): "MALAGA A SU CAUDILLO FRANCO"
Values are for vertical strips of 3 containing examples of each overprint type.

1937 — **Perf. 11½**

10L20	A111	15c Prus grn (R)	5.50 5.50
a.		15c single stamp, ovpt. a	.85 .85
b.		15c single stamp, ovpt. b	1.60 1.60
c.		15c single stamp, ovpt. c	.85 .85
10L21	A113	30c rose red (Bk)	5.50 5.50
a.		30c single stamp, ovpt. a	.85 .85
b.		30c single stamp, ovpt. b	1.60 1.60
c.		30c single stamp, ovpt. c	.85 .85
10L22	A97	50c dk blue (R)	8.75 8.75
a.		50c single stamp, ovpt. a	1.60 1.60
b.		50c single stamp, ovpt. b	3.25 3.25
c.		50c single stamp, ovpt. c	1.60 1.60
10L23	A100	60c apple grn (Bk)	11.00 11.00
a.		60c single stamp, ovpt. a	1.60 1.60
b.		60c single stamp, ovpt. b	3.25 3.25
c.		60c single stamp, ovpt. c	1.60 1.60
		Nos. 10L20-10L23 (4)	30.75 30.75

SPECIAL DELIVERY STAMP

Overprinted like Nos. 10L1-10L19 on Type of Special Delivery Stamp of 1934

1937 — **Perf. 10**

10LE1	SD7	20c rose red (Bk)	.45 .45

ORENSE ISSUE

Stamps of 1931-36 Overprinted in Red, Blue or Black

1936 — **Imperf.**

11L1	A108	1c blue grn (Bl)	.45 .45
a.		Red overprint	1.10 1.10

Perf. 11½, 13½x13

11L2	A108	2c org brn (Bk)	3.50 3.25
11L3	A126	2c org brn (Bk)	.65 .65
11L4	A103	5c brown (R)	1.50 1.50
11L5	A110	10c lt green (Bl)	2.25 2.25
a.		Red overprint	11.00 11.00
11L6	A111	15c Prus grn (R)	3.25 3.25
11L7	A95	20c violet (Bl)	3.25 3.25
11L8	A104	25c lake (Bk)	3.75 3.75
11L9	A113	30c rose red (Bl)	2.75 2.75
a.		Black overprint	5.50 5.50
11L10	A100	40c blue (R)	3.75 3.75
a.		Imperf, pair	50.00
11L11	A97	50c dark blue (R)	6.50 6.50
11L12	A100	60c apple grn (Bk)	4.75 4.75
a.		Red overprint	17.00 17.00
b.		As "a," Imperf, pair	50.00
		Nos. 11L1-11L12 (12)	36.35 36.10

SEMI-POSTAL STAMPS

Stamps of Spain, 1931-36, Surcharged in Blue on front and on back of stamp

1936-37 — **Unwmk.** — **Imperf.**

11LB1	A47	1c + 5c bl grn	2.25 2.25
11LB2	A108	1c + 5c green	.40 .40

Perf. 13½x13, 11½, 11½x11

11LB3	A108	2c + 5c org brn	.45 .45
11LB4	A126	2c + 5c red brn	.45 .45
11LB5	A103	5c + 5c choc	.65 .65
11LB6	A110	10c + 5c emer	.65 .65
11LB7	A111	15c + 5c Prus grn	.95 .95
11LB8	A95	20c + 5c violet	.65 .65
11LB9	A104	25c + 5c lake	.95 .95
11LB10	A113	30c + 5c rose red	2.75 2.75
11LB11	A117	30c + 5c rose red	42.50 42.50
11LB12	A100	60c + 5c apple grn	190.00 190.00
		Nos. 11LB1-11LB12 (12)	242.65 242.65

SPECIAL DELIVERY STAMPS

Type of Special Delivery Stamp of 1934 Overprinted "!VIVA ESPANA!" in Blue or Black

1936

11LE1	SD7	20c rose red (Bl)	1.90 1.90
11LE2	SD7	20c rose red (Bk)	4.25 4.25

Same with Surcharge "+ 5 cts."

11LE3	SD7	20c + 5c rose red	1.00 1.00

Same Surcharge, Overprint Repeated at Right

11LE4	SD7	20c + 5c rose red	1.10 1.10
		Nos. 11LE1-11LE4 (4)	8.25 8.25

SAN SEBASTIAN ISSUE

For Use in Province of Guipuzcoa

Stamps of 1931-36 Overprinted in Red or Blue

1937 — **Unwmk.** — **Imperf.**

12L1	A108	1c bl grn (R)	.65 .65

Perf. 11, 13½

12L2	A108	2c buff (Bl)	1.00 1.50
12L3	A126	2c org brn (Bl)	2.10 2.10
12L4	A95	5c chocolate (R)	5.00 5.00
12L5	A103	5c chocolate (R)	1.75 1.75
12L6	A110	10c emerald (R)	1.75 1.75
12L7	A111	15c Prus grn (R)	2.10 2.10
12L8	A95	20c dk violet (R)	2.75 2.75
12L9	A104	25c car lake (Bl)	2.75 2.75
12L10	A113	30c rose red (Bl)	2.75 2.75
12L11	A100	40c blue (R)	5.50 5.50
12L12	A97	50c dark blue (R)	5.50 5.50
		Nos. 12L1-12L12 (12)	33.60 34.10

SANTA CRUZ DE TENERIFE ISSUE

Stamps of Spain, 1931-36 Overprinted in Black or Red

1936 — **Unwmk.** — **Imperf.**

13L1	A108	1c bl grn (R)	.75 .75
13L2	A108	1c bl grn (Bk)	2.75 2.75

Perf. 11, 13½

13L3	A108	2c buff (Bk)	5.50 5.50
13L4	A126	2c org brn (Bk)	.95 .95
13L5	A103	5c choc (R)	3.00 3.00
13L6	A110	10c green (R)	3.00 3.00
13L7	A104	25c lake (Bk)	11.00 11.00
13L8	A100	40c dk blue (R)	3.25 3.25
13L9	A107	10p dp brn (Bk)	225.00 225.00
		Nos. 13L1-13L9 (9)	255.20 255.20

Many forgeries of #13L9 exist.

SEVILLE ISSUE

Stamps of Spain, 1931-36, Overprinted in Black or Red

1936 — **Imperf.**

14L1	A108	1c blue grn (Bk)	.25 .25

Perf. 13½x13, 11, 11½x11

14L2	A126	2c org brn (Bk)	.30 .30
14L3	A103	5c chocolate (R)	.40 .40
14L4	A110	10c emerald (Bk)	.50 .50
14L5	A111	15c Prus grn (R)	1.25 1.25
14L6	A95	20c violet (R)	1.25 1.25
14L7	A104	25c lake (Bk)	1.25 1.25
14L8	A113	30c carmine (Bk)	1.25 1.25
14L9	A128	30c rose red (Bk)	7.50 7.50
14L10	A100	40c blue (R)	5.00 5.00
14L11	A97	50c dk blue (R)	5.00 5.00
14L12	A100	60c apple grn (Bk)	6.00 6.00
		Nos. 14L1-14L12 (12)	29.95 29.95

Stamps of Spain, 1931-36, Handstamped in Black

1936 — **Imperf**

14L13	A108	1c blue grn	.25 .25

Perf. 13½x13, 11, 11x11½, 11½x11

14L14	A126	2c orange brn	.40 .40
14L15	A103	5c chocolate	.40 .40
14L16	A110	10c emerald	.40 .40
14L17	A111	15c Prus green	.50 .50
14L18	A95	20c violet	.50 .50
14L19	A104	25c lake	.50 .50
14L20	A113	30c carmine	.50 .50
14L21	A128	30c rose red	2.75 2.75
14L22	A100	40c blue	.95 .95
14L23	A97	50c dk blue	2.75 2.75
14L24	A100	60c apple grn	.90 .90
14L25	A105	1p black	2.75 2.75
14L26	AP26	2p gray blue	12.00 12.00
14L27	A106	4p magenta	6.50 6.50
14L28	A107	10p deep brown	9.50 9.50
		Nos. 14L13-14L28,14LE1 (17)	42.00 42.00

The date "Julio-1936" in the overprints of Nos. 14L1-14L28 and 14LE1 marks the beginning of the Franco insurrection.

SPECIAL DELIVERY STAMP

Overprinted like Nos. 14L13-14L25 on Type of Special Delivery Stamp of 1934

1936 — **Perf. 10**

14LE1	SD7	20c rose red	1.75 1.75

SPANISH GUINEA

'spa-nish 'gi-nē

LOCATION — In western Africa, bordering on the Gulf of Guinea
GOVT. — Spanish Colony
AREA — 10,852 sq. mi.
POP. — 212,000 (est. 1957)
CAPITAL — Santa Isabel

Spanish Guinea 1-84 were issued for and used only in the continental area later called Rio Muni. From 1909 to 1960, Spanish Guinea also included Fernando Po, Elobey, Annobon and Corisco.

Fernando Po and Rio Muni united in 1968 to become the Republic of Equatorial Guinea.

100 Centimos = 1 Peseta

Catalogue values for unused stamps in this country are for Never Hinged items, beginning with Scott 319 in the regular postage section, Scott B13 in the semipostal section, and Scott C13 in the airpost section.

King Alfonso XIII
A1   A2

1902   Unwmk.   Typo.   Perf. 14
Blue Control Numbers on Back

1	A1	5c dark green	11.50	6.25
2	A1	10c indigo	11.50	6.25
3	A1	25c claret	85.00	47.50
4	A1	50c deep brown	85.00	47.50
5	A1	75c violet	85.00	47.50
6	A1	1p carmine rose	125.00	47.50
7	A1	2p olive green	165.00	100.00
8	A1	5p dull red	260.00	175.00
		Nos. 1-8 (8)	828.00	477.50
		Set, never hinged	1,500.	

Exists imperf, value set $1,750.

Revenue Stamps Surcharged

1903   Imperf.
Blue or Black Control Numbers on Back

8A		10c on 25c blk (R)	550.00	210.00
8B		10c on 50c org (Bl)	125.00	35.00
8D		10c on 1p 25c car (Bk)	750.00	350.00
8F		10c on 2p cl (Bk)	800.00	550.00
g.		Blue surcharge	1,300.	750.00
8H		10c on 2p 50c red brn (Bl)	1,250.	675.00
8J		10c on 5p ol blk (R)	1,500.	475.00

Nos. 8A-8J are surcharged on stamps inscribed "Posesiones Espanolas de Africa Occidental" and "1903", with arms at left.
This surcharge was also applied to revenue stamps of 10, 15, 25, 50, 75 and 100 pesetas and in other colors.
See Nos. 98-101C.

1903   Typo.   Perf. 14
Blue Control Numbers on Back

9	A2	¼c black	1.25	.75
10	A2	½c blue green	1.25	.75
11	A2	1c claret	1.25	.65
12	A2	2c dark olive	1.25	.65
13	A2	3c dark brown	1.25	.65
14	A2	4c vermilion	1.25	.65
15	A2	5c black brown	1.25	.65
16	A2	10c red brown	2.00	.75
17	A2	15c black blue	7.00	5.75
18	A2	25c orange buff	7.00	5.75

19	A2	50c carmine lake	13.00	12.50
20	A2	75c violet	17.50	12.50
21	A2	1p blue green	30.00	20.00
22	A2	2p dark green	30.00	20.00
23	A2	3p scarlet	80.00	26.00
24	A2	4p dull blue	92.50	45.00
25	A2	5p dark violet	175.00	65.00
26	A2	10p carmine rose	240.00	90.00
		Nos. 9-26 (18)	702.75	308.00
		Set, never hinged	1,300.	

1905
Same, Dated "1905"
Blue Control Numbers on Back

27	A2	1c black	.25	.25
28	A2	2c blue grn	.25	.25
29	A2	3c claret	.25	.25
30	A2	4c bronze grn	.25	.25
31	A2	5c dark brown	.25	.25
32	A2	10c red	1.25	.80
33	A2	15c black brown	3.75	2.60
34	A2	25c chocolate	3.75	2.60
35	A2	50c dark blue	8.25	6.00
36	A2	75c orange buff	9.00	6.00
37	A2	1p carmine rose	9.00	6.00
38	A2	2p violet	22.00	12.50
39	A2	3p blue green	57.50	26.00
40	A2	4p dark green	57.50	37.50
40A	A2	5p vermilion	92.50	40.00
41	A2	10p dull blue	160.00	125.00
		Nos. 27-41 (16)	425.75	266.25
		Set, never hinged	775.00	

Stamps of Elobey, 1905, Overprinted in Violet or Blue

1906

42	A1	1c rose	3.50	2.10
43	A1	2c deep violet	3.50	2.10
44	A1	3c black	3.50	2.10
45	A1	4c orange red	3.50	2.10
46	A1	5c deep green	3.50	2.10
47	A1	10c blue green	8.00	4.75
48	A1	15c violet	14.00	8.25
49	A1	25c rose lake	14.00	8.25
50	A1	50c orange buff	19.00	11.50
51	A1	75c dark blue	23.00	13.50
52	A1	1p red brown	40.00	23.00
53	A1	2p black brown	60.00	35.00
54	A1	3p vermilion	85.00	50.00
55	A1	4p dark brown	400.00	225.00
56	A1	5p bronze green	400.00	225.00
57	A1	10p claret	1,550.	925.00
		Nos. 42-54 (13)	280.50	164.75

King Alfonso XIII
A3   A4

1907   Typo.
Blue Control Numbers on Back

58	A3	1c dark green	.60	.20
59	A3	2c dull blue	.60	.20
60	A3	3c violet	.60	.20
61	A3	4c yellow grn	.60	.20
62	A3	5c carmine lake	.60	.20
63	A3	10c orange	3.25	1.00
64	A3	15c brown	2.50	.65
65	A3	25c dark blue	2.50	.65
66	A3	50c black brown	2.50	.65
67	A3	75c blue green	2.50	.65
68	A3	1p red	4.75	1.10
69	A3	2p dark brown	8.00	5.00
70	A3	3p olive gray	8.00	5.00
71	A3	4p maroon	10.50	5.00
72	A3	5p green	11.00	7.50
73	A3	10p red violet	16.50	9.75
		Nos. 58-73 (16)	75.00	37.95
		Set, never hinged	135.00	

Issue of 1907 Surcharged in Black or Red

1908-09

74	A3	05c on 1c dk grn (R)	2.75	1.50
75	A3	05c on 2c blue (R)	2.75	1.50
76	A3	05c on 3c violet	2.75	1.50
77	A3	05c on 4c yel grn	2.75	1.50

78	A3	05c on 10c orange	2.75	1.50
a.		Red surcharge	5.00	2.75
84	A3	15c on 10c orange	13.50	9.00
		Nos. 74-84 (6)	27.25	16.50

Many stamps of this issue are found with the surcharge inverted, sideways, double and in both black and red. Other stamps of the 1907 issue are known with this surcharge but are not believed to have been put in use. Value, each $17.

1909   Typo.   Perf. 14½
Blue Control Numbers on Back

85	A4	1c orange brown	.20	.20
86	A4	2c rose	.20	.20
87	A4	5c dark green	1.00	.20
88	A4	10c vermilion	.30	.20
89	A4	15c dark brown	.30	.20
90	A4	20c violet	.55	.25
91	A4	25c dull blue	.55	.25
92	A4	30c chocolate	.65	.20
93	A4	40c lake	.40	.20
94	A4	50c dark violet	.40	.20
95	A4	1p blue green	11.00	5.50
96	A4	4p orange	2.75	3.25
97	A4	10p red	2.75	3.25
		Nos. 85-97 (13)	21.05	14.10
		Set, never hinged	37.50	

For overprints see Nos. 102-114.

Revenue Stamps Surcharged like Nos. 8A-8J in Black

1909   Imperf.
With or Without Control Numbers on Back

98		10c on 50c bl grn	80.00	52.50
a.		Red or violet surcharge	100.00	72.50
99		10c on 1p 25c violet	100.00	72.50
100		10c on 2p dk brn	550.00	325.00
100A		10c on 5p dk vio	550.00	325.00
101		10c on 25p red brn	725.00	525.00
101A		10c on 50p brn lil	2,500.	1,450.
101B		10c on 75p carmine	2,500.	1,450.
101C		10c on 100p orange	2,500.	1,450.

Nos. 98-101C are surcharged on undated stamps, arms centered. Stamps inscribed: "Territorios Espanoles del Africa Occidental." Basic revenue stamps similar to Rio de Oro type A3.

Stamps of 1909 Overprinted with Handstamp in Black, Blue, Green or Red

1911

102	A4	1c orange brn (Bl)	.30	.25
103	A4	2c rose (G)	.30	.25
104	A4	5c dk green (R)	1.40	.25
105	A4	10c vermilion	.80	.35
106	A4	15c dk brown (R)	1.40	.55
107	A4	20c violet	1.75	.80
108	A4	25c dull blue (R)	2.00	1.75
109	A4	30c choc (Bl)	2.75	2.50
110	A4	40c lake (Bl)	3.00	2.50
111	A4	50c dark violet	5.00	3.50
112	A4	1p blue grn (R)	40.00	30.00
113	A4	4p orange (R)	21.00	16.50
114	A4	10p red (G)	27.50	30.00
		Nos. 102-114 (13)	107.20	89.20
		Set, never hinged	200.00	

The date "1911" is missing from the overprint on the first stamp in the row, or ten times in each sheet of 100 stamps. This variety occurs on all stamps of the series. Value, set $550.

King Alfonso XIII
A5   A6

1912   Typo.   Perf. 13½
Blue Control Numbers on Back

115	A5	1c black	.20	.20
116	A5	2c dark brown	.20	.20
117	A5	5c deep green	.20	.20
118	A5	10c red	.20	.20
119	A5	15c claret	.20	.20
120	A5	20c red	.30	.20
121	A5	25c dull blue	.20	.20
122	A5	30c lake	2.50	1.40
123	A5	40c car rose	1.60	.25
124	A5	50c brown org	1.40	.25

125	A5	1p dark violet	1.60	.95
126	A5	4p lilac	3.75	1.90
127	A5	10p blue green	7.75	7.00
		Nos. 115-127 (13)	20.10	13.65
		Set, never hinged	32.50	

For overprints and surcharges see Nos. 141-157.

1914   Perf. 13
Blue Control Numbers on Back

128	A6	1c dull violet	.25	.20
129	A6	2c car rose	.25	.20
130	A6	5c deep green	.25	.20
131	A6	10c vermilion	.25	.20
132	A6	15c dark violet	.25	.20
133	A6	20c dark brown	.80	.45
134	A6	25c dark blue	.35	.25
135	A6	30c brown orange	1.25	.45
136	A6	40c blue green	1.25	.45
137	A6	50c dp claret	.60	.30
138	A6	1p vermilion	1.50	1.75
139	A6	4p maroon	5.50	3.50
140	A6	10p olive black	6.00	6.75
		Nos. 128-140 (13)	18.50	14.90
		Set, never hinged	27.50	

Stamps with these or similar overprints are unauthorized and fraudulent.

Stamps of 1912 Overprinted

1917   Perf. 13½

141	A5	1c black	100.00	67.50
142	A5	2c dark brown	100.00	67.50
143	A5	5c deep green	.30	.25
144	A5	10c red	.30	.25
145	A5	15c claret	.30	.25
146	A5	20c red	.25	.25
147	A5	25c dull blue	.25	.25
148	A5	30c lake	.30	.25
149	A5	40c carmine rose	.55	.30
150	A5	50c brown orange	.30	.25
151	A5	1p dark violet	.55	.30
152	A5	4p lilac	6.75	3.25
153	A5	10p blue green	6.75	3.25
		Nos. 141-153 (13)	216.65	143.85
		Set, never hinged	290.00	

Nos. 143-153 exist with overprint double, inverted, in dark blue, reading "9117" and in pairs one without overprint.

Stamps of 1917 Surcharged

1918

154	A5	5c on 40c car rose	29.00	11.50
155	A5	10c on 4p lilac	29.00	11.50
156	A5	15c on 20c red	52.50	20.00
157	A5	25c on 10p bl grn	52.50	20.00
a.		"52" for "25"	400.00	340.00
		Nos. 154-157 (4)	163.00	63.00
		Set, never hinged	275.00	

The varieties "Gents" and "Censt" occur on Nos. 154-157. Values 50 percent more.

King Alfonso XIII
A7   A8

1919   Typo.   Perf. 13
Blue Control Numbers on Back
158	A7	1c lilac	.90	.25
159	A7	2c rose	.90	.25
160	A7	5c vermilion	.90	.25
161	A7	10c violet	1.50	.25
162	A7	15c brown	1.50	.45
163	A7	20c blue	1.50	.70
164	A7	25c green	1.50	.70
a.		25c blue (error)	55.00	
165	A7	30c orange	1.90	.70
166	A7	40c orange	4.00	.70
167	A7	50c red	4.00	.70
168	A7	1p light green	4.00	2.40
169	A7	4p claret	8.75	9.00
170	A7	10p brown	18.00	16.50

Nos. 158-170 (13)   49.35 32.85
Set, never hinged   65.00

1920
Blue Control Numbers on Back
171	A8	1c brown	.25	.20
172	A8	2c dull rose	.25	.20
173	A8	5c gray green	.25	.20
174	A8	10c dull rose	.25	.20
175	A8	15c orange	.25	.25
176	A8	20c yellow	.25	.25
177	A8	25c dull blue	.85	.25
178	A8	30c greenish blue	32.50	20.00
179	A8	40c lt brown	1.40	.25
180	A8	50c lilac	1.60	.25
181	A8	1p light red	1.60	.25
182	A8	4p bright rose	5.00	1.00
183	A8	10p gray lilac	7.25	9.50

Nos. 171-183 (13)   51.70 36.75
Set, never hinged   72.50

A9

Nipa
House — A10

1922
Blue Control Numbers on Back
184	A9	1c dark brown	.55	.20
185	A9	2c claret	.55	.20
186	A9	5c blue green	.55	.20
187	A9	10c pale red	4.00	1.00
188	A9	15c orange	.55	.20
189	A9	20c lilac	2.40	.90
190	A9	25c dark blue	4.00	1.10
191	A9	30c violet	3.75	1.25
192	A9	40c turq blue	2.60	.60
193	A9	50c deep rose	2.60	.60
194	A9	1p myrtle green	2.60	.60
195	A9	4p red brown	11.00	11.00
196	A9	10p yellow	22.00	21.00

Nos. 184-196 (13)   57.15 38.85
Set, never hinged   90.00

1924
Blue Control Numbers on Back
197	A10	5c choc & bl	.20	.20
198	A10	10c gray grn & bl	.20	.20
199	A10	15c rose & blk	.20	.20
200	A10	20c violet & blk	.20	.20
201	A10	25c org red & blk	.40	.25
202	A10	30c orange & blk	.40	.20
203	A10	40c dl bl & blk	.40	.20
204	A10	50c claret & blk	.40	.20
205	A10	60c red brn & blk	.40	.20
206	A10	1p dk vio & blk	1.60	.20
a.		Center inverted	275.00	125.00
207	A10	4p brt bl & blk	3.75	2.25
208	A10	10p bl grn & blk	8.75	6.80

Nos. 197-208 (12)   16.90 8.80
Set, never hinged   25.00

**Seville-Barcelona Issue of Spain,
1929, Overprinted in Red or Blue**

1929   Perf. 11
209	A52	5c rose lake	.30	.35
210	A53	10c green (R)	.30	.35
211	A53	15c Prus bl (R)	.30	.35
212	A51	20c purple (R)	.30	.35
213	A50	25c brt rose	.30	.35
214	A52	30c black brn	.30	.35
215	A53	40c dk blue (R)	.55	.50
216	A51	50c dp orange	.55	.50
217	A52	1p blue blk (R)	9.50	5.00

218	A53	4p deep rose	19.50	9.75
219	A53	10p brown	36.00	19.00

Nos. 209-219 (11)   67.90 36.85
Set, never hinged   132.50

Porter   Drummers
A11   A12

King Alfonso XIII
and Queen
Victoria — A13

1931   Engr.   Perf. 14
220	A11	1c blue green	.20	.20
221	A11	2c red brown	.20	.20

Blue Control Numbers on Back
222	A11	5c brown black	.20	.20
223	A11	10c light green	.20	.20
224	A11	15c dark green	.20	.20
225	A11	20c deep violet	.20	.20
226	A12	25c carmine	.20	.20
227	A12	30c lake	.30	.20
228	A12	40c dark blue	.70	.55
229	A12	50c red orange	1.50	1.10
230	A13	80c blue violet	2.50	1.60
231	A13	1p black	4.50	4.50
232	A13	4p violet rose	30.00	17.00
233	A13	5p dark brown	13.00	12.00

Nos. 220-233 (14)   53.90 38.35
Set, never hinged   110.00

Exist imperf. Value for set, $300.
See Nos. 262-271. For overprints and
surcharges see Nos. 234-277, 282-283, 298.

**Stamps of 1931
Overprinted**

1931
234	A11	1c blue green	.20	.20
235	A11	2c red brown	.20	.20
236	A11	5c brown black	.20	.20
237	A11	10c light green	.20	.20
238	A11	15c dark green	.20	.20
239	A11	20c deep violet	.20	.20
240	A12	25c carmine	.20	.20
241	A12	30c lake	.40	.20
242	A12	40c dark blue	1.40	.45
243	A12	50c red orange	9.75	5.50
244	A12	80c blue violet	3.00	1.60
245	A13	1p black	10.00	3.50
246	A13	4p violet rose	17.50	10.50
247	A13	5p dark brown	17.50	10.50

Nos. 234-247 (14)   60.95 33.65
Set, never hinged   100.00

**Stamps of 1931
Overprinted in Red
or Blue**

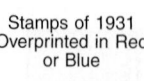

1933
248	A11	1c blue grn (R)	.20	.20
249	A11	2c red brown (Bl)	.20	.20
250	A11	5c brown blk (R)	.20	.20
251	A11	10c lt green (Bl)	.20	.20
252	A11	15c dk green (R)	.20	.20
253	A11	20c dp violet (Bl)	.40	.20
254	A12	25c carmine (Bl)	.40	.20
255	A12	30c lake (Bl)	.45	.20
256	A12	40c dk blue (R)	2.75	.70
257	A12	50c red orange (Bl)	17.00	3.50
258	A12	80c blue vio (R)	5.50	3.00
259	A13	1p black (R)	19.00	3.25
260	A13	4p violet rose (Bl)	35.00	15.00
261	A13	5p dk brown (Bl)	35.00	15.00

Nos. 248-261 (14)   116.50 42.05
Set, never hinged   175.00

**Types of 1931
Without Control Number**
1934-35   Engr.   Perf. 10
262	A11	1c blue green ('35)	9.00	.20
263	A11	2c red brown ('35)	9.00	.20
264	A11	5c black brn	1.75	.20
265	A11	10c light green	1.75	.20
266	A11	15c dark green	3.00	.20
267	A12	30c rose red	3.50	.25
268	A12	50c indigo ('35)	8.00	.85

Nos. 262-268 (7)   36.00 2.10
Set, never hinged   52.50

Types of 1931
1941   Litho.   Unwmk.
269	A11	5c olive gray	2.10	.20
270	A11	20c violet	2.10	.20
271	A12	40c gray green	.85	.20

Nos. 269-271 (3)   5.05 .60
Set, never hinged   6.25

**Stamps of 1931-33 Surcharged in
Black**

a   b

1936-37   Perf. 10, 14
272	A12	30c on 40c (#228)	4.00	2.40
273	A12	30c on 40c (#242)	16.00	3.75
274	A12	30c on 40c (#256)	60.00	18.25

Nos. 272-274 (3)   80.00 24.40
Set, never hinged   115.00

The surcharge on Nos. 272-274 exists in
two types, differing in the "3" which is scarcer
in italic.

No. 268 Surcharged Type "b" in Red
275	A12	1p on 50c indigo	24.00
276	A12	4p on 50c indigo	75.00
277	A12	5p on 50c indigo	45.00

Nos. 275-277 (3)   144.00

Nos. 275-277 were not issued.

**Stamps of Spain,
1936, Overprinted in
Black or Carmine**

1938   Perf. 11
278	A161	10c gray green	1.50	.45
279	A162	15c gray black (C)	1.50	.45
280	A162	20c dark violet	3.50	1.40
281	A162	25c brown lake	3.50	1.40

Nos. 278-281 (4)   10.00 3.70
Set, never hinged   13.00

Nos. 278-281 exist imperf. Value $175.

**Stamps of 1931-33,
Surcharged in Black**

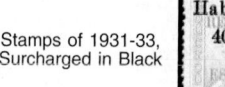

1939
282	A13	40c on 80c (#244)	11.00	7.25
283	A13	40c on 80c (#258)	11.00	4.50

Set, never hinged   30.00

A14   A15

Revenue Stamps Surcharged in Black
1940-41   Perf. 11½
284	A14	5c on 35c pale grn	5.50	1.90
285	A14	25c on 60c org brn	5.75	2.25
286	A14	50c on 75c blk brn	8.00	2.50

Nos. 284-286 (3)   19.25 6.65

Red Surcharge
287	A15	10c on 75c blk brn	8.00	2.50
288	A15	15c on 1.50p lt vio	5.75	2.25
289	A15	25c on 60c org brn	10.00	3.25

Nos. 287-289 (3)   23.75 8.00

A16   A17

Black or Carmine Surcharge
Perf. 11
290	A16	1p on 17p deep red	52.50	15.50
291	A17	1p on 40p yel grn (C)	12.50	4.00

See No. C1.

A18   A19

Black Surcharge
Perf. 11, 13x12½
292	A18	5c carmine	5.25	1.40
293	A19	5c yellow	87.50	32.50

A20   General
                           Francisco
                           Franco — A21

Black Surcharge
294	A20	1p on 15c gray grn	9.50	3.25

1940   Perf. 11½, 13½
295	A21	5c olive brown	3.00	.40
296	A21	40c blue	4.50	.40
297	A21	50c green	5.50	.40
a.		50c greenish gray	23.00	7.25

Nos. 295-297 (3)   13.00 1.20
Set, never hinged   30.00

Nos. 295-297 exist imperf. Value $50.

**No. 270 Surcharged
in Black**

1942
298	A11	3p on 20c vio	8.75	1.25

**Spain, Nos. 702 and
704 Overprinted in
Carmine or Black**

1942   Perf. 9½x10½
299	A166	1p gray blk (C)	.45	.20
300	A166	4p dl rose (Bk)	6.50	.65

The overprint on No. 299 exists in two types:
Spacing between lines of 2mm, and spacing of
3mm. The 3mm spacing sells for about twice
as much.
For surcharges and overprint see #302-303,
C3.

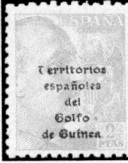

Spain, No. 703
Overprinted in
Carmine

1943
301 A166 2p dull brown .85 .20

Nos. 299 and 301
Surcharged in Green

Habilitado
para quince
cts.

1949 Unwmk. Perf. 9½x10½
302 A166 5c (cinco) on 1p gray blk .25 .20
303 A166 15c on 2p dl brn .25 .20

The two types of No. 299, described in footnote, also exist on No. 302.

Men Poling
Canoe
A22

1949, Oct. 9 Litho. Perf. 12½x13
304 A22 4p dk vio .85 .65
Never hinged 1.25

UPU, 75th anniversary.

San Carlos
Bay — A23

Designs: Various Views

1949-50 Perf. 12½x13
305 A23 2c brown .20 .20
306 A23 5c rose vio .20 .20
307 A23 10c Prussian bl .20 .20
308 A23 15c dp ol gray .25 .20
309 A23 25c red brown .25 .20
309A A23 30c brt yel ('50) .25 .20
310 A23 40c olive gray .25 .20
311 A23 45c rose lake .25 .20
312 A23 50c brn orange .25 .20
312A A23 75c ultra ('50) .25 .20
313 A23 90c dl bl grn .30 .20
314 A23 1p gray 1.00 .20
315 A23 1.35p violet 3.75 1.00
316 A23 2p sepia 10.00 2.10
317 A23 5p lilac rose 13.50 5.25
318 A23 10p light brn 55.00 21.00
Nos. 305-318 (16) 85.90 31.75
Set, never hinged 132.50

Catalogue values for unused stamps in this section, from this point to the end of the section, are for Never Hinged items.

Surveyor
A24

1951, Dec. 5
319 A24 50c orange .40 .20
320 A24 5p indigo 7.50 1.25

Intl. Conference of West Africans, 1951.

Drummer
A25

1952, Mar. 10
321 A25 5c red brown .20 .20
322 A25 50c olive gray .40 .20
323 A25 5p violet 2.40 .25
Nos. 321-323 (3) 3.00 .65

Musician
A26

Design: 60c, Musician facing right.

1953, July 1 Photo.
324 A26 15c sepia .25 .20
325 A26 60c brown .30 .20
Nos. 324-325,B25-B26 (4) 1.10 .85

Woman and
Dove
A27

Drummer
A28

1953, Sept. 5 Perf. 13x12½
326 A27 5c orange .20 .20
327 A27 10c brt lilac rose .20 .20
328 A27 60c brown .20 .20
329 A28 1p dull purple 1.60 .20
330 A28 1.90p greenish blk 2.50 .35
Nos. 326-330 (5) 4.70 1.15

Tragocephala
Nobilis — A29

Butterfly: 60c, Papilio antimachus.

1953, Nov. 23
331 A29 15c dark green .35 .20
332 A29 60c brown .45 .20
Nos. 331-332,B27-B28 (4) 1.35 .85

Colonial Stamp Day.

Hunter
A30

Design: 60c, Hunter and elephant.

1954, June 10 Perf. 12½x13
333 A30 15c dark gray green .35 .20
334 A30 60c dark brown .50 .20
Nos. 333-334,B29-B30 (4) 1.40 .85

Swimming
Turtle
A31

1954, Nov. 23
335 A31 15c shown .30 .20
336 A31 60c Shark .75 .20
Nos. 335-336,B31-B32 (4) 1.65 .85

Colonial Stamp Day.

Manuel
Iradier y
Bulfy, Birth
Cent. (in
1954)
A32

1955, Jan. 18
337 A32 60c orange brown .50 .20
338 A32 1p dark violet 3.25 .30

Priest Saying
Mass — A33

1955, June 1 Photo. Perf. 13x12½
339 A33 50c olive gray .30 .20
Nos. 339,B33-B34 (3) .95 .65

Centenary of the establishment of an Apostolic Prefecture at Fernando Po.

Palace of
Pardo
A34

1955, July 18 Perf. 12½x13
340 A34 5c ol brn .30 .20
341 A34 15c brn lake .30 .20
342 A34 80c Prus grn .35 .20
Nos. 340-342 (3) .95 .60

Treaty of Pardo, 1778.

Red-eared
Guenons — A35

Orchid — A36

1955, Nov. 23 Perf. 13x12½
343 A35 70c gray grn & bl .60 .20
Nos. 343,B35-B36 (3) 1.15 .65

Colonial Stamp Day.

1956, June 1 Unwmk.
Flower: 50c, Strophantus Kombe.
344 A36 20c bluish green .25 .20
345 A36 50c brown .30 .20
Nos. 344-345,B37-B38 (4) 1.10 .85

See Nos. 360-361, B53-B54.

Arms of Santa
Isabel — A37

African Gray
Parrot — A38

1956, Nov. 23 Perf. 13x12½
346 A37 70c light olive green .25 .20
Nos. 346,B39-B40 (3) .70 .65

Colonial Stamp Day.

1957, June 1 Photo.
347 A38 70c olive green .40 .20
Nos. 347,B41-B42 (3) .95 .65

Elephants
A39

Design: 70c, Elephant, vert.

Perf. 12½x13, 13x12½
1957, Nov. 23
348 A39 20c blue green .35 .20
349 A39 70c emerald .45 .20
Nos. 348-349,B43-B44 (4) 1.45 .85

Colonial Stamp Day.

Boxing
A40

Basketball
A41

Preaching
Missionary
A42

Various Sports: 15c, 2.30p, Jumping. 80c, 3p, Runner at finish line.

1958, Apr. 10 Photo. Unwmk.
350 A40 5c violet brn .20 .20
351 A41 10c orange brn .20 .20
352 A40 15c brown .20 .20
353 A41 80c green .20 .20
354 A40 1p orange red .25 .20
355 A41 2p rose lilac .35 .20
356 A40 2.30p dl violet .40 .25
357 A41 3p brt blue .45 .25
Nos. 350-357 (8) 2.25 1.70

1958, June 1 Perf. 13x12½
Design: 70c, Crucifix and missal.
358 A42 20c blue green .30 .20
359 A42 70c green .30 .20
Nos. 358-359,B48-B49 (4) 1.25 .85

Catholic missions in Spanish Guinea, 75th anniv.

Type of 1956 Inscribed: "Pro-Infancia 1959"
1959, June 1 Perf. 13x12½
360 A36 20c Castor bean .25 .20
361 A36 70c Digitalis .30 .25
Nos. 360-361,B53-B54 (4) 1.10 .90

Promoting child welfare.
Stamps of Spanish Guinea were succeeded by those of Fernando Po and Rio Muni in 1960.

SEMI-POSTAL STAMPS

Red Cross Issue
Types of Semi-Postal Stamps of Spain, 1926, Overprinted in Black or Blue

B1ovpt

1926 Unwmk. Perf. 12½, 13
B1 SP3 5c black brown 10.00 6.50
B2 SP4 10c dark green 10.00 6.50
B3 SP1 15c dark vio (Bl) 2.25 1.50

B4	SP4	20c violet brown	2.25	1.50
B5	SP5	25c deep carmine	2.25	1.50
B6	SP1	30c olive green	2.25	1.50
B7	SP3	40c ultra	.50	.20
B8	SP2	50c red brown	.50	.20
B9	SP5	60c myrtle green	.50	.20
B10	SP4	1p vermilion	.50	.20
B11	SP3	4p bister	2.00	1.40
B12	SP5	10p light violet	6.75	4.50
		Nos. B1-B12 (12)	39.75	25.70
		Set, never hinged	57.50	

See Spain No. B6a for No. B4 without overprint. For surcharges see Spain Nos. B70-B71.

> **Catalogue values for unused stamps in this section, from this point to the end of the section, are for Never Hinged items.**

Allegory — SP1   Leopard — SP2

1950, Dec. 1   Photo.   Perf. 13x12½

B13	SP1	50c + 10c ultra	.30	.25
B14	SP1	1p + 25c dk grn	11.00	3.75
B15	SP1	6.50p + 1.65p dp org	2.75	1.75
		Nos. B13-B15 (3)	14.05	5.75

The surtax was to help the native population.

1951, Nov. 23

B16	SP2	5c + 5c brown	.20	.20
B17	SP2	10c + 5c red orange	.20	.20
B18	SP2	60c + 15c olive brn	.35	.25
		Nos. B16-B18 (3)	.75	.65

Colonial Stamp Day, Nov. 23.

Love Lily — SP3   Brown-cheeked Hornbill — SP4

1952, June 1

B19	SP3	5c + 5c brown	.20	.20
B20	SP3	50c + 10c gray	.25	.20
B21	SP3	2p + 30c blue	1.40	1.00
		Nos. B19-B21 (3)	1.85	1.40

The surtax was to help the native population.

1952, Nov. 23   Perf. 12½

B22	SP4	5c + 5c brown	.20	.20
B23	SP4	10c + 5c brown car	.20	.20
B24	SP4	60c + 15c dk green	.45	.30
		Nos. B22-B24 (3)	.85	.70

Colonial Stamp Day, Nov. 23.

Music Type of Regular Issue
1953, July 1   Perf. 12½x13

B25	A26	5c + 5c like #324	.25	.20
B26	A26	10c + 5c like #325	.30	.25

The surtax was to help the native population.

Insect Type of Regular Issue
1953, Nov. 23   Perf. 13x12½

B27	A29	5c + 5c like #331	.25	.20
B28	A29	10c + 5c like #332	.30	.25

Hunter Type of Regular Issue
1954, June 10   Perf. 12½x13

B29	A30	5c + 5c like #333	.25	.20
B30	A30	10c + 5c like #334	.30	.25

The surtax was to help the native population.

Type of Regular Issue
1954, Nov. 23

B31	A31	5c + 5c like #335	.30	.20
B32	A31	10c + 5c like #336	.30	.25

Type of Regular Issue and

Baptism — SP5

Perf. 13x12½
1955, June 1   Photo.   Unwmk.

B33	A33	10c + 5c like #339	.30	.20
B34	SP5	25c + 10c shown	.35	.25

Type of Regular Issue and

Red-eared Guenons SP6

Perf. 13x12½, 12½x13
1955, Nov. 23

B35	A35	5c + 5c like #343	.25	.20
B36	SP6	15c + 5c shown	.30	.25

Flower Type of Regular Issue
1956, June 1   Perf. 13x12½

B37	A36	5c + 5c like #344	.25	.20
B38	A36	15c + 5c like #345	.30	.25

The tax was for native welfare work.

Type of Regular Issue and

Drummers and Arms of Bata SP7

Perf. 13x12½, 12½x13
1956, Nov. 23

B39	A37	5c + 5c like #346	.20	.20
B40	SP7	15c + 5c shown	.25	.25

Type of Regular Issue and

African Gray Parrot SP8

Perf. 13x12½, 12½x13
1957, June 1   Photo.   Unwmk.

B41	A38	5c + 5c like #347	.25	.20
B42	SP8	15c + 5c shown	.30	.25

The surtax was for child welfare.

Type of Regular Issue, 1957
Perf. 12½x13, 13x12½
1957, Nov. 23

B43	A39	10c + 5c like #348	.30	.20
B44	A39	15c + 5c like #349	.35	.25

Pigeons and Arms of Valencia and Santa Isabel SP9

1958, Mar. 6   Perf. 12½x13

B45	SP9	10c + 5c org brn	.20	.20
B46	SP9	15c + 10c bister	.20	.20
B47	SP9	50c + 10c ol gray	.25	.25
		Nos. B45-B47 (3)	.65	.65

The surtax was to aid the victims of the Valencia flood, Oct., 1957.

Type of Regular Issue, 1958
1958, June 1   Photo.   Perf. 13x12½

B48	A42	10c + 5c like #358	.30	.20
B49	A42	15c + 5c like #359	.35	.25

The surtax was to help the native population.

Butterflies SP10   Early Bicycle SP11

Stamp Day: Various butterflies.

1958, Nov. 23   Unwmk.

B50	SP10	10c + 5c brown red	.35	.20
B51	SP10	25c + 10c brt pur	.35	.20
B52	SP10	50c + 10c gray olive	.40	.25
		Nos. B50-B52 (3)	1.10	.65

Type of Regular Issue 1956 Inscribed: "Pro-Infancia 1959"
1959, June 1   Photo.   Perf. 13x12½

B53	A36	10c + 5c like #361	.25	.20
B54	A36	15c + 5c like #360	.30	.25

The surtax was for child welfare.

1959, Nov. 23

Designs: 20c+5c, Bicycle race. 50c+20c, Bicyclist winning race.

B55	SP11	10c + 5c lt rose brn	.25	.20
B56	SP11	20c + 5c turq blue	.25	.20
B57	SP11	50c + 20c olive gray	.30	.25
		Nos. B55-B57 (3)	.80	.65

Stamp Day.

AIR POST STAMPS

AP1

Revenue Stamp Surcharged "Habilitado para / Correo Aéreo / Intercolonial / Una Peseta"

Type I — "Correo Aereo," 20½mm.
Type II — "Correo Aereo," 22mm.

1941   Unwmk.   Perf. 11

C1	AP1	1p on 17p dp red, I	32.50	7.25
a.		Type II	42.50	10.00

Spain No. C113 Overprinted in **Golfo de Guinea.** Red

1942, June 23

C2	AP30	1p chalky blue	1.75	.30

No. 300 Overprinted in Green **Correo Aéreo Viaje Ministerial 10-19 Enero 1948**

1948, Jan. 15   Perf. 10½x9½

C3	A166	4p dull rose	8.25	2.50
		Never hinged	13.50	

The overprint exists in two types: I — The numeral 1's are lower case L's. II — The numeral 1's are actual ones.

Count of Argelejo and Frigate Catalina at Fernando Po, 1778 AP2

1949, Nov. 23   Photo.   Perf. 12½x13

C4	AP2	5p dark slate green	.95	.70
		Never hinged	1.40	

Stamp Day, Nov. 23, 1949.

Manuel Iradier and Native Products — AP3   Woman Holding Dove — AP5

Benito Rapids AP4

1950, Nov. 23   Unwmk.   Perf. 12½

C5	AP3	5p dk brn	2.25	.95
		Never hinged	3.25	

Stamp Day, Nov. 23, 1950.

1951, Mar. 1   Litho.   Perf. 12½x13

Various views.

C6	AP4	25c ocher	.20	.20
C7	AP4	50c lilac rose	.20	.20
C8	AP4	1p green	.20	.20
C9	AP4	2p bright blue	.20	.20
C10	AP4	3.25p rose lilac	.45	.20
C11	AP4	5p gray brown	3.75	1.60
C12	AP4	10p rose red	14.00	5.75
		Nos. C6-C12 (7)	19.00	8.35
		Set, never hinged	32.50	

> **Catalogue values for unused stamps in this section, from this point to the end of the section, are for Never Hinged items.**

1951, Apr. 22   Engr.   Perf. 10

C13	AP5	5p dark blue	19.00	2.50

500th birth anniv. of Queen Isabella I.

Ferdinand the Catholic — AP6   Soccer Players — AP7

1952, July 18   Photo.   Perf. 13x12½

C14	AP6	5p red brown	25.00	6.00

500th birth anniv. of Ferdinand the Catholic of Spain.

1955-56   Unwmk.

C15	AP7	25c blue vio ('56)	.25	.20
C16	AP7	50c olive ('56)	.25	.20
C17	AP7	1.50p brown ('56)	.95	.20
C18	AP7	4p rose car ('56)	3.00	.40
C19	AP7	10p yellow grn	1.60	.40
		Nos. C15-C19 (5)	6.05	1.40

Planes and Arm Holding Spear — AP8

1957, Sept. 19   *Perf. 13x12½*
C20 AP8 25p bister & sepia   7.50 .85

30th anniv. of the Atlantida Squadron flight to Spanish Guinea.

SPECIAL DELIVERY STAMP

View of Fernando Po — SD1

Perf. 12½x13

1951, Mar. 1   Litho.   Unwmk.
E1 SD1 25c rose carmine   .25 .20
    Never hinged   .30

SPANISH MOROCCO

'spa-nish mə-'rä-ˌkō

LOCATION — Northwest coast of Africa
GOVT. — Spanish Protectorate
AREA — 17,398 sq. mi. (approx.)
POP. — 1,010,117 (1950)
CAPITAL — Tetuán

Spanish Morocco was a Spanish Protectorate until 1956 when it, along with the French and Tangier zones of Morocco, became the independent country, Morocco.

100 Centimos = 1 Peseta

> Catalogue values for unused stamps in this country are for Never Hinged items, beginning with Scott 280 in the regular postage section, Scott B27 in the semipostal section, Scott C24 in the airpost section, and Scott E11 in special delivery section.

Spanish Offices in Morocco

Spain No. 221A Overprinted in Carmine

1903-09   Unwmk.   *Imperf.*
1 A21 ¼c blue green   .55 .20
 a. Complete 1c (block 4 ¼c)   2.25 1.50

See Nos. 26, 39, 52, Tetuan 1, 7.

Stamps of Spain Overprinted in Carmine or Blue

a

On Stamps of 1900
Perf. 14
2 A35 2c bister brown   1.40 1.10
3 A35 5c green   1.60 .60
4 A35 10c rose red (Bl)   1.75 .25
5 A35 15c brt violet   2.50 .60
6 A35 20c grnsh black   10.00 2.75

---

7 A35 25c blue   .80 .65
8 A35 30c blue green   6.00 2.75
9 A35 40c rose (Bl)   10.00 4.75
10 A35 50c slate grn   6.00 4.50
11 A35 1p lake (Bl)   12.00 6.25
12 A35 4p dull violet   32.50 11.00
13 A35 10p brown org (Bl)   32.50 27.50
    Nos. 1-13 (13)   117.60 62.90
    Set, never hinged   175.00

Many varieties of overprint exist. Nos. 7-13 exist imperf. Value, $500.
See Tetuan Nos. 2-6, 8-15.

On Stamps of 1909-10

1909-10   *Perf. 13x12½, 14*
14 A46 2c dark brown   .65 .20
15 A46 5c green   3.25 .25
16 A46 10c carmine (Bl)   3.75 .25
17 A46 15c violet   9.00 .55
18 A46 20c olive green   22.50 1.10
19 A46 25c deep blue   77.50
20 A46 30c blue green   7.25 .55
21 A46 40c rose (Bl)   7.25 .55
22 A46 50c slate blue   12.50 12.00
23 A46 1p lake (Bl)   30.00 25.00
24 A46 4p deep violet   77.50
25 A46 10p orange (Bl)   77.50
    Nos. 14-18,20-23 (9)   96.15 40.45
    Set, never hinged   135.00
    Nos. 14-25 (12)   328.65

The stamps overprinted "Correo Espanol Marruecos" were used in all Morocco until the year 1914. After the issue of special stamps for the Protectorate the "Correo Espanol" stamps were continued in use solely in the city of Tangier.

Many varieties of overprint exist.
Nos. 19, 24 and 25 were not regularly issued.
See Nos. 27-38, 40-51, 53-67, 75-76, 78.

Spanish Morocco

Spain No. 221A Overprinted in Carmine

1914   *Imperf.*
26 A21 ¼c green   .20 .20
 a. Complete 1c (block 4 ¼c)   1.25 .90

Stamps of Spain 1909-10 Overprinted in Carmine or Blue

Perf. 13x12½, 14
27 A46 2c dark brown (C)   .25 .20
28 A46 5c green (C)   .25 .20
29 A46 10c carmine (Bl)   .25 .20
30 A46 15c violet (C)   1.25 .85
31 A46 20c olive grn (C)   2.50 1.75
32 A46 25c deep blue (C)   2.50 1.40
33 A46 30c blue grn (C)   5.00 2.50
34 A46 40c rose (Bl)   11.00 3.50
35 A46 50c slate blue (C)   5.75 2.50
36 A46 1p lake (Bl)   5.75 3.50
37 A46 4p dp violet (C)   29.00 23.00
38 A46 10p orange (Bl)   44.00 30.00
    Nos. 26-38,E1 (14)   112.20 71.80
    Set, never hinged   190.00

Many varieties of overprint exist, including inverted.
#27-38 exist imperf. Value for set, $525.

Stamps of Spain 1876 and 1909-10 Overprinted in Red or Blue

1915   *Imperf.*
39 A21 ¼c blue grn (R)   .20 .20
 a. Complete 1c (block 4 ¼c)   1.25 .95

Perf. 13x12½, 14
40 A46 2c dk brown (R)   .20 .25
41 A46 5c green (R)   .25 .25
42 A46 10c carmine (Bl)   .25 .25
43 A46 15c violet (R)   .25 .25
44 A46 20c olive grn (R)   .95 .25
45 A46 25c deep blue (R)   .95 .40
46 A46 30c blue grn (R)   1.10 .45
47 A46 40c rose (Bl)   3.00 .45
48 A46 50c slate blue (R)   5.00 .40
49 A46 1p lake (Bl)   5.00 .45

---

50 A46 4p deep violet (R)   32.50 21.00
51 A46 10p orange (Bl)   47.50 22.50
    Nos. 39-51,E2 (14)   99.65 48.50
    Set, never hinged   155.00

One stamp in the setting on Nos. 39-51 has the first "R" of "PROTECTORADO" inverted. Many other varieties of overprint exist, including double and inverted.
Nos. 40-51 exist imperf. Value, set $650.

Stamps of Spain 1877 and 1909-10 Overprinted in Red or Blue

b

1916-18   *Imperf.*
52 A21 ¼c blue grn (R)   1.10 .20
 a. Complete 1c (block 4 ¼c)   1.75 1.25

Perf. 13x12½, 14
53 A46 2c dk brown (R)   1.10 .20
54 A46 5c green (R)   5.00 .20
55 A46 10c carmine (Bl)   5.50 .20
56 A46 15c violet (R)   125.00
57 A46 20c olive grn (R)   125.00
58 A46 25c dp blue (R)   19.00 3.00
59 A46 30c blue grn (R)   25.00 20.00
60 A46 40c rose (Bl)   26.00 .45
61 A46 50c slate blue (R)   12.00 .20
62 A46 1p lake (Bl)   30.00 2.10
63 A46 4p dp violet (R)   50.00 29.00
64 A46 10p orange (Bl)   100.00 65.00
    Nos. 52-55,58-64 (11)   274.70 120.55
    Set, never hinged   400.00
    Nos. 52-64 (13)   524.70
    Set, never hinged   1,000.

Nos. 56-57 were not regularly issued.
Varieties of overprint, including double and inverted, exist for several denominations.
The 5c exists in olive brown. Value $525.

Same Overprint on Spain No. 310
1920
65 A46 15c ocher (Bl)   5.50 .30

Exists imperf.; also with overprint inverted.

Nos. 44, 46 Perforated through the middle and each half Surcharged "10 céntimos" in Red

1920
66 A46 10c on half of 20c   5.00 1.90
67 A46 15c on half of 30c   11.00 7.25

No. E2 Divided and Surcharged in Black
68 SD1 10c on half of 20c   12.00 7.75
 a. "10/cts." surcharge added   160.00 160.00
    Nos. 66-68 (3)   28.00 16.90

Values of Nos. 66-68 are for pairs, both halves of the stamp. Varieties were probably made deliberately.

"Justice" — A1

Revenue Stamps Perforated through the Middle and each half Surcharged with New Value in Red or Green

1920   *Perf. 11½*
69 A1 5c on 5p lt bl   9.50 1.90
70 A1 5c on 10p green   .40 .20
71 A1 10c on 25p dk grn   .40 .20
 a. Inverted surcharge   11.00 10.00
72 A1 10c on 50p indigo   .45 .30
73 A1 15c on 100p red (G)   .45 .30
74 A1 15c on 500p cl (G)   12.50 6.50
    Nos. 69-74 (6)   23.70 9.40
    Set, never hinged   37.50

Values of Nos. 69-74 are for pairs, both halves of the stamp.

Stamps of Spain 1917-20 Overprinted Type "a" in Blue or Red

1921-24   *Perf. 13*
75 A46 15c ocher (Bl)   1.25 .20
76 A46 20c violet (R)   1.90 .20

Stamps of Spain 1920-21 Overprinted Type "b" in Red
Imperf
77 A47 1c blue green   1.40 .20

Engr.
Perf. 13
78 A46 20c violet   10.00 .20

See No. 92.

Stamps of Spain, 1922 Overprinted Type "a" in Red or Blue

1923-28   *Perf. 13½x12½*
79 A49 2c olive green (R)   3.75 .20
80 A49 5c red violet (Bl)   3.75 .20
81 A49 10c yellow green (R)   4.50 .20
82 A49 20c violet (R)   6.25 .95
    Nos. 79-82 (4)   18.25 1.55

Same Overprinted Type "b"

1923-25
83 A49 2c olive green (R)   .65 .20
84 A49 5c red violet (Bl)   .65 .20
85 A49 10c yellow grn (R)   2.75 .20
86 A49 15c blue (R)   2.75 .20
87 A49 20c violet (R)   6.00 .20
88 A49 25c carmine (R)   12.00 1.40
89 A49 40c deep blue (R)   12.50 4.50
90 A49 50c orange (Bl)   32.50 7.75
91 A49a 1p blue black (R)   50.00 4.50
    Nos. 83-91,E3 (10)   130.30 27.40
    Set, never hinged   210.00

Spain No. 314 Overprinted Type "a" in Red

1927   *Imperf.*
92 A47 1c blue green   .20 .20

Mosque of Alcazarquivir A2   Moorish Gateway at Larache A3

Well at Alhucemas A4

View of Xauen — A5

View of Tetuan — A6

1928-32   Engr.   *Perf. 14, 14½*
93 A2 1c red ("Cs")   .20 .20
94 A2 1c car rose ("Ct") ('32)   .40 .30
95 A2 2c dark violet   .20 .20
96 A2 5c deep blue   .25 .20
97 A2 10c dark green   .25 .20
98 A3 15c orange brown   .60 .25
99 A3 20c olive green   .60 .25
100 A3 25c copper red   .60 .25
102 A3 30c black brown   2.00 .30
103 A3 40c dull blue   2.50 .30
104 A3 50c brown violet   5.50 .30
105 A4 1p yellow green   8.00 .35
106 A5 2.50p red violet   25.00 8.50
107 A6 4p ultra   19.00 5.25
    Nos. 93-107,E4 (15)   69.35 18.25
    Set, never hinged   100.00

For surcharges see Nos. 164-167.

Seville-Barcelona Issue of Spain, 1929, Overprinted in Red or Blue

1929 — Perf. 11, 14

108	A50	1c greenish blue	.30	.25
109	A51	2c pale yel grn	.30	.25
110	A52	5c rose lake (Bl)	.30	.25
111	A53	10c green	.30	.25
112	A50	15c Prussian blue	.30	.25
113	A51	20c purple	.30	.25
114	A50	25c bright rose (Bl)	.30	.25
115	A52	30c black brown (bl)	.80	.65
116	A53	40c dark blue	.80	.65
117	A52	50c deep orange (Bl)	.80	.65
118	A52	1p blue black	6.50	4.75
119	A53	4p deep rose (Bl)	15.00	10.50
120	A53	10p brown (Bl)	32.50	24.00

Nos. 108-120 (13) 58.50 42.95
Set, never hinged 87.50

See Nos. L1-L11.

Stamps of Spain, 1922-31, Overprinted Type "a" in Black, Blue or Red

1929-34 — Perf. 11½, 13x12½

121	A49	5c claret (Bk)	3.25	.20
122	A61	10c green (R)	2.75	.40
123	A61	15c slate grn (R)	97.50	1.00
124	A61	20c violet (R)	2.75	.45
125	A61	30c brown lake (Bl)	3.00	1.00
126	A61	40c dark blue (R)	11.00	5.00
127	A49	50c orange	27.50	4.75
128	A49a	10p brown (Bl)	2.75	4.25

Nos. 121-128 (8) 150.50 17.05
Set, never hinged 210.00

Stamps of Spain, 1922-26, overprinted diagonally as above, and with no control number, or with "A000,000" on back, were not issued but were presented to the delegates at the 1929 UPU Congress in London. Value of complete set of 16, $3,250.

Stamps of Spain 1931-32, Overprinted in Black

1933-34 — Imperf.

130	A108	1c blue green	.20	.20

Perf. 11½

131	A108	2c buff	.20	.20
132	A95	5c brnsh black	.20	.20
133	A96	10c yellow green	.20	.20
134	A97	15c slate green	.20	.20
135	A95	20c dark violet	.25	.20
136	A104	25c lake	.25	.20
137	A99	30c carmine rose	55.00	5.50
138	A100	40c dark blue	.60	.20
139	A97	50c orange	1.10	.25
140	A100	60c apple green	1.10	.25
141	A105	1p blue black	1.10	.45
142	A106	4p magenta	2.40	2.25
143	A107	10p deep brown	3.25	5.00

Nos. 130-143,E7 (15) 67.30 15.50
Set, never hinged 110.00

Street Scene in Tangier — A7

View of Xauen A8

Gate in Town Wall, Arzila — A9

Street Scene in Tangier A10

Mosque of Alcazarquivir A11

Caliph and His Guard A12

View of Tangier A13

Green Control Numbers Printed on Gum

1933-35 — Photo. — Perf. 14, 13½

144	A7	1c brt rose	.25	.20
145	A8	2c green ('35)	.25	.20
146	A9	5c magenta ('35)	.25	.20
147	A10	10c dark green	.35	.20
148	A11	15c yellow ('35)	2.25	.20
149	A7	20c slate green	.90	.20
150	A12	25c crimson ('35)	22.50	.20
151	A10	30c red brown	6.50	.25
152	A13	40c deep blue	10.00	.25
153	A13	50c red orange	32.50	4.00
154	A8	1p slate blk ('35)	14.50	.25
155	A9	2.50p brown ('35)	25.00	4.00
156	A11	4p yel grn ('35)	25.00	4.00
157	A12	5p black ('35)	32.50	4.00

Nos. 144-157,E5 (15) 173.75 18.35
Set, never hinged 255.00

For surcharge see No. CB1.

Mosque — A14

Landscape A15

Green Control Numbers Printed on Gum

1935

158	A14	25c violet	.95	.20
159	A15	30c crimson	13.00	.20
160	A14	40c orange	6.75	.20
161	A15	50c bright blue	6.75	.20
162	A14	60c dk blue green	6.75	.20
163	A15	2p brown lake	32.50	4.75

Nos. 158-163 (6) 66.70 5.80
Set, never hinged 97.50

See No. 174.

Regular Issue and Special Delivery Stamp of 1928, Surcharged in Blue, Green or Red with New Values and Ornaments

1936

164	A6	1c on 4p ultra (Bl)	.30	.20
165	A5	2c on 2.50p red vio (G)	.30	.20
166	A3	5c on 25c cop red (R)	.25	.20
167	A4	10c on 1p yel grn (G)	9.00	3.75
168	SD2	15c on 20c blk (Bl)	7.00	1.90

Nos. 164-168 (5) 16.85 6.25
Set, never hinged 22.50

Caliph and Viziers — A16

View of Bokoia A17

View of Alcazarquivir — A18

Sidi Saida Mosque A19

Caliph and Procession A20

Without Control Numbers

1937 — Photo. — Perf. 13½

169	A16	1c green	.25	.20
170	A17	2c red violet	.25	.20
171	A18	5c orange	.25	.20
172	A16	15c violet	.25	.20
173	A19	30c red	.75	.20
a.		Souvenir sheet of 4, #170-173	20.00	11.00
174	A14	1p ultra	6.75	.25
a.		Souv. sheet of 4, #169-171, 174	20.00	11.00
175	A20	10p brown	55.00	16.00

Nos. 169-175 (7) 63.50 17.25
Set, never hinged 85.00

Nos. 173a, 174a for 1st year of the Spanish Civil War.
Nos. 173a, 174a were privately overprinted "TANGER" in black on each stamp in the sheet for "use" in the International City of Tangier, and "GUINEA" for "use" in Spanish Guinea.

Harkeno Rifleman — A21

Troops Marching A22

Designs: 2c, Legionnaires. 5c, Cavalryman leading his mount. 10c, Moroccan phalanx. 15c, Legion flag-bearer. 20c, Colonial soldier. 25c, Ifni sharpshooters. 30c, Mounted trumpeters. 40c, Cape Juby Dromedary Corps. 50c, Regular infantry. 60c, Caliphate guards. 1p, Orderly on guard. 2p, Sentry. 2.50p, Regular cavalry. 4p, Orderly.

1937 — Perf. 13½

176	A21	1c dull blue	.25	.20
177	A21	2c orange brn	.25	.20
178	A21	5c cerise	.25	.20
179	A21	10c emerald	.25	.20
180	A21	15c brt blue	.25	.20
181	A21	20c red brown	.25	.20
182	A21	25c magenta	.25	.20
183	A21	30c red orange	.25	.20
184	A21	40c orange	.25	.20
185	A21	50c ultra	.25	.25
186	A21	60c yellow grn	.25	.25
187	A21	1p blue violet	.25	.25
188	A21	2p Prus blue	9.25	4.00
189	A21	2.50p gray black	9.25	4.00
190	A21	4p dark brown	9.25	4.00
191	A22	10p black	9.25	4.00

Nos. 176-191,E6 (17) 40.20 18.80
Set, never hinged 60.00

First Year of Spanish Civil War. Exists imperf. Value, set $250.
For overprints see Nos. 214-229.

Spanish Quarter — A25

Designs: 10c, Moroccan quarter. 15c, Street scene, Larache. 20c, Tetuan.

1939 — Unwmk. — Photo. — Perf. 13½

194	A25	5c orange	.25	.20
195	A25	10c brt blue grn	.25	.20
196	A25	15c golden brown	.45	.45
197	A25	20c brt ultra	.45	.25

Nos. 194-197 (4) 1.40 .90

Postman — A26

Mail Box — A27

Landscape A28

Street Scene, Alcazarquivir A29

View of Xauen — A30

Sentry Guarding Palace at Sat — A31

The Chieftain — A32

Market Place, Larache — A33

Tetuán — A34

Ancient Gateway at Xauen — A35

Scene in Alcazarquivir A36

Post Office A37

Spanish War Veterans — A38

Victory Flag Bearers — A39

Cavalry — A40

Day of Court — A41

1940 Unwmk. Photo. Perf. 11½x11

198	A26	1c dark brown	.25	.20
199	A27	2c olive grn	.25	.20
200	A28	5c dk blue	.25	.20
201	A29	10c dk red lilac	.25	.20
202	A30	15c dk green	.30	.25
203	A31	20c purple	.25	.25
204	A32	25c black brown	.25	.25
205	A33	30c brt green	.25	.25
206	A34	40c slate green	2.00	.25
207	A35	45c orange ver	.85	.25
208	A36	50c brown orange	.85	.25
209	A37	70c sapphire	.85	.25
210	A38	1p indigo & brn	2.50	.25
211	A39	2.50p choc & dk grn	14.50	3.50
212	A40	5p dk cerise & sep	2.75	.30
213	A41	10p dk ol grn & brn org	25.00	6.00
		Nos. 198-213,E8 (17)	51.95	13.05
		Set, never hinged	85.00	

"ZONA" printed in black on back.
Exists imperf. Value, set $325.

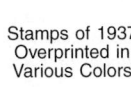

Stamps of 1937 Overprinted in Various Colors

1940 Unwmk. Perf. 13½

214	A21	1c dull blue (Bk)	.70	.55
215	A21	2c org brn (Bk)	.70	.55
216	A21	5c cerise (Bk)	.70	.55
217	A21	10c emerald (Bk)	.70	.55
218	A21	15c brt blue (Bk)	.70	.55
219	A21	20c red brn (Bk)	.70	.55
220	A21	25c mag (Bk)	.70	.55
221	A21	30c red org (V)	.70	.55
222	A21	40c orange (V)	1.25	1.00
223	A21	50c ultra (Bk)	1.25	1.00
224	A21	60c yel grn (Bk)	1.25	1.00
225	A21	1p blue vio (V)	1.25	1.00
226	A21	2p Prus bl (Bl)	38.00	38.00
227	A21	2.50p gray blk (V)	38.00	38.00
228	A21	4p dk brn (Bl)	38.00	38.00
229	A22	10p black (R)	38.00	38.00
		Nos. 214-229,E10 (17)	172.10	167.65
		Set, never hinged	320.00	

4th anniversary of Spanish Civil War.

Larache A42

Alcazarquivir A43

Market Place, Larache — A44

Tangier A45

A46

1941 Unwmk. Photo. Perf. 10½

230	A42	5c dk brn & brn	.25	.20
231	A43	10c dp rose & ver	.25	.20
232	A44	15c sl grn & yel grn	.25	.20
233	A45	20c vio bl & dp bl	.55	.25
234	A46	40c dp plum & claret	1.50	.25
		Nos. 230-234 (5)	2.80	1.10

Exists imperf. Value, set $150.

1943 Perf. 12x12½

234A	A43	5c dark blue	.20	.20
235	A44	40c dull violet brn	55.00	.20

Plowing A47

Harvesting A48

Returning from Work A49

Transporting Wheat — A50

Vegetable Garden A51

Picking Oranges A52

Goat Herd — A53

1944 Unwmk. Photo. Perf. 12½

236	A47	1c choc & lt bl	.20	.20
237	A48	2c sl grn & lt grn	.20	.20
238	A49	5c choc & grnsh blk	.20	.20
239	A50	10c brt ultra & red org	.20	.20
240	A51	15c sl grn & lt grn	.20	.20
241	A52	20c dp cl & blk	.20	.20
242	A53	25c lt bl & choc	.20	.20
243	A47	30c yel grn & brt ultra	.20	.20
244	A48	40c choc & red vio	.20	.20
245	A49	50c brt ultra & red brn	.60	
246	A50	75c yel grn & brt ultra	.80	
247	A51	1p brt ultra & choc	.80	.20
248	A52	2.50p blk & brt ultra	7.00	1.60
249	A53	10p sal & gray blk	10.50	3.25
		Nos. 236-249 (14)	21.50	7.25
		Set, never hinged	35.00	

Exists imperf. Value, set $100.

Potters A54

Dyers A55

Blacksmiths A56

Cobblers A57

Weavers A58

Metal Workers A59

1946 Unwmk. Litho. Perf. 10½x10

250	A54	1c purple & brn	.20	.20
251	A55	2c dk Prus grn & vio blk	.20	.20
252	A54	10c dp org & vio bl	.20	.20
253	A55	15c dk bl & bl grn	.20	.20
254	A54	25c yel grn & ultra	.20	.20
255	A56	40c dk bl & brn, perf. 12½	.20	.20
256	A55	45c black & rose	.50	.20
257	A57	1p dk Prus grn & dp bl	.60	.20
258	A58	2.50p dp org & gray	1.75	.65
259	A59	10p dk bl & gray	3.00	1.50
		Nos. 250-259 (10)	7.05	3.75
		Set, never hinged	9.50	

Control letter "Z" in circle in black on back.
Exists imperf. Value, set $85.

A60

Sanitorium — A61

1946, Sept. 1 Perf. 11½x10½, 10½

260	A60	10c crim & bl grn	.20	.20
261	A61	25c crimson & brn	.25	.20
		Nos. 260-261,B14-B16 (5)	1.70	1.05

Issued to aid anti-tuberculosis work.

A62

A63

1947 Perf. 10

262	A62	10c carmine & blue	.20	.20
263	A63	25c red & chocolate	.20	.20
		Nos. 262-263,B17-B19 (5)	1.65	1.30

Issued to aid anti-tuberculosis work.

Commerce by Railroad A64

Commerce by Truck A65

Urban Market A66

Country Market A67

Caravan A68

Maritime Commerce A69

1948   Litho.   Perf. 10, 10x10½

264	A64	2c purple & brn	.20	.20
265	A65	5c dp cl & vio	.20	.20
266	A66	15c brt ultra & bl grn	.20	.20
267	A67	25c blk & Prus grn	.20	.20
268	A65	35c brt ultra & gray blk	.20	.20
269	A68	50c red & violet	.20	.20
270	A68	70c dk gray grn & ultra	.20	.20
271	A67	90c cer & dk gray grn	.20	.20
272	A68	1p brt ultra & vio	.60	.20
273	A64	2.50p vio brn & sl grn	1.50	.45
274	A69	10p blk & dp ultra	2.75	1.25
		Nos. 264-274 (11)	6.45	3.50
		Set, never hinged	11.00	

Exists imperf. Value, set $90.

Emblem of Tuberculosis Association

A70   A71

Design: 25c, Plane over sanatorium.

1948, Oct. 1   Perf. 10

275	A70	10c car & green	.25	.20
276	A70	25c car & grnsh gray	1.75	.65
		Nos. 275-276,B20-B23 (6)	27.45	9.25

See No. B39.
Exists imperf. Value, set $75.

1949

10c, Road of Health. 25c, Minaret and Palm.

Black Control Number on Back

277	A71	5c car & green	.20	.20
278	A71	10c car & dk vio	.25	.25
279	A71	25c car & black	.90	.30
		Nos. 277-279,B25-B26 (5)	3.15	1.35

> **Catalogue values for unused stamps in this section, from this point to the end of the section, are for Never Hinged items.**

Mail Transport, 1890 — A72   Herald — A73

Designs: 5c, 50c, 90c, Mail transport, 1890. 10c, 45c, 1p, Mail transport, 1906. 15c, 1.50p, Mail transport, 1913. 35c, 75c, 5p, Mail transport, 1914. 10p, Mail transport, 1918.

1950   Litho.   Perf. 10½

280	A72	5c choc & vio bl	.20	.20
281	A72	10c deep bl & sep	.20	.20
282	A72	15c grnsh blk & emer	.20	.20
283	A72	35c pur & gray blk	.20	.20
284	A72	45c dp car & rose lil	.20	.20
285	A72	50c emer & dk brn	.20	.20
286	A72	75c dk vio bl & bl	.20	.20
287	A72	90c grnsh blk & rose car	.20	.20
288	A72	1p blk brn & gray	.20	.20
289	A72	1.50p carmine & blue	.70	.20
290	A72	5p black & vio brn	1.25	.20
291	A72	10p purple & blue	26.00	10.00
		Nos. 280-291,E11 (13)	53.75	21.20

UPU, 75th anniv. (in 1949).
Nos. 280-291 exist imperf. Value $400.

1950   Unwmk.   Perf. 10
Frame and Device in Carmine
Black Control Number on Back

292	A73	5c gray black	.25	.25
293	A73	10c Old fort	.25	.25
294	A73	25c Sanatorium	1.00	.50
		Nos. 292-294,B27-B28 (5)	2.95	1.75

Boar Hunt A74

10c, 1p, Hunters and hounds. 50c, Boar hunt. 5p, Fishermen. 10p, Moorish fishing boat.

1950, Dec. 30   Perf. 10½x10
Black Control Number on Back

295	A74	5c dk brn & rose vio	.20	.20
296	A74	10c carmine & gray	.20	.20
297	A74	50c green & sepia	.20	.20
298	A74	1p bl vio & claret	.45	.20
299	A74	5p dp claret & bl vio	.70	.25
300	A74	10p grnsh blk & dp cl	2.25	.40
		Nos. 295-300 (6)	4.00	1.45

Emblem — A75   Worship — A77

Armed Attack A76

10c, Patients expressing gratitude. 25c, Plane in the Clouds.

Dated "1951"

1951   Litho.   Perf. 12
Frame and Device in Carmine
Black Control Number on Back

301	A75	5c green	.20	.20
302	A75	10c blue violet	.20	.20
303	A75	25c gray black	.85	.30
		Nos. 301-303,B29-B32 (7)	13.55	5.00

Issued to aid anti-tuberculosis work.

1952   Perf. 11

Designs: 10c, Horses on parade. 15c, Holiday procession. 20c, Road to market. 25c, "Brother-hoods." 35c, "Offering." 45c, Soldiers. 50c, On the rooftop. 75c, Teahouse. 90c, Wedding. 1p, Pilgrimage. 5p, Storyteller. 10p, Market corner.

Black Control Number on Back

304	A76	5c dk blue & brn	.20	.20
305	A76	10c dk brn & lil rose	.20	.20
306	A76	15c black & emer	.20	.20
307	A76	20c ol grn & red vio	.20	.20
308	A76	25c red & lt blue	.20	.20
309	A76	35c olive & orange	.20	.20
310	A76	45c red & rose red	.20	.20
311	A76	50c rose car & gray grn	.20	.20
312	A76	75c purple & ultra	.20	.20
313	A76	90c dk bl & rose vio	.20	.20
314	A76	1p dk bl & red brn	.20	.20
315	A76	5p red & blue	1.25	.25
316	A76	10p dk grn & gray blk	1.75	.40
		Nos. 304-316,E12 (14)	5.40	3.05

1952, Oct. 1   Dated "1952"

10c, Distributing alms. 25c, Prickly pear.

Black Control Number on Back

317	A77	5c car & dk ol grn	.20	.20
318	A77	10c car & dk brown	.20	.20
319	A77	25c car & dp blue	.35	.20
		Nos. 317-319,B33-B37 (8)	9.35	3.80

Semi-Postal Types of 1948-49 Dated "1953"

1953   Litho.   Perf. 10
Black Control Number on Back

320	SP7	5c shown	.20	.20
321	SP9	10c like #B26	.20	.20
322	SP7	25c like #B23	.85	.35
		Nos. 320-322,B38-B42 (8)	16.45	5.80

Issued to aid anti-tuberculosis work.

A78

1953, Nov. 15
Black Control Number on Back

323	A78	5c red	.20	.20
324	A78	10c gray green	.20	.20

Mountain Women — A79   Zauia — A80

50c and 2.50p, Water carrier. 90c and 2p, Mountaineers and donkey. 1p and 4.50p, Moorish women and child. 10p, Mounted dignitary.

1953, Dec. 15   Photo.
Black Control Number on Back

334	A79	35c grn & rose vio	.20	.20
335	A79	50c red & green	.20	.20
336	A79	90c dk bl & org	.20	.20
337	A79	1p dk brn & grn	.20	.20
338	A79	1.25p dk grn & car rose	.20	.20
339	A79	2p dk rose vio & bl	.25	.20
340	A79	2.50p black & orange	.65	.25

341	A79	4.50p brt car rose & dk grn	3.25	.35
342	A79	10p green & black	4.25	.65
		Nos. 334-342,E13 (10)	9.60	2.65

25th anniv. of Spanish Morocco's first definitive postage stamps.

1954, Nov. 1   Dated "1954"

10c, "The Family." 25c, Plane, Spanish coast.

Black Control Number on Back

343	A80	5c car & bl grn	.20	.20
344	A80	10c car & dk brn	.20	.20
345	A80	25c car & blue	.20	.20
		Nos. 343-345,B43-B45 (6)	7.50	4.40

Queen's Gate — A81   Honor Guard — A82

1955   Litho.   Perf. 11
Black Control Number on Back
Frames in Black

346	A81	15c shown	.20	.20
347	A81	25c Saida	.20	.20
348	A81	80c like #346	.20	.20
349	A81	1p like #347	.20	.20
350	A81	15p Ceuta	3.00	.65
		Nos. 346-350,E14 (6)	4.00	1.65

**   Perf. 13x12½**
1955, Nov. 8   Photo.   Unwmk.

Designs: 25c, 80c, 3p, Caliph Moulay Hassan ben el-Medi. 30c, 1p, 5p, Caliph and procession. 15p, Coat of arms.

351	A82	15c ol brn & ol	.20	.20
352	A82	25c lil & dp rose	.20	.20
353	A82	30c brn blk & Prus grn	.20	.20
354	A82	70c Prus grn & yel grn	.20	.20
355	A82	80c ol & ol brn	.20	.20
356	A82	1p dk bl & redsh brn	.20	.20
357	A82	1.80p black & bl vio	.20	.20
358	A82	3p blue & gray	.20	.20
359	A82	5p dk grn & brn	1.25	.45

**   Engr.**

360	A82	15p red brn & yel grn	2.75	1.65
		Nos. 351-360 (10)	5.60	3.70

30th anniv. of accession to throne by Caliph Moulay Hassan ben el-Medi ben Ismail.

Succeeding issues, released under the Kingdom, are listed under Morocco.

SEMI-POSTAL STAMPS

Types of Semi-Postal Stamps of Spain, 1926, Overprinted in Black or Blue

1926   Unwmk.   Perf. 12½, 13

B1	SP1	1c orange	7.00	4.50
B2	SP2	2c rose	10.00	8.25
B3	SP3	5c black brn	3.50	3.00
B4	SP4	10c dark grn	3.50	3.00
B5	SP1	15c dk violet (Bl)	.65	.55
B6	SP4	20c violet brn	.65	.55
B7	SP5	25c deep carmine	.65	.55
B8	SP1	30c olive grn	.65	.55
B9	SP3	40c ultra	.20	.20
B10	SP2	50c red brown	.20	.20
B11	SP4	1p vermilion	.20	.20
B12	SP3	4p bister	.65	.55
B13	SP5	10p light violet	2.75	2.25
		Nos. B1-B13,EB1 (14)	33.10	26.45
		Set, never hinged	57.50	

See Spain No. B6a for No. B6 without overprint. For surcharges see Spain Nos. B64-B65.

Tuberculosis Fund Issues

SP1   SP2

SP3

Perf. 10½, 11½x10½

1946, Sept. 1   Litho.   Unwmk.

B14	SP1	25c + 5c crim & rose vio	.20 .20
B15	SP2	50c + 10c crim & blue	.30 .20
B16	SP3	90c + 10c crim & gray brn	.75 .25
		Nos. B14-B16 (3)	1.25 .65

Medical Center — SP4   Nurse and Children — SP5

"Protection" SP6   Herald SP7

1947   Perf. 10

B17	SP4	25c + 5c red & violet	.20 .20
B18	SP5	50c + 10c red & blue	.30 .20
B19	SP6	90c + 10c red & sepia	.75 .50
		Nos. B17-B19 (3)	1.25 .90

1948, Oct. 1

Designs: No. B21, Protection. No. B22, Sun bath. No. B23, Plane over Ben Karrich.

B20	SP7	50c + 10c car & dk vio	.30 .20
B21	SP7	90c + 10c car & dk gray	1.40 .45
B22	SP7	2.50p + 50c car & brn	9.25 3.00
B23	SP7	5p + 1p car & vio bl	14.50 4.75
		Nos. B20-B23 (4)	25.45 8.40

See Nos. 320, 322.

Moulay Hassan ben el-Medi ben Ismail — SP8   Flag — SP9

1949, May 15

B24 SP8 50c + 10c lilac rose   1.00 .40

Wedding of the Caliph at Tetuan, June 5.

Tuberculosis Fund Issues

Design: No. B26, Fight with dragon.

1949

Black Control Numbers on Back

B25	SP9	50c + 10 car & brown	.30 .25
B26	SP9	90c + 10 car & grnsh gray	1.50 .35

See No. 321.

> **Catalogue values for unused stamps in this section, from this point to the end of the section, are for Never Hinged items.**

Crowd at Fountain of Life — SP10   Warrior — SP11

90c+10c, Mohammedan hermit's tomb.

1950, Oct. 1   Litho.   Perf. 10
Black Control Numbers on Back
Frame and Cross in Carmine

B27	SP10	50 + 10c dk brown	.35 .25
B28	SP10	90 + 10c dk green	1.10 .50

1951   Unwmk.   Perf. 12

Designs: 90c+10c, Fort. 1p+5p, Port of Salvation. 1.10p+25c, Road to market.

Black Control Numbers on Back

B29	SP11	50c + 10c car & brn	.20 .20
B30	SP11	90c + 10c car & bl	.35 .20
B31	SP11	1p + 5p car & gray	7.50 2.50
B32	SP11	1.10p + 25p car & gray	4.25 1.40
		Nos. B29-B32 (4)	12.30 4.30

See No. B40.

Pilgrimage SP12   Armed Horseman in Action SP13

Designs: 60c+25c, Palmettos. 90c+10c, Fort. 1.10p+25c, Agave. 5p+2p, Warrior.

1952   Perf. 11
Black Control Numbers on Back

B33	SP12	50 + 10c car & gray	.20 .20
B34	SP12	60 + 25c car & dk grn	.70 .35

B35	SP12	90 + 10c car & vio brn	.70 .35
B36	SP12	1.10p + 25p car & pur	2.00 .70
B37	SP12	5p + 2p car & gray	5.00 1.60
		Nos. B33-B37 (5)	8.60 3.20

1953   Perf. 10

#B39, As #276. #B42, Plane & clouds.

Black Control Numbers on Back

B38	SP13	50c + 10c car & vio	.25 .20
B39	A70	60c + 25c car & brn	2.25 .70
B40	SP11	90c + 10c car & blk	.70 .30
B41	SP13	1.10p + 25c car & vio brn	3.50 1.10
B42	A73	5p + 2p car & bl	8.50 2.75
		Nos. B38-B42 (5)	15.20 5.05

Stork — SP14

50c+10c, Father & Child. 5p+2p, Tomb.

1954   Photo.
Black Control Numbers on Back

B43	SP14	5c + 5c car & rose vio	.20 .20
B44	SP14	50c + 10c car & gray grn	.70 .35
B45	SP14	5p + 2p car & gray	6.00 3.25
		Nos. B43-B45 (3)	6.90 3.80

AIR POST STAMPS

Mosque de Baja and Plane — AP1

View of Tetuán and Plane AP2

10c, Stork of Alcazar. 25c, Shore scene, plane. 40c, Desert tribesmen watching plane. 75c, View of shoreline at Larache. 1p, Arab mailman, plane above. 1.50p, Arab farmers, stork. 2p, Plane at twilight. 3p, Shadow of plane over city.

1938   Unwmk.   Photo.   Perf. 13½

C1	AP1	5c red brown	.20 .20
C2	AP1	10c emerald	.20 .20
C3	AP1	25c crimson	.20 .20
C4	AP1	40c dull blue	1.75 .50
C5	AP2	50c cerise	.20 .20
C6	AP2	75c ultra	.20 .20
C7	AP1	1p dark brown	.20 .20
C8	AP1	1.50p purple	.60 .30
C9	AP1	2p brown lake	.35 .20
C10	AP1	3p gray black	1.60 .20
		Nos. Cdsno=1-C10 (10)	5.50 2.40
		Set, Never Hinged	10.00

Exist imperf. Value, set $100.
For surcharge see No. C32.

Landscape, Ketama — AP3   Mosque, Tangier — AP4

Velez — AP5   Sanjurjo — AP6

Strait of Gibraltar
AP7   AP8

1942   Perf. 12½

C11	AP3	5c deep blue	.20 .20
C12	AP4	10c orange brn	.20 .20
C13	AP5	15c grnsh black	.20 .20
C14	AP6	90c dark rose	.20 .20
C15	AP7	5p black	1.25 .75
		Nos. C11-C15 (5)	2.05 1.55
		Set, Never Hinged	3.00

Exist imperf. Value, set $55.

1949   Litho.   Perf. 10

Designs: 5c, 1.75p, Strait of Gibraltar. 10c, 3p, Market day. 30c, 4p, Kebira Fortress. 6.50p, Airmail arrival. 8p, Horseman.

C16	AP8	5c vio brn & brt grn	.20 .20
C17	AP8	10c blk & rose lil	.20 .20
C18	AP8	30c dk vio bl & grnsh gray	.20 .20
C19	AP8	1.75p car & bl vio	.20 .20
C20	AP8	3p dk blue & gray	.20 .20
C21	AP8	4p grnsh blk & car rose	.25 .20
C22	AP8	6.50p brt grn & brn	.85 .20
C23	AP8	8p rose lil & bl vio	1.40 .40
		Nos. C16-C23 (8)	3.50 1.80
		Set, Never Hinged	5.00

Exist imperf. Value, set $80.

> **Catalogue values for unused stamps in this section, from this point to the end of the section, are for Never Hinged items.**

Road to Tetuan — AP9

Designs: 4p, Arrival of mail from Spain. 8p, Greeting plane. 16p, Shadow of plane.

1952   Perf. 11
Black Frames and Inscriptions
Black Control Numbers on Back

C24	AP9	2p brt blue	.20 .20
C25	AP9	4p scarlet	.25 .20
C26	AP9	8p dk olive green	.40 .20
C27	AP9	16p violet brown	2.00 .85
		Nos. C24-C27 (4)	2.85 1.45

Part of the proceeds was used toward the establishment of a postal museum at Tetuan.

Plane over Boat — AP10

Designs: 60c, Mosques, Sidi Saidi. 1.10p, Plowing. 4.50p, Fortress, Xauen.

1953   Perf. 10
C28 AP10 35c dp bl & car rose   .20   .20
C29 AP10 60c dk car & sl grn   .20   .20
C30 AP10 1.10p dp blue & blk   .25   .20
C31 AP10 4.50p dk car & dk brn   1.10   .35
      Nos. C28-C31 (4)   1.75   .95
      Exist imperf. Value, set $75.

No. C6 Surcharged with New Value in
Black

Type I

Type II

1953   Perf. 13½
C32 AP2 50c on 75c ultra (I)   .45   .20
  a.   50c on 75c ultra (II)   .45   .20
  b.   Vert. gutter pair, types I and II   2.50

   Sheets of 2 panes, 25 stamps each, with
gutter between. Upper pane surcharged type I,
lower type II.

AIR POST SEMI-POSTAL STAMPS

No. 150 Surcharged in Black

1936   Unwmk.   Perf. 14
CB1 A12 25c + 2p on 25c   11.00   4.50
      Never hinged   25.00
  a.   Bars at right omitted   45.00 32.50
  b.   Blue surcharge   35.00 11.50

   25c was for postage, 2p for air post.

   Nos. C1-C10 surcharged "Lucha
Antituberculosa," a Lorraine cross and
surtax are stated to be bogus.

Crowd at
Palace — SPAP1

1949, May 15   Unwmk.   Perf. 10
CB2 SPAP1 1p + 10c gray black   .70   .30
   Wedding of the Caliph at Tetuan, June 5.

SPECIAL DELIVERY STAMPS

Special Delivery Stamp of Spain
Overprinted in Blue

1914   Unwmk.   Perf. 14
E1 SD1 20c red   4.50   2.00

Special Delivery Stamp of Spain
Overprinted in Blue

1915
E2 SD1 20c red   2.50   1.40
   For bisected surcharge see No. 68.

Special Delivery Stamp of Spain
Overprinted in Blue

1923
E3 SD1 20c red   10.50   8.25

Mounted
Courier
SD2

1928   Engr.   Perf. 14, 14½
E4 SD2 20c black   4.25   1.40
   For surcharge see No. 168.

Moorish   Mounted
Postman — SD3   Courier — SD4

1935   Photo.   Perf. 14
Green Control Number on Back
E5 SD3 20c vermilion   1.00   .20
         See No. E9.

1937   Perf. 13½
E6 SD4 20c bright carmine   .20   .20
   1st Year of the Spanish Civil War.
   For surcharge see No. E10.

Spain No. E14 Overprinted in Black

1938   Perf. 10
E7 SD7 20c vermilion   1.25   .20

Arab Postman   Airmail 1935
SD5   SD6

1940   Photo.   Perf. 11½x11
E8 SD5 25c scarlet   .60   .20
   "ZONA" printed on back in black.

Type of 1935
1940   Litho.   Perf. 10
E9 SD3 20c black brown   2.00
   No. E9 was prepared but not issued.
   Exists imperf. Value, $10.

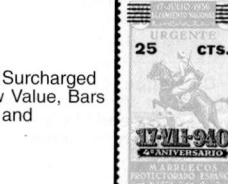

No. E6 Surcharged
with New Value, Bars
and

1940   Perf. 13½
E10 SD4 25c on 20c brt car   9.50   7.25
   4th anniversary of Spanish Civil War.

**Catalogue values for unused
stamps in this section, from this
point to the end of the section, are
for Never Hinged items.**

1950   Unwmk.   Litho.   Perf. 10½
E11 SD6 25c carmine & gray   24.00   9.00
   UPU, 75th anniv. (in 1949).

Moorish
Postrider
SD7

1952   Perf. 11
Black Control Number on Back
E12 SD7 25c car & rose car   .20   .20

Rider with   Gate of
Special Delivery   Tangier — SD9
Mail — SD8

1953   Photo.   Perf. 10
Black Control Number on Back
E13 SD8 25c dk bl & car rose   .20   .20
   25th anniv. of Spanish Morocco's first definitive postage stamps.

1955   Litho.   Perf. 11
Black Control Number on Back
E14 SD9 2p violet & black   .20   .20

SEMI-POSTAL SPECIAL DELIVERY
STAMP

   Type of Semi-Postal Special Delivery
Stamp of Spain, 1926, Overprinted like
#B1-B13
1926   Unwmk.   Perf. 12½, 13
EB1 SPSD1 20c ultra & black   2.50   2.10

POSTAL TAX STAMPS

General Francisco
Franco — PT1

1937-39 Unwmk. Photo.   Perf. 12½
RA1 PT1 10c sepia   .45   .20
  a.   Sheet of 4, imperf.   4.00   1.60
RA2 PT1 10c copper brn ('38)   .45   .20
  a.   Sheet of 4, imperf.   4.00   1.60
RA3 PT1 10c blue ('39)   .45   .20
  a.   Sheet of 4, imperf.   4.00   1.60
      Nos. RA1-RA3 (3)   1.35   .60
      Set, never hinged   3.00
      Set, RA1a-RA3a   13.50

   The tax was used for the disabled soldiers in
North Africa.

Soldiers
PT2

1941   Litho.   Perf. 13½
RA4 PT2 10c brt grn   3.75   .20
RA5 PT2 10c rose pink   3.75   .20
RA6 PT2 10c henna brn   3.75   .20
RA7 PT2 10c ultra   3.75   .20
      Nos. RA4-RA7 (4)   15.00   .80
      Set, never hinged   22.50

   The tax was used for the disabled soldiers in
North Africa.
   Exist imperf. Value, set $60.

General Francisco
Franco — PT3

1943   Photo.   Perf. 10
RA8 PT3 10c chalky blue   7.50   .20
RA9 PT3 10c slate blue   7.50   .20
RA10 PT3 10c dl gray brn   7.50   .20
RA11 PT3 10c blue violet   7.50   .20
      Nos. RA8-RA11 (4)   30.00   .80
      Set, never hinged   42.50

   Exists imperf. Value, set $125.

1944   Perf. 12
RA12 PT3 10c dp mag & brn   5.50   .20
RA13 PT3 10c dp org & dk grn   5.50   .20
      Set, never hinged   14.50

   Exists imperf. Value, set $45.00.

1946   Litho.
RA14 PT3 10c ultra & brown   6.00   .20
RA15 PT3 10c gray blk & rose lil 6.00   .20
      Set, never hinged   16.00

   Exists imperf. Value, set $45.00.

TANGIER

For the International City of Tangier
   Seville-Barcelona Issue of Spain,
   1929, Overprinted in Blue or Red
   TANGER

1929 Perf. 11

L1	A52	5c rose lake	.25	.25
L2	A53	10c green (R)	.25	.25
L3	A50	15c Prus blue (R)	.25	.25
L4	A51	20c purple (R)	.25	.25
L5	A50	25c brt rose	.25	.25
L6	A52	30c black brn	.25	.25
L7	A53	40c dk blue (R)	.65	.65
L8	A51	50c deep org	.65	.65
L9	A52	1p blue blk (R)	7.00	7.00
L10	A53	4p deep rose	19.00	19.00
L11	A53	10p brown	27.50	27.50
		Nos. L1-L11 (11)	56.30	56.30
		Never hinged	95.00	

Overprints of 1937-39
The following overprints on stamps of Spain exist in black or in red:
"TANGER" vertically on Nos. 517-518, 522-523, 528, 532, 534, 539-543, 549.
"Correo Espanol Tanger" horizontally or vertically in three lines on Nos. 540, 592-597 (gray paper), 598-601.
"Tanger" horizontally on Nos. 539-541, 592-601.
"Correo Tanger" horizontally in two lines on five consular stamps.

Woman — A1

Palm Tree — A2

Man — A3

Old Map of Tangier — A4

Tangier Street — A5

Moroccan Women — A6

Head of Moor — A7

Perf. 9½x10½, 12½x13 (1c, 2c, 10c, 20c)

			Photo.	Unwmk.
1948-51				
L12	A1	1c blue grn ('51)	.25	.20
L13	A1	2c red org ('51)	.25	.20

Engr.

L14	A2	5c vio brn ('49)	.25	.20
L15	A3	10c deep blue ('51)	.25	.20
L16	A3	20c gray ('51)	.25	.20
L17	A2	25c green ('51)	.25	.20
L18	A4	30c dk slate grn	.35	.20
L19	A5	45c car rose	.35	.20
L20	A6	50c dp claret	.35	.20
L21	A7	75c deep blue	.70	.25
L22	A7	90c green	.60	.25
L23	A4	1.35p org ver	2.10	.35
L24	A6	2p purple	3.75	.35
L25	A5	10p dk grnsh bl ('49)	4.25	.65
		Nos. L12-L25,LE1 (15)	14.80	4.00
		Never hinged	25.00	

Nos. L18-L25, LE1 exist imperf. Value, set $300.

TANGIER SEMI-POSTAL STAMPS

Types of Semi-Postal Stamps of Spain, 1926, Overprinted

1926 Perf. 12½, 13

LB1	SP1	1c orange	6.00	6.50
LB2	SP2	2c rose	6.00	6.50
LB3	SP3	5c black brn	3.00	3.25
LB4	SP4	10c dk green	3.00	3.25
LB5	SP1	15c dk violet	1.00	1.25
LB6	SP4	20c violet brn	1.00	1.25
LB7	SP5	25c dp carmine	1.00	1.25
LB8	SP1	30c olive grn	1.00	1.25
LB9	SP2	40c ultra	.25	.25
LB10	SP2	50c red brn	.25	.25
LB11	SP4	1p vermilion	.60	.60
LB12	SP3	4p bister	.60	.60
LB13	SP5	10p lt violet	2.75	3.00
		Nos. LB1-LB13,LEB1 (14)	29.70	32.45
		Never hinged	55.00	

For overprints & surcharges see Spain Nos. B66-B67.

TANGIER AIR POST STAMPS

Overprints of 1939
The following overprints on stamps of Spain exist in black or in red:
"Correo Aereo Tanger" in two lines on Nos. 539-541, 596 (gray paper), 600, C72B.
"Via Aerea Tanger" in three lines on Nos. 539-540, 592-597 (gray paper), 599, 601, E14.
"Correo Aereo Tanger" in three lines on four consular stamps.
"Correo Espanol Tanger" in three lines on No. C72B.
"Tanger" on No. C72B.

Plane over Shore — AP1

Twin-Engine Plane — AP2

Passenger Plane in Flight — AP3

Perf. 11x11½, 11½

		Engr.	Unwmk.
1949-50			
LC1	AP1	20c violet brn ('50)	.25	.20
LC2	AP2	25c bright red	.25	.20
LC3	AP3	35c dull green	.25	.20
LC4	AP1	1p violet ('50)	.80	.20
LC5	AP2	2p deep blue	1.50	.25
LC6	AP3	10p brown violet	2.75	1.00
		Nos. LC1-LC6 (6)	5.80	2.05
		Never hinged	9.50	

Nos. LC1, LC4-LC6 exist imperf. Value $100 each.

TANGIER SPECIAL DELIVERY STAMP

Arab Postrider — SD1

1949 Unwmk. Engr. Perf. 13

LE1	SD1	25c red	.85	.35
		Never hinged	1.40	

TANGIER SEMI-POSTAL SPECIAL DELIVERY STAMP

Types of Semi-Postal Special Delivery Stamp of Spain, 1926, Overprinted like #LB1-LB13

1926 Unwmk. Perf. 12½, 13

LEB1	SPSD1	20c ultra & black	3.25	3.25
		Never hinged	5.50	

TETUAN

Stamps of Spanish Offices in Morocco, 1903-09, Handstamped in Black, Blue or Violet

1908 Unwmk. Imperf.

1	A21	¼c blue green	13.00	10.00

Perf. 14

2	A35	2c bister brown	150.00	60.00
3	A35	5c green	140.00	35.00
4	A35	10c rose red	140.00	35.00
5	A35	20c grnsh black	300.00	125.00
6	A35	25c blue	100.00	35.00
		Nos. 1-6 (6)	843.00	300.00

Same Handstamp On Stamps of Spain, 1876 and 1900-05, in Black, Blue or Violet

1908 Imperf.

7	A21	¼c deep green	7.50	3.25

Perf. 14

8	A35	2c bister brn	40.00	13.00
9	A35	5c dark green	55.00	22.50
10	A35	10c rose red	52.50	22.50
11	A35	15c purple	52.50	25.00
12	A35	20c grnsh black	150.00	110.00
13	A35	25c blue	80.00	35.00
14	A35	30c blue green	175.00	60.00
15	A35	40c olive bister	225.00	110.00
		Nos. 7-15 (9)	837.50	401.25

Counterfeits of this overprint are plentiful.

SPANISH SAHARA

ˈspa-nish sə-ˈhar-ə

(Spanish Western Sahara)

LOCATION — Northwest Africa, bordering on the Atlantic Ocean.
GOVT. — Spanish possession
AREA — 102,703 sq. mi.
POP. — 76,425 (1970)
CAPITAL — Aaiún

Spanish Sahara was a subdivision of Spanish West Africa. It included the colony of Rio de Oro and the territory of Saguiet el Hamra. Spanish Sahara was formerly known as Spanish Western Sahara, which superseded the older title of Rio de Oro.

In 1976, Spanish Sahara was divided between Morocco and Mauritania.

100 Centimos = 1 Peseta

Catalogue values for unused stamps in this country are for Never Hinged items, beginning with Scott 51 in the regular postage section, Scott B13 in the semipostal section, Scott C8 in the airpost section, and Scott E1 in the special delivery section.

Tuareg and Camel — A1

1924 Unwmk. Typo. Perf. 13
Control Number on Back

1	A1	5c blue green	2.25	.70
2	A1	10c gray green	2.25	.70
3	A1	15c turq blue	2.25	.70
4	A1	20c dark violet	2.25	1.00
5	A1	25c red	2.25	1.00
6	A1	30c red brown	2.25	1.00
7	A1	40c dark blue	2.25	1.00
8	A1	50c orange	2.25	1.00
9	A1	60c violet	2.25	1.00
10	A1	1p rose	12.00	5.50
11	A1	4p chocolate	55.00	27.50
12	A1	10p claret	140.00	85.00
		Nos. 1-12 (12)	227.25	126.10
		Set, never hinged	300.00	

#1-12 were for use in La Aguera & Rio de Oro.
An unissued set of 10, similar to Nos. 3-12, exists perf. 10 or imperf, and no control number except on 50c. The set also exists perf 14. Value, $300.
Nos. 1-12 also exist perf 14. Value, unused $350.
For overprints see Nos. 24-35.

Seville-Barcelona Issue of Spain, 1929 Overprinted in Blue or Red

1929 Perf. 11

13	A52	5c rose lake	.30	.25
14	A53	10c green (R)	.30	.25
15	A50	15c Prus blue (R)	.30	.25
16	A51	20c purple (R)	.30	.25
17	A50	25c bright rose	.30	.25
18	A52	30c black brown	.30	.25
19	A53	40c dark blue (R)	.75	.40
20	A51	50c deep orange	.75	.40
21	A52	1p blue black (R)	3.00	1.60
22	A53	4p deep rose	24.00	15.00
23	A53	10p brown	45.00	30.00
		Nos. 13-23 (11)	75.30	48.90
		Set, never hinged	110.00	

Stamps of 1924 Overprinted in Red or Blue

1931 Perf. 13

24	A1	5c blue grn (R)	.80	.55
25	A1	10c gray grn (R)	.80	.55
26	A1	15c turq blue (R)	.80	.55
27	A1	20c dark violet (R)	.80	.55
28	A1	25c red	.80	.55
29	A1	30c red brown	.80	.55
30	A1	40c dark blue (R)	4.00	.75
31	A1	50c orange	4.00	1.90
32	A1	60c violet	4.00	1.90
33	A1	1p rose	4.00	1.90

34	A1	4p chocolate	40.00 19.00
35	A1	10p claret	80.00 42.50

Nos. 24-35 (12) 140.80 71.25
Set, never hinged 200.00

The stamps of the 1931 issue exist with the overprint reading upward, downward or horizontally. Some values also exist with double overprint, double overprint, one inverted and diagonal overprint.

Stamps of Spain, 1936-40, Overprinted in Carmine or Blue

1941-46   Unwmk.   Imperf.

36	A159	1c green	1.75	1.50

Perf. 10 to 11

37	A160	2c org brn (Bl)	1.75	1.50
38	A161	5c gray brown	.55	.45
39	A161	10c dk car (Bl)	1.75	1.50
40	A161	15c dark green	.55	.45
41	A166	20c bright violet	.55	.45
42	A166	25c deep claret	1.40	.90
43	A166	30c light blue	1.40	1.10
44	A166	40c Prus grn	.55	.45
45	A166	50c indigo	16.50	1.25
46	A166	70c blue	11.00	1.90
47	A166	1p gray black	21.00	2.75
48	A166	2p dull brown	120.00	60.00
49	A166	4p dull rose (Bl)	300.00	160.00
50	A166	10p lt brown	925.00	250.00

Nos. 36-50 (15) 1,403. 484.20
Set, never hinged 2,150.

Counterfeit overprints exist.

Catalogue values for unused stamps in this section, from this point to the end of the section, are for Never Hinged items.

Dorcas Gazelles — A2

Designs: 2c, 20c, 45c, 3p, Caravan. 5c, 75c, 10p, Camel troops.

1943   Unwmk.   Perf. 12½

51	A2	1c brown & lil rose	.20	.20
52	A2	2c yel grn & sl bl	.20	.20
53	A2	5c magenta & vio	.20	.20
54	A2	15c slate grn & grn	.20	.20
55	A2	20c violet & red brn	.20	.20
56	A2	40c rose vio & vio	.20	.20
57	A2	45c brn vio & red	.35	.20
58	A2	75c indigo & blue	.35	.20
59	A2	1p red & brown	1.25	.70
60	A2	3p bl vio & sl grn	2.75	1.40
61	A2	10p black brn & blk	40.00	21.00

Nos. 51-61,E1 (12) 47.30 25.55

Nos. 51-61, El exist imperf. Value for set, $90.

Gen. Franco and Desert Scene A5

1951   Photo.   Perf. 12½x13

62	A5	50c deep orange	.20	.20
63	A5	1p chocolate	.30	.25
64	A5	5p blue green	27.50	11.00

Nos. 62-64 (3) 28.00 11.45

Visit of Gen. Francisco Franco, 1950.

Allegorical Figure and Globe — A6   Woman Musician — A7

1953, Mar. 2   Perf. 13x12½

65	A6	5c red orange	.20	.20
66	A6	35c dk slate green	.20	.20
67	A6	60c brown	.30	.25

Nos. 65-67 (3) .70 .65

75th anniv. of the founding of the Royal Geographical Society.

1953, June 1

Design: 60c, Man musician.

| 68 | A7 | 15c olive gray | .20 | .20 |
| 69 | A7 | 60c brown | .25 | .20 |

Nos. 68-69,B25-B26 (4) .90 .80

Orange Scorpionfish — A8

Fish: 60c, Banded sargo.

1953, Nov. 23   Perf. 12½x13

| 70 | A8 | 15c dk olive green | .25 | .20 |
| 71 | A8 | 60c orange | .40 | .20 |

Nos. 70-71,B27-B28 (4) 1.10 .80

Colonial Stamp Day.

Hurdlers A9

Runner — A10

1954, June 1   Perf. 12½x13, 13x12½

| 72 | A9 | 15c gray green | .20 | .20 |
| 73 | A10 | 60c brown | .30 | .25 |

Nos. 72-73,B29-B30 (4) .95 .85

Atlantic Flyingfish A11

1954, Nov. 23   Perf. 12½x13

| 74 | A11 | 15c shown | .25 | .20 |
| 75 | A11 | 60c Gilthead | .40 | .20 |

Nos. 74-75,B31-B32 (4) 1.10 .80

Colonial Stamp Day.

Emilio Bonelli A12

1955, June 1   Photo.   Unwmk.

| 76 | A12 | 50c olive gray | .25 | .20 |

Nos. 76,B33-B34 (3) .70 .60

Birth cent. of Emilio Bonelli, explorer.

Scimitar-horned Oryx — A13

1955, Nov. 23

| 77 | A13 | 70c green | .25 | .20 |

Nos. 77,B35-B36 (3) .70 .60

Colonial Stamp Day.

Antirrhinum Romosissimum A14

Design: 50c, Sesiviun portulacastrum.

1956, June 1   Perf. 13x12½

| 78 | A14 | 20c bluish green | .20 | .20 |
| 79 | A14 | 50c brown | .35 | .25 |

Nos. 78-79,B37-B38 (4) 1.00 .85

Arms of Aaiun and Camel Rider A15

1956, Nov. 23   Perf. 12½x13

| 80 | A15 | 70c olive grn & sepia | .25 | .20 |

Nos. 80,B39-B40 (3) .70 .60

Colonial Stamp Day.

Dromedaries A16   Golden Eagle A17

15c, 80c, Ostrich. 50c, 1.80p, Mountain gazelle.

1957, Apr. 10   Perf. 13x12½

81	A16	5c purple	.20	.20
82	A16	15c bister	.20	.20
83	A16	50c dark olive	.25	.20
84	A16	70c yellow green	.70	.20
85	A16	80c blue green	.75	.25
86	A16	1.80p lilac rose	.75	.25

Nos. 81-86 (6) 2.85 1.30

1957, June 1   Photo.   Unwmk.

| 87 | A17 | 70c dark green | .25 | .20 |

Nos. 87,B41-B42 (3) .70 .60

Striped Hyena — A18

Design: 70c, Striped Hyena, horiz.

Perf. 13x12½, 12½x13
1957, Nov. 23

| 88 | A18 | 20c slate green | .20 | .20 |
| 89 | A18 | 70c yellowish green | .25 | .25 |

Nos. 88-89,B43-B44 (4) .90 .85

Stamp Day.

Don Quixote and the Lion A19

Cervantes A20   Gray Heron A21

1958, June 1   Perf. 12½x13, 13x12½

| 90 | A19 | 20c bister brn & grn | .20 | .20 |
| 91 | A20 | 70c dk grn & yel grn | .30 | .25 |

Nos. 90-91,B48-B49 (4) .95 .85

Cervantes Type of 1958

Designs: 20c, Actor as "Peribanez," by Lope de Vega. 70c, Lope de Vega.

1959, June   Photo.   Perf. 13x12½

| 92 | A20 | 20c lt green & brn | .20 | .20 |
| 93 | A20 | 70c yel grn & slate grn | .30 | .25 |

Nos. 92-93,B53-B54 (4) .95 .85

Promoting child welfare.

1959, Oct. 15   Perf. 13x12½

Birds: 50c, 1.50p, 5p, Sparrowhawk. 75c, 2p, 10p, Sea gull.

94	A21	25c dull violet	.20	.20
95	A21	50c dark olive	.20	.20
96	A21	75c dark brown	.20	.20
97	A21	1p red orange	.25	.20
98	A21	1.50p brt green	.30	.20
99	A21	2p brt red lilac	.95	.25
100	A21	3p blue	1.00	.25
101	A21	5p red brown	1.75	.30
102	A21	10p olive green	10.00	4.25

Nos. 94-102 (9) 14.85 6.05

Scene from "The Pilferer Don Pablos" by Quevedo — A22

Francisco Gomez de Quevedo A23

1960, June   Perf. 13x12½, 12½x13

| 103 | A22 | 35c slate green | .20 | .20 |
| 104 | A23 | 80c Prussian green | .25 | .25 |

Nos. 103-104,B58-B59 (4) .90 .85

Francisco Gomez de Quevedo, writer.

Houbara Bustard — A24

Map of Spanish Sahara — A25

Gen. Franco and Camel Rider A26

Design: 50c, 1p, 2p, 5p, Doves.

1961, Apr. 18   Photo.   Perf. 13x12½
105	A24	25c blue violet	.20	.20
106	A24	50c olive gray	.20	.20
107	A24	75c brown violet	.20	.20
108	A24	1p orange ver	.20	.20
109	A24	1.50p blue green	.20	.20
110	A24	2p magenta	.70	.20
111	A24	3p dark blue	.85	.20
112	A24	5p red brown	1.00	.30
113	A24	10p olive	2.75	1.40
		Nos. 105-113 (9)	6.30	3.10

1961, Oct. 1   Perf. 13x12½, 12½x13
Design: 70c, Chapel of Aaiun.
114	A25	25c gray violet	.20	.20
115	A26	50c olive brown	.20	.20
116	A25	70c brt green	.20	.20
117	A26	1p red orange	.25	.25
		Nos. 114-117 (4)	.85	.85

25th anniv. of the nomination of Gen. Francisco Franco as Chief of State.

Neurada Procumbres A27

Clock Fish A28

50c, 1.50p, 10p, Anabasis articulata, flower. 70c, 2p, Euphorbia resinifera, cactus.

1962, Feb. 26   Perf. 13x12½
118	A27	25c black violet	.20	.20
119	A27	50c dark brown	.20	.20
120	A27	70c brt green	.20	.20
121	A27	1p orange ver	.25	.20
122	A27	1.50p blue green	.35	.20
123	A27	2p red lilac	1.10	.20
124	A27	3p slate	1.90	.20
125	A27	10p olive	4.25	1.40
		Nos. 118-125 (8)	8.45	2.85

Perf. 13x12½, 12½x13
1962, July 10   Photo.
Design: 50c, Avia fish, horiz.
126	A28	25c violet black	.20	.20
127	A28	50c dark green	.25	.20
128	A28	1p orange brown	.30	.25
		Nos. 126-128 (3)	.75	.65

Goats A29

Stamp Day: 35c, Sheep.

1962, Nov. 23   Perf. 12½x13
129	A29	15c yellow green	.20	.20
130	A29	35c magenta	.20	.20
131	A29	1p orange brown	.25	.25
		Nos. 129-131 (3)	.65	.65

Seville Cathedral Tower — A30

1963, Jan. 29   Perf. 13x12½
132	A30	50c olive	.20	.20
133	A30	1p brown orange	.25	.20

Issued to help Seville flood victims.

Camel Riders — A31

Hands Releasing Dove and Arms — A32

Design: 50c, Tuareg and camel.

1963, June 1   Unwmk.
134	A31	25c deep violet	.20	.20
135	A31	50c gray	.20	.20
136	A31	1p orange red	.25	.20
		Nos. 134-136 (3)	.65	.65

Issued for child welfare.

1963, July 12
137	A32	50c Prussian green	.20	.20
138	A32	1p orange brown	.25	.20

Issued for Barcelona flood relief.

John Dory A33

Fish: 50c, Plain bonito, vert.

Perf. 12½x13, 13x12½
1964, Mar. 6   Photo.
139	A33	25c purple	.20	.20
140	A33	50c olive green	.25	.20
141	A33	1p brown red	.45	.25
		Nos. 139-141 (3)	.90	.65

Issued for Stamp Day 1963.

Moth and Flowers A34

Design: 50c, Two moths, vert.

Perf. 12½x13, 13x12½
1964, June 1   Unwmk.
142	A34	25c dull violet	.20	.20
143	A34	50c brown black	.25	.20
144	A34	1p orange red	.45	.25
		Nos. 142-144 (3)	.90	.65

Issued for child welfare.

Camel Rider and Microphone A35

Squirrel A36

Designs: 50c, 1.50p, 3p, Boy with flute and camels. 70c, 2p, 10p, Woman with drum.

1964, Sept.   Photo.   Perf. 13x12½
145	A35	25c dull purple	.20	.20
146	A35	50c olive	.20	.20
147	A35	70c green	.20	.20
148	A35	1p dull red brn	.25	.20
149	A35	1.50p bright green	.25	.20
150	A35	2p Prus green	.30	.25
151	A35	3p dark blue	.35	.25
152	A35	10p carmine lake	1.40	.65
		Nos. 145-152 (8)	3.15	2.15

1964, Nov. 23   Unwmk.
Stamp Day: 1p, Squirrel's head, horiz.
153	A36	50c olive gray	.20	.20
154	A36	1p brown carmine	.25	.20
155	A36	1.50p green	.25	.25
		Nos. 153-155 (3)	.70	.65

Tuareg Girl — A37

Wellhead and Camel Rider — A38

25 Years of Peace: 1p, Physician examining patient, horiz.

Perf. 13x12½, 12½x13
1965, Feb. 22   Photo.
156	A37	50c black brown	.20	.20
157	A38	1p dark red	.25	.20
158	A38	1.50p deep blue	.25	.25
		Nos. 156-158 (3)	.70	.65

Anthia Sexmaculata — A39

1p, 3p, Blepharopsis mendica, vert.

Perf. 12½x13, 13x12½
1965, June 1   Photo.   Unwmk.
159	A39	50c slate blue	.20	.20
160	A39	1p blue green	.25	.20
161	A39	1.50p brown	.30	.25
162	A39	3p dark blue	1.25	.55
		Nos. 159-162 (4)	2.00	1.20

Issued for child welfare.

Basketball A40

Arms and Camels A41

1965, Nov. 23   Perf. 13x12½
163	A40	50c rose claret	.20	.20
164	A41	1p deep magenta	.25	.25
165	A40	1.50p slate blue	.25	.25
		Nos. 163-165 (3)	.70	.65

Issued for Stamp Day.

Ship "Rio de Oro" A42

Design: 1.50p, S.S. Fuerte Ventura.

1966, June 1   Photo.   Perf. 12½x13
166	A42	50c olive	.20	.20
167	A42	1p dark red brown	.25	.20
168	A42	1.50p blue green	.30	.25
		Nos. 166-168 (3)	.75	.65

Issued for child welfare.

Ocean Sunfish — A43

A44

Designs: 10c, 1.50p, Bigeye tuna, horiz.

1966, Nov. 23   Photo.   Perf. 13
169	A43	10c bl gray & cit	.20	.20
170	A43	40c slate & pink	.20	.20
171	A43	1.50p brown & olive	.30	.20
172	A43	4p rose vio & gray	.45	.25
		Nos. 169-172 (4)	1.15	.85

Issued for Stamp Day.

1967, June 1   Photo.   Perf. 13
Designs: 40c, 4p, Flower and leaves.
173	A44	10c blk, ocher & gray grn	.20	.20
174	A44	40c emerald & lilac	.20	.20
175	A44	1.50p dk grn & yel grn	.25	.20
176	A44	4p brt blue & org	.30	.25
		Nos. 173-176 (4)	.95	.85

Issued for child welfare.

Aaiun Harbor A45

Design: 4p, Villa Cisneros Harbor.

1967, Sept. 28   Photo.   Perf. 12½x13
177	A45	1.50p brt bl & red brn	.25	.20
178	A45	4p brt bl & bis brn	.25	.25

Modernization of harbor installations.

Ruddy Sheldrake A46

Stamp Day: 1.50p, Flamingo, vert. 3.50p, Rufous bush robin.

1967, Nov. 23   Photo.   Perf. 13
179	A46	1p bister brn & grn	.25	.20
180	A46	1.50p brt rose & gray	.30	.20
181	A46	3.50p brn red & sep	.45	.25
		Nos. 179-181 (3)	1.00	.65

Scorpio — A47

Mailman — A48

Zodiac Issue

1.50p, Aries. 2.50p, Virgo.

1968, Apr. 25   Photo.   Perf. 13
182 A47   1p brt mag, *lt yel*   .20 .20
183 A47   1.50p brown, *pink*   .25 .20
184 A47   2.50p dk vio, *yel*   .40 .25
　　　　Nos. 182-184 (3)   .85 .65

Issued for child welfare.

1968, Nov.   Photo.   Perf. 13x12½
Stamp Day: 1p, Post horn, pigeon, letter and
Spain No. 1. 1.50p, Letter, canceller and vari-
ous stamps of Spain and Ifni.

185 A48   1p dp lil rose & dk bl   .25 .20
186 A48   1.50p green & sl grn   .30 .20
187 A48   2.50p dp org & dk bl   .45 .25
　　　　Nos. 185-187 (3)   1.00 .65

Dorcas Gazelle — A49

Designs: 1.50p, Doe and fawn. 2.50p,
Gazelle and camel. 6p, Leaping gazelle.

1969, June 1   Photo.   Perf. 13
188 A49   1p gldn brn & blk   .20 .20
189 A49   1.50p gldn brn & blk   .25 .20
190 A49   2.50p gldn brn & blk   .30 .25
191 A49   6p gldn brn & blk   .50 .30
　　　　Nos. 188-191 (4)   1.25 .95

Child welfare. See Nos. 196-199, 209-212.

Woman Playing
Drum — A50

Stamp Day: 1.50p, Man with flute. 2p,
Drum and camel rider, horiz. 25p, Flute, horiz.

1969, Nov. 23   Photo.   Perf. 13
192 A50   50c brn red & lt ol   .20 .20
193 A50   1.50p dk bl grn & grnsh
　　　　　　gray   .25 .20
194 A50   2p indigo & bis brn   .30 .25
195 A50   25p brn & lt bl grn   1.00 .30
　　　　Nos. 192-195 (4)   1.75 .95

Animal Type of 1969

Fennec: 50c, Sitting. 2p, Running. 2.50p,
Head. 6p, Vixen and pups.

1970, June 1   Photo.   Perf. 13
196 A49   50c dp bister & blk   .20 .20
197 A49   2p org brn & blk   .25 .20
198 A49   2.50p dp bister & blk   .30 .25
199 A49   6p dp bister & blk   .50 .25
　　　　Nos. 196-199 (4)   1.25 .90

Issued for child welfare.

Grammodes Boisdeffrei — A51

Designs: 1p, like 50c. 2p, 5p, Danaus
chrysippus. 8p, Celerio euphorbiae.

1970, Nov. 23   Photo.   Perf. 12½
200 A51   50c red & multi   .20 .20
201 A51   1p carmine & multi   .25 .20
202 A51   2p green & multi   .30 .20
203 A51   5p Prus bl & multi   .40 .25
204 A51   8p dk blue & multi   .70 .35
　　　　Nos. 200-204 (5)   1.85 1.20

Issued for Stamp Day. See Nos. 233-234.

Gazelle, Arms of　　　Smara
Aaiun — A52　　　Mosque — A53

Designs: 2p, Inn, horiz. 5p, Assembly
building, Aaiun, horiz.

Perf. 12½x13, 13x12½
1971, June 1   Photo.
205 A52   1p multicolored   .20 .20
206 A53   2p gray grn & ol   .20 .20
207 A53   5p lt bl & lt red brn   .30 .20
208 A53   25p lt bl & grnsh gray   .90 .35
　　　　Nos. 205-208 (4)   1.60 .95

Issued for child welfare.

Animal Type of 1969

Birds: 1.50p, 2p, Trumpeter bullfinch. 5p,
Cream-colored courser. 24p, Lanner (falcon).

1971, Nov. 23   Photo.   Perf. 12½
209 A49   1.50p black & multi   .20 .20
210 A49   2p blue & multi   .25 .20
211 A49   5p green & multi   .30 .25
212 A49   24p black & multi   .85 .35
　　　　Nos. 209-212 (4)   1.60 1.00

Stamp Day.

Saharan
Woman — A55

Tuareg
Woman — A56

1.50p, 2p, Saharan man. 8p, 10p, Man's
head. 12p, Woman. 15p, Soldier. 24p, Dancer.

1972, Feb. 18   Photo.   Perf. 13
213 A55   1p blue, pink & brn   .20 .20
214 A55   1.50p brn, lil & blk   .20 .20
215 A55   2p green, buff & sep   .20 .20
216 A55   5p green, pur & vio
　　　　　　brn   .25 .20

217 A55   8p black, lt grn & vio   .25 .20
218 A55   10p black, gray & Prus
　　　　　　bl   .30 .25
219 A55   12p multicolored   .35 .30
220 A55   15p multicolored   .45 .40
221 A55   24p multicolored   .90 .55
　　　　Nos. 213-221 (9)   3.10 2.50

1972, June 1   Photo.   Perf. 13
222 A56   8p shown   .30 .20
223 A56   12p Tuareg man   .40 .25

Child welfare.

Mother and
Child — A57

1972, Nov. 23   Photo.   Perf. 13
224 A57   4p shown   .25 .20
225 A57   15p Saharan man   .45 .25

Stamp Day. See No. 229.

Dunes
A58

Design: 7p, Old Market and Gate, Aaiun.

1973, June 1   Photo.   Perf. 13
226 A58   2p multicolored   .25 .20
227 A58   7p multicolored   .30 .25

Child welfare.

Type of 1972 and

View of
Villa
Cisneros
A59

1973, Nov. 23   Photo.   Perf. 13
228 A59   2p shown   .25 .20
229 A57   7p Tuareg man   .30 .25

Stamp Day.

UPU Monument,
Bern — A60

Gate, Smara
Mosque — A61

1974, May   Photo.   Perf. 13
230 A60   15p multicolored   .55 .20

Centenary of the Universal Postal Union.

1974, May
2p, Court and Minaret, Villa Cisneros
Mosque.

231 A61   1p multicolored   .20 .20
232 A61   2p multicolored   .25 .20

Child welfare.

Animal Type of 1970

1974, Nov.   Photo.   Perf. 13
233 A51   2p Desert eagle owl   .20 .20
234 A51   5p Lappet-faced vulture   .25 .20

Stamp Day.

Espana 75
Emblem, Spain
No. 1084 — A63

Old Man — A65

Children
A64

1975, Apr. 4   Photo.   Perf. 13
235 A63   8p olive, blk & bl   .25 .20

Espana 75 Intl. Phil. Exhib., Madrid, 4/4-13.

1975   Photo.   Perf. 13
236 A64   1.50p shown   .20 .20
237 A64   3p Children's village   .25 .20

Child welfare.

1975, Nov. 7   Photo.   Perf. 13
238 A65   3p blk, lt grn & mar   .20 .20

SEMI-POSTAL STAMPS

Red Cross Issue
Types of Semi-Postal Stamps of
Spain, 1926, Overprinted

1926   Unwmk.   Perf. 12½, 13
B1   SP3   5c black brown   8.00 8.00
B2   SP4   10c dark green   8.00 8.00
B3   SP1   15c dark violet   2.50 2.50
B4   SP4   20c violet brown   2.50 2.50
B5   SP5   25c deep carmine   2.50 2.50
B6   SP1   30c olive green   2.50 2.50
B7   SP3   40c ultra   .20 .20
B8   SP2   50c red brown   .20 .20
B9   SP5   60c myrtle green   .20 .20
B10   SP4   1p vermilion   .20 .20

B11 SP3 4p bister   2.50 1.90
B12 SP5 10p light violet   6.50 5.50
    Nos. B1-B12 (12)   35.80 34.20
    Set, never hinged   52.50

See Spain No. B6a for No. B4 without over-print. For surcharges see Spain #B72-B73.

> Catalogue values for unused stamps in this section, from this point to the end of the section, are for Never Hinged items.

Shepherd and Lamb — SP1   Dromedary and Calf — SP2

1950, Oct. 20   Photo.   Perf. 13x12½
B13 SP1 50c + 10c brown   .30   .20
B14 SP1 1p + 25c rose brn   13.50 6.00
B15 SP1 6.50p + 1.65p dk
    gray grn   7.00 1.75
    Nos. B13-B15 (3)   20.80 7.95

The surtax was for child welfare.

1951, Nov. 23
B16 SP2 5c + 5c brown   .20   .20
B17 SP2 10c + 5 red org   .20   .20
B18 SP2 60c + 15c olive brn   .45   .25
    Nos. B16-B18 (3)   .85   .65

Colonial Stamp Day, Nov. 23.

Child and Protector SP3   Ostrich SP4

1952, June 1
B19 SP3 5c + 5c brown   .20   .20
B20 SP3 50c + 10c gray   .25   .25
B21 SP3 2p + 30c blue   1.50 1.00
    Nos. B19-B21 (3)   1.95 1.45

The surtax was for child welfare.

1952, Nov. 23   Perf. 12½
B22 SP4 5c + 5c brn   .20   .20
B23 SP4 10c + 5c brn car   .20   .20
B24 SP4 60c + 15c dk grn   .40   .25
    Nos. B22-B24 (3)   .80   .65

Colonial Stamp Day, Nov. 23.

Musician Type of Regular Issue
1953, June 1   Perf. 13x12½
B25 A7 5c + 5c like #68   .20   .20
B26 A7 10c + 5c like #69   .25   .20

The surtax was for child welfare.

Fish Type of Regular Issue
1953, Nov. 23   Perf. 12½x13
B27 A8 5c + 5c like #70   .20   .20
B28 A8 10c + 5c like #71   .25   .20

Athlete Types of Regular Issue
1954, June 1   Perf. 12½x13, 13x12½
B29 A9 5c + 5c brn org   .20   .20
B30 A10 10c + 5c purple   .25   .20
The surtax was to help the native population.

Fish Type of Regular Issue
1954, Nov. 23   Perf. 12½x13
B31 A11 5c + 5c like #74   .20   .20
B32 A11 10c + 5c like #75   .25   .20

Type of Regular Issue and

Emilio Bonelli SP5

1955, June 1   Photo.   Unwmk.
B33 A12 10c + 5c red vio   .20   .20
B34 SP5 25c + 10c violet   .25   .20

The surtax was for child welfare.

Antelope Type of Regular Issue
15c+5c, Head of scimitar-horned oryx.
1955, Nov. 23   Perf. 12½x13
B35 A13 5c + 5c org brn   .20   .20
B36 A13 15c + 5c olive bister   .25   .20

Flower Type of Regular Issue
1956, June 1   Perf. 13x12½
B37 A14 5c + 5c like #78   .20   .20
B38 A14 15c + 5c like #79   .25   .20

The tax was for the children.

Aaiun Type of Regular Issue and

Arms of Villa Cisneros and Man — SP6

Perf. 12½x13, 13x12½
1956, Nov. 23   Unwmk.
B39 A15 5c + 5c pur & blk   .20   .20
B40 SP6 15c + 5c bis & grn   .25   .20

Eagle Type of Regular Issue
15c+5c, Lesser spotted eagle in flight.
1957, June 1   Perf. 13x12½
B41 A17 5c + 5c red brown   .20   .20
B42 A17 15c + 5c golden brn   .25   .20

The surtax was for child welfare.

Hyena Type of Regular Issue
Perf. 13x12½, 12½x13
1957, Nov. 23
B43 A18 10c + 5c like #88   .20   .20
B44 A18 15c + 5c like #89   .25   .20

Stork and Arms of Valencia and Aaiun SP7

1958, Mar. 6   Photo.   Perf. 12½x13
B45 SP7 10c + 5c org brn   .20   .20
B46 SP7 15c + 10c bister   .25   .20
B47 SP7 50c + 10c brn olive   .25   .25
    Nos. B45-B47 (3)   .70   .65

The surtax was to aid the victims of the Valencia flood, Oct. 1957.

Cervantes Type of Regular Issue
15c+5c, Don Quixote & Sancho Panza.
1958, June 1   Perf. 13x12½
B48 A20 10c + 5c hn brn & chnt
    brn   .20   .20
B49 A20 15c + 5c dp org & slate
    grn   .25   .20

The surtax was for child welfare.

Hoopoe Lark — SP8   Mailman — SP9

25c+10c, Hoopoe larks, horiz. 50c+10c, Bird.

Perf. 13x12½, 12½x13
1958, Nov. 23   Photo.   Unwmk.
B50 SP8 10c + 5c brn red   .20   .20
B51 SP8 25c + 10c brt pur   .20   .20
B52 SP8 50c + 10c olive   .25   .25
    Nos. B50-B52 (3)   .65   .65

Cervantes Type of Regular Issue
10c+5c, Lope de Vega. 15c+5c, Actress from "Star of Seville," by Lope de Vega.
1959, June   Perf. 12½x13
B53 A20 10c + 5c org brn & ol
    gray   .20   .20
B54 A20 15c + 5c dp ocher &
    choc   .25   .20

The surtax was for child welfare.

1959, Nov. 23   Photo.
Stamp Day: 20c+5c, Mailman. 50c+20c, Mailman on camel.
B55 SP9 10c + 5c rose & brn   .20   .20
B56 SP9 20c + 5c lt grn & brn   .20   .20
B57 SP9 50c + 20c ol gray &
    slate   .25   .20
    Nos. B55-B57 (3)   .65   .60

Quevedo Type of Regular Issue
Designs: 10c+5c, Francisco Gomez de Quevedo. 15c+5c, Winged wheel and hourglass, symbolic of "Hora de Todas."
1960, June 1   Perf. 12½x13, 13x12½
B58 A23 10c + 5c maroon   .20   .20
B59 A22 15c + 5c bister brown   .25   .20

The surtax was for child welfare.

Leopard SP10   Alonso Fernandez de Lugo SP11

Stamp Day: 20c+5c, Desert fox. 30c+10c, Eagle and leopard. 50c+20c, Sand fox.

1960, Nov. 23   Photo.   Perf. 13x12½
B60 SP10 10c + 5c rose lilac   .20   .20
B61 SP10 20c + 5c dk slate grn   .20   .20
B62 SP10 30c + 10c chocolate   .25   .20
B63 SP10 50c + 20c olive gray   .35   .25
    Nos. B60-B63 (4)   1.00   .85

Animal Type of 1961 inscribed: "Pro-Infancia 1961"
Designs: Various Mountain Gazelles.
1961, June 21   Unwmk.
B64 SP10 10c + 5c rose brn   .20   .20
B65 SP10 25c + 10c gray vio   .25   .20
B66 SP10 80c + 20c dk grn   .35   .25
    Nos. B64-B66 (3)   .80   .65

The surtax was for child welfare.

1961, Nov. 23   Perf. 13x12½
Stamp Day: #B68, B70, Diego de Herrera.
B67 SP11 10c + 5c org red   .20   .20
B68 SP11 25c + 10c dk pur   .25   .20
B69 SP11 30c + 10c dk red brn   .25   .20
B70 SP11 1p + 10c red org   .35   .25
    Nos. B67-B70 (4)   1.00   .85

> **AIR POST STAMPS**

In 1942, seven air post stamps of Spain, Nos. C100-C108, were overprinted "SAHARA ESPANOL", but satisfactory information regarding their status is not available.

> Catalogue values for unused stamps in this section are for Never Hinged items.

Ostriches — AP1   Desert Scene — AP2

1943   Unwmk.   Litho.   Perf. 12½
C8 AP1 5c cer & vio brn   .20   .20
C9 AP2 25c yel grn & ol
    grn   .20   .20
C10 AP1 50c ind & turq grn   .20   .20
C11 AP2 1p pur & grnsh bl   .20   .20
C12 AP1 1.40p gray grn & bl   .20   .20
C13 AP2 2p mag & org brn   1.75 1.10
C14 AP1 5p brown & purple   2.40 1.10
C15 AP2 6p brt bl & gray
    grn   47.50 21.00
    Nos. C8-C15 (8)   52.65 24.20

Nos. C8-C15 exist imperf. Value of set $90.

Diego Garcia de Herrera AP3

1950, Nov. 23   Photo.
C16 AP3 5p rose violet   2.50 1.00

Stamp Day.

Woman Holding Dove — AP4

1951, Apr. 22   Engr.   Perf. 10
C17 AP4 5p deep green   22.50 6.50

500th birth anniv. of Queen Isabella I. No. C17 is valued in the grade of fine.

Helmet and Trappings AP5   Plane and Camel Rider AP6

1952, July 18   Photo.   Perf. 13x12½
C18 AP5 5p brown   27.50 6.50

500th birth anniv. of Ferdinand the Catholic, of Spain.

1961, May 16   Unwmk.
C19 AP6 25p gray brown   2.75   .90

SPECIAL DELIVERY STAMPS

Catalogue value for unused stamps in this section are for Never Hinged items.

Type A2 Inscribed "URGENTE"

1943   **Unwmk.**   **Perf. 12½**
E1   A2 25c Camel troops   1.40   .85

Messenger on Motorcycle — SD1

Unwmk.
1971, Sept. 6   **Photo.**   **Perf. 13**
E2   SD1 10p bright rose & olive   .75   .35

SPANISH WEST AFRICA

ˈspa-nish ˈwest ˈa-fri-kə

LOCATION — Northwest Africa bordering on the Atlantic Ocean
GOVT. — Spanish administration
AREA — 117,000 sq. mi.
POP. — 95,000 (1950)
CAPITAL — Sidi Ifni

Spanish West Africa was the major political division of Spanish areas in northwest Africa. It included Spanish Sahara (Rio de Oro and Saguiet el Hamra) Ifni and, for administrative purposes, Southern Morocco. Separate stamp issues have been used for Rio de Oro, Ifni and La Aguera.

Catalogue values for all unused stamps in this country are for Never Hinged items.

Native — A1

Perf. 13x12½
1949, Oct.   **Litho.**   **Unwmk.**
1   A1 4p dark gray green   2.10   .90
UPU, 75th anniversary.

Nomad Camp A2

5c, 30c, 75c, 2p, Tinzgarrentz Oasis. 10c, 40c, 90c, 5p, Desert well. 15c, 45c, 1p, Caravan.

1950, June 5   **Perf. 12½x13**
2	A2	2c brown	.20	.20
3	A2	5c rose violet	.20	.20
4	A2	10c Prussian blue	.20	.20
5	A2	15c deep olive gray	.20	.20
6	A2	25c red brown	.20	.20
7	A2	30c bright yellow	.20	.20
8	A2	40c olive gray	.20	.20
9	A2	45c rose lake	.20	.20
10	A2	50c brown orange	.20	.20

11	A2	75c ultramarine	.20	.20
12	A2	90c dull blue grn	.25	.20
13	A2	1p gray	.25	.20
14	A2	1.35p violet	.80	.45
15	A2	2p sepia	1.40	1.00
16	A2	5p lilac rose	12.50	3.50
17	A2	10p light brown	30.00	20.00
		Nos. 2-17 (16)	47.20	27.35

AIR POST STAMPS

Isabella the Catholic, Queen of Castile — AP1

Perf. 13x12½
1949, Nov. 23   **Photo.**   **Unwmk.**
C1   AP1 5p yellow brown   2.00   .90
Stamp Day, Nov. 23, 1949.

Desert Camp AP2

Designs: Various Desert Scenes.

1951, Mar. 1   **Litho.**   **Perf. 12½x13**
C2	AP2	25c ocher	.25	.20
C3	AP2	50c lilac rose	.25	.20
C4	AP2	1p green	.30	.20
C5	AP2	2p bright blue	.65	.20
C6	AP2	3.25p rose lilac	1.25	.75
C7	AP2	5p gray brown	13.00	2.75
C8	AP2	10p rose red	23.00	17.50
		Nos. C2-C8 (7)	38.70	21.80

SPECIAL DELIVERY STAMP

Tilimenzo Pass and Franco SD1

Perf. 12½x13
1951, Mar. 1   **Litho.**   **Unwmk.**
E1   SD1 25c rose carmine   .35   .25

SRI LANKA

ˌsrē ˈläŋ-kə

LOCATION — Indian Ocean south of India
GOVT. — Democratic Socialist Republic
AREA — 26,244 sq. mi.
POP. — 19,144,875 (1999 est.)
CAPITAL — Colombo

Sri Lanka was named Ceylon until May 22, 1972. Issues inscribed "Ceylon" are listed under that name in Volume 2.

100 Cents = 1 Rupee

Catalogue values for all unused stamps in this country are for Never Hinged items.

Watermark

Wmk. 385 — CARTOR

Wmk. 233 — "Harrison & Sons, London" in Script

Wmk. 388 — Multiple "SPM"

Lotus and Sunrise over Adam's Peak — A162

1972, May 22   **Litho.**   **Perf. 13½x13**
470   A162 15c blue & multi   .60   .60
Inauguration of Ceylon as Republic of Sri Lanka.

A162a

Overprinted "1972" in Red
1972, May 26   **Perf. 14x13½**
471   A162a 5c orange brn & multi   .50   .50
World Fellowship of Buddhists, Sri Lanka, May 22-28.
Supposedly not issued without overprint, copies sell for 25-cents.

Book Year Emblem, Oil Lamp — A163

1972, Sept. 8   **Photo.**   **Perf. 13**
472   A163 20c yellow & dk brn   .40   .40
International Book Year 1972.

Imperial Angelfish A164

Tropical Fish: 3c, Green chromide. 30c, Skipjack bonito. 2r, Black ruby barbs.

Perf. 14x13½
1972, Oct. 12   **Litho.**   **Unwmk.**
473	A164	2c ultra & multi	.20	1.10
474	A164	3c dp orange & multi	.20	1.10
475	A164	30c brt green & multi	2.25	.40
476	A164	2r dp green & multi	6.50	6.75
		Nos. 473-476 (4)	9.15	9.35

3rd Session of Indian Ocean Fisheries Commission, Colombo, Oct. 9-14.

Bandaranaike Memorial Hall — A165

1973, May 17   **Litho.**   **Perf. 14**
477   A165 15c lt ultra & vio blue   .40   .40
Opening of Bandaranaike Memorial International Conference Hall.

Women Holding Lotus A166

Rock and Temple Paintings: 35c, King giving away his children, Degaldoruwa Temple, near Kandy, 18th cent. 50c, Prince and gravedigger, Polonaruwa, 12th cent. 90c, Holy man holding lotus, Polonaruwa, 12th cent. Design of 1.55r is from Sigiriya, 5th cent.

1973, Sept. 3   **Perf. 13½x14**
478	A166	35c lt gray & multi	.45	.20
479	A166	50c gray & multi	.60	.20
480	A166	90c slate & multi	.85	.85
481	A166	1.55r brown & multi	1.00	1.00
a.		Souvenir sheet of 4, #478-481	5.50	5.50
		Nos. 478-481 (4)	2.90	2.25

For surcharges see Nos. 538-540.

Bandaranaike Conference Hall — A167

1974, Sept. 6   **Litho.**   **Perf. 14**
482   A167 85c multicolored   .50   .50
20th Commonwealth Parliamentary Conference, Sri Lanka, Sept. 1-15.

S.W.R.D. Bandaranaike A168

"UPU," "100" and UPU Emblem A170

1974, Sept. 25   **Photo.**   **Perf. 14½**
486   A168 15c ultra & multi   .40   .40
For surcharge see No. 541.

1974, Oct. 9   **Litho.**   **Perf. 13**
490   A170 50c multicolored   1.75   1.50

Parliament,
Colombo
A171

1975, Apr. 1   Litho.   Perf. 13½
491 A171 1r multicolored   .40 .40

Interparliamentary Union, Spring Meeting at
Bandaranaike Memorial International Conference Hall, Sri Lanka, Mar. 31-Apr. 5.

Ponnambalam
Ramanathan
A172

D. J.
Wimalasurendra
A173

1975, Sept. 4   Litho.   Perf. 13½
492 A172 75c multicolored   .40 .40

Sir Ponnambalam Ramanathan (1851-1930), lawyer and educator.

1975, Sept. 17
493 A173 75c ultra & blue blk   .40 .40

Devapura Jayasena Wimalasurendra (1874-1953), engineer and irrigation specialist.

Map, Mrs.
Bandaranaike,
Dove — A174

1975, Dec. 22   Litho.   Perf. 13½
494 A174 1.15r blue & multi   3.75 1.90

International Women's Year 1975.
For surcharge, see No. 1579.

Rhododendron
Zeylanicum
A175

Flowers: 50c, Exacum trinerve. 75c, Daffodil
orchid. 10r, Wormia triquetra.

1976, Jan. 1   Litho.   Perf. 13
495 A175 25c blue & multi   .20 .20
496 A175 50c ocher & multi   .20 .20
497 A175 75c black & multi   .25 .25
498 A175 10r black & multi   4.00 4.00
a.   Souvenir sheet of 4, #495-498   20.00 20.00
       Nos. 495-498 (4)   4.65 4.65

Mahaveli-ganga Sluice — A176

1976, Jan. 8   Litho.   Perf. 13x12½
499 A176 85c lt blue, lt grn & lil   .40 .55
Mahaveli-ganga River diversion.

Radar
Station — A177

1976, May 6   Litho.   Perf. 14
500 A177 1r blue & multi   1.00 1.00
Opening of Satellite Earth Station, Padukka.

Prince Siddhartha as White Elephant
and Sleeping Queen — A178

Birth of Buddha: 10c, King consulting astrologers. 1.50r, King entertaining astrologers at banquet. 2.25r, Flag bearers, musicians in procession. 5r, Queen giving birth to Prince Siddhartha, the Buddha. Designs taken from 18th cent. wall paintings in Dambawa Vihara Temple.

1976, May 7   Litho.   Perf. 13½
501 A178 5c blue & multi   .20 .50
502 A178 10c blue & multi   .20 .50
503 A178 1.50r blue & multi   1.00 1.00
504 A178 2r blue & multi   1.00 1.00
505 A178 2.25r blue & multi   2.00 2.00
506 A178 5r blue & multi   5.00 5.00
a.   Souvenir sheet of 6, #501-506   14.00 14.00
       Nos. 501-506 (6)   9.40 10.00

Blue
Sapphire
A179

Gems of Sri Lanka: 1.15r, Cat's-eye. 2r,
Star sapphire. 5r, Ruby.

1976, June 16   Perf. 12x12½
507 A179 60c multicolored   6.75 .40
508 A179 1.15r multicolored   11.00 2.40
509 A179 2r multicolored   12.50 5.00
510 A179 5r multicolored   17.00 17.00
a.   Souv. sheet of 4, #507-510   70.00 60.00
       Nos. 507-510 (4)   47.25 24.80

Prime Minister
Sirimavo
Bandaranaike
A180

Statue of
Liberty
A181

1976, Aug. 3   Photo.   Perf. 14¼x14½
511 A180 1.15r pink & multi   .40 .40
512 A180 2r pink & multi   .70 .70

5th Summit Conference of Non-aligned
Countries, Colombo, Aug. 9-19.
For surcharges, see Nos. 1347-1348.

1976, Nov. 29   Litho.   Perf. 14
513 A181 2.25r lt blue & indigo   .85 1.00
American Bicentennial.

A. G. Bell,
Telephone and
Telephone Line
A182

Maitreya
Bodhisattva
A183

1976, Dec. 21   Litho.   Perf. 13x13½
514 A182 1r orange & multi   .90 .35
Centenary of first telephone call by Alexander Graham Bell, Mar. 10, 1876.

1977, Jan. 1   Litho.   Perf. 12½x13
Bronze Statues: 1r, Sundara Murti Swami,
11th century. 5r, Goddess Tara.
515 A183 50c multicolored   .45 .45
516 A183 1r multicolored   .45 .45
517 A183 5r multicolored   4.00 4.00
       Nos. 515-517 (3)   4.90 4.90

Colombo Museum, centenary.

Kandyan Crown,
1737-1815
A184

2r, Kandyan throne and footstool, 1693-1815.

1977, Jan. 18
518 A184 1r multicolored   .60 .60
519 A184 2r multicolored   1.90 1.90

Rahula
Thero — A185

Brass
Lamps — A186

No. 521, Ponnambalam Arunachalam.

1977   Litho.   Perf. 13½
520 A185 1r multicolored   1.25 1.25
521 A185 1r multicolored   .80 .80

Sri Rahula Thero, 15th cent. poet and
scholar, and Sir Ponnambalam Arunachalam
(1851-1930), 1st president of Ceylon University Assoc., member of Congress.
Issue dates: #520, Feb. 23; #521, Mar. 10.

1977, Apr. 7   Perf. 13
Handicrafts: 25c, Jewelry box and jewelry.
50c, Caparisoned ivory elephant. 5r, Sinhala
wooden mask.
522 A186 20c multicolored   .20 .20
523 A186 25c multicolored   .20 .20
524 A186 50c multicolored   .45 .45
525 A186 5r multicolored   2.50 2.75
a.   Souvenir sheet of 4, #522-525   5.75 5.75
       Nos. 522-525 (4)   3.35 3.60

Mohammed
Cassim Siddi
Lebbe — A187

1977, June 11   Litho.   Perf. 13
526 A187 1r multicolored   .50 .65
Lebbe (1838-98), lawyer, educator and
Moslem journalist.

Girl Guide
A188

1977, Dec. 13   Litho.   Perf. 15
527 A188 75c multicolored   1.25 .50
60th anniversary of Sri Lanka Girl Guides.

Parliament and
Wheel of
Life — A189

Runners — A190

1978, Feb. 4   Photo.   Perf. 12x12½
528 A189 15c green & gold   .40 .20

J.R. Jayewardene, first elected president,
assumption of office.
See Nos. 559, 611-611A, 847. For
surcharges see Nos. 542, 572, 698A-698B.

1978, Apr. 27   Litho.   Perf. 15
529 A190 15c multicolored   .40 .40

National Youth Service Council.
For surcharge see No. 543.

Bodhisattva
in Royal
Attire in
Lotus
Position
A191

Vesak Festival: 50c, Bodhisattva without
royal attire cutting off his hair with sword. Both
designs from rock carvings in Borobudur Temple, Java.

1978, May 16   Perf. 13
530 A191 15c multicolored   1.10 1.10
531 A191 50c multicolored   1.50 1.50

Veera Puran Appu and his Flag — A192

Birdwing Butterfly — A193

1978, Aug. 8   Litho.   Perf. 13
532 A192 15c multicolored   .40 .20

Veera Puran Appu (1848-1908), revolutionist, 130th birth anniversary.

1978, Nov. 28   Litho.   Perf. 14x13½
Butterflies: 50c, Tamil lacewing. 5r, Blue oakleaf. 10r, Blue mormon.

534 A193 25c multicolored   .90 .20
535 A193 50c multicolored   1.50 .20
536 A193 5r multicolored   2.75 1.75
537 A193 10r multicolored   2.75 2.75
a.   Souvenir sheet of 4, #534-537   20.00 16.00
Nos. 534-537 (4)   7.90 4.90

Nos. 478, 480-481 Surcharged with New Value and Bar

1978   Litho.   Perf. 13½x14
538 A166 5c on 90c multi   3.00 3.00
539 A166 10c on 35c multi   1.00 1.00
540 A166 1r on 1.55r multi   2.00 2.00
Nos. 538-540 (3)   6.00 6.00

Nos. 486, 528 Surcharged with New Value and 2 Bars; No. 529 with New Value on Pink Panel
Perf. 14½, 12x12½, 15

1979, Jan.   Litho.; Engr.
541 A168 25c on 15c multi   6.50 6.50
542 A189 25c on 15c multi   6.50 6.50
543 A190 25c on 15c multi   6.50 6.50
Nos. 541-543 (3)   19.50 19.50

Ceylon No. 390 Overprinted Vertically "SRI LANKA" in Green and Surcharged in Black

1979, Mar. 22   Photo.   Perf. 11½
Granite Paper
544 A118 15c on 10c brt green   4.50 3.00

Arrival of Sacred Tooth — A194

Wrestlers — A195

Wall Paintings from Kelaniya Temple: 25c, Prince Danta and Princess Hema Mala bringing Sacred Tooth from Kalinga, 4th century A.D. 1r, Princess Theri Sanghamitta bringing, by ship, the bodhi tree branch, 3rd century B.C. 10r, King Kirti offering fan of authority to supreme patriarch, 18th century.

1979, May 3   Litho.   Perf. 13½
546 A194 25c multicolored   .20 .20
547 A194 1r multicolored   .20 .20
548 A194 10r multicolored   2.00 2.00
a.   Souvenir sheet of 3, #546-548   4.25 4.25
Nos. 546-548 (3)   2.40 2.40

2523rd Vesak Festival, May 11.

1979, May 18   Litho.   Perf. 14
Design: 50r, Dancer. Woodcarvings from Embekke Temple.
549 A195 20r multicolored   1.60 1.10
550 A195 50r multicolored   4.00 3.50

Piyadasa Sirisena A196

Dudley S. Senanayake A197

1979, May 22   Perf. 13x13½
551 A196 1.25r deep green   .60 .60

Piyadasa Sirisena (1875-1946), patriot, journalist, novelist and poet.

1979, June 19   Photo.
552 A197 1.25r deep green   .40 .40

27th death anniversary of Prime Minister Dudley S. Senanayake.

Mother Feeding Child, IYC Emblem A198

Designs: 3r, Faces and IYC emblem. 5r, Children with rope and ball, IYC emblem.

1979, July 31   Litho.   Perf. 12½
553 A198 5c multicolored   .20 .20
554 A198 3r multicolored   .45 .45
555 A198 5r multicolored   .50 .50
Nos. 553-555 (3)   1.15 1.15

International Year of the Child.

Ceylon No. 2, Rowland Hill — A199

Airlanka Emblem — A200

1979, Aug. 27   Litho.   Perf. 13½
556 A199 3r multicolored   .60 .75

Sir Rowland Hill (1795-1879), originator of penny postage.

1979, Sept. 1   Litho.   Perf. 12½
557 A200 3r red, dk grn & blk   1.25 1.25

Airlanka National Airline, inaugural flight, Colombo-Bangkok.

Coconut Palm — A201

1979, Oct. 9   Litho.   Perf. 13½
558 A201 2r multicolored   1.50 1.50

Asian and Pacific Coconut Community, 10th anniversary.

No. 528 Redrawn Without Date
1979, Oct. 9   Photo.   Perf. 13
Size: 20x24mm
559 A189 25c green & gold   .40 .20

Family in Cogwheel, Parliament A202

1979, Oct.   Litho.   Perf. 13½
560 A202 2r multicolored   1.10 1.10

Intl. Conf. of Parliamentarians on Population & Development, Colombo, Aug. 28-Sept. 1.

Swami Vipulananda (1892-1947), Philosopher & Theologian — A203

1979, Nov. 18   Perf. 12½
561 A203 1.25r multicolored   .40 .40

Text and Crescent A204

1979, Nov. 22
562 A204 3.75r multicolored   .60 .90

Hegira (pilgrimage year).

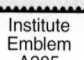

Institute Emblem A205

Blue Magpie A206

1979, Nov. 29   Perf. 13
563 A205 15c multicolored   .40 .40

Ayurveda Medical Institute, 50th anniversary.

1979, Dec. 13   Litho.   Perf. 14
564 A206 10c shown   .20 .20
565 A206 15c Lorikeet   .20 .20
566 A206 75c Arrenga   .20 .20
567 A206 1r Spurfowl   .20 .20
568 A206 5r Yellow-fronted barbet   1.50 1.50
569 A206 10r Yellow-eared bulbul   1.90 1.90
a.   Souvenir sheet of 6, #564-569   10.00 10.00
Nos. 564-569 (6)   4.20 4.20

For surcharges, see Nos. 1062B, 1512.

Rotary Emblem, Map of Sri Lanka A207

1979, Dec. 27   Litho.   Perf. 14½
570 A207 1.50r multicolored   1.10 1.25

Rotary International, 75th anniversary.

A. Ratnayake, Educator and Pres. of Senate — A208

1980, Jan. 7   Photo.   Perf. 14x13½
571 A208 1.25r slate green   .40 .40

No. 559 Surcharged
1980, Mar. 17   Photo.   Perf. 13
572 A189 35c on 25c multi   .40 .40

One position has ".33" instead of ".35."

Leaf, Wheel, Fan (Buddhist Symbols) A209

1980, Mar. 25   Photo.   Perf. 13½x14
573 A209 10c Steeple   .50 1.00
574 A209 35c shown   .50 .40

All Ceylon Buddhist Cong., 60th anniv.

Col. Henry Olcott, Buddhist Emblem — A210

Journey of Patachara, Temple Painting — A211

1980, May 17   Litho.   Perf. 14
575 A210 2r multicolored   1.25 1.25

Col. Henry S. Olcott (1832-1907), American theosophist and Buddhist lecturer, centenary of arrival in Sri Lanka.

1980, May 23   Perf. 13½x14
Vesak Festival (Paintings, life of Buddha): 1.60r, Patachara crossing river.
576 A211 35c multicolored   .40 .40
577 A211 1.60r multicolored   1.90 1.90

George E. De Silva — A212

1980, June 8   Perf. 13x13½
578 A212 1.60r multicolored   .50 .50

George E. de Silva (1879-1950), politician.

Siva Temples, Polonnaruwa — A213

1980, Aug. 25   Litho.   Perf. 13½
579 A213 35c shown   .20 .40
580 A213 35c Cave Temples, Dambulla   .20 .40
581 A213 35c Sacred Tooth Temple, Kandy   .20 .40
582 A213 1.60r Abhayagiri Hill   .80 .80
583 A213 1.60r Jetavanarama Hill   .80 1.25

584 A213 1.60r Sigiri .80 1.25
a. Souvenir sheet of 6, #579-584 4.00 3.50
    Nos. 579-584 (6) 3.00 4.95
UNESCO "Cultural Triangle" Project.

Department of Cooperative Development, 50th Anniversary A214

1980, Oct. 1   Litho.   Perf. 13½
585 A214 20c multicolored .40 .50

Women's Movement Emblem A215

1980, Oct. 16   Photo.   Perf. 14x13½
586 A215 35c multicolored .40 .50
Mahila Samiti (Rural Women's Movement), 50th anniversary.

Nativity — A216

1980, Nov. 20   Litho.   Perf. 13½
587 A216 35c shown .30 .30
588 A216 3.75r Three kings .80 .90
a. Souvenir sheet of 2, #587-588 2.00 2.00
Christmas 1980/Year of the family.

Colombo Public Library Opening A217

1980, Dec. 17   Perf. 12x12½
589 A217 35c multicolored .40 .40

Peacock Banner A218
Designs: Ancient flags.

1980, Dec. 18   Perf. 13
590 A218 10c shown .20 .20
591 A218 25c Elephant banner .20 .20
592 A218 1.60r Sinhalese royal flag .25 .25
593 A218 20r Kings Civil Standard 1.90 1.90
a. Souvenir sheet of 4, #590-593 2.40 2.40
    Nos. 590-593 (4) 2.55 2.55
For surcharge on No. 592, see No. 1550.

Fishing Cat — A219

1981, Feb. 10   Litho.   Perf. 14
594 A219 2.50r on 1.60r, shown .55 .20
595 A219 3r on 1.50r, Golden palm cat .55 .25
596 A219 4r on 2r, Mouse deer .55 .45
597 A219 5r on 3.75r, Rusty-spotted cat .85 .60
a. Souvenir sheet of 4, #594-597 3.00 3.00
    Nos. 594-597 (4) 2.50 1.50
See #728-730A, 928. For surcharge see #731.

Population and Housing Census — A220

1981, Mar. 2   Litho.   Perf. 12½x12
598 A220 50c multicolored 1.00 1.00

Ceylon Light Infantry Centenary A221

1981, Apr. 1   Litho.   Perf. 12
599 A221 2r multicolored 1.60 1.60

The Death of Buddha, Carved Panel, 1st Cent. — A222

1981, May 5   Perf. 13x13½
600 A222 35c shown .20 .20
601 A222 50c Silk banner .20 .20
602 A222 7r Statuette 2.00 1.75
a. Souvenir sheet of 3, #600-602 5.75 5.75
    Nos. 600-602 (3) 2.40 2.15
Vesak Festival.

St. John Baptist de la Salle A223

1981, May 15   Litho.   Perf. 12½x12
603 A223 2r multicolored 2.25 2.25
De la Salle Brothers Order, 300th anniv.

Polwatte Sri Buddadatta A224

Intl. Year of the Disabled — A225

Famous Men: No. 605, Mohottiwatte Gunananda, Buddhist leader. No. 606, Gnanapra Kasar, Catholic missionary. No. 607, Al-Haj T.B. Jayah, Muslim teacher. No. 608, James Peiris. No. 609, N.M. Perera, founded first Marxist Party in Sri Lanka, 1935.

1981   Photo.   Perf. 12
604 A224 50c olive bister .75 .75
605 A224 50c dull red brown .75 .75
606 A224 50c lilac .75 .75
607 A224 50c gray green .75 .75
608 A224 50c brown .75 .75
609 A224 50c crimson rose .75 .75
    Nos. 604-609 (6) 4.50 4.50
Issued: #604-606, 5/22; #607, 5/31; #609, 6/6; #608, 12/20.
See #623-624, 640-642, 646, 672-676, 713-717.

1981, June 19   Litho.   Perf. 12x12½
610 A225 2r multicolored 1.50 1.50

No. 528 Redrawn with Denomination in Upper Right Corner
1981-83   Photo.   Perf. 13   Size: 20x24mm
611 A189 50c green & gold 3.00 .20
611A A189 60c green & gold 10.00 1.40
Issued: 50c, June 6; 60c, Dec. 30, 1983.
For surcharges see Nos. 698A-698B.

Hand Putting Ballot in Box A226

Perf. 12½x12, 12x12½
1981, July 7   Litho.
612 A226 50c shown .30 .30
613 A226 7r Ballot box on map, vert. 2.40 2.40
Universal Franchise, 50th anniv.

Rhys Davids (Society Founder) A227

1981, July 14   Perf. 12½x12
614 A227 35c multicolored 1.25 .60

All Ceylon Buddhist Students' Federation, 25th Anniv. A228

1981, July 21   Litho.   Perf. 13½
615 A228 2r multicolored 1.50 1.50

Family Planning — A229

7th World Acupuncture Cong. — A230

1981, Sept. 25
616 A229 50c multicolored 1.50 1.50

1981, Oct. 20   Litho.   Perf. 12x12½
617 A230 2r multicolored 4.25 4.25

Visit of Queen Elizabeth II, Oct. A231
Designs: Flags of Gt. Britain and Sri Lanka.

1981, Oct. 21   Perf. 14
618 A231 50c multicolored .75 .75
619 A231 5r multicolored 2.25 2.25
a. Souvenir sheet of 2, #618-619 3.50 3.50

Forest Conservation A232

1981, Nov. 27   Perf. 13½x13
620 A232 35c Forest .20 .20
621 A232 50c Tree planting .30 .30
622 A232 5r Jack tree 2.50 2.75
a. Souvenir sheet of 3, #620-622, perf. 14x13 2.75 3.50
    Nos. 620-622 (3) 3.00 3.25

Famous Men Type of 1981
Designs: No. 623, F.R. Senanayaka (1882-1926), lawyer and politician. No. 624, Philip Gunawardhane, politician, 10th death anniv.

1982   Litho.   Perf. 14
623 A224 50c brown 1.00 1.00
624 A224 50c bright rose 1.00 1.00
Issue dates: #623, Jan. 1; #624, Jan. 11.

Dept. of Inland Revenue, 50th Anniv. A233

Natl. Television Inauguration A234

1982, Feb. 9   Litho.   Perf. 14
625 A233 50c multicolored 1.00 1.00

1982, Feb. 15
626 A234 2.50r multicolored 3.75 3.75

Sesquicentennial of Cricket Introduction and Centenary of Sri Lanka vs. England Match — A235

1982, Feb. 17
627 A235 2.50r multicolored   8.00 8.00

Osbeckia Wightiana A236

1982, Apr. 1   *Perf. 12*
628 A236 35c shown   .20   .20
629 A236   2r Mesua nagas-
                  sarium   .35   .25
630 A236   7r Rhodomyrtus to-
                  mentosa   .80   .85
631 A236   20r Phaius tancarvil-
                  leae   2.25   2.25
   a.   Souvenir sheet of 4, #628-
         631   10.00 10.50
         Nos. 628-631 (4)   3.60   3.55

Food and Nutrition Planning A237

World Hindu Conference A238

1982, Apr. 6   Litho.   *Perf. 13*
632 A237 50c multicolored   2.40   2.40

1982, Apr. 21   *Perf. 14x14½*
633 A238 50c multicolored   1.60   1.60

Vesak Festival 1982 A239

Scenes from Jataka Story (Pre-incarnation of Buddha), Cloth Painting, 3rd cent. B.C., Hanguranketa Temple (King Vessantara and): 35c, Giving away white elephant. 50c, Royal Family in Vankagiri Forest. 2.50r, Giving away his children to a Brahmin. 5r, Royal family in chariot.

1982, Apr. 23   *Perf. 14*
634 A239 35c multicolored   .80   .20
635 A239 50c multicolored   .95   .20
636 A239 2.50r multicolored   3.25   2.75
637 A239 5r multicolored   4.25   4.25
   a.   Souvenir sheet of 4, #634-
         637   13.50 13.50
         Nos. 634-637 (4)   9.25   7.40

New Parliament Building Opening A240

1982, Apr. 29
638 A240 50c multicolored   1.40   1.40

Scouting Year A241

1982, May 24   Litho.   *Perf. 12½x12*
639 A241 50c multicolored   2.50   2.25

Famous Men Type of 1981
1982   *Perf. 12x12½*
640 A224 50c C.W.W. Kannan-
               gara   1.50   1.50
641 A224 50c G.P. Malalasekara   1.50   1.50
642 A224 50c John Kotelawala   1.50   1.50
         Nos. 640-642 (3)   4.50   4.50
   Issued: #640, 5/22; #641, 5/26; #642, 6/8.

World Buddhist Leaders Conference — A242

1982, June 10   *Perf. 12½x12*
643 A242 50c multicolored   1.50   1.50

World Environment Day — A243

1982, June 5
644 A243 50c multicolored   2.50   2.10

YMCA Centenary — A244

1982, June 24   Photo.   *Perf. 11½*
645 A244 2.50r multicolored   4.75   4.75

Famous Men Type of 1981
1982, June 14   Litho.   *Perf. 12x12½*
646 A224 50c Waitialingam
               Duraiswamy   1.50   1.50

Weliwita Saranankara Sangharaja A245

1982, July 5
647 A245 50c orange & black   1.50   1.50

25th Anniv. of Sasana Sevaka Samithiya A246

1982, Aug. 8
648 A246 50c multicolored   2.25   2.25

TB Bacillus Centenary A247

1982, Sept. 21
649 A247 50c Koch, microscope,
               bacillus   3.00   2.50

Eye Donation Society — A248

1982, Nov. 16   Litho.   *Perf. 12x12½*
650 A248 2.50r Emblems, map   4.50   4.75

125th Anniv. of Ceylon Postage Stamps — A249

1982, Dec. 1   Litho.   *Perf. 13½*
651 A249   50c Ceylon #5, 302   .60   .60
652 A249 2.50r Ceylon #12, #611   2.40   2.40
   a.   Souv. sheet, #651-652, perf. 12 4.00 4.00
         Natl. Stamp Exhibition.

Sir Oliver Goonetilleke A250

1982, Dec. 17   Litho.   *Perf. 12x12½*
653 A250 50c black & brown   .80   .80

25th Anniv. of Sarvodaya Social Movement A251

1983, Jan. 1   *Perf. 13½*
654 A251 50c multicolored   1.50   1.50

55th Anniv. of Amateur Radio Society A252

1983, Jan. 17
655 A252 2.50r multicolored   4.50   4.50

Customs Cooperation Council and First Intl. Customs Day — A253

1983, Jan. 26   Litho.   *Perf. 12*
656 A253 50c orange & multi   .80   .80
657 A253 5r green & multi   5.25   5.50

Bottlenose Dolphin A254

1983, Feb. 22   *Perf. 14½x14*
658 A254 50c shown   .85   .20
659 A254   2r Dugongs   1.40   .85
660 A254 2.50r Humpback
               whale   4.00   2.50
661 A254 10r Great sperm
               whale   8.75   8.75
         Nos. 658-661 (4)   15.00 12.30

Ceylon Shipping Corp. A255

1983, Mar. 1   *Perf. 12x12½*
662 A255   50c Container ship   .40   .20
663 A255 2.50r Liner services
               map   1.50   .90
664 A255   5r Conventional ship 2.25   2.10
665 A255 20r Oil tanker   3.50   4.25
         Nos. 662-665 (4)   7.65   7.45

Intl. Women's Day — A256

1983, Mar. 8   *Perf. 13½*
666 A256 50c Woman, flag   .40   .20
667 A256 5r Woman, map   1.50   1.90

Commonwealth Day — A257

1983, Mar. 14
668 A257   50c Waterfall   .20   .20
669 A257 2.50r Tea picking   .20   .20
670 A257   5r Harvesting   .35   .50
671 A257 20r Cultural pageant   1.40   1.40
         Nos. 668-671 (4)   2.15   2.30

Famous Men Type of 1981

1983   **Litho.**   **Perf. 12**
672 A224 50c Henry W.
      Amarasuriya   .35   .50
Size: 29x40mm
673 A224 50c Charles A. Lorenz   .35   .50
674 A224 50c Simon G. Perera   .35   .50
675 A224 50c Nordeen H.M. Ab-
      dul Cader   .35   .50
676 A224 50c C.W. Tamother-
      ampillai   1.10 1.10
   Nos. 672-676 (5)   2.50 3.10

No. 676 shows Tamotherampillai looking towards the right of the stamp. A version that was to be issued May 22, showed someone labeled C. W. Tamotherampillai looking straight ahead.
Issued: No. 676, Oct. 1; others, May 22.

25th Anniv. of Lions Club A258

1983, May 7   **Litho.**   **Perf. 14**
677 A258 2.50r multicolored   4.25 2.75

Vesak Festival 1983 — A259

Various Colombo murals.

1983, May 13   **Perf. 12½x12**
678 A259 35c multicolored   .20   .20
679 A259 50c multicolored   .20   .20
680 A259 5r multicolored   1.10 1.10
681 A259 10r multicolored   1.90 1.90
a. Souvenir sheet of 4, #678-681 3.75 3.75
   Nos. 678-681 (4)   3.40 3.40

125th Anniv. of Telecommunication Service — A260

1983, May 17   **Perf. 12x12½**
682 A260 2r shown   1.00   .80
683 A260 10r World Communica-
      tions Year   3.00 3.50

Gam Udawa Village Re-awakening Movement — A261

1983, June 23   **Litho.**   **Perf. 12x12½**
684 A261 50c Family   .25   .30
685 A261 5r Village   .75 1.10

Cattle Transport A262

1983, Aug. 1   **Litho.**   **Perf. 12**
686 A262 35c shown   .20   .20
687 A262 2r Train   3.00 3.00
688 A262 2.50r Cattle cart   1.60 1.60
689 A262 5r Model T Ford   3.25 3.25
   Nos. 686-689 (4)   8.05 8.05

Sir Tikiri Banda Panabokke, 20th Death Anniv. — A263

1983, Sept. 2   **Litho.**   **Perf. 13½x14**
690 A263 50c dark red   1.50 1.50

Ceylon Wood Pigeon A264

1983, Dec. 1   **Litho.**   **Perf. 14½**
691 A264 25c shown   1.40 1.40
692 A264 35c Ceylon white-eye 1.40 1.40
693 A264 2r Dusky-blue fly-
      catcher   2.10 2.10
694 A264 20r Ceylon coucal   3.25 3.25
a. Souvenir sheet of 4, #691-694 7.00 7.00
   Nos. 691-694 (4)   8.15 8.15

See No. 877. For surcharge see No. 780A.

Christmas, Stone Carvings — A265

1983, Dec. 5   **Litho.**   **Perf. 12½x13**
695 A265 50c multicolored   .20   .20
696 A265 5r ultra & bister   .50   .50
a. Souv. sheet, #695-696+label 1.10 2.00

A266

A267

1983, Nov. 25   **Litho.**   **Perf. 14x15**
697 A266 50c brown   1.75 1.75

Rev. Pelene Thero (1878-1955), Buddhist leader.

1983   **Litho.**   **Perf. 13½**
698 A267 50c Ahamed Orabi Al-
      Misri   1.50 1.50

#611 Surcharged with Four Bars, #611A with Three Bars and New Denomination in Black or Green

1983-85   **Photo.**   **Perf. 13**
698A A189 60c on 50c ('83)   8.00 4.00
Size: 20x24mm
698B A189 75c on 60c (G) ('85) .40 .40

Ovpt. on No. 698A also exists with two bars. Value, $13.
Issue dates: both Dec. 1.

World Food Day (Oct. 16) A268

1984, Jan. 2   **Perf. 12½x12**
699 A268 3r Rice paddy   .70 1.10

Colombo Tea Auctions Centenary A269

1984, Jan. 31
700 A269 1r Auction House   .25   .20
701 A269 2r Emblem   .50   .50
702 A269 5r Tea picker   1.25 1.40
703 A269 10r Auction   2.50 2.75
   Nos. 700-703 (4)   4.50 4.85

Mahapola Anniversary (Educational System) — A270

1984, Feb. 10   **Perf. 12**
704 A270 60c Students   .20   .20
705 A270 1r Classroom   .20   .20
706 A270 5.50r Student in library,
      lab   .35   .75
707 A270 6r Emblem   .40   .75
   Nos. 704-707 (4)   1.15 1.90

Vesak Festival 1984 A271

Wooden Casket Paintings, Temple Godapitiya Rajamaha Vihara, Akuressa: Scenes from Daham Sonda Jathaka legend.

1984, Apr. 27   **Litho.**   **Perf. 14**
708 A271 35c multicolored   .20   .20
709 A271 60c multicolored   .80   .70
710 A271 5r multicolored   2.75 2.75
711 A271 10r multicolored   3.25 3.25
a. Souv. sheet of 4, #708-711, perf.
      13x13½   4.00 4.00
   Nos. 708-711 (4)   7.00 6.90

Lions Club Intl., District 306A — A272

1984, May 5   **Litho.**   **Perf. 14x14½**
712 A272 60c multicolored   2.10 1.50

Famous Men Type of 1981

Designs: No. 713, K. Balasingham, lawyer. No. 714, Mohamed Macan Markar (1879-1952), Muslim politician. No. 715, W. Arthur de Silva (d. 1942), industrialist. No. 716, Tissa Mahanayake Thero (1826-1907), Buddhist educator. No. 717, G.P. Wickremarachchi, medical pioneer.

1984, May 22   **Litho.**   **Perf. 12x12½**
713 A224 60c brown   .45   .65
714 A224 60c green   .45   .65
715 A224 60c orange red   .45   .65
716 A224 60c bister   .45   .65
717 A224 60c yellow green   .45   .65
   Nos. 713-717 (5)   2.25 3.25

Public Service Mutual Provident Assoc. Centenary A273

1984, June 16   **Perf. 13x13½**
718 A273 4.60r Emblem   1.00 1.50

Village Re-awakening Movement A274

1984, June 23   **Perf. 12x12½**
719 A274 60c "One Million Hous-
      es"   .60   .60

Asia-Pacific Broadcasting Union, 20th Anniv. — A275

1984, June 30   **Perf. 12½x12**
720 A275 7r Map   3.00 3.00

For surcharge see No. 776.

Cultural Pageant A276

Procession: a, Drummers, elephant. b, Torch bearers, 3 elephants (green or red masks). c, Torch bearers, 3 elephants (orange or yellow masks). d, Dancers. Continuous design.

1984, Aug. 11   **Litho.**   **Perf. 12½x12**
721   Strip of 4   7.00 7.00
a.-d. A276 4.60r any single 1.50 1.50
e.   Souvenir sheet of 4   7.00 7.00

Orchid Circle of Sri Lanka, 50th Anniversary A277

1984, Aug. 31   **Perf. 14**
722 A277 60c Vanda
      memoria   1.50 1.50
723 A277 4.60r Acanthephippi-
      um bicolor   3.00 3.00

724 A277   5r Vanda Tessel-
                  lata   2.00   2.00
725 A277 10r Anoectochillus
                  setaceus   6.50   6.50
  a. Souvenir sheet of 4, #722-
                  725   12.50 12.50
    Nos. 722-725 (4)   13.00 13.00

Wildlife Type of 1981

1982-89   **Litho.**   **Perf. 14**
728 A219 2.50r Felis viverrina   .30   .25
729 A219   3r Paradoxurus
                  zeylonensis   4.25 4.25
730 A219   4r Tragulus
                  meminna   .30   .30
730A A219   5r Felis rubiginosa
                  ('89)   .40   .30
    Nos. 728-730A (4)   5.25 5.10

No. 729 has brown inscriptions. See No.
928 for black inscriptions.
No. 728 is unwatermarked.
Issued: 2.50r, 6/1/83; 3r, 6/21/83; 4r,
11/16/82; 5r, 12/1/89.

No. 728 Surcharged in Brown

1985, Dec. 1 **Litho.** **Perf. 14**
731 A219 5.75r on 2.50r multi 4.00 1.75

The
Observer
Newspaper,
150th
Anniv.
A280

1984, Aug. 31 Litho. Perf. 13x13½
732 A280 4.60r Publisher, Colom-
                  bo   3.25 3.25

Natl. School
Games — A281

1984, Oct. 5   **Perf. 13½x13**
733 A281 60c blue, gray & blk 2.75 2.25

D. S. Senanayake (1884-1952), Prime
Minister — A282

1984, Oct. 20   **Perf. 14½x14**
734 A282 35c Irrigated field   .20   .20
735 A282 60c Statue   .20   .20
736 A282 4.60r Reservoir   .45   .45
737 A282   6r Parliament
                  House, Colom-
                  bo   .65   .65
    Nos. 734-737 (4)   1.50 1.50

World Food   Baari Arabic
Program — A284   College,
                      Weligama,
                     Cent. — A285

1984, Dec. 10 Litho. Perf. 13x13½
738 A284   7r Globe, Sri Lankans
                  working field   2.25 1.60

1984, Dec. 24   **Perf. 13x12½**
739 A285 4.60r dull bl grn & blk 2.00 2.00

Intl. Youth
Year — A286

World Religion
Day — A287

1985, Jan. 1   **Perf. 12½x13**
740 A286 4.60r multicolored   .80   .60
741 A286 20r multicolored   3.00 3.00

For surcharge see No. 790.

1985, Jan. 20   **Perf. 12**
Design: Emblems of World religions.
742 A287 4.60r multicolored   3.25 3.25

Royal College,   Mahapola
Colombo, 150th   Scholarship
Anniv. — A288   Program for
                     Development &
                      Education, 5th
                      Anniv. — A289

1985, Jan. 29   **Perf. 13x12½**
743 A288 60c College crest   .25   .30
744 A288   7r Campus   3.00 3.00

1985, Feb. 7   **Perf. 14**
745 A289 60c Diplomas, freight-
                  er, office build-
                  ings   1.40 1.40

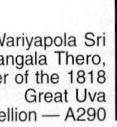

Wariyapola Sri
Sumangala Thero,
Leader of the 1818
Great Uva
Rebellion — A290

1985, Mar. 2   **Perf. 13x13½**
746 A290 60c brown & yellow   1.10 1.10

Victoria
Project
A291

Perf. 12½x12, 12x12½
1985, Apr. 12   **Litho.**
747 A291 60c Victoria Dam   1.00 1.00
748 A291   7r Dam, map, vert. 7.00 7.00

Vesak Festival   Natl.
1985 — A292   Heroes — A293

Designs: 35c, Frontispiece of the Buddhist
Annual golden jubilee issue. 60c, Women wor-
shiping at temple, Vesak Poya Holiday cent.
6r, Bauddha Mandiraya, Colombo. 9r, Buddhist flag cent.

1985, Apr. 26   **Perf. 13x12½**
749 A292 35c multicolored   .20   .20
750 A292 60c multicolored   .20   .20
751 A292   6r multicolored   .85   .85
752 A292   9r multicolored   1.75 1.75
  a. Souvenir sheet of 4, #749-752 7.00 7.00
    Nos. 749-752 (4)   3.00 3.00

1985, May 22   **Perf. 13x12½**
#753,753, Waskaduwe Sri Subhuthi Thero
(1835-1917), Pali scholar, philologist responsible for the Sinhala dictionary. #754, Rev. Fr.
Peter A. Pillai (1904-64), educational & social
reformer. #755, Dr. Senarath Paranavitane (c.
1900-72), epigraphist. #756, A.M. Wapche
Marikar (1829-1925), educational reformer,
architect.

Pale Yellow Orange and

753 A293 60c tan   .45   .45
754 A293 60c brt rose lilac   .45   .45
755 A293 60c brown   .45   .45
756 A293 60c emerald   .45   .45
    Nos. 753-756 (4)   1.80 1.80

Gam Udawa
— Yovur
Udanaya
Village
Reformation
Movement
A294

1985, June 23   **Perf. 13½x13**
757 A294 60c multicolored   1.50 1.50

Colombo Young
Poets Assoc., 50th
Anniv. — A295

1985, June 25   **Perf. 14**
758 A295 60c Emblem   1.75 1.75

Kothmale Project Commission — A296

1985, Aug. 24
759 A296 60c Dam, lake   1.00 1.00
760 A296   6r Hydro-electric
                  power station   5.00 5.00

A297

Child Survival: 35c, Mother breastfeeding.
60c, Infant, oral inoculant. 6r, Weighing toddler. 9r, Infant, intravenous inoculant.

1985, Sept. 1 Wmk. 385 Perf. 13½
761 A297 35c multicolored   .45   .20
762 A297 60c multicolored   .65   .40
763 A297   6r multicolored   2.50 2.75

764 A297   9r multicolored   3.25 3.50
  a. Souvenir sheet of 4, #761-764 7.25 7.25
    Nos. 761-764 (4)   6.85 6.85

1985, Sept. 2   Unwmk.   Perf. 14
765 A298   7r Womb, infant   5.25 5.25

10th Asian & Oceanic Congress of Obstetrics & Gynecology.

World
Tourism
Org., 10th
Anniv.
A299

1985, Sept. 27 Litho. Perf. 14
766 A299   1r Conch shell horn .50   .20
767 A299   6r Parliament complex 1.40 1.40
768 A299   7r Tea plantation   2.00 2.00
769 A299 10r Buddhist monas-
                  tery, Ruwanve-
                  liseya   2.50 2.50
  a. Souv. sheet of 4, #766-769, perf.
                  13½   8.50 8.50
    Nos. 766-769 (4)   6.40 6.10

Land
Development
Ordinance, 50th
Anniv. — A300

Sinhal
Translation,
Koran — A301

1985, Oct. 15   **Perf. 14x15**
770 A300 4.60r Deeds presenta-
                  tion   3.50 3.75

1985, Oct. 17 Wmk. 385 Perf. 13½
771 A301 60c violet & gold   2.75 2.50

Christmas — A302

1985, Nov. 5   **Perf. 12**
772 A302 60c Our Lady of Mata-
                  ra   .40   .20
773 A302   9r Our Lady of
                  Madhu   2.00 2.25
  a. Souvenir sheet of 2, #772-773 8.75 9.25

SAARC
1st
Summit,
Dec. 7-8
A303

1985, Dec. 8   **Perf. 14½x14**
774 A303 60c shown   5.00 5.00
775 A303 5.50r Flags on UN em-
                  blem   5.00 5.00

No. 720 Surcharged in Intense Blue

1986, Jan. 20   **Perf. 12½x12**
776 A275   1r on 7r Map   8.50 3.50

Viceroy Special Train A304

1986, Feb. 2   *Perf. 12½x13*
777 A304 1r multicolored   1.75 1.50
Colombo-Kandy line inauguration.

Students A305

1986, Feb. 14   *Perf. 14*
778 A305 75c multicolored   .80 .80
Mahapola Scholarship Program for development and education, 6th anniv.

Don Richard Wijewardene (1886-1950), Newspaper Publisher — A306

Welitara Gnanatillake Mahanayake Thero (1858-1941), Scientist — A307

1986, Feb. 23   *Perf. 14x15*
779 A306 75c sage grn & brn   .35 .40

1986, Feb. 26   *Wmk. 385*   *Perf. 13½*
780 A307 75c multicolored   1.00 1.10

No. 692 Surcharged

1986, Mar. 10   *Litho.*   *Perf. 14½*
780A A264 7r on 35c   6.50 1.50

Natl. Red Cross Society, 50th Anniv. A308

1986, Mar. 31   *Perf. 12½x13*
781 A308 75c multicolored   3.00 2.50

Halley's Comet A309

1986, Apr. 5   *Perf. 12½*
782 A309 50c Comet is not an omen   .20 .20
783 A309 75c Constellations   .20 .20
784 A309 6.50r Trajectory diagrams   .40 1.00
785 A309 8.50r Edmond Halley   .55 1.50
  a. Souvenir sheet of 4, #782-785, perf. 12½x13   8.00 9.75
    Nos. 782-785 (4)   1.35 2.90

Sinhalese and Tamil New Year — A310

Designs: 50c, Woman lighting lamp. 75c, Woman, holiday foods. 6.50r, Women celebrating around table. 8.50r, Food preparation, feast, anointment ritual.

1986, Apr. 10
786 A310 50c multicolored   .20 .20
787 A310 75c multicolored   .20 .20
788 A310 6.50r multicolored   .50 1.25
789 A310 8.50r multicolored   .80 1.50
  a. Souvenir sheet of 4, #786-789, perf. 13x12½   5.00 5.00
    Nos. 786-789 (4)   1.70 3.15

No. 740 Surcharged

1986, Apr. 29   *Perf. 12½x13*
790 A286 1r on 4.60r multi   6.50 3.25

Vesak Festival A311

Jathaka Story frescoes from the house Samudragiri Vihara, Mirissa, recounting the life of Siddhartha (583-463 B.C.): 50c, King Kurudhamma Jathakaya gives elephant to the brahman. 75c, Vasavarthi heaven. 5r, Sujatha's milk rice offering. 10d, Thapassu and Bhalluka's parched corn and honey offering.

1986, May 16
791 A311 50c multicolored   .20 .20
792 A311 75c multicolored   .20 .20
793 A311 5d multicolored   .60 1.50
794 A311 10d multicolored   .70 2.00
    Nos. 791-794 (4)   1.70 3.90

Natl. Heroes — A312

Natl. Cooperative Movement, 75th Anniv. — A313

#795, Kalukondayave Sri Prajnasekhara Mahanayaka Thero (1895-1977), theologian. #796, Brahmachari Walisinghe Harischandra (1876-1913), historian, social reformer. #797, Martin Wickramasinghe (1890-1970), author. #798, Ganapathipillai Gangaser Ponnambalam (1901-72), diplomat. #799, Aboobucker Mohammed Abdul Azeez (1911-73), scholar.

1986, May 22   *Perf. 13x12½*
795 A312 75c multicolored   .20 .45
796 A312 75c multicolored   .20 .45
797 A312 75c multicolored   .20 .45
798 A312 75c multicolored   .20 .45
799 A312 75c multicolored   .20 .45
    Nos. 795-799 (5)   1.00 2.25

1986, June 23
800 A313 1r multicolored   1.75 2.00

Gam Udawa, Intl. Year of Housing A314

1986, June 23   *Perf. 13½x13*
801 A314 75c multicolored   2.10 2.10

Arthur V. Dias — A315

1986, July 31   *Perf. 14x15*
802 A315 1r multicolored   2.25 2.50

World Wildlife Fund A316

Elephants: a, Adult with tusks. b, Adult, calf. c, Adult. d, Family in river.

1986, Aug. 5   *Perf. 15x14*
803   Strip of 4   72.50 40.00
  a.-d. A316 5r any single   16.00 10.00

2nd Indo-Pacific Congress on Legal Medicine and Forensic Sciences — A317

1986, Aug. 14   *Perf. 13½x13*
804 A317 8.50r multicolored   4.00 4.00

Submarine Cable — A318

1986, Sept. 8   *Perf. 13½x14*
805 A318 5.75r Handset, map   7.25 4.75
South-East Asia, Middle East, Western Europe Submarine Cable System.

Dag Hammarskjold Award — A320

Second Natl. School Games, Sept. 22-27 — A321

1986, Sept. 20   *Litho.*   *Perf. 13x12½*
808 A320 2r multicolored   1.90 1.50

1986, Sept. 22   *Perf. 12*
809 A321 1r multicolored   4.25 2.40

Natl. Surveyor's Institute, 60th Anniv. — A322

1986, Sept. 27   *Perf. 13½x13*
810 A322 75c multicolored   1.00 1.10

Ananda College, Cent. A323

College crest and: 75c, College. 5r, Athletic field. 5.75r, Founders Migettuwatte Gunananda, Hikkaduwe Sumangala and Col. H.S. Olcott, Buddhist flag and College, 1886, 1986. 6r, Crest on flag.

1986, Nov. 1   *Perf. 12*
811 A323 75c multicolored   .20 .20
812 A323 5r multicolored   .50 .60
813 A323 5.75r multicolored   .55 .60
814 A323 6r multicolored   .65 .75
    Nos. 811-814 (4)   1.90 2.15

Wildlife Conservation — A324

1986, Nov. 11
815 A324 35c Mangrove habitat   1.25 1.25
816 A324 50c Rhizophora apiculata   1.40 1.40
817 A324 75c Germinating flower   1.50 1.50
818 A324 6r Fiddler crab   11.00 11.00
    Nos. 815-818 (4)   15.15 15.15
Preservation of mangrove habitats.
For surcharges on Nos. 815 and 818, see Nos. 1513 and 1516.

Intl. Year of Shelter for the Homeless A325

1987, Jan. 1   *Litho.*   *Perf. 13x13½*
819 A325 75c multicolored   3.00 .95

A.I. Thero, 19th
Cent. Theologian
A326

Proctor John De
Silva (b. 1854),
Lawyer and
Playwright
A327

1987, Jan. 29   *Perf. 12*
820 A326 5.75r multicolored   4.25 1.25

1987, Jan. 31
821 A327 5.75r multicolored   1.10 1.10

Mahapola Educational Plan, 7th
Anniv. — A328

1987, Feb. 6
822 A328 75c multicolored   1.25 1.25

Dr. R.L. Brohier,
Historian — A329

1987, Feb. 14
823 A329 5.75r multicolored   3.75 1.75

Sri Lanka
Tire
Corp.,
25th
Anniv.
A330

1987, Mar. 23   *Perf. 14*
824 A330 5.75r multicolored   .80 .80

Sri Lanka
Medical
Assoc.,
Cent.
A331

1987, Mar. 24   *Perf. 13x13½*
825 A331 5.75r multicolored   3.25 3.50

Farmers' Pension
and Social
Security
Plan — A332

AGRO
MAHAWELI '87
Agricultural
Exposition
A333

1987, Mar. 29   *Perf. 14*
826 A332 75c multicolored   1.60 1.60

1987, Apr. 2   *Perf. 12*
827 A333 75c multicolored   .60 .60

Child Immunization Program — A334

1987, Apr. 7   *Perf. 13½*
828 A334 1r multicolored   4.00 1.40

World Health Day.

Sinhalese and
Tamil New
Year — A335

1987, Apr. 9   *Perf. 12*
829 A335 75c Three girls, swing   .20 .20
830 A335 5r Lamp, women   .80 .80

Vesak
Festival
Lanterns
A336

1987, May 4   *Perf. 12*
831 A336 50c Lotus   .20 .20
832 A336 75c Octagonal   .20 .20
833 A336 5r Star   .45 .45
834 A336 10r Gok   .65 .65
   a. Souvenir sheet of 4, #831-834   1.75 1.75
     Nos. 831-834 (4)   1.50 1.50

Natl. Olympic Committee, 50th
Anniv. — A337

1987, May 8   *Perf. 13½*
835 A337 10r multicolored   3.75 1.60

Birds
A338

1987, May 18   *Perf. 14*
836 A338 50c Layard's parakeet   .70 .20
837 A338 1r Legge's
     flowerpecker   1.10 .20
838 A338 5r Sri Lanka white-
     headed starling   1.60 1.75
839 A338 10r Sri Lanka rufous
     babbler   2.10 2.25
   a. Souvenir sheet of 4, #836-839   9.00 9.00
     Nos. 836-839 (4)   5.50 4.40

#837 exists dated "1989." #839 exists dated
"1990."

Natl.
Heroes — A339

#840, Heenatiyana Sri Dhammaloka Thero,
20th cent. theologian. #841, P. de S.
Kularatne, educator. #842, M.C. Abdul
Rahuman, politician.

1987, May 22   *Perf. 12*
840 A339 75c multicolored   .60 .40
841 A339 75c multicolored   .60 .40
842 A339 75c multicolored   .60 .40
     Nos. 840-842 (3)   1.80 1.20

Gam
Udawa
A340

1987, June 23
843 A340 75c multicolored   .50 .50

Village reformation movement.

Natl.
Forestry
Agency,
Cent.
A341

1987, June 25
844 A341 75c Mesua nagassari-
     um   .30 .30
845 A341 5r Elephants in forest   2.00 2.00

Founder
H.S. Olcott
and
College
A342

1987, June 30
846 A342 75c multicolored   3.50 .55

Dharmaraja College, cent.

No. 528 Redrawn with Denomination
in Upper Right Corner
1987, July 1 Photo.   *Perf. 13x13½*
     Size: 20x24mm
847 A189 75c green & gold   .40 .20

Youth
Services
Emblem
A343

1987, July 15 Litho.   *Perf. 12*
848 A343 75c multicolored   .40 .40

Natl. Youth Services Act, 20th anniv.

Mahaweli
Games — A344

Ceylon Bible
Society, 175th
Anniv. — A345

1987, Sept. 5 Litho.   *Perf. 12*
849 A344 75c multicolored   5.00 2.50

1987, Oct. 2
850 A345 5.75r multicolored   .80 .80

Kandy Friend-in-Need Society, 150th
Anniv. — A346

1987, Nov. 4   *Perf. 13½x13*
851 A346 75c multicolored   .40 .40

Christmas
1987 — A347

Sir Ernest de Silva
(1887-1957),
Banker,
Philatelist — A348

1987, Nov. 25 Litho.   *Perf. 12*
852 A347 75c Mother and Child   .20 .20
853 A347 10r Infant, star, dove   .50 .50
   a. Souvenir sheet of 2, #852-853   1.50 1.50

1987, Nov. 25   *Perf. 13x13½*
854 A348 75c multicolored   .40 .40

1st Convocation
Ceremony at
Buddhist and Pali
University — A349

Missionary Work of Fr. Joseph Vaz (1651-1711), 300th Anniv. — A350

1987, Dec. 14 *Perf. 12*
855 A349 75c yel, lake & org yel .40 .40

1987, Dec. 15
856 A350 75c multicolored .40 .40

Buddhist Publication Soc., Kandy, 30th Anniv. — A351

Design: Wheel of Life, dagaba (temple cupola) and Bo (Tree of Life) leaf.

1988, Jan. 1 *Litho.* *Perf. 12*
857 A351 75c multicolored .50 .50

Mahapola Dharmayatra, 5th Anniv. A352

1988, Jan. 4 *Perf. 13½x13*
858 A352 75c multicolored .50 .50

Ceylon Arts Soc., Cent. — A353

1988, Jan. 8 *Perf. 12*
859 A353 75c multicolored 1.00 .90

Opening of the Natl. Youth Center, Maharagama A354

1988, Jan. 31 *Perf. 13½x13*
860 A354 1r multicolored 5.50 .80

Natl. Independence, 40th Anniv. — A355

Mahapola Movement, 8th Anniv. — A356

1988, Feb. 4 *Perf. 12*
861 A355 75c shown .20 .20
862 A355 8.50r Heraldic lion, "40" 1.10 1.10

1988, Feb. 11
863 A356 75c Youth Education Services .35 .35

Transportation Board, 30th Anniv. — A357

1988, Feb. 19
864 A357 5.75r multicolored .80 .80

Weligama Sri Sumangala Maha Nayake Thero (1825-1905), Buddhist Monk, Sanskrit Scholar — A358

1988, Mar. 13
865 A358 75c multicolored .40 .40

Artillery Regiment, Cent. A359

1988, Apr. 20
866 A359 5.75r multicolored 4.25 1.25

Chevalier I.X. Pereira (1888-1951), Politician — A360

1988, Apr. 26 *Litho.* *Perf. 12*
867 A360 5.75r multicolored .50 .50

Vesak Festival A361

Paintings in Suriyagoda Sri Narendraramaya Viharaya temple, Kandy District: 50c, Buddha inviting deities and brahmas to be born into the world as Buddhists. 75c, Buddha walking seven steps on seven lotus flowers, followers paying homage.

1988, May 13 *Perf. 12½x12*
868 A361 50c multicolored .40 .40
869 A361 75c multicolored .40 .40
a. Souvenir sheet of 2, #868-869 2.10 2.10

Natl. Heroes — A362

Designs: No. 870, Rev.-Father Ferdinand Bonnel (1873-1945), Jesuit priest who founded St. Michael's College, Batticaloa. No. 871, Sir Razik Fareed (1893-1984), political and social reformer. No. 872, W.F. Gunawardhana (b. 1861), founder of the Oriental Studies Soc. No. 873, Edward Alexander Nugawela (1898-1972), politician. No. 874, Sir Edwin Arthur Lewis Wijeyewardene (b. 1887), first Ceylonese chief justice, attorney general.

1988, May 22 *Perf. 12x12½*
870 A362 75c multicolored .25 .25
871 A362 75c multicolored .25 .25
872 A362 75c multicolored .25 .25
873 A362 75c multicolored .25 .25
874 A362 75c multicolored .25 .25
Nos. 870-874 (5) 1.25 1.25

Gam Udawa, 10th Anniv. A363

1988, June 23 *Litho.* *Perf. 12*
875 A363 75c multicolored .60 .30
Village reformation movement.

Maliyadeva College, Cent. — A364

1988, June 30 *Perf. 13½x13*
876 A364 75c multicolored .60 .30

Bird Type of 1983
1988, Sept. 28 *Litho.* *Perf. 14½*
877 A264 7r like No. 692 .65 .65

Mohamed J.M. Lafir (1929-1980), World Amateur Billiards Champion — A365

1988, July 5 *Litho.* *Perf. 12½x12*
878 A365 5.75r multicolored .60 .60

Australia Bicentennial — A366

1988, July 19 *Litho.* *Perf. 12*
879 A366 8.50r multicolored 1.00 .70

A367

A368

1988, Aug. 11 *Perf. 12x12½*
880 A367 75c multicolored .50 .30
Gunaratna Maha Nayake Thero (1752-1832), Buddhist and Sinhalese language scholar.

1988, Sept. 3 *Perf. 12*
881 A368 75c multicolored .50 .30
Mahaweli games.

1988 Summer Olympics, Seoul — A369

WHO, 40th Anniv. — A370

1988, Sept. 6 *Perf. 12x12½*
882 A369 75c Running .20 .20
883 A369 1r Swimming .20 .20
884 A369 5.75r Boxing .55 .55
885 A369 8.50r Handshake, map, emblems .95 .95
a. Souvenir sheet of 4, #882-885 2.25 2.25
Nos. 882-885 (4) 1.90 1.90

1988, Sept. 12 *Perf. 12*
886 A370 75c multicolored .50 .50

3rd Natl. School Games, Sept. 20-25 A371

1988, Sept. 20
887 A371 1r multicolored 4.25 .60

Mahatma Gandhi — A372

1988, Oct. 2   *Perf. 12*
888 A372 75c multicolored   2.10   .65

Transportation and Communication Decade, 1978-88 — A373

Modes of transportation and: 75c, Globe. 5.75r, Communication tower.

1988, Oct. 24   Litho.   *Perf. 12½x12*
889 A373   75c multicolored   .75   .20
890 A373   5.75r multicolored   4.00 2.40

For surcharge, see No. 1580.

Randenigala Project — A374

1988, Oct. 31   *Perf. 12*
891 A374   75c Woman, dam,
       power station   .30   .30
892 A374   5.75r Hydrelectric dam   .95   .95

Some copies were distributed at the time the set was originally planned to be issued in 1986.

A375

Christmas — A376

1988, Nov. 17   Litho.   *Perf. 13½*
893 A375 75c multicolored   .50   .50

Opening of Gramodaya Folk Art Center.

1988, Nov. 25   *Perf. 12x12½*
894 A376   75c shown   .20   .20
895 A376   8.50r Shepherds see
       star   1.00 1.00
  a.   Souvenir sheet of 2, #894-895   3.00 3.00

A377

Waterfalls — A378

1988, Dec. 28   *Perf. 12*
896 A377 75c multicolored   .50   .50

E.W. Adikaram (1905-85), educator.

1989, Aug. 11   Litho.   *Perf. 12*
897 A378   75c Dunhinda   .20   .20
898 A378   1r Rawana   .20   .20
899 A378   5.75r Laxapana   1.10 1.10
900 A378   8.50r Diyaluma   1.50 1.50
      Nos. 897-900 (4)   3.00 3.00

Free Distribution of School Text Books, 10th Anniv. A379

1989, Jan. 23   Litho.   *Perf. 13½x13*
901 A379 75c multicolored   .40   .40

Poets — A380

1989, Jan. 27   *Perf. 13*
902 A380   75c Wimalaratne
       Kumaragama   .25   .25
903 A380   75c G.H. Perera   .25   .25
904 A380   75c Sagara Palan-
       suriya   .25   .25
905 A380   75c P.B. Alwis Perera   .25   .25
      Nos. 902-905 (4)   1.00 1.00

Mahapola Educational Plan, 8th Anniv. — A381

1989, Feb.   *Perf. 13½*
906 A381 75c multicolored   .40   .20

Chamber of Commerce, 150th Anniv. — A382

1989, Mar. 25   Litho.   *Perf. 12*
907 A382 75c multicolored   .40   .20

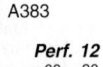

AGRO Mahaweli A383

1989, Sept. 2   Litho.   *Perf. 12*
908 A383 75c multicolored   .60   .30

Famous Men A384

1989, May 22
909 A384   75c Simon Casie Chitty   .35   .35
910 A384   75c Parawahera Sri
       Vajiragnana
       Thero   .35   .35
911 A384   75c Fr. Maurice Le
       Goc   .35   .35
912 A384   75c Hemapala
       Munidasa   .35   .35
913 A384   75c Ananda
       Samarakoon   .35   .35
      Nos. 909-913 (5)   1.75 1.75

Nos. 910-913 vert.

Hartley College, 150th Anniv. (in 1988) — A385

1989, June 5
914 A385 75c multicolored   .40   .20

Vesak Festival A386

Various paintings in Medawala Viharaya, Harispattuwa.

1989, May 15   Litho.   *Perf. 12½x12*
915 A386   50c multicolored   .20   .20
916 A386   75c multicolored   .25   .20
917 A386   5r multicolored   .55   .40
918 A386   5.75r multicolored   .65   .50
  a.   Souvenir sheet of 4, #915-918   2.10 2.10
      Nos. 915-918 (4)   1.65 1.30

For surcharge see No. 953A.

Pres. Premadasa's Declaration Establishing the Ministry of Buddha Sasana — A387

1989, June 18   Litho.   *Perf. 12½x12*
919 A387 75c multicolored   .40   .40

Gam Udawa, 11th Anniv. A388

1989, June 23
920 A388 75c multicolored   .50   .40

Village reformation movement.

French Revolution, Bicent. A389

1989, Aug. 26   Litho.   *Perf. 13½x13*
921 A389 8.50r rose & deep blue 1.50 1.50

Bank of Ceylon, 50th Anniv. A390

1989, Aug. 31
922 A390   75c Old, new head-
       quarters   .20   .20
923 A390   5r Emblem, flowers   .80   .65

Jana Saviya Grants A391

1989, June 23   Litho.   *Perf. 12x11½*
924 A391 75c multicolored   .70   .70

Development program to eliminate poverty and improve the standard of living through education and by providing food, health care, shelter and clothing.
See No. 953. For surcharge see No. 955.

Baptist Mission, 177th Anniv. A392

1989, Aug. 19   *Perf. 12½x12*
925 A392 5.75r James Chater,
       church, 1812   1.00 1.00

For surcharge, see No. 1405.

State Literary Festival — A393

Wilhelm Geiger — A394

1989, Sept. 22   *Perf. 12x11½*
926 A393 75c multicolored   .50 .40

1989, Sept. 30   *Perf. 13x13½*
927 A394 75c multicolored   .50 .40

Wilhelm Geiger (1856-1943), German philologist who studied Sinhalese.

Wildlife Type of 1981
1989, Oct. 11   *Perf. 14*
928 A219 3r like No. 595   4.00 .40

No. 928 has black inscriptions and is dated "1989." See No. 729 for brown inscriptions.

Famous Lawyers — A395

Sir Cyril de Zoysa — A396

1989, Oct. 16   *Perf. 12x11½*
929 A395 75c H.V. Perera (1890-1969)   .25 .25
930 A395 75c Sir Ivor Jennings (1903-1965)   .25 .25

1989, Oct. 26   *Perf. 13x13½*
931 A396 75c multicolored   .50 .40

Sir Cyril de Zoysa (1896-1978), key figure in the Buddhist cultural reformation.

Asia-Pacific Telecommunity, 10th Anniv. — A397

1989, Nov. 1   *Perf. 12x12½*
932 A397 5.75r multicolored   .90 .60

For surcharge, see No. 1574.

Sri Sucharitha Viyaparaya Oratory Children's Soc., 50th Anniv. A398

1989, Nov. 9   *Perf. 13*
933 A398 75c multicolored   .60 .60

1st Moon Landing, 20th Anniv. — A399

Christmas — A400

1989, Nov. 10   *Perf. 12x12½*
934 A399 75c Apollo 11 liftoff, crew   .20 .20
935 A399 1r Astronaut descending ladder   .25 .20
936 A399 2r Astronaut on lunar surface   .45 .40
937 A399 5.75r Lunar surface, view of Earth   1.25 .70
   a. Souvenir sheet of 4, #934-937   3.00 3.00
   Nos. 934-937 (4)   2.15 1.50

For No. 937 surcharged, see No. 1515.

1989, Nov. 21   *Perf. 13½*
938 A400 75c Adoration of the Shepherds   .20 .20
939 A400 8.50r Adoration of the Magi   .80 .80
   a. Souvenir sheet of 2, #938-939   2.10 2.10

Devananda Nayake Thero — A401

1989, Nov. 25   *Perf. 12x11½*
940 A401 75c multicolored   .50 .50

Devananda Nayake Thero (1921-1983), religious scholar, educator, reformer.

Rev. William Ault, College and Crest A402

1989, Nov. 29   *Perf. 11½x12*
941 A402 75c multicolored   .50 .40

Batticaloa Methodist Central College, 175th anniv.

Nuwara Eliya Golf Club, Cent. A403

1989, Dec. 8   *Perf. 14x13½*
942 A403 75c shown   4.00 .50
943 A403 8.50r Course, golf house   11.00 9.50

Raja — A404

1989, Dec. 12   *Perf. 13x13½*
944 A404 75c multicolored   7.25 1.25

Raja (1913-1988), the royal tusker of the Sri Dalada Maligawa that carried the relic casket in the Kandy Esala Procession.

Gampaha Wickamarachchi Ayurveda Medical College, 60th Anniv. — A405

1989, Dec. 14   *Perf. 13½x13*
945 A405 75c Founder, institute   .70 .40

Udunuwara Sri Sarananda Mahanayake Thero (1867-1947), Educator — A406

1989, Dec. 20   *Perf. 12x12½*
946 A406 75c multicolored   .50 .35

Railway Dept., 125th Anniv. — A407

1989, Dec. 27   *Perf. 11½x12, 13 (3r)*
947 A407 75c Train, viaduct   .90 .30
948 A407 2r Train, light signal, Maradana Station   2.10 .50
949 A407 3r Steam locomotive, semaphore signal   2.10 .85
950 A407 7r 1st train in Sri Lanka   4.25 1.75
   Nos. 947-950 (4)   9.35 3.40

A408

A409

1989, Dec. 28   *Perf. 13x13½*
951 A408 75c multicolored   2.00 .35

Thomas Cooray (1901-88), 1st native Sri Lankan Cardinal.

1990, Jan. 14   *Perf. 12x12½*
952 A409 1r multicolored   3.25 .35

Justin Wijayawardena (1904-82), educator, politician.

Jana Saviya Grants Type of 1989
1990, Jan. 31   *Litho.*   *Perf. 12x11½*
953 A391 1r multicolored   .40 .40

No. 918 Surcharged

.25

≡

1990, Feb. 16   *Litho.*   *Perf. 12½x12*
953A A386 25c on 5.75r multi   1.40 .30

Induruwe Uttarananda Mahanayake Thero — A411

1990, Mar. 15   *Litho.*   *Perf. 12*
954 A411 1r multicolored   2.00 1.40

No. 924 Surcharged   **1.00**   ≡

1990, Mar. 22   *Litho.*   *Perf. 12x11½*
955 A391 1r on 75c multi   3.00 1.75

Silver Jubilee of Laksala A413

Traditional handicrafts.

1990, Apr. 2   *Litho.*   *Perf. 12*
956 A413 1r Drums   .40 .20
957 A413 2r Silverware   .55 .20
958 A413 3r Lacquerware   .90 .30
959 A413 8r Dumbara mats   2.40 1.90
   Nos. 956-959 (4)   4.25 2.60

Vesak Festival A414

Various paintings in Wewurukannala Buduraja Maha Viharaya.

1990, May 2   *Perf. 12½x12*
960 A414 75c multicolored   .20 .20
961 A414 1r multicolored   .20 .20
962 A414 2r multicolored   .30 .30

963	A414	8r multicolored	1.10	1.10
a.		Souvenir sheet of 4, #960-963	2.25	2.25
		Nos. 960-963 (4)	1.80	1.80

Famous
Men — A416

A415

1990, May 22   **Perf. 12**
964 A415 1r Rev. T.M.F. Long   .60   .35

Size: 25x39mm
Perf. 12x12½

965	A416	1r D.P.A. Wijewardene	.60	.35
966	A416	1r L.T.P. Manjusri	.60	.35
967	A416	1r M.D. Ratnasuriya	.60	.35
		Nos. 964-967 (4)	2.40	1.40

Gam
Udawa
Program,
12th
Anniv.
A417

1990, June 23   **Perf. 12½x12**
968 A417 1r multicolored   2.50   .60

Dept. of
Archaeology,
Cent. — A418

1r, Gold reliquary from Delivala Temple, c. 200 B.C. 2r, Statuette of Ganesha (the Elephant God) from Polonnaruwa. 3r, Terrace of the Bodhi-tree at Isurumuni Vihara. 8r, Stone seat with inscription of King Nissankamalle, 12th cent. A.D.

1990, July 7   **Perf. 12**

969	A418	1r black & orange	.35	.20
970	A418	2r black & gray	.65	.20
971	A418	3r black, yel grn & gold	.90	.40
972	A418	8r black & gold	2.25	1.50
		Nos. 969-972 (4)	4.15	2.30

Sri Lanka
Tennis
Assoc.,
75th Anniv.
A419

1990, Aug. 14   **Perf. 13½**

973	A419	1r Player ready to volley	1.00	1.00
974	A419	1r Player receiving volley	1.00	1.00
a.		Pair, #973-974	2.25	2.25
975	A419	8r Men players	3.50	3.50
976	A419	8r Women players	3.50	3.50
a.		Pair, #975-976	7.75	7.75
		Nos. 973-976 (4)	9.00	9.00

Fish — A420

1990, Sept. 14   **Perf. 11½**

977	A420	25c Spotted loach	.30	.30
978	A420	2r Ornate paradise fish	.45	.45
979	A420	8r Mountain labeo	1.25	1.25
980	A420	20r Cherry barb	2.50	2.50
a.		Souvenir sheet of 4, #977-980	5.50	5.50
		Nos. 977-980 (4)	4.50	4.50

For No. 979 surcharged, see No. 1303A.

A421

1990, Dec. 26   **Perf. 12**

981	A421	1r Letter box, 1904	.85	.60
982	A421	2r Mail runner, 1815	1.60	.85
983	A421	5r Mail coach, 1832	3.25	2.75
984	A421	10r Nuwara-Eliya Post Office, 1894	4.25	4.25
		Nos. 981-984 (4)	9.95	8.45

Sri Lanka Postal Service, 175th anniv.

A422

1990, Oct. 28   **Litho.**   **Perf. 12**
985 A422 1r multicolored   6.25   1.75

Rukmani Devi (1923-78), actress.

Christmas
A423

1990, Nov. 28   **Perf. 13**

986	A423	1r Mary, Joseph at inn	.75	.45
987	A423	10r Adoration of the Magi	5.25	4.75
a.		Souv. sheet of 2, #986-987, perf. 12	7.00	7.00

World
AIDS Day
A424

1990, Nov. 30

988	A424	1r multicolored	1.25	.20
989	A424	8r AIDS Virus	5.25	3.50

A425

A426

1990, Dec. 8   **Perf. 12**
990 A425 1r multicolored   3.50   1.60

Dharmapala College, 50th anniv.

1990, Dec. 14   **Litho.**   **Perf. 12**
991 A426 1r olive green & brown   4.25   1.50

Peri Sunderam (b. 1890), political & social reformer.

Ceylon Institute
of Chemistry,
50th
anniv. — A427

1991, Jan. 25   **Litho.**   **Perf. 12**
992 A427 1r multicolored   4.00   1.50

Vesak
Festival
A428

Various scenes from Buddha's life.

1991, May 17   **Litho.**   **Perf. 12**

993	A428	75c multicolored	.45	.20
994	A428	1r multicolored	.45	.20
995	A428	2r multicolored	.85	.40
996	A428	11r multicolored	3.75	3.25
a.		Souvenir sheet of 4, #993-996	6.00	6.00
		Nos. 993-996 (4)	5.50	4.05

A429

A430

1991, May 31   **Perf. 12**
997 A429 1r multicolored   2.00   1.10

Mahabodhi Society, cent.

1991, May 22   **Litho.**   **Perf. 12x12½**

Famous men.

998	A430	1r Narada Thero	.75	.65
999	A430	1r Sir Muttu Coomaraswamy	.75	.65
1000	A430	1r Dr. Andreas Nell	.75	.65
1001	A430	1r W.A. Silva	.75	.65
		Nos. 998-1001 (4)	3.00	2.60

Gam
Udawa,
13th
Anniv.
A431

1991, June 23   **Litho.**   **Perf. 12½**
1002 A431 1r multicolored   3.25   .90

Henpitagedera
Gnanaseeha
Nayake Thero
(1909-1981),
Religious
Leader — A432

1991, Aug. 1
1003 A432 1r multicolored   2.50   .95

Colombo
Plan, 40th
Anniv.
A433

1991, July 1   **Litho.**   **Perf. 12**
1004 A433 1r multicolored   3.75   1.40

Survey
Dept.,
190th
Anniv.
A434

1991, Aug. 2   **Perf. 12½**
1005 A434 1r multicolored   3.25   1.25

Police
Service,
125th
Anniv.
A435

1991, Sept. 3   **Litho.**   **Perf. 12½**
1006 A435 1r multicolored   1.75   .65

6th
SAARC
Summit
A436

1991, Dec. 21   **Litho.**   **Perf. 12½**

1007	A436	1r shown	.20	.20
1008	A436	8r Flags encircling bldg.	.70	.60

Kingswood College, Cent. — A437

1991, Oct. 26   **Perf. 12½x12**
1009 A437 1r multicolored   1.00 .50

Christmas — A439

1991, Nov. 19   Litho.   Perf. 12½
1014 A439 1r The Annunciation   .40 .20
1015 A439 10r Nativity scene   1.50 1.50
   a. Sheet of 2, #1014-1015   2.50 2.50

A440

1991, Nov. 23

Telecommunications: 1r, Early telephone network. 2r, Switchboard operations. 8r, Satellite transmitters, cable network. 10r, Telephone, fiber optic cable, computer, cordless telephone, FAX machine.

1016 A440 1r multicolored   .25 .20
1017 A440 2r multicolored   .30 .20
1018 A440 8r multicolored   .90 .90
1019 A440 10r multicolored   .90 .90
   Nos. 1016-1019 (4)   2.35 2.20

5th South Asian Federation Games A441

1991, Dec. 22   **Perf. 14**
1020 A441 1r Mascot   .30 .20
1021 A441 2r Emblem   .60 .25
1022 A441 4r Stadium, Colombo   1.10 1.10
1023 A441 11r Globe and flags   2.50 2.75
   Nos. 1020-1023 (4)   4.50 4.30

Year of Exports A442

1992, Jan. 13   Litho.   Perf. 11½x12
1024 A442 1r multicolored   2.25 .95

Mahinda College, Cent. A443

1992, Mar. 2   Litho.   Perf. 11½x12
1025 A443 1r multicolored   .40 .40

General Ranjan Wijeratne (1931-1991) A444

1992, Mar. 2   Litho.   Perf. 12x12½
1026 A444 1r multicolored   .35 .20

Tea Production, 125th Anniv. A445

Field of tea and: 1r, Tea picker. 2r, Family, cup and glass of tea. 5r, Package of tea. 10r, James Taylor.

1992, Feb. 12   **Perf. 13½**
1027 A445 1r multicolored   .55 .20
1028 A445 2r multicolored   1.10 .25
1029 A445 5r multicolored   2.75 2.40
1030 A445 10r multicolored   3.75 3.25
   Nos. 1027-1030 (4)   8.15 6.10

Newstead College, 175th Anniv. (in 1991) A446

1992, Mar. 13   Litho.   Perf. 11½x12
1031 A446 1r multicolored   .40 .40
Dated 1991.

Mahapola Scholarship Fund, 11th Anniv. — A447

1992, Mar. 30   **Perf. 12**
1032 A447 1r multicolored   .40 .40

Vesak Festival A448

Mural paintings from Kottimbulwala Rajamaha Vihara: 75c, Dukula and Parika retiring to forest. 1r, Sama and parents living in forest. 8r, Sama directing blind parents to hermitage. 11r, Sama's parents approach wounded son.

1992, May 5   Litho.   Perf. 11½x12
1033 A448 75c multicolored   .20 .20
1034 A448 1r multicolored   .30 .20
1035 A448 8r multicolored   1.50 1.50
1036 A448 11r multicolored   2.00 2.00
   a. Souvenir sheet, #1033-1036   4.50 4.50
   Nos. 1033-1036 (4)   4.00 3.90

A449

A450

National Heroes: No. 1037, Wadeebhasinha Dewamottawe Amarawansa Thero. No. 1038, R. A. Mirando. No. 1039, Gate Mudaliyar N. Canaganayagam. No. 1040, I.L.M. Abdul Azeez.

1992, May 22   **Perf. 14**
1037 A449 1r multicolored   .20 .20
1038 A449 1r multicolored   .20 .20
1039 A449 1r multicolored   .20 .20
1040 A449 1r multicolored   .20 .20
   Nos. 1037-1040 (4)   .80 .80

1992, June 14   Litho.   Perf. 12x12½
1041 A450 1r multicolored   .40 .40
Introduction of Buddhism on Sri Lanka by Anubudu Mihindu Jayanthi, 2300th anniv.

Gam Udawa, 14th Anniv. A451

1992, June 23   **Perf. 12**
1042 A451 1r multicolored   .40 .40

Postal Excellence Service Awards A452

Designs: 1r, Award presentation, postal work. 10r, Award of excellence medals, No. 1043 canceled on envelope.

1992, July 11   Litho.   Perf. 14
1043 A452 1r multicolored   .50 .50
1044 A452 10r multicolored   3.75 3.75

A453

A454

Masks of Sri Lanka.

1992, Aug. 19   Litho.   Perf. 13
1045 A453 1r Narilata   .35 .20
1046 A453 2r Mudali   .45 .35
1047 A453 5r Queen   .90 .65
1048 A453 10r King   1.50 1.50
   a. Souvenir sheet, #1045-1048   3.50 3.50
   Nos. 1045-1048 (4)   3.20 2.70

1992, Sept. 15   Litho.   Perf. 14
1049 A454 1r Running   .30 .20
1050 A454 11r Rifle shooting 2.25 2.25
1051 A454 13r Swimming   2.75 2.75
1052 A454 15r Weight lifting 3.00 3.00
   a. Souvenir sheet, #1049-1052 10.00 10.00
   Nos. 1049-1052 (4)   8.30 8.20
1992 Summer Olympics, Barcelona.

Cricket in Sri Lanka, 160th Anniv. A455

1992, Sept. 8   Litho.   Perf. 13
1053 A455 5r multicolored   4.25 3.00

Vijaya Kumaratunga, Entertainer and Political Leader, Birth Anniv. — A456

1992, Oct. 9
1054 A456 1r multicolored   .50 .45

Al-Bahjathul Ibraheemiyyah Arabic College, Cent. — A457

1992, Oct. 24   **Perf. 12**
1055 A457 1r multicolored   .50 .45

A458

1992, Oct. 25   Litho.   Perf. 12x11½
1056 A458 1r multicolored   1.50 .60
Dutch Reformed Church in Sri Lanka, 350th anniv.

Christmas A459

1992, Nov. 17   Litho.   Perf. 12x11½
1057 A459 1r Holy Family   .40 .20
1058 A459 9r Church, family 2.10 2.10
   a. Souvenir sheet, #1057-1058   2.50 2.50

Discovery of America, 500th Anniv. A460

Designs: 1r, Ships at sea, Aug. 1492. 11r, First landing in the Americas, Oct. 1492. 13r, Santa Maria aground, Dec. 1492. 15r, Return to Spain, Apr. 1493.

1992, Dec. 1   **Perf. 14**
1059	A460	1r multicolored	.75 .30
1060	A460	11r multicolored	1.75 1.75
1061	A460	13r multicolored	2.50 2.50
1062	A460	15r multicolored	2.50 2.50
a.		Souvenir sheet, #1059-1062	7.50 7.50
		Nos. 1059-1062 (4)	7.50 7.05

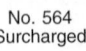

No. 564 Surcharged

1992, Dec. 1   **Litho.**   **Perf. 14**
1062B A206 2r on 10c multi   6.00 .75

Dambagasare Sri Sumedhankara Maha Nayake Thero (1892-1984), Buddhist Monk — A461

1992, Dec. 10   **Litho.**   **Perf. 12**
1063 A461 1r multicolored   .40 .40

University Education in Sri Lanka A462

1992, Dec. 12   **Litho.**   **Perf. 12**
1064 A462 1r multicolored   .40 .40
No. 1064 was not available until Dec. 1993.

University of Colombo, 50th Anniv. (in 1992) A463

1993, Mar. 23   **Litho.**   **Perf. 13**
1065 A463 1r multicolored   1.10 .35

Zahira College, Cent. A464

1993, Apr. 7
1066 A464 1r multicolored   1.25 .40

Vesak Festival — A465

Designs based on verses from the Dhammapada (sermons of Buddha): 75c, Magandiya being presented to Buddha. 1r, Kisa Gotami carrying dead child. 3r, Patachara, dead family members. 10r, Conversion of Angulimala, the murderer.

1993, Apr. 30   **Perf. 12x12½**
1067	A465	75c multicolored	.20 .20
1068	A465	1r multicolored	.30 .30
1069	A465	3r multicolored	.60 .60
1070	A465	10r multicolored	1.40 1.40
a.		Souvenir sheet, #1067-1070	3.00 3.00
		Nos. 1067-1070 (4)	2.50 2.50

A466

A467

1993, May 10   **Perf. 12**
1071 A466 1r Guide, tent, emblem   .80 .35
1072 A466 5r Activities, map   2.40 2.10
Girl Guides in Sri Lanka, 75th Anniv. (in 1992).

1993, May 22   **Perf. 14**
National Heroes: No. 1073, Yagirala Sri Pagnananda Maha Nayaka Thero. No. 1074, C.P. De Silva. No. 1075, Wilmot A. Perera. No. 1076, N.D.H. Abdul Caffoor.
1073	A467	1r multicolored	.45 .45
1074	A467	1r multicolored	.45 .45
1075	A467	1r multicolored	.45 .45
1076	A467	1r multicolored	.45 .45
		Nos. 1073-1076 (4)	1.80 1.80

Gam Udawa, 15th Anniv. A468

1993, June 23   **Litho.**   **Perf. 12½**
1077 A468 1r multicolored   1.90 .50

Co-operative Consumer Service, 50th Anniv. — A469

1993, July 3   **Perf. 13**
1078 A469 1r multicolored   2.25 .50

Birds A470

Designs: 3r, Ashy-headed laughing thrush. 4r, Ceylon brown-capped babbler. 5r, Red-faced malkoha. 10r, Ceylon hill-mynah.

1993, July 14   **Perf. 12½x12**
1079	A470	3r multicolored	.50 .50
1080	A470	4r multicolored	.50 .50
1081	A470	5r multicolored	.75 .75
1082	A470	10r multicolored	1.75 1.75
a.		Souvenir sheet, #1079-1082	3.50 3.50
		Nos. 1079-1082 (4)	3.50 3.50

Talawila Church, 150th Anniv. A471

1993, July 26   **Perf. 13**
1083 A471 1r multicolored   1.50 .50

Postal Excellence Service Awards — A472

1993, Aug. 22
1084 A472 1r multicolored   1.50 .50

Technical Education in Sri Lanka, Cent. A473

1993, Dec. 17
1085 A473 1r multicolored   1.50 .50

Musaeus College, Cent. — A474

1993, Nov. 15
1086 A474 1r multicolored   2.75 .50

Christmas A475

Designs: 1r, Presentation of infant Jesus in Temple of Jerusalem. 17r, Boy Jesus in Temple.

1993, Nov. 30   **Litho.**   **Perf. 14x13½**
1087	A475	1r multicolored	.30 .20
1088	A475	17r multicolored	1.60 1.60
a.		Souvenir sheet, #1087-1088	2.25 2.25

Youth and Health — A476

1993, Dec. 16   **Perf. 14**
1089 A476 1r multicolored   .80 .40

Old Boy's Assoc., Trinity College, Kandy, Cent. — A478

1994, Feb. 11   **Litho.**   **Perf. 12½**
1091 A478 1r multicolored   .50 .45

St. Thomas College, Matara, 150th Anniv. A479

1994, Mar. 10   **Litho.**   **Perf. 13**
1092 A479 1r multicolored   .50 .45

St. Joseph's College, 125th Anniv. A480

1994, Apr. 4   **Litho.**   **Perf. 12½**
1093 A480 1r multicolored   .60 .35

Siyambalangamuwe Sri Gunaratana Thero — A481

1994, Apr. 2   **Litho.**   **Perf. 13**
1094 A481 1r multicolored   2.50 .45

ILO, 75th Anniv. — A482

1994, May. 12
1095 A482 1r multicolored   1.60 .45

Vesak Festival
A483

Designs show actions by Bodhisatva in four of ten perfections: 1r, Dana, displaying generosity. 2r, Sila, morality. 5r, Nekkhamma, ascetic surrounded by worshippers. 17r, Panna, wisdom dispensed by Bodhisatva to others.

1994, May 7   Litho.   Perf. 12½
1096 A483 1r multicolored   .25   .20
1097 A483 2r multicolored   1.25 1.25
1098 A483 5r multicolored   1.25 1.25
1099 A483 17r multicolored   2.25 2.25
  a. Souvenir sheet, #1096-1099   5.50 5.50
      Nos. 1096-1099 (4)   5.00 4.95

Famous People
A484

Designs: No. 1100, Pres. Ranasinghe Premadasa. No. 1101, Ven. Mihiripanne Dhammaratana Thero. No. 1102, E. Periyathambipillai, poet. No. 1103, Dr. Colvin R. De Silva, politician.

1994, May 22   Litho.   Perf. 14
1100 A484 1r multicolored   .35   .20
1101 A484 1r multicolored   .35   .20
1102 A484 1r multicolored   .35   .20
1103 A484 1r multicolored   .35   .20
      Nos. 1100-1103 (4)   1.40   .80

World Conference of Intl. Federation of Social Workers, Colombo
A485

1994, July 9   Litho.   Perf. 12½
1104 A485 8r blue, lt blue & blk   4.25 4.25

Bellanwila Sri Somaratana Nayake Thero — A486

1994, Aug. 2   Litho.   Perf. 12½
1105 A486 1r multicolored   2.60   .40

Infotel Lanka '94
A487

1994, Sept. 8
1106 A487 10r multicolored   3.25 3.25

Intl. Year of Indigenous People — A488

Designs: 1r, Veddah man making bow. 17r, Veddah man seated by rock art paintings.

1994, Sept. 12   Litho.   Perf. 12
1107 A488 1r multicolored   .50   .50
1108 A488 17r multicolored   4.75 3.75

Natl. Wildlife & Nature Protection Society, Cent.
A489

1994, Nov. 24   Litho.   Perf. 12½
1109 A489 1r Emblem   .30   .20
1110 A489 2r Rhino-horned lizard .70   .70
1111 A489 10r Giant squirrel   2.25 2.25
1112 A489 17r Sloth bear   3.50 3.50
  a. Souvenir sheet, #1109-1112 6.75 6.75
      Nos. 1109-1112 (4)   6.75 6.65

Gam Udawa, 16th Anniv.
A490

1994, Sept.   Litho.   Perf. 13
1113 A490 1r multicolored   1.00   .25

A491

A492

1994, Oct. 11   Litho.   Perf. 12½
1114 A491 1r multicolored   2.75   .90

Double entry bookkeeping, 500th anniv.

1995, Feb. 22   Perf. 14
1115 A492 1r Water lily   1.00   .20

Richmond College Old Boys Assoc., Cent.
A493

1994   Perf. 12½
1116 A493 1r multicolored   .40   .20

ICAO, 50th Anniv.
A494

1994, Dec. 7   Litho.   Perf. 13
1117 A494 10r multicolored   4.75 2.40

Christmas
A495

Designs: 1r, Nativity. 17r, Jesus growing up, at home with Joseph and Mary.

1994, Dec. 8   Litho.   Perf. 13
1118 A495 1r multicolored   .30   .20
1119 A495 17r multicolored   3.75 3.25
  a. Souvenir sheet, #1118-1119 4.50 4.50

Assoc. for Advancement of Science, 50th Anniv. — A496

1994, Dec. 19   Litho.   Perf. 13
1120 A496 1r multicolored   3.25   .60

Orchid Circle of Ceylon, 60th Anniv. — A498

Orchids: 50c, Dendrobium maccarthiae. 1r, Cottonia peduncularis. 5r, Bulbophyllum wightii. 17r, Habenaria crinifera.

1994, Dec. 27   Litho.   Perf. 13
1122 A498 50c multicolored   .25   .20
1123 A498 1r multicolored   .40   .30
1124 A498 5r multicolored   .70   .65
1125 A498 17r multicolored   1.60 1.40
  a. Souvenir sheet, #1122-1125 4.50 4.50
      Nos. 1122-1125 (4)   2.95 2.55

Visit of Pope John Paul II, Beatification of Fr. Joseph Vaz — A499

1995, Jan. 20
1126 A499 1r multicolored   5.00   .70

St. Joseph's College, Colombo, Cent.
A500

1995, Mar. 2   Litho.   Perf. 13
1127 A500 1r multicolored   1.60   .30

Royal Asiatic Society of Sri Lanka, 150th Anniv. — A501

1995, Apr. 4
1128 A501 1r multicolored   3.50   .90

Sirimavo Bandaranaike, World's First Woman Prime Minister — A502

1995, Apr. 17   Litho.   Perf. 12
1129 A502 2r multicolored   2.25   .95

A503

A504

M. C. ABDUL CADER

Vesak Festival (Designs show actions by a Bodhisatva in four of ten perfections): 1r, Endeavor, standing on shore. 2r, Forebearance, one holding another. 10r, Veracity, two people listening to truths. 17r, Resolution, man holding hoe.

1995, May 5   Perf. 12x12½
1130 A503 1r multicolored   .35   .20
1131 A503 2r multicolored   .45   .20
1132 A503 10r multicolored   1.40 1.10
1133 A503 17r multicolored   2.50 2.25
  a. Souvenir sheet, #1130-1133 5.00 5.00
      Nos. 1130-1133 (4)   4.70 3.75

1995, June 3   Perf. 11
1134 A504 2r M. C. Abdul Cader   2.40 1.10

St. Aloysius College, Galle, Cent.
A506

1995, June 21   Litho.   Perf. 12½x12
1136 A506 2r multicolored   2.40 1.10

T.B. Ilangaratna (1913-92), Politician
A507

1995, July 7   Litho.   Perf. 13
1137 A507 2r multicolored   2.40 1.10

Dhamma School, Cent.
A508

1995, Aug. 3
1138 A508 2r multicolored   2.40 1.10

General Post Office, Colombo, Cent.
A509

1995, Aug. 22   Litho.   Perf. 13½
1139 A509 1r multicolored   1.75   .45

Help the
Elderly — A510

1995, Oct. 1　Litho.　Perf. 14x13½
1140　A510　2r multicolored　　　　2.50　.95

41st Commonwealth Parliamentary
Conference — A511

1995, Oct. 9　Litho.　Perf. 14x13½
1141　A511　2r multicolored　　　　2.50　.95

UN, 50th
Anniv. — A512

World Thrift
Day — A513

1995, Oct. 24　　　　Perf. 13½x14
1142　A512　2r multicolored　　　　2.50　1.00

1995, Oct. 15
1143　A513　2r multicolored　　　　2.50　.95

Christmas
A514

Designs: 2r, Arms of Colombo and
Kurunegla, Persian cross from Anuradhapura,
Christian church. 20r, Clasping arms, nativity
scene.

1995, Nov. 10　Litho.　Perf. 13
1144　A514　2r multicolored　　　　.50　.20
1145　A514　20r multicolored　　　3.00　2.40
　a.　Souvenir sheet, #1144-1145　4.00　4.00

A515　　　　　　　　A516

1995, Dec. 8
1146　A515　2r multicolored　　　3.00　1.10

SAARC, 10th anniv.

1996, Jan. 22　Litho.　Perf. 12
1147　A516　50c Little Basses　.65　.30
1148　A516　75c Great Basses　.65　.30
1149　A516　2r Devinuwara　1.60　.80
1149A　A516　2.50r like #1149　.65　.30
1150　A516　20r Galle　4.50　2.50
　a.　Souv. sheet, #1147-1149,
　　　　1150　　　　　9.00　9.00
　Nos. 1147-1150 (5)　8.05　4.20

Lighthouses of Sri Lanka.
For surcharges see Nos. 1191-1193,
1282A.

Vincent High
School,
Batticaloa, 175th
Anniv. — A517

1996, Jan. 17　Litho.　Perf. 13
1151　A517　2r multicolored　　　2.50　.95

Handicrafts
A518

1996, Mar. 13　　　　Perf. 12
1152　A518　25c Traditional
　　　　　　sesath　　　.20　.20
1153　A518　8.50r Pottery　.50　.45
1154　A518　10.50r Mats　.80　.70
1155　A518　17r Lace　1.10　1.10
　a.　Souvenir sheet, #1152-1155　4.00　4.00
　Nos. 1152-1155 (4)　2.60　2.45

For surcharges see Nos. 1189-1190, 1548,
1575.

A519

A520

1996, Mar. 21
1156　A519　2r multicolored　　　2.50　.95

Chundikuli Girls' College, Jaffna, cent.

1996, Apr. 30　Litho.　Perf. 12
Vesak Festival: 1r, Capa cradling her son,
teasing her husband. 2r, Dantika, mahout, elephant. 5r, Subha holding her eye in her hand,
man of low morals. 10r, Punna explaining purification by water to Brahmin.

1157　A520　1r multicolored　　.20　.20
1158　A520　2r multicolored　　.50　.50
1159　A520　5r multicolored　　.65　.65
1160　A520　10r multicolored　1.25　1.25
　a.　Souvenir sheet, #1157-1160　3.00　3.00
　Nos. 1157-1160 (4)　2.60　2.60

1996
Summer
Olympic
Games,
Atlanta
A521

1996, July 22　Litho.　Perf. 13½
1161　A521　1r Diving, vert.　.30　.20
1162　A521　2r Volleyball, vert.　1.25　.55
1163　A521　5r Shooting　1.50　1.50
1164　A521　17r Running　3.00　3.00
　Nos. 1161-1164 (4)　6.05　5.25

Sri Lanka, 1996 World Cup Cricket
Champions — A522

1996, Aug. 18
1165　A522　2r Bowler　.55　.55
1166　A522　10.50r Wicketkeeper　1.10　1.10
1167　A522　17r Batsman　1.60　1.60
1168　A522　20r Trophy　1.75　1.75
　a.　Souvenir sheet, #1165-1168　5.25　5.25
　Nos. 1165-1168 (4)　5.00　5.00

No. 1168a contains two se-tenant pairs.

Jaffna
Central
College,
180th
Anniv.
A523

1996, Sept. 7　Litho.　Perf. 13½
1169　A523　2r multicolored　　　2.75　1.00

A524

A525

1996, Nov. 4　Litho.　Perf. 13½x14
1170　A524　2r multicolored　　　3.00　1.10

UNESCO, 50th anniv.

1996, Dec. 2　　　　Perf. 13½x13
Christmas (Scenes of parables from murals,
Trinity College Chapel): 2r, Washing of the
feet. 17r, Good Samaritan.

1171　A525　2r multicolored　　.35　.20
1172　A525　17r multicolored　1.90　1.60
　a.　Souvenir sheet, #1171-1172　2.25　2.25

UNICEF, 50th
Anniv. — A526

Swami
Vivekananda
A527

1996, Dec. 12　Litho.　Perf. 13½x14
1173　A526　5r multicolored　　　1.10　.75

1997, Jan. 15　　　　Perf. 13½x13
1174　A527　2.50r multicolored　1.50　.70

Personalities
A528

Vesak
Festival — A529

Designs: No. 1175, Lt. Gen. Denzil Kobbekaduwa. No. 1176, Ven. Welivitiye Serata
Thero. No. 1177, Dr. S.A. Wickremasinghe.

1997, Apr. 4　Litho.　Perf. 13½x13
1175　A528　2r multicolored　.60　.35
1176　A528　2r multicolored　.60　.35
1177　A528　2r multicolored　.60　.35
　Nos. 1175-1177 (3)　1.80　1.05

1997, May 7　　　　Perf. 12x12½
Cemeteries, monuments to the dead: 1r,
Thuparama. 2.50r, Ruwanvalisaya. 3r,
Abhayagiri Dagaba. 17r, Jetavana Dagaba.

1178　A529　1r multicolored　.20　.20
1179　A529　2.50r multicolored　.20　.20
1180　A529　3r multicolored　.20　.20
1181　A529　17r multicolored　1.25　1.25
　a.　Souvenir Sheet of 4, #1178-
　　　1181　　　2.75　2.75
　Nos. 1178-1181 (4)　1.85　1.85

D.J. Kumarage,
Birth
Cent. — A530

1997, Apr. 4　Litho.　Perf. 13½x14
1182　A530　2.50r multicolored　1.75　.80

Medicinal
Herbs — A531

2.40r, Munronia pinnata. 14r, Rauvolfia
serpentina.

1997, July 22　Litho.　Perf. 13½x14
1183　A531　2.50r multicolored　.30　.20
1184　A531　14r multicolored　1.50　1.00

Tourism
A532

1997, Sept. 11 **Perf. 12**
1185 A532 20r multicolored   3.50 2.25

St.
Servatius
College,
Matara,
Cent.
A533

1997, Nov. 1 **Perf. 12½x12**
1186 A533 2.50r multicolored   .90 .30

Mahagama
Sekera — A534

1997, Apr. 4 **Litho.** **Perf. 13½x13**
1187 A534 2r multicolored   .85 .40

Asterisks obliterate portions of Mahagama
Sekera's name.

Sri Jayawardenapura Vidalaya, Kotte,
175th Anniv. — A535

1997, Jan. 28 **Perf. 12½**
1188 A535 2.50r multicolored   .60 .30

Nos. 1153-1154 Surcharged

1997, May 6 **Litho.** **Perf. 12**
1189 A518 1r on 8.50r, #1153   8.00 1.00
1190 A518 11r on 10.50r, #1154
    (a)   6.50 6.50
  a. Surcharge type b   6.50 6.50

Surcharge Type a on #1190 is 2½mm high.
Type b surcharge is 3mm high.

No. 1149 Surcharged

c   d

e

1997, Feb. 12 **Litho.** **Perf. 12**
1191 A516(c) 2.50r on 2r   6.00 6.00
1192 A516(d) 2.50r on 2r   6.00 6.00
1193 A516(e) 2.50r on 2r   6.00 6.00
    Nos. 1191-1193 (3)   18.00 18.00

A number has been reserved additional
surcharge on No. 1149.

Reptiles
A537

2.50r, Lyre head lizard. 5r, Boie's roughside.
17r, Common Lanka skink. 20r, Great forest
gecko.

1997, Oct. 18 **Litho.** **Perf. 12**
1195 A537 2.50r multicolored   .25 .25
1196 A537 5r multicolored   .40 .40
1197 A537 17r multicolored   .75 .75
1198 A537 20r multicolored   .80 .80
  a. Souvenir sheet, #1195-1198   2.75 2.75
    Nos. 1195-1198 (4)   2.20 2.20

A538

A539

Christmas: 2.50r, Holy Family. 20r, Adoration of the Magi.

1997, Nov. 20 **Perf. 12½x13**
1199 A538 2.50r multicolored   .30 .20
1200 A538 20r multicolored   1.50 .90
  a. Souvenir sheet, #1199-1200   1.90 1.90

1997, Nov. 11 **Litho.** **Perf. 12½**
Personalities: #1201, Hegoda Sri Indasara
Thero (1932-87), religious leader. #1202,
Abdul Aziz (d. 1990), politician. #1203, Sub-
ramaniam Vithiananthan (b. 1924), teacher,
writer. #1204, Vivienne Goonewardene (1916-
96), politician.
1201 A539 2.50r multicolored   .20 .20
1202 A539 2.50r multicolored   .20 .20
1203 A539 2.50r multicolored   .20 .20
1204 A539 2.50r multicolored   .20 .20
  a. Block of 4, #1201-1204   1.25 1.25

Young
Men's
Buddhist
Assoc.,
Colombo,
Cent.
A540

1998, Jan. 1 **Litho.** **Perf. 12½**
1205 A540 2.50r multicolored   .60 .35

Traditional
Jewelry and
Crafts — A541

Designs: 2.50r, Chunam box. 5r, Necklace
of agate. 10r, Bangle and hairpin. 17r, Sigiri
earrings.

1998, Apr. 24 **Litho.** **Perf. 13½**
1206 A541 2.50r multicolored   .25 .20
1207 A541 5r multicolored   .40 .20
1208 A541 10r multicolored   .75 .75
1209 A541 17r multicolored   1.25 1.25
  a. Souvenir sheet, #1206-1209   3.00 3.00

Independence, 50th Anniv. — A542

Natl. flag and: 2r, People holding up arms,
letters and symbols. No. 1211, Ceylon #300.
No. 1212, People standing, images of industry
and technology. 5r, People playing musical
instruments, book, pen, television, musical
instruments. 10r, People holding up items,
symbols of religion, government.

Perf. 13, 13½ (#1211)
1998, Feb. 4 **Litho.**
1210 A542 2r multicolored   .40 .20
1211 A542 2.50r multicolored   .70 .45
1212 A542 2.50r multicolored   .70 .45
1213 A542 5r multicolored   .70 .50
1214 A542 10r multicolored   1.25 1.00
    Nos. 1210-1214 (5)   3.75 2.60

No. 1211 is 28x38mm.

William
Gopallawa, 1st
President
A543

1998 **Litho.** **Perf. 13½**
1215 A543 2.50r multicolored   .60 .20

5th Natl. Scout
Jamboree
A544

Designs: 2.50r, Scouts holding flag,
emblem, campground. 17r, Campground, flag,
emblems, scout saluting.

1998, Feb. 18
1216 A544 2.50r multicolored   1.00 .75
1217 A544 17r multicolored   3.00 2.50

World Health
Organization,
50th
Anniv. — A545

1998, Apr. 7 **Litho.** **Perf. 13x12½**
1218 A545 2.50r multicolored   .70 .20

St. John's College, Jaffna, 175th
Anniv. — A546

1998, May 7 **Litho.** **Perf. 14½x14**
1219 A546 2.50r multicolored   .40 .20

Elephas Maximus Ceylonensis — A547

Designs: 2.50r, Wading in lake. 10r, Female,
calf. 17r, Three standing in plains. 50r, Large
bull.

1998, May 28 **Perf. 13**
1220 A547 2.50r multicolored   .70 .50
1221 A547 10r multicolored   1.00 .80
1222 A547 17r multicolored   1.50 1.10
1223 A547 50r multicolored   2.50 2.00
  a. Souvenir sheet, #1220-1223   6.50 6.50
    Nos. 1220-1223 (4)   5.70 4.40

Vesak
Festival — A548

Kelaniya Rajamaha Vihara paintings: 1r,
Waterfalls, tree. 2.50r, Procession of people,
elephant with rider. 4r, Looking at mother with
newborn baby. 17r, Presenting child for ceremony, laying stone.

1998, Apr. 30 **Litho.** **Perf. 12½**
1224 A548 1r multicolored   .25 .20
1225 A548 2.50r multicolored   .25 .20
1226 A548 4r multicolored   .50 .30
1227 A548 17r multicolored   1.25 .55
  a. Souvenir sheet, #1224-1228   2.50 2.50
    Nos. 1224-1227 (4)   2.25 1.25

SAARC Summit, Colombo — A549

1998 **Litho.** **Perf. 14½x14**
1228 A549 2.50r multicolored   .90 .35

1998, Year of Information Technology A550

1998	Litho.		Perf. 13½
1229	A550 2.50r multicolored	.60	.20

Personalities A551

#1230, Ven. Pannakitti Nayake Thero. #1231, Sir Nicholas Attygalle. #1232, Dr. Samuel Fisk Green. #1233, Prof. Ediriweera Sarachchandra.

1998			Perf. 13
1230	A551 2.50r multicolored	.50	.35
1231	A551 2.50r multicolored	.50	.35
1232	A551 2.50r multicolored	.50	.35
1233	A551 2.50r multicolored	.50	.35
	Nos. 1230-1233 (4)	2.00	1.40

Meteorological Dept., 50th Anniv. — A552

1998	Litho.		Perf. 14x13½
1234	A552 2.50r multicolored	1.00	.30

26th Forum of South Asia, Africa & Middle East Lions Clubs Intl. — A553

1998, Nov. 20	Litho.		Perf. 14x14½
1235	A553 2.50r multicolored	2.40	.80

Christmas A554

1998, Dec. 10			Perf. 13½x14
1236	A554 2.50r Nativity	.30	.20
1237	A554 20r Annunciation	1.50	.95
a.	Souvenir sheet, #1236-1237	1.90	1.90

A555

Kandyan Dancer — A556

S.W.R.D. Bandaranaike, Birth Cent.: No. 1238, Wearing white scarf. No. 1239, Wearing blue scarf.

1999, Jan. 8	Litho.		Perf. 12
1238	A555 3.50r multicolored	.90	.50
1239	A555 3.50r multicolored	.90	.50
a.	Souvenir sheet, #1238-1239, perf. 12½	1.90	1.90

1999, Feb. 3	Photo.		Perf. 12
1240	A556 1r brown	.20	.20
1241	A556 2r green blue	.20	.20
1242	A556 3r plum	.20	.20
1243	A556 3.50r blue	.20	.20
1244	A556 4r dark red	.20	.20

Size: 21x26mm

1245	A556 5r green	.20	.20
1246	A556 10r violet	.35	.30
1247	A556 13.50r bright red	.45	.40
1248	A556 17r blue green	.55	.45
1249	A556 20r olive bister	.65	.55
	Nos. 1240-1249 (10)	3.20	2.90

Telecommunications, 50th Anniv. — A557

Portraits of Sir Arthur C. Clarke, diagrams of Orbital Concept: a, Rocket launch, satellites, space shuttle. b, Satellites, earth from outer space, space capsule.

1999, Feb. 10	Litho.		Perf. 12
1250	A557 3.50r Pair, #a.-b.	2.25	2.25

Dated 1998.

Salvation Army, 116th Anniv. A558

1999, Apr. 28	Litho.		Perf. 11¾x12
1251	A558 3.50r multicolored	.90	.45

British Council, 50th Anniv. — A559

1999, May 20			Perf. 12
1252	A559 3.50r multicolored	.80	.30

Sumithrayo Organization Suicide Hot Line, 25th Anniv. — A560

1999, June 14			Perf. 12½
1253	A560 3.50r multicolored	.60	.30

Vesak Festival — A561

Designs: 2r, Flowers. 3.50r, Leaf, wheel. 13.50r, Nut, flower. 17r, Young people with traditional lanterns.

Unwmk.

1999, May 25	Litho.		Perf. 12
1254	A561 2r multicolored	.20	.20
1255	A561 3.50r multicolored	.20	.20
1256	A561 13.50r multicolored	.70	.35
1257	A561 17r multicolored	.90	.50
	Nos. 1254-1257 (4)	2.00	1.25

Souvenir Sheet
Wmk. 388
Perf. 12½

1258	Sheet of 4	2.25	2.25
a.	A561 2r like #1254	.20	.20
b.	A561 3.50r like #1255	.20	.20
c.	A561 13.50r like #1256	.70	.35
d.	A561 17r like #1257	.90	.50

Independent Television Network, 20th Anniv. — A562

1999, June 5	Unwmk.		Perf. 12¾
1259	A562 3.50r multicolored	.60	.30

Vidyodaya Pirivena, 125th Anniv. A563

Perf. 12¾

1999, Sept. 17	Litho.		Unwmk.
1260	A563 3.50r multicolored	.60	.30

Sri Lankan Cinema, 50th Anniv. — A564

1999, Sept. 17	Litho.		Perf. 12¾
1261	A564 3.50r Handaya, 1979	.20	.20
1262	A564 4r Nidhanaya, 1972	.30	.25
1263	A564 10r Gam Peraliya, 1963	.50	.35
1264	A564 17r Kadawunu Poronduwa, 1947	1.40	1.10
a.	Souvenir sheet, #1261-1264	2.50	2.50
	Nos. 1261-1264 (4)	2.40	1.90

Bhakthi Prabodanaya Magazine, Cent. — A565

1999, Sept.	Litho.		Perf. 12x12¼
1265	A565 3.50r multicolored	.60	.30

Hector Kobbekaduwa, Politician — A566

Perf. 12¾x12½

1999, Sept. 19	Wmk. 388	Litho.	
1266	A566 3.50r multicolored	.60	.30

National Army, 50th Anniv. — A567

1999, Oct. 10	Unwmk.		Perf. 12¾
1267	A567 3.50r multicolored	.80	.35

Convention on the Rights of the Child, 10th Anniv. — A568

1999, Nov. 20			Perf. 12¾x12½
1268	A568 3.50r multicolored	1.25	.60

A569

A570

1999, Nov. 26			Perf. 12¾
1269	A569 3.50r multicolored	.60	.30

Balangoda Ananda Maitreya Mahanyake Thero (b. 1895), Buddhist priest.

1999, Dec. 12			Perf. 12¾

Paintings.

1270	A570 3.50r By David Paynter	.20	.20
1271	A570 4r By Justin Daraniyagala	.20	.20
1272	A570 17r By Ivan Peries	.65	.60
1273	A570 20r By Solias Mendis	.75	.70
a.	Souvenir sheet of 4, #1270-1273	3.00	3.00
	Nos. 1270-1273 (4)	1.80	1.70

Athletic Accomplishments — A571

Designs: 1r, Kumar Anandan's swim across Palk Strait. 3.50r, World champions in cricket. 13.50r, International fame in track and field.

1999			Perf. 12¾	
1274	A571	1r multicolored	.35	.20
1275	A571	3.50r multicolored	.80	.75
1276	A571	13.50r multicolored	1.60	1.40
		Nos. 1274-1276 (3)	2.75	2.35

Natl. Commission
for UNESCO,
50th
Anniv. — A572

Perf. 12¾x12½				
1999, Nov. 16		Litho.	Wmk. 388	
1277	A572	13.50r multi	3.00	2.25

Christmas
A573

1999, Nov. 30			Perf. 12½x12¾	
1278	A573	3.50r shown	.30	.20
1279	A573	20r Magi	1.10	.80
a.		Souvenir sheet, #1278-1279	2.50	2.50

Famous
People — A574

Designs: No. 1280, Dr. Pandithamani S. Kanapathipillai, Tamil scholar. No. 1281, Sunil Santha, musician. No. 1282, Dr. Al Haj Badi-udin Mahmud, Education minister.

1999, Dec. 3			Perf. 12¾x12½	
1280	A574	3.50r multi	1.00	.40
1281	A574	3.50r multi	1.50	.65
1282	A574	3.50r multi	.90	.35
		Nos. 1280-1282 (3)	3.40	1.40

No. 1149A
Surcharged

1999, Dec. 3		Litho.	Perf. 12	
1282A	A516	2r on 2.50r multi	7.50	1.40

Butterflies — A575

Designs: 3.50r, Striped albatross. 13.50r, Ceylon tiger. 17r, Three-spot grass yellow. 20r, Great orange tip.

Perf. 12x11¾				
1999, Dec. 30			Unwmk.	
Granite Paper				
1283	A575	3.50r multi	.45	.25
1284	A575	13.50r multi	1.00	.80
1285	A575	17r multi	1.40	1.10
1286	A575	20r multi	1.60	1.25
a.		Souvenir sheet, #1283-1286	4.50	4.50
		Nos. 1283-1286 (4)	4.45	3.40

Corals
A576

1999, Dec. 30			Perf. 11¾x12	
Granite Paper				
1287	A576	3.50r Boulder	.30	.40
1288	A576	13.50r Blue-tipped	1.40	1.00
1289	A576	14r Brain-boulder	1.40	1.00
1290	A576	22r Elkhorn	1.60	1.25
a.		Souvenir sheet, #1287-1290	5.25	5.25
		Nos. 1287-1290 (4)	4.70	3.65

For surcharge, see No. 1581.

Auditor General's Department,
Bicent. — A576a

Perf. 12½x12¾				
1999, Dec.		Litho.	Unwmk.	
1290B	A576a	3.50r multi	.80	.60

Year 2000 — A577

Satellite and: 10r, Birds, religious symbols. No. 1292, Scales, girl, Red Cross, computer. No. 1293, airplane, satellite dish, man at computer. No. 1294, Hands, symbols of women's equality, crippled and blind.

2000, Jan. 1			Perf. 11¾	
Granite Paper				
1291	A577	10r multi	.25	.25
1292	A577	100r multi	4.00	4.00
1293	A577	100r multi	4.00	4.00
1294	A577	100r multi	4.00	4.00
a.		Souvenir sheet, #1291-1294	12.00	12.00
		Nos. 1291-1294 (4)	12.25	12.25

Kurunagala
Diocese,
50th Anniv.
A578

		Unwmk.		
2000, Feb. 2		Litho.	Perf. 12	
1295	A578	13.50r multi	1.40	1.40

Wesley
College,
Colombo,
125th
Anniv.
A579

2000, Mar. 2			Perf. 11¾x12	
1296	A579	3.50r multi	.60	.30

Panadura Pinwatte Saddharmakara
Vidyayathana Pirivena, Cent. — A580

2000, Mar. 12				
1297	A580	3.50r multi	.60	.30

Vesak
Festival — A581

2r, Arrival of Jaya Sri Maha Bodhi sapling. 3.50r, King Devanampiyatissa carrying sapling on his head. 10r, Venerating sapling. 13.50r, Royal tree planting, Anuradhapura.

2000, Apr. 28	Litho.	Perf. 12¾x12½		
1298-1301	A581	Set of 4	2.40	1.75
1301a		Souvenir sheet, #1298-1301	4.25	4.25

Sri Lanka Bar Association, 25th Anniv.
(in 1999) — A582

2000, June 10			Perf. 12	
1302	A582	3.50r multi	.60	.30

Co-operative Wholesale
Establishment, 50th Anniv. — A583

2000, July 1			Perf. 12¾	
1303	A583	3.50r multi	.60	.30

No. 979
Surcharged

2000, July 21		Litho.	Perf. 11½	
1303A	A420	50c on 8r multi	5.00	3.25

St.
Patrick's
College,
Jaffna,
150th
Anniv.
A584

2000, July 21				
1304	A584	3.50r multi	1.25	.50

Survey
Dept.,
200th
Anniv.
A585

2000, Aug. 2				
1305	A585	3.50r multi	.60	.30

Central Bank of Sri Lanka, 50th
Anniv. — A586

2000, Aug. 27			Perf. 13¼	
1306	A586	3.50r multi	.60	.30

Dr. Maria Montessori (1870-1952),
Educator — A587

2000, Aug. 31			Perf. 11¾	
1307	A587	3.50r multi	.60	.30

2000 Summer
Olympics,
Sydney — A588

Sydney Olympic Games emblem and: a, Hurdler, map. b, Shooter, runners. c, Runners. d, Hurdlers, swimmer.

2000, Sept. 7				
1308	A588	10r Horiz. strip of 4, #a-d	2.50	2.50
e.		Souvenir sheet, #1308	2.75	2.75

All Ceylon Young Men's Muslim
Association Conference, 50th
Anniv. — A589

2000, Sept. 16				
1309	A589	3.50r multi	.60	.30

208 SRI LANKA

Hotel Industry, 25th Anniv. A590

2000. Sept. 18 *Perf. 12¾*
1310 A590 10r multi 2.50 1.10

Immigration and Emigration Dept., 50th Anniv. A591

2000, Oct. 2 *Perf. 11¾*
1311 A591 3.50r multi .70 .35

Traditional Dancer — A592

Perf. 13½x13 Syncopated
2000, Oct. 5 *Litho.*
1312 A592 50r multi 1.75 1.75
1313 A592 100r multi 3.50 3.50
1314 A592 200r multi 6.75 6.75
 Nos. 1312-1314 (3) 12.00 12.00

All-Ceylon Buddhist Congress Natl. Awards Ceremony A593

2000, Aug. 27 *Litho. Perf. 12¾*
1315 A593 3.50r multi .60 .30

Saumiyamoorthy Thondaman, Government Minister — A594

2000, Oct. 30
1316 A594 3.50r multi .60 .30

Famous People — A595

Designs: No. 1317, 3.50r, Most Ven. Baddegama Siri Piyaratana Nayake Thero, educator. No. 1318, 3.50r, Aluthgamage Simon de Silva (1874-1920), writer. No. 1319, 3.50r, Desigar Ramanujam (1907-68), politician.

Perf. 12x12¼ (#1317), 12¾x12½
2000, Nov. 14
1317-1319 A595 Set of 3 1.25 .75

Christmas A596

Designs: 2r, Joseph, Mary, donkey. 17r, Holy family.

2000, Nov. 23 *Perf. 12¾x12½*
1320-1321 A596 Set of 2 2.25 1.75
 1321a Souvenir sheet, #1320-1321, perf. 12 2.25 2.25

Lalith Athulathmudali (1936-93), Politician — A597

2000, Nov. 30 *Perf. 12½x12¾*
1322 A597 3.50r multi .60 .30

Medicina Alternativa Medical Society, 38th Anniv. A598

2000, Dec. 1 *Perf. 12¾*
1323 A598 13.50r multi 1.75 1.10

Ladies' College, Cent. — A599

2000, Dec. 7
1324 A599 3.50r multi .60 .30

Navy, 50th Anniv. A600

2000, Dec. 9
1325 A600 3.50r multi 1.00 .45

Peliyagoda Vidyalankara Pirivena, 125th Anniv. — A601

2000, Dec. 30 *Perf. 12x12¼*
1326 A601 3.50r multi .60 .30

Bishop's College, 125th Anniv. A602

2001, Jan. 19 *Litho.*
1327 A602 3.50r multi .60 .30

St. Thomas' College, 150th Anniv. A603

2001, Feb. 3 *Perf. 12¾*
1328 A603 3.50r multi .60 .30

Lanka Mahila Samiti Women's Training Society, 70th Anniv. A604

2001, Feb. 15
1329 A604 3.50r multi .60 .30

Air Force, 50th Anniv. A605

2001, Mar. 9
1330 A605 3.50r multi 1.00 .45

St. Lawrence's School, Cent. A606

2001, Mar. 15
1331 A606 3.50r multi .60 .30

Bernard Soysa (1914-97), Politician — A607

2001, Mar. 20 *Perf. 12¾*
1332 A607 3.50r multi .60 .30

Vesak Festival — A608

Designs: 2r, Sri Nagadeepa Chaithya, Jaffna. 3.50r, Muthiyangana Chaithya, Badulla. 13.50r, Kirivehera, Kataragama. 17r, Sri Dalada Maligawa, Kandy.

2001, Apr. 7 Litho. *Perf. 13½x13¾*
1333 A608 2r multi .20 .20
 a. Perf. 14¼ .20 .20
 Perf. 14¼
1334 A608 3.50r multi .20 .20
 a. Perf. 13½x13¾ .20 .20
1335 A608 13.50r multi .75 .75
1336 A608 17r multi 1.00 1.00
 a. Souvenir sheet, #1333a, 1334-1336 2.40 2.40

Hansa Jataka, by George Keyt (1901-93) — A609

Illustration reduced.

2001, Apr. 24 *Perf. 13¼*
1337 A609 13.50r multi 1.50 1.10

Coins A610

Designs: 3.50r, Kahavanu gold coin, 9th cent. 13.50r, Vijayabahu I silver coin, 1055-1111. 17r, Sethu copper coin, 13th-14th cent. 20r, Buddha Jayanthi 5r commemorative silver coin, 1957.

Perf. 13¾x13½, 14¼ (17r)
2001, June 18
1338 A610 3.50r multi .25 .20
1339 A610 13.50r multi .80 .55
1340 A610 17r multi 1.10 .90
 a. Perf. 13¾x13½x14¼x13½ 1.10 .90
1341 A610 20r multi 1.40 1.40
 a. Perf. 13¾x13½x14¼x13½ 1.40 1.40
 b. Souvenir sheet, #1338-1339, 1340a, 1341a 4.00 4.00

Colombo Plan, 50th Anniv. — A611

2001, July 2 *Perf. 13½x13¾*
1342 A611 10r multi 1.00 .55

US-Sri Lankan Diplomatic Relations, 150th Anniv. A612

2001, July 3 *Perf. 12¾*
1343 A612 10r multi 1.00 .55

Lance Corporal Gamini Kularatne (1966-91), Military Hero — A613

2001, July 14 *Perf. 13¾x13½*
1344 A613 3.50r multi .60 .30

Prince and Princess of Wales College, Moratuwa, 125th Anniv. A614

2001, Sept. 14 *Perf. 13¼*
1345 A614 3.50r multi .60 .30

Year of Dialogue Among Civilizations A615

2001, Oct. 9   *Perf. 13x13½*
1346 A615 10r multi   .80 .55

No. 511 Surcharged

2001, July 9 Photo.   *Perf. 14¼x14½*
1347 A180   5r on 1.15r multi   4.00 4.00
1348 A180 10r on 1.15r multi   4.00 4.00
   An additional surcharge was released in this set. The editors would like to examine it.

13th Meeting of Parties to the Montreal Protocol — A616

2001, Oct. 18 Litho.   *Perf. 13x13¼*
1349 A616 13.50r multi   .90 .70

Ramakrishna Mission Students' Home, Batticaloa, 75th Anniv. — A617

2001, Oct. 19   *Perf. 12¾*
1350 A617 3.50r multi   .60 .30

Drummer — A618

   Drummer from: 1r, 2r, 3r, 3.50r, Daul. 4r, 5r, 10r, Kandy. 13.50r, 17r, 20r, Low country.

2001, Nov. 8 Litho.   *Perf. 12½x13¼*
1351 A618   1r rose   .20 .20
1352 A618   2r emerald   .20 .20
1353 A618   3r fawn   .20 .20
1354 A618   3.50r dark blue   .20 .20
     Size: 23x28mm
     Perf. 13¼x12½
1355 A618   4r pink   .35 .20
1356 A618   5r orange   .35 .20
1357 A618   10r violet   .75 .30
1358 A618   13.50r dull purple   1.00 .45
1359 A618   17r yel orange   1.25 .50
1360 A618   20r Prus blue   1.50 .60
    Nos. 1351-1360 (10)   6.00 3.05
   For surcharges, see Nos. 1409, 1514, 1549, 1582.

S.W.R.D. Bandaranaike Natl. Memorial Foundation, 25th Anniv. — A619

2001, Nov. 27   *Perf. 13¾x13¼*
1361 A619 3.50r multi   .60 .30

Christmas A620

   Designs: 3.50r, Jesus and children. 17r, The Annunciation.

2001, Nov. 28   *Perf. 13*
1362-1363 A620   Set of 2   1.00 .75
1363a   Souvenir sheet, #1362-1363   1.25 1.25

Frogs A621

   Designs: 3.50r, Conical wart pygmy tree frog. 13.50r, Sharp-snout saddle tree frog. 17r, Round-snout pygmy tree frog. 20r, Sri Lanka wood frog.

2001, Dec. 3   *Perf. 13¼x13*
1364-1367 A621   Set of 4   3.00 2.50
1367a   Souvenir sheet, #1364-1367   3.00 3.00

St. Bridget's Convent, Cent. A622

2002, Feb. 1
1368 A622 3.50r multi   .60 .20

Ceylon Government Gazette, 200th Anniv. — A623

2002, Mar. 15 Litho.   *Perf. 13¾x14*
1369 A623 3.50r multi   .60 .20

D. S. Senanayake (1884-1952), Prime Minister — A624

2002, Mar. 22   *Perf. 14x13¾*
1370 A624 3.50r multi   .60 .20

Gamini Dissanayake (1942-94), Assassinated Government Minister — A625

2002, Mar. 27   *Perf. 13¾x14*
1371 A625 3.50r multi   .60 .20

Lester James Peries (b. 1919), Film Director A626

2002, Apr. 5   *Perf. 13¼x13*
1372 A626 3.50r multi   .60 .20

Natural Beauty of Sri Lanka — A627

   Designs: 5r, Sinharaja Forest Reserve. 10r, Horton Plains National Park. 13.50r, Knuckles Range. 20r, Rumassala Cliff and Bonavista Coral Reef.

2002, Apr. 10   *Perf. 13x13¼*
1373-1376 A627   Set of 4   2.00 1.25

Pres. Ranasinghe Premadasa (1924-93) A628

2002, Apr. 29   *Perf. 13¾x14*
1377 A628 4.50r multi   .60 .20

Sri Lanka - Japan Diplomatic Relations, 50th Anniv. — A629

2002, Apr. 29   *Perf. 14x13¾*
1378 A629 16.50r multi   1.00 .75

Vesak Festival A630

   Dambulla Raja Maha Vihara rock paintings: 3r, Queen Mahamaya's dream. 4.50r, Birth of Prince Siddhartha. 16.50r, Siddhartha's exhibition of archery talents. 23r, Ordination of Prince Siddhartha.

2002, May 17   *Perf. 13¾x14*
1379-1382 A630   Set of 4   2.00 1.50
1382a   Souvenir sheet, #1379-1382   2.00 2.00

Most Venerable Madihe Pannasiha Maha Nayaka Thera, Religious Leader, 90th Birthday — A631

2002, June 23   *Perf. 14x13¾*
1383 A631 4.50r multi   .60 .20

Sri Lanka Oriental Studies Society, Cent. A632

2002, July 24   *Perf. 13¾x14*
1384 A632 4.50r multi   .70 .20

Rifai Thareeq Association, 125th Anniv. — A633

2002, July 26
1385 A633 4.50r multi   .70 .20

14th Asian Track and Field Championships, Colombo — A634

   Designs: 4.50r, Discus thrower. 16.50r, Sprinter. 23r, Hurdler. 26r, Long jumper.

2002, Aug. 8
1386-1389 A634   Set of 4   3.00 2.25

National Museum, 125th Anniv. — A635

   No. 1390: a, Carved lion (sitting). b, Carved lion (standing with head turned). Illustration reduced.

2002, Aug. 27
1390 A635 4.50r Horiz. pair, #a-b 2.00 2.00

Woman's Hand Holding Flower — A636

2002, Aug. 28   *Perf. 14x13¾*
1391 A636 10r multi   1.00 .45
     Tourism promotion.

Dr. A. C. S. Hameed (1929-99), Government Minister — A637

2002, Sept. 3
1392 A637 4.50r multi .70 .20

Freemasons' Hall, Colombo, Cent. — A638

2002, Sept. 5 *Perf. 13¾x14*
1393 A638 4.50r multi .70 .20

Holy Cross College, Kalutara, Cent. A639

2002, Sept. 13
1394 A639 4.50r multi .70 .20

German Dharmaduta Society, 50th Anniv. — A640

2002, Sept. 21 *Perf. 14x13¾*
1395 A640 4.50r multi .70 .20

Intl. Children's Day — A641

2002, Oct. 1
1396 A641 4.50r multi .70 .20

Dr. M. C. M. Kaleel (1899-1995), Government Minister — A642

2002, Oct. 18
1397 A642 4.50r green .70 .20

Dr. Wijayananda Dahanayake (1902-97), Prime Minister — A644

2002, Oct. 22 Litho. *Perf. 14x13¾*
1399 A644 4.50r brown .70 .20

Sri Lanka - Netherlands Relations, 400th Anniv. — A645

2002, Nov. 22 *Perf. 13¾x14*
1400 A645 16.50r multi 1.00 .60

Christmas — A646

Designs: 4.50r, Madonna and Child. 26r, Holy Family.

2002, Dec. 15 *Perf. 13x13¼*
1401-1402 A646 Set of 2 2.00 1.60
1402a Souvenir sheet, #1401-1402 2.00 2.00

Sri Lanka - China Rubber and Rice Pact, 50th Anniv. A647

2002, Dec. 20 *Perf. 13¾x14*
1403 A647 4.50r multi .70 .20

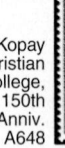

Kopay Christian College, 150th Anniv. A648

2002, Dec. 28
1404 A648 4.50r multi .70 .20

No. 925 Surcharged

2002 ? Litho. *Perf. 12½x12*
1405 A392 25c on 5.75r multi — —

No. 1354 Surcharged

2002 ? Litho. *Perf. 12½x13¼*
1406 A618 4.50r on 3.50r dk bl — —

Teachers' College, Maharagama, Cent. — A649

2003, Jan. 21 *Perf. 13¾x14*
1407 A649 4.50r multi .70 .20

Holy Family Convent, Bambalapitiya, Cent. — A650

2003, Feb. 3 *Perf. 14x13¾*
1408 A650 4.50r multi .70 .20

Drummer Type of 2001 and

No. 1359 Surcharged

Drummer from: 16.50r, Low country.

Perf. 13¼x12½
2003, Feb. 17 Litho.
1409 A618 50c on 5r org yel .40 .30
1410 A618 16.50r purple 1.10 .80

M. D. Banda (1914-74), Government Minister — A651

2003, Mar. 14 *Perf. 13¾x14*
1411 A651 4.50r multi .70 .20

Balagalle Saraswati Maha Pirivena, Cent. A652

2003, Apr. 3
1412 A652 4.50r multi .70 .20

D. B. Welagedara, Politician — A653

2003, Apr. 22 *Perf. 14x13¾*
1413 A653 4.50r multi .70 .20

Vesak Festival — A654

Designs: 2.50r, Paying obeisance to parents. 3r, Dhamma school. 4.50r, Going on alms round. 23r, Meditation.

2003, Apr. 26
1414-1417 A654 Set of 4 1.60 1.10
1417a Souvenir sheet, #1414-1417 1.75 1.75

Dagoba Construction Features — A655

Designs: 4.50r, Stupa. 16.50r, Guard stone, horiz. (58x28mm). 50r, Moonstone, horiz.

2003, Apr. 28 *Perf. 13x13¼, 13¼x13*
1418-1420 A655 Set of 3 2.50 2.00
1420a Souvenir sheet, #1418-1420 2.50 2.50

Second World Hindu Conference, Colombo — A656

2003, May 2 *Perf. 14x13¾*
1421 A656 4.50r multi .60 .20

International Nursing Day — A657

2003, May 12 *Perf. 13¾x14*
1422 A657 4.50r multi .60 .20

Sirimavo Bandaranaike Memorial Exhibition Center — A658

2003, May 17 *Perf. 13¼x12*
1423 A658 4.50r multi .60 .20

SRI LANKA

Al-Haj H. S. Ismail
(1901-73),
Parliament
Speaker — A659

2003, May 18   *Perf. 14x13¾*
1424 A659 4.50r multi   .60 .20

Board of Investment, 25th
Anniv. — A660

2003, May 21   *Perf. 13¾x12*
1425 A660 4.50r multi   .60 .20

World Biodiversity Day — A661

Designs: 4r, Pidurutalagal Mountain Range. 4.50r, Seven Maidens Mountain Range. 16.50r, Kirigalpoththa Mountain. 23r, Ritigala Mountain.

2003, May 22   *Perf. 13¾x12*
1426-1429 A661 Set of 4   2.00 1.50

Saralankara College, Gonapinuwala,
Cent. — A662

2003, June 6   *Perf. 13¾x14*
1430 A662 4.50r multi   .60 .20

A663   A664

First Arab settlement, Beruwala: 4.50r, Masjidul Abrar. 23r, Masjidul Abrar, horiz. (57x22mm).

Perf. 14x13¾, 13¼x12 (23r)
2003, June 8
1431-1432 A663 Set of 2   1.25 .95

2003, June 23   *Perf. 14x13¾*
1433 A664 4.50r multi   .60 .20
Anti-narcotics Week.

Syamopali Maha Nikaya, 250th Anniv. A665

Designs: No. 1434, 4.50r, Asgiri Maha Viharaya. No. 1435, 4.50r, Malwathu Maha Viharaya.

2003, July 13   *Perf. 13¾x14*
1434-1435 A665 Set of 2   1.00 .45

Lanka Philex Intl. Stamp Exhibition,
Colombo — A666

2003, July 31   *Perf. 13¼x12*
1436 A666 16.50r multi   .70 .40
a.   Souvenir sheet of 1   1.25 1.25

Dr. Ananda Tissa de Alwis,
Government Minister — A667

2003, Aug. 21   *Perf. 13¾x14*
1437 A667 4.50r multi   .70 .20

Panadura Controversy, 130th Anniv. — A668

2003, Aug. 24   *Perf. 14x13¾*
1438 A668 4.50r multi   .70 .20

Venerable Haldanduwana Dhammarakkitha Thero — A669

2003, Sept. 3   *Litho.*
1439 A669 4.50r multi   .70 .20

Ragama Walpola Poson Maha Perahara, 75th Anniv. A670

2003, Sept. 10   *Perf. 13¾x14*
1440 A670 4.50r multi   .70 .20

M. H. M. Ashraff (1948-2000), Government Minister — A671

2003, Sept. 18   *Perf. 14x13¾*
1441 A671 4.50r multi   .70 .20

Sisters of the Holy Angels, Cent. A672

2003, Sept. 27   *Perf. 13¾x14*
1442 A672 4.50r multi   .70 .20

Birds — A673

No. 1443: a, Black-necked stork. b, Purple swamphen. c, Gray heron. d, White-throated kingfisher. e, Black-crowned night heron. f, Scarlet minivet. g, White-rumped shama. h, Malabar trogon. i, Asian paradise flycatcher. j, Little green bee-eater. k, Brown wood owl. l, Crested serpent eagle. m, Crested goshawk. n, Jungle owlet. o, Rufous-bellied eagle. p, Black-headed munia. q, Pompadour green pigeon. r, Plum-headed parakeet. s, Coppersmith barbet. t, Emerald dove. u, Blue-faced malkoha. v, Scimitar babbler. w, Painted francolin. x, Red-backed woodpecker. y, Malabar pied hornbill.

2003, Sept. 27   *Perf. 14x13¾*
1443 A673 4.50r Sheet of 25, #a-y   11.00 11.00

World Habitat Day — A674

2003, Oct. 6   *Perf. 13*
1444 A674 4.50r multi   .70 .20

World Post Day A675   Blue Sapphire A676

2003, Oct. 9   *Perf. 14x13¾*
1445 A675 23r multi   1.75 .95

2003, Oct. 21   *Perf. 12x13½*
1446 A676 4.50r multi   .70 .20
See also No. 1497.

Ponificate of Pope John Paul II, 25th Anniv. — A677

2003, Oct. 22   *Perf. 13*
1447 A677 4.50r multi   .70 .20

Deepavali Festival — A678

2003, Oct. 23
1448 A678 4.50r multi   .70 .20

Pinnawala Elephant Orphanage A679

Designs: 4.50r, Two adult and two young elephants. 16.50r, Elephants and caretaker. 23r, Two adult elephants. 26r, Elephants in water.

2003, July 13   *Litho.*   *Perf. 13½x13*
1449-1452 A679 Set of 4   3.00 2.50
1452a   Souvenir sheet, #1449-1452   3.00 3.00
For surcharge, see No. 1576.

Waterfalls — A680

Designs: 2.50r, Ramboda. 4.50r, Saint Clair. 23r, Bopath Ella. 50r, Devon.

2003, Nov. 11   *Perf. 14x13¾*
1453-1456 A680 Set of 4   2.50 2.00

Ukku Banda Wanninayake (1905-73), Finance Minister — A681

2003, Nov. 23   *Perf. 13*
1457 A681 4.50r multi   .60 .20

Christmas A682

Designs: 4.50r, Church. 16.50r, Shepherds and angel, vert.

2003, Nov. 30
1458-1459 A682 Set of 2   .80 .55

Pandith W. D. Amaradeva, Musician, 76th Birthday — A683

2003, Dec. 5
1460 A683 4.50r multi   .60 .20

Gangarama Seemamalakaya — A684

2003, Dec. 20
1461 A684 4.50r multi   .60 .20

Daham Pahana, Sri Pushparamaya, Malegoda — A685

2003, Dec. 31
1462 A685 4.50r multi   .60 .20

Shazuliyathul Fassiya Tharika — A686

2004, Jan. 6
1463 A686 18r multi   .70 .45

Chavakachcheri Hindu College, Cent. — A687

2004, Jan. 30   *Perf. 12x13½*
1464 A687 4.50r multi   .60 .20

Royal-Thomian Cricket Match, 125th Anniv. — A688

2004, Jan. 30   *Perf. 13*
1465 A688 4.50r multi   .60 .20

Pres. Dingiri Banda Wijetunga A689

2004, Feb. 15 Litho. *Perf. 13*
1466 A689 4.50r multi   .60 .20

Planters Association of Ceylon, 150th Anniv. — A690

2004, Feb. 17   *Perf. 13¾x14*
1467 A690 4.50r multi   .60 .20

Kalashuri Most Venerable Mapalagama Vipulasara Thero, Religious Leader — A691

Maithripala Senanayeke A692

Cathiravelu Sittampalam (1898-1964), First Posts and Telecommunications Minister — A693

M. G. Mendis, Communist Leader — A694

2004, Feb. 28   *Perf. 13x13¼*
1468 A691 3.50r multi   .40 .20
1469 A692 3.50r multi   .40 .20
1470 A693 3.50r multi   .40 .20
1471 A694 3.50r multi   .40 .20
    Nos. 1468-1471 (4)   1.60 .80
  Nos. 1468-1471 are dated 2002. They were made available then, but not issued.

75th Ananda-Nalanda Cricket Match — A695

2004, Mar. 7   *Perf. 12x13¼*
1472 A695 4.50r multi   .60 .20

St. Anthony's College, Kandy, 150th Anniv. — A696

2004, Mar. 12   *Perf. 13½x12*
1473 A696 4.50r multi   .60 .20

Vesak Festival — A697

Various scenes of Sittara painting on wooden casket (with white borders on top and bottom): 4r, 4.50r, 16.50r, 20r.
26r, Scene of Sittara painting (no white borders).

2004, Apr. 30
1474-1477 A697 Set of 4   2.00 2.00
      Souvenir Sheet
1478 A697 26r multi   1.50 1.50

Gongalegoda Banda (1809-49), Leader of 1848 Rebellion — A698

2004, May 22   *Perf. 14x13¾*
1479 A698 4.50r multi   .60 .20

World Blood Donor Day — A699

2004, June 15   *Perf. 13*
1480 A699 4.50r multi   .60 .20

2004 Summer Olympics, Athens — A700

Designs: 4.50r, Swimming. 16.50r, Women's track. 17r, Shooting. 20r, Men's track.

2004, Aug. 6   Litho.
1481-1484 A700 Set of 4   1.60 1.60

Sri Siddhartha Buddharakkhita, 18th Cent. Religious Leader — A701

2004, Aug. 16
1485 A701 4.50r brown   .60 .20

Robert Gunawardena, Communist Leader — A702

2004, Aug. 23   *Perf. 14x13¾*
1486 A702 4.50r multi   .60 .20

Pres. Junius Richard Jayewardene (1906-96) A703

2004, Sept. 27   *Perf. 13*
1487 A703 4.50r multi   .60 .20

Intl. Day of Peace — A704

2004, Sept. 21
1488 A704 4.50r multi   .60   .20

Sri Chandrarathna Manawasinghe, Writer — A705

2004, Oct. 6   **Perf. 12x13¼**
1489 A705 4.50r multi   .60   .20

Government Service Buddhist Association, 50th Anniv. — A706

2004, Oct. 7   **Perf. 13**
1490 A706 4.50r multi   .60   .20

World Post Day — A707

2004, Oct. 9   **Perf. 12x13½**
1491 A707 4.50r multi   .80   .20

Raddelle Sri Pannaloka Anunayaka Thero, Religious Leader — A708

2004, Oct. 20   **Perf. 13**
1492 A708 4.50r multi   .60   .20

Christmas A709

2004, Nov. 27   **Perf. 14x13¾**
1493 A709 5r multi   .60   .20

Fathers Jacome Gonsalves and Edmond Peiris — A710

2004, Nov. 27   **Perf. 13¼x12**
1494 A710 20r multi   .75   .75

Information and Communication Technology Week — A711

2004, Nov. 29   **Perf. 13¾x14**
1495 A711 5r multi   .75   .20

De Soysa Hospital for Women, Colombo, 125th Anniv. A712

2004, Dec. 11   **Perf. 13½x14**
1496 A712 5r multi   .60   .20

Blue Sapphire Type of 2003
2004, Dec. 14   Litho.   Perf. 12x13½
1497 A676 5r multi   .75   .20

Most Venerable Talalle Siri Dhammananda Maha Nayaka Thero, Educator — A713

2005, Mar. 13   **Perf. 14x13¾**
1498 A713 5r multi   .60   .20

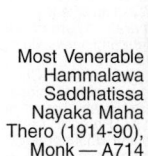

Most Venerable Hammalawa Saddhatissa Nayaka Maha Thero (1914-90), Monk — A714

2005, Mar. 22
1499 A714 5r multi   .60   .20

T. B. Tennakoon, Politician — A715

2005, Mar. 25
1500 A715 5r multi   .60   .20

D. A. Rajapaksa (1905-67), Politician A716

2005, Mar. 25   **Perf. 13¾x14**
1501 A716 5r multi   .60   .20

Vesak Festival — A717

Designs: 4.50r, Ambulatory meditation. 5r, Spiritual bliss through Buddhism. 10r, Meditation in standing posture. 50r, Sedentary meditation.

2005, May 12   **Perf. 14x13¾**
1502-1505 A717   Set of 4   2.00   2.00
1505a   Sheet, #1502-1505   2.00   2.00
   Compare with Type A723.

Rev. Marcelline Jayakody (1902-98) A718

2005, June 3   **Perf. 13**
1506 A718 20r multi   .80   .80

Rana Viru Day — A719

2005, June 7   **Perf. 14x13¾**
1507 A719 50r multi   1.25   1.25

Deshamanya M. A. Bakeer Markar (1917-96), Parliament Speaker — A720

2005, July 20
1508 A720 5r multi   .50   .20

Most Venerable Matara Kithalagama Sri Seelalankara Nayaka Thero — A721

2005, July 21
1509 A721 25r multi   .50   .50

South Asia Tourism Year — A722

2005, July 29   **Perf. 13**
1510 A722 100r multi   2.00   2.00

Kalutara Bodhi Trust A723

2005, Aug. 6   **Perf. 13¾x14**
1511 A723 5r multi   .50   .20

No. 1352 Surcharged Like No. 1409 and Nos. 564, 815, 818 and 937 Surcharged

Methods and Perfs As Before
2005
1512 A206 50c on 10c #564   .20   .20
1513 A324 50c on 35c #815   .20   .20
1514 A618 50c on 2r #1352   .20   .20
1515 A399 50c on 5.75r #937   .20   .20
1516 A324 50c on 6r #818   .20   .20
   Nos. 1512-1516 (5)   1.00   1.00
   Issued: No. 1514, 9/16; others, 3/21.

Postal Headquarters — A725

2005, Sept. 12   Litho.   Perf. 13½x14
1518 A725 5r multi   .20   .20

Ampitiya
National
Seminary
A726

2005, Oct. 1
1519 A726 10r multi .20 .20

World
Post Day
A727

2005, Oct. 9
1520 A727 5r multi .20 .20

General Sir John Kotelawala Defense
Academy, 25th Anniv. — A728

2005, Oct. 11   Litho.   Perf. 13
1521 A728 5r multi .20 .20

Christmas
A729

Cross of Blessed Joseph Vaz, Madonna and
Child and: 5r, Angel. 30r, Star of Bethlehem.

2005, Dec. 3   Litho.   Perf. 13¾x14
1522-1523 A729 Set of 2 .70 .70
1523a   Souvenir sheet, #1522-
1523   .70 .70

Admission to the
UN, 50th
Anniv. — A730

2005, Dec. 13   Litho.   Perf. 14x13½
1524 A730 20r multi .40 .40

Amarapura
Maha
Nikaya,
Bicent.
A731

2005, Dec. 20   Perf. 13½x14
1525 A731 10r multi .20 .20

Ancient Sri Lanka — A732

Designs: 5r, Minhagalkanda and stone
tools. 20r, Extinct animals in Ratnapura gem
gravels and rhinoceros and hippopotamus
bone fragments. 25r, Kuruwita, Batadomba-
lena and human skull from Bellan-bandi
Palassa. 30r, Agriculture on the Horton Plains,
fossilized barley pollen grain.

2005, Dec. 21   Perf. 13¼x12
1526-1529 A732 Set of 4 1.60 1.60

Damage
From Dec.
26, 2004
Tsunami
A733

Designs: 5r, Damaged Kalmunai Post
Office, vehicles. 20r, Train derailed near
Telwatte. 30r, Giant wave breaking along
coast. 33r, Lighthouse and tsunami wave.

2005, Dec. 26   Litho.   Perf. 13¾x14
1530-1533 A733 Set of 4 1.75 1.75
1533a   Souvenir sheet, #1530-
1533   1.75 1.75

Animals of Wilpattu National
Park — A734

Designs: 5r, Barking deer. 10r, White-bellied
sea eagle. 20r, Sloth bear. 50r, Leopard.

2006, Jan. 4   Litho.   Perf. 13½x12
1534 A734 5r multi .20 .20
  a.   Souvenir sheet of 1 .20 .20
1535 A734 10r multi .20 .20
  a.   Souvenir sheet of 1 .20 .20
1536 A734 20r multi .40 .40
  a.   Souvenir sheet of 1 .40 .40
1537 A734 50r multi 1.00 1.00
  a.   Souvenir sheet of 1 1.00 1.00
  Nos. 1534-1537 (4) 1.80 1.80

Institution of
Engineers Sri
Lanka,
Cent. — A735

2006, Jan. 6   Litho.   Perf. 12x13¼
1538 A735 5r black & blue .20 .20

Europa Stamps,
50th Anniv. — A736

Sri Lanka flag and: 100r, Ceylon #336. 500r,
Ship, maps of Europe and Sri Lanka.

2006, Feb. 2   Perf. 12¾x13¼
1539-1540 A736 Set of 2 12.00 12.00
1540a   Souvenir sheet, #1539-
1540   12.00 12.00

Most Venerable
Madithiyawala
Vijithasena
Anunayake
Thero — A737

2006, Mar. 5   Litho.   Perf. 14x13¾
1541 A737 17r multi .35 .35

100th Kingswood-Dharmaraja Cricket
Match — A738

2006, Mar. 24   Perf. 13¾x14
1542 A738 4.50r multi .20 .20

Vesak — A739

No. 1543: a, Wall painting depicting a plea
to the Master to descend from heaven,
Tivamka Image House, Polonnaruva (1/50). b,
Bas-relief of Queen Mahamaya on her way to
visit her parents, Jetavana Vihara,
Anuradhapura (2/50). c, Wall painting depict-
ing birth of Prince Siddhartha, Shai-
labimbarama Vihara, Dodanduwa (3/50). d,
Wall painting of royal teacher Asita visiting
Prince Siddhartha, Purwarama Viharaya,
Kataluva (4/50). e, Bas-relief of Great Renun-
ciation, Girihandu Vihara, Ambalantota (5/50).
f, Rock painting depicting defeat of evils by the
Master, Hindagala Vihara, Hindagala (6/50). g,
Rock painting depicting first sermon of Dham-
machakka, Rangiri Dambulu Vihara, Dambulla
(7/50). h, Wall painting depicting conversion of
Alavaka, Sapugoda Vihara, Beruvala (8/50). i,
Wall painting depicting funeral pyre of the
Master, Veheragalla Samudragiri Vihara,
Mirissa (9/50). j, Tapassu and Bhalluka arriving in Sri Lanka with relics of the Master, Girihandu Seya, Tiriyaya (10/50). k, Wall painting
depicting perfection of generosity, Bodhiruk-
kharama Vihara, Eluvapitiya (11/50). l, Rock
painting depicting perfection of wisdom,
Kaballelena Vihara, Wariyapola (12/50). m,
Wall painting depicting perfection of reunifica-
tion, Degaldoruva Vihara, Kandy (13/50). n,
Wall painting depicting perfection of equanim-
ity, Paramakanda Vihara, Anamaduwa
(14/50). o, Wall painting depicting perfection of
loving kindness, Sunandarama Vihara,
Ambalangoda (15/50). p, Recitation of Chul-
lahastpadopama Sutta by Arhat Mahinda,
Stupa, Mihintale (16/50). q, Establishment of
Buddhism in Sri Lanka, Rajagiri Lena,
Mihintale (17/50). r, Sri Maha Bodhi entering
city, Sri Maha Bodhi, Anuradhapura (18/50). s,
Writing Dhamma on ola leaves, Alu Vihara,
Matale (19/50). t, Arrival of tooth relic of the
Master, Lankapattana, Trincomalee (20/50). u,
Practice of aranyaka, Situlpavuva Vihara
(21/50). v, Symbols of three traditions,
Lovamahapaya, Abhayagiri Vihara, Vajra sym-
bol and lotus (22/50). w, Emergence of
katikavatas, Vatadage, Polonnaruva (23/50). x,
Buddhist discourse between Sri Lanka and
Southeast Asia, Tooth Relic Temple, Kandy
(24/50). y, Translation of the Tripitaka into
Sinhala, Buddhajayanti Vihara, Colombo
(25/50). z, Vesak festival scene, Deepadut-
tarama Vihara, Kotahena (26/50). aa, Serving
of food to Buddhist clergy, Refectory at
Abhayagiriya, Anuradhapura (27/50). ab,
Chanting Paritta, Nishshanka Lata Mandapa,
Polonnaruva (28/50). ac, Combination with vil-
lage, temple tank and stupa, Tissamaharama
Stupa (29/50). ad, Veneration of Bodhi tree,
Bodhighara, Nillakgama (30/50). ae,
Hatthikucchi Vihara, Galgamuva,
Padhanaghara, Anuradhapura (31/50). af, Rit-
ual performance for tooth relic, Atadage,
Polonnaruva (32/50). ag, Perahara,
Subodharma Vihara, Karagampitiya (33/50).
ah, Wall painting of a street market, Mulgiri-
gala Vihara, local coin (34/50). ai, Sanctity of
the temple, Namal Uyana, Ranava (35/50). aj,
Ruvanvalisaya and Thuparama Stupas,

Anuradhapura (36/50). ak, Kirivehera Stupa,
Kataragama, Seruvila Stupa (37/50). al,
Mahiyangana and Nagadipa Stupas, Jaffna
(38/50). am, Kelaniya Stupa and Samantakuta
(39/50). an, Mutiyangana Stupa, Badulla, and
Deeghavapi Stupa (40/50). ao, Painted stupa,
Hanguranketa Raja Maha Vihara, ancient stu-
pas at Kandarodai, Jaffna (41/50). ap, Facade
of Mihintale Stupa, bas-relief of Bahiravas
(42/50). aq, Twin pond, Anuradhapura,
Punkalasa lotus pond, Polonnaruva (43/50).
ar, Moonstone, Mangul Maha Vihara, Lahu-
gala (44/50). as, Bodhisattva Avalokiteshvara,
Muhudumaha Vihara, Potuvil (45/50). at,
Nalanda Gedige, Naula, Satmahal Prasada,
Polonnaruva (46/50). au, Bas-relief of Vimana,
Lankatilaka Vihara, Polonnaruva (47/50). av,
Thuparama Image House, Polonnaruva,
Tampita Vihara, Menikkadawara (48/50). aw,
Wall painting depicting Buddhist cosmos,
Omalpe Vihara, Kolonne (49/50). ax, Depiction
of time in the motif of Makara, Madanvala
Vihara, Hanguranketa (50/50).

2006, May 5   Litho.   Perf. 13¼x12
1543   Sheet of 50 7.75 7.75
  a.-j.   A739 2.50r Any single .20 .20
  k.-t.   A739 4.50r Any single .20 .20
  u.-ad.   A739 5r Any single .20 .20
  ae.-an. A739 10r Any single .20 .20
  ao.-ax. A739 17r Any single .30 .30

Sinhala Bauddhaya Newspaper,
Cent. — A740

2006, May 7   Perf. 13¾x14
1544 A740 5r multi .20 .20

Natl. Cadet Corps,
125th
Anniv. — A741

2006, May 18   Perf. 12x13¼
1545 A741 2r multi .20 .20

Kotte Sri Kalyani Samagridharma
Maha Sanga Sabha, 150th
Anniv. — A742

2006, June 25   Perf. 13¾x14
1546 A742 4.50r multi .20 .20

Sri Lanka
Ramanna Maha
Nikaya — A743

2006, June 29   Perf. 14x13¾
1547 A743 4.50r multi .20 .20

Nos. 592, 1154, and 1353 Surcharged

Methods and Perfs As Before

2006
1548 A518 10r on 10.50r #1154 .20 .20
1549 A618 20r on 3r #1353 .40 .40
1550 A218 50r on 1.60r #592 .95 .95
Nos. 1548-1550 (3) 1.55 1.55

Size, location and style of surcharges vary.

St. Vincent Boys Home, Maggona, 125th Anniv. — A744

2006, July 15 *Litho.* **Perf. 14x13¾**
1551 A744 10r multi .20 .20

Lakshman Kadiragamar (1932-2005), Foreign Minister — A745

2006, Aug. 10
1552 A745 10r multi .20 .20

St. John Dal Bastone Church, Talangama, 125th Anniv. — A746

2006, Aug. 13 **Perf. 13¾x14**
1553 A746 5r multi .20 .20

St. John Ambulance, Cent. — A747

2006, Aug. 15
1554 A747 5r multi .20 .20

Tenth South Asian Games A748

Designs: 10r, High jump. 100r, Cycling.

2006, Aug. 17
1555-1556 A748 Set of 2 2.25 2.25

St. Joseph's Church, Wennappuwa, 125th Anniv. — A749

2006, Aug. 23
1557 A749 2r multi .20 .20

Senaka Bibile (1920-77), Pharmacologist A750

2006, Sept. 29 **Perf. 12x13½**
1558 A750 10r multi .20 .20

World Children's Day A751

2006, Oct. 1 **Perf. 13¾x14**
1559 A751 5r multi .20 .20

Flowers — A752

Designs: No. 1560, Indian laburnum. No. 1561, Sacred lotus. No. 1562, Foxtail orchid. No. 1563, Orange jessamine.

2006, Oct. 2 **Perf. 14x13¾**
1560 A752 4.50r multi .20 .20
1561 A752 4.50r multi .20 .20
1562 A752 50r multi .95 .95
  a. Miniature sheet of 8, 4 each #1560, 1562 4.75 4.75
1563 A752 50r multi .95 .95
  a. Miniature sheet of 8, 4 each #1561, 1563 4.75 4.75
  Nos. 1560-1563 (4) 2.30 2.30

World Post Day A753

2006, Oct. 9 **Perf. 13¾x14**
1564 A753 40r multi .80 .80

Christmas A754

2006, Nov. 13 **Perf. 14x13¾**
1565 A754 5r multi .20 .20

St. Anthony's Shrine, Wahakotte A755

2006, Nov. 13 **Perf. 13¾x14**
1566 A755 20r multi .40 .40

Rugby in Sri Lanka, 125th Anniv. (in 2003) — A756

2006, Dec. 8 **Perf. 13**
1567 A756 4.50r multi .20 .20

D. M. Rajapaksa, Politician — A757

2006, Dec. 14 **Perf. 14x13¾**
1568 A757 5r multi .20 .20

Vee Bissakara Govijana Chaityaya, Ambuluwawa A758

Biodiversity Complex, Ambuluwawa — A759

2006, Dec. 18 **Perf. 12x13½**
1569 A758 5r multi .20 .20
Perf. 13¾x14
1570 A759 25r multi .50 .50

Kande Viharaya A760

2007, Jan. 6 **Perf. 13¾x14**
1571 A760 5r multi .20 .20

Ceylon Nos. 351, 352, 397, 403, and Sri Lanka Nos. 494, 890, 932, 1153, 1290, 1355, and 1452 Surcharged

Methods and Perfs As Before

2007
1572 A86 50c on 35c Ceylon #351 .20 .20
1573 A124 50c on 60c Ceylon #403 .20 .20
1574 A397 50c on 5.75r #932 .20 .20
1575 A518 50c on 8.50r #1153 .20 .20
1576 A679 50c on 26r #1452 .20 .20
1577 A91 4.50r on 50c Ceylon #352 .20 .20
1578 A122 4.50r on 50c Ceylon #397 .20 .20
1579 A174 4.50r on 1.15r #494 .20 .20
1580 A373 4.50r on 5.75r #890 .20 .20
1581 A576 4.50r on 22r #1290 .20 .20
1582 A618 5r on 4r #1355 .20 .20
  Nos. 1572-1582 (11) 2.20 2.20

Issued: Nos. 1572-1576, 1582, 2/13; Nos. 1577-1581, 1/29.

POSTAL-FISCAL STAMP

The editors believe that six additional revenue stamps were authorized for postal use during 1979-98 and would like to examine them.

National Coat of Arms With Sinhalese Characters at Left and Right — PF1

Perf. 13x12
1983, Oct. 14 *Engr.* **Wmk. 233**
AR4 PF1 100r carmine 26.00 25.00

National Coat of Arms — PF2

1984 **Perf. 14½x14**
AR6 PF2 50r vermilion 1.75 1.75
AR7 PF2 100r deep claret 3.25 3.25

A lithographed 500r value exists but was not authorized for postal use.

STELLALAND

'ste-lə-ˌland

LOCATION — South Africa
GOVT. — Republic
AREA — 5,000 sq. mi. (approx.)
CAPITAL — Vryburg

This short-lived republic was set up by the Boers in an effort to annex territory ruled by the Bechuana chiefs. Great Britain refused to recognize it and in 1885 sent an expeditionary force which ended the political career of the country.

Stellaland was annexed by Great Britain in 1885 and became a part of British Bechuanaland.

12 Pence = 1 Shilling

Coat of Arms

A1   A2

1884, Feb.   Unwmk.   Typo.   Perf. 12

1	A1	1p red	225.00	375.00
a.	Horiz. pair, imperf. vert.		4,250.	
b.	Vert. pair, imperf. horiz.		4,600.	
2	A1	3p orange	25.00	375.00
a.	Horiz. pair, imperf. vert.		850.00	
b.	Vert. pair, imperf. horiz.		1,450.	
3	A1	4p gray	24.00	400.00
a.	Horiz. pair, imperf. vert.		750.00	
b.	Vert. pair, imperf. horiz.		2,100.	
4	A1	6p lilac	25.00	400.00
a.	Horiz. pair, imperf. vert.		1,500.	
b.	Vert. pair, imperf. horiz.		1,750.	
5	A1	1sh green	67.50	750.00
	Nos. 1-5 (5)		366.50	2,300.

Imperf. varieties are believed to be proofs.

No. 3 Handstamped "Twee" in Blackish Violet

1885

6	A2	2p on 4p gray	4,000.

The status of No. 6 has long been questioned.

STRAITS SETTLEMENTS

'strāts 'se-təl-mənt

LOCATION — Malay Peninsula in southeastern Asia
GOVT. — British Colony
AREA — 1,356 sq. mi.
POP. — 1,435,895 (estimated)
CAPITAL — Singapore

The colony comprised the settlements of Malacca, Singapore and Penang, which were incorporated under one government in 1826 and the administration transferred from India to the Secretary of State for the Colonies in 1867.

The colony was dissolved in 1946 when Singapore became a separate crown colony. Malacca and Penang were incorporated into the Malayan Union, which became the Federation of Malaya in 1948.

Stamps of India were used in Malacca, Penang and Singapore, 1854-67.

See Malaya for stamps of the Federated Malay States, the Federation of Malaya, Johore, Kedah, Kelantan, Malacca, Negri Sembilan, Pahang, Penang, Perak, Perlis, Selangor, Sungei Ujong and Trengganu.

100 Cents = 1 Dollar

Stamps of India Surcharged in Red, Blue, Black Violet or Green:

Nos. 1-7   Nos. 8-9

1867, Sept. 1   Wmk. 38   Perf. 14

1	A7	1½c on ½a bl (R)	97.50	190.00
2	A7	2c on 1a brn (R)	130.00	75.00
3	A7	3c on 1a brn (Bl)	140.00	80.00
4	A7	4c on 1a brn (Bk)	275.00	250.00
5	A7	6c on 2a yel (V)	625.00	225.00
6	A7	8c on 2a yel (G)	200.00	40.00
7	A9	12c on 4a grn (R)	1,050.	275.00
a.	Double surcharge		2,250.	
8	A7	24c on 8a rose (Bl)	450.00	72.50
9	A7	32c on 2a yel (Bk)	375.00	80.00

Manuscript Surcharge, Pen Bar Across "THREE HALF" of No. 1

9A	A7	2(c) on 1½c on ½a	10,500.	5,000.

Values for Nos. 1-9A are for stamps with perforations touching the frame line on one or two sides. Used values for Nos. 1-9 are for stamps with company chops in addition to postal cancellations. Examples with postal cancels only sell for somewhat lower prices.

A2   A3

A4   A5

1867-72   Typo.   Wmk. 1   Perf. 14

10	A2	2c bister brown	30.00	4.50
11	A2	4c rose	50.00	7.75
12	A2	6c violet	87.50	16.50
13	A3	8c yellow	150.00	10.00
a.	8c orange	150.00	11.00	
14	A3	12c blue	125.00	10.00
15	A3	24c green	125.00	5.75
16	A4	30c claret ('72)	225.00	12.50
17	A5	32c pale red	500.00	75.00
18	A5	96c olive gray	300.00	45.00
	Nos. 10-18 (9)		1,592.	187.00

Corner ornaments of types A2, A3 and A5 differ for each value.
See Nos. 19, 40-44, 48-50, 52-57. For surcharges see Nos. 20-35, 58-59, 61-66, 73-82, 91. For overprints see Malaya, Johore No. 1, Perak Nos. 1, O1-O2, Selangor Nos. 1-2, Sungei Ujong Nos. 2-3.
See the *Scott Classic Catalogue* for other shades.

Stamps of Straits Settlements, 1867-82, overprinted "B" are listed under Bangkok.

1871   Perf. 12½

19	A5	96c olive gray	2,300. 275.00

Stamps of 1867-72 Surcharged:

    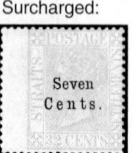

Five Cents.   Seven Cents.

1879, May   Perf. 14

20	A3	5c on 8c yellow	100.00	160.00
a.	No period after "CENTS"		825.00	875.00
21	A5	7c on 32c pale red	125.00	150.00
a.	No period after "CENTS"		1,100.	1,200.

No. 16 Surcharged:

e   f   g

10 10 10 10
j   k   m   h

1880

22	A4(e)	10c on 30c	175.00	55.00
23	A4(f)	10c on 30c	550.00	125.00
24	A4(g)	10c on 30c	190.00	55.00
25	A4(h)	10c on 30c	—	
25A	A4(j)	10c on 30c	3,800.	925.00
25B	A4(k)	10c on 30c	3,800.	925.00
25C	A4(m)	10c on 30c	3,800.	925.00

Surcharges e & f and g, h, j & m are virtually identical. These must have an expert certificate identifying them. Values can be suspect because of misidentifications.
Unused examples are valued without gum.

With Additional Surcharge   *cents*

26	A4(e)	10c on 30c	325.00	82.50
27	A4(f)	10c on 30c	4,750.	700.00
27A	A4(g)	10c on 30c	3,000.	500.00
28	A4(h)	10c on 30c	8,750.	1,425.
28A	A4(j)	10c on 30c	8,750.	1,425.
28B	A4(k)	10c on 30c	8,750.	1,425.
28C	A4(m)	10c on 30c	8,750.	1,425.

Unused examples are valued without gum.

No. 13 Surcharged:

n   o   p

1880

29	A3(n)	5c on 8c yellow	125.00	150.00
30	A3(o)	5c on 8c yellow	450.00	525.00
31	A3(p)	5c on 8c yellow	130.00	160.00

No. 11 Surcharged

1882, Jan.

32	A2	5c on 4c rose	275.00	300.00

Nos. 12, 14a, 16 Surcharged

1880-81

33	A3	10c on 6c violet ('81)	65.00	7.50
a.	Double surcharge		2,100.	
34	A3	10c on 12c blue ('81)	52.50	12.00
35	A4	10c on 30c claret	400.00	97.50
	Nos. 33-35 (3)		517.50	117.00

A6   A7

1882, Jan.   Typo.   Perf. 14

38	A6	5c violet brown	87.50	100.00
39	A7	10c slate	400.00	75.00

See Nos. 45-47, 51. For surcharges see Nos. 60, 67-72, 89-92.

1882-99   Wmk. Crown and C A (2)

40	A2	2c bister brown	250.00	45.00
41	A2	2c car rose ('83)	7.00	1.00
a.	2c rose		40.00	4.00
42	A2	4c rose	125.00	6.00
43	A2	4c car rose ('99)	5.25	1.40
44	A2	4c bister brn ('83)	27.50	1.50
45	A6	5c ultra ('83)	13.00	1.10
46	A6	5c brown ('94)	5.50	1.10
47	A6	5c magenta ('99)	2.75	2.40

48	A2	6c violet	2.25	4.00
49	A3	8c orange	3.50	1.10
50	A3	8c ultra ('94)	5.25	.60
51	A7	10c slate	5.50	1.50
52	A3	12c vio brn ('83)	70.00	12.00
53	A3	12c claret ('94)	12.00	9.75
54	A3	24c blue grn ('83)	4.75	4.50
a.	24c yellow green ('84)		77.50	7.00
55	A4	30c claret ('91)	10.00	11.00
56	A5	32c red org ('87)	8.00	3.00
57	A5	96c olive gray ('88)	82.50	52.50
	Nos. 40-57 (18)		639.75	159.45

For overprints see Malaya, Perak #O3-O9, Selangor #3-4, Sungei Ujong #6-7, 11.

Preceding Issues Surcharged

Surcharged Vertically

1883-84   Wmk. 2, 1

58	A3	2c on 8c orange	125.00	77.50
a.	Double surcharge		2,750.	1,100.
59	A5	2c on 32c pale red	650.00	190.00
a.	Double surcharge			
60	A6	2c on 5c ultra ('84)	130.00	140.00
a.	Pair, one without surcharge			
b.	Double surcharge			
	Nos. 58-60 (3)		905.00	407.50

Five types of surcharge on No. 58, two types on No. 59 and three types on No. 60.

Surcharged in Black

1883   Wmk. 2

61	A2	2c on 4c rose	85.00	97.50
b.	"s" of "Cents." inverted		1,325.	1,425.

**   Wmk. 1**

62	A3	2c on 12c blue	275.00	140.00
a.	"s" of "Cents." inverted		4,000.	2,000.

Surcharged in Black or Blue

1884

63	A3	8c on 12c blue	475.00	130.00

**   Wmk. 2**

64	A3	8c on 12c vio brn	325.00	130.00

With Additional Surcharge Handstamped in Red

65	A3	8c on 8c on 12c vio brn (R + Bk)	275.00	300.00
66	A3	8c on 8c on 12c vio brn (R + Bl)	7,250.	

Surcharged in Black or Red

1884

67	A6	4c on 5c ultra (Bk)	3,250.	4,250.
68	A6	4c on 5c ultra (R)	125.00	110.00

No. 68 Surcharged in Red **4**

69 A6 4c on 4c on 5c ultra 24,000.

No. 69 may be a trial printing. "Usage" seems to been restricted to less than 10 letters known sent from the Postmaster General to his wife.

Surcharged in Black

3 CENTS

1885-87
70 A6 3c on 5c ultra 125.00 *250.00*
 a. Double surcharge 2,500.

Surcharged in Black **3 cents**

71 A6 3c on 5c vio brn
 ('86) 210.00 *225.00*

Surcharged **2 Cents.**

72 A6 2c on 5c ultra ('87) 25.00 *70.00*
 a. Double surcharge 1,200. *1,100.*
 b. "C" omitted 3,000.

In the surcharged issues of 1883 to 1887, Nos. 59, 62, 63 and 71 are on stamps watermarked Crown and C C, the others are watermarked Crown and C A.

Surcharged **THREE CENTS**

1885-94 Wmk. Crown and C A (2)
73 A5 3c on 32c magenta 1.50 1.10
74 A5 3c on 32c rose ('94) 2.75 .85
 a. Without surcharge 4,000.

No. 74a value is for copy with perfs touching frame line.

Surcharged **10 CENTS**

1891
75 A3 10c on 24c green 3.50 1.40
 a. Narrow "0" in "10" 32.50 32.50

Surcharged **THIRTY CENTS**

76 A5 30c on 32c red orange 8.25 4.25

Surcharged **ONE CENT**

1892
77 A2 1c on 2c rose 2.25 *4.25*
78 A2 1c on 4c bister brn 5.75 6.25
 a. Double surcharge 1,300.
79 A2 1c on 6c violet 1.60 *5.50*
 a. Dbl. surch., one invtd. 1,425. *1,325.*
80 A3 1c on 8c orange 1.25 1.50
81 A3 1c on 12c vio brown 5.75 10.50
 Nos. 77-81 (5) 16.60 28.00

Surcharged **ONE CENT**

82 A3 1c on 8c gray green 1.10 *1.75*

Queen Victoria — A13

1892-99 Typo.
83 A13 1c gray green 3.75 .80
84 A13 3c car rose ('95) 12.50 .55
85 A13 3c brown ('99) 6.50 .70
86 A13 25c dk vio & grn 26.00 7.50
87 A13 50c ol grn & car 22.50 3.00
88 A13 $5 org & car ('98) 500.00 275.00
 Nos. 83-88 (6) 571.25 287.55

Denomination of $5, is in color on plain tablet.

Stamps of 1883-94 Surcharged **4 cents.**

1899
89 A6 4c on 5c ultra 4.00 *15.00*
 a. Double surcharge 1,400.
90 A6 4c on 5c brown 3.25 *5.25*
91 A3 4c on 8c brt blue 1.50 *1.25*
 b. Double surcharge 1,100. *1,000.*
 Nos. 89-91 (3) 8.75 21.50

Type of 1882 Issue Surcharged **FOUR CENTS**

92 A6 4c on 5c rose .85 .40
 a. Without surcharge *30,000.*

King Edward VII — A14

Numerals of 5c, 8c, 10c, 30c, $1 and $5, type A14, are in color on plain tablet.

1902 Wmk. 2 Typo.
93 A14 1c green 3.25 *3.50*
94 A14 3c vio & org 4.00 .25
95 A14 4c violet,
 red 5.50 .35
96 A14 5c violet 6.25 .95
97 A14 8c violet,
 blue 4.50 .30
98 A14 10c vio & blk,
 yel 29.00 1.75
99 A14 25c violet &
 grn 14.00 7.00
100 A14 30c gray &
 car rose 21.00 9.25
101 A14 50c grn & car
 rose 22.50 22.50
102 A14 $1 green &
 blk 25.00 *75.00*
103 A14 $2 violet &
 blk 80.00 80.00
104 A14 $5 grn & brn
 org 225.00 190.00
104A A14 $100 dl vio &
 grn, yel 11,000.
 Nos. 93-104 (12) 440.00 390.85

High values of the 1902 and 1904 issues with revenue cancellations are of minimal value. No. 104A is inscribed "Postage & Revenue" but the limit of weight probably precluded its use postally.
See Nos. 113, 115-128B, 133.

A15 A16

A17 A18

1903-04
105 A15 1c gray green 2.00 9.25
106 A16 3c dull violet 12.50 5.25
107 A17 4c violet, red 5.50 .35
108 A18 8c violet, blue 55.00 1.50
 Nos. 105-108 (4) 75.00 16.35

See Nos. 109-112, 114, 129-132, 134.

1904-11 Wmk. 3
Chalky Paper
109 A15 1c gray green 3.25 .20
110 A16 3c dull violet 2.75 .35
111 A17 4c violet, red 11.50 .85
112 A17 4c dull vio
 ('08) 6.25 .20
113 A14 5c violet ('06) 12.50 2.75
114 A18 8c violet, bl 32.50 1.75
115 A14 10c vio & blk,
 yel 9.25 .90
116 A14 10c vio, yel
 ('08) 8.50 1.10
117 A14 25c vio & grn 37.50 24.00
118 A14 25c violet ('09) 16.00 8.00
119 A14 30c gray & car
 rose 55.00 3.00
120 A14 30c vio & org
 ('09) 45.00 4.50
121 A14 50c grn & car
 rose 62.50 17.50
122 A14 50c blk, grn
 ('10) 5.75 *5.50*
123 A14 $1 green & blk 62.50 21.00
124 A14 $1 blk & red,
 bl ('11) 17.00 5.75
125 A14 $2 violet & blk 110.00 97.50
 Revenue cancel 12.00
126 A14 $2 grn & red,
 yel ('09) 27.50 27.50
127 A14 $5 grn & brn
 org 225.00 160.00
128 A14 $5 grn & red,
 grn ('10) 140.00 85.00
 Revenue cancel 5.00
128A A14 $25 green &
 blk 1,725. 1,600.
 Revenue cancel 55.00
128B A14 $100 dl vio &
 grn, yel 12,650.
 Revenue cancel 200.00
 Nos. 109-128 (20) 890.25 467.35

Nos. 125, 128A and 128B are on chalky paper, the other values are on both ordinary and chalky. The note about No. 104A will apply to No. 128B.

1906-11
Ordinary Paper
129 A15 1c blue grn ('10) 26.00 1.25
130 A16 3c carmine ('08) 3.75 .20
131 A17 4c carmine ('07) 6.25 3.00
132 A17 4c lake ('11) 2.25 .95
133 A14 5c orange ('09) 3.25 2.25
134 A18 8c ultra ('06) 4.00 .60
 Nos. 129-134 (6) 45.50 8.25

Stamps of Labuan 1902-03, Overprinted or Surcharged in Red or Black

a b

c

Perf. 12½ to 16 and Compound
1907 Unwmk.
134A A38(a) 1c violet & blk 70.00 *200.00*
135 A38(a) 2c grn & blk 350.00 *350.00*
136 A38(a) 3c brn & blk 22.50 97.50
137 A38(c) 4c on 12c yel
 & blk 2.75 *7.00*
 a. No period after
 "CENTS" 350.00 —
138 A38(c) 4c on 16c org
 brn & grn
 (Bk) 5.25 *9.25*
 a. With additional name in
 red 750.00 800.00
139 A38(c) 4c on 18c bis
 & blk 3.25 *7.50*
 a. No period after
 "CENTS" 325.00
 b. "FOUR CENTS." & bar
 double 8,650.
140 A38(a) 8c org & blk 3.50 *9.25*
141 A38(b) 10c sl bl & brn 8.50 *8.00*
 a. No period after "Settle-
 ments" 375.00
142 A38(a) 25c grnsh bl &
 grn 17.00 45.00
143 A38(a) 50c gray lil &
 vio 18.00 *80.00*
144 A38(a) $1 org & red
 brn 52.50 *125.00*
 Nos. 134A-144 (11) 553.25 938.50

A19

A20

1908-11 Typo. Wmk. 3 Perf. 14
Chalky Paper
145	A19	$25 bl & vio, *bl* ('11)	1,600.	1,250.
146	A19	$500 violet & org	92,000.	
		Revenue cancel		275.

No. 146 is inscribed "Postage-Revenue" but was probably used only for revenue.
Excellent forgeries of No. 146 exist.

1910
Chalky Paper
147	A20	21c maroon & vio	7.50	40.00
148	A20	45c black, *green*	3.00	4.50

King George V
A21   A22

A23   A24

A25   A26

Die I (Type A24).

For description of dies I and II see "Dies of British Colonial Stamps" in Table of Contents. The 25c, 50c and $2 denominations of type A24 show the numeral on horizontally-lined tablet.

1912-18 Chalky Paper Wmk. 3
149	A21	1c green	7.00	1.50
150	A21	1c black ('18)	1.75	1.10
151	A25	2c dp green ('18)	1.10	.60
152	A22	3c scarlet	2.50	.40
a.		3c carmine	3.25	1.00
153	A23	4c gray violet	1.75	.40
154	A23	4c scarlet ('18)	2.75	.20
a.		Booklet pane of 1		
b.		Booklet pane of 12		
c.		4c carmine ('18)	2.75	.20
155	A24	5c orange	2.00	.60
156	A25	6c claret ('18)	2.00	.60
157	A25	8c ultra	2.25	.90
158	A24	10c violet, *yel*	1.75	.60
159	A24	10c ultra ('18)	7.00	.60
160	A26	21c maroon & vio	5.75	11.00
161	A24	25c vio & red vio	14.00	9.75
162	A24	30c vio & org ('14)	9.25	2.25
163	A26	45c blk, *bl grn*, ol back ('14)	3.75	22.50
a.		45c black, *emerald* ('17)	3.75	15.00
164	A24	50c black, *grn* ('14)	6.50	3.25
a.		50c blk, *bl grn*, olive back	21.00	8.50
b.		50c black, *emerald*	14.00	11.00
c.		Die II	3.50	4.50
165	A24	$1 blk & red, *bl* ('14)	10.50	9.75
166	A24	$2 grn & red, *yel* ('15)	11.50	50.00
167	A24	$5 grn & red, *grn* ('15)	92.50	70.00
a.		$5 grn & red, *bl grn*, ol back	175.00	97.50
b.		$5 grn & red, *emer* ('15)	92.50	110.00
c.		Die II	110.00	75.00
		Nos. 149-167 (19)	185.60	186.00

The 1c, 3c, 5c and 8c are on ordinary paper.

Surface-colored Paper
168	A24	10c violet, *yel*	1.75	1.10
169	A26	45c black, *grn* ('14)	7.50	21.00
170	A24	$2 grn & red, *yel* ('14)	9.75	50.00
171	A24	$5 grn & red, *grn*	92.50	50.00
		Nos. 168-171 (4)	111.50	122.10

See Nos. 179-201. For surcharges see Nos. B1-B2.

A27

1915
172	A27	$25 bl & vio, *bl*	1,400.	500.00
		Revenue cancel		5.75
173	A27	$100 red & blk, *bl*	5,750.	
		Revenue cancel		90.00
174	A27	$500 org & dl vio	46,000.	
		Revenue cancel		200.00

Although Nos. 173 and 174 were available for postage, it is probable that they were used only for fiscal purposes.
See Nos. 202-204.

Die II (Type A24)
1921-32 Wmk. 4
Ordinary Paper
179	A21	1c black	.60	.20
180	A25	2c green	.60	.20
181	A25	2c brown	8.00	3.00
182	A22	3c green	1.75	.90
183	A23	4c scarlet	2.25	4.75
184	A23	4c dp violet ('25)	.70	.20
185	A23	4c orange ('29)	1.10	.20
186	A24	5c orange ('23)	2.75	1.50
a.		Die I	1.75	.20
187	A24	5c dk brown ('32)	3.25	.20
a.		Die I ('32)	5.75	.20
188	A25	6c claret	2.25	.25
189	A25	6c scarlet ('27)	3.00	.20
a.		6c rose red ('25)	22.50	11.00
190	A24	10c ultra (I)	2.00	3.00

Chalky Paper
191	A24	10c vio, *yel* ('27)	2.25	.35
a.		Die I ('25)	3.00	7.50
192	A25	12c ultra	1.10	.20
193	A24	21c mar & vio	7.00	55.00
194	A24	25c vio & red vio	5.75	2.00
a.		Die I	32.50	80.00
195	A24	30c violet & org	2.25	1.50
a.		Die I	26.00	40.00
196	A26	35c orange & vio	14.00	7.00
197	A26	35c vio & car ('23)	11.50	8.00
198	A24	50c blk, *emerald*	2.00	.45
199	A24	$1 blk & red, *bl*	7.00	.75
200	A24	$2 grn & red, *yel*	11.50	9.25
201	A24	$5 grn & red, *grn*	100.00	37.50
202	A27	$25 bl & vio, *bl*	800.00	140.00
203	A27	$100 red & blk, *bl*	6,500.	1,900.
204	A27	$500 org & dl vio	37,000.	
		Nos. 179-201 (23)	192.60	136.60

No. 192 is on ordinary paper.
Nos. 203 and 204 were probably used only for fiscal purposes.

Stamps of 1912-21 Overprinted in Black:

"MALAYA-BORNEO EXHIBITION," in Three Lines
1922 Wmk. 3
151d	A25	2c deep green	32.50	85.00
154d	A23	4c scarlet	8.50	26.00
155d	A24	5c orange	5.75	22.50
157d	A25	8c ultra	2.00	8.50
161d	A24	25c vio & red vio	3.75	35.00
163d	A26	45c blk, *bl grn*, ol back	3.50	30.00
165d	A24	$1 blk & red, *bl*	225.00	800.00
166d	A24	$2 grn & red, *yel*	30.00	125.00
167d	A24	$5 grn & red, *grn*	275.00	450.00

Wmk. 4
179d	A21	1c black	3.50	14.00
180d	A25	2c green	2.75	16.00
183d	A23	4c scarlet	4.00	30.00
186d	A24	5c orange (II)	3.25	45.00
190d	A24	10c ultra	2.75	29.00
199d	A24	$1 blk & red, *bl*	22.50	140.00
		Nos. 151d-199d (15)	624.75	1,856.

Industrial fair at Singapore, Mar. 31-Apr. 15, 1922.

Common Design Types
pictured following the introduction.

Silver Jubilee Issue
Common Design Type

George V   George VI
A28   A29

1935, May 6 Engr. Perf. 11x12
213	CD301	5c black & ultra	3.50	.35
214	CD301	8c indigo & green	3.75	3.50
215	CD301	12c ultra & brown	3.75	4.25
216	CD301	25c brown vio & ind	4.00	5.75
		Nos. 213-216 (4)	15.00	13.85
		Set, never hinged	24.00	

1936-37 Typo. Perf. 14
Chalky Paper
217	A28	1c black ('37)	.90	.20
218	A28	2c green	1.00	.80
220	A28	4c orange brn	2.00	.80
221	A28	5c brown	.80	.35
222	A28	6c rose red	1.10	1.25
223	A28	8c gray	1.50	.80
224	A28	10c dull vio	1.75	.70
225	A28	12c ultra	2.00	3.00
226	A28	25c rose red & vio	1.60	.60
227	A28	30c org & dk vio	1.10	3.50
229	A28	40c dk vio & car	1.10	2.75
230	A28	50c blk, *emerald*	4.00	1.40
232	A28	$1 red & blk, *blue*	17.00	1.90
233	A28	$2 rose red & gray grn	37.50	11.50
234	A28	$5 grn & red, *grn* ('37)	80.00	11.50
		Nos. 217-234 (15)	153.35	41.05
		Set, never hinged	290.00	

Coronation Issue
Common Design Type

1937, May 12 Engr. Perf. 13½x14
235	CD302	4c deep orange	.20	.20
236	CD302	8c gray black	.30	.20
237	CD302	12c bright ultra	.50	.65
		Nos. 235-237 (3)	1.00	1.05
		Set, never hinged	2.00	

Two Dies

Die I. Printed in two operations. Lines of background touch outside of central oval. Foliage of palms touches outer frame line. Palm frond in front of King's eye has two points.
Die II. Printed from a single plate. Lines of background separated from central oval by a white line. Foliage of palms does not touch outer frame line. Palm frond in front of King's eye has one point.

1937-41 Typo. Perf. 14
238	A29	1c black (I)	2.75	.20
239	A29	2c green (I)	9.00	.25
c.		Die II ('38)	35.00	.45
239A	A29	2c brown org ('41) (II)	1.25	5.00
239B	A29	3c green ('41) (II)	2.25	3.00
240	A29	4c brown org (I)	8.00	.25
a.		Die II ('38)	50.00	.25
241	A29	5c brown (I)	10.00	.35
a.		Die II ('39)	27.50	.20
242	A29	6c rose red ('38) (I)	5.50	.50
243	A29	8c gray ('38) (I)	19.00	.25
244	A29	10c dull vio (I)	4.00	.20
245	A29	12c ultra ('38) (I)	8.00	.35
245A	A29	15c ultra ('41) (II)	3.25	6.25
246	A29	25c rose red & vio (I)	40.00	1.10
247	A29	30c org & vio (I)	25.00	2.00
248	A29	40c dk vio & rose red (I)	10.00	2.25
249	A29	50c blk, *emer* ('38) (I)	10.00	.45
250	A29	$1 red & blk, *bl* ('38) (I)	15.00	.40
251	A29	$2 rose red & gray grn ('38) (I)	30.00	4.25
252	A29	$5 grn & red, *grn* ('38) (I)	25.00	4.50
		Nos. 238-252 (18)	228.00	31.55
		Set, never hinged	375.00	

For overprints see #256-271, N1-N29 and Malaya, Malacca #N1-N14, Penang #N1-N26.

Stamps and Type of 1937-41 Overprinted in Red or Black

MALAYA

1945-48
256	A29	1c black (R)	.20	.20
257	A29	2c brown org (II)	.25	.20
a.		Die I ('46)	7.50	3.75
258	A29	3c green	.25	.20
259	A29	5c brown	.75	.60
260	A29	6c gray	.25	.20
261	A29	8c rose red	.25	.20
262	A29	10c dull vio (I)	.30	.20
a.		10c claret (II) ('48)	10.00	1.25
263	A29	12c ultra	1.75	3.25
264	A29	15c ultra (Bk)	2.25	4.75
265	A29	15c ultra (R)	.25	.20
266	A29	25c rose red & vio	1.40	.25
a.		Double overprint	400.00	
267	A29	50c blk, *emer* (R)	.60	.20
268	A29	$1 rose red & blk	2.00	.25
269	A29	$2 rose red & gray grn	2.50	.65
270	A29	$5 grn & red, *grn*	72.50	72.50
271	A29	$5 brn org & vio	3.75	2.75
		Nos. 256-271 (16)	89.25	86.65
		Set, never hinged	140.00	

The letters "B M A" are initials of "British Military Administration".
An 8c gray with BMA overprint was prepared but not issued. Value $5.
The 6c gray, 8c rose red and $5 brown orange & violet exist without BMA overprint, but were issued only with it.
No. 262a does not exist without overprint.
No. 262 exists in at least three shades.

SEMI-POSTAL STAMPS

Nos. 152-153 Surcharged

1917 Wmk. 3 Perf. 14
B1	A22	3c + 2c scarlet	3.00	29.00
a.		No period after "C"	375.00	575.00
B2	A23	4c + 2c gray violet	4.00	29.00
a.		No period after "C"	400.00	575.00

POSTAGE DUE STAMPS

D1

1924-26 Typo. Wmk. 4 Perf. 14
J1	D1	1c violet	5.75	7.50
J2	D1	2c black	3.75	1.50
J3	D1	4c green ('26)	2.25	5.50
J4	D1	8c red	5.25	.60
J5	D1	10c orange	7.00	.95
J6	D1	12c ultramarine	8.00	.75
		Nos. J1-J6 (6)	32.00	16.80
		Set never hinged	55.00	

OCCUPATION STAMPS

Issued Under Japanese Occupation
Straits Settlements Nos. 238, 239A, 239B, 243 and 245A Handstamped in Red

1942, Mar. 16 Wmk. 4 Perf. 14
N1	A29	1c black	16.00	20.00
N2	A29	2c brown orange	16.00	16.00
N3	A29	3c green	70.00	85.00

N4	A29	8c gray	27.50	22.50
N5	A29	15c ultra	20.00	20.00
		Nos. N1-N5 (5)	149.50	163.50
		Set never hinged	200.00	

Other denominations with this handstamp are believed to be proofs.

The handstamp reads: "Seal of Post Office of Malayan Military Department."

Stamps of Straits Settlements, 1937-41, Handstamped in Red, Black, Violet or Brown

1942, Apr. 3

N6	A29	1c black	4.00	4.00
N6A	A29	2c green (V)	2,875.	500.00
N7	A29	2c brown org	3.50	3.50
N8	A29	3c green	3.25	3.50
N9	A29	5c brown	25.00	30.00
N10	A29	8c gray	5.00	3.50
N11	A29	10c dull violet	55.00	45.00
N12	A29	12c ultra	92.50	90.00
N13	A29	15c ultra	4.50	4.00
N14	A29	30c orange & vio	2,200.	350.00
N15	A29	40c dk vio & rose red	100.00	125.00
N16	A29	50c blk, *emerald*	60.00	60.00
N17	A29	$1 red & blk, *bl*	87.50	80.00
N18	A29	$2 rose red & gray grn	150.00	150.00
N19	A29	$5 grn & red, *grn*	200.00	165.00

Nos. N6-N7, N9, N11-N12, N15-N19 with red handstamp were used in Sumatra. The 2c green with red handstamp was not regularly issued.

Straits Settlements Nos. 239A, 239B, 243 and 245A Overprinted in Black

1942

N20	A29	2c brown orange	2.00	6.00
a.		Inverted overprint	11.50	21.00
b.		Dbl. ovpt., one invtd.	55.00	70.00
N21	A29	3c green	57.50	62.50
N22	A29	8c gray	5.75	2.75
a.		Inverted overprint	17.00	32.50
N23	A29	15c ultra	15.00	9.25
		Nos. N20-N23 (4)	80.25	80.50
		Set never hinged	100.00	

Straits Settlements Nos. 239A and 243 Overprinted in Black

1942, Nov. 3

N24	A29	2c brown orange	14.00	25.00
a.		Inverted overprint	375.00	375.00
N25	A29	8c gray	15.00	20.00
a.		Inverted overprint	375.00	375.00

Agricultural-Horticultural Exhibition held at Kuala Lumpur, Selangor, Nov. 1-2, 1942. Sold only at a temporary post office at the exhibition.

Straits Settlements Nos. 243, 245 and 248 Overprinted in Black or Red

---

1943

N26	A29	8c gray (Bk)	1.60	.60
a.		Inverted overprint	52.50	62.50
N27	A29	8c gray (R)	2.50	3.00
N28	A29	12c ultramarine	1.40	10.50
N29	A29	40c dk vio & rose red	2.00	4.50
		Nos. N26-N29 (4)	7.50	18.60
		Set never hinged	10.00	

The Japanese characters read: "Japanese Postal Service."

SUDAN

sü-'dan

LOCATION — Northeastern Africa, south of Egypt
GOVT. — Republic
AREA — 967,500 sq. mi.
POP. — 27,953,000 (1997 est.)
CAPITAL — Khartoum

10 Milliemes = 1 Piaster
100 Piasters = 1 Egyptian Pound
Dinar (1992)
100 Qirsh = 1 Pound (2007)

> Catalogue values for unused stamps in this country are for Never Hinged items, beginning with Scott 79 in the regular postage section, Scott C35 in the air post section, Scott CO1 in the air post official section, Scott J12 in the postage due section, and Scott O28 in the officials section.

Watermarks

Wmk. 71 — Rosette

Wmk. 179 — Multiple Crescent and Star

Wmk. 214 — Multiple S G

Wmk. 334 — Rectangles

Wmk. 345 — Rhinoceros

Egyptian Stamps of 1884-93 Overprinted in Black

1897, Mar. 1   Wmk. 119   Perf. 14

1	A18	1m brown	3.50	*2.50*
a.		Inverted overprint	300.00	
2	A19	2m green	2.50	*2.75*
3	A20	3m orange	1.75	*2.10*
4	A22	5m carmine rose	2.50	2.00
a.		Inverted overprint	300.00	
5	A14	1p ultra	9.00	2.50
6	A15	2p orange brown	72.50	19.00
7	A16	5p gray	67.50	22.50
a.		Double overprint	*5,250.*	
8	A23	10p violet	40.00	47.50
		Nos. 1-8 (8)	199.25	100.85

Counterfeits of Nos. 1-8 are plentiful.

Camel Post — A1

1898, Mar. 1   Typo.   Wmk. 71

9	A1	1m rose & brn	1.50	*3.00*
10	A1	2m brown & grn	3.00	3.00
11	A1	3m green & vio	3.25	2.75
12	A1	5m black & rose	2.75	2.00
13	A1	1p yel brn & ultra	7.00	4.75
14	A1	2p ultra & blk	27.50	11.00
15	A1	5p grn & org brn	35.00	21.00
16	A1	10p dp vio & blk	32.50	50.50
		Nos. 9-16 (8)	112.50	50.50

See Nos. 17-27, 43-50. For overprints see Nos. C3, MO1-MO15, O1-O9, O17-O24. For surcharges see Nos. 28, 62, C16.

1902-21   Wmk. 179

17	A1	1m car rose & brn ('05)	1.60	.90
a.		Inverted overprint		
18	A1	2m brown & grn	2.25	.20
19	A1	3m grn & vio ('03)	3.00	.35
20	A1	4m ol brn & bl ('07)	2.00	*3.50*
21	A1	4m brn & red ('07)	2.00	1.00
22	A1	5m blk & rose red ('03)	2.50	.20
23	A1	1p brn & ultra ('03)	3.00	.40
24	A1	2p ultra & blk ('08)	32.50	2.50
25	A1	2p org & vio brn ('21)	6.25	*11.00*
26	A1	5p grn & org brn ('08)	32.50	.45
27	A1	10p dp vio & blk ('11)	32.50	4.75
		Nos. 17-27 (11)	120.10	25.25

No. 15 Surcharged in Black

5 Millièmes

1903, Sept.   Wmk. 71

28	A1	5m on 5p	10.00	*12.00*
a.		Inverted surcharge	325.00	260.00

A2

1921-22   Typo.   Wmk. 179

29	A2	1m orange & blk ('22)	1.25	*5.25*
30	A2	2m dk brn & org ('22)	11.00	*13.50*
31	A2	3m green & vio ('22)	3.00	11.00
32	A2	4m brown & grn ('22)	7.00	6.50
33	A2	5m blk & ol brn ('22)	3.00	.20
34	A2	10m black & car ('22)	5.00	.20
35	A2	15m org brn & ultra	4.00	1.25
		Nos. 29-35 (7)	34.25	37.90

See Nos. 36-42. For overprints see Nos. C1-C2, O10-O16.
For surcharges see Nos. 60-61.

1927-40   Wmk. 214

36	A2	1m org yel & blk	1.00	.20
37	A2	2m dk brn & org	1.00	.20
38	A2	3m green & violet	1.00	.20

39	A2	4m brown & green	.90	.20
40	A2	5m blk & ol brn	.75	.20
a.		Booklet pane of 4		
41	A2	10m black & car	2.00	.20
42	A2	15m org brn & ultra	2.25	.20
43	A1	2p orange & vio brn	3.50	.20
44	A1	3p dk bl & red brn ('40)	4.75	.20
45	A1	4p black & ultra ('36)	4.75	.20
46	A1	5p dk grn & org brn	1.75	.20
47	A1	6p blk & pale bl ('36)	9.00	1.75
48	A1	8p blk & pck grn ('36)	9.50	3.50
49	A1	10p dp vio & blk	5.00	.20
50	A1	20p bl & lt bl ('35)	6.75	.25
		Nos. 36-50 (15)	53.90	7.90

Charles George Gordon — A3

Gordon Memorial College A4

Memorial Service at Khartoum — A5

1935, Jan. 1   Engr.   Perf. 13½x14

51	A3	5m deep green	.50	.20
52	A3	10m brown	1.10	.30
53	A3	13m ultra	1.25	13.50
54	A3	15m carmine	2.25	.30

55	A4	2p deep blue	2.00	.25
56	A4	5p orange	2.25	.50
57	A4	10p dull violet	9.75	10.00
58	A5	20p black	32.50	72.50
59	A5	50p red brown	110.00	155.00
		Nos. 51-59 (9)	161.60	252.55
		Set, never hinged	275.00	

50th anniv. of the death of Gen. Charles George ("Chinese") Gordon (1833-85).

No. 41 Surcharged in Black

5 Mills.

Wmk. Multiple S G (214)

1940, Feb. 25		**Typo.**	***Perf. 14***	
60	A2	5m on 10m black & car	1.00	.60

Nos. 40 and 48 Surcharged in Black

4½ Piastres

a	b

1940-41

61	A2(a)	4½p on 5m ('41)	65.00	12.00
62	A1(b)	4½p on 8p	57.50	14.00

Sudan Landscape A6

Perf. 13½, 14x13½

1941		**Litho.**	**Unwmk.**	
		Size: 21½x17½mm		
63	A6	1m orange & slate bl	1.60	6.00
64	A6	2m chocolate & org	1.60	6.00
65	A6	3m grn & rose vio	1.75	.25
66	A6	4m choc & bl grn	.55	.90
67	A6	5m indigo & ol bis	.20	.20
68	A6	10m indigo & rose pink	7.50	4.50
69	A6	15m chestnut & ultra	1.00	.20
		Size: 29x25mm		
71	A6	2p orange & claret	4.25	.90
72	A6	3p dk blue & fawn	.85	.20
73	A6	4p blk & brt ultra	2.00	.20
74	A6	5p dk grn & brn org	4.00	13.50
75	A6	6p ind & turq bl	14.00	.75
76	A6	8p black & green	11.50	.80
77	A6	10p rose vio & gray	45.00	1.10
78	A6	20p dk & lt blue	42.50	52.50
		Nos. 63-78 (15)	138.30	88.00
		Set, never hinged	240.00	

Catalogue values for unused stamps in this section, from this point to the end of the section, are for Never Hinged items.

Types of 1898-1940 with Changed Arabic Wording Below Camel

A7	A8

Wmk. 214

1948, Jan. 1		**Typo.**	***Perf. 14***	
79	A7	1m dk orange & blk	.45	4.25
80	A7	2m chocolate & org	1.00	5.00
81	A7	3m green & rose lilac	.40	6.00
82	A7	4m choc & sl grn	.65	1.40
83	A7	5m black & ol brn	7.50	2.25

84	A7	10m black & car	7.00	.20
a.		Center inverted	—	
85	A7	15m org brn & ultra	6.50	.20
86	A8	2p org yel & vio brn	11.50	2.75
87	A8	3p dk bl & red brn	9.50	.40
88	A8	4p black & ultra	5.00	2.00
89	A8	5p dk grn & org	5.00	3.75
90	A8	6p blk & pale bl	5.50	3.25
91	A8	8p blk & peacock grn	5.75	3.50
92	A8	10p dp rose lil & blk	13.50	5.00
93	A8	20p dk blue & blue	5.75	.75
a.		Perf. 13	60.00	210.00
94	A8	50p ultra & carmine	8.25	2.75
		Nos. 79-94 (16)	93.25	43.45

Arabic inscription, types A7 and A8: "Berid es-Sudan"; types A1 and A2; "Postai-Sudaniye."
For overprints see Nos. O28-O43.

Stamp of 1898 — A9

1948, Oct. 1			***Perf. 12½x13***	
95	A9	2p dull blue & gray blk	.50	.20

50th anniv. of Sudan's 1st postage stamp.

A10

1948, Dec. 19			***Perf. 13***	
96	A10	10m black & carmine	.75	.20
97	A10	5p dk green & orange	1.50	1.50

Legislative Assembly opening, Dec., 1948.

Nubian Ibex — A11   Cotton Picking — A12

Camel Post — A13

Designs: 2m, Shoebill. 3m, Giraffe. 4m, Baggara girl. 5m, Shilluk warrior. 10m, Hadendowa. 15m, Sudan policeman. 3p, Ambatch canoe. 3½p, Nuba wrestlers. 4p, Weaving. 5p, Saluka farming. 6p, Gum tapping. 8p, Darfur chief. 10p, Stack laboratory. 20p, Nile lechwe.

1951, Sept. 1		**Typo.**	***Perf. 14***	
		Center in Black (#98-104)		
98	A11	1m orange	2.50	1.75
99	A11	2m ultra	2.50	1.10
100	A11	3m dark green	8.50	3.75
101	A11	4m emerald	2.25	3.75
102	A11	5m plum	2.75	.20
103	A11	10m light blue	.40	.20
104	A11	15m dp orange brn	5.25	.20
		Perf. 13		
105	A12	2p lt blue & dk blue	.35	.20
106	A12	3p vio blue & brn	11.00	.20
107	A12	3½p brown & bl grn	3.00	.20
108	A12	4p black & dp blue	2.00	.20

109	A12	5p emer & org brn	.75	.20
110	A12	6p black & blue	10.00	2.75
111	A12	8p brown & dp bl	16.00	4.00
112	A12	10p green & black	1.75	.75
113	A12	20p black & blue	7.50	3.25
114	A13	50p black & carmine	16.50	3.25
		Nos. 98-114 (17)	93.00	25.95

See #159. For overprints see #O44-O61, O75.

Camel Post — A14

1954, Jan. 9			***Perf. 12½x13***	
115	A14	15m emerald & brn org	.55	1.00
116	A14	3p black & blue	.65	1.75
117	A14	5p red violet & blk	.80	1.75
		Nos. 115-117 (3)	2.00	4.50

Self-government in the Sudan.
A quantity of these sets inscribed "1953" was sold in London. They were not valid for postage. Value, set $25.

Independent Republic

Map of Sudan and Sun — A15   Rhinoceros Carrying Globe — A16

Wmk. 214

1956, Sept. 15			***Perf. 14***	
118	A15	15m rose lilac & org	.60	.80
119	A15	3p dk blue & org	.60	1.25
120	A15	5p green & org	.60	.95
		Nos. 118-120 (3)	1.80	3.00

Independence Day, Jan. 1, 1956.

1958, Aug. 2
Center in Orange

121	A16	15m plum	.50	.20
122	A16	3p blue	.75	.35
123	A16	5p green	1.00	.60
		Nos. 121-123 (3)	2.25	1.15

APU Cong., Khartoum, Aug. 2, 1958.

Soldier, Farmer and Map of Nile — A17

Lithographed and Engraved

1959, Nov. 17		**Unwmk.**	***Perf. 14***	
124	A17	15m brown, yel & ultra	.30	.20
125	A17	3p multicolored	.70	.45
126	A17	55m multicolored	.90	.65
		Nos. 124-126 (3)	1.90	1.30

Sudanese army revolution, 1st anniv.

Arab League Center A17a

Uprooted Oak Emblem, Refugee Man and Child — A18

Perf. 13x13½

1960, Mar. 22		**Photo.**	**Wmk. 328**	
127	A17a	15m dull green & blk	.60	.40

Opening of the Arab League Center and the Arab Postal Museum in Cairo.

Wmk. 214

1960, Apr. 7		**Litho.**	***Perf. 14***	
128	A18	15m black, buff & ultra	.25	.20
129	A18	55m black, beige & org	.75	.50

World Refugee Year, 7/1/59-6/30/60.

Soccer Player — A19

Forest — A20

1960, Aug. 25		**Wmk. 214**	***Perf. 14***	
130	A19	15m ultra, blk & yel	.30	.20
131	A19	3p yellow, blk & grn	.65	.45
132	A19	55m emerald, blk & yel	.90	.60
		Nos. 130-132 (3)	1.85	1.25

17th Olympic Games, Rome, 8/25-9/11.

1960, Sept. 6				
133	A19	15m multicolored	.30	.20
134	A20	3p multicolored	.70	.20
135	A20	55m multicolored	.85	.55
		Nos. 133-135 (3)	1.85	.95

5th World Forestry Cong., Seattle, WA, Aug. 29-Sept. 10.

King Tirhaqah, 689-663 B.C. — A21   Girl with Book — A22

Unwmk.

1961, Mar. 1		**Engr.**	***Perf. 14***	
136	A21	15m yellow grn & brown	.30	.25
137	A21	3p salmon & violet	.55	.35
138	A21	55m lt blue & red brown	1.10	.70
		Nos. 136-138 (3)	1.95	1.30

Save historic monuments in Nubia.
An imperf. souvenir sheet exists, not sold at post offices, containing one each of Nos. 136-138. Size: 154x97mm. The sheet was not issued for postal purposes and cancellation requests are declined. Value $9.

1961, Nov. 17		**Litho.**	**Wmk. 214**	
139	A22	15m violet, claret & pink	.30	.20
140	A22	3p orange, blk & blue	.65	.40
141	A22	55m gray grn, blk & och	.90	.65
		Nos. 139-141 (3)	1.85	1.25

50 years of girls' education in the Sudan.

Malaria Eradication Emblem — A23

Arab League Building, Cairo — A24

1962, Apr. 7   Unwmk.   Perf. 14
142 A23 15m black, pur & blue   .55   .20
143 A23 55m dk brown & green   1.25   .75
WHO drive to eradicate malaria.

1962, Apr. 22   Photo.   Perf. 13½x13
144 A24 15m deep orange   .45   .20
145 A24 55m blue green   .80   .75
Arab League Week, Mar. 22-28.

Type of 1951 and

Palace of the Republic, Khartoum — A25

Cotton Picker — A26

Designs: 15m, Straw cover. 35m, 4p, Wild animals. 55m, 6p, Cattle. 8p, Date palms. 10p, Sailboat. 20p, Bohein Temple, 1500 B.C. 50p, Sennar Dam. £1, Camel Post (A13 redrawn).

Perf. 14½x14, 14x14½
1962, Oct. 1   Litho.   Wmk. 345
Size: 23x19mm, 19x23mm
146 A25 5m blue   .20   .20
147 A26 10m blue & lilac   .20   .20
148 A25 15m multicolored   .20   .20
149 A25 2p lt purple   .20   .20
150 A26 3p bl grn, red brn & brn   .40   .20
151 A26 35m yel grn, brn & org brn   .75   .20
152 A26 4p red, lt bl & lil   .75   .30
153 A25 55m gray & yel ol   .75   .30
154 A25 6p brown & lt blue   1.00   .30
155 A25 8p green   1.00   .30

Perf. 14x14½, 13x13½, 14x13½, 13½x14
Size: 24½x30mm, 30x24½mm
156 A26 10p lt bl, red brn & blk   1.50   .50
157 A25 20p gray ol & yel grn   3.00   1.10
158 A25 50p dk gray, ol & bl   7.50   1.75

Engr.
159 A13 £1 green & brn org   15.00   6.50
 b.   Wmk 334   —   —
 Nos. 146-159 (14)   32.45   12.15

The frame of No. 159 has been altered with Arabic inscription on top and English at bottom.
See Nos. 420, 427-428. For surcharge and overprints see Nos. 430, O62-O74, O92, O99-O100.

1975-79   Unwmk.
Perfs, Sizes and Printing Methods as Before
146a A25 5m ('76)   .20   .20
147a A26 10m ('76)   .20   .20
148a A25 15m   .20   .20
149a A25 2p   .20   .20
150a A26 3p ('76)   .30   .20
151a A26 35m   .50   .20
152a A26 4p   .50   .20
153a A26 55m ('79)   .50   .25
154a A26 6p   .60   .25
155a A26 8p ('77)   .75   .25
156a A26 10p   1.00   .40
157a A26 20p   2.00   .90
158a A26 50p   5.50   1.25
159a A13 £1   —   6.00
 Nos. 146a-158a (13)   12.45   4.70

Corn and Millet — A27

Centenary Emblem and Medals — A28

1963, Mar. 21   Litho.   Wmk. 345
160 A27 15m. emerald, gray & brn   .30   .20
161 A27 55m violet, lt & dk blue   .70   .40
FAO "Freedom from Hunger" campaign.

1963, Oct. 1   Perf. 14
162 A28 15m blk, red, gray & gold   .50   .20
163 A28 55m grn, gray, red & gold   1.00   .50
Centenary of the International Red Cross.

Melchior — A29

Khashm El Girba Dam — A30

Designs: 30m, St. Joseph seated, with cross and manuscript, horiz. 55m, Archangel with cross. Designs from frescoes in excavated Faras Church.

1964, Mar. 8   Litho.   Perf. 14
164 A29 15m multicolored   .45   .25
165 A29 30m red brn, blk & brn   .65   .35
166 A29 55m red brn, blk & brn   1.50   .80
 Nos. 164-166 (3)   2.60   1.40
UNESCO world campaign to save historic monuments in Nubia.

Perf. 14x14½, 14½x14
1964, Apr. 22   Wmk. 345
New York World's Fair, 1964-65: 3p, Pavilion. 55m, Illustrated map of Sudan, vert.
167 A30 15m lt vio bl & vio brn   .25   .20
168 A30 3p multicolored   .30   .30
169 A30 55m multicolored   .80   .45
 Nos. 167-169 (3)   1.35   .95

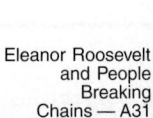

Eleanor Roosevelt and People Breaking Chains — A31

Arab Postal Union Emblem — A32

1964, Dec. 10   Perf. 14
170 A31 15m grnsh blue & blk   .25   .20
171 A31 3p violet & black   .45   .25
172 A31 55m orange brn & blk   .75   .90
 Nos. 170-172 (3)   1.45   1.35
Eleanor Roosevelt (1884-1962), on the 16th anniv. of the Universal Declaration of Human Rights.

1964, Dec. 30   Litho.
173 A32 15m brick red, blk & gold   .25   .20
174 A32 3p gray green, blk & gold   .45   .30
175 A32 55m violet, blk & gold   1.00   .55
 Nos. 173-175 (3)   1.70   1.05
10th anniv. of the Permanent Office of the Arab Postal Union.

ITU Emblem, Old and New Communication Equipment — A33

1965, May 17   Wmk. 345   Perf. 13½
176 A33 15m brown & gold   .40   .20
177 A33 3p black & gold   .75   .30
178 A33 55m green & gold   2.75   .70
 Nos. 176-178 (3)   3.90   1.20
Cent. of the ITU.

"Gurashi" and Revolutionists — A34

1965, Nov. 10   Litho.   Perf. 12
179 A34 15m deep ocher & black   .30   .20
180 A34 3p bright red & black   .55   .25
181 A34 55m dark gray & black   1.00   .55
 Nos. 179-181 (3)   1.85   1.00
1st anniv. of the October 21st Revolution and to honor "Gurashi," one of its heroes.

ICY Emblem — A35

El Siddig el Mahdi — A36

Perf. 14½x14
1965, Dec. 10   Litho.   Wmk. 345
182 A35 15m violet & blk   .45   .20
183 A35 3p yellow green & blk   .55   .30
184 A35 55m vermilion & blk   1.75   .55
 Nos. 182-184 (3)   2.75   1.05
International Cooperation Year, 1965.

1966, Jan. 1   Perf. 13
185 A36 15m lt blue & vio blue   .55   .25
186 A36 3p orange & brown   .85   .35
187 A36 55m gray & red brown   2.00   1.00
 Nos. 185-187 (3)   3.40   1.60
El Siddig el Mahdi (1911-61), imam of Ansar region and political leader.

Mubarak Zaroug A37

1966, Jan. 1   Litho.
188 A37 15m pink & lt olive grn   .60   .25
189 A37 3p brt yel grn & dk grn   .85   .55
190 A37 55m orange brn & dk brn   1.75   .95
 Nos. 188-190 (3)   3.20   1.75
Issued in memory of Mubarak Zaroug (1917-65), lawyer and political leader.

WHO Headquarters, Geneva — A38

1966, June 11   Photo.   Perf. 11½x11
191 A38 15m blue   .40   .20
192 A38 3p magenta   .60   .30
193 A38 55m brown   1.75   .55
 Nos. 191-193 (3)   2.75   1.05
Inauguration of WHO Headquarters, Geneva.

Map of Sudan and Crests of Upper Nile, Blue Nile and Kassala Provinces — A39

Designs: 3p, Map of Sudan and crests of Equatoria, Kordofan and Khartoum Provinces. 55m, Map of Sudan and crests of Bahr El Gazal, Darfur and Northern Provinces.

1967, Apr. 1   Litho.   Perf. 14
194 A39 15m org, pur & lt blue grn   .20   .20
195 A39 3p dp org, vio & lt blue   .50   .35
196 A39 55m yel, dp claret & yel grn   1.50   .65
 Nos. 194-196 (3)   2.20   1.20
Month of the South.

Giraffe and ITY Emblem — A40

Clasped Hands and Arab League Emblem — A41

Perf. 12½x13
1967, Aug. 15   Litho.   Wmk. 345
197 A40 15m multicolored   .50   .25
198 A40 3p multicolored   1.25   .45
199 A40 55m multicolored   2.75   .75
 Nos. 197-199 (3)   4.50   1.45
International Tourist Year 1967.

Perf. 11x11½
1967, Aug. 29   Photo.   Unwmk.
200 A41 15m orange & ultra   .35   .20
201 A41 3p brown org & emer   .45   .35
202 A41 55m lemon & violet   .80   .70
 Nos. 200-202 (3)   1.60   1.25
Arab League Summit Conference.

Emblem of Palestine Liberation
Organization — A42

1967, Aug. 29   **Perf. 11½x11**
203	A42	15m olive, car & yel	.35	.20
204	A42	3p green, car & yel	.90	.25
205	A42	55m brt green, car & yel	1.00	.45
		Nos. 203-205 (3)	2.25	.90

Palestine Liberation Organization.

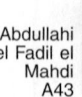

Abdullahi
el Fadil el
Mahdi
A43

1968, Feb. 15   **Photo.**   **Unwmk.**
206	A43	15m ultra & brt purple	.40	.20
207	A43	3p dp ultra & brt grn	.60	.30
208	A43	55m orange & green	1.25	.55
		Nos. 206-208 (3)	2.25	1.05

Issued in memory of Abdullahi el Fadil el
Mahdi (1892-1966), political leader.

Mohammed Nur el Din — A44

1968, Feb. 15
209	A44	15m sl blue & apple grn	.40	.20
210	A44	3p blue & olive	.60	.30
211	A44	55m blue & violet blue	1.25	.55
		Nos. 209-211 (3)	2.25	1.05

Issued in memory of Mohammed Nur el Din
(1898-1964), political leader.

Ahmed
Yousif
Hashim
A45

      Perf. 11½x11
1968, Mar. 5   **Photo.**   **Unwmk.**
212	A45	15m green & brown	.40	.20
213	A45	3p brt blue & sepia	.60	.30
214	A45	55m indigo & violet	1.25	.55
		Nos. 212-214 (3)	2.25	1.05

Ahmed Yousif Hashim (1906-1958),
journalist.

Mohammed Ahmed
el Mardi (1905-
1966), Political
Leader — A46

      Perf. 11x11½
1968, Mar. 5   **Photo.**   **Unwmk.**
215	A46	15m Prus bl & vio bl	.70	.30
216	A46	3p ultra, och & dl rose	.95	.55
217	A46	55m dk blue & brown	1.75	.80
		Nos. 215-217 (3)	3.40	1.65

DC-3
A47

20th anniv. of Sudan Airways: 2p, De Havilland Dove. 3p, Fokker Friendship. 55m, De
Havilland Comet 4C.

1968, Dec. 15   **Litho.**   **Perf. 13½x13**
218	A47	15m multicolored	.45	.20
219	A47	2p multicolored	.75	.20
220	A47	3p multicolored	1.00	.30
221	A47	55m multicolored	1.25	.55
		Nos. 218-221 (4)	3.45	1.25

African Development Bank Emblem
(right) — A48

    Wmk. Rectangles (334)
1969, Dec. 20   **Photo.**   **Perf. 13**
222	A48	2p black, gray & gold	.50	.20
223	A48	4p dark red & gold	.75	.20
224	A48	65m green & gold	1.40	.40
		Nos. 222-224 (3)	2.65	.90

5th anniv. of the African Development Bank.

ILO Emblem
A49

      Unwmk.
1969, Dec. 27   **Litho.**   **Perf. 14**
225	A49	2p blue, blk & pink	.40	.20
226	A49	4p yellow, blk & silver	.55	.30
227	A49	65m green, blk & lilac	1.00	.40
		Nos. 225-227 (3)	1.95	.90

     50th anniv. of the ILO.

Citizens
A50

1970, May 25   **Perf. 11½x11**
228	A50	2p multicolored		
228A	A50	4p multicolored		
228B	A50	55m multicolored		
		Set, 228-228B	90.00	—

First anniv. of May 25th Revolution.
This set was withdrawn on day of issue;
1721 sets of the 2p, 4p and 65m stamps in
same design were sold through the Philatelic
service. A few copies of No. 228 were sold at
Post offices. Nos. 229-231 were issued in
October to replace this set.

Citizens
A51

1970, Oct. 21   **Photo.**   **Perf. 11½x11**
229	A51	2p brown, olive & red	.40	.20
230	A51	4p lt blue, olive & red	.75	.35
231	A51	65m olive, dk blue & red	1.00	.45
		Nos. 229-231 (3)	2.15	1.00

1st anniv. of the May 25th Revolution.

Map and
Flags of
UAR, Libya,
Sudan
A52

1971, Jan. 2   **Unwmk.**   **Perf. 11½**
232	A52	2p lt green, car & blk	.60	.20

Signing of the Charter of Tripoli affirming the
unity of UAR, Libya and the Sudan, Dec. 27,
1970.

Education Year
Emblem — A53

1971, May 2   **Photo.**   **Perf. 11x11½**
233	A53	2p blue, blk & brn	.45	.20
234	A53	4p carmine, blk & brn	.70	.30
235	A53	65m vio brn, blk & brn	1.40	.45
		Nos. 233-235 (3)	2.55	.95

     International Education Year.

Emblem — A54

1971, Nov. 10   **Perf. 11x11½**
236	A54	2p yellow, grn & blk	.40	.20
237	A54	4p blue, grn & blk	.90	.35
238	A54	10½p gray, grn & blk	2.50	.75
		Nos. 236-238 (3)	3.80	1.30

2nd anniversary of May 25th Revolution.

Arab League
and Sudanese
Emblems — A55

UN
Emblem — A56

1972, Feb. 10   **Photo.**   **Perf. 11x11½**
239	A55	2p yellow, grn & blk	.45	.20
240	A55	4p orange, bl & blk	.75	.30
241	A55	10½p orange, brn & blk	2.25	.75
		Nos. 239-241 (3)	3.45	1.25

25th anniv. (in 1971) of the Arab League.

1972, Mar. 12   **Photo.**   **Perf. 11x11½**
242	A56	2p emer, rose red & org	.45	.20
243	A56	4p ultra, rose red & org	.75	.30
244	A56	10½p blk, rose red & org	2.25	.75
		Nos. 242-244 (3)	3.45	1.25

25th anniv. (in 1970) of the UN.

Emblems
and
Measure
A57

1972, Apr. 22   **Photo.**   **Perf. 11½x11**
245	A57	2p multicolored	.50	.20
246	A57	4p lt blue & multi	.80	.30
247	A57	10½p pink & multi	2.00	.75
		Nos. 245-247 (3)	3.30	1.25

World Standards Day, Oct. 14, 1970.

Pres.
Nimeiry
and Arms
of Sudan
A58

1972, May 2   **Litho.**   **Perf. 13x13½**
248	A58	2p vio bl, blk & gold	.50	.20
249	A58	4p dp org, blk & gold	.75	.25
250	A58	10½p ol grn, blk & gold	2.10	.65
		Nos. 248-250 (3)	3.35	1.10

Election of Gaafar al-Nimeiry as President,
Oct. 1971.

Arms of
Sudan
and
Congress
Emblem
A59

1972, Oct. 15   **Photo.**   **Perf. 11x11½**
251	A59	2p blue & multi	.35	.20
252	A59	4p multicolored	.65	.35
253	A59	10½p lt olive & multi	2.25	.50
		Nos. 251-253 (3)	3.25	1.05

Founding Congress of the Sudanese Socialist Union.

Letter and
African
Postal
Union
Emblem
A60

1972, Dec. 16
254	A60	2p yellow & multi	.35	.20
255	A60	4p multicolored	.60	.30
256	A60	10½p blue & multi	2.25	.50
		Nos. 254-256 (3)	3.20	1.00

10th anniv. (in 1971) of the APU.

Emblems of
Sudanese
Provinces
A61

Designs: 4p, Governing Council of Sudan.
10½p, Nat'l Coat of Arms and Unity emblem,
vert.

1973, Jan. 1   **Litho.**   **Perf. 13**
257	A61	2p gold & multi	.35	.20
258	A61	4p dk red brn & blk	.60	.25
259	A61	10½p silver, org & grn	2.25	.50
		Nos. 257-259 (3)	3.20	.95

National Unity Day, March 3, 1972.

Emperor Haile
Selassie — A62

1973, June 25   **Unwmk.**   **Perf. 13**
260	A62	2p tan & multi	.50	.30
261	A62	4p silver & multi	1.00	.40
262	A62	10½p gold & multi	2.40	.75
		Nos. 260-262 (3)	3.90	1.45

80th birthday of Haile Selassie, Emperor of
Ethiopia.

Nasser and Crowd A63

1973, July 15 Photo. Perf. 11½x11
263 A63   2p black   .40   .20
264 A63   4p pale green & blk   .60   .25
265 A63   10½p lilac & blk   2.60   .55
    Nos. 263-265 (3)   3.60 1.00

Gamal Abdel Nasser (1918-70), President of Egypt.

UN and FAO Emblems, Portal and Map of Resettlement Project — A64

1973, Dec. 30 Litho. Perf. 13
266 A64   2p multicolored   .35   .20
267 A64   4p multicolored   .65   .25
268 A64   10½p multicolored   2.75   .50
    Nos. 266-268 (3)   3.75   .95

World Food Program, 10th anniversary.

Scout Emblem, Knotted Rope and Stave — A65

1974, Jan. 15
269 A65   2p multicolored   .70   .20
270 A65   4p multicolored   1.00   .35
271 A65   10½p multicolored   2.75   .75
    Nos. 269-271 (3)   4.45 1.30

24th World Boy Scout Conference.

INTERPOL Emblem A66

1974, Feb. 16 Litho. Perf. 13x13½
272 A66   2p orange & multi   .80   .20
273 A66   4p gray & multi   1.25   .25
274 A66   10½p lt blue & multi   2.00   .55
    Nos. 272-274 (3)   4.05 1.00

50th anniv. of Intl. Criminal Police Organ.

K.S.M. Building A67

1974, July 1 Litho. Perf. 13x13½
275 A67   2p lilac rose & multi   .50   .20
276 A67   4p lt green & multi   1.00   .25
277 A67   10½p vermilion & multi   3.00   .75
    Nos. 275-277 (3)   4.50 1.20

50th anniversary of the Faculty of Medicine, University of Khartoum.

African Postal Union and UPU Emblems — A68

4p, Letters, Arab Postal Union and UPU emblems. 10½p, Letters, UPU and African Postal Union emblems.

1974, Sept. 9 Litho. Perf. 13½
278 A68   2p multicolored   .25   .20
279 A68   4p lt blue & multi   .50   .30
280 A68   10½p lilac & multi   1.90   .50
    Nos. 278-280 (3)   2.65 1.00

Centenary of Universal Postal Union.

Ali Abdel Latif, Abdel Fadil Elmaz, Revolutionary Flag and Nile — A69

1975, July 26 Litho. Perf. 14x13½
281 A69   2½p green & vio blue   .25   .20
282 A69   4p rose & vio blue   .50   .20
283 A69   10½p sepia & vio blue   1.25   .55
    Nos. 281-283 (3)   2.00   .95

50th anniversary of 1924 revolution. Portraits show political and military leaders of the revolution.

ADB Emblem with Map of Africa A70

1975, July 26
284 A70   2½p multicolored   .25   .20
285 A70   4p multicolored   .45   .20
286 A70   10½p multicolored   1.25   .55
    Nos. 284-286 (3)   1.95   .95

African Development Bank, 10th anniv.

Radar Station and Camel Rider — A71

1976, Feb. 2 Litho. Perf. 13½x14
287 A71   2½p lt green & multi   .20   .20
288 A71   4p lilac & multi   .40   .20
289 A71   10½p vio blue & multi   1.50   .55
    Nos. 287-289 (3)   2.15   .95

Umm Haraz Satellite Station.

IWY Emblem, Flag and Woman A72

1976, May 10 Litho. Perf. 14x13½
290 A72   2½p multicolored   .20   .20
291 A72   4p multicolored   .40   .20
292 A72   10½p dk blue & multi   1.25   .55
    Nos. 290-292 (3)   1.85   .95

International Women's Year 1975.

Arms of Sudan, Olympic Rings, Track — A73

1976, July 17 Litho. Perf. 13½x14
293 A73   2½p green & multi   .50   .20
294 A73   4p green & multi   .55   .30
295 A73   10½p green & multi   1.25   .70
    Nos. 293-295 (3)   2.30 1.20

21st Olympic Games, Montreal, Canada, July 17-Aug. 1.

Education, Engineering, Forestry, Agriculture and Defense — A74

1977, July 20 Litho. Perf. 13½x14
296 A74   2½p multicolored   .20   .20
297 A74   4p multicolored   .30   .45
298 A74   10½p multicolored   .90   .40
    Nos. 296-298 (3)   1.40 1.05

5th anniversary of national unity.

Archbishop Capucci — A75

1977, Oct. 22 Photo. Perf. 11x11½
299 A75   2½p black   .75   .20
300 A75   4p black & green   1.00   .45
301 A75   10½p black & red   1.50   .65
    Nos. 299-301 (3)   3.25 1.30

Palestinian Archbishop Hilarion Capucci, jailed by Israel in 1974.

Fair Emblem, Sudanese Flag A76

Perf. 11½x 11
1978, Jan. 19 Photo. Wmk. 342
302 A76   3p multicolored   .25   .20
303 A76   4p multicolored   .40   .20
304 A76   10½p multicolored   .65   .40
    Nos. 302-304 (3)   1.30   .80

International Khartoum Fair, Jan. 19-27.

APU Emblem A77

1978, Mar. 8 Litho. Perf. 14x13½
305 A77   3p black, car & sil   .25   .20
306 A77   4p dk green, blk & sil   .30   .20
307 A77   10½p ultra, blk & sil   .75   .40
    Nos. 305-307 (3)   1.30   .80

APU, 25th anniv. (in 1977).

Jinnah and Sudanese Flag A78

1978, May 6 Litho. Perf. 13
308 A78   3p multicolored   .20   .20
309 A78   4p multicolored   .40   .20
310 A78   10½p multicolored   .70   .40
    Nos. 308-310 (3)   1.30   .80

Mohammed Ali Jinnah (1876-1948), first Governor General of Pakistan.

Desert A79

1978, May 6 Perf. 14x13½
311 A79   3p multicolored   .20   .20
312 A79   4p multicolored   .45   .20
313 A79   10½p multicolored   1.25   .65
    Nos. 311-313 (3)   1.90 1.05

UN Desertification Conference.

Lion God Apedemek, African Unity Emblems — A80

1978, July 18 Litho. Perf. 13½x14
314 A80   3p multicolored   .25   .20
315 A80   4p multicolored   .35   .20
316 A80   10½p multicolored   1.25   .45
    Nos. 314-316 (3)   1.85   .85

15th African Summit Conference, Khartoum, July 18-21.

A81

A82

1979, Oct. 1 Litho. Perf. 13½x14
317 A81   3½p multicolored   .30   .20
318 A81   6p multicolored   .50   .20
319 A81   13p multicolored   1.00   .45
    Nos. 317-319 (3)   1.80   .85

May Revolution, 10th Anniversary.

1980, Jan. 19　Litho.　Perf. 13½x14
320 A82　4½p orange & black　　.40　.20
321 A82　8p olive green & blk　　.75　.40
322 A82　15½p blue & black　　1.50　.55
　　　Nos. 320-322 (3)　　2.65　1.15
UNESCO emblem, children holding globe.

IYC
Emblem,
Hands
Protecting
Child
A83

1980, Mar. 15　　　Perf. 14x13½
323 A83　4½p multicolored　　.40　.25
324 A83　8p multicolored　　.55　.40
325 A83　15½p multicolored　　1.90　.50
　　　Nos. 323-325 (3)　　2.85　1.15
International Year of the Child (1979).

25th Anniv. of Independence — A84

1982, Mar. 4　Photo.　Perf. 11½
326 A84　60m multicolored　　.50　.20
327 A84　120m multicolored　　1.00　.30
328 A84　250m multicolored　　1.75　.75
　　　Nos. 326-328 (3)　　3.25　1.25

World Food
Day, Oct.
16, 1981
A85

1983, Jan. 15　Photo.　Perf. 11½
329 A85　60m Emblem on map,
　　　　　　reaching hands　　.35　.20
330 A85　120m Produce　　.80　.35
331 A85　250m Map, grain　　2.00　.65
　　　Nos. 329-331 (3)　　3.15　1.20

A86

A87

1984, Feb. 20　Litho.　Perf. 13½
332 A86　10p pink & silver　　.20　.20
333 A86　25p lt blue & silver　　.60　.45
334 A86　40p green & silver　　1.10　.80
　　　Nos. 332-334 (3)　　1.90　1.45
25th Anniv. of Economic Commission for
Africa (1983).

1984, June 16　Litho.　Perf. 14
335 A87　10p multicolored　　.30　.20
336 A87　25p multicolored　　.75　.55
337 A87　40p multicolored　　1.40　.70
　　　Nos. 335-337 (3)　　2.45　1.45
Cent. of Shaykan Battle, Kordofan (1983).

Olympic
Week
A88

1984, Dec. 1　Litho.　Perf. 14
338 A88　10p multicolored　　.40　.20
339 A88　25p multicolored　　.80　.45
340 A88　40p multicolored　　1.50　.70
　　　Nos. 338-340 (3)　　2.70　1.35

Sudan-Egypt
Integration
Charter, 2nd
Anniv. — A89

Bakht Erruda,
Teacher Training
Institute — A90

1985, Mar. 16　Photo.　Perf. 13½x13
341 A89　10p multicolored　　.40　.20
342 A89　25p multicolored　　.75　.55
343 A89　40p multicolored　　1.40　.65
　　　Nos. 341-343 (3)　　2.55　1.40

1985, Apr. 1
344 A90　10p multicolored　　.40　.20
345 A90　25p multicolored　　.80　.55
346 A90　40p multicolored　　1.25　.65
　　　Nos. 344-346 (3)　　2.45　1.40

April 6
Uprising,
1st Anniv.
A91

1986, Apr. 1　Litho.　Perf. 14
347 A91　5p multicolored　　.25　.20
348 A91　25p multicolored　　.70　.40
349 A91　40p multicolored　　1.50　.65
　　　Nos. 347-349 (3)　　2.45　1.25

World Food
Day 1986
A92

**Perf. 13x13½, 13½x13 (30p), 14
(50p)**
1988, Jan. 1　　　　　　Litho.
350　A92　25p Net fishermen　　.45　.20
351　A92　30p Two fish, vert.　　.50　.20
352　A92　50p Globe　　.70　.45
353　A92　75p Stylized fish on
　　　　　　　wave　　1.10　.65
354　A92　300p Fish in sea　　4.50　2.00
　　　Nos. 350-354 (5)　　7.25　3.50
Souvenir Sheet
Imperf
354A　A92　75p like 25p　　2.75　2.75

Child
Survival — A93

Perf. 14, Imperf. (No. 357)
1988, Mar. 15　　　　　Litho.
355　A93　50p Breast-feeding,
　　　　　　　vert.　　.70　.30
356　A93　75p Oral rehydration　　1.25　.40
357　A93　75p like 50p, vert.　　1.75　1.75
358　A93　100p Oral vaccine　　1.50　.65
359　A93　150p Growth monitoring　2.25　.95
　　　Nos. 355-359 (5)　　7.45　4.05
No. 357 issued without gum. Size: 63x84mm.

Red Crescent in
Sudan, 30th
Anniv. (in
1987) — A94

World Food Day,
Oct. 16, 1987,
and the Small
Farmer — A95

Designs: 100p, Crescent, candle. 150p,
Crescent, stylized figure of a man.

1988, Oct. 31　Litho.　Perf. 14
360　A94　40p org yel, blk & dk
　　　　　　red　　.50　.30
361　A94　100p blk, blue grn & dk
　　　　　　red　　1.25　.60
362　A94　150p blk, brt blue & dk
　　　　　　red　　1.75　.95
　　　Nos. 360-362 (3)　　3.50　1.85
Nos. 361-362 horiz.

1988, Oct. 31　Perf. 13x13½, 13½x13
FAO emblem and: 40p, Early farming tools,
horiz. 100p, Ox-drawn plow. 150p, Crude public water supply.
363　A95　40p multicolored　　.50　.30
364　A95　100p shown　　1.25　.65
365　A95　150p multicolored　　1.75　.95
　　　Nos. 363-365 (3)　　3.50　1.90

Khartoum
Bank, 75th
Anniv.
A96

Designs: 40p, Anniv. emblem. 100p,
Spheres, emblem, medallion on ribbon. 150p,
Text, emblem.

1988, Oct. 31　　　　　Perf. 14
366　A96　40p multicolored　　.50　.30
367　A96　100p multicolored　　1.25　.65
368　A96　150p multicolored　　1.75　.95
　　　Nos. 366-368 (3)　　3.50　1.90

Declaration of
Palestinian State,
1st Anniv. — A97

#370, 372, 374, Crowd of demonstrators.

1989, Dec. 10　Litho.　Perf. 14
369 A97　100p yellow grn & multi　2.00　.75
370 A97　100p buff & multi　　2.25　.75
371 A97　150p lt vio & multi　　2.75　1.25
372 A97　150p lt blue & multi　　3.00　1.25
373 A97　200p pink & multi　　4.00　1.50
374 A97　200p lt green & multi　　4.00　1.50
　　　Nos. 369-374 (6)　　18.00　7.00
Palestinian Uprising (Nos. 370, 372, 374).

African Development Bank, 25th
Anniv. — A99

1989, Dec. 28　　　　Perf. 13x13½
375 A99　100p yel grn, blk & sil　2.00　.65
376 A99　150p blue, blk & sil　　3.00　1.00
377 A99　200p plum, blk & sil　　4.00　1.50
　　　Nos. 375-377 (3)　　9.00　3.15

Independence,
33rd Anniv. (in
1989) — A100

1990, Jan. 22　Litho.　Perf. 13½x13
378 A100　50p blue & yellow　　.75　.20
379 A100　100p deep claret & yel　1.50　.50
380 A100　150p brt rose & yel　　2.00　.75
381 A100　200p dp rose lil & yel　2.75　1.00
　　　Nos. 378-381 (4)　　7.00　2.45

Mammals
A101

1990, Feb. 20　　　　Perf. 13x13½
382 A101　25p Leopard　　1.00　.25
383 A101　50p Elephant　　1.50　.50
Perf. 14
384 A101　75p Giraffe, vert.　　2.25　.75
385 A101　100p White rhinocer-
　　　　　　　os　　2.75　1.00
386 A101　125p Addax, vert.　　3.75　1.25
　　　Nos. 382-386 (5)　　11.25　3.75
No. 385 inscribed "Rino."

Birds — A102

1990, Mar. 25   Perf. 13½x13
387 A102 25p Zande hornbill   .75   .20
388 A102 50p Marabou stork   1.50   .50
389 A102 75p Buff-crested
                bustard   2.25   .80
390 A102 100p Saddle-bill   3.00 1.00
Perf. 14
391 A102 150p Bald-headed
                ibis   4.00 1.25
   Nos. 387-391 (5)   11.50 3.75

Traditional
Dances
A103

Perf. 13x13½, 13½x13
1990, May 10   Litho.
392 A103 25p Mardoum   .45   .30
393 A103 50p Zandi, vert.   1.00   .40
394 A103 75p Kambala, vert.   1.50   .60
395 A103 100p Nubian, vert.   1.75   .75
396 A103 125p Sword   2.25   .95
   Nos. 392-396 (5)   6.95 3.00

Natl. Salvation
Revolution, 1st
Anniv. — A104

1991, Apr. 14   Litho.   Perf. 13
399 A104 150p multicolored   1.25   .75
400 A104 200p multicolored   1.75 1.00
401 A104 250p multicolored   2.00 1.25
402 A104 £5 multicolored   3.75 2.50
403 A104 £10 multicolored   7.50 4.75
   Nos. 399-403 (5)   16.25 10.25

For surcharge see No. 438.

Type of 1962 and:

Shoebill   Camel Postman
A105   A109

1991, July 1   Perf. 13½x13
404 A105 25p shown   .20   .20
405 A105 50p Sunflower   .40   .25
406 A105 75p Gum Arabic   .60   .40
407 A105 100p Cotton   .80   .50
408 A105 250p Crowned
                crane   1.00   .55
Size: 30x24mm
Perf. 14x14½, 13½x14
409 A105 150p Kenana
                Sugar Co.,
                horiz.   1.25   .75
410 A105 175p Secretary
                bird   1.50   .85
411 A105 £2 Atbara ce-
                ment facto-
                ry, horiz.   2.00   .95
Size: 26x37mm
Perf. 14
412 A105 250p King
                Taharqa
                statue   2.50 1.25
413 A105 £3 Republican
                palace   3.00 1.50
Size: 24x30mm
Perf. 13½x14
414 A105 £4 Hug jar   3.75 2.00
415 A105 £5 Gabana cof-
                fee pot   4.50 2.40

Size: 36x27mm
Litho. & Engr.
Perf. 14
Wmk. 334
416 A109 £8 Pterois
                volitans,
                horiz.   6.50 4.00
417 A109 £10 Animal
                wealth,
                horiz.   9.00 4.75
418 A109 £15 Nubian ibex   12.50 7.00
419 A109 £20 shown   17.50 9.50
   Nos. 404-419 (16)   67.00 36.85

For surcharges on No. 416, see Nos. 605-
606.

1992 Litho. Unwmk. Perf. 14½x14
420 A25 25p Cattle   .20   .20

1990   Unwmk.   Perf. 14x13½
427 A25 £5 Bohein Temple   4.50 2.50
Perf. 13½x14
428 A26 £10 Sailboat   9.00 4.75

This is an expanding set. Numbers will
change if necessary.
   See Nos. O76-O100. For surcharges see
Nos. 430, 436-453, O104-O111.

No. 156a Handstamp Surcharged in
Blue Violet

1990, Sept.   Perf. 13½x14
430 A26 £1 on 10p #156a   35.00 8.00
Surcharge on No. 430 is often incomplete.

Pan-African
Rinderpest
Campaign
A114

Perf. 13½x13
1991, July 27   Litho.   Unwmk.
431 A114 £1 black & brt grn   1.50   .50
432 A114 £2 dp violet & emer   3.00 1.75
433 A114 £5 orange & blue
                grn   7.50 2.50
   Nos. 431-433 (3)   12.00 4.75

Nos. 404, 407, 411, 413-414
Surcharged in Black or Blue Violet

Nos. 406, 409, 420 Surcharged

Nos. 405//420 Surcharged

5d   No. 409 Surcharged
                    in Black

No. 406   No. 412
Surcharged in   Surcharged in Red
Black

35d

No. 408 Surcharged

No. 408 Surcharged

1992?-97
Perfs. & Printing Methods as Before
436 A105   1d on 100p
                #407 (Blk)   5.00 2.50
437 A105   2d on £2 #411   9.00 4.75
438 A104 2.50d on 25p
                #404   12.50 5.75
438A A105 2.50d on 25p
                #420   2.50 1.75
439 A105   3d on £3 #413   15.00 7.00
440 A105   4d on £4 #414   17.50 9.50
441 A105   5d on 50p
                #405   2.75   .90
443 A105 7.50d on 75p
                #406   7.50 5.00
446 A105 1.50d on 150p
                #409   1.50 1.00
447 A105   15d on 150p
                #409   4.00   —
448 A105   25d on 75p
                #406   —   —
449 A105   25d on 250p
                #412   7.00 4.00
451 A105   35d on £8 #416   8.00 5.00
   a. Inverted surcharge
452 A105 100d on 125p
                #408   5.75 5.75
453 A105 100d on 125p
                #408 (R)   50.00   —
   Nos. 436-453 (14)   148.00 52.90

This is an expanding set. Numbers will
change if necessary.

Intl. Human
Rights
Day — A115

Fung Sultanate,
5th Cent. — A116

Designs: £5, Chain links, rainbow of colors,
horiz. 750p, Trellis, rose, inscription.

1993, Dec. 20   Litho.   Perf. 14
454 A115 £4 multicolored   1.00   .65
455 A115 £5 multicolored   1.25   .90
456 A115 750p multicolored   1.75 1.25
   Nos. 454-456 (3)   4.00 2.80

1993, Dec. 20
Designs: £5, Inscription on tablet. 750p,
Inscription in circle, helmet, horiz.
457 A116 £4 multicolored   1.00   .65
458 A116 £5 multicolored   1.25   .90
459 A116 750p multicolored   1.75 1.25
   Nos. 457-459 (3)   4.00 2.80

Wild
Ass — A117

A118

1994, July 15   Litho.   Perf. 14½
460 A117 4d With young   1.25   .50
461 A117 8d Standing   1.75 1.00
462 A117 10d Running   2.25 1.25
463 A117 15d Up close   3.25 2.00
   Nos. 460-463 (4)   8.50 4.75

1994, Aug. 1   Litho.   Perf. 14
464 A118 5d vermilion & multi   .50   .40
465 A118 7d green & multi   1.00   .55
466 A118 15d gray & multi   2.00 1.10
   Nos. 464-466 (3)   3.50 2.05

Intl. Olympic Committee, cent.

A119   A120

1994, Dec. 7   Litho.   Perf. 13½
467 A119 5d lilac & multi   .35   .25
468 A119 7d brown & multi   .60   .45
469 A119 15d brown & multi   1.25   .95
   Nos. 467-469 (3)   2.20 1.65

ICAO, 50th anniv.

1995, July 15   Litho.   Perf. 14
1994 World Cup Soccer Championships,
US: 4d, Goalie, green vest. 5d, Like 4d, blue
vest. 7d, Player about to kick ball, green shirt.
8d, Like 7d, brown shirt. 10d, Player, long-
sleeved shirt. 15d, Player, yellow shirt. 20d,
Player, magenta & blue background. 25d,
Player, white shirt & pants. 35d, Like 20d, blue
& green background.
   75d, Goalie, orange shirt, horiz. 100d,
Player kicking ball, horiz.
470 A120 4d multicolored   .40   .25
471 A120 5d multicolored   .40   .25
472 A120 7d multicolored   .60   .35
473 A120 8d multicolored   .70   .35
474 A120 10d multicolored   .85   .50
475 A120 15d multicolored   1.00   .50
476 A120 20d multicolored   1.75 1.00
477 A120 25d multicolored   2.00 1.25
478 A120 35d multicolored   3.00 1.50
   Nos. 470-478 (9)   10.70 5.95
Souvenir Sheets
479 A120 75d multicolored   7.50 7.50
480 A120 100d multicolored   11.50 11.50

A121

A122

1995, Dec. 16   Litho.   Perf. 13½
481 A121 15d apple grn & blk   1.50   1.00
482 A121 25d blue & black   2.75   1.50
483 A121 30d purple & black   3.25   2.00
  Nos. 481-483 (3)   7.50   4.50

Arab League, 50th anniv.

1996, May 4   Litho.   Perf. 13½
484 A122 15d orange & multi   1.50   1.00
485 A122 25d apple grn & multi   2.75   1.50
486 A122 30d purple & multi   3.25   2.00
  Nos. 484-486 (3)   7.50   4.50

Common Market for East and South Africa (COMESA).

A123

A124

1997, Jan. 22   Photo.   Perf. 13½
487 A123 25d black & violet   2.00   1.75
488 A123 35d black & red brown   3.25   2.00
489 A123 50d black & brown   4.25   3.00
  Nos. 487-489 (3)   9.50   6.75

Abdel Rahman el Mahdi (1885-1959).

1997, June 1   Photo.   Perf. 13½x13
490 A124 5d multicolored   .75   .40

Waiting For Peace.

A125

A126

1997, Oct. 15   Photo.   Perf. 13½
491 A125 25d lilac & multi   1.75   1.50
492 A125 35d apple grn & multi   2.75   2.00
493 A125 50d green, black & sil   3.50   2.75
  Nos. 491-493 (3)   8.00   6.25

Police Commanders, Arab Security Conference, 25th anniv.

1997, Nov. 1

Al-Shaykh Qaribulla's Mosque:Various views of mosque.
494 A126 25d blue & multi   1.50   1.25
495 A126 35d yellow & multi   2.50   1.75
496 A126 50d buff & multi, vert.   3.50   2.50
  Nos. 494-496 (3)   7.50   5.50

A127

A128

1998, Jan. 18   Litho.   Perf. 13½
497 A127 25d multicolored   1.50   1.00
498 A127 35d violet & multi   2.50   2.00
499 A127 50d multicolored   3.25   2.50
  Nos. 497-499 (3)   7.25   5.50

Pan African Postal Union, 18th anniv.

1998, Jan. 25   Perf. 13½x13, 13x13½
Sudanese Archeology: No. 500, Kerma pottery, 2500 BC. No. 501, Fresco, Faras church, 11th cent. No. 502, Close-up of fresco, Faras Church, 11th cent. 60d, C Group church, 2000 BC. No. 504, Meroe pottery, 4000 BC. No. 505, Tomb of Natakamani Meroitic king, 1st cent. BC, vert. 100d, C Group pottery, 2000 BC, diff.

500 A128 50d multicolored   2.00   1.50
501 A128 50d multicolored   2.00   1.50
502 A128 50d multicolored   2.00   1.50
503 A128 60d multicolored   2.25   1.75
504 A128 75d multicolored   3.00   2.00
505 A128 75d multicolored   3.00   2.00
506 A128 100d multicolored   4.00   3.00
  Nos. 500-506 (7)   18.25   13.25

A129

A130

1998, Mar. 1   Perf. 13x13½
507 A129 100d Ruins, Camel
  Post rider   7.00   6.00

First Sudanese Postage Stamp, cent.

1999, May 15   Litho.   Perf. 13¼x13½
508 A130 75d multicolored   4.50   3.00
509 A130 100d green & multi   6.00   5.00
510 A130 150d blue & multi   9.00   3.50
  Nos. 508-510 (3)   19.50   11.50

Battle of Kerreri, cent.

American Bombing of Elshifa Pharmaceuticals Factory, Aug. 20, 1998 — A131

75d, Bomb damage. 100d, Company emblem, falling bombs. 150d, Casualties.

Perf. 13¾x13½, 13¾x13¼
1999, July 1   Litho.
511 A131 75d multi   4.50   3.00
512 A131 100d multi, vert.   6.00   5.00
513 A131 150d multi   9.00   7.00
  Nos. 511-513 (3)   19.50   15.00

A132

A133

Perf. 13¼x13½, 13½x13¼
1999, Oct. 20   Litho.
514 A132 75d shown   4.50   3.00
515 A133 100d shown   6.00   5.00
516 A132 150d 7 people   9.00   7.00
  Nos. 514-516 (3)   19.50   15.00

Intl. Year of the Elderly.

SOS Children's Villages, 50th Anniv. — A134

1999, Oct. 31   Perf. 13½x13¼
517 A134 75d brn & multi   4.50   3.00
518 A134 100d grn & multi   6.00   5.00
519 A134 150d blue & multi   9.00   7.00
  Nos. 517-519 (3)   19.50   15.00

UPU, 125th Anniv. (in 1999) — A134a

2000, Mar. 1   Litho.   Perf. 13½x13¼
Denomination   Color
519A A134a 75d red   4.75   3.50
519B A134a 100d violet   6.25   5.50
519C A134a 150d black   9.50   7.50
  Nos. 519A-519C (3)   20.50   16.50

Common Market for Eastern and Southern Africa Free Trade Area — A135

Panel color: 100d, White. 150d, Pink. 200d, Yellow.

2000, Oct. 31   Litho.   Perf. 13¼x13¾
520-522 A135   Set of 3   25.00   25.00

UN High Commissioner for Refugees, 50th Anniv. — A136

Frame color: 100d, Green. 150d, Red. 200d, Violet.

Perf. 13¼x13½
2001, Aug. 15   Litho.
523-525 A136   Set of 3   25.00   25.00

Al-Zubair Prize for Innovation and Scientific Excellence A137

Frame color: 100d, Yellow. 150d, Red. 200d, Green.

2002, Feb. 14   Perf. 13¼
526-528 A137   Set of 3   27.50   27.50

Association for the Promotion of Scientific Innovation — A138

Frame color: 100d, Black. 150d, Red. 200d, Green.

2002, Feb. 14
529-531 A138   Set of 3   27.50   27.50

Year of Dialogue Among Civilizations A139

Country name in: 100d, Red. 150d, Orange. 200d, Black.

2002, Jan. 28   Litho.   Perf. 13¼x13¾
532-534 A139   Set of 3   — —

Guinea Worm Eradication Campaign A140

Designs: 100d, Infested foot, campaign emblem. 150d, Campaign emblem. 200d, Child, campaign emblem.

2002, Mar. 3   Litho.   Perf. 13¼
535-537 A140   Set of 3   27.50   27.50

Palestinian Intifada — A141

Country name in: 100d, Green. 150d, Red. 200d, Black.

Perf. 13½x13¼
2002, Feb. 14   Litho.
538-540 A141   Set of 3   27.50   27.50

Sudanese postal officials have declared as illegal the following items:
  Sheets of six stamps depicting Pope John Paul II (2 different)
  Miniature sheet of two stamps depicting Pope John Paul II (2 different).

Association of African Banknote and Security Document Printers 11th Annual Conference — A142

Conference emblem and: 100d, Association emblem, circular design. 150d, Banknote rosettes. 200d, Archaeological ruins.

2003, May 10   Litho.   Perf. 13½x13¼
541-543 A142   Set of 3   35.00   35.00

Mango — A143   Nile Perch — A144

Cattle — A145   Soldiers — A146

Muhammad Ahmad (Al-Mahdi, 1844-85), Religious Leader — A147

Butterflyfish — A148

Temple of Amun Ra — A149

Baobab Tree — A150

Doum Palm Tree — A151

Sheep — A152

Grapefruit A153

Oil Rigs A154

Tomb of Sheikh El-Mursi A155

Camel Postman A156

Perf. 13½x13¼, 13¼x13½

2003, July 15

544	A143	50d multi	.75	.75
545	A144	50d multi	.75	.75
546	A145	75d multi	1.25	1.25
547	A146	100d multi	1.50	1.50
548	A147	100d multi	1.50	1.50
549	A148	125d multi	2.00	2.00
550	A149	150d multi	2.25	2.25
551	A150	150d multi	2.25	2.25
552	A151	150d multi	2.25	2.25
553	A152	150d multi	2.25	2.25
554	A153	200d multi	3.00	3.00
555	A154	200d multi	3.00	3.00
556	A155	300d multi	4.50	4.50
557	A156	500d multi	7.50	7.50
a.	Souvenir sheet, #544-557, imperf.		32.50	32.50
	Nos. 544-557 (14)		34.75	34.75

Parliament, 50th Anniv. — A157

Panel colors: 100d, Lilac. 200d, Yellow orange. 250d, Pink.

2004, Jan. 5   **Perf. 13½x13¼**
558-560   A157   Set of 3   9.25 9.25

General Secretariat for Council of Ministers, 50th Anniv. — A158

Panel colors: 100d, Light blue. 200d, Yellow. 250d, Pink.

2004, Jan. 8
561-563   A158   Set of 3   9.25 9.25

Rural Women's Innovation — A159

Panel colors: 100d, Light blue. 200d, Yellow. 250d, Lilac.

2004, Jan. 26
564-566   A159   Set of 3   9.25 9.25

Armed Forces, 50th Anniv. — A160

Background color: 100d, Orange. 200d, Red. 250d, Purple.

2004, Aug. 14   **Litho.**
567-569   A160   Set of 3   10.00 10.00

Peace — A161

Background color: 200d, Dark blue. 300d, Green and yellow, 400d, Light blue.

2005, Jan. 9   **Perf. 13½x13¼**
570-572   A161   Set of 3   15.50 15.50

7th Conference of Sudanese Women's General Union — A162

Panel color: 200d, White. 300d, Lilac. 400d, Light blue.

Perf. 13½x13¼
2005, June 29   **Litho.**
573-575   A162   Set of 3   14.00 14.00

Merowe Dam Project — A163

Background color: 200d, Light blue. 300d, Light green. 400d, Lilac.

2005, June 30
576-578   A163   Set of 3   12.50 12.50

World Summit on the Information Society, Tunis — A164

Background color: 200d, Yellow green. 300d, Blue. 400d, Yellow orange.

2005, Sept. 24
579-581   A164   Set of 3   12.50 12.50

Merowe Dam Housing Rehabilitation Projects — A165

Denomination in: 200d, Black. 300d, Green. 400d, Red.

2005, Oct. 1   **Litho.**   **Perf. 13¼x13¾**
582-584   A165   Set of 3   12.50 12.50

Merowe Dam Archaeology Project — A166

Map and clay pot: 200d, Shown. 300d, With blue panel. 400d, With peach panel.

2005, Dec. 20   **Perf. 13¾x13¼**
585-587   A166   Set of 3   12.50 12.50

A167

A168

Independence, 50th Anniv. — A169

Perf. 13¼x13¾, 13¾x13¼

2006, Jan. 15

588	A167	200d multi	2.25	2.25
589	A168	300d multi	4.00	4.00
590	A169	400d multi	5.00	5.00
	Nos. 588-590 (3)		11.25	11.25

OPEC Intl. Development Fund, 30th Anniv. — A170

Background color: 200d, Red. 300d, Green. 400d, Blue.

2006, Oct. 12   **Litho.**   **Perf. 13¾x13½**
591-593   A170   Set of 3   9.00 9.00

100 qirsh = 1 pound

African Soccer Confederation, 50th Anniv. — A171

Background colors; £2, Pink. £3.50, Pale yellow. £4.50, White.

Perf. 13¾x13½
2007, Feb. 11   **Litho.**
594-596   A171   Set of 3   10.00 10.00

10th Meeting of Regional African Satellite Communications Organization A172

Background colors: £1, Lilac. £2, Light green. £3.50, Yellow. £4.50, Blue.

2007   **Perf. 13½x13¾**
597-600   A172   Set of 4   11.00 11.00

24th Universal Postal Union Congress, Nairobi — A173

Panel color: £1, Lilac. £2, Brown. £3.50, Blue. £4.50, Ocher.

2008   **Perf. 13¾x13½**
601-604   A173   Set of 4   11.00 11.00

Due to political unrest in Kenya, the UPU Congress was moved to Geneva, Switzerland.

No. 416 Surcharged in Black or Red

Methods, Perfs and Watermarks As Before

2008

605	A109	£2 on £8 #416 (Bk)	6.75	6.75
606	A109	£2 on £8 #416 (R)	4.00	4.00

Comprehensive Peace Agreement, 3rd Anniv. — A174

Panel color in: £1, Blue. £2, Black. £3.50, Green. £4.50, Brown.

Perf. 13¾x13½

2008   **Litho.**   **Unwmk.**

607-610	A174	Set of 4	14.50	14.50

AIR POST STAMPS

Nos. 40-41, 43 Overprinted in Black

Nos. C1-C2   No. C3

1931   Wmk. 214   Perf. 11½x12½, 14

C1	A2	5m blk & olive brown	.75	1.00
C2	A2	10m blk & carmine	1.25	4.00
C3	A1	2p org & vio brown	2.00	3.50
		Nos. C1-C3 (3)	4.00	8.50

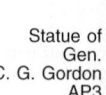

Statue of Gen. C. G. Gordon AP3

1931-35   Engr.   Perf. 14

C4	AP3	3m dk brn & grn ('33)	3.00	7.25
C5	AP3	5m grn & blk	1.10	.20
C6	AP3	10m car rose & blk	1.10	.25
C7	AP3	15m dk brn & brn	.45	.20
C8	AP3	2p org & blk	.40	.20
C9	AP3	2½p bl & red vio ('33)	3.75	.20
C10	AP3	3p gray & blk	.70	.20
C11	AP3	3½p dl vio & blk	1.75	.90
C12	AP3	4½p gray & brn	11.50	16.50
C13	AP3	5p ultra & blk	1.25	.35
C14	AP3	7½p pck grn & dk grn ('35)	11.00	6.00
C15	AP3	10p peacock bl & sep ('35)	10.50	2.00
		Nos. C4-C15 (12)	46.50	34.25

See Nos. C23-C30. For surcharges see Nos. C17-C22, C31-C34.

No. 43 Surcharged in Black

1932, July 18   Typo.

C16	A1	2½p on 2p	2.00	4.00

Nos. C6, C4-C5, C12 Surcharged

1935   Engr.   Perf. 14

C17	AP3	15m on 10m	.45	.20
a.		Double surcharge	700.00	775.00
b.		Arabic characters omitted	650.00	
C18	AP3	2½p on 3m	.95	6.00
a.		"½" 2¼mm high instead of 3mm	2.50	20.00
b.		Second Arabic character of surcharge omitted	55.00	125.00
C19	AP3	2½p on 5m	.60	1.75
a.		"½" 2¼mm high instead of 3mm	2.75	9.00
b.		Second Arabic character of surcharge omitted	30.00	60.00
c.		Inverted surcharge	900.00	900.00
d.		As "a," inverted	5,500.	
e.		As "b," inverted	1,500.	1,600.
f.		Pair, C19c and C19d	5,750.	
C20	AP3	3p on 4½p	2.00	18.50
C21	AP3	7½p on 4½p	7.50	52.50
a.		"7¼" instead of "7½"		
C22	AP3	10p on 4½p	7.50	52.50
		Nos. C17-C22 (6)	19.00	131.45

Type of 1931-35

1936-37   Perf. 11½x12½

C23	AP3	15m dk brn & brn ('37)	4.75	.20
C24	AP3	2p org & blk ('37)	5.25	16.00
C25	AP3	2½p bl & red vio	3.00	.20
C26	AP3	3p gray & blk ('37)	1.00	.40
C27	AP3	3½p dl vio & blk ('37)	2.50	15.00
C28	AP3	5p ultra & blk ('37)	4.25	.40
C29	AP3	7½p pck grn & dk grn ('37)	4.75	11.00
C30	AP3	10p pck bl & sep ('37)	4.75	23.50
		Nos. C23-C30 (8)	30.25	66.70

Nos. C25, C11, C14 and C15 Surcharged as in 1935

1938   Wmk. 214   Perf. 11½x12½, 14

C31	AP3	5m on 2½p	1.25	.25
C32	AP3	3p on 3½p	16.00	52.50
a.		On No. C27	400.00	500.00
C33	AP3	3p on 7½p	6.50	7.25
a.		On No. C29	400.00	500.00
C34	AP3	5p on 10p	1.25	5.50
a.		On No. C30	400.00	500.00
		Nos. C31-C34 (4)	25.00	65.50

Catalogue values for unused stamps in this section, from this point to the end of the section, are for Never Hinged items.

Bridge Over Blue Nile, Khartoum AP4

Designs: 2½p, Kassala Jebel. 3p, Water wheel. 3½p, Port Sudan. 4p, Gordon Memorial College. 4½p, Nile post boat. 6p, Suakin. 20p, General Post Office, Khartoum.

1950, July 1   Engr.   Perf. 12

C35	AP4	2p dk bl grn & blk	5.75	1.75
C36	AP4	2½p red org & bl	1.00	1.50
C37	AP4	3p dp bl & plum	4.25	1.50
C38	AP4	3½p chnt & choc	3.75	4.25
C39	AP4	4p bl & brn	1.75	3.50
C40	AP4	4½p ultra & blk	3.00	4.50

C41	AP4	6p car & blk	3.50	4.00
C42	AP4	20p plum & blk	3.00	6.75
		Nos. C35-C42 (8)	26.00	27.75

For overprints see Nos. CO1-CO8.

AIR POST OFFICIAL

Catalogue values for unused stamps in this section are for Never Hinged items.

Nos. C35 to C42 Overprinted in Carmine or Black

1950, July 1   Wmk. 214   Perf. 12

CO1	AP4	2p dk bl grn & blk (C)	18.50	3.75
CO2	AP4	2½p red org & bl	1.75	2.00
CO3	AP4	3p dp bl & plum	1.00	1.25
CO4	AP4	3½p chnt & choc	1.00	10.00
CO5	AP4	4p bl & brn	1.00	9.50
CO6	AP4	4½p ultra & blk (C)	5.00	21.00
CO7	AP4	6p car & blk (C)	1.25	5.50
CO8	AP4	20p plum & blk (C)	5.50	15.00
		Nos. CO1-CO8 (8)	35.00	68.00

POSTAGE DUE STAMPS

Postage Due Stamps of Egypt, 1889, Overprinted in Black

1897   Wmk. 119   Perf. 14

J1	D3	2m green	2.50	6.00
J2	D3	4m maroon	2.50	6.00
J3	D3	1p ultra	14.00	5.00
J4	D3	2p orange	14.00	10.00
		Nos. J1-J4 (4)	33.00	27.00

Steamboat on Nile River — D1

1901   Typo.   Wmk. 179

J5	D1	2m orange brn & blk	1.00	.85
J6	D1	4m blue green & brn	3.25	1.25
J7	D1	10m blue vio & blue grn	6.50	5.00
J8	D1	20m car rose & ultra	4.75	4.75
		Nos. J5-J8 (4)	15.50	11.85

1927-30   Wmk. Multiple S G (214)

J9	D1	2m org brn & blk ('30)	4.50	3.00
J10	D1	4m blue grn & brn	1.75	1.00
J11	D1	10m violet & blue grn	2.75	2.00
		Nos. J9-J11 (3)	9.00	6.00

Catalogue values for unused stamps in this section, from this point to the end of the section, are for Never Hinged items.

Redrawn

Bottom inscription altered — D2

1948, Jan. 1

J12	D2	2m dp orange & blk	2.75	35.00
J13	D2	4m blue grn & choc	4.50	37.50
J14	D2	10m rose lil & bl grn	26.50	19.00
a.		Wmk. 345 ('71?)		
J15	D2	20m brt car rose & ultra	28.50	30.00
a.		Wmk. 345 ('73)		
		Nos. J12-J15 (4)	62.25	121.50

ARMY OFFICIAL STAMPS

Regular Issues of 1898 and 1902-08 Overprinted in Black:

Nos. MO1, MO3 and MO2, MO4

1905   Wmk. 71   Perf. 14

MO1	A1	1m rose & brown	180.00	190.00
a.		"OFFICIAL"	4,000.	2,500.
b.		Pair, #MO1 and #MO2	4,000.	
MO2	A1	1m rose & brown	1,800.	1,800.
		Wmk. 179		
MO3	A1	1m car rose & brn	4.25	2.50
a.		"OFFICIAL"	45.00	30.00
b.		Inverted overprint	70.00	60.00
c.		Horizontal overprint	375.00	
MO4	A1	1m car rose & brn	40.00	24.00
a.		Inverted overprint	350.00	375.00

Regular Issues of 1902-11 Overprinted in Black

1906-11

MO5	A1	1m car rose & brn	1.75	.30
a.		"Army" and "Service" 14mm apart	450.00	325.00
b.		Inverted overprint	550.00	575.00
c.		Pair, one without ovpt.		5,750.
d.		Double overprint		1,000.
e.		"Service" omitted		4,000.
MO6	A1	2m brn & grn	17.50	1.25
a.		Pair, one without ovpt.	3,450.	
b.		"Army" omitted	3,750.	
MO7	A1	3m green & violet	21.00	.50
a.		Inverted overprint	2,200.	
MO8	A1	5m blk & rose red	1.75	.20
a.		Inverted overprint		275.00
b.		Double overprint	275.00	250.00
c.		Double ovpt., one invtd.	1,100.	500.00
MO9	A1	1p yel brn & ultra	17.00	.40
a.		"Army" omitted	2,500.	2,500.
MO10	A1	2p ultra & blk ('09)	75.00	15.00
a.		Double overprint		3,400.
MO11	A1	5p grn & org brn ('08)	150.00	75.00
MO12	A1	10p dp vio & blk ('11)	625.00	750.00
		Nos. MO5-MO12 (8)	909.00	842.65

Same Overprint On Regular Issue of 1898

Wmk. 71

MO13	A1	2p ultra & black	85.00	11.50
a.		Inverted overprint		
MO14	A1	5p grn & org brn	125.00	250.00
MO15	A1	10p dp vio & blk	175.00	475.00

There are two types of this overprint which may be distinguished by the size and shape of the "y."

OFFICIAL STAMPS

Regular Issue of 1898 Overprinted in Black

1902-06   Wmk. 71   Perf. 14

O1	A1	1m rose & brown	3.00	9.75
a.		Inverted overprint	325.00	400.00
b.		Round periods	8.00	45.00
c.		Double overprint	650.00	

d.	Oval "O" in overprint	90.00		
e.	As "d," inverted overprint	5,500.		
O2	A1 10p dp vio & blk ('06)	15.00	27.50

Same Ovpt. on Stamps of 1902-11

1903-12   **Wmk. 179**

O3	A1	1m car rose & brn ('04)	.60	.20
a.	Double overprint			
O4	A1	3m grn & vio ('04)	3.00	.20
a.	Double overprint			
O5	A1	5m blk & rose red	3.00	.20
O6	A1	1p yel brn & ultra	3.00	.20
O7	A1	2p ultra & blk	27.50	.20
O8	A1	5p grn & org brn	2.75	.40
O9	A1	10p dp vio & blk	5.00	67.50
	Nos. O3-O9 (7)		44.85	68.95

Regular Issue of 1927-40 Overprinted in Black

Perf. 14, 13½x 14

1936-46   **Wmk. 214**

O10	A2	1m dk org & int blk ('46)	2.00	10.00
O11	A2	2m dk brn & dk org ('45)	2.00	.20
O12	A2	3m green & vio ('37)	1.50	.20
O13	A2	4m brown & green	2.75	1.00
O14	A2	5m blk & ol brn ('40)	.70	.20
O15	A2	10m blk & car ('46)	.70	.20
O16	A2	15m org brn & ultra ('37)	7.00	.35

O17	A1	2p org & vio brn	11.00	.20
O18	A1	3p dk bl & red brn ('46)	5.00	3.00
O19	A1	4p blk & ultra ('46)	20.00	5.50
O20	A1	5p dk grn & org brn	7.00	.20
O21	A1	6p blk & pale bl ('46)	5.00	7.00
O22	A1	8p blk & pck grn ('46)	4.00	22.50
O23	A1	10p dp vio & blk ('37)	35.00	6.50
O24	A1	20p bl & lt bl ('46)	24.00	25.00
	Nos. O10-O24 (15)		127.65	82.05

> **Catalogue values for unused stamps in this section, from this point to the end of the section, are for Never Hinged items.**

#79-85 Overprinted Like #O10-O16

1948, Jan. 1

O28	A7	1m dk org & blk	.45	4.50
O29	A7	2m choc & org	1.75	.20
O30	A7	3m grn & rose lil	4.75	10.00
O31	A7	4m choc & sl grn	4.50	5.00
O32	A7	5m blk & ol brn	4.50	.20
O33	A7	10m blk & car	4.00	1.00
O34	A7	15m org brn & ultra	4.75	.20

Nos. 86-94 Overprinted Like Nos. O17-O24

O35	A8	2p org yel & vio brn	4.75	.20
O36	A8	3p dk bl & red brn	4.75	.20
O37	A8	4p blk & ultra	4.00	.20
a.	Perf. 13		10.50	18.00
O38	A8	5p dk grn & org	5.50	.20
O39	A8	6p blk & pale bl	4.00	.20
O40	A8	8p blk & pck grn	4.00	5.00
O41	A8	10p dp rose lil & blk	7.50	.20
O42	A8	20p bl & bl	5.50	1.00
a.	Perf. 13			
O43	A8	50p ultra & car	80.00	70.00
	Nos. O28-O43 (16)		144.70	98.30

Nos. 98-104 Overprinted Liked Nos. O10-O16 in Red

1951, Sept. 1   **Wmk. 214**   **Perf. 14**

Center in Black

O44	A11	1m orange	.70	4.00
O45	A11	2m ultra	.70	1.00
O46	A11	3m dk grn	8.00	16.00
O47	A11	4m emerald	.20	6.00

O48	A11	5m plum	.20	.20
O49	A11	10m light blue	.20	.20
O50	A11	15m dp org & blk	1.00	.20

Nos. 105-114 Overprinted Like Nos. O17-O24 in Black or Red

Perf. 13

O51	A12	2p lt bl & dk bl	.20	.20
a.	Inverted overprint		725.00	
O52	A12	3p vio bl & brn	15.00	.20
O53	A12	3½p brn & dk grn	.80	.40
O54	A12	4p blk & dp bl	2.75	.20
O55	A12	5p emer & org brn	.85	.20
O56	A12	6p blk & bl	1.00	3.00
O57	A12	8p brn & dp bl	1.40	.35
O58	A12	10p grn & blk (R)	1.75	.35
O59	A12	20p blk & car	2.75	1.25
a.	Inverted overprint		700.00	
O60	A13	50p blk & car	8.50	4.00
	Nos. O44-O60 (17)		46.00	37.75

No. 112 Overprinted Like Nos.O17-O24 in Black

1958

O61	A12	10p green & black	20.00	3.00

Nos. 146-159 Overprinted

Perf. 14½x14, 14x14½

1962, Oct. 1   **Litho.**   **Wmk. 345**

Size: 23x19mm, 19x23mm

O62	A25	5m blue	.20	.20
O63	A26	10m blue & lilac	.20	.20
O64	A25	15m yel, vio, org & brn	.20	.20
O65	A25	2p lt pur	.25	.20
O66	A26	3p bl grn, red brn & brn	.50	.20
O67	A26	35m yel grn, brn & org brn	.60	.25
O68	A26	4p red, lt bl & lil	.75	.30
O69	A25	55m gray & yel ol	1.00	.50
O70	A25	6p brn & lt bl	1.00	.50
O71	A25	8p green	1.25	.60

Size: 24½x30mm, 30x24½mm

O72	A26	10p lt bl, red brn & blk	1.50	.65
O73	A25	20p gray ol & yel grn	3.00	1.40
a.	Perf. 13½x12½		2.75	1.10
b.	Perf. 13½x14		8.00	1.90
O74	A25	50p dk gray, ol & bl	7.50	3.50
a.	Perf. 13½x14		6.50	3.25

Engr.

O75	A13	£1 grn & brn org	19.00	12.50
	Nos. O62-O75 (14)		36.95	21.20

The overprint measures 12x4½mm on Nos. O62-O71; 16x6mm on Nos. O72-O75.

1975-79   **Unwmk.**

Same Perfs., Sizes and Printing Methods as Before

O62a	A25	5m	.20	.20
O63a	A26	10m ('76)	.20	.20
O64a	A25	15m	.20	.20
O65a	A25	2p	.20	.20
O66a	A26	3p	.35	.25
O67a	A26	35m	.40	.25
O68a	A26	4p	.45	.20
O69a	A25	55m	.75	.45
O70a	A25	6p ('76)	.80	.45
O71a	A25	8p	1.10	.55
O72a	A26	10p	1.50	.70
O73a	A25	20p	2.50	1.25
O74b	A25	50p	2.50	1.25
O75a	A13	£1 ('79)	19.00	12.50
	Nos. O62a-O75a (14)		30.15	18.70

Nos. 404-419 Overprinted

Perf. 13½x13

1991, July 1   **Litho.**   **Unwmk.**

O76	A105	25p on #404	.20	.20
O77	A105	50p on #405	.20	.20
O78	A105	75p on #406	.40	.25
O79	A105	100p on #407	.50	.35
O80	A105	125p on #408	.60	.40

Size: 30x24mm

Perf. 14x14½, 13½x14

O81	A105	150p on #409	.70	.45
O82	A105	175p on #410	.85	.55
O83	A105	£2 on #411	1.00	.65

Size: 26x37mm

Perf. 14

O84	A105	250p on #412	1.25	.75
O85	A105	£3 on #413	1.40	.95

Size: 24x30mm

Perf. 13½x14

O86	A105	£4 on #414	2.00	1.25
O87	A105	£5 on #415	2.50	1.50

Size: 36x27mm

Perf. 14

Wmk. 334

O88	A105	£8 on #416	4.00	2.75
O89	A105	£10 on #417	4.75	3.75
O90	A105	£15 on #418	7.00	5.75
O91	A105	£20 on #419	9.50	7.50
	Nos. O76-O91 (16)		36.85	27.25

For surcharges see Nos. O104-O111.

Nos. 420, 427-428 Overprinted

1992   **Litho.**   **Unwmk.**   **Perf. 14½**

O92	A25	25p on #420	.25	.20

Perf. 14x13½, 13½x14

O99	A25	£5 on #427	2.50	1.75
O100	A25	£10 on #428	5.25	3.50
	Nos. O92-O100 (3)		8.00	5.45

Nos. O79, O81, O83, O85-O87 Surcharged in Blue Violet or Black

Perf. 13½x13

1993?   **Litho.**   **Unwmk.**

O104	A105	1d on 100p #O79	1.00	.65

Perf. 13½x14

O105	A105	1.50d on 150p #O81	1.50	1.00
O107	A105	2d on £2 #O83	2.00	1.25

Perf. 14

O109	A105	3d on £3 #O85	3.00	2.00

Perf. 14½x14

O110	A105	4d on £4 #O86	4.00	2.75

Perf. 13½x14

O111	A105	5d on £5 #O87 (Blk)	5.00	3.25

Perf. 14

Size: 36x27mm

O112	A109	35d on £8 #O88	14.50	14.50
	Nos. O104-O112 (7)		31.00	25.40

Coat of Arms — O1

2003   **Litho.**   **Perf. 13½x13¼**

O113	O1	50d multi	.50	.50
O114	O1	100d multi	.95	.95
O115	O1	200d multi	1.90	1.90
O116	O1	300d multi	3.00	3.00
	Nos. O113-O116 (4)		6.35	6.35

SURINAM

ˈsur-ə-ˌnam

(Dutch Guiana)

LOCATION — On the northeast coast of South America, bordering on the Atlantic Ocean
GOVT. — Republic
AREA — 63,234 sq. mi.

POP. — 431,156 (1999 est.)
CAPITAL — Paramaribo

The Dutch colony of Surinam became an integral part of the Kingdom of the Netherlands under the Constitution of 1954. It became an independent state November 25, 1975.

100 Cents = 1 Gulden (Florin)
100 Cents = 1 Dollar (2004)

> **Catalogue values for unused stamps in this country are for Never Hinged items, beginning with Scott 168 in the regular postage section, Scott B34 in the semi-postal section, Scott C23 in the airpost section, Scott CB1 in the airpost semi-postal section, and Scott J33 in the postage due section.**

Watermark

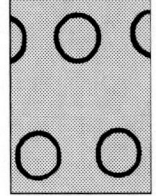

Wmk. 202 — Circles

> Early issues of Surinam were sent to the colony without gum. Many of these were subsequently gummed locally.

King William III — A1   Numeral of Value — A2

Perf. 11½, 11½x12, 12½x12, 13½, 14

1873-89   **Typo.**   **Unwmk.**

Without Gum

1	A1	1c lil gray ('85)	2.10	2.40
2	A1	2c yellow ('85)	1.40	1.40
3	A1	2½c rose	1.40	1.40
4	A1	3c green	17.50	15.00
5	A1	5c dull violet	15.00	4.75
6	A1	10c bister	3.25	2.25
7	A1	12½c sl bl ('85)	17.00	6.75
8	A1	15c gray ('89)	20.00	6.75
9	A1	20c green ('89)	30.00	27.50
10	A1	25c grnsh blue	70.00	8.00
11	A1	25c ultra	240.00	19.00
12	A1	30c red brn ('88)	30.00	32.50
13	A1	40c dk brn ('89)	27.50	26.00
14	A1	50c brown org	26.00	17.00
15	A1	1g red brn & gray ('89)	42.50	42.50
16	A1	2.50g grn & org ('79)	65.00	57.50
	Nos. 1-16 (16)		608.65	271.70

Perf. 14, Small Holes

3b	A1	2½c rose	10.00	11.50
4b	A1	3c green	18.00	24.00
5b	A1	5c dull violet	18.00	15.00
6b	A1	10c bister	17.00	20.00
11b	A1	25c ultra	225.00	60.00
14b	A1	50c brown org	47.50	40.00
	Nos. 3b-14b (6)		335.50	170.50

The paper of Nos. 3-6, 11 and 14 sometimes has an accidental bluish tinge of varying strength. During its manufacture a chemical whitener (bluing agent) was added in varying quantities. No particular printing was made on bluish paper.
"Small hole" varieties have the spaces between the holes wider than the diameter of the holes.
Nos. 1-16 and 3b-14b exist with gum.
For surcharges see Nos. 23, 31-35, 39-42.

1890   **Perf. 11½x11, 12½**

Without Gum

17	A2	1c gray	1.60	1.10
18	A2	2c yellow brn	2.50	2.00
19	A2	2½c carmine	2.00	1.60

20	A2	3c green	4.75	3.25
21	A2	5c ultra	21.00	1.10
		Nos. 17-21 (5)	31.85	9.05

Nos. 17-21 exist with gum.
For surcharges see Nos. 63-64.

A3

1892, Aug. 11   *Perf. 10½*
Without Gum

22	A3	2½c black & org	1.50	1.00
a.		First and fifth vertical words have fancy "F"	22.50	14.00
b.		Imperf.	2.00	
c.		As "a," imperf.	27.50	

No. 14 Surcharged in
Black

2½ CENT.

1892, Aug. 1   *Perf. 14*
Without Gum

23	A1	2½c on 50c	210.00	10.00
a.		Perf. 12½x12	300.00	9.00
b.		Perf. 11½x12	350.00	12.50
c.		Double surcharge	300.00	225.00
d.		Perf. 14, small holes	225.00	12.50

Nos. 23-23c were issued without gum.

Queen
Wilhelmina — A5

1892-93		**Typo.**	*Perf. 12½*	
		Without Gum		
25	A5	10c bister	35.00	2.75
26	A5	12½c rose lilac	40.00	4.75
27	A5	15c gray	3.25	2.25
28	A5	20c green	3.75	2.75
29	A5	25c blue	8.25	4.75
30	A5	30c red brown	4.75	4.00
		Nos. 25-30 (6)	95.00	21.25

Nos. 25-30 exist with gum.
For surcharges see Nos. 65-66.

Nos. 7-12 Surcharged

1898		*Perf. 11½x12, 12½x12, 13½*		
		Without Gum		
31	A1	10c on 12½c sl bl	22.50	3.25
32	A1	10c on 15c gray	52.50	45.00
33	A1	10c on 20c green	4.25	4.25
34	A1	10c on 25c grnsh bl	9.00	5.25
c.		Perf. 11½x12	10.00	10.00
34A	A1	10c on 25c ultra	475.00	425.00
b.		Perf. 11½x12	550.00	475.00
35	A1	10c on 30c red brn	4.25	4.25
a.		Double surcharge	275.00	

Dangerous counterfeits exist.

Netherlands Nos. 80, 83-84
Surcharged

50 Cᵀᵀ

SURINAME
No. 36   Nos. 37-38

1900, Jan. 8   *Perf. 12½*
Without Gum

36	A11	50c on 50c	22.50	8.50

Engr.
Perf. 11½x11

37	A12	100c on 1g dk grn	22.50	13.50
38	A12	2.50g on 2½g brn lil	20.00	12.50
		Nos. 36-38 (3)	65.00	34.50

For surcharge see No. 67.

Nos. 13-16 Surcharged

25 cent

Perf. 11½, 11½x12, 12½x12, 14
1900   **Typo.**
Without Gum

39	A1	25c on 40c	5.00	3.50
40	A1	25c on 50c	5.00	3.50
a.		Perf. 14, small holes	110.00	125.00
b.		Perf. 11½x12	3.75	3.75
41	A1	50c on 1g	40.00	35.00
42	A1	50c on 2.50g	140.00	160.00
		Nos. 39-42 (4)	190.00	202.00

Counterfeits of No. 42 exist.

A9

Queen Wilhelmina
A10   A11

1902-08		**Typo.**	*Perf. 12½*	
		Without Gum		
44	A9	½c violet	1.00	.90
45	A9	1c olive grn	2.10	1.25
46	A9	2c yellow brn	11.50	4.50
47	A9	2½c blue grn	5.00	.45
48	A9	3c orange	8.25	5.25
49	A9	5c red	8.25	.45
50	A9	7½c gray ('08)	18.00	8.25
51	A10	10c slate	12.00	.95
52	A10	12½c deep blue	4.50	.45
53	A10	15c dp brown	30.00	10.50
54	A10	20c olive grn	27.50	5.25
55	A10	22½c brn & ol grn	24.00	13.00
56	A10	25c violet	20.00	1.25
57	A10	30c orange brn	47.50	15.00
58	A10	50c lake brown	37.50	9.25

Engr.
Perf. 11

59	A11	1g violet	60.00	20.00
60	A11	2½g slate blue	60.00	65.00
		Nos. 44-60 (17)	377.10	161.70

Nos. 44-60 exist with gum.

A12

1909 Typeset *Serrate Roulette 13½*
Without Gum

61	A12	5c red	13.50	11.50
a.		Tête bêche pair	190.00	175.00

Perf. 11½x10½

62	A12	5c red	14.50	12.00
a.		Tête bêche pair	140.00	140.00

Nos. 17-18, 29-30, 38 Surcharged in
Red

Nos. 63-64   Nos. 65-66

No. 67

1911, July 15   **Typo.**   *Perf. 12½*
Without Gum

63	A2	½c on 1c	1.75	1.10
64	A2	½c on 2c	12.25	9.00
65	A5	15c on 25c	75.00	57.50
66	A5	20c on 30c	14.00	9.50

Engr.
Perf. 11½x11

67	A12	30c on 2.50g on 2½g	125.00	110.00
		Nos. 63-67 (5)	228.00	187.10

A13

1912, July   **Typeset**   *Perf. 11½*
Without Gum

70	A13	½c lilac	.95	.95
a.		Horiz. pair, imperf. btwn.	200.00	
71	A13	2½c dk green	.95	.95
72	A13	5c pale red	8.75	8.75
a.		Vert. pair, imperf. btwn.	240.00	
73	A13	12½c deep blue	11.00	11.00
		Nos. 70-73 (4)	21.65	21.65

Numeral of
Value — A14

Queen Wilhelmina
A15   A16

1913-31		**Typo.**	*Perf. 12½*	
74	A14	½c violet	.40	.25
75	A14	1c olive green	.40	.20
76	A14	1½c blue, perf 11½ ('21)	.40	.20
a.		Perf. 12½ ('32)	1.10	.85
77	A14	2c yellow brn	1.60	1.10
78	A14	2½c green	.95	.20
79	A14	3c yellow	.80	.65
80	A14	3c green ('26)	3.25	2.50
81	A14	4c chlky bl ('26)	8.25	5.00
82	A14	5c rose	1.60	.20
83	A14	5c green ('22)	2.00	1.00
84	A14	5c lilac ('26)	1.60	.20
85	A14	6c bister ('26)	2.75	2.50
86	A14	6c red org ('31)	2.25	.50
87	A14	7½c drab	1.00	.40
a.		Perf. 11x11½	1.40	
88	A14	7½c orange ('27)	1.40	.40
89	A14	7½c yellow ('31)	9.25	9.25
90	A14	10c violet ('22)	5.00	5.00
91	A14	10c rose ('26)	4.00	.55
92	A15	10c car rose	1.40	.65
93	A15	12½c blue	1.90	.65
94	A15	12½c red ('22)	2.00	2.25
95	A15	15c olive grn	.55	.70
96	A15	15c lt blue ('26)	7.75	4.75
97	A15	20c green	3.50	3.25
98	A15	20c blue ('22)	2.50	2.00
99	A15	20c ol green ('26)	3.50	2.75
100	A15	22½c orange	2.50	2.50
101	A15	25c red violet	4.00	.40
102	A15	30c slate	5.00	1.10
103	A15	32½c vio & org ('22)	15.00	17.50
104	A15	35c sl & red ('26)	5.00	5.00

Perf. 11, 11½, 11½x11, 12½
Engr.

105	A16	50c green	4.00	.85
a.		Perf. 12½ ('32)	14.00	1.60
106	A16	1g brown	5.50	.50
a.		Perf. 12½ ('32)	15.00	1.00
107	A16	1½g dp vio ('26)	35.00	35.00
108	A16	2½g carmine ('23)	30.00	26.00
a.		Perf. 11½x11	35.00	32.50
		Nos. 74-108 (35)	176.00	135.95

Nos. 74, 75, 77-79, 82, 87, 105, 106 and 108 were issued both with and without gum.
Early printings of Nos. 74-104 had water soluble ink.
For surcharges see Nos. 116-120, 139.

Queen
Wilhelmina — A17

1923, Oct. 5		*Perf. 11, 11x11½, 11½*		
109	A17	5c green	1.10	.70
110	A17	10c car rose	1.75	1.50
111	A17	20c indigo	3.50	3.00
112	A17	50c brown org	19.00	19.00
113	A17	1g brown vio	26.00	17.00
114	A17	2½g gray blk	75.00	200.00
115	A17	5g brown	100.00	240.00
		Nos. 109-115 (7)	226.35	481.20

25th anniv. of the assumption of the government of the Netherlands by Queen Wilhelmina, at age 18.
Values for Nos. 114-115 used are for copies clearly dated before July 15, 1924.

Nos. 83, 93-94, 98 Surcharged in
Black or Red:

j   k

m

1925, Dec. 19   Typo.   *Perf. 12½*
116 A14   3c on 5c green   1.10 1.10
117 A15 10c on 12½c red   2.25 2.25
118 A15 15c on 12½c blue (R)   1.60 1.60
119 A15 15c on 20c blue   1.60 1.60
   Nos. 116-119 (4)   6.55 6.55

No. 100 Surcharged in
Blue

1926, Jan. 1
120 A15 12½c on 22½c org   27.50 27.50

Postage Due Stamps Nos. J14 and
J29 Surcharged in Blue or Black:

o   p

121 D2(o) 12½c on 40c (Bl)   3.25 3.25
122 D2(p) 12½c on 40c (Bk)   30.00 30.00
   Nos. 120-122 (3)   60.75 60.75

No. 121 issued without gum.

Queen
Wilhelmina — A21

1927-30   Engr.   *Perf. 11½*
123 A21 10c carmine   1.00   .40
124 A21 12½c red orange   1.75 1.90
125 A21 15c dark blue   2.00   .60
126 A21 20c indigo   2.00   .80
127 A21 21c dk brown ('30)   19.00 19.00
128 A21 22½c brown ('28)   8.00 9.75
129 A21 25c dk violet   3.00   .70
130 A21 30c dk green   3.00 1.10
131 A21 35c black brown   3.00 3.00
   Nos. 123-131 (9)   42.75 37.25

Types of Netherlands
Marine Insurance
Stamps Inscribed
"SURINAME" and
Surcharged

1927, Oct. 26
132 MI1   3c on 15c dk grn   .65   .65
133 MI1 10c on 60c car rose   .65   .65
134 MI1 12½c on 75c gray brn   .65   .65
135 MI2 15c on 1.50 dk blue   2.75 2.75
136 MI2 25c on 2.25g org
                           brn   7.25 7.25
137 MI3 30c on 4⅛g black   9.00 7.25
138 MI3 50c on 7⅛g red   7.25 7.25
   Nos. 132-138 (7)   28.20 26.45

Nos. 135-137 have "FRANKEERZEGEL" in
small capitals in one line. Nos. 135 and 136
have a heavy bar across the top of the stamp.

No. 88 Surcharged

1930, Mar. 1   Typo.   *Perf. 12½*
139 A14   6c on 7½c orange   1.90 1.00

Prince William I
(Portrait by Van
Key) — A22

1933, Apr. 24   Photo.
141 A22   6c deep orange   6.75 1.90

400th birth anniv. of Prince William I, Count
of Nassau and Prince of Orange, frequently
referred to as William the Silent.

Van   Queen
Walbeeck's   Wilhelmina
Ship   A24
A23

1936-41   Litho.   *Perf. 13½x12½*
142 A23   ½c yellow brn   .30   .30
143 A23   1c lt yellow grn   .40   .20
144 A23   1½c brt blue   .55   .40
145 A23   2c black brown   .60   .25
146 A23   2½c green   .25   .20
  a.   Perf. 13 ('41)   9.00 3.25
147 A23   3c dark ultra   .60   .40
148 A23   4c orange   .60   .75
149 A23   5c gray   .60   .20
150 A23   6c red   2.50 2.00
151 A23   7½c red violet   .25   .20
  a.   7½c plum, perf. 13 ('41) 3.00   .25

Engr.
Perf. 14, 12½
Size: 20x30mm
152 A24 10c vermilion   .85   .20
  a.   Perf. 12½ ('39)   60.00 11.50
153 A24 12½c dull green   3.50 1.25
154 A24 15c dark blue   1.25   .60
155 A24 20c yellow org   2.10   .60
156 A24 21c dk gray   3.25 3.00
  a.   Perf. 12½ ('39)   3.75 3.75
157 A24 25c brown lake   2.40 1.00
158 A24 30c brown vio   3.75 1.00
159 A24 35c olive brown   4.00 4.00

Perf. 12½x14
Size: 22x33mm
160 A24 50c dull yel grn   4.00 2.00
161 A24   1g dull blue   8.25 3.00
162 A24   1.50g black brown   22.50 18.00
163 A24   2.50g rose lake   13.50 9.50
   Nos. 142-163 (22)   76.00 49.05

For surcharges see Nos. 181-183, 209-210,
B37-B40.

Queen
Wilhelmina — A25

1938, Aug. 30   Photo.   Wmk. 202
164 A25   2c dull purple   .50   .30
165 A25   7½c red orange   1.50 1.25
166 A25 15c royal blue   3.00 3.00
   Nos. 164-166 (3)   5.00 4.55

Reign of Queen Wilhelmina, 40th anniv.

Catalogue values for unused stamps in this section, from this point to the end of the section, are for Never Hinged items.

Van   Queen
Walbeeck's   Wilhelmina
Ship   A27
A26

1941   Unwmk.   Typo.   *Perf. 12*
168 A26   1c lt yellow grn   .80   .20
169 A26   2c black brown   1.90 1.90

Type A26 is similar to type A23 except for
the white side frame lines which extend to the
base.
For surcharges see No. 180.

1941-46   Photo.   *Perf. 13½x12½*
Size: 18x22½mm
174 A27 12½c royal blue ('46)   .25   .20
          Perf. 12½
175 A27 15c ultra   22.50 8.25

Royal Family — A28

1943, Nov. 2   Engr.   *Perf. 13½x13*
176 A28   2½c deep orange   .25   .35
177 A28   7½c red   .25   .20
178 A28 15c black   2.50 2.10
179 A28 40c deep blue   3.00 2.50
   Nos. 176-179 (4)   6.00 5.15

Birth of Princess Margriet Francisca of the
Netherlands.

Nos. 168, 151, 152 Surcharged with
New Values and Bars in Black
1945   Unwmk.   *Perf. 13, 14, 12*
180 A26   ½c on 1c   .20   .20
181 A23   2½c on 7½c   2.00 1.75
182 A24   5c on 10c   .70   .40
183 A24   7½c on 10c   .80   .40
  a.   Double surcharge   225.00 190.00
   Nos. 180-183 (4)   3.70 2.75

Bauxite
Mine,
Moengo
A29

Queen Wilhelmina
A30   A31

Designs: 1½c, Bush Negroes on Cottica
River near Moengo. 2c, Waterfall in interior.
2½c, Road scene, Coronie District. 3c, Surinam River near Berg en Dahl Plantation. 4c,
Government Square, Paramaribo. 5c, Mining

gold. 6c, Street in Paramaribo. 7½c, Sugar
cane train.

1945, Nov. 5   Engr.   *Perf. 12*
184 A29   1c rose carmine   .25   .25
185 A29   1½c rose lake   1.25 1.25
186 A29   2c violet   .55   .40
187 A29   2½c olive brn   .55   .40
188 A29   3c dull green   1.25   .70
189 A29   4c brown   1.25   .75
190 A29   5c blue   1.25   .25
191 A29   6c olive   2.25 1.60
192 A29   7½c deep orange   .80   .35
193 A30 10c blue   1.60   .20
194 A30 15c brown   2.00   .25
195 A30 20c dull green   3.25   .20
196 A30 22½c gray   3.75   .40
197 A30 25c carmine   10.00 4.50
198 A30 30c olive green   10.00   .55
199 A30 35c brt blue grn   17.00 7.25
200 A30 40c rose lake   9.75   .25
201 A30 50c red orange   9.75   .25
202 A30 60c violet   9.75   .80
203 A31   1g red brown   12.00   .35
204 A31   1.50g lilac   10.00   .80
205 A31   2.50g olive brn   20.00   .95
206 A31   5g rose carmine   45.00 12.50
207 A31 10g red orange   77.50 19.00
   Nos. 184-207 (24)   250.75 54.70

For surcharges see #240, B41-B46, CB2-
CB3.

Nos. 151 and 152 Surcharged with
New Value and Bar in Blue or Black
1947   *Perf. 13½x12½, 14*
209 A23   1½(c) on 7½c (Bl)   .20   .20
  a.   Double surcharge   200.00
210 A24   2½c on 10c (Bk)   .90   .30

Numeral   Queen
A32   Wilhelmina
                             A33

1948, July 21   Unwmk.   Photo.
          Perf. 12½x13½
211 A32   1c dark red   .20   .20
212 A32   1½c plum   .20   .20
213 A32   2c purple   .20   .20
214 A32   2½c olive grn   1.25   .20
215 A32   3c dark green   .20   .20
216 A32   4c red brown   .20   .20
          Perf. 13½x12½
217 A33   5c deep blue   .35   .20
218 A33   6c dark olive   .85   .65
219 A33   7½c scarlet   .35   .20
220 A33 10c blue   .50   .20
221 A33 12½c dark blue   1.10 1.00
222 A33 15c henna brown   1.50   .40
223 A33 17½c dk vio brn   1.60 1.25
224 A33 20c dk blue grn   1.40   .20
225 A33 22½c slate blue   1.40   .65
226 A33 25c crimson   1.40   .30
227 A33 27½c car lake   1.40   .20
228 A33 30c olive green   1.60   .20
229 A33 37½c olive brn   2.75 1.90
230 A33 40c lilac rose   1.90   .30
231 A33 50c red orange   1.90   .30
232 A33 60c purple   2.10   .40
233 A33 70c black   2.50   .65
   Nos. 211-233 (23)   26.85 10.20

See Nos. 241-242.

Wilhelmina - Juliana
A34   A35

1948, Aug. 30   Engr.   *Perf. 12½x14*
234 A34   7½c vermilion   .85 .85
235 A34 12½c deep blue   .85 .85

Reign of Queen Wilhelmina, 50th anniv.

          Perf. 14x13
1948, Sept. 10   Wmk. 202   Photo.
236 A35   7½c deep orange   3.50 3.50
237 A35 12½c ultra   3.50 3.50

Investiture of Queen Juliana, Sept. 6, 1948.
For surcharges see Nos. B53-B54.

Post Horns
Entwined — A36

1949, Oct. 1   Unwmk.   Perf. 11½x12
238 A36 7½c brown red   7.00 3.75
239 A36 27½c dull blue   7.00 2.75
     UPU, 75th anniversary.

No. 192 Surcharged with New Value,
Square and Bar in Black
1950, Aug. 9   Perf. 12
240 A29 1c on 7½c dp org   .60 .60

Numeral Type of 1948
1951, Apr. 5   Perf. 12½x13½
241 A32 5c deep blue   1.25 .20
242 A32 7½c deep orange   3.00 1.60

A37

Queen Juliana — A38

1951, Apr. 5   Perf. 13½x13
243 A37 10c blue   .45 .20
244 A37 15c henna brn   1.00 .20
245 A37 20c dk blue grn   2.40 .20
246 A37 25c crimson   1.50 .40
247 A37 27½c carmine lake   1.50 .20
248 A37 30c olive green   1.50 .40
249 A37 35c olive brown   1.90 1.60
250 A37 40c lilac rose   2.10 .40
251 A37 50c red orange   2.50 .45
         Engr.
         Perf. 12½x12
252 A38 1g red brown   27.50 .50
     Nos. 243-252 (10)   42.35 4.55
     For surcharge see No. 271.

Shooting Fish
A39

Fisherman
A40

Designs: 5c, Bauxite mining. 6c, Log raft.
7½c, Plowing with Water Buffalo. 10c, Woman
picking fruit. 12½c, Armored catfish. 15c,
Macaw. 17½c, Armadillo. 20c, Poling canoe.
25c, Common iguana.

1953-55 Photo.   Perf. 14x13, 13x14
253 A39 2c olive green   .20 .20
254 A40 2½c blue green   .30 .20
255 A40 5c gray   .50 .20
256 A40 6c bright blue   2.50 1.75
257 A40 7½c purple   .20 .20
258 A40 10c bright red   .20 .20
259 A40 12½c dk gray blue   3.25 2.10
260 A40 15c crimson   1.10 .20
261 A40 17½c red brown   5.00 3.00
262 A40 20c Prus green   .90 .20
263 A40 25c olive green   4.50 1.25
  a.   Min. sheet of 4, #259-261, 263 90.00 90.00
     Nos. 253-263 (11)   18.65 9.50

Issued: 2c, 7½c, 10c, 20c, 5/9/53; #263a,
2/14/55; others, 12/1/54.

Queen
Juliana — A41

Harvesting
Bananas — A46

1954, Dec. 15   Perf. 13½
264 A41 7½c dark red brown   .90 .90
     Charter of the Kingdom, adopted Dec. 15,
1954.

1955, May 12   Perf. 14x13
     Designs: 7½c, Pounding rice. 10c, Prepar-
ing cassava. 15c, Fishing.
265 A46 2c dark green   2.10 2.10
266 A46 7½c dull yellow   3.25 3.00
267 A46 10c orange brown   3.25 3.00
268 A46 15c ultra   3.25 3.00
     Nos. 265-268 (4)   11.85 11.10
     4th anniv. of the establishment of the Carib-
bean Tourist Assoc.

Globe and
Mercury's Rod
A47

Flags and Map
of Caribbean
A48

1955, Sept. 19 Unwmk. Perf. 13x12
269 A47 5c bright ultra   .50 .45
     Paramaribo Trade Fair, Oct. 1955.

1956, Dec. 6 Litho.   Perf. 13x14
270 A48 10c lt blue & red   .40 .35
     10th anniv. of Caribbean Commission.

No. 247 Surcharged

1958, Nov. 11 Photo. Perf. 13½x13
271 A37 8c on 27½c car lake   .20 .20

Queen
Juliana — A49

Symbolic
Flowers — A50

Perf. 12½x12
1959, Oct. 15   Unwmk.   Litho.
272 A49 1g magenta   2.00 .20
273 A49 1.50g olive bister   3.25 .80
274 A49 2.50g dk carmine   4.75 .50
275 A49 5g dull blue   9.00 .50
     Nos. 272-275 (4)   19.00 2.00

1959, Dec. 15 Photo. Perf. 12½x13
276 A50 20c multicolored   3.75 2.75
     5th anniv. of the constitution. Flowers in
design symbolize Netherlands, Surinam and
Netherlands Antilles.

Charles Lindbergh's Plane — A51

10c, De Snip plane. 15c, Cessna 170B. 20c,
Super Constellation. 40c, Boeing 707 Jet.

1960, Mar. 12   Perf. 12½
277 A51 8c chalky blue   1.25 1.40
278 A51 10c bright green   1.75 2.00
279 A51 15c rose red   1.75 2.00
280 A51 20c pale violet   2.00 2.40
281 A51 40c light brown   3.00 3.25
     Nos. 277-281 (5)   9.75 11.05
     Inauguration of Zanderij Airport, Mar. 12.
Nos. 277-281 show 25 years of Surinam's civil
aviation.

Flag of Surinam and
Map — A52

Arms of
Surinam — A53

1960, July 1 Litho.   Perf. 12½x13
282 A52 10c multicolored   .70 .70
         Perf. 13x12½
283 A53 15c multicolored   .70 .70
     Day of Freedom, July 1.

Bananas — A54

Finance
Building — A55

1961, Mar. 1 Litho.   Perf. 13½
284 A54 1c shown   .25 .25
285 A54 2c Citrus fruit   .25 .25
286 A54 3c Cacao   .25 .25

---

287 A54 4c Sugar cane   .25 .25
288 A54 5c Coffee   .25 .25
289 A54 6c Coconuts   .25 .25
290 A54 8c Rice   .25 .25
     Nos. 284-290 (7)   1.75 1.75

1961   Perf. 13½x14, 14x13½
     Buildings: 15c, Court of Justice. 20c, Con-
cordia Lodge (Masons). 25c, Neve Shalom
Synagogue, Paramaribo, horiz. 30c, Old
Dutch lock in New Amsterdam. 35c, Government office, horiz. 40c, Governor's palace,
horiz. 50c, Legislative Council, horiz. 60c, Old
Dutch Reformed Church, horiz. 70c, Zeelandia
Fortress, horiz.
291 A55 10c multi   .20 .20
292 A55 15c multi   .20 .20
293 A55 20c multi   .30 .30
294 A55 25c multi   .65 .65
295 A55 30c multi   1.75 1.75
296 A55 35c multi   1.75 1.75
297 A55 40c multi   .90 .90
298 A55 50c multi   .90 .90
299 A55 60c multi   1.00 1.00
300 A55 70c multi   1.10 1.10
     Nos. 291-300 (10)   8.75 8.75
     Issued: 10c, 20c, 25c, 50c, 70c, 4/1; others,
5/15.

Dag
Hammarskjold
(1905-1961)
A56

1962, Jan. 2 Litho. Perf. 11½, 12½
301 A56 10c brt blue & blk   .20 .20
302 A56 20c lilac & blk   .20 .20
     Dag Hammarskjold, Secretary General of
the United Nations, 1953-61.
     Sheets of both perfs. exist either with or
without extension of perforations through the
margins.

A56a

A57

1962, Feb. 1   Photo.   Perf. 14x13
303 A56a 20c olive green   .35 .35
     Silver wedding anniversary of Queen Juli-
ana and Prince Bernhard.

1962, May 2 Litho.   Perf. 13x14
     Malaria eradication emblem.
304 A57 8c bright red   .20 .20
305 A57 10c blue   .20 .20
     WHO drive to eradicate malaria.

Stoelmans Guesthouse — A58

Design: 15c, Torarica Hotel.

1962, July 4   Perf. 14x13½
306 A58 10c multicolored   .40 .40
307 A58 15c multicolored   .40 .40
     Opening of the Torarica Hotel in Paramaribo
and Stoelmans Guesthouse on Stoelman
Island.

Deaconess Residence and Recreation Area — A59

Design: 20c, Deaconess Hospital.

1962, Nov. 30
308 A59 10c multicolored .40 .40
309 A59 20c multicolored .40 .40

Hands Holding Wheat Emblem A60

20c, Farmer harvesting & wheat emblem, vert.

Perf. 14x13, 13x14
1963, Mar. 21 **Photo.**
310 A60 10c deep carmine .20 .20
311 A60 20c dark blue .20 .20

FAO "Freedom from Hunger" campaign.

Broken Chain — A61

1963, June 28 Litho. *Perf. 14x13*
312 A61 10c red & blk .20 .20
313 A61 20c green & blk .20 .20

Centenary of emancipation of the slaves.

Prince William of Orange Landing at Scheveningen A61a

Faja Lobbi Wreath A62

1963, Nov. 21 Photo. *Perf. 13½x14*
Size: 26x26mm
314 A61a 10c dull bl, blk & brn .20 .20

Founding of the Kingdom of the Netherlands, 150th anniv.

1964, Dec. 15 Litho. *Perf. 12½x13*
315 A62 25c multicolored .40 .40

Charter of the Kingdom of the Netherlands, 10th anniv.

Abraham Lincoln (1809-1865) — A63

1965, Apr. 14 Litho. *Perf. 12½x13*
316 A63 25c olive bister & brn .20 .20

ICY Emblem A64

1965, May 26 *Perf. 13x12½*
317 A64 10c orange & blue .20 .20
318 A64 15c red & violet bl .20 .20

International Cooperation Year.

Bauxite Mine, Moengo A65

Red-breasted Blackbird — A66

Designs: 15c, Alum Pottery Works, Paranam. 20c, Hydroelectric plant, Afobaka. 25c, Aluminum smeltery, Paranam.

1965, Oct. 9 Photo. Unwmk.
319 A65 10c ocher .55 .55
320 A65 15c dark green .55 .55
321 A65 20c dark blue .55 .55
322 A65 25c carmine .55 .55
Nos. 319-322 (4) 2.20 2.20

Opening of the Brokopondo Power Station.

1966, Feb. 16 Litho. *Perf. 13x14*
2c, Great kiskadee. 3c, Silver-beaked tanager. 4c, Ruddy ground dove. 5c, Blue-gray tanager. 6c, Glittering-throated emerald (hummingbird). 8c, Turquoise tanager. 10c, Pale-breasted robin.

323 A66 1c brt grn, blk & red .35 .35
324 A66 2c lt ultra, yel & brn .35 .35
325 A66 3c multi .35 .35
326 A66 4c lt ol grn, red brn & blk .35 .35
327 A66 5c org, ultra & blk .35 .35
328 A66 6c multi .35 .35
329 A66 8c gray, vio bl & blk .35 .35
330 A66 10c multi .35 .35
Nos. 323-330 (8) 2.80 2.80

Central Hospital A67

Design: 15c, Hospital, side view.

1966, Mar. 9 Litho. *Perf. 13x12½*
331 A67 10c multi .20 .20
332 A67 15c multi .20 .20

Opening of Central Hospital, Paramaribo.

Father Petrus Donders — A68

Designs: 10c, Church and parsonage, Batavia. 15c, Msgr. Joannes B. Swinkels. 25c, Cathedral, Paramaribo.

1966, Mar. 26 Photo. *Perf. 12½x13*
333 A68 4c org brn & blk .20 .20
334 A68 10c rose brn & blk .20 .20
335 A68 15c yel brn & blk .20 .20
336 A68 25c lt vio & blk .20 .20
Nos. 333-336 (4) .80 .80

Centenary of the Redemptorist Mission in Surinam (Congregation of the Most Holy Redeemer).

100-Year-Old Tree — A69

1966, May 9 Litho. *Perf. 13x12½*
337 A69 25c grn, dp org & blk .20 .20
338 A69 30c red org, grn & blk .20 .20

Centenary of the Surinam Parliament.

Television Transmitter, Eye and Globe — A70

1966, Oct. 20 Litho. *Perf. 12½x13*
339 A70 25c dk bl & ver .20 .20
340 A70 30c brn & ver .20 .20

Inauguration of television service.

Bauxite Industry, 1916 — A71

Design: 25c, Bauxite industry, 1966.

1966, Dec. 19 Litho. *Perf. 13x12½*
341 A71 20c yel, org & blk .20 .20
342 A71 25c org, bl & blk .20 .20

50th anniversary of bauxite industry.

Central Bank, Paramaribo A72

Design: 25c, Central Bank, different view.

1967, Apr. 1 Litho. *Perf. 13x12½*
343 A72 10c dp yel & blk .20 .20
344 A72 25c lil & blk .20 .20

Central Bank of Surinam, 10th anniv.

Amelia Earhart, Lockheed Electra and Paramaribo A73

1967, June 3 Photo. *Perf. 13x12½*
345 A73 20c yel & dk car .20 .20
346 A73 25c yel & grn .20 .20

30th anniv. of Amelia Earhart's visit to Surinam, June 3-4, 1937.

Siva Nataraja, God of Dance, and Ballerina's Foot — A74

Design: 25c, Drummer's mask "Bashi Lele," and scroll of violin.

1967, June 21 Litho. *Perf. 12½x13*
347 A74 10c yel grn & bl .20 .20
348 A74 25c yel grn & brn .20 .20

20th anniv. of the Surinam Cultural Center Foundation.

New Amsterdam, 1660 (New York City) — A75

Designs after 17th Century Engravings: 10c, Fort Zeelandia, Paramaribo, 1670. 25c, Breda Castle, Netherlands, 1667.

1967, July 31 Litho. *Perf. 13½x13*
349 A75 10c yel, blk & bl .30 .30
350 A75 20c red brn, yel & blk .30 .30
351 A75 25c bl grn, yel & blk .30 .30
Nos. 349-351 (3) .90 .90

300th anniv. of the Treaty of Breda between Britain, France and the Netherlands.

WHO Emblem A76

1968, Apr. 7 Litho. *Perf. 13x12½*
352 A76 10c magenta & dk bl .20 .20
353 A76 25c bl & dk pur .50 .50

WHO, 20th anniversary.

Chandelier and Christian Symbols A77

15c, like 10c, reversed. Brass chandelier from the Reformed Church, Paramaribo.

1968, May 29 Litho. *Perf. 13x12½*
354 A77 10c dark blue .20 .20
355 A77 25c dp yel grn .50 .50

Reformed Church of Paramaribo, 300th anniv.

Missionary Store, 1768 — A78

Designs: 25c, Main Church and store, Paramaribo, 1868. 30c, C. Kersten & Co., 1968.

1968, June 29 Litho. *Perf. 13x12½*
356 A78 10c yel & blk .20 .20
357 A78 25c lt grnsh bl & blk .20 .20
358 A78 30c lilac rose & blk .20 .20
Nos. 356-358 (3) .60 .60

200th anniv. of C. Kersten & Co., which is partially owned by the Evangelical Brotherhood Missionary Society.

Joden Savanne Synagogue A79

Mahatma Gandhi A81

Spectacled Caiman A80

Designs: 20c, Map of Joden Savanne and Surinam River. 30c, Gravestone, 1733. The Hebrew inscriptions are quotations from the Bible: 20c, Joshua 24:2; 25c, Isaiah 56:7; 30c, Genesis 31:52.

1968, Aug. 28   **Perf. 12½x13**
359 A79 20c multi   .35   .35
360 A79 25c multi   .50   .50
361 A79 30c multi   .50   .50
    Nos. 359-361 (3)   1.35 1.35

Founding of the first synagogue in the Western Hemisphere in 1685 in Joden Savanne, Surinam.

Perf. 13x12½, 12½x13
1969, Aug. 20   **Litho.**

20c, Squirrel monkey, vert. 25c, Armadillo.

362 A80 10c grn & multi   .90   .75
363 A80 20c bl gray & multi   .90   .75
364 A80 30c vio & multi   .90   .75
    Nos. 362-364 (3)   2.70 2.25

1969, Oct. 2   **Litho.**   **Perf. 12½x13**
365 A81 25c red & blk   .35   .35

Mohandas K. Gandhi (1869-1948), leader in India's fight for independence.

ILO Emblem
A82

1969, Oct. 29   **Litho.**   **Perf. 13x12½**
366 A82 10c brt bl grn & blk   .20   .20
367 A82 25c red & blk   .40   .40

ILO, 50th anniversary.

Queen Juliana
and Rising
Sun — A82a

1969, Dec. 15   **Photo.**   **Perf. 14x13**
368 A82a 25c blue & multi   .50   .50

15th anniv. of the Charter of the Kingdom of the Netherlands. Phosphorescent paper.

"1950-1970"
A83

1970, Apr. 3   **Litho.**   **Perf. 13x12½**
369 A83 10c brn, grn & org   .20   .20
370 A83 25c emer, dk bl & org   .40   .40

20th anniv. of secondary education in Surinam.

Inauguration of UPU Headquarters,
Bern — A84

Design: 25c, UPU Headquarters, sideview and UPU emblem.

1970, May 20   **Litho.**   **Perf. 13x12½**
371 A84 10c sky bl & dk pur   .20   .20
372 A84 25c red & blk   .50   .50

"UNO"
A85

Plane over
Paramaribo
A86

1970, June 26   **Litho.**   **Perf. 12½x13**
373 A85 10c ocher & yel   .20   .20
374 A85 25c dp bl & ultra   .50   .50

25th anniversary of the United Nations.

1970, July 15

Designs: 20c, Plane over map of Totness, 25c, Plane over Nieuw-Nickerie.

375 A86 10c bl, vio bl & gray   .35   .35
376 A86 20c yel, red & gray   .35   .35
377 A86 25c pink, dk red & gray   .35   .35
    Nos. 375-377 (3)   1.05 1.05

40th anniv. of domestic airmail service.

Plan of Soccer
Field and
Ball — A87

Morse
Key — A89

Cocoi Heron
A88

Plan of soccer field with ball in different positions.

1970, Oct. 1
378 A87   4c yel, red brn & blk   .20   .20
379 A87 10c pale lem, red brn &
        blk   .20   .20
380 A87 15c lt yel grn, red brn &
        blk   .20   .20
381 A87 25c lt grn, red brn & blk   .60   .60
    Nos. 378-381 (4)   1.20 1.20

50th anniv. of the Soccer Assoc. of Surinam.

1971, Feb. 14   **Litho.**   **Perf. 13x12½**

Birds in Flight: 20c, Flamingo. 25c, Scarlet macaw.

382 A88 15c gray & multi   1.25 1.25
383 A88 20c ultra & multi   1.25 1.25
384 A88 25c pale grn & multi   1.25 1.25
    Nos. 382-384 (3)   3.75 3.75

25th anniversary of regular air service between the Netherlands, Surinam and Netherlands Antilles.

1971, May 17   **Photo.**   **Perf. 12½x13**

Designs: 20c, Telephone. 25c, Lunar landing module, telescope.

385 A89 15c light green & multi   .45   .40
386 A89 20c blue & multi   .55   .55
387 A89 25c lilac & multi   .75   .60
    Nos. 385-387 (3)   1.75 1.55

3rd World Telecommunications Day.

Prince
Bernhard,
Fokker F27,
Boeing
747B — A89a

Map of
Surinam,
Population
Chart — A90

1971, June 29   **Photo.**   **Perf. 13x14**
388 A89a 25c multi   .60   .50

60th birthday of Prince Bernhard.

1971, July 31   **Litho.**   **Perf. 12½x13**

Design: 30c, Map of Surinam and individual representing population.

389 A90 15c gray bl, blk & ver   .20   .20
390 A90 30c ver, gray bl & blk   .25   .25

50th anniv. of the first census; introduction of civil registration in Surinam.

William
Mogge's Map
of Surinam
A91

1971, Oct. 27   **Perf. 11½x11**
391 A91 30c dull yel & dk brn   .80   .85

300th anniv. of the first map of Surinam.

Map of
Albina
A92

August
Kappler — A93

Drop of
Water — A94

20c, View of Albina from Maroni River.

1971, Dec. 13   **Perf. 13x12½, 12½x13**
392 A92 15c sapphire & blk   .55   .55
393 A92 20c brt grn & blk   .60   .60
394 A93 25c yel & blk   .60   .60
    Nos. 392-394 (3)   1.75 1.75

125th anniv. of the founding of Albina by August Kappler (1815-1887).

1972, Feb. 2   **Perf. 12½x13**

Design: 30c, Faucet and water tower.

395 A94 15c vio & blk   .60   .60
396 A94 30c bl & blk   .75   .75

Surinam water works, 40th anniversary.

Air Mail
Envelope
A95

1972, Aug. 2   **Litho.**   **Perf. 13x12½**
397 A95 15c red & blue   .20   .20
398 A95 30c blue & red   .25   .25

Arrival of the 1st airmail in Surinam, carried by Capt. Dutertre from French Guiana, 50th anniv.

Giant
Tree — A96

Hindu Woman in
Rice Field — A97

Designs: 20c, Wood transport by air lift. 30c, Hands tending seedling.

1972, Dec. 20   **Litho.**   **Perf. 12½x13**
399 A96 15c yel & dk brn   .20   .20
400 A96 20c bl & dp brn   .20   .20
401 A96 30c brt grn & dp brn   .95   .95
    Nos. 399-401 (3)   1.35 1.35

Surinam Forestry Commission, 25th anniv.

1973, June 5   **Litho.**   **Perf. 13½x14**

25c, J. F. A. Cateau van Rosevelt with map of Surinam, ship "Lalla Rookh." 30c, Symbolic bird, flower, sun, flag, factories.

402 A97 15c purple & yel   .45   .45
403 A97 25c maroon & gray   .45   .20
404 A97 30c yel & light blue   .50   .50
    Nos. 402-404 (3)   1.40 1.15

1st immigrants from India, cent.

Queen
Juliana,
Surinam
and House
of Orange
Colors
A97a

Engr. & Photo.
1973, Sept. 4   **Perf. 12½x12**
405 A97a 30c sil, blk & org   .80   .80

25th anniversary of reign of Queen Juliana.

INTERPOL
Emblem — A98

Mailman — A99

Design: 30c, INTERPOL emblem, Surinam visa handstamp.

1973, Nov. 7   **Litho.**   **Perf. 14x14½**
406 A98 15c vio bl & multi   .20   .20
407 A98 30c lt bl, lil & blk   .80   .80

50th anniv. of Intl. Criminal Police Org.

1973, Dec. 12   **Litho.**   **Perf. 12½x13**

15c, Pigeons carrying Letters. 30c, Map of Surinam, plane, ship, train and truck.

408 A99 15c lt yel grn & bl   .20   .20
409 A99 25c sal, blk & bl   .35   .35
410 A99 30c ver & multi   .60   .60
    Nos. 408-410 (3)   1.15 1.15

Centenary of stamps of Surinam.

Patient and Blood Transfusion A100

30c, Cross section of tissue and oscilloscope.

1974, June 1 Litho. Perf. 14½x14
411 A100 15c red brn & multi .20 .20
412 A100 30c lemon & multi .25 .25
75th anniversary of the Medical College.

Crop Dusting A101

1974, July 17 Litho. Perf. 13½
413 A101 15c shown .20 .20
414 A101 30c Fertilizer plant .25 .25
Foundation for Development of Mechanical Agriculture in Surinam, 25th anniv.

Old Title Page — A102

1974, July 31 Perf. 14x14½
415 A102 15c multicolored .20 .20
416 A102 30c multicolored .25 .25
"Weekly Wednesday Surinam Newspaper," bicent. 1st editor was Beeldsnijder Matroos.

Paramaribo Main Post Office A103

Design: 30c, Post Office, different view.

1974, Sept. 11 Litho. Perf. 14½x14
417 A103 15c brown & blk .20 .20
418 A103 30c blue & blk .70 .70
Centenary of Universal Postal Union.

Gold Panner A104

Design: 30c, Modern excavator.

1975, Feb. 5 Litho. Perf. 13x12½
419 A104 15c brown & olive bis .20 .20
420 A104 30c vermilion & maroon .50 .50
Centenary of prospecting policy granting concessions for winning of raw materials.

Symbolic Design A105

1975, June 25 Litho. Perf. 13x12½
421 A105 15c green & multi .55 .55
422 A105 25c blue & multi .60 .60
423 A105 30c red & multi .60 .60
Nos. 421-423 (3) 1.75 1.75
Cent. of Intl. Meter Convention, Paris, 1875.

Hands Holding Saw — A106

Designs: 50c, Book with notes and letter "a." 75c, Hands holding ball.

1975, Nov. 25 Litho. Perf. 13½x14
424 A106 25c yellow, red & brn .60 .60
425 A106 50c yellow, red & pur 1.40 1.40
426 A106 75c dk bl, org & emer 2.00 2.00
Nos. 424-426 (3) 4.00 4.00
Independence. Sheets of 10 (5x2) with ornamental margins.

Oncidium Lanceanum A107

Central Bank, Paramaribo A109

Orchids: 2c, Epidendrum stenopetalum. 3c, Brassia lanceana. 4c, Epidendrum ibaguense. 5c, Epidendrum fragrans.

1975-76 Litho. Perf. 14½x13½
427 A107 1c multicolored .35 .35
428 A107 2c multicolored .35 .35
429 A107 3c multicolored .35 .35
430 A107 4c multicolored .35 .35
431 A107 5c multicolored .35 .35
Perf. 14x13½
436 A109 1g rose lil & blk 1.75 .35
437 A109 1½g brn, dp org & blk 3.00 .35
438 A109 2½g red brn, org red & blk 4.50 .35
439 A109 5g grn, yel grn & blk 8.50 .35
440 A109 10g dk vio bl & blk 19.00 .95
Nos. 427-431,436-440 (10) 38.50 4.10
Issued: #436-439, Nov. 25, 1975; #427-431, Feb. 18, 1976; #440, May 5, 1976.
For surcharges see Nos. 772-774, 810.

Flag of Surinam — A110

Design: 35c, Coat of Arms.

1976, Mar. 3 Perf. 14x13½
445 A110 25c emerald & multi .65 .65
446 A110 35c red orange & multi .85 .85
Sheets of 12 (6x2) with ornamental margins.

Pomacanthus Semicirculatus — A111

Fish: 2c, Adioryx diadema. 3c, Pogonoculius zebra. 4c, Balistes vetula. 5c, Myripristis jacobus.

1976, June 2 Litho. Perf. 12½x13
447 A111 1c multicolored .20 .20
448 A111 2c multicolored .20 .20
449 A111 3c multicolored .20 .20
450 A111 4c multicolored .20 .20
451 A111 5c multicolored .25 .20
Nos. 427-431,C55-C57 (8) 7.25 4.60
See #471-475, 504-508, C72-C74, C85-C87.

19th Century Switchboard and Telephone — A112

35c, Satellite, globe and 1976 telephone.

1976, Aug. 5 Litho. Perf. 13½x14
452 A112 20c yellow & multi .45 .45
453 A112 35c ultra & multi .90 .90
Centenary of first telephone call by Alexander Graham Bell, Mar. 10, 1876.

The Story of Anansi Tori, by A. Baag — A113

Designs: 30c, "Surinam Now" (young people), by R. Chang. 35c, Lamentation, by Nola Hatterman, vert. 50c, Chess Players, by Q. Jan Telting.

Perf. 13½x14, 14x13½
1976, Sept. 29 Photo.
454 A113 20c multicolored .40 .40
455 A113 30c multicolored .70 .60
456 A113 35c multicolored .90 .70
457 A113 50c multicolored 1.25 1.25
Nos. 454-457 (4) 3.25 2.95
Paintings by Surinam artists.

Franklin's Divided Snake Poster, 1754 — A114

1976, Nov. 10 Litho. Perf. 13½x14
458 A114 20c green & blk .65 .65
459 A114 60c orange & blk 2.10 2.10
American Bicentennial.

Ionopsis Utricularioides A115

Surinam Costume A116

Orchids: 30c, Rodiguezia secunda. 35c, Oncidium pusillum. 55c, Sobralia sessilis. 60c, Octomeria surinamensis.

1977, Jan. 19 Litho. Perf. 14½x13½
460 A115 20c vermilion & multi .45 .20
461 A115 30c ultra & multi .65 .25
462 A115 35c magenta & multi .65 .50
463 A115 55c yellow & multi 1.25 .90
464 A115 60c green & multi 1.25 1.00
Nos. 460-464 (5) 4.25 2.85

1977, Mar. 2 Litho. Perf. 14x13½
Various Surinamese women's costumes.
465 A116 10c brt blue & multi .35 .35
466 A116 15c green & multi .35 .35
467 A116 35c violet & multi .45 .45
468 A116 60c orange & multi 1.00 1.00
469 A116 75c ultra & multi 1.25 1.25
470 A116 1g violet & multi 1.60 1.60
Nos. 465-470 (6) 5.00 5.00

Fish Type of 1976
Tropical Fish: 1c, Liopropoma carmabi. 2c, Holacanthus ciliaris. 3c, Opistognathus aurifrons. 4c, Anisotremus virginicus. 5c, Gramma loreto.

1977, June 8 Litho. Perf. 13x13½
471 A111 1c multicolored .20 .20
472 A111 2c multicolored .20 .20
473 A111 3c multicolored .20 .20
474 A111 4c multicolored .20 .20
475 A111 5c multicolored .20 .20
Nos. 471-475,C72-C74 (8) 6.25 4.80

Edison's Phonograph, 1877 — A117

Design: 60c, Modern turntable.

1977, Aug. 24 Litho. Perf. 13½x14
476 A117 20c multicolored .25 .25
477 A117 60c multicolored .60 .60
Invention of the phonograph, cent.

Packet Curacao, 1827 A118

Designs: 15c, Hellevoetsluis Harbor and postmark, 1827. 30c, Sea chart and technical details of packet Curacao. 35c, Logbook and compass rose. 60c, Map of Paramaribo harbor and 1852 postmark. 95c, Modern liner Stuyvesant.

1977, Sept. 28 Litho. Perf. 14x13½
478 A118 5c grnsh bl & dk bl .25 .25
479 A118 15c orange & mar .25 .25
480 A118 30c lt brn & blk .25 .25
481 A118 35c olive & blk .25 .25
482 A118 60c lilac & blk .30 .30
483 A118 95c yel grn & dk grn .70 .70
Nos. 478-483 (6) 2.00 2.00
Regular steamer connection between the Netherlands and Surinam, 150th anniversary.

Passiflora Quad-rangularis A119

Javanese Costume A120

Flowers: 30c, Centropogon surinamensis. 55c, Gloxinia perennis. 60c, Hydrocleis nymphoides. 75c, Clusia grandiflora.

1978, Feb. 8 Litho. Perf. 13x14
484 A119 20c multicolored .60 .60
485 A119 30c multicolored .60 .60
486 A119 55c multicolored .95 .75
487 A119 60c multicolored 1.10 .95
488 A119 75c multicolored 1.25 1.10
Nos. 484-488 (5) 4.50 4.00

1978, Mar. 1   Litho.   Perf. 13x14

People of Surinam, Costumes: 20c, Forest black. 35c, Chinese. 60c, Creole. 75c, Aborigine Indian. 1g, Hindustani.

489	A120	10c multicolored	.35 .35
490	A120	20c multicolored	.35 .35
491	A120	35c multicolored	.35 .35
492	A120	60c multicolored	.55 .55
493	A120	75c multicolored	.65 .65
494	A120	1g multicolored	1.00 1.00
	Nos. 489-494 (6)		3.25 3.25

Air Post Stamps
of 1972
Surcharged

1977, Nov. 15   Litho.   Perf. 13½x14

495	AP6	1c on 25c #C44	.25 .25
496	AP6	4c on 15c #C42	.25 .25
497	AP6	4c on 30c #C45	.25 .25
498	AP6	5c on 40c #C47	.35 .25
499	AP6	10c on 75c #C54	.45 .25
	Nos. 495-499 (5)		1.55 1.25

"Luchtpost" obliterated with 2 bars.

Old Municipal
Church
A121

Johannes
King — A122

Designs: 55c, New Municipal Church. 60c, Johannes Raillard.

1978, May 31   Litho.   Perf. 14x13

500	A121	10c blue, blk & gray	.25 .25
501	A122	20c gray & blk	.25 .25
502	A121	55c rose lil & blk	.40 .40
503	A122	60c orange & blk	.45 .45
	Nos. 500-503 (4)		1.35 1.35

Evangelical Brothers Community Church, Paramaribo, bicentenary.

Tropical Fish Type of 1976

Tropical Fish: 1c, Nannacara Anomala. 2c, Leporinus fasciatus. 3c, Pristella riddlei. 4c, Nannostomus beckfordi. 5c, Rivulus agilae.

1978, June 21   Perf. 12½x13½

504	A111	1c multicolored	.20 .20
505	A111	2c multicolored	.20 .20
506	A111	3c multicolored	.20 .20
507	A111	4c multicolored	.20 .20
508	A111	5c multicolored	.20 .20
	Nos. 504-508,C85-C87 (8)		5.85 4.20

Souvenir Sheet

Commewijne
River
Development
A124

Development: 60c, Map of Surinam and dam. 95c, Planes and world map.

1978, Oct. 18   Litho.   Perf. 14x13

509		Sheet of 3	2.75 2.75
a.	A124	20c multi	.20 .20
b.	A124	60c multi	.35 .35
c.	A124	95c multi	.50 .50

Coconuts   Wright Brothers' Flyer 1
A125   A126

1978-85   Litho.   Perf. 13½x13

510	A125	5c shown	.20 .20
a.		Bklt. pane, 4 #510, 3 #511, 5 #515 ('80)	2.00
511	A125	10c Oranges	.20 .20
512	A125	15c Papayas	.20 .20
a.		Bklt. pane, 5 #512, 6 #514 + label ('79)	2.00
513	A125	20c Bananas	.20 .20
514	A125	25c Soursop	.20 .20
514A	A125	30c Cocoa beans ('85)	.85 .85
b.		Bklt. pane, 6 #514A, 1 #513 + label ('85)	3.25 3.25
515	A125	35c Watermelon	.55 .55
	Nos. 510-515 (7)		2.40 2.40

Perf. 13x14, 14x13

1978, Dec. 13   Litho.

Designs: 20c, Daedalus and Icarus, vert. 95c, DC 8. 125c, Concorde.

516	A126	20c multicolored	.40 .40
517	A126	60c multicolored	.95 .95
518	A126	95c multicolored	1.40 1.40
519	A126	125c multicolored	1.75 1.75
	Nos. 516-519 (4)		4.50 4.50

75th anniversary of 1st powered flight.

Rodriguezia   Javanese
Candida   Dancer
A127   A128

Flowers: 20c, Stanhopea grandiflora. 35c, Scuticaria steelei. 60c, Bollea violacea.

1979, Feb. 7   Litho.   Perf. 13x14

520	A127	10c multicolored	.45 .45
521	A127	20c multicolored	.45 .45
522	A127	35c multicolored	.85 .60
523	A127	60c multicolored	1.10 .90
	Nos. 520-523 (4)		2.85 2.40

1979, Feb. 28

Dancing Costumes: 10c, Forest Negro. 15c, Chinese. 20c, Creole. 25c, Aborigine Indian. 35c, Hindustani.

524	A128	5c multicolored	.20 .20
525	A128	10c multicolored	.20 .20
526	A128	15c multicolored	.20 .20
527	A128	20c multicolored	.20 .20
528	A128	25c multicolored	.20 .20
529	A128	35c multicolored	.70 .70
	Nos. 524-529 (6)		1.70 1.70

Equetus
Pulchellus
A129

Tropical Fish: 2c, Apogon binotatus. 3c, Anisotremus virginicus. 5c, Bodianus rufus. 35c, Microspathodon chrysurus.

1979, May 30   Photo.   Perf. 14x13

530	A129	1c multicolored	.20 .20
531	A129	2c multicolored	.20 .20
532	A129	3c multicolored	.20 .20
533	A129	5c multicolored	.20 .20
534	A129	35c multicolored	.45 .30
	Nos. 530-534,C89-C91 (8)		5.00 3.70

See Nos. 557-561, C92-C94.

Javanese
Wooden
Head — A130

Folkart: 35c, Head ornament, Indian. 60c, Horse's head, Javanese.

1979, Aug. 29   Litho.   Perf. 14x13

535	A130	20c multicolored	.30 .30
536	A130	35c multicolored	.50 .50
537	A130	60c multicolored	.85 .85
	Nos. 535-537 (3)		1.65 1.65

Sir Rowland Hill   Javanese Girl's
A131   Costume
                         A133

SOS Emblem,
House
A132

1979, Oct. 3   Litho.   Perf. 13x14

538	A131	1g yellow & olive	1.50 1.00

Sir Rowland Hill (1795-1879), originator of penny postage.

1979, Oct. 3   Perf. 13x14

Design: 60c, SOS emblem and buildings.

539	A132	20c multicolored	.35 .35
540	A132	60c multicolored	.80 .80

Intl. Year of the Child; SOS Children's Villages, 30th anniv.

1980, Feb. 6   Photo.   Perf. 13x14

541	A133	10c Javanese girl	.40 .40
542	A133	15c Forest Black boy	.40 .40
543	A133	25c Chinese girl	.40 .40
544	A133	60c Creole girl	.95 .65
545	A133	90c Indian girl	1.10 .95
546	A133	1g Hindustani boy	1.25 1.00
	Nos. 541-546 (6)		4.50 3.80

Rotary Intl.,
75th
Anniversary
A134

20c, Handshake, Rotary emblem, vert.

Perf. 13x14, 14x13

1980, Feb. 23   Litho.

547	A134	20c ultra & yellow	.30 .30
548	A134	60c ultra & yellow	.85 .65

Rowland   Weight
Hill — A135   Lifting — A136

1980, May 6   Litho.   Perf. 13x14

549	A135	50c Mailcoach	.50 .50
550	A135	1g shown	1.25 1.25
a.		Souvenir sheet	1.10 1.10
551	A135	2g People mailing letters	2.75 2.75
	Nos. 549-551 (3)		4.50 4.50

London 1980 Intl. Stamp Exhibition, May 6-14. No. 550a contains No. 550 in changed colors. Blue and black margin shows designs of Nos. 549, 551, London 1980 emblem. (No. 550 in lilac rose and multicolored; stamps of No. 550a in light green and multicolored).

1980, June 17

552	A136	20c shown	.25 .25
553	A136	30c Diving	.45 .45
554	A136	50c Gymnast	.55 .55
555	A136	75c Basketball	1.00 1.00
556	A136	150c Running	2.00 2.00
a.		Souvenir sheet of 3, #554-556	3.75 3.75
	Nos. 552-556 (5)		4.25 4.25

22nd Summer Olympic Games, Moscow, July 19-Aug. 3.

Fish Type of 1979

Tropical Fish: 10c, Osteoglossum bicirrhosum. 15c, Colossoma species. 25c,

---

Hemigrammus pulcher. 30c, Petitella georgiae. 45c, Copeina guttata.

1980, Sept. 10   Photo.   Perf. 14x13

557	A129	10c multicolored	.20 .20
558	A129	15c multicolored	.20 .20
559	A129	25c multicolored	.20 .20
560	A129	30c multicolored	.20 .20
561	A129	45c multicolored	.70 .70
	Nos. 557-561,C92-C94 (8)		5.50 4.55

Open Hands   Passiflora
(Reflection)   Laurifolia
A137   A138

Souvenir Sheet

1980, Nov. 19   Litho.   Perf. 13x14

562		Sheet of 3	8.00 8.00
a.	A137	50c shown	.50 .50
b.	A137	1g Shaking hands (cooperation)	.90 .90
c.	A137	2g Victory sign	1.75 1.75

5th anniv. of independence.

1981, Jan. 14   Litho.   Perf. 13x14

Designs: Flower paintings by Maria Sibylle Merian (1647-1717).

563	A138	20c shown	.30 .30
564	A138	30c Aphelandra pectinata	.40 .40
565	A138	60c Caesalpinia pulcherrima	.90 .90
566	A138	75c Hibiscus mutabilis	1.00 1.00
567	A138	1.25g Hippeastrum puniceum	1.90 1.90
	Nos. 563-567 (5)		4.50 4.50

Renovation of
the Economic
Order — A139

1981, Feb. 25   Perf. 14x13

568	A139	30c shown	.25 .25
569	A139	60c Educational Order	.50 .50
570	A139	75c Social Order	.55 .55
571	A139	1g Political Order	.80 .80
a.		Souvenir sheet of 2, #569, 571	3.00 3.00
	Nos. 568-571 (4)		2.10 2.10

Government renovation.

Miniature Sheet

Youths — A140

1981, Apr. 29   Litho.   Perf. 14x13½

572	A140	Sheet of 2	2.75 2.75
a.		1g shown	.95 .95
b.		1.50g Youths, diff.	.95 .95

Youth and its future. Entire sheet in continuous design.

Souvenir Sheet

No. 424,
Exhibition
Hall — A141

1981, May 22   Litho.   Perf. 13½x14

573		Sheet of 3	5.00	5.00
a.	A141	50c shown	.55	.60
b.	A141	1g Penny Black	1.10	1.10
c.	A141	2g Austria #5	2.10	2.25

WIPA '81 Intl. Philatelic Exhibition, Vienna, May 22-31.

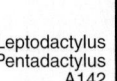

Leptodactylus Pentadactylus
A142

1981, June 24   Photo.   Perf. 14x13

574	A142	40c Phyllomedusa hypochondrialis	.75	.35
575	A142	50c shown	.95	.50
576	A142	60c Hyla boans	1.10	.65
		Nos. 574-576,C95-C97 (6)	9.00	4.80

Child Wearing Earphones
A143

1981, Sept. 16   Litho.   Perf. 14x13

580	A143	50c shown	.60	.60
581	A143	100c Child reading Braille	1.50	1.50
582	A143	150c Woman in wheelchair	2.40	2.40
		Nos. 580-582 (3)	4.50	4.50

Intl. Year of the Disabled.

Planter's House on Parakreek River — A144

Designs: Illustrations from Voyage to Surinam, by P.I. Benoit.

1981, Oct. 21   Photo.   Perf. 14x13

583	A144	20c shown	.20	.20
584	A144	30c Sarameca St., Paramaribo	.40	.40
585	A144	75c Negro Hamlet, Paramaribo	1.00	1.00
586	A144	1g Fish Market, Paramaribo	1.40	1.40
a.		Miniature sheet of 1, perf 13½x13	1.60	1.60
587	A144	1.25g Blaauwe Berg Cascade	2.00	2.00
		Nos. 583-587 (5)	5.00	5.00

Research and Peaceful Uses of Space
A145

1982, Jan. 13   Litho.

588	A145	35c Satellites	.55	.55
589	A145	65c Columbia space shuttle	1.00	1.00
590	A145	1g Apollo-Soyuz	1.50	1.50
		Nos. 588-590 (3)	3.05	3.05

Caretta Caretta
A146

1982, Feb. 17   Photo.   Perf. 14x13

591	A146	5c shown	.25	.25
592	A146	10c Chelonia mydas	.25	.25
593	A146	20c Dermochelys coriacea	.35	.25
594	A146	25c Eretmochelys imbricata	.45	.30
595	A146	35c Lepidochelys olivacea	.60	.35
		Nos. 591-595,C98-C100 (8)	6.15	4.25

25th Anniv. of Lions Intl. in Surinam
A147

1982, May 7   Litho.

596	A147	35c multicolored	.65	.65
597	A147	70c multicolored	1.25	1.25

A148   A149

1982, May 18   Litho.   Perf. 13x14

598	A148	35c Helping the sick	.75	.75
599	A148	65c Birthplace, map	1.50	1.50
a.		Souvenir sheet	1.75	1.75

Beatification of Father Petrus Donders, May 23.

1982, June 9   Litho.   Perf. 13x14

600	A149	50c Stamp designing	.75	.75
601	A149	100c Printing	1.50	1.50
602	A149	150c Collecting	2.25	2.25
a.		Souvenir sheet of 3, #600-602	5.00	5.00
		Nos. 600-602 (3)	4.50	4.50

PHILEXFRANCE '82 Stamp Exhibition, Paris, June 11-21. Nos. 600-602 in continuous design.

TB Bacillus Centenary
A150

1982, Sept. 15   Litho.   Perf. 14x13

603	A150	35c Text	.40	.40
604	A150	65c Microscope	1.10	1.10
605	A150	150c Bacillus	3.00	3.00
		Nos. 603-605 (3)	4.50	4.50

Marienburg Sugar Co. Centenary
A151

1982, Oct. 20   Litho.

606	A151	35c Mill	.50	.50
607	A151	65c Gathering cane	.90	.90
608	A151	100c Rail transport	1.60	1.60
609	A151	150c Gears	2.50	2.50
		Nos. 606-609 (4)	5.50	5.50

A152   Inga Edulis — A153

EBG Missionaries, 250th Anniv. in Caribbean: 35c, Municipal Church, horiz. 65c, St. Thomas Monastery, horiz. 150c, Johan Leonhardt Dober (1706-1766).

Perf. 14x13, 13x14

1982, Dec. 13   Litho.

610	A152	35c multicolored	.50	.50
611	A152	65c multicolored	.95	.95
612	A152	150c multicolored	2.50	2.50
		Nos. 610-612 (3)	3.95	3.95

1983, Jan. 12

Flower Paintings by Maria Sibylle Merian (1647-1717). Nos. 613-618 horiz.

613	A153	1c Erythrina fusca	.25	.25
614	A153	2c Ipomoea acuminata	.25	.25
615	A153	3c Heliconia psittacorum	.25	.25
616	A153	5c Ipomoea	.25	.25
617	A153	10c Herba non denominata	.25	.25
618	A153	15c Anacardium occidentale	.45	.45
619	A153	20c shown	.55	.55
620	A153	25c Abelmoschus moschatus	.80	.80
621	A153	30c Argemone mexicana	1.00	1.00
622	A153	35c Costus arabicus	1.10	1.10
623	A153	45c Muellera frutescens	1.25	1.25
624	A153	65c Punica granatum	2.10	2.10
		Nos. 613-624 (12)	8.50	8.50

Scouting Year — A154   500th Birth Anniv. of Raphael — A155

1983, Feb. 22   Litho.   Perf. 13x14

625	A154	40c Anniv. emblem	1.00	1.00
626	A154	65c Baden-Powell	1.50	1.50
627	A154	70c Tent, campfire	1.60	1.60
628	A154	80c Ax in log	1.75	1.75
		Nos. 625-628 (4)	5.85	5.85

1983, Apr. 13   Photo.

Crayon sketches.

629	A155	5c multicolored	.30	.30
630	A155	10c multicolored	.30	.30
631	A155	40c multicolored	.80	.80
632	A155	65c multicolored	1.25	1.25
633	A155	70c multicolored	1.25	1.25
634	A155	80c multicolored	1.50	1.50
		Nos. 629-634 (6)	5.40	5.40

1982 Coins and Banknotes
A156

1983, June 1   Litho.   Perf. 14x13

635	A156	5c 1-cent coin	.25	.25
636	A156	10c 5-cent coin	.25	.25
637	A156	40c 10-cent coin	.65	.65
638	A156	65c 25-cent coin	1.10	1.10
639	A156	70c 1g note	1.25	1.25
640	A156	80c 2.50g note	1.50	1.50
		Nos. 635-640 (6)	5.00	5.00

For surcharge & overprints see Nos. 751, J59-J60.

25th Anniv. of Dept. of Construction
A157   Manned Ballooning, 200th Anniv.
A159

Local Butterflies
A158

1983, June 15   Litho.   Perf. 13x14

641	A157	25c Map	.40	.40
642	A157	50c Map, bulldozers	.85	.85

Perf. 13x14, 14x13

1983, Sept. 14   Litho.

Drawings by Maria Sibylle Merian (1647-1717). Nos. 643-648 vert.

643	A158	1c Papile anchisiades esper	.25	.25
644	A158	2c Urania leilus	.25	.25
645	A158	3c Morpho deidamia	.25	.25
646	A158	5c Thysania aguippina	.25	.25
647	A158	10c Morpho sp.	.30	.25
648	A158	15c Metamorpha dido	.45	.30
649	A158	20c Morpho menelaus	.60	.40
650	A158	25c Manduca rustica	.85	.55
651	A158	30c Rothschildia sp.	1.00	.55
652	A158	35c Catopsilia ebule	1.25	.80
653	A158	45c Pailio androgeos	1.60	1.10
654	A148	65c Eumorpha vitis	2.40	1.60
		Nos. 643-654 (12)	9.45	6.55

1983, Oct. 19   Litho.   Perf. 13x14

Designs: 5c, 1783, sheep, cock and duck. 10c, first manned flight, d'Arlandes and Pilatre de Rozier. 40c, first hydrogen balloon, Jacques Charles. 65c, 1870, Paris flight, minister Gambetta. 70c, Double Eagle II, transatlantic flight. 80c, Intl. Balloon Festival, Albuquerque.

655	A159	5c multicolored	.20	.20
656	A159	10c multicolored	.20	.20
657	A159	40c multicolored	.95	.95
658	A159	65c multicolored	1.40	1.40
659	A159	70c multicolored	1.50	1.50
660	A159	80c multicolored	2.00	2.00
		Nos. 655-660 (6)	6.25	6.25

Martin Luther, 500th Birth Anniv. — A160

1983, Dec. 7   Litho.

661	A160	25c Portrait	.50	.50
662	A160	50c Engraving	1.25	1.10

Local Flowers
A161   Local Seashells
A162

1984, Jan. 11   Litho.

663	A161	5c Catasetum discolor	.20	.20
664	A161	10c Menadenium labiosum	.20	.20
665	A161	40c Comparettia falcata	.95	.95
666	A161	50c Rodriquezia decora	1.40	1.25
667	A161	70c Oncidium papilio	1.60	1.40
668	A161	75c Epidendrum porpax	1.90	1.50
		Nos. 663-668 (6)	6.25	5.50

1984, Feb. 22   Litho.

669	A162	40c Arca zebra	.95	.65
670	A162	65c Trachycardium egmontianum	1.60	1.10
671	A162	70c Tellina radiata	1.60	1.10
672	A162	80c Vermicularia knorrii	2.00	1.25
		Nos. 669-672 (4)	6.15	4.10

Intl. Civil Aviation Org., 40th Anniv.
A163

1984, May 16   Litho.   Perf. 14x13

673	A163	35c Sea plane	.65	.65
674	A163	65c Surinam Airways jet	1.50	1.50

A164   A165

Greek Art and Artifacts: Ancient Games.

1984, June 13   Perf. 13x14
675 A164   2c Running   .20   .20
676 A164   3c Javelin, discus,
              long jump   .20   .20
677 A164   5c Massage   .20   .20
678 A164   10c Ointment massage   .20   .20
679 A164   15c Wrestling   .20   .20
680 A164   20c Boxing   .20   .20
681 A164   30c Horse racing   .60   .60
682 A164   35c Chariot racing   .65   .65
683 A164   45c Temple of Olympia   .85   .85
684 A164   50c Crypt entrance   .95   .95
685 A164   65c Olympia Stadium   1.50 1.50
686 A164   75c Zeus (bust)   1.50 1.50
  a.   Min. sheet of 3, #675, 682, 686 2.75 2.75
       Nos. 675-686 (12)   7.25 7.25

1984 Summer Olympics.
For overprint see No. 843.

1984, Sept. 18   Litho.   Perf. 13x14
687 A165   50c Ball, net   1.25 1.10
688 A165   90c Ball in net   2.00 1.90

Intl. Council of Military Sports basketball
championship.

World Chess Championship,
Moscow — A166

1984, Oct. 10   Litho.   Perf. 14x13
689 A166   10c Red Square   .35   .35
690 A166   15c Knight, king, pawn   .35   .35
691 A166   30c Kasparov   .65   .65
692 A166   50c Board   1.10 1.10
693 A166   75c Karpov   1.75 1.75
  a.   Souv. sheet of 3 (30c, 50c, 75c),
       perf 13½x13   4.75 4.75
694 A166   90c Game   2.00 2.00
       Nos. 689-694 (6)   6.20 6.20

For overprints see Nos. 742, 796.

World Food
Day, Oct.
16 — A167

1984, Oct. 10
695 A167   50c Children receiving
              milk   1.25 1.25
696 A167   90c Food   2.00 2.00

A168   A169

Cacti.

1985, Jan. 9   Litho.   Perf. 13x14
697 A168   5c Leaf   .25   .25
698 A168   10c Melon   .25   .25
699 A168   30c Pillar   .95   .95
700 A168   50c Fig   1.40 1.40
701 A168   75c Nightqueen   2.25 2.25
702 A168   90c Segment   2.40 2.40
       Nos. 697-702 (6)   7.50 7.50

1985, Feb. 22

Independence, 5th Anniv.: 5c, Star, red
stripe from national flag. 30c, Unified labor.

50c, Perpetual flowering plant. 75c, Growth of
agriculture. 90c, Peace dove and plant.

703 A169   5c multicolored   .20   .20
704 A169   30c multicolored   .60   .60
705 A169   50c multicolored   1.00 1.00
  a.   Min. sheet of 3, 2 #703, #705   3.00
706 A169   75c multicolored   1.60 1.60
707 A169   90c multicolored   2.10 2.10
       Nos. 703-707 (5)   5.50 5.50

Chamber of
Commerce
and Industry,
75th Anniv.
A170

UN Emblem, Natl.
Coat of
Arms — A171

1985, Apr. 17   Litho.   Perf. 14x13
708 A170   50c Chamber emblem   .75   .75
709 A170   90c Chamber, factories   1.50 1.50

1985, Apr. 29   Litho.   Perf. 13x14
710 A171   50c multicolored   .75   .75
711 A171   90c multicolored   1.40 1.40

UN, 40th anniv.

Trains — A172

1985, June 5   Litho.   Perf. 13½
712 A172   5c No. 192   .20   .20
713 A172   5c Monaco, No.
              J50   .20   .20
  a.   Pair, #712-713   .40   .40
714 A172   10c Locomotive
              "Dam"   .20   .20
715 A172   10c Diesel locomo-
              tive   .20   .20
  a.   Pair, #714-715   .60   .60
716 A172   20c Steam locomo-
              tive "No. 3737"   .50   .50
717 A172   20c Netherlands lo-
              comotive "IC
              III"   .50   .50
  a.   Pair, #716-717   1.00 1.00
718 A172   30c Stephenson's lo-
              comotive
              "Rocket"   .85   .85
719 A172   30c French Railways
              high-speed
              TGV   .85   .85
  a.   Pair, #716-717   1.60 1.60
720 A172   50c Stephenson's lo-
              comotive "Ad-
              ler"   1.25 1.25
721 A172   50c French Railways
              commuter train   1.25 1.25
  a.   Pair, #720-721   2.75 2.75
722 A172   75c Locomotive
              "General"   2.00 2.00
723 A172   75c Japanese bullet
              train "Shinkan-
              sen"   2.00 2.00
  a.   Pair, #722-723   4.00 4.00
       Nos. 712-723 (12)   10.00 10.00

For surcharges see Nos. 749-750, 808-809,
928-929.

Birds — A173

1985-95   Litho.   Perf. 14x13
724 A173   10c Toucan   .20   .20
725 A173   1g American
              purple
              fowl   1.10 1.10
  a.   Miniature sheet of 1   3.75 3.75
726 A173   1.50g Tiger bird   1.90 1.90
727 A173   2.50g Red ibis   3.00 3.00

---

728 A173   5g Guyana
              red
              cockerel   5.75 5.75
729 A173   10g Harpy ea-
              gle   11.50 11.50
730 A173   15g Parrot   22.50 22.50
731 A173   25g Owl   35.00 35.00
732 A173   1300g Rose
              lepelaar   32.50 32.50
733 A173   1780g Toucan   9.25 9.25
734 A173   2225g Hum-
              mingbird   11.50 11.50
735 A173   2995g Hoatzin   16.00 16.00
       Nos. 724-735 (12)   150.20 150.20

Nos. 724, 730 inscribed 1990.
  Issued: 1g, 1.50g, 2.50g, 8/21; #725a, 5g,
1/2/86; 10g, 10/1/86; 10c, 15g, 1/30/91; 25g,
1/20/93; 1300g, 3/31/94; 1780g, 2225g,
2995g, 9/6/95.
  See #1040, 1053-1055, 1108-1111, 1136-
1138, 1160, 1194-1195, 1220-1221. For
surcharges & overprint see #963-964, J63.

Mailboxes — A174

1985, Oct. 2   Litho.   Perf. 13x14
736 A174   15c Germany, 1900   .35   .35
737 A174   30c France, 1900   .55   .55
738 A174   50c England, 1932   .95   .95
739 A174   90c Netherlands, 1850   1.90 1.90
       Nos. 736-739 (4)   3.75 3.75

Natl. Independence,
10th Anniv. — A175

1985, Nov. 22
740 A175   50c Agriculture   1.25 1.25
741 A175   90c Industry   2.00 2.00
  a.   Miniature sheet of 2, #740-741 3.25 3.25

No. 691
Ovptd. in Red

1985, Nov. 22   Litho.   Perf. 14x13
742 A166   30c multi   2.25 2.25

Orchids,
World Wildlife
Fund — A177

1986, Feb. 19   Litho.   Perf. 14x13
743 A177   5c Epidendrum
              ciliare   3.00 3.00
744 A177   15c Cycnoches
              chlorochilon   7.50 7.50
745 A177   30c Epidendrum
              anceps   15.00 15.00
746 A177   50c Epidendrum
              vespa   24.00 24.00
       Nos. 743-746 (4)   49.50 49.50

Halley's
Comet
A178

Designs: 50c, The Bayeux Tapestry, c.
1092, France. 110c, Halley's Comet.

1986, Mar. 5   Litho.   Perf. 14x13
747 A178   50c multi   .85   .85
748 A178   110c multi   1.75 1.75

Nos. 720-721 Surcharged in Red
1986, May 28   Litho.   Perf. 13½
749 A172   15c on 50c #720   1.50 1.50
750 A172   15c on 50c #721   1.50 1.50
  a.   Pair, #749-750   3.50 3.50

No. 639
Surcharged

1986, June 25   Litho.   Perf. 14x13
751 A156   30c on 70c multi   2.10 2.10

Finance Building, Paramaribo, 150th anniv.

Surinam
Shipping Co.,
50th Anniv.
A179

1986, Sept. 1   Litho.   Perf. 14x13
752 A179   50c Emblem   .70   .70
753 A179   110c Freighter
              Saramacca   2.00 2.00

Monkeys
A180

1987, Jan. 7   Litho.
755 A180   35c Alouatta   .60   .60
756 A180   60c Aotus   1.00 1.00
757 A180   110c Saimiri   2.00 2.00
758 A180   120c Cacajao   2.25 2.25
       Nos. 755-758 (4)   5.85 5.85

Esperanto,
Cent. — A181

1987, Feb. 4   Litho.
759 A181   60c shown   1.00 1.00
760 A181   110 World map,
              doves   1.90 1.90
761 A181   120c L.L. Zamenhof   2.10 2.10
       Nos. 759-761 (3)   5.00 5.00

10th Pan-   Forestry
American Games,   Commission,
Indianapolis, July   40th
23 — A182   Anniv. — A183

1987, June 3   Litho.   Perf. 13x14
763 A182   90c Soccer   1.50 1.50
764 A182   110c Swimming   1.75 1.75
765 A182   150c Basketball   2.25 2.25
       Nos. 763-765 (3)   5.50 5.50

1987, July 21   Litho.   Perf. 13x14
766 A183   90c Emblem   1.50 1.50
767 A183   120c Logging   2.00 2.00
768 A183   150c Parrot in virgin
              forest   2.75 2.75
       Nos. 766-768 (3)   6.25 6.25

Intl. Year of
Shelter for
the Homeless
A184

1987, Sept. 2   Litho.   Perf. 14x13
769 A184 90c Distressed boy, encampment 1.40 1.40
770 A184 120c Man, ghetto 2.10 2.10

Founders Catherine and William Booth — A185

1987, Sept. 2   Perf. 14x13
771 A185 150c multi 2.25 2.25

Salvation Army in the Caribbean, cent.

Nos. 436-438 Surcharged

1986, Dec. 29   Litho.   Perf. 13½x13
772 A109 35c on 1g 2.25 2.25
773 A109 50c on 1.50g 3.50 3.50
774 A109 60c on 2.50g 4.50 4.50
        Nos. 772-774 (3) 10.25 10.25

Fruits — A186

1987, Oct. 14   Litho.   Perf. 13x13½
775 A186 10c Bananas .20 .20
776 A186 15c Cacao .20 .20
777 A186 20c Pineapple .20 .20
778 A186 25c Papaya .30 .30
779 A186 35c Oranges .40 .40
        Nos. 775-779 (5) 1.30 1.30

Aircraft and Aircraft on Stamps — A187

1987, Oct. 14   Litho.   Perf. 13½
784 A187 25c Degen, 1808 .25 .25
785 A187 25c Ultra Light .25 .25
  a.   Pair, #784-785 .90 .90
786 A187 35c J.C.H. Ellehamner, 1906 .55 .55
787 A187 35c Concorde jet .55 .55
  a.   Pair, #786-787 1.25 1.25
788 A187 60c Fokker F7, 1924 .90 .90
789 A187 60c Fokker F28 jet .90 .90
  a.   Pair, #788-789 2.10 2.10
790 A187 90c Spin Fokker, 1910 1.40 1.40
791 A187 90c DC-10 1.40 1.40
  a.   Pair, #790-791 3.00 3.00
792 A187 110c Orion, 1932 1.75 1.75
793 A187 110c Boeing 747 1.75 1.75
  a.   Pair, #792-793 3.75 3.75
794 A187 120c No. 346 1.90 1.90
795 A187 120c No. 518 1.90 1.90
  a.   Pair, #794-795 4.00 4.00
        Nos. 784-795 (12) 13.50 13.50

No. 693a Overprinted "3e match sevilla 1987" on Stamps in 3 or 4 Lines and with Bar and "sevilla 1987" in Sheet Margin

1987, Nov. 2   Litho.   Perf. 13½x13
Souvenir Sheet
796   Sheet of 3 32.50
  a. A166 30c Kasparov 3.50
  b. A166 50c Board 6.00
  c. A166 75c Karpov 9.00

Alligators and Crocodiles A188

1988, Jan. 20   Litho.   Perf. 14x13
797 A188 50c Gavialis gangeticus .80 .80
798 A188 60c Crocodylus niloticus 1.10 1.10
799 A188 90c Melanosuchus niger 1.50 1.50
800 A188 110c Mississippi alligator 2.10 2.10
        Nos. 797-800 (4) 5.50 5.50

Traditional Wedding Costumes — A189

1988, Feb. 24   Litho.   Perf. 13x14
801 A189 35c Javanese .50 .50
802 A189 60c Bushman .95 .95
803 A189 80c Chinese 1.10 1.10
804 A189 110c Creole 1.60 1.60
805 A189 120c Indian 1.75 1.75
806 A189 130c Hindustan 2.10 2.10
        Nos. 801-806 (6) 8.00 8.00

Nos. 722-723 and 440 Surcharged in Black or Silver

Perf. 13½x13, 13½
1988, Mar. 23   Litho.
808 A172 60c on 75c #722 5.50
809 A172 60c on 75c #723 5.50
  a.   Pair, #808-809 11.00
810 A109 125c on 10g #440 (S) 12.00
        Nos. 808-810 (3) 23.00

1988 Summer Olympics, Seoul — A190

Abolition of Slavery, 125th Anniv. — A191

1988, May 4   Litho.   Perf. 13x14
812 A190 90c Relay 1.10 1.10
813 A190 110c Soccer 1.75 1.75
814 A190 120c Pole vault 1.90 1.90
  a.   Souvenir sheet of 3, #812-814 5.00 5.00
815 A190 250c Women's tennis 4.25 4.25
        Nos. 812-815 (4) 9.00 9.00

1988, June 29   Litho.
816 A191 50c Abaisa Monument .65 .65
817 A191 110c Kwakoe Monument 1.75 1.75
818 A191 120c Home of Anton de Kom 2.10 2.10
        Nos. 816-818 (3) 4.50 4.50

See Netherlands Antilles Nos. 597-598.

Intl. Fund for Agricultural Development (IFAD), 10th Anniv. A192

1988, Sept. 21   Perf. 14x13
819 A192 105c Crop harvest 1.75 1.75
820 A192 110c Net fishing 1.75 1.75
821 A192 125c Agricultural research 2.25 2.25
        Nos. 819-821 (3) 5.75 5.75

FILACEPT '88, The Netherlands, Oct. 18-23 — A193

1988, Oct. 18   Litho.   Perf. 13x14
822 A193 120c Egypt #49 1.50 1.50
823 A193 150c Netherlands #334 2.25 2.25
824 A193 250c Surinam #238 3.50 3.50
        Nos. 822-824 (3) 7.25 7.25

Souvenir Sheet
Same Types, Colors Changed (120c, 150c)
825   Sheet of 3 10.00 10.00
  a. A193 120c Egypt Type A23 (4m green) 1.10 1.10
  b. A193 150c Netherlands Type A81 (10c red brown) 1.40 1.40
  c. A193 250c Surinam No. 239 2.40 2.40

Stylized Butterfly Stroke A194

1988, Nov. 1   Litho.   Perf. 14x13
826 A194 110c multi 1.60 1.60

Anthony Nesty, swimmer and 1st Olympic gold medalist from Surinam.

Otters A195

1989, Jan. 18   Litho.   Perf. 14x13
827 A195 10c Otter .20 .20
828 A195 20c Two on land .20 .20
829 A195 25c Two crossing log .50 .50
830 A195 30c Fishing .60 .60
        Nos. 827-830,C107 (5) 4.50 4.50

Classic and Modern Automobiles — A196

1989, June 7   Litho.   Perf. 13½
Design A196
831   25c 1930 Mercedes Tourenwagen .60 .60
832   25c 1985 Mercedes-Benz 300E .60 .60
  a.   Pair, #831-832 1.00 1.00
833   60c 1897 Daimler 1.25 1.25
834   60c 1986 Jaguar Sovereign 1.25 1.25
  a.   Pair, #833-834 2.50 2.50
835   90c 1898 Renault Voiturette 2.00 2.00
836   90c 1989 Renault 25TX 2.00 2.00
  a.   Pair, #835-836 3.75 3.75
837   105c 1927 Volvo Jacob 2.25 2.25
838   105c 1989 Volvo 440 2.25 2.25
  a.   Pair, #837-838 4.50 4.50
839   110c Left half of Monaco #484 2.40 2.40

840   110c Right half of Monaco #484 2.40 2.40
  a.   Pair, #839-840 5.00 5.00
841   120c 1936 Toyota AA 2.75 2.75
842   120c 1988 Toyota Corolla sedan 2.75 2.75
  a.   Pair, #841-842 5.75 5.75
        Nos. 831-842 (12) 22.50 22.50

No. 686a Ovptd. "PHILEXFRANCE 7t/m 17 juli 1989" on Margin, with Exhibition Emblem on Stamps in Gold

1989, July 7   Litho.   Perf. 13x14
Miniature Sheet
843   Sheet of 3 6.25 6.25
  a. A164 2c on No. 675 .20 .20
  b. A164 35c on No. 682 .40 .40
  c. A164 75c on No. 686 .95 .95

PHILEXFRANCE '89.

Photography, 150th Anniv. A197

1989, Sept. 6   Litho.   Perf. 14x13
844 A197 60c Joseph Niepce 1.00 1.00
845 A197 110c Daguerreotype camera 1.90 1.90
846 A197 120c Louis Daguerre 2.10 2.10
        Nos. 844-846 (3) 5.00 5.00

America Issue — A198

UPAE emblem and pre-Columbian amulets.

1989, Oct. 12   Litho.   Perf. 13x14
847 A198 60c Amazon or Jade Stones 2.10 2.10
848 A198 110c Bisque fertility statue 4.00 4.00

The White House, Washington, DC, and Stamps on Stamps A199

Perf. 13x14, 14x13
1989, Nov. 17   Litho.
849 A199 110c No. 445, vert. 2.00 2.00
850 A199 150c US No. 990 2.50 2.50
851 A199 250c No. 459 4.00 4.00
  a.   Souv. sheet, #849-851, perf 13x14, 14 8.75 8.75
        Nos. 849-851 (3) 8.50 8.50

World Stamp Expo '89 and 20th UPU Congress, Washington, DC.

UNESCO Intl. Literacy Year — A200

Arya Dewaker Temple, 60th Anniv. — A201

1990, Jan. 19   Photo.   Perf. 13x14
852 A200 60c shown 1.10 1.10
853 A200 110c Emblems 2.10 2.10
854 A200 120c Emblems, youth reading 2.25 2.25
        Nos. 852-854 (3) 5.45 5.45

1990, Feb. 14   Litho.
855 A201 60c dk red brn, blk & red 1.10 1.10
856 A201 110c vio blue & blk 2.10 2.10
857 A201 200c emer grn & blk 3.50 3.50
        Nos. 855-857 (3) 6.70 6.70

A202   A203

1990, May 4
858 A202 110c Surinam #C1   1.75   1.75
859 A202 200c Great Britain
             #1   3.00   3.00
860 A202 250c Great Britain
             #208   4.25   4.25
  a.   Souvenir sheet of 3, #858-
         860   11.00 11.00
       Nos. 858-860 (3)   9.00   9.00

Penny Black, 150th anniv. Stamps World London '90.

1990, Aug. 9
861 A203 60c Couple carrying
             baskets   1.00   1.00
862 A203 110c Woman carrying
             bundle   1.90   1.90
863 A203 120c Man carrying
             baskets   2.10   2.10
       Nos. 861-863 (3)   5.00   5.00

Javanese Immigration, cent.

Flowers — A204

1990, Sept. 5   *Perf. 13½*
864 A204 25c Punica
             granatum   .45   .45
865 A204 25c Passiflora
             laurifolia   .45   .45
  a.   Pair, #864-865   .80   .80
866 A204 35c Hippeastrum
             puniceum   .55   .55
867 A204 35c Ipomaea
             batatas   .55   .55
  a.   Pair, #866-867   1.10   1.10
868 A204 60c Hibiscus
             syriacus   1.00   1.00
869 A204 60c Jasminum of-
             ficinale   1.00   1.00
  a.   Pair, #868-869   2.10   2.10
870 A204 105c Musa serapion-
             is   1.75   1.75
871 A204 105c Hibiscus
             mutabilis   1.75   1.75
  a.   Pair, #870-871   3.50   3.50
872 A204 110c Plumiria rubra   1.75   1.75
873 A204 110c Hibiscus diver-
             sifolius   1.75   1.75
  a.   Pair, #872-873   3.50   3.50
874 A204 120c Bixa orellana   2.00   2.00
875 A204 120c Ceasalpinia
             pulcherima   2.00   2.00
  a.   Pair, #874-875   4.00   4.00
       Nos. 864-875 (12)   15.00 15.00

America
Issue — A205

1990, Oct. 10   Litho.   Perf. 14x13
876 A205 60c bluish grn & blk   1.60   1.60
877 A205 110c brn & blk   3.25   3.25

Organization
of American
States,
Cent. — A206

1990, Oct. 10
878 A206 110c multicolored   1.60   1.60

Independence, 15th
Anniv. — A207

1990, Nov. 21   Litho.   Perf. 13x14
879 A207 10c shown   .20   .20
880 A207 60c Passion flower   .95   .95
881 A207 110c Dove with olive
             branch   2.10   2.10
       Nos. 879-881 (3)   3.25   3.25

Architecture
A208

Buildings: 35c, Waterfront warehouse. 60c, Upper class residence. 75c, Labor inspection building. 105c, Plantation supervisor's residence. 110c, Ministry of Labor. 200c, Small residences.

1991, May 15   Litho.   Perf. 14x13
882 A208 35c multicolored   .80   .80
883 A208 60c multicolored   1.10   1.10
884 A208 75c multicolored   1.50   1.50
885 A208 105c multicolored   2.10   2.10
886 A208 110c multicolored   2.25   2.25
887 A208 200c multicolored   4.00   4.00
       Nos. 882-887 (6)   11.75 11.75

Nos. 714-715, 720-721 Surcharged

Methods and Perfs as Before
1991
888 A172 2c on 10c #714   1.00   1.00
889 A172 2c on 10c #715   1.00   1.00
  a.   Pair, #888-889   2.25   2.25
890 A172 3c on 50c #720   1.00   1.00
891 A172 3c on 50c #721   1.00   1.00
  a.   Pair, #890-891   2.25   2.25

Puma
Concolor
A209

Various pictures of pumas.

Perf. 13x14, 14x13
1991, Sept. 12   Litho.
892 A209 10c multi, vert.   .20   .20
893 A209 20c multi, vert.   .25   .25
894 A209 25c multi, vert.   .40   .40
895 A209 30c multi, vert.   .50   .50
896 A209 125c multi   1.90   1.90
897 A209 500c multi   6.75   6.75
       Nos. 892-897 (6)   10.00 10.00

Nos. 896-897 are airmail.

Discovery of America, 500th Anniv. (in
1991) — A210

Diagram showing Columbus' route: 60c, Western Atlantic and Caribbean Sea. 110c, Eastern Atlantic.

1991, Oct. 11   *Perf. 13x14*
898 A210 60c lt bl, red & blk   1.50   1.50
899 A210 110c lt bl, red & blk   3.00   3.00
  a.   A210 Pair, #898-899   5.00   5.00

UPAEP. No. 899a has continous design.

Snakes — A211

#900, Corallus enydris. #901, Corallus caninus. #902, Lachesis muta. #903, Boa constrictor. #904, Micrurus surinamensis. #905, Crotalus durissus. #906, Eunectes murinus. #907, Clelia cloelia. #908, Epicrates cenchris. #909, Chironius carinatus. #910, Oxybelis argenteus. #911, Spilotes pullatus.

1991, Nov. 14   *Perf. 13½*
900 A211 25c multicolored   .30   .30
901 A211 25c multicolored   .30   .30
  a.   Pair, #900-901   .80   .80
902 A211 35c multicolored   .55   .55
903 A211 35c multicolored   .55   .55
  a.   Pair, #902-903   1.10   1.10
904 A211 60c multicolored   .90   .90
905 A211 60c multicolored   .90   .90
  a.   Pair, #904-905   2.10   2.10
906 A211 75c multicolored   1.25   1.25
907 A211 75c multicolored   1.25   1.25
  a.   Pair, #906-907   2.50   2.50
908 A211 110c multicolored   1.75   1.75
909 A211 110c multicolored   1.75   1.75
  a.   Pair, #908-909   3.75   3.75
910 A211 200c multicolored   3.25   3.25
911 A211 200c multicolored   3.25   3.25
  a.   Pair, #910-911   6.75   6.75
       Nos. 900-911 (12)   16.00 16.00

Orchids — A212

A213

Designs: 50c, Cycnoches haagii. 60c, Lycaste cristata. 75c, Galeandra dives, horiz. 125c, Vanilla mexicana. 150c, Cyrtopodium glutiniferum. 250c, Gongora quinquenervis.

1992, Feb. 12   Perf. 13x14, 14x13
912 A212 50c multicolored   .65   .65
913 A212 60c multicolored   .85   .85
914 A212 75c multicolored   1.00   1.00
915 A212 125c multicolored   2.00   2.00
916 A212 150c multicolored   2.50   2.50
917 A212 250c multicolored   4.00   4.00
       Nos. 912-917 (6)   11.00 11.00

Souvenir Sheet

Designs: a, 75c, #847. b, 125c, #848. c, 150c, #898. d. 250c, #899.

1992, Mar. 24   Litho.   Perf. 13x13½
918 A213 Sheet of 4, #a.-d.   11.00 11.00

Granada '92, Intl. Philatelic Exibition.

1992 Summer
Olympics,
Barcelona — A214

1992, Apr. 8   Litho.   Perf. 13x14
919 A214 35c Basketball   .55   .55
920 A214 60c Volleyball   .95   .95
921 A214 75c Running   1.10   1.10
922 A214 125c Soccer   1.90   1.90
923 A214 150c Cycling   2.25   2.25
924 A214 250c Swimming   4.25   4.25
  a.   Souvenir sheet of 3, #921,
         922, 924, perf 13x13½   7.50   7.50
       Nos. 919-924 (6)   11.00 11.00

YWCA, 50th
Anniv.
A215

1992, June 12   Litho.   Perf. 14x13
925 A215 60c red brown & multi   1.00   1.00
926 A215 250c purple & multi   4.00   4.00

Expulsion of
Jews from
Spain, 500th
Anniv.
A216

1992, Aug. 17
927 A216 250c multicolored   4.00   4.00

Nos. 712-713 Surcharged

1992, Aug. 17   *Perf. 13½*
928 A172 1c on 5c multi   .40   .40
929 A172 1c on 5c multi   .40   .40
  a.   Pair, #928-929   .90   .90

A217   A218

1992, Sept. 15   *Perf. 13x14*
930 A217 60c green & multi   1.00   1.00
931 A217 250c pink & multi   4.00   4.00

Jan E. Matzeliger (1852-1889), inventor of shoe lasting machine.

1992, Oct. 12
932 A218 60c blue grn & multi   1.00   1.00
933 A218 250c dp org & multi   4.00   4.00

Discovery of America, 500th anniv.

Christmas — A219

Various abstract designs.

1992, Nov. 15
934 A219 10c multicolored   .50   .50
935 A219 60c multicolored   1.00   1.00
936 A219 250c multicolored   3.50   3.50
937 A219 400c multicolored   6.00   6.00
       Nos. 934-937 (4)   11.00 11.00

Medicinal Plants A220

Designs: 50c, Costus arabicus, vert. 75c, Quassia amara, vert. 125c, Combretum rotundifolium. 500c, Bixa orellana.

Perf. 13x14, 14x13

1993, Feb. 3 Litho.
938	A220	50c multicolored	.85	.85
939	A220	75c multicolored	1.40	1.40
940	A220	125c multicolored	2.25	2.25
941	A220	500c multicolored	9.00	9.00
		Nos. 938-941 (4)	13.50	13.50

Beetles and Grasshoppers — A221

Designs: No. 942, Macrodontia cervicornis. No. 943, Acrididae. No. 944, Curculionidae. No. 945, Acrididae, diff. No. 946, Euchroma gigantea. No. 947, Tettigonidae. No. 948, Tettigonidae. No. 949, Phanaeus festivus. No. 950, Gryllidae. No. 951, Phanaeus lancifer. No. 952, Tettigonidae. No. 953, Batus barbicornis.

1993, June 30 Litho. **Perf. 13½**
942	A221	25c multicolored	.40	.40
943	A221	25c multicolored	.40	.40
a.		Pair, #942-943	.90	.90
944	A221	35c multicolored	.50	.50
945	A221	35c multicolored	.50	.50
a.		Pair, #944-945	1.60	1.60
946	A221	50c multicolored	.70	.70
947	A221	50c multicolored	.70	.70
a.		Pair, #946-947	2.00	2.00
948	A221	100c multicolored	1.40	1.40
949	A221	100c multicolored	1.40	1.40
a.		Pair, #948-949	3.75	3.75
950	A221	175c multicolored	2.75	2.75
951	A221	175c multicolored	2.75	2.75
a.		Pair, #950-951	6.75	6.75
952	A221	220c multicolored	3.25	3.25
953	A221	220c multicolored	3.25	3.25
a.		Pair, #952-953	8.50	8.00
		Nos. 942-953 (12)	18.00	18.00

A222

A223

#956b, 250c, like #955. #956c, 500c, like #956.

1993, July 30 **Perf. 13x14**
954	A222	50c Brazil No. 2	.75	.75
955	A222	250c Brazil No. 3	3.75	3.75
956	A222	500c Brazil No. 1	8.00	8.00
		Nos. 954-956 (3)	12.50	12.50

Souvenir Sheet
956A	A222	Sheet of 2, #b.-c.	10.00	10.00

1st Brazilian postage stamps, 150th Anniv. Brasiliana '93 (#956A).
Nos. 956b-956c have purple border.

1993, Oct. 12 **Perf. 14x13**
America issue: Paleosuchus palpebrosus.
957	A223	50g brown & multi	1.90	1.90
958	A223	100g green & multi	4.00	4.00

Christmas Angels — A224

25g, African angel with drum. 45g, Asian angel holding lamp. 50g, Oriental angel holding lantern. 150g, American Indian angel holding wand.

1993, Nov. 15 Litho. **Perf. 13x14**
959	A224	25g multicolored	1.00	1.00
960	A224	45g multicolored	1.75	1.75
961	A224	50g multicolored	2.00	2.00
962	A224	150g multicolored	6.25	6.25
		Nos. 959-962 (4)	11.00	11.00

The foreign exchange rate of the Surinam florin was allowed to float freely against foreign currencies on Oct. 19, 1994. The florin's value against the dollar has fluctuated dramatically. Stamps may sell for values significantly different from those quoted in the Scott listings.

Nos. 729-730 Surcharged

1993 Litho. **Perf. 14x13**
963	A173	5g on 10g Harpy eagle	1.90	.20
964	A173	5g on 15g Parrot	1.90	1.90

Surcharges differ slightly. Issued: #963, 12/16. #964, 12/28.

Traditional Musical Instruments — A225

1994, Feb. 16 Litho. **Perf. 13x14**
965	A225	25g Indian drum	1.50	1.50
966	A225	50g Bosland Creooise drum	3.00	3.00
967	A225	75g Tambourine	5.00	5.00
968	A225	100g Hindu drum	6.50	6.50
		Nos. 965-968 (4)	16.00	16.00

Environmental Protection A226

1994, June 8 Litho. **Perf. 14x13**
969	A226	50g Smoke stacks	1.75	1.75
970	A226	350g Dying fish	12.50	12.50

Intl. Olympic Committee, Cent. — A227

1994, July 4 Litho. **Perf. 14x13**
971	A227	250g multicolored	7.75	7.75

1994 World Cup Soccer Championships, U.S. — A228

1994, July 4 **Perf. 13x14**
972	A228	100g Goalkeeper's hands	3.00	3.00
973	A228	250g Soccer shoe	7.75	7.75
974	A228	300g Goal	9.00	9.00
a.		Souvenir sheet of 2, #973-974	17.00	17.00
		Nos. 972-974 (3)	19.75	19.75

Butterflies — A229

1994, Sept. 7 Litho. **Perf. 13½**
975	A229	25g Dulcedo	.45	.45
976	A229	25g Ithomia	.45	.45
a.		Pair, #975-976	.90	.90
977	A229	30g Danaus	.50	.50
978	A229	30g Danaus, diff.	.50	.50
a.		Pair, #977-978	1.00	1.00
979	A229	45g Echenais	.75	.75
980	A229	45g Bithijs	.75	.75
a.		Pair, #979-980	1.50	1.50
981	A229	75g Junonia evarette	1.25	1.25
982	A229	75g Anartia jatrophae	1.25	1.25
a.		Pair, #981-982	2.50	2.50
983	A229	250g Heliconius	4.00	4.00
984	A229	250g Heliconius erato	4.00	4.00
a.		Pair, #983-984	8.25	8.25
985	A229	300g Eurytides	5.00	5.00
986	A229	300g Parides	5.00	5.00
a.		Pair, #985-986	10.00	10.00
		Nos. 975-986 (12)	23.90	23.90

For surcharges see #1088-1091.

FEPAPOST '94 — A230

1994, Oct. 1 Litho. **Perf. 14x13**
987	A230	250g Netherlands #B148	6.25	6.25
988	A230	300g #168	7.75	7.75
a.		Souvenir sheet of 2, #987-988, perf. 13½x13	14.00	14.00

America Issue A231

Post vehicles: 50g, Airplane, canoe. 400g, Van, donkey cart.

1994, Oct. 12 Litho. **Perf. 13½**
989	A231	50g multicolored	1.40	1.40
990	A231	400g multicolored	12.00	12.00

A232

A233

Christmas: (A), Angel in sky. 250g, Mother reading to children. 625g, Woman kneeling in prayer.

1994, Nov. 22 **Perf. 13x14**
991	A232	(A) multicolored	.60	.60
992	A232	250g multicolored	1.90	1.90
993	A232	625g multicolored	5.00	5.00
a.		Souvenir sheet, #992-993	13.50	13.50
		Nos. 991-993 (3)	7.50	7.50

No. 991 sold for 37g on day of issue.

1995, Jan. 31 | | |
|---|---|---|---|
| 994 | A233 | 375g shown | 3.25 | 3.25 |
| 995 | A233 | 650g Volleyballs | 5.25 | 5.50 |
| a. | | Souvenir sheet, #994-995 | 9.00 | 9.00 |

Volleyball, cent.

Medicinal Plants — A234

Designs: No. 998, Stachytarpheta jamaicense. No. 999, Ruellia tuberosa. No. 1000, Peperomia pellucida. No. 1001, Ocimum sanctum. No. 1002, Phyllanthus amarus. No. 1003, Portulaca oleracea. No. 1004, Wulffia baccata. No. 1005, Sesamum indicum. No. 1006, Ascelepias curassavica. No. 1007, Heliotropium indicum. No. 1008, Wedelia trilobata. No. 1009, Lantana camara.

1995, Mar. 31 Litho. **Perf. 13½**
998	A234	30g multicolored	.35	.35
999	A234	30g multicolored	.35	.35
a.		Pair, #998-999	.50	.50
1000	A234	50g multicolored	.50	.50
1001	A234	50g multicolored	.50	.50
a.		Pair, #1000-1001	.80	.80
1002	A234	75g multicolored	.75	.75
1003	A234	75g multicolored	.75	.75
a.		Pair, #1002-1003	1.40	1.40
1004	A234	250g multicolored	2.40	2.40
1005	A234	250g multicolored	2.40	2.40
a.		Pair, #1004-1005	4.75	4.75
1006	A234	500g multicolored	4.75	4.75
1007	A234	500g multicolored	4.75	4.75
a.		Pair, #1006-1007	9.50	9.50
1008	A234	600g multicolored	5.75	5.75
1009	A234	600g multicolored	5.75	5.75
a.		Pair, #1008-1009	12.00	12.00
		Nos. 998-1009 (12)	29.00	29.00

World Wildlife Fund — A235

25g, Herpailurus yaguarondi. 30g, same up close. 50g, Leopardus tigrinus. 100g, same up close. 1000g, Leopardus wiedi. 1200g, same up close.

1995, May 31 **Perf. 14x13**
1010	A235	25g multicolored	.90	.40
1011	A235	30g multicolored	.90	.40
1012	A235	50g multicolored	.90	.40
1013	A235	100g multicolored	2.25	1.25
1014	A235	1000g multicolored	5.75	5.75
1015	A235	1200g multicolored	5.75	5.75
		Nos. 1010-1015 (6)	17.70	15.20

Nos. 1014-1015 are airmail and do not contain WWF emblem.

UN, 50th Anniv. — A236

1995, June 26 Litho. **Perf. 13x14**
1016	A236	135g green & multi	.75	.75
1017	A236	740g blue & multi	5.00	5.00

Surinam Police Force, Cent. — A237

1995, June 21　　　**Perf. 14x13**
1018　A237　875g multicolored　9.00 9.00

Nilom Junior Chamber, 25th Anniv. A238

1995, Sept. 6　**Litho.**　**Perf. 14x13**
1019　A238　700g multicolored　3.75 3.75

Environmental Protection A239

1995, Oct. 12
1020　A239　135f multicolored　1.00 1.00
1021　A239　1500f multicolored　11.50 11.50

America issue.

A240　　　　　　A241

Christmas: 70g, Shepherds, star. 135g, Flight into Egypt. 295g, Magi. 1000g, Nativity, horiz.

1995, Nov. 15　　**Perf. 13x14, 14x13**
1022　A240　70g multicolored　.35 .35
1023　A240　135g multicolored　.75 .75
1024　A240　295g multicolored　1.50 1.50
1025　A240　1000g multicolored　6.25 6.25
　a.　Souvenir sheet of 1　4.75 4.75
　　Nos. 1022-1025 (4)　8.85 8.85

For surcharges see #1065A-1065B.

1995, Dec. 5　　　　　**Perf. 13x14**

Paintings of Jesters, by Corneille.

1026　A241　135f With bird　1.00 1.00
1027　A241　615f With cat　4.75 4.75

Orchids — A242

#1028, Cyrtopodium cristatum. #1029, Epidendrum cristatum. #1030, Otostylis lepida. #1031, Cochleanthes guianensis. #1032, Rudolfiella aurantiaca. #1033, Catasetum longifolium. #1034, Maxillaria splendens. #1035, Encyclia granitica. #1036, Catasetum macrocarpum. #1037, Brassia caudata. #1038, Vanilla grandiflora. #1039, Maxillaria rufescens.

1996, Feb. 29　**Litho.**　**Perf. 13½**
1028　A242　10g multicolored　.20 .20
1029　A242　10g multicolored　.20 .20
　a.　Pair, #1028-1029　.25 .25
1030　A242　75g multicolored　.50 .50
1031　A242　75g multicolored　.50 .50
　a.　Pair, #1030-1031　.90 .90
1032　A242　135g multicolored　.85 .85
1033　A242　135g multicolored　.85 .85
　a.　Pair, #1032-1033　1.60 1.60
1034　A242　250g multicolored　1.60 1.60
1035　A242　250g multicolored　1.60 1.60
　a.　Pair, #1034-1035　3.25 3.25
1036　A242　300g multicolored　2.00 2.00
1037　A242　300g multicolored　2.00 2.00
　a.　Pair, #1036-1037　4.00 4.00

1038　A242　750g multicolored　4.75 4.75
1039　A242　750g multicolored　4.75 4.75
　a.　Pair, #1038-1039　10.00 10.00
　　Nos. 1028-1039 (12)　19.80 19.80

Bird Type of 1985
1996, Apr. 16　**Litho.**　**Perf. 14x13**
1040　A173　2000f Kraagpape-
　　　　　gaai　12.50 12.50

Ecotourism A243

Designs: No. 1041, Traditional huts. No. 1042, Butterfly in rain forest. No. 1043, Two natives. No. 1044, Native woman.

Perf. 13½x13 on 3 Sides
1996, Apr. 30　　　　　**Litho.**
Booklet Stamps
1041　A243　70g multicolored　.30 .30
1042　A243　70g multicolored　.30 .30
1043　A243　135g multicolored　.60 .60
1044　A243　135g multicolored　.60 .60
　a.　Booklet pane of 4, #1041-1044　2.75
　　Complete booklet, #1044a　5.75

Radio, Cent. — A244

135g, First wireless radio communication device, vert. 615g, Guglielmo Marconi.

Perf. 13x14, 14x13
1996, May 17　　　　　**Litho.**
1045　A244　135g multicolored　1.00 1.00
1046　A244　615g multicolored　4.50 4.50

1996 Summer Olympic Games, Atlanta — A245

Olymphilex '96, Atlanta — A245a

Stamp on stamp: b, 135f, #678. c, 865f, #683.
Illustration A254a reduced.

1996, June 27　**Litho.**　**Perf. 13x14**
1047　A245　70g Basketball　.50 .50
1048　A245　135g Athletics　.95 .95
1049　A245　195g Badmin-
　　　　　ton　1.40 1.40
1050　A245　200g Swim-
　　　　　ming　1.60 1.60
1051　A245　900g Cycling　7.00 7.00
1052　A245　1000g Hurdles　7.50 7.50
　　Nos. 1047-1052 (6)　18.95 18.95
Souvenir Sheet
1052A　A245a　Sheet of
　　　　　2, #b.-c.　9.00 9.00

Bird Type of 1985
Designs: 75f, Fisman. 160f, Fremusu-aka. 1765f, Roodpoot honingzuiger.

1996, Oct. 2　**Litho.**　**Perf. 14x13**
1053　A173　75f multicolored　.45 .45
1054　A173　160f multicolored　1.00 1.00
1055　A173　1765f multicolored　11.00 11.00
　　Nos. 1053-1055 (3)　12.45 12.45

A246

Women's Traditional Costumes: Various styles.

1996, Oct. 9　**Litho.**　**Perf. 13x14**
1056　135f multicolored　1.25 1.25
1057　990f multicolored　7.75 7.75
　a.　A246 Pair, #1056-1057　10.00 10.00

America issue.

A247

1996, Oct. 30　**Litho.**　**Perf. 13x14**

Christmas: Various stylized designs of Madonna and Child.

1058　A247　10f multicolored　.20 .20
1059　A247　70f multicolored　.50 .50
1060　A247　135f multicolored　.90 .90
1061　A247　285f multicolored　2.40 2.40
1062　A247　750f multicolored　6.00 6.00
　a.　Souvenir sheet, #1062　6.25 6.25
　　Nos. 1058-1062 (5)　10.00 10.00

A248　　　　　　A249

Youth Care: Paintings, by Jan Telting: 135f, Brown dog, child. 865f, White dog, child.

1996, Dec. 4　**Litho.**　**Perf. 13x14**
1063　A248　135f multicolored　1.00 1.00
1064　A248　865f multicolored　6.75 6.75

1996, Dec. 13

City of Albina, 150th Anniv.: August Kappler (1815-87), founder.

1065　A249　875f multicolored　7.25 7.25

Nos. 1024, 1025 Surcharged in Black or Silver

Methods and perfs as before
1996, Dec. 16
1065A　A240　(125g) on 295g　2.40 2.40
1065B　A240　(125g) on 1000g
　　　　　(S)　2.40 2.40

SURALCO (Surinam Aluminum Co.) — A250

10f, Opening of aluminum smelter, Paranam, 1965. 70f, Drilling blasting holes for ore exploration, Moengo, 1947. 130f, Workers'

housing, Moengo, 1919. 150f, Dust-free loading of alumina, Paranam dock, 1995. 160f, Constructing dam, power station, 1960. 730f, Schooner Moengo, 1922.

Perf. 13½x13 on 2 or 3 Sides
1996, Dec. 18
Booklet Stamps
1066　A250　10f multicolored　.20 .20
1067　A250　70f multicolored　.45 .45
1068　A250　130f multicolored　.80 .80
1069　A250　150f multicolored　.90 .90
1070　A250　160f multicolored　1.00 1.00
1071　A250　730f multicolored　4.50 4.50
　a.　Booklet pane, #1066-1071 +
　　label　9.75
　　Complete booklet, #1071a　11.50

Heinrich von Stephan (1831-97) — A251

1997, Jan. 31　**Litho.**　**Perf. 13x14**
1072　A251　275f brown & multi　2.40 2.40
1073　A251　475f dk blue & multi　3.75 3.75

Fauna — A252

#1074, Cebus nigrivittatus. #1075, Cebus apella. #1076, Saguinus midas. #1077, Ateles paniscus. #1078, Ateles geoffroyi panamensis. #1079, Ateles geoffroyi frontatus. #1080, Cacajao calvus. #1081, Lagothrix flavicauda. #1082, Saguinus bicolor. #1083, Saguinus oedipus. #1084, Alouatta seniculus. #1085, Saimiri sciureus.

1997, Feb. 12　**Litho.**　**Perf. 13½**
1074　A252　25f multicolored　.20 .20
1075　A252　25f multicolored　.20 .20
　a.　Pair, #1074-1075　.35 .35
1076　A252　75f multicolored　.55 .55
1077　A252　75f multicolored　.55 .55
　a.　Pair, #1076-1077　1.10 1.10
1078　A252　100f multicolored　.75 .75
1079　A252　100f multicolored　.75 .75
　a.　Pair, #1078-1079　1.50 1.50
1080　A252　275f multicolored　2.00 2.00
1081　A252　275f multicolored　2.00 2.00
　a.　Pair, #1080-1081　4.00 4.00
1082　A252　300f multicolored　2.50 2.50
1083　A252　300f multicolored　2.50 2.50
　a.　Pair, #1082-1083　4.75 4.75
1084　A252　725f multicolored　5.25 5.25
1085　A252　725f multicolored　5.25 5.25
　a.　Pair, #1084-1085　11.00 11.00
　　Nos. 1074-1085 (12)　22.50 22.50

Retracing and Completion of Amelia Earhart's Trans-Global Flight by Linda Finch — A253

1997, Mar. 30　**Litho.**　**Perf. 14x13**
1086　A253　275f multicolored　2.10 2.10

Surinam Museum, 50th Anniv. A254

1997, Apr. 3
1087　A254　625f multicolored　4.75 4.75

Nos. 983-986 Surcharged in Black or Silver

1996-97		**Litho.**		**Perf. 13½**
1088	A229	50f on 250g #983	1.40	1.40
1089	A229	50f on 250g #984	1.40	1.40
a.		Pair, #1088-1089	5.75	5.75
1090	A229	100f on 300g #985 (S)	2.75	2.75
1091	A229	100f on 300g #986 (S)	2.75	2.75
a.		Pair, #1090-1091	6.25	6.25
		Nos. 1088-1091 (4)	8.30	8.30

Issued; #1089a, 11/1; #1091a, 1/1/97.

Orchids — A255

Designs: 25f, Selenipedium steyermarkii. 50f, Phragmipedium schlimii. 75f, Criosantes arietina. 200f, Cypripedium margaritaceum. 775f, Paphiopedilum gratrixianum.

1997, Apr. 3		**Litho.**		**Perf. 13x14**
1092	A255	25f multicolored	.20	.20
1093	A255	50f multicolored	.40	.40
1094	A255	75f multicolored	.55	.55
1095	A255	200f multicolored	1.60	1.60
1096	A255	775f multicolored	6.00	6.00
		Nos. 1092-1096 (5)	8.75	8.75

Souvenir Sheet

PACIFIC 97, San Francisco — A256

Illustration reduced.

1997, May 29		**Litho.**		**Perf. 13½x13**
1097	A256	675f #458-459	5.00	5.00

A257   A258

Mosques: 50f, Great Mosque, Isfahan, Iran. 125f, Dome of the Rock, Jerusalem. 175f, Madrasa of Ulugh beg, Samarkand. 225f, Taj Mahal, Agra, India. 275f, Kaiser St. Mosque, Paramaribo. 325f, Sülçjamiye, Istanbul.

1997, July 7				**Perf. 13x14**
Background Color				
1098	A257	50f pink	.35	.35
1099	A257	125f olive	.90	.90
1100	A257	175f blue	1.25	1.25
1101	A257	225f purple	1.60	1.60
1102	A257	275f green	2.10	2.10
1103	A257	325f brown	2.50	2.50
a.		Souvenir sheet of 1	2.75	2.75
		Nos. 1098-1103 (6)	8.70	8.70

Perf. 13x13½ on 3 Sides

1997, Aug. 16   **Litho.**

State Oil Co. Refinery, Saramacca: 50f, Pumping station. 125f, Derrick, butterfly. #1106, Storage tanks. #1107, Gauge, testing mechanism.

Booklet Stamps

1104	A258	50f multicolored	.25	.25
1105	A258	125f multicolored	.75	.75
1106	A258	275f multicolored	1.75	1.75
1107	A258	275f multicolored	1.75	1.75
a.		Booklet pane, #1104-1107	5.50	
		Complete booklet, #1107a	9.75	

Bird Type of 1985

1997, Sept. 17		**Litho.**		**Perf. 14x13**
1108	A173	50f Krabu-owrukuku	.50	.50
1109	A173	125f Mangrodoifi	1.50	1.50
1110	A173	275f Peprefowru	2.00	2.00
1111	A173	3150f Kroonvink	25.00	25.00
		Nos. 1108-1111 (4)	29.00	29.00

A259   A260

Child Care: 50f, Right side of boy's face. 100f, Left side of boy's face, 175f, Right side of girl's face. 225f, Left side of girl's face. 350f, 675f, Boy's face upside down, girl's face.

1997, Dec. 4		**Litho.**		**Perf. 13x14**
1112	A259	50f multicolored	.40	.40
1113	A259	100f multicolored	.75	.75
1114	A259	175f multicolored	1.25	1.25
1115	A259	225f multicolored	1.75	1.75
1116	A259	350f multicolored	2.75	2.75
		Nos. 1112-1116 (5)	6.90	6.90

Souvenir Sheet

1117	A259	675f multicolored	5.00	5.00

1997, Dec. 4

Christmas: 125f, Madonna and Child. 225f, Children looking at baby. 450f, Angel. 675f, Children singing, horiz.

1118	A260	125f multicolored	1.00	1.00
1119	A260	225f multicolored	1.75	1.75
1120	A260	450f multicolored	3.50	3.50
		Nos. 1118-1120 (3)	6.25	6.25

Souvenir Sheet

1121	A260	675f multicolored	5.00	5.00

America Issue — A261

Designs: 170f, Postal worker, motorcycle. 230f, Postal worker carrying package.

1997, Dec. 10		**Litho.**		**Perf. 13x14**
1122		170f multicolored	1.00	1.00
1123		230f multicolored	1.40	1.40
a.		A261 Pair, #1122-1123	3.25	3.25

Moths & Butterflies — A262

1998, Jan. 26				**Perf. 13½**
1124	A262	50f Alcandor	.30	.30
1125	A262	50f Achilles	.30	.30
a.		Pair, #1124-1125	.85	.85
1126	A262	75f Alphenor	.45	.45
1127	A262	75f Ceres	.45	.45
a.		Pair, #1126-1127	1.25	1.25
1128	A262	100f Cecropia	.60	.60
1129	A262	100f Helenor	.60	.60
a.		Pair, #1128-1129	1.60	1.60

1130	A262	175f Promothea	1.00	1.00
1131	A262	175f Cassiae	1.00	1.00
a.		Pair, #1130-1131	2.75	2.75
1132	A262	275f Ino	2.10	2.10
1133	A262	275f Phidippus	2.10	2.10
a.		Pair, #1132-1133	5.00	5.00
1134	A262	725f Palamedes	5.50	5.50
1135	A262	725f Helenor, diff.	5.50	5.50
a.		Pair, #1134-1135	12.50	12.50
		Nos. 1124-1135 (12)	19.90	19.90

Bird Type of 1985

1998, Mar. 12		**Perf. 14x13, 13x14**		
1136	A173	50f Marjrietje	.40	.40
1137	A173	225f Aka	1.75	1.75
1138	A173	2425f Timmerman, vert.	19.00	19.00
		Nos. 1136-1138 (3)	21.15	21.15

Hindustani Immigration, 125th Anniv. A263

Designs: 175f, Painting showing first immigrants from boat, "Lala Rooch." 200f, Statue of Baba and Mai, first immigrants from India.

1998, June 4		**Litho.**		**Perf. 14x13**
1139	A263	175f multicolored	1.25	1.25
1140	A263	200f multicolored	1.60	1.60

Temples A264

Designs: 50f, Sri Lanka. 75f, Golden Pagoda, Burma, vert. 275f, Swayambhunath, Nepal, vert. 325f, Borobudur, Indonesia. 400f, Wat Phra Kaew, Thailand, vert. 450f, Peking Temple, China, vert.
675f, Statue, Borobudur, Indonesia, vert.

Perf. 13½x12½, 12½x13½

1998, June 4				
1141	A264	50f multicolored	.35	.35
1142	A264	75f multicolored	.55	.55
1143	A264	275f multicolored	2.00	2.00
1144	A264	325f multicolored	2.40	2.40
1145	A264	400f multicolored	2.75	2.75
1146	A264	450f multicolored	3.50	3.50
		Nos. 1141-1146 (6)	11.55	11.55

Souvenir Sheet

1147	A264	675f multicolored	5.00	5.00

No. 1147 is a continuous design.

Ferry Boat A265

1998, Oct. 31				**Perf. 13½x14**
1148	A265	275f blue & multi	2.00	2.00
1149	A265	400f sepia & multi	3.00	3.00

America Issue — A266

Outstanding women: 400f, Sophie Redmond (1907-55). 1000f, Grace Ruth Schneiders-Howard (1869-1968).

1998, Oct. 8		**Litho.**		**Perf. 13x14**
1150	A266	400f multicolored	3.00	3.00
1151	A266	1000f multicolored	7.50	7.50

World Stamp Exhibition, The Hague, Netherlands A267

Designs: 400f, #245, portions of #174, #141. 800f, #174, portions of #245, #141. 2400f, #141, portions of #245, #174.

1998, Oct.		**Litho.**		**Perf. 14x13**
1152	A267	400f multicolored	3.00	3.00
1153	A267	800f multicolored	5.75	5.75

Souvenir Sheet

1154	A267	2400f multicolored	20.00	20.00

A268   A269

Christmas: Various nativity scenes.

1998, Nov. 1				**Perf. 13x14**
1155	A268	50f multicolored	.40	.40
1156	A268	325f multicolored	1.60	1.60
1157	A268	400f multicolored	2.00	2.00
1158	A268	1225f multicolored	7.00	7.00
		Nos. 1155-1158 (4)	11.00	11.00

Souvenir Sheet

1159	A268	675f multicolored	8.00	8.00

Bird Type of 1985

1998, Nov. 16		**Litho.**		**Perf. 14x13**
1160	A173	3800f Butarides striatus	16.00	16.00

1998, Dec. 4		**Litho.**		**Perf. 13x14**
1161	A269	400f Mother, child, foods	2.10	2.10
1162	A269	1000f Mother, child, flower	5.50	5.50

World Health Organization, 50th anniv.

Child Care — A270

1998, Dec. 4		**Litho.**		**Perf. 14x13**
1163	A270	375f shown	2.00	2.00
1164	A270	400f Flying kite, diff.	2.00	2.00
1165	A270	1225f Holding kite	7.00	7.00
		Nos. 1163-1165 (3)	11.00	11.00

Heliconia — A271

#1166, Caribaea kawauchi. #1167, Pastazae. #1168, Rostrata. #1169, Sexy pink. #1170, Collinsiana. #1171, Wagneriana. #1172, Bihai-nappi. #1173, Jaded forest. #1174, Golden torch. #1175, Latispatha-red yellow gyro. #1176, Sexy pink, diff. #1177, Nappi yellow.

1999, Jan. 27		**Litho.**		**Perf. 13½**
1166	A271	50f multicolored	.20	.20
1167	A271	50f multicolored	.20	.20
a.		Pair, #1166-1167	.30	.30
1168	A271	200f multicolored	.65	.65
1169	A271	200f multicolored	.65	.65
a.		Pair, #1168-1169	1.25	1.25
1170	A271	300f multicolored	1.00	1.00
1171	A271	300f multicolored	1.00	1.00
a.		Pair, #1170-1171	2.00	2.00
1172	A271	400f multicolored	1.25	1.25
1173	A271	400f multicolored	1.25	1.25
a.		Pair, 1172-1173	2.50	2.50
1174	A271	750f multicolored	2.50	2.50
1175	A271	750f multicolored	2.50	2.50
a.		Pair, #1174-1175	5.00	5.00

1176	A271	1300f multicolored	4.25	4.25
1177	A271	1300f multicolored	4.25	4.25
a.		Pair, #1176-1177	8.50	8.50
		Nos. 1166-1177 (12)	19.70	19.70

Old Plantation
Houses
A272

1999, Mar. 17   Litho.   Perf. 14x13

1178	A272	75f Katwijk	.25	.25
1179	A272	300f Sorgvliet	1.00	1.00
1180	A272	400f Peperpot	1.25	1.25
1181	A272	2225f Spieringshoek	7.25	7.25
		Nos. 1178-1181 (4)	9.75	9.75

Endangered
Species — A273

1999, June 30   Litho.   Perf. 13x14

1182	A273	75f Flamingo	.20	.20
1183	A273	375f Orangutan	.75	.75
1184	A273	450f Elephant	.90	.90
1185	A273	500f Whale	.95	.95
1186	A273	850f Frog	1.60	1.60
1187	A273	900f Rhinoceros	1.75	1.75
1188	A273	1600f Giant panda	3.00	3.00
1189	A273	7250f Tiger	14.00	14.00
		Nos. 1182-1189 (8)	23.15	23.15

Coppename
Bridge
A274

1999, June 30   Perf. 14x13

1190	A274	850f black & green	1.60	1.60
1191	A274	2250f black & blue	4.25	4.25

A275   A276

1999, July 9   Perf. 13x14

1192	A275	850f multicolored	1.40	1.40
1193	A276	2650f multicolored	4.25	4.25
a.		Souvenir sheet, #1192-1193, perf. 13x13½	5.75	5.75

Surinam Conservation Foundation, 30th
anniv. (No. 1192), Central Surinam Nature
Preserve, 1st anniv. (No. 1193).

Bird Type of 1985-95

1999, Aug. 21   Perf. 14x13

1194	A173	1000f Blauwtje	1.90	1.90
1195	A173	5500f Kepanki	8.75	8.75

A277

1999, Oct. 9   Perf. 13x14

1196	A277	950f Earth	1.75	1.75
1197	A277	1000f Saturn	1.90	1.90

UPU, 125th anniv.

A278

1999, Oct. 9

1198		1000f Gun	1.75	1.75
1199		2250f Flower	3.50	3.50
a.		A278 Pair, #1198-1199	6.00	6.00

America issue, A New Millennium Without
Arms.

Christmas — A279

1999, Nov. 3   Perf. 13x14

1200	A279	500f Star, stable	.80	.80
1201	A279	850f Christmas tree	1.40	1.40
1202	A279	900f Angel	1.50	1.50
1203	A279	1000f Candle	1.60	1.60
		Nos. 1200-1203 (4)	5.30	5.30

Souvenir Sheet

1204	A279	2275f Mother and child	4.25	4.25

Children's
Pictures
A280

1999, Dec. 3   Litho.   Perf. 14x13

1205	A280	1100f multi	1.75	1.75
1206	A280	1400f multi, diff.	2.25	2.25
1207	A280	1600f multi, diff.	2.50	2.50
a.		Souvenir sheet of 1	2.75	2.75
		Nos. 1205-1207 (3)	6.50	6.50

Children's
Drawings
A281

2000, Jan. 3   Litho.   Perf. 14x13

1208	A281	1000f By Tahirih van Kanten	1.75	1.75
1209	A281	2500f By Tirsa Braaf	4.25	4.25

See No. 1224.

Traffic Signs — A282

2000   Perf. 13x14

1210	A282	2000f Turn right	4.00	4.00
1211	A282	2000f No passing	4.00	4.00
1212	A282	2000f Sharp turns	4.00	4.00
1213	A282	2000f Traffic circle	4.00	4.00
		Nos. 1210-1213 (4)	16.00	16.00

Issued: #1210, 1/3; #1211, 4/3; #1212, 5/18.
#1213, 9/29.

Fruits
A283

No. 1214, 50f: a, Citrullus vulgaris. b, Carica
papaya.
No. 1215, 175f: a, Mangifera indica. b,
Garcinia mangostana.
No. 1216, 200f: a, Musa nana. b, Citrus
paradisi.
No. 1217, 250f: a, Punika granatum. b,
Ananas comosus.
No. 1218, 325f: a, Cocos nucifera. b, Pas-
siflora quadrangularis.
No. 1219, 5000f: a, Citrus sinensis. b, Per-
sea gratissima.

2000, Feb. 29   Litho.   Perf. 13¼

Pairs, #a-b

1214-1219	A283	Set of 6	18.00	18.00

No. 1219 is airmail.

Bird Type of 1985

Designs: 1100f, Dendrocygna autumnalis.
4425f, Ceryle torquata.

2000, Apr. 3   Perf. 14x13

1220	A173	1100f multi	1.75	1.75
1221	A173	4425f multi	7.50	7.50

Surinam
River Bridge
A284

Lettering in: 1100f, Red. 1700f, Blue.

2000, May 18

1222-1223	A284	Set of 2	4.75	4.75

Children's Drawings Type
Souvenir Sheet

2000   Perf. 13¼x13

1224	A281	3575f #1208, 1209	5.50	5.50

World Stamp Expo 2000, Anaheim,
Stampin' the Future children's stamp design
contest.

2000
Summer
Olympic,
Sydney
A285

No. 1225, 1100f: a, Soccer. b, Track and
field.
No. 1226, 3900f: a, Tennis. b, Swimming.
No. 1227: a, Soccer, diff. b, Swimming, diff.

2000, Aug. 8   Litho.   Perf. 13¼

Pairs, #a-b

1225-1226	A285	Set of 2	14.50	14.50

Souvenir Sheet

1227	A285	2500f Sheet of 2, #a-b	7.25	7.25

America Issue, Fight Against
AIDS — A286

No. 1228: a, 1100f, Foot with condom
stamping out AIDS, horiz. b, 6400f, People
holding condoms.

2000   Perf. 13x14

1228	A286	Pair, #a-b	10.50	10.50

25th Anniv. of
International
Agencies Ltd. as
Philatelic and
Numismatic
Agent — A287

Designs: 125f, Paper money. 5900f,
Stamps.

2000, Nov. 24

1229-1230	A287	Set of 2	7.00	7.00
1230a		Souvenir sheet, #1229-1230	7.25	7.25

Children — A288

Child: 1100f, Walking. 3900f, Breastfeeding.
2000f, With umbilical cord, horiz.

2000, Dec. 5   Perf. 13x14

1231-1232	A288	Set of 2	6.00	6.00

Souvenir Sheet
Perf. 14x13

1233	A288	2000f multi	2.25	2.25

Fight Against
Poverty
A289

Country name in: 1100f, Green. 4900f, Red.

2000   Perf. 14x13

1234-1235	A289	Set of 2	4.50	4.50

Christmas — A290

Designs: 1100f, Star of Bethlehem. 3900f,
Madonna and Child.
3000f, Magi with gifts, horiz.

2000   Perf. 13x14

1236-1237	A290	Set of 2	6.75	6.75

Souvenir Sheet
Perf. 14x13

1238	A290	3000f multi	4.25	4.25

No. 945a Surcharged

Methods and Perfs as Before

2000 (?)

1238A		Pair	2.50	2.50
b.		A221 1000f on 25c No. 942	.95	.95
c.		A221 1000f on 25c No. 943	.95	.95

1239		Pair	6.75	6.75
a.	A221 3100f on 35c No. 944		2.50	2.50
b.	A221 3100f on 35c No. 945		2.50	2.50

Birds
A291

No. 1240, 50f: a, Rood zwart vink tagara. b, Tyarman.
No. 1241, 175f: a, Sabaku. b, Kolibrie.
No. 1242, 200f: a, Aka. b, Timmerman.
No. 1243, 250f: a, Paarskeel cotinga. b, Zwarte kraag donfowru.
No. 1244, 825f: a, Kees. b, Stonkuyake.
No. 1245, 7500f: a, Guyanese rood cotinga. b, Butabuta.

2001, Jan. 31   Litho.   Perf. 13¼
Pairs, #a-b

1240-1245	A291	Set of 6	18.00	18.00

No. 1245 is airmail.

Traffic Signs Type of 2000

2001   Litho.   Perf. 13x14

1246	A282	2000f No parking	1.90	1.90
1247	A282	4000f Drawbridge	3.75	3.75
1248	A282	4000f Tractor, No entry	3.75	3.75

Issued: 2000f, 3/8; No. 1247, 4/25; No. 1248, 9/12.

UN Women's
Human Rights
Campaign
A292

Youth Philately
A293

Designs: 1400f, Female and male symbols. 4600f, Woman.

2001, Mar. 15   Litho.   Perf. 13x14

1249-1250	A292	Set of 2	6.00	6.00

2001, Apr. 25

Children's art by: 650f, Bhoelai Surender Kumar. 5350f, Sharon Cameron.

1251-1252	A293	Set of 2	6.00	6.00

Bird Type of 1985

Designs: 4500f, Charadrius collaris. 9000f, Bubo virginianus.

2001, May 10   Perf. 14x13

1253	A173	4500f multi	5.25	5.25
1254	A173	9000f multi	10.50	10.50

Fruit — A294

Designs: 150f, Sapotille. 200f, Noni vrucht. 800fr, Baby bananas. 1200f, Mope. 1700f, Pommerak.

2001, July 20   Litho.   Perf. 12¾x13½

1255-1259	A294	Set of 5	3.75	3.75

America Issue — A295

Paramaribo buildings: Nos. 1260a, 1261a, 1700f, Bishop's house. Nos. 1260b, 1261b, 7300f, Presidential palace. Illustration reduced.

2001, Sept. 12   Litho.   Perf. 14x13
Country Name in Red

1260	A295	Pair, #a-b	9.75	9.75

Souvenir Sheet
Country Name in Green
Perf. 13¼x13

1261	A295	Sheet of 2, #a-b	9.75	9.75

Stamp Day — A296

Designs: No. 1262a, 3750f, #648 (green background). No. 1262b, 5250f, #29 (red background).
No. 1263a, 3750f, #648 (red background). No. 1263b, 5250f, #29 (orange background).

2001, Oct. 19   Perf. 13x14

1262	A296	Pair, #a-b	9.75	9.75

Souvenir Sheet
Perf. 13x13¼

1263	A296	Sheet of 2, #a-b	9.75	9.75

Christmas
A297

Children's
Sports — A298

2001, Nov. 2   Perf. 13¼

1264	A297	1700f blue & multi	1.50	1.50

Perf. 14x13

1265	A298	5000f red & multi	4.50	4.50

Souvenir Sheet
Perf. 13¼x13

1266		Sheet of 2	6.00	6.00
a.	A297 1700f green & multi		1.50	1.50
b.	A298 5000f blue & multi		4.50	4.50

No. 947a Surcharged in Gold

2001, Dec. 7   Litho.   Perf. 13½

1266C		Pair	4.50	4.50
d.	A221 2500f on 50c No. 946		2.25	2.25
e.	A221 2500f on 50c No. 947		2.25	2.25

Traffic Signs Type of 2000

2001-02   Perf. 13x14

1267	A282	4000f Pedestrian crossing	3.75	3.75
1268	A282	4000f Yield	3.75	3.75

Issued: No. 1267, 12/7/01; No. 1268, 2/13/02.

Parrots
A299

No. 1269, 150f: a, Deroptyus acciptrinus. b, Amazona achrocephala.
No. 1270, 200f: a, Ara manilata. b, Amazona dufresniana.
No. 1271, 800f: a, Ara severa. b, Pionites melanocephala.
No. 1272, 1200f: a, Ara nobilis. b, Pionus fiscus.
No. 1273, 1700f: a, Ara chloroptera. b, Pionopsitta caicca.
No. 1274, 5325f: a, Ara macao. b, Amazona farinosa.

2002, Jan. 9   Perf. 13¼
Pairs, #a-b

1269-1274	A299	Set of 6	17.50	17.50

No. 1274 is airmail.

Traffic Signs Type of 2000

2002, Apr. 17   Litho.   Perf. 13x14

1275	A282	4000f U turn	3.75	3.75

Traffic Signs Type of 2000

2002-03   Litho.   Perf. 12¾x14

1276	A282	4000f Pedestrian path	3.75	3.75
1277	A282	4000f Train crossing without barriers	3.75	3.75
1278	A282	4000f Motorcycles	3.75	3.75
		Nos. 1276-1278 (3)	11.25	11.25

Issued: No. 1276, 6/19/02; No. 1277, 9/20/02; No. 1278, 2/13/03.

Costumes
A300

Birds
A301

Costumes of: Nos. 1279a, 1279c, 1279e, 1279g, 1279i, 1279k, Various men. Nos. 1279b, 1279d, 1279f, 1279h, 1279j, 1279l, Various women.

2002, May 15   Perf. 12¾x13¼

1279		Horiz. strip of 12	17.00	17.00
a.-b.	A300 150f Either single		.20	.20
c.-d.	A300 200f Either single		.20	.20
e.-f.	A300 800f Either single		.75	.75
g.-h.	A300 1200f Either single		1.10	1.10
i.-j.	A300 1700f Either single		1.60	1.60
k.-l.	A300 4950f Either single		4.50	4.50

2002, June 19   Perf. 12¾x14

1280	A301	5000f Royal flycatcher	4.75	4.75
1281	A301	8500f Swampufowru	7.75	7.75

Amphilex 2002 Intl. Stamp Exhibition, Amsterdam — A302

No. 1282: a, 1700f, Netherlands #244 (yellow background). b, 6800f, Netherlands #103 (maroon background).
No. 1283: a, 1700f, Like No. 1282a (maroon background). b, 6800f, Like No. 1282b (yellow background).
Illustration reduced.

2002, Aug. 30   Perf. 13¼x12¾

1282	A302	Horiz. pair, #a-b	7.75	7.75

Souvenir Sheet

1283	A302	Sheet of 2, #a-b	7.75	7.75

Souvenir Sheet
No. 1230a Overprinted in Gold

2002, Aug. 30   Litho.   Perf. 13x14

1284	A287	Sheet of 2	5.75	5.75
a.	250f on 125f #1229		.25	.25
b.	5900f #1230 overprinted		5.50	5.50

America Issue - Youth, Education and Literacy — A303

No. 1285 — Letters, numbers and: a, 1700f, Stylized head and question mark. b, 7300f, "X" in signature box.

2002, Sept. 20   Perf. 13¼x12¾

1285	A303	Horiz. pair, #a-b	8.25	8.25

Christmas
A304

Designs: No. 1286, 1700f, Unclothed Santa Claus and clothing (light blue background). No. 1287, 5000f, Christmas tree, decorations and gifts (green background).
No. 1288: a, 1700f, Like No. 1286 (yellow background). b, 5000f, Like No. 1287 (blue background).

2002, Nov. 6

1286-1287	A304	Set of 2	6.25	6.25

Souvenir Sheet

1288	A304	Sheet of 2, #a-b	6.25	6.25

Nos. 949a, 953a Surcharged Like No. 1266C in Gold or Silver

2002 ?   Litho.   Perf. 13½

1289		Pair	4.75	4.75
a.	A221 2500f on 100c #948		2.25	2.25
b.	A221 2500f on 100c #949		2.25	2.25
1290		Pair	7.00	7.00
a.	A221 3750f on 220c #952 (S)		3.50	3.50
b.	A221 3750f on 220c #953 (S)		3.50	3.50

Birds — A305

No. 1291: a, Falco deiroleucus. b, Lophornis ornatus. c, Touit purpurata. d, Thanlurania furcata. e, Myrmeciza ferruginea. f, Pteroglossus aracari. g, Cotinga cotinga. h, Granatellus pelzelni. i, Euphonia musica. j, Pitangus lictor. k, Cacicus haemorrhous. l, Columba speciosa.

2003, Jan. 9   Perf. 13¼x14

1291		Block of 12	17.00	17.00
a.-b.	A305 150f Either single		.20	.20
c.-d.	A305 200f Either single		.20	.20
e.-f.	A305 800f Either single		.75	.75
g.-h.	A305 1200f Either single		1.10	1.10
i.-j.	A305 1700f Either single		1.60	1.60
k.-l.	A305 4950f Either single		4.50	4.50

No. 951a Surcharged in Silver Like No. 1266C

2002, Dec. 30   Litho.   Perf. 13½

1292		Pair	5.00	5.00
a.	A221 2750f on 175c #950		2.50	2.50
b.	A221 2750f on 175c #951		2.50	2.50

Dolls — A306

No. 1293: a, A. M. 352/1030. b, S&H 1079, 1892. c, Jumeau, 1895 (denomination in white). d, Jumeau, 1895 (denomination in red). e, A. M. 390, 1900. f, Minerva, 1900. g, K&R 126, 1905. h, K&R, 1905. i, Handwerck, 1905. j, SFBJ, 1907. k, A. M. 980, 1920. l, K&R 1910.

2003, May 12   **Perf. 13½x14**
1293   Block of 12   9.75   9.75
  a.-l. A306 1000f Any single   .80   .80

A307   A308

Designs: 150f, Izaak Enschedé. 800f, Old building of Johann Enschedé Printers, horiz. 1700f, Surinam #7. 3850f, First Surinam banknote printed by Enschedé, horiz.
7500f, Like 150f.

Perf. 12¾x13½, 13½x12¾
2003, June 3
1294-1297 A307   Set of 4   5.25   5.25
Souvenir Sheet
1298 A307   7500f multi   6.00   6.00
Johann Enschedé and Sons, printers, 300th anniv.

2003, Sept. 3   **Perf. 12¾x14**
Birds: 5400f, Anthracothorax viridigula. 6600f, Campephilus melanoleucos.
1299 A308   5400f multi   4.25   4.25
1300 A308   6600f multi   5.25   5.25

Traffic Signs Type of 2000
2003, Sept. 3   Litho.   Perf. 12¾x14
1301 A282   4000f 10% grade   3.25   3.25

America Issue - Flora and Fauna — A309

No. 1302: a, 1700f, Faya lobi. b, 8500f, Puma.
Illustration reduced.

2003, Sept. 20   Litho.   Perf. 14x12¾
1302 A309   Horiz. pair, #a-b   8.25   8.25
  c.   Souvenir sheet, #1302   8.25   8.25

Nos. 889a, 929a Surcharged

Methods and Perfs as Before
2003
1303   Pair   5.50   5.50
  a. A172 3500f on 1c on 5c #928   2.75   2.75
  b. A172 3500f on 1c on 5c #929   2.75   2.75
1304   Pair   5.50   5.50
  a. A172 3500f on 2c on 10c #888   2.75   2.75
  b. A172 3500f on 2c on 10c #889   2.75   2.75

Issued: No. 1303, 11/1; No. 1304, 12/1.

Christmas — A310

Designs: 1700f, Children, dog, toy horse. 5300f, Woman holding candle.

2003, Nov. 6   Litho.   Perf. 12¾x14
1306 A310   1700f multi   1.40   1.40
1307 A310   5300f multi   4.25   4.25
  a.   Horiz. pair, #1306-1307 + central label   5.75   5.75
  b.   Souvenir sheet, #1306-1307   5.75   5.75

Powered Flight, Cent. A311

Designs: 1700f, Santos-Dumont 14bis, first European flight, 1906. 5300f, Replica of 1903 aircraft by Richard Pearse, New Zealand.

2003, Dec. 13   **Perf. 14x12¾**
1308 A311   1700f multi   1.40   1.40
1309 A311   5300f multi   4.25   4.25
  a.   Souvenir sheet, #1308-1309   5.75   5.75

The Surinam dollar replaced the florin in January 2004 at an exchange rate of 1000 florins to 1 dollar. Nos. 1310-1313, though issued after the introduction of the new currency, have denominations expressed in florins.

Butterflies A312

No. 1310: a, Anartia amathea. b, Vanessa carye. c, Papilio demetrius. d, Precis octavia. e, Papilio blumei. f, Papilio aritodemus ponceanus. g, Zerynthia rumina. h, Parides gundlachianus. i, Ornithoptera priamus. j, Lyropteryx apollonia. k, Agrias narcissus. l, Elzunia bonplandii.

2004, Jan. 12   **Perf. 12¾x14**
1310   Block of 12   22.00 22.00
  a.-b. A312 150f Either single   .20   .20
  c.-d. A312 200f Either single   .20   .20
  e.-f. A312 800f Either single   .65   .65
  g.-h. A312 1200f Either single   .95   .95
  i.-j. A312 1700f Either single   1.40   1.40
  k.-l. A312 L Either single   7.50   7.50

Nos. 1310k-1310l sold for 9500f on day of issue.

Traffic Signs Type of 2000
2004   Litho.   Perf. 12¾x14
1311 A282 4000f Horse and rider crossing   3.25   3.25
1312 A282 4000f Large vehicles prohibited   3.25   3.25
  a.   Souvenir sheet, #1278, 1301, 1311, 1312 13.00 13.00

Issued: Nos. 1311-1312, 3/31; No. 1312a, 10/1.

Mailboxes of the World — A313

No. 1313: a, Indonesia. b, Brazil. c, Macao. d, Germany. e, Uruguay. f, Republic of Korea. g, Oman. h, Mexico. i, Australia. j, Switzerland. k, Hong Kong. l, United States.

2004, May 6
1313   Block of 12   25.00 25.00
  a.-b. A313 150f Either single   .20   .20
  c.-d. A313 200f Either single   .20   .20
  e.-f. A313 800f Either single   .65   .65
  g.-h. A313 1200f Either single   .95   .95
  i.-j. A313 1700f Either single   1.40   1.40
  k.-l. A313 K Either single   9.00   9.00

Nos. 1313k-1313l each sold for 11,500f ($11.50) on day of issue.

Greek Amphorae — A314

No. 1314 — Inscriptions: a, Athena en Poseidon. b, Wedren. c, Athena Promachus, 363/62 v. C. d, Hippodamia ontvoerd door Pelops, 415 v. C. e, Winnaar muziekconcours, 440-430 v. C. f, Wedren 485-470 v. C. g, Vaashals: speer-en discuswerpers. h, Wedren vier paarden. i, Heracles met leeuw van Nemea, 520 v. C. j, Amfoor, 566 v. C. k, Winnaar muziekconcours (no handles). l, Winnaar muziekconcours (with handles).
No. 1315 — Portions of an amphora: a, $2, Left. b, $3, Center. c, $5, Right.

2004, July 1
1314   Block of 12   28.00 28.00
  a.-b. A314 5c Either single   .20   .20
  c.-d. A314 15c Either single   .20   .20
  e.-f. A314 20c Either single   .20   .20
  g.-h. A314 45c Either single   .35   .35
  i.-j. A314 80c Either single   .60   .60
  k.-l. A314 M Either single   12.50 12.50

Souvenir Sheet
1315 A314   Sheet of 3, #a-c   8.00   8.00
2004 Summer Olympics, Athens (No. 1315). Nos. 1314k-1314l each sold for $16 on day of issue, and are airmail.

America Issue - Birds — A315

Designs: $1.70, Duck. $12, Parrots.

2004, Sept. 16   **Perf. 14x12¾**
1316-1317 A315   Set of 2   11.00 11.00
1317a   Souvenir sheet, #1316-1317   11.00 11.00

Birds — A316

No. 1318: a, Chloroceryle inda. b, Brotogeris chrysoperus. c, Buteo magnisrostris. d, Buteo albicaudatus. e, Calliphlox amethystina (facing left). f, Calliphlox amethystina (facing right). g, Harpagus diodon. h, Aratinga pertinax. i, Chlorocersyle amazona. j, Galbula galbula. k, Buteogallus aequinoctialis. l, Polyborus plancus.

2004, Oct. 21   **Perf. 12¾x14**
1318   Block of 12   28.00 28.00
  a.-b. A316 5c Either single   .20   .20
  c.-d. A316 15c Either single   .20   .20
  e.-f. A316 20c Either single   .20   .20
  g.-h. A316 45c Either single   .35   .35
  i.-j. A316 80c Either single   .60   .60
  k.-l. A316 M Either single   12.50 12.50

Nos. 1318k-1318l each sold for $16 on day of issue, and are airmail.

Child Care   Christmas
A317   A318

2004, Nov. 18   Litho.   Perf. 12¾x14
1319 A317 $1.70 multi   1.40   1.40
1320 A318 $7.70 multi   6.25   6.25
  a.   Souvenir sheet, #1319-1320   7.75   7.75

Teddy Bears — A319

No. 1321: a, Bing, 1919. b, Steiff "Teddy Clown," 1926. c, Steiff "Teddy Girl," 1905. d, Steiff, 1905. e, Steif "Elliot," 1907. f, Ideal "Aloysius," 1907. g, Steiff, 1936. h, Steif "Zotty," 1951. i, Steiff, 1910. j, Steiff "Titanic," 1912. k, Steiff "Berlin," 1985. l, Aux Nations, 1903.
No. 1322: a, Blue mohair, 1938-52. b, Musical bear, 1937. c, Red mohair, 1908. d, Shaggy beige mohair, 1908. e, Ally bear, 1916. f, National bear, 1917. g, Cowboy, 1940s. h, Coronation bear, 1953. i, Tumbling bear, 1920-30s. j, Messenger bear, 1923. k, Bear on a tricycle, 1958. l, Michi Takahashi, 1999.

2004-05   Litho.   Perf. 12¾x14
1321   Block of 12   21.00 21.00
  a.-b. A319 5c Either single   .20   .20
  c.-d. A319 15c Either single   .20   .20
  e.-f. A319 20c Either single   .20   .20
  g.-h. A319 45c Either single   .35   .35
  i.-j. A319 80c Either single   .65   .65
  k.-l. A319 K Either single   9.00   9.00
1322   Block of 12   30.00 30.00
  a.-b. A319 5c Either single   .20   .20
  c.-d. A319 15c Either single   .20   .20
  e.-f. A319 20c Either single   .20   .20
  g.-h. A319 45c Either single   .35   .35
  i.-j. A319 80c Either single   .65   .65
  k.-l. A319 N Either single   13.50 13.50

Issued: No. 1321, 2004; No. 1322, 3/1/05. Nos. 1321k-1321l each sold for $11.50 on day of issue, and are airmail. Nos. 1322k-1322l each sold for $17 on day of issue, and are airmail.

Butterflies — A320

No. 1323: a, Papilio chikae. b, Iphiclides podalirius. c, Paraphnaeus. d, Morpho didius. e, Delias eucharis. f, Parides sesostris. g, Baronia brevicornis. h, Graphium agamemnon. i, Papilio palinurus. j, Ornithoptera meridionalis. k, Battus bhilenor. l, Eurytides bellerophon.

2005, Jan. 5
1323   Block of 12   30.00 30.00
  a.-b. A320 5c Either single   .20   .20
  c.-d. A320 15c Either single   .20   .20
  e.-f. A320 20c Either single   .20   .20
  g.-h. A320 45c Either single   .35   .35
  i.-j. A320 80c Either single   .60   .60
  k.-l. A320 N Either single   13.50 13.50

Nos. 1323k-1323l each sold for $17 on day of issue, and are airmail.

Ships A321

No. 1324: a, Louis Roux, Altana. b, Fanerom Eni. c, Nafsika. d, Aristeidis Glykas. e, G. D'Esposito. f, G. D'Esposito, diff.

2005, May 4   Litho.   Perf. 14x12¾

1324	Block of 6	17.00	17.00
a.	A321 5c multi	.20	.20
b.	A321 15c multi	.20	.20
c.	A321 20c multi	.20	.20
d.	A321 80c multi	.60	.60
e.	A321 $1.70 multi	1.40	1.40
f.	A321 P multi	14.00	14.00

No. 1324f is airmail and sold for $18 on day of issue.

Orchids — A322

No. 1325: a, Vanda hybrid. b, Phalaenopsis hybrid, dark pink flowers. c, Dendrobium hybrid, pink flowers. d, Dendrobium hybrid, dark red flowers with foliage in background. e, Vanda hybrid, diff. f, Peristeria elata. g, Spathoglottis hybrid. h, Dendrobium hybrid, yellow orange flowers. i, Vanda sanderiana. j, Phalaenopsis hybrid, peach flowers. k, Phalaenopsis hybrid, pink flowers. l, Phalaenopsis hybrid, white flowers.

2005, June 29   Perf. 12¾x14

1325	Block of 12	22.50	22.50
a.-b.	A322 5c Either single	.20	.20
c.-d.	A322 15c Either single	.20	.20
e.-f.	A322 20c Either single	.20	.20
g.-h.	A322 45c Either single	.35	.35
i.-j.	A322 80c Either single	.60	.60
k.-l.	A322 Q Either single	10.00	10.00

Nos. 1325k and 1325 l are airmail and each sold for $12.50 on day of issue. See No. 1337.

America Issue, Fight Against Poverty A323

Designs: $1.70, Teacher and children. $14.50, Farmer, oxen and plow. $14, Teacher and children, diff.

2005   Perf. 14x12¾, 12¾x14

1326-1327	A323 Set of 2	13.00	13.00

Souvenir Sheet
Perf. 12¾x13¼

1328	A323 $14 multi	11.50	11.50

Issued: Nos. 1326-1327, 9/14; No. 1328, 9/17.

Birds Type of 2004

No. 1329: a, Porphyrula flavirostris. b, Asio clamator. c, Herpetotheres cashinnans. d, Jacana jacana. e, Touit batavica. f, Dendrocygna autumnalis. g, Coccyzus minor. h, Busarellus nigricollis. i, Lophostrix cristata. j, Otus choliba. k, Chrysolampis mosquitus. l, Pyrrhula picta.

2005, Oct. 19   Perf. 12¾x14

1329	Block of 12	35.00	35.00
a.-b.	A316 5c Either single	.20	.20
c.-d.	A316 15c Either single	.20	.20
e.-f.	A316 20c Either single	.20	.20
g.-h.	A316 80c Either single	.65	.65
i.-j.	A316 $1.80 Either single	1.40	1.40
k.-l.	A316 P Either single	14.50	14.50

Nos. 1329k and 1329 l are airmail and each sold for $18 on day of issue.

Children — A324

Designs (country name in red): 80c, Girl jumping rope. $9.50, Boy on swing.
No. 1332 — Country name in white: a, Girl jumping rope, diff. b, Boy on swing, diff.

2005, Nov. 16   Perf. 12¾x13¼

1330-1331	A324 Set of 2	7.50	7.50

Souvenir Sheet

1332	A324 $5 Sheet of 2, #a-b	7.50	7.50

No. 891a Surcharged

Methods and Perfs as Before
2005, Dec. 1

1333	Pair	5.25	5.25
a.	A172 $3.50 on 3c on 50c #891a	2.60	2.60
b.	A172 $3.50 on 3c on 50c #891b	2.60	2.60

Europa Stamps, 50th Anniv. — A325

Designs: $1, Netherlands #379. $2, Netherlands #369. $9, Netherlands #375.

2006, Jan. 4   Litho.   Perf. 12¾x13¼

1334-1336	A325 Set of 3	8.75	8.75
1336a	Souvenir sheet, #1334-1336	8.75	8.75

Orchids Type of 2005

No. 1337: a, Dendrobium hybrid, yellow flowers. b, Dendrobium hybrid, white flowers. c, Phalaenopsis hybrid, light purple flowers. d, Phalaenopsis hybrid, pink flowers. e, Vanda hybrid, white flowers. f, Vanda hybrid, purple flowers. g, Dendrobium hybrid, purple and white flowers. h, Arachnis hybrid. i, Vanda hybrid, light orange flowers. j, Vanda hybrid, speckled purple flowers. k, Complex hybrid, orange flowers. l, Vanda hybrid, purple and white flowers.

2006, Feb. 15   Perf. 12¾x14

1337	Block of 12	28.00	28.00
a.-b.	A322 5c Either single	.20	.20
c.-d.	A322 15c Either single	.20	.20
e.-f.	A322 20c Either single	.20	.20
g.-h.	A322 45c Either single	.35	.35
i.-j.	A322 80c Either single	.60	.60
k.-l.	A322 Q Either single	12.50	12.50

Nos. 1337k and 1337 l are airmail and each sold for $17.50 on day of issue.

Birds — A326

No. 1338: a, Phaethornis ruber. b, Threnetes leucurus. c, Podager nacunda. d, Columbina passerina. e, Leptotila rufaxilla. f, Claravis pretiosa. g, Campylopterus largipennis. h, Otus choliba. i, Porzana albicollis. j, Amazilia fimbriata. k, Ciccata virgata. l, Nyctidromus albicollis.

2006, May 15   Litho.   Perf. 14x12¾

1338	Block of 12	28.00	28.00
a.-b.	A326 5c Either single	.20	.20
c.-d.	A326 15c Either single	.20	.20
e.-f.	A326 20c Either single	.20	.20
g.-h.	A326 45c Either single	.30	.30
i.-j.	A326 80c Either single	.55	.55
k.-l.	A326 Q Either single	12.50	12.50

Nos. 1338k-1338l each sold for $17.50, and are airmail.

Nobel Laureates — A327

No. 1339: a, Aung San Suu Kyi, Peace, 1991. b, Milton Friedman, Economics, 1976. c, Marie Curie, Chemistry, 1911. d, Johannes Diderik van der Waals, Physics, 1910. e, Selma Lagerlöf, Literature, 1909. f, Gary S. Becker, Economics, 1992.

2006, June 26   Perf. 12¾x13¼

1339	Block of 6	8.50	8.50
a.	A327 20c multi	.20	.20
b.	A327 $1.20 multi	.85	.85
c.	A327 $1.70 multi	1.25	1.25
d.	A327 $2 multi	1.40	1.40
e.	A327 $3 multi	2.25	2.25
f.	A327 $3.50 multi	2.50	2.50

America Issue, Energy Conservation A328

Designs: 80c, Solar-powered airplane. $16.20, Windmill.
No. 1342: a, $3.50, Glider. b, $12.50, Windmills.

2006, Sept. 15   Perf. 14

1340-1341	A328 Set of 2	12.50	12.50

Souvenir Sheet

1342	A328 Sheet of 2, #a-b	12.00	12.00

Fish — A329

No. 1343: a, Crown betta. b, Barbus barilioides. c, Macropodus opercularis. d, Xiphophorus maculatus. e, Acanthurus lineatus. f, Carassius auratus.

2006, Oct. 15   Perf. 13¼x12¾

1343	Block of 6	14.50	14.50
a.	A329 $1.20 multi	.85	.85
b.	A329 $1.70 multi	1.25	1.25
c.	A329 $2 multi	1.40	1.40
d.	A329 $3 multi	2.25	2.25
e.	A329 $3.50 multi	2.50	2.50
f.	A329 $8.60 multi	6.25	6.25

Child Care — A330

Christmas A331

2006, Nov. 6   Perf. 14

1344	A330 $4 shown	3.00	3.00
1345	A331 $9.20 shown	6.75	6.75

Souvenir Sheet

1346	Sheet of 2	5.00	5.00
a.	A330 80c Children with ball	.60	.60
b.	A331 $6 Stained glass, diff.	4.25	4.25

No. 447 Surcharged in Brown

Methods and Perfs As Before
2006, Dec. 1

1347	A111 $3.25 on 1c #447	2.40	2.40
1348	A111 $3.75 on 1c #447	2.75	2.75

Primates — A332

No. 1349: a, Hylobates lar. b, Leontopithecus rosalia. c, Saguinus imperator. d, Callithrix geoffroyi. e, Callithrix argentata. f, Pygathrix nemaeus nemaeus. g, Saimiri sciureus. h, Douc langur. i, Cercopithecus neglectus. j, Alouatta caraya. k, Verreaux sitaka. l, Pan troglodytes.

2006, Dec. 13   Perf. 12¾x13¼

1349	Block of 12	24.00	24.00
a.	A332 R multi	.20	.20
b.	A332 20c multi	.20	.20
c.	A332 45c multi	.35	.35
d.	A332 80c multi	.60	.60
e.	A332 $1.20 multi	.90	.90
f.	A332 $1.70 multi	1.25	1.25
g.	A332 $2 multi	1.40	1.40
h.	A332 $3 multi	2.25	2.25
i.	A332 $3.50 multi	2.50	2.50
j.	A332 $4 multi	3.00	3.00
k.	A332 $5 multi	3.75	3.75
l.	A332 $10 multi	7.25	7.25

No. 1349a sold for 15c on day of issue.

Bird Type of 2004

2006, Dec. 20   Perf. 12¾x14

1350	A316 $10 Phaethornis suterciliosus	7.25	7.25

Printed in sheets of 2 + label.

Orchids — A333

No. 1351: a, Cattleya labiata. b, Vuylstekeara. c, Cymbidium. d, Odontoglossum pestcatorei. e, Odontocidium f, Odontioda. g, Vanda. h, Cattleya. i, Paphiopedilum insigne. j, Phalaenopsis. k, Thunia. l, Oncidium.

2007, Jan. 3   Perf. 12¾x13¼

1351	Block of 12	24.00	24.00
a.	A333 S multi	.20	.20
b.	A333 20c multi	.20	.20
c.	A333 45c multi	.35	.35
d.	A333 80c multi	.60	.60
e.	A333 $1.20 multi	.90	.90
f.	A333 $1.70 multi	1.25	1.25
g.	A333 $2 multi	1.40	1.40
h.	A333 $3 multi	2.25	2.25
i.	A333 $3.50 multi	2.50	2.50
j.	A333 $4 multi	3.00	3.00
k.	A333 $5 multi	3.75	3.75
l.	A333 $10 multi	7.25	7.25

No. 1351a sold for 10c on day of issue.

Butterflies A334

No. 1352: a, Great spangled fritillary. b, Peacock pansy. c, Viceroy. d, Unidentified taxco. e, Tropical buckeye. f, Limenitis popul.

2007, Feb. 14   Perf. 14

1352	Block of 6	9.00	9.00
a.	A334 T multi	.20	.20
b.	A334 $1.20 multi	.85	.85
c.	A334 $1.70 multi	1.25	1.25
d.	A334 $2 multi	1.40	1.40
e.	A334 $3 multi	2.25	2.25
f.	A334 $4 multi	3.00	3.00

No. 1352a sold for 5c on day of issue.

Reptiles A335

No. 1353: a, Terapene carolina. b, Cuora flavomarginata. c, Chelonia mydas. d, Testudo hermanni. e, Uromastyx acanthinura. f, Physignathus coccincinus. g, Iguana iguana. h, Amblyrhynchus cristatus. i, Chamaeleo jacksoni. j, Crocodylus niloticus. k, Caiman crocodilus. l, Varanus komodensis.

Perf. 13¼x12¾

2007, Mar. 21   **Litho.**

1353	Block of 12	24.00	24.00
a.	A335 S multi	.20	.20
b.	A335 20c multi	.20	.20
c.	A335 45c multi	.30	.30
d.	A335 80c multi	.60	.60
e.	A335 $1.20 multi	.90	.90
f.	A335 $1.70 multi	1.25	1.25
g.	A335 $2 multi	1.50	1.50
h.	A335 $3 multi	2.25	2.25
i.	A335 $3.50 multi	2.60	2.60
j.	A335 $4 multi	3.00	3.00
k.	A335 $5 multi	3.75	3.75
l.	A335 $10 multi	7.25	7.25

No. 1353a sold for 10c on day of issue.

Parrots — A336

No. 1354: a, Callocephalon fimbriatum. b, Cacatua ophthalmica. c, Cacatua galerita. d, Cacatua sulphure amazone. e, Calyporhychus magunificus. f, Cacatua sulphure amazone, diff. g, Eolophus rosicapillus. h, Cacatua sulphure amazone, diff. i, Parrot (inscribed "Pan troglodytes" in error).

2007, Apr. 26   **Perf. 14**

1354	Block of 9	11.50	11.50
a.	A336 T multi	.20	.20
b.	A336 25c multi	.20	.20
c.	A336 55c multi	.40	.40
d.	A336 80c multi	.60	.60
e.	A336 $1.10 multi	.80	.80
f.	A336 $1.20 multi	.90	.90
g.	A336 $2 multi	1.50	1.50
h.	A336 $3 multi	3.00	3.00
i.	A336 $5 multi	3.75	3.75

No. 1354a sold for 5c on day of issue.

Birds — A337

No. 1355: a, Agamia agami. b, Botaurus pinnatus. c, Rallus maculatus. d, Melanerpes cruentatus. e, Piculus chrysochloros. f, Paroaria gularis. g, Gyanicterus cyanicterus. h, Tersina viridis. i, Sicalis floreola.

2007, May 23   **Perf. 12¾x13¼**

1355	Block of 9	18.00	18.00
a.	A337 T multi	.20	.20
b.	A337 20c multi	.20	.20
c.	A337 45c multi	.35	.35
d.	A337 80c multi	.60	.60
e.	A337 $1.20 multi	.90	.90
f.	A337 $2 multi	1.50	1.50
g.	A337 $4 multi	3.00	3.00
h.	A337 $5 multi	3.75	3.75
i.	A337 $10 multi	7.25	7.25

No. 1355a sold for 5c on day of issue.

Fish — A338

No. 1356: a, Brachydanio rerio. b, Pterois miles. c, Pomacanthus annularis. d, Balsitoides conspicillum. e, Plectorhynchus orientalis. f, Chaetodon auriga.

2007, June 27   **Perf. 13¼x12¾**

			Litho.
1356	Block of 6	15.00	15.00
a.	A338 $1.20 multi	.90	.90
b.	A338 $1.70 multi	1.25	1.25
c.	A338 $2 multi	1.50	1.50
d.	A338 $3 multi	2.25	2.25
e.	A338 $3.50 multi	2.60	2.60
f.	A338 $8.60 multi	6.25	6.25

Ferrari Automobiles A339

No. 1357: a, 1947 125 S. b, 1962 250 GTO. c, 1984 GTO. d, 1999 F399. e, 1983 Mondial Cabriolet. f, 1994 F 333 SP. g, 1971 365 GT4 BB. h, 2006 FXX.

2007, July 11   **Perf. 14**

1357	Block of 8 + label	9.75	9.75
a.	A339 10c multi	.20	.20
b.	A339 20c multi	.20	.20
c.	A339 50c multi	.35	.35
d.	A339 $1 multi	.75	.75
e.	A339 $1.60 multi	1.10	1.10
f.	A339 $1.75 multi	1.25	1.25
g.	A339 $3 multi	2.25	2.25
h.	A339 $5 multi	3.50	3.50

No. 1357 was issued in sheets containing two blocks, one of which had the label in the lower right corner, and the other with the label in the upper left corner.

Primates — A340

No. 1358: a, Pan troglodytes. b, Cercopithecus neglectus. c, Nasalis larvatus. d, Macaca fascicularis. e, Mandrillus sphinx. f, Rhinopithecus roxellana.

2007, Aug. 15   **Litho.**   **Perf. 14**

1358	Block of 6	15.00	15.00
a.	A340 $1.20 multi	.90	.90
b.	A340 $1.70 multi	1.25	1.25
c.	A340 $2 multi	1.50	1.50
d.	A340 $3 multi	2.25	2.25
e.	A340 $3.50 multi	2.60	2.60
f.	A340 $8.60 multi	6.25	6.25

America Issue, Education A341

Designs: 80c, Children in classroom. $16.20, Children in classroom, diff.
No. 1361: a, $7, Boy at blackboard. b, $9, Two children.

2007, Sept. 19

1359-1360	A341	Set of 2	12.50	12.50

Souvenir Sheet

1361	A341	Sheet of 2, #a-b	12.00	12.00

Christmas — A342

Designs: $4, Four children at desks. $6, Holy Family.
No. 1364: a, 80c, Children, words and letters. b, $9.20, Holy Family, sheep.

2007, Nov. 7

1362-1363	A342	Set of 2	7.25	7.25

Souvenir Sheet

1364	A342	Sheet of 2, #a-b	7.25	7.25

Frogs A343

No. 1365: a, Agalychnis callidryas. b, Dendrobates pumilio. c, Phaeramia nematoptera. d, Hoffmanni. e, Phaeramia nematoptera, diff. f, Dendrobates histrionicus.

2007, Dec. 12   **Litho.**   **Perf. 14x12¾**

1365	Block of 6	11.00	11.00
a.	A343 T multi	.20	.20
b.	A343 $1.20 multi	.85	.85
c.	A343 $1.70 multi	1.25	1.25
d.	A343 $2 multi	1.40	1.40
e.	A343 $3 multi	2.25	2.25
f.	A343 $7 multi	5.00	5.00

On day of issue, No. 1365a sold for 5c.

Butterflies Type of 2007

No. 1366: a, Anthocharis bella. b, Satyr angelwing. c, Red lacewing. d, Inachis io. e, Purple sapphire. f, Pearly crescentspot. g, Monarch. h, Marpesia berania. i, Darkmuseum swallowtail. j, Byasa alcinous. k, Brown peacock. l, Brown and orange Mexican.

2008, Jan. 2   **Litho.**   **Perf. 14**

1366	Block of 12	24.00	24.00
a.	A334 T multi	.20	.20
b.	A334 25c multi	.20	.20
c.	A334 45c multi	.30	.30
d.	A334 80c multi	.60	.60
e.	A334 $1.20 multi	.90	.90
f.	A334 $1.70 multi	1.25	1.25
g.	A334 $2 multi	1.50	1.50
h.	A334 $3 multi	2.25	2.25
i.	A334 $3.50 multi	2.60	2.60
j.	A334 $4 multi	3.00	3.00
k.	A334 $5 multi	3.75	3.75
l.	A334 $10 multi	7.25	7.25

No. 1366a sold for 5c on day of issue.

Fish — A344

No. 1367: a, Sphaeramia nematoptera. b, Neophrynichthys latus. c, Cheilodipterus isostigmus.

2007, Feb. 13

1367	Horiz. strip of 3	8.75	8.75
a.	A344 $1.20 multi	.90	.90
b.	A344 $3 multi	2.25	2.25
c.	A344 $7.80 multi	5.50	5.50

SEMI-POSTAL STAMPS

SP1   SP2

Green Cross — SP3

Perf. 12½

1927, Aug. 1   **Unwmk.**   **Photo.**

B1	SP1	2c (+ 2c) bl blk & grn	1.10	1.00
B2	SP2	5c (+ 3c) vio & grn	1.10	1.00
B3	SP3	10c (+ 3c) ver & grn	2.00	1.75
		Nos. B1-B3 (3)	4.20	3.75
		Set, never hinged	10.50	

Surtax was given to the Green Cross Society, which promotes public health services.

Nurse and Patient SP4   Good Samaritan SP5

1928, Dec. 1   **Perf. 11½**

B4	SP4	1½c (+ 1½c) ultra	4.50	4.50
B5	SP4	2c (+ 2c) bl grn	4.50	4.50
B6	SP4	5c (+ 3c) vio	4.50	4.50
B7	SP4	7½c (+ 2½c) ver	4.50	4.50
		Nos. B4-B7 (4)	18.00	18.00
		Set, never hinged	67.50	

The surtax on these stamps was for a fund to combat indigenous diseases.

1929, Dec. 1   **Perf. 12½**

B8	SP5	1½c (+ 1½c) grn	6.75	6.75
B9	SP5	2c (+ 2c) scar	6.75	6.75
B10	SP5	5c (+ 3c) ultra	6.75	6.75
B11	SP5	6c (+ 4c) blk	6.75	6.75
		Nos. B8-B11 (4)	27.00	27.00
		Set, never hinged	72.50	

Surtax for the Green Cross Society.

Surinam Mother and Child — SP6

1931, Dec. 14

B12	SP6	1½c (+ 1½c) blk	4.75	4.75
B13	SP6	2c (+ 2c) car rose	4.75	4.75
B14	SP6	5c (+ 3c) ultra	4.75	4.75
B15	SP6	6c (+ 4c) dp grn	4.75	4.75
		Nos. B12-B15 (4)	19.00	19.00
		Set, never hinged	45.00	

The surtax was for Child Welfare Societies.

Designs Symbolical of the Creed of the Moravians
SP7   SP8

1935, Aug. 1   **Perf. 13x14**

B16	SP7	1c (+ ½c) dk brn	6.00	6.00
B17	SP7	2c (+ 1c) dp ultra	6.00	6.00
B18	SP8	3c (+ 1½c) grn	7.50	7.50
B19	SP8	4c (+ 2c) red org	7.50	7.50
B20	SP8	5c (+ 2½c) blk brn	9.00	9.00
B21	SP7	10c (+ 5c) car	9.00	9.00
		Nos. B16-B21 (6)	45.00	45.00
		Set, never hinged	90.00	

200th anniv. of the founding of the Moravian Mission in Surinam.

Surinam Child — SP9

1936, Dec. 14   **Perf. 12½**

B22	SP9	2c (+ 1c) dk grn	2.75	2.75
B23	SP9	3c (+ 1½c) dk bl	2.75	2.75
B24	SP9	5c (+ 2½c) brn blk	4.00	4.00
B25	SP9	10c (+ 5c) lake	4.00	4.00
		Nos. B22-B25 (4)	13.50	13.50
		Set, never hinged	26.50	

Surtax for baby food and the Green Cross Society.

"Emancipation" SP10   Surinam Girl SP11

1938, June 1   **Litho.**   **Perf. 12½x12**

B26	SP10	2½c (+ 2c) dk bl grn	2.40	1.90

Photo.

B27	SP11	3c (+ 2c) vio blk	2.40 1.90
B28	SP11	5c (+ 3c) dk brn	2.60 2.25
B29	SP11	7½c (+ 5c) indigo	2.60 2.25
		Nos. B26-B29 (4)	10.00 8.30
		Set, never hinged	20.00

75th anniv. of the abolition of slavery in Surinam. Surtax to Slavery Remembrance Committee.

Creole Woman — SP12

Javanese Woman — SP13

Hindustani Woman — SP14

American Indian Woman — SP15

1940, Jan. 8   Engr.   Perf. 13x14

B30	SP12	2½c (+ 2c) dk grn	3.00 3.00
B31	SP13	3c (+ 2c) red org	3.00 3.00
B32	SP14	5c (+ 3c) dp bl	3.00 3.00
B33	SP15	7½c (+ 5c) henna brn	3.00 3.00
		Nos. B30-B33 (4)	12.00 12.00
		Set, never hinged	25.00

Surtax to leper care and baby food.

Catalogue values for unused stamps in this section, from this point to the end of the section, are for Never Hinged items.

Netherlands Coat of Arms and Inscription, "Netherlands Shall Rise Again" — SP16

1941, Aug. 30   Litho.   Perf. 12½

B34	SP16	7½c + 7½c dp org, ultra & blk	3.75 3.00
B35	SP16	15c + 15c scar, ultra & blk	3.75 3.00
B36	SP16	1g + 1g gray & ultra	26.00 22.50
		Nos. B34-B36 (3)	33.50 28.50

The surtax was used to buy fighters for Dutch pilots in the Royal Air Force of Great Britain.

Nos. 145, 169, 146, 151 Surcharged in Red:

1942, Jan. 2

B37	A23	2c + 2c blk brn, I	2.50 2.50
a.		Type II	2.50 2.50
B38	A26	2c + 2c blk brn, I	67.50 67.50
a.		Type II	67.50 67.50
B39	A23	2½c + 2c green, I	2.50 2.50
a.		Type II	2.50 2.50
B40	A23	7½c + 5c red vio, III	2.50 2.50
a.		Type IV	8.00 8.00
b.		Type V	20.00 20.00
		Nos. B37-B40,CB1 (5)	77.50 77.50

The surtax was for the Red Cross.

In type III, the "c" may be "large," as illustrated, or "small," as in type II. Value is the same.

The distinctive feature of type IV is the pointed ending of the lower part of the "5."

Types of Regular Issue of 1945 Surcharged in Black

Unwmk.

1945, July 23   Engr.   Perf. 12

B41	A29	7½c + 5c dp org	3.75 2.50
B42	A30	15c + 10c brn	3.00 2.50
B43	A30	20c + 15c dl grn	3.00 2.50
B44	A30	22½c + 20c gray	3.00 2.50
B45	A30	40c + 35c rose lake	3.00 2.50
B46	A30	60c + 50c vio	3.00 2.50
		Nos. B41-B46 (6)	18.75 15.00

Surtax for the National Welfare Fund.

Star — SP17

Marie Curie — SP18

1947, Dec. 16   Photo.   Perf. 13½x13

B47	SP17	7½c + 12½c red org	2.75 2.25
B48	SP17	12½c + 37½c blue	2.75 2.25
		Nos. B47-B48,CB4-CB5 (4)	10.00 8.00

The surtax was used to combat leprosy.

1950, May 15   Perf. 14x13

7½c+22½c, 27½c+12½c, Wm. Roentgen.

B49	SP18	7½c + 7½c	17.50 10.50
B50	SP18	7½c + 22½c	17.50 10.50
B51	SP18	27½c + 12½c	17.50 10.50
B52	SP18	27½c + 97½c	17.50 10.50
		Nos. B49-B52 (4)	70.00 42.00

The surtax was used to combat cancer.

Nos. 236-237 Surcharged in Black (#B53) or Red (#B54)

1953, Feb. 18   Wmk. 202

B53	A35	12½c + 7½c on 7½c	2.75 2.75
B54	A35	20c + 10c on 12½c	2.75 2.75

The surtax was for flood relief in the Netherlands.

Stadium, Paramaribo — SP19

1953, Aug. 29   Unwmk.   Perf. 13½

B55	SP19	10c + 5c claret	11.50 8.25
B56	SP19	15c + 7½c brn	11.50 8.25
B57	SP19	30c + 15c dk grn	11.50 8.25
		Nos. B55-B57 (3)	34.50 24.75

Opening of the new stadium.

Surinam Children — SP20

Doves — SP21

1954, Nov. 1   Perf. 13x14

B58	SP20	7½c + 3c sepia	6.00 4.75
B59	SP20	10c + 5c bl grn	6.00 4.75
B60	SP20	15c + 7½c red brn	6.00 4.75
B61	SP20	30c + 15c blue	6.00 4.75
		Nos. B58-B61 (4)	24.00 19.00

Surtax for the youth center of the Moravian Church.

1955, May 5   Perf. 14x13

B62	SP21	7½c + 3½c brt red	2.75 3.00
B63	SP21	15c + 8c ultra	2.75 3.00

The Netherlands' liberation, 10th anniv.

Queen Juliana and Prince Bernhard SP22

1955, Oct. 27   Unwmk.

B64	SP22	7½c + 2½c dk olive	.55 .55

Royal visit to Surinam, 1955. Surtax for the Royal present.

Theater, 1837 — SP23

Designs: 10c+5c, Theater and car, circa 1920. 15c+7½c, Theater and car, circa 1958. 20c+10c, Theater interior.

1958, Feb. 15   Litho.   Perf. 13x12½

B65	SP23	7½c + 3c lt bl & blk	.45 .45
B66	SP23	10c + 5c rose lil & blk	.45 .45
B67	SP23	15c + 7½c lt grn & blk	.45 .45
B68	SP23	20c + 10c org & blk	.45 .45
		Nos. B65-B68 (4)	1.80 1.80

120th anniv. of the "Thalia" theatrical society.

Carved Eating Utensils and Map of South America SP24

Native Art (Map of So. America and): 10c+5c, Feather headgear. 15c+7c, Clay pottery. 20c+10c, Carved wooden stool.

1960, Jan. 15

B69	SP24	8c + 4c multi	.90 .90
B70	SP24	10c + 5c salmon, red & bl	.90 .90
B71	SP24	15c + 7c red org, grn & sepia	.90 .90
B72	SP24	20c + 10c lt bl, ultra & bis	.90 .90
		Nos. B69-B72 (4)	3.60 3.60

SP25

SP26

Design: Uprooted Oak emblem of WRY.

1960, Apr. 7   Perf. 13x14

B73	SP25	8c + 4c choc & grn	.20 .20
B74	SP25	10c + 5c vio bl & ol grn	.20 .20

World Refugee Year, July 1, 1959-June 30, 1960. The surtax was for aid to refugees.

1960, Aug. 10   Litho.   Perf. 14x13

B75	SP26	8c + 4c Shot put	.55 .55
B76	SP26	10c + 5c Basketball	.55 .55
B77	SP26	15c + 7c Runner	.85 .85
B78	SP26	20c + 10c Swimmer	.85 .85
B79	SP26	40c + 20c Soccer	.85 .85
		Nos. B75-B79 (5)	3.65 3.65

17th Olympic Games, Rome, 8/25-9/11. Surtax for Olympic Committee.

Girl Scout Signaling SP27

Designs: 10c+3c, Scout Saluting, vert. 15c+4c, Brownies around toadstool. 20c+5c, Scouts around campfire, vert. 25c+6c, Scouts cooking outdoors.

Perf. 14x13, 13x14
1961, Aug. 19   Litho.
Multicolored Designs

B80	SP27	8c + 2c blue	.30 .30
B81	SP27	10c + 3c lilac	.35 .35
B82	SP27	15c + 4c yellow	.35 .35
B83	SP27	20c + 5c brn red	.40 .40
B84	SP27	25c + 6c aqua	.40 .40
		Nos. B80-B84 (5)	1.80 1.80

Caribbean Girl Scout Jamborette. Surtax for various charities.

Hibiscus SP28

Flowers: 10c+5c, Caesalpinia pulcherrima. 15c+6c, Heliconia psittacorum. 20c+10c, Lochnera rosea. 25c+12c, Ixora macrothyrsa.

1962, Mar. 7   Photo.   Perf. 14x13
Cross in Red

B85	SP28	8c + 4c dk ol & scar	.32 .30
B86	SP28	10c + 5c dk bl & org	.32 .30
B87	SP28	15c + 6c multi	.32 .30
B88	SP28	20c + 10c multi	.32 .30
B89	SP28	25c + 12c dk bl grn, red & yel	.32 .30
		Nos. B85-B89 (5)	1.60 1.50

The surtax was for the Red Cross.

Hands Protecting Duck — SP29

American Indian Girl — SP30

1962, Dec. 15   Litho.   Perf. 13x14

B90	SP29	2c + 1c shown	.20	.20
B91	SP29	8c + 2c Dog	.20	.20
B92	SP29	10c + 3c Donkey	.20	.20
B93	SP29	15c + 4c Horse	.25	.25
		Nos. B90-B93 (4)	.85	.85

The surtax was for the Organization for Animal Protection.

1963, Oct. 30   Photo.   Unwmk.

Girls: 10c+4c, Negro. 15c+10c, East Indian. 20c+10c, Indonesian. 40c+20c, Caucasian.

B94	SP30	8c + 3c Prus grn	.20	.20
B95	SP30	10c + 4c red brn	.20	.20
a.		Min. sheet, 2 each #B94-B95	1.25	1.25
B96	SP30	15c + 10c dp blue	.25	.25
B97	SP30	20c + 10c brn red	.25	.25
B98	SP30	40c + 20c red vio	.35	.35
		Nos. B94-B98 (5)	1.25	1.25

The surtax was for Child Welfare.

X-15
SP31

Designs: 8c+4c, Flag of the Aeronautical and Astronautical Foundation. 10c+5c, 20c+10c, Agena B Ranger rocket.

1964, Apr. 15   Perf. 13x12½

B99	SP31	3c + 2c blk & rose lake	.20	.20
B100	SP31	8c + 4c blk, ultra & lt ultra	.20	.20
B101	SP31	10c + 5c blk & grn	.20	.20
B102	SP31	15c + 7c blk & yel brn	.20	.20
B103	SP31	20c + 10c blk & vio	.20	.20
		Nos. B99-B103 (5)	1.00	1.00

Surtax for the Aeronautical and Astronautical Foundation of Surinam.

Stylized Campfire amid Trees — SP32

Girls Skipping Rope — SP33

1964, July 29   Litho.   Perf. 13x14

B104	SP32	3c + 1c brn ol, yel bis & lem	.20	.20
B105	SP32	8c + 4c bluish blk, vio bl & yel bis	.20	.20
B106	SP32	10c + 5c dk red, red & yel bis	.20	.20
B107	SP32	20c + 10c grnsh blk, ol grn & yel bis	.20	.20
		Nos. B104-B107 (4)	.80	.80

Jamborette at Paramaribo, Aug. 20-30, marking the 40th anniv. of the Surinam Boy Scout Association.
Surtax for various charities.

1964, Nov. 30   Photo.   Perf. 14x13

10c+4c, Children on swings. 15c+9c, Girl on scooter. 20c+10c, Boy rolling hoop.

B108	SP33	8c + 3c dk blue	.20	.20
B109	SP33	10c + 4c red	.20	.20
a.		Min. sheet, 2 each #B108-B109	.55	.55
B110	SP33	15c + 9c olive grn	.20	.20
B111	SP33	20c + 10c magenta	.20	.20
		Nos. B108-B111 (4)	.80	.80

Issued for Child Welfare.

Mother and Child — SP34

Designs: 4c+2c, Pregnant woman. 15c+7c, Child. 25c+12c, Old man.

1965, Feb. 27   Photo.   Perf. 13x14

B112	SP34	4c + 2c green	.20	.20
B113	SP34	10c + 5c brn & grn	.20	.20
B114	SP34	15c + 7c Prus bl & grn	.20	.20
B115	SP34	25c + 12c brt pur & grn	.20	.20
		Nos. B112-B115 (4)	.80	.80

50th anniv. of the Green Cross Assoc. which promotes public health services.

Girl with Leopard and Spider SP35

Designs: 10c+5c, Boy with monkey and spider. 15c+7c, Girl with tortoise and spider. 25c+10c, Boy with rabbit and spider.

Perf. 13x12½

1965, Nov. 26   Litho.   Unwmk.

B116	SP35	4c + 4c lt grn & blk	.20	.20
B117	SP35	10c + 5c ocher & blk	.20	.20
B118	SP35	15c + 7c dp org & blk	.20	.20
a.		Min. sheet, 2 each #B116, B118	.55	.55
B119	SP35	25c + 10c lt ultra & blk	.20	.20
		Nos. B116-B119 (4)	.80	.80

Issued for Child Welfare.

"Help them to a safe haven" SP35a

1966, Jan. 31   Photo.   Perf. 14x13

B120	SP35a	10c + 5c blk & grn	.20	.20
B121	SP35a	25c + 10c blk & rose brn	.20	.20
a.		Min. sheet of 3, 2 #B120, B121	.45	.45

The surtax was for the Intergovernmental Committee for European Migration (ICEM). The message on the stamps was given and signed by Queen Juliana.

Mary Magdalene, Disciples and "Round Table" Emblem SP36

"New Year's Eve" Boys with Bamboo Gun SP37

Mary Magdalene (John 20:18), and Service Club Emblems: 15c+8c, Toastmasters Intl. 20c+10c, Junior Chamber, Surinam. 25c+12c, Rotary Intl. 30c+15c, Lions Intl.

1966, Apr. 13   Photo.   Perf. 12½x13

B122	SP36	10c + 5c dp crim, blk & gold		.20	.20
B123	SP36	15c + 8c dp vio, blk & bl		.20	.20
B124	SP36	20c + 10c yel org, blk & ultra		.20	.20
B125	SP36	25c + 12c grn, blk & gold		.20	.20
B126	SP36	30c + 15c ultra, blk & gold		.20	.20
		Nos. B122-B126 (5)		1.00	1.00

Easter charities.

1966, Nov. 25   Litho.   Perf. 12½x13

Designs: 15c+8c, "The End of Lent," boys pouring paint over each other. 20c+10c, "Liberation Day," parading children. 25c+12c, "Queen's Birthday," children on hobbyhorses. 30c+15c, "Christmas," Children decorating room with star.

B127	SP37	10c + 5c multi	.20	.20
B128	SP37	15c + 8c multi	.20	.20
B129	SP37	20c + 10c multi	.20	.20
a.		Min. sheet of 3, 2 #B127, B129	.35	.35
B130	SP37	25c + 12c multi	.20	.20
B131	SP37	30c + 15c multi	.20	.20
		Nos. B127-B131 (5)	1.00	1.00

Child welfare.

Good Samaritan Giving His Coat SP38

Children Stilt-walking SP39

The Good Samaritan: 15c+8c, Dressing the wounds. 20c+10c, Feeding the poor man. 25c+12c, Poor man riding Samaritan's horse. 30c+15c, Samaritan taking poor man to the inn.

1967, Mar. 22

B132	SP38	10c + 5c yellow & blk	.20	.20
B133	SP38	15c + 8c lt blue & blk	.20	.20
B134	SP38	20c + 10c buff & blk	.20	.20
B135	SP38	25c + 12c pale rose & blk	.20	.20
B136	SP38	30c + 15c grn & blk	.20	.20
		Nos. B132-B136 (5)	1.00	1.00

Easter charities.

1967, Nov. 21   Litho.   Perf. 12½x13

Children's Games: 15c+8c, Boys playing with marbles. 20c+10c, Girl playing dibs (five stones). 25c+12c, Boy making kite. 30c+15c, Girls play-cooking.

B137	SP39	10c + 5c multi	.20	.20
B138	SP39	15c + 8c multi	.20	.20
B139	SP39	20c + 10c multi	.20	.20
a.		Min. sheet, #B139, 2 #B137	.45	.45
B140	SP39	25c + 12c multi	.20	.20
B141	SP39	30c + 15c multi	.20	.20
		Nos. B137-B141 (5)	1.00	1.00

Child welfare.

Cross, Ash Wednesday SP40

Hopscotch SP41

Easter Symbols: 15c+8c, Palms, Palm Sunday. 20c+10c, Bread and Wine, Maundy Thursday. 25c+12c, Cross, Good Friday. 30c+15c, Chrismon, Easter Sunday.

1968, Mar. 27   Litho.   Perf. 12½x13

B142	SP40	10c + 5c lilac & gray	.20	.20
B143	SP40	15c + 8c brick red & grn		.20
B144	SP40	20c + 10c yellow & dk gray		.20
B145	SP40	25c + 12c gray & blk	.20	.20
B146	SP40	30c + 15c brt yel & brn		.20
		Nos. B142-B146 (5)	1.00	1.00

Easter charities.

1968, Nov. 22   Litho.   Perf. 12½x13

15c+8c, Balancing pyramid. 20c+10c, Handball. 25c+12c, Handicraft. 30c+15c, Tug-of-war.

B147	SP41	10c + 5c fawn & blk	.20	.20
B148	SP41	15c + 8c lt ultra & blk	.20	.20
B149	SP41	20c + 10c pink & blk	.20	.20
a.		Min. sheet, #B149, 2 #B147	.50	.50
B150	SP41	25c + 12c yel grn & blk		.25	.25
B151	SP41	30c + 15c bluish lil & blk		.30	.30
		Nos. B147-B151 (5)		1.15	1.15

Child welfare.

Globe with Map of South America SP42

Pillow Fight SP43

1969, Apr. 2   Litho.   Perf. 12½x13

B152	SP42	10c + 5c bl & lt bl	.25	.25
B153	SP42	15c + 8c sl grn & yel	.25	.25
B154	SP42	20c + 10c sl grn & gray grn		.25	.25
B155	SP42	25c + 12c brn & bis	.25	.25
B156	SP42	30c + 15c vio & gray	.25	.25
		Nos. B152-B156 (5)	1.25	1.25

Easter charities.

1969, Nov. 21   Litho.   Perf. 12½x13

15c+8c, Eating contest. 20c+10c, Pole climbing. 25c+12c, Sack race. 30c+15c, Obstacle race.

B157	SP43	10c + 5c lt ultra & mag		.20	.20
B158	SP43	15c + 8c yel & brn	.25	.25
B159	SP43	20c + 10c gray & dp bl		.20	.20
a.		Min. sheet, #B159, 2 #B157	.80	.80
B160	SP43	25c + 12c pink & brt bl		.25	.25
B161	SP43	30c + 15c emer & brn		.25	.25
		Nos. B157-B161 (5)		1.15	1.15

Child welfare.

Butterfly SP44

Ludwig van Beethoven, 1786 SP45

Designs: 10c+5c, Flower. 20c+10c, Flying bird. 25c+12c, Sun. 30c+15c, Star.

1970, Mar. 25   Litho.   Perf. 12½x13

B162	SP44	10c + 5c multi	.50	.50
B163	SP44	15c + 8c multi	.50	.50
B164	SP44	20c + 10c multi	.50	.50
B165	SP44	25c + 12c multi	.50	.50
B166	SP44	30c + 15c multi	.50	.50
		Nos. B162-B166 (5)	2.50	2.50

Easter.

1970, Nov. 25   Litho.   Perf. 12½x13

Various Portraits of Beethoven: 15c+8c, In 1804. 20c+10c, In 1812. 25c+12c, In 1814. 30c+15c, In 1827 (death mask).

Portrait and Inscription in Gray and Ocher

B167	SP45	10c + 5c green	.50	.50
B168	SP45	15c + 8c scarlet	.50	.50
B169	SP45	20c + 10c blue	.50	.50
a.		Min. sheet, #B169, 2 #B167	1.60	1.60
B170	SP45	25c + 12c red org	.50	.50
B171	SP45	30c + 15c purple	.50	.50
		Nos. B167-B171 (5)	2.50	2.50

Ludwig van Beethoven (1770-1827), composer. The surtax was for child welfare.

Donkey and Palm — SP46 | Leapfrog, by Peter Brueghel — SP47

Easter: 15c+8c, Cock. 20c+10c, Lamb of God. 25c+12c, Cross and Crown of Thorns. 30c+15c, Sun.

1971, Apr. 7   Litho.   Perf. 12½x13

B172	SP46	10c + 5c multi	.50	.50
B173	SP46	15c + 8c blue & multi	.50	.50
B174	SP46	20c + 10c multi	.50	.50
B175	SP46	25c + 12c multi	.50	.50
B176	SP46	30c + 15c multi	.50	.50
		Nos. B172-B176 (5)	2.50	2.50

Easter charities.

1971, Nov. 24   Photo.   Perf. 13x14

Children's Games, by Peter Brueghel: 15c+8c, Girl strewing flowers. 20c+10c, Spinning the hoop. 25c+12c, Ball players. 30c+15c, Stilt walker.

B177	SP47	10c + 5c multi	.60	.60
B178	SP47	15c + 8c multi	.60	.60
B179	SP47	20c + 10c multi	.60	.60
a.		Min. sheet, #B179, 2 #B177	2.00	2.00
B180	SP47	25c + 12c multi	.60	.60
B181	SP47	30c + 15c multi	.60	.60
		Nos. B177-B181 (5)	3.00	3.00

Child welfare.

Easter Candle — SP48 | Toys — SP49

Easter: 15c+8c, Christ teaching Apostles, and crosses. 20c+10c, Cup and folded hands. 25c+12c, Fish in net. 30c+15c, Judas' bag of silver.

1972, Mar. 29   Litho.   Perf. 12½x13

B182	SP48	10c + 5c multi	.45	.45
B183	SP48	15c + 8c multi	.45	.45
B184	SP48	20c + 10c multi	.45	.45
B185	SP48	25c + 12c multi	.45	.45
B186	SP48	30c + 15c multi	.45	.45
		Nos. B182-B186 (5)	2.25	2.25

Easter charities.

1972, Nov. 29   Litho.   Perf. 12½x13

Designs: 15c+8c, Abacus and clock. 20c+10c, Pythagorean theorem. 25c+12c, Model of molecule. 30c+15c, Monkey wrench and drill. Each design represents a different stage of education.

B187	SP49	10c + 5c multi	.50	.50
B188	SP49	15c + 8c multi	.50	.50
B189	SP49	20c + 10c multi	.50	.50
a.		Min. sheet, #B189, 2 #B187	1.50	1.50
B190	SP49	25c + 12c multi	.50	.50
B191	SP49	30c + 15c multi	.50	.50
		Nos. B187-B191 (5)	2.50	2.50

Child welfare.

Jesus Calming the Waves — SP50

Easter: 15c+8c, The washing of the feet. 20c+10c, Jesus carrying Cross. 25c+12c, Cross and "ELI, ELI, LAMA SABACHTHANI?" 30c+15c, on the road to Emmaus.

1973, Apr. 4   Litho.   Perf. 12½x13

B192	SP50	10c + 5c multi	.45	.45
B193	SP50	15c + 8c multi	.45	.45
B194	SP50	20c + 10c multi	.45	.45
B195	SP50	25c + 12c multi	.45	.45
B196	SP50	30c + 15c multi	.45	.45
		Nos. B192-B196 (5)	2.25	2.25

Easter charities.

Red Cross and Florence Nightingale SP51

1973, Oct. 3   Litho.   Perf. 14½x14

B197	SP51	30c + 10c multi	.90	.90

30th anniversary of Surinam Red Cross.

Flower SP52 | Bitterwood SP53

1973, Nov. 28   Litho.   Perf. 14x14½

B198	SP52	10c + 5c shown	.25	.25
B199	SP52	15c + 8c Tree	.45	.45
B200	SP52	20c + 10c Dog	.45	.45
a.		Min. sheet, #B200, 2 #B198	1.25	1.25
B201	SP52	25c + 12c House	.60	.60
B202	SP52	30c + 15c Girl	.60	.60
		Nos. B198-B202 (5)	2.30	2.30

Child welfare.

1974, Apr. 3   Litho.   Perf. 14x14½

Tropical Flowers: 15c+8c, Passion flower. 20c+10c, Wild angelica. 25c+12c, Candlestick senna. 30c+15c, Blood flower.

B203	SP53	10c + 5c multi	.45	.45
B204	SP53	15c + 8c multi	.45	.45
B205	SP53	20c + 10c multi	.45	.45
B206	SP53	25c + 12c multi	.45	.45
B207	SP53	30c + 15c multi	.45	.45
		Nos. B203-B207 (5)	2.25	2.25

Easter charities.

Boy Scout, Tent and Trees — SP54

Designs: 15c+8c, 5th Caribbean Jamboree emblem. 20c+10c, Scouts and emblem.

1974, Aug. 21   Litho.   Perf. 14x14½

B208	SP54	10c + 5c multi	.40	.40
B209	SP54	10c + 8c multi	.40	.40
B210	SP54	20c + 10c multi	.40	.40
		Nos. B208-B210 (3)	1.20	1.20

50th anniversary of Surinam Boy Scouts.

Fruit — SP55

Designs: 15c+8c, Children, birds and nest (security). 20c+10c, Flower, mother and child (protection). 25c+12c, Child and corn (good food). 30c+15c, Dancing children (child care).

1974, Nov. 27   Litho.   Perf. 14½x14

B211	SP55	10c + 5c multi	.25	.25
B212	SP55	15c + 8c multi	.35	.35
B213	SP55	20c + 10c multi	.35	.35
a.		Min. sheet, #B213, 2 #B211	1.00	1.00

B214	SP55	25c + 12c multi	.55	.55
B215	SP55	30c + 15c multi	.60	.60
		Nos. B211-B215 (5)	2.10	2.10

Child welfare.

The Good Shepherd SP56 | Woman and IWY Emblem SP57

Designs: 20c+10c, Peter's denial. 30c+15c, The Women at the Tomb. 35c+20c, Jesus showing His wounds to Thomas.

1975, Mar. 26   Litho.   Perf. 12½x13

B216	SP56	15c + 5c yel grn & grn	.45	.45
B217	SP56	20c + 10c org & dk bl	.60	.60
B218	SP56	30c + 15c yel & red	.60	.60
B219	SP56	35c + 20c bl & pur	.60	.60
		Nos. B216-B219 (4)	2.25	2.25

Easter charities.

1975, May 14   Litho.   Perf. 12½x13

B220	SP57	15c + 5c multi	.65	.65
B221	SP57	30c + 15c multi	.65	.65

International Women's Year.

Carib Indian Water Jug — SP58 | Feeding the Hungry — SP59

Designs: 20c+10c, 35c+20c, Indian arrow head, diff. 30c+15c, Wayana board with animal figures.

1975, Nov. 12   Litho.   Perf. 12½x13

B222	SP58	15c + 5c multi	.20	.20
B223	SP58	20c + 10c multi	.55	.55
a.		Min. sheet, #B223, 2 #B222	1.50	1.50
B224	SP58	30c + 15c multi	.90	.90
B225	SP58	35c + 20c multi	.90	.90
		Nos. B222-B225 (4)	2.55	2.55

Child welfare.

Perf. 14½x13½
1976, Apr. 14   Photo.

Paintings: 25c+15c, Visiting the Sick. 30c+15c, Clothing the Naked. 35c+15c, Burying the Dead. 50c+25c, Giving Water to the Thirsty. Designs after panels in Alkmaar Church, 1504.

B226	SP59	20c + 10c multi	.65	.65
B227	SP59	25c + 15c multi	.80	.80
B228	SP59	30c + 15c multi	1.10	1.10
a.		Souv. sheet, #B228, 2 #B226	3.25	3.25
B229	SP59	35c + 15c multi	1.10	1.10
B230	SP59	50c + 25c multi	1.60	1.60
		Nos. B226-B230 (5)	5.25	5.25

Easter.

Pekingese and Boy's Head — SP60

25c+10c, German shepherd. 30c+15c, Dachshund. 35c+15c, Retriever. 50c+25c, Terrier.

1976   Litho.   Perf. 13½

B231	SP60	20c + 10c multi	.75	.50
B232	SP60	25c + 10c multi	1.00	.70
B233	SP60	30c + 15c multi	1.25	.80
a.		Min. sheet, #B233, 2 #B231	6.75	5.50
B234	SP60	35c + 15c multi	1.25	.85
B235	SP60	50c + 25c multi	2.00	1.25
		Nos. B231-B235 (5)	6.25	4.10

Surtax was for child welfare.

St. Veronica's Veil — SP61 | Descent from the Cross — SP62

Easter: Religious scenes, side panels, front and back, from triptych by Jan Mostaert (1473-1555).

1977, Apr. 6   Litho.   Perf. 13½x14

B236	SP61	20c + 10c multi	.25	.25
B237	SP61	25c + 15c multi	.40	.40
B238	SP61	30c + 15c multi	.45	.45
B239	SP62	35c + 15c multi	.55	.55
B240	SP61	50c + 25c multi	.65	.65
		Nos. B236-B240 (5)	2.30	2.30

Dog and Girl's Head — SP63 | Crosses, Luke 23:43 — SP64

Child's Head and: 25c+15c, Monkey. 30c+15c, Rabbit. 35c+15c, Cat. 50c+25c, Parrot.

1977, Nov. 23   Litho.   Perf. 13x14

B241	SP63	20c + 10c multi	.45	.45
B242	SP63	25c + 15c multi	.55	.55
B243	SP63	30c + 15c multi	.65	.65
a.		Min. sheet, #B243, 2 #B241	1.60	1.60
B244	SP63	35c + 15c multi	.75	.75
B245	SP63	50c + 25c multi	1.10	1.10
		Nos. B241-B245 (5)	3.50	3.50

Surtax was for child welfare.

1978, Mar. 22   Litho.   Perf. 12½x14

Easter: 25c+15c, Serpent and Cross, John 3:14. 30c+15c, Lamb and blood, Exodus 12:13. 35c+15c, Passover plate, chalice and bread. 60c+30c, Cross and solar eclipse.

B246	SP64	20c + 10c multi	.25	.25
B247	SP64	25c + 15c multi	.35	.35
B248	SP64	30c + 15c multi	.40	.40
B249	SP64	35c + 15c multi	.45	.45
B250	SP64	60c + 30c multi	.90	.90
		Nos. B246-B250 (5)	2.35	2.35

Child's Head and White Cat — SP65 | Church, Cross and Chalice — SP66

Child's head and cats in various positions.

1978, Nov. 22   Litho.   *Perf. 14x13*

B251	SP65	20c + 10c multi	.25	.25
B252	SP65	25c + 15c multi	.40	.30
B253	SP65	30c + 15c multi	.45	.35
a.		Min. sheet of 3, #B253, 2 #B251	1.40	1.40
B254	SP65	35c + 15c multi	.50	.40
B255	SP65	60c + 30c multi	.85	.70
		Nos. B251-B255 (5)	2.45	2.00

Surtax was for child welfare.

1979, Apr. 11   Litho.   *Perf. 13x14*

Easter: Cross, chalice and various churches.

B256	SP66	20c + 10c multi	.20	.20
B257	SP66	30c + 15c multi	.35	.35
B258	SP66	35c + 15c multi	.45	.45
B259	SP66	40c + 20c multi	.55	.55
B260	SP66	60c + 30c multi	.80	.80
		Nos. B256-B260 (5)	2.35	2.35

Boy, Bird, Red Cross, Blood Transfusion Bottle — SP67

1979, Nov. 21   Litho.   *Perf. 13x14*

B261	SP67	20c + 10c multi	.20	.20
B262	SP67	30c + 15c multi	.35	.35
B263	SP67	35c + 15c multi	.45	.45
a.		Min. sheet, #B263, 2 #B261	1.90	1.90
B264	SP67	40c + 20c multi	.55	.55
B265	SP67	60c + 30c multi	.80	.80
		Nos. B261-B265 (5)	2.35	2.35

Surtax was for child welfare.

Cross — SP68   Anansi — SP69

Easter: Various symbols.

1980, Mar. 26   Litho.   *Perf. 13x14*

B266	SP68	20c + 10c multi	.30	.30
B267	SP68	30c + 15c multi	.45	.45
B268	SP68	40c + 20c multi	.55	.55
B269	SP68	50c + 25c multi	.70	.70
B270	SP68	60c + 30c multi	.80	.80
		Nos. B266-B270 (5)	2.80	2.80

1980, Nov. 5   Litho.   *Perf. 13x14*

Characters from Anansi and His Creditors.

B271	SP69	20c + 10c shown	.25	.25
B272	SP69	25c + 15c Ba Tigri	.35	.35
B273	SP69	30c + 15c Kakafowroe	.40	.40
B274	SP69	35c + 15c Ontiman	.45	.45
B275	SP69	60c + 30c Mat Kalaka	.80	.80
a.		Min. sheet, #B275, 2 #B271	1.40	1.40
		Nos. B271-B275 (5)	2.25	2.25

Surtax was for child welfare.

Woman Reading SP70

1980, Dec. 10   *Perf. 14x13*

B276	SP70	25c + 10c shown	.30	.30
B277	SP70	50c + 15c Gardening	.55	.55
B278	SP70	75c + 20c With grandchildren	.80	.80
		Nos. B276-B278 (3)	1.65	1.65

Surtax was for the elderly.

Crucifixion SP71   Indian Girl SP72

Easter: Scenes from the Passion of Christ.

1981, Apr. 8   Litho.   *Perf. 13x14*

B279	SP71	20c + 10c multi	.25	.25
B280	SP71	30c + 15c multi	.40	.40
B281	SP71	50c + 25c multi	.70	.70
B282	SP71	60c + 30c multi	.75	.75
B283	SP71	75c + 35c multi	.90	.90
		Nos. B279-B283 (5)	3.00	3.00

Surtax was for the elderly.

1981, Nov. 26   Litho.

B284	SP72	20c + 10c shown	.25	.25
B285	SP72	30c + 15c Black	.45	.45
B286	SP72	50c + 25c Hindustani	.75	.75
B287	SP72	60c + 30c Javanese	.80	.80
B288	SP72	75c + 35c Chinese	.90	.90
a.		Souv. sheet, #B288, 2 #B285	2.50	2.50
		Nos. B284-B288 (5)	3.15	3.15

Surtax was for child welfare.

Easter SP73   Man Pushing Wheelbarrow SP74

Designs: Stained-glass windows, Sts. Peter and Paul Church, Paramaribo.

1982, Apr. 7   Litho.   *Perf. 13x14*

B289	SP73	20c + 10c multi	.35	.35
B290	SP73	35c + 15c multi	.65	.65
B291	SP73	50c + 25c multi	1.00	1.00
B292	SP73	65c + 30c multi	1.00	1.00
B293	SP73	75c + 35c multi	1.25	1.25
		Nos. B289-B293 (5)	4.25	4.25

1982, Nov. 17   Litho.

Children's Drawings of City Cleaning Activities.

B294	SP74	20c + 10c multi	.35	.35
B295	SP74	35c + 15c multi	.65	.65
B296	SP74	50c + 25c multi	1.00	1.00
B297	SP74	65c + 30c multi	1.00	1.00
B298	SP74	75c + 35c multi	1.25	1.25
a.		Souv. sheet, #B298, 2 #B295	3.00	3.00
		Nos. B294-B298 (5)	4.25	4.25

Surtax was for child welfare.

Easter — SP75   Pitcher — SP76

Mosaic Symbols.

1983, Mar. 23   Litho.   *Perf. 13x14*

B299	SP75	10c + 5c Dove	.20	.20
B300	SP75	15c + 5c Bread	.35	.35
B301	SP75	25c + 10c Fish	.65	.65
B302	SP75	50c + 25c Eye	1.40	1.40
B303	SP75	65c + 30c Wine cup	1.60	1.60
		Nos. B299-B303 (5)	4.20	4.20

1983, Nov. 16   Litho.   *Perf. 13x14*

B304	SP76	10c + 5c shown	.30	.30
B305	SP76	15c + 5c Headdress	.30	.30
B306	SP76	25c + 10c Medicine rattle	.55	.55
B307	SP76	50c + 25c Sieve	1.50	1.50

B308	SP76	65c + 30c Basket	1.75	1.75
a.		Min. sheet, #B305, B306, B308	3.00	3.00
		Nos. B304-B308 (5)	4.40	4.40

Easter — SP77   SP78

1984, Apr. 4   Litho.   *Perf. 13x14*

B309	SP77	10c + 5c Cross, rose	.30	.30
B310	SP77	15c + 15c Cemetery	.30	.30
B311	SP77	25c + 10c Candles	.55	.55
B312	SP77	50c + 25c Cross, crown of thorns	1.50	1.50
B313	SP77	65c + 30c Candle	1.75	1.50
		Nos. B309-B313 (5)	4.40	4.15

1984, Aug. 15   Litho.   *Perf. 13x14*

Boy Scouts in Surinam, 60th Anniv.: 30c+10c, 8th Caribbean Jamboree emblem. 35c+10c, Salute. 50c+10c, Gardening. 90c+10c, Campfire in map of Surinam. Surtax was for Boy Scouts.

B314	SP78	30c + 10c multi	.90	.90
B315	SP78	35c + 10c multi	1.10	1.10
B316	SP78	50c + 10c multi	1.40	1.40
B317	SP78	90c + 10c multi	2.25	2.25
		Nos. B314-B317 (4)	5.65	5.65

Children's Games — SP79   Easter — SP80

1984, Nov. 14   Litho.   *Perf. 13x14*

B318	SP79	5c + 5c Kites	.30	.30
B319	SP79	10c + 5c Kites, diff.	.30	.30
B320	SP79	30c + 10c Pingi-pingi-kasi	.70	.70
B321	SP79	50c + 25c Cricket	1.40	1.40
a.		Souv. sheet of 3, #B319-B321	2.50	2.50
B322	SP79	90c + 30c Peroen, peroen	2.10	2.10
		Nos. B318-B322 (5)	4.80	4.80

Surtax was for child welfare.

1985, Mar. 27   Litho.   *Perf. 12½x14*

B323	SP80	5c + 5c multi	.25	.25
B324	SP80	10c + 5c multi	.25	.25
B325	SP80	30c + 15c multi	.65	.65
B326	SP80	50c + 25c multi	1.10	1.10
B327	SP80	90c + 30c multi	1.75	1.75
		Nos. B323-B327 (5)	4.00	4.00

Surtax for child welfare.

Map, Emblem SP81   Literacy SP82

1985, Oct. 22   Litho.   *Perf. 13x14*

B328	SP81	30c + 10c shown	.75	.75
B329	SP81	50c + 10c Crucifix, missionaries	1.10	1.10
B330	SP81	90c + 20c Scroll	1.90	1.90
		Nos. B328-B330 (3)	3.75	3.75

Evangelical Brotherhood Mission in Surinam, 250th anniv. Surtax for mission medical and social work.

1985, Nov. 6

B331	SP82	5c + 5c Boy reading	.35	.35
B332	SP82	10c + 5c Learning alphabet	.35	.35
B333	SP82	30c + 10c Writing	.60	.60

B334	SP82	50c + 25c Girl reading	1.25	1.25
a.		Min. sheet of 3, #B332-B334	2.50	2.50
B335	SP82	90c + 30c Studying	2.25	2.25
		Nos. B331-B335 (5)	4.80	4.80

Surtax for child welfare.

Easter — SP83   Sts. Peter and Paul Cathedral, Cent. — SP84

1986, Mar. 19   Litho.   *Perf. 13x14*

B336	SP83	5c + 5c multi	.25	.25
B337	SP83	10c + 5c multi	.25	.25
B338	SP83	30c + 15c multi	.65	.65
B339	SP83	50c + 25c multi	1.10	1.10
B340	SP83	90c + 30c multi	1.60	1.60
		Nos. B336-B340 (5)	3.85	3.85

1986, May 28   Litho.

B341	SP84	30c + 10c Exterior	.55	.55
B342	SP84	50c + 10c Saints, bas-relief	.80	.80
B343	SP84	110c + 30c Baptismal font	2.00	2.00
		Nos. B341-B343 (3)	3.35	3.35

Ancient Order of Foresters Court Charity, Cent. — SP85

1986, July 29   Litho.   *Perf. 14x13*

B344	SP85	50c + 20c Foresters emblem	.90	.90
B345	SP85	110c + 30c Court building	2.00	2.00

Youth Activities SP86

1986, Nov. 5   Litho.   *Perf. 14x13*

B346	SP86	5c + 5c Hopscotch	.30	.30
B347	SP86	10c + 5c Ballet	.30	.30
B348	SP86	30c + 10c Mobile library	.60	.60
B349	SP86	50c + 25c Crafts	1.10	1.10
a.		Min. sheet of 3, #B347-B349	2.25	2.25
B350	SP86	110c + 30c Education	2.40	2.40
		Nos. B346-B350 (5)	4.70	4.70

Surtax for Children's Charities.

Easter — SP87   Natl. Girl Guides Movement, 40th Anniv. — SP88

Stations of the cross.

1987, Apr. 8   Litho.   *Perf. 13x14*

B351	SP87	5c + 5c Crucifixion	.20	.20
B352	SP87	10c + 5c Christ on cross	.20	.20
B353	SP87	35c + 15c Descent from cross	.60	.60
B354	SP87	60c + 30c Funeral procession	1.10	1.10
B355	SP87	110c + 50c Entombment	1.90	1.90
		Nos. B351-B355 (5)	4.00	4.00

Surtax for annual Easter Charity programs.

1987, May 7   Litho.

Designs: 15c+10c, Mushroom, Brownie's emblem. 60c+10c, Clover, Guides' emblem. 110c+10c, Campfire, Rangers' emblem. 120c+10c, Ivy, Captain's emblem.

B356	SP88	15c + 10c multi	.50	.50
B357	SP88	60c + 10c multi	1.10	1.10
B358	SP88	110c + 10c multi	2.00	2.00
B359	SP88	120c + 10c multi	2.25	2.25
		Nos. B356-B359 (4)	5.85	5.85

Surtax for the Surinam Girl Guides.

Caribbean Manari — SP89

Easter — SP90

1987, Nov. 4   Litho.   Perf. 13x14

B360	SP89	50c + 25c Herring bone	.95	.95
B361	SP89	60c + 30c Tortoise-back	1.00	1.00
B362	SP89	110c + 50c Whirlpool (squares)	1.90	1.90
a.		Min. sheet of 2, #B360, B362	2.75	2.75
		Nos. B360-B362 (3)	3.85	3.85

Surtax to benefit child welfare organizations.

1988, Mar. 23   Perf. 13x13½

B363	SP90	50c + 25c multi	.80	.80
B364	SP90	60c + 30c multi	1.10	1.10
B365	SP90	110c + 50c multi	2.00	2.00
		Nos. B363-B365 (3)	3.90	3.90

Surtax for annual Easter Charity programs.

Intl. Red Cross and Red Crescent Organizations, 125th Anniv. — SP91

#B367, Anniv. & blood donation emblems.

1988, Oct. 26   Litho.   Perf. 13x14

B366	SP91	60c + 30c multi	1.25	1.25
B367	SP91	120c + 60c multi	2.40	2.40

Children's Drawings SP92

1988, Dec. 5   Litho.   Perf. 14x13

B368	SP92	50c + 25c Man and animal	1.00	1.00
B369	SP92	60c + 30c Children and nature	1.10	1.10
B370	SP92	110c + 50c Stop drugs	2.25	2.25
a.		Souv. sheet of 3, #B368-B370, perf 13½x13	3.75	3.75
		Nos. B368-B370 (3)	4.35	4.35

Surtax to benefit children's charities.

Easter 1989 — SP93

Details from Hungarian altarpieces: 60c+30c, Scenes of the Passion, by M.S., 1506. 105c+50c, Crucifixion, by Tamas of Koszvar, 1427. 110c+55c, Miracles, by Tamas of Koszvar, 1427.

1989, Mar. 21   Litho.   Perf. 13½
Size: No. B372, 28½x36½mm

B371	SP93	60c + 30c multi	1.10	1.10
B372	SP93	105c + 50c multi	2.00	2.00
B373	SP93	55c + 55c multi	2.25	2.25
		Nos. B371-B373 (3)	5.35	5.35

Surtax for annual East Charity programs.

Children's Drawings SP94

No. B374, Helping each other. No. B375, Child and nature. No. B376, In the school bus.

1989, Dec. 6   Litho.   Perf. 14x13

B374	SP94	60c + 30c multi	1.40	1.40
B375	SP94	105c + 50c multi	2.40	2.40
B376	SP94	110c + 55c multi	2.50	2.50
a.		Souv. sheet of 2, #B374, B376	3.75	3.75
		Nos. B374-B376 (3)	6.30	6.30

Surtax for children's charities.

Easter — SP95

Designs: No. B377, Mother holding Christ child. No. B378, Christ, follower. No. B379, Mary holding martyred Christ.

1990, Mar. 28   Litho.   Perf. 13x14

B377	SP95	60c + 30c multi	1.00	1.00
B378	SP95	105c + 50c multi	1.75	1.75
B379	SP95	110c + 55c multi	1.90	1.90
		Nos. B377-B379 (3)	4.65	4.65

Children's Drawings SP96

1990, Dec. 4   Litho.   Perf. 14x13

B380	SP96	60c + 30c Children, hammock	1.25	1.25
B381	SP96	105c + 50c Child, animal, palm tree	2.00	2.00
B382	SP96	110c + 55c Child, bird in tree	2.25	2.25
a.		Souv. sheet of 2, #B380, B382, perf. 13½x13	3.00	3.00
		Nos. B380-B382 (3)	5.50	5.50

SP97   SP98

Easter: 60c+30c, Christ carrying cross. 105c+50c, The Crucifixion. 110c+55c, Woman cradling Christ's body.

1991, Mar. 20   Litho.   Perf. 13x14

B383	SP97	60c + 30c multi	1.10	1.10
B384	SP97	105c + 50c multi	1.25	1.25
B385	SP97	110c + 55c multi	2.00	2.00
a.		Souv. sheet of 2, #B383, B385	3.25	3.25
		Nos. B383-B385 (3)	4.35	4.35

1991, Dec. 4   Litho.   Perf. 13x14

Children's Drawings: 60c+30c, Child in wheelchair. 105c+50c, Child beside trees. 110c+55c, Children playing outdoors.

B386	SP98	60c + 30c multi	1.00	1.00
B387	SP98	105c + 50c multi	1.75	1.75
B388	SP98	110c + 55c multi	1.90	1.90
a.		Souv. sheet of 2, #B386, B388	3.00	3.00
		Nos. B386-B388 (3)	4.65	4.65

SP99   SP100

Easter: 60c+30c, Crucifixion. 105c+50c, Taking away body of Christ. 110c+55c, Resurrection.

1992, Mar. 18

B389	SP99	60c + 30c multi	1.00	1.00
B390	SP99	105c + 50c multi	1.75	1.75
B391	SP99	110c + 55c multi	1.90	1.90
		Nos. B389-B391 (3)	4.65	4.65

1992, Dec. 3   Litho.   Perf. 13x14

Children's Drawings: 60c + 30c, Child as tree. 105c + 50c, Face as tree. 110c, + 55c, Boy and girl hanging from tree.

B392	SP100	60c + 30c multi	1.00	1.00
B393	SP100	105c + 50c multi	1.75	1.75
B394	SP100	110c + 55c multi	1.90	1.90
a.		Souv. sheet, #B392, B394	3.00	3.00
		Nos. B392-B394 (3)	4.65	4.65

Surtax for Child Welfare.

SP101   SP102

Easter: 60c+30c, Message from Christ. 110c+50c, Crucifixion. 125c+60c, Resurrection.

1993, Mar. 31   Litho.   Perf. 13x14

B395	SP101	60c + 30c multi	1.10	1.10
B396	SP101	110c + 50c multi	1.75	1.75
B397	SP101	125c + 60c multi	2.10	2.10
		Nos. B395-B397 (3)	4.95	4.95

1993, Dec. 3

Children Playing Hopscotch: 25c+10c, 2 children. 35c+10c, 3 children. 50c+25c, 8 children. 75c+25c, 7 children.

B398	SP102	25c +10c grn & multi	.95	.95
B399	SP102	35c +10c bl & multi	1.25	1.25
B400	SP102	50c +25c grn & multi	2.10	2.10
a.		Souvenir sheet of 2, #B399-B400	4.50	4.50
B401	SP102	75c +25c bl & multi	2.75	2.75
		Nos. B398-B401 (4)	7.05	7.05

Surtax for Child Welfare.
Stamps in No. B400a do not have the 1993 date in lower left corner.

AIR POST STAMPS

Allegory of Flight — AP1

Perf. 12½

1930, Sept. 3   Unwmk.   Engr.

C1	AP1	10c dull red	3.75	.50
C2	AP1	15c ultra	3.75	.75
C3	AP1	20c dull green	.20	.20
C4	AP1	40c orange	.20	.35
C5	AP1	60c brown violet	.55	.40
C6	AP1	1g gray black	1.60	1.75
C7	AP1	1½g deep brown	1.75	1.90
		Nos. C1-C7 (7)	11.80	5.85

Nos. C1-C7 Overprinted in Black or Red

1931, Aug. 8

C8	AP1	10c red (Bk)	19.00	15.00
a.		Double overprint	425.00	
C9	AP1	15c ultra (Bk)	19.00	15.00
C10	AP1	20c dull grn (R)	19.00	15.00
C11	AP1	40c orange (Bk)	29.00	22.50
a.		Double overprint	425.00	
C12	AP1	60c brn vio (R)	62.50	52.50
C13	AP1	1g gray blk (R)	72.50	65.00
C14	AP1	1½g deep brn (Bk)	72.50	67.50
		Nos. C8-C14 (7)	293.50	252.50

The variety with period omitted after "Do" occurs twice on each sheet.
Warning: The red overprint may dissolve in water.

Type of 1930
Thick Paper

1941, Sept. 25   Litho.   Perf. 13

C15	AP1	20c lt green	1.25	.90
C16	AP1	40c lt orange	7.50	5.25
C17	AP1	2½g yellow	7.50	12.50
C18	AP1	5g blue green	300.00	350.00
C19	AP1	10g lt bister	17.50	52.50
		Nos. C15-C19 (5)	333.75	421.15

The lines of shading on Nos. C15 and C16 are not as heavy as on Nos. C3 and C4. For surcharges see Nos. C24-C25.

Type of 1930
Redrawn

1941   Engr.   Perf. 12

C20	AP1	10c light red	1.50	.35
C21	AP1	60c dl brn vio	.85	.45
C22	AP1	1g black	19.00	22.50
		Nos. C20-C22 (3)	21.35	23.30

Redrawn stamps have three horizontal lines through post horn and many minor variations. For surcharges see Nos. C23, CB1.

> Catalogue values for unused stamps in this section, from this point to the end of the section, are for Never Hinged items.

Nos. C21, C17, C19 Surcharged with New Values and Bars in Carmine

1945, Mar. 12   Perf. 13, 12

C23	AP1	22½c on 60c	.45	.70
a.		Inverted surcharge	250.00	250.00
C24	AP1	1g on 2½g	15.00	15.00
C25	AP1	5g on 10g	22.50	22.50
		Nos. C23-C25 (3)	37.95	38.20

Women of Netherlands and Surinam — AP2

Globe and Winged Post Horn — AP3

Perf. 12x12½

1949, May 10   Photo.   Unwmk.

C26	AP2	27½c henna brown	5.75	2.75

Valid only on first flight of Paramaribo-Amsterdam service.

1954, Sept. 25   Perf. 13½x12½

C27	AP3	15c dp ultra & ultra	1.40	1.25

Establishment of airmail service in Surinam, 25th anniv.

Redstone Mercury Rocket and Comdr. Alan B. Shepard, Jr. — AP4

15c, Cosmonaut Gagarin in capsule and globe.

1961, July 3   Litho.   *Perf. 12*

C28	AP4	15c multicolored	.85	.85
C29	AP4	20c multicolored	.85	.85

"Man in Space," Major Yuri A. Gagarin, USSR, and Comdr. Alan B. Shepard, Jr., US. Printed in sheets of 12 (4x3) with ornamental borders and inscriptions. Two printings differ in shades and selvage perforations.

Water Tower — AP5

Eucyane Bicolor — AP6

Designs: 15c, 65c, Brewery. 20c, Boat on lake. 25c, 75c, Wood industry. 30c, Bauxite mine. 35c, 50c, Poelepantje bridge. 40c, Ship in harbor. 45c, Wharf.

1965, July 31   Photo.   *Perf. 14x13½*
Size: 25x18mm

C30	AP5	10c olive grn	.20	.20
C31	AP5	15c ocher	.20	.20
C32	AP5	20c slate blue	.20	.20
C33	AP5	25c violet blue	.20	.20
C34	AP5	30c blue green	.20	.20
C35	AP5	35c red orange	.25	.25
C36	AP5	40c orange	.25	.25
C37	AP5	45c dk carmine	.25	.25
C38	AP5	50c vermilion	.25	.25
C39	AP5	55c emerald	.25	.25
C40	AP5	65c bister	.30	.30
C41	AP5	75c blue	.30	.30
		Nos. C30-C41 (12)	2.85	2.85

See Nos. C75-C82.

1972, July 26   Litho.   *Perf. 13½x14*

C42	AP6	15c shown	.20	.20
C43	AP6	20c Helicopis cupido	.25	.25
C44	AP6	25c Papilio thoas thoas	.25	.20
C45	AP6	30c Urania leilus	.30	.20
C46	AP6	35c Stalachtis calliope	.30	.40
C47	AP6	40c Stalachtis phlegia	.35	.30
C48	AP6	45c Victorina steneles	.45	.20
C49	AP6	50c Papilio neophilus	.50	.20
C50	AP6	55c Anartia amathea	.60	.65
C51	AP6	60c Adelpha cytherea	.65	.95
C52	AP6	65c Heliconius doris metharmina	.65	.65
C53	AP6	70c Nessaea obrinus	.75	.75
C54	AP6	75c Ageronia feronia	.75	.60
		Nos. C42-C54 (13)	6.00	5.60

Surinam butterflies. Valid for regular postage also. For surcharges, see Nos. 495-499. #C42, C45 exist perf 14 with redrawn design.

Fish Type of 1976

Fish: 35c, Chaetodon unimaculatus. 60c, Centropyge loriculus. 95c, Caetodon collare.

1976, June 2   Litho.   *Perf. 12½x13*

C55	A111	35c multicolored	1.00	.55
C56	A111	60c multicolored	1.75	.90
C57	A111	95c multicolored	2.75	1.40
		Nos. C55-C57 (3)	5.50	2.85

Black-headed Sugarbird AP7

Birds of Surinam: 20c, Leistes militaris. 30c, Paradise tangara. 40c, Whippoorwill. 45c, Hemitraupis flavicollis. 50c, White-tailed goldthroated hummingbird. 55c, Saberwing. 60c, Blackcap parrot, vert. 65c, Toucan, vert. 70c, Manakin, vert. 75c, Collared parrot, vert. 80c, Cayenne cotinga, vert. 95c, Trogon, vert. Black-striped tropical tree owl, vert.

1977   Litho.   *Perf. 14x13, 13x14*

C58	AP7	20c multi	.25	.20
C59	AP7	25c multi	.35	.20
C60	AP7	30c multi	.40	.20
a.		Min. sheet of 4, 2 each #C59-C60, perf. 13½x14	3.75	2.00
C61	AP7	40c multi	.70	.40
C62	AP7	45c multi	.70	.40
C63	AP7	50c multi	.80	.50
C64	AP7	55c multi	.95	.55
C65	AP7	60c multi	1.00	.65
C66	AP7	65c multi	1.10	.70
C67	AP7	70c multi	1.25	.70
C68	AP7	75c multi	1.25	.80
C69	AP7	80c multi	1.25	.80
C70	AP7	85c multi	1.40	.95
C71	AP7	95c multi	1.75	1.10
		Nos. C58-C71 (14)	13.15	8.15

A souv. sheet of 4 with same stamps and perf. as No. C60a has marginal inscription "Amphilex 77" with magnifier over No. 424. Sold in folder at phil. exhib. in Amsterdam May 26-June 5, 1977. Value $5.75.
Issued: 25c, 30c, 50c, 60c, 75c, 80c, 95c, Apr. 27; #C60a, May 26; others, Aug. 24.
See Nos. C88, C101. For surcharges and overprints see Nos. C102-C105, C108-C111, J58, J62.

Tropical Fish Type of 1976

60c, Chaetodon striatus. 90c, Bodianus pulchellus. 120c, Centropyge argi.

1977, June 8   Litho.   *Perf. 13x13½*

C72	A111	60c multi	1.00	.80
C73	A111	90c multi	1.75	1.10
C74	A111	120c multi	2.50	1.90
		Nos. C72-C74 (3)	5.25	3.80

Type of 1965 Redrawn

Designs: 5c, Brewery. 10c, Water tower. 20c, Boat on lake. 25c, Wood industry. 30c, Bauxite mine. 35c, Poelepantje bridge. 40c, Ship in harbor. 60c, Wharf.

1976-78   Photo.   *Perf. 12½x13½*
Size: 22x18mm

C75	AP5	5c ocher	.20	.20
a.		Bklt. pane, 4 #C75, 3 #C82 + label	2.50	
C76	AP5	10c olive green	.55	.55
a.		Bklt. pane, 1 #C76, 4 #C80 + label	2.75	
C77	AP5	20c slate green	.20	.20
a.		Bklt. pane, 2 ea #C77-C79	2.75	
b.		Bklt. pane, 6 #C77, 2 #C81	2.50	
C78	AP5	25c vio bl	.55	.55
C79	AP5	30c bl grn	.65	.65
C80	AP5	35c red org	.55	.55
C81	AP5	40c org	.90	.90
C82	AP5	60c dk car	.75	.75
		Nos. C75-C82 (8)	4.35	4.35

Nos. C75-C82 issued in booklets only. Nos. C75a and C77b have inscribed selvage the size of 4 stamps; Nos. C76a and C77a the size of 6 stamps.
Issued: 10c-35c, 12/8; 5c, 40c, 60c, #C77b, 1/11/78.

Tropical Fish Type of 1976

60c, Astyanax species. 90c, Corydoras wotroi. 120c, Gasteropelecus sternicla.

1978, June 21   Litho.   *Perf. 13x13½*

C85	A111	60c multi	1.00	.95
C86	A111	90c multi	1.60	1.00
C87	A111	120c multi	2.25	1.25
		Nos. C85-C87 (3)	4.85	3.20

Bird Type of 1977

Design: 5g, Crested curassow, vert.

1979, Jan. 10   Engr.   *Perf. 13x13½*

C88	AP7	5g violet	6.00	3.00

Tropical Fish Type of 1979

60c, Cantherinus macrocerus. 90c, Holocentrhus rufus. 120c, Holacanthus tricolor.

1979, May 30   Photo.   *Perf. 14x13*

C89	A129	60c multi	.75	.30
C90	A129	90c multi	1.25	.90
C91	A129	120c multi	1.75	1.40
		Nos. C89-C91 (3)	3.75	2.60

Tropical Fish Type of 1979

60c, Symphysodon discus. 75c, Aeqidens curviceps. 90c, Catoprion mento.

1980, Sept. 10   Photo.   *Perf. 14x13*

C92	A129	60c multi	1.00	.80
C93	A129	75c multi	1.50	1.00
C94	A129	90c multi	1.50	1.25
		Nos. C92-C94 (3)	4.00	3.05

Frog Type of 1981

1981, June 24   *Perf. 13x14*

C95	A142	75c Phyllomedusa burmeisteri, vert.	1.60	.80
C96	A142	1g Dendrobates tinctorius, vert.	2.10	1.10
C97	A142	1.25g Bufo guttatus, vert.	2.50	1.40
		Nos. C95-C97 (3)	6.20	3.30

Turtle Type of 1982

1982, Feb. 17   Photo.   *Perf. 14x13*

C98	A146	65c Platemys platycephala	1.00	.65
C99	A146	75c Phrynops gibba	1.25	.80
C100	A146	125c Rhinoclemys punctularia	2.00	1.40
		Nos. C98-C100 (3)	4.25	2.85

Bird Type of 1977

1985, Jan. 9   Litho.   *Perf. 13x14*

C101	AP7	90c Venezuelan Amazon, vert.	4.50	4.50

For overprint see No. J61.

No. C60 Surcharged

1986, Oct. 1   Litho.   *Perf. 14x13*

C102	AP7	15c on 30c multi	3.75	3.75

Nos. C70-C71 and C67 Surcharged

1987, Mar.   Litho.   *Perf. 13x14*

C103	AP7	10c on 85c No. C70	1.90	1.90
C104	AP7	10c on 95c No. C71	1.90	1.90
C105	AP7	25c on 70c No. C67	5.00	5.00
		Nos. C103-C105 (3)	8.80	8.80

Otter Type of 1989

1989, Jan. 18   Litho.   *Perf. 13x14*

C107	A195	185c Otters, vert.	3.00	3.00

No. C63 Surcharged

1993, Jan. 20   Litho.   *Perf. 14x13*

C108	AP7	35c on 50c multi	.40	.40

Nos. C62, C64-C65 Surcharged

1994, Apr. 11   *Perf. 14x13, 13x14*

C109	AP7	( ) on 60c #C65	.20	.20
C110	AP7	( ) on 45c #C62	1.00	1.00
C111	AP7	( ) on 55c #C64	1.50	1.50
		Nos. C109-C111 (3)	1.75	1.75

The face value of Nos. C109-C111 fluctuates with postal rate changes. Face values on day of issue were: No. C109, 2.50f; No. C110, 10f; No. C111, 25f. No. C109 paid the additional 5 grams letter rate to the Netherlands. No. C110 paid the basic rate to North and South America and the Caribbean. No. C111 paid the basic 10-gram letter rate to the Netherlands. Size and location of surcharge varies.

AIR POST SEMI-POSTAL STAMPS

> **Catalogue values for unused stamps in this section are for Never Hinged items.**

No. C20 Surchd. in Red like No. B40
Unwmk.

1942, Jan. 2   Engr.   *Perf. 12*

CB1	AP1	10c + 5c lt red, III	2.50	2.50
a.		Type IV	4.25	5.25
b.		Type V	11.50	14.00

The surtax was for the Red Cross. See note on types III and IV below No. B40.

Nos. 193 and 194 Surcharged in Carmine

1946, Feb. 24   *Perf. 12*

CB2	A30	10c + 40c blue	1.00	1.00
CB3	A30	15c + 60c brown	1.00	1.00

The surtax was for the Red Cross.

Star Type of Semi-Postals
Perf. 13½x12½

1947, Dec. 16   Photo.

CB4	SP17	22½c + 27½c gray	2.25	1.75
CB5	SP17	27½c + 47½c grn	2.25	1.75

POSTAGE DUE STAMPS

D1

D2

Type I — 34 loops. "T" of "BETALEN" over center of loop; top branch of "E" of "TE" shorter than lower branch.
Type II — 33 loops. "T" of "BETALEN" over space between two loops.
Type III — 32 loops. "T" of "BETALEN" slightly to the left of center of loop; top branch of first "E" of "BETALEN" shorter than lower branch.
Type IV — 37 loops and letters of "PORT" larger than in the other 3 types.

Value in Black
Perf. 12½x12

1886-88   Typo.   Unwmk.
Type III

J1	D1	2½c lilac	3.00	3.00
J2	D1	5c lilac	9.00	9.00
J3	D1	10c lilac	100.00	65.00
J4	D1	20c lilac	9.00	9.00
J5	D1	25c lilac	12.50	12.50
J6	D1	30c lilac ('88)	2.50	2.50
J7	D1	40c lilac	6.00	6.00
J8	D1	50c lilac ('88)	3.00	3.00
		Nos. J1-J8 (8)	145.00	110.00

Type I

J1a	D1	2½c	6.00	6.00
J2a	D1	5c	11.00	11.00
J3a	D1	10c	125.00	90.00
J4a	D1	20c	22.50	22.50
J5a	D1	25c	19.00	19.00
J6a	D1	30c	22.50	22.50
J7a	D1	40c	12.50	12.50
J8a	D1	50c	4.00	4.00
		Nos. J1a-J8a (8)	222.50	187.50

Type II

J1b	D1	2½c	5.00	5.00
J2b	D1	5c	10.00	10.00
J3b	D1	10c	1,250.	1,250.
J4b	D1	20c	9.00	9.00
J5b	D1	25c	300.00	300.00
J6b	D1	30c	75.00	75.00
J7b	D1	40c	350.00	350.00
J8b	D1	50c	5.00	5.00

Type IV

J3c	D1	10c	350.00	250.00
J5c	D1	25c	160.00	150.00
J7c	D1	40c	150.00	150.00
		Nos. J3c-J7c (3)	660.00	550.00

Nos. J1-J16 were issued without gum. For surcharges see Nos. J15-J16.

1892-96   Value in Black   Perf. 12½
Type III

J9	D2	2½c lilac	.40	.40
J10	D2	5c lilac	1.25	1.25
J11	D2	10c lilac	24.00	22.50
J12	D2	20c lilac	2.50	2.25
J13	D2	25c lilac	10.00	10.00

Type I

J9a	D2	2½c	.40	.40
J10a	D2	5c	2.00	2.00
J11a	D2	10c	24.00	20.00
J12a	D2	20c	5.00	5.00
J13a	D2	25c	13.00	12.50
J14	D2	40c ('96)	3.25	4.50

Type II

J9b	D2	2½c	.80	.80
J10b	D2	5c	3.00	3.00
J11b	D2	10c	40.00	42.50
J12b	D2	20c	90.00	90.00
J13b	D2	25c	100.00	100.00

For surcharges see Nos. 121-122.

Stamps of 1888
Surcharged in Red

10 cent

1911, July 15

J15	D1	10c on 30c lil (III)	80.00	80.00
a.		10c on 30c lilac (I)	200.00	225.00
b.		10c on 30c lilac (II)	1,800.	1,800.
J16	D1	10c on 50c lil (III)	110.00	110.00
a.		10c on 50c lilac (I)	115.00	115.00
b.		10c on 50c lilac (II)	115.00	115.00

D3

Type I
Value in Color of Stamp

1913-31   Perf. 12½, 13½x12½

J17	D2	½c lilac ('30)	.25	.25
J18	D2	1c lilac ('31)	.25	.35
J19	D2	2c lilac ('31)	.25	.25
J20	D2	2½c lilac	.25	.25
J21	D2	5c lilac	.25	.25
J22	D2	10c lilac	.25	.25
J23	D2	12c lilac ('31)	.25	.25
J24	D2	12½c lilac ('22)	.25	.25
J25	D2	15c lilac ('26)	.55	.45
J26	D2	20c lilac	.85	.45
J27	D2	25c lilac	.45	.25
J28	D2	30c lilac ('26)	.45	.60
J29	D2	40c lilac	14.50	14.00
J30	D2	50c lilac ('26)	1.25	1.25
J31	D2	75c lilac ('26)	1.50	1.50
J32	D3	1g lilac ('26)	1.75	1.50
		Nos. J17-J32 (16)	23.30	22.10

> Catalogue values for unused stamps in this section, from this point to the end of the section, are for Never Hinged items.

D4

1945   Litho.   Perf. 12

J33	D4	1c light brown violet	.20	.30
J34	D4	5c light brown violet	3.00	2.50
J35	D4	25c light brown violet	7.00	.50
		Nos. J33-J35 (3)	10.20	3.30

D5

D6

Perf. 13½x12½

1950   Unwmk.   Photo.

J36	D5	1c purple	3.00	2.50
J37	D5	2c purple	4.50	2.25
J38	D5	2½c purple	3.75	4.50
J39	D5	5c purple	5.50	.50
J40	D5	10c purple	3.00	.50
J41	D5	15c purple	7.50	3.25
J42	D5	20c purple	2.50	4.50
J43	D5	25c purple	15.00	.20
J44	D5	50c purple	25.00	1.90
J45	D5	75c purple	62.50	50.00
J46	D5	1g purple	22.50	9.25
		Nos. J36-J46 (11)	154.75	77.35

1956

J47	D6	1c purple	.20	.20
J48	D6	2c purple	.50	.45
J49	D6	2½c purple	.50	.45
J50	D6	5c purple	.50	.45
J51	D6	10c purple	.50	.45
J52	D6	15c purple	.70	.70
J53	D6	20c purple	.70	.70
J54	D6	25c purple	.80	.40
J55	D6	50c purple	2.10	.50

J56	D6	75c purple	2.75	1.60
J57	D6	1g purple	4.00	1.25
		Nos. J47-J57 (11)	13.25	7.15

For surcharges, see Nos. J64-J69.

Stamps of 1977-1985 Overprinted "TE BETALEN"
Perf. 13x14, 14x13

1987, July   Litho.

J58	AP7	65c No. C66	2.25	2.25
J59	A156	65c No. 638	2.25	2.25
J60	A156	80c No. 640	2.75	2.75
J61	AP7	90c No. C101	3.00	3.00
J62	AP7	95c No. C71	3.50	3.50
J63	A173	1g No. 725	3.75	3.75
		Nos. J58-J63 (6)	17.50	17.50

Nos. J47, J50, J55 and
J57 Surcharged

Methods and Perfs. As Before

2007, Dec. 3

J64	D6	$1 on 1c #J47	.75	.75
J65	D6	$1.50 on 1g #J57	1.10	1.10
J66	D6	$2 on 5c #J50	1.50	1.50
J67	D6	$3 on 50c #J55	2.25	2.25
J68	D6	$3.50 on 1g #J57	2.60	2.60
J69	D6	$4 on 1g #J57	3.00	3.00
		Nos. J64-J69 (6)	11.20	11.20

SWAZILAND

ˈswä-zē-ˌland

LOCATION — Southeast Africa bordered by the Transvaal and Zululand in South Africa and by Mozambique
GOVT. — Constitutional monarchy
AREA — 6,705 sq. mi.
POP. — 985,335 (1999 est.)
CAPITAL — Mbabane

An independent state in the 19th century, Swaziland was administered by Transvaal from 1894 to 1906, when the administration was transferred to the British High Commissioner for South Africa. In 1934 Swaziland and Bechuanaland Protectorate came under the administration of the British High Commissioner for Basutoland. The issuing of individual postage stamps had been resumed in 1933. Internal self-government was introduced in 1967. Independence was proclaimed September 6, 1968.

12 Pence = 1 Shilling
20 Shillings = 1 Pound
100 Cents = 1 Rand (1961)
100 Cents = 1 Emalangeni (1975)

> Catalogue values for unused stamps in this country are for Never Hinged items, beginning with Scott 38 in the regular postage section and Scott J1 in the postage due section.

Coat of Arms — A1

George V — A2

Black Overprint

1889   Unwmk.   Perf. 12½, 12½x12

1	A1	½p gray	10.50	21.00
a.		Inverted overprint	1,250.	725.00
b.		"Swazielan"	1,350.	850.00
c.		As "b," inverted overprint		5,000.
2	A1	1p rose	20.00	19.00
a.		Inverted overprint	800.00	750.00
3	A1	2p olive bister	20.00	18.00
a.		Inverted overprint	900.00	525.00
b.		"Swazielan"	550.00	475.00

---

c.		Perf. 12½x12	100.00	25.00
d.		As "c," "Swazielan"	1,250.	725.00
e.		As "d," inverted overprint		1,250.
f.		As "b," inverted overprint	5,100.	4,600.
		Double overprint	2,600.	
4	A1	6p gray blue	25.00	50.00
5	A1	1sh green	12.50	16.00
a.		Inverted overprint	1,100.	525.00
6	A1	2sh6p yellow	275.00	300.00
7	A1	5sh slate	175.00	225.00
a.		Inverted overprint	1,900.	2,500.
b.		"Swazielan"	5,250.	
c.		As "b," inverted overprint	5,750.	
8	A1	10sh lt brown	5,750.	3,750.

1892   Red Overprint

9	A1	½p gray	8.50	19.00
a.		Inverted overprint	575.00	
b.		Double overprint	525.00	525.00
c.		Pair, one without overprint		1,900.

Beware of counterfeits.
Reprints have a period after "Swaziland."

Stamps of Swaziland were replaced by those of Transvaal in 1895. Swaziland issues were resumed in 1933.

Perf. 14

1933, Jan. 2   Engr.   Wmk. 4

10	A2	½p green	.40	.35
11	A2	1p carmine	.40	.25
12	A2	2p lt brown	.40	.50
13	A2	3p ultra	.55	3.00
14	A2	4p orange	3.50	3.50
15	A2	6p rose violet	1.60	1.10
16	A2	1sh olive green	1.90	3.25
17	A2	2sh6p violet	19.00	25.00
18	A2	5sh gray	37.50	57.50
19	A2	10sh black brown	100.00	140.00
		Nos. 10-19 (10)	165.25	234.45
		Set, never hinged	375.00	

Common Design Types
pictured following the introduction.

Silver Jubilee Issue
Common Design Type

1935, May 4   Perf. 11x12

20	CD301	1p carmine & blue	.70	2.00
21	CD301	2p black & ultra	.70	1.75
22	CD301	3p ultra & brown	.80	6.00
23	CD301	6p brown, vio & ind	1.00	2.00
		Nos. 20-23 (4)	3.20	11.75
		Set, never hinged	6.50	

Coronation Issue
Common Design Type

1937, May 12   Perf. 11x11½

24	CD302	1p dark carmine	.35	.55
25	CD302	2p brown	.35	.20
26	CD302	3p deep ultra	.35	.55
		Nos. 24-26 (3)	1.05	1.30
		Set, never hinged	1.75	

George VI — A3

1938, Apr. 1   Perf. 13, 13x13½

27	A3	½p green	.25	1.50
28	A3	1p rose carmine	.80	1.50
29	A3	1½p light blue	.30	.85
a.		Perf. 14 ('42)	1.40	1.25
		Never hinged	3.25	
30	A3	2p brown	.30	.45
31	A3	3p ultra	2.75	2.00
32	A3	4p red orange	.40	1.60
33	A3	6p rose violet	3.50	1.75
34	A3	1sh olive green	.95	.75
35	A3	2sh6p dark violet	10.50	2.75
36	A3	5sh gray	20.00	15.00
37	A3	10sh black brown	4.75	6.50
		Nos. 27-37 (11)	44.50	34.65
		Set, never hinged	70.00	

> Catalogue values for unused stamps in this section, from this point to the end of the section, are for Never Hinged items.

Peace Issue

South Africa,
Nos. 100-102
Overprinted

Basic stamps inscribed alternately in English and Afrikaans.

1945, Dec. 3   Wmk. 201   Perf. 14

38	A42	1p rose pink & choc, pair	.80	1.25
a.		Single, English	.20	.20
b.		Single, Afrikaans	.20	.20
39	A43	2p vio & sl blue, pair	.80	1.25
a.		Single, English	.20	.20
b.		Single, Afrikaans	.20	.20
40	A43	3p ultra & dp ultra, pair	.80	4.00
a.		Single, English	.20	.25
b.		Single, Afrikaans	.20	.25
		Nos. 38-40 (3)	2.40	6.50

World War II victory of the Allies.

Royal Visit Issue
Type of Basutoland, 1947
Perf. 12½

1947, Feb. 17   Wmk. 4   Engr.

44	A3	1p red	.20	.20
45	A4	2p green	.20	.20
46	A5	3p ultramarine	.20	.20
47	A6	1sh dark violet	.20	.20
		Nos. 44-47 (4)	.80	.80

Visit of the British Royal Family, 3/25/47.

Silver Wedding Issue
Common Design Types

1948, Dec. 1   Photo.   Perf. 14x14½

48	CD304	1½p bright ultra	.20	.20

Perf. 11½x11
Engraved; Name Typographed

49	CD305	10sh violet brown	30.00	40.00

UPU Issue
Common Design Types
Engr.; Name Typo. on 3p, 6p
Perf. 13½, 11x11½

1949, Oct. 10   Wmk. 4

50	CD306	1½p blue	.40	.20
51	CD307	3p indigo	.70	.65
52	CD308	6p red lilac	.90	.65
53	CD309	1sh olive	1.00	.65
		Nos. 50-53 (4)	3.00	2.15

Coronation Issue
Common Design Type

1953, June 3   Engr.   Perf. 13½x13

54	CD312	2p yellow brown & blk	.30	.20

Asbestos Mine — A4

Married Woman — A5

1p, 2sh 6p, Highveld view. 3p, 1sh 3p, Courting couple. 4½p, 5sh, Warrior. 6p, £1, Kudu. 1sh, Asbestos mine. 10sh, Married woman.

Perf. 13x13½, 13½x13

1956, July 2   Engr.   Wmk. 4
Center in Black, except Nos. 63-64

55	A4	½p orange	.20	.20
56	A4	1p emerald	.20	.20
57	A5	2p redsh brown	.40	.20
58	A5	3p rose red	.30	.20
59	A5	4½p ultra	.85	.20
60	A5	6p magenta	.55	.20
61	A4	1sh gray olive	.40	.20
62	A5	1sh3p brown	1.50	10.00
63	A4	2sh6p car & brt grn	1.50	1.50
64	A5	5sh blue gray & vio	9.50	2.75
65	A5	10sh dull violet	20.00	9.00
66	A5	£1 turquoise	47.50	35.00
		Nos. 55-66 (12)	82.90	59.65

Nos. 55-61 and 63-66 Surcharged with New Value

2½c 2½c 4c 4c
I   II   I   II

5c 5c 25c 25c
I   II   I   II

50c 50c 50c
I   II   III

R1 R1 R1 R2 R2
I   II   III   I   II

1961

67	A4	½c on ½p	3.50	3.25
a.		Inverted surcharge	525.00	
68	A4	1c on 1p	.20	.20
a.		"1c" at center	35.00	
b.		Double surcharge	525.00	
69	A5	2c on 2p	.20	.20
70	A5	2½p on 2p	.20	.20
71	A5	2½c on 3p (I)	.20	.20
a.		Type II	.20	.25
72	A5	3½c on 2p	.20	.20
73	A5	4c on 4½p (II)	.20	.20
a.		Type I	.20	.20
74	A5	5c on 6p (II)	.20	.20
a.		Type I	.20	.20
75	A4	10c on 1sh	27.50	9.25
a.		Double surcharge	575.00	
76	A4	25c on 2sh6p (I)	.40	1.50
a.		Type II, "25c" centered	1.60	1.00
b.		Type II, "25c" at lower left	200.00	240.00
77	A5	50c on 5sh (I)	.40	1.90
a.		Type II	7.75	4.25
b.		Type III	400.00	475.00
78	A5	1r on 10sh (I)	2.25	2.50
a.		Type II	5.25	5.25
b.		Type III	72.50	90.00
79	A5	2r on £1 (II, "R2" at middle left)	10.00	8.00
a.		Type I	15.00	15.00
b.		Type II, "R2" at center bottom	35.00	60.00
		Nos. 67-79 (13)	45.45	27.80

The type II "25c" surcharge is nearly centered in the sky on No. 76a, and is at lower left touching the value tablet on No. 76b.

Surcharge types are numbered chronologically.

For surcharges see Nos. J3-J6.

Types of 1956

½c, 10c, Asbestos mine. 1c, 25c, Highveld view. 2c, 1r, Married woman. 2½c, 12½c, Courting couple. 4c, 50c, Warrior. 5c, 2r, Kudu.

Perf. 13x13½, 13½x13

1961   Engr.   Wmk. 4
Center in Black, except Nos. 88-89

80	A4	½c orange	.20	1.10
81	A4	1c emerald	.20	.10
82	A5	2c redsh brown	.20	3.25
83	A5	2½c rose red	.20	1.40
84	A5	4c ultra	.20	1.40
85	A5	5c magenta	.50	.20
86	A4	10c gray olive	.20	.20
87	A5	12½c brown	1.75	.60
88	A4	25c car & brt green	3.00	4.00
89	A5	50c blue gray & vio	3.25	2.10
90	A5	1r dull violet	6.25	13.00
91	A5	2r turquoise	14.00	16.00
		Nos. 80-91 (12)	29.95	42.25

Swazi Shields — A6

Train and Railroad Map — A7

Designs: 1c, Battle axe. 2c, Forestry. 2½c, Ceremonial headdress. 3½c, Musical instrument. 4c, Irrigation. 5c, Widow bird. 7½c, Rock paintings. 10c, Secretary bird. 12½c, Pink arum lily. 15c, Married woman. 20c, Malaria control. 25c, Swazi warrior. 50c, Ground hornbill, horiz. 1r, Aloes. 2r, Msinsi (flame tree), horiz.

Perf. 12½x14, 14x12½

1962, Apr. 24   Photo.   Wmk. 314

92	A6	½c ocher, blk & brn	.20	.20
93	A6	1c gray & orange	.20	.20
94	A6	2c lt yel grn, dk grn & blk	.20	1.25
95	A6	2½c vermilion & blk	.20	.20
96	A6	3½c gray & emerald	.20	.70
97	A6	4c aqua & black	.20	.20
98	A6	5c orange red & blk	.90	.20
99	A6	7½c dull ocher & brn	1.00	.40
100	A6	10c lt blue & black	1.60	.20
101	A6	12½c lt olive & dp car	1.25	2.75
102	A6	15c red lilac & blk	1.75	1.25
103	A6	20c emerald & blk	.50	1.50
104	A6	25c ultra & blk	.60	1.25
105	A6	50c rose red & dk brn	11.00	4.75

106	A6	1r bister & emer	3.75	3.00
107	A6	2r ultra & scar	15.00	11.00
		Nos. 92-107 (16)	38.55	29.05

For surcharge & overprints see #138, 143-159.

Freedom from Hunger Issue
Common Design Type

1963, June 4   Perf. 14x14½
108	CD314	15c lilac	.50	.50

Red Cross Centenary Issue
Common Design Type

1963, Sept. 2   Litho.   Perf. 13
109	CD315	2½c black & red	.30	.30
110	CD315	15c ultra & red	.80	.80

Perf. 11½x12

1964, Nov. 5   Engr.   Wmk. 314
111	A7	2½c purple & brt grn	.60	.20
112	A7	3½c dk olive & blue	.65	1.10
113	A7	15c dk brown & orange	.80	.70
114	A7	25c dk blue & yellow	1.00	.80
		Nos. 111-114 (4)	3.05	2.80

Opening of the Swaziland Railroad linking Ka Dake with Lourenco Marques.

ITU Issue
Common Design Type

Perf. 11x11½

1965, May 17   Litho.   Wmk. 314
115	CD317	2½c blue & bister	.20	.20
116	CD317	15c red lil & rose red	.50	.50

Intl. Cooperation Year Issue
Common Design Type

1965, Oct. 25   Perf. 14½
117	CD318	½c bl grn & claret	.20	.20
118	CD318	15c lt violet & grn	.50	.50

Churchill Memorial Issue
Common Design Type

1966, Jan. 24   Photo.   Perf. 14
Design in Black, Gold and Carmine Rose
119	CD319	½c brt blue	.20	.50
120	CD319	2½c green	.30	.20
121	CD319	15c brown	.50	.60
122	CD319	25c violet	.75	.80
		Nos. 119-122 (4)	1.75	1.90

UNESCO Anniversary Issue
Common Design Type

1966, Dec. 1   Litho.   Perf. 14
123	CD323	2½c "Education"	.20	.20
124	CD323	7½c "Science"	.40	.40
125	CD323	15c "Culture"	.80	.80
		Nos. 123-125 (3)	1.40	1.40

King Sobhuza II and Map of Swaziland A8

Design: 7½c, 25c, King Sobhuza II, vert.

Perf. 14½x14, 14x14½

1967, Apr. 25   Photo.   Wmk. 314
126	A8	2½c multicolored	.20	.20
127	A8	7½c multicolored	.20	.20
128	A8	15c multicolored	.20	.20
129	A8	25c multicolored	.40	.40
		Nos. 126-129 (4)	1.00	1.00

Attainment of internal self-government.

King Sobhuza II, University Buildings and Graduates — A9

Perf. 14x14½

1967, Sept. 1   Photo.   Unwmk.
130	A9	2½c yel, sepia & dp bl	.20	.20
131	A9	7½c blue, sepia & dp bl	.20	.20
132	A9	15c dl rose, sepia & dp bl	.20	.20
133	A9	25c lt vio, sepia & dp bl	.40	.40
		Nos. 130-133 (4)	1.00	1.00

1st conferment of degrees by the University of Botswana, Lesotho and Swaziland at Roma, Lesotho.

Swazi Reed Dance (Umhlanga) — A10

Designs: 3c, 15c, Feast of the First Fruits, Incwala (bull, sun and king), horiz.

Perf. 14½x14, 14x14½

1968, Jan. 5   Photo.   Wmk. 314
134	A10	3c red, blk & silver	.20	.20
135	A10	3c brown, blk, org & sil	.20	.20
136	A10	15c red, blk & gold	.20	.20
137	A10	25c brown, blk, org & gold	.30	.30
		Nos. 134-137 (4)	.90	.90

No. 98 Surcharged with New Value

1968, May 1   Perf. 12½x14
138	A6	3c on 5c org red & blk	.75	.45

Independent Kingdom

Plowing and King Sobhuza II A11

Designs: 4½c, Cable lift carrying asbestos. 17½c, Worker cutting sugar cane. 25c, Iron ore mining and map showing Swaziland railroad.

Perf. 14x12½

1968, Sept. 6   Photo.   Wmk. 314
139	A11	3c gold & multi	.20	.20
140	A11	4½c gold & multi	.20	.20
141	A11	17½c gold & multi	.20	.20
142	A11	25c slate & gold	.50	.50
a.		Strip of 4, #139-142	4.00	4.00
		Nos. 139-142 (4)	1.10	1.10

Swaziland's independence.
Nos. 139-142 printed in sheets of 50. No. 142a printed in sheets of 20 (4x5).

Nos. 92-107 Overprinted; No. 96 Surcharged

1968, Sept. 6   Perf. 12½x14, 14x12½
143	A6	½c ocher, blk & brn	.20	.20
144	A6	1c gray & orange	.20	.20
145	A6	2c multicolored	.20	.20
146	A6	2½c vermilion & blk	1.00	2.25
147	A6	3c on 2½c #146	.20	.20
148	A6	3½c gray & emerald	.20	.20
149	A6	4c aqua & black	.20	.20
150	A6	5c org red & blk	4.75	.20
151	A6	7½c dull ocher & brn	.75	.20
152	A6	10c lt blue & blk	5.25	.20
153	A6	12½c lt olive & dp car	.45	.90
154	A6	15c red lilac & blk	.45	1.10
155	A6	20c emerald & blk	1.25	2.40
156	A6	25c ultra & blk	.60	1.10
157	A6	50c rose red & dk brn	9.75	6.75
a.		Wmk. sideways	4.25	4.25
158	A6	1r bister & emerald	3.50	6.75
159	A6	2r ultra & scarlet	6.75	13.50
a.		Wmk. sideways	7.00	7.00
		Nos. 143-159 (17)	35.70	36.55

Caracal (African Lynx) — A12

Waterbuck — A12a

1c, Cape porcupine. 2c, Crocodile. 3c, Lion. 3½c, African elephants. 5c, Bush pig. 7½c, Impalas. 10c, Chacma baboon. 12½c, Ratel (honey badger). 15c, Leopard. 20c, Blue wildebeest (brindled gnu). 25c, White (square-lipped) rhinoceros. 50c, Burchell's zebra. 2r, Giraffe.

Perf. 13x12½, 12½x13

1969, Aug. 1   Litho.   Wmk. 314
Size: 30½x21½mm
160	A12	½c multicolored	.20	.20
161	A12	1c multicolored	.20	.20
162	A12	2c multicolored	.20	.20

Size: 35x25mm
163	A12	3c multicolored	.50	.20
a.		Wmk. upright ('75)	5.00	5.00
164	A12	3½c multicolored	.70	.20

Size: 30½x21½mm, 21½x30½mm
165	A12	5c multicolored	.35	.20
166	A12	7½c multicolored	.45	.20
167	A12	10c multicolored	.65	.20
168	A12	12½c multicolored	.80	4.25
169	A12	15c multicolored	1.25	.90
170	A12	20c multicolored	1.00	.75
171	A12	25c multicolored	1.60	2.10
172	A12	50c multicolored	2.10	3.50
173	A12a	1r multicolored	5.25	7.50
174	A12a	2r multicolored	11.50	13.00
		Nos. 160-174 (15)	26.75	33.60

See #228-229. For surcharges see #259-260.

King Sobhuza II and Flags — A13

Designs: 7½c, 25c, UN emblem, UN Headquarters, NY, and King Sobhuza II.

1969, Sept. 24   Litho.   Perf. 13½
175	A13	3c dp blue & multi	.20	.20
176	A13	7½c pink & multi	.20	.20
177	A13	12½c yellow & multi	.25	.25
178	A13	25c lt blue & multi	.45	.45
		Nos. 175-178 (4)	1.10	1.10

1st anniv. of admission to the UN.

Walking Racer, Shield and King — A14

Bauhinia Galpinii and King — A15

Designs: 7½c, Runner. 12½c, Hurdler. 25c, Parade of Swaziland team with flag bearer.

Perf. 14x14½

1970, July 16   Litho.   Wmk. 314
179	A14	3c red org & multi	.20	.20
180	A14	7½c yellow & multi	.20	.20
181	A14	12½c lt blue & multi	.35	.35
182	A14	25c multicolored	.55	.55
		Nos. 179-182 (4)	1.30	1.30

Issued to publicize the 9th Commonwealth Games, Edinburgh, July 16-25.

Perf. 14x14½
1971, Feb. 1   Litho.   Wmk. 314

Flowers of Swaziland: 10c, Crocosmia aurea. 15c, Gloriosa superba. 25c, Watsonia densiflora.

183	A15	3c bister & multi	.35	.20
184	A15	10c pale salmon & multi	.40	.20
185	A15	15c pale green & multi	.85	.50
186	A15	25c multicolored	1.25	1.25
		Nos. 183-186 (4)	2.85	2.15

King Sobhuza II — A16

Designs (King Sobhuza II): 3½c, In 1971. 7½c, In tribal costume at gathering of chiefs (Incwala). 25c, Opening Swazi parliament.

1971, Dec. 22

187	A16	3c blue & multi	.20	.20
188	A16	3½c gold, blk, bl & brn	.20	.20
189	A16	7½c gold & multi	.20	.20
190	A16	15c lilac & multi	.30	.30
		Nos. 187-190 (4)	.90	.90

50th anniv. of the reign of Sobhuza II.

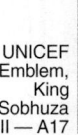

UNICEF Emblem, King Sobhuza II — A17

1972, Apr. 17   Perf. 14½x14

191	A17	15c violet & black	.20	.20
192	A17	25c olive & black	.50	.60

25th anniv. (in 1971) of UNICEF.

Traditional Reed Dancers — A18

Perf. 13½x14
1972, Sept. 11   Wmk. 314

193	A18	3½c shown	.20	.20
194	A18	7½c Swazi beehive hut	.25	.25
195	A18	15c Ezulwini Valley	.55	.55
196	A18	25c Usutu River fishing	.90	.90
		Nos. 193-196 (4)	1.90	1.90

Tourist publicity.

Mosquito Control A19

1973, May 21   Litho.   Perf. 14½

197	A19	3½c shown	.25	.20
198	A19	7½c Anti-malaria vaccination	.75	.50

25th anniv. of WHO.

Mpaka Coal Mines — A20

7½c, Oxen pulling plow. 15c, Weir over Komati River. 25c, Experimental rice plantation.

Perf. 13½x14
1973, June 21   Wmk. 314

199	A20	3½c multicolored	.60	.20
200	A20	7½c multicolored	.30	.20
201	A20	15c multicolored	.40	.25
202	A20	25c multicolored	.60	.60
		Nos. 199-202 (4)	1.90	1.25

Development of natural resources.

Swaziland Coat of Arms — A21

10c, King Sobhuza II in dress uniform. 15c, Parliament. 25c, National Somhlolo Stadium.

1973, Sept. 7   Litho.   Perf. 14

203	A21	3c brick red & black	.20	.20
204	A21	10c dull orange & multi	.20	.20
205	A21	15c blue & multi	.40	.50
206	A21	25c yellow & multi	.50	1.00
		Nos. 203-206 (4)	1.30	1.90

5th anniversary of independence.

Botswana, Lesotho, Swaziland Flags and Cap — A22

12½c, Kwaluseni Campus. 15c, Map of Africa & location of Botswana, Lesotho & Swaziland. 25c, Shield of University.

1974, Mar. 29   Litho.   Perf. 14

207	A22	7½c orange & multi	.25	.20
208	A22	12½c emerald & multi	.35	.20
209	A22	15c yellow & multi	.40	.30
210	A22	25c ultra & multi	.50	.45
		Nos. 207-210 (4)	1.50	1.15

10th anniversary of the University of Botswana, Lesotho and Swaziland.

Sobhuza as Student at Lovedale College, South Africa — A23

1974, July 22   Litho.   Perf. 13x11

211	A23	3c shown	.20	.20
212	A23	9c Sobhuza as middle-aged man	.20	.20
213	A23	50c As old man	.85	.75
		Nos. 211-213 (3)	1.25	1.15

75th birthday of King Sobhuza II.

Mail Carried by Overhead Cable A24

1974, Oct. 9   Perf. 14

214	A24	4c Post Office, Lobamba	.20	.20
215	A24	10c Mbabane temporary P.O., 1902	.25	.20
216	A24	15c shown	.45	.45

217	A24	25c Mule-drawn mail coach	.65	.65
		Nos. 214-217 (4)	1.55	1.50

Centenary of Universal Postal Union.

Animal Type of 1969
"E" instead of "R"

Designs as before.

1975, Jan. 2   Litho.   Perf. 12½x13

228	A12a	1e multicolored	3.75	3.00
229	A12a	2e multicolored	7.50	6.00

Girl's Umcwasho Ceremony — A26

Swazi youth: 10c, Butimba, hunting ceremony. 15c, Lusekwane, ceremony of preparation, horiz. 25c, Gcina Regiment marching with flags.

1975, Mar. 20   Wmk. 314   Perf. 14

232	A26	3c lt green & multi	.20	.20
233	A26	10c lt violet & multi	.25	.20
234	A26	15c brown org & multi	.45	.40
235	A26	25c yellow & multi	.65	.65
		Nos. 232-235 (4)	1.55	1.45

Matsapa Airport Control Tower A27

5c, Fire brigade car and staff. 15c, Douglas C-47 Dakota. 25c, Hawker Siddeley 748.

1975, Aug. 18   Litho.   Perf. 14½

236	A27	4c multicolored	.40	.20
237	A27	5c multicolored	.85	.30
238	A27	15c multicolored	2.00	1.75
239	A27	25c multicolored	2.75	2.75
		Nos. 236-239 (4)	6.00	5.00

10th anniversary of internal air service.

Women in Service — A28   Green Pigeon — A29

4c, Elephant with IWY emblem, horiz. 5c, Queen Labotsibeni, grandmother of King Sobhuza II, horiz. 15c, Handicrafts women.

Wmk. 373
1975, Dec. 22   Litho.   Perf. 14

240	A28	4c ultra, blk & gray	.20	.20
241	A28	5c bister & multi	.20	.20
242	A28	15c multicolored	.40	.40
243	A28	25c multicolored	.50	.70
		Nos. 240-243 (4)	1.30	1.50

International Women's Year 1975.

1976, Jan. 2   Wmk. 373   Perf. 14

Birds: 1c, Black-headed oriole, horiz. 3c, Melba finch, horiz. 4c, Plum-colored starling. 5c, Black-headed heron. 6c, Stonechat. 7c, Chorister robin. 10c, Gorgeous bush shrike. 15c, Black-collared barbet. 20c, Gray heron. 25c, Giant kingfisher. 30c, Black eagle. 50c, Red bishop. 1e, Pin-tailed whydah. 2e, Lilac-breasted roller, horiz.

244	A29	1c orange & multi	.85	1.60
245	A29	2c lilac & multi	.95	1.60
246	A29	3c yel grn & multi	1.40	1.25
247	A29	4c gray blue & multi	.95	.95
248	A29	5c orange & multi	1.10	1.40
249	A29	6c orange & multi	1.90	1.75
250	A29	7c orange & multi	1.90	1.75
251	A29	10c slate & multi	1.90	1.90
252	A29	15c lt green & multi	3.00	1.10
253	A29	20c ocher & multi	4.25	3.75
254	A29	25c orange & multi	4.50	4.00
255	A29	30c orange & multi	4.50	4.00
256	A29	50c sepia & multi	2.50	2.50
257	A29	1e vermilion & multi	3.00	3.25
258	A29	2e lt blue & multi	5.25	6.00
		Nos. 244-258 (15)	37.95	36.55

Nos. 166 and 168 Surcharged in Ultramarine or Brown

1976   Wmk. 314   Perf. 13x12½

259	A12	3c on 7½c multi (U)	1.00	1.25
260	A12	6c on 12½c multi (B)	1.75	1.75

Denomination at lower left on No. 260.

Blindness from Malnutrition — A30

Designs (WHO Emblem and): 10c, Retina, "Operation prevents blindness." 20c, Blind eye, "Blindness from trachoma." 25c, Medicine and syringe, "Medicine and rehabilitation."

Wmk. 373
1976, June 15   Litho.   Perf. 14

261	A30	5c multicolored	.20	.20
262	A30	10c multicolored	.35	.20
263	A30	20c multicolored	.65	.60
264	A30	25c multicolored	.70	.70
		Nos. 261-264 (4)	1.90	1.70

World Health Day: Foresight prevents blindness.

Marathon Runner — A31   Soccer — A32

Designs (Olympic Rings and): 6c, Boxing. 20c, Soccer. 25c, Olympic torch and flame.

1976, July 17   Litho.   Wmk. 373

265	A31	5c lt blue & multi	.20	.20
266	A31	6c olive & multi	.25	.25
267	A31	20c lt violet & multi	.50	.50
268	A31	25c dull orange & multi	.70	.70
		Nos. 265-268 (4)	1.65	1.65

21st Olympic Games, Montreal, Canada, July 17-Aug. 1.

1976, Sept. 13   Litho.   Perf. 14½

Designs: 5c, Player heading ball. 20c, Goalkeeper catching ball. 25c, Player kicking ball.

269	A32	4c blue & multi	.20	.20
270	A32	5c olive & multi	.20	.20
271	A32	20c red & multi	.45	.40
272	A32	25c multicolored	.60	.55
		Nos. 269-272 (4)	1.45	1.35

FIFA membership for Swaziland in 1976 (Federation Internationale de Football Associations).

A. G. Bell and 1976 Telephone — A33

Designs (A. G. Bell and Telephone): 5c, 1895. 10c, 1876. 15c, 1877. 20c, 1905.

1976, Nov. 22   **Perf. 14**
273	A33	4c multicolored	.20	.20
274	A33	5c multicolored	.20	.20
275	A33	10c multicolored	.20	.20
276	A33	15c multicolored	.30	.30
277	A33	20c multicolored	.40	.40
		Nos. 273-277 (5)	1.30	1.30

Centenary of first telephone call by Alexander Graham Bell, Mar. 10, 1876.

Elizabeth II and Sobhuza II — A34

Designs: 25c, Queen's coach at Admiralty Arch. 50c, Queen seated in coach.

1977, Feb. 7   **Perf. 13½**
278	A34	20c silver & multi	.25	.25
279	A34	25c silver & multi	.30	.30
280	A34	50c silver & multi	.65	.65
		Nos. 278-280 (3)	1.20	1.20

25th anniv. of the reign of Elizabeth II.

Matsapa College A35

10c, Men's & Women's uniforms & jeep. 20c, Police badge. 25c, Dog handler & dog.

1977, May 2   **Litho.**   **Perf. 14**
281	A35	5c multi	.35	.35
282	A35	10c multi	.55	.35
283	A35	20c multi, vert.	.85	.85
284	A35	25c multi	1.40	1.25
		Nos. 281-284 (4)	3.15	2.80

50 years of police training in Swaziland.

Various Animals A36

Rock Paintings: 10c, 20c, Groups of men. 15c, Cattle and herdsman.

Perf. 14x14½
1977, Aug. 8   **Wmk. 373**
285	A36	5c multicolored	.30	.20
286	A36	10c multicolored	.40	.35
287	A36	15c multicolored	.60	.55
288	A36	20c multicolored	.80	.75
a.		Souvenir sheet of 4, #285-288	3.75	3.75
		Nos. 285-288 (4)	2.10	1.85

Rock paintings from Highveld area, c. 1700-1850.

Evergreens, Timber, Map of Highveld — A37

Designs: 10c, Pineapple and map of Middleveld. 15c, Map of Lowveld, orange and lemon. 20c, Map of Lubombo and grazing cattle. No. 293, Map of Swaziland and produce, vert.: UL, Evergreens; UR, Orange and lemon; LL, Pineapple; LR, Cattle.

1977, Oct. 17   **Litho.**   **Perf. 13½**
289	A37	5c multicolored	.20	.20
290	A37	10c multicolored	.70	.70
291	A37	15c multicolored	1.00	1.00
292	A37	20c multicolored	1.50	1.50
		Nos. 289-292 (4)	3.40	3.40

Souvenir Sheet
293		Sheet of 4	2.75	2.75
a.-d.		A37 25c single stamp	.65	.65

Nos. 293a-293d are vertical.

Cussonia Spicata Thunb. — A38

Trees: 10c, Sclerocarya birrea. 20c, Pterocarpus angolensis. 25c, Erythrina lysistemon.

1978, Jan. 12   **Litho.**   **Wmk. 373**
294	A38	5c multicolored	.20	.20
295	A38	10c multicolored	.35	.25
296	A38	20c multicolored	.60	.55
297	A38	25c multicolored	.75	1.00
		Nos. 294-297 (4)	1.90	2.00

Rural Electrification, Lobamba — A39

Hydroelectric Power: 10c, Edwaleni Power Station. 20c, Switchgear, Maguduza Power Station. 25c, Hydroturbine hall, Edwaleni.

1978, Mar. 6   **Litho.**   **Perf. 13½**
298	A39	5c black & ocher	.20	.20
299	A39	10c black & yel grn	.20	.20
300	A39	20c black & blue	.30	.30
301	A39	25c black & rose mag	.55	1.00
		Nos. 298-301 (4)	1.25	1.70

Elizabeth II Coronation Anniversary Issue
Souvenir Sheet
Common Design Types

1978, Apr. 21   **Unwmk.**   **Perf. 15**
302		Sheet of 6	2.50	2.50
a.	CD326	25c Queen's lion	.40	.40
b.	CD327	25c Elizabeth II	.40	.40
c.	CD328	25c African Elephant	.40	.40

No. 302 contains 2 se-tenant strips of Nos. 302a-302c, separated by horizontal gutter with commemorative and descriptive inscriptions and showing central part of coronation procession with coach.

Clay Pots A40

Handicrafts: 10c, Basketwork. 20c, Wooden utensils. 30c, Wooden pot with lid.

Wmk. 373
1978, June 26   **Litho.**   **Perf. 13½**
303	A40	5c multicolored	.20	.20
304	A40	10c multicolored	.20	.20
305	A40	20c multicolored	.30	.30
306	A40	30c multicolored	.50	.50
		Nos. 303-306 (4)	1.20	1.20

See Nos. 317-320.

Defense Force A41

Designs: 6c, King's Regiment. 10c, Tinkabi tractor and ox-drawn plow. 15c, Laying water pipe. 25c, Adult literacy class. 50c, Fire engine and ambulance.

1978, Sept. 6   **Litho.**   **Perf. 14**
307	A41	4c multicolored	.20	.20
308	A41	6c multicolored	.20	.20
309	A41	10c multicolored	.20	.20
310	A41	15c multicolored	.40	.20
311	A41	25c multicolored	.55	.50
312	A41	50c multicolored	1.75	1.00
		Nos. 307-312 (6)	3.30	2.30

10th anniversary of independence.

Angel Appearing to the Shepherds — A42

Christmas: 10c, Adoration of the Kings. 15c, Angel warning Joseph in a dream. 25c, Flight into Egypt.

1978, Dec. 12   **Litho.**   **Perf. 14**
313	A42	5c multicolored	.20	.20
314	A42	10c multicolored	.20	.20
315	A42	15c multicolored	.25	.25
316	A42	25c multicolored	.45	.45
		Nos. 313-316 (4)	1.10	1.10

Handicrafts Type of 1978

1979, Jan. 10   **Perf. 13½**
317	A40	5c Sisal bowls	.20	.20
318	A40	15c Clay pots	.30	.30
319	A40	20c Basketwork	.35	.35
320	A40	30c Hide shield	.55	.55
		Nos. 317-320 (4)	1.40	1.40

Prospecting at Phophonyane A43

15c, Early 3-stamp battery mill. 25c, Cyanide tanks at Piggs Peak. 50c, Pouring off molten gold.

Wmk. 373
1979, Mar. 27   **Litho.**   **Perf. 14**
321	A43	5c blue & gold	.35	.30
322	A43	15c brown & gold	.70	.60
323	A43	25c green & gold	.95	.90
324	A43	50c red & gold	1.90	1.90
		Nos. 321-324 (4)	3.90	3.70

Centenary of discovery of gold in Swaziland.

Girls at Piano, 1892, by Renoir A44

Paintings by Renoir: 15c, Madame Charpentier and her Children, 1878. 25c, Girls Picking Flowers, 1889. 50c, Girl with Watering Can, 1876.

1979, May 8   **Litho.**   **Perf. 13½**
325	A44	5c multicolored	.20	.20
326	A44	15c multicolored	.25	.25
327	A44	25c multicolored	.45	.45
328	A44	50c multicolored	.90	.90
a.		Souvenir sheet of 4, #325-328	2.50	2.50
		Nos. 325-328 (4)	1.80	1.80

International Year of the Child.

Swaziland No. 40 and Rowland Hill — A45

Rowland Hill and: 20c, Swaziland #18. 25c, Swaziland #142. 50c, Swaziland #60.

1979, July 17   **Litho.**   **Perf. 14½**
329	A45	10c multicolored	.20	.20
330	A45	20c multicolored	.35	.30
331	A45	25c multicolored	.40	.40
		Nos. 329-331 (3)	.95	.90

Souvenir Sheet
332	A45	50c multicolored	1.25	1.25

Sir Rowland Hill (1795-1879), originator of penny postage.

5c Cupro-Nickel Coin — A46

Coins: 10c, King Sobhuza II and sugar cane. 20c, King and elephant head. 50c, Coat of arms. 1e, Mother and son.

Perf. 13½x14
1979, Sept. 6   **Litho.**   **Wmk. 373**
333	A46	5c multicolored	.20	.20
334	A46	10c multicolored	.25	.20
335	A46	20c multicolored	.40	.25
336	A46	50c multicolored	.65	.65
337	A46	1e multicolored	1.25	1.25
		Nos. 333-337 (5)	2.75	2.55

Big Bend Post Office A47

15c, Mount Ntondozi microwave station, vert. 20c, Swaziland #53. 50c, Swaziland #217.

1979, Nov. 22
338	A47	5c multicolored	.20	.20
339	A47	15c multicolored	.20	.20
340	A47	20c multicolored	.25	.25
341	A47	50c multicolored	.55	.55
		Nos. 338-341 (4)	1.20	1.20

25th anniv. of Post and Telecommunications service (5c, 15c); 10th anniv. of UPU membership (20c, 50c).

Rotary International, 75th Anniversary A48

Wmk. 373
1980, Feb. 23   **Litho.**   **Perf. 14**
342	A48	5c shown	.20	.20
343	A48	15c Hospital equipment	.25	.25
344	A48	50c Rotary principles	.90	.90
345	A48	1e Headquarters, Evanston, IL	1.75	1.75
		Nos. 342-345 (4)	3.10	3.10

Eucomis Autumnalis — A49

Flowers: 1c, Brunsvigia radulosa. 2c, Aloe suprafoliata. 3c, Haemanthus magificus. 4c, Aloe marlothii. 5c, Dicoma zeyheri. 6c, Aloe kniphofioides. 7c, Cyrtanthus bicolor. 15c, Leucospermum gerrardii. 20c, Haemanthus multiflorus. 30c, Acridocarpus natalitius. 50c, Adenium swazicum. 1e, Protea simplex. 2e, Calodendrum capense. 5e, Gladiolus ecklonii. All vert. except. 15c, 20c, 30c, 50c.

1980, Apr. 28   Unwmk.   Perf. 13½
346	A49	1c multicolored	.20	.20
347	A49	2c multicolored	.20	.20
348	A49	3c multicolored	.20	.20
349	A49	4c multicolored	.20	.20
350	A49	5c multicolored	.20	.20
351	A49	6c multicolored	.20	.20
352	A49	7c multicolored	.20	.20
353	A49	10c multicolored	.20	.20
354	A49	15c multicolored	.30	.30
355	A49	20c multicolored	.40	.40
356	A49	30c multicolored	.55	.55
357	A49	50c multicolored	.70	.70

Size: 22x37½mm
358	A49	1e multicolored	1.40	1.40
359	A49	2e multicolored	3.00	3.00
360	A49	5e multicolored	7.00	7.00
		Nos. 346-360 (15)	14.95	14.95

No. 348a does not have a date inscription below design.
For surcharges see Nos. 465-470.

1983   Perf. 12
346a	A49	1c	1.00	.75
347a	A49	2c	1.00	.75
348a	A49	3c	3.50	3.50
349a	A49	4c	1.25	1.25
350a	A49	5c	4.00	2.50
351a	A49	6c	2.00	1.50
353a	A49	10c	2.50	1.00
355a	A49	20c	2.75	1.75
		Nos. 346a-355a (8)	18.00	13.00

Inscribed 1983. Nos. 348a, 350a do not have a date inscription below design.

Mail Runner, London 1980 Emblem A50

1980, May 6   Wmk. 373   Perf. 14
361	A50	10c shown	.20	.20
362	A50	20c Mail truck	.30	.25
363	A50	25c Mail sorting	.40	.30
364	A50	50c Mail ropeway	.80	.80
		Nos. 361-364 (4)	1.70	1.55

London 80 Intl. Stamp Exhib., May 6-14.

Yellow Fish A51

1980, Aug. 25   Litho.   Perf. 14
365	A51	5c shown	.40	.20
366	A51	10c Silver barbel	.40	.20
367	A51	15c Tigerfish	.60	.40
368	A51	30c Squeaker fish	.70	.65
369	A51	1e Bream	2.25	2.25
		Nos. 365-369 (5)	4.35	3.70

Oribi Antelope A52

1980, Oct. 1   Litho.   Perf. 14
370	A52	5c shown	.20	.20
371	A52	10c Nile crocodile, vert.	.50	.20
372	A52	50c Pangolin	1.10	1.00
373	A52	1e Leopard, vert.	2.25	2.10
		Nos. 370-373 (4)	4.05	3.50

Bus A53

1981, Jan. 5   Litho.   Perf. 14½
374	A53	5c shown	.20	.20
375	A53	25c Jet	.50	.50
376	A53	30c Truck	.55	.55
377	A53	1e Train	1.90	1.90
		Nos. 374-377 (4)	3.15	3.15

Mantenga Falls — A54

1981, Apr. 16   Litho.   Perf. 14
378	A54	5c shown	.20	.20
379	A54	15c Mananga Yacht Club	.25	.25
380	A54	30c White rhinoceri, Mlilwane Game Sanctuary	.50	.50
381	A54	1e Gambling	1.65	1.65
		Nos. 378-381 (4)	2.60	2.60

Royal Wedding Issue
Common Design Type
Wmk. 373

1981, July 21   Litho.   Perf. 14
382	CD331	10c Bouquet	.20	.20
383	CD331	25c Charles	.40	.40
384	CD331	1e Couple	1.50	1.50
		Nos. 382-384 (3)	2.10	2.10

Installation of King Sobhuza II, 1921 A55

60th Anniv. of King Sobhuza II's Reign (King and): 10c, Visit of Royal Family, 1947. 15c, Coronation of Queen Elizabeth II, 1953. 25c, Independence ceremony, 1968. 30c, Early portrait. 1e, Parliament buildings.

Wmk. 373

1981, Aug. 24   Litho.   Perf. 14½
385	A55	5c multicolored	.20	.20
386	A55	10c multicolored	.20	.20
387	A55	15c multicolored	.25	.25
388	A55	25c multicolored	.40	.40
389	A55	30c multicolored	.50	.50
390	A55	1e multicolored	1.60	1.60
		Nos. 385-390 (6)	3.15	3.15

Duke of Edinburgh's Awards, 25th Anniv. — A56

Intl. Year of the Disabled — A57

1981, Nov. 5   Litho.   Perf. 14
391	A56	5c Basketball	.20	.20
392	A56	20c Compass reading	.35	.35
393	A56	50c Square	.90	.90
394	A56	1e Duke of Edinburgh	1.75	1.75
		Nos. 391-394 (4)	3.20	3.20

1981, Dec. 7   Perf. 14x14½, 14½x14
395	A57	5c Men learning carpentry, horiz.	.35	.25
396	A57	15c Boy learning Braille	.60	.40
397	A57	25c Carpentry, diff.	.90	.65
398	A57	1e Driving, horiz.	2.75	2.75
		Nos. 395-398 (4)	4.60	4.05

Papilio Demodocus — A58

1982, Jan. 6   Litho.   Perf. 14
399	A58	5c shown	.65	.20
400	A58	10c Charaxes candiope	.70	.35
401	A58	50c Papilio nireus	2.50	2.40
402	A58	1e Eurema desjardinsii	5.00	4.75
		Nos. 399-402 (4)	8.85	7.70

A59

A60

1982, Apr. 27   Litho.   Perf. 14
403	A59	5c Non-smoker, flowers	.75	.70
404	A59	10c Smoker, non-smoker, flag	.90	.85

First Intl. Conference on Smoking and Health, Apr. 25-29

Perf. 13½x13
1982, June 16   Litho.   Wmk. 373

a, Female fishing owl. b, Pair. c, Owl in nest, egg. d, Adult and young owls. e, Male.
405		Strip of 5, multi	125.00	85.00
a.-e.		A60 35c, any single	16.00	10.00

Princess Diana Issue
Common Design Type

1982, July 1   Perf. 14½
406	CD333	5c Arms	.30	.30
407	CD333	20c Diana	.55	.55
408	CD333	50c Wedding	1.40	1.40
409	CD333	1e Portrait	2.75	2.75
		Nos. 406-409 (4)	5.00	5.00

Sugar Industry A61

1982, Sept. 1   Litho.
410	A61	5c Planting sugar cane	.20	.20
411	A61	20c Harvesting cane	.45	.45
412	A61	30c Mhlume Mills	.65	.65
413	A61	1e Rail transport	2.25	2.25
		Nos. 410-413 (4)	3.55	3.55

Baphalali Red Cross Society A62

1982, Nov. 9   Perf. 14
414	A62	5c Immunization	.20	.20
415	A62	20c Red Cross Juniors	.45	.45
416	A62	50c Disaster relief	1.10	1.10
417	A62	1e Red Cross founder Henry Dunant	2.25	2.25
		Nos. 414-417 (4)	4.00	4.00

Scouting Year — A63

Perf. 14½x14
1982, Dec. 6   Litho.   Wmk. 373
418	A63	5c Reciting promise	.20	.20
419	A63	10c Hiking	.25	.25
420	A63	25c Community development	.65	.65
421	A63	75c Baden-Powell	1.90	1.90
		Nos. 418-421 (4)	3.00	3.00

Souvenir Sheet
422	A63	1e Emblem	3.25	3.25

A64

Bearded Vulture — A65

1983, Mar. 14   Litho.   Perf. 14
423	A64	6c Satellite view	.20	.20
424	A64	10c King Sobhuza II, flag	.20	.20
425	A64	50c Beehive huts, horiz.	1.00	1.00
426	A64	1e Spraying sugar crop, horiz.	2.00	2.00
		Nos. 423-426 (4)	3.40	3.40

Commonwealth Day.

Perf. 13½x13
1983, May 16   Litho.   Wmk. 373

Designs: a, Male. b, Pair. c, Nest, egg. d, Female at nest. e, Adult, fledgling.
427		Strip of 5	25.00	25.00
a.-e.		A65 35c, any single	3.50	3.50

Souvenir Sheets

Soccer Tour of Swaziland 1983 — A66

1983, Aug. 20   Litho.   Perf. 14x13½
428	A66	75c Natl. team	1.50	1.50
429	A66	75c Tottenham Hotspur	1.50	1.50
430	A66	75c Manchester United	1.50	1.50
		Nos. 428-430 (3)	4.50	4.50

Manned Flight Bicentenary A67

1983, Sept. 22   Litho.   Perf. 14
431	A67	5c Montgolfiere, 1783, vert.	.20	.20
432	A67	10c Wright brothers' plane	.20	.20
433	A67	25c Royal Swazi Fokker Fellowship	.40	.40
434	A67	50c Bell X-1 jet	.85	.85
		Nos. 431-434 (4)	1.65	1.65

Souvenir Sheet
435	A67	1e Columbia space shuttle take-off, vert.	2.50	2.50

Alfred Nobel, 100th Birth Anniv. A68

1983, Oct. 21
436	A68	6c Albert Schweitzer	3.25	.80
437	A68	10c Dag Hammarskjold	1.25	1.25
438	A68	50c Albert Einstein	4.00	4.00
439	A68	1e shown	8.50	8.50
		Nos. 436-439 (4)	17.00	14.55

World Food Program A69

1983, Nov. 29
440	A69	6c	Maize	.20	.20
441	A69	10c	Rice	.35	.30
442	A69	50c	Cattle	1.00	1.00
443	A69	1e	Tractor	1.90	1.90
			Nos. 440-443 (4)	3.45	3.40

Women's College
A70

Wmk. 373

1984, Mar. 12   Litho.   Perf. 14
444	A70	5c	shown	.20	.20
445	A70	15c	Technical training school	.30	.30
446	A70	50c	University	.90	.90
447	A70	1e	Primary school	1.75	1.75
			Nos. 444-447 (4)	3.15	3.15

Bald Ibis — A71

Designs: a, Male. b, Male, female. c, Nest, egg. d, Female at nest. e, Adult, fledgeling.

1984, May 18   Litho.   Perf. 13½x13
448		Strip of 5	29.00	29.00
a.-e.	A71	35c, any single	4.50	4.50

1984 UPU Congress — A72

Mail Coaches.

1984, June 15   Litho.   Perf. 14½
449	A72	7c	Mule-drawn coach	.35	.20
450	A72	15c	Oxen-drawn post wagon	.50	.30
451	A72	50c	Mule-drawn, diff.	1.10	.90
452	A72	1e	Bristol-London	1.75	1.75
			Nos. 449-452 (4)	3.70	3.15

1984 Summer Olympics A73

1984, July 28   Perf. 14
453	A73	7c	Running	.20	.20
454	A73	10c	Swimming	.25	.20
455	A73	50c	Shooting	.90	.85
456	A73	1e	Boxing	1.75	1.75
a.		Souvenir sheet of 4, #453-456	4.25	4.25
			Nos. 453-456 (4)	3.10	3.00

Local Fungi A74

1984, Sept. 19   Litho.   Perf. 14
457	A74	10c	Suillus bovinus	2.25	.45
458	A74	15c	Langermannia gigantea, vert.	3.25	.80
459	A74	50c	Coriolus versicolor, vert.	3.50	2.50
460	A74	1e	Boletus edulis	4.75	4.75
			Nos. 457-460 (4)	13.75	8.50

20th Anniv. of Swazi Railways A75

1984, Nov. 5   Litho.   Wmk. 373
461	A75	10c	Opening ceremony	.40	.20
462	A75	25c	Type 15A locomotive, Siweni Exchange Yard	.75	.60
463	A75	30c	Container loading, Matsapha Station	.90	.75
464	A75	1e	No. 268, Alto Tunnel	3.00	2.50
a.		Souvenir sheet of 4, #461-464	6.50	6.50
			Nos. 461-464 (4)	5.05	4.05

Nos. 346a, 346-349, 351-352
Surcharged

1984, Dec. 15   Litho.   Perf. 12
465	A49	10c	on 4c #349	.40	.20
a.		Perf. 13½	50.00	50.00

Perf. 13½, 12 (#469)
466	A49	15c	on 7c #352	.50	.30
467	A49	20c	on 3c #348	.45	.25
a.		Perf 12		—
468	A49	25c	on 6c #351	.50	.25
469	A49	30c	on 1c #346a	.60	.30
470	A49	30c	on 2c #347	2.75	2.75
			Nos. 465-470 (6)	5.20	4.05

Rotary Intl., 80th Anniv. A76

1985, Feb. 23   Wmk. 373   Perf. 14
471	A76	10c	Rotary emblem, world map	.60	.40
472	A76	15c	Training scholarships	1.00	.40
473	A76	50c	Two children	1.40	1.40
474	A76	1e	Nurse, children	2.75	2.75
			Nos. 471-474 (4)	5.75	4.95

Life Cycle of the Ground Hornbill — A77

Audubon birth bicentenary.

1985, May 15   Wmk. 373
475		Strip of 5	17.50	17.50
a.-e.	A77	25c, any single	2.50	2.50

Queen Mother 85th Birthday
Common Design Type

Perf. 14½x14

1985, June 7   Wmk. 384
476	CD336	10c	Visit to South Africa, 1947	.40	.20
477	CD336	15c	With Elizabeth II and Margaret	.40	.20
478	CD336	50c	75th birthday celebration	1.10	.75
479	CD336	1e	Holding Prince Henry	1.50	1.50
			Nos. 476-479 (4)	3.40	2.65

Souvenir Sheet
480	CD336	2e	Greeting Prince Andrew	4.00	4.00

Classic Automobiles — A78

Wmk. 373

1985, Sept. 16   Litho.   Perf. 14
481	A78	10c	Buick Tourer	.85	.85
482	A78	15c	Four-cylinder Rover	.90	.85
483	A78	50c	De Dion Bouton	2.10	1.75
484	A78	1e	Ford Model-T	3.50	3.50
			Nos. 481-484 (4)	7.35	6.95

Intl. Youth Year A79

1985, Dec. 2
485	A79	10c	Bridge-building	.20	.20
486	A79	20c	Girl Guides camping	.20	.20
487	A79	50c	Recreation	.75	.65
488	A79	1e	Guides collecting branches	1.40	1.40
			Nos. 485-488 (4)	2.55	2.45

Girl Guide Movement, 20c, 1e. IYY, 10c, 50c.

Halley's Comet A80

1986, Feb. 27   Wmk. 384   Perf. 14½
489	A80	1.50e	multicolored	4.25	4.25

Queen Elizabeth II 60th Birthday
Common Design Type

10c, Princess Anne's christening, 1950. 30c, Wedding of Prince Charles and Lady Diana, 1981. 45c, With George VI, the Dutchess of York and Sobhuza II at Nhlangano, 1947. 1e, At Windsor Polo Ground, 1984. 2e, Visiting Crown Agents' offices, 1983.

1986, Apr. 21   Perf. 14x14½
490	CD337	10c	scar, blk & sil	.20	.20
491	CD337	30c	ultra & multi	.30	.30
492	CD337	45c	green, blk & sil	.45	.45
493	CD337	1e	violet & multi	.95	.95
494	CD337	2e	rose vio & multi	2.00	2.00
			Nos. 490-494 (5)	3.90	3.90

For overprints see Nos. 527-530.

Coronation of Crown Prince Makhosetive A81

10c, Portrait, vert. 20c, Prince and King Sobhuza II at an Incwala ceremony. 25c, Prince at primary school. 30c, At school in England. 40c, Escorted from Matsapha Airport by Guard of Honor. 2e, Dancing the Simemo.

1986, Apr. 25   Perf. 14½
495	A81	10c	multicolored	.50	.50
496	A81	20c	multicolored	.60	.60
497	A81	25c	multicolored	.75	.75
498	A81	30c	multicolored	.90	.90
499	A81	40c	multicolored	1.75	1.10
500	A81	2e	multicolored	5.75	5.75
			Nos. 495-500 (6)	10.25	9.60

Assoc. of Round Tables in Central Africa, 50th Anniv. — A82

Club emblems.

Wmk. 384

1986, Oct. 4   Litho.   Perf. 14
501	A82	15c	Orbis	.40	.20
502	A82	25c	Ehlanzeni 51	.50	.45
503	A82	55c	Mbabane 30	1.10	.90
504	A82	70c	Bulembu 54	1.25	1.25
505	A82	2e	Manzini 44	3.25	3.25
			Nos. 501-505 (5)	6.50	6.05

Butterflies — A83

Unwmk.

1987, Mar. 17   Litho.   Perf. 14
506	A83	10c	Yellow pansy	.50	.50
507	A83	15c	Guineafowl	.60	.50
508	A83	20c	Red forest charaxes	.60	.30
509	A83	25c	Paradise skipper	.60	.60
510	A83	30c	Broad-bordered acraea	.60	.50
511	A83	35c	Veined swallowtail	.60	.50
512	A83	45c	Large striped swordtail	.65	.65
513	A83	50c	Eyed pansy	.70	.50
514	A83	55c	Zebra white	.70	.50
515	A83	70c	Gaudy commodore	.90	1.25
516	A83	1e	Common dotted border	1.25	3.00
517	A83	5e	Queen purple tip	4.25	2.00
518	A83	10e	Natal barred blue	6.75	5.75
			Nos. 506-518 (13)	18.70	16.55

See Nos. 600-611. For surcharges see Nos. 574-577. Compare with design A101.

White Rhinoceros A84

1987, July 1   Wmk. 384   Perf. 14½
519	A84	15c	Two adults	2.50	1.10
520	A84	25c	Adult, calf	3.75	1.75
521	A84	45c	Adult walking	7.25	5.25
522	A84	70c	Adult in mud	8.75	5.75
			Nos. 519-522 (4)	22.25	13.85

World Wildlife Fund.

Flowers — A85

1987, Oct. 19   Litho.   Perf. 14½
523	A85	15c	Blue moon	1.25	.85
524	A85	35c	Danse de feu	2.25	1.50
525	A85	55c	Odin	2.75	2.25
526	A85	2e	Lilium davidii	8.50	8.50
			Nos. 523-526 (4)	14.75	13.10

Nos. 491-494 Ovptd. "40TH WEDDING ANNIVERSARY" in Silver

Perf. 14x14½

1987, Dec. 9   Litho.   Wmk. 384
527	CD337	30c	ultra & multi	.30	.30
528	CD337	45c	green, blk & sil	.45	.45
529	CD337	1e	violet & multi	1.00	1.00
530	CD337	2e	rose vio & multi	2.00	2.00
			Nos. 527-530 (4)	3.75	3.75

Insects A86

Wmk. 384

1988, Mar. 14   Litho.   Perf. 14
531	A86	15c	Zabalius aridus	1.75	.25
532	A86	55c	Callidea bohemani	3.25	1.00
533	A86	1e	Phymateus viridipes	5.50	5.50
534	A86	2e	Nomadacris septemfasciata	8.50	9.50
			Nos. 531-534 (4)	19.00	16.25

1988
Summer
Olympics,
Seoul
A87

1988, Aug. 22   Litho.   Wmk. 384
535 A87 15c Flag-bearer, stadi-
               um   1.00   .40
536 A87 35c Tae kwon do   1.50   .80
537 A87 1e   Boxing   2.00 2.00
538 A87 2e   Tennis   4.00 4.00
        Nos. 535-538 (4)   8.50 7.20
Intl. Tennis Federation, 75th anniv. (2e).

Small
Mammals
A88

Wmk. 384
1989, Jan. 16   Litho.   Perf. 14
539 A88 35c Green monkey   2.10   .50
540 A88 55c Rock dassie   3.00   .95
541 A88 1e   Zorilla   5.50 4.25
542 A88 2e   African wildcat   9.50 11.00
        Nos. 539-542 (4)   20.10 16.70

Intl. Red Cross and Red Crescent
Organizations, 125th Annivs. — A89

Wmk. 373
1989, Sept. 21   Litho.   Perf. 12
543 A89 15c David Hynd   .35   .20
544 A89 60c First aid   .90   .80
545 A89 1e   Sigombeni Clinic   1.50 1.50
546 A89 2e   Relief work   2.50 2.50
        Nos. 543-546 (4)   5.25 5.00

21st Birthday
of King
Mswati III
A90

King Mswati III: 15c, With Prince of Wales,
1987. 60c, With Pope John Paul II, 1988. 1e,
Introduction to the nation while crown prince.
2e, With queen mother.

Perf. 14½x14
1989, Nov. 15   Unwmk.
547 A90 15c multicolored   .20   .20
548 A90 60c multicolored   .55   .55
549 A90 1e   multicolored   .95   .95
550 A90 2e   multicolored   1.90 1.90
        Nos. 547-550 (4)   3.60 3.60

African
Development
Bank, 25th
Anniv. — A91

15c, Manzini-Mahamba Road. 60c,
Mbabane microwave radio link. 1e, Mbabane
Government Hospital. 2e, Ezulwini Power
Switching Station.

Perf. 14x14½
1989, Dec. 18   Wmk. 384
551 A91 15c multicolored   .40   .20
552 A91 60c multicolored   .70   .50
553 A91 1e   multicolored   1.25 1.25
554 A91 2e   multicolored   2.25 2.25
        Nos. 551-554 (4)   4.60 4.20

Stamp
World
London
'90 — A92

Wmk. 384
1990, May 3   Litho.   Perf. 12½
555 A92 15c Intl. priority mail   .35   .30
556 A92 60c Facsimile service   .80   .65
557 A92 1e   Post office   1.50 1.50
558 A92 2e   Ezulwini Earth Sat-
               ellite Station   2.75 2.75
        Nos. 555-558 (4)   5.40 5.20

Souvenir Sheet
559 A92 2e   Mail runner   7.50 7.50
        150th anniv. of the Penny Black.

Queen Mother, 90th Birthday
Common Design Types
1990, Aug. 4   Wmk. 384   Perf. 14x15
565 CD343 75c Queen Mother   .70   .60

Perf. 14½
566 CD344 4e King, Queen vis-
                iting Hatfield
                House   3.50 3.50

Intl.
Literacy
Year
A94

Wmk. 373
1990, Sept. 21   Litho.   Perf. 14
567 A94 15c shown   .20   .20
568 A94 75c Outdoor class   .65   .65
569 A94 1e   Modern instruction   .80   .80
570 A94 2e   Receiving diploma   1.60 1.60
        Nos. 567-570 (4)   3.25 3.25

UN Development
Program, 40th
Anniv. — A95

Perf. 13½x14
1990, Dec. 10   Litho.   Wmk. 373
571 A95 15c Rural water supply   .75   .75
572 A95 1e   Seed production   1.25 1.25
573 A95 2e   Low cost housing   2.25 2.25
        Nos. 571-573 (3)   4.25 4.25

Nos. 509-510, 512, 514 Surcharged

Unwmk.
1990, Dec. 17   Litho.   Perf. 14
574   A83 10c on 25c multi   .20   .20
575   A83 15c on 30c multi   .25   .25
575A A83 15c on 45c multi   50.00 30.00
576   A83 20c on 45c multi   .35   .35
577   A83 40c on 55c multi   .70   .70

National
Heritage
A96

Perf. 14x14½
1991, Feb. 11   Wmk. 233
578 A96 15c Lobamba Hot
               Spring   .40   .20
579 A96 60c Sibebe Rock   .95   .70
580 A96 1e   Jolobela Falls   1.50 1.50
581 A96 2e   Mantjolo Sacred
               Pool   2.40 2.40
        Nos. 578-581 (4)   5.25 4.80

Souvenir Sheet
Perf. 14
581A A96 2e Ushuswana River   5.00 5.00

Coronation
of King
Mswati III,
5th Anniv.
A97

Perf. 14x13½
1991, Apr. 24   Litho.   Wmk. 373
582 A97 15c King making radio
               address   .35   .20
583 A97 75c Butimba royal hunt   1.25   .95
584 A97 1e   King, schoolmates,
               1986   1.25 1.25
585 A97 2e   King opening parlia-
               ment   2.75 2.75
        Nos. 582-585 (4)   5.60 5.15

Elizabeth & Philip, Birthdays
Common Design Types
Wmk. 384
1991, June 17   Litho.   Perf. 14½
586 CD346 1e multicolored   1.50 1.50
587 CD345 2e multicolored   2.40 2.40
  a.   Pair, #586-587 + label   4.25 4.25

Flowers — A98   Christmas — A99

1991, Sept. 30   Wmk. 373   Perf. 14
588 A98 15c Xerophyta retinervis   .60   .40
589 A98 75c Bauhinia galpinii   1.50 1.25
590 A98 1e   Dombeya
               rotundifolia   1.75 1.75
591 A98 2e   Kigelia africana   3.25 3.25
        Nos. 588-591 (4)   7.10 6.65

Wmk. 373
1991, Dec. 18   Litho.   Perf. 13½
592 A99 20c Santa Claus, chil-
               dren   .30   .20
593 A99 70c Carolers   1.00   .90
594 A99 1e   Priest reading Bible   1.40 1.40
595 A99 2e   Nativity Scene   2.50 2.50
        Nos. 592-595 (4)   5.20 5.00

Reptiles
A100

1992, Feb. 25
596 A100 20c Lubombo flat liz-
                ard   1.25   .25
597 A100 70c Natal hinged tor-
                toise   3.00 1.60
598 A100 1e   Swazi thick-toed
                gecko   3.75 3.75
599 A100 2e   Nile monitor   5.25 5.25
        Nos. 596-599 (4)   13.25 10.85

Butterflies
A101

1992-2000   Litho.   Perf. 14
600 A101 5c   Red tip   .20   .20
601 A101 10c like #506   .20   .20
602 A101 15c like #507   .20   .20
603 A101 20c like #508   .25   .20
604 A101 25c like #509   .25   .20
605 A101 30c like #510   .30   .20
606 A101 35c like #511   .35   .30
607 A101 45c like #512   .40   .35
608 A101 50c like #513   .45   .40
609 A101 55c like #514   .50   .45
610 A101 70c like #515   .55   .55
611 A101 1e   like #516   1.00 1.00
612 A101 5e   Like #517   —   —
613 A101 10e Like #518   —   —
        Nos. 600-611 (12)   4.65 4.25
  Issued: Nos. 600-611, 8/26/92. No. 612,
2000.
  Nos. 600-611 dated 1991. Nos. 612 and
613 dated 2000.
  Nos. 600-612 have different portrait of King
Mswati III from Nos. 506-517.

A102   A103

Designs: 20c, Missionaries with royal family.
1e, Pioneer missionaries.

1992, Dec. 16   Litho.   Perf. 13½x14
614 A102 20c multicolored   .75   .65
615 A102 1e   multicolored   3.00 3.00
  Evangelical Alliance Mission in Swaziland,
cent.

1993, Mar. 18   Litho.   Perf. 13½x14
  Cooking Utensils: 20c, Calabashes. 70c,
Contemporary pottery for cooking. 1e,
Wooden bowls. 2e, Quern for grinding seeds.
616 A103 20c multicolored   .65   .20
617 A103 70c multicolored   1.50   .95
618 A103 1e   multicolored   2.10 2.10
619 A103 2e   multicolored   3.25 3.25
        Nos. 616-619 (4)   7.50 6.50

A104   A105

King Mswati, 25th Birthday: 25c, King
Mswati as baby with mother. 40c, King Mswati
III addressing PTA meeting. 1e, King Sobhuza
II receiving Instrument of Independence, 1968.
2e, King Mswati III delivering first speech on
Coronation Day, 1986.

1993, Sept. 6   Litho.   Perf. 13½x14
620 A104 25c multicolored   .25   .20
621 A104 40c multicolored   .35   .25
622 A104 1e   multicolored   .90   .90
623 A104 2e   multicolored   1.75 1.75
        Nos. 620-623 (4)   3.25 3.10
        Independence, 25th anniv.

1993, Nov. 25   Perf. 13½
Common Waxbill
624 A105 25c Male & female   .50   .25
625 A105 40c Nest & eggs   .75   .30
626 A105 1e   Incubating   1.75 1.75
627 A105 2e   Feeding nestlings   2.75 2.75
        Nos. 624-627 (4)   5.75 5.05

A106

A107

1994, Feb. 22   Litho.   Perf. 13½
628	A106	25c Education	.35	.25
629	A106	40c Rural services	.45	.25
630	A106	1e Swazi culture	1.75	1.75
631	A106	2e People to people	2.00	2.00
		Nos. 628-631 (4)	4.55	4.25

US Peace Corps, 25th anniv.

1994, Sept. 15   Perf. 13½x14
Mushrooms.
632	A107	30c Horse mushroom	1.40	.60
633	A107	40c Penny bun bolete	1.40	.60
634	A107	1e Rusulla verdigris	3.00	2.00
635	A107	2e Honey fungus	4.00	4.00
		Nos. 632-635 (4)	9.80	7.20

ICAO, 50th Anniv. A108

1994, Nov. 30   Litho.   Perf. 14
636	A108	30c Natl. airline	.50	.20
637	A108	40c Control tower	.55	.30
638	A108	1e Air rescue service	1.25	1.25
639	A108	2e Air traffic control	1.75	1.75
		Nos. 636-639 (4)	4.05	3.50

A109

A110

Traditional handicrafts.

1995, Apr. 7   Litho.   Perf. 13½
640	A109	35c Wooden bowls	.20	.20
641	A109	50c Chicken nests	.30	.30
642	A109	1e Leather crafts	.55	.55
643	A109	2e Wood carvings	1.10	1.10
		Nos. 640-643 (4)	2.15	2.15

1995, June 5   Litho.   Perf. 13½
FAO, 50th anniv.: 35c, Corn harvest. 50c, Planting vegetables. 1e, Herd of cattle. 2e, Sorghum harvest.
644	A110	35c multicolored	.20	.20
645	A110	50c multicolored	.35	.35
646	A110	1e multicolored	.70	.70
647	A110	2e multicolored	1.40	1.40
		Nos. 644-647 (4)	2.65	2.65

Lourie A111

1995, Sept. 27   Litho.   Perf. 13½x13
648	A111	35c Knysna lourie	.65	.30
649	A111	50c Lourie in flight	.85	.50
650	A111	1e Purple crested lourie	1.25	1.25
651	A111	2e Gray lourie	1.75	1.75
		Nos. 648-651 (4)	4.50	3.80

Reptiles A112

1996, Jan. 17   Litho.   Perf. 13½x13
652	A112	35c Chameleon	.60	.25
653	A112	50c Rock monitor	.75	.40
654	A112	1e African python	1.25	1.25
655	A112	2e Tree agama	2.00	2.00
		Nos. 652-655 (4)	4.60	3.90

Trees — A113

1996, Apr. 23   Litho.   Perf. 13
656	A113	40c Waterberry	.30	.20
657	A113	60c Sycamore fig	.40	.35
658	A113	1e Stem fruit	.70	.70
659	A113	2e Wild medlar	1.25	1.25
		Nos. 656-659 (4)	2.65	2.50

Local Landmarks A114

Designs: 40c, First church, Mahamba Methodist. 60c, Colonial Secretariat, Mbabane. 1e, King Sobhuza II Memorial Monument. 2e, First High Court Building, Hlatikulu.

1996, Aug. 26   Litho.   Perf. 13½x13
660	A114	40c multicolored	.20	.20
661	A114	60c multicolored	.35	.35
662	A114	1e multicolored	.75	.75
663	A114	2e multicolored	1.40	1.40
		Nos. 660-663 (4)	2.70	2.70

UNICEF, 50th Anniv. A115

Designs: 40c, Basic education for all. 60c, Universal child immunization, vert. 1e, No more polio, vert. 2e, Children first, vert.

1996, Dec. 31   Litho.   Perf. 13½x14
664	A115	40c multicolored	.20	.20

Perf. 14x13½
665	A115	60c multicolored	.40	.40
666	A115	1e multicolored	.55	.55
667	A115	2e multicolored	1.25	1.25
		Nos. 664-667 (4)	2.40	2.40

Wild Animals A116

50c, Klipspringer, vert. 70c, Gray duiker, vert. 1e, Antbear. 2e, Cape clawless otter.

Perf. 14x13½, 13½x14
1997, Sept. 22   Litho.
668	A116	50c multicolored	.40	.30
669	A116	70c multicolored	.50	.40
670	A116	1e multicolored	.85	.85
671	A116	2e multicolored	1.50	1.50
		Nos. 668-671 (4)	3.25	3.05

Traditional Costumes — A117

1997, Dec. 1   Litho.   Perf. 13x13½
672	A117	50c Umgaco	.20	.20
673	A117	70c Sigeja	.45	.45
674	A117	1e Umdada	.60	.60
675	A117	2e Ligcebesha	1.25	1.25
		Nos. 672-675 (4)	2.50	2.50

Toads and Frogs A118

1998, June 1   Litho.   Perf. 14
676	A118	55c Olive toad	.35	.20
677	A118	75c African bullfrog	.50	.30
678	A118	1e Water lily frog	.80	.80
679	A118	2e Bushveld rain frog	1.50	1.50
		Nos. 676-679 (4)	3.15	2.80

Independence, 30th Anniv., King Mswati III, 30th Birthday — A119

55c, King Sobhuza II Memorial Park. 75c, King Mswati III taking oath. 1e, King Mswati III delivering 1st speech. 2e, King Sobhuza II receiving instrument of independence.

Perf. 13½x14, 14x13½
1998, Sept. 3   Litho.
680	A119	55c multicolored	.20	.20
681	A119	75c multicolored	.45	.45
682	A119	1e multicolored	.65	.65
683	A119	2e multicolored	1.10	1.10
		Nos. 680-683 (4)	2.40	2.40

Traditional Utensils — A120

1999, May 17   Litho.   Perf. 13¾x13¼
684	A120	60c Grinding stone	.20	.20
685	A120	75c Stirring sticks	.30	.30
686	A120	80c Clay pot	.30	.30
687	A120	95c Swazi spoons	.35	.35
688	A120	1.75e Beer cup	.75	.75
689	A120	2.40e Mortar and pestle	1.00	1.00
		Nos. 684-689 (6)	2.90	2.90

UPU, 125th Anniv. A121

Perf. 13¾x13½
1999, Oct. 9   Litho.   Unwmk.
690	A121	60c Internet service, vert.	.20	.20
691	A121	80c Cellular phone service, vert.	.30	.30

Perf. 13½x13¾
692	A121	1e Intl. mail exchange	.40	.40
693	A121	2.40e Training school	1.00	1.00
		Nos. 690-693 (4)	1.90	1.90

Wildlife A122

Designs: 65c, Lion, vert. 90c, Leopard. 1.50e, Rhinoceros. 2.50e, Buffalo, vert.

Perf. 13½x13¼, 13¼x13½
2000, July 3   Litho.   Unwmk.
694	A122	65c multi	.35	.20
695	A122	90c multi	.60	.30
696	A122	1.50e multi	1.50	1.50
697	A122	2.50e multi	1.25	1.25
		Nos. 694-697 (4)	3.70	3.25

Worldwide Fund for Nature (WWF) — A123

Designs: 65c, Oribi with young. 90c, Oribi. 1.50e, Klipspringers. 2.50e, Klipspringers, diff.

Wmk. 373
2001, Feb. 1   Litho.   Perf. 14
698-701	A123	Set of 4	3.25	3.25
701a		Sheet, 4 each #698-701	13.00	13.00

Environmental Protection — A124

Designs: 70c, Fighting forest fires. 95c, Tree planting. 2.05e Construction of Maguga Dam. 2.80e, Building embankment.

2001, July 30   Litho.   Perf. 14
702-705	A124	Set of 4	1.60	1.60

Reign Of Queen Elizabeth II, 50th Anniv. Issue
Common Design Type

Designs: Nos. 706, 710a, 70c, Princess Elizabeth, Princess Anne, Princes Philip and Charles, 1947. Nos. 707, 710b, 95c, Wearing purple hat. Nos. 708, 710c, 2.05e, Wearing crown. Nos. 709, 710d, 2.80e, Wearing yellow hat, 2001. No. 710e, 22.50e, 1955 portrait by Annigoni (38x50mm).

Perf. 14¼x14½, 13¾ (#710e)
2002, Feb. 6   Wmk. 373
With Gold Frames
706-709	CD360	Set of 4	4.50	4.50

Souvenir Sheet
Without Gold Frames
710	CD360	Sheet of 5, #a-e	7.50	7.50

Tourism A125

Designs: 75c, Swazi chalets. 1e, King Mswati III facing lions, vert. 2.05e, Crocodile. 2.80e, Ostriches.

Perf. 13¼x13¾, 13¾x13¼
2002, Dec. 23   Litho.
711-714	A125	Set of 4	1.90	1.90

Musical Instruments — A126

Designs: 80c, Mouth organ, vert. 1.05e, Rattles. 2.35e, Kudu horn trumpet. 2.80e, Chordphone, vert.

2003, Aug. 12   Litho.   Perf. 14
715-718 A126   Set of 4   1.90 1.90

AIDS Prevention — A127

Designs: 85c, Community home-based care. 1.10e, Know your HIV status. 2.45e, Testing blood samples, vert. 3.35e, Unsterilized instruments can transmit HIV and AIDS, vert.

Perf. 13¼x13¾, 13¾x13¼
2004, Mar. 9   Litho.
719-722 A127   Set of 4   2.40 2.40

Global 2003 Smart Partnership International Dialogue, Ezulwini — A128

Designs: 85c, King Mswati III, Swaziland flag, map of Africa. 1.10e, Map of Africa, Swaziland flag, Smart Partnership International Movement emblems, horiz. 2.45e, Sharing ideas. 3.35e, Man, woman at microphone.

Perf. 13¾x13¼, 13¼x13¾
2004, June 14   Litho.
723-726 A128   Set of 4   2.40 2.40

Birds
A129

Designs: 85c, Purple-crested louries, national bird of Swaziland. 1.10e, Blue cranes, national bird of South Africa. 1.35e, Cattle egrets, national bird of Botswana. 1.90e, African fish eagles, national bird of Zimbabwe. 2e, African fish eagles, national bird of Namibia. 2.45e, Bar-tailed trogons. 3e, African fish eagles, national bird of Zambia. 3.35e, Peregrine falcons, national bird of Angola.

2004, Oct. 11   Litho.   Perf. 14
727-734 A129   Set of 8   5.00 5.00
Sheet of 8

No. 735: a, Cattle egrets, national bird of Botswana. b, African fish eagles, national bird of Namibia. c, Bar-tailed trogons. d, African fish eagles, national bird of Zambia. e, Peregrine falcons, national bird of Angola.

2004, Oct. 11   Litho.   Perf. 14
735   Sheet of 8, #727, 728,
        730, #735a-735e   6.75 6.75
a.-b. A129 1.90e Either single   .90 .90
c. A129 2.25e multi   1.10 1.10
d.-e. A129 2.30e Either single   1.10 1.10

See Angola No. , Botswana Nos. 792-793, Malawi No., Namibia No. 1052, South Africa No. 1342, Zambia No. 1033, and Zimbabwe No. 975.

Road Safety Council A130

Inscriptions: 85c, Stop Killing Them In Traffic. 1.10e, Avoid Accidents. 2.45e, Safe Crossing. 3.35e, No Overloading.

2005, Jan. 25   Litho.   Perf. 13¼x13¾
736-739 A130   Set of 4   2.60 2.60

Snakes
A131

Designs: 85c, Black mamba. 1.10e, Python. 2.45e, Boomslang. 3.35e, Puff adder.

2005, Apr. 5   Litho.   Perf. 13¼x13¾
740-743 A131   Set of 4   2.50 2.50

Pope John Paul II (1920-2005) A132

2005, Aug. 18   Litho.   Perf. 14
744 A132 4.50e multi   1.50 1.50

Locusts
A133

Designs: 85c, Schistocerca solitaria. 1.10e, Red locust. 2.45e, Southern Africa desert locust. 3.35e, African migratory locust.

2005, Oct. 11   Litho.   Perf. 13¼x13¾
745-748 A133   Set of 4   2.40 2.40

Queen Mothers — A134

Designs: 85c, Ntombi Tfwala. 1.10e, Dzeliwe Shongwe. 2e, Lomawa Ndwandwe. 2.45e, Labotsibeni Mduli. 3.35e, Tibati Nkambule.

2006, Jan. 10   Perf. 13¾x13¼
749-753 A134   Set of 5   3.25 3.25

Postal History A135

Designs: 90c, Manzini District Office and Post Office, 1920s. 1.15e, Ox wagon. 2e, Bremersdorp Post Office, 1893. 2.55e, Mail runner, vert. 3.50e, Mbabane Temporary Post Office, 1902.

Perf. 13¾
2006, May 8   Litho.   Unwmk.
754-758 A135   Set of 5   3.50 3.50

Waterfalls — A136

Designs: 90c, Mgubudla Falls. 1.15e, Phophonyane Falls. 1.40e, Mantenga Falls, horiz. 2e, Malolotja Falls. 2.55e, Mabhudlweni Falls. 3.50e, Manzamnyama Falls.

2006, Sept. 26
759-764 A136   Set of 6   3.00 3.00

Trees
A137

Designs: 70c, Common cabbage tree. 85c, Broom cluster fig. 90c, Scented thorn. 1.05e, Natal mahogany. 1.15e, Marula. 1.40e, Stem fruit tree. 2e, Fever tree. 2.40e, Large-leaved coral tree. 2.55e, African teak. 3.50e, Red ivory. 5e, Common coral tree. 10e, Jacketplum. 20e, Sausage tree.

2007, Jan. 23   Litho.   Perf. 13¼x13¾
765 A137   70c multi   .20 .20
766 A137   85c multi   .25 .25
767 A137   90c multi   .25 .25
768 A137   1.05e multi   .30 .30
769 A137   1.15e multi   .30 .30
770 A137   1.40e multi   .40 .40
771 A137   2e multi   .55 .55
772 A137   2.40e multi   .65 .65
773 A137   2.55e multi   .70 .70
774 A137   3.50e multi   1.00 1.00
775 A137   5e multi   1.40 1.40
776 A137   10e multi   2.75 2.75
777 A137   20e multi   5.50 5.50
    Nos. 765-777 (13)   14.25 14.25

Community-based Tourism — A138

Designs: 1e, Rock art at Nsangwini Rock Art Center. 1.20e, Mahamba Gorge Lodge. 2.70e, Shewula Mountain Camp. 3.70e, Khopo Camp, Ngwempisi Hiking Trails.

2008, Jan. 22   Litho.   Perf. 13½x13¾
778-781 A138   Set of 4   2.40 2.40

POSTAGE DUE STAMPS

Catalogue values for unused stamps in this section are for Never Hinged items.

D1   D2

1933   Typo.   Wmk. 4   Perf. 14
J1   D1 1p carmine rose   .30   4.00
a.   Wmk. 4a (error)   275.00
J2   D1 2p violet   2.25 15.00

I   II

No. 57 Surcharged

1961   Engr.   Perf. 13½x13
J3 A5   (2d) on 2p, type I   10.00 12.00
a.   Type II   .40
J4 A5   1c on 2p, type I   2.00   3.25
a.   Type II   1.50 1.50
J5 A5   2c on 2p, type I   2.00   3.25
a.   Type II   1.10 1.10
J6 A5   5c on 2p, type I   2.00   3.25
a.   Type II   1.75 1.75
    Nos. J3-J6 (4)   16.00 21.75
    Nos. J3a-J6a (4)   4.75
    Nos. J4a-J6a (3)   4.35

No. J3a was surcharged after decimal currency was introduced.

Type of 1933
1961   Typo.   Perf. 14
J7   D1 1c carmine rose   .20   .20
J8   D1 2c violet   .30   .30
J9   D1 5c green   .75 1.00
    Nos. J7-J9 (3)   1.25 1.50

Wmk. 314
1971, Feb. 1   Litho.   Perf. 11½
J10   D2 1c carmine rose   .30   .35
J11   D2 2c dull purple   .40   .50
J12   D2 5c green   .70   .80
    Nos. J10-J12 (3)   1.40 1.65

1977, Jan. 17   Wmk. 373
J10a   D2 1c carmine rose   .30   .30
J11a   D2 2c dull purple   .40   .40
J12a   D2 5c green   .70   .70
    Nos. J10a-J12a (3)   1.40 1.40

1978-91   Perf. 15x14
Size: 17½x21mm
J13   D2 1c carmine lake   .20   .20
J14   D2 2c purple   .20   .20
J15   D2 5c green   .20   .20
J16   D2 10c sky blue   .20   .20
J17   D2 25c brown   .30   .20
    Nos. J13-J17 (5)   1.10 1.00

Nos. J14-J15 reissued dated 1991.
Issued: 1c-5c, 4/20; 10c-25c, 7/17/91.

SWEDEN

'swē-dən

LOCATION — Northern Europe, occupying the eastern half of the Scandinavian Peninsula
GOVT. — Constitutional Monarchy
AREA — 173,341 sq. mi.
POP. — 9,182,927 (2007 est.)
CAPITAL — Stockholm

48 skilling banco = 1 riksdaler banco (until 1858)
100 öre = 1 riksdaler (1858 to 1874)
100 öre = 1 krona (since 1874)

> **Catalogue values for unused stamps in this country are for Never Hinged items, beginning with Scott 358 in the regular postage section, and Scott B37 in the semi-postal section.**

Watermarks

Wmk. 180 — Crown

Wmk. 307 — Crown and 1955

Wmk. 181 — Wavy Lines

Values for unused stamps are for examples with original gum as defined in the catalogue introduction except Nos. 1-5, including reprints, and LX1 which are valued without gum.

Coat of Arms
A1　　　　A2

			Unwmk.	Typo. Perf. 14
1855			**Unwmk.**	**Typo.** **Perf. 14**
1	A1	3s blue green	8,000.	3,500.
_a._		3s orange (error)		3,000,000.
2	A1	4s lt blue	1,250.	70.00
3	A1	6s gray	8,500.	1,100.
_b._		Imperf.		—
4	A1	8s orange	4,250.	550.00
_c._		Imperf.		—
5	A1	24s dull red	7,000.	1,750.

Nos. 1-5 were reprinted two or three times perf. 14, once perf. 13. Value of the lowest cost perf. 14 reprints, $375 each. Perf. 13, $325 each.
The reprints were made after Nos. 1-5 were withdrawn, but before being demonetized. Used copies are known.

1858-61				**Perf. 14**
6	A2	5o green	160.00	18.00
_a._		5o deep green	575.00	140.00
7	A2	9o violet	350.00	225.00
_a._		9o lilac	450.00	275.00
8	A2	12o blue	175.00	1.90
9	A2	12o ultra ('61)	310.00	12.50
10	A2	24o orange	400.00	27.50
_a._		24o yellow	400.00	35.00
11	A2	30o brown	400.00	27.50
_a._		30o red brown	450.00	45.00
12	A2	50o rose	500.00	90.00
_a._		50o carmine	550.00	95.00
		Nos. 6-12 (7)	2,295.	402.40

Nos. 6 and 8 exist with double impressions. No. 8 is known printed on both sides. No. 11 exists imperf.
Nos. 6-8, 10-12 were reprinted in 1885, perf. 13. Value $100 each. Also reprinted in 1963,

---

perf. 13½, with lines in stamp color crossing denominations, and affixed to book page. Value $12.50 each.

Lion and Arms
A3　　　　A4

1862-69				
13	A3	3o bister brown	200.00	13.50
_a._		Printed on both sides		2,300.
14	A4	17o red violet ('66)	600.00	160.00
15	A4	17o gray ('69)	650.00	650.00
16	A4	20o vermilion ('66)	225.00	16.00
		Nos. 13-16 (4)	1,675.	839.50

Nos. 13-15 were reprinted in 1885, perf. 13. Values $65, $100 and $65, respectively.

Numeral of Value — A5

Coat of Arms — A6

1872-77				**Perf. 14**
17	A5	3o bister brown	60.00	8.00
18	A5	4o gray ('76)	425.00	135.00
19	A5	5o blue green	310.00	4.50
_a._		5o emerald	500.00	55.00
20	A5	6o violet	325.00	40.00
_a._		6o dark violet	325.00	40.00
21	A5	6o gray ('74)	900.00	87.50
22	A5	12o blue	200.00	1.00
23	A5	20o vermilion	900.00	7.00
_a._		20o dull org yel ('75)	3,500.	35.00
_b._		Double impression, dull yel & ver ('76)	3,250.	45.00
24	A5	24o orange	800.00	35.00
_a._		24o yellow	800.00	35.00
25	A5	30o pale brown	700.00	9.25
_a._		30o black brown	700.00	11.50
26	A5	50o rose	750.00	40.00
_a._		50o carmine	750.00	40.00
27	A6	1rd bister & blue	850.00	75.00
_a._		1rd bister & ultra	850.00	75.00
		Nos. 17-27 (11)	6,220.	442.25

1877-79				**Perf. 13**
28	A5	3o yellow brown	90.00	5.00
29	A5	4o gray ('79)	190.00	3.50
30	A5	5o dark green	125.00	1.00
31	A5	6o lilac	175.00	4.00
_a._		6o red lilac	175.00	4.50
32	A5	12o blue	26.00	.80
33	A5	20o vermilion	225.00	1.00
_a._		"TRETIO" instead of "TJUGO" ('79)	8,250.	5,250.
34	A5	24o yellow ('78)	60.00	25.00
_a._		24o lemon yellow ('83)	400.00	45.00
35	A5	30o pale brown	450.00	1.90
_a._		30o black brown	450.00	2.50
36	A5	50o carmine ('78)	260.00	7.00
37	A6	1rd bister & blue	1,900.	400.00
38	A6	1k bister & bl ('78)	500.00	16.00
		Nos. 28-36,38 (10)	2,101.	65.20

Imperf., Pairs

28a	A5	3o		750.00
29a	A5	4o		750.00
30a	A5	5o		750.00
31b	A5	6o		750.00
32a	A5	12o		750.00
33b	A5	20o		750.00
34b	A5	24o		750.00
35b	A5	30o		750.00
36a	A5	50o		2,900.
38a	A6	1k		750.00

See Nos. 40-44, 46-49. For surcharges see Nos. B1-B10, B22-B31.
No. 37 has been reprinted in yellow brown and dark blue; perforated 13. Value, $325.

King Oscar II — A7

1885				**Typo.**
39	A7	10o dull rose	190.00	.65
_a._		Imperf., pair	2,000.	

Numeral Type with Post Horn on Back

1886-91				
40	A5	2o orange ('91)	2.10	7.50
_a._		Period before "FRIMARKE"	11.00	22.50
_b._		Imperf., pair	725.00	

41	A5	3o yellow brn ('87)	11.00	21.00
42	A5	4o gray	25.00	1.60
43	A5	5o green	55.00	.65
44	A5	6o red lilac ('88)	27.50	55.00
_a._		6o violet	30.00	55.00
45	A7	10o pink	77.50	.25
_a._		10o rose	77.50	.25
_b._		Imperf.		1,750.
46	A5	20o vermilion	100.00	.65
47	A5	30o pale brown	175.00	1.50
48	A5	50o rose	150.00	4.25
49	A6	1k bister & dk bl	82.50	3.00
_a._		Imperf., pair	600.00	
		Nos. 40-49 (10)	705.60	95.40

Nos. 32, 34 with Blue Surcharge

1889, Oct. 1				
50	A5	10o on 12o blue	3.25	4.50
51	A5	10o on 24o orange	11.00	42.50

A9

1891-1904		**Typo.**		**Perf. 13**
52	A9	1o brown & ultra ('92)	1.40	.65
53	A9	2o blue & yellow org	3.25	.30
54	A9	3o brown & orange ('92)	.55	1.50
55	A9	4o carmine & ultra ('92)	4.75	.30

Engr.

56	A10	5o yellow green	2.75	.20
_a._		5o blue green	11.50	.20
_d._		5o brown (error)	6,000.	
_e._		Booklet pane of 6	140.00	
57	A10	8o red violet ('03)	3.25	1.25
58	A10	10o carmine	4.50	.20
_c._		Booklet pane of 6	240.00	
59	A10	15o red brown ('96)	22.50	.30
60	A10	20o blue	22.50	.30
61	A10	25o red orange ('96)	27.50	.40
62	A10	30o brown	50.00	.30
63	A10	50o slate	80.00	.85
64	A10	50o olive gray ('04)	80.00	.85
65	A11	1k car & sl ('00)	140.00	2.25
		Nos. 52-65 (14)	442.95	9.65

Imperf., Pairs

52a	A9	1o		82.50
53a	A9	2o		275.00
54a	A9	3o		275.00
55a	A9	4o		250.00
56b	A10	5o No. 56		82.50
_c._		No. 56a		300.00
57a	A10	8o		325.00
58a	A10	10o		52.50
59a	A10	15o		375.00
60a	A10	20o		140.00
61a	A10	25o		475.00
62a	A10	30o		450.00
63a	A10	50o		525.00
64a	A10	50o		375.00
65a	A11	1k		525.00

No. 56d may be a proof.
A booklet pane of 6 invalid stamps similar to No. 56 but with engraved lines through the denominations was released in 2004 to commemorate the 100th anniversary of the first Swedish booklet. This booklet pane is unwatermarked.
See Nos. 75-76.

Stockholm Post Office — A12

1903, Oct. 26				
66	A12	5k blue	225.00	25.00
_a._		Imperf., pair		1,900.

Opening of the new General Post Office at Stockholm.
For surcharge see No. B11.

Arms — A13

Gustaf V — A14

Perf. 13, 13x13½

1910-14		**Typo.**		**Wmk. 180**
67	A13	1o black ('11)	.65	1.50
68	A13	2o orange	1.75	3.50
69	A13	4o violet	2.50	1.10

Engr.

70	A14	5o green ('11)	14.00	29.00
71	A14	10o carmine	9.50	.50
72	A14	1k black, yel ('11)	87.50	.50
73	A14	5k claret, yel ('14)	1.75	3.00
		Nos. 67-73 (7)	117.65	39.10

See #77-98. For surcharges see #99-104, Q1-Q2.

1911				**Unwmk.**
75	A10	20o blue	20.00	14.00
76	A10	25o red orange	25.00	3.50

1910-19				
77	A14	5o green ('11)	1.90	.20
_a._		Booklet pane of 10	225.00	
_b._		Booklet pane of 4	125.00	
78	A14	7o gray grn ('18)	.20	.20
_a._		Booklet pane of 10	8.75	
79	A14	8o magenta ('12)	.20	.20
80	A14	10o carmine ('10)	1.90	.20
_a._		Booklet pane of 10	225.00	
_b._		Booklet pane of 4	125.00	
81	A14	12o rose lake ('18)	.25	.20
_a._		Booklet pane of 10	8.75	
82	A14	15o red brown ('11)	6.50	.20
_a._		Booklet pane of 10	325.00	
83	A14	20o deep blue ('11)	9.50	.20
_a._		Booklet pane of 10	350.00	
84	A14	25o orange red ('11)	.25	.20
85	A14	27o pale blue ('18)	.40	.90
86	A14	30o claret brn ('11)	20.00	.20
87	A14	35o dk violet ('11)	17.00	.20
88	A14	40o olive green ('17)	32.50	.20
89	A14	50o gray ('12)	57.50	.20
90	A14	55o pale blue ('18)	1,550.	4,750.
91	A14	65o pale ol grn ('19)	.65	1.90
92	A14	80o black ('18)	1,550.	4,750.
93	A14	90o gray green ('18)	.60	.65
94	A14	1k black, yel ('19)	92.50	.30
		Nos. 77-89,91,93-94 (16)	241.85	6.15

Excellent forgeries of Nos. 90 and 92 exist.

1911-19	**Typo.**	**Wmk. 181**		**Perf. 13**
95	A13	1o black	.20	.20
96	A13	2o orange	.20	.20
97	A13	3o pale brown ('19)	.20	.20
98	A13	4o pale violet	.20	.20
		Nos. 95-98 (4)	.80	.80

Remainders of Nos. 95-98 received various private overprints, mostly as publicity for stamp exhibitions. They were not postally valid.

Unwatermarked Stamps with Watermarks

Stamps of these and later issues through the UPU Congress issue of 1924, are frequently found with watermark showing parts of the words "Kungl Postverket" in double-lined capitals. This watermark is normally located in the margins of the sheets of unwatermarked paper or paper watermarked wavy lines or crown.

Nos. 80, 84, 91, 90, 92 Surcharge:

a

b

1918 — Unwmk.

99	A14(a)	7o on 10o	.20	.20
100	A14(b)	12o on 25o	1.90	.40
a.		Inverted surcharge	300.00	500.00
101	A14(a)	12o on 65o	.85	1.40
102	A14(a)	27o on 55o	.75	1.60
103	A14(a)	27o on 65o	1.40	3.50
104	A14(a)	27o on 80o	.85	1.60
		Nos. 99-104 (6)	5.95	8.70

Arms
A15

Heraldic Lion
Supporting
Arms of
Sweden
A16

Two types each of 5o green, 5o copper red and 10o violet, type A16.

1920-25 — Perf. 10 Vertically

			Engr.	Unwmk.
115	A15	3o copper red	.20	.30
116	A16	5o green ('25)	3.75	.25
117	A16	5o cop red ('21)	6.25	.25
118	A16	10o green ('21)	21.00	.30
a.		Tête bêche pair	1,550.	2,500.
119	A16	10o violet ('25)	5.25	.20
120	A16	25o orange ('21)	13.00	.40
121	A16	30o brown	.45	.45

Wmk. 181

122	A16	5o green	2.50	.90
123	A16	5o cop red ('21)	8.25	1.00
124	A16	10o green ('21)	2.50	1.10
125	A16	30o brown	8.25	16.00
		Nos. 115-125 (11)	71.40	21.15

Coil Stamps

Unless part of a booklet pane any stamp perforated only horizontally or vertically is a coil stamp.

1920-26 — Unwmk. — Perf. 10

126	A16	5o green	4.00	1.00
a.		Booklet pane of 10	80.00	
127	A16	10o green ('21)	11.50	3.50
a.		Booklet pane of 10	225.00	
128	A16	10o violet ('25)	6.50	.85
a.		Booklet pane of 10	180.00	
129	A16	30o brown	32.50	3.25

Wmk. 181

130	A16	5o green	11.50	26.00
131	A16	10o green ('21)	45.00	90.00
a.		Booklet pane of 10	425.00	

Perf. 13 Vertically

Unwmk.

132	A16	5o green ('25)	16.00	8.50
133	A16	5o cop red ('21)	425.00	140.00
134	A16	10o violet ('26)	25.00	32.50

Wmk. 181

135	A16	5o green ('25)	1.60	6.50
136	A16	5o copper red ('22)	1.90	5.50
137	A16	10o green ('24)	9.00	35.00
138	A16	10o violet ('25)	8.00	22.50
		Nos. 126-138 (13)	597.50	375.10

The paper used for the earlier printings of types A16, A17, A18, A18a and A20 is usually tinted by the color of the stamp. Printings of 1934 and later are on white paper in slightly different shades.

King Gustaf V — A17

1920-21 — Unwmk. — Perf. 10 Vertically

139	A17	10o rose	32.50	.35
140	A17	15o claret	.30	.45
141	A17	20o blue	35.00	.50

Perf. 10

142	A17	10o rose	12.50	5.50
143	A17	20o blue ('21)	29.00	9.00
a.		Booklet pane of 10	550.00	
		Nos. 139-143 (5)	109.30	15.80

Wmk. 181

144	A17	20o blue	4,000.	

Crown and Post Horn —
A18a

A18

See note after No. 138 regarding paper. There are 2 types of the 35, 40, 45 and 60o.

1920-34 — Unwmk. — Perf. 10 Vert.

145	A18	35o yellow ('22)	42.50	.75
146	A18	40o olive green	32.50	.75
147	A18	45o brown ('22)	1.25	.55
148	A18	60o claret	19.00	.90
149	A18	70o red brn ('22)	.60	2.50
150	A18	80o deep green	.40	.25
151	A18	85o myrtle grn ('29)	3.75	.45
152	A18	90o lt blue ('25)	55.00	.30
153	A18a	1kr dp org ('21)	7.75	.25
154	A18	110o ultra	.50	.40
155	A18	115o red brn ('29)	9.00	.45
156	A18	120o gray blk ('25)	62.50	.60
157	A18	120o lil rose ('33)	14.00	.60
158	A18	140o gray black	.90	.30
159	A18	145o brt grn ('30)	8.50	.55

Wmk. 181

160	A18	35o yellow ('23)	60.00	7.50
161	A18	60o red violet	95.00	110.00
162	A18	80o blue green	8.25	15.00
163	A18	110o ultra	3.50	3.75
		Nos. 145-163 (19)	424.90	145.25

The value for #147 is for the 2nd type, issued in 1925.

Gustavus
Adolphus
A19

King Gustaf V
A20

Perf. 10 Vertically

1920, July 28 — Unwmk.

164	A19	20o deep blue	2.25	.40

Wmk. 181

165	A19	20o blue	150.00	32.50

Unwmk.

Perf. 10

166	A19	20o blue	6.25	2.25
a.		Booklet pane of 10	130.00	
		Nos. 164-166 (3)	158.50	35.15

Tercentenary of Swedish post which first ran between Stockholm and Hamburg.

1921-36 — Unwmk. — Perf. 10 Vert.

See note after No. 138 regarding paper. There are two types each of the 15o rose and 40o olive green.

167	A20	15o violet ('22)	17.00	.30
168	A20	15o rose ('28)	5.50	.45
169	A20	15o brown ('36)	4.75	.45
170	A20	20o violet	.20	.20
171	A20	20o rose ('22)	22.50	.50
172	A20	20o orange ('25)	.20	.35
174	A20	25o rose red ('22)	.55	1.50
175	A20	25o dk bl ('25)	17.00	.20
176	A20	25o ultra ('34)	17.00	.65
177	A20	25o yel org ('36)	32.50	.45
178	A20	30o blue ('23)	19.00	.45
179	A20	30o brown ('25)	22.50	.35
180	A20	30o lt ultra ('36)	6.00	.70
181	A20	35o red vio ('30)	24.00	.45
182	A20	40o blue	.45	.70
183	A20	40o ol grn ('29)	45.00	1.25
184	A20	45o brown ('29)	5.00	.90
185	A20	50o gray	1.75	1.00

186	A20	85o myrtle grn ('25)	17.00	1.75
187	A20	115o brn red ('25)	11.00	1.75
188	A20	145o apple grn ('25)	8.25	1.75
		Nos. 167-188 (21)	277.15	16.10

Wmk. 181

189	A20	15o violet ('22)	2,650.	850.00
189A	A20	20o violet	4,500.	

1922-36 — Unwmk. — Perf. 10

190	A20	15o violet	17.50	.70
a.		Booklet pane of 10	400.00	
191	A20	15o rose red ('25)	22.50	.85
a.		Booklet pane of 10	600.00	
192	A20	15o brown ('36)	5.75	1.25
a.		Booklet pane of 10	175.00	
193	A20	20o violet ('22)	.50	1.50
a.		Booklet pane of 10	10.00	
		Nos. 190-193 (4)	46.25	4.30

Gustavus Vasa — A21

1921, June — Perf. 10 Vertically

194	A21	20o violet	12.50	25.00
195	A21	110o ultra	55.00	7.50
196	A21	140o gray black	30.00	7.50
		Nos. 194-196 (3)	97.50	40.00

400th anniversary of Gustavus Vasa's war of independence from the Danes.

Universal Postal Union Congress

Composite
View of
Stockholm's
Skyline
A22

King
Gustaf V — A23

1924, July 4 — Unwmk. — Perf. 10

197	A22	5o red brown	1.60	3.25
198	A22	10o green	1.60	3.25
199	A22	15o dk violet	1.60	2.50
200	A22	20o rose red	12.50	17.00
201	A22	25o dp orange	15.00	21.00
202	A22	30o deep blue	14.50	21.00
a.		30o greenish blue	87.50	125.00
203	A22	35o black	19.00	26.00
204	A22	40o olive green	29.00	32.50
205	A22	45o deep brown	32.50	32.50
206	A22	50o gray	32.50	32.50
207	A22	60o violet brn	47.50	55.00
208	A22	80o myrtle grn	35.00	35.00
209	A23	1k green	57.50	87.50
210	A23	2k rose red	140.00	250.00
211	A23	5k deep blue	300.00	450.00

Wmk. 181

212	A22	10o green	26.00	55.00
		Nos. 197-212 (16)	765.80	1,124.
		Set, never hinged	1,200.	

Postrider Watching Airplane A24

Carrier Pigeon and Globe — A25

1924, Aug. 16   **Engr.**   **Unwmk.**

213	A24	5o red brown	2.75	4.50
214	A24	10o green	2.75	5.75
215	A24	15o dk violet	3.00	3.00
216	A24	20o rose red	21.00	32.50
217	A24	25o deep orange	26.00	32.50
218	A24	30o deep blue	26.00	32.50
a.		30o greenish blue	90.00	52.50
219	A24	35o black	32.50	47.50
220	A24	40o olive green	32.50	32.50
221	A24	45o deep brown	37.50	35.00
222	A24	50o gray	50.00	62.50
223	A24	60o violet brown	50.00	77.50
224	A24	80o myrtle green	37.50	35.00
225	A25	1k green	75.00	87.50
226	A25	2k rose red	140.00	75.00
227	A25	5k deep blue	275.00	210.00

Wmk. 181

228	A24	10o green	22.50	60.00
		Nos. 213-228 (16)	834.00	833.25
		Set, never hinged	1,450.	

Universal Postal Union issue.

Royal Palace at Stockholm A26

1931, Nov. 26   **Unwmk.**   **Perf. 10**

229	A26	5k dark green	110.00	12.50
		Never hinged	300.00	
a.		Booklet pane of 10	2,500.	

Death of Gustavus Adolphus — A27

1932, Nov. 1

230	A27	10o dark violet	2.50	5.50
a.		Booklet pane of 10	40.00	
231	A27	15o dark red	4.50	1.90
a.		Booklet pane of 10	110.00	

Perf. 10 Vertically

232	A27	10o dark violet	1.90	.20
233	A27	15o dark red	2.50	.20
234	A27	25o dark red	6.00	.95
235	A27	90o dark green	22.50	2.25
		Nos. 230-235 (6)	39.90	11.00
		Set, never hinged	80.00	

300th anniv. of the death of King Gustavus Adolphus II who was killed on the battlefield of Lützen, Nov. 6, 1632.

Catching Sunlight in Bowl — A28

1933, Dec. 6   **Perf. 10**

236	A28	5o green	2.50	1.75
a.		Booklet pane of 10	60.00	

There are two types of No. 236.

Perf. 10 Vertically

237	A28	5o green	2.50	.30

Perf. 13 Vertically

238	A28	5o green	3.50	7.25
		Nos. 236-238 (3)	8.50	9.30
		Set, never hinged	17.50	

Swedish Postal Savings Bank, 50th anniv.

The Old Law Courts — A29

The "Four Estates" and Arms of Engelbrekt A34

Designs: 10o, Stock exchange. 15o, Parish church (Storkyrkan). 25o, House of the Nobility. 35o, House of Parliament.

1935, Jan. 10   **Perf. 10**

239	A29	5o green	2.25	1.40
a.		Booklet pane of 10	55.00	
240	A29	10o dull violet	4.25	5.75
a.		Booklet pane of 10	60.00	
241	A29	15o carmine	4.75	1.10
a.		Booklet pane of 10	125.00	

Perf. 10 Vertically

242	A29	5o green	1.25	.20
243	A29	10o dull violet	5.75	.20
244	A29	15o carmine	2.25	.20
245	A29	25o ultra	6.00	.60
246	A29	35o deep claret	12.00	2.25
247	A34	60o deep claret	17.50	2.50
		Nos. 239-247 (9)	56.00	14.20
		Set, never hinged	110.00	

500th anniv. of the Swedish Parliament.

Chancellor Axel Oxenstierna A35

Post Runner — A36

Mounted Courier — A37

Old Sailing Packet — A38

Mail Paddle Steamship A39

Mail Coach — A40

1855 Stamp Model — A41

Mail Train — A42

Postmaster General A. W. Roos — A43

Mail Truck and Trailer — A44

Modern Swedish Liner — A45

Junkers Plane with Pontoons — A46

1936, Feb. 20   **Engr.**   **Perf. 10**

248	A35	5o green	1.75	.85
a.		Booklet pane of 18	72.50	
249	A36	10o dk violet	2.10	2.75
a.		Booklet pane of 18	95.00	
250	A37	15o dk carmine	3.00	.55
a.		Booklet pane of 18	250.00	

Perf. 10 Vertically

251	A35	5o green	1.75	.20
252	A36	10o dk violet	1.75	.20
253	A37	15o dk carmine	3.25	.20
254	A38	20o lt blue	8.25	5.00
255	A39	25o lt ultra	5.25	.50
256	A40	30o yellow brn	17.50	3.25
257	A41	35o plum	5.50	1.25
258	A42	40o olive grn	5.75	2.75
259	A43	45o myrtle grn	7.75	1.50
260	A44	50o gray	22.50	2.75
261	A45	60o maroon	29.00	.70
262	A46	1k deep blue	8.25	8.50
		Nos. 248-262 (15)	123.35	30.95
		Set, never hinged	300.00	

300th anniv. of the Swedish Postal Service. See Nos. 946-950, B55-B56.

Airplane over Bromma Airport A47

Emanuel Swedenborg — A48

1936, May 23   **Perf. 10 Vert.**

263	A47	50o ultra	5.50	8.50
		Never hinged	10.50	

Opening of Bromma Airport near Stockholm.

Swedish Booklets

Before 1940, booklets were hand-made and usually held two panes of 10 stamps (2x5). About every third booklet contained one row of stamps with straight edges at right or left side. Setenant pairs may be obtained with one stamp perforated on 4 sides and one perforated on 3 sides.

Starting in 1940, booklet stamps have one or more straight edges.

1938, Jan. 29   **Perf. 12½**

264	A48	10o violet	1.50	.35
a.		Perf. on 3 sides	10.00	3.00
		Never hinged	17.00	
b.		Booklet pane of 10	30.00	

Perf. 12½ Vertically

266	A48	10o violet	1.10	.20
267	A48	100o green	3.75	1.95
		Nos. 264-267 (3)	6.35	
		Set, never hinged	12.00	

250th anniv. of the birth of Swedenborg, scientist, philosopher and religious writer.

Johann Printz and Indian Chief — A49

"Kalmar Nyckel" Sailing from Gothenburg A50

Symbolizing the Settlement of New Sweden — A51

Holy Trinity Church, Wilmington, Del. — A52

Queen Christina — A53

1938, Apr. 8   **Perf. 12½ Vert.**

268	A49	5o green	.65	.20
269	A50	15o brown	.90	.20
270	A51	20o red	1.60	.70
271	A52	30o ultra	5.25	.85
272	A53	60o brown lake	8.25	.35

Perf. 12½

273	A49	5o green	1.60	1.00
a.		Perf. on 3 sides	10.00	7.50
		Never hinged	17.00	
b.		Booklet pane of 18	67.50	
274	A50	15o brown	2.75	.70
a.		Perf. on 3 sides	17.00	4.75
		Never hinged	26.00	
b.		Booklet pane of 18	115.00	
		Nos. 268-274 (7)	21.00	4.00
		Set, never hinged	32.50	

Tercentenary of the Swedish settlement at Wilmington, Del. See No. B54.

King Gustaf V — A54

1938, June 16   **Perf. 12½ Vert.**

275	A54	5o green	.65	.20
276	A54	15(o) brown	.75	.20
277	A54	30(o) ultra	17.50	.75

Perf. 12½

278 A54	5o green	1.40	.25
a.	Perf. on 3 sides	13.00	5.50
	Never hinged	22.50	
b.	Booklet pane of 10	45.00	
279 A54	15o brown	1.90	.30
a.	Perf. on 3 sides	20.00	1.40
	Never hinged	32.50	
b.	Booklet pane of 10	65.00	
	Nos. 275-279 (5)	22.20	1.70
	Set, never hinged	29.00	

80th birthday of King Gustaf V.

King Gustaf V — A55

Three Crowns — A56

1939   Perf. 12½ Vertically

280 A55	10o violet	.65	.20
281 A55	20o carmine	2.25	.60
282 A56	60o lake	.65	.20
283 A56	85o dk green	.30	.20
284 A56	90o peacock blue	.30	.20
285 A56	1k orange	.30	.20
286 A56	1.15k henna brn	.30	.20
287 A56	1.20k brt rose vio	1.60	.20
288 A56	1.45k lt yel grn	2.25	.80

Perf. 12½

289 A55	10o violet	1.60	3.00
a.	Perf. on 3 sides	47.50	65.00
	Never hinged	77.50	
b.	Bklt. pane of 10, perf. on 4 sides	30.00	
	Nos. 280-289 (10)	10.20	5.80
	Set, never hinged	17.50	

See Nos. 394-398, 416-417, 425-426, 431, 439-441, 473, 588-591, 656-664.

Per Henrik Ling — A57

1939, Feb. 25   Perf. 12½ Vert.

290 A57	5o green	.20	.20
291 A57	25(o) brown	1.10	.40

Perf. 12½

292 A57	5o green	.90	.40
a.	Perf. on 3 sides	14.00	3.75
	Never hinged	29.00	
b.	Booklet pane of 10	37.50	
	Nos. 290-292 (3)	2.20	1.00
	Set, never hinged	3.50	

Centenary of the death of P. H. Ling, father of Swedish gymnastics.

J. J. Berzelius A58

Carl von Linné A59

Perf. 12½ Vertically

1939, June 2   Engr.

293 A58	10o violet	3.75	.30
294 A59	15o fawn	.20	.20
295 A58	30o ultra	11.50	.45
296 A59	50o gray	13.00	1.00

Perf. 12½

297 A58	10o violet	2.10	.65
a.	Perf. on 3 sides	72.50	19.00
	Never hinged	125.00	
b.	Booklet pane of 10	65.00	
298 A59	15o fawn	3.00	.30
a.	Perf. on 3 sides	11.50	.45
	Never hinged	19.00	
b.	Booklet pane of 10	100.00	
c.	As "a," bklt. pane of 20	450.00	
	Nos. 293-298 (6)	33.55	2.90
	Set, never hinged	60.00	

200th anniv. of the founding of the Royal Academy of Science at Stockholm.

King Gustaf V — A60

Type A55 Re-engraved

1939-46   Perf. 12½

299 A60	5o dp green ('46)	.30	.20
b.	Perf. on 3 sides ('41)	.40	.20
	Never hinged	.50	
c.	As "b," bklt. pane of 20	12.00	
300 A60	10(o) violet ('46)	.20	.20
a.	Bklt. pane of 10, perf. on 4 sides	55.00	
	Never hinged	2.25	
c.	Perf. on 3 sides	2.25	.20
i.	As "c," booklet pane of 20	50.00	
300D A60	15(o) chestnut ('46)	.20	.20
f.	Perf. on 3 sides ('45)	.40	.20
	Never hinged	.65	
j.	As "f," booklet pane of 20	7.75	
300G A60	20(o) red ('42)	.30	.20
h.	Booklet pane of 20	6.50	
	Nos. 299-300G (4)	1.00	.80
	Set, never hinged	1.40	

No. 300 differs slightly from the original due to deeper engraving. No. 300G was issued only in booklets; all copies have one straight edge.

Nos. 299, 300, 300D exist in booklet panes of 20 made from sheets of stamps. These can be collected as booklets.

1940-42   Perf. 12½ Vertically

301 A60	5o dp green ('41)	.25	.20
302 A60	10(o) violet	.20	.20
302A A60	15(o) chestnut ('42)	.20	.20
303 A60	20(o) red	.20	.20
304 A60	25(o) orange	1.00	.20
305 A60	30(o) ultra	.40	.20
306 A60	35(o) red vio ('41)	.60	.20
307 A60	40(o) olive grn	.60	.20
308 A60	45(o) dk brown	.60	.20
309 A60	50(o) gray blk ('41)	3.25	.20
	Nos. 301-309 (10)	7.30	2.00
	Set, never hinged	11.50	

Numerals measure 4½mm high. Less shading around head gives a lighter effect. Horizontal lines only as background for "SVERIGE."
See Nos. 391-393, 399.

Carl Michael Bellman A61

Tobias Sergel A62

1940, Feb. 4   Engr.   Perf. 12½ Vert.

310 A61	5o green	.25	.25
311 A61	35(o) rose red	1.00	.40

Perf. 12½

312 A61	5o green	1.25	.60
a.	Perf. on 3 sides	10.00	.75
	Never hinged	21.00	
b.	Booklet pane of 10	50.00	
c.	As "a," bklt. pane of 20	425.00	
	Nos. 310-312 (3)	2.50	1.25
	Set, never hinged	3.00	

Bellman (1740-95), lyric poet.

1940, Sept. 5   Perf. 12½ on 3 Sides

313 A62	15o lt brown	7.50	.25
a.	Booklet pane of 20	275.00	

Perf. 12½ Vertically

314 A62	15o lt brown	3.25	.20
315 A62	50o gray black	17.00	1.20
	Nos. 313-315 (3)	27.75	1.65
	Set, never hinged	47.50	

Bicentenary of birth of Johan Tobias von Sergel (1740-1814), sculptor.

Reformers Presenting Bible to Gustavus Vasa A63

View of Skansen A64

1941, May 11   Perf. 12½ on 3 Sides

316 A63	15o brown	2.75	.45
a.	Booklet pane of 18	90.00	

Perf. 12½ Vertically

317 A63	15o brown	.30	.20
318 A63	90o ultra	19.00	.95
	Nos. 316-318 (3)	22.05	1.60
	Set, never hinged	35.00	

400th anniv. of the 1st authorized version of the Bible in Swedish.

1941, June 18   Perf. 12½ on 3 Sides

319 A64	10o violet	2.50	.65
a.	Booklet pane of 20	85.00	

Perf. 12½ Vertically

320 A64	10o violet	3.00	.20
321 A64	60o red lilac	8.00	.60
	Nos. 319-321 (3)	13.50	1.45
	Set, never hinged	25.00	

50th anniv. of Skansen, an open air extension of the Nordic Museum.

Royal Palace at Stockholm A65

Artur Hazelius A66

1941   Perf. 12½ on 3 Sides

322 A65	5k blue	1.50	.20
	Never hinged	2.50	
a.	Perf. on 4 sides	29.00	1.00
	Never hinged	57.50	
b.	Bklt. pane of 20, perf. 3 sides	50.00	
c.	Bklt. pane of 10, perf. 4 sides	575.00	

For coil stamp see No. 537.

1941, Aug. 30   Perf. 12½ on 3 Sides

323 A66	5o lt green	2.50	.55
a.	Booklet pane of 20	100.00	

Perf. 12½ Vertically

324 A66	5o lt green	.20	.20
325 A66	1k lt orange	7.00	4.00
	Nos. 323-325 (3)	9.70	4.75
	Set, never hinged	22.50	

Issued to honor Artur Hazelius, founder of Skansen, Nordic museum.

St. Bridget of Sweden — A67

Perf. 12½ on 3 Sides

1941, Oct. 7   Engr.

326 A67	15o deep brown	1.90	.40
a.	Booklet pane of 18	60.00	

Perf. 12½ Horiz.

327 A67	15o deep brown	.20	.20
328 A67	1.20k red vio	21.00	10.50
	Nos. 326-328 (3)	23.10	11.10
	Set, never hinged	47.50	

King Gustavus III — A68

K. G. Tessin, Architect — A69

1942, June 29   Perf. 12½ on 3 Sides

329 A68	20o red	1.25	.45
a.	Booklet pane of 20	45.00	

Perf. 12½ Vertically

330 A68	20o red	.60	.20
331 A69	40o olive green	14.00	1.25
	Nos. 329-331 (3)	15.85	1.90
	Set, never hinged	32.50	

Sesquicentennial of the Swedish National Museum, Stockholm.

Torsten Rudenschold and Nils Mansson — A70

1942, July 1   Perf. 12½ Horiz.

332 A70	10o magenta	.25	.40
a.	Booklet pane of 10	3.50	

Perf. 12½ Vertically

333 A70	10o magenta	.25	.35
334 A70	90o light blue	2.50	6.00
	Nos. 332-334 (3)	3.00	6.75
	Set, never hinged	5.00	

Swedish Public School System, 100th anniv.

Carl Wilhelm Scheele A71

King Gustaf V A72

1942, Dec. 9   Perf. 12½ on 3 Sides

335 A71	5o green	1.50	1.00
a.	Booklet pane of 20	55.00	

Perf. 12½ Vertically

336 A71	5o green	.20	.20
337 A71	60o deep magenta	7.00	.60
	Nos. 335-337 (3)	8.70	1.80
	Set, never hinged	15.00	

200th anniv. of the birth of Carl Wilhelm Scheele, chemist.

Perf. 12½ Horizontally

1943, June 16
338 A72 20o red .60 .45
339 A72 30o ultra .90 2.50
340 A72 60o brt red vio 1.10 3.25

Perf. 12½ on 3 Sides
341 A72 20o red 4.50 1.10
  a. Booklet pane of 20 160.00
    Nos. 338-341 (4) 7.10 7.30
    Set, never hinged 12.00

85th birthday of King Gustaf V, June 16.

Rifle
Federation
Emblem
A73

Oscar
Montelius
A74

1943, July 22   Perf. 12½ Vert.
342 A73 10o rose violet .20 .20
343 A73 90o dp ultra 3.75 .45

Perf. 12½ on 3 Sides
344 A73 10o rose violet .40 .40
  a. Booklet pane of 20 12.50
    Nos. 342-344 (3) 4.35 1.05
    Set, never hinged 8.00

50th anniversary of the Swedish Voluntary Rifle Associations.

1943, Sept. 9   Engr.   Perf. 12½ Vert.
345 A74 5o green .20 .20
346 A74 1.20k brt red vio 6.00 2.50

Perf. 12½ on 3 Sides
347 A74 5o green .55 .40
  a. Booklet pane of 20 19.00
    Nos. 345-347 (3) 6.75 3.10
    Set, never hinged 11.50

Montelius (1843-1921), archaeologist.

Johan Mansson's
Chart of Baltic,
1644 — A75

Perf. 12½ on 3 Sides
1944, Apr. 15   Engr.   Unwmk.
348 A75 5o green .60 .80
  a. Booklet pane of 20 25.00

Perf. 12½ Vertically
349 A75 5o green .20 .20
350 A75 60o lake 4.25 .80
    Nos. 348-350 (3) 5.05 1.80
    Set, never hinged 10.00

1st Swedish Marine Chart, tercentenary.

"The Lion of
Smaland"
A76

Clas Fleming
A77

30o, "Kung Karl." 40o, "Gustaf V." 90o, Stern of "Amphion," Flagship of Gustavus III.

1944, Oct. 13   Perf. 12½ Vert.
351 A76 10o purple .35 .35
352 A77 20o red .30 .20
353 A76 30o blue .50 .80
354 A76 40o olive green .60 1.25
355 A76 90o gray black 6.50 2.25

Perf. 12½ on 3 Sides
356 A76 10o purple .60 2.00
  a. Booklet pane of 20 24.00
357 A77 20o red 2.25 .35
  a. Booklet pane of 20 90.00
    Nos. 351-357 (7) 11.10 7.20
    Set, never hinged 21.00

Issued to honor the Swedish Fleet and mark the tercentenary of the Swedish naval victory at Femern, 1644.

See Nos. B53, B57-B58.

> **Catalogue values for unused stamps in this section, from this point to the end of the section, are for Never Hinged items.**

Red
Cross — A81

Torch and
Quill
Pen — A82

1945, Feb. 27   Perf. 12½ Vert.
358 A81 20o red .60 .20

Perf. 12½ on 3 Sides
359 A81 20o red 3.00 .40
  a. Booklet pane of 20 65.00

Swedish Red Cross Society, 80th anniv.

1945, May 29   Perf. 12½ Vert.
360 A82 5o green .20 .20
361 A82 60o carmine rose 6.00 .45

Perf. 12½ on 3 Sides
362 A82 5o green .35 .45
  a. Booklet pane of 20 7.75
    Nos. 360-362 (3) 6.55 1.10

Tercentenary of Swedish press.

Rydberg
A83

Oak Tree
A84

1945, Sept. 21   Perf. 12½ Vert.
363 A83 20o red .35 .20
364 A83 90o blue 7.00 .45

Perf. 12½ on 3 Sides
365 A83 20o red 1.50 .45
  a. Booklet pane of 20 32.50
    Nos. 363-365 (3) 8.85 1.10

Viktor Rydberg (1828-95), author.

1945, Oct. 27   Perf. 12½ Vert.
366 A84 10o violet .25 .35
367 A84 40o olive 1.60 1.25

Perf. 12½ on 3 Sides
368 A84 10o violet .40 .70
  a. Booklet pane of 20 10.00
    Nos. 366-368 (3) 2.25 2.30

125th anniv. of the Savings Bank movement.

Angel and Lund
Cathedral
A85

View of Lund
Cathedral
A86

Perf. 12½ Vertically
1946, May 28   Unwmk.
369 A85 15o orange brn .70 .55
370 A86 20o red .30 .20
371 A85 90o ultra 8.25 .85

Perf. 12½ on 3 Sides
372 A85 15o orange brn .95 1.10
  a. Booklet pane of 20 19.00
373 A86 20o red 2.25 .45
  a. Booklet pane of 20 45.00
    Nos. 369-373 (5) 12.45 3.15

Lund Cathedral, 800th anniversary.

Mare and
Colt — A87

Esaias
Tegner — A88

1946, June 8   Perf. 12½ Vert.
374 A87 5o green .20 .20
375 A87 60o carmine rose 7.25 .40

Perf. 12½ on 3 Sides
376 A87 5o green .30 .45
  a. Booklet pane of 20 6.50
    Nos. 374-376 (3) 7.75 1.05

Centenary of Swedish agricultural shows.

Perf. 12½ Vertically
1946, Nov. 2   Engr.   Unwmk.
377 A88 10o deep violet .20 .20
378 A88 40o dk olive grn 1.40 .45

Perf. 12½ on 3 Sides
379 A88 10o dp violet .30 .20
  a. Booklet pane of 20 6.00
    Nos. 377-379 (3) 1.90 .85

Esaias Tegner (1782-1846), poet.

Nobel — A89

Geijer — A90

1946, Dec. 10   Perf. 12½ Vert.
380 A89 20o red .80 .20
381 A89 30o ultra 2.25 .60

Perf. 12½ on 3 Sides
382 A89 20o red 1.90 .55
  a. Booklet pane of 20 40.00
    Nos. 380-382 (3) 4.95 1.35

50th anniversary of the death of Alfred Nobel, inventor and philanthropist.

1947, Apr. 23   Perf. 12½ Vert.
383 A90 5o dk yellow grn .25 .20
384 A90 90o ultra 4.25 .25

Perf. 12½ on 3 Sides
385 A90 5o dk yellow grn .30 .45
  a. Booklet pane of 20 7.00
    Nos. 383-385 (3) 4.80 .90

Centenary of the death of Erik Gustaf Geijer, historian, philosopher and poet.

King Gustaf
V — A91

1947, Dec. 8   Engr.   Perf. 12½ Horiz.
386 A91 10o deep violet .20 .20
387 A91 20o red .20 .20
388 A91 60o red violet 1.40 1.40

Perf. 12½ on 3 Sides
389 A91 10o deep violet .20 .30
  a. Booklet pane of 20 4.00
390 A91 20o red .40 .40
  a. Booklet pane of 20 8.00
    Nos. 386-390 (5) 2.40 2.50

40th anniv. of the reign of King Gustaf V.

King and 3-Crown Types of 1939
1948   Unwmk.   Perf. 12½ Vertically
391 A60 5o orange .25 .20
392 A60 10o green .30 .20
393 A60 25o violet 1.50 .20
394 A56 55o orange brown 1.40 .20
395 A56 80o olive green .80 .20
396 A56 1.10k violet 7.00 .20
397 A56 1.40k dk blue green .80 .20
398 A56 1.75k brt grnsh blue 12.50 6.75

Perf. 12½ on 3 Sides
399 A60 10o green .25 .20
  a. Booklet pane of 20 6.00
    Nos. 391-399 (9) 24.80 8.35

Plowman,
Early and
Modern
Buildings
A92

August
Strindberg
A93

1948, Apr. 26   Perf. 12½ Vert.
400 A92 15o orange brown .25 .20
401 A92 30o ultra .50 .55
402 A92 1k orange 1.50 1.25

Perf. 12½ on 3 Sides
403 A92 15o orange brown .40 .50
  a. Booklet pane of 20 8.50
    Nos. 400-403 (4) 2.65 2.50

Centenary of the Swedish pioneers' settlement in the United States.

1949, Jan. 22   Perf. 12½ Vert.
404 A93 20o red .45 .20
405 A93 30o blue .80 .75
406 A93 80o olive green 2.75 .45

Perf. 12½ on 3 Sides
407 A93 20o red .80 .35
  a. Booklet pane of 20 16.00
    Nos. 404-407 (4) 4.80 1.75

Birth centenary of August Strindberg (1849-1912), author and playwright.

Girl and Boy
Gymnasts — A94

Perf. 12½ Horiz.
1949, July 27   Engr.
408 A94 5o ultra .30 .45
409 A94 15o brown .35 .20

Perf. 12½ on 3 Sides
410 A94 15o brown .45 .65
  a. Booklet pane of 20 9.00
    Nos. 408-410 (3) 1.10 1.30

2nd Lingiad or World Gymnastics Festival, Stockholm, July-August 1949.

A95

Symbols of
UPU — A96

1949, Oct. 9   Perf. 12½ Vert.
411 A95 10o green .25 .20
412 A95 20o red .30 .20

Perf. 12½ Horizontally
413 A96 30o lt blue .40 .65

Perf. 12½ on 3 sides
414 A95 10o green .20 .20
  a. Booklet pane of 20 3.50
415 A95 20o red .20 .20
  a. Booklet pane of 20 4.00
    Nos. 411-415 (5) 1.35 1.45

75th anniv. of the formation of the UPU.

Three-Crown Type of 1939
Perf. 12½ Vertically
1949, Nov. 11   Unwmk.
416 A56 65o lt yellow grn .75 .30
417 A56 70o peacock blue 4.00 1.25

Gustaf VI
Adolf (Letters
in color)
A97

Christopher
Polhem
A98

1951, June 6   *Perf. 12½ Vert.*
Without Imprint
418 A97 10o dull green   .25   .20
419 A97 15o chestnut brown   .35   .20
420 A97 20o carmine rose   .35   .20
421 A97 25o gray   .65   .20
422 A97 30o ultra   .45   .20

Perf. 12½ on 3 sides
423 A97 10o dull green   .40   .20
  a.   Booklet pane of 20   8.00
424 A97 25o gray   .50   .25
  a.   Booklet pane of 20   12.00
       Nos. 418-424 (7)   2.95 1.45

See Nos. 435-438, 442-443, 456-461, 502, 505-509, 515-517.

Three-Crown Type of 1939
1951, June 1   *Perf. 12½ Vert.*
425 A56 85o orange brown   5.75 1.60
426 A56 1.70k red   1.25   .20

1951, Aug. 30   *Perf. 12½ Vert.*
427 A98 20o gray   1.40   .20
428 A98 45o brown   .55   .40

Perf. 12½ on 3 sides
429 A98 20o gray   .45   .30
  a.   Booklet pane of 20   9.00
       Nos. 427-429 (3)   2.40   .90

200th anniversary of the death of Christopher Polhem, engineer and technician.

Numeral
(Lettering in
color)
A99

Olaus Petri
Preaching
A100

Type A99 and 3-Crown Type of 1939
1951, Nov.   Engr.   *Perf. 12½ Vert.*
430 A99 5o rose carmine   .25   .20
431 A56 1.50k red violet   1.60 1.25

For other stamps similar to type A99, see type A115a, Nos. 503-504, 513-514, 570, 580, 666-667.

1952, Apr. 19   *Perf. 12½ Horiz.*
432 A100 25o gray black   .45   .20
433 A100 1.40k brown   2.75   .80

Perf. 12½ on 3 sides
434 A100 25o gray black   2.00 2.60
  a.   Booklet pane of 20   50.00
       Nos. 432-434 (3)   5.20 3.60

Olaus Petri (1493-1552), Lutheran clergyman, historian and Bible translator.

King and 3-Crown Types of 1951 and 1939
1952   *Perf. 12½ Vertically*
Without Imprint
435 A97 20o gray   .30   .20
436 A97 25o car rose   1.25   .20
437 A97 30o dk brown   .50   .40
438 A97 40o blue   1.00   .40
439 A56 50o gray   1.75   .20
440 A56 75o orange brown   2.75   .80
441 A56 2k red violet   .90   .20

Perf. 12½ on 3 sides
442 A97 20o gray   .55   .60
  a.   Booklet pane of 20   15.00
443 A97 25o carmine rose   1.25   .40
  a.   Booklet pane of 20   27.50
       Nos. 435-443 (9)   10.25 3.40

Ski Jump
A101

Ice Hockey
A102

40o, Woman throwing slingball. 1.40kr, Wrestlers.

Perf. 12½ Vert. (V), Horiz. (H)
1953, May 27
444 A101 10o green (V)   .50   .20
445 A102 15o brown (H)   .75 1.10
446 A102 40o deep blue (H)   1.50 1.60
447 A101 1.40k red violet (V)   4.50 1.25

Perf. 12½ on 3 sides
448 A101 10o green   .75 1.10
  a.   Booklet pane of 20   17.50
       Nos. 444-448 (5)   8.00 5.25

50th anniv. of Swedish Athletic Association.

Old Stockholm
A103

Original and
Present Seals of
Stockholm
A104

1953, June 17   *Perf. 12½ Vert.*
449 A103 25o blue   .40   .20
450 A104 1.70k red   2.75   .75

Perf. 12½ on 3 sides
451 A103 25o blue   .80   .30
  a.   Booklet pane of 20   17.50
       Nos. 449-451 (3)   3.95 1.25

700th anniv. of the founding of Stockholm.

"Telephone" — A105

1953, Nov. 2   *Perf. 12½ Horiz.*
452 A105 25o shown   .30   .20
453 A105 40o "Radio"   1.00 1.60
454 A105 60o "Telegraph"   2.50 2.75

Perf. 12½ on 3 sides
455 A105 25o shown   .85   .50
  a.   Booklet pane of 20   20.00
       Nos. 452-455 (4)   4.65 5.05

Centenary of the foundation of the Swedish Telegraph Service.

King Type of 1951
1954   *Perf. 12½ Vertically*
Without Imprint
456 A97 10o dark brown   .20   .20
457 A97 25o ultra   .25   .20
458 A97 30o red   9.00   .20
459 A97 40o olive green   .60   .20

Perf. 12½ on 3 sides
460 A97 10o dark brown   .25   .20
  a.   Booklet pane of 10   9.00
  b.   Booklet pane of 20   7.50
461 A97 25o ultra   .25   .20
  a.   Booklet pane of 4   10.00 11.00
  b.   Booklet pane of 8   100.00   —
  c.   Booklet pane of 20   10.00   —
       Nos. 456-461 (6)   10.55 1.20

The booklet pane of 4 contains two copies of No. 461 which are perforated on two adjoining sides.

Skier
A106

Anna Maria
Lenngren
A107

1954, Feb. 13   *Perf. 12½ Vert.*
462 A106 20o shown   .50   .45
463 A106 1k Girl skier   8.50 1.25

Perf. 12½ on 3 sides
464 A106 20o shown   1.25 1.90
  a.   Booklet pane of 20   35.00
       Nos. 462-464 (3)   10.25 3.60

World Ski Championship Matches, 1954.

1954, June 18   *Perf. 12½ Horiz.*
465 A107 20o gray   .30   .30
466 A107 65o dark brown   5.50 3.75

Perf. 12½ on 3 sides
467 A107 20o gray   1.25 1.90
  a.   Booklet pane of 20   35.00
       Nos. 465-467 (3)   7.05 5.95

200th anniversary of the birth of Anna Maria Lenngren, author.

Rock Carvings
A108

Coat of Arms
A109

1954, Nov. 8   *Perf. 12½ Vert.*
468 A108 50o gray   .30   .20
469 A108 60o dp carmine   .50   .20
470 A108 65o dk olive grn   1.25   .20
471 A108 75o dk brown   2.00   .20
472 A108 90o dk blue   .60   .20
       Nos. 468-472 (5)   4.65 1.00

See Nos. 510-512, 655.

Three-Crown Type of 1939
1954, Dec. 10   *Perf. 12½ Vert.*
473 A56 2.10k dp ultra   7.50   .20

1955, May 16   *Perf. 12½ Vert.*
474 A109 25o blue   .20   .20
475 A109 40o green   1.25   .35

Perf. 12½ on 3 sides
476 A109 25o blue   .20   .20
  a.   Booklet pane of 4   9.00 8.50
  b.   Booklet pane of 20   4.00   —
       Nos. 474-476 (3)   1.65   .75

Centenary of Sweden's 1st postage stamps. The booklet pane of 4 contains two copies of No. 476 which are perforated on two adjoining sides.

Crown and
Flag — A110

A111

Perf. 12½
1955, June 6   Unwmk.   Litho.
477 A110 10o green, bl & yel   .30   .20
478 A110 15o lake, bl & yel   .30   .40

National Flag Day.

Wmk. 307
1955, July 1   Typo.   *Perf. 13*
479 A111 3o yellow green   2.25 5.00
480 A111 4o blue   2.25 5.00
481 A111 6o gray   2.25 5.00
482 A111 8o orange yellow   2.25 5.00
483 A111 24o salmon   2.25 5.00
       Nos. 479-483 (5)   11.25 25.00

Cent. of the 1st Swedish postage stamps. Nos. 479-483 were printed in sheets of nine. They were sold in complete sets at the Stockholmia Philatelic Exhibition, July 1-10, 1955. A set cost 45 ore (face value) plus 2k (entrance fee).

Per Atterbom
A112

Greek Horseman
A113

Perf. 12½ Horizontally
1955, July 21   Engr.   Unwmk.
484 A112 20o dark blue   .40   .30
485 A112 1.40k sepia   3.75   .80

Perf. 12½ on 3 sides
486 A112 20o dark blue   1.25 1.40
  a.   Booklet pane of 20   35.00
       Nos. 484-486 (3)   5.40 2.50

Cent. of the death of Per Daniel Amadeus Atterbom, poet.

1956, Apr. 16   *Perf. 12½ Vert.*
487 A113 20o carmine   .85   .60
488 A113 25o ultra   .85   .20
489 A113 40o gray green   2.50 2.10

Perf. 12½ on 3 sides
490 A113 20o carmine   .40   .70
  a.   Booklet pane of 20   10.00
491 A113 25o ultra   .40   .20
  a.   Booklet pane of 20   10.00
       Nos. 487-491 (5)   5.00 3.80

Issued to publicize the Olympic Equestrian Competitions, Stockholm, June 10-17, 1956.

Northern Countries Issue

Whooper
Swans — A113a

Perf. 12½ Vertically
1956, Oct. 30   Engr.   Unwmk.
492 A113a 25o rose red   .20   .20
493 A113a 40o ultra   .75   .65

See footnote after Norway No. 354.

Railroad
Builders — A114

Designs: 25o, First Swedish locomotive and passenger car. 40o, Express train crossing Arsta bridge.

1956, Dec. 1   *Perf. 12½ Vert.*
494 A114 10o olive green   .60   .20
495 A114 25o ultra   .25   .20
496 A114 40o orange   3.00 3.00

Perf. 12½ on 3 sides
497 A114 10o olive green   .45   .45
  a.   Booklet pane of 20   11.00
498 A114 25o ultra   .75   .45
  a.   Booklet pane of 20   18.00
       Nos. 494-498 (5)   5.05 4.30

Centenary of Swedish railroads.

Ship in Distress
and
Lifeboat — A115

Perf. 12½ Vertically
1957, June 1   Engr.   Unwmk.
499 A115 30o blue   3.75   .20
500 A115 1.40k deep rose   4.50 1.25

Perf. 12½ on 3 sides
501 A115 30o blue   1.60 1.25
  a.   Booklet pane of 20   45.00
       Nos. 499-501 (3)   9.85 2.70

Swedish Life Saving Society, 50th anniv.

King Type of 1951
1957, June 1   *Perf. 12½ Vert.*
Without Imprint
502 A97 25o dark brown   1.10 1.60

Re-engraved Types of 1951 and 1954 with Imprint, and

Numeral (Letters in
white) — A115a

1957-64   *Perf. 12½ Vertically*
503 A115a 5o red ('61)   .20   .20
  a.   5o dark red   .20   .20
504 A115a 10o blue ('61)   .20   .20
  a.   10o dark blue   .30   .25

505	A97	15o dark red	.30	.20
506	A97	20o gray	.25	.20
507	A97	25o brown	.60	.20
508	A97	30o blue	.45	.20
509	A97	40o olive green	1.25	.20
510	A108	55o vermilion	1.25	.20
511	A108	70o orange	.60	.20
512	A108	80o yellow green	.80	.20

Perf. 12½ on 3 sides

513	A115a	5o red ('61)	.20	.20
a.		Bklt. pane of 20 ('64)	2.00	
b.		5o dark red	5.00	1.00
c.		Bklt. pane, 5 #513b, 5 #515	22.50	
514	A115a	10o blue ('61)	.20	.20
a.		10o dark blue	20.00	2.50
b.		Bklt. pane, #514a, 3 #517	37.50	18.00
515	A97	15o dark red	.60	.20
a.		Bklt. pane of 20	12.00	
516	A97	20o gray	1.00	.60
a.		Bklt. pane of 20	30.00	
517	A97	30o blue	.75	.20
a.		Bklt. pane of 20	35.00	
		Nos. 503-517 (15)	8.65	3.40

In the redrawn Numeral type A99, "Sverige, ore" and the "g" tail flourishes are white instead of in color.

Booklet pane including #513 is listed as #581b.

The booklet pane of 4, No. 514b, contains two copies of No. 517 which are imperf. on two adjoining sides. No. 514a was issued only in booklet pane No. 514b.

See Nos. 570, 580, 580a, 581b, 584b, 586b-586c, 666-667, 668a, 669b-669c.

Helicopter Mail Service — A116

Perf. 12½ Vertically

1958, Feb. 10   Engr.   Unwmk.

518	A116	30o blue	.40	.20
519	A116	1.40k brown	4.50	1.00

Perf. 12½ on 3 sides

520	A116	30o blue	.80	.55
a.		Booklet pane of 20	20.00	
		Nos. 518-520 (3)	5.70	1.75

10th anniversary of helicopter mail service to the Stockholm archipelago, Feb. 10.

Modern and 17th Century Vessels — A117

1958, Feb. 10   Perf. 12½ Vert.

521	A117	15o dark red	.40	.25
522	A117	40o gray olive	4.25	3.25

Perf. 12½ on 3 sides

523	A117	15o dark red	.50	.60
a.		Booklet pane of 20	12.00	
		Nos. 521-523 (3)	5.15	4.10

3 centuries of transatlantic mail service.

Soccer Player — A118

1958, May 8   Perf. 12½ Vert.

524	A118	15o vermilion	.85	.20
525	A118	20o yellow green	.50	.20
526	A118	1.20k dark blue	1.90	1.10

Perf. 12½ on 3 sides

527	A118	15o vermilion	.55	.45
a.		Booklet pane of 20	9.00	
528	A118	20o yellow green	.50	.65
a.		Booklet pane of 20	12.00	
		Nos. 524-528 (5)	4.30	2.60

Issued to publicize the 6th World Soccer Championships, Stockholm, June 8-29.

Bessemer Converter A119   Selma Lagerlof A120

Perf. 12½ Horizontally

1958, June 18   Engr.   Unwmk.

529	A119	30o gray blue	.35	.20
530	A119	1.70k dull red brown	3.00	.95

Perf. 12½ on 3 sides

531	A119	30o gray blue	.65	.55
a.		Booklet pane of 20	15.00	
		Nos. 529-531 (3)	4.00	1.70

Centenary of the first successful Bessemer blow in Sweden, July 18, 1858.

1958, Nov. 20   Perf. 12½ Horiz.

532	A120	20o dark red	.30	.30
533	A120	30o blue	.40	.20
534	A120	80o olive green	.75	.90

Perf. 12½ on 3 Sides

535	A120	20o dark red	.50	.75
a.		Booklet pane of 20	13.00	
536	A120	30o blue	.50	.60
a.		Booklet pane of 20	16.00	
		Nos. 532-536 (5)	2.45	2.75

Selma Lagerlof, writer, birth cent.

Palace Type of 1941

1958, Sept. 17   Perf. 12½ Vert.

537	A65	5k blue	2.75	.20

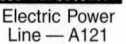

Electric Power Line — A121   Hydroelectric Plant and Dam — A122

Perf. 12½ Horiz. (H), Vert. (V)

1959, Jan. 20   Unwmk.

538	A121	30o ultra (H)	.45	.20
539	A122	90o carmine rose (V)	3.25	2.40

Perf. 12½ on 3 sides

540	A121	30o ultra	.50	.50
a.		Booklet pane of 20	14.00	
		Nos. 538-540 (3)	4.20	3.10

50th anniv. of the establishment of the State Power Board.

Verner von Heidenstam A123   Forest A124

Perf. 12½ Horizontally

1959, July 6   Engr.   Unwmk.

541	A123	15o rose carmine	1.00	.35
542	A123	1k slate	3.00	.90

Perf. 12½ on 3 Sides

543	A123	15o rose carmine	.50	.95
a.		Booklet pane of 20	13.00	
		Nos. 541-543 (3)	4.50	2.20

Verner von Heidenstam, poet, birth cent.

1959, Sept. 4   Perf. 12½ Horiz.

Design: 1.40k, Felling tree.

544	A124	30o green	1.50	.20
545	A124	1.40k brown red	3.50	.60

Perf. 12½ on 3 sides

546	A124	30o green	.90	*1.10*
a.		Booklet pane of 20	25.00	
		Nos. 544-546 (3)	5.90	1.90

Administration of crown lands and forests, cent.

Svante Arrhenius A125   Anders Zorn A126

Perf. 12½ Horizontally

1959, Dec. 10   Engr.   Unwmk.

547	A125	15o dull red brown	.25	.20
548	A125	3.50k dark blue	3.50	.45

Perf. 12½ on 3 sides

549	A125	15o dull red brown	.45	.60
a.		Booklet pane of 20	10.00	
		Nos. 547-549 (3)	4.20	1.25

Arrhenius (1859-1927), chemist and physicist.

1960, Feb. 18   Perf. 12½ Horiz.

550	A126	30o gray	.35	.20
551	A126	80o sepia	3.50	2.25

Perf. 12½ on 3 sides

552	A126	30o gray	1.60	.60
a.		Booklet pane of 20	35.00	
		Nos. 550-552 (3)	5.45	3.05

Zorn (1860-1920), painter and sculptor.

Uprooted Oak Emblem A127   People of Various Races, WRY Emblem A128

Perf. 12½ Vert. (V), Horiz. (H)

1960, Apr. 7   Engr.   Unwmk.

553	A127	20o red brown (V)	.20	.20
554	A128	40o purple (H)	.30	.30

Perf. 12½ on 3 sides

555	A127	20o red brown	.50	.60
a.		Booklet pane of 20	12.00	
		Nos. 553-555 (3)	1.00	1.10

World Refugee Year, 7/1/59-6/30/60.

Target Shooting A129   Gustaf Froding A130

Design: 90o, Parade of riflemen.

1960, June 30   Perf. 12½ Vert.

556	A129	15o rose carmine	.30	.20
557	A129	90o grnsh blue	2.50	2.00

Perf. 12½ on 3 sides

558	A129	15o rose carmine	.35	*.50*
a.		Booklet pane of 20	9.00	
		Nos. 556-558 (3)	3.15	2.70

Centenary of the founding of the Voluntary Shooting Organization.

1960, Aug. 22   Perf. 12½ Horiz.

559	A130	30o red brown	.30	.20
560	A130	1.40k slate green	2.60	.45

Perf. 12½ on 3 sides

561	A130	30o red brown	.45	.35
a.		Booklet pane of 20	10.00	
		Nos. 559-561 (3)	3.35	1.00

Gustaf Froding (1860-1911), poet.

Common Design Types pictured following the introduction.

Europa Issue, 1960
Common Design Type

1960, Sept. 19   Perf. 12½ Vert.
Size: 27x21mm

562	CD3	40o blue	.20	.20
563	CD3	1k red	*.80*	.30

Hjalmar Branting (1860-1925), Labor Party Leader and Prime Minister — A131

Perf. 12½ Horiz.

1960, Nov. 23   Engr.

564	A131	15o rose carmine	.20	.20
565	A131	1.70k slate blue	3.00	.55

Perf. 12½ on 3 sides

566	A131	15o rose carmine	.45	.35
a.		Booklet pane of 20	4.50	
		Nos. 564-566 (3)	3.65	1.10

SAS Issue

DC-8 Airliner — A131a

Perf. 12½ Vertically

1961, Feb. 24   Unwmk.

567	A131a	40o blue	.30	.35

Perf. 12½ on 3 sides

568	A131a	40o blue	.85	*1.25*
a.		Booklet pane of 10	10.00	

Scandinavian Airlines System, SAS, 10th anniv.

Numeral Type of 1957, Three-Crown Type of 1939 and

Gustaf VI Adolf (Letters, numerals in white) A132   Rune Stone, Oland, 11th Century A133

1961-65   Perf. 12½ Vert.

570	A115a	15o green ('62)	.30	.20
571	A132	15o red	.35	.20
572	A132	20o gray	.35	.20
573	A132	25o brown	.65	.20
574	A132	30o ultra	1.50	.20
575	A132	30o lilac ('62)	.55	.20
576	A132	35o lilac	.55	.20
577	A132	35o ultra ('62)	1.10	.20
578	A132	40o emerald	1.00	.20
579	A132	50o gray grn ('62)	.65	.20

Perf. 12½ on 3 sides

580	A115a	15o grn ('65)	.30	.30
a.		Bklt. pane, 2 each #514, 580, 583	2.25	
581	A132	15o red	.25	.20
a.		Bklt. pane, 5 #513, 5 #581	5.00	
b.		Bklt. pane, 5 #513, 5 #581	5.00	
582	A132	20o gray	1.25	.75
a.		Bklt. pane of 20	27.50	
583	A132	25o brown ('62)	.35	.20
a.		Bklt. pane of 20	15.00	
b.		Bklt. pane of 4	2.25	
584	A132	30o ultra	.65	.20
a.		Bklt. pane of 20	15.00	
b.		Bklt. pane, #514 + 3 #584	4.00	
585	A132	30o lilac ('64)	.65	.50
a.		Bklt. pane of 20	14.00	
586	A132	35o ultra ('62)	.55	.20
a.		Bklt. pane of 20	12.50	
b.		Bklt. pane, 3 #514, 2 #586 + blank label	5.00	3.50
c.		As "b," inscribed label	3.50	1.50

Perf. 12½ Vertically

588	A56	1.05k Prus grn ('62)	1.10	.30
589	A56	1.50k brown ('62)	.80	.30
590	A56	2.15k dk sl grn ('62)	4.00	.65
591	A56	2.50k emerald	1.50	.20

Perf. 12½ on 3 sides

592	A133	10k dl red brn	20.00	.50
a.		Bklt. pane of 10 ('68)	250.00	
b.		Bklt. pane of 20	850.00	
		Nos. 570-592 (22)	38.40	6.30

Booklet panes of 4, 5 or 6 (Nos. 580a, 583b, 584b, 586b, 586c) contain two stamps which are imperf. on two adjoining sides.

Combination panes (Nos. 580a, 581b, 584b, 586b, 586c) come in different arrangements of the denominations.

The label of No. 586c is inscribed "ett brev / betyder / sa / mycket" ("a letter means so much"). The label inscription "nord 63 / 5-13 oktober / GÖTEBORG" was privately applied to No. 586b by the Gothenburg Philatelic Society to raise funds for Nord 63 Philatelic Exhibition in Gothenburg. The pane was sold for the equivalent of $1 US, 5 times face value.

See Nos. 648-654A, 666a, 668-672F.

K.-G. Pilo, Self-portrait A134

Jonas Alstromer A135

1961, Apr. 17   **Perf. 12½ Horiz.**

594	A134	30o brown	.35	.25
595	A134	1.40k Prus blue	3.50	1.30

Perf. 12½ on 3 sides

596	A134	30o brown	1.10	.45
a.		Booklet pane of 20	30.00	
		Nos. 594-596 (3)	4.95	2.00

Karl-Gustaf Pilo (1711-1793), painter. Self-portrait from "The Coronation of Gustavus III."

1961, June 2   **Perf. 12½ Vert.**

597	A135	30o dull claret	.20	.20
598	A135	90o grnsh blue	1.60	2.25

Perf. 12½ on 3 sides

599	A135	15o dull claret	.25	.40
a.		Booklet pane of 20	7.00	
		Nos. 597-599 (3)	2.05	2.85

200th anniversary of the birth of Jonas Alstromer, pioneer of agriculture and industry.

17th Century Printer and Student in Library — A136

Perf. 12½ Vert.

1961, Sept. 22   **Engr.**

600	A136	20o dark red	.30	.30
601	A136	1k blue	7.00	1.60

Perf. 12½ on 3 sides

602	A136	20o dark red	.30	.55
a.		Booklet pane of 20	9.00	
		Nos. 600-602 (3)	7.60	2.45

300th anniversary of the regulation requiring copies of all Swedish printed works to be deposited in the Royal Library.

Roentgen, Prudhomme, von Behring, van't Hoff — A137

1961, Dec. 9   **Perf. 12½ Vertically**

603	A137	20o vermilion	.20	.20
604	A137	40o blue	.20	.20
605	A137	50o green	.50	.20

Perf. 12½ on 3 sides

606	A137	20o vermilion	.25	.20
a.		Booklet pane of 20	6.00	
		Nos. 603-606 (4)	1.15	.80

Winners of the 1901 Nobel Prize; Wilhelm K. Roentgen, Rene Sully Prudhomme, Emil von Behring, Jacob van't Hoff.
See Nos. 617-619, 673-676, 689-692, 710-713, 769-772, 804-807.

A138   A139

Footsteps and postmen's badges.

1962, Jan. 29   **Engr.**   **Perf. 12½ Vert.**

607	A138	30o lilac	.40	.20
608	A138	1.70k rose red	3.50	.55

Perf. 12½ on 3 sides

609	A138	30o lilac	.50	.50
a.		Booklet pane of 20	11.00	
		Nos. 607-609 (3)	4.40	1.25

Local mail delivery service in Sweden, cent.

1962, Mar. 21   **Perf. 12½ Horiz.**

610	A139	30o dark blue	.35	.20
611	A139	2k red	4.50	.35

Perf. 12½ on 3 sides

612	A139	30o dark blue	.40	.45
a.		Booklet pane of 20	10.50	
		Nos. 610-612 (3)	5.25	1.00

Centenary of the municipal reform laws.

St. George, Great Church, Stockholm A140

Skokloster Castle A141

Perf. 12½ Horiz. (H), Vert. (V)

1962, Sept. 24

613	A140	20o rose lake (H)	.25	.20
614	A141	50o dk slate grn (V)	.55	.35

Perf. 12½ on 3 sides

615	A140	20o rose lake	.20	.30
a.		Booklet pane of 20	6.00	
616	A141	50o dk slate grn	.90	1.20
a.		Booklet pane of 10	9.00	
		Nos. 613-616 (4)	1.90	2.05

Nobel Prize Winners Type of 1961

Designs: 25o, Theodor Mommsen and Sir Ronald Ross. 50o, Hermann Emil Fischer, Pieter Zeeman and Hendrik Antoon Lorentz.

1962, Dec. 10   **Perf. 12½ Vert.**

617	A137	25o dark red	.30	.30
618	A137	50o blue	.40	.40

Perf. 12½ on 3 sides

619	A142	25o dark red	.40	.65
a.		Booklet pane of 20	10.00	
		Nos. 617-619 (3)	1.10	1.35

Winners of the 1902 Nobel Prize.

Ice Hockey — A143

1963, Feb. 15   **Perf. 12½ Horiz.**

620	A143	25o green	.40	.20
621	A143	1.70k violet bl	3.00	.70

Perf. 12½ on 3 sides

622	A143	25o green	.25	.55
a.		Booklet pane of 20	7.00	
		Nos. 620-622 (3)	3.65	1.45

1963 Ice Hockey World Championships.

Wheat Emblem and Stylized Hands — A144

1963, Mar. 21   **Perf. 12½ Vertically**

623	A144	35o lilac rose	.35	.20
624	A144	50o violet	.30	.35

Perf. 12½ on 3 sides

625	A144	35o lilac rose	.30	.40
a.		Booklet pane of 20	6.00	
		Nos. 623-625 (3)	.95	.95

FAO "Freedom from Hunger" campaign.

Engineering and Industry Symbols — A145

1963, May 27   **Perf. 12½ Vertically**

626	A145	50o gray	.50	.35
627	A145	1.05k orange	3.25	2.75

Perf. 12½ on 3 sides

628	A145	50o gray	2.60	2.75
a.		Booklet pane of 10	27.50	
		Nos. 626-628 (3)	6.35	5.85

Gregoire François Du Reitz — A146

Perf. 12½ Vertically

1963, Sept. 16   **Engr.**   **Unwmk.**

629	A146	25o brown	.40	.45
630	A146	35o dark blue	.30	.20
631	A146	2k dark red	4.00	.55

Perf. 12½ on 3 sides

632	A146	25o brown	.65	.75
a.		Booklet pane of 20	16.00	
633	A146	35o dark blue	.40	.30
a.		Booklet pane of 20	10.00	
		Nos. 629-633 (5)	5.75	2.25

300th anniversary of the Swedish Board of Health. Dr. Du Rietz (1607-1682) was first president of the "Collegium Medicorum," forerunner of the Board of Health.

Hammarby, Home of Carl von Linné (Linnaeus) A147

1963, Oct. 25   **Perf. 12½ Vert.**

634	A147	20o orange red	.30	.20
635	A147	50o yellow grn	.30	.25

Perf. 12½ on 3 sides

636	A147	20o orange red	.30	.35
a.		Booklet pane of 20	6.00	
		Nos. 634-636 (3)	.90	.80

Nobel Prize Winners Type of 1961

Designs: 25o, Svante Arrhenius, Niels Finsen, Bjornstjerne Bjornson. 50o, Antoine Henri Becquerel, Pierre and Marie Curie.

Perf. 12½ Vertically

1963, Dec. 10   **Engr.**   **Unwmk.**

637	A137	25o gray olive	.75	.70
638	A137	50o chocolate	.40	.50

Perf. 12½ on 3 sides

639	A137	25o gray olive	.75	1.10
a.		Booklet pane of 20	16.00	
		Nos. 637-639 (3)	1.90	2.30

Winners of the 1903 Nobel Prize.

A149   A150

"The Assumption of Elijah."

1964, Feb. 3   **Perf. 12½ Horiz.**

640	A149	35o lt ultra	.65	.20
641	A149	1.05k dull red	3.75	3.75

Perf. 12½ on 3 sides

642	A149	35o lt ultra	.45	.35
a.		Booklet pane of 20	10.00	
		Nos. 640-642 (3)	4.85	4.30

Erik Axel Karlfeldt (1864-1931), poet.

1964, June 12   **Perf. 12½ Horiz.**

Seal of Archbishop Stephen.

643	A150	40o slate green	.30	.30
644	A150	60o orange brown	.30	.35

Perf. 12½ Vertically

645	A150	40o slate green	.30	.30
a.		Booklet pane of 10	3.50	
646	A150	60o orange brown	.35	.55
a.		Booklet pane of 10	4.00	
		Nos. 643-646 (4)	1.25	1.50

800th anniv. of the Archbishopric of Uppsala.

Types of Regular Issues, 1939-61, and

Post Horns — A151

Ship Grave, Skane (Bronze Age) — A152

1964-71   **Engr.**   **Perf. 12½ Vert.**

647	A151	20o sl bl & org yel ('65)	.20	.20
648	A132	35o gray	.60	.20
649	A132	40o ultra	.60	.20
650	A132	45o orange	.60	.20
651	A132	45o violet bl ('67)	.60	.20
652	A132	50o green ('68)	.55	.20
652A	A132	55o dark red ('69)	.40	.20
653	A132	60o rose car	.65	.65
653A	A132	65o dull grn ('71)	.80	.20
654	A132	70o lil rose ('67)	.50	.20
654A	A132	85o dp cl ('71)	.80	.30
655	A108	95o violet	3.00	4.00
656	A56	1.20k lt blue	3.50	3.50
657	A56	1.80k dk blue ('67)	1.25	.50
658	A56	1.85k blue ('67)	3.00	1.00
659	A56	2k dp car ('69)	.75	.20
660	A56	2.30k choc ('65)	5.50	.20
661	A56	2.55k red	2.10	2.60
662	A56	2.80k red ('67)	1.40	.20
663	A56	2.85k orange ('65)	2.75	4.00
664	A56	3k brt orange	1.40	.20
665	A152	3.50k grnsh gray ('66)	1.50	.20

Perf. 12½ on 3 Sides

666	A115a	10o brown	.20	.25
a.		Bklt. pane, 2 each #666, 667, 583	3.00	
667	A115a	15o brown	.50	.80
668	A132	30o rose red ('66)	.85	.85
a.		Bklt. pane, 2 each #513, 580, 668	1.40	
b.		Perf. on 3 sides	1.10	1.10

No. 668 is perf. on 2 adjoining sides.

669	A132	40o brown	.65	.20
a.		Bklt. pane of 20	16.00	
b.		Bklt. pane, 2 ea #514, 669	1.50	
c.		Bklt. pane, 2 each #513-514, 580, 668b-669	4.00	
670	A132	45o org ('67)	.65	.20
a.		Bklt. pane of 20	14.00	
671	A132	45o vio bl ('67)	.70	.20
a.		Bklt. pane of 20	14.00	
672	A132	50o green ('69)	.50	.60
a.		Bklt. pane of 10	5.00	
672B	A132	55o dk red ('69)	.50	.20
c.		Bklt. pane of 10	5.00	
672D	A132	65o dull grn ('71)	.85	.50
a.		Bklt. pane of 10	9.00	
672F	A132	85o dp cl ('71)	.90	1.25
g.		Bklt. pane of 10	9.00	
		Nos. 647-672F (32)	38.30	24.40

Some combination booklet panes of 4, 6 or 10 contain two stamps which are imperf. on two adjoining sides. Combination panes come in different arrangements of the denominations.

Fluorescent Paper

Starting in 1967, fluorescent paper was used in printing both definitive and commemorative issues. Its use was gradually eliminated starting in 1976. Numerous definitives and a few commemoratives were printed on both ordinary and fluorescent paper.

Nobel Prize Winners Type of 1961

30o, José Echegaray y Eizaguirre, Frédéric Mistral and John William Strutt, Lord Rayleigh. 40o, Sir William Ramsey and Ivan Petrovich Pavlov.

Perf. 12½ Vertically

1964, Dec. 10		Engr.	
673	A137 30o blue	.45	.45
674	A137 40o red	.70	.25

Perf. 12½ on 3 Sides

675	A137 30o blue	.45	.75
a.	Booklet pane of 20	12.00	
676	A137 40o red	.75	.35
a.	Booklet pane of 20	18.00	
	Nos. 673-676 (4)	2.35	1.80

Winners of the 1904 Nobel Prize.

Visby Town Wall A154   Antenna A155

1965, Apr. 5		Perf. 12½ Horiz.	
677	A154 30o dk car rose	.30	.20
678	A154 2k brt ultra	4.25	.35

Perf. 12½ on 3 Sides

679	A154 30o dk car rose	.40	.35
a.	Booklet pane of 20	9.00	
	Nos. 677-679 (3)	4.95	.90

1965, May 17		Perf. 12½ Horiz.	
680	A155 60o lilac	.45	.45
681	A155 1.40k bluish blk	2.25	1.90

Perf. 12½ on 3 Sides

682	A155 60o lilac	1.10	1.60
a.	Booklet pane of 10	12.50	
	Nos. 680-682 (3)	3.80	3.95

Centenary of the ITU.

Prince Eugen — A156

1965, July 5		Perf. 12½ Horiz.	
683	A156 40o black	.20	.20
684	A156 1k brown	2.10	.35

Perf. 12½ on 3 Sides

685	A156 40o black	.25	.25
a.	Booklet pane of 20	7.00	
	Nos. 683-685 (3)	2.55	.80

Prince Eugen (1865-1947), painter and patron of the arts.

Fredrika Bremer (1801-65), Novelist — A157

Perf. 12½ Vertically

1965, Oct. 25		Engr.	
686	A157 25o violet	.20	.20
687	A157 3k gray green	4.00	.35

Perf. 12½ on 3 Sides

688	A157 25o violet	.25	.20
a.	Booklet pane of 20	5.00	
	Nos. 686-688 (3)	4.45	.75

Nobel Prize Winners Type of 1961

30o, Philipp von Lenard, Adolf von Baeyer. 40o, Robert Koch, Henryk Sienkiewicz.

Perf. 12½ Vertically

1965, Dec. 10		Unwmk.	
689	A137 30o ultra	.35	.45
690	A137 40o dark red	.40	.25

Perf. 12½ on 3 Sides

691	A137 30o ultra	.45	.75
a.	Booklet pane of 20	11.00	
692	A137 40o dark red	.85	.30
a.	Booklet pane of 20	19.00	
	Nos. 689-692 (4)	2.05	1.75

Winners of the 1905 Nobel Prize.

Nathan Soderblom A158   Speed Skater A159

1966, Jan. 15		Perf. 12½ Horiz.	
693	A158 60o brown	.35	.20
694	A158 80o green	.85	.20

Perf. 12½ on 3 Sides

695	A158 60o brown	.75	.90
a.	Booklet pane of 10	8.00	
	Nos. 693-695 (3)	1.95	1.30

Nathan Soderblom (1866-1931), Protestant theologian, who worked for the union of Christian churches and received 1930 Nobel Peace Prize.

Perf. 12½ on 3 Sides

1966, Feb. 18		Engr.	
696	A159 5o rose red	.20	.20
697	A159 25o slate green	.20	.20
698	A159 40o dark blue	.35	.70
a.	Bklt. pane, 4 ea #696-697, 2 #698	2.25	
	Nos. 696-698 (3)	.75	1.10

World Speed Skating Championships for Men, Gothenburg, Feb. 18-20, and 75th anniversary of World Skating Championships.

National Museum, Staircase, 1866 — A160   Baron Louis Gerhard De Geer — A161

1966, Mar. 26		Perf. 12½ Vert.	
699	A160 30o violet	.20	.25
a.	Booklet pane of 10	2.50	
700	A160 2.30k olive green	1.40	1.50
a.	Booklet pane of 10	13.00	

National Gallery, Blasieholmen, Stockholm, cent. The design is from an 1866 woodcut showing the inauguration of the Museum.

1966, May 12		Perf. 12½ Vertically	
701	A161 40o dark blue	.25	.20
702	A161 3k brown carmine	3.75	.65

Perf. 12½ on 3 Sides

703	A161 40o dark blue	.25	.35
a.	Booklet pane of 20	8.00	
	Nos. 701-703 (3)	4.25	1.20

Cent. of the reform of the Representative Assembly under the leadership of Minister of Justice (1858-70) Baron Louis Gerhard De Geer (1818-96).

Stage, Drottningholm Court Theater — A162   Almqvist and Wild Rose — A163

Perf. 12½ on 3 Sides

1966, June 15		Engr.	
	Salmon Paper		
704	A162 5o vermilion	.20	.20
705	A162 25o olive bister	.20	.20
706	A162 40o dark purple	.40	.65
a.	Bkt. pane, 4 ea #704-705, 2 #706	2.00	
	Nos. 704-706 (3)	.80	1.05

Drottningholm Court Theater, 200th anniv.

Perf. 12½ Horizontally

1966, Sept. 26		Engr.	
707	A163 25o magenta	.25	.20
708	A163 1k green	2.25	.30

Perf. 12½ on 3 Sides

709	A163 25o magenta	.20	.20
a.	Booklet pane of 20	4.75	
	Nos. 707-709 (3)	2.70	.70

Carl Jonas Love Almqvist (1793-1866), writer and poet.

Nobel Prize Winner Type of 1961

Designs: 30o, Joseph John Thomson and Giosue Carducci. 40o, Henri Moissan, Camillo Golgi and Santiago Ramon y Cajal.

Perf. 12½ Vertically

1966, Dec. 10		Engr.	
710	A137 30o rose lake	.55	.20
711	A137 40o dark green	.50	.20

Perf. 12½ on 3 Sides

712	A137 30o rose lake	.55	.45
a.	Booklet pane of 20	11.00	
713	A137 40o dark green	.55	.45
a.	Booklet pane of 20	12.00	
	Nos. 710-713 (4)	2.15	1.30

Winners of the 1906 Nobel Prize.

Field Ball Player A164   EFTA Emblem A165

1967, Jan. 12		Perf. 12½ Horiz.	
714	A164 45o dk violet blue	.20	.20
715	A164 2.70k dp rose lilac	2.75	1.50

Perf. 12½ on 3 Sides

716	A164 45o dk violet blue	.25	.30
a.	Booklet pane of 20	6.00	
	Nos. 714-716 (3)	3.20	2.00

World Field Ball Championships, Jan. 12-21.

1967, Feb. 15		Perf. 12½ Horiz.	
717	A165 70o orange	.45	.40

Perf. 12½ on 3 Sides

718	A165 70o orange	1.10	1.25
a.	Booklet pane of 10	15.00	

European Free Trade Association. Tariffs were abolished Dec. 31, 1966, among EFTA members: Austria, Denmark, Finland, Great Britain, Norway, Portugal, Sweden, Switzerland.

"The Fjeld," by Sixten Lundbohm A166   Lion Fortress, Gothenburg A167

Uppsala Cathedral A168   Gripsholm Castle A169

1967		Engr.	Perf. 12½ Vert.	
719	A166 35o dl bl & blk brn		.20	.20

Perf. 12½ Horiz.

720	A167 3.70k violet	2.10	.20
721	A168 4.50k dull red	2.40	.20

Perf. 12½ Vert.

722	A169 7k vio bl & rose red	3.25	.55

Perf. 12½ on 3 Sides

723	A166 35o dl bl & blk brn	.20	.20
a.	Booklet pane of 10	2.50	
	Nos. 719-723 (5)	8.15	1.35

Issued: #719, 721, 723, 3/15; #720, 2/15; #722, 4/11.

Table Tennis — A170

1967, Apr. 11		Perf. 12½ Horiz.	
724	A170 35o bright magenta	.30	.20
725	A170 90o greenish blue	1.30	.50

Perf. 12½ on 3 Sides

726	A170 35o bright magenta	.35	.40
a.	Booklet pane of 20	7.00	
	Nos. 724-726 (3)	1.95	1.10

World Table Tennis Championships, Stockholm.

Man with Axe and Fettered Beast — A171   Double Mortise Corner — A172

Designs: 15o, Man fighting two bears. 30o, Warrior disguised as wolf pursuing enemy. 35o, Two warriors with swords and lances. The designs are taken from 6th century bronze plates (1¾in. x 2½in.) used to decorate helmets; now in Swedish Museum of National Antiquities.

Perf. 12½ on 3 Sides

1967, May 17		Engr.	
727	A171 10o dk brown & dp bl	.20	.20
728	A171 15o dp blue & dk brn	.20	.20
729	A171 30o brt pink & dk brn	.20	.20
730	A171 35o dk brown & brt pink	.20	.20
a.	Bklt. pane, 4 #727, 2 ea #728-730	2.10	2.75
	Nos. 727-730 (4)	.80	2.75

Lithographed and Photogravure

1967, June 16		Perf. 12½	
731	A172 10o olive & multi	.20	.20
732	A172 35o dk blue multi	.30	.30
a.	Bklt. pane, 6 #731, 4 #732	1.75	2.00

Issued to honor generations of Finnish settlers in Sweden.

Right-hand Driving as Seen Through Windshield — A173

1967, Sept. 2	Engr.	Perf. 12½ Vert.	
733	A173 35o dp bl, ocher & blk	.30	.35
734	A173 45o yel grn, ocher & blk	.35	.45

Perf. 12½ Horiz.

735	A173	35o dp bl, ocher & blk	.30	.45
a.		Booklet pane of 10	3.00	
736	A173	45o yel grn, ocher & blk	.20	.20
a.		Booklet pane of 10	2.50	
		Nos. 733-736 (4)	1.15	1.45

Issued to publicize the introduction of right-hand driving in Sweden, Sept. 3, 1967.

Postrider
A174

The Prodigal Son, 13th cent., Rada Church
A174a

Griffin
A174b

Rocky Isles in Bloom, by Harald Lindberg
A175

Dalsland Canal — A176

Log roller — A176a

Gothenburg Harbor — A176b

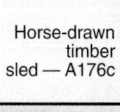
Horse-drawn timber sled — A176c

Nils Holgersson Riding Wild Goose — A176d

Windmills, Öland Island — A176e

Steamer Storskar and Royal Palace, Stockholm
A176f

Elk — A177

Roe deer — A177a

Dancing cranes — A177b

Mail Coach, by Eigil Schwab
A177c

Illustration from Lapponia, by Johannes Schefferus — A177d

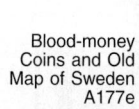
Blood-money Coins and Old Map of Sweden
A177e

Great Seal, 1439 (St. Erik with Banner and Shield) — A177f

10o, Merchant vessel in Oresund, 1661. 20o, St. Stephen as a boy tending horses, medallion from Dädesio Church. #742, Lion, from Grodinge tapestry, 15th cent. 2.55k, Seal of Magnus Ladulas, 1285 (King Magnus Birgersson on throne with lily scepter and orb). 3k, Seal of Duke Erik Magnusson, 1306 (Duke on horseback with standard of Folkunga dynasty). 6k, Gustavus Vasa's silver daler.

1967-72   Perf. 12½ Horiz. or Vert.

737	A174	5o red & blk	.20	.20
738	A174	10o blue & blk	.20	.20
739	A174a	15o sl grn, *grnsh* ('71)	.20	.20
740	A174	20o sep, *buff* ('70)	.20	.20
741	A174b	25o bis & blk ('71)	.20	.20
742	A174b	25o blk & bis ('71)	.20	.20
a.		Pair, #741-742	.40	.50
743	A175	30o ultra & ver	.20	.20
744	A176	40o blk, dk grn & ultra ('68)	.30	.20
745	A176a	45o bl & brn blk ('70)	.30	.20
746	A176b	55o bl & vio, vert. ('71)	.40	.20
747	A176c	60o black brn ('71)	.30	.20
747A	A176d	65o brt blue ('71)	.30	.20
748	A176e	75o slate grn ('71)	.30	.20
749	A176f	80o blue & blk ('71)	.40	.20
750	A177	90o sep & bl gray	.55	.20
750A	A177a	95o sepia ('72)	.40	.20
751	A177b	1k slate grn ('68)	.55	.20
751A	A177c	1.20k multi ('71)	.65	.20
751B	A177d	1.40k lt bl & red ('72)	.75	.20
752	A177f	2.55k brt blue ('70)	1.25	.65
753	A177f	3k dk gray bl ('70)	1.25	.20
754	A177e	4k black ('71)	1.60	.20
755	A177f	5k Prus grn ('70)	2.00	.20
755A	A177d	6k indigo ('72)	3.00	.20

Perf. 12½ on 3 Sides

756	A174	5o red & blk	.20	.20
a.		Booklet pane of 20	.75	
757	A174	10o bl & blk ('69)	.20	.20
a.		Booklet pane of 20	2.10	
758	A175	30o ultra & ver	.30	.30
a.		Booklet pane of 10	3.25	
759	A176	40o blk, dk grn & ultra ('68)	.20	.30
a.		Booklet pane of 10	2.75	
760	A176a	45o bl & brn blk ('70)	.20	.20
a.		Booklet pane of 10	2.75	
761	A176b	55o bl & vio, perf. 12½ horiz. ('71)	.35	.20
a.		Booklet pane of 10	3.50	
762	A176d	65o brt blue ('71)	.40	.40
a.		Booklet pane of 10	4.00	
763	A176e	75o slate grn ('72)	.50	.20
a.		Booklet pane of 10	5.50	
764	A177	90o sepia & bl gray	1.00	1.00
a.		Booklet pane of 10	10.00	
		Nos. 737-764 (33)	19.05	8.25

King Gustaf VI Adolf — A178

Perf. 12½ Horiz.

1967, Nov. 11				**Engr.**
765	A178	45o lt ultra	.30	.20
766	A178	70o green	.30	.30

Perf. 12½ on 3 Sides

767	A178	45o lt ultra	.25	.25
a.		Booklet pane of 20	4.50	
768	A178	70o green	.65	.95
a.		Booklet pane of 10	6.50	
		Nos. 765-768 (4)	1.50	1.70

85th birthday of King Gustaf VI Adolf.

Nobel Prize Winners Type of 1961

35o, Eduard Buchner (Chemistry), Albert A. Michelson (Physics). 45o, Charles L. A. Laveran (Medicine), Rudyard Kipling (Literature).

1967, Dec. 9		**Perf. 12½ Vert.**		
769	A137	35o vermilion	.65	.50
770	A137	45o dark blue	.55	.20

Perf. 12½ on 3 Sides

771	A142	35o vermilion	.70	.95
a.		Booklet pane of 10	7.50	
772	A142	45o dark blue	.45	.50
a.		Booklet pane of 10	6.50	
		Nos. 769-772 (4)	2.35	2.15

Winners of the 1907 Nobel Prize.

Franz Berwald, Violin and His Music — A179

1968, Apr. 3		**Perf. 12½ Horiz.**		
773	A179	35o black & red	.35	.20
774	A179	2k blk, vio bl & org yel	3.00	.80

Perf. 12½ on 3 Sides

775	A179	35o black & red	.45	.60
a.		Booklet pane of 10	4.50	
		Nos. 773-775 (3)	3.80	1.60

Franz Berwald (1796-1868), composer. Design includes opening bar of overture to his opera, "The Queen of Golconda."

National Bank Seal — A180

Perf. 12½ Vertically

1968, May 15				**Engr.**
776	A180	45o dull blue	.25	.20
777	A180	70o black, *pink*	.30	.35

Perf. 12½ on 3 Sides

778	A180	45o dull blue	.35	.50
a.		Booklet pane of 10	4.00	
779	A180	70o black, *pink*	.55	.85
a.		Booklet pane of 10	6.50	
		Nos. 776-779 (4)	1.45	1.90

300th anniv. of the National Bank of Sweden. Nos. 777, 779 are on non-fluorescent paper.

Seal of Lund University — A181

Butterfly Orchid — A182

1968, June 4   Perf. 12½ on 3 sides

780	A181	10o deep blue	.20	.20
781	A181	35o red	.30	.50
a.		Bklt. pane, 6 #780, 4 #781	2.25	2.75

300th anniversary of University of Lund.

1968, June 4

Nordic Wild Flowers: No. 783, Wood anemone. No. 784, Dog rose. No. 785, Prune Cherry. No. 786, Lily of the valley.

782	A182	45o slate green	.90	.55
783	A182	45o gray green	.90	.55
784	A182	45o sl grn & rose car	.90	.55
785	A182	45o gray green	.90	.55
786	A182	45o slate green	.90	.55
a.		Bklt. pane, 2 each #782-786	11.00	
		Nos. 782-786 (5)	4.50	2.75

World Council of Churches' Emblem
A183

Electron Orbits
A184

1968, July 4		**Perf. 12½ Horiz.**		
787	A183	70o plum	.55	.60
788	A183	90o Prus green	1.00	.50

Perf. 12½ on 3 Sides

789	A183	70o plum	.65	.95
a.		Booklet pane of 10	7.50	
		Nos. 787-789 (3)	2.20	2.05

4th General Assembly of the World Council of Churches, Uppsala, July 4-19.

Perf. 12½ Horizontally

1968, Aug. 9				**Engr.**
790	A184	45o rose carmine	.55	.20
791	A184	2k dark blue	2.90	.40

Perf. 12½ on 3 Sides

792	A184	45o rose carmine	.50	.45
a.		Booklet pane of 10	5.00	
		Nos. 790-792 (3)	3.95	1.05

Establishment of the 1st 3 People's Colleges, cent.

"Orienteer" Finding Way through Forest — A185

"Fingerkrok" by Axel Petersson — A186

Perf. 12½ Horizontally

1968, Sept. 5				**Engr.**
793	A185	40o violet & red brn	.35	.40
794	A185	2.80k green & violet	3.00	3.00

Perf. 12½ on 3 Sides

795	A185	40o violet & red brn	.40	.65
a.		Booklet pane of 10	5.00	
		Nos. 793-795 (3)	3.75	4.05

Issued to publicize the World Championships in Orienteering, Linkoping, Sept. 28-29.

Perf. 12½ on 3 Sides

1968, Oct. 28   **Engr.**

796	A186	5o green	.20	.20
797	A186	25o sepia	1.40	1.10
798	A186	45o blk brn & red brn	.20	.25
a.		Bklt. pane, 3 #796, 2 #797, 3 #798	3.00	
		Nos. 796-798 (3)	1.80	1.55

Axel Petersson, called "Doderhultarn" (1868-1925), sculptor.

Black-backed Gull — A187

Designs: No. 799, Varying hare. No. 801, Red fox. No. 802, Hooded crows harassing golden eagle. No. 803, Weasel.

Perf. 12½ on 3 Sides

1968, Nov. 9   **Engr.**

799	A187	30o blue	.65	.80
800	A187	30o black	.65	.80
801	A187	30o dark brown	.65	.80
802	A187	30o black	.65	.80
803	A187	30o blue	.65	.80
a.		Bklt. pane, 2 each #799-803	6.50	
		Nos. 799-803 (5)	3.25	4.00

See Nos. 873-877.

Nobel Prize Winners Type of 1961

35o, Elie Metchnikoff, Paul Ehrlich, Ernest Rutherford. 45o, Gabriel Lippmann, Rudolf Eucken.

1968, Dec. 10   **Perf. 12½ Vertically**

804	A137	35o maroon	.55	.50
805	A137	35o dark green	.50	.20

Perf. 12½ on 3 Sides

806	A137	35o maroon	.50	1.15
a.		Booklet pane of 10	6.00	
807	A137	45o dark green	.45	.50
a.		Booklet pane of 10	5.00	
		Nos. 804-807 (4)	2.00	2.35

Nordic Cooperation Issue

Five Ancient Ships — A187a

1969, Feb. 28   **Engr.**   **Perf. 12½ Vert.**

808	A187a	45o dark gray	.35	.35
809	A187a	70o blue	.55	.90

Perf. 12½ on 3 Sides

810	A187a	45o dark gray	.50	.85
a.		Booklet pane of 10	11.00	
		Nos. 808-810 (3)	1.40	2.10

50th anniv. of the Nordic Society and centenary of postal cooperation among the northern countries. The design is taken from a coin found at the site of Birka, an ancient Swedish town. See also Denmark Nos. 454-455, Finland No. 481, Iceland Nos. 404-405 and Norway Nos. 523-524.

Worker, by Albin Amelin — A188

Perf. 12½ Horiz.

1969, Mar. 31   **Engr.**

811	A188	55o dk carmine rose	.45	.20
812	A188	70o dk blue	.70	.65

Perf. 12½ on 3 Sides

813	A188	55o dk carmine rose	.35	.20
a.		Booklet pane of 10	4.00	
		Nos. 811-813 (3)	1.50	1.05

50th anniv. of the ILO.

Europa Issue, 1969
Common Design Type

1969, Apr. 28   **Photo.**   **Perf. 14 Vert.**
Size: 27x22mm

814	CD12	70o orange & multi	1.50	.45
815	CD12	1k vio blue & multi	1.00	.40

Perf. 14 on 3 Sides

816	CD12	70o orange & multi	1.50	2.00
a.		Booklet pane of 10	17.50	
		Nos. 814-816 (3)	4.00	2.85

Not fluorescent.

Albert Engstrom with Owl, Self-portrait A189

1969, May 12   **Engr.**   **Perf. 12½ Vert.**

817	A189	35o black brown	.30	.20
818	A189	55o blue gray	.30	.20

Perf. 12½ on 3 Sides

819	A189	35o black brown	.35	.55
a.		Booklet pane of 10	3.50	
820	A189	55o blue gray	.30	.30
a.		Booklet pane of 10	3.00	
		Nos. 817-820 (4)	1.25	1.25

Albert Engstrom (1869-1940), cartoonist.

Souvenir Sheet

Paintings by Ivan Agueli — A190

1969, June 6   **Litho.**   **Perf. 13½**

821	A190	Sheet of 6	2.50	4.25
a.		45o Landscape	.40	.45
b.		45o Still life	.40	.45
c.		45o Near East town	.40	.45
d.		55o Young woman	.40	.45
e.		55o Sunny landscape	.40	.45
f.		55o Street at night	.40	.45

Ivan Agueli (1869-1917), painter. Size: #821a-821c, 35x28mm. #821d-821e, 28x44mm. #821f, 48x44mm. Not fluorescent.

Tjorn Bridges — A191

Designs: 15o, 30o, Various bridges.

Perf. 12½ on 3 Sides

1969, Sept. 3   **Engr.**
Size: 20x19mm
Bluish Paper

822	A191	15o deep blue	1.10	.45
823	A191	30o dk grn & blk	1.10	.45

Size: 41x19mm

824	A191	55o blk & dp bl	1.10	.45
a.		Bklt. pane, 2 each #822-824	8.00	
		Nos. 822-824 (3)	3.30	1.35

Tjorn highway bridges connecting the islands of Orust and Tjorn in the Gothenburg Archipelago with the mainland.

Man's Head, Woodcarving — A192

Warship Wasa, 1628 — A193

Designs: No. 826, Crowned lion. No. 827, Great Swedish coat of arms. No. 828, Lion, front view. No. 829, Man's head (different from No. 825).

1969, Sept. 3   **Perf. 12½ on 3 Sides**

825	A192	55o dark red	.40	.20
826	A192	55o brown	.40	.20
827	A193	55o dark blue	.60	.70
828	A192	55o brown	.40	.20
829	A192	55o dark red	.40	.20
830	A193	55o dark blue	.60	.70
a.		Bklt. pane, #827, #830, 2 each #825-826, 828-829	5.50	
		Nos. 825-830 (6)	2.80	2.20

Salvaging in 1961 of the warship Wasa, sunk on her maiden voyage, Aug. 10, 1628.

Soderberg   Bo Bergman
A194   A195

Perf. 12½ Horiz.

1969, Oct. 13   **Engr.**

831	A194	45o brown, *buff*	.40	.30

Perf. 12½ Vert.

832	A195	55o green, *grnsh*	.40	.20

Perf. 12½ on 3 Sides

833	A194	45o brown, *buff*	.50	.85
a.		Booklet pane of 10	5.00	
834	A195	55o green, *grnsh*	.25	.40
a.		Booklet pane of 10	4.00	
		Nos. 831-834 (4)	1.55	1.75

Hjalmar Soderberg (1869-1941), writer; Bo Bergman (1869-1967), poet.

Lever Light, Lightship, Landsort and Svenska Lighthouses — A196

Perf. 12½ Vert.

1969, Nov. 17   **Photo.**

835	A196	30o gray, blk & pink	.25	.20
836	A196	55o lt bl, blk & brn	.35	.20

300th anniversary of Swedish lighthouses.

Pelle's New Suit — A197

The Adventures of Nils — A198

Swedish Fairy Tales: No. 839, Pippi Longstocking (little girl, horse and monkey). No. 840, Vill-Vallareman (boy blowing horn). No. 841, Kattresan (child riding on back of cat).

1969, Nov. 17   **Perf. 12½ on 3 Sides**

				Engr.
837	A197	35o org, red & dk brn	1.60	1.60
838	A198	35o dark brown	1.60	1.60
839	A197	35o org, red & dk brn	1.60	1.60
840	A198	35o dark brown	1.60	1.60
841	A197	35o org, red & dk brn	1.60	1.60
a.		Bklt. pane, 2 each #837-841	20.00	22.50
		Nos. 837-841 (5)	8.00	8.00

Issued for use in Christmas cards.

Dr. Emil T. Kocher and Wilhelm Ostwald — A199

55o, Selma Lagerlof, open book. 70o, Guglielmo Marconi, Carl Ferdinand Braun.

1969, Dec. 10   **Perf. 12½ Vert.**

842	A199	45o dull green	.75	.35
843	A199	55o blk, *pale sal*	.60	.20
844	A199	70o black	.75	1.25

Perf. 12½ on 3 Sides

845	A199	45o dull green	.45	.55
a.		Booklet pane of 10	5.00	
846	A199	55o blk, *pale sal*	.40	.30
a.		Booklet pane of 10	4.50	
		Nos. 842-846 (5)	2.95	2.65

Winners of the 1909 Nobel Prize.

Weather Vane, Soderala Church A200   Door with Iron Fittings, Bjorksta Church, Vastmanland A201

Swedish Art Forgings: 10o, like 5o, facing right. 30o, Memorial cross, Ekshärad churchyard, Varmland.

Perf. 12½ on 3 sides

1970, Feb. 9   **Engr.**

847	A200	5o slate grn & brn	.30	.20
848	A200	10o slate grn & brn	.30	.20
849	A200	30o blk & slate grn	.30	.20

Perf. 12½ Vert.

850	A201	55o brn & slate grn	.30	.20
a.		Bklt. pane, 2 each #847-850	2.00	3.75
		Nos. 847-850 (4)	1.20	.80

Ljusman River Rapids A202

1970, May 11   **Engr.**   **Perf. 12½ Vert.**

851	A202	45o black & multi	.30	.20
852	A202	70o black & multi	.65	.45

European Nature Conservation Year, 1970.

Skiing — A203

"Around the Arctic Circle": No. 853, View of Kiruna. No. 855, Boat on mountain lake in Stora Sjofellet National Park. No. 856, Reindeer herd and herdsman. No. 857, Rocket probe under northern lights.

Perf. 12½ Horiz.

1970, June 5   **Engr.**

853	A203	45o sepia	.50	.85
854	A203	45o violet blue	.50	.85
855	A203	45o dull green	.50	.85
856	A203	45o sepia	.50	.85
857	A203	45o violet blue	.50	.85
a.		Bklt. pane, 2 each #853-857	5.50	
		Nos. 853-857 (5)	2.50	4.25

China Palace, Drottningholm Park, 1769 — A204

Perf. 12½ Vert.
1970, Aug. 28   **Photo.**
858 A204 2k yel, grn & pink   1.50 .25

Glimmingehus, Skane Province, 15th Century — A205

Perf. 12½ Horiz.
1970, Aug. 28   **Engr.**
859 A205 55o gray green   .30 .20

Perf. 12½ on 3 Sides
860 A205 55o gray green   .35 .35
a.   Booklet pane of 10   2.50

Timber Industry A206   Miner A208

Shipping Industry — A207

Designs: No. 863, Heavy industry (propeller). No. 864, Hydroelectric power (dam and diesel). No. 865, Mining (freight train and mine). No. 866, Technical research.

Perf. 12½ on 3 sides
1970, Sept. 28   **Engr.**
861 A206 70o indigo & lt brn   2.00 2.50
862 A207 70o ind, lt brn & dp plum 2.00 2.50
863 A206 70o ind & dp plum   2.00 2.50
864 A206 70o ind & dp plum   2.00 2.50
865 A207 70o ind & dp plum   2.00 2.50
866 A206 70o dp plum & lt brn 2.00 2.50
a.   Booklet pane of 6, #861-866 12.00 15.00
867 A208 1k black, buff   .40 .35
a.   Booklet pane of 10   4.00

Perf. 12½ Vertically
868 A208 1k black, buff   .75 .30
       Nos. 861-868 (8)   13.15 15.65

Swedish trade and industry.

"Love, Not War" A209

Design: 70o, Four-leaf clovers symbolizing efforts for equality and brotherhood.

Engraved and Lithographed
1970, Oct. 24   **Perf. 12½ Horiz.**
869 A209 55o rose red, yel & blk .20 .40
a.   Booklet pane of 4   1.00
870 A209 70o emerald, yel & blk .40 .55
a.   Booklet pane of 4   1.25

Perf. 12½ Vert.
871 A209 55o rose red, yel & blk .35 .30
872 A209 70o emerald, yel & blk .30 .35
       Nos. 869-872 (4)   1.25 1.60

25th anniversary of the United Nations.

Bird Type of 1968
Birds: No. 873, Blackbird. No. 874, Great titmouse. No. 875, Bullfinch. No. 876, Greenfinch. No. 877, Blue titmouse.

Perf. 12½ on 3 Sides
1970, Nov. 20   **Photo.**
873 A187 30o blue grn & multi .85 .85
874 A187 30o bister & multi   .85 .85
875 A187 30o blue & multi   .85 .85
876 A187 30o pink & multi   .85 .85
877 A187 30o org yel & multi   .85 .85
a.   Bklt. pane, 2 each #873-877 8.00 12.50
       Nos. 873-877 (5)   4.25 4.25

Paul Johann Ludwig Heyse A210   Kerstin Hesselgren A211

Designs: 55o, Otto Wallach and Johannes Diderik van der Waals. 70o, Albrecht Kossel.

Perf. 12½ Horiz.
1970, Dec. 10   **Engr.**
878 A210 45o violet   .80 .40
879 A210 55o slate blue   .50 .30
880 A210 70o gray   1.10 1.10

Perf. 12½ on 3 Sides
881 A210 45o violet   .60 1.10
a.   Booklet pane of 10   6.50
882 A210 55o slate blue   .65 .35
a.   Booklet pane of 10   6.50
       Nos. 878-882 (5)   3.65 3.25

Winners of the 1910 Nobel Prize.

Perf. 12½ Horiz.
1971, Feb. 19   **Engr.**
883 A211 45o dp claret, gray   .45 .40
884 A211 1k dp brn, buff   .65 .20

Perf. 12½ on 3 Sides
885 A211 45o dp claret, gray   .30 .85
a.   Booklet pane of 10   3.25
       Nos. 883-885 (3)   1.40 1.45

50th anniv. of woman suffrage; Kerstin Hesselgren, was 1st woman member of Swedish Upper House.

Terns in Flight A212   Abstract Music, by Ingvar Lidholm A213

1971, Mar. 26   **Perf. 13½ Vert.**
886 A212 40o dark red   .40 .35
887 A212 55o violet blue   .80 .20

Perf. 12½ on 3 Sides
888 A212 55o violet blue   .40 .40
a.   Booklet pane of 10   4.50
       Nos. 886-888 (3)   1.60 .75

Joint northern campaign for the benefit of refugees.

Perf. 12½ Horiz.
1971, Aug. 27   **Engr.**
889 A213 55o deep lilac   .40 .20
890 A213 85o green   .45 .20

Perf. 12½ on 3 Sides
891 A213 55o deep lilac   .30 .30
a.   Booklet pane of 10   3.00
       Nos. 889-891 (3)   1.15 .70

The Three Kings, Grotlingbo Church — A214

Flight into Egypt, Stanga Church A215

Designs: 10o, Adam and Eve, Gammelgarn Church. 55o, Saint on horseback and Samson with the lion, Hogrän Church.

Perf. 12½ on 3 Sides
1971, Sept. 28   **Engr.**
892 A214 5o violet & brn   .60 .45
893 A214 10o violet & sl grn   .60 .45

Perf. 12½ Horiz.
894 A215 55o slate grn & brn   .60 .40
895 A215 65o brown & vio blk   .30 .20
a.   Bklt. pane, #892-894, 2 #895 2.50 3.50
       Nos. 892-895 (4)   2.10 1.50

Art of medieval stonemasons in Gotland.

Toddler and Automobile Wheel — A216

1971, Oct. 20   **Perf. 12½ Vert.**
896 A216 35o black & red   .20 .30
897 A216 65o dp blue & multi   .60 .20

Perf. 12½ on 3 Sides
898 A216 65o dp blue & multi   .40 .35
a.   Booklet pane of 10   5.75
       Nos. 896-898 (3)   1.20 .85

Publicity for road safety.

King Gustavus Vasa's Sword, c. 1500 — A217

Swedish Crown Regalia: No. 900, Scepter. No. 901, Crown. No. 902, Orb (Scepter, crown and orb were made in 1561 for Erik XIV). No. 903, Karl IX's anointing horn, 1606.

Perf. 12½ on 3 Sides
1971, Oct. 20   **Engr.**
899 A217 65o lt blue & multi   .50 .30
900 A217 65o lt ol grn & multi .50 .30
901 A217 65o dk blue & multi   .50 .30
902 A217 65o lt ol grn & multi .50 .30
903 A217 65o lt blue & multi   .50 .30
a.   Bklt. pane, 2 each #899-903 5.50 9.50
       Nos. 899-903 (5)   2.50 1.50

Christmas Elf and Goat Bringing Gifts — A218

Christmas Customs (Old Prints): No. 905, Christmas market. No. 906, Dancing children and father playing fiddle. No. 907, Ice-skating on frozen waterways in Stockholm. No. 908, Sleigh ride to church.

1971, Nov. 10
904 A218 35o deep carmine   1.25 1.10
905 A218 35o violet blue   1.25 1.10
906 A218 35o violet brown   1.25 1.10
907 A218 35o violet blue   1.25 1.10
908 A218 35o slate green   1.25 1.10
a.   Bklt. pane, 2 each #904-908 12.50 14.00
       Nos. 904-908 (5)   6.25 5.50

Maurice Maeterlinck A219   Women Athletes A220

Designs: 65o, Wilhelm Wien and Allvar Gullstrand. 85o, Marie Sklodovska Curie.

1971, Dec. 10   **Perf. 12½ Horiz.**
909 A219 65o orange   .65 .55
910 A219 65o green   .65 .20
911 A219 85o dk carmine   .65 .60

Perf. 12½ on 3 Sides
912 A219 55o orange   .60 .80
a.   Booklet pane of 10   6.00
913 A219 65o green   .65 .40
a.   Booklet pane of 10   6.50
       Nos. 909-913 (5)   3.20 2.55

Winners of the 1911 Nobel Prize.

1972, Feb. 23   Perf. 12½ on 3 Sides
914 A220 55o Fencing   .60 .75
915 A220 55o Diving   .60 .75
916 A220 55o Gymnastics   .60 .75
917 A220 55o Tennis   .60 .75
918 A220 55o Figure skating   .60 .75
a.   Bklt. pane, 2 each #914-918 6.25 10.00
       Nos. 914-918 (5)   3.00 3.75

Lars Johan Hierta, by Christian Eriksson — A221   Frans Michael Franzen, by Soderberg and Hultstrom — A222

Hugo Alfven, by Carl Milles — A223

Georg Stiernhielm, by David K. Ehrenstrahl — A224

Photo., Perf 12½ Horiz. (35, 85o); Engr., Perf. 12½ Vert. (50, 65o)
1972 Feb. 23
919 A221 35o multicolored   .30 .25
920 A222 50o violet   .40 .20
921 A223 65o bluish black   .40 .20
922 A224 85o multicolored   .50 .55
       Nos. 919-922 (4)   1.60 1.20

Hierta (1801-72), journalist. Franzen (1772-1847), poet. Alfven (1872-1960), composer. Stiernhielm (1598-1672), poet, writer, scientist.

Lifting Molten Glass A225

Swedish Glassmaking: No. 924, Glass blower. No. 925, Decorating vase. No. 926, Annealing vase. No. 927, Polishing jug.

Perf. 12½ Horiz.
1972, Mar. 22   **Engr.**
923 A225 65o black   .80 .75
924 A225 65o violet blue   .80 .75
925 A225 65o carmine   .80 .75
926 A225 65o black   .80 .75
927 A225 65o violet blue   .80 .75
a.   Bklt. pane, 2 each #923-927 8.00
       Nos. 923-927 (5)   4.00 3.75

Horses and Ruin of Borgholm Castle — A226

Designs: No. 929, Oland Island Bridge. No. 930, Kalmar Castle. No. 931, Salmon fishing. No. 932, Schooner Falken, Karlskrona.

1972, May 8   *Perf. 12½ Horiz.*
928	A226 55o chocolate	.65	.85
929	A226 55o dk violet blue	.65	.85
930	A226 55o dark brown	.65	.85
931	A226 55o blue green	.65	.85
932	A226 55o dk violet blue	.65	.85
a.	Bklt. pane, 2 each #928-932	6.00	
	Nos. 928-932 (5)	3.25	4.25

Tourist attractions in Southeast Sweden.

"Only one Earth" Environment Emblem — A227

"Spring," Bror Hjorth — A228

1972, June 5   *Engr.*   *Perf. 12½ Vert.*
933	A227 65o blue & carmine	.30	.20

Perf. 12½ Horiz.
934	A227 65o blue & carmine	.30	.30
a.	Booklet pane of 10	3.00	

Perf. 12½ Vert.
935	A228 85o brown & multi	.45	.30
a.	Booklet pane of 4	1.80	
	Nos. 933-935 (3)	1.05	.80

UN Conference on Human Environment, Stockholm, June 5-16.

Junkers JU52 — A229

Historic Planes: 5o, Junkers F13. 25o, Friedrichshafen FF49. 75o, Douglas DC-3.

1972, Sept. 8   *Perf. 12½ on 3 Sides*
Size: 20x19mm
936	A229 5o lilac	.20	.20

Size: 44x19mm
937	A229 15o blue	.45	.50
938	A229 25o blue	.45	.50
939	A229 75o gray green	.30	.30
a.	Bklt. pane, #937-938, 2 ea #936, 939	1.60	3.00
	Nos. 936-939 (4)	1.40	1.50

Stockholm from the South, by Johan Fredrik Martin — A230

Amphion Figurehead, by Per Ljung — A231

Lady with Veil, by Alexander Roslin — A232

#941, Anchor Forge, by Pehr Hillestrom. #943, Quadriga, by Johan Tobias von Sergel. #945, (Queen) Sofia Magdalena, by Carl Gustaf Pilo.

1972, Oct. 7   *Engr.*   *Perf. 12½ Horiz.*
940	A230 75o greenish black	.40	.50
941	A230 75o dark brown	.40	.50

Perf. 12½ on 3 Sides
942	A231 75o dark carmine	.45	.55
943	A231 75o dark carmine	.45	.55

Perf. 12½ on 2 Sides
944	A232 75o dk brn, blk & dk car	.45	.60
945	A232 75o dk brn, blk & dk car	.45	.60
a.	Booklet pane of 6, #940-945	2.75	4.50

18th century Swedish art.

Types of 1936
Imprint: "1972"

1972, Oct. 7   *Perf. 12½ on 3 Sides*
946	A36 10o dark carmine	.35	.50
947	A37 15o yellow green	.35	.50
948	A42 40o deep blue	.35	.50
949	A44 50o deep claret	.35	.50
950	A45 60o deep blue	.35	.50
a.	Bklt. pane, 2 each #946-950	3.00	7.00
	Nos. 946-950 (5)	1.75	2.50

Olle Hjortzberg (1872-1959), stamp designer. Booklet sold for 5k of which 1.50k was for Stockholmia 74, Intl. Phil. Exhib., Sept. 21-29, 1973.

Santa Claus — A233

St. Lucia Singers A234

Perf. 14 on 3 Sides
1972, Nov. 6   *Photo.*
951	A233 45o Candles	.35	.25
952	A233 45o shown	.35	.25
a.	Bklt. pane, 5 each #951-952	3.50	

Perf. 12½ Vert.
953	A234 75o gray & multi	.55	.20
	Nos. 951-953 (3)	1.25	.70

Christmas 1972 (children's drawings).

Horse — A235

Viking Ship — A236

Willows, by Peter A. Persson A237

Trosa, by Reinhold Ljunggren A238

Spring Birches, by Oskar Bergman A239

King Gustaf VI Adolf — A240

Perf. 12½ Horiz. or Vert.
1972-73   *Engr.*
954	A235 5o maroon ('73)	.20	.20
955	A236 10o dk blue ('73)	.20	.20
956	A237 40o sepia ('73)	.20	.20
957	A238 50o blk & brn ('73)	.30	.20
958	A239 55o yel grn ('73)	.35	.20
959	A240 75o indigo	.40	.20
960	A240 1k dp carmine	.65	.20

1973   *Perf. 12½ on 3 Sides*
961	A235 5o maroon	.20	.20
a.	Booklet pane of 20	.50	
962	A236 10o dark blue	.20	.20
a.	Booklet pane of 20	.60	
963	A240 75o indigo	.40	.20
a.	Booklet pane of 4	4.00	
	Nos. 954-963 (10)	3.10	2.00

King Gustaf VI Adolf — A245

Chinese Objects — A246

Designs: No. 983, King opening Parliament. No. 984, Etruscan vase and dish. No. 985, King with flowers.

1972, Nov. 11   *Perf. 12½ Vert.*
981	A245 75o violet blue	1.25	2.75
982	A245 75o slate green	1.25	2.75
983	A245 75o maroon	1.25	2.75
984	A246 75o violet blue	1.25	2.75
985	A245 75o slate green	1.25	2.75
a.	Bklt. pane of 5, #981-985	5.75	15.00

90th birthday of King Gustaf VI Adolf. Booklet sold for 4.75k of which 1k was for the King Gustaf VI Adolf Foundation for Swedish Cultural Activities.

Paul Sabatier and Victor Grignard — A247

Dr. Alexis Carrel — A248

75o, Nils Gustaf Dalen. 1k, Gerhart Hauptmann.

1972, Dec. 8   *Engr.*   *Perf. 12½ Vert.*
986	A247 60o olive bister	.60	.40

Perf. 12½ Horiz.
987	A248 65o dark blue	.70	.40
988	A248 75o violet	.90	.20
989	A248 1k redsh brown	1.10	.30
	Nos. 986-989 (4)	3.30	1.30

Winners of the 1912 Nobel Prize.

Mail Coach, 1923 — A249

Design: 70o, Postal autobus, 1972.

Perf. 12½ on 3 Sides
1973, Jan. 18   *Engr.*
990	A249 60o black, *yellow*	.30	.25
a.	Booklet pane of 10	3.00	

Perf. 12½ Vert.
991	A249 70o blue, orange & grn	.45	.25

Tintomara, by Lars Johan Werle — A250

Orpheus and Eurydice, by Christoph W. Gluck — A251

1973, Jan. 18   *Perf. 12½ Horiz.*
992	A250 75o green	.55	.20

Booklet Stamp
993	A251 1k red lilac	.55	.35
a.	Booklet pane of 5	3.00	

Bicentenary of the Royal Theater in Stockholm. The 75o shows a stage setting by Bo-Ruben Hedwall for Tintomara, a new opera, performed for the bicentenary celebration. The 1k shows painting by Pehr Hillestrom of Orpheus and Eurydice, which was first opera performed in Royal Theater.

Vaasa Ski Race, Dalecarlia — A252

Designs: No. 995, "Going to Church in Mora" (church boats), by Anders Zorn. No. 996, Church stables, Rättvik. No. 997, Falun copper mine. No. 998, Midsummer Dance, by Bengt Nordenberg.

1973, Mar. 2   *Perf. 12½ Horiz.*
994	A252 65o slate green	.40	.40
995	A252 65o slate green	.40	.40
996	A252 65o black	.40	.40
997	A252 65o slate green	.40	.40
998	A252 65o claret	.40	.40
a.	Bklt. pane, 2 each #994-998	4.00	
	Nos. 994-998 (5)	2.00	2.00

Tourist attractions in Dalecarlia.

Worker, Confederation Emblem — A253

1973, Apr. 26   *Perf. 12½ Vert.*
999	A253 75o dark carmine	.40	.20
1000	A253 1.40k slate blue	.75	.25

75th anniversary of the Swedish Confederation of Trade Unions (LO).

Observer Reading Temperature A254

Design: No. 1002, Clouds, photographed by US weather satellite.

1973, May 24   *Engr.*   *Perf. 12½ Vert.*
1001	A254 65o slate green	.75	.45
1002	A254 65o black & ultra	.75	.45
a.	Pair, #1001-1002	1.50	2.50

Cent. of the Swedish Weather Organization and of Intl. Meteorological Cooperation.

Nordic Cooperation Issue 1973

Nordic House, Reykjavik A254a

1973, June 26 *Perf. 12½ Vert.*
1003 A254a 75o multicolored .45 .20
1004 A254a 1k multicolored .65 .20

A century of postal cooperation among Denmark, Finland, Iceland, Norway and Sweden and in connection with the Nordic Postal Conference, Reykjavik, Iceland.

Carl Peter Thunberg (1743-1828) — A255

Swedish Explorers: No. 1006, Anders Sparrman (1748-1820) and Polynesian double canoe. No. 1007, Nils Adolf Erik Nordenskjold (1832-1901) and ship in pack ice. No. 1008, Salomon August Andrée (1854-1897) and balloon on snow field. No. 1009, Sven Hedin (1865-1952) and camel riders.

1973, Sept. 22 *Perf. 12½ Horiz.*
1005 A255 1k sl grn, bl & brn .95 1.10
1006 A255 1k bl, sl grn & brn .95 1.10
1007 A255 1k bl, sl grn & brn .95 1.10
1008 A255 1k black & multi .95 1.10
1009 A255 1k black & multi .95 1.10
a.   Bklt. pane of 5, #1005-1009 5.00 8.25

Plower with Ox Team A256

Designs: No. 1011, Woman working flax brake. No. 1012, Farm couple planting potatoes. No. 1013, Women baking bread. No. 1014, Man with horse-drawn sower.

1973, Oct. 24 *Perf. 12½ Horiz.*
1010 A256 75o grnsh black 1.00 .30
1011 A256 75o red brown 1.00 .30
1012 A256 75o grnsh black 1.00 .30
1013 A256 75o plum 1.00 .30
1014 A256 75o red brown 1.00 .30
a.   Bklt. pane, 2 ea #1010-1014 10.00
     Nos. 1010-1014 (5) 5.00 1.50

Centenary of Nordic Museum, Stockholm.

Gray Seal — A257

King Gustaf VI Adolf — A258

Protected Animals: 20o, Peregrine falcon. 25o, Lynx. 55o, Otter. 65o, Wolf. 75o, White-tailed sea eagle.

1973, Oct. 24 *Perf. 12½ on 3 Sides*
1015 A257 10o slate green .20 .20
1016 A257 20o violet .20 .20
1017 A257 25o Prus green .20 .20
1018 A257 55o Prus green .20 .20
1019 A257 65o violet .20 .20
1020 A257 75o slate green .35 .35
a.   Bklt. pane, 2 each #1015-1020 2.50 3.00
     Nos. 1015-1020 (6) 1.35 1.35

1973, Oct. 24 *Perf. 12½ Vert.*
1021 A258 75o dk violet blue .30 .20
1022 A258 1k purple .50 .20

King Gustaf VI Adolf (1882-1973).

The Three Kings A259

Charles XIV John A260

The Goosegirl, by Josephson A261

#1024, Merry country dance. #1026, Basket with stylized Dalecarlian gourd plant.

Perf. 14 Horiz.
1973, Nov. 12 **Photo.**
1023 A259 45o multicolored .35 .30
1024 A259 45o multicolored .35 .30
a.   Bklt. pane, 5 each #1023-1024 3.50

Coil Stamps
1025 A260 75o multicolored 1.40 .20
1026 A260 75o multicolored 1.40 .20
a.   Pair, #1025-1026 5.00
     Nos. 1023-1026 (4) 3.50 1.00

Christmas 1973. Designs are from Swedish peasant paintings.

Perf. 12½ Horiz.
1973, Nov. 12 **Engr.**
1027 A261 10k multicolored 4.50 .35

Ernst Josephson (1851-1906), painter.

Alfred Werner and Heike Kamerlingh-Onnes A262

Charles Robert Richet A263

Design: 1.40k, Rabindranath Tagore.

1973, Dec. 10 **Engr.** *Perf. 12½ Vert.*
1028 A262 75o dark violet .55 .20

Perf. 12½ Horiz.
1029 A263 1k dark brown .55 .30
1030 A263 1.40k green .65 .20
     Nos. 1028-1030 (3) 1.75 .70

Winners of 1913 Nobel Prize.

Ski Jump A264

Skiing: No. 1032, Cross-country race. No. 1033, Relay race. No. 1034, Slalom. No. 1035, Women's cross-country race.

Perf. 12½ Horiz.
1974, Jan. 23 **Engr.**
1031 A264 65o slate green .55 .65
1032 A264 65o violet blue .55 .65
1033 A264 65o slate green .55 .65
1034 A264 65o dk carmine .55 .65
1035 A264 65o violet blue .55 .65
a.   Bklt. pane, 2 each #1031-1035 11.00
     Nos. 1031-1035 (5) 2.75 3.25

Drawing of First Industrial Digester A265

Hans Järta and Quotation from 1809 — A266

Samuel Owen and 19th Century Factory A267

1974, Mar. 5 **Engr.** *Perf. 12½ Vert.*
1036 A265 45o sepia .20 .20
1037 A266 60o green .30 .30
1038 A267 75o dull red .45 .20
     Nos. 1036-1038 (3) .95 .70

Centenary of sulphite pulp process (45o); Hans Järta (1774-1847), statesman responsible for the Instrument of Government Act of 1809 (60o); Samuel Owen (1774-1854), English-born industrialist who introduced new production methods (75o).

Stora Sjofallet (Great Falls) — A268

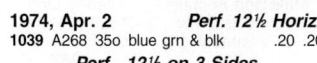

Street in Ystad — A269

1974, Apr. 2 *Perf. 12½ Horiz.*
1039 A268 35o blue grn & blk .20 .20
Perf. 12½ on 3 Sides
1040 A269 75o dull claret .30 .20
a.   Booklet pane of 10 3.00

UPU Type of 1924 A270

1974 **Engr.** *Perf. 12½ on 3 Sides*
1041 A270 20o green .30 .35
1042 A270 25o ultra .30 .35
1043 A270 30o dark brown .30 .35
1044 A270 35o dark red .30 .35
a.   Bklt. pane, 2 each #1041-1044 2.50 3.50
     Nos. 1041-1044 (4) 1.20 1.40

Miniature Sheets
Perf. 12½
1045   Sheet of 4 2.00 3.50
a.   A270 20o ocher, single stamp .40 .75
1046   Sheet of 4 2.00 3.50
a.   A270 25o dk vio, single stamp .40 .75
1047   Sheet of 4 2.00 3.50
a.   A270 30o dk red, single stamp .40 .75
1048   Sheet of 4 2.00 3.50
a.   A270 35o yel grn, single stamp .40 .75

Stockholmia 74 philatelic exhibition, Stockholm, Sept. 21-29. Booklet sold for 3k with surtax going toward financing the exhibition.
Nos. 1045-1048 sold during exhibition in folder with 5k entrance ticket.
Issued: #1041-1044, 4/2; #1045-1048, 9/21.

"Man in Storm," by Bror Marklund — A271

Europa: 1k, Sculpture by Picasso, Lake Vanern, Kristinehamm.

Perf. 12½ Horiz.
1974, Apr. 29 **Engr.**
1049 A271 75o violet brown 1.10 .30
1050 A271 1k slate green 1.25 .30

King Carl XVI Gustaf — A272

1974-78 **Engr.** *Perf. 12½ Vert.*
1068 A272 75o slate grn .40 .20
1069 A272 90o brt blue ('75) .35 .20
1070 A272 1k maroon .45 .20
1071 A272 1.10k rose red ('75) .40 .20
1072 A272 1.30k green ('76) .50 .20
1073 A272 1.40k violet bl ('77) .60 .20
1074 A272 1.50k red lilac ('80) .60 .20
1075 A272 1.70k orange ('78) .75 .20
1076 A272 2k dk brown ('80) .85 .20

Perf. 12½ on 3 Sides
1077 A272 75o slate green .30 .20
a.   Booklet pane of 10 3.00
1078 A272 90o brt blue ('75) .30 .20
a.   Booklet pane of 10 3.00
1079 A272 1k maroon ('76) .40 .20
a.   Booklet pane of 10 4.00
1080 A272 1.10k rose red ('77) .40 .20
a.   Booklet pane of 10 4.00
1081 A272 1.30k green ('78) .50 .20
a.   Booklet pane of 10 5.00
1082 A272 1.50k red lilac ('80) .60 .20
a.   Booklet pane of 10 6.00
     Nos. 1068-1082 (15) 7.40 3.00

A273

Central Post Office, Stockholm A274

Mailman, Northernmost Rural Delivery Route — A275

Perf. 12½ on 3 Sides
1974, June 7 **Engr.**
1084 A273 75o violet brown .70 .30
1085 A274 75o violet brown .70 .30
a.   Bklt. pane, 5 ea #1084-1085 7.00
Perf. 12½ Vert.
1086 A275 1k slate green .65 .20
     Nos. 1084-1086 (3) 2.05 .80

Centenary of Universal Postal Union.

Regatta A276

Scenes from Sweden's West Coast: No. 1088, Vinga Lighthouse. No. 1089, Varberg Fortress. No. 1090, Seine fishing. No. 1091, Fishing village Mollosund.

1974, June 7 *Perf. 12½ Horiz.*
1087 A276 65o crimson .55 .55
1088 A276 65o blue .55 .55
1089 A276 65o dk olive green .55 .55
1090 A276 65o slate green .55 .55
1091 A276 65o brown .55 .55
a.   Bklt. pane, 2 each #1087-1091 4.50
     Nos. 1087-1091 (5) 2.75 2.75

Mr. Simmons, by Axel Fridell — A277

Thread and Spool — A278

Perf. 12½ on 3 Sides
1974, Aug. 28   **Engr.**
1092 A277 45o black   .25 .20
  a.   Booklet pane of 10   2.50

Perf. 12½ Horiz.
1093 A277 1.40k deep claret   .75 .20

Swedish Publicists' Club, centenary.

1974, Aug. 28   **Perf. 12½ Horiz.**
#1095, Sewing machines (abstract).
1094 A278 85o deep violet   .40 .30
1095 A278 85o black & org   .40 .30
  a.   Pair, #1094-1095   .90 .80

Swedish textile and clothing industries.

Tugs in Stockholm Harbor — A279

#1096, Tanker. #1097, Liner "Snow Storm."
#1098, Ice breakers Tor and Atle. #1099,
Skane Train Ferry, Trelleborg-Sassnitz.

1974, Nov. 16   **Perf. 12½ Horiz.**
1096 A279 1k dark blue   .70 .75
1097 A279 1k dark blue   .70 .75
1098 A279 1k dark blue   .70 .75
1099 A279 1k dark blue   .70 .75
1100 A279 1k dark blue   .70 .75
  a.   Bklt. pane of 5, #1096-1100   3.50 6.00

Swedish shipping industry.

Miniature Sheet

Quilt from Skepptuna Church — A280

Deer, Quilt from Hog Church — A281

Designs are from woolen quilts, 15th-16th
centuries. Motifs shown on No. 1101 are stylized deer, griffins, lions, unicorn and horses.

1974, Nov. 16   **Photo.**   **Perf. 14**
1101 A280 Sheet of 10   9.50 13.00
  a.-j. 45o, single stamp   .95   1.00

Perf. 13 Horiz.
1102 A281 75o bl blk, red & yel   .45 .20

Max von Laue — A282

Designs: 70o, Theodore William Richards.
1k, Robert Bárány.

1974, Dec. 10 Engr.   Perf. 12½ Vert.
1103 A282 65o rose red   .35 .20
1104 A282 70o slate   .45 .30
1105 A282 1k indigo   .95 .20
      Nos. 1103-1105 (3)   1.75 .70
Winners of 1914 Nobel Prize.

A283

No. 1106, Sven Jerring's children's program. No. 1107, Televising parliamentary
debate.

1974, Dec. 10   **Perf. 12½ Vert.**
1106 75o dk blue & brn   .65 .20
1107 75o brown & dk bl   .65 .20
  a.   A283 Pair, #1106-1107   1.25 2.00
Swedish Broadcasting Corp., 50th anniv.

Account Holder's Envelope A285

Photogravure and Engraved
1975, Jan. 21   **Perf. 14 Vert.**
1108 A285 1.40k ocher & blk   .65 .35
Swedish Postal Giro Office, 50th anniv.

Male and Female Architects, New Parliament A286

Jenny Lind (1820-87), by J. O. Sodermark A287

1975, Mar. 25 Engr.   Perf. 12½ Vert.
1109 A286 75o slate green   .40 .20

Perf. 12½ Horiz.
1110 A287 1k claret   .60 .20

Perf. 12½ on 3 Sides
1111 A286 75o slate green   .35 .20
  a.   Booklet pane of 10   3.50
      Nos. 1109-1111 (3)   1.35 .60
International Women's Year 1975.

Horseman, Helmet Decoration A288

"Gold Men" A289

Designs: 15o, Scabbard and hilt. 20o,
Shield buckle. 55o, Iron helmet.

1975, Mar. 25   Perf. 12½ on 3 sides
1112 A288 10o dull red   .20 .20
1113 A288 15o slate green   .20 .20
1114 A288 20o violet   .20 .20
1115 A288 55o violet brown   .20 .20
  a.   Bklt. pane, 2 each #1112-1115   .75 1.60

Perf. 12½ Horiz.
1116 A289 25o deep yellow   .20 .20
      Nos. 1112-1116 (5)   1.00 1.00
Treasures from tombs of the Vendel period
(550-800 A.D.), and "gold men" (25o) from
Eketorp II excavations (400-700 A.D.).

Europa Issue 1975

New Year's Eve at Skansen, by Eric Hallstrom — A290

Inferno, by August Strindberg — A291

Perf. 12½ Vert.
1975, Apr. 28   **Photo.**
1117 A290 90o multi   .75 .20

Perf. 12½ Horiz.
1118 A291 1.10k multi   .75 .20

Capercaillie A292

Rok Stone, 9th Century A293

1975, May 20 Engr.   Perf. 12½ Vert.
1119 A292 170o indigo   .70 .20

Perf. 12½ Horiz.
1120 A293 2k deep claret   .85 .20

Metric Tape Measure — A294

Folke Filbyter Statue, by Milles — A296

Hernqvist by Per Krafft the Younger — A295

1975, May 20   **Perf. 12½ Vert.**
1121 A294 55o deep blue   .35 .30
1122 A295 70o yel brn & dk brn   .40 .20

Perf. 12½ Horiz.
1123 A296 75o violet   .40 .20
      Nos. 1121-1123 (3)   1.15 .70
Cent. of Intl. Meter Convention, Paris, 1875;
bicent. of Swedish veterinary medicine,
founded by Peter Hernqvist (1726-1808); Carl
Milles (1875-1955), sculptor.

Officers' Mess, Rommehed, 1798 — A297

No. 1124, Skelleftea Church Village, 17th
cent. No. 1125, Foundry and furnace, Engelsberg, 18th cent. No. 1126, Gunpowder
Tower, Visby. No. 1127, Falun Mine pithead
gear, 1852.

1975, June 13   **Perf. 12½ Horiz.**
1124 A297 75o black   .50 .65
1125 A297 75o dk carmine   .50 .65
1126 A297 75o black   .50 .65
1127 A297 75o dk carmine   .50 .65
1128 A297 75o violet blue   .50 .65
  a.   Bklt. pane, 2 each #1124-1128   5.50
      Nos. 1124-1128 (5)   2.50 3.25
European Architectural Heritage Year 1975.

Rescue at Sea: Helicopter over Ice-
covered Tanker — A298

Designs: No. 1129, Fire fighters: firemen
fighting fire. No. 1130, Customs narcotics service: trained dogs checking cargo. No. 1131,
Police: Officer talking to boy on bridge. No.
1132, Hospital Service: patient arriving by
ambulance.

1975, Aug. 27   **Perf. 12½ Horiz.**
1129 A298 90o dk car rose   .65 .45
1130 A298 90o dk bl   .65 .45
1131 A298 90o dk car rose   .65 .45
1132 A298 90o dk bl   .65 .45
1133 A298 90o green   .65 .45
  a.   Bklt. pane, 2 each #1129-1133   6.50
      Nos. 1129-1133 (5)   3.25 2.25
Public service organizations watching,
guarding, helping.

"Fryckstad" A299

"Gotland" A300

Design: 90o, "Prins August."

1975, Aug. 27 Perf. 12½ on 3 Sides
            Size: 20x19mm
1134 A299 5o green   .20 .20
1135 A300 5o dark blue   .20 .20
            Size: 45x19mm
1136 A299 90o slate green   .55 .20
  a.   Bklt. pane, 2 each #1134-1136   1.75 2.50
      Nos. 1134-1136 (3)   .95 .60

Scouts — A302

1975, Oct. 11   Photo.   Perf. 14 Vert.
1137 90o Around campfire   .50 .20
1138 90o In canoes   .50 .20
  a.   A301 Pair, #1137-1138   1.00 2.00
Nordjamb 75, 14th World Boy Scout Jambo-
ree, Lillehammer, Norway, July 29-Aug. 7.

Hedgehog A303

Old Man Playing Key Fiddle — A304

Romeo and Juliet Ballet — A305

1975, Oct. 11   Engr.   Perf. 12½ Vert.
1139 A303 55o black .30 .20
1140 A304 75o dk red .55 .20

Perf. 12½ Horiz.
1141 A305 7k blue green 3.25 .20

Perf. 12½ on 3 Sides
1142 A303 55o black .25 .20
a. Booklet pane of 10 2.50
Nos. 1139-1142 (4) 4.35 .80

Virgin Mary, 12th Cent. Statue — A306

Chariot of the Sun, from 12th Cent. Altar — A307

Mourning Mary, c. 1280 — A308

Jesse at Foot of Genealogical Tree, c. 1510 — A309

Christmas: #1145, Nativity, from 12th cent. gilt-copper altar. #1148, like #1147.

Perf. 14 Horiz.
1975, Nov. 11   Photo.
1143 A306 55o multi .30 .20

Perf. 12½ on 3 Sides
1144 A307 55o gold & multi .35 .30
1145 A307 55o gold & multi .35 .30
a. Bklt. pane, 5 each #1144-1145 3.00

Perf. 12½ Horiz.   Engr.
1146 A308 90o brown .50 .20

Perf. 12½ on 3 Sides
1147 A309 90o red .60 .30
1148 A309 90o blue .60 .30
a. Bklt. pane, 5 ea #1147-1148 6.00
Nos. 1143-1148 (6) 2.70 1.60

No. 1145a was issued with top row of 5 either No. 1144 or No. 1145.

William H. and William L. Bragg — A310

Designs: 90o, Richard Willstätter. 1.10k, Romain Rolland.

1975, Dec. 10   Engr.   Perf. 12½ Vert.
1149 A310 75o claret .40 .45
1150 A310 90o violet blue .45 .20
1151 A310 1.10k slate green .55 .35
Nos. 1149-1151 (3) 1.40 1.00

Winners of 1915 Nobel Prize.

Cave of the Winds, by Eric Grate — A311

1976, Jan. 27   Perf. 12½ Vert.
1152 A311 1.90k slate green .90 .20

The sculpture by Eric Grate (b. 1896) stands in front of the Town Hall of Vasteras.

Razor-billed Auks and Black Guillemot A312

Bobbin Lace Maker from Vadstena A313

1976, Mar. 10   Engr.   Perf. 12½ Vert.
1153 A312 85o dark blue .55 .20

Perf. 12½ Horiz.
1154 A313 1k claret brn .45 .30

Perf. 12½ on 3 Sides
1155 A312 85o dk bl .30 .30
a. Booklet pane of 10 3.00
1156 A313 1k claret brn .40 .30
a. Booklet pane of 10 4.00
Nos. 1153-1156 (4) 1.70 1.10

Old and New Telephones, Relays — A314

1976, Mar. 10   Perf. 12½ Vert.
1157 A314 1.30k brt violet .75 .20
1158 A314 3.40k red 1.35 .45

Centenary of first telephone call by Alexander Graham Bell, March 10, 1876.

Europa Issue 1976

Lapp Elk Horn Spoon — A315

Tile Stove — A316

Perf. 14½ Horiz.
1976, May 3   Photo.
1159 A315 1k multi .65 .20
1160 A316 1.30k multi .65 .45

Wheat and Cornflower Seeds — A317

Viable and Nonviable Seedlings A318

1976, May 3   Engr.   Perf. 12½ Vert.
1161 A317 65o brown .30 .20
1162 A318 65o choc & grn .30 .20
a. Pair, #1161-1162 .60 .65

Swedish seed testing centenary.

King Carl XVI Gustaf and Queen Silvia — A319

Perf. 12½ Vert.
1976, June 19   Engr.
1163 A319 1k rose car .30 .20
1164 A319 1.30k slate grn .40 .20

Perf. 12½ on 3 Sides
1165 A319 1k rose car .30 .20
a. Booklet pane of 10 3.00
Nos. 1163-1165 (3) 1.00 .60

Wedding of King Carl XVI Gustaf and Silvia Sommerlath.

View from Ringkallen, by Helmer Osslund — A320

Views in Angermanland Province: No. 1167, Tugboat pulling timber. No. 1168, Hay-drying racks. No. 1169, Granvagsnipan slope, Angerman River. No. 1170, Seine fishing.

1976, June 19   Perf. 12½ Horiz.
1166 A320 85o slate grn .40 .55
1167 A320 85o vio bl .40 .55
1168 A320 85o dp brn .40 .55
1169 A320 85o vio bl .40 .55
1170 A320 85o brn red .40 .55
a. Bklt. pane, 2 each #1166-1170 4.50
Nos. 1166-1170 (5) 2.00 2.75

Roman Cross and Ship's Wheel — A321

1976, June 19   Perf. 12½ Horiz.
1171 A321 85o brt bl & bl .45 .30

Swedish Seamen's Church, centenary.

Torgny Segerstedt and 1917 Page of Gothenburg Journal — A322

1976, June 19   Perf. 12½ Vert.
1172 A322 1.90k brn & blk .80 .30

Torgny Segerstedt (1876-1945), editor in chief of the Gothenburg Journal of Commerce and Shipping, birth centenary.

Coiled Snake, Bronze Buckle — A323

Pilgrim's Badge, Adoration of the Magi — A324

Drinking Horn, 14th Century — A325

Chimney Sweep — A326

Girl's Head, by Bror Hjorth, 1922 — A327

Perf. 12½ Horiz., Vert. (30o)
1976, Sept. 8   Engr.
1173 A323 15o bister .20 .20
1174 A324 20o green .20 .20
1175 A325 30o dk rose brn .20 .20
1176 A326 90o indigo .40 .20
1177 A327 9k yel grn & sl grn 3.50 .25
Nos. 1173-1177 (5) 4.50 1.05

Inventors A328

#1178, John Ericsson (1803-1889), ship propeller and "Monitor". #1179, Helge Palmcrantz (1842-80) & reaper. #1180, Lars Magnus Ericsson (1846-1926) & switchboard. #1181, Sven Wingquist (1876-1953) & ball bearing. #1182, Gustaf de Laval (1845-1913) & milk separator.

1976, Oct. 9   Engr.   Perf. 12½ Horiz.
1178 A328 1.30k multi .60 .75
1179 A328 1.30k multi .60 .75
1180 A328 1.30k multi .60 .75
1181 A328 1.30k multi .60 .75
1182 A328 1.30k multi .60 .75
a. Bklt. pane of 5, #1178-1182 3.75 6.00

Swedish inventors and their technological inventions.

Hands and Cogwheels A329

1976, Oct. 9   Perf. 12½ Vert.
1183 A329 85o org & dk vio .40 .20
1184 A329 1k yel grn & brn .55 .20

Industrial safety.

Verner von Heidenstam, Lake Vattern — A330

1976, Nov. 17   Perf. 12½ Vert.
1185 A330 1k yellow green .40 .20
1186 A330 1.30k blue .55 .45

Verner von Heidenstam (1859-1940), Swedish poet, 1916 Nobel Prize winner.

Archangel Michael A331

Virgin Mary Visiting St. Elizabeth A332

Christmas: No. 1189, like No. 1187. No. 1190, St. Nicholas saving 3 children. No. 1191, like No. 1188. No. 1192, Illuminated page, prayer to Virgin Mary. 65o, stamps are from Flemish prayer book, c. 1500. 1k stamps are from Austrian prayer book, late 15th century.

Perf. 12½ Horiz.
1976, Nov. 17   Photo.
1187 A331 65o blue & multi .30 .20
1188 A332 1k gold & multi .30 .20

Perf. 12½ on 3 Sides
1189	A331	65o blue & multi	.20	.40
1190	A331	65o blue & multi	.20	.40
a.		Bklt. pane, 5 each #1189-1190	2.50	

Perf. 12½ Vert.
1191	A332	1k gold & multi	.30	.20
1192	A332	1k gold & multi	.30	.20
a.		Bklt. pane, 5 each #1191-1192	3.00	
		Nos. 1187-1192 (6)	1.60	1.60

Five Water Lilies — A333

Photogravure and Engraved
1977, Feb. 2   **Perf. 12½ Horiz.**
1193	A333	1k brt grn & multi	.45	.20
1194	A333	1.30k ultra & multi	.55	.55

Nordic countries cooperation for protection of the environment and 25th Session of Nordic Council, Helsinki, Feb. 19.

Tailor — A334

1977, Feb. 24   **Perf. 12½ Vert.**
1195	A334	2.10k red brn	.95	.20

Longdistance Skating — A335

Perf. 12½ Horiz.
1977, Mar. 24   **Engr.**
1196	A335	95o shown	.45	.55
1197	A335	95o Swimming	.45	.55
1198	A335	95o Bicycling	.45	.55
1199	A335	95o Jogging	.45	.55
1200	A335	95o Badminton	.45	.55
a.		Bklt. pane, 2 each #1196-1200	4.50	
		Nos. 1196-1200 (5)	2.25	2.75

Physical fitness.

Politeness, by "OA," 1905 — A336

1977, Mar. 24   **Perf. 12½ on 3 Sides**
1201	A336	75o black	.35	.20
a.		Booklet pane of 10	3.50	

Perf. 12½ Horiz.
1202	A336	3.80k red	1.75	.45

Oskar Andersson (1877-1906), cartoonist.

Calle Schewen A337

No. 1204, Seagull. No. 1205, Dancers and accordionist. No. 1206, Fishermen in boat. No. 1207, Tree on shore at sunset.
Designs are illustrations for poem The Calle Schewen Waltz, by Evert Taube, and include bars of music of this song.

1977, May 2   Engr.   Perf. 12½ Horiz.
1203	A337	95o slate grn	.45	.55
1204	A337	95o vio bl	.45	.55
1205	A337	95o grn & blk	.45	.55
1206	A337	95o dark blue	.45	.55
1207	A337	95o red	.45	.55
a.		Bklt. pane, 2 each #1203-1207	4.50	
		Nos. 1203-1207 (5)	2.25	2.75

Tourist publicity for Roslagen (archipelago) and to honor Evert Taube (1890-1976), poet.

Gustavianum, Uppsala University A338

1977, May 2   Photo.   Perf. 12½ Vert.
1208	A338	1.10k multi	.55	.20

Perf. 12½ on 3 Sides
1209	A338	1.10k multi	.35	.20
a.		Booklet pane of 10	3.50	

Uppsala University, 500th anniversary.

Europa Issue 1977

Forest in Snow A339

Rapadalen Valley — A340

1977, May 2   **Perf. 12½ Vert.**
1210	A339	1.10k multi	1.10	.30
1211	A340	1.40k multi	1.10	.65

Owl — A341

Cast-iron Stove Decoration — A342

Gotland Ponies A343

1977, Sept. 8   Engr.   Perf. 12½ Vert.
1212	A341	45o dk slate grn	.40	.30

Perf. 12½ Horiz.
1213	A342	70o dk vio bl	.45	.20

Booklet Stamp
1214	A343	1.40k brown	.55	.35
a.		Booklet pane of 5	2.75	
		Nos. 1212-1214 (3)	1.40	.85

Wild Berries — A344

Perf. 14 on 3 Sides
1977, Sept. 8   **Photo.**
1215	A344	75o Blackberry	.30	.35
1216	A344	75o Cranberry	.30	.35
1217	A344	75o Raspberry	.30	.35
1218	A344	75o Whortleberry	.30	.35
1219	A344	75o Alpine strawberry	.30	.35
a.		Bklt. pane, 2 each #1215-1219	3.00	5.00
		Nos. 1215-1219 (5)	1.50	1.75

Horse-drawn Trolley — A345

Designs: Public transportation.

1977, Oct. 8   Engr.   Perf. 12½ Horiz.
1220	A345	1.10k shown	.55	.65
1221	A345	1.10k Electric trolley	.55	.65
1222	A345	1.10k Ferry	.55	.65
1223	A345	1.10k Tandem bus	.55	.65
1224	A345	1.10k Subway	.55	.65
a.		Bklt. pane of 5, #1220-1224	3.00	5.50

Putting up Sheaf for the Birds — A346

Preparing Dried Soaked Fish — A347

Traditional Christmas Preparations: No. 1227, Children baking ginger snaps. No. 1228, Bringing in Yule tree. No. 1229, Making straw goat. No. 1230, Candle dipping.

Perf. 12½ Horiz.
1977, Nov. 17   **Engr.**
1225	A346	75o violet	.35	.20
1226	A347	1.10k yel grn	.55	.20

Perf. 12½ on 3 Sides
1227	A346	75o ocher	.35	.20
1228	A346	75o slate grn	.35	.20
a.		Bklt. pane, 5 each #1227-1228	2.50	
1229	A347	1.10k dk red	.40	.20
1230	A347	1.10k dk bl	.40	.20
a.		Bklt. pane, 5 each #1229-1230	4.00	
		Nos. 1225-1230 (6)	2.40	1.20

Christmas 1977.

Henrik Pontoppidan, Karl Adolph Gjellerup A348

Design: 1.40k, Charles Glover Barkla.

1977, Nov. 17   **Perf. 12½ Vert.**
1231	A348	1.10k red brn	.60	.30
1232	A348	1.40k yel grn	.65	.65

1917 Nobel Prize winners: Henrik Pontoppidan (1857-1943) and Karl Adolph Gjellerup (1857-1919), Danish writers; Charles Glover Barkla (1877-1944), English X-ray pioneer.

Space Without Affiliation, by Arne Jones — A349

Brown Bear — A350

1978, Jan. 25   **Perf. 12½ Horiz.**
1233	A349	2.50k vio bl	1.00	.20

1978, Apr. 11   **Perf. 12½ Horiz.**
1234	A350	1.15k dark brown	.50	.20

Europa Issue 1978

Örebro Castle — A351

Arch and Stairs — A352

1978, Apr. 11   **Perf. 12½ Vert.**
1235	A351	1.30k slate green	1.35	.20

Perf. 12½ Horiz.
1236	A352	1.70k dull red	1.75	.65

Pentecostal Preacher and Congregation A353

Free Churches: No. 1238, Swedish Missionary Society. No. 1239, Evangelical National Missionary Society. No. 1240, Baptist Society. No. 1241, Salvation Army.

1978, Apr. 11   **Perf. 12½ on 3 sides**
1237	A353	90o purple	.45	.35
1238	A353	90o slate	.45	.35
1239	A353	90o violet	.45	.35
1240	A353	90o slate	.45	.35
1241	A353	90o purple	.45	.35
a.		Bklt. pane, 2 each #1237-1241	4.50	6.00
		Nos. 1237-1241 (5)	2.25	1.75

Independent Christian Associations.

Brosarp Hills — A354

Grindstone Production A355

Red Limestone Cliff — A356

Designs: No. 1243, Avocets. No. 1245, Linnaea borealis (Linné's favorite flower.) No. 1247, Linné with Lapp drum, wearing Lapp clothes and Dutch doctor's hat.

Perf. 12½ Horiz.
1978, May 23   **Engr.**
1242	A354	1.30k gray green	.65	.40
1243	A354	1.30k violet blue	.65	.40

Perf. 12½ on 3 Sides
1244	A355	1.30k violet brown	.65	.60
1245	A355	1.30k brown red	.65	.60

Perf. 12½ on 2 Sides
1246	A356	1.30k violet blue	.65	.60
1247	A356	1.30k violet brown	.65	.60
a.		Bklt. pane of 6, #1242-1247	4.25	5.00

Travels of Carl von Linné (1707-1778), botanist.

Cranes, Lake Hornborgasjon — A357

Designs: No. 1248, Gliding School, Alleberg. No. 1250, Skara Church, Lacko Island. No. 1251, Ancient rock tomb, Luttra. No. 1252, Cloth merchants, sculpture by Nils Sjogren.

1978, May 23   Perf. 12½ Horiz.
1248 A357 1.15k dull green   .55   .45
1249 A357 1.15k maroon   .55   .45
1250 A357 1.15k violet blue   .55   .45
1251 A357 1.15k dk gray grn   .55   .45
1252 A357 1.15k brn & gray grn   .55   .45
  a.   Bklt. pane, 2 each #1284-1252   5.50
    Nos. 1248-1252 (5)   2.75   2.25

Tourist publicity for Vastergotland.

Laurel and Scroll — A358

1978, May 23   Perf. 12½ Vert.
1253 A358 2.50k gray & sl grn   1.00   .20
Stockholm University, centenary.

Homecoming, by Carl Kylberg — A359

Nude, by Karl Isakson A360   Self-portrait, by Ivar Arosenius A361

1978, Sept. 5 Engr. Perf. 12½ Vert.
1254 A359 90o multicolored   .40   .40
Perf. 12½ Horiz.
1255 A360 1.15k multi   .55   .30
1256 A361 4.50k multi   1.75   .40
    Nos. 1254-1256 (3)   2.70   1.10

Swedish painters: Carl Kylberg (1878-1952); Karl Isakson (1878-1922); Ivar Arosenius (1878-1909).

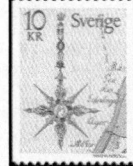

North Arrow (Compass Rose), Map, 1769 — A362

1978, Sept. 5   Perf. 12½ Horiz.
1257 A362 10k lilac   3.75   .20

Coronation Coach, 1699 — A363

1978, Oct. 7 Engr. Perf. 12½ Horiz.
1258 A363 1.70k dk red, yel   .80   .45
  a.   Booklet pane of 5   4.00

Orange Russula — A364

Designs: Edible mushrooms.

1978, Oct. 7   Perf. 12½ on 3 Sides
1259 A364 1.15k shown   .50   .65
1260 A364 1.15k Lycoperdon perlatum   .50   .65
1261 A364 1.15k Macrolepiota procera   .50   .65
1262 A364 1.15k Cantharellus cibarius   .50   .65
1263 A364 1.15k Boletus edulis   .50   .65
1264 A364 1.15k Ramaria botrytis   .50   .65
  a.   Bklt. pane of 6, #1259-1264   3.50   6.50

Toy Ferris Wheel — A365   Rider Drawing Water Cart — A366

Toys: No. 1266, Teddy bear. No. 1267, Dalecarlian wooden horse. No. 1268, Doll. No. 1269, Spinning tops.

Perf. 12½ Horiz.
1978, Nov. 14   Engr.
1265 A365 90o dk red & grn   .45   .20
1266 A365 1.30k brt ultra   .65   .20
Perf. 12½ on 3 Sides
Photo.
1267 A365 90o multicolored   .35   .20
1268 A365 90o multicolored   .35   .20
  a.   Bklt. pane, 5 each #1267-1268   3.50
1269 A366 1.30k multicolored   .55   .20
1270 A366 1.30k multicolored   .55   .20
  a.   Bklt. pane, 5 each #1269-1270   5.50
    Nos. 1265-1270 (6)   2.90   1.20

Christmas 1978.

Fritz Haber — A367

Design: 1.70k, Max Planck.

1978, Nov. 14 Engr. Perf. 12½ Vert.
1271 A367 1.30k dark brown   .65   .50
1272 A367 1.70k dark violet bl   .85   .65

1918 Nobel Prize winners: Fritz Haber (1868-1934), German chemist; Max Planck (1858-1947), German physicist. See #1310-1312, 1341-1344, 1387-1389.

Bandy — A368

1979, Jan. 25 Engr. Perf. 12½ Vert.
1273 A368 1.05k violet blue   .45   .20
1274 A368 2.50k orange   1.10   .20

Child Wearing Gas Mask in Heavy Traffic — A369

1979, Mar. 13   Perf. 12½ Vert.
1275 A369 1.70k dark blue   .85   .60
International Year of the Child.

Drill-weave Tapestry, c. 1855-1860 A370   Carrier Pigeon, Hand with Quill A371

1979, Mar. 13   Perf. 12½ Horiz.
1276 A370 4k gray & red   1.65   .20

Perf. 14x14½ on 3 Sides
1979, Apr. 2   Photo.
1277 A371 (1k) ultra & yel   1.50   .20
  a.   Booklet pane of 20   30.00
    Price of booklet 20k.

DISCOUNT BOOKLETS
Every Swedish household received during Apr. 1979, 2 coupons for the purchase of 2 discount booklets, #1277a. The stamps were for use on post cards and letters within Sweden. The stamps are inscribed "INRIKES POST."
The program continued with numerous changes. The Inscription changed to "PRIVATPOST" in 1981, the same year that denominations were added. At some point the stamps could also be used to Denmark, Norway, Finland and Iceland. In 1991 the discount value of the stamps ended July, 1.
The last stamps inscribed "PRIVAT POST" were issued in 1993.

Mail Service by Boat, Grisslehamn to Echero A372

Europa: 1.70k, Hand on telegraph.

1979, May 7 Engr. Perf. 12½ Vert.
1278 A372 1.30k slate grn & blk   2.25   .35
1279 A372 1.70k ocher & blk   2.25   .85

Woodcutter, Winter — A373

Designs: No. 1281, Sowing, spring. No. 1282, Grazing cattle, summer. No. 1283, Harvester, summer. No. 1284, Plowing, autumn.

1979, May 7   Perf. 12½ Horiz.
1280 A373 1.30k multicolored   .55   .45
1281 A373 1.30k sl grn & dk brn   .55   .45
1282 A373 1.30k dk brn & sl grn   .55   .45
1283 A373 1.30k sl grn & ocher   .55   .45
1284 A373 1.30k multicolored   .55   .45
  a.   Bklt. pane, 2 each #1280-1284   5.75
    Nos. 1280-1284 (5)   2.75   2.25

Tourist Steamer Juno — A374

Roller Bridge, Hajstorp — A375

Sailing Ship — A376

Gota Canal: No. 1286, Borenshult Lock. No. 1288, Hand-drawn gate. No. 1290, Rowboat in Forsvik lock.

1979, May 7   Perf. 12½ Horiz.
1285 A374 1.15k violet blue   .55   .60
1286 A374 1.15k slate green   .55   .60
Perf. 12½ on 3 Sides
1287 A375 1.15k dull purple   .55   .75
1288 A375 1.15k carmine   .55   .75
Perf. 12½ on 2 Sides
1289 A376 1.15k violet blue   .55   .75
1290 A376 1.15k slate green   .55   .75
  a.   Bklt. pane of 6, #1285-1290   3.50   5.00
    Nos. 1285-1290 (6)   3.30   4.20

Strikers and Sawmill A377

1979, Sept. 6 Engr. Perf. 12½ Vert.
1291 A377 90o car & dp brn   .55   .35

Temperance Movement Banner — A378

Jons Jacob Berzelius A379   Johan Olof Wallin A380

Perf. 12½ Horiz.
Litho.
1292 A378 1.30k multi   .55   .30
Engr.
1293 A379 1.70k brown & grn   .75   .40
1294 A380 4.50k slate blue   1.75   .50
    Nos. 1291-1294 (4)   3.60   1.55

Centenaries of Sundsvall strike and Swedish Temperance Movement; birth bicentennials of Jons Jacob Berzelius (1779-1848), physician and chemist; Johan Olof Wallin (1779-1839), Archbishop and poet.

Dragonfly
A381

Green Spotted Toad
A383

Pike
A382

1979, Sept. 6   *Perf. 12½ Horiz.*
1295 A381 60o violet   .40 .40

Perf. 12½ Vert.
1296 A382 65o gray   .50 .35
1297 A383 80o olive green   .50 .55
    Nos. 1295-1297 (3)   1.40 1.30

Swedish Rococo — A384

Designs: 90o, Potpourri pot. 1.15k, Portrait, by Johan Henrik Scheffel. 1.30k, Silver coffee-pot. 1.70k, Bust of Carl Johan Cronstedt.

Souvenir Sheet

Engraved and Photogravure
1979, Oct. 6   *Perf. 12x12½*
1298 A384   Sheet of 4   2.40 3.25
  a.-d.   Any single   .50 .60

No. 1298 sold for 6k; surtax was for philately.

Herrings, Age Determination — A386

Sea Research: No. 1300, Acoustic survey of sea bottom. No. 1301, Water bloom of algae in Baltic Sea. No. 1302, Computer map of herring distribution in South Baltic Sea. No. 1303, Research ship Argos.

1979, Oct. 6   Engr.   *Perf. 12½ Horiz.*
1299 A386 1.70k multicolored   .75 .75
1300 A386 1.70k sepia   .75 .75
1301 A386 1.70k multicolored   .75 .75
1302 A386 1.70k sepia   .75 .75
1303 A386 1.70k multicolored   .75 .75
  a.   Bklt. pane of 5 (1299-1303)   3.75 5.00

Brooch from
Jamtland
A387

Ljusdal Costume
A388

Christmas (Costumes and Jewelry from): #1305, Pendant, Smaland. #1307, Osteraker. #1308, Goinge. #1309, Mora.

Perf. 12½ Horiz.
1979, Nov. 15   Engr.
1304 A387 90o dk Prus blue   .40 .30
1305 A387 1.30k dull red   .40 .20

Perf. 12½ on 3 Sides
Photo.
Size: 22x27mm
1306 A388 90o multicolored   .30 .30
1307 A388 90o multicolored   .30 .30
  a.   Bklt. pane, 5 each #1306-1307   3.00

Perf. 12½ Vert.
Size: 26x44mm
1308 A388 1.30k multicolored   .45 .20
1309 A388 1.30k multicolored   .45 .20
  a.   Bklt. pane, 5 each #1308-1309   4.50
    Nos. 1304-1309 (6)   2.30 1.50

Nobel Prize Winner Type of 1978
1919 Winners: 1.30k, Jules Bordet (1870-1961), Belgian bacteriologist. 1.70k, Johannes Stark (1874-1957), German physicist. 2.50k, Carl Spitteler (1845-1924), Swiss poet.

1979, Nov. 15   Engr.   *Perf. 12½ Vert.*
1310 A367 1.30k lilac   .50 .35
1311 A367 1.70k ultra   .75 .85
1312 A367 2.50k olive green   1.00 .30
    Nos. 1310-1312 (3)   2.25 1.50

Wind
Power — A389

Renewable Energy Sources: No. 1314, Biodegradable material. No. 1315, Solar energy. No. 1316, Geothermal energy. No. 1317, Hydro power.

1980, Jan. 29   *Perf. 12½ on 3 sides*
1313 A389 1.15k dark blue   .65 .65
1314 A389 1.15k dk grn & bis   .65 .65
1315 A389 1.15k yellow orange   .65 .65
1316 A389 1.15k dark green   .65 .65
1317 A389 1.15k dk bl & dk grn   .65 .65
  a.   Bklt. pane, 2 each #1313-1317   6.50 10.00
    Nos. 1313-1317 (5)   3.25 3.25

Crown Princess
Victoria and King
Carl XVI
Gustaf — A390

1980, Feb. 26   *Perf. 12½ on 3 sides*
1318 A390 1.30k brt blue   .40 .20
  a.   Booklet pane of 10   4.00

Perf. 12½ Vert.
1319 A390 1.30k brt blue   .55 .20
1320 A390 1.70k carmine rose   .75 .40
    Nos. 1318-1320 (3)   1.70 .80

Child Holding
Adult's
Hand — A391

Hand Holding
Cane — A392

1980, Apr. 22   *Perf. 12½ Horiz.*
1321 A391 1.40k red brown   .65 .20
1322 A392 1.60k slate green   .75 .20

Parents' insurance system; care for the elderly.

Squirrel — A393

Perf. 15 on 3 Sides
1980, May 12   Photo.
1323 A393 (1k) ultra & yellow   1.50 .20
  a.   Booklet pane of 20   30.00

See note after No. 1277.

Elise Ottesen-
Jensen (1886-
1973), Journalist
A394

Europa: 1.70k, Joe Hill (1879-1915), member of American Workers' Movement and poet.

1980, June 4   Engr.   *Perf. 12½ Vert.*
1324 A394 1.30k green   1.10 .20
1325 A394 1.70k red   1.30 1.10

Banga Farm, Alfta, Halsingland
Province — A395

Tourism (Halsingland Province): No. 1327, Iron Works, Iggesund. No. 1328, Blaxas Ridge, Forsa. No. 1329, Tybling farm, Tyby. No. 1330, Sunds Canal, Hudiksvall.

1980, June 4   *Perf. 12½ Horiz.*
1326 A395 1.15k red   .55 .65
1327 A395 1.15k dark blue   .55 .65
1328 A395 1.15k dark green   .55 .65
1329 A395 1.15k chocolate   .55 .65
1330 A395 1.15k dark blue   .55 .65
  a.   Bklt. pane, 2 each #1326-1330   5.50
    Nos. 1326-1330 (5)   2.75 3.25

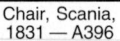
Chair, Scania,
1831 — A396

Cradle, North
Bothnia, 19th
Century — A397

Perf. 12½ Horiz.
1980, Sept. 9   Engr.
1331 A396 1.50k grnsh blue   .65 .20

Perf. 12½ Vert.
1332 A397 2k dk red brown   .95 .45

Norden 80.

Scene from "Diagonal
Symphony,"
1924 — A398

1980, Sept. 9   *Perf. 12½ Horiz.*
1333 A398 3k dark blue   1.10 .30

Viking Eggeling (1880-1925), artist and film maker.

Souvenir Sheet

Gustaf Erikson's
Carriage — A399

Swedish Automobile History: 90o, Gustaf Erikson's carriage. 1.15k, Vabis, 1909. 1.30k, Thulin, 1923. 1.40k, Scania, 1903. 1.50k, Tidaholm, 1917. 1.70k, Volvo, 1927.

Photogravure and Engraved
1980, Oct. 11   *Perf. 12½*
1334 A399   Sheet of 6   4.00 5.00
  a.-f.   Any single   .65 .65

No. 1334 sold for 9k.

Bamse the
Bear — A401

Farmer Kronblom — A402

Christmas 1980 (Comic Strip Characters): No. 1336, Mandel Karlsson, vert. No. 1337, Adamson, vert.

1980, Oct. 11   Engr.   *Perf. 12½ Vert.*
1335 A401 1.15k multicolored   .45 .30

Perf. 12½ on 3 sides
Photo.
1336 A401 1.15k multicolored   .40 .30
  a.   Booklet pane of 10   4.00

Perf. 12½ Horiz.
Engr.
1337 A401 1.50k black   .50 .20

Photo.
1338 A402 1.50k multicolored   .50 .20
  a.   Booklet pane of 10   5.00
    Nos. 1335-1338 (4)   1.85 1.00

Angel Blowing
Horn
A403

Necken, by Ernst
Josephson
A404

Perf. on 3 Sides
1980, Nov. 18   Engr.
1339 A403 1.25k multicolored   .50 .50
  a.   Booklet pane of 12   6.00

Christmas 1980.

1980, Nov. 18   *Perf. 12½ Horiz.*
1340 A404 8k multicolored   3.25 .20

Nobel Prize Winner Type of 1978
1920 Winners: #1341, Knut Hamsun (1859-1953), Norwegian writer. #1342, August Krogh (1874-1949), Danish Physiologist, #1343, Charles-Edouard Guillaume (1861-1938), French physicist. #1344, Walther Nernst (1864-1941), German chemist.

1980, Nov. 18   *Perf. 13 on 3 Sides*
1341 A367 1.40k dk blue gray   .65 .30
1342 A367 1.40k red   .65 .30
  a.   Bklt. pane, 5 each #1341-1342   6.50
1343 A367 2k green   .85 .55
1344 A367 2k brown   .85 .55
  a.   Bklt. pane, 5 each #1343-1344   8.50
    Nos. 1341-1344 (4)   3.00 1.70

Ernst Wigforss
(1881-1977),
Politician & Writer
A405

Freya (Fertility
Goddess)
A406

1981, Jan. 29   Engr.   *Perf. 12½ Vert.*
1345 A405 5k rose carmine   2.25 .35

1981, Jan. 29   *Perf. 12½ on 3 Sides*

Norse Mythological Characters: 10o, Thor (thunder god). 15o, Heimdall (rainbow god). 50o, Frey (god of peace, fertility, weather). 1k, Odin.

1346 A406 10o blue black   .20 .20
1347 A406 15o dk carmine   .20 .20
1348 A406 50o dk carmine   .30 .20
1349 A406 75o deep green   .30 .20
1350 A406 1k blue black   .35 .20
  a.   Bklt. pane, 2 each #1346-1350   2.75
    Nos. 1346-1350 (5)   1.35 1.00

Gyrfalcon
A407

1981, Feb. 26 Engr. *Perf. 12½ Vert.*
1351 A407 50k multicolored 13.50 .75
  a. Booklet pane of 4 55.00

Troll Chasing
Boy — A408

Europa: 2k, Lady of the Woods.

1981, Apr. 28 Engr.
1352 A408 1.50k dk blue & red 1.40 .30
1353 A408 2k dk green & red 1.40 .40

Intl. Year of the
Disabled — A409

1981, Apr. 28
1354 A409 1.50k dk green .65 .20
1355 A409 3.50k purple 1.60 .50

Arms of
Oster-gotland
Province
A410

Sail Boat, Bohuslan
A411

Perf. 14½ on 3 Sides
1981, May 18 Photo.
1356 A410 1.40k shown 1.50 .20
1357 A410 1.40k Jamtland 1.50 .20
1358 A410 1.40k Dalarna 1.50 .20
1359 A410 1.40k Bohuslan 1.50 .20
  a. Bklt. pane, 5 each #1356-
      1359 30.00
  Nos. 1356-1359 (4) 6.00 .80
    See note after No. 1277. See Nos. 1403-
1406, 1456-1459, 1492-1495, 1534-1537,
1592-1595.

Perf. 12½ on 3 Sides
1981, May 26 Engr.
1360 A411 1.65k shown .65 .60
1361 A411 1.65k Blekinge .65 .60
1362 A411 1.65k Norrbotten .65 .60
1363 A411 1.65k Halsingland .65 .60
1364 A411 1.65k Gotland .65 .60
1365 A411 1.65k Skane .65 .60
  a. Bklt. pane of 6, #1360-1365 4.00 6.50

King Carl XVI
Gustaf
A412

Queen Silvia
A413

1981-84 *Perf. 12½ Vert.*
1366 A412 1.65k dark green .65 .20
1367 A413 1.75k dark blue .75 .35
1368 A412 1.80k dark blue ('83) .75 .20
1369 A412 1.90k red ('84) .75 .20
1370 A412 2.40k violet brn .95 .55

1371 A413 2.40k grnsh black
      ('84) .95 .85
1372 A412 2.70k brt lilac ('83) 1.20 1.10
1373 A413 3.20k red ('83) 1.30 1.00
  Nos. 1366-1373 (8) 7.30 4.45

Day and
Night — A414

Scene from Par
Lagerkvist's
Autobiography
Guest of
Reality — A415

Perf. 12½ on 3 Sides
1981, Sept. 9 Engr.
1376 A414 1.65k dark blue .50 .20
  a. Booklet pane of 10 5.00

1981, Sept. 9 *Perf. 12½ Horiz.*
1377 A415 1.50k dark green .75 .20

Conductor Sixten Ehrling and Opera
Singer Birgit Nilsson — A416

Bjorn Borg,
Tennis Player
A417

Baker's Sign
A418

  Designs: No. 1378, Electric locomotive.
No. 1379, Trucks. No. 1381, Oil rig. No. 1383,
Ingemar Stenmark, skier.

**Perf. 12½ on 2 (Type A416) or 3
(Type A417) sides**
1981, Sept. 9
1378 A416 2.40k rose carmine 1.25 .75
1379 A416 2.40k red 1.25 .75
1380 A416 2.40k rose lilac 1.25 .75
1381 A416 2.40k deep violet 1.25 .75
1382 A417 2.40k dark blue 1.25 .75
1383 A417 2.40k dark blue 1.25 .75
  a. Bklt. pane of 6, #1378-1383 7.50 8.50

1981, Sept. 9 *Perf. 12½ Vert.*
1384 A418 2.30k shown 1.50 .20
1385 A418 2.30k Pewter shop
            sign 1.50 .20
  a. Pair, #1384-1385 3.00 1.90

A419

  Swedish Films: a, Olof Ahs in The Coach-
man. b, Ingrid Bergman and Gosta Ekman in
Intermezzo. c, Greta Garbo in The Gosta
Berling Saga, d, Stig Jarrel and Alf Kjellin in
Persecution. e, Kari Sylwan and Harriet
Andersson in Cries and Whispers

Photogravure and Engraved
1981, Oct. 10 *Perf. 13½*
1386 A419 Sheet of 5 3.75 5.50
  a.-e. Any single .75 .90
    No. 1386 sold for 10k.

Nobel Prize Winner Type of 1978
  1921 Winners: 1.35k, Albert Einstein (1879-
1955), German physicist. 1.65k, Anatole
France (1844-1924), French writer. 2.70k,
Frederick Soddy (1877-1956), British chemist.

Christmas
1981 — A421

  Designs: Wooden birds.

1981, Nov. 24 Engr. *Perf. 12½ Vert.*
1387 A367 1.35k red .55 .30
1388 A367 1.65k green .75 .20
1389 A367 2.70k blue 1.10 .75
  Nos. 1387-1389 (3) 2.40 1.25

1981, Nov. 24 *Perf. 12½ on 3 Sides*
1390 A421 1.40k red .55 .20
1391 A421 1.40k green .55 .20
  a. Bklt. pane, 5 each #1390-1391 5.50

Knight on
Horseback,
by John
Bauer
A422

  John Bauer (1882-1918), Fairytale Illustra-
tor: No. 1393, "What a Miserable Little Pale-
face, said the Troll Mother." No. 1394, Marsh
Princess. No. 1395, Now the Dusk of the
Night is already Upon Us.

Perf. 12x12½ on 3 sides
1982, Feb. 16 Engr.
1392 A422 1.65k multicolored .65 .55
1393 A422 1.65k multicolored .65 .55
1394 A422 1.65k multicolored .65 .55
1395 A422 1.65k multicolored .65 .55
  a. Bklt. pane of 4, #1392-1395 2.75 3.50

Impossible
Figures — A423

  Designs: Geometric figures.

1982, Feb. 16 *Perf. 12½ Horiz.*
1396 A423 25o violet brown .20 .20
1397 A423 50o brown olive .20 .20
1398 A423 75o dark blue .30 .20
  Nos. 1396-1398 (3) .70 .60

Newspaper
Distributor, by
Svenolov Ehren
A424

Graziella, by
Carl Larsson
A425

1982, Feb. 16
1399 A424 1.35k deep violet .70 .20
1400 A425 5k violet brown 1.90 .20

Europa Issue 1982

Land
Reform,
19th
Cent.
A426

Anders Celsius
(1701-1744),
Inventor of
Temperature
Scale — A427

1982, Apr. 26 Engr. *Perf. 12½ Vert.*
1401 A426 1.65k dk olive grn 2.75 .20

Perf. 12½ on 3 Sides
1402 A427 2.40k dark green 1.10 .65
  a. Booklet pane of 6 6.50

Provincial Arms Type of 1981
Perf. 14 on 3 Sides
1982, Apr. 26 Photo.
1403 A410 1.40k Dalsland 1.50 .20
1404 A410 1.40k Oland 1.50 .20
1405 A410 1.40k Vastmandland 1.50 .20
1406 A410 1.40k Halsingland 1.50 .20
  a. Bklt. pane, 5 each #1403-
      1406 30.00
  Nos. 1403-1406 (4) 6.00 .80
    See note after No. 1277.

Elin Wagner (1882-
1949), Writer — A428

Perf. 12½ Horiz.
1982, June 3 Engr.
1407 A428 1.35k Sketch by Siri
            Derkert .50 .35

Burgher
House — A429

Embroidered Lace
Ribbon, 19th
Cent. — A430

1982, June 3 *Perf. 12½ Vert.*
1408 A429 1.65k brown .75 .20

Perf. 12½ Horiz.
1409 A430 2.70k bister 1.10 .80
  Cent. of Museum of Cultural History, Lund.

1982 Intl.
Buoyage
System
A431

  Designs: Various buoy signals.

1982, June 3 *Perf. 13 Horiz.*
1410 A431 1.65k shown .60 .45
1411 A431 1.65k Ferry .60 .45
1412 A431 1.65k Six sailboats .60 .45
1413 A431 1.65k One-globed
            buoy .60 .45
1414 A431 1.65k Two-globed
            buoy .60 .45
  a. Bklt. pane, 2 each #1410-1414 6.00
  Nos. 1410-1414 (5) 3.00 2.25

Vietnamese Workers in
Sweden — A432

  Living Together: Swedish emigration and
immigration.

1982, Aug. 26 Engr. *Perf. 13 Horiz.*
1415 A432 1.65k Leaving Swe-
            den, 1880 .65 .55
1416 A432 1.65k shown .65 .55
1417 A432 1.65k Local voting
            right .65 .55

1418 A432 1.65k Girls .65 .55
   a. Bkl. pane, 2 each #1415-1418 5.50
   Nos. 1415-1418 (4) 2.60 2.20

Wild
Orchids — A433

Photogravure and Engraved
1982, Oct. 9   *Perf. 12x13*

Wild Orchids: 1.65k (No. 1419a), Orchis mascula. 1.65k (No. 1419d), Cypripedium calcéolus. 2.40k, Epipactis palustris. 2.70k, Dactylorhiza sambucina.

1419 A433 Sheet of 4 5.00 *6.00*
  a.-d. Any single 1.10 1.30

Sold for 10k for benefit of stamp collecting.

Christmas
1982 — A434

Stained-glass Windows, Church at Lye, Gotland, 14th cent.

Perf. 13 on 3 Sides
1982, Nov. 24   **Photo.**
1420 A434 1.40k Angel .65 .40
1421 A434 1.40k Child in the
    Temple .65 .40
1422 A434 1.40k Adoration of the
    Kings .65 .40
1423 A434 1.40k Tidings to the
    Shepherds .65 .40
1424 A434 1.40k Birth of Christ .65 .40
   a. Bkl. pane, 2 each #1420-1424 6.50 *7.50*
   Nos. 1420-1424 (5) 3.25 2.00

Signature, Atomic Model — A435

Nobel Prizewinners in Physics (Quantum Mechanics). Various Atomic Models: No. 1425, Niels Bohr, Denmark, 1922. No. 1426, Erwin Schrodinger, Austria, 1933. No. 1427, Louis de Broglie, France, 1929. No. 1428, Paul Dirac, England, 1933. No. 1429, Werner Heisenberg, Germany, 1932.

1982, Nov. 24 **Engr.** *Perf. 13 Horiz.*
1425 A435 2.40k multi 1.10 .85
1426 A435 2.40k multi 1.10 .85
1427 A435 2.40k multi 1.10 .85
1428 A435 2.40k multi 1.10 .85
1429 A435 2.40k multi 1.10 .85
   a. Bkl. pane of 5, #1425-1429 6.00 *6.50*
   Nos. 1425-1429 (5) 5.50 4.25

Fruit
A436

Games
A436a

Crown and
Posthorn
A436b

King Carl XVI
Gustaf
A436c

Queen Silvia
A436d

Games
A436e

1983-85 **Engr.**   *Perf. 12½ Vert.*
1430 A436 5o Horse chest-
    nut .20 .20
1431 A436 10o Norway ma-
    ple .20 .20
1432 A436 15o Dogrose .20 .20
1433 A436 20o Sloe .20 .20
1434 A436a 50o Fox and
    cheese .30 .30
1435 A436a 60o Dominoes .30 .30
1436 A436a 70o Ludo .30 .30
1437 A436a 80o Chinese
    checkers .40 .30
1438 A436a 90o Backgammon .45 .40
1439 A436b 1.60k deep blue .75 .30
1440 A436c 2k black .70 .20
1441 A436b 2.50k bister .90 .30
1442 A436c 2.70k dull red brn 1.10 1.00

Perf. 12½ Horiz.
1443 A436e 3k Chess 1.40 .20

Perf. 12½ Vert.
1444 A436d 3.20k brt blue 1.30 1.25
1445 A436b 4k dp car 1.30 .20
   Nos. 1430-1445 (16) 10.00 5.65

Issued: #1430-1433, 2/10/83; #1434-1438, 1443, 10/12/85; #1439-1442, 1444-1445, 1/24/85.
See Nos. 1567-1580, 1783.

Peace Movement
Centenary
A437

1983, Feb. 10
1446 A437 1.35k blue .55 .35

Nils Ferlin (1898-
1961),
Poet — A438

1983, Feb. 10
1447 A438 6k dk grn 2.50 .20

500th
Anniv. of
Printing
in
Sweden
A439

1983, Feb. 10   *Perf. 13 Horiz.*
1448 A439 1.65k Lead type .65 .35
1449 A439 1.65k Dialogus
    Creaturarum,
    1483 .65 .35
1450 A439 1.65k Carolus XII Bi-
    ble, 1703 .65 .35
1451 A439 1.65k ABC Books,
    1760s .65 .35
1452 A439 1.65k Laser photo
    composition .65 .35
   a. Bkl. pane, 2 each #1448-1452 7.50
   Nos. 1448-1452 (5) 3.25 1.75

Sweden-US Relations
Bicentenary — A440

1983, Mar. 24
1453 A440 2.70k Ben Franklin,
    Swedish Arms 1.10 .65
   a. Booklet pane of 5 5.50
    See US No. 2036.

Nordic
Cooperation
Issue — A441

Perf. 12½ Horiz.
1983, Mar. 24   **Engr.**
    Size: 21x27mm
1454 A441 1.65k Bicycling .60 .35

Perf. 13 Vert.
1455 A441 2.40k Sailing 1.00 .85

Provincial Arms Type of 1981
1983, Apr. 25 **Photo.** *Perf. 14½x14*
1456 A410 1.60k Vastergotland 1.50 .20
1457 A410 1.60k Medelpad 1.50 .20
1458 A410 1.60k Gotland 1.50 .20
1459 A410 1.60k Gastrikland 1.50 .20
   a. Bkl. pane, 5 each #1456-
    1459 30.00
   Nos. 1456-1459 (4) 6.00 .80
    See note after No. 1277.

Europa — A442

Perf. 12½ Horiz.
1983, Apr. 25   **Engr.**
1460 A442 1.65k Swedish Ballet
    Co. 1.25 .35
1461 A442 2.70k Sliding-jaw
    wrench 1.25 1.25

A443

Designs: 1k, 3k, 10-ore King Oscar II definitive essays, 1884. 2k, No. 39. 4k, No. 58.

1983, May 25   *Perf. 12½*
1462 A443 1k blue .60 .50
1463 A443 2k red .85 .55
1464 A443 3k blue 1.10 .85
1465 A443 4k green 1.25 1.00
   a. Bkl. pane of 4, #1462-1465 4.25 *4.50*

STOCKHOLMIA Intl. Stamp Exhibition, Aug. 28-Sept. 7, 1986

Red
Cross — A444

Greater
Karlso — A445

1983, Aug. 24   *Perf. 12½ Horiz.*
1466 A444 1.50k red .75 .20
1467 A445 1.60k dk blue .75 .20

Planorbis
Snail — A446

Arctic
Fox — A447

1983, Aug. 24   *Perf. 12½ on 3 Sides*
1468 A446 1.80k green .65 .20
   a. Booklet pane of 10 6.50

Perf. 12½ Horiz.
1469 A447 2.10k grnsh blk .75 .45
    See Nos. 1488-1489, 1526-1527, 1623-1626, 1678-1680, 1762-1763.

Hjalmar Bergman
(1883-1931),
Writer — A448

1983, Aug. 24   *Perf. 13 Horiz.*
1470 A448 1.80k Portrait .75 .20
1471 A448 1.80k Jac the Clown
    illustration by
    Nisse Skoog .75 .20
   a. Pair, #1470-1471 1.50 .95

View of Helgeandsholmen, Stockholm,
by Franz Hogenberg, 1580 — A449

1983, Aug. 24   *Perf. 12½ Vert.*
1472 A449 2.70k dl pur & dk bl 1.25 .70

A450

Photogravure and Engraved
1983, Oct. 1   *Perf. 13½*
1473 A450 Sheet of 5 5.25 *6.00*
   a. 1.80k Wilhelm Stenhammar, pi-
    anist .95 .75
   b. 1.80k Aniara (opera) .95 .75
   c. 1.80k Lars Gullin, jazz saxo-
    phonist .95 .75
   d. 1.80k ABBA, pop music group .95 .75
   e. 2.70k Hins Anders, violinist 1.20 1.20

Sold for 11.50k.

Christmas
1983 — A452

Postcard designs: No. 1474, Christmas Gnomes around the tree. No. 1475, on straw goats. No. 1476, Folk children, Christmas porridge and gingerbread. No. 1477, Gnomes carrying Christmas gifts on a pole.

Perf. 12½ on 3 sides
1983, Nov. 22   **Photo.**
1474 A452 1.60k multi .65 .30
1475 A452 1.60k multi .65 .30
1476 A452 1.60k multi .65 .30
1477 A452 1.60k multi .65 .30
   a. Bkl. pane, 3 each #1474-1477 7.50
   Nos. 1474-1477 (4) 2.60 1.20

Chemistry, Nobel Prize Winners — A453

Designs: No. 1478, Arne Tiselius (1902-1971), Electrophoresis Studies. No. 1479, George De Hevesy (1885-1966), Radioactive isotope tracers. No. 1480 Svante Arrhenius (1859-1927), Theory of Electrolytic Dissociation. No. 1481, Theodor Svedberg (1884-1971), Colloid Studies. No. 1482, Hans Von Euler-Chelpin (1873-1964). Enzyme and Vitamin Structures.

Photogravure and Engraved
1983, Nov. 22   **Perf. 12½ Horiz.**
1478	A453	2.70k slate	1.25	.85
1479	A453	2.70k dp bl vio	1.25	.85
1480	A453	2.70k red lilac	1.25	.85
1481	A453	2.70k blue blk	1.25	.85
1482	A453	2.70k grnsh blk	1.25	.85
a.	Bklt. pane of 5, #1478-1482		6.50	7.00

Postal Savings Centenary — A454

Design: 100o, Three crowns.

1984, Feb. 9   Engr.   Perf. 12½ Vert.
1483	A454	100o orange	.45	.35
1484	A454	1.50k purple	.65	.55
1485	A454	1.80k pink	.75	.20
	Nos. 1483-1485 (3)		1.85	1.10

Europa 1984 A455

Symbolic bridge of communications exchange.

1984, Feb. 9   Perf. 12½ Horiz.
1486	A455	1.80k red	.75	.25
a.	Booklet pane of 10		7.50	

Perf. 13 Vert.
1487	A455	2.70k dp ultra	2.75	1.50

Conservation Type of 1983 and

Angelica — A457

1984, Mar. 27   Perf. 12½ on 3 Sides
1488	A447	1.90k Lemmings	.60	.20
1489	A447	1.90k Musk ox	.60	.20
a.	Bklt. pane, 5 each #1488-1489		6.00	

Perf. 12½ Horiz.
1490	A457	2k shown	1.00	.20
1491	A457	2.25k Alpine birch	1.10	.75
	Nos. 1488-1491 (4)		3.30	1.35

Provincial Arms Type of 1981
1984, Apr. 24   Photo.   Perf. 14½x14
1492	A410	1.60k Sodermanland	1.50	.20
1493	A410	1.60k Blekinge	1.50	.20
1494	A410	1.60k Vasterbotten	1.50	.20
1495	A410	1.60k Skane	1.50	.20
a.	Bklt. pane, 5 ea #1492-1495		30.00	
	Nos. 1492-1495 (4)		6.00	.80

See note after No. 1277.

A458

A459

Swedish Patent System Centenary: No. 1496, Paraffin stove, F.W. Lindqvist, 1892. No. 1497, Industrial robot ASEA-IRB 6. No. 1498, Fan suction vacuum cleaner, Axel Wennergren, 1912. No. 1499, Inboard-outboard motor, AQ-200, No. 1500, SLIC integrated electronic circuit. No. 1501, Tetrahedron container, 1948, 1951.

Perf. 12½ on 3 Sides
1984, June 6   Engr.
1496	A458	2.70k red	1.10	.95
1497	A458	2.70k sepia	1.10	.95
1498	A458	2.70k green	1.10	.95
1499	A458	2.70k green	1.10	.95
1500	A458	2.70k sepia	1.10	.95
1501	A458	2.70k blue	1.10	.95
a.	Bklt. pane of 6, #1496-1501		6.75	8.50

Lithographed and Engraved
1984, June 6   Perf. 12½

Stockholmia '86 (Famous Letters): 1k, Erik XIV's marriage proposal to Queen Elizabeth I, 1561. 2k, Erik Dahlbergh to Sten Bielke, 1684. 3k, Feather letter, 1834. 4k, August Strindberg to Harriet Bosse, 1905.
1502	A459	1k multi	.75	.60
1503	A459	2k multi	.85	.65
1504	A459	3k multi	1.10	.85
1505	A459	4k multi	1.25	1.10
a.	Bklt. pane of 4, #1502-1505		4.25	6.00

Fredrika Bremer Assn. (Women's Rights) Centenary A460

Perf. 12½ Vert.
1984, Aug. 28   Engr.
1506	A460	1.50k pink	.60	.40
1507	A460	6.50k red	2.50	.85

Medieval Towns A461

Engravings by E. Dahlbergh or M. Karl.

1984, Aug. 28   Perf. 12½x13
1508	A461	1.90k Jonkoping	.85	.75
1509	A461	1.90k Karlstad	.85	.75
1510	A461	1.90k Gavle	.85	.75
1511	A461	1.90k Sigtuna	.85	.75
1512	A461	1.90k Norrkoping	.85	.75
1513	A461	1.90k Vadstena	.85	.75
a.	Bklt. pane of 6, #1508-1513		5.25	6.00

Viking Satellite, 1985 A462

1984, Oct. 13   Perf. 12½ Vert.
1514	A462	1.90k Satellite	.70	.30
1515	A462	3.20k Receiving station	1.40	1.10

Souvenir Sheet

Swedish Aviation History — A463

Designs: a, Thulin D Two-Seater, 1915. b, SAAB-90 Scandia, 1946. c, Carl Gustaf Cederstrom (1867-1918, "The Flying Baron"), Bleriot, 1910. d, Tomten, 1927. e, Carl Nyberg's Flugan, 1900.

1984, Oct. 13   Perf. 12½
1516	A463	Sheet of 5	5.75	5.75
a.-d.	1.90k, any single		.90	.85
e.	2.70k, multi		1.10	1.00

Sold for 12k.

Christmas 1984 — A465

Birds.

Lithographed and Engraved
1984, Nov. 29   Perf. 12½ on 3 Sides
1517	A465	1.60k Coccothraustes coccothraustes	.55	.35
1518	A465	1.60k Bombycilla garrulus	.55	.35
1519	A465	1.60k Dendrocopos major	.55	.35
1520	A465	1.60k Sitta europaea	.55	.35
a.	Bklt. pane, 3 each #1517-1520		7.00	
	Nos. 1517-1520 (4)		2.20	1.40

Inner Ear A466

Nobel Prize Winners in Physiology or Medicine: No. 1521, Georg von Bekesy, 1961, hearing. No. 1522, John Eccles, Alan Hodgkin & Andrew Huxley, 1963, Nerve cell activation. No. 1523, Julius Axelrod, Bernard Katz & Ulf von Euler, 1970, nerve cell storage and release. No. 1524, Roger Sperry, 1981, brain functions. No. 1525, David Hubel, Torsten Wiesel, 1981, Visual information processing.

Perf. 12½ Horiz.
1984, Nov. 29   Engr.
1521	A466	2.70k shown	1.10	.85
1522	A466	2.70k Nerve, arrows	1.10	.85
1523	A466	2.70k Nerve (front, side)	1.10	.85
1524	A466	2.70k Brain halves	1.10	.85
1525	A466	2.70k Eye	1.10	.85
a.	Bklt. pane of 5, #1521-1525		6.00	7.00

Conservation Type of 1983 and

A467

Perf. 13 on 3 Sides
1985, Mar. 14   Engr.
1526	A447	2k Muscardinus avellanarius	2.00	.30
1527	A447	2k Salvelinus salvelinus	2.00	.30
a.	Bklt. pane, 5 each #1526-1527		22.50	

World Wildlife Fund.

Perf. 12½ Horiz.
1528	A467	2.20k Nigritella nigra	.75	.20
1529	A467	3.50k Nymphaea alba	1.50	.65
	Nos. 1526-1529 (4)		6.25	1.45

World Table Tennis Championships A468

1985, Mar. 14   Perf. 12½ Vert.
1530	A468	2.70k Jan-Ove Waldner, Sweden	1.30	.90
1531	A468	3.20k Cai Zhenhua, China	1.60	1.20

Clavichord — A469

Key Harp — A470

1985, Apr. 24   Perf. 13 Vert.
1532	A469	2k bluish blk, buff	3.75	.25

Perf. 13 on 3 Sides
1533	A470	2.70k dl red brn, buff	.90	.75
a.	Booklet pane of 6		5.50	

Europa 1985.

Provincial Arms Type of 1981
Perf. 14½x14 on 3 Sides
1985, Apr. 24   Photo.
1534	A410	1.80k Narke	1.50	.20
1535	A410	1.80k Angermanland	1.50	.20
1536	A410	1.80k Varmland	1.50	.20
1537	A410	1.80k Smaland	1.50	.20
a.	Bklt. pane, 5 ea #1534-1537		30.00	
	Nos. 1534-1537 (4)		6.00	.80

See note after No. 1277.

St. Cnut's Land Grant to Lund Cathedral, 900th Anniv. — A471

Seal of St. Cnut and: No. 1538, Lund Cathedral. No. 1539, City of Helsingdorg.

Perf. 12½ on 3 Sides
1985, May 21   Engr.
1538	A471	2k bluish blk & blk	.75	.20
1539	A471	2k blk & dk red	.75	.20
a.	Bklt. pane, 5 each, #1538-1539		8.50	

See Denmark Nos. 777-778.

Stockholmia '86 — A472

Paintings of old Stockholm: No. 1540, A View of Slussen, by Sigrid Hjerten (1919). No. 1541, Skeppsholmen, Winter, by Gosta Adrian-Nilsson (1919). No. 1542, A Summer's Night by the Riddarholmen, by Hilding Linnqvist (1945). No. 1543, Klara Church Tower, by Otte Skold (1927).

Lithographed and Engraved
1985, May 21   Perf. 12½
1540	A472	2k multi	1.10	1.10
1541	A472	2k multi	1.10	1.10
1542	A472	3k multi	1.25	1.00
1543	A472	4k multi	1.40	1.20
a.	Bklt. pane of 4, #1540-1543		5.50	7.50

Swedish Touring
Club
Cent. — A473

#1544, Touring Club Syl Station (c. 1920).
#1545, Af Chapman Hostel, Stockholm.

1985, May 21   Engr.   Perf. 12½ Vert.
1544   2k blk & dp bl   .75   .35

Size: 58x23mm

1545   2k dp bl & blk   .75   .35
a.   A473 Pair, #1544-1545   1.75 1.25

Trade Signs — A474

Perf. 12½ on 3 Sides
1985, Aug. 28   Engr.
1546   A474 10o Music Shop,
                  Slottsgatan   .20   .20
1547   A474 20o Furrier, Stock-
                  holm   .20   .20
1548   A474 20o Coppersmith,
                  Landskrona   .20   .20
1549   A474 50o Haberdasher,
                  Stockholm   .30   .20
1550   A474   2k Shoemaker, Norr-
                  koping   .70   .20
a.   Bklt. pane, #1546-1549, 2
          #1550   2.00 2.50
       Nos. 1546-1550 (5)   1.60 1.00

The Dying Spartan Hero, Otryades,
1779, by Johan Tobias Sergel — A475

Baron Carl Frederik
Adelcrantz, Academy
Pres., 1754, by
Alexander Roslin
(1718-1793) — A476

1985, Aug. 28   Perf. 12½ Vert.
1551   A475 2k slate blue   .85   .30
Perf. 12½ Horiz.
1552   A476 7k dk red brn   2.75   .55
Royal Academy of Fine Arts, 250th anniv.

Intl. Youth Year — A477

Children's drawings: 2k, Participation, by
Marina Karlsson. 2.70k, Development, by
Madeleine Andersson. 3.20k, Peace, by
Charlotta Ankar.

Lithographed and Engraved
1985, Oct. 12   Perf. 12½x13
1553   A477 Sheet of 3   4.25 5.25
a.   2k multi   1.25   .80
b.   2.70k multi   1.25 1.10
c.   3.20k multi   1.50 1.30
       Sold for 10k.

Prime Minister Per Albin Hansson
(1885-1946) — A478

Birger Sjoberg
(1885-1929),
Journalist, Novelist,
Poet — A479

1985, Oct. 12   Engr.   Perf. 12½ Vert.
1556   A478 1.60k black & red   .65 .65
Perf. 12½ Horiz.
1557   A479 4k dk blue grn   1.65 .45

Christmas
1985 — A480

15th cent. religious paintings by Albertus
Pictor.

Perf. 13x12½ on 3 Sides
1985, Nov. 21   Engr.
1558   A480 1.80k Annunciation   .75   .50
1559   A480 1.80k Birth of Christ   .75   .50
1560   A480 1.80k Adoration of the
                    Magi   .75   .50
1561   A480 1.80k Mary as the
                    Apocalyptic
                    Virgin   .75   .50
a.   Bklt. pane, 3 each #1558-1561   9.00
       Nos. 1558-1561 (4)   3.00 2.00

Nobel Laureates in Literature — A481

Authors: No. 1562, William Faulkner (1897-
1962), 1949, Southern United States. No.
1563, Halldor Kiljan Laxness (b.1902), 1955,
Iceland. No. 1564, Miguel Angel Asturias
(1899-1974), 1967, Guatemala. No. 1565,
Yasunari Kawabata (1899-1972), 1968, Japan.
No. 1566, Patrick White (b. 1912), 1973,
Australia.

Lithographed and Engraved
1985, Nov. 21   Perf. 13 Horiz.
1562   A481 2.70k myr grn   1.00   .95
1563   A481 2.70k dp brn, chlky bl
                    & myr grn   1.00   .95
1564   A481 2.70k myr grn & tan   1.00   .95
1565   A481 2.70k chlky bl & myr
                    grn   1.00   .95
1566   A481 2.70k chlky bl & ocher   1.00   .95
a.   Bklt. pane of 5, #1562-1566   6.00 6.25

Types of 1983-85
Engr., Litho. (1.80k, 3.20k, 6k)
1986-89   Perf. 12½ Vert.
1567   A436b 1.70k dk violet   .65   .20
1568   A436b 1.80k brt violet   .65   .20
1569   A436c 2.10k dk blue   .80   .20
1570   A436c 2.20k int blue   .75   .20
1571   A436c 2.30k dk ol grn   .80   .20
1572   A436b 2.80k emerald   1.10   .80
1573   A436c 2.90k dk green   1.20   .60
1574   A436c 3.10k dk brown   1.30   .65
1575   A436c 3.20k yellow brn   1.25   .85
1576   A436c 3.30k dk rose brn   1.25 1.00
1577   A436d 3.40k dk red   1.40   .45
1578   A436d 3.60k green   1.50   .60
1579   A436d 3.90k violet blue   1.65 1.50
1580   A436b   6k blue green   2.00   .35
       Nos. 1567-1580 (14)   16.30 7.80

Issued: 2.10, 2.90, 3.40k, 1/23'; 1.70, 2.80k,
2/20; 1.80, 3.10, 3.20, 3.60, 6k, 1/27/87;
2.20k, 1/29/88; 2.30, 3.30, 3.90k, 4/20/89.
See No. 1796.

Waterbirds
A484

Perf. 13 on 2 or 3 Sides
1986, Jan. 23   Engr.
1582   A484 2.10k Eider   .75   .20
1583   A484 2.10k Smaspov   .75   .20
a.   Bklt. pane, 5 each #1582-1583   7.50
1584   A484 2.30k Storlom   .85   .20
       Nos. 1582-1584 (3)   2.35   .60

STOCKHOLMIA
'86 — A485

Lithographed and Engraved
1986, Jan. 23   Perf. 13
1585   A485 2k #33a, cancel   .95   .95
1586   A485 2k Stamp engraver   .95   .95
1587   A485 3k #268, 271, US
                    #836   1.25 1.10
1588   A485 4k Boy soaking
                    stamps   1.50 1.40
a.   Bklt. pane of 4, #1585-1588   4.75 6.50
       See US Nos. 2198-2201a.

Swedish PO,   Sundial
350th Anniv.   A487
A486

Lithographed and Engraved
1986, Feb. 20   Perf. 13x12½
1589   A486 2.10k org yel & dk bl   .75   .20
a.   Bklt pane of 8   6.00

1986, Feb. 20   Engr.   Perf. 13 Horiz.
No. 1591, Motto of the Swedish Academy.

1590   A487 1.70k dk bl & lake,
                    gray   .75   .60
1591   A487 1.70k grn & dk red,
                    gray   .75   .60
a.   Pair, #1590-1591   1.60 1.50

Royal Swedish Academy of Letters, History
and Antiquities, and Swedish Academy,
bicents.

Provincial Arms Type of 1981
Perf. 15x14½ on 3 Sides
1986, Apr. 23   Photo.
1592   A410 1.90k Harjedalen   1.50   .20
1593   A410 1.90k Uppland   1.50   .20
1594   A410 1.90k Halland   1.50   .20
1595   A410 1.90k Lapland   1.50   .20
a.   Bklt. pane, 5 each #1592-1595   30.00
       Nos. 1592-1595 (4)   6.00   .80

See note after No. 1277.

King Carl XVI   Royal
Gustaf — A488   Cipher — A489

40th birthday: No. 1598, King presenting
Nobel Prize for literature to Czeslaw Milosz,
1980. No. 1600, Royal family at Soldien
palace

Lithographed and Engraved
1986, Apr. 23   Perf. 12 on 3 Sides
1596   A488 2.10k grnsh blk &
                    pale grn   .95   .40
1597   A489 2.10k dk bl, pink &
                    gold   .95   .40
1598   A488 2.10k dk bl & pale
                    bl   .95   .40
1599   A489 2.10k dk bl, pale
                    grn & gold   .95   .40
1600   A488 2.10k blk & pale
                    pink   .95   .40
a.   Bklt. pane, 2 each #1596-
          1600   10.00 11.00
       Nos. 1596-1600 (5)   4.75   2.00

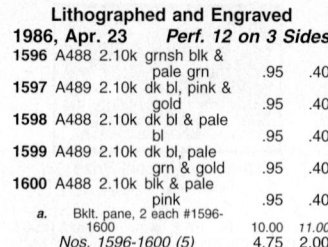

Olof Palme
(1927-1986),
Prime
Minister — A490

Perf. 13 on 3 Sides
1986, Apr. 11   Engr.
1601   A490 2.10k dk lilac rose   .95   .85
1602   A490 2.90k grnsh black   1.25 1.10
a.   Bklt. pane, 5 ea #1601-1602   12.50

Nordic
Cooperation
Issue — A491

Sister towns.

1986, May 27   Engr.   Perf. 13 Vert.
1603   A491 2.10k Uppsala   .85   .30
1604   A491 2.90k Eskilstuna   1.25   .75

Europa
1986 — A492

1986, May 27   Perf. 13 Horiz.
1605   A492 2.10k Automotive pollu-
                    tants   2.10   .40
Perf. 13 on 3 Sides
1606   A492 2.90k Industrial pollu-
                    tants   1.10   .85
a.   Booklet pane of 6   6.75

STOCKHOLMIA
'86 — A493

Designs: No. 1607, Mail handling terminal,
Tomteboda, 1986. No. 1608, Railroad mail car,
19th cent. No. 1609, Post Office, 18th cent.
No. 1610, Postman, 17th cent.

Lithographed and Engraved
1986, Aug. 29   Perf. 13
1607   A493 2.10k multi   1.50   3.00
1608   A493 2.10k multi   1.50   3.00
1609   A493 2.90k multi   1.50   3.00
1610   A493 2.90k multi   1.50   3.00
a.   Bklt. pane of 4, #1607-1610   6.50 16.00

Bklt. sold for 40k, including 30k ticket to
STOCKHOLMIA '86.

Souvenir Sheet

World Class Athletes in Track and Field — A494

Designs: a, Ann-Louise Skoglund, 400-meter hurdle, 1982. b, Dag Wennlund, 1986, and Eric Lemming, c. 1900, javelin. c, Standing high jumper and Patrik Sjoberg, high jump, 1985. d, Anders Garderud, 300-meter steeplechase record-holder.

1986, Oct. 18   Engr.   Perf. 12½
1611	A494	Sheet of 4	4.50	6.00
a.-d.		2.10k, any single	1.10	1.10

No. 1611 sold for 11k to benefit philatelic organizations.

Intl. Peace Year — A495

Amnesty Intl., 25th Anniv. — A496

1986, Oct. 18   Perf. 13 Vert.
1612	A495	3.40k bluish blk & emer grn	1.50	1.50
1613	A496	3.40k dk red & bluish blk	1.50	1.50
a.		Pair, #1612-1613	3.00	3.50

Christmas — A497

Winter village scenes.

Perf. 13x12½ on 3 Sides
1986, Nov. 25   Litho. & Engr.
1614		1.90k Postal van	.85	.35
1615		1.90k Postman on bicycle	.85	.35
1616		1.90k Children, sled	.85	.35
1617		1.90k Child mailing letter	.85	.35
a.		A497 Block of 4, #1614-1617	3.50	4.00
b.		Bklt. pane of 12, 3 #1617a	10.00	—

Nobel Peace Prize Laureates — A498

#1618, Bertha von Suttner, 1905. #1619, Carl von Ossietzky, 1935. #1620, Albert Luthuli, 1960. #1621, Martin Luther King, Jr., 1964. #1622, Mother Teresa, 1979.

1986, Nov. 25   Engr.   Perf. 13 Horiz.
1618	A498	2.90k brt bl, blk & hn brn	1.25	1.10
1619	A498	2.90k blk & hn brn	1.25	1.10
1620	A498	2.90k brt bl, blk & brn blk	1.25	1.10
1621	A498	2.90k brn blk & hn brn	1.25	1.10
1622	A498	2.90k blk, brt bl & hn brn	1.25	1.10
a.		Bklt. pane of 5, #1618-1622	6.75	7.50

Conservation Type of 1983
Perf. 13 on 3 Sides
1987, Mar. 10   Engr.
1623	A447	2.10k Parnassius mnemosyne	.85	.20
1624	A447	2.10k Gentianella campestris	.85	.30
a.		Booklet pane, 5 ea #1623-1624	8.50	

Perf. 13 Horiz.
1625	A447	2.50k Osmoderma eremita	.85	.20
1626	A447	4.20k Arnica montana	1.40	.30
		Nos. 1623-1626 (4)	3.95	1.00

Swedish Aviation Industry A500

1987, Mar. 10   Perf. 13 Vert.
1627	A500	25k Saab SF340	10.00	.40

Europa 1987 — A501

Nos. 1628-1629, City Library, Asplund. No. 1630, Lewerentz Marcus Church.

1987, May 14   Engr.   Perf. 13 Vert.
1628	A501	2.10k int blk & grn	2.75	.35

Perf. 13 on 3 Sides
1629	A501	3.10k emer grn & red brn	1.10	.85
1630	A501	3.10k emer grn & sep	1.10	.85
a.		Bklt. pane, 3 each #1629-1630	7.00	
		Nos. 1628-1630 (3)	4.95	2.05

Illustrations from Children's Novels by Astrid Lindgren (b. 1907) — A502

Perf. 13x12½ on 3 Sides
1987, May 14   Litho. & Engr.
1631	A502	1.90k Karlsson Pa Taket	2.00	.25
1632	A502	1.90k Barnen and Bullerbyn	2.00	.25
1633	A502	1.90k Madicken	2.00	.25
1634	A502	1.90k Mio, Min Mio	2.00	.25
1635	A502	1.90k Nils Karlsson-Pyssling	2.00	.25
1636	A502	1.90k Emil and Lonneberga	2.00	.25
1637	A502	1.90k Ronja Rovardotter	2.00	.25
1638	A502	1.90k Pippi Longstocking	2.00	.25
1639	A502	1.90k Broderna Lejonhjarta	2.00	.25
1640	A502	1.90k Lotta Pa Brakmakargatan	2.00	.25
a.		Bklt. pane, 2 ea #1631-1640	40.00	
		Nos. 1631-1640 (10)	20.00	2.50

See note after No. 1277.

Medieval Towns — A503

#1641, Hans Brask, Bishop of Linkoping, 16th cent. #1642, Nykopingshus Castle.

1987, May 14   Engr.   Perf. 12½ Vert.
1641	A503	2.10k blk, dk vio & yel bis	.85	.55
1642	A503	2.10k dk vio, blk & yel bis	.85	.55
a.		Pair, #1641-1642	1.75	2.00

Swedes in the Service of Mankind A504

Designs: No. 1643, Raoul Wallenberg, Swedish diplomat in Budapest during World War II. No. 1644, Dag Hammarskjold (1905-1961), UN secretary-general. No. 1645, Folke Bernadotte af Wisborg (1895-1948), organizer of the Red Cross operation that saved thousands from Nazi death camps.

Perf. 12½ Horiz.
1987, Aug. 10   Engr.
1643	A504	3.10k blue	1.40	1.10
1644	A504	3.10k green	1.40	1.10
1645	A504	3.10k brown violet	1.40	1.10
a.		Bklt. pane, 2 each #1643-1645	8.50	
		Nos. 1643-1645 (3)	4.20	3.30

Gripsholm Castle, 450th Anniv. — A505

Paintings from the Royal Castle Collection, Gripsholm: No. 1646, King Gustav I Vasa (d. 1560), artist unknown. No. 1647, Blue Tiger, 1673, favorite horse of King Charles XI, by D.K. Ehrenstrahl. No. 1648, Hedvig Charlotta Nordenflycht (1718-1763), poet, by Kopia J.H. Scheffel. No. 1649, Gripsholm Castle Outer Courtyard, 17th Cent., 19th cent. lithograph by C.J. Billmark.

1987, Aug. 10   Perf. 13 Vert.
1646	A505	2.10k multi	.85	.40
1647	A505	2.10k multi	.85	.40
1648	A505	2.10k multi	.85	.40
1649	A505	2.10k multi	.85	.40
a.		Bklt. pane of 8, 2 strips of #1646-1649 with gutter btwn.	7.00	
		Nos. 1646-1649 (4)	3.40	1.60

Botanical Gardens A506

Designs: No. 1650, Victoria cruziana (water lily), Victoria House, Bergian Garden, c. 1790, Stockholm University. No. 1651, Layout of baroque palace garden, by Carl Harleman (1700-1753), Uppsala University. No. 1652, White anemones, rock garden, Gothenberg Botanical Gardens, 1923. No. 1653, Tulip tree blossoms, Academy Garden, c. 1860, Lund University.

1987, Oct. 10   Engr.   Perf. 13 Vert.
1650	A506	2.10k multi	.85	.55
1651	A506	2.10k multi	.85	.55
1652	A506	2.10k multi	.85	.55
1653	A506	2.10k multi	.85	.55
a.		Bklt. pane, 2 each #1650-1653 with gutter between	7.00	
		Nos. 1650-1653 (4)	3.40	2.20

The Circus in Sweden, Bicent. — A507

Litho. & Engr.
1987, Oct. 10   Perf. 13
1654	A507	2.10k Juggler, clown	.95	.95
1655	A507	2.10k High wire	.95	.95
1656	A507	2.10k Equestrian	.95	.95
a.		Bklt. pane of 3, #1654-1656	3.00	4.00

Stamp Day. Sold for 8k.

Christmas A508

Customs: No. 1657, Putting porridge in the stable for the gray Christmas elf. No. 1658, Watering horses at a north-running stream on Boxing Day. No. 1659, Sled-race home from church on Christmas Day. No. 1660, Hanging out sheaves of wheat to foretell a good harvest.

Perf. 13 on 3 Sides
1987, Nov. 25   Litho.
1657	A508	2k multi	.75	.30
1658	A508	2k multi	.75	.30
1659	A508	2k multi	.75	.30
1660	A508	2k multi	.75	.30
a.		Bklt. pane, 3 each #1657-1660	9.50	
		Nos. 1657-1660 (4)	3.00	1.20

Nobel Prize Winners in Physics A509

Space and diagram or formula: No. 1661, Antony Hewish, Great Britain, 1974. No. 1662, Subrahmanyan Chandrasekhar, US, 1983. No. 1663, William Fowler, US, 1983. No. 1664, Arno Penzias and Robert Wilson, US, 1978. No. 1665, Martin Ryle, Great Britain, 1974.

1987, Nov. 25   Engr.   Perf. 13
1661	A509	2.90k dark blue	1.25	1.25
1662	A509	2.90k blk	1.25	1.25
1663	A509	2.90k dark blue	1.25	1.25
1664	A509	2.90k dark blue	1.25	1.25
1665	A509	2.90k blk	1.25	1.25
a.		Bklt. pane of 5, #1661-1665	7.50	9.00

Inland Boats A510

1988, Jan. 29   Engr.   Perf. 13
1666	A510	3.10k Skiff, Lake Hjalmaren	1.25	1.25
1667	A510	3.10k Village boat, Lake Vattern	1.25	1.25
1668	A510	3.10k Rowboat, Byske	1.25	1.25
1669	A510	3.10k Flat-bottomed rowboat, As-nen	1.25	1.25
1670	A510	3.10k Ice boat, Lake Vanern	1.25	1.25
1671	A510	3.10k Church boat, Lake Locknesjon	1.25	1.25
a.		Bklt. pane of 6, #1666-1671	8.00	8.75

A511

A512

Settling of New
Sweden, 350th
Anniv. — A513

Designs: No. 1672, 17th Cent. European
settlers negotiating with American Indians,
map of New Sweden, the Swedish ships *Kalmar Nyckel* and *Fogel Grip*, based on an 18th
cent. illustration from a Swedish book about
the American Colonies. No. 1673, Bishop Hill
and painter Olof Krans. No. 1674, Carl
Sandburg (1878-1967), author, and Jenny
Lind (1820-1867), opera singer known as the
"Swedish Nightingale." No. 1675, Charles
Lindbergh (1902-1974), and *The Spirit of St.
Louis*. No. 1676, American astronaut with
Swedish Hasselblad camera on the Moon. No.
1677, Swedish players in National Hockey
League.

Litho. & Engr., Engr. (#1674-1675)
1988, Mar. 29　　Perf. 13x12½ Horiz
1672　A511　3.60k multi　　　　1.30　1.10
1673　A511　3.60k multi　　　　1.30　1.10

Perf. 13x12½ on 3 Sides
1674　A512　3.60k brn　　　　1.30　1.20
1675　A512　3.60k dk bl & brn　1.30　1.20

Perf. 13x12½ on 2
1676　A513　3.60k dk bl & yel　1.30　1.30
1677　A513　3.60k dk red, dk bl &
　　　　　　　blk　　　　　　1.30　1.30
　a.　Bklt. pane of 6, #1672-1677　8.00　10.50

See US No. C117 and Finland No. 768.

Conservation Type of 1983
Species Inhabiting Coastal Waters

Perf. 13 on 3 Sides
1988, Mar. 29　　　　　　Engr.
1678　A447　2.20k Haliaetus al-
　　　　　　　bicilla　　　　　.75　.30
1679　A447　2.20k Halichoerus
　　　　　　　grypus　　　　　.75　.30
　a.　Bklt. pane, 5 #1678, 5 #1679　8.00

Perf. 13 Horiz.
1680　A446　4.40k Anguilla an-
　　　　　　　guilla　　　　　2.10　.35
　　Nos. 1678-1680 (3)　　　　3.60　.95

Midsummer
Celebration
A515

Skara Township
Millennium
A516

Perf. 12½ on 3 Sides
1988, May 17　　　Litho. & Engr.
1681　A515　2k Wildflowers in
　　　　　　　meadow　　　　1.80　.25
1682　A515　2k Rowing　　　　1.80　.25
1683　A515　2k Children making
　　　　　　　wreaths　　　　1.80　.25
1684　A515　2k Raising maypole　1.80　.25
1685　A515　2k Fiddlers　　　　1.80　.25
1686　A515　2k Ferry　　　　　1.80　.25
1687　A515　2k Dancing　　　　1.80　.25
1688　A515　2k Accordion player　1.80　.25
1689　A515　2k Maypole, resi-
　　　　　　　dence　　　　　1.80　.25

1690　A515　2k Bouquet of flow-
　　　　　　　ers　　　　　　1.80　.25
　a.　Bklt. pane, 2 ea #1681-1690　36.00
　　Nos. 1681-1690 (10)　　　18.00　2.50
　　　　See note after No. 1277.

1988, May 17　　　Perf. 13 Horiz.
Design: Detail from Creation, a Skara
Cathedral stained-glass window by Bo
Beskow, 20th cent.
1691　A516　2.20k multi　　　　.90　.40

Stora Mining Co.,
700th
Anniv. — A517

Royal Dramatic
Theater,
Stockholm,
Founded by King
Gustav III in
1788 — A518

1988, May 17　　　　　　Engr.
1692　A517　4.40k Mine, 18th cent.　1.65　.85

1988, May 17
Design: Scene from *The Queen's Diamond
Ornament*, about the murder of King Gustav
III at the Royal Opera in 1792.
1693　A518　8k grn, red & blk　3.00　1.60

Self-portrait,
1923, by Nils
Dardel (1888-
1943)
A519

Paintings: No. 1695, *Old Age Home in
Autumn*, c. 1930, by Vera Nilsson (1888-
1979). No. 1696, *Self-portrait*, 1912, by Isaac
Grunewald (1899-1979). No. 1697, *Visit of an
Eccentric Lady*, 1921, by Dardel. No. 1698,
Soap Bubbles, 1927, by Nilsson. No. 1699,
The Fair, 1915, by Grunewald.

Perf. 13 on 3 Sides
1988, Aug. 25　　　Litho. & Engr.
Size: 33x35mm (Nos. 1695, 1698)
1694　A519　2.20k shown　　　.95　.90
1695　A519　2.20k multi　　　　.95　.90
1696　A519　2.20k multi　　　　.95　.90
1697　A519　2.20k multi　　　　.95　.90
1698　A519　2.20k multi　　　　.95　.90
1699　A519　2.20k multi　　　　.95　.90
　a.　Bklt. pane of 6, #1694-1699　5.75　7.50

Europa — A520

Transport and communication.

1988, Aug. 25　Engr.　Perf. 13 Vert.
1700　A520　2.20k like No. 1701　2.75　.65
Perf. 13 on 3 Sides
1701　A520　3.10k X2 high-speed
　　　　　　　train　　　　　1.25　1.10
1702　A520　3.10k Steam locomo-
　　　　　　　tive, 1887　　　1.25　1.10
　a.　Bklt. pane, 3 each #1701-1702　7.50
　　Nos. 1700-1702 (3)　　　5.25　2.85

Common
Swift — A521

1988, Aug. 25　　　Perf. 12½ Vert.
1703　A521　20k brt vio & dk vio　6.50　.35

Dan Andersson
(1888-1920),
Poet, and
Manuscript
A522

Forest and Pond, Finnmarken — A523

1988, Oct. 8　Engr.　Perf. 13 Vert.
1704　A522　2.20k vio, dk bl & dk
　　　　　　　bl grn　　　　.90　.45
1705　A523　2.20k vio, dk bl & dk
　　　　　　　bl grn　　　　.90　.45
　a.　Pair, #1704-1705　　　1.90　1.50

Soccer — A524

Match scenes: No. 1706, Dribble (Torbjorn
Nilsson representing local club matches). No.
1707, Heading the ball (Ralf Edstrom of the
national league). No. 1708, Kick (Pia
Sundhage, women's soccer).

1988, Oct. 8　Litho. & Engr.　Perf. 13
1706　A524　2.20k multi　　　1.25　1.00
1707　A524　2.20k multi　　　1.25　1.00
1708　A524　2.20k multi　　　1.25　1.00
　a.　Bklt. pane of 3, #1706-1708　3.75　4.25

No. 1708a sold for 8.50k; surtax benefited
stamp collecting.

Nobel Laureates in
Chemistry
A525

Christmas
A526

Designs: No. 1709, Willard F. Libby, US,
1960, carbon-14 method of dating artifacts.
No. 1710, Karl Ziegler, West Germany, and
Guilio Natta, Italy, 1963, catalysts. No. 1711,
Aaron Klug, South Africa, 1982, electron
microscopy. No. 1712, Ilya Prigogine,
Belgium, 1977, proof that molecular order can
occur spontaneously out of chaos.

1988, Nov. 29　　　Perf. 12½ Vert.
1709　A525　3.10k multi　　　1.25　1.10
1710　A525　3.10k multi　　　1.25　1.10
1711　A525　3.10k multi　　　1.25　1.10
1712　A525　3.10k multi　　　1.25　1.10
　a.　Bklt. pane, 2 each #1709-
　　　1712　　　　　　　10.00
　　Nos. 1709-1712 (4)　　5.00　4.40

Perf. 12½x13 on 3 Sides
1988, Nov. 29
Story of Christ's birth according to Luke
(2:7-20): No. 1713, Angels appear to inform

---

shepherds of Christ's birth. No. 1714, Star of
Bethlehem, angel, horse. No. 1715, Birds
singing. No. 1716, Magi offering gifts. No.
1717, Holy family. No. 1718, Shepherds with
palm offering.

1713　A526　2k multi　　　　.75　.55
1714　A526　2k multi　　　　.75　.55
1715　A526　2k multi　　　　.75　.55
1716　A526　2k multi　　　　.75　.55
1717　A526　2k multi　　　　.75　.55
1718　A526　2k multi　　　　.75　.55
　a.　Bklt. pane, 2 each #1713-1718　9.00
　　Nos. 1713-1718 (6)　　4.50　3.30

Nos. 1713 and 1716, 1714 and 1717, 1715
and 1718 have continuous designs.

Lighthouses
A527

Designs: 1.90k, Twin masonry lighthouses,
1832, and concrete lighthouse, 1946, Nid-
ingen, Kattegat Is. 2.70k, Soderarm, Uppland,
1839. 3.80k, Sydostbrotten, Gulf of Bothnia,
1963. 3.90k, Sandhammaren, Skane, c. 1860.

1989, Jan. 31　Engr.　Perf. 13 Vert.
1719　A527　1.90k multi　　　　.85　.35
1720　A527　2.70k multi　　　1.25　.85
1721　A527　3.80k multi　　　1.60　.85
1722　A527　3.90k multi　　　1.75　.85
　　Nos. 1719-1722 (4)　　5.45　2.80

Endangered
Species — A528

1989, Jan. 31　　Perf. 13 on 3 Sides
1723　A528　2.30k *Gulo gulo*　.85　.25
1724　A528　2.30k *Strix uralensis*　.85　.25
　a.　Bklt. pane, 5 each #1723-1724　8.50

Perf. 13 Horiz.
1725　A528　2.40k *Dendrocopos
　　　　　　　minor*　　　.90　.25
1726　A528　2.60k *Calidris alpina
　　　　　　　schinzii*　　1.25　.85
1727　A528　3.30k *Hyla arborea*　1.40　1.10
1728　A528　4.60k *Ficedula parva*　2.25　1.40
　　Nos. 1723-1728 (6)　　7.50　3.20

Opening of The Globe Arena,
Stockholm — A529

Perf. 13 Horiz.
1989, Apr. 14　　　Litho. & Engr.
1729　A529　2.30k Exterior　　.95　.55
1730　A529　2.30k Ice hockey　.95　.55
1731　A529　2.30k Gymnastics　.95　.55
1732　A529　2.30k Concert　　.95　.55
　a.　Bklt. pane of 4, #1729-1732　4.00

Nordic
Cooperation
Issue — A530

Folk costumes.

Perf. 13 Horiz.
1989, Apr. 20　　　Litho. & Engr.
1733　A530　2.30k Woman's wool
　　　　　　　waist　　　　1.10　.40
1734　A530　3.30k Belt pouch　1.60　.80

Natl. Labor
Movement,
Cent. — A531

1989, May 17   Engr.   Perf. 13 Horiz.
1735 A531 2.30k dk red & blk   1.10   .45

Europa
1989 — A532

Children's games: 2.30k, No. 1738, Sailing
toy boats. No. 1737, Kick-sledding.

1989, May 17   Perf. 13 Vert.
1736 A532 2.30k car lake   3.25   .45

Perf. 13
1737 A532 3.30k greenish blue   1.10   .90
1738 A532 3.30k lilac   1.10   .90
a.   Bklt. pane, 2 ea #1737, 3 #1738   6.60
    Nos. 1736-1738 (3)   5.45   2.25

Summer — A533

Perf. 13 on 3 Sides
1989, May 17   Litho.
1739 A533 2.10k Sailing   1.90   .35
1740 A533 2.10k Beach ball   1.90   .35
1741 A533 2.10k Cycling   1.90   .35
1742 A533 2.10k Canoeing   1.90   .35
1743 A533 2.10k Angling   1.90   .35
1744 A533 2.10k Camping   1.90   .35
1745 A533 2.10k Croquet   1.90   .35
1746 A533 2.10k Badminton   1.90   .35
1747 A533 2.10k Gardening   1.90   .35
1748 A533 2.10k Sand sculp-
            ture   1.90   .35
a.   Bklt. pane, 2 ea #1739-1748   38.00
    Nos. 1739-1748 (10)   19.00   3.50

See note after No. 1277.

Polar Exploration
A534

Swedish polar techniques used in the Arctic
(Nos. 1749-1751) and Antarctic: No. 1749, Aircraft, temperature experiment. No. 1750, Settlement, Arctic pass. No. 1751, Icebreaker,
experiment. No. 1752, Penguins, tall ship and
longboat. No. 1753, Antarctic transports, helicopter. No. 1754, Surveying, albatross.

Perf. 13 on 3 Sides
1989, Aug. 22   Litho. & Engr.
Size: 40x43mm (Nos. 1750, 1753)
1749 A534 3.30k multi   1.40   1.25
1750 A534 3.30k multi   1.40   1.25
1751 A534 3.30k multi   1.40   1.25
1752 A534 3.30k multi   1.40   1.25
1753 A534 3.30k multi   1.40   1.25
1754 A534 3.30k multi   1.40   1.25
a.   Bklt. pane of 6, #1749-1754   8.50   11.00

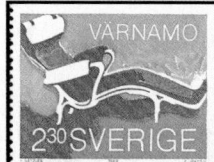

Smaland
Businesses
A535

Perf. 12½x12 on 3 Sides
1989, Aug. 22   Engr.
1755 A535 2.30k Furniture   1.15   .85
1756 A535 2.30k Assembly
            equipment   1.15   .85
1757 A535 2.30k Sewing ma-
            chines   1.15   .85
1758 A535 2.30k Glassware   1.15   .85
1759 A535 2.30k Metal springs   1.15   .85
1760 A535 2.30k Matchsticks   1.15   .85
a.   Bklt. pane of 6, #1755-1760   7.50   9.00

Eagle
Owl,
*Bubo
bubo*
A536

1989, Aug. 22   Perf. 13 Vert.
1761 A536 30k vio, blk & grn blk   8.25   .40

Conservation Type of 1983 and

Birds and
Coastline, Bla
Jungfrun Natl.
Park — A537

Perf. 13x12½ on 3 Sides
1989, Sept. 12   Engr.
1762 A447 2.40k *Rhododendron
            lapponicum*   .90   .25
1763 A447 2.40k *Calypso
            bulbosa*   .90   .25
a.   Bklt. pane, 5 ea #1762-1763   9.00

Perf. 12½ Vert.
1764 A537 4.30k dark blue, blk
            & brn vio   2.10   1.10
    Nos. 1762-1764 (3)   3.90   1.60

See Nos. 1776-1780.

Swedish Kennel Club, Cent. — A538

a, Large spitz. b, Fox hound. c, Small spitz.

1989, Oct. 7   Litho.   Perf. 13x12½
1765 A538   Bklt. pane of 3   3.50   4.50
a.-c.   2.40k any single   1.10   1.00
    Sold for 9.50k.

Christmas — A539

Holiday symbols: No. 1766, Top of Christmas tree, wreath. No. 1767, Candelabrum,
foods. No. 1768, Star, poinsettia plant, grot
pot. No. 1769, Bottom of tree, straw goat, gifts.
No. 1770, Gifts, television, girl. No. 1771, Boy,
grandfather, girl opening gift.

Perf. 12½x13 on 3 Sides
1989, Nov. 24   Litho.
1766 A539 2.10k multi   .85   .50
1767 A539 2.10k multi   .85   .50
1768 A539 2.10k multi   .85   .50
1769 A539 2.10k multi   .85   .50
1770 A539 2.10k multi   .85   .50

1771 A539 2.10k multi   .85   .50
a.   Bklt. pane, 2 each #1766-
            1771   10.50
    Nos. 1766-1771 (6)   5.10   3.00

Nobel Laureates
in Physiology
A540

Genetics: No. 1772, Thomas Morgan (1866-
1945), US, 1933, chromosomal study of fruit
flies to determine laws and mechanism of
heredity. No. 1773, James Watson, US, and
Francis Crick with Maurice Wilkins, Great Britain, 1962, molecular structure of DNA. No.
1774, Werner Arber, Switzerland, Daniel
Nathans and Hamilton Smith, US, 1978, enzy-
matic cutting of nucleotides to create gene
hybrids. No. 1775, Barbara McClintock, botanist, US, 1983, corn color studies that led to
theory of gene jumping.

Perf. 12½ Vert.
1989, Nov. 24   Litho. & Engr.
1772 A540 3.60k multi   1.50   1.10
1773 A540 3.60k multi   1.50   1.10
1774 A540 3.60k multi   1.50   1.10
1775 A540 3.60k multi   1.50   1.10
a.   Bklt. pane, 2 each #1772-
            1775 with gutter between   12.00
    Nos. 1772-1775 (4)   6.00   4.40

Natl. Parks Type of 1989

Designs: No. 1776, Campground, sailboat
on lake, Angso Park. No. 1777, Hiking,
Pieljekaise Park. 3.70k, Three whooper swans
over wetlands, Muddus Park. 4.10k, Deer,
lake, Padjelanta Park. 4.80k, Bears, forest,
Sanfjallet Park.

Perf. 13 on 3 Sides
1990, Jan. 26   Engr.
1776 A537 2.50k multicolored   .95   .20
1777 A537 2.50k multicolored   .95   .20
a.   Bklt. pane, 5 each #1776-1777   9.50

Perf. 13 Vert.
1778 A537 3.70k multicolored   1.50   .30
1779 A537 4.10k multicolored   2.10   1.30
1780 A537 4.80k multicolored   2.10   1.25
    Nos. 1776-1780 (5)   7.60   3.25

**King and Queen Types of 1985-86
and**

Queen
Silvia — A541

King Carl XVI
Gustaf — A542

King Carl XVI
Gustav
A543

Queen Silvia
A544

King Carl XVI
Gustaf — A545

**Perf. 12½ Vert., Horiz. (A541, A542,
A545)**
1990-97   Engr.
1783 A436c 2.50k deep claret   1.00   .20
1784 A542 2.80k dk blue   1.10   .20
1785 A542 2.90k deep green   1.30   .25
1786 A542 3.20k violet   1.50   .20
1787 A543 3.70k dark red
            brown   1.50   .20
1788 A543 3.85k black   1.75   .30
1789 A436d 4.60k bright org   1.75   1.50
1790 A541 5k deep rose vio   2.00   .40
1791 A545 (5k) deep blue   2.10   .30

1792 A541 6k deep claret   2.25   .60
1793 A544 6k dark green   2.75   .95
1794 A541 6.50k purple   3.50   1.25
1795 A544 7.50k purple   3.10   1.65
1796 A544 8k brown red   3.10   1.00
    Nos. 1783-1796 (14)   28.70   9.00
Issued: 2.50k, 4.60k, 1/26; 5k, 3/20/91;
2.80k, 11/20/91; 2.90k, #1792, 1/2/93; 3.20k,
1/17/94; 6.50k, 3/18/94; 3.70k, #1793, 1/2/95;
3.85k, 7.50k, 1/2/96; (5k), 8k, 2/28/97.
No. 1791 is inscribed "BREV."

Viking
Heritage
A546

Designs: No. 1801, Viking head of carved
bone, dragon carving from a molding found in
Birka. No. 1802, Three viking longships. No.
1803, Viking town. No. 1804, Bronze statue of
pagan fertility god, silver filigree cross. No.
1805, Bishop's crosier, southern Russian
carved statue of a deer. No. 1806, Viking longship (stern). No. 1807, Viking longship (bow),
horsemen, woman, warrior, wolf. No. 1808,
Sword hilts.

Perf. 12x13 on 3 Sides
1990, Mar. 28   Litho. & Engr.
1801 A546 2.50k multicolored   1.10   .85
1802 A546 2.50k multicolored   1.10   .85
1803 A546 2.50k multicolored   1.10   .85
1804 A546 2.50k multicolored   1.10   .85
1805 A546 2.50k multicolored   1.10   .85
1806 A546 2.50k multicolored   1.10   .85
1807 A546 2.50k multicolored   1.10   .85
1808 A546 2.50k multicolored   1.10   .85
a.   Bklt. pane of 8, #1801-1808   9.00   10.00

Nos. 1802-1803, 1806-1807 printed in a
continuous design.

Swedish
Industrial Safety,
Cent. — A547

1990, Mar. 28   Engr.   Perf. 13 Horiz.
1809 A547 2.50k Lumberjack   1.10   .30

Europa
1990 — A548

Post offices.

1990, Mar. 28   Perf. 13 Vert.
1810 A548 2.50k Postal Museum,
            1720   3.25   .45

Perf. 13 on 3 Sides
1811 A548 3.80k Sollebrunn,
            1985   1.50   1.10
1812 A548 3.80k Vasteras, 1956   1.50   1.10
a.   Bklt. pane, 3 each #1811-1812   9.00
    Nos. 1810-1812 (3)   6.25   2.65

World
Equestrian
Games,
Stockholm
A549

Litho. & Engr.
1990, May 15   Perf. 12½x13
1813 A549 3.80k Endurance
            riding   1.60   1.40
1814 A549 3.80k Combined
            training   1.60   1.40
1815 A549 3.80k Show jump-
            ing   1.60   1.40
1816 A549 3.80k Dressage   1.60   1.40
1817 A549 3.80k Volting   1.60   1.40
1818 A549 3.80k Four-in-hand   1.60   1.40
a.   Bklt. pane of 6, #1813-1818   10.00   11.50

Apiculture — A550

#1819, Worker bee collecting nectar. #1820, Bee, bilberry flower. #1821, Worker bee. #1822, Apiary hive. #1823, Two bees in honeycomb. #1824, Drone, 7 cells, blue green panel. #1825, Queen bee, 7 cells, yellow panel. #1826, Swarm hanging from tree. #1827, Beekeeper. #1828, Honey.

1990, May 15			Litho.	
1819	A550	2.30k multicolored	1.80	.40
1820	A550	2.30k multicolored	1.80	.40
1821	A550	2.30k multicolored	1.80	.40
1822	A550	2.30k multicolored	1.80	.40
1823	A550	2.30k multicolored	1.80	.40
1824	A550	2.30k multicolored	1.80	.40
1825	A550	2.30k multicolored	1.80	.40
1826	A550	2.30k multicolored	1.80	.40
1827	A550	2.30k multicolored	1.80	.40
1828	A550	2.30k multicolored	1.80	.40
a.		Bklt. pane, 2 ea #1819-1828	36.00	
		Nos. 1819-1828 (10)	18.00	4.00

See note after No. 1277.

Wasa Nautical Museum — A551

Man-of-war *Wasa*: 2.50k, Bow. 4.60k, Stern.

1990, May 15		Engr.	Perf. 13 Vert.	
1829	A551	2.50k org & blk	1.10	.45
1830	A551	4.60k dk bl & org	2.00	1.25

Dearest Brothers, Sisters and Friends — A552

Proud City A553

Allusions to poetry verses of Carl Michael Bellman (No. 1833) and Evert Taube: No. 1833, Fredmen in the gutter. No. 1834, Happy baker in San Remo. No. 1835, At sea. No. 1836, Violava.
Illustration reduced.

Perf. 13 on 3 Sides

1990, Aug. 8		Litho. & Engr.		
1831	A552	2.50k multicolored	1.75	1.20
1832	A553	2.50k multicolored	1.75	1.20
1833	A552	2.50k multicolored	1.75	1.20
1834	A553	2.50k multicolored	1.75	1.20
1835	A552	2.50k multicolored	1.75	1.20
1836	A552	2.50k multicolored	1.75	1.20
a.		Bklt. pane of 6, #1831-1836	7.50	11.00

Paper Production A554

#1837, Paper production c. 1600. #1838, Watermark. #1839, Newspaper mastheads. #1840, Modern paper production.

1990, Aug. 8		Perf. 12½ Vert.		
1837	A554	2.50k multicolored	1.10	.45
1838	A554	2.50k multicolored	1.10	.45
1839	A554	2.50k multicolored	1.10	.45
1840	A554	2.50k multicolored	1.10	.45
a.		Bklt. pane, 2 each #1837-1840 with gutter between	9.00	
		Nos. 1837-1840 (4)	4.40	1.80

Ovedskloster Palace — A555

1990, Aug. 8		Engr.	Perf. 13 Vert.	
1841	A555	40k multicolored	11.00	.30

See Nos. 1874-1877.

Photography A556

Litho. & Engr.

1990, Oct. 6			Perf. 12½	
1842	A556	2.50k Bellows camera	1.10	1.25
1843	A556	2.50k August Strindberg	1.10	1.25
1844	A556	2.50k 35mm camera	1.10	1.25
a.		Bklt. pane of 3, #1842-1844	3.30	5.00

Stamp Day. Booklet of two panes sold for 20k. Surtax benefited stamp collecting.

Clouds — A557

A558

1990, Oct. 6		Engr.	Perf. 12½ Horiz.	
1845	A557	4.50k Cumulus	2.00	.45
1846	A557	4.70k Cumulonimbus	2.25	1.25
1847	A557	4.90k Cirrus	2.50	1.25
1848	A557	5.20k Alto cumulus	2.75	1.50
		Nos. 1845-1848 (4)	9.50	4.45

1990, Oct. 6			Perf. 12½ Vert.	
1849	A558	2.50k shown	1.20	.50
1850	A558	2.50k Women bathing	1.20	.50
a.		Pair, #1849-1850	2.50	2.25

Moa Martinson (1890-1964), author.

Nobel Laureates in Literature — A559

Perf. 13 on 2 Sides

1990, Nov. 27			Engr.	
1851	A559	3.80k Par Lagerkvist, 1951	1.50	1.40
1852	A559	3.80k Ernest Hemingway, 1954	1.50	1.40
1853	A559	3.80k Albert Camus, 1957	1.50	1.40
1854	A559	3.80k Boris Pasternak, 1958	1.50	1.40
a.		Bklt. pane, 2 each #1851-1854 with gutter between	13.00	
		Nos. 1851-1854 (4)	6.00	5.60

See Nos. 1914-1917.

Christmas — A560

Flowers.

Perf. 13 on 3 Sides

1990, Nov. 27			Litho.	
1855	A560	2.30k Schlumbergera x buckleyi	1.00	.55
1856	A560	2.30k Helleborus niger	1.00	.55
1857	A560	2.30k Rhododendron simsii	1.00	.55
1858	A560	2.30k Hippeastrum x hortorum	1.00	.55
1859	A560	2.30k Hyacinthus orientalis	1.00	.55
1860	A560	2.30k Euphorbia pulcherrima	1.00	.55
a.		Bklt. pane, 2 each #1855-1860	12.00	
		Nos. 1855-1860 (6)	6.00	3.30

Carta Marina by Olaus Magnus, 1572 — A561

Scandanavia by A. Bureas and J. Blaeus, 1662 — A562

Maps: No. 1863, Celestial globe by Anders Akerman, 1759. No. 1864, Contour map, 1938. No. 1865, Stockholm, 1989. No. 1866, Bedrock Map, Geological Survey, 1984.
Illustration reduced.

Perf. 13 on 3 Sides

1991, Jan. 30			Litho. & Engr.	
1861	A561	5k multicolored	2.40	1.60
1862	A562	5k multicolored	2.40	1.60
1863	A561	5k multicolored	2.40	1.60
1864	A561	5k multicolored	2.40	1.60
1865	A562	5k multicolored	2.40	1.60
1866	A561	5k multicolored	2.40	1.60
a.		Bklt. pane of 6, #1861-1866	15.00	18.00

Fish — A563

A564

Perf. 13 on 3 Sides

1991, Jan. 30			Engr.	
1867	A563	2.50k shown	1.25	.35
1868	A563	2.50k Siluris glanis, diff.	1.25	.35
b.		Bklt. pane, 5 each #1867-1868	13.50	

Perf. 13 Vert.

1869	A563	5k Cobitis taenia	1.75	.20
1870	A563	5.40k Gobio gobio	2.50	2.50
1871	A563	5.50k Noemacheilus barbatulus	2.40	.25
1872	A563	5.60k Leucaspius delineatus	2.40	1.40
		Nos. 1867-1872 (6)	11.55	5.05

Palace Type of 1990

Designs: 10k, Stromsholm Castle. 20k, Karlberg Castle. 25k, Drottningholm Palace.

1991-92		Engr.	Perf. 13 Vert.	
1874	A555	10k blk & olive brn	4.00	.25
1876	A555	20k multicolored	6.50	.75

Size: 58x23mm

1877	A555	25k multicolored	7.00	.75
		Nos. 1874-1877 (3)	17.50	1.75

Issued: 10k, 4/27; 25k, 3/20; 20k, 5/21/92.

Perf. 12½x13 on 3 Sides

1991, May 15			Litho.	
1883	A564	2.40k Seglora church	.95	.25
1884	A564	2.40k Flag above park	.95	.25
1885	A564	2.40k Wedding	.95	.25
1886	A564	2.40k Animals	.95	.25
b.		Bklt. pane, 5 ea #1883-1886	19.00	
		Nos. 1883-1886 (4)	3.80	1.00

Skansen Park, Stockholm, 100th anniv.
See note after No. 1277. Complete booklet of 20 stamps sold for 46k.

Kolmarden Zoological Park, Ostergotland A565

Perf. 12½ Horiz.

1991, May 15			Engr.	
1887	A565	2.50k Polar bears	1.10	.25
1888	A565	4k Dolphin show	1.75	1.10

Norden '91.

A566

Public Parks, cent.: #1890, Dancing in park.

1991, May 15			Perf. 13 Vert.	
1889	A566	2.50k dark blue	1.10	.50
1890	A566	2.50k dark blue	1.10	.50
a.		Pair, #1889-1890	2.25	2.25

Europa — A567

Litho. & Engr.

1991, May 15			Perf. 13	
1891	A567	4k Hermes space plane	1.75	1.50
1892	A567	4k Freja satellite	1.75	1.50
1893	A567	4k Tele-X satellite	1.75	1.50
a.		Bklt. pane of 3, #1891-1893	5.50	7.50

Olympic Champions A568

Designs: No. 1894, Magda Julin, figure skating, Antwerp, 1920. No. 1895, Toini Gustaffson, cross country skiing, Grenoble, 1968. No. 1896, Agneta Andersson, Anna Olsson, two-person kayak, Los Angeles, 1984. No. 1897, Ulrika Knape, diving, Munich, 1972.
Illustration reduced.

Perf. 12x13 on 3 Sides
1991, Aug. 27   **Litho. & Engr.**

1894	A568	2.50k multicolored	1.10	.70
1895	A568	2.50k multicolored	1.10	.70
1896	A568	2.50k multicolored	1.10	.70
1897	A568	2.50k multicolored	1.10	.70
a.		Bklt. pane, 2 each #1894-1897	9.00	
		Nos. 1894-1897 (4)	*4.40*	*2.80*

See Nos. 1937-1940, 1953-1956.

Iron Mining — A569

#1898, Spetal Mine, Norberg. #1899, Forsmark Mill. #1900, Ironworks forge. #1901, Forge welding. #1902, Dannemora Mine. #1903, Blast furnace, Pershyttan.

Perf. 13 on 2 or 3 Sides
1991, Aug. 27   **Engr.**

1898	A569	2.50k multicolored	1.25	.85
1899	A569	2.50k multicolored	1.25	.85

Size: 31x26mm

1900	A569	2.50k multicolored	1.25	*1.10*
1901	A569	2.50k multicolored	1.25	*1.10*

Size: 31x40mm

1902	A569	2.50k multicolored	1.25	*1.10*
1903	A569	2.50k multicolored	1.25	*1.10*
a.		Bklt. pane of 6, #1898-1903	7.50	6.75

Coronation of King Gustavus III, by Carl Gustaf Pilo — A570

Details from painting: No. 1904, King Gustavus III. No. 1905, Gustavus with crown held above head. No. 1906, Chancellor Arvid Horn, Archbishop Mattias Beronius holding crown above Gustavus III.

1991, Oct. 5   **Engr.**   **Perf. 13**

1904	A570	10k blue	4.00	3.50
1905	A570	10k violet	4.00	3.50

Size: 76x44mm

1906	A570	10k greenish black	5.00	5.00
a.		Bklt. pane of 3, #1904-1906	13.00	13.00

Czeslaw Slania, engraver, 70th birthday. No. 1906a sold for 35k to benefit stamp collecting.

Rock Musicians A571

1991, Oct. 5   **Litho. & Engr.**

1907	A571	2.50k Lena Philipsson	1.75	.85
1908	A571	2.50k Roxette	1.75	.85
1909	A571	2.50k Jerry Williams	1.75	.85
a.		Bklt. pane of 3, #1907-1909	7.50	*4.25*

A572   A573

Christmas: No. 1910, Boy with star, girl with snacks. No. 1911, Family dancing around Christmas tree. No. 1912, Cat beside tree. No. 1913, Child beside bed.

Perf. 12½x13 on 3 Sides
1991, Nov. 20   **Litho.**

1910	A572	2.30k multicolored	.95	.45
1911	A572	2.30k multicolored	.95	.45
1912	A572	2.30k multicolored	.95	.45
1913	A572	2.30k multicolored	.95	.45
b.		Bklt. pane, 3 ea #1910-1913	12.00	
		Nos. 1910-1913 (4)	*3.80*	*1.80*

Nobel Laureates Type of 1990

Nobel Peace Prize Winners: No. 1914, Jean Henri Dunant, founder of Red Cross. No. 1915, Albert Schweitzer, physician and theologian. No. 1916, Alva Myrdal, disarmament negotiator. No. 1917, Andrei Sakharov, physicist.

1991, Nov. 20   **Engr.**   **Perf. 13 Horiz.**

1914	A559	4k carmine	1.60	1.60
1915	A559	4k dk green	1.60	1.60
1916	A559	4k dk ultra	1.60	1.60
1917	A559	4k dk violet	1.60	1.60
a.		Bklt. pane, 2 each #1914-1917 with gutter between	13.00	
		Nos. 1914-1917 (4)	*6.40*	*6.40*

1992, Jan. 30   **Engr.**   **Perf. 13 Horiz.**

1918	A573	2.30k red, grn & blk	1.10	.35

Outdoor Life Assoc., cent.

A574

Wild Animals — A575

1992-96   **Engr.**   **Perf. 13 on 3 Sides**

1920	A574	2.80k Capreolus capreolus	1.00	.20
1921	A574	2.80k Capreolus capreolus (with fawn)	1.00	.20
b.		Bklt. pane, 5 ea #1920-1921	10.00	
1922	A574	2.90k Ursus arctos (2 cubs)	1.10	.30
1923	A574	2.90k Ursus arctos (adult)	1.10	.30
b.		Bklt. pane, 5 ea #1922-1923	11.00	
1924	A574	3.85k Mustela erminea	1.00	.25
1925	A574	3.85k Lutra lutra	1.00	.25
a.		Bklt. pane, 5 ea #1924-1925	16.00	
		Complete booklet, 1 #1925a	16.00	

Perf. 13 Vert. (A574), Horiz. (A575)

1926	A574	1k Erinaeceus eropaeus	.40	.30
1927	A574	2.80k like #1921	1.00	.20
1928	A574	2.90k like #1922	1.25	.20
1929	A574	3k Mustela putorius	1.25	.45
1930	A575	3.20k Castor fiber	1.50	1.25
1931	A574	3.85k like #1924	1.50	.35
1932	A574	5.80k Canis lupus	2.75	.40
1933	A575	6k Sciurus vulgaris	2.50	.50
1934	A575	7k Alces alces	2.75	.50
1935	A574	7.70k Vulpes vulpes	3.00	.60
1936	A575	12k Lynx lynx	3.75	.85
		Nos. 1920-1936 (17)	*27.85*	*7.10*

Issued: #1920-1921, 1930, 6k, 7k, Jan. 30; #1922-1923, 1928-1929, 1932, 1936, Jan. 28, 1993; 1k, 3.20k, 3.85k, 7.70k, 1/2/96.
See Nos. 2207-2209, 2238.

Olympic Champions Type of 1991

No. 1937, Gunde Svan, cross-country skiing, Sarajevo, 1984. No. 1938, Thomas Wassberg, cross-country skiing, Lake Placid, 1980. No. 1939, Tomas Gustafson, speed skating, Sarajevo, 1984. No. 1940, Ingemar Stenmark, slalom skiing, Lake Placid, 1980.

Perf. 12x13 on 3 Sides
1992, Jan. 30   **Litho. & Engr.**

1937	A568	2.80k multicolored	1.10	.60
1938	A568	2.80k multicolored	1.10	.60
1939	A568	2.80k multicolored	1.10	.60
1940	A568	2.80k multicolored	1.10	.60
a.		Bklt. pane, 2 each #1937-1940	9.25	
		Nos. 1937-1940 (4)	*4.40*	*2.40*

European Soccer Championships, Sweden — A576

1992, Mar. 26   **Engr.**   **Perf. 13 Vert.**

1941	A576	2.80k shown	1.00	.35
1942	A576	2.80k Two players	1.00	.35
a.		Pair, #1941-1942	2.00	1.50

Sweden No. 1a A577

1992, Mar. 26   **Litho. & Engr.**   **Perf. 13**

1943	A577	2.80k No. 1	2.50	2.50
1944	A577	4.50k No. 1	2.50	2.50
1945	A577	5.50k shown	2.00	1.60
a.		Bklt. pane, #1943-1944, 2 #1945	7.50	*8.50*
		Nos. 1943-1945 (3)	*7.00*	*6.60*

No. 1945a sold for 25k. Surtax benefited stamp collecting.

Sailing Ships — A578

1992, Mar. 26

1946	A578	4.50k Sprengtporten, 1785	*2.10*	1.50
1947	A578	4.50k Superb, 1855	*2.10*	1.50
1948	A578	4.50k Big T	*2.10*	1.50
a.		Bklt. pane of 3, #1946-1948	*6.50*	6.50

Europa. Discovery Race, Spain-Florida (No. 1948).

Children's Drawings A579

Perf. 13x12½ on 3 Sides
1992, May 21   **Litho.**

1949	A579	2.50k Rabbit	.95	.25
1950	A579	2.50k Horses	.95	.25
1951	A579	2.50k Cat	.95	.25
1952	A579	2.50k Elephant	.95	.25
a.		Bklt. pane, 5 ea #1949-1952	19.00	
		Nos. 1949-1952 (4)	*3.80*	*1.00*

See note after No. 1277.

Olympic Champions Type of 1991

Designs: No. 1953, Gunnar Larsson, swimming, 1972. No. 1954, Bernt Johansson, cycling, 1976. No. 1955, Anders Garderud, steeplechase, 1976. No. 1956, Gert Fredriksson, kayaking, 1948-1956.

Perf. 12x13 on 3 Sides
1992, May 21   **Litho. & Engr.**

1953	A568	5.50k multicolored	2.10	2.10
1954	A568	5.50k multicolored	2.10	2.10
1955	A568	5.50k multicolored	2.10	2.10
1956	A568	5.50k multicolored	2.10	2.10
a.		Bklt. pane, 2 ea #1953-1956	17.00	
		Nos. 1953-1956 (4)	*8.40*	*8.40*

Greetings Stamps — A580

Perf. 13x12 on 3 Sides
1992, Aug. 14   **Litho.**

1957	A580	2.80k Hand with flower	1.10	.85
1958	A580	2.80k Cheese	1.10	.85
1959	A580	2.80k Baby	1.10	.85
1960	A580	2.80k Hand holding pen	1.10	.85
b.		Bklt. pane, 2 each #1957-1960	9.00	
		Nos. 1957-1960 (4)	*4.40*	*3.40*

88th Inter-Parliamentary Union Conference, Stockholm — A581

Swedish Patent and Registration Office, Cent. — A582

#1961, Riksdag building. #1962, First automatic lighthouse, Gustaf Dalen's sun valve.

Perf. 12½ Vert.
1992, Aug. 27   **Engr.**

1961	A581	2.80k violet, *tan*	1.25	.25

Perf. 13 Horiz.

1962	A582	2.80k blue & black	1.25	.35

Kitchen Maid, by Rembrandt A583

The Triumph of Venus, by Francois Boucher A584

Paintings: No. 1965, Portrait of a Girl, by Albrecht Durer. No. 1966, Rorstrand Vase, by Erik Wahlberg. No. 1967, Motif from the Seine/The Tree and the River Bend III, by Carl Fredrik Hill. No. 1968, Sergel in his Studio, by Carl Larsson.

Perf. 12½ on 3 Sides
1992, Aug. 27   **Litho. & Engr.**

1963	A583	5.50k multicolored	2.25	1.75
1964	A584	5.50k multicolored	2.25	1.75
1965	A583	5.50k multicolored	2.25	1.75
1966	A584	5.50k multicolored	2.25	1.75
1967	A584	5.50k multicolored	2.25	1.75
1968	A583	5.50k multicolored	2.25	1.75
a.		Bklt. pane of 6, #1963-1968	13.50	*14.50*

National Museum of Fine Arts, 200th anniv.

Prehistoric
Animals — A585

Perf. 13x12½ on 3 Sides
1992, Oct. 3   **Litho. & Engr.**
1969 A585 2.80k Plateosaurus   1.25   .90
1970 A585 2.80k Thoraco-
    saurus
    scanicus   1.25   .90
1971 A585 2.80k Coelodonta
    antiquitatis   1.25   .90
1972 A585 2.80k Mammuthus
    primigenius   1.25   .90
a.   Bklt. pane, 2 ea #1969-1972   10.40
    Nos. 1969-1972 (4)   5.00 3.60

No. 1972a sold for 27k to benefit stamp
collecting.

1950
Automobiles
A586

1992, Oct. 3   **Engr.**   **Perf. 12½ Vert.**
1973 A586 4k Saab 92   1.50   .75
1974 A586 4k Volvo P 831   1.50   .75
a.   Pair, #1973-1974   3.00 3.00

Birds of the
Baltic
Shores — A587

1992, Oct. 3   **Litho. & Engr.**   **Perf. 13**
1975 A587 4.50k Pandion
    haliaetus   1.75 1.25
1976 A587 4.50k Limosa limosa   1.75 1.25
1977 A587 4.50k Mergus mer-
    ganser   1.75 1.25
1978 A587 4.50k Tadorna
    tadorna   1.75 1.25
a.   Bklt. pane of 4, #1975-1978   7.00 7.50

See Estonia Nos. 231-234, Latvis Nos. 332-
335, and Lithuania Nos. 427-430.

A588   A589

A590   A591
Christmas

Icons: No. 1979, Joachim and Anna, 16th
cent. No. 1980, Madonna and Child, 14th cent.
No. 1981, Archangel Gabriel, 12th cent. No.
1982, St. Nicholas, 16th cent.

Perf. 12½x13 on 3 Sides
1992, Nov. 27   **Litho. & Engr.**
1979 A588 2.30k multicolored   .85   .50
1980 A589 2.30k multicolored   .85   .50
1981 A590 2.30k multicolored   .85   .50
1982 A591 2.30k multicolored   .85   .50
a.   Bklt. pane, 3 ea #1979-1982   10.50
    Nos. 1979-1982 (4)   3.40 2.00

See Russia Nos. 6103-6106.

Derek Walcott,
Nobel Laureate
in Literature,
1992 — A592

1992, Nov. 27 Engr.   **Perf. 12½ Vert.**
1983 A592 5.50k Text   2.25 1.60
1984 A592 5.50k Portrait   2.25 1.60
a.   Pair, #1983-1984   5.00 5.00

1993 Sports Championships — A593

Perf. 12½x13 on 3 Sides
1993, Jan. 28   **Litho. & Engr.**
1985 A593 6k Gliding   2.40 1.90
1986 A593 6k Wrestling   2.40 1.90
1987 A593 6k Table tennis   2.40 1.90
1988 A593 6k Bowling   2.40 1.90
1989 A593 6k Team handball   2.40 1.90
1990 A593 6k Cross-country
    skiing   2.40 1.90
a.   Booklet pane, #1985-1990   14.50 13.50

World Gliding Championships, Borlange
(#1985). World Wrestling Championships,
Stockholm (#1986). World Table Tennis Cham-
pionships, Gothenburg (#1987). European
Bowling Championships, Malmo (#1988).
World Team Handball Championships, Goth-
enburg (#1989). World Cross-Country Skiing
Championships, Falun (#1990).

Uppsala
Convocation,
400th
Anniversary
A594

Litho. & Engr.
1993, Mar. 25   **Perf. 13 Vert.**
1991 A594 2.90k Stone carving   1.25   .45
1992 A594 2.90k Uppsala Cathe-
    dral   1.25   .45
a.   Pair, #1991-1992   2.50 2.00

A595

Tourist Attractions in Gothenburg: No. 1993,
Roller coaster Liseberg Loop, Liseburg
Amusement Park. No. 1994, Fountain of
Poseidon, by Carl Milles.

1993, Mar. 25
1993 A595 3.50k multicolored   1.25 1.40
1994 A595 3.50k multicolored   1.25 1.40
a.   Pair, #1993-1994   2.75 3.25

Fruit
A596   A596a

Perf. 12½ on 3 Sides
1993-95   **Engr.**
1995 A596 2.40k Ribes uva
    crispa   1.10   .75
1996 A596 2.40k Pyrus com-
    munis   1.10   .75
b.   Bklt. pane, 5 ea #1996-1996   11.00
1997 A596 2.80k Victoria plum   1.25   .60
1998 A596 2.80k Opal plum   .95   .60
b.   Bklt. pane, 5 ea #1997-1998   12.50

2001 A596a 3.35k Ribes nigrum   1.40   .60
2002 A596a 3.35k Rubus idaeus   1.40   .60
a.   Bklt. pane, 5 ea #2001-2002   13.50
    Complete booklet, #2002a   13.50

Perf. 12½ Vert.
2004 A596 2.40k Prunus avi-
    um   1.00   .75
2005 A596 2.80k James
    Grieve ap-
    ple   1.40   .50

Perf. 12½ Horiz.
2008 A596a 3.35k Fragaria
    ananassa   1.40   .60
    Nos. 1995-2008 (9)   11.00 5.75

Issued: #1995-1996, 2004, 3/25/93; #1997-
1998, 2005, 1/17/94; #2000-2001, 2008,
1/2/95.
This is an expanding set. Numbers may
change.

Oxe-eye
Daisy — A597

Poppy — A598

Buttercup
A599   Bluebell
     A600

Perf. 12½x13 on 3 Sides
1993, May 21   **Litho.**
2013 A597 2.60k multicolored   .95   .35
2014 A598 2.60k multicolored   .95   .35
2015 A599 2.60k multicolored   .95   .35
2016 A600 2.60k multicolored   .95   .35
b.   Bklt. pane, 5 ea #2013-2016   19.00
    Nos. 2013-2016 (4)   3.80 1.40

See note after No. 1277.

Contemporary
Art — A601

Europa: No. 2017, Oguasark, by Olle
Baertling (1911-81). No. 2018, Ade-Lidic-
Nander II, by Oyvind Fahlstrom (1928-76),
horiz. No. 2019, The Cubist Chair, by Otto G.
Carlsund (1897-1948).

Litho. & Engr.
1993, May 21   **Perf. 13**
2017 A601 5k multicolored   2.10 1.90
2018 A601 5k multicolored   2.10 1.90
2019 A601 5k multicolored   2.10 1.90
a.   Booklet pane of 3, #2017-2019   6.50 7.50

Butterflies — A602

Perf. 12½ Horiz.
1993, May 21
2020 A602 6k Papilio machaon   2.25 2.10
2021 A602 6k Nymphalis anti-
    opa   2.25 2.10
2022 A602 6k Colias palaeno   2.25 2.10
2023 A602 6k Euphydryas
    maturna   2.25 2.10
a.   Booklet pane, 2 each #2020-
    2023 with gutter between   19.00
    Nos. 2020-2023 (4)   9.00 8.40

A603

A604

A605   A606
Greetings

Perf. 13 on 3 Sides
1993, Aug. 6   **Litho.**
2024 A603 2.90k multicolored   1.00   .40
2025 A604 2.90k multicolored   1.25   .75
2026 A605 2.90k multicolored   1.00   .40
2027 A606 2.90k multicolored   1.25   .75
b.   Booklet pane, 3 each #2024,
    2026, 2 each #2025, 2027   11.00
    Nos. 2024-2027 (4)   4.50 2.30

Sea
Birds
A607

Perf. 12½ Horiz.
1993, Aug. 26   **Engr.**
2028 A607 5k Mergus serrator   2.00 1.60
2029 A607 5k Melanitta fusca   2.00 1.60
2030 A607 5k Aythya fuligula   2.00 1.60
2031 A607 5k Somateria mollis-
    sima   2.00 1.60
a.   Booklet pane, 2 each #2028-
    2031 with gutter between   16.00
    Nos. 2028-2031 (4)   8.00 6.40

A608   A609

1993, Oct. 2   **Engr.**   **Perf. 13 Vert.**
2032 A608 2.90k Modern echo
    sounding   1.20   .35
2033 A608 2.90k 1643 Method   1.20   .35
a.   Pair, #2032-2033   2.90 1.75

Hydrographic survey.

1993, Oct. 2   **Engr.**   **Perf. 13**
2034 A609 8k King holding
    flag   3.25 2.75
2035 A609 10k King   3.75 3.50
2036 A609 10k Queen Silvia   3.75 3.50

Size: 75x43mm
2037 A609 12k Royal family   4.50 5.25
a.   Booklet pane, #2034-2037   15.50 15.50
    Nos. 2034-2037 (4)   15.25 15.00

Reign of King Carl XVI Gustaf, 20th anniv.

Christmas — A610

Perf. 12½ on 3 Sides
1993, Nov. 25   **Engr.**
2038 A610 2.40k Plaited heart   .95   .40
2039 A610 2.40k Straw goat   .95   .40
b.   Bklt. pane, 5 ea #2038-2039   9.50

Toni Morrison, Nobel laureate in Literature, 1993 — A611

#2041, Stockholm City Hall.

1993, Nov. 25 Engr. *Perf. 12½ Vert.*
2040	A611	6k red brown & brown	2.40	1.75
2041	A611	6k multicolored	2.40	1.75
a.		Pair, #2040-2041	5.00	4.25

European Economic Assoc. Agreement A612

1994, Jan. 17 *Perf. 12½ Vert.*
2042	A612	5k Mother Svea	2.25	.65

Domestic Animals — A613

No. 2047, North Sweden horse, vert. No. 2048, Two horses, vert. No. 2049, Red polled cattle, vert. No. 2050, Goat, vert. No. 2054, Swedish dwarf poultry. No. 2055, Gotland sheep. No. 2059, Mountain cow. No. 2060, Scanian goose. No. 2060A, Yellow duck.

1994-95 Engr. *Perf. 13 on 3 Sides*
2047	A613	3.20k multicolored	1.25	.25
2048	A613	3.20k multicolored	1.25	.25
a.		Bklt. pane, 5 ea #2047-2048	12.50	
2049	A613	3.70k multicolored	1.40	.30
2050	A613	3.70k multicolored	1.40	.30
a.		Bklt. pane, 5 ea #2049-2050	14.00	
		Complete booklet, #2050a	14.00	

Perf. 13 Vert.
2054	A613	3.10k multicolored	1.40	.45
2055	A613	3.20k multicolored	1.50	.30
2059	A613	6.40k multicolored	3.00	.60
2060	A613	7.40k multicolored	3.00	.60
2060A	A613	7.50k multicolored	3.00	2.10
		Nos. 2047-2060A (9)	17.20	5.15

Issued: #2047-2048, 2055, 2059, 1/17/94; #2049-2050, 2054, 1/2/95; 2060-2060A, 3/17/95.
This is an expanding set. Numbers may change.

Cats — A614

Litho. & Engr.
1994, Mar. 18 *Perf. 13*
2061	A614	4.50k Siamese	1.75	1.60
2062	A614	4.50k Persian	1.75	1.60
2063	A614	4.50k European	1.75	1.60
2064	A614	4.50k Abyssinian	1.75	1.60
a.		Booklet pane of 4, #2061-2064	7.00	8.50

Roman De La Rose — A615

Swedish, French Flags A616

Swedish-French cultural relations: No. 2067, House of the Nobility, designed by Simon and Jean de la Vallee. No. 2068, Household Chores, by Hillestrom. No. 2069, Banquet for Gustavus III at the Trianon, 1784, by Lafrensen. No. 2070, Charles XIV John, by Gerard.

Litho. & Engr., Litho. (#2066)
1994, Mar. 18 *Perf. 13 on 3 Sides*
2065	A615	5k multicolored	2.25	2.25
2066	A616	5k multicolored	2.25	2.25
2067	A615	5k multicolored	2.25	2.25
2068	A615	5k multicolored	2.25	2.25
2069	A616	5k multicolored	2.25	2.25
2070	A615	5k multicolored	2.25	2.25
a.		Booklet pane of 6, #2065-2070	14.00	15.50

See France Nos. 2410-2415.

Roses — A617 Swedish Design — A618

Perf. 12½x13 on 3 Sides
1994, May 11 *Litho.*
2071	A617	3.20k Nyponros rosa dumalis	1.10	.45
2072	A617	3.20k Rosa alba maxima	1.10	.45
2073	A617	3.20k Tuscany superb	1.10	.45
2074	A617	3.20k Peace	1.10	.45
2075	A617	3.20k Quatre saisons	1.10	.45
a.		Bklt. pane, 2 ea #2071-2075	11.00	
		Nos. 2071-2075 (5)	5.50	2.25

Perf. 12½ on 3 Sides
1994, May 11 *Litho. & Engr.*
#2076, Vase with Irises, by Gunnar Wennerberg, 1897. #2077, Table and Chair, by Carl Malmsten; Wallpaper, by Uno Ahren, 1917. #2078, Cabinet, 1940s, and textile, 1920s, by Josef Franck. #2079, Fireworks Bowl, by Edward Hald, 1921. #2080, Silver water jug, by Wiwen Nilsson, 1941. #2081, Towel, by Astrid Sampe; Plate, by Stig Lindberg; Fork and Spoon, by Sigurd Persson, 1955.

2076	A618	6.50k multicolored	2.50	2.25
2077	A618	6.50k multicolored	2.50	2.25
2078	A618	6.50k multicolored	2.50	2.25
2079	A618	6.50k multicolored	2.50	2.25
2080	A618	6.50k multicolored	2.50	2.25
2081	A618	6.50k multicolored	2.50	2.25
a.		Bklt. pane, #2076-2081	15.50	17.50

1994 World Cup Soccer Championships, US — A619

1994, May 11 Engr. *Perf. 12½ Vert.*
2082	A619	3.20k red & blue	1.60	.50

First Manned Moon Landing, 25th Anniv. A620

1994, May 11
2083	A620	6.50k multicolored	2.50	2.25

Greetings A621

Perf. 12½ on 3 Sides
1994, Aug. 5 *Litho.*
2084	A621	3.20k Cat	1.10	.40
2085	A621	3.20k Snail	1.10	.40
2086	A621	3.20k Frog	1.20	.70
2087	A621	3.20k Dog	1.20	.70
a.		Booklet pane, 3 each #2084-2085, 2 each #2086-2087	11.50	
		Nos. 2084-2087 (4)	4.60	2.20

Swedish Explorers A622

Europa: No. 2088, Erland Nordenskiold (1877-1932), explored South America. No. 2089, Eric Von Rosen (1879-1948), explored Africa. No. 2090, Sten Bergman (1895-1975), explored Asia and the Pacific.

Litho. & Engr.
1994, Aug. 26 *Perf. 12½*
2088	A622	5.50k multicolored	2.50	2.00
2089	A622	5.50k multicolored	2.50	2.00
2090	A622	5.50k multicolored	2.50	2.00
a.		Booklet pane of 3, #2088-2090	7.50	8.75

Finland-Sweden Track and Field Meet — A623

#2091, Seppo Raty, Finland, javelin. #2092, Patrick Sjoberg, Sweden, high jump.

1994, Aug. 26 *Perf. 12½ on 3 Sides*
2091	A623	4.50k multicolored	1.75	1.50
2092	A623	4.50k multicolored	1.75	1.50
a.		Bklt. pane, 2 ea #2091-2092	7.50	7.50

See Finland Nos. 942-943.

Johan Helmich Roman (1694-1758), Composer A624

No. 2094, Opera House, Gothenburg.

Perf. 12½ Vert.
1994, Aug. 26 *Engr.*
2093	A624	3.20k multicolored	1.25	.25
2094	A624	3.20k multicolored	1.25	.25

Yes & No Stamps — A625

1994, Oct. 1 Litho. *Perf. 12½ Vert.*
2095	A625	3.20k Ja	1.25	.60
2096	A625	3.20k Nej	1.25	.60

See Nos. 2107-2108.

World Wildlife Fund — A626

#2097, Sterna caspia. #2098, Haliaeetus albicilla. #2099, Dendrocopos leucotos. #2100, Anser erythropus.

Litho. & Engr.
1994, Oct. 1 *Perf. 12½*
2097	A626	5.50k multicolored	2.40	2.00
2098	A626	5.50k multicolored	2.40	2.00
2099	A626	5.50k multicolored	2.40	2.00
2100	A626	5.50k multicolored	2.40	2.00
a.		Booklet pane of 4, #2097-2100	9.75	10.00

Frans G. Bengtsson (1894-1954), Writer — A627

1994, Oct. 1 Engr. *Perf. 12½ Vert.*
2101	A627	6.40k multicolored	2.75	2.00

Nobel Laureates in Literature A628 Christmas A629

Designs: 4.50k, Erik Axel Karlfeldt (1864-1931). 5.50k, Eyvind Johnson (1900-76). 6.50k, Harry Martinson (1904-78).

1994, Nov. 11
2102	A628	4.50k multicolored	1.90	1.00
2103	A628	5.50k multicolored	2.25	1.25
2104	A628	6.50k multicolored	2.75	1.40
		Nos. 2102-2104 (3)	6.90	3.65

Perf. 12½x13 on 3 Sides
1994, Nov. 11 *Litho. & Engr.*
Scenes from medieval altar pieces: No. 2105, Annunciation. No. 2106, Flight to Egypt.

2105	A629	2.80k multicolored	1.25	.40
2106	A629	2.80k multicolored	1.25	.40
a.		Bklt. pane, 5 ea #2105-2106	12.50	

Yes & No Type of 1994
1995, Jan. 2 Litho. *Perf. 12½ Vert.*
2107	A625	3.70k Ja	1.10	.40
2108	A625	3.70k Nej	1.10	.40

Houses A630

Designs: No. 2109, Country cottage. No. 2110, Soldier's log house. No. 2111, Farmhouse courtyard. No. 2112, Timbered farmhouse. No. 2113, Manor house.

Perf. 14 Horiz.
1995, Mar. 17 *Litho. & Engr.*
2109	A630	3.70k multicolored	1.60	.65
2110	A630	3.70k multicolored	1.60	.65
2111	A630	3.70k multicolored	1.60	.65
2112	A630	3.70k multicolored	1.60	.65
2113	A630	3.70k multicolored	1.60	.65
a.		Booklet pane of 5, #2109-2113	8.00	8.00
		Complete booklet, #2113a	8.50	

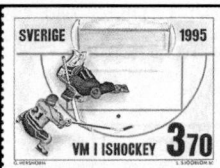

1995 Ice Hockey World
Championships — A631

1995 World
Track & Field
Championships
A632

Litho. & Engr.
1995, Mar. 17   **Perf. 13 Vert.**
2114 A631 3.70k multicolored   3.00 1.00

Perf. 13 Horiz.
2115 A632 3.70k multicolored   1.90 .50

A633

Wood
Sculptures, by
Bror
Hjorth — A634

Europa: Nos. 2116, 2118, Walt Whitman,
Christ, Socrates. Nos. 2117, 2119, Patrice
Lumumba, Albert Schweitzer, children
dancing.

1995, Mar. 17   **Litho.**   **Perf. 13**
2116 A633 5k multicolored   2.25 1.75
2117 A634 5k multicolored   2.25 1.75
2118 A633 6k multicolored   2.50 2.00
2119 A634 6k multicolored   2.50 2.00
   a.   Bklt. pane of 4, #2116-2119   9.50 10.00
     Complete booklet, 2 #2119a   19.00

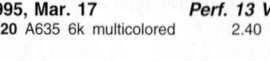

Swedish
Membership in
European
Union — A635

1995, Mar. 17   **Perf. 13 Vert.**
2120 A635 6k multicolored   2.40 1.10

Rock Speedwell   Cloudberry
A636   A637

Mountain   Alpine
Heath — A638   Arnica — A639

Perf. 13 on 3 Sides
1995, May 12   **Litho.**
2121 A636 3.70k multicolored   1.25 .45
2122 A637 3.70k multicolored   1.50 .60
2123 A638 3.70k multicolored   1.25 .45
2124 A639 3.70k multicolored   1.50 .60
  a.   Booklet pane, 3 each #2121,
    2123, 2 each #2122, 2124   13.50
    Complete booklet, #2124a   13.50
   Nos. 2121-2124 (4)   5.50 2.10

Tourist
Attractions — A640

#2125, Canal boat Wilhelm Tham on Gota
Canal. #2126, Sail boat anchored on Lake
Vattern.

1995, May 12   **Engr.**
2125 A640 5k dark green   2.10 1.40
2126 A640 5k dark violet   2.10 1.40
  a.   Bklt. pane, 2 ea #2125-2126   8.50
    Complete booklet, #2126a   8.50

Trams
A641

#2127, Gothenburg, c. 1900. #2128, Norr-
koping, 1905. #2129, Helsingborg, 1921.
#2130, Kiruna, 1958. #2131, Stockholm, 1967.

1995, May 12   **Perf. 13 Horiz.**
2127 A641 7.50k rose claret   3.00 2.75
2128 A641 7.50k dp brown vio   3.00 2.75
2129 A641 7.50k dk green   3.00 2.75
2130 A641 7.50k dk gray violet   3.00 2.75
2131 A641 7.50k dk violet blue   3.00 2.75
  a.   Bklt. pane of 5, #2127-2131   15.00 16.00
    Complete booklet, #2131a   15.00

UN, 50th
Anniv.
A642

1995, Aug. 3   **Engr.**   **Perf. 13 Vert.**
2132 A642 3.70k multicolored   1.75 .35

Greetings
A643

Children's drawings: No. 2133, "The Ball is
Yours," by M. Angesjo. No. 2134, Happy man,
by E. Sandstrom. No. 2135, Teddy Bear saying "I miss you," by L. Nordenhem. No. 2136,
Mussel saying "Hello," by C. Stenbom.

1995, Aug. 3   **Litho.**   **Perf. 13x12½**
2133 A643 3.70k multicolored   1.40 .55
2134 A643 3.70k multicolored   1.40 .55
2135 A643 3.70k multicolored   1.75 1.00
2136 A643 3.70k multicolored   1.75 1.00
  a.   Booklet pane, 3 each #2133-
    2134, 2 each #2135-2136   15.50
    Complete booklet, #2136a   15.50
   Nos. 2133-2136 (4)   6.30 3.10

1995 IAAF World
Track & Field
Championships,
Gothenburg
A644

Perf. 13 Horiz.
1995, Aug. 3   **Litho. & Engr.**
2137 A644 7.50k Maria Akraka   3.00 2.25

Motion
Picture,
Cent.
A645

Scenes from films: No. 2138, Soldier Bom,
1948. No. 2139, Sir Arne's Treasure, 1919.
No. 2140, Wild Strawberries, 1957. No. 2141,
House of Angels, 1992. No. 2142, One Sum-
mer of Happiness, 1951. No. 2143, The Apple
War, 1971.

Litho. & Engr.
1995, Oct. 7   **Perf. 12½x13**
Booklet Stamps
2138 A645 6k multicolored   2.50 2.50
2139 A645 6k multicolored   2.50 2.50
2140 A645 6k multicolored   2.50 2.50
2141 A645 6k multicolored   2.50 2.50
2142 A645 6k multicolored   2.50 2.50
2143 A645 6k multicolored   2.50 2.50
  a.   Booklet pane, #2138-2143   15.00 18.00
    Complete booklet, #2143a   15.00

Fritiof Nilsson
(1895-1972),
Writer — A646

Litho. & Engr.
1995, Oct. 27   **Perf. 13 Vert.**
2144 A646 3.70k blue & claret   1.75 .40

Ancient
Artifacts — A647

Designs: No. 2145, Bronze cult figures of
man with beak, nude woman, Bronze Age. No.
2146, Detail of gold collar, Great Migration
period. No. 2147, Bracteate pendant picturing
figure on horse, Great Migration period. No.
2148, Circular bronze cult object, Bronze Age.

1995, Oct. 27   **Perf. 13**
2145 A647 3.70k multicolored   1.50 1.25
2146 A647 3.70k multicolored   1.50 1.25
2147 A647 3.70k multicolored   1.50 1.25
2148 A647 3.70k multicolored   1.50 1.25
  a.   Booklet pane of 4, #2145-
    2148   6.00 7.50
    Complete booklet, 2 #2148a   12.00

A648   A649

Tycho Brache (1546-1601), Astronomer: 5k,
Uranienborg Observatory, Ven Island. 6k,
Sextant.

Litho. & Engr.
1995, Oct. 27   **Perf. 13 Vert.**
2149 A648 5k multicolored   1.90 1.25
2150 A648 6k multicolored   2.50 2.00

See Denmark Nos. 1035-1036.

Perf. 12½x13 on 3 Sides
1995, Nov. 9   **Litho.**

Christmas candlesticks.

2151 A649 3.35k Santa   1.10 .45
2152 A649 3.35k Apple   1.50 .80
2153 A649 3.35k Wrought iron   1.10 .45
2154 A649 3.35k Red wooden   1.50 .80
  a.   Booklet pane, 3 ea #2151,
    2153, 2 ea #2152, 2154   12.50
    Complete booklet, No. 2151a   12.50
   Nos. 2151-2154 (4)   5.20 2.50

Nobel Prize Fund Established,
Cent. — A650

Designs: No. 2155, Alfred Nobel, last will
and testament. No. 2156, Nobel's home, 59
Avenue de Malakoff, Paris. No. 2157,
Björkborn Laboratory, Karlkoga. No. 2158,
Wilhelm Röntgen receiving the first physics
prize, 1901.

Photo. & Engr.
1995, Nov. 9   **Perf. 13 Horiz.**
2155 A650 6k multicolored   2.40 2.25
2156 A650 6k multicolored   2.40 2.25
2157 A650 6k multicolored   2.40 2.25
2158 A650 6k multicolored   2.40 2.25
  a.   Booklet pane, #2155-2158   9.50 11.00
    Complete booklet, No.
    2158a   9.50

Holly — A651   Rowan
               Berries — A652

Rose Hips &   Lingonberries &
Juniper — A653   Sloe — A654

1996, Jan. 2   **Litho.**   **Perf. 13 Horiz.**
2159 A651 3.50k multicolored   1.50 .75
2160 A652 7.50k multicolored   3.25 1.60
Perf. 13 on 3 Sides
2161 A653 3.50k multicolored   1.25 .55
2162 A654 3.50k multicolored   1.25 .55
  a.   Bklt. pane, 5 ea, #2161-2162   12.50
    Complete booklet, #2162a   12.50
   Nos. 2159-2162 (4)   7.25 3.45

End of Railway Mail Sorting — A655

1996, Mar. 29   **Engr.**   **Perf. 13 Vert.**
2163 A655 6k multicolored   2.50 1.25

King Carl XVI
Gustaf, 50th
Birthday — A656

King Carl XVI Gustaf: No. 2164, In forest.
No. 2165, In front of portrait of King Charles
XIV John. No. 2166, In carriage with King
Albert of Belgium, 1994. 20kr, With family.

Litho. & Engr.
1996, Apr. 19   **Perf. 13x12½**
2164 A656 10k multicolored   3.25 3.50
2165 A656 10k multicolored   3.25 3.50
2166 A656 10k multicolored   3.25 3.50
Size: 80x48mm
2167 A656 20k multicolored   6.75 6.50
  a.   Booklet pane, #2164-2167   16.50 22.50

Historic Buildings — A657

Designs: No. 2168, Railway station, Halsingland. No. 2169, Motala Assembly Hall, Östergotland. No. 2170, Parish storehouse, Smaland. No. 2171, Half-timbered barn, Vasterbotten. No. 2172, Sheep shelter, Gotland. No. 2173, Old Town Hall, Lidkoping.

Perf. 13 on 2 or 3 Sides
1996, Apr. 19
2168	A657	3.85k multicolored	1.50	.60
2169	A657	3.85k multicolored	1.50	.60

Size: 28x29mm
2170	A657	3.85k multicolored	1.50	.85
2171	A657	3.85k multicolored	1.50	.85

Size: 28x38mm
2172	A657	3.85k multicolored	1.50	.85
2173	A657	3.85k multicolored	1.50	.85
a.		Booklet pane of 6, #2168-2173	9.00	10.00

Famous Women — A658

Europa: No. 2174, Karin Kock (1891-1976), economist. No. 2175, Astrid Lindgren (b. 1907), creator of Pippi Longstocking.

Perf. 13 on 3 Sides
1996, May 3   **Engr.**
2174	A658	6k multicolored	3.25	2.25
2175	A658	6k multicolored	3.25	2.25
a.		Bklt. pane, 2 ea #2174-2175	9.00	
		Complete booklet, #2175a	9.00	

Summer Scenes A659

Paintings by: No. 2176, Sven X:Et Erixson (1899-1970). No. 2177, Roland Svensson (b. 1910). No. 2178, Eric Hallström (1893-1946), No. 2179, Thage Nordholm (1927-90). No. 2180, Ragnar Sandberg (1902-72).

Perf. 13 on 2 Sides
1996, May 24   **Litho.**
2176	A659	3.85k multicolored	1.50	.40
2177	A659	3.85k multicolored	1.50	.40
2178	A659	3.85k multicolored	1.50	.40
2179	A659	3.85k multicolored	1.50	.40
2180	A659	3.85k multicolored	1.50	.40
a.		Bklt. pane, 2 ea #2176-2180	15.00	
		Complete booklet, #2180a	15.00	
		Nos. 2176-2180 (5)	7.50	2.00

Golf — A660

1996, Aug. 23   Engr.   Perf. 13 Horiz.
2181	A660	3.50k dark green, *buff*	2.25	1.25

Greetings Stamps — A661

Designs: No. 2182, Masks of comedy, tragedy, "don't worry, be happy." No. 2183, Hearts, "Var Glad (Be happy)," vert. No. 2184, Posthorn. No. 2185, Hearts, person, "Minns du mig? (Do you remember me?)."

Perf. 13x12½ on 3 Sides
1996, Aug. 23   **Litho.**
2182	A661	3.85k multicolored	1.40	.40
2183	A661	3.85k multicolored	1.40	.40
2184	A661	3.85k multicolored	1.60	.75
2185	A661	3.85k multicolored	1.60	.75
a.		Booklet pane, 3 each #2182-2183, 2 each #2184-2185	15.00	
		Complete booklet, #2185a	15.00	
		Nos. 2182-2185 (4)	6.00	2.30

Mushrooms — A662

3.85k, Boletus edulis. #2187, Russula integra. #2188, Cantharellus cibarius. #2189, Craterellus cornucopioides. #2190, Coprinus comatus.

Perf. 13 Horiz.
1996, Aug. 23   **Litho. & Engr.**
2186	A662	3.85k multicolored	1.75	.45

Perf. 12½x13 on 3 Sides
2187	A662	5k multicolored	1.75	1.25
2188	A662	5k multicolored	1.75	1.25
2189	A662	5k multicolored	1.75	1.25
2190	A662	5k multicolored	1.75	1.25
a.		Booklet pane of 4, #2187-2190	7.00	8.50
		Complete booklet, #2190a	7.00	
		Nos. 2186-2190 (5)	8.75	5.45

Ecopark, Stockholm A663

Designs: No. 2191, Pelousen, grassy area, Haga Park. No. 2192, Copper tents, Haga Park. No. 2193, Rosendals Palace, roe deer. No. 2194, Isbladskarret, marsh birds.

Litho. & Engr.
1996, Aug. 23   **Perf. 12½Vert.**
2191	A663	7.50k multicolored	2.50	2.50
2192	A663	7.50k multicolored	2.50	2.50
2193	A663	7.50k multicolored	2.50	2.50
2194	A663	7.50k multicolored	2.50	2.50
a.		Booklet pane of 4, #2191-2194	10.50	12.50
		Complete booklet, #2194a	10.50	

Four Decades A664

Designs: No. 2195, Errand boy, 1930's. No. 2196, Flower child, 1960's. No. 2197, Zootsuiter, 1940's. No. 2198, Biker, 1950's.

Perf. 12½x13 on 3 Sides
1996, Oct. 5   **Litho. & Engr.**
2195	A664	3.85k multicolored	1.75	.65
2196	A664	3.85k multicolored	2.25	1.50
2197	A664	3.85k multicolored	1.75	.65
2198	A664	3.85k multicolored	2.25	1.50
a.		Bklt. pane, 3 ea #2195, 2197, 2 ea #2196, 2198	17.50	
		Complete booklet, #2198a	17.50	
		Nos. 2195-2198 (4)	8.00	4.30

The Baroque Chair, by Endre Nemes — A665

1996, Oct. 5   **Perf. 12½ Horiz.**
2199	A665	6k multicolored	2.25	1.60
		See Czech Republic #2995, Slovakia #255.		

Christmas A666

Illustrations from Book of Hours (15th cent.): No. 2200, The Annunciation. No. 2201, The Birth. No. 2202, Adoration of the Magi.

Perf. 12½ Vert.
1996, Nov. 8   **Litho. & Engr.**
2200	A666	3.50k multicolored	1.50	.90

Perf. 12½x13 on 3 Sides
2201	A666	3.50k multicolored	1.10	.45
2202	A666	3.50k multicolored	1.10	.45
a.		Bklt. pane, 5 ea #2201-2202	11.00	
		Complete booklet, #2202a	11.00	
		Nos. 2200-2202 (3)	3.70	1.80

Nobel Laureates in Physiology or Medicine — A667

#2203, Sune Bergström (b. 1916), medical chemist. #2204, Bengt Samuelsson (b. 1934), medical chemist. #2205, Hugo Theorell (1903-82), biochemist. #2206, Ragnar Granit (1900-91), neurophysiologist.

Perf. 13x12½ on 3 Sides
1996, Nov. 8   **Engr.**
2203	A667	5k blue, grn & blk + label	2.00	1.50
2204	A667	5k grn, blue & blk+ label	2.00	1.50
2205	A667	5k blue, grn & blk+ label	2.75	2.25
2206	A667	5k green & black+ label	2.75	2.25
a.		Booklet pane, 3 each #2203-#2204, 2 each #2205-2206	23.00	
		Complete booklet, #2206a	23.00	
		Nos. 2203-2206 (4)	9.50	7.50

Wild Animal Types of 1992
1997, Jan. 2   Engr.   Perf. 13 Vert.
2207	A574	3.20k Gulo gulo	1.25	1.10
2208	A574	3.50k Nyclea scandiaca	1.25	.70

Perf. 13 Horiz.
2209	A575	7.70k Ciconia ciconia	3.25	2.75
		Nos. 2207-2209 (3)	5.75	4.55

Churches — A668

Illustration reduced.

Perf. 13 Horiz.
1997, Jan. 2   **Litho. & Engr.**
2210	A668	3.85k Dalby	1.25	1.25
2211	A668	3.85k Vendel	1.25	1.25

Size: 27x23mm
Perf. 13x12½ on 2 or 3 Sides
2212	A668	3.85k Hagby	1.50	*1.60*
2213	A668	3.85k Overtornea	1.50	*1.60*

Size: 27x37mm
2214	A668	3.85k Varnhem	1.50	*1.60*
2215	A668	3.85k Ostra Amtervik	1.50	*1.60*
a.		Booklet pane of 6, #2210-2215	8.50	*11.50*
		Complete booklet, #2215a	8.50	

Kalmar Union, 600th Anniv. — A669

Design: Queen Margareta, Erik of Pomerania, coronation document. Illustration reduced.

1997, Jan. 2   Engr.   Perf. 12½ Vert.
2216	A669	3.85k dark blue	1.50	.50

Love Stamps — A670

Perf. 13x12½ on 3 Sides
1997, Jan. 2   **Litho.**
2217	A670	3.85k gray & multi	1.75	.75
2218	A670	3.85k yellow & multi	1.75	.75
a.		Bklt. pane, 5 ea #2217-2218	17.50	
		Complete booklet, #2218a	17.50	

Stamps that follow, with denominations in parenthesis, are inscribed "Brev," "Ekonomibrev," "Foreningsbrev," etc.

Wild Animals — A671

Perf. 13 on 2 Sides
1997, Feb. 28   **Engr.**
2219	A671	(4.50k) Alopex lagopus	1.60	.55
2220	A671	(5k) Equus przewalskii	2.25	.35

Perf. 13 on 3 Sides
2221	A671	(5k) Panthera unica, adult	1.75	.35
2222	A671	(5k) same, cubs	1.75	.35
a.		Bklt. pane, 3 ea #2221-2222	11.00	
		Complete booklet, #2222a	11.00	
		Complete booklet, 1 ea #2221-2222	7.00	
		Nos. 2219-2222 (4)	7.35	1.60

No. 2220 is 28x21mm.

Easter Stamps — A672

Perf. 13x12½ on 3 Sides
1997, Feb. 28   **Litho.**
2223	A672	(5k) Rooster	2.10	.55
2224	A672	(5k) Daffodils	2.10	.55
a.		Bklt. pane, 3 ea #2223-2224	12.50	
		Complete booklet, #2224a	12.50	

Pheasants A673

Designs: No. 2225, Phasianus colchicus. No. 2226, Chrysolophus amherstiae.

Perf. 12½ Horiz.
1997, May 9   **Litho. & Engr.**

2225	A673	2k multicolored	.85	.60
2226	A673	2k multicolored	.85	.60
a.		Pair, #2225-2226	1.75	1.40

See China (PRC) Nos. 2763-2764.

Garden Flowers — A674

#2227, Iris sibirica. #2228, Lonicera periclymenum. #2229, Aquilegia vulgaris. #2230, Hemerocallis flava. #2231, Viola x wittrokiana.

1997, May 9   **Litho.**   **Perf. 12½x13**

2227	A674	(5k) multicolored	2.10	.45
2228	A674	(5k) multicolored	2.10	.45
2229	A674	(5k) multicolored	2.10	.45
2230	A674	(5k) multicolored	2.10	.45
2231	A674	(5k) multicolored	2.10	.45
a.		Bklt. pane, 2 ea #2227-2231	21.00	
		Complete booklet, #2231a	21.00	
		Nos. 2227-2231 (5)	10.50	2.25

A675   A676

6k, Ship's figurehead, 18th cent., Naval Museum, Karlskrona. 7k, Compass rose, 18th cent. atlas. 8k, Compass rose, 1568 atlas.

Perf. 12½ Vert.
1997, May 9   **Litho. & Engr.**

2232	A675	6k multicolored	2.10	1.20

Litho.
Perf. 12½ Horiz.

2233	A676	7k multicolored	2.40	1.50
2234	A676	8k multicolored	2.90	1.75
		Nos. 2232-2234 (3)	7.40	4.45

18th Intl. Cartographic Conf. (#2233-2234).

Gnomes and Trolls — A677

Illustrations from "Among Trolls and Sprites," by John Bauer: No. 2235, Troll looking through treasure chest, gnome. No. 2236, Trolls looking at girl seated on rock. No. 2237, Troll talking with boy.

Litho. & Engr.
1997, May 9   **Perf. 12x13**

2235	A677	7k multicolored	2.75	2.00
2236	A677	7k multicolored	2.75	2.00
2237	A677	7k multicolored	2.75	2.00
a.		Bklt. pane, 2 ea, #2235-2237	16.50	
		Complete booklet, #2237a	16.50	
		Nos. 2235-2237 (3)		

Europa.

Wild Animal Type of 1992
Perf. 12½ Horiz.
1997, Aug. 21   **Engr.**

2238	A575	(3.50k) Ailurus fulgens, vert.	1.75	1.20

Construction of High Coast Bridge — A678

1997, Aug. 21

2239	A678	(5k) multicolored	2.25	.55

Swedish Elk A679

Designs: No. 2240, Elk as fantasy character. No. 2241, Bar code elk. No. 2242, Swedish elk, yellow bars. No. 2243, Forest elk, green background. No. 2244, Road sign elk, black silhouette against yellow. No. 2245, Old Norse elks, adult & calf.

1997, Aug. 21   **Litho.**   **Perf. 13**

2240	A679	(5k) multicolored	2.10	.85
2241	A679	(5k) multicolored	2.10	.85
2242	A679	(5k) multicolored	2.10	.85
2243	A679	(5k) multicolored	2.10	.85
2244	A679	(5k) multicolored	2.10	.85
2245	A679	(5k) multicolored	2.10	.85
a.		Booklet pane, #2240-2245	12.00	13.50
		Complete booklet, #2245a	12.00	

Perforations at each corner of Nos. 2240-2245 end in a large hole within the pane or semi-circles at the edges of the pane, giving the corners of each stamp a slightly concave appearance.

King Gustav III's Museum of Antiquities, Stockholm Palace — A680

Perf. 13x12½ on 3 Sides
1997, Aug. 21   **Engr.**

2246	A680	8k Muses Gallery	3.00	2.10
2247	A680	8k Endymion	3.00	2.10
a.		Booklet pane, 2 each #2246-2247 + 4 labels	12.00	
		Complete booklet, #2247a	12.00	

Classic Cars A681

#2248, 1958 Volvo Duett. #2249, 1955 Chevrolet Bel-Air. #2250, 1959 Porsche 356A Coupé. #2251, 1952, Citroen B11. #2252, 1963 Saab 96. #2253, 1961 E-Type Jaguar.

Perf. 12½x13 on 3 Sides
1997, Oct. 4   **Litho. & Engr.**
Booklet Stamps

2248	A681	(5k) multicolored	2.25	2.25
2249	A681	(5k) multicolored	2.25	2.25
2250	A681	(5k) multicolored	2.25	2.25
2251	A681	(5k) multicolored	2.25	2.25
2252	A681	(5k) multicolored	2.25	2.25
2253	A681	(5k) multicolored	2.25	2.25
a.		Booklet pane, #2248-2253	13.50	15.00
		Complete booklet, #2253a	13.50	

Alfred Nobel (1833-1896), Founder of Nobel Prize — A682

Design: No. 2255, Paul Karrer (1889-1971), winner of Nobel prize for chemistry, 1937.

Perf. 12½x13 on 3 Sides
1997, Nov. 13   **Litho. & Engr.**

2254	A682	7k lt pink & black	3.00	2.50
2255	A682	7k gray & black	3.00	2.50
a.		Bklt. pane, 2 ea #2254-2255	12.00	14.50
		Complete booklet, #2255a	12.00	

See Switzerland Nos. 1004-1005.

Christmas Gingerbread A683

Perf. 12½ Vert.
1997, Nov. 20   **Litho.**

2256	A683	(3.50k) Heart	1.75	1.50

Perf. 12½ on 3 Sides

2257	A683	(3.50k) Animals	1.50	1.00
2258	A683	(3.50k) People	1.50	1.00
a.		Bklt. pane, 5 ea #2257-2258	15.00	
		Complete booklet, #2258a	15.00	

Christmas Angels — A684

Angels from altarpiece, Litslena Church: No. 2259, Playing horn, mandolin. No. 2260, Playing pipes, harp.

1997, Nov. 20   **Perf. 13x12½**

2259	A684	6k multicolored	2.25	1.70
2260	A684	6k multicolored	2.25	1.70
a.		Booklet pane, 5 each #2259-2260 + 10 labels	22.50	
		Complete booklet, #2260a	22.50	

Photographer Jan Lindblad (1932-87) and His Tigers — A685

Perf. 12½ Horiz.
1998, Jan. 15   **Litho. & Engr.**

2261	A685	(3.50k) shown	1.60	1.00
2262	A685	(3.50k) Two tigers on rock	1.60	1.00
a.		Pair, #2261-2262	3.25	2.50

New Modern Museum of Art, Stockholm A686

#2263, Fungus Sculpture, by Yves Klein. #2264, Skeppsholmen, by Göran Gidenstam. #2265, Monogram, by Robert Rauschenberg.

1998, Jan. 15   **Perf. 12½ Vert.**

2263	A686	(5k) multicolored	2.25	.65
2264	A686	(5k) multicolored	2.25	.65
2265	A686	(5k) multicolored	2.25	.65
a.		Booklet pane of 3, #2263-2265	6.75	7.00
		Complete booklet, 2 #2265a	13.50	

Valentine's Day — A687

Perf. 13 (on 3 Sides)
1998, Jan. 15   **Litho.**

2266	A687	(5k) dp grn & org red	2.00	.50
2267	A687	(5k) dp blue & rose red	2.00	.50
a.		Bklt. pane, 3 ea #2266-2267	12.00	
		Complete booklet, #2267a	12.00	

Swedish Confederation of Trade Unions, Cent. — A688

Perf. 12½ Horiz.
1998, Mar. 19   **Engr.**

2268	A688	(5k) multicolored	2.10	.50

Public Buildings A689

#2269, Fire station, Gävle. #2270, Shoe shop, Askersund. #2271, Fish halls, Gothenburg. #2272, Rödalvarm (Red Mill) Cinema, Halmstad. #2273, Town Hotel, Eksjö.

1998, Mar. 19   **Perf. 12½ Horiz.**

2269	A689	(5k) multicolored	2.00	.60
2270	A689	(5k) multicolored	2.00	.60
2271	A689	(5k) multicolored	2.00	.60
2272	A689	(5k) multicolored	2.00	.60
2273	A689	(5k) multicolored	2.00	.60
a.		Booklet pane, #2269-2273	10.00	
		Complete booklet, #2273a	10.00	

Queen Christina, Medallion Commemorating the Peace of Westphalia, 1648 — A690

1998, Mar. 19   **Engr.**   **Perf. 12½ Vert.**

2274	A690	7k rose brn & dp grn	2.75	1.25

Handicrafts A691

Designs: (4.50k), Apron from costume, Dalecarlia. (5k), Wrought iron ornamental designs. No. 2277, Lovikka mitten. No. 2278, Boxes made from wood shavings.

1998, Mar. 19   **Perf. 13 Vert.**

2275	A691	(4.50k) multicolored	1.60	1.10
2276	A691	(5k) multicolored	1.60	.40

Perf. 12½ on 3 Sides

2277	A691	8k multicolored	2.75	2.75
2278	A691	8k multicolored	2.75	2.75
a.		Bklt. pane, 2 ea #2277-2278	11.00	
		Complete booklet, #2278a + 4 labels	11.00	

Wetland Flowers
A692   A693

Perf. 13 on 3 Sides

1998, May 14   **Litho.**
2279 A692 (5k) Marsh violet   2.00   .35
2280 A693 (5k) Great willow-
              herb   2.00   .35
a.   Bklt. pane, 5 ea #2279-2280 20.00
         Complete booklet, #2280a   20.00

City of Stockholm — A694

Designs: Nos. 2281, 2287, Stockholm Palace. Nos. 2282, 2288, Skerry boats. No. 2283, Opera House, cent. No. 2284, Sail boats. No. 2285, Langholmen Beach, vert. No. 2286, Fireworks over City Hall, vert.
Illustration reduced.

Perf. 13 on 2 or 3 Sides

1998, May 14   **Litho. & Engr.**
2281 A694 (5k) multicolored   2.10   1.25
2282 A694 (5k) multicolored   2.10   1.25

Size: 27x22mm

2283 A694 (5k) multicolored   2.25   1.60
2284 A694 (5k) multicolored   2.25   1.60

Size: 27x36mm

2285 A694 (5k) multicolored   2.25   1.60
2286 A694 (5k) multicolored   2.25   1.60
a.   Booklet pane, #2281-2286   13.00 14.50
     Complete booklet, #2286a   13.00 14.50

Size: 58x23mm

2287 A694 7k multicolored   2.10   1.50
2288 A694 7k multicolored   2.10   1.50
a.   Bklt. pane, 2 ea #2287-2288 8.50
     Complete booklet, #2288a   8.50

Cruise Ship Albatros in Stockholm
Harbor — A695

1998, May 14   **Perf. 13 Vert.**
Coil Stamp
2289 A695 6k multicolored   2.25   2.25

Festivals and
Holidays — A696

Europa: No. 2290, Crayfish party, paper moon. No. 2291, Dancing around maypole, Midsummer in June.

Perf. 13 on 3 Sides

1998, May 14   **Litho.**
2290 A696 7k multicolored   2.75   2.75
2291 A696 7k multicolored   2.75   2.75
a.   Bklt. pane, 2 ea #2289-2290 11.00 13.00
     Complete booklet, #2291a +
     4 labels   11.00 13.00

King Carl XVI
Gustaf, 25th
Anniv. of
Accession to the
Throne — A697

1998, May 14   Engr.   Perf. 13 Vert.
2292 A697 (5k) multicolored   2.25   .50

Vilhelm Moberg (1898-1973),
Writer — A698

Litho. & Engr.
1998, Aug. 20   **Perf. 13 Vert.**
Coil Stamp
2293 A698 (5k) multicolored   2.25   .65

Pastries
A699

Designs: No. 2294, Princess cake. No. 2295, Gustav Adolf pastry. No. 2296, Napoleon pastry. No. 2297, Mocha cake. No. 2298, National pastry. No. 2299, Lent bun (semla).

Perf. 13 on 3 Sides

1998, Aug. 20   **Litho.**
2294 A699 (5k) multicolored   2.25   1.25
2295 A699 (5k) multicolored   2.25   1.25
2296 A699 (5k) multicolored   2.25   1.25
2297 A699 (5k) multicolored   2.25   1.25
2298 A699 (5k) multicolored   2.25   1.25
2299 A699 (5k) multicolored   2.25   1.25
a.   Booklet pane, #2294-2299   13.50 14.50
     Complete booklet, #2299a   13.50

The Millennium — A700

Swedish developments during 1900's: No. 2300, Painting, "Flowers on the Window Sill," by Carl Larsson. No. 2301, Stockholm Stadium, poster for 1912 Olympic Games. No. 2302, Power plant, Porjus, Lapland. No. 2303, Inventions; zippers, ball bearings, vacuum cleaners, refrigerators. No. 2304, Johnson (shipping) Line. No. 2305, AB Radiotjänst, 1924. No. 2306, Jazz music, Charleston dance. No. 2307, Ellen Key, Kerstin Hesselgren, pioneers for women's rights. No. 2308, Arne Borg, swimmer, Gillis Grafström, figure skater, world champions. No. 2309, Ernst Rolf, entertainer, 1920's.

Perf. 12½ Horiz.

1998, Oct. 3   **Litho. & Engr.**
2300 A700 (5k) multicolored   2.50   2.50
2301 A700 (5k) multicolored   2.50   2.50
2302 A700 (5k) multicolored   2.50   2.50
2303 A700 (5k) multicolored   2.50   2.50
2304 A700 (5k) multicolored   2.50   2.50
2305 A700 (5k) multicolored   2.50   2.50
2306 A700 (5k) multicolored   2.50   2.50
2307 A700 (5k) multicolored   2.50   2.50
2308 A700 (5k) multicolored   2.50   2.50
2309 A700 (5k) multicolored   2.50   2.50
a.   Booklet pane, #2300-2309   25.00 30.00
     Complete booklet, #2309a   25.00

See Nos. 2327-2336, 2379-2388.

Nobel Laureates
A701

Perf. 13x12½ on 3 Sides

1998, Oct. 3   **Engr.**
2310 A701 6k Nadine Gordimer,
              1991   2.25   1.75
2311 A701 6k Sigrid Undset,
              1928   2.25   1.75
a.   Bklt. pane, 2 ea #2310-2311 9.00
     Complete booklet, #2311a + 4
     labels   9.00

Sigismund
(1566-1632),
King of Sweden
and
Poland — A702

Perf. 12½ Horiz.

1998, Oct. 3   **Litho. & Engr.**
2312 A702 7k multicolored   2.75   2.00

See Poland No. 3421.

A703   A704

Perf. 12½ Horiz.

1998, Nov. 19   **Litho.**
2313 A703 (4k) Hyacinth   2.00   1.25

Perf. 12½ on 3 Sides

2314 A703 (4k) Mistletoe   1.60   .50
2315 A703 (4k) Amaryllis   1.60   .50
a.   Bklt. pane, 5 ea #2314-2315 16.00
     Complete booklet, #2315a   16.00
2316 A703 6k Wreath   2.10   1.50
2317 A703 6k Azalea   2.10   1.50
a.   Bklt. pane, 5 ea #2316--2317 21.00
     Complete booklet, #2317a   21.00
     Nos. 2313-2317 (5)   9.40   5.25

Christmas.

1999, Jan. 14   Litho.   Perf. 13 Vert.
2318 A704 (5k) multicolored   2.10   .40

Swedish Cooperative Union, cent.

A705   A706

Swedish Coins: No. 2319, Gustav Vasa daler. No. 2320, Carl XIV John riksdaler.

1999, Jan. 14   Engr.   Perf. 12½ Vert.
2319 A705 (4.50k) dark green   1.60   1.00
2320 A705   (5k) dark blue   2.00   .40

Perf. 12½ on 3 Sides

1999, Jan. 14   **Litho.**

Easter Eggs: No. 2321, Sugar egg. No. 2322, Egg filled with marzipan chicks.

Panel Color

2321 A706 (5k) green   2.25   1.00
2322 A706 (5k) red   2.25   1.00
a.   Bklt. pane, 3 ea #2321-2322 13.50
     Complete booklet, #2322a   13.50

"Little Sister
Rabbit," by Ulf
Nilsson — A707

Rabbits: No. 2323, Preparing meal over fireplace. No. 2324, Feeding Little Sister. No. 2325, Dancing to music. No. 2326, Hopping through thicket.

Perf. 12½ Vert.

1999, Jan. 14   **Litho. & Engr.**
2323 A707 (5k) multicolored   2.00   1.00
2324 A707 (5k) multicolored   2.00   1.00
2325 A707 (5k) multicolored   2.00   1.00
2326 A707 (5k) multicolored   2.00   1.00
a.   Booklet pane, #2323-2326   8.00   7.50
     Complete booklet, #2326a   8.00

The Millennium Type of 1998

Sweden in years 1939-1969: No. 2327, Scene from Bergman's film "Smiles of a Summer Night," 1955. No. 2328, Vällingby Centre. No. 2329, Silhouette of soldier, singer Ulla Bilquist. No. 2330, Cobra telephone, three-point seat belt, ASEA high voltage cables and breakers, Tetra Pak's milk carton. No. 2331, Scandinavian Airlines System formed, DC-4 over New York City, 1946. No. 2332, "Hyland's Corner," Carl-Gustaf Lindstedt, Prime Minister Tage Erlander on television. No. 2333, Protests of the 60's, Hep Stars band. No. 2334, Volvo Amazon car, family picnic. No. 2335, Ingemar Johansson, heavy-weight boxing champion, 1959, Mora-Nisse Karlsson, skiing champion, Gunder Hägg, running champion, 1941-45. No. 2336, Jazz singer Alice Babs, opera singer Jussi Björling.

Perf. 12½ Horiz.

1999, Mar. 11   **Litho.**
2327 A700 (5k) multicolored   2.10   1.25
2328 A700 (5k) multicolored   2.10   1.25
2329 A700 (5k) multicolored   2.10   1.25
2330 A700 (5k) multicolored   2.10   1.25
2331 A700 (5k) multicolored   2.10   1.25
2332 A700 (5k) multicolored   2.10   1.25
2333 A700 (5k) multicolored   2.10   1.25
2334 A700 (5k) multicolored   2.10   1.25
2335 A700 (5k) multicolored   2.10   1.25
2336 A700 (5k) multicolored   2.10   1.25
a.   Booklet pane, #2327-2336   21.00 21.00
     Complete booklet, #2336a   21.00

Construction of
the Oresund
Bridge — A708

(5k), Swan Pontoon Crane. 6k, Building bridge.

1999, Mar. 11   **Perf. 12½ Vert.**
2337 A708 (5k) multicolored   2.00   .40
2338 A708 6k multicolored   2.25   2.00

Swedish
Ships
A709

Perf. 12½x13 on 3 Sides

1999, Mar. 11   **Litho. & Engr.**
2339 A709 8k East Indiaman   2.50   2.10
2340 A709 8k Mary Anne   2.50   2.10
2341 A709 8k Beatrice   2.50   2.10
2342 A709 8k SS Austalic   2.50   2.10
a.   Booklet pane, #2339-2342   10.00 12.50
     Complete booklet, #2342a +
     4 labels   10.00

Australia '99 World Stamp Expo.

Pyramid
Orchid — A710

Lady's
Slipper — A711

Marsh
Helleborine
A712

Green-Winged
Ordhid
A713

Perf. 12½ on 3 Sides

1999, May 20   **Litho.**

2343	A710	(5k) multicolored	2.10	.40
2344	A711	(5k) multicolored	2.50	.75
2345	A712	(5k) multicolored	2.10	.40
2346	A713	(5k) multicolored	2.50	.75
a.	Booklet pane, 3 each #2343, 2345, 2 each #2344, #2346	22.50	
	Complete booket, #2346a	22.50	
	Nos. 2343-2346 (4)	9.20	2.30

Council of Europe,
50th Anniv. — A714

1999, May 20   **Perf. 12½ Horiz.**

2347 A714 7k multicolored   2.75 1.75

Europa — A715

Perf. 12½x13 on 3 Sides

1999, May 20

2348	A715 7k	Tyresta Natl. Park	2.50	2.00
2349	A715 7k	Gotska Sandön Natl. Park	2.50	2.00
a.		Bklt. pane, 2 ea #2348-2349	10.00	11.00
		Complete bklt., #2349a+4 labels	10.00	

Post Bike — A716

Racing
Bike — A717

Town
Bike — A718

Messenger
Bike — A719

Engr., Litho. (#2351)

1999, May 20   **Perf. 12½ Horiz.**

2350 A716 (3.50k) multicolored   1.75 1.40

Perf. 12½ Vert.

2351	A717	(5k) multicolored	2.00	.90
2352	A718	6k multicolored	2.25	1.50
2353	A719	8k multicolored	2.75	2.25
		Nos. 2350-2353 (4)	8.75	6.05

Signs of
the
Zodiac
A720

No. 2354: a, Aquarius. b, Pisces. c, Aries. d, Taurus. e, Gemini. f, Cancer.
No. 2355: a, Leo. b, Virgo. c, Libra. d, Scorpio. e, Sagittarius. f, Capricorn.

Litho. & Engr.

1999, Aug. 12   **Perf. 13**

2354	Booklet pane of 6	15.00	10.00
a.-f.	A720 (5k) any single	2.50	1.60
2355	Booklet pane of 6	15.00	10.00
a.-f.	A720 (5k) any single	2.50	1.60
	Complete booklet, #2354-2355	30.00	

Perforations at each corner of Nos. 2354a-2354f, 2355a-2355f end in a large hole within the pane or semi-circles at the edges of the pane, giving the corners of each stamp a slightly concave appearance.

Butterflies
A721

a, Inachis io. b, Junonia orithya wallacei. c, Hypolimnas bolina. d, Vanessa atalanta.

1999, Aug. 12   **Perf. 12½x13**

2356	Booklet pane of 4	9.00	10.50
a.-d.	A721 6k any single	2.25	1.75
	Complete bklt., #2356 + 4 labels	9.00	

See Singapore Nos. 903-907.

Nobel Laureates
in Peace — A722

#2357, Auguste Beernaert (1829-1912).
#2358, Henri La Fontaine (1854-1943).

Perf. 13x12½ on 3 sides

1999, Sept. 30   **Litho. & Engr.**

2357	A722 7k gold & blue	2.75	2.25
2358	A722 7k gold & red	2.75	2.25
a.	Bklt. pane, 2 ea #2357-2358	11.00	
	Complete booklet, #2358a + 4 labels	11.00	

See Belgium Nos. 1749-1750.

Dance
Bands
A723

Designs: a, Thorleifs. b, Arvingarna. c, Lotta Engbergs. d, Sten & Stanley.

Litho. & Engr.

1999, Oct. 2   **Perf. 12¾**

2359	Booklet pane of 4	9.00	9.50
a.-d.	A723 (5k) any single	2.90	1.60
	Complete booklet, 2 #2359	18.00	

A724

Christmas
A725

Stained glass: No. 2360, Nativity, Klinte Church. No. 2361, Nativity, Hablingbro Church. No. 2362, Three kings, Hablingbro Church.
Madonna and child icons from: No. 2363, Bälinge Church. No. 2364, Skänninge Church.

Perf. 12½ Vert.

1999, Nov. 18   **Litho.**

2360 A724 (4.50k) multicolored   1.75 1.25

Perf. 12¾ on 3 sides

2361	A724 (4.50k) multicolored	1.50	.60
2362	A724 (4.50k) multicolored	1.50	.60
a.	Bklt. pane, 5 ea #2361-2362	15.00	
	Complete booklet, # 2362a	15.00	

Litho. & Engr.

2363	A725	6k multicolored	2.25	1.60
2364	A725	6k multicolored	2.25	1.60
a.		Booklet pane, 5 each #2363-2364 + 10 labels	22.50	
		Complete booklet, # 2364a	22.50	
		Nos. 2360-2364 (5)	9.25	5.65

Millennium — A726

Sun rays touching Heligholmen Island: No. 2365, Island rocks. No. 2366, Island map.

Perf. 12¾ Horiz.

1999, Dec. 27   **Litho. & Engr.**

2365	A726 5k multicolored	2.25	1.75
2366	A726 5k multicolored	2.25	1.75
a.	Bklt. pane, 2 ea #2365-2366	9.00	
	Complete booklet # 2366a	18.00	

New Year
2000
(Year of
the
Dragon)
A727

Dragon from children's book "The Dragon with Red Eyes," by Astrid Lindgren: No. 2367, In flight (shown). No. 2368, With basket. No. 2369, In flight.

Perf. 12¾ Horiz.

2000, Jan. 13   **Litho.**

2367	A727 (5k) multi	2.25	1.10
2368	A727 (5k) multi	2.25	1.10
2369	A727 (5k) multi	2.25	1.10
a.	Bklt. pane, 2 ea #2367-2369	13.50	
	Complete booklet, #2369a	13.50	

A728

A729

Love.

2000, Jan. 13   **Perf. 12¾ on 3 sides**

2370	A728 (5k) shown	2.00	1.00
2371	A728 (5k) Heart, diff.	2.00	1.00
a.	Bklt. pane, 3 ea #2370-2371	12.00	
	Complete booklet, #2371a	12.00	

2000, Jan. 13 Engr. Perf. 12½ Vert.

Watch of King Karl XII, 1701: (4.50k), Works. (5k), Face.

2372	A729 (4.50k) blue	1.60	1.00
2373	A729 (5k) claret brown	2.25	.45

Souvenir Sheet

Detail of "Great Deeds by Swedish Kings," by David Ehrenstrahl — A730

Litho. & Engr.

2000, Mar. 17   **Perf. 12¾**

2374 A730 50k multi   11.50 14.50

Czeslaw Slania's 1000th postage stamp.

Forests — A731

Designs: (3.80k), People in forest. No. 2376, Elk in forest. No. 2377, Bird in forest. 6k, Birch forest.

Perf. 12¾ Vert.

2000, Mar. 17   **Litho.**

2375	A731 (3.80k) multi	1.75	1.10
2376	A731 (5k) multi	1.90	.55
2377	A731 (5k) multi	1.90	.55
a.	Pair, #2376-2377	3.75	3.50
2378	A731 6k multi	2.25	1.75
	Nos. 2375-2378 (4)	7.80	3.95

Millennium Type of 1998

Sweden in the years 1970-99: No. 2379, Art in Stockholm subway stations. No. 2380, Swedish UN forces, postal clerk. No. 2381, Computer, mouse and mobile phone. No. 2382, Cullberg Ballet, Svenska Ord repertory company. No. 2383, Jönköping railway station. No. 2384, Youth with spiked hair, musical group ABBA. No. 2385, European Union flag, map of member countries. No. 2386, Scene from film, "The Apple War." No. 2387, Skiiers Pernilla Wiberg, Ingemar Stenmark, tennis player Björn Borg. No. 2388, Photo of child in womb, taken by Lennart Nilsson.

Perf. 12¾ Horiz.

2000, Mar. 17   **Litho.**

2379	A700 (5k) multi	2.00	1.40
2380	A700 (5k) multi	2.00	1.40
2381	A700 (5k) multi	2.00	1.40
2382	A700 (5k) multi	2.00	1.40
2383	A700 (5k) multi	2.00	1.40
2384	A700 (5k) multi	2.00	1.40
2385	A700 (5k) multi	2.00	1.40
2386	A700 (5k) multi	2.00	1.40

2387	A700	(5k) multi	2.00	1.40
2388	A700	(5k) multi	2.00	1.40
a.	Booklet pane, #2379-2388	20.00	20.00
	Complete booklet, #2388a	20.00	

Art by Philip von Schantz (1928-98) — A732

Designs: No. 2389, A Peck of Apples. No. 2390, A Bowl of Blueberries.

Perf. 12¾ on 3 sides

2000, May 9			**Litho.**
2389	A732	(5k) multi	1.75	.60
2390	A732	(5k) multi	1.75	.60
a.	Bklt. pane, 5 ea #2389-2390	19.00	
	Complete booklet, #2390a	19.00	

A733

Oresund Bridge, Sweden-Denmark — A734

Illustration A734 reduced.

2000, May 9	**Engr.**	**Perf. 12½ Vert.**
2391	A733	(5k) blue & ultra	2.25	.75

		Litho.	
		Perf. 12¾ Horiz.	
2392	A734	6k shown	2.50	1.75
2393	A734	6k Map	2.50	1.75
a.	Booklet pane, 2 each #2392-2393, + 4 etiquettes	10.00	
	Complete booklet, #2393a	10.00	

See Denmark Nos. 1187-1188.

Europa Issue
Common Design Type

2000, May 9	**Litho.**	**Perf. 12¾ Horiz.**
2394	CD17	7k multi	2.25	2.25

2000 Summer Olympics, Sydney — A735

No. 2395: a, Hurdler Ludmila Engquist. b, Archer Magnus Petersson. c, Windsurfer Fredrik Palm. d, Beach volleyball player Lena Malm.

Perf. 12¾x12½ on 3 sides

2000, Aug. 17		**Litho.**
2395	A735	Booklet pane of 4	11.00	12.50
a.-d.	8k Any single	2.75	2.25
	Booklet, #2395 + 4 etiquettes	11.00	

Sky Conditions A736

No. 2396: a, Clouds and sun. b, Clouds and lightning. c, Clouds and rainstorm. d, Aurora borealis. e, Rainbow. f, Cumulus clouds.

2000, Aug. 17	**Die Cut Perf. 9¾x10**
	Self-Adhesive
2396	Booklet of 6	12.00	
a.-f.	A736 (5k) Any single	2.00	1.25

King Carl XVI Gustaf — A737

Design: 8k, Queen Silvia.

2000, Aug. 17		**Engr.**
		Perf. 12¾ Vert.
2397	A737	(5k) blue	2.25	.50
2398	A737	8k red	2.75	2.00

Nobel Laureates for Literature — A738

a, Wislawa Szymborska. b, Nelly Sachs. Illustration reduced.

Perf. 12¾x12½ on 3 sides

2000, Oct. 7		**Engr.**
2399	A738	Pair	5.00	5.00
a.-b.	7k Any single	2.50	2.40
c.	Booklet pane, 2 #2399	10.00	
	Booklet, #2399c + 4 etiquettes	10.00	

Toys — A739

No. 2400: a, Doll, tea set, teddy bear. b, Marbles, tin soldier, yo-yo, jump rope. c, Pine cone cow, doll, horse-drawn wagon. d, Cars and policeman. e, Model train, mechanical men. f, Lego car, robot, Furbee.

Perf. 12¾ on 3 sides

2000, Oct. 7		**Litho. & Engr.**
2400	Booklet of 6	13.50	15.00
a.-f.	A739 (5k) Any single	2.25	2.25

Christmas Songs — A740

Christmas Snowflakes — A741

Designs: No. 2401, Hey, Santas.
No. 2402, vert.: a, It's Christmas Again (four children, tree). b, Three Gingerbread Men. c,

---

The Fox Runs Over the Ice. d, Christmas Has Come to Our House (three children, candles).
No. 2403: a, White background. b, Blue background.
Illustration A741 reduced.

Perf. 12¾ Vert.

2000, Nov. 16		**Litho.**
2401	A740	(4.30k) multi	1.50	1.00

Perf. 12¾ on 3 sides

2402	Block of 4	6.00	5.50
a.-d.	A740 (4.30k) Any single	1.50	.70
e.	Booklet pane, 3 ea #2402a, 2402c, 2 ea #2402b, 2402d	15.00	
	Booklet, #2402e	15.00	
2403	A741	Pair	4.50	5.50
a.-b.	6k Any single	2.25	2.25
c.	Booklet pane, 5 #2403 + 10 etiquettes	22.50	
	Booklet, #2403c	22.50	
	Nos. 2401-2403 (3)	12.00	12.00

Rock Carvings, Tanum World Heritage Site — A742

Swedish World Heritage Site A743

Designs: (4.50k), Rock carvings of animals and people. (5k), Rock carvings of ships.
No. 2406: a, Gammelstad Church Village. b, Karlskrona Naval Port. c, Theater, Drottningholm Palace. d, Engelsberg Ironworks.

2001, Jan. 31	**Engr.**	**Perf. 12½ Vert.**
2404	A742	(4.50k) blue, *gray*	1.75	1.25
2405	A742	(5k) red, *gray*	1.90	.45

Perf. 12½x12¾ on 3 sides

2406	Booklet pane of 4	8.00	10.00
a.-d.	A743 6k Any single	2.00	2.00
	Booklet, #2406 + 4 etiquettes	8.00	

New Year 2001 (Year of the Snake) — A744

No. 2407: a, Snake with tongue extended. b, Snake curled up.
Illustration reduced.

Perf. 12¾ on 3 sides

2001, Jan. 31		**Litho.**
2407	A744	Pair	4.00	2.75
a.-b.	(5k) Any single	2.00	1.00
c.	Booklet pane, 3 #2407	12.00	
	Booklet, #2407c	12.00	

Dogs — A745

No. 2408: a, Golden retriever. b, German shepherd. c, Labrador retriever. d, Dachshund.

2001, Jan. 31		**Perf. 12¾ Vert.**
2408	Booklet of 4	8.00	7.50
a.-d.	A745 (5k) Any single	2.00	1.00

Birds — A746

Designs: (3.80k), Vanellus vanellus. (5k), Pica pica. 6k, Larus argentatus. 7k, Aegithalos caudatus.

2001, Mar. 22	**Engr.**	**Perf. 12¾ Vert.**
2409	A746	(3.80k) multi	1.75	1.25
2410	A746	(5k) multi	1.90	.50
2411	A746	6k multi	2.00	1.50
2412	A746	7k multi	2.25	1.75
	Nos. 2409-2412 (4)	7.90	5.00

Europa — A747

No. 2413: a, Waterways of northern Sweden. b, Large ship in Trollhätte Canal, trees. c, Waterways of southern Sweden. d, Ship "Juno" in Trollhätte Canal, duck.
Illustration reduced.

Perf. 12¾ on 3 Sides

2001, Mar. 22		**Litho.**
2413	A747	Booklet pane of 4	11.00	12.00
a.-d.	7k Any single	2.75	2.25
	Booklet, #2413 + 4 etiquettes	11.00	

Easter A748

No. 2414: a, Orange egg. b, Purple egg. c, Chick.

2001, Mar. 22	**Die Cut Perf. 9¾x10**
	Self-Adhesive
2414	A748	Booklet pane of 3	6.00	6.00
a.-c.	(5k) Any single	1.90	1.60
	Booklet, 2 #2414	12.00	

Nobel Prize, Cent. A749

No. 2415: a, Alfred Nobel, Peace medal, obverse of Physics, Chemistry, Physiology or Medicine, Literature medal. b, Reverse of Physiology or Medicine medal. c, Reverse of medal for Physics or Chemistry. d, Reverse of Literature medal.

Perf. 12¾x13½ on 3 Sides
2001, Mar. 22   **Litho. & Engr.**

2415	Vert. strip of 4	10.00	12.50
a.-d.	A749 8k Any single	2.50	2.50
e.	Booklet pane, #2415 + 4 eti-		
	quettes + 4 blank labels	10.00	
	Booklet, #2415e	10.00	

See United States No. 3504.

Ivar Lo-Johansson (1901-90),
Writer — A750

No. 2416: a, Portrait. b, Lo-Johansson, truck.
Illustration reduced.

2001, May 17   **Engr.**   **Perf. 12¾ Vert.**

2416	A750 Pair	3.75	3.50
a.-b.	(5k) Any single	1.90	.90

Peonies — A751

No. 2417: a, Fernleaf peony (two flowers, one bud). b, Chinese peony "Mons Jules Elie." c, Herbaceous peony (yellow). d, Common peony (flower and bud). e, Tree peony.

Perf. 12¾ on 3 Sides
2001, May 17   **Litho.**

2417	Horiz. strip of 5	9.25	6.00
a.-e.	A751 (5k) Any single	1.90	1.10
f.	Booklet pane, 2 #2417	19.00	
	Booklet, #2417f	19.00	

Nobel Prize, Cent. — A752

Past winners: a, Doctors Without Borders. b, Red Cross.
Illustration reduced.

Perf. 12¾ Vert.
2001, Aug. 16   **Litho.**

2418	A752 Horiz. pair	5.50	6.50
a.-b.	8k Any single	2.75	2.75

Daniel Solander (1733-82), Botanist on Endeavour A753

No. 2419: a, Barringtonia calyptrata and Solander. b, Cochlospermum gillivraei and Endeavour.

Perf. 12½x12¾ on 3 Sides
2001, Aug. 16   **Litho. & Engr.**

2419	A753 Vert. pair	5.00	5.50
a.-b.	8k Any single	2.50	2.25
c.	Booklet pane, 2 #2419	10.00	
	Booklet, #2419c + 4 eti-		
	quettes	10.00	

See Australia Nos. 1996-1997.

Fish
A754

Designs: a, Perca fluviatilis. b, Abramis brama. c, Triglopsis quadricornis.

Die Cut Perf. 13½ Horiz.
2001, Aug. 16   **Litho. & Engr.**
Self-Adhesive

2420	Booklet pane of 3	5.75	5.50
a.-c.	A754 (5k) Any single	1.90	1.20
d.	Booklet, 2 #2420	11.50	

Souvenir Sheet

Aviation — A755

No. 2421: a, Lilienthal glider, 1895. b, Royal Swedish Aero Club. c, Saab J-29, 1962. d, Friedrichshafen FF49. e, Trike ultralight, 1999. f, Douglas DC-3, 1938.

Perf. 12½x12¾
2001, Oct. 6   **Litho. & Engr.**

2421	A755 Sheet of 6	18.00	13.50
a.-f.	5k Any single	2.00	1.75

Stamp Design Contest Winners — A756

No. 2422: a, Rollerblader, by Emilie Kilström, Kikebo School, Oskarshamn. b, The Letter, by Thomas Fröhling.
Illustration reduced.

Perf. 12¾ on 3 Sides
2001, Oct. 6   **Litho.**

2422	A756 Horiz. pair	4.00	4.50
a.-b.	(5k) Any single	2.00	1.25
c.	Booklet pane, 3 #2422	12.00	
	Booklet, #2422c	12.00	

A757

Christmas — A758

Designs: No. 2423, Christmas tree.
No. 2424 — Tree ornaments (26x20mm): a, Star. b, Cracker. c, Angel. d, Heart e, Cone.
No. 2425 — Crumpled paper art by Yrjö Edelmann: a, Straw goat. b, Christmas tree.
Illustration A758 reduced.

Perf. 12¾ Vert.
2001, Nov. 21   **Litho.**

2423	A757 (4.50k) multi	1.90	1.25

Self-Adhesive
Die Cut Perf. 10¾x11¼

2424	Vert. strip of 5	8.25	8.25
a.-e.	A757 (4.50k) Any single	1.60	.80
	Booklet, 2 #2424	16.50	

Water-Activated Gum
Perf. 12¾ on 3 Sides

2425	A758 Horiz. pair	4.50	5.25
a.-b.	6k Any single	2.25	2.25
c.	Booklet pane, 5 #2425 + 10		
	etiquettes	22.50	
	Booklet, #2425c	22.50	
	Nos. 2423-2425 (3)	14.65	

World Ice Hockey Championships A759

2002, Jan. 24   **Litho.**   **Perf. 12¾ Vert.**

2426	A759 (5k) multi	2.00	1.10

Pandion Haliaetus A760

2002, Jan. 24   **Engr.**

2427	A760 10k multi	2.25	1.25

New Year 2002 (Year of the Horse) — A761

No. 2428 — The Stones Family, by Bertil Almqvist: a, Boy and girl on horse. b, Girl on, and boy leading horse, dog running.
Illustration reduced.

Perf. 12¾ on 3 Sides
2002, Jan. 24   **Litho.**

2428	A761 Horiz. pair	4.00	2.50
a.-b.	(5k) Any single	2.00	1.00
c.	Booklet pane, 5 #2428	20.00	
	Booklet, #2428c	20.00	

Love and Miss Terrified, by Joanna Rubin Dranger A762

No. 2429: a, "Det tror. . ." b, "Men jag. . ." c, "Anej!!!"

Die Cut Perf. 13¾ Horiz.
2002, Jan. 24   **Litho.**
Self-Adhesive

2429	A762 Booklet pane of 3	6.00	5.00
a.-c.	(5k) Any single	2.00	1.25
d.	Booklet, 2 #2429	12.00	

Antarctic Expedition of Otto Nordenskjöld, Cent. — A763

No. 2430: a, Scientists, ship, gull. b, Ship, penguin.

Litho. & Engr., Litho. (#2430b)
2002, Jan. 24   **Perf. 12¾ Horiz.**

2430	A763 Vert. pair	6.00	6.25
a.-b.	10k Any single	3.00	2.75
c.	Booklet pane, 2 #2430	12.00	
	Booklet, #2430c + 4 eti-		
	quettes	12.00	

Astrid Lindgren (1907-2002), Children's Book Writer — A764

Designs: a, Pippi Langstrump (Pippi Longstocking). b, Karlsson pa Taket. c, Bröderna Lejonhjärta, vert. d, Lindgren (24x29mm). e, Emil i Lönneberga, vert. f, Lotta pa Brakmakargatan. g, Madicken.

2002, Mar. 5   **Litho.**   **Perf. 13x13¼**

2431	A764 Booklet pane of 7	14.00	17.50
a.-g.	5k Any single	2.00	2.50
	Booklet, #2431	14.00	

Stockholm, 750th Anniv. — A765

Painting of Stockholm, 1535: (5k), Town and Lake Mälaren. 10k, Close-up view of Cathedral and palace.

2002, Mar. 21   **Engr.**   **Perf. 12¾ Vert.**

2432	A765 (5k) shown	1.75	1.10

Size: 28x28mm

2433	A765 10k claret	3.00	2.25

A766

Swedish World Heritage Sites A767

Artifacts from Birka archaeological site: (3.80k), Cross. (4.50k), Runic stone. (5k), Man's face.
No. 2437 — Scenes from Visby: a, Town and ring wall. b, Wall towers. c, Burmeister

building, flowers. d, Square, walls of St. Cathe-rine's Church.

2002, Mar. 21   Engr.   Perf. 12½ Vert.
2434	A766	(3.80k) purple	1.40	1.10
2435	A766	(4.50k) blue	1.75	.75
2436	A766	(5k) brn & claret	1.75	.75
	Nos. 2434-2436 (3)		4.90	2.60

Litho. & Engr.
Perf. 12½x12¾ on 3 Sides
2437		Booklet pane of 4	7.25	8.00
a.-d.	A767 (5k) Any single	1.75	1.20
	Booklet, #2437	7.25	

Kristianstad Sculptures — A768

No. 2438: a, Structure by Takashi Naraha. b, Sprung From, by Pal Svensson. Illustration reduced.

Perf. 12¾ Vert.
2002, Mar. 23   Litho. & Engr.
2438	A768	Horiz. pair	5.50	5.50
a.-b.		8k Any single	2.75	2.50

Europa — A769

No. 2439: a, Charlie Rivel (1896-1983), clown. b, Clowns Without Borders (boy and clown). c, Cirkus Cirkör (performer with balloon). d, Cirkus Scott (woman on elephant). Illustration reduced.

Perf. 12¾ on 3 Sides
2002, May 2   Litho.
2439	A769	Booklet pane of 4	11.00	12.50
a.-d.		8k Any single	2.75	3.00
		Booklet, #2439 + 4 eti-quettes	11.00	

Art From Sweden and New Zealand A770

No. 2440: a, Rain Forest, glass vase blown by Ola Höglund, Sweden. b, Maori basket, by Willa Rogers, New Zealand.

Perf. 12½x12¾ on 3 Sides
2002, May 2   Litho. & Engr.
2440	A770	Vert. pair	10.00	12.00
a.-b.		10k Any single	5.00	4.50
c.		Booklet pane, 2 #2440	20.00	
		Booklet, #2440c + 4 eti-quettes	20.00	

See New Zealand Nos. 1780, 1786.

A771

Summer in Bohuslän — A772

Designs: No. 2441, Waterfront building. No. 2442: a, Lighthouse and gull. b, Light-house and three birds. c, Bridge, sailboat, waterfront buildings. d, Boat with outboard motor. Illustration A772 reduced.

2002, May 10   Engr.   Perf. 12¾ Vert.
2441	A771	(5k) multi	1.75	.85

Litho.
Self-Adhesive
Serpentine Die Cut 6¾
2442	A772	Block of 4	7.00	7.50
a.-d.		(5k) Any single	1.75	1.00
e.		Booklet, #2442c-2442d, 2 #2442	17.50	

Grönköpings Veckoblad Satirical Newspaper, Cent. — A773

No. 2443: a, Newspaper and fictitious Post-master of Grönköping. b, Fictitious police chief and criminal. Illustration reduced.

Perf. 12¾ Vert.
2002, Aug. 29   Litho. & Engr.
2443	A773	Pair	4.00	3.75
a.-b.		(5k) Either single	2.00	1.75

Chefs A774

No. 2444: a, Charles Emil Hagdahl (1809-97) and Cajsa Warg (1703-69). b, Marit "Hiram" Huldt, cook with cauldron and bird, flowers. c, Tore Wretman and medal. d, Leif Mannerström, fish and lobster. e, Gert Klötzke and Swedish Culinary Team. f, Christer Ling-ström, poultry, peas and apples.

Perf. 12½x12¾ on 3 Sides
2002, Aug. 29   Litho.
2444		Booklet pane of 6	10.50	10.50
a.-f.		A774 (5k) Any single	1.75	1.25
		Booklet, #2444	10.50	

Royal Palaces A775

No. 2445: a, Sweden. b, Thailand.

Perf. 12½x13 on 3 Sides
2002, Oct. 5   Litho. & Engr.
2445	A775	Vert. pair	8.00	8.00
a.-b.		5k Either single	4.00	3.50
c.		Booklet pane, 2 #2445	16.00	
		Booklet, #2445c	16.00	

See Thailand Nos. 2040-2041.

Motorcycle Racers — A776

No. 2446: a, Hakan Carlqvist. b, Sten Lun-din. c, Anders Eriksson. d, Ulf Karlsson.
No. 2447: a, Ove Fundin. b, Tony Rickard-sson. c, Peter Linden. d, Varg-Olle Nygren.

2002, Oct. 5   Litho.   Perf. 12¾
2446	A776	Booklet pane of 4	6.50	9.00
a.-d.		5k Any single	1.60	2.00

Litho. & Engr.
2447	A776	Booklet pane of 4	6.50	9.00
a.-d.		5k Any single	1.60	2.00
		Booklet, #2446-2447	13.00	

Animated Film Karl-Bertil Jonsson's Christmas A777

Designs: No. 2448, Man with arm on Karl-Bertil's shoulder.
No. 2449: a, Karl-Bertil and mail sack of Christmas parcels. b, Karl-Bertil asleep with Robin Hood hat. c, Karl-Bertil giving parcel to poor man. d, Karl-Bertil with man, woman and child.

Perf. 12¾ Vert.
2002, Nov. 21   Litho.
2448	A777	(4.50k) multi	1.50	1.50

Self-Adhesive
Serpentine Die Cut 6½x6 on 3 Sides
2449		Block of 4	5.50	6.50
a.-d.		A777 (4.50k) Any single	1.40	1.00
e.		Booklet pane, 3 #2449a-2449b, 2 #2449c-2449d	14.00	

Churches — A778

No. 2450: a, Kiruna Church. b, Habo Church. c, Sundborn Church. d, Tensta Bell Tower. Illustration reduced.

2002, Nov. 21   Perf. 12¾ on 3 Sides
2450	A778	Block of 4	11.00	11.00
a.-d.		8k Any single	2.50	2.25
e.		Booklet pane, 3 #2450a-2450b, 2 #2450c-2450d	27.50	—
		Booklet, #2450e	27.50	

St. Bridget (1303-73) — A779

2003, Jan. 20   Engr.   Perf. 12¾ Vert.
2451	A779	(5.50k) red & brown	1.90	1.25

Swedish Sports Federation, Cent. — A780

No. 2452: a, Woman and child. b, Wheel-chair racer. c, Snowboarder and sign lan-guage. d, Girl running.

Serpentine Die Cut 8½
2003, Jan. 20   Litho.
Self-Adhesive
2452		Booklet pane, 3 each #2452a, 2452c, 2 each #2452b, 2452d	15.00	
a.-d.		A780 (5.50k) Any single	1.50	1.10

Europa — A781

Posters by: a, Anders Beckman, 1935. b, Georg Magnusson, 1930. c, Owe Gustafson, 1984. d, Carina Länk, 1993. Illustration reduced.

Perf. 12¾x12½ on 3 Sides
2003, Jan. 20
2453	A781	Booklet pane of 4	11.00	12.50
a.-d.		10k Any single	2.75	2.50
		Booklet, #2453 + 4 eti-quettes	11.00	

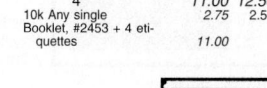

Knots — A782

Various knots.

2003, Jan. 20   Engr.   Perf. 12½ Vert.
2454	A782	(4.80k) green	1.40	1.75
2455	A782	(5k) blue	1.50	1.00
2456	A782	(5.50k) red	1.75	.65
	Nos. 2454-2456 (3)		4.65	3.40

Regional Houses — A783

Perf. 12¼ Vert. Syncopated
2003, Mar. 20   Engr.
2457	A783	2k Närke	.75	.55
2458	A783	4k Bohuslän	1.25	1.10
2459	A783	5k Medelpad	1.50	1.40
	Nos. 2457-2459 (3)		3.50	3.05

Nobel Prize Winners For Physiology or Medicine From Spain — A784

No. 2460: a, Santiago Ramón y Cajal, 1906. b, Severo Ochoa, 1959.

Perf. 12 Vert. Syncopated

2003, Mar. 20		Litho. & Engr.	
2460	A784 Horiz. pair	5.50	6.00
a.-b.	10k Either single	2.75	2.75

See Spain No. 3204.

Flowers — A785

No. 2461: a, Hepatica nobilis. b, Primula veris. c, Tussilago farfara.

Die Cut Perf. 9¾x10

2003, Mar. 20		Litho.	
	Self-Adhesive		
2461	Booklet pane of 3	4.50	5.50
a.-c.	A785 (5.50k) Any single	1.50	1.25
	Booklet, 2 #2461	9.00	

Oland Moorland, UNESCO World Heritage Site A786

No. 2462: a, Windmills. b, Megaliths and windmill. c, Cow and linear village. d, Sheep and lighthouse.

Perf. 12¾ Horiz.

2003, Mar. 20		Litho. & Engr.	
2462	Booklet pane of 4	7.75	7.00
a.-d.	A786 (5.50k) Any single	1.90	1.50
	Booklet, #2462	7.75	

A787

Garden Pavilions A788

Designs: No. 2463, 1820s pavilion, by Frederik Blom.
No. 2464: a, Pavilion of Emanuel Swedenborg. b, Pavilion of Ebba Brahe. c, Västana farm pavilion, Borensberg. d, Godegard pavilion.

Perf. 12½ Vert. Syncopated

2003, May 16		Engr.	
2463	A787 (5.50k) multi	1.75	1.40
	Litho.		
	Self-Adhesive		

Serpentine Die Cut 6½ on 3 Sides

2464	Block of 4	7.00	7.50
a.-d.	A788 (5.50k) Any single	1.75	1.25
e.	Booklet pane, 3 #2464a-2464b, 2 #2464c-2464d	17.50	

Souvenir Sheet

St. Bridget (1303-73) — A789

Litho. & Engr.

2003, May 31		**Perf. 13**	
2465	A789 40k multi	10.50	12.50

No. 2465 exists with and without numbers printed in LL and LR corners of the margin.

Royalty Type of 2000

Designs: (5.50k), King Carl XVI Gustaf. 10k, Queen Silvia.

Perf. 13 Vert. Syncopated

2003, Aug. 21		Engr.	
2466	A737 (5.50k) red brown	1.50	.75
2467	A737 10k purple	2.50	2.00

Harvest Time — A790

No. 2468: a, Tree, radicchio, parsnip, cucumber, beet, onion. b, Pitchfork, artichoke, pear, gourd, raspberries, apple, plum, pumpkin, eggplant. c, Trowel, garlic, peas, cabbage, tomato, potato, turnip, carrots. d, Strawberries, sunflower, cherries, plums, apple, pear.

Serpentine Die Cut 6½ on 3 Sides

2003, Aug. 21		Litho.	
	Self-Adhesive		
2468	A790 Block of 4	6.50	7.50
a.-d.	(5.50k) Any single	1.60	1.25
e.	Booklet pane, 2 each #2468a-2468b, 2 each #2468c-2468d	16.00	

Birds — A791

No. 2469: a, Recurvirostra avosetta. b, Podiceps auritus. c, Gavia arctica. d, Podiceps cristatus.
Illustration reduced.

Perf. 12½x12¾ on 3 Sides

2003, Oct. 4		Litho. & Engr.	
2469	A791 Booklet pane of 4	12.00	13.50
a.-d.	10k Any single	3.00	2.75
	Complete booklet, #2469 + 4 etiquettes	12.00	

See Hong Kong Nos. 1052-1055.

Building of East Indiaman "Götheborg" — A792

No. 2470: a, Figurehead (19x23mm). b, Ship under construction (19x23mm). c, Side view of ship, horiz. (23x40mm). d, Ship at sea (39x50mm).
Illustration reduced.

Perf. 12½x12¾

2003, Oct. 4		Perf. 12½x12¾	
2470	A792 Booklet pane of 4	19.00	25.00
a.-b.	5.50k Either single	2.50	2.50
c.	10k multi	3.50	4.00
d.	30k multi	10.00	12.00
	Complete booklet, #2470 + label	19.00	

Christmas at Sundborn, by Carl Larsson — A793

No. 2471: a, Martina med Frukostbrickan. b, Kerstis Slädfärd.
Illustration reduced.

Perf. 12¾ on 3 Sides

2003, Nov. 10		Litho.	
2471	A793 Horiz. pair	5.25	6.00
a.-b.	9k Either single	1.75	2.25
c.	Booklet pane, 5 #2471 +10 etiquettes	26.50	
	Complete booklet, #2471c	26.50	

Christmas Paintings by Carl Larsson — A794

Designs: No. 2472, Aftonvarden.
No. 2473, vert.: a, Esbjörn pa Skidor. b, Brita med Julljus. c, Farfar och Esbjörn. d, Garden och Brygghuset.

Perf. 12¾ Vert. Syncopated

2003, Nov. 10			
2472	A794 (5k) multi	1.50	1.40
	Self-Adhesive		

Serpentine Die Cut 6½x6 on 3 Sides

2473	A794 Block of 4	6.50	7.50
a.-d.	(5k) Any single	1.60	1.40
e.	Booklet pane, #2473b, 2473d, 2 #2473	16.00	

Anna Lindh (1957-2003), Murdered Minister of Foreign Affairs — A795

Perf. 12¾ on 3 Sides

2003, Nov. 11		Engr.	
2474	A795 Pair	4.50	5.50
a.	(5.50k) claret	1.60	1.60
b.	10k blue	2.75	2.75

---

c.	Booklet pane, 2 each #2474a-2474b	9.00	—
	Complete booklet, #2474c	9.00	—

No. 2474c sold for 35k, 4k of which went to the Anna Lindh Memorial Fund.

Woodworking Tools — A796

Designs: (4.80k), Brace and bit. (5k), Saw. (5.50k), Plane.

Perf. 12 Vert. Syncopated

2004, Jan. 26		Engr.	
2475	A796 (4.80k) green	1.40	1.40
2476	A796 (5k) blue	1.40	1.00
2477	A796 (5.50k) claret	1.60	.60
	Nos. 2475-2477 (3)	4.40	3.00

Flowers A797

No. 2478: a, Tulip. b, Lily. c, Hibiscus. d, Amaryllis. e, Calla lily.

Perf. 12¾ Horiz.

2004, Jan. 26		Litho.	
2478	Vert. strip of 5	7.75	7.75
a.-e.	A797 (5.50k) Any single	1.50	1.25
f.	Booklet pane, 2 #2478	15.50	
	Complete booklet, #2478f	15.50	

Europa A798

No. 2479 — Views of Lapland: a, Mountain with purple sky. b, Tents near lake.

Perf. 12¾x13½ on 3 Sides

2004, Jan. 26			
2479	A798 Pair	5.75	6.50
a.-b.	10k Either single	2.75	2.75
c.	Booklet pane, 2 #2479	11.50	
	Complete booklet, #2479c + 4 etiquettes	11.50	

Souvenir Sheet

Norse Mythology — A799

No. 2480 — Return to Valhalla: a, Return of a warrior (denomination at LR). b, Welcoming Valkyrie (denomination at UR).

Litho. & Engr.

2004, Mar. 26		Perf. 12¾	
2480	A799 Sheet of 2	5.75	7.00
a.-b.	10k Either single	2.75	3.00

Falun, UNESCO World Heritage Site — A800

No. 2481: a, Excavation pit, red mine shaft entrance building. b, Yellow green and green copper weighing building, red, white and purple mining operations building. c, Gray mine entrance building. d, Miners and houses. Illustration reduced.

Perf. 12½x12¾ on 3 Sides
2004, Mar. 26 Litho.
2481 A800 Block of 4 9.50 8.50
a.-d. (5.50k) Any single 1.50 1.75
e. Booklet pane, #2481b, 2481d,
2 each #2481a, 2481c 9.00 —
Complete booklet, #2481e 9.00

Swedish Soccer Association, Cent. — A801

No. 2482: a, Nils Liedholm. b, Hanna Ljungberg. c, Fredrik Ljungberg. d, Henrik Larsson. e, Victoria Svensson. f, Thomas Ravelli.

Serpentine Die Cut 7x6¼ on 3 Sides
2004, Mar. 26
Self-Adhesive
2482 Booklet pane of 6 10.50 13.00
a.-f. A801 (5.50k) Any single 1.75 1.75

Sunset Scenes — A802

No. 2483: a, Fisherman. b, Lighthouse. Illustration reduced.

Perf. 12½ Vert. Syncopated
2004, May 13 Engr.
2483 A802 Horiz. pair 3.50 3.00
a.-b. (5.50k) Either single 1.75 1.25

Stockholm Archipelago A803

No. 2484: a, Sailboat, red house, Gillöga. b, Rowboat, houses, Langviksskär. c, Ferry, Stora Nassa. d, Sailboat, lighthouse, Nämdöfjärden.

Serpentine Die Cut 6¾ on 3 Sides
2004, May 13 Litho.
Self-Adhesive
2484 Block of 4 7.00 7.50
a.-d. A803 (5.50k) Any single 1.75 1.50
e. Booklet pane, 3 #2484a-2484b,
2 #2484c-2484d 15.00

Cottages A804

Designs: 3k, Blacksmith's cottage, Uppland. 6k, Dalsland cottage. 8k, Stone cottage, Gotland.

Perf. 12¾ Vert. Syncopated
2004, Aug. 19 Engr.
2485 A804 3k multi .80 .60
2486 A804 6k multi 1.60 .90
2487 A804 8k multi 2.10 1.50
Nos. 2485-2487 (3) 4.50 3.00

Birds — A805

Designs: (5k), Streptopelia decaocto. (5.50k), Swedish tumbler. 10k, Columba palumbus.

2004, Aug. 19
2488 A805 (5k) multi 1.40 1.25
2489 A805 (5.50k) multi 1.50 .60
2490 A805 10k multi 2.75 2.50
Nos. 2488-2490 (3) 5.65 4.35

Forest Larder — A806

No. 2491: a, Mushrooms, lingonberries. b, Wild strawberries, butterfly, basket of blueberries. c, Juniper berries, basket of mushrooms. d, Cloudberries, cranberries.

Serpentine Die Cut 6½ on 3 Sides
2004, Aug. 19 Litho.
Self-Adhesive
2491 A806 Block of 4 7.25 6.00
a.-d. (5.50k) Any single 1.75 1.25
e. Booklet pane, 3 each
#2491a-2491b, 2 each
#2491c-2491d 15.00

Nobel Prize Winners for Literature from Ireland — A807

No. 2492: a, William Butler Yeats, 1923. b, George Bernard Shaw, 1925. c, Samuel Beckett, 1969. d, Seamus Heaney, 1995. Illustration reduced.

Perf. 12½x13½ on 3 Sides
2004, Oct. 1 Litho. & Engr.
2492 A807 Booklet pane of 4 11.00 12.50
a.-d. 10k Any single 2.75 2.75
Complete booklet, #2492 +
4 etiquettes 11.00

See Ireland Nos. 1576-1579.

Rock Music, 50th Anniv. — A808

No. 2493: a, Jerry Williams (29x39mm). b, Elvis Presley (36x39mm). c, Eva Dahlgren (29x39mm). d, Ulf Lundell (36x39mm). e, Tomas Ledin (29x39mm). f, Pugh Rogefeldt (29x33mm). g, Sahara Hotnights (36x33mm). h, Louise Hoffsten (29x33mm).

Litho., Litho. & Engr. (#2493b, 2493d)
2004, Oct. 2 **Perf. 12x12¾**
2493 Booklet pane of 8 + 2
labels 14.00 16.50
a.-h. A808 5.50k Any single 1.75 1.75
Complete booklet, #2493 14.00
i. Sheet of 9 #2493b 17.00 —

Labels and margins of Nos. 2493 and 2493i have perforations reading "Rock 54-04." No. 2493i sold for 55c.

Regional Houses Type of 2003 and

Log Cabin — A809 · Scanian Farm House — A810

Designs: 1k, Miner's house. 9k, Blekinge cottage.

Perf. 12 Vert. Syncopated
2004, Nov. 11 Engr.
2494 A809 50o multi .30 .25
Perf. 12¼ Vert. Syncopated
2495 A783 1k multi .35 .30
2496 A810 7k multi 2.00 1.25
2497 A810 9k multi 2.75 2.00
Nos. 2494-2497 (4) 5.40 3.80

Birds — A811

No. 2498: a, Parus major. b, Emberiza citrinella. c, Pinicola enucleator. d, Pyrrhula pyrrhula. Illustration reduced.

Perf. 12¾ on 3 Sides
2004, Nov. 11 Litho.
2498 A811 Booklet pane of 4 12.00 13.00
a.-d. 10k Any single 3.00 2.75
Complete booklet, #2498 +
4 etiquettes 12.00

Christmas A812

Designs: No. 2499, Gnomes playing leap frog.
No. 2500: a, Three gnomes. b, Gnome with Christmas tree. c, Two gnomes with chair on skis. d, Gnome, birds at mail box.

Perf. 12¼ Vert. Syncopated
2004, Nov. 11
2499 A812 (5k) multi 1.50 1.50
Self-Adhesive
Serpentine Die Cut 6¼x6 on 3 Sides
2500 Block of 4 6.00 6.75
a.-d. A812 (5k) Any single 1.50 1.50
e. Booklet pane, 3 each #2500a-
2500b, 2 each #2500c-2500d 15.00

King Carl XVI Gustaf — A813

Queen Silvia — A814

Perf. 12½ Vert. Syncopated
2005, Jan. 27 Engr.
2501 A813 (5.50k) multi 1.60 1.00
2502 A814 10k multi 3.00 2.50

High Coast, UNESCO World Heritage Site — A815

No. 2503: a, Högbonden Lighthouse, birds on rocks. b, Cliffs and eagles, Storön Nature Reserve. c, Fishing boat at dock, Ulvön. d, Lakes near Häggvik. Illustration reduced.

Perf. 12¾x13½ on 3 Sides
2005, Jan. 27 Litho. & Engr.
2503 A815 Booklet pane of 4 12.00 14.00
a.-d. 10k Any single 3.00 3.00
Complete booklet, #2503 +
4 etiquettes 12.00

Swedish Design A816

No. 2504: a, Glassware, by Ingegerd Raman. b, Turn-o-matic number ticket machine, by A/E Design. c, Speedway 9000 welding helmet, by Carl-Göran Crafoord and Hakan Bergkvist. d, Camilla chair and Pilaster shelving unit, by John Kandell. e, Women's watch, by Vivianna Torun Bülow-Hübe. f, Streamliner toy car, by Ulf Hanses.

Die Cut Perf. 12½ Horiz.
2005, Jan. 27
Self-Adhesive
2504 Booklet pane of 6 9.75 10.00
a.-f. A816 (5.50k) Any single 1.60 1.25

Oriolus Oriolus A817

Perf. 12½ Vert. Syncopated
2005, Mar. 10 Litho. & Engr.
2505 A817 11k multi 3.25 2.50

Dag Hammarskjold (1905-61), UN Secretary General — A818

No. 2506: a, Hammarskjold. b, United Nations flag. Illustration reduced.

2005, Mar. 10   **Engr.**
2506 A818   Horiz. pair   3.25 3.25
a.-b.   (5.50k) Either single   1.60 1.60

Europa
A819

No. 2507: a, Lemon, star anise, elderberry
marmalade. b, Apples, rosemary, Jerusalem
artichokes. c, Chives, goat cheese, beets.

2005, Mar. 10   Litho.   Perf. 12¾
2507 A819   Vert. strip of 3   5.00 5.00
a.-c.   (5.50k) Any single   1.60 1.00
d.   Booklet pane, 2 #2507   10.00   —
             Complete booklet, #2507d   10.00

Spring
Flowers
A820

No. 2508: a, Convallaria majalis. b, Gagea
lutea. c, Pulsatilla vulgaris. d, Anemone
nemorosa.

Serpentine Die Cut 10 on 3 Sides
2005, Mar. 10
Self-Adhesive
2508 A820   Block of 4   6.50 6.50
a.-d.   A820 (5.50k) Any single   1.60 1.10
e.   Booklet pane, 3 each #2508a-
             2508b, 2 each #2508c-2508d   16.00
f.   As "a," serpentine die cut 6¾
             on 3 sides   17.50   —
g.   As "b," serpentine die cut 6¾
             on 3 sides   17.50   —
h.   As "c," serpentine die cut 6¾
             on 3 sides   17.50   —
i.   As "d," serpentine die cut 6¾
             on 3 sides   17.50   —
j.   Booklet pane, 3 each #2508f-
             2508g, 2 each #2508h-2508i   70.00

Nos. 2508f-2508i issued 9/6.

Mother
Svea
A821

Perf. 12½ Vert. Syncopated
2005, May 26   Litho. & Engr.
2509 A821   15k multi   4.00 4.00

Tumba Bruk, manufacturer of Swedish
banknotes, 250th anniv.

A822

Allotment Gardens — A823

No. 2511: a, Girl near shrub, man tending
vegetable garden. b, Woman at table. b, Man
tending garden, woman with basket of vegetables. c, Man watering garden.

Perf. 12¾ Vert. Syncopated
2005, May 26   **Litho.**
2510 A822   (5.50k) multi   1.50 1.50
Self-Adhesive
Serpentine Die Cut 10 on 3 Sides
2511 A823   Block of 4   6.00 7.50
a.-d.   (5.50k) Any single   1.50 1.50
e.   Complete booklet, 3 each
             #2511a, 2511c, 2 each
             #2511b, 2511d   15.00

A824

Swedish Postage Stamps, 150th
Anniv. — A825

No. 2512 — Details from stamps: a, #944
(1972). b, #430 (1951). c, #250 (1936). d,
#1490 (1984).
No. 2513: a, Count Pehr Ambjörn Sparre,
#2, printing press. b, Woman reading letter,
cover. c, Airplane, train. d, Mailman in van at
mailbox.
Illustrations reduced.

2005, May 26   Litho.   Perf. 12¾
2512 A824   Booklet pane of 4   6.00 8.50
a.-d.   (5.50k) Any single   1.50 1.50
Litho. & Engr.
2513 A825   Booklet pane of 4   6.00 8.50
a.-d.   (5.50k) Any single   1.50 1.50
e.   Miniature sheet, 9 #2513a   15.00   —
             Complete booklet, #2512-
             2513   12.00

No. 2513e sold for 55k.

Souvenir Sheet

Dissolution of Union of Sweden and
Norway, Cent. — A826

No. 2514 — Svinesund Bridge: a, View of
roadway with cars. b, View from valley.

Perf. 12½x12¾
2005, May 27   Litho. & Engr.
2514 A826   Sheet of 2   6.50 6.75
a.-b.   10k Either single   3.25 2.75

See Norway Nos. 1430-1431.

Varberg Radio
Station World
Heritage
Site — A827

Skogskyrkogarden Cemetery World
Heritage Site — A828

Perf. 12½ Vert. Syncopated
2005, Sept. 23   **Engr.**
2515 A827   (4.80k) grn & violet   1.40 1.40
2516 A828   (5k) multi   1.60   .50

Greta Garbo (1905-90),
Actress — A829

No. 2517: a, Portrait. b, Caricature and
"Greta."

Perf. 12¾x12½ on 3 Sides
2005, Sept. 23   Litho. & Engr.
2517 A829   Pair   5.50 6.50
a.-b.   10k Either single   2.75 2.75
c.   Booklet pane, 2 each
             #2517a-2517b   11.00   —
             Complete booklet,
             #2517c + 4 etiquettes   11.00
d.   Souvenir sheet of 4
             #2517a, perf.
             12¾x12½   110.00 125.00

No. 2517d sold for 45k and has a lithographed sheet margin. Single stamps from
#2517d are perforated on all four sides.
See United States No. 3943.

Juvenile Wild Animals — A830

No. 2518: a, Lynx. b, Bear. c, Wolf. d, Fox.

Serpentine Die Cut 10 on 3 Sides
2005, Sept. 23   **Litho.**
Self-Adhesive
2518 A830   Block of 4   6.00
a.-d.   (5.50k) Any single   1.60 1.60
e.   Complete booklet, 3 each
             #2518a-2518b, 2 each
             #2518c-2518d   16.00

A831

Mopeds — A832

No. 2519: a, Man, woman, Fram moped. b,
Husqvarna moped. c, Kuli moped engine and
wheel. d, Two men sitting on mopeds.
No. 2520: a, Man repairing hoisted moped.
b, Three-wheeled platform scooter. c,
Zundapp moped engine. d, Man riding moped.

**Litho., Litho. & Engr. (#2519b,
2519c, 2520b, 2520c)**
2005, Sept. 24   **Perf. 12¾**
2519 A831   Booklet pane of
             4   6.00 7.50
a.-d.   5.50k Any single   1.50 1.50
e.   Sheet of 9 #2519d   14.50 14.50
2520 A832   Booklet pane of
             4   6.00 7.50
a.-d.   5.50k Any single   1.50 1.50
             Complete booklet, #2519-
             2520   12.00

No. 2519e sold for 55k.

Christmas
A833

Illustrations from Christmas in a Noisy Village, by Astrid Lindgren: No. 2521, Dog, child
on skis.
No. 2522: a, Children near fence. b, Dog,
children with sled. c, Girl wrapping gifts. d,
Children looking at Christmas tree.

Perf. 12¾ Vert. Syncopated
2005, Nov. 10   **Litho.**
2521 A833   (5k) multi   1.25 1.25
Self-Adhesive
Serpentine Die Cut 10 on 3 Sides
2522   Block of 4   6.50 6.50
a.-d.   A833 (5k) Any single   1.50 1.25
e.   Booklet pane, 3 each #2522a-
             2522b, 2 each #2522c-2522d   12.50

Angel Musicians, Sculptures by Carl Milles — A834

No. 2523: a, Angel with horn facing right. b, Angel with horn facing left. c, Angel with flute facing right. d, Angel with flute facing forward.

Perf. 12¾ on 3 Sides

2005, Nov. 10		Litho. & Engr.	
2523	A834	Booklet pane of 4	10.00 13.00
a.-d.		10k Any single	2.50 2.50
		Complete booklet, #2523 + 4 etiquettes	10.00

Swedish Railroads, 150th Anniv. — A835

Designs: 10k, X40 train.

No. 2525: a, Mallet steam locomotive (green). b, Gasoline-powered Rail bus (tan). c, SJ Class D electric locomotive (orange). d, R steam locomotive (black). e, RC electric locomotive (red).

Perf. 12½ Vert. Syncopated

2006, Jan. 26		Litho.	
2524	A835	10k multi	2.60 1.90

Litho. & Engr.
Booklet Stamps
Perf. 12½ Horiz.

2525		Vert. strip of 5	8.00 8.00
a.-e.	A835	(5.50k) Any single	1.60 1.50
f.		Booklet pane, 2 #2525	16.00 —
		Complete booklet, #2525f	16.00

Hearts — A836

No. 2526: a, Tattooed heart. b, Red heart. c, Heart-shaped leaf. d, Heart carved in tree trunk.

Serpentine Die Cut 10 on 3 Sides

2006, Jan. 26		Litho.	
		Self-Adhesive	
2526	A836	Block of 4, #a-d	6.00 5.00
a.-d.		(5.50k) Any single	1.50 1.40
e.		Booklet pane, 2 each #2526c-2526d, 3 each #2526a-2526b	15.00

Souvenir Sheet

Norse Mythology — A837

No. 2527: a, Skogsraet, reindeer, goats and bird. b, Näcken, horse and violin.

Litho. & Engr.

2006, Mar. 29			Perf. 12¾	
2527	A837	Sheet of 2	5.25 6.25	
a.-b.		10k Either single	2.60 2.60	

Souvenir Sheet

King Carl XVI Gustaf, 60th Birthday — A838

2006, Mar. 29	Engr.	Perf. 13x12¾	
2528	A838	Sheet, #2528a, 2 #2528b	8.00 8.00
a.		10k blue	2.60 2.60
b.		10k black	2.60 2.60

Coffee — A839

No. 2529: a, Coffee cups stacked on coffeemaker. b, Glass of cappucino. c, Espresso machine and cup, sugar dispenser and spoon. d, Steamed milk dispenser and measuring cup.

Serpentine Die Cut 10 on 3 Sides

2006, Mar. 29			Litho.	
		Self-Adhesive		
2529	A839	Block of 4	6.25 7.00	
a.-d.		(5.50k) Any single	1.60 1.25	
e.		Booklet pane, 3 each #2529a-2529b, 2 each #2529c-2529d	15.50	

Suomenlinna (Sveaborg) Fortress, Helsinki, Finland — A840

No. 2530: a, Ship without oars, flagpole at fortress. b, Ship with oars facing fortress. c, Ship with oars, windmill.

Litho. & Engr.

2006, May 4			Perf. 12¾	
2530	A840	Booklet pane of 3	8.25 9.00	
a.-c.		10k Any single	2.75 3.25	
		Complete booklet, #2530	8.25	

See Finland No. 1266.

Track and Field Athletes — A841

Designs: (4.80k), Stefan Holm, high jump. 10k, Christian Olsson, triple jump.

No. 2533: a, Carolina Klüft, heptathlon. b, Kajsa Bergqvist, high jump.

Perf. 13¼ Vert. Syncopated

2006, May 4			Litho.	
2531	A841	(4.80k) grn & multi	1.40 1.40	
2532	A841	10k gray & multi	3.00 2.75	
2533		Horiz. pair	3.00 3.00	
a.-b.		A841 (5.50k) Either single	1.50 1.00	
		Nos. 2531-2533 (3)	7.40 7.15	

Europa A842

No. 2534 — Children's art by: a, Alexandros Terzis. b, Linda Wong.

Perf. 12¾x12½ on 3 Sides

2006, May 4				
2534	A842	Pair	5.50 6.50	
a.-b.		10k Either single	2.75 2.75	
c.		Booklet pane, 2 each #2534a-2534b	11.00	
		Complete booklet, #2534c + 4 etiquettes	11.00	

Summer by the Lake — A843

No. 2536: a, Elk and immigrant women's picnic. b, Father and daughter fishing. c, Dog watching swimmers. d, Frog and boaters.

Perf. 12¼ Vert. Syncopated

2006, May 4				
2535	A843	(5.50k) shown	1.50 1.50	

Self-Adhesive
Size: 34x24mm

2536		Block of 4	6.00 7.00	
a.-d.	A843	(5.50k) Any single	1.50 1.00	
e.		Booklet pane, 3 each #2536a-2536b, 2 each #2536c-2536d	15.00	

Famous Men — A844

Designs: (4.80k,) Carl Michael Bellman (1740-95), poet. (5k), Joseph Martin Kraus (1756-92), composer. (5.50k), Wolfgang Amadeus Mozart (1756-91), composer.

2006, Sept. 7		Engr.	Perf. 12¾	
2537	A844	(5.50k) multi	1.75 1.75	

Coil Stamps
Perf. 12½ Vert. Syncopated

2538	A844	(4.80k) multi	1.40 1.40
2539	A844	(5k) multi	1.40 1.40
2540	A844	(5.50k) multi	1.50 1.50
		Nos. 2537-2540 (4)	6.05 6.05

No. 2537 was issued in a sheet of 6 stamps that sold for 38k.

Hanseatic League, 650th Anniv. — A845

Designs: No. 2541, Hanseatic cog, 1380. No. 2542, Building and ships, Visby. No. 2543, City seal, shopper and salesman, Stockholm.

Perf. 12½x13½ on 3 Sides

2006, Sept. 7		Litho. & Engr.	
2541	A845	10k multi	2.75 2.75
2542	A845	10k multi	2.75 2.75
2543	A845	10k multi	2.75 2.75
a.		Booklet pane, #2542-2543, 2 #2541	11.00 —
		Complete booklet, #2543a	11.00

Souvenir Sheets

A846

Characters from Swedish Children's Television Shows — A847

No. 2544: a, Andy Pandy (marionette), Humle and Dumle (puppets). b, Anita on Television, Captain Zoom. c, Fablernas Värld (owl), Teskedsgumman (woman). d, Kalles Klätterträd (cartoon), Beppe Wolgers Godnattstunden (man in pajamas).

No. 2545: a, Trazan and Banarne, pink elephant. b, Pippi Longstockings, bear. c, Dinosaur, characters from Tjet och Allram Eest. d, Loophole, Bananas in Pajamas.

Litho. & Engr.

2006, Sept. 30			Perf. 12½x13	
2544	A846	Sheet of 4	6.00 6.00	
a.-d.		5.50k Any single	1.50 1.50	
2545	A847	Sheet of 4	6.00 6.00	
a.-d.		5.50k Any single	1.50 1.50	
e.		Booklet pane, #2544-2545	12.00 —	
		Complete booklet, #2545e	12.00	
f.		Sheet of 9 #2545a	15.00 15.00	

No. 2545e has a row of rouletting separating No. 2544 from No. 2545, and has a wider margin where the pane is attached to the booklet cover.

Winter Scenes in Art — A848

No. 2546: a, Bourdelle's Heracles in Snow, by Prince Eugen. b, Lelle-Kalle, by Sven Ljundberg. c, Modification of a Winter Landscape by W. O. Petersen, by Philip von Schantz. d, Rime Frost on Ice, by Gustaf Adolf Fjaestad.
Illustration reduced.

Perf. 12¾ on 3 Sides

2006, Nov. 9		Litho.
2546 A848	Booklet pane of 4	12.00
a.-d.	10k Any single	3.00 3.00
	Complete booklet, #2546 + 4 etiquettes	12.00

Christmas A849

Designs: No. 2547, Santa Claus, New Year's ornament, candles.
No. 2548: a, Star ornament. b, Spherical and New Year's ornaments. c, Bird at feeder, poinsettia. d, Candles.

Perf. 12½ Vert. Syncopated

2006, Nov. 9		
2547 A849	(5k) multi	1.50 1.50

Self-Adhesive
Size: 25x25mm
Serpentine Die Cut 10 on 3 Sides

2548	Block of 4	6.00
a.-d.	A849 (5k) Any single	1.50 1.50
e.	Booklet pane, 3 each #2548a-2548b, 2 each #2548c-2548d	15.00

Linnaea Borealis — A850

Enneandria and Carl von Linné (1707-78), Creator of Linnaean Taxonomic System — A851

Perf. 12½ Vert. Syncopated

2007, Jan. 25		Engr.
2549 A850	(5.50k) multi	1.60 1.60

Litho. & Engr.

| 2550 A851 | 11k multi | 3.25 3.25 |

Spring — A852

No. 2551: a, Birds, heart, musical notes. b, Sun, cloud, person. c, Flower, heart, person. d, Bird, sun, musical notes.

Serpentine Die Cut 10 on 3 Sides

2007, Jan. 25		Litho.
2551 A852	Block of 4	6.25
a.-d.	(5.50k) Any single	1.50 1.50
e.	Booklet pane, 3 each #2551a-2551b, 2 each #2551c-2551d	15.50

Souvenir Sheet

Intl. Polar Year — A853

No. 2552: a, Stenfragment I, etching by Svenerik Jakobsson. b, Arctic Ocean 2001 88 Degrees North, 145 Degrees East, by Johan Petterson.

Perf. 13, 12¾x13¼ (#2552b)

2007, Jan. 25		Litho. & Engr.
2552 A853	Sheet of 2	5.75 5.75
a.-b.	10k Either single	2.75 2.75

Wing of Maculinea Arion Butterfly — A854

Serpentine Die Cut 9 Vert. Syncopated
2007, Mar. 22   Litho. & Engr.
Self-Adhesive

| 2553 A854 | 20k multi | 5.75 5.75 |

Printed in sheets of 40.

Swedish Sea Rescue Society, Cent. — A855

Designs: (4.80k), Rowboat, rescuer on jetski. (5k), Helicopter rescue. (5.50k), Nautical chart, rescue boat.

Litho. & Engr., Engr. (#2554, 2557)

2007, Mar. 22		Perf. 13x12¾
2554 A855	(5.50k) multi	1.90 1.90

Perf. 12½ Vert. Syncopated

2555 A855	(4.80k) multi	1.40 1.40
2556 A855	(5k) multi	1.40 1.40
2557 A855	(5.50k) multi	1.60 1.60
	Nos. 2554-2557 (4)	6.30 6.30

No. 2554 was printed in sheets of 6 that sold for 38k.

Europa A856

No. 2558: a, "Jamboree", globe and airplane. b, Scouts.

Perf. 13½x12¾ on 3 Sides

2007, Mar. 22		Litho.
2558 A856	Horiz. or vert. pair	3.25 3.25
a.-b.	(5.50k) Either single	1.60 1.60
c.	Booklet pane, 2 each #2558a-2558b	6.50 —

Scouting, cent.

Swedish Inventions — A857

No. 2559: a, Wall anchor for screws, by Oswald Thorsman. b, Allergy globe for flowers, by Elisabeth Gagnemyhr. c, Cooling food cover, by Birgitta Folcker-Sundell. d, Adjustable wrench, by Johan Petter Johansson.

Serpentine Die Cut 9 Horiz.

2007, Mar. 22		
2559	Horiz. strip or block of 4	5.75
a.-d.	(5k) Any single	1.40 1.40
e.	Booklet paneof 20, 5 each #2559a-2559d	29.00

Queen Silvia Type of 2005
Perf. 12½ Vert. Syncopated

2007, May 10		Engr.
2560 A814	11k grn & blue	3.25 3.25

Souvenir Sheet

Botanical Illustrations by Georg Dionys Ehret — A858

No. 2561: a, Musa x paradisiaca. b, Podophyllum peltatum.

Litho. & Engr.

2007, May 10		Perf. 13
2561 A858	Sheet of 2	6.50 6.50
a.-b.	11k Either single	3.25 3.25

Exists with serial number in margin.

Children Fishing — A859

Designs: No. 2562, Boy fishing in pail.
No. 2563: a, Boy on dock. b, Child kissing fish. c, Girls holding caught fish. d, Boys with fishing pole and caught fish.

Perf. 12½ Vert. Syncopated

2007, May 10		Litho.
2562 A859	(5.50k) multi	1.60 1.60

Size: 34x24mm
Self-Adhesive
Booklet Stamps
Serpentine Die Cut 10 on 3 Sides

2563	Block of 4	6.50
a.-d.	A859 (5.50k) Any single	1.60 1.60
e.	Booklet pane, 3 each #2563a-2563b, 2 each #2563c-2563d	16.00

Landscapes — A860

No. 2564: a, Rape field and house, Skane. b, Duck on lake, Muddus National Park. c, Elk in forest, Sveafallen. d, Hay field and Kallsjön Lake, Jämtland.
Illustration reduced.

Perf. 12¾x13½

2007, May 10		Litho. & Engr.
2564 A860	Booklet pane of 4	13.00
a.-d.	11k Any single	3.25 3.25
	Complete booklet, #2564 + 4 etiquettes	13.00

Wing of Papilio Machaon A861

Serpentine Die Cut 9¼ Vert. Syncopated
2007, Sept. 27   Litho. & Engr.
Self-Adhesive

| 2565 A861 | 50k multi | 15.50 15.50 |

Chocolate A862

Designs: No. 2566, Chocolate candy.
No. 2567: a, Chocolate bonbon with whipped cream and cherry. b, Chocolate-dipped strawberry. c, Cacao pod. d, Cup of cocoa.

Perf. 12½ Vert. Syncopated
2007, Sept. 27   Litho.
Coil Stamp

| 2566 A862 | (5.50k) multi | 1.75 1.75 |

Self-Adhesive
Booklet Stamps
Serpentine Die Cut 10 on 3 Sides
Size: 25x26mm

2567	Block of 4	7.00
a.-d.	A862 (5.50k) Any single	1.75 1.75
e.	Booklet pane of 10, 3 each #2567a-2567b, 2 each #2567c-2567d	17.50

Swedish Fashion — A863

No. 2568 — Clothing designs by: a, Lars Wallin. b, Ann-Sofie Back. c, Katja of Sweden. d, Behnaz Aram. e, Gunilla Pontén. f, Carin Rodebjer. g, Rohdi Heintz. h, Nakkna.

Litho. & Engr.
2007, Sept. 29   **Perf. 12½x13**

2568	Booklet pane of 8	14.00	
a.-h.	A863 5.50k Any single	1.75	1.75
	Complete booklet, #2568	14.00	
i.	Miniature sheet, 4 each #2568a, 2568g	15.50	—

No. 2568i sold for 49k.

Sami Culture — A864

Designs: No. 2569, Reindeer from ceremonial drum, country name in red. No. 2570, Silver button, country name in green. No. 2571, Glass dish, country name in blue.

2007, Nov. 8   **Perf. 12¾x13**

2569	A864 11k multi	4.00	4.00

Booklet Stamps
Perf. 12¾x13 on 3 Sides

2570	A864 11k multi	3.50	3.50
2571	A864 11k multi	3.50	3.50
a.	Booklet pane of 6, 2 each #2569-2571	21.00	—
	Complete booklet, #2571a	21.00	
	Nos. 2569-2571 (3)	11.00	11.00

No. 2569 was printed in sheets of 4 that sold for 49k. Examples of No. 2569 from booklet pane are perforated on 3 sides like Nos. 2570-2571. No. 2571a sold for 66k.

Souvenir Sheet

Astrid Lindgren (1907-2002), Writer — A865

Litho. & Engr.
2007, Nov. 8   **Perf. 12¾**

2572	A865 11k multi	10.00	10.00

See Germany No. 2462.

Christmas — A866

Scenes from children's stories by Astrid Lindgren: No. 2573, Pippi Longstocking rolling gingerbread dough on floor.

No. 2574: a, Houses in winter. b, Children in snowball fight. c, Lotta and father roping Christmas tree to sled. d, Children and horse-drawn sleigh.

Perf. 12½ Vert. Syncopated
2007, Nov. 8   **Litho.**
Coil Stamp

2573	A866 (5k) multi	1.60	1.60

Self-Adhesive
Booklet Stamps
Serpentine Die Cut 10 on 3 Sides

2574	Block of 4	6.50	
a.-d.	A866 (5k) Any single	1.60	1.60
e.	Booklet pane of 10, 3 each #2574a-2574b, 2 each #2574c-2574d	16.00	

Olof von Dalin (1708-63), Historian — A867

No. 2575: a, Illuminated letter "D." b, Illustration from first edition of *The Swedish Argus.* Illustration reduced.

Perf. 13¼ Vert. Syncopated
2008, Jan. 24   **Engr.**

2575	A867 Horiz. pair	7.00	7.00
a.-b.	11k Either single	3.50	3.50

Ingmar Bergman (1918-2007), Film Director — A868

Scene From "Fanny and Alexander" — A869

Perf. 13 Vert. Syncopated
2008, Jan. 24   **Engr.**

2576	A868 (5.50k) indigo	1.75	1.75

Souvenir Sheet
Litho. & Engr.
Perf. 12¾x13¼

2577	A869 11k multi	3.50	3.50

A book containing an imperf example of No. 2577, an imperf example of the litho portions of No. 2577 and an imperf example of the engraved portions of No. 2577 sold for 299k.

A870

Insects — A871

Designs: (4.80k), Bombus hypnorum (bee). (5k), Formica rufa (ants). (5.50k), Coccinella (ladybug).

2008, Jan. 24   **Litho.**   **Perf. 13½**

2578	A870 (5.50k) multi	2.00	2.00

Coil Stamps
Engr.
Perf. 12½ Vert. Syncopated
Size: 27x21mm

2579	A871 (4.80k) multi	1.50	1.50

Size: 28x24mm

2580	A871 (5k) multi	1.60	1.60

Litho.
Perf. 13¼ Vert. Syncopated
Size: 27x28mm

2581	A870 (5.50k) multi	1.75	1.75
	Nos. 2578-2581 (4)	6.85	6.85

Coil Stamp
Perf. 13¼ Horiz. Syncopated

2581A	A870 (5.50k) multi	6.00	6.00

No. 2578 was printed in a sheet of 6 that sold for 38k.

Dogs — A872

No. 2582: a, Lagotto Romagnolo (light green background). b, Saluki (pink background). c, Pug (yellow background). d, Great Dane (light blue background).

Serpentine Die Cut 10 on 3 Sides
2008, Jan. 24   **Litho.**

2582	A872 Block of 4	7.00	
a.-d.	(5.50k) Any single	1.75	1.75
e.	Booklet pane of 10, 3 each # 2582a, 2582c, 2 each #2582b, 2582d	17.50	

Trees — A873

No. 2583: a, Juniperus communis tree. b, Juniperus communis berries.

No. 2584: a, Betula pendula tree. b, Betula pendula catkins.
Illustration reduced.

Perf. 12 Vert. Syncopated
2008, Mar. 27   **Litho.**

2583	A873 Horiz. pair	.70	.70
a.-b.	1k Either single	.35	.35
2584	A873 Horiz. pair	1.40	1.40
a.-b.	2k Either single	.70	.70

Eyes and Hearts — A874

No. 2585: a, Eye with heart-shaped pupil. b, Eye with heart on cheek. c, Eye with hearts as eyebrow. d, Eye with hearts as teardrops. Illustration reduced.

Serpentine Die Cut 10 on 3 Sides
2008, Mar. 27
Self-Adhesive

2585	A874 Block of 4	7.50	
a.-d.	(5.50k) Any single	1.75	1.75
e.	Booklet pane of 10, 3 each #2585a-2585b, 2 each #2585c-2585d	19.00	

Europa — A875

No. 2586: a, Semicolon. b, Comma.

Perf. 12¾ on 3 Sides
2008, Mar. 27   **Litho. & Engr.**

2586	A875 Pair	7.50	7.50
a.-b.	11k Either single	3.75	3.75
c.	Booklet pane of 4, 2 each #2586a-2586b	15.00	
	Complete booklet, #2586c + 4 etiquettes	15.00	

Souvenir Sheet

Blakulla — A876

No. 2587: a, Woman riding backwards on ram. b, Bats.

2008, Mar. 27   **Perf. 12¾**

2587	A876 Sheet of 2	7.50	7.50
a.-b.	11k Either single	3.75	3.75

Butterfly Wings — A877

Wings of: 5k, Argynnis aglaja. 10k, Parnassius apollo.

Serpentine Die Cut 9¼ Vert. Syncopated
2008, May 15   **Litho. & Engr.**
Self-Adhesive

2588	A877 5k multi	1.75	1.75

Size: 24x34mm

2589	A877 10k multi	3.50	3.50

Food Served Outdoors — A878

Designs: No. 2590, Plate of crawfish, glasses of wine.

No. 2591: a, Strawberry cake, potatoes, cheese, pickled herring in sour cream and chives. b, Fish on grill. c, Coffee and pastries. d, Ham, bread, watermelon, tomatoes, wine.

Perf. 12¾ Vert. Syncopated
2008, May 15   **Litho.**
Coil Stamp

2590	A878 (5.50k) multi	1.90	1.90

Booklet Stamps
Self-Adhesive
Size: 34x23mm
Serpentine Die Cut 10 on 3 Sides

2591	Block of 4	7.75	
a.-d.	A878 (5.50k) Any single	1.90	1.90
e.	Booklet pane of 10, 3 each #2591a-2591b, 2 each #2591c-2591d	19.00	

Sailing Ships — A879

Designs: No. 2592, Tre Kronor af Stockholm.

No. 2593: a, Training ship Gunilla. b, Like #2592. c, Gratitude. d, Gladan and Falken.

Litho. & Engr.

2008, May 15   **Perf. 13½x13**
2592 A879 11k multi   4.25 4.25

Perf. 12½x12¾ on 3 Sides
2593   A879 Booklet pane of 4   15.00
a.-d. A879 11k Any single   3.75 3.75
    Complete booklet, #2593 + 4
    etiquettes   15.00

No. 2592 was printed in sheets of 4 that sold for 49k.

SEMI-POSTAL STAMPS

Type of 1872-91 Issues
Surcharged in Dark
Blue

Perf. 13x13½
1916, Dec. 21   **Wmk. 181**
B1	A5	5o + 5o on 2o org	5.50	7.75
B2	A5	5o + 5o on 3o yel brn	5.50	7.75
B3	A5	5o + 5o on 4o gray	5.50	7.75
B4	A5	5o + 5o on 5o brn	5.50	7.75
B5	A5	5o + 5o on 6o lilac	5.50	7.75
B6	A5	10o + 10o on 12o pale bl	5.50	7.75
B7	A5	10o + 10o on 20o red org	5.50	7.75
B8	A5	10o + 10o on 24o yel	5.50	7.75
B9	A5	10o + 10o on 30o brn	5.50	7.75
B10	A5	10o + 10o on 50o rose red	5.50	7.75
		Nos. B1-B10 (10)	55.00	77.50

The surtax on Nos. B1-B31 was for the militia. See note after No. B21.
For surcharges see Nos. B22-B31.

No. 66 Surcharged
in Dark Blue

1916, Dec. 21   **Wmk. 180**   **Perf. 13**
B11 A12 10o + 4.90k on 5k   150.00 *325.00*

Nos. J12-J22
Surcharged in Dark
Blue

1916, Dec. 21   **Unwmk.**   **Perf. 13**
B12	D1	5o + 5o on 1o	18.50	10.50
B13	D1	5o + 5o on 3o	5.00	5.50
B14	D1	5o + 5o on 5o	8.25	5.50
B15	D1	5o + 10o on 6o	5.00	6.00
B16	D1	5o + 15o on 12o	42.50	27.50
B17	D1	10o + 20o on 20o	15.00	21.00
B18	D1	10o + 40o on 24o	60.00	82.50
B19	D1	10o + 20o on 30o	5.50	6.00
B20	D1	10o + 40o on 50o	22.50	37.50
B21	D1	10o + 90o on 1kr	140.00	375.00
		Nos. B12-B21 (10)	322.25	577.00

The surtax on Nos. B12-B21 is indicated not in figures, but in words at bottom of surcharge: Fem, 5; Tio, 10; Femton, 15; Tjugo, 20; Fyrtio, 40; Nittio, 90.

Nos. B1-B10
Surcharged

1918, Dec. 18   **Wmk. 181**
B22	A5	7o + 3o on #B1	8.75	8.25
B23	A5	7o + 3o on #B2	2.75	1.25
B24	A5	7o + 3o on #B3	2.75	1.25
B25	A5	7o + 3o on #B4	2.75	1.25
B26	A5	7o + 3o on #B5	2.75	1.25
B27	A5	12o + 8o on #B6	2.75	1.25
B28	A5	12o + 8o on #B7	2.75	1.25
B29	A5	12o + 8o on #B8	2.75	1.25

B30	A5	12o + 8o on #B9	2.75	1.25
B31	A5	12o + 8o on #B10	2.75	1.25
		Nos. B22-B31 (10)	33.50	19.50

The 12o+8o surcharge exists on Nos. B1-B5 and the 7o+3o surcharge exists on Nos. B6-B10. Value, each $72.50.
Nos. B24, B26, B28 and B30 exist with surcharge inverted. Value unused, each $140.

SP1

King Gustaf V — SP2

Unwmk.
1928, June 16   **Engr.**   **Perf. 10**
B32	SP1	5o (+ 5o) yel grn	2.75	6.00
B33	SP1	10o (+ 5o) dk vio	2.75	6.00
B34	SP1	15o (+ 5o) car	2.75	4.50
		Complete booklet, pane of 8 ea. #B32, B33, B34	275.00	
B35	SP1	20o (+ 5o) org	4.75	2.75
B36	SP1	25o (+ 5o) dk bl	4.75	3.25
		Nos. B32-B36 (5)	17.75	22.50
		Set, never hinged	27.50	

70th birthday of King Gustaf V. The surtax was used for anti-cancer work.

> **Catalogue values for unused stamps in this section, from this point to the end of the section, are for Never Hinged items.**

1948, June 16   **Perf. 12½ Vertically**
B37	SP2	10o + 10o green	.55	.60
B38	SP2	20o + 10o red	.80	.75
B39	SP2	30o + 10o ultra	.55	.60

Perf. 12½ on 3 Sides
B40	SP2	10o + 10o green	.65	.70
a.		Booklet pane of 20	10.00	
B41	SP2	20o + 10o red	.80	.90
a.		Booklet pane of 20	12.00	
		Nos. B37-B41 (5)	3.35	3.55

90th anniv. of the birth of King Gustaf V. The surtax provided aid for Swedish youth.

King Gustaf VI
Adolf — SP3

Henri
Dunant — SP4

1952, Nov. 11   **Perf. 12½ Horiz.**
B42	SP3	10o + 10o green	.35	.40
B43	SP3	25o + 10o car rose	.35	.40
B44	SP3	40o + 10o ultra	.65	.60

Perf. 12½ on 3 Sides
B45	SP3	10o + 10o green	.35	.40
a.		Booklet pane of 20	6.50	
B46	SP3	25o + 10o car rose	.35	.40
a.		Booklet pane of 20	7.00	
		Nos. B42-B46 (5)	2.05	2.20

70th birthday of King Gustaf VI Adolf. The surtax was used to promote Swedish culture.

1959, May 8   **Perf. 12½ Horizontally**
B47	SP4	30o + 10o red	.50	.75

Perf. 12½ on 3 Sides
B48	SP4	30o + 10o red	1.00	1.25
a.		Booklet pane of 20	18.00	

Centenary of the Red Cross idea. The surtax went to the Swedish Red Cross.

King Gustav VI Adolf — SP5

Perf. 12½ Vertically
1962, Nov. 10   **Engr.**   **Unwmk.**
Size: 58x24mm
B49	SP5	20o + 10o brown	.30	.30
B50	SP5	35o + 10o blue	.30	.30

Perf. 12½ Horizontally
B51	SP5	20o + 10o brown	.30	.40
a.		Booklet pane of 10	3.00	
B52	SP5	35o + 10o blue	.30	.40
a.		Booklet pane of 10	3.00	
		Nos. B49-B52 (4)	1.20	1.40

80th birthday of King Gustaf VI Adolf. The surtax went to the King Gustaf VI Adolf 80th anniv. Foundation for Swedish Cultural Activities.

Ship Types of Regular Issues
Imprint: "1966"

Designs (Ships): 10o, "The Lion of Smaland." 15o, "Kalmar Nyckel." 20o, Old Sailing Packet. 25o, Mail Paddle Steamship. 30o, "Kung Karl." 40o, Stern of "Amphion."

1966, Nov. 15   **Perf. 12½ on 3 Sides**
B53	A76	10o vermilion	.30	.45
B54	A50	15o vermilion	.30	.45
B55	A38	20o slate grn	.30	.45
B56	A39	25o ultra	.20	.20
B57	A76	30o vermilion	.30	.55
B58	A76	40o vermilion	.30	.55
a.		Bkt. pane. #B53-B54, B57-B58, 2 #B55, 4 #B56	2.75	
		Nos. B53-B58 (6)	1.70	2.65

The booklet sold for 3.50k and the surtax of 1.15k went to the National Cancer Fund.

AIR POST STAMPS

Official Stamps
Surcharged in Dark
Blue

1920, Sept. 17   **Wmk. 181**   **Perf. 13**
C1	O3	10o on 3o brn	2.75	7.75
a.		Inverted surcharge	275.00	700.00
C2	O3	20o on 2o org	4.50	11.00
a.		Inverted surcharge	275.00	700.00
C3	O3	50o on 4o vio	20.00	25.00
a.		Inverted surcharge	275.00	700.00
		Nos. C1-C3 (3)	27.25	43.75
		Set, never hinged	55.00	

Wmk. 180
C4	O3	20o on 2o org	2,250.	
C5	O3	50o on 4o vio	160.00	*350.00*

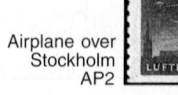

Airplane over
Stockholm
AP2

Perf. 10 Vertically
1930, May 9   **Engr.**   **Unwmk.**
C6	AP2	10o deep blue	.20	.60
C7	AP2	50o dark violet	.65	1.75
		Set, never hinged	1.50	

Flying
Swans — AP3

1942-53   **Perf. 12½ on 3 Sides**
C8	AP3	20k brt ultra ('53)	4.50	.65
		Never hinged	7.00	
a.		Bkt. pane of 20 ('53)	725.00	
b.		Bkt. pane of 10 ('68)	65.00	

c.	Perf. on 4 sides	75.00	13.50
	Never hinged	140.00	
d.	As "c," bkt. pane of 10	1,350.	

Issued: #C8c, May 4, 1942; #C8, July 7.

POSTAGE DUE STAMPS

D1

1874   **Unwmk.**   **Typo.**   **Perf. 14**
J1	D1	1o black	50.00	40.00
J2	D1	3o rose	50.00	40.00
J3	D1	5o brown	50.00	35.00
J4	D1	6o yellow	100.00	77.50
J5	D1	12o pale red	7.75	5.25
J6	D1	20o blue	62.50	40.00
J7	D1	24o violet	450.00	260.00
J8	D1	24o gray	55.00	52.50
J9	D1	30o dk grn	52.50	40.00
J10	D1	50o brown	175.00	57.50
J11	D1	1k blue & bister	225.00	72.50
		Nos. J1-J11 (11)	1,277.	720.25

1877-86   **Perf. 13**
J12	D1	1o black ('80)	2.75	4.00
J13	D1	3o rose	6.25	7.25
J14	D1	5o brown	4.50	4.50
J15	D1	6o yellow	4.50	4.50
a.		Printed on both sides	1,000.	
J16	D1	12o pale red ('82)	14.50	17.00
J17	D1	20o pale blue ('78)	5.25	4.50
J18	D1	24o red lilac ('86)	26.00	29.00
a.		24o violet ('84)	26.00	29.00
J19	D1	24o gray lil ('82)	125.00	150.00
J20	D1	30o yellow green	6.50	4.50
J21	D1	50o yellow brown	10.50	5.75
J22	D1	1k blue & bister	30.00	17.50
		Nos. J12-J22 (11)	235.75	248.50

Nos. J12-J17, J19-J22 exist imperf. Value, pairs, each $400.
For surcharges see Nos. B12-B21.

STAMPS FOR CITY POSTAGE

S1

Perf. 14x13½
1856-62   **Typo.**   **Unwmk.**
LX1	S1	(1sk or 3o) blk	950.00	450.00
LX2	S1	(3o) bis brn ('62)	600.00	475.00

From 1856 to 1858 No. LX1 was sold at 1sk, from 1858 to 1862 at 3o. The paper of the 1sk black is thin while the paper of the 3o black is medium thick.
No. LX1 was reprinted three times with perf. 14, once with perf. 13. No. LX2 was reprinted once with each perforation. Value of lowest-cost Perf. 14 reprints, $250 each. Perf. 13, $175 each.

OFFICIAL STAMPS

O1

O3

1874-77   **Unwmk.**   **Typo.**   **Perf. 14**
O1	O1	3o bister	72.50	40.00
O2	O1	4o gray ('77)	250.00	70.00
O3	O1	5o yel green	140.00	52.50
O4	O1	6o lilac	250.00	65.00
O5	O1	6o gray	525.00	175.00
O6	O1	12o blue	160.00	21.00

O7	O1	20o pale red	950.00	90.00
O8	O1	24o yellow	950.00	20.00
a.		24o orange	950.00	22.50
O9	O1	30o pale brn	425.00	35.00
O10	O1	50o rose	575.00	125.00
O11	O1	1k bl & bis	1,650.	65.00
		Nos. O1-O11 (11)	5,947.	740.00

Imperf., Pairs

O1a	O1	3o	575.
O2a	O1	4o	575.
O3a	O1	5o	900.
O4a	O1	6o	900.
O6a	O1	12o	575.
O7a	O1	20o	2,350.
O8b	O1	24o	1,800.
O9a	O1	30o	1,050.
O10a	O1	50o	1,300.
O11a	O1	1k	3,250.

1881-95   Perf. 13

O12	O1	2o org ('91)	1.40	2.00
O13	O1	3o bis brn	1.40	2.25
O14	O1	4o gray blk ('93)	2.50	.70
a.		4o gray ('82)	16.00	2.25
O15	O1	5o grn ('84)	5.25	.60
O16	O1	6o red lil ('82)	40.00	60.00
a.		6o lilac ('81)	45.00	65.00
O17	O1	10o car ('95)	3.00	.20
b.		10o rose ('85)	45.00	1.25
O18	O1	12o blue	57.50	21.00
O19	O1	20o ver ('82)	200.00	2.50
O20	O1	20o dk bl ('91)	5.75	.60
O21	O1	24o yellow	72.50	22.50
a.		24o orange	65.00	22.50
O22	O1	30o brown	26.00	.70
O23	O1	50o pale rose	140.00	22.50
O24	O1	50o pale gray ('93)	18.00	1.90
O25	O1	1k dk bl & yel brn	9.00	6.50
		Nos. O12-O25 (14)	582.30	143.95

Imperf., Pairs

O12a	O1	2o	250.00
O17a	O1	10o No. O17	300.00
c.		No. O17b	300.00
O20a	O1	20o	45.00
O24a	O1	50o	250.00

Surcharged in Dark Blue

1889

O26	O1	10o on 12o blue	11.50	15.00
a.		Inverted surcharge	1,000.	2,250.
b.		Perf. 14	—	3,500.
O27	O1	10o on 24o yel	15.00	22.00
a.		Inverted surcharge	3,000.	2,500.
b.		Perf. 14	3,000.	3,000.

1910-12   Wmk. 180   Typo.

O28	O3	1o black	.20	.45
O29	O3	2o orange	1.40	3.00
O30	O3	4o pale violet	2.10	4.00
O31	O3	5o green	.65	1.10
O32	O3	8o claret	.65	1.10
O33	O3	10o red	12.00	.70
O34	O3	15o red brown	1.10	.85
O35	O3	20o deep blue	8.25	1.60
O36	O3	25o red orange	8.25	2.10
O37	O3	30o chocolate	8.00	3.25
O38	O3	50o gray	8.25	3.25
O39	O3	1k black, *yellow*	7.75	7.75
O40	O3	5k claret, *yellow*	11.00	4.00
		Nos. O28-O40 (13)	69.60	33.15

1910-19   Wmk. Wavy Lines (181)

O41	O3	1o black	3.00	*3.25*
O42	O3	2o orange	.30	*.40*
O43	O3	3o pale brown	.40	*1.00*
O44	O3	4o pale violet	.30	*.40*
O45	O3	5o green	.30	*.40*
O46	O3	7o gray green	.45	*1.25*
O47	O3	8o rose	20.00	*27.50*
O48	O3	10o red	.30	.20
O49	O3	12o rose red	.30	.30
O50	O3	15o org brown	.30	.30
O51	O3	20o deep blue	.45	.30
O52	O3	25o orange	1.00	.50
O53	O3	30o chocolate	.55	.55
O54	O3	35o dark violet	.85	*1.00*
O55	O3	50o gray	3.25	2.10
		Nos. O41-O55 (15)	31.75	39.45

For surcharges see Nos. C1-C5.

Use of official stamps ceased on 7/1/20.

PARCEL POST STAMPS

Regular Issue of 1914
Surcharged

1917   Wmk. 180   *Perf. 13*

Q1	A14	1.98k on 5k claret, *yel*	1.40	*5.25*
Q2	A14	2.12k on 5k claret, *yel*	1.40	*5.25*

SWITZERLAND

'swit-sər-lənd

(Helvetia)

LOCATION — Central Europe, between France, Germany and Italy
GOVT. — Republic
AREA — 15,943 sq. mi.
POP. — 7,062,400 (1998 est.)
CAPITAL — Bern

100 Rappen or Centimes = 1 Franc

Catalogue values for unused stamps in this country are for Never Hinged items, beginning with Scott 365 in the regular postage section, Scott B272 in the semi-postal section, Scott C46 in the airpost section, Scott CB1 in the airpost semi-postal section, and Scott 3O94, 4O40, 5O26, 7O31, 8O1, 9O1, 10O1, 11O1, 12O1 in the official sections.

Watermarks

Wmk. 182 — Cross in Oval   Wmk. 183 — Swiss Cross

Watermark 182 is not a true watermark, having been impressed after the paper was manufactured. There are two types:
Type 1 — width just under 9mm.
Type 2 — width just under 8½mm.
There are many other differences of ¹⁄₁₀mm to ⅛mm.

CANTONAL ADMINISTRATION

Unused values of Nos. 1L1-3L1 are for stamps without gum.
Counterfeit and repaired copies of Nos. 1L1-3L1 abound.

Zurich

Numerals of Value — A1   A2

1843   Unwmk.   Litho.   Imperf.
Red Vertical Lines
1L1	A1	4r black	20,000.	17,500.
1L2	A2	6r black	6,500.	1,750.

1846   Red Horizontal Lines
1L3	A1	4r black	17,500.	22,500.
1L4	A2	6r black	1,900.	1,600.

Five varieties of each value.

Reprints of the Zurich stamps show signs of wear and lack the red lines. Values 4r, $5,500; 6r, $1,800.

Coat of Arms — A3

1850   Unwmk.   Imperf.
1L5	A3	2½r black & red	6,500.	4,000.

No. 1L5 has separation designs in the margins between stamps as shown. Values are for stamps showing part of the separation design on all four sides.

Geneva

Coat of Arms — A4

1843   Unwmk.   Litho.   Imperf.
2L1	A4	10c blk, *yel grn*	60,000.	40,000.
a.		Either half	22,500.	9,000.
b.		Stamp composed of right half at left & left half at right	85,000.	62,500.

A5   A6

1845-48
2L2	A5	5c blk, *yel grn*	2,750.	1,750.
2L3	A6	5c blk, *yel grn* ('46)	2,100.	1,750.
2L4	A6	5c blk, *dk grn* ('48)	4,000.	3,000.

Coat of A7   Arms — A8

1849-50
2L5	A7	4c black & red	35,000.	21,000.
2L6	A7	5c blk & red ('50)	2,500.	1,750.

1851
2L7	A8	5c black & red	9,750.	4,000.

ENVELOPE STAMP USED AS ADHESIVE

E1

1847   Unwmk.   Imperf.
2LU1	E1	5c yel grn, see footnote	21,000.

Authorized for use from Feb. 19, 1847. Value is for cut-out stamp used on folded letters. Value of unused envelope (1846) or cut-

---

out, from $400. Value of used cut-out off cover, $2,800.

Basel

Dove of Basel — A9

Typo. & Embossed
1845   Unwmk.   Imperf.
3L1	A9	2½r blk, crim & bl	14,000.	12,500.

Proofs are black, vermilion and green. Value, $3,600.

FEDERAL ADMINISTRATION

Due to its tendency to damage the paper and/or the color of the stamps, the gum on Nos. 1-40 very often is removed. Unused values for Nos. 1-40 are for stamps without gum. Stamps with original gum sell for about the same prices.

A10   A11

1850   Unwmk.   Litho.   Imperf.
Full Black Frame Around Cross
1	A10	2½r black & red	3,000.	1,600.
2	A11	2½r black & red	2,500.	1,500.

Without Frame Around Cross
3	A10	2½r black & red	5,750.	2,750.
4	A11	2½r blk & red	42,500.	25,000.

Forty types of each.

A12   A13

1850
Full Black Frame Around Cross
5	A12	5r dk bl, blk & red	5,000.	1,250.
a.		5r dk grayish bl, blk & red	5,000.	1,250.
6	A13	10r yel, blk & red		110,000.

No. 6 used, with only parts of frame around cross showing, value $175 to $900.
Beware of copies of Nos. 7-8 with faked frame added.

Without Frame Around Cross
7	A12	5r lt bl, blk & red	1,750.	500.00
a.		5r dp bl, blk & red	3,500.	1,000.
b.		5r pur bl, blk & red	—	5,500.
c.		5r grnsh bl, blk & red	2,000.	575.00

8	A13	10r yel, blk & red	925.00	125.00
a.		10r buff, blk & red	1,275.	225.00
b.		10r org yel, blk & red	1,250.	250.00
c.		Half used as 5r on cover		12,500.

1851
Full Blue Frame Around Cross
9	A12	5r light blue & red	140,000.

No. 9 used, with only parts of frame around cross showing, value $180 to $3,750.
Beware of copies of No. 10 with faked frame added.

Without Frame Around Cross
10	A12	5r lt blue & red	575.00	125.00

Forty types of each.

A14   A15

A16

1852
Vermilion Frame Around Cross
11	A14	15r vermilion	15,000.	700.00
12	A15	15r vermilion	2,500.	125.00
13	A16	15c vermilion	14,000.	1,000.

Ten types of each.
On October 1st, 1854, all stamps of the preceding issues were declared obsolete.

Helvetia — A17

1854   Embossed.   Unwmk.
Thin Paper, Fine Impressions
Emerald Silk Threads
14	A17	5r orange brn	8,000.	1,600.
15	A17	5r red brown	550.00	140.00
16	A17	10r blue	775.00	80.00
17	A17	15r carmine rose	1,250.	175.00
a.		15r pale rose	1,250.	175.00
18	A17	40r pale yel grn	10,000.	1,250.
19	A17	40r yellow grn	1,250.	275.00

1854-55
Emerald Silk Threads
Medium Thick Paper
Fine Impressions
20	A17	5r pale yel brn	650.00	150.00
21	A17	10r blue	1,600.	110.00
22	A17	15r rose	925.00	100.00
23	A17	20r pale orange	1,400.	175.00

1855-57
Colored Silk Threads
Medium Thick Paper
Fine to Rough Impressions

24	A17	5r yel brn (yel)	575.00	100.00
25	A17	5r dk brown (blk)	325.00	35.00
26	A17	10r mlky bl (red)	925.00	175.00
27	A17	10r blue (car)	300.00	45.00
a.		Thin paper	5,000.	425.00
28	A17	15r rose (bl)	550.00	65.00
29	A17	40r yel grn (mar)	1,000.	100.00
30	A17	1fr lav (blk)	1,400.	925.00
31	A17	1fr lav (yel)	1,400.	925.00
a.		Thin paper	20,000.	7,250.

1857
Thin (Emergency) Paper
Rough Impressions
Green Silk Threads

32	A17	5r pale gray brn	4,500.	1,000.
32A	A17	10r blue	6,500.	925.
33	A17	15r pale dl rose	3,250.	325.
34	A17	20r pale dl org	3,250.	250.

1858-62
Thick Ordinary Paper
Rough Impressions
Green Silk Threads

35	A17	2r gray	250.00	550.00
a.		One and one-half used as 3r on newspaper or wrapper		14,000.
c.		Half used as 1r on cover		
36	A17	5r brown	225.00	20.00
a.		5r black brown	275.00	40.00
b.		Half used as 2r on cover		1,400.
37	A17	10r dark blue	240.00	20.00
a.		Half used as 5r on cover		7,250.
38	A17	15r dark rose	375.00	65.00
39	A17	20r dark orange	475.00	70.00
a.		Half used as 10r on cover		17,500.
40	A17	40r dk yellow grn	450.00	85.00
a.		Half used as 20r on cover		27,500.
		Nos. 35-40 (6)	2,015.	810.00

Helvetia — A18

Double embossing errors, Nos. 43c, 44a, 55b, 60a, 61a, 61b, 67b, have the design impressed twice. These do not refer to the "embossed" watermark.

Embossed
1862-64   Wmk. 182   Perf. 11½
White Wove Paper

41	A18	2c gray	140.00	4.25
42	A18	3c black	14.50	115.00
43	A18	5c dark brown	3.50	.85
a.		5c bister brown	110.00	6.75
b.		5c gray brown	110.00	32.50
c.		Dbl. embossing, one invtd.	4,000.	425.00
d.		Double impression of lower left "5"		1,450.
44	A18	10c blue	725.00	.85
a.		Dbl. embossing, one invtd.		8,000.
45	A18	20c orange	2.50	2.75
a.		20c yellow orange	350.00	2.90
46	A18	30c vermilion	1,700.	40.00
47	A18	40c green	1,600.	65.00
48	A18	60c bronze	1,450.	150.00
50	A18	1fr gold	20.00	120.00
a.		1fr yellowish bronze ('64)	1,450.	425.00

1867-78

52	A18	2c bister brown	2.50	1.80
a.		2c red brown	675.00	275.00
53	A18	10c carmine	3.50	1.00
54	A18	15c lemon	4.25	42.50
55	A18	25c blue green	1.80	4.25
a.		25c yellow green	60.00	40.00
b.		Dbl. embossing, one invtd.		575.00
56	A18	30c ultra	575.00	10.00
a.		30c blue	2,000.	250.00
58	A18	40c gray	1.80	160.00
59	A18	50c violet	57.50	65.00
		Nos. 52-59 (7)	646.35	284.55

1881
Granite Paper

60	A18	2c bister	.55	25.00
a.		Dbl. embossing, one invtd.	350.00	
61	A18	5c brown	.55	13.00
a.		Dbl. embossing, one invtd.	30.00	425.00
b.		Double embossing of lower left "5"		1,150.

62	A18	10c rose	5.00	10.50
63	A18	15c lemon	10.50	475.00
64	A18	20c orange	.55	160.00
65	A18	25c green	.55	105.00
66	A18	40c gray	1.80	3,400.
67	A18	50c deep violet	18.00	575.00
b.		Dbl. embossing, one invtd.	250.00	4,500.
68	A18	1fr gold	21.50	1,300.

The granite paper contains fragments of blue and red silk threads.

Forged or backdated cancellations are found frequently on Nos. 42, 50, 54, 58 and 60-68.

All stamps of the preceding issues were declared obsolete on October 1st, 1883. Some of the remainders of Nos. 41-68 were overprinted "AUSSER KURS" (Obsolete) diagonally in black.

Numeral — A19

1882-99   Typo.   Perf. 11½
Granite Paper

69	A19	2c bister	1.80	.60
70	A19	3c gray brown	3.00	8.50
a.		3c gray	47.50	45.00
71	A19	5c maroon	18.00	.60
a.		Tête bêche pair		
72	A19	5c deep grn ('99)	8.00	.60
73	A19	10c red	7.25	.60
a.		10c carmine	55.00	.90
b.		10c light rose	250.00	5.00
74	A19	12c ultra	8.00	.60
a.		12c chalky blue	22.50	19.00
b.		12c greenish blue	450.00	
75	A19	15c yellow	140.00	29.00
a.		15c orange	14,500.	4,000.
b.		Tête bêche pair		
76	A19	15c violet ('89)	45.00	2.25
		Nos. 69-76 (8)	231.05	42.75

Nos. 69-74, 76 are watermark type 1. Nos. 70a, 73a-73b, 75-75a are type 2.

1882
White Paper

77	A19	2c bister	375.00	300.00
78	A19	5c maroon	825.00	100.00
79	A19	10c rose	2,100.	70.00
80	A19	12c chalky blue	150.00	26.00
81	A19	15c yellow	225.00	250.00

Watermark type 1.
See Nos. 113-118.

Helvetia (Large numerals) A20	Helvetia (Small numerals) A21

1882-1904   Engr.   Perf. 11½ - 11¾

82	A20	20c orange	150.00	5.50
83	A20	25c green	82.50	3.00
95b	A20	30c brown	—	16,750.
84	A20	40c gray	120.00	40.00
85	A21	40c gray ('04)	37.50	21.00
86	A20	50c blue	125.00	21.00
87	A20	1fr claret	210.00	6.00
88	A20	3fr yel brn ('91)	180.00	19.00

1888   Perf. 9½

89	A20	20c orange	800.00	100.00
90	A20	25c yellow grn	150.00	15.00
91	A20	40c gray	800.00	650.00
92	A20	50c blue	1,100.	325.00
93	A20	1fr claret	850.00	87.50

Values for Nos. 89-93 are for well-centered stamps with slightly uneven perforations. Stamps missing perforations sell for much less.

1891-99   Perf. 11½x11

82a	A20	20c orange	47.50	1.75
83a	A20	25c green	10.00	1.75
94	A20	25c blue ('99)	11.00	1.75
95	A20	30c red brn ('92)	30.00	1.90
84a	A20	40c gray	67.50	4.75
86a	A20	50c blue	40.00	11.00
96	A20	50c green ('99)	42.50	21.00
87a	A20	1fr claret	37.50	4.00
97	A20	1fr carmine	80.00	8.00
88a	A20	3fr yellow brown	135.00	25.00

1901-03   Perf. 11½x12

82b	A20	20c orange	25.00	1.60
94a	A20	25c blue	12.00	1.10
95a	A20	30c red brown	35.00	1.90
84b	A20	40c gray	75.00	30.00

96a	A20	50c green	60.00	7.00
87b	A20	1fr claret	2,000.	250.00
97a	A20	1fr carmine ('03)	375.00	32.50
88b	A20	3fr yellow brown	180.00	19.00

Numerous retouches and plate flaws exist on all values of this issue.

Nos. 82-88 have wmk. type 1 and are ½mm taller (paper size) than Nos. 82b-88b, which have wmk. type 2.

See Nos. 105-112, 119-125.

UPU Allegory — A22

1900   Perf. 11½

98	A22	5c gray green	30.00	1.60
99	A22	10c carmine rose	10.00	1.60
100	A22	25c blue	25.00	30.00
		Nos. 98-100 (3)	65.00	33.20

Re-engraved

101	A22	5c gray green	3.00	1.50
102	A22	10c carmine rose	45.00	35.00
103	A22	25c blue	700.00	10,000.

Universal Postal Union, 25th anniv.

The impression of the re-engraved stamps is much clearer, especially in the horizontally lined background. The figures of value are lined instead of being solid.

Helvetia Types of 1882-1904
1905   Wmk. 183   Perf. 11½x11
White Paper

105	A20	20c orange	3.75	2.25
106	A20	25c blue	5.00	9.00
107	A20	30c brown	5.00	2.00
108a	A21	40c gray	90.00	140.00
109	A20	50c green	30.00	7.25
110	A20	1fr carmine	77.50	3.00
111	A20	3fr yellow brn	200.00	110.00

Some clichés in the plates of the 20c, 25c, 30c, 50c and 3fr have been retouched.

1906   Re-engraved   Perf. 11½x11

112	A20	25c pale blue	6.00	2.25

In the re-engraved stamp the stars are larger and the background below "FRANCO" is of horiz. or horiz. and vert. crossed lines, instead of horiz. and curved lines.

1906   Perf. 11½

112a	A20	25c pale blue	85.00	7.50
108	A21	40c gray	27.50	11.00

1907   Perf. 11½x12

105a	A20	20c orange	6.00	6.00
109a	A20	50c green	37.50	12.00
110a	A20	1fr carmine	100.00	9.00
111a	A20	3fr yellow brown	240.00	190.00

Numeral Type of 1882-99
1905   Typo.   Perf. 11½
Granite Paper

113	A19	2c dull bister	4.25	1.90
114	A19	3c gray brown	4.50	60.00
115	A19	5c green	4.25	.50
116	A19	10c scarlet	4.25	.50
117	A19	12c ultra	5.50	2.00
118	A19	15c brown vio	60.00	13.50
		Nos. 113-118 (6)	82.75	78.40

Helvetia Types of 1882-1904
1907   Engr.   Perf. 11½x12
Granite Paper

119	A20	20c orange	2.25	3.75
120	A20	25c blue	7.75	10.00
121	A20	30c red brown	6.50	17.50
122	A20	40c gray	21.00	45.00
a.		Helvetia without diadem	300.00	1,050.
123	A20	50c gray green	5.50	17.50
124	A21	1fr carmine	19.00	9.25
125a	A20	3fr yellow brown		10,500.

There are retouches and plate flaws on all values.

Perf. 11½x11

120a	A20	25c deep blue	10.00	6.50
121a	A20	30c red brown	140.00	325.00
122b	A21	40c gray		13,000.
124a	A20	1fr carmine		10,000.
125	A20	3fr yel brn	100.00	65.00

William Tell's Son — A23

Helvetia
A24   A25

1907-25   Typo.   Perf. 11½
Granite Paper

126	A23	2c pale bister	.30	.55
127	A23	3c lilac brn	.25	10.00
128	A23	5c yellow grn	2.25	.50
129	A24	10c rose red	1.50	.50
130	A24	12c ocher	.30	3.50
131	A24	15c red vio	3.00	13.00
132	A25	20c red & yel ('08)	2.25	1.00
133	A25	25c dp blue ('08)	1.90	.65
a.		Tête bêche pair	17.00	55.00
134	A25	30c yel brn & pale grn ('08)	1.60	.50
135	A25	35c yel brn & yel ('08)	1.90	1.40
136	A25	40c red vio & yel ('08)	12.50	1.00
a.		Designer's name in full on the rock ('08)	6.00	82.50
137	A25	40c deep blue ('22)	1.75	.50
		40c light blue ('21)	5.50	1.90
138	A25	40c red vio & grn ('25)	25.00	.50
139	A25	50c dp grn & pale grn ('08)	11.00	.50
140	A25	60c brn org & buff ('08)	9.25	.65
141	A25	70c dk brn & buff ('08)	55.00	17.00
142	A25	70c vio & buff ('24)	14.50	2.25
143	A25	80c slate & buff ('15)	9.75	1.10

144	A25	1fr dp cl & pale grn ('08)	7.00	.55
145	A25	3fr bis & yel ('08)	275.00	2.10
		Nos. 126-145 (20)	436.00	57.75

No. 136 has two leaves and "CL" below sword hilt. No. 136a has three leaves and designer's full name below hilt.

For surcharges and overprints see Nos. 189, 199, O10-O13, O15, 1O6-1O8, 1O14-1O16, 2O18-2O26, 3O14-3O22.

1933
With Grilled Gum

135a	A25	35c yel grn & yel	1.40	12.50
138a	A25	40c red vio & grn	32.50	1.50
139a	A25	50c dp grn & pale grn	9.00	1.50
140a	A25	60c brn org & buff	12.00	1.50
142a	A25	70c vio & buff	17.50	3.75
143a	A25	80c slate & buff	13.00	4.25
144a	A25	1fr dp cl & pale grn	19.00	6.50
		Nos. 135a-144a (7)	104.40	31.50

"Grilled" Gum

In 1930-44 many Swiss stamps were treated with a light grilling process, applied with the gumming to counteract the tendency to curl. It resembles a faint grill of vertical and horizontal ribs covering the entire back of the stamp, and can be seen after the gum has been removed. Listings of the grilled gum varieties begin with No. 135a.

William Tell's Son — A26

Bow-string in front of stock

1909
Perf. 11½, 12
Granite Paper

146	A26	2c bister	.25	1.40
a.		Tête bêche pair	3.25	17.50
147	A26	3c dark violet	.25	14.00
148	A26	5c green	3.75	.20
a.		Tête bêche pair	14.00	50.00
		Nos. 146-148 (3)	4.25	15.60

See Nos. 149-163. For surcharges and overprints see Nos. 186, 193-195, 207-208, 1O1-1O3, 1O9-1O11, 2O1-2O7, 3O1-3O5.

First Redrawing

Bow-string behind stock. Thin loop above crossbow. Letters of "HELVETIA" without serifs.

1910-17
Granite Paper

149	A26	2c bister ('10)	8.75	8.00
150	A26	3c dk violet ('10)	.20	.20
a.		Tête bêche pair	2.75	2.75
b.		Booklet pane of 6	12.50	
151	A26	3c brown org ('17)	.20	.20
a.		Tête bêche pair	8.25	11.00
152	A26	5c green ('10)	21.00	6.50
a.		Tête bêche pair	92.50	175.00
		Nos. 149-152 (4)	30.15	14.90

Second Redrawing

Bow-string behind stock. Thick loop above crossbow. Letters of "HELVETIA" have serifs.
7½ CENTIMES:
Type I — Top of "7" is ½mm thick. The "1" of "½" has only traces of serifs. The two base plates of the statue are of even thickness.
Type II — Top of "7" is 1mm thick. The "1" of "½" has distinct serifs. The upper base plate is thinner than the lower.

1911-30
Granite Paper

153	A26	2c bister ('11)	.20	.20
a.		Tête bêche pair	3.25	1.60
154	A26	2½c claret ('18)	.20	1.10
155	A26	2½c ol, buff ('28)	.55	2.10
156	A26	3c ultra, buff ('30)	2.75	6.00
157	A26	5c green ('11)	1.75	.20
a.		Tête bêche pair	5.50	10.00
158	A26	5c org, buff ('21)	.20	.20
a.		Bklt. pane of 6 (5 #158, 168)	14.00	47.50

159	A26	5c gray vio, buff ('24)	.20	.20
a.		Bklt. pane of 6 (5 #159, 168)	6.50	19.00
160	A26	5c red vio, buff ('27)	.20	.20
a.		Bklt. pane 6 (5 #160, 168)	30.00	65.00
161	A26	5c dk grn, buff ('30)	.30	.25
a.		Bklt. pane 6 (5 #161, 169)	27.50	70.00
162	A26	7½c gray (I) ('18)	1.10	.20
a.		Tête bêche pair (I)	13.00	45.00
c.		7½c slate (II)	4.50	2.75
163	A26	7½c dp grn, buff (I) ('28)	.30	3.25
		Nos. 153-163 (11)	7.75	13.90

1933
With Grilled Gum

156a	A26	3c ultra, buff	4.75	17.50
161b	A26	5c dark green, buff	.55	5.00

Helvetia
A27

William Tell
A28

1909
Granite Paper

164	A27	10c carmine	.60	.40
a.		Tête bêche pair	2.25	6.00
165	A27	12c bister brn	.85	.40
166	A27	15c red violet	26.00	1.10
		Nos. 164-166 (3)	27.45	1.90

For surcharge see No. 187.

1914-30　Granite Paper　Perf. 11½

TEN CENTIMES:
Type I — Bust 16½mm high. "HELVETIA" 15½mm wide. Cross bar of "H" at middle of the letter.
Type II — Bust 15mm high. "HELVETIA" 15mm wide. Cross bar of "H" above middle of the letter.

167	A28	10c red, buff (type II)	.75	.20
a.		10c red, buff (type I)	2.50	26.00
b.		Tête bêche pair (II)	3.25	4.25
d.		Bklt. pane, #172, 167	50.00	160.00
168	A28	10c grn, buff (type II) ('21)	.20	.20
a.		Tête bêche pair	1.10	1.40
168C	A28	10c bl grn, buff (type II) ('28)	.20	.20
d.		Tête bêche pair	2.50	2.50
169	A28	10c vio, buff (type II) ('30)	2.25	.20
a.		Tête bêche pair	9.25	1.40
170	A28	12c brn, buff	.20	3.25
171	A28	13c ol grn, buff ('15)	1.40	.50
172	A28	15c red, buff	3.50	.20
b.		15c dk vio, buff	32.50	4.25
c.		Tête bêche pair	87.50	125.00
173	A28	15c brn red, buff ('28)	2.50	2.75
174	A28	20c red vio, buff ('21)	3.25	.20
a.		Tête bêche pair	6.50	7.50
175	A28	20c ver, buff ('24)	1.00	.50
a.		Tête bêche pair	5.75	9.25
176	A28	20c car, buff ('25)	.25	.20
a.		Tête bêche pair	2.50	.55
177	A28	25c ver, buff ('21)	2.25	1.60
178	A28	25c car, buff ('22)	1.10	.85
179	A28	25c brn, buff ('25)	3.25	1.25
180	A28	30c dp bl, buff ('24)	9.25	.50
		Nos. 167-180 (15)	31.35	12.60

1932-33　With Grilled Gum

169c	A28	10c violet, buff	4.50	1.50
173a	A28	15c brn red, buff ('33)	50.00	52.50
176c	A28	20c carmine, buff	7.25	1.50
179a	A28	25c brown, buff ('33)	125.00	35.00
180a	A28	30c deep blue, buff	72.50	2.50
		Nos. 169c-180a (5)	259.25	93.00

For surcharges and overprints see Nos. 188, 196-198, 1O4-1O5, 1O12-1O13, 2O8-2O17, 3O6-3O13.

The Mythen
A29

The Rütli — A30

The Jungfrau
A31

1914-30　Engr.　Granite Paper

181	A29	3fr dk green	650.00	6.50
182	A29	3fr red ('18)	87.50	1.40
183	A30	5fr dp ultra	35.00	3.00
184	A31	10fr dull violet	100.00	3.25
185	A31	10fr gray grn ('30)	225.00	37.50
		Nos. 181-185 (5)	1,097.	51.65

See No. 206. For overprints see Nos. 2O27-2O30, 3O23-3O26.

Stamps of 1909-14 Surcharged

a

b

c

1915

186	A26(a)	1c on 2c bister	.25	1.25
187	A27(b)	13c on 12c bis brn	.25	9.25
188	A28(c)	13c on 12c brn, buff	.30	.90
		Nos. 186-188 (3)	.80	11.40

No. 141 Surcharged

| 189 | A25 | 80c on 70c | 25.00 | 17.50 |

Significant of Peace
A32

"Peace"
A33

"Dawn of Peace"
A34

Perf. 11½

1919, Aug. 1		Typo.		Unwmk.
190	A32	7½c olive drab & blk	.80	2.25
191	A33	10c red & yel	1.10	8.75
192	A34	15c violet & yel	1.90	2.75
		Nos. 190-192 (3)	3.80	13.75

Commemorating Peace after World War I.

Nos. 151, 149, 162, 171-172, 133 Surcharged in Black, Red or Dark Blue

a

---

b

c

1921
Wmk. 183

193	A26(a)	2½c on 3c (Bl)	.20	1.10
a.		Tête bêche pair	1.10	3.25
b.		Inverted surcharge	800.00	1,550.
c.		Double surcharge	550.00	775.00
194	A26(a)	5c on 2c (R)	.20	4.50
a.		Double surcharge	450.00	450.00
195	A26(a)	5c on 7½c (R)	.20	.55
a.		Tête bêche pair	6.50	1.00
b.		Double surcharge	550.00	550.00
c.		5c on 7½c slate (II)	2,200.	4,500.
196	A28(b)	10c on 13c (R)	.20	2.25
a.		Double surcharge	550.00	550.00
197	A28(c)	20c on 15c (Bk)	.55	2.75
a.		Tête bêche pair	2.50	55.00
198	A28(c)	20c on 15c (Bl)	2.25	5.50
b.		Double surcharge	875.00	875.00
199	A25(c)	20c on 25c dp bl (R)	.20	.55
a.		Tête bêche pair	1.50	4.50
		Nos. 193-199 (7)	3.80	17.20

A36

1924　Typo.　Perf. 11½
Granite Paper, Surface Colored

200	A36	90c grn & red, grn	15.00	2.75
201	A36	1.20fr brn rose & red, rose	5.25	5.25
202	A36	1.50fr bl & red, bl	37.50	6.50
203	A36	2fr gray blk & red, gray	47.50	6.75
		Nos. 200-203 (4)	105.25	21.25
		Set, never hinged	325.00	

1933　With Grilled Gum

200a	A36	90c	17.50	3.25
201a	A36	1.20fr	47.50	5.50
202a	A36	1.50fr	32.50	6.50
203a	A36	2fr	27.50	8.25
		Nos. 200a-203a (4)	125.00	23.50
		Set, never hinged	300.00	

For overprints see Nos. O16-O18, 2O31-2O34, 3O27-3O30.

Building in Bern, Location of 1st UPU Congress, 1874
A37　　　　　　A38

1924, Oct. 9　Engr.　Wmk. 183
Granite Paper

204	A37	20c vermilion	.55	1.60
205	A38	30c dull blue	1.10	6.25
		Set, never hinged	3.25	

50th anniv. of the UPU.

The Rütli — A39

Type of 1914 Issue

1928   Re-engraved   Perf. 11½

206 A39 5fr blue   110.00 9.75
    Never hinged   300.00
a. Imperf., pair, never hinged   *10,000.*

In the re-engraved stamp the picture is clearer and lighter than on No. 183. "HELVETIA" is in smaller letters. The names at foot of the stamp are "Grasset-J. Sprenger" instead of "E. GRASSET-A. BURKHARD."
For overprints see Nos. 2O35, 3O31.

Nos. 155 and 163 Surcharged

1930, June   Perf. 11½

207 A26 3c on 2½c ol grn, *buff*   .20 2.75
208 A26 5c on 7½c dp grn, *buff*   .20 8.00
    Set, never hinged   1.10

The Mythen
A40

1931   Engr.   Granite Paper

209 A40 3fr orange brown   65.00 5.25
    Never hinged   150.00

For overprints see Nos. 2O56, 3O47.

Dove on Broken
Sword — A41

"Peace"
A42

1932, Feb. 2   Typo.   Perf. 11½
Granite Paper

210 A41 5c peacock blue   .20 .20
211 A41 10c orange   .20 .20
212 A41 20c cerise   .25 .20
213 A41 30c ultra   2.25 1.60
214 A41 60c olive brown   17.50 8.75

Unwmk.
Photo.

215 A42 1fr olive gray & bl   17.50 8.75
    Nos. 210-215 (6)   37.90 19.70
    Set, never hinged   95.00

Intl. Disarmament Conf., Geneva, Feb. 1932.
For overprints see #2O36-2O41, 3O32-3O37.

Louis   Alfred
Favre — A43   Escher — A44

Design: 30c, Emil Welti.

Wmk. 183

1932, May 31   Engr.   Perf. 11½
Granite Paper

216 A43 10c red brown   .20 .20
217 A44 20c vermilion   .25 .20
218 A44 30c deep ultra   .55 2.10
    Nos. 216-218 (3)   1.00 2.50
    Set, never hinged   3.00

Completion of the St. Gotthard tunnel, 50th anniv.
Nos. 216-218 exist imperforate.

Staubbach   Mt. Pilatus
Falls   A47
A46

Chillon   Rhone
Castle   Glacier
A48   A49

St. Gotthard   Via Mala
Railroad   Gorge
A50   A51

Rhine Falls — A52

1934, July 2   Typo.   Perf. 11½
Granite Paper

219 A46 3c olive   .20 3.00
220 A47 5c emerald   .20 .20
221 A48 10c brt violet   .40 .20
222 A49 15c orange   .50 3.25
223 A50 20c red   .60 .45
224 A51 25c brown   7.75 8.25
225 A52 30c ultra   25.00 2.10
    Nos. 219-225 (7)   34.65 17.45
    Set, never hinged   100.00

Tête bêche Pairs

220a A47 5c   1.60 1.60
221a A48 10c   1.50 .85
222a A49 15c   1.75 3.00
223a A50 20c   3.50 2.25

Souvenir Sheet

1934, Sept. 29

226   Sheet of 4   500.00 550.00
    Never hinged   900.00

No. 226 was issued in connection with the Swiss National Philatelic Exhibition at Zurich, Sept. 29 to Oct. 7, 1934. It contains one each of Nos. 220-223. Size: 62x72mm.
For overprints see Nos. 2O42-2O46, 3O48.

Staubbach   Mt. Pilatus
Falls   A54
A53

Chillon   Rhone
Castle   Glacier
A55   A56

St. Gotthard   Via Mala
Railroad   Gorge
A57   A58

Rhine   Balsthal
Falls — A59   Pass — A60

Alpine Lake of
Säntis — A61

Two types of 10c red violet:
  I — Shading inside "0" of 10 has only vertical lines.
  II — Shading in "0" includes two diagonal lines.

1936-42   Unwmk.   Engr.   Perf. 11½

227 A53 3c olive   .20 .20
228 A54 5c blue green   .20 .20
229 A55 10c red vio (II)   .85 .20
b. Type I   .85 .20
230 A55 10c dk red brn ('39) .20 .20
230B A55 10c org brn ('42)   .20 .20
231 A56 15c orange   .40 1.10
232 A57 20c carmine   4.75 .20
233 A58 25c lt brown   .50 1.10
234 A59 30c ultra   .90 .20
235 A60 35c yellow grn   1.10 1.25
236 A61 40c gray   6.00 .20
    Nos. 227-236 (11)   15.30 5.05
    Set, never hinged   37.50

Two types of the 20c. See Nos. 316-321.
For overprints see Nos. O1-O4, O6-O9, O19-O19-O22, O24-O27, 2O47-2O55, 2O68-2O68A, 2O70-2O73, 2O75-2O78, 3O38-3O46, 3O60-3O60A, 3O62-3O65, 3O67-3O70, 4O1-4O4, 4O6-4O9, 4O23-4O24, 4O27-4O28, 5O1-5O2, 5O5.

Tête bêche Pairs

228a A54 5c blue green   .45 .30
229a A55 10c red violet (II) 4.50 5.50
230a A55 10c dark red brown 1.75 1.10
230d A55 10c orange brown   .50 .60
232a A57 20c carmine   25.00 35.00

1936-40   With Grilled Gum

227a A53 3c olive   .65 6.25
228d A54 5c blue green   .30 .25
229d A55 10c red violet (II) .30 .25
e. Type I   1.00 .25
230e A55 10c dark red brn ('40) 1.90 25.00
231a A56 15c orange   .30 1.10
232c A57 20c carmine   6.75 .25
233a A58 25c light brown   1.00 5.00
234a A59 30c ultra   .95 .25
235a A60 35c yellow green   1.40 3.25
236a A61 40c gray   9.25 .50
    Nos. 227a-236a (10)   22.80 42.10
    Set, never hinged   47.50

Mobile
Post Office
A62

1937, Sept. 5   Photo.
Granite Paper

237 A62 10c black & yellow   .25 .50
    Never hinged   .55

No. 237 was sold exclusively by the traveling post office. It exists on two kinds of granite paper, black and red fibers or blue and red fibers. See No. 307 for type A62 redrawn.

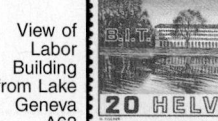

View of
Labor
Building
from Lake
Geneva
A63

Palace of
League of
Nations
A64

Main
Building,
Palace of
League of
Nations
A65

Labor
Building
and Albert
Thomas
Monument
A66

1938, May 2   Perf. 11½
Granite Paper

238 A63 20c red & buff   .20 .20
239 A64 30c blue & lt blue   .45 .20
240 A65 60c brown & buff   1.75 2.25
241 A66 1fr black & buff   7.50 17.00
    Nos. 238-241 (4)   9.90 19.65
    Set, never hinged   25.00

Opening of Assembly Hall of the Palace of the League of Nations.
For overprints see #O2O57-2O64, 3O49-3O56.

Souvenir Sheet

A67

Engraved and Typographed
1938, Sept. 17   Unwmk.   Perf. 11½
Granite Paper

242 A67 Sheet of 3   37.50 32.50
    Never hinged   70.00
a. 10c on 65c gray bl & dp bl 19.00 25.00
b. A68 20c red   1.10 2.50

Natl. Phil. Exhib. at Aarau, Sept. 17-25, and 25th anniv. of Swiss air mail. No. 242 contains 2 No. 243, but on granite paper, and a 10c on 65c similar to No. C22 but redrawn, with wing tips 1½mm from side frame lines; overall size 37x20½mm; no watermark.
On No. C22, wing tips touch frame lines; size is 36x21½mm; Wmk. 183.

Lake Lugano — A68

First
Federal
Pact, 1291
A69

Diet of
Stans,
1481
A70

Citizens
Voting
A71

1938, Sept. 17   Engr.   Perf. 11½

243	A68	20c red	.25	.25
a.		Tête bêche pair	.50	.85
c.		Grilled gum	.40	.40
d.		As "c," tête bêche pair	1.40	15.00

Granite Paper

244	A69	3fr brn car, grnsh	11.00	8.75
245	A70	5fr slate bl, grnsh	7.50	6.00
246	A71	10fr grn, grnsh	47.50	35.00
		Nos. 243-246 (4)	66.25	50.00
		Set, never hinged	190.00	

No. 243 is printed on ordinary paper. Nos. 244-246 are on granite surface-colored paper. The greenish surface coating has faded on most copies.

For type A68 in orange brown, see No. 318.

See Nos. 242b, 284-286. For overprints see Nos. O5, O23, 2O65-2O67, 2O69, 2O74, 2O88-2O90, 3O57-3O59, 3O61, 3O66, 3O80-3O82, 4O5, 4O19-4O21, O4O25, 5O3, 5O23-5O25, 7O18-7O20.

Deputation of Trades and Professions — A72

Swiss Family A73

Alpine Scenery A74

Engr., Photo. (30c)

1939, Feb. 1   Perf. 11½

Inscribed in French

247	A72	10c dl pur & red	.20	.20
248	A73	20c lake & red	.50	.20
249	A74	30c dp blue & red	2.50	3.00

Inscribed in German

250	A72	10c dl pur & red	.20	.20
251	A73	20c lake & red	.40	.20
252	A74	30c dp blue & red	2.50	8.25

Inscribed in Italian

253	A72	10c dl pur & red	.20	.20
254	A73	20c lake & red	1.90	.20
255	A74	30c dp blue & red	2.50	9.25
		Nos. 247-255 (9)	10.90	21.70
		Set, never hinged	35.00	

National Exposition of 1939, Zurich.

Tree and Crossbow — A75

1939, May 6   Photo.   Perf. 11½

Granite Paper

Inscribed in French

256	A75	5c deep green	.55	1.60
257	A75	10c gray brown	.55	1.90
258	A75	20c brt carmine	1.10	1.60
259	A75	30c violet blue	3.00	8.00

Inscribed in German

260	A75	5c deep green	.55	2.50
261	A75	10c gray brown	.55	2.50
262	A75	20c brt carmine	1.10	3.50
263	A75	30c violet blue	8.75	9.50

Inscribed in Italian

264	A75	5c deep green	.85	4.50
265	A75	10c gray brown	.55	3.50
266	A75	20c brt carmine	1.10	4.25
267	A75	30c violet blue	3.25	11.00
		Nos. 256-267 (12)	21.90	54.35
		Set, never hinged	32.50	

National Exposition of 1939.

The 5c, 10c and 20c stamps in the three languages exist se-tenant in coils. On the 10c coil stamp, the inscription "COURVOISIER S.A." beneath is design is smaller, with the "A" just left of the point on the "V" of "HELVETIA."

On the sheet stamp, the 'A' is just right of the 'V.' Value about three times that of the sheet stamp.

1939   With Grilled Gum

256a	A75	5c deep green	.75	2.25
257a	A75	10c gray brown	.75	2.25
258a	A75	20c bright carmine	1.90	3.00
260a	A75	5c deep green	.75	1.60
262a	A75	20c bright carmine	1.90	1.60
264a	A75	5c deep green	1.10	3.75
265a	A75	10c gray brown	1.00	3.00
266a	A75	20c bright carmine	1.90	3.25
		Nos. 256a-266a (8)	10.05	20.70

View of Geneva A76

Perf. 11½

1939, Aug. 22   Photo.   Unwmk.

Granite Paper

268	A76	20c red, car & buff	.20	.20
269	A76	30c blue, car & gray	.30	2.75
		Set, never hinged	1.40	

75th anniv. of the founding of the Intl. Red Cross Society.

"The Three Swiss" — A77

William Tell — A78

Fighting Soldier — A79

Standard Bearer — A81

Jürg Jenatsch — A83

Dying Warrior — A80

Ludwig Pfyffer — A82

Francois de Reynold — A84

Joachim Forrer — A85

1941-59   Engr.   Perf. 11½

Granite Paper

270	A77	50c dp pur, grnsh	4.25	.20
271	A78	60c red brn, buff	5.50	.20
272	A79	70c rose vio, pale lil	2.75	1.00
273	A80	80c blk, pale gray	1.10	.20
a.		80c black, pale lilac ('58)	.80	.50
274	A81	90c dk red, pale rose	1.00	.20
a.		90c dark red, buff ('59)	1.00	1.25
275	A82	1fr dk grn, grnsh	1.00	.20
276	A83	1.20fr red vio, pale gray	1.10	.20
a.		1.20fr red vio, pale lil ('58)	1.90	.75

277	A84	1.50fr dk bl, buff	1.50	.25
278	A85	2fr mar, pale rose	2.25	.20
a.		2fr maroon, buff ('59)	2.25	.50
		Nos. 270-278 (9)	20.45	2.65
		Set, never hinged	47.50	

For overprints see Nos. O28-O36, 2O79-2O87, 3O71-3O79, 4O10-4O18, 5O17-5O22, 6O6-6O8, 7O12-7O17.

Farmer Plowing A86

1941, Mar. 21   Photo.

Granite Paper

279	A86	10c brown & buff	.20	.50
		Never hinged		.20

Natl. Agriculture Development Plan of 1941.

Masons, Knight and Bern Coat of Arms A87

1941, Sept. 6

Granite Paper

280	A87	10c multicolored	.20	.75
		Never hinged		.20

750th anniversary of Bern.

"In order to Endure, Reclaim Used Materials" Inscribed in French A88

1942, Mar. 21   Unwmk.   Perf. 11½

281	A88	10c shown	.35	.50
282	A88	10c German	.40	1.00
283	A88	10c Italian	6.25	4.00
		Nos. 281-283 (3)	7.00	5.50
		Set, never hinged	14.00	
		Sheet of 25	90.00	550.00

Printed in sheets of 25, containing 8 No. 281, 12 No. 282 and 5 No. 283.

Types of 1938

1955   Engr.

Cream-surfaced Granite Paper

284	A69	3fr brown car	7.00	.75
285	A70	5fr slate blue	5.00	.80
286	A71	10fr green	7.00	3.00
		Nos. 284-286 (3)	19.00	4.55
		Set, never hinged	27.50	

1942   Cream paper

284a	A69	3fr	22.50	.50
285a	A70	5fr	10.00	.50
286a	A71	10fr	32.50	2.00
		Nos. 284a-286a (3)	65.00	3.00
		Set, never hinged	160.00	

The 1955 set is on cream-surfaced granite paper with white back, and blue and red fibers. The 1942 set is on colored-through cream paper with black and red fibers.

Zurich Stamps of 1843 A91

1943, Feb. 26

287	A91	10c blk & salmon	.20	.20
		Never hinged		.20

Centenary of postage stamps of Switzerland. See Nos. B130-B131.

Apollo Statue — A94

1944, Mar. 21   Photo.

Granite Paper

290	A94	10c org yel & gray blk	.20	1.00
291	A94	20c cer & gray blk	.30	1.00
292	A94	30c lt bl & gray blk	.60	6.00
		Nos. 290-292 (3)	1.10	8.00
		Set, never hinged	2.50	

Olympic Jubilee.

Numeral of Value — A95

Olive Branch A96

Designs: 60c, Keys of peace. 80c, Horn of plenty. 1fr, Dove of peace. 2fr, Plowing. 3fr, Field of crocus. 5fr, Clasped hands. 10fr, Aged couple.

1945, May 9   Unwmk.   Perf. 12

Granite Paper

293	A95	5c gray & green	.20	.50
294	A95	10c gray & brown	.25	.25
295	A95	20c gray & car rose	.35	.25
296	A95	30c gray & ultra	.70	3.00
297	A95	40c gray & orange	2.00	10.00
298	A96	50c dark red	2.75	19.00
299	A96	60c dull gray	2.75	6.75
300	A96	80c slate green	6.25	85.00
301	A96	1fr blue	8.75	95.00
302	A96	2fr red brown	22.50	160.00

Engr.

303	A96	3fr dk sl grn, buff	30.00	65.00
304	A96	5fr brn lake, buff	100.00	325.00
305	A96	10fr rose vio, buff	110.00	125.00
		Nos. 293-305,B145 (14)	286.80	895.50
		Set, never hinged	525.00	

End of war in Europe.

Johann Heinrich Pestalozzi — A104

1946, Jan. 12   Engr.   Perf. 11½

306	A104	10c rose violet	.20	.20
		Never hinged		.20

200th anniversary of the birth of J. H. Pestalozzi, educational reformer.

For overprint see No. 4O22.

Mobile P.O. Type of 1937

Redrawn

1946, July 6   Photo.

Granite Paper

307	A62	10c black & yellow	1.10	.20
		Never hinged		3.00

The designer's and printer's names are larger on the redrawn stamp. There are many minor differences in the two designs. Sizes: 1937, 37½x21mm. 1946, 38x22½mm.

First Swiss Steam Locomotive — A105

Modern Steam Locomotive — A106

Electric Gotthard Express A107

Electric Trains Passing on Bridge A108

1947, Aug. 6   Photo.   Perf. 11½
Granite Paper

308	A105	5c dk grn, blk & yel	.40	.50
309	A106	10c dk brn, gray & blk	.40	.50
310	A107	20c dk red & red	.35	.50
311	A108	30c dk bl & bl gray	.90	1.75
		Nos. 308-311 (4)	2.05	3.25
		Set, never hinged	5.00	

Centenary of the opening of the first Swiss railroad, between Zurich and Baden.

Johann Rudolf Wettstein A109

Castle at Neuchatel A110

"Helvetia" A111

Symbol of Swiss Federal State A112

1948, Feb. 27   Granite Paper

312	A109	5c dp grn	.20	.50
313	A110	10c gray blk	.20	.20
314	A111	20c dk red	.30	.20
315	A112	30c dk bl & red	.45	1.25
		Nos. 312-315 (4)	1.15	2.15
		Set, never hinged	2.00	

Tercentenary of the acknowledgment of independence of the Swiss Confederation, and the centenaries of the Neuchatel Revolution and the Swiss Federal State.
See Nos. B178a and B178b for 10c and 20c denominations, type A109.

Types of 1936-42 and

Grisons National Park — A113

1948, Mar. 1   Engr.

316	A54	5c chocolate	.20	.20
a.		Tête bêche pair	1.25	1.25
317	A55	10c green	.20	.20
a.		Tête bêche pair	1.25	1.50

318	A68	20c org brn	.30	.20
a.		Tête bêche pair	1.65	2.25
319	A113	25c carmine	1.50	1.50
320	A59	30c grnsh bl	6.25	4.00
321	A61	40c ultra	11.00	.75
		Nos. 316-321 (6)	19.45	6.85
		Set, never hinged	42.50	

For overprints see Nos. 4O26, 5O4.

Figures Encircling Globe A114

Designs: 25c, Globe and inscribed ribbon. 40c, Globe and pigeons.

Perf. 11½
1949, May 16   Photo.   Unwmk.

322	A114	10c green	.20	.20
323	A114	25c dark red	.40	6.25
324	A114	40c brt blue	.60	4.00
		Nos. 322-324 (3)	1.20	10.45
		Set, never hinged	2.00	

75th anniv. of the UPU.

Post Horn A115

Horse Drawn Mail Coach A116

Design: 30c, Post bus with trailer.

1949, May 16

325	A115	5c gray, yel & pink	.20	.50
326	A116	20c pur, gray & yel	.25	.30
327	A116	30c dk org brn, gray & yel	.45	6.75
		Nos. 325-327 (3)	.90	7.55
		Set, never hinged	1.50	

Centenary of the establishment of the Federal Post in Switzerland.

High Tension Conductors A117

Viaducts — A118

Mountain Railway — A119

Rotary Snow Plow — A120

Reservoir, Grimsel — A121

Lake Dam — A122

Dam and Power Station — A123

Alpine Postal Road — A124

Harbor of the Rhine — A125

Suspension Railway — A126

Railway Viaduct — A127

Triangulation Point — A128

Two types of 20c:
Type I — Three lines above curved rock.
Type II — Two lines above rock.

Perf. 12x11½
1949, Aug. 1   Engr.   Unwmk.

328	A117	3c gray	1.50	4.00
329	A118	5c orange	.20	.20
a.		Tête bêche pair	.90	.20
330	A119	10c yel grn	.20	.20
a.		Tête bêche pair	.60	.20
331	A120	15c aqua	.20	.50
332	A121	20c brown car (II)	.30	.20
a.		Tête bêche pair	1.75	.75
c.		Type I	2,000.	67.50
		Type I, never hinged	3,750.	
333	A122	25c red	.25	.20
334	A123	30c olive	.25	.20
335	A124	35c red brown	.45	.60
336	A125	40c deep blue	1.40	.20
337	A126	50c slate gray	1.40	.20
338	A127	60c blue green	4.00	.50
339	A128	70c purple	1.10	.30
		Nos. 328-339 (12)	11.25	7.30
		Set, never hinged	22.50	

For use in vending machines, some printings of the 5c, 10c, 20c (II), 25c, 30c and 40c carry a control number on the back of every fifth stamp. The number was applied on top of the gum.
For overprints see Nos. O37-O47, 3O83-3O93, 4O29-4O39, 5O6-5O16, 6O1-6O5, 7O1-7O11.

Symbolical of the Telegraph — A129

10c, Telephone. 20c, Radio. 40c, Television.

Zurich Airport and Tail of Plane A130

1952, Feb. 1   Photo.   Perf. 11½

340	A129	5c org & yel	.25	.50
341	A129	10c brt grn & pink	.30	.20
342	A129	20c dp red lil & gray bl	.45	.20
343	A129	40c dp bl & lt bl	1.40	4.75
		Nos. 340-343 (4)	2.40	5.65
		Set, never hinged	5.25	

"A century of telecommunications."

1953, Aug. 29

344	A130	40c blue, red & gray	3.25	10.50
		Never hinged	5.50	

Opening of Zurich-Kloten airport.

Alpine Post Bus, Winter Background — A131

Design: 20c, Same, summer background.

1953, Oct. 8

345	A131	10c dk grn, grn & yel	.20	.20
346	A131	20c dk red, red brn & yel	.30	.20
		Set, never hinged	1.00	

Sold only on Swiss alpine post buses.

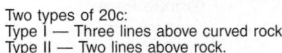

Symbols of Agriculture, Forestry and Horticulture — A132

Map and Nautical Emblems A133

Alphorn Blower A135

Lausanne Cathedral A134

20c, Winged spoon. 40c, Football and map.

1954, Mar. 15   Perf. 14

347	A132	10c multicolored	.20	.25
348	A132	20c multicolored	.40	.25
349	A133	25c red, dk ol grn & gray	1.00	3.00
350	A132	40c bl, yel & brn	1.60	3.50
		Nos. 347-350 (4)	3.20	7.00
		Set, never hinged	6.00	

Nos. 347-348 were issued to publicize exhibitions at Lucerne and Bern; No. 349, fifty years of navigation on the Rhine; No. 350, the 1954 World Soccer Championships in Switzerland.

1955, Feb. 15   *Perf. 11½*

Designs: 10c, Vaud costume hat. 40c, Automobile steering wheel.

351	A134	5c multi	.20	.60
352	A134	10c grn, yel & red	.25	.50
a.		Souvenir sheet of 2	60.00	80.00
		Never hinged	90.00	
353	A135	20c red & sepia	.55	.50
354	A134	40c bl, pink & gray	1.25	2.10
		Nos. 351-354 (4)	2.25	3.70
		Set, never hinged	5.50	

No. 352a contains 10c and 20c multicolored, imperf. stamps of Cathedral type A134. Size: 104x52mm.

National Philatelic Exhibition (5c, #352a), Winegrowers' Festival (10c), Alpine Herdsman and Costume Festival (20c) and 25th Intl. Automobile Show (40c).

First Swiss Post Bus — A136

10c, North Gate of Simplon Tunnel and Stockalper Palace. 20c, Children crossing street and road signs. 40c, Planes and emblem of Swissair, vert.

1956, Mar. 1   Photo.
Granite Paper

355	A136	5c ol gray, blk & yel	.20	.50
356	A136	10c brt grn, gray & red	.25	.50
357	A136	20c multi	.45	.50
358	A136	40c blue & red	1.00	1.40
		Nos. 355-358 (4)	1.90	2.60
		Set, never hinged	4.50	

50th anniv. of the Swiss Motor Coach Service (#355); 50th anniv. of the opening of Simplon Tunnel (#356); Accident prevention (#357); 25th anniv. of the founding of Swissair (#358).

Inking Device, Printing Machine A137

10c, Train on southern ramp of Gotthard Railroad. 20c, Shield of civil defense and coat of arms. 40c, Munatius Plancus and view of Basel.

Two types of 10c:
I — "Black" bottom line on train.
II — Brown bottom line.

1957, Feb. 27   *Perf. 11½*
Granite Paper

359	A137	5c multicolored	.20	.20
360	A137	10c lt bl grn, dk grn & red brn (I)	1.10	.50
a.		Type II	1.00	.50
		Never hinged	2.75	
361	A137	20c red org & gray	.25	.50
362	A137	40c multi	.75	1.25
		Nos. 359-362 (4)	2.30	2.15
		Set, never hinged	4.50	

Intl. Exhibition for Graphic Arts, Lausanne, June 1-16, 1957 (#359). 75th anniv. of St. Gotthard railroad (#360). Civil defense (#361). 2000th anniv. of Basel (#362).

Rope and Symbol of European Unity — A138

1957, July 15   Engr.   *Perf. 11½*

363	A138	25c lt red	.50	.35
364	A138	40c blue	.80	.35
		Set, never hinged	4.50	

Issued to emphasize European unity.

Catalogue values for unused stamps in this section, from this point to the end of the section, are for Never Hinged items.

Nyon Castle and Corinthian Capital A139

Designs: 10c, Woman's head and ribbons in Swiss colors. 20c, Crossbow emblem. 40c, Salvation Army hat.

1958, Mar. 5   Photo.   Unwmk.
Granite Paper

365	A139	5c ol bis & dl pur	.20	.20
366	A139	10c grn, dk grn & red	.20	.20
367	A139	20c ver, lil & car	.50	.20
368	A139	40c multicolored	1.40	1.25
		Nos. 365-368 (4)	2.30	1.85

2000th anniv. of Nyon (#365). Saffa Exhibition, Zurich, July 17-Sept. 15 (#366). 25th anniv. of Swiss manufacturing emblem (#367). 75th anniv. of the Salvation Army in Switzerland (#368).

Symbol of Nuclear Fission A140

1958, Aug. 25   *Perf. 11½*
Granite Paper

369	A140	40c blue, yel & red	.60	.60

2nd UN Atomic Conf. for peaceful uses of atomic power, Geneva, Sept. 1958.

"Transportation" — A141

Designs: 10c, Fasces and post horn. 20c, Owl, rabbit and fish. 30c, Jean Calvin, Theodore de Beze and University of Geneva.

1959, Mar. 9   Photo.   Unwmk.
Granite Paper

370	A141	5c multicolored	.20	.20
371	A141	10c emer, yel & lt gray	.30	.20
a.		Souvenir sheet of 2, imperf.	14.00	14.00
372	A141	20c multicolored	.60	.20
373	A141	50c multicolored	1.25	.75
		Nos. 370-373 (4)	2.35	1.35

Opening of the Swiss House of Transport and Communications (5c). Natl. Phil. Exhib., St. Gall, Aug. 21-30 (10c and #371a). Protection of animals (20c). 400th anniv. of the University of Geneva (50c).

No. 371a contains a 10c green, gold and light gray and a 20c deep carmine. Sold for 2fr; the money went for the St. Gall Phil. Exhib.

Chain Symbolizing European Unity — A142

1959, June 22   Engr.   *Perf. 11½*

374	A142	30c brick red	*1.60*	.30
375	A142	50c lt ultra	*2.75*	.45

Issued to emphasize European Unity.

Overprinted "REUNION DES PTT D'EUROPE 1959" in Ultramarine or Red

1959, June 22

376	A142	30c brick red	*37.50*	6.50
377	A142	50c lt ultra	*37.50*	6.50

European Conference of PTT Administrations, Montreux, June 22-July 31. Nos. 376-377 were on sale only during the conference at a special P. O. in Montreux.

"Cancer Control" A143

Designs: 20c, Founding charter and scepter of University of Basel. 50c, Uprooted Oak Emblem. 75c, Swissair Jet DC-8.

1960, Apr. 7   Photo.   *Perf. 11½*
Granite Paper

378	A143	10c brt grn & red	.55	.20
379	A143	20c car rose, gray blk & yel	.55	.20
380	A143	50c ultra & yel	.75	1.25
381	A143	75c lt bl, gray & red	3.50	4.00
		Nos. 378-381 (4)	5.35	5.65

50th anniv. of the Swiss League for Cancer Control (10c). 500th anniv. of the University of Basel (20c). World Refugee Year, July 1, 1959-June 30, 1960 (50c). Swissair's entry into the jet age (75c).

Messenger, Fribourg A144   Cathedral, Lausanne A145

Designs: 10c, Messenger, Schwyz. 15c, Messenger and pack animal. 20c, Postilion on horseback. 30c, Grossmünster (church), Zürich. 35c, 1.30fr, Woodcutters' Guildhall, Biel. 40c, Cathedral, Geneva. 50c, Spalen Gate, Basel. 60c, Clock Tower, Berne. 70c, 2.80fr, Sts. Peter and Stephen Church, Bellinzona (tower omitted on 2.80fr). 75c, Bridge and water tower, Lucerne. 80c, Cathedral, St. Gallen. 90c, Munot tower, Schaffhausen. 1fr, Townhall, Fribourg. 1.20fr, Basel gate, Solothurn. 1.50fr, Reding house, Schwyz. 1.70fr, 2fr, 2.20fr, Church, Einsiedeln.

Two types of 5c, 10c, 20c, 50c:
5 Centimes:
Type I — Four lines on pike at left of hand.
Type II — Three lines.
10 Centimes:
Type I — Dot on pike below head.
Type II — No dot.
20 Centimes:
Type I — Ten dots on horiz. harness strip.
Type II — Nine dots.
50 Centimes:
Type I — 3 shading lines at right above arch.
Type II — 2 shading lines.

1960-63   Engr.   *Perf. 11½*
1.30fr, 1.70fr, 2.20fr, 2.80fr on Granite Paper, Red and Blue Fibers

382	A144	5c lt ultra (I)	.20	.20
c.		Tête bêche pair	.20	.20
383	A144	10c blue grn (I)	.20	.20
c.		Tête bêche pair	.40	.20
384	A144	15c lt red brn	.20	.20
385	A145	20c rose pink (I)	.30	.20
c.		Tête bêche pair	.90	.45
386	A145	25c emerald	.35	.20
387	A145	30c vermilion	.45	.20
388	A145	35c orange red	.50	.30
389	A145	40c lilac	.60	.20
390	A145	50c lt vio bl (I)	.75	.20
c.		Tête bêche pair	2.75	2.75
391	A145	60c rose red	.90	.20
392	A145	70c orange	1.10	.40
393	A145	75c lt blue	1.20	.20
394	A145	80c dp claret	1.25	.20
395	A145	90c olive green	1.30	.20
396	A144	1fr dull orange	1.50	.20
397	A144	1.20fr dull red	1.75	.30
397A	A145	1.30fr red brn, *pink ('63)*	1.90	.20
398	A144	1.50fr brt green	2.25	.20
398A	A144	1.70fr rose lil, *pink ('63)*	2.50	.20
399	A144	2fr brt blue	3.25	.50
399A	A145	2.20fr bl grn, *grn ('63)*	3.25	.50
399B	A145	2.80fr org, *buff ('63)*	3.75	.40
		Nos. 382-399B (22)	29.45	5.90

See Nos. 440-455.

1963-76
Violet Fibers, Fluorescent Paper

382d	A144	5c lt ultra (I)	.20	.20
g.		Tête bêche pair ('68)	.20	.20
383d	A144	10c bl grn (I)	.20	.20
e.		Bkt. pane of 2 + 2 labels ('68)	.65	.65
g.		Tête bêche pair ('68)	.35	.20

384a	A144	15c lt red brn	.55	.55
385d	A144	20c rose pink (I)	.30	.20
g.		Tête bêche pair ('68)	.70	.20
386a	A145	25c emerald	.35	.20
387a	A145	30c vermilion	.35	.20
c.		Tête bêche pair ('68)	1.00	.75
389a	A145	40c lilac ('67)	.55	.20
c.		Tête bêche pair ('76)	1.25	1.10
390d	A145	50c lt vio bl (I)	.75	.20
391a	A145	60c rose red ('67)	.80	.30
393a	A145	75c lt blue ('68)	1.25	.20
394a	A145	80c dp claret	1.00	.20
395a	A145	90c olive grn ('67)	1.00	.20
396a	A144	1fr dull org ('67)	2.00	.20
397b	A144	1.20fr dl red ('68)	3.00	1.75
398b	A145	1.50fr brt green ('68)	3.00	1.75
		Nos. 382d-398b (15)	15.30	6.95

Coil Stamps

1960   **White Paper**

382b	A144	5c lt ultra (II)	1.40	1.40
383b	A144	10c blue grn (II)	.85	.85
385b	A145	20c rose pink (II)	.85	.85
390b	A145	50c lt vio bl (II)	4.00	4.00
		Nos. 382b-390b (4)	7.10	7.10

The coil stamps were printed in sheets (available to collectors) and pasted into coils. Every fifth stamp has a control number on the back.

Other denominations issued in coils on white paper are: 40c, 60c, 90c, 1fr, 1.30fr, 1.70fr, 2.20fr and 2.80fr.

Denominations issued in coils on granite paper (red & blue fibers) are: 1.30fr, 1.70fr, 2.20fr and 2.80fr.

Coil Stamps

1965-68
Violet Fibers, Fluorescent Paper

382e	A144	5c lt ultra (II)	1.25	1.25
383h	A144	10c blue grn (II)	.60	.60
385e	A144	20c rose pink (II)	.60	.30
390e	A145	50c lt vio bl (II)	4.00	4.00
		Nos. 382e-390e (4)	6.45	5.85

Other denominations issued in coils on violet-fiber paper are: 40c, 60c, 90c and 1fr.

Common Design Types pictured following the introduction.

Europa Issue, 1960
Common Design Type

1960, Sept. 19   Unwmk.   *Perf. 11½*
Size: 33x23mm

400	CD3	30c vermilion	.50	.25
401	CD3	50c ultra	.75	.40

Wall under Construction and Globe — A146

Designs: 10c, Symbolic sun (HYSPA Emblem). 20c, Ice hockey stick and puck. 50c, Wiring diagram on map of Switzerland.

1961, Feb. 20   Photo.   *Perf. 11½*
Granite Paper

402	A146	5c gray, brick red & grnsh bl	.35	.20
403	A146	10c aqua & yel	.35	.20
404	A146	20c multicolored	1.50	.60
405	A146	50c ultra, gray & car rose	1.25	1.00
		Nos. 402-405 (4)	3.45	2.00

Development aid to new nations (5c). HYSPA 1961, Health and Sports Exhibition, Bern, May 18-July 17 (10c). Intl. Ice Hockey Championships, Lausanne and Geneva, Mar. 2-12 (20c). Fully automatic Swiss telephone service (50c).

St. Matthew and Angel — A147

Evangelists: 5fr, St. Mark and winged lion. 10fr, St. Luke and winged ox. 20fr, St. John and eagle.

Perf. 11½
1961, Sept. 18   Unwmk.   Engr.
Granite Paper

406	A147	3fr rose carmine	4.00	.20
407	A147	5fr dark blue	6.50	.20
408	A147	10fr dark brown	8.25	.45
409	A147	20fr red	20.00	3.00
		Nos. 406-409 (4)	38.75	3.85

Designs are after 15th century wood carvings from St. Oswald's church, Zug.

Europa Issue, 1961
Common Design Type
1961, Sept. 18
Size: 26x21mm

410	CD4	30c vermilion	.50	.20
411	CD4	50c blue	.75	.35

Trans-Europe Express A148

10c, Rower. 20c, Jungfrau railroad station and Mönch. 50c, WHO Anti-malaria emblem.

1962, Mar. 19   Photo.   Perf. 11½

412	A148	5c multicolored	.50	.20
413	A148	10c brt grn, lem & lil	.45	.20
414	A148	20c rose lil, pale bl & bis	.90	.25
415	A148	50c ultra, lt grn & rose lil	.90	.60
		Nos. 412-415 (4)	2.75	1.25

Introduction of Swiss electric TEE trains (5c). Rowing world championship, Lucerne, Sept. 6-9 (10c). 50th anniv. of the railroad station on the Jungfrau mountain (20c). WHO Anti-Malaria campaign (50c).

Europa Issue, 1962
Common Design Type
1962, Sept. 17   Unwmk.   Perf. 11½
Size: 33x23mm

416	CD5	30c orange, yel & brn	.65	.40
417	CD5	50c ultra, lt grn & brn	1.00	.60

Boy Scout — A149

Designs: 10c, Swiss Alpine Club emblem. 20c, Luegelkinn viaduct. 30c, Wheat Emblem. No. 426, Red Cross Jubilee Emblem. No. 427, Post Office Building, Paris, 1863.

1963, Mar. 21   Photo.

422	A149	5c gray, dk red & brn	.55	.20
423	A149	10c dk grn, gray & red	.40	.20
424	A149	20c dk car, brn & gray	1.10	.20
425	A149	30c yel grn, yel & org	1.60	1.60
426	A149	50c blue, sil & red	.85	.80
427	A149	50c ultra, pink, yel & gray	.90	.75
		Nos. 422-427 (6)	5.40	3.75

Souvenir Sheet
Imperf

428		Sheet of 4	7.00	6.00
a.		A149 50c bl, lt bl, sil & red	1.75	1.25

50 years of Swiss Boy Scouts (5c). Cent. of Swiss Alpine Club (10c). 50 years Lötschberg Railroad (20c). FAO "Freedom from Hunger" campaign (30c). Red Cross Cent. (#426, 428). 1st Intl. Postal Conf., Paris 1863 (#427). No. 428 sold for 3fr.

Europa Issue, 1963
Common Design Type
1963, Sept. 16   Unwmk.   Perf. 11½
Granite Paper
Size: 26x21mm

429	CD6	50c ultra & ocher	.90	.60

EXPO Emblem A150

50c, EXPO emblem on globe & moon ("Outlook"). 75c, EXPO emblem on globe ("Insight").

1963, Sept. 16   Unwmk.   Perf. 11½
Granite Paper

430	A150	10c brt grn & dk grn	.30	.20
431	A150	20c red & maroon	.35	.20
432	A150	50c ultra & red	.65	.40
433	A150	75c purple & red	1.00	.45
		Nos. 430-433 (4)	2.30	1.25

Issued to publicize the Swiss National Exhibition, Lausanne, Apr. 30-Oct. 25, 1964.

Road Tunnel Through Great St. Bernard A151

10c, Symbolic water god & waves. 20c, Soldiers of 1864 & 1964. 50c, Standards of Swiss Confederation & Geneva.

1964, Mar. 9   Photo.
Granite Paper

434	A151	5c ol, ultra & red	.20	.20
435	A151	10c Prus bl & grn	.20	.20
436	A151	20c red, ultra, blk & sal	.40	.20
437	A151	50c rose, yel & blk	.95	.65
		Nos. 434-437 (4)	1.75	1.25

1st Trans-Alpine Automobile route from Switzerland to Italy (5c). "Pro Aqua" water conservation campaign (10c). Centenary of the Swiss Noncommissioned Officers' Association (20c). Sesqui. of union of Geneva with Swiss Confederation (50c).

Europa Issue, 1964
Common Design Type
1964, Sept. 14   Engr.   Perf. 11½
Size: 21x26mm
Violet Fibers, Fluorescent Paper

438	CD7	20c vermilion	.40	.20
439	CD7	50c ultra	.85	.25

Type of Regular Issue, 1960-63

Designs: 5c, Lenzburg. 10c, Freuler Mansion, Näfels. 15c, St. Mauritius Church, Appenzell. 20c, Planta House, Samedan. 30c, Gabled houses, Gais. 50c, Castle and Abbey Church, Neuchâtel. 70c, Lussy House, Wolfenschiessen. 1fr, Santa Croce Church, Riva San Vitale. 1.20fr, Abbey Church, Payerne. 1.30fr, Church of St. Pierre de Clages. 1.50fr, La Porte de France, Porrentruy. 1.70fr, Frauenfeld Castle. 2fr, A Pro Castle, Seedorf. 2.20fr, Thomas Tower and Gate. Liestal. 2.50fr, St. Oswald's Church, Zug. 3.50fr, Benedictine Abbey, Engelberg.

1964-68   Engr.   Perf. 11½
Violet Fibers, Fluorescent Paper

440	A144	5c car rose ('68)	.20	.20
441	A144	10c violet bl ('68)	.20	.20
b.		Tête bêche pair	.25	.20
c.		Booklet pane of 2 + 2 labels	.70	
442	A144	15c brown red ('68)	.20	.20
b.		Tête bêche pair	.35	.35
443	A144	20c blue grn ('68)	.30	.20
b.		Tête bêche pair	.65	.35
444	A144	30c vermilion ('68)	.45	.20
b.		Tête bêche pair	1.00	.80
445	A144	50c ultra ('68)	.75	.20
446	A145	70c brown ('68)	1.50	.20
447	A145	1fr dk green ('68)	1.50	.20
448	A145	1.20fr brown red ('68)	1.75	.25
449	A145	1.30fr violet bl ('66)	1.75	.75
450	A145	1.50fr green ('68)	2.25	.40
451	A145	1.70fr brown org ('66)	2.50	1.25
452	A145	2fr orange ('67)	3.00	.40
453	A145	2.20fr green	3.25	.80
454	A145	2.50fr Prus grn ('67)	3.50	.55
455	A145	3.50fr purple ('67)	4.25	.60
		Nos. 440-455 (16)	26.85	6.60

The 15c was issued in coils in 1972 (?) with control number on the back of every fifth stamp.

Nurse and Patient A152

Seated Helvetia, 1854 — A153

Women's Army Auxiliary A154

Intercontinental Communications Map — A155

1965, Mar. 8   Photo.   Perf. 11½
Violet Fibers, Fluorescent Paper

462	A152	5c lt ultra & red	.20	.20
463	A153	10c emer, brn & blk	.20	.20
464	A154	20c red & multi	.30	.20

Granite Paper, Red and Blue Fibers

465	A155	50c dl bl grn & mar	.75	.50
		Nos. 462-465 (4)	1.45	1.10

Nursing and auxiliary medical professions (5c). Natl. Postage Stamp Exhibition, NABRA, Bern, Aug. 27-Sept. 5, 1965 (10c). 20th anniv. of Women's Army Auxiliary Corps (20c). Cent. of ITU (50c).
See No. B344.

Swiss Arms, Cantonal Emblems of Valais, Neuchatel, Geneva A156

1965, June 1   Unwmk.   Perf. 11½
Granite Paper, Red and Blue Fibers

466	A156	20c multicolored	.30	.20

150th anniversary of the entry of the cantons of Valais, Neuchatel and Geneva in the Swiss Confederation.

Matterhorn A157

30c, like 10c but inscribed in French "Cervin."

1965, June 1   Photo.
Granite Paper, Red and Blue Fibers

467	A157	10c grn, slate & dk red	.20	.20

Violet Fibers, Fluorescent Paper

468	A157	30c dk red, grn & slate	.45	.40

Year of the Alps; the cent. of the 1st wintertime visitors to the Alps and cent. of the 1st ascent of the Matterhorn. Nos. 467-468 on sale only at Swiss Alpine post buses.

Europa Issue, 1965
Common Design Type
1965, Sept. 14   Unwmk.   Perf. 11½
Violet Fibers, Fluorescent Paper

469	CD8	50c bl, dk bl & grn	.75	.25

Figure Skating A159

1965, Sept. 14   Photo.
Violet Fibers, Fluorescent Paper

470	A159	5c grn, dl bl & blk	.20	.20

Issued to publicize the World Figure Skating Championships, Davos, Feb. 22-27, 1966.

ITU Emblem and Atom Diagram A160

Cent. of the ITU: 30c, Symbol of communications, waves.

1965, Sept. 14
Violet Fibers, Fluorescent Paper

471	A160	10c ultra & multi	.20	.20

Granite Paper, Red and Blue Fibers

472	A160	30c org, red & gray	.45	.40

Violet Fibers, Fluorescent Paper Paper from No. 473 onward is fluorescent and has violet fibers, unless otherwise noted.

European Kingfisher A161

Mercury's Helmet and Laurel A162

Flags of 13 Member Nations and Nuclear Fission A163

1966, Feb. 21   Photo.

473	A161	10c emer & multi	.20	.20
474	A162	20c dp mag, red & brt grn	.30	.20
475	A163	50c slate blue & multi	.70	.40
		Nos. 473-475 (3)	1.20	.80

Intl. Cong. for Conservation "Pro Natura," Lucerne (10c). 50th anniv. of Swiss Trade Fair, Basel, Apr. 16-26 (20c). European Organization for Nuclear Research, CERN (50c).

Emblem of Society of Swiss Abroad — A164

1966, June 1   Photo.   Perf. 11½

476	A164	20c ultra & ver	.30	.25

50th anniv. of the Society of Swiss Abroad.

Europa Issue, 1966
Common Design Type
1966, Sept. 26   Engr.   Perf. 11½
Size: 21x26mm

477	CD9	20c vermilion	.25	.20
478	CD9	50c ultra	.80	.35

Finsteraarhorn — A165

1966, Sept. 26   **Photo.**
479 A165 10c lt grnsh bl, dk bl & dk red   .30 .25

Automobile Wheels and White Cane — A166

Flags of EFTA Members A167

1967, Mar. 13   **Photo.**   *Perf. 11½*
480 A166 10c bl grn, blk & yel   .20 .20
481 A167 20c multicolored   .30 .20

No. 480 issued to publicize the white cane as a distinguishing mark for blind pedestrians. No. 481 publicizes the European Free Trade Association, EFTA. See note after Norway No. 501.

Europa Issue, 1967
Common Design Type
1967, Mar. 13
482 CD10 30c blue gray   .60 .25

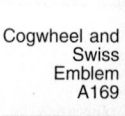

Cogwheel and Swiss Emblem A169

Hourglass and Sun — A170

San Bernardino, from North — A171

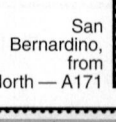

Railroad Wheel A172

1967, Sept. 18   **Photo.**   *Perf. 11½*
483 A169 10c multicolored   .20 .20
484 A170 20c red, yel & blk   .25 .20
485 A171 30c multicolored   .40 .25
486 A172 50c multicolored   .65 .50
     Nos. 483-486 (4)   1.50 1.15

50th anniv. of Swiss Week (10c). 50th anniv. of the Foundation for the Aged (20c). Opening of the San Bernardino Road Tunnel (30c). 75th anniv. of the Central Office for Intl. Railroad Transportation (50c).

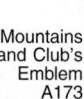

Mountains and Club's Emblem A173

Pegasus Constellation A182

Golden Key with CEPT Emblem A174

Rook and Chessboard A175

Aircraft Tail and Satellites A176

1968, Mar. 14   **Photo.**   *Perf. 11½*
487 A173 10c grn, lt ultra & red   .20 .20
488 A174 20c Prus bl, yel & brn   .35 .20
489 A175 30c dk ol bis & vio bl   .45 .20
490 A176 50c dk blue & red   .70 .35
     Nos. 487-490 (4)   1.70 .95

50th anniv. of the Swiss Women's Alpine Club (10c). A unified Europe through postal cooperation (20c). 18th Chess Olympics, Lugano, Oct. 17-Nov. 6 (30c). Inauguration of the new Geneva-Cointrin Air Terminal (50c).

Worker's Protective Helmet A177

Double Geneva and Zurich Stamps of 1843 — A178

Map Showing Systematic Planning A179

Flag of Rhine Navigation Committee A180

1968, Sept. 12   **Photo.**   *Perf. 11½*
491 A177 10c bl grn & yel   .20 .20
492 A178 20c dp car, blk & yel grn   .30 .20
493 A179 30c multicolored   .45 .20
494 A180 50c bl, yel & blk   .70 .50
     Nos. 491-494 (4)   1.65 1.10

50th anniv. of the Swiss Accident Insurance comp., SUVA (10c). 125th anniv. of 1st Swiss postage stamps (20c). 25th anniv. of the Swiss Society for Territorial Planning (30c). Cent. of the Rhine Navigation Act (50c).

Swiss Girl Scouts' Emblem and Camp — A181

Comptoir Suisse Emblem and Beaulieu Building, Lausanne A183

Gymnaestrada Emblem (Man in Circle) — A184

Swissair DC-8 and DH-3 — A185

1969, Feb. 12   **Photo.**   *Perf. 11½*
495 A181 10c multicolored   .20 .20
496 A182 20c dark blue   .30 .20
497 A183 30c red, ocher, grn & gray   .45 .20
498 A184 50c vio bl, bl, red, grn & sil   .70 .50
499 A185 2fr bl, dk bl & red   2.50 2.00
     Nos. 495-499 (5)   4.15 3.10

50th anniv. of Swiss Girl Scouts (10c). Opening of 1st Swiss Planetarium, Lucerne, July 1 (20c). 50th anniv. of the Comptoir Suisse (trade fair, 30c). 5th Gymnaestrada (gymnastic meet), Basel, July 1-5 (50c). 50th anniv. of Swiss airmail service (2fr).

Europa Issue, 1969
Common Design Type
1969, Apr. 28
Size: 32½x23mm
500 CD12 30c brn org & multi   .40 .25
501 CD12 50c chlky bl & multi   .60 .35

Huldreich Zwingli (1484-1531) A186

Famous Swiss: 20c, Gen. Henri Guisan (1874-1960). 30c, Francesco Borromini, architect (1599-1667). 50c, Othmar Schoeck, musician (1886-1957). 80c, Germaine de Stael, writer (1766-1817).

1969, Sept. 18   **Engr.**   *Perf. 11½*
502 A186 10c brt purple   .20 .20
503 A186 20c green   .30 .20
504 A186 30c deep carmine   .45 .20
505 A186 50c deep blue   .90 .60
506 A186 80c red brown   1.20 1.00
     Nos. 502-506 (5)   3.05 2.20

Kreuzberge, Alpstein Mountains A187

Children Crossing Street — A188

Steelworker A189

Telex Tape — A190

1969, Sept. 18   **Photo.**
507 A187 20c blue & multi   .40 .20
508 A188 30c car & multi   .40 .20
509 A189 50c violet & multi   .70 .45
     Nos. 507-509 (3)   1.50 .85

No. 508 publicizes the traffic safety campaign; No. 509 for 50th anniv. of the ILO.

Fireman Rescuing Child — A191

Pro Infirmis Emblem A192

United Nations Emblem A193

New UPU Headquarters A194

1970, Feb. 26   **Photo.**   *Perf. 11½*
510 A190 20c dk grn, yel & blk   .25 .20
511 A191 30c dk car & multi   .45 .20
512 A192 30c red & multi   .45 .20
513 A193 50c dk bl, lt grnsh bl & sil   .65 .35
514 A194 80c dk pur, sep & tan   1.10 .70
     Nos. 510-514 (5)   2.90 1.65

75th anniv. of the Swiss Telegraph Agency (20c). Cent. of the Swiss Firemen's Assoc. (No. 511). 50th anniv. of the Pro Infirmis Foundation (No. 512). UN, 5th anniv. (50c). New Headquarters of the UPU in Bern (80c).

Europa Issue, 1970
Common Design Type
1970, May 4   **Engr.**   *Perf. 11½*
Size: 21x26mm
515 CD13 30c vermilion   .45 .20
516 CD13 50c brt blue   .65 .35

Soccer A195

Census Form — A196

Piz Palu, Grisons A197

"Nature Conservation" A198 — Numeral A199

1970, Sept. 17   Photo.   Perf. 11½
517 A195 10c green & multi   .40   .20
518 A196 20c dk grn & multi   .30   .20
519 A197 30c slate bl & multi   .50   .20
520 A198 50c dk bl & multi   .70   .65
      Nos. 517-520 (4)   1.90 1.25

75th anniv. of Swiss Soccer Association (10c). Federal Census of 1970 (20c). Swiss Alps (30c). Nature Conservation Year (50c).

Coil Stamps
1970, Sept. 17   Engr.   Perf. 11½
521 A199 10c brown lake   .20   .20
522 A199 20c olive grn   .35   .20
523 A199 50c ultra   .70   .60
      Nos. 521-523 (3)   1.25 1.00

Control number in stamp's color on back of every fifth stamp. Nos. 521-523 were regularly issued only in coils, but exist in sheets of 50.

Gymnastic Trio — A200

Rose — A201

Switzerland No. 8 — A202

Rising Spiral — A203

Intelsat 4 Satellite A204

NABA 1971 BASEL

Adaptation of 1850 Design — A205

Design: No. 525, Runners (men).

1971, Mar. 11   Photo.   Perf. 11½
524 A200 10c ol, brn & bl   .25   .30
525 A200 10c gray, brn & yel   .25   .30
  a.   Pair, #524-525   .50   .30
526 A201 20c dk grn & multi   .30   .20
527 A202 30c dp car & multi   .45   .30
528 A203 50c dk bl & bis   .70   .60
529 A204 80c multicolored   1.10 1.00
      Nos. 524-529 (6)   3.05 2.70

Souvenir Sheet
Typo.
Imperf
530 A205 2fr blue & multi   3.00 3.00

New article on gymnastics and sports in Swiss Constitution (10c); Intl. Child Welfare Org. (20c); NABA Natl. Postage Stamp Exhibition, Basel, June 4-13 (30c, 2fr); 2nd decade of development aid (50c); Intl. Space Communications Conf., Geneva, June-July, 1971 (80c).

#525a printed checkerwise. #530 sold for 3fr.

Europa Issue, 1971
Common Design Type
1971, May 3   Engr.   Perf. 11½
Size: 26x21mm
531 CD14 30c rose car & org   .45   .20
532 CD14 50c blue & org   .65   .40

Les Diablerets, Vaud — A206

Telecommunications Symbols — A207

1971, Sept. 23   Photo.   Perf. 11½
533 A206 30c rose lil & bl gray   .50   .30
534 A207 40c ultra, yel & brt pink .65   .55

No. 534 for the 50th anniv. of Radio-Suisse, which is also in charge of air traffic control.

Alexandre Yersin (1863-1943) Bacteriologist A208

Physicians: 20c, Auguste Forel (1848-1931), psychiatrist. 30c, Jules Gonin (1870-1935), ophthalmologist. 40c, Robert Koch (1843-1910), German bacteriologist. 80c, Frederick G. Banting (1891-1941), Canadian physiologist.

1971, Sept. 23   Engr.
535 A208 10c gray olive   .20   .20
536 A208 20c bluish green   .30   .20
537 A208 30c carmine rose   .40   .20
538 A208 40c dark blue   .60   .55
539 A208 80c brt purple   1.10   .90
      Nos. 535-539 (5)   2.60 2.05

Wrench, Road Sign, Club Emblems A209

Electronic Switch Panel — A210

Boy's Head and Radio Waves A211

Symbolic Tree — A212

1972, Feb. 17   Photo.   Perf. 11½
540 A209 10c multicolored   .20   .20
541 A210 20c olive & multi   .30   .20
542 A211 30c orange & maroon   .45   .30
543 A212 40c blue, grn & pur   .60   .60
      Nos. 540-543 (4)   1.55 1.30

75th anniv. of the touring and automobile clubs of Switzerland (10c). 125th anniv. of Swiss railroads (20c). 50th anniv. of Swiss radio (30c). 50th annual congress of Swiss citizens living abroad, Bern, Aug. 25-27 (40c).

Europa Issue 1972
Common Design Type
1972, May. 2
Size: 21x26mm
544 CD15 30c multicolored   .45   .20
545 CD15 40c multicolored   .90   .35

Alberto Giacometti (1901-66), Painter and Sculptor — A213

Portraits and Signatures: 20c, Charles Ferdinand Ramuz (1878-1947), writer. 30c, Le Corbusier (Charles Edouard Jeanneret; 1887-1965) architect. 40c, Albert Einstein (1879-1955), physicist. 80c, Arthur Honegger (1892-1955), composer.

Engraved & Photogravure
1972, Sept. 21   Perf. 11½
546 A213 10c ocher & blk   .20   .20
547 A213 20c lt olive & multi   .30   .20
548 A213 30c pink & blk   .45   .20
549 A213 40c lt blue & blk   .60   .60
550 A213 80c lil rose & blk   1.10   .75
      Nos. 546-550 (5)   2.65 1.95

Civil Defense Emblem A214

Spannörter, Swiss Alps — A215

Red Cross Rescue Helicopter A216

Clean Air, Fire, Earth and Water — A217

1972, Sept. 21   Photo.
551 A214 10c org, bl & yel   .20   .20
552 A215 20c bl grn & multi   .40   .30
553 A216 30c lilac, red & indigo   .75   .20
554 A217 40c lt blue & multi   .70   .60
      Nos. 551-554 (4)   2.05 1.30

Earth Satellite Station, Leuk, World Map — A218

Quill Pen and Arrows in Circle — A219

INTERPOL Emblem A220

1973, Feb. 15   Photo.   Perf. 11½
555 A218 15c gray, yel & bl   .25   .25
556 A219 30c multicolored   .40   .20
557 A220 40c dp bl, lt bl & gray   .60   .50
      Nos. 555-557 (3)   1.25   .95

Opening of the satellite station at Leuk; Swiss Association of Commercial Employees, cent. (30c); International Criminal Police Organization (INTERPOL), 59th anniv.

Sottoceneri A221

Sign of Inn "Zur Sonne," Toggenburg A222

Villages: 10c, Graubunden. 15c, Central Switzerland. 25c, Jura. 30c, Simme Valley. 35c, Central Switzerland (2 buildings). 40c, Vaud. 50c, Valais. 60c, Engadine. 70c, Sopraceneri. 80c, Eastern Switzerland.
Designs: 1fr, Rose window, Lausanne Cathedral. 1.10fr, Gallus Portal, Basel Cathedral. 1.20fr, Romanesque capital (eagle), St. Jean Baptiste Church, Grandson. 1.50fr, Ceiling medallion (bird feeding nestlings), Stein am Rhein Convent. 1.70fr, Romanesque capital (St. George and dragon), St. Jean Baptiste, Grandson. 1.80fr, Gargoyle, Bern Cathedral. 2fr, Bay window, Schaffhausen. 2.50fr, Cock weather vane, St. Ursus Cathedral, Solothurn. 3fr, Font, St. Maurice Church, Saanen. 3.50fr, Astronomical clock, Bern clock tower.

1973-80   Engr.   Perf. 11½
Fluorescent, No Violet Fibers
558 A221 5c dl yel & dk bl   .20   .20
559 A221 10c rose lil & ol grn   .20   .20
560 A221 15c org & vio bl   .20   .20
561 A221 25c emer & vio bl   .35   .20
562 A221 30c brick red & dk bl   .45   .20
563 A221 35c red org & brt vio
             ('75)   .45   .20
564 A221 40c brt bl & blk   .55   .20
565 A221 50c ol grn & org   .70   .25
566 A221 60c yel brn & gray   .85   .25
567 A221 70c sep & dk grn   1.00   .25
568 A221 80c brt grn & brick red 1.10   .25

Violet Fibers, Fluorescent Paper
569 A222 1fr pur ('74)   1.40   .20
  a. Without fibers, fluorescent pa-
        per ('78)   2.00 1.50
570 A222 1.10fr Prus bl ('75)   1.50   .40
571 A222 1.20fr rose red ('74)   1.60 1.25
572 A222 1.30fr ocher   2.00   .90
573 A222 1.50fr grn ('74)   2.00 1.25
574 A222 1.70fr gray   2.25   .60
575 A222 1.80fr dp org   2.50   .60
576 A222 2fr ultra ('74)   2.75   .40
  a. Without fibers, fluorescent pa-
        per ('78)   4.50 3.50

577 A222 2.50fr gldn brn ('75)　3.25　.60
578 A222　3fr dk car ('79)　4.00　1.00
579 A222 3.50fr ol grn ('80)　4.50　1.25
　　Nos. 558-579 (22)　33.80 10.85

No. 577 exists without tagging. Value, $60 unused, $30 used.

Europa Issue 1973
Common Design Type
1973, Apr. 30　Engr. and Photo.
　　Size: 38x28mm
580 CD16 25c brown & yel　.40　.25
581 CD16 40c ultra & yel　.70　.35

"Man and Time" — A223

Skier and Championship Emblem A224

Child — A225

1973, Aug. 30　Photo.　Perf. 11½
582 A223 15c multicolored　.25　.20
583 A224 30c pink & multi　.40　.20
584 A225 40c blue vio & blk　.60　.50
　　Nos. 582-584 (3)　1.25　.90

Opening of the Intl. Clock Museum, La Chaux-de-Fonds, 1974 (15c); Intl. Alpine Skiing Championships, St. Moritz, Feb. 2-10, 1974 (30c); "Terre des hommes" children's aid program (40c).

Souvenir Sheet

Medieval Postal Couriers — A226

1974, Jan. 29　Photo.　Perf. 11½
585 A226　Sheet of 4　5.50　5.50
　a.　30c Basel (with staff)　1.10　1.10
　b.　30c Zug (without staff)　1.10　1.10
　c.　60c Uri　1.10　1.10
　d.　80c Schwyz　1.10　1.10

Cent. of UPU and for INTERNABA 74 Intl. Phil. Exhib., Basel, June 7-16. No. 585 sold for 3fr.

Pine and Cabin on Globe — A227

Gymnast and Hurdlers A228

Target and Pistol — A229

1974, Jan. 29
586 A227 15c lt green & multi　.20　.20
587 A228 30c red & multi　.40　.20
588 A229 40c blue & multi　.70　.30
　　Nos. 586-588 (3)　1.30　.70

50th anniv. of Swiss Youth Hostels (15c); Cent. of Swiss Workers' Gymnast and Sports Association (SATUS) (30c); World Marksmanship Championships, Thun and Bern, Sept. 1974 (40c).

Old Houses, Parliament RR Station, Bern — A230

Eugéne Borel — A231

Designs: No. 590, Castle, Town Hall, Chauderon Center, Lausanne. 40c, Heinrich von Stephan. 80c, Montgomery Blair.

1974, Mar. 28　Photo.　Perf. 11½
589 A230 30c orange & multi　.50　.25
590 A230 30c scarlet & multi　.50　.25
　　Engr.
591 A231 30c rose & blk　.40　.25
592 A231 40c gray & blk　.60　.50
593 A231 80c lt yel grn & blk　1.10　.75
　　Nos. 589-593 (5)　3.10　2.00

Cent. of the UPU. Nos. 589-590 publicize the Cent. Cong., Lausanne, May 22-July 5; Nos. 591-593 honor the founders of the UPU.

"Continuity," by Max Bill — A232

Europa: 40c, "Amazon," bronze sculpture by Carl Burckhardt.

1974, Mar. 28　Photo.
594 A232 30c red & black　.45　.20
595 A232 40c ultra & sepia　.75　.35

Oath of Allegiance, by Werner Witschi — A233

Sports Foundation Emblem A234

Conveyor Belts, Paths of Mail Transport and Delivery A235

1974, Sept. 19　Photo.　Perf. 11½
596 A233 15c lil, ol & dk ol　.20　.20
597 A234 30c silver & multi　.40　.20
598 A235 40c plum & multi　.40　.20
　　Nos. 596-598 (3)　1.00　.60

Centenary of Swiss Constitution (15c); Swiss Sports Foundation (No. 597); 125th anniversary of Swiss Federal Post (No. 598).

Standard Meter, Krypton Spectrum A236

Women of Four Races A237

Red Cross Flag, Barbed Wire — A238

"Ville de Lucerne" Dirigible A239

1975, Feb. 13　Photo.　Perf. 11½
599 A236 15c grn, org & ultra　.25　.25
600 A237 30c brown & multi　.45　.20
601 A238 60c ultra, blk & red　.75　.40
602 A239 90c blue & multi　1.20　1.00
　　Nos. 599-602 (4)　2.65　1.85

Cent. of Intl. Meter Convention, Paris, 1875 (15c); Intl. Women's Year 1975 (30c); 2nd Session of Diplomatic Conf. on Humanitarian Intl. Law, Geneva, Feb. 1975 (60c); Aviation and Space Travel exhibition in Museum of Transport and Communications, Lucerne (90c).

Mönch, by Ferdinand Hodler — A240

Vineyard Worker, by Maurice Barraud — A241

Europa: 50c, Still Life with Guitar, by René Auberjonois.

1975, Apr. 28　Photo.　Perf. 12x11½
603 A240 30c gray & multi　.45　.20
604 A241 50c multicolored　.75　.50
605 A241 60c bl gray & multi　.90　.80
　　Nos. 603-605 (3)　2.10　1.50

Man Pulling Wheel Chair Upstairs A242

"The Helping Hand" A243

Architectural Heritage Year Emblem A244

Beat Fischer von Reichenbach A245

1975, Sept. 11　Photo.
606 A242 15c lilac, blk & grn　.25　.20
607 A243 30c red, blk & car　.40　.20
608 A244 50c yel brn & mar　.70　.60
609 A245 60c blue & multi　.80　.75
　　Nos. 606-609 (4)　2.15　1.75

Special building features for the handicapped (15c); interdenominational telephone pastoral counseling (30c); European Architectural Heritage Year 1975 (50c); Fischer Post, Bern, tercentenary (60c).

Forest A246

Fruits and Vegetables A247

Black Infant — A248

Telephones of 1876 and 1976 — A249

1976, Feb. 12　Photo.　Perf. 11½
Fluorescent, No Violet Fibers
610 A246 20c green & multi　.50　.25
611 A247 40c car & multi　.60　.20
612 A248 40c lil rose & multi　.60　.20
　　Engr.
Violet Fibers, Fluorescent Paper
613 A249 80c lt bl & dk bl　1.10　1.00
　　Nos. 610-613 (4)　2.80　1.65

Centenary of Federal forest laws (20c); healthy nutrition to combat alcoholism (No. 611); fight against leprosy (No. 612); telephone centenary (80c).

Cotton and Gold Lace, St. Gall — A250

Pocket Watch, 18th Century — A251

1976, May 3   **Engr.**   **Perf. 11½**
614   A250   40c red brn & multi   .65   .25
615   A251   80c black & multi   1.40   .90
    Europa. Both 40c and 80c are on fluorescent paper, the 80c having violet fibers.

Fawn, Frog and Swallow
A252

"Conserve Energy"
A253

St. Gotthard Mountains
A254

Skater
A255

1976, Sept. 16   **Photo.**   **Perf. 11½**
Fluorescent, No Violet Fibers
616   A252   20c multicolored   .75   .30
617   A253   40c multicolored   .60   .20
618   A254   40c multicolored   .65   .30
619   A255   80c multicolored   1.10   .90
    Nos. 616-619 (4)   3.10   1.70
    Wildlife protection (20c); energy conservation (No. 617); Pizzo Lucendro to Pizzo Rotondo, seen from Altanca (No. 618); World Men's Skating Championships, Davos, Feb. 5-6, 1977 (80c).

Oskar Bider, Bleriot Monoplane
A256

    Swiss Aviation Pioneers: 80c, Eduard Spelterini and balloon gondola. 100c, Armand Dufaux and Dufaux plane. 150c, Walter Mittelholzer and Dornier hydroplane.

1977, Jan. 27   **Engr.**   **Perf. 11½**
620   A256   40c multicolored   .65   .65
621   A256   80c multicolored   1.50   1.25
622   A256   100c multicolored   1.25   1.00
623   A256   150c multicolored   2.00   1.75
    Nos. 620-623 (4)   5.40   4.65

Blue Cross — A257

Festival Emblem
A258

Balloons Carrying Letters
A259

1977, Jan. 27   **Photo.**
624   A257   20c gray, bl & blk   .30   .25
625   A258   40c red, gold & brn   .50   .20
626   A259   80c lt bl & multi   1.10   1.00
    Nos. 624-626 (3)   1.90   1.45
    Blue Cross Society (care of alcoholics and fight against alcoholism), centenary (20c); Vintage Festival, Vevey, July 30-Aug. 14 (40c); JUPHILEX 77 Youth Philatelic Exhibition, Bern, Apr. 7-11 (80c).

Fluorescent Paper
    From No. 624 onward the paper lacks violet fibers but is fluorescent, unless otherwise noted.

St. Ursanne on Doubs River — A260

    Europa: 80c, Sils-Baselgia on Inn River.

1977, May 2   **Engr.**   **Perf. 11½**
627   A260   40c multicolored   .65   .25
628   A260   80c multicolored   1.40   .70

Worker and Factories
A261

Ionic Column and Shield
A262

Swiss Cross, Arrow and Butterfly
A263

1977, Aug. 25   **Photo.**   **Perf. 11½**
629   A261   20c multicolored   .30   .20
630   A262   40c multicolored   .55   .40
631   A263   80c multicolored   1.10   1.00
    Nos. 629-631 (3)   1.95   1.65
    Federal Factories Act, centenary (20c); protection of cultural monuments (40c); Swiss hiking trails (80c).

Star Singer, Bergün — A264

    Folk Customs: 10c, Horse race, Zürich. 20c, New Year's Eve costumes, Herisau. 25c, Chesslete, Solothurn. 30c, Rollelibutzen, Altstatten. 35c, Cutting of the goose, Sursee. 40c, Herald reading proclamation and men scaling wall, Geneva. 45c, Klausjagen, Kussnacht. 50c, Masked men, Laupen. 60c, Schnabelgeissen, Ottenbach. 70c, Procession (horse and masked men), Mendrisio. 80c, Griffins, Basel. 90c, Masked men, Lotschental.

1977-84   **Engr.**   **Perf. 11½**
632   A264   5c blue grn   .20   .20
   a.   Bklt. pane of 4 ('84)   .25
633   A264   10c dark red   .20   .20
   a.   Bklt. pane of 2 + 2 labels ('79)   .45
   b.   Bklt. pane of 4 ('84)   .50
634   A264   20c orange   .30   .20
   a.   Booklet pane of 4 ('79)   1.20
635   A264   25c brown   .35   .20
636   A264   30c brt green   .45   .20
637   A264   35c olive   .50   .20
   a.   Bklt. pane of 4 ('84)   2.00
638   A264   40c brown lake   .60   .20
   a.   Booklet pane of 4 ('79)   2.50
   b.   Violet fibers, fluorescent paper ('78)   .60   .20
639   A264   45c gray blue   .60   .30
640   A264   50c red brown   .75   .20
   a.   Bklt. pane of 2+2 labels ('84)   1.50
   b.   Bklt. pane of 4 ('84)   3.00

---

641   A264   60c gray brown   .90   .45
642   A264   70c purple   1.00   .30
643   A264   80c steel blue   1.10   .75
644   A264   90c deep brown   1.25   .90
    Nos. 632-644 (13)   8.20   4.30
    Issue dates: 30c, Nov. 25, 1982; 25c, 40c, 60c, Sept. 11, 1984; others, Aug. 25, 1977.

Arms of Vaud Canton
A265

Old Lucerne
A266

Title Page of "Melusine"
A267

Stylized Lens and Bellows
A268

Steamers on Swiss Lakes — A269

1978, Mar. 9   **Photo.**   **Perf. 11½**
652   A265   20c multicolored   .30   .20
653   A266   40c multicolored   .75   .25
654   A267   70c multicolored   .90   .80
655   A268   80c multicolored   1.10   1.00
    Nos. 652-655 (4)   3.05   2.25

Miniature Sheet
656   A269   Sheet of 8   7.00   7.00
   a.   20c La Suisse, 1910   .30   .30
   b.   20c Il Verbano, 1826   .30   .30
   c.   40c MS Gotthard, 1970   .85   .85
   d.   40c Ville de Neuchatel, 1972   .85   .85
   e.   40c MS Romanshorn, 1958   .85   .85
   f.   40c Le Winkelried, 1871   .85   .85
   g.   70c DS Loetschberg, 1914   .90   .90
   h.   80c DS Waedenswil, 1895   1.25   1.25
    LEMANEX 78 Philatelic Exhibition, Lausanne, May 26-June 4 (#652); Founding of Lucerne, 800th anniv. (#653); printing in Geneva, 500th anniv. (#654); 2nd Intl. Triennial Photography Exhibition, Fribourg, June 17-Oct. 22 (#655).
    Size of No. 656: 134x129mm. Sold for 5fr.

Stockalper Palace, Brig — A270

    Europa: 80c, Diet Hall, Bern.

1978, May 2   **Engr.**   **Perf. 11½**
657   A270   40c multicolored   .75   .30
658   A270   80c multicolored   1.50   .75

Machinist
A271

Joseph Bovet (1879-1951), Composer — A272

    #660, Chemical worker (French inscription). #661, Construction worker (Italian inscription).

1978, Sept. 14   **Photo.**   **Perf. 11½**
659   A271   40c multicolored   .65   .45
660   A271   40c multicolored   .65   .45
661   A271   40c multicolored   .65   .45
   a.   Strip of 3, #659-661   2.25   2.25
    Industrial safety.

1978, Sept. 14   **Engr.**
    Portraits: 40c, Henri Dunant (1828-1910), founder of Red Cross. 70c, Carl Gustave Jung (1875-1961), psychologist. 80c, Auguste Piccard (1884-1962), physicist and balloonist.
662   A272   20c dull green   .30   .20
663   A272   40c rose lake   .55   .20
664   A272   70c gray   1.00   .75
665   A272   80c blue gray   1.10   .90
    Nos. 662-665 (4)   2.95   2.05

Arms of Switzerland and Jura — A273

1978, Sept. 25   **Photo.**   **Perf. 11½**
666   A273   40c buff, red & blk   .55   .35
    Admission of Jura as 23rd Canton.

Rainer Maria Rilke (1875-1926), Poet, Muzot Castle — A274

    Designs: 40c, Paul Klee (1879-1940), painter and "heroic roses." 70c, Hermann Hesse (1877-1962), writer, and vines. 80c, Thomas Mann (1875-1955), writer, and Lubeck buildings.

1979, Feb. 21   **Engr.**   **Perf. 11½**
667   A274   20c gray green   .30   .20
668   A274   40c red   .60   .30
669   A274   70c brown   .90   .70
670   A274   80c gray blue   1.10   1.00
    Nos. 667-670 (4)   2.90   2.20

O. H. Ammann, Verrazano-Narrows Bridge, NY — A275

Target Hit with Pole and Lucerne Flag — A276

Hot Air
Balloon
A277

Airport,
Swissair and
Air France
Jets — A278

1979, Feb. 21   **Photo.**
671 A275 20c multicolored   .30   .20
672 A276 40c multicolored   .60   .25
673 A277 70c multicolored   .90   .70
674 A278 80c multicolored   1.10   1.00
        Nos. 671-674 (4)   2.90   2.15

Othmar H. Ammann (1879-1965), engineer,
bridge builder in US; 50th Federal Riflemen's
Festival, Lucerne, July 7-22; World Esperanto
Congress, Lucerne; new runway at Basel-Mul-
house Intl. Airport.

Letter Box, 1845,
Spalentor,
Basel — A279

Europa: 80c, Microwave radio relay station
on Jungfraujoch.

1979, Apr. 30   **Engr.**   **Perf. 11½**
675 A279 40c multicolored   .65   .35
676 A279 80c multicolored   1.40   .90

Helvetian Gold
Quarter Stater,
2nd Century
B.C. — A280

Three-stage
Launcher
Ariane — A283

Child and
Dove — A281

Morse Key
and Satellite
A282

1979, Sept. 6   **Photo.**
677 A280 20c multicolored   .30   .20
678 A281 40c multicolored   .55   .25
679 A282 70c multicolored   .90   .70
680 A283 80c multicolored   1.10   .90
        Nos. 677-680 (4)   2.85   2.05

Centenary of Swiss Numismatic Society;
International Year of the Child; Union of Swiss
Radio Amateurs, 50th anniv.; European Space
Agency (ESA).

Tree in Bloom
A284

Hand Carved
Milk Bucket
A285

Winterthur
Town
Hall — A286

"Pic-Pic,"
1930 — A287

1980, Feb. 21   **Photo.**
681 A284 20c multicolored   .30   .20
682 A285 40c multicolored   .55   .25
683 A286 70c multicolored   1.00   .80
684 A287 80c multicolored   1.10   1.00
        Nos. 681-684 (4)   2.95   2.25

Green '80, Swiss Horticultural & Gardening
Expo., Basel, 4/12-9/9/12; Swiss Arts Crafts
Centers, 50th anniv.; Soc. for Swiss Art His-
tory, cent.; 50th Intl. Automobile Show,
Geneva, 3/16.

Johann Konrad
Kern (1808-
1888), Politician
A288

Europa: 80c, Gustav Adolf Hasler (1830-
1900), communications pioneer.

1980, Apr. 28   **Lith. & Engr.**
        Granite Paper
685 A288 40c multicolored   .50   .20
686 A288 80c multicolored   1.00   .90

Postal Giro
System
A289

Postal Bus
System
A290

Security
Printing Plant,
50th
Anniversary
A291

Swiss
Telephone
Service
Centenary
A292

Photo., Photo. & Engr. (70c)
1980, Sept. 5   **Perf. 12**
687 A289 20c multicolored   .30   .20
688 A290 40c multicolored   .55   .25
689 A291 70c multicolored   1.00   .75
690 A292 80c multicolored   1.20   1.10
        Nos. 687-690 (4)   3.05   2.30

Swiss
Meteorological
Office
Centenary
A293

Swiss Trade
Union
Federation
Centenary
A294

Opening of
St. Gotthard
Tunnel for
Year-round
Traffic — A295

1980, Sept. 5   **Photo.**
691 A293 20c multicolored   .35   .20
692 A294 40c multicolored   .55   .20
693 A295 80c multicolored   1.25   1.00
        Nos. 691-693 (3)   2.15   1.40

Granary,
Kiesen, 17th
Century
A296

International
Year of the
Disabled
A297

The Parish Clerk, by
Albert
Anker — A298

Theodolite
and
Rod — A299

DC-9 (50th
Anniversary of
Swissair)
A300

1981, Mar. 9   **Photo.**   **Perf. 11½**
694 A296 20c multicolored   .30   .20
695 A297 40c multicolored   .55   .20
696 A298 70c multicolored   1.00   .80
697 A299 80c multicolored   1.10   .90
698 A300 110c multicolored   1.60   1.10
        Nos. 694-698 (5)   4.55   3.20

Ballenberg Open-air Museum of Rural
Architecture, Furnishing and Crafts; Albert
Anker (1831-1910), artist (70c); 16th Congress of the International Federation of Surveyors, Montreux, Aug. (80c).

Europa Issue 1981

Couple Dancing in
Native
Costumes — A301

1981, May 4   **Photo.**   **Perf. 11½**
699 A301 40c shown   .45   .35
700 A301 80c Stone putting   1.25   1.00

Seal of
Fribourg
A302

1981, Sept. 3   **Photo. & Engr.**
701 A302 40c shown   .55   .25
702 A302 40c Seal of Solothurn   .55   .25
703 A302 80c Old Town Hall,
              Stans   1.25   1.00
        Nos. 701-703 (3)   2.35   1.50

Diet of Stans, 50th anniv., and entry of Fribourg & Solothurn into the Swiss
Confederation.

Voltage
Regulator
A303

Crossbow
Quality
Emblem
A304

Youths
A305

Flower
Mosaic, St.
Peter's
Cathedral,
Geneva
A306

1981, Sept. 3   **Photo.**
704 A303 20c multi   .30   .20
705 A304 40c multi   .55   .30
706 A305 70c multi   .90   .75
707 A306 1.10fr multi   1.40   1.25
        Nos. 704-707 (4)   3.15   2.50

Technorama Industrial Fair, Winterthur;
Crossbow Quality Emblem, 50th anniv.; Swiss
Youth Assoc., 50th anniv.; restoration of St.
Peter's Cathedral.

Gotthard
Railway
Centenary
A307

Designs: Locomotives. Nos. 708-709 se-
tenant with label showing workers' monument.

1982, Feb. 18   **Photo.**
708 A307 40c Steam   .60   .30
709 A307 40c Electric   .60   .30

Swiss
Hoteliers'
Assoc.
Centenary
A308

Federal Gymnastic Society
Sesquicentennial — A309

Intl. Gas
Union, 50th
Anniv.
Convention,
Lausanne
A310

Bern Museum of Natural History
Sesquicentennial — A311

Society of
Chemical
Industries
Centenary
A312

1982, Feb. 18

710	A308	20c multicolored	.30	.20
711	A309	40c multicolored	.60	.30
712	A310	70c multicolored	.90	.75
713	A311	80c multicolored	1.10	1.00
714	A312	110c multicolored	1.50	1.10
		Nos. 710-714 (5)	4.40	3.35

Europa
1982 — A313

1982, May 3   Photo.   Perf. 11½

715	A313	40c Oath of Eternal Fealty	.75	.30
716	A313	80c Pact of 1291	1.50	1.00

Virgo, Schwarzee
above
Zermatt — A314

Signs of the Zodiac and City Views.

Photogravure and Engraved
1982-86   Perf. 11½

717	A314	1fr Aquarius, Old Bern	1.25	.30
718	A314	1.10fr Pisces, Nax near Sion	1.40	.30
719	A314	1.20fr Aries, Graustock	1.60	.30
719A	A314	1.40fr Gemini, Bischofszell	2.00	1.40
720	A314	1.50fr Taurus, Basel Cathedral	2.10	.30
721	A314	1.60fr Gemini, Schonengrund	2.10	1.10
722	A314	1.70fr Cancer, Wetterhorn, Grindelwald	2.25	.30
723	A314	1.80fr Leo, Areuse Gorge, Neuchatel	2.25	1.00
724	A314	2fr Virgo, Jungfrau Monch Eiger Mts.	2.75	2.25
725	A314	2fr shown	2.75	.30
726	A314	2.50fr Libra, Fechy	3.25	.80
727	A314	3fr Scorpio, Corippo	4.00	1.25
728	A314	4fr Sagittarius, Glarus	5.50	1.50

728A	A314	4.50fr Capricorn, Schuls	5.75	2.00
		Nos. 717-728A (14)	38.95	13.10

Issued: #717-719, 720-721, 8/23/82; #719,
2/11/86; #722-724, 2/17/83; #725, 11/24/83;
#726-727, 2/19/85; #728-728A, 2/21/84.

Zurich Tram
Centenary
A315

Centenary of
Salvation
Army in
Switzerland
A316

World Dressage Championship,
Lausanne, Aug. 25-29 — A317

Intl. Water
Supply
Assoc., 14th
World
Congress,
Zurich, Sept.
6-10 — A318

1982, Aug. 23   Photo.

729	A315	20c multicolored	.40	.20
730	A316	40c multicolored	.55	.25
731	A317	70c multicolored	1.00	.90
732	A318	80c multicolored	1.10	1.00
		Nos. 729-732 (4)	3.05	2.35

Fishing and
Pisciculture
Fed.
Centenary
A319

Zurich University
Sesquicentennial — A320

Journalists'
Fed.
Centenary
A321

Machine Manufacturers' Assoc.
Centenary — A322

1983, Feb. 17   Photo.
Granite Paper

733	A319	20c Perch	.45	.20
734	A320	40c multicolored	.55	.30
735	A321	70c Computer print outs	1.00	.90
736	A322	80c Micrometer, cycloidal computer pattern	1.10	1.00
		Nos. 733-736 (4)	3.10	2.40

Europa 1983   Basel Seal,
A323   1832-1848
                     A324

Photogravure and Engraved
1983, May 3   Perf. 11½

737	A323	40c Celestial globe, 1594	.50	.25
738	A323	80c Cog railway, 1871	1.40	1.00

1983, May 26   Photo.

739	A324	40c multicolored	.60	.35

Basel Canton sesquicentennial (land
division).

Octodurus
Martigny
Bimillenium
A325

Swiss Kennel
Club
Centenary
A326

Bicycle and
Motorcycle
Federation
Centenary
A327

World Communications Year — A328

1983, Aug. 22   Photo.

740	A325	20c multicolored	.30	.20
741	A326	40c multicolored	.65	.25
742	A327	70c multicolored	1.00	.90
743	A328	80c multicolored	1.10	.90
		Nos. 740-743 (4)	3.05	2.25

NABA-ZURI'84 Natl. Stamp Show,
Zurich, June 22-July 1 — A329

1100th Anniv.
of Saint
Imier — A330

Upper City,
Lausanne
A331

1984, Feb. 21   Photo.

744	A329	25c multicolored	.40	.25
745	A330	50c multicolored	.70	.35
746	A331	80c multicolored	1.40	1.10
		Nos. 744-746 (3)	2.50	1.70

Selection of Lausanne as permanent headquarters for the Intl. Olympic Committee (80c).

Europa (1959-
1984)
A332

1984, May 2   Photo.   Perf. 11½

747	A332	50c lilac rose	.80	.50
748	A332	80c ultra	1.60	1.00

Souvenir Sheet

Panoramic View of Zurich — A333

1984, May 24

749	A333	Sheet of 4	5.00	5.00
a.-d.		50c any single	1.20	1.20

NABA-ZURI '84 Stamp Show. Sold for 3fr.

Fire
Prevention
A334

1984, Sept. 11   Photo.

750	A334	50c Flames, match	.70	.35

Railway Staff
Association,
Cent. — A335

Rheto-Roman
Culture
Bimillennium
A336

Lake Geneva
Rescue Soc.,
Cent. — A337

Intl. Congress
on Large
Dams,
Lausanne
A338

1985, Feb. 19   Photo.   Perf. 12x11½

751	A335	35c Conductor's hat, paraphernalia	.50	.25
752	A336	50c Engraved artifact, Chur	.65	.25
753	A337	70c Rescuing drowning victim	1.10	.90
754	A338	80c Grande Dizence Dam, Canton Valais	1.25	1.10
		Nos. 751-754 (4)	3.50	2.50

Europa
1985 — A339

Designs: 50c, Ernest Ansermet (1883-1969), composer, conductor. 80c, Frank Martin (1890-1974), composer.

1985, May 7   Photo.   Perf. 11½x12
755 A339 50c multicolored   .60   .20
756 A339 80c multicolored   1.40 1.00

Swiss Master Bakers and Confectioners Federation, Bern, Cent. — A340

Swiss Radio Intl., 50th Anniv. A341

Postal, Telegraph & Telephone Intl. Congress, Sept. 16-21, Interlaken A342

1985, Sept. 10 Photo.   Perf. 12x11½
757 A340 50c Baker   .65   .20
758 A341 70c multi   1.00   .75
759 A342 80c PTTI 75th anniv.   1.20   .90
      Nos. 757-759 (3)   2.85 1.85

Swiss Worker's Relief Org., 50th Anniv. A343

Battle of Sempach, 600th Anniv. A344

Roman Chur Bimillennium A345

Vindonissa Bimillennium A346

Zurich Bimillennium A347

1986, Feb. 11   Photo.   Perf. 12
772 A343 35c Knot   .50   .40
773 A344 50c Military map,
            1698   .65   .20

774 A345 80c Mercury statue   1.10   .90
775 A346 90c Gallic head   1.25 1.00
776 A347 1.10fr Augustus coin   1.60 1.25
      Nos. 772-776 (5)   5.10 3.75

Europa 1986   Mail Handling
A348   A349

1986, Apr. 22   Photo.   Perf. 13½
777 A348 50c Woman   .65   .30
778 A348 90c Man   1.60 1.25

Photo. & Engr.
1986-89   Perf. 13½x13
779 A349 5c Franz mail van,
            1911   .20   .20
780 A349 10c Parcel sorting   .20   .20
781 A349 20c Mule post   .30   .20
782 A349 25c Letter-facing, can-
            celing   .40   .20
783 A349 30c Mail coach, 1735-
            1960   1.10   .90
784 A349 35c Counter service   .55   .40
785 A349 45c Packet steamer,
            1837-40   .65   .45
786 A349 50c Postman, 1986   .75   .35
  a.   Bklt. pane of 10 ('88)   7.50
787 A349 60c Loading airmail,
            1986   .90   .45
788 A349 75c 17th Cent. courier   1.10   .75
789 A349 80c Postman, ca. 1900   1.25   .80
790 A349 90c Railroad mail car   1.40 1.00
      Nos. 779-790 (12)   8.80 5.90

Issued: 5c, 10c, 25c, 35c, 80c, 90c, 9/9/86; 20c, 30c, 45c, 50c, 60c, 3/10/87; 75c, 3/7/89. For surcharge see No. B535.

Intl. Peace Year — A351

Swiss Winter Relief Fund, 50th Anniv. A352

Berne Convention for the Protection of Literary and Artistic Copyrights, Cent. — A353

25th Intl. Red Cross Conference, Geneva, Oct. 23-31 A354

1986, Sept. 9   Photo.   Perf. 12x11½
799 A351 35c multicolored   .50   .30
800 A352 50c multicolored   .70   .25
801 A353 80c multicolored   1.25 1.00
802 A354 90c multicolored   1.30 1.10
      Nos. 799-802 (4)   3.75 2.65

Mobile P.O., 50th Anniv. A355

Lausanne University, 450th Anniv. A356

Swiss Engineers & Architects Assoc., Sesquicent. A357

Cointrin Airport-Geneva, Rail Link Opening, June 1, 1987 — A358

Baden Hot Springs, 2000th Anniv. A359

1987, Mar. 10   Photo.
803 A355 35c multicolored   .55   .35
804 A356 50c multicolored   .70   .20
805 A357 80c multicolored   1.20 1.00
806 A358 90c multicolored   1.40 1.25
807 A359 1.10fr multicolored   1.60 1.50
      Nos. 803-807 (5)   5.45 4.30

Europa 1987 — A360

Sculpture: 50fr, Scarabaeus, 1979, by Bernard Luginbuhl. 90fr, Carnival Fountain, 1977, by Jean Tinguely, Basel Theater.

1987, May 26   Photo.   Perf. 11½
808 A360 50c multicolored   .75   .30
809 A360 90c multicolored   1.90 1.25

Swiss Master Butchers' Federation, Cent. — A361

Stamp Day, 50th Anniv. A362

Swiss Dairy Assoc., Cent. — A363

1987, Sept. 4   Photo.   Perf. 12x11½
810 A361 35c multicolored   .50   .40
811 A362 50c multicolored   .75   .40
812 A363 90c Cheesemaker   1.50 1.00
      Nos. 810-812 (3)   2.75 1.80

Tourism Industry, Bicent. — A364

Switzerland's four language regions: 50c, Clock Tower, Zug, German. 80c, Church of San Carlo, Blenio Valley, Italian. 90c, Witches' Tower, Sion Castle, French. 140c, Jorgenberg Castle ruins, Waltensburg/Vuorz, Surselva, Rhaeto-Romansh.

1987, Sept. 4   Perf. 11½
813 A364 50c multicolored   .70   .40
814 A364 80c multicolored   1.25   .75
815 A364 90c multicolored   1.50 1.00
816 A364 140c multicolored   2.00 1.50
  a.   Souvenir sheet of 4, #813-816   5.00
      Nos. 813-816 (4)   5.45 3.65

Swiss Women's Benevolent Soc., Cent. — A365

Swiss Hairdressers Assoc., Cent. — A366

Battle of Naefels, 600th Anniv. A367

European Campaign to Protect Undeveloped and Developing Lands A368

Intl. Music Festival, Lucerne, 50th Anniv. A369

1988, Mar. 8   Photo.   Perf. 12x11½
817 A365 25c multicolored   .40   .25
818 A366 35c multicolored   .55   .40
819 A367 50c Banner of St.
            Fridolin, medieval
            manuscript   .80   .25
820 A368 80c multicolored   1.25   .90
821 A369 90c Girl playing a
            shawm   1.40 1.25
      Nos. 817-821 (5)   4.40 3.05

Europa 1988 — A370

1988, May 24   Photo.   Perf. 11½
822 A370 50c Arrows (transport)   .65   .40
823 A370 90c Circuitry (commu-
            nication)   1.75 1.25

Swiss Accident Prevention Office, 50th Anniv. A371

Assoc. of Metalworkers and Watchmakers, Cent. — A372

Federal Topography Office, 150th Anniv. A373

Intl. Red Cross Museum, Geneva A374

1988, Sept. 13   Photo.   Perf. 12x11½
824 A371 35c multicolored   .45   .40
825 A372 50c multicolored   .70   .25
826 A373 80c Triangulation pyramid, theodolite, map   1.10   .90
827 A374 90c multicolored   1.30 1.10
    Nos. 824-827 (4)   3.55 2.65

Metamecanique, by Jean Tinguely — A375

1988, Nov. 25   Photo.   Perf. 13x12½
828 A375 90c multicolored   3.75 3.00
    See France No. 2137.

Military Post, Cent. — A376

Delemont Municipal Charter, 700th Anniv. A377

Public Transport Assoc., Cent. — A378

Rhaetian Railway, Cent. — A379

Great St. Bernard Pass Bimillennium A380

25c, Army postman. 35c, Fontaine du Sauvage & the Porte au Loup, Delemont. 50c, Eye, modes of transportation. 80c, Train, viaduct. 90c, St. Bernard dog, statue of saint, hospice on summit.

1989, Mar. 2   Photo.   Perf. 12x11½
829 A376 25c multicolored   .45   .25
830 A377 35c multicolored   .55   .40
831 A378 50c multicolored   .75   .25
832 A379 80c multicolored   1.25 1.00
833 A380 90c multicolored   1.50 1.10
    Nos. 829-833 (5)   4.50 3.00

Europa — A381

Industry — A382

Children's games: 50c, Hopscotch. 90c, Blindman's buff.

1989, May 23   Perf. 11½
834 A381 50c multicolored   .60   .50
835 A381 90c multicolored   1.50 1.25

Engr., Litho. & Eng. (2.80, 3, 3.60, 4, 5fr)
1989-94   Perf. 13x13½
842 A382 2.75fr Bricklayer   3.50 2.25
843 A382 2.80fr Cook   3.75 2.40
844 A382 3fr   Cabinet maker   3.75 1.75
845 A382 3.60fr Pharmacist   4.75 3.00
846 A382 3.75fr Fisherman   4.50 3.50
847 A382 4fr   Wine grower   5.25 3.00
848 A382 5fr   Cheesemaker   6.50 4.00
849 A382 5.50fr Dressmaker   6.50 4.00
    Nos. 842-849 (8)   38.50 23.90

Issued: 2.75fr, 5.50fr, 8/29/89; 3.75fr, 3/6/90; 2.80fr, 3.60fr, 1/24/92; 5fr, 9/7/93; 4fr, 3/15/94; 3fr, 7/5/94.

Swiss Electricians' Assoc., Cent. — A383

Swiss Travel Fund, 50th Anniv. A384

Fribourg University, Cent. — A385

Opening of the Natl. Sound-Recording Archives, 1st Anniv. — A386

Interparliamentary Union, Cent. — A387

1989, Aug. 25   Photo.   Perf. 11½
851 A383 35c multicolored   .55   .45
852 A384 50c multicolored   .75   .25
853 A385 80c "Wisdom" and "Science"   1.20   .80
854 A386 90c multicolored   1.30 1.00
855 A387 140c multicolored   1.75 1.25
    Nos. 851-855 (5)   5.55 3.75

Union of Swiss Philatelic Societies, Cent. — A388

Urban Railway System, Zurich A389

Assistance for Mountain Communities, 50th Anniv. A390

1990 World Ice Hockey Championships — A391

1990, Mar. 6
856 A388 25c 5c maroon type A19, 50c stamp type A20   .40   .20
857 A389 35c Locomotives   .75   .40
858 A390 50c Mountain farmer   .70   .30
859 A391 90c Athletes   1.25 1.00
    Nos. 856-859 (4)   3.10 1.90

Europa 1990 — A393

Post offices.

Litho. & Engr.
1990, May 22   Perf. 13½
861 A393 50c Lucerne   .75   .25
862 A393 90c Geneva   1.90 1.25

Conrad Ferdinand Meyer (1825-1898), Writer — A394

Designs: 50c, Angelika Kaufmann (1741-1807), painter. 80c, Blaise Cendrars (1887-1961), journalist. 90c, Frank Buchser (1828-1890), artist.

1990, Sept. 5   Litho.
863 A394 35c green & blk   .55   .40
864 A394 50c blue & blk   .75   .30
865 A394 80c yellow & blk   1.20   .80
866 A394 90c vermilion & blk   1.50 1.10
    Nos. 863-866 (4)   4.00 2.60

Swiss Confederation, 700th Anniv. in 1991 — A395

1990, Sept. 5   Photo.   Perf. 11½
867 A395 50c shown   .75   .40
868 A395 90c multi, diff.   1.60 1.25

Natl. Census A396

1990, Nov. 20
869 A396 50c multicolored   .75   .40

Animals — A397

1990-95   Litho. & Engr.   Perf. 13
870 A397 10c Cow   .30   .25
871 A397 50c House cats   .70   .30
872 A397 70c Rabbit   1.00   .65
  a.   Booklet pane of 10   12.00
        Complete booklet, #872a   12.00
873 A397 80c Barn owls   1.10   .60
874 A397 100c Horses   1.30   .80
875 A397 110c Geese   1.60   .60
876 A397 120c Dog   1.75 1.00
877 A397 140c Sheep   2.00   .75
878 A397 150c Goats   2.00   .75
879 A397 160c Turkey   2.00 1.25
880 A397 170c Donkey   2.50   .90
881 A397 200c Chickens   3.00 1.75
    Nos. 870-881 (12)   19.25 9.60

Issued: 50c, 3/6/90; 70c, 80c, 1/15/91; 10c, 160c, 1/24/92; 100c, 120c, 3/16/93; 150c, 200c, 7/5/94; #872a, 110c, 140c, 170c, 11/28/95.

This is an expanding set. Nos. 882-883 will be used for high values if necessary.

Swiss Confederation, 700th Anniv. — A398

Swiss Parliament, US Capitol A399

1991, Feb. 22   Photo.   Perf. 12
884 A398 50c "700 jahre"   .80   .25
885 A398 50c "700 onns"   .80   .25
886 A398 50c "700 ans"   .80   .25
887 A398 50c "700 anni"   .80   .25
  a.   Block of 4, #884-887   3.25 1.00
888 A399 1.60fr multicolored   2.50   .80
    Nos. 884-888 (5)   5.70 1.80

    See US No. 2532.

Bern, 800th Anniv. — A400

1991, Feb. 22   *Perf. 11½*
889 A400 80c multicolored   1.25   .60

Europa — A401

1991, May 14   *Litho.*   *Perf. 11½*
890 A401 50c Ariane payload
            fairing   1.00   .25
891 A401 90c Giotto probe   1.75 1.00

Union of Postal, Telephone and Telegraph Officials, Cent. — A402

1991, Sept. 10   *Photo.*   *Perf. 11½*
892 A402 80c multicolored   1.20   .70

Bridges A403

Designs: 50c, Stone bridge near Lavertezzo. 70c, Wooden "New Bridge" near Bremgarten. 80c, Railway bridge between Koblenz and Felsenau. 90c, Ganter Bridge, Simplon Pass.

1991, Sept. 10
893 A403 50c multicolored   .75   .25
894 A403 70c multicolored   1.10   .55
895 A403 80c multicolored   1.30   .75
896 A403 90c multicolored   1.50   .90
    Nos. 893-896 (4)   4.65 2.45

Mountain Lakes — A404   A404a

A404b

Design: 60c, Lake de Tanay.

Litho., Litho. & Engr. (60c, #908)
1991-95   *Perf. 13½x13*
904 A404 50c blue & multi   .70   .20
905 A404 60c blue & multi   .90   .25
  a.   Booklet pane of 10   8.50
907 A404 80c red & multi, diff.   1.10   .50
908 A404a 80c multicolored   1.10   .40
909 A404b 90c multicolored   1.50   .75
  a.   Booklet pane of 10   15.00
     Complete booklet, #909a   15.00
    Nos. 904-909 (5)   5.30 2.10

Issued: 50c, #907, 12/16/91; 60c, #908, 1/19/1993; 90c, 11/28/95.
See No. 1102.

Bird Over Rhine River — A405

Faces of Parents, Child — A406

Molecular Formula, Structure and Model A407

1992, Mar. 24   *Photo.*   *Perf. 11½*
911 A405 50c multicolored   .70   .25
912 A406 80c multicolored   1.20   .60
913 A407 80c multicolored   1.20 1.00
    Nos. 911-913 (3)   3.10 1.85

Intl. Rhine Regulation, cent. (No. 911), Pro Familia Switzerland, 50th anniv. (No. 912), Intl. Chemical Nomenclature Conf., Geneva, cent. (No. 913).

A408   A409

Europa: 90c, Columbus, map of voyage.

1992, Mar. 24
914 A408 50c multicolored   1.00   .50
915 A408 90c multicolored   2.00 1.10

Discovery of America, 500th anniv.

1992, May 22   *Photo.*   *Perf. 12*
916 A409 90c multicolored   1.30   .90

Protect the Alps.
See Austria No. 1571.

Comic Strips A410

1992, May 22   *Perf. 11½*
917 A410 50c Cosey   .70   .30
918 A410 80c Zep   1.20   .60
919 A410 90c Aloys   1.40 1.00
    Nos. 917-919 (3)   3.30 1.90

World of the Circus A411

50c, Clowns on trapeze. 70c, Sea lion, clown. 80c, Clown, elephant. 90c, Lipizzaner, harlequin.

1992, Aug. 25   *Photo.*   *Perf. 12x11½*
920 A411 50c multicolored   .75   .30
921 A411 70c multicolored   1.10   .60
922 A411 80c multicolored   1.20   .60
923 A411 90c multicolored   1.40 1.00
    Nos. 920-923 (4)   4.45 2.50

Central Office for Intl. Carriage by Rail, Cent. (in 1993) — A412

1992, Nov. 24   *Photo.*   *Perf. 11½*
924 A412 90c multicolored   1.40   .75

First Swiss Postage Stamps, 150th Anniv. — A413

Designs: 60c, Zurich Types A1, A2, Geneva Type A1. 80c, Stylized canceled stamp. 100c, Stylized stamps on album page.

1993, Mar. 16   *Photo.*   *Perf. 11½*
925 A413 60c multicolored   1.00   .50
926 A413 80c multicolored   1.25   .60
927 A413 100c multicolored   1.50 1.00
    Nos. 925-927 (3)   3.75 2.10

Paracelsus (1493-1541), Physician A414   Opening of Olympic Museum, Lausanne A415

Intl. Metalworkers' Federation, Cent. — A416

1993, Mar. 16   *Photo.*   *Perf. 11½*
928 A414 60c blue & sepia   .90   .35
929 A415 80c multicolored   1.20   .75
930 A416 180c multicolored   2.60 1.75
    Nos. 928-930 (3)   4.70 2.85

Lake Constance Steamer Hohentwiel A417

1993, May 5   *Photo.*   *Perf. 11½x12*
931 A417 60c multicolored   .95   .50
See Austria No. 1598, Germany No. 1786.

Contemporary Architecture A418

Europa: 60c, Media House, Villeurbanne, France. 80c, House, Breganzona, Switzerland.

Litho. & Engr.
1993, May 5   *Perf. 13½*
932 A418 60c multicolored   .90   .40
933 A418 80c red & black   1.30   .90

Works of Art by Swiss Women A419

Designs: 60c, Work No. 095, by Emma Kunz. 80c, Grande Cantatrice Lilas Goergens, by Aloise Corbaz. 100c, Under the Rain Cloud, by Meret Oppenheim. 120c, Four Spaces in Horizontal Bands, by Sophie Taeuber-Arp.

1993, Sept. 7   *Photo.*   *Perf. 11½*
934 A419 60c multicolored   .90   .40
      Size: 33x33 ½mm
935 A419 80c multicolored   1.20   .75
936 A419 100c multicolored   1.50 1.00
937 A419 120c multicolored   2.00 1.25
    Nos. 934-937 (4)   5.60 3.40

Swiss Sports School, 50th Anniv. A420

Jakob Bernoulli (1654-1705), Mathematician A421

Swiss Telecom PTT Participation in Unisource A422

ICAO, 50th Anniv. A423

1994, Mar. 15   *Photo.*   *Perf. 11½*
938 A420 60c multicolored   .90   .40
939 A421 80c multicolored   1.25   .45
940 A422 100c multicolored   1.50   .85
941 A423 180c multicolored   2.75 1.25
    Nos. 938-941 (4)   6.40 2.95

Intl. Congress of Mathematicians, Zurich (#939).

"Books and the Press" Exhibition, Geneva A424

1994, Mar. 15
942 A424 60c Early manuscripts   .95   .40
943 A424 80c Letterpress   1.25   .75
944 A424 100c Electronic pub-
            lishing   1.50 1.00
    Nos. 942-944 (3)   3.70 2.15

1994 World Cup Soccer Championships, U.S. — A425

1994, Mar. 15
945 A425 80c multicolored   1.20   .65

Research Vehicles
of August &
Jacques
Piccard — A426

Europa: 60c, Bathyscaphe Trieste. 100c,
Stratospheric balloon.

1994, May 17   Photo.   Perf. 12
946 A426 60c multicolored   1.00   .50
947 A426 100c multicolored   1.90 1.00

Georges
Simenon
(1903-89),
Writer
A427

Litho. & Engr.
1994, Oct. 15   Perf. 13
948 A427 100c multicolored   1.50   .90
See Belgium No. 1567, France No. 2443.

A428   A429

1994, Oct. 15   Photo.   Perf. 11½
949 A428 60c multicolored   .95   .35
Campaign to stop AIDS.

1995, Mar. 7   Photo.   Perf. 11½
Endangered species.
950 A429 60c European beaver   .90   .30
951 A429 80c Map butterfly   1.25   .50
952 A429 100c Green tree frog 1.50   .75
953 A429 120c Litte owl   1.90   .90
        Nos. 950-953 (4)   5.55 2.45

Swiss Wrestling
Assoc.,
Cent. — A430

Swiss Assoc.
of Producers
& Distributors
of Electricity,
Cent. — A431

Swiss News
Agency,
Cent. — A432

UN, 50th
Anniv.
A433

1995, Mar. 7
954 A430 60c blue & black   1.00   .55
955 A431 60c multicolored   1.00   .55
956 A432 80c multicolored   1.25 1.50
957 A433 180c multicolored   2.50 1.75
        Nos. 954-957 (4)   5.75 4.35

Peace &
Freedom
A434

Europa: 60c, Dove, faces. 100c, Zeus disguised as bull, abducting Europa, daughter of
King of Phoenicia.

Litho., Engr. & Embossed
1995, May 16   Perf. 13
958 A434 60c lt blue & dk blue 1.00   .40
959 A434 100c orange & brown   1.75   .85

Switzerland-
Liechtenstein
Postal
Relationship
A435

Litho. & Engr.
1995, Sept. 5   Perf. 13½
960 A435 60c multicolored   .90   .50

See Liechtenstein No. 1055.
No. 960 and Liechtenstein No. 1055 are
identical. This issue was valid for postage in
both countries.

Motion
Pictures,
Cent. — A436

Scenes from motion pictures: 60c, La Voca-
tion d'Andre Carrel. 80c, Anna Goldin-The
Last Witch. 150c, Pipilotti's Mistakes-
Absolution.

1995, Sept. 5   Photo.   Perf. 11½
961 A436 60c multicolored   .90   .40
962 A436 80c multicolored   1.20   .70
963 A436 150c multicolored   2.00 1.25
        Nos. 961-963 (3)   4.10 2.35

Telecom '95,
Geneva — A437

1995, Sept. 5
964 A437 180c multicolored   3.00 1.00

Swiss
Charities,
Solidarity
Chain, 50th
Anniv.
A438

Touring Club,
Cent. — A439

Federal Music
Festival,
Interlaken
A440

Swiss Natl.
Assoc. Pro
Filia,
Cent. — A441

Jean Piaget
(1896-1980),
Psychologist
A442

1996, Mar. 12   Photo.   Perf. 11½
965 A438 70c multicolored   1.00   .50
966 A439 70c multicolored   1.00   .50
967 A440 90c multicolored   1.40   .60
968 A441 90c multicolored   1.40   .60
969 A442 180c multicolored   2.50 2.00
        Nos. 965-969 (5)   7.30 4.20

Famous
Women — A443

Europa: 70c, S. Corinna Bille (1912-79),
author. 110c, Iris von Roten-Meyer (1917-90),
writer, painter.

Litho. & Engr.
1996, May 14   Perf. 13½
970 A443 70c multicolored   1.00   .50
971 A443 110c multicolored   1.60 1.10

Modern
Olympic
Games,
Cent. — A444

1996, May 14   Litho.   Perf. 13½
972 A444 180c multicolored   3.00 1.50

Guinness Record
Stamp — A445

Design: Aerial view of 11,000 gymnasts
arranged as No. 909, making record as
world's largest living postage stamp.

1996, June 27   Litho.   Perf. 13½x13
973 A445 90c multicolored   1.75   .80

Greeting
Stamps
A446

Various ornate or floral patterns.

Serpentine Die Cut 7 Vert.
1996, Sept. 10   Typo.
Self-Adhesive
Booklet Stamps
974 A446 90c yellow & black   1.50 1.00
975 A446 90c blue & multi   1.50 1.00
976 A446 90c red & multi   1.50 1.00

977 A446 90c green & multi   1.50 1.00
  a.   Booklet pane of 4, #974-977   6.00
        Complete booklet, 2 #977a   12.00

Music Boxes
and Automata
A447

Designs: 70c, Ring with mechanical figures,
musical movement, by Isaac-Daniel Piguet.
90c, Basso-piccolo mandolin cylinder music
box, by Eduard Jaccard. 110c, Station autom-
aton, by Paillard and Co. 180c, Kalliope disk
music box.

1996, Sept. 10   Photo.   Perf. 11½
978 A447 70c multicolored   1.10   .40
979 A447 90c multicolored   1.40   .60
980 A447 110c multicolored   1.75 1.00
981 A447 180c multicolored   2.75 1.50
        Nos. 978-981 (4)   7.00 3.50

Stamp Design
Competition
Winners — A448

Designs: 70c, Golden cow. 90c, Smiling
creature. 110c, Leaves. 180c, Dove.

1996, Nov. 26   Photo.   Perf. 11½
982 A448 70c blue & bister   1.10   .55
983 A448 90c multicolored   1.40   .80
984 A448 110c multicolored   1.75 1.00
985 A448 180c multicolored   2.75 1.75
        Nos. 982-985 (4)   7.00 4.10

"Globi" as
Postman
A449

1997, Mar. 11   Litho.   Perf. 13x13½
986 A449 70c multicolored   1.20   .45

Swiss
Railways,
150th Anniv.
A450

Designs: 70c, Locomotive 2000, 1990's.
90c, Red Arrow, 1930's. 140c, Pullman coach,
1920's-30's. 170c, Limmat steam locomotive,
1800's.

1997, Mar. 11   Photo.   Perf. 11½
987 A450 70c multicolored   1.10   .40
988 A450 90c multicolored   1.40   .55
989 A450 140c multicolored   2.25 1.25
990 A450 170c multicolored   2.50 1.75
        Nos. 987-990 (4)   7.25 3.95

Gallo-Roman
Art — A451

Archaeological finds: 70c, Venus of
Octodurus. 90c, Bronze bust of Bacchus.
110c, Ceramic fragment depicting Victoria.
180c, Mosaic theatrical mask.

1997, Mar. 11
991 A451 70c multicolored   1.10   .40
992 A451 90c multicolored   1.40   .50
993 A451 110c multicolored   1.60   .80
994 A451 180c multicolored   2.50 1.25
        Nos. 991-994 (4)   6.60 2.95

Swiss Air's North Atlantic Service, 50th Anniv. — A452

1997, Mar. 11   Litho.   Perf. 13½
995 A452 180c multicolored   2.75 1.10

Swiss Farmers' Union, Cent. — A453

1997, May 13   Litho.   Perf. 13½
996 A453 70c shown   1.10 .35
997 A453 90c Street map   1.30 .65
Swiss Municipalities' Union, cent. (#997).

Stories and Legends — A454

Europa: Devil and Billy Goat from legend of the "Devil's Bridge."

1997, May 13   Litho. & Engr.
998 A454 90c multicolored   1.40 1.10

King of Thailand's Visit to Switzerland, Cent. — A455

King Chulalongkorn (Rama V), Pres. Adolf Deucher.

1997, Sept. 12   Litho.   Perf. 13½
999 A455 90c multicolored   1.25 .75

Energy 2000 — A456

1997, Sept. 12   Photo.   Perf. 11½
1000 A456 70c Air (clouds)   1.00 .35
1001 A456 90c Fire   1.40 .65
1002 A456 110c Water   1.60 .95
1003 A456 180c Earth   2.75 1.50
    Nos. 1000-1003 (4)   6.75 3.45

Paul Karrer (1889-1971), Winner of Nobel Prize for Chemistry, 1937 — A457

Design: 110c, Alfred Nobel (1833-96), founder of Nobel Prize.

Litho. & Engr.
1997, Nov. 13   Perf. 13
1004 A457 90c gray & blk   1.40 .50
1005 A457 110c lt gray brn & blk   1.75 .75
Nos. 1004-1005 each issued in sheets of 8.
See Sweden Nos. 2254-2255.

Swiss Postal Service A458

Various people from different generations, cultures. Each stamp inscribed in one of Switzerland's four national languages with message to keep in touch.

1997, Nov. 20   Litho.   Perf. 13
Color of Denomination
1006 A458 70c blue   1.00 .40
1007 A458 70c yellow   1.00 .40
1008 A458 70c green   1.00 .40
1009 A458 70c red   1.00 .40
    a.   Strip of 4, #1006-1009   3.25 1.40

Division of Swiss PTT — A459

1998, Jan. 7   Litho.   Perf. 13½
1010 A459 90c Swisscom   1.10 .40
1011 A459 90c Swiss Post   1.10 .40

Confederation, 150th Anniv. and Helvetic Republic, Bicent. — A460

Stylized design, proclamation in one of four languages, location of denomination: No. 1012, German, LL. No. 1013, Romansch, LR. No. 1014, French, UL. No. 1015, Italian, UR.

1998, Mar. 10   Photo.   Perf. 11½
1012 A460 90c multicolored   1.40 1.00
1013 A460 90c multicolored   1.40 1.00
1014 A460 90c multicolored   1.40 1.00
1015 A460 90c multicolored   1.40 1.00
    a.   Block of 4, #1012-1015   5.75 5.00

Printed in continuous design.

Swiss Old Age and Survivors' Insurance, 50th Anniv. A461

Opening of Natl. Museum, Prangins Castle A462

St. Gallen University, Cent. — A463

1998, Mar. 10
1016 A461 70c multicolored   1.00 .40
1017 A462 70c multicolored   1.00 .40
1018 A463 90c multicolored   1.40 .80
    Nos. 1016-1018 (3)   3.40 1.60

View of Switzerland A464

Designs: 10c, Simplon Pass. 20c, Snow-covered winter scene. 50c, Fence posts along country road. 70c, Hobbyhorses, posts. 90c, Stream, route marker. 110c, Lake, shoreline.

1998, Mar. 10   Litho.   Perf. 13x13½
1019 A464 10c multicolored   .20 .20
1020 A464 20c multicolored   .30 .20
1021 A464 50c multicolored   .70 .30
1022 A464 70c multicolored   1.00 .30
1023 A464 90c multicolored   1.40 .30
1024 A464 110c multicolored   1.60 .75
    Nos. 1019-1024 (6)   5.20 2.05
    See Nos. 1027-1029.

Sion, Candidate for 2006 Winter Olympic Games — A465

1998, Feb. 12   Litho.   Perf. 13½
1025 A465 90c multicolored   1.40 .75

National Day — A466

1998, May 12
1026 A466 90c multicolored   1.25 1.10
    Europa.

View of Switzerland Type of 1998
140c, City of Zug. 170c, Olive grove, Castagnola. 180c, Road, mountains outside Reutigen.

1998, Sept. 8   Litho.   Perf. 13
1027 A464 140c multicolored   1.90 .50
1028 A464 170c multicolored   2.50 .60
1029 A464 180c multicolored   2.75 .75
    Nos. 1027-1029 (3)   7.15 1.85

Youth Sports — A467

Die Cut x Serpentine Die Cut
1998, Sept. 8   Photo.
Self-Adhesive
Booklet Stamps
1030 A467 70c Roller blading   1.10 .50
1031 A467 70c Snow boarding   1.10 .50
1032 A467 70c Mountain biking   1.10 .50
1033 A467 70c Street basketball   1.10 .50
1034 A467 70c Beach volleyball   1.10 .50
    a.   Booklet pane, #1030-1034 + label   5.50
    Complete booklet, 2 #1034a   11.00

Universal Declaration of Human Rights, 50th Anniv. — A468

1998, Nov. 25   Litho.   Perf. 13½
1035 A468 70c multicolored   1.10 .50

Christmas A469

1998, Nov. 25
1036 A469 90c multicolored   1.40 .75

Bridge 24, Slender West Lake, Yangzhou A470

Chillon Castle, Lake Geneva A470A

Photo. & Engr.
1998, Nov. 25   Perf. 13½
1037 A470 20c multicolored   .30 .20

Photo.
1038 A470A 70c multicolored   1.00 .55
    a.   Sheet of 4 each, #1038-1039   5.25 5.00

Souvenir Sheet
Perf. 11½
1039 A470A 90c Castle, Bridge 24   1.50 1.50

No. 1039 contains one 53x45mm stamp. See China (PRC) Nos. 2920-2921.
No. 1039 exists with China 1999 World Philatelic Exhibition emblem and a hologram in margin. These were sold for 3.50fr only canceled on cover.

Switzerland Post, 150th Anniv. A471

1999, Jan. 21   Photo.   Perf. 12
1040 A471 90c multicolored   1.40 .75

Pingu the Penguin as Postman A472

1999, Mar. 9   Litho.   Perf. 13½
1041 A472 70c Carrying package   1.00 .50
1042 A472 90c In delivery cart   1.40 .65
See Nos. 1064-1065 for redrawn designs.

Comic Book, "Les Amours de Monsieur Vieux Bois," by Rodolphe Töpffer (1799-1846) A473

Vieux Bois: No. 1043, Waving out of window, lady walking away. No. 1044, Down on knees, lady. No. 1045, In air after knocking over furniture. No. 1046, Pulling lady up to lift her over wall. No. 1047, Standing with his lady to be married.

Die Cut x Serpentine Die Cut
1999, Mar. 9
Self-Adhesive
Booklet Stamps
1043 A473 90c multicolored   1.40 .55
1044 A473 90c multicolored   1.40 .55
1045 A473 90c multicolored   1.40 .55
1046 A473 90c multicolored   1.40 .55
1047 A473 90c multicolored   1.40 .55
    a.   Booklet pane, #1043-1047 + label   7.00
    Complete booklet, 2 #1047a   15.00

First Non-stop Balloon Flight Around World by Bertrand Piccard and Brian Jones — A473a

1999, Mar. 24   Litho.   Perf. 13½
1047B A473a 90c multicolored   1.40   .55

UPU, 125th Anniv. — A474

1999, May 5   Photo.   Perf. 12
1048 A474 20c shown   .35   .25
1049 A474 70c UPU emblem   1.00   .65
a.   Pair, #1048-1049   1.35   1.25

No. 1049 is 56x30mm. Issued in sheets of 8 stamps.

SOS Children's Village, Wabern, 50th Anniv. — A475

1999, May 5   Litho.   Perf. 13½
1050 A475 70c multicolored   1.00   .45

Vintners Festival, Vevey — A476

1999, May 5
1051 A476 90c multicolored   1.40   .55
Complete booklet, 10 #1051   14.00

Council of Europe, 50th Anniv. — A477

1999, May 5   Photo.   Perf. 11½
1052 A477 90c multicolored   1.40   .55

Swiss National Park — A478

1999, May 5   Litho.   Perf. 13½
1053 A478 90c Horns of an ibex   1.40   1.10

Europa.

Geneva Convention, 50th Anniv. — A479

1999, May 5
1054 A479 110c multicolored   1.75   .85

Field Marshal Aleksandr Suvorov's Alpine Campaign, 200th Anniv. A481

Designs: 70c, Suvorov and soldiers, monument at Schöllenen Gorge. 110c, Suvorov's vanguard by Lake Klöntal.

1999, Sept. 24   Photo.   Perf. 11¾
1056 A481 70c multicolored   1.10   .50
1057 A481 110c multicolored   1.75   .70

Nos. 1056-1057 each issued in sheets of 8 stamps.
See Russia Nos. 6534-6535.

Rights of the Child — A482

1999, Sept. 24   Litho.   Perf. 13½
1058 A482 70c multicolored   1.00   .45

Carl Lutz (1895-1975), Diplomat, Rescuer of Jews — A483

1999, Sept. 24
1059 A483 90c multicolored   1.40   .55

Christian Friedrich Schönbein (1799-1868), Discoverer of Ozone — A484

1999, Sept. 24
1060 A484 1.10fr multicolored   1.60   .60

Midday in the Alps, by Giovanni Segantini (1858-99) A485

1999, Sept. 24
1061 A485 180c multicolored   2.75   1.25

Christmas — A486

Perf. 13½x13¼
1999, Nov. 23   Litho.
1062 A486 90c multicolored   1.40   .75

Millennium A487

Perf. 11¾x11½
1999, Nov. 23   Photo.
1063 A487 90c multicolored   1.40   .55

No. 1063 was printed in sheets of 8 stamps and 8 se-tenant labels with text or blank. Swiss Post offered to print photos or artwork sent in by customers on the blank labels. Personalized sheets sold for 14fr per sheet.

Pingu The Penguin Type of 1999
Redrawn to Omit Strings on Packages
1999, Dec. 6   Litho.   Perf. 13¼x13½
1064 A472 70c Like #1041   1.10   .55
1065 A472 90c Like #1042   1.40   .70

Intl. Cycling Union, Cent. — A488

2000, Mar. 7   Litho.   Perf. 13¼x13½
1066 A488 70c multicolored   1.00   .40

Swiss Souvenirs — A489

Souvenirs in snow domes: 10c, Alphorn. 20c, Fondue pot. 30c, Wine pitchers. 50c, Figurine of ibex. 60c, Neuchâtel "Pendule" wall clock. 70c, St. Bernard dog.

2000, Mar. 7   Litho.   Perf. 13x13¼
1067 A489 10c multicolored   .20   .20
1068 A489 20c multicolored   .30   .20
1069 A489 30c multicolored   .45   .35
1070 A489 50c multicolored   .75   .45
1071 A489 60c multicolored   .85   .50
1072 A489 70c multicolored   1.10   .60
    Nos. 1067-1072 (6)   3.65   2.30
See No. 1101.

National Council of Women, Cent. A490

2000, May 10   Litho.   Perf. 13¼
1073 A490 70c multi   1.10   .55

Europa, 2000
Common Design Type
2000, May 10
1074 CD17 90c multi   1.25   .75

Embroidery — A491

Illustration reduced.

Embroidered
2000, June 21   Imperf.
Self-Adhesive
1075 A491 5fr multi   12.00   12.00
a.   Sheet of 4   175.00   175.00

A492

Designs: 120c, Payerne Church, violin. 130c, Church of St. Saphorin, waiter's tray. 180c, Vals hot springs, bather.

2000, June 21   Litho.   Perf. 13x13¼
1076 A492 120c multi   1.75   .75
1077 A492 130c multi   1.90   .80
1078 A492 180c multi   2.50   1.00
    Nos. 1076-1078 (3)   6.15   2.55
See Nos. 1089-1092.

2000 Census — A493

2000, Sept. 15   Perf. 13¼x13½
1079 A493 70c multi   1.00   .55

A Perfect World, by Sandra Dobler A494

My Town, by Stephanie Aerschmann A495

Stampin' the Future children's stamp design contest winners: No. 1080, Alien From Outer Space, by Yannik Kehrli. No. 1081, Looks Below the Sun, by Charlotte Bättig.

Serpentine Die Cut 5¾ Vert.
2000, June 15
Booklet Stamps
Self-Adhesive
1080 A494 70c multi   1.20   .60
1081 A494 70c multi   1.20   .60
1082 A494 70c shown   1.20   .60
1083 A495 70c shown   1.20   .60
a.   Booklet pane, #1080-1083   4.75
    Booklet, 2 #1083a   9.50

The booklet, which was sold unfolded, has rouletting between panes.

2000 Summer Olympics, Sydney A496

2000, Sept. 15   Photo.   Die Cut
Booklet Stamps
Self-Adhesive
1084 A496 90c Swimmer   1.50   .60
1085 A496 90c Cyclist   1.50   .60
1086 A496 90c Runner   1.50   .60
a.   Booklet pane, #1084-1086   4.50
    Booklet, #1086a   4.50

No. 1086a is separated from booklet cover by rouletting. The booklet was sold folded. See Nos. 12O1-12O2.

Stamp
Day — A497

Perf. 13¼x13½

2000, Nov. 21			**Litho.**
1087	A497	70c multi	1.10 .40

Christmas — A498

2000, Nov. 21		**Photo.**	**Perf. 11½**
Granite Paper			
1088	A498	90c multi	1.60 .50

Type of 2000

Designs: 200c, Mountain, hiker. 300c, Cyclist, bridge and church, Biasca.

2000-01		**Litho.**	**Perf. 13x13¼**
1089	A492	200c multi	3.00 2.00
1090	A492	220c multi	3.25 2.25
1091	A492	300c multi	4.50 3.00
1092	A492	400c multi	6.00 3.75

Issued: 200c, 300c, 11/21/00. 220c, 400c, 3/13/01.

Alice Rivaz
(1901-98),
Writer — A499

Perf. 13¼x13½

2001, Mar. 13			**Litho. & Engr.**
1093	A499	70c multi	1.10 .40

Aero Club,
Cent.
A500

2001, Mar. 13		**Litho.**	**Perf. 13¼**
1094	A500	90c multi	1.40 .55

Congratulations
A501

2001, Mar. 13			**Perf. 13¼x13½**
1095	A501	90c multi	1.50 .60

Caritas,
Cent. — A502

2001, Mar. 13			
1096	A502	110c multi	1.60 .75

UN High
Commissioner
for Refugees,
50th
Anniv. — A503

2001, Mar. 13			
1097	A503	130c multi	1.90 1.00

Vela Museum,
Ligornetto
A504

2001, May 9			
1098	A504	70c multi	1.10 .50

Europa — A505

2001, May 9			
1099	A505	90c multi	1.40 .60

Chocosuisse,
Cent. — A506

2001, May 9		**Photo.**	**Perf. 11½**
Granite Paper			
1100	A506	90c multi	1.40 .50

No. 1100 has a scratch-and-sniff coating with a chocolate aroma.

Swiss Souvenirs Type of 2000
Serpentine Die Cut 5¾ Horiz.

2001, May 9			**Litho.**
Self-Adhesive			
1101	A489	70c Like #1072	1.10 .40
a.		Booklet of 12	13.00

Type of 1995
Serpentine Die Cut 5¾ Vert.

2001, May 9			**Typo.**
Self-Adhesive			
1102	A404b	90c multi	1.40 .45
a.		Booklet of 12	16.50

Type of 2000

Designs: 90c, Farm house, Willisau, people feeding horse. 100c, Boat on Lake Geneva, woman at water's edge. 110c, Kleine Matterhorn Glacier, skier.

2001, Sept. 20		**Litho.**	**Perf. 13x13¼**
1103	A492	90c multi	1.40 .50
1104	A492	100c multi	1.50 .50
1105	A492	110c multi	1.60 .60
		Nos. 1103-1105 (3)	4.50 1.60

The Birth of Venus,
by Arnold Böcklin
(1827-1901)
A507

2001, Sept. 20			**Perf. 13½**
1106	A507	180c multi	2.50 2.00

Souvenir Sheet

Flowers — A508

2001, Sept. 20			**Perf. 13¼x12¾**
1107	A508	Sheet of 4	5.75 5.50
a.		70c Melastoma malabathricum	1.00 .80
b.		90c Saraca cauliflora	1.40 .90
c.		110c Leontopodium alpinum	1.60 1.25
d.		130c Gentiana clusii	1.75 1.50

See Singapore Nos. 984-988.

Illustrations from
Children's Book,
"The Rainbow
Fish," by Marcus
Pfister — A509

2001, Sept. 20		**Photo.**	**Perf. 12¾x14**
1108	A509	70c Fish, coral	1.10 .40
1109	A509	90c Fish, starfish	1.40 .50

Stamp Day
Stamp Design
Competition
Winner — A510

Perf. 13¼x13½			
2001, Nov. 20			**Litho.**
1110	A510	70c multi	1.10 .45

Christmas — A511

2001, Nov. 20			**Perf. 11½**
Granite Paper			
1111	A511	90c multi	1.50 .60

Geneva
Escalade, 400th
Anniv. — A512

Perf. 13¼x13½			
2002, Mar. 12			**Litho.**
1112	A512	70c multi	1.10 .40

Federal
Parliament
Building,
Cent. — A513

2002, Mar. 12			
1113	A513	90c multi	1.40 .50

Rega Air
Rescue
Foundation
A514

Litho. with Hologram Affixed

2002, Mar. 12			**Perf. 13x13¾**
1114	A514	180c multi	2.75 2.00

Expo.02, Switzerland — A515

No. 1115: a, "E." b, Backwards "P." c, "0." d, "2."

2002, Mar. 12		**Photo.**	**Perf. 14x13¼**
Granite Paper			
1115	A515	Block of 4	4.50 4.50
a.-d.		70c Any single	1.10 .80

Swiss Railways,
Cent. — A516

Designs: 70c, RABDe 500 Inter-city tilting train. 90c, Inter-city 2000 double-deck train. 120c, Seetal line railcar. 130c, Re 460 locomotive.

2002, Mar. 12			**Perf. 12¾x14**
1116	A516	70c multi	1.20 .40
1117	A516	90c multi	1.60 .70
1118	A516	120c multi	1.75 .75
1119	A516	130c multi	2.00 1.00
		Nos. 1116-1119 (4)	6.55 2.85

Souvenir Sheet

Arteplage Mobile du Jura — A517

2002, May 15		**Photo.**	**Perf. 14**
1120	A517	90c multi	1.40 1.25

Expo.02, Switzerland.

Europa
A518

2002, May 15		**Litho.**	**Perf. 13¼**
1121	A518	70c Clown	1.10 .40
1122	A518	90c Clown, diff.	1.40 .50

Teddy Bears, Cent. — A519

No. 1123 — Teddy bear from: a, France, 1925 (round, with tan frame, 26mm diameter).

b, Switzerland, 1950s (square with cut in corners, 25x25mm). c, Germany, 1904 (oval, 23x33mm). d, Switzerland, 2002 (rectangular, 26x23mm). e, England, c. 1920 (round, with blue and red frame, 26mm diameter).

2002, May 15   *Die Cut*
Self-Adhesive
1123 A519 Booklet pane of 5   7.00
a.-e. 90c Any single   1.40   1.00
f. Booklet, 2 #1123   14.00

Cessation of Production at Swiss Post Stamp Printers — A520

Litho. & Engr.
2002, Sept. 17   *Perf. 13¼*
1124 A520 70c multi   1.10   .40

Ladybug — A521

Illustration reduced.

Serpentine Die Cut 12¼ Vert.
2002, Sept. 17   Litho.
Self-Adhesive
1125 A521 90c multi + label   1.40   .55
a. Booklet pane of 10   14.00

Insects — A522

Designs: 10c, Anax imperator. 20c, Mesoacidalia aglaja. 50c, Rosalia alpina. 100c, Graphosoma lineatum.

Perf. 13¾x14¼
2002, Sept. 17   Litho.
1126 A522 10c multi   .20   .20
1127 A522 20c multi   .30   .20
1128 A522 50c multi   .75   .20
1129 A522 100c multi   1.50   .30
   Nos. 1126-1129 (4)   2.75   .90

Minerals — A523

Designs: 200c, Quartz crystal. 500c, Titanite.

2002-05   Litho.   *Perf. 13¾*
1130 A523 200c multi   3.00   1.50
1131 A523 500c multi   7.50   2.75
a. Perf. 13¾x14¼   8.00   2.75

Issued: Nos. 1130-1131, 9/17/02. No. 1131a, 5/10/05.

Switzerland's Entry Into United Nations — A524

Perf. 13¾x14¼
2002, Sept. 10   Litho.
1132 A524 90c multi   1.40   .50

Stamp Day — A525

2002, Nov. 19   *Perf. 13¾x14*
1133 A525 70c multi   1.10   .45

World Alpine Skiing Championships, St. Moritz — A526

2002, Nov. 19   *Perf. 14x13¾*
1134 A526 90c multi   1.40   .50

Emblem of Switzerland Tourism — A527

Serpentine Die Cut 13¼ Vert.
2002, Nov. 19
Self-Adhesive
1135 A527 (1.30fr) blue & multi   2.00   .50
a. Booklet pane of 6   12.00
1136 A527 (1.80fr) red & multi   2.75   .75
a. Booklet pane of 6   16.50

Nos. 1135-1136 were valid only on post cards sent to European (#1135) or non-European (#1136) addresses, and could not be used in combination with other stamps. No. 1135a sold for 7.20fr, and No. 1136a for 10fr.

Christmas — A528

2002, Nov. 19   Photo.   *Perf. 11½*
Granite Paper
1137 A528 90c multi   1.40   .50

Swiss Natl. Association of and for the Blind, Cent. — A529

Litho. & Embossed
2003, Mar. 6   *Perf. 14¾x14½*
1138 A529 70c red & carmine   1.10   .45

100th Natl. Horse Market and Show, Saignelégier — A530

2003, Mar. 6   Litho.   *Perf. 13¼x13½*
1139 A530 90c multi   1.40   .50

2003 World Orienteering Championships, Rapperswil and Jona — A531

2003, Mar. 6
1140 A531 90c multi   1.40   .50

Intl. Year of Water — A532

2003, Mar. 6   *Perf. 13x13¼*
1141 A532 90c multi   1.40   .50

Medicinal Plants — A533

Designs: 70c, Hypericum perforatum. 90c, Vinca minor. 110c, Valeriana officinalis. 120c, Arnica montana. 130c, Centaurium minus. 180c, Malva sylvestris. 220c, Matricaria chamomilla.

2003-05   *Perf. 14x13¾*
1142 A533 70c multi   1.10   .50
1143 A533 90c multi   1.40   .50
1144 A533 110c multi   1.60   .65
1145 A533 120c multi   1.75   .75
a. Perf. 14x14½   1.90   .40
1146 A533 130c multi   1.90   .90
1147 A533 180c multi   2.60   1.10
a. Perf. 14x14½   3.00   .60
1148 A533 220c multi   3.25   1.50
a. Perf. 14x14½   3.50   .70
   Nos. 1142-1148 (7)   13.60   5.90

Issued: Nos. 1142-1148, 3/6/03; Nos. 1145a, 1147a, 1148a, 2005.

Europa — A534

2003, May 8   Litho.   *Perf. 13¼x13*
1149 A534 90c multi   1.40   .50

Comic Strip Art — A535

No. 1150 — Envelope and: a, Woman, birthday cake. b, Man, heart. c, Man, thunder cloud. d, Woman, musical note.
90c, Envelope, woman, duck.

2003, May 8   *Perf. 14¾*
1150 A535 Block of 4   4.75   4.00
a.-d. 70c Any single   1.10   .50
Souvenir Sheet
1151 A535 90c multi   1.50   1.25
   20th Intl. Comics Festival, Sierre.

Souvenir Sheet

Trilateral Stamp Exhibition, Ticino — A536

2003, May 8   *Perf. 14¾*
1152 A536 Sheet of 2   1.50   1.25
a. 20c Eagle   .30   .20
b. 70c Gentian   1.20   .40

Switzerland's Victory in 2003 America's Cup Yacht Races — A537

2003, Mar 7   Litho.   *Perf. 13x13¼*
1153 A537 90c multi   1.40   .45

No. 1153 was not sent to standing order subscribers until September.

Minerals Type of 2002

Designs: 300c, Rutilated quartz. 400c, Green fluorite.

2003, Sept. 9   *Perf. 13¾x14¼*
1154 A523 300c multi   4.50   2.00
1155 A523 400c multi   5.75   3.00

Comic Strip "Diddl," by Thomas Goletz — A538

Designs: 70c, Mice reading love letters. 90c, Mouse chasing flying envelopes.

2003, Sept. 9   *Perf. 13¼x13½*
1156 A538 70c multi   1.10   .45
1157 A538 90c multi   1.40   .55

UNESCO World Heritage Sites — A539

Designs: No. 1158, Jungfrau-Aletsch-Bietschhorn. No. 1159, Three Castles, Bellinzona. No. 1160, Old City, Bern. No. 1161, Convent of St. Gall. No. 1162, Benedictine Convent of St. John, Müstair.

2003, Sept. 9   *Perf. 12¾*
1158 A539 90c multi   1.40   .55
1159 A539 90c multi   1.40   .55
1160 A539 90c multi   1.40   .55
1161 A539 90c multi   1.40   .55
1162 A539 90c multi   1.40   .55
   Nos. 1158-1162 (5)   7.00   2.75

Nos. 1158-1162 each issued in sheets of 6.

Stamp Day — A540

Perf. 13¼x13½
2003, Nov. 19   Litho.
1163 A540 70c multi   1.10   .45

Four-leaf Clover — A541

Illustration reduced.

Serpentine Die Cut 12¼ Vert.
2003, Nov. 19
Self-Adhesive

1164	A541	130c multi + label	1.90	.65
a.		Booklet of 10	19.00	

Christmas — A542

Ornaments: 70c, Horseman. 90c, Santa Claus.

2003, Nov. 19   Photo.   Perf. 11½

1165	A542	70c multi	1.10	.45
1166	A542	90c multi	1.40	.55

Swiss Design — A543

Designs: 15c, Rex potato peeler, 1947, designed by Alfred Neweczeral. 50c, Zipper, 1924, designed by M.O. Winterthaler. 85c, Station clock, 1944, designed by Hanls Hilfiker. No. 1169, Le Fauteuil Grand Confort (black armchair), 1928, designed by Le Corbusier. No. 1170, Landi chair (aluminum chair), 1938, designed by Hans Coray.

Serpentine Die Cut 12
2003-04   Litho.
Self-Adhesive

1167	A543	15c multi	.25	.20
a.		Booklet pane of 10	2.50	
1168	A543	85c multi	1.40	.30
a.		Booklet pane of 10	14.00	
1169	A543	100c multi + etiquette	1.60	.30
a.		Booklet pane of 10 + 10 etiquettes	16.00	
b.		Nos. 1167-1169 on translucent paper	3.25	
1170	A543	100c multi + etiquette	1.60	.30
a.		Booklet pane of 10 + 10 etiquettes	16.00	

Coil Stamp

1171	A543	50c multi	.80	.20
		Nos. 1167-1171 (5)	5.65	1.30

Issued: 15c, 85c, No. 1169, 12/30; No. 1170, 3/31/04; 50c, 9/7/04.
See No. 1206.

FIFA (Fédération Internationale de Football Association), Cent. — A544

2004, Mar. 9   Perf. 13¼

1172	A544	100c multi	1.60	.55

UEFA (European Football Union), 50th Anniv. — A545

2004, Mar. 9   Perf. 13¼x13½

1173	A545	130c multi	2.00	.65

CERN (European Organization for Nuclear Research), 50th Anniv. — A546

2004, Mar. 9   Perf. 13½x13¼

1174	A546	180c multi	2.75	.90

Comic Strip "Titeuf," by Zep — A547

Titeuf: No. 1175, Giving spring flower to Nadia. No. 1176, Sitting in refrigerator. No. 1177, Running through raked leaves. No. 1178, Pointing at snowman.

2004, Mar. 9   Perf. 14x13½

1175	A547	85c multi	1.40	.45
1176	A547	85c multi	1.40	.45
1177	A547	85c multi	1.40	.45
1178	A547	85c multi	1.40	.45
		Nos. 1175-1178 (4)	5.60	1.80

Souvenir Sheet

Cycling — A548

No. 1179 — Cyclists and marker for: a, Route 5. b, Route 3.

2004, Mar. 9   Perf. 14x13½

1179	A548	Sheet of 2	3.25	1.10
a.-b.		100c Either single	1.60	.55

Doorbell Button — A549

2004, May 6   Perf. 14½x14¼

1180	A549	85c multi	1.40	.45

Europa A550

2004, May 6   Perf. 14¼x14½

1181	A550	100c multi	1.60	.55

2004 Summer Olympics, Athens A551

2004, May 6   Perf. 13x13¼

1182	A551	100c multi	1.60	.55

See No. 12O3.

Zeppelin NT — A552

2004, May 6   Perf. 14x13½

1183	A552	180c multi	2.75	.90

Diddl Type of 2003

Designs: 85c, Diddl with teddy bear, Pimboli, and butterflies. 100c, Diddl with flower.

2004, May 6   Perf. 13¼x13½

1184	A538	85c multi	1.40	.45
1185	A538	100c multi	1.60	.55

UNESCO World Heritage Type of 2003

Design: Monte San Giorgio.

2004, Sept. 7   Perf. 13¾x14¼

1186	A539	100c multi	1.60	.55

Issued in sheets of 6.

Suisse Balance Health Program A553

2004, Sept. 7   Perf. 13¼x13½

1187	A553	85c multi	1.40	.45

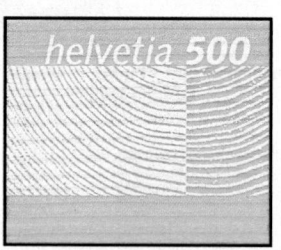

Wood — A554

Silk-screened on Wood
2004, Sept. 7   Imperf.
Self-Adhesive

1188	A554	500c white	8.00	2.75

Cheesemaking A555

Designs: 100c, Cheesemaker inspecting curds and whey. 130c, Cheeses, grapes and nuts.

2004, Sept. 7   Litho.   Perf. 13¼x13½

1189	A555	100c multi	1.60	.55
1190	A555	130c multi	2.10	.70

Animal Protection A556

2004, Sept. 7   Perf. 14x13½

1191	A556	85c Cat	1.40	.45
1192	A556	100c Hedgehog	1.60	.55
1193	A556	130c Pig	2.10	.70
		Nos. 1191-1193 (3)	5.10	1.70

Nos. 1191-1193 each issued in sheets of 6.

Souvenir Sheet

Sitting Helvetia Stamps and Coins, 150th Anniv. — A557

No. 1194: a, Type A17. b, Coin.

Litho. (#1194a), Litho. & Embossed (#1194b)
Perf. 14¼x13¾ on 3 Sides
2004, Sept. 7

1194	A557	Sheet of 2	2.80	.90
a.-b.		85c Either single	1.40	.45

Stamp Day — A558

Perf. 13¼x13½
2004, Nov. 23   Litho.

1195	A558	85c multi	1.50	.50

Sports A559

2004, Nov. 23   Litho.   Perf. 13x13½

1196	A559	180c multi	3.25	1.10

No. 1196 is identical to United Nations Offices in Geneva No. 433. The stamp, available for use throughout Switzerland, also served as an official stamp for the International Olympic Committee.

Christmas Ornaments Types of 2000-2003

2004, Nov. 23   Photo.   Perf. 13x13½

1197		Sheet of 5	8.50	8.50
a.	A511	85c Snowflake	1.50	.50
b.	A528	85c Church	1.50	.50
c.	A498	100c Angel	1.75	.60
d.	A542	100c Horseman	1.75	.60
e.	A542	100c Santa Claus	1.75	.60

Photographs by René Burri — A560

No. 1198: a, Children kissing, German inscription. b, Teenagers on bicycle, French inscription. c, Man and woman kissing, Italian inscription. d, Man and woman in bumper car, Romansch inscription.

Serpentine Die Cut 12

2005, Jan. 3   **Litho.**

Self-Adhesive

1198	Block of 4, #a-d + 4 etiquettes	6.75	
a.-d.	A560 100c Any single	1.60	.35
e.	Booklet pane, 2 each #1198a-1198d + 8 etiquettes	13.50	

No. 1198 lacks self-adhesive selvage, and is on a translucent paper that is rouletted on the left and right sides. No. 1198e has a white paper backing, has each stamp and its setenant etiquette surrounded by self-adhesive selvage, and is rouletted through the selvage and backing paper.

Swiss Federal Institute of Technology, Zurich, 150th Anniv. — A561

2005, Mar. 8   **Perf. 13**

1199	A561 85c multi	1.50	.50

Matterhorn Superimposed Over Inverted Map of Africa — A562

2005, Mar. 8   **Perf. 13x13¼**

1200	A562 85c multi	1.50	.50

Discovery of rocks from Africa making up top of the Matterhorn.

Unspunnen Traditional Costume and Alpine Herdsman's Festival, Bicent. — A563

2005, Mar. 8   **Perf. 13¼x13**

1201	A563 100c multi	1.75	.60

Albert Einstein's Theory of Relativity, Cent. — A564

2005, Mar. 8   **Perf. 13½x13¼**

1202	A564 130c multi	2.25	.75

Cartoon Mouse, by Uli Stein — A565

Mouse with: 85c, Slice of Swiss cheese in typewriter. 100c, Golf club and letter on tee.

2005, Mar. 8   **Perf. 13¼x13½**

1203	A565 85c multi	1.50	.50
1204	A565 100c multi	1.75	.60

Souvenir Sheet

Geneva International Auto Show, Cent. — A566

2005, Mar. 8   **Perf. 13¾x14¼**

1205	A566 Sheet of 2	4.00	4.00
a.	100c Front of car	1.75	.60
b.	130c Side of car	2.25	.75

Swiss Design Type of 2003-04

Design: Fixpencil, by Caran d'Ache.

2005, May 10 Serpentine Die Cut 12

Self-Adhesive

1206	A543 220c multi + etiquette	3.75	.75
a.	Serpentine die cut 12¼x12 + etiquette	3.75	.75
b.	Booklet pane, 6 #1206, 4 #1206a + 10 etiquettes	37.50	

Europa A567

2005, May 10   **Perf. 13x13¼**

1207	A567 100c multi	1.75	.60

Soccer for the Visually Impaired A568

2005, May 10   **Perf. 13¾x14¼**

1208	A568 100c multi	1.75	.60

Printed in sheets of 6.

Opening of Paul Klee Center, Bern — A569

2005, May 10   **Perf. 13¼x14**

1209	A569 100c multi	1.75	.60

Printed in sheets of 6.

Stylized Butterflies A570

Serpentine Die Cut 11¾

2005, May 10

Self-Adhesive

1210	A570 100c multi	1.75	.60
a.	Booklet pane of 10 + 10 labels	17.50	

Felix the Bunny, by Annette Langen A571

Felix and: 85c, Lambs, cows. 100c, Swans and Chillon Castle.

2005, May 10   **Perf. 13x13¼**

1211	A571 85c multi	1.50	.50
1212	A571 100c multi	1.75	.60

Subtractive Color Combinations — A572

Additive Color Combinations — A573

Serpentine Die Cut 12½

2005, Sept. 6   **Litho.**

Self-Adhesive

1213	A572 50c multi	.80	.30
1214	A573 100c multi	1.60	.55

Swiss Timepieces A574

Designs: 100c, Watchmaker, pocket watch and mechanism. 130c, Woman, wristwatches.

2005, Sept. 6   **Perf. 13¼x13½**

1215	A574 100c multi	1.60	.55
1216	A574 130c multi	2.10	.70

Cell Phone Pictures A575

Images: 85c, On Horseback, by Brigit Rohrbach. 100c, Mountain Hike, by Peter Schumacher. 130c, On Top of the World, by Rémy Sager. 180c, Tracks in the Snow, by Debora Ronchi.

2005, Sept. 6   **Perf. 14¼x14**

1217	A575 85c multi	1.40	.45
1218	A575 100c multi	1.60	.55
1219	A575 130c multi	2.10	.70
1220	A575 180c multi	3.00	1.00
	Nos. 1217-1220 (4)	8.10	2.70

Souvenir Sheet

Friends of Nature Switzerland, Cent. — A576

2005, Sept. 6   **Perf. 13½**

1221	A576 Sheet of 4	7.00	7.00
a.	85c Skiers	1.40	1.40
b.	100c Chalet, vert.	1.60	1.60
c.	110c People fording stream	1.75	1.75
d.	130c Mountain climber, vert.	2.10	2.10

Stamp Day — A577

Perf. 13¼x13½

2005, Nov. 22   **Litho.**

1222	A577 85c multi	1.40	.45

2006 Winter Olympics, Turin, Italy — A578

2005, Nov. 22   **Perf. 13¾**

1223	A578 100c Curling	1.60	.55

Issued in sheets of 6. See No. 12O4.

Swiss Papal Guards, 500th Anniv. A579

Designs: 85c, Guard and drummers. 100c, Guards and St. Peter's Basilica.

2005, Nov. 22   **Perf. 14x14¼**

1224	A579 85c multi	1.40	.45
1225	A579 100c multi	1.60	.55

Nos. 1224-1225 each issued in sheets of 6. See Vatican City Nos. 1315-1316.

Christmas — A580

Designs: 85c, Crozier and miter. 100c, Gingerbread man.

2005, Nov. 22   **Perf. 13½x13¼**

1226	A580 85c multi	1.40	.45
1227	A580 100c multi	1.60	.55

Reintroduction of Alpine Ibex in Switzerland, Cent. — A581

2006, Mar. 7   Litho.   Perf. 13¼x13
1228 A581 85c multi   1.40   .45

Youth Soccer — A582

2006, Mar. 7   Perf. 13¼x13½
1229 A582 85c multi   1.40   .45

Cuculus Canorus A583

Serpentine Die Cut 12
2006, Mar. 7   Photo.
Self-Adhesive
1230 A583 240c multi + eti-
             quette   3.75   .75
   a.   Block of 10 + 10 etiquettes   37.50

No. 1230a is on a backing paper with bar codes on the reverse.
See Nos. 1273-1276.

Railroad Anniversaries A584

Designs: 85c, Simplon Tunnel, cent. 100c, Bern-Lötschberg-Simplon Railway, cent.

2006, Mar. 7   Perf. 14x13¾
1231 A584 85c multi   1.40   .45
1232 A584 100c multi   1.60   .55

Art Nouveau Exhibition, La Chaux-de-Fonds — A585

Designs: 100c, "Fir." 180c, "Petal."

2006, Mar. 7
1233 A585 100c multi   1.60   .55
1234 A585 180c multi   2.75   .90

Post Buses, Cent. — A586

Various post buses and passengers.

Serpentine Die Cut 10¾x11
2006, Mar. 7   Litho.
Self-Adhesive
1235 A586 85c blue & multi   1.40   .45
   a.   Block of 4 on backing paper   5.75
1236 A586 100c red & multi   1.60   .55
   a.   Block of 4 on backing paper   6.50
1237 A586 130c grn & multi   2.00   .65
   a.   Block of 4 on backing paper   8.00
   b.   Block of 3, #1235-1237 on
          backing paper   5.00
      Nos. 1235-1237 (3)   5.00 1.65

Nos. 1235-1237 each were issued in sheets of 20. Stamps are adjacent on Nos. 1235a-1237a and on a shiny, but opaque backing paper.

Kasperli, Children's Theater Puppet — A587

2006, May 9   Litho.   Perf. 14x13¾
1238 A587 85c multi   1.40   .45

Europa A588

2006, May 9   Perf. 13x13¼
1239 A588 100c multi   1.75   .60

Mountains — A589

No. 1240: a, Eiger (35x36mm). b, Monch (30x36mm). c, Jungfrau (39x36mm). Illustration reduced.

2006, May 9   Perf. 13¼x13½
1240 A589 Horiz. strip of 3   4.25 4.25
   a.-c.   85c Any single   1.40   .45

Caricatures of Cows by Patrice Killoffer A590

Cow: 85c, On back. 100c, In water. 130c, Seated. 180c, In snow.

2006, May 9   Perf. 14x14¼
1241 A590 85c multi   1.40   .45
1242 A590 100c multi   1.75   .60
1243 A590 130c multi   2.25   .75
1244 A590 180c multi   3.00 1.00
      Nos. 1241-1244 (4)   8.40 2.80

First Session of United Nations Human Rights Council A591

Perf. 13¾x14¼
2006, June 19   Litho.
1245 A591 100c multi   1.75   .60

Dimitri the Clown — A592

2006, Sept. 7   Perf. 13¼x13
1246 A592 100c multi   1.60   .55

Victorinox Swiss Army Knives — A593

Designs: 100c, First model, 1897, khaki pants. 130c, Modern model, blue jeans.

2006, Sept. 7   Perf. 14x13¾
1247 A593 100c multi   1.60   .55
1248 A593 130c multi   2.10   .70

Cocolino the Cooking Cat, by Oskar Weiss — A594

Serpentine Die Cut 10¾x11
2006, Sept. 7
Self-Adhesive
1249 A594 85c multi   1.40   .45
   a.   Booklet pane of 10   14.00

Fruit — A595

Designs: 200c, Gelterkinder cherries. 300c, Spätlauber apple. 400c, Hauszwetschge plums.

2006 Photo. Serpentine Die Cut 12
Self-Adhesive
1250 A595 200c multi   3.25 1.10
1251 A595 300c multi   5.00 1.60
   a.   Pair, #1250-1251 on backing
          paper   8.25
1252 A595 400c multi   6.75 2.25
      Nos. 1250-1252 (3)   15.00 4.95

Issued: 200c, 300c, 9/7; 400c, 11/21.Nos. 1250-1252 each were printed in sheets of 50.

Town of Olten, Boy Wearing Train Conductor's Hat — A596

Perf. 13½x13¼
2006, Nov. 21   Litho.
1253 A596 85c multi   1.50   .50

Stamp Day.

Christmas — A597

Designs: 85c, Star singers. 100c, Advent wreath.

2006, Nov. 21
1254 A597 85c multi   1.50   .50
1255 A597 100c multi   1.75   .60

Women's Soccer — A598

2007, Mar. 6   Litho.   Perf. 13¼x13½
1256 A598 85c multi   1.40   .45
      Printed in sheets of 6.

Leonhard Euler (1707-83), Mathematician A599

2007, Mar. 6
1257 A599 130c multi   2.10   .70

Stein am Rhein, 1000th Anniv. — A600

No. 1258: a, Town Hall (28x36mm). b, Houses on Town Hall Square (40x36mm). c, Municipal Fountain (34x36mm). Illustration reduced.

2007, Mar. 6   Perf. 13¾x13½
1258 A600 Horiz. strip of 3   4.25 3.50
   a.-c.   85c Any single   1.40   .45

Legends A601

Designs: 85c, Charlemagne and the Snake. 100c, Fenetta, the Island Maiden. 130c, The Judge of Bellinzona. 180c, Margaretha.

2007, Mar. 6   Perf. 13½x14
1259 A601 85c multi   1.40   .45
1260 A601 100c multi   1.60   .55
1261 A601 130c multi   2.10   .70
1262 A601 180c multi   3.00 1.00
      Nos. 1259-1262 (4)   8.10 2.70

Swiss Club for Bernese Mountain Dogs, Cent. — A602

Serpentine Die Cut 11x10¾
2007, Mar. 6
Self-Adhesive
1263 A602 85c multi   1.40   .45
   a.   Block of 4 on backing paper   5.75

No. 1263 was issued in sheets of 20.

Swiss National Bank, Cent. — A603

Designs: 85c, Banknote security devices.
100c, Artwork from 100-franc banknote.

2007, Mar. 6   **Litho.**
Self-Adhesive
1264 A603 85c multi   1.40   .45
1265 A603 100c multi   1.60   .55
  a.   Horiz. pair, #1264-1265   3.00
  b.   Block of 4 on backing paper 6.50
  Nos. 1264-1265 each were printed in sheets
of 12.

Roger Federer,
Tennis
Player — A604

2007, Apr. 10   **Perf. 13¾x14¼**
1266 A604 100c multi   1.75   .60

Swiss Assoc.
of Day Care
Centers,
Cent. — A605

2007, Apr. 27   **Perf. 13½x13¾**
1267 A605 85c multi   1.40   .45

Europa — A606

2007, Apr. 27   **Perf. 14**
1268 A606 100c multi   1.75   .60
  Scouting, cent. Printed in sheets of 18 + 12
labels.

Art Brut
Movement — A607

Designs: 100c, Saint Adolf-Throne-Rock
Face-Flower, by Adolf Wölfli. 180c, Untitled
work by Carlo Zinelli.

2007, Apr. 27   **Perf. 14¼x14**
1269 A607 100c multi   1.75   .60
1270 A607 180c multi   3.00   1.00

Museum of Communications,
Cent. — A608

  People with: 85c, Lake in background. 100c,
Building in background.

Litho. With Three-Dimensional Plastic Affixed
Serpentine Die Cut 10½
2007, Apr. 27
Self-Adhesive
1271 A608 85c multi   1.40   .45
1272 A608 100c multi   1.75   .60

Bird Type of 2006
Designs: 85c, Fringilla coelebs. 100c, Parus
major. 110c, Tichodroma muraria. 180c,
Aegolius funereus.

Serpentine Die Cut 12¼x12
2007, Sept. 6   **Photo.**
Self-Adhesive
1273 A583 85c multi   1.50   .30
  a.   Booklet pane of 10   15.00
1274 A583 100c multi + eti-
         quette   1.75   .35
  a.   Booklet pane of 10 + 10 eti-
         quettes   17.50
1275 A583 110c multi   1.90   .40
1276 A583 180c multi + eti-
         quette   3.25   .65
  a.   Block of 4, #1273-1276, + 2
    etiquettes on backing paper 8.50
  Nos. 1273-1276 (4)   8.40   1.70

The Dance, by
Nina
Corti — A609

2007, Sept. 6   Litho.   Perf. 14¼x14
1277 A609 85c multi   1.50   .50

Illustration for Children's Book
"Schnellen-Ursli," by Alois
Carigiet — A610

Serpentine Die Cut 10½x11
2007, Sept. 6
Self-Adhesive
1278 A610 85c multi   1.50   .50
  a.   Booklet pane of 10   15.00

Congratulations
A611

Designs: 85c, Children and hearts. 100c,
Boy and stars. 130c, Woman and starbursts.

2007, Sept. 6   **Litho.**
Self-Adhesive
1279 A611 85c multi   1.50   .30
1280 A611 100c multi   1.75   .35
1281 A611 130c multi   2.25   .45
  a.   Block of 3, #1279-1281, on
    backing paper   5.50
  Nos. 1279-1281 (3)   5.50   1.10

Swiss Settings
in British
Literature
A612

Designs: 85c, Mönch, from *Frankenstein*, by
Mary Shelley. 100c, Staubbach Falls, from "At
Staubbach Falls," by William Wordsworth, vert.
130c, Lake Leman, from "The Prisoner of Chil-
lon," by Lord Byron, vert. 180c, Reichenbach
Waterfall, from *The Final Problem*, by Sir
Arthur Conan Doyle.

Litho. With Foil Application
Perf. 13¼x13½, 13½x13¼
2007, Sept. 6
1282 A612 85c black & silver   1.50   .50
1283 A612 100c black & silver   1.75   .60
1284 A612 130c black & silver   2.25   .75
1285 A612 180c black & silver   3.25   1.10
  Nos. 1282-1285 (4)   8.75   2.95

Skiers and Swiss Post
BeeTagg — A613

Serpentine Die Cut 10¾x10½
2007, Oct. 31   **Litho.**
Self-Adhesive
1286 A613 100c multi   1.75   .60
  The BeeTagg design can be read by camera
phones to connect the phones to client
websites.

Souvenir Sheet

Einsiedeln Abbey — A614

2007, Nov. 20   **Perf. 13¼x14**
1287 A614 85c multi   1.50   1.50

Paper Cuttings
A615

  Paper cuttings: 85c, Heart, by Christian
Schwizgebel. 100c, Spring, by Pia Arm. 130c,
Family Trip, by Christiane and Jacqueline
Saugy. 180c, Minuet, by Verena Kühni.

Serpentine Die Cut 10¾
2007, Nov. 20
Self-Adhesive
1288 A615 85c red & black   1.50   .50
1289 A615 100c green & black   1.75   .60
1290 A615 130c blue & black   2.40   .80
1291 A615 180c org & black   3.25   1.10
  a.   Block of 4, #1288-1291 on
    backing paper   9.00
  Nos. 1288-1291 (4)   8.90   3.00

Christmas — A616

Designs: 85c, Berne Christmas Fair. 100c,
Christmas tree. 130c, Gifts.

2007, Nov. 20   **Perf. 13½x13¼**
1292 A616 85c multi   1.50   .50
1293 A616 100c multi   1.75   .60
1294 A616 130c multi   2.40   .80
  Nos. 1292-1294 (3)   5.65   1.90

Intl. Year of the
Potato — A617

2008, Mar. 4   **Litho.**
1295 A617 85c multi   1.75   .60

Albrecht von
Haller (1708-
77),
Physiologist
A618

2008, Mar. 4   **Perf. 13¼x13½**
1296 A618 85c multi   1.75   .60

The Little Polar
Bear, by Hans
de
Beer — A619

Serpentine Die Cut 10½x11
2008, Mar. 4
Self-Adhesive
1297 A619 85c multi   1.75   .60
  a.   Booklet pane of 10   17.50

Euro 2008 Soccer Championships,
Austria and Switzerland — A620

Serpentine Die Cut 12x12¼
2008, Mar. 4   **Photo.**
Self-Adhesive
1298 A620 100c green & black   2.00   .65
  Printed in sheets of 10.

Men's
Soccer — A621

2008, Mar. 4 Litho.   Perf. 13¾x14¼
1299 A621 100c multi   2.00   .65
  Printed in sheets of 6.

Ice Hockey in Switzerland,
Cent. — A622

2008, Mar. 4   **Perf. 13x13¼**
1300 A622 100c multi   2.00   .65

Horse Foundation, 50th Anniv. — A623

No. 1301 — Horses and: a, Sun (35x37mm). b, Path and fence (38x37mm). c, Building (31x37mm)

2008, Mar. 4			**Perf. 13½**	
1301	A623	Horiz. strip of 3	5.25	5.25
a.-c.		85c Any single	1.75	.80

Musical Instruments
A624

Designs: 85c, Violin. 100c, Swiss accordion. 130c, Electric guitar. 180c, Saxophone.

2008, Mar. 4		**Litho.**	**Perf. 13x14**	
1302	A624	85c multi	1.75	.60
1303	A624	100c multi	2.00	.65
1304	A624	130c multi	2.60	.85
1305	A624	180c multi	3.50	1.10
		Nos. 1302-1305 (4)	9.85	3.20

SEMI-POSTAL STAMPS

Nos. B1-B76, B81-B84 were sold at premiums of 2c for 3c stamps, 5c for 5c-20c stamps and 10c for 30c-40c stamps.

Helvetia and Matterhorn — SP2

Perf. 11½, 12

1913, Dec. 1   Typo.   Wmk. 183
Granite Paper

B1	SP2	5c green	2.75	8.25
		Never hinged		7.75

Boy (Appenzell) SP3   Girl (Lucerne) SP4

1915, Dec. 1			**Perf. 11½**	
B2	SP3	5c green, buff	3.25	8.25
a.		Tête bêche pair	82.50	875.00
I		Never hinged	160.00	
B3	SP4	10c red, buff	100.00	87.50
		Set, never hinged	225.00	

Girl (Fribourg) SP5   Dairy Boy (Bern) SP6

Girl (Vaud) — SP7

1916, Dec. 1

B4	SP5	3c vio, buff	5.00	37.50
B5	SP6	5c grn, buff	11.00	9.25
B6	SP7	10c brn red, buff	47.50	77.50
		Nos. B4-B6 (3)	63.50	124.25
		Set, never hinged	175.00	

Girl (Valais) SP8   Girl (Unterwalden) SP9

Girl (Ticino) — SP10

1917, Dec. 1

B7	SP8	3c vio, buff	3.25	50.00
B8	SP9	5c green, buff	7.75	5.50
B9	SP10	10c red, buff	19.00	22.50
		Nos. B7-B9 (3)	30.00	78.00
		Set, never hinged	87.50	

Uri SP11   Geneva SP12

1918, Dec. 1
Straw-Surfaced Paper

B10	SP11	10c red, org & blk	7.75	25.00
B11	SP12	15c vio, red, org & blk	9.25	11.00
		Set, never hinged	52.50	

Nidwalden SP13   Vaud SP14

Obwalden — SP15

1919, Dec. 1
Cream-Surfaced Paper

B12	SP13	7½c gray, red & blk	2.50	14.00
B13	SP14	10c lake, grn & blk	2.50	14.00
B14	SP15	15c pur, red & blk	5.00	7.25
		Nos. B12-B14 (3)	10.00	35.25
		Set, never hinged	22.50	

Schwyz SP16   Zürich SP17

Ticino — SP18

1920, Dec. 1
Cream-Surfaced Paper

B15	SP16	7½c gray & red	2.75	11.50
B16	SP17	10c red & lt bl	5.00	12.50
B17	SP18	15c violet, red & bl	2.75	6.00
		Nos. B15-B17 (3)	10.50	30.00
		Set, never hinged	25.00	

Valais SP19   Bern SP20

Switzerland — SP21

1921, Dec. 1
Cream-Surfaced Paper

B18	SP19	10c grn, red & blk	.65	3.00
B19	SP20	20c vio, red, org & blk	1.90	3.50
B20	SP21	40c blue & red	7.25	47.50
		Nos. B18-B20 (3)	9.80	54.00
		Set, never hinged	25.00	

Zug SP22   Fribourg SP23

Lucerne SP24   Switzerland SP25

1922, Dec. 1
Cream-Surfaced Paper

B21	SP22	5c org, pale bl & blk	.50	5.50
B22	SP23	10c ol grn & blk	.60	2.50
B23	SP24	20c vio, pale bl & blk	1.00	2.50
B24	SP25	40c bl & red	8.75	47.50
		Nos. B21-B24 (4)	10.85	58.00
		Set, never hinged	26.00	

Basel SP26   Glarus (St. Fridolin) SP27

Neuchâtel SP28   Switzerland SP29

1923, Dec. 1
Cream-Surfaced Paper

B25	SP26	5c org & blk	.40	3.50
B26	SP27	10c multi	.40	1.90
B27	SP28	20c multi	.45	1.90
B28	SP29	40c dk bl & red	7.75	37.50
		Nos. B25-B28 (4)	9.00	44.80
		Set, never hinged	21.00	

Appenzell SP30   Solothurn SP31

Schaffhausen SP32   Switzerland SP33

1924, Dec. 1
Cream-Surfaced Paper

B29	SP30	5c dk vio & blk	.25	1.60
B30	SP31	10c grn, red & blk	.40	1.00
B31	SP32	20c car, yel & blk	.65	1.00
B32	SP33	30c bl, red & blk	1.40	11.00
		Nos. B29-B32 (4)	2.70	14.60
		Set, never hinged	6.50	

St. Gallen (Canton) SP34   Appenzell-Ausser-Rhoden SP35

Grisons SP36   Switzerland SP37

1925, Dec. 1
Cream-Surfaced Paper

B33	SP34	5c vio, grn & blk	.25	1.10
B34	SP35	10c grn & blk	.25	.85
B35	SP36	20c multi	.25	.85
B36	SP37	30c dk bl, red & blk	1.10	8.25
		Nos. B33-B36 (4)	1.85	11.05
		Set, never hinged	4.50	

Thurgau SP38   Basel SP39

Aargau SP40   Switzerland SP41

1926, Dec. 1
Cream-Surfaced Paper

B37	SP38	5c vio, bis & grn	.25	1.40
B38	SP39	10c gray grn, red & blk	.25	1.40
B39	SP40	20c red, blk & bl	.25	1.40
B40	SP41	30c dk bl & red	1.10	12.50
		Nos. B37-B40 (4)	1.85	16.70
		Set, never hinged	4.50	

Orphan SP42   Orphan at Pestalozzi School SP43

SP44

J. H. Pestalozzi
SP45

1927, Dec. 1   Typo.   Wmk. 183
Granite Paper
B41 SP42 5c red vio & yel,
                grysh   .20 1.60
B42 SP43 10c grn & fawn, grnsh   .20   .60
Engr.
B43 SP44 20c red   .20   .60
Unwmk.
Photo.
B44 SP45 30c gray bl & blk   1.10 6.50
        Nos. B41-B44 (4)   1.70 9.30
        Set, never hinged   3.25

Nos. B43-B44 for the centenary of the death of Johann Heinrich Pestalozzi, the Swiss educational reformer.

Lausanne
SP46

Winterthur
SP47

St. Gallen
(City) — SP48

J. H. Dunant
SP49

1928, Dec. 1   Typo.   Wmk. 183
Cream-Surfaced Paper.
B45 SP46 5c dk vio, red & blk   .20 1.60
B46 SP47 10c bl grn, org red &
                blk   .20   .90
B47 SP48 20c brn red, blk & yel .20   .90
Unwmk.
Photo.
Thick White Paper
B48 SP49 30c dl bl & red   1.10 7.00
        Nos. B45-B48 (4)   1.70 10.40
        Set, never hinged   3.50

No. B48 for the centenary of the birth of Jean Henri Dunant, Swiss author, philanthropist and founder of the Red Cross Society.

Lake Lugano and Mt. Salvatore
SP50

Lake Engstlen and Mt. Titlis
SP51

Mt. Lyskamm
SP52

Nicholas von der Flüe
SP53

1929, Dec. 1   Perf. 11x11½
B49 SP50 5c dk vio & red org   .20 1.40
B50 SP51 10c ol brn & gray bl .20 1.10
B51 SP52 20c brn garnet & bl   .25 1.10
B52 SP53 30c dk blue   1.25 12.50
        Nos. B49-B52 (4)   1.90 16.10
        Set, never hinged   4.50

No. B52 for Nicholas von der Flüe, the Swiss patriot. By his advice the Swiss Confederation was continued and Swiss independence was saved.

Fribourg
SP54

Altdorf
SP55

Schaffhausen
SP56

Jeremias Gotthelf
SP57

Wmk. 183
1930, Dec. 1   Typo.   Perf. 11½
Cream-Surfaced Paper
B53 SP54 5c dp grn, dl bl & blk .20 1.40
B54 SP55 10c multicolored   .20   .90
B55 SP56 20c multicolored   .30   .90
Engr.
White Paper
B56 SP57 30c slate blue   1.25 6.00
        Nos. B53-B56 (4)   1.95 9.20
        Set, never hinged   4.00

No. B56 for Jeremias Gotthelf, pen name of Albrecht Bitzius, pastor and author.

Lakes Silvaplana and Sils
SP58

Wetterhorn
SP59

Lake Geneva
SP60

Alexandre Vinet
SP61

1931, Dec. 1   Photo.   Unwmk.
Granite Paper
B57 SP58 5c dp grn   .45 1.60
B58 SP59 10c dk vio   .40   .85
B59 SP60 20c brn red   .55 1.10
Wmk. 183
Engr.
B60 SP61 30c ultra   4.50 19.00
        Nos. B57-B60 (4)   5.90 22.55
        Set, never hinged   14.00

No. B60 for Alexandre Rudolph Vinet, critic and theologian.

Flag Swinger
SP62

Putting the Stone
SP63

Wrestling
SP64

Eugen Huber
SP65

1932, Dec. 1   Typo.   Unwmk.
Granite Paper
B61 SP62 5c dk grn & red   .30 1.90
B62 SP63 10c orange   .45 2.25
B63 SP64 20c scarlet   .55 1.90
Wmk. 183
Engr.
B64 SP65 30c ultra   2.25 8.75
        Nos. B61-B64 (4)   3.55 14.80
        Set, never hinged   9.50

No. B64 for Eugen Huber, jurist and author of the Swiss Civil Law Book.

Girl of Vaud — SP66

Girl of Bern — SP67

Girl of Ticino
SP68

Jean Baptiste Girard (Le Père Grégoire)
SP69

1933, Dec. 1   Photo.   Unwmk.
Granite Paper
B65 SP66 5c grn & buff   .30 1.50
B66 SP67 10c vio & buff   .30 1.10
B67 SP68 20c red & buff   .45 2.10
Wmk. 183
Engr.
B68 SP69 30c ultra   2.50 8.50
        Nos. B65-B68 (4)   3.55 13.20
        Set, never hinged   8.25

Girl of Appenzell
SP70

Girl of Valais
SP71

Girl of Grisons
SP72

Albrecht von Haller
SP73

1934, Dec. 1   Photo.   Unwmk.
B69 SP70 5c grn & buff   .30 1.60
B70 SP71 10c vio & buff   .45 1.10
B71 SP72 20c brn & buff   .45 1.60
Wmk. 183
Engr.
B72 SP73 30c ultra   2.50 8.75
        Nos. B69-B72 (4)   3.70 13.05
        Set, never hinged   8.25

Girl of Basel
SP74

Girl of Lucerne
SP75

Girl of Geneva
SP76

Stefano Franscini
SP77

1935, Dec. 1   Photo.   Unwmk.
Granite Paper
B73 SP74 5c grn & buff   .25 1.75
B74 SP75 10c vio & buff   .45 1.10
B75 SP76 20c red & buff   .45 2.75
Wmk. 183
Engr.
B76 SP77 30c ultra   2.50 8.75
        Nos. B73-B76 (4)   3.65 14.35
        Set, never hinged   8.25

No. B76 honors Stefano Franscini (1796-1857), political economist and educator.

Alpine Herdsman — SP78

Perf. 11½
1936, Oct. 1   Photo.   Unwmk.
Granite Paper
B77 SP78 10c + 5c vio   .55 1.00
B78 SP78 20c + 10c dk red   .85 4.25
B79 SP78 30c + 10c ultra   3.75 20.00
        Nos. B77-B79 (3)   5.15 25.25
        Set, never hinged   11.00

Souvenir Sheet
B80 SP78   Sheet of 3   35.00 125.00
        Never hinged   70.00
a.   Block of 4 sheets   190.00 875.00
        Never hinged   300.00

Swiss National Defense Fund Drive.
No. B80 contains stamps similar to Nos. B77-B79, but on grilled granite paper with blue and red fibers instead of black and red. Sold for 2fr. Size: 120x130mm.

Johann Georg Nägeli
SP79

Girl of Neuchâtel
SP80

Girl of Schwyz
SP81

Girl of Zurich
SP82

Wmk. 183

1936, Dec. 1   **Engr.**   *Perf. 11½*

Granite Paper

B81 SP79 5c green   .25   .70

Unwmk.

Photo.

B82 SP80 10c vio & buff   .55   .70
B83 SP81 20c red & buff   .25   1.90
B84 SP82 30c ultra & buff   3.50   30.00
   Nos. B81-B84 (4)   4.55   33.30
   Set, never hinged   11.00

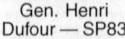

Gen. Henri Dufour — SP83   Nicholas von der Flüe — SP84

Boy SP85

Girl SP86

Perf. 11½

1937, Dec. 1   **Unwmk.**   **Engr.**

B85 SP83 5c + 5c bl grn   .20   .55
B86 SP84 10c + 5c red vio   .20   .55

Photo.

Granite Paper

B87 SP85 20c + 5c red & silver   .30   .55
B88 SP86 30c + 10c ultra & sil   1.25   5.50
   Nos. B85-B88 (4)   1.95   7.15
   Set, never hinged   3.75

25th anniv. of the Pro Juventute (child welfare) stamps.

Souvenir Sheet

1937, Dec. 20   *Imperf.*

B89   Sheet of 2   6.50   57.50
  a. SP85 20c + 5c red & silver   1.60   17.00
  b. SP86 30c + 10c ultra & silver   1.60   17.00
   Never hinged   7.50

Simulated perforation in silver. Sheet sold for 1fr.

Tell Chapel, Lake Lucerne SP87

1938, June 15   *Perf. 11½*

Granite Paper

B90 SP87 10c + 10c brt vio & yel   .45   1.10
   Never hinged   1.10
  a. Grilled gum   22.50   77.50
   Never hinged   32.50

National Fête Day.

Salomon Gessner SP88   Girl of St. Gallen SP89

Girl of Uri — SP90   Girl of Aargau — SP91

1938, Dec. 1   **Engr.**   *Perf. 11½*

B91 SP88 5c + 5c dp bl grn   .20   .50

Photo.

Granite Paper

B92 SP89 10c + 5c pur & buff   .25   .55
B93 SP90 20c + 5c red & buff   .25   .55
B94 SP91 30c + 10c ultra   1.60   6.50
   Nos. B91-B94 (4)   2.30   8.10
   Set, never hinged   4.50

Castle at Laupen SP92

1939, June 15

B95 SP92 10c + 10c brn, gray & red   .30   1.10
   Never hinged   1.10

600th anniversary of the Battle of Laupen. The surtax was used to aid needy mothers.

Hans Herzog SP93   Girl of Fribourg SP94

Girl of Nidwalden SP95   Girl of Basel SP96

Perf. 11½

1939, Dec. 1   **Unwmk.**   **Engr.**

B96 SP93 5c + 5c dk grn   .20   .45

Photo.

Granite Paper

B97 SP94 10c + 5c rose vio & buff   .20   .45
B98 SP95 20c + 5c org red   .30   1.40
B99 SP96 30c + 10c ultra & buff   1.60   11.50
   Nos. B96-B99 (4)   2.30   13.80
   Set, never hinged   5.00

Sempach, 1386 — SP97   Giornico, 1478 — SP98

Calven, 1499 SP99   WWI Ranger SP100

1940, Mar. 20   **Photo.**

Granite Paper

B100 SP97 5c + 5c emer, blk & red   .30   1.25
B101 SP98 10c + 5c brn org, blk & car   .30   .55
B102 SP99 20c + 5c brn red, blk & car   2.25   .95
B103 SP100 30c + 10c brt bl, brn blk & red   1.60   8.25

National Fête Day. The surtax was for the National Fund and the Red Cross.

Redrawn

B104 SP99 20c + 5c brn red, blk & car   9.75   6.50
   Nos. B100-B104 (5)   14.20   17.50
   Set, never hinged   26.00

The base of statue has been heavily shaded "Calven 1499" moved nearer to bottom line of base. Top line of base removed.

Souvenir Sheet

Unwmk.

1940, July 16   **Photo.**   *Imperf.*

Granite Paper

B105   Sheet of 4   250.00   575.00
   Never hinged   425.00
  a. SP97 5c+5c yel grn, blk & red   11.00   26.00
  b. SP98 10c+5c org yel, blk & red   47.50   210.00
  c. SP99 20c+5c brn red, blk & red (redrawn)   47.50   210.00
  d. SP100 30c+10c chlky bl, blk & red   11.00   26.00

National Fete Day. Sheets measure 125x65mm and sold for 5fr.

Gottfried Keller SP102   Girl of Thurgau SP103

Girl of Solothurn SP104   Girl of Zug SP105

1940, Dec. 1   **Engr.**   *Perf. 11½*

B106 SP102 5c + 5c dk bl grn   .20   .40

Photo.

B107 SP103 10c + 5c brn & buff   .20   .30
B108 SP104 20c + 5c org red & buff   .20   .40
B109 SP105 30c + 10c dp ultra & buff   1.40   9.50
   Nos. B106-B109 (4)   2.00   10.60
   Set, never hinged   4.00

Lake Lucerne, Arms of Cantons SP106

Tell Chapel at Chemin Creux SP107

1941, June 15

B110 SP106 10c + 10c multi   .30   .75
B111 SP107 20c + 10c org, red & lt buff   .30   1.25
   Set, never hinged   2.00

Natl. Fête Day and 650th anniv. of Swiss Independence.

Johann Lavater SP108   Girl of Schaffhausen SP109

Girl of Obwalden SP110   Daniel Jean Richard SP111

1941, Dec. 1   **Engr.**

B112 SP108 5c + 5c dk grn   .20   .30
B113 SP111 30c + 10c dp ultra   .25   .40

Photo.

B114 SP109 10c + 5c chnt & buff   .25   .40
B115 SP110 20c + 5c ver & buff   .80   5.00
   Nos. B112-B115 (4)   1.50   6.10
   Set, never hinged   3.50

Souvenir Sheet

Imperf

B116   Sheet of 2   60.00   350.00
  a. SP109 10c +5c chnt & buff   17.00   125.00
  b. SP110 20c +5c ver & buff   17.00   125.00
   Never hinged   100.00

Issued in sheets measuring 75x70mm and sold for 2fr. The surtax was used for charity.

Ancient Geneva SP113

Soldiers' Monument, Forch SP114

1942, June 15   *Perf. 11½*

B117 SP113 10c + 10c gray blk, red & yel   .25   .50
B118 SP114 20c + 10c cop red, red & buff   .25   .85
   Set, never hinged   1.25

National Fête Day, 1942. No. B117 for the 2000th anniv. of the City of Geneva.

Souvenir Sheet

Imperf

B119   Sheet of 2   50.00   225.00
  a. SP113 10c +10c gray black, red & yellow   14.00   80.00
  b. SP113 20c +10c copper red, red & buff   14.00   80.00
   Never hinged   82.50

Issued in sheets measuring 105x63mm in commemoration of National Fete and the 2000th anniv. of the City of Geneva. Sold for 2fr. The surtax was divided between the Swiss Alliance of Samaritans and the National Community Chest.

Niklaus
Riggenbach
SP116

Girl of
Appenzell
SP117

Girl of Glarus
SP118

Konrad Escher
von der Linth
SP119

1942, Dec. 1   **Engr.**   **Perf. 11½**
B120 SP116   5c + 5c deep grn   .20   .50
B121 SP119   30c + 10c royal bl   1.10   4.50

Photo.
B122 SP117   10c + 5c dp brn &
     buff   .25   .50
B123 SP118   20c + 5c org red   .20   .50
   Nos. B120-B123 (4)   1.75   6.00
   Set, never hinged   3.75

Intragna
SP120

Parliament
Buildings,
Bern
SP121

1943, June 15   **Photo.**   **Perf. 11½**
B124 SP120   10c + 10c blk brn,
     buff & dk red   .25   .75
B125 SP121   20c + 10c cop red,
     buff & dk red   .30   1.50
   Set, never hinged   1.25

National Fête Day, 1943.

Emanuel von
Fellenberg
SP122

Silver Thistle
SP123

20c+5c, Lady slipper. 30c+10c, Gentian.

1943, Dec. 1   **Engr.**
B126 SP122   5c + 5c green   .20   .50

Photo.
B127 SP123   10c + 5c sl grn &
     ocher   .20   .50
B128 SP123   20c + 5c copper
     red & yel   .25   .50
B129 SP123   30c + 10c royal bl
     & lt bl   1.10   8.50
   Nos. B126-B129 (4)   1.75   10.00
   Set, never hinged   3.25

Souvenir Sheets

SP126

1943   **Engr.**   **Imperf.**
B130 SP126   Sheet of 12   37.50   60.00
   a.   10c black, single stamp   1.10   3.75
     Never hinged   77.50

Sold for 5fr. Size: 165x140mm.

SP127

Red Horizontal Lines
B131 SP127   Sheet of 2   42.50   52.50
   a.   4c black & red   13.00   20.00
   b.   6c black & red   13.00   20.00
     Never hinged   75.00

Sold for 3fr. Size: 70x75mm.

Arms of Geneva — SP128

B132 SP128   Sheet of 2   40.00   40.00
   a.   5c green & black   11.50   15.00
     Never hinged   65.00

Sold for 3fr. Size: 72x72mm. Centenary of
Swiss postage stamps. The surtax aided the
Swiss Red Cross.

Heiden
SP129

St. Jacob
SP130

Mesocco
SP131

Basel
SP132

Perf. 11½
1944, June 15   **Photo.**   **Unwmk.**
B133 SP129   5c + 5c dk bl grn,
     red & buff   .20   2.25
B134 SP130   10c + 10c gray blk,
     red & buff   .20   .50
B135 SP131   20c + 10c hn, red
     & buff   .20   1.00
B136 SP132   30c + 10c brt ultra
     & red   2.10   17.50
   Nos. B133-B136 (4)   2.70   21.25
   Set, never hinged   6.00

National Fete Day.

Numa Droz
SP133

Edelweiss
SP134

Designs: 20c+5c, Lilium martagon.
30c+10c, Aquilegia alpina.

1944, Dec. 1   **Engr.**
B137 SP133   5c + 5c green   .20   .35

Photo.
B138 SP134   10c + 5c dk sl grn,
     yel & gray   .25   .40
B139 SP134   20c + 5c red, yel &
     gray   .35   .40
B140 SP134   30c + 10c bl, gray
     & lt bl   1.10   8.50
   Nos. B137-B140 (4)   1.90   9.65
   Set, never hinged   4.00

Symbol of Faith,
Hope and
Love — SP137

Lifeboat Making a Rescue — SP138

1945, Feb. 20   **Perf. 11½**
B141 SP137   10c + 10c multi   .30   .50
B142 SP137   20c + 60c multi   .90   5.75
   Set, never hinged   2.50

Imperf
Souvenir Sheet
B143 SP138   3fr + 7fr bl gray   110.00   225.00
     Never hinged   200.00

Issued in sheets measuring 70x110mm.
Surtax for the benefit of war victims.

Souvenir Sheet

Dove of Basel — SP139

1945, Apr. 14   **Typo.**
B144 SP139   Sheet of 2   70.00   95.00
   a.   10c gray, maroon &
     black   16.00   26.00
     Never hinged   150.00

Cent. of the Basel Cantonal Stamp. The
sheets measure 71x63mm and sold for 3fr.
The surtax was for the Pro Juventute
Foundation.

Numeral of Value
and Red
Cross — SP140

1945   **Photo.**   **Perf. 12**
B145 SP140   5c + 10c grn & red   .30   .75
     Never hinged   .65

Weaver
SP141

Farm of
Jura
SP142

Farm of
Emmental
SP143

Frame House, Eastern
Switzerland — SP144

1945, June 15   **Engr.**   **Perf. 11½**
B146 SP141   5c + 5c bl grn &
     red   .35   2.00

Photo.
B147 SP142   10c + 10c brn,
     gray bl &
     red   .35   .75
B148 SP143   20c + 10c hn brn,
     buff & red   .55   .75
B149 SP144   30c + 10c saph &
     red   5.50   35.00
   Nos. B146-B149 (4)   6.75   38.50
   Set, never hinged   14.50

The surtax was for needy mothers.

Ludwig Forrer — SP145

Susanna Orelli — SP146

Alpine Dog-Rose SP147

Crocus SP148

1945, Dec. 1   **Engr.**
B150 SP145   5c + 5c dk grn   .20   .50
B151 SP146   10c + 10c dk red   brn   .20   .50

Photo.
B152 SP147   20c + 10c rose brn,   rose & yel org   .30   .50
B153 SP148   30c + 10c dk bl,   gray & lil   1.50   7.50
    Nos. B150-B153 (4)   2.20   9.00
    Set, never hinged   4.50

Cheese Making SP149

Farm Buildings and Vineyards SP150

House in Appenzell SP151

House in Engadine SP152

1946, June 15   **Engr.**
B154 SP149   5c + 5c bl grn &   red   .35   2.00

Photo.
B155 SP150   10c + 10c brn,   buff & red   .25   .75
B156 SP151   20c + 10c henna,   buff & red   .35   .75
B157 SP152   30c + 10c saph &   red   3.00   9.50
    Nos. B154-B157 (4)   3.95   13.00
    Set, never hinged   9.50

Rodolphe Toepffer SP153

Narcissus SP154

20c+10c, Mountain sengreen. 30c+10c, Blue thistle.

1946, Nov. 30   **Engr.**
B158 SP153   5c + 5c green   .20   .50

Photo.
B159 SP154   10c + 10c dk sl grn,   gray & red org   .20   .50
B160 SP154   20c + 10c brn car,   gray & yel   .30   .75
B161 SP154   30c + 10c bl,   gray & pink   1.40   6.00
    Nos. B158-B161 (4)   2.10   7.75
    Set, never hinged   3.75

Railroad Laborers SP157

Railroad Station, Rorschach SP158

Lüen-Castiel Station — SP159

Flüelen Station SP160

Perf. 11½
1947, June 14   **Engr.**   **Unwmk.**
B162 SP157   5c + 5c dk grn   & red   .25   2.10

Photo.
B163 SP158   10c + 10c gray   blk, cream &   red   .30   .75
B164 SP159   20c + 10c rose lil,   cream & red   .30   1.00
B165 SP160   30c + 10c bl, gray   & red   3.50   9.00
    Nos. B162-B165 (4)   4.35   12.85
    Set, never hinged   10.00

The surtax was for professional education of invalids and for the fight against cancer.

Jakob Burckhardt SP161

Alpine Primrose SP162

20c+10c, Red lily. 30c+10c, Cyclamen.

1947, Dec. 1   **Engr.**
B166 SP161   5c + 5c dk grn   .20   .45

Photo.
B167 SP162   10c + 10c sl blk,   gray & yel   .20   .45
B168 SP162   20c + 10c red brn,   gray & cop red   .30   .40
B169 SP162   30c + 10c dk bl,   gray & pink   1.25   5.75
    Nos. B166-B169 (4)   1.95   7.05
    Set, never hinged   3.50

Sun and Olympic Emblem SP165

Icehockey Player SP167

10c+10c, Snowflake and Olympic Emblem. 30c+10c, Ski-runner.

1948, Jan. 15
B170 SP165   5c + 5c dk bl grn &   yel   .25   1.50
B171 SP165   10c + 10c choc & bl   .30   1.00
B172 SP167   20c + 10c dp mag,   gray & org yel   .40   1.50
B173 SP167   30c + 10c bl, bl   & gray blk   1.25   5.50
    Nos. B170-B173 (4)   2.20   9.50
    Set, never hinged   5.50

Issued to publicize the 5th Olympic Winter Games, St. Moritz, Jan. 30-Feb. 8, 1948.

Frontier Guard SP169

House of Fribourg SP170

House of Valais SP171

House of Ticino SP172

1948, June 15   **Engr.**
B174 SP169   5c + 5c dk grn &   red   .20   1.25

Photo.
B175 SP170   10c + 10c sl &   gray   .20   .75
B176 SP171   20c + 10c brn red   & pink   .30   1.00
B177 SP172   30c + 10c bl &   gray   2.25   7.50
    Nos. B174-B177 (4)   2.95   10.50
    Set, never hinged   6.00

Johann R. Wettstein — SP173

1948, Aug. 21   **Perf. 11x12½**
B178 SP173   Sheet of 2   50.00   65.00
   a.   10c rose lilac   14.00   25.00
   b.   20c chalky blue   14.00   25.00
     Never hinged   77.50

Intl. Phil. Expo., Basel, Aug. 21-29, 1948. Sheet, size 110x60mm, sold for 3fr, of which the surtax was used for the exhibition and charitable purposes.

Gen. Ulrich Wille SP174

Foxglove SP175

20c+10c, Alpine rose. 40c+10c, Lily of paradise.

1948, Dec. 1   **Engr.**   **Perf. 11½**
B179 SP174   5c + 5c dk vio brn   .20   .45

Postman SP176

Mountain Farmhouse SP177

House of Lucerne SP178

House of Prattigau SP179

Photo.
B180 SP175   10c + 10c dk grn,   yel grn & yel   .25   .45
B181 SP175   20c + 10c brn, crim   & buff   .30   .45
B182 SP175   40c + 10c bl, gray &   org   1.25   5.50
    Nos. B179-B182 (4)   2.00   6.85
    Set, never hinged   4.50

Engraved and Photogravure
1949, June 15
Shield in Carmine
B183 SP176   5c + 5c rose vio   .30   1.50

Photo.
B184 SP177   10c + 10c bl grn &   car   .30   .75
B185 SP178   20c + 10c dk brn   & cr   .30   .75
B186 SP179   40c + 10c bl &   pale bl   2.50   10.00
    Nos. B183-B186 (4)   3.40   13.00
    Set, never hinged   7.25

The surtax was for professional education of Swiss youth.

Niklaus Wengi SP180

Anemone Sulphureous SP181

20c+10c, Alpine clematis. 40c+10c, Superb pink.

1949, Dec. 1   **Engr.**   **Perf. 11½**
B187 SP180   5c + 5c vio brn   .20   .45

Photo.
B188 SP181   10c + 10c grn, gray   & yel   .20   .45
B189 SP181   20c + 10c brn, bl &   yel   .25   .45
B190 SP181   40c + 10c bl, lav &   yel   1.40   5.50
    Nos. B187-B190 (4)   2.05   6.85
    Set, never hinged   4.00

Adaptation of 1850 Design SP182

Putting the Stone SP183

Designs: 20c+10c, Wrestlers. 30c+10c, Runners. 40c+10c, Target shooting.

1950, June 1   **Engr. & Photo.**
Shield in Red
B191 SP182 5c + 5c black   .20   .75

Photo.
Inscribed: "I. VIII. 1950"
B192 SP183 10c + 10c green   .50   .80
B193 SP183 10c + 10c brown ol   .50   1.25
B194 SP183 30c + 10c rose lil   3.75   17.00
B195 SP183 40c + 10c dull bl   4.75   11.00
Nos. B191-B195 (5)   9.70   30.80
Set, never hinged   20.00

The surtax was for the Red Cross and the Society of Swiss History of Art.

Theophil Sprecher von Bernegg SP184

Admiral Butterfly SP185

Designs: 20c+10c, Blue Underwing Butterfly. 30c+10c, Bee. 40c+10c, Sulphur Butterfly.

1950, Dec. 1   **Engr.**
B196 SP184 5c + 5c sepia   .20   .30

Photo.
B197 SP185 10c + 10c multi   .25   .40
B198 SP185 20c + 10c multi   .30   .50
B199 SP185 30c + 10c rose lil, gray & dk brn   3.00   13.50
B200 SP185 40c + 10c bl, dk brn & yel   3.00   9.25
Nos. B196-B200 (5)   6.75   23.95
Set, never hinged   13.50

Arms of Switzerland and Zurich — SP186

Valaisan Polka SP187

20c+10c, Flag-swinging. 30c+10c, Hornussen (natl. game). 40c+10c, Blowing alphorn.

1951, June 1   **Engr.**
Shield in Red
B201 SP186 5c + 5c gray   .20   .50

Photo.
Inscribed: "1. VIII. 1951"
Shield in Red, Figure Shaded in Gray
B202 SP187 10c + 10c green   .40   .50
B203 SP187 20c + 10c ol bis   .60   .85
B204 SP187 30c + 10c red vio   4.50   11.50
B205 SP187 40c + 10c brt blue   4.50   13.50
Nos. B201-B205 (5)   10.20   26.85
Set, never hinged   20.00

The surtax was used primarily for needy mothers.

Souvenir Sheet
1951, Sept. 29   **Imperf.**
B206 SP187 40c brt bl, sheet   175.00   190.00
Never hinged   275.00

No. B206 sold for 3fr, size: 74x56mm. Natl. Phil. Exhib., LUNABA, Sept. 29-Oct. 7, 1951, Lucerne. The net proceeds were used for Swiss schools abroad.

Johanna Spyri SP189   Dragonfly SP190

Butterflies: 20c+10c, Black-Veined. 30c+10c Orange-Tip. 40c+10c, Saturnia pyri.

1951, Dec. 1   **Engr.**   **Perf. 11½**
B207 SP189 5c + 5c red brn   .20   .30

Photo.
B208 SP190 10c + 10c grn & dk bl   .20   .30
B209 SP190 20c + 10c rose lil, cr & blk   .30   .50
B210 SP190 30c + 10c ol grn, gray & org   2.00   8.50
B211 SP190 40c + 10c bl, dk brn & car   2.50   8.50
Nos. B207-B211 (5)   5.20   18.10
Set, never hinged   10.00

Arms of Switzerland, Glarus and Zug — SP191

Doubs River — SP192

Designs: 20c+10c, Lake of St. Gotthard. 30c+10c, Moesa River. 40c+10c, Lake of Marjelen.

1952, May 31   **Engr. & Typo.**
B212 SP191 5c + 5c gray & red   .25   1.00

Photo.
B213 SP192 10c + 10c blue green   .25   .50
B214 SP192 20c + 10c brown car   .30   .50
B215 SP192 30c + 10c brown   2.50   6.50
B216 SP192 40c + 10c blue   3.00   8.75
Nos. B212-B216 (5)   6.30   17.25
Set, never hinged   12.50

The surtax was used primarily for historical research and popular culture.
See Nos. B222-B226, B233-B236, B243-B246, B253-B256.

Portrait of a Boy, by Albert Anker SP193   Ladybug SP194

20c+10c, Barred-wing butterfly. 30c+10c, Argus butterfly. 40c+10c, Silkworm moth.

Perf. 11½
1952, Dec. 1   **Unwmk.**   **Engr.**
B217 SP193 5c + 5c brown car   .20   .35

Photo.
B218 SP194 10c + 10c bluish grn, blk & org red   .20   .35
B219 SP194 20c + 10c rose lil, cr & blk   .30   .50
B220 SP194 30c + 10c brn, blk & gray bl   2.00   8.25
B221 SP194 40c + 10c pale vio, brn & buff   1.90   8.75
Nos. B217-B221 (5)   4.60   18.20
Set, never hinged   10.00
See Nos. B227-B231, B238-B241.

Types Similar to 1952
Designs: 5c+5c, Arms of Switzerland and Bern. 10c+10c, Reuss River. 20c+10c, Sihl Lake. 30c+10c, Bisse River. 40c+10c, Lake of Geneva.

Engraved and Photogravure
1953, June 1
B222 SP191 5c + 5c gray & red   .20   .75

Photo.
B223 SP192 10c + 10c blue green   .25   .50
B224 SP192 20c + 10c brown car   .30   .75
B225 SP192 30c + 10c brown   2.50   7.00
B226 SP192 40c + 10c blue   2.50   6.50
Nos. B222-B226 (5)   5.75   15.50
Set, never hinged   12.50

The surtax was used for Swiss nationals abroad and for disabled persons.

Booklet Panes
Panes consisting of blocks, strips or pairs removed from large sheets of regular issue and fastened or enclosed within a cover or folder, often by stapling or sewing in the sheet margin, are no longer being listed. Such panes contain no straight edges and can easily be made privately.

Types Similar to 1952, Dated "1953"
5c+5c, Portrait of a girl, by Albert Anker. 10c+10c, Camberwell beauty butterfly. 20c+10c, Purple longicorn beetle. 30c+10c, Self-portrait, Ferdinand Hodler, facing left.

1953, Dec. 1   **Engr.**   **Perf. 11½**
B227 SP193 5c + 5c rose brown   .20   .35

Photo.
B228 SP194 10c + 10c multi   .25   .30
B229 SP194 20c + 10c multi   .30   .50
a. Sheet of 24   200.00
Never hinged   375.00
b. Bklt. pane, 4 #B229, 2 #B230   32.50
B230 SP194 30c + 10c ol, blk & red   1.90   8.25

Engr.
B231 SP193 40c + 10c bl· blue   2.75   7.00
Nos. B227-B231 (5)   5.40   16.40
Set, never hinged   12.00

No. B229a consists of 16 No. B229 and 8 No. B230, arranged to include four se-tenant pairs and four pairs which are both se-tenant and tête bêche.

Opening Bars of "Swiss Hymn" SP195   Jeremias Gotthelf SP196

Types Similar to 1952, Dated "1954"
Views: 10c+10c, Neuchatel lake. 20c+10c, Maggia river. 30c+10c, Cascade, Taubenloch gorge. 40c+10c, Sils lake.

1954, June 1   **Engr.**   **Perf. 11½**
B232 SP195 5c + 5c dk bl grn   .25   .75

Photo.
B233 SP192 10c + 10c blue grn   .25   .50
B234 SP192 20c + 10c deep plum   .35   .50
B235 SP192 30c + 10c dk brown   2.00   6.75

B236 SP192 40c + 10c dp blue   2.25   7.25
Nos. B232-B236 (5)   5.10   15.75
Set, never hinged   12.00

The surtax was used to aid vocational training and home nursing.
No. B232 commemorates the centenary of the death of Alberik Zwyssig, composer of the "Swiss Hymn."

Types Similar to 1952, Dated "1954"
Insects: 10c+10c, Garden tiger. 20c+10c, Bumble bee. 30c+10c, Ascalaphus. 40c+10c, Swallow-tail.

1954, Dec. 1   **Engr.**
B237 SP196 5c + 5c dk red brn   .20   .30

Photo.
B238 SP194 10c + 10c multi   .20   .30
B239 SP194 20c + 10c multi   .35   .50
B240 SP194 30c + 10c rose vio, brn & yel   2.00   6.75
B241 SP194 40c + 10c multi   2.25   7.25
Nos. B237-B241 (5)   5.00   15.10
Set, never hinged   11.00

Type Similar to 1952, Dated "1955," and

Federal Institute of Technology, Zurich — SP197

Views: 10c+10c, Saane river. 20c+10c, Lake of Aegeri. 30c+10c, Grappelen Lake. 40c+10c, Lake of Bienne.

1955, June 1   **Engr.**   **Perf. 11½**
B242 SP197 5c + 5c gray   .20   .75

Photo.
B243 SP192 10c + 10c dp green   .25   .50
B244 SP192 20c + 10c rose brn   .35   .50
B245 SP192 30c + 10c brown   2.00   6.00
B246 SP192 40c + 10c dp blue   2.25   7.50
Nos. B242-B246 (5)   5.05   15.25
Set, never hinged   11.50

The surtax aided mountain dwellers.
No. B242 for the centenary of the Federal Institute of Technology in Zurich.

Charles Pictet de Rochemont SP198   Peacock Butterfly SP199

Insects: 20c+10c, Great Horntail. 30c+10c, Yellow Bear moth. 40c+10c, Apollo butterfly.

1955, Dec. 1   **Engr.**   **Unwmk.**
B247 SP198 5c + 5c brn car   .20   .30

Photo.
Insects in Natural Colors
B248 SP199 10c + 10c yel grn   .20   .30
B249 SP199 20c + 10c red   .30   .50
B250 SP199 30c + 10c dk ocher   2.50   4.75
B251 SP199 40c + 10c ultra   2.25   5.75
Nos. B247-B251 (5)   5.45   11.60
Set, never hinged   11.50

Types Similar to 1952, Dated "1956", and

"Woman's Work" — SP200

Designs: 10c+10c, Rhone at St. Maurice. 20c+10c, Katzensee. 30c+10c, Rhine at Trin. 40c+10c, Lake Wallen.

1956, June 1   **Engr.**   **Perf. 11½**
B252 SP200 5c + 5c turq bl   .20   1.00

Photo.

B253	SP192	10c + 10c green	.25	.50
B254	SP192	20c + 10c brn car	.30	.75
B255	SP192	30c + 10c brown	2.00	4.75
B256	SP192	40c + 10c ultra	1.75	5.75
	Nos. B252-B256 (5)		4.50	12.75
	Set, never hinged		10.00	

The surtax was for the National Day Collection, the National Library and Academy of Arts and Letters. No. B252 was issued in honor of Swiss women.

Carlo Maderno SP201 Burnet Moth SP202

Insects: 20c+10c, Purple Emperor. 30c+10c, Blue ground beetle. 40c+10c, Cabbage butterfly.

1956, Dec. 1 Engr. Perf. 11½

B257	SP201	5c + 5c brn car	.20	.30

Photo.
Granite Paper

B258	SP202	10c + 10c grn, dk grn & car rose	.20	.30
B259	SP202	20c + 10c multi	.30	.30
B260	SP202	30c + 10c yel & dp bl	1.40	4.50
B261	SP202	40c + 10c lt ultra, pale yel & sep	1.40	5.00
	Nos. B257-B261 (5)		3.50	10.40
	Set, never hinged		7.50	

Red Cross and Swiss Emblems SP203

"Charity" — SP204

Engraved and Photogravure
1957, June 1 Unwmk. Perf. 11½

B262	SP203	5c + 5c gray & red	.20	.55

Photo.
Granite Paper
Cross in Deep Carmine

B263	SP204	10c + 10c brt grn & gray	.20	.30
B264	SP204	20c + 10c red & bl gray	.30	.30
B265	SP204	30c + 10c brn & vio gray	1.75	4.50
B266	SP204	40c + 10c brt bl & bis	1.90	5.75
	Nos. B262-B266 (5)		4.35	11.40
	Set, never hinged		10.00	

The surtax went to the Red Cross for the needs of the sick and to combat cancer.

Leonhard Euler — SP205 Clouded Yellow — SP206

Insects: 20c+10c, Magpie moth. 30c+10c, Rose Chafer. 40c+10c, Red Underwing.

1957, Nov. 30 Engr. Perf. 11½

B267	SP205	5c + 5c brn car	.20	.30

Photo.
Granite Paper

B268	SP206	10c + 10c multi	.20	.30
B269	SP206	20c + 10c lil rose, blk & yel	.30	.50

B270	SP206	30c + 10c rose brn, ind & brt grn	1.40	4.50
B271	SP206	40c + 10c multi	1.40	3.50
	Nos. B267-B271 (5)		3.50	9.10
	Set, never hinged		7.50	

> **Catalogue values for unused stamps in this section, from this point to the end of the section, are for Never Hinged items.**

Mother and Child — SP207

Fluorite — SP208

Designs: 20c+10c, Ammonite. 30c+10c, Garnet. 40c+10c, Rock Crystal.

Perf. 11½

1958, May 31 Unwmk. Engr.

B272	SP207	5c + 5c brn car	.40	.40

Photo.
Granite Paper

B273	SP208	10c + 10c multi	.55	.55
B274	SP208	20c + 10c blk, red & ol bis	.75	.75
B275	SP208	30c + 10c blk, dl yel & mag	3.25	5.25
B276	SP208	40c + 10c blk, chlky bl & sl bl	3.25	5.00
	Nos. B272-B276 (5)		8.20	11.95

The surtax was for needy mothers. See #B283-B286, B292-B295, B304-B307.

Albrecht von Haller — SP209 Pansy — SP210

Flowers: 20c+10c, China aster. 30c+10c, Morning glory. 40c+10c, Christmas rose.

1958, Dec. 1 Engr. Perf. 11½

B277	SP209	5c + 5c brn car	.25	.30

Photo.
Granite Paper

B278	SP210	10c + 10c grn, yel & brn	.25	.30
B279	SP210	20c + 10c multi	.55	.30
B280	SP210	30c + 10c multi	2.00	3.50
B281	SP210	40c + 10c dk bl, yel	2.00	3.50
	Nos. B277-B281 (5)		5.05	7.90

See Nos. B287-B291.

Mineral Type of 1958 and

Globe and Swiss Flags — SP211

Designs: 10c+10c, Agate. 20c+10c, Tourmaline. 30c+10c, Amethyst. 40c+10c, Fossil salamander (andrias).

1959, June 1 Engr. Perf. 11½

B282	SP211	5c + 5c dl grn & red	.40	.50

Photo.
Granite Paper

B283	SP208	10c + 10c gray, yel grn & ver	.50	.50
B284	SP208	20c + 10c blk, lil rose & bl grn	.65	.50
B285	SP208	30c + 10c blk, lt brn & vio	2.25	3.00

B286	SP208	40c + 10c blk, bl & gray	2.50	3.00
	Nos. B282-B286 (5)		6.30	7.50

Types of 1958

Designs: 5c+5c, Karl Hilty. 10c+10c, Marigold. 20c+10c, Poppy. 30c+10c, Nasturtium. 50c+10c, Sweet pea.

1959, Dec. 1 Engr. Perf. 11½

B287	SP209	5c + 5c brn car	.20	.25

Photo.
Granite Paper

B288	SP210	10c + 10c dk grn, grn & yel	.30	.25
B289	SP210	20c + 10c mag, red & grn	.50	.25
B290	SP210	30c + 10c multi	2.25	3.00
B291	SP210	50c + 10c multi	2.25	3.00
	Nos. B287-B291 (5)		5.50	6.75

Mineral Type of 1958 and

Owl, T-Square and Hammer — SP212

Designs: 5c+5c, Smoky quartz. 10c+10c, Feldspar. 20c+10c, Gryphaea, fossil. 30c+10c, Azurite.

1960, June 1 Photo. Perf. 11½
Granite Paper

B292	SP208	5c + 5c blk, bl & ocher	.55	.75
B293	SP208	10c + 10c blk, yel grn & pink	.60	.50
B294	SP208	20c + 10c blk, lil rose & yel	.85	.50
B295	SP208	30c + 10c multi	4.00	3.75

Engr.

B296	SP212	50c + 10c bl & gold	4.75	3.50
	Nos. B292-B296 (5)		10.75	9.00

Souvenir Sheet
Imperf
Typo.

B297	Sheet of 4		40.00	20.00

#B297 contains 4 50c+10c stamps of design SP212 in gold & blue. Size: 84x75mm. Sold for 3fr.

Alexandre Calame SP213 Dandelion SP214

Flowers: 20c+10c, Phlox. 30c+10c, Larkspur. 50c+10c, Thorn apple.

1960, Dec. 1 Engr. Unwmk.

B298	SP213	5c + 5c grnsh bl	.25	.20

Photo.
Granite Paper

B299	SP214	10c + 10c grn, yel & gray	.30	.20
B300	SP214	20c + 10c mag, grn & gray	.45	.20
B301	SP214	30c + 10c org brn, grn & bl	3.50	3.50
B302	SP214	50c + 10c ultra & grn	3.50	3.50
	Nos. B298-B302 (5)		8.00	7.60

See Nos. B308-B312, B329-B333, B339-B343.

Mineral Type of 1958 and

Book of History with Symbols of Time and Eternity — SP215

Designs: 10c+10c, Fluorite. 20c+10c, Petrified fish. 30c+10c, Lazulite. 50c+10c, Petrified fern.

1961, June 1 Engr. Perf. 11½

B303	SP215	5c + 5c lt blue	.35	.50

Photo.
Granite Paper

B304	SP208	10c + 10c gray, grn & pink	.50	.35
B305	SP208	20c + 10c gray & car rose	.60	.35
B306	SP208	30c + 10c gray, org & grnsh bl	1.60	2.50
B307	SP208	50c + 10c gray, bl & bis	2.25	3.50
	Nos. B303-B307 (5)		5.30	7.20

Types of 1960

Designs: 5c+5c, Jonas Furrer. 10c+10c, Sunflower. 20c+10c, Lily of the valley. 30c+10c, Iris. 50c+10c, Silverweed.

1961, Dec. 1 Engr. Perf. 11½

B308	SP213	5c + 5c dk blue	.20	.20

Photo.
Granite Paper

B309	SP214	10c + 10c grn, yel & org	.20	.20
B310	SP214	20c + 10c dk red, grn & gray	.30	.20
B311	SP214	30c + 10c multi	1.75	2.00
B312	SP214	50c + 10c dk bl, yel & grn	2.00	2.50
	Nos. B308-B312 (5)		4.45	5.10

Jean Jacques Rousseau SP216 Half-Thaler, Obwalden, 1732 SP217

Coins: 20c+10c, Ducat, Schwyz, ca. 1653. 30c+10c, "Steer Head" Batzen, Uri, 1659. 50c+10c, Nidwalden Batzen.

Perf. 11½

1962, June 1 Unwmk. Engr.

B313	SP216	5c + 5c dk blue	.20	.20

Photo.
Granite Paper

B314	SP217	10c + 10c grn & stl bl	.20	.20
B315	SP217	20c + 10c car rose & yel	.50	.50
B316	SP217	30c + 10c org & sl bl	1.25	1.65
B317	SP217	50c + 10c ultra & vio bl	1.25	1.65
	Nos. B313-B317 (5)		3.40	4.20

Apple Blossoms SP218 Mother and Child SP219

Designs: 10c+10c, Boy chasing duck. 30c+10c, Girl and sunflowers. 50c+10c, Forsythia. 1fr+20c, Mother and child, facing right.

1962, Dec. 1 Perf. 11½
Granite Paper

B318	SP218	5c + 5c bl gray, pink, grn & yel	.20	.20
B319	SP218	10c + 10c grn, pink & dk grn	.20	.20
B320	SP219	20c + 10c org red, brn, grn & pink	.60	.50
B321	SP218	30c + 10c org, red & yel	1.10	2.00
B322	SP218	50c + 10c dp bl, yel & brn	1.50	2.50
	Nos. B318-B322 (5)		3.60	5.40

Souvenir Sheet
Imperf

B323	SP219	1fr + 20c Sheet of 2	5.25	5.25

50th anniv. of the Pro Juventute (Youth Aid) Foundation. No. B323 sold for 3fr.

Anna Heer,
M.D. — SP220

Bandage
Roll — SP221

Designs: 20c+10c, Gift parcel. 30c+10c,
Plasma bottles. 50c+10c, Red Cross
armband.

1963, June 1   Engr.   Perf. 11½
B324 SP220 5c + 5c dk blue   .20   .20
Photo.
Granite Paper
Cross in Red
B325 SP221 10c + 10c lt & dk
              grn & gray   .20   .20
B326 SP221 20c + 10c rose,
              gray & blk   .50   .20
B327 SP221 30c + 10c mul-
              ticolored   1.10 1.50
B328 SP221 50c + 10c bl, gray &
              blk   1.25 1.50
  Nos. B324-B328 (5)   3.25 3.60

Types of 1960
Designs: 5c+5c, Portrait of a Boy by Albert
Anker. 10c+10c, Daisy. 20c+10c, Geranium.
30c+10c, Cornflower. 50c+10c, Carnation.

1963, Nov. 30   Engr.   Perf. 11½
B329 SP213 5c + 5c blue   .20   .30
  a.   Booklet pane of 4   3.00
Photo.
B330 SP214 10c + 10c grn,
              gray & yel   .30 1.25
  a.   Booklet pane of 4   4.00
B331 SP214 20c + 10c multi   1.40 2.50
  a.   Booklet pane of 4   5.75
B332 SP214 30c + 10c multi   1.40 1.50
B333 SP214 50c + 10c ultra, lil
              rose & grn   1.75 1.50
  Nos. B329-B333 (5)   5.05 7.05

Nos. B329-B331 were printed on two kinds
of paper: I. Fluorescent, with violet fibers. II.
Non-fluorescent, the 10c+10c and 20c+10c
with mixed red and blue fibers. Nos. B332-
B333 exist only on violet-fibered, fluorescent
paper. The booklet panes, Nos. B329a, B330a
and B331a, exist only on non-fluorescent
paper.

Johann Georg
Bodmer
SP222

Copper Coin,
Zurich
SP223

Coins: 20c+10c, Doppeldicken, Basel.
30c+10c, Silver taler, Geneva. 50c+10c, Gold
half florin, Bern.

Violet Fibers, Fluorescent Paper
1964, June 1   Engr.   Perf. 11½
B334 SP222 5c + 5c blue   .20   .20
Photo.
B335 SP223 10c + 10c grn, bis &
              blk   .20   .20
B336 SP223 20c + 10c rose car,
              gray & blk   .30   .25
B337 SP223 30c + 10c org, gray
              & blk   .55   .50
Granite Paper, Red and Blue Fibers
B338 SP223 50c + 10c ultra, yel
              & brn   .80   .65
  Nos. B334-B338 (5)   2.05 1.80

Fluorescent Paper
Paper of Nos. B334-B425, B427 and
B429 is fluorescent and has violet
fibers.
Nos. B426, B428 and all semipostals
from No. B430 onward are fluorescent
but lack violet fibers, unless otherwise
noted.

Types of 1960
Designs: 5c+5c, Portrait of a Girl by Albert
Anker. 10c+10c, Daffodil. 20c+10c, Rose.
30c+10c, Clover. 50c+10c, Water lily.

1964, Dec. 1   Engr.   Perf. 11½
B339 SP213 5c + 5c grnsh bl   .20   .20
Photo.
B340 SP214 10c + 10c dp grn,
              yel & org   .20   .20
B341 SP214 20c + 10c dp car,
              rose & grn   .30   .20
B342 SP214 30c + 10c brn, lil &
              grn   .55   .55
B343 SP214 50c + 10c multi   .75   .75
  Nos. B339-B343 (5)   2.00 1.90

Type of Regular Issue, 1965
Souvenir Sheet
10c, 20r Seated Helvetia. 20c, 40r Seated
Helvetia.

1965, Mar. 8   Photo.   Imperf.
Granite Paper, Nonfluorescent
B344 A153 Sheet of 2   1.50 1.00
  a.   10c grn, pale orange & blk   .75   .50
  b.   20c dark red, yel grn & blk   .75   .50

Natl. Postage Stamp Exhib., NABRA, Bern,
Aug. 27-Sept. 5, 1965. Sold for 3fr, the net
proceeds were used to cover expenses of the
exhibition and to promote philately.

Father
Theodosius
Florentini
SP224

The Temptation
of Christ
SP225

Ceiling Paintings from Church of St. Martin
at Zillis, 12th century: 10c+10c, Symbol of evil
(goose with fishtail). 20c+10c, Magi on horseback. 30c+10c, Fishermen on Sea of Galilee.

Perf. 11½
1965, June 1   Unwmk.   Engr.
B345 SP224 5c + 5c blue   .20   .20
Photo.
B346 SP225 10c + 10c ol grn,
              ocher & bl   .20   .20
B347 SP225 20c + 10c dk brn,
              red & buff   .30   .20
B348 SP225 30c + 10c dk brn,
              sep & bl   .50   .30
B349 SP225 50c + 10c vio bl, bl
              & brn   .60   .30
  Nos. B345-B349 (5)   1.80 1.20

See Nos. B355-B359, B365-B369.

Hedgehogs — SP226

Designs: 10c+10c, Alpine marmots.
20c+10c, Red deer. 30c+10c, European
badgers. 50c+10c, Varying hares.

1965, Dec. 1   Photo.   Perf. 11½
B350 SP226 5c + 5c multi   .20   .20
B351 SP226 10c + 10c multi   .20   .20
B352 SP226 20c + 10c multi   .30   .20
B353 SP226 30c + 10c multi   .50   .20
B354 SP226 50c + 10c multi   .60   .30
  Nos. B350-B354 (5)   1.80 1.10

See Nos. B360-B364.

Types of 1965
5c+5c, Heinrich Federer (1866-1928),
writer. 10c+10c, Joseph's dream. 20c+10c,
Joseph on his way. 30c+10c, Virgin and Child
fleeing to Egypt. 50c+20c, Angel leading the
way. Nos. B356-B359 from ceiling paintings,
Church of St. Martin at Zillis.

1966, June 1   Engr.   Perf. 11½
B355 SP224 5c + 5c dp blue   .20   .20
Photo.
B356 SP225 10c + 10c multi   .20   .20
B357 SP225 20c + 10c multi   .30   .20
B358 SP225 30c + 10c multi   .50   .25
B359 SP225 50c + 10c multi   .60   .35
  Nos. B355-B359 (5)   1.80 1.20

Animal Type of 1965
5c+5c, Ermine. 10c+10c, Red squirrel.
20c+10c, Red fox. 30c+10c, Hares. 50c+10c,
Two chamois.

1966, Dec. 1   Photo.   Perf. 11½
Animals in Natural Colors
B360 SP226 5c + 5c grnsh bl   .20   .20
B361 SP226 10c + 10c emer   .20   .20
B362 SP226 20c + 10c ver   .30   .20
B363 SP226 30c + 10c brt lemon   .50   .20
B364 SP226 50c + 10c org   .60   .35
  Nos. B360-B364 (5)   1.80 1.15

Types of 1965
Designs: 5c+5c, Dr. Theodor Kocher.
10c+10c, Annunciation to the Shepherds.
20c+10c, Jesus and the Samaritan Woman at
the Well. 30c+10c, Adoration of the Magi.
50c+10c, St. Joseph. (Ceiling paintings, St.
Martin at Zillis).

Perf. 11½
1967, June 1   Unwmk.   Engr.
B365 SP224 5c + 5c blue   .20   .20
Photo.
B366 SP225 10c + 10c multi   .20   .20
B367 SP225 20c + 10c multi   .30   .20
B368 SP225 30c + 10c multi   .50   .20
B369 SP225 50c + 10c multi   .60   .35
  Nos. B365-B369 (5)   1.80 1.15

Roe
Deer — SP227

Hunter, Month
of
May — SP228

Designs: 20c+10c, Pine marten. 30c+10c,
Alpine ibex. 50c+20c, Otter.

1967, Dec. 1   Photo.   Perf. 11½
Animals in Natural Colors
B370 SP227 10c + 10c yel grn   .20   .20
B371 SP227 20c + 10c dp car   .30   .20
B372 SP227 30c + 10c ol bis   .50   .25
B373 SP227 50c + 20c ultra   .75   .50
  Nos. B370-B373 (4)   1.75 1.15

1968, May 30   Photo.   Perf. 11½
Designs from Rose Window, Lausanne
Cathedral: 10c+10c, Leo. 30c+10c, Libra.
50c+20c, Pisces.

B374 SP228 10c + 10c multi   .20   .20
B375 SP228 20c + 10c multi   .30   .20
B376 SP228 30c + 10c multi   .50   .30
B377 SP228 50c + 10c multi   .70   .70
  Nos. B374-B377 (4)   1.70 1.40

Capercaillie
SP229

St. Francis
SP230

Birds: 20c+10c, Bullfinch. 30c+10c, Wood-
chat shrike. 50c+20c, Firecrest.

1968, Nov. 28   Photo.   Perf. 11½
Birds in Natural Colors
B378 SP229 10c + 10c dull yel   .20   .20
B379 SP229 20c + 10c olive grn   .30   .20
B380 SP229 30c + 10c lilac rose   .40   .20
B381 SP229 50c + 20c dp violet   .70   .50
  Nos. B378-B381 (4)   1.60 1.10

See Nos. B386-B389.

1969, May 29   Photo.   Perf. 11½
Designs: 10c+10c, St. Francis Preaching to
the Birds, Königsfelden Convent Church.
20c+10c, Israelites Drinking from Spring of
Moses, Berne Cathedral. 30c+10c, St. Christopher, Laufelfinger Church (now Basel
Museum). 50c+20c, Virgin and Child, Chapel
at Grapplang (now National Museum).

B382 SP230 10c + 10c multi   .20   .20
B383 SP230 20c + 10c multi   .30   .20
B384 SP230 30c + 10c multi   .50   .25
B385 SP230 50c + 20c multi   .70   .45
  Nos. B382-B385 (4)   1.70 1.10

Bird Type of 1968
Birds: 10c+10c, European goldfinch.
20c+10c, Golden oriole. 30c+10c, Wall
creeper. 50c+20c, Eurasian jay.

1969, Dec. 1   Photo.   Perf. 11½
Birds in Natural Colors
B386 SP229 10c + 10c gray   .20   .20
B387 SP229 20c + 10c green   .30   .20
B388 SP229 30c + 10c plum   .40   .25
B389 SP229 50c + 20c ultra   .70   .55
  Nos. B386-B389 (4)   1.60 1.20

Sailor, by Gian
Casty, Gellert
Schoolhouse,
Basel
SP231

Blue Titmice
SP232

Contemporary Stained Glass Windows:
20c+10c, Abstract composition, by Celestino
Piatti. 30c+10c, Bull (Assyrian god Marduk),
by Hans Stocker. 50c+20c, Man and Woman,
by Max Hunziker and Karl Ganz.

1970, May 29   Photo.   Perf. 11½
B390 SP231 10c + 10c multi   .20   .20
B391 SP231 20c + 10c multi   .30   .20
B392 SP231 30c + 10c multi   .50   .25
B393 SP231 50c + 10c multi   .70   .50
  Nos. B390-B393 (4)   1.70 1.15

See Nos. B398-B401.

1970, Dec. 1   Photo.   Perf. 11½
Birds: 20c+10c, Hoopoe. 30c+10c, Greater
spotted woodpecker. 50c+20c, Crested
grebes.

Birds in Natural Colors
B394 SP232 10c + 10c orange   .20   .20
B395 SP232 20c + 10c emerald   .30   .20
B396 SP232 30c + 10c brt rose   .50   .20
B397 SP232 50c + 20c blue   .80   .75
  Nos. B394-B397 (4)   1.80 1.35

See Nos. B402-B405.

Art Type of 1970
Contemporary Stained Glass Windows:
10c+10c, "Composition," by Jean-François
Comment. 20c+10c, Cock, by Jean Prahin.
30c+10c, Fox, by Kurt Volk. 50c+20c, "Composition," by Bernard Schorderet.

1971, May 27   Photo.   Perf. 11½
B398 SP231 10c + 10c multi   .20   .20
B399 SP231 20c + 10c multi   .30   .20
B400 SP231 30c + 10c multi   .40   .25
B401 SP231 50c + 20c multi   .70   .45
  Nos. B398-B401 (4)   1.60 1.10

Bird Type of 1970
Birds: 10c+10c, European redstarts.
20c+10c, White-spotted bluethroats. 30c+
10c, Peregrine falcon. 40c+20c, Mallards.

1971, Dec. 1
B402 SP232 10c + 10c multi   .20   .20
B403 SP232 20c + 10c multi   .30   .20
B404 SP232 30c + 10c multi   .50   .20
B405 SP232 40c + 20c multi   .75   .60
  Nos. B402-B405 (4)   1.75 1.20

Harpoon Heads,
Late Stone Age
SP233

McGredy's
Sunset
SP234

Archaeological Treasures: 20c+10c, Bronze
hydria, Hallstadt period. 30c+10c, Gold bust of
Emperor Marcus Aurelius, Roman period.
40c+20c, Horseback rider (decorative disk),
early Middle Ages.

1972, June 1

B406	SP233 10c + 10c multi	.20	.20
B407	SP233 20c + 10c multi	.35	.20
B408	SP233 30c + 10c multi	.50	.20
B409	SP233 40c + 20c multi	1.25	.70
	Nos. B406-B409 (4)	2.30	1.30

1972, Dec. 1   Photo.   *Perf. 11½*

Famous Roses: 20c+10c, Miracle. 30c+10c, Papa Meilland. 40c+20c, Madame Dimitriu.

B410	SP234 10c + 10c multi	.25	.20
B411	SP234 20c + 10c multi	.30	.20
B412	SP234 30c + 10c multi	.50	.20
B413	SP234 40c + 20c multi	1.25	1.10
	Nos. B410-B413 (4)	2.30	1.70

Rauraric
(Gallic)
Jug — SP235

Chestnut — SP236

Archeologic Finds: 30c+10c, Bronze head of a Gaul. 40c+20c, Alemannic dress fasteners (fish), 6th century. 60c+20c, Gold bowl, 6th century B.C.

1973, May 29   Photo.   *Perf. 11½*

B414	SP235 15c + 5c multi	.20	.20
B415	SP235 30c + 10c multi	.50	.20
B416	SP235 40c + 20c multi	1.00	.60
B417	SP235 60c + 20c multi	1.25	.85
	Nos. B414-B417 (4)	2.95	1.85

See Nos. B422-B425.

1973, Nov. 29   Photo.   *Perf. 11½*

Fruits of the Forest: 30c+10c, Sweet cherries. 40c+20c, Blackberries. 60c+20c, Blueberries.

B418	SP236 15c + 5c multi	.20	.20
B419	SP236 30c + 10c multi	.30	.20
B420	SP236 40c + 20c multi	.75	.60
B421	SP236 60c + 20c multi	1.25	.70
	Nos. B418-B421 (4)	2.50	1.70

Archaeological Type of 1973

Archaeological Finds: 15c+5c, Polychrome glass bowl. 30c+10c, Bull's head. 40c+20c, Gold fibula. 60c+20c, Ceramic bird.

1974, May 30   Photo.   *Perf. 11½*

B422	SP235 15c + 5c multi	.20	.20
B423	SP235 30c + 10c multi	.50	.30
B424	SP235 40c + 20c multi	.90	.55
B425	SP235 60c + 20c multi	1.25	.70
	Nos. B422-B425 (4)	2.85	1.75

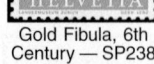

Laurel — SP237   Gold Fibula, 6th
                       Century — SP238

Designs: 30c+20c, Belladonna. 50c+20c, Laburnum. 60c+25c, Mistletoe.

1974, Nov. 29   Photo.   *Perf. 11½*

B426	SP237 15c + 10c multi	.20	.20
B427	SP237 30c + 20c multi	.50	.30
B428	SP237 50c + 20c multi	.80	.60
B429	SP237 60c + 25c multi	1.10	.80
	Nos. B426-B429 (4)	2.60	1.80

1975, May 30   Photo.   *Perf. 11½*

Archaeological Treasures: 30c+20c, Bronze head of Bacchus, 2nd century. 50c+20c, Bronze daggers, 1800-1600 B.C. 60c+25c, Colored glass bottle, 1st century.

B430	SP238 15c + 10c multi	.35	.20
B431	SP238 30c + 20c multi	.60	.25
B432	SP238 50c + 20c multi	1.00	.70
B433	SP238 60c + 25c multi	1.10	.75
	Nos. B430-B433 (4)	3.05	1.90

Mail Bucket   Hepatica
SP239.   SP240

Forest Plants: 30c+20c, Mountain ash berries. 50c+20c, Yellow nettle. 60c+25c, Sycamore maple.

1975, Nov. 27   Photo.   *Perf. 11½*

B434	SP239 10c + 5c multi	.20	.20
B435	SP240 15c + 10c multi	.20	.20
B436	SP240 30c + 20c multi	.50	.30
B437	SP240 50c + 20c multi	.80	.65
B438	SP240 60c + 25c multi	1.00	.75
	Nos. B434-B438 (5)	2.70	2.10

See Nos. B443-B446.

Castles
SP241

1976, May 28   Photo.   *Perf. 11½*

B439	SP241 20c + 10 Kyburg	.40	.20
B440	SP241 40c + 20 Grandson	.75	.30
B441	SP241 40c + 20 Murten	.75	.30
B442	SP241 80c + 40 Bellinzona	2.25	.85
	Nos. B439-B442 (4)	4.15	1.65

See #B447-B450, B455-B458, B463-B466.

Plant Type of 1975

Medicinal Forest Plants: 20c+10c, Barberry. No. B444, Black elder. No. B445, Linden. 80+40c, Pulmonaria.

1976, Nov. 29   Photo.   *Perf. 11½*

B443	SP240 20c + 10c multi	.30	.20
B444	SP240 40c + 20c lil & multi	.55	.20
B445	SP240 40c + 20c terra cotta & multi	.55	.20
B446	SP240 80c + 40c multi	1.25	.80
	Nos. B443-B446 (4)	2.65	1.40

Castle Type of 1976

1977, May 26   Photo.   *Perf. 11½*

B447	SP241 20c + 10c Aigle	.40	.25
B448	SP241 40c + 20c Pratteln	.60	.35
B449	SP241 70c + 30c Sargans	1.25	.90
B450	SP241 80c + 40c Hallwil	1.50	1.00
	Nos. B447-B450 (4)	3.75	2.50

Wild   Communal
Rose — SP242   Arms — SP243

Designs: Roses.

1977, Nov. 28   Photo.   *Perf. 11½*

B451	SP242 20c + 10c multi	.30	.20
B452	SP242 40c + 20c multi	.60	.20
B453	SP242 70c + 30c multi	1.00	.80
B454	SP242 80c + 40c multi	1.25	1.00
	Nos. B451-B454 (4)	3.15	2.20

See Nos. B492-B496.

Castle Type of 1976

1978, May 26   Photo.   *Perf. 11½*

B455	SP241 20c + 10c Hagenwil	.30	.30
B456	SP241 40c + 20c Burgdorf	.60	.60
B457	SP241 70c + 30c Tarasp	1.25	1.25
B458	SP241 80c + 40c Chillon	1.50	1.50
	Nos. B455-B458 (4)	3.65	3.65

1978, Nov. 28   Photo.   *Perf. 11½*

B459	SP243 20c + 10c multi	.30	.20
B460	SP243 40c + 20c Gruyeres	.60	.25
B461	SP243 70c + 30c Castasegna	1.00	1.00
B462	SP243 80c + 40c Wangen an der Aare	1.50	1.25
	Nos. B459-B462 (4)	3.40	2.70

See #B467-B470, B475-B478, B484-B487.

Castle Type of 1976

1979, May 25   Photo.   *Perf. 11½*

B463	SP241 20c + 10c Oron	.30	.30
B464	SP241 40c + 20c Spiez	.60	.45
B465	SP241 70c + 30c Porrentruy	1.10	1.00
B466	SP241 80c + 40c Rapperswil	1.50	1.50
	Nos. B463-B466 (4)	3.50	3.25

Arms Type of 1978

1979, Nov. 28   Photo.   *Perf. 11*

B467	SP243 20c + 10c Cadro	.30	.20
B468	SP243 40c + 20c Rute	.60	.25
B469	SP243 70c + 30c Schwamendingen	1.00	.85
B470	SP243 80c + 40c Perroy	1.50	1.10
	Nos. B467-B470 (4)	3.40	2.40

Masons' and
Carpenters'
Sign — SP244

1980, May 29   Photo.   *Perf. 11½*

B471	SP244 20c + 10c shown	.30	.30
B472	SP244 40c + 20c Barber	.45	.30
B473	SP244 70c + 30c Hat maker	1.00	1.00
B474	SP244 80c + 40c Baker	1.25	1.25
	Nos. B471-B474 (4)	3.00	2.85

Arms Type of 1978

1980, Nov. 26   Photo.   *Perf. 11½*

B475	SP243 20c + 10c Cortaillod	.30	.20
B476	SP243 40c + 20c Sierre	.55	.25
B477	SP243 70c + 30c Scuol	1.00	.90
B478	SP243 80c + 40c Wolfenschiessen	1.25	.95
	Nos. B475-B478 (4)	3.10	2.30

Icarus in
Flight
SP245

1981, Mar. 9   Photo.

B479	SP245 2fr + 1fr multi	3.00	3.00

Swissair, 50th Anniversary. Surtax was for Pro Aero Foundation Issued in sheet of 8.

Post Office Sign,
Aarburg,
1685 — SP246

Post Office Signs (c. 1849).

1981, May 4   Photo.

B480	SP246 20c + 10c shown	.30	.30
B481	SP246 40c + 20c Fribourg	.60	.50
B482	SP246 70c + 30c Gordola	1.10	1.10
B483	SP246 80c + 40c Splugen	1.25	1.25
	Nos. B480-B483 (4)	3.25	3.15

Arms Type of 1978

1981, Nov. 26   Photo.   *Perf. 11½*

B484	SP243 20c + 10c Uffikon	.30	.20
B485	SP243 40c + 20c Torre	.60	.30
B486	SP243 70c + 30c Benken	1.00	.60
B487	SP243 80c + 40c Preverenges	1.10	.75
	Nos. B484-B487 (4)	3.00	1.85

Sonne Inn
Sign, Willisau
SP247

1982, May 27   Photo.   *Perf. 11½*

B488	SP247 20c + 10c shown	.30	.20
B489	SP247 40c + 20c A L'Onde, St. Saphorin	.55	.30
B490	SP247 70c + 30c Three Kings, Rheinfelden	.90	.55
B491	SP247 80c + 40c Krone, Winterthur	1.25	.70
	Nos. B488-B491 (4)	3.00	1.75

See Nos. B497-B500.

Rose Type of 1977

Designs: 10c+10c, Letter balance. 20c+10c, La Belle Portugaise. 40c+20c, Hugh Dickson. 70c+30c, Mermaid. 80c+40c, Madame Caroline.

1982, Nov. 25   Photo.

B492	SP242 10c + 10c multi	.25	.20
B493	SP242 20c + 10c multi	.40	.20
B494	SP242 40c + 20c multi	.70	.30
B495	SP242 70c + 30c multi	1.25	.80
B496	SP242 80c + 40c multi	1.40	1.10
	Nos. B492-B496 (5)	4.00	2.60

Inn Sign Type of 1982

1983, May 26   Photo.

B497	SP247 20c + 10c Lion Inn, Heimiswil, 1669	.40	.30
B498	SP247 40c + 20c Cross Hotel, Sachseln, 1489	.75	.50
B499	SP247 70c + 30c Tankard Inn, 1830	1.25	.80
B500	SP247 80c + 40c Au Cavalier Inn, Vaud	1.40	1.00
	Nos. B497-B500 (4)	3.80	2.60

Antique
Toys — SP248

1983, Nov. 24

B501	SP248 20c + 10c Kitchen stove, 1850	.35	.20
B502	SP248 40c + 20c Rocking horse, 1826	.70	.35
B503	SP248 70c + 30c Doll, 1870	1.10	.55
B504	SP248 80c + 40c Steam locomotive, 1900	1.40	.70
	Nos. B501-B504 (4)	3.55	1.80

Ceramic Tiled
Stoves — SP249

1984, May 24   Photo.   *Perf. 11½*

B505	SP249 35c + 15c 1566	.55	.40
B506	SP249 50c + 20c 1646	.70	.50
B507	SP249 70c + 30c 1768	1.00	.70
B508	SP249 80c + 40c 18th cent.	1.25	.90
	Nos. B505-B508 (4)	3.50	2.50

See Nos. B660-B663.

Children's
Stories
SP250

1984, Nov. 26   Photo.

B509	SP250 35c + 15c Heidi	.60	.40
B510	SP250 50c + 20c Pinocchio	.75	.50
B511	SP250 70c + 30c Pippi Longstocking	1.10	.70
B512	SP260 80c + 40c Max and Moritz	1.40	.90
	Nos. B509-B512 (4)	3.85	2.60

Musical Museum Exhibits SP251

1985, May 28 **Photo.** *Perf. 11½*
B513 SP251 25c + 10c Music box, 1895 .30 .20
B514 SP251 35c + 15c Rattle box, 18th cent. .50 .20
B515 SP251 50c + 20c Emmenthal necked zither, 1828 .70 .20
B516 SP251 70c + 30c Drum, 1571 1.00 .30
B517 SP251 80c + 40c Diatonic accordion, 20th cent. 1.25 .35
Nos. B513-B517 (5) 3.75 1.25
Surtax for Swiss cultural programs.

Hansel and Gretel SP252

Fairy tales by Jakob (1785-1863) and Wilhelm (1786-1859) Grimm.

1985, Nov. 26 **Photo.**
B518 SP252 35c + 15c shown .55 .20
B519 SP252 50c + 20c Snow White .80 .20
B520 SP252 80c + 40c Little Red Riding Hood 1.25 .35
B521 SP252 90c + 40c Cinderella 1.40 .40
Nos. B518-B521 (4) 4.00 1.15
Surtax for Pro Juventute Foundation and youth welfare orgs.

Man, Vitality and Movement SP253

1986, Feb. 11 **Photo.** *Perf. 12*
B522 SP253 50c + 20c multi .90 .25
Surtax for Natl. Sports Federation and cultural programs.

Paintings in Natl. Museums SP254

Swiss art: 35c+15c, Bridge in the Sun, 1907, by Giovanni Giacometti (1868-1933). 50c+20c, The Violet Hat, 1907, by Cuno Amiet (1868-1961). 80c+40c, After the Funeral, 1905, by Max Buri (1868-1915). 90c+40c, Still Life, 1914, by Felix Vallotton (1865-1925).

1986, Apr. 22 **Photo.** *Perf. 11½*
B523 SP254 35c + 15c multi .50 .20
B524 SP254 50c + 20c multi .70 .25
B525 SP254 80c + 40c multi 1.25 .40
B526 SP254 90c + 40c multi 1.40 .45
Nos. B523-B526 (4) 3.85 1.30
Surtax for Natl. Day Collection &monuments preservation, social & cultural organizations.

Children's Toys — SP255

1986, Nov. 25 **Photo.**
B527 SP255 35c + 15c Teddy bear .60 .20
B528 SP255 50c + 20c Top .90 .30
B529 SP255 80c + 40c Steamroller 1.50 .50
B530 SP255 90c + 40c Doll 1.60 .55
Nos. B527-B530 (4) 4.60 1.55
Surtax was for youth welfare organizations and the Pro Juventute Foundation.

Antique Furniture SP256

Designs: 35c+15c, Saane Valley wall cabinet, 1764, Vieux Pays d'Enhaut Museum, Chateau d'Oex. 50c+20c, Raised chest, 16th cent., Rhaetian Museum, Chur. 80c+40c, Ticino canton cradle, 1782, Valmaggia Museum, Cevio. 90c+40c, Appenzell region wardrobe, 1698, St. Gallen Historical Museum.

1987, May 26 **Photo.**
B531 SP256 35c + 15c multi .55 .25
B532 SP256 50c + 20c multi .80 .35
B533 SP256 80c + 40c multi 1.40 .60
B534 SP256 90c + 40c multi 1.50 .60
Nos. B531-B534 (4) 4.25 1.80
Surtax for Red Cross and patriotic funds.

No. 786 Surcharged with Clasped Hands and "7.9.87" in Red

Photo. & Engr.
1987, Sept. 7 *Perf. 13½x13*
B535 A349 50c + 50c multi 1.25 .45
Surtaxed to benefit flood victims.

Christmas SP257   Child Development SP258

1987, Nov. 24 **Photo.** *Perf. 11½*
B536 SP257 25c +10c shown .50 .20
B537 SP258 35c +15c shown .70 .20
B538 SP258 50c +20c Boy, building blocks .95 .30
B539 SP258 80c +40c Boy, girl in sandbox 1.60 .55
B540 SP258 90c +40c Father, child 1.75 .60
Nos. B536-B540 (5) 5.50 1.85
Surtax for national youth welfare projects and the Pro Juventute Foundation.
See Nos. B555-B558.

Junkers JU-52, 1939, and the Matterhorn SP259

1988, Mar. 8 **Photo.**
B541 SP259 140c +60c multi 2.50 2.50
Pro Aero Foundation, Zurich, 50th Anniv. Issued in sheets of 8.

SP260   SP261

Minnesingers.

1988, May 24 **Photo.**
B542 SP260 35c +15c Count Rudolf of Neuchatel .60 .25
B543 SP260 50c +20c Rudolf von Rotenburg .85 .35
B544 SP260 80c +40c Master Johannes Hadlaub 1.50 .60
B545 SP260 90c +40c The Hardegger 1.60 .65
Nos. B542-B545 (4) 4.55 1.85
700 Years of art and culture.

1988, Nov. 25 *Perf. 11½*
B546 SP261 35c +15c Reading .65 .20
B547 SP261 50c +20c Music .95 .30
B548 SP261 80c +40c Math 1.65 .55
B549 SP261 90c +40c Art 1.75 .60
Nos. B546-B549 (4) 5.00 1.65
Child development. Surtax for natl. youth welfare projects and the Pro Juventute Foundation.

700 Years of Art and Culture SP262

Illuminations in Zurich Central, Bern Burgher and Lucerne Central libraries: No. B550, King Friedrich II presenting Bern municipal charter, 1218, *Bendicht Tschachtlan Chronicle*, 1470. No. B551, Capt. Adrian von Bubenberg and troops passing through Murten town gate, 1476, *Bern Chronicle*, by Diebold Schilling, 1483. No. B552, Official messenger of Schwyz before the Council of Zurich, c. 1440, *Gerold Edlibach Chronicle*, 1485. No. B553, Schilling presenting manuscript to the mayor and councilmen in the council chamber, Lucerne, c. 1500, *Diebold Schilling's Lucerne Chronicle*, 1513.

1989, May 23
B550 SP262 35c +15c multi .65 .20
B551 SP262 50c +20c multi .90 .30
B552 SP262 80c +40c multi 1.50 .50
B553 SP262 90c +40c multi 1.75 .55
Nos. B550-B553 (4) 4.80 1.55
Surtax to benefit women's and cultural organizations.

Gymnastics SP263

1989, Aug. 25 **Photo.** *Perf. 11½*
B554 SP263 50c +20c multi .80 .30
Surtax to benefit Swiss Natl. Sports Federation, cultural and social work.

Child Development Type of 1987
1989, Nov. 24
B555 SP258 35c +15c Community work .60 .20
B556 SP258 50c +20c Friendship .85 .25
B557 SP258 80c +40c Vocational training 1.50 .50
B558 SP258 90c +40c Higher education and research 1.60 .55
Nos. B555-B558 (4) 4.55 1.50
Surtax for natl. youth welfare projects and the Pro Juventute Foundation.

700 Years of Art and Culture — SP264

Street criers: No. B559, Fly swatter and starch-sprinkler vendor. No. B560, Clock vendor. No. B561, Knife grinder. No. B562, Pinewood sellers.

1990, May 22 **Photo.**
B559 SP264 35c +15c multi .70 .25
B560 SP264 50c +20c multi .95 .30
B561 SP264 80c +40c multi 1.60 .55
B562 SP264 90c +40c multi 1.75 .60
Nos. B559-B562 (4) 5.00 1.70

Souvenir Sheet

Natl. Philatelic Exhibition, Geneva '90 — SP265

a, Brass badge worn by Geneva Cantonal post drivers before 1849. b, Place du Bourg-de-Four and entrance to Rue Etienne-Dumont. c, Ile Rousseau and Pont des Bergues. d, No. 2L1 on cover.

1990, Sept. 5
B563 SP265 Sheet of 4 4.00 1.40
a.-d. 50c +25c any single 1.00 .35

Child Development SP266

1990, Nov. 20
B564 SP266 35c +15c Model making .70 .25
B565 SP266 50c +20c Youth groups 1.00 .30
B566 SP266 80c +40c Sports 1.70 .55
B567 SP266 90c +40c Music 1.85 .60
Nos. B564-B567 (4) 5.25 1.70

700 Years of Art and Culture SP267

Contemporary paintings by: 50c+20c, Wolf Barth. 70c+30c, Helmut Federle. 80c+40c, Matthias Bosshart. 90c+40c, Werner Otto Leuenberger.

1991, May 14 **Photo.** *Perf. 11½*
B568 SP267 50c +20c multi 1.00 .30
B569 SP267 70c +30c multi 1.40 .45
B570 SP267 80c +40c multi 1.75 .55
B571 SP267 90c +40c multi 1.75 .60
Nos. B568-B571 (4) 5.90 1.90

Woodland Flowers SP268

50c+25c, Allium ursinum. 70c+30c, Geranium sylvaticum. 80c+40c, Campanula trachelium. 90c+40c, Hieracium murorum.

1991, Nov. 26
B572 SP268 50c +25c multi 1.00 .40
B573 SP268 70c +30c multi 1.40 .45
B574 SP268 80c +40c multi 1.60 .55
B575 SP268 90c +40c multi 1.80 .60
Nos. B572-B575 (4) 5.80 2.00
Surtax for youth and family welfare projects and the Pro Juventute Foundation.

Swiss Folk Art — SP269

50c + 20c, Earthenware plate, Heimberg, 18th cent. 70c + 40c, Paper cutout by Johann Jakob Hauswirth (1809-1871). 80c + 40c, Cream spoon, Gruyeres. 90c + 40c, Embroidered silk carnation, Grisons.

1992, May 22   Photo.   Perf. 11½

B576	SP269	50c +20c multi	.95	.30
B577	SP269	70c +30c multi	1.25	.45
B578	SP269	80c +40c multi	1.60	.50
B579	SP269	90c +40c multi	1.75	.60
	Nos. B576-B579 (4)		5.55	1.85

Surtax for preservation of cultural heritage.

Unfinished Work, by Jean Tinguely SP270

1992, Aug. 25   Photo.   Perf. 12

B580	SP270	50c +20c blue & black	1.10	.40

Surtax for Natl. Sports Federation and sports-related social and cultural activities.

Wood Puppet of Melchior, 18th Cent. — SP271

Trees — SP272

1992, Nov. 24   Photo.   Perf. 11½

B581	SP271	50c +25c multi	1.00	.35
B582	SP272	50c +25c Copper beech	1.00	.35
B583	SP272	70c +30c Norway maple	1.40	.50
B584	SP272	80c +40c Common oak	1.60	.55
B585	SP272	90c +40c Spruce	1.75	.60
	Nos. B581-B585 (5)		6.75	2.35

Christmas. Surtax for youth and family welfare projects and the Pro Juventute Foundation.

Swiss Folk Art — SP273

Designs: No. B586, Appenzell dairyman's earring. No. B587, Fluhli glassware. 80c + 40c, Painting of cattle drive, by Sylvestre Pidoux. 100c + 40c, Straw hat ornament.

1993, May 5   Photo.   Perf. 11½

B586	SP273	60c +30c multi	1.25	.40
B587	SP273	60c +30c multi	1.25	.40
B588	SP273	80c +40c multi	1.10	.35
B589	SP273	100c +40c multi	2.00	.70
	Nos. B586-B589 (4)		5.60	1.85

Architectural Heritage Type of 1960

Design: 80c+20c, Kapell Bridge and Water Tower, Lucerne.

1993, Sept. 7   Litho.   Perf. 13½x13

B590	A145	80c +20c orange & red	1.40	.45

Surtax for reconstruction of Kapell Bridge with any excess for preservation of architectural heritage.

SP274   SP275

Woodland plants.

1993, Nov. 23   Photo.   Perf. 11½

B591	SP274	60c +30c Christmas wreath	1.25	.40
B592	SP274	60c +30c Male fern	1.25	.40
B593	SP274	80c +40c Guelder rose	1.60	.55
B594	SP274	100c +40c Mnium punctatum	2.00	.65
	Nos. B591-B594 (4)		6.10	2.00

Christmas. Surtax for youth and family welfare projects and the Pro Juventute Foundation.

1994, May 17   Photo.   Perf. 11½

Swiss Folk Art: No. B595, Weight-driven Neuchatel clock. No. B598, Linen-embroidered pomegranate. 80c+40c, Biscuit mold for Krafli. 100c+40c, Paper bird mobile for child's cradle.

B595	SP275	60c +30c multi	1.25	.40
B596	SP275	60c +30c multi	1.25	.40
B597	SP275	80c +40c multi	1.60	.55
B598	SP275	100c +40c multi	1.90	.65
	Nos. B595-B598 (4)		6.00	2.00

Christmas SP276

Mushrooms SP277

Designs: No. B600, Wood blewit. 80c+40c, Red boletus. 100c+50c, Shaggy pholiota.

1994, Nov. 28   Litho.   Perf. 11½

B599	SP276	60c +30c multi	1.10	.45
B600	SP277	60c +30c multi	1.10	.45
B601	SP277	80c +40c multi	1.40	.60
B602	SP277	100c +40c multi	1.75	.80
	Nos. B599-B602 (4)		5.35	2.30

Surtax for youth and family welfare projects and the Pro Juventute Foundation.

Swiss Folk Art — SP278

Designs: No. B603, Wooden cream pail. No. B604, Straw hat. 80c+40c, Chest lock, c. 1580. 100c+40c, Langnau pottery sugar bowl.

1995, May 16   Photo.   Perf. 11½

B603	SP278	60c +30c multi	1.10	.50
B604	SP278	60c +30c multi	1.10	.50
B605	SP278	80c +40c multi	1.50	.70
	Complete booklet, 10 #B605		15.00	
B606	SP278	100c +40c multi	1.90	.80
	Nos. B603-B606 (4)		5.60	2.50

Surtax for Swiss Pro Patria Foundation and special cultural, social projects.

Souvenir Sheet

Basler Taube '95 Philatelic Exhibition, Basel — SP279

Designs: a, 80c+30c, like Switzerland #3L1. Engraved panorama of Basel, by Matthaus Merian, 17th cent.: b, 60c+30c, Buildings, twin church steeples. c, 100c+50c, Buildings. d, 100c+50c, Buildings, bridge.

1995, May 16   Photo.   Perf. 13x14

B607	SP279	Sheet of 4	7.00	3.00
a.		80c +30c multi	1.25	.60
b.		60c +30c black & blue	1.25	.55
c.-d.		100c +50c any single	2.50	.90

Nos. B607b-B607d are a continuous design.

Christmas SP280

Life In and Around Water — SP281

#B608, Angel from "The Annunciation," by Bartolome. #B609, River trout. 80c+40c, Grey wagtail. 100c+50c, Spotted salamander.

1995, Nov. 28   Photo.   Perf. 11½

B608	SP280	60c +30c multi	1.10	.50
	Complete booklet, 10 #B608		11.00	
B609	SP281	60c +30c multi	1.10	.50
B610	SP281	80c +40c multi	1.40	.65
B611	SP281	100c +50c multi	1.75	.80
	Nos. B608-B611 (4)		5.35	2.45

Surtax for Pro Juventute Foundation.

For Sports SP282

1996, Mar. 12   Photo.   Perf. 11½

B612	SP282	70c +30c multi	1.60	.85
	Complete booklet, 10 #B612		16.00	

SP283

Restorations, projects: No. B613, Magdalena Chapel, Wolfenschiessen. No. B614, Underground mills, Col-des-Roches. 90c+40c, Pfäfers Baroque spa complex. 110c+50c, Roman road over Great St. Bernhard.

1996, May 14   Photo.   Perf. 11½

B613	SP283	70c +35c multi	1.25	.60
B614	SP283	70c +35c multi	1.25	.60
B615	SP283	90c +40c multi	1.75	.75
	Complete booklet, 10 #B615		17.50	
B616	SP283	110c +50c multi	2.10	.90
	Nos. B613-B616 (4)		6.35	2.85

Christmas SP284

Life In and Around Water — SP285

1996, Nov. 26   Photo.   Perf. 11½

B617	SP284	70c +35c Star, constellations	1.25	.55
B618	SP285	70c +35c Grayling	1.25	.55
	Complete booklet, 10 #B618		12.50	
B619	SP285	90c +45c Crayfish	1.60	.70
B620	SP285	110c +55c Otter	1.90	.80
	Nos. B617-B620 (4)		6.00	2.60

SP286

Designs: No. B621, St. Valbert Church, Soubey. No. B622, Culture Mill, Lützelflüh. 90c+40c, Ittingen Charterhouse, Thurgau. 110c+50c, Municipal Building, Onsernone Valley.

1997, May 13   Photo.   Perf. 11½

B621	SP286	70c +35c multi	1.25	1.25
B622	SP286	70c +35c multi	1.25	1.25
B623	SP286	90c +40c multi	1.60	1.60
	Complete booklet, 10 #B623		16.00	
B624	SP286	110c +50c multi	2.00	2.00
	Nos. B621-B624 (4)		6.10	6.10

Christmas SP287

Life In and Around Water — SP288

Designs: No. B625, Mistletoe twig. No. B626, Three-spined stickleback. 90c+45c, Yellow-bellied toad. 110c+55c, Ruff.

1997, Nov. 20   Photo.   Perf. 11½

B625	SP287	70c +35c multi	1.25	1.25
B626	SP288	70c +35c multi	1.25	1.25
	Complete booklet, 10 #B626		12.50	
B627	SP288	90c +45c multi	1.60	1.60
B628	SP288	110c +55c multi	1.90	1.90
	Nos. B625-B628 (4)		6.00	6.00

Surtax for Pro Juventute Foundation.

Pro Patria Stamps, 60th Anniv. SP289

Heritage and landscapes: No. B629, St. Gall Rhine Valley. No. B630, Round Church, Saas Balen. No. B631, Natural forest preserves, Bödmeren. No. B632, St. Gotthard Refuge. 110c +50c, Blacksmiths, Corcelles.

1998, May 12	Photo.		Perf. 11½	
B629	SP289	70c + 35c multi	1.25	1.25
B630	SP289	70c + 35c multi	1.25	1.25
B631	SP289	90c + 40c multi	1.50	1.50
	Complete booklet, 10 #B631		15.00	
B632	SP289	90c + 40c multi	1.50	1.50
B633	SP289	110c + 50c multi	1.90	1.90
	Nos. B629-B633 (5)		7.40	7.40

Christmas
SP290

Life Near Water — SP291

No. B634, Bell, holly on ribbon. No. B635, Ramshorn snail. 90c+45c, Great crested grebe. 110c+55c, Pike.

1998, Nov. 25	Photo.		Perf. 11½	
B634	SP290	70c +35c multi	1.25	1.25
B635	SP291	70c +35c multi	1.25	1.25
B636	SP291	90c +45c multi	1.60	1.60
	Complete booklet, 6 #B634, 4 #B636		16.00	
B637	SP291	110c +55c multi	1.90	1.90
	Nos. B634-B637 (4)		6.00	6.00

Pro Patria — SP292

Heritage and landscapes: No. B638, Chestnut groves, Malcantone. No. B639, La Sarraz Castle. 90c+40c, Lake Lucerne steamship. 110c+50c, St. Paul's Chapel, Rhäzüns.

1999, May 5	Litho.		Perf. 13½	
B638	SP292	70c +35c multi	1.40	1.40
B639	SP292	70c +35c multi	1.40	1.40
B640	SP292	90c +40c multi	1.75	1.75
	Complete booklet, 10 #B640		17.50	
B641	SP292	110c +50c multi	2.10	2.10
	Nos. B638-B641 (4)		6.65	6.65

Souvenir Sheet

NABA 2000 Philatelic Exhibition, St. Gallen — SP293

a, 70c+30c, St. Laurenzen Church spire. b, 20c+10c, Top of town house. c, 90c+30c, Oriel window.
Illustration reduced.

1999, Sept. 9	Photo.	Perf. 11¾	
	Sheet of 3		
B642	SP293 #a.-c. + label	3.50	3.50
a.	70c+30c multicolored	1.25	1.25
b.	20c+10c multicolored	.40	.40
c.	90c+30c multicolored	1.60	1.60

Christmas
SP294

Nicolo the Clown From Children's Book by Verena Pavoni SP295

Designs: No. B643, Children, snowman. No. B644, Nicolo, circus tent. 90c+45c, Nicolo and his father. 110c+55c, Nicolo and donkey.

1999, Nov. 23		Litho.	
B643	SP294 70c +35c multi	1.40	1.40
B644	SP295 70c +35c multi	1.40	1.40
B645	SP295 90c +45c multi	1.75	1.75
	Complete booklet, 6 #B644, 4 #B645	16.00	
B646	SP295 110c +55c multi	2.10	2.10
	Nos. B643-B646 (4)	6.65	6.65

Perf. 13½x13¼

Surtax for Pro Juventute Foundation.

Cities With Pro Patria Foundation Renovation Projects SP296

Perf. 13¼x13½

2000, May 10		Litho. & Engr.	
B647	SP296 70c +35c Näfles	1.25	1.25
B648	SP296 70c +35c Tengia	1.25	1.25
B649	SP296 90c +40c Brugg	1.60	1.60
B650	SP296 90c +40c Carouge	1.60	1.60
	Booklet, 10 #B650	16.00	
	Nos. B647-B650 (4)	5.70	5.70

Souvenir Sheet

NABA 2000 Philatelic Exhibition, St. Gallen — SP297

Quadrants of stylized No. 5: a, UL. b, UR. c, LL. d, LR.
Illustration reduced.

2000, May 10	Photo.	Perf. 11¾	
B651	SP297 Sheet of 4	3.75	3.75
a.	70c+35c multicolored	1.25	1.25
b.-c.	20c+10c any single	.35	.35
d.	90c+45c multicolored	1.75	1.75

Christmas
SP298

Illustrations from Little Albert, by Albert Manser SP299

Designs: No. B652, St. Nicholas and Schmutzli in sleigh. No. B653, Children at fence. No. B654, Little Albert with umbrella. No. B655, Children on sleds.

Perf. 13¼x13½

2000, Nov. 21		Litho.	
B652	SP298 70c +35c multi	1.25	1.25
B653	SP299 70c +35c multi	1.25	1.25
B654	SP299 90c +45c multi	1.50	1.50
	Booklet, 6 #B653, 4 #B654	13.50	
B655	SP299 90c +45c multi	1.50	1.50
	Nos. B652-B655 (4)	5.50	5.50

Surtax for Pro Juventute Foundation.

Landmarks SP300

Designs: No. B656, Hauterive Abbey. No. B657, La Chaux-de-Fonds Theater. No. B658, Granary, Rorschach. No. B659, Bishop's Castle, Leuk.

2001, May 9	Litho.	Perf. 13¼x13½	
B656	SP300 70c +35c multi	1.25	1.25
B657	SP300 70c +35c multi	1.25	1.25
B658	SP300 90c +40c multi	1.50	1.50
B659	SP300 90c +40c multi	1.50	1.50
	Booklet, 10 #B659	15.00	
	Nos. B656-B659 (4)	5.50	5.50

Surtax for Pro Patria Foundation.

Pro Juventute Types of 1999

Art from children's books: No. B660, What's Santa Claus Doing?, by Karin von Oldershausen. No. B661, Leopold the Leopard, from Leopold and the Sun, by Stephan Brülhart. No. B662, Honeybear, from Leopold and the Sun. No. B663, Tom the Monkey, from Leopold and the Sun.

Perf. 13½x13¼

2001, Nov. 20		Litho.	
B660	SP294 70c +35c multi	1.25	1.25
B661	SP295 70c +35c multi	1.25	1.25
B662	SP295 90c +45c multi	1.60	1.60
	Booklet, 6 #B661, 4 #B662	14.00	
B663	SP295 90c +45c multi	1.60	1.60
	Nos. B660-B663 (4)	5.70	5.70

Surtax for Pro Juventute Foundation.

Mills — SP301

Location: No. B664, Bruzella. No. B665, Oberdorf. No. B666, Büren an der Aare. No. B667, Lussery-Villars.

2002, May 15	Litho.	Perf. 13¼x13½	
B664	SP301 70c +35c multi	1.40	1.40
B665	SP301 70c +35c multi	1.40	1.40
B666	SP301 90c +40c multi	1.60	1.60
	Booklet, 10 #B666	16.00	
B667	SP301 90c +40c multi	1.60	1.60
	Nos. B664-B667 (4)	6.00	6.00

Surtax for Pro Patria Foundation.

Roses — SP302

Designs: No. B668, Christmas rose (gold background). No. B669, Ingrid Bergman rose (white background). No. B670, Belle Vaudoise rose (orange petals). No. B671, Charmian

---

rose (pink petals). 130c+65c, Frühlingsgold rose.

Perf. 13¾x13¼

2002, Nov. 19		Litho.	
B668	SP302 70c +35c multi	1.40	1.40
B669	SP302 70c +35c multi	1.40	1.40
B670	SP302 90c +45c multi	1.90	1.90
	Booklet, 6 #B669, 4 #B670	16.00	
B671	SP302 90c +45c multi	1.90	1.90
B672	SP302 130c +65c multi	2.60	2.60
	Nos. B668-B672 (5)	9.20	9.20

Surtax for Pro Juventute Foundation. No. B668 is impregnated with a pine needle, cinnamon and clove scent, and Nos. B669-B672 with a rose scent.

Bridges SP303

Designs: No. B673, Wynigen Bridge, Burgdorf, 1776. No. B674, Salginatobel Bridge, Schiers, 1929. No. B675, Pont St. Jean, Saint Ursanne, 15th cent. No. B676, Reuss Bridge, Rottenschwil, 1907.

2003, May 8	Litho.	Perf. 13¼x13½	
B673	SP303 70c +35c multi	1.60	1.60
B674	SP303 70c +35c multi	1.60	1.60
B675	SP303 90c +40c multi	2.00	2.00
	Booklet, 10 #B675	20.00	
B676	SP303 90c +40c multi	2.00	2.00
	Nos. B673-B676 (4)	7.20	7.20

Rights of the Child — SP304

Children: 70c+35c, Christmas tree, toy tractor, gift. 85c+35c, Playing as storekeeper and shopper. 90c+45c, Skateboarding with dog. 100c+45c, Playing guitar and drums.

Serpentine Die Cut 10½x11

2003, Nov. 19		Litho.	
	Self-Adhesive		
B677	SP304 70c +35c multi	1.75	1.75
a.	Block of 4 on translucent backing paper	7.00	
B678	SP304 85c +35c multi	1.90	1.90
a.	Block of 4 on translucent backing paper	7.60	
B679	SP304 90c +45c multi	2.10	2.10
a.	Block of 4 on translucent backing paper	8.40	
B680	SP304 100c +45c multi	2.25	2.25
a.	Block of 4 on translucent backing paper	9.00	
b.	Nos. B677-B680 on translucent backing paper	8.00	
c.	Booklet, 6 each #B678, B680	22.50	
	Nos. B677-B680 (4)	8.00	8.00

Nos. B677-B680 each were printed in sheets of 20 stamps with a white paper backing.

Small Buildings SP305

Designs: No. B681, Bathing pavilion, Gorgier. No. B682, Granary, Oberramsern. No. B683, Ossuary, Gentilino. No. B684, Dock house, Lucerne.

2004, May 6	Litho.	Perf. 13¾x14¼	
B681	SP305 85c +40c multi	1.90	1.90
B682	SP305 85c +40c multi	1.90	1.90
B683	SP305 100c +50c multi	2.40	2.40
B684	SP305 100c +50c multi	2.40	2.40
	Complete booklet, 6 #B681, 4 #B684	22.50	

Complete booklet sold for 14.50fr.

Rights of the Child — SP306

Designs: No. B685, Children playing card game. No. B686, Children, man, giraffe. No. B687, Children, teacher. No. B688, Child, elderly man and woman.

Serpentine Die Cut 10½x11
2004, Nov. 23   Litho.
Self-Adhesive

B685	SP306	85c +40c multi	2.25	2.25
a.		Block of 4 on translucent paper	9.00	
B686	SP306	85c +40c multi	2.25	2.25
a.		Block of 4 on translucent paper	9.00	
B687	SP306	100c +50c multi	2.75	2.75
a.		Block of 4 on translucent paper	11.00	
b.		Booklet pane, 6 each #B685, B687	30.00	
B688	SP306	100c +50c multi	2.75	2.75
a.		Block of 4 on translucent paper	11.00	
b.		Nos. B685-B688 on translucent paper	10.00	
		Nos. B685-B688 (4)	10.00	10.00

Nos. B685-B688 were each printed in sheets of 20 stamps. No. B687b sold for 17fr.

Historic Buildings SP307

Designs: No. B689, Rotach Houses, Zurich. No. B690, Monte Carasso Abbey, Monte Carasso. No. B691, St. Katharinental Abbey, Diessenhofen. No. B692, Palais Wilson, Geneva.

2005, May 10   Litho.   Perf. 13¼x13½

B689	SP307	85c +40c multi	2.10	2.10
B690	SP307	85c +40c multi	2.10	2.10
B691	SP307	100c +50c multi	2.50	2.50
		Complete booklet, 6 #B690, 4 #B691	23.00	
B692	SP307	100c +50c multi	2.50	2.50
		Nos. B689-B692 (4)	9.20	9.20

Surtax for Pro Patria Foundation.

Children's Rights SP308

Children and: No. B693, Life preserver. No. B694, Cherries. No. B695, Computer. No. B696 Candle in window.

Serpentine Die Cut 10½x11
2005, Nov. 22   Photo.
Self-Adhesive

B693	SP308	85c +40c multi	1.90	1.90
a.		Block of 4 on translucent paper	7.75	
B694	SP308	85c +40c multi	1.90	1.90
a.		Block of 4 on translucent paper	7.75	
B695	SP308	100c +50c multi	2.25	2.25
a.		Block of 4 on translucent paper	9.00	
b.		Booklet pane, 2 each #B693, B695	8.50	
		Complete booklet, 3 #B695b	26.00	
B696	SP308	100c +50c multi	2.25	2.25
a.		Block of 4 on translucent paper	9.00	
b.		Nos. B693-B696 on translucent paper	8.50	
		Nos. B693-B696 (4)	8.30	8.30

Nos. B693-B696 were each printed in sheets of 20. Complete booklet sold for €17.

Gardens and Parks — SP309

Designs: No. B697, Prangins Castle, Prangins. No. B698, Heidegg Castle, Gelfingen. No. B699, Birseck Castle, Arlesheim. No. B700, Villa Garbald, Castasegna.

2006, May 9   Litho.   Perf. 14x13¾

B697	SP309	85c +40c multi	2.10	2.10
B698	SP309	85c +40c multi	2.10	2.10
B699	SP309	100c +50c multi	2.50	2.50
B700	SP309	100c +50c multi	2.50	2.50
		Complete booklet, 6 #B698, 4 #B700	24.00	
		Nos. B697-B700 (4)	9.20	9.20

Complete booklet sold for €14.50.

Souvenir Sheet

Wettingen Monastery — SP310

No. B701: a, Building, country name at left. b, Building and bridge, country name at right. c, Main building.

2006, May 9   Perf. 13¾x14¼

B701	SP310	Sheet of 3	6.00	6.00
a.-b.		85c+15c Either single	1.75	1.75
c.		100c+50c multi	2.50	2.50

NABA Baden 2006.

Souvenir Sheet

NABA Baden 2006 Philatelic Exhibition — SP311

No. B702: a, Baden City Tower. b, Fountain.

Perf. 14¼x13¾ on 3 Sides
2006, Sept. 7   Litho.

B702	SP311	Sheet of 2	5.00	5.00
a.-b.		100c +50c Either single	2.50	2.50

Children's Art Competition SP312

Designs: No. B703, Singer, by Veronica Jesus Garcia Pinto. No. B704, Car in garage, by Stephane Arada. No. B705, Bandaged dog, by Lea Mayer. No. B706, Angel, by Ted Scapa, judge of competition.

Serpentine Die Cut 10¾x11
2006, Nov. 21
Self-Adhesive

B703	SP312	85c +40c multi	2.10	2.10
a.		Block of 4, #B703	8.50	
B704	SP312	85c +40c multi	2.10	2.10
a.		Block of 4, #B704	8.50	
B705	SP312	100c +50c multi	2.50	2.50
a.		Booklet pane, 6 each #B704-B705	28.00	
b.		Block of 4, #B705	10.00	
B706	SP312	100c +50c multi	2.50	2.50
a.		Block of 4, #B703-B706	9.25	
b.		Block of 4, #B706	10.00	
		Nos. B703-B706 (4)	9.20	9.20

Surtax for Pro Juventute Foundation. See Nos. B711-B714.

Historic Roads SP313

Designs: No. B707, Via Jura, Chateau de Vorbourg. No. B708, Via Jacobi, Chapel of St. Apollonia. No. B709, Via Cook, Grandhotel Giessbach. No. B710, Via Gottardo, Alte Sust.

2007, Apr. 27   Litho.   Perf. 13½x13¼

B707	SP313	85c +40c multi	2.10	2.10
B708	SP313	85c +40c multi	2.10	2.10
B709	SP313	100c +50c multi	2.50	2.50
		Complete booklet, 6 #B708, 4 #B709	23.00	
B710	SP313	100c +50c multi	2.50	2.50
		Nos. B707-B710 (4)	9.20	9.20

Surtax for Pro Patria Foundation.

Children's Art Competition Type of 2006

Designs: No. B711, Camping, by Christine Fischer. No. B712, Mountains, by Jonathan Balest. No. B713, Sunshine, by Morena Rufatti. No. B714, Angels, by Ted Scapa, judge of competition.

Serpentine Die Cut 10½x11
2007, Nov. 20   Litho.
Self-Adhesive

B711	SP312	85c +40c multi	2.25	2.25
B712	SP312	85c +40c multi	2.25	2.25
B713	SP312	100c +50c multi	2.75	2.75
a.		Booklet pane, 6 each #B711, B713	30.00	
B714	SP312	100c +50c multi	2.75	2.75
a.		Block of 4, #B711-B714 on backing paper	10.00	10.00
		Nos. B711-B714 (4)	10.00	10.00

Surtax for Pro Juventute Foundation.

AIR POST STAMPS

Nos. 134 and 139 Overprinted in Carmine

1919-20   Wmk. 183   Perf. 11½
Granite Paper

C1	A25	30c yel brn & pale grn ('20)	110.00	1,250.
C2	A25	50c dp & pale grn	32.50	110.00
		Set, never hinged	350.00	

Counterfeits of overprint and fraudulent cancellations exist.

Airplane AP1

Pilot at Controls of Airplane AP2

Biplane against Sky — AP3

Allegorical Figure of Flight AP4

Perf. 11½, 12 and Compound
1923-25   Typo.

C3	AP1	15c brn red & ap grn	2.25	8.25
C4	AP1	20c grn & lt grn ('25)	.90	6.00
C5	AP1	25c dk bl & bl	7.75	22.50
C6	AP2	35c brn & buff	11.00	42.50
C7	AP2	40c vio & gray vio	14.50	45.00
C8	AP3	45c red & ind	1.60	7.25
C9	AP3	50c blk & red	12.50	17.00

Perf. 11½

C10	AP4	65c gray bl & dp bl ('24)	3.25	16.00
C11	AP4	75c org & brn red ('24)	15.00	55.00
C12	AP4	1fr vio & dp vio ('24)	42.50	32.50
		Nos. C3-C12 (10)	111.25	252.00
		Set, never hinged	275.00	

For surcharges see Nos. C19, C22, C26.

1933-37   With Grilled Gum

C4a	AP1	20c grn & lt grn ('37)	.30	.40
C5a	AP1	25c dk bl & bl ('34)	5.00	50.00
C8a	AP3	45c red & indigo ('37)	2.50	52.50
C9a	AP3	50c gray grn & scar ('35)	1.10	1.60
C10a	AP4	65c gray bl & dp bl ('37)	2.75	8.50
C11a	AP4	75c org & brn red ('36)	27.50	175.00
C12a	AP4	1fr vio & deep vio ('36)	2.10	3.25
		Nos. C4a-C12a (7)	41.25	291.25
		Set, never hinged	65.00	

See Grilled Gum note after No. 145.

Allegory of Air Mail — AP5

Bird Carrying Letter AP6

1929-30   Granite Paper

C13	AP5	35c red brn, bis & claret	15.00	42.50
C14	AP5	40c dl grn, yel grn & bl	57.50	82.50
C15	AP6	2fr blk brn & red brn, gray ('30)	85.00	85.00
		Nos. C13-C15 (3)	157.50	210.00
		Set, never hinged	425.00	

1933-35   With Grilled Gum

C13a	AP5	35c red brn, bis & cl	5.00	50.00
C14a	AP5	40c dk grn, yel grn & bl	37.50	77.50
C15a	AP6	2fr blk brn & red brn ('35)	7.25	12.00
		Nos. C13a-C15a (3)	49.75	139.50
		Set, never hinged	140.00	

Front View of Airplane AP7

1932, Feb. 2   Granite Paper

C16	AP7	15c dp grn & lt grn	.55	1.60
C17	AP7	20c dk red & buff	1.10	2.50
C18	AP7	90c dp bl & gray	7.25	30.00
		Nos. C16-C18 (3)	8.90	34.10
		Set, never hinged	22.50	

Intl. Disarmament Conf., Geneva, Feb. 1932. For surcharges see Nos. C20-C21, C23-C25.

Nos. C3, C10, C16-C18 Surcharged with New Values and Bars in Black or Red

1935-38

C19	AP1	10c on 15c	4.75	32.50
C20	AP7	10c on 15c	.40	.55
a.		Inverted surcharge	6,500.	12,000.
C21	AP7	10c on 20c ('36)	.45	2.25
C22	AP4	10c on 65c ('38)	.20	.40
C23	AP7	30c on 90c ('36)	3.00	14.00
C24	AP7	40c on 20c ('37)	3.75	15.00

C25 AP7 40c on 90c ('36)
    (R)   3.25   14.50
  a. Vermilion surcharge 92.50 800.00
     Never hinged, #C25a 150.00
  Nos. C19-C25 (7)   15.80 79.20
  Set, never hinged   40.00

Stamp similar to No. C22, but from souvenir sheet, is listed as No. 242a.

Type of Air Post Stamp of 1923 Surcharged in Black

1938, May 22   Wmk. 183   Perf. 11½
C26 AP3 75c on 50c gray & scar 6.50

"Pro Aero" Meeting, May 21-22.
No. C26 was not sold to the public in the ordinary way, but affixed to air mail letters by postal officials. It was not regularly obtainable unused.

Jungfrau — AP8

Designs: 40c, View of Valais. 50c, Lake Geneva. 60c, Alpstein. 70c, View of Ticino. 1fr, Lake Lucerne. 2fr, The Engadine. 5fr, Churfirsten.

Perf. 11½
1941, May 1   Unwmk.   Engr.
Tinted Granite Paper
C27 AP8 30c ultra   .55   .25
C28 AP8 40c gray blk   .55   .25
C29 AP8 50c slate grn   .55   .30
C30 AP8 60c chestnut   .85   .30
C31 AP8 70c plum   .90   .55
C32 AP8 1fr Prus grn   1.75   .60
C33 AP8 2fr car lake   5.75 3.50
C34 AP8 5fr deep blue 19.00 15.00
  Nos. C27-C34 (8) 29.90 20.75
  Set, never hinged   80.00

See Nos. C43-C44.

Type of 1941 Overprinted in Red

1941, May 12
C35 AP8 1fr blue green   5.50 19.00
  Never hinged   10.00

Issued to commemorate special flights between Payerne and Buochs, May 28, 1941.

Parliament Buildings, Bern AP16

1943, July 13   Photo.
C36 AP16 1fr cop red, buff & blk   1.60 10.00
  Never hinged   3.75

30th anniv. of the 1st Alpine flight, by Oscar Bider, July 13, 1913.

DH-3 Haefeli AP17

Fokker AP18

Lockheed-Orion — AP19

1944, Sept. 1
C37 AP17 10c gray brn & pale grn   .20 .50
C38 AP18 20c rose car & buff   .30 .50
C39 AP19 30c ultra & pale gray .35 1.25
  Nos. C37-C39 (3)   .85 2.25
  Set, never hinged   1.50

25th anniv. of the 1st regular air route in Switzerland.

Douglas DC-3 AP20

1944, Sept. 20   Granite Paper
C40 AP20 1.50fr multi   5.50 17.50
  Never hinged   11.00

25th anniv. of the Zurich-Geneva air route.

Zoegling Training Glider AP21

1946, May 1   Granite Paper
C41 AP21 1.50fr henna brn & gray   11.50 27.50
  Never hinged   20.00

Valid for use only on two special flights.

Douglas DC-4 Linking Geneva and New York AP22

1947, Mar. 17   Granite Paper
C42 AP22 2.50fr bl gray, dk bl & red   7.00 20.00
  Never hinged   13.00

Valid only on the Geneva-New York flight of May 2, 1947.
Because of bad weather at NYC the flight ended at Washington.

Types of 1941

1948, Oct. 1   Engr.
Tinted Granite Paper
C43 AP8 30c dk slate bl   4.50 12.50
C44 AP8 40c deep ultra 21.00 2.75
  Set, never hinged   57.50

Glider in Symbolized Aerodynamic Buoyancy — AP23

1949, Apr. 11   Engr. & Typo.
C45 AP23 1.50fr dk vio & yel 16.00 37.50
  Never hinged   30.00

Valid only on special flights, Apr. 27-29, 1949. Proceeds were for the advancement of national aviation.

> **Catalogue values for unused stamps in this section, from this point to the end of the section, are for Never Hinged items.**

Glider and Jets AP24

1963, June 1   Photo.   Perf. 11½
Granite Paper
C46 AP24 2fr multicolored 4.00 3.50

50th anniversary of the first Alpine flight by Oscar Bider, July 13, 1913. Valid for postage on July 13, 1963, on flights from Bern to Locarno and Langenbruck to Bern. Proceeds went to the Pro Aero Foundation.

AIR POST SEMI-POSTAL STAMP

> **Catalogue values for unused stamps in this section are for Never Hinged items.**

Boeing 747 — SPAP1

1972, Feb. 17   Photo.   Perf. 12½
Violet Fibers, Fluorescent Paper
CB1 SPAP1 2fr + 1fr dp bl, red & gray   2.50 2.25

50th anniv. of 1st Swiss Intl. flight, Zurich to Nuremberg, and 25th anniv. of 1st Swissair trans-Atlantic flight, Zurich to NYC. Valid on all mail but obligatory on special flights from Geneva to NYC in May, and from Geneva to Nuremberg in June, 1972.
Surtax was for Pro Aero Foundation and the training of young airmen, and for the Swiss Air Rescue Service.

POSTAGE DUE STAMPS

D1   D2

1878-80   Typo.   Perf. 11½
             Wmk. 182
J1 D1 1c ultra   1.90   1.60
J2 D2 2c ultra   1.90   1.60
J3 D2 3c ultra   17.00 16.00
J4 D2 5c ultra   17.00   6.75
J5 D2 10c ultra   180.00   6.00
J6 D2 20c ultra   210.00   6.00
J7 D2 50c ultra   400.00 20.00
J8 D2 100c ultra 525.00 17.00
J9 D2 500c ultra 475.00 27.50
  Nos. J1-J9 (9) 1,827. 102.45

A 5c in design D1 exists.

1882-83
          Granite Paper
J10 D2 10c ultra   175.00 40.00
J11 D2 20c ultra   400.00 52.50
J12 D2 50c ultra 2,400. 525.00
J13 D2 100c ultra 800.00 400.00
J14 D2 500c ultra 13,750. 210.00

1883-84
Numerals in Red
J15 D2 5c blue green   42.50 30.00
J16 D2 10c blue green 65.00 25.00
J17 D2 20c blue green 120.00 22.50
J18 D2 50c blue green 140.00 72.50
J19 D2 100c blue green 350.00 350.00
J20 D2 500c blue green 775.00 190.00
  Nos. J15-J20 (6) 1,492. 690.00

1884-97
Numerals in Red
J21 D2 1c olive green   .65   .65
J22 D2 3c olive green   5.75 6.50
J23 D2 5c olive green   1.60   .65
  a. 5c yellow green 25.00 12.50
J24 D2 10c olive green 3.75   .85
  a. 10c yellow green 110.00 16.00
J25 D2 20c olive green 8.25 1.30
  a. 20c yellow green 110.00 16.00
J26 D2 50c olive green 12.00 2.50
  a. 50c yellow green 100.00 32.50
J27 D2 100c olive green 14.00 2.75
  a. 100c yellow green 100.00 80.00
J28 D2 500c olive green 150.00 160.00
  a. 500c yellow green 125.00 60.00

Numerous shades of Nos. J21-J28 exist.

1908-09   Wmk. 183
Numerals in Red
J29 D2 1c olive green   .30 1.10
J30 D2 5c olive green   .60   .90
J31 D2 10c olive green   1.50 2.25
J32 D2 20c olive green   3.00 5.00
J33 D2 50c olive green 15.00 1.10
J34 D2 100c olive green 30.00 2.25
  Nos. J29-J34 (6) 50.40 12.60

D3

1910   Perf. 11½, 12
Numerals in Red
J35 D3 1c blue green   .20 .20
J36 D3 3c blue green   .20 .20
J37 D3 5c blue green   .20 .20
J38 D3 10c blue green 11.00 .20
J39 D3 15c blue green   .65 1.10
J40 D3 20c blue green 17.50 .20
J41 D3 25c blue green   1.25 .65
J42 D3 30c blue green   1.25 .55
J43 D3 50c blue green   1.50 1.10
  Nos. J35-J43 (9) 33.75 4.40

See Nos. S1-S12.

No. J36 Surcharged

1916
J44 D3 5c on 3c bl grn & red   .40 .25

Nos. J35-J36, J43 Surcharged

1924
J45 D3 10c on 1c   .25 8.25
J46 D3 10c on 3c   .25 1.50
J47 D3 20c on 50c   .95 1.50
  Nos. J45-J47 (3)   1.45 11.25

D4   D5

Wmk. 183
1924-26   Typo.   Perf. 11½
Granite Paper
J48 D4 5c ol grn & red   .65 .25
J49 D4 10c ol grn & red 2.75 .20
J50 D4 15c ol grn & red ('26) 2.50 .55

J51	D4	20c ol grn & red	6.00	.20
J52	D4	25c ol grn & red	2.75	.55
J53	D4	30c ol grn & red	2.75	.85
J54	D4	40c ol grn & red ('26)	3.75	.70
J55	D4	50c ol grn & red	3.75	.70
		Nos. J48-J55 (8)	24.90	4.00

1924
With Grilled Gum

J48a	D4	5c olive green & red	.65	.60
J49a	D4	10c olive green & red	2.50	1.10
J51a	D4	20c olive green & red	4.75	1.50
J52a	D4	25c olive green & red	7.25	65.00
		Nos. J48a-J52a (4)	15.15	68.20

See Grilled Gum note after No. 145.

Nos. J50, J53 and J55 Surcharged with New Value in Black

1937

J56	D4	5c on 15c	.90	4.25
J57	D4	10c on 30c	.90	1.50
J58	D4	20c on 50c	1.50	5.00
J59	D4	40c on 50c	2.50	12.00
		Nos. J56-J59 (4)	5.80	22.75
		Set, never hinged	10.50	

1938   Engr.   Unwmk.

J60	D5	5c scarlet	.40	.20
J61	D5	10c scarlet	.55	.20
J62	D5	15c scarlet	1.25	2.25
J63	D5	20c scarlet	.95	.20
J64	D5	25c scarlet	1.40	1.90
J65	D5	30c scarlet	1.40	1.25
J66	D5	40c scarlet	1.60	.45
J67	D5	50c scarlet	1.90	2.25
		Nos. J60-J67 (8)	9.45	8.70
		Set, never hinged	19.00	

1938
With Grilled Gum

J60a	D5	5c scarlet	.65	1.60
J61a	D5	10c scarlet	.65	1.25
J62a	D5	15c scarlet	1.40	2.50
J63a	D5	20c scarlet	1.25	.55
J64a	D5	25c scarlet	1.40	9.50
J65a	D5	30c scarlet	1.40	2.25
J66a	D5	40c scarlet	2.10	2.10
J67a	D5	50c scarlet	2.50	3.50
		Nos. J60a-J67a (8)	11.35	23.25
		Set, never hinged	29.00	

See Grilled Gum note after No. 145.

OFFICIAL STAMPS

For General Use

With Perforated Cross
In 1935 the government authorized the use of regular postage issues perforated with a nine-hole cross for all government departments. Twenty-seven different stamps were so perforated. These were succeeded in 1938 by the cross overprints.

Values for canceled Official Stamps are for those canceled to order. Postally used stamps sell for considerably less. This note does not apply to Nos. 1O1-1O16, 2O27-2O30, 3O23-3O26.

Counterfeit overprints exist of most official stamps.

Official stamps without unused values were not made available to the public unused.

Regular Issues of 1908-36 Overprinted in Black

1938   Unwmk.   Perf. 11½

O1	A53	3c olive	.20	.20
O2	A54	5c blue green	.20	.20
O3	A55	10c red violet	.95	.45
O4	A56	15c orange	.25	1.60
O5	A68	20c red	.45	.25
O6	A58	25c brown	.45	1.40
O7	A59	30c ultra	.60	1.00
O8	A60	35c yellow green	.60	1.25
O9	A61	40c gray	.60	1.00

Wmk. 183
With Grilled Gum

O10	A25	50c dp grn & pale grn	.60	1.50
O11	A25	60c brn org & buff	1.25	2.50
O12	A25	70c vio & buff	1.25	4.25
O13	A25	80c sl & buff	1.25	3.25
O14	A36	90c grn & red, *grn*	3.00	3.25
O15	A25	1fr dp cl & pale grn	1.50	3.25
O16	A36	1.20fr brn rose & red, *rose*	1.50	4.50
O17	A36	1.50fr bl & red, *bl*	2.50	6.00
O18	A36	2fr gray blk & red, *gray*	3.00	7.00
		Nos. O1-O18 (18)	20.15	42.85
		Set, never hinged	65.00	

Nos. O14, O16, O17 and O18 are on surface-colored paper.

1938   Unwmk.   With Grilled Gum

O1a	A53	3c olive	4.50	.45
O2a	A54	5c blue green	1.25	.25
O3a	A55	10c red violet	1.50	.55
O4a	A56	15c orange	2.75	1.25
O5a	A68	20c red	1.50	.70
O6a	A58	25c brown	75.00	7.75
O7a	A59	30c ultra	2.50	1.10
O8a	A60	35c yellow green	1.90	1.90
O9a	A61	40c gray	2.50	1.00
		Nos. O1a-O9a (9)	93.40	14.95
		Set, never hinged	190.00	

See Grilled Gum note after No. 145.

Postage Stamps of 1936-42 Overprinted in Black

1942-45   Unwmk.   Perf. 11½

O19	A53	3c olive	.30	2.10
O20	A54	5c blue green	.30	.20
O21	A55	10c dk red brn	.55	.55
O21A	A55	10c orange brn ('45)	.20	.45
O22	A56	15c orange	.60	1.90
O23	A68	20c red	.60	.45
O24	A58	25c lt brown	.60	2.25
O25	A59	30c ultra	.95	.90
O26	A60	35c yellow grn	1.25	2.75
O27	A61	40c gray	1.25	.60
O28	A77	50c dp pur, *grnsh*	3.75	4.25
O29	A78	60c red brn, *buff*	4.50	4.25
O30	A79	70c rose vio, *pale lil*	5.00	8.25
O31	A80	80c blk, *pale gray rose*	1.40	1.60
O32	A81	90c dk red, *pale rose*	1.60	2.25
O33	A82	1fr dk grn, *grnsh*	1.60	1.60
O34	A83	1.20fr red vio, *pale gray*	2.25	2.75
O35	A84	1.50fr dk bl, *buff*	2.25	3.25
O36	A85	2fr mar, *pale rose*	3.25	4.00
		Nos. O19-O36 (19)	32.20	44.35
		Set, never hinged	60.00	

Same Overprint on Nos. 329-339

1950   Unwmk.   Perf. 12x11½

O37	A118	5c orange	.40	.55
O38	A119	10c yellow grn	.65	.55
O39	A120	15c aqua	5.50	15.00
O40	A121	20c brown car	2.10	.65
O41	A122	25c red	3.25	8.25
O42	A123	30c olive	2.50	3.25
O43	A124	35c red brown	3.50	11.00
O44	A125	40c deep blue	2.75	3.25
O45	A126	50c slate gray	4.50	5.75
O46	A127	60c blue green	5.50	7.75
O47	A128	70c purple	16.00	22.50
		Nos. O37-O47 (11)	46.65	78.50
		Set, never hinged	77.50	

FOR THE WAR BOARD OF TRADE

Regular Issues of 1908-18 Overprinted

1918   Wmk. 183   Perf. 11½, 12

1O1	A26	3c brown org	110.00	225.00
1O2	A26	5c green	10.00	32.50
1O3	A26	7½c gray (I)	300.00	450.00
a.		7½c slate (II)	550.00	950.00
1O4	A28	10c red, *buff*	15.00	40.00
1O5	A28	15c vio, *buff*	12.50	45.00
1O6	A25	20c red & yel	125.00	500.00
1O7	A25	25c dp bl	125.00	500.00

1O8	A25	30c yel brn & pale grn	125.00	450.00
		Nos. 1O1-1O8 (8)	822.50	2,242.

Most unused copies of Nos. 1O1-1O8 are reprints made using the original overprint forms.
Counterfeits exist.

Overprinted

1918

1O9	A26	3c brown orange	4.25	35.00
1O10	A26	5c green	12.00	52.50
1O11	A26	7½c gray	4.50	22.50
1O12	A28	10c red, *buff*	45.00	87.50
1O13	A28	15c vio, *buff*	87.50	
1O14	A25	20c red & yel	8.75	52.50
1O15	A25	25c dp blue	8.75	52.50
1O16	A25	30c yel brn & pale grn	14.50	87.50
		Nos. 1O9-1O16 (8)	185.25	

No. 1O13 was never placed in use.
Fraudulent cancellations are found on Nos. 1O1-1O16.

FOR THE LEAGUE OF NATIONS

Regular Issues Overprinted

On 1908-30 Issues

1922-31   Wmk. 183   Perf. 11½, 12

2O1	A26	2½c ol, *buff* ('28)		.45
2O2	A26	3c ultra, *buff* ('30)		8.25
2O3	A26	5c orange, *buff*		5.50
2O4	A26	5c gray vio, *buff* ('26)		2.75
2O5	A26	5c red vio, *buff* ('27)		2.25
2O6	A26	5c dk grn, *buff* ('31)		25.00
2O7	A28	7½c dp grn, *buff* ('28)		.55
2O8	A28	10c green, *buff*		.55
2O9	A28	10c bl grn, *buff* ('28)		1.10
2O10	A28	10c vio, *buff* ('31)		2.75
2O11	A28	15c brn red, *buff* ('28)		1.10
2O12	A28	20c red vio, *buff*		8.25
2O13	A28	20c car, *buff* ('26)		2.25
2O14	A28	25c ver, *buff*		8.25
2O15	A28	25c car, *buff*		1.10
2O16	A28	25c brn, *buff* ('27)		17.00
2O17	A29	30c dp bl, *buff* ('25)		8.25
2O18	A25	30c yel brn & pale grn		14.00
2O19	A25	35c yel grn & yel		10.00
2O20	A25	40c deep blue		1.40
2O21	A25	40c red vio & grn ('28)		14.00
2O22	A25	50c dp grn & pale grn		11.00
2O23	A25	60c brn org & buff	30.00	1.60
2O24	A25	70c vio & buff ('25)		26.00
2O25	A25	80c slate & buff		2.75
2O26	A25	1fr dp cl & pale grn		6.75
2O27	A29	3fr red		32.50
2O28	A30	5fr ultra		60.00
2O29	A31	10fr dull violet		140.00
2O30	A31	10fr gray grn ('30)		140.00
		Nos. 2O1-2O30 (30)		555.35

1930-44   With Grilled Gum

2O2a	A26	3c ultra, *buff* ('33)		10.00
2O6a	A26	5c dk grn, *buff* ('33)		19.00
2O17a	A29	30c dp bl, *buff*		425.00
2O22a	A25	50c dp grn & pale grn ('35)	.90	2.25
2O23a	A25	60c brn org & buff ('44)	25.00	225.00
2O24a	A25	70c violet & buff ('42)	1.60	2.25
2O25a	A25	80c slate & buff ('42)	2.75	2.50
2O26a	A25	1fr dp cl & pale grn ('42)		5.25

1935-36
With Grilled Gum

2O31	A36	90c grn & red, *grn* ('36)		5.00
2O32	A36	1.20fr brn rose & red, *rose* ('36)	2.75	4.50
b.		Inverted overprint		4,250.
2O33	A36	1.50fr bl & red, *bl*	2.75	4.50
2O34	A36	2fr gray blk & red, *gray* ('36)	2.75	5.25

1922-25   Ordinary Gum

2O31a	A36	90c		14.00
2O32a	A36	1.20fr ('25)		14.00
2O33a	A36	1.50fr ('25)		13.00
2O34a	A36	2fr ('25)		12.00

1928

2O35	A39	5fr blue		87.50

On 1932 Issue

1932

2O36	A41	5c peacock bl		19.00
2O37	A41	10c orange		1.60
2O38	A41	20c cerise		1.60
2O39	A41	30c ultra		55.00
2O40	A41	60c olive brn		15.00

Unwmk.

2O41	A42	1fr ol gray & bl		15.00
		Nos. 2O36-2O41 (6)		107.20

On 1934 Issue

1934-35   Wmk. 183

2O42	A46	3c olive		.25
2O43	A47	5c emerald		.65
2O44	A49	15c orange ('35)		1.50
2O45	A51	25c brown		19.00
2O46	A52	30c ultra		1.60
		Nos. 2O42-2O46 (5)		23.00

On 1936 Issue

1937   Unwmk.

2O47	A53	3c olive	.20	.25
2O48	A54	5c blue green	.25	.25
2O49	A55	10c red violet		1.10
2O50	A56	15c orange	.45	.55
2O51	A57	20c carmine		1.90
2O52	A58	25c brown	.65	1.10
2O53	A59	30c ultra	.65	1.00
2O54	A60	35c yellow green	.65	1.00
2O55	A61	40c gray	.95	1.25
		Nos. 2O47-2O55 (9)		8.40

1937   With Grilled Gum

2O47a	A53	3c olive		.30
2O48a	A54	5c blue green		.45
2O49a	A55	10c red violet		6.25
2O50a	A56	15c orange		.70
2O51a	A57	20c carmine		2.25
2O52a	A58	25c brown		1.40
2O53a	A59	30c ultra		1.10
2O54a	A60	35c yellow green		4.25
2O55a	A61	40c gray		4.25
		Nos. 2O47a-2O55a (9)		20.95

On 1931 Issue

1937   Wmk. 183

2O56	A40	3fr orange brown		190.00

On 1938 Issue

1938   Unwmk.   Perf. 11½
Granite Paper

2O57	A63	20c red & buff		1.90
2O58	A64	30c blue & lt blue		3.00
2O59	A65	60c brown & buff		5.75
2O60	A66	1fr black & buff		9.25
		Nos. 2O57-2O60 (4)		19.90

Regular Issue of 1938 Overprinted in Black or Red

Granite Paper

2O61	A63	20c red & buff		2.25
2O62	A64	30c blue & lt blue		4.00
2O63	A65	60c brown & buff		7.25
2O64	A66	1fr black & buff (R)		12.50
		Nos. 2O61-2O64 (4)		26.00

Regular Issue of 1938 Overprinted in Black

1939
2O65	A69	3fr brn car, *buff*	3.25	11.00
2O66	A70	5fr slate bl, *buff*	5.50	15.00
2O67	A71	10fr green, *buff*	11.00	32.50
		Nos. 2O65-2O67 (3)	19.75	58.50

Same Overprint in Black on Regular
Issues of 1939-42

1942-43
2O68	A55	10c dk red brown		.85
2O68A	A55	10c orange brn ('43)	.40	.85
2O69	A68	20c red	.50	1.00
		Nos. 2O68-2O69 (3)		2.70

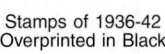

Stamps of 1936-42
Overprinted in Black

1944
2O70	A53	3c olive	.20	.25
2O71	A54	5c blue green	.20	.25
2O72	A55	10c orange brown	.80	.40
2O73	A56	15c orange	.20	.50
2O74	A68	20c red	.40	.75
2O75	A58	25c lt brown	.40	1.00
2O76	A59	30c ultra	.50	1.00
2O77	A60	35c yellow green	.50	1.00
2O78	A61	40c gray	.55	1.25

Nos. 2O73-2O75 and 2O78 exist with grilled gum. Value each $2,000 unused, $2,250 used.

Stamps of 1941
Overprinted in Black

2O79	A77	50c dp pur, *grnsh*	1.00	1.75
2O80	A78	60c red brn, *buff*	1.25	2.50
2O81	A79	70c rose vio, *pale lil*	1.25	2.50
2O82	A80	80c blk, *pale gray*	1.10	2.00
2O83	A81	90c dk red, *pale rose*	1.10	2.00
2O84	A82	1fr dk grn, *grnsh*	1.10	2.25
2O85	A83	1.20fr red vio, *pale gray*	1.75	3.00
2O86	A84	1.50fr dk bl, *pale rose*	2.00	3.50
2O87	A85	2fr mar, *pale rose*	2.50	4.00

Stamps of 1942 Overprinted in Black

		Unwmk.	**Perf. 11½**	
2O88	A69	3fr brn car, *cr*	4.50	9.00
2O89	A70	5fr slate bl, *cr*	7.00	12.50
2O90	A71	10fr green, *cr*	12.00	24.00
		Nos. 2O70-2O90 (21)	40.30	75.40
		Set, never hinged	65.00	

FOR THE INTERNATIONAL LABOR BUREAU

Regular Issues
Overprinted

On 1908-30 Issues
		Wmk. 183	**Perf. 11½, 12**	
3O1	A26	2½c ol grn, *buff* ('28)		.30
3O2	A26	3c ultra, *buff* ('30)		1.10
3O3	A26	5c org, *buff*		.55
3O4	A26	5c red vio, *buff* ('28)		.20
3O5	A26	7½c dp grn, *buff* ('28)		.45
3O6	A28	10c grn, *buff*		.55
3O7	A28	10c bl grn, *buff* ('28)		1.10
3O8	A28	15c brn red, *buff* ('28)		1.10
3O9	A28	20c red vio, *buff*		17.00

3O10	A28	20c car, *buff* ('27)		5.00
3O11	A28	25c car, *buff*		1.25
3O12	A28	25c brn, *buff* ('28)		3.00
3O13	A28	30c dp bl, *buff* ('25)		2.50
3O14	A25	30c yel brn & pale grn		65.00
3O15	A25	35c yel grn & yel		11.00
3O16	A25	40c deep blue		1.25
3O17	A25	40c red vio & grn ('28)		17.00
3O18	A25	50c dp grn & pale grn		5.00
3O19	A25	'60c brn org & buff	1.60	1.90
3O20	A25	70c vio & buff ('24)		26.00
3O21	A25	80c slate & buff	14.00	2.25
3O22	A25	1fr dp cl & pale grn		2.75
3O23	A29	3fr red		25.00
3O24	A30	5fr ultra		37.50
3O25	A31	10fr dull violet		150.00
3O26	A31	10fr gray grn ('30)		150.00
		Nos. 3O1-3O26 (26)		528.75

1937-44   **With Grilled Gum**
3O18a	A25	50c dp grn & pale grn ('42)	1.75	2.25
3O20a	A25	70c vio & buff	1.75	2.25
3O21a	A25	80c slate & buff ('44)	25.00	175.00
3O22a	A25	1fr dp cl & pale grn ('42)		3.25

1925-42   **With Grilled Gum**
3O27	A36	90c grn & red, *grn* ('37)		9.75
a.		Ordinary gum		5.00
3O28	A36	1.20fr brn rose & red, *rose* ('42)	14.00	4.00
a.		Ordinary gum		4.50
3O29	A36	1.50fr bl & red, *bl* ('37)	2.75	3.00
a.		Ordinary gum		14.00
3O30	A36	2fr gray blk & red, *gray* ('36)	3.25	6.25
a.		Ordinary gum		32.50
		Nos. 3O27-3O30 (4)		23.00

1928
3O31	A39	5fr blue		82.50

On 1932 Issue

1932
3O32	A41	5c peacock blue		1.10
3O33	A41	10c orange		.90
3O34	A41	20c cerise		1.25
3O35	A41	30c ultra		7.75
3O36	A41	60c olive brown		7.75

Unwmk.
3O37	A42	1fr ol gray & bl		10.00
		Nos. 3O32-3O37 (6)		28.75

On 1936 Issue

1937
3O38	A53	3c olive	.20	.55
3O39	A54	5c blue green	.20	.55
3O40	A55	10c red violet		2.75
3O41	A56	15c orange	.45	1.10
3O42	A57	20c carmine		2.25
3O43	A58	25c brown	.60	1.40
3O44	A59	30c ultra	.60	1.10
3O45	A60	35c yellow green	.60	1.60
3O46	A61	40c gray	.95	1.90
		Nos. 3O38-3O46 (9)		13.20

1937   **With Grilled Gum**
3O38a	A53	3c olive		1.10
3O39a	A54	5c blue green		1.10
3O40a	A55	10c red violet		1.60
3O41a	A56	15c orange		1.90
3O42a	A57	20c carmine		1.60
3O43a	A58	25c brown		2.25
3O44a	A59	30c ultra		2.25
3O45a	A60	35c yellow green		2.75
3O46a	A61	40c gray		2.25
		Nos. 3O38a-3O46a (9)		16.80

On 1931 Issue

1937   **Wmk. 183**
3O47	A40	3fr orange brown		175.00

On 1934 Issue
3O48	A46	3c olive		5.50

On 1938 Issue

1938   **Unwmk.**   **Perf. 11½**
Granite Paper
3O49	A63	20c red & buff		1.60
3O50	A64	30c blue & lt blue		3.25
3O51	A65	60c brown & buff		6.00
3O52	A66	1fr black & buff		8.75
		Nos. 3O49-3O52 (4)		19.60

Regular Issue of 1938 Overprinted in
Black or Red

3O53	A63	20c red & buff (Bk)		3.25
3O54	A64	30c bl & lt bl (Bk)		3.25
3O55	A65	60c brn & buff (Bk)		6.50
3O56	A66	1fr blk & buff (R)		7.00
		Nos. 3O53-3O56 (4)		20.00

Regular Issue of 1938 Overprinted in
Black

1939
3O57	A69	3fr brn car, *buff*	4.50	8.25
3O58	A70	5fr slate bl, *buff*	5.50	17.00
3O59	A71	10fr green, *buff*	10.00	30.00
		Nos. 3O57-3O59 (3)	20.00	55.25

Same Overprint in Black on Regular
Issues of 1939-42

1942-43
3O60	A55	10c dark red brown		.80
3O60A	A55	10c orange brn ('43)	.50	.80
3O61	A68	20c red	.55	.80
		Nos. 3O60-3O61 (3)		2.40

Stamps of 1936-42
Overprinted in Black

1944
3O62	A53	3c olive	.20	.20
3O63	A54	5c blue green	.20	.20
3O64	A55	10c orange brn	.20	.25
3O65	A56	15c orange	.50	.50
3O66	A68	20c red	.35	.50
3O67	A58	25c lt brown	.55	.70
3O68	A59	30c ultra	.50	1.10
3O69	A60	35c yellow grn	.70	1.25
3O70	A61	40c gray	.75	1.40

Stamps of 1941
Overprinted

3O71	A77	50c dp pur, *grnsh*	1.50	8.00
3O72	A78	60c red brn, *buff*	1.50	8.00
3O73	A79	70c rose vio, *pale lil*	1.75	8.00
3O74	A80	80c blk, *pale gray*	.45	1.40
3O75	A81	90c dk red, *pale rose*	.45	1.40
3O76	A82	1fr dk grn, *grnsh*	.45	1.40
3O77	A83	1.20fr red vio, *pale gray*	.75	1.75
3O78	A84	1.50fr dull bl, *buff*	1.00	2.25
3O79	A85	2fr mar, *pale rose*	1.25	3.00

Stamps of 1942 Overprinted

3O80	A69	3fr brown car, *cr*	3.25	6.00
3O81	A70	5fr slate blue, *cr*	5.00	10.50
3O82	A71	10fr green, *cr*	10.00	20.00
		Nos. 3O62-3O82 (21)	31.30	77.80
		Set, never hinged	60.00	

Nos. 329-339
Overprinted in
Black

1950   **Unwmk.**   **Perf. 12x11½**
3O83	A118	5c orange	4.00	4.75
3O84	A119	10c yellow green	4.00	5.25
3O85	A120	15c aqua	5.00	7.50
3O86	A121	20c brown carmine	5.00	7.50
3O87	A122	25c red	6.00	7.75
3O88	A123	30c olive	6.00	7.75
3O89	A124	35c red brown	6.00	7.75
3O90	A125	40c deep blue	6.00	7.75
3O91	A126	50c slate gray	7.50	8.25
3O92	A127	60c blue green	9.00	12.50
3O93	A128	70c purple	10.00	17.50
		Nos. 3O83-3O93 (11)	68.50	94.25
		Set, never hinged	110.00	

> **Catalogue values for unused stamps in this section, from this point to the end of the section, are for Never Hinged items.**

Miners — O1   Globe, Chimney
and Wheel — O2

1956-60   **Unwmk.**   **Engr.**   **Perf. 11½**
3O94	O1	5c dark gray	.20	.20
3O95	O1	10c green	.20	.20
3O96	O2	20c vermilion	1.25	2.25
3O97	O2	20c car rose ('60)	.20	.20
3O98	O2	30c orange ver ('60)	.25	.40
3O99	O1	40c blue	1.25	2.75
3O100	O1	50c lt ultra ('60)	.25	.50
3O101	O2	60c reddish brown	.30	.50
3O102	O2	2fr rose violet	1.10	1.50
		Nos. 3O94-3O102 (9)	5.00	8.50

Type of 1960 Overprinted: "Visite du / Pape Paul VI / Genève / 10 juin 1969"

1969, June 10
Violet Fibers, Fluorescent Paper
3O103	O2	30c orange vermilion	.30	.30

Visit of Pope Paul VI to the Intl. Labor Bureau to celebrate its 50th anniv., Geneva, June 10.

ILO
Headquarters,
Geneva — O3

1974, May 30   **Photo.**   **Perf. 11½**
Violet Fibers, Fluorescent Paper
3O104	O3	80c blue, yellow & gray	.85	.80

Inauguration of the new International Labor Organization Building.

Young Man at
Lathe,
Cogwheels
O4

Designs: 60c, Woman at drilling machine. 90c, Welder and lab assistant using protective devices and clothing. 100c, Surveyor with theodolite and topographical map. 120c, Professional education for youth.

1975-88   **Photo.**   **Perf. 11½**
3O105	O4	30c red brn & dk brn	.30	.30
3O106	O4	60c ultra & blk	.60	.60
3O107	O4	100c dk green & blk	1.00	1.00
3O108	O4	120c multicolored	1.25	1.25

Perf. 12x11½

3O109	O4	90c multicolored	1.00	1.00
		Nos. 3O105-3O109 (5)	4.15	4.15

Issued: 30c-100c, 2/13; 120c, 8/22/83; 90c, 9/13/88.

ILO, 75th Anniv. — O5

1994, May 17   Litho.   Perf. 13

3O110	O5	180c multicolored	2.00	2.00

FOR THE INTERNATIONAL BUREAU OF EDUCATION

Regular Issues of 1936-42, Overprinted in Black

1944   Unwmk.   Perf. 11½

4O1	A53	3c olive	.40	1.00
4O2	A54	5c blue grn	.55	1.25
4O3	A55	10c orange brn	.55	1.50
4O4	A56	15c orange	.55	1.50
4O5	A68	20c red	.55	1.50
4O6	A58	25c lt brown	.65	1.75
4O7	A59	30c ultra	.85	2.25
4O8	A60	35c yellow grn	.85	2.25
4O9	A61	40c gray	1.10	2.50

Regular Issue of 1941, Overprinted in Black

4O10	A77	50c dp pur, *grnsh*	5.00	13.00
4O11	A78	60c red brn, *buff*	5.00	13.00
4O12	A79	70c rose vio, *pale lil*	5.00	13.00
4O13	A80	80c blk, *pale gray*	.60	1.50
4O14	A81	90c dk red, *pale rose*	.70	1.75
4O15	A82	1fr dk grn, *grnsh*	.85	2.25
4O16	A83	1.20fr red vio, *pale gray*	1.00	2.50
4O17	A84	1.50fr dk bl, *buff*	1.25	3.00
4O18	A85	2fr mar, *pale rose*	1.60	4.00

Regular Issue of 1942, Overprinted in Black

4O19	A69	3fr brn car, *cr*	7.00	17.00
4O20	A70	5fr slate bl, *cr*	10.00	25.00
4O21	A71	10fr green, *cr*	15.00	40.00
		Nos. 4O1-4O21 (21)	59.05	151.50
		Set, never hinged	110.00	

No. 306 Overprinted in Carmine

1946

4O22	A104	10c rose violet	.20	.50
		Never hinged	.50	

Nos. 316-321 Overprinted in Black

1948   Unwmk.   Perf. 11½

4O23	A54	5c chocolate	1.75	3.00
4O24	A55	10c green	1.75	3.00
4O25	A68	20c orange brn	1.75	3.00
4O26	A113	25c carmine	1.75	3.00
4O27	A59	30c grnsh blue	2.00	3.00
4O28	A61	40c ultra	2.00	3.00
		Nos. 4O23-4O28 (6)	11.00	18.00
		Set, never hinged	20.00	

Same Overprint on Nos. 329-339

1950   Perf. 12x11½

Overprint 18mm wide

4O29	A118	5c orange	.65	1.75
4O30	A119	10c yellow grn	.65	2.10
4O31	A120	15c aqua	.65	2.10
4O32	A121	20c brown car	2.00	5.75
4O33	A122	25c red	4.50	10.50
4O34	A123	30c olive	4.50	10.50
4O35	A124	35c red brn	3.50	8.75
4O36	A125	40c deep blue	3.50	8.75
4O37	A126	50c slate gray	4.00	9.75
4O38	A127	60c blue green	4.75	11.50
4O39	A128	70c purple	5.50	13.50
		Nos. 4O29-4O39 (11)	34.20	84.95
		Set, never hinged	60.00	

> Catalogue values for unused stamps in this section, from this point to the end of the section, are for Never Hinged items.

Globe and Books — O1

Designs: 20c, 30c, 60c, 2fr, Pestalozzi Monument at Yverdon.

1958-60   Engr.   Perf. 11½

4O40	O1	5c dark gray	.20	.20
4O41	O1	10c green	.20	.20
4O42	O1	20c vermilion	2.25	2.25
4O43	O1	20c car rose ('60)	.20	.20
4O44	O1	30c org ver ('60)	.20	.35
4O45	O1	40c blue	2.75	2.75
4O46	O1	50c lt ultra ('60)	.30	.50
4O47	O1	60c reddish brn	.30	.50
4O48	O1	2fr rose violet	1.10	1.50
		Nos. 4O40-4O48 (9)	7.50	8.45

FOR THE WORLD HEALTH ORGANIZATION

No. 316-319, 321 Overprinted in Black

1948   Unwmk.   Perf. 11½

5O1	A54	5c chocolate	2.25	2.50
5O2	A55	10c green	2.25	3.50
5O3	A68	20c orange brn	2.25	3.50
5O4	A113	25c carmine	2.25	4.50
5O5	A61	40c ultra	2.50	5.00
		Nos. 5O1-5O5 (5)	11.50	19.00
		Set, never hinged	20.00	

Regular Issues of 1941, 1942 and 1949 Overprinted in Black

1948-50

5O6	A118	5c orange	.50	1.00
5O7	A119	10c yellow grn	.65	1.50
5O8	A120	15c aqua	.90	2.00
5O9	A121	20c brown car	2.25	6.00
5O10	A122	25c red	2.25	6.00
5O11	A123	30c olive	1.50	5.00
5O12	A124	35c red brown	2.10	7.00
5O13	A125	40c deep blue	2.10	3.50

5O14	A126	50c slate gray	2.25	6.00
5O15	A127	60c blue green	2.50	7.00
5O16	A128	70c purple	3.00	7.00
5O17	A80	80c blk, *pale gray* ('48)	2.00	3.75
5O18	A81	90c dk red, *pale rose*	4.25	8.50
5O19	A82	1fr dk grn, *grnsh* ('48)	2.50	4.50
5O20	A83	1.20fr red vio, *pale gray*	5.50	12.00
5O21	A84	1.50fr dk bl, *buff*	11.00	12.00
5O22	A85	2fr mar, *pale rose* ('48)	3.50	6.50
5O23	A69	3fr brn car, *cr*	22.50	37.50
5O24	A70	5fr sl bl, *cr* ('48)	7.50	11.50
5O25	A71	10fr grn, *cr*	45.00	65.00
		Nos. 5O6-5O25 (19)	121.25	208.75
		Set, never hinged	250.00	

> Catalogue values for unused stamps in this section, from this point to the end of the section, are for Never Hinged items.

WHO Emblem — O2

1957-60   Unwmk.   Engr.   Perf. 11½

5O26	O2	5c gray	.20	.20
5O27	O2	10c lt grn	.20	.20
5O28	O2	20c vermilion	2.25	2.25
5O29	O2	20c car rose ('60)	.25	.25
5O30	O2	30c org ver ('60)	.35	.35
5O31	O2	40c blue	2.75	2.75
5O32	O2	50c lt ultra ('60)	.50	.50
5O33	O2	60c red brn	.50	.50
5O34	O2	2fr rose lilac	1.50	1.50
		Nos. 5O26-5O34 (9)	8.50	8.50

No. 5O32 Overprinted: "ERADICATION DU PALUDISME"

1962, Mar. 19

5O35	O2	50c lt ultra	.75	.75

WHO drive to eradicate malaria.

World Health Organization Emblem — O3

1975-95   Typo.   Perf. 11½

5O36	O3	30c multi	.30	.30
5O37	O3	60c lt bl & multi	.60	.30
5O38	O3	90c lilac & multi	.90	.90
5O39	O3	100c orange & multi	1.00	1.00

Litho.

Perf. 12

5O40	O3	140c lt grn, scar & grn	1.50	1.50

Perf. 13½x13

5O41	O3	180c multicolored	2.10	2.10
		Nos. 5O36-5O41 (6)	6.40	6.10

Issued: 140c, 5/27/86; 180c, 11/28/95; others, 2/13/75.

FOR THE INTERNATIONAL ORGANIZATION FOR REFUGEES

Stamps of 1941 and 1949 Overprinted in Black

1950   Unwmk.   Perf. 12x11½, 11½

6O1	A118	5c orange	11.00	14.00
6O2	A119	10c yellow green	11.00	14.00
6O3	A121	20c brown carmine	11.00	14.00
6O4	A122	25c red	11.00	14.00
6O5	A125	40c deep blue	11.00	14.00
6O6	A80	80c blk, *pale gray*	11.00	14.00
6O7	A82	1fr dk grn, *grnsh*	11.00	14.00

6O8	A85	2fr mar, *pale rose*	11.00	14.00
		Nos. 6O1-6O8 (8)	88.00	112.00
		Set, never hinged	150.00	

FOR THE UNITED NATIONS EUROPEAN OFFICE

See No. 513 for postage issue commemorating the United Nations.

Stamps of 1941-49 Overprinted in Black

1950   Unwmk.   Perf. 12x11½, 11½

7O1	A118	5c orange	.20	2.25
7O2	A119	10c yellow grn	.35	2.25
7O3	A120	15c aqua	.55	3.00
7O4	A121	20c brown car	.85	4.25
7O5	A122	25c red	1.10	7.50
7O6	A123	30c olive	1.40	7.50
7O7	A124	35c red brown	1.40	7.50
7O8	A125	40c deep blue	2.10	8.75
7O9	A126	50c slate gray	2.50	10.50
7O10	A127	60c blue green	2.75	12.50
7O11	A128	70c purple	3.50	12.50
7O12	A80	80c blk, *pale gray*	5.50	10.00
7O13	A81	90c dk red, *pale rose*	5.50	10.00
7O14	A82	1fr dk grn, *grnsh*	5.50	10.00
7O15	A83	1.20fr red vio, *pale gray*	6.50	13.00
7O16	A84	1.50fr dk bl, *buff*	6.50	13.00
7O17	A85	2fr mar, *pale rose*	6.50	13.00
7O18	A69	3fr brn car, *cr*	65.00	125.00
7O19	A70	5fr sl bl, *cr*	67.50	125.00
7O20	A71	10fr grn, *cr*	90.00	160.00
		Nos. 7O1-7O20 (20)	275.20	557.50
		Set, never hinged	500.00	

UN Emblem — O1

Statue from UN Building, Geneva — O2

1955-59   Engr.   Perf. 11½

7O21	O1	5c dk violet brn	.20	.20
7O22	O1	10c green	.20	.20
7O23	O2	20c vermilion	2.00	4.00
7O24	O2	20c car rose ('59)	.20	.20
7O25	O2	30c org ver ('59)	.20	.30
7O26	O1	40c ultra	2.25	4.50
7O27	O1	50c ultra ('59)	.20	.40
7O28	O2	60c red brown	.25	.50
7O29	O2	2fr lilac	.80	1.60
		Nos. 7O21-7O29 (9)	6.30	11.90
		Set, never hinged	12.50	

See Nos. 7O34-7O37. For overprints see Nos. 7O31-7O32.

United Nations Emblem — O3

1955, Oct. 24   Photo.

7O30	O3	40c dark blue & bister	1.60	3.75
		Never hinged	3.00	

10th anniv. of the UN, Oct. 24, 1955.

> Catalogue values for unused stamps in this section, from this point to the end of the section, are for Never Hinged items.

Nos. 7O24 and 7O27 Overprinted in Black or Red: "ANNÉE MONDIALE DU RÉFUGIE 1959 1960"

1960

7O31	O2	20c carmine rose	.20	.20
7O32	O1	50c ultra (R)	.50	.50

World Refugee Year, 7/1/59-6/30/60.

Palace of Nations, Geneva O4

1960   Granite Paper   Perf. 11½

7O33	O4	5fr blue	3.75	4.00

Types of 1955 Inscribed: "MUSÉE PHILATÉLIQUE" (O1) or "ONU MUSÉE PHILATÉLIQUE" (O2)

Engraved; Inscription Typographed

1962, Oct. 24   Unwmk.   Perf. 11½

7O34	O1	10c green & red	.20	.20
7O35	O2	30c org ver & ultra	.30	.30
7O36	O1	50c ultra & org	.50	.50
7O37	O2	60c red brn & emer	.60	.60
		Nos. 7O34-7O37 (4)	1.60	1.60

Opening of the Philatelic Museum, UN European Office, Geneva.

O5   O6

UNCSAT Emblem

1963, Feb. 4   Engr.   Perf. 11½

7O38	O5	50c ultra & car rose	.50	.50
7O39	O6	2fr lilac & emer	2.00	2.00

UN Conf. on the Application of Science and Technology for the Benefit of the Less Developed Areas (UNCSAT), Geneva, Feb. 4-20.

Stamps issued, starting Oct. 4, 1969, by the UN in Swiss currency for use by UN staff members or the public are listed under "United Nations" in Vol. 1 of this catalogue and in Scott's U.S. Specialized Catalogue. These stamps are on sale in various UN post offices, but are valid only in the UN enclave in Geneva. They are not inscribed "Helvetia."

FOR THE WORLD METEOROLOGICAL ORGANIZATION

Catalogue values for unused stamps in this section are for Never Hinged items.

Sun, Cloud, Rain and Snow — O1

Design: 20c, 30c, 60c, 2fr, Direction indicator and anemometer.

1956-60   Unwmk.   Engr.   Perf. 11½

8O1	O1	5c dark gray	.20	.20
8O2	O1	10c green	.20	.20
8O3	O1	20c vermilion	2.25	2.25
8O4	O1	20c car rose ('60)	.25	.25
8O5	O1	30c org ver ('60)	.35	.35
8O6	O1	40c blue	2.75	2.75
8O7	O1	50c lt ultra ('60)	.50	.50
8O8	O1	60c reddish brn	.60	.60
8O9	O1	2fr rose violet	2.00	2.00
		Nos. 8O1-8O9 (9)	9.10	9.10

WMO Emblem O2

1973, Aug. 30   Engr.   Perf. 11½
Violet Fibers, Fluorescent Paper

8O10	O2	30c carmine	.20	.30
8O11	O2	40c blue	.20	.30
8O12	O2	1fr ocher	1.00	1.00
		Nos. 8O10-8O12 (3)	1.40	1.60

Type O2 Inscribed: "OMI / OMM / 1873 / 1973"

1973, Aug. 30   Photo.   Perf. 11½
Violet Fibers, Fluorescent Paper

8O13	O2	80c deep violet & gold	.80	.80

Intl. meteorological cooperation, cent.

FOR THE INTERNATIONAL BUREAU OF THE UNIVERSAL POSTAL UNION

Catalogue values for unused stamps in this section are for Never Hinged items.

See Nos. 98-103, 204-205, 514, 589-590 for postage issues commemorating the UPU.

UPU Monument, Bern — O1

Design: 10c, 20c, 30c, 60c, Pegasus.

1957-60   Unwmk.   Engr.   Perf. 11½

9O1	O1	5c gray	.20	.20
9O2	O1	10c lt grn	.20	.20
9O3	O1	20c vermilion	2.25	2.25
9O4	O1	20c car rose ('60)	.20	.20
9O5	O1	30c org ver ('60)	.35	.35
9O6	O1	40c blue	2.75	2.75
9O7	O1	50c lt ultra ('60)	.50	.50
9O8	O1	60c red brn	.60	.60
9O9	O1	2fr rose lilac	2.00	2.00
		Nos. 9O1-9O9 (9)	9.05	9.05

First Class Mail — O2

Parcel Post — O3

Money Orders — O4

Technical Cooperation O5

Intl. Reply and Notication Service — O6

Express Mail Service — O7

Post NET System O8

1976-95   Photo.   Perf. 11½
Fluorescent Paper

9O10	O2	40c multi	.40	.40
9O11	O3	80c multi	.80	.80
9O12	O4	90c multi	.90	.90
9O13	O5	100c multi	1.00	1.00
9O14	O6	120c multi	1.25	1.25
9O15	O7	140c multi	1.50	1.50

Perf. 13½x13

9O16	O8	180c multicolored	2.10	2.10
		Nos. 9O10-9O16 (7)	7.95	7.95

Issued: 120c, 8/22/83; 140c, 3/7/89; 180c, 11/28/95; others, 9/16/76.

UPU, 125th Anniv. O9

1999, Mar. 9   Perf. 13

9O17	O9	20c shown	.30	.20
9O18	O9	70c Hand holding rainbow	.85	.65

Service Quality Improvement O10

2003, Sept. 9   Litho.   Perf. 13¾x14¼

9O19	O10	90c multi	1.40	.45

Methods of Mail Transport O11

2005, Sept. 6   Litho.   Perf. 13½x14¼

9O20	O11	100c multi	1.60	1.60

Postman O12

2007, Sept. 6   Litho.   Perf. 13¼x13½

9O21	O12	180c multi	3.25	3.25

See United Nations No. 944, United Nations Offices in Geneva No. 475, and United Nations Offices in Vienna No. 403.

FOR THE INTERNATIONAL TELECOMMUNICATION UNION

Catalogue values for unused stamps in this section are for Never Hinged items.

Transmitter — O1

ITU Headquarters, Geneva — O2

Designs: 20c, 30c, 60c, 2fr, Antenna.

1958-60   Unwmk.   Engr.   Perf. 11½

10O1	O1	5c dark gray	.20	.20
10O2	O1	10c green	.20	.20
10O3	O1	20c vermilion	2.25	2.25
10O4	O1	20c car rose ('60)	.20	.20
10O5	O1	30c org ver ('60)	.35	.35
10O6	O1	40c blue	2.75	2.75
10O7	O1	50c lt ultra ('60)	.50	.50
10O8	O1	60c redsh brn	.60	.60
10O9	O1	2fr rose vio	2.00	2.00
		Nos. 10O1-10O9 (9)	9.05	9.05

1973, Aug. 30   Photo.   Perf. 11½
Violet Fibers, Fluorescent Paper

10O10	O2	80c blue & black	.80	.80

Sound Waves, ITU Emblem O3

Airplane, Ocean Liner — O4

Radio Waves, Face on TV, Microphone O5

Photogravure and Engraved

1976, Feb. 12   Perf. 11½
Violet Fibers, Fluorescent Paper

10O11	O3	40c dp org & vio bl	.40	.40
10O12	O4	90c bl, vio bl & yel	.90	.90
10O13	O5	1fr grn & multi	1.00	1.00
		Nos. 10O11-10O13 (3)	2.30	2.30

ITU activities: world telecommunications, mobile radio and mass media.

Fiber Optic Communication Links — O6

1988, Sept. 13   Litho.   Perf. 12x11½

10O14	O6	1.40fr multi	1.40	1.40

Radio Waves, ITU Emblem — O7

1994, May 17   Litho.   Perf. 13½
10O15 O7 1.80fr multicolored   2.10 2.10

Telecommunications — O8

1999, Mar. 9   Photo.   Perf. 11½
10O16 O8 10c Teleeducation   .20 .20
10O17 O8 100c Telemedicine   1.10 1.10

Stylized Face — O9

2003, Sept. 9   Litho.   Perf. 13¾x14¼
10O18 O9 90c multi   1.40 .45

FOR THE WORLD INTELLECTUAL PROPERTY ORGANIZATION

Catalogue values for unused stamps in this section are for Never Hinged items.

WIPO Emblem O1

1982, May 27   Photo.   Perf. 12x11½
1101 O1 40c shown   .40 .40
1102 O1 80c Headquarters, Geneva   .80 .80
1103 O1 100c Industrial symbols 1.00 1.00
1104 O1 120c Educational and artistic symbols 1.25 1.25

1985, Sept. 10   Photo.   Perf. 12x11½
1105 O1 50c Mind in action   .55 .55
      Nos. 1101-1105 (5)   4.00 4.00

This is an expanding set. Numbers will change if necessary.

FOR THE INTERNATIONAL OLYMPIC COMMITTEE

Catalogue values for unused stamps in this section are for Never Hinged items.

Olympics Type of Regular Issue

Hand and plant with leaves of Olympic rings and: 20c, Orange frame. 70c, Green frame.

2000, Sept. 15   Photo.   Die Cut
Booklet Stamps
Self-Adhesive
1201 A496 20c multi   .25 .25
1202 A496 70c multi   .80 .80
   a.   Booklet pane, #1201-1202   1.10
        Booklet, #1202a   1.10

No. 1202a is separated from booklet cover by rouletting. The booklet was sold folded.

Olympics Type of Regular Issue, 2004

Design: Runner, "40," Olympic rings, scene from 1896 Athens Olympics.

2004, May 6   Litho.   Perf. 13x13¼
1203 A551 100c multi   1.60 1.60

2006 Winter Olympics Type of 2005
2005, Nov. 22   Litho.   Perf. 13½x13
1204 A578 130c Ice hockey   2.00 2.00

Issued in sheets of 6.

FRANCHISE STAMPS

These stamps were distributed to many institutions and charitable societies for franking their correspondence.

F1

Control Figures Overprinted in Black
214

Perf. 11½, 12
1911-21   Typo.   Wmk. 183
Blue Granite Paper
S1 F1 2c ol grn & red   .20 .25
S2 F1 3c ol grn & red   2.50 .55
S3 F1 5c ol grn & red   1.10 .20
S4 F1 10c ol grn & red   1.40 .20
S5 F1 15c ol grn & red   21.00 4.00
S6 F1 20c ol grn & red   5.00 .60
     Nos. S1-S6 (6)   31.20 5.80

Without Control Figures
S1a F1 2c olive green & red   .55 19.00
S2a F1 3c olive green & red   .55 25.00
S3a F1 5c olive green & red   4.75 32.50
S4a F1 10c olive green & red   8.25 50.00
S5a F1 15c olive green & red   5.25 125.00
S6a F1 20c olive green & red   9.50 50.00
     Nos. S1a-S6a (6)   28.85 301.50

Control Figures Overprinted in Black

1926
S7 F1 5c ol grn & red   12.50 4.50
S8 F1 10c ol grn & red   7.75 3.25
S9 F1 20c ol grn & red   10.00 3.75
     Nos. S7-S9 (3)   30.25 11.50

Control Figures Overprinted in Black

1927
White Granite Paper
S10 F1 5c green & red   5.00 .40
S11 F1 10c green & red   2.50 .20
   b.   Grilled gum   325.00 725.00
S12 F1 20c green & red   3.50 .30
     Nos. S10-S12 (3)   11.00 .90

Without Control Figures
S10a F1 5c green & red   32.50 140.00
S11a F1 10c green & red   32.50 140.00
   c.   Grilled gum   150.00 650.00
S12a F1 20c green & red   32.50 140.00

Nurse — F2

Nun — F3

J. H. Dunant — F4

Control Figures Overprinted in Black

1935   **Perf. 11½**
S13 F2 5c turq green   2.25 5.50
   b.   Grilled gum   3.25 .40
S14 F3 10c lt violet   2.25 5.50
   b.   Grilled gum   3.25 .20
S15 F4 20c scarlet   2.25 6.50
   b.   Grilled gum   3.75 .45
     Nos. S13-S15 (3)   6.75 17.50
     Nos. S13b-S15b (3)   10.25 1.05

Without Control Figures
S13a F2 5c turquoise green   1.40 3.75
   c.   Grilled gum   15.00 1.40
S14a F3 10c light violet   1.40 3.75
   c.   Grilled gum   15.00 1.40
S15a F4 20c scarlet   1.40 5.00
   c.   Grilled gum   15.00 1.50
     Nos. S13a-S15a (3)   4.20 12.50
     Nos. S13c-S15c (3)   45.00 4.30

SYRIA
ˈsir-ē-ə

LOCATION — Asia Minor, bordering on Turkey, Iraq, Lebanon, Israel and the Mediterranean Sea
GOVT. — Republic
AREA — 71,498 sq. mi.
POP. — 14,972,000 (1997 est.)
CAPITAL — Damascus

Syria was originally part of the Turkish province of Sourya conquered by British and Arab forces in late 1918 and later partitioned. The British assumed control of the Palestine and Transjordan regions; the French were permitted to occupy the sanjaks of Lebanon, Alaouites and Alexandretta; and the remaining territory, including the vilayets of Damascus and Aleppo, was established as an independent Arab kingdom, under which the first Syrian stamps were issued.

French forces from Beirut deposed King Faisal in July 1920, and two years of military occupation followed until Syria was mandated to France in July 1922. Syrian autonomy was substituted for the mandate in 1934, but full independence was not again achieved until 1946. In 1958, Syria and Egypt merged to form the United Arab Republic. Syria left this union in 1961, adopting the name Syrian Arab Republic. UAR issues for Syria are listed following Syria's 1919-20 Issues of the Arabian Government.

10 Milliemes = 1 Piaster
40 Paras = 1 Piaster (Arabian Govt.)
100 Centimes = 1 Piaster (1920)
100 Piasters = 1 Syrian Pound

Catalogue values for unused stamps in this country are for Never Hinged items, beginning with Scott 314 in the regular postage section, Scott B13 in the semipostal section, Scott C124 in the airpost section, Scott CB5 in the airpost semipostal section, Scott J40 in the postage due section, and all of the items in the UAR sections.

Watermarks

Wmk. 291 — National Emblem Multiple

Carrier Pigeon — Wmk. 403

Issued under French Occupation
Stamps of France, 1900-07, Surcharged

Perf. 14x13½
1919, Nov. 21   **Unwmk.**
1 A16 1m on 1c gray   200.00 200.00
2 A16 2m on 2c vio brn   550.00 550.00
3 A16 3m on 3c red org   240.00 240.00
4 A20 4m on 15c gray grn   47.50 47.50
5 A22 5m on 5c dp grn   25.00 22.50
6 A22 1p on 10c red   37.50 32.50
7 A22 2p on 25c blue   17.50 15.00
8 A18 5p on 40c red & pale bl 25.00 22.50
9 A18 9p on 50c bis brn & lav 55.00 50.00
10 A18 10p on 1fr cl & ol grn 87.50 80.00
     Nos. 1-10 (10)   1,285. 1,260.

The letters "T.E.O." are the initials of "Territoires Ennemis Occupés." There are two types of the numerals in the surcharges on Nos. 2, 3, 8 and 9.

Stamps of French Offices in Turkey, 1902-03, Surcharged

1919
11 A2 1m on 1c gray   1.10 .80
12 A2 2m on 2c violet brn   1.10 .80
13 A2 3m on 3c red orange   2.50 1.40
14 A3 4m on 15c pale red   1.10 .80
15 A2 5m on 5c green   1.10 .80

Overprinted

16 A5 1p on 25c blue   1.00 .75
17 A6 2p on 50c bis brn & lav 1.90 1.25
18 A6 4p on 1fr claret & ol grn 3.25 2.50
19 A6 8p on 2fr gray vio & yel 10.00 8.00
   a.   "T.E.O." double   75.00 75.00
20 A6 20p on 5fr dk bl & buff 300.00 210.00
     Nos. 11-20 (10)   323.05 227.10

On Nos. 17-20 "T.E.O." reads vertically up.
Nos. 1-20 were issued in Beirut and mainly used in Lebanon. Nos. 16-20 were also used in Cilicia.
Inverted surcharges exist on several values of this issue.

Stamps of France, 1900-07, Surcharged

1920
21 A16 1m on 1c gray   5.00 4.50
   a.   Inverted surcharge   45.00 45.00
   b.   Double surcharge

22	A16	2m on 2c vio brn	6.00	4.75
a.		Double surcharge	25.00	
23	A22	3m on 5c green	12.00	12.00
a.		Double surcharge	40.00	40.00
24	A18	20p on 5fr dk bl & buff	450.00	450.00
		Nos. 21-23 (3)	23.00	21.25

The letters "O.M.F." are the initials of "Occupation Militaire Francaise."

Stamps of France, 1900-07, Surcharged in Black or Red

1920

25	A16	1m on 1c gray	1.10	.95
26	A16	2m on 2c violet brn	1.25	1.00
27	A22	3m on 5c green	2.00	2.00
28	A22	5m on 10c red	2.25	2.25
a.		Inverted surcharge		
29	A18	20p on 5fr dk bl & buff	70.00	70.00
30	A18	20p on 5fr dk bl & buff (R)	275.00	250.00
		Nos. 25-30 (6)	351.60	326.20

Stamps of France, 1900-21, Surcharged in Black or Red:

1920-22

31	A16	25c on 1c gray	1.75	1.00
32	A16	50c on 2c vio brn	1.75	1.00
33	A16	75c on 3c red org	1.75	1.00
34	A22	1p on 5c green (R)	2.00	2.00
35	A22	1p on 5c green	1.00	1.00
36	A22	1p on 20c red brn ('21)	.50	.25
37	A22	1.25p on 25c bl ('22)	1.25	.95
38	A22	1.50p on 30c org ('22)	1.40	.80
39	A22	2p on 10c red	1.00	1.00
40	A22	2p on 25c bl (R)	1.00	1.00
41	A18	2p on 40c red & pale bl ('21)	1.40	.75
42	A20	2.50p on 50c dl bl ('22)	1.10	1.10
a.		Final "S" of "Piastres" omitted	10.00	10.00
43	A22	3p on 25c bl (R)	1.10	1.10
44	A18	3p on 60c vio & ultra ('21)	1.50	1.10
45	A20	5p on 15c gray grn	2.25	2.25
46	A18	5p on 1fr cl & ol grn ('21)	2.50	1.50
47	A18	10p on 40c red & pale bl	3.25	3.25
48	A18	10p on 2fr org & pale bl ('21)	5.00	3.00
49	A18	25p on 50c bis brn & lav	4.50	4.00
50	A18	25p on 5fr dk bl & buff ('21)	100.00	95.00
51	A18	50p on 1fr cl & ol grn	22.50	20.00
a.		"PIASRTES"	1,650.	1,650.
52	A18	100p on 5fr dk bl & buff (R)	45.00	45.00
53	A18	100p on 5fr dk bl & buff (Bk)	240.00	225.00
a.		"PIASRTES"	1,650.	1,650.
		Nos. 31-53 (23)	443.50	413.05

In first printing, space between "Syrie" and numeral is 2mm, second printing, 1mm.

Surcharge is found inverted on Nos. 32, 35-38, 42, 44-45. Value, each $2-$3.

Surcharge is found double on Nos. 31, 37, 40, 42. Value, each $2.

For overprints see Nos. C1-C9.

Surcharged in Black or Red

1920-23

54	A16	10c on 2c violet ('23)	1.10	.90
55	A22	10c on 5c org (R) ('23)	.80	.65
56	A16	25c on 1c dk gray	.90	.90
a.		50c on 1c dk gray (error)	4.50	4.50
57	A22	25c on 5c green ('21)	.90	.60
58	A22	25c on 5c orange ('22)	.80	.80
a.		"CENTIEMES" omitted	26.00	26.00
59	A16	50c on 2c vio brn	.90	.90
60	A22	50c on 10c red ('21)	1.00	.55
61	A22	50c on 10c green ('22)	1.25	1.25
62	A16	75c on 3c red orange	2.50	2.00
63	A20	75c on 15c sl grn ('21)	1.10	.90
		Nos. 54-63 (10)	11.25	9.45

Surcharge is found inverted on Nos. 54-55, 58-59, 62-63; double on Nos. 60, 62. Value $1.50-$2.

Preceding Issues Overprinted

1920

Black Overprint

64	A16	25c on 1c sl gray	11.00	10.00
65	A16	50c on 2c vio brn	12.00	11.00
66	A22	1p on 5c green	10.00	9.00
67	A22	2p on 25c blue	16.00	14.50
68	A20	5p on 15c gray grn	50.00	47.50
69	A18	10p on 40c red & pale bl	77.50	75.00
70	A18	25p on 50c bis brn & lav	200.00	190.00
71	A18	50p on 1fr cl & ol grn	650.00	625.00
72	A18	100p on 5fr dk bl & buff	2,000.	1,900.
		Nos. 64-72 (9)	3,026.	2,882.

Red Overprint

73	A16	25c on 1c sl gray	11.00	10.00
74	A16	50c on 2c vio brn	9.50	8.50
75	A22	1p on 5c green	9.50	8.50
76	A22	2p on 25c blue	7.50	6.50
77	A20	5p on 15c gray grn	50.00	47.50
78	A18	10p on 40c red & pale bl	77.50	75.00
79	A18	25p on 50c bis brn & lav	200.00	180.00
80	A18	50p on 1fr cl & ol grn	450.00	425.00
81	A18	100p on 5fr dk bl & buff	1,650.	1,650.
		Nos. 73-81 (9)	2,465.	2,411.

Nos. 64-81 were used only in the vilayet of Aleppo where Egyptian gold currency was still in use.

A1

Black or Red Surcharge

1921   **Perf. 11½**

82	A1	25c on ⅒p lt brn	1.00	.85
a.		"25 Centiemes" omitted		
83	A1	50c on ⅗p grn	1.00	.85
84	A1	1p on ⅗p yel	1.40	.85
a.		"⁹⁄₁₀" for "³⁄₁₀"	12.50	12.50
85	A1	1p on 5m rose	1.75	1.10
86	A1	2p on 5m rose	2.25	1.25
a.		Tête bêche pair	110.00	110.00
87	A1	3p on 1p gray bl	2.75	1.25
88	A1	5p on 2p bl grn	4.75	3.50
89	A1	10p on 5p vio brn	10.00	5.75
90	A1	25p on 10p gray (R)	12.00	8.00
		Nos. 82-90 (9)	36.90	23.40

Nos. 82-90 are surcharged on stamps of the Arabian Government Nos. 85, 87-93 and have the designs and sizes of those stamps.

Surcharge is found inverted on Nos. 84-88, 90; double on No. 86.

Kilis Issue

A2

Sewing Machine Perf. 9

1921   **Handstamped**

Pelure Paper

91	A2	(1p) violet	50.00	45.00

Issued at Kilis to meet a shortage of the regular issue, caused by the sudden influx of a large number of Armenian refugees from Turkey. The Kilis area was restored to Turkey in Oct. 1923.

Stamps of France, Surcharged

1921-22   **Perf. 14x13½**

92	A18	2p on 40c red & pale bl	1.00	.90
93	A18	2.50p on 50c bis brn & lav ('22)	1.10	1.00
a.		2p on 50c bister brown & lavender (error)	60.00	47.50
94	A18	3p on 60c vio & ultra	1.00	.90
95	A18	5p on 1fr cl & ol grn	6.50	6.00
96	A18	10p on 2fr org & pale bl	13.00	11.00
97	A18	25p on 5fr dk bl & buff	12.00	10.00
		Nos. 92-97 (6)	34.60	29.80

On No. 93 the surcharge reads: "2 PIASTRES 50."

Surcharge is found inverted on Nos. 92-95; double on No. 94. Value $2-$3.

For overprints see Nos. C10-C17.

French Mandate

French Stamps of 1900-23 Surcharged

1923

104	A16	10c on 2c vio brn	.40	.25
105	A22	25c on 5c orange	.75	.75
106	A22	50c on 10c green	.90	.85
a.		25c on 10c green (error)	170.00	
107	A20	75c on 15c sl grn	1.60	1.50
108	A22	1p on 20c red brn	.75	.70
109	A22	1.25p on 25c blue	1.40	1.25
110	A22	1.50p on 30c orange	1.10	.90
111	A22	1.50p on 30c red	1.10	.90
112	A20	2.50p on 50c dl bl	.70	.60

On Pasteur Stamps of 1923

113	A23	50c on 10c green	2.00	1.75
114	A23	1.50p on 30c red	1.75	1.50
115	A23	2.50p on 50c bl green	.90	.60

Surcharge is found inverted on #104-108, 110, 115; double on #104, 106. Value $1.50-$2.

Surcharged

116	A18	2p on 40c red & pale bl	.75	.70
a.		Inverted surcharge	14.00	
b.		Double surcharge	17.00	
c.		"Liabn"	450.00	450.00
117	A18	2p on 60c vio & ultra	1.50	1.25
a.		"Liabn"	450.00	450.00
118	A18	5p on 1fr cl & ol grn	2.00	1.50
a.		"Liabn"	450.00	450.00
119	A18	10p on 2fr org & pale bl	7.50	7.00
a.		"Liabn"	450.00	450.00
120	A18	25p on 5fr dk bl & buff	22.50	20.00
a.		Inverted surcharge		
		Nos. 104-120 (17)	48.70	43.15

Stamps of France, 1900-21, Surcharged

1924   **Perf. 14x13½**

121	A16	10c on 2c vio brn	.40	.25
a.		Double surcharge	—	
122	A22	25c on 5c orange	.70	.60
a.		"25" omitted	16.50	
123	A22	50c on 10c green	.70	.60
124	A20	75c on 15c sl grn	.70	.60
125	A22	1p on 20c red brn	.60	.50
a.		"1 PIASTRES"	15.00	
126	A22	1.25p on 25c blue	1.10	.90
127	A22	1.50p on 30c orange	1.10	.90
128	A22	1.50p on 30c red	1.00	.85
129	A20	2.50p on 50c dl bl	1.00	.85

Same on Pasteur Stamps of France, 1923

1924

130	A23	50c on 10c grn	.90	.70
131	A23	1.50p on 30c red	1.40	1.10
132	A23	2.50p on 50c blue	.75	.70
		Nos. 121-132 (12)	10.35	8.55

Olympic Games Issue

Stamps of France, 1924, Surcharged "SYRIE" and New Values

1924

133	A24	50c on 10c gray grn & yel grn	30.00	27.50
134	A25	1.25p on 25c rose & dk rose	30.00	27.50
135	A26	1.50p on 30c brn red & blk	30.00	27.50
136	A27	2.50p on 50c ultra & dk bl	30.00	27.50
		Nos. 133-136 (4)	120.00	110.00

See Nos. 166-169.

Stamps of France 1900-20 Surcharged

137	A18	2p on 40c red & pale bl	.90	.50
138	A18	3p on 60c vio & ultra	.70	.65
139	A18	5p on 1fr claret & ol grn	3.50	3.25
140	A18	10p on 2fr org & pale bl	3.50	3.00
141	A18	25p on 5fr dk bl & buff	5.25	4.50
		Nos. 137-141 (5)	13.85	11.90

For overprints see Nos. C18-C21.

Stamps of France 1900-21, Surcharged

or

1924-25

143	A16	10c on 2c vio brn	.40	.25
a.		Double surcharge	20.00	
b.		Inverted surcharge	22.50	
144	A22	25c on 5c orange	.40	.25
a.		Double surcharge	20.00	
b.		Inverted surcharge	22.50	
145	A22	50c on 10c green	.75	.50
a.		Double surcharge	20.00	
b.		Inverted surcharge	22.50	
146	A20	75c on 15c gray grn	.90	.70
a.		Double surcharge	20.00	
b.		Inverted surcharge	22.50	
147	A22	1p on 20c red brn	.60	.40
a.		Inverted surcharge	22.50	
148	A22	1.25p on 25c blue	.95	.75
a.		Inverted surcharge	22.50	
149	A22	1.50p on 30c red	.90	.70
150	A22	1.50p on 30c orange	26.00	25.00
151	A22	2p on 35c violet ('25)	1.00	.80
152	A18	2p on 40c red & pale bl	.75	.50
a.		Arabic "Piastre" in singular	1.75	1.75
153	A18	2p on 45c grn & bl ('25)	5.00	4.00

154	A18	3p on 60c vio & ul-tra	1.10	.75
155	A20	3p on 60c lt vio ('25)	1.25	.75
156	A20	4p on 85c ver	.45	.25
157	A18	5p on 1fr cl & ol grn	1.25	.75
158	A18	10p on 2fr org & pale bl	2.00	1.50
159	A18	25p on 5fr dk bl & buff	2.75	1.50
		Nos. 143-159 (17)	46.45	39.35

On No. 152a, the surcharge is as illustrated. The correct fourth line ("2 Piastres" -plural), as it appears on Nos. 151, 152 and 153, has four characters, the third resembling "9."
For overprints see Nos. C22-C25.

Same Surcharge on Pasteur Stamps of France

1924-25

160	A23	50c on 10c green	1.25	1.00
161	A23	75c on 15c grn ('25)	1.25	1.00
162	A23	1.50p on 30c red	1.25	1.00
163	A23	2p on 45c red ('25)	1.25	1.00
164	A23	2.50p on 50c blue	1.75	1.25
165	A23	4p on 75c blue	1.75	1.25
		Nos. 160-165 (6)	8.50	6.50

Olympic Games Issue
Stamps of France, 1924, Surcharged "Syrie" and New Values in French and Arabic

1924

Same Colors as #133-136

166	A24	50c on 10c	29.00	29.00
167	A25	1.25p on 25c	29.00	29.00
168	A26	1.50p on 30c	29.00	29.00
169	A27	2.50p on 50c	29.00	29.00
		Nos. 166-169 (4)	116.00	116.00

Ronsard Issue
Same Surcharge on France No. 219

1925

| 170 | A28 | 4p on 75c bl, bluish | 1.00 | .75 |

Mosque at Hama A3 — Mosque at Damascus A5

View of Merkab A4

Designs: 50c, View of Alexandretta. 75c, View of Hama. 1p, Omayyad Mosque, Damascus. 1.25p, Latakia Harbor. 1.50p, View of Damascus. 2p, View of Palmyra. 2.50p, View of Kalat Yamoun. 3p, Bridge of Daphne. 5p, View of Aleppo. 10p, View of Aleppo. 25p, Columns at Palmyra.

Perf. 12½, 13½

| 1925 | | Litho. | Unwmk. | |
| 173 | A3 | 10c dark violet | .35 | .20 |

Photo.

174	A4	25c olive black	1.00	.55
175	A4	50c yellow green	.50	.25
176	A4	75c brown orange	.60	.20
177	A5	1p magenta	.60	.20
178	A4	1.25p deep green	2.25	1.10
179	A4	1.50p rose red	.75	.20
180	A4	2p dark brown	2.00	.20
181	A4	2.50p peacock blue	1.50	.50
182	A4	3p orange brn	1.50	.20
183	A4	5p violet	1.25	.20
184	A4	10p violet brown	3.50	.30
185	A4	25p ultra	3.50	.20
		Nos. 173-185 (13)	21.55	8.60

For surcharges see Nos. 186-206, B1-B12, C26-C45, CB1-CB4.

Surcharged in Black or Red

1926-30

186	A4	1p on 3pi org brn ('30)	2.00	.50
187	A4	2p on 1p25 dp grn (R) ('28)	1.25	.35
a.		Double surcharge	16.00	16.00
188	A4	3.50p on 75c org brn	1.00	.35
a.		Double surcharge	16.00	16.00
189	A4	4p on 25c ol blk	1.50	.35
190	A4	4p on 25c ol blk ('27)	1.40	.45
191	A4	4p on 25c ol blk (R) ('28)	1.25	.35
192	A4	4.50p on 75c brn org	1.40	.35
193	A4	6p on 2p50 pck bl	1.00	.35
194	A4	7.50p on 2p50 pck bl	1.10	.35
195	A4	7.50p on 2p50 pck bl (R) ('28)	3.50	.90
a.		Double surcharge	29.00	
196	A4	12p on 1p25 dp grn	1.50	.40
a.		Surcharge on face and back	50.00	42.50
197	A4	15p on 25p ultra	2.75	.90
198	A4	20p on 1p25 dp grn	2.25	.70
		Nos. 186-198 (13)	21.90	6.35

Size of numerals and arrangement of this surcharge varies on the different denominations.
No. 189 has slanting foot on "4."
No. 190, foot straight.

No. 173 Surcharged in Red

1928

| 199 | A3 | 05c on 10c dk vio | 1.00 | .20 |

Stamps of 1925 Issue Overprinted in Red or Blue

1929 | | | **Perf. 13½** |
200	A4	50c yellow grn (R)	3.50	2.75
201	A5	1p magenta (Bl)	3.50	2.75
202	A4	1.50p rose red (Bl)	3.50	2.75
203	A4	3p orange brn (Bl)	3.50	2.75
204	A4	5p violet (R)	3.50	2.75
205	A4	10p violet brn (Bl)	3.50	2.75
206	A4	25p ultra (R)	3.50	2.75
		Nos. 200-206 (7)	24.50	19.25

Industrial Exhibition, Damascus, Sept. 1929.

View of Hama — A6

View of Alexandretta — A9

Citadel at Aleppo A10

Great Mosque of Damascus A11

Ruins of Bosra A13

Mosque at Homs A15

View of Sednaya A16

Citadel at Aleppo A17

Ancient Bridge at Antioch A18

Mosque at Damascus A22

Designs: 20c, Great Mosque, Aleppo. 25c, Minaret, Hama. 2p, View of Antioch. 4p, Square at Damascus. 15p, Mosque at Hama. 25p, Monastery of St. Simeon the Stylite (ruins). 50p, Sun Temple (ruins), Palmyra.

Perf. 12x12½

1930-36		Litho.	Unwmk.	
208	A6	10c red violet	.50	.20
209	A6	10c vio brn ('33)	.50	.35
209A	A6	10c vio brn, redrawn ('35)	.50	.20
210	A6	20c dark blue	.50	.20
211	A6	20c brn org ('33)	.50	.20
212	A6	25c gray green	.50	.20
213	A6	25c dk bl gray ('33)	.80	.45

Photo.
Perf. 13

214	A9	50c violet	.50	.20
215	A15	75c org red ('32)	.50	.20
216	A10	1p green	.75	.20
217	A10	1p bis brn ('36)	1.75	.40
218	A11	1.50p bister brown	7.50	3.00
219	A11	1.50p dp grn ('33)	1.00	.50
220	A9	2p dark violet	.75	.25
221	A13	3p yellow green	2.00	.70
222	A10	4p yellow orange	.75	.25
223	A15	4.50p rose carmine	1.75	.55
224	A16	6p grnsh black	2.25	.50
225	A17	7.50p dull blue	2.25	.70
226	A18	10p dark brown	2.00	.50
227	A10	15p deep green	3.50	1.00
228	A18	25p violet brown	3.25	1.10
229	A15	50p olive brown	11.50	4.50
230	A22	100p red orange	22.50	9.75
		Nos. 208-230 (24)	68.30	26.10

On No. 209A Arabic inscriptions, upper right, are entirely redrawn with lighter lines. Hyphen added in "Helio-Vaugirard" imprint. Lines in buildings and background more distinct.
On No. 215 the letters of "VAUGIRARD" in the imprint are reversed as in a mirror.
For overprints and surcharges see Nos. 253-268, 346, M1-M2.

Autonomous Republic

Parliament Building A23

abu-al-Ala al-Maarri — A24 — President Ali Bek el Abed — A25

Saladin — A26

1934, Aug. 2	Engr.		Perf. 12½	
232	A23	10c olive green	1.25	1.50
233	A23	20c black	1.25	1.50
234	A23	25c red orange	1.40	1.50
235	A23	50c ultra	1.50	1.50
236	A23	75c plum	1.50	1.50
237	A24	1p vermilion	3.75	3.00
238	A24	1.50p green	4.50	3.50
239	A24	2p red brown	4.50	3.50
240	A24	3p Prus blue	4.50	3.50
241	A24	4p brt violet	4.75	3.50
242	A24	4.50p carmine	5.00	3.75
243	A24	5p dark blue	5.00	3.75
244	A24	6p dark brown	5.00	3.75
245	A24	7.50p dark ultra	5.25	3.75
246	A25	10p dark brown	7.25	6.00
247	A25	15p dull blue	10.00	8.50
248	A25	25p rose red	15.00	13.00
249	A26	50p dark brown	25.00	20.00
250	A26	100p lake	37.50	32.50
		Nos. 232-250 (19)	143.90	119.50

Proclamation of the Republic. See Nos. C57-C66. For surcharge see No. M3.

Stamps of 1930-36 Overprinted in Red or Black

1936, Apr. 15

253	A9	50c violet (R)	2.75	1.50
254	A10	1p bister brn (Bk)	2.75	1.50
255	A9	2p dk violet (R)	2.75	1.50
256	A13	3p yellow grn (Bk)	3.25	1.50
257	A10	4p yellow org (Bk)	3.25	1.50
258	A15	4.50p rose car (Bk)	3.25	1.50
259	A16	6p grnsh blk (R)	4.00	2.00
260	A17	7.50p dull blue (R)	4.75	2.75
261	A18	10p dk brown (Bk)	5.75	3.75
		Nos. 253-261 (9)	32.50	17.50

Industrial Exhibition, Damascus, May 1936. See Nos. C67-C71.

Stamps of 1930 Surcharged in Black

1937-38 | | | **Perf. 13½x13** |
| 262 | A10 | 2.50p on 4p yel org ('38) | .55 | .40 |
| 263 | A22 | 10p on 100p red orange | 1.00 | .90 |

Stamps of 1930-33 Surcharged in Red or Black

1938   **Perf. 13½**
264 A15 25c on 75c org red (Bk)   .50   .20
265 A11 50c on 1.50p dp grn (R)   .60   .30
266 A17 2p on 7.50p dl bl (R)   1.00   .60
267 A17 5p on 7.50p dl bl (R)   1.75   .90
268 A15 10p on 50p ol brn (Bk)   2.25   .95
     Nos. 264-268 (5)   6.10   2.95

President Hashem Bek el Atassi — A27

1938-43   **Photo.**   **Unwmk.**
268A A27 10p dp blue ('43)   1.25   .85
269 A27 12.50p on 10p dp bl (R)   1.50   .90
270 A27 20p dark brown   1.25   .85
     Nos. 268A-270 (3)   4.00   2.60

The 10pi and 20pi exist imperf.

Columns at Palmyra A28

1940   **Litho.**   **Perf. 11½**
271 A28 5p pale rose   2.00   .65

Exists imperf.

Museum at Damascus — A29

Hotel at Bloudan A30

Kasr-el-Heir A31

1940   **Typo.**   **Perf. 13x14**
272 A29 10c bright rose   .50   .20
273 A29 20c light blue   .50   .20
274 A29 25c fawn   .55   .20
275 A29 50c ultra   .55   .20
     Engr.
     Perf. 13
276 A30 1p peacock blue   .70   .20
277 A30 1.50p chocolate   1.25   .70
278 A30 2.50p dark green   .70   .30
279 A31 5p violet   .75   .40
280 A31 7.50p vermilion   1.75   .40
281 A31 50p sepia   3.00   1.25
     Nos. 272-281 (10)   10.25   4.05

For overprints see Nos. 298-299.

President Taj Eddin Hassani A32

1942, Apr. 6   **Litho.**   **Perf. 11½**
282 A32 50c sage green   4.00   2.50
283 A32 1.50p dull gray brn   4.25   2.50
284 A32 6p fawn   4.50   2.50
285 A32 15p light blue   4.75   2.50
     Nos. 282-285,C96-C97 (6)   25.75   18.25

Proclamation of independence by the Allies, Sept. 27, 1941.

President Taj Eddin Hassani — A33   President Hassani and Map of Syria — A34

1942   **Photo.**   **Unwmk.**
286 A33 6p rose lake & salmon rose   3.50   1.25
287 A33 15p dull blue & blue   3.50   1.25
     Nos. 286-287,C98 (3)   11.00   6.50

Nos. 286-287 exist imperf.

1943   **Litho.**
288 A34 1p light green   3.50   1.50
289 A34 4p buff   3.50   1.50
290 A34 8p pale violet   3.50   1.50
291 A34 10p salmon   3.50   1.50
292 A34 20p dull chalky blue   3.50   1.50
     Nos. 288-292,C99-C102 (9)   29.50   19.50

Proclamation of a United Syria. Exist imperf.

Stamps of 1943 Overprinted with Border in Black

1943
293 A34 1p light green   3.50   1.50
294 A34 4p buff   3.50   1.50
295 A34 8p pale violet   3.50   1.50
296 A34 10p salmon   3.50   1.50
297 A34 20p dl chalky bl   3.50   1.50
     Nos. 293-297,C103-C106 (9)   29.50   19.50

Mourning for President Hassani. Exist imperf.

Nos. 278 and 280 Overprinted in Carmine or Black

1944   **Unwmk.**   **Perf. 13**
298 A30 2.50p dk green (C)   3.75   2.50
299 A31 7.50p vermilion (Bk)   4.00   2.75
     Nos. 298-299,C114-C116 (5)   36.25   33.75

1000th anniv. of the Arab poet and philosopher, abu-al-Ala al-Maarri.

President Shukri el Kouatly — A35

1945, Mar. 15   **Litho.**   **Perf. 11½**
300 A35 4p pale lilac   .75   .35
301 A35 6p dull blue   .95   .40
302 A35 10p salmon   .95   .40
303 A35 15p dark brown   1.50   .50
304 A35 20p slate green   1.50   .50
305 A35 40p orange   2.50   1.00
     Nos. 300-305,C117-C123 (13)   24.25   10.25

Resumption of constitutional government.

A36   A37

A38   A39

Fiscal Stamps Overprinted or Surcharged in Black

1945   **Typo.**   **Perf. 11, 11½x11**
306 A36 12½p on 15p yel grn   3.75   1.25
307 A37 25p buff   7.50   1.75
307A A38 25p on 25s lt vio brn   4.50   1.40
308 A39 50p on 75p brn org   8.50   2.50
309 A39 75p brown org   11.00   3.25
310 A37 100p yellow grn   17.50   4.00
     Nos. 306-310 (6)   52.75   14.15

Type of 1945 and Nos. 308 and 310 Overprinted in Black

a   b

1945   **Unwmk.**   **Perf. 11**
311 A37(b) 50p magenta   5.50   1.50
312 A39(a) 50p on 75p brn org   4.00   .90
313 A37(b) 100p yellow green   7.00   1.50
     Nos. 311-313 (3)   16.50   3.90

> **Catalogue values for unused stamps in this section, from this point to the end of the section, are for Never Hinged items.**

Independent Republic

A40

Fiscal Stamp Overprinted in Carmine

1946
314 A40 200p light blue   27.50   10.00

Sun and Ears of Wheat — A41   President Shukri el Kouatly — A42

1946   **Litho.**   **Perf. 13x13½**
315 A41 50c brown orange   .50   .20
316 A41 1p violet   .95   .20
317 A41 2.50p blue gray   1.10   .30

---

318 A41 5p lt blue green   1.75   .20
     Photo.
     Perf. 13½x13, 13x13½
319 A42 7.50p dark brown   .50   .20
320 A42 10p Prussian green   .75   .20
321 A42 12.50p deep violet   2.00   .20
     Nos. 315-321 (7)   7.55   1.50

For overprints see Nos. 328-329, 335-336.

Arab Horse A44

1946-47   **Litho.**
325 A44 50p olive brown   5.25   .90
326 A44 100p dk blue grn ('47)   11.00   2.00
327 A44 200p rose violet ('47)   60.00   5.50
     Nos. 325-327 (3)   76.25   8.40

For overprints and surcharges see Nos. 330, 337, 356-357.

Nos. 320, 321 and 325 Overprinted in Black or Green

1946, Apr. 17
328 A42 10p Prus green   1.00   .45
329 A42 12.50p deep violet   1.50   .65
330 A44 50p olive brown (G)   3.50   1.60
     Nos. 328-330,C135 (4)   8.50   3.70

Evacuation of British and French troops from Syria. For surcharge see No. 347.

President Shukri el Kouatly — A45

1946   **Unwmk.**   **Litho.**   **Perf. 13½x13**
331 A45 15p red   .90   .20
332 A45 20p violet   1.25   .25
333 A45 25p ultra   2.00   .30
     Nos. 331-333 (3)   4.15   .75

No. 333 Overprinted in Magenta

1946, Aug. 28
334 A45 25p ultra   2.75   1.10
     Nos. 334,C136-C138 (4)   14.25   7.10

8th Arab Medical Cong., Aleppo, 8/28-9/4.

Nos. 328 to 330 With Additional
Overprint in Black

e

f

Perf. 13½x13, 13x13½
1947, June 10
335 A42(e) 10p Prus green 1.25 .20
336 A42(e) 12.50p deep violet 1.40 .25
337 A44(f) 50p olive brown 4.00 .75
Nos. 335-337,C139 (4) 9.15 2.45

Evacuation of British and French troops, 1st
anniv.

Hercules and the
Lion — A46

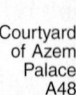

Mosaics
from
Omayyad
Mosque,
Damascus
A47

1947, Nov. 15 Litho. Perf. 11½
338 A46 12.50p slate green 2.00 .40
339 A47 25p gray blue 3.25 .85
Nos. 338-339,C140-C141 (4) 11.75 3.75

1st Arab Archaeological Cong., Damascus,
Nov.
See No. C141a.

Courtyard
of Azem
Palace
A48

Telephone
Building
A49

1947, Nov. 15
340 A48 12.50p deep claret 2.00 .50
341 A49 25p brt blue 2.75 .70
Nos. 340-341,C142-C143 (4) 10.25 3.95

3rd Congress of Arab Engineers, Damascus, Nov.
See No. C143a.

House of
Parliament
A50

Pres. Shukri el
Kouatly — A51

1948, June 23 Unwmk. Perf. 10½
342 A50 12.50p black & org .75 .20
343 A51 25p deep rose 1.60 .45
Nos. 342-343,C144-C145 (4) 5.50 1.90

Reelection of Pres. Shukri el Kouatly. See
No. C145a.

National
Emblem — A52

Syrian Flag and
Soldier — A53

1948, June 23 Litho.
344 A52 12.50p gray & choc 1.25 .25
345 A53 25p multicolored 1.75 .45
Nos. 344-345,C146-C147 (4) 5.75 1.75

Inauguration of compulsory military training.
See No. C147a.

Nos. 215 and 327 Surcharged with
New Value and Bars in Black
1948 Perf. 13, 13x13½
346 A15 50c on 75c org red .40 .20
347 A44 25p on 200p rose vio 2.50 .30

Col. Husni
Zayim — A54

Palmyra — A56

Ain el
Arous
A55

1949, June 20 Litho. Perf. 11½
348 A54 25p blue 1.75 .40

Revolution of Mar. 30, 1949. See No. C153.
A souvenir sheet comprises Nos. 348 and
C153, imperf. Value $80.

1949, June 20
349 A55 12.50p violet 3.50 1.50
350 A56 25p blue 6.00 2.75
Nos. 349-350,C154-C155 (4) 36.00 22.75

UPU, 75th anniv. See note after #C155.

Pres. Husni
Zayim and
Map — A57

Wmk. 291
1949, Aug. 6 Litho. Perf. 11½
351 A57 25p blue & brown 6.00 1.25

Election of President Husni Zayim. See
Nos. C156, C156a.

Tel-Chehab
Waterfall — A58

Damascus
Scene
A59

1949
352 A58 5p gray .60 .20
353 A58 7.50p olive gray .85 .20
354 A59 12.50p violet brown 1.00 .20
355 A59 25p blue 1.75 .40
Nos. 352-355 (4) 4.20 1.00

See No. 376.

Nos. 327 and 326 Surcharged with
New Value and Bars in Black
1950 Unwmk. Perf. 13x13½
356 A44 2.50p on 200p rose vio .40 .20
357 A44 10p on 100p dk bl grn .50 .20

National
Emblem — A60

Road to
Damascus
A61

Postal Administration Building,
Damascus — A62

1950-51 Litho. Perf. 11½
358 A60 50c orange brn .30 .20
359 A60 2.50p pink .40 .20
360 A61 10p purple ('51) .50 .20
361 A61 12.50p sage grn ('51) .75 .40
362 A62 25p blue ('51) 1.75 .20
363 A62 50p black ('51) 5.25 .60
Nos. 358-363 (6) 8.95 1.80

Nos. 358 to 363 exist imperforate.

Parliament
Building,
Damascus
A63

1951, Apr. 14
364 A63 12.50p gray blk .40 .20
365 A63 25p blue .75 .35
Nos. 364-365,C162-C163 (4) 2.80 1.75

New constitution adopted Sept. 5, 1950.
Nos. 364-365 exist imperforate.

Palace of
Justice,
Damascus
A65

Perf. 11½
1952, Apr. 22 Litho. Unwmk.
366 A64 50c dark brown .30 .20
367 A64 2.50p dark blue .35 .20
368 A64 5p blue green .40 .20
369 A64 10p red .45 .20
370 A65 12.50p gray black .75 .20
371 A65 15p lilac rose 4.00 .25
372 A65 25p deep blue 2.00 .35
373 A65 100p olive brown 7.50 2.00
Nos. 366-373 (8) 15.75 3.60

Nos. 366-373 exist imperforate.

Type of 1949 and

Crusaders'
Fort — A66

Crusaders'
Fort — A67

1953 Photo.
374 A67 50c rose red .40 .20
375 A66 2.50p dark brown .40 .20
376 A58 7.50p green .50 .20
377 A67 12.50p deep blue 1.75 .20
Nos. 374-377 (4) 3.05 .80

Farm Workers — A68

Family
Group
A69

Designs: 1pi, 5pi, Farm workers. 10pi,
12½p, Family group. 20pi, 25pi, 50pi, Factory
and construction workers.

1954 Perf. 11½
378 A68 1p olive .25 .20
379 A68 2½p brown red .30 .20
380 A68 5p deep blue .40 .20
381 A69 7½p brown red .50 .20
382 A69 10p black .60 .20
383 A69 12½p violet .70 .20
384 A69 20p deep plum .85 .20
385 A69 25p violet 1.25 .35
386 A69 50p dark green 3.00 .75
Nos. 378-386 (9) 7.85 2.50

For overprints see #387-388, UAR 20, 34.

Nos. 382 and 385 Overprinted in
Carmine

1954, Oct. 9
387 A69 10p black 1.25 .35
388 A69 25p violet 1.50 .45
Nos. 387-388,C185-C186 (4) 5.85 3.40

Cotton Festival, Aleppo, October 1954.

Water
Wheel,
Hama
A64

Globe — A69a

Mother and Child — A70

Arab Postal Union Issue

1955   **Photo.**   **Perf. 13½x13**
389 A69a 12½p green .50 .20
390 A69a 25p violet .95 .35
    Nos. 389-390,C191 (3) 1.85 .80

Founding of the APU, 7/1/54. Exist imperf. For overprints see #396-399, C203, C207.

1955, May 13   **Litho.**   **Perf. 11½**
391 A70 25p red .80 .25
    Nos. 391,C194-C195 (3) 3.30 1.80

Mother's Day.

United Nations Emblem A71

1955   **Photo.**
392 A71 7½p crimson .50 .25
393 A71 12½p Prus green 1.00 .50
    Nos. 392-393,C200-C201 (4) 3.75 1.75

UN, 10th anniv., Oct. 24. For overprints see Nos. 401-402.

Aqueduct at Aleppo A72

1955   **Litho.**   **Unwmk.**
394 A72 7.50p lilac .55 .25
395 A72 12.50p carmine 1.00 .35
    Nos. 394-395,C202 (3) 3.55 1.70

New aqueduct bringing water from the Euphrates to Northern Syria. Exist imperf.

Nos. 389-390 Overprinted in Ultramarine or Green

1955   **Photo.**   **Perf. 13½x13**
396 A69a 12½p green .40 .20
397 A69a 25p vio (G) 1.25 .40
    Nos. 396-397,C203 (3) 2.15 .80

APU Congress held at Cairo, Mar. 15.

Nos. 389-390 Overprinted in Black

1956
398 A69a 12½p green .50 .25
399 A69a 25p violet 1.25 .55
    Nos. 398-399,C207 (3) 2.25 1.00

Visit of King Hussein of Jordan to Damascus, Apr. 1956.

Cotton — A73

1956   **Unwmk.**   **Litho.**   **Perf. 11½**
400 A73 2½p bluish green .50 .25

Issued to publicize a Cotton Festival.

Nos. 392-393 Overprinted in Black

1956   **Photo.**   **Perf. 11½**
401 A71 7½p crimson .50 .20
402 A71 12½p Prussian green .75 .35
    Nos. 401-402,C221-C222 (4) 4.00 2.40

UN, 11th anniv.

People's Army A74

1957   **Litho.**   **Perf. 11½**
403 A74 5p lilac rose .30 .20
404 A74 20p gray green .50 .25

Formation of the Popular Resistance Movement.
For overprints see Nos. 405-406, 413-414.

Nos. 403-404 Overprinted in Black or Red

1957
405 A74 5p lilac rose .30 .20
406 A74 20p gray green (R) .65 .30

Evacuation of Port Said by British and French troops, Dec. 22, 1956.

Azem Palace, Damascus A75

1957   **Litho.**   **Perf. 11½**
407 A75 12½p lilac .30 .20
408 A75 15p gray .50 .20

For overprint see UAR No. 33.

Map of Near East, Scales and Damascus Skyline — A76

Cotton, Bale and Ship — A77

1957   **Wmk. 291**   **Perf. 11½**
409 A76 12½p bright green .40 .20
    Nos. 409,C240-C241 (3) 1.70 1.00

3rd Congress of the Union of Arab Lawyers, Damascus, Sept. 21-25.

1957
410 A77 12½p lt bl grn & blk .50 .20
    Nos. 410,C242-C243 (3) 2.50 1.10

Cotton Festival, Aleppo, Oct. 3-5.

Children — A78

1957, Oct. 7
411 A78 12½p olive 1.00 .20
    Nos. 411,C244-C245 (3) 3.75 1.20

Intl. Children's Day, Oct. 7.
For overprint see UAR Nos. 13A, C10-C11.

Mailing and Receiving Letter A79

1957   **Unwmk.**
412 A79 5p magenta .50 .20

Intl. Letter Writing Week, Oct. 6-12. See No. C246.

Nos. 403-404 Overprinted in Black or Red

1957   **Perf. 11½**
413 A74 5p lilac rose .40 .20
414 A74 20p gray green (R) .50 .20

Digging of fortifications along the Syrian-Israeli frontier.

Scales, Torch and Map A80

1957, Nov. 8   **Wmk. 291**
415 A80 20p olive gray .55 .20
    Nos. 415,C247-C248 (3) 1.80 1.05

Congress of Afro-Asian Jurists, Damascus.

Glider A81

1957, Nov. 8   **Litho.**   **Perf. 11½**
416 A81 25p red brown 1.10 .30
417 A81 35p green 1.50 .40
418 A81 40p ultra 3.00 .70
    Nos. 416-418 (3) 5.60 1.40

Issued to commemorate a glider festival.

Khaled ibn el Walid Mosque, Homs — A82

1957   **Unwmk.**   **Perf. 12**
419 A82 2½p dull brown .40 .20

Scroll, Communications Building and Telephone — A83

1958   **Wmk. 291**   **Perf. 11½**
420 A83 25p ultra .30 .20
    Nos. 420,C249-C250 (3) 1.05 .65

Issues of 1958-61 released by the United Arab Republic are listed following the listings of Syria, Issues of the Arabian Government.

Syrian Arab Republic

Hall of Parliament, Damascus A83a

1961   **Unwmk.**   **Litho.**   **Perf. 12**
420A A83a 15p magenta .40 .25
420B A83a 35p olive gray .75 .25

Establishment of Syrian Arab Republic.

Water Wheel, Hama — A84

Roman Arch of Triumph, Latakia — A85

Qalb Lozah Church, Aleppo A86

7½p, 10p, Khaled ibn el Walid Mosque, Homs.

Perf. 11½x11
1961-62   **Unwmk.**   **Litho.**
421 A84 2½p rose red .30 .20
422 A84 5p blue .30 .20
423 A84 7½p blue grn ('62) .30 .20
424 A84 10p orange ('62) .35 .20
     Perf. 12x11½
425 A85 12½p gray brn .60 .20
426 A86 17½p olive gray ('62) .50 .20
427 A85 25p dull red brown .70 .20
428 A86 35p dull green ('62) .70 .20
    Nos. 421-428 (8) 3.70 1.60

Types of 1961, Regular and Air Post

Designs: 2½p, 5p, 7½p, 10p, Arch, Jupiter Temple. 12½p, 15p, 17½p, 22½p, "The Beauty of Palmyra."

1962   **Perf. 11½x11**
429 A84 2½p gray blue .30 .20
430 A84 5p brown orange .30 .20
431 A84 7½p olive bister .30 .20
432 A84 10p claret .30 .20
     Perf. 12x11½
     Size: 26x38mm
433 AP68 12½p gray olive .35 .20
434 AP68 15p ultra .50 .20
435 AP68 17½p brown .50 .20
436 AP68 22½p grnsh blue .70 .20
    Nos. 429-436 (8) 3.25 1.60

Martyrs' Memorial — A87

Pres. Nazem el-Kodsi — A88

1962, June 11   Litho.
440 A87 12½p tan & sepia   .30 .20
441 A87 35p green & bl grn   .35 .20

1925 Revolution.

1962, Dec. 14   Perf. 12x11½
442 A88 12½p sepia & lt bl   .30 .20

1st anniv. of the election of Pres. Nazem el-Kodsi. See No. C278.

Queen Zenobia — A89

Central Bank of Syria A90

Designs: 2½p, 5p, "The Beauty of Palmyra." 17½p, Hejaz Railway Station, Damascus. 22½p, Mouassat Hospital, Damascus. 35p, P.T.T. Jalaa Avenue Office, Damascus.

1963   Unwmk.   Perf. 11½x11
443 A89 2½p dk bl gray   .30 .20
444 A89 5p rose lilac   .30 .20
445 A89 7½p dull blue   .35 .20
446 A89 10p olive gray   .70 .20
447 A89 12½p ultra   1.00 .20
448 A89 15p violet brn   1.50 .20

     Perf. 11½x12
449 A90 17½p dull violet   .60 .20
450 A90 22½p brt violet   .30 .20
451 A90 25p bister brown   .30 .20
452 A90 35p bright pink   .35 .20
   Nos. 443-452 (10)   5.70 2.00

Wheat Emblem and Globe — A91

Boy Playing Ball and UN Emblem — A92

1963, Mar. 21   Litho.   Perf. 12x11½
453 A91 12½p ultra & blk   .30 .20

FAO "Freedom from Hunger" Campaign. See No. C291 and souvenir sheet No. C291a.

Cotton Festival Type of Air Post Issue, 1962, Inscribed "1963"

1963, Sept. 26   Perf. 12x11½
455 AP75 17½p multi   .30 .20
456 AP75 22½p multi   .35 .20

The 1963 Cotton Festival, Aleppo.

1963, Oct. 24   Perf. 12x11½
457 A92 12½p emer & sl grn   .30 .20
458 A92 22½p rose red & dk grn   .30 .20

Issued for International Children's Day.

Ugharit Princess — A93

1964   Litho.   Perf. 11½x11
459 A93 2½p gray   .30 .20
460 A93 5p brown   .30 .20
461 A93 7½p rose claret   .30 .20
462 A93 10p emerald   .30 .20
463 A93 12½p light violet   .30 .20
464 A93 17½p ultra   .30 .20
465 A93 20p rose carmine   .45 .20
466 A93 25p orange   .75 .20
   Nos. 459-466 (8)   3.00 1.60

Map of North Africa and Middle East, Flag of Syria, and Crowd A94

1965, Mar. 8   Litho.   Perf. 11½x12
467 A94 12½p multicolored   .30 .20
468 A94 17½p multicolored   .30 .20
469 A94 20p multicolored   .30 .20
   Nos. 467-469 (3)   .90 .60

Mar. 8 Revolution, 2nd anniv.

Weather Map and Anemometer — A95

1965, Mar. 23   Litho.   Unwmk.
470 A95 12½p dl lilac & blk   .30 .20
471 A95 27½p lt blue & blk   .30 .20

Fifth World Meteorological Day.

"Evacuation of Apr. 17, 1946" — A96

Peasants' Union Emblem — A97

1965, Apr. 17   Litho.   Perf. 12x11½
472 A96 12½p bl & brt yel grn   .30 .20
473 A96 27½p rose red & lt lil   .30 .20

19th anniv. of the evacuation of British and French troops from Syria.

1965, Aug.   Unwmk.   Perf. 11½x11
474 A97 2½p blue green   .30 .20
475 A97 12½p purple   .30 .20
476 A97 15p maroon   .30 .20
   Nos. 474-476 (3)   .90 .60

Issued to publicize the Peasants' Union.

Torch, Map of Arab Countries and Farmer, Soldier, Woman, Intellectual and Worker — A98

Workers, Factory and Emblem — A99

1965, Nov. 23   Perf. 12x11½
477 A98 12½p multicolored   .30 .20
478 A98 25p multicolored   .30 .20

National Council of the Revolution, a legislative body working for a socialist and democratic society.

1966, Jan.   Litho.   Perf. 11½x11
479 A99 12½p blue   .30 .20
480 A99 15p carmine   .30 .20
481 A99 20p dull violet   .30 .20
482 A99 25p olive gray   .30 .20
   Nos. 479-482 (4)   1.20 .80

Establishment of the General Union of Trade Unions.

Roman Lamp A100

Islamic Vessel, 12th Century A101

1966   Litho.   Perf. 11½x11
483 A100 2½p slate green   .30 .20
484 A100 5p magenta   .30 .20
485 A101 7½p brown   .30 .20
486 A101 10p brt rose lilac   .30 .20
   Nos. 483-486 (4)   1.20 .80

"Evacuation of Troops" — A102

Bust of Core, Terra Cotta Vase — A103

1966, Apr. 17   Litho.   Perf. 12x11½
487 A102 12½p multi   .30 .20
488 A102 27½p multi   .30 .20

20th anniv. of the evacuation of British and French troops from Syria.

1967   Perf. 11½x11

Design: 15p, 20p, 25p, 27½p, Bronze vase in form of seated African woman.

489 A103 2½p brt green   .30 .20
490 A103 5p salmon pink   .30 .20
491 A103 10p grnsh blue   .30 .20
492 A103 12½p dull brown   .30 .20
493 A103 15p brt pink   .30 .20
494 A103 20p brt blue   .30 .20
495 A103 25p green   .30 .20
496 A103 27½p violet blue   .30 .20
   Nos. 489-496 (8)   2.40 1.60

Arab Revolution Monument, Damascus A104

1968, Mar. 8   Litho.   Perf. 12x12½
497 A104 12½p black, yel & brn   .30 .20
498 A104 25p blk, pink & car rose   .30 .20
499 A104 27½p blk, lt grn & grn   .30 .20
   Nos. 497-499 (3)   .90 .60

Mar. 8 Revolution, 5th anniversary.

Map of Syria — A105

Hands Holding Wrench, Gun and Torch — A106

1968, Apr. 4   Litho.   Perf. 12x12½
500 A105 12½p pink & multi   .30 .20
501 A105 60p gray & multi   .40 .20

Arab Baath Socialist Party, 21st anniv.

1968, Apr. 13
502 A106 12½p tan & multi   .30 .20
503 A106 17½p rose & multi   .30 .20
504 A106 25p yellow & multi   .30 .20
   Nos. 502-504 (3)   .90 .60

Issued to publicize the mobilization effort.

Rising Sun, Power Lines and Railroad Tracks A107

1968, Apr. 17   Litho.   Perf. 12½x12
505 A107 12½p multicolored   .30 .20
506 A107 27½p violet & multi   .30 .20

22nd anniv. of the evacuation of British and French troops from Syria.

Oil Wells and Oil Pipe Line on Map — A108

1968, May 1
507 A108 12½p lt & dk grn & ultra .30 .20
508 A108 17½p pink, brn & ultra .30 .20

Syrian oil exploitation; completion of the oil pipe line to Tartus.

Map of Palestine and Torch — A109

Citadel of Aleppo, Wheat and Cogwheel A110

1968, May   Litho.   Perf. 12x12½
509 A109 12½p ultra, blk & red .50 .35
510 A109 25p ol bis, blk & red .65 .35
511 A109 27½p gray, blk & red .80 .50
    Nos. 509-511 (3) 1.95 1.20

Issued for Palestine Day.

1968, July 18   Litho.   Perf. 12x12½
512 A110 12½p multi .30 .20
513 A110 27½p multi .30 .20

Industrial and Agricultural Fair, Aleppo.

Fair Emblem, Globe, Grain, Wheel and Horse — A111

Woman Carrying Cotton, and Castle of Aleppo — A112

Design: 27½p, Syrian flag, hand with torch, fair emblem, globe, grain and wheel.

Perf. 12x12½, 12½x12
1968, Aug. 25   Litho.
514 A111 12½p dp brn, blk & emer .30 .20
515 A111 27½p multicolored .30 .20
516 A111 60p bl gray, blk & dp org .30 .20
    Nos. 514-516 (3) .90 .60

15th Intl. Damascus Fair, Aug. 25-Sept. 20.

1968, Oct. 3   Litho.   Perf. 12x12½
517 A112 12½p multi .30 .20
518 A112 27½p multi .30 .20

13th Cotton Festival, Aleppo.

Al Jahez — A113

Oil Derrick and Pipe Line — A114

1968, Nov. 9   Litho.   Perf. 12x12½
519 A113 12½p black & buff .30 .20
520 A113 27½p black & gray .60 .20

9th Science Week; Al Jahez Abu Uthman Amr ben Bahr (776-868).

1968   Perf. 12x11
521 A114 2½p grnsh bl & dk grn .30 .20
522 A114 5p grn & vio bl .30 .20
523 A114 7½p lt yel grn & bl .30 .20
524 A114 10p brt yel & grn .30 .20
525 A114 12½p yellow & ver .30 .20
526 A114 15p ol bis & dk brn .30 .20
527 A114 27½p dl org & dk red brn .30 .20
    Nos. 521-527 (7) 2.10 1.40

Broken Chains and Sun A115

1969, Mar. 8   Litho.   Perf. 12½x12
Sun in Yellow and Red
528 A115 12½p vio bl & blk .30 .20
529 A115 25p gray & blk .30 .20
530 A115 27½p dull grn & blk .30 .20
    Nos. 528-530 (3) .90 .60

March 8 Revolution, 6th anniversary.

"Sun of Freedom, Young Man and Woman" — A116

Liberation through Knowledge and Construction A117

1969, Mar. 29   Perf. 12x12½
531 A116 12½p multi .30 .20
532 A116 25p multi .30 .20

Youth Week; 5th Youth Festival, Homs, 4/18-24.

1969, Apr. 17   Litho.   Perf. 12x12½
533 A117 12½p yellow & multi .30 .20
534 A117 27½p gray & multi .30 .20

23rd anniv. of the evacuation of British and French troops from Syria.

Mahatma Gandhi — A118

Cotton — A119

1969, Oct. 7   Litho.   Perf. 12x12½
535 A118 12½p brown & dull yel .30 .20
536 A118 27½p green & yellow .30 .20

Mohandas K. Gandhi (1869-1948), leader in India's fight for independence.

1969, Oct. 10
537 A119 12½p multi .30 .20
538 A119 17½p multi .30 .20
539 A119 25p multi .30 .20
    Nos. 537-539 (3) .90 .60

14th Cotton Festival, Aleppo.

Map of Arab Countries A120

Designs: 25p, Arab Academy. 27½p, Damascus University.

1969, Nov. 2   Litho.   Perf. 12½x12
540 A120 12½p ultra & lt grn .30 .20
541 A120 25p dk pur & dp pink .30 .20
542 A120 27½p dp bis & yel grn .30 .20
    Nos. 540-542 (3) .90 .60

10th Science Week, and 6th Arab Scientific Conf. No. 541 also for 50th anniv. of the Arab Academy and No. 542, the 50th anniv. of the Medical School of the Damascus University.

Symbols of Progress A121

1970, Mar. 8   Litho.   Perf. 12½x12
543 A121 12½p brt bl, blk & bis brn .30 .20
544 A121 25p red, blk & dp bl .30 .20
545 A121 27½p lt grn, blk & tan .30 .20
    Nos. 543-545 (3) .90 .60

March 8 Revolution, 7th anniversary.

Map of Arab League Countries, Flag and Emblem A122

1970, Mar. 22
546 A122 12½p multi .30 .20
547 A122 25p gray & multi .30 .20
548 A122 27½p multi .35 .20
    Nos. 546-548 (3) .95 .60

25th anniversary of the Arab League.

Sultan Saladin and Battle of Hattin, 1187, between Saracens and Crusaders — A123

1970, Apr. 17   Litho.   Perf. 12½x12
549 A123 15p brn & buff .30 .20
550 A123 35p lilac & buff .35 .20

24th anniv. of the evacuation of British and French troops from Syria.

Development of Agriculture and Industry — A124

1970-71   Litho.   Perf. 11x11½
551 A124 2½p brn & red ('71) .30 .20
552 A124 5p orange & bl .30 .20
553 A124 7½p lil & gray ('71) .30 .20
554 A124 10p lt & dk brn .30 .20
555 A124 12½p blue & org ('71) .30 .20
556 A124 15p grn & red lil .30 .20
557 A124 20p vio & red brn .30 .20
558 A124 22½p red brn & blk ('71) .30 .20
559 A124 25p gray & vio bl ('71) .30 .20
560 A124 27½p brt grn & dk brn ('71) .30 .20
561 A124 35p rose red & emer ('71) .35 .20
    Nos. 551-561 (11) 3.35 2.20

Young Man and Woman, Map of Arab Countries A125

1970, May 7   Unwmk.   Perf. 12½x12
569 A125 15p green & ocher .30 .20
570 A125 25p brown & ocher .30 .20

First Youth Week, Latakia, Apr. 23-29. Inscribed "Youth's First Weak" (sic.).

Refugee Family A126

1970, May 15
571 A126 15p multicolored .30 .20
572 A126 25p gray & multi .30 .20
573 A126 35p green & multi .30 .20
    Nos. 571-573 (3) .90 .60

Issued for Arab Refugee Week.

Cotton — A127

1970, Aug. 18   Litho.   Perf. 12½
574 A127 5p shown .30 .20
575 A127 10p Tomatoes .30 .20
576 A127 15p Tobacco .30 .20
577 A127 20p Beets .30 .20
578 A127 35p Wheat .75 .25
a.   Strip of 5, #574-578 2.00 2.00

Industrial and Agricultural Fair, Aleppo.

Boy Scout, Tent, Emblem and Map of Arab Countries A128

1970, Aug. 25
579 A128 15p gray green   .40 .20
   9th Pan-Arab Boy Scout Jamboree, Damascus.

Olive Tree and Emblem A129

1970, Sept. 28 Litho. Perf. 11½x12
580 A129 15p gray grn, yel & blk   .30 .20
581 A129 25p red brn, yel & blk   .50 .20
   Issued to publicize World Olive Year.

Protection of Industry, Agriculture, Arts and Commerce — A130

1971, Mar. 8 Litho. Perf. 12½x12
582 A130 15p olive, yel & bl   .30 .20
583 A130 22½p red brn, yel & ol   .30 .20
584 A130 27½p bl, yel & red brn   .30 .20
   Nos. 582-584 (3)   .90 .60
   March 8 Revolution, 8th anniversary.

Workers Memorial, Hands with Wrench and Olive Branch A131

1971, May 1 Litho. Perf. 12½x12
585 A131 15p brn vio, yel & bl   .30 .20
586 A131 25p dk bl, bl & yel   .30 .20
   Labor Day.

Child and Traffic Lights A132

   World Traffic Day: 25p, Road signs, traffic lights, children, vert.

1971, May 4 Perf. 11½x12, 12x11½
587 A132 15p black, red & bl   .30 .20
588 A132 25p gray & multi   .30 .20
589 A132 45p black, red & yel   .30 .20
   Nos. 587-589 (3)   .90 .60

Factories, Cogwheel and Cotton A133

1971, July 15 Litho. Perf. 12½x12
590 A133 15p lt grn, bl & blk   .30 .20
591 A133 30p red & black   .30 .20
   11th Industrial and Agricultural Fair, Aleppo.

Arab Postal Union Emblem — A134

Flag, Map of Syria, Egypt and Libya — A135

1971, Sep. 1 Perf. 12x12½
592 A134 15p claret & multi   .30 .20
593 A134 20p vio bl & multi   .30 .20
   25th anniv. of the Conference of Sofar, Lebanon, establishing the APU.

1971, Aug. 13 Perf. 12x11½
594 A135 15p car, dl grn & blk   .30 .20
   Confederation of the Arab states of Syria, Libya and Egypt.

Red Pepper and Chemical Factory (Fertilizer Industry) — A136

   18th Intl. Damascus Fair: 15p, Electronics industry (TV, telephone, computer). 35p, Glass industry (old map and glass manufacture). 50p, Carpet industry (carpet and looms).

1971, Aug. 25 Perf. 12½
595 A136 5p violet & multi   .30 .20
596 A136 15p dull grn & multi   .30 .20
597 A136 35p multicolored   .30 .20
598 A136 50p yel grn & multi   .50 .20
   Nos. 595-598 (4)   1.40 .80

Pres. Hafez al Assad and Crowd — A137

UNESCO Emblem, Radar, Spacecraft, Telephone A138

1971, Nov. Litho. Perf. 12x12½
599 A137 15p vio bl, blk & car   .30 .20
600 A137 20p dk & lt grn, car & blk   .30 .20
   1st anniv. of Correctionist Movement of Nov. 16, 1970.

1971, Dec. 8
601 A138 15p vio bl & multi   .30 .20
602 A138 50p green & multi   .30 .20
   25th anniv. of UNESCO.

UNICEF Emblem and Playing Children — A139

1971, Dec. 21
603 A139 15p ultra, dk bl & dp car   .30 .20
604 A139 25p grnsh bl, ocher & dk bl   .30 .20
   UNICEF, 25th anniv.

Conference Emblem — A140

1971, Dec. Perf. 12½x12
605 A140 15p blk, grnsh bl & org   .30 .20
   Scholars' Conference.

Book Year Emblem A141

1972, Jan. 2
606 A141 15p tan, lt bl & vio   .30 .20
607 A141 20p brn, lt grn & grn   .30 .20
   International Book Year.

Wheel, "8" and Scales of Justice — A142

Baath Party Emblem — A143

1972, Mar. 8 Litho. Perf. 12x12½
608 A142 15p blue grn & vio   .30 .20
609 A142 20p olive bis & car   .30 .20
   March 8 Revolution, 9th anniversary.

1972, Mar. 7
610 A143 15p dk blue & multi   .30 .20
611 A143 20p violet & multi   .30 .20
   Arab Baath Socialist Party, 25th anniv.

Eagle, Chimneys, Grain and Oil Rigs — A144

1972, Apr. 17 Perf. 12½x12
612 A144 15p gold, blk & car   .30 .20
   Federation of Arab Republics, 1st anniv.

Symbolic Flower, Broken Chain — A145

Hand Holding Wrench and Spade — A146

1972, Apr. 17 Perf. 12x11½
613 A145 15p rose red & gray   .30 .20
614 A145 50p pale bl grn & gray   .30 .20
   26th anniv. of the evacuation of British and French troops from Syria.

1972, May 1
615 A146 15p ol grn, bl & blk   .30 .20
616 A146 50p vio bl, brn & blk   .30 .20
   Labor Day.

Environment Emblem, Crystals, Microscope A147

Dove over Factory — A148

1972, June 5
617 A147 15p multicolored   .30 .20
618 A147 50p blue & multi   .35 .20
   UN Conference on Human Environment, Stockholm, June 5-16.

1972, July 17 Litho. Perf. 12x11½
619 A148 15p yellow & multi   .30 .20
620 A148 20p yellow & multi   .30 .20
   Agricultural and Industrial Fair, Aleppo.

Folk Dance — A149

1972, Aug. 25   Litho.   Perf. 12x12½
621 A149 15p shown   .30   .20
622 A149 20p Women and tam-
              bourine player   .30   .20
623 A149 50p Men and drummer   .50   .20
      Nos. 621-623 (3)   1.10   .60

19th International Damascus Fair.

Olympic Rings, Discus, Soccer,
Swimming — A150

Warriors on Horseback, Olympic
Emblems — A151

Design: 60p, Olympic rings, running, gymnastics, fencing.

1972   Litho.   Perf. 12½x12
624 A150 15p ol bis, blk & vio   .50   .20
625 A150 60p dull bl, blk & org   .60   .20

Souvenir Sheet
Imperf
626 A151 75p lt grn, bl & blk   2.00   2.00

20th Olympic Games, Munich, Aug. 26-
Sept. 11, 1972.

Emblem
of
Revolution
and
Prancing
Horse
A152

1973, Mar. 8   Litho.   Perf. 11½x12
627 A152 15p brt grn, blk & red   .30   .20
628 A152 20p dull org, blk & red   .30   .20
629 A152 25p blue, blk & red   .30   .20
      Nos. 627-629 (3)   .90   .60

March 8 Revolution, 10th anniversary.

Heart and
WHO
Emblem
A153

1973, Mar. 21
630 A153 15p gray & multi   .30   .20
631 A153 50p lt brown & multi   .35   .20

WHO, 25th anniversary.

Cogwheel and
Grain
Emblem — A154

1973, Apr. 17   Perf. 12x12½
632 A154 15p blue & multi   .30   .20
633 A154 20p multicolored   .30   .20

27th anniv. of the evacuation of British and
French troops from Syria.

Workers
and Globe
A155

1973, May 1   Perf. 11½x12
634 A155 15p rose & multi   .30   .20
635 A155 50p blue & multi   .35   .20

Labor Day.

UN, FAO
Emblems, People
and
Symbols — A156

Stock — A157

1973, May 7   Perf. 12x11½
636 A156 15p lt grn & red brn   .30   .20
637 A156 50p lilac & blue   .35   .20

World food program, 10th anniv.

1973, May 15
638 A157 5p shown   .30   .20
639 A157 10p Gardenia   .30   .20
640 A157 15p Jasmine   .30   .20
641 A157 20p Rose   .30   .20
642 A157 25p Narcissus   .30   .20
  a. Strip of 5, #638-642   1.50   1.50

Intl. Flower Show, Damascus.

Children and
Flame — A158

Children's Day: 3 children's heads and
flame in different arrangements; 25p, 35p,
70p, vertical.

Perf. 11½x12, 12x11½
1973-74   Litho.
643 A158 2½p lt olive grn   .30   .20
644 A158 5p orange   .30   .20
645 A158 7½p dk brown   .30   .20
646 A158 10p crimson   .30   .20
647 A158 15p ultra   .30   .20
648 A158 25p gray   .30   .20
649 A158 35p brt blue   .30   .20
650 A158 55p green   .30   .20
651 A158 70p rose lilac   .35   .20
      Nos. 643-651 (9)   2.75   1.80

Issued: 15p, 55p, 70p, 5/73; others, 3/74.

Fair
Emblem
A159

1973, June 17   Perf. 11½x12
652 A159 15p multicolored   .30   .20

13th Agricultural and Industrial Fair, Aleppo.

Euphrates Dam and Power
Plant — A160

1973, July 5   Perf. 12½x12
653 A160 15p green & multi   .30   .20
654 A160 50p brown & multi   .30   .20

Euphrates River diversion and dam project.

Woman from Deir
Ezzor — A161

Map of Palestine,
Barbed Wire,
Human Rights
Emblem — A162

Women's Costumes from: 10p, Hassaké.
20p, As Sahel. 25p, Zakié. 50p, Sarakeb.

1973, July 25   Litho.   Perf. 12
655 A161 5p multicolored   .30   .20
656 A161 10p multicolored   .30   .20
657 A161 20p multicolored   .30   .20
658 A161 25p multicolored   .30   .20
659 A161 50p multicolored   .30   .20
  a. Strip of 5, #655-659   1.50   1.50

20th International Damascus Fair.

1973, Aug. 20   Perf. 12x11½
660 A162 15p lt green & multi   .40   .40
661 A162 50p lt blue & multi   .95   .40

25th anniversary of the Universal Declaration of Human Rights.

Citadel of
Ja'abar
A163

15p, Minaret of Meskeneh, vert. 25p, Statue
of Psyche at Anab al Safinah, vert.

Perf. 11½x12, 12x11½
1973, Sept. 5   Litho.
662 A163 10p black, org & blue   .30   .20
663 A163 15p black, org & blue   .30   .20
664 A163 25p black, org & blue   .30   .20
      Nos. 662-664 (3)   .90   .60

Salvage of monuments threatened by
Euphrates Dam.

WMO
Emblem
A164

1973, Sept. 12   Perf. 11½x12
665 A164 70p yellow & multi   .50   .20

Intl. meteorological cooperation, cent.

Maalula
A165

Design: 50p, Ruins of Afamia.

1973, Oct. 22   Litho.   Perf. 11½x12
666 A165 15p gray blue & blk   .30   .20
667 A165 50p brown & blk   .30   .20

Arab Emigrants' Congress, Buenos Aires.

Workers
and
Soldiers
A166

1973, Nov. 16   Litho.   Perf. 12½x12
668 A166 15p ultra & yellow   .30   .20
669 A166 25p purple & red brn   .30   .20

3rd anniv. of Correctionist Movement of
Nov. 16, 1970.

Nicolaus
Copernicus
A167

UPU
Emblem — A169

Arms of
Syria and
Emblems
A168

Design: 25p, Abu-al-Rayhan al-Biruni.

1973, Dec. 15   Perf. 12x11½
670 A167 15p gold & black   .30   .20
671 A167 25p gold & black   .30   .20

14th Science Week.

1974, Mar. 8   Perf. 11x12
672 A168 20p gray & blue   .30   .20
673 A168 25p lt green & vio   .30   .20

11th anniversary of March 8th Revolution.

1974, Mar. 15 *Perf. 12x11½, 11½x12*

20p, Air mail letter and UPU emblem, horiz.

674	A169	15p gray & multi	.30	.20
675	A169	20p multicolored	.30	.20
676	A169	70p gray & multi	.50	.20
		Nos. 674-676 (3)	1.10	.60

Centenary of Universal Postal Union.

Arab Postal Institute A170

1974, Apr. 10 *Perf. 11½x12*

677	A170	15p multicolored	.30	.20

Inauguration of the Higher Arab Postal Institute, Damascus, Apr. 10.

Sun and Monument A171

1974, Apr. 10

678	A171	15p emerald, blk & org	.30	.20
679	A171	20p dp org, blk & org	.30	.20

28th anniversary of the evacuation of British and French troops from Syria.

Machine Shop Worker A172 — Abulfeda A173

1974, May 1 *Perf. 12x12½*

680	A172	15p black, yel & bl	.30	.20
681	A172	50p black, buff & bl	.30	.20

Labor Day.

1974 *Litho.* *Perf. 11½x11*

Design: 200p, al-Farabi.

682	A173	100p pale green	.50	.20
683	A173	200p lt brown	1.00	.45

Damascus Fair Emblem — A174

Figs — A175

Design: 25p, Cog wheel and sun.

1974, July 25 *Perf. 11½x11*

684	A174	15p multicolored	.30	.20
685	A174	25p blue, blk & yel	.30	.20

21st International Damascus Fair.

1974, Aug. 21 *Perf. 12x12½*

Fruits: 15p, Grapes. 20p, Pomegranates. 25p, Cherries. 35p, Rose hips.

686	A175	5p gray & multi	.30	.20
687	A175	15p gray & multi	.30	.20
688	A175	20p gray & multi	.30	.20
689	A175	25p gray & multi	.30	.20
690	A175	35p gray & multi	.30	.20
a.		Strip of 5, #686-690	2.50	2.50

Agricultural and Industrial Fair, Aleppo.

Burning Fuse and Flowers — A176

Rook and Knight — A177

20p, Bomb and star-shaped holes in target.

1974, Oct. 6 *Litho.* *Perf. 12x12½*

691	A176	15p multicolored	.75	.20
692	A176	20p multicolored	1.00	.20

First anniv. of October Liberation War (Yom Kippur War).

1974, Nov. 23

Design: 50p, Knight and chess board.

693	A177	15p blue & black	.75	.20
694	A177	50p orange, blk & bl	2.25	.80

Chess Federation, 50th anniversary.

WPY Emblem — A178 — Ishtup, Ilum — A179

1974, Dec. 4 *Litho.* *Perf. 12x12½*

695	A178	50p black, slate & red	.30	.20

World Population Year.

1975 *Perf. 12x11½*

Ancient Statuettes: 55p, Woman holding pitcher. 70p, Ur-Nina.

696	A179	20p brt green	.30	.20
697	A179	55p brown	.30	.20
698	A179	70p gray blue	.50	.20
		Nos. 696-698 (3)	1.10	.60

"A," People and Sun — A180

Postal Savings Bank Emblem, Family — A181

1975, Mar. 8 *Litho.* *Perf. 12x11½*

699	A180	15p gray & multi	.30	.20

12th anniversary, March 8th Revolution.

1975, Mar. 17

Design: 20p, Family depositing money, and stamped envelope.

700	A181	15p brt green & multi	.30	.20
701	A181	20p orange & black	.30	.20

Publicity for Savings Certificates and Postal Savings Bank.

"Sun" and Dove — A182

1975, Apr. 17 *Litho.* *Perf. 12x11½*

702	A182	15p bister, red & blk	.30	.20
703	A182	25p bister, grn & blk	.30	.20

29th anniversary of the evacuation of British and French troops from Syria.

"Worker and Industry" — A183

Camomile A184

1975, May 1 *Litho.* *Perf. 12x11½*

704	A183	15p blue grn & blk	.30	.20
705	A183	25p brown, yel & blk	.30	.20

Labor Day.

1975, May 17

Flowers: 10p, Chincherinchi. 15p, Carnation. 20p, Poppy. 25p, Honeysuckle.

706	A184	5p ultra & multi	.30	.20
707	A184	10p lilac & multi	.30	.20
708	A184	15p blue & multi	.35	.20
709	A184	20p gray grn & multi	.40	.20
710	A184	25p vio bl & multi	.75	.25
a.		Strip of 5, #706-710	2.10	2.10

International Flower Show, Damascus.

Kuneitra Destroyed and Rebuilt — A185

1975, June 5 *Perf. 12½*

711	A185	50p black & multi	.35	.20

Re-occupation of Kuneitra by Syria.

Apples A186

1975, July 7

712	A186	5p shown	.30	.20
713	A186	10p Quince	.30	.20
714	A186	15p Apricots	.35	.20
715	A186	20p Grapes	.40	.20
716	A186	25p Figs	.50	.20
a.		Strip of 5, #712-716	1.90	1.90

Agricultural and Industrial Fair, Aleppo.

22nd Intl. Damascus Fair — A187

Farm Woman — A189

Pres. Hafez al Assad A188

1975, July 25 *Litho.* *Perf. 12x11½*

717	A187	15p olive grn & multi	.30	.20
718	A187	35p brown & multi	.30	.20

1975, Nov. 29 *Litho.* *Perf. 11½x12*

719	A188	15p green & multi	.30	.20
720	A188	50p blue & multi	.30	.20

5th anniv. of Correctionist Movement of Nov. 16, 1970.

1975, Nov. 29 *Perf. 12x11½*

IWY Emblem and: 15p, Mother. 25p, Student. 50p, Laboratory technician.

721	A189	10p buff & multi	.30	.20
722	A189	15p rose & black	.30	.20
723	A189	25p dull green & blk	.35	.20
724	A189	50p orange & blk	.50	.20
		Nos. 721-724 (4)	1.45	.80

International Women's Year.

Horse-shaped Bronze Lamp A190

Man's Head Inkstand A191

Designs: 10p, 25p, like 20p. 35p, like 30p. 50p, 60p, Nike. 75p, Hera. 100p, Imdugug-Mari (winged animal). 500p, Palmyrene coin of Vasalathus. 1000p, Abraxas coin.

1976   *Perf. 11½x12, 12x11½*
725	A190	10p brt bluish grn	.30	.20
726	A190	20p lilac rose	.30	.20
727	A190	25p violet blue	.30	.20
728	A191	30p brown	.30	.20
729	A191	35p olive	.30	.20
730	A191	50p brt blue	.30	.20
731	A191	60p violet	.30	.20
732	A191	75p orange	.35	.20
733	A191	100p lilac rose	.50	.20
734	A191	500p grnsh gray	2.00	1.75
735	A191	1000p dk green	4.00	2.25
		Nos. 725-735 (11)	8.95	5.80

See Nos. 798-803.

National Theater, Damascus and Pres. al Assad A192

1976, Mar. 8   Litho.   *Perf. 11½x12*
736	A192	25p brt grn, sil & blk	.30	.20
737	A192	35p olive, sil & blk	.30	.20

13th anniversary of March 8 Revolution.

Syria, Arabian Government #85 — A193

1976, Apr. 12   *Perf. 12x12½*
738	A193	25p brt green & multi	.30	.20
739	A193	35p blue & multi	.30	.20

Post's Day.

Nurse and Emblem — A194

Eagle and Stars — A195

1976, Apr. 8   *Perf. 12x11½*
740	A194	25p blue, blk & red	.30	.20
741	A194	100p violet, blk & red	.50	.30

Arab Red Cross and Red Crescent Societies, 8th Conference, Damascus.

1976, Apr. 17
742	A195	25p blk, red & brt grn	.30	.20
743	A195	35p blk, red & brt grn	.30	.20

30th anniversary of the evacuation of British and French troops from Syria.

Hand Holding Wrench — A196

Cotton and Factory — A197

May Day: 60p, Hand holding globe.

1976, May 1
744	A196	25p blue & black	.30	.20
745	A196	60p citron & multi	.40	.20

1976, July 1
746	A197	25p vio & multi	.30	.20
747	A197	35p bl & multi	.30	.20

Agricultural and Industrial Fair, Aleppo.

Tulips — A198

1976, July 26
748	A198	5p shown	.30	.20
749	A198	15p Yellow daisies	.30	.20
750	A198	20p Turk's-cap lilies	.30	.20
751	A198	25p Irises	.50	.20
752	A198	35p Freesia	.75	.20
a.		Strip of 5, #748-752	2.25	2.25

Intl. Flower Show, Damascus.

People, Globe and Olive Branch A199

60p, Symbolic arrow piercing darkness.

1976, Sept. 2   *Perf. 11½x12*
753	A199	40p yel & multi	.30	.20
754	A199	60p multi	.35	.20

5th Summit Conference of Non-aligned Countries, Colombo, Sri Lanka, Aug. 9-19.

Soccer, Pan Arab Games Emblem A200

1976, Oct. 6   Litho.   *Perf. 12½*
755	A200	5p shown	.30	.20
756	A200	10p Swimming	.30	.20
757	A200	25p Running	.30	.20

758	A200	35p Basketball	.30	.20
759	A200	50p Javelin	.30	.20
a.		Strip of 5, #755-759	1.50	1.50

Souvenir Sheet
Imperf
760	A200	100p Steeplechase	2.00	2.00

5th Pan Arab Sports Tournament. Size of stamp of No. 760: 55x35mm.

"Development" A201

The Fox and the Crow — A202

1976, Nov. 16   *Perf. 12½x12½*
761	A201	35p multi	.30	.20

Correctionist Movement pof Nov. 16, 1970.

1976, Dec. 7   *Perf. 12x12½, 12½x12*

Fairy Tales: 15p, The Hare and the Tortoise, horiz. 20p, Little Red Riding Hood. 25p, The Lamb and the Wolf, horiz. 35p, The Lamb and the Wolf.

762	A202	10p multi	.30	.20
763	A202	15p multi	.30	.20
764	A202	20p multi	.30	.20
765	A202	25p multi	.30	.20
766	A202	35p multi	.30	.20
		Nos. 762-766 (5)	1.50	1.00

Children's literature.

Syrian Airlines Boeing 747 — A203

1977, Feb.   Litho.   *Perf. 12½x12*
767	A203	35p multi	.30	.20

Civil Aviation Day.

Muhammad Kurd-Ali (1876-1953), Philosopher, Birth Cent. — A204

1977, Feb.   *Perf. 12x12½*
768	A204	25p lt grn & multi	.30	.20

Woman Holding Syrian Flag — A205

APU Emblem — A207

Warrior on Horseback — A206

1977, Mar. 8   Litho.   *Perf. 12x12½*
769	A205	35p multi	.30	.20

14th anniversary of March 8 Revolution.

1977, Apr. 10   Litho.   *Perf. 12½*
770	A206	100p multi	.30	.20

31st anniversary of the evacuation of British and French troops from Syria.

1977, Apr. 12   Litho.   *Perf. 12x12½*
771	A207	35p silver & multi	.30	.20

Arab Postal Union, 25th anniversary.

Tools and Factories A208

1977, May 1   *Perf. 12½x12*
772	A208	60p multi	.35	.20

Labor Day.

ICAO Emblem, Plane and Globe A209

1977, May 11
773	A209	100p multi	.50	.25

Intl. Civil Aviation Org., 30th anniv.

Pioneers A210

Citrus Fruit A211

1977, Aug. 15   Litho.   *Perf. 12½x12½*
774	A210	35p multi	.30	.20

Al Baath Pioneer Organization.

1977, Aug. 1
775	A211	10p Lemon	.30	.20
776	A211	20p Lime	.30	.20
777	A211	25p Grapefruit	.30	.20
778	A211	35p Oranges	.30	.20
779	A211	60p Tangerines	.40	.20
a.		Strip of 5, #775-779	1.60	1.60

Agricultural and Industrial Fair, Aleppo.

Flowers
A212

1977, Aug. 6　Litho.　Perf. 12½x12
780	A212	10p Mallow	.30	.20
781	A212	20p Coxcomb	.30	.20
782	A212	25p Morning glories	.30	.20
783	A212	35p Almond blossoms	.30	.20
784	A212	60p Lilacs	.30	.20
a.		Strip of 5, #780-784	1.50	1.50

Intl. Flower Show, Damascus.

Coffeepot and
Ornament
A213

1977, Sept. 10　　Perf. 12x12½
785	A213	25p blk, bl & red	.30	.20
786	A213	60p blk, grn & brn	.35	.20

24th Intl. Damascus Fair.

Blind Man, Globe
and Eye — A214

Globe and
Measures
A215

1977, Nov. 17　Litho.　Perf. 12x12½
787	A214	55p multi	.30	.20
788	A214	70p multi	.30	.20

World Blind Week.

1977, Nov. 5
789	A215	15p grn & multi	.30	.20

World Standards Day, Oct. 14.

Microscope, Book, Harp, UNESCO
Emblem — A216

1977, Nov. 5　　Perf. 12½x12
790	A216	25p multi	.30	.20

30th anniversary of UNESCO.

Archbishop
Capucci, Map of
Palestine,
Bars — A217

Fight Cancer
Shield, Crab and
Surgeon — A218

1977, Nov. 17　　Perf. 12x12½
791	A217	60p multi	1.00	.50

Palestinian Archbishop Hilarion Capucci,
jailed by Israel in 1974.

1977, Nov. 17
792	A218	100p multi	1.00	.50

Fight Cancer Week.

Dome of the Rock, Jerusalem — A219

1977, Dec. 6　　Perf. 12
793	A219	5p multi	.50	.20
794	A219	10p multi	.75	.20

Palestinian fighters and their families.

Mural — A220

Pres. Hafez al
Assad — A221

Designs: 10p, 15p, Murals from Dura-Euro-
pos, in National Museum, Damascus.

1978, Jan. 22　Litho.　Perf. 12x11½
795	A220	5p gray grn	.30	.20
796	A220	10p vio bl	.30	.20
797	A220	15p brown, horiz.	.30	.20
		Nos. 795-797 (3)	.90	.60

Types of 1976

Designs: 40p, Man's head inkstand. 55p,
Nike. 70p, 80p, Hera. 200p, Arab-Islamic
astrolabe. 300p, Palmyrene (Herod) coin.

1978　Litho.　Perf. 12x11½, 11½x12
798	A191	40p pale org	.30	.20
799	A191	55p brt rose	.30	.20
800	A191	70p vermilion	.35	.20
801	A191	80p green	.35	.20
802	A191	200p lt ultra	1.00	.30
803	A190	300p rose lil	1.50	.50
		Nos. 798-803 (6)	3.80	1.60

1978　　Perf. 12x11½
805	A221	50p multi	.40	.20

Anniversary of "Correction Movement."

Blood Circulation,
WHO
Emblem — A222

Factory — A223

1978, Apr. 7　Litho.　Perf. 12x11½
806	A222	100p multi	.50	.20

World Health Day, fight against hypertension.

1978, Apr. 17
807	A223	35p multi	.30	.20

32nd anniversary of the evacuation of British and French troops from Syria.

Rosette — A224

Map of Arab
Countries, Police,
Flag and
Eye — A225

1978, Apr. 21
808	A224	25p blk & grn	.30	.20

14th Arab Engineering Conference, Damascus, Apr. 21-26.

1978, May
809	A225	35p multi	.30	.20

6th Conf. of Arab Police Commanders.

European
Goldfinch
A226

Birds: 20p, Peregrine falcon. 25p, Rock
dove. 35p, Eurasian hoopoe. 60p, Old World
quail.

1978　　Perf. 11½x12
810	A226	10p multi	.40	.20
811	A226	20p multi	.40	.20
812	A226	25p multi	.40	.20
813	A226	35p multi	.50	.20
814	A226	60p multi	.60	.20
a.		Strip of 5, #810-814	2.40	2.40

Trout
A227

Designs: Various fish.

1978, July　Litho.　Perf. 11½x12
815	A227	10p multi	.40	.20
816	A227	20p multi	.40	.20
817	A227	25p multi	.40	.20
818	A227	35p multi	.50	.20
819	A227	60p multi	.55	.25
a.		Strip of 5, #815-819	2.25	2.25

Pres. Assad Type of Air Post, 1978
Miniature Sheet

1978, Sept.　Litho.　Imperf.
820	AP161	100p gold & multi	1.00	1.00

Reelection of President Assad. Size of
stamp: 58x80mm.

Flowering
Cactus
A228

Fair
Emblem — A229

Designs: Flowering cacti.

1978　　Litho.　　Perf. 12½
821	A228	25p multi	.50	.20
822	A228	30p multi	.50	.20
823	A228	35p multi	.50	.20
824	A228	50p multi	.50	.20
825	A228	60p multi	.50	.20
a.		Strip of 5, #821-825	2.50	2.50

International Flower Show, Damascus.

1978　　Litho.　　Perf. 12x12½
826	A229	25p sil & multi	.30	.20
827	A229	35p sil & multi	.30	.20

Miniature Sheet
Imperf
828	A229	100p sil & multi	1.00	1.00

25th Intl. Damascus Fair. No. 828 shows
different ornament, size of stamp: 40x46mm.

Euphrates Dam and Pres.
Assad — A230

1978, Dec.　Litho.　Perf. 12½x12
829	A230	60p multi	.50	.20

Inauguration of Euphrates Dam.

Pres. Hafez al Assad — A231

1978, Nov. 16   Litho.   Perf. 12x12½
830 A231 60p multi   .40 .20
Nov. 16 Movement.

Racial Equality Emblem A232

1978, Mar.   Litho.   Perf. 12½
831 A232 35p multi   .40 .20
International Year to Combat Racism.

Averroes — A233

Human Rights Flame and Globe — A234

1979, Mar.
832 A233 100p multi   .75 .25
Averroes (1126-1198), Spanish-Arabian philosopher and physician.

1978, Dec.   Perf. 12x12½
833 A234 60p multi   .50 .20
30th anniversary of Universal Declaration of Human Rights (in 1978).

Symbolic Design — A235

Princess, 2nd Century Shield — A236

1979, Mar.
834 A235 100p multi   .50 .20
16th anniversary of March 8 Revolution.

1979   Litho.   Perf. 11½
Designs: 20p, Helmet of Homs. 35p, Ishtar.
836 A236 20p green   .30 .20
837 A236 25p rose car   .30 .20
838 A236 35p sepia   .30 .20
   Nos. 836-838 (3)   .90 .60

Molar, Emblem with Mosque — A237

Flame Emblem — A238

1979   Litho.   Perf. 12x11½
846 A237 35p multi   .30 .20
Intl. Middle East Dental Congress.

1979
847 A238 35p multi   .30 .20
33rd anniversary of evacuation.

Ibn Assaker, 900th Anniv. A239

1979   Perf. 11½x12
848 A239 75p multi   .30 .20

Telephone Lineman — A240

Girl with IYC Emblem — A242

Wright Brothers' Plane A241

1979, May 1   Litho.   Perf. 12x11½
849 A240 50p multi   .30 .20
850 A240 75p multi   .30 .20
May Day.

1979   Perf. 11½x12
Designs: 75p, Bleriot's plane crossing English Channel. 100p, Spirit of St. Louis.
851 A241 50p multi   .30 .20
852 A241 75p multi   .30 .20
853 A241 100p multi   .50 .20
   Nos. 851-853 (3)   1.10 .60
75th anniversary of 1st powered flight.

1979   Perf. 12x11½
Design: 15p, Boy, globe, IYC emblem.
854 A242 10p multi   .30 .20
855 A242 15p multi   .35 .20
International Year of the Child.

Power Plant — A243

Flags and Pavilion — A244

1979   Perf. 11x11½
856 A243 5p blue   .30 .20
857 A243 10p lil rose   .30 .20
858 A243 15p gray grn   .30 .20
   Nos. 856-858 (3)   .90 .60

1979   Photo.   Perf. 12x11½
Design: 75p, Lamppost and flags.
859 A244 60p multi   .30 .20
860 A244 75p multi   .35 .20
26th International Damascus Fair.

Correction Movement, 9th Anniversary — A245

1979   Photo.   Perf. 11½x12
861 A245 100p multi   .50 .20

Games Emblem, Running A246

1979, Nov.
862 A246 25p shown   .30 .20
863 A246 35p Diving   .30 .20
864 A246 50p Soccer   .30 .20
   Nos. 862-864 (3)   .90 .60
8th Mediterranean Games, Split, Yugoslavia, Sept. 15-29.

Butterfly — A247

Damascus Intl. Flower Show A248

Designs: Various butterflies.

1979, Dec.   Litho.   Perf. 12x11½
865 A247 20p multi   .50 .20
866 A247 25p multi   .50 .20
867 A247 30p multi   .50 .20
868 A247 35p multi   .50 .20
869 A247 50p multi   .50 .20
   Nos. 865-869 (5)   2.50 1.00

1980, Jan. 9   Litho.   Perf. 12½
Design: Roses.
870 A248 5p multi   .50 .20
871 A248 10p multi   .50 .20
872 A248 15p multi   .50 .20
873 A248 50p multi   .50 .20
874 A248 75p multi   .50 .20
875 A248 100p multi   .80 .20
   Nos. 870-875 (6)   3.30 1.20

March 8 Revolution, 17th Anniv. — A249

Astrolabe A250

1980, Mar. 25   Litho.   Perf. 12x11½
876 A249 40p multi   .30 .20

1980, May 2   Perf. 12½
877 A250 50p violet   .30 .20
878 A250 100p sepia   .50 .20
879 A250 1000p gray grn   4.00 1.25
   Nos. 877-879 (3)   4.80 1.65
2nd International History of Arabic Sciences Symposium, Apr. 5.

Lit Cigarette, Skull — A251

Evacuation, 34th
Anniversary
A252

1980, June 25   Photo.   Perf. 12x11½
880 A251   60p Smoker   .60   .25
881 A251   100p shown   1.00   .30

World Health Day; anti-smoking campaign.

1980, June 25   Litho.
882 A252   40p multi   .30   .20
883 A252   60p multi   .35   .20

Moscow
'80
Emblem
and
Wrestling
A253

1980, July   Litho.   Perf. 11½x12
884 A253   15p shown   .30   .20
885 A253   25p Fencing   .30   .20
886 A253   35p Weight lifting   .35   .20
887 A253   50p Judo   .50   .20
888 A253   75p Boxing   1.00   .25
  a.   Strip of 5, #884-888   2.50 2.50

Souvenir Sheet
Imperf

888B A253 300p Discus, running   5.00 5.00

22nd Summer Olympic Games, Moscow,
July 19-Aug. 3.

Sinbad
the Sailor
A254

1980   Litho.   Perf. 11½x12
889 A254   15p shown   .30   .20
890 A254   25p Scheherezade
             and Shahrayar   .30   .20
891 A254   35p Ali Baba and the
             Forty Thieves   .35   .20
892 A254   50p Hassan the Clev-
             er   .50   .20
893 A254   100p Aladdin's Lamp   1.00   .30
  a.   Strip of 5, #889-893   2.50 2.50

Popular stories.

Savings Certificates — A255

1980
894 A255   25p multi   .30   .20

Hegira, 1500th Anniv. — A256

1980
895 A256   35p multi   .35   .20

Intl. Flower Show,
Damascus
A257

1980   Perf. 12x11½
896 A257   20p Daffodils   .50   .20
897 A257   30p Chrysanthemums   .50   .20
898 A257   40p Clematis   .55   .20
899 A257   60p Yellow roses   .60   .20
900 A257   100p Chrysanthe-
             mums, diff.   .75   .25
  a.   Strip of 5, #896-900   3.00 3.00

May Day — A258

Children's
Day — A259

1980, May
901 A258   35p multi   .40   .20

1980
902 A259   25p multi   .40   .20

November 16th Movement, 10th
Anniv. — A260

1980   Perf. 11½x12
903 A260   100p multi   1.00   .25

Steam-powered Passenger
Wagon — A261

1980
904 A261   25p shown   .35   .20
905 A261   35p Benz, 1899   .40   .20
906 A261   40p Rolls-Royce, 1903 .60   .20
907 A261   50p Mercedes, 1906   .75   .25
908 A261   60p Austin, 1915   1.00   .30
  a.   Strip of 5, #904-908   3.25 3.25

Mother's
Day — A262

1980   Perf. 12x11½
909 A262   40p shown   .50   .20
910 A262   100p Mother and child 1.00   .20

27th International Damascus
Fair — A263

1981, Jan. 24   Perf. 11½x12
911 A263   50p multi   .45   .20
912 A263   100p multi   .80   .20

Army Day — A264

1981, Jan. 24   Perf. 12½x12
913 A264   50p multi   .45   .20

A265

A266

1981, Mar. 8   Litho.   Perf. 12x11½
914 A265   50p multi   .35   .20

18th anniv. of March 8th revolution.

1981, Apr. 17   Litho.   Perf. 12x11½
915 A266   50p multi   .35   .20

35th anniversary of evacuation.

World Conference on History of Arab
and Islamic Civilization,
Damascus — A267

1981, May 30   Photo.   Perf. 12½x12
916 A267   100p multi   .60   .20

Intl. Workers'
Solidarity
Day — A268

Housing and
Population
Census — A269

1981, May 30   Litho.   Perf. 12x11½
917 A268   100p multi   .60   .20

1981, June 1
918 A269   50p multi   .35   .20

Umayyad
Window
A270

Abdul Malik Gold
Coin
A270a

10p, figurine. 15p, Rakkla's cavalier, Abbcid
ceramic. 160p, like 5p. 500p, Umar B. Abdul
Aziz gold coin.

1981   Perf. 12x11½, 11½x12
919 A270   5p crim rose   .20   .20
920 A270   10p brt grn   .20   .20
921 A270   15p dp rose lil   .20   .20
922 A270a   75p blue   .35   .20
923 A270   160p dk grn   .70   .35
924 A270a   500p dk brn   2.50 1.10
  Nos. 919-924 (6)   4.15 2.25

Olives
A270b

Harbor
A270c

1982   Perf. 12x11½
925 A270b   50p ol grn   .40   .20
926 A270b   60p bl gray   .45   .20
929 A270c   100p lilac   .55   .25
930 A270c   180p red   1.10   .55
  Nos. 925-930 (4)   2.50 1.20

Saving
Certificates
Plan — A271

Avicenna (980-
1037),
Philosopher and
Physician
A272

1981, June 22
931 A271 50p gldn brn & blk   .35 .20

1981, Aug.
932 A272 100p multi   .60 .20

Syria-P.L.O.
Solidarity, Intl.
Conference
A273

1981, June 22
933 A273 160p multi   3.50 .90

Grand Mosque, Damascus — A274

1981   *Perf. 12½*
934 A274 50p Glass lamp, 13th
               cent.   .30 .20
935 A274 180p shown   1.40 .40
936 A274 180p Hunter   1.40 .40
       Nos. 934-936 (3)   3.10 1.00

Youth
Festival
A275

1981   *Perf. 12½*
937 A275 60p multi   .40 .20

28th Intl.
Damascus
Fair — A276

Intl. Palestinian
Solidarity
Day — A277

1981   *Perf. 12x11½*
938 A276 50p Ornament   .30 .20
939 A276 160p Emblem   1.00 .45

1981
940 A277 100p multi   .75 .20

1300th
Anniv. of
Bulgaria
A278

1981   *Perf. 11½x12*
941 A278 380p multi   2.25 1.00

Intl.
Children's
Day
A279

1981
942 A279 180p multi   1.10 .45

World
Food Day,
Oct. 16
A280

1981
943 A280 180p multi   1.10 .45

9th Intl. Flower
Show, Damascus
A281

Designs: Flowers.

1981   *Perf. 12x11½*
944 A281 25p multi   .25 .20
945 A281 40p multi   .40 .25
946 A281 50p multi   .50 .30
947 A281 60p multi   .75 .35
948 A281 100p multi   1.10 .50
   a.   Strip of 5, #944-948   3.00 2.00

Souvenir Sheet

Koran Competition — A282

1981   **Litho.**   *Imperf.*
949 A282 500p multi   5.00 5.00

11th Anniv. of
Correction
Movement
A283

1981, Nov.   *Perf. 12x11½*
950 A283 60p multi   .45 .30

TB
Bacillus
Centenary
A284

1982   **Litho.**   *Perf. 11½x12*
951 A284 180p multi   1.25 .65

Mothers'
Day — A285

Mar. 8th
Revolution, 19th
Anniv. — A286

1982   *Perf. 11½*
952 A285 40p green   .25 .20
953 A285 75p brown   .50 .25

1982, Mar.   *Perf. 12x11½*
954 A286 50p multi   .35 .20

Intl. Year of the
Disabled
(1981) — A287

1982   *Perf. 12x11½*
955 A287 90p multi   .75 .30

1982   *Perf. 11½*
956 A288 150p ultra   .90 .50

Pres. Hafez al
Assad — A288

36th Anniv. of
Evacuation
A289

World Traffic
Day — A290

1982   *Perf. 12x11½*
957 A289 70p multi   .50 .25

1982
958 A290 180p multi   1.25 .65

Intl. Workers'
Solidarity
Day — A291

1982
959 A291 180p multi   1.25 .65

World Telecommunication Day,
May 17 — A292

1982
960 A292 180p multi   1.25 .65

Soldier Holding
Rifles — A293

Arab Postal
Union, 30th
Anniv. — A294

1982   **Photo.**   *Perf. 12x11½*
961 A293 50p multi   .30 .20

1982
962 A294 60p multi   .45 .20

1982 World Cup — A295

Various soccer players. 300p, Ball.

1982, July *Perf. 12½*
963 A295 40p multi .25 .20
964 A295 60p multi .40 .20
965 A295 100p multi .65 .40
Nos. 963-965 (3) 1.30 .80
Size: 75x55mm
Imperf
966 A295 300p multi 10.00 10.00

10th Intl. Flower
Show, Damascus
A297

1982 *Perf. 12x11½*
967 A297 50p Honeysuckle .45 .20
968 A297 60p Geraniums .60 .30

Scouting
Year
A298

1982, Nov. 4 *Perf. 11½x12*
969 A298 160p green 1.40 .75

Ladybug
A299

1982 *Perf. 12x12½*
970 Strip of 5 .75 .40
a. A299 5p Dragonfly .20 .20
b. A299 10p Stag Beetle .20 .20
c. A299 20p shown .20 .20
d. A299 40p Grasshopper .20 .20
e. A299 50p Honeybee .30 .20

ITU Plenipotentiaries Conference,
Nairobi, Sept — A300

1982 *Perf. 11½x12*
971 A300 50p Map .30 .25
972 A300 180p Dish antenna 1.40 .75

12th
Anniv. of
Correction
Movement
A301

1982, Nov.
973 A301 50p dk bl & sil .35 .20

A302
Factory —
A302a

Walled Arch —
A302b

Ruins — A302c

1982-83 Litho. *Perf. 11½*
974 A302 30p brown .20 .20
975 A302a 50p dark green .25 .20
976 A302b 70p green .35 .20
977 A302c 200p red 1.00 .55
Nos. 974-977 (4) 1.80 1.15
Issued: 50p, 11/16/83; others, 11/4/82.

Dove and
Satellite — A303

Intl. Palestinian
Solidarity
Day — A304

1982 Litho. *Perf. 12x11½*
978 A303 50p multi .50 .30
2nd UN Conference on Peaceful Uses of
Outer Space, Vienna, Aug. 9-21.

1982
979 A304 50p multi .90 .20

20th Anniv. of March 8th
Revolution — A305

1983 *Perf. 12½x12*
980 A305 60p multi 1.00 .50

World Communications Year — A305a

1983
981 A305a 180p multi 1.25 .65

9th Anniv. of
Liberation of Al-
Kuneitra
A306

25th Anniv. of Intl.
Maritime Org.
A308

Arab Pharmacists' Day, Apr. 2 — A307

1983, June 26 Litho. *Perf. 11½*
982 A306 50p View 1.50 .50
983 A306 100p View, diff. 3.00 .65

1983, Apr. 2 *Perf. 11½x12*
984 A307 100p multi .75 .30

1983, June *Perf. 12x11½*
985 A308 180p multi 1.40 .75

Namibia
Day, Aug.
26
A309

1983, Aug. 26 *Perf. 11½x12*
986 A309 180p multi 1.40 .75

Eibla
Sculpture,
3rd Cent.
BC
A310

1983
987 A310 380p ol & brn 2.50 1.40

World Standards
Day — A311

11th Intl. Flower
Show, Damascus
A312

1983, Oct. 14 Photo. *Perf. 11½*
988 A311 50p Factory, emblem .40 .20
989 A311 100p Measuring equipment .80 .40

1983, Oct. 14 Litho. *Perf. 11½*
990 A312 50p multi .40 .20
991 A312 60p multi, diff. .50 .25

World
Food Day
A313a

1983, Oct. 16 Litho. *Perf. 11½x12*
992A A313a 180p multi 1.50 .75

Waterwheels of
Hama — A314

Perf. 11x11½, 11½x11
1982-84 Litho.
993 A314 5p sepia .20 .20
994 A314 10p violet .20 .20
995 A314 20p red .25 .20
997 A314 50p dk grn .60 .30
Nos. 993-997 (4) 1.25 .90
Issued: 50p, 11/25/82; others, 1/15/84.
On No. 997 "50" is in outlined numbers.

Statue — A316

View of
Aleppo — A317

1983 *Perf. 12*
1003 A316 225p brown 2.00 1.00
Intl. Symposium on History and Archaeology of Deir Ez-zor.

1983 *Perf. 12x12½*
1004 A317 245p multi 2.25 1.10
Intl. Symposium on Conservation of Old City
of Aleppo, Sept. 26-30.

Mar. 8th Revolution, 21st
Anniv. — A318

1984, Mar. 8 *Perf. 12½x12*
1005 A318 60p Alassad Library .75 .35

Massacre
at Sabra
and
Shatilla
A319

Intl. Palestinian day

1983 Litho. *Perf. 11½x12*
1006 A319 225p Victims, mother &
child 2.00 .50

World Heritage
Day — A313

1983, Oct. 14 Photo. *Perf. 11½*
992 A313 60p dk brn .50 .25

Mothers'
Day — A320

12th Intl. Flower
Show, Damascus
A321

1984, Mar. 21 *Perf. 12x11½*
1007 A320 245p Mother & child 2.50 1.25

1984, May 25

Various flowers.

1008 A321 245p multi 2.50 1.25
1009 A321 285p multi 2.75 1.40

1984 Summer
Olympics — A322

Aleppo
Agricultural &
Industrial
Fair — A324

9th
Regional
Pioneers'
Festival
A323

1984 **Litho.** *Perf. 12x11½*
1010 Strip of 5 3.00 2.40
 a. A322 30p Swimming .30 .20
 b. A322 50p Wrestling .50 .25
 c. A322 60p Running .60 .30
 d. A322 70p Boxing .65 .35
 e. A322 90p Soccer .90 .45
 Souvenir Sheet
 Imperf
1011 A322 200p Soccer, diff. 3.50 3.50

1984 *Perf. 11½x12*
1012 A323 50p Pioneers .50 .25
1013 A323 60p Pioneers, diff. .60 .30

1984, June 12 Litho. *Perf. 12x12½*
1014 A324 150p Peppers, Aleppo
 Castle 1.25 .50

Supreme
Council of
Science,
25th Anniv.
A325

1985, Feb. 23 *Perf. 12½x12*
1015 A325 65p multi .40 .20

Aleppo
University,
25th
Anniv.
A326

1985, Feb. 23
1016 A326 45p multi .25 .20

Syrian
Arab
Army,
39th
Anniv.
A327

1985, Feb. 23
1017 A327 65p brn & gldn brn .40 .20

Pres.
Assad,
Soldier
Saluting,
Troops
A328

1984, Aug. 1 *Perf. 11½x12*
1018 A328 60p multi .60 .30

4th General Revolutionary Youth Conference.

ITU Emblem,
Satellite
Dish,
Telephone
A329

1984, Oct. 2 *Perf. 12½*
1019 A329 245p multi 1.75 .90

Intl. Telecommunications Day.

APU Emblem and Administration
Building, Damascus — A330

1984, Oct. 9
1020 A330 60p multi .60 .30

Arab Postal Union Day.

Gearwheel,
Arabesque
Pattern — A331

Gold
Necklace — A332

1984, Oct. 27 *Perf. 12x12½, 12x11½*
1021 A331 45p multi .45 .20
1022 A332 100p multi 1.00 .45

Intl. Fair, Damascus.

Intl. Civil
Aviation
Org., 40th
Anniv.
A333

1984, Oct. 27 *Perf. 11½x12*
1023 A333 45p brt bl & lt bl .25 .20
1024 A333 245p brt ultra, brt bl &
 lt bl 1.25 .60

14th
Anniv. of
11-16-70
Movement
A334

1984, Dec. 3 *Perf. 12½x12*
1025 A334 65p red brn, blk & org .65 .35

Pres. Assad,
Text on Scroll
A335

1984, Nov. 29 *Perf. 12½*
1026 A335 50p grn, brn org & sep .50 .25

Vow of Dedication taken by Youth of the
Revolution.

Agricultural Exhibition — A336

1984, June 12 *Perf. 12½x12*
1027 A336 65p multi .65 .35

Al-Kuneitra Memorial, Rose — A337

1984
1028 A337 70p multi 1.25 .35

Roman Arch and Colonnades,
Palmyra — A338

1984, Dec. 3
1029 A338 100p multi 1.00 .50

Intl. Tourism Day.

Woodland Conservation — A339

1984
1030 A339 45p multi .25 .20

March 8
Revolution, 22nd
Anniv. — A340

UPU Emblem,
Postal
Headquarters,
Damascus
A341

1985, Apr. 27
1031 A340 60p multi .40 .20

1985, Apr. 27
1032 A341 285p multi 3.00 1.50

World Post Day.

APU Building, Damascus — A342

1985, Apr. 27 *Perf. 12½*
1033 A342 245p multi 2.50 1.25

Arab Parliamentary Union, 10th Anniv.

Natl. Flag, Map of Arab Countries A343

1985   **Perf. 12½x12**
1034 A343 50p multi   .50 .25
Arab League.

Re-election of President Assad A344

1985, Mar. 12   **Perf. 12½**
1035 A344 200p multi   1.25 .70
1036 A344 300p multi   2.00 1.00
1037 A344 500p multi   3.25 1.75
  a.   Souvenir sheet of 3, #1035-
       1037, imperf.   7.00 5.50
     Nos. 1035-1037 (3)   6.50 3.45

Arab Postal Union, 12th Congress, Damascus A345

1985, Aug. 12   **Perf. 12x12½**
1038 A345 60p multi   .60 .30

Labor Day — A346

1985, Aug. 12   **Perf. 12½**
1039 A346 60p Order of Labor   .60 .30

32nd Intl. Fair, Damascus A347

1986, Feb. 1   Litho.   **Perf. 12½**
1040 A347 60p multi   .50 .25

2nd Scientific Symposium — A348

1985, Nov. 16   **Perf. 12½**
1041 A348 60p Locomotives   .60 .30

UN Child Survival Campaign A349

1985, Nov. 16   **Perf. 12½x12**
1042 A349 60p Malnourished child   .50 .25

UN, 40th Anniv. — A350

1985, Nov. 16   **Perf. 12x12½**
1043 A350 245p multi   2.25 1.10

November 16th Movement, 15th Anniv. — A351

1985, Nov. 16   **Perf. 12½**
1044 A351 60p Pres. Assad, high-
             way   .50 .25

Abdul Rahman Dakhei in Andalusia, 1200th Anniv. A352

1986, Feb. 1   **Perf. 12½x12**
1045 A352 60p beige & brn   .60 .30

Tulips — A353

World Traffic Day — A355

Dental Congress, Damascus — A354

1986, Feb. 1   **Perf. 12½**
1046 A353 30p multi   .30 .20
1047 A353 60p multi, diff.   .60 .30
       Intl. Flower Show, Damascus.

1986   **Perf. 12½x12**
1048 A354 110p yel, grysh grn &
             bl   1.10 .55

1986   **Perf. 12x12½**
1049 A355 330p multi   3.00 1.50

Syrian Investment Certificates, 15th Anniv. — A357

Day of Internal Security Forces — A359

Liberation of Al-Kuneitra, 12th Anniv. — A358

1986   Litho.   **Perf. 12x11½**
1055 A357 100p multi   1.00 .50

1986   Litho.   **Perf. 11½x12**
1056 A358 110p Government Build-
             ing   .75 .40

1986   **Perf. 12x11½**
1057 A359 110p multi   .75 .40

Labor Day — A360

1986 World Cup Soccer Championships, Mexico — A361

1986, Aug. 12
1058 A360 330p multi   1.25 .60

1986, July 7
1059 A361 330p multi   3.25 1.75
1060 A361 370p multi   3.50 1.90
            Booklet Stamp
            Size: 105x80mm
               Imperf
1061 A361 500p Hemispheres,
             ball   5.00 2.50
     Nos. 1059-1061 (3)   11.75 6.15

Pres. Hafez al Assad — A362

1986-90   Litho.   **Perf. 12x11½**
1068 A362 10p rose   .20 .20
1069 A362 30p dl ultra   .20 .20
1070 A362 50p claret   .40 .20
1071 A362 100p brt lt bl   .65 .30
1072 A362 150p brn vio   1.40 .65
1073 A362 175p violet   1.60 .80
1074 A362 200p pale red brn   1.40 .65
1075 A362 300p brt rose lil   2.00 1.00
1076 A362 500p orange   3.25 1.60
1077 A362 550p pink   5.00 2.50
1078 A362 600p dull grn   5.25 2.75
1079 A362 1000p brt pink   6.50 3.25
1080 A362 2000p pale grn   13.00 6.50
     Nos. 1068-1080 (13)   40.85 20.60
  Issued: 150p, 175p, 550p, 600p, 1988; 50p,
9/30/90.

Intl. Day for Solidarity with the Palestinian People — A363

Mothers' Day — A364

1986, Aug. 7   **Litho.**
1081 A363 110p multi   1.10 .55

1986, Aug. 7
1082 A364 100p multi   1.00 .50

March 8 Revolution, 23rd Anniv. — A365

1986, Aug. 7   **Perf. 11½x12**
1083 A365 110p multi   1.10 .55

Arab Post
Day
A366

1986, Aug. 7
1084 A366 110p multi   1.10 .55

A367

33rd Intl.
Damascus
Fair
A368

1986, Dec. 9   Litho.   Perf. 11½x12
1085 A367 110p multi   .90 .45
1086 A368 330p multi   2.50 .60

14th Intl. Flower Show,
Damascus — A369

Various flowers.

1986, Oct. 11   Perf. 12½
1087   Strip of 5   6.50 5.00
a.   A369 10p multi   .20   .20
b.   A369 50p multi   .50   .25
c.   A369 100p multi   1.00   .50
d.   A369 110p multi   1.10   .60
e.   A369 330p multi   3.50 1.75

Syria-Soviet Joint
Space
Project — A370

World Children's
Day — A371

1986, Nov. 16   Litho.   Perf. 12½
1088 A370 330p multi   3.50 1.75

1986   Perf. 12x12½, 12½x12
1089 A371 330p shown   1.75   .90
1090 A371 330p Youth art exhibi-
            tion, horiz.   1.75   .90

World
Post Day
A372

1986, Jan. 28   Perf. 12½x12
1091 A372 330p multi   1.75   .90

Intl.
Tourism
Day
A373

Women wearing folk costumes, landmarks.

1986
1092 A373 330p multi   1.75   .90
1093 A373 370p multi   2.00 1.00

Pres. Assad, Tishreen Palace — A374

1986, Nov. 16   Litho.   Perf. 12½
1094 A374 110p multi   1.25   .60

Nov. 16 Corrective Movement.

March 8th Revolution, 24th
Anniv. — A375

1987, Mar. 6
1095 A375 100p multi   .60   .30

Intl. Peace
Year — A376

1987, Mar. 8   Perf. 12x11½
1096 A376 370p multi   2.25 1.25

Arab Baath
Socialist
Party, 40th
Anniv.
A377

1987, Apr. 7   Litho.   Perf. 12½
1097 A377 100p multi   .60   .30

Arab Post
Day, 35th
Anniv.
A378

1987, May 1   Perf. 11½x12
1098 A378 110p multi   .70   .35

Evacuation, Day, 41st Anniv. — A379

1987, Apr. 17   Perf. 12½x12
1099 A379 100p multi   .60   .30

Labor
Day — A380

Al-Kuneitra
Monument
A382

Hitteen's Battle, 800th Anniv. — A381

1987, May 1   Perf. 12x11½
1100 A380 330p multi   2.00 1.00

1987, June 25   Litho.   Perf. 12½
1101 A381 110p multi   1.00   .45

1987, June 25   Perf. 12x11½
1102 A382 100p multi   .65   .30

Child Vaccination Campaign — A383

1987, June 25   Perf. 11½x12
1103 A383 100p multi   .50   .30
1104 A383 330p multi   2.00 1.10

A384

A385

Syrian-Soviet Joint
Space Flight, July
22-30 — A386

Designs: No. 1105, Launch, July 22. No.
1106, Docking at space station, July 24. No.
1107, Landing, July 30, vert. No. 1108a, Lift-
off. No. 1108b, Parachute landing. No.
1108c, Docked at space station. No. 1108d,
Cosmonauts.

Perf. 12½, 11½x12, 12x11½
1987   Litho.
1105 A384 330p multi   2.00 1.00
1106 A385 330p multi   2.00 1.00
1107 A385 330p multi   2.00 1.00
      Nos. 1105-1107 (3)   6.00 3.00
          Souvenir Sheet
              Imperf
1108   Sheet of 4   10.00 10.00
a.-d.   A386 300p, any single   2.25 2.25

6th
Conference
of Arab
Ministers of
Culture
A387

1987, Apr. 21   Litho.   Perf. 12½
1109 A387 330p dull blue grn &
            blk   3.00 1.50

President Assad Conversing with
Syrian Cosmonaut — A388

1987, Aug. 12
1110 A388 500p multi   3.50 1.75

10th Mediterranean Games,
Latakia — A389

Designs: 100p, Gymnastic rings, weight lifting, vert. 330p, Phoenician sailing ship. 370p,
Flags spelling "SYRIA." No. 1115a, Emblem,
gymnastics. No. 1115b, Emblem, weight lifting. No. 1115c, Emblem, tennis. No. 1115d,
Emblem, soccer.

Perf. 12x11½, 11½x12
1987, Sept. 10
1111 A389 100p brt rose lil & blk   .70   .35
1112 A389 110p shown   .75   .40

Size: 58x28mm
Perf. 12½
1113 A389 330p multi   2.25 1.10
1114 A389 370p multi   2.50 1.25
       Nos. 1111-1114 (4)   6.20 3.10
Souvenir Sheet
Imperf
1115   Sheet of 4   7.75 7.75
a.-d. A389 300p any single   1.90 1.90

34th Intl.
Damascus
Fair — A390

Arbor
Day — A392

Intl.
Flower
Show,
Damascus
A391

1987   **Perf. 12x11½**
1116 A390 330p multi   2.00 1.00

1987, Oct. 20   **Perf. 11½x12**
1117 A391 330p Poppies   1.90 1.00
1118 A391 370p Gentian   2.00 1.00

1987, Oct. 20   **Perf. 12x11½**
1119 A392 330p multi   2.00 1.00

Army
Day — A393

Intl. Palestine
Day — A394

1987, Oct. 20 Litho. Perf. 12x11½
1120 A393 100p multi   .60   .30

1987, Nov. 16
1121 A394 500p multi   3.50 1.75

Corrective Movement, 17th
Anniv. — A395

1987, Nov. 16   **Perf. 12½**
1122 A395 150p Assad waving to
              crowd   1.00   .50

World Post Day — A396

1988, Mar. 8 Litho. Perf. 12½x12
1123 A396 500p multi   3.00 1.50

Intl.
Tourism
Day
A397

Women wearing folk costumes and: No.
1124, Palmyra Ruins. No. 1125, Reconstructed Roman amphitheater, Busra.

1988, Feb. 25 Litho. Perf. 11½x12
1124 A397 500p multi   3.00 1.50
1125 A397 500p multi   3.00 1.50

       See Nos. 1147-1148, 1178-1179.

Intl. Children's Day — A398

1988, Feb. 27   **Perf. 12½**
1126 A398 500p multi   3.00 1.50

March 8th
Revolution, 25th
Anniv. — A399

Mothers'
Day — A400

1988, Mar. 15 Litho. Perf. 12x11½
1127 A399 150p multi   1.00   .50
       Size: 110x81mm
       Imperf
1128 A399 500p multi, diff.   4.75 4.75
       No. 1128 pictures vignette like 150p without
denomination, in diff. colors, and Arab Revolt

flag, text, outline map; denomination at LR in
sheet.

1988, Apr. 12 Litho. Perf. 12x12½
1129 A400 500p multi   3.00 1.50

Arab Post
Day
A401

1988, Apr. 17   **Perf. 12½x12**
1130 A401 150p multi   1.00   .50

1946 Evacuation
A402

Labor
Day — A403

1988, Apr. 17   **Perf. 12x12½**
1131 A402 150p multi   1.00   .50

1988, May 1
1132 A403 550p multi   3.00 1.50

Intl. Flower
Show, Damascus
A404

Arab Engineers'
Union — A405

1988, May 25   **Perf. 12x11½**
1133 A404 550p Tiger Lily   3.25 1.60
1134 A404 600p Carnations   3.75 1.90

1988, May 25
1135 A405 150p multi   1.00   .50

A406

A407

1988, Aug. 28 Litho. Perf. 12x11½
1136 A406 600p blk, grn & olive   3.50 1.75
       Intl. Children's Day.

1988, Aug. 28   **Perf. 12½**
1137 A407 550p multi   3.00 1.50

Restoration of San'a, Yemen Arab Republic.

Ebla Intl. Symposium on Archaeology
of Idlib — A408

1988, Aug. 28
1138 A408 175p Hieroglyphic
              tablet   1.00   .50
1139 A408 550p Bas-relief (votive
              basin)   3.00 1.50
1140 A408 600p Gold statue,
              3000 B.C.   3.50 1.75
       Nos. 1138-1140 (3)   7.50 3.75

1988
Summer
Olympics,
Seoul
A409

1988, Sept. 17   **Perf. 11½x12**
1141 A409 550p Cycling   3.50 1.60
1142 A409 600p Soccer   3.75 1.75
       Size: 81x61mm
       Imperf
1143 A409 1200p Emblem,
              character
              trademark   12.50 12.50
       Nos. 1141-1143 (3)   19.75 15.85

35th Intl. Fair,
Damascus
A410

WHO, 40th
Anniv. — A411

1988, Aug. 28   **Perf. 12x11½**
1144 A410 600p multi   3.50 1.75

1988, Aug. 28 Litho. Perf. 12x11½
1145 A411 600p multi   3.25 1.60

Arab Scouting Movement, 50th
Anniv. — A412

1988, Sept. 17   **Perf. 12½x12**
1146 A412 150p multi   1.50 .75

Tourism Type of 1988

Women wearing folk costumes and: 550p,
Euphrates Bridge, Deir-ez-Zor. 600p, The Tet-
rapylon, Latakia.

1988, Oct. 18
1147 A397 550p multi   3.25 1.60
1148 A397 600p multi   3.50 1.75

World Post
Day — A413

Arbor
Day — A414

1988, Dec. 7   **Litho.**   **Perf. 12x12½**
1149 A413 600p multi   3.50 1.75

1988, Nov. 16
1150 A414 600p multi   3.50 1.75

Shelter for the Homeless — A415

1988-89   **Perf. 12½x12**
1151 A415 150p Arab Housing
   Day   .65 .35
1151A A415 175p Intl. Year of
   Shelter for
   the Homeless 1.25 .60
1152 A415 550p World Housing
   Day   2.50 1.25
1153 A415 600p as No. 1151A 2.75 1.50
   Nos. 1151-1153 (4)   7.15 3.70

The IYSH emblem is pictured on the 175p,
550p and 600p.
Issued: 175p, 2/6/89; others, 10/18/88.

Al-Assad University Hospital — A416

1988, Nov. 16   **Litho.**   **Perf. 12½**
1154 A416 150p multi   .90 .45

Corrective Movement, 18th anniv.

World Food
Day — A417

1988, Oct. 18   **Perf. 12x12½**
1155 A417 550p multi   2.75 1.40

Birds
A418

1989, Mar. 21   **Litho.**   **Perf. 11½x12**
1156 A418 600p Goldfinch   1.50 .75
1157 A418 600p Turtledove   1.50 .75
1158 A418 600p Bee eater   1.50 .75
   Nos. 1156-1158 (3)   4.50 2.25

Jawaharlal
Nehru, 1st
Prime
Minister of
Independent
India — A419

1989, Mar. 8   **Perf. 12½**
1159 A419 550p brn & chest 1.10 .55

Mothers'
Day — A420

1989, Mar. 21
1160 A420 550p multi   1.10 .55

Teacher's
Day
A421

1989, Mar. 8   **Litho.**   **Perf. 11½x12**
1161 A421 175p multi   .70 .35

5th General
Congress of
the Union of
Women
A422

1989, Mar. 8   **Perf. 12½**
1162 A422 150p multi   .30 .20

March 8th Revolution, 26th
Anniv. — A423

1989, Mar. 8   **Perf. 11½x12**
1163 A423 150p multi   .30 .20

Arab Board for Medical
Specializations, 10th Anniv. — A424

1989, Feb. 6   **Perf. 12½**
1164 A424 175p multi   .60 .30

1946 Evacuation of British and French
Troops — A425

1989, Apr. 17   **Litho.**   **Perf. 11½x12**
1165 A425 150p multi   .40 .20

Intl. Flower
Show,
Damascus
A426

1989, June 3   **Perf. 12½**
1166   Strip of 5   5.00 4.00
a. A426 150p Snapdragon   .30 .20
b. A426 150p Canaria   .30 .20
c. A426 450p Compositae   .90 .45
d. A426 850p Clematis sackmani 1.75 .85
e. A426 900p Gesneriaceae 1.75 .90

A427

A428

1989, May 1   **Perf. 12x11½**
1167 A427 850p blue grn & blk 1.75 .90

Labor Day.

1989, June 6   **Litho.**   **Perf. 12x11½**
1168 A428 175p multi   .50 .25

13th General Congress of the Arab Teachers' Union.

Arab Post
Day — A429

Liberation of Al-
Kuneitra, 15th
Anniv. — A430

1989, June 6
1169 A429 175p multi   .50 .25

1989, June 26
1170 A430 450p multi   1.25 .60

17th
Congress
of the
Arab
Advocates
Union
A431

1989, June 19   **Perf. 11½x12**
1171 A431 175p multi   .50 .25

World
Post Day
A432

1989, June 26
1172 A432 550p multi   1.50 .75

World Telecommunications
Day — A433

1989, June 6
1173 A433 550p multi   1.50   .75

Interparliamentary Union,
Cent. — A434

1989. July 12   Perf. 12½
1174 A434 900p multi   2.50 1.25

Butterflies
A435

1989, June 6
1175 A435 550p Small white   1.50   .75
1176 A435 550p Clouded yellow 1.50   .75
1177 A435 550p Painted Lady   1.50   .75
      Nos. 1175-1177 (3)   4.50 2.25

Intl. Tourism Day Type of 1988

Women wearing folk costumes and: 550p,
Jaabar Castle, Rakka. 600p, Temple of the
Bell, Palmyra.

1989, Oct. 16   Litho.   Perf. 11½x12
1178 A397 550p multicolored   3.75 1.75
1179 A397 600p multicolored   4.00 2.00

36th Intl. Fair,
Damascus
A436

1989, Oct. 16   Perf. 12x11½
1180 A436 450p multicolored   3.00 1.50

Fish
A437

1989, Oct. 24   Perf. 11½x12
1181 A437 550p Carp   3.75 1.75
1182 A437 600p Trout   4.00 2.00

2nd Anniv. of the
Palestinian
Uprising — A438

1989, Oct. 24   Perf. 12x11½
1183 A438 550p Child's drawing 3.75 1.75

Corrective Movement, 19th
Anniv. — A439

1989, Nov. 16   Litho.   Perf. 12½x12
1184 A439 150p multicolored   1.00   .50

A440

A441

1990, Feb. 13   Litho.   Perf. 12x11½
1185 A440 850p multicolored   1.00   .50
      World Children's Day.

1990
1186 A441 600p multicolored   .70   .35
      March 8th Revolution, 27th anniv.

Revolutionary
Youth Union
A442

1990   Perf. 12½
1187 A442 150p multicolored   .20   .20

World
Food Day
A443

1990, Feb. 13   Litho.   Perf. 11½x12
1188 A443 850p multicolored   1.00   .50
      Dated 1989.

Evacuation of
British and French
Troops,
1946 — A444

1990, Apr. 17   Perf. 12x11½
1189 A444 175p multicolored   .20   .20

Mother's
Day — A445

1990, Apr. 17   Perf. 12½
1190 A445 550p multicolored   .65   .30

Labor
Day — A446

1990, May 1   Litho.   Perf. 12x12½
1191 A446 550p multicolored   .75   .35

World Cup Soccer Championships,
Italy — A447

Perf. 11½x12, 12x11½
1990, June 8   Litho.
1192 A447 550p shown   .40   .20
1193 A447 550p Denomination
                at right   .40   .20
1194 A447 600p Map, soccer
                ball, vert.   .45   .25
      Nos. 1192-1194 (3)   1.25   .65
            Miniature Sheet
               Imperf
1195 A447 1300p Stadium   3.50 1.75

Intl. Flower Show,
Damascus
A448

1990, May 27   Perf. 12x11½
1196 A448 600p Lily   1.10   .50
1197 A448 600p Pastelkleurig 1.10   .50
1198 A448 600p Marigold   1.10   .50
1199 A448 600p Viburnum opu-
               lus   1.10   .50
1200 A448 600p Swan river daisy 1.10 .50
      Nos. 1196-1200 (5)   5.50 2.50

World Health
Day — A449

1990, May 1   Litho.   Perf. 12½
1201 A449 600p multicolored   2.50 1.25

Liberation of Al-
Kuneitra, 16th
Anniv. — A450

Intl. Literacy
Year — A451

1990, June 26   Perf. 12x11½
1202 A450 550p multicolored   2.50 1.25

1990, June 26
1203 A451 550p multicolored   2.25 1.10

UN Conference on Least Developed
Countries — A452

1990, July 10   Perf. 11½x12
1204 A452 600p multicolored   2.40 1.25

37th Damascus
Intl. Fair — A453

Arbor
Day — A455

World Meteorology Day — A454

1990, Aug. 28   *Perf. 12x11½*
1205 A453 550p multicolored   2.25 1.10

1990, Aug. 28   *Perf. 11½x12*
1206 A454 450p multicolored   1.90 .95

1990, Oct. 30   *Perf. 12x11½*
1207 A455 550p multicolored   2.25 1.10

World Food Day — A456

1990, Oct. 30   *Perf. 12½*
1208 A456 850p multicolored   3.25 1.75

Al Maqdisi, Cartographer A457

1990, Nov. 6   *Perf. 12x11½*
1209 A457 550p multicolored   2.25 1.10

A458   A459

Pres. Hafez al Assad A460

1990, Nov. 16   Litho.   *Perf. 11½*
1210 A458 50p claret   .20 .20
1211 A458 70p gray   .25 .20
1212 A458 100p blue   .35 .20
1213 A458 150p brown   .60 .30
    Perf. 12x11½
1214 A459 175p multicolored   .70 .35
1215 A459 300p multicolored   1.25 .55
1216 A459 550p multicolored   2.25 1.10
1217 A459 600p multicolored   2.40 1.25
    Perf. 11½x12
1219 A460 1000p multicolored   4.00 2.00
1220 A460 1500p multicolored   6.00 3.00
1222 A460 2000p multicolored   8.00 4.00
1224 A460 2500p multicolored   10.00 5.00
    Nos. 1210-1224 (12)   36.00 18.15

This may be an expanding set. Numbers will change if necessary.

1992, May 19   Litho.   *Perf. 11½*
    Without Date at Right
1225   A458 150p brown   .60 .30
1225A A458 300p violet   1.25 .60
1225B A458 350p gray   1.40 .70
1225C A458 400p red   1.60 .80
    Nos. 1225-1225C (4)   4.85 2.40

     Souvenir Sheet

Corrective Movement, 20th Anniv. — A461

a, Pres. Assad with children. b, Assad addressing crowd. c, Assad, memorial. d, Assad, dam.

1990, Nov. 16   *Imperf.*
1227 A461 550p Sheet of 4, #a.- d.   9.00 9.00

UN Development Program, 40th Anniv. — A462

1990, Dec. 11   *Perf. 11½x12*
1228 A462 550p multicolored   2.25 1.10

Arab Civil Aviation Day A463

1990, Dec. 11
1229 A463 175p multicolored   1.00 .50

World Post Day — A464

Intl. Children's Day — A465

1990, Dec. 11   *Perf. 12x11½*
1230 A464 550p multicolored   2.25 1.10

1990, Dec. 11
1231 A465 550p multicolored   2.25 1.10

Arab-Spanish Cultural Symposium A466

World AIDS Day — A467

1990, Dec. 24
1232 A466 550p multicolored   2.25 1.10

1990, Dec. 24
1233 A467 550p multicolored   2.25 1.10

March 8th Revolution, 28th Anniv. — A468

1991, Mar. 8   Litho.   *Perf. 11½x12*
1234 A468 150p multicolored   .60 .30

Butterflies A469

1991, Mar. 17   *Perf. 12½*
1235 A469 550p Small tortoise-shell   2.25 1.10
1236 A469 550p Changeful great mars   2.25 1.10
1237 A469 550p Papillion machaon   2.25 1.10
    Nos. 1235-1237 (3)   6.75 3.30

Birds — A470

Mother's Day — A471

1991, Mar. 17   *Perf. 12x11½*
1238 A470 600p Golden oriole   2.40 1.25
1239 A470 600p European roller   2.40 1.25
1240 A470 600p House sparrow   2.40 1.25
    Nos. 1238-1240 (3)   7.20 3.75

1991, Mar. 21
1241 A471 550p multicolored   2.25 1.10

1946 Evacuation of British and French Troops — A472

1991, Apr. 17   *Perf. 11½x12*
1242 A472 150p multicolored   .60 .30

Labor Day A473

1991, May 1
1243 A473 550p multicolored   2.25 1.10

Intl. Flower Show, Damascus — A474

1991, July 8   *Perf. 12x12½*
1244 A474 550p Narcissus   2.25 1.10
1245 A474 600p Monarda didyma   2.40 1.25

Liberation of Kuneitra, 17th Anniv. A475

1991, July 22   *Perf. 11½x12*
1246 A475 550p multicolored   2.25 1.10

11th Mediterranean Games, Athens — A476

1991, July 22
1247 A476 550p Running   2.25 1.10
1248 A476 550p Soccer   2.25 1.10
1249 A476 600p Equestrian   2.25 1.25
    Size: 80x64mm
    Imperf
1250 A476 1300p Dolphins play-ing water polo   5.25 5.25
    Nos. 1247-1250 (4)   12.00 8.70

38th Damascus
Intl. Fair — A477

1991, Aug. 28 *Perf. 12x12½*
1251 A477 550p multicolored 2.25 1.10

Intl.
Tourism
Day
A478

Designs: 450p, Woman at Khan Asaad
Pasha El Azem. 550p, Woman at Castle of
Arwad Island.

1991, Sept. 27 *Perf. 11½x12*
1252 A478 450p multicolored 1.90 .95
1253 A478 550p multicolored 2.25 1.10

Housing
Day — A479

1991, Oct. 7 *Perf. 12x11½*
1254 A479 175p multicolored 1.00 .50

1991, Oct. 16
1255 A480 600p multicolored 2.40 1.25

Intl. Children's
Day — A480

Physician
Abu Bakr
Al Razi
(Rhazes),
Patient
A481

1991, Nov. 2 Litho. *Perf. 12½x12*
1256 A481 550p multicolored 2.25 1.10
31st Science Week.

World
Post Day
A482

1991, Nov. 12
1257 A482 550p multicolored 2.25 1.10

World
Food Day
A483

1991, Nov. 12
1258 A483 550p multicolored 2.25 1.10

Tomb of
Unknown
Soldier,
Damascus
A484

1991, Nov. 16 *Perf. 12½*
1259 A484 600p multicolored 2.40 1.25
Size: 65x80mm
Imperf
1260 A484 1000p multicolored 4.00 2.00

Corrective Movement, 21st
Anniv. — A485

Illustration reduced.

1991, Nov. 16 *Imperf.*
1261 A485 2500p multicolored 10.00 5.00

Protect the Environment — A486

1991, Nov. 20 *Perf. 12½x12*
1262 A486 175p multicolored .70 .35

World Telecommunications
Fair — A487

1991, Nov. 20 *Perf. 12x12½*
1263 A487 600p multicolored 2.40 1.25

March 8th
Revolution,
29th Anniv.
A488

1992, Mar. 8 Litho. *Perf. 12½*
1264 A488 600p multicolored 2.40 1.25

Re-election of Pres. Assad — A489

1992, Mar. 12 Litho. *Imperf.*
1265 A489 5000p shown 20.00 10.00
Size: 100x85mm
1266 A489 5000p inscription at
right 20.00 10.00
Nos. 1265-1266 incorporate designs of
#1036, C496 & C506.

Baath
Party,
45th
Anniv.
A490

1992, Apr. 7 *Perf. 12½x12*
1267 A490 850p multicolored 3.50 1.75

Labor
Day — A491

Mother's
Day — A492

1992, May 1 *Perf. 12x12½*
1268 A491 900p multicolored 3.50 1.75

1992, May 19
1269 A492 900p multicolored 3.50 1.75

Evacuation of British and French
Troops, 46th Anniv. — A493

1992, May 19 *Perf. 12½x12*
1270 A493 900p multicolored 3.50 1.75

Traffic Safety
Day — A494

Intl. Flower Show,
Damascus
A495

1992, May 19 *Perf. 12x12½*
1271 A494 850p multicolored 3.50 1.75

Perf. 11½x12, 12x11½
1992, July 5 *Litho.*
Designs: 300p, Linum mucronatum, horiz.
800p, Yucca filamentosa. 900p, Zinnia
elegans.
1272 A495 300p multicolored 1.25 .65
1273 A495 800p blue & multi 3.25 1.60
1274 A495 900p multicolored 3.50 1.75
Nos. 1272-1274 (3) 8.00 4.00

1992 Summer
Olympics,
Barcelona
A496

No. 1275: a, 150p, Team handball. b, 150p,
Running. c, 450p, Swimming. d, 750p, Wrestling. 5000p, Incorporates designs of Nos.
1275a-1275d.

1992, July 25 Litho. *Perf. 12x11½*
1275 A496 Strip of 4, #a.-d. 6.00 5.00
Imperf
Size: 80x124mm
1276 A496 5000p multicolored 20.00 10.00

Anti-Smoking
Campaign
A497

39th Intl. Damascus Fair — A498

1992, Aug. 28 *Perf. 12x12½*
1277 A497 750p multicolored 3.00 1.50

1992, Aug. 28
1278 A498 900p multicolored 3.50 1.75

7th Arab Games, Damascus — A499

Designs: a, 750p, Soccer. b, 850p, Pommel horse. c, 900p, Pole vault.

1992, Sept. 4 *Perf. 12½*
1279 A499 Strip of 3, #a.-c. 10.00 5.00

World Post Day — A500

World Children's Day — A501

1992, Oct. 9 *Perf. 12x12½*
1280 A500 600p multicolored 2.40 1.25

1992, Nov. 7 *Perf. 12x11½*
1281 A501 850p multicolored 3.50 1.75

Sebtt El Mardini (826-912) A502

1992, Nov. 7 Litho. *Perf. 12x11½*
1282 A502 850p multicolored 3.50 1.75

1992 Special Olympics, Madrid A503

1992, Nov. 7 *Perf. 12½*
1283 A503 850p multicolored 3.50 1.75

Corrective Movement, 22nd Anniv. — A504

1992, Nov. 16 *Perf. 11½x12*
1284 A504 450p multicolored 1.75 .90

Arbor Day — A505

1992, Dec. 31 *Perf. 12x12½*
1285 A505 600p multicolored 2.40 1.25

2nd Intl. Conference of PACO — A506

Design: 1150p, Eye surrounded by scenes of day and night, rainbow.

1993, May 12 Litho. *Perf. 12*
1286 A506 1100p multicolored 1.00 .50
Size: 35½x24mm
Perf. 11½x12
1287 A506 1150p multicolored 1.10 .55
Syrian Ophthamological Society, 25th anniv. (#1287).

March 8th Revolution, 30th Anniv. — A507

1993, Mar. 8 Litho. *Perf. 11½x12*
1288 A507 1100p multicolored .80 .40

Butterflies A508

Designs: a, 1000p, Common blue. b, 1500p, Silver-washed fritillary. c, 2500p, Precis orithya.

1993, Mar. 13
1289 A508 Strip of 3, #a.-c. 4.75 4.75

Mother's Day — A509

1993, Apr. 17 *Perf. 12x11½*
1290 A509 1100p multicolored .80 .40

Evacuation of British and French Troops, 47th Anniv. — A510

1993, Apr. 17 *Perf. 11½x12*
1291 A510 1100p multicolored .80 .40

A511

1993, Apr. 17 Litho. *Perf. 11½x12*
1292 A511 2500p multicolored 1.75 .85

Agricultural Reform, 25th Anniv. — A512

1993, Apr. 20 Litho. *Perf. 11½x12*
1293 A512 1150p multicolored .90 .45

A513

A514

1993, May 1 *Perf. 12x11½*
1294 A513 1100p multicolored .80 .40
Labor day.

1993, June 17 Litho. *Perf. 12x11½*
Intl. Flower Show, Damascus: a, 1000p, Alcea setosa. b, 1100p, Primulaceae. c, 1150p, Gesneriaceae.
1295 A514 Strip of 3, #a.-c. 2.25 2.25

Tourism A515

1993, Sept. 27 *Perf. 11½x12*
1296 A515 1000p Woman, prism tomb 1.00 .50

World Post Day A516

1993, Oct. 9 *Perf. 12½x12*
1297 A516 1000p multicolored 1.00 .50

World Child Day A517

1993, Nov. 6 *Perf. 11½x12*
1298 A517 1150p multicolored 1.10 .55

Ibn El Bittar, Chemist — A518

1993, Nov. 6 *Perf. 12x11½*
1299 A518 1150p multicolored 1.10 .55

Corrective Movement, 23rd Anniv. — A519

Illustration reduced.

1993, Nov. 16 Litho. *Imperf.*
1300 A519 2500p multicolored 2.50 2.50

Arabian
Horses
A520

1994, Jan.　　Litho.　　Perf. 12½
1301　A520　1000p shown　　　　　.60　.30
1302　A520　1000p White horse　　.60　.30
1303　A520　1500p Tan horse　　　.90　.45
1304　A520　1500p Black horse　　.90　.45
　　　a.　　Strip of 4, #1301-1304　3.00　3.00

Arbor Day
A521

1994, Jan.　　Litho.　　Perf. 12½x12
1305　A521　1100p multicolored　　1.75　.85

40th Intl.
Damascus
Fair
A522

1994, Jan.
1306　A522　1100p multicolored　　1.75　.85

Basel Al Assad
(1962-94) — A523

1994, Mar. 1　　　　Perf. 12x12½
1307　A523　2500p multicolored　　4.00　2.00

March 8th Revolution, 31st
Anniv. — A524

a, Oranges. b, Mandarin oranges. c,
Lemons.

1994, Mar. 8　　　　Perf. 12½x12
1308　A524　1500p Strip of 3, #a.-
　　　　　　　c.　　　　　　　7.50　7.50

Evacuation of British and French
Troops, 48th Anniv. — A525

1994, Apr. 17
1309　A525　1800p multicolored　　2.75　1.40

Mother's
Day
A526

1994, May 1　　Litho.　　Perf. 12½x12
1310　A526　1800p multicolored　　2.75　1.40

Labor Day
A527

1994, May 1
1311　A527　1700p multicolored　　2.75　1.40

ILO, 75th
Anniv.
A528

1994, June 1
1312　A528　1700p multicolored　　2.75　1.40

1994 World Cup Soccer
Championships, U.S. — A529

Various soccer plays.

1994, June 17　　　　Perf. 12½
1313　A529　1700p Pair, #a.-b.　5.75　2.75
　　　Size: 80x80mm
　　　　　Imperf
1314　A529　4000p multicolored　6.75　6.75

41st Intl. Fair,
Damascus
A530

1994, Aug. 3　　Litho.　　Perf. 12x12½
1315　A530　1800p multicolored　　1.60　.80

1994, Aug. 3　　　　Perf. 12x11½
　　a, Daisies. b, Red flowers. c. Yellow flowers.
1316　A531　1800p Strip of 3, #a.-
　　　　　　　c.　　　　　　　4.50　4.50

Intl. Flower Show,
Damascus
A531

Intl. Olympic Committee,
Cent. — A532

1994, Aug. 3　　　　Perf. 11½x12
1317　A532　1700p multicolored　　1.50　.75

Butterflies
A533

a, Apollo (shown). b, Purple emperor, value
at right. c, Birdwing, value at left.

1994, Aug. 9　　Litho.　　Perf. 11½x12
1318　A533　1700p Strip of 3, #a.-
　　　　　　　c.　　　　　　　8.25　8.25

4th Natl.
Census
A534

1994, Aug. 15
1319　A534　1000p multicolored　　1.50　.75

Science
Week
A535

Design: £10, Al Kindi, philosopher.

1994, Nov. 5　　　　Perf. 12½
1320　A535　£10 multicolored　　1.50　.75

Corrective Movement, 24th
Anniv. — A536

Illustration reduced.

1994, Nov. 16　　　　Imperf.
1321　A536　£25 multicolored　　6.50　6.50

ICAO, 50th Anniv. — A537

1994, Dec. 7　　Litho.　　Perf. 12½
1322　A537　17p multicolored　　1.50　.75

Martyr's
Square
A538

1994, Dec. 7　　Litho.　　Perf. 11½x12
1323　A538　£50 purple　　　7.25　3.75
　　　See Nos. 1472-1474, 1518, 1538.

Intl. Children's
Day — A539

World Post
Day — A540

1994, Dec. 19　　　　Perf. 12x11½
1324　A539　£10 multicolored　　1.50　.75

1994, Dec. 19
1325　A540　£10 multicolored　　1.50　.75

Intl. Tourism
Day — A541

1994, Dec. 19
1326　A541　£17 multicolored　　2.50　1.25

March 8 Revolution, 32nd
Anniv. — A542

1995, Mar. 8　　Litho.　　Perf. 11½x12
1327　A542　£18 multicolored　　2.75　1.40

Arab League,
50th Anniv.
A543

1995, Mar. 22   *Perf. 12½*
1328 A543 £17 multicolored   2.50 1.25

World Water
Day — A544

1995, Apr. 9   Litho.   *Perf. 12x12½*
1329 A544 £17 multicolored   1.25 .60

Mother's
Day
A545

1995, Apr. 9   Litho.   *Perf. 12½x12*
1330 A545 £17 multicolored   2.00 1.00

Arbor
Day — A546

1995, Apr. 9   Litho.   *Perf. 12x12½*
1331 A546 1800p multicolored   1.50 .75

A547

A548

1995, Aug. 13   Litho.   *Perf. 12x11½*
1332 A547 £18 multicolored   2.75 1.40
UN, 50th anniv.

1995, Aug. 21
1333 A548 £18 multicolored   2.75 1.40
4th World Conference on Women, Beijing.

Desert
Festival,
Tourism
Day
A549

1995, June 25   *Perf. 12½x12*
1334 A549 £18 multicolored   1.25 .65

A550

A551

1995, June 25   *Perf. 12x12½*
1335 A550 £10 Labor Day   .75 .40

1995, Apr. 30   Litho.   *Perf. 12x11½*
1336 A551 £17 multicolored   1.25 .60
Evacuation of British & French Troops, 49th
anniv.

A552   A553

1995, Apr. 30   Litho.   *Perf. 12x11½*
1337 A542 £17 multicolored   1.40 .70
Intl. Year of the Family.

1995, Apr. 30   Litho.   *Perf. 12x12½*
1338 A553 £17 multicolored   2.00 1.00
Arab Apiculture Union, 1st anniv.

FAO, 50th
Anniv.
A554

1995, June 25   *Perf. 12½x12*
1339 A554 £15 multicolored   1.75 .85

42nd Intl.
Fair,
Damascus
A555

1995, Aug. 28   Litho.   *Perf. 11½x12*
1340 A555 £15 multicolored   1.50 .75

Int'l Flower
Show,
Damascus
A556

1995, July 30   Litho.   *Perf. 12½*
1341 A556 £10 Astilbe   .50 .25
1342 A556 £10 Evening prim-   .50 .25
    rose
1343 A556 £10 Blue carpet   .50 .25
  a.   Strip of 3, #1341-1343   1.50 1.50

Second Congress
of Arab Dentists'
Assoc. — A557

1995, Sept. 16   Litho.   *Perf. 12x11½*
1344 A557 £18 multicolored   1.50 .75

Syrian
Army,
50th
Anniv.
A558

1995, Oct. 2   Litho.   *Perf. 11½x12*
1345 A558 £18 multicolored   1.40 .70

World
Post Day
A559

1995, Oct. 2   Litho.   *Perf. 11½x12*
1346 A559 £15 multicolored   1.60 .85

World Children's
Day — A560

1995, Oct. 2   *Perf. 12x11½*
1347 A560 £18 multicolored   2.00 1.00

Ahmed ben Maged, Cartographer,
500th Death Anniv. — A561

1995, Nov. 4   Litho.   *Perf. 11½x12*
1348 A561 £18 multicolored   2.00 1.00

Corrective
Movement,
25th Anniv.
A562

Design: £50, like #1349 with Nos. 1044,
720, 1227b, 903.

1995, Nov. 11   Litho.   *Perf. 12½*
1349 A562 £10 multicolored   1.10 .55
   Imperf
   Size: 100x64mm
1350 A562 £50 multicolored   5.50 2.75

Songbirds
A563

Designs: a, Group on tree branch. b, One in
snow, flower. c, One on fence rail.

1995, Dec. 5   Litho.   *Perf. 12½*
1351 A563 £18 Strip of 3, #a.-c. 7.25 7.25

Louis
Pasteur
(1822-95)
A564

1995, Dec. 21   *Perf. 12½x12*
1352 A564 £18 multicolored   2.00 1.00

March 8 Revolution, 33rd
Anniv. — A565

1996, Mar. 8   Litho.   *Perf. 11½x12*
1353 A565 £25 Hydro-electric   2.00 1.00
    plant

Evacuation Day, 50th Anniv. — A566

1996, Apr. 17   *Perf. 12½*
1354 A566 £10 black & multi   .85 .40
1355 A566 £25 bister & multi   2.00 1.00
   Size: 57x46mm
   Imperf
1356 A566 £25 bis, blk, & multi   *5.25 2.75*

Liberation of Kuneitra
A567

1996, June 26   Litho.   Perf. 11½x12
1357 A567 £10 multicolored   .60   .30

1996 Summer Olympic Games, Atlanta
A568

1996, July 19   Perf. 11½x12
1358 A568 £17 Wrestling   1.10   .55
1359 A568 £17 Swimming   1.10   .55
1360 A568 £17 Running   1.10   .55
  a.   Strip of 3, #1358-1360   3.25 3.25
Size: 55x41mm
Imperf
1361 A568 £25 Soccer   1.60   .80
  Nos. 1358-1361 (4)   4.90 2.45

Intl. Flower Show, Damascus
A569

Cactus: No. 1362, Notocactus graessnerii.
No. 1363, Mammilaria erythosperma.

1996, July 1   Litho.   Perf. 12½
1362 A569 £18 multicolored   1.25   .65
1363 A569 £18 multicolored   1.25   .65

Ba'ath Party, 50th Anniv.
A570

1996, July 1   Perf. 11½x12
1364 A570 £18 multicolored   1.25   .65

Pres. Hafez al-Assad — A571

1995   Litho.   Perf. 11½
1365 A571 100p bright blue   .20   .20
1366 A571 500p bright orange   .55   .25
1367 A571 £10 bright lilac   1.10   .55
1368 A571 £17 rose lake   1.90   .95
1369 A571 £18 slate green   2.00 1.00
  Nos. 1365-1369 (5)   5.75 2.95

Issued: £10, 5/3; 100p, 500p, £17, £18, 12/31.

Arbor Day — A572

Mother's Day — A573

1996, Mar. 8   Litho.   Perf. 12¼x12½
1370 A572 £17 multicolored   .80   .40

1996, May 1   Perf. 12x11½
1370A A573 £10 multicolored   .50   .25

Labor Day — A574

1996, May 1   Perf. 12¼x12½
1371 A574 £15 multicolored   .70   .35

Radio, Cent. — A575

1996, Aug. 18   Litho.   Perf. 12½
1372 A575 £17 multicolored   1.10   .55

World AIDS Day — A576

43rd Intl. Fair, Damascus
A577

1996, Aug. 18   Perf. 12x11½
1373 A576 £17 multicolored   1.10   .55

1996, Aug. 28
1374 A577 £17 multicolored   1.10   .55

NICE, 5th Anniv.
A578

1996, Sept. 5   Perf. 11½x12
1375 A578 £18 multicolored   1.10   .60

World Child Day — A579

World Post Day — A580

1996, Oct. 9   Perf. 12x11½
1376 A579 £10 multicolored   .65   .30

1996, Oct. 9
1377 A580 £17 multicolored   1.10   .55

UNICEF, 50th Anniv. — A581

1996, Nov. 20
1378 A581 £17 multicolored   1.10   .55

36th Science Week — A582

Design: Musa Iben Shaker's sons.

1996, Nov. 2   Perf. 12½x12
1379 A582 £10 multicolored   .65   .35

Corrective Movement, 26th Anniv.
A583

1996, Nov. 16   Perf. 12½
1380 A583 £10 multicolored   .65   .35
Size: 65x90mm
Imperf
1381 A583 £50 like No. 1380   3.25 1.60

Natl. Advance Party — A584

March 8 Revolution, 34th Anniv. — A585

1997, Mar. 7   Litho.   Perf. 12x11½
1382 A584 £3 multicolored   .20   .20

1997, Mar. 8
1383 A585 £15 multicolored   1.00   .50

Arbor Day — A586

1996, Apr. 8   Litho.   Perf. 12x12½
1384 A586 £10 multicolored   .75   .40

Fish — A587

1996, Apr. 8   Perf. 12½x12
1385 A587 £17 Two dorsal fins 1.00   .50
1386 A587 £17 One dorsal fin   1.00   .50
  a.   Pair, #1385-1386   2.00 2.00

Mother's
Day — A588

1997, Apr. 8 **Perf. 12x11½**
1387 A588 £15 multicolored 1.00 .50

Baath Party
Revolution,
50th Anniv.
A589

1997, Apr. 3 **Perf. 12½**
1388 A589 £25 multicolored 1.60 .80
Size: 90x65mm
Imperf
1389 A589 £25 multicolored 1.60 .80

World Tourism
Day — A590

1997, Apr. 8 **Perf. 12x11½**
1390 A590 £17 multicolored 1.10 .60

Evacuation Day, 51st Anniv. — A591

1997, Apr. 17 **Perf. 11½x12**
1391 A591 £15 multicolored 1.00 .50

Labor
Day — A592

1997, May 1 **Perf. 12x11½**
1392 A592 £15 multicolored 1.00 .50

World Book
Day —
A592a

1997, June 16 **Litho.** **Perf. 12½**
1392A A592a £10 multicolored .50 .25

A592b

1997, June 16 **Perf. 12x11½**
1392B A592b £18 multicolored .70 .35
No smoking day.

A593

1997, June 21 **Litho.** **Perf. 12x11½**
No. 1393, Echino ereus. No. 1394, Iris.
1393 A593 £18 multicolored 1.10 .60
1394 A593 £18 multicolored 1.10 .60
a. Pair, #1393-1394 2.25 2.25
Intl. Flower Show, Damascus.
See Nos. 1412-1413.

4th Congress of
Arab
Denistry — A594

44th Intl. Fair,
Damascus
A595

1997, Sept. 4
1395 A594 £10 multicolored .65 .35
1997, Sept. 4
1396 A595 £17 multicolored 1.10 .55

World
Post Day
A596

1997, Sept. 27 **Perf. 11½x12**
1397 A596 £17 multicolored 1.10 .55

World
Children's
Day
A597

1997, Sept. 27
1398 A597 £17 multicolored 1.10 .55

Intl.
Tourism
Day
A598

1997, Sept. 27
1399 A598 £17 multicolored 1.10 .55

37th Science
Week — A599

1997, Nov. 1 **Litho.** **Perf. 12x11½**
1400 A599 £17 multicolored 1.10 .55

Corrective
Movement,
27th Anniv.
A600

1997, Nov. 16 **Perf. 12½**
1401 A600 £10 multicolored .70 .35
Size: 92x67mm
Imperf
1402 A600 £50 like #1401 3.25 3.25

Islamic Conference, 30th
Anniv. — A601

1997, Dec. 9 **Litho.** **Perf. 11½x12**
1403 A601 £10 multicolored .70 .35

March 8 Revolution, 35th
Anniv. — A602

1998, Mar. 8 **Litho.** **Perf. 12½x12**
1404 A602 £17 multicolored 1.10 .55

Mother's
Day
A603

1998, March 21 **Perf. 11½x12**
1405 A603 £10 multicolored .70 .35

Evacuation Day,
52nd
Anniv. — A604

Labor
Day — A605

1998, Apr. 17 **Litho.** **Perf. 12x11½**
1406 A604 £10 multicolored .70 .35
1998, May 1
1407 A605 £18 multicolored 1.10 .55

World Tourism
Day — A606

Mother Teresa
(1910-97)
A607

1998, July 22 **Litho.** **Perf. 12x11½**
1408 A606 £17 Princess of
Banias 1.10 .55
1998, July 22
1409 A607 £18 multicolored 1.10 .55

1998 World Cup
Soccer
Championships,
France — A608

1998, June 22 **Perf. 12x12½**
1410 A608 £10 shown .60 .30

Size: 60x55mm
Imperf
1411 A608 £25 Soccer players,
              diff.   2.25 1.10

Intl. Flower Show Type of 1997
Flowers: No. 1412, Plum-colored with yellow
centers. No. 1413, Red hibiscus.

1998, June 22   Perf. 12x11½
1412 A593 £17 multicolored   1.10 1.10
1413 A593 £17 multicolored   1.10 1.10
  a. Pair, #1412-1413   2.25 2.25

45th Intl.
Damascus
Fair
A609

1998, Sept. 26 Litho. Perf. 11½x12
1414 A609 £18 multicolored   1.10 .55

World Children's
Day — A610

1998, Sept. 26   Perf. 12x11½
1415 A610 £18 multicolored   1.10 .55

World
Post Day
A611

1998, Sept. 26 Litho. Perf. 11½x12
1416 A611 £18 multicolored   1.10 .55

Day to Stop
Smoking — A612

1998, Sept. 26   Perf. 12x11½
1417 A612 £15 multicolored   .95 .50

Arab Post Day — A613

1998, Sept. 26   Perf. 12½
1418 A613 £10 multicolored   .60 .30

Arab-Israeli October War, 25th
Anniv. — A614

Illustration reduced.

1998, Oct. 6   Imperf.
1419 A614 £25 multicolored   1.60 .80

Science
Week
A615

1998, Nov. 3   Perf. 11½x12
1420 A615 £10 multicolored   .65 .35

Camels
A616

1998, Nov. 25   Perf. 12½
1421 A616 £17 multicolored   1.10 .55

Corrective
Movement,
28th Anniv.
A617

1998, Nov. 16 Litho. Perf. 12½
1422 A617 £10 multicolored   .65 .30

Size: 99x65mm
Imperf
1423 A617 £25 multicolored   .65 .30

Jerusalem — A618

1998, Nov. 25   Perf. 12½
1424 A618 £10 multicolored   .65 .30

Re-election
of Pres.
Assad
A619

£50, Portrait with designs from Nos. 1036,
C496, C506, & portrait from No. 1265.

1999, Feb. 11 Litho. Perf. 12½
1425 A619 £10 red brn & multi   .50 .25
1426 A619 £17 pale yel & multi   .90 .45
1427 A619 £18 pale grn & multi   .95 .45

Size: 140x110mm
Imperf
1428 A619 £50 pale grn & multi   2.50 2.50
  Nos. 1425-1428 (4)   4.85 3.65

Arbor
Day — A620

1999, Apr. 29 Litho. Perf. 12½
1429 A620 £17 multicolored   1.10 .55

Evacuation Day,
53rd.
Anniv. — A621

Mother's
Day — A622

1999, Apr. 29   Perf. 12x11½
1430 A621 £18 multicolored   1.10 .55

1999, Apr. 29
1431 A622 £17 multicolored   1.10 .55

Intl. Flower Show,
Damascus
A623

Designs: a, Jasminum. b, Acanthaceae.

1999, June 20 Litho. Perf. 12x11½
1432 A623 £10 Pair, #a.-b.   .85 .45

March 8 Revolution, 36th
Anniv. — A624

1999, Mar. 8   Litho. Perf. 12¼x12½
1433 A624 £25 shown   1.50 .75
Size: 75x110mm
Imperf
1434 A624 £25 Building, monu-
              ment   1.50 .75

Declaration of Human Rights, 50th
Anniv. — A625

1999, June 5   Perf. 11½x12
1435 A625 £18 multicolored   .95 .45

Labor
Day — A626

1999, June 5   Litho. Perf. 12x11½
1436 A626 £10 multicolored   .55 .30

10th
Amity
Festival
A627

1999, Aug. 1   Litho. Perf. 11½x12
1437 A627 £10 multicolored   .65 .30

A628

A630

A629

1999, Oct. 12 Litho. Perf. 12x11½
1438 A628 £10 multi   .65 .30
  Arab Post Day.

1999, Aug. 28   Perf. 11½x12
1439 A629 £15 multi   .95 .45
  46th Intl. Fair, Damascus.

1999, Sept. 21   Perf. 12x11½
1440 A630 £17 multi   1.10 .55
  Arab Dentists Assoc., 7th Congress.

A631

A632

1999, Nov. 16
1441 A631 £18 multi   1.10   .55
World Children's Day.

1999, Oct. 12
1442 A632 £17 multi   1.10   .55
UPU, 125th anniv.

Corrective Movement, 29th
Anniv. — A633

#1443, Building, statue. #1444, Close-up of
statue. £25, Building statue, fountain.

1999, Nov. 16   **Perf. 12½**
1443 A633 £17 multi   1.10   .55
1444 A633 £17 multi, vert.   1.10   .55
          Imperf
          Size: 115x76mm
1445 A633 £25 multi   1.60 1.60
     Nos. 1443-1445 (3)   3.80 2.70

Abu Hanifah al-Deilouri,
Botanist — A634

1999, Oct. 12   **Perf. 11½x12**
1446 A634 £17 multi   1.10   .55

Christianity, 2000th Anniv. — A635

1999, Nov. 16   **Perf. 12½**
1447 A635 £17 multi   1.10   .55

March 8
Revolution,
37th Anniv.
A636

2000, Mar. 8 **Litho.** **Perf. 12½**
1448 A636 £18 multi   1.10   .55

Mother's
Day — A637

2000, Mar. 21
1449 A637 £17 multi   1.00   .50

Evacuation Day, 54th Anniv. — A638

Illustration reduced.

2000, Apr. 17   **Imperf.**
1450 A638 £25 multi   1.50 1.50

Labor
Day — A639

2000, May 1 **Litho.** **Perf. 12x11½**
1451 A639 £10 multi   .40   .20

Installation of
Bashar al-
Assad as
President
A640

2000, July 17   **Perf. 12¼**
1452   Strip of 4   1.90 1.90
  a. A640 £3 lt blue & multi   .20   .20
  b. A640 £10 tan & multi   .40   .20
  c. A640 £17 bl gray & multi   .65   .30
  d. A640 £18 gray & multi   .65   .35

          Imperf
          Size: 110x74mm
1453 A640 £50 multi   1.90 1.90

Arab Post
Day
A641

2000, Aug. 20 **Litho.** **Perf. 11½x12**
1454 A641 £18 multi   1.10   .55

47th Damascus Fair — A642

2000, Aug. 20
1455 A642 £15 multi   .90   .45

2000 Summer Olympics,
Sydney — A643

No. 1456: a, £17, Weight lifting. b, £18,
Women's shot put.
Illustration reduced.

2000, Oct. 1 **Litho.** **Perf. 12x11½**
1456 A643 Pair, #a-b   1.40   .70
          Imperf
          Size: 80x77mm
1457 A643 £25 Javelin   .95   .50

World Tourism Day — A644

Illustration reduced.

2000, Dec. 6 **Litho.** **Imperf.**
1458 A644 £50 Mosaic   3.00 3.00

World
Post Day
A645

2000, Aug. 20   **Perf. 11½x12**
1459 A645 £18 multi   1.10   .55

Nasir ad-Din
at-Tusi (1201-
74), Scientist
A646

2000, Nov. 1 **Litho.** **Perf. 12½x12¼**
1460 A646 £15 multi   .60   .30
Science week.

Arbor
Day — A647

2000, May 15   **Perf. 12x11½**
1461 A647 £18 multi   .65   .35

Butterflies — A648

a, £17, Charaxes jasius. b, £18, Apaturairis.
Illustration reduced.

2000, May 15   **Perf. 12½**
1462 A648 Pair, #a-b   1.40   .70

World Children's
Day — A649

2000, Aug. 20 **Litho.** **Perf. 12x11½**
1463 A649 £10 multi   .60   .30

World
Meteorological
Organization,
50th
Anniv. — A650

2000, Dec. 6
1464 A650 £10 multi   .60   .30

March 8
Revolution, 38th
Anniv. — A651

2001   **Litho.**   **Perf. 12x11½**
1465   A651   £25 multi   .95   .50

Mother's
Day — A652

2001
1466   A652   £10 multi   .40   .20

Evacuation Day,
55th
Anniv. — A653

2001
1467   A653   £25 multi   .95   .50

Book and
Author's
Rights — A654

2001
1468   A654   £10 multi   .40   .20

Intl. Flower Show, Damascus — A655

No. 1469: a, Weigela. b, Mertensia.
Illustration reduced.

2001
1469   A655   £10 Horiz. pair, #a-b   .75   .40

Syrian
Engineering
Syndicate,
50th Anniv.
A656

2001, Feb. 1   **Litho.**   **Perf. 12½**

1470   A656   £17 multi   .65   .35

Size: 95x85mm
Imperf
1471   A656   £25 multi   .95   .50

Martyr's Square Type of 1994
2001   **Perf. 11½x12**
1472   A538   100p brt blue grn   .20   .20
1473   A538   £10 red   .35   .20
1474   A538   £50 blue   1.90   .95
     Nos. 1472-1474 (3)   2.45   1.35

Labor Day — A657

2001   **Litho.**   **Perf. 12x11½**
1475   A657   £18 multi   .75   .40

48th Damascus
Fair — A658

2001   **Litho.**   **Perf. 12x11½**
1476   A658   £10 multi   .40   .20

Re-occupation of Kuneitra by Syria,
27th Anniv. — A659

2001   **Perf. 11½x12**
1477   A659   £17 multi   .65   .35

Anti-Smoking Campaign — A660

2001
1478   A660   £18 multi   .70   .35

UN High Commissioner for Refugees,
50th Anniv. — A661

2001
1479   A661   £17 multi   .65   .35

Tooth Cross-
section
A662

2001   **Perf. 12x11½**
1480   A662   £10 multi   .40   .20

World Children's
Day — A663

2001   **Perf. 12x11½**
1481   A663   £18 multi   .70   .35

A664

2001   **Perf. 12x11½**
1482   A664   £10 multi   .40   .20

Size: 84x111mm
Imperf
1483   A664   £25 multi   1.00   1.00

A665

Aga Khan Award for
Architecture — A666

2001   **Perf. 11½x12**
1484   A665   £10 multi   .40   .20
1485   A666   £17 multi   .65   .35
1486   A666   £18 multi   .70   .35
     Nos. 1484-1486 (3)   1.75   .90

Installation of Bashar al-Assad as
President, 1st Anniv. — A667

Assad and: a, £10, Silver frame. b, £17,
Gold frame.
Illustration reduced.

2001   **Litho.**   **Perf. 12½x12¼**
1487   A667   Horiz. pair, #a-b   1.10   .55

Arab Post
Day
A668

2001   **Perf. 11½x12**
1488   A668   £18 multi   .75   .35

World Post
Day
A669

2001
1489   A669   £10 multi   .40   .20

Arbor Day — A670

2001   **Perf. 12x11½**
1490   A670   £5 multi   .20   .20

World Tourism
Day — A671

2001   **Perf. 12½**
1491   A671   £17 multi   .70   .35

Palestinian
Intifada — A672

2001   **Perf. 12x11½**
1492   A672   £17 multi   .70   .35

Pres. Hafez al-Assad (1930-
2000) — A673

2001   **Perf. 12¼x12½**
1493   A673   £25 multi   1.00   .50

Correctionist Movement, 31st Anniv. — A674

Text color: £5, Black. £15, Red.

2001   *Perf. 11½x12*
1494-1495 A674   Set of 2   .80   .40

Evacuation Day, 56th Anniv. — A675

2002, Apr. 7   Litho.   *Perf. 12x11½*
1496 A675   £15 multi   .65   .30

Labor Day — A676

2002, May 1   *Perf. 12x12½*
1497 A676   £10 multi   .45   .20

Intl. Flower Show, Damascus — A677

No. 1498: a, £15, Yellow flowers. b, £17, White lilies.

2002, May 1   *Perf. 12x11½*
1498 A677   Horiz. pair, #a-b   1.40   .70

March 8 Revolution, 39th Anniv. A678

2002, Mar. 8   Litho.   *Perf. 11½x12*
1499 A678   £15 multi   .65   .30

Mother's Day — A679

2002, Mar. 21   *Perf. 12x11½*
1500 A679   £25 multi   1.10   .55

Gazelle A680

2002, Mar. 8   *Perf. 12½*
1501 A680   £15 multi   .65   .30

Baath Party, 55th Anniv. A681

2002, Apr. 7   *Perf. 11½x12*
1502 A681   £15 multi   .65   .30

2002 World Cup Soccer Championships, Japan and Korea — A682

No. 1503 — Various players: a, £5. b, £10. £25, Goalie making save, horiz. Illustration reduced.

2002, May 31   *Perf. 12½*
1503 A682   Horiz. pair, #a-b   .65   .30
    Size: 78x65mm
    Imperf
1504 A682   £25 multi   1.10   .55

World Tourism Day — A683

2002, Sep. 27   *Perf. 12½*
1505 A683   £10 multi   .40   .20

First Syrian Railroad, Cent. — A684

2002, Nov. 9
1506 A684   £10 multi   .40   .20

Abd al-Rahman al-Kawakibi (1849-1902), Arab Nationalist — A685

2002, Aug. 13   *Perf. 12x11½*
1507 A685   £10 multi   .40   .20

Intifada — A686

Designs: £10, Flag bearer, four rock throwers, tank. £25, Flag bearer, rock thrower, tank.

2002, Sep. 28   *Perf. 12x11½*
1508 A686   £10 multi   .40   .20
    Size: 66x79mm
    Imperf
1509 A686   £25 multi   1.10   .55

Birds A687

2002, Sep. 27   *Perf. 11½x12*
1510   Vert. strip of 4   1.40   .70
a. A687 £3 Sand grouse   .20   .20
b. A687 £5 Francolin   .20   .20
c. A687 £10 Duck   .40   .20
d. A687 £15 Goose   .65   .30

Arab Post Day A688

Frame color: £5, Blue. £10, Red violet.

2002, Aug. 3   *Perf. 11½x12*
1511-1512 A688   Set of 2   .65   .30

49th Intl. Damascus Fair — A689

Emblem and: a, £5, "X's." b, £10, Squares and diamonds.

2002, Aug. 28   *Perf. 12x11½*
1513 A689   Horiz. pair, #a-b   .65   .30

World Post Day — A690

No. 1514: a, Dove, envelope, rainbow. b, Envelope, UPU emblem, horiz.

Perf. 12x11½, 11½x12 (#1514b)
2002, Oct. 9
1514 A690   £10 Horiz. pair, #a-b   .80   .40

Arbor Day — A691

2002, Dec. 26   *Perf. 12x11½*
1515 A691   £10 multi   .40   .20

Intl. Children's Day — A692

2002, Oct. 16   *Perf. 12½*
1516 A692   £10 multi   .40   .20

Corrective Movement, 32nd Anniv. A693

2002, Oct. 16   *Perf. 11½x12*
1517 A693   £10 multi   .40   .20

Martyr's Square Type of 1994
2003, May 5   Litho.   *Perf. 11½x12*
1518 A538   300p brown   .20   .20

March 8 Revolution, 40th Anniv. — A694

2003, Mar. 8   *Perf. 12¼x12½*
1519 A694   £15 multi   .65   .30

Teacher's Day — A695

2003, Mar. 8 **Perf. 12x11½**
1520 A695 £17 multi .75 .40

Mother's Day — A696

2003, Mar. 21
1521 A696 £32 multi 1.40 .70

Evacuation Day, 57th Anniv. — A697

2003, Apr. 17
1522 A697 £15 multi .65 .30

Labor Day — A698

2003, May 1
1523 A698 £25 multi 1.10 .55

Intl. Flower Show, Damascus A699

No. 1524: a, Damask roses and violets. b, Anemones. c, Daisies. d, Damask roses and gillyflowers. e, Sunflowers.

2003, June 15 **Perf. 12½x12¼**
1524 Horiz. strip of 5 2.25 1.10
a.-e. A699 £10 Any single .45 .20

50th Intl. Damascus Fair — A700

Designs: £32, Flags, emblems. £50, Open orbs, horiz.

2003, Sep. 3 **Perf. 12x12½**
1525 A700 £32 multi 1.40 .70
Size: 89x66mm
Imperf
1526 A700 £50 multi 2.25 2.25

World Tourism Day — A701

2003, Sep. 27 **Perf. 12¼x12½**
1527 A701 £32 multi 1.40 .70

Election of Pope John Paul II, 25th Anniv. — A702

2003, Oct. 16 **Perf. 12½x12¼**
1528 A702 £32 multi 1.40 .70

World Post Day A703

2003, Oct. 14 Litho. Perf. 11½x12
1529 A703 £10 multi .45 .20

Corrective Movement, 33rd Anniv. — A704

2003, Nov. 16 **Perf. 12x11½**
1530 A704 £15 multi .65 .30

Intl. Children's Day A705

2003, Dec. 8 **Perf. 11½x12**
1531 A705 £15 multi .65 .30

Birds A706

2003, Dec. 8 **Perf. 12½x12¼**
1532 Horiz. strip of 5 2.75 2.75
a. A706 £5 Woodcock .20 .20
b. A706 £10 Lapwing .45 .20
c. A706 £15 European roller .65 .30
d. A706 £17 Teal .70 .35
e. A706 £18 Bustard .75 .40

Pres. Bashar al-Assad — A707

Perf. 11¾x11¼
2003, Dec. 8 **Unwmk.**
1533 A707 £15 brt blue green .65 .30
1534 A707 £25 blue 1.10 .55
1535 A707 £50 lilac 2.10 1.10
Nos. 1533-1535 (3) 3.85 1.95
See Nos. 1585-1594.

World Summit on the Information Society, Geneva — A708

2003, Dec. 10 **Perf. 12x11½**
1536 A708 £15 multi .65 .30

Arbor Day — A709

2003, Dec. 25 **Litho.**
1537 A709 £25 multi 1.10 .55

Martyr's Square Type of 1994
2004 **Perf. 11½x12**
1538 A538 £5 blue .20 .20

March 8 Revolution, 41st Anniv. — A710

2004, Mar 8 **Perf. 12½x12**
1539 A710 £10 multi .40 .20

Teacher's Day — A711

2004, Mar. 13 **Perf. 12x11½**
1540 A711 £5 multi .20 .20

Mother's Day A712

2004, Mar. 21 **Perf. 11½x12**
1541 A712 £15 multi .65 .30

Evacuation Day, 58th Anniv. — A713

2004, Apr. 17 **Litho.**
1542 A713 £10 multi .40 .20

Labor Day A714

2004, May 1
1543 A714 £10 multi .40 .20

A715

A716

A717

A718

FIFA (Fédération Internationale de Football Association), Cent. — A719

Illustration A719 reduced.

2004, May 21   **Perf. 11½x12**
1544 A715 £5 multi   .20 .20
1545 A716 £10 multi   .40 .20
    Perf. 12½x12¼
1546 A717 £15 multi   .60 .30
    Perf. 12¼x12½
1547 A718 £32 multi   1.25 .60
   Nos. 1544-1547 (4)   2.45 1.30
    Imperf
1548 A719 £25 multi   1.00 1.00

Intl. Flower Show, Damascus A720

No. 1549: a, Gladiola lavender. b, Jasmine. c, Iris. d, Orange nesrien. e, Tulip.

2004, June 15   **Perf. 12x11½**
1549   Horiz. strip of 5   1.00 1.00
a.-e. A720 £5 Any single   .20 .20

Children and War Campaign of Intl. Committee of the Red Cross — A721

2004, June 17   **Perf. 12¼x12½**
1550 A721 £32 red & black   1.25 .60

2004 Summer Olympics, Athens — A722

Designs: £5, Track. £10, Boxing, horiz. £25, Swimming, horiz.

    Perf. 12x11½, 11½x12
2004, Aug. 13
1551-1553 A722 Set of 3   1.60 .80

51st Intl. Damascus Fair — A723

2004, Sept. 3   **Perf. 12x11½**
1554 A723 £25 multi   1.00 .50

2004 Census A724

2004, Sept. 14   **Perf. 12½**
1555 A724 £10 multi   .45 .20

World Tourism Day A725

Designs: £5, Locomotive. No. 1557, £10, Building. No. 1558, £10, Train.

    Perf. 11½x12
2004, Sept. 27   **Litho.**   **Unwmk.**
1556-1558 A725 Set of 3   1.00 .50

World Post Day — A726

2004, Oct. 9   **Litho.**   **Perf. 12x11½**
1559 A726 £17 multi   .70 .35

Intl. Children's Day A727

2004, Oct. 16   **Perf. 11½x12**
1560 A727 £18 multi   .70 .35

Corrective Movement, 34th Anniv. — A728

2004, Nov. 16   **Perf. 12½x12**
1561 A728 £25 multi   1.00 .50

Arbor Day — A729

2004, Dec. 30   **Perf. 12x11½**
1562 A729 £10 multi   .40 .20

Northern Bald Ibis — A730

    Perf. 12½x12¼
2004, Dec. 30   **Litho.**   **Unwmk.**
1563 A730 £10 multi   .40 .20

Farm Animals A731

2004, Dec. 30   **Perf. 11½x12**
1564   Vert. strip of 4   2.10 1.10
a. A731 £5 Shami goat   .20 .20
b. A731 £15 Awassi ewe   .55 .25
c. A731 £17 Bull   .65 .30
d. A731 £18 Shami cow   .70 .35

March 8 Revolution, 42nd Anniv. — A732

    Perf. 12¼x12½
2005, Mar. 8   **Wmk. 403**
1565 A732 £17 multi   .65 .30

Teacher's Day A733

2005, Mar. 13   **Perf. 11½x12**
1566 A733 £25 multi   1.00 .50

Mother's Day — A734

2005, Mar. 21   **Perf. 12x11½**
1567 A734 £18 multi   .70 .35

Arab League, 60th Anniv. — A735

2005, Mar. 22
1568 A735 £10 multi   .40 .20

National Day — A736

2005, Apr. 17
1569 A736 £17 multi   .65 .30

Labor Day — A737

2005, May 1   **Wmk. 403**
1570 A737 £15 multi   .60 .30

Intl. Flower Show, Damascus A738

2005, June 15   **Litho.**
1571   Horiz. strip of 5   2.50 1.25
a. A738 £5 Hyacinth   .20 .20
b. A738 £10 Sternbergia clusiana   .40 .20
c. A738 £15 Primula obconica   .55 .30
d. A738 £17 Primula malacoides   .65 .30
e. A738 £18 Canaria   .70 .35

Butterflies A739

No. 1572: a, Papilio ulysses. b, Monarch. c, Baeotus baeotus. d, Lacewing. e, Tiger swallowtail.

2005, Aug. 7   **Perf. 12½**
1572   Horiz. strip of 5   2.00   1.00
a.-e.   A739 £10 Any single   .40   .20

52nd Intl. Damascus Fair — A740

2005, Sept. 3   **Perf. 12x11½**
1573   A740   £15 multi   .60   .30

Mevlana Jalal ad-Din ar-Rumi (1207-73), Islamic Philosopher A741

2005, Sept. 25   **Perf. 12½x12¼**
1574   A741   £25 multi   1.00   .50

See Afghanistan No. , Iran No. 2911, and Turkey No. 2971.

World Tourism Day A742

2005, Sept. 27   **Perf. 11½x12**
1575   A742   £17 multi   .65   .30

World Post Day — A743

2005, Oct. 9   **Perf. 12x11½**
1576   A743   £18 multi   .70   .35

Intl. Children's Day — A744

2005, Oct. 16   **Perf. 12¼x12½**
1577   A744   £17 multi   .65   .30

Corrective Movement, 35th Anniv. — A745

2005, Nov. 16   **Perf. 11½x12**
1578   A745   £25 multi   1.00   .50

World Summit on the Information Society, Tunis — A746

2005, Nov. 16   **Perf. 12¼x12½**
1579   A746   £17 multi   .65   .30

Poets A747

No. 1580: a, Nizar Kabbani (1923-98). b, Sadalah Wannous (1941-97). c, Omar Abu Reisheh (1910-90).

2005, Dec. 20   **Perf. 12½x12¼**
1580   Horiz. strip of 3   1.75   .85
a.   A747 £10 multi   .40   .20
b.   A747 £17 multi   .65   .30
c.   A747 £18 multi   .70   .35

Arbor Day — A748

2005, Dec. 25   **Wmk. 403**
1581   A748   £17 multi   .65   .30

March 8 Revolution, 43rd Anniv. — A749

Perf. 12x11½
2006, Mar. 8   **Litho.**   **Wmk. 403**
1582   A749   £18 multi   .70   .35

Aleppo, 2006 Capital of Islamic Culture A750

No. 1583: a, £17, Aleppo Castle. b, £18, Mosque, vert. £25, Emblem and buildings.

2006, Mar. 16 **Perf. 11½x12, 12x11½**
1583   A750   Pair, #a-b   1.40   .70
Imperf
Size: 79x60mm
1584   A750   £25 multi   .95   .50

Pres. Bashir al-Assad Type of 2003
2006   **Wmk. 403**   **Perf. 11¾x11¼**
1585   A707   £1 brt blue   .20   .20
1586   A707   £3 lilac rose   .20   .20
1587   A707   £5 brown   .20   .20
1588   A707   £10 purple   .40   .20
1589   A707   £15 brt blue grn   .60   .30
1590   A707   £17 orange brn   .65   .35
1591   A707   £18 dark blue   .70   .35
1592   A707   £25 blue   .95   .50
1593   A707   £50 lilac   1.90   .95
1594   A707   £100 green   4.00   2.00
       Nos. 1585-1594 (10)   9.80   5.25

Issued: £1, 9/7; £3, 8/24; £5, 8/1; £10, 6/2; £15, £25, £50, 3/19; £17, 5/11; £18, 6/8; £100, 9/27.

Mother's Day — A751

Perf. 12x11½
2006, Mar. 21   **Wmk. 403**
1595   A751   £17 multi   .65   .35

National Day — A752

No. 1596: a, Sultan Pasha al-Atrach (1889-1982). b, Yousef al-Azmeh (1884-1920). c, Sheikh Saleh al-Ali (1885-1950). d, Ibrahim Hanano (1889-1935). e, Ahmad Moraiwed (1886-1926).

2006, Apr. 17
1596   Horiz. strip of 5   1.90   .95
a.-e.   A752 £10 Any single   .35   .20

Labor Day — A753

2006, May 1
1597   A753   £17 multi   .65   .35

Intl. Flower Show, Damascus — A754

No. 1598: a, £5, Hyoscyamus aureus. b, £10, Cistus salviaefolius.

2006, May 15   **Perf. 11½x12**
1598   A754   Vert. pair, #a-b   .60   .30

2006 World Cup Soccer Championships, Germany — A755

No. 1599: a, £17, Players, aerial view of stadium. b, £18, Players under stadium roof. £50, Players, vert.

2006, June 25   **Perf. 11½x12**
1599   A755   Vert. pair, #a-b   1.40   .70
Imperf
Size: 60x80mm
1600   A755   £50 multi   1.90   .95

Diplomatic Relations Between Syria and People's Republic of China, 50th Anniv. — A756

2006, Aug. 1   **Perf. 12½x12¼**
1601   A756   £10 multi   .40   .20

Intl. Year of Deserts and
Desertification — A757

2006, Aug. 13 **Wmk. 403**
602 A757 £10 multi .40 .20

53rd Intl.
Damascus
Fair — A758

2006, Sept. 3 **Perf. 12x11½**
603 A758 £10 multi .40 .20

A759

2006, Sept. 27 **Perf. 11½x12**
604 A759 £10 multi .40 .20
Perf. 12¼x12½
605 A760 £10 multi .40 .20

World Tourism
Day — A760

World Post
Day — A761

2006, Oct. 19 **Perf. 12x11½**
606 A761 £17 multi .65 .35

Artists — A762

No. 1607: a, Fateh Almudarres (1922-99). b,
Adham Ismail (1922-63). c, Saeed Makhlouf

(1925-2000). d, Burhan Karkutli (1932-2003).
e, Michael Kirsheh (1900-73).

2006, Nov. 12 **Litho.**
1607 Horiz. strip of 5 1.90 .95
a.-e. A762 £10 Any single .35 .20

Corrective Movement, 36th
Anniv. — A763

2006, Nov. 16 **Perf. 12½x12¼**
1608 A763 £15 multi .60 .30

Arbor Day — A764

2006, Dec. 28 **Perf. 12¼x12½**
1609 A764 £15 multi .60 .30

Fish
A765

No. 1610: a, Light-colored fish, green and
violet seaweed. b, Dark-colored fish, green
and violet seaweed. c, Light-colored fish,
green seaweed.

2006, Dec. 28 **Perf. 11½x12**
1610 A765 £15 Vert. strip of 3,
#a-c 1.75 .85

March 8 Revolution, 44th
Anniv. — A766

Perf. 12¼x12½
2007, Mar. 8 **Litho.** **Wmk. 403**
1611 A766 £17 multi .65 .35

Mother's
Day — A767

2007, Mar. 21 **Perf. 12½x12¼**
1612 A767 £15 multi .60 .30

Baath Party,
60th Anniv.
A768

2007, Apr. 7
1613 A768 £25 multi 1.00 .50

National
Day — A769

2007, Apr. 14
1614 A769 £15 multi .60 .30

Labor
Day — A770

2007, May 1 **Perf. 12½**
1615 A770 £10 multi .40 .20

Intl. Flower Show, Damascus — A771

No. 1616: a, Freesia. b, Ipomoea purpurea.
c, Plumbago capensis.

2007, June 27 **Perf. 12¼x12½**
1616 A771 £15 Vert. strip of 3,
#a-c 1.75 .90

Second Term of Pres. Bashar al-
Assad — A772

No. 1617: a, £10, Portrait of Assad. b, £15,
Portrait of Assad, diff.
£25, Assad taking oath, horiz.
Illustration reduced.

Perf. 12½x12¼
2007, July 17 **Litho.** **Wmk. 403**
1617 A772 Horiz. pair, #a-b 1.00 .50
Size: 85x70mm
Imperf
1618 A772 £25 multi 1.00 .50

SEMI-POSTAL STAMPS

Nos. 174-185 Surcharged in Red or
Black

1926		**Unwmk.**	**Perf. 12½, 13½**	
B1	A4	25c + 25c ol blk (R)	2.25	2.00
B2	A4	50c + 25c yel grn	2.25	2.00
B3	A4	75c + 25c brown org	2.25	2.00
B4	A5	1p + 50c magenta	2.25	2.00
B5	A4	1.25p + 50c dp grn (R)	2.25	2.00
B6	A4	1.50p + 50c rose red	2.25	2.00
B7	A4	2p + 75c dk brn (R)	2.25	2.00
B8	A4	2.50p + 75c pck bl (R)	2.25	2.00
B9	A4	3p + 1p org brn (R)	2.25	2.00
B10	A4	5p + 1p violet	2.25	2.00
B11	A4	10p + 2p vio brn	2.25	2.00
B12	A4	25p + 5p ultra (R)	2.25	2.00
		Nos. B1-B12 (12)	27.00	24.00
		Set, never hinged	36.00	

On No. B4 the surcharge is set in six lines to
fit the shape of the stamp.

The surcharge was a contribution to the relief of refugees from the Djebel Druze War. See Nos. CB1-CB4.

Catalogue values for unused stamps in this section, from this point to the end of the section, are for Never Hinged items.

Syrian Arab Republic

Jordanian Flags on Map of Israel, and Arabs — SP1

1965, June 12   Litho.   Perf. 12x11½

B13	SP1	12½p + 5p multi	.20	.20
B14	SP1	25p + 5p multi	.20	.20

Issued for Palestine Week.

Father with Children and Red Crescent SP2

1968, May   Litho.   Perf. 12½x12

B15	SP2	12½p + 2½p multi	.25	.25
B16	SP2	27½p + 7½p multi	.25	.25

The surtax was for refugees.

AIR POST STAMPS

a

b

Nos. 35, 45, 47 Handstamped Type "a" in Violet

1920, Dec.   Unwmk.   Perf. 13½

C1	A22	1p on 5c	160.00	40.00
C2	A20	5p on 15c	290.00	47.50
C3	A18	10p on 40c	425.00	77.50
		Nos. C1-C3 (3)	875.00	165.00

Nos. 36, 46, 48 Overprinted Type "a" in Violet

1921, June 12

C4	A22	1p on 20c	87.50	40.00
C5	A18	5p on 1fr	425.00	150.00
C6	A18	10p on 2fr	425.00	150.00
		Nos. C4-C6 (3)	937.50	340.00

Excellent counterfeits exist of Nos. C1-C6.

Nos. 36, 46, 48 Overprinted Type "b"

1921, Oct. 5

C7	A22	1p on 20c	60.00	18.50
C8	A18	5p on 1fr	150.00	37.50
a.		Inverted overprint	325.00	240.00
C9	A18	10p on 2fr	200.00	47.50
a.		Double overprint	475.00	400.00
		Nos. C7-C9 (3)	410.00	103.50

Nos. 92, 94-96 Overprinted

c

1922, May 28

C10	A18	2p on 40c	25.00	25.00
a.		Inverted overprint		
C11	A18	3p on 60c	25.00	25.00
C12	A18	5p on 1fr	25.00	25.00
C13	A18	10p on 2fr	25.00	25.00
		Nos. C10-C13 (4)	100.00	100.00

Nos. 116-119 Overprinted Type "c"

1923, Nov. 22

C14	A18	2p on 40c	29.00	29.00
b.		Inverted surcharge		
C15	A18	3p on 60c	29.00	29.00
C16	A18	5p on 1fr	29.00	29.00
C17	A18	10p on 2fr	29.00	29.00
b.		Double overprint		
		Nos. C14-C17 (4)	116.00	116.00

Overprinted "Liabn"

C14a	A18	2p on 40c	400.00	400.00
C15a	A18	3p on 60c	400.00	400.00
C16a	A18	5p on 1fr	400.00	400.00
C17a	A18	10p on 2fr	400.00	400.00

Nos. 137-140 Overprinted Type "c"

1924, Jan. 13

C18	A18	2p on 40c	4.50	4.50
a.		Double overprint	27.50	
C19	A18	3p on 60c	4.50	4.50
a.		Inverted overprint	47.50	
C20	A18	5p on 1fr	4.50	4.50
a.		Double overprint	50.00	30.00
C21	A18	10p on 2fr	4.50	4.50
		Nos. C18-C21 (4)	18.00	18.00

Nos. 152, 154, 157-158 Overprinted

1924, July 17

C22	A18	2p on 40c	7.00	7.00
a.		Inverted overprint	32.50	
C23	A18	3p on 60c	7.00	7.00
a.		Inverted overprint	32.50	
b.		Double overprint	20.00	
C24	A18	5p on 1fr	7.00	7.00
C25	A18	10p on 2fr	7.00	7.00
a.		Inverted overprint	32.50	
		Nos. C22-C25 (4)	28.00	28.00

Regular Issue of 1925 Overprinted in Green

1925, Mar. 1

C26	A4	2p dark brown	2.25	2.25
C27	A4	3p orange brown	2.25	2.25
C28	A4	5p violet	2.25	2.25
C29	A4	10p violet brown	2.25	2.25
		Nos. C26-C29 (4)	9.00	9.00

Regular Issue of 1925 Overprinted in Red

f

1926

C30	A4	2p dark brown	2.00	2.00
a.		Inverted overprint	32.50	
C31	A4	3p orange brown	2.00	2.00
a.		Inverted overprint	32.50	
C32	A4	5p violet	2.50	2.50
a.		Inverted overprint	32.50	
C33	A4	10p violet brown	2.50	2.50
a.		Inverted overprint	32.50	
b.		Double overprint		
		Nos. C30-C33 (4)	9.00	9.00

Nos. C30-C33 received their first airmail use June 16, 1929, at the opening of the Beirut-Marseille line.
For surcharges see Nos. CB1-CB4.

Regular Issue of 1925 Overprinted Type "f" in Red or Black

1929

C34	A4	50c yellow green (R)	1.25	1.25
a.		Inverted overprint	40.00	
b.		Overprinted on face and back	22.50	
c.		Double overprint	40.00	
d.		Double overprint, one inverted	60.00	
e.		Pair, one without overprint		
C35	A5	1p magenta (Bk)	1.75	1.75
a.		Reversed overprint		
b.		Red overprint		
C36	A4	25p ultra (R)	5.50	5.50
a.		Inverted overprint	82.50	
b.		Pair, one without overprint		
		Nos. C34-C36 (3)	8.50	8.50

On No. C35, the overprint is vertical, with plane nose down.

No. 197 Overprinted Type "f" in Red

1929, July 9

C37	A4	15p on 25p ultra	4.25	4.25
a.		Inverted overprint		

Air Post Stamps of 1926-29 Overprinted in Various Colors

1929, Sept. 5

C38	A4	50c yellow grn (R)	3.00	3.00
C39	A5	1p magenta (Bl)	3.00	3.00
C40	A4	2p dk brown (V)	3.00	3.00
C41	A4	3p orange brn (Bl)	3.00	3.00
a.		Inverted overprint	70.00	
C42	A4	5p violet (R)	3.00	3.00
C43	A4	10p violet brn (Bl)	3.00	3.00
C44	A4	25p ultra (R)	3.00	3.00
		Nos. C38-C44 (7)	21.00	21.00

Damascus Industrial Exhibition.

AP1

Red Surcharge

1930, Jan. 30

C45	AP1	2p on 1.25p dp grn	3.00	3.00
a.		Inverted surcharge		
b.		Double surcharge	60.00	

Plane over Homs AP2

Designs: 1pi, City Wall, Damascus. 2pi, Euphrates River. 3pi, Temple Ruins, Palmyra. 5pi, Deir-el-Zor. 10pi, Damascus. 15pi, Aleppo, Citadel. 25pi, Hama. 50pi, Zebdani. 100pi, Telebisse.

1931-33   Photo.   Unwmk.

C46	AP2	50c ocher	1.00	.90
C47	AP2	50c black brn ('33)	1.25	1.00
C48	AP2	1p chestnut brown	1.10	.95
C49	AP2	2p Prus blue	2.75	1.75
C50	AP2	3p blue grn	1.75	1.25
C51	AP2	5p red violet	1.25	1.25
C52	AP2	10p slate grn	1.25	1.25
C53	AP2	15p orange red	2.10	1.50
C54	AP2	25p orange brn	2.75	2.00
C55	AP2	50p black	3.00	2.25
C56	AP2	100p magenta	3.75	2.50
		Nos. C46-C56 (11)	21.95	16.60

Nos. C46 to C56 exist imperforate. Value, $425.
For overprints see Nos. C67-C71, C110-C112, C114-C115, MC1-MC4.

Village of Bloudan AP12

1934, Aug. 2   Engr.   Perf. 12½

C57	AP12	50c yel brown	2.25	2.25
C58	AP12	1p green	2.50	2.50
C59	AP12	2p peacock bl	2.75	2.75
C60	AP12	3p red	3.00	3.00
C61	AP12	5p plum	3.00	3.00
C62	AP12	10p brt violet	27.50	27.50
C63	AP12	15p orange brn	30.00	30.00
C64	AP12	25p dk ultra	35.00	35.00
C65	AP12	50p black	45.00	45.00
C66	AP12	100p red brown	90.00	90.00
		Nos. C57-C66 (10)	241.00	241.00

Proclamation of the Republic. Exist imperf. Value, set $1,200.
Also exists without figures of value. Value, set $900.

Air Post Stamps of 1931-33 Overprinted in Red or Black

1936, Apr. 15   Perf. 13½x13, 13½

C67	AP2	50c black brown	5.25	4.75
C68	AP2	1p chnt brown (Bk)	5.25	4.75
C69	AP2	2p Prus blue	5.25	4.75
C70	AP2	3p blue green	5.25	4.75
C71	AP2	5p red violet (Bk)	5.25	4.75
		Nos. C67-C71 (5)	26.25	23.75

Damascus Fair, May 1936.

Syrian Pavilion at Paris Exposition AP13

1937, July 1   Photo.   Perf. 13½

C72	AP13	½p yellow green	2.75	2.75
C73	AP13	1p green	2.75	2.75
C74	AP13	2p lt brown	2.75	2.75
C75	AP13	3p rose red	2.75	2.75
C76	AP13	5p brown orange	2.75	2.75
C77	AP13	10p grnsh black	4.75	4.75
C78	AP13	15p blue	5.25	5.25
C79	AP13	25p dark violet	6.25	6.25
		Nos. C72-C79 (8)	30.00	30.00

Paris International Exposition. Exist imperf.

Ancient Citadel at Aleppo AP14

Omayyad Mosque and Minaret of Jesus at Damascus AP15

1937   Engr.   Perf. 13

C80	AP14	½ dark violet	.65	.65
C81	AP15	1p black	.65	.65
C82	AP14	2p deep green	.65	.65
C83	AP15	3p deep ultra	.65	.65
C84	AP15	5p rose lake	2.00	2.00
C85	AP15	10p red brown	1.10	1.10
C86	AP14	15p lake brown	4.75	4.75
C87	AP15	25p dark blue	6.00	6.00
		Nos. C80-C87 (8)	16.45	16.45

No. C80 to C87 exist imperforate. Value, set $175.
For overprint see No. C109.

Maurice Noguès and Route of France-Syria Flight — AP16

1938, July   Photo.   Perf. 11
C88 AP16 10p dark green   3.00 3.00
  a. Souv. sheet of 4, perf. 13½   32.50 32.50
  b. Perf. 13½   8.00 8.00

10th anniversary of first Marseille-Beirut flight, by Maurice Noguès.
No. C88a exists imperf.; value $800.

Bridge at Deir-el-Zor AP17

1940   Engr.   Perf. 13
C89 AP17 25c brown black   .20 .20
C90 AP17 50c peacock blue   .25 .25
C91 AP17 1p deep ultra   .30 .30
C92 AP17 2p dk orange brn   .45 .45
C93 AP17 5p green   .95 .95
C94 AP17 10p rose carmine   1.40 1.00
C95 AP17 50p dark violet   3.00 2.25
  Nos. C89-C95 (7)   6.55 5.40

Exist imperf. Value, set $125.

President Taj Eddin Hassani AP18

1942   Litho.   Perf. 11½
C96 AP18 10p blue gray   4.00 4.00
C97 AP18 50p gray lilac   4.25 4.25

Proclamation of Independence by the Allies, Sept. 27, 1941.

President Taj Eddin Hassani AP19

President Hassani and Map of Syria AP20

1942   Photo.
C98 AP19 10p sl grn & yel grn   4.00 4.00

Exists imperforate. Value, $30.

1943   Litho.
C99 AP20 2p dull brown   3.00 3.00
C100 AP20 10p red violet   3.00 3.00
C101 AP20 20p aqua   3.00 3.00
C102 AP20 50p rose pink   3.00 3.00
  Nos. C99-C102 (4)   12.00 12.00

Proclamation of United Syria.

Same, Overprinted with Black Border
1943, May 5
C103 AP20 2p dull brown   3.00 3.00
C104 AP20 10p red violet   3.00 3.00
C105 AP20 20p aqua   3.00 3.00
C106 AP20 50p rose pink   3.00 3.00
  Nos. C103-C106 (4)   12.00 12.00

Mourning for President Hassani. Exist imperf.

President Shukri el Kouatly — AP21

1944
C107 AP21 200p sepia   9.50 7.50
C108 AP21 500p dull blue   14.00 11.00

For overprints see Nos. C113, C116.

Stamps of 1931-44 Overprinted in Black, Blue or Carmine

1944   Perf. 13, 13½, 11½
C109 AP15 10p red brn (Bk)   2.50 2.50
C110 AP2 15p orange red   2.75 2.75
C111 AP2 25p org brown   2.75 2.75
C112 AP2 100p magenta   8.00 6.75
C113 AP21 200p sepia (C)   15.00 12.00
  Nos. C109-C113 (5)   31.00 26.75
  Set, never hinged   50.00

1st congress of Arab lawyers held in Damascus, Sept. 1944.

Nos. C53-C54, C108 Overprinted in Black or Orange

1944
C114 AP2 15p orange red   3.00 3.00
C115 AP2 25p org brown   3.00 3.00
C116 AP21 500p dull blue (O)   22.50 22.50
  Nos. C114-C116 (3)   28.50 28.50
  Set, never hinged   40.00

See note after No. 299.

President Shukri el Kouatly AP22

1945, Mar. 15   Litho.   Perf. 11½
C117 AP22 5p pale green   .50 .20
C118 AP22 10p dull red   .50 .20
C119 AP22 15p orange   .60 .25
C120 AP22 25p lt blue   1.25 .50
C121 AP22 50p lt violet   1.75 .70
C122 AP22 100p deep brown   3.50 1.25
C123 AP22 200p fawn   8.00 4.00
  Nos. C117-C123 (7)   16.10 7.10
  Set, never hinged   25.00

Resumption of constitutional government.

> **Catalogue values for unused stamps in this section, from this point to the end of the section, are for Never Hinged items.**

Plane and Flock of Sheep AP23

Kattineh Dam AP24

Kanawat, Djebel Druze AP25

Sultan Ibrahim Mosque AP26

1946-47   Perf. 13x13½
C124 AP23 3p rose brown   .50 .20
C125 AP23 5p lt bl grn ('47)   .50 .20
C126 AP23 6p dp org ('47)   .50 .20
C127 AP24 10p sl gray ('47)   .35 .20

C128 AP24 15p scarlet ('47)   .35 .20
C129 AP24 25p blue   .45 .20
C130 AP25 50p violet   .75 .20
C131 AP25 100p blue green   1.75 .40
C132 AP25 200p brown ('47)   4.00 1.25
C133 AP26 300p red brn ('47)   16.00 2.50
C134 AP26 500p ol gray ('47)   17.50 3.50
  Nos. C124-C134 (11)   42.65 9.10

For overprints and surcharges see Nos. C135-C139, C148-C152, C157, C172.

No. C129 Overprinted in Red

1946, Apr. 17
C135 AP24 25p blue   2.50 1.00

Evacuation of British and French troops from Syria.

Nos. C129-C131 Overprinted in Magenta

1946, Aug. 28
C136 AP24 25p blue   2.50 1.25
C137 AP25 50p violet   3.00 1.75
C138 AP25 100p blue green   6.00 3.00
  Nos. C136-C138 (3)   11.50 6.00

See note after No. 334.

No. C135 with Additional Overprint in Black

1947, June 10   Perf. 13x13½
C139 AP24 25p blue   2.50 1.25

1st anniv. of the evacuation of British and French troops from Syria.

Window at Kasr El-Heir El-Gharbi AP27

Ram-headed Sphinxes Carved in Ivory, from King Hazael's Bed — AP28

1947, Nov. 15   Litho.   Perf. 11½
C140 AP27 12.50p dark violet   1.50 .50
C141 AP28 50p brown   5.00 2.00
  a. Souv. sheet of 4, #338-339, C140-C141   60.00 60.00

1st Arab Archaeological Cong., Damascus, Nov.
No. C141a sold for 125 piasters.

Kasr El-Heir El-Charqui AP29

Congress Emblem — AP30

1947, Nov. 15
C142 AP29 12.50p olive black   1.00 .50
C143 AP30 50p dull violet   4.50 2.25
  a. Souv. sheet of 4, #340, 341, C142, C143   60.00 60.00

3rd Cong. of Arab Engineers, Damascus, Nov.
No. C143a sold for 125 piasters.

Kouatly Types of Regular Issue
1948, June 22   Litho.   Perf. 10½
C144 A50 12.50p dp bl & vio brn   .65 .25
C145 A51 50p violet brn & grn   2.50 1.00
  a. Souv. sheet of #342, 343, C144, C145, imperf   150.00 150.00

Reelection of Pres. Shukri el Kouatly.

Military Training Types of Regular Issue
1948, June 22
C146 A52 12.50p blue & dk bl   .75 .25
C147 A53 50p green, car & blk   2.00 .80
  a. Souv. sheet of 4, #344, 345, C146, C147, imperf.   140.00 140.00

Inauguration of compulsory military training.

Nos. C124, C126 and C132 to C134 Surcharged with New Value and Bars in Black or Carmine
1948, Oct. 18   Perf. 13x13½
C148 AP23 2.50p on 3p   .30 .20
C149 AP23 2.50p on 6p   .35 .20
C150 AP25 25p on 200p (C)   .80 .25
C151 AP26 50p on 300p   10.00 .75
C152 AP26 50p on 500p   10.00 .75
  Nos. C148-C152 (5)   21.45 2.15

Husni Zayim Type of Regular Issue
1949, June 20   Litho.   Perf. 11½
C153 A54 50p brown   3.75 2.50

Revolution of March 30, 1949.

Pigeons and Globe AP36

Husni Zayim and View of Damascus AP37

1949, June 20   Unwmk.
C154 AP36 12.50p claret   7.50 6.00
C155 AP37 50p gray black   19.00 12.50

UPU, 75th anniv. A souvenir sheet of 4 contains #349, 350, C154, C155. Value $125.

Election Type of Regular Issue
Wmk. 291
1949, Aug. 6   Litho.   Perf. 11½
C156 A57 50p car rose & dk grnsh bl   3.75 2.50
  a. Souv. sheet of 2, #351, C156, imperf.   175.00 175.00

Election of Pres. Husni Zayim.

No. C131 Surcharged with New Value and Bars in Black
1950   Unwmk.   Perf. 13x13½
C157 AP25 2.50p on 100p bl grn   .40 .20

Port of
Latakia
AP38

1950, Dec. 25   *Perf. 11½*
C158 AP38 2.50p dull lilac   .50 .20
C159 AP38 10p grnsh blue   1.10 .20
C160 AP38 15p orange brown   2.50 .40
C161 AP38 25p bright blue   5.50 .35
   Nos. C158-C161 (4)   9.60 1.15

Exist imperf. Value, $35. See No. C173. For
overprint see No. C169.

Symbolical
of
Constitution
AP39

1951, Apr. 14   **Unwmk.**
C162 AP39 12.50p crimson rose   .40 .20
C163 AP39 50p brown violet   1.25 1.00

New constitution adopted Sept. 5, 1950.
Exist imperf.

Ruins,
Palmyra
AP40

Citadel at
Aleppo
AP41

1952, Apr. 22   Litho.   *Perf. 11½*
C164 AP40 2.50p vermilion   .30 .20
C165 AP40 5p green   .35 .20
C166 AP40 15p violet   .50 .20
C167 AP41 25p deep blue   .75 .35
C168 AP41 100p lilac rose   5.50 1.00
   Nos. C164-C168 (5)   7.40 1.95

Nos. C164-C168 exist imperforate.
For overprints see Nos. C170-C171, C186.

Stamps of 1946-52 Overprinted in
Black

U.N.S.W.S.
Damascus
8-20 Dec. 1952.

1953, Feb. 16   *Perf. 13x13½, 11½*
C169 AP38 10p grnsh blue   2.00 1.00
C170 AP40 15p violet   2.25 1.10
C171 AP41 25p deep blue   3.25 1.60
C172 AP25 50p violet   8.00 2.25
   Nos. C169-C172 (4)   15.50 5.95

UN Social Welfare Seminar, Damascus,
Dec. 8-20, 1952.

Type of 1950 and

Post Office,
Aleppo
AP42

1953, Oct.   Photo.   *Perf. 11½*
C173 AP38 10p violet blue   .50 .20
C174 AP42 50p red brown   1.60 .30

For overprint see No. C185.

Building at Hama and
PTT Emblem — AP43

University
of Syria,
Damascus
AP44

1954
C175 AP43 5p violet   .25 .20
C176 AP43 10p brown   .30 .20
C177 AP43 15p dull green   .35 .20
C178 AP44 30p dark brown   .45 .20
C179 AP44 35p blue   .80 .25
C180 AP44 40p orange   1.75 .40
C181 AP44 50p deep plum   1.25 .60
C182 AP44 70p purple   3.25 .70
   Nos. C175-C182 (8)   8.40 2.75

For overprints see UAR Nos. C27-C28.

Monument,
Damascus
Square
AP45

Mosque and Syrian
Flag — AP46

1954, Sept. 2
C183 AP45 40p carmine rose   1.00 .45
C184 AP46 50p green   1.25 .55

Damascus Fair, Sept. 1954.
Nos. C183-C184 exist imperforate.

Nos. C174 and C168 Overprinted in
Blue or Black

REP. SYRIENNE
FESTIVAL du COTON Alep oct.1954

1954, Oct. 9
C185 AP42 50p red brown (Bl)   1.10 1.00
C186 AP41 100p lilac rose   2.00 1.60

Cotton Festival, Aleppo, October 1954.

Virgin of
Sednaya
Convent
AP47

Omayyad
Mosque
AP48

1955, Mar. 27   Photo.   *Perf. 11½*
C187 AP47 25p deep purple   .60 .40
C188 AP47 75p deep blue green   1.75 1.25

50th anniv. of the founding of Rotary Intl.
Exist imperforate.

1955, Mar. 26
C189 AP48 35p cerise   .95 .60
C190 AP48 65p deep green   1.75 1.10

1955 Regional Cong. of Rotary Intl.,
Damascus.

Arab Postal Union Type of Regular
Issue

1955, Jan. 1   *Perf. 13½x13*
C191 A69a 5p yellow brown   .40 .25

Founding of the APU, July 1, 1954.
For overprints see Nos. C203, C207.

Young
Couple and
View of
Damascus
AP49

60p, Tank and planes leading advancing
troops.

1955, Apr. 16   Litho.   *Perf. 11½*
C192 AP49 40p dark rose lake   .60 .30
C193 AP49 60p ultra   2.25 .35

9th anniv. of the evacuation of British and
French troops from Syria.

Mother's Day Type of Regular Issue

1955, May 13   Unwmk.
C194 A70 35p violet   1.00 .60
C195 A70 40p black   1.50 .95

Issued to publicize Mother's Day.

Emigrants
under Syrian
Flag — AP51

Mother and
Child — AP52

15p, Airplane over globe and fountain.

1955, July 26   *Perf. 11½*
C196 AP51 5p magenta   .55 .25
C197 AP51 15p light blue   .75 .40

Emigrants' Congress. Exist imperf.

1955, Oct. 3   Photo.
C198 AP52 25p deep blue   .75 .50
C199 AP52 50p plum   1.25 .90

International Children's Day.

Globe,
Scales and
Dove
AP53

1955, Oct. 30
C200 AP53 15p ultra   .75 .40
C201 AP53 35p brown black   1.50 .60

10th anniv. of the UN, Oct. 24, 1955.
For overprints see Nos. C221-C222.

Aqueduct Type of Regular Issue

1955, Nov. 21   Litho.   Unwmk.
C202 A72 30p dark blue   2.00 1.10

No. C191
Overprinted in
Ultramarine

1955, Dec. 29 Photo.   *Perf. 13½x13*
C203 A69a 5p yellow brown   .50 .20

APU Congress, Cairo, Mar. 15, 1955.

Liberation
Monument — AP54

Designs: 65p, Winged figure with shield
and sword. 75p, President Shukri el Kouatly.

1956, Apr. 17   Litho.   *Perf. 11½*
C204 AP54 35p black brown   .60 .40
C205 AP54 65p rose red   1.00 .60
C206 AP54 75p dk slate green   1.90 1.00
   Nos. C204-C206 (3)   3.50 2.00

10th anniv. of the evacuation of British and
French troops from Syria.

No. C191
Overprinted in Black

1956, Apr. 11 Photo.   *Perf. 13½x13*
C207 A69a 5p yellow brown   .50 .20

Visit of King Hussein of Jordan to Damascus, Apr. 1956.

President
Shukri el
Kouatly
AP55

Gate of Kasr el
Heir, Palmyra
AP56

1956, July 7   Litho.   *Perf. 11½*
C208 AP55 100p black   1.25 1.00
C209 AP55 200p violet   2.50 1.25
C210 AP55 300p dull rose   4.00 2.75
C211 AP55 500p dk bl grn   7.50 5.00
   Nos. C208-C211 (4)   15.25 10.00

Nos. CB5-CB8 Overprinted with 3
Bars Obliterating Surtax

1956
C212 SPAP1 25p gray black   .60 .20
C213 SPAP2 35p ultra   .75 .25
C214 SPAP2 40p rose lilac   1.50 .60
C215 SPAP1 70p Prus green   1.75 .90
   Nos. C212-C215 (4)   4.60 1.95

1956, Sept. 1   Unwmk.

Designs: 20p, Hand loom and modern mill.
30p, Ox-drawn plow and tractor. 35p, Cogwheels and galley. 50p, Textiles and vase.

C216 AP56 15p gray   .50 .50
C217 AP56 20p brt ultra   .75 .75
C218 AP56 30p blue green   1.00 1.00

C219 AP56 35p blue   1.25 1.25
C220 AP56 50p rose lilac   1.50 1.50
Nos. C216-C220 (5)   5.00 5.00

3rd International Fair, Damascus.

#C200-C201 Overprinted in Red or Green

1956, Oct. 30   Photo.   Perf. 11½
C221 AP53 15p ultra (R)   1.00 .60
C222 AP53 35p brown blk (G)   1.75 1.25

United Nations, 11th anniversary.

Clay Tablet
with First
Alphabet
AP57

Helmet of Syrian
Legionary and
Ornament — AP58

50p, Lintel from Temple of the Sun, Palmyra.

1956, Oct. 8   Typo.
C223 AP57 20p gray   1.00 .40
C224 AP58 30p magenta   1.25 .50
C225 AP57 50p gray brown   1.90 1.00
Nos. C223-C225 (3)   4.15 1.90

Intl. Museum Week (UNESCO), Oct. 8-14.

Trees and
Mosque
AP59

1956, Dec. 27   Litho.   Perf. 11½
C226 AP59 10p olive bister   .40 .25
C227 AP59 40p slate green   .90 .45

Day of the Tree, Dec. 27, 1956.
See UAR #36. For overprint see UAR #49.

Mother and
Child
AP60

Sword and
Shields
AP61

Design: 60p, Mother holding infant.

1957, Mar. 21   Unwmk.
C228 AP60 40p ultra   .75 .60
C229 AP60 60p vermilion   1.25 .85

Mother's Day, 1957.

1957, Apr. 20   Wmk. 291
Designs: 15p, 35p, Map and "Syria" holding
torch. 25p, Pres. Kouatly.

C230 AP61 10p redsh brn   .30 .20
C231 AP61 15p bl grn   .40 .25
C232 AP61 25p violet   .50 .35
C233 AP61 35p cerise   .75 .50
C234 AP61 40p gray   1.10 .90
Nos. C230-C234 (5)   3.05 1.90

British-French troop evacuation, 11th anniv.

Ship
Loading — AP62

Sugar
Production
AP63

30p, 40p, Harvesting grain and cotton.

1957, Sept. 1   Unwmk.   Perf. 11½
C235 AP62 25p magenta   .50 .30
C236 AP62 30p light red brown   .60 .35
C237 AP63 35p light blue   .75 .40
C238 AP62 40p blue green   1.00 .50
C239 AP62 70p olive bister   1.25 .90
Nos. C235-C239 (5)   4.10 2.45

4th International Fair, Damascus.

Arab Lawyers Type of Regular Issue
1957, Sept. 21   Litho.   Wmk. 291
C240 A76 17½p red   .40 .30
C241 A76 40p black   .90 .50

Cotton Festival Type of Regular Issue
1957, Oct. 17
C242 A77 17½p org & blk   .75 .40
C243 A77 40p lt bl & blk   1.25 .50

Children's Day Type of Regular Issue
1957, Oct. 3
C244 A78 17½p ultra   1.25 .50
C245 A78 20p red brn   1.50 .50

International Children's Day, Oct. 7.
For overprints see UAR Nos. C10-C11.

Family
Writing
and
Reading
Letters
AP64

1957, Oct. 18   Litho.   Unwmk.
C246 AP64 5p brt grn   .40 .20

Intl. Letter Writing Week Oct. 6-12.
For overprint see No. C26.

Afro-Asian Jurists Type of Regular
Issue
1957, Nov.   Wmk. 291   Perf. 11½
C247 A80 30p lt bl grn   .50 .35
C248 A80 50p lt vio   .75 .50

Type of Regular Issue and

Radio, Telegraph and
Telephone — AP65

1958, Feb. 12   Perf. 11½
C249 A83 10p brt grn   .35 .20
C250 AP65 15p brown   .40 .25

Syrian Arab Republic

Syrian Flag — AP67

Souvenir Sheet
1961   Unwmk.   Litho.   Imperf.
C253 AP67 50p multi   2.75 2.75

Establishment of Syrian Arab Republic.

"The Beauty of
Palmyra" — AP68

Archway,
Palmyra — AP69

Design: 200p, 300p, 500p, 1000p, Niche,
King Zahir Bibar's tomb.

1961-63   Litho.   Perf. 12x11½
C255 AP68 45p citron   .40 .20
C256 AP68 50p red org   .50 .25
C257 AP69 85p sepia   1.00 .30
C258 AP69 100p lilac   1.25 .35
C259 AP69 200p slate grn
    ('62)   2.25 .65
C260 AP69 300p dk bl ('62)   2.75 .75
C261 AP69 500p lilac ('63)   4.00 1.50
C262 AP69 1000p dk gray
    ('63)   8.25 2.75
Nos. C255-C262 (8)   20.40 6.75

See Nos. 433-436.

Arab League
Building, Cairo,
and
Emblem — AP70

Malaria
Eradication
Emblem — AP71

1962, Apr. 1   Perf. 12x11½
C264 AP70 17½p Prus grn & yel
    grn   .30 .20
C265 AP70 22½p dk & lt bl   .30 .20
C266 AP70 50p dk brn & dl org   .75 .30
Nos. C264-C266 (3)   1.35 .70

Arab League Week, Mar. 22-28.

1962, Apr. 7
C267 AP71 12½p ol, lt bl & pur   .40 .20
C268 AP71 50p brn, yel & grn   .75 .40

WHO drive to eradicate malaria.

Rearing
Horse — AP72

Gen. Yusef al-
Azmeh
AP73

1962, Apr. 17
C269 AP72 45p vio & org   .55 .20
C270 AP73 55p vio bl & lt bl   .75 .20

Evacuation Day, 1962.

Martyrs' Square
Memorial, Globe
and Handshake
AP74

Cotton and
Cogwheel
AP75

Design: 40p, 45p, Eastern Gate at Fair.

1962, Aug. 25   Litho.   Perf. 12x11½
C271 AP74 17½p rose cl & brn   .30 .20
C272 AP74 22½p ver & magenta   .30 .20
C273 AP74 40p vio brn & lt brn   .30 .20
C274 AP74 45p grnsh bl & lt grn   .50 .20
Nos. C271-C274 (4)   1.40 .80

9th International Damascus Fair.

1962, Sept. 20   Perf. 12x11½
C275 AP75 12½p multi   .35 .20
C276 AP75 50p multi   .50 .20

Cotton Festival, Aleppo. See Nos. 455-456.

President Type of Regular Issue
1962, Dec. 14   Unwmk.
C278 A88 50p bl gray & tan   .75 .25

1st anniv. of the election of Pres. Nazem el-
Kodsi.

Queen Zenobia
of
Palmyra — AP76

Saad Allah El
Jabri — AP77

1962, Dec. 28   *Perf. 12x11½*
C279 AP76 45p violet   1.00 .25
C280 AP76 50p rose red   1.00 .25
C281 AP76 85p blue green   1.00 .30
C282 AP76 100p rose claret   1.25 .55
   Nos. C279-C282 (4)   4.25 1.35

1962, Dec. 30   **Litho.**
C283 AP77 50p dull blue   .50 .20

Saad Allah El Jabri (1894-1947), a leader in Syria's struggle for independence.

Woman from
Mohardé — AP78

Eagle in
Flight — AP79

Regional Costumes: 40p, Marje Sultan. 45p, Kalamoun. 55p, Jabal-Al-Arab. 60p, Afrine. 65p, Hauran.

1963   *Perf. 12*
Costumes in Original Colors
C285 AP78 40p pale lil & blk   .55 .20
C286 AP78 45p pink & blk   .60 .20
C287 AP78 50p lt grn & blk   .60 .20
C288 AP78 55p lt bl & blk   .75 .30
C289 AP78 60p tan & blk   .80 .30
C290 AP78 65p pale grn & blk   1.00 .40
   Nos. C285-C290 (6)   4.30 1.60

Hunger Type of Regular Issue

50p, Wheat emblem & bird feeding nestlings.

    Perf. 12x11½
1963, Mar. 21   **Unwmk.**
C291 A91 50p ver & blk   .45 .20
  a.   Souv. sheet of 2, #453, C291, imperf.   1.50 1.50

FAO "Freedom from Hunger" campaign.

1963, Apr. 18   **Litho.**
C292 AP79 12½p brt grn   .30 .20
C293 AP79 50p lilac rose   .35 .20

   Revolution of Mar. 8, 1963.

Faris el
Khouri — AP80

Arms and
Wreath — AP81

1963, Apr. 27   *Perf. 12x11½*
C294 AP80 17½p gray   .30 .20
C295 AP81 22½p bl grn & blk   .30 .20

   Evacuation Day, 1963.

abu-al-Ala al-
Maarri — AP82

Copper Pitcher,
Arch and
Fair — AP83

1963, Aug. 19   *Perf. 12x11½*
C296 AP82 50p violet blue   .40 .20

   abu-al-Ala al-Maarri (973-1057), poet and philosopher.

1963, Aug. 25
C297 AP83 37½p ultra, yel & brn   .45 .20
C298 AP83 50p brt bl, yel & brn   .50 .20

   10th International Damascus Fair.

Centenary
Emblem — AP84

Abou Feras al
Hamadani
AP85

50p, Centenary emblem and globe.

1963, Sept. 19   **Litho.**
C299 AP84 15p chlky bl, red & blk   .40 .20
C300 AP84 50p yel grn, blk & red   .50 .20

   Centenary of the International Red Cross.

1963, Nov. 13   *Perf. 12x11½*
C301 AP85 50p yel ol & dk brn   .50 .20

   Abou Feras (932-968), poet.

Heads of Three
Races and
Flame — AP86

1964, Jan. 6   **Unwmk.**
C302 AP86 17½p multi   .30 .20
C303 AP86 22½p grn, blk & red   .30 .20
C304 AP86 50p vio, blk & red   .40 .20
  a.   Souv. sheet of 3   1.10 1.10
   Nos. C302-C304 (3)   1.00 .60

Universal Declaration of Human Rights, 15th anniv. #C304a contains 3 imperf. stamps similar to #C302-C304 with simulated perforations.

Flag,
Torch and
Map of
Arab
Countries
AP87

1964, Mar. 8   **Unwmk.**   *Perf. 11½*
C305 AP87 15p multi   .30 .20
C306 AP87 17½p multi   .30 .20
C307 AP87 22½p multi   .30 .20
   Nos. C305-C307 (3)   .90 .60

   Revolution of Mar. 8, 1963, 1st anniv.

Kaaba,
Mecca,
and
Mosque,
Damascus
AP88

1964, Mar. 14   **Litho.**   *Perf. 11½x12*
C308 AP88 12½p bl & blk   .30 .20
C309 AP88 22½p rose lil & blk   .30 .20
C310 AP88 50p lt grn & blk   .35 .20
   Nos. C308-C310 (3)   .95 .60

First Arab Conference of Moslem Wakf Ministers, Damascus.

Young
Couple
and View
of
Damascus
AP89

1964, Apr. 17   **Unwmk.**
C311 AP89 20p blue   .30 .20
C312 AP89 25p rose car   .30 .20
C313 AP89 60p emerald   .35 .20
   Nos. C311-C313 (3)   .95 .60

   Evacuation Day, Apr. 17, 1964.

Abul Kasim
(Albucasis)
AP90

1964, Apr. 21   *Perf. 12x11½*
C314 AP90 60p brown   .40 .20

4th Arab Congress of Dental and Oral Surgery, Damascus.

Mosaic,
Chahba,
Thalassa
AP91

    Perf. 11½x12
1964, June-July   **Litho.**
C315 AP91 27½p car rose   .30 .20
C316 AP91 45p gray   .30 .20
C317 AP91 50p brt grn   .40 .20
C318 AP91 55p slate grn   .40 .20
C319 AP91 60p ultra   .50 .20
   Nos. C315-C319 (5)   1.90 1.00

Hanging Lamp,
Fair
Emblem — AP92

Globe and Fair
Emblem — AP93

1964, Aug. 28   *Perf. 12x11½*
C320 AP92 20p multi   .30 .20
C321 AP93 25p multi   .30 .20

   11th International Damascus Fair.

Industrial and
Agricultural
Symbols — AP94

1964, Sept. 22   **Litho.**   **Unwmk.**
C322 AP94 25p multi   .30 .20

**Same Overprinted with two Red
Lines in Arabic**

C323 AP94 25p multi   .30 .20

Cotton Festival, Aleppo. Overprint on No. C323 translates: "Market for Industrial and Agricultural Products."

Arms of Syria and Aero Club Emblem AP95

1964, Oct. 8   Litho.   Perf. 11½x12
C324 AP95 12½p emer & blk   .30   .20
C325 AP95 17½p crim & blk   .30   .20
C326 AP95 20p brt bl & blk   .40   .20
Nos. C324-C326 (3)   1.00   .60

10th anniversary of Syrian Aero Club.

Arab Postal Union Emblem — AP96

1964, Nov. 12   Litho.   Perf. 12x11½
C327 AP96 12½p org & blk   .30   .20
C328 AP96 20p emer & blk   .30   .20
C329 AP96 25p dp lil rose & blk   .30   .20
Nos. C327-C329 (3)   .90   .60

10th anniv. of the permanent office of the APU.

Grain and Hands Holding Book — AP97

1964, Nov. 30   Unwmk.
C330 AP97 12½p emer & blk   .30   .20
C331 AP97 17½p mar & blk   .30   .20
C332 AP97 20p dp bl & blk   .30   .20
Nos. C330-C332 (3)   .90   .60

Burning of the library of Algiers, 6/7/62.

Tennis Player — AP98

17½p, Wrestlers and drummer. 20p, Weight lifter. 100p, Wrestlers and drummer.

1965, Feb. 7   Perf. 12x11½
C333 AP98 12½p multi   .30   .20
C334 AP98 17½p multi   .30   .20
C335 AP98 20p multi, horiz.   .30   .20
Nos. C333-C335 (3)   .90   .60
Souvenir Sheet
C336 AP98 100p multi   1.25   1.25

18th Olympic Games, Tokyo, 10/10-25/64. #C336 contains one 45x33mm stamp.

Ramses Battling the Hittites AP99

Design: 50p, Two statues of Ramses II.

1965, Mar. 21   Litho.   Perf. 11x12
C337 AP99 22½p emer, ultra & blk   .30   .20
C338 AP99 50p ultra, emer & blk   .40   .20

UNESCO world campaign to save historic monuments in Nubia.

Al-Sharif Al-Radi — AP100

Dagger in Map of Palestine AP102

Hippocrates and Avicenna — AP101

1965, Apr. 3   Litho.   Perf. 12x11½
C339 AP100 50p gray brn   .50   .20

5th Poetry Festival held in Latakia; Al-Sharif Al-Radi (970-1015), poet.

1965, Apr. 19   Perf. 11½
C340 AP101 60p dl bl grn & blk   .55   .30

"Medical Days of the Near and Middle East," a convention held at Damascus Apr. 19-25.

1965, May 15
C341 AP102 12½p multi   .30   .20
C342 AP102 60p multi   .35   .20

Deir Yassin massacre, Apr. 9, 1948.

ITU Emblem, Old and New Communication Equipment — AP103

Perf. 11½x12
1965, May 24   Litho.   Unwmk.
C343 AP103 12½p multi   .30   .20
C344 AP103 27½p multi   .30   .20
C345 AP103 60p multi   .50   .25
Nos. C343-C345 (3)   1.10   .65

ITU, centenary.

Syrian Welcoming AP104

Bridge and Gate — AP105

1965, Aug.   Unwmk.   Perf. 12x11½
C346 AP104 25p pur & multi   .30   .20
C347 AP104 100p blk & multi   .75   .25

Issued to welcome Arab immigrants.

1965, Aug. 28   Litho.
27½p, Fair emblem. 60p, Jug & ornaments.
C348 AP105 12½p blk, brt ultra & brn   .30   .20
C349 AP105 27½p multi   .30   .20
C350 AP105 60p multi   .40   .20
Nos. C348-C350 (3)   1.00   .60

12th International Damascus Fair.

Fair Emblem and Cotton Pickers — AP106

1965, Sept. 30   Perf. 12x11½
C351 AP106 25p olive & multi   .30   .20

10th Cotton Festival, Aleppo.

Same with Red Overprint

1965, Sept. 30
C352 AP106 25p olive & multi   .30   .20

Industrial and Agricultural Fair, Aleppo.

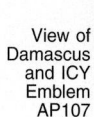

View of Damascus and ICY Emblem AP107

1965, Oct. 24   Perf. 11½x12
C353 AP107 25p multi   .30   .20

International Cooperation Year.

Radio Transmitter, Globe, Syrian Flag and View of Damascus AP108

Hand (shaped like a dove) Holding Flower — AP109

1966, Feb. 16   Litho.   Perf. 12x11½
C354 AP108 25p multi   .30   .20
C355 AP108 60p multi   .35   .20

3rd Conference of Arab Information Ministers, Damascus, Feb. 14-18.

1966, Mar. 8   Perf. 12x11½, 11½x12
Design: 17½p, Stylized people, horiz.
C356 AP109 12½p multi   .30   .20
C357 AP109 17½p multi   .30   .20
C358 AP109 50p multi   .75   .25
Nos. C356-C358 (3)   1.35   .65

March 8 Revolution, 3rd anniversary.

Statues of Ramses II from Abu Simbel — AP110

1966, Mar. 15   Perf. 12x11½
C359 AP110 25p dark blue   .30   .20
C360 AP110 60p dark slate green   .40   .20

Arab "Save the Nubian Monument Week."

UN Headquarters Building and Emblem — AP111

Design: 100p, UN Flag.

1966, Apr. 11   Litho.   Perf. 11½x12
C361 AP111 25p blk & gray   .30   .20
C362 AP111 50p blk & pale grn   .35   .20
Souvenir Sheet
Imperf
C363 AP111 100p yel, brt bl & blk   1.25   1.25

20th anniv. (in 1965) of the UN. No. C363 contains one stamp 42x36mm.

Marching Workers AP112

1966, May 1   Litho.   Perf. 11½x12
C364 AP112 60p multi   .40   .20

Issued for May Day.

Inauguration of WHO Headquarters, Geneva — AP113

1966, May 3
C365 AP113 60p blk, bl & yel .40 .20

Map of Arab Countries and Traffic Signals — AP114

Astarte & Tyche, 1st cent. Basrelief, Palmyra AP115

1966, May 4 *Perf. 12x11½*
C366 AP114 25p gray & multi .30 .20
Issued to publicize Traffic Day.

1966, July 26 Litho. *Perf. 12x11½*
C367 AP115 50p pale brn .35 .20
C368 AP115 60p slate .50 .25

Symbolic Flag, Wheat, Globe and Fair Emblem AP116

Shuttle and Symbols of Agriculture, Industry and Cotton — AP117

1966, Aug. 25 Litho. *Perf. 12x11½*
C369 AP116 12½p multi .30 .20
C370 AP116 60p multi .35 .20
13th Intl. Damascus Fair, Aug. 25-Sept. 20.

1966, Sept. 9 Litho. *Perf. 12x11½*
C371 AP117 50p sil, blk & plum .35 .20
11th Cotton Festival, Aleppo.

Symbolic Water Cycle — AP118

Abd-el Kader — AP119

1966, Oct. 24 Litho. *Perf. 12x11½*
C372 AP118 12½p emer, blk & org .30 .20
C373 AP118 60p ultra, blk & org .35 .20
Hydrological Decade (UNESCO), 1965-74.

1966, Nov. 7
C374 AP119 12½p brt grn & blk .30 .20
C375 AP119 50p brt grn & red brn .35 .20
Transfer from Damascus to Algiers of the ashes of Abd-el Kader (1807?-1883), Emir of Mascara.

Clasped Hands over Map of South Arabia — AP120

Pipelines and Pigeons AP121

1967, Feb. 8 Litho. *Perf. 12x11½*
C376 AP120 20p pink & multi .30 .20
C377 AP120 25p multi .30 .20
3rd Congress of Solidarity with the Workers and People of Aden, Damascus, Jan. 15-18.

1967, Mar. 8 Litho. *Perf. 12x11½*
C378 AP121 17½p multi .30 .20
C379 AP121 25p multi .30 .20
C380 AP121 27½p multi .30 .20
Nos. C378-C380 (3) .90 .60
4th anniversary of March 8 Revolution.

Soldier, Woman and Man Holding Flag — AP122

Workers' Monument, Damascus AP123

1967, Apr. 17 Litho. *Perf. 12x11½*
C381 AP122 17½p green .30 .20
C382 AP122 25p dp claret .30 .20
C383 AP122 27½p vio blue .30 .20
Nos. C381-C383 (3) .90 .60
21st anniv. of the evacuation of British and French troops from Syria.

1967, May 1
C384 AP123 12½p bl grn .30 .20
C385 AP123 50p brt pink .35 .20
Issued for Labor Day, May 1.

Fair Emblem and Gate, Minaret, Omayyad Mosque — AP124

1967, Aug. 25 Litho. *Perf. 12x12½*
C386 AP124 12½p multi .30 .20
C387 AP124 60p multi .35 .20
14th Intl. Damascus Fair, Aug. 25-Sept. 20.

Statue of Ur-Nina and ITY Emblem AP125

1967, Sept. 2 *Perf. 12½x12*
C388 AP125 12½p lt bl, brt rose lil & blk .30 .20
C389 AP125 25p lt bl, ver & blk .30 .20
C390 AP125 27½p lt bl, dk bl & blk .30 .20
Nos. C388-C390 (3) .90 .60
Souvenir Sheet
Imperf
C391 AP125 60p lt bl & vio bl 1.00 1.00
Intl. Tourist Year.

Cotton Boll and Cogwheel Segment AP126

1967, Sept. 28 Litho. *Perf. 12x12½*
C392 AP126 12½p ocher, brn & blk .30 .20
C393 AP126 60p ap grn, brn & blk .40 .20
12th Cotton Festival, Aleppo.

Same with Red Overprint

1967, Sept. 28
C394 AP126 12½p multi .30 .20
C395 AP126 60p multi .35 .20
Industrial and Agricultural Production Fair, Aleppo.

Head of Young Man, Amrith, 4th-5th Century B.C. — AP127

1967, Oct. 7
100p, 500p, Bronze bust of a Princess, 2nd cent.
C396 AP127 45p orange .30 .20
C397 AP127 50p brt pink .40 .20
C398 AP127 60p grnsh bl .50 .20
C399 AP127 100p green .60 .30
C400 AP127 500p brn red 2.25 1.50
Nos. C396-C400 (5) 4.05 2.40

Ibn el-Naphis AP128

1967, Dec. 28 Litho. *Perf. 12x12½*
C401 AP128 12½p grn & org .30 .20
C402 AP128 27½p dk bl & lil rose .30 .20
700th death anniv. of Ibn el-Naphis (1210-1288), Arab physician.

Human Rights Flame and People AP129

Design: 100p, Heads of various races and Human Rights flame.

1968, Feb. 21 Litho. *Perf. 12½x12*
C403 AP129 12½p lt grnsh bl, bl & blk .30 .20
C404 AP129 60p pink, blk & dl red .40 .20
Souvenir Sheet
Imperf
C405 AP129 100p multi 1.00 1.00
20th anniv. of the Declaration of Human Rights; Intl. Human Rights Year.

Old Man and Woman Reading AP130

Design: 17½p, 45p, Torch and book.

1968, Mar. 3 *Perf. 12½x12½*
C406 AP130 12½p rose car, blk & org .30 .20
C407 AP130 17½p multi .30 .20
C408 AP130 25p grn, blk & org .30 .20
C409 AP130 45p bl & multi .30 .20
Nos. C406-C409 (4) 1.20 .80
Issued to publicize the literacy campaign.

Euphrates Dam Project — AP131

1968, Apr. 11 Litho.   Perf. 12½x12
C410 AP131 12½p multi   .30 .20
C411 AP131 17½p multi   .30 .20
C412 AP131 25p multi   .30 .20
      Nos. C410-C412 (3)   .90 .60
Proposed dam across Euphrates River.

WHO Emblem and Avenzoar (1091-1162) — AP132

WHO Emblem and: 25p, Rhazes (Razi, 850-923). 60p, Geber (Jabir 721-776).

1968, June 10 Litho.   Perf. 12½x12
C413 AP132 12½p brn, grn & sal   .30 .20
C414 AP132 25p brn, gray & sal   .30 .20
C415 AP132 60p brn, gray bl &
             sal   .40 .20
      Nos. C413-C415 (3)   1.00 .60
WHO, 20th anniv.

Monastery of St. Simeon the Stylite AP133

Designs: 17½p, El Tekkieh Mosque, Damascus, vert. 22½p, Columns, Palmyra, vert. 45p, Chapel of St. Paul, Bab Kisan. 50p, Theater of Bosra.

Perf. 12½x12, 12x12½
1968, Oct. 10   Litho.
C416 AP133 15p pale grn &
             rose brn   .30 .20
C417 AP133 17½p redsh brn &
             dk red brn   .30 .20
C418 AP133 22½p grn gray & dk
             red brn   .30 .20
C419 AP133 45p yel & dk red
             brn   .30 .20
C420 AP133 50p lt bl & dk red
             brn   .30 .20
      Nos. C416-C420 (5)   1.50 1.00

Hammer Throw — AP134

Designs: 25p, Discus. 27½p, Running. 60p, Basketball. 50p, Polo, horiz.

1968, Dec. 19 Litho.   Perf. 12x12½
C421 AP134 12½p brt pink, blk &
             grn   .30 .20
C422 AP134 25p red, grn & blk   .30 .20
C423 AP134 27½p blk, gray &
             grn   .30 .20
C424 AP134 60p multi   .30 .20
      Nos. C421-C424 (4)   1.20 .80
Souvenir Sheet
Imperf
C425 AP134 50p multi   1.00 1.00

19th Olympic Games, Mexico City, Oct. 12-27. #C425 contains one 52x80mm horiz. stamp.

Construction of Damascus Intl. Airport — AP135

1969, Jan. 20 Litho.   Perf. 12½x12
C426 AP135 12½p yel, brt bl &
             grn   .30 .20
C427 AP135 17½p org, pur & lt
             grn   .30 .20
C428 AP135 60p car, blk & yel   .40 .20
      Nos. C426-C428 (3)   1.00 .60

Baal Shamin Temple, Palmyra AP136

Designs: 45p, Interior of Omayyad Mosque, Damascus, vert. 50p, Amphitheater, Palmyra. 60p, Khaled ibn al-Walid Mosque, Homs, vert. 100p, Ruins of St. Simeon, Djebel Samaan.

1969, Jan. 20 Photo.   Perf. 12x11½
C429 AP136 25p multi   .30 .20
C430 AP136 45p bl & multi   .30 .20
C431 AP136 50p multi   .30 .20
C432 AP136 60p multi   .30 .20
C433 AP136 100p vio & multi   .60 .25
      Nos. C429-C433 (5)   1.80 1.05

Workers, ILO Emblem, Cogwheel AP137

Design: 60p, ILO emblem.

1969, May 1 Litho.   Perf. 12½x12
C434 AP137 12½p multi   .30 .20
C435 AP137 27½p multi   .30 .20
Miniature Sheet
Imperf
C436 AP137 60p multi   .60 .60
ILO, 50th anniv. No. C436 contains one stamp 53½x47mm.

Ballet Dancers AP138

Designs: 12½p, Russian dancers. 45p, Lebanese singer and dancers. 55p, Egyptian dancer and musicians. 60p, Bulgarian dancers.

1969, Aug. 25 Litho.   Perf. 12½x12
C437 AP138 12½p multi   .30 .20
C438 AP138 27½p bl & multi   .30 .20
C439 AP138 45p multi   .30 .20
C440 AP138 55p multi   .30 .20
C441 AP138 60p multi   .40 .20
  a.   Strip of 5, #C437-C441   1.75 1.75
16th Intl. Fair, Damascus, Aug. 25-Sept. 20.

Children Playing — AP139

Fortuna — AP140

1969, Oct. 6 Litho.   Perf. 12x12½
C442 AP139 12½p aqua, dk bl &
             emer   .30 .20
C443 AP139 25p brn red, dk bl &
             lt vio   .30 .20
C444 AP139 27½p ultra, dk bl &
             gray   .30 .20
      Nos. C442-C444 (3)   .90 .60
      Issued for Children's Day.

1969, Oct. 10
Designs: 25p, Seated woman from Palmyra. 60p, Motherhood. All sculptures from Greco-Roman period.
C445 AP140 17½p blk, yel grn &
             grn   .30 .20
C446 AP140 25p dk brn, red brn
             & lt grn   .30 .20
C447 AP140 60p blk, lt gray & bl
             gray   .40 .20
      Nos. C445-C447 (3)   1.00 .60
9th Intl. Congress for Classical Archaeology, Oct. 11-20.

Damascus Agricultural Museum — AP141

1969, Dec. 24 Litho.   Perf. 12½x12
C448 AP141 12p Cock   .30 .20
C449 AP141 17½p Cow   .30 .20
C450 AP141 20p Corn   .30 .20
C451 AP141 50p Olives   .30 .20
  a.   Strip of 4, #C448-C451 + la-
        bel   1.25 1.25

Weather Balloon Tracking and UN Emblem AP142

1970, Mar. 23 Litho.   Perf. 12½x12
C452 AP142 25p blk, sl grn & yel .30 .20
C453 AP142 60p blk, dk bl & yel   .35 .20
10th World Meteorological Day.

Lenin (1870-1924) AP143

1970, Apr. 15 Litho.   Perf. 12x12½
C454 AP143 15p red & dk brn   .30 .20
C455 AP143 60p red & grn   .35 .20

Workers' Syndicate Emblem AP144

1970, May 1 Litho.   Perf. 12½x12
C456 AP144 15p dk brn & brt grn .30 .20
C457 AP144 60p dk brn & org   .35 .20
Issued for Labor Day.

Radar and Open Book AP145

1970, May 17
C458 AP145 15p brt pink & blk   .30 .20
C459 AP145 60p bl & blk   .35 .20
International Telecommunications Day.

Opening of UPU Headquarters, Bern — AP146

1970, May 30
C460 AP146 15p multi   .30 .20
C461 AP146 60p multi   .35 .20

"Zahier Piebers and Maarouf" — AP147

Folk Tales: 10p, Two warriors on horseback. 15p, Two warriors on white horses. 20p, Lady and warrior on horseback. 60p, Warriors, woman and lion.

1970, Aug. 12 Litho.   Perf. 12½
C462 AP147 5p lt bl & multi   .30 .20
C463 AP147 10p lt bl & multi   .30 .20
C464 AP147 15p lt bl & multi   .30 .20
C465 AP147 20p lt bl & multi   .30 .20
C466 AP147 60p lt bl & multi   .50 .20
  a.   Strip of 5, #C462-C466   1.75 1.75

Al Aqsa Mosque on Fire AP148

1970, Aug. 21   Perf. 12½x12
C467 AP148 15p multi   .30 .20
C468 AP148 60p multi   .35 .20
1st anniv. of the burning of Al Aqsa Mosque, Jerusalem.

Wood Carving — AP149

Handicrafts: 20p, Jewelry. 25p, Glass making. 30p, Copper engraving. 60p, Shellwork.

1970, Aug. 25   Perf. 12½
C469	AP149	15p vio & multi	.30	.20
C470	AP149	20p ol & multi	.30	.20
C471	AP149	25p multi	.30	.20
C472	AP149	30p multi	.30	.20
C473	AP149	60p multi	.50	.20
a.		Strip of 5, #C469-C473	1.75	1.75

17th Intl. Fair, Damascus.

Education Year
Emblem
AP150

1970, Nov. 2   Litho.   Perf. 12
C474	AP150	15p dl grn & dk brn	.30	.20
C475	AP150	60p vio bl & dk brn	.35	.20

International Education Year.

UN Emblem, Symbols of Progress,
Justice and Peace
AP151

1970, Nov. 3
C476	AP151	15p lt ultra, red & blk	.30	.20
C477	AP151	60p bl, yel & blk	.35	.20

United Nations, 25th anniversary.

Khaled ibn-al-
Walid
AP152

Woman with
Garland
AP153

1970-71   Perf. 12x11½, 12½x12½
C478	AP152	45p brt pink	.30	.20
C479	AP152	50p green	.35	.20
C480	AP152	60p vio brn	.50	.20
C481	AP152	100p dk bl	.60	.20
C482	AP152	200p grnsh gray ('71)	1.10	.50
C483	AP152	300p lil ('71)	1.50	.95
C484	AP152	500p gray ('71)	3.00	1.60
		Nos. C478-C484 (7)	7.35	3.85

1971, Apr. 17   Litho.   Perf. 12
C485	AP153	15p dl red, blk & grn	.30	.20
C486	AP153	60p grn, blk & dk red	.35	.20

25th anniv. of the evacuation of British and
French troops from Syria.

People
Dancing
Around
Globe
AP154

1971, Apr. 28   Litho.   Perf. 12½x12
C487	AP154	15p vio & multi	.30	.20
C488	AP154	60p grn & multi	.30	.20

Intl. Year against Racial Discrimination.

Pres. Hafez al Assad and Council
Chamber — AP155

1971, Sept. 30   Litho.   Perf. 12½x12
C489	AP155	15p grn & multi	.30	.20
C490	AP155	65p bl & multi	.60	.20

People's Council and presidential election.

Gamal Abdel
Nasser (1918-
1970), President
of
Egypt — AP156

1971, Oct. 17   Perf. 12x12½
C491	AP156	15p lt ol grn & brn	.30	.20
C492	AP156	20p gray & brn	.30	.20

Globe
and
Arrows
AP157

1972, May 17   Litho.   Perf. 11½
C493	AP157	15p bl, vio bl & pink	.30	.20
C494	AP157	50p org, yel & sep	.30	.20

4th World Telecommunications Day.

Pres. Hafez al
Assad — AP158

Airline Emblem,
Eastern
Hemisphere
AP159

1972, July   Litho.   Perf. 12x11½
C495	AP158	100p dk grn	.60	.25
C496	AP158	500p dk brn	3.00	1.10

1972, Sept. 16   Litho.   Perf. 12x11½
C497	AP159	15p blk, lt bl & Prus bl	.30	.20
C498	AP159	50p blk, gray & Prus bl	.30	.20

Syrianair, Syrian airline, 25th anniversary.

Pottery — AP160

Handicraft Industries: 25p, Rugs. 30p,
Metal (weapons). 35p, Straw (baskets, mats).
100p, Wood carving.

1976, July   Litho.   Perf. 12x12½
C499	AP160	10p multi	.30	.20
C500	AP160	25p multi	.30	.20
C501	AP160	30p multi	.30	.20
C502	AP160	35p multi	.30	.20
C503	AP160	100p multi	.50	.30
a.		Strip of 5, #C499-C503	1.75	1.75

23rd Intl. Damascus Fair.

Pres. Hafez
al Assad
AP161

1978, Sept.   Litho.   Perf. 12½x12
C504	AP161	25p sil & multi	.50	.20
C505	AP161	35p grn & multi	.50	.20
C506	AP161	60p gold & multi	.50	.20
		Nos. C504-C506 (3)	1.50	.60

Reelection of Pres. Assad. See No. 820.

AIR POST SEMI-POSTAL STAMPS

Nos. C30-C33 Surcharged Like Nos.
B1-B12 in Black and Red

1926, Apr. 1   Unwmk.   Perf. 13½
CB1	A4	2p + 1p dk brown	3.00	2.75
CB2	A4	3p + 2p org brn	2.75	2.75
CB3	A4	5p + 3p violet	2.75	2.75
CB4	A4	10p + 5p vio brn	2.75	2.75
		Nos. CB1-CB4 (4)	11.25	11.00

The new value is in red and rest of the
surcharge in black on Nos. CB1-CB3. The
entire surcharge is black on No. CB4.
See note following Nos. B1-B12.

**Catalogue values for unused
stamps in this section, from this
point to the end of the section, are
for Never Hinged items.**

Fair
Entrance
SPAP1

Industry,
Handicraft
and
Farming
SPAP2

Design: 70p+10p, Fairgrounds.

Perf. 11½, Imperf.
1955   Litho.   Unwmk.
CB5	SPAP1	25p + 5p gray black	.40	.40
CB6	SPAP2	35p + 5p ultra	.40	.40
CB7	SPAP2	40p + 10p rose lilac	.60	.60
CB8	SPAP1	70p + 10p Prus grn	1.10	1.10
		Nos. CB5-CB8 (4)	2.50	2.50

Intl. Fair, Damascus, Sept. 1955.
For overprint see Nos. C212-C215.

United
Nations
Refugee
Emblem
SPAP3

1966, Dec. 12   Litho.   Perf. 11½x12
CB9	SPAP3	12½p + 2½p ultra & blk	.25	.20
CB10	SPAP3	50p + 5p grn & blk	.50	.25

UN Day, 21st anniv.; Refugee Week, Oct.
24-31.

POSTAGE DUE STAMPS

Under French Occupation

Stamps of French
Offices in the Turkish
Empire, 1902-03,
Surcharged

O. M. F
Syrie
Ch. taxe
1 PIASTRE

1920   Unwmk.   Perf. 14x13½
J1	A3	1p on 10c rose red	160.00	160.00
J2	A3	2p on 20c brn vio	160.00	160.00
J3	A3	3p on 30c lil	160.00	160.00
J4	A4	4p on 40c red & pale bl	160.00	160.00
		Nos. J1-J4 (4)	640.00	640.00

Postage Due Stamps of
France, 1893-1920,
Surcharged in Black or
Red

O. M. F
Syrie
2
PIASTRES

1920
J5	D2	1p on 10c brown	3.25	3.25
J6	D2	2p on 20c ol grn (R)	3.25	3.25
a.		"PIASTRE"	900.00	900.00
J7	D2	3p on 30c red	3.25	3.25
a.		"PIASTRE"		
J8	D2	4p on 50c brn vio	4.75	4.75
a.		3p in setting of 4p	525.00	525.00
		Nos. J5-J8 (4)	14.50	14.50

1921-22
J9	D2	50c on 10c brown	1.40	1.40
a.		"75" instead of "50"	90.00	
b.		"CENTI MES" instead of "CEN- TIEMES"	7.50	
J10	D2	1p on 20c ol grn	1.40	1.40
J11	D2	2p on 30c red	3.25	3.25
J12	D2	3p on 50c brn vio	3.50	3.50
J13	D2	5p on 1fr red brn, straw	5.00	5.00
		Nos. J9-J13 (5)	14.55	14.55

D3

D4

1921   Perf. 11½
Red Surcharge
J14	D3	50c on 1p black	3.75	3.75
J15	D3	1p on 1p black	3.75	3.75

1922
J16	D4	2p on 5m rose	10.00	6.50
a.		"AX" of "TAXE" inverted	175.00	175.00
J17	D4	3p on 1p gray bl	15.00	12.00

French Mandate

Postage Due Stamps of France, 1893-1920, Surcharged

1923
J18	D2	50c on 10c brown	1.50	1.50
J19	D2	1p on 20c ol grn	2.25	2.25
J20	D2	2p on 30c red	1.90	1.90
J21	D2	3p on 50c vio brn	1.90	1.90
J22	D2	5p on 1fr red brn, *straw*	3.75	3.75
		Nos. J18-J22 (5)	11.30	11.30

Postage Due Stamps of France, 1893-1920, Surcharged

1924
J23	D2	50c on 10c brown	1.00	1.00
J24	D2	1p on 20c ol grn	1.00	1.00
J25	D2	2p on 30c red	1.10	1.10
J26	D2	3p on 50c vio brn	1.50	1.50
J27	D2	5p on 1fr red brn, *straw*	1.50	1.50
		Nos. J23-J27 (5)	6.10	6.10

Postage Due Stamps of France, 1893-1920, Surcharged

1924
J28	D2	50c on 10c brown	.75	.75
J29	D2	1p on 20c ol grn	.75	.75
J30	D2	2p on 30c red	1.00	1.00
J31	D2	3p on 50c vio brn	1.40	1.40
J32	D2	5p on 1fr red brn, *straw*	1.75	1.75
		Nos. J28-J32 (5)	5.65	5.65

Water Wheel at Hama — D5

Bridge at Antioch — D6

Designs: 2p, The Tartous. 3p, View of Banias. 5p, Chevaliers' Castle.

1925   **Photo.**   *Perf. 13½*
J33	D5	50c brown, *yel*	.25	.25
J34	D6	1p violet, *rose*	.25	.25
J35	D5	2p black, *blue*	.55	.55
J36	D5	3p black, *red org*	1.25	1.25
J37	D5	5p black, *bl grn*	1.50	1.50
		Nos. J33-J37 (5)	3.80	3.80

D7

Lion — D8

1931
J38	D7	8p black, *gray blue*	3.50	3.50
J39	D8	15p black, *dull rose*	6.00	6.00

> Catalogue values for unused stamps in this section, from this point to the end of the section, are for Never Hinged items.

Syrian Arab Republic

D9

1965   Unwmk. Litho.   *Perf. 11½x11*
J40	D9	2½p violet blue	.20	.20
J41	D9	5p black brown	.20	.20
J42	D9	10p green	.20	.20
J43	D9	17½p carmine rose	.20	.20
J44	D9	25p blue	.20	.20
		Nos. J40-J44 (5)	1.00	1.00

MILITARY STAMPS

Free French Administration
Syria No. 222 Surcharged in Black

1942   Unwmk.   *Perf. 13*
M1	A10	50c on 4p yel org	5.75	5.75

Lebanon Nos. 155 and 142A Surcharged in Carmine

M2	A13	1fr on 5p grnsh bl	4.25	4.25
M3	A25	2.50fr on 12½p dp ultra	4.25	4.25

Camel Corps, Palmyra — M1

1942   Unwmk. Litho.   *Perf. 11½*
M4	M1	1fr deep rose	.40	.30
M5	M1	1.50fr bright violet	.40	.30
M6	M1	2fr orange	.40	.30
M7	M1	2.50fr brown gray	.40	.30
M8	M1	3fr Prussian blue	.75	.60
M9	M1	4fr deep green	1.10	1.10
M10	M1	5fr deep claret	1.75	1.75
		Nos. M4-M10 (7)	5.20	4.65

Nos. M4 to M10 exist imperforate.
For surcharges see Nos. MB1-MB2, MC10.

MILITARY SEMI-POSTAL STAMPS

Free French Administration

Military Stamps of 1942 Surcharged in Black

+9F

1943   Unwmk.   *Perf. 11½*
MB1	M1	1fr + 9fr deep rose	5.00	5.00
MB2	M1	5fr + 20fr deep claret	5.00	5.00

MILITARY AIR POST STAMPS

Free French Administration
Syria Nos. C55-C56 Surcharged in Black, Carmine or Orange

1942   Unwmk.   *Perf. 13*
MC1	AP2	4fr on 50p blk (C)	4.00	4.00
MC2	AP2	6.50fr on 50p blk (C)	4.00	4.00
MC3	AP2	8fr on 50p blk (O)	4.00	4.00
MC4	AP2	10fr on 100p mag	4.00	4.00
		Nos. MC1-MC4 (4)	16.00	16.00

Winged Shields and Cross of Lorraine MAP1

1942   Litho.   *Perf. 11½*
MC5	MAP1	6.50fr pale pink & rose car	1.25	1.25
MC6	MAP1	10fr lt bl & dl vio	1.75	1.75

Nos. MC5 and MC6 exist imperforate.
See Nos. MC7-MC8. For surcharges see Nos. MC9, MCB1-MCB2.

Souvenir Sheets

1942   Without Gum   *Perf. 11*
MC7		Sheet of 2	11.00	11.00
a.		MAP1 6.50fr pale pink & rose carmine	3.50	3.50
b.		MAP1 10fr lt bl & dl violet	3.50	3.50

Imperf
MC8		Sheet of 2	11.00	11.00
a.		MAP1 6.50fr pale pink & rose carmine	3.50	3.50
b.		MAP1 10fr lt bl & dl violet	3.50	3.50

No. MC5 Surcharged in Rose Carmine With New Value and Bars

1942   *Perf. 11½*
MC9	MAP1 4fr on 6.50fr	2.00	2.00

Military Stamp of 1942 Surcharged in Black

1943
MC10	M1 4fr on 3fr Prus blue	2.00	2.00

MILITARY AIR POST SEMI-POSTAL STAMPS

Free French Administration
Military Air Post Stamps of 1942 Surcharged in Black

1943   Unwmk.   *Perf. 11½*
MCB1	MAP1	6.50fr + 48.50fr	15.00	15.00
MCB2	MAP1	10fr + 100fr	15.00	15.00

POSTAL TAX STAMPS

Revenue Stamps Overprinted in Red or Black

R1

a   b

1945   Unwmk.   *Perf. 10½x11½*
RA1	R1(a) 5p dark blue (R)	100.00	22.50

On Stamps Overprinted

RA2	R1(a) 5p dk bl (Bk+Bk)	90.00	27.50
RA3	R1(a) 5p dk bl (Bk+R)	90.00	27.50
RA4	R1(a) 5p dk bl (R+R)	100.00	27.50
RA5	R1(b) 5p dk bl (R+R)	95.00	24.00

On Stamps Overprinted

RA6	R1(a) 5p dk bl (Bk+Bk)	90.00	30.00
RA7	R1(a) 5p dk bl (Bk+R)	90.00	30.00
RA8	R1(a) 5p dk bl (R+R)	90.00	30.00
RA9	R1(b) 5p dk bl (R+R)	110.00	30.00
	Nos. RA1-RA9 (9)	855.00	249.00

The tax was for national defense.

R2

Revenue Stamp Surcharged in Black
1945   Unwmk.   *Perf. 11*
RA10	R2 5p on 25c on 40c rose red	90.00	32.50

The surcharge reads "Tax (postal) for Syrian Army."

Revenue Stamp
Surcharged in
Black

1945
RA11 R2 5p on 25c on 40c
rose red   100.00 32.50

No. RA11 Overprinted in
Black

RA12 R2 5p on 25c on 40c
rose red   80.00

The tax on #RA11-RA12 was for the army.
This overprint exists on No. RA10.

Revenue stamps without overprints
occasionally were used as postage on
covers through at least 1948.

___

ISSUES OF THE ARABIAN GOVERNMENT

The following issues replaced the
British Military Occupation (E.E.F.)
stamps (Palestine Nos. 2-14) which
were used in central and eastern Syria
from Nov. 1918 until Jan. 1920.

Turkish Stamps of
1913-18
Handstamped in
Various Colors

Also Handstamp Surcharged with New
Values as:

1 millieme   1 Egyptian
                           piaster

The Seal reads: "Hakuma al Arabie"
(The Arabian Government)
Perf. 11½, 12, 12½, 13½

1919-20			Unwmk.	
1	A24	1m on 2pa red lil (254)	.85	.85
2	A25	1m on 4pa dk brn (255)	.85	.85
3	A26	2m on 5pa vio brn (256)	1.40	1.40
4	A15	2m on 5pa on 10pa gray grn (291)	.95	.95
5	A18	2m on 5pa ocher (304)	22.50	22.50
6	A41	2m on 5pa grn (345)	275.00	250.00
7	A18	2m on 5pa ocher (378)	47.50	47.50
8	A28	4m on 10pa grn (258)	6.50	6.50
9	A28	4m on 10pa grn (271)	.85	.85
10	A22	4m on 10pa bl grn (329)	1.75	1.75
11	A41	4m on 10pa car (346)	37.50	37.50
12	A23	4m on 10pa grn (415)	7.25	7.25
13	A44	4m on 10pa grn (424)	1.25	1.25
14	A11	4m on 10pa on 20pa vio brn (B38)	1.25	1.25
15	A41	4m on 10pa car (B42)	.85	.85

16	SP1	4m on 10pa red vio (B46)	1.40	1.40
17	SP1	4m on 10pa on 20pa car rose (B47)	1.40	1.40
19	A21	5pa ocher (317)		
21	A21	20pa car rose (153)	92.50	110.00
22	A29	20pa red (259)	1.40	1.40
23	A29	20pa red (272)	275.00	275.00
24	A17	20pa car (299)	2.75	2.75
25	A21	20pa car rose (318)	2.75	2.75
26	A22	20pa car rose (330)	11.00	11.00
27	A21	20pa car rose (342)	5.00	5.00
28	A41	20pa ultra (347)	2.75	2.75
29	A16	20pa mag (363)	11.00	11.00
30	A17	20pa car (371)		
31	A18	20pa car (379)	7.75	7.75
32	A45	20pa dp rose (425)	3.75	3.75
33	A21	20pa car rose (B8)	2.75	2.75
34	A22	20pa car rose (B33)	2.75	2.75
35	A22	20pa car rose (B36)	13.00	13.00
36	A41	20pa ultra (B43)	.55	.55
37	A16	20pa mag (P140)	2.75	2.75
38	A17	20pa car (P144)	250.00	250.00
39	A30	1pi bl (260)	2.75	2.75
40	A31	1pi on 1½pi car & blk (261)	375.00	375.00
41	A30	1pi bl (273)	92.50	92.50
42	A30	1pi on 1pi bl (273)	125.00	125.00
43	A17	1pi blue (300)	4.75	4.75
44	A18	1pi blue (307)	57.50	57.50
45	A22	1pi ultra (331)	5.75	5.75
46	A21	1pi ultra (343)	10.00	10.00
47	A41	1pi vio & blk (348)	1.75	1.75
48	A18	1pi brt bl (389)	5.75	5.75
49	A46	1pi dl vio (426)	1.75	1.75
50	A47	1pi on 50pa ultra (428)	1.10	1.10
51	A21	1pi ultra (B9)	6.00	6.00
52	A21	1pi ultra (B15)	10.00	10.00
53	A18	1pi brt bl (B21)	6.00	6.00
54	A18	1pi blue (B23)	15.00	15.00
55	A22	1pi ultra (B34)	12.50	12.50
56	A41	1pi vio & blk (B44)	2.75	2.75
57	A33	2pi grn & blk (263)	72.50	72.50
58	A13	2pi brn org (289)	2.00	2.00
59	A18	2pi slate (308)	27.50	27.50
60	A18	2pi slate (314)	27.50	27.50
61	A21	2pi bl blk (320)	5.25	5.25
62	A17	2pi org (373)	4.25	4.25
63	A18	2pi brn (310)	12.00	12.00
64	A22	5pi dl vio (333)	23.50	23.50
65	A41	5pi yel brn & blk (349)	4.75	4.75
66	A41	5pi yel brn & blk (418)	4.75	4.75
67	A53	5pi on 2pa Prus bl (547)	7.75	7.75
68	A21	5pi dk vio (B10)	275.00	275.00
69	A17	5pi lil rose (B20)	47.50	47.50
70	A41	5pi yel brn & blk (B45)	4.75	4.75
72	A50	10pi dk grn (431)	130.00	130.00
73	A50	10pi dk vio (432)	110.00	110.00
74	A50	10pi dk brn (433)	375.00	
75	A18	10pi org brn (B2)	350.00	350.00
76	A37	25pi ol grn (267)	350.00	350.00
77	A40	25pi on 200pi grn & blk (287)	500.00	500.00
78	A17	25pi brn (303)	375.00	375.00
79	A51	25pi car, *straw* (434)	92.50	92.50
81	A52	50pi ind (438)	200.00	200.00

The variety "surcharge omitted" exists on
Nos. 1-5, 12-13, 16, 32, 49-50, 67.
A few copies of No. 377 (50pi) and No. 269
(100pi) were overprinted but not regularly
issued.

Overprinted

The Inscription reads "Hakum Soria
Arabie" (Syrian-Arabian Government)
On Stamp of 1913

83	A26	2m on 5pa vio brn (256)	5.00	5.00

On Stamp of 1916-18

84	A45	20pa dp rose (425)	.55	.55

A1

		Litho.	*Perf. 11½*	
85	A1	5m rose	.55	.55
a.	Tête bêche pair		22.50	10.00
b.	Imperf.			

Independence Issue
Arabic Overprint in Green:
"Souvenir of Syrian Independence
March 8, 1920"

86	A1	5m rose	250.00	150.00
a.	Tête bêche pair			
b.	Inverted overprint		375.00	375.00

A2

Litho.
Size: 22x18mm

87	A2	¹/₁₀pi lt brn	.25	.20

Size: 28x22mm

88	A2	²/₁₀pi yel grn	.30	.20
a.	²/₁₀pi yellow (error)		10.00	10.00
89	A2	³/₁₀pi yellow	.40	.30
90	A2	1pi gray blue	.35	.25
91	A2	2pi blue grn	2.00	1.00

Size: 31x25mm

92	A2	5pi vio brn	2.75	1.50
93	A2	10pi gray	2.75	2.00
		Nos. 86-93 (8)	258.80	155.45

Nos. 86-93 exist imperf.
For overprint see No. J5.

PF1   PF2

Revenue Stamps Surcharged as on
Postage Stamps, for Postal Use

1920		Unwmk.	*Perf. 11½*	
94	PF1	5m on 5pa red	.50	.35
95	PF2	1m on 5pa red	.50	.20
96	PF2	2m on 5pa red	.40	.25
97	PF2	1pi on 5pa red	1.00	.65

Surcharged in Syrian
Piasters

98	PF2	2pi on 5pa red	.35	.20
99	PF2	3pi on 5pa red	.35	.20
		Nos. 94-99 (6)	3.10	1.85

___

ISSUES OF THE ARABIAN GOVERNMENT POSTAGE DUE STAMPS

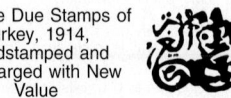

Postage Due Stamps of
Turkey, 1914,
Handstamped and
Surcharged with New
Value

1920		Unwmk.	*Perf. 12*	
J1	D1	2m on 5pa claret	6.75	6.75
J2	D2	20pa red	6.75	6.75
J3	D3	1pi dark blue	6.75	6.75
J4	D4	2pi slate	6.75	6.75
		Nos. J1-J4 (4)	27.00	27.00

Type of Regular Issue
Perf. 11½
Litho.

5	A2	1pi black	1.25	1.25

UNITED ARAB REPUBLIC

Catalogue values for unused
stamps in this section are for
Never Hinged items.

___

See Egypt for stamps of types A1,
A4, A7, A8, A14, A17, A19, A20, A24
with denomination in "M" (milliemes).

Issues for Syria

Linked Maps of
Egypt and
Syria — A1

Perf. 11½

1958, Feb. 1		Unwmk.	Litho.	
1	A1	12½p yellow & green	.20	.20

Establishment of UAR. See No. C1.
See also Egypt No. 436.

Freedom
Monument
A2

1958, May

2	A2	5p yel & vio	.40	.20
3	A2	15p yel grn & brn red	.65	.35
		Nos. 2-3,C2-C3 (4)	3.00	1.30

British-French troop evacuation, 12th anniv.

Bronze Rattle — A3   Hand Holding
                          Torch, Broken
                          Chain and
                          Flag — A4

Antique Art: 15p, Goddess. 20p, Lamgi
Mari. 30p, Mithras fighting bull. 40p, Aspasia.
60p, Minerva. 75p, Flask. 100p, Enameled
Vase. 150p, Mosaic from Omayyad Mosque,
Damascus.

1958, Sept. 14		Litho.	*Perf. 12*	
4	A3	10p lt ol grn	.20	.20
5	A3	15p brown org	.20	.20
6	A3	20p rose lilac	.20	.20
7	A3	30p lt brown	.20	.20
8	A3	40p gray	.30	.20
9	A3	60p green	.50	.20
10	A3	75p blue	.80	.20

11	A3	100p brown car	1.20 .40
12	A3	150p dull purple	2.25 .60

Nos. 4-12 (9)   5.85 2.50

Archaeological collections and museums.

1958, Oct. 14   *Perf. 11½*
13   A4   12.50p car rose   .20 .20

Establishment of Republic of Iraq.
See Egypt No. 454.

Syria No. 411
Overprinted

RAU

1958, Oct. 6   **Wmk. 291**   *Perf. 11½*
13A   A78   12½p olive   37.50 35.00

Nos. 13A,C10-C11 (3)   87.50 85.00

Intl. Children's Day, 1958.

View of Damascus — A5

1958, Dec. 10   **Unwmk.**
14   A5   12½p green   .20 .20

4th Near East Regional Conference,
Damascus, Dec. 10-20. See No. C14.

Secondary School, Damascus — A6

1959, Feb. 26   **Litho.**   *Perf. 12*
15   A6   12½p dull green   .20 .20

See No. 26.

Flags of
UAR and
Yemen
A7

1959, Mar. 8   **Photo.**   **Wmk. 318**
16   A7   12½p grn, red & blk   .20 .20

1st anniversary of United Arab States.
See Egypt No. 465.

Arms of   Mother and
UAR — A8   Children — A9

Perf. 12x11½
1959, Feb. 22   **Litho.**   **Wmk. 291**
17   A8   12½p grn, blk & red   .20 .20

United Arab Republic, 1st anniv.
See Egypt No. 462.

1959, Mar. 21   *Perf. 11½*
18   A9   15p carmine rose   .20 .20
19   A9   25p dk slate grn   .30 .25

Arab Mother's Day, Mar. 21.
For overprints see Nos. 41-42.

Syria No. 378 Surcharged "U.A.R." in
Arabic and English, and New Value in
Red

1959, Apr. 6   **Photo.**   **Unwmk.**
20   A68   2½p on 1p olive   .20 .20

Type of 1959 and

A10

Boys' School, Damascus — A11

Designs: 5p,   7½p,   10p,   Various
arabesques. 12½p, St. Simeon's Monastery.
17½p, Hittin school. 35p, Normal School for
Girls, Damascus.

1959-61   **Unwmk.**   **Litho.**   *Perf. 11½*
21	A10	2½p violet	.20 .20
22	A10	5p olive bister	.20 .20
23	A10	7½p ultra	.20 .20
24	A10	10p bl grn	.20 .20
25	A11	12½p lt bl ('61)	.20 .20
26	A6	17½p brt lilac ('60)	.20 .20
27	A11	25p brt grnsh bl	.30 .20
28	A11	35p brown ('60)	.40 .20

Nos. 21-28 (8)   1.90 1.60

Male Profile and
Fair Emblem — A12

Fair Emblem and Globe — A13

1959, Aug. 30   **Unwmk.**   *Perf. 11½*
30   A12   35p gray, grn & vio   .40 .20
Souvenir Sheet
Imperf
31   A13   30p dl yel & grn   1.50 1.50

6th International Damascus Fair.

Shield and
Cogwheel — A14

Perf. 13½x13
1959, Oct. 20   **Wmk. 328**
32   A14   50p sepia   .60 .35

Issued for Army Day, 1959.

See Egypt No. 491.

Syria Nos.
408 and
386 with
Red
Overprint
Similar to

1959   **Unwmk.**   **Litho.**   *Perf. 11½*
33   A75   15p gray   .20 .20
Photo.
34   A69   50p dk grn   .60 .40

The overprints differ in size and lettering:
No. 33 is 28x8½mm; No. 34 is 21x6mm. A
period follows "R" on Nos. 33-34. The Arabic
overprint means "United Arab Republic."

Cogwheel,   A. R.
Wheat and   Kawakbi — A16
Cotton — A15

1959, Oct. 30   **Litho.**
35   A15   35p gray, bl & ocher   .40 .20

Industrial and Agricultural Production Fair,
Aleppo. For overprint see No. 46.

Type of Syria Air Post, 1956, Inscribed
"U.A.R."

1959, Dec. 31   **Unwmk.**   *Perf. 13½*
36   AP59   12½p gray ol & bister   .20 .20

Day of the Tree. For overprint see No. 49.

1960, Jan. 11   *Perf. 12x11½*
37   A16   15p dark green   .20 .20

Kawakbi, Arabic writer, 50th death anniv.

Arms and
Flag — A17

Perf. 13½x13
1960, Feb. 22   **Photo.**   **Wmk. 328**
38   A17   12½p red & dk sl grn   .20 .20

United Arab Republic, 2nd anniversary.
See Egypt No. 499.

Diesel Train and Old Town — A18

Perf. 11½x11
1960, Mar. 15   **Litho.**   **Unwmk.**
39   A18   12½p brn & brt bl   .35 .20

Construction of the Latakia-Aleppo railroad.

Arab
League
Center,
Cairo,
and Arms
of UAR
A19

Perf. 13x13½
1960, Mar. 22   **Photo.**   **Wmk. 328**
40   A19   12½p dl grn & blk   .20 .20

Opening of the Arab League Center and the
Arab Postal Museum in Cairo.
See Egypt No. 502.

Nos. 18-19
Overprinted in
Black or Magenta

Wmk. 291
1960, Apr. 3   **Litho.**   *Perf. 11½*
41   A9   15p car rose   .20 .20
42   A9   25p dk slate grn (M)   .35 .20

Issued for Arab Mother's Day.

Refugees
Pointing
to Map of
Palestine
A20

Perf. 13x13½
1960, Apr. 7   **Photo.**   **Wmk. 328**
43   A20   12½p car rose   .40 .20
44   A20   50p green   .70 .30

World Refugee Year, 7/1/59-6/30/60.
See Egypt Nos. 503-504.

A21

Perf. 11½
1960, May 12   **Unwmk.**   **Litho.**
45   A21   12½p vio, rose & pale grn   .20 .20

Evacuation Day, 1960.

No. 35 Overprinted
in Red

1960
46   A15   35p gray, bl & ocher   .30 .20

1960 Industrial and Agricultural Production
Fair, Aleppo.

Souvenir Sheet

Flags in Symbolic Design — A22

1960   Unwmk.   Imperf.
47   A22 100p gray, brn & lt bl   1.50 1.50
   7th Intl. Damascus Fair.

Child — A23

1960   Litho.   Perf. 11½
48   A23 35p dk grn & fawn   .40 .20
   Issued for Children's Day.

No. 36 Overprinted in Carmine

1960   Unwmk.   Perf. 11½
49   AP59 12½p gray ol & bis   .20 .20
   Issued to publicize the Day of the Tree.

Coat of Arms   Cogwheel, Retort
and Victory   and Ear of
Wreath — A24   Wheat — A25

Perf. 13½x13
1961, Feb. 22   Photo.   Wmk. 328
50   A24 12½p lt vio   .20 .20
   United Arab Republic, 3rd anniversary.
   See Egypt No. 517.

Perf. 11½
1961, June 8   Unwmk.   Litho.
51   A25 12½p multi   .20 .20
   Industrial and Agricultural Fair, Aleppo.

UAR SEMI-POSTAL STAMP

Catalogue values for unused stamp in this section is for a Never Hinged item.

Postal Emblem — SP1

Perf. 13½x13
1959, Jan. 2   Photo.   Wmk. 318
B1   SP1 20p + 10p bl grn, red & blk   .40 .40
   Issued for Post Day. The surtax went to the social fund for postal employees.
   See Egypt No. B18 for similar stamp with denomination in "M" (milliemes).

UAR AIR POST STAMPS

Catalogue values for unused stamps in this section are for Never Hinged items.

Map Type of Regular Issue
Perf. 11½
1958, Apr. 3   Unwmk.   Litho.
C1   A1 17½p ultra & brn   .35 .20

Broken Chain, Dove and Olive Branch AP1

1958, May 17
C2   AP1 35p rose & blk   .70 .35
C3   AP1 45p bl & brn   1.25 .40
   British-French troop evacuation, 12th anniv.

Scout Putting up Tent AP2

1958, Aug. 31   Perf. 12
C4   AP2 35p dk brn   3.00 1.50
C5   AP2 40p ultra   4.00 2.00
   3rd Pan-Arab Boy Scout Jamboree.

View of Damascus Fair — AP3

UAR Flag and Fair Emblem — AP4

Designs: 30p, Minaret, vase and emblem, vert. 45p, Mosque, chimneys and wheel, vert.

1958, Sept. 1   Litho.   Perf. 11½
C6   AP3 25p vermilion   .70 .60
C7   AP3 30p brt grn   1.00 .60
C8   AP3 45p violet   .80 .55
   Nos. C6-C8 (3)   2.50 1.75
Souvenir Sheet
Imperf
C9   AP4 100p brt grn, car & blk   50.00 50.00
   Fifth Damascus International Fair.

Syria Nos. C244-C245
Overprinted

RAU

1958, Oct. 6   Wmk. 291   Perf. 11½
C10 A78 17½p ultra   25.00 25.00
C11 A78 20p red brn   25.00 25.00
   International Children's Day.

Cotton and Cotton Material — AP5

1958, Oct. 10   Unwmk.   Perf. 12
C12 AP5 25p brn & yel   .40 .40
C13 AP5 35p brn & brick red   .70 .50
   Cotton Festival, Aleppo, Oct. 9-11.

Type of Regular Issue, 1958
1958, Dec. 10
C14 A5 17½p brt vio   .20 .20

Children and Glider — AP6

1958, Dec. 1   Litho.   Perf. 12
C15 AP6 7½p gray green   .50 .30
C16 AP6 12½p olive   2.00 1.25
   1958 glider festival.

UN Emblem — AP7

1958, Dec. 10
C17 AP7 25p dl pur   .20 .20
C18 AP7 35p light blue   .35 .25
C19 AP7 40p brn red   .45 .30
   Nos. C17-C19 (3)   1.00 .75
   10th anniv. of the signing of the Universal Declaration of Human Rights.

Globe, Radio and Telegraph — AP8

1959, Mar. 1   Perf. 12
C20 AP8 40p grn & blk   .50 .35
   Arab Union of Telecommunications.
   See Egypt No. 464 for similar stamp with denomination in "M" (milliemes).

Same Overprinted in Red

1959, Mar. 1
C21 AP8 40p grn & blk   .40 .20
   2nd Conference of the Arab Union of Telecommunications, Damascus.

Laurel and Map of Syria — AP9

Design: 35p, Torch and broken chain.

1959, Apr. 17   Perf. 12x11½
C22 AP9 15p ocher & green   .20 .20
C23 AP9 35p gray & carmine   .40 .20
   British-French troop evacuation, 13th anniv.

"Emigration" — AP10

1959, Aug. 4   Unwmk.   Perf. 11½x12
C24 AP10 80p brt grn, blk & red   .70 .40
   Convention of the Assoc. of Arab Emigrants in the US.

Refinery
AP11

1959, Aug. 12   **Litho.**
C25 AP11 50p bl, blk & car   .90 .40
Opening of first oil refinery in Syria.

Syria Nos. C246 and C181-C182
Overprinted like Nos. 33-34
1959   **Perf. 11½**
C26 AP64   5p bright green   .20 .20
C27 AP44 50p deep plum   .40 .20
C28 AP44 70p purple   .70 .30
     Nos. C26-C28 (3)   1.30 .70
The overprints differ in size and lettering:
#C26 is 25½x9½mm; #C27-C28 are 27x8mm.
A period follows "R" on #C27-C28.

Cotton Boll and   Boy and Building
Thread — AP12   Blocks — AP13

1959, Oct. 1   **Litho.**   **Perf. 11½**
C29 AP12 45p gray blue   .40 .20
C30 AP12 50p claret   .40 .30
Cotton Festival, Aleppo.
For overprints see Nos. C33-C34.

1959, Oct. 5
C31 AP13 25p dl lil, red & dk bl   .20 .20
Issued for Children's Day.

Crane and
Compass
AP14

1960   **Unwmk.**   **Perf. 11½**
C32 AP14 50p lt brn, crim & blk   .40 .30
7th Damascus International Fair.

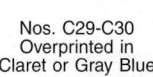

Nos. C29-C30
Overprinted in
Claret or Gray Blue

1960   **Litho.**   **Perf. 11½**
C33 AP12 45p gray blue (C)   .40 .20
C34 AP12 50p claret (GB)   .45 .30
1960 Cotton Festival, Aleppo.

17th Olympic
Games,
Rome — AP15

Globe, Laurel and
"UN" — AP16

1960, Dec. 27   **Unwmk.**   **Perf. 12**
C35 AP15 15p Basketball   .20 .20
C36 AP15 20p Swimmer   .35 .20
C37 AP15 25p Fencing   .35 .20
C38 AP15 40p Horsemanship   .60 .30
     Nos. C35-C38 (4)   1.50 .90

1960, Dec. 31
C39 AP16 35p multi   .35 .20
C40 AP16 50p bl, red & yel   .40 .20
United Nations, 15th anniversary.

Ibrahim
Hanano — AP17

Soldier with
Flag — AP18

1961   **Litho.**   **Perf. 12x11½**
C41 AP17 50p buff & slate grn   .35 .20
Hanano, leader of liberation movement.

1961, Apr. 17   **Wmk. 291**   **Perf. 11½**
C42 AP18 40p gray green   .35 .20
Issued for Evacuation Day, 1961.

Arab and Map of
Palestine — AP19

Abu-Tammam
AP20

1961, May 15   **Perf. 12**
C43 AP19 50p ultra & blk   .50 .25
Issued for Palestine Day.

1961, July 20   **Unwmk.**   **Perf. 11½**
C44 AP20 50p brown   .40 .20
Abu-Tammam (807-845?), Arabian poet.

Discus
Thrower
and Lyre
AP21

1961, Aug. 23   **Litho.**   **Perf. 11½**
C45 AP21 15p crimson & blk   .20 .20
C46 AP21 35p bl grn & vio   .50 .20
5th University Youth Festival.
A souvenir sheet contains one each of Nos.
C45-C46 imperf.

Fair
Emblem — AP22

UAR
Pavilion — AP23

1961, Aug. 25
C47 AP22 17½p vio & grn   .20 .20
C48 AP23   50p brt lil & blk   .35 .20
     a.   Black omitted
8th International Damascus Fair.

St. Simeon's
Monastery
AP24

1961, Oct.   **Litho.**   **Perf. 12**
C49 AP24 200p violet blue   1.50 .90
No. C49 was issued by the Syrian Arab
Republic after dissolution of the UAR.

UAR AIR POST SEMI-POSTAL STAMP

Catalogue value for the unused
stamp in this section is for a Never
Hinged item.

Eye, Hand and
UN Emblem
SPAP1

Perf. 12x11½
1961, Apr. 29   **Litho.**   **Wmk. 291**
CB1 SPAP1 40p + 10p sl grn &
     blk   .30 .30
UN welfare program for the blind.

TAHITI

tə-'hēt-ē

LOCATION — An island in the South Pacific Ocean, one of the Society group
GOVT. — A part of the French Oceania Colony
AREA — 600 sq. mi.
POP. — 19,029
CAPITAL — Papeete

The stamps of Tahiti were replaced by those of French Oceania (see French Polynesia in Vol. 2).

100 Centimes = 1 Franc

Counterfeits exist of surcharges and overprints on Nos. 1-31.

Stamps of French Colonies Surcharged in Black:

25c a

TAHITI 25c b

TAHITI 5c c

TAHITI 10c d

1882		**Unwmk.**		*Imperf.*
1	A8(a)	25c on 35c dk vio, *org*	350.	300.
1A	A8(b)	25c on 35c dk vio, *org*	4,250.	4,250.
1B	A8(a)	25c on 40c ver, *straw*	6,250.	6,750.

Nos. 1-1B exist with surcharges inverted. Values for Nos. 1 and 1A are approximately the same as for normal copies; No. 1B with surcharge inverted is worth about half the value of a normal copy.
Surcharge exists reading either up or down on Nos. 1 and 1A, and double, one inverted on No. 1B. See *Scott Classic Specialized Catalogue of Stamps and Covers* for detailed listings of these and later Tahiti issues.

1884			*Perf. 14x13½*	
2	A9(c)	5c on 20c red, *grn*	260.00	210.00
3	A9(d)	10c on 20c red, *grn*	300.00	275.00
		Imperf		
4	A8(b)	25c on 1fr brnz grn, *straw*	725.00	600.00

Inverted and vertical surcharges on Nos. 2-4 are same value as normally placed surcharges.

Handstamped in Black

1893			*Perf. 14x13½*	
5	A9	1c blk, *lil bl*	850.00	775.00
6	A9	2c brown, *buff*	3,100.	2,500.
7	A9	4c claret, *lav*	1,500.	1,250.
8	A9	5c green, *grnsh*	50.00	45.00
9	A9	10c black, *lav*	50.00	45.00
10	A9	15c blue	50.00	45.00
11	A9	20c red, *green*	70.00	60.00
12	A9	25c yel, *straw*	8,250.	6,500.
13	A9	25c blk, *rose*	50.00	45.00
14	A9	35c violet, *org*	2,500.	2,000.
15	A9	75c carmine, *rose*	77.50	77.50
16	A9	1fr brnz grn, *straw*	80.00	77.50

Nearly all values of this set are known with overprint inverted, sloping up, sloping down and horizontal. Some occur double. Values the same as for the listed stamps.
Nos. 6, 12 and 14 are valued in the grade of Fine.

Overprinted in Black

1893				
17	A9	1c blk, *lil bl*	850.	750.
18	A9	2c brn, *buff*	3,750.	2,750.
19	A9	4c claret, *lav*	1,850.	1,500.
20	A9	5c grn, *grnsh*	1,100.	950.
21	A9	10c black, *lav*	325.	325.
22	A9	15c blue	50.	45.
23	A9	20c red, *grn*	50.	45.
24	A9	25c yel, *straw*	50,000.	42,500.
25	A9	25c black, *rose*	50.	45.
26	A9	35c violet, *org*	2,500.	2,000.
27	A9	75c carmine, *rose*	50.	45.
b.		Double overprint	350.	
28	A9	1fr brnz grn, *straw*	50.	45.

No. 18 is valued in the grade of Fine.

Inverted Overprint

17a	A9	1c blk, *lil bl*	1,250.	1,150.
18a	A9	2c brn, *buff*	4,000.	3,900.
19a	A9	4c claret, *lav*	2,000.	1,900.
20a	A9	5c grn, *grnsh*	1,400.	1,400.
21a	A9	10c black, *lav*	900.	825.
22a	A9	15c blue	210.	190.
23a	A9	20c red, *grn*	210.	190.
25a	A9	25c black, *rose*	210.	190.
26a	A9	35c violet, *org*	2,900.	2,700.
27a	A9	75c carmine, *rose*	210.	190.
28a	A9	1fr brnz grn, *straw*	210.	190.

Stamps of French Polynesia Surcharged in Black or Carmine:

g　　　　　h

1903				
29	A1 (g)	10c on 15c bl (Bk)	10.00	10.00
a.		Double surcharge	57.50	57.50
b.		Inverted surcharge	57.50	57.50
30	A1 (h)	10c on 25c blk, *rose* (C)	10.00	10.00
a.		Double surcharge	62.50	62.50
b.		Inverted surcharge	72.50	72.50
31	A1 (h)	10c on 40c red, *straw* (Bk)	11.50	11.50
a.		Double surcharge	57.50	57.50
b.		Inverted surcharge	62.50	62.50
		Nos. 29-31 (3)	31.50	31.50

In the surcharges on Nos. 29-31 there are two varieties of the "1" in "10," i. e. with long and short serif.

SEMI-POSTAL STAMPS

Stamps of French Polynesia Overprinted in Red

1915		**Unwmk.**	*Perf. 14x13½*	
B1	A1	15c blue	275.00	275.00
a.		Inverted overprint	1,100.	1,100.
B2	A1	15c gray	35.00	35.00
a.		Inverted overprint	400.00	400.00

Counterfeits exist.

POSTAGE DUE STAMPS

Counterfeits exist of overprints on Nos. J1-J26.
Inverted overprints exist on most, and double overprints on many, Tahiti postage due stamps. See the *Scott Classic Specialized Catalogue of Stamps and Covers* for detailed listings.

Postage Due Stamps of French Colonies
Handstamped in Black like Nos. 5-16

1893		**Unwmk.**	*Imperf.*	
J1	D1	1c black	375.	375.
J2	D1	2c black	400.	400.
J3	D1	3c black	425.	425.
J4	D1	4c black	425.	425.
J5	D1	5c black	425.	425.
J6	D1	10c black	425.	425.
J7	D1	15c black	425.	425.
J8	D1	20c black	350.	350.
J9	D1	30c black	425.	425.
J10	D1	40c black	425.	425.
J11	D1	60c black	500.	500.
J12	D1	1fr brown	1,000.	1,000.
J13	D1	2fr brown	1,000.	1,000.
		Nos. J1-J13 (13)	6,600.	6,600.

Overprinted in Black like Nos. 17-28

1893				
J14	D1	1c black	2,400.	2,400.
a.		Inverted overprint	3,250.	3,250.
J15	D1	2c black	550.	550.
J16	D1	3c black	550.	550.
J17	D1	4c black	550.	550.
J18	D1	5c black	550.	550.
J19	D1	10c black	550.	550.
J20	D1	15c black	550.	550.
J21	D1	20c black	550.	550.
J22	D1	30c black	550.	550.
J23	D1	40c black	550.	550.
J24	D1	60c black	550.	550.
J25	D1	1fr brown	550.	550.
J26	D1	2fr brown	550.	550.
		Nos. J14-J26 (13)	9,000.	9,000.

Nos. J15-J20, J22-J26 exist with overprint inverted, double or both. Value, each $600.

TAJIKISTAN

tä-jik-i-'stan

(Tadzhikistan)

LOCATION — Asia, bounded by Uzbekistan, Kyrgyzstan, People's Republic of China and Afghanistan
GOVT. — Republic
AREA — 55,240 sq. mi.
POP. — 6,102,854 (1999 est.)
CAPITAL — Dushanbe

With the breakup of the Soviet Union on Dec. 26, 1991, Tajikistan became independent.

100 Kopecks = 1 Ruble
100 Tanga = 1 Ruble
100 Dinars = 1 Somoni (2000)

Catalogue values for all unused stamps in this country are for Never Hinged items.

Gold Statue of Man on Horse — A1

1992, May 20		**Litho.**	*Perf. 12x12½*	
1	A1	50k multicolored	.30	.30

For surcharge see No. 12.

Sheik Muslihiddin Mosque A2

1992, May 25		**Photo.**	*Perf. 11½*	
2	A2	50k multicolored	.30	.30

For surcharges, see Nos. 13-14.

Musical Instruments of Tajikistan — A3

Photo. & Engr.				
1992, Aug. 15			*Perf. 12x11½*	
3	A3	35k multicolored	.30	.30

For surcharges see Nos. 5-7.

Ram — A4

1992, Aug. 21		**Photo.**	*Perf. 12x12½*	
4	A4	30k multicolored	.30	.30

No. 3 Surcharged in Black or Blue

Photo. & Engr.				
1992, Nov. 12			*Perf. 12x11½*	
5	A3	15r on 35k	.75	.75
6	A3	15r on 35k (Bl)	2.50	2.50
7	A3	50r on 35k	.75	.75
		Nos. 5-7 (3)	4.00	4.00

Russia No. 5838 Surcharged

1992, Jan. 4		**Litho.**	*Perf. 12x12½*	
8	A2765	3r on 1k	.35	.35
9	A2765	100r on 1k	2.10	2.10

No. 1 Surcharged in Black and Russia No. 5984 Surcharged in Violet Blue or Green

1992, May 7		**Litho.**	*Perf. 12x12½*	
10	A2765	10r on 2k (VB)	.75	.20
11	A2765	15r on 2k (Gr)	.75	.20
12	A1	60r on 50k	1.50	1.50
		Nos. 10-12 (3)	3.00	1.90

Location and size of lettering on Nos. 10-11 varies.

No. 2 Surcharged

Methods and Perfs as Before				
1992, Sept. 18				
13	A2	5r on 50k multi	.40	.40
14	A2	25r on 50k multi	1.00	1.00

Wild Animals A5

Designs: 3r, Ursus arctos. 10r, Cervas elaphus. 15r, Capra falconeri. 25r, Hystrix leucura. 100r, Uncia uncia.

1993, June 8   Litho.   Perf. 13½

15	A5	3r multicolored	.20	.20
16	A5	10r multicolored	.30	.20
17	A5	15r multicolored	.30	.20
18	A5	25r multicolored	.55	.25
19	A5	100r multicolored	1.90	.40
		Nos. 15-19 (5)	3.25	1.25

Fortress, 19th Cent. — A6

Academy — A6a

1r, Statue of Rudaki, poet, vert. 5r, Mountains, river. 10r, Statue with oriental inscription, vert. 15r, Mausoleum of Aini, poet, vert. 20r, Map, flag. 35r, Post office. 50r, Aini Opera House. #29, Theater. #30, Flag, map, diff. #31, Observatory. #32, Academy.

1993-94

20	A6	1r multicolored	.20	.20
22	A6	5r multicolored	.20	.20
23	A6	10r multicolored	.20	.20
24	A6	15r multicolored	.20	.20
25	A6	20r green & multi	.20	.20
26	A6	25r multicolored	.35	.35
27	A6	35r multicolored	.20	.20
28	A6	50r multicolored	.55	.50
29	A6	100r multicolored	.50	.50
30	A6	100r blue & multi	1.00	1.00
31	A6	160r multicolored	.60	.60
32	A6a	160r shown	.60	.60
		Nos. 20-32 (12)	4.80	4.80

Issued: 1r, 5r, 15r, 20r, 25r, 50r, No. 30, 6/8/93, others, 9/8/94.

This is an expanding set. Numbers will change if necessary.

For surcharge, see No. 301.

Souvenir Sheet

1992 Summer Olympics, Barcelona — A7

1993, June 8

33	A7	50r multicolored	5.75	5.75

For surcharge see No. 52A.

Epic Poem "Book of Kings", by Ferdowsi, 1000th Anniv. A8

Designs: 5r, Combat with swords. 20r, Two men on horseback fighting with spears. 30r, Men in combat stopped by guide on giant bird, vert. 50r, Ferdowsi (c. 935-c. 1020), vert.

1993, June 8   Litho.   Perf. 13½

34	A8	5r multicolored	.25	.25
35	A8	20r multicolored	.75	.75
36	A8	30r multicolored	1.00	1.00
a.		Sheet, 2 each # 34-36, + 4 labels	12.00	—
		Nos. 34-36 (3)	2.00	2.00

Souvenir Sheet

37	A8	50r multicolored	2.00	2.00

No. 37 contains one 30x45mm stamp.

Traditional Art Pattern — A8a

1993, July 1   Litho.   Perf. 12x11½

37A	A8a	1.50r multicolored	.60	.60

Dated 1992.

For surcharges see Nos. 62-65.

Ali Hamadani (1314-85), Persian Mystic — A9

1994, Feb. 22   Litho.   Perf. 13½

38	A9	1000r multicolored	2.50	2.50
39	A9	1000r multicolored	2.50	2.50

Name in latin letters on No. 38 and in cyrillic letters on No. 39.

Natl. Arms — A10

1994, Feb. 22

40	A10	10r black brown & multi	.20	.20
41	A10	15r purple & multi	.20	.20
43	A10	35r olive & multi	.20	.20
44	A10	50r red & multi	.25	.25
46	A10	100r green & multi	.30	.30
47	A10	160r blue & multi	.50	.50

Size: 23x36mm

50	A10	500r blue & multi	.75	.75
52	A10	1000r brown & multi	1.25	1.25
		Nos. 40-52 (8)	3.65	3.65

This is an expanding set. Numbers will change if necessary.

No. 33 Ovptd.

1994, Apr. 13   Litho.   Perf. 13½

52A	A7	50r multicolored	8.50	8.50

Prehistoric Animals A11

Designs: No. 53, Diatryma. No. 54, Triceratops. No. 55, Anatosaurus. No. 56, Tyrannosaurus. No. 57, Parasaurolophus. No. 58, Incorrectly inscribed "Tyrannosaurus," with

horns, resembling an Ankalysaurus. No. 59, Spinosaurus. No. 60, Stegosaurus.

1994, Sept. 8   Litho.   Perf. 13½

53-60	A11	500r Set of 8	6.50	2.50

Issued both in separate sheetlets of nine and together in a se-tenant sheetlet of nine, containing Nos. 53-60 and one label. Values: set of nine sheetlets, $50; se-tenant sheetlet, $35.

No. 37A Surcharged in Green

1995, Mar. 10   Litho.   Perf. 12x11½

62	A8a	100r on 1.50r multi	.20	.20
63	A8a	600r on 1.50r multi	.50	.50
64	A8a	1000r on 1.50r multi	.90	.90
65	A8a	5000r on 1.50r multi	3.75	3.75
a.		Strip, #64-65, 2 ea #62-63	8.00	8.00
		Nos. 62-65 (4)	5.35	5.35

Issued in sheets of 36 stamps. Each vertical and horizontal strip has stamps in different order.

For surcharges see Nos. 111-114.

Membership Admissions — A13

Designs: No. 66, Member of UN. No. 67, Member of UPU, vert. No. 68, Member of OSCE (Organization of Security & Cooperation in Europe), vert.

1995, May 4   Litho.   Perf. 13½

66	A13	1000r multicolored	1.10	.95
67	A13	1000r multicolored	1.10	.95
68	A13	1000r multicolored	1.10	.95
		Nos. 66-68 (3)	3.30	2.85

Lizards A14

#69, Alsophylax loricatus. #70, Varanus griseus. #71, Phrynocephalus mystaceus. #72, Phrynocephalus helioscopus. #73, Phrynocephalus sogdianus. #74, Teratoscincus scineus.

5000r, Eumeces schneideri.

1995, May 4   Litho.   Perf. 13½

69	A14	500r multicolored	.55	.55
70	A14	500r multicolored	.55	.55
71	A14	500r multicolored	.55	.55
72	A14	500r multicolored	.55	.55
73	A14	500r multicolored	.55	.55
74	A14	500r multicolored	.55	.55
		Nos. 69-74 (6)	3.30	3.30

Souvenir Sheet

75	A14	5000r multicolored	5.50	3.25

For overprints see Nos. 77-78.

Souvenir Sheet

End of World War II, 50th Anniv. — A15

Illustration reduced.

1995, May 8   Litho.   Perf. 13½

76	A15	5000r multicolored	4.00	4.00
a.		As #76, color diff.	3.00	3.00

On No. 76 emblem in margin is bister, black & red. No. 76a emblem is yellow, black & red with missing letter "E" from second line of text.

No. 70 Ovptd.

No. 71 Ovptd.

1995, Dec. 1   Litho.   Perf. 13½

77	A14	500r on #70	2.75	2.75
78	A14	500r on #71	2.75	2.75

Singapore '95 (#77), Beijing '95 (#78).

New Natl. Arms — A16

1995, Dec. 20

79	A16	1r olive & multi	.20	.20
80	A16	2r brown & multi	.20	.20
81	A16	5r green & multi	.20	.20
82	A16	12r red & multi	.30	.30
83	A16	40r green blue & multi	.70	.70
		Nos. 79-83 (5)	1.60	1.50

Birds A17

Designs: No. 84, Syrrhaptes tibetana. No. 85, Perdix daurica turcomana. No. 86, Tetraogallus tibetanus. No. 87, Otis undulata macqueeni. No. 88, Larus brunnicephalus. No. 89, Anser indicus.

600r, Phasianus colchicus.

1996, Feb. 1

84	A17	200r multicolored	1.25	1.25
85	A17	200r multicolored	1.25	1.25
86	A17	200r multicolored	1.25	1.25
87	A17	200r multicolored	1.25	1.25
88	A17	200r multicolored	1.25	1.25
89	A17	200r multicolored	1.25	1.25
		Nos. 84-89 (6)	7.50	7.50

Souvenir Sheet

90	A17	600r multicolored	6.00	6.00

Two each of Nos. 84-89 were issued in sheet of 12 + label.

UN, 50th Anniv. A18

Designs: 100r, UN headquarters, New York. 500r, Headquarters at night.

1996

90A	A18	100r multicolored	1.00	1.00

Souvenir Sheet

90B	A14	500r multicolored	4.00	4.00

Issued: 100r, 4/10; 500r, 2/1.

Souvenir Sheet

Save the Aral Sea — A19

Designs: a, Felis caracal. b, Salmo trutta aralensis. c, Hyaena hyaena. d, Pseudoscaphirhynchus kaufmanni. e, Aspiolucius esocinus.

1996, May 3   Litho.   Perf. 14
91   A19 100r Sheet of 5, #a.-e.   6.00 6.00

See Kazakhstan No. 145, Kyrgyzstan No. 107, Turkmenistan No. 52, Uzbekistan No. 113.

A20

A20a

Designs: Nos. 92-95, 98, Otocolobus manul (different views). No. 96, Felis chaus oxiana. No. 97, Felix lynx isabellina.

1996, June 28   Litho.   Perf. 13½
92   A20 100r brown & multi   2.00 2.00
93   A20 100r yellow & multi   2.00 2.00
94   A20 150r blue & multi   2.00 2.00
95   A20 150r lilac & multi   2.00 2.00
96   A20 200r multicolored   2.00 2.00
97   A20 200r multicolored   2.00 2.00
        Nos. 92-97 (6)   12.00 12.00

Souvenir Sheet

98   A20a 500r multicolored   8.00 8.00
        World Wildlife Fund (#92-95).

1996 Summer Olympic Games, Atlanta A21

1996, July 12   Litho.   Perf. 13½
99   A21 200r Judo   1.75 1.75
100   A21 200r Diving   1.75 1.75
101   A21 200r Hammer throw   1.75 1.75
102   A21 200r Soccer   1.75 1.75
103   A21 200r Pierre de Coubertin   1.75 1.75
        Nos. 99-103 (5)   8.75 8.75

Kamol Khujandi, Poet — A22

1996, Sept. 7   Litho.   Perf. 13½
104   A22 500r Cyrillic name 14mm long   3.75 3.75
a.   Cyrillic name 13mm long   8.50 8.50
105   A22 500r English inscriptions   3.75 3.75

Central Asian Postal Union, 5th Anniv. A23

1996, Dec. 25   Perf. 12¾
106   A23 100r multicolored   4.50 4.50

Mountains A24

1997, July 16   Perf. 13x12¾
107   A24 100r Communism Peak   1.50 1.50
108   A24 100r Peak Korzhenevskoj   1.50 1.50
109   A24 100r Lenin Peak   1.50 1.50
a.   Strip of 3, #107-109   6.00 6.00

Souvenir Sheet

110   A24 500r Mountain climber   6.00 6.00

Nos. 62-65 Surcharged

1997, Oct. 27   Litho.   Perf. 12x11½
111   A8a (A) on 100r #62   .75   .75
112   A8a (A) on 600r #63   .75   .75
113   A8a (A) on 1000r #64   .75   .75
114   A8a (A) on 5000r #65   .75   .75
a.   Strip, #113-114, 2 ea #111-112   4.50 4.50
        Nos. 111-114 (4)   3.00 3.00

A25

Traditional Costumes: #115, Woman with red shawl draped over head, carrying pitcher. #116, Woman in long formal dress, cape, tiara. #117, Man wearing long striped coat. #118, Man wearing long blue coat.

1998, Feb. 20   Litho.   Perf. 12½x13
115   A25 100r multicolored   1.00 1.00
116   A25 100r multicolored   1.00 1.00
117   A25 150r multicolored   1.50 1.50
a.   Pair, #115, 117   2.50 2.50
118   A25 150r multicolored   1.50 1.50
a.   Pair, #116, 118   2.50 2.50
        Nos. 115-118 (4)   5.00 5.00

Handicrafts — A26

1998, Feb. 20   Litho.   Perf. 12¾
119   A26 30r Urn   .50   .50
119A A26 100r Cradles   1.50 1.50

Size: 64x64mm
Imperf
120   A26 300r Ceramic tile   4.00 4.00
        Nos. 119-120 (3)   6.00 6.00

A27

1998, Apr. 3   Litho.   Perf. 12½x13
Flowers: 12r, Tulipa greigii. 30r, Crocus korolkowii. 70r, Iris darwasica. 150r, Petilium eduardii. 300r, Juno nicolai.

121   A27 12r multicolored   .40   .40
122   A27 30r multicolored   .60   .60
123   A27 70r multicolored   1.25 1.25
124   A27 150r multicolored   2.75 2.75
a.   Sheet of 4, #121-124   5.50 5.50
        Nos. 121-124 (4)   5.00 5.00

Souvenir Sheet

125   A27 300r multicolored   5.00 5.00

Stamps in No. 124a have margins continuing the background design of the sheet.

Butterflies A28

12r, Catocala timur. 30r, Celerio chamyla apocyni. 70r, Colias sieversi. 150r, Papilio alexanor. 300r, Anthocharis tomyris.

1998, Apr. 3   Perf. 13x12½
126   A28 12r multicolored   .75   .75
127   A28 30r multicolored   .90   .90
128   A28 70r multicolored   1.25 1.25
129   A28 150r multicolored   2.50 2.50
a.   Sheet of 4, #126-129   7.00 7.00
        Nos. 126-129 (4)   5.40 5.40

Souvenir Sheet

130   A28 300r multicolored   6.50 6.50

Stamps in No. 129a have margins continuing the background design of the sheet.

Gems A29

1998, Aug. 21   Litho.   Perf. 13x12¾
131   A29 1r Sapphire   .20   .20
132   A29 1r Ruby   .20   .20
133   A29 12r Lapis lazuli   .30   .30
134   A29 12r Tourmaline   .30   .30
135   A29 150r Spinel   1.75 1.75
136   A29 150r Amethyst   1.75 1.75
a.   Sheet of 6, #131-136, + 2 labels   4.50 4.50
        Nos. 131-136 (6)   4.50 4.50

Souvenir Sheet

137   A29 350r Agate   4.50 4.50

Bobojon Ghafurov, Academician (1908-98) — A30

1998, Aug. 21   Perf. 12¾x13
138   A30 12r blue & multi   .25   .25
139   A30 150r red & multi   2.00 2.00

Each printed in sheets of 10.

Aleksander Pushkin (1799-1837), Russian Poet — A31

1999, June   Litho.   Perf. 13¼x13½
140   A31 100r Self-portrait drawing   .50   .50
141   A31 270r Painting by Kiprensky   1.50 1.50
a.   Pair, #140-141   2.00 2.00

"ILLEGAL" STAMPS

Tajikistan postal officials have declared as "illegal" the following items.

Sheets of nine stamps of various denominations depicting:

Elvis Presley, Barry White, Michael Douglas, Robert DeNiro, Grace Kelly, the television show "Ally McBeal," Harry Potter, Batman, Superman (two different sheets), Warner Brothers cartoon characters, U.S. Political Cartoons concerning the 2000 Presidential election, Mushrooms, Mushrooms in Art, Major League Baseball players, Sydney 2002 Olympic Games (two different sheets), Various golfers, U.S. Open Golf Championship, Golfer Eduardo Romero, Tiger Woods (two different sheets), Pope John Paul II, and Masonic emblems.

Sheet of 3 stamps of various denominations depicting Marilyn Monroe.

A32

A32a

A32b

1999, June 5   Litho.   Perf. 13½
142   A32   (40r) multi   .20   .20
143   A32a (100r) multi   .55   .55
144   A32b (270r) multi   1.40 1.40
        Nos. 142-144 (3)   2.15 2.15

Samanid Dynasty — A33

1999, Aug.   Litho.   Perf. 12¾x13
145   A33 30r Lion figurine   .20   .20
146   A33 50r Round emblem   .45   .45
147   A33 100r Handled figurine   .90   .90
148   A33 270r Three figurines   2.50 2.50
        Nos. 145-148 (4)   4.05 4.05

Souvenir Sheet

149   A33 500r King   5.50 5.50
a.   Sheet, #149, 2 ea #145-148   10.00 10.00

Samanid Dynasty, 1100th Anniv. — A34

Illustration reduced.
No. 150: a, 100r, King. b, 500r, Pres. Emomali Rakhmonov.

1999, Oct.   **Litho.**   *Perf. 13½x13*
150   A34   Sheet of 2, #a.-b.   8.00 8.00

Mushrooms A35

Designs: Nos. 151, 153a, 100r, Pleurotus eryngii. Nos. 152, 153b, 270r, Lepista nuda. 500r, Morchella steppicola.

1999, Nov.   *Perf. 13¼x13*
151   A35   100r multi   1.00 1.00
152   A35   270r multi   3.00 3.00
Miniature Sheet
153   A35   Sheet, 2 ea #153a-153b   2.75 2.75
Souvenir Sheet
154   A35   500r multi   2.25 2.25

Nos. 151-152 have white borders, while Nos. 153a-153b have borders which continue the sheet's central design.

Fish — A36

Designs: 40r, Ophiocephalus argus. 100r, Barbus brachycephalus. 230r, Schizopygopsis stoliczkai. 270r, Pseudoscaphirhynchus fedtschenkoi.
500r, Pseudoscaphirhynchus kaufmanni. Illustration reduced.

2000   **Litho.**   *Perf. 13¼x13*
155-158   A36   Set of 4   3.00 3.00
158a   Souvenir sheet, #155-158   3.50 3.50
Souvenir Sheet
159   A36   500r multi   3.50 3.50

On Nos. 158-159, Pseudoscaphirhynchus is misspelled "Pseudoscaphiynchus."

UPU, 125th Anniv. (in 1999) — A37

2000
160   A37   270r multi   1.10 1.10

---

100 Dinars = 1 Somoni (2000)

Birds of Prey A38

Designs: 10d, Pandion haliaetus. 27d, Aquila chrysaetus, vert. 50d, Gyps himalayensis. 70d, Circaetus ferox, vert. 1s, Falco peregrinus, vert.

2001, Jan. 23   **Litho.**   *Perf. 14*
161-164   A38   Set of 4   5.25 5.25
Souvenir Sheet
165   A38   1s multi   3.25 3.25

No. 165 contains one 42x56mm stamp. Dated 2000.

Chess — A39

Designs: 15d, Mikhail Botvinnik. 41d, Bobby Fischer.
No. 168: a, 10d, Wilhelm Steinitz. b, 25d, Chess board, five people. c, 50d, José Raul Capablanca. d, 70d, Emanuel Lasker. e, 90d, Chess board, four people. f, 1s, Alexander Alekhine.

2001, May 29   *Perf. 14¼x14*
166-167   A39   Set of 2   2.00 2.00
Souvenir Sheet
168   A39   Sheet of 6, #a-f   8.00 8.00

No. 26 Surcharged in Green, Red or Black

a

b

c

2001, June 4   *Perf. 13½*
169   A6(a)   (6d) multi (G)   .45 .45
170   A6(b)   (15d) multi (R)   .80 .80
171   A6(c)   (41d) multi (Bk)   2.50 2.50
   Nos. 169-171 (3)   3.75 3.75

Souvenir Sheet

Satellite Communications — A40

2001, July 25   *Perf. 13¼x13*
172   A40   1.50s multi   3.50 3.50

Souvenir Sheets

Nurec Hydroelectric Station — A41

Pres. Emomali Rakhmonov — A42

Independence, 10th Anniv. — A43

No. 175: a, 41d, Map, flag and arms (29x29mm). b, 54d, Emblem (29x29mm). c, 95d, Ratification of constitution (49x29mm).

2001, Sept. 7   *Perf. 13¼x13¾*
173   A41   2.50s multi   19.00 19.00
   Perf. 12¾x13¼
174   A42   3s multi   22.50 22.50
   Perf. 14x13¾
175   A43   Sheet of 3, #a-c   16.00 16.00
   Independence, 10th anniv.

Tajikistan postal officials have declared as "illegal" the following items:
Sheets of nine stamps of various denominations depicting Bruce Lee, Michael Jordan, Osama bin Laden, Captain America, Fantastic Four, Queen Mother's 100th Birthday, Formula 1 Racing, Motor Sports and the Netherlands Royal Wedding.
Sheets of six stamps of various denominations depicting Pope John Paul II and Motorcycle racers.
Sheet of three stamps of various denominations depicting Pope John Paul II.

Transportation — A44

Designs: 1s, Tu-154M Airplane.
No. 177: a, 41d, Vehicles on road. b, 90d, Locomotive.

2001, Dec. 12   **Litho.**   *Perf. 14x13¼*
176   A44   1s multi   2.50 2.50
Souvenir Sheet
177   A44   Sheet of 3, #176, 177a, 177b   6.00 6.00

Commonwealth of Independent States, 10th Anniv. — A45

2001, Dec. 17   *Perf. 14¼x14*
178   A45   50d multi   1.75 1.75

Souvenir Sheet

Regional Communications Accord — A46

2001, Dec. 17
179   A46   1s multi + 2 labels   3.25 3.25

Avesta, 2700th Anniv. — A47

Zoroastrian: 2d, Goddess Anahita. 3d, Priest.
No. 182: a, 70d, Goddess Haoma. b, 90d, God Farroh. c, 1s, God Surush. d, 2s, Goddess Din.

2002, Jan. 1   **Litho.**   *Perf. 10*
180-181   A47   Set of 2   1.50 1.50
Souvenir Sheet
182   A47   Sheet of 4, #a-d   10.00 10.00

No. 182 contains four 27x44mm stamps. Dated 2001.

Miniature Sheet

UN High Commissioner for Refugees, 50th Anniv. (in 2001) — A48

No. 183: a, Mothers holding children, refugees. b, Military helicopter, sun, refugees. c, Cloud, rainbow, moon, soldier, child.

2002, Jan. 1
183 A48 50d Sheet of 3, #a-c   3.50 3.50
            Dated 2001.

Flora and Fauna of Central Asia — A49

No. 184: a, Bird facing right. b, Bird facing left. c, Mushrooms and snail. d, Rodent. e, Butterfly. f, Butterfly and tulip. g, Cat. h, Cat and tulip.

2002, Apr. 12 Litho. Perf. 13¾x13½
184   Miniature sheet of 8   7.50 7.50
   a.   A49 6d multi   .45   .45
   b.   A49 15d multi   .45   .45
   c.   A49 41d multi   .45   .45
   d.   A49 50d multi   .55   .55
   e.   A49 95d multi   .95   .95
   f.-h. A49 1.50s any single   1.50 1.50

Worldwide Fund for Nature (WWF) — A50

Reed cats: a, 1s, Two cats. b, 1.50s, One cat walking. c, 2s, One cat resting. d, 2s, Three kittens.
Illustration reduced.

2002, Apr. 12   Perf. 14x14¼
185 A50   Block of 4, #a-d   6.50 6.50
   e.   Sheet, 2 #185   15.00 15.00

Dushanbe Zoo, 40th Anniv. — A51

Designs: 2d, Pan troglodytes. 3d, Cervus nippon hortulorum. 10d, Panthera tigris altaice. 41d, Diceros bicornis michaeli. 50d, Giraffa camelopardis reticulata. 1s, Panthera leo.

2002, Aug. 29 Litho. Perf. 14¼x14
186-191 A51   Set of 6   5.75 5.75

Souvenir Sheet

Navruz — A52

No. 192: a, 1s, Wheat bundle. b, 50d, Dancers in red costumes. c, 1s, Dancer in purple costume.

2002, Aug. 29
192 A52   Sheet of 3, #a-c   5.00 5.00

A53   A54

Istravashan, 2500th Anniv.
A55   A56

2002, Sept. 6
193 A53 50d brown & multi   .90   .90
194 A54 50d green & multi   .90   .90
195 A55 50d brown & multi   .90   .90
196 A56 50d green & multi   .90   .90
        Nos. 193-196 (4)   3.60 3.60

No. 168 Overprinted "2002" on Stamps and With Text in Margin
Souvenir Sheet

Designs as before.

2002, Sept. 20 Litho. Perf. 14¼x14
197 A39   Sheet of 6, #a-f   9.00 9.00

No. 197 is overprinted in bottom sheet margin "Chess Super Championship / between teams of the World and Russia / 08-11.09.2002. Moscow" and in left sheet margin with similar text in Cyrillic characters.
No. 197 exists imperf. Value $300.
No. 197 also exists with violet overprint. Value: perf, $30; imperf $350.

Tajikistan postal officials have declared as "illegal" the following items.
Sheets of nine stamps of various denominations depicting: 20th Century Dreams (6 different sheets), Elephants and Rotary Intl. emblem, Owls, mushrooms and Rotary International emblem, Pandas, Chess, The Beatles, Locomotives, Princess Diana, the movie The Blair Witch Project, Defenders of Peace and Freedom, 2002 Brazilian World Cup Soccer Team, Harry Potter, Cartoon characters from South Park (Christmas), Warner Brothers Cartoon Characters (Christmas).
Sheets of six stamps of various denominations depicting Pokemon characters (eight sheets), Pope John Paul II, Dinosaurs.
Sheet of three stamps of various denominations depicting Elvis Presley.
Souvenir sheets of one stamp with 25.00 denomination depicting Harry Potter (2 different sheets), Penguins,
Souvenir sheet of one stamp with 20.00 denomination depicting Pope John Paul and New York fireman.

New Year 2002 (Year Of the Horse) — A57

No. 198: a, 2d, Thoroughbred racing. b, 3d, Harness racing. c, 95d, Troika. d, 95d, Polo.
No. 199: a, 50d, Dressage. b, 50d, Fox hunting. c, 1s, Steeplechase. d, 1s, Show jumping.
1.50s, Horses in circus act, vert.
Illustration reduced.

2002, Oct. 15 Litho. Perf. 14x14¼
Blocks of 4, #a-d
198-199 A57   Set of 2   7.50 7.50
Souvenir Sheet
Perf. 14¼x14
200 A57 1.50s multi + 2 labels   4.00 4.00

Oriental Bazaar — A58

No. 201: a, Man in donkey cart. b, Man on donkey. c, Melon vendor. d, Man cooking shashliks.

2002, Dec. 25 Litho. Perf. 14¼x14
201 A58 65d Block of 4, #a-d   4.50 4.50

Traditional Sports A59

Designs: 1d, Archery. 20d, Horse racing. 53d, Polo. 65d, Stone throwing. 1s, Buzkashi. 1.24s, Wrestling.

2002, Dec. 25   Perf. 14x14¼
202-207 A59   Set of 6   6.00 6.00

Lunar Calendar — A60

Designs: 53d, Sun and zodiac animals. 65d, Zodiac animals and ram. 1s, Ram in circle. 1.50s, Ram.

2003, Mar. 11   Perf. 14¼x14
208-210 A60   Set of 3   4.75 4.75
Souvenir Sheet
211 A60 1.50s multi + 2 labels   3.75 3.75

Monument to Ismail Somoni — A61

2003, Mar. 11   Perf. 13¼x14
212 A61 1d emerald   .40   .40
213 A61 2d red violet   .40   .40
214 A61 3d blue green   .40   .40
215 A61 4d purple   .40   .40
216 A61 12d brown   .40   .40
217 A61 20d blue   .40   .40
        Nos. 212-217 (6)   2.40 2.40

Souvenir Sheet
No. 158 Surcharged in Purple

No. 218: a, 8d on 40r, Ophiocephalus argus. b, 20d on 100r, Barbus brachycephalus. c, 53d on 230r, Schizopygopsis stoliczkai. d, 66d on 270r, Pseudoscaphihynchus fedtschenkoi.

2003, May 12 Litho. Perf. 13¼x13
218 A36   Sheet of 4, #a-d   7.75 7.75

2004 Summer Olympics, Athens and 2008 Summer Olympics, Beijing — A62

No. 219: a, 53d, Archery. b, 1s, Track and field. c, 1.23s, Soccer. d, 2s, Gymnastics.

2003, May 20   Perf. 14x13½
219 A62   Sheet of 4, #a-d, +
            2 labels   10.00 10.00

No. 219 exists imperf. with additional designs in margin. Value $27.50.

Philatelic Exhibitions and Fauna — A63

No. 220: a, 8d, 16th Asian Intl. Stamp Exhibition, China. b, 20d, Panthera tigris. c, 53d, Inachis io. d, 66d, Bangkok 2003 World Philatelic Exhibition. e, 1s, Rupicapra rupicapra. f, 1.50s, Ailuropoda melanoleuca. g, 1.50s, Leontopithecus rosalia. h, 2s, Elephas maximus.

2003, May 20
220 A63   Sheet of 8, #a-h   14.00 14.00

No. 220 exists imperf. Value $30.

Intl. Forum on Fresh Water — A64

Designs: No. 221, 1.50s, Peak of Moskvin. No. 222, 1.50s, Iskanderkul.

2003, June 7　　　**Perf. 13½**
221-222 A64　Set of 2　　6.00 6.00
Nos. 221-222 were printed setenant, both vertically and horiziontally, in one sheet.

Famous Men — A65

Designs: No. 223, 1.23s, Nosir Khusrav (1004-88), poet. No. 224, 1.23s, Sadridin Aini (1878-1954), writer.

2003, Sept. 1
223-224 A65　Set of 2　　4.75 4.75

Intl. Association of Academies of Science, 10th Anniv. — A66

No. 225: a, Head, satellite dish, airplane, chemicals. b, Association emblem, cosmonaut, robotic hand, computer.
Illustration reduced.

2003, Sept. 1
225 A66　1.23s Horiz. pair, #a-b　5.50 5.50

Intl. Year of Fresh Water — A67

Children's art: a, Fish above lake. b, Sun, river, tree and hills. c, River, hills and trees. d, Waterfalls.
Illustration reduced.

2003, Oct. 20　　　**Perf. 14x14¼**
226 A67　66d Block of 4, #a-d　5.00 5.00

Racing Airplanes — A68

No. 227: a, Aero L-29A Delfin Akrobat. b, Yak-55. c, Cessna 172. d, SIAI-Marchetti SF-

260. e, Europa XS. f, MBB BO 209 Monsun. g, Mudry Cap 10. h, Soko 2.

2003, Oct. 28　　　**Perf. 14x13½**
227 A68　1s Sheet of 8, #a-h　14.00 14.00
No. 227 exists imperf. Value $35.

Fauna of Central Asia — A69

No. 228: a, 8d, Mimas tiliae. 20d, Mustela erminea. 53d, Testudo horsfieldii. 64d, Mantis religiosa. 1.23s, Lanius collurio. 1.27s, Canis aureus. 1.76s, Capra falconeri. 2.29s, Alcedo atthis.

2003, Oct. 28
228 A69　Sheet of 8, #a-h　14.00 14.00
No. 228 exists imperf. Value $35.

No. 153 Surcharged in Red

2004, Jan. 4　Litho.　Perf. 13¼x13
229 A35　Miniature sheet, 2
　　　each #a-b　　7.00 7.00
a.　20d on 100r #153a　1.75 1.75
b.　66d on 270r #153b　3.25 3.25

National Dances — A70

No. 230 — Various dancers and frame color of: a, Brown. b, Purple. c, Green. d, Bright pink.

2004, Jan. 19　Litho.　Perf. 14¼x14
230 A70　53d Block of 4, #a-d　4.75 4.75
Adjacent blocks in sheet are tete-beche. No. 230 exists with visible tagging that reads "Belarus."

No. 28 Surcharged in Black and Red

2004, Apr. 26　Litho.　Perf. 13½
231 A6　A on 50r multi　　.90 .90
Sold for 8d on day of issue.

No. 31 Surcharged in Black

2004, Apr. 26
232 A6　b on 160r multi　　.90 .90
Sold for 20d on day of issue.

Miniature Sheet

New Year 2004 (Year of the Monkey) — A71

No. 233: a, 1s, Monkey covering eyes. b, 1.20s, Monkey covering ears. c, 1.50s, Monkey covering mouth.

2004, Aug. 13　　　**Perf. 13¾x13½**
233 A71　Sheet of 3, #a-c　6.50 6.50

Dushanbe Buildings — A72

Designs: 1d, National Circus. 2d, Ferdowsi National Library. 3d, National Bank. 8d, Finance Ministry. 20d, Communications Ministry. 50d, City Government Building.

2004, Aug. 13　　　**Perf. 13¾x13¼**
234 A72　1d multi　　.60 .60
235 A72　2d multi　　.60 .60
236 A72　3d multi　　.60 .60
237 A72　8d multi　　.60 .60
238 A72　20d multi　　.60 .60
239 A72　50d multi　　1.25 1.25
　　Nos. 234-239 (6)　4.25 4.25

FIFA (Fédération Internationale de Football Association), Cent. — A73

Designs: 50d, Goalie, World Cup. 70d, FIFA General Secretariat Building, Zurich. 1s, Player with red shirt, vert. 2s, Player with yellow shirt, vert.

Perf. 13½x13¾, 13¾x13½
2004, Aug. 30
240-243 A73　Set of 4　　8.00 8.00
Nos. 240-243 exist imperf. Value, set $35.

Miniature Sheet

2004 Summer Olympics, Athens — A74

No. 244: a, 30d, Wrestling. b, 45d, Track. c, 55d, Basketball. d, 60d, Shooting. e, 75d,

Equestrian. f, 80d, Women's archery. g, 1.50s, Soccer. h, 2.50s, Rhythmic gymnastics.

2004, Sept. 6　　　**Perf. 14x13½**
244 A74　Sheet of 8, #a-h　13.00 13.00
No. 244 exists imperf. Value $35.

Miniature Sheet

Dushanbe Circus — A75

No. 245: a, 20d, Circus building. b, 50d, Tightrope walkers. c, 1s, Elephant and trainer. d, 1.10s, Genie, lamp and cat. e, 1.50s, Man riding donkey, dog. f, 1.70s, Bareback rider.

2004, Dec. 21　　　**Perf. 14x13½**
245 A75　Sheet of 6, #a-f　10.00 10.00
No. 245 exists imperf. Value $25.

Miniature Sheet

Vehicles — A76

No. 246: a, Fire engine. b, Ambulance and helicopter. c, Police cars. d, Postal van and train. e, Wrecker and damaged car. f, School bus.

2004, Dec. 21
246 A76　1s Sheet of 6, #a-f　10.00 10.00
No. 246 exists imperf. Value $25.

Miniature Sheet

Dushanbe as Capital City, 80th Anniv. — A77

No. 247: a, 20d, New apartment buildings on Rudaki Ave. b, 46d, Aini State Opera and Ballet Theater. c, 53d, National Bank. d, 62d, City Government Building. e, 1.27s, Parliament Building. f, 1.76s, Presidential Palace.

2004, Nov. 16　Litho.　Perf. 11½
247 A77　Sheet of 6, #a-f　13.00 13.00

Musical Instruments — A78

No. 248: a, Gejak and bow. b, Adirna.
Illustration reduced.

2004, Nov. 29   Perf. 11½x11¾
248 A78 2.50s Horiz. pair, #a-b 11.00 11.00
        See Kazakhstan No. 470.

Fruit — A79

Designs: Nos. 249, 255, Apples. Nos. 250,
256, Apricots. Nos. 251, 257, Plums. Nos.
252, 258, Pears. Nos. 253, 259, Quince. Nos.
254, 260, Pomegranates.

2005, Mar. 19   Perf. 14x14¼
Panel Color
White Background
249 A79   6d lilac   .20   .20
250 A79   7d blue   .20   .20
251 A79   8d brn orange   .20   .20
252 A79 10d rose   .20   .20
253 A79 11d green   .20   .20
254 A79 12d yel orange   .20   .20
Pale Yellow Background
255 A79 20d purple   .45   .45
256 A79 50d violet   .90   .90
257 A79 55d red   1.00   1.00
258 A79 75d red violet   1.25   1.25
259 A79   2s dk olive   3.50   3.50
260 A79   3s brown red   5.50   5.50
        Nos. 249-260 (12)   13.80 13.80

Lake Sarez — A80

No. 261: a, Katta Nardjonoi Bay (denomination in white). b, Iriht Bay (denomination in
black).
Illustration reduced.

2005, Apr. 4   Perf. 13½
261 A80 2s Horiz. pair, #a-b   7.00 7.00

Souvenir Sheet

End of World War II, 60th
Anniv. — A81

No. 262: a, 18d. b, 75d.

2005, Apr. 15   Perf. 14¼x14
262 A81 Sheet of 2, #a-b, +
            central label   4.25 4.25

Souvenir Sheet

Hunting — A82

No. 263: a, 1s, Hunter facing left. b, 1.70s,
Hunter facing right. c, 2.30s, Like 1s.

2005, July 27   Perf. 13¾x13½
263 A82 Sheet of 3, #a-c   10.00 10.00
        Compare with Type A89.

Airbus A-380 — A83

No. 264 — Inset of airplane and: a, 1.50s,
Left wing. b, 1.50s, Nose. c, 1.80s, Tail. d,
1.80s, Right wing.
Illustration reduced.

2005, July 27   Perf. 13½x14
264 A83 Block of 4, #a-d   12.50 12.50
        No. 264 exists imperf. Value $25.

Miniature Sheet

Mammals — A84

No. 265: a, 20d, Hyena on cliff. b, 20d, Turkestan lynx on tree branch. c, 75d, Badger. d,
75d, Fox. e, 80d, Snow leopard. f, 1s, Bear. g,
1.50s, Leopard. h, 1.80s, Tiger.

2005, Aug. 10   Perf. 13½x14
265 A84 Sheet of 8, #a-h   12.50 12.50
        No. 265 exists imperf. Value $25.

Worldwide Fund for Nature
(WWF) — A85

No. 266 — Various views of bharals: a, 1s.
b, 1.45s. c, 1.70s. d, 2.25s.
Illustration reduced.

2005, Aug. 26   Perf. 13½x14
266 A85 Block of 4, #a-d   7.50 7.50
        No. 266 exists imperf. Value $15.

Avicenna (980-1037),
Scientist — A86

2005, Oct. 3   Perf. 13¼x13¾
267 A86   6d Prus bl & blk   .20   .20
268 A86   8d brn & black   .20   .20
269 A86 10d purple & lilac .20   .20
270 A86 12d blue   .35   .35
271 A86 50d blue green   1.10   1.10
272 A86   1s orange   2.25   2.25
        Nos. 267-272 (6)   4.30   4.30

World Post
Day — A87

2005, Oct. 3   Perf. 13¼x13¾
273 A87   5d blue & black   .20   .20
274 A87   7d brown   .20   .20
275 A87 11d green & lt grn .20   .20
276 A87 20d purple   .35   .35
277 A87 55d gray blue   1.10   1.10
278 A87 75d orange   2.25   2.25
        Nos. 273-278 (6)   4.30   4.30

Mountains — A88

No. 279: a, 1s, Pendjikent. b, 1.50s,
Muminabod. c, 2s, Pamir. d, 2.50s, Isfara.
Illustration reduced.

2005, Dec. 6   Perf. 13½
279 A88 Block of 4, #a-d   12.50 12.50

Souvenir Sheet

Hunting — A89

No. 280: a, Hunter holding falcon. b, Hunter
killing leopard.

2005, Dec. 31   Perf. 13¾x13½
280 A89 2.50s Sheet of 2, #a-b,
            + central label   9.50 9.50
        Compare with type A82.
        No. 280 exists imperf. Value $20.

Fairy Tales — A90

No. 281: a, 55d, The Peasant and the Bear.
b, 75d, Three Brothers. c, 2s, Iradj-bogatyr. d,
3s, The Gold Fox.

2006, Mar. 20   Perf. 14¼x14
281 A90 Block of 4, #a-d   9.50 9.50
        Stamps in vertical columns are tete-beche.

Traditional Costumes — A91

No. 282: a, 75d, Man from Samarkand
wearing red headdress. b, 75d, Man from
Sugd wearing blue headdress. c, 1s, Woman
from Bukhara with arms together. d, 1s,
Woman from Kalayhum with arms apart.

2006, June 20 Litho. Perf. 14¼x14
282 A91 Block or horiz. strip of
            4, #a-d   6.00 6.00
        Printed in sheets of eight containing two of
each stamp.

Miniature Sheet

Fauna of Asia — A92

No. 283: a, 8d, Aquila chrysaetos. b, 20d,
Panthera tigris longipilis. c, 55d, Hystrix hirsu-
tirostris. d, 70d, Alluropoda melanoleuca. e,
75d, Meles meles. f, 1.60s, Ursus arctos. g,
1.92s, Mustela erminea. h, 2s, Bubo
coromandus.

2006, June 29   Perf. 13¾x13½
283 A92 Sheet of 8, #a-h   12.00 12.00
        No. 283 exists imperf. Value $25.

2006 World Cup Soccer
Championships, Germany — A93

No. 284: a, 1.50s, Five players. b, 1.50s,
Three players and goalie. c, 1.50s, Four play-
ers. d, 2s, Three players and goalie, diff.
Illustration reduced.

2006, June 29   Perf. 13½x13¾
284 A93 Block of 4, #a-d   10.00 10.00
   e.   Miniature sheet, 2 each
            #284a-284d   20.00 20.00

Souvenir Sheet

Kulob, 2700th Anniv. — A94

No. 285: a, Anniversary emblem, flag of Tajikistan. b, Mausoleum of Mir Said Ali Hamadoni.

2006, Aug. 30
285 A94 2s Sheet of 2, #a-b   7.50 7.50

Miniature Sheet

Independence, 15th Anniv. — A95

No. 286: a, 1.50s, Presidential Palace. b, 2.50s, Arms of Tajikistan. c, 3s, Flag of Tajikistan, Pres. Emomali Rakhmonov.

2006, Aug. 30   **Perf. 14x14¼**
286 A95   Sheet of 3, #a-c, +   13.00 13.00
    3 labels

Souvenir Sheet

Commonwealth of Independent States, 15th Anniv. — A96

No. 287: a, Emblem of Commonwealth of Independent States, flags of member nations. b, Emblem of Regional Communications Commonwealth.

2006, Sept. 12   **Perf. 14¼x14**
287 A96 1.50s Sheet of 2, #a-b,   6.25 6.25
    + central label

Cotton — A97

2006, Dec. 15   **Perf. 13½x13¾**
Background Color
288 A97 5d olive green   .30 .30
289 A97 6d rose   .30 .30
290 A97 7d lilac   .30 .30
291 A97 8d light blue   .30 .30
292 A97 20d green   .50 .50
293 A97 75d blue   1.40 1.40
    Nos. 288-293 (6)   3.10 3.10

Headdresses — A98

No. 294 — Various headdresses with gray geometrical design at: a, LR. b, LL. c, UR. d, UL.

2006, Dec. 28   **Perf. 14x14¼**
294 A98 1.50s Block of 4, #a-d   9.00 9.00
No. 294 exists imperf. Value $20.

Dogs — A99

Designs: 20d, West Siberian laika. 55d, Perdiguero de burgos. 75d, Afghan hound. 1s, Sredneasiatckaia ovtcharka. 2s, Saluki. 3s, Tosa.

2006, Dec. 28   **Perf. 13¾x13½**
295-300 A99   Set of 6   12.00 12.00
Nos. 295-300 exist imperf. Value, set $25.

No. 32
Surcharged

Methods and Perfs As Before
2007, Mar. 31
301 A6a 75d on 160r #32   1.60 1.60

Souvenir Sheet

Snakes — A100

No. 302: a, Echis carinatus. b, Naja oxiana.

2007, Apr. 30   **Litho.**   **Perf. 14**
302 A100 2s Sheet of 2, #a-b   6.25 6.25

A101   A102

Mevlana (c. 1207-73),
Poet — A103

2007, Aug. 30   **Perf. 13¼x13¾**
303 A101   5d red   .20 .20
304 A101   10d bright blue   .20 .20
305 A101   20d green   .20 .20
306 A101 (25d) dark blue   .30 .30
307 A102 (1.35s) brown violet   1.60 1.60
308 A103 (2.15s) red violet   2.60 2.60
    Nos. 303-308 (6)   5.10 5.10

Jewelry — A104

No. 309: a, 50d, Earring. b, 2s, Necklace. c, 2.50s, Necklace, diff. d, 3s, Earring, diff.

2007, Dec. 18   **Perf. 14¼x14**
309 A104   Block of 4, #a-d   7.50 7.50

Miniature Sheet

Transportation — A105

No. 310: a, 50d, Camels. b, 60d, Steam locomotive. c, 70d, Airplane and helicopter. d, 80d, Pickup truck. e, 90d, Donkey cart. f, 1.50s, Train. g, 1.70s, Bus. h, 2s, Dump truck.

2007, Dec. 27   **Perf. 14x13½**
310 A105   Sheet of 8, #a-h   8.00 8.00

Birds — A106

Designs: Nos. 311, 317a, 1s, Aquila chrysaetos. Nos. 312, 317b, 1.10s, Phasianinae. Nos. 313, 317c, 1.20s, Aix galericulata. Nos. 314, 317d, 1.30s, Otididae. Nos. 315, 317e, 1.40s, Falco cherrug. Nos. 316, 317f, Haliaeetus albicilla.

2007, Dec. 27   **Perf. 14x13½**
Stamps With White Frames
311-316 A106   Set of 6   8.00 8.00
Stamps With Colored Frames
317 A106   Sheet of 6, #a-f   8.00 8.00

TANGANYIKA

ˌtan-gə-ˈnyē-kə

LOCATION — Southeastern Africa bordering on the Indian Ocean
GOVT. — Republic within British Commonwealth
AREA — 362,688 sq. mi.
POP. — 9,404,000 (est. 1961)
CAPITAL — Dar es Salaam

Before World War I, this area formed part of German East Africa. It was mandated to Britain after World War I and (in 1946) became a trust territory under the United Nations. In 1935, stamps of the mandate were replaced by those

---

used jointly by Kenya, Uganda and Tanganyika (see Kenya, Uganda and Tanzania). On Dec. 9, 1961, Tanganyika became independent. On Dec. 9, 1962, it became a republic. April 26, 1964, it joined Zanzibar to form the United Republic of Tanganyika and Zanzibar (later renamed Tanzania). See Tanzania.

100 Cents = 1 Rupee
100 Cents = 1 Shilling (1922)
20 Shillings = 1 Pound

> **Catalogue values for unused stamps in this country are for Never Hinged items, beginning with Scott 45 in the regular postage section and Scott O1 in the officials section.**

Stamps of Kenya,
Uganda & Tanganyika
Overprinted

1921   **Wmk. 4**   **Perf. 14**
1 A1 12c gray   7.50 110.00
2 A1 15c ultra   3.75 6.25
3 A1 50c dull violet & blk   11.50 97.50

Overprinted

4 A2 2r black & red, *blue*   37.50 140.00
5 A2 3r gray green & violet   85.00 210.00
7 A2 5r dull violet & ultra   120.00 290.00
    Nos. 1-7 (6)   265.25 853.75

Overprinted in Red or
Black

1922
8 A1 1c black (R)   1.25 21.00
9 A1 10c orange (Bk)   1.60 16.00

Giraffe
A3   A4

Perf. 14½x14
1922-25   **Engr.**   **Wmk. 4**
10 A3 5c dk violet & blk   2.75 .20
11 A3 5c grn & blk ('25)   3.75 1.75
12 A3 10c green & blk   2.75 .95
13 A3 10c yel & blk ('25)   5.25 1.75
14 A3 15c carmine & blk   2.25 .20
15 A3 20c orange & blk   2.00 .20
16 A3 25c black   6.25 7.50
17 A3 25c blue & blk ('25)   4.50 20.00
18 A3 30c blue & blk   5.75 5.75
19 A3 30c dull vio & blk   4.75 16.00
    ('25)
20 A3 40c brown & black   3.25 5.25
21 A3 50c gray black   2.75 1.75
22 A3 75c bister & black   3.75 21.00
    Perf. 14
23 A4 1sh green & black   3.50 12.50
   a. Wmk. sideways   4.75 16.00
24 A4 2sh brn vio & blk   5.25 29.00
   a. Wmk. sideways   6.25 17.50
25 A4 3sh blk, wmk. sideways   21.00 32.50
26 A4 5sh red & black   18.00 85.00
   a. Wmk. sideways   37.50 97.50
27 A4 10sh dp blue & blk   62.50 125.00
   a. Wmk. sideways   140.00 250.00

28 A4   £1 orange & black   200.00   *375.00*
  a.   Wmk. sideways   225.00   *400.00*
    Nos. 10-28 (19)   360.00   *741.30*

On No. 28 the words of value are in a curve between the circle and "POSTAGE & REVENUE."

King George V
A5   A6

1927-31   Typo.

29	A5	5c green & black	2.00	.20
30	A5	10c yellow & black	2.25	.20
31	A5	15c red & black	2.00	.20
32	A5	20c orange & black	3.00	.20
33	A5	25c ultra & black	4.25	2.25
34	A5	30c dull violet & blk	3.25	3.00
35	A5	30c ultra & blk ('31)	29.00	.35
36	A5	40c brown & black	2.25	5.25
37	A5	50c gray & black	2.90	1.10
38	A5	75c olive grn & blk	2.25	17.50
39	A6	1sh green & black	4.75	3.25
40	A6	2sh violet brn & blk	24.00	5.25
41	A6	3sh black	29.00	70.00
42	A6	5sh scarlet & blk	22.50	21.00
43	A6	10sh ultra & black	67.50	110.00
44	A6	£1 brown org & blk	190.00	350.00
		Nos. 29-44 (16)	390.90	589.75

> **Catalogue values for unused stamps in this section, from this point to the end of the section, are for Never Hinged items.**

Independent State

Nurse and Infant — A7   Torch above Mt. Kilimanjaro — A8

5c, Teacher instructing villagers, horiz. 15c, Coffee picker. 20c, Harvesting corn. 30c, Flag, horiz. 50c, Serengeti lions. 1sh, Nurse showing infant to mother & hospital. 2sh, Dar es Salaam harbor. 5sh, Tractor & field workers. 10sh, Diamond mine & rose diamond. 1sh, 2sh, 5sh, 10sh, horiz.

Perf. 14x14½, 14½x14

1961, Dec. 9 **Photo.** **Unwmk.**

45	A7	5c sepia & yel grn	.30	.30
46	A7	10c Prussian green	.30	.30
47	A7	15c sepia & blue	.30	.30
b.		Blue omitted	400.00	
48	A7	20c orange brown	.30	.30
49	A7	30c dp green, blk & yel	.30	.30
50	A7	50c sepia & yellow	.30	.30

Perf. 14½

51	A8	1sh cit brn & gray bl	.30	.30
52	A8	1sh30c multicolored	3.50	.30
53	A8	2sh multicolored	1.10	.30
54	A8	5sh Prus grn & dp org	1.10	.30
55	A8	10sh blk, bl & rose	17.50	5.25
a.		Rose (diamond) omitted	125.00	
56	A8	20sh multicolored	4.50	18.25
		Nos. 45-56 (12)	29.80	18.25

Tanganyika's independence, Dec. 9, 1961.
For overprints see Nos. O21-O28.

Pres. Julius Nyerere with Pickax — A9

Designs: 50c, Flag hoisting on Mt. Kilimanjaro. 1sh30c, Presidential emblem. 2sh50c, Independence monument, Mnazi Moja.

1962, Dec. 9   **Perf. 14½x14**

57	A9	30c bright green	.20	.20
58	A9	50c multicolored	.20	.20
59	A9	1sh30c multicolored	.20	.20
60	A9	2sh50c dk blue, blk & red	.75	.50
		Nos. 57-60 (4)	1.35	1.10

Issued to commemorate the establishment of the Republic of Tanganyika, Dec. 9, 1962.

OFFICIAL STAMPS

> **Catalogue values for unused stamps in this section are for Never Hinged items.**

Issued for use by the Tanganyika Government

Stamps of Kenya, Uganda & Tanganyika, 1954-59, Overprinted

Perf. 12½x13, 13x12½

1959   **Engr.**   **Wmk. 4**

O1	A18	5c choc & blk	.20	1.25
O2	A19	10c carmine	.20	1.25
O3	A20	15c lt bl & blk (on #106)	.35	1.25
O4	A19	20c org & blk	.20	.20
a.		Double overprint	700.00	
O5	A18	30c ultra & black	.20	.95
O6	A19	50c dp red lilac	.25	.20
O7	A19	1sh dp mag & blk	.25	.85
O8	A20	1sh30c pur & red org	3.75	2.25
O9	A20	2sh dp grn & gray	1.40	1.10
O10	A20	5sh black & org	4.00	3.50
O11	A20	10sh ultra & blk	2.25	4.00
O12	A21	£1 black & ver	7.50	17.50
		Nos. O1-O12 (12)	20.55	34.30

Stamps of Kenya, Uganda & Tanganyika, 1960, Overprinted

Perf. 14½x14

1960, Oct. 1 **Photo.** **Wmk. 314**

O13	A23	5c dull blue	.20	1.75
O14	A23	10c lt olive green	.20	1.75
O15	A23	15c dull purple	.20	1.75
O16	A23	20c brt lilac rose	.20	.55
O17	A23	30c brt vermilion	.20	.20
O18	A23	50c dull violet	.35	1.10

Overprinted

Engr.   **Perf. 14**

O19	A24	1sh violet & lilac red	.45	.30
O20	A24	5sh rose red & lilac	16.00	1.50
		Nos. O13-O20 (8)	17.80	8.90

Nos. 45-51 and 54 Overprinted "OFFICIAL" in Sans-serif Type of Various Sizes

Perf. 14x14½, 14½x14

1961, Dec. 9   **Unwmk.**

O21	A7	5c sepia & yellow grn	.20	.20
O22	A7	10c Prussian green	.20	.20
O23	A7	15c sepia & blue	.20	.20
O24	A7	20c orange brown	.20	.20
O25	A7	30c dp grn blk & yel	.20	.20
O26	A7	50c sepia & yellow	.20	.20
O27	A8	1sh citron brn & gray bl	.20	.20
O28	A8	5sh Prus grn & dp org	1.00	1.00
		Nos. O21-O28 (8)	2.40	2.40

TANNU TUVA

ˈtä-nə ˈtü-və

(Tuva People's Republic)

LOCATION — Between Siberia and northwestern Mongolia at the sources of the Yenisei, in the basin formed by the Tannu-Ola and Sayan Mountains.
GOVT. — A former republic closely identified with Soviet Russia in Asia
AREA — 64,000 sq. mi. (approx.)
POP. — 95,000 (1941 est.)
CAPITAL — Kyzyl

This region, traditionally called Uriankhai, was ruled by the Mongols until the mid-18th century, when it became part of the Chinese Empire. Russia and China struggled for control of the country 1914-21, until it became independent as the Tannu Tuva People's Republic in 1921. In 1944 it was incorporated into the U.S.S.R. as an autonomous region of the Russian Soviet Federated Socialist Republic.

Russian, later Soviet, stamps were used in Tuva prior to 1926 and after 1944.

100 Mongo=1 Tugrik
100 Kopecks = 1 Ruble
100 Kopecks = 1 Tugrik (1934)
100 Kopecks = 1 Aksha (1936)

Watermark

Wmk. 204 — Stars and Diamonds

Wmk. 170 — Greek Border and Rosettes

Most used examples of Nos. 1-38, 45-52a, 54-92 and C1-C18 on the market are cancelled to order, and the used values below are for such stamps.

Tuvan stamps, except for Nos. 117-123 and most of the overprints, were

printed by the State Security Printers in Moscow.

Wheel of Truth — A1

1926 **Litho.** **Wmk. 204** **Perf. 13½**
Size: 20x26mm

1	A1	1k red	1.25	1.00
2	A1	2k light blue	1.50	1.00
3	A1	5k orange	1.50	1.00
4	A1	8k yel green	1.75	1.00
5	A1	10k violet	2.00	1.00
6	A1	30k dark brown	1.75	1.00
7	A1	50k gray black	2.00	1.25

Size: 22½x30mm
Perf. 10½

8	A1	1r blue green	5.50	2.50
9	A1	3r red brown	8.00	4.00
10	A1	5r dark ultra	13.50	6.00
		Nos. 1-10 (10)	38.75	19.75

Nos. 1-10 have crackled white gum. Reprints can be distinguished by their smooth gum.
Nos. 1-10 in different colors are proofs.

Nos. 7-10 Surcharged in Red or Black

1927   **Perf. 13½**

11	A1	8k on 50k	25.00	12.50

    Perf. 10½

12	A1	14k on 1r	25.00	12.50
13	A1	18k on 3r (Bk)	25.00	12.50
14	A1	28k on 5r (Bk)	25.00	12.50
		Nos. 11-14 (4)	100.00	50.00

Nos. 11-14 were surcharged with a shiny ink. Reprints are overprinted with a dull ink and are often smudged.
Nos. 11-14 exist with surcharge inverted and No. 14 with surcharge double. Value $35.00 each.
Reprints exist of Nos. 1-14.

Tuvan Woman — A3

Map of Tannu Tuva A8

Sheep Herding — A11

Fording a Stream — A13

Tuvans Riding Reindeer — A16

Designs: 2k, Stag. 3k, Mountain goat. 4k, Tuvan and tent. 5k, Tuvan man. 10k, Archery competition. 14k, Camel caravan. 28k, Landscape. 50k, Weaving. 70k, Tuvan on horseback.

			1927	Typo.		Perf. 12½
15	A3	1k	blk, lt brn & red		1.00	.60
16	A3	2k	pur, dp brn & grn		1.20	.55
17	A3	3k	blk, bl grn & yel		2.00	.60
18	A3	4k	vio bl & choc		.90	.60
19	A3	5k	org, blk & dk bl		.90	.65
			Perf. , 12½x12			
20	A8	8k	ol brn, pale bl & red brn		1.00	.65
21	A8	10k	blk, grn & brn red		5.50	1.00
22	A8	14k	vio bl & red org		10.00	3.50
			Perf. 10, 10½			
23	A11	18k	dk bl & red brn		10.00	5.00
24	A11	28k	emer & blk brn		7.25	2.75
25	A13	40k	rose & bl grn		5.00	2.50
26	A13	50k	blk, grn & red brn		3.50	2.00
27	A13	70k	dl red & bis		7.00	4.00
28	A16	1r	yel brn & vio		16.00	6.75
			Nos. 15-28 (14)		71.25	31.15

Nos. 15-28 were issued with a crackled white gum. Reprints of the 1k-5k values exist and can be distinguished by their smooth gum. Nos. 15-28 in different colors are proofs.

Nos. 25-27, 20-22 Surcharged "Tuva", "Posta" and New Values in Various Colors

			1932			
29	A13	1k on 40k (Bk)			9.00	10.00
30	A13	2k on 50k (Br)			10.00	10.00
31	A13	3k on 70k (Bl)			10.00	10.00
a.		Inverted surcharge			300.00	
32	A8	5k on 8k (Bk)			10.00	10.00
33	A8	10k (Bk)			10.00	10.00
34	A8	15k on 14k (Bk)			15.00	15.00
		Nos. 29-34 (6)			64.00	65.00

Issued in connection with the Romanization of the alphabet.

#23-24 Surcharged in Black

No. 37

No. 38

			1933		Wmk. 204	
35	A8	10k on 8k			180.00	100.00
36	A8	15k on 14k			300.00	200.00
37	A11	35k on 18k			150.00	100.00
38	A11	35k on 28k			150.00	100.00
		Nos. 35-38 (4)			780.00	500.00

A19

Revenue Stamps Surcharged "Posta" and New Values

Three types: type 1, figures of value 6.7mm high; type 2, figures of value 6.7mm high, letter "p" lengthened at bottom; type 3, figures of value 5.1mm high.

		1933		Perf. 12x12½	
39	A19	15k on 6k org yel, type 1		300.00	150.00
40	A19	15k on 6k org yel, type 2		300.00	150.00
41	A19	15k on 6k org yel, type 3		500.00	300.00
42	A19	35k on 15k red brn, type 1		—	4,000.
43	A19	35k on 15k red brn, type 2		—	4,000.
44	A19	35k on 15k red brn, type 3		1,500.	800.00

Mounted Hunter — A20

Tuvan Inside of Yurt — A21

Tuvan Milking Yak — A22

Designs: 2k, Hunter stalking game. 4k, Tractor. 10k, Camel caravan. 15k, Herdsman lassoing reindeer. 20k, Hunter shooting fox with arrow.

Two dies on 10k: Die I, Crown at center top is light and matches the shade of the sky below; Die II, Crown at center top is bold, consistent with rest of design and darker than the sky.

Printed by State Security Printers, Moscow.

		1934, Apr.	Photo.	Perf. 12	
45	A20	1k red orange		1.50	1.00
46	A20	2k olive green		1.50	1.00
47	A21	3k rose red		1.50	1.00
48	A21	4k slate purple		3.50	1.75
49	A22	5k ultramarine		3.50	1.75
50	A22	10k brown, die II		3.50	1.75
c.		10k brown, die I		8.00	2.00
51	A22	15k dark lilac		3.50	1.75
52	A22	20k gray black		4.75	2.75
		Nos. 45-52 (8)		23.25	12.75
		Set, never hinged		50.00	
		Set, Imperf		50.00	
		Set, imperf, never hinged		100.00	

Nos. 45-52 are inscribed "REGISTERED," but were used as regular postage stamps.

Nos. 46, 48 and 50 exist perf 11, and No. 50 also exists perf 11x10. No. 48 exists perf 11½, reportedly as a color trial proof.

#51 Surcharged in Black
Surcharged by numbering machine in Kyzyl.

		1935			
53	A22	20k on 15k		175.00	325.00
a.		Inverted surcharge			400.00

Map of Tuva — A23

Rocky Outcropping — A24

Designs: 3k, 5k, 10k, Different scenes of Yenisei River. 25k, Bei-kem rapids. 50k, Mounted hunters.
Printed by State Security Printers, Moscow.

			Wmk. 170			
		1935, Mar.	Photo.		Perf. 14	
54	A23	1k yellow orange			2.25	1.75
55	A23	3k deep green			2.25	1.75
56	A23	5k carmine red			3.00	2.00
57	A23	10k violet			3.25	2.00
b.		Pair, imperf between				
58	A24	15k olive green			3.50	2.50
59	A24	25k violet blue			4.00	2.50
60	A24	50k dark brown			5.75	2.75
		Nos. 54-60 (7)			24.00	15.25
		Set, never hinged			45.00	

Nos. 54-60 in different colors, perf and imperf, are proofs.

Badger A25

Squirrel — A26

Fox — A27

Elk — A28

Yak — A29

Designs: 5k, Ermine. 25k, Otter. 50k, Lynx. 3t, Bactrian camels. 5t, Bear.
Printed by State Security Printers, Moscow.

		1935, Mar.			
61	A25	1k orange		1.60	1.00
62	A26	3k emerald green		1.60	1.00
a.		Imperf, pair		300.00	
63	A25	5k rose red		1.60	1.10
64	A27	10k crimson red		1.60	1.10
65	A27	25k orange red		2.50	1.20
66	A27	50k deep blue		2.50	1.20
67	A28	1t violet		2.50	1.20
a.		Pair, imperf between			
68	A29	2t royal blue		3.50	1.20
69	A29	3t red brown		4.00	1.35
70	A28	5t indigo		5.00	1.75
a.		Imperf, pair		300.00	
b.		Pair, imperf between		—	
		Nos. 61-70 (10)		26.40	12.10
		Set, never hinged		50.00	

Nos. 61-70 in different colors are proofs.

Tuvan Arms — A30

Wrestlers — A31

Herdsman on Bull — A32

Athletic Competitions — A33

Soldiers A34

Designs: 2k, Pres. Ch(aumlaut char='u')rmit-Dazhy. 3k, Tuvan with Bactrian camel. 5k, 8k, Archer. 10k, 15k, Spearfishing. 12k, 20k, Bear-hunting. 30k, Camel and train. 40k, 50k, Horse race. 80k, Partisans. 3t, Partisans confiscating cattle. 5t, 1921 battle scene.

Printed by State Security Printers, Moscow.

1936, July			Perf. 11, 14	
71	A30	1k bronze green	2.00	.70
72	A30	2k dark brown	2.50	1.50
73	A30	3k indigo blue	2.75	.75
74a	A31	4k orange red	3.50	.75
75	A31	5k brown purple	5.00	.70
76	A31	6k myrtle green	4.75	.70
77	A31	8k plum	4.75	.70
78	A31	10k rose red	5.75	1.00
79	A31	12k black brown	7.00	1.25
80a	A31	15k bronze green	8.50	1.25
81	A31	20k deep blue	8.50	1.20
82a	A32	25k orange red	8.50	.90
83	A32	30k plum	27.50	1.25
84a	A32	35k rose red	8.50	1.25
85	A32	40k deep brown	8.50	1.50
86a	A32	50k indigo blue	8.50	1.50
87	A33	70k plum	10.00	2.00
88	A33	80k green	9.50	2.00
89	A34	1a orange red	9.50	2.00
a.		1a rose red (error)	—	—
90	A34	2a rose red	9.50	3.00
91	A33	3a indigo blue	15.00	2.00
92	A33	5a black brown	11.00	2.50
		Nos. 71-92 (22)	181.00	30.40
		Set, never hinged	325.00	

15th anniversary of independence.
Values for Nos. 71-92 are for the most common varieties. For detailed listings, see the *Scott Classic Specialized Catalogue*.
Imperfs are remainders, later sold by the Soviet Postal Museum.

Values for Nos. 93-98 and 104-116 are for genuine examples. Expertization is essential for these issues.

Issues of 1934-36 Handstamped with Large Numerals and Old Values Obliterated with Bars or Blocks

1938, Aug.				
93	A34	5k on 2a (#90a)		300.00
94	AP5	5k on 2a (#C17)		225.00
95	AP1	10k on 1t (#C8)		200.00
96	A24	20k on 50k (#60)		200.00
		On cover		
97	AP5	30k on 2a (#C17)		200.00
98	AP5	30k on 3a (#C18)		175.00

Types of 1935-36 with Modified Designs and New Colors

1938, Dec.		Unwmk.	Perf. 12½	
99	A25	5k deep green	60.00	—
100	A31	10k indigo (dates removed)	60.00	—
101	AP3	15k red brown ("AIR MAIL," dates removed)	60.00	—
102	A31	20k brown (dates removed)	85.00	—
103	A33	30k maroon (dates removed)	60.00	—
		Nos. 99-103 (5)	325.00	
		Set, never hinged	500.00	

Some experts believe that these stamps were issued in March 1941.

Stamps of 1934-35 Handstamp Surcharged with New Values in Black or Violet at Kyzyl

1939				
104	AP1	10k on 1t (#C8)		225.00
105	AP1	10k on 1t (#C8) (V)		225.00
106	A24	20k on 50k (#60) (V)		200.00

Old values obliterated on Nos. 104-106.

Stamps of 1934-36 Handstamp Surcharged with New Values at Kyzyl

1940, Oct.-1941				
107	AP1	10k on 1t (#C8)	—	90.00
a.		Double surcharge		—
108	A24	20k on 50k (#60)	—	100.00
109	A27	20k on 50k (#66)	—	300.00
110	A32	20k on 50k (#86a)	—	300.00
111	AP4	20k on 50k (#C14)	—	65.00
112	A33	20k on 70k (#87a)	—	
113	AP4	20k on 75k (#C15)	—	75.00
114	A33	20k on 80k (#88)	—	500.00

The old values are not obliterated on Nos. 107 or 108.

Nos. 91, 92 Handstamp Surcharged with New Values at Kyzyl

1942				
115	A33	25k on 3a (#91)	1,200.	—
116	A33	25k on 5a (#92)	—	—

Government House — A35

Exhibition Hall — A36

Tuvan Woman — A37

1942		Typo.	Unwmk.	Imperf.
117	A35	25k steel blue	750.00	100.00
118	A36	25k steel blue	750.00	100.00
119	A37	25k steel blue	750.00	150.00
		Nos. 117-119 (3)	2,250.	350.00

21st anniversary of independence.
Nos. 117-119 were hand-printed together in small sheetlets of five (117+119+118+117+119), so various se-tenant combinations are possible. Value, pane $2,000.
Two additional values, a 25k depicting a Tuvan man and a 50k depicting a soldier on a horse, were prepared, but not issued. A collective proof sheetlet of five, containing Nos. 117-119 and these two values, in the same color as the issued stamps, is also known.

Coat of Arms — A38

Government Building — A39

1943		*Perf. 11 (1 or 2 Sides)*		
		Buff Paper		
120	A38	25k slate blue	—	—
121	A38	25k black	100.00	—
122	A38	25k blue green	90.00	—
123	A39	50k blue green	90.00	—
		Nos. 120-123 (3)	280.00	
		White Paper		
120a	A38	25k slate blue	90.00	—
b.		Strip of 3, imperf between		
			250.00	

121a	A38	25k black	125.00	—
122a	A38	25k blue green	95.00	—
123a	A39	50k blue green	95.00	—
		With gum	175.00	
		Nos. 120a-123a (4)	405.00	

22nd anniversary of independence.
Nos. 120 and 121 were each printed in vertical strips of five, perforated 11 between stamps and imperf on outside edges, so that these stamps may be perforated on top edge only, bottom edge only, or on both top and bottom edges. To make maximum use of limited wartime paper supplies, they were sometimes printed in strips of four. These smaller strips are rare.

Nos. 122 and 123 were printed together in blocks of four, containing a vertical pair of the 25k and a vertical pair of the 50k, perforated internally both vertically and horizontally and imperf on the outer edges. Setenant pairs, Value $225 (#122+123), $275 (#122a+123a).

Nos. 121 and 123a were issued with gum, No. 123a both with and without gum, and the balance of the set without gum.

Used examples and covers exist but are extremely rare.

AIR POST STAMPS

Airplane and Yaks — AP1

Airplane and Capercaillie — AP2

Designs, airplane over: 5k, 15k, Camels. 25k, Argali (wild sheep). 75k, Ox and cart. 2t, Roe deer.
Printed by State Security Printers, Moscow.

Wmk. 170

1934, Apr. 4		Photo.	Perf. 14	
C1	AP1	1k orange red	1.40	1.00
C2	AP1	5k emer green	1.40	1.00
C3	AP2	10k purple brown	4.50	3.00
C4	AP1	15k rose red	2.75	1.00
C5	AP2	25k slate purple	2.75	1.00
C6	AP1	50k dp bl green	2.75	1.00
C7	AP2	75k lake	2.75	1.75
C8	AP1	1t royal blue	3.50	2.00
C9	AP2	2t ultra, 61x31mm	20.00	25.00
a.		54.5x29mm	40.00	
		Nos. C1-C9 (9)	41.80	36.75
		Set, never hinged	55.00	

Nos. C1-C9 imperf or perf 11½ and stamps printed in different colors are proofs.

Tuvan Leading Laden Yak — AP3

Horseman and Zeppelin AP4

Seaplane Above Dragon — AP5

Designs: 10k, Tuvan plowing. 50k, Villagers with biplane overhead.
Printed by State Security Printers, Moscow.

1936			Unwmk.	
C10	AP3	5k indigo & beige	3.00	1.50
C11	AP3	10k purple & cinnamon	4.50	1.50
C12	AP3	15k black brown & pale gray	4.50	1.75
C13	AP4	25k plum & cream	6.00	2.50
c.		Horiz. pair, perf 11, imperf between	—	—
C14	AP4	50k rose red & cream	6.50	2.50
C15	AP4	75k emer grn & pale yellow	10.00	4.00
C16	AP5	1a blue green & pale bl grn	12.00	3.75
C17	AP5	2a rose red & cream	9.50	3.75
C18	AP5	3a dark brown & beige	9.50	3.75
		Nos. C10-C18 (9)	65.50	25.00
		Set, never hinged	120.00	

15th anniversary of independence.

Nos. C10-C18 exist imperf.

TANZANIA

ˌtan-zə-ˈnē-ə

(Tanganyika and Zanzibar)

LOCATION — Southeastern Africa bordering on the Indian Ocean, and a group of islands about 20 miles off the coast
GOVT. — United republic in British Commonwealth
AREA — 364,886 sq. mi.
POP. — 31,270,820 (1999 est.)
CAPITAL — Dodoma

Tanganyika joined Zanzibar on April 26, 1964, to form the United Republic of Tanganyika and Zanzibar. In October 1965 the name was changed to United Republic of Tanzania.
Zanzibar stamps include two (Nos. 331, 334) inscribed "Tanzania."

100 Cents = 1 Shilling

Catalogue values for all unused stamps in this country are for Never Hinged items.

Watermark

Wmk. 387 — Squares and Rectangles

Map — A1

Design: 30c, 1sh30c, Emblem (hands holding torch and spear).

Perf. 14x14½

1964, July 7   Photo.   Unwmk.
1	A1	20c blue & emerald	.20 .20
2	A1	30c brn, dk & lt bl	.20 .20
3	A1	1.30sh ultra, blk & org	.35 .35
4	A1	2.50sh ultra & purple	.75 .75
		Nos. 1-4 (4)	1.50 1.50

Union of Tanganyika and Zanzibar. Not sold in Zanzibar, nor valid there.

Flag
A2

Native Handicraft
A3

Designs: 5c, Hale hydroelectric plant. 15c, Army squad. 20c, Road building. 40c, Giraffes. 50c, Zebras. 65c, Mt. Kilimanjaro. 1sh, Dar es Salaam harbor. 1.30sh, Zinjanthropus skull and Olduvai Gorge excavation. 2.50sh, Sailfish, dhow and map of Mafia Island. 5sh, Sisal industry. 10sh, State House, Dar es Salaam. 20sh, Tanzania coat of arms.

Perf. 14x14½, 14½x14

1965, Dec. 9   Photo.   Unwmk.
Size: 21x17½mm, 17½x21mm
5	A2	5c orange & ultra	.45 .60
6	A2	10c ultra, grn, yel & blk	.45 .60
7	A3	15c grn, bl, brn & buff	.45 .60
8	A2	20c blue & brown	.45 .60
9	A3	30c black & red brn	.45 .60
10	A3	40c blue, yel grn & brn	.45 .60
11	A2	50c yellow grn & blue	.45 .60
12	A2	65c ultra, grn & red brn	.55 .75

Perf. 14½
Size: 41½x25, 25x41½mm
13	A2	1sh bl, grn, yel & brn	.70 .60
14	A2	1.30sh multicolored	1.00 .60
15	A2	2.50sh blue & red brn	1.50 .95
16	A2	5sh bl, brt grn & red brn	3.00 1.40
17	A2	10sh blue & yellow	6.00 3.75
18	A3	20sh gray & multi	12.00 8.50
		Nos. 5-18 (14)	27.90 20.75

For overprints see Nos. O1-O8.

Turkeyfish — A4

Fish: 5c, Cardinalfish. 10c, Mudskipper. 15c, Toby puffer. 20c, Two sea horses. 30c, Batfish. 40c, Sweetlips. 50c, Birdfish. 65c, Butterflyfish. 70c, Grouper. 1.30sh, Surgeonfish. 1.50sh, Caesio xanthonotus. 2.50sh, Emperor snapper. 5sh, Moorish idol. 10sh, Striped triggerfish. 20sh, Squirrelfish.

1967-71   Photo.   Perf. 14x14½
Size: 21x17½mm
Fish in Natural Colors
19	A4	5c black & citron	.20 .20
20	A4	10c brown & olive	.20 .20
21	A4	15c brown & blue	.20 .20
22	A4	20c brn & dk bl grn	.20 .20
23	A4	30c black & yel grn	.20 .20
24	A4	40c brown & emerald	.20 .20
25	A4	50c blk & dull bl grn	.20 .20
26	A4	65c blk & gray grn	.70 .70
27	A4	70c blk & olive ('69)	.55 .55

Perf. 14½
Size: 41x25mm
28	A4	1sh brown & multi	.45 .20
29	A4	1.30sh black & olive	.70 .20
30	A4	1.50sh black & ol ('69)	.80 .20
31	A4	2.50sh brn yel & grn	1.40 .20
32	A4	5sh black & bl grn	2.25 .20
33	A4	10sh brn & gray grn	5.25 .60
34	A4	20sh blk & gray olive	11.50 1.40
		Nos. 19-34 (16)	25.00 5.65

Issued: #27, 30, 9/15/69; others, 12/9/67.
Values of Nos. 28-34 are for canceled-to-order stamps with printed cancellations. Postally used examples sell for higher prices.
For overprints see Nos. O9-O16.

Papilio Hornimani
A5

Euphaedra Neophron
A6

Butterflies: 10c, Colotis ione. 15c, Amauris makuyuensis. 20c, Libythea laius. 30c, Danaus chrysippus. 40c, Sallya rosa. 50c, Axiocerses styx. 60c, Eurema hecabe. 70c, Acraea insignis. 1.50sh, Precis octavia. 2.50sh, Charaxes eupale. 5sh, Charaxes pollux. 10sh, Salamis parhassus. 20sh, Papilio ophidicephalus.

1973, Dec. 3   Photo.   Perf. 14½x14
35	A5	5c yellow grn & multi	.35 .35
a.		Booklet pane of 4	.20
36	A5	10c lt brown & multi	.35 .35
a.		Booklet pane of 4	.20
37	A5	15c ultra & multi	.35 .35
a.		Booklet pane of 4	.20
38	A5	20c fawn & multi	.35 .35
a.		Booklet pane of 4	.20
39	A5	30c yellow & multi	.35 .35
a.		Booklet pane of 4	.30
40	A5	40c multicolored	.35 .35
a.		Booklet pane of 4	.35
41	A5	50c citron & multi	.35 .35
a.		Booklet pane of 4	.52
42	A5	60c multicolored	.35 .35
43	A5	70c brt green & multi	.35 .35
a.		Booklet pane of 4	.70

Perf. 14½
44	A6	1sh green & multi	.60 .60
45	A6	1.50sh orange & multi	1.00 1.00
46	A6	2.50sh multicolored	1.75 1.75
47	A6	5sh multicolored	4.00 4.00
48	A6	10sh lt green & multi	7.50 7.50
49	A6	20sh blue & multi	15.00 15.00
		Nos. 35-49 (15)	33.00 33.00

For surcharges and overprints see Nos. 50-53, 135-136, O17-O26.

Nos. 42, 45-46, 49 Surcharged with New Value and 2 Bars
Perf. 14½x14, 14½
1975, Nov. 17   Photo.
50	A5	80c on 60c multi	3.25 3.25
51	A6	2sh on 1.50sh multi	6.00 6.00
52	A6	3sh on 2.50sh multi	21.00 21.00
53	A6	40sh on 20sh multi	10.00 10.00
		Nos. 50-53 (4)	40.25 40.25

Designs: 50c, Microwave tower. 1sh, Cordless switchboard and operators, horiz. 2sh, Telephones of 1880, 1930 and 1976. 3sh, Message switching center, horiz.

1976, Apr. 15   Litho.   Perf. 14½
54	A6a	50c blue & multi	.20 .20
55	A6a	1sh red & multi	.20 .20
56	A6a	2sh yellow & multi	.30 .25
57	A6a	3sh multicolored	.45 .35
a.		Souvenir sheet of 4	2.00 2.00
		Nos. 54-57 (4)	1.15 1.00

Telecommunications development in East Africa. No. 57a contains 4 stamps similar to Nos. 54-57 with simulated perforations.
Exist imperf. from Format International liquidation stock.

Designs: 50c, Akii Bua, Ugandan hurdler. 1sh, Filbert Bayi, Tanzanian runner. 2sh, Steve Muchoki, Kenyan boxer. 3sh, Olympic torch, flags of Kenya, Tanzania and Uganda.

1976, July 5   Litho.   Perf. 14½
58	A6b	50c blue & multi	.20 .20
59	A6b	1sh red & multi	.20 .20
60	A6b	2sh yellow & multi	.30 .25
61	A6b	3sh blue & multi	.40 .35
a.		Souv. sheet of 4, #58-61, perf. 13	4.50 4.50
		Nos. 58-61 (4)	1.10 1.00

21st Olympic Games, Montreal, Canada, July 17-Aug. 1.
Exist imperf. from Format International liquidation stock.

Rail Transport in East Africa: 50c, Tanzania-Zambia Railway. 1sh, Nile Bridge, Uganda. 2sh, Nakuru Station, Kenya. 3sh, Class A locomotive, 1896.

1976, Oct. 4   Litho.   Perf. 14½
62	A6c	50c lilac & multi	.20 .20
63	A6c	1sh emerald & multi	.30 .20
64	A6c	2sh brt rose & multi	.60 .35
65	A6c	3sh yellow & multi	.90 .60
a.		Souv. sheet of 4, #62-65, perf. 13	9.00 9.00
		Nos. 62-65 (4)	2.00 1.35

A6d

1977, Jan. 10   Litho.   Perf. 14½
66	A6d	50c Nile perch	.20 .20
67	A6d	1sh Tilapia	.50 .45
68	A6d	3sh Sailfish	1.40 1.00
69	A6d	5sh Black marlin	2.40 2.40
a.		Souvenir sheet of 4, #66-69	4.50 3.50
		Nos. 66-69 (4)	4.50 4.05

A6e

50c, Masai tribesmen bleeding cow. 1sh, Dancers from Uganda. 2sh, Makonde sculpture. 3sh, Tribesmen skinning hippopotamus.

1977, Jan. 15   Perf. 13½x14
70	A6e	50c multicolored	.20 .20
71	A6e	1sh multicolored	.25 .20
72	A6e	2sh multicolored	.45 .30
73	A6e	3sh multicolored	.75 .45
a.		Souvenir sheet of 4, #70-73	2.75 2.75
		Nos. 70-73 (4)	1.65 1.15

2nd World Black and African Festival, Lagos, Nigeria, Jan. 15-Feb. 12.

A6f

50c, Automobile passing through village. 1sh, Winner at finish line. 2sh, Car going through washout. 5sh, Car, elephants and Mt. Kenya.

1977, Apr. 5   Litho.   Perf. 14
74	A6f	50c multicolored	.20 .20
75	A6f	1sh multicolored	.20 .20
76	A6f	2sh multicolored	.60 .30
77	A6f	5sh multicolored	1.50 .85
a.		Souvenir sheet of 4, #74-77	3.75 3.75
		Nos. 74-77 (4)	2.50 1.55

25th Safari rally, Apr. 7-11.

A6g

Designs: 50c, Rev. Canon Apolo Kivebulaya. 1sh, Uganda Cathedral. 2sh, Early grass-topped Cathedral. 5sh, Early tent congregation, Kigezi.

1977, June 20   Litho.   Perf. 14
78	A6g	50c multicolored	.20 .20
79	A6g	1sh multicolored	.20 .20
80	A6g	2sh multicolored	.25 .20
81	A6g	5sh multicolored	.75 .55
a.		Souvenir sheet of 4, #78-81	3.00 3.00
		Nos. 78-81 (4)	1.40 1.15

Church of Uganda, centenary.

A6h

Endangered species: 50c, Pancake tortoise. 1sh, Nile crocodile. 2sh, Hunter's hartebeest. 3sh, Red Colobus monkey. 5sh, Dugong.

1977, Sept. 26   Litho.   *Perf. 14x13½*
82	A6h	50c multicolored	.60	.20
83	A6h	1sh multicolored	1.75	.40
84	A6h	2sh multicolored	4.25	1.50
85	A6h	3sh multicolored	7.00	2.00
86	A6h	5sh multicolored	8.00	4.00
a.		Souvenir sheet of 4, #83-86	14.00	10.00
		Nos. 82-86 (5)	21.60	8.10

Prince Philip and Julius Nyerere, 1961 — A7

5sh, Queen Elizabeth II, Prince Philip, Prime Minister Nyerere in London, 1975. 10sh, Royal crown, flags of Tanzania and Commonwealth nations. 20sh, Coronation.

1977, Nov. 23   Litho.   *Perf. 14x13½*
87	A7	50c multicolored	.20	.20
88	A7	5sh multicolored	.20	.20
89	A7	10sh multicolored	.30	.30
90	A7	20sh multicolored	.55	.55
a.		Souvenir sheet of 4, #87-90	1.25	1.25
		Nos. 87-90 (4)	1.25	1.25

25th anniv. of reign of Elizabeth II.
For overprints see Nos. 99-102, 179-180.

Women Fetching Water from Stream and Tap — A8

1sh, Flag raising. 3sh, Health care, laboratory and hospital. 5sh, Pres. Julius Nyerere.

1978, Feb. 5   Litho.   *Perf. 13½x14*
91	A8	50c multicolored	.20	.20
92	A8	1sh multicolored	.20	.20
93	A8	3sh multicolored	.35	.30
94	A8	5sh multicolored	.60	.50
a.		Souvenir sheet of 4, #91-94	1.25	1.25
		Nos. 91-94 (4)	1.35	1.30

First anniversary of the New Revolutionary Party (Chama cha Mapinduzi).

A8a

50c, Soccer scene and Joe Kadenge. 1sh, Mohammed Chuma receiving trophy, and his portrait. 2sh, Shot on goal and Omari S. Kidevu. 3sh, Backfield defense and Polly Ouma.

1978, Apr. 17   Litho.   *Perf. 14x13½*
95	A8a	50c green & multi	.20	.20
96	A8a	1sh lt brown & multi	.20	.20
97	A8a	2sh lilac & multi	.35	.30
98	A8a	3sh dk blue & multi	.55	.40
a.		Souvenir sheet of 4, #95-98	2.50	2.50
		Nos. 95-98 (4)	1.30	1.10

World Soccer Cup Championships, Argentina '78, June 1-25.

Nos. 87-90a Overprinted in Large Serifed Letters: "25th ANNIVERSARY / CORONATION / 2nd JUNE 1953"

1978, June 2
99	A7	50c multicolored	.20	.20
100	A7	5sh multicolored	.20	.20
101	A7	10sh multicolored	.30	.30
102	A7	20sh multicolored	.55	.55
a.		Souvenir sheet of 4, #99-102	1.00	1.00
		Nos. 99-102 (4)	1.25	1.25

25th anniv. of coronation of Elizabeth II. Nos. 99-102a also exist overprinted with smaller, sans serif letters, perf. 12. Same values or less. The perf. 12 set does not exist without overprint.

"Do not Drink when Driving" — A9

Designs: 1sh, "Courtesy to the young, old and handicapped." 3sh, "Observe highway code." 5sh, "Do not drive faulty vehicle."

1978, July 1   Litho.   *Perf. 13½x13*
103	A9	50c multicolored	.20	.20
104	A9	1sh multicolored	.25	.25
105	A9	3sh multicolored	.60	.60
106	A9	5sh multicolored	2.50	2.50
a.		Souv. sheet #103-106, perf. 14	3.00	3.00
		Nos. 103-106 (4)	3.55	3.55

Road Safety Campaign.

Lake Manyara Hotel — A10

Designs: 1sh, Lobo Wildlife Lodge. 3sh, Ngorongoro Crater Lodge. 5sh, Ngorongoro Wildlife Lodge. 10sh, Mafia Island Lodge. 20sh, Mikumi Wildlife Lodge.

1978, Sept. 11   Litho.   *Perf. 13½*
107	A10	50c multicolored	.20	.20
108	A10	1sh multicolored	.20	.20
109	A10	3sh multicolored	.30	.30
110	A10	5sh multicolored	.55	.55
111	A10	10sh multicolored	1.10	1.10
112	A10	20sh multicolored	2.25	2.25
a.		Souvenir sheet of 6, #107-112	8.00	8.00
		Nos. 107-112 (6)	4.60	4.60

Game Lodges of Tanzania.

Chained African — A11

1sh, Division of races (black and white heads). 2.50sh, Racial harmony (black and white handshake and heads). 5sh, End of suppression and rise of freedom (hands breaking loose from chains).

1978, Oct. 24   Litho.   *Perf. 14½x14*
113	A11	50c multicolored	.20	.20
114	A11	1sh multicolored	.20	.20
115	A11	2.50sh multicolored	.45	.45
116	A11	5sh multicolored	.90	.90
a.		Souvenir sheet of 4, #113-116	2.25	2.25
		Nos. 113-116 (4)	1.75	1.75

Anti-Apartheid Year.

Fokker Friendship at Dar Es Salaam Airport — A12

Designs: 1sh, Single-engine Dragon, 1930, Zanzibar. 2sh, British Airways Concorde. 5sh, Wright Brothers' Flyer 1, 1903.

1978, Dec. 28   Litho.   *Perf. 13½*
117	A12	50c multicolored	.30	.30
118	A12	1sh multicolored	.45	.45
119	A12	2sh multicolored	.85	.85

120	A12	5sh multicolored	2.10	2.10
a.		Souvenir sheet of 4, #117-120	4.25	4.25
		Nos. 117-120 (4)	3.70	3.70

75th anniversary of 1st powered flight.

Emblem A13

Design: 5sh, Headquarters buildings.

1979, Feb. 3   Litho.   *Perf. 14½x14*
121	A13	50c multicolored	.20	.20
122	A13	5sh multicolored	.75	.75
a.		Souvenir sheet of 2, #121-122	1.60	1.60

Tanzania Post and Telecommunications Corporation, 1st anniversary.

Pres. Nyerere and Children — A14

Designs (UNICEF and Tanzanian IYC Emblems and): 1sh, Kindergarten. 2sh, Vaccination of infant. 3sh, Emblems.

1979, June 25   Litho.   *Perf. 14½*
123	A14	50c multicolored	.20	.20
124	A14	1sh multicolored	.20	.20
125	A14	2sh multicolored	.25	.25
126	A14	5sh multicolored	.60	.60
a.		Souvenir sheet of 4, #123-126	2.50	2.50
		Nos. 123-126 (4)	1.25	1.25

International Year of the Child.

Tree Planting — A15

Forest Preservation and Expansion: 1sh, Seedling. 2sh, Rainfall. 5sh, Forest fire.

1979, Sept. 29   Litho.   *Perf. 14½*
127	A15	50c multicolored	.20	.20
128	A15	1sh multicolored	.35	.35
129	A15	2sh multicolored	.70	.70
130	A15	5sh multicolored	1.75	1.75
		Nos. 127-130 (4)	3.00	3.00

Mwenge Satellite Earth Station Opening A16

1979, Dec. 3   Litho.   *Perf. 13½*
131	A16	10c multicolored	.20	.20
132	A16	40c multicolored	.20	.20
133	A16	50c multicolored	.20	.20
134	A16	1sh multicolored	.25	.20
		Nos. 131-134 (4)	.85	.80

Nos. 36, 43 Surcharged

1979   Litho.   *Perf. 14½x14*
135	A5	40c (10 + 30) multi	2.25	2.25
136	A5	50c on 70c multi	4.00	4.00

Tabata Dispensary, Dar-es-Salaam, Rotary Emblem — A17

1980, Mar. 1   Litho.   *Perf. 13x13½*
137	A17	50c shown	.20	.20
138	A17	1sh Ngomvu water project	.20	.20
139	A17	5sh Flying doctor service	.45	.45
140	A17	20sh Torch, anniversary emblem	2.25	2.25
a.		Souvenir sheet of 4, #137-140	3.25	3.25
		Nos. 137-140 (4)	3.10	3.10

Rotary International, 75th anniversary. For overprints see Nos. 149-152.

Zanzibar Nos. 49 and 309, "Stamp History" Cancel A18

Cancel and: 50c, Tanganyika #58, postal worker, vert. 10sh, Tanganyika #16, 52. 20sh, Penny Black, Rowland Hill, vert.

1980, Apr.   *Perf. 14*
141	A18	40c multicolored	.20	.20
142	A18	50c multicolored	.20	.20
143	A18	10sh multicolored	.70	.70
144	A18	20sh multicolored	1.40	1.40
a.		Souvenir sheet of 4, #141-144	3.00	3.00
		Nos. 141-144 (4)	2.50	2.50

Sir Rowland Hill (1795-1879), originator of penny postage; Tanzanian stamp history.

Overprinted: "LONDON 1980" / PHILATELIC EXHIBITION

1980, May 6   Litho.   *Perf. 14*
145	A18	40c multicolored	.20	.20
146	A18	50c multicolored	.20	.20
147	A18	10sh multicolored	.70	.70
148	A18	20sh multicolored	1.40	1.40
a.		Souvenir sheet of 4, #145-148	3.25	3.25
		Nos. 145-148 (4)	2.50	2.50

London 80 Intl. Stamp Exhib., May 6-14.

Nos. 137-140a with Additional Inscription on 1 or 2 Lines: "District 920-55th Annual / Conference, Arusha, Tanzania"

1980, June 23   Litho.   *Perf. 13x13½*
149	A17	50c multicolored	.20	.20
150	A17	1sh multicolored	.20	.20
151	A17	5sh multicolored	.85	.85
152	A17	20sh multicolored	3.50	3.50
a.		Souvenir sheet of 4, #149-152	5.00	5.00
		Nos. 149-152 (4)	4.75	4.75

District 920 Rotary Club, 55th Annual Conference, Arusha.

Pan African Postal Union and U.P.U. Emblems A19

1980, July 1   *Perf. 13x13½*
153	A19	50c purple & blk	.20	.20
154	A19	1sh ultra & blk	.20	.20
155	A19	5sh red orange & blk	.75	.75
156	A19	10sh green & blk	1.50	1.50
		Nos. 153-156 (4)	2.65	2.65

Pan African Postal Union Plenipotentiary Conference, Arusha, Jan. 8-18.

Gidamis Shahanga, Marathon — A20

Tanzanian Olympic Team: 1sh, Nzael Kyomo and sprinters. 10sh, Zakayo Malekwa and javelin. 20sh, William Lyimo and boxers.

1980, Aug. 18 Litho. Perf. 13x13½
157	A20	50c multicolored	.20	.20
158	A20	1sh multicolored	.20	.20
159	A20	1.10sh multicolored	1.10	1.10
160	A20	20sh multicolored	2.25	2.25
a.		Souvenir sheet of 4, #157-160	4.00	4.00
		Nos. 157-160 (4)	3.75	3.75

22nd Summer Olympic Games, Moscow, July 19-Aug. 3.
Issued also in sheets of 20 (5 of each value).

Spring Hare — A21

1980, Oct. 1 Litho. Perf. 14
161	A21	10c shown	.20	.20
162	A21	20c Genet	.20	.20
163	A21	40c Mongoose	.20	.20
164	A21	50c Ratel	.20	.20
165	A21	75c Rock hyrax	.20	.20
166	A21	80c Leopard	.20	.20

Perf. 14½
Size: 40x24mm
167	A21	1sh Impalas	.20	.20
168	A21	1.50sh Giraffes	.20	.20
169	A21	2sh Zebras	.20	.20
170	A21	3sh Buffalo	.25	.25
171	A21	5sh Lions	.40	.40
172	A21	10sh Rhinoceros	.80	.80
173	A21	20sh Elephants	1.60	1.60
174	A21	40sh Cheetahs	3.25	3.25
		Nos. 161-174 (14)	8.10	8.10

For overprints see Nos. O27-O36.

National Parks Emblem A22

1981, Jan. 26 Litho. Perf. 13x13½
175	A22	50c Ngorongoro Park	.20	.20
176	A22	1sh shown	.20	.20
177	A22	5sh Friends of Serengeti	.70	.70
178	A22	20sh Friends of Ngorongoro	3.00	3.00
		Nos. 175-178 (4)	4.10	4.10

Ngorongoro & Serengeti Parks, 60th anniv. For overprints see Nos. 299-302.

Nos. 89-90 Overprinted: "ROYAL WEDDING/ H.R.H. PRINCE CHARLES/ 29th JULY 1981"

1981, July 29 Litho. Perf. 14x13½
179	A7	10sh multicolored	.35	.35
180	A7	20sh multicolored	.65	.65
a.		Souvenir sheet of 2, #179-180	6.00	6.00

Mail Runner A23

1981, Oct. 23 Litho. Perf. 12½x12
181	A23	50c shown	.20	.20
182	A23	1sh Letter sorting	.20	.20
183	A23	5sh Post horn, carrier pigeon	.70	.70
184	A23	10sh Commonwealth members' flags	1.50	1.50
a.		Souvenir sheet of 4, #181-184	3.00	3.00
		Nos. 181-184 (4)	2.60	2.60

Commonwealth Postal Administrations Conference, Arusha, June 29-July 10.

Intl. Year of the Disabled A24

1981, Nov. 30 Litho. Perf. 14
185	A24	50c Morris Nyunyusa, blind drummer	.30	.30
186	A24	1sh Sewing	.40	.40
187	A24	5sh Prostheses	1.60	1.60
188	A24	10sh Children	3.00	3.00
		Nos. 185-188 (4)	5.30	5.30

20th Anniv. of Independence — A25

1982, Jan. 13 Litho. Perf. 13x13½
189	A25	50c Pres. Nyerere, flag	.20	.20
190	A25	1sh Zanzibar Electricity Plant	.20	.20
191	A25	3sh Sisal plant, weaver	.50	.50
192	A25	10sh Pupils	1.75	1.75
a.		Souvenir sheet of 4, #189-192	3.25	3.25
		Nos. 189-192 (4)	2.65	2.65

Ostrich — A26

1982, Jan. 25 Litho. Perf. 13½
193	A26	50c shown	.65	.65
194	A26	1sh Secretary bird	1.00	1.00
195	A26	5sh Kori bustard	4.50	4.50
196	A26	10sh Saddle-bill stork	8.50	8.50
		Nos. 193-196 (4)	14.65	14.65

1982 World Cup A27

1982, June 2 Litho. Perf. 14
197	A27	50c Jella Mtagwa	.35	.35
198	A27	1sh Stadium	.35	.35
199	A27	10sh Diego Armando Maradona	3.20	3.20
200	A27	20sh Globe	7.00	7.00
a.		Souvenir sheet of 4, #197-200	11.00	11.00
		Nos. 197-200 (4)	10.90	10.90

Jade of Seronera and her Cubs A28

Animals Appearing in Movies or TV Shows: 1sh, Wild dog and puppies, Havoc. 5sh, Fifi and sons, Gombe. 10sh, Bahati and twins Rashidi and Ramadhani, Lake Manyara.

1982, July 15 Litho. Perf. 14
201	A28	50c multicolored	.20	.20
202	A28	1sh multicolored	.30	.30
203	A28	5sh multicolored	1.50	1.50
204	A28	10sh multicolored	3.00	3.00
a.		Souv. sheet, #201-204, perf. 14½	6.00	6.00
		Nos. 201-204 (4)	5.00	5.00

Scouting Year A29

1982, Aug. 25
205	A29	50c Brick laying	.20	.20
206	A29	1sh Camping	.20	.20
207	A29	10sh Tracing marks	2.00	2.00

208	A29	20sh Baden-Powell	4.00	4.00
a.		Souvenir sheet of 4, #205-208	7.00	7.00
		Nos. 205-208 (4)	6.40	6.40

For overprint see No. 303.

World Food Day — A30

1982, Oct. 16 Litho. Perf. 14
209	A30	50c Plowing	.20	.20
210	A30	1sh Dairy cows	.20	.20
211	A30	5sh Corn harvest	1.00	1.00
212	A30	10sh Grain storage	2.00	2.00
a.		Souvenir sheet of 4, #209-212	3.50	3.50
		Nos. 209-212 (4)	3.40	3.40

TB Bacillus Centenary A31

1982, Dec. 5 Perf. 12½x12
213	A31	50c Child immunization	.20	.20
214	A31	1sh Koch	.20	.20
215	A31	5sh TB emblem	1.00	1.00
216	A31	10sh WHO emblem	2.00	2.00
		Nos. 213-216 (4)	3.40	3.40

A31a

1983, Mar. 14 Litho. Perf. 14
217	A31a	50c Pres. Nyerere	.20	.20
218	A31a	1sh Running, boxing	.20	.20
219	A31a	5sh Flags	1.00	1.00
220	A31a	10sh Pres. Nyerere, Royal Family	2.00	2.00
a.		Souvenir sheet of 4, #217-220	3.50	3.50
		Nos. 217-220 (4)	3.40	3.40

Commonwealth Day. For overprint see #407.

5th Anniv. of Posts and Telecommunications Dept. — A32

1983, Feb. 3 Litho. Perf. 12½x12
221	A32	50c Letter post	.20	.20
222	A32	1sh Training Institute	.20	.20
223	A32	5sh Satellite communications	1.00	1.00
224	A32	10sh Emblems	2.00	2.00
a.		Souvenir sheet of 4, #221-224	3.50	3.50
		Nos. 221-224 (4)	3.40	3.40

25th Anniv. of Economic Commission for Africa — A33

1983, Sept. 12 Litho. Perf. 12½x12
225	A33	50c Eastern & Southern African Management Institute, Arusha	.45	.45
226	A33	1sh Emblems	.60	.60
227	A33	5sh Mineral collections	2.40	2.40
228	A33	10sh Emblems, diff.	4.75	4.75
a.		Souvenir sheet of 4, #225-228	8.25	8.25
		Nos. 225-228 (4)	8.20	8.20

World Communications Year — A34

1983, Oct. 17 Litho. Perf. 14
229	A34	50c Rural telephone service	.20	.20
230	A34	1sh Emblems	.20	.20
231	A34	5sh Post Office	1.10	1.10
232	A34	10sh Microwave tower	2.25	2.25
a.		Souvenir sheet of 4, #229-232	3.75	3.75
		Nos. 229-232 (4)	3.75	3.75

Historical Buildings A35

1983, Dec. 12 Litho. Perf. 12½x12
233	A35	1sh Bagamoyo Boma	.20	.20
234	A35	1.50sh Beit-El-Ajaib	.30	.30
235	A35	5sh Anglican Church	.90	.90
236	A35	10sh State House, old and new	1.75	1.75
a.		Souvenir sheet of 4, #233-236	3.50	3.50
		Nos. 233-236 (4)	3.15	3.15

20th Anniv. of Revolution A36

1984, June 18 Litho. Perf. 14
237	A36	1sh Muasisi Kwanza	.20	.20
238	A36	1.50sh Clove farming	.30	.30
239	A36	5sh Industrial development	1.00	1.00
240	A36	10sh Housing developments	2.00	2.00
		Nos. 237-240 (4)	3.50	3.50

Souvenir Sheet
241	A36	15sh Map, ship	3.50	3.50

1984 Summer Olympics A37

1984, Aug. 6 Perf. 12½x12
242	A37	1sh Boxing	.20	.20
243	A37	1.50sh Running	.20	.20
244	A37	5sh Basketball	.75	.75
245	A37	20sh Soccer	2.25	2.25
a.		Souvenir sheet of 4, #242-245	3.50	3.50
		Nos. 242-245 (4)	3.40	3.40

For overprints see Nos. 275-278.

Intl. Civil Aviation Org. 40th Anniv. A38

1984, Nov. 15 Litho. Perf. 13
246	A38	1sh Icarus	.20	.20
247	A38	1.50sh Air Tanzania jets, traffic controller	.20	.20
248	A38	5sh Aircraft maintenance	1.00	1.00
249	A38	10sh ICAO emblem	1.60	1.60
a.		Souvenir sheet of 4, #246-249	3.50	3.50
		Nos. 246-249 (4)	3.00	3.00

Traditional
Houses
A39

1984, Dec. 20   *Perf. 12½x12*
250 A39   1sh Sochi   .20   .20
251 A39   1.50sh Isyenga   .20   .20
252 A39   5sh Tembe   .65   .65
253 A39   15sh Banda   1.25   1.25
a.   Souvenir sheet of 4, #250-253   2.75   2.75
   Nos. 250-253 (4)   2.30   2.30

Textile
Industry
A40

5th anniversary of the Southern Africa
Development Coordination Conference.

1985, Apr. 1   *Perf. 14*
254 A40   1.50sh shown   .50   .50
255 A40   4sh Mining   1.25   1.25
256 A40   5sh Transportation
         and commu-
         nications   1.40   1.40
257 A40   20sh Flags of mem-
         ber nations   6.00   6.00
a.   Souvenir sheet of 4, #254-257   10.00   10.00
   Nos. 254-257 (4)   9.15   9.15

Rare
Species
of
Zanzibar
A41

Perf. 13½x13, 13x13½

1985, May 8   *Litho.*
258 A41   1sh Tortoise   .50   .50
259 A41   4sh Leopard   1.50   1.50
260 A41   10sh Civet cat   3.00   3.00
261 A41   17.50sh Red colobus,
         vert.   4.75   4.75
   Nos. 258-261 (4)   9.75   9.75

Souvenir Sheet
262   Sheet of 2   3.75   3.75
a.   A41 15sh Black rhinoceros   1.50   1.50
b.   A41 20sh Giant ground pangolin   2.25   2.25

For overprints see Nos. 408-409, 411.

Automobile Centenary — A42

Classic autos manufactured by Rolls-Royce.

1985, May 14   *Perf. 14½x14*
263 A42   1.50sh 1936 20/25   .20   .20
264 A42   5sh 1933 Phantom II   .20   .20
265 A42   10sh 1926 Phantom I   .20   .20
266 A42   30sh 1907 Silver
         Ghost   .70   .70
a.   Souvenir sheet of 4, #263-266   1.10   1.10
   Nos. 263-266 (4)   1.30   1.30

Queen Mother, 85th Birthday — A43

1985, Sept. 30
267 A43   20sh Waving   .20   .20
268 A43   20sh Facing left   .20   .20
269 A43   100sh Wearing green
         hat   .20   .20
a.   Souvenir sheet, #267, 269   .75   .75
270 A43   100sh Facing right   .20   .20
a.   Souvenir sheet, #268, 270   .75   .75
   Nos. 267-270 (4)   .80   .80

For overprints see Nos. 295-298.

Tanzania Railways Locomotives — A44

1985, Oct. 7   *Litho.*   *Perf. 14½x14*
271 A44   5sh No. 3022   .20   .20
272 A44   10sh No. 3107   .20   .20
273 A44   20sh No. 6004   .45   .45
274 A44   30sh No. 3129   .65   .65
a.   Souvenir sheet of 4, #271-274   1.50   1.50
   Nos. 271-274 (4)   1.50   1.50

Nos. 242-245 Ovptd. with Winners and
"GOLD MEDAL" in 2 or 3 Lines

1985, Oct. 22   *Perf. 12½x12*
275 A37   1sh Henry Tillman, USA   .20   .20
276 A37   1.50sh USA   .20   .20
277 A37   5sh USA   .60   .60
278 A37   20sh France   2.25   2.25
a.   Souvenir sheet of 4, #275-278   8.75   8.75
   Nos. 275-278 (4)   3.25   3.25

Pottery
A45

1985, Nov. 4
279 A45   1.50sh Water and cook-
         ing pots   .20   .20
280 A45   2sh Frying pot and cal-
         dron   .20   .20
281 A45   5sh Woman selling pots   .50   .50
282 A45   40sh Beer pot   3.75   3.75
   Nos. 279-282 (4)   4.65   4.65

Souvenir Sheet
283 A45   30sh Water pot   4.25   4.25

Locomotives — A46

1985, Nov. 25
284 A46   1.50sh Class 64   .20   .20
285 A46   2sh Class 36   .20   .20
286 A46   5sh Shunting DFH1013   .60   .60
287 A46   10sh Diesel Electric
         DE1001   1.25   1.25
288 A46   30sh Zanzibar, 1906   3.50   3.50
   Nos. 284-288 (5)   5.75   5.75

Souvenir Sheet
289   Sheet of 2   10.00   10.00
a.   A46 15sh Class 30 steam   4.50   4.50
b.   A46 20sh Class 11 steam   5.50   5.50

For overprints see Nos. 381A-381E.

Intl. Youth
Year — A47

1986, Jan. 20   *Perf. 14*
290 A47   1.50sh Young Pioneers   .20   .20
291 A47   4sh Health care   .50   .50
292 A47   10sh Uhuru torch race   1.00   1.00
293 A47   20sh World map   1.75   1.75
   Nos. 290-293 (4)   3.45   3.45

Souvenir Sheet
294 A47   30sh Agriculture   3.50   3.50

Nos. 267-270 Ovptd. "CARIBBEAN/
ROYAL VISIT/ 1985" in Silver or Gold

1986, Feb. 10   *Perf. 14½x14*
295 A43   20sh on #267   7.50   7.50
296 A43   20sh on #268   7.50   7.50
297 A43   100sh on #269   7.50   7.50
a.   Souvenir sheet, #295, 297   20.00
298 A43   100sh on #270   7.50   7.50
a.   Souvenir sheet, #296, 298   20.00
   Nos. 295-298 (4)   30.00   30.00

See footnote following No. 303.

Nos. 175-178, 208a Ovptd.
"75th ANNIVERSARY GIRL GUIDES/
1910-1985" in Silver or Black

1986, Feb.   *Litho.*   *Perf. 13x13½, 14*
299 A22   50c multicolored (S)   15.00   15.00
300 A22   1sh multicolored   15.00   15.00
301 A22   10sh multicolored   15.00   15.00
302 A22   20sh multicolored   15.00   15.00

Souvenir Sheet
303   Sheet of 4   45.00   45.00
a.   A29 50c multicolored   —   —
b.   A29 1sh multicolored   —   —
c.   A29 10sh multicolored   —   —
d.   A29 20sh multicolored   —   —

The status of this set, the Caribbean Royal
Visit set and at least 12 stamps overprinted
congratulating the Duke and Duchess of York
on their marriage are in question.

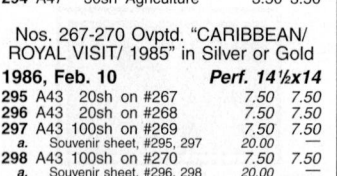

Rotary Intl., World Chess
Championships — A48

1986, Mar. 17   *Perf. 14*
304 A48   20sh shown   .25   .25
305 A48   100sh Chess board   1.25   1.25
a.   Souvenir sheet of 2, #304-305   1.75   1.75

Audubon Birth Bicent. — A49

Illustrations of American bird species by
Audubon.

1986, May 22
306 A49   5sh Mallard   .20   .20
307 A49   10sh American eider   .20   .20
308 A49   20sh Scarlet ibis   .45   .45
309 A49   30sh Roseate spoonbill   .70   .70
a.   Souvenir sheet of 4, #306-309   2.00   2.00
   Nos. 306-309 (4)   1.55   1.55

Gemstones
A50

1986, May 22
310 A50   1.50sh Pearls   .65   .65
311 A50   2sh Sapphires   .80   .80
312 A50   5sh Tanzanite   2.25   2.25
313 A50   40sh Diamonds   12.50   12.50
   Nos. 310-313 (4)   16.20   16.20

Souvenir Sheet
314 A50   30sh Rubies   18.00   18.00

Indigenous
Flowers — A51

Endangered
Wildlife — A52

1986, June 2
315 A51   1.50sh Hibiscus
         calyphyllus   .20   .20
316 A51   5sh Aloe graminicola   .20   .20
317 A51   10sh Nersium olean-
         der   .20   .20
318 A51   30sh Nymphaea
         caerulea   .50   .50
a.   Souvenir Sheet of 4, #315-318   1.25   1.25
   Nos. 315-318 (4)   1.10   1.10

1986, June 30   *Litho.*   *Perf. 14x14½*
319 A52   5sh Oryx   .20   .20
320 A52   10sh Giraffe   .20   .20
321 A52   20sh Rhinoceros   .25   .25
322 A52   30sh Cheetah   .35   .35
a.   Miniature sheet of 4, #319-322   1.10   1.10
   Nos. 319-322 (4)   1.00   1.00

UN Child
Survival
Campaign
A53

1986, July 29   *Perf. 12½x12*
323 A53   1.50sh Immunization   .35   .35
324 A53   2sh Growth monitor-
         ing   .35   .35
325 A53   5sh Oral rehydration
         therapy   .35   .35
326 A53   40sh Breast feeding   3.00   3.00
   Nos. 323-326 (4)   4.05   4.05

Souvenir Sheet
327 A53   30sh Healthy child   2.00   2.00

For overprints see Nos. 406, 410, 412.

Marine
Life
A54

1986, Aug. 20
328 A54   1.50sh Butterflyfish   .80   .80
329 A54   4sh Parrotfish   1.75   1.75
330 A54   10sh Sea turtle   3.00   3.00
331 A54   20sh Octopus   4.50   4.50
   Nos. 328-331 (4)   10.05   10.05

Souvenir Sheet
332 A54   30sh Coral   3.75   3.75

Queen Elizabeth II, 60th
Birthday — A55

Photographs: 5sh, Royal family, Buckingham Palace balcony. 10sh, With princes in open carriage. 40sh, Elizabeth II. 60sh, Greeting crowd.

1987, Mar. 24   Litho.   Perf. 14

333	A55	5sh multicolored		.20
334	A55	10sh multicolored		.20
335	A55	40sh multicolored		.60
336	A55	60sh multicolored		1.00
a.		Souvenir sheet of 4, #333-336		2.00
		Nos. 333-336 (4)		2.00

1986 World Cup Soccer
Championships, Mexico — A57

Designs: 1.50sh, Map, team captains, officials. 2sh, Foul. 10sh, Goal. 20sh, Goalie save. 30sh, Argentine natl. team.

1986, Oct. 30   Litho.   Perf. 14

341	A57	1.50sh multicolored	.30	.30
342	A57	2sh multicolored	.30	.30
343	A57	10sh multicolored	.75	.75
344	A57	20sh multicolored	1.40	1.40
		Nos. 341-344 (4)	2.75	2.75

Souvenir Sheet

345	A57	30sh multicolored	1.50	1.50

Hair Styles — A58

1987, Mar. 16   Perf. 14½

346	A58	1.50sh Nungu Nungu	.40	.40
347	A58	2sh Upanga wa Jogoo	.60	.60
348	A58	10sh Morani	1.25	1.25
349	A58	20sh Twende Kilioni	1.75	1.75
		Nos. 346-349 (4)	4.00	4.00

Souvenir Sheet

350	A58	30sh Kusuka Nywele	4.00	4.00

Intl. Peace
Year
A59

Designs: 1.50sh, Julius K. Nyerere, Beyond War Award winner. 2sh, Peace among nations. 10sh, Peaceful use of outer space. 20sh, Emblem, UN building. 30sh, Emblem, handshake.

1986, Dec. 22   Litho.   Perf. 14½

351	A59	1.50sh multicolored	.55	.55
352	A59	2sh multicolored	.85	.85
353	A59	10sh multicolored	2.10	2.10
354	A59	20sh multicolored	3.00	3.00
		Nos. 351-354 (4)	6.50	6.50

Souvenir Sheet

355	A59	30sh multicolored	2.75	2.75

Natl. Bank of Commerce, 20th
Anniv. — A60

1987, Feb. 6   Litho.   Perf. 14

356	A60	1.50sh Mobile bank	.50	.50
357	A60	2sh Headquarters	.85	.85
358	A60	5sh Pres. Mwinyi laying foundation stone	1.40	1.40
359	A60	20sh Cotton harvest	3.50	3.50
		Nos. 356-359 (4)	6.25	6.25

New Revolutionary Party (CCM), 10th
Anniv. — A61

1987, Apr. 10   Perf. 14½x14

360	A61	2sh Soldiers in formation	.20	.20
361	A61	3sh Woman picking coffee beans	.20	.20
362	A61	10sh Speaker at podium	.45	.45
363	A61	30sh Nyerere, Mwinyi	1.25	1.25
		Nos. 360-363 (4)	2.10	2.10

Arush Declaration, 20th anniv.

Insects
A62

1987, Apr. 22   Perf. 12½x12

364	A62	1.50sh Bees	.70	.70
365	A62	2sh Greater grain borer	.95	.95
366	A62	10sh Tse-tse fly	2.10	2.10
367	A62	20sh Wasp	3.50	3.50
		Nos. 364-367 (4)	7.25	7.25

Souvenir Sheet

368	A62	30sh Mosquito	6.00	6.00

Reptiles
A63

1987, July 2

369	A63	2sh Crocodiles	.70	.70
370	A63	3sh Black-striped grass snake	.70	.70
371	A63	10sh Adder	1.40	1.40
372	A63	20sh Green mamba	2.75	2.75
		Nos. 369-372 (4)	5.55	5.55

Souvenir Sheet

373	A63	30sh Tortoise	2.00	2.00

Posts and Telecommunications,
Railways Emblems — A64

1987, July 27   Perf. 14

374	A64	2sh shown	.60	.60
375	A64	8sh Air Tanzania, Port Authority	1.40	1.40

Souvenir Sheet

376	A64	20sh Modes of communication and transportation	5.00	5.00

Traditional
Crafts
A65

1987, Dec. 15   Litho.   Perf. 12½x12

377	A65	2sh Baskets	.30	.30
378	A65	3sh Gourds	.30	.30
379	A65	5sh Stools	.50	.50
380	A65	20sh Makonde carvings	.90	.90
		Nos. 377-380 (4)	2.00	2.00

Souvenir Sheet

381	A65	40sh Makonde carver at work	2.00	2.00

Nos. 284-288 Ovptd.

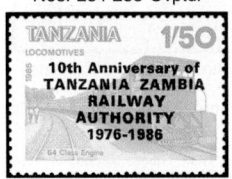

1987, Dec. 30   Litho.   Perf. 12½x12

381A	A46	1.50sh multicolored	.85	.85
381B	A46	2sh multicolored	.85	.85
381C	A46	5sh multicolored	1.00	1.00
381D	A46	10sh multicolored	2.10	2.10
381E	A46	30sh multicolored	6.25	6.25
		Nos. 381A-381E (5)	11.05	11.05

Plateosaurus — A66

1988, Apr. 22   Perf. 12½

382	A66	2sh shown	.65	.65
383	A66	3sh Pteranodon	.65	.65
384	A66	5sh Brontosaurus	.65	.65
385	A66	7sh Lions	.70	.70
386	A66	8sh Tiger	.70	.70
387	A66	12sh Orangutans	.80	.80
388	A66	20sh Elephants	1.10	1.10
389	A66	100sh Stegosaurus	3.00	3.00
		Nos. 382-389 (8)	8.25	8.25

Traditional
Games
A67

1988, Feb. 15   Litho.   Perf. 12½x12

390	A67	2sh Mdako (marbles)	.50	.50
391	A67	3sh Mieleka (wrestling)	.50	.50
392	A67	8sh Bull fight	.50	.50
393	A67	20sh Bao (African chess)	.80	.80
		Nos. 390-393 (4)	2.30	2.30

Souvenir Sheet

394	A67	30sh Kulenga shabaha (archery)	2.00	2.00
		Dated 1987.		

Statue of Liberty, Cent. (in
1986) — A68

No. 395: 1sh, Re-opening gala (evening), 1986. 2sh, Musicians performing. 3sh, Cheerleaders. 15sh, Statue holding tablet. 30sh, Tablet inscription. 40sh, Liberty Island. 50sh, Re-opening gala (afternoon), 1986. 60sh, Blimps over Liberty Island.

No. 396: 4sh, Statue, blimp. 5sh, Torch. 6sh, Torch and crown observatories lit at night, scaffolding. 7sh, Worker gilding torch. 8sh, Statue shrouded in scaffolding. 10sh, Two workers, torch. 12sh, Head, scaffolding. 18sh, Celebrant at re-opening (evening). 20sh, Goodyear blimp, skirt of Statue. 25sh, Boys' choir, statue. 35sh, Torch held aloft, full moon. 45sh, Worker cleaning tablet.

1988, June 15   Litho.   Perf. 14

395	Sheet of 8 + label	9.00	9.00
a.	A68 1sh multicolored	.25	.25
b.	A68 2sh multicolored	.25	.25
c.	A68 3sh multicolored	.25	.25
d.	A68 15sh multicolored	.60	.60
e.	A68 30sh multicolored	1.25	1.25
f.	A68 40sh multicolored	1.60	1.60
g.	A68 50sh multicolored	2.00	2.00
h.	A68 60sh multicolored	2.40	2.40
396	Sheet of 12	9.00	9.00
a.	A68 4sh multicolored	.25	.25
b.	A68 5sh multicolored	.25	.25
c.	A68 6sh multicolored	.25	.25
d.	A68 7sh multicolored	.25	.25
e.	A68 8sh multicolored	.35	.35
f.	A68 10sh multicolored	.40	.40
g.	A68 12sh multicolored	.45	.45
h.	A68 18sh multicolored	.75	.75
i.	A68 20sh multicolored	.80	.80
j.	A68 25sh multicolored	1.00	1.00
k.	A68 35sh multicolored	1.40	1.40
l.	A68 45sh multicolored	1.75	1.75

No. 395 contains a center label inscribed "THE STATUE / OF LIBERTY / 100th ANNIVERSARY."

Natl.
Monuments — A69

1988, June 15   Litho.

397	A69	5sh Independence Torch	.25	.25
398	A69	12sh Arusha Declaration	.25	.25
399	A69	30sh Askari	.30	.30
400	A69	60sh Independence	.60	.60
		Nos. 397-400 (4)	1.40	1.40

Souvenir Sheet

401	A69	100sh Soldier (Askari detail)	2.75	2.75

3rd Natl.
Census,
Aug.
28 — A70

1988, Aug. 8

402	A70	2sh shown	.20	.20
403	A70	3sh Enumeration	.20	.20
404	A70	10sh Health care	.30	.30
405	A70	20sh Population figures	.55	.55
		Nos. 402-405 (4)	1.25	1.25

Souvenir Sheet

405A	A70	40sh Segments of economy and society	1.25	1.25

Stamps of 1983-86 Ovptd:

A53 "125TH ANNIVERSARY / INTERNATIONAL RED CROSS / AND RED CRESCENT"

CD334 "40TH WEDDING ANNIVERSARY / H.M. QUEEN ELIZABETH II / H.R.H. THE DUKE OF EDINBURGH"
A41 "63RD ANNIVERSARY / ROTARY INTERNATIONAL / IN AFRICA"

1988, Aug. 15   *Perfs. as Before*

406	A53	5sh on #325	.80	.80
407	A31a	10sh on #220	11.00	11.00
a.		Souv. sheet of 4, #218-220, 407	2.50	2.50
408	A41	15sh on #260	4.00	4.00
409	A41	17.50sh on #261	7.50	7.50
410	A53	40sh on #326	9.75	9.75
		Nos. 406-410 (5)	33.05	33.05

Souvenir Sheets

411		Sheet of 2	5.00	5.00
a.		A41 15sh on #262a	1.25	1.25
b.		A41 20sh on #262b	2.75	2.75
412	A53	30sh on #327	5.00	5.00

1988 Olympics, Seoul and Calgary — A71

1988, Aug. 29   *Perf. 14*

414	A71	5sh Biathlon	.50	.50
415	A71	10sh Soccer	.20	.20
416	A71	20sh Cycling	.80	.80
417	A71	25sh Pairs figuring skating	.90	.90
418	A71	50sh Fencing	.85	.85
419	A71	50sh Downhill skiing	1.60	1.60
420	A71	70sh Volleyball	1.00	1.00
421	A71	75sh Bobsled	1.90	1.90
		Nos. 414-421 (8)	7.75	7.75

Souvenir Sheets

422	A71	100sh Flags, hockey sticks	4.00	4.00
423	A71	100sh Gymnastics	4.00	4.00

For overprint see No. 534A-534J.

1988 Summer Olympics, Seoul A71a

1988, Sept. 5   **Litho.**   *Perf. 12½x12*

423A	A71a	2sh Javelin	.90	.90
423B	A71a	3sh Hurdles	.95	.95
423C	A71a	7sh Long distance running	1.50	1.50
423D	A71a	12sh Relay race	2.00	2.00
		Nos. 423A-423D (4)	5.35	5.35

A souvenir sheet exists.

Disney Characters, Special Occasions — A72

1988, Sept. 9   *Perf. 14*

424	A72	4sh Love You, Dad	.30	.30
425	A72	5sh Happy Birthday	.30	.30
426	A72	10sh Trick or Treat	.45	.45
427	A72	12sh Be Kind to Animals	.45	.45
428	A72	15sh Love	.55	.55
429	A72	20sh Let's Celebrate	.80	.80
430	A72	30sh Keep In Touch	1.75	1.75
431	A72	50sh Love You, Mom	3.50	3.50
		Nos. 424-431 (8)	8.10	8.10

Souvenir Sheets

432	A72	150sh Let's Work Together	4.50	4.50
433	A72	150sh Have a Super Sunday	4.50	4.50

Mickey Mouse, 60th anniv.

Domestic Animals A73

1988, Sept. 9

434	A73	4sh Goat, vert.	.60	.60
435	A73	5sh Rabbit	.60	.60
436	A73	8sh Cows	.85	.85
437	A73	10sh Cat	1.10	1.10
438	A73	12sh Horse, vert.	1.50	1.50
439	A73	20sh Dog, vert.	2.25	2.25
		Nos. 434-439 (6)	6.90	6.90

Souvenir Sheet

440	A73	100sh Chicken	4.50	4.50

Traditional Musical Instruments — A74

1988, Sept. 30   **Litho.**   *Perf. 14*

441	A74	2sh Drums	.60	.60
442	A74	3sh Xylophones	.60	.60
443	A74	10sh Thumb pianos	1.25	1.25
444	A74	20sh Fiddles	1.90	1.90
		Nos. 441-444 (4)	4.35	4.35

Souvenir Sheet

445	A74	40sh Violins with calabash resonators	1.75	1.75

Dated 1987.

Butterflies A75

1988, Oct. 17   *Perf. 14½*

446	A75	8sh Charaxes varanes	.70	.70
447	A75	30sh Neptis melicerta	1.25	1.25
448	A75	40sh Mylothris chloris	1.25	1.25
449	A75	50sh Charaxes bohemani	1.60	1.60
450	A75	60sh Myrina ficedula	2.00	2.00
451	A75	75sh Papilio phorcas	2.50	2.50
452	A75	90sh Cyrestis camillus	3.00	3.00
453	A75	100sh Salamis temora	3.00	3.00
		Nos. 446-453 (8)	15.30	15.30

Souvenir Sheets

454	A75	200sh Asterope rosa	7.00	7.00
455	A75	250sh Kallima rumia	8.00	8.00

Intl. Lions Club at Dar es Salaam, 25th Anniv. A76

1988, Nov, 30   **Litho.**   *Perf. 14½*

456	A76	2sh Eye operation	.40	.40
457	A76	3sh Shallow water well	.40	.40
458	A76	7sh Map, rhinoceros	1.25	1.25
459	A76	12sh Donating school desks	.50	.50
		Nos. 456-459 (4)	2.55	2.55

Souvenir Sheet

460	A76	40sh Emblem	2.00	2.00

Community services: Matibabu Ya Macho Eye Camp (2sh); sanitary water supply in Dar es Salaam (3sh); wildlife conservation (7sh); aid to local schools (12sh).

Intl. Red Cross and Red Crescent Organizations, 125th Annivs. — A77

Design: 2sh, Assisting the wounded and sick. 3sh, Postnatal care clinic. 7sh, Red Cross flag. 12sh, Jean-Henry Dunant, founder. 40sh, Dunant, Thomas Maunier, Louis Appia, Gustave Moynier and Gen. Guillaume Henri Dufour, members of intl. committee that sponsored the conference in 1863 where the Red Cross was founded.

1988, Dec. 30   **Litho.**   *Perf. 12½x12*

461	A77	2sh multicolored	.60	.60
462	A77	3sh multicolored	.60	.60
463	A77	7sh multicolored	.65	.65
464	A77	12sh multicolored	.90	.90
		Nos. 461-464 (4)	2.75	2.75

Souvenir Sheet

465	A77	40sh multicolored	2.25	2.25

Miniature Sheet

Paradise Whydah — A78

Birds: a, Paradise whydah. b, Black-collared barbet. c, Bateleur eagle. d, Openbill storks. lilac-breasted roller. e, Scarlet-tufted malachite sunbird. f, Dark chanting goshawk. g, White-fronted bee-eater, little bee-eater, carmine bee-eater. h, Marabou stork, Narina's trocon. i, African gray parrot. j, Hoopoe. k, Yellow-collared lovebird. l, Yellow-billed hornbill. m, Hammerkop. n, Flamingos, violet-crested turaco. o, Malachite kingfisher. p, Greater flamingo. q, Yellow-billed stork. r, Shoebill stork. s, Saddle-billed stork, blacksmith plover. t, Crowned crane.

1989, Jan. 10   *Perf. 14*

466		Sheet of 20	30.00	30.00
a.-t.		A78 20sh any single	.75	.75

Souvenir Sheets

467	A78	350sh Helmeted guineafowl	8.00	8.00
467A	A78	350sh Ostrich	8.00	8.00

No. 466 has a continuous design.

Endangered Species
A79   A80

World Wildlife Fund: Various bushbabies, *Galago zanzibaricus*. 350sh, African palm civet.

1989, Jan. 24   *Perf. 14*

468	A79	5sh shown	.80	.80
469	A79	10sh multi, horiz.	.85	.85
470	A79	20sh multi, diff.	1.25	1.25
471	A79	45sh multi, diff., horiz.	2.50	2.50
		Nos. 468-471 (4)	5.40	5.40

Souvenir Sheet

472	A79	350sh multi, horiz.	9.50	9.50

1989, Jan. 24

30sh, Black cobra, umbrella acacia. 70sh, Red-tailed tropic bird, tree fern. 100sh, African tree frog, cocoa tree. 150sh, African black-necked heron, Egyptian papyrus. 350sh, Pink-backed pelicans, baobab tree.

473	A80	30sh shown	1.00	1.00
474	A80	70sh multicolored	4.50	4.50
475	A80	100sh multicolored	4.50	4.50
476	A80	150sh multicolored	8.00	8.00
		Nos. 473-476 (4)	18.00	18.00

Souvenir Sheet

477	A80	350sh multicolored	8.75	8.75

Steam Locomotives — A81

1989, Jan. 31

478	A81	10sh Class P36, USSR	.95	.95
479	A81	25sh Class 12, Belgium	1.00	1.00
480	A81	60sh Class C62, Japan	1.50	1.50
481	A81	75sh Class T1, Pennsylvania R.R.	1.75	1.75
482	A81	80sh Class WP, India	1.90	1.90
483	A81	90sh Class 59, East African Railways	2.25	2.25
484	A81	150sh People Class 4-6-2, China	3.50	3.50
485	A81	200sh Southern Pacific *Daylight Express*, US	3.50	3.50
		Nos. 478-485 (8)	16.35	16.35

Souvenir Sheets

486	A81	350sh Stephenson's *Planet*, Britain	6.75	6.75
487	A81	350sh *Coronation Scot*, Britain	6.75	6.75

Nos. 486-487 vert.

World-Class Athletes — A82

Designs: 4sh, Juma Ikangaa, Tanzania, marathon. 8.50sh, Steffi Graf, West Germany, tennis. 12sh, Yannick Noah, France, tennis. 40sh, Pele, Brazil, soccer. 100sh, Erhard Keller, West Germany, speed skater. 125sh, Sadanoyama, Japan, Sumo wrestler. 200sh, Taino, Japan, Sumo wrestler. 250sh, I. Aoki, Japan, golfer. No. 496, Joe Louis, US, world heavyweight boxing champion, 1937-1949. No. 497, T. Nakajima, Japan, golfer.

1989, Feb. 7

488	A82	4sh multicolored	.40	.40
489	A82	8.50sh multicolored	.40	.40
490	A82	12sh multicolored	.40	.40
491	A82	40sh multicolored	1.25	1.25
492	A82	100sh multicolored	3.00	3.00
493	A82	125sh multicolored	3.50	3.50
494	A82	200sh multicolored	5.25	5.25
495	A82	250sh multicolored	6.75	6.75
		Nos. 488-495 (8)	20.95	20.95

Souvenir Sheets

496	A82	350sh multicolored	8.50	8.50
497	A82	350sh multicolored	8.50	8.50

History of Space Exploration and 20th Anniv. of the 1st Moon Landing — A83

1989, July 20

498	A83	20sh Luna 3	.55	.55
499	A83	30sh Rendezvous of Gemini 6&7	.65	.65
500	A83	40sh 1st US space walk	.70	.70

501	A83	60sh	First man on Moon	1.00	1.00
502	A83	70sh	Experiments on Moon	1.10	1.10
503	A83	100sh	Apollo 15 lunar rover	1.50	1.50
504	A83	150sh	Apollo-Soyuz	2.00	2.00
505	A83	200sh	Spacelab	2.50	2.50

Nos. 498-505 (8) 10.00 10.00

Souvenir Sheets

506	A83	250sh	Futuristic space station	4.25	4.25
507	A83	250sh	*Eagle* lunar module	4.25	4.25

History of space exploration (Nos. 498-500, 503-506); others 20th anniv. of 1st Moon Landing.

St. Mary Magdalene in Penitence A84

Details from paintings by Titian: 10sh, Averoldi Polyptych. 15sh, St. Margaret. 50sh, Venus and Adonis. 75sh, Venus and the Lutenist. 100sh, Tarquin and Lucretia. 125sh, St. Jerome. 150sh, Madonna and Child with Saints. No. 516, St. Catherine of Alexandria at Prayer. No. 517, Adoration of the Holy Trinity. No. 517A, The Supper at Emmaus.

1989, Nov. 15   Litho.   Perf. 13½x14

508	A84	5sh	multicolored	.40	.40
509	A84	10sh	multicolored	.40	.40
510	A84	15sh	multicolored	.40	.40
511	A84	50sh	multicolored	.90	.90
512	A84	75sh	multicolored	1.40	1.40
513	A84	100sh	multicolored	1.60	1.60
514	A84	125sh	multicolored	2.00	2.00
515	A84	150sh	multicolored	2.50	2.50

Nos. 508-515 (8) 9.60 9.60

Souvenir Sheets

516	A84	300sh	multicolored	4.00	4.00
517	A84	300sh	multicolored	4.00	4.00
517A	A84	300sh	multicolored	4.00	4.00

500th birth anniv. of Titian.
#517A was not available until Jan. 8, 1991.

World Cup Soccer Championships, Italy — A85

1989, Nov. 15   Perf. 14

Uniform colors

518	A85	25sh	green, red & yel	1.00	1.00
519	A85	60sh	green, yel & blue	2.10	2.10
520	A85	75sh	orange & blue	2.75	2.75
521	A85	200sh	blue & white	7.00	7.00

Nos. 518-521 (4) 12.85 12.85

Souvenir Sheets

522	A85	350sh	orange & bl, diff.	5.75	5.75
523	A85	350sh	grn, yel & bl, diff.	5.75	5.75

Souvenir Sheet

Union Station, Washington, DC — A86

1989, Nov. 17

524	A86	500sh	multicolored	9.50	9.50

World Stamp Expo '89.

Fish A87

1989, Dec. 14

525	A87	9sh	Tiger tilapia	.35	.35
526	A87	13sh	Picasso fish	.35	.35
527	A87	20sh	Powder-blue surgeonfish	.50	.50
528	A87	40sh	Butterflyfish	.90	.90
529	A87	70sh	Guenther's notho	1.60	1.60
530	A87	100sh	Ansorge's noelebias	2.40	2.40
531	A87	150sh	Lyretail panchax	3.75	3.75
532	A87	200sh	Regal angelfish	5.00	5.00

Nos. 525-532 (8) 14.85 14.85

Souvenir Sheets

533	A87	350sh	Batfish	7.00	7.00
534	A87	350sh	Jewel cichlid	7.00	7.00

Nos. 533-534 each contain one 38x51mm stamp.

Nos. 414-423 Ovptd. and Similarly

Perfs. as Before

1989, Dec. 19   Litho.

534A	A71	5sh	shown	.55	.55
534B	A71	10sh	"Gold - USSR / Silver - Brazil / Bronze - W. Germany"	.75	.75
534C	A71	20sh	"Men's Match Sprint / Lutz Hesslich, DDR"	3.00	3.00
534D	A71	25sh	"Pairs, Gordeeva & Grinkov, USSR"	1.50	1.50
534E	A71	50sh	"Epee, Schmitt, W. Germany"	2.40	2.40
534F	A71	50sh	"Zurbriggen, Switzerland"	2.40	2.40
534G	A71	70sh	"Men's Team, USA"	3.75	3.75
534H	A71	75sh	"Gold-USSR / Silver-DDR / Bronze-DDR"	3.00	3.00

Nos. 534A-534H (8) 17.35 17.35

Souvenir Sheets

534I	A71	100sh	"Ice Hockey: / Gold-USSR"	11.00	11.00
534J	A71	100sh	"Women's Team, / Gold-USSR"	4.00	4.00

Silver and Bronze medalists overprinted on margins of souvenir sheets.

Inter-Parliamentary Union, Cent. — A88

Designs: 9sh, Secret ballot. 13sh, Parliament, Dar Es Salaam. 40sh, Sir William Randal Cremer, Frederic Passy. 80sh, Parliament in session. 100sh, IPU emblem.

1989, Dec. 22   Perf. 12½x12

535	A88	9sh	multicolored	.20	.20
536	A88	13sh	multicolored	.20	.20
537	A88	80sh	multicolored	.85	.85
538	A88	100sh	lt bl, dp bl & blk	1.00	1.00

Nos. 535-538 (4) 2.25 2.25

Souvenir Sheet

539	A88	40sh	multicolored	1.40	1.40

Pan-African Postal Union, 10th Anniv. A89

1990, Jan. 17   Perf. 13½

540	A89	9sh	PAPU emblem	.40	.40
541	A89	13sh	Post offices boxes	.40	.40
542	A89	70sh	Mail early, prompt delivery	1.50	1.50
543	A89	100sh	Modes of mail delivery	2.75	2.75

Nos. 540-543 (4) 5.05 5.05

Souvenir Sheet

544	A89	40sh	Tanzania Post, PAPU, UPU emblems	1.60	1.60

Extinct Animals A90

1990, Feb. 4   Perf. 14

545	A90	25sh	Tecopa pupfish	.75	.75
546	A90	40sh	Thylacine	1.10	1.10
547	A90	50sh	Quagga	1.50	1.50
548	A90	60sh	Passenger pigeon	1.75	1.75
549	A90	75sh	Rodriguez saddleback tortoise	2.25	2.25
550	A90	100sh	Toolache wallaby	2.75	2.75
551	A90	150sh	Texas red wolf	4.25	4.25
552	A90	200sh	Utah lake sculpin	5.50	5.50

Nos. 545-552 (8) 19.85 19.85

Souvenir Sheets

553	A90	350sh	Hawaiian O-O, vert.	8.00	8.00
554	A90	350sh	South island whekau	8.00	8.00

Nina, Admiral's Flag A91

1990, Feb. 20

555	A91	50sh	shown	2.10	2.10
556	A91	60sh	Pinta, flag	2.50	2.50
557	A91	75sh	Santa Maria, flag	3.00	3.00
558	A91	200sh	Map of Columbus' first voyage	8.25	8.25

Nos. 555-558 (4) 15.85 15.85

Souvenir Sheet

559	A91	350sh	Ships, bird's head	9.50	9.50

Discovery of America, 500th anniv. (in 1992).

Modern Discoveries — A92

Designs: 9sh, Bell X-1 breaking the sound barrier. 13sh, Bathyscaph Trieste reaches the deepest ocean bottom. 150sh, Transistor and computer chips. 250sh, Discovery of DNA structure. 350sh, Voyager 2 visits Neptune.

1990, Feb. 20

560	A92	9sh	multicolored	.65	.65
561	A92	13sh	multicolored	.65	.65
562	A92	150sh	multicolored	1.50	1.50
563	A92	250sh	multicolored	2.50	2.50

Nos. 560-563 (4) 5.30 5.30

Souvenir Sheet

564	A92	350sh	multicolored	5.75	5.75

Girl Guides, 60th Anniv. A93

1990, Feb. 22   Perf. 12½x12

565	A93	9sh	Hiking	.20	.20
566	A93	13sh	Planting trees	.20	.20
567	A93	50sh	Teaching writing	.85	.85
568	A93	100sh	Teaching health care	1.75	1.75

Nos. 565-568 (4) 3.00 3.00

Souvenir Sheet

Perf. 12x12½

569	A93	40sh	Nursing school, vert.	2.00	2.00

Disney Characters, Automobiles — A94

1990, Mar. 20   Perf. 14x13½

570	A94	20sh	Herbie, The Love Bug	.45	.45
571	A94	30sh	The Absent-Minded Professor's car	.50	.50
572	A94	45sh	Chitty-Chitty Bang-Bang	.65	.65
573	A94	60sh	Mr. Toad's wild ride	.90	.90
574	A94	75sh	Scrooge's limousine	1.10	1.10
575	A94	100sh	Shaggy dog's car	1.50	1.50
576	A94	150sh	Donald Duck's car	2.40	2.40
577	A94	200sh	Firetruck in "Dumbo"	2.50	2.50

Nos. 570-577 (8) 10.00 10.00

Souvenir Sheets

578	A94	350sh	Cruella de Vil	6.00	6.00
579	A94	350sh	Mickeymobile	6.00	6.00

Black Entertainers A95

1990, Mar. 30   Litho.   Perf. 14

580	A95	9sh	Miriam Makeba	.25	.25
581	A95	13sh	Manu Dibango	.25	.25
582	A95	25sh	Fela	.25	.25

583	A95	70sh	Smokey Robin- son	1.00	1.00
584	A95	100sh	Gladys Knight	1.25	1.25
585	A95	150sh	Eddie Murphy	2.25	2.25
586	A95	200sh	Sammy Davis, Jr.	3.00	3.00
587	A95	250sh	Stevie Wonder	3.00	3.00
		Nos. 580-587 (8)		11.25	11.25

Souvenir Sheets
Perf. 14½

588	A95	350sh	Bill Cosby	3.75	3.75
589	A95	350sh	Michael Jack- son	3.75	3.75

Union of Tanganyika and Zanzibar,
25th Anniv. (in 1989) — A95a

Designs: 9sh, Fishing. 13sh, Grapes. 50sh,
Cloves. 100sh, Presidents Nyerere and
Karume exchanging Union instruments, vert.
40sh, Natl. arms, vert.

Perf. 12½x12, 12x12½

1990, Apr. 25				**Litho.**	
589A	A95a	9sh	multicolored	.55	.55
589B	A95a	13sh	multicolored	.55	.55
589C	A95a	50sh	multicolored	1.75	1.75
589D	A95a	100sh	multicolored	3.50	3.50
		Nos. 589A-589D (4)		6.35	6.35

Souvenir Sheet

589E	A95a	40sh	multicolored	2.75	2.75

Southern Africa Development
Coordinating Conf. (SADCC), 10th
Anniv. — A96

1990, Aug. 8				**Perf. 13½**	
590	A96	8sh	Railway trans- port	.50	.50
591	A96	11.50sh	Paper industry	.50	.50
592	A96	25sh	Tractor produc- tion	.90	.90
593	A96	100sh	Flags, map	3.00	3.00
		Nos. 590-593 (4)		4.90	4.90

Souvenir Sheet
Perf. 12½

594	A96	50sh	Map	2.50	2.50

A97　　　　　　　　　A98

Pope John Paul II's Visit to Tanzania: 15sh,
Wearing red vestments. 20sh, Wearing miter.
100sh, Papal arms. No. 599: a, Pope with
arms outstretched. b, St. Joseph's Cathedral,
Dar Es Salaam. c, Christ the King Cathedral,
Moshi. d, Saint Theresa's Cathedral, Tabora.
e, Cathedral of the Epiphany, Bugando
Mwanza. f, St. Mathias Mulumba Kalemba
Cathedral, Songea.

1990, Sept. 1				**Litho.**	**Perf. 14**
595	A97	10sh	shown	.30	.30
596	A97	15sh	multicolored	.45	.45
597	A97	20sh	multicolored	.50	.50
598	A97	100sh	multicolored	1.25	1.25
		Nos. 595-598 (4)		2.50	2.50

Souvenir Sheet

599			Sheet of 6	7.00	7.00
a.-f.	A97 50sh any single			.60	.60

1990, Sept. 28

Players from participating countries.

600	A98	10sh	West Germany	1.00	1.00
601	A98	60sh	Italy	1.75	1.75
602	A98	100sh	Scotland	3.00	3.00
603	A98	300sh	Yugoslavia	5.25	5.25
		Nos. 600-603 (4)		11.00	11.00

Souvenir Sheets

604	A98	400sh	Costa Rica	6.50	6.50
605	A98	400sh	Belgium	6.50	6.50

World Cup Soccer Championships, Italy.

Birds — A99

1990-91				**Litho.**	**Perf. 14**
606	A99	5sh	Masked weaver	.45	.45
607	A99	9sh	Emerald cuckoo	.45	.45
608	A99	13sh	Little bee- eater	.80	.80
609	A99	15sh	Red bishop	.80	.80
610	A99	20sh	Bateleur	1.00	1.00
611	A99	25sh	Scarlet- chested sunbird	1.00	1.00
a.	Bklt. pane, 2 ea #606-611			9.00	9.00
611B	A99	30sh	Pigeons	1.00	1.00

Size: 42x28mm

612	A99	40sh	Lesser fla- mingo	1.00	1.00
613	A99	70sh	Helmeted guineafowl	1.10	1.10
614	A99	100sh	White peli- can	1.25	1.25
615	A99	170sh	Saddle-billed stork	1.75	1.75
616	A99	200sh	Crowned crane	2.00	2.00
616A	A99	300sh	Pied crow	2.25	2.25
616B	A99	400sh	White-head- ed vulture	2.50	2.50
617	A99	500sh	Ostrich	2.50	2.50
		Nos. 606-617 (15)		19.85	19.85

Souvenir Sheet
Stamp size: 42x28mm

617A			Sheet of 2	6.25	6.25
b.	A99 40sh Superb starling			1.10	1.10
c.	A99 60sh Lilac-breasted roller			1.60	1.60

Issued: 30sh, 300sh, 400sh, 1991; others,
10/1/90.
For surcharges, see Nos. 1723A, 1723B,
2157-2159C.

Boats
A100

1990, Oct. 10				**Litho.**	**Perf. 12½x12**
618	A100	9sh	Canoe	.55	.55
619	A100	13sh	Outrigger canoe	.55	.55
620	A100	25sh	Dhow	.85	.85
621	A100	100sh	Freighter	4.00	4.00
		Nos. 618-621 (4)		5.95	5.95

Souvenir Sheet

622	A100	40sh	Boat	4.00	4.00

Commonwealth Games, New
Zealand — A101

1990, Oct. 22					**Perf. 14**
623	A101	9sh	Sprinting	.50	.50
624	A101	13sh	Netball, vert.	.90	.90
625	A101	25sh	Pole vault	1.25	1.25
626	A101	100sh	Long jump, vert.	4.00	4.00
		Nos. 623-626 (4)		6.65	6.65

Souvenir Sheet

627	A101	40sh	Boxing	2.50	2.50

Orchids — A102

1990, Nov. 12					
628	A102	10sh	Phalaenopsis	.40	.40
629	A102	25sh	Lycaste	.40	.40
630	A102	30sh	Vuylstekeara, Cambria "Plush"	.45	.45
631	A102	50sh	Vuylstekeara, Monica "Burnham"	.70	.70
632	A102	90sh	Odontocidium	1.25	1.25
633	A102	100sh	Oncidioda	1.60	1.60
634	A102	250sh	Sophrolaelio- cattleya	4.00	4.00
635	A102	300sh	Laeliocattleya	4.50	4.50
		Nos. 628-635 (8)		13.30	13.30

Souvenir Sheets

636	A102	400sh	Cymbidium, Baldoyle "Melbury"	6.25	6.25
637	A102	400sh	Cymbidium, Tapestry "Long Beach"	6.25	6.25

Expo '90, the Intl. Garden and Greenery
Exposition, Osaka, Japan.

1990 World Cup Soccer
Championships, Italy — A102a

1990, Nov. 17				**Litho.**	**Perf. 14**
637A	A102a	9sh	Long throw-in	.75	.75
637B	A102a	13sh	Penalty kick	.75	.75
637C	A102a	25sh	Dribbling	1.25	1.25
637D	A102a	100sh	Corner kick	4.25	4.25
		Nos. 637A-637D (4)		7.00	7.00

Souvenir Sheet

637E	A102a	50sh	Trophy, map	4.50	4.50

Racing
A103

5sh, Olympic Soling Class Yacht racing.
20sh, Olympic downhill ski racing. 30sh, Tour
de France bicycle race. 40sh, Le Mans 24
hour endurance auto race. 75sh, Olympic 2-
man bobsled. 100sh, Belgian Grand Prix
motorcycle race. 250sh, Indianapolis 500 auto
race. 300sh, Power boat gold cup racing.
#646, Colorado 500 enduro motorcycle race.
#647, Schneider Trophy air races.

1990, Nov. 19					
638	A103	5sh	multicolored	.45	.45
639	A103	20sh	multicolored	.85	.85
640	A103	30sh	multicolored	1.40	1.40
641	A103	40sh	multicolored	1.40	1.40
642	A103	75sh	multicolored	1.60	1.60
643	A103	100sh	multicolored	2.40	2.40
644	A103	250sh	multicolored	3.00	3.00
645	A103	300sh	multicolored	3.25	3.25
		Nos. 638-645 (8)		14.35	14.35

Souvenir Sheets

646	A103	400sh	multicolored	7.00	7.00
647	A103	400sh	multicolored	7.00	7.00

1992 Summer
Olympics,
Barcelona — A104

1990, Nov. 30					
648	A104	5sh	Archery	.30	.30
649	A104	10sh	Women's gymnastics	.30	.30
650	A104	25sh	Boxing	.30	.30
651	A104	50sh	Two-man kay- ak race	.55	.55
652	A104	100sh	Men's volley- ball	1.10	1.10
653	A104	150sh	Mens' gym- nastics	1.75	1.75
654	A104	200sh	4x100 meter relay	2.25	2.25
655	A104	300sh	Judo	3.50	3.50
		Nos. 648-655 (8)		10.05	10.05

Souvenir Sheets

656	A104	400sh	Men's 400 meter hur- dles	5.50	5.50
657	A104	400sh	Men's cycling	5.50	5.50

Cog
Railroads
A105

Cog locomotives: 8sh, Petersberg Cog Railway, West Germany. 25sh, Engine *Waumbek*
on Mt. Washington Cog Railway, US. 50sh,
Doubleheaded cog engines on Dubrovnik-
Sarajevo line, Yugoslavia. 100sh, Cog Railway, Budapest, Hungary 1874. 150sh,
Vordenberg-Eisenerz line, Austria. 200sh,
Rimutaka Incline, New Zealand, 1955. 250sh,
John Stevens' cog engine, Hoboken, NJ,
1825. 300sh, Pilatusbahn Cog Railway, Switzerland, 1889. No. 666, Schneebergbahn of
the OBB, Austria. No. 667, Sylvester Marsh,
Mt. Washington Cog Railway, 1869.

1990, Dec. 8					
658	A105	8sh	multicolored	.30	.30
659	A105	25sh	multicolored	.30	.30
660	A105	50sh	multicolored	.60	.60
661	A105	100sh	multicolored	1.10	1.10
662	A105	150sh	multicolored	1.75	1.75
663	A105	200sh	multicolored	2.25	2.25
664	A105	250sh	multicolored	3.25	3.25
665	A105	300sh	multicolored	3.75	3.75
		Nos. 658-665 (8)		13.30	13.30

Souvenir Sheets

666	A105	400sh	multicolored	6.50	6.50
667	A105	400sh	multicolored	6.50	6.50

First
Postage
Stamps,
150th
Anniv.
A106

Designs: No. 668, German Post Office at
Dar Es Salaam, German East Africa No. 16.
No. 669, Mailboat S.S. Reichstag, 1890, Germany No. 40 cancelled in Zanzibar. No. 670,
Dhows used as mailboats, Zanzibar No. 1. No.
671, Mailplane Singapore I on Lake Victoria,
1928, Tanganyika No. 22. No. 672, Mailplane,
Livingston's House, Zanzibar No. 316. No.
673, Passenger-mail train at Moshi Station,
Tanganyika No. 52. No. 674, Royal mail
coach, 1840. 150sh, Stephenson's *Rocket*,
mail car, 1838. 200sh, Handley Page HP-42
mailplane. No. 677, Hand delivery of mail,
Thurn & Taxis No. 44 on cover. No. 678, Sir
Rowland Hill.

1990, Dec. 12					
668	A106	50sh	multicolored	1.10	1.10
669	A106	50sh	multicolored	1.10	1.10
a.	Pair, #668-669			1.10	1.10
670	A106	75sh	multicolored	1.40	1.40
671	A106	75sh	multicolored	1.40	1.40
a.	Pair, #670-671			1.50	1.50
672	A106	100sh	multicolored	2.10	2.10
673	A106	100sh	multicolored	2.10	2.10
a.	Pair, #672-673			2.25	2.25

674	A106	100sh multicolored	2.10	2.10
675	A106	150sh multicolored	3.00	3.00
676	A106	200sh multicolored	3.00	3.00

Nos. 668-676 (9) 17.30 17.30

Souvenir Sheets

677	A106	350sh multicolored	6.75	6.75
678	A106	350sh multicolored	6.75	6.75

500th anniv. of Thurn and Taxis Post (No. 677).

For overprints see Nos. 928-934.

Intl. Literacy
Year — A107

Nos. 679a-681i depict various Walt Disney characters and a letter of the alphabet. No. 682, Mickey's train hauls Russian alphabet. No. 683, Children learning Hebrew.

1990, Dec. 27   *Perf. 13½x14*

Miniature Sheets

679		Sheet of 9	7.50	7.50
a.	A107	1sh "ABC"	.20	.20
b.	A107	2sh "A"	.20	.20
c.	A107	3sh "B"	.20	.20
d.	A107	15sh "C"	.20	.20
e.	A107	55sh "D"	.45	.45
f.	A107	80sh "E"	.65	.65
g.	A107	120sh "F"	.95	.95
h.	A107	145sh "G"	1.10	1.10
i.	A107	200sh "H"	1.60	1.60
680		Sheet of 9	7.25	7.25
a.	A107	10sh "I"	.20	.20
b.	A107	20sh "J"	.20	.20
c.	A107	30sh "K"	.25	.25
d.	A107	40sh "L"	.30	.30
e.	A107	50sh "M"	.40	.40
f.	A107	60sh "N"	.50	.50
g.	A107	100sh "O"	.80	.80
h.	A107	125sh "P"	1.00	1.00
i.	A107	150sh "Q"	1.25	1.25
681		Sheet of 9	7.50	7.50
a.	A107	5sh "R"	.20	.20
b.	A107	18sh "S"	.20	.20
c.	A107	25sh "T"	.20	.20
d.	A107	35sh "U"	.30	.30
e.	A107	45sh "V"	.35	.35
f.	A107	75sh "W"	.60	.60
g.	A107	90sh "X"	.70	.70
h.	A107	160sh "Y"	1.25	1.25
i.	A107	175sh "Z"	1.40	1.40

Souvenir Sheets

682	A107	600sh multicolored	8.50	8.50
683	A107	600sh multicolored	8.50	8.50

Intl.
Literacy
Year
A108

1991, Mar. 15   **Litho.**   *Perf. 14*

684	A108	9sh Learning to read	.35	.35
685	A108	13sh Learning to write	.50	.50
686	A108	25sh Blackboard, books	.65	.65
687	A108	100sh Reading newspapers	3.00	3.00

Nos. 684-687 (4) 4.50 4.50

Souvenir Sheet

688	A108	50sh Adult education	2.75	2.75

For surcharge see No. 1431A.

Mickey Mouse — A109

Character roles: 5sh, Western cowboy. 10sh, Boxer. 15sh, Astronaut. 20sh, Romantic lead with Minnie. 100sh, Swashbuckling hero. 200sh, Detective with Donald Duck and Pistol Pete. 350sh, King with Donald as court jester.

450sh, Sailor with Donald and Goofy. No. 697, Minnie, Mickey as archaeologists in Egypt, Donald as a mummy. No. 698, Mickey as Canadian Mountie.

1991, Feb. 11   **Litho.**   *Perf. 14x13½*

689	A109	5sh multicolored	.45	.45
690	A109	10sh multicolored	.50	.50
691	A109	15sh multicolored	.50	.50
692	A109	20sh multicolored	.50	.50
693	A109	100sh multicolored	2.00	2.00
694	A109	200sh multicolored	4.00	4.00
695	A109	350sh multicolored	4.50	4.50
696	A109	450sh multicolored	4.50	4.50

Nos. 689-696 (8) 16.95 16.95

Souvenir Sheets

697	A109	600sh multicolored	8.50	8.50
698	A109	600sh multicolored	8.50	8.50

Craters
and
Caves —
A109a

Designs: 3sh, Ngorongoro Crater. 5sh, Kondoa Caves, prehistoric rock paintings. 9sh, Mount Kilimanjaro's inner crater. 12sh, Olduvai Gorge.

Amboni Caves: No. 698f, Open area of cave. g, People viewing cave, large stalactite. h, Woman seated beside welcome sign. i, Man climbing up to view cave.

1991, Mar. 28   **Litho.**   *Perf. 14½*

698A	A109a	3sh multicolored	3.75	3.75
698B	A109a	5sh multicolored	3.75	3.75
698C	A109a	9sh multicolored	4.75	4.75
698D	A109a	12sh multicolored	6.75	6.75

Nos. 698A-698D (4) 19.00 19.00

Souvenir Sheet

698E	A109a	10sh Sheet of 4, #f.-i.	8.00	8.00

Nos. 698A-698E were not available to the philatelic community until Mar. 1994.

Miniature Sheet

Peter Paul Rubens, 350th Death
Anniv. — A110

Cycle of Decius Mus: No. 699a, Proclamation of the Vision. b, Divining of the Entrails. c, Dispatch of the Lictors. d, Dedication to Death. e, Victory and Death of Decius Mus. f, Funeral Rites. No. 700, Trophy of War, vert.

1991, Apr. 10   **Litho.**   *Perf. 14x13½*

699	A110	85sh Sheet of 6, #a.-f.	14.00	14.00

Souvenir Sheet

Perf. 13½x14

700	A110	500sh multicolored	12.00	12.00

Tanzania Investment Bank, 20th
Anniv. — A111

Designs: 10sh, Dairy farming. 13sh, Industrial development. 25sh, Engineering. 100sh, Tea harvesting.

1991, June 7   *Perf. 14*

701	A111	10sh multicolored	.50	.50
702	A111	13sh multicolored	.50	.50
703	A111	25sh multicolored	.50	.50
704	A111	100sh multicolored	3.25	3.25
a.		Souvenir sheet of 4, #701-704	3.25	3.25

Nos. 701-704 (4) 4.75 4.75

Phila
Nippon
'91
A112

Japanese locomotives: 10sh, First Japanese steam. 25sh, Series 4500 steam. 35sh, C 62 steam. 50sh, Mikado steam. 75sh, Series 6250 steam. 100sh, C 11 steam. 200sh, E 10 steam. 300sh, Series 8550 steam. No. 713, EF 58 electric. No. 714, DD 51 diesel. No. 715, Series 400 electric. No. 716, EH 10 electric.

1991, Aug. 15   **Litho.**   *Perf. 14*

705	A112	10sh multicolored	1.00	1.00
706	A112	25sh multicolored	1.50	1.50
707	A112	35sh multicolored	1.75	1.75
708	A112	50sh multicolored	2.00	2.00
709	A112	75sh multicolored	2.75	2.75
710	A112	100sh multicolored	3.25	3.25
711	A112	200sh multicolored	3.75	3.75
712	A112	300sh multicolored	5.00	5.00

Nos. 705-712 (8) 21.00 21.00

Souvenir Sheets

713	A112	400sh multicolored	4.75	4.75
714	A112	400sh multicolored	4.75	4.75
715	A112	400sh multicolored	4.75	4.75
716	A112	400sh multicolored	4.75	4.75

Fauna in
Natl.
Game
Parks
A113

Species and park: 10sh, Common zebra, golden-winged sunbird, Ngorongoro Crater Conservation Area. 25sh, Greater kudu, African elephant, Ruaha. 30sh, Sable antelope, red and yellow barbet, Mikumi. 50sh, Wildebeest, leopard, Serengeti. 90sh, Giraffe, white-starred bush robin, Ngurdoto Crater. 100sh, Eland, Abbot's duiker, Kilimanjaro. 250sh, Lion, impala, Lake Manyara. 300sh, Black rhinoceros, ostrich, Tarangire. No. 725, Paradise whydah, oryx, Mkomazi Game Reserve. No. 726, Blue-breasted kingfisher, defassa waterbuck, Selous Game Reserve.

1991, Aug. 22   **Litho.**   *Perf. 14*

717	A113	10sh multicolored	.30	.30
718	A113	25sh multicolored	.65	.65
719	A113	30sh multicolored	.80	.80
720	A113	50sh multicolored	1.25	1.25
721	A113	90sh multicolored	2.10	2.10
722	A113	100sh multicolored	2.50	2.50
723	A113	250sh multicolored	6.00	6.00
724	A113	300sh multicolored	7.50	7.50

Nos. 717-724 (8) 21.10 21.10

Souvenir Sheets

725	A113	400sh multicolored	9.75	9.75
726	A113	400sh multicolored	9.75	9.75

Butterflies — A114

Designs: 10sh, Vine leaf vagrant. 15sh, Blue spot commodore. 35sh, Orange admiral. 75sh, Wanderer. 100sh, Jackson's leaf. 150sh, Painted empress. 200sh, Double-banded orange. 300sh, Crawshay's sapphire blue. No. 735, Noble swallowtail. No. 736, Club-tailed charaxes. No. 737, Satyr charaxes. No. 738, Green patch swallowtail.

1991, Aug. 28   **Litho.**   *Perf. 14*

727	A114	10sh multicolored	.40	.40
728	A114	15sh multicolored	.40	.40
729	A114	35sh multicolored	.85	.85
730	A114	75sh multicolored	1.75	1.75
731	A114	100sh multicolored	2.25	2.25
732	A114	150sh multicolored	3.50	3.50
733	A114	200sh multicolored	4.50	4.50
734	A114	300sh multicolored	7.00	7.00

Nos. 727-734 (8) 20.65 20.65

Souvenir Sheets

735	A114	400sh multicolored	5.50	5.50
736	A114	400sh multicolored	5.50	5.50
737	A114	400sh multicolored	5.50	5.50
738	A114	400sh multicolored	5.50	5.50

While Nos. 727-736 have the same issue date as Nos. 737-738, the dollar value of Nos. 737-738 was lower when they were released.

Intelsat,
25th
Anniv.
A115

Designs: 10sh, Microwave link. 25sh, Earth. 100sh, Mwenge standard "B" Earth station. 500sh, Mwenge standard "A" Earth station. 50sh, World map.

1991, Sept. 5   **Litho.**   *Perf. 14*

739	A115	10sh multicolored	.40	.40
740	A115	25sh multicolored	.55	.55
741	A115	100sh multicolored	2.50	2.50
742	A115	500sh multicolored	9.00	9.00

Nos. 739-742 (4) 12.45 12.45

Souvenir Sheet

743	A115	50sh multicolored	4.00	4.00

UN Development Program, 40th
Anniv. — A116

Designs: 10sh, Irrigated rice farming. 15sh, Vocational training. 100sh, Terrace farming. 500sh, Architectural renovations, vert. 40sh, Helping people to help themselves, vert.

1991, Sept. 16   *Perf. 13½*

744	A116	10sh multicolored	.30	.30
745	A116	15sh multicolored	.30	.30
746	A116	100sh multicolored	1.50	1.50
747	A116	500sh multicolored	7.00	7.00

Nos. 744-747 (4) 9.10 9.10

Souvenir Sheet

Perf. 13x12½

748	A116	40sh black & blue	2.00	2.00

All Africa Games,
Cairo — A117

Perf. 12x12½, 12½x12

1991, Sept. 20

749	A117	10sh Netball	.50	.50
750	A117	15sh Soccer, horiz.	.50	.50
751	A117	100sh Tennis	2.75	2.75
752	A117	200sh Running	3.50	3.50
753	A117	500sh Baseball, horiz.	8.25	8.25

Nos. 749-753 (5) 15.50 15.50

Souvenir Sheet

754	A117	500sh Basketball	11.50	11.50

Telecom
'91 — A118

1991, Oct. 1   Perf. 13½x14, 14x13½
755 A118 10sh shown   .30   .30
756 A118 15sh Telecom '91,
                horiz.   .30   .30
757 A118 35sh arrows   .40   .40
758 A118 100sh like #757, horiz. 1.10   1.10
       Nos. 755-758 (4)   2.10 2.10
World Telecommunications Day (Nos. 757-758).

Dinosaurs
A119

1991, Oct. 28   Perf. 12x12½
759 A119 10sh Stegosaurus   .30   .30
760 A119 15sh Triceratops   .30   .30
761 A119 25sh Edmontosaurus   .45   .45
762 A119 30sh Plateosaurus   .60   .60
763 A119 35sh Diplodocus   .70   .70
764 A119 100sh Iguanodon   1.90 1.90
765 A119 200sh Silviasaurus   3.75 3.75
       Nos. 759-765 (7)   8.00 8.00

Souvenir Sheet
766 A119 150sh Rhampho-
                rhynchus   4.75 4.75

Animals
and Fish
A120

No. 767 — Horses: a, Shire. b, Thorough-
bred. c, Kladruber. d, Appaloosa. e, Hanove-
rian. f, Arab. g, Breton. h, Exmoor. i, Con-
nemara. j, Lipizzaner. k, Shetland. l,
Percheron. m, Pinto. n, Orlov. o, Palomino. p,
Welsh cob.
No. 768 — Cats: a, Japanese bobtail. b,
Cornish rex. c, Malayan. d, Tonkinese. e,
Abyssinian. f, Russian blue. g, Cymric. h,
Somali. i, Siamese. j, Himalayan. k, Sin-
gapura. l, Manx. m, Oriental shorthair. n,
Maine coon. o, Persian. p, Birman.
No. 769, vert. — African elephants: a, One
walking left. b, Two with tusks entangled. c,
One facing forward. d, One under tree. e, Adult
and calf in water, zebra. f, Adult and calf walk-
ing into water. g, Two adults and calf in water.
h, Adult and calf standing in water. i, One
walking right. j, Two, one raising trunk in air. k,
One raising trunk in air. l, One facing forward,
trunk down, zebra. m, Adult, calf at edge of
water, antelope. n, Adult and calf, two more in
background. o, One walking toward water. p,
Adult with trunk on calf.
No. 770 — Aquarium fish: a, Jewel tetra. b,
Five-banded barb. c, Simpson platy. d, Guppy,
e, Zebra danio. f, Neon tetra. g, Siamese fighting fish. h, Tiger barb. i, Red lyretail. j, Goldfish. k, Pearl gourami. l, Angelfish. m, Clown
loach. n, Red swordtail. o, Brown discus. p,
Rosy barb.
No. 771 — Birds: a, Budgerigar. b, Rainbow
bunting. c, Golden-fronted leafbird. d, Black-
headed caique. e, Java sparrow. f, Diamond
sparrow. g, Peach-faced lovebird. h, Golden
conure. i, Military macaw. j, Celestial parrotlet.
k, Sulphur-crested cockatoo. l, Spectacled
Amazon parrot. m, Paradise tanager. n,
Gouldian finch. o, Masked lovebird. p, Hill
mynah.

1991, Oct. 28   Litho.   Perf. 14
767 A120 50sh Sheet of 16,
          #a.-p.   19.00 19.00
768 A120 50sh Sheet of 16,
          #a.-p.   19.00 19.00
769 A120 75sh Sheet of 16,
          #a.-p.   19.00 19.00
770 A120 75sh Sheet of 16,
          #a.-p.   19.00 19.00
771 A120 75sh Sheet of 16,
          #a.-p.   19.00 19.00
       Nos. 767-771 (5)   95.00 95.00

For overprints see Nos. 1529-1530.

Paintings by
Vincent Van
Gogh
A121

Designs: 10sh, Peasant Woman Sewing.
15sh, Head of a Peasant Woman with Greenish Lace Cap. 35sh, Flowering Orchard. 75sh,
Portrait of a Girl. 100sh, Portrait of a Woman
with a Red Ribbon. 150sh, Vase with Flowers.
200sh, Houses in Antwerp. 400sh, Seated
Peasant Woman with White Cap. No. 780, The
Parsonage Garden at Nuenen in the Snow,
horiz. No. 781, Bulb Fields, horiz.

1991, Nov. 20   Litho.   Perf. 13½x14
772 A121 10sh multicolored   .30   .30
773 A121 15sh multicolored   .30   .30
774 A121 35sh multicolored   .80   .80
775 A121 75sh multicolored   1.60 1.60
776 A121 100sh multicolored   2.00 2.00
777 A121 150sh multicolored   3.00 3.00
778 A121 200sh multicolored   4.00 4.00
779 A121 400sh multicolored   8.00 8.00
       Nos. 772-779 (8)   20.00 20.00

Size: 127x102mm

Imperf
780 A121 400sh multicolored   8.50 8.50
781 A121 400sh multicolored   8.50 8.50

Walt Disney Christmas Cards — A122

Design and date of card: 10sh, "Joy," 1968.
25sh, Mickey, Pluto and Goofy at fireplace,
1981. 35sh, Robin Hood and merry men celebrating, 1973. 75sh, Tree of greetings, Mickey,
1967. 100sh, Goofy, Mickey and Donald trying
to catch Santa coming down chimney, 1969,
vert. 150sh, Mickey on top of Christmas ornament, 1976, vert. 200sh, Clarabelle Cow with
bells, 1935, vert. 300sh, Orphan mice reading
book of tricks, 1935, vert. No. 790, Mickey
wearing Santa hat and surrounded by Disney
characters, 1968, vert. No. 791, Mickey with
present for Donald, 1935, vert.

Perf. 13½x14, 14x13½
1991, Dec.   Litho.
782 A122 10sh multicolored   .30   .30
783 A122 25sh multicolored   .55   .55
784 A122 35sh multicolored   .70   .70
785 A122 75sh multicolored   1.40 1.40
786 A122 100sh multicolored   2.00 2.00
787 A122 150sh multicolored   2.50 2.50
788 A122 200sh multicolored   3.00 3.00
789 A122 300sh multicolored   4.00 4.00
       Nos. 782-789 (8)   14.45 14.45

Souvenir Sheets
790 A122 500sh multicolored   9.50 9.50
791 A122 500sh multicolored   9.50 9.50

Elephants
A123

Designs: 10sh, 15sh, 25sh, 100sh, Various
pictures of elephas maximus. 30sh, 35sh,
200sh, Various pictures of loxodonta africana.
400sh, Mammut mammuthus.

Perf. 12x12½, 12½x12
1991, Nov. 28   Litho.
792 A123 10sh multi, vert.   .60   .60
793 A123 15sh multi, vert.   .60   .60
794 A123 25sh multi, vert.   .90   .90
795 A123 30sh multi, vert.   1.25 1.25
796 A123 35sh multicolored   1.50 1.50

797 A123 100sh multicolored   4.00 4.00
798 A123 200sh multicolored   7.50 7.50
       Nos. 792-798 (7)   16.35 16.35
Souvenir Sheet
799 A123 400sh multicolored   7.25 7.25

Locomotives — A124

1991, Dec. 10   Perf. 12½x12, 12x12½
800 A124 10sh USSR 1930   .25   .25
801 A124 15sh Japan 1964   .25   .25
802 A124 25sh Russia 1834,
                vert.   .40   .40
803 A124 35sh France 1979   .65   .65
804 A124 60sh France 1972   1.10 1.10
805 A124 100sh United Kingdom
                1972   1.60 1.60
806 A124 300sh Russia 1837,
                vert.   5.25 5.25
       Nos. 800-806 (7)   9.50 9.50

Souvenir Sheet
807 A124 100sh France, 1952,
                vert.   2.50 2.50

Entertainers — A125

Nos. 808a-808i, 812, Various portraits of
Elvis Presley.
Nos. 809a-809i, 813, Various portraits of
Marilyn Monroe.
Nos. 810a-810i, 814, Various portraits of
Bruce Lee.
Black entertainers: No. 811: a, Scott Joplin.
b, Sammy Davis, Jr. c, Joan Armatrading. d,
Louis Armstrong. e, Miriam Makeba. f, Lionel
Ritchie. g, Whitney Houston, h, Bob Marley. i,
Tina Turner. No. 815, Kouyate family.

1992, Feb. 15   Perf. 14
808 A125 75sh Sheet of 9,
          #a.-i.   9.75 9.75
809 A125 75sh Sheet of 9,
          #a.-i.   9.75 9.75
810 A125 75sh Sheet of 9,
          #a.-i.   9.75 9.75
811 A125 75sh Sheet of 9,
          #a.-i.   9.75 9.75
       Nos. 808-811 (4)   39.00 39.00

Souvenir Sheets
812 A125 500sh multicolored   8.75 8.75
813 A125 500sh multicolored   8.75 8.75
814 A125 500sh multicolored   8.75 8.75
815 A125 500sh multicolored   8.75 8.75
       Nos. 812-815 (4)   35.00 35.00

Nos. 812-815 each contain one 29x43mm
stamp.
See #949 for #808 inscribed "15th
Anniversary."

Fish of
Tanzania
A126

Designs: 10sh, Malacanthus latovittatus.
15sh, Lamprologus tretocephalus. 25sh, Lamprologus calvus. 35sh, Hemichromis bimacu-
latusl. 60sh, Aphyosemion bivittatum. No. 821,
Synanceia verrucosa. 300sh, Aphyosemion
ahli. No. 823, Regalecus glesne.

1992, Mar. 8   Perf. 12½x12
816 A126 10sh multicolored   .55   .55
817 A126 15sh multicolored   .70   .70
818 A126 25sh multicolored   .90   .90

819 A126 35sh multicolored   1.10 1.10
820 A126 60sh multicolored   1.50 1.50
821 A126 200sh multicolored   2.00 2.00
822 A126 300sh multicolored   5.25 5.25
       Nos. 816-822 (7)   12.00 12.00

Souvenir Sheet
823 A126 100sh multicolored   3.00 3.00

World War II
in the Pacific
A127

Designs: No. 824a, British-designed radar
at Pearl Harbor. b, Churchill declares war on
Japan. c, Repulse destroyed. d, Prince of
Wales sunk. e, Singapore falls to Japanese. f,
Hermes is sunk off Ceylon. g, Airfields in
Malaya attacked. h, Hong Kong falls to Japa-
nese. i, Japanese Daihatsu landing craft. j,
Japanese cruiser Haguro in Java Sea.

1992, Apr. 27   Perf. 14½x15
824 A127 75sh Sheet of 10,
          #a.-j.   22.50 22.50

Visits of Pope
John Paul
II — A128

No. 825, 100sh: a, Dominican Republic,
1979. b, Mexico, 1979. c, Poland, 1979. d,
Ireland, 1979. e, UN, New York, 1979. f, US,
1979. g, Turkey, 1979. h, Zaire, 1980. i,
Congo, 1980. j, Kenya, 1980. k, Ghana, 1980.
l, Upper Volta, 1980.
No. 826, 100sh: a, Ivory Coast, 1980. b,
France, 1980. c, Brazil, 1980. d, West Ger-
many, 1980. e, Pakistan, 1981. f, Philippines,
1981. g, Guam, 1981. h, Japan, 1981. h,
Alaska, 1981. i, Nigeria, 1982. j, Benin, 1982.
l. Gabon, 1982.
No. 827, 100sh: a, Equatorial Guinea, 1982.
b, Portugal, 1982. c, Great Britain, 1982. d,
Argentina, 1982. e, UN, Geneva, 1982. f, San
Marino, 1982. g, Spain, 1982. h, Costa Rica,
1983. i, Panama, 1983. j, El Salvador, 1983. k,
Nicaragua, 1983. l, Guatemala, 1983.
No. 828, 100sh: a, Honduras, 1983. b,
Belize, 1983. c, Haiti, 1983. d, Poland, 1983.
e, France, 1983. f, Austria, 1983. g, Alaska,
1984. h, South Korea, 1984. i, Papua New
Guinea, 1984. j, Solomon Islands, 1984. k,
Thailand, 1984. l, Switzerland, 1984.
No. 829, 100sh: a, Canada, 1984. b, Domin-
ican Republic, 1984. c, Puerto Rico, 1984. d,
Venezuela, 1985. e, Ecuador, 1985. f, Peru,
1985. g, Trinidad & Tobago, 1985. h, Netherlands, 1985. i, Luxembourg, 1985. j, Belgium,
1985. k, Togo, 1985. l, Ivory Coast, 1985.
No. 830, 100sh: a, Cameroun, 1985. b,
Central African Republic, 1985. c, Zaire, 1985.
d, Kenya, 1985. e, Morocco, 1985. f, Liechten-
stein, 1985. g, India, 1986. h, Colombia, 1986.
i, St. Lucia, 1986. j, France, 1986. k, Bangladesh, 1986. l, Singapore, 1986.
No. 831, 100sh: a, Fiji, 1986. b, New Zealand, 1986. c, Australia, 1986. d, Seychelles,
1986. e, Uruguay, 1987. f, Chile, 1987. g,
Argentina, 1987. h, West Germany, 1987. i,
Poland, 1987. j, US, 1987. k, Canada, 1987. l,
Uruguay, 1988.
No. 832, 100sh: a, Bolivia, 1988. b, Peru,
1988. c, Paraguay, 1988. d, Austria, 1988. e,
Zimbabwe, 1988. f, Botswana, 1988. g,
Lesotho, 1988. h, Swaziland, 1988. i,
Mozambique, 1988. j, France, 1988. k, Mada-
gascar, 1989. l, France, 1989.
No. 833, 100sh: a, Zambia, 1989. b, Malawi,
1989. c, Norway, 1989. d, Iceland, 1989. e,
Finland, 1989. f, Denmark, 1989. g, Sweden,
1989. h, Spain, 1989. i, South Korea, 1989. j,
Indonesia, 1989. k, Mauritius, 1989. l, Cape
Verde, 1990.
No. 834, 100sh: a, Mali, 1990. b, Guinea-
Bissau, 1990. c, Burkina Faso, 1990. d, Chad,
1990. e, Czechoslovakia, 1990. f, Mexico,
1990. g, Curacao, 1990. h, Malta, 1990. i,
Tanzania, 1990. j, Burundi, 1990. k, Rwanda,
1990. l, Ivory Coast, 1990.

1992, Apr. 13   Perf. 14
Sheets of 12 + 4 Labels
825-834 A128 Set of 10   200.00 200.00

Zanzibar
Stone
Town
A129

Designs: No. 839a, 150sh, Old fort. b, 300sh, Maruhubi ruins.

1992, Apr. 15 *Perf. 12x12½, 12½x12*
835	A129	10sh	Balcony	.60 .60
836	A129	20sh	Bahlnara mosque	1.40 1.40
837	A129	30sh	High Court bldg.	2.00 2.00
838	A129	200sh	Natl. museum	8.00 8.00
		Nos. 835-838 (4)		12.00 12.00

Souvenir Sheet
839	A129	Sheet of 2, #a.-b.		10.00 10.00

Nos. 835-837 are vert.

Wolfgang
Amadeus
Mozart,
Death
Bicent.
A130

Designs: 10sh, Marcella Sembrich as Zerlina in Don Giovanni. 50sh, Symphony Number 41, Jupiter. 300sh, Luciano Pavarotti as Idamente in Idomeneo. 500sh, Wolfgang Amadeus Mozart, vert.

1992, Aug. 1 *Perf. 14*
840	A130	10sh	violet & blk	1.50 1.50
841	A130	50sh	multicolored	3.50 3.50
842	A130	300sh	violet & blk	8.00 8.00
		Nos. 840-842 (3)		13.00 13.00

Souvenir Sheet
843	A130	500sh	olive brn & blk	13.00 13.00

While No. 843 has the same issue date as Nos. 840-842, the dollar value was lower when it were released.
No. 843 contains one 38x50mm stamp.

1992, Aug. 1

Designs: 10sh, Insignia, giraffe and elephant. 15sh, Scouts in canoe. 400sh, John Glenn's Gemini space capsule orbiting Earth. 500sh, Boy scout, vert.

844	A130	10sh	multicolored	.45 .45
845	A130	15sh	multicolored	.45 .45
846	A130	400sh	multicolored	10.50 10.50
		Nos. 844-846 (3)		11.40 11.40

Souvenir Sheet
847	A130	500sh	multicolored	8.50 8.50

Lord Robert Baden-Powell, Founder of Boy Scouts, 50th Death Anniv. (in 1991).
While No. 847 has the same issue date as Nos. 844-846, the dollar value was lower when it were released.
No. 847 contains one 38x50mm stamp.

1992, Aug. 1

Charles de Gaulle (1890-1970): 25sh, French Resistance Monument and medal. 30sh, First Free French tank at Omaha beach, Normandy. 150sh, Concorde at de Gaulle Airport. 500sh, France #439 with Cross of Lorraine overprint and Free French stamp, vert.

848	A130	25sh	multicolored	.90 .90
849	A130	30sh	multicolored	1.00 1.00
850	A130	150sh	multicolored	10.00 10.00
		Nos. 848-850 (3)		11.90 11.90

Souvenir Sheet
851	A130	500sh	multicolored	13.00 13.00

While No. 851 has the same issue date as Nos. 848-850, the dollar value was lower when it was released.
No. 851 contains one 38x50mm stamp.

Common
Chimpanzee
A131

Various chimpanzees in natural habitat.

1992
852	A131	10sh	multicolored	.35 .35
853	A131	15sh	multicolored	.35 .35
854	A131	35sh	multicolored	.85 .85
855	A131	75sh	multicolored	1.90 1.90
856	A131	100sh	multicolored	2.25 2.25
857	A131	150sh	multicolored	3.50 3.50
858	A131	200sh	multicolored	4.50 4.50
859	A131	300sh	multicolored	7.00 7.00
		Nos. 852-859 (8)		20.70 20.70

Souvenir Sheets
860	A131	400sh	Swinging from tree	6.25 6.25
861	A131	400sh	Eating termites	6.25 6.25

Spanish Art — A132

Drawings by Goya: 25sh, A Picador mounted on the shoulders of a Chulo, spears a Bull. 100sh, The Dream of Reason brings forth Monsters, vert. 150sh, Another Madness (of Martincho) in the Plaza de Zaragoza. 200sh, Recklessness of Martincho in the Plaza de Zaragoza.
No. 866, Seascape, by Mariano Salvador Maella.

1992 *Perf. 13*
862	A132	25sh	blk & red brn	.50 .50
863	A132	100sh	black & brn	1.75 1.75
864	A132	150sh	blk & red brn	2.75 2.75
865	A132	300sh	blk & red brn	3.00 3.00

Size: 120x95mm
Imperf
866	A132	400sh	multicolored	5.00 5.00
		Nos. 862-866 (5)		13.00 13.00

Granada '92.

1992 *Perf. 13*

Drawings by Diego da Silva Velazquez: 35sh, Philip IV at Fraga. 50sh, The Head of the Stag. 75sh, The Cardinal Infante Don Fernando as a Hunter. 300sh, Pablo de Valladolid. No. 871, Two Men at Table.

867	A132	35sh	multicolored	.75 .75
868	A132	50sh	multicolored	.90 .90
869	A132	75sh	multicolored	1.40 1.40
870	A132	300sh	multicolored	4.00 4.00

Size: 120x95mm
Imperf
871	A132	400sh	multicolored	5.50 5.50
		Nos. 867-871 (5)		12.55 12.55

Granada '92.

A133

Chimpanzees of
Gombe — A134

Designs: No. 872, Melisa and Mike. No. 873, Leakey and David Greybeard. No. 874, Fifi eating termites. No. 875 Galahad.
No. 876a, 10sh, Leakey. b, 15sh, Fifi. c, 20sh, Faben. d, 30sh, David Greybeard. e, 35sh, Mike. f, 50sh, Galahad. g, 100sh, Melisa. h, 200sh, Flo.
No. 877, Fifi, Flo, and Faben.

1992, May 29 Litho. *Perf. 14*
872	A133	10sh	multicolored	1.00 1.00
873	A133	15sh	multicolored	1.25 1.25
874	A133	30sh	multicolored	1.75 1.75
875	A133	35sh	multicolored	2.00 2.00
		Nos. 872-875 (4)		6.00 6.00

Miniature Sheet
876	A134	Sheet of 8, #a.-h.		12.00 12.00

Souvenir Sheet
877	A133	100sh	multicolored	4.50 4.50

Natl. Bank of Commerce, 25th
Anniv. — A135

Designs: 10sh, Sorghum plants. 15sh, Samora Avenue branch, computer operator, vert. 30sh, Head office. 35sh, Bankers Training Center. 40sh, Batik tie dyeing.

1992, June 22
878	A135	10sh	multicolored	.70 .70
879	A135	15sh	multicolored	.80 .80
880	A135	35sh	multicolored	1.25 1.25
881	A135	40sh	multicolored	1.25 1.25
		Nos. 878-881 (4)		4.00 4.00

Souvenir Sheet
882	A135	30sh	multicolored	2.50 2.50

Traditional
Dress — A136

Designs: 3sh, Gogo, central area. 5sh, Swahili, coastal area. 9sh, Hehe, southern highlands and Makonde, southern area. 12sh, Maasai, northern area. 40sh, Mwarusha.

1992, Apr. 30 Litho. *Perf. 14½*
883	A136	3sh	multicolored	.80 .80
884	A136	5sh	multicolored	.90 .90
885	A136	9sh	multicolored	1.10 1.10
886	A136	12sh	multicolored	1.40 1.40
		Nos. 883-886 (4)		4.20 4.20

Souvenir Sheet
887	A136	40sh	multicolored	4.50 4.50

Dated 1989.

1992 Summer
Olympics,
Barcelona
A137

1992, July 23 *Perf. 12x12½*
888	A137	40sh	Basketball	.80 .80
889	A137	100sh	Billiards	1.25 1.25
890	A137	200sh	Table tennis	2.00 2.00
891	A137	400sh	Darts	4.25 4.25
		Nos. 888-891 (4)		8.30 8.30

Souvenir Sheet
892	A137	500sh	Weight lifting	6.00 6.00

Fish
A138

No. 893: a, Tilapia mariae. b, Capoeta hulstaerti. c, Tropheus moorii. d, Synodontis angelicus. e, Julidochromis dickfeldi. f, Tilapia nilotica. g, Nothobranchius rachovii. h, Pseudotropheus crabro. i, Lamprologus leleupi. j, Pseudotropheus zebra. k, Julidochromis marlieri. l, Chalinochromis brichardi.
Designs: No. 894, Haplochromis "electric blue." No. 895, Lamprologus brevis. No. 896, Nothobranchius palmqvisti.

1992, Oct. Litho. *Perf. 13½*
893	A138	100sh	Sheet of 12, #a.-l.	19.00 19.00

Souvenir Sheets
894	A138	500sh	multicolored	6.50 6.50
895	A138	500sh	multicolored	6.50 6.50
896	A138	500sh	multicolored	6.50 6.50

Discovery
of
America,
500th
Anniv.
A139

1992, Oct. Litho. *Perf. 14*
897	A139	70sh	Sailing ship	1.75 1.75
898	A139	300sh	Columbus	6.00 6.00

Souvenir Sheet
899	A139	500sh	Columbus, diff.	5.00 5.00

Miniature Sheet

Flowers in Rio de
Janeiro Botanical
Garden — A140

No. 900: a, Couroupita guianensis. b, Jacaranda acutifolia. c, Psychopsis papilio. d, Nelumbo nucifera. e, Brownea grandiceps. f, Coffea arabica. g, Monodora myristica. h, Calaranthus rosea. i, Hibiscus schizopetalus. j, Carpobrotus edulis. k, Adenium obesum. l, Delonix regia. m, Agapanthus praecox. n, Zantedeschia aethiopica. o, Protea cynaroides. p, Cassia fistula. q, Aganisia cyanea. r, Heliconia rostrata. s, Cattelya luteola. t, Lagerstroemia speciosa.
500sh, Avenue of Royal Palms, Rio.

1992, Nov. 5 Litho. *Perf. 14½*
900	A140	70sh	Sheet of 20, #a.-t.	24.00 24.00

Souvenir Sheet
901	A140	500sh	multicolored	7.50 7.50

Dinosaurs
A141

No. 902: a, Iguanodon. b, Saltasaurus. c, Cetiosaurus. d, Camarasaurus. e, Spinosaurus. f, Stegosaurus. g, Allosaurus. h, Ceratosaurus. i, Lesothosaurus. j, Anchisaurus. k, Ornithomimus. l, Baronyx. m, Pachycephalosaurus. n, Heterodontosaurus. o, Dryosaurus. p, Coelophysis.

1992, Nov. 5   Litho.   Perf. 14
902 A141 100sh Sheet of
16, #a.-p.   24.00 24.00

1992
Olympics,
Albertville
and
Barcelona
A142

Designs: 20sh, 4000-meter pursuit cycling,
vert. 40sh, Double sculls. 50sh, Water polo.
70sh, Women's single luge. 100sh, Marathon.
150sh, Uneven parallel bars. 200sh, Ice
hockey, vert, 400sh, Rings, vert.
No. 911, Tennis, vert. No. 912, Soccer, vert.

1992, Nov. 16   Litho.   Perf. 14
903 A142 20sh multicolored   .35   .35
904 A142 40sh multicolored   .55   .55
905 A142 50sh multicolored   .60   .60
906 A142 70sh multicolored   .85   .85
907 A142 100sh multicolored   1.25   1.25
908 A142 150sh multicolored   1.75   1.75
909 A142 200sh multicolored   2.40   2.40
910 A142 400sh multicolored   4.75   4.75
    Nos. 903-910 (8)   12.50 12.50

Souvenir Sheets
911 A142 500sh multicolored   7.25   7.25
912 A142 500sh multicolored   7.25   7.25

Mickey's
Portrait
Gallery
A142a

Donald Duck in scenes from Disney movies:
No. 915, Sea Scouts, 1939. 35sh, Fire Chief,
1940. 50sh, Truant Officer Donald, 1941.
500sh, With Daisy in Mr. Duck Steps Out,
1940.
No. 925, Daisy in Don Donald, 1937.
Disney characters in scenes from Disney
movies: No. 913, Hawaiian Holiday, 1937. No.
914, Society Dog Show, 1939. 75sh, Clock
Cleaners, 1937. No. 919, Magician Mickey,
1937. No. 920, Goofy and Wilbur, 1939.
200sh, The Nifty Nineties, 1941. 300sh, Society Dog Show, 1939. 400sh, Pluto's Quin-
Puplets, 1937. No. 926, Brave Little Tailor,
1938, horiz. No. 927, Forever Goofy.

1992, Nov. 30   Litho.   Perf. 13½x14
913 A142a 25sh multicolored   .50   .50
914 A142a 25sh multicolored   .50   .50
915 A142a 25sh multicolored   .50   .50
916 A142a 35sh multicolored   .65   .65
917 A142a 50sh multicolored   .90   .90
918 A142a 75sh multicolored   1.10   1.10
919 A142a 100sh multicolored   1.25   1.25
920 A142a 100sh multicolored   1.25   1.25
921 A142a 200sh multicolored   2.00   2.00
922 A142a 300sh multicolored   2.75   2.75
923 A142a 400sh multicolored   3.00   3.00
924 A142a 500sh multicolored   3.00   3.00
    Nos. 913-924 (12)   17.40 17.40

Souvenir Sheets
925 A142a 600sh multicolored   6.00   6.00

Perf. 14x13½
926 A142a 600sh multicolored   6.00   6.00

Perf. 13½x14
927 A142a 600sh multicolored   6.00   6.00

Nos. 668-
673 &
678
Ovptd. in
Black or
Red

1992   Litho.   Perf. 14
928 A106 50sh on #668   .35   .35
929 A106 50sh on #669   .35   .35
  a.   Pair, #928-929   .70   .70
930 A106 75sh on #670   .55   .55
931 A106 75sh on #671   .55   .55
  a.   Pair, #930-931   1.10   1.10

---

932 A106 100sh on #672   .75   .75
933 A106 100sh on #673   .75   .75
  a.   Pair, #932-933   1.50   1.50
    Nos. 928-933 (6)   3.30   3.30

Souvenir Sheet
934 A106 350sh on #678 (R)   2.50   2.50
    Overprint appears on one line in sheet mar-
gin of No. 934.

Traditional
Hunting
A143

Designs: 20sh, Slingshots used on birds.
40sh, Various weapons. 70sh, Bow and arrow
used on gazelles. 100sh, Long knife, wooden
club used on gazelles. 150sh, Spear and
shield used on lion.

1992   Litho.   Perf. 13½
935 A143 20sh multicolored   1.40   1.40
936 A143 70sh multicolored   1.75   1.75
937 A143 100sh multicolored   3.00   3.00
938 A143 150sh multicolored   4.25   4.25
    Nos. 935-938 (4)   10.40 10.40

Souvenir Sheet
Perf. 12½
939 A143 40sh multicolored   3.25   3.25

Shells — A144

Designs: 10sh, Lambis truncata Humphrey.
15sh, Cypraecassis rufa. 25sh, Vexillum
rugosum. 30sh, Conus litteratus. 35sh,
Corculum cardissa. 50sh, Murex ramosus.
250sh, Melo melo. 300sh, Tridacha gigas.

1992, June 30   Perf. 12x12½
940 A144 10sh multicolored   .45   .45
941 A144 15sh multicolored   .55   .55
942 A144 25sh multicolored   .75   .75
943 A144 30sh multicolored   .75   .75
944 A144 35sh multicolored   .75   .75
945 A144 50sh multicolored   1.10   1.10
946 A144 250sh multicolored   4.50   4.50
    Nos. 940-946 (7)   8.85   8.85

Souvenir Sheet
947 A144 300sh multicolored   6.00   6.00

No. 808 Inscribed Vertically "15th
Anniversary"

1992   Litho.   Perf. 14
949 A125 75sh Sheet of 9,
#a.-i.   12.00 12.00

Marine
Life
A145

1992   Litho.   Perf. 14
950 A145 20sh Seal   1.00   1.00
951 A145 30sh Whale   2.50   2.50
952 A145 70sh Shark   1.50   1.50
953 A145 100sh Walrus   2.50   2.50
    Nos. 950-953 (4)   7.50   7.50

Souvenir Sheet
954 A145 500sh Sea turtle   9.25   9.25

A146

Anniversaries and
Events — A147

Designs: 30sh, Count Ferdinand von
Zeppelin. 70sh, Apollo-Soyuz. No. 957, Child
being offered apple. No. 958, African elephant.
No. 959, Lions Intl. emblem, man being given
glasses. No. 960, Zebra. 300sh, Graf
Zeppelin. No. 962, Space shuttle in Earth
orbit. No. 963, Wolfgang Amadeus Mozart.
No. 964, Voyager 2. No. 965, Unidentified
zeppelin. No. 966, African elephant, diff. No.
967, Scene from "The Magic Flute."

1992   Litho.   Perf. 14
955 A146 30sh multicolored   3.25   3.25
956 A146 70sh multicolored   4.50   4.50
957 A146 150sh multicolored   2.00   2.00
958 A146 150sh multicolored   3.25   3.25
959 A146 200sh multicolored   2.40   2.40
960 A146 200sh multicolored   3.25   3.25
961 A146 300sh multicolored   3.25   3.25
962 A146 400sh multicolored   4.50   4.50
963 A147 400sh multicolored   3.25   3.25
    Nos. 955-963 (9)   29.65 29.65

Souvenir Sheets
964 A146 500sh multicolored   4.50   4.50
965 A146 500sh multicolored   4.50   4.50
966 A146 500sh multicolored   4.50   4.50
967 A147 800sh multicolored   6.50   6.50

Count Zeppelin, 75th death anniv. (#955,
961, 965). Intl. Space Year (#956, 962, 964).
Intl. Conference on Nutrition (#957). Earth
Summit, Rio de Janeiro (#958, 960, 966).
Lions Intl., 75th anniv. (#959). Wolfgang
Amadeus Mozart, bicent. of death (in 1991)
(#963, 967).
Issued: Nos. 955-956, 961-962, 964-965,
Nov.; Nos. 957-960, 966, Dec.

Cats — A147a

1992, Dec. 3   Litho.   Perf. 12x12½
967A A147a 20sh Abyssini-
an   .85   .85
967B A147a 30sh Havana   .85   .85
967C A147a 50sh Persian
black   1.00   1.00
967D A147a 70sh Persian
blue   1.25   1.25
967E A147a 100sh European
silver
tabby   1.50   1.50
967F A147a 150sh Persian
silver
tabby   1.75   1.75
967G A147a 200sh Maine   2.25   2.25
    Nos. 967A-967G (7)   9.45   9.45

Souvenir Sheet
967H A147a 300sh European   5.00   5.00

Model
Trains
A148

Lionel models: 10sh, B & O Tunnel locomotive #5, 2⅞-inch gauge, 1904. 20sh, Liberty
Bell #385E, standard gauge, 1930. 30sh,
Armored motor car #203, standard gauge,
1917. 50sh, Open trolley #202, standard
gauge, 1910-14. 70sh, Macy special #450,
standard gauge. 100sh, Milwaukee Road bi-
polar electric #381E, standard gauge, 1929.
200sh, New York Central "S" type, standard
gauge, 1912. 300sh, 4-4-0 American #7 (thick
rim), standard gauge, 1914.
No. 976, Wind-up hand car with Mickey and
Minnie Mouse, O-27 gauge, 1936. No. 977,
Clear plastic F-3 display model, O gauge,
1947.

1992, Dec. 10   Litho.   Perf. 14
968 A148 10sh multicolored   .65   .65
969 A148 20sh multicolored   .75   .75
970 A148 30sh multicolored   .80   .80
971 A148 50sh multicolored   1.25   1.25
972 A148 70sh multicolored   1.50   1.50
973 A148 100sh multicolored   1.60   1.60
974 A148 200sh multicolored   2.25   2.25
975 A148 300sh multicolored   3.00   3.00
    Nos. 968-975 (8)   11.80 11.80

Souvenir Sheets
976 A148 500sh multicolored   5.00   5.00
977 A148 500sh multicolored   5.00   5.00

Genoa '92.

Birds — A149

1992, Dec. 10   Litho.   Perf. 12x12½
978 A149   5sh Superb starling   .90   .90
979 A149 10sh Canary   1.10   1.10
980 A149 15sh Four-colored
bush shrike   1.10   1.10
981 A149 25sh Grey-headed
kingfisher   1.25   1.25
982 A149 30sh Common kingfisher   1.25   1.25
983 A149 35sh Yellow-billed ox-
pecker   1.25   1.25
984 A149 150sh Black throated
honeyquide   3.00   3.00
    Nos. 978-984 (7)   9.85   9.85

Souvenir Sheet
Perf. 12½x12
985 A149 300sh European cuckoo, horiz.   5.50   5.50

Makonde
Art — A149a

Various carved faces.

1992, Dec. 24   Litho.   Perf. 12x12½
985A A149a 20sh multicolored   .30   .30
985B A149a 30sh multicolored   .30   .30
985C A149a 50sh multicolored   .50   .50
985D A149a 70sh multicolored   .70   .70
985E A149a 100sh multicolored   1.00   1.00
985F A149a 150sh multicolored   1.50   1.50
985G A149a 200sh multicolored   2.00   2.00
    Nos. 985A-985G (7)   6.30   6.30

Souvenir Sheet
985H A149a 350sh multicolored   5.00   5.00

Bicycles
A149b

1992, Dec. 30   Litho.   Perf. 12½x12
985I A149b 20sh Russia,
1813   .45   .45
985J A149b 30sh Germany,
1840   .45   .45
985K A149b 50sh Germany,
1818   .65   .65
985L A149b 70sh Germany,
1850   .65   .65
985M A149b 100sh Italy, 1988   .70   .70
985N A149b 150sh Sweden,
1982   1.50   1.50
985O A149b 300sh Italy, 1989   1.75   1.75
    Nos. 985I-985O (7)   6.15   6.15

Souvenir Sheet
985P A149b 350sh Great Britain, 1887   5.00   5.00

Discovery of America, 500th Anniv. — A150

Designs: 10sh, Symbols of luck. 15sh, "Is this course right?," compass, chart. 25sh, "Earth!," first sight of land. 30sh, First meetings, horiz. 35sh, Nina, horiz. 75sh, Santa Maria, horiz. 250sh, Ship running aground, vert. 200sh, Columbus.

Perf. 12x12½, 12½x12
1992, Sept. 30   **Litho.**
986 A150 10sh multicolored .35 .35
987 A150 15sh multicolored .40 .40
988 A150 25sh multicolored .55 .55
989 A150 30sh multicolored .60 .60
990 A150 35sh multicolored .70 .70
991 A150 75sh multicolored 1.25 1.25
992 A150 250sh multicolored 2.25 2.25
   Nos. 986-992 (7) 6.10 6.10
Souvenir Sheet
993 A150 200sh multicolored 6.00 6.00

Louvre Museum, Bicent. A151

No. 994 — Paintings by Jean-Baptiste-Simeon Chardin (1699-1779): a, Young Artist. b, The Buffet. c, The Provider. d, A Mother Working. e, Grace. f, The Copper Fountain. g, House of Cards. h, Child with Teetotum. 500sh, The Ray, horiz.

1993, Mar. 8   **Litho.**   **Perf. 12**
994 A151 100sh Sheet of 8, #a.-h. + label 12.00 12.00
Souvenir Sheet
Perf. 14½
995 A151 500sh multicolored 6.00 6.00
No. 995 contains one 88x55mm stamp.

Coronation of Queen Elizabeth II, 40th Anniv. A152

No. 996: a, 100sh, Official coronation photograph. b, 150sh, Exeter salt. c, 200sh, Photograph of ceremony, 1953. d, 300sh, Queen, Prince Andrew.
500sh, Princess Elizabeth Opening the New Broadgate Coventry, by Dame Laura Knight, 1948.

1993, June 2   **Litho.**   **Perf. 13½x14**
996 A152 Sheet, 2 ea #a.-d. 14.00 14.00
Souvenir Sheet
Perf. 14
997 A152 500sh multicolored 6.00 6.00
No. 997 contains one 28x43mm stamp.

Famous Women — A153

Designs: a, 20sh, Valentina Tereshkova. b, 40sh, Marie Curie. c, 50sh, Indira Gandhi. d, 70sh, Wilma Rudolph. e, 100sh, Margaret Mead. f, 150sh, Golda Meir. g, 200sh, Dr. Elizabeth Blackwell. h, 400sh, Margaret Thatcher. No. 999, Mother Teresa.

1993, July 15   **Perf. 14**
998 A153 Sheet of 8, #a.-h. 17.00 17.00
Souvenir Sheet
999 A153 500sh multicolored 7.00 7.00

Wildlife — A154

No. 1000 — Wildlife at watering hole: No. 1000: a, Elephant. b, Gazelles. c, Hartebeest. d, Duiker. e, Genet. f, Civet. g, Pelicans. h, Waterbuck. i, Blacksmith plovers. j, Pied kingfisher. k, Black-winged stilts. l, Bush pig.
No. 1000M: n, Brown-hooded kingfisher. o, Sable antelope (n). p, Impala (q). q, Buffalo. r, Leopard. s, Aardvark (t). t, Hippopotamus. u, Spotted hyena. v, Crowned crane (w). w, Crocodile. x, Flamingo. y, Baboon.
No. 1001 — Wildlife on the plains: No. 1001: a, Potto. b, Flamingos. c, Grey-headed kingfisher. d, Red colobus monkey. e, Dik-dik. f, Aardwolf. g, Black-backed jackal. h, Tree pangolin. i, Serval. j, Yellow-billed hornbill. k, Pygmy mongoose. l, Bat-eared fox.
No. 1001M: n, Bushbaby. o, Egyptian vulture. p, Ostrich. q, Greater kudu. r, Diana monkey. s, Giraffe (w). t, Cheetah (s). u, Wildebeeest (t). v, Chimpanzee. w, Warthog. x, Zebra. y, Rhinoceros.
No. 1002, Lions, horiz. No. 1003, African elephants, horiz.

1993, June 30
1000 A154 100sh Sheet of 12, #a.-l. 12.00 12.00
1000M A154 100sh Sheet of 12, #n.-y. 12.00 12.00
1001 A154 100sh Sheet of 12, #a.-l. 12.00 12.00
1001M A154 100sh Sheet of 12, #n.-y. 12.00 12.00
   Nos. 1000-1001M (4) 48.00 48.00
Souvenir Sheets
1002 A154 500sh multi 6.50 6.50
1003 A154 500sh multi 6.50 6.50
For overprints see Nos. 1531, 1534.

Pancake Tortoise A155

1993, June 30
1004 A155 20sh On rock .60 .60
1005 A155 30sh Drinking .80 .80
1006 A155 50sh Crawling from under rocks 1.10 1.10
1007 A155 70sh Hatchling 1.40 1.40
   Nos. 1004-1007 (4) 3.90 3.90
World Wildlife Federation.

Mushrooms A156

Designs: 20sh, Macrolepiota rhacodes. 40sh, Mycena pura. 50sh, Chlorophyllum molybdites. 70sh, Agaricus campestris. 100sh, Volvariella volvacea. 150sh, Leucoagaricus naucinus. 200sh, Oudemansiella radicata. 300sh, Clitocybe nebularis.
No. 1016, Omphalotus olearius. No. 1017, Lepista nuda.

1993, June 18   **Litho.**   **Perf. 14**
1008 A156 20sh multicolored .35 .35
1009 A156 40sh multicolored .55 .55
1010 A156 50sh multicolored .60 .60
1011 A156 70sh multicolored .85 .85
1012 A156 100sh multicolored 1.40 1.40
1013 A156 150sh multicolored 1.75 1.75
1014 A156 200sh multicolored 2.40 2.40
1015 A156 300sh multicolored 4.00 4.00
   Nos. 1008-1015 (8) 11.90 11.90
Souvenir Sheets
1016 A156 500sh multicolored 5.00 5.00
1017 A156 500sh multicolored 5.00 5.00

Sports — A157

1992, May 28   **Litho.**   **Perf. 12x12½**
1018 A157 20sh Boxing .35 .35
1019 A157 50sh Field hockey .80 .80
1020 A157 70sh Horse racing .65 .65
1021 A157 100sh Marathon .75 .75
1022 A157 150sh Soccer .95 .95
1023 A157 200sh Diving 1.25 1.25
1024 A157 400sh Basketball 2.40 2.40
   Nos. 1018-1024 (7) 7.15 7.15
Souvenir Sheet
Perf. 12½x12
1025 A157 300sh High jump, horiz. 4.25 4.25

Animals A158

No. 1026: a, Female Grant's zebra, running. b, Male Grant's zebra, standing. c, Female Grant's gazelle. d, Male Grant's gazelle. e, Thompson's gazelle. f, White-bearded gnu, calf.
No. 1027: a, Female cheetah, cubs. b, Young cheetah. c, Lioness carrying her cub. d, Two hunting dogs. e, Three hunting dogs. f, Hunting dogs before an attack.
No. 1028, African rhinoceros. No. 1029, African elephant.

1993, June 30   **Litho.**   **Perf. 14**
1026 A158 100sh Sheet of 6, #a.-f. 9.00 9.00
1027 A158 100sh Sheet of 6, #a.-f. 9.00 9.00
Souvenir Sheets
1028 A158 500sh multicolored 10.00 10.00
1029 A158 500sh multicolored 10.00 10.00
For overprints see Nos. 1532-1533, 1535.

A159   A160

1994 Winter Olympics, Lillehammer, Norway: 300sh, Matti Nykanen, ski jumping, 1988. 400sh, Stefan Krause, Jan Behrendt, double luge, 1992. 500sh, Downhill skiing, 1972.

1993, June 10   **Litho.**   **Perf. 14**
1030 A159 300sh multicolored 2.25 2.25
1031 A159 400sh multicolored 2.75 2.75
Souvenir Sheet
1032 A159 500sh multicolored 3.50 3.50

1993, June 10
1033 A160 100sh Telescope .70 .70
1034 A160 300sh Radio telescope 2.25 2.25
Souvenir Sheet
1035 A160 500sh Copernicus 3.50 3.50
Copernicus, 450th anniv. of death.

Picasso (1881-1973) A160a

Various details of painting, Guernica, 1937.

1993, June 10   **Litho.**   **Perf. 14**
1035A A160a 30sh multi .20 .20
1035B A160a 200sh multi 1.40 1.40
1035C A160a 300sh multi 2.00 2.00
   Nos. 1035A-1035C (3) 3.60 3.60
Souvenir Sheet
1035D A160a 500sh multi 3.50 3.50

Flowers — A161   Polska '93 — A162

Designs: 20sh, Leopard orchid. 30sh, African violet. 40sh, Stapelia semota lutea. 50sh, Busy Lizzie. 60sh, Senecio petraeus. 70sh, Kalanchoe velutina. 100sh, Dwarf ginger lily. 150sh, Nymphaea colorata. 200sh, Thunbergia battiscombei. 250sh, Crossandra nilotica. 300sh, African tulip tree. 350sh, Ruttya fruticosa.
No. 1048, False African violet. No. 1049, Glory lily.

1993, Nov. 8   **Litho.**   **Perf. 13½**
1036 A161 20sh multicolored .50 .50
1037 A161 30sh multicolored .55 .55
1038 A161 40sh multicolored .55 .55
1039 A161 50sh multicolored .55 .55
1040 A161 60sh multicolored .80 .80
1041 A161 70sh multicolored .90 .90
1042 A161 100sh multicolored 1.00 1.00
1043 A161 150sh multicolored 1.60 1.60
1044 A161 200sh multicolored 1.90 1.90
1045 A161 250sh multicolored 1.90 1.90
1046 A161 300sh multicolored 2.25 2.25
1047 A161 350sh multicolored 2.25 2.25
   Nos. 1036-1047 (12) 14.75 14.75
Souvenir Sheets
Perf. 13
1048 A161 500sh multicolored 4.50 4.50
1049 A161 500sh multicolored 4.50 4.50

1993   **Litho.**   **Perf. 14**

Paintings: 200sh, Stone Masons, by Aleksander Kobzdej, 1952. 300sh, Child Wearing Plumed Helmut, by Z. Waliszewski, 1932.

500sh, In the Marketplace, by Stanislaw Ossotowicz, 1939.

| 1050 | A162 | 200sh multicolored | 1.75 | 1.75 |
| 1051 | A162 | 300sh multicolored | 2.50 | 2.50 |

Souvenir Sheet

| 1052 | A162 | 500sh multicolored | 3.75 | 3.75 |

Butterflies
A163

No. 1053: a, Gold-banded forester. b, Twin dotted border. c, Aphnaeus flavescens. d, Orange-and-lemon. e, Club-tailed charaxes. f, Broad blue-banded swallowtail. g, African map. h, Buxton's hairstreak. i, Bush charaxes. j, Lilac nymph. k, Large striped swordtail. l, Charaxes acuminatus. m, African leaf. n, African wood white. o, Trimen's false acraea. p, Red line sapphire. q, Mother-of-pearl. r, Flame-bordered charaxes. s, Large blue charaxes. t, Emperor swallowtail.

No. 1054: a, Angled grass yellow. b, Figtree blue. c, Iolaus ismenias. d, Green-veined charaxes. e, Commodore. f, African monarch. g, Bush scarlet. h, Eyed pansy. i, Zebra white. j, Azure hairstreak. k, Yellow pansy. l, Regal purple tip.

No. 1054M: n, Iolaus aphnaeoides. o, Green charaxes. p, Beautiful monarch. q, Short-tailed admiral. r, Dusky dotted border. s, Charaxes anticlea. t, Blue salamis. u, Nepheronia argia. v, Acraea pseudolycia. w, Blue-banded diadem. x, Golden tip. y, Acraea bonasia.

No. 1055, Blood-red cymothoe. No. 1056, Precis octavia. No. 1056A, Noble swallowtail. No. 1056B, Violet-spotted charaxes.

1993, Nov. 8   **Litho.**   **Perf. 13**

1053	A163	100sh Sheet of 20, #a.-t.	30.00	30.00
1054	A163	100sh Sheet of 12, #a.-l.	20.00	20.00
1054M	A163	100sh Sheet of 12, #n.-y.	20.00	20.00

Souvenir Sheets

1055	A163	500sh multi	7.00	7.00
1056	A163	500sh multi	7.00	7.00
1056A	A163	500sh multi	7.00	7.00
1056B	A163	500sh multi	7.00	7.00

A164   A165

Players, country: 20sh, Gullit, Holland. 30sh, Sheehy, Ireland. 50sh, Giannini, Italy. 70sh, Cesar, Brazil. 250sh, Barnes, England; Grun, Belgium. 300sh, Chendo, Spain. 350sh, Rijkaard, Holland. 400sh, Matthaeus, Germany.

No. 1065, 500sh, Berti, Italy; Caligiuri, US. No. 1066, 500sh, Walker, England; Gilhaus, Holland.

1993, Dec.   **Perf. 14**

| 1057-1064 | A164 | Set of 8 | 9.50 | 9.50 |

Souvenir Sheets

| 1065-1066 | A164 | Set of 2 | 9.50 | 9.50 |

1994 World Cup Soccer Championships, US.

1994, Feb. 10

Hummel Figurines: 20sh, Boy with accordian. 40sh, Girl with guitar, boy with banjo. 50sh, Boy with tuba. 70sh, Boy with harmonica, bird. 100sh, Bird in tree, boy seated on fence. 150sh, Boy playing horn. 200sh, Boy with horn, bird. 300sh, Girl playing banjo. 350sh, Boy with cello on back. 400sh, Girls with banjo and sheet music.

No. 1077, 500sh, Four carolers. No. 1078, 500sh, Two figures in tower blowing horns at angel below.

| 1067-1076 | A165 | Set of 10 | 12.50 | 12.50 |

Souvenir Sheets

| 1077-1078 | A165 | Set of 2 | 11.00 | 11.00 |

Black
Athletes — A166

No. 1079: a, 20sh, Arthur Ashe. b, 40sh, Michael Jordan. c, 50sh, Daley Thompson. d, 70sh, Jackie Robinson. e, 100sh, Kareem Abdul-Jabbar. f, 150sh, Florence Joyner. g, 200sh, Jesse Owens. h, 400sh, Jack Johnson. 500sh, Muhammad Ali, horiz.

1993, July 15

| 1079 | A166 | Sheet of 8, #a.-h. | 9.00 | 9.00 |

Souvenir Sheet

| 1080 | A166 | 500sh multicolored | 5.50 | 5.50 |

First US
Gas
Balloon
Flight,
Bicent.
A167

Designs: 200sh, Balloons filling with hot air. 400sh, Jean-Pierre Blanchard (1753-1809), balloon. 500sh, Hot air balloons in flight, vert.

1994, Apr. 25   **Litho.**   **Perf. 14**

| 1081 | A167 | 200sh multicolored | 2.25 | 2.25 |
| 1082 | A167 | 400sh multicolored | 4.25 | 4.25 |

Souvenir Sheet

| 1083 | A167 | 500sh multicolored | 6.50 | 6.50 |

Royal Air
Force,
75th
Anniv.
A168

Designs: 200sh, Sopwith Camel. 400sh, BAE Harrier. 500sh, Supermarine Spitfire.

1993, Dec.

| 1084 | A168 | 200sh multicolored | 2.75 | 2.75 |
| 1085 | A168 | 400sh multicolored | 5.25 | 5.25 |

Souvenir Sheet

| 1086 | A168 | 500sh multicolored | 7.00 | 7.00 |

Automotive Anniversaries — A171

Designs: No. 1099, 200sh, 1893 Benz, 1993 500 SEL. No. 1100, 200sh, Henry Ford, 1922 Model T. No. 1101, 400sh, Karl Benz, emblem. No. 1102, 400sh, 1893 Ford, Mustang Cobra.

No. 1103, 500sh, Emblem, 1937 540 K. No. 1104, 500sh, Henry Ford, first Ford factory.

1994, Apr. 25   **Litho.**   **Perf. 14**

| 1099-1102 | A171 | Set of 4 | 11.00 | 11.00 |

Souvenir Sheets

| 1103-1104 | A171 | Set of 2 | 10.00 | 10.00 |

First Benz 4-wheel motor car, cent. (#1099, 1101, 1103). First Ford motor, cent. (#1100, 1102, 1104).

Birds
A172

No. 1105, vert.: a, 20sh, African hawk eagle. b, 30sh, Shoe-bill stork. c, 50sh, Harrier eagle. d, 70sh, Casqued hornbill. e, 100sh, Crowned crane. f, 150sh, Greater flamingo.

No. 1106: a, 200sh, Pelican. b, 250sh, Jacana, black crake. c, 300sh, Ostrich. d, 350sh, Helmeted guinea fowl. e, 400sh, Malachite kingfisher. f, 500sh, Saddle-billed stork.

1994, May 11

| 1105 | A172 | Sheet of 6, #a.-f. | 10.50 | 10.50 |
| 1106 | A172 | Sheet of 6, #a.-f. | 12.50 | 12.50 |

Hong
Kong '94
A173

Red-cap white pearl-scale goldfish and: No. 1107, Scarus ghobban. No. 1108, Regal angelfish.

1994, Feb. 18

1107	A173	350sh multicolored	2.25	2.25
1108	A173	350sh multicolored	2.25	2.25
a.		Pair, #1107-1108	4.50	4.50

Nos. 1107-1108 issued in sheets of 5 pairs. No. 1108a is a continuous design.

Mickey Mouse, 65th Anniv. — A176

Disney characters on tour: 10sh, Boarding plane. 20sh, Dancing, Tonga. 30sh, Lawn bowling, Australia. 40sh, Building igloo, Arctic region. 50sh, Royal Palace Guard, London. 60sh, Esna bazaar, Egypt. 70sh, Zsambox cowboys, Hungary, vert. 100sh, Grand Canal, Venice, vert. 150sh, Dancing, Bali, Indonesia, vert. 200sh, Monks studying text, Bangkok, Thailand, vert. 300sh, Water skiing, Taj Mahal, India, vert. 400sh, Himalayas, Nepal.

No. 1125, Kilimanjaro Uhuru Peak, Kibo, Tanzania, vert. No. 1126, Kigoma railway station, Dar es Salaam, Tanzania, vert. No. 1127, Memorial to Dr. Livingstone, shores of Lake Tanganyika, Tanzania.

1994, Apr. 6   **Perf. 14x13½, 13½x14**

1113	A176	10sh multicolored	.35	.35
1114	A176	20sh multicolored	.35	.35
1115	A176	30sh multicolored	.35	.35
1116	A176	40sh multicolored	.55	.55
1117	A177	50sh multicolored	.60	.60
1118	A176	60sh multicolored	.65	.65
1119	A176	70sh multicolored	.85	.85
1120	A176	100sh multicolored	1.25	1.25
1121	A176	150sh multicolored	1.75	1.75
1122	A176	200sh multicolored	2.50	2.50
1123	A176	300sh multicolored	3.50	3.50
1124	A176	400sh multicolored	4.75	4.75
		Nos. 1113-1124 (12)	17.45	17.45

Souvenir Sheets

1125	A176	500sh multicolored	5.50	5.50
1126	A176	500sh multicolored	5.50	5.50
1127	A176	500sh multicolored	5.50	5.50

Reptiles
A177

Designs: 20sh, Geochelone elephantopus, vert. 50sh, Iguana iguana, vert. 70sh, Varanus salvator. 100sh, Naja oxiana, vert. 150sh, Chamaeleo jacksonii. 200sh, Eunectes murinus. 250sh, Alligator mississippensis.

500sh, Vipera berus, vert.

Perf. 12x12½, 12½x12

1993, June 28   **Litho.**

| 1128-1134 | A177 | Set of 7 | 6.75 | 6.75 |

Souvenir Sheet

| 1135 | A177 | 500sh multicolored | 5.25 | 5.25 |

Nos. 1128-1135 were were not available until July 1994.

Sharks
A178

Designs: 20sh, Isurus oxyrinchus. 30sh, Etmopterus hillianus. 50sh, Galeocerdo cuvier. 70sh, Squatina africana. 100sh, Pristiophorus cirratus. 150sh, Triaenodon obesus. 200sh, Sphyrna lewini.

350sh, Hexanchus griseus, vert.

1993, July 27   **Perf. 12½x12**

| 1136-1142 | A178 | Set of 7 | 5.25 | 5.25 |

Souvenir Sheet

Perf. 12½x12½

| 1143 | A178 | 350sh multicolored | 3.25 | 3.25 |

Nos. 1136-1143 were not available until July 1994.

Dogs — A179

Designs: 20sh, Gordon setter. 30sh, Zwergschnauzer. 50sh, Labrador retriever. 70sh, Wire fox terrier. 100sh, English springer spaniel. 150sh, Newfoundlander. 200sh, Moscow toy terrier.

350sh, Doberman pinscher.

1993, Sept. 27   **Perf. 12x12½**

| 1144-1150 | A179 | Set of 7 | 5.75 | 5.75 |

Souvenir Sheet

| 1151 | A179 | 350sh multicolored | 2.75 | 2.75 |

Nos. 1144-1151 were not available until July 1994.

Horses
A180

Designs: 20sh, Norman-Arab. 40sh, Nonius. 50sh, Boulonnais. 70sh, Arab. 100sh, Anglo-Arab. 150sh, Tarpan. 200sh, Thoroughbred.

No. 1159, Anglo-Norman.

1993, Nov. 30   **Perf. 12½x12**

| 1152-1158 | A180 | Set of 7 | 6.50 | 6.50 |

Souvenir Sheet

Perf. 12x12½

| 1159 | A180 | 400sh multicolored | 3.00 | 3.00 |

Nos. 1152-1159 were not available until July 1994.

Military
Aircraft
A181

Designs: 20sh, ALFA jet. 30sh, Northrup F-5E. 50sh, Mirage 3NG. 70sh, MB-339C. 100sh, MIG-31. 150sh, C-101 AVIOJET. 200sh, F-16B.

500sh, EAP fighter, vert.

1994, Apr. 25 Litho. Perf. 12½x12
1160-1166 A181 Set of 7   6.00 6.00
Souvenir Sheet
Perf. 12x12½
1167 A181 500sh multicolored   3.50 3.50

A182

Customs Co-operation Council
Meeting, Arusha — A183

Designs: 20sh, Trans-border trade. 50sh, Customs-international trade by ship. 100sh, Customs-air transportation. 150sh, Postal service-customs co-operation, Customs and UPU emblems.
500sh, Emblem.

1994, Aug. 23 Litho. Perf. 13½
1168-1171 A182 Set of 4   5.00 5.00
Souvenir Sheet
Perf. 12½
1172 A183 500sh multicolored   6.00 6.00

1994 World Cup
Soccer
Championships,
US — A184

No. 1173: a, Giuseppe Signori. b, Ruud Gullit. c, Roberto Mancini. d, Marco Van Basten. e, Dennis Bergkamp. f, Oscar Ruggeri. g, Frank Rijkaard. h, Peter Schmeichel.
1000sh, World Cup trophy.

1994, Sept. 26 Perf. 14
1173 A184 300sh Sheet of 8, #a.-h.   11.00 11.00
Souvenir Sheet
1174 A184 1000sh multicolored   6.00 6.00

1994 World Cup Soccer
Championships, US — A184a

Letter in soccer ball: 40sh, B. 50sh, C. 70sh, D. 100sh, E. 170sh, A. 200sh, none. 250sh, F. 500sh, Two players and goalie.

1994, Sept. 30 Litho. Perf. 12½x12
1174A-1174G A184a Set of 7   10.00 10.00
    i. Souv. sheet of 6, #1174A-1174E, 1174G + 3 labels   8.00 8.00
Souvenir Sheet
1174H A184a 500sh multi   6.00 6.00

Dogs — A185

No. 1175, 120sh: a, Alsatian (German Shepherd). b, Japanese chin. c, Shetland sheepdog. d, Italian spinone. e, Great dane. f, English setter. g, Pembroke (welsh corgi). h, St. Bernard. i, Irish wolfhound.
No. 1176, 120sh: a, Afghan hound. b, Basenji (Congo dog). c, Siberian husky. d, Irish setter. e, Norwegian elkhound. f, Bracco Italiano (Italian hound). g, Australian cattle dog. h, German short haired pointer. i, Rhodesian ridgeback.
No. 1177, 120sh: a, Alaskan malamute. b, Scottish cairn terrier. c, American foxhound. d, British bulldog. e, Boston terrier. f, Borzoi (Russian wolfhound). g, Shar pei (Chinese fighting dog). h, Saluki (Persian greyhound). i, Bernese mountain dog.
No. 1178, 120sh: a, Doberman pinscher. b, Chihuahua. c, Bloodhound. d, Keeshond (Dutch barge dog). e, Tibetan spaniel. f, Japanese akita. g, Tervueren (Belgian shepherd dog). h, Chow chow (Chinese Spitz). i, Pharaoh hound.
No. 1179, 1000sh, Like #1175e. No. 1180, 1000sh, Like #1176b.

1994, Sept. 30
Sheets of 9, #a-i
1175-1178 A185 Set of 4   25.00 25.00
Souvenir Sheets
1179-1180 A185 Set of 2   15.00 15.00

Miniature Sheets of 8

Orchids — A186

No. 1181, 200sh: a, Rangaeris amaniensis. b, Eulophia macowanii. c, Cyrtorchis arcuata. d, Centrostigma occultans. e, Cirrhopetalum umbellatum. f, Ansellia gigantea. g, Angraecum ramosum. h, Disa englerana.
No. 1182, 200sh: a, Nervilia stolziana. b, Satyrium orbiculare. c, Schzochilus sulphureus. d, Disa stolzii. e, Platycoryne mediocris. f, Satyrium breve. g, Eulophia nuttii. h, Disa ornithantha.
No. 1183, 1000sh, Eulophia thomsonii, horiz. No. 1184, 1000sh, Phaius P. tankervilliae, horiz.

1994, Oct. 7
Sheets of 8, #a-h
1181-1182 A186 Set of 2   30.00 30.00
Souvenir Sheets
1183-1184 A186 Set of 2   17.50 17.50

Natl.
Parks
A187

Designs: 20sh, Ngorongoro Crater. 50sh, Ngurdoto Crater. 70sh, Kilimanjaro Natl. Park. 100sh, Gombe Natl. Park. 150sh, Selous Natl. Park. 200sh, Mikumi Natl. Park. 250sh, Serengeti Natl. Park.
500sh, Lake Manyara Natl. Park, vert.

1993, Oct. 29 Litho. Perf. 12
1185-1191 A187 Set of 7   5.00 5.00
Souvenir Sheet
1192 A187 500sh multicolored   2.75 2.75

Nos. 1185-1192 are dated 1993 but were not available until Oct. 1994.

Historical African
Costumes
A188

Designs: 20sh, Berts style. 40sh, Galla style. 50sh, Guinean warrior. 70sh, Goloff style. 100sh, Peul style. 150sh, Abyssinian warrior. 200sh, Pahuin style.
350sh, Zulu style.

1993, Dec. 30
1193-1199 A188 Set of 7   4.00 4.00
Souvenir Sheet
1200 A189 350sh multicolored   2.50 2.50

Nos. 1193-1200 are dated 1993 but were not available until Oct. 1994.

1994 Winter
Olympics,
Lillehammer
A189

Designs: 40sh, Downhill skiing. 50sh, Ice hockey. 70sh, Speed skating. 100sh, Bobsled. 120sh, Figure skating. 170sh, Free style skiing. 250sh, Biathlon.
500sh, Slalom skiing.

1994, Feb. 12
1201-1207 A189 Set of 7   4.50 4.50
Souvenir Sheet
1208 A189 500sh multicolored   2.50 2.50

Sailing
Ships — A190

Designs: 40sh, Jahazi. 50sh, Caravel. 70sh, Carrack. 100sh, Galeas. 170sh, Line of battle ship. 200sh, Frigate. 250sh, Brig.
No. 1210, Bark.

1994, Apr. 20
1209-1215 A190 Set of 7   4.00 4.00
Souvenir Sheet
1216 A190 500sh multicolored   2.50 2.50

Prehistoric
Animals — A191

Designs: 40sh, Diatruma. 50sh, Tyranosaurus. 100sh, Uintaterius. 120sh, Stiracosaurus. 170sh, Diplodocus. 250sh, Archaeopteryx. 300sh, Sordes.
500sh, Dimetrodon, vert.

1994, June 30
1217-1223 A191 Set of 7   9.00 9.00
Souvenir Sheet
1224 A191 500sh multicolored   3.25 3.25

Intl. Year of the
Family — A192

Designs: 40sh, Family. 120sh, Father playing ball with children. 170sh, People at clinic, horiz. 250sh, Woman harvesting in field.
300sh, Emblem.

Perf. 12x12½, 12½x12
1994, Aug. 30 Litho.
1225-1228 A192 Set of 4   4.00 4.00
Souvenir Sheet
1229 A192 300sh multicolored   4.00 4.00

Zanzibar
Revolution, 30th
Anniv. — A193

Designs: 40sh, Pres. Salmin Amour. 70sh, Abeid Amani Karume, first president. 120sh, Processing cloves, horiz. 250sh, Zanzibar door.
500sh, Hands clasped over map.

1994, Aug. 1
1230-1233 A193 Set of 4   4.75 4.75
Souvenir Sheet
1234 A193 500sh multicolored   3.50 3.50

Arachnids
A194

Designs: 40sh, Trombidium. 50sh, Eurypelma. 100sh, Salticus. 120sh, Micrommata rosea, vert. 170sh, Araneus. 250sh, Micrathena, vert. 300sh, Araneus diadematus, vert.
500sh, Hadogenes, vert.

Perf. 12½x12, 12x12½
1994, Aug. 31
1235-1241 A194 Set of 7   5.25 5.25
Souvenir Sheet
1242 A194 500sh multicolored   2.50 2.50

Butterflies
and
Flowers
A195

No. 1243, 120sh: a, Lunaria biennis, papilio glaucus. b, Phlox paniculata, danaus plexippus. c, Rudbeckia gloriosa, papilio troilus. d, Tithonia rotundifolia, hypolimnas antevorta. e, Osteospermum, cirrochroa imperatrix. f, Ursinia anethoides, vanessa atalanta. g, Wahlenbergia gloriosa, limenitis archippus. h, Mentzelia lindleyi, hypolimnas pandarus. i, Paeonia suffruticosa, anthocharis belia.
No. 1244, 120sh: a, Coreopsis laneolata, limenitis sydyi. b, Lantana camara, agraulis vanillae. c, Asclepias tuberosa, danaus chrysippus. d, Verbena canadensis, eurytides marcellus. e, Lonicera japonica, artopoetes pryeri. f, Pentas bussei, heliconius charitonius. g, Echinacea purpurea, limenitis weidemeyerii. h, Myosotis alpestris, phoebis sennae. i, Aster amellus, timelaea albescens.
No. 1245, 1000sh, Buddleia davidii, papilio polyxenes. No. 1246, 1000sh, Helianthus annuus, vanessa cardui.

1994, Nov. 19   *Perf. 14*
Sheets of 9, #a-i
1243-1244 A195 Set of 2   20.00 20.00
Souvenir Sheets
1245-1246 A195 Set of 2   13.50 13.50

First Manned Moon Landing, 25th Anniv. A196

No. 1247, 150sh: a, Map of landing site. b, Location of Sea of Tranquility shown on Moon. c, Craters. d, Launch. e, Second stage separation. f, Separation of lunar modules. g, Command module, "Columbia," landing module, "Eagle." h, "Eagle" descending. i, Inside module.

No. 1248, 150sh: a, Michael Collins, Neil Armstrong, Edwin "Buzz" Aldrin. b, "Eagle" on lunar surface. c, Stepping foot on moon. d, Erecting solar wind devices. e, Gathering soil samples. f, Reflection in helmet. g, Astronaut, US flag. h, Carrying equipment. i, "Eagle" ascending from lunar surface.

No. 1249, 150sh: a, "Columbia" above lunar surface, Earth on horizon. b, "Eagle" above lunar surface. c, Release of S-4B rocket. d, Heading toward Earth. e, Re-entering atmosphere. f, Splashdown. g, Pickup at sea. h, Helicopter lifting men on board. i, Astronauts in quarantine.

1994, Nov. 30
Sheets of 9, #a-i
1247-1249 A196 150sh Set of
                        3   30.00 30.00

A197

Dinosaurs — A198

No. 1250: a, Brontosaurus (e). b, Albertosaurus. c, Parasaurolophus. d, Pteranodon. e, Stegosaurus. f, Tyrannosaurus. g, Triceratops. h, Ornitholestes. i, Camarasaurus. j, Ankylosaurus. k, Trachodon. l, Allosaurus. m, Corythosaurus. n, Struthiomimus. o, Camptosaurus. p, Heterodontosaurus.

No. 1251: a, Deinonychus. b, Styracosaurus. c, Anatosaurus. d, Plateosaurus. e, Iguanodon. f, Oviraptor. g, Dimorphodon. h, Ornithomimus. i, Lambeosaurus. j, Megalosaurus. k, Cetiosaurus. l, Hypsilophodon. m, Rhamphorhynchus. n, Scelidosaurus. o, Antrodemus. p, Dimetrodon.

1000sh, Brachiosaurus, vert.

1994, Dec. 26
1250 A197 120sh Sheet of
             16, #a.-p.   16.00 16.00
1251 A198 120sh Sheet of
             16, #a.-p.   16.00 16.00
Souvenir Sheet
1252 A197 1000sh multi   8.00   8.00
No. 1250 is a continuous design.

Mickey Mouse, Safari Club — A199

Designs: No. 1253, 70sh, Donald, Mickey, lion cubs. No. 1254, 70sh, Goofy leaning on Donald. No. 1255, 100sh, Donald wearing tree disguise. No. 1256, 100sh, Donald under elephant. No. 1257, 120sh, Donald, hippopotamus. No. 1258, 120sh, Mickey writing in diary. No. 1259, 150sh, Goofy carrying gear, Donald, Mickey. No. 1260, 150sh, Mickey, elephant, Donald, Goofy in rain. No. 1261, 200sh, Donald, Goofy, Mickey reading book, lion. No. 1262, 200sh, Goofy, zebras. No. 1263, 250sh, Mickey, giraffe. No. 1264, 250sh, Donald filming picture.

No. 1265, 1000sh, Goofy hanging from tree, vert. No. 1266, 1000sh, Goofy holding camera, Donald, vert. No. 1267, 1000sh, Mickey holding camera, vert.

1994, Dec. 26   *Perf. 14x13½*
1253-1264 A199 Set of 12   13.00 13.00
Souvenir Sheets
Perf. 13½x14
1265-1267 A199 Set of 3   16.00 16.00

A200

Olympic Gold Medalists — A201

Designs: 350sh, Kristin Otto, Germany, 50m free-style swimming, 1988. 500sh, Carl Lewis, US, track & field, 1984, 1988. 1000sh, Oksana Baiul, Ukraine, women's figure skating, 1994.

1994, Dec. 12   **Litho.**   *Perf. 14*
1268 A200 350sh multicolored   1.75   1.75
1269 A200 500sh multicolored   2.50   2.50
Souvenir Sheet
1270 A201 1000sh multicolored 5.00   5.00
Intl. Olympic Committee, cent. (#1270).

D-Day, 50th Anniv. A202

350sh, Combined forces attack Atlantic wall. 600sh, Waterproofed tanks support Marines at Omaha Beach.

No. 1273, 200sh: a, Gen. Eisenhower, US forces, Omaha Beach. b, P-51 Mustang, D-Day armada. c, US Coast Guard cutter, landing craft. d, US troops approaching Omaha Beach. e, US troops landing on Omaha Beach. f, US forces on Omaha Beach.

No. 1274, 200sh: a, Gen. Montgomery, White Ensign flies over Normandy beach. b, British forces with Churchill Avre tank, Gold Beach. c, USS Thompson refueled en route to Omaha Beach. d, HMS Warspite fires on German positions, Sword Beach. e, Royal Marine commandoes landing, Juno Beach. f, Sherman Crab flail tank landing on Normandy beach.

No. 1275, 200sh: a, Supermarine Spitfire over Normandy beaches. b, Bren gun carriers, Gold Beach. c, Le Regiment de la Chaudiere, Juno Beach. d, Canadian forces land on Juno Beach. e, Sherman forces on Normandy beach. f, German artillery fires on D-Day Armada.

No. 1276, 1000sh, US forces prepare to embark from England to Normandy beaches. No. 1277, 1000sh, US forces on Utah Beach. No. 1278, 1000sh, Beach obstacles.

1994, Dec. 12   **Litho.**   *Perf. 14*
1271 A202 350sh multicolored   1.75   1.75
1272 A202 600sh multicolored   3.25   3.25
Sheets of 6, #a-f
1273-1275 A202 Set of 3   20.00 20.00
Souvenir Sheets
1276-1278 A202 Set of 3   16.00 16.00

Raptors A203

Designs: 40sh, Terathopius ecaudatus, vert. 50sh, Spizaetus ornatus, vert. 100sh, Pandion haliaetus, vert. 120sh, Vultur gryphus, vert. 170sh, Haliaeetus vocifer. 250sh, Sarcoramphus papa, vert. 400sh, Falco peregrinus.

500sh, Pseudogyps africanus, vert.

Perf. 12x12½, 12½x12
1994, Sept. 30
1279-1285 A203 Set of 7   9.25   9.25
Souvenir Sheet
1286 A203 500sh multicolored   3.50   3.50

Endangered Species — A204

Designs: 40sh, Phascolasctos cinereus. 70sh, Ailurus fulgens. 100sh, Aguila. 120sh, Loxodonta africana. 250sh, Monachus tropicalis. 400sh, Eschrichtius gibbosus. 500sh, Cetacea.

500sh, Panthera tigris, vert.

1994, July 29   *Perf. 12½x12*
1287-1293 A204 Set of 7   8.50   8.50
Souvenir Sheet
Perf. 12x12½
1294 A204 500sh multicolored 4.00   4.00
No. 1288 shows a Giant Panda, and is incorrectly inscribed with the scientific name of the Lesser Panda.

Crabs — A205

Designs: 40sh, Astacus leptodactytus, horiz. 100sh, Eriocheir sinensis. 120sh, Caneer opillo. 170sh, Cardisoma quanhumi, horiz. 250sh, Birgus latro. 300sh, Menippe mercenaria, horiz. 400sh, Dromia vulgaris. No. 1302, Callinectes sapidus, horiz.

Perf. 12½x12, 12x12½
1994, Nov. 30   **Litho.**
1295-1301 A205 Set of 7   7.25   7.25
Souvenir Sheet
1302 A205 500sh multicolored 2.50   2.50

Flowers — A206

Designs: 40sh, Dicentra spectabilis. 100sh, Thunbergia alata. 120sh, Cyrtanthus minimiflorus. 170sh, Nepenthes hybrida. 250sh, Allamanda cathartica. 300sh, Encyclia pentotis. 400sh, Protea lacticolor. 500sh, Tradescantia.

1995, Oct. 31   *Perf. 12x12½*
1303-1309 A206 Set of 7   6.50   6.50
Souvenir Sheet
1310 A206 500sh multicolored 2.50   2.50
Dated 1994.

Woodstock Music Festival, 25th Anniv. — A207

Illustration reduced.

1995   **Litho.**   *Imperf.*
Size: 124x84mm
1311 A207 2000sh Jimi Hendrix   10.00 10.00
Souvenir Sheet
Self-Adhesive
1312 A207 2000sh Carlos
            Santana   10.00 10.00
Size: 115x122mm
Imperf
Self-Adhesive
1313 A207 2000sh John Lee
            Hooker   10.00 10.00
Issued: #1311, 2/27; #1312, 5/15; #1313, 8/22.

Space Probes and Satellites A208

Designs: 40sh, Hubble telescope. 100sh, Mariner. 120sh, Voyager 2. 170sh, Work Package 03. 250sh, Orbiting solar observatory (OSO). 300sh, Magellan. 400sh, Galileo. 500sh, FOBOS.

1994, Dec. 30 **Litho.** *Perf. 12½x12*
1319-1325 A208 Set of 7   6.75   6.75
Souvenir Sheet
1326 A208 500sh multicolored 3.50   3.50

Sierra Club, Cent. A209

No. 1327, 150sh, vert: a, Black rhinoceros. b, Aye-aye. c, Aye-aye, holding claw at mouth.

d, Giraffes, Masai Mara Reserve. e, Red lechwe, group. f, Red lechwe running. g, White-handed gibbon, white coat. h, White-handed gibbon, dark coat. i, White-handed gibbon, ready to climb tree.

No. 1328, 150sh: a, Aye-aye. b, Black rhinoceros facing each other. c, Black rhinoceros. d, Red lechwe. e, Lions fighting, Masai Mara Reserve. f, Hyena, Masai Mara Reserve. g, Nile crocodile in water. h, Nile crocodile, mouth open. i, Nile crocodile in grass.

1995, July 6 **Litho.** *Perf. 14*
Sheets of 9, #a-i
1327-1328 A209 Set of 2 18.00 18.00

Fruit
A210

Designs: 70sh, Coconuts. 100sh, Pineapple. 150sh, Pawpaw. 200sh, Tomato. 500sh, Coconuts.

1995, June 30
1329-1332 A210 Set of 4 6.00 6.00
Souvenir Sheet
1333 A210 500sh multicolored 5.25 5.25

Miniature Sheets of 9

The Beatles — A211

No. 1334, 100sh: a, George Harrison. b, d, e, f, h, Various group portraits. c, Ringo Starr. g, Paul McCartney. i, John Lennon.

No. 1335, 100sh, vert.: a-i, Various portraits of John Lennon.

No. 1336, 500sh, John Lennon, vert. No. 1337, 500sh, Paul McCartney.

1995 *Perf. 12½*
Sheets of 9, #a-i
1334-1335 A211 100sh Set of 2 13.00 13.00
Souvenir Sheets
1336-1337 A211 500sh Set of 2 13.00 13.00

No. 1336 contains one 51x76mm stamp. No. 1337 contains one 57x51mm stamp.

Trains
A212

No. 1338, 200sh: a, 0-6-0 Italy. b, 0-4-4-OT Mallet, Germany. c, 4-8-0 Tender Engine, Ghana. d, Mallet Tanks, Germany. e, 0-6-2T on the Zillertalbahn, Switzerland. f, Rack Lines, Austria. g, Sweden Jodemans Railway, Norway. h, 4-6-0 Portugal. i, 60CM gauge, Mine Railway, Spain.

No. 1339, 200sh: a, 640 Class 2-6-0s, Italy. b, Norway electric. c, Gordon Highlander 4-40s. d, High Line 9600 class 2-8-0 Japan. e, 4-6-0 Henschel, Portugal. f, Federal German State Railway 220 hydraulic. g, Caledonian 4-2-2, Scotland. h, M2 Locomotive, Denmark. i, Denver & Rio Grande, Western US.

No. 1340, 1000sh, Karl Golsdorf 2-6-0 tank engine, "Germany." No. 1341, 1000sh, High speed ET 403, Germany. No. 1342, 1000sh, AKO 1920, US. No. 1343 1000sh, Porter 2-4-0S, Hawaii.

1995, July 5 **Litho.** *Perf. 14*
Sheets of 9, #a-i
1338-1339 A212 Set of 2 25.00 25.00
Souvenir Sheets
1340-1343 A212 Set of 4 27.50 27.50
Singapore '95.

FAO, 50th Anniv.— A213

No. 1344: a, Boy eating. b, Baby, mother eating. c, Two young people eating. 1000sh, Woman picking fruit, horiz.

1995, Aug. 14
1344 A213 250sh Strip of 3, #a.-c. 4.75 4.75
Souvenir Sheet
1345 A213 1000sh multicolored 5.25 5.25
No. 1344 is a continuous design.

Rotary International, 90th Anniv. — A214

Designs: 600sh, Paul Harris, Rotary emblem. 1000sh, Natl. flag, Rotary emblem.

1995, Aug. 14
1346 A214 600sh multicolored 3.25 3.25
Souvenir Sheet
1347 A214 1000sh multicolored 5.25 5.25

Queen Mother, 95th Birthday A215

No. 1348: a, Drawing. b, With Queen Elizabeth II. c, Formal portrait. d, In black outfit. 1000sh, Blue dress with pearls.

1995, Aug. 14 *Perf. 13½x14*
1348 A215 250sh Block or strip of 4, #a.-d. 5.00 5.00
Souvenir Sheet
1349 A215 1000sh multicolored 5.25 5.25
No. 1348 was issued in sheets of 8 stamps. Sheets of Nos. 1348-1349 exist with black borders overprinted in sheet margins and text "In Memoriam 1900-2002."

End of World War II, 50th Anniv. A216

No. 1350 — Flags of countries shaped as "VJ:" a, Singapore. b, Fiji. c, Malaysia. d, Marshall Islands. e, Philippines. f, Solomon Islands.

No. 1351: a, Pearl Harbor. b, North Africa. c, Battle of Atlantic. d, War in Soviet Union. e, "D" Day, June 6, 1944. f, Holocaust. g, War in Pacific. h, Hiroshima, Enola Gay, mushroom cloud.

No. 1352, 1000sh, Battle of Britain. No. 1353, 1000sh, British soldier, donkey with backpack.

1995, Aug. 14 **Litho.** *Perf. 14*
1350 A216 250sh Sheet of 6, #a.-f. + label 8.50 8.50

1351 A216 250sh Sheet of 8, #a.-h. + label 8.50 8.50
Souvenir Sheets
1352-1353 A216 Set of 2 17.50 17.50

Reptiles
A217

No. 1354: a, African rock python. b, Bell's hinged tortoise. c, Gaboon viper. d, Royal python. e, Savannah monitor. f, Nile monitor. g, Three-horned chameleon. h, Nile crocodile. i, Rough-scaled bush viper. j, Puff adder. k, Rhinocerous viper. l, Leopard tortoise.

No. 1355, 1000sh, Bush viper. No. 1356, 1000sh, Spitting cobra.

1995, Sept. 5
1354 A217 200sh Sheet of 12, #a.-l. 13.00 13.00
Souvenir Sheets
1355-1356 A217 Set of 2 11.00 11.00

UN, 50th Anniv. — A218

No. 1357 — Various races of people, within group: a, Woman holding baby on shoulders. b, Man holding child in arms. c, One child standing. 1000sh, UN soldier using binoculars.

1995, Aug. 14 **Litho.** *Perf. 14*
1357 A218 250sh Strip of 3, #a.-c. 5.25 5.25
Souvenir Sheet
1358 A218 1000sh multicolored 5.25 5.25
No. 1357 is a continuous design.

Summer Olympics Gold Medal Winners — A219

No. 1359, 200sh, : a, Tommie Smith, US, 1968. b, Jack Lovelock, New Zealand, 1936. c, Al Oerter, US, 1956-68. d, Daley Thompson, Great Britain, 1980. e, Greg Louganis, US, 1984-88. f, Sammy Lee, US, 1948. g, Dan Gable, US, 1972. h, Helen Meany, US, 1928. i, Sugar Ray Leonard, US, 1976.

No. 1360, 200sh: a, Robert Mathias, US, 1948-52 . b, Larissa Latynina, USSR, 1956. c, Martin Sheridan, US, 1904-08. d, Vera Caslavska, Czechoslovakia, 1968. e, Edwin Moses, US, 1984. f, Jesse Owens, US, 1936. g, Mary Lou Retton, US, 1984. h, Bobby Morrow, US, 1956. i, Joan Benoit, US, 1984.

No. 1361, 1000sh, Florence Griffith Joyner, Jackie Joyner-Kersee, US, 1988. No. 1362, 1000sh, Vasily Alexeyev USSR, 1972-76.

1995, Sept. 18
Sheets of 9, #a-i
1359-1360 A219 Set of 2 16.00 16.00
Souvenir Sheets
1361-1362 A219 Set of 2 10.00 10.00

Wild Animals A220

No. 1363: a, Snake, vulture. b, Vulture. c, Giraffe (d, g, h, k, l). d, African bateleur. e, Elephants (f). f, Kob, rhino (b, e, i, j, n). g, Rhinos. h, Baboon. i, Kob (m, n). j, Saddle billed stork, warthog (n). k, Cheetahs (g, j, n). l, African lion (h, k, o, p). m, Vulture. n, Dikdiks. o, Lion cubs. p, Lions (o).

No. 1364: a, Elands. b, Zebras. c, Lions. d, Baboons.

No. 1365, 1000sh, Rhinoceros. No. 1366, 1000sh, Leopard.

1995, Sept. 15
1363 A220 100sh Sheet of 16, #a.-p. 8.50 8.50
1364 A220 250sh Sheet of 4, #a.-d. 5.50 5.50
Souvenir Sheets
1365-1366 A220 Set of 2 10.00 10.00

UN, 50th Anniv. A221

Designs: 70sh, Corn farming, vert. 100sh, Cultivating land. 150sh, Women spinning cotton in factory. 200sh, Boy drawing at desk, vert. 500sh, UN emblem, "50."

Wmk. 387
1995, Oct. 24 **Litho.** *Perf. 14*
1367-1371 A221 Set of 4 4.75 4.75
Souvenir Sheet
1372 A221 500sh multicolored 5.25 5.25

East African Treaty, 2nd Anniv. A222

Designs: 100sh, Heads of State. 150sh, Map, flags, vert. 180sh, Map, cotton, vert. 200sh, Fishing on Lake Victoria. 500sh, Heads of State.

1995, Oct. 24
1373-1376 A222 Set of 4 6.00 6.00
Souvenir Sheet
1377 A222 500sh multicolored 6.00 6.00

Hoofed Animals — A224

Designs: 70sh, Hippopotamus amphibius, horiz. 100sh, Litocranius walleri. 150sh, Sincerus caffer, horiz. 180sh, Antilocapridae, horiz. 200sh, Alcelphus buselaphus. 260sh, Taurotragus oryx. 380sh, Strepsiceros. 500sh, Giraffa camelopardalis.

Perf. 12½x12, 12x12½
1995, May 31 **Litho.**
1380-1386 A224 Set of 7 7.00 7.00
Souvenir Sheet
1387 A224 500sh multicolored 6.50 6.50

Cactus Flowers — A225

Designs: 70sh, Weingartia fidaiana. 100sh, Rebutia spegazziniana. 150sh, Caralluma lugarii. 180sh, Cerochlamys pachyphylla. 200sh, Schlumbergera orssighiana. 260sh, Epiphyllum darrahii. 380sh, Ceropegia nilotica. 500sh, Neoporteria nigrihorrida.

1995, Aug. 31   *Perf. 12x12½*
1388-1394 A225 Set of 7   7.00 7.00
Souvenir Sheet
1395 A225 500sh multicolored   6.50 6.50

Bats
A226

Designs: 70sh, Cheiromeles torquatus, vert. 100sh, Hypsignatus monstrosus, vert. 150sh, Rhinolophus, ferrum-equinum, vert. 180sh, Plecotus auritus. 200sh, Syconycteris australis, vert. 260sh, Plecotus auritus, vert. 380sh, Otomops martiensseni.
500sh, Pteropus.

1995, July 31   *Perf. 12x12½, 12½x12*
1396-1402 A226 Set of 7   7.00 7.00
Souvenir Sheet
1403 A226 500sh multicolored   6.50 6.50

Marine
Life of
Coral
Reefs
A227

Designs: 70sh, Medusa. 100sh, Surgeonfish. 150sh, Angelfish. 180sh, Octopus. 200sh, Zebra fish. 260sh, Shark. 380sh, Ray. 500sh, Turtle.

1995, June 15   *Perf. 12½x12*
1404-1410 A227 Set of 7   7.00 7.00
Souvenir Sheet
1411 A227 500sh multicolored   6.50 6.50

Jerry Garcia
(d. 1995),
Musician
A228

Scenes of Grateful Dead performing on stage and: No. 1413A, Bears. No. 1413B, Skeletons.

1995   **Litho.**   *Perf. 12½*
1412 A228 200sh mul-
            ticolored   10.00 10.00
Souvenir Sheet
1413 A228 1000sh mul-
            ticolored   9.50   9.50
Size: 140x92mm
Imperf
Self-Adhesive
1413A A228 2000sh mul-
             ticolored   8.25   8.25
1413B A228 2000sh mul-
             ticolored   8.25   8.25

No. 1412 was issued in sheets of 9. No. 1413 contains one 51x57mm stamp.
Issued: #1412-1413, 11/15/95; #1413A-1413B, 12/21/95.

Rock and
Roll Stars
A229

No. 1414: a, Chuck Berry. b, Bob Dylan. c, Aretha Franklin. d, The Supremes. e, Buddy Holly. f, Bruce Springsteen. g, Elton John. h, The Rolling Stones. i, Michael Jackson.
1000sh, The Beach Boys (Al Jardin, Mike Love, Brian Wilson, Carl Wilson, Dennis Wilson), horiz.

1995, Dec. 1   *Perf. 13½x14*
1414 A229 250sh Sheet of 9,
            #a.-i.   15.00 15.00
Souvenir Sheet
Perf. 14x13½
1415 A229 1000sh multi   8.50   8.50

Motion
Pictures,
Cent.
A230

No. 1416: a, Noah's Ark, Dolores Costello. b, Ben-Hur, 1926, Ramon Novarro. c, Ben-Hur, 1926, Francis X. Bushman. d, Ben-Hur, 1959, Charlton Heston. e, Ben-Hur, 1959, Haya Harareet. f, Ben-Hur, 1959, Sam Jaffe. g, The Ten Commandments, 1923, Theodore Roberts. h, Samson and Delilah, Victor Mature. i, Samson and Delilah, Hedy Lamarr.
No. 1417, The Ten Commandments, Theodore Roberts.

1995, Dec. 1   *Perf. 13½x14*
1416 A230 250sh Sheet of 9,
            #a.-i.   19.00 19.00
Souvenir Sheet
1417 A230 1000sh multi   8.50   8.50

World Tourism Organization, 20th
Anniv. — A231

Designs: 100sh, Olduvai Gorge, "Cradle of Mankind." 300sh, First State House, Bagamoyo. 400sh, Mount Kilimanjaro.
500sh, Rhinoceroses, Ngorongoro Crater.

1995, Dec. 18 **Litho.**   *Perf. 14*
1418-1420 A231 Set of 3   6.50 6.50
Souvenir Sheet
1421 A231 500sh multicolored   6.00 6.00

Predatory
Animals
A232

Designs: 70sh, Acinonyx jubatus. 100sh, Felus serval. 150sh, Huaena buana. 200sh, Otocyon megalotis. 250sh, Lucaon pictus. 280sh, Pantera pardus. 300sh, Pantera leo. 500sh, Alligator.

1995, Sept. 30 Litho.   *Perf. 12½x12*
1422-1428 A232 Set of 7   10.50 10.50
Souvenir Sheet
1429 A232 500sh multicolored 5.25 5.25

Horses — A233

No. 1430: a, True black Freisian. b, Appaloosa. c, Arab. d, Paint. e, Chestnut saddlebred. f, Standard thoroughbred. g, Belgian. h, Liver chestnut quarter. i, Hackney.
1000sh, Clydesdale.

1995   *Perf. 14*
1430 A233 250sh Sheet of 9,
            #a.-i.   19.00 19.00
Souvenir Sheet
1431 A233 1000sh multi   10.50 10.50

No. 685 Surcharged

70/-

X

1995, May 30   Litho.   *Perf. 14*
1431A A108 70sh on 13sh #685

Paintings from
the
Metropolitan
Museum of
Art — A234

No. 1432, 200sh: a, La Orana Maria, by Gauguin. b, Young Herdsman with Cows, by Cuyp. c, Moses and the Burning Bush by, Domenichino. d, Path in the Ile Saint-Martin, Vétheuil, by Monet. e, Dances, Pink and Green, by Degas. f, Terrace at Sainte-Adresse, by Monet. g, The Rehearsal Onstage, by Degas. h, Study for "A Sunday on La Grande Jatte," by Seurat.
No. 1433, 200sh: a, Madame Marsollier and Daughter, by Nattier. b, Christ and the Woman of Samaria, by Rembrandt. c, Rubens and His Wife and Son, by Rubens. d, Portrait of a Young Woman, by Vermeer. e, Portrait of a Man, by Van Dyck. f, Young Woman with a Water Jug, by Vermeer. g, Self Portrait, by Rembrandt. h, Young Man and Woman in an Inn, by Hals.
No. 1434, 1000sh, On the Beach at Trouville, by Boudin. No. 1435, 1000sh, A Dance in the Country, by G.D. Tiepolo.

1996, Mar. 7   *Perf. 13½x14*
Sheets of 8, #a-h, + Label
1432-1433 A234 Set of 2   32.50 32.50
Souvenir Sheets
Perf. 14
1434-1435 A234 Set of 2   20.00 20.00
Nos. 1434-1435 each contain one 81x53mm stamp.

Miniature Sheet

Cats
and
Dogs — A235

No. 1436 — Cats: a, Siberian. b, Classic silver tabby Persian. c, Brown Burmese. d, Norwegian forest. e, Tabby. f, Blue & white maine coon. g, Brown California spangled cat. h, Black & white bicolor Persian. i, Shaded silver American shorthair.
No. 1437 — Dogs: a, Red labrador. b, St. Bernard. c, Cocker spaniel. d, Black labrador. e, Bernese mountain dog. f, Beagle. g, Miniature pincher. h, Basset hound. i, German shepherd.
No. 1438, Silver tabby British shorthair. No. 1439, Alaskan malamute.

1996, Mar. 4   **Litho.**   *Perf. 14*
1436 A235 250sh Sheet of 9,
            #a.-i.   14.50 14.50
1437 A235 250sh Sheet of 9,
            #a.-i.   14.50 14.50
Souvenir Sheets
1438 A235 1000sh multi   8.50   8.50
1439 A235 1000sh multi   8.50   8.50

Souvenir Sheets

Janis Joplin (1943-70), Rock
Musician — A235a

Design: No. 1439B, Joplin seated atop a psychedelically-painted Porsche, horiz. Illustration reduced.

1996, Apr. 10 **Litho.**   *Imperf.*
Self-Adhesive
1439A A235a 2000sh shown   20.00 20.00
1439B A235a 2000sh multi   20.00 20.00

Elvis Presley (1935-77) — A235b

Various photographs with EPE (Elvis Presley Enterprises) official product emblem.

1996, Mar. 13   Litho.   Perf. 12½
1439C A235b 200sh Sheet of
9, #d.-l.   13.00 13.00

New
Year
1996
(Year of
the Rat)
A236

No. 1440: a, Arvicola oryzivora. b, Meriones
hudsonicus. c, Mus missouriensis. d, Mus
aureolus.
500sh, Fiber zibethicus.

1996, Apr. 12
1440 A236 200sh Block of 4, #a.-
d.   4.25 4.25
e.   Souvenir sheet of 1 #1440   4.25 4.25
Souvenir Sheet
1442 A236 500sh multicolored   4.25 4.25
No. 1440 was issued in sheets of 16 stamps.

Deng
Xiaoping,
Chinese
Communist
Leader
A237

Various portraits.

1996, May 6   Litho.   Perf. 13
1443 A237 250sh Sheet of 6,
#a.-f.   13.00 13.00
Souvenir Sheet
1444 A237 500sh multicolored   5.50 5.50
CHINA '96, 9th Asian Intl. Philatelic Exhibition (#1443).

Butterflies
A238

Designs: 70sh, Dirphia multicolor. 100sh,
Inachis io, vert. 150sh, Automerisio. 200sh,
Saturnia pyri. 250sh, Arctia villica. 260sh, Arctia caja. 300sh, Celerio euforbiae, vert.
500sh, Zygaena laeta.

Perf. 12½x12, 12x12½
1996, Jan.   Litho.
1445-1451 A238 Set of 7   11.00 11.00
Souvenir Sheet
1452 A238 500sh multicolored   5.50 5.50

Frogs
A239

Designs: 100sh, Bufo bufo laur. 140sh, Pyx-
icephalus adspersus. 180sh, Megalixalus
laevis. 200sh, Xenopus laevis. 210sh,
Hemisus marmoratus. 260sh, Rana beccarii.
300sh, Hyperolius cinctiventrus.
500sh, Rana goliath.

1996, Jan. 31   Perf. 12½x12
1453-1459 A239 Set of 7   8.50 8.50
Souvenir Sheet
1460 A239 500sh multicolored   7.00 7.00

Souvenir Sheet

China 1996 Intl. Philatelic
Exhibition — A239a

1996, June 5   Litho.   Perf. 12½
1460A A239a 300sh multi   5.00 5.00

Souvenir Sheet

Shanghai Intl. Tea Culture
Festival — A239b

1996   Litho.   Perf. 12½
1460B A239b 300sh multi   5.00 5.00

Queen Elizabeth II, 70th
Birthday — A240

No. 1461: a, Portrait. b, As young woman in
evening dress. c, Wearing tiara, jewels.
1000sh, Portrait as young woman.

1996, July 3   Litho.   Perf. 13½x14
1461 A240 300sh Strip of 3,
#a.-c.   7.00 7.00
Souvenir Sheet
1462 A240 1000sh multicolored   8.00 8.00
No. 1461 was issued in sheets of 9 stamps.

Crocodiles, Alligators — A241

Designs: 100sh, Melanosuchus niger.
150sh, Caiman latirostris. 200sh, Alligator mis-
sisspiensis. 250sh, Gavialis gangeticus.
260sh, Crocodylus niloticus. 300sh, Crocodylus cataphractus. 380sh, Crocodylus
rhombifer.
500sh, Crocodile.

1996   Perf. 12½x12
1463-1469 A241 Set of 7   9.50 9.50
Souvenir Sheet
1470 A241 500sh multicolored   7.50 7.50

Snakes
A242

Designs: 100sh, Naja pallida. 140sh, Agkistrodon contortrix. 180sh, Bungarus fasciatus.
200sh, Micrurus frontalis, vert. 260sh, Bitis
gabonica, vert. 300sh, Elaphe moellendorffi,
vert. 400sh, Vipera ursini, vert.
700sh, Corallus caninus, vert.

1996   Perf. 12½x12, 12x12½
1471-1477 A242 Set of 7   9.50 9.50
Souvenir Sheet
1478 A242 700sh multicolored   7.50 7.50

Famous People,
Events — A243

No. 1479, 250sh: a, Gandhi. b, Mao Tse-
tung. c, Jonas Salk. d, John F. Kennedy. e,
Neil Armstrong. f, Mikhail Gorbachev. g, Nelson Mandela. h, Gen. Colin Powell.
No. 1480, 250sh: a, Orville, Wilbur Wright.
b, Battle of Verdun, 1916. c, Charles
Lindbergh. d, Al Jolson. e, Alexander Fleming.
f, Amelia Earhart. g, Franklin Roosevelt,
Joseph Stalin, Winston Churchill, Yalta Conference, 1945. h, Atomic bomb blast, 1945,
Enrico Fermi.
1000sh, Deng Xiaoping.

1996, July 15   Litho.   Perf. 14
Sheets of 8, #a-h
1479-1480 A243 250sh Set of
2   17.00 17.00
Souvenir Sheet
1481 A243 1000sh multicolored   8.00 8.00

A244   Birds — A245

Fruits of East Africa: 140sh, Pineapple.
180sh, Orange, lime. 200sh, Pear, apple.
300sh, Bananas.

1996, Sept. 4   Litho.   Perf. 13
1482-1485 A244 Set of 4   7.50 7.50
1485a   Souv. sheet of 1 #1485   4.25 4.25

1996, Sept. 16   Perf. 14
No. 1486, 300sh: a, Vidua macroura. b,
Tockus erythrorynchus. c, Trachyphonus
erythrocephalus. d, Bubo capensis. e, Gyps
ruppellii. f, Sarkidiornis melanotus. g, Dendrocygna bicolor. h, Struthio camelus.
No. 1487, 300sh: a, Gypohierax angolensis.
b, Aquila chrysaetos. c, Spilornis rufipectus. d,
Eutriorchis astur. e, Haliaeetus albicilla. f,
Ichthyophaga ichthyaetus. g, Spilornis holospi-
lus. h, Dryotriorchis spectabilis.
No. 1488, African paradise flycatcher. No.
1489, Haliaeetus leucocephala, horiz.

Sheets of 8, #a-h
1486-1487 A245 300sh Set of
2   27.50 27.50
Souvenir Sheets
1488 A245 1000sh multicolored   9.00 9.00
1489 A245 1000sh multicolored   9.00 9.00

Reef Fish
A246

Designs: 100sh, Yellowtail wrasse. 150sh,
Jewel grouper. 250sh, Barred thick-lipped
wrasse. 500sh, Bullethead parrotfish.
No. 1494: a, Golden cardinal fish. b, Yel-
lowhead butterfly fish. c, Common banner fish
(diver). d, Zanzibar butterfly fish. e, Lemon
damsel. f, Blue and gold fusilier. g, Red
firegoby. h, Threadfin fairy basslet. i, Rein rock
basslet.
No. 1495, 1000sh, African pygmy angelfish.
No. 1496, 1000sh, Blue green chromis.

1996, Sept. 23
1490-1493 A246 Set of 4   8.50 8.50
1494 A246 200sh Sheet of 9,
#a.-i.   13.00 13.00
Souvenir Sheets
1495-1496 A246 Set of 2   8.50 8.50

Ferrari
Cars
A247

No. 1497: a, 1964 250LM. b, 1992 456 GT.
c, 1995 F50. d, 1995 F512 M "Testarossa." e,
1984 BB 512. f, 1955 410 S coupe.
1000sh, 1964 250 GTO.

1996, Sept. 27   Litho.   Perf. 14
1497 A247 250sh Sheet of 6,
#a.-f.   12.50 12.50
Souvenir Sheet
1498 A247 1000sh multi   8.50 8.50
No. 1498 contains one 85x28mm stamp.

Radio, Cent.
A248

Designs: 70sh, Franklin D. Roosevelt, 1st
fireside chat, 1933. 100sh, Harry S. Truman
announces US use of atomic bomb, 1945.
150sh, Orson Welles, "Alien Invasion" broadcast, 1938. 200sh, Fiorello La Guardia reads
newspaper comics via radio.
1000sh, Robin Williams as Adrian
Cronauer, "Good Morning Viet Nam."

1996, July 15   Litho.   Perf. 13½x14
1499-1502 A248 Set of 4   4.25 4.25
Souvenir Sheet
1503 A248 1000sh multicolored   8.50 8.50

Mercedes-Benz Automobiles — A249

No. 1504: a, 1952 300SL Coupè 1. b, 1932 680S. c, 1934 500K. d, 1934 Type 150. e, 1934 Type 150 Sport Roadster "Heck." f, 1937 W125.
1000sh, 1936 540K Roadster Class A.

1996, Sept. 27   **Perf. 14**
1504 A249   250sh Sheet of 6,
     #a.-f.   12.00 12.00
Souvenir Sheet
1505 A249 1000sh multi   8.50   8.50

UNICEF, 50th
Anniv. — A250

Designs: 200sh, Child holding bowl. 250sh, Mother breastfeeding infant. 500sh, Tetsuko Kuroyanaga holding child.
1000sh, Girl.

1996, Oct. 4
1506-1508 A250   Set of 3   7.50   7.50
Souvenir Sheet
1509 A250 1000sh multicolored   7.75   7.75

UNESCO, 50th Anniv. — A251

Designs: 200sh, Ngorongoro Conservation Area, Tanzania. 250sh, Los Katios Natl. Park, Colombia. 600sh, Kilwa Kisiwani Makutani Complex, Tanzania.
1000sh, Kilimanjaro Natl. Park, Tanzania.

1996, Oct. 4
1510-1512 A251   Set of 3   10.00 10.00
Souvenir Sheet
1513 A251 1000sh mul-
     ticolored   10.00 10.00

Flowers — A252

No. 1514, 300sh: a, Lily of the valley. b, Spanish iris. c, Spiderwort. d, Morning glory. e, Gazania. f, Pansy. g, Begonia. h, Madonna lily.
No. 1515, 300sh: a, Snowdrop. b, Treesia. c, Cosmos. d, Daffodil. e, Blue himalayan poppy. f, Blue daisy. g, Zinnia flore-pleno. h, Oriental poppy.
No. 1516, 1000sh, Fuchsia. No. 1517, 1000sh, Hanson's lily.

1996, Oct. 25
Sheets of 8, #1-h + Label
1514-1515 A252   Set of 2   32.50 32.50
Souvenir Sheets
1516-1517 A252   Set of 2   18.00 18.00

Domestic
Cats
A253

Designs: 100sh, Lilac point Siamese. 150sh, Somali. 200sh, British blue shorthair.
No. 1521: a, American shorthair silver tabby. b, Scottish fold. c, Persian blue. d, Ocicat.
1000sh, Ragdoll.

1996, Dec. 10   **Litho.**   **Perf. 14**
1518-1520 A253   Set of 3   3.50   3.50
1521 A253   300sh Sheet of 4,
     #a.-d.   8.00   8.00
Souvenir Sheet
1522 A253 1000sh multicolored   8.50   8.50

Dogs
A254

Designs: 70sh, Shar-pei. 250sh, Beagle. 600sh, Keeshond.
No. 1527: a, St. Bernard. b, Shetland sheepdog. c, Samoyed. d, Australian cattle dog.
1000sh, Collie.

1996, Dec. 10   **Litho.**   **Perf. 14**
1524-1526 A254   Set of 3   6.50   6.50
1527 A254   300sh Sheet of 4,
     #a.-d.   9.50   9.50
Souvenir Sheet
1528 A254 1000sh multicolored   8.50   8.50

Nos. 767-768, 1001-1002, 1026-1028 Ovptd.

a

b

c

1996, Dec. 16
1529 A120(a-b)   50sh Sheet
     of 16,
     #a.-p.
     (#767)   9.75   9.75
1530 A120(c)   50sh Sheet
     of 16,
     #a.-p.
     (#768)   9.75   9.75
1531 A154(a-b)   100sh Sheet
     of 12,
     #a.-l.
     (#1001) 14.50 14.50
1532 A158(c)   100sh Sheet
     of 6,
     #a.-f.
     (#1026)   7.25   7.25
1533 A158(c)   100sh Sheet
     of 6,
     #a.-f.
     (#1027)   7.25   7.25
Souvenir Sheets
1534 A154(c)   500sh on
     #1002   6.00   6.00
1535 A158(a)   500sh on
     #1028   6.00   6.00
Size and location of overprint varies.

Overprints types a-b appear on alternating stamps of Nos. 1529, 1531.
Nos. 1529-1533 have additional overprints in sheet margin.

Mushrooms
A255

No. 1536, 300sh: a, Amanita phalloides. b, Amanita muscaria. c, Morchella vulgaris. d, Tricholoma aurantium. e, Amanita caesarea. f, Psalliota haemorrhoidaria. g, Russula virescens. h, Boletus crocipodius.
No. 1537, 300sh: a, Coprinus comatus. b, Amanitopsis vaginata. c, Clitocybe geotropa. d, Cortinarius violaceus. e, Russula sardonia. f, Cortinarius collinitus. g, Boletus aereus. h, Lepiota procera.
No. 1538, 1000sh, Ganoderma lucidum. No. 1539, 1000sh, Collybia distorta.

1996, Dec. 17
Sheets of 8, #a-h
1536-1537 A255   Set of 2   32.50 32.50
Souvenir Sheets
1538-1539 A255   Set of 2   18.00 18.00

Souvenir Sheet

Watercolor Painting — A256

Illustration reduced.

1996, May 6   **Litho.**   **Perf. 13**
1540 A256 500sh multicolored   4.75   4.75
China '96. No. 1540 was not available until March 1997.

Sun Yat-Sen
(1866-1925)
A257

Various portraits.

1997   **Perf. 14**
1541 A257   300sh Sheet of 6,
     #a.-f.   13.00 13.00
Souvenir Sheet
1542 A257 1000sh multi   8.50   8.50
Hong Kong '97.

Horses
A258

No. 1543: a, Blue Arabian horse. b, English thoroughbred. c, Tennessee walking horse. d, Anglo-Arab horse.
No. 1544: a, Trakehner. b, American saddlebred. c, Morgan. d, Frederiksborg. e, Mirror

of #d. f, Mirror of #c. g, Mirror of #b. h, Mirror of #a.
No. 1545, 1000sh, Wielkopolski. No. 1546, 1000sh, Thiawari, vert.

1997, Mar. 20   **Litho.**   **Perf. 14**
1543 A258 250sh Strip of 4,
     #a.-d.   8.50   8.50
1544 A258 250sh Sheet of 8,
     #a.-h.   15.00 15.00
Souvenir Sheets
1545-1546 A258   Set of 2   15.00 15.00
No. 1543 was issued in sheets of 8 stamps with second strip in reverse order.

COMESA
A259

Designs140sh, Tourism. 180sh, Fishing. 200sh, Dar es Salaam Port. 300sh, TAZARA Railway.

1997   **Perf. 13**
1547-1550 A259   Set of 4   7.00   7.00
Souvenir Sheet
1551 A259 500sh Cotton   4.75   4.75

UN
Volunteers,
25th Anniv.
A260

Designs: 140sh, Health of mother and child. 200sh, Food distribution. 260sh, Clean water distribution. 300sh, Public education.
500sh, Refugee camp.

1997
1552-1555 A260   Set of 4   7.50   7.50
Souvenir Sheet
1556 A260 500sh multicolored   5.50   5.50

Birds
A261

Designs: 150sh, Mockingbird. 200sh, House finch. 410sh, Bridled titmouse. 500sh, Cactus wren.
No. 1561: a, Sooty tern. b, Nunbird. c, Mottled wood owl. d, Turquoise-browed mot mot. e, Emerald toucanet. f, Dusky-headed conure.
No. 1562: a, Maguari stork. b, Spoonbills. c, Flamingo. d, Hammerkop. e, Limpkin. f, Pink-backed pelican.
No. 1563, 1000sh, Masked booby. No. 1564, 1000sh, Brown pelican.

1997, May 5   **Litho.**   **Perf. 14**
1557-1560 A261   Set of 4   8.50   8.50
1561 A261 140sh Sheet of 6,
     #a.-f.   5.00   5.00
1562 A261 370sh Sheet of 6,
     #a.-f.   13.00 13.00
Souvenir Sheets
1563-1564 A261   Set of 2   14.00 14.00

Flowers
A262   A263

Designs: 100sh, Plumeria rubra acutifolia. 140sh, 150sh, Liliaceae. 180sh, Alamanda. 200sh, Lilaceae, diff. 210sh, Zinnia. 260sh, Malvaviscus penduliflorus. 300sh, Carna. 380sh, Nerium oleander carneum. 400sh, Hibiscus rosa sinensis. 500sh, Catharanthus

roseus. 600sh, Cartharanthus roseus. 700sh, Bougainvillea formosa. 750sh, Acalypha.
No. 1577: a, like #1571. b, like #1569. c, like #1572. d, like #1575.

1997-2004(?)		Perf. 14½x15		
1565	A262	100sh	multi	.40	.40
1566	A262	140sh	multi	.60	.60
1566A	A262	150sh	multi		
1567	A262	180sh	multi	.75	.75
1568	A262	200sh	multi	.80	.80
1569	A262	210sh	multi	.85	.85
1570	A262	260sh	multi	1.00	1.00
1571	A262	300sh	multi	1.25	1.25
1572	A262	380sh	multi	1.50	1.50
1573	A262	400sh	multi	1.60	1.60
1573A	A262	500sh	multi	1.00	1.00
1574	A262	600sh	multi	2.50	2.50
1575	A262	700sh	multi	3.00	3.00
1576	A262	900sh	multi	3.50	3.50

Nos. 1565-1566,1567-1576 (13) 18.75 18.75

Souvenir Sheet
Perf. 14½x14

1577 A263 125sh Sheet of 4,
    #a.-d. 2.00 2.00

Issued: #1566A, 1997; #1573A, 2004(?); others, 5/19.
For overprint see No. O49.

Modern Olympic Games, Cent., 1996
Summer Olympic Games,
Atlanta, — A264

1996		Litho.	Perf. 11½	
1578	A264	100sh	Tennis	.90	.90
1579	A264	150sh	Baseball	1.40	1.40
1580	A264	200sh	Soccer	1.60	1.60
1581	A264	300sh	Boxing	2.75	2.75

Nos. 1578-1581 (4) 6.65 6.65

Chernobyl
Disaster,
10th Anniv.
A265

Designs: No. 1582, Chabad's Children of Chernobyl. No. 1583, UNESCO.

1997, Apr. 25		Litho.	Perf. 13½x14	
1582	A265	700sh	multicolored	5.50	5.50
1583	A265	700sh	multicolored	5.50	5.50

Flowers
A266

No. 1583A: b, Prunus dulcis. c, Spassky Clock tower. d, Crataegus monogyna. e, Amica montana. f, Campanula patula. g, Papaver orientalis.
No. 1584: a, Malus niedzwetzkayana. b, Golden domes of the Cathedral of the Annunciation, Moscow. c, Polygonatum multiflorum. d, Leucanthemum vulgare, e, Hypencum perforatum. f, Pulsatilla vulgaris.
No. 1585, 1000sh, Laburnum anagyroides, St. Basil's Cathedral, vert. No. 1585A, 1000sh, Rosa canina, Church of Christ Resurrection, Moscow.

1997		Perf. 14x14½	
1583A	A266	200sh	Sheet of 6,
			#b.-g.	9.50	9.50

1584	A266	300sh	Sheet of 6,
			#a.-f.	14.50	14.50

Souvenir Sheets

1585-1585A	A266	Set of 2	17.50	17.50

No. 1585 contains one 30x38mm stamp.

World
AIDS Day
A267

Designs: 140sh, Condom protects against AIDS, vert. 310sh, Caution, you may contract AIDS. 370sh, Control of AIDS is our responsibility. 410sh, Care and support AIDS orphans. 500sh, Like #1586.

1997		Litho.	Perf. 13	
1586-1589	A267	Set of 4		9.50	9.50

Souvenir Sheet

1590	A267	500sh	multicolored	5.00	5.00

Paintings by
Hiroshige
(1797-1858)
A268

No. 1591: a, Aoi Slope, Outside Toranomon Gate. b, Bikuni Bridge in Snow. c, Mount Atago, Shiba. d, Akasaka Kiribatake. e, Zojoji Pagoda & Akabane. f, Hibiya & Soto-Sakurada from Yamashita-cho.
No. 1592, 1000sh, Shiba Shinmei Shrine. No. 1593, 1000sh, Kanasugibashi Shibaura.

1997, July 21		Litho.	Perf. 13½x14	
1591	A268	250sh	Sheet of 6,
			#a.-f.	10.50	10.50

Souvenir Sheets

1592-1593	A268	Set of 2	7.00	7.00

Queen
Elizabeth II
and Prince
Philip, 50th
Anniv.
A269

No. 1594: a, Engagement picture of Queen. b, Royal arms. c, Queen, Prince in casual attire. d, Prince, Queen. e, Balmoral Castle. f, Prince Philip.
1500sh, Formal portrait.

1997, July 21		Litho.	Perf. 14	
1594	A269	370sh	Sheet of 6,
			#a.-f.	10.50	10.50

Souvenir Sheet

1595	A269	1500sh	multi-
			ticolored	10.50	10.50

Return of Hong Kong to
China — A270

No. 1596 — Split design comparing modern and early photographs of: a, Clock Tower, Tsim Sha Tsu, former terminal of Kowloon-Canton Railways. b, Legislative Council Building, previously Supreme Court.
No. 1597: a, Signing of Sino-British Joint Declaration on Question of Hong Kong, 1984. b, Deng Xiaoping, Chinese leaders, c, C.F. Tung, first Chinese chief executive of Hong Kong, 1996.
Illustration reduced.

1997, July 21			Perf. 14½
1596	A270	1000sh	Sheet of 2,
			#a.-b.	10.00	10.00
1597	A270	1000sh	Sheet of 3,
			#a.-c.	15.00	15.00

No. 1597 contains 3 59x28mm stamps.

Grimm's
Fairy Tales
A271

Mother Goose — A272

No. 1598 — Rumpelstiltskin: a, Woman at spinning wheel, Prince. b, Woman, Rumpelstiltskin at spinning wheel. c, Prince, woman playing mandolin.
No. 1599, Girl whistling. No. 1600, Rumpelstiltskin.

1997			Perf. 13½x14
1598	A271	400sh	Sheet of 3,
			#a.-c.	7.00	7.00

Souvenir Sheets
Perf. 14

1599	A272	1000sh	multicolored	7.00	7.00

Perf. 13½x14

1600	A271	1500sh	multicolored	7.00	7.00

1998 Winter
Olympic Games,
Nagano — A273

Designs: 100sh, Torvill & Dean, ice dancing. 200sh, Katarina Witt, figure skating. 500sh, First Olympic winter games, 1924, curling introduced. 600sh, Pirmin Zurbriggen, downhill skiing.
No. 1605: a, Dan Jansen, 1000m speed skating. b, Alberto Tomba, slalom & giant slalom skiing. c, Herma Plank-Szabo, figure skating. d, Donna Weinbrecht, mogul skiing.
No. 1606, 1000sh, Yukio Kasaya, ski jump. No. 1607, 1000sh, Barbara Ann Scott, figure skating.

1997, Oct. 6		Litho.	Perf. 14	
1601-1604	A273	Set of 4		9.00	9.00
1605	A273	250sh	Block or
			strip of 4,
			#a.-d.	6.00	6.00

Souvenir Sheets

1606-1607	A273	Set of 2	12.50	12.50

Sinking of
MV Bukoba
A274

Designs: 140sh, Ship sinking. 350sh, Removing bodies. 370sh, Identification of the dead. 410sh, Mass funeral.
500sh, MV Bukoba.

1997, May 21		Litho.	Perf. 14	
1608-1611	A274	Set of 4		8.50	8.50

Souvenir Sheet
Perf. 14½

1612	A274	500sh	multicolored	4.25	4.25

Tourist Attractions of East
Africa — A275

Designs: 140sh, Mount Kilimanjaro. 310sh, Masai. 370sh, Zanzibar old stonetown. 410sh, Buffalo, plains of Ruaha.
500sh, Mount Kilimanjaro Kibo Peak.

1997, Oct. 9			Perf. 13½
1613-1616	A275	Set of 4	8.50	8.50

Souvenir Sheet

1617	A275	500sh	multicolored	4.25	4.25

1998 World Cup Soccer
Championships, France — A276

Teams: 100sh, Italy, 1938. 150sh, Brazil, 1970. 200sh, Uruguay, 1930. 250sh, W. Germany, 1954. 500sh, Argentina, 1978. 600sh, England, 1966.
No. 1624, 250sh, vert. — Players: a, Muller, W. Germany. b, Kocsis, Hungary. c, Pele, Brazil. d, Schillaci, Italy. e, Fontaine, France. f, Nejedly, Czechoslovakia. g, Rahn, W. Germany. h, Lineker, England.
No. 1625, 250sh — Stadiums: a, The Rose Bowl, US, 1994. b, Torino Stadium, Italy, 1934. c, Olympia Stadium, Germany, 1974. d, Azteca Sadtium, Mexico, 1970, 1986. e, Wembley, England, 1966. f, Maracana, Brazil, 1950. g, Centenary Stadium, Uruguay, 1930. h, Bernabeu Stadium, Spain, 1982.
No. 1626, 1000sh, Pele, Brazil. No. 1627, 1000sh, Eusebio, Portugal.

1997, Oct. 20	Perf. 14x13½, 13½x14		
1618-1623	A276	Set of 6	6.50	6.50

Sheets of 8, #a-h, + Label

1624-1625	A276	Set of 2	14.50	14.50

Souvenir Sheet

1626-1627	A276	Set of 2	8.50	8.50

Endangered
Species
A277

Fauna
A278

Aircraft
A281

No. 1628, 250sh — Animals of Asia: a, Tiger. b, Japanese macaque. c, Slender loris. d, Musk deer. e, Przewalski's horse. f, Red panda.

No. 1629, 250sh — Animals of Latin America: a, Night monkey. b, Woolly opossum. c, Jaguar. d, Red uakaris. e, Ringtailed coati. f, Cotton-top tamarin.

No. 1630, 250sh — Animals of North America: a, Bobcat. b, Moose. c, American bison. d, Mountain goat. e, Walrus. f, Common racoon.

No. 1630G — Animals of Africa: h, Cheetah. i, Zebra. j, Gorilla. k, Brown lesser mouse lemur. l, Rhinoceros. m. Chimpanzee.

No. 1631, 250sh — Northern wilderness animals: a, Great horned owl. b, Bald eagle. c, Coyotes. d, Grizzly bear. e, Caribou (d). f, Walrus. g, Hooded seal. h, Humpback whale (g). i, Harp seal.

No. 1632, 250sh — African safari animals a, Barbary macaque. b, Turaco. c, Giraffe (f). d, Mountain gorilla, African elephant (a, b, e, g, h). e, Zebra. f, Grant's gazelle. g, Monarch butterfly, meerkat. h, African lion. i, Rhinoceros (f).

No. 1633, 1500sh, Maned wolf. No. 1634, 1500sh, Giant panda. No. 1635, 1500sh, Gray wolf. No. 1636, 1500sh, African elephant, diff.

1997, Oct. 30   *Perf. 14*
Sheets of 6, #a-f

1628-1630	A277	Set of 3	45.00	45.00
1630G	A277	250sh Sheet of 6, #h.-m.	15.00	15.00

Sheets of 9, #a-i

1631-1632	A278	250sh Set of 2	40.00	40.00

Souvenir Sheets

1633-1636	A277	1500sh Set of 4	50.00	50.00

A279   A280

No. 1637 — Modern architecture: a, Sydney Opera House, Australia. b, Brasilia Cathedral, Brazil. c, Metropolitan Cathedral of Christ the King, Liverpool, England. d, Einstein Tower, Potsdam, Berlin, Germany. e, Solomon Guggenheim Museum, New York City, US. f, Palace of the Natl. Congress, Brasilia.

No. 1638 — Ancient wonders of the world, vert.: a, Temple of Artemis at Ephesus. b, Great Pyramid of Cheops. c, Mausoleum at Halicarnassus. d, Statue of Zeus at Olympia. e, Hanging Gardens of Babylon. f, Colossus of Rhodes.

No. 1639, 1000sh, Notre Dame Du Haut Chapel, Ronchamp, France. No. 1640, 1000sh, Lighthouse of Alexandria.

1997, Nov. 5   *Perf. 14*

1637	A279	140sh Sheet of 6, #a.-f.	6.00	6.00
1638	A279	370sh Sheet of 6, #a.-f.	16.00	16.00

Souvenir Sheets

1639-1640	A279	Set of 2	15.00	15.00

Nos. 1639-1640 contain one 42x57mm or 57x42mm stamp, respectively.

1997, Nov. 28   *Wmk. 233*

Coastal Birds: 140sh, Red hornbill. 350sh, Sacred ibis, horiz. 370sh, Sea gulls, horiz. 410sh, Ring-necked dove, horiz. 500sh, Hornbill, ibis, gulls, doves, horiz.

1641-1644	A280	Set of 4	9.00	9.00

Souvenir Sheet

1645	A280	500sh multicolored	3.75	3.75

Fighter Planes: 100sh, P-51D. 200sh, Lockheed P-38J Lightning. 300sh, B-29 Superfortress. 400sh, Lockheed P-80 Shooting Star P-80 A1. 500sh, Curtiss P-36A.

No. 1651, 150sh — Spitfires: a, MK IX providing altitude cover for bomber formations. b, MK Vc dog fighting. c, PRMK XIX, Photographic Reconnaissance Development Unit, RAF. d, MK Vb over North Africa. e, FR XIVE firing rockets. f, MK VIII (ZPZ), Japanese bomber. g, Supermarine Seafire being catapulted from HMS Indomitable. h, MK IX during D-Day landings. i, MK XII attacking V1 Flying Bomb.

No. 1652, 150sh — Spitfires: a, MK IXc, excorting crippled Lancaster Bomber. b, MK 1a dog fighting. c, PR MK XI, 14th Photo Sqdn., US 8th Air Force. d, MK Vb, North Africa. e, MK VIII with lightning bolt on nose. f, MK Vc with RAF, Yugoslav, American markings. g, Supermarine Seafire landing on British carrier. h, MK IXc D-Day. i, MK XII destroying V-1 Flying Bomb.

No. 1653, 150sh — a, MKII in desert. b, Hurribomber dog fighting. c, MK 24, photo reconnaissance. d, Canadian MK 1 foreign squadron. e, Mark IXC convoy protection. f, Spitfire with clipped wings flanked by MK 22. g, Hurricanes MKII in desert. h, Hurribomber.

No. 1654, 1000sh, Boeing P-26. No. 1655, 1000sh, SR-71A. No. 1656, 1000sh, MK Vb. No. 1657, 1000sh,MK V Float plane. No. 1658, 1000sh, MK 1.

1997, Dec. 23   *Litho.*   *Perf. 14*

1646-1650	A281	Set of 5	11.00	11.00

Sheets of 9, #a-i

1651-1652	A281	Set of 2	15.00	15.00
1653	A281	250sh Sheet of 8, #a.-h.	25.00	25.00

Souvenir Sheets

1654-1658	A281	Set of 5	40.00	40.00

No. 1656 contains one 85x28mm stamp. Nos. 1657-1658 each contain one 57x42mm stamp.

Jackie Chan, Movie Star A282

Various portraits.

1997, Dec. 30

1659	A282	370sh Sheet of 6, #a.-f.	15.00	15.00

PAPU (Pan African Postal Union), 18th Anniv. A283

Designs: 150sh, Natl. flag of Tanzania, flag of PAPU. 250sh, PAPU emblem. 400sh, Delivery by EMS motorcycles. 500sh, Giraffes.

1998, Jan. 18   *Perf. 13½*

1660-1663	A283	Set of 4	9.50	9.50

A284   A285

1998   *Litho.*   *Perf. 14*

1664	A284	410sh Mt. Kilimanjaro	3.00	3.00

1998, Jan. 23

Diana, Princess of Wales (1961-97): 150sh, In red jacket. 250sh, In lilac dress. 1000sh, In teal suit with Prince Harry (in sheet margin).

1665	A285	150sh multicolored	1.10	1.10
1666	A285	250sh multicolored	1.90	1.90

Souvenir Sheet

1667	A285	1000sh multicolored	7.00	7.00

Nos. 1665-1666 were each issued in sheets of 9.

Marine Life and Sea Birds A286

No. 1668: a, Black-browed albatross. b, Unidentified bird. c, Xantusi murrelet. d, Empress angelfish. e, Bottle nosed dolphins. f, Queen angelfish. g, Red sponge. h, Unidentified red and tan fish. i, Reef shark. j, Sea star. k, Unidentified white and black fish. l, Stingray.

No. 1669, 250sh: a, Black-saddled pufferfish. b, Harlequin tuskfish. c, Emperor angelfish. d, Foxface. e, Yellow tang. f, Catalina goby. g, Fifteen-spined stickleback. h, Banded pipefish. i, Weather loach.

No. 1670, 250sh, vert.: a, Octopus. b, Pantherfish. c, Hawksbill turtle. d, Skate. e, Jellyfish. f, White tip shark. g, Blue starfish. h, Brain coral. i, Anemone.

No. 1671, 1000sh, Clown fish. No. 1672, 1000sh, Shark. No. 1673, 1000sh, Yellow seahorse, vert.

1998, Jan. 30

1668	A286	200sh Sheet of 12, #a.-l.	17.00	17.00

Sheets of 9, #a-i

1669-1670	A286	Set of 2	37.50	37.50

Souvenir Sheets

1671-1673	A286	Set of 3	22.50	22.50

For overprints see #1697-1702.

Traditional Weapons — A287

Designs: 150sh, Slingshot. 250sh, Cutlass and club. 400sh, Gun. 500sh, Bow, arrows.

1998, Mar. 16   *Litho.*   *Perf. 14*

1674-1677	A287	Set of 4	9.00	9.00

New Year 1998 (Year of the Tiger) — A288

No. 1678 — Stylized tiger: a, Walking right. b, Walking left. c, Lying down. d, Seated. 1500sh, Tiger standing.

1998, Mar. 30   *Litho.*   *Perf. 13½*

1678	A288	370sh Sheet of 4, #a.-d.	10.00	10.00

Souvenir Sheet

1679	A288	1500sh multicolored	10.00	10.00

John Denver (1943-97), Rock Musician — A288a

No. 1679A: c, Wearing green sweater. d, Wearing brown sweater (shoulders in middle of stamp). e, Wearing brown sweater (shoulder near corner of stamp). f, Wearing green sweater, hand at face. 1500sh, Wearing blue shirt.

1998, Apr. 30   *Litho.*   *Perf. 14*

1679A	A288a	370sh Sheet of 4, #c-f	5.00	5.00

Souvenir Sheet

1679B	A288a	1500sh multi	5.00	5.00

Most examples of Nos. 1679A-1679B were not available in the philatelic marketplace until Dec. 2002.

Antique Automobiles — A289

No. 1680, 370sh: a, 1901 Mercedes 35hp. b, 1903 Ford Model A. c, 1908 Legnano Type A. d, 1908-09 Rolls Royce 40-50hp Silver Ghost. e, 1910 Renault Petit Duc. f, 1913 Fischer Torpedo.

No. 1681, 370sh: a, 1923-24 Peugeot 18cv. b, 1926 Daimler 25-85hp. c, 1932 Bugatti Type 50T. d, 1933 Pierce-Arrow V12 "Silver Arrow." e, 1934 Tatra V8. f, 1937 Grosser Mercedes Benz.

No. 1682, 1000sh, 1900 Benz. No. 1683, 1000sh, 1893 Duryea.

1998, Aug. 4   *Litho.*   *Perf. 14*
Sheets of 6, #a-f

1680-1681	A289	Set of 2	35.00	35.00

Souvenir Sheets

1682-1683	A289	Set of 2	17.50	17.50

Nos. 1682-1683 each contain one 64x48mm stamp.

Flowers and Insects A290

No. 1684, vert: a, Euanthe sanderiana, teirataenia surinama. b, "Clown Mixed." c, Pansies, caterpiller of papilio polyxenes. d, "Prelude." e, Dendrobium primulinum, wasp beetle. f, Carrion beetle, clematis "Lasurstern." g, Sunflowers, "Autumn Beauty" & "Italian White," elder borer, painted daisy. h, Grape hyacinth.

No. 1685, 250sh: a, Platinum sun. b, Vespid wasp, oriental poppy. c, Anemone. d, Ipomoea alba, king's bee hawkmoth. e, Aussie delight, potter wasp. f, Colorado potato beetle, Japanese iris. g, Bomarea caldasii, azure damselfly. h, Hybrid macranthe, queen bumblebee. i, Love with lace iris, click beetle.

No. 1686, 250sh: a, Golden ray lily, South African longhorn beetle. b, Oncidium macianthum. c, Agelia petali, dendrobium. c, Cobaea scandens. d, Goldsmith beetle, paphiopedilum gilda. e, Iceland poppies, potter wasp. f, Pink beauty. g, Annual chrysanthemums. h, Little mal, m. femurrubrum.

No. 1687, 1500sh, Carolina Queen. No. 1688, 1500sh, Robert E. Lee daffodils. No.

1689, 1500sh, Orange scarlet hybrid "Tempo." No. 1690, 1500sh, Pansies.

1998, Aug. 18   Litho.   Perf. 14
1684 A290 250sh Sheet of 8,
             #a.-h.   22.50 22.50
Sheets of 9, #a-i
1685-1686 A290 Set of 2   25.00 25.00
Souvenir Sheets
1687-1690 A290 Set of 2   40.00 40.00

A291

Endangered Species — A292

No. 1691: a, Hyacinth macaw. b, Gibbon. c, Bosman's potto. d, Scarlet crowned barbets. e, Giant anteater. f, Cacomistle. g, Tiger. h, Mara. i, Mandrill. j, Crocodile. k, Wood turtle. l, Baribusa.

No. 1692: a, Giant sable antelope. b, Cheetah. c, Giraffe. d, Black bear. e, African elephant. f, Giant panda.

No. 1693: a, Tiger. b, Bald eagle (a, c). c, Mountain gorilla. d, Sea lion. e, Green sea turtle. f, Hippopotamus.

No. 1694, Emerald tanager.

No. 1695, 1500sh, Florida manatee. No. 1696, 1500sh, Orangutan.

1998, Aug. 31   Litho.   Perf. 14
1691 A291 200sh Sheet of
             12, #a.-l.   17.00 17.00
1692 A292 370sh Sheet of 6,
             #a.-f.   15.00 15.00
1693 A292 370sh Sheet of 6,
             #a.-f.   15.00 15.00
Souvenir Sheets
1694 A291 1500sh multi   13.50 13.50
1695-1696 A292 Set of 2   27.00 27.00

Nos. 1692, 1695 each contain 51x38mm stamps. No. 1696 contains 43x28mm stamps.

Nos. 1668-1673 Ovptd.

1998, Sept. 2   Litho.   Perf. 14
1697 A286 200sh Sheet of 12,
             #a.-l.
             (#1668)   22.50 22.50
1698 A286 250sh Sheet of 9
             #a.-i.
             (#1669)   11.00 11.00
1699 A286 250sh Sheet of 9
             #a.-i.
             (#1670)   11.00 11.00
Souvenir Sheets
1700 A286 1000sh multi
             (#1671)   7.00   7.00
1701 A286 1000sh multi
             (#1672)   7.00   7.00
1702 A286 1000sh multi
             (#1673)   7.00   7.00

The stamps of Nos. 1697-1699, 1701-1702 were ovptd. with Intl. Year of the Ocean emblem and the sheet margins contain one or two emblems with words "INTERNATIONAL YEAR OF THE OCEAN." No. 1700 has overprint only on sheet margin.

Aircraft
A293

No. 1703, 300sh: a, Antoinette IV, 1908. b, Deperdussin Racer, 1912. c, Demoiselle, 1909. d, Bleriot XI, 1909. e, Avro FAV Roe, 1912. f, Breguet IV, 1910.

No. 1704, 300sh: a, Deperdussin. b, Ultralight, 1979-86. c, Amphibian, 1929-30. d, Pitts Special, 1930. e, BAC-221, 1960. f, Avro Tutor, 1931.

No. 1705, 300sh: a, KI-44 Tojo. b, Hawker Fury. c, Mustang. d, Zero. e, Travel Air Mystery Ship. f, F8F Bearcat.

No. 1706, 1000sh, USAAF Curtiss P-40M. No. 1707, 1000sh, Biplane. No. 1708, 1000sh, Balloon.

1998, Aug. 4   Litho.   Perf. 14
Sheets of 6, #a-f
1703-1705 A293 Set of 3   35.00 35.00
Souvenir Sheets
1706-1708 A293 Set of 3   22.50 22.50

No. 1704a incorrectly inscribed 1900.

Eagles
A294

No. 1709: a, Pallas's fish. b, Bateleur. c, Martial. d, Golden. e, Wedge-tailed. f, Java hawk.

1500sh, Wedge-tailed, diff.

1998, Aug. 31
1709 A294 370sh Sheet of 6,
             #a.-f.   15.00 15.00
Souvenir Sheet
1710 A294 1500sh multi-
             ticolored   11.00 11.00

Fauna and
Flora
A295

Designs: 250sh, Takahe. 410sh, Lear's macaw. 500sh, Ring-tailed lemur. 600sh, Arabian oryx.

No. 1715, 370sh, : a, Japanese crested ibis. b, Kuai O'o. c, Bourke's hairstreak. d, Quokka. e, Tahitian lorikeet. f, Black-faced tamarin.

No. 1716, 370sh: a, Loggerhead turtle. b, Snow leopard. c, Gurney's pitta. d, Lowland gorilla. e, Echo parakeet. f, Orangutan.

No. 1717, 1500sh, Giant panda. No. 1718, 1500sh, Bengal tiger.

1998, Aug. 31   Perf. 14x14½
1711-1714 A295 Set of 4   13.50 13.50
Sheets of 6, #a-f
1715-1716 A295 Set of 2   22.50 22.50
Souvenir Sheets
1717-1718 A295 Set of 2   15.00 15.00

Children's
Rights
A296

Designs: 150sh, Equal rights for boys and girls. 250sh, Right to education. 400sh, Right not to be beaten, vert. No. 1722, 500sh, Right to be loved, vert.

No. 1723, Right to education.

1998   Perf. 13
1719-1722 A296 Set of 4   8.00   8.00
Souvenir Sheet
1723 A296 500sh multicolored 3.25   3.25

Nos. 608, 610
Surcharged

1998   Method and Perf. as Before
1723A A99 150sh on 13sh #608
1723B A99 150sh on 20sh #610   — —

Issued: No. 723A, 1/26; No. 1723B, 3/16.

World
Stamp
Day — A297

Designs: 150sh, UPU Emblem. 250sh, Letter facing and date stamping. 400sh, Trusted messenger. 500sh, Letter posting. No. 1728, Trusted messenger, letter posting, UPU emblem.

1998, Oct. 9   Wmk. 387   Perf. 14
1724-1727 A297 Set of 4   8.00   8.00
Souvenir Sheet
1728 A297 500sh multicolored 3.25   3.25

A298

Marine
Life, Sea
Birds
A299

Designs: 150sh, Equal sea star. 250sh, Mountain crab. 400sh, Wolffish. 500sh, Purple sea urchin.

No. 1733: a, Barred antshrike. b, Yellow-nosed albatross, common tern. c, Common tern, killer whale. d, Crimson-rumped toucanet. e, French angelfish. f, Grey shark (e). g, Manta ray (f, h). h, Yellow-backed damselfish. i, Green parrot wrasse. j, Silver badgerfish, pyjama wrasse. k, Skate, red-knobbed starfish (h). l, Striped snapper.

No. 1734: a, Common dolphin. b, Blue marlin. c, Arctic tern. d, Blackedge moray. e, Loggerhead turtle. f, Blacktip shark. g, Two-spotted octopus. h, Manta ray. i, Sailfin tang.

No. 1735, 1000sh, Aequipecten opercularis. No. 1736, 1000sh, Chrysaora quinquecirrha. 1500sh, Skate.

1998, Oct. 12
1729-1732 A298 Set of 4   9.00   9.00
1733 A299 200sh Sheet of 12,
             #a.-l.   17.00 17.00
1734 A298 300sh Sheet of 9,
             #a.-i.   21.00 21.00
Souvenir Sheets
1735-1736 A298 Set of 2   12.00 12.00
1737 A299 1500sh multi   9.00   9.00

Intl. Year of the Ocean (#1733-1737).

Mushrooms and Insects — A300

Designs: 140sh, Cardinal beetle, tricholoma batschii. 150sh, Tricholoma catigatum, painted lady. 200sh, Lyophylum decastes, speckled wood butterfly. 250sh, Tricholoma flavovfrens, speckled bush cricket. 370sh, Boletus chrysenteron, shieldbug. 410sh, Boletus zelleri, darter dragonfly. 500sh, Gyroporus castaneus, tortoise beetle. 600sh, Hissing cockroach, boletus satanas.

No. 1746, 250sh: a, Hygrocybe miniata, shieldbug. b, Peacock butterfly, cystolepiata adulterina. c, Collybia dryophila, bush cricket. d, Omphalotus olearius, halloween pennant butterfly. e, Macrolepiota rhacodes, helicon butterfly. f, Macrole piota puellaris, hornet. g, Carpenter bee. h, Mycena epipteryia, South African longhorn beetle. i, Amanita muscaria, skipper butterfly.

No. 1747 250sh, vert.: a, Leaf hopper cicadia, pleurotus ostreatus. b, Amanita muscaria, froghopper beetle. c, Wasp, amanita umbrinolutea. d, Butterfly, onnia tomentosa. e, Monarch butterfly, ganoderma lucidum. f, Broad-bodied libellua, macrolepiota procera. g, Butterfly anthocharis, suillus granulatus. h, Egyptian grasshopper, cortinarius praestans. i, Flying bush cricket, marasmius ramealis.

No. 1748, 1500sh, Coprinus silvaticus, thornbug. No. 1749, 1500sh, Black swallowtail, chroogomphus rutilus.

1998, Nov. 27
1738-1745 A300 Set of 8   17.00 17.00
Sheets of 9, #a-i
1746-1747 A300 Set of 2   35.00 35.00
Souvenir Sheets
1748-1749 A300 Set of 2   22.50 22.50

Rudolph the
Red-Nosed
Reindeer
A301

No. 1752, 200sh: a, Milo. b, Rudolph (face). c, Leonard. d, Stormella. e, Ridley. f, Boone.

No. 1753, 200sh: a, Santa. b, Rudolph. c, Doggle. d, Edgar. e, Baby Rudolph. f, Toys.

No. 1754, 1000sh, Leonard, horiz. No. 1755, 1000sh, Rudolph. No. 1756, 1000sh, Baby Rudolph with ball on nose, diff. No. 1757, 1000sh, Santa with Rudolph.

Perf. 13½x14, 14x13½
1998, Dec. 15   Litho.
Sheets of 6, #a-f
1752-1753 A301 Set of 2   10.00 10.00
Souvenir Sheets
1754-1757 A301 Set of 2   17.50 17.50

Ferrari Automobiles — A301a

No. 1757A: c, GTO. d, F40. e, 512S. 100sh, Breadvan.
Illustration reduced.

1998, Dec. 16   Litho.   Perf. 14
1757A A301a 500sh Sheet of
              3, #c-e   9.00   9.00
Souvenir Sheet
Perf. 13¾x14¼
1757B A301a 1000sh multi   6.00   6.00

No. 1757A contains three 39x25mm stamps.

Diana, Princess
of Wales (1961-
97)
A302

1998, Dec. 16   Perf. 14
1758 A302 600sh multicolored 3.50   3.50

No. 1758 was issued in sheets of 6.

Picasso — A303

Paintings: No. 1759, 400sh, Jacquelin with Crossedhand, 1954. No. 1760, 400sh, Straw Hat with Blue Foilage, 1936. 500sh, Reading the Letter, 1921.
1500sh, Woman Writing, 1934.

1998, Dec. 16   *Perf. 14½*
1759-1761 A303   Set of 3   7.50 7.50
Souvenir Sheet
1762 A303 1500sh multicolored   8.50 8.50

Mohandas Gandhi — A304

1998, Dec. 16   *Perf. 14*
1763 A304   370sh Portrait   3.00 3.00
Souvenir Sheet
1764 A304 1500sh Jawaharlal Nehru   10.00 10.00

No. 1763 was issued in sheets of 4.

1998 World Scout Jamboree, Chile A305

No. 1765: a, US Pres. William Howard Taft greets scouts during early years, 1908. b, Early Cub Scout pack enjoys musical camp break, 1930's. c, Dan Beard demonstrates tomahawk throw at Silver Bay, 1912.
1500sh, Ernest Thompson Seton (1860-1946), first Chief Scout.

1998, Dec. 16   *Litho.*   *Perf. 14*
1765 A305   600sh Sheet of 3, #a.-c.   10.50 10.50
Souvenir Sheet
1766 A305 1500sh multicolored   9.50 9.50

Royal Air Force, 80th Anniv. A306

No. 1767: a, Panavia Tornado F3. b, Sepecat Jaguar GR1A. c, Jaguar GR1A. d, Jaguar GR1A, diff.
No. 1768, 1000sh, Harrier, Eurofighter. No. 1769, 1000sh, Biplane, hawk.

1998, Dec. 16   *Perf. 14*
1767 A306   500sh Sheet of 4, #a.-d.   12.50 12.50
Souvenir Sheets
1768-1769 A306   Set of 2   14.00 14.00

New Year 1999 (Year of the Rabbit) A307

No. 1770 - Color of rabbit : a, Red brown. b, Spotted. c, Yellow. d, Brown.
1500sh, White.

1999, Jan. 18   *Perf. 14*
1770 A307   250sh Sheet of 4, #a.-d.   7.00 7.00
Souvenir Sheet
1771 A307 1500sh multicolored   9.00 9.00

Tourism in Zanzibar A308

Designs: 100sh, Dhow Harbor, vert. 150sh, Girl on giant tortoise, vert. 250sh, Children with giant tortoise. 300sh, Street in Stone Town, vert. 400sh, Old fort. 500sh, Red colobus monkeys.
600sh, Girl on tortoise, street in Stone Town.

1998, Nov. 10   *Litho.*   *Perf. 14*
1772-1777 A308   Set of 6   11.00 11.00
Souvenir Sheet
1778 A308 600sh multicolored   4.75 4.75

Tanzanian Posts Corp., 5th Anniv. A309

Designs: 150sh, Rural post office. 250sh, Overnight mail service. 350sh, Money fax service. 400sh, Post shop business.
500sh, Exterior view of high rise building, vert.

1999, Jan. 1
1779-1782 A309   Set of 4   7.00 7.00
Souvenir Sheet
1783 A309 500sh multicolored   3.50 3.50

Butterflies A310

200sh, Calycopis cecrops. 250sh, Heliconis melpomena, vert. 370sh, Citherias menander, vert. 410sh, Heliconis antiochus, vert.
No. 1788, 200sh: a, Acraea cerasa. b, Acraea semivitrea. c, Euchrysops scintilla. d, Papilio phorcas. e, Euphaedra eusemoides. f, Acraea masamba. g, Phyciodes emerantia. h, Hypothiris tricolor. i, Orimba jansoni.
No. 1789, 200sh: a, Papilio zagreus. b, Chlosyne narva. c, Phyciodes alsina. d, Pyronia bathseba. e, Eurema daira. f, Eurytides xanticles. g, Clossiana titania. h, Euphydryas cynthia. i, Polygonia c-album.
No. 1790, 1500sh, Ornithoptera priamus, vert. No. 1791, 1500sh, Phyciodes, vert.

1999, Feb. 18
1784-1787 A310   Set of 4   7.50 7.50
Sheets of 9, #a-i
1788-1789 A310   Set of 2   15.00 15.00
Souvenir Sheets
1790-1791 A310   Set of 2   19.00 19.00

Birds A311

No. 1792, 370sh: a, Yellow billed stork. b, Black egret. c, Crowned lapwing. d, Snowy plover. e, Crowned crane. f, Saddlebilled stork.
No. 1793, 370sh: a, Great blue heron. b, Chinese egret. c, Horned puffins. d, White faced ibis. e, Greater flamingo. f, Blue footed boobie.
No. 1794, 370sh: a, Blacksmith plover. b, Brolga crane. c, Green-backed heron. d, Straw-necked ibis. e, Little bittern. f, Marabou stork.
No. 1795, 370sh, vert.: a, Sandhill crane. b, Great egret. c, Spoonbill. d, Yellow-crowned night heron. e, Glossy ibis. f, Willet.
No. 1796, 1500sh, Purple heron. No. 1797, 1500sh, Kittliz's sandplover, vert. No. 1798, 1500sh, Black-crowned night heron. No. 1799, 1500sh, Black-headed heron.

1999, Feb. 18
Sheets of 6, #a-f
1792-1795 A311   Set of 4   40.00 40.00
Souvenir sheets
1796-1799 A311   Set of 4   35.00 35.00

A312   A313

Cats A314

Designs: No. 1800, 200sh, Bengal, horiz. No. 1801, 250sh, Seal lynx point birman. No. 1802, 370sh, Calico British shorthair, horiz. No. 1803, 420sh, Blue & white cornish rex.
Nos. 1804, 100sh, Burmese. No. 1805, 140sh, Burmilla. No. 1806, 150sh, Turkish van. No. 1807, 200sh, Snowshoe. No. 1808, 250sh, Bombay. No. 1809, 370sh, Seychellois longhair.
No. 1810: a, Silver classic tabby. b, Auburn Turkish van. c, Seal bicolor ragdoll. d, European shorthair. e, Black & white British shorthair. f, Gold California spangled. g, Chocolate tipped Burmilla. h, Red classic tabby manx.
No. 1811, 370sh: a, Pekeface Persian. b, American curl shorthair. c, Korat. d, Himalayan Persian. e, Exotic shorthair. f, Scottish fold.
No. 1812, 370sh: a, European shorthair. b, Chartreux. c, British shorthair. d, Maine coon. e, Japanese bobtail. f, Birman.
No. 1813 - Kittens chasing butterflies: a, Black & white kitten, butterfly UL. b, Black & white kitten, butterfly UR. c, Black & yellow kitten, butterfly UR. d, Yellow kitten, butterfly UL.
No. 1814, 1500sh, Black & white Persian, horiz. No. 1815, 1500sh, Cream tabby European shorthair.
No. 1816, 1500sh, American shorthair. No. 1817, 1500sh, American wirehair. No. 1818, Kitten, butterfly, vert.

1999, Feb. 23
1800-1803 A312   Set of 4   9.00 9.00
1804-1809 A313   Set of 6   9.00 9.00
1810 A312   250sh Sheet of 8, #a.-h.   11.00 11.00
Sheets of 6, #a-f
1811-1812 A312   Set of 2   24.00 24.00
1813 A314   500sh Sheet of 4, #a.-d.   11.00 11.00
Souvenir Sheets
1814-1815 A312   Set of 2   20.00 20.00
1816-1817 A313   Set of 2   20.00 20.00
1818 A314 1500sh multi   10.00 10.00

Military Helicopters — A316

No. 1823: a, Germany DF 4. b, Germany. c, France. d, US, with rocket pods. e, US, with suspended lift sling. f, France, red on tail boom & stabilizers.

1999
1823 A316 370sh Sheet of 6, #a.-f.   14.00 14.00

Unidentified Flying Objects (UFOs) — A317

No. 1824, 370sh: a, US, 1968. b, Trinidad, 1958. c, Belgium, 1990. d, Finland, 1970. e, New Zealand, 1951. f, Australia, 1954.
No. 1825, 370sh: a, McMinnville, 1950. b, Albuquerque, 1963. c, Gulf Breeze, 1988. d, Madre de Dios, 1952. e, Merlin, 1964. f, Mexico City, 1991.
No. 1826, 1500sh, The Arnold Sighting, 1947. No. 1827, 1500sh, The Mantell case, 1948.

1999
Sheets of 6, #a-f
1824-1825 A317   Set of 2   16.00 16.00
Souvenir Sheets
1826-1827 A317   Set of 2   18.00 18.00

Dogs A318

No. 1828: a, Boston terrier. b, Tyrolean hound. c, Rottweiler. d, Golden retriever. e, English bulldog. f, Spanish greyhound. g, Long-haired dachshund. h, Scottish terrier. i, Pekingese.
1500sh, English cocker spaniel.

1999
1828 A318   200sh Sheet of 9, #a.-i.   10.00 10.00
Souvenir Sheet
1829 A318 1500sh multicolored   9.00 9.00

Dinosaurs — A319

Designs: 200sh, Stegosaurus (inscribed Edmontonia). 250sh, Archaeopteryx. 370sh, Stegosaurus. 410sh, Lagosuchus.
No. 1834, 370sh: a, Dromiceiomimus. b, Saurolophus. c, Camarasaurus. d, Protoceratops. e, Psittacosaurus. f, Stegoceras.
No. 1835, 370sh: a, Gallimimus. b, Peteinosaurus. c, Lambeosaurus. d, Coelophysis. e, Parasaurolophus. f, Tyrannosaurus rex.
No. 1836, 1500sh, Quetzalcoatlus. No. 1837, 1500sh, Rhomaleosaurus.

1999, Apr. 30   *Litho.*   *Perf. 14*
1830-1833 A319   Set of 4   7.50 7.50

19th Century Ships A315

No. 1819, 370sh: a, Prince Consort (1). b, USS Kearsage (2). c, HMS Victoria (3). d, USS Brooklyn (4). e, Mount Stewart (5). f, Hougomont (6).
No. 1820, 370sh: a, Charles W. Morgan (1). b, RMS Britannia (2). c, Great Britain (3). d, Flying Cloud (4). e, HMS Warrior (5). f, Lightning (6).
No. 1821, 1500sh, Cutty Sark. No. 1822, 1500sh, Great Eastern.

1999, Feb. 9   *Litho.*   *Perf. 14*
Sheets of 6, #a-f
1819-1820 A315   Set of 2   29.00 29.00
Souvenir Sheets
1821-1822 A315   Set of 2   19.00 19.00
Nos. 1821-1822 each contain one 57x43mm stamp.

Sheets of 6, #a-f

1834-1835 A319 Set of 2   29.00 29.00

Souvenir Sheets

1836-1837 A319 Set of 2   19.00 19.00

Tourism
A320

No. 1838: a, Hoofed animals. b, Mount Kilimanjaro, crater. c, Animal life. d, Sacred ibis. e, Ngorongoro crater. f, Giraffe. g, Lions. h, Dik diks. i, Vulture. j, Lion cubs. k, Elephants. l, African lion. m, Stone Town, Zanzibar. n, National Museum. o, Carved door, Zanzibar. p, Map showing Zanzibar, Pemba, Indian Ocean. q, Herding animals. r, Fishing. s, Lion cub. t, Buildings, boats along shore. u, Masai. v, Birds wading in water. w, Buffalo stampede. x, Like #1838b, closer view.

1999   **Perf. 14½x14**

Booklet Stamps

1838	A320	Souvenir Booklet	11.00	
a.-x.		150sh any single	.45	.45
y.		Booklet pane, #1838a-1838f	2.75	
z.		Booklet pane, #1838g-1838l	2.75	
aa.		Bklt. pane, #1838m-1838r	2.75	
ab.		Bklt. pane, #1838s-1838x	2.75	

Space Exploration — A321

Designs: 70sh, Edward White. 100sh, Gemini 7. 150sh, Mir, Russian space station, vert. 200sh, Laika, Russian space dog. 250sh, Apollo Command & Service Modules. 370sh, Apollo Lunar Module.
1500sh, Saturn V Moon Rocket, vert.

1999   **Perf. 14**

1839-1844 A321 Set of 6   8.00 8.00

Souvenir Sheet

1845 A321 1500sh multicolored   10.00 10.00

Airships, Balloons — A322

No. 1846: a, Graf Zeppelin, 1935 (b). b, Knabenshue Airship, 1905. c, British R-100, 1931. d, Hindenburg, 1937 (c). e, French Balloon, 1783. f, French Balloon, 1912.
1500sh, Sport ballooning.

1999

1846 A322 370sh Sheet of 6, #a.-f.   12.00 12.00

Souvenir Sheet

1847 A322 1500sh multicolored   8.00 8.00

Marine Life
A323

Designs: 200sh, Powder blue surgeon. 250sh, Frilled anemone. 310sh, Red-finned batfish. 410sh, Red beard sponge.
No. 1852, 250sh: a, Right whale. b, Fin whale. c, Humpback whale. d, Tucuxi. e, Gray's beaked whale. f, Sperm whale. g, Bottlenose dolphin. h, Hector's dolphin. i, Hourglass dolphin.

No. 1853, 250sh: a, Horn shark. b, Nurse shark. c, Bonnethead. d, Tiger shark. e, Bull shark. f, Leopard shark. g, Blue shark. h, Zebra shark. i, Oceanic whitetip.
No. 1854, 1500sh, Pacific Electric ray, vert.
No. 1855, 1500sh, Loggerhead turtle, vert.

1999, Feb. 9   **Litho.**   **Perf. 14**

1848-1851 A323 Set of 4   5.50 5.50

Sheets of 9, #a.-i.

1852-1853 A323 Set of 2   27.50 27.50

Souvenir Sheets

1854-1855 A323 Set of 2   16.00 16.00

Airplanes
A324

Designs: 20sh, Oiseau Bleu, 1929. 100sh, Beechcraft Model 17, 1934. No. 1858, 140sh, US Army Air Corps Beechcraft YC-43. No. 1859, 140sh, Deperdussin, 1913. 150sh, Beechcraft E17B, 1937. 200sh, Beechcraft B17L, 1936. 250sh, Beechcraft Model-G175, 1946. 370sh, Beechcraft Staggerwing Model-C17L.
No. 1864: a, Bird of Passage, Voisin Brothers, 1909. b, BS1, Geoffrey de Havilland, 1913. c, Taube-IGO Etrich, 1910. d, Curtiss Rheims Flyer, Glenn Curtiss, 1909. e, Wright Flyer III, Wright Brothers. f, Russky Vityas, Igor Sikorsky, 1913.
No. 1865: a, Sikorsky S-38. b, EFA Eurofighter. c, F-16. d, Hawker Hurricane. e, Artiplast. f, Islander.
No. 1866, 1500sh, Piper Cherokee. No. 1867, 1500sh, MiG.

1999, Feb. 14

1856-1863 A324 Set of 8   8.00 8.00

Sheets of 6

1864 A324 370sh Sheet of 6, #a.-f.   10.00 10.00
1865 A324 370sh Sheet of 6, #a.-f.   10.00 10.00

Souvenir Sheets

1866-1867 A324 Set of 2   18.00 18.00

Nos. 1866-1867 contain one 56x42mm stamp.
Stamp inscriptions are incorrect on Nos. 1865b, 1865c, and perhaps others.

African Wildlife
A325

Designs: 100sh, Black rhinoceros. 140sh, Zebra, vert. 150sh, Hippopotomus. 200sh, Nile crocodile. 250sh, African elephant, vert. 370sh, Cape buffalo.
No. 1874, 1500sh, Royal python. No. 1875, 1500sh, Giraffe.

1999, Feb. 18

1868-1873 A325 Set of 6   7.75 7.75

Souvenir Sheets

1874-1875 A325 Set of 2   18.00 18.00

Millennium — A326

Designs: 350sh, High quality health care. 400sh, Good upbringing. 700sh, An abundance of food. 750sh, Clean water for all.
1500sh, Ostrich, "Enhancement of tourism promotion," vert.

1999, Mar. 29

1876-1879 A326 Set of 4   12.00 12.00

Souvenir Sheet

1880 A326 1500sh multicolored   9.50 9.50

Sharks
A327

Designs: 200sh, Sand tiger. 250sh, Mako. 370sh, Great white. 410sh, Bull.
No. 1885: a, Basking. b, Whale. c, Tiger. d, Thresher. e, Caribbean reef. f, Nurse.
No. 1886, 1500sh, Scalloped hammerhead. No. 1887, 1500sh, Blue.

1999   **Litho.**   **Perf. 14**

1881-1884 A327 Set of 4   6.50 6.50
1885 A327 370sh Sheet of 6, #a.-f.   13.00 13.00

Souvenir Sheets

1886-1887 A327 Set of 2   17.50 17.50

Rotary Club of Dar Es Salaam, 50th Anniv.
A328

Designs: 150sh, Emblem. 250sh, Polio plus immunization, vert. 350sh, Paul P. Harris, founder of Rotary, Intl., vert. 400sh, Water supply.
500sh, Emblem, vert.

1999, June 30

1888-1891 A328 Set of 4   6.50 6.50

Souvenir Sheet

1892 A328 500sh multicolored   3.00 3.00

Endangered or Extinct Species — A330

No. 1898: a, Atitlan grebe. b, Cabot's tragopan. c, Spider monkey. d, Dibatag. e, Right whale. f, Imperial parrot. g, Cheetah. h, Brown-eared pheasant. i, Leatherback turtle. j, Imperial woodpecker. k, Andean condor. l, Barbary deer. m, Gray gentle lemur. n, Cuban parrot. o, Numbat. p, Short-tailed albatross. q, Green turtle. r, White rhinoceros. s, Diademed sifaka. t, Galapagos penguin.
No. 1899 — Tigers, horiz.: a, Caspian. b, Bengal. c, Javan. d, Indochinese. e, In white phase. f, Sumatran. g, Chinese. h, Bali. i, Siberian.
No. 1900, 1500sh, Rabbit-eared bandicoot. No. 1901, 1500sh, Grenada dove.

1999, Feb. 18

1898 A330 100sh Sheet of 20, #a.-t.   10.00 10.00
1899 A330 250sh Sheet of 9, #a.-i.   11.00 11.00

Souvenir Sheets

1900-1901 A330 Set of 2   15.00 15.00

Queen Mother (b. 1900) — A331

No. 1902: a, In Kenya, 1959. b, In 1980. c, With Prince Charles, 1950. d, lin 1990.
1500sh, In Kenya, 1959, diff.

1999, Aug. 4   **Litho.**   **Perf. 14**

1902 A331 600sh Sheet of 4, #a.-d. + label   10.00 10.00

Souvenir Sheet

Perf. 13¾

1903 A331 1500sh black   6.75 6.75

No. 1903 contains one 38x51mm stamp.

UPU, 125th Anniv.
A332

Designs: 150sh, Mail conveyance. 300sh, Letter writing competition. 350sh, UPU committee meeting. 400sh, EMS Post net track and trace.
500sh, UPU emblem.

Wmk. 387

1999, Aug. 10   **Litho.**   **Perf. 14**

1904-1907 A332 Set of 4   5.50 5.50

Souvenir Sheet

1908 A332 500sh multicolored   2.50 2.50

Souvenir Sheets

Philex France 99 — A333

Illustration reduced.
Trains: No. 1909, 1500sh, 4-8-2 compound express locomotive. No. 1910, 1500sh, TGV.

1999, Aug. 20   **Litho.**   **Perf. 13¾**

1909-1910 A333 Set of 2   14.00 14.00

Inscriptions are misspelled on Nos. 1909-1910.

Birds of Japan
A334

No. 1911, 250sh: a, Steller's sea eagle. b, Japanese blue flycatcher. c, Great gray shrike. d, Kingfisher. e, Hen harrier. f, Siberian meadow bunting. g, Mandarin duck. h, Red-necked grebe. i, Fairy pitta.
No. 1912, 250sh: a, Black paradise flycatcher. b, Laysan albatross. c, Collared Scops owl. d, Ryukyu robin. e, Japanese green woodpecker. f, Lidth's jay. g, White-naped crane. h, Copper pheasant. i, Okinawa rail.
No. 1913, 1500sh, Gyrfalcon. No. 1914, 1500sh, Japanese yellow bunting.

1999, Aug. 20

Sheets of 9, #a.-i.

1911-1912 A334 Set of 2   22.50 22.50

Souvenir Sheets

1913-1914 A334 Set of 2   15.00 15.00

Inscription on No. 1912b, and perhaps others, is misspelled.
APS StampShow '99 (#1911-1912).

Hokusai Paintings — A335

No. 1915: a, A Ferry Boat at Onmayagashi. b, A Drum Bridge at Kameido. c, Sea Life (fish). d, Sea Life (Octopus). e, Measuring a Pine Tree at Mishima Pass. f, Mount Fuji Seen From the Banks of Minobu River.
1500sh, Mount Fuji and Edo Castle Seen From Nihonbashi, horiz.

1999, Aug. 20
1915 A335 400sh Sheet of 6,
#a.-f. 12.00 12.00
Souvenir Sheet
1916 A335 1500sh mul-
ticolored 7.50 7.50

Masks — A336

Military Scenes — A337

Various masks: 150sh, 250sh, 300sh, 350sh.

1999, Aug. 20 **Perf. 14**
1917-1920 A336 Set of 4 5.00 5.00
Souvenir Sheet
1921 A336 1500sh multicolored 7.00 7.00

1999, Sept. 30
150sh, British defeat Spanish Armada, 1588, horiz. No. 1923, 250sh, Battle of Waterloo. No. 1924, 250sh, Rorke's Drift, 24th Regiment, South Wales Borderers. No. 1925, 250sh, Special Air Services, Desert Storm. No. 1926, 300sh, Soldier on horseback. No. 1927, 300sh, World War I, horiz. No. 1928, 300sh, Bland's Dragoons, Battle of Dettingen. No. 1929, 350sh, Battle of Trafalgar, horiz. No. 1930, 350sh, Light Brigade. No. 1931, 350sh, Squadron 617, the "Dam Busters." No. 1932, 400sh, World War I tank, horiz. No. 1933, 400sh, Battle of Inkerman. No. 1934, 400sh, Battle of Salamanca, horiz. No. 1935, 500sh, Gen. James Wolfe, Battle of Quebec. No. 1936, 500sh, Parachute Regiment, Battle of Arnhem. No. 1937, 500sh, Battle of the Bulge.
No. 1938, 1500sh, Battle of the Nile. No. 1939, 1500sh, Battle of Albuhera.

1922-1937 A337 Set of 16 28.00 28.00
Souvenir Sheets
1938-1939 A337 Set of 2 14.00 14.00

Ships A338

No. 1940, 400sh: a, Bayan. b, Flying Cloud. c, Mayflower. d, Santa Maria. e, Morning Star. f, Ben Venue.
No. 1941, 400sh: a, Georg Stag. b, E. Starr Jones. c, Indiana. d, Brazilian coasting vessel. e, Nova Queen. f, Rainbow.
No. 1942, 1500sh, Dutch East Indiaman. No. 1943, 1500sh, Junk.

1999, Sept. 30
Sheets of 6, #a.-f.
1940-1941 A338 Set of 2 22.50 22.50
Souvenir Sheets
1942-1943 A338 Set of 2 14.00 14.00

Trains A339

No. 1944, 400sh: a, Adler 2-2-2, 1835. b, Beuth 2-2-2, 1843. c, Class 500 4-6-0, 1900. d, Northumbrian 0-2-2, 1830. e, Class 4-6-2, 1901. f, Claud Hamilton class 4-4-0.
No. 1945, 400sh: a, Firefly class 2-2-2, 1840. b, Single, 1854. c, 4-4-0, 1891. d, Medoc class 2-4-0, 1857. e, 4-4-0, 1893. f, Numar, 1846.
No. 1946, 1500sh, Planet class 2-2-0, 1830. No. 1947, 1500sh, Vauxhall 2-2-0, 1834. No. 1948, 1500sh, Class PB 4-6-0, 1906. No. 1949, 1500sh, 4-4-0, 1855.

1999, Sept. 30
Sheets of 6, #a.-f.
1944-1945 A339 Set of 2 22.50 22.50
Souvenir Sheets
1946-1949 A339 Set of 4 15.00 15.00

Airplanes A340

Designs: 200sh, Amref. No. 1951, 250sh, Westwind 2. 300sh, Morning Star. 400sh, Piper Warrior III.
No. 1954: a, Glasair Super II. b, Glastar. c, Cessna 120. d, Europa XS. e, Beechcraft Bonanza. f, Comache GTO. g, Lancir IV. h, Comanche 400.
No. 1955, 250sh, Glastar, diff. No. 1956, 1500sh, Piper Archer III.

1999, Sept. 30 **Litho.** **Perf. 14**
1950-1953 A340 Set of 4 6.00 6.00
1954 A340 250sh Sheet of 8,
#a.-h. 10.00 10.00
Souvenir Sheets
1955-1956 A340 Set of 2 14.00 14.00

Automobiles — A341

No. 1957, 400sh: a, Audi TT Coupe. b, Mitsubishi SST Spyder. c, Honda Dream. d, Renault 20. e, Renault Spider. f, Hyundai Euro I.
No. 1958, 400sh: a, Pininfarina Ethos. b, Jaguar XK120. c, Pininfarina Ethos II. d, Rinspeed E-GO Rocket. e, Volkswagen W12 Roadster. f, Chrysler Pronto Cruiser.
No. 1959, 1500sh, Ferrari Mythos. No. 1960, 1500sh, Hyundai Euro I, diff.

1999, Sept. 30
Sheets of 6, #a.-f.
1957-1958 A341 Set of 2 22.50 22.50
Souvenir Sheets
1959-1960 A341 Set of 2 14.00 14.00

Flowers A342

Designs: 150sh, Lilium longiflorum. 250sh, Strelitzia reginea. 400sh, Zantedeschia anim lily. 600sh, Iris.
600sh, Like 400sh.

1999, Oct. 6 **Litho.** **Perf. 14**
1961-1964 A342 Set of 4 6.00 6.00
Souvenir Sheet
1965 A342 600sh multicolored 3.00 3.00

Butterflies — A343

No. 1966: a, Basilarchia archippus. b, Eueides isabella. c, Colobura dirce. d, Papilio cresphontes. e, Agrias claudia. f, Callicore maimuna.
No. 1967, 1500sh, Anteos clorinade, horiz. No. 1968, 1500sh, Tithorea harmonia, horiz.

1999, Nov. 15
1966 A343 400sh Sheet of 6,
#a.-f. 11.50 11.50
Souvenir Sheets
1967-1968 A343 Set of 2 15.00 15.00

Sea Birds A344

Designs: 150sh, Rockhopper penguin, vert. No. 1970, 250sh, Jackass penguin, vert. 300sh, Adelie penguin, vert. 350sh, White tern. 400sh, Great frigatebird. 500sh, Brown pelican.
No. 1975, 250sh: a, Manx shearwater. b, Ring-billed gull. c, Herring gull. d, Red-tailed tropic bird. e, Laysan albatross. f, Black-headed gull. g, Blue-footed booby. h, Parakeet auklet. i, Red-legged cormorant.
No. 1976, 250sh: a, Razorbill. b, Southern giant petrel. c, Atlantic puffin. d, Great cormorant. e, Northern gannet. f, Masked booby. g, Tufted puffin. h, Galapagos penguin. i, Macaroni penguin.
No. 1977, 1500sh, King penguin, vert. No. 1978, 1500sh, Emperor penguin, vert.

1999, Nov. 15
1969-1974 A344 Set of 6 10.00 10.00
Sheets of 9, #a.-i.
1975-1976 A344 Set of 2 22.50 22.50
Souvenir Sheets
1977-1978 A344 Set of 2 14.00 14.00

Dogs A345

No. 1979: a, Boxer. b, Mixed breed. c, Afghan hound. d, Chihuahua. e, Basset hound. f, Cavalier King Charles.
1500sh, Cocker spaniel.

1999, Nov. 15
1979 A345 400sh Sheet of 6,
#a.-f. 10.00 10.00
Souvenir Sheet
1980 A345 1500sh mul-
ticolored 7.50 7.50

Paintings by Xu Beihong (1895-1953) A346

No. 1981: a, Chang K'uei. b, Fisherman. c, Orchid. d, Cock and Sunflower. e, Eagle. f,

Sprite of the Mountain. g, Horse. h, Geese. i, Pigeon and Bamboo. j, Cat and Bamboo.
No. 1982: a, Spring Rain of Li River, horiz. b, The Himalayas, horiz.

1999 **Perf. 12½**
1981 A346 150sh Sheet of 10,
#a.-j. 7.50 7.50
Perf. 13
1982 A346 600sh Sheet of 2,
#a.-b. 6.00 6.00
China 1999 World Philatelic Exhibition.

Return of Macao to People's Republic of China — A347

No. 1983 — Nam Van: a, In 1850s. b, In 1930s. c, At present. d, View of lakes project.

1999 **Litho.** **Perf. 13¾**
1983 A347 300sh Sheet of 4,
#a.-d. 6.00 6.00
China 1999 World Philatelic Exhibition.

Animals of the Central American Rain Forest — A348

No. 1984: a, Red howler monkey. b, Scarlet macaw. c, Rainbow boa, tree sloth. d, Iguana. e, Fruit bat. f, Rainbow boa. g, Crocodile. h, Manatee. i, Jaguar.
1500sh, Jaguar, diff.

1999, Nov. 15 **Litho.** **Perf. 14**
1984 A348 350sh Sheet of 9,
#a.-i. 9.00 9.00
Souvenir Sheet
1985 A348 1500sh multi 4.25 4.25

Dinosaurs — A349

No. 1986: a, Tyrannosaurus. b, Coelurus. c, Stegosaurus. d, Corythosaurus. e, Thadeosaurus. f, Brachiosaurus.
1500sh, Ceratosaurus.

1999, Nov. 15
1986 A349 400sh Sheet of 6,
#a.-f. 6.50 6.50
Souvenir Sheet
1987 A349 1500sh multi 4.25 4.25
Nos. 1986-1987 dated 1998. Inscription on No. 1986f is misspelled.

Cats A350

No. 1988: a, Si-Rex. b, Spotted Mist. c, Angora. d, Persian. e, Sphynx. f, Alaskan Snow.
1500sh, Ragdoll.

1999, Nov. 15
1988 A350 400sh Sheet of 6,
#a.-f. 6.75 6.75
Souvenir Sheet
1989 A350 1500sh multi 4.50 4.50

Mushrooms
A351

150sh, Tricholoma portentosum. 250sh, Tricholomopsis rutilans. 300sh, Russula foetens. 350sh, Russula aeruginea. #1994, 400sh, Cortinarius varius. 500sh, Hygrocybe coccineocrenata.

No. 1996, 400sh: a, Agaricus abruptibulbus. b, Anellaria semiovata. c, Cystoderma carcharias. d, Amanita rubescens. e, Amanita fulva. f, Tricholoma sulphureum.

No. 1997, 400sh: a, Xerocomus rubellus. b, Geastrum rufescens. c, Lactarius salmonicolor. d, Gomphus clavatus. e, Russula rhodopoda. f, Russula paludosa.

No. 1998, 1500sh, Owl. No. 1999, 1500sh, Chipmunk and Stropharia hornemanii, horiz.

1999, Nov. 15

1990-1995	A351	Set of 6	5.50	5.50

Sheets of 6, #a.-f.

1996-1997	A351	Set of 2	13.00	13.00

Souvenir Sheets

1998-1999	A351	Set of 2	7.75	7.75

Flora and Fauna
A352

Designs: No. 2000, 150sh, Lion, vert. No. 2001, 150sh, Mountain gorilla, vert. No. 2002, 250sh, Pygmy hippopotamus, vert. No. 2003, 250sh, Japanese macaque, vert. No. 2004, 300sh, Cheetah. No. 2005, 300sh, Desert hare, vert. No. 2006, 350sh, Horned puffin. No. 2007, 350sh, Salvin's Amazon parrot. No. 2008, 400sh, Blueberries. No. 2009, 400sh, Bird's foot violet. No. 2010, 500sh, Orange groundsel. No. 2011, 500sh, Iguana.

No. 2012, 400sh: a, Polar bear. b, Woodland caribou. c, Snowy owl. d, Arctic fox. e, Willow ptarmigan. f, Arctic hare.

No. 2013, 400sh: a, White-tailed deer. b, Monarch butterfly. c, Yellow trumpet pitcher plants. d, Great blue heron. e, Yellow mud turtle. f, American alligator.

No. 2014, 400sh: a, Three-toed sloth. b, Emerald toucan. c, Praying mantis. d, Mouse opossum. e, Green palm viper. f, Phyllomedusa lemur.

No. 2015, 400sh: a, Ficus stupenda. b, Slow loris. c, Sambar deer. d, Thick-billed green pigeon. e, Bush cricket. f, Monitor lizard.

No. 2016, 1500sh, Three-toed jacamar. No. 2017, 1500sh, Chuckwallas. No. 2018, 1500sh, Swallowtail butterfly. No. 2019, 1500sh, Otter, vert.

1999, Nov. 15

2000-2011	A352	Set of 12	11.00	11.00

Sheets of 6, #a.-f.

2012-2015	A352	Set of 4	17.50	17.50

Souvenir Sheets

2016-2019	A352	Set of 4	15.00	15.00

Flowers — A353

Designs: 150sh, Foxglove. 250sh, Chrysanthemum. 400sh, Amaryllis. 500sh, Hidden lilies.

No. 2024, 350sh, horiz.: a, Gerbera daisies. b, Begonias. c, Clematis. d, Violas. e, Southern magnolia. f, Dwarf balloon flowers. g, Camellias. h, Day lilies. i, Roses.

No. 2025, 350sh, horiz.: a, Daffodils. b, Columbines. c, Nasturtiums. d, Gazanias. e, Rose. f, Crocuses. g, Trumpet vine. h, Dahlia. i, Oriental poppies.

No. 2026, 1500sh, Siberian iris. No. 2027, 1500sh, Water lily, horiz.

1999, Nov. 15   **Litho.**   **Perf. 14**

2020-2023	A353	Set of 4	3.25	3.25

Sheets of 9, #a.-i.

2024-2025	A353	Set of 2	16.00	16.00

Souvenir Sheets

2026-2027	A353	Set of 2	7.50	7.50

Military Vehicles — A354

Illustration reduced.

No. 2028, 400sh: a, French Hotchkiss H35 tank. b, German Panzer IV tank. c, US M4 tank. d, German Tiger tank. e, US Half track. f, British Cromwell tank.

No. 2029, 400sh: a, British MK IV tank. b, Japanese Type 95 tank. c, German Hunting Panther tank. d, French AMX30 tank. e, Israeli Merkava tank. f, US M1 tank.

No. 2030, 1500sh, AH-64A Apache helicopter. No. 2031, 1500sh, Austin armored car, vert.

1999, Sept. 30   **Litho.**   **Perf. 14**

Sheets of 6, #a.-f.

2028-2029	A354	Set of 2	12.00	12.00

Souvenir Sheets

2030-2031	A354	Set of 2	7.50	7.50

African Flowers — A355

Designs: 150sh, Canarina abyssinica. 250sh, Diaphananthe kamerunensis. 350sh, Protea barbigera. 500sh, Angraecum scottianum.

No. 2036, 400sh: a, Bolusanthus speciosus. b, Cassia abbreviata. c, Erythrina lysistemon. d, Leucodendron discolor. e, Romulea fischeri. f, Lupinus princei.

No. 2037, 400sh: a, Ansellia africana. b, Kigelia africana. c, Aerangis brachycarpa. d, Brachcorythis kalbreyeri. e, Begonia meyerii-johannis. f, Saintpaulia ionantha.

No. 2038, 1500sh, Nymphaea caerulea. No. 2039, 1500sh, Aloe petricola.

1999, Nov. 15

2032-2035	A355	Set of 4	3.25	3.25

Sheets of 6, #a.-f.

2036-2037	A355	Set of 2	12.00	12.00

Souvenir Sheets

2038-2039	A355	Set of 2	7.50	7.50

African Wildlife — A356

Illustration reduced.

No. 2040, horiz.: a, Mountain gorilla. b, Zebras. c, East African elephant. d, Crowned cranes. e, Cheetah. f, Tiger. g, Pygmy chimpanzee. h, Hippopotamus.

No. 2041, 1500sh, Giraffes. No. 2042, 1500sh, Rhinoceros.

1999, Nov. 15

2040	A356	300sh Sheet of 8, #a.-h.	10.00	10.00

Souvenir Sheets

2041-2042	A356	Set of 2	9.00	9.00

Marine Life
A357

Designs: 350sh, Beluga whale. 400sh, Ghost crab. 500sh, Emperor penguin, vert.

No. 2046: a, Herring gulls. b, Dusky dolphin. c, Sandwich tern. d, Humpback whale. e, Right whale. f, Dusky dolphin, sergeant major. g, White-tipped shark. h, Manta ray, trunkfish. i, Purple moon angel. j, Scalloped hammerhead shark. k, Manatee. l, Striped fingerfish.

No. 2047, 1500sh, Humpback whales. No. 2048, 1500sh, Tiger shark.

1999, Nov. 15

2043-2045	A357	Set of 3	4.50	4.50
2046	A357	250sh Sheet of 12, #a.-l.	10.00	10.00

Souvenir Sheets

2047-2048	A357	Set of 2	10.00	10.00

Ballet A358

Designs: 300sh, Romeo and Juliet. 350sh, The Dying Swan. 400sh, Giselle, vert. 500sh, Spartacus, vert.

No. 2053, 1500sh, The Firebird, vert. No. 2054, 1500sh, Swan Lake, vert.

1999, Aug. 20   **Litho.**   **Perf. 14**

2049-2052	A358	Set of 4	5.00	5.00

Souvenir Sheets

2053-2054	A358	Set of 2	9.00	9.00

17th and 18th Century Indian Art — A359

No. 2055, 500sh: a, Krishna and the Gopis (large tree). b, Krishna Painting the Feet of Radha. c, Krishna Yearning for the Moon (woman with fan). d, Games of Krishna and Radha (boat).

No. 2056, 500sh: a, Balwant Singh Having His Beard Cut. b, Ragini Bialvali (woman with fan, woman on seat). d, Krishna Holding a Ball of Butter.

No. 2057, 1500sh, Portrait of Emperor Jahanoir (man with necklace), vert. No. 2058, 1500sh, Krishna and the Gopis, diff., vert.

Illustration reduced.

1999, Aug. 20   **Perf. 13¾**

Sheets of 4, #a-d

2055-2056	A359	Set of 2	10.00	10.00

Souvenir Sheets

2057-2058	A359	Set of 2	7.50	7.50

Fashion Designers — A360

No. 2059: a, Christian Dior. b, Model wearing Dior fashions. c, Bottle of Chanel No. 5, model wearing Chanel Fashions. d, Gabrielle "Coco" Chanel. e, Gianni Versace. f, Model wearing Versace fashions. g, Model wearing Yves Saint Laurent fashions. h, Yves Saint Laurent.

1500sh, Valentino Garavani.

1999, Aug. 20   **Perf. 14**

2059	A360	300sh Sheet of 8, #a-h	6.00	6.00

Souvenir Sheet

2060	A360	1500sh multi	3.75	3.75

Nos. 2059b-2059c, 2059f-2059g are 53x39mm.

Locomotives — A361

No. 2061: a, Class EF 81 Bo-Bo, Japan. b, Class 120 Bo-Bo, West Germany. c, Shao Shan I Co-Co, China. d, TGV, France. e, F40 PH Bo-Bo, US. f, LRC Bo-Bo, Canada. 1500sh, Class 401 Intercity Express, Germany.
Illustration reduced.

1999, Sept. 30
2061 A361 400sh Sheet of 6,
#a-f   6.00 6.00
Souvenir Sheet
2062 A361 1500sh multi   3.75 3.75

Marine Life A362

Designs: 150sh, Great barracuda. 250sh, Common squid. No. 2065, 300sh, Atlantic salmon. 350sh, Ocean sunfish. 400sh, Lobster. 500sh, Yellowfin tuna.
No. 2069, 300sh: a, Flying fish. b, Sailfish. c, Common dolphin. d, Sperm whale. e, Spinner dolphin. f, Manta ray. g, Green turtle. h, Hammerhead shark. i, Marlin.
No. 2070, 300sh: a, Walrus. b, Killer whale. c, Arctic tern. d, White shark. e, Narwhal. f, Blue whale. g, Giant clam. h, Octopus. i, Conger eel.
No. 2071, 1500sh, Whale shark. No. 2072, 1500sh, Beluga, vert.

1999, Nov. 15
2063-2068 A362 Set of 6   6.00 6.00
Sheets of 9, #a-i
2069-2070 A362 Set of 2   14.00 14.00
Souvenir Sheets
2071-2072 A362 Set of 2   7.50 7.50

Pres. Julius K. Nyerere (1922-99) A363

Nyerere: 200sh, As young man and old man. 500sh, With Edward Moringe Sokoine. 600sh, The Compassionate leader, vert. 800sh, During the early days of independence, vert.
1000sh, Mausoleum.

2000, Apr. 13   Perf. 13
2073-2076 A363 Set of 4   5.25 5.25
Souvenir Sheet
Perf. 13x13½
2077 A363 1000sh multi   2.50 2.50
No. 2077 contains one 35x28mm stamp.

Tourism A364

Designs: 400sh, Lion, Seronera Wildlife Lodge. No. 2079, 800sh, Hippopotami and hyenas, Selous Game Reserve. No. 2080, 800sh, Fish, Mafia Island. No. 2081, 800sh, Giraffes, Lobo Wildlife Lodge. No. 2082, 800sh, Rhinoceros, Ngorongoro Crater Wildlife Lodge. No. 2083, 800sh, Elephant, Mikumi Natl. Park. No. 2084, 800sh, Elephant, Lake Manyara Natl. Park. No. 2085, 800sh, Elephants, rhinoceros, Kibo Peak, Mt. Kilimanjaro.

1000sh, Lion, giraffes, elephant, rhinoceros, Lake Manyara Natl. Park, vert.

Perf. 13x13½, 13½x13
2000, June 10   Litho.
2078-2085 A364 Set of 8   18.00 18.00
Souvenir Sheet
2086 A364 1000sh multi   4.00 4.00
See Nos. 2102-2125.

Activities of World Vision A365

Designs: 200sh, Children with water pots on heads. 600sh, Family preparing food. 800sh, Nurse, family. 1000sh, Education of children.

2000, July 20   Litho.   Perf. 13x13¼
2087-2090 A365 Set of 4   6.50 6.50
Souvenir Sheet
2091 A365 500sh Two children   1.25 1.25

2000 Summer Olympics, Sydney A366

Designs: 150sh, Soccer. 350sh, Basketball, vert. 400sh, Women's 1500-meter race, vert. 800sh, Boxing.
500sh, Medal ceremony, vert.

2000, Sept. 15   Perf. 13¾
2092-2095 A366 Set of 4   4.50 4.50
Souvenir Sheet
2096 A366 500sh multi   1.25 1.25

Universities of East Africa A367

Designs: 150sh, Medical students, Muhimbili University College of Health Sciences. 200sh, Zanzibar University. 600sh, Makerere University, Uganda, vert. 800sh, Egerton University, Kenya.
500sh, Emblem of Inter-university Council for East Africa.

2000   Perf. 13x13¼, 13¼x13
2097-2100 A367 Set of 4   4.50 4.50
Perf. 14½
Size: 84x83mm
2101 A367 500sh multi   1.25 1.25

Tourism Type of 2000

No. 2102, 400sh, No. 2110, 500sh, No. 2118, 600sh, Like #2079. No. 2103, 400sh, No. 2111, 500sh, No. 2119, 600sh, Like #2080. No. 2104, 400sh, No. 2112, 500sh, No. 2120, 600sh, Like #2081. No. 2105, 400sh, No. 2113, 500sh, No. 2121, 600sh, Like #2082. No. 2106, 400sh, No. 2114, 500sh, No. 2122, 600sh, Like #2083. No. 2107, 400sh, No. 2115, 500sh, No. 2123, 600sh, Like #2084. No. 2108, 400sh, No. 2116, 500sh, No. 2124, 600sh, Like #2085. No. 2109, 500sh, No. 2117, 600sh, 800sh, Like #2078.

2000, June 1   Litho.   Perf. 13x13½
2102-2125 A364 Set of 24   45.00 45.00

Flowers A368

150sh, Bacciflava. 250sh, Hybridus pendulus. #2128, 300sh, Rhaphiolepis umbellata. 350sh, Magnoliaeflora. 400sh, Magnolia, vert. 500sh, Margot Koster, vert.

No. 2132, 300sh: a, Viola pedata. b, Magnolia. c, Felicia amelloides. d, Lythrum. e, Hemerocallis. f, Tithonia rotundifolia. g, Lilium. h, Iris. i, Stokesia laevis.
No. 2133, 300sh, vert.: a, Prunus subhirtella. b, Sanguinaria canadensis. c, Rosa palustris. d, Gordonia lasianthius. e, Aquilegia caerulea. f, Fremontodendron. g, Hypericum calycinum. h, Anemone vitifolia. i, Clematis.
No. 2134, Iris cristata, vert. No. 2134A, Aster prikartil.

2000   Perf. 14
2126-2131 A368 Set of 6   5.00 5.00
Sheets of 9, #a-i
2132-2133 A368 Set of 2   13.50 13.50
Souvenir Sheet
2134-2134A A368 Set of 2   7.50 7.50

Social Security Fund A369

Designs: 200sh, Retirement. 350sh, Employment injury. 600sh, Invalidity. 800sh, Health insurance.

2000   Wmk. 387   Perf. 13¾
2135-2138 A369 Set of 4   5.00 5.00
Souvenir Sheet
2139 A369 500sh Maternity   1.25 1.25

Environmental Care — A370

Designs: 200sh, Tree planting campaign. 400sh, Water sources protection. 600sh, Cleaning sewage. 800sh, Protecting forests.

2000   Wmk. 387   Perf. 13x13¼
2140-2143 A370 Set of 4   5.00 5.00
Souvenir Sheet
2144 A370 1000sh Mountain   2.50 2.50

Zanzibar Millennium A371

Designs: 150sh, Fishing industry. 200sh, Trade and tourism. 400sh, Child and emblem, vert. 800sh, Right to higher learning, vert.
500sh, Peace and tranquility, vert.

2000   Wmk. 387   Perf. 13¾
2145-2148 A371 Set of 4   4.50 4.50
Souvenir Sheet
2149 A371 500sh multi   1.25 1.25

Orchids A372

Designs: 200sh, Vanilla planifolia. 250sh, Pleurothallis tuerckheimii. No. 2152, 370sh, Trichopilia fragrans.
No. 2153, 370sh: a, Cyrtopodium andersonii. b, Cochleanthes discolor. c, Catasetum barbatum. d, Caularthron bicornutum. e, Broughtonia sanguinea. f, Brassavola nodosa.
No. 2154, 370sh: a, Oeceoclades maculata. b, Isochilus linearis. c, Eulophia alta. d, Ionopsis utricularioides. e, Epidendrum ciliare. f, Dimerandra emarginata.
No. 2155, 1500sh, Brassavola cucullata. No. 2156, 1500sh, Epidendrum nocturnum.

2000   Litho.   Perf. 14
2150-2152 A372 Set of 3   3.00 3.00

Sheets of 6, #a-f
2153-2154 A372 Set of 2   13.00 13.00
Souvenir Sheets
2155-2156 A372 Set of 2   7.50 7.50

Nos. 607, 610, 612, 615, 617 Surcharged

Methods and perfs as before
1998-2001
2157 A99 100sh on 40sh multi
2158 A99 150sh on 9sh multi
2159 A99 200sh on 170sh multi
2159A A99 230sh on 20sh multi   —   —
2159B A99 230sh on 170sh multi
2159C A99 800sh on 500sh multi 2.00 2.00

Issued: No. 2158, 1/26/98; No. 2157, 8/6/98; No. 2159, 6/4/00; No. 2159C, 4/6/00; No. 2159B, 11/20/00; No. 2159A, 11/20/01.

Rare Birds A373

Designs: 150sh, Taita falcon. 300sh, Banded green. 400sh, Spotted ground thrush. 500sh, Fischer's turaco. 600sh, Blue swallow.

2000   Litho.   Perf. 14
2160 A373 150sh multi
2161 A373 300sh multi
2162 A373 400sh multi
2163 A373 500sh multi
Souvenir Sheet
2164 A373 600sh multi

Architecture — A374

Designs: 150sh, Ruins of Great Mosque, Kilwa Kisiwani. 200sh, German Boma, Mikindani. 250sh, German Boma, Bagamoyo. 300sh, Butiama Museum, Mara. 350sh, Chief Government Chemist Office. 400sh, Old Post Office, Dar es Salaam. 500sh, Dr. David Livingstone Lodge, Kwihara Tabora. 600sh, Original and present State Houses, vert. 700sh, Ngoni-Nyamwezi traditional houses. 800sh, The People's Palace Beit Elajaib, Zanzibar. 900sh, Tongoni Ruins, Tanga. 1000sh, Karimjee Hall, Dar es Salaam.
1500sh, Old Boma, Mikindani.

2000 (?)		**Litho.**		**Perf. 13**
2165	A374	150sh	multi	
2166	A374	200sh	multi	
2166A	A374	250sh	multi	
2167	A374	300sh	multi	
2167A	A374	350sh	multi	
2168	A374	400sh	multi	
2168A	A374	500sh	multi	
2169	A374	600sh	multi	
2169A	A374	700sh	multi	
2170	A374	800sh	multi	
2170A	A374	900sh	multi	
2171	A374	1000sh	multi	
Souvenir Sheet				
2172	A374	1500sh	multi	

Flora and Fauna — A375

Designs: 100sh, Common babbler. 140sh, Eastern blue darner. 150sh, Cavalier mushroom. 200sh, Orange-barred sulphur. 250sh, Harlequin bug. No. 2179, 370sh, Brassolae liocattleya.
No. 2180, 370sh: a, Common yellowthroat. b, Great orange tip. c, Tiger lily. d, Shaggy mane. e, Sri Lanka grasshopper. f, Woodhouse's toad.
No. 2181, 370sh: a, Golden-crowned warbler. b, Fuchsia. c, Alfalfa butterfly. d, Lycaste aquila. e, Snail. f, Ground beetle.
No. 2182, 1500sh, Rufous-collared sparrow, horiz. No. 2183, 1500sh, Monarch butterfly, horiz.

2000		**Litho.**		**Perf. 14**
2174-2179	A375	Set of 6	3.00	3.00
Sheets of 6, #a-f				
2180-2181	A375	Set of 2	11.00	11.00
Souvenir Sheets				
2182-2183	A375	Set of 2	7.50	7.50

Activities of World Vision — A375a

Design: 200sh, Children have a right to education, horiz. 600sh, Children have a right to happiness, horiz. 800sh, Children have a right not to be exploited. 1000sh, Children have a right to be heard.

2001, Apr. 30		**Litho.**		**Perf. 13**
2183A	A375a	200sh	multi	— —
2183B	A375a	600sh	multi	— —
2183C	A375a	800sh	multi	— —
2183D	A375a	1000sh	multi	— —
Souvenir Sheet				
2183E	A375a	500sh	multi	— —

Endangered Animals A376

Designs: 200sh, Leopard. 400sh, Rhinoceros. No. 2186, 600sh, Crocodile. 800sh, Hunting wild dogs.
No. 2188, 600sh, Cheetah.

2001, June 15		**Litho.**		**Perf. 13**
2184-2187	A376	Set of 4	4.50	4.50
Souvenir Sheet				
2188	A376	600sh	multi	1.40 1.40

UN High Commissioner for Refugees, 50th Anniv. — A377

Designs: 200sh, Refugee child being vaccinated. 400sh, Refugees crossing Lake Tanganyika. 600sh, Refugee woman, vert. 800sh, Fleeing refugees, vert.

2001, July 31				
2189-2192	A377	Set of 4	4.50	4.50
2191a		Souvenir sheet of 1	1.40	1.40

Landscapes A378

Designs: 200sh, Rufiji River, Selous Game Reserve. 400sh, Mangapwani Beach, Zanzibar. 600sh, Mountains, Mikumi Natl. Park. 800sh, Balancing Stones, Shore of Lake Victoria, Mwanza, vert.
700sh, Ruaha Natl. Park, vert.

2001, Nov. 30		**Litho.**		**Perf. 13**
2193-2196	A378	Set of 4	4.50	4.50
Souvenir Sheet				
2197	A378	700sh	multi	1.50 1.50

Year of Dialogue Among Civilizations A379

Designs: 200sh, Talking with children. 400sh, Formal dress. 600sh, Exchanging ideas. 800sh, Letter writing.
700sh, Communication linkages, vert.

2001, Oct. 9			**Litho.**	
2198-2201	A379	Set of 4	4.50	4.50
Souvenir Sheet				
2202	A379	700sh	multi	1.50 1.50

Conservation of Zanzibar Rare Species — A380

Designs: 250sh, Dolphins. 300sh, Coral reefs. 450sh, Coral reefs, diff. 800sh, Zanzibar red colobus, vert.
700sh, Zanzibar red colobus, diff.

2002, Aug. 30		**Litho.**		**Perf. 13**
2203-2206	A380	Set of 4	4.00	4.00
Souvenir Sheet				
2207	A380	700sh	multi	1.60 1.60

Historic Sites of East Africa A381

Designs: 250sh, Fort Kilwa. 300sh, Maruhubi Palace ruins, Zanzibar. 400sh, Old Provincial Office, Nairobi, 1913. 800sh, Mparu Tombs, Hoima, Uganda.
700sh, Map of East Africa, ship.

2001, Oct. 19				
2208-2211	A381	Set of 4	3.75	3.75
Souvenir Sheet				
2212	A381	700sh	multi	1.50 1.50

Independence, 40th Anniv. — A382

Designs: 180sh, Tea estates. 230sh, Regional integration with Uganda and Kenya, vert. 350sh, University graduates, vert. 450sh, 1000sh, Lion, elephant, buffalo, cheetah, rhinoceros, Mt. Kilimanjaro. 650sh, Referral hospitals. 950sh, Mining industry.

2001, Dec. 30		**Litho.**		**Perf. 14**
2213-2218	A382	Set of 6	6.00	6.00
Souvenir Sheet				
2219	A382	1000sh	multi	2.10 2.10

Ceremonial Costumes — A383

Designs: 250sh, Makonde mask dance. 350sh, Zanzibar Mwaka koga festival. 400sh, Lizombe dancer. 450sh, Zaramo bride's celebration.
500sh, Like 400sh.

		Wmk. 387		
2002, Mar. 30		**Litho.**		**Perf. 13¾**
2220-2223	A383	Set of 4	3.00	3.00
Souvenir Sheet				
2224	A383	500sh	multi	1.00 1.00

Mountains A384

Designs: 250sh, Mt. Kilimanjaro. 350sh, Usambara Mountains. 400sh, Uluguru Mountains. 450sh, Mwanihana Peak, Udzungwa Mountains.
500sh, Like 250sh.

2002, June 30		**Wmk. 387**		
2225-2228	A384	Set of 4	3.00	3.00
Souvenir Sheet				
2229	A384	500sh	multi	1.10 1.10

National Census A385

Census emblem and: 200sh, School children, vert. 250sh, Group of people. 350sh, Family. 600sh, Boy, census figures. 800sh, Group of people, vert.

Perf. 13x13¼ Sync., 13¼x13 Sync.

2002, Aug. 13			**Unwmk.**	
2230-2233	A385	Set of 4	3.00	3.00
Souvenir Sheet				
Perf. 13x13¼				
2234	A385	800sh	multi	1.60 1.60

Arts of Zanzibar A386

Designs: 200sh, Mat making. 250sh, Handsewn hats. 350sh, Chair making. 600sh, Hina painting.
800sh, Zanzibar door.

2002, Sept. 13		**Unwmk.**		**Perf. 13¼**
2235-2238	A386	Set of 4	3.00	3.00
Souvenir Sheet				
Perf. 13				
2239	A386	800sh	multi	1.60 1.60

Souvenir Sheet

Wildlife — A387

No. 2240: a, Leopard. b, Elephant. c, Rhinoceros. d, Lion. e, Buffalo.

Perf. 13x14

2002, Apr. 30			**Wmk. 387**	
2240	A387	250sh Sheet of 5, #a-e	2.60	2.60

Compare No. 2240 with No. 2251.

Archaeology A388

Designs: 250sh, Ancient city of Kisimkazi, Zanzibar, vert. 400sh, Ruins of Kaole town, Bagamoyo. 450sh, Kondoa Irangi rock paintings, vert. 600sh, Great Mosque, Kilwa Kisiwani.
1000sh, Like 450sh.

Perf. 13¼

2002, Sept. 30		**Unwmk.**		**Litho.**
2241-2244	A388	Set of 4	3.50	3.50
Souvenir Sheet				
Perf. 13				
2245	A388	1000sh	multi	2.10 2.10

Wildlife A389

Designs: 400sh, Rhinoceroses. 500sh, Elephant. 600sh, Lion. 800sh, Leopard, vert. 1000sh, Buffalo.
1500sh, Rhinoceros, elephant, lion, leopard, buffalo, vert.

Perf. 13¼x12¾, 12¾x13¼
2003, Apr. 22 **Litho.** **Wmk. 387**
2246-2250 A389 Set of 5 6.50 6.50
Size: 85x115mm
Imperf
2251 A389 1500sh multi 3.00 3.00
Compare No. 2251 with No. 2240.

Cash Crops — A390

Designs: 250sh, Cotton. 300sh, Cashews. 600sh, Sisal. 800sh, Cloves. 1000sh, Tea, horiz.

Perf. 13x13¼ Syncopated
2003, June 10 **Unwmk.**
2252-2255 A390 Set of 4 3.75 3.75
Souvenir Sheet
Perf. 13¼x13 Syncopated
2256 A390 1000sh multi 1.90 1.90

Activities of World Vision A391

Designs: 300sh, Better nutrition with vitamin A. 600sh, Education opportunity for all children. 800sh, Clean and safe water for all, vert. 1000sh, Malaria prevention with treated mosquito nets.
500sh, Children have a right to be heard.

2003, July 3 *Perf. 13*
2257-2260 A391 Set of 4 5.25 5.25
Souvenir Sheet
2261 A391 500sh multi .95 .95

Traditional Dances A392

Dances: 300sh, Nyamwezi. 500sh, Luo. 600sh, Pemba. 800sh, Baganda. 1000sh, Masai.

Perf. 13¼x13 Syncopated
2003, July 25
2262-2265 A392 Set of 4 4.25 4.25
Souvenir Sheet
2266 A392 1000sh multi 1.90 1.90

Nos. 612 and 1567 Surcharged

Methods and Perfs As Before
2002
2267 A99 250sh on 40sh #612 .50 .50
2268 A262 250sh on 180sh #1567 .50 .50
Issued: No. 2267, 7/23/02; No. 2268, 8/30/02.

Northern Circuit Tourist Attractions A393

Designs: 300sh, Lion, lioness, Mt. Kilimanjaro. 350sh, Kibo Peak, Mt. Kilimanjaro. 400sh, Zebras, Serengeti Natl. Park. 500sh, Elephants, Kilimanjaro Natl. Park. 600sh, Leopards, Serengeti Natl. Park. 800sh, Rhinoceros, Ngorongoro Crater.
1000sh, Buffalo, Arusha Natl. Park.

2003, Apr. 30 **Litho.** *Perf. 13¼x13*
2269-2274 A393 Set of 6 5.75 5.75
Souvenir Sheet
2275 A393 1000sh multi 2.00 2.00

Landscapes A394

Designs: 300sh, Rufiji Delta. 400sh, Zanzibar shore. 500sh, Lake Manyara, Rift Valley. 800sh, Kalambo Falls, vert.
1000sh, Coastal mangroves.

2003, July 22 **Litho.** *Perf. 13¼x13*
2276-2279 A394 Set of 4 4.00 4.00
Souvenir Sheet
2280 A394 1000sh multi 1.90 1.90

Zanzibar Tourist Attractions A395

Designs: 300sh, Old Fort. 500sh, Door, Beit al Ajaib, vert. 600sh, Coconut palm tree, Michamvi Beach, vert. 800sh, Dhow, Beit al Ajaib.

Perf. 13¼x13, 13x13¼
2003, Sept. 30 **Litho.**
2281-2284 A395 Set of 4 4.25 4.25
2284a Souvenir sheet, #2281, 2283, 2284 3.25 3.25

Marine Mammals A396

Designs: 300sh, Common dolphin. 350sh, Sperm whale. 400sh, Southern right whale. 600sh, Dugong.
500sh, Bottlenose dolphin.

2003, Oct. 11 **Litho.** *Perf. 13¼x13*
2285-2288 A396 Set of 4 3.25 3.25
Souvenir Sheet
2289 A396 500sh multi .95 .95

Religious Festivals — A396a

Designs: 300sh, Muslims on pilgrimage to Mecca. 500sh, Choir at Christmas. 600sh, Prophet Mohammed's Birthday. 800sh, Church at Christmas.
1000sh, Crucifixion of Jesus.

Wmk. 387
2003, Nov. 4 *Perf. 14*
2289A-2289D A396a Set of 4 4.25 4.25
Souvenir Sheet
2289E A396a 1000sh multi 1.90 1.90

Tanzania Posts Corporation, 10th Anniv. — A397

Designs: 350sh, Counter automation. 400sh, Overnight mail delivery services. 600sh, Workers' participation. 800sh, Expedited mail services.
1000sh, Post Cargo.

Unwmk.
2004, Jan. 19 **Litho.** *Perf. 13*
2290-2293 A397 Set of 4 4.00 4.00
2293a Souvenir sheet, #2290-2293 4.00 4.00
Souvenir Sheet
2294 A397 1000sh multi 1.90 1.90

Western Union Money Transfer A398

Designs: 300sh, Exchange of American and Tanzanian currency. 400sh, Busalanga Primary School. 500sh, Woman, child, Tanzanian currency, vert. 600sh, World map.
800sh, Like 300sh, without Western Union emblem.

Perf. 13¼x13, 13x13¼
2004, Feb. 3 **Litho.**
2295-2298 A398 Set of 4 3.25 3.25
Souvenir Sheet
2299 A398 800sh multi 1.50 1.50

Girl Guides in Tanzania, 75th Anniv. A399

Designs: 300sh, Guides demonstrating solar cookers. 400sh, Camp training. 600sh, Bravery training. 800sh, Guides assisting at a mother and child clinic session.
1000sh, Like 800sh.

2004, May 15 *Perf. 13¼x13*
2300-2303 A399 Set of 4 3.75 3.75
Souvenir Sheet
2304 A399 1000sh multi 1.90 1.90

Tanganyika Christian Refugee Service, 40th Anniv. A400

Designs: 350sh, Truck carrying refugees and bicycles. 600sh, Public water source. 800sh, Students in classroom. 1000sh, Afforestation campaign.
1200sh, Four vignettes combined.

Unwmk.
2004, May 24 **Litho.** *Perf. 14*
2305-2308 A400 Set of 4 5.00 5.00
Souvenir Sheet
Perf. 14¼
2309 A400 1200sh multi 2.25 2.25
No. 2309 contains one 44x34mm stamp.

Zanzibar Watercraft Races A401

Designs: 350sh, Crowd cheering race winners. 400sh, Punt race. 600sh, Dhow race. 800sh, Sailboat race.
1000sh, Dhow, vert.

2004, June 25 *Perf. 13*
2310-2313 A401 Set of 4 4.00 4.00
2313a Souvenir sheet, #2310-2313 4.00 4.00
Souvenir Sheet
2314 A401 1000sh multi 1.90 1.90

Flora, Fauna and Mushrooms — A402

No. 2315, 550sh, horiz. — Animals: a, Red colobus monkey. b, Leopard. c, Giraffe. d, Eland. e, Zebra. f, African elephant.
No. 2316, 550sh, horiz. — Birds: a, European roller. b, Little swift. c, African gray parrot. d, Bateleur. e, European bee-eater. f, Hoopoe.
No. 2317, 550sh, horiz. — Butterflies: a, Gold-banded forester. b, Two-tailed pasha. c, Plain tiger. d, Common dotted border. e, African migrant. f, Forest queen.
No. 2318, 550sh, horiz. — Orchids: a, Cynorkis kassnerana. b, Habenaria rhodocheila. c, Vanilla planifolia. d, Ansellia africana. e, Disa uniflora. f, Calathe rosea.
No. 2319, 550sh, horiz. — Mushrooms: a, Fly mushroom. b, Rosy-gill fairy helmet. c, Purple coincap. d, Velvet shank. e, Thick-footed morel. f, King bolete.
No. 2320, 2000sh, Olive baboon. No. 2321, 2000sh, Gray crowned crane. No. 2322, 2000sh, Blue diadem butterfly. No. 2323, 2000sh, Disa uniflora, diff. No. 2324, 2000sh, Sharp-scaled parasol mushroom.

2004, July 19 *Perf. 14*
Sheets of 6, #a-f
2315-2319 A402 Set of 5 30.00 30.00
Souvenir Sheets
2320-2324 A402 Set of 5 18.50 18.50

Mining A403

Designs: 350sh, Diamond mining at Williamson Diamond Mwadui. 500sh, Semi-processed jewels. No. 2327, 600sh, Drillers in deep mine. 800sh, Gold miners.
No. 2329, Unprocessed gemstones.

2004, July 30 *Perf. 13¼x12¾*
2325-2328 A403 Set of 4 4.25 4.25
2328a Souvenir sheet, #2325-2328 4.25 4.25
Souvenir Sheet
2329 A403 600sh multi 1.10 1.10

Southern African Development Community, 24th Anniv. A404

Designs: 350sh, Removal of water hyacinths from beach. 500sh, Irrigation ditch in corn field. 600sh, irrigation ditch at rice paddy. 800sh, Workers installing pipe in borehole, vert.
1000sh, Farm workers hoeing corn field irrigation ditches.

2004, Aug. 17   *Perf. 14x13, 13x14*
2330-2333 A404 Set of 4   4.25   4.25
2333a   Souvenir sheet, #2330-
               2333, perf. 13½x13,
               13x13½   4.25   4.25
Souvenir Sheet
2334 A404 1000sh multi   1.90   1.90

Nos. 1565, 1569 and 2166
Surcharged

#2335   #2336

Methods and Perfs As Before
2004, Nov. 13
2335 A262 350sh on 100sh
           #1565   —   —
2336 A374 350sh on 200sh
           #2166   —   —
2337 A262 350sh on 210sh
           #1569   —   —

Children's
Rights
A405

Inscriptions: No. 2338, 350sh, Involve children in school development. No. 2339, 350sh, Let's equip children with life skills. 400sh, Children need education before employment. 500sh, 1000sh, Disabled children need to be educated.

2004, Nov. 4 Litho.   Perf. 13¼x12¾
2338-2341 A405 Set of 4   3.00   3.00
Souvenir Sheet
2342 A405 1000sh multi   1.90   1.90

Law and
Peace in
the Great Lakes
Zone —
A405a

Designs: 350sh, Julius K. Nyerere acting as facilitator in Burundi peace negotiations. 500sh, Burundi refugees at border. No. 2342C, 600sh, Nelson Mandela and Tanzania Pres. Banjamin W. Mkapa at Arusha peace talks. 800sh, Pres. Mkapa with Uganda Pres. Yoweri Musaveni and Burundi Pres. Domitien Ndayizeye at Dar es Salaam peace talks. No. 2342E, 600sh, Arusha Intl. Conference Center.

2004, Oct. 15 Litho.   Perf. 14x13
2342A-2342D A405a Set of 4   4.25   4.25
2342Df   Souvenir sheet, #2342A-
               2342D   4.25   4.25
Souvenir Sheet
2342E A405a 600sh multi   1.10   1.10

Rotary International, Cent. — A406

Designs: 350sh, Rotary officials honor Tanzania Pres. Julius Nyerere. 500sh, Emblem of Dar es Salaam North Tanzania Club, vert. No. 2345 600sh, Eradication of polio. 800sh, Map and flags of District 9200 countries, Eritrea, Ethiopia, Uganda, Kenya and Tanzania, vert.
No. 2347: a, Environmental project. b, Self-reliance to the handicapped. c, Basic health care project, vert. d, Jaipur foot project. e, Malaria project. f, Eradication of river blindness project.
1000sh, Centenary emblem, vert.

2005, Feb. 23 Litho.   Perf. 13
2343-2346 A406 Set of 4   4.25   4.25

2347 A406 600sh Sheet of 6,
           #a-f   6.50   6.50
Souvenir Sheet
2348 A406 1000sh multi   1.90   1.90

Safari Circuit
Animals — A407

Designs: 350sh, Lionesses. 500sh, Cheetahs, horiz. No. 2351, 600sh, Red colobus monkey. 800sh, Zebras, horiz.
No. 2353, horiz.: a, Elephants. b, Rhinoceroses. c, Giraffes. d, Crocodile. e, Chimpanzees. f, Buffaloes.
No. 2354, horiz.: a, Leopard. b, Wild hunting dogs.

Perf. 12¾x13¼, 13¼x12¾
2005, Apr. 30
2349-2352 A407 Set of 4   4.25   4.25
2353 A407 600sh Sheet of 6,
           #a-f   6.50   6.50
2354 A407 1000sh Sheet of 2,
           #a-b   3.75   3.75

Zanzibar
Heritage and
Culture
A408

Designs: 350sh, Bull fighting. 400sh, Narrow street in Stone Town, vert. No. 2357, 600sh, Women's traditional dress, vert. 800sh, Clove harvesting, vert.
No. 2359, 600sh: a, House of Wonders. b, Local Taarabu musicians. c, Man holding fish. d, Coconut palm. e, Women's indoor traditional dress. f, Old museum building.
500sh, Pemba-Zanzibar ferry boat.

Perf. 13½x13, 13x13½
2005, June 30   **Litho.**
2355-2358 A408 Set of 4   4.00   4.00
2359 A408 600sh Sheet of 6,
           #a-f   6.50   6.50
Souvenir Sheet
2360 A408 500sh multi   .90   .90

2004 Summer Olympics,
Athens — A409

Designs: No. 2361, 350sh, Greco-Roman wrestlers. No. 2362, 350sh, Baron Godefroy de Blonay, vert. 500sh, Commemorative medal for 1928 Amsterdam Summer Olympics, vert. 1000sh, Greek javelin thrower sculpture, vert.

2005, May 2 Litho.   Perf. 13¼
2361-2364 A409 Set of 4   4.00   4.00

Souvenir Sheet

Reign of Pope John Paul, 25th Anniv.
(in 2003) — A410

No. 2365: a, Pope as boy, with mother, 1921. b, Visit to Poland, 1979. c, Meeting with Pres. George W. Bush, 2001. d, In Armenia, 2001.

2005, May 2   **Perf. 13½**
2365 A410 1000sh Sheet of 4,
           #a-d   7.25   7.25

Locomotives, Bicent. — A411

No. 2366: a, West Side Lumber 3-truck shay, Georgetown Loop Railroad. b, LK&P 0-4-0 Saddletanker. c, Double-headed C&T steam locomotive. d, Baldwin 4-6-0, Huckleberry Railroad.
2500sh, Heber Valley Railroad 2-8-0.

2005, May 2
2366 A411 1000sh Sheet of 4,
           #a-d   7.25   7.25
Souvenir Sheet
2367 A411 2500sh multi   4.50   4.50

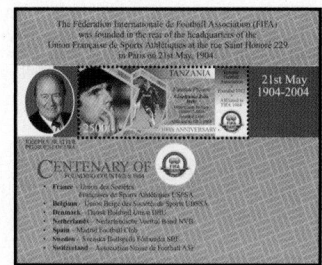

FIFA (Fédération Internationale de
Football Association) Cent. (in
2004) — A412

No. 2368: a, Franco Baresi. b, Daniel Passarella. c, Miroslav Klose. d, Michel Platini. 2500sh, Gianfranco Zola.

2005, May 2 Litho.   Perf. 13½
2368 A412 1000sh Sheet of 4,
           #a-d   7.25   7.25
Souvenir Sheet
2369 A412 2500sh multi   4.50   4.50

D-Day, 60th Anniv. (in 2004) — A413

No. 2370, vert.: a, Map of invasion. b, Gen. Dwight D. Eisenhower. c, American troops landing at Omaha Beach. d, British Mosquitos. e, Fleet Admiral Ernest J. King. f, Gen. George C. Marshall.
2500sh, Battle for Fox Green Beach.

2006, May 2
2370 A413 600sh Sheet of 6,
           #a-f   6.50   6.50
Souvenir Sheet
2371 A413 2500sh multi   4.50   4.50

Jules Verne (1828-1905),
Writer — A414

No. 2372, 800sh: a, Voyages Extraordinaires. b, Twenty Thousand Leagues Under the Sea. c, A Floating City (book cover). d, Adventures of Three Englishmen and Three Russians in South Africa.
No. 2373, 800sh: a, Mathias Sandorf. b, The Steam House, The Demon of Cawnpore. c, Hector Servadec on the Career of a Comet. d, An Antarctic Mystery.
No. 2374, 800sh: a, Around the World in Eighty Days. b, Dr. Ox's Experiment. c, The Purchase of the North Pole. d, Adrift in the Pacific.
No. 2375, 800sh: a, The Archipelago on Fire. b, The Vanished Diamond. c, Mistress Branican. d, The Castle of the Carpathians.
No. 2376, 800sh: a, The Invasion of the Sea. b, The Floating Island. c, A Floating City (men near ship railing). d, Dick Sands, Boy Captain.
No. 2377, 2000sh, Around the World in Eighty Days, diff. No. 2378, 2000sh, Five Weeks in a Balloon. No. 2379, 2000sh, The Mysterious Island. No. 2380, 2000sh, The Adventures of a Chinaman. No. 2381, 2000sh, The Invasion of the Sea, diff.

2005, May 16   **Perf. 13½**
Sheets of 4, #a-d
2372-2376 A414 Set of 5   29.00 29.00
Souvenir Sheets
2377-2381 A414 Set of 5   18.00 18.00

Fish of
Lake
Victoria
A415

Designs: No. 2382, 350sh, Labeo victorianus. 400sh, Lates niloticus. 600sh, Pundamilia nyererei. 800sh, Brycinus sadleri.
No. 2386, 350sh: a, Haplochromis sharpsnout. b, Haplochromis chilotes. c, Mormyrus kannume. d, Clarias gariepinus. e, Synodontis afrofischeri. f, Protopterus aethiopicus.
500sh, Oreochromis niloticus.

2005, Aug. 30　　　*Perf. 13¼x13¾*
2382-2385　A415　Set of 4　　3.75　3.75
2386　A415　350sh Sheet of 6, #a-
　　　　f　　　　　　　　　　　3.75　3.75
Souvenir Sheet
2387　A415　500sh multi　　　　.90　.90

Pope John Paul II
(1920-2005), and
Pres. Bill
Clinton — A416

2005, Sept. 22　　　*Perf. 12¾*
2388　A416　1500sh multi　　2.75　2.75

Printed in sheets of 4, with each stamp having a slightly different background.

Rotary International, Cent. — A417

No. 2389: a, Child receiving polio vaccine.
b, Dr. Jonas E. Salk, polio researcher. c,
Hands, test tube.
　2500sh, Salk and Rotary International centenary emblem.

2005, Sept. 22
2389　A417　1200sh Sheet of 3,
　　　　#a-c　　　　　　　　　6.50　6.50
Souvenir Sheet
2390　A417　2500sh multi　　4.50　4.50

Albert Einstein (1879-1955),
Physicist — A418

No. 2391 — Sketch of Einstein and: a, 1979
Swiss 5-franc coin. b, Time Magazine cover. c,
Israel #117.
　2500sh, Portrait of Einstein.

2005, Sept. 22
2391　A418　1300sh Sheet of 3,
　　　　#a-c　　　　　　　　　7.00　7.00
Souvenir Sheet
2392　A418　2500sh multi　　4.50　4.50

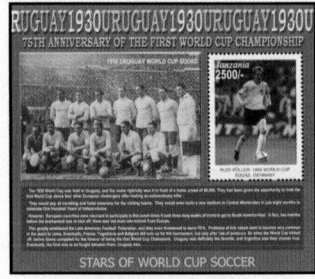

First World Cup Soccer
Championships, 75th Anniv. — A419

No. 2393: a, Christian Ziege. b, Marko
Rehmer. c, Jens Nowotny.
　2500sh, Rudi Völler.

2005, Sept. 22　　　*Perf. 13¼*
2393　A419　1200sh Sheet of 3,
　　　　#a-c　　　　　　　　　6.50　6.50
Souvenir Sheet
2394　A419　2500sh multi　　4.50　4.50

Butterflies
A420

Designs: 350sh, Papilio ufipa. No. 2396,
500sh, Mylothris sagala mahale. No. 2397,
600sh, Amauris tartarea tukuyuensis. 800sh,
Charaxes lucyae gabriellae.
　No. 2399, 600sh: a, Like 350sh. b,
Euphaedra neophron kiellandi. c, Like 800sh.
d, Abisara zanzibarica. e, Acrae utengulensis.
　No. 2400, 500sh, Charaxes usambarae
maridadi.

2005, Oct. 27　　　*Perf. 13¾x13½*
2395-2398　A420　Set of 4　　4.00　4.00
2399　A420　600sh Sheet of 6,
　　　　　　　　　#2397,
　　　　　　　　　2399a-2399e　6.50　6.50
Souvenir Sheet
2400　A420　500sh multi　　　　.90　.90

Anniversaries
and Events
A421

Designs: 350sh, Person with amputated leg.
No. 2402, 500sh, Line of people at polling station. No. 2403, 600sh, Pope John Paul II,
kneeling at airport. 800sh, Laurean Cardinal
Rugambwa, Pope John Paul II and Pres. Alis
Hassan Mwinyi.
　No. 2405, 600sh: a, Pres. Julius Nyerere
and Abeid Aman Karume signing Union
Treaty. b, Woman holding child, casting ballot.
c, Pope John Paul II, Pres. Mwinyi and Julius
and Maria Nyerere. d, Pope John Paul II and
Cardinal Rugambwa and car roof. e, Majimaji
Museum, Songea. f, President B. W. Mkapa at
fire.
　No. 2406, 500sh, Majimaji Monument, vert.

2005, Dec. 9　　　*Perf. 13¼x12¾*
2401-2404　A421　Set of 4　　4.00　4.00
2405　A421　600sh Sheet of 6, #a-
　　　　f　　　　　　　　　　　6.25　6.25
Souvenir Sheet
Perf. 12¾x13¼
2406　A421　500sh multi　　　　.90　.90

World Diabetes Day (350sh); 2005 general
elections (#2402, 2405b), Visit of Pope John
Paul II, 15th anniv. (800sh, #2405c, 2405d).

Birds
A422

Designs: 350sh, Rufous-winged sunbird.
No. 2408, 500sh, Pemba white-eye. No. 2409,
600sh, Kilombero weaver. 800sh, Usambara
eagle owl.
　No. 2411, 600sh: a, Pemba scops owl. b,
Spike-heeled lark. c, Pemba green pigeon. d,
Uluguru bush shrike. e, Yellow-collared love
birds. f, Usambara nightjar.
　No. 2412, 500sh, Moreau's sunbird, vert.

2006, Mar. 25　　　*Perf. 13*
2407-2410　A422　Set of 4　　3.75　3.75
2411　A422　600sh Sheet of 6, #a-
　　　　f　　　　　　　　　　　6.00　6.00
Souvenir Sheet
2412　A422　500sh multi　　　　.85　.85

No. 2412 contains one 39x49mm stamp.

2006 World Cup Soccer
Championships, Germany — A423

Designs: 350sh, New National Stadium, Dar
es Salaam. 500sh, Map of Africa and flags of
participating countries, vert. No. 2415, 600sh,
Pres. Jakaya Kikwete holding World Cup trophy. 800sh, Mascot for 2006 World Cup, vert.
No. 2417, 600sh, World Cup Trophy and
2006 World Cup emblem.

Perf. 13¼x12¾, 12¾x13¼
2006, Mar. 25
2413-2416　A423　Set of 4　　3.75　3.75
2416a　　　Miniature sheet, #2413-
　　　　　　2416　　　　　　　3.75　3.75
Souvenir Sheet
2417　A423　600sh multi　　1.00　1.00

Miniature Sheet

Wolfgang Amadeus Mozart (1756-91),
Composer — A424

No. 2418: a, Portrait of Mozart (blue panel).
b, Mozart's birthplace, Salzburg. c, Poster for
Don Giovanni. d, Portrait of Mozart (purple
panel).

2006, June 13　　　*Perf. 12¾*
2418　A424　1200sh Sheet of 4,
　　　　#a-d　　　　　　　　8.00　8.00

Release of Elvis Presley Movie,
Jailhouse Rock, 50th Anniv. — A425

No. 2419 — Presley with: a, Both arms at
side. b, Arm raised above head. c, Arms outstretched and jacket pulled up behind head. d,
Hand in front of chest.

2006, June 13　　　*Perf. 13½*
2419　A425　1200sh Sheet of 4,
　　　　#a-d　　　　　　　　8.00　8.00

Queen Elizabeth II, 80th
Birthday — A426

No. 2420 — Queen: a, Wearing blue robe.
b, On reviewing stand. c, On horse. d, Wearing
feathered hat.
　2500sh, Wearing tiara.

2006, June 13　　　*Perf. 14¼*
2420　A426　1200sh Sheet of 4,
　　　　#a-d　　　　　　　　8.00　8.00
Souvenir Sheet
2421　A426　2500sh multi　　4.25　4.25

Rembrandt (1606-69), Painter — A427

No. 2422 — Painting details: a, Jan Pellicorne and His Son Caspar (Jan Pellicorne).
b, Jan Pellicorne and His Son Caspar (Caspar). c, Susanna Van Collen, Wife of Jan Pellicorne, and Her Daughter, Eva Susanna
(Susanna). d, Susanna Van Collen, Wife of
Jan Pellicorne, and Her Daughter, Eva
Susanna (Eva Susanna).
　3000sh, A Turk.

2006, June 13　　　*Perf. 13¼*
2422　A427　1000sh Sheet of 4,
　　　　#a-d　　　　　　　　6.75　6.75
Imperf
Size: 70x100mm
2423　A427　3000sh multi　　5.00　5.00

Beauty of
Zanzibar
A428

Designs: 350sh, Man and woman in traditional Zanzibar dress. No. 2425, 500sh, Zanzibar Museum. No. 2426, 600sh, Maruhubi Palace ruins. 800sh, Man climbing coconut tree.
　No. 2428, 600sh: a, Green turtle at Mnemba
Island. b, Red colobus monkey. c, Giant tortoise at Changuu Island. d, Dhow, Zanzibar
sunset. e, Dhow sailing near Matemwe. f,
Coconut crab, Chumbe Island.
　No. 2429, 500sh, vert.: a, Clove foliage and
enlargement of flower buds. b, Light Signal
Tower.

2006, June 30　　　*Perf. 13½x13*
2424-2427　A428　Set of 4　　4.00　4.00
2428　A428　600sh Sheet of 6, #a-
　　　　f　　　　　　　　　　　6.00　6.00
Souvenir Sheet
Perf. 13x13½
2429　A428　500sh Sheet of 2, #a-
　　　　b　　　　　　　　　　　1.75　1.75

Mountains — A429

Designs: 350sh, Mt. Kenya. 400sh,
Udzungwa Mountain Range. 600sh, Sanje
Falls, vert. 800sh, Ruwenzori Range.
　No. 2434, 1000sh: a, Kiko Summit and
Mawenzi, Mt. Kilimanjaro. b, Giraffe and Mt.
Kilimanjaro.
　No. 2435, 1000sh: a, Cattle, herder and Ol
Doinyo Lengai. b, Ol Doinyo Lengai summit
and crater, vert.

Perf. 13½x13¾, 13¾x13½
2006, Aug. 24
2430-2433 A429 Set of 4 3.50 3.50
Sheets of 2, #a-b
2434-2435 A429 Set of 2 6.75 6.75

Miniature Sheet

Tazara Railway, 30th Anniv. — A430

No. 2436: a, 350sh, Map of Tanzania and Zambia, waterfall, mountain, people waving, and men signing agreement. b, 350sh, Men and train, elephant and antelope. c, 600sh, Dar es Salaam Station, sign and wreaths with Chinese inscriptions. d, 600sh, New Kapiri Mposhi Station, people near train. e, 800sh, Train, bridge and tunnel, zebra and giraffe. f, 800sh, Train on bridge, lion and lioness.

2006, Oct. 25 *Perf. 12*
2436 A430 Sheet of 6, #a-f 6.00 6.00

Worldwide Fund for Nature (WWF) — A431

No. 2437 — Damaliscus lunatus jimela: a, Males butting heads. b, Close-up view of head. c, Adult and juvenile. d, Adult on mound.

2006, Nov. 24 *Perf. 13¼*
2437 Horiz. or vert. strip 4.00 4.00
a.-d. A431 600sh Any single .95 .95
e. Miniature sheet, 2 each #2437a-2437d 8.00 8.00

Zanzibar Flora and Fauna — A432

No. 2438, 1000sh: a, Coconut crab. b, Frangipane. c, Sykes monkey. d, Green sea turtle. No. 2439, 1000sh: a, African civet. b, Fourtoed elephant shrew. c, Lesser bushbaby. d, Pemba sunbird.
No. 2440, 3000sh, Protoreaster lincki. No. 2441, 3000sh, Tauraco fischeri.

2006, Nov. 24 *Perf. 13¼*
Sheets of 4, #a-d
2438-2439 A432 Set of 2 13.50 13.50
Souvenir Sheets
2440-2441 A432 Set of 2 10.00 10.00

Space Achievements — A433

No. 2442 — Intl. Space Station: a, Two rows of solar panels at top, part of Space Station at bottom. b, Connection point for arms holding solar panels. c, Main junction of Space Station. d, Space Station, denomination at UR. e, Space Shuttle with cargo door open. f, Space Station, "International Space Station" just above country name.
No. 2443 — Mars Reconnaissance Orbiter: a, Mars, launch of rocket. b, Orbiter, country name in white at UR. c, Orbiter, country name in red and black at LL. d, Orbiter, country name in white at UL.
No. 2444, 2500sh, Calipso and Cloudsat satellites. No. 2445, 2500sh, Muses-C probe.

2006, June 13 *Litho.* *Perf. 14*
2442 A433 800sh Sheet of 6, #a-f 7.75 7.75
2443 A433 1150sh Sheet of 4, #a-d 7.50 7.50
Souvenir Sheets
2444-2445 A433 Set of 2 8.00 8.00

Phila Africa 06 Stamp Exhibition, Dar es Salaam A434

2006, Aug. 24 *Perf. 13¾*
2446 A434 (700sh) multi 1.10 1.10
Souvenir Sheet
2447 A434 600sh multi .90 .90
No. 2447 contains one 47x32mm stamp.

Independence, 45th Anniv. — A435

Designs: 350sh, Pres. Julius K. Nyerere with torch. No. 2449, 400sh, University of Dar es Salaam, horiz. No. 2450, 600sh, Vice-president Abeid A. Karume, country name in green. 800sh, Nyerere.
No. 2452, 600sh: a, Prime Minister Rashidi Mfaume Kawawa. b, Nyerere, diff. c, Karume, country name in blue. d, Pres. Ali Hassan Mwinyi. e, Pres. Benjamin W. Mkapa. f, Pres. Jakaya Mrisho Kikwete.
No. 2453, National Uhuru Monument.

2006, Dec. 9 *Perf. 13½*
2448-2451 A435 Set of 4 3.50 3.50
2452 A435 600sh Sheet of 6, #a-f 5.75 5.75
Souvenir Sheet
2453 A435 400sh multi .65 .65

Safari Hunt Animals A436

Designs: 400sh, Wild dog. 600sh, Warthog. No. 2456, 700sh, Zebras. 800sh, Female monkeys and young.

No. 2458, 700sh: a, Elephant. b, Leopard in grass. c, Buffaloes. d, Lion and lioness. e, Leopard in foliage (66x46mm).
1000sh, Lionesses.

2007, Feb. 23 *Perf. 13¾*
2454-2457 A436 Set of 4 4.00 4.00
2458 A436 700sh Sheet of 5, #a-e 5.75 5.75
Souvenir Sheet
2459 A436 1000sh multi 1.60 1.60
No. 2459 contains one 47x32mm stamp.

Historical Zanzibar — A437

Designs: 400sh, Ruins. 600sh, Coral reef and fish west of Pemba, horiz. No. 2462, 700sh, Bet El Ajaib, cloves. 800sh, Coral reef and fish, diff.
No. 2464, 700sh, horiz.: a, Beach. b, Kizimbani Persian Bath. c, Maruhubi Ruins. d, Livingstone House. e, Old Dispensary. f, Cave.
No. 2465, 700sh, Colobus monkey, horiz.

2007, Apr. 26
2460-2463 A437 Set of 4 4.00 4.00
2464 A437 700sh Sheet of 6, #a-f 6.75 6.75
Souvenir Sheet
2465 A437 700sh multi 1.10 1.10

Environmental Care — A439

Designs: No. 2473, 400sh, Prof. Mark Mwandosya planting tree at Kiroka Secondary School, Morogoro. No. 2474, 500sh, Shinyanga. 700sh, Kihansi Waterfall, Nectophrynoides aspergins. 800sh, Natural regeneration of the land.
No. 2477, 400sh: a, Illegal mining. b, Tree planting, Morogoro. c, Planted trees in degraded areas. d, Traditional soil and moisture conservation method. e, Tree seedlings for rehabilitating degraded areas. f, Agriculture on steep mountains.
No. 2478, 500sh, Nguru Mountains catchment area.

2007, June 5 *Litho.* *Perf. 14*
2473-2476 A439 Set of 4 4.00 4.00
2477 A439 400sh Sheet of 6, #a-f 4.00 4.00
Souvenir Sheet
2478 A439 500sh multi .80 .80

Reign of Aga Khan, 50th Anniv. A441

Designs: 400sh, Zanzibar Madrasa Resource Center. No. 2486, 600sh, Aga Khan Hospital, Dar es Salaam, gold frame. 700sh, Lake Manyara Serena Safari Lodge. 800sh, Zanzibar Serena Inn.
No. 2489, 600sh: a, Exterior of Stone Town Cultural Center, Zanzibar. b, View from balcony of Stone Town Cultural Center. c, Medical personnel treating patient at Aga Khan Hospital. d, Aga Khan Hospital, white frame.
1000sh, Women at Zanzibar Madrasa Resource Center, vert.

2007, Aug. 18 *Litho.* *Perf. 14½*
2485-2488 A441 Set of 4 4.00 4.00
2489 A441 600sh Sheet of 4, #a-d 3.75 3.75
Souvenir Sheet
2490 A441 1000sh multi 1.60 1.60

Pope Benedict XVI — A444

2007, Oct. 24 *Litho.* *Perf. 13½*
2503 A444 600sh multi 1.10 1.10
Printed in sheets of 8.

Wedding of Queen Elizabeth II and Prince Philip, 60th Anniv. — A445

No. 2504: a, Queen and flowers. b, Couple.

2007, Oct. 24
2504 A445 750sh Pair, #a-b 2.60 2.60
Printed in sheets containing three of each stamp.

Princess Diana (1961-97) — A446

No. 2505 — Diana wearing: a, Purple and red hat, close-up. b, Blue and beige hat, close-up. c, Black and white hat. d, Blue and beige hat. e, Purple and red hat. f, Black and white hat, close-up.
3500sh, Blue and white hat.

2007, Oct. 24
2505 A446 750sh Sheet of 6, #a-f 7.75 7.75
Souvenir Sheet
2506 A446 3500sh multi 6.00 6.00

First Helicopter Flight, Cent. — A447

No. 2507: a, Hiller UH-12 Raven. b, Kamov Ka-25 Hormone. c, Cierva autogyro. d, Eurocopter Tiger.
3000sh, Bristol Sycamore.

2007, Oct. 24
2507 A447 1200sh Sheet of 4, #a-d 8.25 8.25
Souvenir Sheet
2508 A447 3000sh multi 5.25 5.25

Paintings by Qi Baishi (1864-1957) — A448

No. 2509: a, Wisteria and Bees. b, Pine and Cicada. c, Narcissus, Rock and Quail. d, Pumpkins.
3000sh, Begonias and Butterfly.

2007, Oct. 24   *Perf. 12½*
2509 A448 1000sh Sheet of 4, #a-d   7.00 7.00

Souvenir Sheet
Perf. 13½
2510 A448 3000sh multi   5.25 5.25

No. 2509 contains four 32x80mm stamps.

SEMI-POSTAL STAMPS

Natl. Solidarity Walk — SP1

1988, July 1   *Litho.*   *Perf. 14½*
B1 SP1 2sh +1sh Flag, crowd   .70 .70
B2 SP1 3sh +1sh Map, Pres. Mwinyi   .70 .70

Souvenir Sheet
B3 SP1 50sh +1sh Flag, Pres. Mwinyi   1.75 1.75

Surtax for Chama Cha Mapinduzi party activities.

Natl. Solidarity Walk — SP2

1989, July 1   *Litho.*   *Perf. 14½*
B4 SP2 5sh +1sh Party flag   .45 .45
B5 SP2 10sh +1sh Pres. Mwinyi, walk   .45 .45

Souvenir Sheet
B6 SP2 50sh +1sh Pres. Mwinyi   1.40 1.40

Natl. Solidarity Walk SP3

Designs: 4sh + 1sh, Pres. Mwinyi marching with crowd. 9sh + 1sh, Crowd around party flag. 13sh + 1sh, Pres. Mwinyi. 30sh + 1sh, Pres. Mwinyi planting tree. No. B11, Pres. Mwinyi sorting cloves. No. B12, Handshake across map, vert.

1991-92   *Litho.*   *Perf. 13½*
B7 SP3 4sh +1sh multicolored ('92)   .65 .65
B8 SP3 9sh +1sh multicolored   .85 .85
B9 SP3 13sh +1sh multicolored   .85 .85
B10 SP3 30sh +1sh multicolored ('92)   1.50 1.50
   Nos. B7-B10 (4)   3.85 3.85

Souvenir Sheets
Perf. 12½
B11 SP3 50sh +1sh multicolored   2.75 2.75
B12 SP3 50sh +1sh multicolored   2.25 2.25

Issued: Nos. B8-B9, 7/6/90. Nos. B7, B10, 7/5/91.

POSTAGE DUE STAMPS

D1   D2

Perf. 13
1978, July 31   *Litho.*   *Unwmk.*
J1 D1 5c red   .75 1.00
J2 D1 10c green   .75 1.00
J3 D1 20c dark blue   .75 1.00
J4 D1 30c reddish brown   .75 1.00
J5 D1 40c bright rose lilac   .75 1.00
J6 D1 1sh orange   1.25 2.25
   Nos. J1-J6 (6)   5.00 7.25

1967, Jan. 3   *Perf. 14x13½*
J1a D1 5c red   .35 3.00
J2a D1 10c green   .35 3.00
J3a D1 20c dark blue   .55 5.25
J4a D1 30c reddish brown   .90 7.50
J5a D1 40c bright rose lilac   1.25 10.50
J6a D1 1sh orange   3.25 22.50
   Nos. J1a-J6a (6)   6.65 51.75

1969-71   *Perf. 14x15*
J1b D1 5c red   .60 3.00
J2b D1 10c green   .60 3.00
J3b D1 20c dark blue   1.25 5.25
J4b D1 30c reddish brown   1.75 7.50
J5b D1 40c bright rose lilac   2.40 10.50
J6b D1 1sh orange ('71)   6.00 22.50
   Nos. J1b-J6b (6)   12.60 51.75

1973, Dec. 12   *Perf. 15*
J1c D1 5c red   .40 3.00
J2c D1 10c green   .40 3.00
J3c D1 20c dark blue   .60 6.00
J4c D1 30c reddish brown   .90 9.00
J5c D1 40c bright rose lilac   1.25 12.00
J6c D1 1sh orange   3.00 30.00
   Nos. J1c-J6c (6)   6.55 63.00

1984?   *Perf. 14¾x14*
J4d D1 30c reddish brown

Additional stamps of this type with this perforation have been reported. The editors would like to examine any examples.

1990   *Litho.*   *Perf. 15x14*
J7 D2 50c dark green   .35 .35
J8 D2 80c bright blue   .35 .35
J9 D2 1sh orange brown   .35 .35
J10 D2 2sh light olive green   .35 .35
J11 D2 3sh purple   .35 .35
J12 D2 5sh gray   .35 .35
J13 D2 10sh brown   .35 .35
J14 D2 20sh bister   .35 .35
   Nos. J7-J14 (8)   2.80 2.80

OFFICIAL STAMPS

Nos. 5-9, 11, 13 and 16 Overprinted: "OFFICIAL"
Perf. 14x14½, 14½x14
1965, Dec. 9   *Photo.*   *Unwmk.*
Size: 21x17½mm, 17½x21mm
O1 A2 5c orange & ultra   .20 .20
O2 A2 10c multicolored   .20 .20
O3 A3 15c grn bl, brn & buff   .20 .20
O4 A2 20c blue & brown   .20 .20
O5 A3 30c black & red brn   .20 .20
O6 A2 50c yellow grn & blk   .20 .20

Perf. 14½
Size: 41½x25
O7 A2 1sh multicolored   .30 .20
O8 A2 5sh bl, brt grn & red brn   1.50 1.00
   Nos. O1-O8 (8)   3.00 2.40

Overprint size: 17mm on 5c, 10c, 20c, 50c. 14mm on 15c, 30c. 29x3½mm on 1sh, 5sh. The overprint was also applied in 1967 in Dar es Salaam to 50c, 1sh and 5sh. Size: 29x3mm.

Nos. 19-23, 25, 27 and 30 Overprinted: "OFFICIAL"
1967, Dec. 9   *Photo.*   *Perf. 14x14½*
Fish in Natural Colors
Size: 21x17½mm
Overprint Litho., 17mm Wide
O9 A4 5c black & citron   .40 1.25
O10 A4 10c brown & olive   .40 .60
O11 A4 15c brown & blue   .40 .40
O12 A4 20c brown & dk blue grn   .40 .40
O13 A4 30c black & yel grn   .40 .40
O14 A4 50c black & dull bl grn   .40 1.00

Perf. 14½
Size: 41x25mm
Overprint 29mm Wide
O15 A4 1sh brown & multi   .80 2.00
O16 A4 5sh black & blue grn   3.50 8.00
   Nos. O9-O16 (8)   6.70 14.05

1970-73   Overprint Typo., 17½mm Wide
O9a A4 5c black & citron   .55 .55
O10a A4 10c brown & olive   .55 .55
O12a A4 20c brn & dk bl grn   .55 .55
O13a A4 30c blk & yel grn   .80 .55
O13B A4 40c multicolored ('73)
   Nos. O9a-O13a (4)   2.45 2.20

The overprint was also applied in 1973 to 15c, 50c, 1sh (28mm wide), and 5sh.

Nos. 35-36, 38, 40-41, 43-47 Overprinted

a   b

1973, Dec. 10   *Photo.*   *Perf. 14½x14*
O17 A5(a) 5c multicolored   1.00 4.00
O18 A5(a) 10c multicolored   1.25 .70
O19 A5(a) 20c multicolored   1.40 .70
O20 A5(a) 40c multicolored   2.00 .70
O21 A5(a) 50c multicolored   2.00 .70
O22 A5(a) 70c multicolored   2.00 .70

Perf. 14½
O23 A6(b) 1sh multicolored   3.00 .80
O24 A6(b) 1.50sh multicolored   3.50 4.00
O25 A6(b) 2.50sh multicolored   5.00 6.00
O26 A6(b) 5sh multicolored   7.00 10.00
   Nos. O17-O26 (10)   28.15 28.30

A larger overprint (17½mm wide instead of 14½mm) was applied locally to 10c, 20c, 40c, and 50c.
Provisional use of some values for regular postage is known.

Nos. 161-171 Overprinted: OFFICIAL
1980, Oct. 1   *Perf. 14*
O27 A21 10c multicolored   .60 .60
O28 A21 20c multicolored   .60 .60
O29 A21 40c multicolored   .60 .60
O30 A21 50c multicolored   .60 .60
O31 A21 75c multicolored   .60 .60
O32 A21 80c multicolored   .60 .60

Perf. 14½
O33 A21 1sh multicolored   .60 .60
O33A A21 1.50sh multicolored
O34 A21 2sh multicolored   1.25 1.25
O35 A21 3sh multicolored   1.75 1.75
O36 A21 5sh multicolored   3.00 3.00
   Nos. O27-O33, O34-O36 (10)   10.20 10.20

Overprint measures 13mm on Nos. O33-O36; reads up or down.

Nos. 606-614 Inscribed "OFFICIAL"
1990-91   *Litho.*   *Perf. 14*
O37 A99 5sh multi   .60 .60
O38 A99 9sh multi   .60 .60
O39 A99 13sh multi   .60 .60
O40 A99 15sh multi   .60 .60
O41 A99 20sh multi   .90 .90
O42 A99 25sh multi   1.00 1.00
O42A A99 30sh multi ('91)   1.40 1.40
O43 A99 40sh multi   1.75 1.75
O44 A99 70sh multi   3.00 3.00
O45 A99 100sh multi   4.50 4.50
   Nos. O37-O45 (10)   14.95 14.95

Inscription on Nos. O37-O42A is 15½mm long. Inscription on Nos. O43-O45 is 19mm long.

Nos. 1565, 1566, 1568, 1570, 1571, and 1572 Overprinted "OFFICIAL"

1997 (?)   *Litho.*   *Perf. 14½x15*
O47 A262 100sh multi   — —
O48 A262 140sh multi   — —
O49 A262 200sh multi   — —
O50 A262 260sh multi   — —
O51 A262 300sh multi   — —
O52 A262 380sh multi   — —

The editors suspect there are additional stamps in this set, and would like to examine any examples.

TETE

'tāt-ə

LOCATION — In southeastern Africa between Nyasaland and Southern Rhodesia
GOVT. — A district of the Portuguese East Africa Colony
AREA — 46,600 sq. mi. (approx.)
POP. — 367,000 (approx.)
CAPITAL — Tete

This district was formerly a part of Zambezia. Stamps of Mozambique replaced those of Tete. See Mozambique.

100 Centavos = 1 Escudo

Vasco da Gama Issue of Various Portuguese Colonies Surcharged as

1913   *Unwmk.*   *Perf. 12½, 16*
On Stamps of Macao
1 CD20 ¼c on ½a bl grn   5.00 5.00
2 CD21 ½c on 1a red   1.75 3.00
3 CD22 1c on 2a red vio   1.75 3.00
4 CD23 2½c on 4a yel grn   1.75 3.00
6 CD25 7½c on 12a vio brn   2.40 3.00
7 CD26 10c on 16a bis brn   1.75 2.10
8 CD27 15c on 24a bister   1.75 2.10
   Nos. 1-8 (8)   17.90 23.30

On Stamps of Portuguese Africa
9 CD20 ¼c on 2½r bl grn   1.75 2.10
10 CD21 ½c on 5r red   1.75 2.10
11 CD22 1c on 10r red vio   1.75 2.10
12 CD23 2½c on 25r yel grn   1.75 2.10
13 CD24 5c on 50r dk blue   1.75 2.10
14 CD25 7½c on 75r vio brn   2.40 3.00
15 CD26 10c on 100r bis brn   1.75 2.10
16 CD27 15c on 150r bister   1.75 2.10
   Nos. 9-16 (8)   14.65 17.70

On Stamps of Timor
17 CD20 ¼c on ½a bl grn   1.75 2.10
18 CD21 ½c on 1a red   1.75 2.10
19 CD22 1c on 2a red vio   1.75 2.10
a. Inverted overprint   30.00 30.00
20 CD23 2½c on 4a yel grn   1.75 2.10
21 CD24 5c on 8a dk blue   1.75 2.10
22 CD25 7½c on 12a vio brn   2.40 3.00
23 CD26 10c on 16a bis brn   1.75 2.10
24 CD27 15c on 24a bister   1.75 2.10
   Nos. 17-24 (8)   14.65 17.70
   Nos. 1-24 (24)   47.20 58.70

Common Design Types pictured following the introduction.

Ceres — A1

1914   Typo.   Perf. 15x14
Name and Value in Black

25	A1	¼c olive brn	1.40	2.25
26	A1	½c black	1.40	2.25
27	A1	1c blue grn	1.40	2.25
28	A1	1½c lilac brn	1.40	2.25
29	A1	2c carmine	1.40	2.25
30	A1	2½c light vio	1.40	2.25
31	A1	5c deep blue	1.40	2.25
32	A1	7½c yel brn	2.25	3.25
33	A1	8c slate	2.25	3.25
34	A1	10c org brn	2.75	4.00
35	A1	15c plum	3.25	4.50
36	A1	20c yel green	3.25	4.50
37	A1	30c brn, *green*	3.25	4.50
38	A1	40c brn, *pink*	4.00	7.00
39	A1	50c org, *salmon*	7.00	9.00
40	A1	1e grn, *blue*	10.00	10.00
		Nos. 25-40 (16)	47.80	65.75

THAILAND

'tī-,land

(Siam)

LOCATION — Western part of the Malay peninsula in southeastern Asia
GOVT. — Republic
AREA — 198,250 sq. mi.
POP. — 60,609,046 (1999 est.)
CAPITAL — Bangkok

32 Solot = 16 Atts = 8 Sio =
4 Sik = 2 Fuang = 1 Salung
4 Salungs = 1 Tical
100 Satangs (1909) = 1 Tical
= 1 Baht (1912)

Catalogue values for unused stamps in this country are for Never Hinged items, beginning with Scott 264 in the regular postage section, Scott B34 in the semi-postal section, Scott C20 in the airpost section, and Scott O1 in the official section.

Watermarks

Wmk. 176 — Chakra

Wmk. 233 — Harrison & Sons, London in Script Letters

Wmk. 299 — Thai Characters and Wavy Lines

Wmk. 329 — Zigzag Lines

Wmk. 334 — Rectangles

Wmk. 340 — Alternating Interlaced Wavy Lines

Wmk. 356 — POSTAGE

Wmk. 368 — JEZ Multiple

Wmk. 371 — Wavy Lines

Wmk. 374 — Circles and Crosses

Wmk. 375 — Letters

Wmk. 377 — Interlocking Circles

Wmk. 385 — CARTOR

Wmk. 387 — Squares and Rectangles

King Chulalongkorn
A1   A2

A4

Perf. 14½, 15
1883, Aug. 4   Unwmk.   Engr.

1	A1	1sol blue	10.00	10.00
b.		Imperf., pair		4,500.
2	A1	1att carmine	10.00	10.00
3	A1	1sio vermilion	32.50	20.00
4	A2	1sik yellow	13.50	17.00
5	A4	1sa orange	50.00	50.00
a.		1sa ocher	55.00	55.00
		Nos. 1-5 (5)	116.00	107.00

There are three types of No. 1, differing mainly in the background of the small oval at the top.

A 1 fuang red, of similar design to the foregoing, was prepared but not placed in use. Value, $900.
For surcharges see Nos. 6-8, 19.

No. 1 Handstamp Surcharged in Red:

1 TICAL
a

1 Tical   **1 Tical**
b   *c*

1 Tical   **1 Tical**
d   *e*

1885, July 1

6	A1	(a) 1t on 1sol blue	425.	425.
7	A1	(b) 1t on 1sol blue	350.	350.
c.		"1" inverted	1,100.	1,100.
8	A1	(c) 1t on 1sol blue	450.	450.

Surcharges of Nos. 6-8 have been counterfeited.
Types "d" and "e" are typeset *official reprints.*
As is usual with handstamps, double impressions, etc., exist.

King Chulalongkorn — A7

1887-91 Typo. Wmk. 176 *Perf. 14*

11	A7	1a green ('91)	3.00	1.00
12	A7	2a green & car	5.00	1.00
13	A7	3a grn & blue	12.00	4.00
14	A7	4a grn & org brn	10.00	3.00
15	A7	8a green & yel	10.00	7.00
16	A7	12a lilac & car	17.00	2.00
17	A7	24a lilac & blue	22.50	3.00
18	A7	64a lil & org brn	85.00	27.50
		Nos. 11-18 (8)	164.50	48.50

The design of No. 11 has been redrawn and differs from the illustration in many minor details.
Issue dates: #12-18, Apr. 1; #11, Feb.
For surcharges see Nos. 20-69, 109, 111, 126.

No. 3 Handstamp Surcharged

1889, Aug.   Unwmk.   Perf. 15

19	A1	1a on 1sio	18.00	18.00

Three different handstamps were used. Doubles, etc. exist.

Nos. 12 and 13 Handstamp Surcharged

1889-90   Wmk. 176   Perf. 14

20	A7	1a on 2a	4.00	3.00
a.		"1" omitted	275.00	275.00
c.		1st Siamese character invtd.		
d.		First Siamese character omitted	300.00	300.00
21	A7	1a on 3a ('90)	9.00	9.00
a.		Inverted "1"	150.00	150.00

For surcharge see No. 29.

๑ ฮู 1

22	A7	1a on 2a grn & car	450.00	450.00

๑ ฮู 1

24	A7	1a on 2a grn & car	200.00	200.00

| 25 | A7 | 1a on 2a grn & car | 1,000. | 1,000. |

| 26 | A7 | 1a on 3a grn & bl | | |

Some authorities consider No. 26 a forgery. Doubles, etc., exist in this issue.
Issue dates: Nov. 1889. Sept. 1890.

No. 13 Handstamp Surcharged

1891

| 27 | A7 | 2a on 3a grn & bl | 60.00 | 60.00 |

28	A7	2a on 3a grn & bl	50.00	50.00
a.		Double surcharge	250.00	250.00
b.		"2" omitted	250.00	

No. 21 with Additional 2 Att Surcharge

| 29 | A7 | 2a on 1a on 3a grn & bl | 1,500. | 1,500. |

On No. 29 the 2a surcharge consists of Siamese numeral like No. 27 and English numeral like No. 28.
Most examples of No. 29 show attempts to remove the "1" of the first surcharge.

Typeset Surcharge

| 30 | A7 | 2a on 3a grn & bl | 40.00 | 40.00 |

There are 7 types of this surcharge in the setting.
Issued: #27-28, Jan.; #29, Feb.; #30, Mar.

No. 17 Handstamp Surcharged:

f   g

1892, Oct.

| 33 | A7 (f) | 4a on 24a lil & bl | 50.00 | 50.00 |
| 34 | A7 (g) | 4a on 24a lil & bl | 35.00 | 35.00 |

Surcharges exist double on Nos. 33-34 and inverted on No. 33.

Nos. 33-34 Handstamp Surcharged in English

4 atts

1892, Nov.

| 35 | A7 | 4a on 24a lil & bl | 8.50 | 8.50 |
| c. | | Inverted "s" | 45.00 | 45.00 |

| 36 | A7 | 4a on 24a lil & bl | 14.00 | 9.50 |
| a. | | Inverted "s" | 40.00 | 40.00 |

| 37 | A7 | 4a on 24a lil & bl | 12.50 | 12.50 |

4 atts.

| 38 | A7 | 4a on 24a lil & bl | 14.00 | 15.00 |

Numerous inverts., doubles, etc., exist.

Nos. 18 and 17 Typeset Surcharged in English (Shown) and Siamese

1 Atts

1894

39	A7	1a on 64a lil & org brn	3.50	3.50
a.		Inverted "s"	45.00	45.00
b.		Inverted surcharge	900.00	900.00
d.		Italic "s"	57.50	57.50
e.		Italic "1"	57.50	57.50

1 Att.

| 40 | A7 | 1a on 64a lil & org brn | 2.00 | 2.00 |
| a. | | Inverted capital "S" added to the surcharge | 175.00 | 200.00 |

2 Atts. (h) **2 Atts.** (i)

2 Atts. (j) **2 Atts.** (k)

2. Atts. (l) **2 Atts.** (m)

41	A7 (h)	2a on 64a	26.00	26.00
a.		Inverted "s"	42.50	42.50
b.		Double surcharge	100.00	100.00
42	A7 (i)	2a on 64a	3,000.	3,000.
43	A7 (j)	2a on 64a	62.50	62.50
44	A7 (k)	2a on 64a	37.50	37.50
45	A7 (l)	2a on 64a	57.50	57.50
46	A7 (m)	2a on 64a	2.50	2.50
a.		"Att.s"	45.00	45.00

Nos. 41-46 were in one plate of 120 subjects. The quanrtities were: h, 38; i, 1; j, 8; k, 18; l, 11 and m, 44.

1 Att.

1894, Oct. 12

47	A7	1a on 64a	2.50	2.50
a.		Surcharged on face and back	150.00	
b.		Surcharge on back inverted	200.00	
c.		Double surcharge	475.00	
d.		Inverted surcharge	500.00	
e.		Siamese surcharge omitted	400.00	

2 Atts.

48	A7	2a on 64a	3.00	3.00
a.		"Att"	35.00	35.00
b.		Inverted surcharge	300.00	300.00
c.		Surch. on face and back	400.00	400.00
d.		Surcharge on back inverted	400.00	400.00
e.		Double surcharge	300.00	300.00
f.		Double surch., one inverted	1,100.	1,100.
g.		Inverted "s"	42.50	42.50

10 Atts.

1895, July 23

49	A7	10a on 24a lil & bl	7.00	2.00
a.		Inverted "s"	45.00	45.00
b.		Surch. on face and back	175.00	175.00
c.		Surch. on back inverted	175.00	175.00

No. 16 Surcharged in English (Shown) and Siamese

4 Atts.

1896

50	A7	4a on 12a lil & car	15.00	8.00
a.		Inverted "s"	50.00	50.00
b.		Surch. on face and back	175.00	175.00
c.		Double surcharge on back	175.00	175.00

Two types of surcharge.

Nos. 16-18 Surcharged in English (Shown) and Siamese
Antique Surcharges:

1 Atts. (a) **1 Att.** (b) **2 Atts.** (c)

3 Atts. (d) **4 Atts.** (e) **10 Atts.** (f)

Atts.
Antique Letters

Atts.
Roman Letters

1898-99

51	A7 (a)	1a on 12a	350.00	350.00
52	A7 (b)	1a on 12a	18.00	7.00
53	A7 (c)	2a on 64a ('99)	30.00	9.00
54	A7 (d)	3a on 12a	12.00	4.00
a.		Double surcharge	350.00	350.00
55	A7 (e)	4a on 12a	12.00	5.00
a.		Double surcharge	350.00	350.00
56	A7 (e)	4a on 24a ('99)	35.00	12.00
57	A7 (f)	10a on 24a ('99)	775.00	775.00

Roman Surcharges:

1 Atts. (g) **1 Att.** (h) **2 Atts.** (i)

3 Atts. (j) **4 Atts.** (k) **10 Atts.** (l)

58	A7 (g)	1a on 12a	450.00	450.00
59	A7 (h)	1a on 12a	42.50	20.00
60	A7 (i)	2a on 64a ('99)	35.00	10.00
61	A7 (j)	3a on 12a	85.00	19.00
62	A7 (k)	4a on 12a	40.00	14.00
a.		Double surcharge	175.00	175.00
b.		No period after "Atts."	35.00	35.00
63	A7 (k)	4a on 24a ('99)	60.00	27.50
64	A7 (l)	10a on 24a ('99)	750.00	750.00
		Nos. 58-64 (7)	1,462.	1,290.

In making the settings to surcharge Nos. 51 to 64 two fonts were mixed. Antique and Roman letters are frequently found on the same stamp.
Issued: #54-55, 61-62, Feb. 22; #51-52, 58-59, June 4; #56-57, 63-64, Oct. 3.

Nos. 16 and 18 Surcharged in English (Shown) and Siamese
Surcharged:

1 Att. (m) **1 Att.** (n)

1 Att. (o)

2 Atts. (p) **2 Atts.** (r)

1894-99

65	A7 (m)	1a on 12a	20.00	6.00
66	A7 (n)	1a on 12a	20.00	6.00
a.		Inverted "l"	150.00	150.00
b.		Inverted 1st "t"	150.00	150.00
67	A7 (o)	1a on 64a	5.00	5.00
68	A7 (p)	2a on 64a	9.00	9.00
a.		"1 Atts."	500.00	500.00
69	A7 (r)	2a on 64a	24.00	8.00
		Nos. 65-69 (5)	78.00	34.00

Issued: #67, 10/12/94; others, 2/14/99.

A13   A14

1899, Oct.   Typo.   Unwmk.

70	A13	1a dull green	140.	85.
71	A13	2a dl grn & rose	250.	125.
72	A13	3a carmine & blue	350.	190.
73	A13	4a black & grn	2,100.	650.
74	A13	10a carmine & grn	2,500.	950.
		Nos. 70-74 (5)	5,340.	2,000.

The King rejected Nos. 70-74 in 1897, but some were released by mistake to three post offices in Oct. 1899. Used values are for copies canceled to order at Korat in Dec. 1899. Postally used examples sell for more.

1899-1904

75	A14	1a gray green	2.00	1.00
76	A14	2a yellow green	2.25	1.25
77	A14	2a scarlet & bl	4.00	2.00
78	A14	3a red & blue	7.00	2.00
79	A14	3a green	20.00	12.00
80	A14	4a dark rose	4.00	1.50
81	A14	4a vio brn & rose	8.00	2.00
82	A14	6a dk rose	35.00	14.00
83	A14	8a dk grn & org	9.00	1.50
84	A14	10a ultra	9.00	3.00
85	A14	12a brn vio & rose	40.00	2.00
86	A14	14a ultra	22.50	18.00
87	A14	24a brn vio & bl	375.00	29.00
88	A14	28a brn vio & bl	25.00	25.00
89	A14	64a brn vio & org brn	70.00	11.00
		Nos. 75-89 (15)	632.75	125.25

Two types of 1a differ in size and shape of Thai "1" are in drawing of spandrel ornaments.
Issue dates: 6a, 14a, 28a, Nos. 77, 79, 81, Jan. 1, 1904; others, Sept. 1899.

For surcharges see Nos. 90-91, 112, 125, 127.

Nos. 78 and 85 With Typewritten Surcharge of 6 or 7 Siamese Characters (1 line) in Violet

1902

78a	A14	2a on 3a	4,000.	4,500.
85a	A14	10a on 12a	4,000.	4,500.

Nos. 78a and 85a were authorized provisionals, surcharged and issued by the Battambang postmaster.

Nos. 86 and 88 Surcharged in Black

1905, Feb.

90	A14	1a on 14a	10.00	10.00
a.		No period after "Att"	35.00	35.00
91	A14	2a on 28a	12.00	12.00
a.		Double surcharge	125.00	125.00

King Chulalongkorn — A15

King Chulalongkorn — A16

1905-08 Engr.

92	A15	1a orange & green	2.00	1.00
93	A15	2a violet & slate	3.00	1.00
94	A15	2a green ('08)	11.00	4.00
95	A15	3a green	3.00	2.00
96	A15	3a vio & sl ('08)	10.00	5.00
97	A15	4a gray & red	4.00	1.00
98	A15	4a car & rose ('08)	6.00	1.50
99	A15	5a carmine & rose	8.00	3.00
100	A15	8a blk & ol bis	8.00	1.50
101	A15	9a blue ('08)	22.50	9.00
102	A15	12a blue	18.00	4.00
103	A15	18a red brn ('08)	55.00	16.00
104	A15	24a red brown	32.50	8.00
105	A15	1t dp bl & brn org	45.00	10.00
		Nos. 92-105 (14)	228.00	67.00

Issue dates: Dec. 1905, Apr. 1, 1908. For surcharges and overprints see Nos. 110, 113-117, 128-138, 161-162, B15, B21.

1907, Apr. 24

Black Surcharge

106	A16	10t gray green	325.	100.
107	A16	20t gray green	3,300.	290.
108	A16	40t gray green	2,400.	450.
		Nos. 106-108 (3)	6,025.	840.00

Counterfeits of Nos. 106-108 exist. In the genuine, the surcharged figures correspond to the Siamese value inscriptions on the basic revenue stamps.

No. 17 Surcharged

1907, Dec. 16

109	A7	1a on 24a lil & bl	2.00	1.00
a.		Double surcharge	400.00	

No. 99 Surcharged

1908, Sept.

110	A15	4a on 5a car & rose	11.00	4.00

The No. 110 surcharge is found in two spacings of the numerals: normally 15mm apart, and a narrow, scarcer spacing of 13½mm.

Nos. 17 and 84 Surcharged in Black:

111	A7	2a on 24a lil & bl	2.00	1.00
a.		Inverted surcharge	325.00	325.00
112	A14	9a on 10a ultra	12.00	5.00
a.		Inverted surcharge	325.00	325.00

Jubilee Issue

Nos. 92, 95, 110, 100 and 103 Overprinted in Black or Red

1908, Nov. 11

113	A15	1a	2.00	1.00
a.		Siamese date "137" instead of "127"	950.00	950.00
b.		Pair, one without ovpt.		
114	A15	3a	3.00	2.00
115	A15	4a on 5a	5.00	3.00
a.		Horiz. pair, imperf. btwn.	500.00	
116	A15	8a (R)	21.00	21.00
117	A15	18a	30.00	20.00
		Nos. 113-117 (5)	61.00	47.00

40th year of the reign of King Chulalongkorn. Nos. 113 to 117 exist with a small "i" in "Jubilee."

Statue of King Chulalongkorn A19

1908, Nov. 11 Engr. Perf. 13½

118	A19	1t green & vio	29.00	3.00
119	A19	2t red vio & org	60.00	11.00
120	A19	3t pale ol & bl	85.00	14.00
121	A19	5t dl vio & dk grn	120.00	25.00
122	A19	10t bister & car	1,250.	87.50
123	A19	20t gray & red brn	325.00	87.50
124	A19	40t sl bl & blk brn	500.00	300.00
		Nos. 118-124 (7)	2,369.	528.00

The inscription at the foot of the stamps reads: "Coronation Commemoration-Forty-first year of the reign-1908."

Stamps of 1887-1904 Surcharged

1909 Perf. 14

125	A14	6s on 6a dk rose	2.00	2.00
126	A7	14s on 12a lil & car	100.00	100.00
127	A14	14s on 14a ultra	18.00	18.00
		Nos. 125-127 (3)	120.00	120.00

Nos. 92-102 Surcharged with Bar and

1909, Aug. 15

128	A15	2s on 1a #92	2.00	1.00
129	A15	2s on 2a #93	60.00	60.00
130	A15	2s on 2a #94	2.00	1.00
a.		"2" omitted	85.00	
131	A15	3s on 3a #95	3.00	1.00
132	A15	3s on 3a #96	3.00	1.00
133	A15	6s on 4a #97	62.50	62.50
134	A15	6s on 4a #98	4.00	1.00
135	A15	6s on 5a #99	3.00	3.00
136	A15	12s on 8a #100	7.00	1.00
137	A15	14s on 9a #101	11.00	3.00
138	A15	14s on 12a #102	21.00	21.00
		Nos. 128-138 (11)	178.50	155.50

King Chulalongkorn — A20

1910 Engr. Perf. 14x14½

139	A20	2s org & green	1.50	.50
140	A20	3s green	2.00	.50
141	A20	6s carmine	3.00	.50
142	A20	12s blk & ol brn	6.00	1.00
143	A20	14s blue	19.00	2.00
144	A20	28s red brown	47.50	10.00
		Nos. 139-144 (6)	79.00	14.50

Issue dates: 12s, June 5. Others, May 5. For surcharges see Nos. 163, 223-224.

A21

King Vajiravudh — A22

Printed at the Imperial Printing Works, Vienna

1912 Perf. 14½

145	A21	2s brown orange	1.25	.20
a.		Vert. pair, imperf. btwn.	500.00	500.00
b.		Horiz. pair, imperf. btwn.	500.00	500.00
146	A21	3s yellow green	1.25	.20
a.		Horiz. pair, imperf. btwn.	500.00	500.00
147	A21	6s carmine rose	2.25	.55
148	A21	12s gray blk & brn	3.25	.60
149	A21	14s ultramarine	5.25	.80
150	A21	28s chocolate	20.00	8.00
151	A22	1b blue & blk	20.00	2.00
a.		Pair, imperf. btwn.	1,250.	1,250.
152	A22	2b car rose & ol brn	24.00	3.00
153	A22	3b yel grn & bl blk	35.00	6.00
154	A22	5b vio & blk	50.00	7.00
155	A22	10b ol grn & vio brn	275.00	90.00
156	A22	20b sl bl & red brn	450.00	90.00
		Nos. 145-156 (12)	887.25	208.35

See Nos. 164-175. For surcharges and overprints see Nos. 157-160, 176-186, 206, B1-B14, B16-B20, B22, B31-B33.

Nos. 147-150 Surcharged in Red or Blue

1914-15

157	A21	2s on 14s (R) ('15)	2.00	.50
a.		Vert. pair, imperf. btwn.	900.00	900.00
b.		Double surcharge	62.50	40.00
158	A21	5s on 6s (Bl)	3.25	.50
a.		Horiz. pair, imperf. btwn.	900.00	900.00
b.		Double surcharge	67.50	67.50

159	A21	10s on 12s (R)	4.00	.45
a.		Double surcharge	67.50	67.50
160	A21	15s on 28s (Bl)	5.00	.60
		Nos. 157-160 (4)	14.25	2.05

The several settings of the surcharges on Nos. 157 to 160 show variations in the figures and letters.

Nos. 92-93 Surcharged

1915, Apr. 3

161	A15	2s on 1a org & grn	5.00	3.00
a.		Pair, one without surcharge	350.00	350.00
162	A15	2s on 2a vio & slate	5.00	3.00

No. 143 Surcharged in Red

1916, Oct.

163	A20	2s on 14s blue	2.50	1.10

Printed by Waterlow & Sons, London Types of 1912 Re-engraved

1917, Jan. 1 Perf. 14

164	A21	2s orange brown	.65	.40
165	A21	3s emerald	.95	.35
166	A21	5s rose red	2.50	.25
167	A21	10s black & olive	2.00	.25
168	A21	15s blue	4.00	.50
170	A22	1b bl & gray blk	17.50	2.00
171	A22	2b car rose & brn	70.00	26.00
172	A22	3b yel grn & blk	525.00	275.00
173	A22	5b dp violet & blk	140.00	87.50
174	A22	10b ol gray & vio brn	425.00	11.00
a.		Perf. 12½	500.00	37.50
175	A22	20b sea grn & brn	500.00	50.00
a.		Perf. 12½	600.00	85.00
		Nos. 164-175 (11)	1,687.	453.10

The re-engraved design of the satang stamps varies in numerous minute details from the 1912 issue. Four lines of the background appear between the vertical strokes of the "M" of "SIAM" in the 1912 issue and only three lines in the 1917 stamps. The 1912 stamps with value in bahts are 37½mm high; those of 1917 are 39mm. In the latter the king's features, especially the eyes and mouth, are more distinct and the uniform and decorations are more sharply defined.

The 1912 stamps have seven pearls between the earpieces of the crown. On the 1917 stamps there are nine pearls in the same place. Nos. 174 and 175 exist imperforate.

Nos. 164-173 Overprinted in Red

1918, Dec. 2

176	A21	2s orange brown	.55	.45
a.		Double overprint	110.00	110.00
177	A21	3s emerald	.85	.75
178	A21	5s rose red	1.40	1.25
a.		Double overprint	150.00	150.00
179	A21	10s black & olive	1.40	1.25
180	A21	15s blue	2.75	2.50
181	A22	1b bl & gray blk	22.50	17.00
182	A22	2b car rose & brn	45.00	35.00
183	A22	3b yel grn & blk	125.00	67.50
184	A22	5b dp vio & blk	400.00	300.00
		Nos. 176-184 (9)	599.45	425.70

Counterfeits of this overprint exist.

Nos. 147-148 Surcharged in Green or Red

1919-20
185	A21	5s on 6s (G)	2.00	.50
186	A21	10s on 12s (R) ('20)	6.00	1.00

Issue dates: 5s, Nov. 11. 10s, Jan. 1.

King Vajiravudh A23   Throne Room A24

1920-26   Engr.   Perf. 14-15, 12½
187	A23	2s brn, *yel* ('21)	2.00	.40
188	A23	3s grn, *grn* ('21)	3.25	.55
189	A23	3s chocolate ('24)	3.25	.40
190	A23	5s rose, *pale rose*	3.75	.40
191	A23	5s green ('22)	32.50	5.50
192	A23	5s dk vio, *lil* ('26)	7.50	.40
193	A23	10s blk & org ('21)	5.75	.40
194	A23	15s bl, *bluish* ('21)	7.50	.40
195	A23	15s carmine ('22)	42.50	6.00
196	A23	25s chocolate ('21)	24.00	2.00
197	A23	25s dk blue ('22)	27.50	1.00
198	A23	50s och & blk ('21)	25.00	2.00
		Nos. 187-198 (12)	185.50	19.45

For overprints see Nos. 205, B23-B30.

1926, Mar. 5   Perf. 12½
199	A24	1t gray vio & grn	12.00	2.00
200	A24	2t car & org red	27.50	6.00
201	A24	3t ol grn & bl	45.00	25.00
202	A24	5t dl vio & ol grn	65.00	19.00
203	A24	10t red & ol bis	325.00	25.00
204	A24	20t gray bl & brn	350.00	70.00
		Nos. 199-204 (6)	824.50	147.00

This issue was intended to commemorate the fifteenth year of the reign of King Vajiravudh. Because of the King's death the stamps were issued as ordinary postage stamps.

Nos. 195 and 150 with Surcharge similar to 1914-15 Issue in Black or Red

1928, Jan.
205	A23	5s on 15s car	4.00	2.00
206	A21	10s on 28s choc (R)	9.00	1.00

King Prajadhipok
A25   A26

1928   Engr.   Perf. 12½
207	A25	2s deep red brown	.60	.20
208	A25	3s deep green	.75	.20
209	A25	5s dark violet	.60	.20
210	A25	10s deep rose	.75	.20
211	A25	15s dark blue	.90	.40
212	A25	25s black & org	3.50	.60
213	A25	50s brn org & blk	1.75	1.25
214	A25	80s blue & black	3.00	.80
216	A26	1b dk blue & blk	6.00	1.25
217	A26	2b car rose & blk brn	12.00	3.00
218	A26	3b yellow grn & blk	9.00	3.00
219	A26	5b dp vio & gray	20.00	5.00
220	A26	10b ol grn & red vio	37.50	10.00

221	A26	20b Prus grn & brn	80.00	17.50
222	A26	40b dk grn & ol brn	160.00	47.50
		Nos. 207-222 (15)	336.35	91.10
		Set, never hinged	475.00	

On the single colored stamps, type A25, the lines in the background are uniform; those of the bicolored values are shaded and do not extend to the frame.

Issue dates: 5s, 10s, 2b-40b, Apr. 15; 2s, 3s, 15s, 25s, 50s, May 1; 1b, June 1; 80s, Nov. 15.

For overprints & surcharge see #300-301, B34.

Nos. 142, 144 Surcharged in Red or Blue

1930   Perf. 14
223	A20	10s on 12s	6.00	1.00
224	A20	25s on 28s (Bl)	30.00	2.00
		Set, never hinged	40.00	

King Prajadhipok and Chao P'ya Chakri
A27   A28

Statue of Chao P'ya Chakri — A29

1932, Apr. 1   Engr.   Perf. 12½
225	A27	2s dark brown	1.00	.30
226	A27	3s deep green	2.00	.40
227	A27	5s dull violet	1.25	.25
228	A28	10s red brn & blk	2.00	.25
229	A28	15s dull blue & blk	7.75	.95
230	A28	25s violet & black	11.00	1.40
231	A28	50s claret & black	52.50	5.50
232	A29	1b blue black	77.50	15.00
		Nos. 225-232 (8)	155.00	24.00
		Set, never hinged	225.00	

150th anniv. of the Chakri dynasty, the founding of Bangkok in 1782, and the opening of the memorial bridge across the Chao Phraya River.

Assembly Hall, Bangkok A30

1939, June 24   Litho.   Perf. 11, 12
233	A30	2s dull red brown	3.25	1.00
234	A30	3s green	6.75	2.25
235	A30	3s dark violet	3.25	1.00
236	A30	10s carmine	14.00	.50
237	A30	15s dark blue	32.50	2.00
		Nos. 233-237 (5)	59.75	6.25
		Set, never hinged	75.00	

7th anniv. of the Siamese Constitution.

Chakri Palace, Bangkok — A31

1940   Typo.   Perf. 12½
238	A31	2s dull brown	3.25	1.00
239	A31	3s dp yellow grn	6.25	2.25
a.		Cliché of 5s in plate of 3s	900.00	725.00
240	A31	5s dark violet	5.00	.50
241	A31	10s carmine	18.00	.50
242	A31	15s dark blue	37.50	1.00
		Nos. 238-242 (5)	70.00	5.25
		Set, never hinged	90.00	

Issued: 2s, 3s, 5/13; 5s, 5/24; 15s, 5/28; 10s, 5/30.

King Ananda Mahidol — A32   Plowing Rice Field — A33

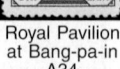

Royal Pavilion at Bang-pa-in A34   King Ananda Mahidol A35

1941, Apr. 17   Engr.
243	A32	2s brown	.40	.25
244	A32	3s deep green	.40	.40
245	A32	5s violet	.40	.25
246	A32	10s dark red	.40	.25
247	A33	15s dp bl & gray blk	.55	.25
248	A33	25s slate & org	.70	.40
249	A33	50s red org & gray	.80	.40
250	A34	1b brt ultra & gray	7.75	.90
251	A34	2b dk car rose & gray	14.00	2.00
252	A34	3b dp grn & gray	17.50	4.25
253	A34	5b blk & rose red	47.50	20.00
a.		Horiz. pair, imperf. btwn.		
254	A34	10b ol blk & yel	70.00	47.50
		Nos. 243-254 (12)	160.40	76.85
		Set, never hinged	250.00	

1943, May 1   Unwmk.   Perf. 11
255	A35	1b dark blue	19.00	2.00
a.		Horiz. pair, imperf. btwn.	90.00	90.00
b.		Vert. pair, imperf. btwn.	90.00	90.00

See No. 274.

Indo-China War Monument A36   Bangkhaen Monument A37

1943   Engr.   Perf. 11, 12½
256	A36	3s dark green	17.50	17.50

Litho.
Perf. 12½x11
257	A36	3s dull green	3.00	1.00

Issue dates: #256, June 1. #257, Nov. 2.

1943, Nov. 25   Perf. 12½, 12½x11

Two types of 10s:
I — Size 19½x24mm.
II — Size 20¾x25¼mm.
258	A37	2s brown orange	2.50	1.75
259	A37	10s car rose (I)	4.00	.60
a.		Type II	8.00	5.00

10th anniv. of the quelling of a counter-revolution led by a member of the royal family on Oct. 11, 1933.

Stamps of similar design, but with values in "cents," are listed under Malaya, Occupation Stamps. See Nos. 2N1-2N6.

King Bhumibol Adulyadej
A38   A39

1947, Dec. 5   Pin-perf. 12½x11
260	A38	5s orange	1.75	1.25
261	A38	10s olive ('48)	1.75	1.25
a.		10s light brown	77.50	77.50

262	A38	20s blue	7.00	1.25
263	A38	50s blue green	14.00	2.50
		Nos. 260-263 (4)	24.50	6.25

Coming of age of King Bhumibol Adulyadej. Issued with and without gum.

> **Catalogue values for unused stamps in this section, from this point to the end of the section, are for Never Hinged items.**

1947-49   Unwmk.   Engr.   Perf. 12½
Size: 20x25mm
264	A39	5s violet	1.50	.20
265	A39	10s red	2.00	.50
266	A39	20s chocolate	2.00	.20
267	A39	50s olive	2.50	.20

Size: 22x27mm
268	A39	1b vio & dp bl	14.00	.30
269	A39	2b ultra & green	27.50	1.40
270	A39	3b brn red & blk	47.50	2.50
271	A39	5b bl grn & brn red	87.50	6.00
272	A39	10b dk brn & pur	325.00	3.00
273	A39	20b blk & rose brn	400.00	9.00
		Nos. 264-273 (10)	909.50	23.30

Issued: 5s, 20s, 11/15/47; 10s, 50s, 1/3/49; 1b-20b, 11/1/48.
For surcharges see Nos. 302-303.

Type of 1943
Perf. 11½, 12½x11½
1948, Jan.   Litho.
274	A35	1b chalky blue	50.00	8.00
a.		Horiz. pair, imperf. btwn.	150.00	150.00
b.		Vert. pair, imperf. btwn.	150.00	150.00

King Bhumibol Adulyadej and Palace
A40   A41

Perf. 12½
1950, May 5   Unwmk.   Engr.
275	A40	5s red violet	1.40	.30
276	A40	10s red	1.40	.30
277	A40	15s purple	5.00	3.25
278	A40	20s chocolate	1.75	.30
279	A40	80s green	14.00	3.75
280	A40	1b deep blue	5.00	.30
281	A40	2b orange yellow	22.50	2.00
282	A40	3b gray	90.00	11.00
		Nos. 275-282 (8)	141.05	21.20

Coronation of Bhumibol Adulyadej as Rama IX, May 5, 1950.

1951-60   Perf. 12½, 13x12½
283	A41	5s rose lilac	.30	.20
284	A41	10s deep green	.30	.20
285	A41	15s red brown	.90	.20
285A	A41	20s chocolate	.90	.20
286	A41	25s carmine	.30	.20
287	A41	50s gray olive	.90	.20
288	A41	1b deep blue	1.25	.20
289	A41	1.15b deep blue	.30	.50
290	A41	1.25b orange brn	4.50	.30
291	A41	2b dull blue grn	5.50	.35
292	A41	3b gray	9.00	.30
293	A41	5b aqua & red	45.00	2.00
294	A41	10b black brn & vio	325.00	6.00
295	A41	20b gray & olive	300.00	21.00
		Nos. 283-295 (14)	694.15	32.10

Issued: 25s, 2/15; 5s, 10s, 1b, 6/4; 2b, 3b, 10/1; 15s, 2/15/52; 1.15b, 9/1/53; 1.25b, 10/1/54; 5b, 10b, 20b, 2/1/55; 50s, 10/15/56; 20s, 1960.

United Nations Day — A42

1951, Oct. 24
296	A42	25s ultramarine	3.75	2.50

Overprinted "1952" in Carmine
1952, Oct.
297	A42	25s ultramarine	2.75	2.00

Overprinted "1953" in Carmine
1953, Oct.
298 A42 25s ultramarine   1.75 1.10

Overprinted "1954" in Carmine
1954, Oct. 24
299 A42 25s ultramarine   4.75 3.50
  Nos. 296-299 (4)   13.00 9.10
For more overprints see Nos. 315, 320.

Nos. 209 and 210
Overprinted in Black

1955, Jan. 4   **Perf. 12½**
300 A25 5s dark violet   8.50 7.50
301 A25 10s deep rose   8.50 7.50
No. 266 Surcharged with New Value in Black or Carmine
302 A39 10s on 20s choc   2.00 .75
303 A39 10s on 20s choc (C)   3.00 .75
  Nos. 300-303 (4)   22.00 16.50

King Naresuan (1555-1605), on War Elephant — A43

Tao Suranari — A44

          Perf. 13½
1955, Feb. 15 Unwmk.   Engr.
304 A43 25s brt carmine   1.75 .20
305 A43 80s rose violet   20.00 5.00
306 A43 1.25b dark olive grn   50.00 3.00
307 A43 2b deep blue   12.50 2.00
308 A43 3b henna brown   35.00 3.00
  Nos. 304-308 (5)   119.25 13.20

1955, Apr. 15   Perf. 12x13½
309 A44 10s purple   2.50 .40
310 A44 25s emerald   1.75 .20
311 A44 1b brown   40.00 3.00
  Nos. 309-311 (3)   44.25 3.60
Lady Mo, called Tao Suranari (Brave Woman) for her role in stopping an 1826 rebellion.

King Taksin Statue at Thonburi A45

Don Jedi Monument A46

1955, May 1   Perf. 12½x12
312 A45 5s violet blue   1.50 .30
313 A45 25s Prus green   11.00 .20
314 A45 1.25b red   37.50 3.00
  Nos. 312-314 (3)   50.00 3.50
King Somdech P'ya Chao Taksin (1734-1782).

No. 296 Overprinted "1955" in Red
1955, Oct. 24   Perf. 12½
315 A42 25s ultramarine   5.00 3.00
United Nations Day, Oct. 24, 1955.

1956, Feb. 1   Perf. 13½x13
316 A46 10s emerald   3.50 2.50
317 A46 50s reddish brown   22.50 2.00
318 A46 75s violet   7.00 .75
319 A46 1.50b brown orange   19.00 1.25
  Nos. 316-319 (4)   52.00 6.50

No. 296 Overprinted "1956" in Red Violet
1956, Oct. 24
320 A42 25s ultramarine   2.00 1.60
United Nations Day, Oct. 24, 1956.

Dharmachakra and Deer — A47

20s, 25s, 50s, Hand of peace and Dharmachakra. 1b, 1.25b, 2b, Pagoda of Nakon Phatom.

Wmk. 329
1957, May 13 Photo.   Perf. 13½
321 A47 5s dark brown   1.50 .55
322 A47 10s rose lake   1.50 .55
323 A47 15s brt green   3.00 1.50
324 A47 20s orange   3.00 1.75
325 A47 25s reddish brown   1.10 .55
326 A47 50s magenta   2.50 .65
327 A47 1b olive brown   2.75 .75
328 A47 1.25b slate blue   35.00 6.00
329 A47 2b deep claret   8.00 1.00
  Nos. 321-329 (9)   58.35 13.30
2500th anniversary of birth of Buddha.

UN Day — A48   Thai Archway — A49

1957, Oct. 24   Perf. 13½
330 A48 25s olive   1.00 .30
331 A48 25s bright ocher ('58)   1.00 .30
332 A48 25s indigo ('59)   1.40 .30
  Nos. 330-332 (3)   3.40 .90
Issued: Oct. 24.

1959, Oct. 15 Photo.   Perf. 13½
Designs (inscribed "SEAP Games 1959"): 25s, Royal tiered umbrellas. 1.25b, Thai archer, ancient costume. 2b, Wat Arun pagoda and prow of royal barge.
333 A49 10s orange   1.10 .20
334 A49 25s dk carmine rose   1.40 .20
335 A49 1.25b bright green   5.50 1.25
336 A49 2b light blue   4.75 .80
  Nos. 333-336 (4)   12.75 2.45
Issued to publicize the South-East Asia Peninsula Games, Bangkok, Dec. 12-17.

Wat Arun, WRY Emblem — A50

Wat Arun, Bangkok — A51

1960, Apr. 7
337 A50 50s chocolate   .85 .20
338 A50 2b yellow green   2.00 .70
WRY, July 1, 1959-June 30, 1960.

1960, Aug. Wmk. 329   Perf. 13½
339 A51 50s carmine rose   .75 .20
340 A51 2b ultramarine   4.75 1.00
Anti-leprosy campaign.

Elephants in Teak Forest — A52

Globe and SEATO Emblem — A53

1960, Aug. 29 Photo.   Perf. 13½
341 A52 25s emerald   1.25 .20
5th World Forestry Cong., Seattle, WA, Aug. 29-Sept. 10.

1960, Sept. 8
342 A53 50s chocolate   1.40 .20
SEATO Day, Sept. 8.

Siamese Child — A54

Hand with Pen and Globe — A55

1960, Oct. 3   Wmk. 329
343 A54 50s magenta   1.75 .20
344 A54 1b orange   5.00 .75
Children's Day, 1960.

1960, Oct. 3
345 A55 50s carmine rose   1.50 .20
346 A55 2b blue   5.50 .90
Intl. Letter Writing Week, Oct. 3-9.

UN Emblem and Globe A56

King Bhumibol Adulyadej A57

1960, Oct. 24   Perf. 13½
347 A56 50s purple   1.75 .25
15th anniversary of the United Nations. See Nos. 369, 390.

          Perf. 13½x13
1961-68   Engr.   Wmk. 334
348 A57 5s rose cl ('62)   .30 .20
349 A57 10s green ('62)   .30 .20
350 A57 15s red brn ('62)   .55 .20
351 A57 20s brown ('62)   .30 .20
352 A57 25s carmine ('63)   .55 .20
353 A57 50s olive ('62)   .60 .20
354 A57 80s orange ('62)   2.50 1.00
355 A57 1b vio bl & brn   2.25 .20
355A A57 1.25b red & citron ('65)   8.25 1.25
356 A57 1.50b dk vio & yel green   2.25 .35
357 A57 2b red & violet   2.50 .20
358 A57 3b brn & bl   8.00 .35
358A A57 4b olive bis & blk ('68)   11.00 1.40
359 A57 5b blue & green   32.50 2.00
360 A57 10b red org & blk   90.00 3.00
361 A57 20b emer & ultra   80.00 6.00
362 A57 25b green & blue   45.00 5.00
362A A57 40b yellow & blk ('65)   85.00 9.00
  Nos. 348-362A (18)   371.85 30.95
For overprint see No. 588.

Children in Garden — A58

Pen and Envelope with Map — A59

Wmk. 329
1961, Oct. 2 Photo.   Perf. 13½
363 A58 20s indigo   1.25 .25
364 A58 2b purple   4.25 .70
Issued for Children's Day.

1961, Oct. 9
1b, 2b, Pen and letters circling globe.
365 A59 25s gray green   .65 .20
366 A59 50s rose lilac   .35 .20
367 A59 1b bright rose   2.00 .40
368 A59 2b ultramarine   2.50 .55
  Nos. 365-368 (4)   5.50 1.35
Intl. Letter Writing Week, Oct. 2-8.

UN Type of 1960
1961, Oct. 24 Wmk. 329 Perf. 13½
369 A56 50s maroon   1.00 .25
Issued for United Nations Day, Oct. 24.

Scout Emblem — A60

Scouts Saluting and Tents — A61

Design: 2b, King Vajiravudh and Scouts.
1961, Nov. 1   Photo.
370 A60 50s carmine rose   .60 .30
371 A61 1b bright green   1.75 .50
372 A61 2b bright blue   2.00 .65
  Nos. 370-372 (3)   4.35 1.45
Thai Boy Scouts, 50th anniversary.

Malaria Eradication Emblem and Siamese Designs
A62   A63

1962, Apr. 7 Wmk. 329   Perf. 13
373 A62 5s orange brown   .30 .20
374 A62 10s sepia   .30 .20
375 A62 20s blue   .50 .20
376 A62 50s carmine rose   .30 .20
377 A63 1b green   1.25 .25
378 A63 1.50b dk car rose   3.50 .55
379 A63 2d dark blue   2.00 .35
380 A63 3b violet   5.50 2.50
  Nos. 373-380 (8)   13.65 4.45
WHO drive to eradicate malaria.

View of Bangkok and Seattle Fair Emblem A64

1962, Apr. 21 Wmk. 329   Perf. 13
381 A64 50s red lilac   1.00 .30
382 A64 2b deep blue   7.00 .75
"Century 21" Intl. Expo., Seattle, WA, Apr. 21-Oct. 12.

Mother and
Child
A65

Globe,
Letters,
Carrier
Pigeons
A66

Wmk. 329

1962, Oct. 1   Photo.   Perf. 13
383	A65	25s lt blue green	1.25	.30
384	A65	50s bister brown	1.50	.20
385	A65	2b bright pink	6.75	.75
		Nos. 383-385 (3)	9.50	1.25

Issued for Children's Day.

1962, Oct. 8

Design: 1b, 2b, Quill pen and scroll.
386	A66	25s violet	.70	.30
387	A66	50s red	.50	.20
388	A66	1b lemon	3.50	.60
389	A66	2b lt bluish green	6.75	.70
		Nos. 386-389 (4)	11.45	1.80

Intl. Letter Writing Week, Oct. 7-13.

UN Type of 1960

1962, Oct. 24   Perf. 13½
390	A56	50s carmine rose	1.00	.25

United Nations Day, Oct. 24.

Exhibition
Emblem — A67

Temple
Lion — A69

Woman Harvesting Rice — A68

1962, Nov. 1   Unwmk.
391	A67	50s olive bister	1.90	.20

Students' Exhibition, Bangkok.

Wmk. 334

1963, Mar. 21   Engr.   Perf. 14
392	A68	20s green	2.00	.45
393	A68	50s ocher	1.50	.25

FAO "Freedom from Hunger" campaign.

1963, Apr. 1   Wmk. 329   Perf. 13½
394	A69	50s green & bister	1.40	.20

1st anniv. of the formation of the Asian-Oceanic Postal Union, AOPU.

New and Old Post and Telegraph
Buildings — A70

Wmk. 334

1963, Aug. 4   Engr.   Perf. 14
395	A70	50s org, bluish blk & grn	.85	.25
396	A70	3b grn, dk red & brn	6.50	1.50

80th anniv. of the Post and Telegraph Dept.

King Bhumibol
Adulyadej
A71

Child with Dolls
A72

Perf. 13x13½
1963-71   Wmk. 329   Photo.
397	A71	5s dk car rose	.30	.20
398	A71	10s dark green	.30	.20
399	A71	15s red brown	.30	.20
400	A71	20s black brown	.30	.20
401	A71	25s carmine	.35	.20
402	A71	50s olive gray	.40	.20
402A	A71	75s brt vio ('71)	.50	.20
403	A71	80s dull orange	2.00	.45
404	A71	1b dk bl & dk		
		brn	1.75	.20
404A	A71	1.25b org brn & ol		
		('65)	6.25	1.00
405	A71	1.50b vio bl & grn	1.75	.50
406	A71	2b dk red & vio	1.00	.20
407	A71	3b brn & dk bl	2.00	.20
407A	A71	4b dp bis & blk		
		('68)	2.75	.25
408	A71	5b blue & green	13.00	.25
409	A71	10b orange & blk	25.00	1.00
410	A71	20b brt grn & ind	175.00	6.00
411	A71	25b dk grn & bl	6.00	.50
411A	A71	40b yel & blk		
		('65)	160.00	9.00
		Nos. 397-411A (19)	398.95	21.00

Nos. 397-403 were issued in 1963; Nos. 404, 405-407, 408-411 in 1964.
For overprint see No. 589.

1963, Oct. 7   Litho.   Perf. 13½
412	A72	50s rose red	2.00	.20
413	A72	2b dull blue	6.50	.75

Issued for Children's Day.

Garuda Carrying Letter — A73

Design: 2b, 3b, Thai women writing letters.

1963, Oct. 7   Wmk. 329
414	A73	50s lt blue & claret	1.50	.20
415	A73	1b lt grn & vio brn	4.75	.80
416	A73	2b yel brn & turq bl	32.50	3.00
417	A73	3b org brn & yel grn	18.00	3.00
		Nos. 414-417 (4)	56.75	7.00

Intl. Letter Writing Week, Oct. 6-12.

UN
Emblem — A74

UNICEF
Emblem — A76

King Bhumibol Adulyadej — A75

1963, Oct. 24   Wmk. 329   Perf. 13½
418	A74	50s bright blue	1.00	.20

United Nations Day, Oct. 24.

1963, Dec. 5   Photo.   Perf. 13½
419	A75	1.50b blue, org & ind	4.00	.50
420	A75	5b brt lil rose, org & blk	23.00	3.00

King Bhumibol's 36th birthday.

1964, Jan. 13   Litho.
421	A76	50s blue	.75	.20
422	A76	2b olive green	4.25	.45

17th anniv. of UNICEF.

Hand (flags), Pigeon and Globe — A77

Designs: 1b, Girls and world map. 2b, Pen, pencil and unfolded world map. 3b, Globe and hand holding quill.

1964, Oct. 5   Wmk. 329   Perf. 13½
423	A77	50s lilac & grn	.25	.20
424	A77	1b red brown & grn	5.50	.80
425	A77	2b yellow & vio bl	13.50	1.00
426	A77	3b blue & dk brown	7.25	2.50
		Nos. 423-426 (4)	26.50	4.50

Intl. Letter Writing Week, Oct. 5-11.

UN Emblem
and
Globe — A78

King and
Queen — A79

1964, Oct. 24   Photo.   Perf. 13½
427	A78	50s gray	1.40	.20

United Nations Day, Oct. 24.

1965, Apr. 28   Wmk. 329   Perf. 13½
428	A79	2b brown & multi	14.00	.40
429	A79	5b violet & multi	21.00	2.00

15th wedding anniversary of King Bhumibol Adulyadej and Queen Sirikit.

ITU Emblem, Old and New
Communications Equipment — A80

1965, May 17   Photo.
430	A80	1b bright green	4.50	.50

Cent. of the ITU.

World Map, Letters and
Goddess — A81

2b, 3b, World map, letters and handshake.

1965, Oct. 3   Wmk. 329   Perf. 13½
431	A81	50s dp plum, gray & sal	.25	.25
432	A81	1b dk vio bl, lt vio & yel	2.75	.60
433	A81	2b dk gray, bis & dp org	11.00	.60
434	A81	3b multicolored	16.00	2.75
		Nos. 431-434 (4)	30.00	4.20

Intl. Letter Writing Week, Oct. 3-9.

A82

A83

Gates of Royal Chapel of Emerald Buddha.

Engr. & Litho.
Perf. 13½x14
1965, Oct. 24   Wmk. 356
435	A82	50s slate grn, bl & ocher	1.75	.30

International Cooperation Year, 1965.

Wmk. 329
1965, Nov. 1   Litho.   Perf. 13½

Map of Thailand and UPU monument, Bern.
436	A83	20s dk blue & lilac	.75	.20
437	A83	50s gray & blue	2.25	.20
438	A83	1b orange brn & vio bl	5.00	.35
439	A83	3b green & bister	13.00	2.25
		Nos. 436-439 (4)	21.00	3.00

80th anniv. of Thailand's admission to the UPU.

Lotus Blossom and Child — A84

Design: 1b, Boy with book walking up steps.

1966, Jan. 8   Wmk. 334   Perf. 13½
440	A84	50s henna brn & blk	.30	.20
441	A84	1b green & black	3.25	.60

Issued for Children's Day, 1966.

Bicycling — A85

1966, Aug. 4   Photo.   Wmk. 329
442	A85	20s shown	.70	.20
443	A85	25s Tennis	1.00	.30
444	A85	50s Running	.70	.20
445	A85	1b Weight lifting	3.00	.60
446	A85	1.25b Boxing	4.50	2.50
447	A85	2b Swimming	8.00	.45
448	A85	3b Netball	19.00	4.00
449	A85	5b Soccer	52.50	14.00
		Nos. 442-449 (8)	89.40	22.25

5th Asian Games, Bangkok.

Trade Fair Emblem
and Temple of
Dawn — A86

1966, Sept. 1   Litho.   Perf. 13½
450	A86	50s lilac	1.50	.40
451	A86	1b brown red	3.00	.75

1st Intl. Asian Trade Fair, Bangkok.

Letter
Writer
A87

Design: 50s, 1b, Letters, maps and pen.

1966, Oct. 3   Photo.   Wmk. 329
452 A87 50s scarlet   .30   .20
453 A87 1b orange brown   1.90   .60
454 A87 2b brt violet   9.50   .60
455 A87 3b brt blue grn   6.00 2.25
    Nos. 452-455 (4)   17.70 3.65

Intl. Letter Writing Week, Oct. 6-12.

UN Emblem — A88

Pra Buddha Bata Monastery, UNESCO Emblem — A90

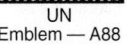

Rice Field A89

Wmk. 334
1966, Oct. 24   Litho.   Perf. 13½
456 A88 50s ultramarine   1.25   .20

United Nations Day, Oct. 24.

1966, Nov. 1   Engr.   Wmk. 329
457 A89 50s dp bl & grnsh bl   1.50   .60
458 A89 3b plum & pink   13.50 4.00

Intl. Rice Year under sponsorship of the FAO.

1966, Nov. 4   Photo.   Wmk. 329
459 A90 50s black & yel grn   1.25   .20

20th anniv. of UNESCO.

Thai Boxing A91

Designs: 1b, Takraw (three men playing ball). 2b, Kite fighting. 3b, Cudgel play.

1966, Dec. 9   Wmk. 329   Perf. 13½
460 A91 50s black, brn & red   1.50   .25
461 A91 1b black, brn & red   5.00 2.00
462 A91 2b black, brn & red   29.00 4.50
463 A91 3b black, brn & red   27.50 14.00
    Nos. 460-463 (4)   63.00 20.75

5th Asian Games.

Snakehead — A92

Pigmy Mackerel — A93

Fish: 3b, Barb. 5b, Siamese fighting fish.

1967, Jan. 1   Photo.
464 A92 1b brt blue & multi   6.00 1.50
465 A93 2b multicolored   26.00 3.00
466 A93 3b yel grn & multi   15.00 7.00
467 A92 5b pale grn & multi   18.00 8.00
    Nos. 464-467 (4)   65.00 19.50

Dharmachakra, Globe and Temples — A94

Wmk. 329
1967, Jan. 15   Litho.   Perf. 13½
468 A94 2b black & yellow   4.75   .90

Establishment of the headquarters of the World Fellowship of Buddhists in Thailand.

Great Hornbill A95

Ascocentrum Curvifolium A96

Birds: 25s, Hill myna. 50s, White-rumped shama. 1b, Diard's fireback pheasant. 1.50b, Spotted dove. 2b, Sarus crane. 3b, White-breasted kingfisher. 5b, Asiatic open-bill (stork).

1967, Feb. 1   Photo.
469 A95 20s tan & multi   .70   .60
470 A95 25s lt gray & multi   1.00   .90
471 A95 50s yel grn & multi   1.75   .30
472 A95 1b olive & multi   4.25 1.25
473 A95 1.50b dull yel & multi   4.25 1.50
474 A95 2b pale sal & multi   27.50 2.00
475 A95 3b gray & multi   17.50 7.75
476 A95 5b multicolored   27.50 8.00
    Nos. 469-476 (8)   84.45 22.30

1967, Apr. 1   Wmk. 329   Perf. 13½

Orchids: 20s, Vandopsis parishii. 80s, Rhynchostylis retusa. 1b, Rhynchostylis gigantea. 1.50b, Dendrobium falconerii. 2b, Paphiopedilum callosum. 3b, Dendrobium formosum. 5b, Dendrobium primulinum.

477 A96 20s black & multi   .50   .45
478 A96 50s brt blue & multi   1.00   .30
479 A96 80s black & multi   1.75 1.40
480 A96 1b blue & multi   5.25 1.25
481 A96 1.50b black & multi   3.50 1.25
482 A96 2b ver & multi   24.00 2.00
483 A96 3b brown & multi   17.50 7.75
484 A96 5b multicolored   27.50 6.25
    Nos. 477-484 (8)   81.00 20.65

Thai Architecture — A97

1967, Apr. 6   Engr.
485 A97 50s Mansion   1.40   .40
486 A97 1.50b Pagodas   4.00 1.50
487 A97 2b Bell tower   22.50 2.00
488 A97 3b Temple   14.00 5.00
    Nos. 485-488 (4)   41.90 8.90

Grand Palace and Royal Barge on Chao Phraya River — A98

1967, Sept. 15   Wmk. 329   Perf. 13½
489 A98 2b ultra & sepia   6.00 1.00

International Tourist Year, 1967.

Globe, Dove, People and Letters A99

2b, 3b, Clasped hands, globe and doves.

1967, Oct. 8   Photo.
490 A99 50s dk blue & multi   .85   .20
491 A99 1b multicolored   2.00   .60
492 A99 2b brt yel grn & blk   6.00   .75
493 A99 3b brown & blk   10.00 3.00
    Nos. 490-493 (4)   18.85 4.55

Intl. Letter Writing Week, Oct. 6-12.

UN Emblem — A100

1967, Oct. 24   Wmk. 329   Perf. 13½
494 A100 50s multicolored   1.00   .20

Issued for United Nations Day, Oct. 24.

Flag and Map of Thailand — A101

1967, Dec. 5   Photo.   Perf. 13½
495 A101 50s greenish blue, red
          & vio bl   1.00   .20
496 A101 2b ol gray, red & vio
          bl   6.00 1.25

50th anniversary of the flag.

Elephant Carrying Teakwood — A102

1968, Mar. 1   Engr.   Wmk. 329
497 A102 2b rose claret & gray ol   4.75   .75

See Nos. 537, 566.

Syncom Satellite over Thai Tracking Station — A103

1968, Apr. 1   Photo.   Perf. 13
498 A103 50s multicolored   .50   .20
499 A103 3b multicolored   3.00 1.25

Earth Goddess — A104

1968, May 1   Wmk. 329   Perf. 13
500 A104 50s blk, gold, red & bl
          grn   1.00   .20

Hydrological Decade (UNESCO), 1965-74.

Snake-skinned Gourami — A105

Fish: 20s, Red-tailed black "shark." 25s, Tor tambroides. 50s, Pangasius sanitwongsei. 80s, Bagrid catfish. 1.25b, Vaimosa rambaiae. 1.50b, Catlocarpio siamensis. 4b, Featherback.

1968, June 1   Photo.   Perf. 13
501 A105 10s multicolored   .55   .20
502 A105 20s multicolored   .55   .20
503 A105 25s multicolored   .75   .35
504 A105 50s multicolored   .95   .20
505 A105 80s multicolored   2.50 1.50
506 A105 1.25b multicolored   4.75 3.25
507 A105 1.50b multicolored   24.00 4.00
508 A105 4b multicolored   50.00 17.50
    Nos. 501-508 (8)   84.05 27.20

Arcturus Butterfly — A106

Various butterflies.

1968, July 1   Wmk. 329   Perf. 13
509 A106 50s lt blue & multi   5.00   .30
510 A106 1b multicolored   8.00 1.50
511 A106 3b multicolored   19.00 7.00
512 A106 4b buff & multi   32.50 12.00
    Nos. 509-512 (4)   64.50 20.80

Queen Sirikit — A107

Designs: Various portraits of Queen Sirikit.

Photogravure and Engraved
Perf. 13½x14
1968, Aug. 12   Wmk. 334
513 A107 50s gold & multi   .70   .35
514 A107 2b gold & multi   3.00 1.25
515 A107 3b gold & multi   8.00 3.00
516 A107 5b gold & multi   14.00 3.25
    Nos. 513-516 (4)   25.70 7.85

Queen Sirikit's 36th birthday, or third 12-year "cycle."

WHO Emblem and Medical Apparatus — A108

1968, Sept. 1   Photo.   Perf. 12½
517 A108 50s olive, blk & gray   .80   .20

20th anniv. of the WHO.

Globe, Pen and Envelope — A109

1b, 3b, Pen nib, envelope and globe.

1968, Oct. 6   Wmk. 329   Perf. 13½
518 A109 50s brown & multi   .30   .20
519 A109 1b pale brown &
         multi   1.40   .25
520 A109 2b multicolored   2.75   .45
521 A109 3b violet & multi   6.75 1.60
    Nos. 518-521 (4)   11.20 2.45

Intl. Letter Writing Week, Oct. 7-13.

UN Emblem   King Rama
and   II — A112
Flags — A110

Human Rights Flame and Bas-
relief — A111

1968, Oct. 24
522 A110 50s multicolored   .80   .20
    Issued for United Nations Day.

1968, Dec. 10   Photo.   Perf. 13½
523 A111 50s sl grn, red & vio   .90   .20
    International Human Rights Year.

1968, Dec. 30   Engr.   Wmk. 329
524 A112 50s sepia & bister   1.25   .30
Rama II (1768-1824), who reigned 1809-24.

National Assembly Building — A113

Photogravure and Engraved
1969, Feb. 10   Wmk. 329   Perf. 13½
525 A113 50s multicolored   1.00   .20
526 A113 2b multicolored   4.00   .70

    First constitutional election day.

ILO Emblem and Cogwheels — A114

1969, May 1   Photo.   Perf. 13½
527 A114 50s rose vio & dk bl   .50   .20
    50th anniv. of the ILO.

Ramwong Dance — A115

Designs: 1b, Candle dance. 2b, Krathop Mai
dance. 3b, Nohra dance.

1969, July 15   Wmk. 329   Perf. 13
528 A115 50s multicolored   .30   .20
529 A115 1b multicolored   1.25   .50
530 A115 2b multicolored   2.75   .35
531 A115 3b multicolored   5.25 1.50
    Nos. 528-531 (4)   9.55 2.55

Posting and Receiving Letters — A116

Design: 2b, 3b, Writing and posting letters.

1969, Oct. 5   Photo.   Wmk. 334
532 A116 50s multicolored   .25   .20
533 A116 1b multicolored   1.00   .35
534 A116 2b multicolored   1.90   .50
535 A116 3b multicolored   3.25 1.25
    Nos. 532-535 (4)   6.40 2.30

International Letter Writing Week.

  Hand Holding
Globe — A117

1969, Oct. 24   Wmk. 329   Perf. 13
536 A117 50s multicolored   .80   .20
    Issued for United Nations Day.

Teakwood Type of 1968
1969, Nov. 18   Engr.   Perf. 13½
537 A102 2b Tin mine   3.75   .40
    Issued to publicize tin export, and the 2nd
Technical Conf. of the Intl. Tin Council,
Bangkok.

Loy Krathong Festival — A118

Designs: 1b, Marriage ceremony. 2b,
Khwan ceremony. 5b, Songkran festival.

1969, Nov. 23   Wmk. 329
538 A118 50s gray & multi   .30   .20
539 A118 1b multicolored   1.10   .30
540 A118 2b multicolored   1.50   .40
541 A118 5b multicolored   5.50 1.40
    Nos. 538-541 (4)   8.40 2.30

Biplane, Mailmen and Map of First
Thai Airmail Flight, 1919 — A119

1969, Dec. 10   Engr.   Perf. 13½
542 A119 1b multicolored   1.75   .40
50th anniversary of Thai airmail service.

Shadow Play — A120

Photogravure and Engraved
1969, Dec. 18   Wmk. 329
543 A120 50s Phra Rama   .25   .20
544 A120 2b Ramasura   3.50   .30
545 A120 3b Mekhala   3.00 1.10
546 A120 5b Ongkhot   4.25 1.40
    Nos. 543-546 (4)   11.00 3.00

Symbols of Agriculture, Industry and
Shipping — A121

1970, Jan. 1   Photo.
547 A121 50s multicolored   .60   .20
    Productivity Year 1970.

World Map, Thai Temples and
Emblem — A122

1970, Jan. 31   Litho.
548 A122 50s brt blue & blk   .80   .20
    19th triennial meeting of the Intl. Council of
Women, Bangkok.

Earth Station Radar
and Satellite — A123

Perf. 14½x15
1970, Apr. 1   Litho.   Wmk. 356
549 A123 50s multicolored   .60   .20
    Communication by satellite.

Household and Population
Statistics — A124

Perf. 13x13½
1970, Apr. 1   Photo.   Wmk. 329
550 A124 1b multicolored   .65   .20
    Issued to publicize the 1970 census.

Inauguration of New UPU
Headquarters, Bern — A125

Lithographed and Engraved
1970, June 15   Wmk. 334   Perf. 13½
551 A125 50s lt bl, lt grn & grn   .60   .20

Khun Ram Kamhang Teaching
(Mural) — A126

1970, July 1   Litho.
552 A126 50s black & multi   .80   .20
    Issued for International Education Year.

Swimming Stadium — A127

1.50b, Velodrome. 3b, Subhajalasaya Stadium. 5b, Kittikachorn Indoor Stadium.

Lithographed and Engraved
1970, Sept. 1   Wmk. 329   Perf. 13½
553 A127 50s yellow, red & pur   .70   .20
554 A127 1.50b ultra, grn & dk
          red   1.25   .40
555 A127 3b gold, black & dk
          red   2.00   .55
556 A127 5b brt grn, ultra &
          dk red   3.50   .85
    Nos. 553-556 (4)   7.45 2.00

    6th Asian Games, Bangkok.

Children Writing Letters — A128

Designs: 1b, Woman writing letter. 2b, Two
women reading letters. 3b, Man reading letter.

1970, Oct. 4   Photo.   Perf. 13½
557 A128 50s black & multi   .35   .20
558 A128 1b black & multi   .90   .35
559 A128 2b black & multi   2.00   .35
560 A128 3b black & multi   2.75 1.10
    Nos. 557-560 (4)   6.00 2.00

Intl. Letter Writing Week, Oct. 6-12.

Royal Palace,
Bangkok, and UN
Emblem — A129

1970, Oct. 24   Photo.   Perf. 13½
561 A129 50s multicolored   .90   .20
    25th anniversary of the United Nations.

Heroes of Bangrachan — A130

1b, Monument to Thao Thepkrasatri & Thao Srisunthorn. 2b, Queen Suriyothai riding elephant. 3b, Phraya Phichaidaphak and battle scene.

1970, Oct. 25   Engr.   Perf. 13½
562 A130 50s pink & violet   .30   .20
563 A130 1b violet & maroon   1.00   .65
564 A130 2b rose & brown   3.50   1.00
565 A130 3b blue & green   3.25   1.10
     Nos. 562-565 (4)   8.05   2.95

Heroes from Thai history.

Teakwood Type of 1968
1970, Nov. 1   Engr.
566 A102 2b Rubber plantation   2.50   .30

Issued to publicize rubber export.

King Bhumibol Lighting Flame — A131

1970, Dec. 9   Photo.   Wmk. 329
567 A131 1b multicolored   1.25   .30

Opening of 6th Asian Games, Bangkok.

Woman Playing So Sam Sai — A132

Women Playing Classical Thai Musical Instruments: 2b, Khlui Phiang-O. 3b, Krachappi. 5b, Thon Rammana.

1970, Dec. 20
568 A132 50s multicolored   .50   .20
569 A132 2b multicolored   1.10   .30
570 A132 3b multicolored   2.50   .70
571 A132 5b multicolored   5.00   1.25
     Nos. 568-571 (4)   9.10   2.45

Chocolate Point Siamese Cats — A133

Siamese Cats: 1b, Blue point. 2b, Seal point. 3b, Pure white cat and kittens.

Perf. 13½x14
1971, Mar. 15   Litho.   Wmk. 356
572 A133 50s multicolored   .40   .20
573 A133 1b multicolored   4.50   .50
574 A133 2b multicolored   6.00   .55
575 A133 3b multicolored   8.50   1.75
     Nos. 572-575 (4)   19.40   3.00

Muang Nakhon Temple — A134

Temples: 1b, Phanom. 3b, Pathom Chedi. 4b, Doi Suthep.

Lithographed and Engraved
1971, Mar. 30   Wmk. 329   Perf. 13½
576 A134 50s rose, black & brn   .50   .20
577 A134 1b emerald, bis & pur   .90   .30
578 A134 3b org, brn & dk brn   2.00   .40
579 A134 4b ultra, ocher & brn   3.75   2.10
     Nos. 576-579 (4)   7.15   3.00

Corn and Tractor in Field A135

1971, Apr. 20   Engr.   Wmk. 329
580 A135 2b multicolored   1.75   .30

Export promotion.

Buddha's Birthplace, Lumbini, Nepal — A136

Buddha's: 1b, Place of Enlightenment, Bihar. 2b, Place of first sermon, Benares. 3b, Place of death, Kusinara.

1971, May 9   Engr.   Perf. 13½
581 A136 50s violet blue & blk   .40   .20
582 A136 1b green & black   1.25   .30
583 A136 2b dull yellow & blk   2.75   .50
584 A136 3b red & black   2.75   1.25
     Nos. 581-584 (4)   7.15   2.25

20th anniv. of World Fellowship of Buddhists.

King Bhumibol and Subjects — A137

Perf. 13½
1971, June 9   Unwmk.   Litho.
585 A137 50s silver & multi   1.25   .20

King Bhumibol's Silver Jubilee.

Floating Market — A138

1971, June 20   Photo.   Wmk. 329
586 A138 4b gold & multi   2.25   .50

Visit Asia Year.

Boy Scouts Saluting — A139

1971, July 1   Litho.
587 A139 50s orange & multi   1.25   .20

60th anniversary of Thai Boy Scouts.

Blocks of four of Nos. 354 and 403 Overprinted in Dark Blue

a

b

Perf. 13½x13
1971, Aug.   Wmk. 334   Engr.
588 A57 (a) Block of 4   5.50   5.50
  a.   80s orange, single stamp 1.00   1.00

Perf. 13x13½
Photo.   Wmk. 329
589 A71 (b) Block of 4   5.50   5.50
  a.   80s dull orange, single stamp 1.00 1.00

THAILANDPEX '71, Philatelic Exhib., Aug. 4-8.

Woman Writing Letter — A140

Designs: 1b, Women reading mail. 2b, Woman sitting on porch. 3b, Man handing letter to woman.

Wmk. 334
1971, Oct. 3   Litho.   Perf. 13½
590 A140 50s gray & multi   .70   .20
591 A140 1b red brown & multi   1.00   .25
592 A140 2b ultra & multi   1.75   .50
593 A140 3b lt gray & multi   2.75   1.25
     Nos. 590-593 (4)   6.20   2.20

Intl. Letter Writing Week, Oct. 6-12.

Wat Benchamabopit (Marble Temple), Bangkok — A141

Perf. 13½x14
1971, Oct. 24   Litho.   Unwmk.
594 A141 50s multicolored   .90   .20

United Nations Day, Oct. 24.

Duck Raising — A142

Rural occupations: 1b, Raising tobacco. 2b, Fishermen. 3b, Rice winnowing.

Wmk. 329
1971, Nov. 15   Photo.   Perf. 12½
595 A142 50s lt blue & multi   .50   .20
596 A142 1b multicolored   .75   .30
597 A142 2b blue & multi   1.60   .40
598 A142 3b buff & multi   2.25   1.25
     Nos. 595-598 (4)   5.10   2.15

UNICEF Emblem, Mother and Child — A143

1971, Dec. 11   Wmk. 334   Perf. 13½
599 A143 50s blue & multi   .60   .20

25th anniv. of UNICEF.

Thai Costumes, 17th Century — A144

Thai Costumes: 1b, 13th-14th cent. 1.50b, 14th-17th cent. 2b, 18th-19th cent.

Perf. 13½x14
1972, Jan. 12   Litho.   Unwmk.
600 A144 50s multicolored   .65   .20
601 A144 1b multicolored   1.10   .30
602 A144 1.50b multicolored   2.25   .50
603 A144 2b blue & multi   3.00   .90
     Nos. 600-603 (4)   7.00   1.90

Globe A145

Perf. 13x13½
1972, Apr. 1   Photo.   Wmk. 334
604 A145 75s violet blue   .65   .20

Asian-Oceanic Postal Union, 10th anniv.

King Bhumibol
Adulyadej — A146

Perf. 13½x13
1972-77   Litho.   Wmk. 329
Size: 21x26mm
605	A146	10s yellow green	.30	.20
606	A146	20s blue	.30	.20
607	A146	25s rose red	.30	.20
608	A146	75s lilac	.30	.20

Engr.
609	A146	1.25b yel grn & pink	1.25	.20
610	A146	2.75b red brn & blue grn	.55	.20
611	A146	3b brn & dk blue ('74)	2.50	.25
612	A146	4b blue & org red ('73)	1.25	.20
613	A146	5b dk vio & red brown	1.25	.35
614	A146	6b green & vio	2.50	.45
615	A146	10b ver & black	2.00	.65
616	A146	20b org & yel grn	4.00	1.10
617	A146	40b dp bis & lilac ('74)	55.00	3.25
618	A146	50b pur & brt grn ('77)	30.00	2.75
619	A146	100b dp org & dk bl ('77)	52.50	5.25
		Nos. 605-619 (15)	154.00	15.45

See Nos. 835-838, 907-908.
For surcharges, see Nos. 2281-2282.

Iko Women — A147

Hill Tribes: 2b, Musoe musician. 4b, Yao weaver. 5b, Maeo farm woman.

Wmk. 334
1972, May 11   Photo.   Perf. 13½
620	A147	50s multicolored	.70	.20
621	A147	2b dark gray & multi	2.50	.30
622	A147	4b multicolored	7.00	3.50
623	A147	5b multicolored	8.00	1.00
		Nos. 620-623 (4)	18.20	5.00

Ruby
A148

Precious Stones: 2b, Yellow sapphire. 4b, Zircon. 6b, Star sapphire.

1972, June 7   Litho.
624	A148	75s gray & multi	1.00	.25
625	A148	2b multicolored	6.00	.55
626	A148	4b multicolored	10.00	4.50
627	A148	6b crimson & multi	15.00	5.00
		Nos. 624-627 (4)	32.00	10.30

Prince
Vajiralongkorn
A149

Thai Costume
A150

Perf. 13½x13
1972, July 28   Photo.   Wmk. 329
628	A149	75s tan & multi	1.00	.30

20th birthday of Prince Vajiralongkorn, heir apparent.

Perf. 14x13½
1972, Aug. 12   Litho.   Wmk. 356
Designs: Costumes of Thai women.
629	A150	75s tan & multi	1.00	.20
630	A150	2b multicolored	2.00	.40
631	A150	4b yellow & multi	3.25	2.75
632	A150	5b gray & multi	4.75	1.50
a.		Souvenir sheet of 4, #629-632	37.50	22.50
		Nos. 629-632 (4)	11.00	4.85

Rambutan — A151

Fruits: 1b, Mangosteen. 3b, Durian. 5b, Mango.

1972, Sept. 7   Wmk. 334   Perf. 13½
633	A151	75s multicolored	1.00	.20
634	A151	1b multicolored	2.40	.55
635	A151	3b pink & multi	6.00	1.00
636	A151	5b lt ultra & multi	12.00	2.50
		Nos. 633-636 (4)	21.40	4.25

Lod Cave, Phangnga — A152

1.25b, Kang Krachara Reservoir. 2.75b, Erawan Waterfalls, Kanchanaburi. 3b, Nok-Kaw Cliff, Loei.

1972, Nov. 15   Litho.   Wmk. 334
637	A152	75s multicolored	.80	.20
638	A152	1.25b multicolored	1.40	.20
639	A152	2.75b multicolored	3.50	.65
640	A152	3b multicolored	4.50	1.75
		Nos. 637-640 (4)	10.20	2.80

Intl. Letter Writing Week, Oct. 9-15.

Princess Mother Visiting Old
People — A153

1972, Oct. 21   Photo.   Wmk. 329
641	A153	75s dk green & ocher	2.25	1.00

Princess Mother Sisangwan, 72nd birthday.

UN Emblem and
Globe — A154

Wmk. 334
1972, Nov. 15   Litho.   Perf. 14
642	A154	75s blue & multi	.70	.20

25th anniversary of the Economic Commission for Asia and the Far East (ECAFE).

Educational Center and Book Year
Emblem — A155

1972, Dec. 8   Perf. 13½
643	A155	75s multicolored	.65	.20

International Book Year 1972.

Crown Prince
Vajiralongkorn
A156

1972, Dec. 28   Photo.   Wmk. 329
644	A156	2b brt blue & multi	1.50	.20

Investiture of Prince Vajiralongkorn Salayacheevin as Crown Prince.

Flag, Soldiers and Civilians — A157

1973, Feb. 3   Wmk. 334   Perf. 13½
645	A157	75s multicolored	.70	.20

25th anniversary of Veterans Day.

Savings Bank,
Emblem and
Coin — A158

1973, Apr. 1   Wmk. 329
646	A158	75s emerald & multi	.65	.20

60th anniv. of Government Savings Bank.

WHO Emblem and Deity — A159

1973, Apr. 1   Wmk. 329
647	A159	75s brt green & multi	.70	.20

25th World Health Organization Day.

Water
Lily
A160

Designs: Various water lilies (Thai lotus).

Perf. 11x13
1973, May 15   Litho.   Wmk. 356
648	A160	75s violet & multi	1.00	.25
649	A160	20s blue	2.00	.35
650	A160	2b dull grn & multi	2.75	.75
651	A160	4b black & multi	9.00	2.50
		Nos. 648-651 (4)	14.75	3.85

King Bhumibol
Adulyadej — A161

Perf. 14x13½
1973-81   Photo.   Wmk. 334
652	A161	5s purple	.50	.20
653	A161	20s blue	.55	.20
a.		Perf. 14½, wmk. 233	.55	.20
654	A161	25s rose carmine	.65	.20

Wmk. 233   Perf. 14½
655	A161	25s brown red ('81)	.65	.25
656	A161	50s dk olive grn ('79)	1.25	.20
657	A161	75s violet	1.25	.20
a.		Perf. 14x13½, wmk. 334	1.25	.20

Wmk. 334
Engr.   Perf. 13
658	A161	5b violet & brown	5.50	.65
659	A161	6b green & violet	3.50	1.00
660	A161	10b red & black	11.00	1.10
661	A161	20b org & yel grn ('75)	125.00	6.00
		Nos. 652-661 (10)	149.85	10.00

For surcharges see Nos. 1168A, 1548.

Silversmiths — A162

1973, June 15   Litho.   Perf. 13½
662	A162	75s shown	.50	.20
663	A162	2.75b Lacquerware	2.25	.55
664	A162	4b Pottery	4.00	3.00
665	A162	5b Paper umbrellas	5.75	1.00
		Nos. 662-665 (4)	12.50	4.75

Thai handicrafts.

Fresco from Temple of the Emerald
Buddha — A163

Designs: Frescoes illustrating Ramayana in Temple of the Emerald Buddha.

1973, July 17   Photo.   Wmk. 329
666	A163	25s multicolored	.20	.20
667	A163	75s multicolored	.40	.20
668	A163	1.50b multicolored	2.10	.20
669	A163	2b multicolored	3.00	1.00
670	A163	2.75b multicolored	2.75	.35
671	A163	3b multicolored	9.25	1.50
672	A163	5b multicolored	13.50	3.50
673	A163	6b multicolored	4.75	1.50
		Nos. 666-673 (8)	35.95	8.45

Development of Postal
Service — A164

2b, Telecommunications development.

1973, Aug. 4   *Perf. 13½*
674 A164 75s multicolored   .65 .20
675 A164 2b multicolored   1.40 .65

90th anniv. of Post and Telegraph Dept.

No. 1 and Other Stamps — A165

Various Stamps and: 1.25b, No. 147. 1.50b,
No. 209. 2b, No. 244.

1973, Aug. 4   **Photo. & Engr.**
676 A165 75s dp rose & dk
   bl   1.10 .20
677 A165 1.25b blue & dp rose   2.25 .50
678 A165 1.50b olive & vio blk   2.50 1.25
679 A165 2b orange & sl
   grn   3.75 1.25
  a. Souvenir sheet of 4   18.00 15.00
   Nos. 676-679 (4)   9.60 3.20

2nd Natl. Phil. Exhib., THAIPEX '73, Aug. 4-
8. No. 679a contains 4 stamps with simulated
perforations similar to Nos. 676-679.

INTERPOL Emblem — A166

1973, Sept. 3   **Photo.**
680 A166 75s gray & multi   1.00 .20

Intl. Criminal Police Organization, 50th anniv.

"Lilid Pralaw" — A167

Designs: Scenes from Thai literature.

Perf. 11x13
1973, Oct. 7   **Litho.**   **Wmk. 368**
681 A167 75s green & multi   .65 .30
682 A167 1.50b blue & multi   1.60 .60
683 A167 2b multicolored   3.50 1.10
684 A167 5b blue & multi   7.00 2.00
  a. Souvenir sheet of 4, #681-
   684, perf. 13x14   40.00 27.50
   Nos. 681-684 (4)   12.75 4.00

Intl. Letter Writing Week, Oct. 7-13.

Wat Suan Dok,
Chiangmai; UN
Emblem — A168

1973, Oct. 24   *Perf. 13x11*
685 A168 75s blue & multi   .90 .35

United Nations Day.

Schomburgk's Deer — A169

Wmk. 329
1973, Nov. 14   **Photo.**   *Perf. 13½*
686 A169 20s shown   .30 .20
687 A169 25s Kouprey   .40 .20
688 A169 75s Gorals   .65 .20
689 A169 1.25b Water buffalos   1.90 .30
690 A169 1.50b Javan rhinocer-
   os   7.00 1.50
691 A169 2b Eld's deer   7.00 1.50
692 A169 2.75b Asiatic 2-
   horned rhi-
   noceros   8.00 .50
693 A169 4b Serows   12.00 3.00
   Nos. 686-693 (8)   37.25 7.40

Protected animals.

Human Rights Flame — A170

Wmk. 371
1973, Dec. 10   **Litho.**   *Perf. 12½*
694 A170 75s multicolored   1.00 .20

25th anniversary of the Universal Declaration of Human Rights.

Children and
Flowers — A171

1974, Jan. 12   **Litho.**   *Perf. 13*
695 A171 75s multicolored   .90 .30

Children's Day.

Siriraj Hospital and Statue of Prince
Nakarin — A172

Perf. 13x13½
1974, Mar. 17   **Photo.**   **Wmk. 368**
696 A172 75s multicolored   .75 .20

84th anniversary of Siriraj Hospital, oldest
medical school in Thailand.

Phala Piang
Lai — A173

Classical Thai Dances: 2.75b, Phra Lux
Phlaeng Rit. 4b, Chin Sao Sai. 5b, Charot
Phra Sumen.

Wmk. 334
1974, June 25   **Litho.**   *Perf. 14*
697 A173 75s pink & multi   .85 .20
698 A173 2.75b gray bl & multi   2.25 .30
699 A173 4b gray & multi   3.50 2.40
700 A173 5b yellow & multi   4.25 .95
   Nos. 697-700 (4)   10.85 3.85

Large Teak Tree in Uttaradit
Province — A174

1974, July 5   **Wmk. 329**   *Perf. 12½*
701 A174 75s multicolored   .65 .20

15th Arbor Day.

People and WPY Emblem — A175

Perf. 10½x13
1974, Aug. 19   **Litho.**   **Wmk. 368**
702 A175 75s multicolored   .55 .20

World Population Year, 1974.

Ban Chiang Painted Vase — A176

75s, Royal chariot. 2.75b, Avalokitesavara
Bodhisattva. 3b, King Mongkut, Rama IV.

1974, Sept. 19   **Wmk. 262**   *Perf. 12½*
703 A176 75s blue & multi   .75 .20
704 A176 2b black, brn & bis   1.50 .60
705 A176 2.75b black, brn & tan   1.75 .65
706 A176 3b black & multi   2.50 1.25
   Nos. 703-706 (4)   6.50 2.70

Centenary of National Museum. Inscribed
"BATH" in error.

Purging Cassia — A177

1974, Oct. 6   **Wmk. 368**   *Perf. 11x13*
707 A177 75s shown   .75 .20
708 A177 2.75b Butea   2.25 .35
709 A177 3b Jasmine   2.50 .40

710 A177 4b Lagerstroemia   2.75 1.00
  a. Souvenir sheet of 4, #707-
   710, perf. 13½x14   30.00 30.00
   Nos. 707-710 (4)   8.25 1.95

Intl. Letter Writing Week, Oct. 6-12.

"UPU" and UPU Emblem — A178

1974, Oct. 9   **Wmk. 371**   *Perf. 12½*
711 A178 75s dk green & multi   .65 .25

Centenary of Universal Postal Union.

Wat Suthat Thepvararam — A179

Wmk. 329
1974, Oct. 24   **Photo.**   *Perf. 13*
712 A179 75s multicolored   .65 .25

United Nations Day.

Elephant Roundup — A180

Wmk. 371
1974, Nov. 16   **Engr.**   *Perf. 12½*
713 A180 4b multicolored   3.25 1.60

Tourist publicity.

Vanda Coerulea — A181

Orchids: 2.75b, Dendrobium aggregatum.
3b, Dendrobium scabrilingue. 4b, Aerides
falcata.

Perf. 11x13
1974, Dec. 5   **Wmk. 368**
714 A181 75s red & multi   .75 .20
715 A181 2.75b multicolored   1.75 .30
716 A181 3b olive & multi   2.75 .80
717 A181 4b green & multi   3.50 1.75
  a. Souvenir sheet of 4, #714-
   717, perf. 13½x14   37.50 37.50
   Nos. 714-717 (4)   8.75 3.05

See Nos. 745-748.

Boy — A182

Perf. 14x13½
1975, Jan. 11   **Litho.**   **Wmk. 374**
718 A182 75s vermilion & multi   1.00 .25

Children's Day.

Democracy Monument — A183

Designs: 2b, Mother with children and animals, bas-relief from Democracy Monument. 2.75b, Workers, bas-relief from Democracy Monument. 5b, Top of Democracy Monument and quotation from speech of King Rama VII.

Perf. 14x14½

1975, Jan. 26   **Wmk. 233**

719	A183	75s dull grn & multi	.50	.20
720	A183	2b multicolored	1.40	.20
721	A183	2.75b blue & multi	2.00	.35
722	A183	5b multicolored	3.75	1.40
		Nos. 719-722 (4)	7.65	2.15

Movement of Oct. 14, 1973, to re-establish democratic institutions.

Marbled Tiger Cat — A184

1975, Mar. 5   **Wmk. 334**   **Perf. 13½**

723	A184	20s shown	.50	.20
724	A184	75s Gaurs	1.90	.20
725	A184	2.75b Asiatic elephant	5.50	.60
726	A184	3b Clouded leopard	7.00	1.60
		Nos. 723-726 (4)	14.90	2.60

Protected animals.

White-eyed River Martin — A185

Birds: 2b, Paradise flycatchers. 2.75b, Long-tailed broadbills. 5b, Sultan tit.

Wmk. 371

1975, Apr. 2   **Litho.**   **Perf. 12½**

727	A185	75s ocher & multi	.90	.20
728	A185	2b lt blue & multi	2.25	.20
729	A185	2.75b lt violet & multi	3.50	.45
730	A185	5b rose & multi	7.00	1.50
		Nos. 727-730 (4)	13.65	2.35

King Bhumibol Adulyadej and Queen Sirikit — A186

3b, King, Queen, different background design.

Perf. 10½x13

1975, Apr. 28   **Photo.**   **Wmk. 368**

731	A186	75s violet bl & multi	.55	.20
732	A186	3b multicolored	2.40	.85

25th wedding anniversary of King Bhumibol Adulyadej and Queen Sirikit.

Round-house Kick — A187

Thai Boxing: 2.75b, Reverse elbow. 3b, Flying knee. 5b, Ritual homage.

Wmk. 371

1975, May 20   **Litho.**   **Perf. 12½**

733	A187	75s green & multi	.90	.20
734	A187	2.75b blue & multi	3.25	.35
735	A187	3b orange & multi	4.75	1.25
736	A187	5b orange & multi	7.00	2.40
		Nos. 733-736 (4)	15.90	4.20

Tosakanth Mask — A188

Masks: 2b, Kumbhakarn. 3b, Rama. 4b, Hanuman.

1975, June 10   **Litho.**   **Wmk. 371**

737	A188	75s dark gray & multi	.95	.20
738	A188	2b dull vio & multi	2.75	.35
739	A188	3b purple & multi	5.00	.90
740	A188	4b multicolored	10.00	4.50
		Nos. 737-740 (4)	18.70	5.95

Thai art and literature.

THAIPEX 75 Emblem — A189

THAIPEX 75 Emblem and: 2.75b, Stamp designer. 4b, Stamp printing plant. 5b, Stamp collector.

1975, Aug. 4   **Wmk. 371**   **Perf. 12½**

741	A189	75s yellow & multi	.50	.20
742	A189	2.75b orange & multi	1.60	.40
743	A189	4b lt blue & multi	2.50	1.25
744	A189	5b carmine & multi	3.00	1.00
		Nos. 741-744 (4)	7.60	2.85

THAIPEX 75, Third National Philatelic Exhibition, Aug. 4-10.

Orchid Type of 1974

Orchids: 75s, Dendrobium cruentum. 2b, Dendrobium parishii. 2.75b, Vanda teres. 5b, Vanda denisoniana.

Perf. 11x13

1975, Aug. 12   **Photo.**   **Wmk. 368**

745	A181	75s olive & multi	.75	.20
746	A181	2b multicolored	1.75	.40
747	A181	2.75b scarlet & multi	2.75	.40
748	A181	5b ultra & multi	4.25	1.25
a.		Souv. sheet, #745-748, perf 13½	45.00	45.00
		Nos. 745-748 (4)	9.50	2.25

Mytilus Smaragdinus — A190

Sea Shells: 1b, Turbo marmoratus. 2.75b, Oliva mustelina. 5b, Cypraea moneta.

Perf. 14x14½

1975, Sept. 5   **Litho.**   **Wmk. 375**

749	A190	75s yellow & multi	.85	.40
750	A190	1b ver & multi	1.40	.20
751	A190	2.75b blue & multi	4.00	.30
752	A190	5b green & multi	11.00	3.00
		Nos. 749-752 (4)	17.25	3.90

Yachting and Games Emblem — A191

Designs: 1.25b, Badminton. 1.50b, Volleyball. 2b, Target shooting.

Perf. 11x13

1975, Sept. 20   **Litho.**   **Wmk. 368**

753	A191	75s ultra & black	.60	.20
754	A191	1.25b brt rose & blk	1.40	.45
755	A191	1.50b red & black	2.50	1.10
756	A191	2b apple grn & blk	3.50	1.10
a.		Souv. sheet, #753-756, perf 13½	30.00	30.00
		Nos. 753-756 (4)	8.00	2.85

8th SEAP Games, Bangkok, Sept. 1975.

Pataya Beach A192

Views: 2b, Samila Beach. 3b, Prachuap Bay. 5b, Laem Singha Bay.

1975, Oct. 5   **Wmk. 371**   **Perf. 12½**

757	A192	75s orange & multi	1.10	.20
758	A192	2b orange & multi	2.00	.45
759	A192	3b orange & multi	2.25	.40
760	A192	5b orange & multi	6.75	2.00
		Nos. 757-760 (4)	12.10	3.25

Intl. Letter Writing Week, Oct. 6-12.

"u n," UN Emblem, Food and Education for Children — A193

1975, Oct. 24   **Litho.**   **Wmk. 371**

761	A193	75s ultra & multi	.70	.25

United Nations Day.

Morse Telegraph — A194

Design: 2.75b, Teleprinter and radar.

Perf. 14x14½

1975, Nov. 4   **Litho.**   **Wmk. 334**

762	A194	75s multicolored	.60	.20
763	A194	2.75b blue & multi	1.75	.30

Centenary of telegraph system.

Sukhrip Khrong Mueang Barge — A195

Thai ceremonial barges: 1b, Royal escort barge Anekchat Phuchong. 2b, Royal barge Anantanakarat. 2.75b, Krabi Ran Ron Rap barge. 3b, Asura Wayuphak barge. 4b, Asura paksi barge. 5b, Royal barge Sri Suphanahong. 6b, Phali Rang Thawip barge.

Wmk. 371

1975, Nov. 18   **Litho.**   **Perf. 12½**

764	A195	75s multicolored	.55	.20
765	A195	1b multicolored	.65	.30
766	A195	2b lilac & multi	2.75	.40
767	A195	2.75b multicolored	4.00	.45
768	A195	3b yellow & multi	5.00	.45
769	A195	4b multicolored	6.25	1.25
770	A195	5b gray & multi	11.00	4.00
771	A195	6b blue & multi	10.00	2.50
		Nos. 764-771 (8)	40.20	9.55

Thai Flag, Arms of Chakri Royal Family — A196

King Bhumibol Adulyadej — A197

Perf. 15x14

1975, Dec. 5   **Litho.**   **Wmk. 375**

772	A196	75s multicolored	1.25	.40
773	A197	5b multicolored	3.50	.80

King Bhumibol's 48th birthday.

Shot Put and SEAP Emblem — A198

2b, Table tennis. 3b, Bicycling. 4b, Relay race.

1975, Dec. 9   **Wmk. 368**   **Perf. 11x13**

774	A198	1b orange & black	.80	.20
775	A198	2b brt green & blk	1.75	1.25
776	A198	3b ocher & blk	2.75	.65
777	A198	4b violet & blk	3.25	1.25
a.		Souvenir sheet of 4, #774-777, perf. 13½	37.50	37.50
		Nos. 774-777 (4)	8.55	3.35

8th SEAP Games, Bangkok, Dec. 9-20.

IWY Emblem and Globe — A199

Perf. 14x14½

1975, Dec. 20   **Wmk. 375**
778 A199 75s blk, org & vio bl   .60 .20
International Women's Year.

Children Writing on Slate — A200

Perf. 13x14

1976, Jan. 10   **Litho.**   **Wmk. 368**
779 A200 75s lt green & multi   1.10 .20
Children's Day.

Macrobrachium Rosenbergii — A201

Designs: 2b, Penaeus merguiensis. 2.75b, Panulirus ornatus. 5b, Penaeus monodon.

1976, Feb. 18   **Perf. 11x13**
780 A201 75s multicolored   2.25 .20
781 A201 2b multicolored   3.75 .85
782 A201 2.75b multicolored   4.75 .20
783 A201 5b multicolored   9.00 1.75
    Nos. 780-783 (4)   19.75 3.00
Shrimp and lobster exports.

Golden-backed Three-toed Woodpecker A202

Ban Chiang Vase — A203

Birds: 1.50b, Greater green-billed malcoha. 3b, Pomatorhinus hypoleucos. 4b, Green magpie.

Wmk. 371

1976, Apr. 2   **Litho.**   **Perf. 12½**
784 A202 1b multicolored   .80 .20
785 A202 1.50b multicolored   1.50 .20
786 A202 3b yellow & multi   2.75 .75
787 A202 4b rose & multi   3.00 .75
    Nos. 784-787 (4)   8.05 1.90

Perf. 14½x14

1976, May 5   **Litho.**   **Wmk. 375**
Designs: Ban Chiang painted pottery, various vessels, Bronze Age.

788 A203 1b olive & multi   1.10 .20
789 A203 2b dp blue & multi   2.40 .20
790 A203 3b green & multi   4.50 .40
791 A203 4b org red & multi   6.00 2.10
    Nos. 788-791 (4)   14.00 2.90

Mailman, 1883 — A204

Designs: 3b, Mailman, 1935. 4b, Mailman, 1950. 5b, Mailman, 1974.

Wmk. 377

1976, Aug. 4   **Litho.**   **Perf. 12½**
792 A204 1b multicolored   .70 .20
793 A204 3b multicolored   2.75 .65
794 A204 4b multicolored   4.25 1.00
795 A204 5b multicolored   4.50 1.25
    Nos. 792-795 (4)   12.20 3.10
Development of mailmen's uniforms.

Kinnari — A205

Thai Mythology: 2b, Suphan-mat-cha. 4b, Garuda. 5b, Naga.

1976, Oct. 3   **Wmk. 368**   **Perf. 11x13**
796 A205 1b green & multi   .70 .20
797 A205 2b ultra & multi   2.75 .20
798 A205 4b gray & multi   4.25 .60
799 A205 5b slate & multi   4.50 .65
    Nos. 796-799 (4)   12.20 1.65
International Letter Writing Week.

UN Emblem, Drug Addicts, Alcohol, Cigarettes, Drugs — A206

Wmk. 329

1976, Oct. 24   **Photo.**   **Perf. 13½**
800 A206 1b ultra & multi   .65 .25
United Nations Day.

Old and New Telephones — A207

Perf. 14x14½

1976, Nov. 10   **Litho.**   **Wmk. 375**
801 A207 1b multicolored   .65 .25
Centenary of first telephone call by Alexander Graham Bell, Mar. 10, 1876.

Sivalaya-Mahaprasad Hall — A208

Royal Houses: 2b, Cakri-Mahaprasad. 4b, Mahisra-Prasad. 5b, Dusit-Mahaprasad.

Perf. 14x15

1976, Dec. 5   **Wmk. 375**   **Litho.**
802 A208 1b multicolored   1.50 .20
803 A208 2b multicolored   2.00 .75
804 A208 4b multicolored   5.50 1.00
805 A208 5b multicolored   6.00 1.10
    Nos. 802-805 (4)   15.00 3.05

Banteng — A209

Protected animals: 2b, Tapir and young. 4b, Sambar deer and fawn. 5b, Hog deer family.

Wmk. 334

1976, Dec. 26   **Litho.**   **Perf. 11**
806 A209 1b multicolored   1.25 .20
807 A209 2b multicolored   1.50 .40

Wmk. 368

808 A209 4b multicolored   3.75 .75
809 A209 5b multicolored   4.50 1.25
    Nos. 806-809 (4)   11.00 2.60

Child Casting Shadow of Man — A210

Wmk. 329

1977, Jan. 8   **Photo.**   **Perf. 13½**
810 A210 1b multicolored   .90 .25
National Children's Day.

Alsthom's Electric Engine — A211

Locomotives: 2b, Davenport's electric engine. 4b, Pacific's steam engine. 5b, George Egestoff's steam engine.

Perf. 11x13

1977, Mar. 26   **Litho.**   **Wmk. 368**
811 A211 1b multicolored   1.90 .20
812 A211 2b multicolored   4.75 .35
813 A211 4b multicolored   13.50 2.00
814 A211 5b multicolored   19.00 .80
    Nos. 811-814 (4)   39.15 3.35
80th anniv. of State Railroad of Thailand.

Chulalongkorn University Auditorium — A212

1977, Mar. 26   **Photo.**
815 A212 1b multicolored   .90 .20
Chulalongkorn University, 60th anniversary.

Flags of AOPU Members — A213

Wmk. 371

1977, Apr. 1   **Litho.**   **Perf. 12½**
816 A213 1b multicolored   .90 .20
Asian-Oceanic Postal Union (AOPU), 15th anniv.

Invalid in Wheelchair and Soldiers — A214

Wmk. 329

1977, Apr. 2   **Photo.**   **Perf. 13½**
817 A214 5b multicolored   1.60 .45
Sai-Jai-Thai Day, to publicize Sai-Jai-Thai Foundation which helps wounded soldiers.

Phra Aphai Mani and Phisua Samut A215

Puppets: 3b, Rusi and Sutsakhon. 4b, Nang Vali and Usren. 5b, Phra Aphai Mani and Nang Laweng's portrait.

Perf. 11x13

1977, June 16   **Wmk. 368**
818 A215 2b multicolored   .55 .20
819 A215 3b multicolored   .75 .25
820 A215 4b multicolored   1.50 .45
821 A215 5b multicolored   2.00 .55
    Nos. 818-821 (4)   4.80 1.45
Thai plays and literature.

Drum Dance — A216

Designs: 3b, Dance of dip nets. 4b, Harvest dance. 5b, Kan dance.

1977, July 14   **Photo.**   **Perf. 13x11**
822 A216 2b rose & multi   .70 .20
823 A216 3b lt green & multi   .80 .20
824 A216 4b yellow & multi   1.40 .40
825 A216 5b lt violet & multi   1.60 .40
    Nos. 822-825 (4)   4.50 1.20

Thailand No. 609, Various Stamps and Thaipex Emblem — A217

Wmk. 377

1977, Aug. 4   Litho.   Perf. 12½
826 A217 75s multicolored   .90 .25
THAIPEX 77, 4th National Philatelic Exhibition, Aug. 4-12.

Scenes from Thai Literature — A218

Perf. 11x13
1977, Oct. 5   Photo.   Wmk. 368
827 A218 75s multicolored   .85 .20
828 A218 2b multi, diff.   1.25 .20
829 A218 5b multi, diff.   3.50 .50
830 A218 6b multi, diff.   4.75 .80
     Nos. 827-830 (4)   10.35 1.70
Intl. Letter Writing Week, Oct. 6-12.

Old and New Buildings, UN Emblem — A219

1977, Oct. 5   Litho.   Perf. 11x13
831 A219 75s multicolored   .90 .20
United Nations Day.

King Bhumibol as Scout Leader, Camp and Emblem — A220

1977, Nov. 21   Photo.   Wmk. 368
832 A220 75s multicolored   1.75 .20
9th National Jamboree, Nov. 21-27.

Diseased Hand and Elbow — A221

1977, Dec. 20   Perf. 11x13
833 A221 75s multicolored   .90 .25
World Rheumatism Year.

Map of South East Asia and ASEAN Emblem — A222

Wmk. 377
1977, Dec. 1   Litho.   Perf. 12½
834 A222 5b multicolored   1.75 .35
ASEAN, 10th anniv.

King Type of 1972-74 Redrawn
1976   Perf. 12½x13
            Size: 21x27mm
835 A146 20s blue   2.50 .20
836 A146 75s lilac   2.50 .20
            Engr.
837 A146 10b vermilion & blk   25.00 1.00
838 A146 40b bister & lilac   20.00 2.25
     Nos. 835-838 (4)   50.00 3.65
Numerals are taller and thinner and leaves in background have been redrawn.

Children Carrying Flag of Thailand — A223

Wmk. 329
1978, Jan. 9   Photo.   Perf. 13½
839 A223 75s multicolored   1.00 .25
Children's Day.

Dendrobium Heterocarpum — A224

Orchids: 1b, Dendrobium pulchellum. 1.50b, Doritis pulcherrima. 2b, Dendrobium hercoglossum. 2.75b, Aerides odorata. 3b, Trichoglottis fasciata. 5b, Dendrobium wardianum. 6b, Dendrobium senile.

Perf. 11x14
1978, Jan. 18   Wmk. 368
840 A224 75s multicolored   .20 .20
841 A224 1b multicolored   .30 .20
842 A224 1.50b multicolored   .50 .20
843 A224 2b multicolored   1.00 .75
844 A224 2.75b multicolored   3.25 .20
845 A224 3b multicolored   1.50 .40
846 A224 5b multicolored   2.00 .70
847 A224 6b multicolored   6.00 .80
     Nos. 840-847 (8)   14.75 3.45
9th World Orchid Conference.

Census Chart, Symbols of Agriculture — A225

Wmk. 377
1978, Mar. 1   Litho.   Perf. 12½
848 A225 75s multicolored   .65 .20
Agricultural census, Apr. 1978.

Anabas Testudineus — A226

Fish: 2b, Datnioides microlepis. 3b, Kryptopterus apogon. 4b, Probarbus Jullieni.

Perf. 11x13
1978, Apr. 13   Photo.   Wmk. 368
849 A226 1b multicolored   .45 .20
850 A226 2b multicolored   1.00 .20
851 A226 3b multicolored   1.90 .50
852 A226 4b multicolored   2.75 .85
     Nos. 849-852 (4)   6.10 1.75

Birth of Prince Siddhartha — A227

Murals: 3b, Prince Siddhartha cuts his hair. 5b, Buddha descending from Tavatimsa Heaven. 6b, Buddha entering Nirvana.

Wmk. 329
1978, June 15   Photo.   Perf. 13½
853 A227 2b multicolored   2.00 .35
854 A227 3b multicolored   3.00 .70
855 A227 5b multicolored   8.75 1.25
856 A227 6b multicolored   6.50 1.60
     Nos. 853-856 (4)   20.25 3.90
Story of Gautama Buddha, murals in Puthi Savan Hall, National Museum, Bangkok.

Bhumibol Dam — A228

Dams and Reservoirs: 2b, Sirikit dam. 2.75b, Vajiralongkorn dam. 6b, Ubol Ratana dam.

Perf. 14x14½
1978, July 28   Litho.   Wmk. 233
857 A228 75s multicolored   1.10 .20
858 A228 2b multicolored   1.40 .20
859 A228 2.75b multicolored   2.75 .20
860 A228 6b multicolored   4.25 1.50
     Nos. 857-860 (4)   9.50 2.10

Idea Lynceus — A229

Butterflies: 3b, Sephisa chandra. 5b, Charaxes durnfordi. 6b, Cethosia penthesilea methypsia.

Perf. 11x13
1978, Aug. 25   Litho.   Wmk. 368
861 A229 2b lilac, blk & red   1.75 .20
862 A229 3b multicolored   2.25 .40
863 A229 5b multicolored   3.75 .75
864 A229 6b multicolored   6.00 1.50
     Nos. 861-864 (4)   13.75 2.85

Chedi Chai Mongkhon Temple — A230

Mother and Children, UN Emblem — A231

Temples: 2b, That Hariphunchai. 2.75b, Borom That Chaiya. 5b, That Choeng Chum.

1978, Oct. 8   Perf. 13x11
865 A230 75s multicolored   1.25 .20
866 A230 2b multicolored   1.75 .20
867 A230 2.75b multicolored   2.25 .20
868 A230 5b multicolored   3.75 1.25
     Nos. 865-868 (4)   9.00 1.85
Intl. Letter Writing Week, Oct. 6-12.

Perf. 14½x14
1978, Oct. 24   Litho.   Wmk. 375
869 A231 75s multicolored   .70 .20
United Nations Day.

Boxing, Soccer, Pole Vault — A232

Designs: 2b, Javelin, weight lifting, running. 3b, Ball games and sailing. 5b, Basketball, hockey stick and boxing gloves.

Perf. 14x14½
1978, Oct.   Wmk. 233   Litho.
870 A232 75s multicolored   .60 .20
871 A232 2b multicolored   1.50 .40
872 A232 3b multicolored   2.10 .50
873 A232 5b multicolored   3.00 1.50
     Nos. 870-873 (4)   7.20 2.60
8th Asian Games, Bangkok.

Five Races and World Map A233

1978, Nov.
874 A233 75s multicolored   .70 .25
Anti-Apartheid Year.

Children Painting Thai Flag — A234

Children and Children's SOS Village, Tambol Bangpu — A235

1979, Jan. 17   Perf. 14x14½
875 A234 75s multicolored   .80 .20
876 A235 75s multicolored   .80 .20
International Year of the Child.

Matuta Lunaris — A236

Crabs: 2.75b, Matuta planipes fabricius. 3b, Portunus pelagicus. 5b, Scylla serrata.

Wmk. 377
1979, Mar. 22   Litho.   *Perf. 12½*
877	A236	2b multicolored	1.50 .20
878	A236	2.75b multicolored	4.75 .20
879	A236	3b multicolored	3.00 .25
880	A236	5b multicolored	5.25 .70
		Nos. 877-880 (4)	14.50 1.35

A237

1979, June 25
881	A237	1b Sweetsop	1.25 .20
882	A237	2b Pineapple	1.00 .20
883	A237	5b Bananas	4.00 .45
884	A237	6b Longans (litchi)	3.75 1.25
		Nos. 881-884 (4)	10.00 2.10

See Nos. 1145-1148.

A238

Perf. 13x11
1979, July 10   Litho.   Wmk. 368
Young man and woman planting tree.

885   A238   75s multicolored   .75 .20

20th Arbor Day.

Pencil, Pen, Thaipex '79
Emblem — A239

Thaipex '79 Emblem and: 2b, Envelopes. 2.75b, Stamp album. 5b, Magnifying glass and tongs.

1979, Aug. 4   *Perf. 11x13*
886	A239	75s multicolored	.40 .20
887	A239	2b multicolored	1.10 .20
888	A239	2.75b multicolored	1.75 .20
889	A239	5b multicolored	2.75 .50
		Nos. 886-889 (4)	6.00 1.10

Thaipex '79, 5th National Philatelic Exhibition, Bangkok, Aug. 4-12.

Floral
Arrangement
A240

UN Day — A241

Designs: Decorative arrangements.

Perf. 14½x14
1979, Oct. 7   Litho.   Wmk. 233
890	A240	75s multicolored	.65 .20
891	A240	2b multicolored	1.10 .20
892	A240	2.75b multicolored	1.75 .20
893	A240	5b multicolored	2.50 .85
		Nos. 890-893 (4)	6.00 1.45

Intl. Letter Writing Week, Oct. 8-14.

1979, Oct. 24   Litho.   *Perf. 14½x14*
894   A241   75s multicolored   .60 .20

Frigate Makut Rajakumarn — A242

Thai Naval Ships: 3b, Frigate Tapi. 5b, Fast strike craft, Prabparapak. 6b, Patrol boat T-91.

Wmk. 329
1979, Nov. 20   Photo.   *Perf. 13½*
895	A242	2b multicolored	.85 .20
896	A242	3b multicolored	1.40 .40
897	A242	5b multicolored	5.75 .90
898	A242	6b multicolored	7.00 1.25
		Nos. 895-898 (4)	15.00 2.75

Thai Royal Orders (Medallions and
Ribbons) — A243

Designs: #900a, Rajamitrabhorn Order. #902a, House of Chakri. #904a, The nine gems. #906a, Chula Chom Klao. Pairs have continuous design.

Perf. 13x11
1979, Dec. 5   Litho.   Wmk. 368
899		1b multicolored	.75 .35
900		1b multicolored	.75 .35
a.	A243	Pair, #899-900	1.50 .70
901		2b multicolored	1.50 .30
902		2b multicolored	1.50 .30
a.	A243	Pair, #901-902	3.00 .60
903		5b multicolored	3.00 .70
904		5b multicolored	3.00 .70
a.	A243	Pair, #903-904	6.00 1.40
905		6b multicolored	3.75 1.00
906		6b multicolored	3.75 1.00
a.	A243	Pair, #905-906	7.50 2.00
		Nos. 899-906 (8)	18.00 4.70

See Nos. 1278-1285.

King Type of 1972-77
Perf. 13½x13
1979, Dec. 23   Litho.   Wmk. 329
Size: 21x26mm
907   A146   50s olive green   .60 .20

Engr.
908   A146   2b org red & lilac   1.25 .20

Rice
Planting — A245

Children's Day: No. 910, Family in rice field.

Perf. 13x11
1980, Jan. 12   Litho.   Wmk. 368
909	A245	75s multicolored	.55 .20
910	A245	75s multicolored	.55 .20

Family, House,
Map of
Thailand — A246

Gold-fronted
Leafbird — A247

Perf. 15x14
1980, Feb. 1   Litho.   Wmk. 233
911   A246   75s multicolored   .65 .30

Natl. Population & Housing Census, Apr.

Perf. 13x11
1980, Feb. 26   Wmk. 368
912	A247	75s shown	.60 .20
913	A247	2b Yellow-cheeked tit	1.00 .25
914	A247	3b Chestnut-tailed si-va	2.00 .40
915	A247	5b Scarlet minivet	3.25 1.10
		Nos. 912-915 (4)	6.85 1.95

Intl. Commission for Bird Preservation, 9th Conf. of Asian Section, Chieng-mai, 2/26-29.

Smokers and Lungs, WHO
Emblem — A248

1980, Apr. 7   Wmk. 329   *Perf. 13½*
916   A248   75s multicolored   .60 .25

World Health Day; fight against cigarette smoking.

Garuda and
Rotary
Emblem — A249

1980, May 6   Wmk. 368   *Perf. 13x11*
917   A249   5b multicolored   1.50 .25

Rotary International, 75th anniversary.

Sai Yok Falls, Kanchanaburi — A250

Perf. 14x15
1980, July 1   Litho.   Wmk. 233
918	A250	1b shown	.45 .20
919	A250	2b Punyaban Falls, Ra-nong	.75 .25
920	A250	5b Heo Suwat Falls, Nakhon Ratch-asima	2.25 .85
921	A250	6b Siriphum Falls, Chi-ang Mai	2.10 1.25
		Nos. 918-921 (4)	5.55 2.55

Queen
Sirikit — A251

Family with Cattle, Ceres Medal
(Reverse) — A252

No. 524, Ceres medal (obverse), potters.

Perf. 13½, 11x13 (5b)
Wmk. 329, 368 (5b)
1980, Aug. 12   Litho.
922	A251	75s multicolored	.50 .20
923	A252	5b multicolored	1.75 .80
924	A252	5b multicolored	1.75 .80
		Nos. 922-924 (3)	4.00 1.80

Queen Sirikit's 48th birthday.

Khao Phanomrung Temple, Buri
Ram — A253

Intl. Letter Writing Week, Oct. 6-12 (Temples): 2b, Prang Ku, Chaiiyaphum. 2.75b, Phimai, Nakhon Ratchasima. 5b, Sikhoraphum, Surin.

Perf. 11x13

1980, Oct. 5		**Litho.**	**Wmk. 368**	
925	A253	75s multicolored	.30	.20
926	A253	2b multicolored	.80	.25
927	A253	2.75b multicolored	1.10	.30
928	A253	5b multicolored	2.40	1.00
		Nos. 925-928 (4)	4.60	1.75

Princess Mother — A254

Golden Mount, Bangkok — A255

Perf. 15x14

1980, Oct. 21		**Litho.**	**Wmk. 233**	
929	A254	75s multicolored	2.00	.45

Princess Mother, 80th birthday.

1980, Oct. 24

930	A255	75s multicolored	.65	.25

United Nations Day.

King Bhumibol Adulyadej — A256

Perf. 11x13

1980-84(?)		**Litho.**	**Wmk. 368**	
932	A256	25s salmon	2.00	.20
933	A256	50s olive green	.20	.20
b.		Wmk. 233, perf. 14x15	5.00	.20
c.		Wmk. 387, perf. 11x13	1.00	.20
934	A256	75s lilac	.50	.20
935	A256	1.25b yellow green	.50	.20
a.		Wmk. 387, perf. 11x13	2.00	.20
b.		Wmk. 233, perf. 14x15	6.00	.20

Perf. 13½x13

		Engr.	**Wmk. 329**	
936	A256	3b brown & dk bl	4.75	.20
937	A256	5b purple & brn	7.25	.30
938	A256	6b dk green & pur	9.50	.35
939	A256	8.50b grn & brn org	2.00	.50
940	A256	9.50b olive & dk grn	2.50	.55
		Nos. 932-940 (9)	29.20	2.70

Issued: 50s, 1.25b, 1981. 3b-9.50b, 1983.
See Nos. 1080-1093. For surcharges see Nos. 1226-1226A.

King Rama VII Monument Inauguration A257

Perf. 15x14

1980, Dec. 10			**Wmk. 233**	
946	A257	75s multicolored	.75	.25

Bencharongware Bowl — A258

Perf. 11x13

1980, Dec. 15			**Wmk. 368**	
947	A258	2b shown	.90	.40
948	A258	2.75b Covered bowls	.90	.40
949	A258	3b Covered jar	1.75	.60
950	A258	5b Stem plates	1.75	1.00
		Nos. 947-950 (4)	5.30	2.40

King Vajiravudh Birth Centenary A259

Children's Day — A260

1981, Jan. 1		**Wmk. 233**	**Perf. 15x14**	
951	A259	75s multicolored	1.00	.25

Perf. 13x11

1981, Jan. 16			**Wmk. 368**	
952	A260	75s multicolored	.60	.20

Hegira, 1500th Anniv. — A261

Wmk. 377

1981, Jan. 18		**Litho.**	**Perf. 12½**	
953	A261	5b multicolored	2.40	.75

Dolls in Native Costumes — A262

Wmk. 368

1981, Feb. 6		**Litho.**	**Perf. 13½**	
954	A262	75s Palm-leaf fish mobile	.45	.20
955	A262	75s Teak elephants	.45	.20
956	A262	2.75b shown	1.25	.60
957	A262	2.75b Baskets	1.25	.60
		Nos. 954-957 (4)	3.40	1.60

CONEX '81 International Crafts Exhibition.

Scout Leader and Boy on Crutches — A263

1981, Feb. 28			**Perf. 13x11**	
958	A263	75s shown	.40	.20
959	A263	5b Diamond cutter in wheelchair	1.60	.60

International Year of the Disabled.

Dindaeng-Tarua Expressway Opening — A264

1981, Oct. 29			**Perf. 13½**	
960	A264	1b Klongtoey	.25	.20
961	A264	5b Vipavadee Rangsit Highway	2.25	.65

Ongkhot, Khon Mask — A265

Designs: Various Khon masks.

1981, July 1		**Litho.**	**Perf. 13x11**	
962	A265	75s shown	.45	.25
963	A265	2b Maiyarab	.70	.30
964	A265	3b Sukrip	1.60	.50
965	A265	5b Indrajit	2.00	1.10
		Nos. 962-965 (4)	4.75	2.15

Exhibition Emblem, No. 83 — A266

Wmk. 370

1981, Aug. 4		**Litho.**	**Perf. 12**	
966	A266	75s shown	.40	.20
967	A266	75s No. 144	.40	.20
968	A266	2.75b No. 198	1.25	.60
969	A266	2.75b No. 226	1.25	.60
		Nos. 966-969 (4)	3.30	1.60

A267

A268

Perf. 15x14

1981, Aug. 26			**Wmk. 233**	
970	A267	1.25b multicolored	.65	.25

Luang Praditphairo, court Musician, birth centenary. THAIPEX '81 Intl. Stamp Exhibition.

1981, Oct. 4   **Wmk. 329**

Designs: Dwarfed trees.

971	A268	75s Mai hok-hian	.45	.20
972	A268	2b Mai kam-ma-lo	.75	.40
973	A268	2.75b Mai khen	1.10	.25
974	A268	5b Mai khabuan	2.75	1.25
		Nos. 971-974 (4)	5.05	2.10

25th Intl. Letter Writing Week, Oct. 6-12.

World Food Day A269

Wmk. 370

1981, Oct. 16		**Litho.**	**Perf. 12**	
975	A269	75s multicolored	.65	.25

United Nations Day — A270

1981, Oct. 24		**Wmk. 368**	**Perf. 13½**	
976	A270	1.25b Samran Mukhamat Pavilion	.65	.25

King Cobra A271

1981, Dec. 1		**Wmk. 329**	**Perf. 13½**	
977	A271	75s shown	.45	.20
978	A271	2b Banded krait	1.40	.55
979	A271	2.75b Thai cobra	1.40	.25
980	A271	5b Malayan pit viper	2.75	1.00
		Nos. 977-980 (4)	6.00	2.00

Children's Day — A272

Scouting Year — A273

1982, Jan. 9   Wmk. 370   Perf. 12
981 A272 1.25b multicolored   .75 .25

1982, Feb. 22
982 A273 1.25b multicolored   .60 .25

Bicentenary of Bangkok (Thai Capital) A274

Chakri Dynasty kings. (Rama I-Rama IX).

1982, Apr. 4   Litho.   Perf. 12
983 A274   1b Buddha Yod-Fa (1736-1809)   .45 .25
984 A274 1.25b shown   .60 .30
985 A274   2b Buddha Lert La Naphalai (1767-1824)   .90 .25
986 A274   3b Nang Klao (1787-1851)   1.60 .35
987 A274   4b Mongkut (1804-1868)   1.25 .50
988 A274   5b Chulalongkorn (1853-1910)   2.00 .75
989 A274   6b Vajiravudh (1880-1925)   2.50 .75
990 A274   7b Prachathipok (1893-1941)   5.25 2.50
991 A274   8b Ananda Mahidol (1925-1946)   2.75 1.50
992 A274   9b Bhumibol Adulyadej (b. 1927)   2.75 1.00
a.   Souv. sheet of 10, 205x142mm   45.00 45.00
b.   Souv. sheet of 10, 195x180mm   45.00 45.00
Nos. 983-992 (10)   20.05 8.15
Nos. 992a-992b each contain Nos. 983-992. No. 992a sold for 60b, No. 992b for 70b. Values for #992a-992b include folder.

TB Bacillus Centenary — A275

Wmk. 368
1982, Apr. 7   Litho.   Perf. 13½
993 A275 1.25b multicolored   .70 .25

Local Flowers — A276

Perf. 14x14½
1982, June 30   Wmk. 233
994 A276 1.25b Quisqualis indica   .35 .20
995 A276 1.50b Murraya anicu-lata   .55 .30
996 A276 6.50b Mesua ferrea   2.00 .80

997 A276   7b Desmos chinensis   1.60 .50
Nos. 994-997 (4)   4.50 1.80

Buddhist Temples in Bangkok — A277

1982, Aug. 4   Wmk. 368   Perf. 13½
998 A277 1.25b shown   .45 .20
999 A277 4.25b Wat Pho   1.10 .40
1000 A277 6.50b Mahathat Yuwarat Rangsarit   1.40 .75
1001 A277   7b Phra Sri Rattana Satsadaram   2.25 .55
a.   Souv. sheet of 4, #998-1001, perf. 12½   90.00 90.00
Nos. 998-1001 (4)   5.20 1.90
BANGKOK '83 Intl. Stamp Exhibition, Aug. 4-13, 1983. No. 1001a sold for 30b. See Nos. 1025-1026.

A278

A279

1982, Aug. 9   Wmk. 370   Perf. 12
1002 A278 1.25b LANDSAT Satellite   .60 .25
2nd UN Conference on Peaceful Uses of Outer Space, Vienna, Aug. 9-21.

1982, Sept. 14   Wmk. 233   Perf. 14
Prince Purachatra of Kambaengbejra (1882-1936).
1003 A279 1.25b multicolored   .60 .25

26th Intl. Letter Writing Week, Oct. 6-12 — A280

Sangalok Pottery.
1982, Oct. 3   Wmk. 329   Perf. 13½
1004 A280 1.25b Covered glazed jar   .50 .25
1005 A280   3b Painted jar   1.75 .50
1006 A280 4.25b Glazed plate   1.00 .65
1007 A280   7b Painted plate   2.25 1.00
Nos. 1004-1007 (4)   5.50 2.40

UN Day — A281

1982, Oct. 24
1008 A281 1.25b Loha Prasat Tower   .60 .25

Musical Instruments — A282

1982, Nov. 30   Wmk. 370   Perf. 12
1009 A282 50s Chap, ching   .20 .20
1010 A282   1b Pi nai, pi nok   .60 .25
1011 A282 1.25b Klong that, taphon   .40 .20
1012 A282 1.50b Khong mong, krap   .40 .30
1013 A282   6b Khong wong yai   5.00 1.75
1014 A282   7b Khong wong lek   2.00 .60
1015 A282   8b Ranat ek   1.75 .60
1016 A282   9b Ranat thum   1.75 .60
Nos. 1009-1016 (8)   12.10 4.50

Pileated Gibbon — A283

ASEAN Members' Flags — A284

1982, Dec. 26
1017 A283 1.25b shown   .60 .25
1018 A283   3b Pig-tailed macaque   2.90 .45
1019 A283   5b Slow loris   1.75 1.00
1020 A283   7b Silvered leaf monkey   2.25 1.10
Nos. 1017-1020 (4)   7.50 2.80

1982, Dec. 26   Wmk. 233
1021 A284 6.50b multicolored   1.75 .40
15th Anniv. of Assoc. of Southeast Asian Nations.

Children's Day — A285

Perf. 14½x14
1983, Jan. 8   Litho.   Wmk. 233
1022 A285 1.25b multicolored   .60 .25

First Anniv. of Postal Code A286

1983, Feb. 25   Wmk. 329   Perf. 13½
1023 A286 1.25b Codes   .60 .25
1024 A286 1.25b Code on envelope   .60 .25

BANGKOK '83 Type of 1982
Design: Old General Post Office.
1983, Feb. 25   Wmk. 368   Photo.
1025 A277   7b multicolored   1.75 .30
1026 A277   10b multicolored   2.75 .50
a.   Souv. sheet of 2, #1025-1026, perf. 12½   25.00 25.00

25th Anniv. of Intl. Maritime Org. — A287

Perf. 14x14½
1983, Mar. 17   Litho.   Wmk. 233
1029 A287 1.25b Chinese junks   .60 .25

Civil Servants' Day — A288

Prince Sithiporn Kridakara (1883-1971) A289

1983, Apr. 1   Wmk. 370   Perf. 12
1030 A288 1.25b multicolored   .60 .25

Perf. 14½x14
1983, Apr. 11   Wmk. 233
1031 A289 1.25b multicolored   .60 .25

Domestic Satellite Communications System Inauguration — A290

Wmk. 368

1983, Aug. 4   Litho.   Perf. 13½
1032 A290 2b Map, dish antenna, satellite   .80 .25

BANGKOK '83 Intl. Stamp Show, Aug. 4-13 — A291

1983, Aug. 4   Wmk. 370   Perf. 12
1033 A291 1.25b Mail collection   .25 .20
1034 A291 7.50b Posting letters   1.75 .60
1035 A291 8.50b Mail transport   1.25 .75
1036 A291 9.50b Mail delivery   1.25 .75
a.   Souv. sheet of 4, #1033-1036   32.50 32.50
Nos. 1033-1036 (4)   4.50 2.30

No. 1036a exist imperf, sold for 50b. Value, $200.

A292

Perf. 15x14
1983, Aug. 4   Litho.   Wmk. 233
1037 A292 1.25b multicolored   .60 .25

A293

Prince Bhanurangsi memorial statue.

Wmk. 370
1983, Sept. 27   Litho.   Perf. 12
1038 A293 1.25b multicolored   .25 .20
1039 A293 7b multicolored   1.50 .75

Malaysia/ Thailand/ Singapore submarine cable inauguration.

Intl. Letter Writing Week — A294

1983, Oct. 6   Wmk. 329   Perf. 13½
1040 A294 2b Acropora asper   .70 .25
1041 A294 3b Platygyra lamellina   1.60 .25
1042 A294 4b Fungia   .70 .70
1043 A294 7b Pectinia lactuca   2.00 1.25
Nos. 1040-1043 (4)   5.00 2.30

Prince Mahidol of Songkhla — A295

Wmk. 370
1983, Oct. 10   Litho.   Perf. 12
1044 A295 9.50b multicolored   1.50 .75

Siriraj Hospital Faculty of Medicine and Rockefeller Foundation, 60th Anniv. of cooperation.

World Communications Year — A296

3b, Telecommunications equipment, diff.

Perf. 14x14½
1983, Oct. 24   Litho.   Wmk. 233
1045 A296 2b multicolored   .70 .25
1046 A296 3b multicolored   .70 .25

United Nations Day — A297

1983, Oct. 24
1047 A297 1.25b multicolored   .60 .25

Thai Alphabet, 700th Anniv. — A298

Designs: 3b, Painted pottery, Sukothai period. 7b, Thai characters, reign of King Ramkamhaeng. 8b, Buddha, Sukothai period. 9b, Mahathat Temple, Sukothai province.

1983, Nov. 17   Wmk. 370   Perf. 12
1048 A298 3b multicolored   1.00 .25
1049 A298 7b multicolored   1.90 .45
1050 A298 8b multi, vert.   1.00 .50
1051 A298 9b multi, vert.   1.00 .50
Nos. 1048-1051 (4)   4.90 1.70

National Development Program — A299

#1052, King and Queen initiating Royal Projects. #1053, Technical aid. #1054, Terrace farming, Irrigation dam. #1055, Gathering grain. #1056, Receiving the peoples' gratitude.

1984, May 5
1052 A299 1.25b multicolored   .60 .25
1053 A299 1.25b multicolored   .60 .25
1054 A299 1.25b multicolored   .60 .25
1055 A299 1.25b multicolored   .60 .25
1056 A299 1.25b multicolored   .60 .25
a.   Strip of 5, #1052-1056   3.00 1.50

Children's Day — A300

1984, Jan. 14   Wmk. 329   Perf. 13½
1057 A300 1.25b multicolored   .60 .25

17th Natl. Games, Jan. 22-28 — A301

1984, Jan. 22
1058 A301 1.25b Running   .75 .20
1059 A301 3b Soccer   .50 .25

5th Rheumatology Congress, Jan. 22-27 — A302

Perf. 14x15
1984, Jan. 22   Wmk. 233
1060 A302 1.25b Rheumatic joints   .75 .25

Armed Forces Day — A303

1984, Jan. 25   Perf. 15x14
1061 A303 1.25b King Naresuan, tanks, jet, ship   .60 .25

50th Anniv. of Royal Institute — A304

1984, Mar. 31
1062 A304 1.25b multicolored   .60 .25

Thammasat University, 50th Anniv. — A305

1984, June 27   Perf. 14x15
1063 A305 1.25b Dome Building   .60 .25

Asia-Pacific Broadcasting Union, 20th Anniv. — A306

1984, July 1   Wmk. 387   Perf. 12
1064 A306 4b Map, emblem   1.25 .40

Seated Buddha, Chiang Saen Style — A307

Intl. Letter Writing Week — A308

Seated Buddhas in various styles.

Perf. 14½x14
1984, July 12   Wmk. 233
1065 A307 1.25b shown   .35 .20
1066 A307 7b Sukhothai   2.25 .80
1067 A307 8.50b U-Thong   1.10 1.00
1068 A307 9.50b Ayutthaya   1.10 1.00
Nos. 1065-1068 (4)   4.80 3.00

Wmk. 385
1984, Oct. 7   Litho.   Perf. 13½

Medicinal Succulents: 1.50b, Alocasia indica. 2b, Aloe barbadensis. 4b, Gynura pseudochina DC. 10b, Rhoeo spathacea.

1069 A308 1.50b multicolored   .40 .25
1070 A308 2b multicolored   .65 .25
1071 A308 4b multicolored   1.10 .45
1072 A308 10b multicolored   3.00 1.25
Nos. 1069-1072 (4)   5.15 2.20

Princess Mother (b. 1900) — A309

UN Day — A310

Perf. 15x14

1984, Oct. 21   **Wmk. 233**
1073 A309 1.50b Portrait   .60 .25

1984, Oct. 24   **Wmk. 233**
1074 A310 1.50b Woman threshing rice   .60 .25

Local Butterflies — A311

Wmk. 329
1984, Nov. 27   **Photo.**   **Perf. 13½**
1075 A311 2b Bhutanitis lidderdalei   .65 .30
1076 A311 3b Stichophthalma louisa   .65 .30
1077 A311 5b Parthenos sylvia   1.40 .90
1078 A311 7b Stichophthalma godfreyi   2.40 .90
Nos. 1075-1078 (4)   5.10 2.40

King Type of 1980
Perf. 13½x13, 14x15 (1.50b, 2b)
Wmk. 329, 233 (1.50b, 2b)
1984-87   **Litho.**
1080 A256 1b Prus blue   .25 .20
1081 A256 1.50b brt yel org ('85)   .35 .20
1082 A256 2b dk car ('85)   .45 .20
   a. Wmk. 387, perf. 11x13½ ('86?)   4.00 .50
   b. Wmk. 387, perf. 14½x14 ('87)   1.50 .30

Engr.
1083 A256 2b hn brn & gray vio   5.50 .20
1084 A256 4b turq bl & hn brn   .75 .25
1085 A256 6.50b dk yel grn & ol brn   1.00 .35
1086 A256 7b dl red brn & sep   1.25 .40
1087 A256 7.50b dk org & saph ('85)   1.25 .50
1088 A256 8b brn vio & ol grn ('85)   1.40 .50
1089 A256 9b int bl & dk ol bis ('85)   1.75 .60
1090 A256 10b hn brn & sl grn   2.25 .65
1091 A256 20b dk org & grn   7.50 1.25
1092 A256 50b dp vit & grn   9.00 3.00
1093 A256 100b dp org & dk bl   18.00 6.00
Nos. 1080-1093 (14)   50.70 14.30
For surcharge see No. 1212.

Children's Day — A313

Children's drawings.

Wmk. 385
1985, Jan. 12   **Litho.**   **Perf. 13½**
1101 A313 1.50b Pedestrians, overpass   .40 .20
1102 A313 1.50b Climbing overpass, vert.   .40 .20

Bangkok Mail Center Opening — A314

1985, Feb. 25
1103 A314 1.50b multicolored   .60 .25

Phuket Province Heroes Bicent. — A315

Perf. 15x14
1985, Mar. 13   **Litho.**   **Wmk. 233**
1104 A315 2b multicolored   .60 .25
Tao-Thep-Krasattri, Tao-Sri-Sundhorn Monument.

Government Savings Bank, 72nd Anniv. — A316

1985, Apr. 1   **Perf. 14x15**
1105 A316 1.50b King Rama VI, headquarters   .60 .25

Intl. Telecommunications Satellite Org., 20th Anniv. — A317

1985, Apr. 6   **Wmk. 387**   **Perf. 12**
1106 A317 2b multicolored   .60 .25

Thai Airways Intl., 25th Anniv. — A318

Wmk. 385
1985, May 1   **Litho.**   **Perf. 13**
1107 A318 2b DC-6   .30 .20
1108 A318 7.50b DC-10   1.40 .65
1109 A318 8.50b Airbus A-300   1.60 .90
1110 A318 9.50b Boeing 747   1.60 1.00
Nos. 1107-1110 (4)   4.90 2.75

Natl. Flag and UPU Emblem — A319

1985, July 1   **Wmk. 387**   **Perf. 12**
1111 A319 2b shown   .25 .20
Perf. 13½
Wmk. 385
1112 A319 10b Flag and ITU emblem   1.25 .90
Thai membership to UPU and Intl. Telecommunications Union, cent.

Natl. Communications Day, Aug. 5 — A320

1985, Aug. 4   **Wmk. 329**   **Perf. 13½**
1113 A320 2b multicolored   .60 .25

THAIPEX '85, Aug. 4-13 — A321

1985, Aug. 4   **Wmk. 385**
1114 A321 2b Aisvarya Pavilion, vert.   .50 .20
1115 A321 3b Varopas Piman Pavilion   .75 .25
1116 A321 7b Vehas Camrun Pavilion   1.25 .60
1117 A321 10b Vitoon Tassana Tower, vert.   1.50 .95
  a. Souv. sheet of 4, #1114-1117   57.50
Nos. 1114-1117 (4)   4.00 2.00
No. 1117a exists imperf, sold for 40b. Value, $700.

Natl. Science Day, Aug. 18 — A322

1985, Aug. 18   **Wmk. 387**   **Perf. 12**
1118 A322 2b King Rama IV, solar eclipse   .60 .60

1885 Seal, Modern Map and Crest — A323

Perf. 14½x15
1985, Sept. 3   **Wmk. 233**
1119 A323 2b multicolored   .60 .25
Royal Thai Survey Department, Cent.

13th SEA Games, Bangkok, Dec. 8-17 — A324

Designs: a, Boxing. b, Shot put. c, Badminton. d, Javelin. e, Weight lifting.

1985, Oct. 1   **Wmk. 387**   **Perf. 12**
1120 Strip of 5   2.75 2.50
  a.-e. A324 2b, any single   .50 .20
  f. Souv. sheet of 5, #a.-e. + label   27.50 22.50
No. 1120f sold for 20b.

Climbing Plants — A325

UN Child Survival Campaign A326

1985, Oct. 6   **Wmk. 385**   **Perf. 13½**
1121 A325 2b Allemanda cathartica   .65 .25
1122 A325 3b Jasminum auriculatum   .90 .25
1123 A325 7b Passiflora laurifolia   1.40 .70
1124 A325 10b Antigonon leptopus   1.60 .80
Nos. 1121-1124 (4)   4.55 2.00
International Letter Writing Week.

1985, Oct. 24
1125 A326 2b multicolored   .60 .25
UN Day.

Prince Kromamun Bidyalabh Bridhyakorn (1885-1974), Govt. Minister — A327

Rangsit (1885-1951), Prince of Jainad — A328

1985, Nov. 7
1126 A327 2b multi   7.00   1.25
1126A A327 2b multi, diff.   1.75   .25
  b.   Pair, #1126-1126A   37.50 37.50

No. 1126A has flower design framing portrait reversed.

Perf. 15x14½
1985, Nov. 12   **Wmk. 233**
1127 A328 1.50b multicolored   .60   .25

Asian-Pacific Postal Union, 5th
Congress, Nov. 25-Dec. 4 — A329

1985, Nov. 25 Wmk. 385   Perf. 13½
1128 A329 2b multicolored   .20   .20
1129 A329 10b multicolored   1.25   .50

Intl.
Youth
Year
A330

Perf. 14x15
1985, Nov. 26   **Wmk. 233**
1130 A330 2b multicolored   .75   .25

12th Asian-Pacific Dental Congress,
Bangkok, Dec. 5-10 — A331

1985, Dec. 5
1131 A331 2b multicolored   .60   .25

13th SEA
Games — A332

French
Envoys — A333

1985, Dec. 8   Wmk. 387   Perf. 12
1132 A332 1b Volleyball   .60   .30
1133 A332 2b Sepak-takraw   .60   .30
1134 A332 3b Women's gym-
            nastics   .60   .30
1135 A332 4b Bowling   1.00   .60
  a.   Souv. sheet, #1132-1135 +
       label   27.50 27.50
       Nos. 1132-1135 (4)   2.80   1.50

No. 1135a sold for 20b.

1985, Dec. 12   Wmk. 385   Perf. 13½
1136 A333 2b shown   .35   .20
1137 A333 8.50b Thai envoys   1.40   .70

Diplomatic relations with France, 300th anniv.

Domestic Express Mail Service
Inauguration — A334

1986, Jan. 1
1138 A334 2b multicolored   .60   .25

Intl. Express Mail Service, EMS, 3rd anniv.

Wildlife Conservation — A335

Marine turtles.

1986, Jan. 8   **Wmk. 329**
1139 A335 1.50b Chelonia mydas   .55   .25
1140 A335 3b Eretmochelys
            imbricata   1.00   .25
1141 A335 5b Dermochelys
            coriacea   3.00   .45
1142 A335 10b Lepidochelys
            olivacea   2.40   .65
       Nos. 1139-1142 (4)   6.95   1.60

Natl. Children's
Day — A336

Statue of Sunthon
Phu,
Poet — A337

Design: Children picking lotus, by Areeya
Makarabhundhu, age 12.

1986, Jan. 11   **Wmk. 385**
1143 A336 2b multicolored   .75   .25

1986, June 26
1144 A337 2b multicolored   .75   .25

Fruit Type of 1979

1986, June 26   **Wmk. 385**
1145 A237 2b Watermelon   1.50   .25
1146 A237 2b Malay apple   1.50   .25
1147 A237 6b Pomelo   2.00   .65
1148 A237 6b Papaya   2.00   .65
       Nos. 1145-1148 (4)   7.00   1.80

Nos. 1145-1148 horiz.

Natl.
Year
of the
Trees
A338

1986, July 21
1149 A338 2b multicolored   .50   .25

Communications Day — A339

1986, Aug. 4
1150 A339 2b multicolored   .50   .25

Bamboo
Baskets — A340

1986, Oct. 5
1151 A340 2b Chalom   .50   .20
1152 A340 2b Krabung   .50   .20
1153 A340 6b Kratib   1.00   .45
1154 A340 6b Kaleb   1.00   .45
       Nos. 1151-1154 (4)   3.00   1.30

Intl. Letter Writing Week.

Intl.
Peace
Year
A341

1986, Oct. 24
1155 A341 2b multicolored   .60   .25

Productivity Year — A342

1986, Oct. 24   **Wmk. 329**
1156 A342 2b multicolored   .50   .25

6th ASEAN Orchid Congress — A343

1986, Nov. 7   **Wmk. 385**
1157 A343 2b Vanda varavuth,
            vert.   .60   .25
1158 A343 3b Ascocenda em-
            ma, vert.   .60   .30
1159 A343 4b Dendrobium sri-
            siam   1.10   .85

1160 A343 5b Dendrobium
            ekapol panda   1.10   .60
  a.   Souv. sheet of 4, #1157-
       1160   90.00 90.00
       Nos. 1157-1160 (4)   3.40   2.00

No. 1160a sold for 25b.

Fungi
A344

Perf. 13x13½
1986, Nov. 26   Wmk. 329   Photo.
1161 A344 2b Volvariella
            volvacea   .90   .20
1162 A344 2b Pleurotus os-
            treatus   .90   .20
1163 A344 6b Auricularia poly-
            tricha   2.50   .65
1164 A344 6b Pleurotus cystidi-
            osus   2.50   .65
       Nos. 1161-1164 (4)   6.80   1.70

Fisheries Dept., 60th Anniv. — A345

Wmk. 385
1986, Dec. 16   Litho.   Perf. 13½
1165 A345 2b Morulius
            chrysophekadion   .60   .25
1166 A345 2b Notopterus blanci   .60   .25
1167 A345 7b Scleropages
            formosus   1.10   .65
1168 A345 7b Pangasianodon gi-
            gas   1.10   .65
       Nos. 1165-1168 (4)   3.40   1.80

No. 653 Surcharged in
Dark Olive Green

Perf. 14x13½
1986, Dec.   Photo.   Wmk. 233
1168A A161 1b on 20s blue   .60   .25

Children's Day — A346

Child's drawing.

Perf. 14½x15
1987, Jan. 10   Litho.   Wmk. 387
1169   2b School, playground   .60   .25
1170   2b Pool   .60   .25
  a.   A346 Pair, #1169-1170   1.25   1.00

No. 1170a has continuous design.

F-16 & F-5 Fighter Planes,
Pilot — A347

1987, Mar. 27 Wmk. 385 *Perf. 13½*
1171 A347 2b multicolored .70 .25
Royal Thai Air Force, 72nd anniv.

King Rama III (Nang Klao, 1787-
1851) — A348

Perf. 15x14½
1987, Mar. 31 Wmk. 387
1172 A348 2b multicolored .60 .25

Ministry of Communications, 75th
Anniv. — A349

1987, Apr. 1
1173 A349 2b multicolored .60 .25

Forestry Year — A350

1987, July 11 Wmk. 385 *Perf. 13½*
1174 A350 2b multicolored .50 .25

THAIPEX '87 — A351

Gold artifacts.

1987, Aug. 4 Wmk. 385
1175 A351 2b Peacock, vert. .40 .20
1176 A351 2b Hand mirrors,
vert. .40 .20
1177 A351 6b Water urn, finger bowls 1.10 .55
1178 A351 6b Dragon vase 1.10 .55
a. Souv. sheet of 4, #1175-
1178 52.50 52.50
Nos. 1175-1178 (4) 3.00 1.50
No. 1178a exists imperf. Value, $450.

ASEAN, 20th Anniv. — A352

1987, Aug. 20
1179 A352 2b multicolored .30 .20
1180 A352 3b multicolored .60 .30
1181 A352 4b multicolored .60 .40
1182 A352 5b multicolored .90 .45
Nos. 1179-1182 (4) 2.40 1.35

Natl. Communications Day — A353

1987, Aug. 4
1183 A353 2b multicolored .50 .25

Chulachamklao Royal Military
Academy, Cent. — A354

Design: School crest, King Rama V, and
King Rama IX conferring sword on graduating
officer.

1987, Aug. 5
1184 A354 2b multicolored 1.50 .25

Intl. Literacy
Day — A355

1987, Sept. 8
1185 A355 2b multicolored .50 .25

Tourism
Year — A356

1987, Sept. 18
2b, Flower-offering ceremony, Saraburi
province. 3b, Duan Sib Festival, Nakhon Si
Thammarat province. 5b, Bang Fai Festival,
Yasothon province. 7b, Loi Krathong Festival,
Sukhothai province.
1186 A356 2b multicolored .25 .20
1187 A356 3b multicolored .60 .30
1188 A356 5b multicolored .90 .40
1189 A356 7b multicolored 1.25 .60
Nos. 1186-1189 (4) 3.00 1.50

Auditor General's Office, 72nd
Anniv. — A357

1987, Sept. 18
1190 A357 2b multicolored .50 .25

Diplomatic Relations Between
Thailand and Japan, Cent. — A358

1987, Sept. 26 Wmk. 329
1191 A358 2b multicolored .60 .25

Intl. Letter Writing
Week — A359

Floral garlands.

1987, Oct. 4 Wmk. 385
1192 A359 2b Floral tassel .35 .20
1193 A359 3b Tasselled garland .65 .30
1194 A359 5b Wrist garland .75 .40
1195 A359 7b Double-ended garland 1.25 .65
Nos. 1192-1195 (4) 3.00 1.55

Thai Pavilion — A360

1987, Oct. 9 Wmk. 387 *Perf. 15*
1196 A360 2b multicolored .50 .25
Social Education and Cultural Center
inauguration.

A361

A362

King Bhumibol Adulyadej, 60th
Birthday — A363

Royal ciphers and: #1197, Adulyadej as a
child. #1198, King and Queen, wedding portrait, 1950. #1199, King taking the Oath of
Accession, 1950. #1200, King dressed as a
monk, collecting alms. #1201, Greeting 100
year-old woman. #1202, In military uniform
holding pen and with hill tribes. #1203, Royal
couple visiting wounded serviceman. #1204,
Visiting farm. #1205, Royal family. #1206,

King, Queen Sirikit. #1207, Princess Mother
Somdej Phra Sri Nakarindra Boromrajjonnani,
emblem of Medical Volunteer Assoc. #1208,
Crown Prince Maha Vajiralongkorn, crown
prince's royal standard. #1209, Princess Maha
Chakri Sirindhorn, emblem of Sai Jai Thai
Foundation. #1210, Princess Chulabhorn,
Albert Einstein gold medal awarded by
UNESCO.

Wmk. 329
1987, Dec. 5 Photo. *Perf. 13½*
1197 A361 2b shown .55 .25
1198 A361 2b multicolored .55 .25
1199 A361 2b multicolored .55 .25
1200 A361 2b multicolored .55 .25
1201 A361 2b multicolored .55 .25
1202 A361 2b multicolored .55 .25
1203 A361 2b multicolored .55 .25
1204 A361 2b multicolored .55 .25
a. Souv. sheet, #1197-1204 35.00 30.00

Litho.
Wmk. 385
1205 A362 2b multicolored 1.10 .30
1206 A362 2b multicolored 1.10 .30
1207 A362 2b multicolored 1.10 .30
1208 A362 2b multicolored 1.10 .30
1209 A362 2b multicolored 1.10 .30
1210 A362 2b multicolored 1.10 .30

Litho. & Embossed
1211 A363 100b vio blue &
gold 65.00 65.00
Nos. 1197-1211 (15) 76.00 68.80

Size of Nos. 1206-1210: 45x27mm. No.
1211 printed in sheets of 10. No. 1204a sold
for 40b.

No. 1081 Surcharged

1987 Litho. Wmk. 233 *Perf. 14x15*
1212 A256 2b on 1.50b brt yel org .60 .25

Children's
Day — A364

Thai Agricultural
Cooperatives,
72nd
Anniv. — A365

Perf. 14x14½
1988, Jan. 9 Litho. Wmk. 387
1213 A364 2b multicolored .50 .25

1988, Feb. 26 Wmk. 387
1214 A365 2b Prince Bridhy-
alongkorn, founder .50 .25

Royal
Siam
Soc.,
84th
Anniv.
A366

1988, Mar. 10 *Perf. 14½x14*
1215 A366 2b multicolored .50 .25

Cultural Heritage Preservation — A367

Ruins in Sukhothai Historic Park.

1988, Apr. 2   Perf. 14½x14
1216 A367 2b Wat Phra Phai
              Luang   .25   .20
1217 A367 3b Wat Traphang
              Thonglang   .60   .30
1218 A367 4b Wat Maha That   .90   .60
1219 A367 6b Thewalai Maha
              Kaset   1.25   .70
     Nos. 1216-1219 (4)   3.00 1.80

Red Cross Fair A368

1988, Apr.   Wmk. 387   Perf. 14
1220 A368 2b Prevention of rabies   .50 .25

King Rama V, Founder — A369

Intl. Council of Women, Cent. — A371

Pheasants — A370

Perf. 14x14½
1988, Apr. 26   Wmk. 387
1221 A369 5b multicolored   2.75 .70

Siriraj Hospital, cent.

Wmk. 329
1988, June 15   Photo.   Perf. 13½
1222 A370 2b Crested fireback   .30 .20
1223 A370 3b Kalij   .60 .25
1224 A370 6b Silver pheasant   1.25 .60
1225 A370 7b Hume's pheasant   1.50 .75
     Nos. 1222-1225 (4)   3.65 1.80

Nos. 935a, 935 Surcharged

     a   b

Perf. 11x13
1988-92   Litho.   Wmk. 387
1226 A256(a) 1b on 1.25b   .60 .25
1226A A256(b) 1b on 1.25b   .75 .25
   b.   Wmk. 368   1.40 1.10
Issued: #1226, 1988; #1226A, Dec. 5, 1992.

1988, June 26 Wmk. 385 Perf. 13½
1227 A371 2b multicolored   .60 .25

King Bhumibol Adulyadej
A372   A372a

Perf. 13½x13
1988-95   Litho.   Wmk. 387
1228 A372 25s brown   .20 .20

Perf. 14x14½
1229 A372 50s olive   .20 .20
   a.   Wmk. 329   .60 .20
1230 A372 1b brt blue   .20 .20
     Complete booklet, 5 #1230   1.25
   a.   Photo, wmk. 233   1.00 .20
   b.   Photo., wmk. 340, perf.
        13½x13¾   .20 .20
1233 A372 2b scarlet   .75 .20
     Complete booklet, 5 #1233   1.25
   a.   Wmk. 329   .75 .20
   b.   Photo., wmk. 340, perf.
        13½x13¾   .25 .25
     Complete booklet, 5 #1233b   1.25

Photo.
Wmk. 233
Perf. 14½
1236 A372 1b bright blue   .20 .20
     Nos. 1228-1236 (5)   1.55 1.00

No. 1236 has blue background without halo
effect around head. See #1230.
   Issued: 25s, 8/12/92; 1b-2b, 7/2/88; 50s,
7/28/93; #1230a, 1236, 1990; #1233a, 1992;
#1230b, 1233b, 12/5/94; #1229a, 1995.

Perf. 13½x13
1988-90   Engr.   Wmk. 329
1241 A372a 3b brn & bluish gray   .35 .25
1242 A372a 4b brt bl & red brn   .45 .30
1243 A372a 5b violet & brn   .40 .30
1244 A372a 6b green & vio   .45 .35
1245 A372a 7b red brn & dk brn   .80 .55
1246 A372a 8b red brn & gray ol   .65 .40
1247 A372a 9b dk blue & brn   .70 .40
1248 A372a 10b henna brn &
            blk   1.00 .25
1249 A372a 20b brn org &
            sage grn   2.00 .65
1250 A372a 25b olive grn &
            dark blue   2.50 .90
1251 A372a 50b violet & grn   5.00 1.00
1252 A372a 100b brn org &
            bluish blk   10.00 2.00
     Nos. 1241-1252 (12)   24.30 7.35

Issued:3b, 10b, 50b, 100b, 12/5; 5b, 6b, 8b,
9b, 7/1/89; 4b, 7b, 20b, 12/5/89; 25b, 1/9/90.

A373

A375

King Bhumibol's Reign (since 1950) — A374

Designs: No. 1253, King Bhumibol.
Regalia: No. 1254, Great Crown of Victory.
No. 1255, Sword of Victory and matching
scabbard. No. 1256, Scepter. No. 1257, Fan
and feather fly swatter. No. 1258, Royal
slippers.
   Canopied thrones in the Grand Palace: No.
1259, Queen's round ottoman on 1-tier dais in
front of decorative screen. No. 1260, King's
throne on 1-tier dais in front of decorative
screen. No. 1261, 3-Tier throne with 3 gilded
trees. No. 1262, 3-Canopy throne on high gold
dais. No. 1263, 3-Tier throne with 4 gilded
trees, altar in background. No. 1264, 3-Can-
opy throne on 5-stair dais, in front of arch
flanked by columns.

Wmk. 385
1988, July 2   Litho.   Perf. 13½
1253 A373 2b shown   2.00 .25

Photo.
Wmk. 329
1254 A374 2b multi, vert.   .60 .30
1255 A374 2b multicolored   .60 .30
1256 A374 2b multicolored   .60 .30
1257 A374 2b multicolored   .60 .30
1258 A374 2b multicolored   .60 .30

Litho.
Perf. 14x14½
Wmk. 387
1259 A375 2b multicolored   .60 .30
1260 A375 2b multicolored   .60 .30
1261 A375 2b multicolored   .60 .30
1262 A375 2b multicolored   .60 .30
1263 A375 2b multicolored   .60 .30
1264 A375 2b multicolored   .60 .30
   a.   Souv. sheet of 6, #1259-
        1264   57.50 57.50
     Nos. 1253-1264 (12)   8.60 3.55

No. 1264a sold for 25b.

Arbor Year A376

Perf. 14½x14
1988, July 29   Litho.   Wmk. 387
1265 A376 2b multicolored   .45 .25

Natl. Communications Day — A377

Wmk. Alternating Interlaced Wavy Lines (340)
1988, Aug. 4   Perf. 13½
1266 A377 2b multicolored   .60 .25

Intl. Letter Writing Week — A378

Designs: Coconut leaf sculptures.

Perf. 14½x14
1988, Oct. 9   Wmk. 387
1267 A378 2b Grasshopper   .40 .20
1268 A378 2b Fish   .40 .20
1269 A378 6b Bird   1.10 .50
1270 A378 6b Takro (box)   1.10 .50
     Nos. 1267-1270 (4)   3.00 1.40

Housing Development — A379

Wmk. 233
1988, Oct. 24   Litho.   Perf. 14
1271 A379 2b multicolored   .50 .25

Traffic Safety — A380

King's Bodyguard, 120th Anniv. — A381

1988, Nov. 11   Wmk. 329   Perf. 13½
1272 A380 2b multicolored   .50 .25

1988, Nov. 11   Wmk. 385
1273 A381 2b Chulalongkorn   3.50 .40

New Year — A382

Flowers.

1988, Dec. 1   Wmk. 387
1274 A382 1b Crotalaria ses-
              siliflora   .45 .30
1275 A382 1b Uvaria grandiflora   .45 .30
1276 A382 1b Reinwardtia tri-
              gyna   .45 .30
1277 A382 1b Impatiens griffithii   .45 .30
     Nos. 1274-1277 (4)   1.80 1.20

Thai Royal Orders Type of 1979

Floral background: Nos. 1278-1279, Knight
Grand Commander, Order of Rama, 1918.
Nos. 1280-1281, Knight Grand Cordon, Order
of the White Elephant, 1861. Nos. 1282-1283,
Knight Grand Cordon, Order of the Crown of
Thailand, 1869. Nos. 1284-1285, Ratana
Varabhorn Order of Merit, 1911. Pairs have
continuous designs.

1988, Dec. 5   Wmk. 385
1278 A243 2b multicolored   .25 .20
1279 A244 2b multicolored   .25 .20
   a.   Pair, #1278-1279   .50 .40
1280 A243 3b multicolored   .50 .25
1281 A244 3b multicolored   .50 .25
   a.   Pair, #1280-1281   .50 .50
1282 A243 5b multicolored   1.00 .75
1283 A244 5b multicolored   .75 .30
   a.   Pair, #1282-1283   1.50 1.10
1284 A243 7b multicolored   1.00 .40
1285 A244 7b multicolored   1.00 .40
   a.   Pair, #1284-1285   2.00 1.50
     Nos. 1278-1285 (8)   5.25 2.75

A383

Buddha Monthon
Celebrations,
Tambol
Salaya — A384

Perf. 14x15, 15x14

1988, Dec. 5   Wmk. 233

1286	A383	2b Birthplace	.35	.20
1287	A383	3b Enlightenment place	.45	.25
1288	A383	4b Location of 1st sermon	.65	.45
1289	A383	5b Place Buddha achieved nirva-na	.85	.40
1290	A384	6b Statue	1.00	.50
		Nos. 1286-1290 (5)	3.30	1.80

Souvenir Sheet
Perf. 14½x14

1291	A384	6b like No. 1290	24.00	20.00

No. 1291 sold for 15b.

Children's Day — A385

"Touch" paintings by blind youth: No. 1292, *Floating Market*, by Thongbai Siyam. No. 1293, *Flying Bird*, by Kwanchai Kerd-Daeng. No. 1294, *Little Mermaid*, by Chalermpol Jiengmai. No. 1295, *Golden Fish*, by Natetip Korsantirak.

Wmk. 387

1989, Jan. 14   Litho.   Perf. 13½

1292	A385	2b multicolored	.45	.25
1293	A385	2b multicolored	.45	.25
1294	A385	2b multicolored	.45	.25
1295	A385	2b multicolored	.45	.25
		Nos. 1292-1295 (4)	1.80	1.00

Communications Authority of Thailand,
12th Anniv. — A386

1989, Feb. 25   Perf. 14½x14

1296	A386	2b multicolored	.60	.25

Chulalongkorn University, 72nd
Anniv. — A387

Design: 2b, Statue of Chulalongkorn and King Vajiravudh in front of university auditorium.

1989, Mar. 26

1297	A387	2b multicolored	.75	.25

A388

A389

Perf. 15x14

1989, Mar. 31   Litho.   Wmk. 233

1298	A388	2b shown	.50	.30

Wmk. 387
Perf. 13½

1299	A388	10b Emblem	1.50	.60

Thai Red Cross Society, 96th anniv. (2b); Intl. Red Cross and Red Crescent organizations, 125th annivs. (10b).

Perf. 14x14½

1989, Apr. 2   Wmk. 387

Phra Nakhon Khiri Historical Park: 2b, Wat Phra Kaeo. 3b, Chatchawan Wiangchai Observatory. 5b, Phra That Chom Phet Stupa. 6b, Wetchayan Wichian Phrasat Throne Hall.

1300	A389	2b multicolored	.30	.20
1301	A389	3b multicolored	.90	.40
1302	A389	5b multicolored	1.25	.90
1303	A389	6b multicolored	1.25	.90
		Nos. 1300-1303 (4)	3.70	2.40

Natl. Lottery Office, 50th
Anniv. — A390

1989, Apr. 5   Perf. 13½

1304	A390	2b multicolored	.50	.25

Seashells — A391

1989, June 28   Wmk. 329   Perf. 13½

1305	A391	2b Conus thailandis	.30	.20
1306	A391	3b Spondylus princeps	.60	.30
1307	A391	6b Cyprea guttata	.95	.75
1308	A391	10b Nautilus pompilius	3.00	1.50
		Nos. 1305-1308 (4)	4.85	2.75

Arts
and
Crafts
Year
A392

Wmk. 387

1989, June 28   Litho.   Perf. 13½

1309	A392	2b Ceramic figurines	.40	.20
1310	A392	2b Gold niello ginger jar, chicken	.40	.20
1311	A392	6b Textiles	1.10	.50
1312	A392	6b Gemstone flower ornament	1.10	.50
		Nos. 1309-1312 (4)	3.00	1.40

Asia-Pacific Telecommunications
Organization, 10th Anniv. — A393

APT emblem, map of submarine cable network and satellites of member nations.

1989, July 1   Wmk. 329   Perf. 13½

1313	A393	9b multicolored	1.00	.50

Phya Anuman
Rajadhon (1888-1969),
Ethnologist
A394

9th Natl. Phil.
Exhib., Aug. 4-
13 — A395

1989, July 1   Wmk. 387   Perf. 13½

1314	A394	2b multicolored	.50	.20

1989, Aug. 4   Wmk. 233   Perf. 15x14

Various mailboxes.

1315	A395	2b multicolored	.30	.20
1316	A395	3b multi, diff.	.45	.25
1317	A395	4b multi, diff.	.60	.35
1318	A395	5b multi, diff.	.75	.40
1319	A395	6b multi, diff.	.90	.50
a.		Souv. sheet, #1315-1319, perf 14	35.00	35.00
		Nos. 1315-1319 (5)	3.00	1.70

No. 1319a sold for 30b. No. 1319a exists imperf. Value, $125.

A396

A398

A397

Wmk. 387

1989, June 26   Litho.   Perf. 13½

1320	A396	2b multicolored	.50	.20

Intl. Anti-drug Day.

1989, Aug. 4   Wmk. 233   Perf. 14x15

1321	A397	2b multicolored	.50	.20

Post and Telecommunications School, cent.

1989, Aug. 4   Wmk. 387   Perf. 13½

1322	A398	2b multicolored	.50	.20

Natl. Communications Day.

Dragonflies — A399

Wmk. 329

1989, Oct. 8   Photo.   Perf. 13½

1323	A399	2b shown	.40	.20
1324	A399	5b multi, diff.	.75	.50
1325	A399	6b multi, diff.	1.25	.60
1326	A399	10b Damselfly	1.60	1.50
a.		Souv. sheet of 4, #1323-1326	30.00	30.00
		Nos. 1323-1326 (4)	4.00	2.80

Intl. Letter Writing Week. #1326a sold for 40b.

Transport and Communications
Decade for Asia and the
Pacific — A400

Perf. 14½x14

1989, Oct. 24   Litho.   Wmk. 387

1327	A400	2b multicolored	.50	.20

Mental Health
Care,
Cent. — A401

New Year
1990 — A402

1989, Nov. 1   Wmk. 233   Perf. 15x14

1328	A401	2b multicolored	.50	.20

Perf. 14x14½

1989, Nov. 15   Wmk. 387

Flowering plants.

1329	A402	1b Hypericum uralum	.30	.25
1330	A402	1b Uraria rufescens	.30	.25
1331	A402	1b Manglietia garrettii	.30	.25
1332	A402	1b Aeschynanthus macranthus	.30	.25
a.		Souv. sheet of 4, #1329-1332	6.00	6.00
		Nos. 1329-1332 (4)	1.20	1.00

No. 1332a sold for 14b.

Insects — A403

Wmk. 329

1989, Nov. 15   Photo.   Perf. 13½

1333	A403	2b Catacanthus incarnatus	.40	.20
1334	A403	3b Aristobia approximator	.60	.30
1335	A403	6b Chrysochroa chinensis	.90	.50
1336	A403	10b Enoplotrupes sharpi	1.60	1.25
		Nos. 1333-1336 (4)	3.50	2.25

Population and Housing Census of 1990 — A404

Wmk. 387

1990, Jan. 1   Litho.   Perf. 13½

1337	A404	2b multicolored	.50	.20

Children's Day   Emblems
A405   A406

Perf. 15x14

1990, Jan. 13   Wmk. 233

1338	A405	2b Jumping rope, horiz.	.45	.20
1339	A405	2b Sports	.45	.20

1990, Mar. 29   Wmk. 387   Perf. 13½

1340	A406	2b multicolored	.50	.20

WHO Fight AIDS Worldwide campaign and the Natl. Red Cross Soc.

Thai Heritage Conservation Day — A407

Prize-winning inlaid mother-of-pearl containers: No. 1341, Tiap (footed bowl with lid), vert. No. 1342, Phan waenfa (two-tiered vessel), vert. No. 1343, Lung (lidded bowl). No. 1344, Chiat klom (spade-shaped lidded container signifying noble rank).

1990, Apr. 2   Photo.   Wmk. 329

1341	A407	2b multicolored	.40	.20
1342	A407	2b multicolored	.40	.20
1343	A407	8b multicolored	1.10	.90
1344	A407	8b multicolored	1.10	.90
		Nos. 1341-1344 (4)	3.00	2.20

A408

A409

Minerals.

Perf. 14x14½

1990, June 29   Litho.   Wmk. 387

1345	A408	2b Tin	.45	.25
1346	A408	3b Zinc	.70	.40
1347	A408	5b Lead	.85	.60
1348	A408	6b Fluorite	1.00	.80
a.		Souv. sheet of 4, #1345-1348	6.25	6.25
		Nos. 1345-1348 (4)	3.00	2.05

No. 1348a sold for 30b. Exists imperf, value same as perf.

1990, May 16

1349	A409	2b multicolored	.50	.20

Faculty of Dentistry, Chulalongkorn Univ., 50th anniv.

Communications Day — A410

1990, Aug. 4   Perf. 14½x14

1350	A410	2b multicolored	.50	.20

Asian-Pacific Postal Training Center, 20th Anniv. — A411

1990, Sept. 10

1351	A411	2b multicolored	.35	.20
1352	A411	8b multicolored	.90	.65

Rotary Intl. in Thailand, 60th Anniv. — A412

1990, Sept. 16   Perf. 13½

1353	A412	2b Health care	.45	.25
1354	A412	3b Immunizations	.60	.30
1355	A412	6b Literacy project	.90	.55
1356	A412	8b Thai museum project	1.50	1.00
		Nos. 1353-1356 (4)	3.45	2.10

Intl. Letter Writing Week, 1990 — A413

Illustration reduced.

1990, Oct. 7   Perf. 14

1357	A413	2b multicolored	.45	.25
1358	A413	3b multi, diff.	.70	.40
1359	A413	5b multi, diff.	.85	.60
1360	A413	6b multi, diff.	1.00	.80
a.		Souv. sheet of 4, #1357-1360	6.25	6.25
		Nos. 1357-1360 (4)	3.00	2.05

No. 1360a sold for 30b. Exists imperf, value same as perf.

Dept. of Comptroller-General, Cent. — A414

1990, Oct. 7   Perf. 14½x14

1361	A414	2b multicolored	.50	.20

A415   A416

1990, Oct. 21   Perf. 14x14½

1362	A415	2b multicolored	2.50	.50

Princess Mother, 90th birthday.

1990, Nov. 15   Wmk. 233   Perf. 14½

Flowers: No. 1363, Cyrtandromoea grandiflora. No. 1364, Rhododendron arboreum. No. 1365, Merremia vitifolia. No. 1366, Afgekia mahidolae.

1363	A416	1b multicolored	.30	.25
1364	A416	1b multicolored	.30	.25
1365	A416	1b multicolored	.30	.25
1366	A416	1b multicolored	.30	.25
a.		Sheet of 4, #1363-1366	3.75	3.75
		Nos. 1363-1366 (4)	1.20	1.00

New Year 1991. No. 1366a sold for 10b. Exists imperf, value same as perf. See Nos. 1417-1420.

Wiman Mek Royal Hall — A417

Royal Throne Rooms in the Dusit Palace: 3b, Ratcharit Rungrot Royal House. 4b, Aphisek Dusit Royal Hall. 5b, Amphon Sathan Palace. 6b, Udon Phak Royal Hall. 8b, Anantasamakhom Throne Hall.

Wmk. 329

1990, Dec. 5   Photo.   Perf. 13½

1367	A417	2b multicolored	.30	.20
1368	A417	3b multicolored	.65	.25
1369	A417	4b multicolored	.65	.40
1370	A417	5b multicolored	.75	.50
1371	A417	6b multicolored	.95	.50
1372	A417	8b multicolored	1.10	.75
		Nos. 1367-1372 (6)	4.40	2.60

Somdet Phra Maha Samanachao Kromphra Paramanuchitchinorot (1790-1853), Supreme Patriarch — A418

1990, Dec. 11   Wmk. 387   Perf. 13½

1373	A418	2b multicolored	.50	.20

Petroleum Authority, 12th Anniv. — A419

Perf. 14½x14

1990, Dec. 29   Litho.   Wmk. 387

1374	A419	2b multicolored	.50	.20

Locomotives — A420

Designs: 2b, No. 6, Krauss & Co., Germany, 1908. 3b, No. 32, Kyosan Kogyo, Japan, 1949. 5b, No. 715, C56, Japan, 1946. 6b, No. 953, Mikado, Japan, 1949-1951.

Perf. 14½x14

1990, Dec. 29   Litho.   Wmk. 387

1375	A420	2b multicolored	.35	.25
1376	A420	3b multicolored	.70	.35
1377	A420	5b multicolored	1.00	1.00
1378	A420	6b multicolored	1.40	1.10
a.		Souv. sheet of 4, #1375-1378	7.50	7.50
		Nos. 1375-1378 (4)	3.45	2.70

No. 1378a sold for 25b. Exists imperf, value same as perf.

Children's Day — A421

Children's games: 2b, Tops. 5b, Race. 6b, Blind-man's buff.

1991, Jan. 12

1379	A421	2b multicolored	.35	.25
1380	A421	3b shown	.35	.30
1381	A421	5b multicolored	.70	.40
1382	A421	6b multicolored	1.10	.50
		Nos. 1379-1382 (4)	2.50	1.45

A422

A423

1991, Feb. 17   *Perf. 14x14½*
1383 A422 2b multicolored   .50   .20

Land titling project.

Perf. 14x14½
1991, Mar. 30   Litho.   Wmk. 387
1384 A423 2b Princess Maha   1.00   .20
    a.   Souvenir sheet of 1   5.00   5.00

Red Cross. No. 1384a sold for 8b. Exists imperf, value same as perf.

Cultural
Heritage
A424

Floral decorations: 2b, Indra's heavenly abode. 3b, Celestial couch. 4b, Crystal ladder. 5b, Crocodile.

Wmk. 329
1991, Apr. 2   Photo.   *Perf. 13½*
1385 A424 2b multicolored   .40   .25
1386 A424 3b multicolored   .50   .30
1387 A424 4b multicolored   .75   .50
1388 A424 5b multicolored   .85   .60
    a.   Souv. sheet of 4, #1385-1388   8.00   8.00
     Nos. 1385-1388 (4)   2.50   1.65

No. 1388a sold for 30b. Exists imperf, value same as perf.

Songkran
Day — A425

Perf. 14x14½
1991, Apr. 13   Wmk. 387   Litho.
1389 A425 2b Demon on
     sheep   2.50   1.00
    a.   Souvenir sheet of 1   17.00   17.00

No. 1389a sold for 8b. Exists imperf, value same as perf.
   See #1467, 1530, 1566, 1606, 1662, 1724, 1801, 1869, 1940, 1970, 2017.

Prince Narisranuvattivongs (1863-1947) — A426

1991, Apr. 28   *Perf. 14½x14*
1390 A426 2b brown & yellow   .50   .25

Mosaics — A427

Various lotus flowers.

1991, May 28   *Perf. 13½*
1391 A427 2b multi, vert.   .30   .20
1392 A427 3b multi, vert.   .40   .25
1393 A427 5b multi   .65   .45
1394 A427 6b multi   .80   .55
     Nos. 1391-1394 (4)   2.15   1.45

Natl. Communications Day — A428

Wmk. 387
1991, Aug. 4   Litho.   *Perf. 13½*
1395 A428 2b multicolored   .60   .25

Thaipex '91, Natl.
Philatelic
Exhibition
A429

Various fabric designs.

1991, Aug. 4   *Perf. 14x14½*
1396 A429 2b multicolored   .45   .25
1397 A429 4b multicolored   .70   .35
1398 A429 6b multicolored   .85   .50
1399 A429 8b multicolored   1.00   .90
    a.   Souv. sheet of 4, #1396-1399   6.00   6.00
     Nos. 1396-1399 (4)   3.00   2.00

No. 1399a sold for 30b. Exists imperf, value $32.50. No. 1399a overprinted with Philanippon emblem in lower left corner of margin sold for 200b. Value, $190.

Intl. Productivity Congress — A430

Perf. 14½x14
1991, Sept. 3   Litho.   Wmk. 387
1400 A430 2b multicolored   .50   .25

26th Intl. Council
of Women
Triennial — A431

Wmk. 387
1991, Sept. 23   Litho.   *Perf. 13½*
1401 A431 2b multicolored   .50   .25

Bantam Chickens — A432

Wmk. 329
1991, Oct. 6   Photo.   *Perf. 13½*
1402 A432 2b Black bantams   .35   .25
1403 A432 3b Black-tailed buff
     bantams   .65   .30
1404 A432 6b Fancy bantams   1.00   .45
1405 A432 8b White bantams   1.25   1.00
    a.   Souv. sheet of 4, #1402-1405   7.50   7.50
     Nos. 1402-1405 (4)   3.25   2.00

No. 1405a sold for 35b. Exists imperf, value same as perf.
Intl. Letter Writing Week.

World Bank/Intl. Monetary Fund
Annual Meetings — A433

Temples, meeting emblem and: 2b, Silver coin of King Rama IV. 4b, Pod Duang money. 8b, Chieng and Hoi money. 10b, Funan, Dvaravati and Srivijaya money.

Perf. 14½x14
1991, Oct. 15   Litho.   Wmk. 387
1406 A433   2b multicolored   .20   .20
1407 A433   4b multicolored   .45   .30
1408 A433   8b multicolored   .90   .60
1409 A433 10b multicolored   1.10   .75
    a.   Souv. sheet of 4, #1406-1409   6.25   6.25
     Nos. 1406-1409 (4)   2.65   1.85

No. 1409a sold for 35b. Exists imperf, value same as perf.

1993 World
Philatelic
Exhibition,
Bangkok — A434

1991, Oct. 23   *Perf. 14x14½*
1410 A434   2b No. 118   .20   .20
1411 A434   3b No. 119   .30   .20
1412 A434   4b No. 120   .40   .30
1413 A434   5b No. 121   .55   .40
1414 A434   6b No. 122   .65   .45
1415 A434   7b No. 123   .75   .50
1416 A434   8b No. 124   .85   .60
    a.   Souvenir sheet of 1   5.00   5.00
     Nos. 1410-1416 (7)   3.70   2.65

No. 1416a sold for 15b. Exists imperf, value same as perf.

Flower Type of 1990
1991, Nov. 5   *Perf. 13½*
1417 A416 1b Dillenia obovata   .20   .20
1418 A416 1b Melastoma
     sanguineum   .20   .20
1419 A416 1b Commelina diffusa   .20   .20
1420 A416 1b Plumbago indica   .20   .20
    a.   Souv. sheet of 4, #1417-1420   5.00   5.00
     Nos. 1417-1420 (4)   .80   .80

No. 1420a sold for 10b. Exists imperf, value same as perf.

Asian Elephants — A435

Wmk. 329
1991, Nov. 5   Photo.   *Perf. 13½*
1421 A435 2b shown   .30   .20
1422 A435 4b Pulling logs   .55   .30
1423 A435 6b Lying down   .80   .45
1424 A435 8b In river   1.10   .60
    a.   Souvenir sheet of 1, litho.   7.50   7.50
     Nos. 1421-1424 (4)   2.75   1.55

No. 1424a sold for 22b and stamp does not have border. No. 1424a exists imperf, value same as perf.

Wild Animals — A436

Perf. 14½x14
1991, Dec. 26   Wmk. 387   Litho.
1425 A436 2b Viverra zibetha   .25   .20
1426 A436 3b Prionodon linsang   .40   .25
1427 A436 6b Felis temmincki   .80   .50
1428 A436 8b Ratufa bicolor   1.10   .65
    a.   Sheet of 4, #1425-1428   8.50   8.50
     Nos. 1425-1428 (4)   2.55   1.60

No. 1428a sold for 30b. Exists imperf, value same as perf.

Prince Mahidol of
Songkla (1891-
1929), Medical
Pioneer — A437

1992, Jan. 1   *Perf. 14x14½*
1429 A437 2b multicolored   .35   .25

Department of Mineral Resources,
Cent. — A438

No. 1430, Locating fossils. No. 1431, Mining excavation. No. 1432, Drilling for natural gas and petroleum. No. 1433, Digging artesian wells.

Perf. 14½x14
1992, Jan. 1   Litho.   Wmk. 387
1430 A438 2b multicolored   .35   .20
1431 A438 2b multicolored   .35   .20
1432 A438 2b multicolored   .35   .20
1433 A438 2b multicolored   .35   .20
     Nos. 1430-1433 (4)   1.40   .80

Children's Day — A439

Children's drawings on "World Under the Sea": 2b, Divers, fish. 3b, Fish, sea grass. 5b, Mermaid.

1992, Jan. 11　Wmk. 329　Perf. 13½
1434　A439　2b multicolored　　　　.30　.20
1435　A439　3b multicolored　　　　.40　.30
1436　A439　5b multicolored, vert.　.65　.50
　　　Nos. 1434-1436 (3)　　　　　1.35　1.00

Duel on Elephants, 400th Anniv. — A440

Perf. 14½x14
1992, Jan. 18　Litho.　Wmk. 387
1437　A440　2b multicolored　　　　.50　.20

Orchids (Paphiopedilum) — A441

1992, Jan. 20
1438　A441　2b Bellatulum　　　.25　.20
1439　A441　2b Exul　　　　　　.25　.20
1440　A441　3b Concolor　　　　.35　.30
1441　A441　3b Godefroyae　　　.35　.30
1442　A441　6b Niveum　　　　　.70　.55
1443　A441　6b Villosum　　　　.70　.55
1444　A441　10b Parishii　　　　1.25　.90
　a.　Souv. sheet of 4, #1438, 1440,
　　　1442, 1444　　　　　　5.00　5.00
1445　A441　10b Sukhakulii　　　1.25　.90
　a.　Souv. sheet of 4, #1439, 1441,
　　　1443, 1445　　　　　　5.00　5.00
　　　Nos. 1438-1445 (8)　　　5.10　3.90

Fourth Asia Pacific Orchid Conference. Nos. 1444a-1445a each sold for 30b. Each exists imperf, value same as perf.

21st Intl. Society of Sugar Cane Technologists Conf. — A442

1992, Mar. 5　　　　Perf. 14x14½
1446　A442　2b multicolored　　　.50　.25

Intl. Red Cross A443

Perf. 14½x14
1992, Mar.　Litho.　Wmk. 387
1447　A443　2b multicolored　　　.50　.20

Ministry of Justice, Cent. — A444

Designs: 3b, Prince Rabi Badhanasakdi of Ratchaburi, founder of Thailand's School of Law. 5b, King Rama V, reformer of court system.

1992, Mar. 25　　　　Perf. 13½
1448　A444　3b multicolored　　　.65　.30
1449　A444　5b multicolored　　　1.10　.40

Ministry of Agriculture and Cooperatives, Cent. — A445

1992, Apr. 1　　　　Perf. 14½x14
1450　A445　2b gray & multi　　　.25　.20
1451　A445　3b lil & multi　　　.40　.30
1452　A445　4b pink & multi　　　.45　.35
1453　A445　5b gray bl & multi　.60　.40
　　　Nos. 1450-1453 (4)　　　1.70　1.25

A446

A447

Ministry of Interior, Cent.: No. 1454, Prince Damrong Rajanubharb, first Minister of the Interior. No. 1455, People voting. No. 1456, Police and fire protection. No. 1457, Water and electricity provided to remote areas.

1992, Apr. 1　　　　Perf. 14x14½
1454　A446　2b multicolored　　　.35　.20
1455　A446　2b multicolored　　　.35　.20
1456　A446　2b multicolored　　　.35　.20
1457　A446　2b multicolored　　　.35　.20
　　　Nos. 1454-1457 (4)　　　1.40　.80

1992, Apr. 1
1458　A447　2b Ships, truck　　　.25　.20
1459　A447　3b Truck, bus, train　.40　.30
1460　A447　5b Airplanes　　　　.60　.40
1461　A447　6b Truck, satellites　.75　.50
　　　Nos. 1458-1461 (4)　　　2.00　1.40

Ministry of Transport and Communications, 80th anniv.

Ministry of Education, Cent. — A448

Perf. 14x14½
1992, Apr. 1　Litho.　Wmk. 387
1462　A448　2b multicolored　　　.30　.20

Carts A449

1992, Apr. 2　　　　Perf. 14½x14
1463　A449　2b West　　　　　　.25　.20
1464　A449　3b North　　　　　　.35　.25
1465　A449　5b Northeast　　　　.55　.40
1466　A449　10b East　　　　　　1.10　.90
　a.　Souv. sheet of 4, #1463-1466　4.50
　　　Nos. 1463-1466 (4)　　　2.25　1.75

Heritage Conservation Day. No. 1466a sold for 30b. Exists imperf without sheet price in margin, value same as perf.

Songkran Day Type of 1991
1992, Apr. 13　　　　Perf. 14x14½
1467　A425　2b Demon on mon-
　　　　　key, zodiac　　　.60　.25
　a.　Souvenir sheet of 1　　3.75

No. 1467a sold for 8b. Exists imperf with sale price in different colors, value same as perf.

Department of Livestock Development, 50th Anniv. — A451

Perf. 14½x14
1992, May 5　Litho.　Wmk. 387
1468　A451　2b multicolored　　　.30　.20

Wisakhabucha Day — A452

Scenes from Buddha's life: 2b, Birth. 3b, Enlightenment. 5b, Death.

Wmk. 387
1992, May 16　Litho.　Perf. 14½
1469　A452　2b multicolored　　　.30　.20
1470　A452　3b multicolored　　　.35　.25
1471　A452　5b multicolored　　　.60　.40
　　　Nos. 1469-1471 (3)　　　1.25　.85

Meteorological Department, 50th Anniv. — A453

1992, June 23　　　Perf. 14x14½
1472　A453　2b multicolored　　　.30　.20

1993 World Philatelic Exhibition, Bangkok — A454

Visit ASEAN Year — A455

Perf. 14x14½
1992, July 1　Litho.　Wmk. 387
1473　A454　2b No. 18　　　　　.25　.20
1474　A454　3b No. 156　　　　　.35　.25
1475　A454　5b No. 222　　　　　.55　.40
1476　A454　7b No. 255　　　　　.85　.50
1477　A454　8b No. 273　　　　　1.00　.65
　a.　Souv. sheet of 5, #1473-1477
　　　+ label　　　　　　　6.00　6.00
　　　Nos. 1473-1477 (5)　　　3.00　2.00

No. 1477a sold for 35b. Exists imperf. with sheet price in blue, value same as #1477a.

1992, July 1

Designs: 2b, Bua Tong field, Mae Hong Son Province. 3b, Klong Larn Waterfall, Kamphaeng Phet Province. 4b, Coral, Chumphon Province. 5b, Khao Ta-Poo, Phangnga Province.

1478　A455　2b multicolored　　　.30　.20
1479　A455　3b multicolored　　　.40　.25
1480　A455　4b multicolored　　　.50　.35
1481　A455　5b multicolored　　　.60　.40
　　　Nos. 1478-1481 (4)　　　1.80　1.20

Prince Chudadhuj Dharadilok of Bejraburna (1892-1923) A456

Wmk. 368
1992, July 5　Litho.　Perf. 13½
1482　A456　2b multicolored　　　.30　.20

Natl. Communications Day — A457

Perf. 14½x14

1992, Aug. 4	**Litho.**		**Wmk. 387**
1483	A457 2b multicolored	.30	.20

ASEAN, 25th Anniv. — A458

Flags and: 2b, Cultures and sports. 3b, Tourist attractions. 5b, Transportation, communications. 7b, Agriculture.

1992, Aug. 8	**Wmk. 368**	**Perf. 13½**	
1484	A458 2b multicolored	.25	.20
1485	A458 3b multicolored	.35	.25
1486	A458 5b multicolored	.55	.40
1487	A458 7b multicolored	.85	.55
	Nos. 1484-1487 (4)	2.00	1.40

Queen Sirikit, 60th Birthday — A459

#1488, Wedding, with King, Queen being anointed. #1489, Coronation, King and Queen on throne. #1490, Being crowned, Queen with crown, being anointed. #1491, Formal portrait, Queen seated. #1492, Visiting wounded. #1493, Visiting public.

Wmk. 329

1992, Aug. 12	**Photo.**	**Perf. 13½**	
1488	A459 2b multicolored	.30	.20
1489	A459 2b multicolored	.30	.20
1490	A459 2b multicolored	.30	.20
1491	A459 2b multicolored	.30	.20
1492	A459 2b multicolored	.30	.20
1493	A459 2b multicolored	.30	.20
a.	Souv. sheet of 6, #1488-1493	7.00	7.00
	Nos. 1488-1493 (6)	1.80	1.20

No. 1493a sold for 30b. Exists imperf with sale price in different colors, value same as perf.

Royal Regalia of Queen Sirikit — A460

No. 1494, Tray. No. 1495, Kettle. No. 1496, Bowl. No. 1497, Box. No. 1498, Covered dish.

1992, Aug. 12
Background Colors

1494	A460 2b dark blue	.25	.20
1495	A460 2b violet	.25	.20
1496	A460 2b yellow green	.25	.20
1497	A460 2b Prussian blue	.25	.20
1498	A460 2b dark green	.25	.20
	Nos. 1494-1498 (5)	1.25	1.00

Opening of Sirikit Medical Center — A461

Perf. 14½x14

1992, Aug. 12	**Litho.**		**Wmk. 387**
1499	A461 2b multicolored	.30	.20

Queen Sirikit, 60th Birthday — A462

Litho. & Embossed

1992, Aug. 12			**Perf. 13½**
1500	A462 100b blue & gold	10.00	10.00

No. 1500 printed in sheets of 10.

A463

A464

Wmk. 387

1992, Aug. 25	**Litho.**		**Perf. 13½**
1501	A463 2b multicolored	.30	.20

Prince Wan Waithayakon Krommun Naradhip Bongsprabandh (1891-1976).

1992, Sept. 15			**Perf. 14x14½**
1502	A464 2b multicolored	.30	.20

Professor Silpa Bhirasri, Sculptor, cent. of birth.

Coral — A465

Perf. 14½x14

1992, Oct. 4	**Litho.**		**Wmk. 387**
1503	A465 2b Catalaphyllia jardinei	.25	.20
1504	A465 3b Porites lutea	.30	.25
1505	A465 6b Tubastraea coccinea	.65	.50
1506	A465 8b Favia pallida	.90	.70
a.	Souv. sheet of 4, #1503-1506	5.25	
	Nos. 1503-1506 (4)	2.10	1.65

Intl. Letter Writing Week. No. 1506a sold for for 30b.

New Year 1993 — A466

Flowers: No. 1507, Rhododendron simsii. No. 1508, Cynoglossum lanceolatum. No. 1509, Tithonia diversifolia. No. 1510, Agapetes parishii.

Perf. 14x13½

1992, Nov. 15	**Wmk. 368**		**Litho.**
1507	A466 1b multicolored	.20	.20
1508	A466 1b multicolored	.20	.20
1509	A466 1b multicolored	.20	.20
1510	A466 1b multicolored	.20	.20
a.	Souv. sheet of 4, #1507-1510	3.00	
	Nos. 1507-1510 (4)	.80	.80

Nos. 1510a sold for 10b. Exists imperf with sheet price in green, value same as perf.

1st Asian Congress of Allergies and Immunology A467

1992, Nov. 22			**Perf. 13½**
1511	A467 2b black, red & yellow	.30	.20

Natl. Assembly, 60th Anniv. — A468

Wmk. 387

1992, Dec. 10	**Litho.**		**Perf. 13½**
1512	A468 2b multicolored	.30	.20

Bank of Thailand, 50th Anniv. — A469

1992, Dec. 10			**Perf. 14½x14**
1513	A469 2b multicolored	.30	.20

Children's Day — A470

Children's drawings: No. 1514, River scene. No. 1515, Wild animals, forest. No. 1516, Trains, planes, monorail.

1993, Jan. 9	**Wmk. 368**	**Perf. 13½**	
1514	A470 2b multicolored	.25	.20
1515	A470 2b multicolored	.25	.20
1516	A470 2b multicolored	.25	.20
	Nos. 1514-1516 (3)	.75	.60

Pottery — A471

Designs: 3b, Jug with bird's neck spout, two bottles. 6b, Pear-shaped vase, two jars. 7b, Three bowls. 8b, Three jars.

1993, Jan. 9	**Photo.**	**Wmk. 329**	
1517	A471 3b multicolored	.35	.25
1518	A471 6b multicolored	.70	.50
1519	A471 7b multicolored	.80	.55
1520	A471 8b multicolored	.95	.70
a.	Souv. sheet of 4, #1517-1520	4.00	
	Nos. 1517-1520 (4)	2.80	2.00

1993 World Philatelic Exhibition, Bangkok. No. 1520a sold for 35b.

Thai Teachers' Training Institute, Cent. — A472

Perf. 13½x14

1993, Jan. 16	**Litho.**		**Wmk. 368**
1521	A472 2b multicolored	.30	.25

Kasetsart University, 50th Anniv. — A473

1993, Feb. 2	**Wmk. 329**	**Perf. 13½**	
1522	A473 2b multicolored	.50	.25

Maghapuja Day — A474

Wmk. 387

1993, Mar. 7	**Litho.**		**Perf. 14½**
1523	A474 2b multicolored	.30	.20

Queen Sri Bajarindra A475

1993, Mar. 27			**Perf. 14x14½**
1524	A475 2b multicolored	.50	.20

Thai Red Cross, cent.

Office of Attorney General,
Cent. — A476

1993, Apr. 1   Wmk. 368   Perf. 12½
1525 A476 2b multicolored   .40   .20

Heritage Conservation Day — A477

Historical landmarks, Si Satchanalai Park:
3b, Wat Chedi Chet Thaeo. 4b, Wat Chang
Lom. 6b, Wat Phra Si Rattanamahathat
(Chaliang). 7b, Wat Suan Kaeo Utthayan Noi.

Wmk. 368
1993, Apr. 2   Litho.   Perf. 13½
1526 A477 3b multicolored   .30   .25
1527 A477 4b multicolored   .45   .30
1528 A477 6b multicolored   .65   .50
1529 A477 7b multicolored   .75   .55
  a. Souv. sheet of 4, #1526-1529   4.00
    Nos. 1526-1529 (4)   2.15   1.60

No. 1529a sold for 25b.
See Nos. 1561-1564, 1650-1653, 1797-
1800.

Songkran Day Type of 1991
Perf. 14x14½
1993   Litho.   Wmk. 387
1530 A425 2b Demon on roost-
    er's back, zodiac   .40   .20
  a. Souvenir sheet of 1   2.50
  b. #1530a ovptd. in gold   13.00

No. 1530b overprinted on sheet margin in
both Thai and Chinese for Chinpex '93.
Nos. 1530a-1530b sold for 8b and exist
imperf. with sale price in different colors.
Issued: #1530, 1530a, Apr. 13.

Mushrooms — A478

Wmk. 368
1993, July 1   Litho.   Perf. 13½
1531 A478 2b Marasmius   .25   .20
1532 A478 4b Coprinus   .50   .30
1533 A478 6b Mycena   .70   .45
1534 A478 8b Cyathus   .90   .60
  a. Souv. sheet of 4, #1531-1534   4.25
    Nos. 1531-1534 (4)   2.35   1.55

No. 1534a sold for 30b.

Natl. Communications Day — A479

1993, Aug. 4   Wmk. 387   Perf. 13½
1535 A479 2b multicolored   .30   .20

Post and Telegraph Department, 110th
Anniv. — A480

Wmk. 387
1993, Aug. 4   Litho.   Perf. 13½
1536 A480 2b multicolored   .75   .20

Queen Suriyothai's Monument — A481

1993, Aug. 12
1537 A481 2b multicolored   .50   .25

Fruit — A482

Wmk. 368
1993, Oct. 1   Photo.   Perf. 13½
1538 A482 2b Citrus reticulata   .25   .20
1539 A482 3b Musa sp.   .40   .25
1540 A482 6b Phyllanthus dis-
    tichus   .75   .45
1541 A482 8b Bouea burmanica   1.00   .60
    Nos. 1538-1541 (4)   2.40   1.50

Thai Ridgeback Dogs — A483

Various dogs.

1993, Oct. 1
1542 A483 2b multicolored   .20   .20
1543 A483 3b multicolored   .30   .20
1544 A483 5b multicolored   .50   .40
1545 A483 10b multicolored   1.00   .75
  a. Souv. sheet of 4, #1542-1545   3.75
    Nos. 1542-1545 (4)   2.00   1.55

Intl. Letter Writing Week. No. 1545a sold for
30b.

5th Conference & Exhibition of ASEAN
Council on Petroleum
(ASCOPE) — A484

Wmk. 387
1993, Nov. 2   Litho.   Perf. 13½
1546 A484 2b multicolored   .50   .20

King Rama VII
(1893-1941)
A485

1993, Nov. 8   Perf. 14x14½
1547 A485 2b multicolored   .60   .20

No. 655 Surcharged

1993   Photo.   Wmk. 233   Perf. 14½
1548 A161 1b on 25s brown red   .50   .20

Bencharong and
Lai Nam Thong
Wares — A486

Designs: 3b, Bencharong cosmetic jar,
divinity design. 5b, Bencharong cosmetic jar,
gold knob. 6b, Lai Nam Thong cosmetic jar,
floral design. 7b, Lai Nam Thong cosmetic jar,
floral design, diff.

Wmk. 368
1993, Oct. 1   Photo.   Perf. 13½
1549 A486 3b multicolored   .30   .20
1550 A486 5b multicolored   .55   .40
1551 A486 6b multicolored   .65   .45
1552 A486 7b multicolored   .75   .55
  a. Souv. sheet of 4, #1549-1552   4.00
    Nos. 1549-1552 (4)   2.25   1.60

Bangkok '93. No. 1552a sold for 30b.
No. 1552a exists imperf. Value, $22.50.

New Year
1994 — A487

Perf. 14½x14
1993, Nov. 15   Litho.   Wmk. 387
1553 A487 1b Ipomoea cairica   .20   .20
1554 A487 1b Decaschistia
    parviflora   .20   .20
1555 A487 1b Hibiscus tiliaceus   .20   .20
1556 A487 1b Passiflora foetida   .20   .20
  a. Souv. sheet of 4, #1553-1556   1.25
    Nos. 1553-1556 (4)   .80   .80

No. 1556a sold for 10b.

THAICOM, Natl.
Satellite
Project — A488

1993, Dec. 1   Perf. 14x14½
1557 A488 2b multicolored   .50   .20

Children's Day — A489

1994, Jan. 8   Perf. 14½x14
1558 A489 2b Play land   .40   .20

Administrative Building, Chulalongkorn
Hospital, 80th Anniv. — A490

Perf. 14½x14
1994, Mar. 30   Litho.   Wmk. 387
1559 A490 2b multicolored   .40   .20

Thai Red Cross.

Royal Institute,
60th
Anniv. — A491

1994, Mar. 31   Perf. 14x14½
1560 A491 2b multicolored   .40   .20

Heritage Conservation Day Type of
1993

Historical landmarks, Phra Nakhon Si
Ayutthaya Park: 2b, Wat Ratchaburana. 3b,
Wat Maha That. 6b, Wat Maheyong. 9b, Wat
Phra Si Samphet.

1994, Apr. 2   Perf. 14½x14
1561 A477 2b multicolored   .20   .20
1562 A477 3b multicolored   .35   .25
1563 A477 6b multicolored   .65   .50
1564 A477 9b multicolored   1.25   .95
  a. Souv. sheet of 4, #1561-1564   2.50
    Nos. 1561-1564 (4)   2.45   1.90

No. 1564a sold for 25b.

Opening of Friendship Bridge,
Thailand-Laos — A492

1994, Apr. 8
1565 A492 9b multicolored   1.00   .75

Songkran Day Type of 1991
1994, Apr. 13   Litho.
1566 A425 2b Demon on dog's
    back, zodiac   .25   .20
  a. Souvenir sheet of 1   1.00
  b. As "a," inscribed in margin   4.50

No. 1566a sold for 8b and exists imperf with
frame around stamp and sale price in different
color. Value same as perf.
Sheet margin of No. 1566b has no value
inscription and is overprinted in violet with Thai
and Chinese inscriptions for Beijing Stamp
Exhibition. Issued: May 1994. No. 1566b also
exists imperf. Value same as perf.

Intl. Olympic Committee, Cent. — A493

Wmk. 387

1994, June 23   Litho.   *Perf. 14*
1567	A493	2b Soccer	.20	.20
1568	A493	3b Running	.30	.20
1569	A493	5b Swimming	.50	.40
1570	A493	6b Weight lifting	.60	.45
1571	A493	9b Boxing	.90	.75
		Nos. 1567-1571 (5)	2.50	2.00

Thammasat University, 60th Anniv. — A494

Wmk. 387

1994, June 27   Litho.   *Perf. 14*
1572	A494	2b multicolored	.35	.20

Asalhapuja Day — A495

1994, July 22   Wmk. 329   *Perf. 13½*
1573	A495	2b multicolored	.35	.20

Natl. Communications Day — A496

1994, Aug. 4   Wmk. 368
1574	A496	2b multicolored	.35	.20

Crabs A497

3b, Phricotelphusa limula. 5b, Thaipotamon chulabhorn. 6b, Phricotelphusa sirindhorn. 10b, Thaiphusa sirikit.

Wmk. 340 (340)

1994, Aug. 12   Photo.   *Perf. 13½x13*
1575	A497	3b multicolored	.30	.20
1576	A497	5b multicolored	.50	.40
1577	A497	6b multicolored	.60	.45
1578	A497	10b multicolored	1.00	.75
a.		Souv. sheet of 4, #1575-1578	3.00	
b.		As "a," inscribed in margin	3.00	
		Nos. 1575-1578 (4)	2.40	1.80

No. 1578b has PHILAKOREA '94 Exhibition emblem added to sheet margin.

Intl. Letter Writing Week — A498

Winning paintings in design contest: 2b, Gold niello bowls, octagonal footed tray. 6b, Pumpkin shaped bowls. 8b, Silver niello betelnut set. 9b, Covered square bowl with gold finial, small lotus-shaped footed tray.

Wmk. 368

1994, Oct. 9   Photo.   *Perf. 13½*
1579	A498	2b multicolored	.20	.20
		Complete booklet, 5 #1579	.80	
1580	A498	6b multicolored	.50	.35
1581	A498	8b multicolored	.60	.50
1582	A498	9b multicolored	.70	.55
a.		Souv. sheet of 4, #1579-1582	2.50	
		Nos. 1579-1582 (4)	2.00	1.60

No. 1582a sold for 30b.

ILO, 75th Anniv. A499

Perf. 15x14

1994, Oct. 29   Litho.   Wmk. 387
1583	A499	2b multicolored	.30	.20
		Complete booklet, 5 #1583	1.60	

New Year 1995 — A500

Herbs: No. 1584, Utricularia delphinioides. No. 1585, Utricularia minutissima. No. 1586, Eriocaulon odoratum. No. 1587, Utricularia bifida.

1994, Nov. 15   *Perf. 14x14½*
1584	A500	1b multicolored	.20	.20
1585	A500	1b multicolored	.20	.20
1586	A500	1b multicolored	.20	.20
1587	A500	1b multicolored	.20	.20
a.		Souv. sheet of 4, #1584-1587	1.25	
		Nos. 1584-1587 (4)	.80	.80

No. 1587a sold for 10b.

Suan Dusit Teachers College, 60th Anniv. — A501

Perf. 14½x14

1994, Dec. 4   Litho.   Wmk. 387
1588	A501	2b multicolored	.30	.20
		Complete booklet, 5 #1588	1.60	

Council of State, 120th Anniv. — A502

1994, Dec. 5   Wmk. 368   *Perf. 13½*
1589	A502	2b multicolored	.75	.20
		Complete booklet, 5 #1589	4.00	

ICAO, 50th Anniv. A503

Perf. 14½x14

1994, Dec. 7   Wmk. 387
1590	A503	2b multicolored	.30	.20
		Complete booklet, 5 #1590	1.60	

Pharmacy in Thailand, 80th Anniv. — A504

Grinding stones: 2b, Dvaravati, 7th-11th cent. 6b, Lopburi Period, 11th-13th cent. 9b, Bangkok Period, 18th-20th cent.

1994, Dec. 13
1591	A504	2b multicolored	.30	.20
		Complete booklet, 5 #1591	1.60	
1592	A504	6b multicolored	.45	.35
1593	A504	9b multicolored	.70	.55
		Nos. 1591-1593 (3)	1.45	1.10

Bar Assoc., 80th Anniv. — A505

Design: 2b, First Bar Assoc. headquarters, King Vajiravudh, King Bhumibol.

1995, Jan. 1   Wmk. 368   *Perf. 13½*
1594	A505	2b multicolored	.30	.20
		Complete booklet, 5 #1594	1.60	

A506

A507

Children's drawings: No. 1595, Kites Decorate the Summer Sky. No. 1596, Trees and Streams, horiz. No. 1597, Youths and Religion, horiz.

1995, Jan. 14   Wmk. 387   *Perf. 14*
1595	A506	2b multicolored	.20	.20
		Complete booklet, 5 #1595	1.10	
1596	A506	2b multicolored	.20	.20
		Complete booklet, 5 #1596	1.10	
1597	A506	2b multicolored	.20	.20
		Complete booklet, 5 #1597	1.10	
		Nos. 1595-1597 (3)	.60	.60

Children's Day.

1995, Mar. 4
1598	A507	2b multicolored	.25	.20
		Complete booklet, 5 #1598	1.40	

First Thai newspaper, Bangkok Recorder, 150th anniv.

Royal Thai Air Force, 80th Anniv. A508

1995, Mar. 27   Wmk. 368   *Perf. 13½*
1599	A508	2b multicolored	.25	.20
		Complete booklet, 5 #1599	1.40	

Red Cross Floating Clinic, Wetchapha — A509

1995, Mar. 30
1600	A509	2b multicolored	.25	.20
		Complete booklet, 5 #1600	1.40	

Phimai Historical Park — A510

Paintings: 3b, Naga Bridge. 5b, Brahmin Hall. 6b, Gateway of the Inner Wall. 9b, Main Pagoda.

Perf. 14½x14

1995, Apr. 2   Wmk. 387
1601	A510	3b multicolored	.25	.20
1602	A510	5b multicolored	.40	.30
1603	A510	6b multicolored	.50	.35
1604	A510	9b multicolored	.75	.55
a.		Souv. sheet of 4, #1601-1604	2.50	
		Nos. 1601-1604 (4)	1.90	1.40

Heritage Conservation Day.
No. 1604a sold for 30b.

Ministry of Defense, 108th Anniv. — A511

Design: 2b, Admin. building, King Rama V.

1995, Apr. 8   Wmk. 387   *Perf. 14*
1605	A511	2b multicolored	.30	.20
		Complete booklet, 5 #1605	1.60	

Songkran Day Type of 1991

1995, Apr. 13   *Perf. 11x13*
1606	A425	2b Demon on boar's back, zodiac	.30	.20
a.		Souvenir sheet of 1	1.25	
		Complete booklet, 5 #1606	1.60	

No. 1606a sold for 8b and exists imperf with sale price in different color. Value same as perf. No. 1606a and the similar imperf sheet exist with a red marginal inscription in Thai and Chinese (without sale price). Value, each $4.75.

Ministry of Foreign Affairs, 120th
Anniv. — A512

2b, Saranrom Palace, King Rama V.

1995, Apr. 14   **Perf. 14**
1607 A512 2b multicolored   .50 .20
    Complete booklet, 5 #1607   2.75

Visakhapuja
Day — A513

Sculptures of Buddha: 2b, Emerald Buddha,
temple of Wat Phra Si Rattana Satsadaram,
Bangkok. 6b, Phra Phuttha Chinnarat, Wat
Phra Si Rattana Maha That, Phitsanulok Prov-
ince. 8b, Phra Phuttha Sihing, Wat Phra Sing,
Chiang Mai Province. 9b, Phra Sukhothai
Traimit, Wat Traimit Witthayaram, Bangkok.

         Wmk. 340
1995, May 13   **Photo.**   **Perf. 13½**
1608 A513 2b multicolored   .20 .20
1609 A513 6b multicolored   .45 .35
1610 A513 8b multicolored   .60 .50
1611 A513 9b multicolored   .75 .55
   a.   Souv. sheet of 4, #1608-1611   2.75
    Nos. 1608-1611 (4)   2.00 1.60

   No. 1611a sold for 35b.

ASEAN
Environment
Year — A514

1995, June 5   **Litho.**   **Wmk. 368**
1612 A514 2b multicolored   .25 .20
    Complete booklet, 5 #1612   1.40

Information Technology Year — A515

1995, June 9   **Wmk. 340**
1613 A515 2b multicolored   .25 .20
    Complete booklet, 5 #1613   1.40

Thailand-People's Republic of China
Diplomatic Relations, 20th
Anniv. — A516

#1614, Elephants walking right into water.
#1615, Elephants walking left into water.

         Wmk. 340
1995, July 1   **Photo.**   **Perf. 13½**
1614 A516 2b multicolored   .50 .20
1615 A516 2b multicolored   .50 .20
   a.   Pair, Nos. 1614-1615   1.75 1.75
   b.   Souv. sheet, #1614-1615   3.50
   c.   As "b," diff. inscriptions in
      sheet margin   18.00

   No. 1615c contains Jakarta '95 exhibition
emblem and does not have sheet value in
margin.
   #1615b sold for 8b. #1615c sold for 28b.
   No. 1615b exists with serial number in sheet
margin, The same number is on China (PRC)
No. 2462a. These two souvenir sheets were
sold as a set. Value, set $26.50.
   See People's Republic of China Nos. 2579-
2580.

Natl. Communications Day — A517

1995, Aug. 4   **Litho.**   **Perf. 14½x14**
1616 A517 2b multicolored   .30 .20
    Complete booklet, 5 #1616   1.60

A518

   Domestic cats: 3b, Khoa Manee. 6b, Korat
or Si-Sawat. 7b, Seal point Siamese. 9b,
Burmese.

1995, Aug. 4   **Photo.**   **Perf. 13½**
1617 A518 3b multicolored   .25 .20
1618 A518 6b multicolored   .50 .40
1619 A518 7b multicolored   .55 .45
1620 A518 9b multicolored   .70 .55
   a.   Souv. sheet, Nos. 1617-1620   2.75
   b.   As "a," diff. inscriptions in
      margin   10.00
    Nos. 1617-1620 (4)   2.00 1.60

       Thaipex '95.
   No. 1620b contains Singapore '95 exhibition
emblem added to sheet margin and does not
have value inscription.
   No. 1620a sold for 35b. No. 1620b sold for
46b.

1995, Sept. 2   **Litho.**   **Perf. 14x14½**
1621 A519 2b multicolored   .25 .20
    Complete booklet, 5 #1621   1.40

     Revenue Department, 80th anniv.

Natl. Auditing & Office of Auditor
General, 120th Anniv. — A520

1995, Sept. 18   **Perf. 14½x14**
1622 A520 2b multicolored   .25 .20
    Complete booklet, 5 #1622   1.40

Intl. Letter Writing
Week — A521

   Wicker: No. 1623, Vase with handles, legs.
No. 1624, Oval-shaped container. No. 1625,
Lamp shade. No. 1626, Vase.

         Wmk. 340
1995, Oct. 8   **Photo.**   **Perf. 13½**
1623 A521 2b multicolored   .20 .20
    Complete booklet, 5 #1623   1.10
1624 A521 2b multicolored   .20 .20
    Complete booklet, 5 #1624   1.10
1625 A521 9b multicolored   .75 .55
1626 A521 9b multicolored   .75 .55
   a.   Souv. sheet, #1623-1626   1.75
    Nos. 1623-1626 (4)   1.90 1.50

FAO,
50th
Anniv.
A522

1995, Oct. 16   **Litho.**   **Perf. 14½x14**
1627 A522 2b multicolored   .25 .20
    Complete booklet, 5 #1627   1.40

Total Solar Eclipse in Thailand — A523

1995, Oct. 24   **Perf. 13½**
1628 A523 2b multicolored   .25 .20
    Complete booklet, 5 #1628   1.40

UN,
50th
Anniv.
A524

       Perf. 13½x14
1995, Oct. 24   **Wmk. 387**
1629 A524 2b multicolored   .25 .20
    Complete booklet, 5 #1629   1.40

World Agricultural and Industrial
Exhibition, Nkhon Ratchasima
Province — A525

   2b, Worldtech '95 Thailand Symbol Tower,
vert. 5b, Farming equipment, food products,
vert. 6b, Computers, equipment. 9b, Factory,
beach.

    Perf. 14x14½, 14½x14
1995, Nov. 4   **Wmk. 340**
1630 A525 2b multicolored   .25 .20
    Complete booklet, 5 #1630   1.40

1631 A525 5b multicolored   .40 .30
1632 A525 6b multicolored   .50 .40
1633 A525 9b multicolored   .75 .55
    Nos. 1630-1633 (4)   1.90 1.45

New Year
1996 — A526

   #1634, Adenium obesum. #1635, Bauhinia
acuminata. #1636, Cananga odorata. #1637,
Thumbergia erecta.

1995, Dec. 9   **Perf. 13½**
1634 A526 2b multicolored   .20 .20
1635 A526 2b multicolored   .20 .20
   a.   Souvenir sheet, #1634-1635   4.50
1636 A526 2b multicolored   .20 .20
1637 A526 2b multicolored   .20 .20
   a.   Souvenir sheet, #1634-1637   1.25
   b.   As "a," inscribed in margin   5.00
   c.   Souvenir sheet, #1636-1637   4.50
    Nos. 1634-1637 (4)   .80 .80

   No. 1637a sold for 15b.
   Nos. 1635a, 1637c have "CHINA '96"
emblem inscribed in sheet margin and sold for
22b each. No. 1637b is inscribed in sheet margin with "Indonesia '96" emblem and has the
gold 15b value removed. No. 1637b sold for
14b.
   Issued: #1635a, 1637b-1637c, 5/18/96.

Veterinary Science in Thailand, 60th
Anniv. — A527

1995, Dec. 9   **Perf. 14½x14**
1638 A527 2b multicolored   .25 .20
    Complete booklet, 5 #1638   1.40

A528

A529

       Perf. 14x14½
1996, Jan. 12   **Litho.**   **Wmk. 340**
1639 A528 2b multicolored   .40 .20
    Complete booklet, 5 #1639   2.25

   Siriraj School of Nursing and Midwifery, cent.

1996, Jan. 13   **Wmk. 387**   **Perf. 13½**

   Paintings of Buddha instructing people with:
No. 1640, Bright light, deer. No. 1641, Chil-
dren, animal, person reclined, horiz. No. 1642,
Followers, large tree, river.

1640 A529 2b multicolored   .20 .20
    Complete booklet, 5 #1640   1.10
1641 A529 2b multicolored   .20 .20
    Complete booklet, 5 #1641   1.10
1642 A529 2b multicolored   .20 .20
    Complete booklet, 5 #1642   1.10
    Nos. 1640-1642 (3)   .60 .60

     Natl. Children's Day.

Natl. Aviation Day — A530

Perf. 14½x14

1996, Jan. 13   **Wmk. 340**
1643 A530 2b multicolored   .30   .20
    Complete booklet, 5 #1643   1.60

Asia-Europe Economic Meeting — A531

Perf. 14x14½

1996, Mar. 1   **Litho.**   **Wmk. 340**
1644 A531 2b multicolored   .25   .20
    Complete booklet, 5 #1644   1.40

Maghapuja Day — A532

Scenes from the Ten Jataka stories: 2b, Man on knee, another holding chariot. 6b, Two people flying over sea. 8b, Archer approaching man with arrow in side. 9b, Charioteer pointing.

Wmk. 340

1996, Mar. 3   **Photo.**   **Perf. 13½**
1645 A532 2b multicolored   .20   .20
1646 A532 6b multicolored   .50   .35
1647 A532 8b multicolored   .60   .50
1648 A532 9b multicolored   .70   .50
   a.   Souvenir Sheet, #1645-1548   2.75
     Nos. 1645-1648 (4)   2.00   1.55

No. 1648a sold for 36b.

Cremation of Princess Mother Somdej Phra Sri Nakharindra Barommarajjonnani — A533

Litho. & Embossed
Perf. 14½x14

1996, Mar. 10   **Wmk. 340**
1649 A533 2b gold & multi   .50   .20
    Complete booklet, 5 #1649   3.00

Heritage Conservation Day Type of 1993

Historical landmarks, Kamphaeng Phet Park: 2b, Wat Phra Kaeo. 3b, Wat Phra Non. 6b, Wat Chang Rop. 9b, Wat Phra Si Iriyabot.

Wmk. 387

1996, Apr. 2   **Litho.**   **Perf. 13½**
1650 A477 2b multicolored   .20   .20
    Complete booklet, 5 No. 1650   1.10
1651 A477 3b multicolored   .25   .20
1652 A477 6b multicolored   .50   .35
1653 A477 9b multicolored   .70   .50
   a.   Souvenir sheet, #1650-1653   2.25
     Nos. 1650-1653 (4)   1.65   1.25

No. 1653a sold for 28b.

Chiang Mai, 700th Anniv. — A534

Anniv. logo of Chiang Mai and: 2b, Buddhist Pagoda of Wat Chiang Man. 6b, Sculpted angel on wall, Wat Chet Yot's Pagoda. 8b, Insignia of Wat Phan Tao's Vihara. 9b, Sattaphanta.

Wmk. 340

1996, Apr. 12   **Photo.**   **Perf. 13½**
1654 A534 2b multicolored   .20   .20
    Complete booklet, 5 #1654   1.10
1655 A534 6b multicolored   .50   .35
1656 A534 8b multicolored   .60   .45
1657 A534 9b multicolored   .70   .50
   a.   Souvenir sheet, #1654-1657   2.90
     Nos. 1654-1657 (4)   2.00   1.50

No. 1657a sold for 37b.

Second Intl. Asian Hornbill Workshop A535

#1658, White-crowned. #1659, Rufous-necked. #1660, Plain-pouched. #1661, Rhinoceros.

1996, Apr. 12
1658 A535 3b multicolored   .25   .20
1659 A535 3b multicolored   .25   .20
1660 A535 9b multicolored   .70   .50
1661 A535 9b multicolored   .70   .50
   a.   Souvenir sheet, #1658-1661   2.75
   b.   As "a," inscribed in margin   6.50
     Nos. 1658-1661 (4)   1.90   1.40

No. 1661a sold for 35b. No. 1661b was issued 6/8/96, contains CAPEX '96 exhibition emblem in sheet margin, no value inscription, and sold for 47b.

Songkran Day Type of 1991
Perf. 13½x14

1996, Apr. 13   **Litho.**   **Wmk. 387**
1662 A425 2b Demon on rat's   back, zodiac   .25   .20
    Complete booklet, 5 #1662   1.40
   a.   Souvenir sheet of 1   1.50
   b.   Souv. sheet, #1389, 1467,   1530, 1566, 1606, 1662   2.75
   c,   As "a," inscribed in margin   5.50
   d.   As "b," inscribed in margin   11.00

No. 1662c contains CHINA '96 exhibition emblem and "CHINA '96-9th Asian International Philatelic Exhibition" in Chinese and English and no value inscription in sheet margin. No. 1662d contains CHINA '96 and Hong Kong '96 exhibition emblems in margin and no value inscription.
#1662a sold for 8b. #1662b sold for 20b. #1662c, issued 5/15/96, sold for 14b. #1662d, issued 5/10/96, sold for 25b. #1662a-1662d exist imperf.

A536

King Bhumibol Adulyadej, 50th Anniv. of Assession to the Throne A537

Designs: No. 1663, Royal Ablutions Ceremony. No. 1664, Pouring of the Libation. No. 1665, Grand Audience. No. 1666, Royal Progress by Land. No. 1667, Audience from Balcony.

1996, June 9   **Photo.**   **Perf. 11½**
Granite Paper
1663 A536 3b multicolored   .35   .20
   a.   Souvenir sheet   1.00
1664 A536 3b multicolored   .35   .20
   a.   Souvenir sheet   1.00
1665 A536 3b multicolored   .35   .20
   a.   Souvenir sheet   1.00
1666 A536 3b multicolored   .35   .20
   a.   Souvenir sheet   1.00
1667 A536 3b multicolored   .35   .20
   a.   Souvenir sheet   1.00

Litho. & Typo.
Wmk. 387
Perf. 13½
1668 A537 100b gold & multi   8.00 6.00
     Nos. 1663-1668 (6)   9.75 7.00

Nos. 1663a 1664a, 1665a, 1666a, 1667a have a continuous design and each sold for 8b.

Development Programs of King Bhumibol Adulyadej — A538

#1669, Using Vetiver grass to prevent soil erosion. #1670, Chai pattana aerator to improve water quality. #1671, Rain making project to counter droughts. #1672, Dam, natural water resource development. #1673, Reforestation.

Wmk. 340

1996, June 9   **Litho.**   **Perf. 13½**
1669 A538 3b multicolored   .25   .20
1670 A538 3b multicolored   .25   .20
1671 A538 3b multicolored   .25   .20
1672 A538 3b multicolored   .25   .20
1673 A538 3b multicolored   .25   .20
   a.   Souv. sheet, #1669-1673+label   2.00
     Nos. 1669-1673 (5)   1.25 1.00

No. 1671 has a holographic image. Soaking in water may affect the hologram. No. 1673a sold for 25b.

Royal Utensils — A539

#1674, Gold-enameled cuspidor, golden spittoon. #1675, Royal betel, areca-nut set, vert. #1676, Royal water urn, vert.

Wmk. 329
1996, June 9   **Photo.**   **Perf. 13½**
1674 A539 3b green & multi   .25   .20
1675 A539 3b blue & multi   .25   .20
1676 A539 3b purple & multi   .25   .20
   a.   Souvenir sheet, #1674-1676   1.30
     Nos. 1674-1676 (3)   .75   .60

No. 1676a sold for 17b.

Modern Olympic Games, Cent. — A540

2b, Pierre de Coubertin, grave site. 3b, 1st lighting of Olympic torch, Olympia, Greece. 5b, Olympic Stadium, Athens, Olympic flag. 9b, Discus thrower, medal from 1896 games.

Perf. 14x14½

1996, June 23   **Litho.**   **Wmk. 340**
1677 A540 2b multicolored   .20   .20
    Complete booklet, 5 #1677   1.25
1678 A540 3b multicolored   .25   .20
1679 A540 5b multicolored   .40   .30
1680 A540 9b multicolored   .75   .55
     Nos. 1677-1680 (4)   1.60 1.25

Nat. Communications Day — A541

1996, Aug. 4   **Wmk. 340**
1681 A541 2b King using radio   .30   .20
    Complete booklet, 5 #1681   1.60

Royal Forest Department, Cent. — A542

Perf. 14½x14

1996, Sept. 18   **Litho.**   **Wmk. 340**
Type of Forest
1682 A542 3b Tropical rain   .25   .20
1683 A542 6b Hill evergreen   .50   .40
1684 A542 7b Swamp   .55   .30
1685 A542 9b Mangrove   .70   .55
   a.   Souvenir sheet, #1682-1685   2.75
     Nos. 1682-1685 (4)   2.00 1.45

No. 1685a sold for 35b.

Intl. Letter Writing Week — A543

Classical Thai novels, characters: No. 1686, "Ramayana," King Rama following deer. No. 1687, "Inao," Inao kidnapping Budsaba, taking her to cave. No. 1688, "Ngao Pa," Lumhap touring forest. No. 1689, "Mathanapatha," Nang Mathana being cursed.

Wmk. 340

1996, Oct. 6   **Photo.**   **Perf. 13½**
1686 A543 3b multicolored   .25   .20
1687 A543 3b multicolored   .25   .20
1688 A543 9b multicolored   .70   .55
1689 A543 9b multicolored   .70   .55
   a.   Souvenir sheet, #1686-1689   1.90 1.50

No. 1689a sold for 36b.

Rotary Intl. 1996
Asia Regional
Conference
A544

Perf. 14x14½

1996, Oct. 25   Litho.   Wmk. 340
1690 A544 2b multicolored   .25   .20
        Complete booklet, 5 #1609   1.40

UNESCO, 50th Anniv. — A545

1996, Nov. 4   Perf. 14½x14
1691 A545 2b multicolored   .25   .20
        Complete booklet, 5 #1691   1.40

Royal Barge — A546

Illustration reduced.

1996, Nov. 7   Unwmk.   Perf. 11½
                  Granite Paper
1692 A546 9b multicolored   1.00   .65
    a.   Souvenir sheet of 1   2.25   2.25

No. 1692a sold for 16b.

New Year
1997 — A547

Designs: No. 1693, Limnocharis flava. No.
1694, Crinum thaianum, vert. No. 1695,
Monochoria hastata, vert. No. 1696, Nymphoides indicum.

Perf. 14x14½, 14½x14

1996, Nov. 15   Litho.   Wmk. 387
1693 A547 2b multicolored   .20   .20
1694 A547 2b multicolored   .20   .20
1695 A547 2b multicolored   .20   .20
1696 A547 2b multicolored   .20   .20
    a.   Souvenir sheet, #1693-1696   1.20
    b.   As "a," inscribed in margin   7.50
        Nos. 1693-1696 (4)   .80   .80

No. 1696a sold for 15b. No. 1696b inscribed
in sheet margin with Hong Kong '97 emblem
and vertical Chinese inscription.
No. 1696b issued 2/12/97.

Ducks
A548

#1697, Sarkidiornis melanotos. #1698, Den-
drocygna javanica, vert. #1699, Cairina scutu-
lata, vert. #1700, Nettapus coromandelianus.

Wmk. 340

1996, Dec. 1   Photo.   Perf. 13½
1697 A548 3b multicolored   .25   .20
1698 A548 3b multicolored   .25   .20
1699 A548 7b multicolored   .55   .40
1700 A548 7b multicolored   .55   .40
    a.   Souvenir sheet, #1697-1700   2.50
        Nos. 1697-1700 (4)   1.60   1.20

No. 1700a sold for 33b.

UNICEF, 50th Anniv. — A549

Perf. 14½x14

1996, Dec. 11   Litho.   Wmk. 340
1701 A549 2b multicolored   .25   .20
        Complete booklet, 5 #1701   1.40

King Bhumibol
Adulyadej — A550

Perf. 14x14½

1996, Dec. 5   Litho.   Wmk. 340
1702 A550 2b carmine   .25   .20
        Complete booklet, 5 #1702   1.40
    a.   Unwmkd., granite paper   .20   .20

No. 1702a issued 9/1/98.
See Nos. 1725-1729, 1743-1745, 1756-
1757, 1794-1795, 1819-1820, 1876-1879,
2067, 2212-2213.

Thailand's 1st Olympic Gold Medal,
1996 — A552

Litho. & Embossed
Perf. 14½x14

1996, Dec. 16   Wmk. 340
1704 A552 6b multicolored   .45   .35

Mahavajiravudh
School,
Songkhla,
Cent. — A553

Perf. 14x14½

1997, Jan. 1   Wmk. 387
1705 A553 2b multicolored   .25   .20
        Complete booklet, 5 #1705   1.40

Children's
Day — A554

Children' paintings: No. 1706, Children
processing fish. No. 1707, Monument, children
in praise.

1997, Jan. 11   Wmk. 340
1706 A554 2b multicolored   .25   .20
        Complete booklet, 5 #1706   1.40
1707 A554 2b multicolored   .25   .20
        Complete booklet, 5 #1707   1.40

Communications Authority of Thailand,
20th Anniv. — A555

Perf. 14½x14

1997, Feb. 25   Litho.   Wmk. 340
1708 A555 2b multicolored   .25   .20
        Complete booklet, 5 #1708   1.40

Statue of Prince
Bhanurangsi
A556

1997, Feb. 25   Perf. 14x14½
1709 A556 2b multicolored   .25   .20
        Complete booklet, 5 #1709   1.40

Laksi
Mail
Center
A557

#1710, Outside view of building. #1711,
Computerized mail sorting machine.

1997, Feb. 25   Perf. 14½x14
1710 A557 2b multicolored   .20   .20
1711 A557 2b multicolored   .20   .20
    a.   Pair, #1710-1711   .30   .25

State Railway, Cent. — A558

3b, 0-6-0 Type. 4b, Garratt. 6b, Sulzer diesel. 7b, Hitachi diesel leaving tunnel.

Wmk. 387

1997, Mar. 26   Litho.   Perf. 13
1712 A558 3b multicolored   .25   .20
    a.   Souvenir sheet of 1   1.50   1.50
1713 A558 4b multicolored   .30   .25
1714 A558 6b multicolored   .45   .35
1715 A558 7b multicolored   .55   .40
    a.   Souv. sheet of 4, #1712-1715   2.25
        Nos. 1712-1715 (4)   1.55   1.20

No. 1712a sold for 20b, No. 1715a sold for
30b.

Chulalongkorn University, 80th
Anniv. — A559

Designs: No. 1716, Palace of Prince Maha
Vajirunhis. No. 1717, Faculty of Arts building.

Perf. 14½x14

1997, Mar. 26   Wmk. 340
1716 A559 2b yellow & multi   .20   .20
        Complete booklet, 5 #1716   1.00
1717 A559 2b rose & multi   .20   .20
        Complete booklet, 5 #1717   1.00

Thai
Red
Cross
A560

1997, Mar. 28
1718 A560 3b Rajakarun building   .25   .20

Govt. Savings Bank, 84th
Anniv. — A561

1997, Apr. 1
1719 A561 2b multicolored   .25   .20
        Complete booklet, 5 #1719   1.40

Heritage Conservation Day — A562

Phanomrung historical Park: No. 1720,
Outer stairway. No. 1721, Pavilion. No. 1722,
Passage, stairway to sanctuary. No. 1723,
Naga balustrade, Central Gate of Eastern
Gallery.

1997, Apr. 2
1720 A562 3b multicolored   .25   .20
1721 A562 3b multicolored   .25   .20
1722 A562 7b multicolored   .55   .40
1723 A562 7b multicolored   .55   .40
    a.   Souvenir sheet, #1720-1723   2.25
        Nos. 1720-1723 (4)   1.60   1.20

No. 1723a sold for 30b.

Songkran Day Type of 1991

1997-2002   Wmk. 340   Perf. 14x14½
1724 A425 2b Demon on ox's
                  back, zodiac   .30   .20
        Complete booklet, 5 #1724   1.60   1.25
    a.   Souvenir sheet of 1   1.50
    b.   Unwmkd., granite paper   .20   .20

Issued: Nos. 1724, 1724a, 4/13/97; No.
1724b, 4/13/02. No. 1724b issued only in No.
2017b.
No. 1724a sold for 8b and exists imperf.

King Bhumibol Adulyadej Type of 1996
**Litho, Litho & Engraved (#1728-
1729)**
Perf. 14x14½

1997, May 5   Wmk. 340
1725 A550 4b blue & red brown   .30   .25
    a.   Perf. 13¼, unwmkd.   .30   .25
    b.   Unwmkd., granite paper   .20   .20
1726 A550 5b pur & org brn   .40   .30
    a.   Perf. 13½, unwmk., granite pa-
          per   .25   .20
    b.   Unwmkd., granite paper   .20   .20
1727 A550 7b pink & green   .55   .40
                  Wmk. 329
                  Perf. 13½x13
1728 A550 10b orange & brown   .80   .60
1729 A550 20b violet & maroon   1.60   1.25
        Nos. 1725-1729 (5)   3.65   2.80

Issued: No. 1726a, 12/28/98; No. 1725a,
10/8/99. 1725b, 1726b, 12/1/00.

Waterfowl — A563

Designs: No. 1730, Pheasant-tailed jacana.
No. 1731, Bronze-winged jacana. No. 1732,
Painted stork. No. 1733, Black-winged stilt.

Perf. 11½x12
1997, May 15 Photo. Unwmk.
Granite Paper

1730	A563	3b multicolored	.25	.20
1731	A563	3b multicolored	.25	.20
1732	A563	5b multicolored	.55	.40
1733	A563	7b multicolored	.55	.40
a.		Souvenir sheet, #1730-1733	5.00	
b.		As "a," with added inscription	7.50	
		Nos. 1730-1733 (4)	1.60	1.20

No. 1733a sold for 30b. No. 1733b has PACIFIC 97 emblem in sheet margin, while sales price has been removed from sheet margin. No. 1728b sold for 42b.

King Bhumibol Adulyadej, National Telecommunications — A564

2b, King using hand-held radio, "Suthee" aerial. 3b, King using hand-held radio for communication in local areas. 6b, King using computer. 9b, King, classroom using satellite information.

Perf. 14½x14
1997, June 9 Litho. Wmk. 340

1734	A564	2b multicolored	.20	.20
		Complete booklet, 5 #1734	1.00	
1735	A564	3b multicolored	.25	.20
1736	A564	6b multicolored	.50	.40
1737	A564	9b multicolored	.70	.50
a.		Souvenir sheet, #1734-1737	2.40	
		Nos. 1734-1737 (4)	1.65	1.30

No. 1737a sold for 30b.

Motion Pictures in Thailand, Cent. — A565

Designs: No. 1738, King Rama VII filming movie, film showing King Chulalongkorn's state visit to Europe. No. 1739, Early motion picture equipment, advertisement, Prince Sanbassatra, founder of Thai motion picures. No. 1740, Poster from "Double Luck," band playing in front of movie theater. No. 1741, Open air theater, poster from "Going Astray."

1997, June 10

1738	A565	3b multicolored	.25	.20
1739	A565	3b multicolored	.25	.20
1740	A565	5b multicolored	.55	.40
1741	A565	7b multicolored	.55	.40
		Nos. 1738-1741 (4)	1.60	1.20

Faculty of Medicine, Chulalongkorn University, 50th Anniv. — A566

King Rama VIII, building, operating room.

1997, June 11

1742	A566	2b multicolored	.25	.20
		Complete booklet, 5 #1742	1.40	

King Bhumibol Adulyadej Type of 1996
Perf. 14½x14
1997, July 19 Litho. Wmk. 340

1743	A550	6b grn & gray vio	.40	.30
1744	A550	9b dk bl & brn org	.60	.45

Litho. & Engr.
Wmk. 329
Perf. 13½x13

1745	A550	100b lem & dk bl grn	6.25	4.75
		Nos. 1743-1745 (3)	7.25	5.50

Thai-Russian Diplomatic Relations, Cent. — A567

Design: Peterhof Palace, King Chulalongkorn (King Rama V).

1997, July 3 Litho. Perf. 14½x14

1746	A567	2b multicolored	.25	.20
		Complete booklet, 5 #1746	1.00	

Asalhapuja Day — A568

3b, Mahosathajataka (scene with man on elephant). 4b, Bhuridattajataka (scene with two men, large snake). 6b, Candakumarajataka (scene with pot of fire, three men on knees, man in sky, Buddha). 7b, Naradajataka (scene with people praising human figure with four arms hovering above roof).

Perf. 11½ Syncopated
1997, July 19 Photo. Unwmk.
Granite Paper

1747	A568	3b multicolored	.25	.20
a.		Souvenir sheet of 1	.50	
b		As "a," inscribed in margin	7.50	
1748	A568	4b multicolored	.30	.20
a.		Souvenir sheet of 1	.60	
b		As "a," inscribed in margin	7.50	
1749	A568	6b multicolored	.50	.25
a.		Souvenir sheet of 1	.90	
b		As "a," inscribed in margin	7.50	
1750	A568	7b multicolored	.55	.35
a.		Souvenir sheet of 1	1.00	
b.		As "a," #1747-1750	1.90	
c		As "a," inscribed in margin	7.50	6.00
		Nos. 1747-1750 (4)	1.60	1.00

#1747a sold for 6b; #1748a for 8b; #1749a for 10b; #1750a for 12b; #1750b for 30b. Sheet margins of lack value inscriptions, but contain Shanghai '97 exhibition emblem (#1747b, 1748b), Chinese insription; Bangkok '97 exhibition emblem (#1749b, 1750c).

1997 Thailand Philatelic Exhibition — A569

Houses from: 2b, Northern region. 5b, Central region. 6b, Northeastern region. 9b, Southern region.

Wmk. 329
1997, Aug. 2 Litho. Perf. 13½

1751	A569	2b multicolored	.20	.20
		Complete booklet, 5 #1751	1.00	
1752	A569	5b multicolored	.30	.25
1753	A569	6b multicolored	.40	.30
1754	A569	9b multicolored	.55	.45
a.		Souvenir sheet, #1751-1754	2.00	
		Nos. 1751-1754 (4)	1.45	1.20

No. 1754a sold for 32b.
No. 1754a exists imperf, sold with an exhibition book. Value, $15.

Natl. Communications Day — A570

Perf. 14x14½
1997, Aug. 4 Wmk. 340

1755	A570	2b multicolored	.25	.20
		Complete booklet, 5 #1755	1.25	

Greeting Stamps — A570a

Lotus flowers: No. 1755A, Nymphaea capensis. No. 1755B, Nymphaea stellata.

Perf. 14x14½
1997, Aug. 4 Wmk. 387
Booklet Stamps

1755A	A570a	(2b) multicolored	1.50	1.50
1755B	A570a	(2b) multicolored	1.50	1.50
c.		Bklt. pane, 5 ea #1755A-1755B + 4 labels	15.00	
		Complete bklt., #1755Bc	15.00	

Nos. 1755A-1755B were sold only at 7-11 stores, not at post offices or philatelic agencies.

King Bhumibol Adulyadej Type of 1996
Litho. & Engr.
Perf. 13½x13
1997, Aug. 8 Wmk. 329

1756	A550	25b bl grn & ol blk	1.60	1.25
1757	A550	200b lil rose & vio blk	12.50	6.25

ASEAN, 30th Anniv. — A571

Designs: No. 1758, Thi Lo Su Falls, Tak. No. 1759, Luang Chiang Dao Mountain, Chiang Mai. No. 1760, Phromthep Cape, Phuket. No. 1761, Thalu Island, Chumphon.

Perf. 14½x14
1997, Aug. 8 Wmk. 340

1758	A571	2b multicolored	.20	.20
		Complete booklet, 5 #1758	1.00	
1759	A571	2b multicolored	.20	.20
		Complete booklet, 5 #1759	1.00	
1760	A571	9b multicolored	.60	.45
1761	A571	9b multicolored	.60	.45
		Nos. 1758-1761 (4)	1.60	1.30

Dinosaurs — A572

Designs: 2b, Phuwiangosaurus sirindhornae. 3b, Siamotyrannus isanensis. 6b, Siamosaurus suteethorni. 9b, Psittacosaurus sattayaraki.

Perf. 13½x13 Syncopated
1997, Aug. 28 Photo. Unwmk.

1762	A572	2b multicolored	.20	.20
		Complete booklet, 5 #1762	1.00	
1763	A572	3b multicolored	.20	.20
1764	A572	6b multicolored	.50	.25
1765	A572	9b multicolored	.85	.35
a.		Souvenir sheet, #1762-1765	2.25	
		Nos. 1762-1765 (4)	1.75	1.00

No. 1765a sold for 30b.

King Chulalongkorn's Visit to Switzerland, Cent. — A573

Perf. 14x14½
1997, Sept. 12 Litho. Wmk. 340

1766	A573	2b multicolored	.25	.20
		Complete booklet, 5 #1766	1.00	

Intl. Letter Writing Week — A574

Winning drawings: No. 1767, Tricycle, combining rickshaw and tricycle. No. 1768, Tricycle with side seat. No. 1769, Motor tricycle. No. 1770. Motor tricycle with light on roof.

Perf. 11½x12
1997, Oct. 5 Photo. Unwmk.
Granite Paper

1767	A574	3b multicolored	.20	.20
1768	A574	3b multicolored	.20	.20
1769	A574	9b multicolored	.65	.30
1770	A574	9b multicolored	.65	.30
a.		Souvenir sheet, #1767-1770	2.25	
		Nos. 1767-1770 (4)	1.70	1.00

No. 1770a sold for 30b.

Shells of Thailand and Singapore A575

Designs: No. 1771, Drupa morum. No. 1772, Nerita chamaelon. No. 1773, Littoraria melanostoma. No. 1774, Cryptospira elgans.

1997, Oct. 9 Litho. Perf. 11½
Granite Paper

1771	A575	2b multicolored	.20	.20
		Complete booklet, 5 #1771	1.00	
1772	A575	2b multicolored	.20	.20
		Complete booklet, 5 #1772	1.00	
1773	A575	9b multicolored	.60	.30
1774	A575	9b multicolored	.60	.30
a.		Souvenir sheet, #1771-1774	2.25	
		Nos. 1771-1774 (4)	1.60	1.00

No. 1774a sold for 30b. See Singapore Nos. 825-828A.

Chalerm Prakiat Energy Conserving Building — A576

Perf. 14½x14
1997, Nov. 10 Litho. Wmk. 340

1775	A576	2b multicolored	.25	.20
		Complete booklet, 5 #1775	1.25	

Christening of Suphannahong Royal
Barge, 86th Anniv. — A577

Illustration reduced.

Perf. 11½
1997, Nov. 13   Photo.   Unwmk.
Granite Paper
1776	A577	9b multicolored	.75	.40
a.		Souvenir sheet of 1	1.50	
b.		As "a," ovptd. in margin	6.00	
c.		As "a," ovptd. in margin	20.00	

#1776a, 1776b, 1776c sold for 20b.
The sheet margin of #1776b is ovptd in gold
with Thai and Chinese inscriptions for Bang-
kok/China 98. Issued 10/16/98.
No. 1776c overprinted in margin with World
Stamp Expo 2000 emblem in gold. Issued
7/7/00.

New Year
1998 — A578

Flowers: No. 1777, Cassia alata. No. 1778,
Strophanthus caudatus. No. 1779, Clina-
canthus nutans. No. 1780, Acanthus ilicifolius.

1997, Nov. 15   Litho.   Perf. 13½x13
Granite Paper
1777	A578	2b multicolored	.20	.20
1778	A578	2b multicolored	.20	.20
1779	A578	2b multicolored	.20	.20
1780	A578	2b multicolored	.20	.20
a.		Souvenir sheet, #1777-1780	1.00	
b.		As "a," with added inscription	1.25	
		Nos. 1777-1780 (4)	.80	.80

No. 1780a sold for 15b. No. 1780b contains
Indepex '97 exhibition emblem, but no value
inscription in sheet margin.

King Bhumibol Adulyadej's 70th
Birthday — A579

#1781, Playing saxophone. #1782, Painting
picture. #1783, Building sailboat. #1784,
Wearing gold medal, sailboats. 6b, Taking
photograph. 7b, Writing book. 9b, Working at
computer.

1997, Dec. 5   Photo.   Perf. 11½
Granite Paper
1781	A579	2b multicolored	.20	.20
1782	A579	2b multicolored	.20	.20
1783	A579	2b multicolored	.20	.20
1784	A579	2b multicolored	.20	.20
1785	A579	6b multicolored	.25	.20
1786	A579	7b multicolored	.30	.25
1787	A579	9b multicolored	.40	.30
		Nos. 1781-1787 (7)	1.75	1.55

A580

A581

Winners in Yuvabadhana Foundation,
"Sports Develop Mind and Body" drawing
competition: No. 1788, Children in wheelchair
race. No. 1789, Flying kites. No. 1790, Gymnastics. No. 1791, Windsurfing.

Perf. 14x14½
1998, Jan. 10   Litho.   Wmk. 340
1788	A580	2b multicolored	.20	.20
		Complete booklet, 5 #1788	.45	
1789	A580	2b multicolored	.20	.20
		Complete booklet, 5 #1789	.45	
1790	A580	2b multicolored	.20	.20
		Complete booklet, 5 #1790	.45	
1791	A580	2b multicolored	.20	.20
a.		Complete booklet, 5 #1791	.45	
		Nos. 1788-1791 (4)	.80	.80

Natl. Childrens' Day.

1998, Jan. 17   Unwmk.
Granite Paper
1792	A581	2b multicolored	.25	.20
		Complete booklet, 5 #1792	.60	

20th Asia Pacific Dental Congress.

A582

A583

1998, Feb. 3   Wmk. 340
1793	A582	2b multicolored	.25	.20

Veteran's Day, 50th anniv.

King Bhumibol Adulyadej Type of 1996
1998, Feb. 25   Photo.   Perf. 11½x12
Granite Paper
1794	A550	50s dk ol & lt ol	.50	.20

Litho. & Engr.
Wmk. 329
Perf. 13½x13
1795	A550	50b dp vio & dk grn	2.50	1.90

Perf. 14x14½
1998, Mar. 27   Litho.   Wmk. 340
1796	A583	2b Queen Sirikit	.25	.20
		Complete booklet, 5 #1796	.65	

1998 Thai Red Cross Fair.

Heritage Conservation Day Type of
1993

Paintings of Phanomrung Historical Park:
3b, Main Tower. 4b, Minor Tower. 6b, Scripture
Repository. 7b, Lintel depicting Vishnu sleeping in ocean, doorway of Main Tower.

Perf. 14½x14
1998, Apr. 2   Litho.   Wmk. 340
1797	A477	3b multicolored	.20	.20
1798	A477	4b multicolored	.20	.20
1799	A477	6b multicolored	.40	.25
1800	A477	7b multicolored	.45	.30
a.		Souvenir sheet, #1797-1800	1.75	

No. 1800a sold for 27b.

Songkran Day Type of 1991
1998-2002   Perf. 14x14½
1801	A425	2b Demon on tiger's back, zodiac	.25	.20
a.		Complete booklet, 5 #1801	.60	
b.		Souvenir sheet of 1	1.00	
c.		As "a," inscribed in margin	5.00	
c.		Unwmkd., granite paper	.20	.20

Issued: Nos. 1801-1801b, 4/13/98. No.
1801c, 4/13/02. No. 1801c issued only in No.
2017b.
No. 1801a sold for 8b and exists imperf.
Sheet margin of No. 1801b contains flags of
Thailand and China (PRC), Thai and Chinese
inscriptions, no value inscription, and exists
imperf.
No. 1801b sold for 8b and was issued
10/16/98.

Wild
Cats
A584

Paintings: 2b, Felis viverrina. 4b, Panthera
tigris. 6b, Panthera pardus. 8b, Felis chaus.

1998, Apr. 13   Perf. 14½x14
1802	A584	2b multicolored	.25	.20
		Complete booklet, 5 #1802	.60	
1803	A584	4b multicolored	.30	.20
1804	A584	6b multicolored	.50	.35
1805	A584	8b multicolored	.60	.45
a.		Souvenir sheet, #1802-1805	2.25	
		Nos. 1802-1805 (4)	1.65	1.20

No. 1805a sold for 30b.

AEROTHAI (Aeronautical Radio of
Thailand, Ltd.), 50th Anniv. — A585

1998, Apr. 15
1806	A585	2b multicolored	.25	.20
		Complete booklet, 5 #1806	.60	

Visakhapuja Day — A586

Paintings of the "Ten Jataka Stories:" 3b,
Riding horse above buildings, Vidhurajataka.
4b, In chariot, Vessantarajataka. 6b, Two
figures seated before larger figure, Vessantarajataka. 7b, Figures in front of building,
Vessantarajataka.

1998, May 10   Perf. 13½
1807	A586	3b multicolored	.20	.20
1808	A586	4b multicolored	.30	.25
1809	A586	6b multicolored	.50	.35
1810	A586	7b multicolored	.60	.40
a.		Souvenir sheet, #1807-1810	2.25	
		Nos. 1807-1810 (4)	1.60	1.20

No. 1810a sold for 30b.

Adm. Abhakara Kiartiwongse (1880-
1923), Father of Royal Thai
Navy — A587

1998, May 19   Perf. 14½x14
1811	A587	2b multicolored	.25	.20
		Complete booklet, 5 #1811	.60	

Educational Development — A588

Perf. 14½x14
1998, June 15   Litho.   Wmk. 340
1812	A588	2b multicolored	.25	.20
		Complete booklet, 5 #1812	.60	

King Chulalongkorn's 1st State Visit to
Europe, Cent. — A589

Illustration reduced.

Unwmk.
1998, July 1   Litho.   Perf. 13
Granite Paper
1813	A589	6b multicolored	.35	.25

Litho. & Embossed
1814	A589	20b multicolored	1.40	.90

Intl.
Year
of the
Ocean
A590

2b, Orchaella brevirostris. 3b, Tursiops truncatus. 6b, Physeter catodon. 9b, Dugong
dugon.

1998, July 19   Litho.   Perf. 14½x14
Granite Paper
1815	A590	2b multicolored	.20	.20
		Complete booklet, 5 #1815	.50	
1816	A590	3b multicolored	.20	.20
1817	A590	6b multicolored	.30	.30
1818	A590	9b multicolored	.45	.45
a.		Souvenir sheet, #1815-1818	2.25	
		Nos. 1815-1818 (4)	1.15	1.15

No. 1818a sold for 30b.

King Bhumibol Adulyadej Type of 1996
1998   Photo.   Unwmk.   Perf. 11½x12
Granite Paper
1819	A550	2b carmine	.20	.20
1820	A550	9b dark bl & brn org	.60	.45

Irrigation Engineering in Thailand, 60th
Anniv. — A591

Perf. 14½x14
1998, Aug. 1   Litho.   Unwmk.
Granite Paper
1821 A591 2b multicolored   .25 .20
  Complete booklet, 5 #1821   .60

Natl. Communications Day — A592

1998, Aug. 4
Granite Paper
1822 A592 2b multicolored   .25 .20
  Complete booklet, 5 #1822   .60

School of Political Science, Chulalongkorn University, 50th Anniv. — A593

1998, Aug. 19
Granite Paper
1823 A593 2b multicolored   .25 .20
  Complete booklet, 5 #1823   .60

Sukhothai Thammathirat Open University, Award for Excellence — A594

1998, Sept. 5   Litho.   Perf. 14½x14
Granite Paper
1824 A594 2b multicolored   .25 .20
  Complete booklet, 5 #1824   .60

Amazing Thailand, 1998-99, Thai Arts and Culture A595

1998, Sept. 15   Perf. 13½
Granite Paper
1825 A595 3b With bow & arrow   .20 .20
1826 A595 3b Combat   .20 .20
1827 A595 7b Seizing opponent   .45 .25
1828 A595 7b Sky hovering   .45 .25
  Nos. 1825-1828 (4)   1.30 .90

Chinese Stone Statues — A596

Warriors holding: No. 1829, Staff with loop. No. 1830, Spear with slightly curved blade.

No. 1831, Mace. No. 1832, Spear with jagged blade.

1998, Sept. 15   Perf. 14x14½
Granite Paper
1829 A596 2b multicolored   .20 .20
  Complete booklet, 5 #1829   .50
1830 A596 2b multicolored   .20 .20
  Complete booklet, 5 #1830   .50
1831 A596 10b multicolored   .50 .40
1832 A596 10b multicolored   .50 .40
  a. Souvenir sheet, #1829-1832, perf 13¼   2.50
  b. As "a," with added marginal inscription 11.00
  Nos. 1829-1832 (4)   1.40 1.20

China 1999 World Philatelic Exhibition (#1832b). #1832a-1832b sold for 35b. #1832 is perf 13¼ and was issued 8/21/99.

Intl. Letter Writing Week — A597

Himavanta mythical animals created by ancient Thai artists: #1836, Kraisara Rajasiha, 3 king lions, white body, golden collars. #1837, Gajasiha, 2 tusked lions. #1838, Kesara Singha, 2 hoofed lions. #1839, Singha, 3 gray lions.

Perf. 11½
1998, Oct. 3   Photo.   Unwmk.
Granite Paper
1836 A597 2b multicolored   .20 .20
  Complete booklet, 5 #1836   .55
1837 A597 2b multicolored   .20 .20
  Complete booklet, 5 #1837   .55
1838 A597 12b multicolored   .65 .50
1839 A597 12b multicolored   .65 .50
  a. Souvenir sheet, #1836-1839   2.75
  Nos. 1836-1839 (4)   1.70 1.40

No. 1839a sold for 40b.

Thai Presidency of the Intl. Assoc. of Lions Clubs — A598

1998, Oct. 8   Litho.   Perf. 14½x14
Granite Paper
1840 A598 2b multicolored   .25 .20
  Complete booklet, 5 #1840   .60

New Year 1999 — A599

Flowers: No. 1841, Barleria lupulina. No. 1842, Gloriosa superba. No. 1843, Asclepias curassavica. No. 1844, Sesamum indicum.

Perf. 14½x14
1998, Nov. 15   Photo.   Unwmk.
Granite Paper
1841 A599 2b multicolored   .25 .20
1842 A599 2b multicolored   .25 .20
1843 A599 2b multicolored   .25 .20
1844 A599 2b multicolored   .25 .20
  a. Souvenir sheet, #1841-1844   1.25
  Nos. 1841-1844 (4)   1.00 .80

No. 1844a sold for 15b.

Knight Grand Cross, Most Admirable Order of the Direkgunabhorn — A600

Perf. 14x14½
1998, Dec. 5   Litho.   Unwmk.
Granite Paper
1845 15b shown   .95 .70
1846 15b Decoration   .95 .70
  a. A600 Pair, #1845-1846   1.90 1.60

Children's Day — A601

Paintings from competition, "Sports develop body and mind:" No. 1847, Sepak Takraw (game of kicking ball over net). No. 1848, Swimming. No. 1849, Volleyball. No. 1850, Equestrian sports.

Perf. 14½x14
1999, Jan. 9   Litho.   Unwmk.
Granite Paper
1847 A601 2b multicolored   .20 .20
  Complete booklet, 5 #1847   .55
1848 A601 2b multicolored   .20 .20
  Complete booklet, 5 #1848   .55
1849 A601 2b multicolored   .20 .20
  Complete booklet, 5 #1849   .55
1850 A601 2b multicolored   .20 .20
  Complete booklet, 5 #1850   .55
  Nos. 1847-1850 (4)   .80 .80

Asian and Pacific Decade of Disabled Persons — A602

1999, Jan. 10
Granite Paper
1851 A602 2b multicolored   .25 .20
  a. Complete booklet, 5 #1851   .60

Thai Rice Production — A603

#1852, Planting rice. #1853, Harvesting rice by hand. #1854, Harvesting rice with machinery. #1855, Rice in field, bowl of rice.

1999, Feb. 25   Litho.   Perf. 14½x14
Granite Paper
1852 A603 6b multicolored   .35 .25
1853 A603 6b multicolored   .35 .25
1854 A603 12b multicolored   .65 .50
1855 A603 12b multicolored   .65 .50
  a. Souvenir sheet, #1852-1855   3.00
  Nos. 1852-1855 (4)   2.00 1.50

No. 1855a sold for 45b.

Maghapuja Day (Buddhist Holiday) — A604

Designs: 3b, Birth of Mahajanaka. 6b, Mani Mekkhala carrying Mahajanaka to Mithila City. 9b, Two mango trees. 15b, Mahajanaka founding an educational institution.

1999, Mar. 1   Litho.   Perf. 13½
Granite Paper
1856 A604 3b multicolored   .30 .25
1857 A604 6b multicolored   .35 .25
1858 A604 9b multicolored   .55 .40
1859 A604 15b multicolored   .80 .60
  a. Souvenir sheet, #1856-1859   3.00
  Nos. 1856-1859 (4)   2.00 1.50

No. 1859a sold for 45b.

Somdetch Phra Sri Savarindira Baromma Raja Devi Phra Phan Vassa Ayika Chao, Queen Grandmother A605

Perf. 14x14½
1999, Mar. 30   Litho.   Wmk. 340
1860 A605 2b multicolored   .25 .20
  Complete booklet, 5 #1860   .60

1999 Red Cross Fair.

Bangkok 2000 World Youth Stamp Expo, 13th Asian Intl. Stamp Expo — A606

Thai children's games: No. 1861, Kite flying. No. 1862, Wheel rolling. No. 1863, Catching last one in line (children going under arms). No. 1864, Snatching baby from mother snake.

Perf. 14½x14
1999, Mar. 30   Unwmk.
Granite Paper
1861 A606 2b multicolored   .20 .20
1862 A606 2b multicolored   .20 .20
1863 A606 15b multicolored   .80 .60
1864 A606 15b multicolored   .80 .60
  a. Souvenir sheet, #1861-1864, perf. 13½   3.00
  Nos. 1861-1864 (4)   2.00 1.60

No. 1864a sold for 45b.

Heritage Conservation Day — A607

Various Thai silk designs for "Mudmee" textiles.

1999, Apr. 2   *Perf. 14x14½*
Granite Paper
1865 A607   2b bl grn & multi   .20   .20
      Complete booklet, 5 #1865   .55
1866 A607   4b red & multi   .20   .20
1867 A607   12b vermilion & multi   .75   .55
1868 A607   15b black & multi   1.00   .70
   a. Souvenir sheet, #1865-1868   3.00
      Nos. 1865-1868 (4)   2.15 1.65

No. 1868a sold for 45b.

Songkran Day Type of 1991
1999, Apr. 13
Granite Paper
1869 A425   2b Woman on rabbit's
             back, zodiac   .20   .20
      Complete booklet, 5 #1869   .55
   a. Souvenir sheet of 1   1.00
   b. As "a," with added marginal in-
      scription   5.00

China 1999 World Philatelic Exhibition
(#1869b). #1869a-1869b sold for 8b and exist
imperf.
Issued: #1869b, 8/21.

Consumer Protection Years, 1998-
99 — A608

1999, Apr. 30   *Perf. 14½x14*
Granite Paper
1870 A608   2b multicolored   .25   .20
      Complete booklet, 5 #1870   .60

King Bhumibol Adulyadej's 72nd
Birthday — A609

Royal palaces: No. 1871, Chitralada Villa,
Dusit Palace, Bangkok, tree branch at UL. No.
1872, Phu Phing Ratchaniwet Palace, circular
drive, white fence. No. 1873, Phu Phan Ratchaniwet Palace, adjoining buildings, light posts.
No. 1874, Thaksin Ratchaniwet Palace, four
trees reaching to second story windows.
Illustration reduced.

1999, May 5   **Photo.**   *Perf. 11½*
Granite Paper
1871 A609   6b multicolored   .45   .30
1872 A609   6b multicolored   .45   .30
1873 A609   6b multicolored   .45   .30
1874 A609   6b multicolored   .45   .30
   a. Souvenir sheet, #1871-1874   3.25
      Nos. 1871-1874 (4)   1.80 1.20

No. 1874a sold for 40b.

Political Science
Dept.,
Thammasat
University, 50th
Anniv. — A610

1999, June 14 Litho.   Perf. 14x14½
1875 A610   3b multicolored   .25   .20

**King Bhumibol Adulyadej Type of
1996**
Litho. & Engr.
1999   **Wmk. 329**   *Perf. 13*
1876 A550   12b bl grn & bl   .60   .40
1877 A550   15b yel brn & grn   .80   .60
1878 A550   30b pink & brown   1.60 1.40

Size: 25x30mm
          Perf. 12¾x13¼
1879 A550 500b org & claret   30.00 19.00
      Nos. 1876-1879 (4)   33.00 21.40

Issued: 12b, 15b, 30b, 7/1; 500b, 9/10.

UPU,
125th
Anniv.
A611

Designs: 2b, Floating Vessel of Light Festival. 15b, Buddhist Candle Festival, Ubon
Ratchathani.

1999, July 1 Litho.   Perf. 14½x14
Granite Paper
1880 A611   2b multicolored   .20   .20
      Complete booklet, 5 #1880   .55
1881 A611   15b multicolored   .80   .60

Customs Dept., 125th Anniv. — A612

1999, July 3
1882 A612   6b multicolored   .30   .20

Natl. Communications Day — A613

1999, Aug. 4   Litho.   Perf. 14½x14
Granite Paper
1883 A613   4b multicolored   .25   .20

Thaipex '99 — A614

1999, Aug. 4   Granite Paper
Color of Rabbits
1884 A614   6b black & white   .30   .20
1885 A614   6b golden brown,
             brown   .30   .20
1886 A614   12b white   .60   .40
1887 A614   12b gray   .60   .40
   a. Souvenir sheet, #1884-1887,
      perf. 13½   3.50
      Nos. 1884-1887 (4)   1.80 1.20

No. 1887a sold for 50b and exists imperf.
Value, $15.

Bangkok 2000 Stamp
Exhibition — A615

Scenes from Thai folk tales and literature:
No. 1888, Boy on dragon-like horse. No. 1889,
Rishi transforming tiger cub and calf into
humans. No. 1890, Boy exiting conch shell.
No. 1891, Children playing with kitchenware.

1999, Aug. 4   Perf. 14½x14
Granite Paper
1888 A615   2b multicolored   .20   .20
1889 A615   2b multicolored   .20   .20
1890 A615   15b multicolored   .80   .55
1891 A615   15b multicolored   .80   .55
   a. Souvenir sheet, #1888-1891,
      perf. 13½   3.25
      Nos. 1888-1891 (4)   2.00 1.50

No. 1891a sold for 45b.

King
Bhumibol
Adulyadej's
72nd Birthday
A616

King: No. 1892, On father's knee. No. 1893,
With mother, sister and brother. No. 1894,
With brother, in suits. No. 1895, With brother,
in military uniforms. No. 1896, With wife on
wedding day. No. 1897, At coronation ceremony. No. 1898, As Buddhist monk. No. 1899,
With Queen, Prince and Princesses. No.
1900, Wearing royal robe.

1999, Sept. 10   Photo.   Perf. 11¾
Granite Paper
1892 A616   3b multicolored   .20   .20
1893 A616   3b multicolored   .20   .20
1894 A616   3b multicolored   .20   .20
1895 A616   6b multicolored   .30   .20
1896 A616   6b multicolored   .30   .20
1897 A616   6b multicolored   .30   .20
1898 A616   12b multicolored   .60   .40
1899 A616   12b multicolored   .60   .40
1900 A616   12b multicolored   .60   .40
   a. Souvenir sheet, #1892-1900   7.00
      Nos. 1892-1900 (9)   3.30 2.40

No. 1900a sold for 90b.

Intl. Year of Older Persons — A617

1999, Oct. 1   Litho.   Perf. 14½x14
Granite Paper
1901 A617   2b multi   .25   .20
      Complete booklet, 5 #1901   1.25

Bauhinia
Variegata — A618

Intl. Letter Writing Week: No. 1903, Bombax
ceiba. No. 1904, Radermachera ignea (orange
flowers). No. 1905, Bretschneidera sinensis
(pink flowers).

1999, Oct. 2   Perf. 14x14½
Granite Paper
1902 A618   2b shown   .20   .20
      Complete booklet, 5 #1902   .55
1903 A618   2b multi   .20   .20
      Complete booklet, 5 #1903   .55
1904 A618   12b multi   .65   .45
1905 A618   12b multi   .65   .45
   a. Souvenir sheet, #1902-1905,
      perf. 13¼   2.75
      Nos. 1902-1905 (4)   1.70 1.30

No. 1905a sold for 35b.

King Bhumibol Adulyadej's 72nd
Birthday — A619

King: #1906, And vehicle. #1907, And Buddhist monks. #1908, And Queen. #1909, And
soldiers. #1910, And crowd. #1911, And disabled boy. #1912, Wearing green army uniform. #1913, In white suit with camera. #1914,
With crowd waving flags.

1999, Oct. 21   Photo.   Perf. 14½
Granite Paper
1906 A619   3b multi   .20   .20
1907 A619   3b multi   .20   .20
1908 A619   3b multi   .20   .20
1909 A619   6b multi   .30   .20
1910 A619   6b multi   .30   .20
1911 A619   6b multi   .30   .20
1912 A619   12b multi   .65   .45
1913 A619   12b multi   .65   .45
1914 A619   12b multi   .65   .45
   a. Souvenir sheet, #1906-1914   6.50
      Nos. 1906-1914 (9)   3.45 2.55

No. 1914a sold for 90b. Numbers have been
reserved for additional stamps in this set.

Design
A39 — A620

**Litho. & Embossed with Foil
Application**
1999, Dec. 5   Wmk. 387   Perf. 13¼
1915 A620   100b blue & bronze   7.00 3.50
1916 A620   100b blue & silver   7.00 3.50
1917 A620   100b blue & gold   7.00 3.50
   a. Souvenir sheet, #1915-1917   25.00
      Nos. 1915-1917 (3)   21.00 10.50

King Bhumibol Adulyadej's 72nd birthday.
No. 1917a sold for 350b.

New Year
2000 — A621

Medicinal plants: No. 1918, Thunbergia
laurifolia. No. 1919, Gmelina arborea. No.
1920, Prunus cerasoides. No. 1921, Fagraea
fragrans.

          Perf. 14½x14¼
1999, Nov. 15   Litho.
Granite Paper
1918 A621   2b multi   .20   .20
1919 A621   2b multi   .20   .20
1920 A621   2b multi   .20   .20
   a. Souv. sheet, 5 ea #1918-1920
      + 10 labels   5.00
1921 A621   2b multi   .20   .20
   a. Souvenir sheet, #1918-1921   1.00   .70
      Nos. 1918-1921 (4)   .80   .80

No. 1921a sold for 15b.
No. 1920a was issued 3/25/00 and sold for
60b. For an additional fee the blank labels
could be personalized with photos taken at a
booth not operated by the Thailand postal
authorities at the Bangkok 2000 Stamp
Exhibition.

Investiture of Crown Prince Vajiralongkorn, 27th Anniv. — A622

1999, Dec. 28   *Perf. 14x14½*
Granite Paper
1922 A622 3b multi   .60 .20

Lake of Lilies, Thale Noi — A623

Kulap Khao Flowers, Doi Chang Dao — A624

Krachieo Flowers, Pa Hin Ngam — A625

Bua Tong Flowers, Doi Mae Ukor — A626

Illustrations reduced.

Perf. 14½x14¼
2000   Litho.   Unwmk.
Granite Paper
1923 A623   Sheet of 12, #a-l   1.75 1.75
a.-l.   3b Any single   .20 .20
1924 A624   Sheet of 12, #a-l   1.75 1.75
a.-l.   3b Any single   .20 .20
1925 A625   Sheet of 12, #a-l   1.75 1.75
a.-l.   3b Any single   .20 .20
1926 A625   Sheet of 12, #a-l   1.75 1.75
a.-l.   3b Any single   .20 .20
    Nos. 1923-1926 (4)   7.00 7.00

Issued: #1923, 1/1; #1924, 2/25; #1925, 7/16. #1926, 11/15.

Bees — A627

#1927, Apis andreniformis. #1928, Apis florea. #1929, Apis cerana. #1930, Apis dorsata.

2000, Mar. 19   Photo.   *Perf. 11¾*
Granite Paper
1927-1930 A627 3b Set of 4   .90 .65
Souvenir Sheets of 1
1927a-1930a   Set of 4   2.25

Nos. 1927a-1930a do not have white margin on stamps and sold for 8b each.

Bangkok 2000 Stamp Exhibition — A628

Ceremonies: #1931, 2b, 1st month blessing (family & baby). #1932, 2b, Tonsure. #1933, 15b, Teacher respect (teacher, 3 children). #1934, 15b, Novice ordination.

2000, Mar. 25   Litho.   *Perf. 14½x14*
Granite Paper
1931-1934 A628   Set of 4   2.25 2.00
1934a   Souvenir sheet, #1931-1934,
   perf. 13½x14   4.00

No. 1934a sold for 45b. Exists imperf, value $15.

Thai Red Cross Fair — A629

2000, Mar. 30   *Perf. 14½x14*
Granite Paper
1935 A629 3b multi   .30 .20

Thai Heritage Conservation — A630

Chok cloths from: 3b, Hat Seio. 6b, Mae Chaem. 8b, Ban Rai. 12b, Khu Bua.

2000, Apr. 2   Wmk. 387   *Perf. 13¼*
1936-1939 A630   Set of 4   2.00 1.40
1939a   Souvenir sheet, #1936-1939   2.75

No. 1939a sold for 40b.

Songkran Day Type of 1991
Perf. 14x14½
2000, Apr. 13   Litho.   Unwmk.
Granite Paper
1940 A425 2b Angel on serpent   .20 .20
   Booklet, 5 #1940   .50
a.   Souvenir sheet of 1   .75

No. 1940a sold for 8b and exists imperf.

Asalhapuja Day — A632

2000, July 16   Litho.   *Perf. 14x14½*
Granite Paper
1942 A632 3b multi   .25 .20

Crown Prince Maha Vajiralongkorn, 48th Birthday — A633

2000, July 28   *Perf. 14½x14*
Granite Paper
1943 A633 2b multi   .25 .20
   Booklet, 5 #1943   .60
a.   Souvenir sheet of 1, perf. 13¼   .60

No. 1943a sold for 8b.

Natl. Communications Day — A634

2000, Aug. 4
Granite Paper
1944 A634 3b multi   .25 .20

A635

Intl. Letter Writing Week — A636

Various tea sets.

Perf. 14½x14
2000, Oct. 7   Litho.   Unwmk.
Granite Paper
1945 A635   6b shown   .30 .20
1946 A635   6b multi, diff.   .30 .20
1947 A636   12b shown   .70 .50
1948 A636   12b multi, diff.   .70 .50
a.   Souvenir sheet, #1945-1948,
   perf. 13¼   3.25
   Nos. 1945-1948 (4)   2.00 1.40

No. 1948a sold for 45b.

Princess Srinagarindra, Birth Cent. — A637

2000, Oct. 21   **Granite Paper**
1949 A637 2b multi   .25 .20
   Booklet, 5 #1949   .60
a.   Souvenir sheet of 1, perf. 13¼   .75

No. 1949a sold for 8b.

Royal Barge Anantanakkharat — A638

Illustration reduced.

Perf. 13¼x14
2000, Nov. 15   Photo.   Wmk. 340
1950 A638 9b multi   .60 .50
a.   Souvenir sheet of 1   1.25

No. 1950a sold for 15b.

New Year 2001 — A639

Flowers: No. 1951, 2b, Clerodendrum philippinum. No. 1952, 2b, Capparis micracantha. No. 1953, 2b, Belamcanda chinensis. No. 1954, 2b, Memecylon caeruleum.

Perf. 14½x14¼
2000, Nov. 15   Litho.   Unwmk.
Granite Paper
1951-1954 A639   Set of 4   .65 .45
1954a   Souvenir sheet, #1951-
   1954   1.10

No. 1954a sold for 15b.

Parrots — A640

Designs: 2b, Psittacula alexandri. 5b, Psittacula eupatria. 8b, Psittinus cyanurus. 10b, Psittacula roseata.

2001, Jan. 13   *Perf. 14x14½*
Granite Paper
1955-1958 A640   Set of 4   1.75 1.25
   Booklet, 5 #1955   .60
a.   Souvenir sheet, #1955-
   1958, perf. 13¼   4.00
b.   As "a," without price
   and with show em-
   blem in margin   20.00

No. 1955a sold for 35b. No. 1955b, Hong Kong 2001 Stamp Exhibition, sold for 50b.

King Chulalongkorn and Land Deed — A641

2001, Feb. 17   **Granite Paper**
1959 A641 5b multi   .50 .20

Dept. of Lands, cent.

Marine Life — A642

Designs: a, Ray. b, Turtle. c, Jellyfish, fish. d, Lionfish. e, Black, yellow fish, coral. f, Eel. g, School of striped fish, angelfish, coral, vert. h, Pufferfish, blue fish, vert. i, Shark, fish.
Stamp sizes: Nos. 1960a-1960f, 29x24mm, Nos. 1960g-1960h, 29x48mm. No. 1960i, 58x42mm.

Perf. 13¾x14¼

2001, Mar. 15 **Photo.**
Granite Paper
1960 A642 Sheet of 9 3.00 3.00
a.-f. 3b Any single .40 .20
g.-i. 6b Any single .45 .20

Gems A643

Designs: 3b, Diamond. 4b, Green sapphire. 6b, Pearl. 12b, Blue sapphire.

2001 **Litho.** **Perf. 14½x14**
Granite Paper
1961-1964 A643 Set of 4 2.25 2.00
a. Souvenir sheet, #1961-1964, perf. 13½x14 4.00
b. As "a," ovptd. in margin in gold 10.00

Issued, Nos. 1961-1964a, 3/30; No. 1964b, 6/9.
No. 1964a sold for 35b.
No. 1964b has Belgica 2001 emblem overprint.

Red Cross A644

Perf. 14½x14
2001, Apr. 1 **Litho.** **Unwmk.**
Granite Paper
1965 A644 4b multi .60 .20

Ancient Brocades From Nakhon Si Thammarat National Museum — A645

Colors of brocade: 2b, Orange red, lilac, and gold. 3b, Green and gold. No. 1968, 10b, Orange and gold. No. 1969, 10b, Bright pink and gold.

2001, Apr. 2 **Perf. 14x14½**
Granite Paper
1966-1969 A645 Set of 4 2.00 1.50
Booklet, 5 #1966 1.50
a. Souvenir sheet, #1966-1969, perf. 13¼ 3.50

Heritage Conservation Day.
No. 1969a sold for 35b.

Songkran Day Type of 1991
Perf. 13½x13¾

2001-2002 **Wmk. 387**
1970 A425 2b Man on snake, zo-diac .60 .20
Booklet, 5 #1970 1.50
a. Souvenir sheet of 1 1.50 1.50
b. Unwmkd., granite paper, perf. 14x14½ 3.00 3.00

Issued: Nos. 1970-1970a, 4/13/01. No. 1970b, 4/13/02. No. 1970b issued only in No. 2017b.
No. 1970a sold for 8b and exists imperf.

Visakhapuja Day — A646

2001, May 7 **Unwmk.** **Perf. 14x14½**
Granite Paper
1971 A646 3b multi .50 .20

Demon Statues — A647

Designs: 2b, Maiyarap. 5b, Wirunchambang. 10b, Thotsakan. 12b, Sahatsadecha.

Perf. 14x14½
2001, June 13 **Litho.** **Unwmk.**
Granite Paper
1972-1975 A647 Set of 4 2.25 1.75
Booklet, 5 #1972 2.25
1975a Souvenir sheet, #1972-1975, perf. 13½ 3.00
No. 1975a sold for 33b.

Prince Purachartra Jayakara and Rotary Intl. Emblem — A648

2001, July 1 **Granite Paper**
1976 A648 3b multi .50 .20
Rotary Intl. in Thailand, 66th anniv.

Mushrooms — A649

Designs: 2b, Schizophyllum commune. 3b, Lentinus giganteus. 5b, Pleurotus citri-nopileatus. 10b, Pleurotus flabellatus.

2001, July 4 **Photo.** **Perf. 13¾x14**
1977-1980 A649 Set of 4 2.25 2.00
Booklet, 5 # 1977 2.00
1980a Souvenir sheet, #1977-1980, perf. 13½ 3.75
No. 1980 sold for 26b.

Insects A650

Designs: 2b, Cheirotonus parryi. 5b, Mouho-tia batesi. 6b, Cladognathus giraffa. 12b, Mormolyce phyllodes.

2001, July 4 **Wmk. 329** **Perf. 13½**
1981-1984 A650 Set of 4 2.25 1.75
Booklet, 5 #1981 2.00
a. Souvenir sheet, #1981-1984 3.75
b. As "a," with Phila Nip-pon '01 emblem in margin 3.75 —
No. 1984a sold for 34b.
No. 1984b sold for 34b, and was issued 8/1.

Natl. Communications Day — A651

Perf. 14½x14
2001, Aug. 4 **Litho.** **Unwmk.**
Granite Paper
1985 A651 4b multi .50 .20

Thaipex '01 — A652

Various domesticated fowl: 3b, 4b, 6b, 12b.

2001, Aug. 4 **Photo.** **Perf. 13¼**
Granite Paper
1986-1989 A652 Set of 4 2.25 1.75
1989a Souvenir sheet, #1986-1989 4.00 —
No. 1989 sold for 33b, also exists imperf.

Queen Suriyothai, Heroine of Thailand — A653

2001, Aug. 12 **Litho.** **Perf. 14x14¾**
Granite Paper
1990 A653 3b multi .50 .20
a. Souvenir sheet of 1, perf. 13¼ 1.60
No. 1990a sold for 10b.

Queen Sirikit's Visit to the People's Republic of China — A654

2001, Aug. 12 **Perf. 14¾x14**
Granite Paper
1991 A654 5b multi .75 .20

Butterflies — A655

Designs: 2b, Pachliopta aristolochiae goni-opeltis. 4b, Rhinopalpa polynice. 10b, Poritia erycinoides. 12b, Spindasis lohita.

Perf. 13½ Syncopated
2001, Sept. 10 **Photo.**
1992-1995 A655 Set of 4 3.00 2.25
Booklet, 5 #1992 2.25
1995a Souvenir sheet, #1992-1995 4.50 4.50
1995b As "a," with Hafnia '01 emblem in margin 16.00 16.00
No. 1995a sold for 40b.
No. 1995b issued 11/16. No. 1995b sold for 43b.

Intl. Letter Writing Week — A656

Medicinal herbs: 2b, Piper nigrum. 3b, Sola-num trilobatum. 5b, Boesenbergia rotunda. 10b, Ocimum tenuiflorum.

Perf. 14x14½
2001, Oct. 6 **Litho.** **Unwmk.**
Granite Paper
1996-1999 A656 Set of 4 2.00 1.75
Booklet, 5 #1996 2.00
1999a Souvenir sheet, #1996-1999, perf. 13½x13¼ 2.75 2.75
No. 1999a sold for 25b.

Police Cadet Academy, Cent. — A657

2001, Oct. 13 **Litho.** **Perf. 14½x14**
Granite Paper
2000 A657 5b multi .50 .20

Royal Barge Anekkachat Puchong — A658

Illustration reduced.

2001, Nov. 15 **Photo.** **Perf. 14¼**
Granite Paper
2001 A658 9b multi 1.00 .90
a. Souvenir sheet of 1 1.50 1.50
No. 2001a sold for 17b.

New Year 2002 — A659

Flowers: No. 2002, 2b, Pedicularis siamensis. No. 2003, 2b, Schoutenia glomerata. No. 2004, 2b, Gentiana crassa. No. 2005, 2b, Colquhounia coccinea.

2001, Nov. 15   Litho.   Perf. 14x14½
Granite Paper
2002-2005 A659   Set of 4   1.10 1.00
2005a   Souvenir sheet, #2002-
               2005   1.75 1.75
        No. 2005a sold for 11b.

Laying of Foundation Stone for Suvarnabhumi Airport Passenger Terminal — A660

2002, Jan. 19   Litho.   Perf. 14½x14
Granite Paper
2006 A660 3b multi   .50 .20

Rose — A661

2002, Feb. 1   Perf. 13¾
Granite Paper
2007 A661 4b multi   .75 .20

12th World Congress of Gastroenterology A662

2002, Feb. 24   Perf. 14x14½
Granite Paper
2008 A662 3b multi   .50 .20

Communications Authority of Thailand, 25th Anniv. — A663

No. 2009: a, Satellite dish, CAT Telecom Co. emblem. b, Envelope, mailbox, Thailand Post emblem.
Illustration reduced.

2002, Feb. 25   Perf. 14½x14
Granite Paper
2009 A663 3b Horiz. pair, #a-b   .75 .20
   c.   Souvenir sheet, #2009, perf.
           13¼x13½   1.00 1.00
        No. 2009c sold for 10b.

Maghapuja Day — A664

2002, Feb. 26   Perf. 14½x14
Granite Paper
2010 A664 3b multi   .50 .20

2002 Red Cross Fair A665

2002, Mar. 30   Granite Paper
2011 A665 4b multi   .50 .20

Ministry of Transport and Communications, 90th Anniv. — A666

2002, Apr. 1   Litho.   Perf. 14½x14
Granite Paper
2012 A666 3b multi   .50 .20

Heritage Conservation Day — A667

String puppets: No. 2013, 3b, Man. No. 2014, 3b, Woman. 4d, Demon. 15b, Monkey.

2002, Apr. 2   Perf. 14x14½
Granite Paper
2013-2016 A667   Set of 4   2.50 1.75
2016a   Souvenir sheet, #2013-
               2016, perf. 13¼   3.50 3.50
        No. 2016a sold for 30b.

Songkran Day Type of 1991
2002, Apr. 13   Perf. 14x14½
Granite Paper
2017 A425 2b Angel on horse,
                zodiac   .60 .20
   a.   Souvenir sheet of 1   2.00 2.00
   b.   Souvenir sheet, #1724b,
           1801c, 1869, 1940,
           1970b, 2017   3.00 3.00
   c.   As "b," with Beijing 2002
           emblem in margin and
           selling price removed 17.50 17.50
        Nos. 2017a and 2017b sold for 8b and 14b respectively. Both exist imperf.
        Issued: No. 2017c, 9/29. No. 2017c sold for 30b.

Fighting Fish A668

Designs: No. 2018, 3b, Betta imbellis. No. 2019, 3b, Betta splendens. 4b, Betta splendens, diff. 15b, Betta splendens, diff.

2002, May 15   Litho.   Perf. 14½x14
Granite Paper
2018-2021 A668   Set of 4   2.75 2.00
2021a   Souvenir sheet, #2018-
               2021, perf. 13½   4.00 4.00
2021b   As "a," with Amphilex
               2002 emblem and sell-
               ing price removed 15.00 15.00
        Issued: No. 2021b, 8/30. No. 2021a sold for 30b; No. 2021b sold for 31b.

Temples — A669

Designs: No. 2022, 3b, Wat Phra Si Rattanasatsadaram. No. 2023, 3b, Wat Phra Chetuphon Wimon Mangkhalaram. 4b, Wat Arun Ratchawararam. 12b, Wat Benchamabophit Dusit Wanaram.

2002, June 17   Perf. 14½x14
Granite Paper
2022-2025 A669   Set of 4   2.25 1.75
2025a   Souvenir sheet, #2022-
               2025, perf. 13½   2.75 2.75
2025b   As "a," with Philakorea
               2002 emblem and sell-
               ing price removed 15.00 15.00
        Issued: No. 2025b, 8/2. Nos. 2025a and 2025b each sold for 27b.

Crown Prince Maha Vajiralongkorn, 50th Birthday — A670

2002, July 28   Perf. 14x14½
Granite Paper
2026 A670 3b multi   .50 .20

Natl. Communications Day — A671

2002, Aug. 4   Granite Paper
2027 A671 4b multi   .50 .20

Thailand — Australia Diplomatic Relations, 50th Anniv. — A672

Designs: No. 2028, 3b, Nelumbo nucifera (pink flower). No. 2029, 3b, Nymphaea immutabilis (purple flower).

2002, Aug. 6   Perf. 14½x14
Granite Paper
2028-2029 A672   Set of 2   1.00 .75
2029a   Souvenir sheet, #2028-
               2029, perf. 13½   1.50 1.50
        See Australia Nos. 2072-2073. No. 2029a sold for 9b.

Queen Sirikit, 70th Birthday — A673

Designs: No. 2030, 3b, Queen and roses. No. 2031, 3b, Queen Sirikit rose. 4b, Queen Sirikit orchid. 15b, Queen Sirikit dona shrub.

2002, Aug. 12   Perf. 14½x14
Granite Paper
2030-2033 A673   Set of 4   2.25 1.60
2033a   Souvenir sheet, #2030-
               2033   3.50 3.50
        No. 2033a sold for 31b.

National Archives, 50th Anniv. — A674

2002, Aug. 18   Perf. 14½x14
2034 A674 3b multi   .50 .20

Thai Bank Notes, Cent. A675

2002, Sept. 7   Engr.   Perf. 13½
Granite Paper
2035 A675 5b org & brown   .50 .20
   a.   Souvenir sheet of 1   1.25 1.25
        No. 2035a sold for 11b.

Vimanmek Mansion Art Objects — A676

Designs: No. 2036, 3b, Round, lidded betel nut box. No. 2037, 3b, Bowl. 4b, Bowl, diff. 12b, Rectangular betel nut box.

2002, Sept. 7   Litho.   Perf. 14½x14
Granite Paper
2036-2039 A676   Set of 4   2.25 1.60
2039a   Souvenir sheet, #2036-
               2039, perf. 13½   3.25 3.25
        No. 2039a sold for 26b.

Royal Palaces A677

Designs: No. 2040, 4b, Thailand. No. 2041, 4b, Sweden.

Perf. 12½x13½ Syncopated
2002, Oct. 5   Litho. & Engr.
2040-2041 A677   Set of 2   .75 .60
        See Sweden No. 2445.

Intl. Letter Writing Day A678

Designs: No. 2042, 3b, Animal-shaped coconut grater. No. 2043, 3b, Strainer. 4b, Coconut shell ladle. 15b, Earthenware stove and pot.

2002, Oct. 5   Litho.   Perf. 14½x14
Granite Paper
2042-2045 A678   Set of 4   2.75 2.00
2045a   Souvenir sheet, #2042-
               2045, perf. 13½   3.25 3.25
        No. 2045a sold for 31b.

Bangkok 2003 World Philatelic Exhibition — A679

Foods from: No. 2046, 3b, Central Thailand (red tablecloth). No. 2047, 3b, Southern Thailand (brown and yellow tablecloth). 4b, Northeastern Thailand. 15b, Northern Thailand.

2002, Oct. 5   *Perf. 14½x14*
2046-2049	A679	Set of 4	2.25	1.60
2049a		Souvenir sheet, #2046-2049, perf. 13½	3.50	3.50

No. 2049a sold for 30b.

New Year 2003 — A680

Flowers: No. 2050, 3b, Guaiacum officinale. No. 2051, 3b, Nyctanthes arbor-tristis. No. 2052, 3b, Barleria cristata. No. 2053, 3b, Thevetia peruviana.

Perf. 14½x14¼
2002, Nov. 15   **Litho.**
Granite Paper
2050-2053	A680	Set of 4	1.50	1.10
2053a		Souvenir sheet, #2050-2053	2.25	2.25

No. 2053a sold for 16b.

20th World Scout Jamboree — A681

Designs: 3b, Scouts. 12b, Jamboree site.

2002, Dec. 28   *Perf. 14½x14*
Granite Paper
2054-2055	A681	Set of 2	1.40	1.25

New Year 2003 (Year of the Goat) — A682

2003, Jan. 1   *Perf. 13*
Granite Paper
2056	A682	3b multi	.50	.20

National Children's Day — A683

Pangpond and his: a, Dog, Big (blue background). b, Friend, Hanuman (orange background). c, Girlfriend, Namo (green background). d, Teacher (red background). Illustration reduced.

2003, Jan. 11   *Perf. 14½x14*
Granite Paper
2057	A683	3b Block of 4, #a-d	1.25	1.00

Rose — A684

2003, Feb. 1   *Perf. 13*
Granite Paper
2058	A684	4b multi	.75	.20

No. 2058 is impregnated with rose scent. Compare with Type A716.

Blue Green, by Fua Haribhitak A685

Portrait of Chira Chongkon, by Chamras Kietkong A686

Moonlight, by Prasong Padmanuja A687

Lotus Flowers, by Thawee Nandakwang — A688

2003, Feb. 24   *Perf. 13¼*
Granite Paper
2059	A685	3b multi	.35	.20
2060	A686	3b multi	.35	.20
2061	A687	3b multi	.35	.20
2062	A688	15b multi	1.40	1.10
		Nos. 2059-2062 (4)	2.45	1.70

Bangkok 2003 World Philatelic Exhibition — A689

Tourist attractions: No. 2063, 3b, Doi Inthanon Temple, Chiang Mai. No. 2064, 3b, River Kwai Bridge, Kanchanaburi. No. 2065, 3b, Phu Kradung (cliff), Loei. 15b, Maya Bay, Krabi.

2003, Mar. 3   *Perf. 14½x14*
Granite Paper
2063-2066	A689	Set of 4	2.25	1.75
2066a		Souvenir sheet, #2063-2066, perf. 13¼	3.00	3.00

No. 2066a sold for 29b.

King Bhumibol Adulyadej Type of 1996
Perf. 14x14½
2003, Mar. 14   **Litho.**   **Unwmk.**
Granite Paper
2067	A550	1b blue	.20	.20

2003 Red Cross Fair — A690

2003, Mar. 28   *Perf. 14x14½*
Granite Paper
2068	A690	3b multi	.50	.20

Kick Boxing — A691

Designs: No. 2069, 3b, Boxers punching. No. 2070, 3b, Boxer in black trunks with knee raised. No. 2071, 3b, Boxer in red trunks kicking. 15b, Boxer in red trunks kicking, diff.

2003, Apr. 2   **Litho.**   *Perf. 13¼*
Granite Paper
2069-2072	A691	Set of 4	2.25	1.75
2072a		Souvenir sheet, #2069-2072	3.50	3.50
2072b		As "a," with China 2003 Philatelic Exhibition emblem in margin	10.00	10.00

No. 2072a sold for 29b.
Issued: No. 2072b, 11/20. No. 2072b sold for 29b.

Princess Maha Chakri Sirindhorn, 48th Birthday — A692

2003, Apr. 2   *Perf. 14x14½*
Granite Paper
2073	A692	3b multi	.50	.20

Princess Galyani Vadhana, 80th Birthday — A693

2003, May 6   **Granite Paper**
2074	A693	3b multi	.50	.20

Kings Chulalongkorn and Vajiravudh A694

2003, May 6   **Granite Paper**
2075	A694	3b multi	.50	.20

Inspector General Dept., cent.

King Prajadhipok Day — A695

2003, May 30   *Perf. 14½x14*
Granite Paper
2076	A695	3b multi	.50	.20

Bantam Chickens — A696

Designs: No. 2077, 3b, White ears jungle fowl. No. 2078, 3b, Sugarcane husk colored. No. 2079, 3b, Black-tailed white. 15b, Dark gray.

2003   **Litho.**   *Perf. 13*
Granite Paper
2077-2080	A696	Set of 4	2.25	1.75
2080a		Souvenir sheet, #2077-2080	3.00	3.00
2080b		As "a," with Lanka Philex 2003 emblem in margin	8.00	8.00

Issued: Nos. 2077-2080, 2080a, 6/10; No. 2080b, 7/31. Nos. 2080a and 2080b each sold for 29b.

Asalhapuja Day — A697

2003, July 13   *Perf. 14x14½*
Granite Paper
2081	A697	3b multi	.50	.20

National Communications Day — A698

2003, Aug. 4   *Perf. 14½x14*
Granite Paper
2082	A698	3b multi	.50	.20

Communications Organization
Emblems — A699

No. 2083: a, Thailand Post Company Limited. b, Communications Authority of Thailand (23x27mm). c, CAT Telecom Public Company Limited.
Illustration reduced.

Perf. 14¼x14½
2003, Aug. 14   Litho.   Wmk. 340
2083 A699 3b Horiz. strip of 3,
#a-c   1.10   .80

King Chulalongkorn (1853-1910) A700

Litho. & Embossed
2003, Sept. 20   Unwmk.   Perf. 13¼
2084 A700 100b gold & multi   8.00   6.00
a.   Souvenir sheet of 4   32.50 32.50

No. 2084a issued 9/30.
No. 2084a exists imperf. with Bangkok 2003 emblem at lower left. Value, $50.

Government Housing Bank, 50th
Anniv. — A701

2003, Sept. 24   Litho.   Perf. 14½x14
Granite Paper
2085 A701 3b multi   .50   .20

Bangkok 2003 World Philatelic
Exhibition — A702

Handicrafts: No. 2086, 3b, Basketry. No. 2087, 3b, Pottery. No. 2088, 3b, Leatherwork. 15b, Wood carving.

2003, Oct. 4
Granite Paper
2086-2089 A702   Set of 4   2.25   1.75
2089a   Souvenir sheet, #2086-
         2089, perf. 13¼   3.25   3.25

A varnish with a rough surface was applied to portions of the designs. No. 2089a sold for 29b, and exists imperf.

Trees of Thailand and Canada — A703

No. 2090: a, Cassia fistula (Thailand). b, Maple leaves (Canada).

2003, Oct. 4   Perf. 14x14½
Granite Paper
2090 A703 3b Horiz. pair, #a-b   1.25   1.10
c.   Souvenir sheet, #2090, perf.
      13¼   2.50   2.50

No. 2090c sold for 9b.

Lychees — A704

Rose
Apples — A705

Fruit: No. 2093, Coconuts. 15b, Jackfruit.

2003, Oct. 4
Granite Paper
2091 A704 3b shown   .30   .20
2092 A705 3b shown   .30   .20
2093 A704 3b multi   .30   .20
2094 A704 15b multi   1.50   1.10
a.   Souvenir sheet, #2091-2094,
      perf. 13¼   2.75   2.75

International Letter Writing Week. No. 2094a sold for 29b.

Oct. 14, 1973 Student Uprisings, 30th
Anniv. — A706

2003, Oct. 14   Perf. 14½x14
Granite Paper
2095 A706 3b multi   .50   .20

Asia-Pacific Economic Cooperation
Meeting — A707

2003, Oct. 20   Granite Paper
2096 A707 3b multi   .50   .20

New Year
2004 — A708

Flowers: No. 2097, 3b, Bougainvillea spectabilis. No. 2098, 3b, Eucrosia bicolor. No. 2099, 3b, Canna x generalis. No. 2100, 3b, Zinnia violacea.

2003, Nov. 15   Perf. 14½x14¼
Granite Paper
2097-2100 A708   Set of 4   1.25   .90
2100a   Souvenir sheet, #2097-
         2100   1.75   1.75

2100b   As "a," with 2004 Hong
         Kong Stamp Expo em-
         blem in margin   5.00   5.00

No. 2100a sold for 16b.
Issued: No. 2100b, 1/30/04. No. 2100b sold for 16b.

Thailand Flag
A709

Thai Pavilion
A710

Elephants
A711

Cassia Fistula
A712

2003, Dec. 1   Perf. 14¼x14½
Granite Paper
2101 A709 3b multi   .35   .25
2102 A710 3b multi   .35   .25
2103 A711 3b multi   .35   .25
2104 A712 3b multi   .35   .25
     Nos. 2101-2104 (4)   1.40 1.00

Elephants — A713

No. 2105: a, Asian elephant. b, African elephants.
Illustration reduced.

2003, Dec. 9   Perf. 14½x14
Granite Paper
2105 A713 3b Horiz. pair, #a-b   1.00   .75
c.   Souvenir sheet, #2105a, perf.
      13¼   1.50   1.50

No. 2105c sold for 9b.
Thailand-South Africa diplomatic relations, 10th anniv. See South Africa No. 1330.

King Bhumibol Adulyadej Type of 1996
2003-04   Litho.   Perf. 14x14½
Granite Paper
2106 A550 50s olive brown   .60   .20

Issued: 50s, 12/3. 1b, 1/22/04.

Zodiac Animal Type of 2003
2004, Jan. 1   Litho.   Perf. 13
Granite Paper
2108 A682 3b Monkey   .50   .20

Children's Day — A714

2004, Jan. 10   Perf. 14½x14
Granite Paper
2109 A714 3b multi   .50   .20

Paintings of
Hem Vejakorn
A715

Designs: No. 2110, 3b, A Scene in Thai History (dancers). No. 2111, 3b, Maha Bharatayudh (charioteer). No. 2112, 3b, Khun Chang — Khun Phaen (women with horse). No. 2113, 3b, Phra Lor (woman and rooster).

2004, Jan. 17   Perf. 13¼
Granite Paper
2110-2113 A715   Set of 4   1.40   1.10
2113a   Souvenir sheet, #2110-
         2113   1.75   1.75

No. 2113a sold for 16b.

Rose — A716

2004, Feb. 1   Perf. 13
Granite Paper
2114 A716 4b multi   .60   .20

Compare with type A684. No. 2114 is impregnated with rose scent.

Turtles — A717

Designs: No. 2115, 3b, Cuora amboinensis. No. 2116, 3b, Platysternon megacephalum. No. 2117, 3b, Indotestudo elongata. No. 2118, 3b, Heosemys spinosa.

2004, Mar. 1   Perf. 14½x14
Granite Paper
2115-2118 A717   Set of 4   1.60   1.25
2118a   Souvenir sheet, #2115-
         2118, perf. 13¼   3.00   3.00
2118b   Similar to "a," with 2004
         Singapore World Stamp
         Championship emblem in
         margin   5.00   5.00

Issued: No. 2118b, 8/28.
Nos. 2118a and 2118b sold for 16b.

Siam Society, Cent. — A718

2004, Mar. 10   Perf. 14½x14
2119 A718 3b multi   .50   .20

2004 Red Cross Fair — A719

2004, Mar. 29   *Perf. 14x14½*
Granite Paper
2120 A719 3b multi   .50 .20

Heritage Conservation Day — A720

Fringe colors of hand woven clothes: No. 2121, 3b, Rose red. No. 2122, 3b, Blue. No. 2123, 3b, Green. No. 2124, 3b, Orange red. Denomination at LL on Nos. 2122, 2124.

2004, Apr. 2   Litho.   *Perf. 14x14½*
Granite Paper
2121-2124 A720   Set of 4   1.60 1.25
2124a   Souvenir sheet, #2121-2124, perf. 13¼   1.75 1.75
2124b   As "a," with España 2004 emblem in margin, perf. 13¼   7.00 7.00

Issued: No. 2124b, 5/22. No. 2124a sold for 16b; No. 2124b for 18b.

Architecture in Thailand and Italy — A721

No. 2125: a, Golden Mountain Temple, Bangkok. b, Colosseum, Rome. Illustration reduced.

2004, Apr. 21   *Perf. 14½x14*
Granite Paper
2125 A721 3b Horiz. pair, #a-b   2.50 2.50
2125c   Souvenir sheet, #2125, perf. 13¼   20.00 20.00

No. 2125c sold for 10b.
See Italy No. 2602.

Sculpture A722

Designs: No. 2126, 3b, One-sided Drum, by Chit Rienpracha (yellow green background). No. 2127, 3b, Dance Drama, by Sitthidet Saenghiran (rose red background). No. 2128, 3b, Heavenly Flute, by Khien Yimsiri (Prussian blue background). No. 2129, 3b, The Calf, by Paitun Muangsomboom, horiz.

2004, May 3   *Perf. 13¼*
2126-2129 A722   Set of 4   1.40 .95

Unseen Tourist Attractions — A723

No. 2130: a, Non Ngai Buddha, Suphan Buri. b, Khao Laem Dam, Kanchanaburi. c, Mural, Temple fo the Emerald Buddha, Bangkok. d, Ko Li-Pe, Satun. e, Buddha, Wat Phra Thong, Phuket. f, Khao Luang National Park, Nakhon Si Thammarat. g, Miracle Beach, Ko Damikhwan, Krabi. h, Hornbill, Hala-Bala Forest, Narathiwat. i, Long Ru Waterfall, Ubon Ratchathani. j, Prasat Hin Phanom Rung, Buri Ram. k, Red maple leaves, Phu Kradueng National Park, Loei. l, Phukhao Ya, Ranong. m, Ko Kradat, Trat. n, Op Luang National Park, Chiang Mai. o, Dusky leaf monkey, Phetchaburi. p, Lalu, Sra Kaeo. q, Pu Kai, Mu Ko Similan, Phang-Nga. r, Tha Le Noi Waterfowl Park, Phatthalung. s, Phu Pha Thoep, Mukdahan National Park. t, Phi Maen Cave, Mae Hong Son.

2004, May 31   *Perf. 13*
Granite Paper
2130 A723 3b Sheet of 20, #a-t   6.00 4.25
See Nos. 2137, 2147, 2158.

Buddha Sculptures A724

No. 2131: a, Phra Nangpaya. b, Phra Kampaeng Soumkhor. c, Phra Somdej Wat Rakangkhositaram. d, Phar Rod. e, Phra Phongsuphan.

Litho. & Embossed
2004, June 1   *Perf. 13¼*
Granite Paper
2131   Horiz. strip of 5   10.00 7.00
a.-e.   A724 9b Any single   2.00 1.40
f.   Souvenir sheet, #2131a-2131e   20.00 20.00

No. 2131f sold for 53b.

Visakhapuja Day — A725

2004, June 2   Litho.   *Perf. 14x14½*
Granite Paper
2132 A725 3b multi   .50 .20

Bridges — A726

Designs: No. 2133, 5b, Phra Buddha Yodfa Bridge. No. 2134, 5b, Rama VI Bridge. No. 2135, 5b, Rama VIII Bridge. No. 2136, 5b, Rama IX Bridge. Illustration reduced.

2004, July 1   Litho.   *Perf. 14¼x14½*
Granite Paper
2133-2136 A726   Set of 4   1.75 1.10

On Nos. 2135 and 2136 portions of the design were produced by a thermographic process which produces a shiny, raised effect.

Unseen Tourist Attractions Type of 2004

No. 2137: a, Wat Pho Prathap Chang, Phichit. b, Phra Prathan Chaturathit, Wat Phumin, Nan. c, Thalenai, Angthong Archipelago, Surat Thani. d, Wat Na Phra Men, Phra Nakhon Si Ayutthaya. e, Sanam Chan Palace, Nakhon Pathom. f, Piyamitr Tunnel, Yala. g, Ban Khamchanot, Udon Thani. h, Rail line along Pasak Cholasit Dam, Lop Buri. i, Khlong Lan Waterfall, Khlong Lan National Park, Kamphaeng Phet. j, Mo-I-Daeng Cliff, Khao Phra Wihan National Park, Si Sa Ket. k, Changkra Wild Orchid Park, Khon Kaen. l, Canoeists at Ti Lo Re, Tak. m, Khao Ta Mong Lai, Prachuap Khiri Khan. n, Suriya Patithin solar calendar, Prasat Phu Phek, Sakon Nakhon. o, Traditional boat racing, Chumphon. p, Mokochu Range Mae Wong National Park, Nakhon Sawan. q, Ordination by elephant in the sixth month, Surin. r, Rock climbing, Tan Rattana Waterfall, Khao Yai National Park, Prachin Buri. s, Monks collecting alms on horseback, Chiang Rai. t, Cycling in Thung Salaeng Luang, Phitsanulok.

2004, July 28   *Perf. 13*
Granite Paper
2137 A723 3b Sheet of 20, #a-t   6.00 4.25

Jasmine Flower — A727

Litho. & Embossed
2004, Aug. 2   *Perf. 13*
Granite Paper
2138 A727 5b multi   .50 .20

No. 2138 is impregnated with a jasmine scent.

Princess Maha Chakri Sirindhorn Information Technology Program — A728

2004, Aug. 4   Litho.   *Perf. 14x14½*
Granite Paper
2139 A728 3b multi   .50 .20

National Communications Day — A729

2004, Aug. 4   *Perf. 14½x14*
Granite Paper
2140 A729 3b multi   .50 .20

Opening of First Subway Line — A730

2004, Aug. 12   Litho.   *Perf. 14½x14*
Granite Paper
2141 A730 3b multi   .50 .20

Queen Sirikit, 72nd Birthday A731

Litho. & Embossed
2004, Aug. 12   *Perf. 13¼*
2142 A731 100b multi   6.50 4.25

Boats A732

Designs: No. 2143, 3b, Thai junk. No. 2144, 3b, Sampan boat. No. 2145, 3b, Krachaeng boat. 15b, Packet boat.

2004-05   Litho.   *Perf. 14½x14*
2143-2146 A732   Set of 4   2.00 1.40
2146a   Souvenir sheet, #2143-2146, perf. 13¼   3.00 3.00
b.   As "a," with Pacific Explorer 2005 emblem in margin   8.00 8.00

No. 2146a sold for 29b. No. 2146b sold for 30b.
Issued: Nos. 2143-2146a, 9/1/04; No. 2146b, 4/21/05.

Unseen Tourist Attractions Type of 2004

No. 2147: a, Phra Nang Din, Phayad. b, Phra That Kong Khao Noi, Yasothon. c, Phra Atchana, Wat Sri Chum, Sukothai. d, Wat Bang Kung, Samut Songkhram. e, Ku Kut, Wat Phrathat Chamthewi, Lamphun. f, Dolphin watching, Chachoengsao. g, Tak Bat Dok Mai tradition, Saraburi. h, Hat Chao Lao, Chanthaburi. i, Phu Kum Khao dinosaur fossils, Kalasin. j, Reversed stupa, Wat Phra That Lampang Luang, Lampang. k, Khu Khut Waterfowl Park, Songkhla. l, Plant Market Khlong 15, Nakhon Nayok. m, Huppatad, Uthai Thani. n, Thai Muang Beach, Nakhon Phanom. o, Wild gaur, Khao Yai National Park, Nakhon Ratchasima. p, Canoeing, Le Khao Kop Cave, Trang. q, Sea of flowers, Pru Soi Dao, Uttaradit. r, Kolae boat, Ban Paseyawo, Pattani. s, Sea of Mist, Thap Boek, Phu Hin Rongkla National Park, Phetchabun. t, Bats, Khao Chung Phran, Ratchaburi.

2004, Sept. 28   *Perf. 13*
Granite Paper
2147 A723 3b Sheet of 20, #a-t   6.00 4.25

Intl. Letter Writing Week — A733

Kites: No. 2148, 3b, Snake. No. 2149, 3b, Star-shaped. No. 2150, 3b, Diamond-shaped with tail. 15b, Buffalo.

2004, Oct. 9   Litho.   Perf. 14x14½
Granite Paper
2148-2151 A733   Set of 4   2.00 1.40
2151a   Souvenir sheet, #2148-
         2151, perf. 13¼   3.00 3.00
2151b   Similar to "a," with Beijing
         2004 emblem in margin   7.00 7.00

Issued: No. 2151b, 10/28. No. 2151a sold for 29b; No. 2151b for 30b.

King Mongkut (1804-68) A734

2004, Oct. 18   Perf. 14x14½
Granite Paper
2152 A734 4b multi   .50 .20

E-customs System — A735

2004, Nov. 15   Perf. 14½x14
Granite Paper
2153 A735 3b multi   .50 .20

New Year 2005 — A736

Flowers: No. 2154, 3b, Wrightia sirikitiae. No. 2155, 3b, Eria amica. No. 2156, 3b, Burmannia coelestris. No. 2157, 3b, Utricularia bifida.

2004, Nov. 15   Perf. 14¼x14½
Granite Paper
2154-2157 A736   Set of 4   3.00 2.00
2157a   Souvenir sheet, #2154-
         2157, perf. 14¼x14½   5.00 5.00

No. 2157a sold for 16b.

Unseen Tourist Attractions Type of 2004

No. 2158: a, Phra That Cho Hae, Phrae. b, Wat Karuna, Chai Nat. c, Wat Nang Sao, Samut Sakhon. d, Phra Mutao Pagoda, Nonthaburi. e, Phu Kao Phu Phan Kham National Park, Nong Bua Lam Phu. f, Airvata (three-headed elephant), Erawan Museum, Samut Prakan. g, Wat Chedi Hoi, Pathum Thani. h, White krajiaw field, Chaiyaphum. i, Chet Si Waterfall, Nong Khai. j, Summer Palace, Ko Si Chang, Choi Buri. k, Traditional Drum-making village (Ban Bang Phae), Ang Thong. l, Ko Thalu, Rayong. m, Kosamphi Forest Park, Maha Sarakham. n, Cannonball tree, Wat Phra Non Chaksi, Sing Buri. o, Tung Kula Rong Hai, Roi Et. p, Phu Sra Dok Bua, Amnat Charoen.

2004, Nov. 26   Perf. 13
Granite Paper
2158 A723 3b Sheet of 16, #a-p,
         + 4 labels   6.00 6.00

Bangkok Fashion City Initiative — A737

No. 2159: a, 3b, Man and woman. b, 3b, Woman in pink dress. c, 3b, Woman with green shirt. d, 15b, Woman with brown eyeshade.
Illustration reduced.

2004, Dec. 5   Perf. 14x14½
Granite Paper
2159 A737 Horiz. strip of 4, #a-
           d   2.25 2.25
e.   Souvenir sheet, #2159a-2159d,
      perf. 13½   2.50 2.50

No. 2159e sold for 30b.

Queen Rambhai Bharni (1904-84) A738

2004, Dec. 20   Perf. 14x14½
Granite Paper
2160 A738 3b multi   .50 .20

Zodiac Animal Type of 2003
2005, Jan. 1   Perf. 13
Granite Paper
2161 A682 3b Cock   .50 .20

Children's Day — A739

2005, Jan. 8   Perf. 14½x14
Granite Paper
2162 A739 3b multi   .50 .20

Thailand - Argentina Diplomatic Relations, 50th Anniv. — A740

No. 2163: a, Tango dancers, Argentina. b, Tom-tom dancers, Thailand.
Illustration reduced.

2005, Feb. 2   Perf. 13¼
Granite Paper
2163 A740 3b Horiz. pair, #a-b   1.00 1.00
      See Argentina Nos. 2312-2313.

Rose — A741

2005, Feb. 10   Perf. 12½
Flocked Paper
2164 A741 10b multi   1.10 .80
No. 2164 is impregnated with rose scent.

Maghapuja Day — A742

2005, Feb. 23   Perf. 14x14½
Granite Paper
2165 A742 3b multi   .50 .20

Rotary International, Cent. — A743

2005, Feb. 23   Perf. 14½x14
Granite Paper
2166 A743 3b multi   .50 .20

Red Cross A744

2005, Mar. 30   Litho.
Granite Paper
2167 A744 3b multi   .50 .20

Princess Maha Chakri Sirindhorn, 50th Birthday — A774a

2005, Apr. 2   Litho.   Perf. 13¼
Granite Paper
2167A A774a 3b multi   .50 .20

A745

Hanging Art — A746

2005, Apr. 2   Litho.   Perf. 13¼
Granite Paper
2168 A745 3b shown   .30 .20
2169 A746 3b shown   .30 .20
2170 A746 3b multi, diff.   .30 .20
2171 A745 15b multi, diff.   1.25 .90
a.   Souvenir sheet, #2168-2171   2.50 2.50
      Nos. 2168-2171 (4)   2.15 1.50

Heritage Conservation Day. No. 2171 sold for 30b.

Authors Born in 1905 — A747

Designs: No. 2172, 3b, Dokmaisod (olive green background). No. 2173, 3b, Sri Burapha (Prussian blue background). No. 2174, 3b, Maimuangderm (dark blue background). No. 2175, 3b, Arkatdumkeung Rabibhadana (rose pink background).

2005, May 5   Perf. 14½x14
Granite Paper
2172-2175 A747   Set of 4   1.40 1.00
2175a   Souvenir sheet, #2172-
         2175, perf. 13¼   1.60 1.60

No. 2175a sold for 17b.

Insects — A748

No. 2176: a, Coccinella transversalis. b, Chrysochroa buqueti rugicollis (47x28mm). c, Sagra femorata. d, Chrysochroa maruyamai (47x28mm).

Litho. & Embossed
2005, May 31   Perf. 14¼x14½
Granite Paper
2176   Horiz. strip or block of
       4   1.75 1.10
a.-d. A748 5b Any single   .40   .20
e.   Sheet, 2 each #2176a-2176d   3.00 3.00

Embossed portions of stamps are covered with a glossy varnish.
No. 2176e issued May 2006, Washington 2006 World Philatelic Exhibition. No. 2176e sold for 54b.

Heart Balloons and Mail Truck — A749

Balloons — A749a

2005 **Litho.** **Perf. 13**
Granite Paper
2177 A749 3b multi .75 .50
2177A A749a 3b multi .75 .50

Issued: No. 2177, June; No. 2177A, 7/15. Nos. 2177 and 2177A were issued in sheets of 12 + 12 personalizable labels the same size as the stamp.

Buddha Amulets A750

No. 2178: a, Phra Ruang Lang Rang Rang Puen. b, Phra Hu Yan. c, Phra Chinnarat Bai Sema. d, Phra Mahesuan. e, Phra Tha Kradan.

Litho. & Embossed
2005, June 19 **Perf. 13¼**
Granite Paper
2178 Horiz. strip of 5 4.50 3.00
a.-e. A750 9b Any single .90 .60
f. Souvenir sheet, #2178a-2178e 5.00 5.00
g. As "f," with Taipei 2005 emblem in margin 12.00 12.00

No. 2178f sold for 55b. No. 2178g issued 8/19/05. No. 2178g sold for 85b.

Thailand - People's Republic of China Diplomatic Relations, 30th Anniv. — A751

Panda: a, Showing tongue. b, Feeding on bamboo.
Illustration reduced.

2005, July 1 **Litho.** **Perf.**
Granite Paper
2179 A751 Horiz. pair 1.00 .65
a.-b. 3b Either single .30 .30
c. Souvenir sheet, #2179a-2179b 2.00 2.00

No. 2179 has perf. 13¼ line of perforations between the two stamps, and the surrounding selvage is rouletted 11¾. No. 2179c, which sold for 15b, lacks the perforations between the stamps and has no rouletting.

Thaipex 2005 — A752

Dancers in play "Chuck Nark": No. 2180, 3b, Pra Rama and Princess Srida. No. 2181, 3b, Hanuman (white mask). No. 2182, 3b, Thotsakan (green mask). 15b, Pra Rama and Thotsakan.

Litho. with Foil Application
2005, Aug. 3 **Perf. 13¼**
Granite Paper
2180-2183 A752 Set of 4 2.00 1.50
2183a Souvenir sheet, #2180-2183 2.75 2.75

No. 2183a sold for 30b.

Natl. Communications Day — A753

2005, Aug. 4 **Litho.** **Perf. 14½x14**
Granite Paper
2184 A753 3b multi .50 .20

Building Gables — A754

No. 2185: a, Prasat Phanom Rung. b, Phra Prang at Wat Phra Phai Luang. c, Uposatha Hall at Wat Khao Bandai It. d, Scripture Library at Wat Phra Sing Woramahawihan.

Perf. 13¼x13½
2005, Aug. 4 **Photo.** **Wmk. 340**
2185 Horiz. strip of 4 + central label 2.00 1.40
a.-d. A754 5b Any single .50 .30

Orchids — A755

Designs: No. 2189, 3b, Rhynchostylis gigantea Alba (white flowers). No. 2190, 3b, Rhynchostylis gigantea (pink and red flowers). No. 2191, 3b, Dendrobium gratiosissimum. 15b, Dendrobium thyrsiflorum.

Perf. 14½
2005, Sept. 1 **Litho.** **Unwmk.**
Granite Paper
2189-2192 A755 Set of 4 2.50 1.75
2192a Souvenir sheet, #2189-2192, perf. 13¼ 3.50 3.50

No. 2192a sold for 30b.

Intl. Day of Peace — A756

2005, Sept. 21 **Perf. 13**
Granite Paper
2193 A756 3b multi .50 .20

Intl. Letter Writing Week — A757

Water buffalo: No. 2194, 3b, Head. No. 2195, 3b, Standing in field. No. 2196, 3b, In mud. 15b, Attached to plow.

Perf. 14½x14
2005, Oct. 8 **Unwmk.**
Granite Paper
2194-2197 A757 Set of 4 2.50 1.75
2197a Souvenir sheet, #2194-2197, perf. 13¼ 3.00 3.00

National Library, Cent. — A758

2005, Oct. 12 **Perf. 14½x14**
Granite Paper
2198 A758 3b multi .50 .20

Abolition of Slavery, Cent. — A759

2005, Oct. 23 **Litho.**
Granite Paper
2199 A759 3b multi .50 .20

New Year 2006 — A760

Flowers: No. 2200, 3b, Beaumontia murtonii. No. 2201, 3b, Hibiscus mutabilis. No. 2202, 3b, Hibiscus rosa-sinensis. No. 2203, 3b, Cochlospermum religiosum.

2005, Nov. 15 **Perf. 14x14½**
Granite Paper
2200-2203 A760 Set of 4 1.25 .90
2203a Souvenir sheet, #2200-2203 2.00 2.00

No. 2203a sold for 17b.

Princess Bejaratana, 80th Birthday — A761

2005, Nov. 24 **Perf. 14x14½**
Granite Paper
2204 A761 3b multi .50 .20

Siamese Roosters — A762

Designs: No. 2205, 3b, Golden Rooster, by Pichai Nirand (olive green panel). No. 2206, 3b, Rooster at Dawn, by Prayat Pongdam (black panel). No. 2207, 3b, Legendary Rooster, by Chakrabhand Posayakrit (dancing woman, brown panel). No. 2208, 3b, Divine Rooster, by Chalermchai Kositpipat (blue panel), horiz.

Perf. 14x14½, 14½x14
2005, Nov. 24
2205-2208 A762 Set of 4 1.25 .80

King Bhumibol Adulyadej's "New Theory" Agriculture — A763

No. 2209: a, King, easel, farmers, animals. b, King and farmers.

2005, Dec. 5 **Perf. 14¼x14½**
Granite Paper
2209 Horiz. pair, #a-b, + central label .75 .40
a.-b. A763 3b Either single .30 .20

Buddhist Monks A764

No. 2210: a, Somdet Phra Phutthachan (1788-1872). b, Phra Ratchamuni Samiram Khunupamachan (1582-1682). c, Phra Achan Man Bhuridatto (1870-1949). d, Khruba Si wichai (1877-1938).

Litho. & Engr.
2005, Dec. 5 **Perf. 13½**
Granite Paper
2210 Horiz. strip of 4 2.00 1.25
a.-d. A764 5b Any single .50 .30
e. Souvenir sheet, #2210a-2210d 3.50 3.50

No. 2210e sold for 30b.

Dec. 26, 2004 Tsunami, 1st
Anniv. — A765

No. 2211: a, Wave. b, Undivided Kindness
of Thai People, by Chanipa Temprom.
Illustration reduced.

2005, Dec. 26   Litho.   Perf. 14½x14
Granite Paper
2211 A765 3b Horiz. pair, #a-b   2.50 1.75

**King Bhumibol Adulyadej Type of
1996**
2006   Litho.   Perf. 14x14½
Granite Paper
2212 A550 10b orange & brown   2.00 1.00
2213 A550 15b yel brn & green   3.00 1.50

New Year 2006
(Year of the
Dog) — A766

2006, Jan. 1   Litho.   Perf. 13
Granite Paper
2214 A766 3b multi   .50 .20

Prince Chaturantarasmi Krom Phra
Chakrabardibongse (1856-1900),
Finance Minister — A767

2006, Jan. 13   Perf. 14x14½
Granite Paper
2215 A767 3b multi   .50 .20

Natl. Children's Day — A768

Winning designs in children's stamp design
competition with panel colors of: No. 2216, 3b,
Orange brown. No. 2217, 3b, Blue. No. 2218,
3b, Red violet. No. 2219, 3b, Green.

2006, Jan. 14   Perf. 14½x14
Granite Paper
2216-2219 A768 Set of 4   1.25 .80

Rose — A769

Litho. & Embossed
2006, Feb. 7   Perf. 13
Granite Paper
2220 A769 5b multi   .75 .20

Diplomatic Relations Between
Thailand and Iran, 50th Anniv. — A770

2006, Feb. 11   Litho.   Perf. 14½x14
Granite Paper
2221 A770 3b multi   .50 .20

Queen Sirikit Center for Breast
Cancer — A771

2006, Mar. 29   Perf. 14½x14
Granite Paper
2222 A771 3b multi   .50 .20

Heritage
Conservation
Day — A772

Sites in Phu Phrabat Historical Park: No.
2223, 3b, Buddha's Footprint (monument). No.
2224, 3b, Upright rocks and trees, horiz. No.
2225, 3b, Thao Barot horse stable (rock over-
hang), horiz. 15b, Nang Usa rock pillar.

2006, Apr. 2   Perf. 14x14½, 14½x14
Granite Paper
2223-2226 A772   Set of 4   2.50 1.75
2226a   Souvenir sheet, #2223-
         2226, perf. 13¼   2.75 2.75
No. 2226a sold for 36b.

Thon Buri Palace — A773

No. 2227: a, Throne Hall. b, King Taksin's
Shrine. c, Two Chinese-style residences. d,
King Pinklao's residence.

2006, Apr. 2   Perf. 14½x14
Granite Paper
2227 A773 3b Block of 4, #a-d   1.40 1.00
  e.   Souvenir sheet, #2227, perf.
        13¼   1.60 1.60
No. 2227e sold for 17b.

A774

King Bhumibol Adulyadej, 60th Anniv.
of Accession — A775

King Bhumibol Adulyadej: No. 2228, 3b,
Wearing tie, red brown background (shown).
No. 2229, 3b, Wearing tie, blue background.
No. 2230, 3b, Wearing tie, olive brown background. No. 2231, 3b, Without tie, blue violet
background. No. 2232, Without tie, green
background. No. 2233, 3b, Without tie, brown
background.

2006   Photo.   Perf. 13¼
Granite Paper
2228-2233 A774   Set of 6   8.00 7.00
2233a   Miniature sheet, #2228-
         2233   10.00 10.00
**Litho. & Embossed With Foil
Application**
2234 A775 100b gold & multi   6.50 4.50
Issued: Nos. 2228-2233, 2233a, 5/5; No.
2234, 6/9. No. 2233a sold for 30b.

Visakhapuja
Day — A776

2006, May 12   Litho.   Perf. 14x14½
Granite Paper
2235 A776 3b multi   .50 .20

Buddhadasa
Bhikkhu (1906-
93), Buddhist
Philosopher
A777

No. 2236: a, Buddhadasa seated between
trees. b, Profile of Buddhadasa. c, Gathering
of monks. d, Stone fence.

2006, May 27   Perf. 13
Granite Paper
2236   Horiz. strip of 4   1.40 1.00
  a.-d. A777 3b Any single   .45 .30
  e.   Miniature sheet, #2236a-2236d   2.00 2.00
No. 2236e sold for 17b.

Anemonefish — A778

Designs: No. 2237, 3b, Amphiprion clarkii.
No. 2238, 3b, Amphiprion perideraion. No.
2239, 3b, Amphiprion ocellaris. No. 2240, 3b,
Amphiprion polymnus.

2006   Perf. 14½x14
Granite Paper
2237-2240 A778   Set of 4   1.40 1.00
2240a   Miniature sheet, #2237-
         2240, perf. 13½   2.00 2.00
2240b   As "a", with Belgica '06
         emblem in margin   10.00 10.00
Issued: Nos. 2237-2240, 2240a, 6/24; No.
2240b, Dec. No. 2240a sold for 20b; No.
2240b, for 30b.

Natl. Communications Day — A779

2006, Aug. 4   Litho.
Granite Paper
2241 A779 3b multi   .50 .20

Mitrephora
Sirikitiae — A780

Litho. & Embossed
2006, Aug. 12   Perf. 13
Granite Paper
2242 A780 5b multi   .50 .20

Royal Dog
Tongdaeng
A781

Dog: No. 2243, 3b, Sitting. No. 2244, 3b,
Standing. No. 2245, 3b, Laying down. No.
2246, 3b, With puppies.

2006   Litho.   Perf. 13½
Granite Paper
2243-2246 A781   Set of 4   1.40 1.10
2246a   Miniature sheet, #2243-
         2246   1.50 1.50
2246b   As "a", with MonacoPhil
         2006 emblem in margin   9.00 9.00
Issued: Nos. 2243-2246, 2246a, 9/1; No.
2246b, Dec. No. 2246a sold for 17b; No.
2246b, for 26b.

Suvarnabhumi Airport — A782

2006, Sept. 28   Perf. 14½x14
Granite Paper
2247 A782 3b multi   .50 .20

Nos, 606, 653a, 934 and 1081 Surcharged

Methods, Perfs and Watermarks As Before

2006, Sept. ?
2248	A146	2b on 20s #606	1.00	.75
2249	A161	2b on 20s #653a	1.00	.75
2250	A256	2b on 75s #934	1.00	.75
2251	A256	2b on 1.50b #1081	1.00	.75
		Nos. 2248-2251 (4)	4.00	3.00

Location and size of surcharges differs.

Intl. Letter Writing Week — A784

Carnivorous plants: No. 2253, 3b, Nepenthes mirabilis. No. 2254, 3b, Rafflesia kerrii. No. 2255, 3b, Sapria poilanei. 15b, Drosera burmannii.

2006 Litho. Unwmk. *Perf. 14½x14*
Granite Paper
2253-2256	A784	Set of 4	2.50	1.60
2256a		Miniature sheet, #2253-2256, perf. 13½	2.25	2.25
2256b		As "a," with Beijing 2006 emblem in margin	8.00	8.00

Issued: Nos. 2253-2256, 2256a, 10/9; No. 2256b, Dec. No. 2256a sold for 29b; No. 2256b, for 44b.

New Year 2007 — A785

Flowers: No. 2257, 3b, Hypoxis aurea. No. 2258, 3b, Murdannia gigantea. No. 2259, 3b, Impatiens phuluangensis. No. 2260, 3b, Caulokaempferia alba.

2006, Nov. 15　　　*Perf. 14½x14*
Granite Paper
2257-2260	A785	Set of 4	1.25	.80
2260a		Miniature sheet, #2257-2260	1.50	1.50

No. 2260a sold for 16b.

Royal Thai Naval Academy, Cent. — A786

2006, Nov. 20
Granite Paper
2261	A786	3b multi		.50	.20

King Bhumibol Adulyadej, 60th Anniv. of Accession A787

King Bhumibol Adulyadej: No. 2262, 5b, Standing in forest. No. 2263, 5b, Seated on walkway, taking notes. No. 2264, 5b, Standing on wooden plank over water. No. 2265, 5b, Pointing to ground. No. 2266, 5b, Riding cow. No. 2267, 5b, Walking up hill.

2006, Dec. 5　　Photo.　*Perf. 13½*
Granite Paper
2262-2267	A787	Set of 6	3.50	2.50
2267a		Miniature sheet, #2262-2267	3.75	3.75

No. 2267a sold for 44b.

Opening of Second Thai-Lao Friendship Bridge — A788

No. 2268 — Bridge and flag of: a, Thailand (denomination at LL). b, Laos (denomination at LR).
Illustration reduced.

2006, Dec. 20　Litho.　*Perf. 14½x14*
Granite Paper
2268	A788	3b Horiz. pair, #a-b	1.00	.75

New Year 2007 (Year of the Pig) — A789

2007, Jan. 1　　　　　*Perf. 13*
Granite Paper
2269	A789	3b multi		.50	.20

Natl. Children's Day — A790

No. 2270 — Children's drawings: a, Rainbow, birds and butterflies. b, Cat with green face and butterflies. c, Spotted animals. d, Birds, cloud, sun and girl riding horse.
Illustration reduced.

2007, Jan. 13　　　*Perf. 14½x14*
Granite Paper
2270	A790	3b Block of 4, #a-d	1.00	.65

Siam Commercial Bank Public Company, Cent. — A791

2007, Jan. 30　　　*Perf. 14x14½*
Granite Paper
2271	A791	3b multi		.50	.20

Bangkok 2007 Intl. Stamp Exhibition — A792

Various carved wooden dolls depicting Thai children with background colors of: No. 2272, 5b, Blue. No. 2273, 5b, Olive green. No. 2274, 5b, Brown olive. No. 2275, 5b, Rose.
Illustration reduced.

Litho. With Foil Application
2007, Feb. 1　　　　　*Perf. 13*
Granite Paper
2272-2275	A792	Set of 4	2.00	.95
2275a		Miniature sheet, #2272-2275	2.25	2.25

No. 2275a sold for 33b.

Yellow Rose — A793

2007, Feb. 7　　Litho.　*Perf. 13*
Granite Paper
2276	A793	5b multi		.50	.20

No. 2276 is impregnated with a rose scent.

A794

A795

A796

A797

Carved Fruits and Vegetables — A797

2007, Mar. 1　　Litho.　*Perf. 14½x14*
Granite Paper
2277	A794	5b multi	.30	.20
2278	A795	5b multi	.30	.20
2279	A796	5b multi	.30	.20
2280	A797	5b multi	.30	.20
a.		Souvenir sheet, #2277-2280, perf. 13¼	1.60	1.60
		Nos. 2277-2280 (4)	1.20	.80

No. 2280a sold for 26b.

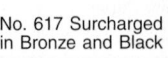

No. 617 Surcharged in Bronze and Black

Methods, Perfs and Watermarks As Before

2007, Mar. 29
2281	A146	50b on 40b #617	3.25	2.50
2282	A146	100b on 40b #617	6.25	4.75

Postman on Scooter — A798

Unwmk.
2007, Mar. 29　Litho.　*Perf. 13*
Granite Paper
2283	A798	3b multi		.20	.20

Thailand Red Cross Tuberculosis Laboratory — A799

2007, Mar. 29　Litho.　*Perf. 14½x14*
2285	A799	3b multi		.20	.20

A800

A801

A802

Buddhist Ecclesiastical Ceremonial Fans of King Chulalongkorn Era — A803

Litho. With Foil Application
2007, Apr. 2   **Perf. 13¼**
Granite Paper
2286	A800	5b multi	.30	.20
2287	A801	5b multi	.30	.20
2288	A802	5b multi	.30	.20
2289	A803	5b multi	.30	.20
a.		Souvenir sheet, #2286-2289	1.75	1.75
		Nos. 2286-2289 (4)	1.20	.80

No. 2289a sold for 27b.

Flowers — A804

No. 2290: a, Lotus flower at UR, sunflowers in center and LR. b, Sunflower at UR, two lotus flowers. c, Rose, sunflower and lotus flowers. d, Three roses.

2007, Apr. 23   **Litho.**   **Perf. 13**
Granite Paper
2290		Vert. strip of 4	.80	.60
a.-d.	A804	3b Any single	.20	.20

King Bhumibol Adulyadej, 80th Birthday — A805

Litho. & Embossed With Foil Application
2007, May 5   **Perf. 13¼**
Granite Paper
2291	A805	9b multi	.55	.40

Princess Galyani Vadhana, 84th Birthday — A806

2007, May 6   **Litho.**   **Perf. 14x14½**
2292	A806	3b multi	.20	.20

Visakhapuja Day — A807

Illustration reduced.

2007, May 31   **Perf. 14x14½**
Granite Paper
2293	A807	3b multi	.20	.20

Seaside Tourist Areas — A808

No. 2294: a, Mu Ko Similan National Park. b, Ko Khai. c, Ko Chang. d, Khao Tapu. e, Hat Cha-am. f, Ao Maya. g, Ko Panyi. h, Hat Chao Mai. i, Thale Waek. j, Hat Pattaya.

2007, June 1   **Perf. 14½x14**
Granite Paper
2294		Sheet of 10	9.25	9.25
a.-j.		A808 15b Any single	.90	.70

Waterfalls — A809

Waterfall at: No. 2295, 3b, Doi Inthanon National Park. No. 2296, 3b, Thung Salaeng Luang National Park. No. 2297, 3b, Khuean Srinagarindra National Park. No. 2298, 3b, Phu Hin Rong Kla National Park.

2007, June 1   **Perf. 14½x14**
Granite Paper
2295-2298	A809	Set of 4	.80	.60
2298a		Souvenir sheet, #2295-2298, perf. 13½	1.00	1.00

No. 2298a sold for 16b.

Phi Takhon Masks — A810

No. 2299 — Masks with rice steamer hat in: a, White, black background. b, Black, white background. c, Red, black background. d, White, white background.
10b, Two people wearing masks.

2007, June 23   **Perf. 13¼**
Granite Paper
2299	A810	3b Horiz. strip of 4, #a-d	.80	.60

Souvenir Sheet
Perf. 14x14½
2300	A810	10b multi	.65	.50

No. 2300 contains one 60x48mm stamp.

A811

A812

A813

Rock Formations in Pa Hin Ngam National Park — A814

2007, July 2   **Litho.**   **Perf. 13¼x12¾**
2301	A811	5b multi	.35	.25
2302	A812	5b multi	.35	.25
2303	A813	5b multi	.35	.25
2304	A814	5b multi	.35	.25
a.		Souvenir sheet, #2301-2304	2.50	2.50
		Nos. 2301-2304 (4)	1.40	1.00

No. 2304a sold for 39b. Portions of the designs of Nos. 2301-2304 and 2304a were printed with a thermographic process producing a shiny, raised effect. A gritty substance was added to these areas to produce a rough texture.

Temples — A815

Designs: No. 2305, 5b, Wat Rajaorasaram. No. 2306, 5b, Wat Rajapradit Sathitmahasimaram. No. 2307, 5b, Wat Rajabopit Sathitmahasimaram. No. 2308, 5b, Wat Suthatthepwararam.

2007, July 2   **Litho.**   **Perf. 14½x14**
Granite Paper
2305-2308	A815	Set of 4	1.40	1.00
2308a		Souvenir sheet, #2305-2308, perf. 13¼	1.75	1.75

No. 2308a sold for 27b.

Bird Figurines A816

Bird figurines covered with beetle wing: No. 2309, 5b, Duck with wings spread. No. 2310, 5b, Bird on rock. No. 2311, 5b, Bird with long tail feathers. No. 2312, 5b, Rooster.

Litho. With Foil Application
2007, Aug. 3   **Perf. 14x14½**
Granite Paper
2309-2312	A816	Set of 4	1.40	1.00
2312a		Souvenir sheet, #2309-2312	2.10	2.10

No. 2312a sold for 33b. Bangkok 2007 Intl. Stamp Exhibition.

Natl. Communications Day — A817

2007, Aug. 4   **Litho.**   **Perf. 14½x14**
Granite Paper
2313	A817	3b multi	.20	.20

24th Summer Universiade, Bangkok — A818

2007, Aug. 8   **Perf. 13¼**
Granite Paper
2314	A818	3b multi	.20	.20

Miniature Sheet

Association of South East Asian Nations (ASEAN), 40th Anniv. — A819

No. 2315: a, Secretariat Building, Bandar Seri Begawan, Brunei. b, National Museum of Cambodia. c, Fatahillah Museum, Jakarta, Indonesia. d, Typical house, Laos. e, Malayan Railway Headquarters Building, Kuala Lumpur, Malaysia. f, Yangon Post Office, Myanmar (Burma). g, Malacañang Palace, Philippines. h, National Museum of Singapore. i, Vimanmek Mansion, Bangkok. j, Presidential Palace, Hanoi, Viet Nam.

2007, Aug. 8   **Perf. 13¼**
Granite Paper
2315	A819	3b Sheet of 10, #a-j	2.00	1.40

See Brunei Nos. , Burma No. 370, Cambodia Nos. , Indonesia Nos. , Laos Nos. , Malaysia No. 1170, Philippines Nos. 3103-3105, Singapore No. 1265, and Viet Nam Nos. 3302-3311.

Miniature Sheet

People at Work — A823

No. 2323: a, People in palm tree. b, Cook feeding people on wooden walkway. c, People near elephant carving. d, Buddhist monk in canoe. e, People under lanterns. f, Artisan with hammer. g, Woman with flowers. h, Man weaving fishing basket. i, People in boats filled with fruits and vegetables. j, People logging with elephants.

2007, Oct. 26   **Litho.**   **Perf. 13**
Granite Paper
2323	A823	3b Sheet of 10, #a-j	2.00	1.40

Ministry of Defense, 120th Anniv. — A824

2007, Nov. 11   **Perf. 14x14½**
Granite Paper
2324 A824 3b multi   .20   .20

New Year 2008 — A825

Designs: No. 2325, 3b, Pink Plumeria rubra. denomination in red. No. 2326, 3b, Plumeria obtusa. No. 2327, 3b, White and yellow Plumeria rubra, denomination in pink. No. 2328, 3b, Red Plumeria rubra, denomination in red.

2007, Nov. 15   **Perf. 14x14½**
Granite Paper
2325-2328	A825	Set of 4	.80 .60
2328a		Souvenir sheet, #2325-2328	1.25 1.25

No. 2328a sold for 18b.

SEMI-POSTAL STAMPS

Nos. 164-175 Overprinted in Red

1918, Jan. 11   **Unwmk.**   **Perf. 14**
B1	A21	2s orange brown	2.00	1.00
B2	A21	3s emerald	2.00	1.00
B3	A21	5s rose red	4.50	2.00
B4	A21	10s black & olive	7.00	3.00
B5	A21	15s blue	7.00	3.00
B6	A21	1b bl & gray blk	35.00	15.00
B7	A22	2b car rose & brn	60.00	25.00
B8	A22	3b yel grn & blk	90.00	40.00
B9	A22	5b dp vio & blk	225.00	65.00
a.		Double overprint	775.00	400.00
B10	A22	10b ol grn & vio brn	575.00	175.00
B11	A22	20b sea grn & brn	2,100.	600.00
		Nos. B1-B11 (11)	3,107.	930.00

Excellent counterfeit overprints are known.
These stamps were sold at an advance over face value, the excess being given to the Siamese Red Cross Society.

Stamps of 1905-19 Handstamp Overprinted

1920, Feb.
On Nos. 164, 146, 168
B12	A21	2s (+ 3s) org brn	37.50	37.50
B13	A21	3s (+ 2s) green	40.00	40.00
B14	A21	15s (+ 5s) blue	90.00	90.00

On No. 105
B15	A15	1t (+ 25s)	325.00	290.00

On Nos. 185-186
B16	A21	5s (+ 5s) on 6s	55.00	55.00
a.		Overprint inverted		
B17	A21	10s (+ 5s) on 12s	60.00	60.00
		Nos. B12-B17 (6)	607.50	572.50
		Set, never hinged	850.00	

Sold at an advance over face value, the excess being for the benefit of the Wild Tiger Corps. Counterfeits exist.

Stamps of 1905-20 Handstamp Overprinted

On Nos. 164, 146, 168
B18	A21	2s (+ 3s) org brn	35.00	35.00
B19	A21	3s (+ 2s) green	35.00	35.00
a.		Pair, one without ovpt.		
B20	A21	15s (+ 5s) blue	52.50	52.50

On No. 105
B21	A15	1t (+ 25s)	260.00	260.00

On No. 186
B22	A21	10s on 12s (+ 5s)	55.00	55.00

On No. 190
B23	A23	5s (+ 5s)	85.00	85.00
		Nos. B18-B23 (6)	522.50	522.50
		Set, never hinged		

Sold at an advance over face value, the excess being for the benefit of the Wild Tiger Corps. Counterfeits exist.

Nos. 187-188, 190, 193-194, 196, 198 Overprinted in Blue or Red

1920, Dec. 21
B24	A23	2s brown, *yel*	13.00	13.00
B25	A23	3s grn, *grn* (R)	13.00	13.00
B26	A23	5s rose, *pale rose*	13.00	13.00
B27	A23	10s blk & org (R)	13.00	13.00
B28	A23	15s bl, *bluish* (R)	25.00	25.00
B29	A23	25s chocolate	85.00	85.00
B30	A23	50s ocher & blk (R)	190.00	190.00
		Nos. B24-B30 (7)	352.00	352.00
		Set, never hinged	550.00	

Sold at an advance over face value, the excess being for the benefit of the Wild Tiger Corps. Counterfeits exist.

Nos. 170-172 Surcharged in Red

1939, Apr. 6   **Unwmk.**   **Perf. 14**
B31	A22	5s + 5s on 1b	20.00	20.00
B32	A22	10s + 5s on 2b	26.00	26.00
B33	A22	15s + 5s on 3b	26.00	26.00
		Nos. B31-B33 (3)	72.00	72.00
		Set, never hinged	110.00	

Founding of the Intl. Red Cross Soc., 75th anniv.
Bottom line of overprint is different on Nos. B32-B33.

> **Catalogue values for unused stamps in this section, from this point to the end of the section, are for Never Hinged items.**

No. 214 Surcharged in Carmine

1952   **Unwmk.**   **Perf. 12½**
B34	A25	80s + 20s blue & blk	21.00	12.00

New constitution.

Red Cross and Dancer — SP1

Lithographed, Cross Typographed
1953, Apr. 6   **Wmk. 299**   **Perf. 11**
Cross in Red, Dancer Dark Blue
B35	SP1	25s + 25s yellow grn	11.00	4.00
B36	SP1	50s + 50s brt rose	22.50	7.00
B37	SP1	1b + 1b lt blue	29.00	8.00
		Nos. B35-B37 (3)	62.50	19.00

60th anniv. of the founding of the Siamese Red Cross Society.

Nos. B35-B37 Overprinted with Year Date "24 98," in Black

1955, Apr. 3
Cross in Red, Dancer Dark Blue
B38	SP1	25s + 25s yel grn	55.00	15.00
B39	SP1	50s + 50s brt rose	120.00	25.00
B40	SP1	1b + 1b lt blue	140.00	35.00
		Nos. B38-B40 (3)	315.00	75.00

Counterfeits exist.

Red Cross Cent. Emblem — SP2

1963   **Wmk. 334**   **Litho.**   **Perf. 13½**
B41		50s + 10s cross at right	.30	.20
B42		50s + 10s cross at left	.30	.20
a.		SP2 Pair, #B41-B42	.60	

Cent. of the Intl. Red Cross.

Nos. B41-B42 Surcharged

1973, Feb. 15
B43	SP2	75s + 25s on 50s + 10s	.75	.75
B44	SP3	75s + 25s on 50s + 10s	.75	.75
a.		Pair, #B43-B44	2.00	

Red Cross Fair, Feb. 15-19.

Nos. B41-B42 Surcharged

1974, Feb. 2
B45	SP2	75s + 25s on 50s + 10s	.40	.30
B46	SP3	75s + 25s on 50s + 10s	.40	.30
a.		Pair, #B45-B46	1.50	

Red Cross Fair, Feb. 1974. Position of surcharge reversed on No. B46.

Nos. B41-B42 Surcharged

1975, Feb 11 52
B47	SP2	75s + 25s on 50s + 10s	.50	.30
B48	SP3	75s + 25s on 50s + 10s	.50	.30
a.		Pair, #B47-B48		

Red Cross Fair, Feb. 1975. Position of surcharge reversed on No. B48.

Nos. B41-B42 Surcharged

1976, Feb. 26
B49	SP2	75s + 25s on 50s + 10s	.40	.40
B50	SP3	75s + 25s on 50s + 10s	.40	.40
a.		Pair, #B49-B50	1.50	

Red Cross Fair, Feb. 16-Mar. 1. Position of surcharge reversed on #B50.

Nos. B41-B42 Surcharged

1977, Apr. 6   **Wmk. 334**   **Perf. 13½**
B51	SP2	75s + 25s on 50s + 10s	.45	.30
B52	SP3	75s + 25s on 50s + 10s	.45	.30
a.		Pair, #B51-B52	1.50	

Red Cross Fair 1977.

Red Cross Blood Collection SP4   Eye and Blind People SP5

Wmk. 329
1978, Apr. 6   **Photo.**   **Perf. 13**
B53	SP4	2.75b + 25s multi	1.00	.25

"Give blood, save life."
For surcharge see No. B58.

Perf. 14x13½
1979, Apr. 6   **Litho.**   **Wmk. 368**
B54	SP5	75s + 25s multi	.55	.20

"Give an eye, save new life." Red Cross Fair. Surtax was for Thai Red Cross.
For surcharge see No. B59.

Extracting Snake Venom, Red Cross — SP6

1980, Apr.   **Perf. 11x13**
B55	SP6	75s + 25s multi	.90	.90

Red Cross Fair. Surtax was for Thai Red Cross.
For surcharge see No. B60.

Nurse Helping Victim — SP7

1981, Apr. 6   Wmk. 377   Perf. 12½
B56 SP7 75 + 25s red & gray grn 1.25 1.25
Red Cross Fair (canceled). Surtax was for
Thai Red Cross.
For surcharge see No. B65.

Red
Cross
Fair
SP8

Perf. 13x13½
1983, Apr. 6   Litho.   Wmk. 329
B57 SP8 1.25b + 25s multi   .75 .75
Surtax was for Thai Red Cross.

No. B53 Surcharged

1984, Apr.   Photo.   Perf. 13
B58 SP4 3.25b + 25s on 2.75b +
25s   2.00 2.00
Red Cross Fair. Surtax was for Thai Red
Cross. Overprint translates: Red Cross
Donation.

No. B54
Surcharged

Wmk. 387

1985, Mar. 30   Litho.   Perf. 13
B59 SP5 2b + 25c on 75s + 25s   1.50 1.50
Surtax for the Thai Red Cross.

No. B55 Overprinted and Surcharged

1986, Apr. 6   Wmk. 368   Perf. 11x13
B60 SP6 2b + 25s on 75s + 25s   1.50 1.50
Natl. Children's Day. Surtax for Natl. Red
Cross Society. Overprint translates "Red
Cross Donation."

Natl. Scouting Movement, 75th Anniv.,
15th Asia-Pacific Conference,
Thailand — SP9

#B61, Scouts, saluting, community service.
#B62, Scout activities. #B63, King & queen at
ceremony. #B64, 15th Asia-Pacific conf.

1986, Nov. 7   Wmk. 385   Perf. 13½
B61 SP9 2b + 50s multi   .35 .35
B62 SP9 2b + 50s multi   .35 .35
B63 SP9 2b + 50s multi   .35 .35
B64 SP9 2b + 50s multi   .35 .35
Nos. B61-B64 (4)   1.40 1.40
Surtax for the Natl. Scouting Fund.

No. B56 Surcharged

1987, Apr.   Wmk. 377   Perf. 12½
B65 SP7 2b + 50s on 75s + 25s   .95 .20

Sports
SP10   SP11

Designs: No. B66, Hurdles, medal winners.
No. B67, Race, nurse treating injured cyclist.
No. B68, Boxers training. No. B69, Soccer.

1989, Dec. 16   Wmk. 387   Perf. 13½
B66 SP10 2b +1b multi   .40 .25
B67 SP10 2b +1b multi   .40 .25
B68 SP10 2b +1b multi   .40 .25
B69 SP10 2b +1b multi   .40 .25
Nos. B66-B69 (4)   1.60 1.00
Surtax for sports welfare organizations.

1990, Dec. 16
B70 SP11 2b +1b Judo   .40 .25
B71 SP11 2b +1b Archery   .40 .25
B72 SP11 2b +1b High jump   .40 .25
B73 SP11 2b +1b Windsurfing   .40 .25
Nos. B70-B73 (4)   1.60 1.00
Surtax for sports welfare organization.

Sports — SP12

Wmk. 387
1991, Dec. 16   Litho.   Perf. 13½
B74 SP12 2b +1b Jogging   .30 .20
B75 SP12 2b +1b Cycling   .30 .20
B76 SP12 2b +1b Soccer, jump-
ing rope   .30 .20
B77 SP12 2b +1b Swimming   .30 .20
Nos. B74-B77 (4)   1.20 .80
Surtax for sports welfare organizations.

18th South East
Asian Games,
Chiang
Mai — SP13

No. B78: a, Water polo. b, Tennis. c, Hur-
dles. d, Gymnastics.
No. B79: a, Fencing. b, Pool. c, Diving. d,
Pole vault.

1994, Dec. 16   Wmk. 340
B78 SP13 2b +1b Strip of 4,
#a.-d.   1.00 .75
e.   Souvenir sheet, #B78   1.25 1.00
Wmk. 387
B79 SP13 2b +1b Strip of 4,
#a.-d.   1.00 .75
e.   Souvenir sheet, #B79   1.25 1.25
Nos. B78e, B79e sold for 15b.
Issued: #B78, 12/16/94; #B79, 12/9/95.

SP14

13th Asian Games, Bangkok — SP15

1998, Mar. 27   Perf. 14½x14
B80 SP14 2b +1b Shooting   .20 .20
B81 SP14 3b +1b Rhythmic
gymnastics   .20 .20
B82 SP14 4b +1b Swimming   .25 .20
B83 SP14 7b +1b Wind-surfing   .35 .30
Nos. B80-B83 (4)   1.00 .90

Perf. 14½x14
1998, Dec. 6   Litho.   Unwmk.
Granite Paper
B84 SP15 2b +1b Field hockey   .20 .20
B85 SP15 3b +1b Wrestling   .20 .20
B86 SP15 4b +1b Rowing   .25 .20
B87 SP15 7b +1b Equestrian   .35 .30
Nos. B84-B87 (4)   1.00 .90

AIR POST STAMPS

Garuda — AP1

1925   Unwmk.   Engr.   Perf. 14, 14½
C1 AP1 2s brown, yel   2.00 .50
C2 AP1 3s dark brown   2.00 .50
C3 AP1 5s green   6.00 .50
C4 AP1 10s black & org   17.50 1.00
C5 AP1 15s carmine   5.00 1.50
C6 AP1 25s dark blue   5.00 1.50
C7 AP1 50s brown org & blk   35.00 9.00
C8 AP1 1b blue & brown   32.50 11.00
Nos. C1-C8 (8)   105.00 25.50
Set, never hinged   165.00
Issued: 2s, 50s, 4/21; others, 1/3.

Nos. C1-C8 received this overprint
("Government Museum 2468") in 1925,
but were never issued. The death of
King Vajiravudh caused cancellation of
the fair at which this set was to have
been released.
They were used during 1928 only in
the interdepartmental service for
accounting purposes of the money-
order sections of various Bangkok post
offices, and were never sold to the public. Value for canceled set, $25.

1930-37   Perf. 12½
C9 AP1 2s brown, yel   5.00 1.00
C10 AP1 5s green   1.25 .20
C11 AP1 10s black & org   2.50 .20
C12 AP1 15s carmine   25.00 6.00
C13 AP1 25s dark blue ('37)   1.50 1.00
a.   Vert. pair, imperf. btwn.   450.00
C14 AP1 50s brn org & blk
('37)   3.00 1.50
Nos. C9-C14 (6)   38.25 9.90
Set, never hinged   62.50

Monument of
Democracy,
Bangkok
AP2

1942-43   Engr.   Perf. 11
C15 AP2 2s dk org brn
('43)   1.75 .80
C16 AP2 3s dk grn ('43)   32.50 19.00
a.   Vert. pair, imperf. btwn.   100.00 100.00
C17 AP2 5s deep claret   2.00 .25
a.   Horiz. pair, imperf. btwn.   75.00 75.00
b.   Vert. pair, imperf. btwn.   75.00 75.00
C18 AP2 10s carmine ('43)   15.00 .60
a.   Vert. pair, imperf. btwn.   100.00 100.00
C19 AP2 15s dark blue   3.00 2.00
a.   Vert. pair, imperf. btwn.   100.00 100.00
Nos. C15-C19 (5)   54.25 22.65
Set, never hinged   80.00

**Catalogue values for unused
stamps in this section, from this
point to the end of the section, are
for Never Hinged items.**

Garuda and
Bangkok
Skyline — AP3

1952-53   Perf. 13x12½
C20 AP3 1.50b red violet ('53)   4.75 .25
C21 AP3 2b dark blue   11.00 2.50
C22 AP3 3b gray ('53)   16.00 1.10
Nos. C20-C22 (3)   31.75 3.85
Issue dates: June 15, 1952. Sept. 15, 1953.

OFFICIAL STAMPS

**Catalogue values for unused
stamps in this section are for
Never Hinged items.**

O1   O2

Perf. 10½ Rough
1963, Oct. 1   Typo.   Unwmk.
Without Gum
O1 O1 10s pink & dp car   .20 .20
O2 O1 20s brt grn & car rose   .20 .20
O3 O1 25s blue & dp car   .30 .35
O4 O1 50s deep carmine   1.00 2.00
O5 O2 1b silver & car rose   1.00 3.00
O6 O2 2b bronze & car rose   2.00 1.50
Nos. O1-O6 (6)   4.70 7.25

Issued as an official test from Oct. 1, 1963,
to Jan. 31, 1964, to determine the amount of
mail sent out by various government
departments.
Nos. O5, O9, O10 exist with oval frame of
type O1.

1964   Without Gum
O7 O1 20s green   .50 .50
O8 O1 25s blue   .50 .50
O9 O2 1b silver   1.00 1.00
O10 O2 2b bister   2.50 2.50
Nos. O7-O10 (4)   4.50 4.50

Others values exist printed in one color.

THRACE

'thrās

LOCATION — In southeastern Europe between the Black and Aegean Seas
GOVT. — Former Turkish Province
AREA — 89,361 sq. mi. (approx.)

Thrace underwent many political changes during the Balkan Wars and World War I. It was finally divided among Turkey, Greece and Bulgaria.

100 Lepta = 1 Drachma
40 Paras = 1 Piaster
100 Stotinki = 1 Leva (1919)

Giumulzina District Issue

Turkish Stamps of 1909 Surcharged in Blue or Red

1913		**Unwmk.**	**Perf. 12, 13½**
1	A21	10 l on 20pa rose (Bl)	20.00 30.00
2	A21	25 l on 10pa bl grn	47.50 47.50
3	A21	25 l on 20pa rose (Bl)	60.00 60.00
4	A21	25 l on 1pi ultra	80.00 92.50
		Nos. 1-4 (4)	207.50 230.00

Counterfeits exist of Nos. 1-4.

Turkish Inscriptions
A1   A2

1913		**Litho.**	**Imperf.**
		Laid Paper	
		Control Mark in Rose	
		Without Gum	
5	A1	1pi blue	17.00 17.00
6	A1	2pi violet	20.00 20.00
		Wove Paper	
7	A2	10pa vermilion	35.00 32.50
8	A2	20pa blue	35.00 32.50
9	A2	1pi violet	37.50 32.50
		Nos. 5-9 (5)	144.50 134.50

Turkish Stamps of 1908-13 Surcharged in Red or Black

1913			**Perf. 12**
10	A22	1pi on 2pa ol grn (R)	12.00 12.00
10A	A22	1pi on 2pa ol grn	12.00 12.00
11	A22	1pi on 5pa ocher	16.00 14.50
11A	A22	1pi on 5pa ocher (R)	17.50 17.00
12	A22	1pi on 20pa rose	26.00 25.00
13	A21	1pi on 5pi dk vio (R)	60.00 60.00
13A	A21	1pi on 5pi dk vio	55.00 55.00
14	A21	1pi on 10pi dl red	90.00 90.00
15	A19	1pi on 25pi dk grn	425.00 425.00
		Nos. 10-15 (9)	713.50 710.50

On Nos. 13-15 the surcharge is vertical, reading up. No. 15 exists with double surcharge, one black, one red.
Nos. 10-15 exist with forged surcharges.

Bulgarian Stamps of 1911 Handstamp Surcharged in Red or Blue

1913			
16	A20	10pa on 1s myr grn (R)	20.00 20.00
17	A21	20pa on 2s car & blk	20.00 20.00
18	A23	1pi on 5s grn & blk (R)	20.00 20.00
19	A22	2pi on 3s lake & blk	26.00 26.00
20	A24	2½pi on 10s dp red & blk	40.00 40.00
21	A25	5pi on 15s brn bis	62.50 62.50
		Nos. 16-21 (6)	188.50 188.50

Same Surcharges on Greek Stamps
On Issue of 1911

1913		**Serrate Roulette 13½**	
22	A24	10pa on 1 l grn (R)	21.00 21.00
23	A24	10pa on 1 l grn (R)	22.50 22.50
25	A25	10pa on 25 l ultra (R)	30.00 30.00
26	A25	20pa on 2 l car rose	20.00 20.00
27	A24	1pi on 3 l ver	20.00 20.00
28	A26	2pi on 5 l grn (R)	47.50 47.50
29	A24	2½pi on 10 l car rose	47.50 47.50
30	A25	5pi on 40 l dp bl (R)	82.50 82.50
		Nos. 22-30 (8)	291.00 291.00

On Occupation Stamps of 1912

31	O1	10pa on 1 l brn	14.00 14.00
32	O1	20pa on 1 l brn	14.00 14.00
33	O1	1pi on 1 l brn	14.00 14.00
		Nos. 31-33 (3)	42.00 42.00

These surcharges were made with handstamps, two of which were required for each surcharge. One or both parts may be found inverted, double or omitted.
Nos. 16-33 exist with forged surcharges.

OCCUPATION STAMPS

Issued under Allied Occupation

Bulgarian Stamps of 1915-19 Handstamped in Violet Blue

Perf. 11½, 11½x12, 14

1919				**Unwmk.**
N1	A43	1s black	2.00	2.00
N2	A43	2s olive green	2.00	2.00
N3	A44	5s green	.75	.75
N4	A44	10s rose	.75	.75
N5	A44	15s violet	.85	.85
N6	A26	25s indigo & black	.85	.85
		Nos. N1-N6 (6)	7.20	7.20

The overprint on Nos. N1-N6 is frequently inverted and known in other positions.

Bulgarian Stamps of 1911-19 Overprinted in Red or Black

1919				
N7	A43	1s black (R)	.20	.20
N8	A43	2s olive green	.20	.20
N9	A44	5s green	.20	.20
N10	A44	10s rose	.20	.20
N11	A44	15s violet	.20	.20
N12	A26	25s indigo & black	.25	.25
N13	A29	1 l chocolate	4.00	4.00
N14	A37a	2 l brown orange	6.00	6.00
N15	A38	3 l claret	10.00	10.00
		Nos. N7-N15 (9)	21.25	21.25

Overprint is vertical, reading up, on Nos. N9-N13.

The following varieties are found in the setting of "INTERALLIEE": Inverted "V" for "A," second "L" inverted, "F" instead of final "E."

Bulgarian Stamps of 1919 Overprinted

1920				
N16	A44	5s green	.25	.25
N17	A44	10s rose	.25	.25
N18	A44	15s violet	.25	.25
N19	A44	50s yellow brown	.70	.70
		Nos. N16-N19 (4)	1.45	1.45

The varieties: "Irteralliee" and final "e" inverted are found on all values.

Bulgarian Stamps of 1919 Overprinted

1920		**Perf. 12x11½**		
N20	A44	5s green	.25	.25
a.		Inverted overprint	19.00	
N21	A44	10s rose	.25	.25
a.		Inverted overprint	19.00	
N22	A44	15s violet	.25	.25
N23	A44	25s deep blue	.25	.25
N24	A44	50s ocher	.25	.25
		Imperf		
N25	A44	30s chocolate	.75	.75
		Nos. N20-N25 (6)	2.00	2.00

No. N25 is not known without overprint.

ISSUED UNDER GREEK OCCUPATION

For Use in Western Thrace

Greek Stamps of 1911-19 Overprinted

		Serrate Roulette 13½		
1920		**Litho.**		**Unwmk.**
N26	A24	1 l green	.20	.35
a.		Inverted overprint	15.00	
N27	A25	2 l rose	.20	.35
N28	A24	3 l vermilion	.20	.35
N29	A26	5 l green	.20	.35
N30	A24	10 l rose	.30	.50
N31	A25	15 l dull blue	.35	.65
a.		Inverted overprint	16.00	
b.		Dbl. ovpt., one inverted	24.00	
N32	A25	25 l blue	.40	.75
N33	A26	30 l rose	29.00	50.00
N34	A25	40 l indigo	1.90	4.00
N35	A26	50 l violet brn	1.90	5.00
N36	A27	1d ultra	6.50	14.00
N37	A27	2d vermilion	17.50	32.50
		Engr.		
N38	A25	2 l car rose	.60	.60
N39	A24	3 l vermilion	.60	.60
N40	A27	1d ultra	25.00	52.50
N41	A27	2d vermilion	25.00	55.00
N42	A27	3d car rose	37.50	70.00
N43	A27	5d ultra	14.50	22.50
N44	A27	10d deep blue	14.00	20.00
		Nos. N26-N44 (19)	175.85	330.00

Nos. N42-N44 are overprinted on the reissues of Greece Nos. 210-212. See footnote below Greece No. 213. Counterfeits exist of Nos. N26-N84.

ΔΙΟΙΚΗΣΙΣ
ΔΥΤΙΚΗΣ
Overprinted   ΘΡΑΚΗΣ

N45	A28	25d deep blue	40.00 65.00

This overprint reads: "Administration Western Thrace."

With Additional Overprint

		Litho.		
N46	A24	1 l green	.55	1.10
N47	A25	2 l rose	.20	.40
a.		Inverted overprint	77.50	
N48	A24	10 l rose	.55	.65
N49	A25	20 l slate	.55	.65
N50	A26	30 l rose	.65	1.00
		Engr.		
N51	A27	2d vermilion	19.00	32.50
N52	A27	3d car rose	8.50	22.50
N53	A27	5d ultra	25.00	42.50
N54	A27	10d deep blue	19.00	32.50
a.		Double overprint	45.00	
		Nos. N46-N54 (9)	74.00	133.40

For Use in Eastern and Western Thrace

Greek Stamps of 1911-19 Overprinted

1920		**Litho.**		
N55	A24	1 l green	.20	.30
a.		Pair, one without ovpt.	22.50	
N56	A25	2 l rose	.20	.30
N57	A24	3 l vermilion	.20	.30
N58	A26	5 l green	.25	.45
a.		Pair, one without ovpt.	24.00	
N59	A24	10 l rose	.40	.70
a.		Double overprint	27.50	
N60	A25	20 l slate	.65	1.25
a.		Inverted overprint	15.00	
N61	A25	25 l blue	1.25	2.00
N62	A25	40 l indigo	2.40	6.50
N63	A26	50 l violet brn	3.00	8.50
N64	A27	1d ultra	12.00	20.00
N65	A27	2d vermilion	22.50	35.00
		Engr.		
N66	A24	3 l vermilion	2.75	4.75
N67	A25	20 l gray lilac	9.50	22.50
N68	A28	25d deep blue	47.50	90.00
		Nos. N55-N68 (14)	102.80	192.55

This overprint reads "Administration Thrace."

With Additional Overprint as Nos. N46-N54

		Litho.		
N69	A25	2 l car rose	.25	.50
N70	A26	5 l green	1.50	3.00
N71	A25	20 l slate	.25	.50
N72	A26	30 l rose	.25	.50
		Engr.		
N73	A27	3d car rose	7.50	14.00
N74	A27	5d ultra	18.00	30.00
N75	A27	10d deep blue	32.50	60.00
		Nos. N69-N75 (7)	60.25	108.50

Turkish Stamps of 1916-20 Surcharged in Blue, Black or Red

1920			**Perf. 11½, 12½**	
N76	A43	1 l on 5pa org (Bl)	.40	.50
N77	A32	5 l on 3pi blue	.40	.50
N78	A30	20 l on 1pi bl grn	.50	.70
N79	A53	25 l on 5pi on 2pa Prus bl (R)	.60	.75
N80	A49	50 l on 5pi bl & blk (R)	4.75	4.75
N81	A45	1d on 20pa dp rose (Bl)	1.60	1.40
N82	A22	5d on 10pa on 2pa ol grn (R)	2.50	2.50
N83	A57	3d on 1pi dp bl (R)	9.50	9.50
N84	A23	5d on 20pa rose	9.00	9.00
		Nos. N76-N84 (9)	29.25	29.60

Nos. N77, N78 and N84 are on the 1920 issue with designs modified. Nos. N81, N82 and N83 are on stamps with the 1919 overprints.

Varieties found on some values of this issue include: inverted surcharge, double surcharge with one inverted, and surcharge on both face and back.

POSTAGE DUE STAMPS

Issued under Allied Occupation

Bulgarian Postage Due Stamps of 1919 Overprinted like Nos. N7-N15 Reading Vertically Up

				Perf. 12x11½
1919		**Unwmk.**		
NJ1	D6	5s emerald	.30	.30
NJ2	D6	10s purple	.70	.70
NJ3	D6	50s blue	.70	.60
		Nos. NJ1-NJ3 (3)	1.70	1.60

Type of Bulgarian Postage Due Stamps of 1919-22 Overprinted

1920				*Imperf.*
NJ4	D6	5s emerald	.20	.20
NJ5	D6	10s deep violet	1.40	1.40
NJ6	D6	20s salmon	.25	.25
NJ7	D6	50s blue	1.25	1.10
		Perf. 12x11½		
NJ8	D6	10s deep violet	1.00	.80
		Nos. NJ4-NJ8 (5)	4.10	3.75

TIBET

tə-'bet

LOCATION — A high tableland in Central Asia

GOVT. — A semi-independent state, nominally under control of China (under Communist China since 1950-51). In 1965 Tibet became a nominally autonomous region of the People's Republic of China.

AREA — 463,200 sq. mi.

POP. — 1,500,000 (approx.)

CAPITAL — Lhasa

Tibet's postage stamps were valid only within its borders.

6 ⅔ Trangka = 1 Sang

"Stamps" produced by the "Tibetan Government in Exile" have no postal value. These include four-value sets for Himalayan animals and the UPU that were put on sale in the early 1970s.

Excellent counterfeits of Nos. 1-18 exist. Numerous shades of all values.

All stamps issued without gum

Small bits of foreign matter (inclusions) are to be expected in Native Paper. These do not reduce the value of the stamp unless they have caused serious damage to the design or paper.

Lion
A1   A2

1912-50		**Unwmk. Typo.**		*Imperf.*
		Native Paper		
1	A1	⅛t green	35.00	40.00
2	A1	⅛t blue	40.00	45.00
a.		⅛t ultramarine	45.00	55.00
3	A1	¼t violet	40.00	45.00
4	A1	⅔t carmine	45.00	50.00
a.		"POTSAGE"	140.00	150.00

5	A1	1t vermilion	50.00	60.00
6	A1	1s sage green ('50)	90.00	100.00
		Nos. 1-6 (6)	300.00	340.00

The "POTSAGE" error is found on all shades of the ⅔t (positions 6 and 7).
Pin-perf. copies of Nos. 1 and 3 exist.
Issued in sheets of 12.
Beware of private reproductions of #1-5 that were printed in the US around 1986. Sheets of 12 bear "J. Crow Co." imprint. The set of 5 sheets was sold for $5.

Printed Using Shiny Enamel Paint

1920				
1a	A1	⅛t green	50.00	30.00
2b	A1	⅛t blue	450.00	450.00
3d	A1	¼t purple	90.00	100.00
4h	A1	⅔t carmine	90.00	100.00
i.		"POTSAGE"	200.00	225.00
5c	A1	1t carmine	300.00	300.00

In some 1920-30 printings, European enamel paint was used instead of ink. It has a glossy surface.

1914				
7	A2	4t milky blue	675.	725.
a.		4t dark blue	1,000.	1,000.
8	A2	8t carmine rose	160.	160.
a.		8t carmine	1,000.	1,100.

Issued in sheets of 6.

Printed Using Shiny Enamel Paint

1920				
7b	A2	4t blue	1,200.	1,250.
8b	A2	8t carmine	1,200.	1,250.

See note following No. 5c.

A3

Thin White Native Paper

1933				*Pin-perf.*
9	A3	½t orange	82.50	95.00
10	A3	⅔t dark blue	82.50	110.00
11	A3	1t rose carmine	82.50	110.00
12	A3	2t scarlet	82.50	110.00
13	A3	4t emerald	82.50	110.00
		Nos. 9-13 (5)	412.50	535.00

Issued in sheets of 12.
Exist imperf.

Heavy Toned Native Paper

1934				*Imperf.*
14	A3	½t yellow	13.00	16.00
15	A3	⅔t blue	10.00	11.00
16	A3	1t orange ver	8.75	10.00
a.		1t carmine	11.00	11.00
17	A3	2t red	10.00	10.00
a.		2t orange vermilion	7.75	7.75
18	A3	4t green	7.75	7.75
a.		25x25mm instead of 24x24mm	50.00	60.00
		Nos. 14-18 (5)	49.50	54.75

Nos. 14-18 are also known with a private pin-perf.
The ½t and 1t exist printed on both sides.
Issued in sheets of 12.

OFFICIAL STAMPS

O1

O2

Various Designs and Sizes Inscribed "STAMP"

Sizes: No. O1, 32½x32½mm. No. O2, 38x28½mm. No. O3, 34x33mm. No. O4, 44x44mm. No. O5, 66x66mm.

1945		**Unwmk. Typo.**		*Imperf.*
		Native Paper		
O1	O1	⅛t bronze green		
O2	O2	⅛t slate black		
O3	O1	⅔t reddish brown		
O4	O1	1 ⅛t olive green		
O5	O1	1s dark gray blue		

The status of Nos. O1-O5 is in question. Other values exist.

TIMOR

'tē-,mor

LOCATION — The eastern part of Timor island, Malay archipelago

GOVT. — Former Portuguese Overseas Territory

AREA — 7,330 sq. mi.

POP. — 660,000 (est. 1974)

CAPITAL — Dili

The Portuguese territory of Timor was annexed by Indonesia May 3, 1976. Timor-Leste achieved independent statehood status on May 20, 2002.

1000 Reis = 1 Milreis
78 Avos = 1 Rupee (1895)
100 Avos = 1 Pataca
100 Centavos = 1 Escudo (1960)
100 Cents = 1 Dollar (2000)

Catalogue values for unused stamps in this country are for Never Hinged items, beginning with Scott 256 in the regular postage section, Scott J31 in the postage due section, and Scott RA11 in the postal tax section.

Watermark

Wmk. 232 —
Maltese Cross

Stamps of Macao Overprinted in Black or Carmine   **TIMOR**

1885		**Unwmk.**	**Perf. 12½, 13½**	
1	A1	5r black (C)	5.50	1.60
a.		Double overprint	37.50	37.50
b.		Triple overprint	115.00	
2	A1	10r green	8.00	3.50
a.		Overprint on Mozambique stamp	22.50	14.00
b.		Overprinted on Portuguese India stamp	210.00	150.00
3	A1	20r rose, perf. 13½	9.00	4.50
a.		Double overprint	22.50	
b.		Perf. 12½	9.50	5.00
4	A1	25r violet	2.25	1.10
a.		Perf. 13½	22.00	11.00
5	A1	40r yellow	5.50	3.00
a.		Double overprint	17.50	
b.		Inverted overprint	21.00	21.00
c.		Perf. 13½	14.00	11.00
6	A1	50r blue	4.50	1.50
a.		Perf. 13½	12.00	9.50
7	A1	80r slate	11.00	3.00
8	A1	100r lilac	5.50	1.50
a.		Double overprint	22.50	
b.		Perf. 13½	9.00	3.50
9	A1	200r org, perf. 13½	9.00	3.50
a.		Perf. 12½	11.00	3.50
10	A1	300r brown	8.00	3.00
		Nos. 1-10 (10)	68.25	26.20

The 20r brown, 25r rose and 50r green were prepared for use but not issued.
The reprints are printed on a smooth white chalky paper, ungummed, with rough perforation 13½, and on thin white paper with shiny white gum and clean-cut perforation 13½.

King Luiz — A2   King Carlos — A3

1887		**Embossed**	*Perf. 12½*	
11	A2	5r black	2.00	1.75
12	A2	10r green	3.50	3.00
13	A2	20r bright rose	3.50	3.00
14	A2	25r violet	6.75	3.50
15	A2	40r chocolate	11.50	4.50
16	A2	50r blue	14.00	5.50
17	A2	80r gray	14.00	7.50
18	A2	100r yellow brown	20.00	9.00
19	A2	200r gray lilac	25.00	16.00
20	A2	300r orange	25.00	16.00
		Nos. 11-20 (10)	125.25	69.75

Reprints of Nos. 11, 16, 18 and 19 have clean-cut perforation 13½.
For surcharges see Nos. 34-43, 83-91.

Macao No. 44 Surcharged in Black

1892		**Without Gum**	**Perf. 12½, 13**	
21	A7	30r on 300r orange	8.25	5.50

For surcharge see No. 44.

1894		**Typo.**	*Perf. 11½*	
22	A3	5r yellow	1.10	.65
23	A3	10r red violet	1.50	.65
24	A3	15r chocolate	2.75	.95
25	A3	20r lavender	3.50	1.10
26	A3	25r green	4.25	.80
27	A3	50r light blue	5.50	3.50
a.		Perf. 13½	150.00	125.00
28	A3	75r rose	6.75	2.75
29	A3	80r light green	7.25	4.25
30	A3	100r brown, *buff*	5.50	2.75
31	A3	150r car, *rose*	12.00	6.75
32	A3	200r dk bl, *lt bl*	12.50	8.00
33	A3	300r dk bl, *salmon*	14.00	9.50
		Nos. 22-33 (12)	76.60	41.65

For surcharges and overprints see Nos. 92-102, 120-122, 124-128, 131-133, 183-193, 199.

Stamps of 1887 Surcharged in Red, Green or Black

1895		**Without Gum**	*Perf. 12½*	
34	A2	1a on 5r black (R)	1.00	.85
35	A2	2a on 10r green	1.25	.85
a.		Double surcharge	17.50	
36	A2	3a on 20r brt rose (G)	2.75	1.75
37	A2	4a on 25r violet	2.75	1.10
38	A2	6a on 40r choc	4.50	2.50
39	A2	8a on 50r blue (R)	4.00	2.25
40	A2	13a on 80r gray	14.00	9.00
41	A2	16a on 100r yellow brn	15.00	6.75
42	A2	31a on 200r gray lilac	27.50	17.50
43	A2	47a on 300r org (G)	27.50	20.00
		Nos. 34-43 (10)	100.25	62.55

5 avos
PROVISORIO
仙伍

No. 21 Surcharged

1895		**Without Gum**	*Perf. 12½, 13*	
44	A7	5a on 30r on 300r org	8.50	5.00

Common Design Types pictured following the introduction.

Vasco da Gama Issue
Common Design Types

		1898	**Engr.**	**Perf. 14 to 15**	
45	CD20	½a blue green		1.50	.85
46	CD21	1a red		1.50	.85
47	CD22	2a red violet		1.50	.85
48	CD23	4a yellow green		1.50	.85
49	CD24	8a dark blue		3.00	1.25
50	CD25	12a violet brown		3.50	1.40
51	CD26	16a bister brown		4.00	1.90
52	CD27	24a bister		5.00	2.50
		Nos. 45-52 (8)		21.50	10.45

400th anniversary of Vasco da Gama's discovery of the route to India.
For overprints and surcharge see Nos. 148-155.

King Carlos
A5   A6

		1898-1903	**Typo.**	**Perf. 11½**	

Name & Value in Black Except #79

53	A5	½a gray		.35	.25
a.		Perf. 12½		2.50	1.75
54	A5	1a orange		.35	.30
a.		Perf. 12½		2.50	1.75
55	A5	2a light green		.35	.30
56	A5	2½a brown		1.25	1.10
57	A5	3a gray violet		1.25	1.10
58	A5	3a gray green ('03)		1.50	1.00
59	A5	4a sea green		1.60	1.00
60	A5	5a rose ('03)		1.50	1.00
61	A5	6a pale yel brn ('03)		1.50	1.00
62	A5	8a blue		2.00	1.10
63	A5	9a red brown ('03)		1.50	1.25
64	A5	10a slate blue ('00)		2.00	1.10
65	A5	10a gray brown ('03)		1.50	1.00
66	A5	12a rose		4.25	3.00
67	A5	12a dull blue ('03)		15.00	8.50
68	A5	13a violet		4.50	3.75
69	A5	13a red lilac ('03)		3.50	1.75
70	A5	15a gray lilac ('03)		5.50	3.75
71	A5	16a dark bl, *bl*		4.50	3.75
72	A5	20a brn, *yelsh* ('00)		5.25	3.75
73	A5	22a brn org, *pink* ('03)		5.25	3.50
74	A5	24a brown, *buff*		5.50	3.75
75	A5	31a red lil, *pinkish*		5.50	3.75
76	A5	31a brn, *straw* ('03)		5.75	3.50
77	A5	47a dk blue, *rose* ('03)		9.00	4.25
78	A5	47a red vio, *pink* ('03)		6.50	3.50
79	A5	78a blk & red, *bl* ('00)		11.00	6.00
80	A5	78a dl bl, *straw* ('03)		14.00	8.00
		Nos. 53-80 (28)		121.65	76.00

Most of Nos. 53-80 were issued without gum.
For surcharges & overprints see #81-82, 104-119, 129-130, 134-147, 195-196.

1899

Black Surcharge

81	A6	10a on 16a dk bl, *bl*	3.00	2.50
82	A6	20a on 31a red lil, *pnksh*	3.00	2.50

Surcharged in Black

1902

On Issue of 1887

83	A2	5a on 25r violet	2.50	1.75
84	A2	5a on 200r gray lil	4.00	2.50
85	A2	6a on 10r blue grn	75.00	40.00
86	A2	6a on 300r orange	3.75	3.50
87	A2	9a on 40r choc	4.50	3.50
88	A2	9a on 100r yel brn	4.50	3.50
89	A2	15a on 20r rose	4.50	3.50
90	A2	15a on 50r blue	75.00	40.00
91	A2	22a on 80r gray	7.50	5.00
		Nos. 83-91 (9)	181.25	103.25

Reprints of Nos. 83-88, 90-91, 104A have clean-cut perf. 13½.

On Issue of 1894

92	A3	5a on 5r yellow	1.90	1.10
a.		Inverted surcharge	40.00	30.00
93	A3	5a on 25r green	2.25	1.10
94	A3	5a on 50r lt blue	2.25	1.40
95	A3	6a on 20r lavender	2.25	1.40
96	A3	9a on 15r choc	2.25	1.40
97	A3	9a on 75r rose	2.25	1.40
98	A3	15a on 10r red vio	4.00	2.25
99	A3	15a on 100r brn, *buff*	4.00	2.25

100	A3	15a on 300r bl, *sal*	4.00	2.25
101	A3	22a on 80r lt green	6.00	4.00
102	A3	22a on 200r bl, *blue*	8.00	4.00

On Newspaper Stamp of 1893

103	N2	6a on 2½r brn	1.00	.85
a.		Inverted surcharge	27.50	27.50
		Nos. 92-103 (12)	40.15	23.40

Nos. 93-97, 99-102 issued without gum.

Stamps of 1898
Overprinted in Black

104	A5	3a gray violet	3.00	1.40
104A	A5	12a rose	6.00	3.75

Reprint noted after No. 91.

No. 67 Surcharged in Black

1905

105	A5	10a on 12a dull blue	3.50	2.50

Stamps of 1898-1903
Overprinted in
Carmine or Green

1911

106	A5	½a gray	.30	.30
a.		Inverted overprint	20.00	20.00
107	A5	1a orange	.30	.30
a.		Perf. 12½	16.00	16.00
108	A5	2a light green	.40	.35
109	A5	3a gray green	.50	.35
110	A5	5a rose (G)	.50	.35
111	A5	6a yel brown	.50	.35
112	A5	9a red brown	.75	.45
113	A5	10a gray brown	.75	.45
114	A5	13a red lilac	.80	.50
115	A5	15a gray lilac	1.60	1.25
116	A5	22a brn org, *pink*	1.60	1.25
117	A5	31a brown, *straw*	1.60	1.25
118	A5	47a red vio, *pink*	3.00	2.50
119	A5	78a dl bl, *straw*	4.75	3.50
		Nos. 106-119 (14)	17.35	13.15

Preceding Issues
Overprinted in Red

1913

Without Gum
On Provisional Issue of 1902

120	A3	5a on 5r yellow	4.00	4.00
121	A3	5a on 25r green	4.00	4.00
122	A3	5a on 50r lt bl	6.00	7.00
123	N2	6a on 2½r brn	6.00	7.00
124	A3	6a on 20r lavender	4.00	4.00
125	A3	9a on 15r choc	4.00	4.00
126	A3	15a on 100r brn, *buff*	6.00	5.50
127	A3	22a on 80r lt grn	9.00	8.00
128	A3	22a on 200r bl, *bl*	8.00	7.50

On Issue of 1903

129	A5	3a gray green	5.00	7.50

On Issue of 1905

130	A5	10a on 12a dull bl	4.50	4.00
		Nos. 120-130 (11)	60.50	62.50

Overprinted in Green
or Red

1913
On Provisional Issue of 1902

131	A3	9a on 75r rose (G)	4.50	4.50
132	A3	15a on 10r red vio (G)	3.75	3.75
133	A3	15a on 300r bl, *sal* (R)	6.50	6.50
a.		"REUBPLICA"	19.00	19.00
b.		"REPBLICAU"	19.00	19.00

On Issue of 1903

134	A5	5a rose (G)	3.00	3.00
		Nos. 131-134 (4)	17.75	17.75

Stamps of 1898-1903
Overprinted in Red

1913

135	A5	6a yellow brown	4.00	1.75
136	A5	9a red brown	4.00	1.75
137	A5	10a gray brown	4.00	1.75
138	A5	13a violet	6.00	2.50
a.		Inverted overprint	40.00	40.00
139	A5	13a red lilac	5.00	2.50
140	A5	15a gray lilac	6.00	3.25
141	A5	22a brn org, *pnksh*	7.00	3.50
142	A5	31a red lil, *pnksh*	7.00	3.50
143	A5	31a brown, *straw*	9.00	5.50
144	A5	47a blue, *pink*	10.00	5.50
145	A5	47a red vio, *pink*	12.00	8.00
146	A5	78a dl bl, *straw*	12.00	6.50

No. 79 Overprinted in
Red

147	A5	78a blk & red, *bl*	12.00	8.00
		Nos. 135-147 (13)	98.00	54.00

Vasco da Gama Issue of 1898
Overprinted or Surcharged in Black:

1913

148	CD20	½a blue green	.65	.60
149	CD21	1a red	.65	.60
150	CD22	2a red violet	.65	.60
151	CD23	4a yellow green	.65	.60
152	CD24	8a dark blue	1.40	1.10
153	CD25	10a on 12a vio brn	2.50	2.00
154	CD26	16a bister brown	2.00	1.75
155	CD27	24a bister	2.75	2.25
		Nos. 148-155 (8)	11.25	9.50

Ceres — A7

1914-23   Typo.   Perf. 15x14, 12x11½
Name and Value in Black

156	A7	½a olive brown	.20	.20
157	A7	1a black	.20	.20
158	A7	1½a yel grn ('23)	1.00	1.10
159	A7	2a blue green	.25	.25
160	A7	3a lilac brown	1.00	.75
161	A7	4a carmine	1.00	.75
162	A7	6a light violet	1.00	.75
163	A7	7a lt green ('23)	1.75	1.75
164	A7	7½a ultra ('23)	3.25	3.50
165	A7	9a blue ('23)	4.00	6.75
166	A7	10a deep blue	1.25	.75

167	A7	11a gray ('23)	4.00	6.75
168	A7	12a yellow brown	1.50	1.25
169	A7	15a lilac ('23)	8.00	7.25
170	A7	16a slate	2.00	3.75
171	A7	18a dp blue ('23)	10.00	6.25
172	A7	19a gray grn ('23)	10.00	5.50
173	A7	20a org brown	15.00	6.00
174	A7	36a turq blue ('23)	9.00	4.25
175	A7	40a plum	9.00	4.50
176	A7	54a choc ('23)	10.00	6.25
177	A7	58a brown, *grn*	10.00	5.00
178	A7	72a brt rose ('23)	16.00	16.00
179	A7	76a brown, *rose*	11.50	6.50
180	A7	1p org, *salmon*	20.00	11.00
181	A7	3p green, *blue*	35.00	25.00
182	A7	5p car rose ('23)	70.00	52.50
		Nos. 156-182 (27)	255.50	184.50

For surcharges see Nos. 200-201, MR1.

Preceding Issues
Overprinted in
Carmine

1915   Perf. 11½
On Provisional Issue of 1902

183	A3	5a on 5r yellow	1.00	.55
184	A3	5a on 25r green	1.00	.55
185	A3	5a on 50r lt blue	1.00	.55
186	A3	6a on 20r lavender	1.00	.55
187	A3	9a on 15r chocolate	1.00	.55
188	A3	9a on 75r rose	1.50	.55
189	A3	15a on 10r red vio	1.50	1.50
190	A3	15a on 100r brn, *buff*	2.00	1.50
191	A3	15a on 300r bl, *sal*	2.00	3.00
192	A3	22a on 80r lt grn	3.25	2.75
193	A3	22a on 200r bl, *bl*	5.00	5.00

On No. 103

194	N2	6a on 2½r, perf. 13½	1.00	.55
a.		Perf. 12½	2.00	1.25
b.		Perf. 11½	4.00	1.75

On No. 104

195	A5	3a gray violet	1.00	.60

On No. 105

196	A5	10a on 12a dull bl	1.10	.60
		Nos. 183-196 (14)	23.35	18.80

Type of 1915 with
Additional Surcharge
in Black

Perf. 11½

199	A3	½a on 5a on 50r lt bl	12.50	7.00
a.		Perf. 13½	35.00	12.50

Nos. 178 and 169
Surcharged

1932   Perf. 12x11½

200	A7	6a on 72a brt rose	1.50	1.25
201	A7	12a on 15a lilac	1.50	1.25

"Portugal" and Vasco
da Gama's Flagship
"San Gabriel" — A8

Perf. 11½x12

		1935	**Typo.**	**Wmk. 232**	
202	A8	½a bister		.20	.20
203	A8	1a olive brown		.20	.20
204	A8	2a blue green		.20	.20
205	A8	3a red violet		.60	.60
206	A8	4a black		.60	.60
207	A8	5a gray		.70	.65
208	A8	6a brown		.85	.65
209	A8	7a bright rose		1.00	1.00
210	A8	8a bright blue		1.10	1.10
211	A8	10a red orange		1.60	1.20
212	A8	12a dark blue		2.75	2.10
213	A8	14a olive green		3.25	2.10
214	A8	15a maroon		3.00	2.75
215	A8	20a orange		3.50	2.75
216	A8	30a apple green		4.00	2.75
217	A8	40a violet		7.50	4.50

218	A8	50a olive bister	8.75	4.50
219	A8	1p light blue	21.00	12.00
220	A8	2p brn orange	42.50	22.50
221	A8	3p emerald	52.50	32.50
222	A8	5p dark violet	82.50	45.00
		Nos. 202-222 (21)	*238.30*	*139.85*

Common Design Types

1938   Unwmk. Engr. Perf. 13½x13
Name and Value in Black

223	CD34	1a gray green	.20	.20
224	CD34	2a orange brown	.20	.30
225	CD34	3a dk violet brn	.20	.30
226	CD34	4a brt green	.20	.65
227	CD35	5a dk carmine	.20	1.75
228	CD35	6a slate	.45	.20
229	CD35	8a rose violet	.65	1.10
230	CD37	10a brt red violet	.65	1.75
231	CD37	12a red	1.10	2.50
232	CD37	15a orange	1.75	2.50
233	CD36	20a blue	1.75	.80
234	CD36	40a gray black	3.75	1.25
235	CD36	50a brown	3.75	1.25
236	CD38	1p brown carmine	7.00	4.50
237	CD38	2p olive green	14.00	3.50
238	CD38	3p blue violet	17.50	8.00
239	CD38	5p red brown	35.00	11.50
		Nos. 223-239 (17)	*88.35*	*42.05*

For overprints see Nos. 245A-245K.

Mozambique Nos. 273, 276, 278, 280, 282 and 283 Surcharged in Black

1946   Perf. 13½x13

240	CD34	1a on 15c dk vio brn	6.75	5.00
241	CD35	4a on 35c brt grn	6.75	5.00
242	CD35	8a on 50c brt red vio	6.75	5.00
243	CD36	10a on 70c brn vio	6.75	5.00
244	CD36	12a on 1e red	6.75	5.00
245	CD37	20a on 1.75e blue	6.75	5.00
		Nos. 240-245 (6)	*40.50*	*30.00*

Nos. 223-227 and 229-234
Overprinted "Libertacao"

1947

245A	CD34	1a gray green	18.00	12.50
245B	CD34	2a org brown	28.00	11.50
245C	CD34	3a dk vio brn	11.50	6.75
245D	CD34	4a brt green	11.50	9.00
245E	CD35	5a dark car	5.00	2.40
245F	CD35	8a rose violet	2.50	1.75
245G	CD37	10a brt red vio	7.00	3.75
245H	CD37	12a red	7.25	3.00
245I	CD37	15a orange	5.75	3.00
245J	CD36	20a blue	62.50	40.00
	m.	Inverted overprint	90.00	77.50
245K	CD36	40a gray black	17.50	9.25
		Nos. 245A-245K (11)	*176.50*	*102.90*

Timor Woman — A9   UPU Symbols — A10

Designs: 3a, Gong ringer. 4a, Girl with basket. 8a, Aleixo de Ainaro. 10a, 1p, 3p, Heads of various chieftains. 20a, Warrior and horse.

1948   Litho.   Perf. 14

246	A9	1a aqua & dk brn	.50	.50
247	A9	3a gray & dk brn	1.10	.60
248	A9	4a pink & dk grn	1.40	.60
249	A9	8a red & blue blk	.80	.35
250	A9	10a blue grn & org	.80	.50
251	A9	20a ultra, aqua & bl	.85	.45
252	A9	1p org, bl & ultra	16.00	5.00
253	A9	3p vio & dk brn	16.00	5.00
	a.	Sheet of 8, #246-253	55.00	55.00
		Nos. 246-253 (8)	*37.45*	*11.00*

No. 253a sold for 5p.

Lady of Fatima Issue
Common Design Type

1948, Oct.

254	CD40	8a slate gray	3.00	3.00

UPU Issue

1949   Unwmk.   Perf. 14.

255	A10	16a brown & buff	4.00	*5.00*

UPU, 75th anniversary.

> **Catalogue values for unused stamps in this section, from this point to the end of the section, are for Never Hinged items.**

Craftsman A11   Timor Woman A12

1950   Perf. 14½

256	A11	20a dull vio blue	1.10	.70
257	A12	50a dull brown	4.50	1.40

Holy Year Issue
Common Design Types

1950, May   Perf. 13x13½

258	CD41	40a green	1.50	1.25
259	CD42	70a black brown	2.25	2.00

Blackberry Lily — A13

Designs: Various flowers.

1950   Unwmk.   Litho.   Perf. 14½

260	A13	1a multicolored	.35	.30
261	A13	3a multicolored	1.40	1.00
262	A13	10a multicolored	1.75	1.00
263	A13	16a multicolored	3.50	1.25
264	A13	20a multicolored	1.40	1.00
265	A13	30a multicolored	1.75	1.10
266	A13	70a multicolored	2.25	1.25
267	A13	1p multicolored	3.75	2.00
268	A13	2p multicolored	6.00	3.50
269	A13	5p multicolored	9.50	4.50
		Nos. 260-269 (10)	*31.65*	*16.90*

Holy Year Extension Issue
Common Design Type

1951   Perf. 14

270	CD43	86a bl & pale bl + label	2.00	1.75

Stamp without label attached sells for much less.

Medical Congress Issue
Common Design Type

Design: Weighing baby.

1952   Litho.   Perf. 13½

271	CD44	10a ol blk & brn	.90	.85

St. Francis Xavier Issue

Statue of St. Francis Xavier — A14

Designs: 16a, Miraculous Arm of St. Francis. 1p, Tomb of St. Francis.

1952, Oct. 25   Perf. 14

272	A14	1a black	.25	.20
273	A14	16a blk brn & brn	1.00	.80
274	A14	1p dk car & gray	5.00	2.00
		Nos. 272-274 (3)	*6.25*	*3.00*

400th death anniv. of St. Francis Xavier.

Madonna and Child — A15   Stamp of Portugal and Arms of Colonies — A16

1953   Perf. 13x13½

275	A15	3a dk brn & dull gray	.25	.20
276	A15	16a dk brown & cream	1.00	.60
277	A15	50a dk bl & dull gray	3.00	1.40
		Nos. 275-277 (3)	*4.25*	*2.20*

Exhibition of Sacred Missionary Art, Lisbon, 1951.

Stamp Centenary Issue

1953   Photo.   Perf. 13

278	A16	10a multicolored	1.10	1.00

Sao Paulo Issue
Common Design Type

1954   Litho.   Perf. 13½

279	CD46	16a dk brn red, bl & blk	.85	.70

Map of Timor — A17

1956   Unwmk.   Perf. 14x12½
Inscription and design in brown, red, green, ultramarine & yellow

280	A17	1a pale salmon	.20	.20
281	A17	3a pale gray blue	.25	.20
282	A17	8a buff	.30	.20
283	A17	24a pale green	.40	.20
284	A17	32a lemon	.50	.20
285	A17	40a pale gray	.75	.30
286	A17	1p yellow	1.75	1.10
287	A17	3p pale blue	4.25	1.50
		Nos. 280-287 (8)	*8.40*	*3.90*

For surcharges see Nos. 291-300.

Brussels Fair Issue

Exhibition Emblems and View — A18

1958   Perf. 14½

288	A18	40a multicolored	.50	.40

Tropical Medicine Congress Issue
Common Design Type

Design: Calophyllum inophyllum.

1958   Perf. 13½

289	CD47	32a multicolored	3.00	2.75

Symbolical Globe — A19

Carved Elephant Jar — A20

1960   Unwmk.   Litho.   Perf. 13½

290	A19	4.50e multicolored	.50	.35

500th death anniv. of Prince Henry the Navigator.

Nos. 280-287 Surcharged with New Value and Bars

1960   Unwmk.   Perf. 14x12½
Inscription and design in brown, red, green, ultramarine & yellow

291	A17	5c on 1a pale salmon	.20	.20
292	A17	10c on 3a pale gray bl	.20	.20
293	A17	20c on 8a buff	.25	.20
294	A17	30c on 24a pale grn	.30	.20
295	A17	50c on 32a lemon	.40	.20
296	A17	1e on 40a pale gray	.50	.20
297	A17	2e on 40a pale gray	.60	.20
298	A17	5e on 1p yellow	.75	1.00
299	A17	10e on 3p pale blue	1.75	2.50
300	A17	15e on 3p pale blue	2.50	2.00
		Nos. 291-300 (10)	*7.45*	*6.90*

1961   Litho.   Perf. 11½x12

Native Art: 10c, House on stilts. 20c, Madonna and Child. 30c, Silver rosary. 50c, Two men in boat, horiz. 1e, Silver box in shape of temple. 2.50e, Archer. 4.50e, Elephant. 5e, Man climbing tree. 10e, Woman carrying pot on head. 20e, Cockfight. 50e, House on stilts and animals.

Multicolored Designs

301	A20	5c pale violet	.20	.30
302	A20	10c pale green	.20	.30
	a.	Value & legend inverted	72.50	72.50
303	A20	20c pale blue	.20	.30
304	A20	30c rose	.25	.20
305	A20	50c pale grnsh bl	.20	.20
306	A20	1e bister	.70	.20
307	A20	2.50e pale ol bis	.50	.20
308	A20	4.50e lt salmon	.50	.20
309	A20	5e lt gray	.60	.20
310	A20	10e gray	1.40	.30
311	A20	20e yellow	2.75	1.00
312	A20	50e lt bluish gray	9.25	2.50
		Nos. 301-312 (12)	*16.75*	*5.90*

Sports Issue
Common Design Type

Sports: 50c, Duck hunting. 1e, Horseback riding. 1.50e, Swimming. 2e, Gymnastics. 2.50e, Soccer. 15e, Big game hunting.

1962, Mar. 22   Unwmk.   Perf. 13½
Multicolored Designs

313	CD48	50c gray & bis	.25	.20
314	CD48	1e olive bister	.60	.30
315	CD48	1.50e gray & bl grn	.70	.40
316	CD48	2e buff	.85	.35
317	CD48	2.50e gray	1.00	.50
318	CD48	15e salmon	3.00	1.90
		Nos. 313-318 (6)	*6.40*	*3.65*

Anti-Malaria Issue
Common Design Type

Design: Anopheles sundaicus.

1962   Litho.   Perf. 13½

319	CD49	2.50e multicolored	.75	.60

National Overseas Bank Issue
Common Design Type

Design: 2.50e, Manuel Pinheiro Chagas.

1964, May 16   Unwmk.   Perf. 13½

320	CD51	2.50e grn, gray, yel, lt bl & blk	.75	.60

ITU Issue
Common Design Type

1965, May 17   Litho.   Perf. 14½

321	CD52	1.50e multicolored	1.50	.90

National Revolution Issue
Common Design Type

Design: 4.50e, Dr. Vieira Machado Academy and Dili Health Center.

1966, May 28   Litho.   Perf. 11½

322	CD53	4.50e multicolored	1.50	.90

Navy Club Issue
Common Design Type

10c, Capt. Gago Coutinho and gunboat Patria. 4.50e, Capt. Sacadura Cabral and seaplane Lusitania.

1967, Jan. 31   Litho.   Perf. 13
323 CD54 10c multicolored   2.00 1.00
324 CD54 4.50e multicolored   2.00 1.00

Sepoy Officer,   Our Lady of
1792 — A21   Fatima — A22

Designs: 1e, Officer, 1815. 1.50e, Infantry soldier, 1879. 2e, Infantry soldier, 1890. 2.50e, Infantry officer, 1903. 3e, Sapper, 1918. 4.50e, Special forces soldier, 1964. 10e, Paratrooper, 1964.

1967, Feb. 12   Photo.   Perf. 13½
325 A21 35c multicolored   .25 .30
326 A21 1e multicolored   1.50 1.00
327 A21 1.50e multicolored   .60 .30
328 A21 2e multicolored   .60 .30
329 A21 2.50e multicolored   .60 .25
330 A21 3e multicolored   .75 .35
331 A21 4.50e multicolored 1.10 .45
332 A21 10e multicolored   2.25 .65
    Nos. 325-332 (8)   7.65 3.50

1967, May 13   Litho.   Perf. 12½x13
333 A22 3e multicolored   .60 .30

Apparition of the Virgin Mary to three shepherd children at Fatima, Portugal, 50th anniv.

Cabral Issue

Map of Brazil, by Lopo Homem-
Reinéis, 1519 — A23

1968, Apr. 22   Litho.   Perf. 14
334 A23 4.50e multicolored   .80 .50

See note after Macao No. 416.

Admiral Coutinho Issue
Common Design Type

Design: 4.50e, Adm. Coutinho and frigate Adm. Gago Coutinho.

1969, Feb. 17   Litho.   Perf. 14
335 CD55 4.50e multicolored 1.10 .85

View of Dili,
1834 — A24

1969, July 25   Litho.   Perf. 14
336 A24 1e multicolored   .30 .20

Bicentenary of Dili as capital of Timor.

da Gama Medal   Emblem of King
in St. Jerome's   Manuel, St.
Convent — A25   Jerome's
                    Convent — A26

Vasco da Gama Issue

1969, Aug. 29   Litho.   Perf. 14
337 A25 5e multicolored   .40 .30

Vasco da Gama (1469-1524), navigator.

Administration Reform Issue
Common Design Type

1969, Sept. 25   Litho.   Perf. 14
338 CD56 5e multicolored   .40 .25

King Manuel I Issue

1969, Dec. 1   Litho.   Perf. 14
339 A26 4e multicolored   .40 .25

King Manuel I, 500th birth anniv.

Capt. Ross Smith, Arms of Great
Britain, Portugal and Australia, and
Map of Timor
A27

1969, Dec. 9
340 A27 2e multicolored   .50 .40

50th anniv. of the first England to Australia flight of Capt. Ross Smith and Lt. Keith Smith.

Marshal Carmona Issue
Common Design Type

Antonio Oscar Carmona in civilian clothes.

1970, Nov. 15   Litho.   Perf. 14
341 CD57 1.50e multicolored .20 .20

Lusiads Issue

Sailing Ship and
Monks Preaching
to
Islanders — A28

1972, May 25   Litho.   Perf. 13
342 A28 1e brown & multi   .20 .35

4th centenary of publication of The Lusiads by Luiz Camoens.

Olympic Games Issue
Common Design Type

Design: 4.50e, Soccer, Olympic emblem.

1972, June 20   Perf. 14x13½
343 CD59 4.50e multicolored .50 .50

Lisbon-Rio de Janeiro Flight Issue
Common Design Type

Design: 1e, Sacadura Cabral and Gago Coutinho in cockpit of "Lusitania."

1972, Sept. 20   Litho.   Perf. 13½
344 CD60 1e multicolored   .25 .40

WMO Centenary Issue
Common Design Type

1973, Dec. 15   Litho.   Perf. 13
345 CD61 20e multicolored   1.75 2.00

United Nations Transitional Authority in East Timor

A30

2000, Apr. 29   Litho.   Perf. 12x11¾
350 A30 Dom. red & multi   8.50 8.50
351 A30 Int. blue & multi   17.50 17.50

No. 350 sold for 10c and No. 351 sold for 50c on day of issue.

INDEPENDENT STATE OF TIMOR-LESTE

Independence — A31

Designs: 25c, Crocodile. 50c, Palm fronds. $1, Coffee beans and picker. $2, Flag.

2002, May 20   Litho.   Perf. 14½x14
352-355 A31   Set of 4   20.00 20.00

A32

Flag and: 10c, Pres. Xanana Gusmao. 50c, Map of country.

2002   Litho.   Perf. 13x13¼
356-357 A32   Set of 2   9.50 9.50

AIR POST STAMPS

Common Design Type
1938   Unwmk.   Engr.   Perf. 13½x13
Name and Value in Black

C1 CD39 1a red orange   .85   .45
C2 CD39 2a purple   .90   .55
C3 CD39 3a orange   .90   .60
C4 CD39 5a ultra   1.00   .65
C5 CD39 10a lilac brown 1.60 1.10
C6 CD39 20a dark green   3.00 1.40
C7 CD39 50a red brown   6.00 4.00
C8 CD39 70a rose carmine 7.00 5.25
C9 CD39 1p magenta   13.00 6.00
    Nos. C1-C9 (9)   34.25 20.00

No. C7 exists with overprint "Exposicao Internacional de Nova York, 1939-1940" and Trylon and Perisphere. Counterfeits exist. For overprints see Nos. C15-C23.

Mozambique Nos.
C3, C4, C6, C7 and
C9 Surcharged in
Black

TIMOR
8
AVOS

1946   Unwmk.   Perf. 13½x13
C10 CD39 8a on 50c orange   6.25 4.00
C11 CD39 12a on 1e ultra   6.25 4.00
C12 CD39 40a on 3e dk green 6.25 4.00
C13 CD39 50a on 5e red brn   6.25 4.00
C14 CD39 1p on 10e mag   6.25 4.00
    Nos. C10-C14 (5)   31.25 20.00

Nos. C1-C9 Overprinted "Libertacao"

1947
C15 CD39 1a scarlet   20.00 15.00
C16 CD39 2a purple   20.00 15.00
C17 CD39 3a orange   20.00 15.00
C18 CD39 5a ultra   20.00 15.00
C19 CD39 10a lilac brown 6.50 3.75
C20 CD39 20a dark green   6.50 4.25
C21 CD39 50a red brown   6.75 3.75
C22 CD39 70a rose carmine 27.50 9.00
C23 CD39 1p magenta   10.50 3.75
    Nos. C15-C23 (9)   137.75 84.50

POSTAGE DUE STAMPS

D1

1904   Unwmk.   Typo.   Perf. 12
Without Gum
Name and Value in Black

J1 D1 1a yellow green   .50   .50
J2 D1 2a slate   .50   .50
J3 D1 5a yellow brown 2.25 1.50
J4 D1 6a red orange   2.25 2.25
J5 D1 10a gray brown   2.50 2.00
J6 D1 15a red brown   3.75 2.75
J7 D1 24a dull blue   6.25 5.50
J8 D1 40a carmine   7.50 5.50
J9 D1 50a orange   10.50 7.50
J10 D1 1p dull violet 17.00 13.00
    Nos. J1-J10 (10)   53.00 41.00

Overprinted in
Carmine or Green

1911   Without Gum
J11 D1 1a yellow green   .25   .25
J12 D1 2a slate   .30   .25
  a. Inverted overprint
J13 D1 5a yellow brown   .60   .40
J14 D1 6a deep orange   .80   .50
J15 D1 10a gray brown   1.50 1.00
J16 D1 15a brown   1.75 1.10
J17 D1 24a dull blue   2.50 2.00
J18 D1 40a carmine (G) 3.25 2.25
J19 D1 50a orange   3.75 2.50
J20 D1 1p dull violet   7.50 7.00
    Nos. J11-J20 (10)   22.20 17.20

Nos. J1-J10
Overprinted in Red or
Green

1913   Without Gum
J21 D1 1a yellow green   8.00 9.00
J22 D1 2a slate   8.00 9.00
J23 D1 5a yellow brown   4.50 4.50
J24 D1 6a deep orange   4.50 4.50
  a. Inverted surcharge   30.00
J25 D1 10a gray brown   4.50 6.00
J26 D1 15a red brown   4.50 6.00
J27 D1 24a dull blue   6.00 6.00
J28 D1 40a carmine (G)   6.00 6.00
J29 D1 50a orange   10.00 12.00
J30 D1 1p gray violet   10.00 12.00
    Nos. J21-J30 (10)   66.00 75.00

> **Catalogue values for unused stamps in this section, from this point to the end of the section, are for Never Hinged items.**

Common Design Type
1952   Photo. & Typo.   Perf. 14
Numeral in Red, Frame Multicolored

J31 CD45 1a chocolate   .40 .40
J32 CD45 3a brown   .40 .40
J33 CD45 5a dark green   .40 .40
J34 CD45 10a green   .40 .40
J35 CD45 30a purple   .65 .65
J36 CD45 1p brown carmine 1.25 1.25
    Nos. J31-J36 (6)   3.50 3.50

WAR TAX STAMP

Regular Issue of 1914
Surcharged in Red

1919   **Unwmk.**   **Perf. 15x14**
Without Gum

MR1   A7   2a on ½a ol brn   22.50   20.00
   See note after Macao No. MR2.

NEWSPAPER STAMPS

King Luiz — N1

Stamps of Macao Surcharged in Black
1892   **Unwmk.**   **Perf. 12½**
Without Gum

P1	N1	2½r on 20r brt rose	2.00	.75
a.		"TIMOR" inverted		
P2	N1	2½r on 40r chocolate	2.00	.75
a.		"TIMOR" inverted		
b.		Perf. 13½	4.50	3.00
c.		As "a," perf. 13½		
P3	N1	2½r on 80r gray	2.00	.75
a.		"TIMOR" inverted		
b.		Perf. 13½	12.50	8.00
		Nos. P1-P3 (3)	6.00	2.25

N2   N3

1893-95   **Typo.**   **Perf. 11½, 13½**

P4	N2	2½r brown	.40	.35
a.		Perf. 12½	2.00	1.50
P5	N3	½a on 2½r brn ('95)	.45	.30

For surcharges see Nos. 103, 123, 194.

POSTAL TAX STAMPS

Pombal Issue
Common Design Types
1925   **Unwmk.**   **Perf. 12½**

RA1	CD28	2a lake & black	.30	.30
RA2	CD29	2a lake & black	.30	.30
RA3	CD30	2a lake & black	.30	.30
		Nos. RA1-RA3 (3)	.90	.90

Type of War Tax Stamp of Portuguese
India Overprinted in Red

1934-35   **Perf. 12**

RA4	WT1	2a green & blk	6.50	8.00
RA5	WT1	5a green & blk	8.00	8.00

Surcharged in Black

RA6	WT1	7a on ½a rose & blk ('35)	9.00	7.50
		Nos. RA4-RA6 (3)	23.50	23.50

The tax was for local education.

Type of War Tax Stamp of Portuguese
India Overprinted in Black

1936   **Perf. 12x11½**

RA7	WT1	10a rose & black	7.00	9.00

1937   **Perf. 11½**

RA8	WT1	10a green & blk	5.50	8.25

PT1   PT2

1948   **Unwmk.**   **Typo.**   **Perf. 11½**
Without Gum

RA9	PT1	10a dark blue	3.00	2.00
RA10	PT1	20a green	3.50	3.00

The 20a bears a different emblem.

> **Catalogue values for unused stamps in this section, from this point to the end of the section, are for Never Hinged items.**

1960   **Without Gum**   **Perf. 11½**

RA11	PT2	70c dark blue	1.50	1.25
RA12	PT2	1.30e green	2.25	2.25

See Nos. RA13-RA16. For surcharges see Nos. RA20-RA25.

Type of 1960 Redrawn
1967   **Typo.**   **Perf. 10½**
Without Gum

RA13	PT2	70c deep blue	12.00	12.00
RA14	PT2	1.30e emerald	3.00	2.50

The denominations of Nos. RA13-RA14 are 2mm high. They are 2½mm high on Nos. RA11-RA12. Other differences exist. The printed area of No. RA13 measures 18x31mm; "Republica" 16mm.

Type of 1960
Serif Type Face
1967

RA14A	PT2	70c deep blue	12.00	10.00

Type of 1960, 2nd Redrawing
1967-68   **Typo.**   **Perf. 10½**
Without Gum

RA15	PT2	70c violet blue	.60	.60
RA16	PT2	1.30e bluish grn ('68)	1.25	1.25

The printed area measures 13x30mm on Nos. RA15-RA16; "Republica" measures 10½mm.

Woman and Star — PT3

1969-70   **Litho.**   **Perf. 13½**

RA17	PT3	30c vio bl & lt bl ('70)	.20	.20
RA18	PT3	50c dl org & maroon	.20	.20
RA19	PT3	1e yellow & brown	.20	.20
		Nos. RA17-RA19 (3)	.60	.60

The 2.50e and 10e in design PT3 were revenue stamps. Value $1.50 each.

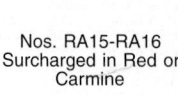

Nos. RA15-RA16
Surcharged in Red or
Carmine

1970   **Typo.**   **Perf. 10½**
Without Gum

RA20	PT2	30c on 70c	7.00	6.00
RA21	PT2	30c on 1.30e	6.00	6.00
RA22	PT2	50c on 70c	225.00	175.00
RA23	PT2	50c on 1.30e	6.00	6.00

RA24	PT2	1e on 70c (C)	225.00	175.00
RA25	PT2	1e on 1.30e	8.00	7.25
		Nos. RA20-RA25 (6)	477.00	375.25

POSTAL TAX DUE STAMPS

Pombal Issue
Common Design Types
1925   **Unwmk.**   **Perf. 12½**

RAJ1	CD28	4a lake & black	.40	1.00
RAJ2	CD29	4a lake & black	.40	1.00
RAJ3	CD30	4a lake & black	.40	1.00
		Nos. RAJ1-RAJ3 (3)	1.20	3.00

TOBAGO

tə-'bā-ˌgō

LOCATION — An island in the West Indies lying off the Venezuelan coast north of Trinidad
GOVT. — British Colony
AREA — 116 sq. mi.
POP. — 25,358
CAPITAL — Scarborough (Port Louis)

In 1889 Tobago, then an independent colony, was united with Trinidad under the name of Colony of Trinidad and Tobago. It became a ward of that colony January 1, 1899.

12 Pence = 1 Shilling
20 Shillings = 1 Pound

Queen Victoria
A1   A2

Wmk. Crown and C C (1)
1879   **Typo.**   **Perf. 14**

1	A1	1p rose	110.00	82.50
2	A1	3p blue	110.00	82.50
3	A1	6p orange	47.50	72.50
4	A1	1sh green	425.00	77.50
a.		Half used as 6p on cover		
5	A1	5sh slate	775.00	775.00
6	A1	£1 violet	4,500.	

Stamps of the above set with revenue cancellations sell for a small fraction of the price of postally used copies.
Stamps of Type A1, watermarked Crown and C A, are revenue stamps.

1880
Manuscript Surcharge

7	A1	1p on half of 6p org	5,250.	875.

1880

8	A2	½p brown violet	50.00	77.50
9	A2	1p red brown	125.00	67.50
a.		Half used as ½p on cover		2,250.
10	A2	4p yellow green	325.00	30.00
a.		Half used as 2p on cover		2,250.
11	A2	6p bister brown	400.00	125.00
12	A2	1sh bister	77.50	87.50
a.		Imperf.		
		Nos. 8-12 (5)	977.50	387.50

No. 11 Surcharged in Black

1883

13	A2	2½p on 6p bister brn	67.50	67.50
a.		Double surcharge	3,750.	1,900.

1882-96   **Wmk. Crown and C A (2)**

14	A2	½p brown vio ('82)	2.25	14.50
15	A2	½p dull green ('86)	2.75	1.40
16	A2	1p red brown ('82)	5.75	2.50
a.		Diagonal half used as ½p on cover		
17	A2	1p rose ('89)	3.75	1.40
18	A2	2½p ultra ('83)	9.50	1.10
a.		2½p dull blue ('83)	42.50	2.50
b.		2½p bright blue	9.50	1.10

19	A2	4p yel grn ('82)	210.00	100.00
20	A2	4p gray ('85)	3.75	2.75
a.		Imperf., pair	2,250.	
21	A2	6p bis brn ('84)	625.00	550.00
a.		Imperf.		
22	A2	6p brn org ('86)	2.75	5.75
23	A2	1sh olive bis ('94)	3.25	22.50
24	A2	1sh brn org ('96)	12.00	77.50

Stamps of 1882-96 Surcharged in Black:

Nos. 25-29   No. 30

1886-92

25	A2	½p on 2½p ultra	7.00	17.00
a.		Inverted surcharge		
b.		Pair, one without surcharge	15,000.	
c.		Space between "½" and "PENNY" 3mm	30.00	67.50
d.		Double surcharge	2,400.	1,900.
26	A2	½p on 4p gray	23.00	67.50
a.		Space between "½" and "PENNY" 3mm	3,000.	
b.		Double surcharge		
27	A2	½p on 6p bis brn	3.50	22.50
a.		Inverted surcharge	2,750.	
b.		Space between "½" and "PENNY" 3mm	30.00	125.00
c.		Double surcharge	3,250.	
28	A2	½p on 6p brn org	115.00	160.00
a.		Space between "½" and "PENNY" 3mm	350.00	375.00
b.		Double surcharge		2,750.
29	A2	1p on 2½p ultra	82.50	19.00
a.		Space between "1" and "PENNY" 4mm	210.00	87.50
b.		Half used as ½p on cover		1,650.
30	A2	2½p on 4p gray	12.00	9.00
a.		Double surcharge	3,250.	3,250.
		Nos. 25-30 (6)	243.00	295.00

Revenue Stamp Type A1 Surcharged in Black

1896

31	A1	½p on 4p lilac & rose	77.50	42.50
a.		Space between "½" and "d" 1½ to 2½mm	150.00	82.50

Tobago stamps were replaced by those of Trinidad or Trinidad and Tobago.

TOGO

'tō-ˌgō

LOCATION — Western Africa, border-
ing on the Gulf of Guinea
GOVT. — Republic
AREA — 20,400 sq. mi.
POP. — 4,320,000 (1997 est.)
CAPITAL — Lome

The German Protectorate of Togo
was occupied by Great Britain and
France in World War I, and later mandated to them. The British area became
part of Ghana. The French area was
granted internal autonomy in 1956 and
achieved independence in 1958.

100 Pfennig = 1 Mark
12 Pence = 1 Shilling
100 Centimes = 1 Franc

**Catalogue values for unused
stamps in this country are for
Never Hinged items, beginning
with Scott 309 in the regular postage section, Scott B11 in the semi-
postal section, Scott C14 in the
airpost section, Scott J32 in the
postage due section, and Scott O1
in the official section.**

Watermark

Wmk. 125 —
Lozenges

German Protectorate

AREA — 34,934 sq. mi.
POP. — 1,000,368 (1913)

Stamps of Germany
Overprinted in Black

1897　Unwmk.　Perf. 13½x14½

1	A9	3pf dark brown	5.50	7.25
a.		3pf yellow brown	9.25	25.00
b.		3pf reddish brown	42.50	140.00
2	A9	5pf green	5.00	2.90
3	A10	10pf carmine	6.00	3.25
4	A10	20pf ultra	6.00	13.50
5	A10	25pf orange	35.00	60.00
6	A10	50pf red brown	35.00	60.00
		Nos. 1-6 (6)	92.50	146.90

A3

Kaiser's Yacht, the
"Hohenzollern" — A4

1900　Typo.　Perf. 14

7	A3	3pf brown	1.00	1.25
8	A3	5pf green	12.00	2.00
9	A3	10pf carmine	22.00	1.75
10	A3	20pf ultra	1.00	1.50
11	A3	25pf org & blk, yel	1.00	10.00
12	A3	30pf org & blk, sal	1.40	10.00
13	A3	40pf lake & blk	1.00	10.00
14	A3	50pf pur & blk, sal	1.40	7.50
15	A3	80pf lake & blk, rose	2.50	17.00

Engr.
Perf. 14½x14

16	A4	1m carmine	3.50	55.00
17	A4	2m blue	5.50	85.00
18	A4	3m black vio	7.25	150.00
19	A4	5m slate & car	110.00	500.00
		Nos. 7-19 (13)	169.55	851.00

Counterfeit cancellations are found on Nos.
10-19 and 22.

1909-19　Wmk. 125　Typo.　Perf. 14

20	A3	3pf brown ('19)	.85	
21	A3	5pf green	1.25	2.25
22	A3	10pf carmine ('14)	1.75	110.00

Engr.
Perf. 14½x14

23	A4	5m slate & car ('19)	24.00	
		Nos. 20-23 (4)	27.85	

Nos. 20 and 23 were never placed in use.

British Protectorate

Nos. 7, 10-19, 21-22 Overprinted or
Surcharged

First (Wide) Setting
3mm between Lines
2mm between "Anglo" & "French"
Wmk. 125 (5pf, 10pf); Unwmkd.
1914, Oct. 1　　　Perf. 14, 14½

33	A3	½p on 3pf brown	225.00	175.00
a.		Thin "y" in "penny"	500.00	450.00
34	A3	1p on 5pf green	225.00	175.00
a.		Thin "y" in "penny"	500.00	500.00
35	A3	3pf brown	130.00	100.00
36	A3	5pf green	125.00	100.00
37	A3	10pf carmine	150.00	110.00
a.		Inverted overprint	8,500.	4,000.
b.		Unwmk.		6,250.
38	A3	20pf ultra	30.00	37.50
39	A3	25pf org & blk, yel	30.00	30.00
40	A3	30pf org & blk, sal	32.50	47.50
41	A3	40pf lake & blk	275.00	275.00
42	A3	50pf pur & blk, sal	10,000.	8,500.
43	A3	80pf lake & blk, rose	275.00	300.00
44	A4	1m carmine	5,750.	2,800.
45	A4	2m blue	9,000.	10,000.
a.		Inverted overprint	—	—
b.		"Occupation" double	—	—

On Nos. 33-34, the surcharge line ("Half
penny" or "One penny") was printed separately
and its position varies in relation to the 3-line
overprint. On Nos. 46-47, the surcharge and
overprint lines were printed simultaneously.

Second (Narrow) Setting
2mm between Lines
2mm between "Anglo" & "French"
1914, Oct.

46	A3	½p on 3pf brown	40.00	30.00
a.		Thin "y" in "penny"	70.00	70.00
b.		"TOG"	475.00	350.00
47	A3	1p on 5pf green	5.00	5.00
a.		Thin "y" in "penny"	15.00	17.50
b.		"TOG"	150.00	125.00
48	A3	3pf brown	5,250.	1,000.
a.		"Occupation" omitted		
49	A3	5pf green	1,400.	800.00
50	A3	10pf carmine		3,100.
51	A3	20pf ultra	20.00	14.00
a.		"TOG"	4,750.	4,750.
b.		Vert. pair, #51 & #38	7,250.	
52	A3	25pf org & blk, yel	27.50	35.00
a.		"TOG"	13,750.	
53	A3	30pf org & blk, sal	22.50	32.50
54	A3	40pf lake & blk	5,250.	1,750.
55	A3	50pf pur & blk, sal		6,750.
56	A3	80pf lake & blk, rose	2,100.	2,100.
57	A4	1m carmine	8,500.	4,500.
58	A4	2m blue		10,000.
59	A4	3m black violet		45,000.
60	A4	5m slate & car		45,000.

Third Setting
1 ¼mm btwn. "Anglo" & "French"
2mm between Lines
"Anglo-French" 15mm Wide

1915, Jan. 7

61	A3	3pf brown	8,500.	3,250.
62	A3	5pf green	225.	150.
63	A3	10pf carmine	225.	150.
64	A3	20pf ultra	1,600.	600.
64A	A3	40pf lake & blk		8,500.
65	A3	50pf pur & blk, sal	14,000.	11,000.

Stamps of Gold Coast
Overprinted Locally

1915, May　Wmk. 3　Perf. 14

66	A7	½p green	.35	1.90
a.		Double overprint	525.00	550.00
67	A8	1p scarlet	.35	.55
a.		Double ovpt.	375.00	500.00
b.		Inverted ovpt.	200.00	275.00
		As "b," "Togo" omitted		
68	A7	2p gray	.35	1.40
69	A7	2½p ultra	2.25	4.00

Chalky Paper

70	A7	3p violet, yel	2.25	3.00
71	A7	6p dl vio & red		
		vio	1.60	2.00
72	A7	1sh black, grn	2.50	6.00
a.		Double overprint	1,300.	
73	A7	2sh vio & bl, bl	11.00	16.00
74	A7	2sh6p blk & red, bl	5.25	25.00
75	A7	10sh grn & red, grn	42.50	70.00
76	A7	20sh vio & bk, red	150.00	175.00

Surfaced-Colored Paper

77	A7	3p violet, yel	4.50	20.00
78	A7	5sh grn & red, yel	9.25	17.50
		Nos. 66-78 (13)	232.15	342.35

Nos. 66-78 exist with small "F" in "French"
and thin "G" in "Togo." Several values are
known without the hyphen between "Anglo-
French" and all but No. 77 without the first "O"
in "Occupation."

Stamps of Gold Coast
Overprinted in London

1916, Apr.
Ordinary Paper

80	A7	½p green	.35	2.90
81	A8	1p scarlet	.35	1.00
a.		Inverted overprint		
82	A7	2p gray	.60	.90
83	A7	2½p ultra	.65	1.75

Chalky Paper

84	A7	3p violet, yel	3.00	.80
85	A7	6p dl vio & red vio	2.25	1.10
86	A7	1sh black, grn	4.00	7.50
a.		1sh black, emerald	350.00	750.00
b.		1sh black, bl grn, ol back	7.50	17.50
87	A7	2sh vio & ultra, bl	5.25	9.75
88	A7	2sh6p blk & red, bl	5.25	8.00
89	A7	5sh grn & red, yel	21.00	30.00
90	A7	10sh grn & red, bl grn, ol back	20.00	80.00
a.		10sh green & red, grn	27.50	75.00
91	A7	20sh vio & blk, red	150.00	180.00
		Nos. 80-91 (12)	212.70	323.70

The overprint on Nos. 80-91 is in heavier
letters than on Nos. 66-78 and the 2nd and 3rd
lines are each ½mm longer. The letter "O" on
Nos. 80-91 is narrower and more oval.

Issued under French Occupation
Stamps of German Togo Surcharged:

c　　　　　　　　d

e　　　　　　　　f

g　　　　　　　　h

i

**Wmk. Lozenges (5pf and 10pf)
(125), Unwmk. (other values)**
1914　　　　Perf. 14, 14½

151	A3(c+d)	5c on 3pf brn	57.50	57.50
152	A3(c+e)	5c on 3pf brn	57.50	57.50
153	A3(c+f)	5c on 3pf brn	60.00	60.00
154	A3(c+g)	10c on 5pf grn	19.00	19.00
a.		Double surcharge	1,050.	1,050.
155	A3(c+h)	10c on 5pf grn	19.00	19.00
156	A3(c+i)	10c on 5pf grn	26.00	26.00
158	A3(c)	20pf ultra	45.00	45.00
a.		3½mm between "TOGO" and "Occupation"	750.00	700.00
159	A3(c)	25pf org & blk, yel	52.50	52.50
160	A3(c)	30pf org & blk, sal	95.00	95.00
161	A3(c)	40pf lake & blk	575.00	525.00
162	A3(c)	80pf lake & blk, rose	575.00	525.00
		Nos. 151-162 (11)	1,581.	1,481.

Surcharged or Overprinted in Sans-
Serif Type:

1915

164	A3	5c on 3pf brown	14,000.	4,400.
165	A3	5pf green	900.	425.
166	A3	10pf carmine	1,050.	425.
a.		Inverted overprint	27,000.	15,000.
167	A3	20pf ultra	1,300.	900.
168	A3	25pf org & blk, yel	14,000.	7,000.
169	A3	30pf org & blk, sal	14,000.	7,000.
170	A3	40pf lake & blk	14,000.	7,000.
171	A3	50pf pur & blk, sal	20,000.	12,000.
172	A4	1m carmine		75,000.
173	A4	2m blue		21,000.
174	A4	3m black vio		29,000.
175	A4	5m slate & car	27,000.	29,000.

Stamps of Dahomey, 1913-17, Overprinted

1916-17 Unwmk. Perf. 13½x14
176	A5	1c violet & blk	.25	.25
177	A5	2c choc & rose	.25	.25
178	A5	4c black & brn	.35	.35
a.		Double overprint	425.00	425.00
179	A5	5c yel grn & bl grn	.60	.60
180	A5	10c org red & rose	.55	.55
181	A5	15c brn org & dk vio	1.50	1.50
182	A5	20c gray & choc	.60	.60
183	A5	25c ultra & dp bl	.90	.90
184	A5	30c choc & vio	.90	.90
185	A5	35c brown & blk	1.50	1.50
186	A5	40c blk & red org	1.25	1.25
187	A5	45c gray & ultra	1.40	1.40
188	A5	50c choc & brn	1.40	1.40
189	A5	75c blue & vio	6.00	6.00
190	A5	1fr bl grn & blk	7.50	7.50
191	A5	2fr buff & choc	11.00	11.00
192	A5	5fr vio & do bl	13.00	13.00
		Nos. 176-192 (17)	48.95	48.95

All values of the 1916-17 issue exist on chalky paper and all but the 15c, 25c and 35c on ordinary paper.

French Mandate

AREA — 21,893 sq. mi.
POP. — 780,497 (1938)

Type of Dahomey, 1913-39, Overprinted

1921
193	A5	1c gray & yel grn	.20	.20
a.		Overprint omitted	100.00	
194	A5	2c blue & org	.20	.20
195	A5	4c ol grn & org	.25	.25
196	A5	5c dull red & blk	.25	.25
a.		Overprint omitted	325.00	
197	A5	10c bl grn & yel grn	.55	.55
198	A5	15c brown & car	.60	.60
199	A5	20c bl grn & org	1.00	1.00
200	A5	25c slate & org	1.00	1.00
201	A5	30c dp rose & ver	1.10	1.10
202	A5	35c red brn & yel grn	1.00	1.00
203	A5	40c bl grn & ol	1.40	1.40
204	A5	45c red brn & ol	1.25	1.25
205	A5	50c deep blue	1.25	1.25
206	A5	75c dl red & ultra	1.40	1.40
207	A5	1fr gray & ultra	1.60	1.60
208	A5	2fr ol grn & rose	5.00	5.00
209	A5	5fr orange & blk	9.00	9.00
		Nos. 193-209 (17)	27.05	27.05

Stamps and Type of 1921 Surcharged

1922-25
210	A5	25c on 15c ol brn & rose red	.30	.30
211	A5	25c on 2fr ol grn & rose	.45	.45
212	A5	25c on 5fr org & blk	.45	.45
213	A5	60c on 75c vio, pnksh	.75	.75
a.		"60" omitted	175.00	175.00
214	A5	65c on 45c red brn & ol	1.25	1.25
a.		"TOGO" omitted	150.00	
215	A5	85c on 75c dull red & ultra	2.00	2.00
		Nos. 210-215 (6)	5.20	5.20

Issue years: #213, 1922; #211-212, 1924; others, 1925.

Coconut Grove A6

Cacao Trees — A7

Oil Palms A8

1924-38 Typo.
216	A6	1c yellow & blk	.20	.20
217	A6	2c dp rose & blk	.20	.20
218	A6	4c dk blue & blk	.20	.20
219	A6	5c dp org & blk	.20	.20
220	A6	10c red vio & blk	.20	.20
221	A6	15c green & blk	.20	.20
222	A7	20c gray & blk	.25	.25
223	A7	25c grn & blk, yel	.55	.55
224	A7	30c gray grn & blk	.25	.25
225	A7	30c dl grn & lt grn ('27)	.40	.40
226	A7	35c lt brown & blk	.60	.60
227	A7	35c dp bl grn & grn ('38)	.55	.45
228	A7	40c red org & blk	.25	.25
229	A7	45c carmine & blk	.25	.25
230	A7	50c ocher & blk, bluish	.40	.40
231	A7	55c vio bl & car rose ('38)	.75	.60
232	A7	60c brn & blk, pnksh	.25	.25
233	A7	60c dp red ('26)	.40	.40
234	A7	65c gray lil & brn	.55	.55
235	A7	75c blue & black	.55	.55
236	A7	80c ind & dl vio ('38)	1.60	1.50
237	A7	85c brn org & brn	1.00	1.00
238	A7	90c brn red & cer ('27)	.75	.75
239	A8	1fr red brn & blk, bluish	.70	.70
240	A8	1fr blue ('26)	.60	.60
241	A8	1fr gray lil & grn ('28)	2.25	1.90
242	A8	1fr dk red & red org ('38)	.75	.55
243	A8	1.10fr vio & dk brn ('28)	3.50	3.50
244	A8	1.25fr mag & rose ('33)	1.25	1.25
245	A8	1.50fr bl & lt bl ('27)	.60	.60
246	A8	1.75fr bis & pink ('33)	7.50	4.25
247	A8	1.75fr vio bl & ultra ('38)	1.25	1.00
248	A8	2fr bl blk & blk, bluish	1.00	1.00
249	A8	3fr bl grn & red org ('27)	1.25	1.25
250	A8	5fr red org & blk, bluish	1.75	1.75
251	A8	10fr ol brn & rose ('26)	2.25	2.25
252	A8	20fr brn red & blk, yel ('26)	2.50	2.50
		Nos. 216-252 (37)	37.70	33.30

For surcharges see #253, 301-302, B8-B9.

No. 240 Surcharged with New Value and Bars in Red

1926
253	A8	1.25fr on 1fr lt bl	.60	.60

Common Design Types pictured following the introduction.

Colonial Exposition Issue
Common Design Types
Engr., "TOGO" Typo. in Black
1931, Apr. 13 Perf. 12½
254	CD70	40c deep green	5.00	5.00
255	CD71	50c violet	5.00	5.00
256	CD72	90c red orange	5.00	5.00
257	CD73	1.50fr dull blue	5.00	5.00
		Nos. 254-257 (4)	20.00	20.00

Paris International Exposition Issue
Common Design Types
1937 Perf. 13
258	CD74	20c deep violet	1.50	1.50
259	CD75	30c dark green	1.50	1.50
260	CD76	40c carmine rose	1.50	1.50
261	CD77	50c dark brown	1.50	1.50

262	CD78	90c red	1.50	1.50
263	CD79	1.50fr ultra	1.50	1.50
		Nos. 258-263 (6)	9.00	9.00

Colonial Arts Exhibition Issue
Souvenir Sheet
Common Design Type
1937 Imperf.
264	CD77	3fr Prus bl & blk	6.00	7.50

Caillié Issue
Common Design Type
1939, Apr. 5 Perf. 12½x12
265	CD81	90c org brn & org	.75	.75
266	CD81	2fr brt violet	.75	.75
267	CD81	2.25fr ultra & dk bl	.75	.75
		Nos. 265-267 (3)	2.25	2.25

New York World's Fair Issue
Common Design Type
1939, May 10
268	CD82	1.25fr carmine lake	.90	.90
269	CD82	2.25fr ultra	.90	.90

Togolese Women
A9   A12

Mono River Bank A10

Hunters A11

1941 Engr. Perf. 12½
270	A9	2c brown vio	.20	.20
271	A9	3c yellow grn	.20	.20
272	A9	4c brown blk	.20	.20
273	A9	5c lilac rose	.20	.20
274	A9	10c light blue	.20	.20
275	A9	15c chestnut	.20	.20
276	A10	20c plum	.20	.20
277	A10	25c violet blue	.20	.20
278	A10	30c brown blk	.20	.20
279	A10	40c dk carmine	.25	.25
280	A10	45c dk green	.25	.25
281	A10	50c chestnut	.25	.25
282	A10	60c red violet	.55	.55
283	A11	70c black	.75	.75
284	A11	90c lt violet	1.10	1.10
285	A11	1fr yellow grn	.40	.40
286	A11	1.25fr cerise	1.00	1.00
287	A11	1.40fr orange brn	.60	.60
288	A11	1.60fr orange	.60	.60
289	A11	2fr lt ultra	.75	.75
290	A12	2.25fr ultra	1.10	1.10
291	A12	2.50fr lilac rose	.75	.75
292	A12	3fr brown vio	.90	.90
293	A12	5fr vermilion	.90	.90
294	A12	10fr rose violet	1.50	1.50
295	A12	20fr brown blk	2.00	2.00
		Nos. 270-295 (26)	15.45	15.45

For surcharges see Nos. 303-308, B7, B10.

Mono River Bank and Marshal Pétain A12a

1941 Engr. Perf. 12½x12
296	A12a	1fr green	.55	
297	A12a	2.50fr blue	.55	

Nos. 296-297 were issued by the Vichy government in France, but were not placed on sale in Togo.
For surcharges, see Nos. B10D-B10E.

Types of 1941 Without "RF"
1942-44 Perf. 12½
298	A9	10c blue green	.25
299	A9	15c yel brn & black	.60
300	A10	20c lilac brn & black	.75
300A	A11	1fr yellow grn	.85
300B	A11	1.50fr lilac & green	.60
300C	A12	3fr brown violet	.85
300D	A12	5fr red brown	.85
300E	A12	10fr rose violet	1.40
300F	A12	20fr black	1.50
		Nos. 298-300F (9)	7.65

Nos. 298-300F were issued by the Vichy government in France, but were not placed on sale in Togo.

Nos. 231, 238, 284 Surcharged with New Values in Various Colors

a

b

Perf. 14x13½, 12½
1943-44 Unwmk.
301	A7(a)	1.50fr on 55c (Bk)	.85	.85
302	A7(a)	1.50fr on 90c (Bk)	.85	.85
303	A11(b)	3.50fr on 90c (Bk)	.70	.70
304	A11(b)	4fr on 90c (R)	.85	.85
305	A11(b)	5fr on 90c (Bl)	1.50	1.50
306	A11(b)	5.50fr on 90c (Br)	1.50	1.50
307	A11(b)	10fr on 90c (G) ('44)	1.50	1.50
308	A11(b)	20fr on 90c (R)	2.00	2.00
		Nos. 301-308 (8)	9.75	9.75

Catalogue values for unused stamps in this section, from this point to the end of the section, are for Never Hinged items.

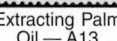
Extracting Palm Oil — A13

Hunter — A14

Cotton Spinners — A15

Village of Atakpamé A16

Red-fronted Gazelles — A17

Houses of
the Cabrais
A18

1947, Oct. 6		Engr.		Perf. 12½	
309	A13	10c dark red		.40	.20
310	A13	30c brt ultra		.40	.20
311	A13	50c bluish green		.40	.20
312	A13	60c lilac rose		.40	.20
313	A14	1fr chocolate		.70	.35
314	A14	1.20fr yellow grn		.90	.40
315	A15	1.50fr brown org		.90	.45
316	A15	2fr olive		.90	.45
317	A15	2.50fr gray blk		2.10	.90
318	A16	3fr slate		1.00	.45
319	A16	3.60fr rose car		1.50	.75
320	A16	4fr Prus green		1.10	.35
321	A17	5fr black brn		2.50	.35
322	A17	6fr ultra		2.50	1.00
323	A17	10fr orange red		3.50	.35
324	A14	15fr dp yel grn		3.25	.50
325	A18	20fr grnsh black		3.25	.75
326	A18	25fr lilac rose		3.50	.75
		Nos. 309-326 (18)		29.20	8.60

Military Medal Issue
Common Design Type
Engr. & Typo.

1952, Dec. 1			Perf. 13	
327	CD101	15fr multicolored	4.50	4.00

Gathering
Palm Nuts
A19

1954, Nov. 29			Engr.	
328	A19	8fr vio & vio brn	1.00	.60
329	A19	15fr indigo & dk brn	1.25	.60

Goliath
Beetle — A20

1955, May 2				
330	A20	8fr black & green	2.25	1.75

Intl. Exhibition for Wildlife Protection, Paris,
May 1955.

FIDES Issue
Common Design Type

Design: 15fr, Teacher and children planting
tree.

1956		Unwmk.	Perf. 13x12½	
331	CD103	15fr dk vio brn & org brn	4.50	2.25

Republic

Woman
Holding
Flag — A21

1957, June 8			Engr.	Perf. 13	
332	A21	15fr dk bl grn, sepia & red	.65	.20

Konkomba
Helmet — A22

Teak Forest
A23

Design: 4fr, 5fr, 6fr, 8fr, 10fr, Buffon's kob.

1957, Oct.			Unwmk.	
333	A22	30c violet & claret	.30	.20
334	A22	50c indigo & blue	.30	.20
335	A22	1fr pur & lil rose	.30	.20
336	A22	2fr dk brn & olive	.30	.20
337	A22	3fr black & green	.30	.20
338	A22	4fr blue & gray	.60	.20
339	A22	6fr bluish gray & mag	.60	.20
340	A22	6fr crim rose & bl gray	.65	.20
341	A22	8fr bluish gray & vio	.65	.25
342	A22	10fr grn & red brn	.65	.25
343	A23	15fr multicolored	.45	.20
344	A23	20fr violet, mar & org	.50	.20
345	A23	25fr indigo & bis brn	.65	.25
346	A23	40fr dk brn, ol & dk grn	1.10	.35
		Nos. 333-346 (14)	7.35	3.10

See Nos. 350-363.

Flags, Dove and UN
Emblem — A24

1958, Dec. 10			Engr.	Perf. 13	
347	A24	20fr dk grn & rose red		.65	.20

Universal Declaration of Human Rights,
10th anniversary.

Flower Issue
Common Design Type

Designs: 5fr, Flower of Bombax tree
(kapok). 20fr, Tectona grandis (teakwood)
flower, horiz.

Perf. 12x12½, 12½x12

1959, Jan. 15		Photo.	Unwmk.	
348	CD104	5fr dp bl, rose & grn	.50	.20
349	CD104	20fr black, yel & grn	.50	.20

Types of 1957 Inscribed: "Republique
du Togo"

1959, Jan. 15		Engr.	Perf. 13	
Designs as Before				
350	A22	30c ultra & gray	.35	.20
351	A22	50c org & brt grn	.35	.20
352	A22	1fr red lil & lt ol grn	.35	.20
353	A22	2fr olive & bl grn	.35	.20
354	A22	3fr vio & rose car	.35	.20
355	A22	4fr lil rose & pale pur	.35	.20
356	A22	5fr green & brown	.35	.20
357	A22	6fr ultra & gray bl	.35	.20
358	A22	8fr sl grn & bis	.35	.20
359	A22	10fr vio & lt brn	.35	.20
360	A23	15fr dk brn, bis & cl	.35	.20
361	A23	20fr blk, bl grn & brn	.35	.20
362	A23	25fr sep, red brn, ol & vio	.45	.20
363	A23	40fr dk grn, org brn & bl	.45	.20
		Nos. 350-363 (14)	5.10	2.80

Skier
A26

Bicyclist
A27

Sports: 50c, Ice Hockey. 1fr, Tobogganing.
15fr, Discus thrower, vert. 20fr, Boxing, vert.
25fr, Runner.

1960		Unwmk.	Perf. 13	
369	A26	30c sl grn, car & bl grn	.45	.20
370	A26	50c red & black	.45	.20
371	A26	1fr red, blk & emer	.45	.20
372	A27	10fr brown, ultra & sl	.45	.20
373	A27	15fr dk red brn & grn	.45	.20
374	A27	20fr dk grn, gldn brn & brn	.55	.20
375	A27	25fr orange, mag & brn	.65	.20
		Nos. 369-375 (7)	3.45	1.40

8th Winter Olympic Games, Squaw Valley,
Calif. (Nos. 369-371); 17th Olympic Games,
Rome (Nos. 372-375).

Prime Minister
Sylvanus Olympio
and Togo
Flag — A28

1960, Apr. 27			Litho.	
Center in Green, Red, Yellow & Brown				
376	A28	30c black & buff	.20	.20
377	A28	50c brown & buff	.20	.20
378	A28	1fr lilac & buff	.20	.20
379	A28	10fr blue & buff	.20	.20
380	A28	20fr red & buff	.20	.20
381	A28	25fr green & buff	.20	.20
		Nos. 376-381 (6)	1.20	1.20

Proclamation of Togo's full independence,
Apr. 27, 1960.
See Nos. C31-C33.

Flags of
"Big Four,"
and British
Flag — A29

1960, May 21			Perf. 14x14½	
382	A29	50c shown	.35	.20
383	A29	1fr USSR	.35	.20
384	A29	20fr France	.35	.20
385	A29	25fr US	.35	.20
		Nos. 382-385 (4)	1.40	.80

Summit Conference of France, Great Britain, United States and USSR, Paris, May 16.

Flag of
Togo and
UN
Emblem
A30

1961, Jan. 6			Perf. 14½x15	
Flag in red, olive green & yellow				
386	A30	30c red	.30	.20
387	A30	50c brown	.30	.20
388	A30	1fr ultramarine	.30	.20
389	A30	10fr maroon	.30	.20
390	A30	25fr black	.30	.20
391	A30	30fr violet	.30	.20
		Nos. 386-391 (6)	1.80	1.20

Togo's admission to United Nations.

Crowned
Cranes over
Map — A31

Augustino de
Souza — A32

1961, Apr. 1			Perf. 14½x15	
392	A31	1fr multicolored	.40	.20
393	A31	1fr multicolored	.40	.20
394	A31	25fr multicolored	.50	.20
395	A31	30fr multicolored	.70	.20
		Nos. 392-395 (4)	2.00	.80

1961, Apr. 27			Litho.	Perf. 15	
396	A32	50c yellow, red & blk		.35	.35
397	A32	1fr emerald, brn & blk		.35	.35
398	A32	10fr grnsh bl, vio & blk		.35	.35
399	A32	25fr salmon, grn & blk		.35	.35
400	A32	30fr rose lil, bl & blk		.35	1.00
		Nos. 396-400 (5)		1.75	1.00

1st anniv. of independence; "Papa" Augustino de Souza, leader of the independence
movement.

Daniel
C.
Beard
A33

Designs: 1fr, Lord Baden-Powell. 10fr,
Togolese Scout and emblems. 25fr, Togolese
Scout and flag, vert. 30fr, Symbolic tents and
fire, vert. 100fr, Three hands of different races
giving Scout sign.

1961, Oct. 7		Photo.	Perf. 13	
401	A33	50c brt rose & grn	.45	.20
402	A33	1fr dp violet & car	.45	.20
403	A33	10fr dk gray & brn	.45	.20
404	A33	25fr multicolored	.45	.20
405	A33	30fr grn, red & org brn	.55	.20
406	A33	100fr rose car & bl	1.25	.25
		Nos. 401-406 (6)	3.60	1.25

Togolese Boy Scouts; 20th anniv. of the
deaths of Daniel C. Beard and Lord Baden-
Powell.

Four imperf. souvenir sheets each contain
the six stamps, Nos. 401-406. Two sheets
have a solid background of bright yellow, two a
background of pale grayish brown. One yellow
and one brown sheet have simulated perforations around the stamps. Size: 120x145mm.
"REPUBLIQUE DU TOGO" is inscribed in
white on bottom sheet margin. Value, each $4.

Plane, Ship
and Part of
Map of
Africa — A34

Part of Map of Africa and: 25fr, Electric train
and power mast. 30fr, Tractor and oil derricks.
85fr, Microscope and atomic symbol.

1961, Oct. 24			Litho.	
Black Inscriptions; Map in Ocher				
407	A34	20fr vio bl, org & yel	.45	.20
408	A34	25fr gray, org & yel	.45	.20
409	A34	30fr dk red, yel & org	.55	.20
410	A34	85fr blue, yel & org	1.00	.20
a.		Souvenir sheet of 4	3.50	2.50
		Nos. 407-410 (4)	2.45	.80

UN Economic Commission for Africa. No.
410a contains one each of Nos. 407-410,
imperf., printed without separating margin
between the individual stamps to show a complete map of Africa.

Issued for United Nations Day

"Five Continents,"
Ceiling Painting,
Palais des
Nations,
Geneva — A25

1959, Oct. 24		Engr.	Perf. 12½	
Centers in Dark Ultramarine				
364	A25	15fr brown	.35	.20
365	A25	20fr purple	.35	.20
366	A25	25fr dark orange	.35	.20
367	A25	40fr dark green	.55	.25
368	A25	60fr carmine rose	.60	.30
		Nos. 364-368 (5)	2.20	1.15

Issued for United Nations Day, Oct. 24.

Children Dancing
around
Globe — A35

Cmdr. Alan B.
Shepard — A36

UNICEF Emblem, children and globe.

1961, Dec. 9   Unwmk.   Perf. 13½
**Black Inscription; Multicolored
Design**

411	A35	1fr ultra	.40	.20
412	A35	10fr red brown	.40	.20
413	A35	20fr lilac	.40	.20
414	A35	25fr gray	.40	.20
415	A35	30fr bright blue	.45	.20
416	A35	85fr deep lilac	.85	.25
		Nos. 411-416 (6)	2.90	1.25

UNICEF, 15th anniv.
Nos. 411-416 assembled in two rows show
the globe and children of various races dancing around it.

1962, Feb. 24   Perf. 15x14

Design: 1fr, 30fr, Yuri A. Gagarin.

417	A36	50c green	.40	.20
418	A36	1fr carmine rose	.40	.20
419	A36	25fr blue	.40	.20
420	A36	30fr purple	.40	.20
		Nos. 417-420 (4)	1.60	.80

Astronauts of 1961.
Issued in sheets of 50 and in miniature
sheets of 12 stamps plus four central labels
showing photographs of Alan B. Shepard
(US), Virgil I. Grissom (US), Yuri A. Gagarin
(USSR), Gherman S. Titov (USSR).

No. 417 Surcharged: "100F COL.
JOHN H. GLENN USA VOL ORBITAL
20 FEVRIER 1962" and Bars in Black

1962, Apr. 7

421	A36	100fr on 50c green	2.40	.50
a.		Carmine surcharge	2.40	.50

Orbital flight of Lt. Col. John H. Glenn, Jr.,
US, Feb. 20, 1962.

Independence
Monument,
Lomé — A37

Woman
Carrying Fruit
Basket — A38

1962, Apr. 27   Litho.   Perf. 13½x14

422	A37	50c multicolored	.30	.20
423	A38	1fr green & pink	.30	.20
424	A37	5fr multicolored	.30	.20
425	A38	20fr purple & yel	.30	.20
426	A37	25fr multicolored	.30	.20
427	A38	30fr red & yellow	.30	.20
a.		Souv. sheet of 3, #424-425, 427,		
		imperf.	2.00	1.50
		Nos. 422-427 (6)	1.80	1.20

2nd anniversary of Togo's independence.

Malaria
Eradication
Emblem
A39

1962, June 2   Perf. 13½x13
Multicolored Design

428	A39	10fr yellow green	.55	.20
429	A39	25fr pale lilac	.55	.20
430	A39	30fr ocher	.55	.20
431	A39	85fr light blue	1.10	.20
		Nos. 428-431 (4)	2.75	.80

WHO drive to eradicate malaria.

Capitol, Pres. John F. Kennedy and
Pres. Sylvanus Olympio — A40

1962, July 4   Unwmk.   Perf. 13
**Inscription and Portraits
in Slate Green**

432	A40	50c yellow	.20	.20
433	A40	1fr blue	.20	.20
434	A40	2fr vermilion	.20	.20
435	A40	5fr lilac	.20	.20
436	A40	25fr pale violet	.45	.20
437	A40	100fr brt green	1.75	.80
a.		Souvenir sheet, imperf.	6.00	5.75
		Nos. 432-437 (6)	3.00	1.80

Visit of Pres. Sylvanus Olympio of Togo to
the US, Mar. 1962.

Mail Coach and Stamps of
1897 — A41

50c, Mail ship, stamps of 1900. 1fr, Mail
train, stamps of 1915. 5fr, Motorcycle truck,
stamp of 1924. 25fr, Mail truck, stamp of 1941.
30fr, DC-3, stamp of 1947.

1963, Jan. 12   Photo.   Perf. 13

438	A41	30c multicolored	.50	.20
439	A41	50c multicolored	.50	.20
440	A41	1fr multicolored	.50	.20
441	A41	10fr vio, dp org & blk	.50	.20
442	A41	25fr dk red brn, blk &		
		yel grn	.50	.20
443	A41	30fr ol brn & lil rose	.50	.20
		Nos. 438-443,C34 (7)	4.40	1.50

65th anniv. of Togolese mail service.
For souvenir sheet see No. C34a.

Hands
Reaching
for FAO
Emblem
A42

1963, Mar. 21   Perf. 14

444	A42	50c bl, org & dk brn	.60	.20
445	A42	1fr ol grn, org & dk brn	.60	.20
446	A42	25fr brn, dk brn & org	.60	.20
447	A42	30fr vio, dk brn & org	.80	.20
		Nos. 444-447 (4)	2.60	.80

FAO "Freedom from Hunger" campaign.

Togolese Flag and Lomé
Harbor — A43

1963, Apr. 27   Litho.   Perf. 13x12½
Flag in Red, Green and Yellow

448	A43	50c red brn & blk	.30	.20
449	A43	1fr dk car rose & blk	.30	.20
450	A43	25fr dull bl & blk	.30	.20
451	A43	50fr bister & blk	.40	.20
		Nos. 448-451 (4)	1.30	.80

3rd anniversary of independence.

Centenary
Emblem — A44

1963, June 1   Photo.   Perf. 14
Flag in Red, Olive Green, Yellow

452	A44	25fr blue, blk & red	1.10	.20
453	A44	30fr dull grn, blk & red	1.50	.20

International Red Cross centenary.

Lincoln,
Broken
Fetters,
Maps of
Africa and
US. — A45

1963, Oct.   Unwmk.   Perf. 13x14

454	A45	50c multicolored	.35	.20
455	A45	1fr multicolored	.35	.20
456	A45	25fr multicolored	.35	.20
		Nos. 454-456,C35 (4)	2.30	.90

Centenary of the emancipation of the American slaves. See souvenir sheet No. C35a.
For overprints see Nos. 473-475, C41.

UN Emblem and
"15" — A46

Hibiscus — A47

1963, Dec. 10   Photo.   Perf. 14x13

457	A46	50c ultra, dk bl & rose		
		red	.30	.20
458	A46	1fr yel grn, dk bl &		
		rose red	.30	.20
459	A46	25fr lil, dk bl & rose red	.30	.20
460	A46	85fr gold, dk bl & rose		
		red	1.10	.25
		Nos. 457-460 (4)	2.00	.85

15th anniv. of the Universal Declaration of
Human Rights.

1964   Perf. 14

Designs: 50c, Orchid. 2fr, Butterfly. 5fr,
Hinged tortoise. 8fr, Ball python. 10fr, Bunea
alcinoe (moth). 20fr, Octopus. 25fr, John Dory
(fish). 30fr, French angelfish. 40fr, Hippopotamus. 60fr, Bohor reedbuck. 85fr, Anubius
baboon.

Size: 22½x31mm

461	A47	50c multicolored	1.25	.20
462	A47	1fr yellow, car & grn	1.25	.20
463	A47	2fr lilac, yel & blk	1.25	.20
464	A47	5fr gray & multi	1.25	.20
465	A47	8fr cit, red brn & blk	1.25	.20
466	A47	10fr multicolored	1.25	.20
467	A47	20fr dl bl, yel & brn	1.25	.20
468	A47	25fr dl bl, grn & yel	1.25	.20
469	A47	30fr multicolored	1.55	.20
470	A47	40fr grn, red brn & blk	1.90	.20
471	A47	60fr grnsh bl & red brn	2.75	.20
472	A47	85fr lt grn, brn & org	4.00	.25
		Nos. 461-472 (12)	20.20	2.45

See Nos. 511-515, C36-C40, J56-J63.

Nos. 454-456 Overprinted Diagonally:
"En Mémoire de / JOHN F. KENNEDY
/ 1917-1963"

1964, Mar. 7   Perf. 13x14

473	A45	50c multicolored	.35	.20
474	A45	1fr multicolored	.35	.20
475	A45	25fr multicolored	.35	.20
		Nos. 473-475 (3)	1.05	.60

Issued in memory of John F. Kennedy.
See No. C41 and note on souvenir sheets
following it.

Isis of
Kalabsha
A48

Designs: 25fr, Head of Ramses II. 30fr, Colonnade of Birth House at Philae.

1964, Mar. 8   Litho.   Perf. 14

476	A48	20fr blk, pale grn & red	.45	.20
477	A48	25fr black & lil rose	.45	.20
478	A48	30fr black & citron	.55	.20
a.		Souvenir sheet of 3	2.40	2.00
		Nos. 476-478 (3)	1.45	.60

UNESCO world campaign to save historic
monuments in Nubia. No. 478a contains three
imperf. stamps similar to Nos. 476-478 with
simulated perforations.

Phosphate
Mine,
Kpeme
A49

25fr, Phosphate plant, Kpeme. 60fr,
Phosphate train. 85fr, Loading ship with
phosphate.

1964, Apr. 27   Unwmk.   Perf. 14

479	A49	5fr brown & bis brn	.30	.20
480	A49	25fr dk pur & brn car	.30	.20
481	A49	60fr dk green & olive	.70	.20
482	A49	85fr vio blk & Prus bl	1.00	.25
		Nos. 479-482 (4)	2.30	.85

Fourth anniversary of independence.

African Breaking
Slavery Chain, and
Map — A50

1964, May 25   Photo.   Perf. 14x13

483	A50	5fr dp orange & brn	.40	.20
484	A50	25fr olive grn & brn	.40	.20
485	A50	85fr rose car & brn	1.00	.20
		Nos. 483-485,C42 (4)	3.30	.90

1st anniv. of the meeting of African heads of
state at Addis Ababa.

Pres.
Nicolas
Grunitzky
and
Butterfly
A51

1964, Aug. 18   Litho.   Perf. 14

486	A51	1fr shown	.55	.20
487	A51	5fr Dove	.55	.20
488	A51	25fr Flower	.55	.20
489	A51	45fr as 1fr	.90	.25
490	A51	85fr Flower	1.75	.25
		Nos. 486-490 (5)	4.30	1.05

National Union and Reconciliation.

Soccer
A52

1964, Oct.   Photo.   Perf. 14

491	A52	1fr shown	.50	.20
492	A52	5fr Runner	.50	.20
493	A52	25fr Discus	.50	.20
494	A52	45fr as 1fr	.65	.20
		Nos. 491-494,C43 (5)	4.05	1.10

18th Olympic Games, Tokyo, Oct. 10-25.
For souvenir sheet see No. C43a.

Cooperation Issue
Common Design Type

1964, Nov. 7   Engr.   Perf. 13

495	CD119	25fr mag, dk brn & ol		
		bis	.80	.20

Dirigible and Balloons — A53

25fr, 45fr, Otto Lilienthal's glider, 1894; Wright Brothers' plane, 1903; Boeing 707.

1964, Dec. 5   Photo.   Perf. 14x13
496 A53 5fr org lil & grn   .55 .20
497 A53 10fr brt grn, dl bl & dk
          red   .55 .20
498 A53 25fr bl, vio bl & org   .55 .20
499 A53 45fr brt pink, vio bl &
          grn   .70 .20
  a.   Souv. sheet of 4   5.50 4.50
          Nos. 496-499,C44 (5)   3.15 1.10

Inauguration of the national airline, Air Togo. #499a contains 4 imperf. stamps similar to #497-499 and #C44 with simulated perfs.

Orbiting Geophysical Observatory and Mariner — A54

Space Satellites: 15fr, 25fr, Tiros, Telstar and Orbiting Solar Observatory. 20fr, 50fr, Nimbus, Syncom and Relay.

1964, Dec. 12   Litho.   Perf. 14
500 A54 10fr dp rose, bl & yel   .40 .20
501 A54 15fr multi   .40 .20
502 A54 20fr yel, grn & vio   .40 .20
503 A54 25fr multi   .40 .20
504 A54 45fr brt grn, dk bl & yel   .55 .20
505 A54 50fr yel, grn & org   .75 .20
  a.   Souv. sheet, #502-505, imperf. 3.00 2.50
          Nos. 500-505 (6)   2.90 1.20

Intl. Quiet Sun Year.

Togo Olympic Stamps Printed in Israel — A55

Arms of Israel and Togo — A56

Pres. Nicolas Grunitzky of Togo and: 20fr, Church of the Mount of Beatitudes. 45fr, Ruins of Synagogue at Capernaum.

Perf. 13½x14½, 14x13½
1964, Dec. 26   Photo.
506 A55 5fr rose violet   .40 .20
507 A56 20fr grnsh bl, grn & dl
          pur   .40 .20
508 A56 25fr red & bluish grn   .40 .20
509 A56 45fr dl yel, ol & dl pur   .85 .20
510 A56 85fr mag & bluish grn   .65 .20
  a.   Souv. sheet of 4, imperf.   4.50 3.50
          Nos. 506-510 (5)   2.70 1.05

Israel-Togo friendship.

Type of Regular Issue, 1964
1965, June   Unwmk.   Perf. 14
Designs: 3fr, Morpho aega butterfly. 4fr, Scorpion. 6fr, Bird-of-paradise flower. 15fr,

---

Flap-necked chameleon. 45fr, Ring-tailed palm civet.

Size: 23x31mm
511 A47 3fr bister & multi   1.40 .20
512 A47 4fr org & bluish blk   1.40 .20
513 A47 6fr multi   1.40 .20
514 A47 15fr brt pink, yel & brn   1.40 .20
515 A47 45fr dl grn, org & brn   2.00 .20
          Nos. 511-515 (5)   7.60 1.00

Syncom Satellite, Radar Station and ITU Emblem — A57

1965, June   Perf. 13x14
516 A57 10fr Prus blue   .45 .20
517 A57 20fr olive bister   .45 .20
518 A57 25fr bright blue   .45 .20
519 A57 45fr crimson   .65 .20
520 A57 50fr green   .75 .20
          Nos. 516-520 (5)   2.75 1.00

ITU, centenary.

Abraham   Discus Thrower,
Lincoln — A58   Flags of Togo
                       and
                       Congo — A59

1965, June 26   Photo.   Perf. 13x14
521 A58 1fr magenta   .40 .20
522 A58 5fr dull green   .40 .20
523 A58 20fr brown   .40 .20
524 A58 25fr slate   .40 .20
          Nos. 521-524,C45 (5)   3.50 1.10

Death cent. of Abraham Lincoln. For souvenir sheet see No. C45a.

1965, July   Unwmk.   Perf. 14x13

Flags and: 10fr, Javelin thrower. 15fr, Handball player. 25fr, Runner.

Flags in Red, Yellow and Green
525 A59 5fr deep magenta   .40 .20
526 A59 10fr dark blue   .40 .20
527 A59 15fr brown   .40 .20
528 A59 25fr dark purple   .40 .20
          Nos. 525-528,C46 (5)   3.20 1.10

1st African Games, Brazzaville, July 18-25.

Winston Churchill
and "V" — A60

Stalin, Roosevelt and Churchill at Yalta — A61

Perf. 13½x14, 14x13½
1965, Aug. 7   Photo.
529 A60 5fr dull green   .40 .20
530 A61 10fr brt vio & gray   .40 .20
531 A60 20fr brown   .40 .20
532 A61 45fr Prus bl & gray   .70 .20
          Nos. 529-532,C47 (5)   3.50 1.10

Sir Winston Spencer Churchill (1874-1965), British statesman and World War II leader.

Unisphere and New York Skyline — A62

10fr, Togolese dancers & drummer, Unisphere. 50fr, Michelangelo's Pieta & Unisphere.

1965, Aug. 28   Photo.   Perf. 14
533 A62 5fr grnsh bl & vio blk   .35 .20
534 A62 10fr yel grn & dk brn   .35 .20
535 A62 25fr brn org & dk grn   .35 .20
536 A62 50fr vio & sl grn   .50 .20
537 A62 85fr rose red & brn   1.10 .30
  a.   Souvenir sheet of 2   2.75 1.75
          Nos. 533-537 (5)   2.65 1.10

New York World's Fair, 1964-65. No. 537a contains two imperf. stamps similar to Nos. 536-537 with simulated perforations.

"Constructive Cooperation" and Olive Branch — A63

Designs: 25fr, 40fr, Hands of various races holding globe and olive branch. 85fr, Handclasp, olive branch and globe.

1965, Sept. 25   Unwmk.   Perf. 14
538 A63 5fr violet, lt bl & org   .35 .20
539 A63 15fr brn, org & gray   .35 .20
540 A63 25fr blue & orange   .35 .20
541 A63 40fr dp car, gray & org   .55 .20
542 A63 85fr green & org   1.00 .30
          Nos. 538-542 (5)   2.60 1.10

International Cooperation Year.

Major White and Gemini 4 — A64

25fr, Lt. Col. Alexei Leonov and Voskhod 2.

1965, Nov. 25 Photo. Perf. 13½x14
543 A64 25fr dp bl & brt car rose   .60 .20
544 A64 50fr green & brown   1.00 .20

"Walks in Space" of Lt. Col. Alexei Leonov (USSR), and Major Edward H. White (US). Printed in sheets of 12 with ornamental borders.
For overprints and surcharges see Nos. 563-566.

Adlai E. Stevenson and UN Headquarters — A65

5fr, "ONU" and doves. 10fr, UN emblem and headquarters. 20fr, "ONU" and orchids.

1965, Dec. 15   Perf. 14x13½
545 A65 5fr dk brn, yel & lt bl   .40 .20
546 A65 10fr org, dk bl & grn   .40 .20
547 A65 20fr dk grn, yel grn &
          org brn   .40 .20
548 A65 25fr brt yel, dk bl & blu-
          ish grn   .40 .20
          Nos. 545-548,C48 (5)   3.35 1.20

UN, 20th anniv.; Adlai E. Stevenson (1900-1965), US ambassador to the UN.

Pope Paul VI, Plane and UN Emblem — A66

15fr, 30fr, Pope addressing UN General Assembly & UN emblem, vert. 20fr, Pope, NYC skyline with UN Headquarters.

1966, Mar. 5   Litho.   Perf. 12
549 A66 5fr blue & multi   .40 .20
550 A66 15fr lt violet & multi   .40 .20
551 A66 20fr bister & multi   .40 .20
552 A66 30fr lt ultra & multi   .40 .20
          Nos. 549-552,C49-C50 (6)   3.60 1.20

Visit of Pope Paul VI to the UN, New York City, Oct. 4, 1965.

Surgical Operation and Togolese Flag — A67

Togolese Flag and: 10fr, 30fr, Blood transfusion. 45fr, Profiles of African man and woman.

1966, May 7   Litho.   Perf. 12
553 A67 5fr multicolored   .40 .20
554 A67 10fr multicolored   .40 .20
555 A67 15fr multicolored   .40 .20
556 A67 30fr multicolored   .40 .20
557 A67 45fr multicolored   .60 .20
          Nos. 553-557,C51 (6)   4.10 1.30

Togolese Red Cross, 7th anniversary.

Talisman Roses and WHO
Headquarters, Geneva — A68

Various flowers & WHO Headquarters.

1966, May   Litho.   Perf. 12

558 A68	5fr lt yel grn & multi	.45	.20
559 A68	10fr pale pink & multi	.45	.20
560 A68	15fr dull yel & multi	.45	.20
561 A68	20fr pale gray & multi	.45	.20
562 A68	30fr tan & multi	.45	.20
	Nos. 558-562,C52-C53 (7)	4.65	1.40

Inauguration of WHO Headquarters, Geneva.

Nos. 543-544 Overprinted or
Surcharged in Red

1966, July 11   Photo.   Perf. 13½x14

563 A64	50fr Envolée Surveyor 1	.55	.20
564 A64	50fr Envolée Gemini 9	.55	.20
a.	Pair, #563-564	1.25	.50
565 A64	100fr on 25fr Envolée Luna 9	1.25	.20
566 A64	100fr on 25fr Envolée Venus 3	1.25	.20
a.	Pair, #565-566	3.00	.75
	Nos. 563-566 (4)	3.60	.80

US and USSR achievements in Space.

Wood
Carver — A69

Togolese
Dancer — A70

Arts and Crafts: 10fr, Basket maker. 15fr,
Woman weaver. 30fr, Woman potter.

1966, Sept.   Photo.   Perf. 13x14

567 A69	5fr blue, yel & dk brn	.40	.20
568 A69	10fr emer, org & dk brn	.40	.20
569 A69	15fr ver, yel & dk brn	.40	.20
570 A69	30fr lilac, dk brn & yel	.40	.20
	Nos. 567-570,C55-C56 (6)	4.00	1.20

1966, Nov.   Photo.   Perf. 13x14

Designs: 5fr, Togolese man. 20fr, Woman
dancer from North Togo holding branches.
25fr, Male dancer. 30fr, Male dancer from
North Togo with horned helmet. 45fr,
Drummer.

571 A70	5fr emerald & multi	.40	.20
572 A70	10fr dl yel & multi	.40	.20
573 A70	20fr lt ultra & multi	.40	.20
574 A70	25fr dp orange & multi	.40	.20
575 A70	30fr red violet & multi	.40	.20
576 A70	45fr blue & multi	.50	.20
	Nos. 571-576,C57-C58 (8)	4.30	1.60

Soccer Players and Jules Rimet
Cup — A71

Various Soccer Scenes.

1966, Dec. 14   Photo.   Perf. 14x13

577 A71	5fr blue, brn & red	.50	.20
578 A71	10fr brick red & multi	.50	.20
579 A71	20fr ol, brn & dk grn	.50	.20
580 A71	25fr vio, brn & org	.50	.20
581 A71	30fr ocher & multi	.50	.20
582 A71	45fr emerald, brn & mag	.60	.20
	Nos. 577-582,C59-C60 (8)	5.20	1.60

England's victory in the World Soccer Cup
Championship, Wembley, July 30. For souvenir sheet see No. C60a.

African Mouthbreeder and
Sailboat — A72

Designs: 10fr, Yellow jack and trawler. 15fr,
Banded distichodus and seiner.   25fr,
Jewelfish and galley. 30fr, like 5fr.

1967, Jan. 14   Photo.   Perf. 14
Fish in Natural Colors

583 A72	5fr lt ultra & blk	.45	.20
584 A72	10fr brn org & brn	.45	.20
585 A72	15fr brt rose & dk bl	.45	.20
586 A72	25fr olive & blk	.45	.20
587 A72	30fr grnsh bl & blk	.60	.20
	Nos. 583-587,C61-C62 (7)	5.40	1.50

African Boy and Greyhound — A73

UNICEF Emblem and: 10fr, Boy and Irish
setter. 20fr, Girl and doberman.

1967, Feb. 11   Photo.   Perf. 14x13½

588 A73	5fr orange, plum & blk	.45	.20
589 A73	10fr yel grn, red brn & dk grn	.45	.20
590 A73	15fr brt rose, brn & blk	.45	.20
591 A73	20fr bl, vio bl & blk	.45	.20
592 A73	30fr ol, sl grn & blk	.45	.20
	Nos. 588-592,C63-C64 (7)	4.75	1.45

UNICEF, 20th anniv. (in 1966).

French A-1 Satellite — A74

5fr, Diamant rocket, vert. 15fr, Fr-1 satellite,
vert. 20fr, D-1 satellite. 25fr, A-1 satellite.

Perf. 14x13½, 13½x14

1967, Mar. 18   Photo.

593 A74	5fr multi	.40	.20
594 A74	10fr multi	.40	.20
595 A74	15fr multi	.40	.20
596 A74	20fr multi	.40	.20
597 A74	25fr multi	.40	.20
598 A74	40fr multi	.50	.20
	Nos. 593-598,C65-C66 (8)	5.00	1.65

French achievements in space.

Johann Sebastian Bach and
Organ — A75

UNESCO Emblem and: 10fr, Ludwig van
Beethoven, violin and oboe. 15f, Duke Elling-
ton, saxophone, trumpet, drums. 20fr, Claude
A. Debussy, piano and harp. 30fr, like 15fr.

1967, Apr. 15   Photo.   Perf. 14x13½

599 A75	5fr org & multi	.50	.20
600 A75	10fr multi	.50	.20
601 A75	15fr multi	.50	.20
602 A75	20fr lt bl & multi	.50	.20
603 A75	30fr lil & multi	.50	.20
	Nos. 599-603,C67-C68 (7)	5.40	1.40

20th anniv. (in 1966) of UNESCO.

EXPO Emblem, British Pavilion and
Day Lilies — A76

10fr, French pavilion, roses. 30fr, African village, bird-of-paradise flower.

1967, May 30   Photo.   Perf. 14

604 A76	5fr brt pink & multi	.45	.20
605 A76	10fr dull org & multi	.45	.20
606 A76	30fr blue & multi	.45	.20
	Nos. 604-606,C69-C72 (7)	6.00	1.55

EXPO '67 Intl. Exhibition, Montreal, Apr. 28-
Oct. 27.
For overprints see Nos. 628-630, C86-C89.

Lions
Emblem — A77

20fr, 45fr, Lions emblem and flowers.

1967, July 29   Photo.   Perf. 13x14

607 A77	10fr yellow & multi	.45	.20
608 A77	20fr multicolored	.45	.20
609 A77	30fr green & multi	.55	.20
610 A77	45fr blue & multi	.80	.20
	Nos. 607-610 (4)	2.25	.80

50th anniversary of Lions International.

Montagu's Harriers — A78

5fr, Bohor reedbucks. 15fr, Zebras. 20fr,
30fr, Marsh harriers. 25fr, Leopard.

1967, Aug. 19   Photo.   Perf. 14x13½

611 A78	5fr lilac & org brn	.55	.20
612 A78	10fr dk red, yel & dl bl	.55	.20
613 A78	15fr grn, blk & lil	.55	.20
614 A78	20fr dk brn, yel & dl bl	.55	.20
615 A78	25fr brn, ol & yel	.55	.20
616 A78	30fr vio, yel & dl bl	.65	.20
	Nos. 611-616,C79-C80 (8)	6.10	1.60

Stamp Auction and Togo Nos. 16 and
C42 — A79

10fr, 45fr, Exhibition, #67 (British) & 520.
15fr, 30fr, Stamp store, #230. 20fr, Stamp
packet vending machine, #545.

1967, Oct. 14   Photo.   Perf. 14x13
Stamps on Stamps in Original
Colors

617 A79	5fr purple	.30	.20
618 A79	10fr dk brown	.30	.20
619 A79	15fr deep blue	.30	.20
620 A79	20fr slate green	.35	.20
621 A79	30fr red brown	.50	.20
622 A79	45fr Prus blue	.50	.20
	Nos. 617-622,C82-C83 (8)	5.80	1.85

70th anniv. of the 1st Togolese stamps. For
souvenir sheet see No. C82a.
See Nos. 853-855, C205.

Monetary Union Issue
Common Design Type

1967, Nov. 4   Engr.   Perf. 13

623 CD125	30fr dk bl, vio bl & brt grn	.60	.20

Broad Jump, Summer Olympics
Emblem and View of Mexico
City — A80

15fr, Ski jump, Winter Olympics emblem, ski
lift. 30fr, Runners, Summer Olympics emblem,
view of Mexico City. 45fr, Bobsledding, Winter
Olympics emblem, ski lift.

1967, Dec. 2   Photo.   Perf. 13x14

624 A80	5fr orange & multi	.45	.20
625 A80	15fr multicolored	.45	.20
626 A80	30fr multicolored	.45	.20
627 A80	45fr multicolored	.55	.20
	Nos. 624-627,C84-C85 (6)	4.35	1.60

1968 Olympic Games. For souvenir sheet
see No. C85a.

Nos. 604-606 Overprinted: "JOURNÉE
NATIONALE / DU TOGO / 29
SEPTEMBRE 1967"

1967, Dec.   Perf. 14

628 A76	5fr multicolored	.30	.20
629 A76	10fr multicolored	.30	.20
630 A76	30fr blue & multi	.45	.20
	Nos. 628-630,C86-C89 (7)	5.40	1.60

National Day, Sept. 29, 1967.

The Gleaners, by François Millet and
Phosphate Works, Benin — A81

Industrialization of Togo: 20fr, 45fr, 90fr,
The Weaver at the Loom, by Vincent van
Gogh, and textile plant, Dadia.

1968, Jan.   Photo.   Perf. 14

631 A81	10fr olive & multi	.35	.20
632 A81	20fr multicolored	.35	.20
633 A81	30fr brown & multi	.45	.20
634 A81	45fr multicolored	.50	.20

635 A81 60fr dk blue & multi   .75   .20
636 A81 90fr multicolored   1.25   .25
        Nos. 631-636 (6)   3.65 1.25

Togolese Women Brewing Beer — A82

The Beer
Drinkers, by
Edouard
Manet — A83

Design: 45fr, Modern beer bottling plant.

1968, Mar. 26   Litho.   Perf. 14
637 A82 20fr emerald & multi   .55   .20
638 A83 30fr dk car & multi   .70   .20
639 A82 45fr orange & multi   .85   .20
        Nos. 637-639 (3)   2.10   .60

Publicity for local beer industry.

Symbolic Water
Cycle, Flower
and Cogwheels
A84

1968, Apr. 6
640 A84 30fr multicolored   .65 .20
Hydrological Decade (UNESCO), 1965-74.
See No. C90.

Viking Ship and Portuguese
Brigantine — A85

10fr, Fulton's steamship and modern steamship. 20fr, Harbor activities and map of Africa.

1968, Apr. 26   Photo.   Perf. 14x13½
641 A85   5fr brt green & multi   .40 .20
642 A85 10fr dp orange & multi   .40 .20
643 A85 20fr green & multi   .40 .20
644 A85 30fr yel grn & multi   .40 .20
        Nos. 641-644,C91-C92 (6)   4.00 1.20

Inauguration of Lomé Harbor.

Adenauer and 1968
Europa
Emblem — A86

1968, May 25   Photo.   Perf. 14
645 A86 90fr olive grn & brn org   1.90 .20
Konrad Adenauer (1876-1967), chancellor
of West Germany (1949-63).

Adam and Eve Expelled from
Paradise, by Michelangelo — A87

Paintings: 20fr, The Anatomy Lesson of Dr.
Tulp, by Rembrandt. 30fr, The Anatomy Lesson, by Rembrandt (detail). 45fr, Jesus Healing the Sick, by Raphael.

1968, June 22   Photo.   Perf. 14
646 A87 15fr crimson & multi   .45 .20
647 A87 20fr multicolored   .45 .20
648 A87 30fr green & multi   .45 .20
649 A87 45fr multicolored   .55 .20
        Nos. 646-649,C93-C94 (6)   4.60 1.20

WHO, 20th anniv.

Olympic Monument, San Salvador
Island, Bahamas — A88

1968, July 27   Perf. 14x13½
650 A88 15fr Wrestling   .40 .20
651 A88 20fr Boxing   .40 .20
652 A88 30fr Judo   .40 .20
653 A88 45fr Running   .50 .20
        Nos. 650-653,C95-C96 (6)   4.05 1.20

19th Olympic Games, Mexico City, 10/12-27.

Chick Holding   Scout Before
Lottery   Tent — A90
Ticket — A89

45fr, Lottery ticket, horseshoe & 4-leaf
clover.

1968, Oct. 5   Litho.   Perf. 14
654 A89 30fr dk green & multi   .65 .20
655 A89 45fr multicolored   .75 .20

2nd anniversary of National Lottery.

1968, Nov. 23
10fr, 45fr, Scout leader training cub scouts,
horiz. 20fr, First aid practice, horiz. 30fr,
Scout game.

656 A90   5fr dp org & multi   .30 .20
657 A90 10fr emerald & multi   .30 .20
658 A90 20fr multicolored   .30 .20
659 A90 30fr multicolored   .40 .20
660 A90 45fr blue & multi   .50 .20
        Nos. 656-660,C97-C98 (7)   4.20 1.60

Issued to honor the Togolese Boy Scouts.

Adoration of the Shepherds, by
Giorgione — A91

Paintings: 20f, Adoration of the Magi, by
Pieter Brueghel. 30fr, Adoration of the Magi,
by Botticelli. 45fr, Adoration of the Magi, by
Durer.

1968, Dec. 28   Litho.   Perf. 14
661 A91 15fr green & multi   .40 .20
662 A91 20fr multicolored   .40 .20
663 A91 30fr multicolored   .50 .20
664 A91 45fr multicolored   .60 .20
        Nos. 661-664,C100-C101 (6)   5.05 1.30

Christmas.

Martin Luther
King, Jr. — A92

Portraits and Human Rights Flame: 20fr,
Professor René Cassin (author of Declaration
of Human Rights). 45fr, Pope John XXIII.

1969, Feb. 1   Photo.   Perf. 13½x14
665 A92 15fr brn org & sl grn   .45 .20
666 A92 20fr grnsh bl & vio   .45 .20
667 A92 30fr ver & slate bl   .45 .20
668 A92 45fr olive & car rose   .60 .20
        Nos. 665-668,C102-C103 (6)   4.20 1.30

International Human Rights Year.
For overprints see Nos. 683-686, C110-
C111.

Omnisport Stadium and Soccer — A93

Stadium and: 15fr, Handball. 20fr, Volleyball. 30fr, Basketball. 45fr, Tennis.

1969, Apr. 26   Photo.   Perf. 14x13½
669 A93 10fr emer, dp car & dk
                brn   .45 .20
670 A93 15fr org, ultra & dk brn   .45 .20
671 A93 20fr yel, ol & dk brn   .45 .20
672 A93 30fr dl grn, bl & dk brn   .45 .20
673 A93 45fr org, lil & dk brn   .55 .20
        Nos. 669-673,C105-C106 (7)   4.70 1.45

Opening of Omnisport Stadium, Lomé.

Astronaut
and Eagle
on Moon,
Earth and
Stars in
Sky — A94

Designs: 1f, 30f, Lunar Module Eagle Landing on Moon. 45fr, Astronaut and Eagle on
moon, earth and stars in sky.

1969, July 21   Litho.   Perf. 14
674 A94   1fr green & multi   .40 .20
675 A94 20fr brown & multi   .40 .20
676 A94 30fr scarlet & multi   .40 .20
677 A94 45fr ultra & multi   .70 .20
        Nos. 674-677,C107-C108 (6)   4.10 1.40

Man's 1st landing on the moon, 7/20/69. US
astronauts Neil A. Armstrong & Col. Edwin E.
Aldrin, Jr., with Lieut. Col. Michael Collins
piloting Apollo 11.
For overprints see #710-712, C120-C121.

Christ at
Emmaus,
by
Velazquez
A95

Paintings: 5fr, The Last Supper, by Tintoretto. 20fr, Pentecost, by El Greco. 30fr, The
Annunciation, by Botticelli. 45fr, Like 10fr.

1969, Aug. 16   Litho.   Perf. 14
678 A95   5fr red, gold & multi   .50 .20
679 A95 10fr multicolored   .50 .20
680 A95 20fr grn, gold & multi   .50 .20
681 A95 30fr multicolored   .50 .20
682 A95 45fr pur, gold & multi   .70 .20
        Nos. 678-682,C109 (6)   5.10 1.40

Nos. 665-668
Overprinted

1969, Sept. 1   Photo.   Perf. 13½x14
683 A92 15fr brn org & sl grn   .50 .20
684 A92 20fr grnsh bl & vio   .50 .20
685 A92 30fr ver & slate bl   .50 .20
686 A92 45fr olive & car rose   .60 .20
        Nos. 683-686,C110-C111 (6)   4.60 1.25

Gen. Dwight D. Eisenhower (1890-1969),
34th President of the US.

African
Development
Bank and
Emblem — A96

Designs: 45fr, Bank emblem and hand
holding railroad bridge and engine.

1969, Sept. 10 Photo.   Perf. 13x14
687 A96 30fr ultra, blk gold & grn 1.00 .20
688 A96 45fr grn, dk bl, gold &
                dk red   1.40 .20

5th anniv. of the African Development Bank.
See No. C112.

Louis Pasteur and Help for 1968 Flood
Victims — A97

Designs: 15fr, Henri Dunant and Red Cross workers meeting Biafra refugees at airport. 30fr, Alexander Fleming and help for flood victims. 45fr, Wilhelm C. Roentgen and Red Cross workers with children in front of Headquarters.

1969, Sept. 27   Litho.   Perf. 14

689	A97	15fr red & multi	.50	.20
690	A97	20fr emerald & multi	.50	.20
691	A97	30fr purple & multi	.50	.20
692	A97	45fr brt blue & multi	.70	.20
		Nos. 689-692,C113-C114 (6)	4.90	1.40

League of Red Cross Societies, 50th anniv.

Glidji Agricultural Center A98

Designs (Emblem of Young Pioneer and Agricultural Organization and): 1fr, Corn harvest. 3fr, Founding meeting of Agricultural Pioneer Youths, Mar. 7, 1967. 4fr, Class at Glidji Agricultural School. 5fr, Boys forming human pyramid. 7fr, Farm students threshing. 8fr, Instruction in gardening. 10fr, Cooperative village. 15fr, Gardening School. 20fr, Cattle breeding. 25fr, Chicken farm. 30fr, Independence parade. 40fr, Boys riding high wire. 45fr, Tractor and trailer. 60fr, Instruction in tractor driving.

1969-70   Litho.   Perf. 14

693	A98	1fr multi ('70)	.45	.20
694	A98	2fr multi	.45	.20
695	A98	3fr multi ('70)	.45	.20
696	A98	4fr multi ('70)	.45	.20
697	A98	5fr ultra & multi	.45	.20
698	A98	7fr multi ('70)	.45	.20
699	A98	8fr red & multi	.45	.20
700	A98	10fr bl & multi ('70)	.45	.20
701	A98	15fr red & multi ('70)	.45	.20
702	A98	20fr lilac & multi	.45	.20
703	A98	25fr multi ('70)	.45	.20
704	A98	30fr brt bl & multi	.45	.20
705	A98	40fr brt yel & multi	.45	.20
706	A98	45fr rose lil & multi	.60	.20
707	A98	50fr blue & multi	.60	.20
708	A98	60fr orange & multi	.60	.20
		Nos. 693-708,C115-C119 (21)	24.30	5.35

Books and Map of Africa A99

1969, Nov. 27   Litho.   Perf. 14

709	A99	30fr lt blue & multi	.60	.20

12th anniv. of the Intl. Assoc. for the Development of Libraries in Africa.

Christmas Issue
Nos. 674-675, 677 Overprinted "JOYEUX NOEL"

1969, Dec.   Litho.   Perf. 14

710	A94	1fr green & multi	.55	.20
711	A94	20fr brown & multi	1.90	.35
712	A94	45fr ultra & multi	3.50	.65
		Nos. 710-712,C120-C121 (5)	14.70	2.20

George Washington — A100

Portraits: 20fr, Albert Luthuli. 30fr, Mahatma Gandhi. 45fr, Simon Bolivar.

1969, Dec. 27   Photo.   Perf. 14x13½

713	A100	15fr dk brn, emer & buff	.50	.20
714	A100	20fr dk brn, org & buff	.50	.20
715	A100	30fr dk brn, grnsh bl & ocher	.50	.20
716	A100	45fr dk brn, sl grn & dl yel	.50	.20
		Nos. 713-716,C122-C123 (6)	4.60	1.30

Issued to honor leaders for world peace.

For overprint & surcharges see #764-766, C143.

Plower, by M.K. Klodt and ILO Emblem A101

Paintings and ILO Emblem: 10fr, Gardening, by Camille Pissarro. 20fr, Fruit Harvest, by Diego Rivera. 30fr, Spring Sowing, by Vincent van Gogh. 45fr, Workers, by Rivera.

1970, Jan. 24   Litho.   Perf. 12½x13

717	A101	5fr gold & multi	.80	.20
718	A101	10fr gold & multi	.80	.20
719	A101	20fr gold & multi	.80	.20
720	A101	30fr gold & multi	1.00	.20
721	A101	45fr gold & multi	1.40	.20
		Nos. 717-721,C124-C125 (7)	8.70	1.40

ILO, 50th anniversary.

Togolese Hair Styles — A102

Various hair styles. 20fr, 30fr, vertical.

1970, Feb. 21   Perf. 13x12½, 12½x13

722	A102	5fr multicolored	.60	.20
723	A102	10fr ver & multi	.60	.20
724	A102	20fr purple & multi	.60	.20
725	A102	30fr yellow grn & multi	.80	.20
		Nos. 722-725,C126-C127 (6)	5.00	1.30

Togo No. C127 and Independence Monument, Lomé — A103

30fr, Pres. Etienne G. Eyadéma, Presidential Palace and Independence Monument. 50fr, Map of Togo, dove and Independence Monument, vert.

Perf. 13x12½, 12½x13

1970, Apr. 27   Litho.

726	A103	20fr multicolored	.65	.20
727	A103	30fr multicolored	.65	.20
728	A103	50fr multicolored	.95	.20
		Nos. 726-728,C128 (4)	3.20	.80

10th anniv. of independence.

Inauguration of UPU Headquarters, Bern — A104

1970, May 30   Photo.   Perf. 14x13½

729	A104	30fr orange & pur	1.25	.20
		See No. C129.		

Soccer, Jules Rimet Cup and Flags of Italy and Uruguay — A105

Designs (Various Scenes from Soccer, Rimet Cup and Flags of): 10fr, Great Britain and Brazil. 15fr, USSR and Mexico. 20fr, Germany and Morocco. 30fr, Romania and Czechoslovakia.

1970, June 27   Litho.   Perf. 13x14

730	A105	5fr olive & multi	.55	.20
731	A105	10fr pink & multi	.55	.20
732	A105	15fr yellow & multi	.55	.20
733	A105	20fr multicolored	.55	.20
734	A105	30fr emerald	.80	.20
		Nos. 730-734,C130-C132 (8)	6.40	1.70

Soccer Championships for the Jules Rimet Cup, Mexico City, May 30-June 21, 1970.

Lenin and UNESCO Emblem A106

1970, July 25   Litho.   Perf. 12½

735	A106	30fr fawn & multi	1.90	.20

Lenin (1870-1924), Russian communist leader. See No. C133.
For surcharge see No. C179.

EXPO '70 Emblem and View of US Pavilion — A107

Designs: 2fr, Paper carp flying over Sanyo pavilion. 30fr, Russian pavilion. 50fr, Tower of the Sun pavilion. 60fr, French and Japanese pavilions.

1970, Aug. 8   Litho.   Perf. 13

Size: 56½x35mm

736	A107	2fr gray & multi	.45	.20

Size: 50x33mm

737	A107	20fr blue & multi	.45	.20
738	A107	30fr blue & multi	.45	.20
739	A107	50fr blue & multi	.55	.20
740	A107	60fr blue & multi	.65	.20
a.		Strip of 4, #737-740	2.25	1.25
		Nos. 736-740 (5)	2.55	1.00

EXPO '70 Intl. Exhibition, Osaka, Japan, Mar. 15-Sept. 13. No. 740a has continuous view of EXPO. See No. C134.

Neil A. Armstrong, Michael Collins and Edwin E. Aldrin, Jr. — A108

Designs: 2fr, US flag, moon rocks and Apollo 11 emblem. 20fr, Astronaut checking Surveyor 3 on moon, and Apollo 12 emblem. 30fr, Charles Conrad, Jr., Richard F. Gordon, Jr., Alan L. Bean and Apollo 12 emblem. 50fr, US flag, moon rocks and Apollo 12 emblem.

1970, Sept. 26

741	A108	1fr multi	.50	.20
742	A108	2fr multi	.50	.20
743	A108	20fr multi	.50	.20
744	A108	30fr multi	.65	.20
745	A108	50fr multi	1.25	.20
		Nos. 741-745,C135 (6)	5.90	1.55

Moon landings of Apollo 11 and 12.
For overprints see Nos. 746-750, C136.

Nos. 741-745 Inscribed: "FELICITATIONS / BON RETOUR APOLLO XIII"

1970, Sept. 26

746	A108	1fr multi	.50	.20
747	A108	2fr multi	.50	.20
748	A108	20fr multi	.50	.20
749	A108	30fr multi	.65	.20
750	A108	50fr multi	1.10	.20
		Nos. 746-750,C136 (6)	5.75	1.55

Safe return of the crew of Apollo 13.

Forge of Vulcan, by Velazquez, and ILO Emblem — A109

Paintings and Emblems of UN Agencies: 15fr, Still Life, by Delacroix, and FAO emblem. 20fr, Portrait of Nicholas Kratzer, by Holbein, and UNESCO emblem. 30fr, UN Headquarters, New York, and UN emblem. 50fr, Portrait of a Little Girl, by Renoir, and UNICEF emblem.

1970, Oct. 24   Litho.   Perf. 13x12½

751	A109	1fr car, gold & dk brn	.65	.20
752	A109	15fr ultra, gold & blk	.65	.20
753	A109	20fr grnsh bl, gold & dk grn	.65	.20
754	A109	30fr lil & multi	.80	.20
755	A109	50fr org brn, gold & sepia	1.25	.20
		Nos. 751-755,C137-C138 (7)	6.85	1.50

United Nations, 25th anniversary.

Euchloron Megaera — A110

Butterflies and Moths: 2fr, Cymothoe chrysippus. 30fr, Danaus chrysippus. 50fr, Morpho.

1970, Nov. 21   Litho.   Perf. 13x14

756	A110	1fr yellow & multi	2.00	.20
757	A110	2fr lt vio & multi	2.00	.20
758	A110	30fr multicolored	2.00	.20
759	A110	50fr orange & multi	3.75	.20
		Nos. 756-759,C139-C140 (6)	20.25	1.20

For surcharge see No. 859.

Nativity, by Botticelli — A111

Paintings: 20fr, Adoration of the Shepherds, by Veronese. 30fr, Adoration of the Shepherds, by El Greco. 50fr, Adoration of the Kings, by Fra Angelico.

1970, Dec. 26　Litho.　Perf. 12½x13

760	A111 15fr gold & multi	.65	.20
761	A111 20fr gold & multi	.65	.20
762	A111 30fr gold & multi	.65	.20
763	A111 50fr gold & multi	1.10	.20
	Nos. 760-763,C141-C142 (6)	6.80	1.30

Christmas.

Nos. 715, C123, 714 Surcharged and Overprinted: "EN MEMOIRE / Charles De Gaulle / 1890-1970"

1971, Jan. 9　Photo.　Perf. 14x13½

764	A100 30fr multicolored	2.00	.20
765	A100 30fr on 90fr multi	2.00	.20
766	A100 150fr on 20fr multi	8.50	.35
	Nos. 764-766,C143 (4)	24.00	1.35

"Aerienne" obliterated with heavy bar on No. 765.

De Gaulle and Churchill A112

De Gaulle and: 30fr, Dwight D. Eisenhower. 40fr, John F. Kennedy. 50fr, Konrad Adenauer.

1971, Feb. 20　Photo.　Perf. 13x14

767	A112 20fr blk & brt blue	.90	.20
768	A112 30fr blk & crimson	.90	.20
769	A112 40fr blk & dp green	1.40	.20
770	A112 50fr blk & brown	1.60	.20
	Nos. 767-770,C144-C145 (6)	10.00	1.25

Nos. 764-770 issued in memory of Charles de Gaulle (1890-1970), President of France.

Resurrection, by Raphael — A113

Easter: 30fr, Resurrection, by Master of Trebon. 40fr, like 1fr.

1971, Apr. 10　Litho.　Perf. 10½x11½

771	A113 1fr gold & multi	.50	.20
772	A113 30fr gold & multi	.50	.20
773	A113 40fr gold & multi	.50	.20
	Nos. 771-773,C146-C148 (6)	5.20	1.30

Cmdr. Alan B. Shepard, Jr. — A114

Designs: 10fr, Edgar D. Mitchell and astronaut on moon. 30fr, Stuart A. Roosa, module on moon. 40fr, Take-off from moon, and spaceship.

1971, May　Litho.　Perf. 12½

774	A114 1fr blue & multi	.30	.20
775	A114 10fr green & multi	.30	.20
776	A114 30fr dull red & multi	.30	.20
777	A114 40fr dk green & multi	.35	.20
	Nos. 774-777,C149-C151 (7)	4.65	2.00

Apollo 14 moon landing, Jan. 31-Feb. 9. For overprints see Nos. 788, C162-C164.

Cacao Tree and Pods — A115

Designs: 40fr, Sorting and separating beans and pods. 50fr, Drying cacao beans.

1971, June 6　Litho.　Perf. 14

778	A115 30fr multicolored	.60	.20
779	A115 40fr ultra & multi	.65	.20
780	A115 50fr multicolored	.65	.20
	Nos. 778-780,C152-C154 (6)	5.15	1.45

International Cacao Day, June 6.

Napoleon, Death Sesquicentennial — A115a

Die Cut Perf. 12

1971, June 11　　　　　Embossed

780A	A115a 1000fr gold	40.00	40.00
b.	Sheet of 1, imperf.	26.00	26.00

No. 780Ab contains one 48x69mm stamp.

Control Tower and Plane — A116

1971, June 26　Litho.　Perf. 14

781	A116 30fr multicolored	1.00	.20

10th anniv. of the Agency for the Security of Aerial Navigation in Africa and Madagascar (ASECNA). See No. C155.

Great Market, Lomé — A117

Tourist publicity: 30fr, Bird-of-paradise flower and sculpture of a man. 40fr, Aledjo Gorge and anubius baboon.

1971, July 17

782	A117 20fr multicolored	.45	.20
783	A117 30fr multicolored	.45	.20
784	A117 40fr multicolored	.55	.20
	Nos. 782-784,C156-C158 (6)	4.50	1.35

For surcharge and overprint see Nos. 804, C172.

Great Fetish of Gbatchoume — A118

Religions of Togo: 30fr, Chief Priest in front of Atta Sakuma Temple. 40fr, Annual ceremony of the sacred stone.

1971, July 31　Litho.　Perf. 14½

785	A118 20fr multicolored	.40	.20
786	A118 30fr multicolored	.40	.20
787	A118 40fr multicolored	.50	.20
	Nos. 785-787,C159-C161 (6)	3.65	1.25

No. 777 Overprinted in Silver: "EN MEMOIRE / DOBROVOLSKY — VOLKOV — PATSAYEV / SOYUZ 11"

1971, Aug.　　　　Perf. 12½

788	A114 40fr multicolored	.40	.20
	Nos. 788,C162-C164 (4)	4.60	1.25

Russian astronauts Lt. Col. Georgi T. Dobrovolsky, Vladislav N. Volkov and Victor I. Patsayev, who died during the Soyuz 11 space mission, June 6-30, 1971.

Sapporo '72 Emblem and Speed Skating — A119

Sapporo '72 Emblem and: 10fr, Slalom skiing. 20fr, Figure skating, pairs. 30fr, Bobsledding. 50fr, Ice hockey.

1971, Oct. 30　　　　Perf. 14

789	A119 1fr multicolored	.30	.20
790	A119 10fr multicolored	.30	.20
791	A119 20fr multicolored	.30	.20
792	A119 30fr multicolored	.30	.20
793	A119 50fr multicolored	.55	.20
	Nos. 789-793,C165 (6)	4.00	1.50

11th Winter Olympic Games, Sapporo, Japan, Feb. 3-13, 1972.

Toy Crocodile and UNICEF Emblem — A120

Toys and UNICEF Emblem: 30fr, Fawn and butterfly. 40fr, Monkey. 50fr, Elephants.

1971, Nov. 27

794	A120 20fr multicolored	.35	.20
795	A120 30fr violet & multi	.35	.20
796	A120 40fr green & multi	.45	.20
797	A120 50fr bister & multi	.65	.20
	Nos. 794-797,C167-C168 (6)	3.60	1.25

UNICEF, 25th anniv. For overprints see Nos. 918, C263-C264.

Virgin and Child, by Botticelli A121

Virgin and Child by: 30fr, Master of the Life of Mary. 40fr, Dürer. 50fr, Veronese.

1971, Dec. 24　　　　Perf. 14x13

798	A121 10fr purple & multi	.50	.20
799	A121 30fr green & multi	.50	.20
800	A121 40fr brown & multi	.75	.20
801	A121 50fr dk blue & multi	1.00	.20
	Nos. 798-801,C169-C170 (6)	5.50	1.45

Christmas.

St. Mark's Basilica — A122

Design: 40fr, Rialto Bridge.

1972, Feb. 26　Litho.　Perf. 14

802	A122 30fr multicolored	.55	.20
803	A122 40fr multicolored	.70	.20
	Nos. 802-803,C171 (3)	3.25	.80

UNESCO campaign to save Venice.

No. 784 Surcharged with New Value, Two Bars and "VISITE DU PRESIDENT / NIXON EN CHINE / FEVRIER 1972"

1972, Mar.　Litho.　Perf. 14

804	A117 300fr on 40fr multi	3.50	1.25

Visit of Pres. Richard M. Nixon to the People's Republic of China, Feb. 20-27. See No. C172.

Crucifixion, by Master MS — A123

Easter (Paintings): 30fr, Pietà, by Botticelli.

1972, Mar. 31

805	A123 25fr gold & multi	.80	.20
806	A123 30fr gold & multi	.80	.20
807	A123 40fr gold & multi	1.00	.20
	Nos. 805-807,C173-C174 (5)	7.25	1.05

Heart, Smith, WHO Emblem A124

Video Telephone A125

Org. of African and Malagasy Union Conf. — A124a

Heart, WHO Emblem and: 40fr, Typist. 60fr, Athlete with javelin.

1972, Apr. 4
808	A124	30fr multicolored	.40	.20
809	A124	40fr multicolored	.55	.20
810	A124	60fr multicolored	.85	.20
		Nos. 808-810,C175 (4)	3.20	1.00

"Your heart is your health," World Health Day.

Die Cut Perf. 12x12½
1972, Apr. 24   Litho. & Embossed
Self-adhesive
810A	A124a	1000fr gold, red & grn	8.00	8.00

On No. 810A embossing may cut through stamp and embossed backing paper may not adhere well to the unused stamps.
For overprint see No. 893A.

1972, June 24   Litho.   Perf. 14
811	A125	40fr violet & multi	1.00	.25

4th World Telecommunications Day. See No. C176.
For overprints see Nos. 880, C229.

Grating Cassava A126

Basketball A127

25fr, Cassava collection by truck, horiz.

1972, June 30
812	A126	25fr yellow & multi	.45	.20
813	A126	40fr multicolored	.60	.20
		Nos. 812-813,C177-C178 (4)	3.40	.90

Cassava production.
For overprint & surcharge see #866-867.

1972, Aug. 26   Litho.   Perf. 14
814	A127	30fr shown	.35	.20
815	A127	40fr Running	.40	.20
816	A127	50fr Discus	.55	.20
		Nos. 814-816,C180-C181 (5)	4.70	1.60

20th Olympic Games, Munich, 8/26-9/11.
For overprints see Nos. C234-C235.

Pin-tailed Whydah — A128

Paul P. Harris, Rotary Emblem — A129

Birds: 30fr, Broad-tailed widowbird. 40fr, Yellow-shouldered widowbird. 60fr, Yellow-tailed widowbird.

1972, Sept. 9
817	A128	25fr citron & multi	.80	.20
818	A128	30fr lt blue & multi	1.00	.20
819	A128	40fr multicolored	1.00	.20
820	A128	60fr lt green & multi	1.60	.20
		Nos. 817-820,C182 (5)	6.90	1.15

1972, Oct. 7   Litho.   Perf. 14
50fr, Flags of Togo and Rotary Club.
821	A129	40fr green & multi	.30	.20
822	A129	50fr multicolored	.55	.20
a.		Souvenir sheet of 2	2.00	1.25
		Nos. 821-822,C183-C185 (5)	3.20	1.35

Rotary International, Lomé. No. 822a contains 2 stamps with simulated perforations similar to Nos. 821-822.
For overprints see Nos. 862, 898, C212-C213, C244-C235.

Mona Lisa, by Leonardo da Vinci A130

40fr, Virgin and Child, by Giovanni Bellini.

1972, Oct. 21
823	A130	25fr gold & multi	.90	.20
824	A130	40fr gold & multi	1.10	.20
		Nos. 823-824,C186-C188 (5)	9.50	1.25

West African Monetary Union Issue
Common Design Type
Design: 40fr, African couple, city, village and commemorative coin.

1972, Nov. 2   Engr.   Perf. 13
825	CD136	40fr red brn, rose red & gray	.60	.20

Presidents Pompidou and Eyadema, Party Headquarters — A131

1972, Nov. 23   Litho.   Perf. 14
826	A131	40fr purple & multi	1.90	.20

Visit of Pres. Georges Pompidou of France to Togo, Nov. 1972. See No. C189.

Christmas A132

Paintings: 25fr, Anunciation, Painter Unknown. 30fr, Nativity, Master of Vyshchibrod. 40fr, Like 25fr.

1972, Dec. 23
827	A132	25fr gold & multi	.50	.20
828	A132	30fr gold & multi	.50	.20
829	A132	40fr gold & multi	.60	.20
		Nos. 827-829,C191-C193 (6)	6.00	1.50

Raoul Follereau and Lepers — A133

1973, Jan. 23   Photo.   Perf. 14x13½
830	A133	40fr violet & green	2.00	.20

World Leprosy Day and 20th anniv. of the Raoul Follereau Foundation. See No. C194.

WHO Emblem — A134

Christ on the Cross — A135

1973, Apr. 7   Photo.   Perf. 14x13
831	A134	30fr blue & multi	.50	.20
832	A134	40fr dp yellow & multi	.65	.20

WHO, 25th anniv.

1973, Apr. 21   Litho.   Perf. 14
833	A135	25fr shown	.50	.20
834	A135	30fr Pietá	.50	.20
835	A135	40fr Ascension	.60	.20
		Nos. 833-835,C195 (4)	3.00	1.00

Easter.

Eugene Cernan, Ronald Evans, Harrison Schmitt, Apollo 17 Badge — A136

Design: 40fr, Lunar rover on moon.

1973, June 2   Litho.   Perf. 14
836	A136	30fr multicolored	.45	.20
837	A136	40fr multicolored	.55	.20
		Nos. 836-837,C196-C197 (4)	5.40	1.40

Apollo 17 moon mission, Dec. 7-19, 1972.

Scouts Pitching Tent — A137

Nicolaus Copernicus, 500th Anniv. Birth — A138

20fr, Campfire, horiz. 30fr, Rope climbing.

1973, June 30
838	A137	10fr multicolored	.40	.20
839	A137	20fr multicolored	.40	.20
840	A137	30fr violet & multi	.40	.20
841	A137	40fr ocher & multi	.55	.20
		Nos. 838-841,C198-C199 (6)	6.40	1.85

24th Boy Scout World Conference (1st in Africa), Nairobi, Kenya, July 16-21.
For overprints see Nos. C265-C266.

1973, July 18
Designs: 10fr, Heliocentric system. 20fr, Nicolaus Copernicus. 30fr, Seated figure of Astronomy and spacecrafts around earth and moon. 40fr, Astrolabe.
842	A138	10fr multicolored	.60	.20
843	A138	20fr multicolored	.60	.20
844	A138	30fr multicolored	.60	.20
845	A138	40fr lilac & multi	.75	.20
		Nos. 842-845,C200-C201 (6)	6.40	1.50

Red Cross Ambulance Crew A139

1973, Aug. 4
846	A139	40fr multicolored	1.60	.20

Togolese Red Cross. See No. C202.
For overprints see Nos. 846, C294.

Teacher and Students — A140

40fr, Hut and man reading under tree, vert.

1973, Aug. 18   Litho.   Perf. 14
847	A140	30fr multicolored	.50	.20
848	A140	40fr multicolored	.65	.20
		Nos. 847-848,C203 (3)	2.65	.75

Literacy campaign.

African Postal Union Issue
Common Design Type
1973, Sept. 12   Engr.   Perf. 13
849	CD137	100fr yel, red & claret	1.25	.35

INTERPOL Emblem and Headquarters A141

Weather Vane and WMO Emblem A142

1973, Sept. 29   Photo.   Perf. 13½x14
850	A141	30fr yel, brn & gray grn	.55	.20
851	A141	40fr yel grn, bl & mag	.65	.20

50th anniv. of Intl. Criminal Police Org.

1973, Oct. 4   Perf. 14x13
852	A142	40fr yel, dp brn & grn	1.00	.20

Intl. meteorological cooperation, cent. See No. C204.

Type of 1967
Designs: 25fr, Old and new locomotives, No. 795. 30fr, Mail coach and bus, No. 613. 90fr, Mail boat and ship, Nos. C61 and 469.

516   TOGO

1973, Oct. 20   Photo.   Perf. 14x13
853 A79 25fr multicolored   .55   .20
854 A79 30fr purple & green   .70   .20
855 A79 90fr dk blue & multi   1.90   .30
      Nos. 853-855,C205 (4)   5.40 1.00
Togolese postal service, 75th anniv.

John F. Kennedy
and Adolf
Schaerf — A143

Virgin and Child,
Italy, 15th
Century — A144

Designs: 30fr, Kennedy and Harold MacMillan. 40fr, Kennedy and Konrad Adenauer.

1973, Nov. 22   Litho.   Perf. 14
856 A143 20fr blk, gray & vio   .40   .20
857 A143 30fr blk, rose & brn   .40   .20
858 A143 40fr blk, lt grn & grn   .50   .20
      Nos. 856-858,C206-C208 (6)   6.95 2.00
John F. Kennedy (1917-1963).

No. 758 Surcharged with New Value, 2
Bars and Overprinted in Ultramarine:
"SECHERESSE SOLIDARITE
AFRICAINE"
1973, Dec.   Photo.   Perf. 13x14
859 A110 100fr on 30fr multi   1.40   .50
African solidarity in drought emergency.

1973, Dec. 22   Litho.   Perf. 14
30fr, Adoration of the Kings, Italy, 15th cent.
860 A144 25fr gold & multi   .40   .20
861 A144 30fr gold & multi   .50   .20
      Nos. 860-861,C210-C211 (4)   3.40 1.00
Christmas.

No. 821 Overprinted: "PREMIERE
CONVENTION / 210eme DISTRICT /
FEVRIER 1974 / LOME"
1974, Feb. 21   Litho.   Perf. 14
862 A129 40fr green & multi   .40   .20
      Nos. 862,C212-C213 (3)   2.05   .75
First convention of Rotary Intl., District 210,
Lomé, Feb. 22-24.

Soccer and
Games'
Cup
A145

Various soccer scenes and games' cup.

1974, Mar. 2   Litho.   Perf. 14
863 A145 20fr lt blue & multi   .25   .20
864 A145 30fr yellow & multi   .30   .20
865 A145 40fr lilac & multi   .35   .20
      Nos. 863-865,C214-C216 (6)   4.65 2.10
World Soccer Championships, Munich, Germany, June 13-July 7.

Nos. 812-813 Overprinted and
Surcharged: "10e ANNIVERSAIRE DU
P.A.M."
1974, Mar. 25   Litho.   Perf. 14
866 A126 40fr multicolored   .65   .20
867 A126 100fr on 25fr multi   1.40   .50
10th anniv. of World Food Program. Overprint on No. 866 is in one line; 2 lines on No. 867 and 2 bars through old denomination.

Girl Before Mirror,
by Picasso — A146

Mailman, UPU
Emblem — A148

Kpeme
Village and
Wharf
A147

Paintings by Picasso: 30fr, The Turkish
Shawl. 40fr, Mandolin and Guitar.

1974, Apr. 6
868 A146 20fr vio blue & multi   .40   .20
869 A146 30fr maroon & multi   .55   .20
870 A146 40fr multicolored   .65   .20
      Nos. 868-870,C217-C219 (6)   7.35 1.90
Pablo Picasso (1881-1973), Spanish painter.

1974, Apr. 20
Design: 40fr, Tropicana tourist village.
871 A147 30fr multicolored   .45   .20
872 A147 40fr multicolored   .45   .20
      Nos. 871-872,C220-C221 (4)   3.25 1.00

1974, May 10   Litho.   Perf. 14
Design: 40fr, Mailman, different uniform.
873 A148 30fr salmon & multi   .45   .20
874 A148 40fr multicolored   .50   .20
      Nos. 873-874,C222-C223 (4)   2.90   .95
UPU, centenary.

Map and
Flags of
Members
— A148a

1974, May 29   Litho.   Perf. 13x12½
875 A148a 40fr blue & multi   .60   .25
15th anniversary of the Council of Accord.

Fisherman
with Net
A149

40fr, Fisherman casting net from canoe.

1974, June 22   Litho.   Perf. 14
876 A149 30fr multicolored   .55   .20
877 A149 40fr multicolored   .65   .20
      Nos. 876-877,C224-C226 (5)   5.70 1.55
Lagoon fishing.

Pioneer Communicating with
Earth — A150

30fr, Radar station and satellite, vert.

1974, July 6   Perf. 14
878 A150 30fr multicolored   .35   .20
879 A150 40fr multicolored   .40   .20
      Nos. 878-879,C227-C228 (4)   3.65 1.40
US Jupiter space probe.

No. 811 Overprinted with INTERNABA
Emblem in Silver Similar to No. C229
1974, July
880 A125 40fr multicolored   3.00   .55
   INTERNABA 1974 Intl. Philatelic Exhibition,
Basel, June 7-16. See No. C229.
   No. 880 exists overprint in black. Value,
unused $10.

Tympanotomus
Radula — A151

Designs: Seashells.

1974, July 13   Litho.   Perf. 14
881 A151 10fr shown   .75   .20
882 A151 20fr Tonna galea   .75   .20
883 A151 30fr Conus mercator   .90   .20
884 A151 40fr Cardium costatum   1.25   .20
      Nos. 881-884,C230-C231 (6)   7.25 1.40

Groom with
Horses
A152

Design: 40fr, Trotting horses.

1974, Aug. 3   Litho.   Perf. 14
885 A152 30fr multicolored   .80   .20
886 A152 40fr multicolored   .95   .20
      Nos. 885-886,C232-C233 (4)   5.90 1.00
Horse racing.

Leopard
A153

1974, Sept. 7   Litho.   Perf. 14
887 A153 20fr shown   .65   .20
888 A153 30fr Giraffes   .65   .20
889 A153 40fr Elephants   .85   .20
      Nos. 887-889,C236-C237 (5)   6.05 1.25
Wild animals of West Africa.

1974, Oct. 14
890 A153 30fr Herding cattle   .40   .20
891 A153 40fr Milking cow   .55   .20
      Nos. 890-891,C238-C239 (4)   3.30 1.00
Domestic animals.

Churchill
and Frigate
F390
A154

Design: 40fr, Churchill and fighter planes.

1974, Nov. 1   Photo.   Perf. 13x13½
892 A154 30fr multicolored   .50   .20
893 A154 40fr multicolored   .60   .20
      Nos. 892-893,C240-C241 (4)   4.60 1.30
Winston Churchill (1874-1965).

No. 810A Ovptd. "Inauguration de
l'hotel de la Paix 9-1-75"
Litho. & Embossed
1975, Jan. 9   Perf. 12½
Self-adhesive
893A A124a 1000fr gold, red &
                grn   8.00 8.00
On No. 893A embossing may cut through
stamp and embossed backing paper may not
adhere well to the unused stamps.

Chlamydocarya Macrocarpa — A155

Flowers of Togo: 25fr, Strelitzia reginae,
vert. 30fr, Storphanthus sarmentosus, vert.
60fr, Clerodendrum scandens.

1975, Feb. 15   Litho.   Perf. 14
894 A155 25fr multicolored   .55   .20
895 A155 30fr multicolored   .55   .20
896 A155 40fr multicolored   .70   .20
897 A155 60fr multicolored   .95   .20
      Nos. 894-897,C242-C243 (6)   7.25 1.55

No. 821 Overprinted: "70e
ANNIVERSAIRE / 23 FEVRIER 1975"
1975, Feb. 23   Litho.   Perf. 14
898 A129 40fr green & multi   .55   .20
      Nos. 898,C244-C245 (3)   2.45   .80
Rotary Intl., 70th anniv.

Radio
Station,
Kamina
A156

30fr, Benedictine Monastery, Zogbegan.
40fr, Causeway, Atchinedji. 60fr, Ayome
Waterfalls.

1975, Mar. 1   Photo.   Perf. 13x14
899 A156 25fr multicolored   .36   .20
900 A156 30fr multicolored   .36   .20
901 A156 40fr multicolored   .45   .20
902 A156 60fr multicolored   .65   .25
      Nos. 899-902 (4)   1.82   .85

Jesus Mocked, by
El Greco — A157

Paintings: 30fr, Crucifixion, by Master
Janoslet. 40fr, Descent from the Cross, by
Bellini. 90fr, Pietà, painter unknown.

1975, Apr. 19   Litho.   Perf. 14
903 A157 25fr black & multi   .35   .20
904 A157 40fr black & multi   .45   .20
905 A157 40fr black & multi   .55   .20
906 A157 90fr black & multi   1.10   .30
      Nos. 903-906,C246-C247 (6)   5.45 1.70
Easter.

Stilt
Walking,
Togolese
Flag
A158

Design: 30fr, Flag and dancers.

1975, Apr. 26   **Litho.**   *Perf. 14*
907 A158 25fr multicolored   .40 .20
908 A158 30fr multicolored   .40 .20
  Nos. 907-908,C248-C249 (4) 2.00 .80

15th anniv. of independence.

Rabbit
Hunter with
Club
A159

40fr, Beaver hunter with bow and arrow.

1975, May 24   **Photo.**   *Perf. 13x13½*
909 A159 30fr multicolored   .65 .20
910 A159 40fr multicolored   .85 .20
  Nos. 909-910,C250-C251 (4) 5.00 .90

Pounding
Palm Nuts
A160

Design: 40fr, Man extracting palm oil, vert.

1975, June 28   **Litho.**   *Perf. 14*
911 A160 30fr multicolored   .45 .20
912 A160 40fr multicolored   .45 .20
  Nos. 911-912,C252-C253 (4) 2.65 .90

Palm oil production.

Apollo-Soyuz Link-up — A161

1975, July 15
913 A161 30fr multicolored   .40 .20
  Nos. 913,C254-C258 (6) 5.80 1.70

Apollo Soyuz space test project (Russo-
American cooperation), launching July 15;
link-up July 17.

Women's Heads, IWY
Emblem — A162

1975, July 26   **Litho.**   *Perf. 12½*
914 A162 30fr blue & multi   .50 .20
915 A162 40fr multicolored   .60 .20

International Women's Year.

Dr. Schweitzer and Children — A163

1975, Aug. 23   **Litho.**   *Perf. 14x13½*
916 A163 40fr multicolored   .65 .20
  Nos. 916,C259-C261 (4) 4.00 1.10

Dr. Albert Schweitzer (1875-1965), medical
missionary and musician.

Merchant Writing
Letter, by Vittore
Carpaccio
A164

Virgin and Child,
by Mantegna
A165

1975, Oct. 9   **Litho.**   *Perf. 14*
917 A164 40fr multicolored   .60 .20

Intl. Letter Writing Week. See No. C262.

No. 797 Overprinted: "30ème
Anniversaire / des Nations-Unies"

1975, Oct. 24   **Litho.**   *Perf. 14*
918 A120 50fr multi   .50 .25
  Nos. 918,C263-C264 (3) 1.85 .70

UN, 30th anniv.

1975, Dec. 20   **Litho.**   *Perf. 14*
Paintings of the Virgin and Child: 30fr, El
Greco. 40fr, Barend van Orley.
919 A165 20fr red & multi   .35 .20
920 A165 30fr bl & multi   .40 .20
921 A165 40fr red & multi   .50 .20
  Nos. 919-921,C267-C269 (6) 4.70 1.60

Christmas.

Crashed
Plane and
Pres.
Eyadema
A166

1976, Jan. 24   **Photo.**   *Perf. 13*
922 A166 50fr multi   10.00 .40
923 A166 60fr multi   14.00 .45

Airplane crash at Sara-kawa, Jan. 24, 1974,
in which Pres. Eyadema escaped injury.

1976
Summer
Olympics,
Montreal
— A166a

Litho. & Embossed
1976, Feb. 24   *Perf. 11*
923A A166a 1000fr Diving   15.00 —
923B A166a 1000fr Track   15.00 —
923C A166a 1000fr Pole vault   15.00 —
923D A166a 1000fr Equestrian   15.00 —
923E A166a 1000fr Cycling   15.00 —
  Nos. 923A-923E (5) 75.00

Exist imperf.

Frigates on the Hudson — A167

American Bicentennial: 50fr, George Washington, by Gilbert Stuart, and Bicentennial
emblem, vert.

1976, Mar. 3   **Litho.**   *Perf. 14*
924 A167 35fr multicolored   .45 .20
925 A167 50fr multicolored   .65 .25
  Nos. 924-925,C270-C273 (6) 5.50 1.65

For overprints see Nos. C280-C283.

ACP and
CEE
Emblems
A168

50fr, Map of Africa, Europe and Asia.

1976, Apr. 24   **Photo.**   *Perf. 13x14*
926 A168 10fr orange & multi   .25 .20
927 A168 50fr pink & multi   .40 .25
  Nos. 926-927,C274-C275 (4) 1.65 .85

First anniv. of signing of treaty between
Togo and European Common Market, Lomé,
Feb. 28, 1975.

Cable-laying Ship — A169

30fr, Telephone, tape recorder, speaker.

1976, Mar. 10   **Photo.**   *Perf. 13x14*
928 A169 25fr ultra & multi   .25 .20
929 A169 30fr pink & multi   .25 .20
  Nos. 928-929,C276-C277 (4) 1.80 1.00

Centenary of first telephone call by Alexander Graham Bell, Mar. 10, 1876.

Blind Man and
Insect — A170

Marine
Exhibition
Hall — A171

1976, Apr. 8   *Perf. 14x13*
930 A170 50fr brt grn & multi   .60 .20

World Health Day: "Foresight prevents blindness." See No. C278.

Air Post Type, 1976, and Type A171

10fr, Pylon, flags of Ghana, Togo and
Dahomey.

1976   **Litho.**   *Perf. 14*
931 A171 5fr multicolored   .30 .20
932 AP19 10fr multicolored   .30 .20
933 A171 50fr multicolored   .45 .25
  Nos. 931-933,C279 (4) 1.60 .85

Marine Exhibition, 10th anniv. (5fr, 50fr).
Ghana-Togo-Dahomey electric power grid, 1st
anniversary (10fr).
Issue dates: 50fr, May 8; 5fr, 10fr, August.

Running — A172

Montreal Olympic Emblem and: 30fr, Kayak.
50fr, High jump.

1976, June 15   **Photo.**   *Perf. 14x13*
934 A172 25fr multicolored   .30 .20
935 A172 30fr multicolored   .30 .20
936 A172 50fr multicolored   .45 .20
  Nos. 934-936,C284-C286 (6) 4.10 1.90

21st Olympic Games, Montreal, Canada,
July 17-Aug. 1.
For overprints see Nos. 947, C298-C299.

Titan 3 and Viking Emblem — A173

50fr, Viking trajectory, Earth to Mars.

1976, July 15   **Litho.**   *Perf. 14*
937 A173 30fr blue & multi   .30 .20
938 A173 50fr rose & multi   .45 .20
  Nos. 937-938,C287-C290 (6) 4.25 1.70

US Viking Mars missions.

Young Routy at
Celeyran, by
Toulouse-Lautrec
A174

Mohammed Ali
Jinnah, Flags of
Togo and
Pakistan — A176

Adoration of the Shepherds, by
Pontormo — A175

Paintings by Toulouse-Lautrec: 20fr, Model
in Studio. 35fr, Louis Pascal, portrait.

1976, Aug. 7   **Litho.**   *Perf. 14*
939 A174 10fr black & multi   .45 .20
940 A174 20fr black & multi   .45 .20
941 A174 35fr black & multi   .60 .20
  Nos. 939-941,C291-C293 (6) 5.70 1.60

Henri Toulouse-Lautrec (1864-1901),
French painter, 75th death anniversary.

No. 846 Overprinted: "Journée / Internationale / de l'Enfance"

1976, Nov. 27   Litho.   Perf. 14
942 A139 40fr multi   .40   .20
Intl. Children's Day. See No. C294.

1976, Dec. 18
Paintings: 30fr, Nativity, by Carlo Crivelli. 50fr, Virgin and Child, by Jacopo da Pontormo.
943 A175 25fr multi   .35   .20
944 A175 30fr multi   .35   .20
945 A175 50fr multi   .50   .20
Nos. 943-945,C295-C297 (6)   4.45 1.70
Christmas.

1976, Dec. 24   Litho.   Perf. 13
946 A176 50fr multi   .60   .20
Jinnah (1876-1948), first Governor General of Pakistan.

No. 936 Overprinted: "CHAMPIONS OLYMPIQUES / SAUT EN HAUTEUR / POLOGNE"

1976, Dec.   Photo.   Perf. 14x13
947 A172 50fr multi   .50   .20
Nos. 947,C298-C299 (3)   2.70 1.00
Olympic winners.

Queen Elizabeth II, Silver Jubilee — A176a

Designs: No. 947A, Portrait. No. 947B, Wearing coronation regalia.

Litho. & Embossed
1977, Jan. 10   Perf. 11
947A A176a 1000fr silver & multi   6.50

Souvenir Sheet
947B A176a 1000fr silver & multi   9.00
Exist imperf.

Kpeme Phosphate Mine, Sarakawa Crash A177

1977, Jan. 13   Photo.   Perf. 13x14
948 A177 50fr multi   .45   .20
Nos. 948,C300-C301 (3)   1.85   .70
Presidency of Etienne Eyadema, 10th anniv.

Musical Instruments A178

1977, Feb. 7   Litho.   Perf. 14
949 A178 5fr Gongophone   .45   .20
950 A178 10fr Tamtam, vert. .45   .20
951 A178 25fr Dondon   .45   .20
Nos. 949-951,C302-C304 (6)   4.30 1.25

Victor Hugo and his Home A179

1977, Feb. 26   Perf. 13x14
952 A179 50fr multi   .65   .20
Victor Hugo (1802-1885), French writer, 175th birth anniversary. See No. C305.

For overprints see Nos. 959, C316.

Beethoven and Birthplace, Bonn A180

50fr, Bronze bust, 1812, & Heiligenstadt home.

1977, Mar. 7   Perf. 14
953 A180 30fr multi   .40   .20
954 A180 60fr multi   .60   .20
Nos. 953-954,C306-C307 (4)   4.20 3.75

Benz, 1894, Germany — A181

Early Automobiles: 50fr, De Dion Bouton 1903, France.

1977, Apr. 11   Litho.   Perf. 14
955 A181 35fr multi   .50   .20
956 A181 50fr multi   .70   .20
Nos. 955-956,C308-C311 (6)   6.05 1.75

Lindbergh, Ground Crew and Spirit of St. Louis — A182

50fr, Lindbergh and Spirit of St. Louis.

1977, May 9
957 A182 25fr multi   .30   .20
958 A182 50fr multi   .55   .20
Nos. 957-958,C312-C315 (6)   4.20 1.25
Charles A. Lindbergh's solo transatlantic flight from New York to Paris, 50th anniv.

No. 952 Overprinted: "10ème ANNIVERSAIRE DU / CONSEIL INTERNATIONAL / DE LA LANGUE FRANCAISE"

1977, May 17   Litho.   Perf. 14
959 A179 50fr multi   .60 .20
Intl. French Language Council, 10th anniv. See No. C316.

African Slender-snouted Crocodile — A183

Endangered wildlife: 15fr, Nile crocodile.

1977, June 13
960 A183 5fr multi   .35   .20
961 A183 15fr multi   .35   .20
Nos. 960-961,C317-C320 (6)   5.90 1.35

Agriculture School, Tove A184

1977, July 11   Litho.   Perf. 14
962 A184 50fr multi   .45   .20
Nos. 962,C321-C323 (4)   3.25 1.00
Agricultural development.

Landscape with Cart, by Peter Paul Rubens (1577-1640) — A185

Rubens Painting: 35fr, Exchange of the Princesses at Hendaye, 1623.

1977, Aug. 8
963 A185 15fr multi   .35   .20
964 A185 35fr multi   .45   .20
Nos. 963-964,C324-C325 (4)   2.60   .80

Orbiter 101 on Ground — A186

Designs: 30fr, Launching of Orbiter, vert. 50fr, Ejection of propellant tanks at take-off.

1977, Oct. 4   Litho.   Perf. 14
965 A186 20fr multi   .30   .20
966 A186 30fr multi   .40   .20
967 A186 50fr multi   .50   .20
Nos. 965-967,C326-C328 (6)   4.50 1.35
Space shuttle trials in the US.

Lafayette Arriving in Montpelier, Vt. — A187

Design: 25fr, Lafayette, age 19, vert.

1977, Nov. 7   Perf. 14x13, 13x14
968 A187 25fr multi   .25   .20
969 A187 50fr multi   .45   .20
Nos. 968-969,C329-C330 (4)   2.05   .80
Arrival of the Marquis de Lafayette in North America, 200th anniv.

Lenin, Cruiser Aurora, Red Flag A188

1977, Nov. 7   Litho.   Perf. 12
970 A188 50fr multi   1.20   .20
Russian October Revolution, 60th anniv.

Virgin and Child, by Lorenzo Lotto — A189

Edward Jenner — A190

Virgin and Child by: 30fr, Carlo Bellini. 50fr, Cosimo Tura.

1977, Dec. 19   Perf. 14
971 A189 25fr multi   .25   .20
972 A189 30fr multi   .30   .20
973 A189 50fr multi   .45   .20
Nos. 971-973,C331-C333 (6)   4.30 1.35
Christmas.

Perf. 14x13, 13x14
1978, Jan. 9   Litho.
Design: 20fr, Vaccination clinic, horiz.
974 A190 5fr multi   .20   .20
975 A190 20fr multi   .20   .20
Nos. 974-975,C334-C335 (4)   1.15   .80
Worldwide eradication of smallpox.

Orville and Wilbur Wright — A191

Design: 50fr, Wilbur Wright flying at Kill Devil Hill, 1902.

1978, Feb. 6   Litho.   Perf. 14
976 A191 35fr multi   .35   .20
977 A191 50fr multi   .50   .20
Nos. 976-977,C336-C339 (6)   7.10 1.75
75th anniversary of first motorized flight.

Anniversaries and Events — A192

Designs: No. 978, High jump. No. 979, Westminster Abbey. No. 980, Soccer players, World Cup. No. 981, Apollo 8. No. 982, Duke of Wellington, by Goya. No. 983, Hurdles. No. 984, Coronation coach. No. 985, Soccer players. No. 986, Apollo launch. No. 987, Dona Isabel Cobos de Porcel, by Goya.

1978, Mar. 13   Litho.   Perf. 11
978 A192 1000fr gold & multi   8.00
979 A192 1000fr gold & multi   8.00
980 A192 1000fr gold & multi   8.00
981 A192 1000fr gold & multi   8.00
982 A192 1000fr gold & multi   8.00

Souvenir Sheets
983 A192 1000fr gold & multi   8.00
984 A192 1000fr gold & multi   8.00
985 A192 1000fr gold & multi   8.00
986 A192 1000fr gold & multi   8.00
987 A192 1000fr gold & multi   8.00
Nos. 978, 983, 1980 Summer Olympics, Moscow. Nos. 979, 984, Coronation of Queen Elizabeth II, 25th anniv. Nos. 980, 985, 1978 World Cup Soccer Championships, Argentina. Nos. 981, 986, 1st manned lunar orbit, 10th anniv. Nos. 982, 987, Death sesquicent. of Francisco Goya.
For overprints see Nos. 1056A-1056B, 1094A-1094B.
Exist imperf.

John, the Evangelist and Eagle — A197

Evangelists: 10fr, Luke and ox. 25fr, Mark and lion. 30fr, Matthew and angel.

1978, Mar. 20   Litho.   Perf. 13½x14
988 A197 5fr multi   .20   .20
989 A197 10fr multi   .20   .20
990 A197 25fr multi   .20   .20
991 A197 30fr multi   .25   .20
a.   Souvenir sheet of 4   .90   .60
Nos. 988-991 (4)   .85   .80
No. 991a contains one each of Nos. 988-991 with simulated perforations.

Anchor, Fishing Harbor, Lomé A199

1978, Apr. 26   Photo.   *Perf. 13*
997 A199 25fr multi   .25   .20
  Nos. 997,C340-C342 (4)   3.05 1.00

Venera I, USSR — A200

Soccer — A201

Designs: 30fr, Pioneer, US, horiz. 50fr, Venera, fuel base and antenna.

1978, May 8   Litho.   *Perf. 14*
998 A200 20fr multi   .25   .20
999 A200 30fr multi   .30   .20
1000 A200 50fr multi   .40   .20
  Nos. 998-1000,C343-C345 (6)   3.90 1.35
US Pioneer and USSR Venera space missions.

1978, June 5   *Perf. 14*
50fr, Soccer players and Argentina '78 emblem.
1001 A201 30fr multi   .30   .20
1002 A201 50fr multi   .45   .20
  Nos. 1001-1002,C346-C349 (6)   5.55 1.65
11th World Cup Soccer Championship, Argentina, June 1-25.

Celerifère, 1818 A202

History of the Bicycle: 50fr, First bicycle sidecar, c. 1870, vert.

**   *Perf. 13x14, 14x13***
1978, July 10   Photo.
1003 A202 25fr multi   .25   .20
1004 A202 50fr multi   .45   .20
  Nos. 1003-1004,C350-C353 (6)   3.65 1.30

Thomas A. Edison, Sound Waves — A203

Dunant's Birthplace, Geneva — A204

Design: 50fr, Victor's His Master's Voice phonograph, 1905, and dancing couple.

1978, July 8   Photo.   *Perf. 14x13*
1005 A203 30fr multicolored   .30   .20
1006 A203 50fr multicolored   .40   .20
  Nos. 1005-1006,C354-C357 (6)   5.35 1.65
  Centenary of the phonograph, invented by Thomas Alva Edison.

1978, Sept. 4   Photo.   *Perf. 14x13*
Designs: 10fr, Henri Dunant and red cross. 25fr, Help on battlefield, 1864, and red cross.
1007 A204 5fr Prus bl & red   .25   .20
1008 A204 10fr red brn & red   .25   .20
1009 A204 25fr grn & red   .25   .20
  Nos. 1007-1009,C358 (4)   1.20   .80
Dunant (1828-1910), founder of Red Cross.

Threshing, by Raoul Dufy — A205

50fr, Horsemen on Seashore, by Paul Gauguin.

1978, Nov. 6   Litho.   *Perf. 14*
1010 A205 25fr multi   .25   .20
1011 A205 50fr multi   .45   .20
  Nos. 1010-1011,C359-C362 (6)   4.25 1.85

Eiffel Tower, Paris — A206

Virgin and Child, by Antonello da Messina — A207

1978, Nov. 27   Photo.   *Perf. 14x13*
1012 A206 50fr multi   .40   .20
  Nos. 1012,C365-C367 (4)   3.25 1.40
  Centenary of the Congress of Paris.

1978, Dec. 18   Litho.   *Perf. 14*
Paintings (Virgin and Child): 30fr, by Carlo Crivelli. 50fr, by Francesco del Cossa.
1013 A207 20fr multi   .25   .20
1014 A207 30fr multi   .35   .20
1015 A207 50fr multi   .45   .20
  Nos. 1013-1015,C368-C370 (6)   4.20 1.90
  Christmas.

Capt. Cook's Ship off New Zealand — A208

Entry into Jerusalem A209

Design: 50fr, Endeavour in drydock, N.E. Coast of Australia, horiz.

1979, Feb. 12   Litho.   *Perf. 14*
1016 A208 25fr multi   .25   .20
1017 A208 50fr multi   .45   .20
  Nos. 1016-1017,C371-C374 (6)   4.25 2.40
200th death anniv. of Capt. James Cook.

1979, Apr. 9
Easter: 40fr, The Last Supper, horiz. 50fr, Descent from the Cross, horiz.
1018 A209 30fr multi   .25   .20
1019 A209 40fr multi   .30   .20
1020 A209 50fr multi   .35   .20
  Nos. 1018-1020,C375-C377 (6)   3.35 1.80

Einstein Observatory, Potsdam — A210

Design: 50fr, Einstein and James Ramsay MacDonald, Berlin, 1931.

1979, July 2   Photo.   *Perf. 14x13*
1021 A210 35fr multi   .25   .20
1022 A210 50fr multi   .35   .20
  Nos. 1021-1022,C380-C383 (6)   3.65 1.90
  Albert Einstein (1879-1955), theoretical physicist.

Children and Children's Village Emblem — A211

Man Planting Tree — A212

IYC: 10fr, Mother and children. 15fr, Map of Africa, Children's Village emblem, horiz. 20fr, Woman and children walking to Children's Village, horiz. 25fr, Children sitting under African fan palm. 30fr, Map of Togo with location of Children's Villages.

1979, July 30   Photo.   *Perf. 14x13*
1023 A211 5fr multi   .20   .20
1024 A211 10fr multi   .20   .20
1025 A211 15fr multi   .20   .20
1026 A211 20fr multi   .20   .20
1027 A211 25fr multi   .20   .20
1028 A211 30fr multi   .25   .20
  a.   Souv. sheet of 2, #1027-1028   .75   .45
  Nos. 1023-1028 (6)   1.25 1.20

1979, Aug. 13   *Perf. 14x13*
1029 A212 50fr lilac & green   .60   .20
  Second Arbor Day. See No. C384.

Sir Rowland Hill (1795-1879), Originator of Penny Postage — A213

Olympic Flame, Lake Placid 80 Emblem, Slalom — A215

Norris Locomotive, 1843 — A214

30fr, French mail-sorting office, 18th cent., horiz. 50fr, Mailbox, Paris, 1850.

1979, Aug. 27
1030 A213 20fr multi   .25   .20
1031 A213 30fr multi   .30   .20
1032 A213 50fr multi   .40   .20
  Nos. 1030-1032,C385-C387 (6)   3.80 1.90

1979, Oct. 1   Litho.   *Perf. 14*
35fr, Stephenson's "Rocket," 1829, vert.
1033 A214 35fr multi   .35   .20
1034 A214 50fr multi   .50   .20
  Nos. 1033-1034,C388-C391 (6)   4.10 1.90

1979, Oct. 18   Litho.   *Perf. 13½*
1980 Olympic Emblems, Olympic Flame and: 30fr, Yachting 50fr, Discus.
1035 A215 20fr multi   .25   .20
1036 A215 30fr multi   .30   .20
1037 A215 50fr multi   .40   .20
  Nos. 1035-1037,C392-C394 (6)   3.90 1.90
13th Winter Olympic Games, Lake Placid, NY, 2/12-24/80 (90fr); 22nd Summer Olympic Games, Moscow, 7/19-8/3/80.

Catholic Priests A216

Design: 30fr, Native praying, vert.

1979, Oct. 29   *Perf. 13x14*
1038 A216 30fr multi   .30   .20
1039 A216 50fr multi   .40   .20
  Nos. 1038-1039,C396-C397 (4)   1.65   .85
  Religions in Togo.

Astronaut Walking on Moon — A217

Design: 50fr, Space capsule orbiting moon.

1979, Nov. 5

1040	A217	35fr multi	.30	.20
1041	A217	50fr multi	.40	.20
	Nos. 1040-1041,C398-C401 (6)		5.25	2.50

Apollo 11 moon landing, 10th anniversary.

Telecom
79 — A218

1979, Nov. 26   Photo.   Perf. 13x14

| 1042 | A218 | 50fr multi | .40 | .20 |

3rd World Telecommunications Exhibition, Geneva, Sept. 20-26. See No. C402.

Holy
Family — A219

Rotary
Emblem — A220

Christmas: 30fr, Virgin and Child. 50fr, Adoration of the Kings.

1979, Dec. 17   Litho.   Perf. 14

1043	A219	20fr multi	.25	.20
1044	A219	30fr multi	.30	.20
1045	A219	50fr multi	.45	.20
	Nos. 1043-1045,C403-C405 (6)		4.05	1.90

1980, Jan. 14

Rotary Emblem and: 30fr, Anniversary emblem. 40fr, Paul P. Harris, Rotary founder.

1046	A220	25fr multi	.20	.20
1047	A220	30fr multi	.25	.20
1048	A220	40fr multi	.30	.20
	Nos. 1046-1048,C406-C408 (6)		3.25	1.90

Rotary International, 75th anniversary.

Biathlon, Lake
Placid '80
Emblem — A221

1980, Jan. 31   Litho.   Perf. 13½

| 1049 | A221 | 50fr multi | .40 | .20 |
| | *Nos. 1049,C409-C411 (4)* | | 3.00 | 1.40 |

13th Winter Olympic Games, Lake Placid, NY, Feb. 12-24. See No. C412.

1980 Winter Olympics, Lake Placid —
A221a

Gold medalist: No. 1049F, Hanni Wenzel, Liechtenstein, women's slalom. No. 1049G, Eric Heiden, US, men's speed skating. No. 1049H, Jouko Tormanen, Finland, 90-meter ski jumping. No. 1049I, Erich Schaerer, Josef Benz, Switzerland, 2-man bobsled. No. 1049J, US, ice hockey.

1980   Litho.   Perf. 11

1049A	A221a	1000fr multi	20.00	4.50
1049B	A221a	1000fr multi	20.00	4.50
1049C	A221a	1000fr multi	20.00	4.50
1049D	A221a	1000fr multi	20.00	4.50
1049E	A221a	1000fr multi	20.00	4.50
	Nos. 1049A-1049E (5)		100.00	22.50

Souvenir Sheets

1049F	A221a	1000fr gold & multi	—
1049G	A221a	1000fr gold & multi	—
1049H	A221a	1000fr gold & multi	—
1049I	A221a	1000fr gold & multi	—
1049J	A221a	1000fr gold & multi	—

Exist imperf.

Swimming, Moscow '80
Emblem — A222

1980, Feb. 29   Litho.   Perf. 13½

1050	A222	20fr shown	.20	.20
1051	A222	30fr Gymnastics	.25	.20
1052	A222	50fr Running	.45	.25
	Nos. 1050-1052,C413-C415 (6)		5.90	3.15

22nd Summer Olympic Games, Moscow, July 19-Aug. 3.

Christ and the
Angels, by
Andrea Mantegna
A223

Easter 1980 (Paintings by): 40fr, Carlo Crivelli. 50fr, Jacopo Pontormo.

1980, Mar. 31   Perf. 14

1053	A223	30fr multi	.35	.20
1054	A223	40fr multi	.40	.20
1055	A223	50fr multi	.45	.20
	Nos. 1053-1055,C416-C418 (6)		3.90	1.80

Jet over
Map of
Africa
A224

1980, Mar. 24   Litho.   Perf. 12½

| 1056 | A224 | 50fr multi | .60 | .20 |

ASECNA (Air Safety Board), 20th anniv. See No. C419.

Nos. 979, 984 Ovptd. "Londres / 1980"

Litho. & Embossed

1980, May 6   Perf. 11

| 1056A | A192 | 1000fr gold & multi | 6.50 | — |

Souvenir Sheet

| 1056B | A192 | 1000fr gold & multi | 7.25 | — |

12th World Telecommunications
Day — A225

1980, May 17   Photo.   Perf. 14x13½

| 1057 | A225 | 50fr multi | .50 | .20 |

See No. C420.

Red Cross over
Globe Showing
Lomé, Togo — A226

1980, June 16   Photo.   Perf. 14x13

| 1058 | A226 | 50fr multi | .60 | .20 |

Togolese Red Cross. See No. C421.

Jules Verne
(1828-1905),
French Science
Fiction
Writer — A227

Baroness James
de Rothschild, by
Ingres — A228

50fr, Shark (20,000 Leagues Under the Sea).

1980, July 14   Litho.   Perf. 14

1059	A227	30fr multi	.30	.20
1060	A227	50fr multi	.45	.20
	Nos. 1059-1060,C422-C425 (6)		4.20	1.85

1980, Aug. 29   Litho.   Perf. 14

Paintings by Jean Auguste Dominique Ingres (1780-1867): 30fr, Napoleon I on Imperial Throne. 40fr, Don Pedro of Toledo and Henri IV.

1061	A228	25fr multi	.25	.20
1062	A228	30fr multi	.35	.20
1063	A228	40fr multi	.40	.20
	Nos. 1061-1063,C426-C428 (6)		4.25	1.90

Minnie
Holding
Mirror for
Leopard
A229

Disney Characters and Animals from Fazao Reserve: 2fr, Goofy (Dingo) cleaning teeth of hippopotamus. 3fr, Donald holding snout of crocodile. 4fr, Donald dangling over cliff from horn of rhinoceros. 5fr, Goofy riding water buffalo. 10fr, Monkey taking picture of Mickey. 100fr, Mickey as doctor examining giraffe with sore throat. 200fr, Pluto in party hat. No. 1071, Elephant giving shower to Goofy. No. 1072, Lion carrying Goofy by seat of his pants. No. 1072A, Pluto.

1980, Sept. 15   Perf. 11

1064	A229	1fr multi	.20	.20
1065	A229	2fr multi	.20	.20
1066	A229	3fr multi	.20	.20
1067	A229	4fr multi	.20	.20
1068	A229	5fr multi	.20	.20
1069	A229	10fr multi	.20	.20
1070	A229	100fr multi	.75	.35
1070A	A229	200fr multi	1.50	.75
1071	A229	300fr multi	2.25	1.10
	Nos. 1064-1071 (9)		5.70	3.40

Souvenir Sheets

| 1072 | A229 | 300fr multi | 3.00 | 1.10 |
| 1072A | A229 | 300fr multi | 3.00 | 1.10 |

50th anniv. of the Disney character Pluto.

Market
Activities,
Women
Preparing
Meat
A230

1980-81   Perf. 14

1073	A230	1fr Grinding savo	.20	.20
1074	A230	2fr shown	.20	.20
1075	A230	3fr Truck going to market	.20	.20
1076	A230	4fr Unloading produce	.20	.20
1077	A230	5fr Sugar cane vendor	.20	.20
1078	A230	6fr Barber curling child's hair, vert.	.20	.20
1079	A230	7fr Vegetable vendor	.20	.20
1080	A230	8fr Sampling mangos, vert.	.20	.20
1081	A230	9fr Grain vendor	.20	.20
1082	A230	10fr Spiced fish vendor	.20	.20
1083	A230	15fr Clay pot vendor	.20	.20
1084	A230	20fr Straw baskets	.20	.20
1085	A230	25fr Selling lemons and onions, vert.	.20	.20
1086	A230	30fr Straw baskets, diff.	.25	.20
1087	A230	40fr Shore market	.30	.20
1087A	A230	45fr Vegatable stall	.30	.20
1088	A230	50fr Women carrying produce, vert.	.40	.20
1088A	A230	60fr Rice wine	.40	.20
	Nos. 1073-1088A (18)		4.25	3.60

Issued: 45fr, 60fr, 3/8/81; others, 3/17/80. Nos. 1087A, 1088A dated 1980. See Nos. C440-C445, J68-J71. For overprints see Nos. C486-C487.

Commemorative Wreath — A231

Famous Men of the Decade: 40fr, Mao Tse-tung, vert.

1980, Feb. 11   **Perf. 14x13**
1089 A231 25fr multi   .40 .20
1090 A231 40fr emer grn & dk
     grn   .60 .20
Nos. 1089-1090,C429-C431 (5)   5.10 1.70

World Tourism Conference, Manila,
Sept. 27 — A232

1980, Sept. 15   **Litho.**   **Perf. 14**
1091 A232 50fr Hotel tourism
     emblem, vert.   .50 .25
1092 A232 150fr shown   1.50 .75

Map of
Australia
and Human
Rights
Flame
A233

1980, Oct. 13   **Photo.**   **Perf. 13x14**
1093 A233 30fr shown   .30 .20
1094 A233 50fr Europe and Asia
     map   .50 .25
Nos. 1093-1094,C432-C433 (4)   2.20 1.15

Declaration of Human Rights, 30th anniv.

#980, 985 Ovptd. in Gold & Black

Litho. & Embossed
1980, Nov. 24   **Perf. 11**
1094A A192 1000fr gold & multi   8.00 —
     Souvenir Sheet
1094B A192 1000fr gold & multi   7.25 —
No. 1094B ovptd. with additional text and
black bars in sheet margin.

Melk
Monastery,
Austria, 18th
Century
A234

    Perf. 14½x13½
1980, Dec. 22   **Litho.**
1095 A234 20fr shown   .25 .20
1096 A234 30fr Tarragon Cathe-
     dral, Spain, 12th
     cent.   .35 .20

1097 A234 50fr St. John the Bap-
     tist, Florence,
     1964   .55 .25
Nos. 1095-1097,C435-C437 (6)   4.35 2.15
Christmas.

African Postal
Union, 5th
Anniversary
A235

1980, Dec. 24   **Photo.**   **Perf. 13½**
1098 A235 100fr multi   .75 .35

February
2nd Hotel
Opening
A236

1981, Feb. 2   **Litho.**   **Perf. 12½x13**
1099 A236 50fr multi   .60 .25
See No. C437B.

A236a

A237

1981, Dec. 21   **Litho.**   **Perf. 12½**
1100 A236a 70fr lt grn & multi   .70 .35
West African Rice Development Assoc.
See No. C461.

1981, Apr. 13   **Perf. 14½x13½**
Easter (Rembrandt Paintings): 30fr, Rembrandt's Father. 40fr, Self-portrait. 50fr, Artist's
father as an old man. 60fr, Rider on
Horseback.

1101 A237 30fr multi   .30 .20
1102 A237 40fr multi   .35 .20
1103 A237 50fr multi   .45 .20
1104 A237 60fr multi   .55 .25
Nos. 1101-1104,C438-C439 (6)   4.05 1.85

Wedding of Prince Charles and Lady
Diana Spencer — A237a

1981, July 29   **Litho.**   **Perf. 11**
1105 A237a 1000fr gold & multi   5.75 3.00
    Souvenir Sheet
    Litho. & Embossed
1106 A237a 1000fr Charles & Di-
     ana, diff.   7.25 3.50
No. 1105 printed with embossed se-tenant
label.
For overprints see Nos. 1143A-1143B.

Red-headed Rock Fowl — A238

1981, Aug. 10   **Perf. 13½x14½**
1107 A238 30fr shown   .45 .20
1108 A238 40fr Splendid sunbird   .55 .20
1109 A238 60fr Violet-backed
     starling   .90 .20
1110 A238 90fr Red-collared
     widowbird   1.40 .30
Nos. 1107-1110,C446-C447 (6)   5.60 1.45

1982 World Soccer Championships,
Spain — A238a

Flags (Nos. 1110A-1110E) or Players (Nos.
1110F-1110J) and stadiums: Nos. 1110A,
1110F, Athletico de Madrid. Nos. 1110B,
1110G, Real Madrid C.F. Nos. 1110C, 1110H,
R.C.D. Espanol. Nos. 1110D, 1110I, Real
Zaragoza. Nos. 1110E, 1110J, Valencia.

    Litho. & Embossed
1981, Aug. 17   **Perf. 11**
1110A-1110E A238a 1000fr Set
     of
     5   37.50 9.00
    Souvenir Sheets
1110F-1110J A238a 1000fr Set
     of
     5   30.00 9.00

African
Postal
Union
Ministers,
6th Council
Meeting,
July 28-20
A239

1981, Aug. 31   **Litho.**   **Perf. 12½**
1111 A239 70fr Dish antenna   .50 .25
1112 A239 90fr Computer oper-
     ator, vert.   .70 .35
1113 A239 105fr Map   .80 .40
Nos. 1111-1113 (3)   2.00 1.00

Intl. Year of
the
Disabled
A240

1981, Aug. 31   **Perf. 14**
1114 A240 70fr Blind man   .75 .35
Nos. 1114,C448-C449 (3)   2.80 1.30
See No. C449A.

Woman with
Hat, by
Picasso,
1961 — A241

Picasso Birth Centenary: Sculptures.

1981, Sept. 14   **Perf. 14½x13½**
1116 A241 25fr shown   .25 .20
1117 A241 50fr She-goat   .45 .20
1118 A241 60fr Violin, 1915   .50 .20
Nos. 1116-1118,C450-C452 (6)   4.45 1.90

Aix-la-Chapelle Cathedral,
Germany — A242

World Heritage Year: 40fr, Geyser, Yellow-
stone Natl. Park. 50fr, Nahanni Natl. Park,
Canada. 60fr, Stone churches, Ethiopia.

1981, Sept. 28   **Perf. 13½x14½**
1119 A242 30fr multi   .25 .20
1120 A242 40fr multi   .30 .20
1121 A242 50fr multi   .35 .20
1122 A242 60fr multi   .45 .30
Nos. 1119-1122,C453-C454 (6)   3.60 2.00

Yuri Gagarin's Vostok I, 20th. — A243

Space Anniversaries: 50fr, 20th Anniv. of
Alan Shepard's Flight. 60fr, Lunar Orbiter I,
15th.

1981, Nov.   **Perf. 14**
1123 A243 25fr multi   .20 .20
1124 A243 50fr multi   .35 .20
1125 A243 60fr multi   .45 .25
Nos. 1123-1125,C455-C456 (5)   2.45 1.40

Christmas A244

Rubens Paintings: 20fr, Adoration of the Kings. 30fr, Adoration of the Shepherds. 50fr, St. Catherine.

Perf. 14½x13½

1981, Dec. 10			**Litho.**	
1126	A244	20fr multi	.25	.20
1127	A244	30fr multi	.25	.20
1128	A244	50fr multi	.40	.20
Nos. 1126-1128,C457-C459 (6)			5.20	2.60

15th Anniv. of Natl. Liberation — A245

1982, Jan. 13		**Litho.**	**Perf. 12½**	
1129	A245	70fr Dove, flag	.70	.35
1130	A245	90fr Citizens, Pres. Eyadema, vert.	.90	.45
Nos. 1129-1130,C462-C463 (4)			3.20	1.55

Scouting Year A246

1982, Feb. 25		**Litho.**	**Perf. 14**	
1131	A246	70fr Pitching tent	.55	.25
Nos. 1131,C464-C467 (5)			4.50	1.80

Easter — A247

Designs: The Ten Commandments.

1982, Mar. 15			**Perf. 14x14½**	
1132	A247	10fr multi	.20	.20
1133	A247	25fr multi	.20	.20
1134	A247	30fr multi	.20	.20
1135	A247	45fr multi	.30	.20
1136	A247	50fr multi	.35	.20
1137	A247	70fr multi	.45	.25
1138	A247	90fr multi	.60	.30
Nos. 1132-1138,C469-C470 (9)			3.80	2.30

Papilio Dardanus A248

1982, July 15		**Litho.**	**Perf. 14½x14**	
1139	A248	15fr shown	.45	.20
1140	A248	20fr Belenois calypso	.45	.20
1141	A248	25fr Palla decius	.45	.20
Nos. 1139-1141,C474-C475 (5)			4.35	1.25

1982 World Cup — A249

Designs: Various soccer players.

1982, July 26			**Perf. 14x14½**	
1142	A249	25fr multi	.25	.20
1143	A249	45fr multi	.35	.20
Nos. 1142-1143,C477-C479 (5)			4.90	2.40

For overprints see Nos. 1150-1155.

Nos. 1105-1106 Ovptd. "BEBE ROYALE 21 JUIN 1982" on one or two lines

1982, Oct. 28		**Litho.**	**Perf. 11**	
1143A	A237a	1000fr gold & multi	7.25	3.50

Souvenir Sheet

Litho. & Embossed

1143B	A237a	1000fr gold & multi	9.25	3.50

Christmas A250

Madonna of Baldacchino, by Raphael. #1144-1148 show details; #1149 entire painting.

1982, Dec. 24		**Litho.**	**Perf. 14½x14**	
1144	A250	45fr multi	.35	.20
1145	A250	70fr multi	.55	.25
1146	A250	105fr multi	.85	.35
1147	A250	130fr multi	1.10	.40
1148	A250	150fr multi	1.20	.50
Nos. 1144-1148 (5)			4.05	1.70

Souvenir Sheet

Perf. 14x14½

1149	A250	500fr multi, vert.	4.00	1.60

Nos. 1142-1143, C477-C480 Overprinted: VAINQUER / COUPE DU MONDE / FOOTBALL 82 / "ITALIE"

1983, Jan. 31		**Litho.**	**Perf. 14x14½**	
1150	A249	25fr multi	.20	.20
1151	A249	45fr multi	.30	.20
1152	A249	105fr multi	.70	.35
1153	A249	200fr multi	1.40	.65
1154	A249	300fr multi	2.00	1.00
Nos. 1150-1154 (5)			4.60	2.40

Souvenir Sheet

1155	A249	500fr multi	4.25	2.50

Italy's victory in 1982 World Cup. Nos. 1152-1155 airmail.

20th Anniv. of West African Monetary Union (1982) — A251

1983, May		**Litho.**	**Perf. 12½x12**	
1156	A251	70fr Map	.60	.25
1157	A251	90fr Emblem	.80	.30

Visit of Pres. Mitterand of France, Jan. 13-15 — A252

1983, Jan. 13		**Litho.**	**Perf. 13**	
1158	A252	35fr Sokode Regional Hospital	.30	.20
a.		Souvenir sheet, imperf.	.85	.45
1159	A252	45fr Citizens joining hands	.35	.20
a.		Souvenir sheet, imperf.	.85	.45
1160	A252	70fr Soldiers, vert.	.50	.25
a.		Souvenir sheet, imperf.	.85	.45
1161	A252	90fr Pres. Mitterand, vert.	.70	.30
a.		Souvenir sheet, imperf.	.85	.45
1162	A252	105fr Pres. Eyadema, Mitterand, vert.	.80	.35
a.		Souvenir sheet, imperf.	.85	.45
1163	A252	130fr Greeting crowd	1.00	.40
a.		Souvenir sheet, imperf.	.85	.45
Nos. 1158-1163 (6)			3.65	1.70

Nos. 1161-1163 airmail.

Easter — A253

Paintings: 35fr, Mourners at the Death of Christ, by Bellini. 70fr, Crucifixion, by Raphael. 90fr, Descent from the Cross, by Carracci. 500fr Christ, by Reni.

1983		**Litho.**	**Perf. 13½x14½**	
1164	A253	35fr multi	.25	.20
1165	A253	70fr multi, vert.	.50	.20
1166	A253	90fr multi	.75	.20
Nos. 1164-1166 (3)			1.50	.60

Souvenir Sheet

Perf. 14½x13½

1167	A253	500fr multi	4.00	1.50

90fr, 500fr airmail.

Folkdances — A254

1983, Dec. 1			**Perf. 14½x14**	
1168	A254	70fr Kondona	.55	.20
1169	A254	90fr Kondona, diff.	.65	.20
1170	A254	105fr Toubole	.80	.20
1171	A254	130fr Adjogbo	.90	.20
Nos. 1168-1171 (4)			2.90	.80

90fr, 105fr, 130fr airmail.

World Communications Year — A255

1983, June 20		**Litho.**	**Perf. 14x14½**	
1172	A255	70fr Drummer	.60	.20
1173	A255	90fr Modern communication	.70	.20

90fr airmail.

Christmas — A256

1983, Dec.			**Perf. 13½x14½**	
1174	A256	70fr Catholic Church, Kante	.25	.20
1175	A256	90fr Altar, Dapaong Cathedral	.30	.20
1176	A256	105fr Protestant Church, Dapaong	.35	.20
Nos. 1174-1176 (3)			.90	.60

Souvenir Sheet

1177	A256	500fr Ecumenical Church, Pya	4.00	1.50

90fr, 105fr, 500fr airmail.

Sarakawa Presidential Assassination Attempt, 10th Anniv. — A257

1984, Jan. 24		**Litho.**	**Perf. 13**	
1178	A257	70fr Wrecked plane	.55	.20
1179	A257	90fr Plane, diff.	.65	.20
1180	A257	120fr Memorial Hall	.90	.20
1181	A257	270fr Pres. Eyadema statue, vert.	2.00	.40
Nos. 1178-1181 (4)			4.10	1.00

120fr, 270fr airmail.

20th Anniv. of World Food Program (1983) A258

1984, May 2		**Litho.**	**Perf. 13**	
1182	A258	35fr Orchard	.20	.20
1183	A258	70fr Fruit tree	.25	.20
1184	A258	90fr Rice paddy	.30	.20
Nos. 1182-1184 (3)			.75	.60

Souvenir Sheet

1185	A258	300fr Village, horiz.	2.25	1.50

25th Anniv. of Council of Unity — A259

Easter
1984 — A260

1984, May 29 — *Perf. 12*
1186 A259 70fr multi .50 .20
1187 A259 90fr multi .65 .20

1984 — *Litho.* *Perf. 14x14½*
Various stained-glass windows.
1188 A260 70fr multi .50 .20
1189 A260 90fr multi .60 .20
1190 A260 120fr multi .75 .20
1191 A260 270fr multi 1.75 .45
1192 A260 300fr multi 1.90 .20
Nos. 1188-1192 (5) 5.50 1.55

Souvenir Sheet
1193 A260 500fr multi 4.00 3.00
Nos. 1189-1193 airmail.

Centenary of German-Togolese
Friendship — A261

#1194, Degbenou Catholic Mission, 1893.
#1195, Kara Bridge, 1911. #1196, Treaty Site,
Baguida, 1884. #1197, Degbenou Students,
1893. #1198, Sansane Administrative Post,
1908. #1199, Adjido Official School.
#1200, Sokode Cotton Market, 1910.
#1201, William Fountain, Atakpame, 1906.
#1202, Lome Main Street, 1895, No. 19.
#1203, Police, 1905. #1204, Lome Railroad
Construction. #1205, Governor's Palace,
Lome, 1905. #1206, No. 9, Commerce Street,
Lome.
#1207, Nos. 10, 17. #1208, Lome Wharf,
1903. #1209, G. Nachtigal. #1210, Wilhelm II.
#1211, O.F. de Bismark. #1212, J. de
Puttkamer. #1213, A. Koehler. #1214, W.
Horn. #1215, J.G. de Zech. #1216, E. Bruck-
ner. #1217, A.F. de Mecklenburg. #1218, H.G.
de Doering. #1219, Land Development, 1908.
#1220, Postal Courier, No. 8. #1221, Treaty
Signers, 1885. 150fr, German & Togolese
Children, Flags. #1223, Aneho Line Locomo-
tive, 1905. #1224, Mallet Locomotive, 1907.
#1225, German Ship "Mowe," 1884. #1226,
"La Sophie," 1884. 300fr, Pres. Eyadema,
Helmut Kohl.

1984, July 5 — *Litho.* *Perf. 13*
1194 A261 35fr multi .50 .20
1195 A261 35fr multi .50 .20
1196 A261 35fr multi, vert. .50 .20
1197 A261 35fr multi .50 .20
1198 A261 35fr multi .50 .20
1199 A261 35fr multi .50 .20
1200 A261 35fr multi .50 .20
1201 A261 45fr multi, vert. .50 .20
1202 A261 45fr multi .50 .20
1203 A261 45fr multi .50 .20
1204 A261 45fr multi .50 .20
1205 A261 45fr multi .50 .20
1206 A261 45fr multi, vert. .50 .20
1207 A261 70fr multi .60 .20
1208 A261 70fr multi .60 .20
1209 A261 90fr multi .75 .20
1210 A261 90fr multi, vert. .75 .20
1211 A261 90fr multi, vert. .75 .20
1212 A261 90fr multi, vert. .75 .20
1213 A261 90fr multi, vert. .75 .20
1214 A261 90fr multi, vert. .75 .20
1215 A261 90fr multi, vert. .75 .20
1216 A261 90fr multi .75 .20
1217 A261 90fr multi, vert. .75 .20
1218 A261 90fr multi, vert. .75 .20
1219 A261 90fr multi, vert. .75 .20
1220 A261 120fr multi, vert. 1.00 .20
1221 A261 120fr multi 1.00 .20
1222 A261 150fr multi, vert. 1.25 .25
1223 A261 270fr multi 2.25 .45
1224 A261 270fr multi 2.25 .45
1225 A261 270fr multi 2.25 .45

1226 A261 270fr multi 2.25 .45
1227 A261 300fr multi 2.40 .50
Nos. 1194-1227 (34) 30.60 8.15
Souvenir sheets of one exist for each
design. Stamp size: 65x80mm. Value, set of
34, $35.

Donald
Duck, 50th
Anniv.
A262

1984, Sept. 21 — *Litho.* *Perf. 11*
1230 A262 1fr Donald, Chip .55 .20
1231 A262 2fr Donald, Chip
and Dale .55 .20
1232 A262 3fr Louie, Chip
and Dale .55 .20
1233 A262 5fr Donald, Chip .55 .20
1234 A262 10fr Daisy Duck,
Donald .55 .20
1235 A262 15fr Goofy, Donald .55 .20
1236 A262 105fr Huey, Dewey
and Louie .80 .20
1237 A262 500fr Nephews,
Donald 3.75 .70
1238 A262 1000fr Nephews,
Donald 8.25 1.40
Nos. 1230-1238 (9) 16.10 3.50

Souvenir Sheets
Perf. 14
1239 A262 1000fr Surprised
Donald 7.50 7.50
1240 A262 1000fr Perplexed
Donald 7.50 7.50
Nos. 1236-1240 airmail.
For overprints see Nos. C551-C554.

Endangered Mammals — A263

1984, Oct. 1 — *Litho.* *Perf. 15x14½*
1241 A263 45fr Manatee
swimming 1.25 .50
1242 A263 70fr Manatee eating 2.00 .50
1243 A263 90fr Manatees
floating 3.00 1.00
1244 A263 105fr Young manatee, mother 5.00 1.00
Nos. 1241-1244 (4) 11.25 3.00

Souvenir Sheets
Perf. 14x15, 15x14
1245 A263 1000fr Olive Colobus
monkey,
vert. 10.00 6.00
1246 A263 1000fr Galago
(Bushbaby) 10.00 6.00
Nos. 1243-1246 airmail. See #1444-1447.

Birth
Centenary
of Eleanor
Roosevelt
A264

1984, Oct. 10 — *Litho.* *Perf. 13½*
1247 A264 70fr shown .55 .20
1248 A264 90fr Mrs. Roosevelt,
Statue of Liberty .70 .20
No. 1248 airmail.

Classic Automobiles — A265

1984, Nov. 15 — *Litho.* *Perf. 15*
1249 A265 1fr 1947 Bristol .85 .20
1250 A265 2fr 1925 Frazer
Nash .85 .20
1251 A265 3fr 1950 Healey .85 .20
1252 A265 4fr 1925 Kissell .85 .20
1253 A265 50fr 1927 La Salle .85 .20
1254 A265 90fr 1921 Minerva 1.00 .20
1255 A265 500fr 1950 Morgan 5.75 .20
1256 A265 1000fr 1921 Napier 12.00 1.40
Nos. 1249-1256 (8) 23.00 3.30

Souvenir Sheets
1257 A265 1000fr 1941 Nash 9.00 2.00
1258 A265 1000fr 1903 Peugeot 9.00 2.00
Nos. 1254-1258 airmail.
For overprints see Nos. 1328-1331, C542-
C544, C564-C565.

Christmas
A266

Perf. 14½x13½
1984, Nov. 23 — *Litho.*
1259 A266 70fr Connestable
Madonna .50 .20
1260 A266 290fr Cowper Madonna 1.90 .40
1261 A266 300fr Alba Madonna 1.90 .45
1262 A266 500fr Madonna of
the Curtain 3.25 .70
Nos. 1259-1262 (4) 7.55 1.75

Souvenir Sheet
1263 A266 1000fr Madonna with
Child 7.25 6.00
Nos. 1260-1263 airmail.

African Locomotives — A267

1984, Nov. 30 — *Litho.* *Perf. 15*
1264 A267 1fr Decapod,
Madeira .45 .20
1265 A267 2fr 2-6-0, Egypt .45 .20
1266 A267 3fr 4-8-2+2-8-4,
Algeria .45 .20
1267 A267 4fr Congo-Ocean
diesel .45 .20
1268 A267 50fr 0-4-0+0-4-0,
Libya .45 .20
1269 A267 90fr #49, Malawi .55 .20
1270 A267 105fr 1907 Mallet,
Togo .65 .20
1271 A267 500fr 4-8-2, Rhodesia 3.00 .70
1272 A267 1000fr Beyer-Garratt,
East Africa 5.75 1.40
Nos. 1264-1272 (9) 12.20 3.50

Souvenir Sheets
1273 A267 1000fr 2-8-2, Ghana 9.00 6.00
1274 A267 1000fr Locomotive,
Senegal 9.00 6.00
Nos. 1269-1274 airmail.
For overprints see Nos. 1343-1346, 1356-
1360, C541, C566.

Economic Convention, Lome — A268

1984, Dec. 8 — *Litho.* *Perf. 12½*
1275 A268 100fr Map of the Americas .65 .20
1276 A268 130fr Map of Eurasia, Africa .95 .20
1277 A268 270fr Map of Asia, Australia 1.60 .40
a. A268 Strip of 3, #1275-1277 3.50 3.50

Souvenir Sheet
1278 A268 500fr President
Eyadema 4.00 3.50
No. 1277a has continuous design.

Intl. Civil
Aviation
Org., 40th
Anniv.
A269

Map of Togo, ICAO emblem and: 70fr, Lockheed Constellation, 1944. 105fr, Boeing 707,
1954. 200fr, Doublas DC-8-61, 1966. 500fr,
Bac/Sud Concorde, 1966. 1000fr, Icarus, by
Hans Erni.

1984, Oct. 15 — *Litho.* *Perf. 15x14*
1279 A269 70fr multi .55 .20
1280 A269 105fr multi .70 .20
1281 A269 200fr multi 1.10 .20
1282 A269 500fr multi 2.75 .50
Nos. 1279-1282 (4) 5.10 1.10

Souvenir Sheet
1283 A269 1000fr multi 6.50 6.00
Nos. 1280-1283 airmail.

Fresco of the 12
Apostles, Baptistry
of the Aryans,
Ravenna,
Italy, — A270

Designs: 1fr, St. Paul. 2fr, St. Thomas. 3fr,
St. Matthew. 4fr, St. James the Younger. 5fr,
St. Simon. 70fr, St. Thaddeaus Judas. 90fr, St.
Bartholomew. 105fr, St. Philip. 200fr, St. John.
270fr, St. James the Greater. 400fr, St.
Andrew. 500fr, St. Peter. No. 1296, The Last
Supper, by Andrea del Castagno, c. 1421-
1457, horiz. No, 1297, Coronation of the Vir-
gin, by Raphael, 1483-1520, horiz.

1984, Dec. 14 — *Perf. 15*
1284 A270 1fr multi 1.00 .20
1285 A270 2fr multi 1.00 .20
1286 A270 3fr multi 1.00 .20
1287 A270 4fr multi 1.00 .20
1288 A270 5fr multi 1.00 .20
1289 A270 70fr multi 1.00 .20
1290 A270 90fr multi 1.00 .20
1291 A270 105fr multi 1.00 .20
1292 A270 200fr multi 2.25 .20
1293 A270 270fr multi 3.00 .30
1294 A270 400fr multi 4.25 .40
1295 A270 500fr multi 5.25 .50
Nos. 1284-1295 (12) 22.75 3.00

Souvenir Sheets
1296-1297 A270 1000fr each 14.00 4.00
Nos. 1290-1297 airmail.
For overprints see Nos. C545-C547.

Race
Horses
A271

1985, Jan. 10

1298	A271	1fr Allez France	.70	.20
1299	A271	2fr Arkle, vert.	.70	.20
1300	A271	3fr Tingle Creek, vert.	.70	.20
1301	A271	4fr Interco	.70	.20
1302	A271	50fr Dawn Run	.70	.20
1303	A271	90fr Seattle Slew, vert.	.70	.20
1304	A271	500fr Nijinsky	3.25	.50
1305	A271	1000fr Politician	6.50	1.00
		Nos. 1298-1305 (8)	13.95	2.70

Souvenir Sheets

1306	A271	1000fr Shergar	9.00	6.50
1307	A271	1000fr Red Rum	9.00	6.50

Nos. 1303-1307 airmail.
For overprints see Nos. 1353-1355A.

Easter — A272

Paintings by Raphael (1483-1520).

Perf. 13½x14½, 14½x13½

1985, Mar. 7

1308	A272	70fr Christ and His Flock	.70	.20
1309	A272	90fr Christ and the Fishermen	.70	.20
1310	A272	135fr The Blessed Christ, vert.	.85	.20
1311	A272	150fr The Entombment, vert.	1.00	.20
1312	A272	250fr The Resurrection, vert.	1.75	.25
		Nos. 1308-1312 (5)	5.00	1.05

Souvenir Sheet

1313	A272	1000fr The Resurrection, diff.	7.50	6.00

Nos. 1309-1313 airmail.

Technical & Cultural Cooperation Agency, 15th Anniv. — A273

1985, Mar. 20   *Perf. 12½*

1314	A273	70fr multi	.60	.20
1315	A273	90fr multi	.60	.20

Philexafrica '85, Lome — A274

1985, May 9   *Perf. 13*

1316	A274	200fr Woman carrying fruit basket	1.90	.20
1317	A274	200fr Man plowing field	1.90	.20
a.		Pair, #1316-1317 + label	4.00	3.50

Scarification
Ritual — A275

1985, May 14   *Perf. 14x15*

1318	A275	25fr Kabye (Pya)	.60	.20
1319	A275	70fr Mollah (Kotokoli)	.60	.20
1320	A275	90fr Maba (Dapaong)	.60	.20
1321	A275	105fr Kabye (Pagouda)	.75	.20
1322	A275	270fr Peda	1.75	.30
		Nos. 1318-1322 (5)	4.30	1.10

Nos. 1320-1322 airmail.

Seashells
A276

70fr, Clavatula muricata. 90fr, Marginella desjardini. 120fr, Clavatula nifat. 135fr, Cypraea stercoraria. 270fr, Conus genuanus. 1000fr, Dancers wearing traditional shell decorations.

1985, June 1   *Perf. 15x14*

1323	A276	70fr multi	1.00	.20
1324	A276	90fr multi	1.00	.20
1325	A276	120fr multi	1.25	.20
1326	A276	135fr multi	1.25	.20
1327	A276	270fr multi	2.75	.30
		Nos. 1323-1327 (5)	7.25	1.10

Souvenir Sheet

1327A	A276	1000fr multi	7.50	6.00

Nos. 1324-1327A airmail.

Nos. 1253, 1256-1258 Overprinted
"Exposition Mondiale 1985 / Tsukuba, Japon"

1985, June   *Perf. 15*

1328	A265	50fr #1253	1.10	.20
1329	A265	1000fr #1256	10.50	3.00

Souvenir Sheets

1330	A265	1000fr #1257	9.00	3.50
1331	A265	1000fr #1258	9.00	3.50

EXPO '85.

Audubon Birth
Bicent. — A277

Illustrations by artist-naturalist J.J. Audubon (1785-1851).

1985, Aug. 13   *Perf. 13*

1332	A277	90fr Larus bonapartii	.85	.20
1333	A277	120fr Pelecanus occidentalis	1.10	.20
1334	A277	135fr Cassidix mexicanus	1.10	.20
1335	A277	270fr Aquila chrysaetos	2.40	.30
1336	A277	500fr Picus erythrocephalus	4.25	.50
		Nos. 1332-1336 (5)	9.70	1.40

Souvenir Sheet

1337	A277	1000fr Dendroica petechia	7.50	6.00

Nos. 1332, 1334 and 1336-1337 airmail.

Dove, UN Emblem — A278

Kara Port Construction — A279

Designs: 115fr, Hands, UN emblem. 250fr, Millet crop, Atalote Research Facility. 500fr, UN, Togo flags, statesmen.

1985, Oct. 24   Litho.   *Perf. 13*

1338	A278	90fr multi	.60	.20
1339	A278	115fr multi	.75	.20
1340	A279	150fr multi	.90	.20
1341	A279	250fr multi	1.50	.25
1342	A279	500fr multi	3.00	.50
		Nos. 1338-1342 (5)	6.75	1.35

UN, 40th anniv. Nos. 1340-1342 are airmail.

Nos. 1267, 1270, 1272, 1273 Ovptd. with Rotary Emblem and "80e ANNIVERSAIRE DU / ROTARY INTERNATIONAL"

1985   Litho.   *Perf. 15*

1343	A267	4fr multi	.65	.40
1344	A267	105fr multi	1.25	1.10
1345	A267	1000fr multi	12.50	6.50
		Nos. 1343-1345 (3)	14.40	8.00

Souvenir Sheet

1346	A267	1000fr multi	12.50	6.50

Nos. 1344-1346 are airmail.

Christmas
A280

Religious paintings and statuary: 90fr, The Garden of Roses Madonna. 115fr, Madonna and Child, Byzantine, 11th cent. 150fr, Rest During the Flight to Egypt, by Gerard David (1450-1523). 160fr, African Madonna, 16th cent. 250fr, African Madonna, c. 1900. 500fr, Mystic Madonna, by Sandro Botticelli (1444-1510).

Perf. 14½x13½

1985, Dec. 10   Litho.

1347	A280	90fr multi	.75	.20
1348	A280	115fr multi	.90	.20
1349	A280	150fr multi	1.25	.20
1350	A280	160fr multi	1.25	.20
1351	A280	250fr multi	1.90	.35
		Nos. 1347-1351 (5)	6.05	1.15

Souvenir Sheet

1352	A280	500fr multi	4.00	3.00

Nos. 1348-1352 air airmail. No. 1352 contains one stamp 36x51mm.

Nos. 1302, 1305-1307 Ovptd. "75e Anniversaire / du Scoutisme Feminin"

1986, Jan.   *Perf. 15*

1353	A271	50fr multi	1.40	.25
1354	A271	1000fr multi	13.00	3.00

Souvenir Sheet

1355	A271	1000fr multi	7.50	6.00
1355A	A271	1000fr multi	7.50	6.00

Nos. 1354-1355A airmail.

Nos. 1268-1269, 1271, 1273-1274 Ovptd. "150e ANNIVERSAIRE / DE CHEMIN FER 'LUDWIG'"

1985, Dec. 27   Litho.   *Perf. 15*

1356	A267	50fr multi	1.25	.35
1357	A267	90fr multi	1.25	.60
1358	A267	500fr multi	8.00	3.50
		Nos. 1356-1358 (3)	10.50	4.45

Souvenir Sheets

1359	A267	1000fr No. 1273	9.00	6.50
1360	A267	1000fr No. 1274	9.00	6.50

Halley's
Comet
A281

Designs: 70fr, Suisei space probe, comets. 90fr, Vega-1 probe. 150fr, Space telescope. 200fr, Giotto probe, comet over Togo. 1000fr, Edmond Halley, Sir Isaac Newton.

1986, Mar. 27   *Perf. 13*

1361	A281	70fr multi	.60	.20
1362	A281	90fr multi	.75	.25
1363	A281	150fr multi	1.25	.40
1364	A281	200fr multi	1.75	.55
		Nos. 1361-1364 (4)	4.35	1.40

Souvenir Sheet

1365	A281	1000fr multi	7.50	6.00

Nos. 1362-1365 are airmail.
For overprints see Nos. 1405-1409.

Flowering
and Fruit-
bearing
Plants
A282

1986, June   *Perf. 14*

1366	A282	70fr Anacardium occidentale	.60	.20
1367	A282	90fr Ananas comosus	.75	.25
1368	A282	120fr Persea americana	1.00	.35
1369	A282	135fr Carica papaya	1.10	.40
1370	A282	290fr Mangifera indica, vert.	2.40	.80
		Nos. 1366-1370 (5)	5.85	2.00

Nos. 1368-1370 airmail.

1986 World Cup Soccer
Championships, Mexico — A283

Various soccer plays.

1986, May 5   Litho.   *Perf. 15x14*

1371	A283	70fr multi	.55	.20
1372	A283	90fr multi	.60	.25
1373	A283	130fr multi	.90	.35
1374	A283	300fr multi	2.10	.80
		Nos. 1371-1374 (4)	4.15	1.60

Souvenir Sheet

1375	A283	1000fr multi	7.50	6.00

Nos. 1372-1375 are airmail.
For overprints see Nos. 1394-1397.

Mushrooms — A284

1986, June 9   *Perf. 13x12½*

1376	A284	70fr Ramaria moelleriana	1.00	.20
1377	A284	90fr Hygrocybe firma	1.25	.25
1378	A284	150fr Kalchbrennera corallocephala	2.00	.40
1379	A284	200fr Cookeina tricholoma	2.75	.55
		Nos. 1376-1379 (4)	7.00	1.40

Intl. Youth Year — A285

1986, June　　　**Perf. 13½x14½**
1380 A285 25fr shown　　.75 .20
1381 A285 90fr Youths, doves　1.90 .25
　　Dated 1985.

Wrestling — A286

Wedding of Prince
Andrew and Sarah
Ferguson — A287

1986, July 16　**Perf. 14x15, 15x14**
1382 A286 15fr Single-leg take-
　　　　　down move　　.30 .20
1383 A286 20fr Completing take-
　　　　　down　　　　.30 .20
1384 A286 70fr Pinning combina-
　　　　　tion　　　　.50 .20
1385 A286 90fr Riding　　.70 .25
　　Nos. 1382-1385 (4)　1.80 .85
　Nos. 1384-1385 horiz. No. 1385 is airmail.

1986, July 23　　　**Perf. 14**
1386 A287 10fr Sarah Fergu-
　　　　　son　　　　.45 .20
1387 A287 1000fr Prince An-
　　　　　drew　　11.50 2.75
　　Souvenir Sheet
1388 A287 1000fr Couple　7.50 6.00
　　Nos. 1387-1388 are airmail.

Easter
A288

　Paintings (details): 25fr, 1000fr, The Resurrection, by Andrea Mantegna (1431-1506),
vert. 70fr, The Calvary, by Paolo Veronese
(1528-1588), vert. 90fr, The Last Supper, by
Jacopo Tintoretto (1518-1594). 200fr, Christ
at the Tomb, by Alonso Berruguette (1486-
1561).

1986, Mar. 24　**Perf. 14x15, 15x14**
　　　　　　　　　　　　Litho.
1389 A288 25fr multi　　.40 .20
1390 A288 70fr multi　　.55 .20
1391 A288 90fr multi　　.65 .25
1392 A288 200fr multi　1.50 .55
　　Nos. 1389-1392 (4)　3.10 1.20
　　Souvenir Sheet
1393 A288 1000fr multi　7.50 5.00
　　Nos. 1391-1393 are airmail.

Nos. 1371-1374 Ovptd. or Inscribed
"DEMI-FINALE / ARGENTINE 2 /
BELGIQUE 0,"
"DEMI-FINALE / ALLEMAGNE / DE
L'OUEST 2 / FRANCE 0,"
"3 eme et 4 eme PLACE / FRANCE 4
/ BELGIQUE 2,"
& "FINALE / ARGENTINE 3 /
ALLEMAGNE / DE L'OUEST 2"

1986, Aug. 4　**Litho.**　**Perf. 15x14**
1394 A283 70fr multi　　.55 .20
1395 A283 90fr multi　　.65 .25
1396 A283 130fr multi　　.90 .35
1397 A283 300fr multi　2.10 .80
　　Nos. 1394-1397 (4)　4.20 1.60
　　Nos. 1395-1397 are airmail.

Hotels — A289

1986, Aug. 18　　　**Perf. 12½**
1398 A289 70fr Fazao　　.50 .20
1399 A289 90fr Sarakawa　.60 .25
1400 A289 120fr Le Lac　　.80 .30
　　Nos. 1398-1400 (3)　1.90 .75
　　Nos. 1399-1400 are airmail.

Keran
Natl.
Park
A290

1986, Sept. 15　**Litho.**　**Perf. 14½**
1401 A290 70fr Wild ducks　.95 .25
1402 A290 90fr Antelope　1.10 .25
1403 A290 100fr Elephant　1.25 .30
1404 A290 130fr Waterbuck　1.75 .35
　　Nos. 1401-1404 (4)　5.05 1.10
　　Nos. 1402-1404 are airmail.

Nos. 1361-1365 Ovptd. with Halley's
Comet Emblem in Silver

1986, Oct. 9　　　　**Perf. 13**
1405 A281 70fr multi　1.50 .20
1406 A281 90fr multi　1.75 .25
1407 A281 150fr multi　3.00 .40
1408 A281 200fr multi　4.00 .55
　　Nos. 1405-1408 (4)　10.25 1.40
　　Souvenir Sheet
1409 A281 1000fr multi　18.00 6.00
　　Nos. 1406-1409 are airmail.

Frescoes from
Togoville
Church — A291

Togoville Church — A292

1986, Dec. 22　**Litho.**　**Perf. 14½x15**
1410 A291 45fr Annunciation　.40 .20
1411 A291 120fr Nativity　1.00 .30
1412 A291 130fr Adoration of
　　　　　the Magi　1.10 .35
1413 A291 200fr Flight into
　　　　　Egypt　1.75 .55
　　Nos. 1410-1413 (4)　4.25 1.40
　　Souvenir Sheet
1414 A292 1000fr multi　7.50 6.00
　Christmas. Nos. 1411-1414 are airmail.

Phosphate Mining — A293

Natl. Liberation, 20th Anniv. — A294

1987, Jan. 13　**Litho.**　**Perf. 12½**
1415 A293 35fr shown　　.25 .20
1416 A293 50fr Sugar refinery,
　　　　　Anie　　.30 .20
1417 A293 70fr Nangbeto Dam　.40 .20
1418 A293 90fr Hotel, post of-
　　　　　fice in Lome　.55 .30
1419 A293 100fr Post office, Kara　.60 .30
1420 A293 120fr Peace monu-
　　　　　ment　　.70 .35
1421 A293 130fr Youth vaccina-
　　　　　tion campaign　.80 .45
　　Nos. 1415-1421 (7)　3.60 2.00
　　Souvenir Sheet
　　　　Perf. 13
1422 A294 500fr shown　3.25 3.00
　　Nos. 1419-1422 are airmail.

Easter — A295

　Paintings in Nadoba Church, Keran: 90fr,
The Last Supper. 130fr, Christ on the Cross.
300fr, The Resurrection. 500fr, Evangelization
in Tamberma, fresco, horiz.

1987, Apr. 13　**Litho.**　**Perf. 14½x15**
1423 A295 90fr multi　　.60 .30
1424 A295 130fr multi　　.85 .40
1425 A295 300fr multi　1.90 .90
　　Nos. 1423-1425 (3)　3.35 1.60

　　Souvenir Sheet
　　　Perf. 15x14½
1426 A295 500fr multi　3.25 3.00
　　Nos. 1424-1426 are airmail.

World
Rugby Cup
A296

1987, May 11　　**Perf. 15x14½**
1427 A296 70fr Dive　　.60 .20
1428 A296 130fr Running with
　　　　　the ball　1.25 .40
1429 A296 300fr Scrimmage　2.50 .90
　　Nos. 1427-1429 (3)　4.35 1.50
　　Souvenir Sheet
　　　Perf. 14½x15
1430 A296 1000fr Stands, goal,
　　　　　vert.　7.50 7.50
　　Nos. 1427-1429 are horiz. Nos. 1428-1430
are airmail.

Indigenous
Flowers
A297

1987, June 22　**Litho.**　**Perf. 13**
1431 A297 70fr Adenium
　　　　　obesum　.70 .20
1432 A297 90fr Amorphophallus
　　　　　abyssinicus,
　　　　　vert.　.85 .25
1433 A297 100fr Ipomoea
　　　　　mauritana　.95 .30
1434 A297 120fr Salacia togoica,
　　　　　vert.　1.25 .35
　　Nos. 1431-1434 (4)　3.75 1.10
　　Nos. 1432-1434 are airmail.

Fish
A298

1987, Sept. 8　**Litho.**　**Perf. 13**
1435 A298 70fr Chaetodon
　　　　　hoefleri　.60 .25
1436 A298 90fr Tetraodon
　　　　　lineatus　.70 .30
1437 A298 120fr Chaetodipterus
　　　　　goreensis　.90 .40
1438 A298 130fr Labeo parvus　1.00 .45
　　Nos. 1435-1438 (4)　3.20 1.40

1988 Summer Olympics,
Seoul — A299

Buddha and athletes

1987, Sept. 14　　　**Perf. 12½**
1439 A299 70fr Long jump　.55 .25
1440 A299 90fr Relay　　.65 .30
1441 A299 200fr Cycling　1.50 .70
1442 A299 250fr Javelin　2.00 .85
　　Nos. 1439-1442 (4)　4.70 2.10
　　Souvenir Sheet
1443 A299 1000fr Tennis　7.50 5.50
　　Nos. 1440-1443 are airmail.

World Wildlife Fund Type of 1984

1987, Dec. 15   Litho.   Perf. 14
Size: 32x24mm

1444	A263	60fr like 45fr	3.25	.50
1445	A263	75fr like 70fr	3.75	.75
1446	A263	80fr like 90fr	3.75	1.00
1447	A263	100fr like 105fr	5.00	1.50
	Nos. 1444-1447 (4)		15.75	3.75

No. 1447 is airmail.

Christmas
A300

Eradication of
Tuberculosis
A301

Paintings: 40fr, Springtime in Paradise, horiz.. 45fr, Creation of Man, Sistine Chapel, by Michelangelo, horiz.. 105fr, Presentation in the Temple. 270fr, Original Sin. 500fr, Nativity, horiz.

Perf. 15x14, 14x15
1987, Dec. 15   Litho.

1448	A300	40fr multi	.35	.20
1449	A300	45fr multi	.40	.20
1450	A300	105fr multi	1.00	.40
1451	A300	270fr multi	2.50	.95
	Nos. 1448-1451 (4)		4.25	1.75

Souvenir Sheet

1452	A300	500fr multi	4.50	4.00

Nos. 1450-1452 are airmail.

1987, Dec. 28   Perf. 12½x13, 13x12½

1453	A301	80fr Inoculation, horiz.	.55	.30
1454	A301	90fr Family under umbrella	.65	.30
1455	A301	115fr Hospital, horiz.	.80	.40
	Nos. 1453-1455 (3)		2.00	1.00

Health for all by the year 2000. Nos. 1454-1455 are airmail.

Intl. Fund for Agricultural Development
(IFAD), 10th Anniv. — A302

1988, Feb. 25   Litho.   Perf. 13½

1456	A302	90fr multi	.75	.30

Easter
1988 — A303

Stained-glass windows: 70fr, Jesus and the Disciples at Emmaus. 90fr, Mary at the Foot of the Cross. 120fr, The Crucifixion. 200fr, St. Thomas Touching the Resurrected Christ. 500fr, The Agony of Jesus on the Mount of Olives.

1988, June 6   Litho.   Perf. 14x15

1457	A303	70fr multi	.45	.20
1458	A303	90fr multi	.70	.30
1459	A303	120fr multi	.90	.40
1460	A303	200fr multi	1.60	.70
	Nos. 1457-1460 (4)		3.65	1.60

Souvenir Sheet

1461	A303	500fr multi	3.75	3.00

Nos. 1459-1461 are airmail.

Paintings by Picasso (1881-
1973) — A304

Designs: 45fr, The Dance. 160fr, Portrait of a Young Girl. No. 1464, Gueridon. No. 1465, Mandolin and Guitar.

1988, Apr. 25   Litho.   Perf. 12½x13

1462	A304	45fr multi	.35	.20
1463	A304	160fr multi	1.10	.50
1464	A304	300fr multi	2.25	1.00
	Nos. 1462-1464 (3)		3.70	1.70

Souvenir Sheet

1465	A304	300fr multi	2.25	1.90

Nos. 1464-1465 are airmail.

A305

A306

1988, Aug. 30   Perf. 14x15

1466	A305	70fr Basketball	.50	.25
1467	A305	90fr Tennis	.65	.30
1468	A305	120fr Archery	.85	.40
1469	A305	200fr Discus	1.40	.65
	Nos. 1466-1469 (4)		3.40	1.60

Souvenir Sheet

1470	A305	500fr Marathon	3.50	2.75

1988 Summer Olympics, Seoul. Nos. 1468-1470 are airmail.

1988, Oct. 28   Litho.   Perf. 13

1471	A306	80fr shown	.55	.30
1472	A306	125fr Emblems	.85	.40

WHO, 40th anniv.

Traditional
Costumes
A307

1988, July 25   Litho.   Perf. 13½

1473	A307	80fr Watchi chief	.55	.20
1474	A307	90fr Watchi woman	.85	.40
1475	A307	165fr Kotokoli	1.10	.50
1476	A307	175fr Ewe	1.25	.60
	Nos. 1473-1476 (4)		3.75	1.70

Souvenir Sheet

1477	A307	500fr Moba	3.50	2.75

PHILTOGO 3,
Aug. 11-
12 — A308

Children's drawings by: 10fr, B. Gossner. 35fr, K. Ekoue-Kouvahey. 70fr, A. Abbey. 90fr, T.D. Lawson. 120fr, A. Tazzar.

1988, Dec. 3

1478	A308	10fr multi	.25	.20
1479	A308	35fr multi	.35	.20
1480	A308	70fr multi	.60	.25
1481	A308	90fr multi	.65	.30
1482	A308	120fr multi	.90	.40
	Nos. 1478-1482 (5)		2.75	1.35

Christmas — A309

Paintings: 80fr, Adoration of the Magi, by Brueghel. 150fr, The Virgin, Infant Jesus, Sts. Jerome and Dominic, by Lippi. 175fr, Madonna, Infant Jesus, St. Joseph and Infant John the Baptist, by Barocci. 195fr, Virgin and Child, by Bellini. 750fr, The Holy Family and a Shepherd, by Titian.

1988, Dec. 15   Perf. 14½x15

1483	A309	80fr multi	.55	.25
1484	A309	150fr multi	1.00	.45
1485	A309	175fr multi	1.25	.55
1486	A309	195fr multi	1.50	.60
	Nos. 1483-1486 (4)		4.30	1.85

Souvenir Sheet

1487	A309	750fr multi	4.75	3.50

Nos. 1484-1487 are airmail.

Natl.
Industries
A310

1988, May 28   Litho.   Perf. 13

1488	A310	125fr Cement factory	.80	.40
1489	A310	165fr Bottling plant	1.25	.55
1490	A310	195fr Phosphate mine	1.25	.65
1491	A310	200fr Plastics factory	1.50	.70
1492	A310	300fr Manufacturing plant	2.00	1.00
	Nos. 1488-1492 (5)		6.80	3.30

John F.
Kennedy
A311

Designs: 125fr, Arrival in Paris, 1961. 155fr, At Hotel de Ville, vert. 165fr, With De Gaulle at Elysee Palace, vert. 180fr, Boarding Air Force One with Jackie at Orly, France. 750fr, Kennedy and De Gaulle, natl. colors, vert.

1988, July 30   Litho.   Perf. 14

1493	A311	125fr multi	.85	.35
1494	A311	155fr multi	1.10	.50
1495	A311	165fr multi	1.25	.55
1496	A311	180fr multi	1.50	.60
	Nos. 1493-1496 (4)		4.70	2.00

Souvenir Sheet
Perf. 13½x13

1497	A311	750fr multi	5.00	4.00

Hairstyles
A312

1988, Nov. 20   Perf. 13

1498	A312	80fr shown	.55	.25
1499	A312	125fr multi, diff.	.85	.40
1500	A312	170fr multi, diff.	1.25	.55
1501	A312	180fr multi, diff., vert.	1.50	.60
	Nos. 1498-1501 (4)		4.15	1.80

Souvenir Sheet
Perf. 14

1502	A312	500fr multi, diff.	3.50	2.75

Sarakawa
Plane Crash,
15th Anniv.
A313

Portrait and various views of the wreckage.

1989, Jan. 24   Perf. 13½

1503	A313	10fr multi	.20	.20
1504	A313	80fr multi, vert.	.50	.25
1505	A313	125fr multi	.80	.40
	Nos. 1503-1505 (3)		1.50	.85

1990 World Cup Soccer
Championships, Italy — A314

ITALIA '90 emblem, flag of Togo, athletes and architecture: 80fr, Cathedral of St. Januarius, Naples. 125fr, Milan Cathedral. 165fr, Bevilacqua Palace, Verona. 175fr, Baptistery of San Giovanni, Florence. 380fr, Madama Palace, Turin. 425fr, Cathedral of San Lorenzo, Genoa. 650fr, The Colosseum, Rome.

1989, Jan. 10   Litho.   Perf. 13½

1506	A314	80fr multi	.55	.25
1507	A314	125fr multi	.85	.40
1508	A314	165fr multi	1.10	.50
1509	A314	175fr multi	1.25	.55
1510	A314	380fr multi	2.50	1.25
1511	A314	425fr multi	3.00	1.25
	Nos. 1506-1511 (6)		9.25	4.20

Souvenir Sheet

1512	A314	650fr multi	4.00	4.00

Nos. 1510-1512 are airmail.

Prince Emanuel of Liechtenstein
Foundation — A316a

1988 Summer Olympics, Seoul: Flags of Liechtenstein, Togo, athletes, Pres. Eyadema.

No. 1522A, Olympic rings. No. 1522B, Tennis players Miroslav Mecir, Steffi Graf, vert.

1989, May 25   Litho.   Perf. 13½
1520	A316	80fr Boxing	1.10	.25
1521	A316	125fr Long jump	.90	.40
1522	A316	165fr Running	2.25	.50
		Nos. 1520-1522 (3)	4.25	1.15

Litho. & Embossed
1522A	A316a	1500fr gold & multi	10.00
1522B	A316a	1500fr gold & multi	10.00

Nos. 1522A-1522B are airmail and exist imperf. and in souvenir sheets of 1 both perf. and imperf.

Federal Republic of Germany, 40th Anniv. A317

1989, June 1
1523	A317	90fr Palace	.60	.25
1524	A317	125fr Statesmen, vert.	.80	.40
1525	A317	180fr Natl. flag, crest	1.00	.50
		Nos. 1523-1525 (3)	2.40	1.15

Council for Rural Development, 30th Anniv. — A318

1989, June 19   Perf. 15x14
1526	A318	75fr Flags, well, tractor, field	.50	.25

See Ivory Coast No. 874.

Intl. Red Cross, 125th Anniv. A319

1989, June 30   Perf. 13½
1527	A319	90fr shown	.60	.30
1528	A319	125fr Geneva Convention, 1864	.80	.40

French Revolution, Bicent. A320

Designs: 90fr, Storming of the Bastille, vert. 125fr, Tennis Court Oath. 180fr, Abolition of privileges. 1000fr, Declaration of Human Rights and Citizenship, vert.

1989, July 15
1529	A320	90fr multi	.65	.30
1530	A320	125fr multi	.85	.40
1531	A320	180fr multi	1.25	.55
		Nos. 1529-1531 (3)	2.75	1.25

Souvenir Sheet
1532	A320	1000fr multi	7.50	2.50

Electric Corp. of Benin, 20th Anniv. A321

1989, July 15
1533	A321	80fr multi	.60	.25
1534	A321	125fr multi	1.00	.40

A322

PHILEXFRANCE '89, French Revolution, Bicent. — A322a

Figures and scenes from the revolution: 90fr, Jacques Necker (1732-1804), financier, statesman, and The Three Estates. 190fr, Guy Le Chapelier (1754-1794), politician, and abolition of feudalism (seigniorial privileges), Aug. 4, 1789. 425fr, Talleyrand-Perigord (1754-1838), statesman, and Lafayette's Oath at the Festival of Federation, July 14, 1790. 480fr, Paul Barras (1755-1829), revolutionary, and overthrowing of Robespierre during the Revolution of 9th Thermidor, July 27, 1794. 750fr, Georges Jacques Danton (1759-1794), revolutionary leader, and arrest of Louis XVI at Varennes, June 21, 1791, horiz. Nos. 1537-1539 are airmail.

No. 1539A, Assassination of Jean-Paul Marat (1743-93). No. 1539B, Fabré d'Eglantine (1750-94), making of the calendar of the republic.

1989   Litho.   Perf. 13½
1535	A322	90fr multi	.65	.30
1536	A322	125fr multi	1.25	.65
1537	A322	425fr multi	3.00	1.50
1538	A322	480fr multi	3.50	1.75
		Nos. 1535-1538 (4)	8.40	4.20

Souvenir Sheet
1539	A322	750fr multi	6.00	1.50

Litho. & Embossed
1539A	A322a	1500fr gold & multi	15.00

Souvenir Sheet
1539B	A322a	1500fr gold & multi	8.00

#1539A-1539B are airmail and exist imperf. Nos. 1535-1538 exist in souvenir sheets of 1, No. 1539A in souvenir sheets of 1, perf. and imperf.

Issued: 90fr-750fr, 6/12; 1500fr, 7/15.

Gen. Kpalime's Role in Natl. Unity and Peace Struggle, 20th Anniv. A323

1989, Aug. 21
1540	A323	90fr shown	.65	.30
1541	A323	125fr Giving speech	.90	.45

A324

A325

Butterflies.

1990, Apr. 30   Litho.   Perf. 13½
1542	A324	5fr Danaus chrysippus	.40	.20
1543	A324	10fr Morpho aega	.40	.20
1544	A324	15fr Papilio demodocus	.40	.20
1545	A324	90fr Papilio dardanus	1.40	.40
		Nos. 1542-1545 (4)	2.60	1.00

Souvenir Sheet
1545A	A324	500fr Papilio zalmoxis	3.75	1.90

No. 1545A is airmail.

1989, Dec. 1   Litho.   Perf. 13½
1546	A325	40fr Apollo 11 liftoff	.45	.20
1547	A325	90fr Module transposition	.90	.30
1548	A325	150fr Eagle	1.40	.50
1549	A325	250fr Splashdown	2.50	.90
		Nos. 1546-1549 (4)	5.25	1.90

Souvenir Sheet
1550	A325	500fr Astronaut on Moon	3.50	2.50

1st Moon Landing, 20th anniv.

Lome IV Conference, Dec. 1989 — A326

1989, Dec. 15   Litho.   Perf. 13
1551	A326	100fr "Dec. 89"	.70	.35
1552	A326	100fr "15 Dec. 89"	.70	.35

A327

Boy Scouts, Flora and Fauna A327a

#1559A, *Kalchbrennera corallocephala.* #1559B, *Spindasis mozambica.*

1990, Jan. 8   Litho.   Perf. 13½
1553	A327	80fr *Myrina silenus*	.60	.30
1554	A327	90fr *Phlebobus silvaticus*	.65	.35
1555	A327	125fr *Volvariella esculenta*	.90	.45
1556	A327	165fr *Hypolicaena antifaunus*	1.10	.65
1557	A327	380fr *Termitomyces striatus*	2.75	1.25
1558	A327	425fr *Axiocerces harpax*	3.00	1.50
		Nos. 1553-1558 (6)	9.00	4.50

Souvenir Sheet
1559	A327	750fr *Cupidopsis jobates*	5.50	1.00

Litho. & Embossed
1559A	A327a	1500fr gold & multi	10.00

Souvenir Sheet
1559B	A327a	1500fr gold & multi	10.00

Nos. 1557-1559B are airmail. Nos. 1559A-1559B exist imperf. No. 1559A exists in souvenir sheet of 1 both perf. and imperf.

People's Republic of Togo, 20th Anniv. — A328

1990, Jan. 8
1560	A328	45fr Government House, Kara	.35	.20
1561	A328	90fr Pres. Eyadema, House	.65	.30

Pan-African Postal Union, 10th Anniv. — A329

1990, Jan. 1   Perf. 13½
1562	A329	125fr bronze, blk & bl	1.00	.45

Ninth Convention of Lions Club International Multidistrict 403, Lome — A329a

Frame color: 90fr, Blue. 125fr, Rose. 165fr, Yellow.

1990, May 5   Litho.   Perf. 13½
1562A-1562C	A329a	Set of 3	—	—

US-Togo Relations A330

180fr, Pres. Bush, Pres. Eyadema, horiz.

1990, July 20   Litho.   Perf. 13½
1563	A330	125fr multicolored	.95	.50
1564	A330	180fr multicolored	1.40	.70

Size: 90 x 75mm
1565	A330	125fr multicolored	1.00	.50
1566	A330	180fr multicolored	1.40	.70
		Nos. 1563-1566 (4)	4.75	2.40

Nos. 1565-1566 printed in sheets of 1.

Reptiles A331

1990, May 22
1567	A331	1fr Varanus niloticus	.20	.20
1568	A331	25fr Vipere bitis arietans	.20	.20
1569	A331	60fr Naja melaneulo-ca	.50	.25
1570	A331	90fr Python de sebae	.70	.35
		Nos. 1567-1570 (4)	1.60	1.00

Cowrie Shell Ornaments A332

1990, July, 20   Litho.   Perf. 13½
1571	A332	90fr shown	.70	.35
1572	A332	125fr Shell necklace	1.00	.50
1573	A332	180fr Shells on horned helmet	1.40	.70
		Nos. 1571-1573 (3)	3.10	1.55

Stamp Day A333

1990, Aug. 23
1574	A333	90fr multicolored	.75	.35

Traditional Homes A334

1990, Sept. 9
1575	A334	90fr shown	.70	.35
1576	A334	125fr multi, diff.	1.00	.50
1577	A334	190fr multi, diff.	1.50	.75
		Nos. 1575-1577 (3)	3.20	1.60

Charles de Gaulle (1890-1970), Speech at Brazzaville, 1944 — A335

1990, Aug. 30   Litho.   Perf. 14
1578	A335	125fr multicolored	1.00	.50

New Lome Airport A336

1990, Sept. 17   Perf. 13½
1579	A336	90fr multicolored	.75	.35

Children's Art — A337

1990, Sept. 28   Litho.   Perf. 13½
1580	A337	90fr multicolored	.75	.35

Forest Wildlife — A342

1991, June 5   Litho.   Perf. 13½x14
1593	A342	90fr Chimpanzee	.70	.30
1594	A342	170fr Green parrot	1.25	.60
1595	A342	185fr White parrot	1.25	.65
		Nos. 1593-1595 (3)	3.20	1.55

Python Regius A343

Various snakes emerging from eggs.

1992, Aug. 24   Litho.   Perf. 13½
1596	A343	90fr multicolored	.70	.35
1597	A343	125fr multicolored	1.00	.50
1598	A343	190fr multicolored	1.50	.75
1599	A343	300fr multicolored	2.25	1.10
		Nos. 1596-1599 (4)	5.45	2.70

Dated 1991.

Voodoo Dances A344

Various women dancing.

1992, Aug. 24
1600	A344	90fr multicolored	.70	.35
1601	A344	125fr multicolored	1.00	.50
1602	A344	190fr multicolored	1.50	.75
		Nos. 1600-1602 (3)	3.20	1.60

Dated 1991.

A345

1994 World Cup Soccer Championships, US — A346

Various soccer players in action: 5fr, 10fr, 25fr, 60fr, 90fr, 100fr, 200fr, 1000fr. 1500fr, Player in white & green uniform. 3000fr, Two players in air, horiz.

1994, Nov. 15   Litho.   Perf. 14
1603-1610	A345	Set of 8	5.75	3.00

Souvenir Sheets
1611	A346	1500fr multicolored	5.75	3.00
1612	A346	3000fr multicolored	11.50	5.75

UPU, 120th Anniv. — A347

Stamp Day — A348

1994, July 29   Perf. 13½
1613	A347	180fr multicolored	.70	.35

A miniature sheet may exist.

1994, Oct. 9
1614	A348	90fr pale bl & multi	.35	.20
1615	A348	125fr pale yel & multi	.50	.25

Intl. Olympic Committee, Cent. — A348a

Designs, each 300fr: b, Pierre de Coubertin, Olympic Hymn. c, Original members of IOC. d, Olympic flame. 900fr, Pierre de Coubertin holding document.

1994, Oct.   Litho.   Perf. 13½
1615A	A348a	Strip of 3, #b.-d.	3.50	3.50

Souvenir Sheet
1615E	A348a	900fr multicolored	3.50	1.75

Nos. 1615A, 1615E exist imperf. No. 1615c is 60x51mm. No. 1615E is airmail and contains one 36x51mm stamp.

Birds A349

Designs: #1616, 5fr, Secretary bird, vert. #1617, 10fr, Paradise flycather, vert. #1618, 25fr, African spoonbill. #1619, 60fr, Cordon bleu waxbill. #1620, 90fr, Orange-breasted sunbird, vert. #1621, 100fr, Yellow-billed hornbill, vert. #1621A, 180fr, Barn owl. #1622,

200fr, African hoopoe. #1622A, 300fr, Fire-crowned bishop, vert. #1623, 1000fr, Red-throated bee eater, vert.

1995   Litho.   Perf. 14
1616-1623	A349	Set of 10	7.75	3.75

Souvenir Sheet
1624	A349	1500fr Vulture	5.75	2.75

Issued: 180fr, 300fr, 8/7; others, 1/23.

A350   A351

Motion Picture, Alien: a, Alien creature. b, Humans in combat with creature. c, Sigourney Weaver.

1994   Litho.   Perf. 13½
1625	A350	600fr Strip of 3, #a.-c.	7.50	3.75

No. 1625b is 60x48mm. No. 1625 is a continuous design and exists in souvenir sheets of 1.

1994

No. 1626, each 600fr: a, Edwin "Buzz" Aldrin. b, Eagle, olive branch, Neil Armstrong. c, Michael Collins.
No. 1627, each 600fr: a, Apollo emblem, footprint. b, Crew of Apollo 11. c, Moon rock, NASA emblem.

Strips of 3, #a.-c.
1626-1627	A351	Set of 2	15.00	7.50

First manned Moon landing, 25th anniv.
Nos. 1626b, 1627b are each 60x47mm. Nos. 1626-1627 are continuous designs and exist in souvenir sheets of 1.

Dinosaurs — A352

125fr, Polacanthus. 180fr, Pachycephalosaurus. 425fr, Coelophysis. 480fr, Brachiosaurus. 500fr, Dilophosaurus. 1500fr, Scutellosaurus.
No. 1634, Velociraptor, vert.

1994
1628-1633	A352	Set of 6	13.00	6.50

Souvenir Sheet
1634	A352	1500fr multicolored	6.25	3.00

No. 1634 is airmail.

Flowers — A353

Easter — A354

Designs: 15fr, Belvache de Madagascar. 90fr, Oeuillets. 125fr, Agave, horiz.

1995, May 12
1635-1637 A353 Set of 3   .90 .45

1995, May 12

Details or entire paintings: 90fr, The Resurrection, by A. Mantegna. 180fr, Calvary, by Veronese. 190fr, The Last Supper, by Tintoretto, horiz.

1638-1640 A354 Set of 3   1.75 .90

Fish
A355

10fr, Pike. 90fr, Capitaine. 180fr, Carp.

1995, May 12
1641-1643 A355 Set of 3   1.10 .55

Miniature Sheets of 6 and 8

VJ Day, 50th Anniv. A356

Japanese leaders: No. 1644a, Adm. Isoroko Yamamoto. b, Gen. Hideki Tojo. c, Vice Adm. Shigeru Fukudome. d, Adm. Shigetaro Shimada. e, Contre-Adm. Chuichi Nagumo. f, Gen. Shizu Ichi Tanaka.
No. 1646, Japanese signing peace agreement.
VE Day: No. 1645a, 200fr, German fighter planes making final attacks. b, 200fr, Allies win Battle of the Atlantic. c, 200fr, Ludendorf Bridge at Remagen is taken intact. d, 200fr, Russian rockets fired at Berlin. e, 45fr, Hostilities suspended in Italy. f, 90fr, Russians capture devastated Warsaw. g, 125fr, Russian tanks enter Berlin. h, 500fr, UN flag.
No. 1647, German U-236 surrenders.

1995, July 20   Litho.   Perf. 14
1644 A356 200fr #a.-f.   4.75 2.50
1645 A356   #a.-h.   6.25 3.25
    Souvenir Sheets
1646 A356 1500fr multicolored   6.00 3.00
1647 A356 1500fr multicolored   6.00 3.00

UN, 50th Anniv. — A357

No. 1648: a, 25fr, Doves, earth from space. b, 90fr, Doves, UN headquarters. c, 400fr, Doves, earth from space.
1000fr, Earth, dove.

1995, June 26
1648 A357 Strip of 3, #a.-c.   1.25 .65
    Souvenir Sheet
1649 A357 1000fr multicolored   4.00 2.00

1995 Boy Scout Jamboree, Holland — A358

Designs: 90fr, Nat. flag. 190fr, Scout oath. 300fr, Lord Baden-Powell. 1500fr, Scout salute.

1995, July 20
1650-1652 A358 Set of 3   1.60 .80
    Souvenir Sheet
1653 A358 1500fr multicolored   6.00 3.00

Queen Mother, 95th Birthday A359

No. 1654: a, Formal portrait. b, Cutting cake. c, As younger woman wearing jewels, waving. d, Drawing.
No. 1654E, Holding umbrella. No. 1654F, Formal portrait as young woman.
No. 1655, Royal attire, pearls.
No. 1655A, Early picture of King George VI, Queen Mother.

1995, July 20   Perf. 13½x14
1654 A359 250fr Strip of 4,   5.00 2.50
     #a.-d.
1654E A359 250fr multicolored   1.25 .65
1654F A359 250fr multicolored   1.25 .65
  g.   Block or strip of 4, #1654a,   5.00 2.50
     1654d, 1654E, 1654F
    Nos. 1654-1654F (3)   7.50 3.80
    Souvenir Sheets
1655 A359 1000fr multicolored   4.00 2.00
1655A A359 1000fr multicolored   4.00 2.00
Nos. 1654, 1654Fg were issued in sheets of 8 stamps.
Issued: #1654, 1655, 7/20; # 1654E, 1654F, 1655A, 11/22.

FAO, 50th Anniv. — A360

No. 1656: a, 45fr, Cattle. b, 125fr, Water buffalo. c, 200fr, Boy, man with water buffaloes.
1000fr, Woman milking cow.

1995, Mar. 3   Litho.   Perf. 14
1656 A360 Strip of 3, #a.-c.   1.50 .75
    Souvenir Sheet
1657 A360 1000fr multicolored   4.25 2.00
    No. 1656 is a continuous design.

A361

A362

No. 1658, each 200fr: a, Elihu Root, peace, 1912. b, Alfred Fried, peace, 1911. c, Henri Moissan, chemistry, 1906. d, Charles Barkla, physics, 1917. e, Rudolf Eucken, literature, 1908. f, Carl von Ossietzky, peace, 1935. g, Sir Edward Appleton, physics. 1947. h, Camillo Golgi, physiology, 1906. i, Wilhelm Roentgen, physics, 1901.
No. 1659, each 200fr: a, Manfred Eigen, chemistry, 1967. b, Donald J. Cram, chemistry, 1987. c, Paul J. Flory, chemistry, 1974. d, Johann Deisenhofer, chemistry, 1988. e, P.W. Bridgman, physics, 1946. f, Otto Stern, physics, 1943. g, Arne Tiselis, chemistry, 1948. h, J. Georg Bednorz, physics, 1987. i, Albert Claude, medicine, 1974.
Each 1500fr: No. 1660, Albert Einstein, physics, 1921. No. 1661, Woodrow Wilson, peace, 1919.

1995, Aug. 21
    Miniature Sheets of 9, a-i
1658-1659 A361 Set of 2   14.50 7.00
    Souvenir Sheets
1660-1661 A361 Set of 2   12.00 6.00
    Nobel Prize winners.

1995, July 20
1662 A362 1000fr shown   4.25 2.00
    Souvenir Sheet
1663 A362 1000fr Natl. flag, Ro-   4.25 2.00
      tary emblem
    Rotary Intl., 90th anniv.

Miniature Sheets

Fauna
A363

Primates, each 200fr, vert: No. 1664a, Black-faced monkey in tree. b, Brown monkey in tree. c, Black monkey. d, Baboon.
Wild animals, each 200fr: No. 1665a, Hyena. b, Hyrax. c, Mongoose. d, Elephant. e, Mandrill. f, Okapi. g, Hippopotamus. h, Flamingo. i, Wild boar.
1500fr, Potto.

1995, Oct. 2   Litho.   Perf. 14
1664 A363 Sheet of 4, #a.-d.   3.25 1.60
1665 A363 Sheet of 9, #a.-i.   7.25 3.50
    Souvenir Sheet
1666 A363 1500fr multicolored   6.00 3.00

FAO, 50th Anniv. A364

1995, Mar. 3   Litho.   Perf. 14
1667 A364 125fr shown   .50 .25
    Souvenir Sheet
1668 A364 300fr like No. 1667   1.25 .60

Sir Rowland Hill (1795-1879) A365

UN, 50th Anniv. — A366

1995, June 3   Perf. 13½
1669 A365 125fr multicolored   .50 .25

1995, June 26
1670 A366 180fr multicolored   .75 .40

Miniature Sheets of 8

Mushrooms
A367

No. 1671: a, Cortinarius violaceus. b, Hygrocybe flavescens. c, Mycena haematopus. d, Coprinus micaceus. e, Helvella lacunosa. f, Flammulina velutipes. g, Aleuria aurantia. h, Geastrum triplex.
No. 1672: a, Russula laurocerasi. b, Phyllotopsis nidulans. c, Xeromphalina campanella. d, Psathyrella hydrophila. e, Entoloma murraii. f, Hygrophorus speciosus. g, Mycena leaiana. h, Cystoderma amianthinum.
No. 1673, each 200fr: a, Amanita muscaria. b, Amanita virosa. c, Galerina autumnalis. d, Omphalotus illudens. e, Naematoloma fasciculare. f, Paxillus involutus. g, Russula emetica. h, Scleroderma citrinum.
No. 1674, each 200fr: a, Armillaria ponderosa. b, Agaricus augustus. c, Gomphidius subroseus. d, Morchella esculenta. e, Stropharia rugoso. f, Boletus edulis. g, Clitocybe nuda. h, Lactarius deliciosus.
Each 1500fr: No. 1675, Trametes versicolor. No. 1676, Collybia iocephala.

1995, Nov. 1   Perf. 14
1671 A367 180fr #a.-h.   5.75 2.75
1672 A367 195fr #a.-h.   6.25 3.00
1673-1674 A367 Set of 2, #a.-   13.00 6.50
     h.
    Souvenir Sheets
1675-1676 A367 Set of 2   12.00 6.00

Miniature Sheets

History of Transportation — A368

Steam locomotives: No. 1677, each 200fr: a, SNCF Class 231 D Le Havre-Paris Express. b, Princess Royal Class Pacific, England. c, Class 52 2-10-0, German Railroad. d, Class "15A" 4-6-4+4-6-4 Beyer-Garratt, Rhodesia. e, Japanese 2-8-0. f, Class 940, 2-8-2 engine, Italy.
Various vehicles: No. 1678, each 200fr: a, Semi truck. b, Roman chariot. c, Motorcycle. d, Hummer 4-wheel drive. e, Bicycle. f, London autobus. g, Lunar rover. h, 1954 Jaguar XK 140. i, Ski-doo.
No. 1679, First land vehicle to break sound barrier.

1995, Dec. 1   Litho.   Perf. 14
1677 A368 Sheet of 6, #a.-f.   4.75 2.50
1678 A368 Sheet of 9, #a.-i.   7.25 3.50
    Souvenir Sheet
1679 A368 1500fr multicolored   6.00 3.00
    No. 1679 contains one 85x28mm stamp.

World Post Day
A369

Designs: 220fr, Selling stamps. 315fr, Sorting stamps. 335fr, Post office workers handling large sacks of mail.

1995	**Litho.**		**Perf. 13½**
1680-1682	A369	Set of 3	4.50 2.25

Christmas
A370

Paintings: 90fr, Nativity scene, vert. 325fr, Adoration of the Magi, vert. 340fr, 500fr, Adoration of the shepherds.

1995, Sept. 13	**Litho.**		**Perf. 13½**
1683-1685	A370	Set of 3	3.00 1.50
	Souvenir Sheet		
	Perf. 12½		
1686	A370	500fr multi, vert.	2.00 1.00

Sheets of 6

Wildlife of Africa
A371

No. 1687: a, Gorilla. b, Uroota suraka. c, Pan troglodytes. d, Panthera pardus. e, Crocodylus niloticus. f, Leptailurus serval.
No. 1688a, Papilio tynderaeus. b, Bongo taurotragus. c, Epiphora aldiba. d, Cephalophus zebra. e, Cercopithecus cephus. f, Arctocebus calabarensis.

1996, May 10	**Litho.**		**Perf. 14**
1687	A371	150fr #a.-f.	3.50 1.75
1688	A371	180fr #a.-f.	4.25 2.25

China '96, 9th Asian Intl. Philatelic Exhibition.

A372

1996 Summer Olympics, Atlanta — A373

Designs: 50fr, Olympic Stadium, Mexico, 1968, horiz. 90fr, Yevgeny Petrov, skeet shooter, Mexico, 1968, horiz. 220fr, Lia Manoliu, women's discus, Mexico, 1968, horiz. 325fr, Dumb-bell lifting, discontinued sport.
Medal winners from past games: No. 1693, each 200fr: a, China, Women's Volleyball, 1984. b, Wayne Wells, wrestling, 1972. c, Bob Beaman, long jump, 1968. d, Victor Kurentsov, weight lifting, 1968. e, Shirley Strong, 100m hurdles, 1984. f, Nadia Comaneci, balance beam, 1976. g, Giovanni Parisi, boxing, 1988. h, Emil Zatopek, 10,000m, 1948. i, USSR, Brazil, Germany, soccer, 1988.
1000fr, Helen Mayer, fencing, 1936.

1996, July 8	**Litho.**		**Perf. 14**
1689-1692	A372	Set of 4	2.75 1.40
1693	A372	Sheet of 9, #a.-i.	7.25 3.50
	Souvenir Sheet		
1694	A372	1000fr multicolored	4.00 2.00

1996, Mar. 25		**Perf. 12½**

100fr, Women's gymnastics. 150fr, Women's tennis. 200fr, Javelin. 300fr, Men's field hockey. 400fr, Weight lifting. 500fr, Men's soccer.
1000fr, Synchronized swimming.

1695-1700	A373	Set of 6	7.50 3.75
	Souvenir Sheet		
1701	A373	1000fr multicolored	5.50 2.75

Butterflies
A374

Designs: 40fr, Euphaedra eleus, vert. 90fr, Papilio dardanus, vert. 220fr, Iolaus timon. 315fr, Charaxes cynthia.

1996, June 17	**Litho.**		**Perf. 13**
1702-1705	A374	Set of 4	2.75 1.50

Beetles — A375

Designs: 100fr, Purpuricenus kaehleri. 150fr, Carabus auronitens. 200fr, Semanotus rassicus. 300fr, Rosalia alpina. 400fr, Mylabris variabilis. 500fr, Odontolabis cuvera.
1000fr, Psalidognathus atys.

1996, May 5			
1706-1711	A375	Set of 6	7.75 3.75
	Souvenir Sheet		
	Perf. 12½		
1712	A375	1000fr multicolored	5.50 2.75

No. 1712 contains one 40x32mm stamp.

1998 World Cup Soccer Championships, France — A376

French flag, various action scenes: 100fr, 150fr, 200fr, 300fr, 400fr, 500fr.

1996, Apr. 10			**Perf. 12½**
1713-1718	A376	Set of 6	7.75 3.75
	Souvenir Sheet		
1719	A376	1000fr multicolored	5.50 2.75

World Wildlife Fund — A377

Designs: a, 325fr, Cephalophus drosalis. b, 220fr, Cephalophus maxwelli. c, 180fr, Cephalophus rufilatus. d, 370fr, Cephalophus syvicultor.
1500fr, Cephalophus drosalis, diff.

1996, July 30			**Perf. 14**
1720	A377	Block of 4, #a.-d.	7.00 3.00
	Souvenir Sheet		
1721	A377	1500fr multicolored	8.25 4.00

No. 1720 was issued in sheets of 16 stamps.

Endangered Species — A378

Designs, vert: 220fr, Zebra. 315fr, Leopard. 325fr, Antelope. 335fr, Madoqua Kirki.
No. 1726, each 200fr: a, African elephants. b, Toucan (c, d, e, f.) c, Mamba (f). d, Lionesses. e, Impala. f, Nyala. g, Hippopptamus. h, Crocodile. i, Kingfisher.
Each 1500 fr: No. 1727, Buphagus erythrorhynchus, vert. No. 1728, Leopard, vert.

1996, July 30			
1722-1725	A378	Set of 4	6.50 3.25
1726	A378	Sheet of 9, #a.-i.	8.00 4.00
	Souvenir Sheets		
1727-1728	A378	Set of 2	13.00 7.00

Endangered Species
A379

75fr, Elephant. 90fr, Crocodile. 315fr, Deer.

1996, July 30	**Litho.**		**Perf. 13**
1729-1731	A379	Set of 3	2.25 1.25

Traditional Musical Instruments
A380

90fr, Gongs. 220fr, Cymbals (balafon). 325fr, String instrument. 500fr, Drums.

1996, July 15			
1732-1735	A380	Set of 4	4.50 2.25

Traditional Dances
A381

Designs: 10fr, Kamou dance, Kabyes. 90fr, Kondona dance, Kabyes. 220fr, Bassar. 315fr, Kloto. 335fr, Voudoussis.

1996, June 30			
1736-1740	A381	Set of 5	4.00 2.00

New Year 1997 (Year of the Ox) — A382

Paintings, by Ren Bonian (1840-95): No. 1741: a, Herdboy on Buffalo. b, Return from the Pasture. c, Grazing by the Pond. 500fr, Reading Beside an Ox.

1997, Jan. 2	**Litho.**		**Perf. 14**
1741	A382	180fr Strip of 3, #a.-c.	2.25 2.25
d.		Souvenir sheet of 6, 2x #a-c	4.50 4.50
	Souvenir Sheet		
	Perf. 13½x14		
1742	A382	500fr multicolored	2.00 2.00

No. 1741 was issued in sheets of 6 stamps. No. 1742 contains one 34x46mm stamp.

Fruits
A383

100fr, Mango. 150fr, Bananas. 200fr, Peaches. 300fr, Papaya. 400fr, Lemon. 500fr, Coconuts.
1000fr, Various fruits.

1996, June 2	**Litho.**		**Perf. 12½**
1743-1748	A383	Set of 6	7.25 7.25
	Souvenir Sheet		
	Perf. 13		
1749	A383	1000fr multicolored	5.25 5.25

No. 1749 contains one 40x32mm stamp.

Souvenir Sheet

Chinese Stone Carving — A384

Illustration reduced.

1996, May 10	**Litho.**		**Perf. 12**
1750	A384	370fr multicolored	1.50 1.50

China '96. No. 1750 was not available until March 1997.

Jaffar Ballogou, Boxer — A384a

1996	**Litho.**		**Perf. 13**
1750B	A384a	220fr blk & multi	—
1750C	A384a	315fr red & multi	—

An additional stamp was issued in this set. The editors would like to examine it. World Telecommunications Day.

UNESCO, 50th Anniv.
A385

World Heritage Sites: No. 1751, each 235fr: a, Axum archaeological site, Ethiopia. b, Victoria Falls, Zambia. c, Archaeological site, Zimbabwe. d, Nature reserve, Niger. e, Arguin Natl. Park, Mauritania. f, Goree Island, Senegal. g, Timgad Ruins, Algeria. h, Ait Ben-Haddou, Morocco.
No. 1752, each 235fr: a, Kyoto, Japan. b, Waterfalls, Colombia. c, Necropolis, Egypt. d, Old Rama Church, Finland. e, Palladian villa, Vicenza, Italy. f, Rock paintings, China. g, Church, Ouro Preto, Brazil. h, Rhodes, Greece.

No. 1753, each 235fr: a, Exterior of Cistercian Abbey, Fontenay, France. b, Dubrovnik Village, Croatia. c, Interior of Cistercian Abbey, Fontenay. d, e, Quedlinburg, Germany. f, Ironbridge Gorge, England. g, Grand Canyon, US. h, Village, Ironbridge Gorge, England.

Each 1000fr: No. 1754, Kyoto, Japan, horiz. No. 1755, Mt. Huangshan, China, horiz. No. 1756, Village, Ironbridge, England, horiz.

1997, Mar. 24   Litho.   Perf. 14
Sheets of 8, a-h, + Label
1751-1753 A385 Set of 3   22.50 22.50
Souvenir Sheets
1754-1756 A385 Set of 3   12.00 12.00

Cats
A386

150fr, American shorthair. 200fr, Siamese, vert. 300fr, Java. 400fr, "Ocicat," vert. 500fr, Scottish fold. No. 1762, 1000fr, Persian, vert. No. 1763, Colorpoint shorthair, vert.

1997   Litho.   Perf. 12½
1757-1762 A386 Set of 6   8.50 8.50
Souvenir Sheet
1763 A386 1000fr multicolored   3.50 3.50
No. 1763 contains one 32x40mm stamp.

Military
Uniforms — A387

Designs: 150fr, Officer of cuirassiers. 200fr, Norman regiment officer. 300fr, Volunteer battalion foot soldier. 400fr, Berlin Campaign Militiaman. 500fr, Foot soldier. No. 1769, 1000fr, Musketeer.

No. 1770, Belling Regiment Hussar.

1997   Perf. 13x12½
1764-1769 A387 Set of 6   8.50 8.50
Souvenir Sheet
1770 A387 1000fr multicolored   3.50 3.50
No. 1770 contains one 40x32mm stamp.

Return of Hong Kong to China —
A388

Deng Xiaoping (1904-97) — A388a

Views of city: 220fr, Chinese flag as inscription, skyscraper. 315fr, Chinese flag as inscription, night scene. 325fr, Circular stair railing, skyscraper at night. 340fr, Chinese flag, view of city through inscription. 370fr, Deng Xiaoping (1904-97), fireworks over city.
#1775A: a, shown. b, Looking left.
Illustration reduced.

1997, June 2   Perf. 14
1771-1775 A388 Set of 5   6.50 6.50
Sheet of 2
Perf. 13½
1775A A388a 500fr #a.-b.   3.75 3.75
Nos. 1771-1773 are 28x44mm and were each issued in sheets of 4. Nos. 1774-1775 were each issued in sheets of 3.

Queen Elizabeth II and Prince Philip, 50th Wedding Anniv. A389

No. 1776: a, Queen. b, Royal arms. c, Queen in yellow hat, Prince in military uniform. d, Queen in white hat, Prince. e, Windsor Castle. f, Prince.
1000fr, Portrait of Queen, Prince.

1997, June 25
1776 A389 315fr Sheet of 6, #a.-
   f.   6.50 6.50
Souvenir Sheet
1777 A389 1000fr multicolored   3.50 3.50

Locomotives — A390

150fr, Light locomotive, Adams Bridges. 200fr, Norris Type, England 1866. 300fr, Jones and Ports locomotive with long boiler, 1848. 400fr, Cargo and passenger locomotive, Ansaldo, 1850. 500fr, Birkenhead, Italy, 1863. #1783, 1000fr, Quarter locomotive, New York, 1890.
#1783A, Six-wheeled locomotive, Robert Stephenson, 1830, vert.

1996, Dec. 5   Litho.   Perf. 12½x12
1778-1783 A390 Set of 6   8.75 8.75
Souvenir Sheet
Perf. 12½
1783A   A390 1000fr multi   3.50 3.50

Birds — A391

150fr, Poephila guttata. 200fr, Lonchura malacca. 300fr, Acanthis cannabina. 400fr, Fringilla coelebs. 500fr, Emblema guttata. #1789, 1000fr, Passerina amoena. #1789A, Chloebia gouldiae.

1996, Nov. 27   Perf. 13
1784-1789 A391 Set of 6   8.75 8.75
Souvenir Sheet
1789A A391 1000fr multicolored   3.50 3.50
Nos. 1784-1789 are dated 1996.
No. 1789A contains one 32x40mm stamp.

Turtles
A392

Designs: 150fr, Asterochelys yniphora. 200fr, Stauротypus triporcatus. 300fr, Puxidea mouhoti. 400fr, Geomyda spengleri. 500fr, Cuora galbinifrons. #1795, 1000fr, Malaclemys terrapin.
#1795A, Asterochelys radiata.

1996, Nov. 30
1790-1795 A392 Set of 6   6.50 6.50
Souvenir Sheet
1795A A392 1000fr multicolored   3.50 3.50
Nos. 1790-1795 are dated 1996.
No. 1795A contains one 40x32mm stamp.

Natl. Liberation, 30th Anniv. — A393

1997   Litho.   Perf. 13½
1796 A393 90fr yellow & multi   .30 .30
1797 A393 220fr green & multi   .75 .75

Diana, Princess of Wales (1961-97) A394

Nos. 1798a-1798i: Various portraits of Princess Diana in designer gowns, each 180fr.
Views up close, each 180fr: No. 1799, like #1798a. No. 1799A, Like #1798b. No. 1800, like #1798c. No. 1801, like #1798d. No. 1802, like #1798e. No. 1802A, Like #1798f. No. 1802B, Like #1798g. No. 1803, like #1798h. No. 1804, like #1798i.

1997
1798 A394 Sheet of 9, #a.-i.   7.50 7.50
Souvenir Sheets
1799-1804 A394 Set of 9   50.00 50.00

Diana, Princess of Wales (1961-97) — A395

Nos. 1805-1807, Various pictures of Diana during her lifetime as Princess of Wales.
Each 1000fr: Pictures of Diana with (in margin): No. 1808, French Pres. Giscard d'Estaing. No. 1809, Mother Teresa. No. 1810, US First Lady Hillary Clinton.

1998, Jan. 2   Perf. 14
Sheets of 6
1805 A395 240fr #a.-f.   5.00 5.00
1806 A395 315fr #a.-f.   6.50 6.50
1807 A395 340fr #a.-f.   7.25 7.25
Souvenir Sheets
1808-1810 A395 Set of 3   10.50 10.50

Souvenir Sheet

Marilyn Monroe (1926-62) — A396

Illustration reduced.

1997   Litho.   Perf. 13½
1811 A396 2000fr multicolored   7.25 7.25

New Year 1998 (Year of the Tiger) — A397

Various paintings of tigers, by Liu Jiyou (1918-83): No. 1812: a, 180fr. b, 200fr. No. 1813: a, 90fr. b, 100fr. c, 180fr. d, 200fr.

1998, Jan. 5   Litho.   Perf. 14
1812 A397 Sheet of 2, #a.-b.   1.25 1.25
1813 A397 Sheet of 4, #a.-d.   2.00 2.00
No. 1812 contains two 26x65mm stamps.

Hiroshige (1797-1858), Painter — A398

Paintings: No. 1814: a, Sixty-Nine Stations of the Kisokaido Road: Mochizuki. b, Eight Views of Lake Biwa Evening Snow at Mt. Hira. c, Kinkizan Temple on Enoshima Island, Sagami Provence. d, Cherry Blossoms. e, Evening Snow at Asakusa. f, Myhankoshi.
No. 1815: a, Two Terrapins (Fan print). b, Swimming Carp. c, Takanawa by Moonlight. d, Night Rain at Karasaki. e, Chiryu: The Summer Horse Fair. f, Shower over the Nihonbashi.
No. 1816, vert: a, Takata Riding Grounds. b, Sugatami & Omokage Bridges & Jariba at Takata. c, Dam on the Otonashi River at Oji. d, Basho's Hermitage and Camellia Hill. e, Fudo Falls, Oji. f, Takinogawa Oji.
Each 1000fr: No. 1817, Bird in a Tree. No. 1818, Title Page for Hiroshige's One Hundred Views of Edo, by Baisotei. No. 1819, Memorial Portrait of Hiroshige, by Utagawa. No. 1820, Street Stalls and Tradesmen in Jouricho. No. 1821, Cherry Blossom, Morning Glory, Cranes and Rabbits. No. 1822, Three Wild Geese Flying Across the Moon. No. 1823, Suwa Bluff, Nippori. Nos. 1817-1823 are vert.

Perf. 14x13½, 13½x14
1998, Mar.   Litho.
Sheets of 6
1814 A398 220fr #a.-f.   4.50 4.50
1815 A398 315fr #a.-f.   6.50 6.50
1816 A398 370fr #a.-f.   7.50 7.50
Souvenir Sheets
Perf. 13½x14
1817-1823 A398 Set of 7   25.00 25.00
Nos. 1817-1823 each contain one 26x72mm stamp.

Fauna, Flora, Minerals — A399

Dolphins and whales: No. 1824: a, Souffleur nesarnack. b, Lagenorhynque. c, Sotalie du cameroun. d, Petit rorqual. e, Rorqual commun. f, Faux orque.
Insects and spiders: No. 1825: a, Lasius niger. b, Sceliphron spirifex. c, Peucetia. d, Mygale. e, Theraphoside. f, Dynaste hercule.
Precious stones, minerals: No. 1826: a, Ruby. b, Diamond in kimberlite. c, Cut diamond. d, Rock salt. e, Tiger's eye. f, Uraninite.

Moths and butterflies: No. 1827: a, Pirate. b, Euchromie des liserons. c, Asterope. d, Psalis de kiriakoff. e, Sphinx de fabricius. f, Pensee bleue.

Mushrooms: No. 1828: a, Lepiote. b, Hypholome. c, Lactaire. d, Russule fetide. e, Russule doree. f, Strophaire.

Each 2000fr: No. 1829, Tricholome a odeur de savon. No. 1830, Potto.

1998(?)   Litho.   *Perf. 13½*
Sheets of 6

1824	A399	180fr #a.-f.	4.00	4.00
1825	A399	250fr #a.-f.	5.75	5.75
1826	A399	300fr #a.-f.	6.75	6.75
1827	A399	400fr #a.-f.	9.00	9.00
1828	A399	450fr #a.-f.	10.25	10.25

Souvenir Sheets

| 1829-1830 | A399 | Set of 2 | 15.50 | 15.50 |

Intl. Scouting, 90th Anniv. (#1825, 1827-1830). Nos. 1829-1830 each contain one 41x60mm stamp.

Jerry Garcia (1942-95) — A400

Various portraits.

1998   Litho.   *Perf. 13½*

| 1831 | A400 | 250fr Sheet of 9, #a.-i. | 7.75 | 7.75 |

Souvenir Sheet

| 1832 | A400 | 2000fr multicolored | 7.00 | 7.00 |

No. 1832 contains one 42x51mm stamp.

Dinosaurs — A401

Various unidentified dinosaurs.

1998

| 1833 | A401 | 290fr Sheet of 9, #a.-i. | 10.00 | 10.00 |

Souvenir Sheet

| 1834 | A401 | 2000fr multicolored | 7.50 | 7.50 |

No. 1834 contains one 42x51mm stamp.

1998 Winter Olympic Games, Nagano — A402

No. 1835: a, Hockey. b, Speed skating. c, Pairs figure skating. d, Luge. e, Curling. f, Bobsledding.

No. 1836: a, Downhill skiing. b, Freestyle ski jumping (blue skis). c, Ski jumping. d, Downhill skiier in tuck. e, Snow boarding. f, Freestyle skiing (red skis).

1998
Sheets of 6

| 1835 | A402 | 250fr #a.-f. | 5.75 | 5.75 |
| 1836 | A402 | 300fr #a.-f. | 6.75 | 6.75 |

Nos. 1835-1836 each have 3 labels.

1998 World Cup Soccer Championships, France — A403

Player, country, vert: No. 1837, Kluivert, Netherlands. No. 1838, Asprilla, Colombia. No. 1839, Bergkamp, Netherlands. No. 1840, Gascoigne, England. No. 1841, Ravanelli, Italy. No. 1842, Sheringham, England.

No. 1843: a, Paul Gascoigne, England, diff. b, Ryan Giggs, Wales. c, Roy Keane, Ireland. d, Stuart Pearce, England. e, Tony Adams, England. f, Teddy Sheringham, England, diff. g, Paul Ince, England. h, Steve McManaman, England.

No. 1844: a, Rossi, Italy. b, Lineker, England. c, Lato, Poland. d, Futre, Poland. e, Klinsmann, Germany. f, Hurst, England. g, Kempes, Argentina. h, McCoist, Scotland.

World Cup Champions, year, vert.— #1845: a, Argentina, 1978. b, Italy, 1982. c, England, 1966. d, Uruguay, 1930. e, Germany, 1954. f, Argentina, 1986. g, Brazil, 1994.

Each 1500fr: No. 1846, Ronaldo, Brazil, vert. No. 1847, Gary Lineker, England, vert. No. 1848, Shearer, England, vert.

**   *Perf. 13½x14, 14x13½***
1998, July 10   Litho.

| 1837-1842 | A403 | 370fr Set of 6 | 7.50 | 7.50 |

Sheets of 8 + Label

| 1843 | A403 | 220fr #a.-h. | 5.00 | 6.00 |
| 1844 | A403 | 315fr #a.-h. | 8.50 | 8.50 |

Sheet of 7 + 2 Labels

| 1845 | A403 | 325fr #a.-g. | 7.75 | 7.75 |

Souvenir Sheets

| 1846-1848 | A403 | Set of 3 | 15.00 | 15.00 |

Bella Bellow (d. 1973), Singer — A403a

1998-2002   Litho.   *Perf. 13½*

1848A	A403a	5fr yel orange
1848B	A403a	10fr olive green
1848C	A403a	25fr emerald
1848D	A403a	40fr violet
1848E	A403a	50fr black
1848F	A403a	75fr yel orange
1848G	A403a	100fr orange
1848H	A403a	125fr blue
1848I	A403a	200fr brt purple
1848J	A403a	240fr red violet
1848K	A403a	280fr green
1848L	A403a	300fr Prus blue
1848M	A403a	320fr red orange
1848N	A403a	340fr car lake
1848O	A403a	390fr car rose

| 1848P | A403a | 450fr brt blue ('02) | — | — |
| 1848R | A403a | 500fr gray olive ('02) | — | — |

At least four additional values were issued in this set. The editors would like to examine any examples.

Star Wars Movies — A404

Return of the Jedi — #1849: a, Princess Leia. b, Darth Vader. c, Han Solo. d, R2-D2, C-3PO. e, Emperor Palpatine. f, Chewbacca. g, Leia on speeder. h, Luke Skywalker. i, Storm trooper on speeder.

Empire Strikes Back — #1850: a, Lando Calrissian. b, Yoda. c, Chewbacca. d, C-3PO, R2-D2. e, Luke Skywalker. f, Darth Vader. g, Battle on snow planet. h, Leia. i, Rider on snow planet.

2000fr, Han Solo, Luke Skywalker, Princess Leia, R2-D2.

1997   Litho.   *Perf. 13½*
Sheets of 9

| 1849 | A404 | 190fr #a.-i. | 5.75 | 5.75 |
| 1850 | A404 | 350fr #a.-i. | 10.50 | 10.50 |

Souvenir Sheet

| 1851 | A404 | 2000fr multicolored | 7.00 | 7.00 |

No. 1851 contains one 42x60mm.

Jacqueline Kennedy Onassis (1929-94) — A405

No. 1852: Various portraits.
No. 1853: Various portraits of John F. Kennedy (1917-63).

1997
Sheets of 9

| 1852 | A405 | 250fr #a.-i. | 7.50 | 7.50 |
| 1853 | A405 | 400fr #a.-i. | 12.00 | 12.00 |

Diana, Princess of Wales (1961-97) — A406

No. 1854: Various portraits.
2000fr, Diana in black (Mother Teresa in sheet margin).

1997
Sheet of 8 + Label

| 1854 | A406 | 500fr #a.-h. | 15.00 | 15.00 |

Souvenir Sheet

| 1854I | A406 | 2000fr multicolored | 8.25 | 8.25 |

Marilyn Monroe (1926-62) — A407

Various portraits, each 300fr.

1997   Litho.   *Perf. 13½*

| 1855 | A407 | Sheet of 9, #a.-i. | 9.00 | 9.00 |

Minerals — A408

Designs: 100fr, Calcite. 150fr, Turquoise, vert. 200fr, Pyrite, vert. 300fr, Tourmaline, vert. 400fr, Pyrargirite, vert. 500fr, Malachite. 1000fr, Beryl, vert.

1999   Litho.   *Perf. 12¾*

| 1856-1861 | A408 | Set of 6 | 5.00 | 5.00 |

Souvenir Sheet
**   *Perf. 13***

| 1861A | A408 | 1000fr multicolored | 3.00 | 3.00 |

No. 1861A contains one 32x40mm stamp.

Flowers — A409

Designs: No. 1862, Caralluma burchardii. No. 1863, Dimorphotheca barberiae. No. 1864, Hoya carnosa. No. 1865, Amaryllis belladonna. No. 1866, Watsonia beatricis. No. 1867, Anthurium schezerianum. No. 1868, Thumbergia alata. No. 1869, Arctotis breviscapa. No. 1870, Glaucium flavum. No. 1871, Impatiens petersiana. No. 1872, Chrysanthemum segetum. No. 1873, Zantedeschia aethiopica, horiz.

1999			Perf. 12¼	
1862	A409	100fr brown	.30	.30
1863	A409	100fr violet	.30	.30
1864	A409	100fr pale red	.30	.30
1865	A409	150fr dark grn bl	.45	.45
1866	A409	150fr red brown	.45	.45
1867	A409	150fr violet blue	.45	.45
1868	A409	200fr orange	.60	.60
1869	A409	200fr bright grn bl	.60	.60
1870	A409	300fr olive	.90	.90
1871	A409	300fr blue	.90	.90
1872	A409	500fr brown	1.50	1.50
1873	A409	1000fr bright pink	3.00	3.00
		Nos. 1862-1873 (12)	9.75	9.75

1998 World Cup Soccer Championship, France — A410

Predominant colors of player's shirts. No. 1874: a, Yellow. b, White. c, Blue. d, Red.
No. 1875: a, White. b, Blue. c, Red. d, Green.
No. 1876: a, White, with black shorts. b, Yellow, with blue shorts. c, Yellow, with yellow shorts. d, White, with white shorts.
No. 1877: a, Red. b, Green. c, White. d, Red & white striped.
No. 1878: a, Blue. b, Yellow. c, Red. d, White.
No. 1879: a, Orange. b, White. c, Red. d, Multicolored diamonds.
No. 1880: a, White, with black shorts. b, White, with blue and red chest stripes. c, White, with green trim. d, White, with red and blue arm stripes.
No. 1881: a, Blue & white stripes. b, Red & white checks. c, Yellow & green, d, Blue.
2000fr, Player, map of France.

1998		Litho.	Perf. 13¼	
		Sheets of 4		
1874	A410	180fr #a.-d.	2.40	2.40
1875	A410	200fr #a.-d.	2.60	2.60
1876	A410	250fr #a.-d.	3.25	3.25
1877	A410	290fr #a.-d.	3.75	3.75
1878	A410	300fr #a.-d.	4.00	4.00
1879	A410	350fr #a.-d.	4.75	4.75
1880	A410	400fr #a.-d.	5.25	5.25
1881	A410	425fr #a.-d.	5.50	5.50
		Nos. 1874-1881 (8)	31.50	31.50
		Souvenir Sheet		
1882	A410	2000fr multicolored	6.50	6.50

Birds
A410a

Designs: 100fr, Luscinia svecica. 150fr, Oriolus oriolus. 200fr, Carduelis carduelis. 300fr, Parus caeruleus. 400fr, Fringilla coelebs. 500fr, Parus montanus.
1000fr, Regulus ignicapillus.

1999		Litho.	Perf. 12¾	
1882A-1882F	A410a	Set of 6	4.00	4.00
		Souvenir Sheet		
		Perf. 13x13¼		
1882G	A410a	1000fr multi	2.40	2.40

No. 1882G contains one 40x32mm stamp.

Antique Automobiles — A410b

Designs: 100fr, 1913 Peugeot Bebe. 150fr, 1950 Rolls-Royce. 200fr, 1921 Stutz Bearcat. 300fr, 1923 Ford Model T. 400fr, 1907 Packard. 500fr, 1950 Citroen II Legere sedan.
1000fr, 1929 Ford Model A Tudor sedan.

1999			Perf. 12¾	
1882H-1882M	A410b	Set of 6	4.00	4.00
		Souvenir Sheet		
		Perf. 13		
1882N	A410b	1000fr multi	2.40	2.40

No. 1882N contains one 40x32mm stamp.

Cats — A411

No. 1883: a, 100fr, Colorpoint. b, 150fr, British shorthair.
No. 1884: a, 200fr, Ocicat. b, 300fr, Ragdoll.
No. 1885: a, 400fr, Balinese. b, 500fr, California Spangled.
1000fr, Somali.

1999		Litho.	Perf. 12½	
1883	A411	Pair, #a.-b.	.75	.75
1884	A411	Pair, #a.-b.	1.50	1.50
1885	A411	Pair, #a.-b.	2.75	2.75
		Nos. 1883-1885 (3)	5.00	5.00
		Souvenir Sheet		
1886	A411	1000fr multicolored	3.00	3.00

Millennium
A412

No. 1886A, Invention of Paper by Chinese (with millennium emblem).
No. 1887 — Chinese Science & Technology: a, Lacquerware. b, Counting rods. c, Sericulture. d, Acupuncture. e, "Tuned chime bell." f, Piston bellows. g, Compass. h, Manufacture of steel. i. Crossbow. j, Spinning wheel. k, Water conservancy. l, Pulse taking. m, Multi-tube seed drill. n, Rotary winnowing fan. o, Like #1886A (no millennium emblem). p, Silk loom (60x40mm). q, Wheelbarrow.
No. 1888 — Highlights of the 11th Century: a, Chinese invent gunpowder. b, Islamic bronze griffin. c, Battle of Clontarf. d, William becomes Duke of Normandy. e, Norman knight. f, Spinning wheels in use in China. g, Yaroslav becomes Grand Prince of Kiev. h, Polyphonic singing introduced. i, Macbeth becomes King of Scotland. j, Edward the Confessor becomes King of England. k, Astrolabe. l, Harp introduced in Europe. m, Trier Cathedral. n, Mandingo Empire founded in Africa. o, Toltecs invade Yucatan. p, Vikings reach North Americam (60x40mm). q, Movable type used in China.
No. 1889 — Western Paintings of the 20th century by: a, Henri Matisse. b, Pablo Picasso. c, Marc Chagall. d, Wassily Kandinsky. e, Fernand Léger. f, Piet Mondrian. g, George Bellows. h, Georgia O'Keeffe. i, Salvador Dali. j, Francis Bacon. k, Edward Hopper. l, Andy Warhol. m, Helen Frankenthaler. n, Richard Anuszkiewicz. o, Audrey Flack. p, Jackson

Pollack, Lee Krasner (60x40mm). q, Jean-Michel Basquiat.

1999		Litho.	Perf. 13¼x13	
1886A	A412	120fr multi	.35	.35
		Sheets of 17		
		Perf. 12½		
1887	A412	120fr #a.-q. + label	6.75	6.75
1888	A412	130fr #a.-q. + label	7.00	7.00
1889	A412	140fr #a.-q. + label	7.75	7.75

Inscriptions on Nos. 1887b, 1887e, 1888i, and perhaps others, are incorrect or misspelled.
Issued: 130fr, 7/20.

US Civil War Photographs
A413

Various Civil War photographs making up a photomosaic of Abraham Lincoln, each 300fr.

1999, July 20		Litho.	Perf. 13½	
1890	A413	Sheet of 8, #a.-h.	7.50	7.50

See Nos. 1939-1940.

Free Trade Zone, 10th Anniv. — A414

Symbol and: 125fr, Map. 240fr, Clouds. 340fr, Wall.

1999		Litho.	Perf. 12¾	
1891	A414	125fr multi	.35	.35
1892	A414	240fr multi	.65	.65
1893	A414	340fr multi	.90	.90
		Nos. 1891-1893 (3)	1.90	1.90

Rural Development Council, 40th Anniv. — A414a

1999		Litho.	Perf. 13x13¼	
1893A	A414a	240fr red & multi		
1893B	A414a	380fr vio & multi		
1893C	A414a	390fr blk & multi		

Other stamps for this subject may exist. The editors would like to examine any examples. Numbers may change.

Goldfish
A415

Various depictions of Carassius auratus auratus: 100fr, 150fr, 200fr, 300fr, 400fr, 500fr.

1999				
1894-1899	A415	Set of 6	4.75	4.75
		Souvenir Sheet		
		Perf. 13		
1899A	A415	1000fr multi	3.00	3.00

No. 1899A contains one 40x31mm stamp.

SOS Children's Villages, 50th Anniv. — A416

1999		Litho.	Perf. 13¼x13	
1900	A416	125fr multi ('01)	.35	.35
1901	A416	240fr multi		
1902	A416	340fr multi		

Additional stamps may have been issued in this set. The editors would like to examine any examples.

Sailing Vessels — A417

Designs: 100fr, Phoenician boat. 150fr Roman cargo boat. 200fr, New Guinea fishing boat. 300fr, Caravel, vert. 400fr, 16th cent. English ship, vert. 500fr, 17th cent. English ship, vert.
1000fr, Steamship with sails.

1999		Litho.	Perf. 12½	
1905-1910	A417	Set of 6	4.50	4.50
		Souvenir Sheet		
		Perf. 12¼x12		
1911	A417	1000fr multi	2.75	2.75

No. 1911 contains one 42x30mm stamp.

Dogs — A417a

Designs: 100fr, St. Bernard. 150fr, Teckel. 200fr, German shepherd. 300fr, Italian hound. 400fr, Yorkshire terrier. 500fr, Schnauzer.

1999		Litho.	Perf. 12¾	
1911A-1911F	A417a	Set of 6	4.00	4.00
		Souvenir Sheet		
		Perf. 12½		
1911G	A417a	1000fr Afghan hound	2.40	2.40

No. 1911G contains one 40x31mm stamp.

Trains
A417b

Designs: 100fr, Baldwin 0-4-0. 150fr, Baldwin 2-6-2. 200fr, Baldwin gasoline locomotive. 300fr, H.K. Porter 0-4-0. 400fr, H.K. Porter 2-6-2. 500fr, Vulcan 0-4-0.

1999		Litho.	Perf. 12¾	
1911H-1911M	A417b	Set of 6	4.00	4.00
		Souvenir Sheet		
1911N	A417b	1000fr Jordanian locomotive	2.40	2.40

No. 1911N contains one 40x31mm stamp.

Orchids
A417c

Designs: 100fr, Gramangis ellisii. 150fr, Habenaria columbae. 200fr, Epidendrum atroporpureum. 300fr, Odontoglossum majale. 400fr, Oncidium splendidum. 500fr, Zygopetalum mackai.
1000fr, Paphiopedilum pairieanum.

1999, Nov. 8   Perf. 12x12¼
1911O-1911T A417c   Set of 6   5.25 5.25
Souvenir Sheet
Perf. 12½
1911U A417c 1000fr multi   3.25 3.25
No. 1911U contains one 31x39mm stamp.

New Year 2000
(Year of the
Dragon) — A418

Various views of dragon: 100fr, 150fr, 200fr, 300fr, 400fr, 500fr.
1000fr, Head of dragon, horiz.

2000   Perf. 12¾x12
1912-1917 A418 Set of 6   4.50 4.50
Souvenir Sheet
Perf. 13¼
1918 A418 1000fr multi   2.75 2.75
No. 1918 contains one 40x32mm stamp.

Wild
Cats
A419

Designs: 100fr, Panthera tigris. 150fr, Acinonyx jubatus. 200fr, Felis concolor. 300fr, Panthera leo, female. 400fr, Felis pardalis. 500fr, Panthera leo, male.
1000fr, Panthera tigris, diff.

2000   Perf. 13
1919-1924 A419 Set of 6   4.50 4.50
Souvenir Sheet
1925 A419 1000fr multi   2.75 2.75
No. 1925 contains one 40x32mm stamp.

Flowers — A420

No. 1926, 290fr: a, Cyrtanthus contractus. b, Sandersonia aurantiaca. c, Anomateca grandiflora. d, Helichrysum ecklonis. e, Striga elegans. f, Nymphaea odorata.
No. 1927, 290fr: a, Leomotis leonii. b, Strelitzia reginae. c, Freesia refracta. d, Garzania nivea. e, Dimophotheca sinuata. f, Pelargonium domesticum.
No. 1928, 290fr: a, Gloriosa rothchiliana. b, Clematis vitalba. c, Rochea falcato. d, Plumbago capensis. e, Thunbergia alata. f, Lampranthus coccineus.
No. 1929, 1500fr, Epiphyllum hybrid. No. 1930, 1500fr, Agapanthus africanus.
Illustration reduced.

2000, July 28   Litho.   Perf. 14
Sheets of 6, #a-f
1926-1928 A420 Set of 3   13.50 13.50
Souvenir Sheets
1929-1930 A420 Set of 2   7.75 7.75

Wildlife
A421

Designs: 200fr, Thompson's gazelle. 300fr, Felis margarita. 400fr, Blesbok. 500fr, Kob.
No. 1935, 290fr, vert.: a, Hoopoe. b, Harpactira spider. c, Marabou. d, Bee-eater. e, Oryx. f, Okapi. g, Wart hog. h, Baboon.
No. 1936, 290fr, vert.: a, Hornbill. b, Pygmy kingfisher. c, Vulture. d, Bataleur eagle. e, Kudu. f, Hyena. g, Gorilla. h, Lizard.
No. 1937, 1500fr, Eland, vert. No. 1938, 1500fr, Mongoose, vert.

2000, July 28
1931-1934 A421 Set of 4   3.75 3.75
Sheets of 8, #a-h
1935-1936 A421 Set of 2   12.00 12.00
Souvenir Sheets
1937-1938 A421 Set of 2   7.75 7.75

Mushrooms
A421a

Designs: 100fr, Hebeloma crustuliniforme. 150fr, Polyporellus squamosus, horiz. 200fr, Morchella deliciosa. 300fr, Disciotis venosa, horiz. 400fr, Cantharellus tubiformis. 500fr, Otidea onotica, horiz.
1000fr, Ixocomus granulatus, horiz.

2000, July 30   Litho.   Perf. 12¾
1938A-1938F A421a Set of 6   4.75 4.75
Souvenir Sheet
Perf. 13
1938G A421a 1000fr multi   2.75 2.75
No. 1938G contains one 39x31mm stamp.

Civil War Photographs Type of 1999

No. 1939, 290fr: Various photographs with a science theme making up a photomosaic of Albert Einstein.
No. 1940, 290fr: Various photographs with an Oriental theme making up a photomosaic of Mao Zedong.

2000, Sept. 5   Perf. 13¾
Sheets of 8, #a-h
1939-1940 A413 Set of 2   12.00 12.00

Queen Mother, 100th Birthday — A422

No. 1941: a, With Princesses Elizabeth and Margaret, 1931. b, With daughter, 1940. c, Black and white photo. d, In 1990.
1500fr, With Princess Margaret, 1939.
Illustration reduced.

2000, Sept. 5   Perf. 14
1941 A422   650fr Sheet of 4, #a-d, + label   6.75 6.75
Souvenir Sheet
Perf. 13¾
1942 A422 1500fr With Princess Margaret, 1939   4.00 4.00
No. 1942 contains one 38x51mm stamp.

Popes — A423

No. 1943, 400fr: a, Anastasius I, 399-401. b, Boniface I, 418-22. c, Gaius, 283-96. d, Hilarius, 461-68. e, Hyginus, 136-40. f, Innocent I, 402-17.
No. 1944, 400fr: a, Martin I, 649-55. b, Nicholas I, 858-67. c, Paschal I, 817-24. d, Paul I, 757-67. e, Pelagius, 556-61. f, Pelagius II, 579-90.
No. 1945, 400fr: a, Sergius, 687-701. b, Sergius II, 844-47. c, Severinus, 640. d, Sisinnius, 708. e, Stephen II, 752-57. f, Stephen IV, 816-17.
No. 1946, 1500fr, Pontian, 230-35. No. 1947, 1500fr, Pelagius II, diff. No. 1948, 1500fr, Stephen V, 885-91.
Illustration reduced.

2000, Sept. 5   Perf. 12x12¼
Sheets of 6, #a-f
1943-1945 A423 Set of 3   19.00 19.00
Souvenir Sheets
1946-1948 A423 Set of 3   11.50 11.50

British Monarchs — A424

No. 1949, 400fr: a, Charles II, 1660-85. b, Anne, 1702-14. c, George I, 1714-27. d, George IV, 1820-30. e, James II, 1685-88. f, George II, 1727-60.
No. 1950, 400fr: a, Elizabeth II, 1952-present. b, Edward VIII, 1936. c, George VI, 1936-52. d, George V, 1910-36. e, Edward VII, 1901-10. f, William IV, 1830-37.
No. 1951, 1500fr, William III and Mary, 1689-1702. No. 1952, 1500fr, Victoria, 1837-1901.
Illustration reduced.

2000, Sept. 5
Sheets of 6, #a-f
1949-1950 A424 Set of 2   12.50 12.50
Souvenir Sheets
1951-1952 A424 Set of 2   7.75 7.75

Millennium Type of 1999

Highlights of 1950-59: a, US sends troops to defend South Korea. b, Rock and roll hits the air waves. c, Death of Eva Peron. d, Structure of DNA revealed by Watson and Crick. e, Sir Edmund Hillary and Tenzing Norgay reach peak of Mt. Everest. f, John F. Kennedy marries Jacqueline Bouvier. g, Coronation of Queen Elizabeth II. h, Millionth Volkswagen produced. i, German soccer team wins World Cup. j, Roger Bannister runs 1st 4-minute mile. k, Dr. Jonas Salk develops polio vaccine. l, 1st McDonald's franchise. m, New phone lines cross Atlantic. n, Soviet Union launches Sputnik. o, Jack Kerouac writes "On the Road." p, China begins "Great Leap Forward." q, Communist revolution in Cuba. r, Computer chip patented.

2000   Perf. 12¾x12½
1953 A412   200fr Sheet of 18, #a-r, + label   9.25 9.25

36th Organization of African Unity
Summit, Lomé — A425

OAU emblem, map of Africa, doves and panel color of: 10fr, Bright yellow. 25fr, Green. 100fr, Dull yellow. 125fr, Blue violet. 250fr, Red violet. 375fr, Red. 400fr, Brown. 425fr, Orange.
No. 1954: a, Peace dove statue. b, Hotel du 2 Février. c, Congress building, Lomé. d, Alédjo Fault. e, Temberma hut. f, Cacao plantation.
No. 1955: a, Pres. Gnassingbé Eyadema, map of Europe and Africa, handshakes. b, Algerian Pres. Abdelaziz Boutefilka, Pres. Eyadema, and map of Africa. c, Pres. Eyadema and OAU emblem. d, Map of Africa, doves, OAU emblem.
Illustration reduced.

2000, Litho.   Perf. 14x13¾
1953S-1953Z A425 Set of 8   5.00 5.00
Sheets of 6 and 4
1954 A425 350fr #a-f   5.50 5.50
1955 A425 550fr #a-d   6.00 6.00

Trains — A426

No. 1956, 425fr: a, Richard Trevethick's engine. b, Stephenson's Adler. c, Crampton Continent. d, Atlantic Coastlines 4-4-2. e, Great Northern Railway Ivatt Atlantic. f, Great Western Railway City of Truro 4-4-0.
No. 1957, 425fr: a, Paris-Lyon-Mediterranean Railway, compound 4-8-2. b, Canadian Pacific Railway Royal Hudson 4-6-4. c, London-Midland Railway Duchess. d, New York Central Twentieth Century Limited. e, New Zealand Government Railway J class 4-8-4. f, British Railways Evening Star 5-10-0.

No. 1958, 1800fr, Eurostar. No. 1959, 1800fr, TGV Atlantique.
Illustration reduced.

2000, Sept. 8   Litho.   Perf. 14
Sheets of 6, #a-f
1956-1957 A426 Set of 2   14.50 14.50

Souvenir Sheets
1958-1959 A426 Set of 2   10.50 10.50

Ships — A427

No. 1960, 425fr: a, Norse knaar. b, Hanseatic cog. c, Iberian caravel. d, Henri Grace à Dieu. e, Ark Royal. f, Dutch Hooker.
No. 1961, 425fr: a, HMS Victory. b, HMS Warrior. c, Cutty Sark. d, USS Olympia. e, Empress of Canada. f, James Clark Ross.
No. 1962, 1800fr, Discovery. No. 1963, 1800fr, Sea Cat ferry.
Illustration reduced.

2000, Sept. 8   Litho.   Perf. 14
Sheets of 6, #a-f
1960-1961 A427 Set of 2   14.50 14.50

Souvenir Sheets
1962-1963 A427 Set of 2   10.50 10.50

Dogs and
Cats — A428

Designs: 275fr, Bloodhound. 300fr, Sphinx cat. 325fr, Basset hound. 350fr, Cocker spaniel. No. 1968, 375fr, American curl cat. 400fr, Scottish fold cat.
No. 1970, 375fr, horiz. — Dogs: a, Bearded collie. b, Chow chow. c, Boxer. d, Irish setter. e, Bracco Italiano. f, Pointer.
No. 1971, 375fr, horiz. — Cats: a, Devon Rex. b, Cornish Rex. c, Siamese. d, Balinese. e, Birman. f, Korat.
No. 1972, 1500fr, Yorkshire terrier. No. 1973, 1500fr, Chinchilla cat.

Perf. 13½x13¼, 13¼x13½
2001, Dec. 17   Litho.
1964-1969 A428 Set of 6   5.50 5.50

Sheets of 6, #a-f
1970-1971 A428 Set of 2   12.50 12.50

Souvenir Sheets
1972-1973 A428 Set of 2   8.25 8.25

Marine Life — A429

No. 1974, 200fr (31x31mm): a, Priacanthus arenatus. b, Diplodus annularis. c, Lithognathus mormgrus. d, Selene nomer. e, Perraeus duorarum. f, Arbacia lixula. g, Serranus scriba. h, Trachurus trachurus. i, Lepas amatifera. j, Octopus vulgaris. k, Scorpaena scrofa. l, Dardenus arroser.
No. 1975, 250fr (31x31mm): a, Porcupine fish. b, Blue shark. c, Sting ray. d, Physalia physalis. e, Turtles. f, Coryphaena hippurus. g, Carranx hippos. h, Sawfish. i, Todarupsis eblanae. j, Pompano. k, Diplodus cervinus. l, Barracuda.

No. 1976, 1500fr, Octopus vulgaris, diff. No. 1977, 1500fr, Blue shark, diff.

2001, Dec. 17   Perf. 12½
Sheets of 12, #a-l
1974-1975 A429 Set of 2   15.00 15.00

Souvenir Sheets
Perf. 13¼x13½
1976-1977 A429 Set of 2   8.25 8.25

African Wildlife A430

Designs: 150fr, Okapia johnstoni, vert. 200fr, Sagittarius serpentarius. 250fr, Lemur catta, vert. 300fr, Gorilla gorilla. 350fr, Genetta genetta, vert. 400fr, Fennecus zerda.
No. 1984, 380fr: a, Papio hamadryas. b, Felis serval. c, Suricata suricatta. d, Orycteropus afer. e, Connochataetes taurinus. f, Tragelaphus strepsiceros.
No. 1985, 380fr: a, Panthera pardus. b, Loxodonta africana. c, Cercopithecus hamlyni. d, Ephippiorhynchuus senegalensis. e, Hippopotamus amphibius. f, Hippotragus niger.
No. 1986, 415fr: a, Equus burchelli boehmi. b, Ceratotherium simum. c, Achionyx jubatus. d, Gazella dama. e, Crocuta crocuta. f, Lyacon pictus.
No. 1987, 1500fr, Crocodylus niloticus. No. 1988, 1500fr, Panthera leo, vert. No. 1989, 1500fr, Giraffa camelopardalis.

Perf. 13½x13¼, 13¼x13½
2001, Dec. 17
1978-1983 A430 Set of 6   4.50 4.50

Sheets of 6, #a-f
1984-1986 A430 Set of 3   19.00 19.00

Souvenir Sheets
1987-1989 A430 Set of 3   12.50 12.50

United We Stand A431

2002, Mar. 18   Litho.   Perf. 14
1990 A431 400fr multi   1.10 1.10

Bella Bellow Type of 1998-2002
2002   Litho.   Perf. 13½
1990A A403a 20fr yel green   — —
1990B A403a 30fr brown   — —
1990C A403a 110fr blue green   — —
    Numbers may change.

2004 Summer Olympics, Athens — A432

Designs: 150fr, Chariot rider and horses. 300fr, Pin from 1960 Rome Olympics, vert. 450fr, Emblem of 1960 Squaw Valley Winter Olympics, vert. 500fr, Diver, vert.

2004, Aug. 25   Litho.   Perf. 13¼
1991-1994 A432 Set of 4   5.25 5.25

Pres. Gnassingbé Eyadema (1935-2005)
A433

2004   Perf. 13½x13¼
Panel Color
1995 A433 25fr dark blue   .20 .20
1996 A433 50fr yel green   .20 .20
1997 A433 150fr olive green   .60 .60
1998 A433 400fr dull brown   1.60 1.60
1999 A433 550fr green   2.25 2.25
2000 A433 650fr brt blue   2.75 2.75
2001 A433 1000fr lilac   4.25 4.25
2002 A433 2000fr salmon pink   8.25 8.25
2003 A433 3000fr blue green   12.50 12.50
    Nos. 1995-2003 (9)   32.60 32.60

Pope John Paul II (1920-2005) A435

2006, Jan. 24   Litho.   Perf. 13½
2007 A435 550fr multi   2.00 2.00
    Printed in sheets of 4.

Jules Verne (1828-1905), Writer — A436

No. 2008:, a, Home of Verne from 1882-1900. b, Monument to Verne, Amiens, France. c, Sculpture of Verne, Amiens. d, Mysterious Island.

2006, Jan. 24   Litho.   Perf. 13½
2008 A436 550fr Sheet of 4, #a-d 8.25 8.25

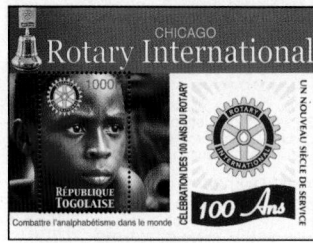

Rotary International, Cent. (in 2005) — A437

No. 2009 — Children and denomination in: a, Yellow in upper right. b, Red. c, Yellow in upper left.
1000fr, Child.

2006, Jan. 24
2009 A437 700fr Sheet of 3, #a-c   7.75 7.75

Souvenir Sheet
2010 A437 1000fr multi   3.75 3.75

Friedrich von Schiller (1759-1805), Writer — A438

No. 2011, vert. — Schiller: a, Monument. b, Bust. c, Portrait.
1000fr, Birthplace of Schiller.

2006, Jan. 24
2011 A438 700fr Sheet of 3, #a-c   7.75 7.75

Souvenir Sheet
2012 A438 1000fr multi   3.75 3.75

World Cup Soccer Championships, 75th Anniv. (in 2005) — A439

No. 2013: a, David Beckham. b, Ronaldo Nazario. c, Fernando Hierro.
1000fr, Eusebio.

2006, Jan. 24
2013 A439 700fr Sheet of 3, #a-c   7.75 7.75

Souvenir Sheet
2014 A439 1000fr multi   3.75 3.75

V-E Day, 50th Anniv. (in 2005) — A440

No. 2015, vert.: a, Monument to victory. b, New York Times front page with war reports. c, Soldiers at Battle of the Bulge, 1944. d, Airplanes. e, Sculpture of Holocaust victim.
1000fr, DUKW.

2006, Jan. 24   Litho.   Perf. 13¼
2015 A440 400fr Sheet of 5, #a-e   7.50 7.50

Souvenir Sheet
2016 A440 1000fr multi   3.75 3.75

V-J Day, 50th Anniv. (in 2005) — A441

No. 2017: a, USS Charles Carroll. b, BB-35. c, LCT-515. d, LST-388. e, Destroyer Thompson DD-627. f, USS Thomas Jefferson.
1000fr, Battle of Iwo Jima.

2006, Jan. 24
2017 A441　350fr Sheet of 6, #a-
　　　　　　f　　　　　　　7.75　7.75
Souvenir Sheet
2018 A441　1000fr multi　　　3.75　3.75

Railroads, Bicent. — A442

No. 2019: a, DX5287. b, W192. c, Central Pacific Jupiter. d, LWDHAM.
No. 2020, 1000fr, Rovos Ralf Class 25NC.
No. 2021, 1000fr, Class 242 streamlined tank locomotive.

2006, Jan. 24
2019 A442　550fr Sheet of 4, #a-
　　　　　　d　　　　　　　8.25　8.25
Souvenir Sheets
2020-2021 A442　Set of 2　7.50　7.50

Léopold Sédar Senghor Year — A443

2006, July 28
2022 A443　150fr multi　　　.60　.60
2023 A443　550fr multi　　　2.25　2.25
2024 A443　650fr multi　　　2.60　2.60
2025 A443　1000fr multi　　　4.00　4.00
2026 A443　2000fr multi,
　　　　　　horiz.　　　　　8.00　8.00
2027 A443　3000fr multi,
　　　　　　horiz.　　　　　12.00　12.00
2028 A443　5000fr multi,
　　　　　　horiz.　　　　　20.00　20.00
2029 A443　10,000fr multi,
　　　　　　horiz.　　　　　40.00　40.00
　　Nos. 2022-2029 (8)　89.45　89.45

Souvenir Sheet

Wolfgang Amadeus Mozart (1756-91), Composer — A444

2006, Dec. 21　　　　*Perf. 14*
2030 A444　1500fr multi　　6.00 6.00

Space Achievements — A445

Designs: 150fr, Luna 9. 300fr, Hayabusa probe. 450fr, Venus Express. 500fr, Space Shuttle Discovery, vert.
No. 2035: a, Intl. Space Station. b, Deep Impact probe. c, Muse Asteroid. d, Artist's view of L1 spacecraft. e, Odyssey. f, Calipso.
No. 2036: a, Viking 1 in oribit around Mars. b, Viking 1. c, Phobos. d, Viking Lander 1.
No. 2037, 1500fr, Mars Reconnaissance Orbiter. No. 2038, 1500fr, Apollo 11, vert.

2006, Dec. 21　　　　*Perf. 13¼*
2031-2034 A445　Set of 4　5.75　5.75
2035 A445　400fr Sheet of 6,
　　　　　　#a-f　　　　　9.50　9.50
2036 A445　550fr Sheet of 4,
　　　　　　#a-d　　　　　8.75　8.75
Souvenir Sheets
2037-2038 A445　Set of 2　12.00 12.00

Worldwide Fund for Nature (WWF) — A446

No. 2039 — Cyclanorbis senegalensis: a, On sand, facing left. b, With foliage, facing left. c, Head. d, With foliage, facing right.
Illustration reduced.

2006, Dec. 28
2039 A446　350fr Block or strip
　　　　　　of 4, #a-d　　5.75　5.75
　e.　Minature sheet, 2 each #a-d　11.50 11.50

Birds — A447

No. 2040: a, Platnea alba. b, Ceryle rudis. c, Ardea alba. d, Ephipphorhynchus senegalensis.
1500fr, Ephipphorhynchus senegalensis, diff.

2006, Dec. 28　　　　*Perf. 14*
2040 A447　450fr Sheet of 4, #a-
　　　　　　d　　　　　　7.25　7.25
Souvenir Sheet
2041 A447　1500fr multi　　6.00 6.00

Mushrooms — A448

No. 2042: a, Coprinus micaceus. b, Cookeina sulcipes. c, Hygrocybe firma. d, Chlorophyllum molybdites.
1500fr, Volvariella esculenta.

2006, Dec. 28
2042 A448　450fr Sheet of 4, #a-
　　　　　　d　　　　　　7.25　7.25
Souvenir Sheet
2043 A448　1500fr multi　　6.00 6.00

Butterflies — A449

No. 2044, horiz.: a, Papilio nobilis. b, Colotis celimene. c, Salamis anacardii. d, Eronia cleodora.
1500fr, Colotis regina.

2006, Dec. 28　　　　*Perf. 14*
2044 A449　450fr Sheet of 4, #a-
　　　　　　d　　　　　　7.25　7.25
Souvenir Sheet
2045 A449　1500fr multi　　6.00 6.00

Orchids — A450

No. 2046, vert.: a, Triphora trianthophora. b, Amerorchis rotundifolia. c, Cypripedium x andrewsii. d, Pogonia ophioglossoides.
1500fr, Platanthera x keenanii.

2006, Dec. 28　　　　*Perf. 14*
2046 A450　450fr Sheet of 4, #a-
　　　　　　d　　　　　　7.25　7.25
Souvenir Sheet
2047 A450　1500fr multi　　6.00 6.00

Rembrandt (1606-69), Painter — A451

Designs: 50fr, Three Oriental Figures (Jacob and Laban). 100fr, The Pancake Woman. 150fr, The Goldsmith. 250fr, The Golf Player. 325fr, The Persian. 350fr, Jacob and Rachel Listening to an Account of Joseph's Dreams.
1250fr, The Conspiracy of Julius Civilis, horiz.

2006　　　　　　*Perf. 14¼*
2048-2053 A451　Set of 6　5.00　5.00
Imperf
Size: 106x76mm
2054 A451　1250fr multi　　5.00　5.00

Souvenir Sheets

A452

Elvis Presley (1935-77) — A453

No. 2055 — Country name in: a, Pale blue. b, Pale yellow. c, Pink. d, Pale green.
No. 2056 — Country name in: a, Pale blue. b, Pale yellow. c, Pink. d, Pale green.

2006, Dec. 21　*Litho.*　*Perf. 14*
2055 A452　550fr Sheet of 4, #a-d　8.75　8.75
2056 A453　550fr Sheet of 4, #a-d　8.75　8.75

New Year 2007 (Year of the Pig) A454

2008, Jan. 21　*Litho.*　*Perf. 13½*
2057 A454　275fr multi　　1.25　1.25
　　　　　Printed in sheets of 4.

Pope Benedict
XVI — A455

2008, Jan. 21   *Perf. 12½x12¾*
2058 A455 300fr multi   1.40 1.40
Printed in sheets of 8.

Miniature Sheet

Inauguration of Pres. John F.
Kennedy, 47th Anniv. — A456

No. 2059: a, Band passing reviewing stand.
b, Kennedy taking oath of office. c, Capitol. d,
Kennedy giving inaugural address.

2008, Jan. 21   *Perf. 13¼*
2059 A456 450fr Sheet of 4, #a-d 8.00 8.00

Wedding of Queen Elizabeth II and
Prince Philip, 60th Anniv. — A457

No. 2060: a, Couple, white frame. b, Queen,
pink frame. c, Couple, light blue frame. d,
Queen, light blue frame. e, Couple, pink frame.
f, Queen, white frame.
   1250fr, Couple, diff., green frame.

2008, Jan. 21   *Perf. 12¾*
2060 A457 400fr Sheet of 6,
          #a-f   11.00 11.00
Souvenir Sheet
2061 A457 1250fr multi   5.75 5.75

Princess Diana (1961-97) — A458

No. 2062, vert.: a, Wearing double-stranded
pearl necklace, large photo. b, Wearing white
hat, cropped photo. c, Wearing black and
white houndstooth dress, large photo. d,

Wearing double-stranded pearl necklace,
cropped photo. e, Wearing white hat, large
photo. f, Wearing black and white houndstooth
dress, cropped photo.
   1500fr, Wearing black jacket.

2008, Jan. 21
2062 A458 400fr Sheet of 6,
          #a-f   11.00 11.00
Souvenir Sheet
2063 A458 1500fr multi   6.75 6.75

Campaign to
Prevent
AIDS — A459

Red AIDS ribbon and: 200fr, Colored
squares. 350fr, Hand, horiz. 650fr, Man and
woman carrying Togo flags, horiz.

2008, Feb. 8   *Perf. 11½*
2064-2066 A459   Set of 3   5.75 5.75
          Dated 2007.

SEMI-POSTAL STAMPS

Curie Issue
Common Design Type
1938   Unwmk.   Engr.   Perf. 13
B1 CD80 1.75fr + 50c brt ultra 16.00 16.00

French Revolution Issue
Common Design Type
**Photo., Name and Value Typo. in
Black**
1939
B2 CD83   45c + 25c green   8.00 8.00
B3 CD83   70c + 30c brown   8.00 8.00
B4 CD83   90c + 35c red org 8.00 8.00
B5 CD83   1.25fr + 1fr rose
                      pink   8.00 8.00
B6 CD83   2.25fr + 2fr blue 8.00 8.00
       Nos. B2-B6 (5)   40.00 40.00
French Revolution, 150th anniv. Surtax for
defense of the colonies.

Nos. 281, 236, 245,
289 Surcharged in Red
or Black
**SECOURS
+ 1 fr.
NATIONAL**

1941   *Perf. 14 x 13½, 12½*
B7 A10   50c + 1fr   1.50 1.50
B8 A7   80c + 2fr   4.50 4.50
B9 A8   1.50fr + 2fr   4.50 4.50
B10 A11   2fr + 3fr (R)   4.50 4.50
       Nos. B7-B10 (4)   15.00 15.00

**Catalogue values for unused
stamps in this section, from this
point to the end of the section, are
for Never Hinged items.**

Common Design Type and

Togolese
Militiaman
SP1

Military
Infirmary
SP2

1941   Photo.   Perf. 13½
B10A SP1   1fr + 1fr red   .75
B10B CD86   1.50fr + 3fr maroon .75
B10C SP2   2.50fr + 1fr blue   .75
       Nos. B10A-B10C (3)   2.25
Nos. B10A-B10C were issued by the Vichy
government in France, but were not placed on
sale in Togo.

Nos. 296-297
Surcharged in Black or Red

1944   Engr.   Perf. 12x12½
B10D 50c + 1.50fr on 2.50fr deep
        blue (R)   .55
B10E + 2.50fr on 1fr green   .55
Colonial Development Fund.
Nos. B10D-B10E were issued by the Vichy
government in France, but were not placed on
sale in Togo.

Tropical Medicine Issue
Common Design Type
1950   Engr.   Perf. 13
B11 CD100 10fr + 2fr indigo & dk
        bl   3.00 3.00
The surtax was for charitable work.

Republic

Patient on   Uprooted Oak
Stretcher — SP3   Emblem — SP4

Designs: 30fr+5fr, Feeding infant.
50fr+10fr, Blood transfusion.

1959   Engr.   Perf. 13
B12 SP3 20fr + 5fr multicolored   .75 .75
  a. Souvenir sheet of 4   5.00 5.00
B13 SP3 30fr + 5fr bl, car & brn .75 .75
  a. Souvenir sheet of 4   5.00 5.00
B14 SP3 50fr + 10fr emer, brn &
        car   .75 .75
  a. Souvenir sheet of 4   5.00 5.00
       Nos. B12-B14 (3)   2.25 2.25
Issued for the Red Cross.
Nos. B12a, B13a, B14a exist imperf.; same
values.

1960   Unwmk.   Perf. 13
#B16 similar to #B15, with emblem on top.
B15 SP4 25fr + 5fr dk bl, brn &
        yel grn   .45 .45
B16 SP4 45fr + 5fr dk bl, brn & ol .80 .80
World Refugee Year, July 1, 1959-June 30,
1960. The surtax was for aid to refugees.

AIR POST STAMPS

Common Design Type
1940 Unwmk. Engr. Perf. 12½x12
C1 CD85 1.90fr ultra   .25 .25
C2 CD85 2.90fr dark red   .45 .25
C3 CD85 4.50fr dk gray grn   .60 .40
C4 CD85 4.90fr yellow bister .60 .60
C5 CD85 6.90fr deep orange   1.00 1.00
       Nos. C1-C5 (5)   2.90 2.50

Common Design Type
Inscribed "Togo" across top
1942
C6 CD88 50c car & bl   .20
C7 CD88 1fr brn & blk   .25
C8 CD88 2fr grn & red brn   .30
C9 CD88 3fr dk bl & scar   .45
C10 CD88 5fr vio & brn red   .60

**Frame Engraved, Center
Typographed**
C11 CD89 10fr ultra, ind & org .75
C12 CD89 20fr rose car, mag &
        gray blk   .75

C13 CD89 50fr yel grn, dl grn & lt
          vio   1.25 2.25
       Nos. C6-C13 (8)   4.55
There is doubt whether Nos. C6-C12 were
officially placed in use.

**Catalogue values for unused
stamps in this section, from this
point to the end of the section, are
for Never Hinged items.**

Elephants — AP1

Plane — AP2

Plane — AP3

Post Runner and Plane — AP4

1947, Oct. 6   Engr.   Perf. 12½
C14 AP1 40fr blue   6.00 3.00
C15 AP2 50fr lt ultra, & red vio 3.50 1.25
C16 AP3 100fr emer & dk brn   5.00 1.75
C17 AP4 200fr lilac rose   8.50 3.00
       Nos. C14-C17 (4)   23.00 9.00

UPU Issue
Common Design Type
1949, July 4   Perf. 13
C18 CD99 25fr multi   6.00 6.00

Liberation Issue
Common Design Type
1954, June 6
C19 CD102 15fr indigo & pur   4.50 4.50

Freight
Highway — AP5

1954, Nov. 29
C20 AP5 500fr indigo & dk grn 42.50 37.50

Republic

Independence Allegory — AP6

Unwmk.

1957, Oct. 29   Engr.   Perf. 13
C21 AP6 25fr bl, olive bister & ver   .60 .30
    1st anniv. of Togo's autonomy.

Flag and Torch — AP7

Great White Egret — AP8

1957, Oct. 29
C22 AP7 50fr multi   .65   .35
C23 AP7 100fr multi   1.10   .60
C24 AP7 200fr multi   2.25 1.00
C25 AP8 500fr ind, lt bl & grn 18.00 6.75
    Nos. C22-C25 (4)   22.00 8.70

Types of 1957 inscribed:
"Republique du Togo" and

Flag, Plane and
Map — AP9

1959, Jan. 15   Engr.   Perf. 13
C26 AP9 25fr ultra, emer & vio
        brn   .35   .20
C27 AP7 50fr dk bl, dl grn &
        red   .55   .30
C28 AP7 100fr multi   1.20   .55
C29 AP7 200fr dk grn, red & ul-
        tra   3.00 1.10
C30 AP8 500fr blk brn, rose lil &
        grn   13.00 3.00
    Nos. C26-C30 (5)   18.10 5.15

Hotel Le
Benin
AP10

Eagle and Map of
Togo — AP11

Perf. 14½x15, 15x14½
1960, Apr. 27   Litho.   Unwmk.
C31 AP10 100fr crim, emer &
        yel   1.75   .25
C32 AP10 200fr multi   4.00   .40
C33 AP11 500fr grn & gldn brn 8.50 1.00
    Nos. C31-C33 (3)   14.25 1.65
    Proclamation of Togo's full independence,
Apr. 27, 1960.

Mail Service Type
100fr, Boeing 707 and stamps of 1960.

1963, Jan. 12   Photo.   Perf. 13
C34 A41 100fr multi   1.40   .30
   a. Souvenir sheet of 4   4.25 3.50
    No. C34a contains 4 stamps similar to Nos.
441-443 and C34, with simulated perforations.

Emancipation Type
1963, Oct.   Unwmk.   Perf. 13x14
C35 A45 100fr multi   1.25   .30
   a. Souv. sheet of 4, #454-456, C35,
      imperf.   2.40 2.10
    For overprint see No. C41.

Type of 1964 Regular Issue
50fr, Black-bellied seed-cracker. 100fr, Blue-billed mannikin. 200fr, Redheaded lovebird. 250fr, African gray parrot. 500fr, Yellow-breasted barbet.

1964-65   Photo.   Perf. 14
Size: 22½x31mm
Birds in Natural Colors
C36 A47 50fr yel grn   2.75   .25
C37 A47 100fr ocher   5.50   .25
C38 A47 200fr dl bl grn   10.50   .80
C39 A47 250fr dl rose ('65)   14.00 1.00
C40 A47 500fr violet   27.50 1.50
    Nos. C36-C40 (5)   60.25 3.85

    No. C35 Overprinted Diagonally: "En
Mémoire de / JOHN F. KENNEDY /
1917-1963"
1964, Feb.   Perf. 13x14
C41 A45 100fr multi   2.25   .30
    Issued in memory of John F. Kennedy.
Same overprint was applied to stamps of
No. C35a, with black border and commemorative inscription added. Two sheets exist: with
and without gray silhouetted head of Kennedy
covering all four stamps. Value: without silhouette, $17.50; with silhouette, $25.

Liberation Type
1964, May 25   Perf. 14x13
C42 A50 100fr dl bl grn & dk brn 1.50 .30

Olympic Games Type
1964, Oct.   Photo.   Perf. 14
C43 A52 100fr Tennis   1.90   .30
   a. Souv. sheet of 3, #493-494, C43,
      imperf.   3.25 2.50

Flag of Togo and Jet — AP12

1964, Dec. 5   Unwmk.   Perf. 14x13
C44 AP12 100fr multi   .80   .30
    Inauguration of the national airline "Air
Togo." For souvenir sheet see No. 499a.

Lincoln Type
1965, June   Photo.   Perf. 13½x14
C45 A58 100fr ol gray   1.90   .30
   a. Souv. sheet, #545, C45, imperf 2.75 2.00

Sports Type
100fr, Soccer player, flags of Togo and Congo.

1965, July   Unwmk.   Perf. 14x13
C46 A59 100fr multi   1.60   .30

Churchill Type
1965, Aug. 7   Photo.   Perf. 13½x14
C47 A60 85fr car rose   1.60   .30
   a. Souv. sheet, #532, C47, imperf 2.50 2.00

UN Type
100fr, Apple, grapes, wheat and "ONU."

1965, Dec. 15   Perf. 14x13½
C48 A65 100fr dk bl & bis   1.75   .40
   a. Souvenir sheet of 2   2.40 1.75
    No. C48a contains two imperf. stamps similar to Nos. 548 and C48 with simulated perforations.

Pope Type
Designs: 45fr, Pope speaking at UN rostrum, world map and UN emblem. 90fr, Pope, plane and UN emblem.

1966, Mar. 5   Litho.   Perf. 12
C49 A66 45fr emer & multi   .60   .20
C50 A66 90fr gray & multi   1.40   .20
   a. Souvenir sheet of 2, #C49-C50 3.00 1.75

Red Cross Type
Jean Henri Dunant and Togolese Flag.

1966, May 7   Litho.   Perf. 12
C51 A67 100fr multi   1.90   .30

WHO Type
Flowers: 50fr, Daisies and WHO Headquarters. 90fr, Talisman roses and WHO Headquarters.

1966, May   Litho.   Perf. 12
C52 A68 50fr lt bl & multi   .90   .20
C53 A68 90fr gray & multi   1.50   .20
   a. Souvenir sheet of 2, #C52-C53 3.00 2.00

Air Afrique Issue
Common Design Type
1966, Aug. 31   Photo.   Perf. 13
C54 CD123 30fr brt grn, blk & lem .65 .20

Arts and Crafts Type
60fr, Basket maker. 90fr, Wood carver.

1966, Sept.   Perf. 13x14
C55 A69 60fr ultra, org & blk .90   .20
C56 A69 90fr brt rose, yel & blk 1.50 .20

Dancer Type
50fr, Woman from North Togo holding branches. 60fr, Man from North Togo with horned helmet.

1966, Nov.   Photo.   Perf. 13x14
C57 A70 50fr multi   .80   .20
C58 A70 60fr olive & multi   1.00   .20

Soccer Type
Designs: Different Soccer Scenes.

1966, Dec. 14   Photo.   Perf. 14x13
C59 A71 50fr org, brn & pur   1.00   .20
C60 A71 60fr ultra, brn & org 1.10   .20
   a. Souv. sheet of 3, #582, C59-
      C60, imperf.   3.00 2.25

Fish Type
Designs: 45fr, Yellow jack and trawler. 90fr, Banded distichodus and seiner.

1967, Jan. 14   Photo.   Perf. 14
Fish in Natural Colors
C61 A72 45fr org & brn   .90   .20
C62 A72 90fr emer & dk bl   2.10   .30

UNICEF Type
UNICEF Emblem and: 45fr, Girl and miniature poodle. 90fr, African boy and greyhound.

1967, Feb. 11   Photo.   Perf. 14x13½
C63 A73 45fr yel, red brn & blk 1.00 .20
C64 A73 90fr ultra, dk grn & blk 1.50 .25
   a. Souvenir sheet of 2   3.00 1.75
    No. C64a contains 2 imperf., lithographed stamps with simulated perforations similar to Nos. C63-C64.

Satellite Type
50fr, Diamant rocket. 90fr, Fr-1 satellite.

1967, Mar. 18   Photo.   Perf. 13½x14
C65 A74 50fr multi, vert.   .90   .20
C66 A74 90fr multi, vert.   1.60   .25
   a. Souvenir sheet of 2   2.50 1.75
    No. C66a contains 2 imperf. stamps similar to Nos. C65-C66 with simulated perforations.

Musician Type
UNESCO Emblem and: 45fr, Johann Sebastian Bach and organ. 90fr, Ludwig van Beethoven, violin and oboe.

1967, Apr. 15   Photo.   Perf. 14x13½
C67 A75 45fr multi   .90   .20
C68 A75 90fr pink & multi   2.00   .20
   a. Souvenir sheet of 2   3.50 2.50
    No. C68a contains 2 imperf. stamps similar to Nos. C67-C68 with simulated perforations.

EXPO '67 Type
EXPO '67 Emblem and: 45fr, French pavilion, roses. 60fr, British pavilion, day lilies. 90fr, African village, bird-of-paradise flower. 105fr, US pavilion, daisies.

1967, May 30   Photo.   Perf. 14
C69 A76 45fr multi   .65   .20
C70 A76 60fr multi   1.00   .20
C71 A76 90fr yel & multi   1.25   .20
   a. Souv. sheet, #C69-C71, imperf 3.50 2.50
C72 A76 105fr multi   1.75   .30
    Nos. C69-C72 (4)   4.65   .95
    For overprints see Nos. C86-C89.

Mural by José Vela Zanetti — AP13

    The designs are from a mural in the lobby of the UN Conf. Building, NYC. The mural depicting mankind's struggle for a lasting peace is shown across 3 stamps twice in the set: on the 5fr, 15fr, 30fr and 45fr, 60fr, 90fr.

1967, July 15   Litho.   Perf. 14
C73 AP13 5fr multi   .35   .20
C74 AP13 15fr org & multi   .35   .20
C75 AP13 30fr multi   .40   .20
C76 AP13 45fr multi   .65   .20
C77 AP13 60fr car & multi   1.00   .20
C78 AP13 90fr ind & multi   1.50   .25
   a. Souvenir sheet of 3, #C76-C78 3.50 2.50
    Nos. C73-C78 (6)   4.25 1.25
    Issued to publicize general disarmament.

Animal Type
1967, Aug. 19   Photo.   Perf. 14x13½
C79 A78 45fr Lion   1.10   .20
C80 A78 60fr Elephant   1.60   .20

African Postal Union Issue, 1967
Common Design Type
1967, Sept. 9   Engr.   Perf. 13
C81 CD124 100fr bl, brt grn & ol
      brn   1.90   .30

Stamp Anniversary Type
Designs: 90fr, Stamp auction and Togo Nos. 16 and C42. 105fr, Father and son with stamp album and No. 474.

1967, Oct. 14   Photo.   Perf. 14x13
**Stamps on Stamps in Original
Colors**
C82 A79 90fr olive   1.25   .25
   a. Souvenir sheet of 3   3.00 2.50
C83 A79 105fr dk car rose   2.00   .40
    No. C82a contains 3 imperf. stamps similar to Nos. 621-622 and C82 with simulated perforations.

Pre-Olympics Type
View of Mexico City, Summer Olympics emblem and: 60fr, Runners. 90fr, Broad jump.

1967, Dec. 2   Perf. 13x14
C84 A80 60fr pink & multi   1.25   .35
C85 A80 90fr multi   1.20   .45
   a. Souv. sheet of 3, #627, C84-
      C85, imperf.   4.25 2.50

    Nos. C69-C72 Overprinted:
"JOURNÉE NATIONALE / DU TOGO /
29 SEPTEMBRE 1967"
1967, Dec.   Photo.   Perf. 14
C86 A76 45fr multi   .60   .20
C87 A76 60fr multi   .90   .20
C88 A76 90fr yel & multi   1.40   .25
C89 A76 105fr multi   1.50   .35
    Nos. C86-C89 (4)   4.40 1.00
    Issued for National Day, Sept. 29, 1967.

Hydrological Decade Type
1968, Apr. 6   Litho.   Perf. 14
C90 A84 60fr multi   1.00   .20

Ship Type

Designs: 45fr, Fulton's and modern steamships. 90fr, US atomic ship Savannah and atom symbol.

1968, Apr. 26   Photo.   *Perf. 14x14½*
C91 A85 45fr yel & multi   .80   .20
C92 A85 90fr bl & multi   1.60   .20
  a.   Souvenir sheet of 2   3.50 1.75

No. C92a contains 2 imperf. stamps similar to Nos. C91-C92 with simulated perforations.

WHO Type

Paintings: The Anatomy Lesson, by Rembrandt (detail). 90fr, Jesus Healing the Sick, by Raphael.

1968, June 22   Photo.   *Perf. 14*
C93 A87 60fr multi   1.10   .20
C94 A87 90fr pur & multi   1.60   .20
  a.   Souvenir sheet of 2   3.00 2.50

No. C94a contains 2 imperf. stamps with simulated perforations.

Olympic Games Type

1968, July 27   Photo.   *Perf. 14x13½*
C95 A87 60fr Wrestling   .95   .20
C96 A88 90fr Running   1.40   .20
  a.   Souvenir sheet of 2   2.50 2.00

No. C96a contains 2 imperf. stamps similar to Nos. C95-C96 with simulated perforations.

Boy Scout Type

60fr, First aid practice, horiz. 90fr, Scout game.

1968, Nov. 23   Litho.   *Perf. 14*
C97 A90 60fr ol & multi   1.00   .25
C98 A90 90fr org & multi   1.40   .35
  a.   Souvenir sheet of 2   3.00 1.75

No. C98a contains 2 imperf. stamps with simulated perforations similar to Nos. C97-C98.

PHILEXAFRIQUE Issue

The Letter, by Jean Auguste Franquelin AP14

1968, Nov. 9   Photo.   *Perf. 12½x12*
C99 AP14 100fr multi   2.75 1.75

PHILEXAFRIQUE Philatelic Exhibition in Abidjan, Feb. 14-23. Printed with alternating light ultramarine label.

Christmas Type

Paintings: 60fr, Adoration of the Magi, by Pieter Brueghel. 90fr, Adoration of the Magi, by Dürer.

1968, Dec. 28   Litho.   *Perf. 14*
C100 A91 60fr red & multi   1.25   .20
C101 A91 90fr multi   1.90   .30
  a.   Souvenir sheet   3.50 1.75

No. C101a contains 2 imperf. stamps similar to Nos. C100-C101 with simulated perforations.

Human Rights Type

Human Rights Flame and: 60fr, Robert F. Kennedy. 90fr, Martin Luther King, Jr.

1969, Feb. 1   Photo.   *Perf. 13½x14*
C102 A92 60fr brt rose lil & vio bl 1.00   .20
C103 A92 90fr emer & brn   1.25   .30
  a.   Souvenir sheet   2.50 1.75

No. C103a contains 2 imperf. stamps similar to Nos. C102-C103 with simulated perforations.
For overprints see Nos. C110-C111.

2nd PHILEXAFRIQUE Issue
Common Design Type

Design: 50fr, Togo #16 and Aledjo Fault.

1969, Feb. 14   Engr.   *Perf. 13*
C104 CD128 50fr red brn, grn &
                     car rose   2.00   .40

Sports Type

Stadium and: 60fr, Boxing. 90fr, Bicycling.

1969, Apr. 26   Photo.   *Perf. 14x13½*
C105 A93 60fr multi   .85   .20
C106 A93 90fr ultra, brt pink & dk
                     brn   1.50   .25
  a.   Souvenir sheet   2.50 1.75

No. C106a contains 2 imperf. stamps similar to Nos. C105-C106 with simulated perforations.

Lunar Type

Designs: 60fr, Astronaut exploring moon surface. 100fr, Astronaut gathering rocks.

1969, July 21   Litho.   *Perf. 14*
C107 A94 60fr dk bl & multi   .80   .20
C108 A94 100fr multi   1.40   .40
  a.   Souvenir sheet   12.00 6.00

No. C108a contains 4 imperf. stamps with simulated perforations similar to Nos. 676-677 and C107-C108, magenta margin. No. C108a also exists with colors of 30fr and 100fr stamps changed, and margin in orange. Value, unused $6, used $2.
For overprints see Nos. C120-C121.

Painting Type

Painting: 90fr, Pentecost, by El Greco.

1969, Aug. 16   Litho.   *Perf. 14*
C109 A95 90fr multi   2.40   .40
  a.   Souvenir sheet   2.75 1.50

No. C109a contains two imperf. stamps with simulated perforations similar to Nos. 682 and C109.

Nos. C102-C103 Overprinted Like Nos. 683-686

1969, Sept. 1   Photo.   *Perf. 13½x14*
C110 A92 60fr brt rose lil & vio bl 1.00   .20
C111 A92 90fr emer & brn   1.50   .20
  a.   Souv. sheet of 2   3.00 2.00

#C111a is #C103a with Eisenhower overprint.

Bank Type

Design: 100fr, Bank emblem and hand holding cattle and farmer.

1969, Sept. 10   Photo.   *Perf. 13x14*
C112 A96 100fr multi   1.25   .40

Red Cross Type

60fr, Wilhelm C. Roentgen & Red Cross workers with children in front of Togo Headquarters. 90fr, Henri Dunant & Red Cross workers meeting Biafra refugees at airport.

1969, Sept. 27   Litho.   *Perf. 14*
C113 A97 60fr brn & multi   1.10   .25
C114 A97 90fr ol & multi   1.60   .35
  a.   Souv. sheet of 2   2.75 2.00

No. C114a contains 2 imperf. stamps with simulated perforations similar to Nos. C113-C114.

Agricultural Center Type

Emblem of Young Pioneer and Agricultural Organization and: 90fr, Manioc harvest. 100fr, Instruction in gardening. 200fr, Corn harvest. 250fr, Marching drum corps. 500fr, Parade of Young Pioneers.

1969-70   Litho.   *Perf. 14*
C115 A98 90fr multi   1.25   .20
C116 A98 100fr org & multi   1.40   .25
C117 A98 200fr multi ('70)   3.00   .35
C118 A98 250fr ol & multi   3.50   .60
C119 A98 500fr multi ('70)   7.50   .75
      Nos. C115-C119 (5)   16.65 2.15

Christmas Issue
Nos. C107-C108, C108a Overprinted:
"JOYEUX NOEL"

1969, Dec.   Litho.   *Perf. 14*
C120 A94 60fr multi   3.50   .40
C121 A94 100fr multi   5.25   .60
  a.   Souvenir sheet of 4   55.00 55.00

Peace Leaders Type

60fr, Friedrich Ebert. 90fr, Mahatma Gandhi.

1969, Dec. 27   Litho.   *Perf. 14x13½*
C122 A100 60fr dk brn, dk red &
                      yel   1.00   .20
C123 A100 90fr dk brn, vio bl &
                      ocher   1.60   .30

For surcharges see Nos. 765, C143.

ILO Type

Paintings and ILO Emblem: 60fr, Spring Sowing, by Vincent van Gogh. 90fr, Workers, by Diego de Rivera.

1970, Jan. 24   Litho.   *Perf. 12½x13*
C124 A101 60fr gold & multi   1.40   .20
C125 A101 90fr gold & multi   2.50   .20
  a.   Souvenir sheet of 2   3.00 1.25

No. C125a contains two stamps similar to Nos. C124-C125, with simulated perforations.

Hair Styles Type

Various hair styles. 45fr, vert. 90fr, horiz.

1970, Feb. 21   Photo.   *Perf. 12½x13, 13x12½*
C126 A102 45fr car & multi   .80   .20
C127 A102 90fr multi   1.60   .30

Independence Type

Design: 60fr, Togo No. C33 and Independence Monument, Lomé.

1970, Apr. 27   Litho.   *Perf. 13x12½*
C128 A103 60fr yel & multi   .95   .20

UPU Type

1970, May 30   Photo.   *Perf. 14x13½*
C129 A104 50fr grnsh bl & dk car   .90   .20

Soccer Type

Various Scenes from Soccer, Rimet Cup and Flags of: 50fr, Sweden and Israel. 60fr, Bulgaria and Peru. 90fr, Belgium and Salvador.

1970, June 27   Litho.   *Perf. 13x14*
C130 A105 50fr multi   .80   .20
C131 A105 60fr lil & multi   1.10   .20
C132 A105 90fr multi   1.50   .30
  a.   Souvenir sheet   3.50 3.50
      Nos. C130-C132 (3)   3.40   .70

No. C132a contains 4 stamps similar to Nos. 734, C130-C132, but imperf. with simulated perforations.

Lenin Type

Design: 50fr, Lenin Meeting Peasant Delegation, by V. A. Serov, and UNESCO emblem.

1970, July 25   Litho.   *Perf. 12½*
C133 A106 50fr multi   2.00   .20

For overprint see No. C179.

EXPO '70 Type
Souvenir Sheet

150fr, Mitsubishi pavilion, EXPO '70 emblem.

1970, Aug. 8   Litho.   *Perf. 13*
C134 A107 150fr yel & multi   3.50 2.25
  a.   Inscribed "AERINNE"

No. C134 contains one stamp 86x33mm.

Astronaut Type

Design: 200fr, James A. Lovell, Fred W. Haise, Jr. and Tom Mattingly (replaced by John L. Swigert, Jr.) and Apollo 13 emblem.

1970, Sept. 26
C135 A108 200fr multi   2.50   .55
  a.   Souv. sheet of 3   3.50 2.50

Space flight of Apollo 13. No. C135a contains 3 stamps similar to Nos. 741, 744 and C135, with simulated perforations.
For overprint see No. C136.

Nos. C135, C135a Inscribed: "FELICITATIONS / BON RETOUR APOLLO XIII"

1970, Sept. 26
C136 A108 200fr multi   2.50   .55
  a.   Souvenir sheet of 3   3.50 2.50

Safe return of the crew of Apollo 13.

UN Type

Paintings and Emblems of UN Agencies: 60fr, The Mailman Roulin, by van Gogh, and UPU emblem. 90fr, The Birth of the Virgin, by Vittore Carpaccio, and WHO emblem.

1970, Oct. 24   Photo.   *Perf. 13x12½*
C137 A109 60fr grn, gold & blk   1.10   .20
C138 A109 90fr red org, gold &
                      brn   1.75   .30
  a.   Souvenir sheet of 4   3.50 2.50

No. C138a contains one each of Nos. 754-755 and C137-C138 with simulated perforations.

Moth Type

Moths: 60fr, Euchloron megaera. 90fr, Pseudacraea boisduvali.

1970, Nov. 21   Photo.   *Perf. 13x14*
C139 A110 60fr multi   5.25   .20
C140 A110 90fr multi   5.25   .20

Christmas Type

Paintings: 60fr, Adoration of the Shepherds, by Botticelli. 90fr, Adoration of the Kings, by Tiepolo.

1970, Dec. 26   Litho.   *Perf. 12½x13*
C141 A111 60fr gold & multi   1.50   .20
C142 A111 90fr gold & multi   2.25   .30
  a.   Souv. sheet of 2, #C141-C142 3.50 1.75

No. C122 Surcharged and Overprinted: "EN MEMOIRE / Charles De Gaulle / 1890-1970"

1971, Jan. 9   Photo.   *Perf. 14x13½*
C143 A100 200fr on 60fr   11.50   .60

De Gaulle Type

Designs: 60fr, De Gaulle and Pope Paul VI. 90fr, De Gaulle and satellite.

1971, Feb. 20   Photo.   *Perf. 13x14*
C144 A112 60fr blk & dp vio   2.20   .20
C145 A112 90fr blk & bl grn   3.00   .25
  a.   Souvenir sheet of 4   8.50 3.00

Nos. C143-C145 issued in memory of Charles De Gaulle (1890-1970), President of France. No. C145a contains 4 imperf. stamps similar to Nos. 769-770, C144-C145.

Easter Type

Paintings: 50fr, Resurrection, by Matthias Grunewald. 60fr, Resurrection, by Master of Trebon. 90fr, Resurrection, by El Greco.

1971, Apr. 10   Litho.   *Perf. 10½x11½*
C146 A113 50fr gold & multi   .85   .20
C147 A113 60fr gold & multi   1.25   .20
C148 A113 90fr gold & multi   1.60   .30
  a.   Souvenir sheet of 4, #773,
             C146-C148   4.50 2.50
      Nos. C146-C148 (3)   3.70   .70

Apollo 14 Type

Designs: 50fr, 200f, Apollo 14 badge 100fr, Take-off from moon, and spaceship.

1971, May   Litho.   *Perf. 12½*
C149 A114 50fr grn & multi   .50   .20
C150 A114 100fr multi   .90   .35
C151 A114 200fr gold & multi   2.00   .65
  a.   Souv. sheet of 4   4.50 4.50
      Nos. C149-C151 (3)   3.40 1.20

No. C151a contains 4 stamps similar to Nos. 777 and C149-C151 with simulated perforations.
For surcharge and overprints see Nos. C162-C164.

Cacao Type

60fr, Ministry of Agriculture. 90fr, Cacao tree and & pods. 100fr, Sorting & separating beans from pods.

1971, June 6   Litho.   *Perf. 14*
C152 A115 60fr multi   .75   .20
C153 A115 90fr multi   1.10   .30
C154 A115 100fr multi   1.40   .35
      Nos. C152-C154 (3)   3.25   .85

ASECNA Type

1971, June 26
C155 A116 60fr multi   1.60   .35

Tourist Type

Designs: 50fr, Château Viale and antelope. 60fr, Lake Togo and crocodile. 100fr, Old lime furnace, Tokpli, and hippopotamus.

1971, July 17
C156 A117 50fr multi   .75   .20
C157 A117 60fr multi   .90   .20
C158 A117 100fr multi   1.40   .35
      Nos. C156-C158 (3)   3.05   .75

For overprint see No. C172.

Religions Type

Designs: 50fr, Mohammedans praying in front of Lomé Mosque. 60fr, Protestant service. 90fr, Catholic bishop and priests.

1971, July 31   Litho.   *Perf. 14½*
C159 A118 50fr multi   .60   .20
C160 A118 60fr multi   .65   .20
C161 A118 90fr multi   1.10   .25
  a.   Souvenir sheet of 4, #787,
             C159-C161   4.25 2.50
      Nos. C159-C161 (3)   2.35   .65

Nos. C149-C151 Overprinted and Surcharged in Black or Silver: "EN MEMOIRE / DOBROVOLSKY — VOLKOV — PATSAYEV / SOYUZ 11"

C162	A114	90fr on 50fr multi	.95	.25
C163	A114	100fr multi (S)	1.00	.30
C164	A114	200fr multi	2.25	.50
a.		Souvenir sheet of 4, #788, C162-C164	5.50	5.50
		Nos. C162-C164 (3)	4.20	1.05

See note after No. 788.

Olympic Type

200fr, Sapporo '72 emblem and Ski jump.

1971, Oct. 30   Litho.   Perf. 14

C165	A119	200fr multi	2.25	.50
a.		Souvenir sheet of 4	4.25	3.50

No. C165 contains 4 stamps with simulated perforations similar to Nos. 791-793 and C165 printed on glazed paper.

African Postal Union Issue, 1971
Common Design Type

Design: 100fr, Adjogbo dancers and UAMPT Building, Brazzaville, Congo.

1971, Nov. 13   Photo.   Perf. 13x13½

C166	CD135	100fr bl & multi	1.25	.40

Intl. Organization for the Protection of Children (U.I.P.E.) — AP14a

Die Cut Perf. 10½

1971, Nov. 13   Embossed

C166A	AP14a	1500fr gold	20.00

UNICEF Type

Toys: 60fr, Turtle. 90fr, Parrot.

1971, Nov. 27   Litho.   Perf. 14

C167	A120	60fr lt bl & multi	.70	.20
C168	A120	90fr multi	1.10	.25
a.		Souvenir sheet of 4	2.75	2.50

No. C168a contains 4 stamps with simulated perforations similar to Nos. 796-797 and C167-C168.
For overprints see Nos. C263-C264.

Christmas Type

Virgin and Child by: 60fr, Giorgione. 100fr, Raphael.

1971, Dec. 24   Perf. 14x13

C169	A121	60fr olive & multi	1.00	.25
C170	A121	100fr multi	1.75	.40
a.		Souvenir sheet of 4	5.25	2.25

No. C170a contains 4 stamps with simulated perforations similar to Nos. 800-801, C169-C170.

Venice Type

Design: 100fr, Ca' d'Oro, Venice.

1972, Feb. 26   Litho.   Perf. 14

C171	A122	100fr multi	2.00	.40
a.		Souvenir sheet of 3	5.25	2.50

No. C171a contains 3 stamps similar to Nos. 802-803, C171 with simulated perforations.

No. C156 Overprinted "VISITE DU PRESIDENT / NIXON EN CHINE / FEVRIER 1972"

1972, Mar.   Litho.   Perf. 14

C172	A117	50fr multi	.80	.20

Visit of Pres. Richard M. Nixon to the People's Republic of China, Feb. 20-27.

Easter Type

Paintings: 50fr, Resurrection, by Thomas de Coloswa. 100fr, Ascension by Andrea Mantegna.

1972, Mar. 31

C173	A123	90fr gold & multi	1.90	.20
C174	A123	100fr gold & multi	2.75	.25
a.		Souvenir sheet of 4	3.50	1.90

No. C174a contains 4 stamps similar to Nos. 806-807, C173-C174 with simulated perforations.

Heart Type

100fr, Heart, WHO emblem and smith.

1972, Apr. 4

C175	A124	100fr multi	1.40	.40
a.		Souvenir sheet of 2	3.00	1.25

No. C175a contains 2 stamps similar to Nos. 810 and C175 with simulated perforations.

Telecommunications Type

Design: 100fr, Intelsat 4 over Africa.

1972, June 24   Perf. 14

C176	A125	100fr multi	1.60	.30

For overprint see No. C229.

Cassava Type

60fr, Truck and cassava processing factory, horiz. 80fr, Children, mother holding tapioca cake.

1972, June 30

C177	A126	60fr multi	1.10	.25
C178	A126	80fr multi	1.25	.25

No. C133 Surcharged in Deep Carmine: "VISITE DU PRESIDENT / NIXON EN RUSSIE / MAI 1972"

1972, July 15   Litho.   Perf. 12½

C179	A106	300fr on 50fr multi	4.75	1.40

President Nixon's visit to the USSR, May 1972. Old denomination obliterated with 6x5mm rectangle.

Olympic Type

1972, Aug. 26   Perf. 14

C180	A127	90fr Gymnastics	1.00	.35
a.		Souv. sheet of 2	3.50	1.75
C181	A127	200fr Basketball	2.40	.65

No. C180a contains 2 stamps with simulated perforations similar to Nos. 816 and C180.
For overprints see Nos. C234-C235.

Bird Type

Bird: 90fr, Rose-ringed parakeet.

1972, Sept. 9

C182	A128	90fr multi	2.50	.35
a.		Souvenir sheet of 4	12.00	2.25

No. C182a contains 4 stamps similar to Nos. 818-820, C182 with simulated perforations.

Rotary Type

Rotary Emblem and: 60fr, Map of Togo, olive branch. 90fr, Flags of Togo and Rotary Club. 100fr, Paul P. Harris.

1972, Oct. 7   Litho.   Perf. 14

C183	A129	60fr brn & multi	.55	.20
C184	A129	90fr multi	.80	.35
C185	A129	100fr multi	1.00	.40
		Nos. C183-C185 (3)	2.35	.95

For overprints see Nos. C212-C213, C244-C245.

Painting Type, 1972

Designs: 60fr, Mystical Marriage of St. Catherine, by Assistant to the P. M. Master. 80fr, Self-portrait, by Leonardo da Vinci. 100fr, Sts. Mary and Agnes by Botticelli.

1972, Oct. 21

C186	A130	60fr gold & multi	1.75	.20
C187	A130	80fr gold & multi	2.00	.25
C188	A130	100fr gold & multi	3.75	.40
a.		Souvenir sheet of 4	4.50	2.00
		Nos. C186-C188 (3)	7.50	.85

No. C188a contains 4 stamps with simulated perforations similar to Nos. 824, C186-188.

Presidential Visit Type

Design: 100fr, Pres. Pompidou and Col. Etienne Eyadema, front view of party headquarters.

1972, Nov. 23   Litho.   Perf. 14

C189	A131	100fr multi	2.40	.40

Johann Wolfgang von Goethe (1749-1832), German Poet and Dramatist
AP15

1972, Dec. 2   Photo.   Perf. 13x14

C190	AP15	100fr grn & multi	1.60	.40

Christmas Type

Paintings: 60fr, Nativity, by Master Vyshchibrod. 80fr, Adoration of the Kings, anonymous. 100fr, Flight into Egypt, by Giotto.

1972, Dec. 23   Litho.   Perf. 14

C191	A132	60fr gold & multi	1.10	.20
C192	A132	80fr gold & multi	1.40	.30
C193	A132	100fr gold & multi	1.90	.40
a.		Souvenir sheet of 4	4.50	2.50
		Nos. C191-C193 (3)	4.40	.90

No. C193a contains 4 stamps with simulated perforations similar to Nos. 829, C191-C193.

Leprosy Day Type

Design: 100fr, Dr. Armauer G. Hansen, apparatus, microscope and Petri dish.

1973, Jan. 23   Photo.   Perf. 14x13½

C194	A133	100fr rose car & bl	3.00	.40

World Leprosy Day and centenary of the discovery of the Hansen bacillus, the cause of leprosy.

Miniature Sheets

1972 Summer Olympics, Munich — AP15a

Medalists, each 1500fr.: #C194A, Mark Spitz, US, swimming. #C194B, L. Linsenhoff, West Germany, equestrian. #C194C, D. Morelon, France, cycling.

Litho. & Embossed

1973, Jan.   Perf. 13½

C194A-C194C	AP15a	Set of 3	375.00

Exist imperf.

Miniature Sheet

Apollo 17 Moon Landing — APb15

1973, Jan.

C194D	AP15b	1500fr gold & multi	55.00

Exists imperf.

Easter Type

1973, Apr. 21   Litho.   Perf. 14

C195	A135	90fr Christ in Glory	1.40	.40
a.		Souvenir sheet of 2	2.75	1.75

No. C195a contains one each of Nos. 835 and C195 with simulated perforations.

Apollo 17 Type

Designs: 100fr, Astronauts on moon and orange rock. 200fr, Rocket lift-off at Cape Kennedy and John F. Kennedy.

1973, June 2   Litho.   Perf. 14

C196	A136	100fr multi	1.40	.40
C197	A136	200fr multi	3.00	.60
a.		Souvenir sheet of 2	4.25	3.00

No. C197a contains 2 stamps similar to Nos. C196-C197 with simulated perforations.

Boy Scout Type

100fr, Canoeing, horiz. 200fr, Campfire, horiz.

1973, June 30   Litho.   Perf. 14

C198	A137	100fr bl & multi	1.40	.40
C199	A137	200fr bl & multi	3.25	.65
a.		Souvenir sheet of 2	4.00	2.25

No. C199a contains 2 stamps similar to Nos. C198-C199 with simulated perforations.
For overprints see Nos. C265-C266.

Copernicus Type

Designs: 90fr, Heliocentric system. 100fr, Nicolaus Copernicus.

1973, July 18

C200	A138	90fr multi	1.75	.30
C201	A138	100fr bis & multi	2.10	.40
a.		Souv. sheet of 2, #C200-C201	3.50	1.75

Red Cross Type

Design: 100fr, Dove carrying Red Cross letter, sun, map of Togo.

1973, Aug. 4

C202	A139	100fr multi	3.25	.35

For overprint see No. C294.

Literacy Type

Design: 90fr, Woman teacher in classroom.

1973, Aug. 18   Litho.   Perf. 14

C203	A140	90fr multi	1.50	.35

WMO Type

1973, Oct. 4   Photo.   Perf. 14x13

C204	A142	200fr dl bl, pur & brn	2.00	.40

Type 1967

Early & contemporary planes, #758, C36.

1973, Oct. 20   Photo.   Perf. 14x13

C205	A79	100fr multi	2.25	.30
a.		Souvenir sheet of 2	2.75	1.50

75th anniversary of Togolese postal service. No. C205a contains 2 stamps similar to Nos. 855 and C205 with simulated perforations.

Kennedy Type

Designs: 90fr, Kennedy and Charles De Gaulle. 100fr, Kennedy and Nikita Krushchev. 200fr, Kennedy and model of Apollo spacecraft.

1973, Nov. 22   Litho.   Perf. 14

C206	A143	90fr blk & pink	1.25	.35
C207	A143	100fr blk, lt bl & bl	1.40	.45
C208	A143	200fr blk, buff & brn	3.00	.60
a.		Souvenir sheet of 2	4.00	2.00
		Nos. C206-C208 (3)	5.65	1.40

No. C208a contains 2 stamps similar to Nos. C207-208 with simulated perforations.

Human Rights
Flame and
People — AP16

1973, Dec. 8   Photo.   Perf. 13x14
C209 AP16 250fr lt bl & multi   2.40   .80
25th anniversary of the Universal Declaration of Human Rights.

Christmas Type

Paintings: 90fr, Virgin and Child. 100fr, Adoration of the Kings. Both after 15th century Italian paintings.

1973, Dec. 22   Litho.   Perf. 14
C210 A144 90fr gold & multi   1.10   .25
C211 A144 100fr gold & multi   1.40   .35
  a.   Souvenir sheet of 2   2.75   1.50
No. C211a contains 2 stamps with simulated perforations similar to Nos. C210-C211.

Nos. C183 and C185 Overprinted: "PREMIERE CONVENTION / 210eme DISTRICT / FEVRIER 1974 / LOME"

1974, Feb. 21   Litho.   Perf. 14
C212 A129 60fr brn & multi   .65   .20
C213 A129 100fr multi   1.00   .35
First convention of Rotary International, District 210, Lomé, Feb. 22-24.

Soccer Type

Various soccer scenes and games' cup.

1974, Mar. 2   Litho.   Perf. 14
C214 A145 90fr multi   .85   .35
C215 A145 100fr multi   1.00   .40
C216 A145 200fr multi   1.90   .55
  a.   Souvenir sheet of 2   4.00   2.50
  Nos. C214-C216 (3)   3.75   1.50
No. C216a contains 2 stamps with simulated perforations similar to Nos. C215-C216.

Picasso Type

Paintings: 90fr, The Muse. 100fr, Les Demoiselles d'Avignon. 200fr, Sitting Nude.

1974, Apr. 6   Litho.   Perf. 14
C217 A146 90fr brn & multi   1.25   .30
C218 A146 100fr pur & multi   1.50   .35
C219 A146 200fr multi   3.00   .65
  a.   Souvenir sheet of 3   5.50   3.00
  Nos. C217-C219 (3)   5.75   1.30
No. C219a contains 3 stamps with simulated perforations similar to Nos. C217-C219.

Coastal Views Type

Designs: 90fr, Fishermen on Lake Togo. 100fr, Mouth of Anecho River.

1974, Apr. 20
C220 A147 90fr multi   1.10   .25
C221 A147 100fr multi   1.25   .35
  a.   Souvenir sheet of 2   2.50   1.25
No. C221a contains 2 stamps similar to Nos. C220-C221 with simulated perforations.

UPU Type

Designs: Old mailmen's uniforms.

1974, May 10   Litho.   Perf. 14
C222 A148 50fr multi   .70   .20
C223 A148 100fr multi   1.25   .35
  a.   Souvenir sheet of 2   40.00   17.00
No. C223a contains 2 stamps similar to Nos. C222-C223, rouletted.

Fishing Type

Designs: 90fr, Fishermen bringing in net with catch. 100fr, Fishing with rod and line. 200fr, Fishing with basket, vert.

1974, June 22   Litho.   Perf. 14
C224 A149 90fr multi   1.00   .25
C225 A149 100fr multi   1.10   .25
C226 A149 200fr multi   2.40   .65
  a.   Souvenir sheet of 3   5.25   2.50
  Nos. C224-C226 (3)   4.50   1.15
No. C226a contains 3 stamps with simulated perforations similar to Nos. C224-C226.

Jupiter Probe Type

Designs: 100fr, Rocket take-off, vert. 200fr, Satellite in space.

1974, July 6   Perf. 14
C227 A150 100fr multi   .90   .35
C228 A150 200fr multi   2.00   .65
  a.   Souvenir sheet of 2   5.50   4.00
No. C228a contains 2 stamps similar to Nos. C227-C228 with simulated perforations; imperf. or rouletted.

No. C176
Overprinted in Black

1974, July   Perf. 14
C229 A125 100fr multi   3.50   1.20
INTERNABA 1974 Intl. Philatelic Exhibition, Basel, June 7-16.
No. C229 exists overprinted in silver. Value, unused $11.

Seashell Type

1974, July 13   Litho.   Perf. 14
C230 A151 90fr Alcithoe ponsonbyi   1.60   .25
C231 A151 100fr Casmaria iredalei   2.00   .35
  a.   Souvenir sheet of 2   4.00   1.25
No. C231a contains 2 stamps similar to Nos. C230-C231 with simulated perforations.

Horse Racing Type

90fr, Steeplechase. 100fr, Galloping horses.

1974, Aug. 3   Litho.   Perf. 14
C232 A152 90fr multi   1.90   .25
C233 A152 100fr multi   2.25   .35
  a.   Souvenir sheet of 2   6.00   2.00
No. C233a contains one each of Nos. C232-C233 with simulated perforations.

Nos. C180, C180a and C181 Overprinted: "COUPE DU MONDE / DE FOOTBALL / VAINQUEURS / REPUBLIQUE FEDERALE / d'ALLEMAGNE"

1974, Aug. 19
C234 A127 90fr multi   .75   .25
  a.   Souvenir sheet of 2   18.00   —
C235 A127 200fr multi   1.50   .65
World Cup Soccer Championship, Munich, 1974, victory of German Federal Republic. For description of No. C234a see note after No. C181.

Animal Type

1974, Sept. 7   Litho.   Perf. 14
C236 A153 90fr Lions   1.90   .30
C237 A153 100fr Rhinoceroses   2.00   .35
  a.   Souvenir sheet of 3   3.50   1.75
Wild animals of West Africa. No. C237a contains 3 stamps similar to Nos. 889, C236-C237 with simulated perforations.

1974, Oct. 14
C238 A153 90fr Herd at waterhole   1.10   .25
C239 A153 100fr Village and cows   1.25   .35
  a.   Souvenir sheet of 2   2.50   1.25
Domestic animals. No. C239a contains 2 stamps with simulated perforations similar to Nos. C238-C239.

Churchill Type

Designs: 100fr, Churchill and frigate. 200fr, Churchill and fighter planes.

1974, Nov. 1   Photo.   Perf. 13x13½
C240 A154 100fr multi   1.10   .30
C241 A154 200fr org & multi   2.40   .60
  a.   Souvenir sheet of 2   4.00   1.90
No. C241a contains 2 stamps with simulated perforations similar to Nos. C240-C241; perf. or imperf.

Flower Type

Flowers of Togo: 100fr, Clerodendrum thosonae. 200fr, Gloriosa superba.

1975, Feb. 15   Litho.   Perf. 14
C242 A155 100fr multi   1.50   .25
C243 A155 200fr multi   3.00   .50
  a.   Souvenir sheet of 2   7.50   2.50
No. C243a contains one each of Nos. C242-C243, perf. 13x14 or imperf.

Nos. C184-C185 Overprinted: "70e ANNIVERSAIRE / 23 FÉVRIER 1975"

1975, Feb. 23   Litho.   Perf. 14
C244 A129 90fr multi   .90   .25
C245 A129 100fr multi   1.00   .35
Rotary International, 70th anniversary.

Easter Type

Paintings: 100fr, Christ Rising from the Tomb, by Master MS. 200fr, Holy Trinity (detail), by Dürer.

1975, Apr. 19   Litho.   Perf. 14
C246 A157 100fr multi   1.00   .25
C247 A157 200fr multi   2.00   .55
  a.   Souvenir sheet of 2   3.50   2.00
No. C247a contains 2 stamps similar to Nos. C246-C247 with simulated perforations.

Independence Type

50fr, National Day parade, flag and map of Togo. 60fr, Warriors' dance and flag of Togo.

1975, Apr. 26   Litho.   Perf. 14
C248 A158 50fr multi, vert.   .50   .20
C249 A158 60fr multi   .70   .20
  a.   Souvenir sheet of 2   1.50   .75
No. C249a contains 2 stamps similar to Nos. C248-C249 with simulated perforations.

Hunt Type

Designs: 90fr, Running deer. 100fr, Wild boar hunter with shotgun.

1975, May 24   Photo.   Perf. 13x13½
C250 A159 90fr multi   1.60   .25
C251 A159 100fr multi   1.90   .25

Palm Oil Type

Designs: 85fr, Selling palm oil in market, vert. 100fr, Oil processing plant, Alokoegbe.

1975, June 28   Litho.   Perf. 14
C252 A160 85fr multi   .80   .25
C253 A160 100fr multi   .95   .25

Apollo-Soyuz Type and

Soyuz Spacecraft
AP17

Designs: 60fr, Donald K. Slayton, Vance D. Brand and Thomas P. Stafford. 90fr, Aleksei A. Leonov and Valery N. Kubasov. 100fr, Apollo-Soyuz link-up, American and Russian flags. 200fr, Apollo-Soyuz emblem and globe.

1975, July 15
C254 AP17 50fr yel & multi   .50   .20
C255 A161 60fr lil & multi   .70   .20
C256 A161 90fr bl & multi   .85   .25
C257 A161 100fr grn & multi   1.25   .40
C258 A161 200fr yel & multi   2.10   .45
  a.   Souv. sheet of 4, #C255-C258   6.00   3.50
  Nos. C254-C258 (5)   5.40   1.50
See note after No. 913.

Schweitzer Type

Dr. Schweitzer: 80fr, playing organ, vert. 90fr, with pelican, vert. 100fr, and Lambarene Hospital.

1975, Aug. 23   Litho.   Perf. 14x13½
C259 A163 80fr multi   1.00   .25
C260 A163 90fr multi   1.10   .30
C261 A163 100fr multi   1.25   .35
  Nos. C259-C261 (3)   3.35   .90

Letter Writing Type

80fr, Erasmus Writing Letter, by Hans Holbein.

1975, Oct. 9   Litho.   Perf. 14
C262 A164 80fr multi   1.00   .25

Nos. C167-C168a Overprinted: "30ème Anniversaire / des Nations-Unies"

1975, Oct. 24   Litho.   Perf. 14
C263 A120 60fr multi   .60   .20
C264 A120 90fr multi   .75   .25
  a.   Souvenir sheet of 4   3.00   1.90
UN, 30th anniv. #C264a contains Nos. 796 (with overprint), 918, C263-C264.

Nos. C198-C199 Overprinted: "14ème JAMBORÉE / MONDIAL / DES ÉCLAIREURS"

1975, Nov. 7
C265 A137 100fr multi   .55   .25
C266 A137 200fr multi   1.10   .50
  a.   Souvenir sheet of 2   3.25   2.00
14th World Boy Scout Jamboree, Lillehammer, Norway, July 29-Aug. 7. No. C266a contains one each of Nos. C265-C266 with simulated perforations.

Christmas Type

Paintings of the Virgin and Child: 90fr, Nativity, by Federico Barocci. 100fr, Bellini. 200fr, Correggio.

1975, Dec. 20   Litho.   Perf. 14
C267 A165 90fr bl & multi   .80   .25
C268 A165 100fr red & multi   .90   .25
C269 A165 200fr bl & multi   1.75   .50
  a.   Souv. sheet of 2, #C268-C269   3.50   2.00
  Nos. C267-C269 (3)   3.45   1.00

Bicentennial Type

Paintings (and Bicentennial Emblem): 60fr, Surrender of Gen. Burgoyne, by John Trumbull. 70fr, Surrender at Trenton, by Trumbull, vert. 100fr, Signing of Declaration of Independence, by Trumbull. 200fr, Washington Crossing the Delaware, by Emanuel Leutze.

1976, Mar. 3   Litho.   Perf. 14
C270 A167 60fr multi   .65   .20
C271 A167 70fr multi   .75   .20
C272 A167 100fr multi   1.00   .25
C273 A167 200fr multi   2.00   .55
  a.   Souv. sheet of 2, #C272-C273   4.00   2.00
  Nos. C270-C273 (4)   4.40   1.20
No. C273a also exists imperf. Value $22.50. For overprints see Nos. C280-C283.

Common Market Type

Designs: 60fr, ACP and CEE emblems. 70fr, Map of Africa, Europe and Asia.

1976, Apr. 24   Photo.   Perf. 13x14
C274 A168 60fr lt bl & multi   .45   .20
C275 A168 70fr yel & multi   .55   .20

Telephone Type

Designs: 70fr, Thomas A. Edison, old and new communications equipment. 105fr, Alexander Graham Bell, old and new telephones.

1976, Mar. 10   Photo.   Perf. 13x14
C276 A169 70fr multi   .55   .20
C277 A169 105fr multi   .75   .40
  a.   Souv. sheet of 2, #C276-C277   1.75   1.10
No. C277a exists imperf. Value $10.00.

Eye Examination
AP18

Pylon, Flags of
Ghana, Togo,
Dahomey
AP19

1976, Apr. 8   Perf. 14x13
C278 AP18 60fr dk red & multi   .60   .20
World Health Day: "Foresight prevents blindness."

1976, May 8   Litho.   Perf. 14
C279 AP19 60fr multi   .55   .20
Ghana-Togo-Dahomey electric power grid, 1st anniv. See No. 932.

Nos. C270-C273, C273a, Overprinted:
"INTERPHIL / MAI 29-JUIN 6, 1976"

1976, May 29

C280	A167	60fr multi	.50	.20
C281	A167	70fr multi	.55	.20
C282	A167	100fr multi	.80	.25
C283	A167	200fr multi	1.60	.55
a.		Souvenir sheet of 2	3.00	3.00
		Nos. C280-C283 (4)	3.45	1.20

Interphil 76 Intl. Philatelic Exhibition, Philadelphia, Pa., May 29-June 6. Overprint on No.
C281 in 3 lines; overprint on No. C283a
applied to each stamp.

Olympic Games Type

Montreal Olympic Emblem and: 70fr,
Yachting. 105fr, Motorcycling. 200fr, Fencing.

1976, June 15   Photo.   Perf. 14x13

C284	A172	70fr multi	.60	.25
C285	A172	105fr multi	.85	.40
C286	A172	200fr multi	1.60	.65
a.		Souvenir sheet of 2, #C285-C286, perf. 14	3.00	2.25
		Nos. C284-C286 (3)	3.05	1.30

For overprints see Nos. C298-C299.

Viking Type

60fr, Viking landing on Mars. 70fr, Nodus
Gordii (view on Mars). 105fr, Lander over
Mare Tyrrhenum. 200fr, Landing on Mars.

1976, July 15   Litho.   Perf. 14

C287	A173	60fr bis & multi	.50	.20
C288	A173	70fr multi	.60	.20
C289	A173	105fr bl & multi	.80	.35
C290	A173	200fr multi	1.60	.55
a.		Souv. sheet of 2, #C289-C290, perf. 14x13½	3.00	2.00
		Nos. C287-C290 (4)	3.50	1.30

Toulouse-Lautrec Type, 1976

Paintings: 60fr, Carmen, portrait. 70fr, Maurice at the Somme. 200fr, "Messalina."

1976, Aug. 7   Litho.   Perf. 14

C291	A174	60fr blk & multi	.80	.20
C292	A174	70fr blk & multi	.90	.25
C293	A174	200fr blk & multi	2.50	.55
a.		Souv. sheet of 2, #C292-C293, perf. 13½x14	4.50	2.00
		Nos. C291-C293 (3)	4.20	1.00

No. C202 Overprinted: "Journeé /
Internationale / de l'Enfance"

1976, Nov. 27   Litho.   Perf. 14

C294	A139	100fr multi	.55	.35

International Children's Day.

Christmas Type

Paintings: 70fr, Holy Family, by Lorenzo
Lotto. 105fr, Virgin and Child with Saints, by
Jacopo da Pontormo. 200fr, Virgin and Child
with Saints, by Lotto.

1976, Dec. 18

C295	A175	70fr multi	.60	.20
C296	A175	105fr multi	.90	.35
C297	A175	200fr multi	1.75	.55
a.		Souv. sheet of 2, #C296-C297	3.50	2.00
		Nos. C295-C297 (3)	3.25	1.10

No. C284 Overprinted: "CHAMPIONS
OLYMPIQUES / YACHTING —
FLYING DUTCHMAN / REPUBLIQUE
FEDERALE ALLEMAGNE"
No. C286 Overprinted: "CHAMPIONS
OLYMPIQUES / ESCRIME FLEURET
PAR EQUIPES / REPUBLIQUE
FEDERALE ALLEMAGNE"

1976, Dec.   Photo.   Perf. 14x13

C298	A172	70fr multi	.60	.20
C299	A172	200fr multi	1.60	.60
a.		Souvenir sheet of 2	3.25	2.25

Olympic winners. No. C299a (on No.
C286a) contains Nos. C285 and C299.

Eyadema Anniversary Type

60fr, National Assembly Building. 100fr,
Pres. Eyadema greeting people at Aug. 30th
meeting.

1977, Jan. 13   Photo.   Perf. 13x14

C300	A177	60fr multi	.55	.20
C301	A177	100fr multi	.85	.30
a.		Souv. sheet of 2, #C300-C301	1.75	1.10

Musical Instrument Type

Musical Instruments: 60fr, Atopani. 80fr,
African violin, vert. 105fr, African flutes, vert.

1977, Feb. 7   Litho.   Perf. 14

C302	A178	60fr multi	.80	.20
C303	A178	80fr multi	.90	.20
C304	A178	105fr multi	1.25	.25
a.		Souv. sheet of 2, #C303-C304	2.50	1.40
		Nos. C302-C304 (3)	2.95	.65

Victor Hugo Type

Victor Hugo in exile on Guernsey Island.

1977, Feb. 26   Perf. 13x14

C305	A179	60fr multi	.80	.20
a.		Souvenir sheet of 2, #952, C305	1.25	.75

For overprint see No. C316.

Beethoven Type

Designs: 100fr, Beethoven's piano and
1818 portrait. 200fr, Beethoven on his death-
bed and Holy Trinity Church, Vienna.

1977, Mar. 7   Perf. 14

C306	A180	100fr multi	1.10	.35
C307	A180	200fr multi	2.10	3.00
a.		Souv. sheet of 2, #C306-C307	3.00	1.60

Automobile Type

Early Automobiles: 60fr, Cannstatt-Daimler,
1899, Germany. 70fr, Sunbeam, 1904,
England. 100fr, Renault, 1908, France. 200fr,
Rolls Royce, 1909, England.

1977, Apr. 11   Litho.   Perf. 14

C308	A181	60fr multi	.70	.20
C309	A181	70fr multi	.80	.20
C310	A181	100fr multi	1.10	.30
C311	A181	200fr multi	2.25	.65
a.		Souv. sheet of 2, #C310-C311	4.50	1.75
		Nos. C308-C311 (4)	4.85	1.35

Lindbergh Type

Designs: 60fr, Lindbergh and son Jon, birds
in flight. 85fr, Lindbergh home in Kent,
England. 90fr, Spirit of St. Louis over Atlantic
Ocean. 100fr, Concorde over NYC.

1977, May 9

C312	A182	60fr multi	.60	.20
C313	A182	85fr multi	.85	.20
C314	A182	90fr multi	.90	.20
C315	A182	100fr multi	1.00	.25
a.		Souv. sheet of 2, #C314-C315	2.25	1.25
		Nos. C312-C315 (4)	3.35	.85

No. C305 Overprinted: "10ème
ANNIVERSAIRE DU / CONSEIL
INTERNATIONAL / DE LA LANGUE
FRANCAISE"

1977, May 17   Litho.   Perf. 14

C316	A179	60fr multi	.70	.20

10th anniv. of the French Language Council.

Wildlife Type

60fr, Colobus monkeys. 90fr, Chimpanzee,
vert. 100fr, Leopard. 200fr, West African
manatee.

1977, June 13

C317	A183	60fr multi	.70	.20
C318	A183	90fr multi	1.00	.20
C319	A183	100fr multi	1.10	.20
C320	A183	200fr multi	2.40	.35
a.		Souv. sheet of 2, #C319-C320	4.40	1.75
		Nos. C317-C320 (4)	5.20	.95

Agriculture Type

Designs: 60fr, Corn silo. 100fr, Hoeing and
planting by hand. 200fr, Tractor on field.

1977, July 11   Litho.   Perf. 14

C321	A184	60fr multi	.45	.20
C322	A184	100fr multi	.75	.20
C323	A184	200fr multi	1.60	.40
a.		Souv. sheet of 2, #C322-C323, perf. 13x14	3.00	1.50
		Nos. C321-C323 (3)	2.80	.80

Rubens Type

Paintings: 60fr, Heads of Black Men, 1620.
100fr, Anne of Austria, 1624.

1977, Aug. 8

C324	A185	60fr multi	.70	.20
C325	A185	100fr multi	1.10	.20
a.		Souv. sheet of 2, #C324-C325, perf. 14x13	2.10	1.25

Orbiter Type

90fr, Retrieval of unmanned satellite in
space. 100fr, Satellite's return to space after
repairs. 200fr, Manned landing of Orbiter.

1977, Oct. 4   Litho.   Perf. 14

C326	A186	90fr multi, vert.	.75	.20
C327	A186	100fr multi	.80	.20
C328	A186	200fr multi	1.75	.35
a.		Souv. sheet of 2, #C327-C328	3.00	1.50
		Nos. C326-C328 (3)	3.30	.75

Lafayette Type

60fr, Lafayette landing in New York, 1824.
105fr, Lafayette and Washington at Valley
Forge.

1977, Nov. 7   Perf. 13x14

C329	A187	60fr multi	.50	.20
C330	A187	105fr multi	.85	.20
a.		Souv. sheet of 2, #C329-C330	1.75	1.00

Christmas Type

Virgin & Child by: 90fr, 200fr, Carlo Crivelli,
diff. 100fr, Bellini.

1977, Dec. 19   Perf. 14

C331	A189	90fr multi	.75	.20
C332	A189	100fr multi	.80	.20
C333	A189	200fr multi	1.75	.35
a.		Souv. sheet of 2, #C332-C333	3.25	1.50
		Nos. C331-C333 (3)	3.30	.75

Jenner Type

Designs: 50fr, Edward Jenner. 60fr, Smallpox vaccination clinic, horiz.

1978, Jan. 9   Perf. 14x13, 13x14

C334	A190	50fr multi	.35	.20
C335	A190	60fr multi	.40	.20
a.		Souvenir sheet of 2	1.40	.65

No. C335a contains 2 stamps with simulated perforations similar to Nos. C334-C335.

Wright Brothers Type

Designs: 60fr, Orville Wright's 7½-minute
flight. 70fr, Orville Wright injured in first aircraft
accident, 1908. 200fr, Wrights' bicycle shop,
Dearborn, Mich. 300fr, First flight, 1903.

1978, Feb. 6   Litho.   Perf. 14

C336	A191	60fr multi	.60	.20
C337	A191	70fr multi	.65	.20
C338	A191	200fr multi	2.00	.35
C339	A191	300fr multi	3.00	.60
a.		Souvenir sheet of 2	9.25	5.25
		Nos. C336-C339 (4)	6.25	1.35

No. C339a contains one each of Nos. C338-
C339 with simulated perforations.

Port of Lomé Type, 1978

Anchor and: 60fr, Industrial harbor. 100fr,
Merchant marine harbor. 200fr, Bird's-eye
view of entire harbor.

1978, Apr. 26   Photo.   Perf. 13

C340	A199	60fr multi	.45	.20
C341	A199	100fr multi	.75	.20
C342	A199	200fr multi	1.60	.40
a.		Souv. sheet of 2, #C341-C342	3.00	1.50
		Nos. C340-C342 (3)	2.80	.80

Space Type

Designs: 90fr, Module camera, horiz. 100fr,
Module antenna. 200fr, Pioneer, US, in orbit.

1978, May 8   Litho.   Perf. 14

C343	A200	90fr multi	.70	.20
C344	A200	100fr multi	.75	.20
C345	A200	200fr multi	1.50	.35
a.		Souv. sheet of 2, #C344-C345, perf. 13½x14	2.50	1.50
		Nos. C343-C345 (3)	2.95	.75

Soccer Type

Various soccer scenes & Argentina '78
emblem.

1978, June 5   Perf. 14

C346	A201	60fr multi	.45	.20
C347	A201	80fr multi	.60	.20
C348	A201	200fr multi	1.50	.35
C349	A201	300fr multi	2.25	.50
a.		Souv. sheet of 2, #C348-C349, perf. 13½x14	3.75	2.25
		Nos. C346-C349 (4)	4.80	1.25

Bicycle Type

History of Bicycle: 60fr, Bantam, 1896, vert.
85fr, Fold-up bicycle for military use, 1897.
90fr, Draisienne, 1816, vert. 100fr, Penny-far-
thing, 1884, vert.

Perf. 14x13, 13x14

1978, July 10   Photo.

C350	A202	60fr multi	.55	.20
C351	A202	85fr multi	.75	.20
C352	A202	90fr multi	.80	.25
C353	A202	100fr multi	.85	.25
a.		Souv. sheet of 2, #C352-C353	2.00	1.10
		Nos. C350-C353 (4)	2.95	.90

Phonograph Type

60fr, Edison's original phonograph, horiz.
80fr, Emile Berliner's phonograph, 1888.
200fr, Berliner's improved phonograph, 1894,
horiz. 300fr, His Master's Voice phonograph,
1900, horiz.

Perf. 13x14, 14x13

1978, July 8   Photo.

C354	A203	60fr multi	.45	.20
C355	A203	80fr multi	.60	.20
C356	A203	200fr multi	1.40	.35
C357	A203	300fr multi	2.20	.50
a.		Souv. sheet of 2, #C356-C357	3.50	2.00
		Nos. C354-C357 (4)	4.65	1.25

Red Cross Type

Design: 60fr, Red Cross and other pavilions
at Paris Exhibition, 1867.

1978, Sept. 4   Photo.   Perf. 14x13

C358	A204	60fr pur & red	.45	.20
a.		Souv. sheet, #1009, C358	1.10	.55

Paintings Type

60fr, Langlois Bridge, by Vincent van Gogh.
70fr, Witches' Sabbath, by Francisco Goya.
90fr, Jesus among the Doctors, by Albrecht
Dürer. 200fr, View of Arco, by Dürer.

1978, Nov. 6   Litho.   Perf. 14

C359	A205	60fr multi	.55	.20
C360	A205	70fr multi	.60	.25
C361	A205	90fr multi	.80	.35
C362	A205	200fr multi	1.60	.65
a.		Souv. sheet of 2, #C361-C362	3.00	1.25
		Nos. C359-C362 (4)	3.55	1.45

Birth and death anniversaries of famous
painters.

Philexafrique II — Essen Issue
Common Design Types

#C363, Warthog and Togo No. C36. #C364,
Firecrest and Thurn and Taxis No. 1.

1978, Nov. 1   Litho.   Perf. 13x12½

C363	CD138	100fr multi	2.50	2.00
C364	CD139	100fr multi	2.50	2.00
a.		Pair, #C363-C364 + label	5.00	5.00

Congress of Paris Type

60fr, Mail ship "Slieve Roe" 1877, post horn.
105fr, Congress of Paris medal. 200fr, Locomotive, 1870. All horizontal.

1978, Nov. 27   Photo.   Perf. 14x13

C365	A206	60fr multi	.45	.20
C366	A206	105fr multi	.80	.35
C367	A206	200fr multi	1.60	.65
a.		Souv. sheet of 2, #C366-C367	2.50	1.25
		Nos. C365-C367 (3)	2.85	1.20

Christmas Type

Paintings (Virgin and Child): 90fr, 200fr, by
Carlo Crivelli, diff. 100fr, by Cosimo Tura.

1978, Dec. 18

C368	A207	90fr multi	.70	.30
C369	A207	100fr multi	.85	.35
C370	A207	200fr multi	1.60	.65
a.		Souv. sheet of 2, #C369-C370	3.00	1.25
		Nos. C368-C370 (3)	3.15	1.30

Capt. Cook Type

Designs: 60fr, "Freelove," Whitby Harbor,
horiz. 70fr, Trip to Antarctica, 1773, horiz.
90fr, Capt. Cook. 200fr, Sails of Endeavour.

1979, Feb. 12   Litho.   Perf. 14

C371	A208	60fr multi	.50	.20
C372	A208	70fr multi	.55	.25
C373	A208	90fr multi	.75	.30
C374	A208	200fr multi	1.75	.65
a.		Souv. sheet of 2, #C373-C374	3.00	1.75
		Nos. C371-C374 (4)	3.55	2.00

Easter Type

60fr, Resurrection. 100fr, Ascension. 200fr,
Jesus appearing to Mary Magdalene.

1979, Apr. 9

C375	A209	60fr multi	.40	.20
C376	A209	100fr multi	.65	.35
C377	A209	200fr multi	1.40	.65
a.		Souv. sheet of 2, #C376-C377	2.50	1.25
		Nos. C375-C377 (3)	2.45	1.20

UPU Emblem, Drummer — AP20

Design: 100fr, UPU emblem, hands passing
letter, satellites.

1979, June 8   Engr.   *Perf. 13*
C378 AP20 60fr multi   1.40 .50
C379 AP20 100fr multi   1.20 1.00

Philexafrique II, Libreville, Gabon, June 8-17.

Einstein Type
Designs: 60fr, Sights and actuality diagram. 85fr, Einstein playing violin, vert. 100fr, Atom symbol and formula of relativity, vert. 200fr, Einstein portrait, vert.

Perf. 14x13, 13x14
1979, July 2   Photo.
C380 A210 60fr multi   .40 .20
C381 A210 85fr multi   .60 .30
C382 A210 100fr multi   .65 .35
C383 A210 200fr multi   1.40 .65
  a.   Souv. sheet of 2, #C382-C383 2.50 1.25
      Nos. C380-C383 (4)   3.05 1.50

Tree Type
Design: 60fr, Man watering tree.

1979, Aug. 13   *Perf. 14x13*
C384 A212 60fr blk & brn   .40 .20

Rowland Hill Type
Designs: 90fr, Bellman, England, 1820. 100fr, "Centercycles" used for parcel delivery, 1883, horiz. 200fr, French P.O. railroad car, 1848, horiz.

1979, Aug. 27   Photo.
C385 A213 90fr multi   .65 .30
C386 A213 100fr multi   .70 .35
C387 A213 200fr multi   1.50 .65
  a.   Souv. sheet of 2, #C386-C387 2.50 1.25
      Nos. C385-C387 (3)   2.85 1.30

Train Type
Historic Locomotives: 60fr, "Le General," 1862. 85fr, Stephenson's, 1843. 100fr, "De Witt Clinton," 1831. 200fr, Joy's "Jenny Lind," 1847.

1979, Oct. 1   Litho.   *Perf. 14*
C388 A214 60fr multi   .55 .20
C389 A214 85fr multi   .80 .30
C390 A214 100fr multi   .90 .35
C391 A214 200fr multi   1.00 .65
  a.   Souv. sheet of 2, #C390-C391 4.25 2.25
      Nos. C388-C391 (4)   3.25 1.50

Olympic Type
1980 Olympic Emblems and: 90fr, Ski jump. No. C393, Doubles canoeing, Olympic flame. No. C394, Rings. No. C395a, Bobsledding, horiz. No. C395b, Gymnast, horiz.

1979, Oct. 18   Litho.   *Perf. 13½*
C392 A215 90fr multi   .65 .30
C393 A215 100fr multi   .70 .35
C394 A215 200fr multi   1.60 .65
      Nos. C392-C394 (3)   2.95 1.30

Souvenir Sheet
C395   Sheet of 2   2.50 1.25
  a.   A215 100fr multi   .65 .35
  b.   A215 200fr multi   1.40 .65

Religion Type
Designs: 60fr, Moslems praying. 70fr, Protestant ministers.

1979, Oct. 29   *Perf. 13x14*
C396 A216 60fr multi   .45 .20
C397 A216 70fr multi   .50 .25
  a.   Souv. sheet of 2, #C396-C397 1.40 .55

Apollo 11 Type
60fr, Astronaut leaving Apollo 11. 70fr, US flag. 200fr, Sun shield. 300fr, Lunar take-off.

1979, Nov. 5
C398 A217 60fr multi   .45 .20
C399 A217 70fr multi   .50 .25
C400 A217 200fr multi   1.50 .65
C401 A217 300fr multi   2.10 1.00
  a.   Souv. sheet of 2, #C400-C401 4.00 1.75
      Nos. C398-C401 (4)   4.55 2.10

Telecom Type
Design: 60fr, Telecom 79, dish antenna.

1979, Nov. 26   Photo.   *Perf. 14x13*
C402 A218 60fr multi   .70 .20

Miniature Sheets

President Eyadema, 10th Anniv. of the People's Republic — AP21

Illustration reduced.

Litho. & Embossed
1979, Nov. 30   *Perf. 13½*
C402A AP21 1000fr In uniform 6.00 —

Imperf.
C402B AP21 1000fr In suit, vert. 6.00 —
      Exist imperf.

Christmas Type
90fr, Adoration of the Kings. 100fr, Presentation of Infant Jesus. 200fr, Flight into Egypt.

1979, Dec. 17   Litho.   *Perf. 14*
C403 A219 90fr multi   .75 .30
C404 A219 100fr multi   .80 .35
C405 A219 200fr multi   1.50 .65
  a.   Souv. sheet of 2, #C404-C405 3.00 1.25
      Nos. C403-C405 (3)   3.05 1.30

Rotary Type
3-H Emblem and: 90fr, Man reaching for sun. 100fr, Fish, grain. 200fr, Family, globe.

1980, Jan. 14
C406 A220 90fr multi   .60 .30
C407 A220 100fr multi   .65 .35
C408 A220 200fr multi   1.25 .65
  a.   Souv. sheet of 2, #C407-C408 2.50 1.25
      Nos. C406-C408 (3)   2.50 1.30

Rotary Intl., 75th anniv.; 3-H program (health, hunger, humanity).

Winter Olympic Type, 1980
1980, Jan. 31   Litho.   *Perf. 13½*
C409 A221 60fr Downhill skiing .45 .20
C410 A221 100fr Speed skating   .75 .35
C411 A221 200fr Cross-country
                  skiing   1.40 .65
      Nos. C409-C411 (3)   2.60 1.20

Souvenir Sheet
C412   Sheet of 2   2.50 1.25
  a.   A221 100fr Ski jump, horiz. .65 .35
  b.   A221 200fr Hockey, horiz.   1.25 .65

Olympic Type
1980, Feb. 29   Litho.   *Perf. 13½*
C413 A222 100fr Fencing   .90 .45
C414 A222 200fr Pole vault   1.60 .80
C415 A222 300fr Hurdles   2.50 1.25
  a.   Souv. sheet of 3, #C414-C415 4.75 2.50
      Nos. C413-C415 (3)   5.00 2.50

Easter Type
Easter 1980 (Paintings by): 60fr, Lorenzo Lotto. 100fr, El Greco. 200fr, Carlo Crivelli.

1980, Mar. 31   *Perf. 14*
C416 A223 60fr multi   .50 .20
C417 A223 100fr multi   .70 .35
C418 A223 200fr multi   1.50 .65
  a.   Souv. sheet of 3, #C417-C418 2.50 1.25
      Nos. C416-C418 (3)   2.70 1.20

ASECNA Type
1980, Mar. 24   Litho.   *Perf. 12½*
C419 A224 60fr multi   .60 .20

Telecommunications Type
1980, May 17   Photo.   *Perf. 13½x14*
C420 A225 60fr "17 MAI", vert. .60 .20

Red Cross Type
1980, June 16   Photo.   *Perf. 14x13*
C421 A226 60fr Nurses, patient .60 .20

Jules Verne Type
Designs: 60fr, Rocket (From Earth to Moon). 80fr, Around the World in 80 Days. 100fr, Rocket and moon (From Earth to Moon). 200fr, Octopus (20,000 Leagues Under the Sea).

1980, July 14   Litho.   *Perf. 14*
C422 A227 60fr multi   .50 .20
C423 A227 80fr multi   .65 .25
C424 A227 100fr multi   .80 .35

C425 A227 200fr multi   1.50 .65
  a.   Souv. sheet of 2, #C424-C425,
       perf. 13½x14   2.50 1.25
      Nos. C422-C425 (4)   3.45 1.45

Ingres Type
Ingres Paintings: 90fr, Jupiter and Thetis. 100fr, Countess d'Hassonville. 200fr, "Tu Marcellus Eris."

1980, Aug. 29   Litho.   *Perf. 14*
C426 A228 90fr multi   .80 .30
C427 A228 100fr multi   .85 .35
C428 A228 200fr multi   1.60 .65
  a.   Souv. sheet of 2, #C427-C428 3.00 1.25
      Nos. C426-C428 (3)   3.25 1.30

Famous Men Type
90fr, Salvador Allende, vert. 100fr, Pope Paul VI, vert. 200fr, Jomo Kenyatta, vert.

1980, Feb. 11   Litho.   *Perf. 14x13*
C429 A231 90fr ultra & lt bl grn 1.00 .30
C430 A231 100fr pur & pink   1.10 .35
C431 A231 200fr brn & yel bis 2.00 .65
  a.   Souv. sheet of 2, #C430-C431 2.50 1.25
      Nos. C429-C431 (3)   4.10 1.30

Human Rights Type
1980, Oct. 13   *Perf. 13x14*
C432 A233 60fr Map of Ameri-
                cas   .40 .20
C433 A233 150fr Map of Africa 1.00 .50
  a.   Souv. sheet of 2, #C432-C433 1.75 1.25

American Order of Rosicrucians Emblem — AP22

1980, Nov. 17   Litho.   *Perf. 13*
C434 AP22 60fr multi   .60 .20

General Conclave of the American Order of Rosicrucians, meeting of French-speaking countries, Lome, Aug.

Christmas Type
Designs: 100fr, Cologne Cathedral, Germany, 13th cent. 150fr, Notre Dame, Paris, 12th cent. 200fr, Canterbury Cathedral, England, 11th cent.

1980, Dec. 22   *Perf. 14½x13½*
C435 A234 100fr multi   .70 .35
C436 A234 150fr multi   1.10 .50
C437 A234 200fr multi   1.40 .65
  a.   Souv. sheet of 2, #C436-C437 3.00 1.40
      Nos. C435-C437 (3)   3.20 1.50

Hotel Type of 1981
1981, Feb. 2   Litho.   *Perf. 12½x13*
C437B A236 60fr multi   .60 .20

Easter Type of 1981
Rembrandt Paintings: 100fr, Artist's Mother. 200fr, Man in a Ruff.

1981, Apr. 13   Litho.   *Perf. 14½x13½*
C438 A237 100fr multi   .80 .35
C439 A237 200fr multi   1.60 .65
  a.   Souv. sheet of 2, #C438-C439 3.00 1.25

Market Type
1981, Mar. 8   Litho.   *Perf. 14*
C440 A230 90fr Fabric dealer .60 .30
C441 A230 100fr Bananas   .65 .35
C442 A230 200fr Clay pottery 1.40 .65
C443 A230 250fr Setting up   1.60 .80
C444 A230 500fr Selling   3.50 1.60
C445 A230 1000fr Measuring
                   grain   6.50 3.50
      Nos. C440-C445 (6)   14.25 7.20

For overprints see Nos. C486-C487.

Bird Type
Perf. 13½x14½
1981, Aug. 10   Litho.
C446 A238 50fr Violet-backed
                sunbird   .80 .20
C447 A238 100fr Red bishop   1.50 .35
  a.   Souv. sheet, #C446-C447 5.50 2.50

IYD Type
1981, Aug. 31   *Perf. 14*
C448 A240 90fr Carpenter   .65 .30

C449 A240 200fr Basketball
                  players   1.40 .65

Souvenir Sheet
C449A A240 300fr Weaver   2.25 1.25

Picasso Type
1981, Sept. 14   *Perf. 14½x13½*
C450 A241 90fr Violin and Bot-
                tle on Table,
                1916   .75 .30
C451 A241 100fr Baboon and
                  Young   .75 .35
C452 A241 200fr Mandolin and
                  Clarinet, 1914 1.75 .65
  a.   Souv. sheet of 2, #C451-C452 3.00 1.25
      Nos. C450-C452 (3)   3.25 1.30

World Heritage Year Type
1981, Sept. 28   *Perf. 13½x14½*
C453 A242 100fr Cracow Muse-
                  um, Poland   .75 .35
C454 A242 200fr Goree Isld., Se-
                  negal   1.50 .75
  a.   Souv. sheet of 2, #C453-C454 2.50 1.25

Space Type
1981, Nov.   *Perf. 14*
C455 A243 90fr multi   .70 .35
C456 A243 100fr multi   .75 .40

Souvenir Sheet
Perf. 13x14
C456A A243 300fr multi, vert. 2.25 1.25

10th anniv. of Soyuz 10 (90fr) and Apollo 14 (100fr).

Christmas Type
Rubens Paintings: 100fr, Adoration of the Kings. 200fr, Virgin and Child. 300fr, Virgin giving Chasuble to St. Idefonse.

Perf. 14½x13½
1981, Dec. 10   Litho.
C457 A244 100fr multi   .70 .35
C458 A244 200fr multi   1.50 .65
C459 A244 300fr multi   2.10 1.00
  a.   Souv. sheet of 3, #C458-C459 4.00 1.90
      Nos. C457-C459 (3)   4.30 2.00

West African Rice Development Assoc. Type
1981, Dec. 21   Litho.   *Perf. 12½*
C461 A236a 105fr yel & multi .70 .35

Liberation Type
Designs: 105fr, Citizens holding hands, Pres. Eyadema, vert. 130fr, Hotel.

1982, Jan. 13   Litho.   *Perf. 12½*
C462 A245 105fr multi   .70 .35
C463 A245 130fr multi   .90 .40

Scouting Year Type
1982, Feb. 25   Litho.   *Perf. 14*
C464 A246 90fr Semaphore   .75 .30
C465 A246 120fr Tower   1.00 .40
C466 A246 130fr Scouts, canoe 1.10 .40
C467 A246 135fr Scouts, tent   1.10 .45
      Nos. C464-C467 (4)   3.95 1.55

Souvenir Sheet
Perf. 13x14
C468 A246 500fr Baden-Powell 4.25 1.60

Easter Type
1982, Apr.   *Perf. 14x14½*
C469 A247 105fr multi   .70 .35
C470 A247 120fr multi   .80 .40

Souvenir Sheet
C471 A247 500fr multi   4.00 1.60

PHILEXFRANCE '82 Intl. Stamp Exhibition, Paris, June 11-21 — AP23

1982   Litho.   *Perf. 13*
C472 AP23 90fr shown   .70 .30
C473 AP23 105fr ROMOLYMPHIL
                  '82, vert.   .90 .35

Issue dates: 90fr, June 11; 105fr, May 19.

Butterfly Type

1982, July 15			**Perf.**	**14½x14**
C474	A248	90fr Euxanthe eurio-nome	1.40	.30
C475	A248	105fr Mylothris rhodo-pe	1.60	.35

Souvenir Sheet

C476	A248	500fr Papilio zalmoxis	4.25	1.60

World Cup Type

1982, July 26			**Perf.**	**14x14½**
C477	A249	105fr multi	.80	.35
C478	A249	200fr multi	1.40	.65
C479	A249	300fr multi	2.10	1.00
		Nos. C477-C479 (3)	4.30	2.00

Souvenir Sheet

C480	A249	500fr multi	4.00	1.65

For overprints see Nos. 1152-1155.

Pre-Olympics, 1984 Los Angeles — AP24

1983, Oct. 3		**Photo.**	**Perf.**	**12½**
C481	AP24	70fr Boxing	.55	.20
C482	AP24	90fr Hurdles	.70	.20
C483	AP24	105fr Pole vault	.80	.20
C484	AP24	130fr Runner	.90	.20
		Nos. C481-C484 (4)	2.95	.80

Souvenir Sheet

C485	AP24	500fr Runner, diff.	4.00	1.50

Nos. C443-C444 Overprinted: "19E CONGRES UPU HAMBOURG 1984"

1984, June		**Litho.**	**Perf.**	**14**
C486	A230	250fr multi	1.75	1.00
C487	A230	500fr multi	3.75	2.00

1984 Summer Olympics — AP25

1984, July 27			**Perf.**	**13**
C488	AP25	70fr Pole vault	.45	.20
C489	AP25	90fr Bicycling	.45	.20
C490	AP25	120fr Soccer	.75	.20
C491	AP25	250fr Boxing	1.50	.40
C492	AP25	400fr Running	2.25	.65
		Nos. C488-C492 (5)	5.40	1.65

Souvenir Sheet

C493	AP25	1000fr like 120fr, without flag	7.50	6.50

Nos. C488-C490, C493 vert.

Olympic Champions AP26

Peace and Human Rights — AP28

1984, Nov. 15		**Litho.**	**Perf.**	**15**
C494	AP26	500fr Jim Thorpe, US	7.25	3.25
C495	AP26	500fr Jesse Owens, US	7.25	3.25
C496	AP26	500fr Muhammad Ali, US	40.00	3.25
C497	AP26	500fr Bob Beamon, US	7.25	3.25
		Nos. C494-C497 (4)	61.75	13.00

Souvenir Sheets

C498	AP26	500fr Bill Steinkraus, US	7.25	3.25
C499	AP26	500fr New Zealand rowing team	7.25	3.25
C500	AP26	500fr Pakistani hockey team	7.25	3.25
C501	AP26	500fr Yukio Endo, Japan	7.25	3.25

West German Olympians

1984, Nov. 15				
C502	AP26	500fr Dietmar Mogenburg	7.25	3.25
C503	AP26	500fr Fredy Schmidtke	7.25	3.25
C504	AP26	500fr Matthias Behr	7.25	3.25
C505	AP26	500fr Sabine Everts	7.25	3.25
		Nos. C502-C505 (4)	29.00	13.00

Souvenir Sheets

C506	AP26	500fr Karl-Heinz Radschinsky	7.25	3.25
C507	AP26	500fr Pasquale Passarelli	7.25	3.25
C508	AP26	500fr Michale Gross	7.25	3.25
C509	AP26	500fr Jurgen Hingsen	7.25	3.25

For overprints see Nos. C521-C536, C563.

1985, Jan. 14		**Litho.**	**Perf.**	**13½x14**

230fr, Map of Togo, globe, doves. 270fr, Palm tree, emblem. 500fr, Opencast mining operation. 1000fr, Human Rights Monument, UN, NYC.

C510	AP28	230fr multi	1.50	.20
C511	AP28	270fr multi	1.90	.30
C512	AP28	500fr multi	3.50	.50
C513	AP28	1000fr multi	7.00	1.00
		Nos. C510-C513 (4)	13.90	2.00

Tribal Dances AP29

1985, July			**Perf.**	**15x14**
C514	AP29	120fr Adifo, Adangbe	.85	.20
C515	AP29	135fr Fouet (whip), Kente	.85	.20
C516	AP29	290fr Idjombi, Pagouda	2.00	.30
C517	AP29	500fr Moba, Dapaong	3.50	.50
		Nos. C514-C517 (4)	7.20	1.20

Visit of Pope John Paul II — AP30

90fr, The Pope outside Lome Cathedral. 130fr, Blessing crowd in St. Peter's Square. 500fr, Greeting Pres. Eyadema.

1985, Aug. 9			**Perf.**	**13**
C518	AP30	90fr multi	.75	.20
C519	AP30	130fr multi, vert.	1.25	.25
C520	AP30	500fr multi	3.50	.50
		Nos. C518-C520 (3)	5.50	.95

Nos. C495, C497, C499, C502, C505-508 Overprinted with Winners Names, Country and Type of Olympic Medal

1985, Aug.			**Perf.**	**15**
C521	AP26	500fr Kirk Baptiste, US	6.50	1.50
C522	AP26	500fr Carl Lewis, US	6.50	1.50
C523	AP26	500fr Patrik Sjoborg, Sweden	6.50	1.50
C524	AP26	500fr Glynis Nunn, Australia	6.50	1.50
		Nos. C521-C524 (4)	26.00	6.00

Souvenir Sheets

C525	AP26	500fr Rowing eights, Canada	3.50	3.00
C526	AP26	500fr Rolf Milser, W. Germany	3.50	3.00
C527	AP26	500fr Takashi Irie, Japan	3.50	3.00
C528	AP26	500fr Frederic Delcourt, France	3.50	3.00

Nos. C494, C496, C503-C504, C498, C500, C501, C509 Ovptd. with Winners Names, Country and Type of Olympic Medal

1985, Sept. 19		**Litho.**	**Perf.**	**15**
C529	AP26	500fr Italy	6.50	1.50
C530	AP26	500fr Kevin Barry	6.50	1.50
C531	AP26	500fr Rolf Golz	6.50	1.50
C532	AP26	500fr Philippe Boisse	6.50	1.50
		Nos. C529-C532 (4)	26.00	6.00

Souvenir Sheets

C533	AP26	500fr Karen Stives	3.50	3.00
C534	AP26	500fr R.F.A. (West Germany)	3.50	3.00
C535	AP26	500fr Koji Gushiken	3.50	3.00
C536	AP26	500fr Daley Thompson	3.50	3.00

Traditional Instruments — AP31

Youth and Development — AP32

Designs: No. C537, Xylophone, Kante horn, tambour. No. C538, Bongo drums, castanets, bassar horn. No. C539, Communications. No. C540, Agriculture and industry.

1985		**Litho.**	**Perf.**	**13**
C537	AP31	100fr multi	.90	.60
C538	AP31	100fr multi	.90	.60
a.		Pair, #C537-C538	3.00	3.00
C539	AP32	200fr multi	1.75	1.25
C540	AP32	200fr multi	1.75	1.25
a.		Pair, #C539-C540	7.50	7.50
		Nos. C537-C540 (4)	5.30	3.70

PHILEXAFRICA '85, Lome, Togo, 11/16-24. Issued: 100fr, Nov. 4; 200fr, Nov. 16.

No. 1274 Ovptd. with Organization Emblem and "80e Anniversaire du Rotary International."

1985, Nov. 15		**Litho.**	**Perf.**	**15**

Souvenir Sheet

C541	A267	1000fr multi	20.00	6.50

Nos. 1254-1255, 1258 Ovptd. "10e ANNIVERSAIRE DE APOLLO-SOYUZ" in 1 or 2 lines

1985, Dec. 27		**Litho.**	**Perf.**	**15**
C542	A265	90fr multi	1.25	.40
C543	A265	500fr multi	6.75	2.00

Souvenir Sheet

C544	A265	1000fr multi	8.50	2.90

Nos. 1294-1295, 1297 Ovptd. "75e ANNIVERSAIRE DE LA MORT DE HENRI DUNANT FONDATEUR DE LA CROIX ROUGE" in 2 or 4 lines

1985, Dec. 27				
C545	A270	400fr multi	4.75	1.50
C546	A270	500fr multi	6.25	2.00

Souvenir Sheet

C547	A270	1000fr multi	7.50	6.00

Statue of Liberty, Cent. — AP33

1986, Apr. 10			**Perf.**	**13**
C548	AP33	70fr Eiffel Tower	.55	.20
C549	AP33	90fr Statue of Liberty	.65	.25
C550	AP33	500fr Empire State Building	3.75	1.40
		Nos. C548-C550 (3)	4.95	1.85

Nos. 1237-1240 Ovptd. with AMERIPEX '86 Emblem

1986, May 22			**Perf.**	**11**
C551	A262	500fr multi	6.50	1.40
C552	A262	1000fr multi	12.50	2.75

Souvenir Sheets

		Perf.	**14**	
C553	A262	1000fr No. 1239	8.50	3.50
C554	A262	1000fr No. 1240	8.50	3.50

Air Africa, 25th Anniv. AP34

1986, Dec. 29		**Litho.**	**Perf.**	**12½x13**
C555	AP34	90fr multi	.75	.25

Konrad Adenauer (1876-1967) West German Chancellor — AP35

1987, July 15		**Litho.**	**Perf.**	**12½x13**
C556	AP35	120fr At podium	.90	.60
C557	AP35	500fr With Pres. Kennedy, 1962	3.50	3.00

Souvenir Sheet

		Perf.	**13x12½**	
C558	AP35	500fr Portrait, vert.	3.50	3.00

Berlin, 750th Anniv. AP36

Designs: 90fr, Wilhelm I (1781-1864) coin, Victory statue. 150fr, Frederick III (1831-1888) coin, Brandenburg Gate. 300fr, Wilhelm II (1882-1951) coin, Reichstag building. 750fr, Otto Leopold von Bismarck (1815-1898), first chancellor of the German empire, and Charlottenburg Palace.

1987, Aug. 31 Litho. Perf. 13½
C559	AP36	90fr multi	.60	.30
C560	AP36	150fr multi	1.00	.50
C561	AP36	300fr multi	2.00	1.00
	Nos. C559-C561 (3)		3.60	1.80

Souvenir Sheet
C562	AP36	750fr multi	5.50	4.25

Nos. C506, 1258, 1273 and 1274 Overprinted in Black for Philatelic Exhibitions

a

b

c

d

Additional overprints appear on souvenir sheets away from stamps.

1988, Apr. 25 Litho. Perf. 15
Souvenir Sheets
C563	AP26 (a)	500fr #C506	9.50	3.00
C564	A265 (b)	1000fr #1258	10.00	5.50
C565	A265 (c)	1000fr #1273	10.00	5.50
C566	A267 (d)	1000fr #1274	10.00	5.50
	Nos. C563-C566 (4)		39.50	19.50

AIR POST SEMI-POSTAL STAMPS

Nursery — SPAP1

Perf. 13½x12½
1942, June 22 Unwmk. Photo.
CB1	SPAP1	1.50fr + 3.50fr green	.60
CB2	SPAP1	2fr + 6fr brown	.60

Native children's welfare fund.
Nos. CB1-CB2 were issued by the Vichy government in France, but were not placed on sale in Togo

Colonial Education Fund
Common Design Type
1942, June 22 Engr.
CB3	CD86a	1.20fr + 1.80fr blue & red	.60

No. CB3 was issued by the Vichy government in France, but was not placed on sale in Togo.

POSTAGE DUE STAMPS

Postage Due Stamps of Dahomey, 1914 Overprinted

1921 Unwmk. Perf. 14x13½
J1	D2	5c green	.60	.60
J2	D2	10c rose	.60	.60
J3	D2	15c gray	1.25	1.25
J4	D2	20c brown	2.25	2.25
J5	D2	30c blue	2.50	2.50
J6	D2	50c black	2.00	2.00
J7	D2	60c orange	2.00	2.00
J8	D2	1fr violet	3.75	3.75
	Nos. J1-J8 (8)		14.95	14.95

Cotton Field — D3

1925 Typo. Unwmk.
J9	D3	2c blue & blk	.20	.20
J10	D3	4c dl red & blk	.20	.20
J11	D3	5c ol grn & blk	.20	.20
J12	D3	10c cerise & blk	.25	.25
J13	D3	15c orange & blk	.60	.60
J14	D3	20c red vio & blk	.40	.40
J15	D3	25c gray & blk	.75	.75
J16	D3	30c ocher & blk	.40	.40
J17	D3	50c brown & blk	.85	.85
J18	D3	60c green & blk	.85	.85
J19	D3	1fr dk vio & blk	.85	.85
	Nos. J9-J19 (11)		5.55	5.55

Type of 1925 Issue Surcharged

1927
J20	D3	2fr on 1fr rose red & vio	5.00	5.00
J21	D3	3fr on 1fr org brn, blk & ultra	5.00	5.00

Mask — D4   Carved Figures — D5

1941 Engr. Perf. 13
J22	D4	5c brown black	.20	.20
J23	D4	10c yellow green	.20	.20
J24	D4	15c carmine	.20	.20
J25	D4	20c ultra	.25	.25
J26	D4	30c chestnut	.55	.55
J27	D4	50c olive green	1.40	1.40
J28	D4	60c violet	.55	.55
J29	D4	1fr light blue	.85	.85
J30	D4	2fr orange vermilion	.75	.75
J31	D4	3fr rose violet	.90	.90
	Nos. J22-J31 (10)		5.85	5.85

For type D4 without "RF," see Nos. J31A-J31F.

Type of 1941 Without "RF"
1942-44
J31A	D4	5c brown black	.20
J31B	D4	10c green & violet	.20
J31C	D4	15c car rose & brn	.25
J31D	D4	30c brown & black	.45

J31E	D4	2fr brn org & brn vio	.55
J31F	D4	3fr violet & green	.55
	Nos. J31A-J31F (6)		2.20

Nos. J31A-J31F were issued by the Vichy government in France, but were not placed on sale in Togo.

Catalogue values for unused stamps in this section, from this point to the end of the section, are for Never Hinged items.

1947
J32	D5	10c brt ultra	.20	.20
J33	D5	30c red	.20	.20
J34	D5	50c dp yellow grn	.20	.20
J35	D5	1fr chocolate	.40	.40
J36	D5	2fr carmine	.40	.40
J37	D5	3fr gray blk	.40	.40
J38	D5	4fr ultra	.70	.70
J39	D5	5fr sepia	.85	.85
J40	D5	10fr dp orange	.90	.90
J41	D5	20fr dk blue vio	1.25	1.25
	Nos. J32-J41 (10)		5.50	5.50

Republic

Konkomba Helmet
D6   D7
1957 Engr. Perf. 14x13
J42	D6	1fr brt violet	.25	.25
J43	D6	2fr brt orange	.25	.25
J44	D6	3fr dk gray	.25	.25
J45	D6	4fr brt red	.25	.25
J46	D6	5fr ultra	.25	.25
J47	D6	10fr dp green	.35	.35
J48	D6	20fr dp claret	.50	.50
	Nos. J42-J48 (7)		2.10	2.10

1959 Perf. 14x13
J49	D7	1fr orange brn	.20	.35
J50	D7	2fr lt blue grn	.20	.35
J51	D7	3fr orange	.20	.35
J52	D7	4fr blue	.20	.45
J53	D7	5fr lilac rose	.20	.45
J54	D7	10fr violet blue	.45	.65
J55	D7	20fr black	.80	.85
	Nos. J49-J55 (7)		2.25	3.45

Type of Regular Issue
Shells: 1fr, Conus papilionaceus. 2fr, Marginella faba. 3fr, Cypraea stercoraria. 4fr, Strombus latus. 5fr, Costate cockle (sea shell). 10fr, Cancellaria cancellata. 15fr, Cymbium pepo. 20fr, Tympanotomus radula.

1964-65 Unwmk. Photo. Perf. 14
Size: 20x25½mm
J56	A47	1fr gray grn & red brn ('65)	.40	.20
J57	A47	2fr tan & ol grn ('65)	.40	.20
J58	A47	3fr gray, brn & yel ('65)	.40	.20
J59	A47	4fr tan & multi ('65)	.40	.20
J60	A47	5fr sep, org & grn	.60	.30
J61	A47	10fr sl bl, brn & bis	.80	.40
J62	A47	15fr grn & brn	1.90	1.00
J63	A47	20fr sl, dk brn & yel	2.40	1.25
	Nos. J56-J63 (8)		7.30	3.75

Tomatoes — D8

1969-70 Litho. Perf. 14
J64	D8	5fr yellow & multi	.45	.20
J65	D8	10fr blue & multi	.45	.20
J66	D8	15fr multi ('70)	.65	.30
J67	D8	20fr multi ('70)	.90	.40
	Nos. J64-J67 (4)		2.45	1.10

Market Type
1981, Mar. 8 Litho. Perf. 14
Size: 23x32mm, 32x23mm
J68	A230	5fr Millet, vert.	.25	.20
J69	A230	10fr Packaged goods	.25	.20
J70	A230	25fr Chickens	.25	.20
J71	A230	50fr Ivory vendor	.30	.20
	Nos. J68-J71 (4)		1.05	.80

OFFICIAL STAMPS

Catalogue values for unused stamps in this section are for never hinged items.

O1

1991? Litho. Perf. 13½
O1	O1	15fr multicolored	.20	—
O2	O1	100fr multicolored	.35	—
O3	O1	125fr multicolored	.40	—
O4	O1	500fr multicolored	1.40	—

1991?
O5	O1	10fr multicolored	—	—
O6	O1	90fr yellow & multi	.30	—

1991?
O7	O1	180fr ap grn & multi	.50	—

1991
O8	O1	50fr yellow & multi	.20	.20
O9	O1	300fr ap grn & multi	1.00	1.00

The editors would like information on dates of issue and stamps of other denominations. The catalogue numbers will change.

TOKELAU

'tō-kə-ˌlau

(Union Islands)

LOCATION — Pacific Ocean 300 miles north of Apia, Western Samoa
GOVT. — A dependency of New Zealand
AREA — 4 sq. mi.
POP. — 1,487 (1996)

The Tokelau islands consist of three atolls: Atafu, Nukunono and Fakaofo, which span 100 miles of ocean.

12 Pence = 1 Shilling
100 Cents = 1 Dollar (1967)

Catalogue values for all unused stamps in this country are for Never Hinged items.

Map and Scene on Atafu — A1

Nukunono Dwelling and Map — A2

Fakaofo Shore Line and Map — A3

Perf. 13½x13

1948, June 22   **Wmk. 253**   **Engr.**
1	A1	½p red brown & rose lilac	.20	.40
2	A2	1p dp green & orange brn	.25	.30
3	A3	2p deep ultra & green	.30	.30
		Nos. 1-3 (3)	.75	1.00

For surcharges see Nos. 5, 9-11.

Coronation Issue

Queen Elizabeth II — A3a

1953, May 25   **Photo.**   **Perf. 14x14½**
4	A3a	3p brown	3.50	2.50

No. 1 Surcharged in Black:

Perf. 13½x13

1956, Mar. 27   **Engr.**   **Wmk. 253**
5	A1	1sh on ½p	4.25	4.25

Postal-Fiscal Type of New Zealand, 1950, Surcharged

Wmk. 253

1966, Nov.   **Typo.**   **Perf. 14**
6	A109	6p light blue	.75	.35
7	A109	8p light green	1.40	.75
8	A109	2sh pink	2.50	1.90
		Nos. 6-8 (3)	4.65	3.00

Nos. 1-3 Surcharged with New Value and Dots Obliterating Old Denomination

1967, July 10   **Engr.**   **Perf. 13½x13**
9	A2	1c on 1p	.60	.60
10	A3	2c on 2p	1.40	1.40
11	A1	10c on ½p	4.75	4.75
		Nos. 9-11 (3)	6.75	6.75

The 1c and 2c surcharges include two dots, the 10c surcharge has only one.

Postal Fiscal Type of New Zealand, 1950, Surcharged

1967, July 10   **Typo.**   **Perf. 14**
12	A109	3c light lilac	.35	.35
13	A109	5c light blue	.70	.70
14	A109	7c light green	1.10	1.10
15	A109	20c pink	2.50	2.50
		Nos. 12-15 (4)	4.65	4.65

1877, British Protectorate — A4

History of Tokelau: 10c, 1916, part of Gilbert and Ellice Islands Colony. 15c, 1925, administration transferred to New Zealand. 20c, 1948, New Zealand Territory.

Perf. 13x12½

1969, Aug. 8   **Litho.**   **Wmk. 253**
16	A4	5c ultra, yellow & blk	.80	.45
17	A4	10c rose red, yel & blk	1.00	.85
18	A4	15c dull grn, yel & blk	1.10	1.40
19	A4	20c brown, yel & blk	1.75	1.75
		Nos. 16-19 (4)	4.65	4.45

Nativity, by Federico Fiori — A4a

Adoration, by Correggio — A4b

1969, Oct. 1   **Photo.**   **Perf. 13½x14**
20	A4a	2c multicolored	.40	.40

Christmas.

Perf. 12½

1970, Oct. 1   **Unwmk.**   **Litho.**
21	A4b	2c multicolored	.40	.40

Christmas.

"Dolphin," 1765, Map of Atafu — A5

Fan — A6

Designs: 10c, "Pandora," 1791, and map of Nukunono. 25c, "General Jackson," 1835, and map of Fakaofo, horiz.

1970, Dec. 9   **Unwmk.**   **Perf. 13½**
22	A5	5c yellow & multi	1.00	.90
23	A5	10c multicolored	2.40	1.60
24	A5	25c pink & multi	5.75	4.75
		Nos. 22-24 (3)	9.15	7.25

Discovery of Tokelau Islands.

1971, Oct. 20   **Litho.**   **Perf. 14**

Native Handicrafts: 2c, Round vessel. 3c, Hexagonal box. 5c, Shoulder bag. 10c, Handbag. 15c, Jewelry box with beads. 20c, Outrigger canoe model. 25c, Fish hooks.
25	A6	1c olive & multi	.20	.20
26	A6	2c red & multi	.20	.20
27	A6	3c dk violet & multi	.20	.20
28	A6	5c dull blue & multi	.20	.20
29	A6	10c dp orange & multi	.55	.30
30	A6	15c emerald & multi	.85	.55
31	A6	20c multicolored	1.10	.70
32	A6	25c violet blue & multi	1.25	.90
		Nos. 25-32 (8)	4.55	3.25

Windmill Pump, Map of Atafu — A7

Horny Coral — A8

South Pacific Commission Emblem and: 10c, Community well, map of Fakaofo. 15c, Eradication of rhinoceros beetle, map of Nukunono. 20c, members.

1972, Sept. 6   **Litho.**   **Perf. 14x13½**
33	A7	5c lt blue grn & multi	.35	.25
34	A7	10c grnsh blue & multi	.75	.45
35	A7	15c lilac & multi	1.10	.60
36	A7	20c violet bl & multi	1.50	.95
		Nos. 33-36 (4)	3.70	2.25

South Pacific Commission, 25th anniversary. On 15c, "PACIFIC" reads "PACFIC."

1973, Sept. 12   **Litho.**   **Perf. 13x13½**
37	A8	3c shown	1.25	1.10
38	A8	5c Soft coral	1.25	1.25
39	A8	15c Mushroom coral	2.00	2.10
40	A8	25c Staghorn coral	2.50	2.50
		Nos. 37-40 (4)	7.00	6.95

Cowrie (Cypraea Mauritiana) A9

Cowrie shells: 5c, Cypraea tigris. 15c, Cypraea talpa. 25c, Cypraea argus.

1974, Nov. 13   **Litho.**   **Perf. 14**
41	A9	3c apple grn & multi	1.25	1.10
42	A9	5c dk blue & multi	1.50	1.10
43	A9	15c blue & multi	2.00	2.25
44	A9	25c green & multi	2.25	2.50
		Nos. 41-44 (4)	7.00	6.95

Moorish Idol — A10

Fish: 10c, Long-nosed butterflyfish. 15c, Lined butterflyfish. 25c, Red firefish.

1975, Nov. 19   **Litho.**   **Perf. 14**
45	A10	5c blue & multi	.50	.30
46	A10	10c brown & multi	1.10	.65
47	A10	15c lilac & multi	1.90	1.10
48	A10	25c multicolored	3.25	2.10
		Nos. 45-48 (4)	6.75	4.15

Canoe Making A11

Designs: 2c, Reef fishing. 3c, Woman preparing pandanus leaves for weaving. 5c, Communal kitchen (umu). 9c, Wood carving. 20c, Husking coconuts. 50c, Wash day. $1, Meal time. 9c, 20c, 50c, $1, vertical.

1976, Oct. 27   **Litho.**   **Perf. 14**
49	A11	1c pink & multi	.55	1.70
50	A11	2c multicolored	.40	1.40
51	A11	3c lt blue & multi	.35	.70
52	A11	5c yellow & multi	.40	.70
53	A11	9c bister & multi	.25	.85
54	A11	20c multicolored	.25	.70
55	A11	50c tan & multi	.35	.85
56	A11	$1 multicolored	.70	2.10
		Nos. 49-56 (8)	3.25	8.40

1981, July 17   **Perf. 15**
49a	A11	1c	.40	.65
51a	A11	3c	.40	.65
52a	A11	5c	.40	.65
53a	A11	9c	.65	.65
54a	A11	20c	.65	.90
55a	A11	50c	.85	.90
56a	A11	$1	1.25	1.25
		Nos. 49a-56a (7)	4.60	5.40

White Tern — A12

Birds of Tokelau: 10c, Turnstone. 15c, White-capped noddy. 30c, Brown noddy.

1977, Nov. 16   **Litho.**   **Perf. 14½x15**
57	A12	8c multicolored	.50	.35
58	A12	10c multicolored	.65	.40
59	A12	15c multicolored	.80	.65
60	A12	30c multicolored	1.75	1.40
		Nos. 57-60 (4)	3.70	2.80

Westminster Abbey — A13

10c, King Edward's Chair. 15c, Scepter, Crown, Orb, Bible and Staff of State. 30c, Elizabeth II.

1978, June 28   **Litho.**   **Perf. 14**
61	A13	8c multicolored	.25	.25
62	A13	10c multicolored	.35	.35
63	A13	15c multicolored	.55	.55
64	A13	30c multicolored	1.00	1.00
		Nos. 61-64 (4)	2.15	2.15

25th anniv. of coronation of Elizabeth II.

Canoe Racing A14

Designs: Various canoe races.

1978, Nov. 8   **Litho.**   **Perf. 13½x14**
65	A14	8c multicolored	.40	.40
66	A14	12c multicolored	.55	.55
67	A14	15c multicolored	.65	.65
68	A14	30c multicolored	1.10	1.10
		Nos. 65-68 (4)	2.70	2.70

1979, Nov. 7   **Photo.**   **Perf. 14**
69	A14	10c Rugby	.35	.35
70	A14	15c Cricket	.70	.70
71	A14	20c Rugby, diff.	.70	.70
72	A14	30c Cricket, diff.	.85	.85
		Nos. 69-72 (4)	2.60	2.60

1980, Nov. 5   Litho.   Perf. 13½
73	A14	10c Surfing	.25	.25
74	A14	20c Surfing, diff.	.30	.25
75	A14	30c Swimming	.45	.40
76	A14	50c Swimming, diff.	.60	.55
		Nos. 73-76 (4)	1.60	1.45

1981, Nov. 4   Photo.   Perf. 14
77	A14	10c Pole vaulting, vert.	.35	.35
78	A14	20c Volleyball, vert.	.40	.35
79	A14	30c Running, vert.	.50	.40
80	A14	50c Volleyball, vert., diff.	.60	.60
		Nos. 77-80 (4)	1.85	1.70

Wood Carving — A15

Octopus Lure Fishing — A16

1982, May 5   Litho.   Perf. 13½x13
81	A15	10s shown	.35	.35
82	A15	22s Bow-drilling sea shells	.35	.35
83	A15	34s Bowl finishing	.50	.50
84	A15	60s Basket weaving	1.00	1.00
		Nos. 81-84 (4)	2.20	2.20

1982, Nov. 3   Litho.   Perf. 14

Designs: Fishing Methods.
85	A16	5s shown	.20	.20
86	A16	18s Multiple-hook	.20	.20
87	A16	23s Ruvettus	.25	.25
88	A16	34s Netting flying fish	.40	.40
89	A16	63s Noose	.70	.70
90	A16	75s Bonito	.85	.85
		Nos. 85-90 (6)	2.60	2.60

Outrigger Canoe A17

1983, May 4   Litho.   Perf. 13½x14
91	A17	5s shown	.25	.25
92	A17	18s Whale boat	.25	.25
93	A17	23s Aluminium whale boat	.25	.25
94	A17	34s Alia fishing boat	.30	.30
95	A17	63s Cargo ship	.65	.65
96	A17	75s Seaplane	.90	.90
		Nos. 91-96 (6)	2.60	2.60

Traditional Games A18

1983, Nov. 2   Litho.   Perf. 14
97	A18	5s Javelin throwing	.25	.25
98	A18	18s Tifaga string game	.25	.25
99	A18	23s Fire making	.25	.25
100	A18	34s Shell throwing	.30	.30
101	A18	63s Handball	.65	.65
102	A18	75s Mass wrestling	.90	.90
		Nos. 97-102 (6)	2.60	2.60

Planting, Harvesting Copra — A19

Local Fish — A20

Copra Industry: b, Husking, splitting. c, Drying, cutting. d, Bagging, weighing. e, Shipping. Continuous design.

1984, May 2   Litho.   Perf. 13½x13
103		Strip of 5	3.00	3.00
a.-e.		A19 48s any single	.45	.45

1984, Dec. 5   Litho.   Perf. 14½x14
104	A20	1c Manini	.30	.30
105	A20	2c Hahave	.30	.30
106	A20	5c Uloulo	.30	.30
107	A20	9c Ume Ihu	.30	.30
108	A20	23c Lifilafi	.40	.40
109	A20	34c Fagamea	.55	.55
110	A20	50c Kakahi	.70	.70
111	A20	75c Palu Po	1.25	1.25
112	A20	$1 Mokoha	1.60	1.60
113	A20	$2 Hakula	2.75	2.75
		Nos. 104-113 (10)	8.45	8.45

Trees, Fruits and Herbs — A21

1985, June 26   Litho.   Perf. 13½
114	A21	5c Mati	.20	.20
115	A21	18c Nonu	.20	.20
116	A21	32c Ulu	.45	.45
117	A21	48c Fala	.65	.65
118	A21	60c Kanava	.85	.85
119	A21	75c Niu	1.00	1.00
		Nos. 114-119 (6)	3.35	3.35

Public Buildings and Churches A22

Designs: 5c, Administration Center, Atafu. 18c, Administration Center, Nukunonu. 32c, Administration Center, Fakaofo. 48c, Congregational Church, Atafu. 60c, Catholic Church, Nukunonu. 75c, Congregational Church, Fakaofo.

1985, Dec. 4
120	A22	5c multicolored	.20	.20
121	A22	18c multicolored	.20	.20
122	A22	32c multicolored	.45	.45
123	A22	48c multicolored	.65	.65
124	A22	60c multicolored	.85	.85
125	A22	75c multicolored	1.00	1.00
		Nos. 120-125 (6)	3.35	3.35

Hospitals and Schools A23

Designs: 5c, Atafu Hospital. 18c, St. Joseph's Hospital, Nukunonu. 32c, Fenuafala Hospital, Fakaofo. 48c, Matauala School, Atafu. 60c, Matiti School, Nukunonu. 75c, Fenuafala School, Fakaofo.

1986, May 7   Perf. 13½
126	A23	5c multicolored	.20	.20
127	A23	18c multicolored	.20	.20
128	A23	32c multicolored	.45	.45
129	A23	48c multicolored	.65	.65
130	A23	60c multicolored	.85	.85
131	A23	75c multicolored	1.00	1.00
		Nos. 126-131 (6)	3.35	3.35

Fauna A24

1986, Dec. 3   Litho.   Perf. 14
132	A24	5c Coconut crab	.20	.20
133	A24	18c Pigs	.20	.20
134	A24	32c Chickens	.50	.50
135	A24	48c Turtles	.75	.75
136	A24	60c Goats	.90	.90
137	A24	75c Ducks	1.10	1.10
		Nos. 132-137 (6)	3.65	3.65

Flora A25

1987, May 6
138	A25	5c Gahu	.60	.60
139	A25	18c Puka	.85	.85
140	A25	32c Higano	1.10	1.10
141	A25	48c Tialetiale	1.50	1.50
142	A25	60c Gagie	1.75	1.75
143	A25	75c Puapua	1.90	1.90
		Nos. 138-143 (6)	7.70	7.70

Olympic Sports A26

1987, Dec. 2   Litho.   Perf. 14x14½
144	A26	5c Javelin	.40	.40
145	A26	18c Shot put	.70	.70
146	A26	32c Long jump	.90	.90
147	A26	48c Hurdles	1.00	1.00
148	A26	60c Running	1.25	1.25
149	A26	75c Wrestling	1.75	1.75
		Nos. 144-149 (6)	6.00	6.00

Australia Bicentennial, SYDPEX '88 — A27

Re-enactment of the arrival of the First Fleet in Sydney Harbor, Jan. 26, 1988 (in a continuous design): a, Ships in harbor, building (LL). b, Ships in harbor, tall ship (LR). c, Ships in harbor, Sydney Opera House. d, Bridge. e, North Sydney.

1988, July 30   Litho.   Perf. 13½x13
150		Strip of 5	14.00	14.00
a.-e.		A27 50c any single	2.40	2.40

Political Development A28

Designs: 5c, Transfer of administration from the New Zealand Department of Maori and Island Affairs to the Ministry of Foreign Affairs, 1975. 18c, The General Fono empowered as the decision-making body of Tokelau, 1977. 32c, 1st Visit of New Zealand's prime minister, 1985. 48c, 1st Visit of UN representatives, 1976. 60c, 1st Tokelau delegation to go to the UN, 1987. 75c, 1st Tokelau appointed to the office of Official Secretary, 1987.

1988, Aug. 10   Perf. 14½
151	A28	5c multicolored	.20	.20
152	A28	18c multicolored	.40	.40
153	A28	32c multicolored	.85	.85
154	A28	48c multicolored	1.25	1.25
155	A28	60c multicolored	1.50	1.50
156	A28	75c multicolored	2.00	2.00
		Nos. 151-156 (6)	6.20	6.20

Island Christmas A29

Designs: 5c, Three Wise Men (Na Makoi). 20c, Holy family (He Tala). 40c, Escape into Egypt (Fakagagalo ki Aikupito). 60c, Christmas presents (Meaalofa Kilihimahi). 70c, Christ child (Pepe ko Iesu). $1, Christmas parade (Holo Tamilo).

1988, Dec. 7   Litho.   Perf. 13½
157	A29	5c multicolored	.30	.30
158	A29	20c multicolored	.30	.30
159	A29	40c multicolored	.70	.70
160	A29	60c multicolored	1.10	1.10
161	A29	70c multicolored	1.25	1.25
162	A29	$1 multicolored	1.75	1.75
		Nos. 157-162 (6)	5.40	5.40

Food Gathering A30

Fishing and gathering coconuts. Printed se-tenant in continuous designs.

No. 163: a, Launching outrigger canoe. b, Outrigger canoe and sailboat starboard side. c, Outrigger canoe and sailboat stern.

No. 164: a, Outrigger and sailboat port side. b, Islander carrying baskets of coconuts. c, Gathering coconuts on palm trees.

1989, June 28   Litho.   Perf. 14x14½
163		Strip of 3	5.25	5.25
a.-c.		A30 50c any single	1.60	1.60
164		Strip of 3	5.25	5.25
a.-c.		A30 50c any single	1.60	1.60

Women's Work and Leisure — A31

1990, May 2   Litho.   Perf. 14½
165	A31	5c Weavers	.85	.65
166	A31	20c Washing clothes	1.25	1.25
167	A31	40c Resting among palm trees	2.10	1.75
168	A31	60c Weaving mat	2.50	2.75
169	A31	80c Weaving, diff.	3.50	3.75
170	A31	$1 Basket weaver	3.75	4.00
		Nos. 165-170 (6)	13.95	14.15

Souvenir Sheet

Penny Black, 150th Anniv. — A32

1990, May 3   Litho.   Perf. 11½
171	A32	$3 multicolored	22.50	22.50

Men's Handicrafts — A33

1990, Aug. 1   Photo.   Perf. 13
172	A33	50c shown	1.75	1.50
173	A33	50c Carving pots	1.75	1.50
174	A33	50c Tying rope on pot	1.75	1.50
a.		Strip of 3, #172-174	6.75	6.75

175 A33 50c Finishing pots   1.75 1.50
176 A33 50c Shaping a canoe   1.75 1.50
177 A33 50c Three men working 1.75 1.50
   a.   Strip of 3, #175-177   6.75 6.75

1992 Summer
Olympics,
Barcelona — A34

1992, July 8   **Litho.**   *Perf. 13½*
178 A34 40c Swimming   1.00 1.00
179 A34 60c Long jump   1.50 1.50
180 A34 $1 Volleyball   3.25 3.25
181 A34 $1.80 Running   4.25 4.25
    Nos. 178-181 (4)   10.00 10.00

Discovery
of America,
500th
Anniv.
A35

1992, Dec. 18
182 A35 40c Santa Maria   1.25 1.25
183 A35 60c Columbus   1.50 1.50
184 A35 $1.20 Columbus' fleet 3.50 3.50
185 A35 $1.80 Landfall   4.75 4.75
    Nos. 182-185 (4)   11.00 11.00

Coronation
of Queen
Elizabeth II,
40th Anniv.
A36

1993, July 8   **Litho.**   *Perf. 13½*
186 A36 25c Queen, early por-
     trait   .85 .85
187 A36 40c Prince Philip   1.40 1.40
188 A36 $1 Queen, recent por-
     trait   2.50 2.50
189 A36 $2 Queen & Prince
     Philip   4.25 4.25
    Nos. 186-189 (4)   9.00 9.00

Birds
A37

25c, Numenius tahitiensis. 40c, Phaethon
rubricauda. $1, Egretta sacra. $2, Pluvialis
fulva.

1993-94   **Litho.**   *Perf. 13½*
190 A37 25c multicolored   1.10 1.10
191 A37 40c multicolored   1.60 1.60
192 A37 $1 multicolored   2.75 2.75
193 A37 $2 multicolored   3.50 3.50
   a.   Souvenir sheet of 4, #190-193,
     perf. 14x14 ½   8.95 8.95
    Nos. 190-193 (4)   8.95 8.95

No. 193a contains Hong Kong '94 emblem,
inscription in Chinese and English in sheet
margin and sold for $20 HK at the show.
Issued: #190-193, 12/15/93; #193a, 2/1/94.

PHILAKOREA '94 — A38

1994, Aug. 16   **Litho.**   *Perf. 12*
194 A38 $2 White heron   4.50 4.50
   a.   Souvenir sheet of 1   7.00 7.00
No. 194a has a continuous design.

Handicrafts
A39

1995   **Litho.**   *Perf. 13½*
195 A39 5c Outrigger canoe   .30 .30
196 A39 25c Plaited fan   .40 .40
197 A39 40c Plaited baskets   .65 .65
198 A39 50c Fishing box   .85 .85
199 A39 80c Water bottle   1.25 1.25
200 A39 $1 Fishing hook   1.75 1.75
201 A39 $2 Coconut gourds   3.25 3.25
202 A39 $5 Shell necklace   8.50 8.50
    Nos. 195-202 (8)   16.95 16.95

Souvenir Sheet

New Year 1995 (Year of the
Boar) — A40

Illustration reduced.

1995, Feb. 3   **Litho.**   *Perf. 14*
203 A40 $5 multicolored   10.00 10.00
   a.   Ovptd. in sheet margin   16.00 16.00
   b.   Ovptd. in sheet margin   9.50 9.50

No. 203a ovptd. in red in sheet margin
"POST'X 95 / 3-6 February / 1995 / AUCK-
LAND" surrounded by simulated perforations.
No. 203b ovptd. in red in sheet margin with
Singapore '95 exhibition emblem.

Pacific
Imperial
Pigeon
A41

1995, Apr. 27   **Litho.**   *Perf. 13½*
204 A41 25c shown   .85 .85
205 A41 40c Full view   1.40 1.40
206 A41 $1 In tree, red ber-
     ries   2.25 2.25
207 A41 $2 Nesting   4.00 4.00
    Nos. 204-207 (4)   8.50 8.50

World Wildlife Fund.

Reef
Fish — A42

Designs: 25c, Long nosed butterfly fish. 40c,
Emperor angelfish. $1, Moorish idol. $2, Lined
butterfly fish.
$3, Red fire fish.

1995, Sept. 1   **Litho.**   *Perf. 12*
208 A42 25c multicolored   .55 .55
209 A42 40c multicolored   .85 .85
210 A42 $1 multicolored   2.10 2.10
211 A42 $2 multicolored   4.50 4.50
    Nos. 208-211 (4)   8.00 8.00

Souvenir Sheet

212 A42 $3 multicolored   6.00 6.00
No. 212 contains one 40x35mm stamp and
is inscribed in sheet margin for Singapore '95.

Butterflies — A43

Designs: 25c, Danaus plexippus. 40c, Precis villida samoensis. $1, Hypolimnas bolina.
$2, Euploea lewenii.

1995, Oct. 16   **Litho.**   *Perf. 12*
213 A43 25c multicolored   .75 .75
214 A43 40c multicolored   1.25 1.25
215 A43 $1 multicolored   3.00 3.00
216 A43 $2 multicolored   4.50 4.50
    Nos. 213-216 (4)   9.50 9.50

Sea Turtles
A44

1995, Nov. 27   **Litho.**   *Perf. 12*
217 A44 25c Hawksbill   .85 .85
218 A44 40c Leatherback   1.25 1.25
219 A44 $1 Green   3.00 3.00
220 A44 $2 Loggerhead   4.50 4.50
    Nos. 217-220 (4)   9.60 9.60

Souvenir Sheet

221 A44 $3 like #220   6.50 6.50
No. 221 contains one 50x40mm stamp and
is a continuous design.

Souvenir Sheet

New Year 1996 (Year of the
Rat) — A45

Illustration reduced.

1996, Feb. 19   **Litho.**   *Perf. 12*
222 A45 $3 Pacific rat   6.00 6.00
   a.   Ovptd. in sheet margin   6.00 6.00
   b.   Ovptd. in sheet margin   6.00 6.00

Overprinted in sheet margin with red exhibition emblem: No. 222a, CHINA '96; No. 222b,
TAIPEI '96.

Common Design Types
pictured following the introduction.

Queen Elizabeth II, 70th Birthday
Common Design Type

Various portraits of Queen, scenes of Tokelau: 40c, Nukunonu. $1, Atafu, silhouette of
island, boat. $1.25, Atafu, building on island,
boat. $2, Atafu, huts.
$3, Queen wearing tiara, formal dress.

1996, Apr. 22   **Litho.**   *Perf. 13½*
223 CD354 40c multicolored   .65 .65
224 CD354 $1 multicolored   2.10 2.10
225 CD354 $1.25 multicolored   2.40 2.40
226 CD354 $2 multicolored   3.25 3.25
    Nos. 223-226 (4)   8.40 8.40

Souvenir Sheet

227 CD354 $3 multicolored   6.00 6.00

Dolphins — A46

1996, July 15   **Litho.**   *Perf. 14*
228 A46 40c Fraser's   1.50 1.50
229 A46 $1 Common   3.25 3.25
230 A46 $1.25 Striped   3.25 3.25
231 A46 $2 Spotted   4.75 4.75
    Nos. 228-231 (4)   12.75 12.75

Shells
A47

Designs: 40c, Cypraea talpa. $1, Cypraea
mauritiana. $1.25, Cypraea argus. $2,
Cypraea tigris.
$3, Cypraea mauritiana, diff.

1996, Oct. 16   **Litho.**   *Perf. 12*
232 A47 40c multicolored   .85 .85
233 A47 $1 multicolored   1.90 1.90
234 A47 $1.25 multicolored   2.50 2.50
235 A47 $2 multicolored   3.75 3.75
    Nos. 232-235 (4)   9.00 9.00

Souvenir Sheet

236 A47 $3 multicolored   6.00 6.00
No. 236 contains one 50x40mm stamp with
a continuous design.

Souvenir Sheet

New Year 1997 (Year of the
Ox) — A48

Illustration reduced.

1997, Feb. 12   **Litho.**   *Perf. 15x14*
237 A48 $2 multicolored   4.25 4.25
   a.   Overprinted in gold   4.00 4.00
   b.   Overprinted in red   4.25 4.25

No. 237a ovptd. in sheet margin HONG
KONG '97 / STAMP EXHIBITION" in English
and Chinese.
No. 237b overprinted in sheet margin with
Pacific 97 emblem. Issued 5/29.

Humpback
Whale
A49

Designs: 40c, With school of fish. $1, Calf,
adult, young adult. $1.25, With mouth open,
school of fish. $2, Adult, calf.
$3, Mouth, head of whale.

1997, May 29   **Litho.**   *Perf. 12*
238 A49 40c multicolored   .75 .75
239 A49 $1 multicolored   1.75 1.75
240 A49 $1.25 multicolored   2.50 2.50
241 A49 $2 multicolored   3.50 3.50
    Nos. 238-241 (4)   8.50 8.50

Souvenir Sheet

242 A49 $3 multicolored   4.75 4.75
   a.   Ovptd. in sheet margin   5.00 5.00

No. 242a ovptd. in sheet margin, "AUPEX
'97 / 13-16 NOVEMBER / NZ NATIONAL /
STAMP EXHIBITION." Issued: 11/13.

South Pacific Commission, 50th
Anniv. — A50

1997, Sept. 17   Litho.   Perf. 14
243	A50	40c Church, waterfront	.70	.70
244	A50	$1 Beach, child	1.75	1.75
245	A50	$1.25 Island	2.25	2.25
246	A50	$2 Atoll	3.50	3.50
		Nos. 243-246 (4)	8.20	8.20

Year of the
Coral
Reef — A51

Designs: No. 247, Gorgonian coral, emperor
angelfish. No. 248, Soft coral. No. 249, Mushroom coral. No. 250, Staghorn coral. No. 251,
Staghorn coral, Moorish idol.

1997, Oct. 20   Litho.   Perf. 13½
247	A51	$1 multicolored	1.40	1.40
248	A51	$1 multicolored	1.40	1.40
249	A51	$1 multicolored	1.40	1.40
250	A51	$1 multicolored	1.40	1.40
251	A51	$1 multicolored	1.40	1.40
a.		*Strip of 5, #247-251*	7.00	7.00

Souvenir Sheet

New Year 1998 (Year of the
Tiger) — A52

Illustration reduced.

1998, Jan. 28   Litho.   Perf. 14x14½
| 252 | A52 | $2 multicolored | 2.75 | 2.75 |
| a. | | *Ovptd. in sheet margin* | 3.00 | 3.00 |

No. 252a overprinted in sheet margin with
emblem of Singpex '98 Stamp Exhibition,
Singapore.

Diana, Princess of Wales (1961-97)
Common Design Type

Designs: No. 252B, Holding yellow flowers.
No. 253: a, Wearing high-collared ruffled
blouse. b, Wearing red beret. c, Wearing pink
and yellow jacket.

1998, May 15   Litho.   Perf. 14½x14
| 252B | CD355 | $1 multi | 1.25 | 1.25 |

Souvenir Sheet
253	CD355	$1 Sheet of 4,		
		#252B, 253a-		
		253c	5.00	5.00

No. 253 sold for $4 + 50c, with surtax from
international sales being donated to the Princess Diana Memorial Fund and surtax from
national sales being donated to designated
local charity.

Souvenir Sheet

First Stamps of Tokelau, 50th
Anniv. — A53

Designs: a, #3. b. #1. c, #2.

1998, June 22   Litho.   Perf. 14½
| 254 | A53 | $1 Sheet of 3, #a.-c. | 4.50 | 4.50 |

Beetles
A54

Designs: 40c, Oryctes rhinoceros. $1,
Tribolium castaneum. $1.25, Coccinella
repanda. $2, Amarygmus hyrophiloides.
$3, Coccinella repanda, diff.

1998, Aug. 24   Litho.   Perf. 14
255	A54	40c multicolored	.65	.65
256	A54	$1 multicolored	1.75	1.75
257	A54	$1.25 multicolored	2.25	2.25
258	A54	$2 multicolored	3.25	3.25
		Nos. 255-258 (4)	7.90	7.90

Souvenir Sheet
| 259 | A54 | $3 multicolored | 4.25 | 4.25 |

Tropical
Flowers
A55

40c, Ipomoea pes-caprae. $1, Ipomoea littoralis. $1.25, Scaevola taccada. $2, Thespesia populnea.

1998, Nov. 19   Litho.   Perf. 14
260	A55	40c multicolored	.55	.55
261	A55	$1 multicolored	1.40	1.40
262	A55	$1.25 multicolored	1.75	1.75
263	A55	$2 multicolored	2.75	2.75
		Nos. 260-263 (4)	6.45	6.45

Souvenir Sheet

New Year 1999 (Year of the
Rabbit) — A56

Illustration reduced.

1999, Feb. 16   Litho.   Perf. 14
| 264 | A56 | $3 multicolored | 4.50 | 4.50 |
| a. | | *Ovptd. in sheet margin* | 4.50 | 4.50 |

No. 264a overprinted in sheet margin with
emblem of IBRA '99 Intl. Stamp Exhibtion,
Nuremburg. Issued: 4/27.

Souvenir Sheet

Australia '99, World Stamp
Exhibition — A57

Illustration reduced.

1999, Mar. 19
| 265 | A57 | $3 HMS Pandora | 5.00 | 5.00 |

First Manned
Moon Landing,
30th Anniv. — A58

Designs: 25c, Lift-off. 50c, Separation of
stages. 75c, Aldrin deploying instruments on
moon. $1, Planting flag. $1.25, Returning to
Earth. $2, Splashdown.
$3, Apollo 11, Moon, Earth.

Perf. 13½x13¼
1999, Aug. 31   Litho.
266	A58	25c multicolored	.35	.35
267	A58	50c multicolored	.70	.70
268	A58	75c multicolored	1.00	1.00
269	A58	$1 multicolored	1.50	1.50
270	A58	$1.25 multicolored	2.00	2.00
271	A58	$2 multicolored	3.00	3.00
		Nos. 266-271 (6)	8.55	8.55

Souvenir Sheet
272	A58	$3 multicolored	4.25	4.25
a.		*Ovptd. in silver "World Stamp*		
		Expo 2007 7-16 July		
		Anaheim - U.S.A." on sheet		
		margin	3.00	*4.00*

Crabs
A59

1999   Litho.   Perf. 14¼x14½
273	A59	40c Coconut	.65	.65
274	A59	$1 Ghost	1.60	1.60
275	A59	$1.25 Land hermit	2.10	2.10
276	A59	$2 Purple hermit	3.25	3.25
		Nos. 273-276 (4)	7.60	7.60

Souvenir Sheet
| 277 | A59 | $3 Ghost, diff. | 4.25 | 4.25 |

Black-naped
Tern — A60

Designs: 40c, Chick and egg. $1, On nest.
$1.25, Pair near water. $2, Pair in flight.

Perf. 13½x14
1999, Dec. 31   Litho.   Unwmk.
| 278-281 | A60 | Set of 4 | 7.00 | 7.00 |

Souvenir Sheet

New Year 2000 (Year of the
Dragon) — A61

Illustration reduced.

2000   Litho.   Perf. 14x14¼
| 282 | A61 | $3 multi | 5.00 | 5.00 |
| a. | | *Overprinted in sheet margin* | 4.50 | 4.50 |

No. 282a overpritned in sheet margin with
emblem "Bangkok 2000," "World Youth Stamp
Exhibition" and Thai text.

Souvenir Sheet

The Stamp Show 2000,
London — A62

Illustration reduced.

Unwmk.
2000, May 22   Litho.   Perf. 14
| 283 | A62 | $6 multi | 9.00 | 9.00 |

Queen Mother,
100th
Birthday — A63

Various photos. Denominations 40c, $1.20,
$1.80, $3.

Perf. 14½x14¼
2000, Aug. 4   Wmk. 373
| 284-287 | A63 | Set of 4 | 10.00 | 10.00 |

Lizards
A64

Designs: 40c, Gehyra oceanica. $1,
Lepidodactylus lugubris. $1.25, Gehyra mutilata. $2, Emoia cyanura.

2001, Feb. 1   Litho.   Perf. 14
| 288-291 | A64 | Set of 4 | 7.00 | 7.00 |

Souvenir Sheet

New Year 2001 (Year of the
Snake) — A65

2001, Feb. 1
292 A65 $3 multi   6.50 6.50
  a. With gold ovpt. in margin 6.50 6.50

Overprint in margin on No. 292a is for Hong Kong 2001 Stamp Exhibition.

Hippocampus Histrix — A66

Various views of seahorses. Denominations: 40c, $1, $1.25, $2.

2001, Aug. 23 Litho. *Perf. 14*
293-296 A66 Set of 4   7.00 7.00
Souvenir Sheet
297 A66 $3 multi   4.50 4.50

Island Scenery A67

Designs: 40c, Sky over Atafu. $1, Waters of Fakaofo. $2, Sunrise over Nukunonu village. $2.50, Ocean, Nukunonu.

Unwmk.
2001, Dec. 17 Litho. *Perf. 14*
298-301 A67 Set of 4   9.00 9.00
  'a. Souvenir sheet, #298-301 9.00 9.00

Issued: No. 301a issued 5/27/06 for Washington 2006 World Philatelic Exhibition.

Reign Of Queen Elizabeth II, 50th Anniv. Issue
Common Design Type

Designs: Nos. 302, 306a, 40c, Princess Elizabeth, Prince Philip on honeymoon, 1947. Nos. 303, 306b, $1, Wearing purple hat. Nos. 304, 306c, $1.25, Holding Prince Charles, 1948. Nos. 305, 306d, $2, In 1996. No. 306e, $3, 1955 portrait by Annigoni (38x50mm).

Perf. 14¼x14½, 13¾ (#306e)
2002, Feb. 6 Litho. Wmk. 373
With Gold Frames
302-305 CD360 Set of 4   7.00 7.00
Souvenir Sheet
Without Gold Frames
306 CD360 Sheet of 5, #a-e 11.00 11.00

Souvenir Sheet

New Year 2002 (Year of the Horse) — A68

2002, Feb. 12 Litho. *Perf. 14*
307 A68 $4 multi   6.00 6.00
  a. As #307, with gold ovpt. in margin 6.00 6.00

No. 307a was issued 2/22 and has overprint reading "STAMPEX 2002 / HONG KONG / 22-24 FEBRUARY 2002."

Worldwide Fund for Nature (WWF) — A69

Various views of Pelagic thresher shark: 40c, $1, $2, $2.50.

2002, July 2 Litho. *Perf. 14¼*
308-311 A69 Set of 4   9.50 9.50

Queen Mother Elizabeth (1900-2002)
Common Design Type

Designs: 40c, Wearing broad-brimmed hat (black and white photograph). $2, Wearing blue hat.
No. 314: a, $2.50, Wearing hat (black and white photograph). b, $4, Wearing purple hat.

Wmk. 373
2002, Aug. 5 Litho. *Perf. 14¼*
With Purple Frames
312-313 CD361 Set of 2   4.75 4.75
Souvenir Sheet
Without Purple Frames
Perf. 14½x14¼
314 CD361 Sheet of 2, #a-b 10.50 10.50

New Zealand Navy Ships That Have Stopped at Tokelau A70

Designs: 40c, HMNZS Kaniere. $1, HMNZS Endeavour. $2, HMNZS Wellington. $2.50, HMNZS Monowai.

2002, Dec. Litho. Unwmk. *Perf. 14*
315-318 A70 Set of 4   9.00 9.00

Souvenir Sheet

New Year 2003 (Year of the Ram) — A71

2003, Feb. 3
319 A71 $4 multi   6.00 6.00
  a. With Bangkok 2003 overprint in gold in margin 5.00 5.00

Issued: No. 319a, 10/13.

Coronation of Queen Elizabeth II, 50th Anniv.
Common Design Type

Designs: Nos. 320, 322a, $2.50, Queen with maids of honor. Nos. 321, 322b, $4, Queen with Prince Philip.

Perf. 14¼x14½
2003, June 2 Litho. Wmk. 373
Vignettes Framed, Red Background
320-321 CD363 Set of 2 12.00 12.00
Souvenir Sheet
Vignettes Without Frame, Purple Panel
322 CD363 Sheet of 2, #a-b 12.00 12.00

Prince William, 21st Birthday
Common Design Type

No. 323: a, Color photograph at right. b, Color photograph at left.

Wmk. 373
2003, June 21 Litho. *Perf. 14¼*
323 Horiz. pair   6.25 6.25
  a. CD364 $1.50 multi 2.00 2.00
  b. CD364 $3 multi 4.25 4.25

Souvenir Sheet

Welpex 2003 Stamp Show, Wellington, New Zealand — A72

Unwmk.
2003, Nov. 7 Litho. *Perf. 14*
324 A72 $4 multi   6.00 6.00

Souvenir Sheet

New Year 2004 (Year of the Monkey) — A73

2004 Litho. with Foil Application
325 A73 $4 multi   6.00 6.00
  a. With 2004 Hong Kong Stamp Expo emblem in gold in margin 6.00 6.00

Issued: No. 325, 1/22; No. 325a, 1/28.

Island Scenes A74

Designs: 40c, Atafu dawn. $1, Return of the fishermen, Nukunonu. $2, A Fakaofo calm evening glow. $2.50, Solitude in Atafu.

2004, June 30 Litho. *Perf. 14¼x14*
326-329 A74 Set of 4   9.00 9.00

No. 324 Overprinted in Silver

2004, Aug. 8 Litho. *Perf. 14*
330 A72 $4 multi   6.25 6.25

Fregata Ariel A75

Designs: 40c, Bird on nest. $1, Birds in flight. $2, Birds on nest and in flight. $2.50, Bird on nest, diff.

2004, Dec. 20 Litho. *Perf. 14*
331-334 A75 Set of 4   9.00 9.00

Souvenir Sheet

New Year 2005 (Year of the Rooster) — A76

2005, Feb. 9
335 A76 $4 multi   6.00 6.00
  a. Ovptd. in gold in margin with Pacific Explorer 2005 emblem 6.00 6.00

No. 335a issued 4/21/05.

Pope John Paul II (1920-2005) A77

2005, Aug. 18 Litho. *Perf. 14*
336 A77 $1 multi   1.50 1.50

Visit of HMNZS Te Kaha A78

Various views of ship: 40c, $1, $2, $2.50.

2005, Dec. 15 Litho. *Perf. 14*
337-340 A78 Set of 4   9.00 9.00

Souvenir Sheet

New Year 2006 (Year of the Dog) — A79

2006, Jan. 29
341 A79 $4 multi   6.00 6.00

Queen Elizabeth II, 80th Birthday A80

Queen: 40c, With head on hands. $1, In wedding gown. No. 344, $2, Wearing tiara. No. 345, $2.50, Wearing blue hat.
No. 346: a, $2, Like $1. b, $2.50, Like #344.
No. 347: a, #346a overprinted "KIWIPEX." b, #346b overprinted "2006"

2006 Litho. *Perf. 14*
With White Frames
342-345 A80 Set of 4   9.00 9.00
Souvenir Sheets
Without White Frames
346 A80 Sheet of 2, #a-b 6.00 6.00
Overprinted in Metallic Blue
347 A80 Sheet of 2, #a-b 6.00 6.00

Issued: Nos. 342-346, 4/21; No. 347, 11/2. No. 347 is also overprinted in sheet margin

"National Stamp Exhibition, Christchurch, New Zealand."

Souvenir Sheet

New Year 2007 (Year of the Pig) — A81

2007, Feb. 18	**Litho.**		**Perf. 14**
348	A81	$4 multi	6.00 6.00

Worldwide Fund for Nature (WWF) A82

Pacific golden plover: 40c, Flock of birds. $1, Head. $2, Bird standing on one leg. $2.50, Birds and driftwood.

2007, Oct. 19	**Litho.**		**Perf. 14**
349-352	A82	Set of 4	9.00 9.00
352a		Miniature sheet of 16, 4 each #349-352	36.00 36.00

Marine Life — A83

Designs: 10c, Bicolor angelfish. 20c, Staghorn coral. 40c, Black-tipped reef sharks. 50c, Sea star. $1, Porcupine fish. $1.50, Thorny seahorses. $2, Spotted eagle rays. $2.50, Small giant clams. $5, Green turtles. $10, Slate pencil urchin.

2007, Dec. 19			**Perf. 14½x14¼**
353	A83	10c multi	.20 .20
354	A83	20c multi	.30 .30
355	A83	40c multi	.65 .65
356	A83	50c multi	.80 .80
357	A83	$1 multi	1.60 1.60
358	A83	$1.50 multi	2.40 2.40
359	A83	$2 multi	3.25 3.25
360	A83	$2.50 multi	4.00 4.00
361	A83	$5 multi	7.75 7.75
362	A83	$10 multi	15.50 15.50
a.		Miniature sheet, #353-362	37.50 37.50
		Nos. 353-362 (10)	36.45 36.45

Souvenir Sheet

New Year 2008 (Year of the Rat) — A84

2008, Feb. 7			**Perf. 14**
363	A84	$4 multi	6.50 6.50

TONGA

ˈtäŋgə

LOCATION — A group of islands in the south Pacific Ocean, south of Samoa
GOVT. — Kingdom in British Commonwealth
AREA — 289 sq. mi.
POP. — 109,082 (1999 est.)
CAPITAL — Nuku'alofa

This group, also known as the Friendly Islands, became a British Protectorate in 1900 under the Anglo-German Agreement of 1899. On June 4, 1970, the United Kingdom ceased to have any responsibility for the external relations of Tonga.

12 Pence = 1 Shilling
20 Shillings = 1 Pound
100 Seniti = 1 Pa'anga (1967)

> Catalogue values for unused stamps in this country are for Never Hinged items, beginning with Scott 87 in the regular postage section, Scott B1 in the semipostal section, Scott C1 in the air post section Scott CE1 in the air post special delivery section, Scott CO1 in the air post official section, and Scott O11 in the officials section.

Watermarks

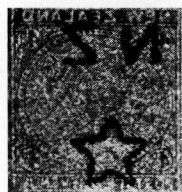

Wmk. 62 — NZ and Small Star Wide Apart

Wmk. 79 — Turtles

King George I — A1

		Perf. 12x11½		
1886-92		**Typo.**		**Wmk. 62**
1	A1	1p car rose ('87)	11.50	4.00
a.		Perf. 12½	450.00	7.00
b.		Perf. 12½x10		
2	A1	2p violet ('87)	32.50	3.50
a.		Perf. 12½	57.50	14.00
3	A1	6p ultra ('88)	57.50	2.75
a.		Perf. 12½	67.50	4.00
4	A1	6p org yel ('92)	18.00	30.00
5	A1	1sh blue grn ('88)	62.50	7.25
a.		Perf. 12½	110.00	4.50
b.		Half used as 6p on cover		
		Nos. 1-5 (5)	182.00	47.50

For surcharges and overprints see #6-9, 24.

Nos. 1 and 2 Surcharged or Overprinted in Black:

a

b

1891, Nov. 10			**Perf. 12x11½**	
6	A1(a)	4p on 1p car rose	3.50	12.50
a.		No period after "PENCE"	57.50	125.00
7	A1(a)	8p on 2p violet	40.00	100.00

1891, Nov. 23			**Perf. 12½**	

Two types of overprint:
I — Solid stars, rays pointed and short.
II — Open-center stars, rays blunt and long.

8	A1(b)	1p car rose (I)	5.00	57.50
a.		Overprinted with 3 stars (I)	375.00	
b.		Overprinted with 4 stars (I)	475.00	
c.		Overprinted with 5 stars (I)	750.00	
d.		Type II	50.00	57.50
e.		Perf. 12x11½ (I or II)	350.00	

9	A1(b)	2p violet (I)	80.00	42.50
a.		Type II	80.00	42.50
b.		Perf. 12x11½ (I or II)	425.00	

Coat of Arms
A4

George I
A5

1892, Nov. 10		**Typo.**	**Perf. 12x11½**	
10	A4	1p rose	14.00	19.00
a.		Diagonal half used as ½p on cover		975.00
11	A5	2p olive gray	18.00	18.00
12	A4	4p red brown	55.00	80.00
13	A5	8p violet	62.50	200.00
14	A5	1sh brown	90.00	125.00
		Nos. 10-14 (5)	239.50	442.00

For surcharges and overprints see Nos. 15-23, 25-28, 36-37, O1-O10.

Types A4 and A5 Surcharged in Carmine or Black:

c

d

f

FIVE PENCE.

1893				
15	A4	½p on 1p ultra (C)	26.00	30.00
a.		Surcharge omitted		
16	A4	½p on 1p ultra	50.00	55.00
17	A5	2½p on 2p blue grn (C)	16.00	13.50
18	A5	2½p on 2p blue grn	19.00	19.00
a.		Double surcharge		2,000.
19	A4	5p on 4p org yel (C)	4.50	7.50
20	A5	7½p on 8p rose (C)	27.50	85.00
		Nos. 15-20 (6)	143.00	210.00

Stamps of 1886-92 Surcharged in Blue or Black:

g

h

1894				
21	A4	½p on 4p red brn (Bl)	2.25	8.00
a.		"SURCHARCE"	10.00	22.50
b.		Pair, one without surcharge		
c.		"HALF PENNY" omitted		
22	A5	½p on 1sh brn (Bk)	2.75	12.50
a.		Double surcharge	310.00	
b.		"SURCHARCE"	11.50	45.00
c.		As "b," double surcharge	1,000.	
23	A5	2½p on 8p vio (Bk)	5.75	9.25
a.		No period after "SURCHARGE"	35.00	62.50
24	A1	2½p on 1sh blue grn (Bk)	62.50	27.50
a.		No period after "SURCHARGE"	200.00	
b.		Perf. 12x11½	17.50	47.50
		Nos. 21-24 (4)	73.25	57.25

Type A5 with Same Surcharges in Carmine

1895			**Unwmk.**	
25	A5(g)	1p on 2p lt blue	50.00	25.00
26	A5(h)	1½p on 2p lt bl, perf. 12x11	55.00	32.50
a.		Perf. 12	70.00	32.50

27	A5(h)	2½p on 2p lt blue	45.00	50.00
b.		Without period	250.00	250.00
28	A5(h)	7½p on 2p lt bl, perf. 12x11	70.00	50.00
a.		Perf. 12	450.00	
		Nos. 25-28 (4)	220.00	157.50

King George II — A13

1895, Aug. 16			**Perf. 12**	
29	A13	1p gray green	22.50	30.00
a.		Diagonal half used as ½p on cover		850.00
b.		Horiz. pair, imperf. btwn.	—	6,900.
30	A13	2½p dull rose	22.50	15.00
31	A13	5p brt blue, perf. 12x11	26.00	57.50
a.		Perf. 12	25.00	57.50
b.		Perf. 11	400.00	
32	A13	7½p yellow	35.00	55.00
		Nos. 29-32 (4)	106.00	157.50

Type A13 Redrawn and Surcharged "g" or "h" in Black

33	A13(g)	½p on 2½p red	35.00	37.50
a.		"SURCHARCE"	80.00	
b.		Period after "Postage"	85.00	
34	A13(g)	1p on 2½p red	70.00	45.00
a.		Period after "Postage"	125.00	
35	A13(h)	7½p on 2½p red	62.50	70.00
a.		Period after "Postage"	110.00	
		Nos. 33-35 (3)	167.50	152.50

Nos. 26 and 28 with Additional Surcharge in Violet and Black

1896, May			**Perf. 12x11**	
36	A5	½p on 1½p on 2p	500.00	
a.		Tongan surch. reading up	475.00	475.00
b.		Perf. 12	475.00	475.00
c.		As "a," perf. 12	500.00	500.00
d.		"Haalf"	2,100.	
37	A5	½p on 7½p on 2p	97.50	125.00
a.		"Half penny" inverted	2,100.	
b.		"Half penny" double		
c.		Tongan surch. reading up	97.50	125.00
d.		Tongan surcharge as "c" and double		
e.		"Hafl Penny"	1,750.	1,800.
f.		"Hafl" only	3,750.	
g.		"Hwlf"		
h.		Periods instead of hyphens after words	1,000.	
j.		Perf. 12	925.00	

Coat of Arms — A17

Ovava Tree — A18

George II — A19

Prehistoric Trilithon, Tongatabu — A20

Breadfruit
A21

Coral Formations
A22

View of
Haabai
A23

Red-breasted Musk
Parrot — A24

View of
Vavau — A25

Two types of 2p:
I — Top of sword hilt shows above "2."
II — No hilt shows.

Wmk. 79 Sideways

		1897-1934	Engr.	Perf. 14	
38	A17	½p dark blue	4.75	3.00
39	A17	½p green ('34)	1.10	1.40
40	A18	1p dp red & blk	.90	.90
41	A19	2p bis & sep (I)	18.00	6.25
a.		bister & gray, type II	35.00	3.75
42	A19	2½p lt blue & blk	7.00	1.60
a.		"½" without fraction bar	110.00	75.00
43	A20	3p ol grn & blk	4.00	9.75
44	A21	4p dull vio & grn	4.25	4.50
45	A19	5p orange & blk	35.00	16.00
46	A22	6p red	15.00	7.00
47	A19	7½p green & blk	18.00	26.00
a.		Center inverted	5,500.	
48	A19	10p carmine & blk	50.00	55.00
49	A19	1sh red brn & blk	16.00	8.50
50	A23	2sh dk ultra & blk	70.00	75.00
51	A24	2sh6p dk violet	57.50	35.00
52	A25	5sh dull red & blk	55.00	55.00
		Nos. 38-52 (15)	356.50	304.90

See Nos. 73-74, 77-78, 80-81. For surcharges see Nos. 63-69.

Stamp of 1897
Overprinted in
Black

1899, June 1

53	A18	1p red & black	35.00	72.50
a.		"1889" instead of "1899"	225.00	400.00
b.		Comma omitted after June		
c.		Double overprint		

Marriage of George II to Lavinia, June 1, 1899. The letters "T L" are the initials of Taufa'ahau, the King's family name, and Lavinia.

Queen
Salote — A26

Dies of 2p:
Die I — Ball of "2" smaller.
Die II — Ball of "2" larger. "U" has spur at left.

		1920-35	Engr.	Wmk. 79	
54	A26	1½p gray blk ('35)	.55	3.50
55	A26	2p violet & sepia	9.75	15.00
56	A26	2p dl vio & blk (I) ('24)	9.75	2.75
a.		Die II	5.00	7.50
57	A26	2½p blue & black	5.50	45.00
58	A26	2½p ultra ('34)	2.25	1.10
59	A26	5p red org & blk	3.75	5.50
60	A26	7½p green & blk	2.00	2.00
61	A26	10p carmine & blk	2.90	5.50
62	A26	1sh red brown & blk	1.40	2.90
		Nos. 54-62 (9)	37.85	83.25

See Nos. 75-76, 79.

Stamps of 1897 Surcharged in Dark Blue or Red

TWO PENCE
PENI-E-UA

1923

63	A19	2p on 5p org & blk	1.10	1.00
64	A19	2p on 7½p grn & blk	20.00	32.50
65	A19	2p on 10p car & blk	12.50	57.50
66	A19	2p on 1sh red brn & blk	55.00	25.00
67	A23	2p on 2sh ultra & blk (R)	22.50	22.50
68	A24	2p on 2sh6p dk vio (R)	35.00	7.50
69	A25	2p on 5sh dull red & blk (R)	16.00	16.00
		Nos. 63-69 (7)	162.10	162.00

Queen
Salote — A27

Inscribed "1918-1938"

1938, Oct. 12 — Perf. 14

70	A27	1p carmine & blk	.50	4.00
71	A27	2p violet & blk	4.50	3.00
72	A27	2½p ultra & blk	4.50	3.75
		Nos. 70-72 (3)	9.50	10.75
		Set, never hinged	18.00	

Accession of Queen Salote Tupou, 20th anniv.
See Nos. 82-86.

Types of 1897-1920

1942 — Engr. — Wmk. 4

Die III of 2p:
Foot of "2" longer than in Die II, extending beyond curve of loop.

73	A17	½p green	.30	2.75
74	A18	1p scarlet & blk	1.25	2.75
75	A26	2p dull vio & blk (II)	2.25	3.00
a.		Die III	4.25	8.25
76	A26	2½p ultra	.90	2.00
77	A20	3p green & black	.30	3.75
78	A22	6p orange red	1.50	2.25
79	A26	1sh red brown & gray blk	1.40	3.50
80	A24	2sh6p dk violet	22.50	24.00
81	A25	5sh dull red & brn blk	14.00	50.00
		Nos. 73-81 (9)	44.40	94.00
		Set, never hinged	62.50	

Type of 1938, Inscribed "1918-1943"

1944, Jan. 25

82	A27	1p rose car & blk	.20	1.10
83	A27	2p purple & blk	.20	1.10
84	A27	3p dk yel grn & blk	.20	1.10
85	A27	6p red orange & blk	.25	2.00
86	A27	1sh dk red brn & blk	.25	2.00
		Nos. 82-86 (5)	1.10	7.30
		Set, never hinged	2.00	

25th anniv. of the accession of Queen Salote.

Catalogue values for unused stamps in this section, from this point to the end of the section, are for Never Hinged items.

UPU Issue
Common Design Types
Engr.; Name Typo. on 3p, 6p
Perf. 13½, 11x11½

1949, Oct. 10 — Wmk. 4

87	CD306	2½p ultra	.40	.90
88	CD307	3p deep olive	1.75	3.25
89	CD308	6p deep carmine	.55	.55
90	CD309	1sh red brown	.55	.55
		Nos. 87-90 (4)	3.25	5.25

Common Design Types pictured following the introduction.

A28

A29

Queen
Salote — A30

1950, Nov. 1 — Photo. — Perf. 12½

91	A28	1p cerise	1.00	2.25
92	A29	5p green	1.00	2.50
93	A30	1sh violet	1.00	3.00
		Nos. 91-93 (3)	3.00	7.75

50th anniv. of the birth of Queen Salote.

Map and Island
Scene — A31

Badges
and Royal
Palace
A32

2½p, Queen Salote & coastal scene. 3p, Queen Salote & ship "Bellona." 5p, Flag of Tonga, island view. 1sh, Arms of Tonga & Great Britain.

1951, July 2 — Engr. — Wmk. 4

94	A31	½p deep green	.30	3.00
95	A32	1p carmine & black	.30	3.00
96	A32	2½p choc & dp grn	.60	3.00
97	A31	3p ultra & org yel	2.25	3.00
98	A32	5p dp green & car	1.75	1.10
99	A32	1sh purple & orange	2.50	1.10
		Nos. 94-99 (6)	7.70	14.20

50th anniv. of the treaty of friendship between Tonga and Great Britain.

Royal
Palace,
Nukualofa
A33

Map of Tonga
Islands — A34

Designs: 1½p, Fisherman. 2p, Canoe and schooners. 3p, Swallows' Cave, Vavau. 3½p, Map of Tongatabu. 4p, Vavau harbor. 5p, Post Office, Nukualofa. 6p, Fuaamotu airport. 8p, Wharf, Nukualofa. 2sh, Beach at Lifuka, Haapai. 5sh, Mutiny on the Bounty. 10sh, Queen Salote. £1, Arms of Tonga.

Perf. 11½x11, 11x11½

1953, July 1 — Wmk. 79

100	A33	1p chocolate & blk	.30	.20
101	A33	1½p emerald & ultra	.30	.20
102	A33	2p black & aqua	.30	.20
103	A34	3p dk grn & ultra	.30	.20
104	A33	3½p carmine & yel	.30	.20
105	A33	4p rose car & yel	.30	.20
106	A33	5p choc & ultra	.30	.20
107	A33	6p black & dp ultra	.40	.20
108	A33	8p purple & emer	.45	.25
109	A34	1sh black & ultra	.75	.40
110	A33	2sh choc & ol grn	5.00	.90
111	A33	5sh purple & yel	15.00	5.00
112	A34	10sh black & yellow	9.00	6.00
113	A34	£1 ultra, car & yel	11.00	10.50
		Nos. 100-113 (14)	43.70	24.65

For surcharges and overprints see Nos. 119-126, 158-174, 182-202, 210-215, 218-221, 237, 269-273, C34-C39, C47-C54, C87-C91, CO4-CO6, CO11-CO20, CO27-CO43.

Whaling
Ship and
Longboat
A35

1p, Stamp of 1886. 4p, Post Office, Customs & Treasury Building & Queen Salote. 5p, Diesel-driven ship Aoniu. 1sh, Plane over Tongatabu.

1961, Dec. 1 — Photo. — Perf. 14½x13½

114	A35	1p brn org & car rose	.30	.20
115	A35	2p ultra	.90	.30
116	A35	4p bright green	.30	.20
117	A35	5p purple	.90	.30
118	A35	1sh red brown	1.00	.60
		Nos. 114-118 (5)	3.40	1.70

75th anniversary of postal service.
For surcharges & overprints see #146-151, 216-221, C16-C21, C55-C57, CO1-CO3, CO9-CO10.

Stamps of 1953 and 1961 Overprinted in Red: "1862 / TAU'ATAINA / EMANCIPATION / 1962"

Perf. 11½x11, 11x11½, 14½x13
Engr.; Photo. (4p)

1962, Feb. 7 — Wmk. 79

119	A33	1p choc & blk	.20	.60
120	A35	4p brt green	.20	.65
121	A33	5p choc & ultra	.20	.65
122	A33	6p black & dp ultra	.20	1.10
123	A33	8p purple & emer	.50	1.60
124	A34	1sh black & ultra	.35	.80
125	A34	2sh on 3p dk grn & ultra	.60	3.75
126	A33	5sh purple & yellow	6.25	3.75
		Nos. 119-126 (8)	8.50	12.90

Cent. of emancipation. See Nos. CO1-CO6.

Freedom from Hunger Issue
Common Design Type with Portrait of Queen Salote
Perf. 14x14½

1963, June 4 — Wmk. 79 — Photo.

127	CD314	11p ultra	.70	.35

Coat of
Arms,
¼ Koula
Coin,
Reverse
A36

Designs: 2p, 9p, 2sh, Queen Salote (head), ¼-koula coin, obverse.

Litho.; Embossed on Gilt Foil
1963, July 15 — Unwmk. — Die Cut
Diameter: 40mm

128	A36	1p dp carmine	.20	.20
129	A36	2p violet blue	.20	.20
130	A36	6p dp green	.30	.30
131	A36	9p magenta	.35	.35

132 A36 1sh6p violet .70 .70
133 A36 2sh emerald .75 .75
Nos. 128-133,C1-C6,CO7 (13) 13.45 13.50

1st gold coinage of Polynesia. Backed with paper inscribed in salmon-colored alternating rows: "TONGA" and "THE FRIENDLY ISLANDS" in multiple.

For surcharges see #140-145, C11-C15, CO8.

Red Cross Centenary Issue
Common Design Type with Portrait of Queen Salote
Wmk. 79

1963, Sept. 2		Litho.	Perf. 13
134	CD315	2p black & red	.25 .20
135	CD315	11p ultra & red	.75 1.00

Queen Salote on ¼-Koula Coin A37

Litho.; Embossed on Gilt Foil

1964, Oct. 19		Unwmk.	Die Cut
136	A37	3p pink	.20 .20
137	A37	9p light blue	.20 .20
138	A37	2sh yellow green	.50 .50
139	A37	5sh pale lilac	1.50 1.50
		Nos. 136-139,C7-C10 (8)	5.50 5.50

Pan-Pacific and Southeast Asia Women's Association Conf., Nukualofa, Aug. 1964. See note on paper backing after No. 133.

For surcharges & overprints see #152-157, 263-268.

Nos. 128-133 Surcharged in Red, White or Black

1965, Mar. 18
140	A36	1sh3p on 1sh6p (R)	.20 .20
141	A36	1sh9p on 9p (W)	.20 .20
142	A36	2sh6p on 6p (R)	.25 .25
143	A36	5sh on 1p	22.50 22.50
144	A36	5sh on 2p	4.00 4.00
145	A36	5sh on 2sh	.90 .90
		Nos. 140-145,C11-C15,CO8 (12)	82.00 82.00

Nos. 114-115 Overprinted and Surcharged in Purple or Red

Perf. 14½x13½
1966, June 18		Photo.	Wmk. 79
146	A35	1p (P)	.20 .20
147	A35	3p on 1p (P)	.20 .20
148	A35	6p on 2p (R)	.20 .20
149	A35	1sh2p on 2p (R)	.20 .20
150	A35	2sh on 2p (R)	.35 .20
151	A35	3sh on 2p (R)	.35 .20
		Nos. 146-151,C16-C21,CO9-CO10 (14)	5.55 3.10

Centenary of Tupou College and of secondary education.

Nos. 136-137 Overprinted and Surcharged in Silver on Black or Ultramarine

Illustration reduced.

Litho.; Embossed on Gilt Foil
1966, Dec. 16		Unwmk.	Die Cut
152	A37	3p pink (U)	.20 .20
153	A37	5p on 9p lt blue	.20 .20
154	A37	9p lt bl	.20 .20
155	A37	1sh7p on 3p pink (U)	.55 .55
156	A37	3sh6p on 9p lt blue	.95 .95
157	A37	6sh6p on 3p pink (U)	1.75 1.75
		Nos. 152-157,C22-C26 (11)	9.25 9.25

Nos. 100-110, 147 and 151 Surcharged in Black or Red

Perf. 11½x11, 11x11½, 14½x13½
1967, Mar. 25			Wmk. 79
158	A33	1s on 1p	.20 .20
159	A33	3s on 4p	.20 .20
160	A33	3s on 5p	.20 .20
161	A33	4s on 5p	.20 .20
162	A33	5s on 3½p	.20 .20
163	A33	6s on 8p	.20 .20
164	A33	7s on 1½p	.20 .20
165	A33	8s on 6p	.20 .20
166	A34	9s on 3p	.20 .20
167	A34	10s on 1sh	.25 .25
168	A35	11s on 3p on 1p	.35 .35
169	A35	21s on 3sh on 2p	.55 .55
170	A33	23s on 1p	.60 .60
171	A33	30s on 2sh (R) (1-line surcharge)	1.25 1.25
172	A33	30s on 2sh (R) (3-line surcharge)	1.40 1.40
173	A33	50s on 6p (R)	1.60 1.60
174	A33	60s on 2p (R)	2.00 2.00
		Nos. 158-174 (17)	9.80 9.80

The size, typeface and arrangement of surcharge vary on the different denominations.

King Taufa'ahau IV — A38

Designs: 1s, 4s, 28s, 1pa, Coat of Arms, reverse of new palladium coins.

Litho.; Embossed on Palladium Foil
1967, July 4 Unwmk. Die Cut

Diameter: 1s, 44mm; 2s, 50s, 52mm; 4s, 59mm; 15s, 68mm; 28s, 40mm; 1pa, 74mm

175	A38	1s orange & brt bl	.20 .20
176	A38	2s brt bl & dp mag	.20 .20
177	A38	4s emerald & mag	.20 .20
178	A38	15s blue grn & vio	.35 .35
179	A38	28s blk & brt red lil	.60 .60
180	A38	50s red & vio bl	1.10 1.10
181	A38	1pa ultra & brt rose	2.75 2.75
		Nos. 175-181,C27-C33 (14)	13.00 13.00

Coronation of King Taufa'ahau IV, July 4, 1967. Backed with paper inscribed in yellow

---

alternating rows: "Tonga The Friendly Islands" and "Historically The First Palladium Coinage." For surcharges and overprints see Nos. 203-209, C40-C46, CO21-CO24.

Types of Regular Issue, 1953, Surcharged

Wmk. 79
1967, Dec. 15		Engr.	Die Cut
182	A33	1s on 1p yellow & blk	.20 .20
183	A33	2s on 2p carmine & ultra	.20 .20
184	A34	3s on 3p brown org & yel	.20 .20
185	A33	4s on 4p purple & yel	.20 .20
186	A33	5s on 5p green & yel	.20 .20
187	A34	10s on 10p rose red & yel	.20 .20
188	A33	20s on 2sh carmine & ultra	.25 .25
189	A33	50s on 5sh sepia & yel	2.00 2.00
190	A34	1pa on 10sh orange yel	.75 .75
		Nos. 182-190,C34-C36,CO12-CO14 (15)	7.70 7.70

Arrival of US Peace Corps.

Nos. 100-111 Surcharged in Red, Black or Ultramarine

Perf. 11½x11, 11x11½
1968, Apr. 6		Engr.	Wmk. 79
191	A33	1s on 1p (R)	.20 .20
192	A33	2s on 4p	.20 .20
193	A34	3s on 3p (U)	.20 .20
194	A33	4s on 5p (R)	.20 .20
195	A33	5s on 2p (R)	.20 .20
196	A33	6s on 6p (R)	.20 .20
197	A33	7s on 1½p (R)	.20 .20
198	A33	8s on 8p (R)	.20 .20
199	A33	9s on 3½p	.30 .30
200	A34	10s on 1sh (R)	.30 .30
201	A33	20s on 5sh (R)	1.25 1.25
202	A33	2pa on 2sh (R)	2.75 2.75
		Nos. 191-202,C37-C39,CO15-CO18 (19)	13.10 13.10

Surcharge on 3s and 10s is vertical.

Nos. 175-181 Overprinted: "H.M'S BIRTHDAY / 4 July 1968" in Gold on Red Panel on 1s, 4s, 28s and 1pa. "HIS MAJESTY'S 50th BIRTHDAY" in Silver on Blue Panel on 2s, 15s and 50s

Litho.; Embossed on Palladium Foil
1968, July 4		Unwmk.	Die Cut
203	A38	1s orange & brt bl	.20 .20
204	A38	2s brt bl & dp mag	.20 .20
205	A38	4s emerald & mag	.20 .20
206	A38	15s blue grn & vio	.55 .55
207	A38	28s blk & brt red lil	1.10 1.10
208	A38	50s red & vio bl	1.90 1.90
209	A38	1pa ultra & brt rose	4.00 4.00
		Nos. 203-209,C40-C46,CO21-CO24 (18)	31.25 27.75

Types of 1953 Surcharged in Red, Black or Green: "Friendly Islands / Field & Track Trials / South Pacific Games / Port Moresby 1969"

Designs as before.

Wmk. 79
1968, Dec. 19		Engr.	Die Cut
210	A33	5s on 5p green & yel (R)	.20 .20
211	A34	10s on 1sh cer & buff	.20 .20
212	A33	15s on 2sh rose car & bl	.30 .30
213	A33	25s on 2p rose car & bl	.30 .20
214	A33	50s on 1p yel & blk	.50 .30
215	A34	75s on 10sh org (G)	.85 .45
		Nos. 210-215,C47-C54,CO19-CO20 (16)	8.00 4.75

Issued to publicize the field and track trials for the third South Pacific Games, Port Moresby, 1969. The overprint is in 5 lines on the horizontal stamps, in 7 lines on vertical stamps. On the vertical stamps "Trial" is printed on the line ahead of "Field & Track." On #215 the denomination is spelled out.

Nos. 149-150 and Types of 1953 Surcharged
Perf. 14½x13½
1968		Photo.	Wmk. 79
216	A35	1s on 1sh2p on 2p	1.60 1.60
217	A35	1s on 2sh on 2p	1.60 1.60

		Engr.	Die Cut
218	A33	1s on 6p yellow & blk	.90 .90
219	A33	2s on 3½p dk blue	1.00 1.00
220	A33	3s on 1½p lt green	1.00 1.00
221	A33	4s on 8p black & pale grn	1.10 1.10
		Nos. 216-221,C55-C57 (9)	12.00 10.20

Banana — A39

Unwmk.
1969, Apr. 21		Typo.	Die Cut
		Self-adhesive	
222	A39	1s yellow, black & red	1.00 .85
223	A39	2s yel, black & emer	1.10 1.00
224	A39	3s yellow, black & lil	1.25 1.10
225	A39	4s yellow, black & ultra	1.40 1.10
226	A39	5s yel, blk & ol grn	1.75 1.75
		Nos. 222-226 (5)	6.50 5.80

Packed in boxes of 200. See Nos. 248-252, 297-301, O11-O15, design A75.

Peelable Backing Inscribed
Starting in 1969, self-adhesive stamps are attached to peelable paper backing printed with "TONGA where time begins" in multiple rows and various colors, unless otherwise stated.

Shot-putter — A40

1969, Aug. 13		Litho.	Die Cut
		Self-adhesive	
227	A40	1s bister, red & blk	.20 .20
228	A40	3s bis, red & emer	.20 .20
229	A40	6s bister, red & bl	.20 .20
230	A40	10s bister, red & pur	.20 .20
231	A40	30s bister, red & bl	.30 .30
		Nos. 227-231,C58-C62,CO25-CO26 (12)	5.50 5.50

3rd Pacific Games, Port Moresby, Papua and New Guinea, Aug. 13-23.

Oil Derrick and Map of Tonga Islands — A41

1969, Dec. 23		Litho.	Die Cut
		Self-adhesive	
232	A41	3s brown & multi	.20 .20
233	A41	7s brt blue & multi	.20 .20
234	A41	20s multicolored	.55 .55
235	A41	25s orange & multi	.80 .80
236	A41	35s henna brn & multi	1.10 1.10

Type of Regular Issue, 1953,
Surcharged in Red: "1969 / OIL /
SEARCH / T$1.10" and Oil Derrick
Obliterating Old Denomination

Wmk. 79   Die Cut

237 A34 1.10pa on £1 green &
        multi   3.50   3.50
*Nos. 232-237,C63-C67,CO27
        (12)   12.70 12.70*

First scientific search for oil in Tonga.

British and Tongan Royal
Families — A42

Litho.; Gold Embossed
1970, Mar. 7 Self-adhesive Die Cut

238 A42 3s multicolored   .20   .20
239 A42 5s multicolored   .20   .20
240 A42 10s multicolored   .55   .40
241 A42 25s multicolored   1.25   .90
242 A42 50s multicolored   2.75 2.00
*Nos. 238-242,C68-C72,CO28-
        CO30 (13)   27.45 18.75*

Visit of Elizabeth II, Prince Philip and Princess Anne, Mar. 1970.

Open Book, George Tupou I and II,
Salote Tupou III, Taufa'ahau Tupou IV
and Tonga Flag — A43

Litho.; Gold Embossed
1970, June 4   Die Cut
Self-adhesive

243 A43 3s multicolored   .20   .20
244 A43 7s multicolored   .25   .25
245 A43 15s multicolored   .60   .60
246 A43 25s multicolored   .70   .70
247 A43 50s multicolored   1.25 1.25
*Nos. 243-247,C73-C77,CO31-
        CO33 (13)   13.25 13.25*

Tonga's independence and entry into the
British Commonwealth of Nations.
For surcharges see Nos. CO49-CO51,
CO71.

Banana Type of 1969 redrawn and

Coconut — A44

1970, June 9   Typo.
Self-adhesive

248 A39 1s yellow, blk & mag .40   .40
249 A39 2s yellow, blk & bl   .50   .50
250 A39 3s yellow, blk & brn .50   .50
251 A39 4s yellow, blk & grn .50   .50
252 A39 5s yellow, blk & org .55   .55

Typo.; Embossed on Gilt Foil
Coconut Brown

253 A44 6s blue, grn & mag   .65   .65
254 A44 7s purple & green   .70   .70
255 A44 8s gold, grn & vio bl .75 .75
256 A44 9s carmine & green   .85   .85
257 A44 10s gold, grn & org .85   .85
Nos. 248-257,O11-O20 (20)   16.00 16.00

Nos. 248-252 have no white shading in
upper part of the banana, Nos. 222-226 have
white shading. Nos. 253-256 have self-adhesive control numbers in lower left corner of

paper backing. Paper backing is green on
Nos. 253-257.
See Nos. 302-306, O26-O30.

Red
Cross
and
Arms of
Tonga
A45

1970, Oct. 17   Litho.   Die Cut
Self-adhesive

258 A45 3s red, black & grn   .20   .20
259 A45 7s red, blk & vio bl .20   .20
260 A45 15s red, blk & red lil .55 .55
261 A45 25s red, black & brt
             grn   .90   .90
262 A45 75s red, black & brn 4.50 4.50
*Nos. 258-262,C78-C82,CO34-
        CO36 (13)   28.25 28.25*

Centenary of the British Red Cross.

Nos. 153, 152
Surcharged

15s

Litho.; Embossed on Gilt Foil
1971, Jan. 31   Die Cut

263 A37 2s on 9p lt blue   .20   .20
264 A37 3s on 9p lt blue   .20   .20
265 A37 5s on 3p pink   .35   .20
266 A37 15s on 9p lt blue   1.10   .65
267 A37 25s on 3p pink   1.50 1.00
268 A37 50s on 3p pink   3.50 2.10
*Nos. 263-268,C83-C86,CO37-
        CO40 (14)   35.00 24.35*

In memory of Queen Salote (1900-65). The
"In Memoriam" inscription is in silver on black
panel on the 2s, 3s and 15s; in silver on
ultramarine panel on the 5s, 25s and 50s. The
dates and denominations are all on black
panels in silver and metallic red, green,
bronze, magenta or gold respectively.

Type of
Regular
Issue, 1953,
Surcharged
in Red and
Black

1971   Engr.   Wmk. 79   Imperf

269 A33 3s on 8p black &
             pale grn   .20   .20
270 A33 7s on 4p pur & yel   .25   .24
271 A33 25s on 1p yel & blk .55   .40
272 A33 75s on 2sh car & ultra 3.25 2.10
*Nos. 269-272,C87-C89,CO41-
        CO43 (10)   14.00   9.20*

Philatokyo 71, Philatelic Exposition, Tokyo,
Apr. 19-29.

Type of Regular
Issue, 1971,
Surcharged

1971

273 A34 15s on 1sh car & buff .50 .50
Nos. 273,C90-C91 (3)   4.00 4.00

Centenary of Japanese postal service.

Self-adhesive & Imperf.
Starting with Nos. 274-278, all issues
are self-adhesive and imperforate,
unless otherwise stated.

Pole Vault — A46   Gold Medal
                             of
                         Merit — A47

1971, July   Litho.   Unwmk.

274 A46 3s green, blk & brn .20   .20
275 A46 7s red, blk & brn   .20   .20
276 A46 15s green, blk & brn .35   .35
277 A46 25s rose lil, blk &
             brn   .45   .45
278 A46 50s dk bl, blk & brn .95   .95
*Nos. 274-278,C92-C96,CO44-
        CO46 (13)   8.50   8.50*

4th South Pacific Games, Papeete, French
Polynesia, Sept. 8-19.
For surcharges see Nos. 332, C140.

1971, Oct. 30   Litho; Embossed

24s, Silver Medal of Merit. 38s, Bronze
Medal of Merit, obverse (King Taufa'ahau IV).

279 A47 3s gold & multi   .20   .20
280 A47 24s silver & multi   .35   .35
281 A47 38s bronze & multi   .75   .75
*Nos. 279-281,C99-C101,CO49-
        CO51 (9)   8.70   8.70*

First investiture of Tongan Medal of Merit.
For surcharges see Nos. 333-336.

Juggler,
UNICEF
Emblem
A48

1971, Dec.   Litho.

282 A48 2s violet & multi   .20   .20
283 A48 4s multicolored   .20   .20
284 A48 8s blue & multi   .20   .20
285 A48 16s emerald & multi .35   .35
286 A48 30s lil rose & multi .65   .65
*Nos. 282-286,C102-
        C106,CO52-CO54 (13) 13.00 13.00*

25th anniv. of UNICEF.

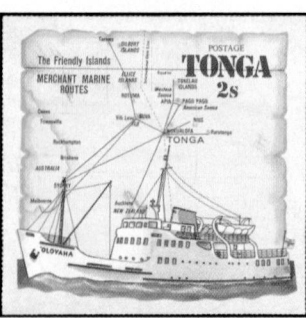

Merchant Marine Routes from Tonga
and "Olovaha" — A49

1972, Apr. 14

287 A49 2s blue & multi   .35   .35
288 A49 10s magenta & multi .85   .35
289 A49 17s brown & multi   1.25   .35
290 A49 21s dk green & multi 1.40   .50
291 A49 60s multicolored   6.50 4.00
*Nos. 287-291,C107-
        C111,CO55-CO57 (13) 41.95 28.75*

Togan Merchant Marine publicity
For surcharges see Nos. C124, CO66-
CO69.

King Taufa'ahau IV Coronation Coin,
¼ Hau — A50

Litho.; Embossed on Metallic Foil
1972, July 15

292 A50 5s silver & multi   .20   .20
293 A50 7s silver & multi   .20   .20
294 A50 10s silver & multi   .20   .20
295 A50 17s silver & multi   .40   .40
296 A50 60s silver & multi 1.40 1.40
*Nos. 292-296,C112-
        C116,CO58-CO60 (13) 12.75 12.75*

Coronation of King Taufa'ahau IV, 5th anniv.

Coconut Type of 1970 and

Banana
A51

Watermelon — A52

1972, Sept. 30   Typo.

297 A51 1s brt yel, red & blk .35 .20
298 A51 2s brt yel, bl & blk .40   .20
299 A51 3s brt yel, emer &
             blk   .45   .20
300 A51 4s brt yel & blk   .45   .25
301 A51 5s brt yel & brn blk .45   .25
302 A44 6s brn & grn   .50   .25
303 A44 7s brn, ultra & grn   .55   .30
304 A44 8s brn, mag & grn   .55   .30
305 A44 9s brn, red & grn   .55   .30
306 A44 10s brn, bl & grn   .65   .35
307 A52 15s green, org brn &
             ultra   1.40   .50
308 A52 20s grn, bl & red   1.50   .70
309 A52 25s grn, red & brn   1.75   .80
310 A52 40s grn, bl & org   3.00 1.75
311 A52 50s grn, dk bl & yel 3.00 2.00
Nos. 297-311,O21-O35 (30)   27.85 16.70

Paper backing is brown on Nos. 302-311.
Nos. 302-306 have self-adhesive control number in lower left corner of paper backing.

Flag Raising, Minerva Reef — A53

1972, Dec. 9   Litho.

312 A53 5s black & multi   .20   .20
313 A53 7s green & multi   .20   .20
314 A53 10s purple & multi   .20   .20
315 A53 15s orange & multi   .35   .35
316 A53 40s ultra & multi   1.40 1.40
*Nos. 312-316,C119-
        C123,CO63-CO65 (13) 12.00 12.00*

Tonga's proclamation of sovereignty over
the Minerva Reefs, June 1972.

Tongan Coins and Bank
Building — A54

1973, Mar. 30   **Litho.**
317	A54	5s	silver & multi	.20	.20
318	A54	7s	silver & multi	.20	.20
319	A54	10s	silver & multi	.20	.20
320	A54	20s	silver & multi	.45	.20
321	A54	30s	silver & multi	.60	.35

Nos. 317-321,C125-
C129,CO66-CO68 (13)   15.30 14.00

Establishment of Bank of Tonga.

Handshake, Outrigger Canoe — A55

1973, June 29
322	A55	5s	silver & multi	.30	.20
323	A55	7s	silver & multi	.45	.20
324	A55	15s	silver & multi	1.40	.55
325	A55	21s	silver & multi	1.90	.70
326	A55	50s	silver & multi	6.75	3.25

Nos. 322-326,C130-
C134,CO69-CO71 (13)   135.00 70.00

Tongan Boy Scout Movement, 25th anniv.

Capt. Cook's Report and Tongan
Rulers — A56

Litho.; Embossed on Gilt Foil
1973, Oct. 2
327	A56	6s	multicolored	.50	.45
328	A56	8s	multicolored	.50	.45
329	A56	11s	multicolored	.70	.55
330	A56	35s	multicolored	4.75	1.90
331	A56	40s	multicolored	4.75	2.25

Nos. 327-331,C135-
C139,CO72-CO74 (13)   60.00 31.45

Bicentenary of Capt. Cook's arrival. Design
is from the manuscript in British Museum.

Nos. 278, 281, C100-C101 and 280
Surcharged and Overprinted in Silver
or Gold on Red (12s, 14s) or Black
Panels (5s, 20s, 50s): "Commonwealth
Games Christchurch 1974"

1973, Dec. 19   **Litho.**
| 332 | A46 | 5s on 50s (G) | .20 | .20 |

Litho.; Embossed
333	A47	12s on 38s (S)	.45	.20
334	A47	14s on 75s (G)	.45	.20
335	A47	20s on 1pa (G)	.80	.35
336	A47	50s on 24s (S)	1.60	1.25

Nos. 332-336,C140-
C144,CO75-CO77 (13)   13.95 10.45

10th British Commonwealth Games, Christchurch, N.Z., Jan. 24-Feb. 2, 1974.

Letter Addressed to Tonga, Names
of UPU Members — A57

1974, June 20   **Typo.**
337	A57	5s	tan & multi	.20	.20
338	A57	10s	tan & multi	.20	.20
339	A57	15s	tan & multi	.45	.45
340	A57	20s	tan & multi	.50	.50
341	A57	50s	tan & multi	1.60	1.60

Nos. 337-341,C154-
C158,CO87-CO89 (13)   13.80 13.80

Centenary of Universal Postal Union.

Girl Guide Badges — A58

1974, Sept. 11   **Litho.**
342	A58	5s	multicolored	.45	.30
343	A58	10s	multicolored	.85	.50
344	A58	20s	multicolored	2.00	1.25
345	A58	40s	multicolored	4.00	2.40
346	A58	60s	multicolored	5.50	3.25

Nos. 342-346,C159-
C163,CO90-CO92 (13)   49.00 29.20

Girl Guides of Tonga.
For surcharges see Nos. C189, C192.

Sailing
Ship
and
Anchors
A59

1974, Dec. 11
347	A59	5s	blue & multi	.40	.35
348	A59	10s	blue & multi	.90	.45
349	A59	25s	blue & multi	2.00	.80
350	A59	50s	blue & multi	4.00	2.75
351	A59	75s	blue & multi	6.00	4.50

Nos. 347-351,C164-
C168,CO93-CO95 (13)   47.00 27.00

Establishment of Royal Marine Institute.

Dateline Hotel, Nukualofa — A60

1975, Mar. 11
352	A60	5s	blue & multi	.20	.20
353	A60	10s	green & multi	.20	.20
354	A60	15s	scarlet & multi	.35	.35
355	A60	30s	purple & multi	.75	.75
356	A60	1pa	orange & multi	2.75	2.75

Nos. 352-356,C169-
C173,CO96-CO98 (13)   15.00 15.00

First meeting of South Pacific area Prime
Ministers. See note after No. 226.

Boxing and Games' Emblem — A61

1975, June 11   **Litho.**
357	A61	5s	black & multi	.25	.25
358	A61	10s	green & multi	.35	.35
359	A61	20s	brown & multi	.55	.55
360	A61	25s	orange & multi	.65	.65
361	A61	65s	violet & multi	1.40	1.40

Nos. 357-361,C174-
C178,CO99-CO101 (13)   12.50 12.50

5th South Pacific Games, Guam, Aug. 1-10.
See note after No. 226.
For surcharges see Nos. 412, 482.

King
Taufa'ahau IV
Coin — A62

Designs (FAO Coins): 5s, Chicken. 20s, like
1pa, (small coin, 27mm). 50s, School of fish.
2pa, Animals and plants on reverse, King on
obverse (large coin, 42mm.).

1975, Sept. 3
362	A62	5s	red, sil & blk	.25	.25
363	A62	20s	ultra, grn, sil & blk	.55	.55
364	A62	50s	blue, sil & blk	1.10	1.10
365	A62	1pa	silver & black	2.25	2.25
366	A62	2pa	silver & black	3.75	3.75

Nos. 362-366,C179-C183 (10)   13.00 13.00

Coinage issued for the benefit of the FAO.
Size of paper backing of 2pa: 82x50mm;
others 45x45mm. See note after No. 226.
For surcharge see Nos. 413.

Coat of Arms, 5pa Coin,
Reverse — A63

George Tupou I Coin, Reverse and
Obverse — A64

Coins: 20s, King Taufa'ahau IV. 50s, King
George Tupou II, 50pa obverse and reverse.
75s, 20pa reverse.

Litho.; Embossed on Gilt Foil
1975, Nov. 4
Pink Background
367	A63	5s	black, sil & vio bl	.20	.20
368	A64	10s	gold, blk & red	.35	.20
369	A63	20s	black, sil & grn	.60	.35
370	A64	50s	gold, blk & vio	1.25	1.25
371	A63	75s	black, sil & red lil	2.25	2.25

Nos. 367-371,C184-
C188,CO102-CO104 (13)   14.90 13.25

Centenary of Constitution of Tonga. Size of
paper backing of Nos. 367 and 369:
65x60mm; of No. 371, 87x78mm. See note
after No. 226.
For surcharges see Nos. C232, C296.

Montreal Olympic Games
Emblem — A65

1976, Feb. 24   **Litho.**
372	A65	5s	red, ultra & blk	.40	.35
373	A65	10s	red, green & blk	.60	.35
374	A65	25s	red, lt brown & blk	1.40	.80
375	A65	35s	red, lilac & blk	1.75	1.10
376	A65	70s	red, bister & blk	3.50	2.75

Nos. 372-376,C189-
C193,CO105-CO107 (13)   31.00 20.05

21st Olympic Games, Montreal, Canada,
July 17-Aug. 1. See note after No. 226.
For surcharges see Nos. 414, 478.

William Hooper, William Floyd, John
Penn, Francis Lightfoot Lee — A66

Signers of Declaration of Independence,
Flags of US and Tonga: 10s, Benjamin Frank-
lin, Thomas Nelson, Jr., Benjamin Harrison,
William Ellery. 15s, Oliver Wolcott, Lyman
Hall, William Whipple, Carter Braxton. 25s,
George Taylor, Thomas Stone, Arthur Middle-
ton, Richard Stockton. 75s, Stephen Hopkins,
Eldridge Gerry, James Wilson, Francis
Hopkinson.

1976, May 26   **Litho.**
377	A66	9s	buff & multi	.45	.20
378	A66	10s	buff & multi	.45	.20
379	A66	15s	buff & multi	.65	.50
380	A66	25s	buff & multi	1.00	1.00
381	A66	75s	buff & multi	5.75	4.50

Nos. 377-381,C194-
C198,CO108-CO110 (13)   31.00 20.50

American Bicentennial. Printed on peelable
buff paper backing, inscribed in carmine with
facsimile of Declaration of Independence.
For surcharges see #481, C233, C236-
C237, C297.

Nathaniel Turner and John Thomas — A67

1976, Aug. 25
382	A67	5s yellow & multi	.25	.25
383	A67	10s multicolored	.40	.25
384	A67	20s multicolored	.90	.50
385	A67	25s multicolored	1.00	.55
386	A67	85s multicolored	2.75	2.75

Nos. 382-386,C199-
C203,CO111-CO113 (13)   18.75 16.65

Sesquicentennial of the arrival of Methodist missionaries and establishment of Christianity in Tonga. Printed on peelable paper backing inscribed in manuscript with segments of John Thomas's Tonga diary.

For surcharges see Nos. 415-416, 479-480.

Wilhelm I and George Tupou I — A68

1976, Nov. 1
387	A68	9s yellow & multi	.35	.30
388	A68	15s yellow & multi	.55	.50
389	A68	22s yellow & multi	.80	.70
390	A68	50s yellow & multi	1.40	1.25
391	A68	73s yellow & multi	1.90	1.75

Nos. 387-391,C204-
C208,CO114-CO116 (13)   14.85 13.50

Tonga-Germany Friendship Treaty, centenary. Printed on peelable paper backing showing reproduction of original treaty.

Queen Salote in Coronation Procession, 1953 — A69

1977, Feb. 7   **Litho.**
392	A69	11s blue & multi	.40	.40
393	A69	20s green & multi	.50	.50
394	A69	30s vio blue & multi	.30	.30
395	A69	50s lt green & multi	.45	.45
396	A69	75s violet & multi	.80	.80

Nos. 392-396,C209-
C213,CO117-CO119 (13)   20.00 15.50

25th anniv. of the reign of Elizabeth II. Printed on peelable paper backing showing replica of handwritten Proclamation of Accession.

For surcharge see No. 417.

Various Coins — A70

1977, July 4
397	A70	10s multicolored	.20	.20
398	A70	15s multicolored	.30	.30
399	A70	25s multicolored	.40	.40
400	A70	50s multicolored	.85	.85
401	A70	75s multicolored	1.50	1.50

Nos. 397-401,C214-
C218,CO120-CO122 (13)   10.75 10.75

10th anniversary of coronation of King Taufa'ahau IV. Printed on peelable paper backing showing multicolored replicas of Tongan stamps.

Capt. Cook's Resolution — A71

1977, Sept. 27   **Litho.**
402	A71	10s multicolored	1.00	.75
403	A71	17s multicolored	2.25	1.25
404	A71	25s multicolored	2.50	2.50
405	A71	30s multicolored	3.50	3.00
406	A71	40s multicolored	3.50	3.00

Nos. 402-406,C219-
C223,CO123-CO125 (13)   81.95 61.90

Bicentenary of Capt. Cook's farewell voyage.

Humpback Whale — A72

1977, Dec. 16
407	A72	15s ultra & black	4.25	.85
408	A72	22s green & black	4.50	1.50
409	A72	31s orange & black	5.25	2.00
410	A72	38s lilac & black	5.50	5.25
411	A72	64s red & black	9.25	5.50

Nos. 407-411,C224-
C228,CO126-CO128 (13)   87.25 38.15

Whale protection.

Stamps of 1975-77 Surcharged in Black, Green, Brown or Black on Silver

1978, Feb. 17
412	A61	15s on 20s		
		(#359;B)	2.00	1.75
413	A62	15s on 5s		
		(#362;B)	2.00	1.75
414	A65	15s on 10s		
		(#373;G)	2.00	1.75
415	A67	15s on 5s		
		(#382;Br)	2.00	1.75
416	A67	15s on 10s		
		(#383;B)	2.00	1.75
417	A69	15s on 11s		
		(#392;B on S)	2.00	3.00

418	OA11	15s on 38s		
		(#CO99;B)	2.00	1.75

Nos. 412-418,C229-C238
(17)   79.75 70.50

The surcharge on No. 413 is only the "1," and on No. 418 includes "postage."

Flags of Canada and Tonga — A73

1978, May 5   **Litho.**
419	A73	10s red & multi	.20	.20
420	A73	15s red & multi	.35	.35
421	A73	20s red & multi	.45	.45
422	A73	25s red & multi	.60	.60
423	A73	45s red & multi	2.00	2.00

Nos. 419-423,C239-
C243,CO129-CO131 (13)   14.00 14.00

11th Commonwealth Games, Edmonton, Canada, Aug. 3-12. See note after No. 226.

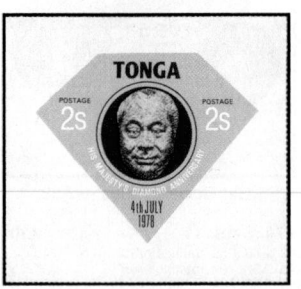

King Taufa'ahau IV — A74

1978, July 4
424	A74	2s multicolored	.20	.20
425	A74	5s multicolored	.20	.20
426	A74	10s multicolored	.25	.25
427	A74	25s multicolored	.65	.65
428	A74	75s multicolored	2.00	2.00

Nos. 424-428,C244-
C248,CO132-CO134 (13)   13.00 13.00

60th birthday of King Taufa'ahau IV. See note after No. 226.

Two Bananas A75

Coconut — A76

Designs: 1s to 5s, Bananas. 6s to 10s, Coconuts. 15s to 1pa, Pineapples.

1978, Sept. 29   **Typo.**
429	A75	1s yellow & black	.25	.25
430	A75	2s yellow & dk blue	.25	.25
431	A75	3s multicolored	.35	.35
432	A75	4s multicolored	.35	.35
433	A75	5s multicolored	.35	.35
434	A76	6s multicolored	.50	.50
435	A76	7s multicolored	.50	.50
436	A76	8s multicolored	.50	.50
437	A76	9s multicolored	.50	.50
438	A76	10s brown & green	.50	.50
439	A76	15s green & lt brown	1.50	1.50
440	A76	20s multicolored	1.75	1.75
441	A76	30s multicolored	2.00	2.00
442	A76	50s multicolored	2.50	2.50
443	A76	1pa multicolored	3.00	3.00

Nos. 429-443,O36-O50 (30)   28.00 28.00

Nos. 429-443 issued in coils; self-adhesive control numbers on paper backing, except on 1s and 5s. See note after No. 226.

See No. 529.

Whale — A77

1978, Dec. 15   **Litho. & Typo.**
444	A77	15s shown	3.50	1.75
445	A77	18s Bat	3.50	1.75
446	A77	25s Turtle	3.50	1.75
447	A77	28s Parrot	5.50	2.50
448	A77	60s like 15s	9.00	6.00

Nos. 444-448,C249-
C253,CO150-CO152 (13)   73.25 40.25

Wildlife conservation. See note after No. 226.

Introduction of Metric System — A78

Shipping Routes, South Pacific Map — A79

Peace Corps A80

22s, New church buildings. 50s, Air routes to Auckland, Suva, Apia & Pago Pago.

1979, Feb. 16   **Litho.**
449	A78	5s multicolored	.20	.20
450	A79	11s multicolored	.35	.20
451	A80	18s multicolored	.50	.40
452	A79	22s multicolored	.60	.50
453	A79	50s multicolored	1.50	.80

Nos. 449-453,C254-
C258,CO153-CO155 (13)   14.25 9.15

Decade of Progress. Paper backing shows map of Tonga.

Tongan First Day Covers — A81

1979, June 1
454	A81	5s multicolored	.20	.20
455	A81	10s multicolored	.25	.25
456	A81	25s multicolored	.60	.60
457	A81	50s multicolored	1.25	1.25
458	A81	1pa multicolored	1.75	1.75
	Nos. 454-458,C259-C263,CO156-CO158 (13)		11.55	11.55

10th anniversary of introduction of self-adhesive stamps and for Bernard Mechanick, inventor of self-adhesive, free-form stamps; death centenary of Sir Rowland Hill.

Printed on peelable paper backing showing advertisement.

For surcharges and overprints see Nos. 469-473.

Eua Island through Camera Lens — A82

1979, Nov. 23 Litho.
459	A82	10s multicolored	.20	.20
460	A82	18s multicolored	.45	.45
461	A82	31s multicolored	.75	.75
462	A82	50s multicolored	1.10	1.10
463	A82	60s multicolored	1.40	1.40
	Nos. 459-463,C275-C279,CO170-CO172 (13)		11.80	11.80

Printed on peelable paper backing showing film and camera.

King George Tupou I, Admiral du Bouzet, Map of Tonga — A83

1980, Jan. 9 Litho.
464	A83	7s multicolored	.20	.20
465	A83	10s multicolored	.35	.35
466	A83	14s multicolored	.45	.45
467	A83	50s multicolored	1.40	1.40
468	A83	75s multicolored	1.90	1.90
	Nos. 464-468,C280-C284,CO173-CO175 (13)		13.50	13.50

Tongan-French Friendship Treaty, 125th anniversary. Printed on peelable paper; multicolored backing shows map of Tonga.

Nos. 454-458 Surcharged and Overprinted in Black on Silver: "1980 OLYMPIC GAMES," Moscow '80 and Bear Emblems

1980, Apr. 30 Litho.
469	A81	13s on 5s multi	.50	.50
470	A81	20s on 10s multi	.75	.75
471	A81	25s multicolored	.90	.90
472	A81	33s on 50s multi	1.10	1.10
473	A81	1pa multicolored	3.50	3.50
	Nos. 469-473,C285-C289,CO176-CO178 (13)		17.50	17.50

Boy Scout Cooking over Campfire — A84

1980, Sept. 30 Litho.
474	A84	9s multicolored	.25	.25
475	A84	13s multicolored	.40	.40
476	A84	15s multicolored	.45	.45
477	A84	30s multicolored	.90	.90
	Nos. 474-477,C290-C293,CO179-CO180 (10)		14.75	14.75

Boy Scout Jamboree; Rotary Intl., 75th anniv. Peelable backing shows map of Tonga.

Nos. 361, 375, 380, 384-385 Surcharged

1980, Dec. 3 Litho.
478	A65	9s on 35s multi	.20	.20
479	A67	13s on 20s multi	.30	.30
480	A67	13s on 25s multi	.30	.30
481	A66	19s on 25s multi	.45	.45
482	A61	1pa on 65s multi	2.50	2.50
	Nos. 478-482,C294-C299,CO181 (12)		13.70	13.70

Intl. Year of the Disabled — A85

1981, Sept. 9 Litho.
483	A85	2pa multicolored	3.25	3.25
484	A85	3pa multicolored	5.00	5.00
	Nos. 483-484,C300-C302 (5)		10.05	10.05

Prince Charles and Lady Diana — A86

Designs: 13s, Charles, King Taufa'ahau. 47s, 1.50pa, Couple, diff.

1981, Oct. 21 Litho.
485	A86	13s multicolored	.20	.20
486	A86	47s multicolored	.50	.50
487	A86	1.50pa multicolored	1.75	1.75
488	A86	3pa multicolored	3.50	3.50
	Nos. 485-488 (4)		5.95	5.95

Royal Wedding and Gt. Britain-Tonga Friendship Treaty centenary. Issued in sheets of 20 (2x10) and 5 labels in vert. center row. For surcharge see No. B1.

Bicentenary of Discovery of Vavau by Francisco Maurelle A87

18th century Spanish engravings and maps.

1981, Nov. 25 Litho.
489	A87	9s multicolored	.60	.50
490	A87	13s multicolored	.90	.60
491	A87	47s multicolored	2.75	1.40
492	A87	1pa multicolored	6.75	6.75
a.	Souvenir sheet, imperf.		13.00	13.00
	Nos. 489-492 (4)		11.00	9.25

No. 492a contains one No. 492 (32x25mm).

Bible Class, 1830 Print — A88

1981, Nov. 25
493	A88	9s Open book	.30	.30
494	A88	13s Book, diff.	.50	.40
495	A88	1.10 Type	1.10	1.10
496	A88	47s shown	1.60	1.60
	Nos. 493-496 (4)		3.50	3.40

Christmas 1981 and sesquicentennial of books printed in Tonga.

175th Anniv. of Capture of The Port-au-Prince — A89

1981, Dec. 16 Litho.
497	A89	29s Battle	1.00	.75
498	A89	32s Battle, diff.	1.25	.90
499	A89	32s Map	1.60	1.50
500	A89	47s Sinking ship	1.60	1.50
a.	Pair, #499-500		3.25	
501	A89	1pa Ship	3.50	3.50
	Nos. 497-501 (5)		8.95	8.15

Nos. CO179-CO180 Surcharged

1982, Jan. 4 Litho.
502	OA19	5pa on 25s multi	10.00	10.00
503	OA19	5pa on 2pa multi	10.00	10.00

Scouting Year — A90

1982, Feb. 22 Litho.
504	A90	29s Brownsea Isld. Camp, 1907	1.00	.60
505	A90	32s Baden-Powell, horse	1.00	.65
506	A90	47s Imperial Jamboree, 1924	1.50	1.00
507	A90	1.50pa "Scouting for Boys"	4.50	3.00
508	A90	2.50pa Mafeking stamp	8.00	5.00
	Nos. 504-508 (5)		16.00	10.25

1982 World Cup — A91

Designs: Various soccer players, map showing match sites.

1982, July 7 Litho.
509	A91	32s multicolored	.85	.60
510	A91	47s multicolored	1.25	.85
511	A91	75s multicolored	1.90	1.40
512	A91	1.50pa multicolored	3.50	2.50
	Nos. 509-512 (4)		7.50	5.35

Inter-island Transport A92

9s, 13s, Ferry Olovaha. 47s, 1pa SPIA Twin Otter (Niuatoputapu Airport opening).

1982, Aug. 11
513	A92	9s multicolored	.40	.20
514	A92	13s multicolored	.50	.25
515	A92	47s multicolored	1.75	.90
516	A92	1pa multicolored	3.50	2.50
	Nos. 513-516 (4)		6.15	3.85

Tin Can Mail Centenary A93

13s, 32s, 47s, Collecting mail. 2pa, Map. Nos. 517-519 form continuous design.

1982, Sept. 29 Litho.
517	A93	13s multicolored	.20	.20
518	A93	32s multicolored	.45	.45
519	A93	47s multicolored	.75	.75
a.	Souv. sheet of 3 (13s, 32s, 47s)		1.50	1.50
520	A93	2pa multicolored	3.25	3.25
a.	Souvenir sheet of 1		3.25	3.25
	Nos. 517-520 (4)		4.65	4.65

No. 520 comes with different labels. For surcharges see Nos. 526-528.

Tonga College Centenary — A94

1982, Oct. 25   Size: 42x30mm (5s)
521	A94	5s Students	.35	.35
522	A94	29s King George Tupou I	2.25	2.25
523	A94	29s Monument	2.25	2.25
a.	Pair, #522-523		5.00	
	Nos. 521-523 (3)		4.85	4.85

Nos. 521-523 inscribed in English or Tongan.

12th Commonwealth Games, Brisbane, Australia, Sept. 30-Oct. 9 — A95

1982, Oct. 25

524	A95	32s Decathlon, vert.	1.25	.60
525	A95	1.50pa Opening ceremony	6.50	6.50

Nos. 517-519 Overprinted in Red or Silver in 1 or 2 Lines: "Christmas / Greetings / 1982"

1982, Nov. 17

526	A93	13s multicolored	.30	.30
527	A93	32s multicolored	.70	.70
528	A93	47s multicolored	1.00	1.00
		Nos. 526-528 (3)	2.00	2.00

Pineapple Type of 1978 and

Fruit — A96

1982, Nov. 17

529	A76	13s multicolored	.35	.25
530	A96	2pa multicolored	5.75	4.00
531	A96	8pa multicolored	8.75	6.00
		Nos. 529-531 (3)	14.85	10.25

Capt. Cook's Resolution, 1777 and Canberra, 1983 — A96a

32s, like 29s. 47s, 1.50pa, Montgolfier Bros. balloon, 1783, Concorde. 2.50pa, Concorde, Canberra. 29s se-tenant with label showing Resolution.

1983, Feb. 22   **Litho.**

532	A96a	29s multicolored	2.25	1.50
533	A96a	32s multicolored	3.00	1.50
534	A96a	47s multicolored	4.25	2.50
535	A96a	1.50pa multicolored	11.00	11.00
		Nos. 532-535 (4)	20.50	16.50

Souvenir Sheet

536	A96a	2.50pa multicolored	6.50	6.50

Pacific Forum of Sea and Air Transport (29s, 32s, 2.50pa); manned flight bicentenary (47s, 1.50pa).
For overprints see Nos. O68-O70.

A96b

1983, Mar. 14

537	A96b	29s Map	1.40	1.40
538	A96b	32s Dancers	1.60	1.60
539	A96b	47s Fishermen	2.25	2.25
540	A96b	1.50pa King Taufa'ahau IV, flag	7.00	7.00
		Nos. 537-540 (4)	12.25	12.25

Commonwealth Day.

Niuafo'ou Airport Opening A97

1983, May 11   **Litho.**

541	A97	32s De Havilland Otter	.90	.50
542	A97	47s like 32s	1.25	.50
543	A97	1pa Boeing 707	2.10	1.40
544	A97	1.50pa like 1pa	3.75	2.10
		Nos. 541-544 (4)	8.00	4.50

World Communications Year — A98

1983, June 22   **Litho.**

545	A98	29s Intelsat IV	.40	.40
546	A98	32s Intelsat IV-A	.50	.50
547	A98	75s Intelsat V	1.25	1.25
		Size: 45x32mm		
548	A98	2pa Apollo 15 Moon post cover	3.25	3.25
		Nos. 545-548 (4)	5.40	5.40

10th Anniv. of Bank of Tonga A99

Various banknotes.

1983, Aug. 3   **Litho.**

549	A99	1pa multicolored	2.25	2.25
550	A99	2pa multicolored	4.25	4.25

Printing Press, 1830 — A100

1983, Sept. 22   **Litho.**

551	A100	13s shown	.25	.25
552	A100	32s Woon's arrival, 1831	.65	.65
553	A100	1pa Print	1.60	1.60
554	A100	2pa Tonga Chronicle	3.50	3.50
		Nos. 551-554 (4)	6.00	6.00

Sesquicentennial of printing in Tonga (by missionary William Woon).

Christmas 1983 A101

Designs: Various sailboats off Vava'u.

1983, Nov. 17   **Litho.**

555	A101	29s multicolored	.50	.40
556	A101	32s multicolored	.60	.50
557	A101	1.50pa multicolored	2.40	2.40
558	A101	2.50pa multicolored	4.25	4.25
		Nos. 555-558 (4)	7.75	7.55

Abel Tasman, Discoverer of Tonga, and his Zeehan — A102

Navigators and Explorers of the Pacific and their Ships.

1984, Mar. 12   **Litho.**

559	A102	32s shown	2.00	2.00
560	A102	47s Samuel Wallis, Dolphin	2.75	2.75
561	A102	90s William Bligh, Bounty	5.00	5.00
562	A102	1.50pa James Cook, Resolution	9.00	9.00
		Nos. 559-562 (4)	18.75	18.75

See Nos. 593-596.

Swainsonia Casta — A103

Shells, fish.

1984-85   **Litho.**

563	A103	1s shown	.45	1.75
564	A103	2s Porites (coral)	1.10	1.75
565	A103	3s Holocentrus ruber	1.40	2.00
566	A103	5s Cypraea mappa viridis	.55	1.75
567	A103	6s Dardanus megistos (crab)	1.40	2.00
568	A103	9s Stegostoma fasciatum	1.40	.80
a.		Perf. 14½ ('85)	1.40	.80
569	A103	10s Conus bullatus	1.10	1.75
570	A103	13s Pterois volitans	1.75	.85
571	A103	15s Conus textile	1.10	2.00
572	A103	20s Dascyllus aruanus	2.60	2.60
573	A103	29s Conus aulicus	2.00	1.10
574	A103	32s Acanthurus leucosternon	3.50	1.10
575	A103	47s Lambis truncata	3.50	1.75
		Size: 39x25mm		
576	A103	1pa Millepora dichotama (coral)	11.00	11.00
577	A103	2pa Birgus latro (crab)	16.00	17.50
578	A103	3pa Chicoreus palma-rosae	10.00	17.50
579	A103	5pa Thunnus albacares	12.50	20.00
		Nos. 563-579 (17)	71.35	87.20

See Nos. 682-692, 701-709, 756-759. For surcharges and overprints see Nos. 618-625, 808-810, O52-O67, O71-O77.

Tonga Chronicle, 20th Anniv. A104

1984 Summer Olympics A105

1984, June 26

580	A104	3s multicolored	.20	.20
a.		Sheet of 12	.75	
581	A104	32s multicolored	.50	.50
a.		Sheet of 12	7.00	

Nos. 580-581 issued in sheets of 12; sheet backgrounds show pages of Chronicle, giving each stamp a different background.

1984, July 23

582	A105	29s Running	.40	.40
583	A105	47s Javelin	.65	.65
584	A105	1.50pa Shot put	2.00	2.00
585	A105	3pa Torch	4.25	4.25
		Nos. 582-585 (4)	7.30	7.30

Intl. Dateline Centenary — A106

1984, Aug. 20

586	A106	47s George Airy, Greenwich Meridian pioneer	1.75	1.25
587	A106	2pa Sandford Fleming, time zone pioneer	8.00	5.50

Ausipex '84 — A107

1984, Sept. 17

588	A107	32s Australia #18	1.00	.75
589	A107	1.50pa Tonga #51	5.00	3.50

Souvenir Sheet

589A		Sheet of 2, #588-589	5.00	5.00

Nos. 588-589 each printed se-tenant with label showing exhibition emblem.
No. 589A contains two imperf. stamps similar to Nos. 588-589, but with denomination replacing logo. No. 589A without denominations was not valid for postage.

Christmas 1984 — A108

1984, Nov. 12   **Litho.**

Christmas Carols in local settings.

590	A108	32s Silent Night	.90	.50
591	A108	47s Away in a Manger	1.60	.80
592	A108	1pa I Saw Three Ships	3.25	3.25
		Nos. 590-592 (3)	5.75	4.55

Famous Mariners

Designs: 32s, Willem Schouten (c. 1580-1625), The Eendracht, 1616. 47s, Jakob Le Maire (1585-1616), The Hoorn, 1615. 90s, Lt. Fletcher Christian, The Bounty, 1789. 1.50pa, Francisco Maurelle, La Princessa, 1781.

1985, Feb. 27   **Litho.**   **Die Cut**

593	A102	32s multicolored	2.50	1.50
a.		Perf. 14	50.00	
594	A102	47s multicolored	3.75	1.75
595	A102	90s multicolored	6.75	5.00
596	A102	1.50pa multicolored	12.00	7.75
		Nos. 593-596 (4)	25.00	16.00

Nos. 593-596 each printed se-tenant with self-adhesive label picturing anchor.

Geological Survey of Tonga Trench for Oil — A110

Designs: 29s, Tonga Trench and islands. 32s, Marine exploration, seismic surveying. 47s, Search for oil off Tongatapu, vert. No. 600, Exploration of sea bed, vert. No. 601, Angler fish.

1985, Apr. 10
597	A110	29s multicolored	1.50	1.10
598	A110	32s multicolored	1.60	1.10
599	A110	47s multicolored	2.50	1.60
600	A110	1.50pa multicolored	8.25	8.25
		Nos. 597-600 (4)	13.85	12.05

Souvenir Sheet
601	A110	1.50pa multicolored	13.00	7.75
a.		Perf. 14	13.00	7.75

Nos. 597-600 printed in sheets of 40, 2 panes of 20 separated by labels inscribed "Proof 1," etc.

Adventures of Will Mariner — A111

29s, Readying Port au Prince for sail, Gravesend, 1805. 32s, Captured & set afire, 1806. 47s, Mariner taken prisoner by Chief Finow, Tonga. 1.50pa, Passage to China aboard brig Favourite. 2.50pa, Returning to England aboard East Indiaman Cuffnells, 1810.

1985, June 18   *Die Cut*
602	A111	29s multicolored	.60	.50
a.		Perf. 14	.60	.50
603	A111	32s multicolored	.65	.55
a.		Perf. 14	.65	.55
604	A111	47s multicolored	1.00	.80
a.		Perf. 14	1.00	.80
605	A111	1.50 pa multicolored	3.75	3.75
a.		Perf. 14	3.75	3.75
606	A111	2.50pa multicolored	6.00	6.00
a.		Perf. 14	6.00	6.00
		Nos. 602-606 (5)	12.00	11.60
		Nos. 602a-606a (5)	12.00	11.60

Mutiny on the Bounty, Film 50th Anniv. A112

Designs: a, Byron Russell (Quintal), Stanley Fields (Muspratt) and Charles Laughton (Capt. Bligh). b, Laughton, Donald Crisp (Burkitt), Eddie Quillon (Ellison) and David Thursby (Maxwell). c, Clark Gable (Fletcher Christian). d, Russell, Alec Craig (McCoy), Laughton and Fields. e, Laughton and Franchot Tone (Roger Byam).

1985, July 16   *Perf. 14*
607		Strip of 5	62.50	62.50
a.-e.		A112 47s, any single	10.00	5.00

Sheets consist of four strips of 5 and a central strip of labels showing film credits.

Queen Mother, 85th Birthday A113

Designs: 32s, Age 10. 47s, At Hadfield Girl Guides rally, 1931. 1.50pa, In Guide uniform. 2.50pa, Portrait by Norman Parkinson, 1985.

1985, Aug. 20   *Imperf.*
608	A113	32s multicolored	1.25	.90
a.		Perf. 14	2.00	1.50
609	A113	47s multicolored	2.00	1.50
a.		Perf. 14	3.25	2.40
610	A113	1.50pa multicolored	6.00	6.00
a.		Perf. 14	9.25	9.25
611	A113	2.50pa multicolored	9.75	9.75
a.		Perf. 14	15.00	15.00
		Nos. 608-611 (4)	19.00	18.15
		Nos. 608a-611a (4)	29.50	28.15

Girl Guides movement, 75th anniv.

Christmas — A114

1985, Nov. 12
612	A114	32s No room at the inn	.50	.35
613	A114	42s Shepherds follow star	.75	.50
614	A114	1.50pa The three kings	2.75	2.75
615	A114	2.50pa Holy family	4.25	4.25
		Nos. 612-615 (4)	8.25	7.85

Self-adhesive Discontinued

In 1986, imperforate self-adhesive stamps attached to peelable paper backing were no longer issued, unless otherwise stated.

Halley's Comet A115

Designs: Nos. 616a, 617a, Comet. Nos. 616b, 617b, Edmond Halley. Nos. 616c, 617c, Solar system. Nos. 616d, 617d, Telescope. Nos. 616e, 617e, Giotto space probe.

1986, Mar. 26   *Perf. 14*
616		Strip of 5	19.00	19.00
a.-e.		A115 42s, any single	3.00	3.00
617		Strip of 5	19.00	19.00
a.-e.		A115 57s, any single	3.00	3.00

Nos. 564, 570, 565, 568, 567, 572, 577 and 579 Surcharged

1986, Apr. 16   *Litho.*   *Imperf.*
Self-adhesive
618	A103	4s on 2s, #564	1.10	2.25
619	A103	4s on 13s, #570	1.10	2.25
620	A103	42s on 3s, #565	2.90	1.75
621	A103	42s on 9s, #568	2.90	1.75
622	A103	57s on 6s, #567	3.50	2.50
623	A103	57s on 20s, #572	3.50	2.50
624	A103	2.50pa on 2pa, #577	11.00	11.00
625	A103	2.50pa on 5pa, #579	11.00	11.00
		Nos. 618-625 (8)	37.00	35.00

Royal Links with the United Kingdom A116

1986, May 22   *Perf. 14*
626	A116	57s Taufa'ahau IV	1.25	1.25
627	A116	57s Elizabeth II	1.25	1.25
a.		Pair, #626-627	3.00	3.00

Size: 40x40mm
628	A116	2.50pa King and queen	5.50	5.50
		Nos. 626-628 (3)	8.00	8.00

Queen Elizabeth II, 60th birthday. No. 628 printed in sheets of 5 plus one label.

AMERIPEX '86, Chicago, May 22-June 1 — A117

Peace Corps activities: No. 629, Health care. No. 630, Education.

1986, May 22
629	A117	57s multicolored	1.00	1.00
630	A117	1.50pa multicolored	2.75	2.75
a.		Souv. sheet, #629, 630, imperf	4.50	4.50
b.		Pair, #629-630	5.50	5.50

Peace Corps in Tonga, 20th anniv.

Intl. Sporting Events — A118

Designs: 42s, 1986 Field Hockey World Cup, London. 57s, Women's basketball, 13th Commonwealth Games, Scotland. 1pa, Boxing, Commonwealth Games. 2.50pa, 1986 World Cup Soccer Championships, Mexico.

1986, July 23   *Litho.*   *Perf. 14*
631	A118	42s multicolored	1.25	1.25
632	A118	57s multicolored	2.00	2.00
633	A118	1pa multicolored	3.25	3.25
634	A118	2.50pa multicolored	8.00	8.00
		Nos. 631-634 (4)	14.50	14.50

Postage Stamp Cent. A119

Stamps on stamps: No. 635, #1. No. 636, #47a. No. 637, #91. No. 638, #628. No. 639a, #40, UL portion of #C29. No. 639b, UR portion of #C29, left side #245. No. 639c, Center of #245, Type AP10. No. 639d, Left side #245, #C148. No. 639e, LL portion of #C29, #429, #440. No. 639f, LR portion of #C29, #C135. No. 639g, #507. No. 639h, #514. Nos. 639a-639h, vert.

1986, Aug. 27
635	A119	32s multi	2.50	1.75
636	A119	42s multi	2.75	2.00
637	A119	57s multi	3.50	2.00
638	A119	2.50pa multi	5.75	5.75
		Nos. 635-638 (4)	14.50	11.50

Souvenir Sheet
639		Sheet of 8	15.00	15.00
a.-h.		A119 50s, any single	1.50	1.50

Christmas — A120

Designs: 32s, Girls wearing shell jewelry. 42s, Boy, totem poles, vert. 57s, Folk dancers, vert. 2pa, outrigger canoe.

1986, Nov. 12   *Litho.*   *Perf. 14*
640	A120	32s multicolored	2.50	.75
641	A120	42s multicolored	2.75	1.00
642	A120	57s multicolored	3.00	1.50
643	A120	2pa multicolored	6.25	6.25
		Nos. 640-643 (4)	14.50	9.50

Nos. 641-642 Ovptd. with Jamboree Emblem and "BOY SCOUT / JAMBOREE / 5th-10th DEC '86" in Silver

1986, Dec. 2   *Litho.*   *Perf. 14*
644	A120	42s multicolored	3.50	3.50
645	A120	57s multicolored	3.75	3.75

Dumont d'Urville's Second Voyage A121

Designs: 32s, D'Urville and ship Astrolabe. 42s, Four Tongan girls, detail from D'Urville's

engraving, Voyage au Pole et dans l'Oceanie. 1pa, Map of voyage. 2.50pa, Wreck of the Astrolabe.

1987, Feb. 24
646	A121	32s multicolored	4.25	2.00
647	A121	42s multicolored	4.25	2.00
648	A121	1pa multicolored	10.00	6.00
649	A121	2.50pa multicolored	16.00	16.00
		Nos. 646-649 (4)	34.50	26.00

Dumont d'Urville (1790-1842), explorer and admiral.

Wildlife Conservation — A122

Fauna: a, Noah's Ark. b, Eagles. c, Giraffes, birds. d, Seagulls. e, Elephants, ostriches. f, Elephant. g, Lions, zebras, antelopes. h, Chimpanzees. i, Antelope, frogs. j, Tigers, lizard. k, Tiger, snake. l, Butterfly.

1987, May 6   *Perf. 13½*
650		Sheet of 12	62.50	62.50
a.-l.		A122 42s any single	4.00	4.00

1st Inter-island Canoe Race, Tonga to Samoa — A123

1987, July 1   *Perf. 14*
651	A123	32s Two paddlers	.55	.45
652	A123	42s Five paddlers	.85	.70
653	A123	57s Three paddlers	1.10	.90
654	A123	1.50pa Two, diff.	3.00	3.00
a.		Souvenir sheet of 4, #651-654	9.50	9.50
		Nos. 651-654 (4)	5.50	5.05

Coronation of King Taufa'ahau IV, 20th Anniv. — A124

Booklet Stamps
1987-88   *Imperf.*
Self-Adhesive
655	A124	1s green & yel grn	.30	.75
655A	A124	2s blk & pale yel org	3.50	3.50
656	A124	5s black & brt pink	.30	.75
a.		Bklt. pane of 12 (6 5s plus 1 5s, 2 10s, 3 15s with gutter between)		4.50
657	A124	10s black & bluish lil	.40	.85
658	A124	15s brn blk & org ver	.55	.85
a.		Bklt. pane of 12 (1s, 2 2s, 3 10s, plus 2 5s, 10s, 3 15s with gutter between) ('88)		12.50
659	A124	32s Prus bl & aqua	.65	.90
a.		Bklt. pane, 4 32s, 2 15s + 4 10s, 2 1s with gutter between)		6.25
b.		Bklt. pane, 6 32s + 2 2s, 4 1s with gutter btwn. ('88)		12.50
		Nos. 655-659 (6)	5.70	7.60

Issued: 2s, 7/4/88; others, 7/1/87.

Parliament, 125th Anniv. — A125

1987, Sept. 2   **Litho.**   **Perf. 14½**

660	A125	32s multicolored	.50	.50
661	A125	42s multicolored	.75	.75
662	A125	75s multicolored	1.50	1.50
663	A125	2pa multicolored	3.00	3.00
		Nos. 660-663 (4)	5.75	5.75

Christmas 1987 — A126

Cartoons featuring Octopus as Santa Claus and mouse as his helper.

1987, Nov. 18   **Litho.**   **Perf. 14**

664	A126	42s Sack of gifts	1.50	.80
665	A126	57s Delivering them by canoe	1.75	1.75
666	A126	1pa By automobile	3.25	3.25
667	A126	3pa Sipping tropical drinks	8.00	8.00
		Nos. 664-667 (4)	14.50	13.80

King Taufa'ahau Tupou IV, 70th Birthday — A127

Portrait and: 32s, M.V. *Olovaha* inter-island ship, athlete pole vaulting and offshore oil derrick. 42s, Banknote and coins, Ha'Amonga Trilithon and traditional craftsman. 57s, Rowing, Red Cross nurse and communications satellite. 2.50pa, Tonga Scouts emblem, No. 506 and Friendly Islands Airways passenger plane.

1988, July 4   **Litho.**   **Perf. 11½**

668	A127	32s multicolored	2.00	.90
669	A127	42s multicolored	1.40	1.00
670	A127	57s multicolored	1.50	1.00
671	A127	2.50pa multicolored	7.50	7.50
		Nos. 668-671 (4)	12.40	10.40

See Nos. 744-747 for stamps inscribed for the silver jubilee.

Souvenir Sheet

Australia Bicentennial — A128

Designs: a, Cook and his journal. b, List of stores shipped aboard the *Lady Juliana*, the ship, Arthur Philip, 1st gov. of New South Wales, 1788, and left half of the list of sentences of all the prisoners tried at Glo'ster Assizes. c, Right half of list of sentences, Australia Type A59 redrawn and aerial view of an early settlement. d, Robert O'Hara Burke (1820-61) and W.J. Wills (1834-61), the 1st explorers to cross Australia from south to north. e, Emu pictured on a Player's cigarette card, U.R. Stuart's (gold) prospecting license and opals. f, Australian Commonwealth Military Forces emblem, WW I recruit on cigarette card, and war poster. g, Souv. card commemorating 1st overland mail delivery by transcontinental railway, and Australia Type A4 on cover. h, Hand-canceled cover commemorating the 1st England-Australia transcontinental airmail flight, Nov. 12-Dec.10, 1919, aviator Capt. Ross Smith (1892-1922) and Great Britain #588. i, Don Bradman and Harold

Larwood, cricket champions of the 1930s, on cigarette cards, and era newspaper frontispiece. j, Frontispiece of Hulton's natl. weekly *Picture Post* Victory Special issue, and WW II campaign medals. k, Australia #676 and a sheep station. l, Sydney Harbor Bridge, Opera House and theater tickets to *The Bartered Bride*.

1988, July 11   **Litho.**   **Perf. 13½**

672	A128	Sheet of 12	45.00	45.00
a.-l.		42s any single	3.00	3.00

1988 Summer Olympics, Seoul — A129

1988, Aug. 11   **Perf. 14**

673	A129	57s Running	.90	.90
674	A129	75s Yachting	1.10	1.10
675	A129	2pa Cycling	5.50	5.50
676	A129	3pa Women's tennis	6.50	6.50
		Nos. 673-676 (4)	14.00	14.00

Music of Tonga A130

1988, Sept. 9   **Litho.**   **Perf. 14**

677	A130	32s shown	.55	.45
678	A130	42s Choir	.75	.60
679	A130	57s Tonga Police Band	.95	.80
680	A130	2.50pa The Jets	4.25	4.25
		Nos. 677-680 (4)	6.50	6.10

Souvenir Sheet

681		Sheet of 2	3.00	3.00
a.		A130 57s like 2.50pa	1.00	1.00
b.		A130 57s Olympic eternal flame	1.00	1.00

SPORT AID '88.

Marine Type of 1984

Two types of background shading on No. 690:

Type I: Shading at top and sides extends to vert. & horiz. edges of design.

Type II: Shading is oval shaped.

1988   **Litho.**   **Perf. 14½**

Size: 27x34mm

682	A103	1s like No. 563	.25	.25
683	A103	2s like No. 564	.35	.35
684	A103	5s like No. 566	.45	.45
685	A103	6s like No. 567	.90	.90
686	A103	10s like No. 569	.55	.55
687	A103	15s like No. 571	.55	.55
688	A103	20s like No. 572	.80	.80
689	A103	32s like No. 574	.90	.90
690	A103	42s Fregata ariel, type I	3.25	.80
a.		Type II	30.00	
691	A103	57s Sula leucogaster	4.00	1.00

Size: 41x27mm

Perf. 14

692	A103	3pa Like No. 578	2.50	*7.50*
		Nos. 682-692 (11)	14.50	14.05

Issued: 1s, 5s, 10s, 20s, 32s, Oct. 4; 2s, 6s, 15s, 42s, 57s, 3pa, Oct. 18.

Nos. 683-684, 686, 689 exist inscribed "1990."

See #701-709. For surcharge see #808.

Tonga-US Treaty, Cent. A131

1988, Oct. 20   **Perf. 14**

693	A131	42s *Resolution*	1.00	.75
694	A131	57s *Santa Maria*	1.50	1.10
695	A131	2pa Capt. Cook, Columbus	5.50	5.50
a.		Souvenir sheet of 3, #693-695	6.75	6.75
		Nos. 693-695 (3)	8.00	7.35

Christmas — A132

Designs (a, Intl. Red Cross, b, Natl. Red Cross): 15s, Girl, teddy bear. 32s, Nurse reading to child. 42s, Checking pulse. 57s, Tucking child into bed. 1.50pa, Boy in wheelchair.

1988, Nov. 17   **Litho.**   **Perf. 14½**

696	A132	15s Pair, #a.-b.	.50	.50
697	A132	32s Pair, #a.-b.	1.00	1.00
698	A132	42s Pair, #a.-b.	1.10	1.10
699	A132	57s Pair, #a.-b.	1.90	1.90
700	A132	1.50pa Pair, #a.-b.	4.75	4.75
		Nos. 696-700 (5)	9.25	9.25

Intl. Red Cross 125th anniv. and 25th anniv. of the natl. Red Cross.

Marine Type of 1984

1989, Mar. 2   **Litho.**

Size: 27x34mm

701	A103	4s like No. 570	1.60	1.60
702	A103	7s Diomedea exulans	3.75	2.50
703	A103	35s Hippocampus	3.25	2.75
704	A103	50s like No. 573	3.75	2.00

Size: 41x27mm

Perf. 14

705	A103	1pa Chelonia mydas	6.00	4.50
706	A103	1.50pa Megaptera novaeangliae	12.00	7.50
707	A103	2pa like No. 577	8.75	8.75
709	A103	5pa like No. 579	14.00	*17.00*
		Nos. 701-709 (8)	53.10	46.60

Mutiny on the *Bounty*, Bicent. — A133

32s, Map of Tofua & Kao Isls., breadfruit. 42s, *Bounty*, chronometer. 57s, William Bligh & castaways in longboat. 2pa, Mutineers on the *Bounty*, vert. 3pa, Castaways.

Perf. 13½x14, 14x13½

1989, Apr. 28   **Photo.**

710	A133	32s multicolored	4.50	2.50
711	A133	42s multicolored	7.50	3.25
712	A133	57s multicolored	10.00	4.75
		Nos. 710-712 (3)	22.00	10.50

Souvenir Sheet

713		Sheet of 2	17.00	17.00
a.		A133 2pa multicolored	5.00	5.00
b.		A133 3pa multicolored	7.50	7.50

Butterflies A134

1989, May 15   **Litho.**   **Perf. 14½**

714	A134	42s *Hypolimnas bolina*	1.10	.75
715	A134	57s *Jamides bochus*	1.40	1.00
716	A134	1.20pa *Melanitis leda solandra*	3.25	2.50
717	A134	2.50pa *Danaus plexippus*	6.25	6.25
		Nos. 714-717 (4)	12.00	10.50

Opening of the Natl. Sports Stadium and the South Pacific Mini Games, Aug. 22 A135

Rugby (No. 718): a, Rugby Public School, 1870. b, Dave Gallaher and the Springboks vs. East Midlands, 1906. c, King George V inspecting Cambridge team of 1922 and Wavell Wakefield, captain of England. d, Ernie Crawford, captain of Ireland, Danie Craven demonstrating the dive pass and cigarette cards from the 1930's. e, Sioni Mafi, captain of Tonga, and match scene.

Tennis (No. 719): a, Royal tennis, 1659. b, Walter Clopton Wingfield and game of lawn tennis, 1873. c, Oxford and Cambridge teams of 1884. d, Bunny Ryan in 1910 and cigarette cards. e, Tennis players, 1980's.

Cricket (No. 720): a, Match in 1743 and bronze memorial to Fuller Pilch. b, W.G. Grace, 19th cent. c, *The Boys Own Paper*, 1909. d, Australian team of 1909 and cigarette cards. e, The Ashes trophy and modern match scene.

1989, Aug. 22   **Litho.**   **Perf. 14**

718		Strip of 5	6.25	6.25
a.-e.	A135	32s any single	1.00	1.00
719		Strip of 5	9.50	9.50
a.-e.	A135	42s any single	1.50	1.50
720		Strip of 5	14.50	14.50
a.-e.	A135	57s any single	2.50	2.50
		Nos. 718-720 (3)	30.25	30.25

Printed in sheets of 10 containing descriptions and emblem.

Natl. Aviation History — A136

Designs: 42s, Short S30. 57s, Vought F4U Corsair. 90s, Boeing 737. 3pa, Montgolfier brothers' hot-air balloon, the Wright Flyer, Concorde jet and space shuttle.

1989, Oct. 23   **Litho.**   **Perf. 14½x14**

721	A136	42s multicolored	3.25	1.60
722	A136	57s multicolored	3.75	2.00
723	A136	90s multicolored	6.50	6.00

Size: 97x126½mm

724	A136	3pa multicolored	16.00	16.00
		Nos. 721-724 (4)	29.50	25.60

1st Flight to Tonga, 1939 (42s); military base on the island, 1943 (57s); civil aviation, Fua'amotu Airport (90s); aviation through the ages (3pa).

Flying Home for Christmas A137

1989, Nov. 9   **Perf. 14x13½**

725	A137	32s Aircraft landing	2.00	.90
726	A137	42s Islanders waving, aircraft	2.25	.90
727	A137	57s Tongan in outrigger canoe, aircraft	2.50	1.25
728	A137	3pa Islanders waving, aircraft, diff.	6.75	6.75
		Nos. 725-728 (4)	13.50	9.80

World
Stamp
Expo '89
A138

20th UPU Congress, Washington,
DC — A139

Postal history and communications (No.
730): a, Sir Rowland Hill, penny blacks on
Mulready envelope. b, Clipper ship, early train.
c, Pony Express advertisement, stagecoach,
post rider. d, Hot-air balloon and flight cover.
e, Samuel Morse, miniature, telegraph key. f,
Early Royal Mail truck, mailbox. g, Biplane and
early aviators. h, Zeppelin flight cover, HMS
Queen Mary. i, Helicopter, truck. j, Computer
operator, facsimile machine. k, Apollo 11 mission emblem, flight cover, planetary bodies. l,
American space shuttle, UPU monument.

1989, Nov. 17   Litho.   Perf. 14
729   A138 Pair, #730k-
                730 l   3.50   3.50
Souvenir Sheet
Perf. 13½
730   A139   Sheet of 12   42.50 42.50
a.-l. A139 57s any single   2.50   2.50

A140   A141

1990, Feb. 14   Litho.   Perf. 14
731   A140   42s Boxing   1.25   .75
732   A140   57s Archery   2.25   1.50
733   A140   1pa Bowls   3.00   3.00
734   A140   2pa Swimming   5.00   5.00
     Nos. 731-734 (4)   11.50 10.25
1990 Commonwealth Games.

1990, Apr. 11   Litho.   Perf. 14
Protect the Environment: 32s, Wave power,
ocean pollution. 57s, Wind power, acid rain.
$1.20, Solar power, ozone layer. $2.50, Green
earth, rain forests.
735   A141   32s multicolored   2.50   .90
736   A141   57s multicolored   3.50   1.50
737   A141   1.20pa multicolored 7.00   7.00
     Nos. 735-737 (3)   13.00   9.40
Souvenir Sheet
738   A141 2.50pa multicolored 13.00 13.00

First
Postage
Stamps,
150th
Anniv.
A142

1990   Litho.   Perf. 14
739   A142   42s G. B. #1   2.10   1.50
740   A142   42s G. B. #2   2.10   1.50
a.   Pair, #739-740   3.75   3.75
741   A142   57s Tonga #1   2.50   1.50
742   A142   1.50pa Tonga
                    #CO180   6.00   6.00
743   A142   2.50pa Tonga #736   9.00   9.00
     Nos. 739-743 (5)   21.70 19.50

King's Birthday Type of 1988 Inscribed
"Silver Jubilee of His Majesty King
Taufa'ahau Tupou IV 1965-1990"
1990, July 4   Litho.   Perf. 11½
744   A127   32s like No. 668   1.50   1.00
745   A127   42s like No. 669   1.50   1.00
746   A127   57s like No. 670   2.25   1.25
747   A127 2.50pa like No. 671 7.75   7.75
     Nos. 744-747 (4)   13.00 11.00

Native
Catamaran — A143

1990, June 6   Perf. 14½
748   A143   32s buff & green   1.60   .75
749   A143   42s buff & bl, diff. 1.60   .85
750   A143 1.20pa buff & brn,
                       diff.   4.25   4.25
751   A143   3pa buff & vio,
                       diff.   8.50   8.50
     Nos. 748-751 (4)   15.95 14.35

Banded
Iguana
A144

1990, Sept. 12   Litho.   Perf. 14
752   A144   32s multicolored   2.00   1.25
753   A144   42s multi, diff.   2.50   1.75
754   A144   57s multi, diff.   3.25   2.25
755   A144 1.20pa multi, diff. 4.25   4.75
     Nos. 752-755 (4)   16.00 10.00

Marine Type of 1984
1990, July 6   Litho.   Perf. 14
Size: 20x22mm
756   A103   2s like No. 564   1.10   .75
a.   Booklet pane of 10   11.00 11.00
757   A103   5s like No. 566   1.10   .75
a.   Booklet pane of 10   11.00 11.00
758   A103   10s like No. 569   1.10   .75
a.   Booklet pane of 10   11.00 11.00
759   A103   32s like No. 574   2.00   2.00
a.   Booklet pane of 10   20.00 20.00
     Nos. 756-759 (4)   5.30   4.25

Nos. 756-758 exist inscribed "1992."
For surcharge see No. 810.
Issue date: #756a-759a, Sept. 4.

UN Development Program, 40th
Anniv. — A145

1990, Oct. 25   Litho.   Perf. 14
760   A145   57s Tourism   2.00   2.00
761   A145   57s Agriculture,
                   fisheries   2.00   2.00
a.   Pair, #760-761   4.50   4.50
762   A145   3pa Education   10.00 10.00
763   A145   3pa Healthcare   10.00 10.00
a.   Pair, #762-763   22.50 22.50
     Nos. 760-763 (4)   24.00 24.00

Rotary
Intl. — A146

Accident
Prevention
A147

1990, Nov. 28
764   A146   32s shown   1.00   .55
765   A146   42s Two boys   1.50   .80
766   A146   2pa Three children 5.00   5.00
767   A146   3pa Two girls   6.50   6.50
     Nos. 764-767 (4)   14.00 12.85

1991, Apr. 10   Litho.   Perf. 14½
No. 768: a, d, Care at work; hard hats save
lives. b, c, Keep matches and medicines out of
children's reach. e, as "d," corrected
inscription
No. 769: a, d, Don't drink and drive. b, c,
Crash helmets save lives; mind cyclists and
children.
No. 770: a, d, Listen to forecasts; learn to
swim. b, c, Swim from safe beaches; beware
of broken glass.
"a" and "b" have English inscriptions,
denominations at top; "c" and "d" have Tongan
inscriptions, denominations at bottom.
Strips of 4 + Label
768   A147   32s #a.-d.   5.25   5.25
f.   Strip of 4, #a.-c.,   32.50
769   A147   42s #a.-d.   7.50   7.50
770   A147   57s #a.-d.   9.25   9.25
     Nos. 768-770 (3)   22.00 22.00
Center label is a progressive proof.
No. 768d was incorrectly inscribed, "Ngauo
tokanga." No. 768e was issued 8/11/91 with
correct inscription, "Ngaue tokanga."
For surcharges see No. 811, 1124.

A148

A149

1991, July 2   Litho.   Perf. 14½
771   A148   42s Fish   .80   .70
772   A148   57s Island, boat   .95   .85
773   A148   2pa Fruit, island 3.50   3.50
774   A148   3pa Turtle, beach 6.25   6.25
     Nos. 771-774 (4)   11.50 11.30
Heilala week.

1991, July 2
Racing yachts: a, Red spinnaker. b, Yellow
spinnaker. c, Green striped spinnaker. d,
Yacht at sunset. e, Yacht, moon.
Miniature Sheet of 5 + Label
775   A149   1pa #775a-775e   13.00 13.00
Around the world yacht race.

Church of Jesus
Christ of Latter
Day Saints in
Tonga,
Cent. — A150

1991, Aug. 19
776   A150   42s Tonga Temple   1.75   1.75
777   A150   57s Temple at night 2.75 2.75

Rowing
Festival
A151

1991, Oct. 29   Litho.   Perf. 14
778   A151   42s Women's coxed
                     eight   1.00   1.00
779   A151   57s Men's longboat 1.50   1.50
780   A151   1pa Outrigger   2.75   2.75
781   A151   2pa Bow of large
                     canoe   5.25   5.25
782   A151   2pa Stern of large
                     canoe   5.25   5.25
a.   Pair, #781-782   11.00 11.00
     Nos. 778-782 (5)   15.75 15.75
For surcharges see Nos. 898-899C.

Telecommunications — A152

No. 783: a, Recording television program. b,
Communications Satellite. c, Watching television program.
No. 784: a, Man on telephone, woman at
computer. b, Communications satellite, diff. c,
Man in city on telephone.
No. 785: a, Seaman on sinking ship broadcasting SOS. b, Man on telephone, satellite
relay station. c, Rescue missions.
No. 786: a, Weather satelite. b, Men at computers. c, Television weather report, storm.

1991, Oct. 15   Litho.   Perf. 14½
783   A152   15s Strip of 3, #a.-c. 1.50 1.50
784   A152   32s Strip of 3, #a.-c. 3.00 3.00
785   A152   42s Strip of 3, #a.-c. 4.25 4.25
786   A152   57s Strip of 3, #a.-c. 6.00 6.00
     Nos. 783-786 (4)   14.75 14.75
For surcharges, see 1095-1098.

Christmas — A153

Designs: 32s, Turtles pulling Santa's sleigh.
42s, Santa on roof. 57s, Family with presents.
3.50pa, Waving goodbye to Santa.

1991, Nov. 11   Perf. 14
787   A153   32s multicolored   1.00   .70
788   A153   42s multicolored   1.25   .90
789   A153   57s multicolored   1.75   1.75
790   A153 3.50pa multicolored 10.00 10.00
     Nos. 787-790 (4)   14.00 13.35
For surcharges, see 1120-1122.

Armed Forces — A154

1991, Dec. 15
791   A154   42s Royal Tonga Marine 1.00 1.00
792   A154   42s Patrol boat Pangai 1.00 1.00
a.   A154 Pair, #791-792   2.50   2.50
793   A154   57s Patrol boat Neiafu 1.50 1.50
794   A154   57s Tonga Royal Guards 1.50 1.50
a.   A154 Pair, #793-794   3.50   3.50
795   2pa King Tupou IV, mili-
                   tary parade   5.25   5.25

796	2pa Patrol boat Savea		5.25	5.25
a.	A154 Pair, #795-796		11.00	11.00
	Nos. 791-796 (6)		15.50	15.50

Miniature Sheet

Discovery of
America, 500th
Anniv. — A155

Designs: a, Columbus. b, Monastery of Santa Maria de la Chevas. c, Obverse and reverse of coin of Ferdinand and Isabella. d, Spain #C48, #426. e, Compass, astrolabe. f, Santa Maria. g, Map, Columbus' signature. h, Columbus arriving in New World. i, Lucayan artifacts, parrot. j, Pineapple, artifacts. k, Columbus announcing his discovery. l, Medal of Columbus, signature.

1992, Apr. 28　Litho.　Perf. 13½

797	A155 57s Sheet of 12, #a.-l.		40.00	40.00

Marine Type of 1984 and

A155a

Perf. 13x13½, 14 (15s, 20s, 10pa)
1992-93　　　　　　　　Litho.

798	A155a	1s Swainsonia casta	.20	.20
799	A155a	3s Holocentrus ruber	.20	.20
800	A155a	5s Cypraea mappa viridis	.20	.20
801	A155a	10s Conus bullatus	.20	.20
802	A103	15s like #567	.25	.25
803	A155a	20s Dascyllus aruanus	.30	.30
804	A155a	45s Lambis truncata	.70	.70
805	A155a	60s Conus aulicus	.90	.90
806	A155a	80s Pterois volitans	1.25	1.25

Size: 27x41mm

807	A103	10pa like #568	18.00	18.00
	Nos. 798-807 (10)		22.20	22.20

Issued: 1s, 3s, 5s, 10s, 20s, 45s, 60s, 80s, May 12, 1993. 15s, 10pa, May 5, 1992.

See Nos. 874-884. Area covered by background colors on Nos. 874, 876-879 has been reduced in size. See Nos. 920-924.

For inscribed stamps see Nos. O78-O87.

Surcharges

XXX

xx

On #688

10s
On #756
in Blue

45s　45s

On #759

On #769 in Red
and Black

1992-93　　Litho.　　Perf. 14½, 14

808	A103	1s on 20s #688	.20	.20
809	A103	10s on 2s #756		
810	A103	45s on 32s #759	4.00	4.00
811	A147	60s on 42s Strip of 4, #a.-d. + label	16.00	16.00

Issued: 1s, 5/19; 45s, 60s, 8/11; 10s, 1993.

Miniature Sheet

World
War II in
Pacific,
50th
Anniv.
A156

Designs: a, Newspaper headline, Japanese attack on Pearl Harbor. b, Map of Bataan, Corregidor, and Manila, pilot's wings, airplanes. c, Newspaper headline, troops landing in Gilbert Islands, Marine Corps emblem, dogtags. d, Uniform patch, B-29 "Enola Gay," troops landing on Iwo Jima. e, Map of Battle of Midway, Admiral Nimitz. f, Southwest Pacific campaign map, Gen. MacArthur. g, Map of Saipan and Tinian, Lt. Gen. Holland Smith. h, Map outlining bombing of Japan, Maj. Gen. Curtis Lemay. i, Mitsubishi A6M Zero. j, Douglas SBD Dauntless. k, Grumman F4F Wildcat. l, Supermarine Seafire.

1992, May 26　Litho.　Perf. 14

814	A156 42s Sheet of 12, #a.-l.		30.00	30.00

1992 Summer
Olympics,
Barcelona — A157

1992, June 16

815	A157	42s Boxing	1.25	.85
816	A157	57s Diving	1.75	1.10
817	A157	1.50pa Tennis	4.50	4.50
818	A157	3pa Cycling	9.50	9.50
	Nos. 815-818 (4)		17.00	15.95

For surcharges, see 1123, 1125.

King
Taufa'ahau
IV, 25th
Anniv. of
Coronation
A158

Designs: 45s, 2pa, King, Queen Halaevalu. No. 820a, King, crown. b, Extract from investiture ceremony. c, King, #C33.

1992, July 4　　　Perf. 13½x13

819	A158 45s multicolored		1.25	.90

Size: 51x38mm
Perf. 12½x12

820	A158 80s Strip of 3, #a.-c.		6.50	6.50
821	A158 2pa multicolored		5.25	5.25
	Nos. 819-821 (3)		13.00	12.65

Sacred Bats of
Kolovai — A159

Designs: No. 822a, Bats in flight. b, Close-up of flying bat. c, Flying bats, tree. d, Bats hanging in tree. e, Bat hanging from tree limb. Origin of sacred bats: No. 823a, Kula leaving for Upolu to be tattooed as Tongan chief. b, 45s, Kula looking through path of fires. c, 2pa, Kula walking down path, Hina. d, 2pa, Hina waving, Kula leaving with pet fruit bats.

Nos. 823a-823d are horiz.

1992, Oct. 20　Litho.　Perf. 14

822	A159 60s Strip of 5, #a.-e.		13.00	13.00

Souvenir Sheet
Perf. 14½

823	A159 Sheet of 4, #a.-d.		14.00	14.00

60
Greetings
from
TONGA

Christmas
A160

1992, Nov. 10　　　Perf. 14

824	A160	60s Pearls	1.50	1.10
825	A160	80s Reef fish	2.00	1.40
826	A160	2pa Pacific orchids	4.75	4.75
827	A160	3pa Eua parrots	7.25	7.25
	Nos. 824-827 (4)		15.50	14.50

For surcharges see Nos. 894-897.

Anniversaries and Events — A161

Designs: 60s, Tonga flag, Rotary emblem. 80sh, John F. Kennedy, Peace Corps emblem. 1.50pa, FAO, WHO emblems. 3.50pa, Globe, Rotary Foundation emblem.

1992, Dec. 15　　　Perf. 14½

828	A161	60s multicolored	1.40	1.00
829	A161	80s multicolored	1.90	1.40
830	A161	1.50pa multicolored	3.50	3.50
831	A161	3.50pa multicolored	8.50	8.50
	Nos. 828-831 (4)		15.30	14.40

Rotary Intl. in Tonga, 25th anniv. (#828). Peace Corps in Tonga, 25th anniv. (#829). Intl. Conference of FAO and WHO (#830). Rotary Foundation of Rotary Intl., 75th anniv. (#831). For overprint see No. 868.

Family Planning — A163

Outdoor silhouette scenes: No. 832, Mother, girl, butterflies. No. 833, Child on tricycle pulling kite. No. 834, Girl, kittens. No. 835, Adult, child playing chess.

1993, Jan. 26　　　Perf. 14x13½

832	A163	15s Pair, #a.-b.	2.50	2.50
833	A163	45s Pair, #a.-b.	3.50	3.50
834	A163	60s Pair, #a.-b.	5.00	5.00
835	A163	2pa Pair, #a.-b.	15.00	15.00
	Nos. 832-835 (4)		26.00	26.00

Nos. 832a-835a have Tongan inscriptions. Nos. 832b-835b have English inscriptions and are mirror images of Nos. 832a-835a.

Health and Fitness — A164

Designs: 60s, Fresh fruit, fish, anti-smoking and anti-drug symbols. 80s, Anti-smoking symbol, weight training. 1.50pa, Anti-drug symbol, water sports. 2.50pa, Fresh fruit, fish, cyclist, jogger. Illustration reduced.

1993, Mar. 16　Litho.　Perf. 14

836	A164	60s multicolored	2.00	2.00
837	A164	80s multicolored	2.75	2.75
838	A164	1.50pa multicolored	5.25	5.25
839	A164	2.50pa multicolored	8.50	8.50
	Nos. 836-839 (4)		18.50	18.50

Tonga
Fire
Service,
25th
Anniv.
A165

1993, May 18　Litho.　Perf. 14

840	A165	45s Fireman's badge	2.00	2.00
841	A165	45s Police van, badge	2.00	2.00
a.		Pair, #840-841	3.50	3.50
842	A165	60s Police band	2.50	2.50
843	A165	60s Putting out fire	2.50	2.50
a.		Pair, #842-843	4.50	4.50
844	A165	2pa Fire truck at station	9.00	9.00
845	A165	2pa Policeman, police dog	9.00	9.00
a.		Pair, #844-845	15.00	15.00
	Nos. 840-845 (6)		27.00	27.00

Tonga Police Training College, 25th anniv. (#841-842, 845).

For surcharges see Nos. 943-948.

A166

A167

Abel Tasman's Voyage to Eua, 350th Anniv.: 30s, Map of islands. 60s, Sailing ships, Heemskirk and Zeehaen. 80s, Sailing ships, natives in canoes. 3.50pa, Landing on Eua.

1993, June 21

846	A166	30s multicolored	.80	.50
847	A166	60s multicolored	1.75	1.10
848	A166	80s multicolored	2.25	2.25
849	A166	3.50pa multicolored	10.00	10.00
	Nos. 846-849 (4)		14.80	13.85

1993, July 1　Litho.　Perf. 13x13½

King Taufa'ahau IV, 75th Birthday: 45s, 2pa, Musical instruments.

No. 851a, Sporting events. b, Ancient landmarks. c, Royal Palace.

850	A167 45s multicolored		.65	.65

Perf. 12x12½
Size: 37x48mm

851	A167	80s Strip of 3, #a.-c.	5.00	5.00
852	A167	2pa multicolored	3.00	3.00
	Nos. 850-852 (3)		8.65	8.65

A168

A168a

Children's Stamp Designs: Nos. 853a, 854a, Beach scene. Nos. 853b, 854b, "Maui-The Fisher of the Islands." Nos. 853c, 854c, Raft on ocean. Nos. 853d, 854d, Woman with hands in mixing bowl. Nos. 853e, 854e, "Maui and his Hook." Nos. 853f, 854f, "Communication in the South Pacific."

1993, Dec. 1　Litho.　Perf. 14

853	A168	10s Strip of 6, #a.-f.	3.00	3.00
854	A168	80s Strip of 6, #a.-f.	14.00	14.00

1993, Nov. 10   Litho.   Perf. 14

Christmas traditions: 60s, Festive dinner. 80s, Shooting cannon. 1.50pa, Musicians. 3pa, Going to church.

855	A168a	60s multicolored	1.50	1.25
856	A168a	80s multicolored	2.00	1.50
857	A168a	1.50pa multicolored	3.75	3.75
858	A168a	3pa multicolored	7.75	7.75
		Nos. 855-858 (4)	15.00	14.25

Miniature Sheet

Kindness to Animals — A169

Designs: a, 80s, Boy holding puppy. b, 80s, Girl holding kitten. c, 60s, Boy holding rooster (b). d, 60s, Girl with butterfly. e, 60s, Three dogs. f, 60s, Boy, puppy.

1994, Jan. 14   Perf. 14½

859	A169	Sheet of 6, #a.-f.	17.50	17.50

For overprint see No. 868.

Game Fishing — A170

1994, Feb. 28   Litho.   Perf. 12

860	A170	60s Tiger shark	1.50	1.00
861	A170	80s Dolphin fish	2.00	1.40
862	A170	1.50pa Yellow fin tuna	4.00	4.00
863	A170	2.50pa Pacific blue marlin	6.50	6.50
		Nos. 860-863 (4)	14.00	12.90

1994 World Cup Soccer Championships, US — A171

Designs: No. 864a, Player's legs. No. 864b, World Cup trophy. No. 865a, American player in red, white, & blue. No. 865b, German player in black shorts, white shirt.

1994, June 1   Perf. 14x14½

864	A171	80s Pair, #a.-b.	4.00	4.00
865	A171	2pa Pair, #a.-b.	10.00	10.00

Pan Pacific & South East Asia Women's Assoc. Conference — A172

Career women: No. 866a, Lawyer. No. 866b, Policewoman. No. 867a, Doctor. No. 867b, Nurse.

1994, Aug. 18   Litho.   Perf. 14

866	A172	45s Pair, #a.-b.	3.50	3.50
867	A172	2.50pa Pair, #a.-b.	10.50	10.50

Nos. 859a, 859c-859f Ovptd. "MERRY / CHRISTMAS"
No. 859b Ovptd. "KILISIMASI FIEFIA"

1994, Nov. 10   Litho.   Perf. 14½

868	A169	Sheet of 6, #a.-f.	8.50	8.50

No. 831 Ovptd. in Dark Blue

1994, Nov. 17   Litho.   Perf. 14½

869	A161	60s on 3.50pa multi	4.00	4.00

Types of 1969-85 and

Tongastar 1 Satellite — A173

Design: a, 10s, Type A39 banana, size 22x11mm. b, 25s, Type AP12. c, Booklet pane, 12 #870a, 3 #870b. d, 45s, like #608. e, 45s, like #609. f, 45s, like #610. g, 45s, like #611. h, Booklet pane of 3 each #870d-870e, 2 #870f, 1 #870g. i, 60s, Type A72. j, 60s, Type OA19. k, 80s, Type OA17. l, Booklet pane, #870i-870k. m, 2pa, Tongastar 1. n, Booklet pane of 1 #870m.

Unwmk.
1994, Dec. 14   Litho.   Die Cut
Self-adhesive

870	A173	Souvenir booklet	26.50

First full-scale production of self-adhesive stamps by Tonga, 25th anniv. (#870). Satellite communications network for Tongan Islands (#870m).
No. 870b is airmail. Nos. 870j-870k are air post official stamps.
No. 870m contains a holographic image. Soaking in water may affect the hologram.

Marine Type of 1992-93 Redrawn

1994-95   Litho.   Perf. 14

874	A155a	10s like #799A	.20	.20
876	A155a	20s like #801	.30	.30
877	A155a	45s like #803	.70	.70
878	A155a	60s like #804	.95	.95
879	A155a	80s like #806	1.25	1.25

Size: 41x27mm, 41x27mm

880	A155a	1pa like #705, horiz.	1.90	1.90
881	A155a	2pa like #577, horiz.	3.75	3.75
882	A155a	3pa like #578, horiz.	5.75	5.75
883	A155a	5pa like #706	9.50	9.50
884	A155a	10pa like #568	20.00	20.00
		Nos. 874-884 (10)	44.30	44.30

Area covered by background colors on Nos. 874, 876-879 has been reduced in size.
Issued: 1pa, 2pa, 3pa, 6/21/94; 5pa, 9/21/94; 10pa, 1/18/95; 10s, 20s, 45s, 60s, 80s, 9/25/95.
This is an expanding set. Numbers may change.

FAO, 50th Anniv. A174

1995, May 16   Litho.   Perf. 14

886	A174	5pa multicolored	17.00	17.00

Tonga's Entry into British Commonwealth, 25th Anniv. — A175

Children with bicycles from parts of Commonwealth.

1995, June 6

887	A175	45s Polynesia	1.10	.90
888	A175	60s Asia	1.50	1.25
889	A175	80s Africa	1.75	1.75
890	A175	2pa India	4.50	4.50
891	A175	2.50pa Europe	6.00	6.00
		Nos. 887-891 (5)	14.85	14.40

1995 Rugby World Cup, South Africa — A176

Designs: No. 892a, Player running right with ball, two others. b, Two players. No. 893a, Three players. b, Player ready to catch ball.

1995, June 20   Perf. 14½

892	A176	80s Pair, #a.-b.	6.00	6.00
893	A176	2pa Pair, #a.-b.	13.50	13.50

Nos. 892-893 were each issued in sheets of 4 stamps.
For surcharges see Nos. 954A, 956A.

Nos. 824-827 Surcharged

i

j

1995, June 30   Litho.   Perf. 14

894		60s Pair	4.00	4.00
a.	A160(i)	on #824	1.75	1.75
b.	A160(j)	on #824	1.75	1.75
895		60s Pair	4.00	4.00
a.	A160(i)	on 80s #825	1.75	1.75
b.	A160(j)	on 80s #825	1.75	1.75
896		60s Pair	4.00	4.00
a.	A160(i)	on 2pa #826	1.75	1.75
b.	A160(j)	on 2pa #826	1.75	1.75
897		60s Pair	4.00	4.00
a.	A160(i)	on 3pa #827	1.75	1.75
b.	A160(j)	on 3pa #827	1.75	1.75
		Nos. 894-897 (4)	16.00	16.00

Nos. 779-782 Surcharged

1995, June 30   Litho.   Perf. 14

898	A151	60s on 57s #779	1.40	1.40
899	A151	80s on 2pa #781	1.75	1.75
899A	A151	80s on 2pa #782	1.75	1.75
b.		Pair, #899-899A	3.50	3.50
899C	A151	1pa on #780	2.25	2.25
		Nos. 898-899C (4)	7.15	7.15

Victory in the Pacific, 50th Anniv. — A177

Nos. 900, 901: a, Soldier climbing from rope ladder. b, Ship, soldiers. c, Ship, landing craft with troops, soldiers up close. d, Ship, landing craft with troops. e, Map.

1995, Aug. 1   Litho.   Perf. 14x14½

900	A177	60s Strip of 5, #a.-e.	10.00	10.00
901	A177	80s Strip of 5, #a.-e.	12.00	12.00

Nos. 900-901 are continuous designs and were issued together in sheet containing ten stamps.

Singapore '95 — A178

Designs: No. 902a, 45s, #887. b, 60s, #888. 2pa, Boy cycling in Singapore.

1995, Sept. 1   Litho.   Perf. 12

902	A178	Pair, #a.-b.	3.75	3.75

Souvenir Sheet

903	A178	2pa multicolored	5.25	5.25

Souvenir Sheet

Beijing Intl. Coin & Stamp Show '95 — A179

Design: 1.40pa, Mount Song, Henan Province, China. Illustration reduced.

1995, Sept. 14   Perf. 14½

904	A179	1.40pa multicolored	5.00	5.00

End of World War II, UN, 50th Anniv. — A180

No. 905a, Holocaust survivors. b, UN emblem, "50." c, Children of Holocaust survivors in celebration.
No. 906a, Mushroom cloud from atom bomb explosion. b, Like #905b. c, Space shuttle.

1995, Oct. 20   Litho.   Perf. 13

905	A180	60s Strip of 3, #a.-c.	4.00	4.00
906	A180	80s Strip of 3, #a.-c.	7.50	7.50

Nos. 905b, 906b are 23x31mm.

Christmas and New Year — A181

Orchids: 20s, Calanthe triplicata. Nos. 908, Spathoglottis plicata, inscribed "MERRY CHRISTMAS." No. 909, like #908, inscribed "A HAPPY 1996." No. 910, Dendrobium platygastrium, inscribed "MERRY CHRISTMAS." No. 911, like #910, inscribed "A HAPPY 1996." 80s, Goodyera rubicunda. 2pa, Dendrobium toki. 2.50pa, Phaius tankervilliae.

1995, Nov. 15   Litho.   *Perf. 14x14½*
907	A181	20s multicolored	.75	.75
908	A181	45s multicolored	1.00	1.00
909	A181	45s multicolored	1.00	1.00
910	A181	60s multicolored	1.25	1.25
911	A181	60s multicolored	1.25	1.25
912	A181	80s multicolored	1.75	1.75
913	A181	2pa multicolored	5.00	5.00
914	A181	2.50pa multicolored	6.00	6.00
	Nos. 907-914 (8)		18.00	18.00

Humpback Whale — A182

1996, Jan. 7   *Perf. 14*
915	A182	45s In water	2.10	2.10
916	A182	60s With calf	3.25	3.25
917	A182	1.50pa Sounding	6.50	6.50
918	A182	2.50pa Breaching	9.25	9.75
	Nos. 915-918 (4)		21.10	21.60

World Wildlife Fund.

Miniature Sheet

New Year 1996 (Year of the Rat) — A183

Denomination: a, UR. b, UL. c, LR. d, LL.

1996, Feb. 23
919	A183	60s Sheet of 4,		
		#a.-d.	7.50	7.50

No. 919 is a continuous design. See Nos. 930-932, 932E, 942, 986.

Marine Type of 1992-93 Redrawn
1996, May 31   Litho.   *Perf. 14*
Size: 40x26mm
920	A155a	1pa like #880	2.10	2.10
921	A155a	2pa like #881	4.25	4.25
922	A155a	3pa like #882	6.75	6.75
923	A155a	5pa like #883	11.00	11.00
924	A155a	10pa like #884	22.50	22.50
	Nos. 920-924 (5)		46.60	46.60

Size of "TONGA" on Nos. 920-923 is smaller than on Nos. 880-883. Name of species appears at top instead of bottom on Nos. 920-924. Background colors vary. Inscribed "1996."

1996 Summer Olympic Games, Atlanta — A184

Statues of classical Greek figures, modern athletes: 45s, Zeus, runner. 80s, The Discus Thrower. 2pa, The Javelin Thrower. 3pa, The Horseman, dressage competitor.

1996, July 2   Litho.   *Perf. 14*
925	A184	45s multicolored	1.25	.80
926	A184	80s multicolored	2.00	1.90
927	A184	2pa multicolored	5.75	5.75
928	A184	3pa multicolored	9.00	9.00
	Nos. 925-928 (4)		18.00	17.45

For surcharges & overprint see Nos. 949-952.

13th Congress of Intl. Union of Preshistoric and Protohistoric Sciences — A185

a, Prehistoric man using fire, knife, bow & arrow, animals. b, Ancient Egyptians, Greeks, Romans.

1996, Sept. 5   Litho.   *Perf. 12*
929	A185	1pa Pair, #a.-b.	7.50	7.50

No. 929 was issued in sheets of 6 stamps.

New Year 1996 (Year of the Rat) Type
Denomination: a, UR. b, UL. c, LR. d, LL.

1996, June 27   Litho.   *Perf. 14*
Sheets of 4
930	A183	10s #a.-d.	1.40	1.40
931	A183	20s #a.-d.	2.75	2.75
932	A183	45s #a.-d.	6.75	6.75
932E	A183	60s #a.-d.	10.00	10.00

The denominations are larger on No. 932E than those on No. 919.

Christmas A186

Paintings: 20s, Virgin and Child, by Sassoferrato. 60s, Adoration of the Shepherds, by Murillo. 80s, Virgin and Child, by Delaroche. 1pa, Adoration of the Shepherds, by Champaigne.

1996, Oct. 29   Litho.   *Perf. 14*
933	A186	20s multicolored	.75	.50
934	A186	60s multicolored	2.50	1.50
935	A186	80s multicolored	2.75	2.50
936	A186	1pa multicolored	8.50	8.50
	Nos. 933-936 (4)		14.50	13.00

UNICEF, 50th Anniv. — A187

Children in sports activities: a, Running, playing rugby. b, Tennis. c, Cycling.

1996, Oct. 29
937	A187	80s Strip of 3, #a.-c.	9.00	9.00

No. 937 is a continuous design.

Queen Halaevalu Mata'aho, 70th Birthday — A188

Designs: 60s, Queen, natl. flag. No. 939a, Queen, coin with portrait. No. 939b, Coin with natl. arms, Queen.

1996, Nov. 27   Litho.   *Perf. 12*
938	A188	60s multicolored	3.50	3.50
939	A188	2pa Pair, #a.-b.	10.50	10.50

Towards the Year 2000 — A189

Year "2000" rising out of Pacific, Tonga landmarks: Nos. 940a, 941a, The Ha'amonga stone monument, globe, Kao Island. Nos. 941b, 941b, Mount Talau overlooking Port of Reguge, Royal Palance, Tongatapu, communication satellite.

1996, Dec. 9
940	A189	80s Pair, #a.-b.	4.00	4.00
941	A189	2pa Pair, #a.-b.	9.50	9.50

New Year Type of 1996 Redrawn with Ox

Denomination located: a, 60s, UR. b, 60s, UL. c, 80s, LR. d, 2pa, LL.

1997, Jan. 24   Litho.   *Perf. 14*
942	A183	Sheet of 4, #a.-d.	11.00	11.00

New Year 1997 (Year of the Ox).

Nos. 840-845 Surcharged

1997, Mar. 3   Litho.   *Perf. 14*
943	A165	10s on 45s #840	3.50	3.25
944	A165	10s on 45s #841	3.50	3.25
a.		Pair, #943-944	6.00	6.00
945	A165	10s on 60s #842	3.50	3.25
946	A165	10s on 60s #843	3.50	3.25
a.		Pair, #945-946	6.00	6.00
947	A165	20s on 2pa #844	4.00	3.75
948	A165	20s on 2pa #845	4.00	3.75
a.		Pair, #947-948	7.00	7.00
	Nos. 943-948 (6)		22.00	20.50

Nos. 925-928 Surcharged, Ovptd.

1997, Mar. 24   Litho.   *Perf. 14*
949	A184	10s on 45s #925	.90	.90
950	A184	10s on 80s #926	.90	.90
951	A184	10s on 2pa #927	.90	.90
952	A184	3pa #928	9.25	9.25
	Nos. 949-952 (4)		11.95	11.95

Size and location of surcharge varies.

Nos. 892-893 Surcharged

     a   b

1997, Mar. 24   *Perf. 14½*
Sheets of 4
954A	A176	10s on 80s	2.00	2.00
956A	A176	1pa on 2pa	15.00	15.00

#954A contains #892a (a), #892b (a), #892b (b), #892a (b). #956A contains #893a (a), #893b ((a), #893b (b), #893a (b).

Christianity in Tonga, Birth of King George Tupou I, Bicent. — A190

#957, 961a, 962a, Arrival of missionary ship, Duff, Captain James Wilson. #958, King George Tupou I, village. #959, 961b, 962b, People in water, rowboats coming ashore from Duff. #960, 961c, 962c, Natives, missionaries, Duff.

1997, Apr. 28   *Perf. 14*
957	A190	10s multicolored	.20	.20
958	A190	10s multicolored	.20	.20
959	A190	10s multicolored	.20	.20
960	A190	10s multicolored	.20	.20
a.		Sheet of 6, #957, 959-960, 3 #958	3.75	3.75
961	A190	60s Strip of 3, #a.-c.	4.50	4.50
962	A190	80s Strip of 3, #a.-c.	6.50	6.50

Nos. 961-962 were each issued in sheets of 9 stamps.
See Nos. 972-975.

Souvenir Sheet

Pacific Swallow, Golden Gate Bridge — A191

Illustration reduced.

1997, May 30
963	A191	2pa multicolored	7.50	7.50

Pacific '97.

Tonga High School, 50th Anniv. A192

Designs: 20s, Students in uniforms outside of school. 60s, Dressed for sports. 80s, Brass band. 3.50pa, Running competition.

1997, June 4

964	A192	20s multicolored	.75	.40
965	A192	60s multicolored	1.75	1.10
966	A192	80s multicolored	2.25	1.50
967	A192	3.50pa multicolored	9.25	9.25
		Nos. 964-967 (4)	14.00	12.25

A193

A194

Nos. 968, 970: a, Queen, King with bowed heads, royal escorts. b, Coronation ceremony. c, Queen, King. 45s, 2pa, King's crown.

1997, June 30   Litho.   Perf. 13x13½

968	A193	10s Strip of 3, #a.-		
		c.	1.25	1.25
969	A193	45s multicolored	1.75	1.75

Size: 34x47mm

Perf. 12

970	A193	60s Strip of 3, #a.-		
		c.	7.00	7.00
971	A193	2pa multicolored	8.50	8.50

King Taufa'ahau IV, Queen Halaevalu Mata'aho, 50th wedding anniv., coronation, 30th anniv.

Christianity in Tonga Type of 1997

1997, Aug. 27   Perf. 14

Size: 27x18mm

972	A190	10s like #957	.20	.20
973	A190	10s like #958	.20	.20
974	A190	10s like #959	.20	.20
975	A190	10s like #960	.20	.20
a.		Sheet of 12, 6 #973, 2 each #972, 974-975	6.00	6.00

1997, Oct. 1   Litho.   Perf. 14

Mushrooms: Nos. 976a, 977a, Lenzites elegans. Nos. 976b, 977b, Marasmiellus semiustus. No. 976c, 978a, Aseroe rubra. Nos. 976d, 978b, Podoscypha involuta. Nos. 976e, 979a, Microporus xanthopus. Nos. 976f, 979b, Lentinus tuberregium.

976	A194	10s Strip of 6, #a.-		
		f.	2.25	2.25

Size: 26x40mm

977	A194	20s Pair, #a.-b.	2.00	2.00
978	A194	60s Pair, #a.-b.	6.00	6.00
979	A194	2pa Pair, #a.-b.	19.00	19.00
c.		Sheet of 6, #977-979	26.50	26.50

No. 976 is a continuous design.

Diana, Princess of Wales (1961-97)
Common Design Type

Various portraits: a, 10s. b, 80s, c, 1pa. d, 2.50pa.

Perf. 13½x14

1998, May 29   Litho.   Unwmk.

980	CD355	Strip of 4, #a.-d.	6.75	6.75

No. 980 sold for 4.40pa + 50s with surtax from international sales going to the Princess Diana Memorial Fund and surtax from local sales going to designated local charity.

Flying Home for Christmas
A195

Designs: 60s, Airplane on ground, people waving. 80s, People waving, house, plane overhead. 1.50pa, Man in outrigger canoe waving to airplane. 3.50pa, Man, woman, people in boat on lake waving, airplane overhead.

1997, Oct. 20   Litho.   Perf. 14x13½

981	A195	60s bister & red	.90	.90
982	A195	80s bister & red	1.20	1.20
983	A195	1.50pa bister & red	2.20	2.20
984	A195	3.50pa bister & red	5.20	5.20
		Nos. 981-984 (4)	9.50	9.50

King Taufa'ahau Tupou IV, 80th Birthday — A196

1998, July 4   Litho.   Perf. 14

985	A196	2.70pa multicolored	7.00	7.00
a.		Souv. sheet, #985, Niuafo'ou #207	10.00	10.00

New Year 1998 (Year of the Tiger)

Tiger: a, 55s, Leaping down. b, 80s, Lying down. c, 1pa, Leaping upward. d, 1pa, Stalking.

1998, July 23

986	A183	Sheet of 4, #a.-d.	6.00	6.00

No. 986 is a continuous design. Singpex '98. For surcharges, see No. 1098.

Birds
A197

5s, Fairy tern, vert. 10s, Tongan whistler, vert. 15s, Common barn owl, vert. 20s, Purple swamp hen, vert. 30s, Red-footed booby, vert. 40s, Banded rail. 50s, Swamp harrier. 55s, Blue-crowned lorikeet, vert. 60s, Great frigate bird, vert. 70s, Friendly ground dove. 80s, Red-tailed tropic bird, vert. 1pa, Red shining parrot, vert. 2pa, Pacific pigeon, vert. 3pa, Pacific golden plover. 5pa, Tongan megapode.

Perf. 14x14½, 14½x14

			Litho.
992	A197	5s multicolored	.20	.20
993	A197	10s multicolored	.20	.20
994	A197	15s multicolored	.20	.20
995	A197	20s multicolored	.25	.25
996	A197	30s multicolored	.45	.45
997	A197	40s multicolored	.60	.60
998	A197	50s multicolored	.70	.70
999	A197	55s multicolored	.80	.80
1000	A197	60s multicolored	.85	.85
1001	A197	70s multicolored	1.00	1.00
1002	A197	80s multicolored	1.10	1.10
1003	A197	1pa multicolored	1.40	1.40
1004	A197	2pa multicolored	2.75	2.75
1005	A197	3pa multicolored	4.25	4.25
1006	A197	5pa multicolored	7.25	7.25
		Nos. 992-1006 (15)	22.00	22.00

For surcharges, see Nos. 1077A, 1077B, 1099-1114, 1126.

Fish
A198

Designs: a, 10s, Chaetodon pelewensis. b, 55s, Chaetodon lunula. c, 1pa, Chaetodon ephippium.

1998, Sept. 23   Litho.   Perf. 14

1008	A198	Strip of 3, #a.-c.	4.00	4.00

Intl. Year of the Ocean. No. 1008 was issued in sheets of 9 stamps.

Christmas
A199

Designs: 10s, Angel, "Kilisimasi Fiefia." 80s, Angel, "Merry Christmas." 1pa, Children, candle, "Ta'u Fo'ou Monu'ia." 1.60pa, Children, candle, "Happy New Year."

1998, Nov. 12   Litho.   Perf. 14x14½

1009	A199	10s multicolored	.60	.40
1010	A199	80s multicolored	2.50	1.25
1011	A199	1pa multicolored	2.75	2.25
1012	A199	1.60pa multicolored	3.50	3.50
		Nos. 1009-1012 (4)	9.35	7.40

New Year 1999 (Year of the Rabbit) A200

a, 10s, Three rabbits. b, 55s, Rabbit eating. c, 80s, Rabbit looking upward. d, 1pa, Rabbit hopping.

1999, Feb. 16   Perf. 14

1013	A200	Sheet of 4, #a.-d.	4.50	4.50

Explorers — A201

Explorer, ship: 55s, Tasman, Heemsberck, 1643. 80s, La Perouse, Astrolabe, 1788. 1pa, William Bligh, Bounty, 1789. 2.50pa, James Cook, Resolution, 1777.

1999, Mar. 19   Litho.   Perf. 14

1014	A201	55s multicolored	1.00	.60
1015	A201	80s multicolored	1.50	1.00
1016	A201	1pa multicolored	2.00	1.75
1017	A201	2.50pa multicolored	4.75	4.75
a.		Souvenir sheet of 1	5.00	5.00
		Nos. 1014-1017 (4)	9.25	8.10

Australia '99 World Stamp Expo (#1017a).

Scenic Views, Vava'u
A202

Designs: 10s, Neiafu. 55s, Boats on water, Port of Refuge. 80s, Aerial view, Port of Refuge. 1pa, Sunset, Neiafu. 2.50pa, Mounu Island.

1999, May 19   Perf. 14½

1018	A202	10s multicolored	.50	.40
1019	A202	55s multicolored	1.00	.60
1020	A202	80s multicolored	1.60	.80
1021	A202	1pa multicolored	1.75	1.40
1022	A202	2.50pa multicolored	3.50	3.50
		Nos. 1018-1022 (5)	8.35	6.70

Flowers
A203

Designs: 10s, Fagraea berteroana. 80s, Garcinia pseudoguttfera. 1pa, Phlaeria disperma, vert. 2.50pa, Gardenia taitensis, vert.

Perf. 13¼x13, 13x13¼

1999, Sept. 29   Litho.

1023	A203	10s multicolored	.25	.25
1024	A203	80s multicolored	1.25	1.25
1025	A203	1pa multicolored	1.60	1.60
1026	A203	2.50pa multicolored	4.00	4.00
		Nos. 1023-1026 (4)	7.10	7.10

Millennium — A204

Designs: a, 55s, Ha'amonga monument, people, clocks at 11:15 to 11:25. b, 80s, Monument, people, clocks at 11:30 to 11:40. c, 1pa, People, clocks at 11:45 to 11:55. d, 2.50pa, King Taufa'ahau IV, clocks at 12:00, 12:05.

1999, Dec. 1

1027	A204	Strip of 4, #a.-d.	7.00	7.00

Millennium — A205

Clock, dove and: 10s, Flowers. 1pa, Ha'amonga Monument. 2.50pa, Native boat. 2.70pa, Crown.

Litho. & Embossed

2000, Jan. 1   Perf. and Die Cut

1028	A205	10s multi	.25	.25
1029	A205	1pa multi	1.50	1.50
1030	A205	2.50pa multi	3.50	3.50
1031	A205	2.70pa multi	4.00	4.00
a.		Souv. sheet, #1030-1031	7.50	7.50
		Nos. 1028-1031 (4)	9.25	9.25

Values are for stamps with attached selvage.

Souvenir Sheet

New Year 2000 (Year of the Dragon) — A206

Illustration reduced.
Various dragons; a, 10s. b, 55s, c, 80s. d, 1pa.

Litho. with Foil Application

2000, Feb. 4   Perf. 14½

1032	A206	Sheet of 4, #a.-d.	4.75	4.75

Souvenir Sheet

The Stamp Show 2000, London — A207

Illustration reduced.

Litho. with Foil Application
2000, May 22   *Perf. 13x13¼*
1033 A207 Sheet of 2   5.50 5.50
a.   1pa Queen Mother   1.50 1.50
b.   2.50pa Queen Salote Tupou III   3.50 3.50

Geostationary Orbital Slot Program — A208

Designs: 10s, Proton RU500 lauch vehicle, vert. 1pa, LM3 launch vehicle. 2.50pa, Apstar 1. 2.70pa, Gorizont.

Litho. with Foil Application
2000, July 5   *Perf. 14½x15, 15x14½*
1034-1037 A208 Set of 4   9.00 9.00
1037a   Souvenir sheet, #1036-1037   8.25 8.25

World Stamp Expo 2000, Anaheim.

2000 Summer Olympics, Sydney — A209

No. 1038: a, Runner, koalas, sailboats. b, Boxers, kangaroos, Ayers Rock. c, Torchbearers, Ayers Rock, Sydney Opera House (60x45mm). d, Discus thrower, Sydney Harbour Bridge, flower. e, Weight lifter, kookaburra, fish.

2000, Sept. 15   Litho.   *Perf. 14*
1038   Horiz. strip of 5   5.50 5.50
a.-e.   A209 80s Any single   1.00 1.00

Commonwealth Membership, 30th Anniv. — A210

Designs: 10s, Education. 55s, Arts. 80s, Health. 2.70pa, Agriculture.

2000, Oct. 25
1039-1042 A210 Set of 4   5.50 5.50

Souvenir Sheet

New Year 2001 (Year of the Snake) — A211

No. 1043 — Various snakes: a, 10s. b, 55s, c, 80s, d, 1pa.

Litho. with Foil Application
2001, Feb. 1   *Perf. 14¼*
1043 A211 Sheet of 4, #a-d   4.50 4.50
Hong Kong 2001 Stamp Exhibition.

Dance — A212

Designs: 10s, Ma'ulu'ulu. 55s, Me'etupaki. 80s, Tau'olunga. 2.70pa, Faha'iula.

2001, Apr. 4   Litho.   *Perf. 13¼*
1044-1047 A212 Set of 4   5.50 5.50

Year of the Mangrove A213

Designs: 10s, Fiddler crab. 55s, Black duck, gray mullet, vert. 80s, Red mangrove, emperor fish, vert. 1pa, Reef heron, mangrove. 2.70pa, Mangrove crab.

2001, May 5   Litho.   *Perf. 13¾*
1048-1052 A213 Set of 5   6.50 6.50
1052a   Souvenir sheet, #1048-1052, perf. 13½   7.00 7.00

Sport Fishing — A214

2001, July 31   *Perf. 14¾x14*
1053   Horiz. strip of 4 with central label   8.25 8.25
a.   A214 45s Sailfish   .50 .50
b.   A214 80s Blue marlin   1.00 1.00
c.   A214 2.40pa Wahoo   3.00 3.00
d.   A214 2.60pa Dorado   3.25 3.25

Fruit — A215

2001, Sept. 19   *Serpentine Die Cut*
Self-Adhesive
1054   Horiz. strip of 5   6.00
a.   A215 10s Banana   .25 .25
b.   A215 45s Coconut   .50 .50
c.   A215 60s Pineapple   .75 .75
d.   A215 80s Watermelon   .85 .85
e.   A215 2.40pa Passion fruit   2.40 2.40

Shells A216

Designs: 10s, Haliotis ovina. 80s, Turbo petholatus. 1pa, Trochus niloticus. 2.70pa, Turbo marmoratus.

Perf. 12¾
2001, Dec. 13   Litho.   Unwmk.
1055-1058 A216 Set of 4   6.25 6.25
Values are for copies with surrounding selvage.

Reign Of Queen Elizabeth II, 50th Anniv. Issue
Common Design Type
Souvenir Sheet

No. 1059: a, 15s, Princess Elizabeth as child. b, 90s, Wearing yellow hat. c, 1.20pa, With Princess Anne and Prince Charles. d, 1.40pa, Wearing crown. e, 2.25pa, 1955 portrait by Annigoni (38x50mm).

Perf. 14¼x14½, 13¾ (2.25pa)
2002, Feb. 6   Litho.   Wmk. 373
1059 CD360 Sheet of 5, #a-e   8.00 8.00

Souvenir Sheet

New Year 2002 (Year of the Horse) — A217

Various horses: a, 65s. b, 80s. c, 1pa. d, 2.50pa.

Litho. With Foil Application
2002, Feb. 12   Unwmk.   *Perf. 14*
1060 A217 Sheet of 4, #a-d   6.75 6.75

Intl. Year of Ecotourism — A218

Designs: 5s, Whale, surfer. 15s, Woman, shoreline. 70s, Beach, fish. 1.40pa, Arch, man. 2.25pa, Boats, man.

2002, Apr. 9   Litho.   *Perf. 13¼x13¾*
1061-1065 A218 Set of 5   6.50 6.50

Pearls A219

Pearls and: 90s, Workers preparing oysters for pearl cultivation. 1pa, Diver checking strung oysters. 1.20pa, Woman, pearl on necklace. 2.50pa, Islands.

2002, June 12   Litho.   *Perf. 13½*
1066-1069 A219 Set of 4   7.50 7.50
1069a   Souvenir sheet, #1068-1069   5.00 5.00
Values are for copies with surrounding selvage.

Participation of Tongan Team in Rugby Sevens Tournament — A220

Designs: 15s, Player leaping for ball. 30s, Players ready for scrum. 90s, Player attempting tackle. 4pa, Players on ground.

2002, July 27
1070-1073 A220 Set of 4   7.25 7.25
Values are for copies with surrounding selvage.

Weaving — A221

Designs: 30s, Woman and young girl. 90s, Woman with work hanging on line, boy with baskets. 1.40pa, Women weaving baskets. 2.50pa, Woman weaving basket lid.

2002, Sept. 17   *Perf. 12¼*
1074-1077 A221 Set of 4   7.00 7.00

Nos. 999, 1003 Surcharged

Type 1 — Slash Over First "5"

Methods and Perfs As Before
2002, Sept.
1077A A197 5s on 55s #999, Type 1   — —
1077B A197 15(s) on $1 #1003   — —
See Nos. 1099-1114 for additional surcharges on No. 999.

'Eua National Park, 10th Anniv. — A222

Various depictions of red shining parrots 45s, 1pa, 1.50pa, 2.50pa.

2002, Nov. 27   Litho.   *Perf. 12¼*
1078-1081 A222 Set of 4   7.50 7.50

New Year 2003 (Year of the Ram) — A223

No. 1082: a, 65s, One ram. 80s, Three sheep. 1pa, Three sheep, diff. 2.50pa, Two sheep.

2003, Apr. 14   Litho.   Perf. 13¼
1082 A223   Sheet of 4, #a-d   4.75 4.75

Coronation of Queen Elizabeth II, 50th Anniv. — A224

Designs: 90s, Queen Elizabeth II in coach. 1.20pa, Queen Salote of Tonga. 1.40pa, Queen Salote in coach. 2.50pa, Queen Elizabeth II.

Litho. With Foil Application
2003, June 2
1083-1086 A224   Set of 4   10.00 10.00

Boats of Abel Tasman — A225

Various boats: 15s, 75s, 90s, 2.50pa.

2003, Aug. 7   Litho.   Perf. 13¼
1087-1090 A225   Set of 4   7.75 7.75
1090a   Souvenir sheet, #1087-1090   8.00 8.00

Beaches — A226

Flower and: 15s, Euakafa Beach. 90s, Pangaimotu Beach. 1.40pa, Fafa Beach. 2.25pa, Nuku Beach.

2003, Sept. 11
1091-1094 A226   Set of 4   8.50 8.50

Nos. 784, 785a, 785b, 785c, 786 Surcharged

Methods and Perfs As Before
2003, Sept.
1095   A152   10s on 32s Horiz.
            strip of 3,
            #784a-784c   — —
1096   A152   10s on 42s #785a   —
1097   A152   10s on 42s #785b   —
1097A   A152   10s on 42s #785c   —

1098   A152   10s on 57s Horiz.
            strip of 3,
            #786a-786c   — —

No. 999 Surcharged

Type 2 — Small numerals and cent sign

Type 3 — Small numerals and "s"

Type 4 — Thin numerals and "s"

Type 5 — Large numerals and "s"

Type 6 — Medium-sized numerals and "s"

Type 7 — Very large, bold numerals and "c"

Methods and Perfs As Before
2003-04
1099   A197   05s on 55s, Type 3   — —
a.   Obliterators 2x1 ½mm
1100   A197   05s on 55s, Type 4   — —
1101   A197   5s on 55s, Type 5   — —
1102   A197   5c on 55s, Type 7   — —
1103   A197   10s on 55s, Type 4   — —
1104   A197   10s on 55s, Type 5   — —
1105   A197   10c on 55s, Type 7   — —
1106   A197   15s on 55s, Type 2   — —
1107   A197   15s on 55s, Type 4   — —
1108   A197   15s on 55s, Type 5   — —
1109   A197   15c on 55s, Type 7   — —
1110   A197   20s on 55s, Type 2   — —
1111   A197   20s on 55s, Type 4   — —
1112   A197   20s on 55s, Type 5   — —
1113   A197   45c on 55s, Type 2   — —
1114   A197   45s on 55s, Type 6   — —

Earliest known uses: Nos. 1099, 1106, 1110, 10/03; Nos. 1100, 1103, 1107, 1111, 12/03; Nos. 1101, 1108, 2/04; Nos. 1113, 4/04; Nos. 1104, 1112, 1114, 6/04; Nos. 1105, 1109, 8/04; No. 1102, 9/04;

Churches A227

Designs: 15s, Catholic Church, Neiafu, Vava'u. 90s, Wesleyan Church, Uiha, Ha'apai. 1.40pa, Cathedral of the Immaculate Conception of Mary. 2.25pa, Free Wesleyan Church, Nuku'alofa.

2003, Nov. 10
1115-1118 A227   Set of 4   8.50 8.50
Christmas.

New Year 2004 (Year of the Monkey) — A228

No. 1119: a, 60s, Spider monkey. b, 80s, Ring-tailed lemur. c, 1pa, Cotton-top tamarin. d, 2.50pa, White-cheeked gibbon.

2004, Feb. 12   Litho.   Perf. 13¼
1119 A228   Sheet of 4, #a-d   5.75 5.75

Nos. 770, 787, 788, 815, 816, 1001, Niuafo'ou Nos. 140, 141 and 145 Surcharged

Type 1 — Small denomination and obliterator

Type 2 — Large denomination and obliterator

Methods and Perfs As Before
2004
1120   A153   10s on 32s #787   — —
1121   A153   10s on 42s #788,
            Type 1   — —

1122   A153   10s on 42s #788,
            Type 2   — —
1123   A157   10s on 42s #815   — —
1124   A147   10s on 57s Horiz.
            strip of 4, + central label, #770a-
            770d   — —
1125   A157   10s on 57s #816   — —
1126   A197   60s on 70s #1001   — —

On Stamps of Niuafo'ou

1127   A25   10s on 42s #140   — —
1128   A26   10s on 42s #145   — —
1129   A25   10s on 57s #141   — —

Size and location of obliterators and new denominations varies. Earliest known use: No. 1126, 3/04; Nos. 1120, 1121, 4/04; Nos. 1122, 1123, 1124, 1125, 1127, 1128, 1129, 6/04. The surcharged Niuafo'ou stamps were not necessarily sent only to Niuafo'ou for sale there.

Fruit Plants — A229

Designs: 45s, Mango. 60s, Pineapple. 80s, Coconut. 1.80pa, Banana.

2004, Sept. 21   Litho.   Perf. 14¼x14
1130-1133 A229   Set of 4   3.75 3.75

Christmas A230

Designs: 65s, Madonna and Child. 80s, Journey to Bethlehem. 1.20pa, Annunciation to the Shepherds. 2.50pa, Magi.

2004, Dec.   Perf. 14
1134-1137 A230   Set of 4   5.50 5.50

Royalty — A231

Designs: 65s, King George Tupou I. 90s, King George Tupou II. 1.40pa, Queen Salote Tupou III. 3.05pa, King Taufa'ahau Tupou IV.

2004, July 7   Litho.   Perf. 14
1138-1141 A231   Set of 4   6.25 6.25

Souvenir Sheet

New Year 2005 (Year of the Rooster) — A232

No. 1142 — Various roosters with panel color of: a, 65s, Yellow orange. b, 80s, Light green. c, 1pa, Tan. d, 2.50pa, Gray blue.

2005, Feb. 12
1142 A232   Sheet of 4, #a-d   5.25 5.25

Souvenir Sheet

Whales — A233

No. 1143 — Various whales with denominations in: a, 65s, Purple. b, 80s, Yellow. c, 1pa, Green. d, 2.50pa, Pink.

2005, May 4   *Perf. 13¼*
1143 A233   Sheet of 4, #a-d   5.25 5.25

SEMI-POSTAL STAMP

Catalogue values for unused stamps in this section are for Never Hinged items.

No. 488 Surcharged in Silver for Cyclone Relief

1982, Apr. 14   **Litho.**
B1   A86   3pa + 50s multi   3.00 3.00

AIR POST STAMPS

Catalogue values for unused stamps in this section are for Never Hinged items.

Type of Regular Gold Coin Issue

Designs: 10p, 1sh1p, Queen Salote standing, ½-koula coin, obverse. 11p, Coat of arms, ½-koula coin, reverse. 2sh1p, 2sh9p, Queen Salote standing, 1-koula coin, obverse. 2sh4p, Coat of arms, 1-koula coin, reverse.

Litho.; Embossed on Gilt Foil
1963, July 15   Unwmk.   *Die Cut*
Diameter: 54mm
C1   A36   10p dp carmine   .45   .45
C2   A36   11p green   .55   .55
C3   A36   1sh1p violet blue   .50   .55
Diameter: 80mm
C4   A36   2sh1p magenta   1.10 1.10
C5   A36   2sh4p emerald   1.10 1.10
C6   A36   2sh9p violet   1.50 1.50
       Nos. C1-C6 (6)   5.20 5.25

See note after No. 133.

Map of Tongatabu and ¼-Koula Coin — AP1

Litho.; Embossed on Gilt Foil
1964, Oct. 19
C7   AP1   10p deep green   .20   .20
C8   AP1   1sh2p black   .20   .20
C9   AP1   3sh6p carmine   .95   .95
C10 AP1   6sh6p purple   1.75 1.75
       Nos. C7-C10 (4)   3.10 3.10

Pan-Pacific and Southeast Asia Women's Association Conf., Nukualofa, Aug. 1964. See note after No. 133.

Nos. C1-C2, C4-C6 Surcharged like Regular Issue, 1965, in Black, White or Red

1965, Mar. 18
C11 A36   2sh3p on 10p (B)   .20   .20
C12 A36   2sh9p on 11p (W)   .25   .25
C13 A36   4sh6p on 2sh1p   18.00 18.00

C14 A36   4sh6p on 2sh4p   18.00 18.00
C15 A36   4sh6p on 2sh9p   11.00 11.00
       Nos. C11-C15 (5)   47.45 47.45

Nos. 114-115, 117-118 Overprinted or Surcharged

Perf. 14½x13½
1966, June 18   Wmk. 79
C16 A35   5p purple   .25   .20
C17 A35   10p on 1p brn org & car
             rose   .25   .20
C18 A35   1sh red brown   .30   .20
C19 A35   2sh9p on 2p ultra   .35   .20
C20 A35   3sh6p on 5p purple   .35   .20
C21 A35   4sh6p on 1sh red brn   .75   .20
       Nos. C16-C21 (6)   2.25 1.20

Centenary of Tupou College and secondary education. The overprint or surcharge is spaced differently on other values.

Nos. C7-C8 Overprinted and Surcharged in Silver or Gold on Black, or in Black on Gold

Litho.; Embossed on Gilt Foil
1966, Dec. 16   Unwmk.   *Die Cut*
C22 AP1   10p (S on B)   .20   .20
C23 AP1   1sh2p (B on G)   .20   .20
C24 AP1   4sh on 10p (S on B)   1.00 1.00
C25 AP1   5sh6p on 1sh2p (B on
             G)   1.50 1.50
C26 AP1   10sh6p on 1sh2p (G on
             B)   2.50 2.50
       Nos. C22-C26 (5)   5.40 5.40

In memory of Queen Salote (1900-65).

King Taufa'ahau Type of Regular Issue, 1967

Designs: 7s, 11s, 23s, 2pa, Taufa'ahau IV, obverse of new palladium coins. 9s, 21s, 29s, Coat of Arms, plane.

Litho.; Embossed on Palladium Foil
1967, July 4
Diameter: 7s, 44mm; 9s, 29s, 52mm; 11s, 59mm; 21s, 68mm; 23s, 40mm; 2pa, 74mm.
C27 A38   7s red & black   .20   .20
C28 A38   9s maroon & emer   .25   .25
C29 A38   11s brt blue & org   .30   .30
C30 A38   21s black & emer   .55   .55
C31 A38   23s magenta & emer   .60   .60
C32 A38   29s vio blue & emer   .70   .70
C33 A38   2pa magenta & orange   5.00 5.00
       Nos. C27-C33 (7)   7.60 7.60

See note after No. 181.

Type of Regular Issue, 1953 Surcharged in Red or Black

Wmk. 79
1967, Dec. 15   Engr.   *Die Cut*
C34 A33   11s on 3½p ultra (R)   .30   .30
C35 A33   21s on 1½p emerald   .30   .30
C36 A33   23s on 3½p ultra (R)   .30   .30
       Nos. C34-C36 (3)   .90   .90

Arrival of the United States Peace Corps.

No. 112 Surcharged in Red

1968, Apr. 6   Engr.   *Perf. 11x11½*
C37 A34   11s on 10sh blk & yel   .45   .45
C38 A34   21s on 10sh blk & yel   .60   .60
C39 A34   23s on 10sh blk & yel   .60   .60
       Nos. C37-C39 (3)   1.65 1.65

Nos. C27-C33 Overprinted: "HIS MAJESTY'S 50th BIRTHDAY" in Silver on Blue Panel on 7s, 11s, 23s and 2pa. "H.M.'s BIRTHDAY / 4 . JULY . 1968" in Gold on Red Panel on 9s, 21s and 29s

Litho.; Embossed on Palladium Foil
1968, July 4   Unwmk.   *Die Cut*
C40 A38   7s red & black   .20   .20
C41 A38   9s maroon & emer   .20   .20
C42 A38   11s brt blue & org   .25   .20
C43 A38   21s black & emerald   .75   .35
C44 A38   23s mag & emerald   .75   .35
C45 A38   29s vio blue & emer   1.00   .40
C46 A38   2pa magenta & org   6.75 6.00
       Nos. C40-C46 (7)   9.90 7.70

50th birthday of King Taufa'ahau IV.

Types of 1953 Surcharged: "Friendly Islands / Field & Track Trials / South Pacific Games / Port Moresby 1969 / AIRMAIL"

Designs as before.

1968, Dec. 19   Engr.   Wmk. 79
C47 A33   6s on 6p yel& blk   .20   .20
C48 A33   7s on 4p purple & yel   .20   .20
C49 A33   8s on 8p blk & lt grn   .20   .20
C50 A33   9s on 1½p emerald   .20   .20
C51 A34   11s on 3p brn org & yel .20   .20
C52 A33   21s on 3½p dk blue   .30   .30
C53 A33   38s on 5sh sepia & yel 2.10   .50
C54 A34   1pa on 10sh orange yel 1.00   .60
       Nos. C47-C54 (8)   4.40 2.40

Issued to publicize the field and track trials for the third South Pacific Games, Port Moresby, 1969. The overprint is in 5 lines on the horizontal stamps, in 7 lines on the vertical stamps. On the vertical stamps "Trial" is printed on the line ahead of "Field & Track." On No. C54 the denomination is spelled out.

Nos. C19-C21 Surcharged

Perf. 14½x13½
1968   Photo.   Wmk. 79
C55 A35   1s on 2sh9p on 2p ultra 1.60 1.00
C56 A35   1s on 3sh6p on 5p pur 1.60 1.00
C57 A35   1s on 4sh6p on 1sh red
             brown   1.60 1.00
       Nos. C55-C57 (3)   4.80 3.00

Pacific Games Type of Regular Issue

Design: Boxer.

1969, Aug. 13   Litho.   *Die Cut*
Self-adhesive
C58 A40   9s orange, blk & pur   .20   .20
C59 A40   11s orange, blk & dk bl .20   .20
C60 A40   20s org, blk & yel grn .25   .25
C61 A40   60s orange, blk & scar .75   .75
C62 A40   1pa orange, blk & grn 1.25 1.25
       Nos. C58-C62 (5)   2.65 2.65

See note after No. 231.

Oil Derrick on Map of Tongatabu and King Taufa'ahau IV — AP2

Litho.; Gold Embossed
1969, Dec. 23   Self-adhesive
C63 AP2   9s multicolored   .25   .25
C64 AP2   10s multicolored   .25   .25
C65 AP2   24s multicolored   .70   .70
C66 AP2   29s multicolored   .80   .80
C67 AP2   38s multicolored   1.10 1.10
       Nos. C63-C67 (5)   3.10 3.10

1st scientific search for oil in Tonga.

King Taufa'ahau IV and Queen Elizabeth II — AP3

Litho.; Gold Embossed
1970, Mar. 7   Self-adhesive
C68 AP3   7s multicolored   .40   .30
C69 AP3   9s multicolored   .50   .35
C70 AP3   24s multicolored   1.25   .65
C71 AP3   29s multicolored   1.50   .75
C72 AP3   38s multicolored   2.10 1.00
       Nos. C68-C72 (5)   5.75 3.05

See note after No. 242.

King Taufa'ahau Tupou IV Medal — AP4

Litho.; Gold Embossed
1970, June 4
C73 AP4   9s grnsh bl, ver &
             gold   .25   .25
C74 AP4   10s lilac, bl & gold   .25   .25
C75 AP4   24s yel, grn & gold   .70   .70
C76 AP4   29s ultra, org & gold   .80   .80
C77 AP4   38s ocher, emer & gold 1.00 1.00
       Nos. C73-C77 (5)   3.00 3.00

See note after No. 247.

Red Cross Type of Regular Issue Without Coat of Arms

1970, Oct. 17   Litho.   *Die Cut*
Self-adhesive
C78 A45   9s red & silver   .25   .25
C79 A45   10s red & magenta   .25   .25
C80 A45   18s red & brt green   .75   .75
C81 A45   38s red & brt blue   2.25 2.25
C82 A45   1pa red & green   5.50 5.50
       Nos. C78-C82 (5)   9.00 9.00

Centenary of the British Red Cross.

Nos. C22-C24 Surcharged

Lithographed; Embossed on Gilt Foil
1971, Jan. 31   *Die Cut*
C83 AP1   9s on #C22 (S on B)   .70   .20
C84 AP1   24s on #C24 (G on B)   1.50 1.00
C85 AP1   29s on #C23 (R on B)   2.10 1.25
C86 AP1   38s on #C23 (G on B)   3.25 1.60
       Nos. C83-C86 (4)   7.55 4.05

In memory of Queen Salote (1900-1965).

Type of Regular Issue, 1953,
Surcharged in Red and Black

1971	**Engr.**	**Wmk. 79**	***Imperf***
C87	A33 9s on 1½p green	.25	.20
C88	A33 10s on 4p purple & yel	.25	.20
C89	A33 38s on 1p yellow & blk	1.10	.60
	Nos. C87-C89 (3)	1.60	1.00

See note after No. 272.

Types of Regular Issue Surcharged in
Purple or Black: "AIRMAIL," New
Denomination and "HONOURING
JAPANESE POSTAL CENTENARY
1871-1971"

1971

C90	A34 18s on 1sh car & buff		
	(P)	.50	.50
C91	A33 1pa on 2sh car & ultra	3.00	3.00

Surcharge on #C90 in 6 lines, on #C91 in 4.

Self-adhesive & Imperf.
Starting with Nos. C92-C96, all airmail issues are self-adhesive and
imperforate, unless otherwise stated.

High Jump — AP5

1971, July		**Litho.**	**Unwmk.**
C92	AP5 9s brown, mag & blk	.20	.20
C93	AP5 10s brown, blue & blk	.20	.20
C94	AP5 24s brn, dk grn & blk	.45	.45
C95	AP5 29s brown, vio & blk	.60	.60
C96	AP5 38s brown, red & blk	.80	.80
	Nos. C92-C96 (5)	2.25	2.25

4th South Pacific Games, Papeete, French
Polynesia, Sept. 8-19.
For surcharges see Nos. C141-C142.

Prehistoric
Trilithon,
King's Watch
and Portrait
AP6

Litho. and Embossed

1971, July 20			
C97	AP6 14s dk brown & multi	.65	.65
C98	AP6 21s ocher & multi	.90	.90

2nd anniversary of man's first landing on the
moon and the placement of a Bulova Accutron
there. See Nos. C117-118, CO47-CO48,
CO61-CO62. Advertisement on peelable
paper backing.

Medal Type of Regular Issue

Designs: 10s, Gold Medal of Merit, obverse
(King Taufa'ahau IV). 75s, Silver Medal of
Merit, obverse (King Taufa'ahau IV). 1pa,
Bronze Medal of Merit, reverse.

1971, Oct. 30		**Litho. & Embossed**	
C99	A47 10s gold & multi	.20	.20
C100	A47 75s silver & multi	1.50	1.50
C101	A47 1pa bronze & multi	1.60	1.60
	Nos. C99-C101 (3)	3.30	3.30

Girl with Blocks
and UNICEF
Emblem — AP7

1971, Dec.		**Litho.**	
C102	AP7 10s multicolored	.20	.20
C103	AP7 15s multicolored	.35	.35
C104	AP7 25s multicolored	.60	.60
C105	AP7 50s multicolored	1.25	1.25
C106	AP7 1pa multicolored	2.50	2.50
	Nos. C102-C106 (5)	4.90	4.90

25th anniversary of UNICEF.

Ship Type of Regular Issue

Design: Map of Merchant Marine routes
from Tonga and cargo ship "Niuvakai."

1972, Apr. 14			
C107	A49 9s ver & multi	.85	.35
C108	A49 12s multicolored	1.10	.35
C109	A49 14s dk purple & multi	1.25	.35
C110	A49 75s olive & multi	6.75	5.00
C111	A49 90s black & multi	7.00	6.50
	Nos. C107-C111 (5)	16.95	12.55

For surcharge and overprint see No. C124.

Coin Type of Regular Issue

Design: Coins on top; panel at bottom
inscribed "5th anniversary world's first palladium coinage."

Litho.; Embossed on Metallic Foil

1972, July 15			
C112	A50 9s silver & multi	.20	.20
C113	A50 12s silver & multi	.30	.30
C114	A50 14s silver & multi	.35	.35
C115	A50 21s silver & multi	.50	.50
C116	A50 75s silver & multi	1.75	1.75
	Nos. C112-C116 (5)	3.10	3.10

Watch Type of 1971
Litho. and Embossed

1972, July 20			
C117	AP6 17s multicolored	.75	.75
C118	AP6 38s multicolored	1.50	1.50

Advertisement on peelable paper backing.

Proclamation of Sovereignty — AP8

1972, Dec. 9		**Litho.**	
C119	AP8 9s ultra & multi	.20	.20
C120	AP8 12s red brown & multi	.25	.25
C121	AP8 14s magenta & multi	.35	.35
C122	AP8 38s brn org & multi	.95	.95
C123	AP8 1pa olive & multi	2.50	2.50
	Nos. C119-C123 (5)	4.25	4.25

Tonga's proclamation of sovereignty over
the Minerva Reefs, June 1972.

No. C107 Surcharged

1972, Nov.		**Litho.**	
C124	A49 7s on 9s multicolored	1.50	1.50

Inauguration of internal airmail service
Nukualofa-Vavau, Nov. 1972.

Tongan Bank Notes and Bank
Building — AP9

1973, Mar. 30		**Litho.**	
C125	AP9 9s multicolored	.25	.20
C126	AP9 12s ultra & multi	.25	.20
C127	AP9 17s dp car & multi	.40	.20
C128	AP9 50s lt blue & multi	1.50	1.25
C129	AP9 90s multicolored	2.75	2.75
	Nos. C125-C129 (5)	5.15	4.60

Establishment of Bank of Tonga.

Boy Scout Emblem — AP10

1973, June 29		**Litho.**	
C130	AP10 9s silver & multi	.70	.35
C131	AP10 12s silver & multi	.85	.45
C132	AP10 14s silver & multi	1.25	.70
C133	AP10 17s silver & multi	1.40	.85
C134	AP10 1pa silver & multi	15.00	9.25
	Nos. C130-C134 (5)	19.20	11.60

See note after No. 326.
For surcharges see Nos. C143-C144.

"Resolution" — AP11

1973, Oct. 2		**Litho.**	
C135	AP11 9s multicolored	.80	.40
C136	AP11 14s multicolored	1.50	.60
C137	AP11 29s multicolored	4.50	2.75
C138	AP11 38s multicolored	5.50	3.00
C139	AP11 75s multicolored	10.50	4.25
	Nos. C135-C139 (5)	22.80	11.00

Bicentenary of Capt. Cook's arrival.

Nos. 277, C96, C94, C130 and C132
Surcharged in Silver, Violet or Black:
"Commonwealth Games Christchurch
1974"

1973, Dec. 19			
C140	A46 7s on 25s multi (S)	.20	.20
C141	AP5 9s on 38s multi (V)	.25	.20
C142	AP5 24s multicolored (B)	.95	.35
C143	AP10 29s on 9s multi (V)	1.10	.50
C144	AP10 40s on 14s multi (B)	1.60	1.10
	Nos. C140-C144 (5)	4.10	2.35

10th British Commonwealth Games, Christchurch, New Zealand, Jan. 24-Feb. 2, 1974.
No. C140 is overprinted "AIRMAIL" in black;
the silver surcharge and overprint are on black
panels.

Parrot of
Eua — AP12

1974, Mar. 20		**Litho.**	
C145	AP12 7s multicolored	.50	.25
C146	AP12 9s multicolored	.60	.30
C147	AP12 12s multicolored	.60	.30
C148	AP12 14s multicolored	.90	.45
C149	AP12 17s multicolored	1.00	.50
C150	AP12 29s multicolored	1.75	.90
C151	AP12 38s multicolored	2.50	1.25
C152	AP12 50s multicolored	3.00	1.50
C153	AP12 75s multicolored	4.50	2.25
	Nos. C145-C153 (9)	15.35	7.70

Printed in rolls of 500. Self-adhesive rose
red control number in upper left corner.

Carrier Pigeon Scattering Letters over
Tonga — AP13

1974, June 20		**Typo.**	
C154	AP13 14s lt blue & multi	.45	.45
C155	AP13 21s lt blue & multi	.55	.55
C156	AP13 60s lt blue & multi	1.75	1.75
C157	AP13 75s lt blue & multi	1.90	1.90
C158	AP13 1pa lt blue & multi	2.50	2.50
	Nos. C154-C158 (5)	7.15	7.15

Centenary of Universal Postal Union.

Girl Guide Leaders — AP14

1974, Sept. 11   **Litho.**
C159 AP14 14s blue & multi   .80   .50
C160 AP14 16s blue & multi   1.40   .80
C161 AP14 29s blue & multi   2.75   1.60
C162 AP14 31s blue & multi   3.50   2.10
C163 AP14 75s blue & multi   7.50   4.50
      Nos. C159-C163 (5)   15.95   9.50
            Girl Guides of Tonga.
    For surcharges and overprints see Nos.
C190-C191, C193.

Freighter "James Cook" and List of
Tongan Merchantmen — AP15

1974, Dec. 11
C164 AP15   9s blue & multi   .80   .30
C165 AP15 14s blue & multi   1.40   .55
C166 AP15 17s blue & multi   1.50   .60
C167 AP15 60s blue & multi   5.50   3.75
C168 AP15 90s blue & multi   8.75   4.75
      Nos. C164-C168 (5)   17.95   9.95
      Establishment of Royal Marine Institute.

Beach
AP16

Designs: 12s, 14s, like 9s. 17s, 38s, Surf.

1975, Mar. 11   **Litho.**
C169 AP16   9s gold & multi   .20   .20
C170 AP16 12s gold & multi   .25   .25
C171 AP16 14s gold & multi   .30   .30
C172 AP16 17s gold & multi   .30   .30
C173 AP16 38s gold & multi   .95   .95
      Nos. C169-C173 (5)   2.00   2.00
    First meeting of South Pacific area Prime
Ministers. See note after No. 226.
    For surcharges see Nos. C229, C298.

Women's Discus and Games'
Emblem — AP17

1975, June 11
C174 AP17   9s multicolored   .35   .35
C175 AP17 12s multicolored   .45   .45
C176 AP17 14s multicolored   .45   .45
C177 AP17 17s black & multi   .55   .55
C178 AP17 90s olive & multi   2.00   2.00
      Nos. C174-C178 (5)   3.80   3.80
    5th South Pacific Games, Guam, Aug. 1-10.
See note after No. 226.
    For surcharges see Nos. C230-C231.

            FAO Type of 1975

    Designs (FAO Coins): 12s, Coins showing
cattle, corn and pig. 14s, Cornucopias; coins
showing king, family planning emblem and
melons. 25s, Bananas and treasure chest.
50s, King Taufa'ahau. 1pa, Palms.

1975, Sept. 3
C179 A62 12s multicolored   .45   .45
C180 A62 14s blue & multi   .45   .45
C181 A62 25s silver, blk & org   .70   .70
C182 A62 50s car, sil & blk   1.25   1.25
C183 A62 1pa silver & black   2.25   2.25
      Nos. C179-C183 (5)   5.10   5.10
    Size of paper backing of 14s: 82x50mm;
others 45x45mm. See note after No. 226.

            Coin Type of 1975

    Coins: 9s, King Taufa'ahau IV, obverse. 12s,
Queen Salote III, 75pa reverse and obverse.
14s, 10pa reverse. 38s, King Taufa'ahau IV,
10pa reverse and observe. 1pa, Heads of four
constitutional monarchs.

1975, Nov. 4
      Light Blue Background
C184 A63   9s black, sil & red   .35   .20
C185 A63 12s gold, blk & grn   .45   .35
C186 A63 14s black, sil & ol   .45   .35
C187 A63 38s gold, blk & org   1.00   .50
C188 A63 1pa black, sil & blue   2.60   2.60
      Nos. C184-C188 (5)   4.85   4.00
    Size of paper backing of 1pa: 87x78mm,
others 65x60mm. See note after No. 226.

       Nos. 344-345, C160, C163
      Surcharged and Overprinted in
      Carmine on Silver, Green or Gold

a

b

1976, Feb. 24   **Litho.**
C189 A58 (a) 12s on 20s (S)   .80   .50
C190 AP14 (b) 14s on 16s
                    (Gr)   .80   .50
C191 AP14 (b) 16s (G)   1.00   .50
C192 A58 (a) 38s on 40s (G)   2.50   .70
C193 AP14 (b) 75s (S)   4.50   2.75
      Nos. C189-193 (5)   9.60   4.95
    21st Olympic Games, Montreal, Canada,
July 17-Aug. 1. See note after No. 226.

         Bicentennial Type of 1976

    Signers of Declaration of Independence,
Flags of US and Tonga: 12s, Abraham Clark,
George Ross, Thomas Lynch, Jr., Charles
Carroll, Roger Sherman (no flags). 14s, Rob-
ert Treat Paine, Thomas Jefferson, Thomas
McKean, John Adams. 17s, Button Gwinnett,
Lewis Morris, Caesar Rodney, Richard Henry
Lee. 38s, John Hart, Samuel Huntington,
Philip Livingstone, John Morton. 1pa, John
Hancock, Joseph Hewes, Josiah Bartlett, John
Witherspoon.

1976, May 26
C194 A66 12s buff & multi   .65   .20
C195 A66 14s buff & multi   .75   .20
C196 A66 17s buff & multi   .80   .45

C197 A66 38s buff & multi   3.50   1.00
C198 A66 1pa buff & multi   6.00   3.75
      Nos. C194-C198 (5)   11.70   5.60
         See note after No. 381.

Missionary Ship "Triton" — AP18

1976, Aug. 25   **Litho.**
C199 AP18   9s pink & multi   .35   .30
C200 AP18 12s multicolored   .55   .40
C201 AP18 14s multicolored   .60   .45
C202 AP18 17s buff & multi   .80   .55
C203 AP18 38s multicolored   1.40   .90
      Nos. C199-C203 (5)   3.70   2.60
         See note after No. 386.
    For surcharges see Nos. C234, C294,
C299.

Treaty Signing Ceremony,
Nukualofa — AP19

1976, Nov. 1
C204 AP19 11s multicolored   .45   .40
C205 AP19 17s multicolored   .60   .55
C206 AP19 18s multicolored   .65   .60
C207 AP19 31s multicolored   1.10   1.00
C208 AP19 39s multicolored   1.40   1.25
      Nos. C204-C208 (5)   4.20   3.80
         See note after No. 391.
    For surcharges see Nos. C235, C295.

Elizabeth II and Taufa'ahau IV — AP20

1977, Feb. 7
C209 AP20 15s gray & multi   .20   .20
C210 AP20 17s gray & multi   .35   .35
C211 AP20 22s gray & multi   10.00   6.50
C212 AP20 31s gray & multi   .50   .50
C213 AP20 39s gray & multi   .50   .50
      Nos. C209-C213 (5)   11.55   8.05
         See note after No. 396.

Coronation Coin — AP21

1977, July 4   **Litho.**
C214 AP21 11s multicolored   .30   .30
C215 AP21 17s multicolored   .40   .40
C216 AP21 18s multicolored   .40   .40
C217 AP21 39s multicolored   .65   .65
C218 AP21 1pa multicolored   2.00   2.00
      Nos. C214-C218 (5)   3.75   3.75
         See note after No. 401.
         See Nos. CO120-CO122.

Capt. Cook Medal and Journal
Quotation — AP22

1977, Sept. 27
C219 AP22 15s multicolored   .90   .75
C220 AP22 22s multicolored   1.40   1.25
C221 AP22 31s multicolored   3.50   3.00
C222 AP22 50s multicolored   10.00   5.00
C223 AP22 1pa multicolored   21.00   9.00
      Nos. C219-C223 (5)   36.80 19.00
    Bicentenary of Capt. Cook's farewell voyage.
    See Nos. CO123-CO125.

Sei and Fin Whales — AP23

1977, Dec. 16
C224 AP23 11s blk, vio & bl   4.25   .80
C225 AP23 17s blk, red & bl   4.75   .90
C226 AP23 18s blk, grn & bl   4.75   1.10
C227 AP23 39s blk, brn & bl   5.75   2.25
C228 AP23 50s blk, mag & bl   7.25   3.50
      Nos. C224-C228 (5)   26.75   8.55
         Whale protection.
         See Nos. CO126-CO128.

    Stamps of 1975-77 Surcharged in
              Various Colors
1978
C229 AP16 17s on 38s
               (#C173;Gr)   2.25   1.50
C230 AP17 17s on 9s
               (#C174;B)   2.25   1.50
C231 AP17 17s on 12s
               (#C175;DBl)   2.25   1.50
C232 A63   17s on 38s
               (#C187;B)   2.25   1.50
C233 A66   17s on 12s
               (#C194; R on
               G)   2.25   1.50
C234 AP18 17s on 9s (#C199;
               B)   2.25   1.50
C235 AP19 17s on 18s
               (#C206; G on
               Brn)   2.25   1.50
C236 A66   1pa on 75s (#381;
               Gr on S)   11.75   9.50
C237 A66   1pa on 38s
               (#C197; DBl
               on G)   11.75   9.50

C238 OA15 1pa on 1.10pa
(#CO119; S
on DBI) 26.50 27.50

Edmonton Games Type of 1978

Canadian Maple leaf and Tongan coat of arms.

1978, May 5   **Litho.**
C239 A73 17s red & multi   .45 .45
C240 A73 35s red & multi   .90 .90
C241 A73 38s red & multi   .95 .95
C242 A73 40s red & multi   2.00 2.00
C243 A73 65s red & multi   1.50 1.50
    Nos. C239-C243 (5)   5.80 5.80

See note after No. 423.

King Type of 1978

Design: Head of King Taufa'ahau IV within 6-pointed star.

1978, July 4
C244 A74 11s multicolored   .25 .25
C245 A74 15s multicolored   .35 .35
C246 A74 17s multicolored   .45 .45
C247 A74 39s multicolored   1.00 1.00
C248 A74 1pa multicolored   2.50 2.50
    Nos. C244-C248 (5)   4.55 4.55

See note after No. 226.

Wildlife Type of 1978

1978, Dec. 15   **Litho. & Typo.**
C249 A77 17s Whale   3.50 1.75
C250 A77 22s Bat   3.50 1.75
C251 A77 31s Turtle   3.50 1.75
C252 A77 39s Parrot   7.00 3.00
C253 A77 45s like 17s   7.50 3.50
    Nos. C249-C253 (5)   25.00 11.75

Wildlife conservation. See note after No. 226.

Types of 1979

Designs: 15s, like No. 453. 17s, like No. 450. 31s, Rotary emblem. 39s, Ministry and tourism buildings, Bank of Tonga, GPO. 1pa, Dish antenna and map of Tonga.

1979, Feb. 16   **Litho.**
C254 A79 15s multicolored   .40 .30
C255 A79 17s multicolored   .50 .35
C256 A78 31s vio blue & gold   .75 .45
C257 A79 39s multicolored   1.10 .95
C258 A79 1pa multicolored   2.75 1.60
    Nos. C254-C258 (5)   5.50 3.35

Decade of Progress. Paper backing shows map of Tonga.

Type of 1979

Tongan self-adhesive, free-form stamps.

1979, June 1
C259 A81 15s multicolored   .35 .35
C260 A81 17s multicolored   .45 .45
C261 A81 18s multicolored   .50 .50
C262 A81 31s multicolored   .75 .75
C263 A81 39s multicolored   .95 .95
    Nos. C259-C263 (5)   3.00 3.00

See note after No. 458.

Jet — AP24

1979, Aug. 17
C264 AP24 5s multicolored   .20 .20
C265 AP24 11s multicolored   .35 .25
C266 AP24 14s multicolored   .50 .35
C267 AP24 15s multicolored   .50 .35
C268 AP24 17s multicolored   .65 .45
C269 AP24 18s multicolored   .70 .50
C270 AP24 22s multicolored   .75 .55
C271 AP24 31s multicolored   1.10 .75
C272 AP24 39s multicolored   1.40 .95
C273 AP24 75s multicolored   2.50 1.75
C274 AP24 1pa multicolored   3.50 2.50
    Nos. C264-C274 (11)   12.15 8.60

Nos. C264-C274 issued in coils; self-adhesive control number in lower left corner of paper backing except on 14s, 18s, 22s, 75s. See note after No. 226.
See Nos. C303-C305.

View Type of 1979

Design: Kao Island. See note after No. 463.

1979, Nov. 23
C275 A82 5s multicolored   .20 .20
C276 A82 15s multicolored   .35 .35
C277 A82 17s multicolored   .45 .45

C278 A82 39s multicolored   .95 .95
C279 A82 75s multicolored   1.75 1.75
    Nos. C275-C279 (5)   3.70 3.70

Friendship Treaty Type of 1980

George Tupou I, Admiral du Bouzet, Adventure. See notes over #464 & after #468.

1980, Jan. 9   **Litho.**
C280 A83 15s multicolored   .45 .45
C281 A83 17s multicolored   .55 .55
C282 A83 22s multicolored   .60 .60
C283 A83 31s multicolored   .85 .85
C284 A83 39s multicolored   1.00 1.00
    Nos. C280-C284 (5)   3.45 3.45

Nos. C259-C263 Surcharged and Overprinted in Black on Silver: "1980 OLYMPIC GAMES," Moscow '80 and Bear Emblems

1980, Apr. 30   **Litho.**
C285 A81 9s on 15s multi   .30 .30
C286 A81 16s on 17s multi   .65 .65
C287 A81 29s on 18s multi   1.00 1.00
C288 A81 32s on 31s multi   1.10 1.10
C289 A81 47s on 39s multi   1.60 1.60
    Nos. C285-C289 (5)   4.65 4.65

22nd Summer Olympic Games, Moscow, July 19-Aug. 3.

Scouting Activities in Rotary Emblem — AP25

1980, Sept. 30   **Litho.**
C290 AP25 29s multicolored   .90 .90
C291 AP25 32s multicolored   1.00 1.00
C292 AP25 47s multicolored   1.40 1.40
C293 AP25 1pa multicolored   3.00 3.00
    Nos. C290-C293 (4)   6.30 6.30

Boy Scout Jamboree; Rotary International, 75th anniversary. Peelable backing shows map of Tonga.

Nos. C170, C185, C195, C200-C201, C208 Surcharged

1980, Dec. 3   **Litho.**
C294 AP18 29s on 14s multi   .70 .70
C295 AP19 29s on 39s multi   .70 .70
C296 A63 32s on 12s multi   .80 .80
C297 A66 32s on 14s multi   .80 .80
C298 AP16 47s on 12s multi   1.10 1.10
C299 AP18 47s on 12s multi   1.10 1.10
    Nos. C294-C299 (6)   5.20 5.20

IYD Type of 1981

1981, Sept. 9   **Litho.**
     Size: 25x32mm
C300 A85 29s multicolored   .45 .45
C301 A85 32s multicolored   .55 .55
C302 A85 47s multicolored   .80 .80
    Nos. C300-C302 (3)   1.80 1.80

Jet Type of 1979

1982, Nov. 17   **Litho.**
C303 AP24 29s pink & black   1.25 .85
C304 AP24 32s pale yel & blk   1.40 1.00
C305 AP24 47s lt brown & blk   2.25 1.50
    Nos. C303-C305 (3)   4.90 3.35

AIR POST SPECIAL DELIVERY

Catalogue values for unused stamps in this section are for Never Hinged items.

Owl — APSD1

1990, Feb. 21   **Litho.**   **Perf. 11½**
CE1 APSD1 10pa multi   15.00 15.00

AIR POST OFFICIAL STAMPS

Catalogue values for unused stamps in this section are for Never Hinged items.

Nos. 115, 117-118, 111-113 Overprinted "OFFICIAL AIR MAIL / 1862 / TAU'ATAINA / EMANCIPATION / 1962" in Red

Engr.; Photo. (A35)
1962, Feb. 7   **Wmk. 79**
CO1 A35 2p ultra   10.00 7.50
CO2 A35 5p purple   11.00 8.00
CO3 A35 1sh red brown   8.00 4.00
CO4 A33 5sh pur & yel   85.00 50.00
CO5 A34 10sh black & yel   40.00 20.00
CO6 A34 £1 ultra, car & yel   65.00 30.00
    Nos. CO1-CO6 (6)   219.00 119.50

Centenary of emancipation.

Type of Regular Gold Coin Issue

Design: 15sh, Queen Salote standing, 1-koula coin, obverse.

Litho.; Embossed on Gilt Foil
1963, July 15   **Unwmk.**   **Die Cut**
     Diameter: 80mm
CO7 A36 15sh black   5.75 5.75

Note after No. 133 also applies to No. CO7.

No. CO7 Surcharged like Regular Issue of 1965 in Black

1965, Mar. 18
CO8 A36 30s on 15sh black   6.50 6.50

No. 116 Surcharged in Italic Letters Similarly to Nos. C16-C21

Perf. 14½x13½
1966, June 18   **Wmk. 79**
CO9 A35 10sh on 4p brt green   .80 .30
CO10 A35 20sh on 4p brt green   1.00 .40

Centenary of Tupou College and secondary education.

No. 111 Surcharged in Red: "OFFICIAL / AIRMAIL / ONE PA'ANGA"

1967, Mar. 25   **Engr.**   **Perf. 11½x11**
CO11 A33 1p on 5sh pur & yel   3.00 3.00

Type of Regular Issue Surcharged

1967, Dec. 15   **Wmk. 79**   **Die Cut**
CO12 A34 30s on £1 multi   .55 .55
CO13 A34 70s on £1 multi   .80 .80
CO14 A34 1.50pa on £1 multi   1.25 1.25
    Nos. CO12-CO14 (3)   2.60 2.60

Arrival of US Peace Corps.

No. 113 Surcharged with New Value and "OFFICIAL/AIRMAIL"

1968, Apr. 6   **Engr.**   **Perf. 11x11½**
CO15 A34 40s on £1 multi   .75 .75
CO16 A34 60s on £1 multi   1.00 1.00
CO17 A34 1pa on £1 multi   1.25 1.25
CO18 A34 2pa on £1 multi   2.25 2.25
    Nos. CO15-CO18 (4)   5.25 5.25

Type of 1953 Surcharged: "Friendly Islands / Trials / Field & Track / South Pacific / Games / Port Moresby / 1969 / OFFICIAL AIRMAIL"

Wmk. 79
1968, Dec. 19   **Engr.**   **Die Cut**
CO19 A34 20s on £1 grn & multi   .35 .20
CO20 A34 1pa on £1 grn & multi   1.00 .60

No. 176 Overprinted and Surcharged in Gold on Colored Panels (Green, Emerald, Violet or Lilac) like Nos. 203-209.

Litho.; Embossed on Palladium Foil
1968   **Unwmk.**
CO21 A38 40s on 2s (G)   1.60 .80
CO22 A38 60s on 2s (E)   2.10 1.60
CO23 A38 1pa on 2s (V)   3.50 3.50
CO24 A38 2pa on 2s (L)   6.00 6.00
    Nos. CO21-CO24 (4)   13.20 11.90

50th birthday of King Taufa'ahau IV.

Pacific Games Type of Regular Issue

Design: Boxer.

1969, Aug. 13   **Litho.**   **Die Cut**
     Self-adhesive
CO25 A40 70s gray, red & grn   .80 .80
CO26 A40 80s gray, red & org   .95 .95

See note after No. 231.

Type of Regular Issue, 1953, Surcharged: "OFFICIAL AIRMAIL / 1969 OIL / SEARCH / 90s" and Oil Derrick Obliterating Old Denomination

1969, Dec. 23   **Die Cut Wmk. 79**
CO27 A34 90s on £1 grn & multi   3.25 3.25

First scientific search for oil in Tonga.

Type of Regular Issue, 1953, Surcharged: "Royal Visit / MARCH / 1970 / OFFICIAL / AIRMAIL" in Black, Violet Blue or Emerald

1970, Mar. 7   **Engr.**   **Wmk. 79**
CO28 A34 75s on 1sh   4.25 3.00
CO29 A34 1pa on 1sh (VBl)   5.50 4.00
CO30 A34 1.25pa on 1sh (E)   7.00 5.00
    Nos. CO28-CO30 (3)   16.75 12.00

See note after No. 242.

Type of Regular Issue Surcharged in Black, Red or Emerald

1970, June 4   **Wmk. 79**   **Die Cut**
CO31 A33 50s on 5sh (B)   1.50 1.50
CO32 A33 90s on 5sh (R)   2.25 2.25
CO33 A33 1.50pa on 5sh (E)   3.50 3.50
    Nos. CO31-CO33 (3)   7.25 7.25

See note after No. 247.

Type of Regular Issue, 1953, Surcharged in Red and Purple or Black:

1970, Oct. 17　Engr.　　Die Cut
CO34　A33　30s on 1½p (B & R)　　1.90　1.90
CO35　A33　80s on 5sh (P & R)　　5.00　5.00
CO36　A33　90s on 5sh (P & R)　　6.00　6.00
　Nos. CO34-CO36 (3)　　12.90　12.90
Centenary of the British Red Cross.

Type of Regular Issue, 1953, Surcharged in Black, Purple, Blue or Green

1971, Jan. 31　Engr.　　Die Cut
CO37　A34　20s on 10sh (Bk)　　1.25　.85
CO38　A34　30s on 10sh (P)　　2.10　1.25
CO39　A34　50s on 10sh (Bl)　　3.50　2.10
CO40　A34　2pa on 10sh (G)　　13.75　11.75
　Nos. CO37-CO40 (4)　　20.60　15.95
In memory of Queen Salote (1900-1965).

Type of Regular Issue, 1953, Surcharged in Red and Blue, Black or Purple

1971　Engr.　Wmk. 79　Imperf
Colors: Green & Yellow
CO41　A33　30s on 5p (R & Bl)　　1.40　.80
CO42　A33　80s on 5p (R & R)　　3.25　2.10
CO43　A33　90s on 5p (R & P)　　3.50　2.40
　Nos. CO41-CO43 (3)　　8.15　5.30
See note after No. 272.

Self-adhesive & Imperf.
Starting with Nos. CO44-CO46, all airmail official issues are self-adhesive and imperforate, unless otherwise stated.

Soccer Ball — OA1

1971, July　Litho.　Unwmk.
CO44　OA1　50s multi　　.95　.95
CO45　OA1　90s multi　　1.25　1.25
CO46　OA1　1.50pa multi　　1.90　1.90
　Nos. CO44-CO46 (3)　　4.10　4.10
4th South Pacific Games, Papeete, French Polynesia, Sept. 8-19.
For overprints see Nos. CO75-CO77.

Watch Type of Air Post Issues
Litho. and Embossed
1971, July 20
CO47　AP6　14s brown & multi　　.65　.65
CO48　AP6　21s brn red & multi　　.90　.90
Advertisement on peelable paper backing.

Nos. 243-244, 246 Surcharged

Reduced illustration.

Litho.; Gold Embossed
1971, Oct. 30
CO49　A43　60s on 3s multi　　1.10　1.10
CO50　A43　80s on 25s multi　　1.40　1.40
CO51　A43　1.10pa on 7s multi　　1.60　1.60
　Nos. CO49-CO51 (3)　　4.10　4.10
First investiture of Tongan Medal of Honor.

"UNICEF" — OA2

1971, Dec.　　Litho.
CO52　OA2　70s black & multi　　2.00　2.00
CO53　OA2　80s multicolored　　2.25　2.25
CO54　OA2　90s multicolored　　2.25　2.25
　Nos. CO52-CO54 (3)　　6.50　6.50
25th anniversary of UNICEF.
For overprint see No. CO70.

Ship Type of Regular Issue
Design: Map of Merchant Marine routes from Tonga and tanker "Aoniu."

1972, Apr. 14
CO55　A49　20s multi　　1.90　.90
CO56　A49　50s multi　　4.00　2.75
CO57　A49　1.20pa multi　　8.75　7.00
　Nos. CO55-CO57 (3)　　14.65　10.65

Coin Type of Regular Issue
Design: Coins in center, inscription panel above, date below coins.

Litho.; Embossed on Metallic Foil
1972, July 15
CO58　A50　50s silver & multi　　1.50　1.50
CO59　A50　70s silver & multi　　2.00　2.00
CO60　A50　1.50pa silver & multi　　3.75　3.75
　Nos. CO58-CO60 (3)　　7.25　7.25

Watch Type of Air Post Issue
1972, July 20　Litho.; Embossed
CO61　AP6　17s multicolored　　.60　.60
CO62　AP6　38s ocher & multi　　1.25　1.25
Advertisement on peelable paper backing.

Flags and Map of Tonga Islands — OA3

1972, Dec. 9　　Litho.
CO63　OA3　25s black & multi　　.55　.55
CO64　OA3　75s multicolored　　1.60　1.60
CO65　OA3　1.50pa multicolored　　3.25　3.25
　Nos. CO63-CO65 (3)　　5.40　5.40
Tonga's proclamation of sovereignty over the Minerva Reefs, June 1972.

No. 290 Surcharged in Black, Ultramarine or Green

1973
ESTABLISHMENT BANK OF TONGA
40s
OFFICIAL AIRMAIL

1973, Mar. 30　　Litho.
CO66　A49　40s on 21s (B)　　1.50　1.25
CO67　A49　85s on 21s (U)　　3.25　3.25
CO68　A49　1.25pa on 21s (G)　　3.75　3.75
　Nos. CO66-CO68 (3)　　8.50　8.25
Establishment of Bank of Tonga.

Nos. CO55, CO53 and 247 Overprinted or Surcharged in Silver:
No. CO69: New value, 4 wavy lines, fleur-de-lis and "SILVER JUBILEE/ TONGAN SCOUTING / 1948-1973"
No. CO70: "SILVER / JUBILEE" (vertically), fleur-de-lis and "1948 1973"
No. CO71: Silver surcharge and overprint on dark blue panels "OFFICIAL AIRMAIL / T$1.40," "1948-1973" "SILVER / JUBILEE/ TONGAN / SCOUTING," "1948-1973" in dark blue

1973, June 29
CO69　A49　30s on 20s　　15.00　4.00
CO70　OA2　80s multi　　37.50　14.50
CO71　A43　1.40pa on 80s　　52.50　35.00
　Nos. CO69-CO71 (3)　　105.00　53.50
25th anniv. of Tongan Boy Scout movement.

Tanker James Cook and Cook Medal — OA4

1973, Oct. 2　　Litho.
CO72　OA4　25s multi　　4.00　1.60
CO73　OA4　80s multi　　10.00　5.00
CO74　OA4　1.30pa multi　　12.00　8.25
　Nos. CO72-CO74 (3)　　26.00　14.85
Bicentenary of Capt. Cook's arrival.

Nos. CO44-CO46 Overprinted in Dark Blue, Black or Green with Games' Emblems and: "1974 / Commonwealth / Games / Christchurch"

1973, Dec. 19
CO75　OA1　50s multi (DBl)　　1.25　1.25
CO76　OA1　90s multi (B)　　2.10　1.90
CO77　OA1　1.50pa multi (G)　　3.00　2.75
　Nos. CO75-CO77 (3)　　6.35　5.90
10th British Commonwealth Games, Christchurch, N.Z., Jan. 24-Feb. 2, 1974.

Peace Dove OA5

1974, Mar. 20　　Litho.
CO78　OA5　7s multicolored　　.40　.25
CO79　OA5　9s multicolored　　.50　.30
CO80　OA5　12s multicolored　　.50　.30
CO81　OA5　14s multicolored　　.75　.45
CO82　OA5　17s multicolored　　.80　.50
CO83　OA5　29s multicolored　　1.50　.90
CO84　OA5　38s multicolored　　2.00　1.25

CO85　OA5　50s multicolored　　2.50　1.50
CO86　OA5　75s multicolored　　3.75　2.25
　Nos. CO78-CO86 (9)　　12.70　7.70
Printed in rolls of 500. Self-adhesive lilac control number in upper left corner.

"UPU Centenary" — OA6

1974, June 20　　Typo.
CO87　OA6　25s red, green & blk　　.85　.85
CO88　OA6　35s yel, red lil & blk　　.95　.95
CO89　OA6　70s dp org, bl & blk　　1.90　1.90
　Nos. CO87-CO89 (3)　　3.70　3.70
Centenary of Universal Postal Union.

Lady Baden-Powell — OA7

1974, Sept. 11　　Litho.
CO90　OA7　45s emer & multi　　4.50　2.75
CO91　OA7　55s emer & multi　　6.50　3.75
CO92　OA7　1pa emer & multi　　9.25　5.50
　Nos. CO90-CO92 (3)　　20.25　12.00
Girl Guides of Tonga.
For overprints see Nos. CO105-CO107.

Handshake and Institute's Emblem — OA8

Institute's Emblem and Banknotes — OA9

1974, Dec. 11
CO93　OA8　30s multicolored　　3.25　1.60
CO94　OA8　35s multicolored　　3.75　2.10
CO95　OA9　80s red & multi　　8.75　4.50
　Nos. CO93-CO95 (3)　　15.75　8.20
Establishment of Royal Marine Institute.

Arch and Palms — OA10

Designs: 75s, 1.25pa, Dawn over lagoon.

1975, Mar. 11				Litho.	
CO96	OA10	50s multi		1.75	1.75
CO97	OA10	75s multi		3.00	3.00
CO98	OA10	1.25pa multi		4.00	4.00
	Nos. CO96-CO98 (3)			8.75	8.75

First meeting of South Pacific area Prime Ministers. See note after No. 226.

Track and Games' Emblem — OA11

1975, June 11					
CO99	OA11	38s multi		1.00	1.00
CO100	OA11	75s multi		1.75	1.75
CO101	OA11	1.20pa multi		2.75	2.75
	Nos. CO99-CO101 (3)			5.50	5.50

5th South Pacific Games, Guam, Aug. 1-10. See note after No. 226.
For surcharge see No. 418.

Four Constitutional Monarchs — OA12

Litho.; Embossed on Gilt Foil
1975, Nov. 4					
CO102	OA12	17s multicolored		.80	.65
CO103	OA12	60s multicolored		2.00	1.75
CO104	OA12	90s multicolored		2.60	2.60
	Nos. CO102-CO104 (3)			5.40	5.00

No. CO90-CO92 Overprinted in Carmine on Blue, Silver or Gold

1976, Feb. 24				Litho.	
CO105	OA7	45s multicolored (B)		3.50	1.40
CO106	OA7	55s multicolored (S)		3.50	1.60
CO107	OA7	1pa multicolored (G)		6.75	6.75
	Nos. CO105-CO107 (3)			13.75	9.75

21st Olympic Games, Montreal, Canada, July 17-Aug. 1. See note after No. 226.

Bicentennial Type of 1976

Signers of Declaration of Independence: 20s, William Paca, Francis Lewis, George Read, Edward Rutledge, Thomas Heyward, Jr. 50s, George Walton, Matthew Thornton, Robert Morris, William Williams, James Smith. 1.15pa, Benjamin Rush, Samuel Adams, Samuel Chase, George Wythe, George Clymer.

1976, May 26					
CO108	A66	20s buff & multi		1.00	.75
CO109	A66	50s buff & multi		3.25	2.50
CO110	A66	1.15pa buff & multi		6.75	5.25
	Nos. CO108-CO110 (3)			11.00	8.50

See note after No. 381.

Inside View of Lifuka Chapel — OA13

1976, Aug. 25				Litho.	
CO111	OA13	65s multicolored		2.75	2.75
CO112	OA13	85s multicolored		3.00	3.00
CO113	OA13	1.15pa multicolored		4.00	4.00
	Nos. CO111-CO113 (3)			9.75	9.75

See note after No. 386.
For surcharge see No. CO181.

OA14

1976, Nov. 1					
CO114	OA14	30s silver & multi		.80	.70
CO115	OA14	60s silver & multi		1.60	1.50
CO116	OA14	1.25pa silver & multi		3.25	3.00
	Nos. CO114-CO116 (3)			5.65	5.20

See note after No. 391.

Flags and Arms of Great Britain and Tonga — OA15

1977, Feb. 7				Litho.	
CO117	OA15	35s multi		4.00	3.25
CO118	OA15	45s multi		.50	.50
CO119	OA15	1.10pa multi		1.50	1.25
	Nos. CO117-CO119 (3)			6.00	5.00

See note after No. 396.
For surcharge see No. C238.

Coin Type of Air Post Stamps 1977

Design: Coronation coin, inscriptions in round upper panel.

1977, July 4					
CO120	AP21	20s multicolored		.55	.55
CO121	AP21	40s multicolored		1.10	1.10
CO122	AP21	80s multicolored		2.10	2.10
	Nos. CO120-CO122 (3)			3.75	3.75

See note after No. 401.

Capt. Cook Type of Air Post Stamps 1977

Design: Inscription and flying dove.

1977, Sept. 27					
CO123	AP22	20s gold & multi		1.40	1.40
CO124	AP22	55s on 20s multi		10.00	10.00
CO125	AP22	85s on 20s multi		21.00	21.00
	Nos. CO123-CO125 (3)			32.40	32.40

Printed on peelable paper backing showing dark brown replica of entry in Capt. Cook's diary.

Whale Type of Air Post Stamps 1977

Design: Blue whale.

1977, Dec. 16					
CO126	AP23	45s multicolored		7.75	3.50
CO127	AP23	65s multicolored		11.00	5.00
CO128	AP23	85s multicolored		13.00	6.00
	Nos. CO126-CO128 (3)			31.75	14.50

Whale protection.

Games' Emblem and Athletes OA16

1978, May 5				Litho.	
CO129	OA16	30s red & multi		.70	.70
CO130	OA16	60s red & multi		1.40	1.40
CO131	OA16	1pa red & multi		2.50	2.50
	Nos. CO129-CO131 (3)			4.60	4.60

See note after No. 423.

King Type of 1978

Head of King Taufa'ahau IV on medal.

1978, July 4					
CO132	A74	26s multicolored		.65	.65
CO133	A74	85s multicolored		2.00	2.00
CO134	A74	90s multicolored		2.50	2.50
	Nos. CO132-CO134 (3)			5.15	5.15

See note after No. 226.

Wildlife Type of 1978

1978, Dec. 15				Litho. & Typo.	
CO150	A77	40s Whale		7.00	3.50
CO151	A77	50s Bat		7.00	3.50
CO152	A77	1.10pa Turtle		9.25	7.75
	Nos. CO150-CO152 (3)			23.25	14.75

Wildlife conservation. See note after No. 226.

Types of 1979

Designs: 38s, Red Cross and star. 74s, like No. 451. 80s, like No. 450.

1979, Feb. 16				Litho.	
CO153	A78	38s multicolored		1.10	.70
CO154	A80	74s multicolored		2.00	1.40
CO155	A79	80s multicolored		2.50	1.60
	Nos. CO153-CO155 (3)			5.60	3.70

Decade of Progress. Paper backing shows map of Tonga.

Hands Peeling off No. CO118 — OA17

1979, June 1					
CO156	OA17	45s multicolored		1.10	1.10
CO157	OA17	65s multicolored		1.50	1.50
CO158	OA17	80s multicolored		1.90	1.90
	Nos. CO156-CO158 (3)			4.50	4.50

See note after No. 458.
For surcharges see Nos. CO176-CO178.

Parrot — OA18

1979, Aug. 1					
CO159	OA18	5s multicolored		.20	.20
CO160	OA18	11s multicolored		.25	.25
CO161	OA18	14s multicolored		.35	.35
CO162	OA18	15s multicolored		.35	.35
CO163	OA18	17s multicolored		.45	.45
CO164	OA18	18s multicolored		.50	.50
CO165	OA18	22s multicolored		.55	.55
CO166	OA18	31s multicolored		.75	.75
CO167	OA18	39s multicolored		.95	.95
CO168	OA18	75s multicolored		1.75	1.75
CO169	OA18	1pa multicolored		2.25	2.25
	Nos. CO159-CO169 (11)			8.35	8.35

Nos. CO159-CO169 issued in coils. See note after No. 226.
The 5s exists with denomination in magenta and the leaves behind the bird missing. This seems to be a special printing that was not available for postal purposes.

View Type of 1979

Design: Niuatoputapu and Tafahi Islands. See note after No. 463.

1979, Nov. 23				Litho.	
CO170	A82	35s multicolored		.85	.85
CO171	A82	45s multicolored		1.10	1.10
CO172	A82	1pa multicolored		2.25	2.25
	Nos. CO170-CO172 (3)			4.20	4.20

Friendship Treaty Type of 1980

Design: Church. See note after No. 468.

1980, Jan. 9				Litho.	
CO173	A83	40s multicolored		1.10	1.10
CO174	A83	55s multicolored		1.40	1.40
CO175	A83	1.25pa multicolored		3.25	3.25
	Nos. CO173-CO175 (3)			5.75	5.75

Nos. CO156-CO158 Surcharged and Overprinted in Black on Silver: "1980 OLYMPIC GAMES," Moscow '80 and Bear Emblems

1980, Apr. 30				Litho.	
CO176	OA17	26s on 45s		.95	.95
CO177	OA17	40s on 65s		1.40	1.40
CO178	OA17	1.10pa on 80s		3.75	3.75
	Nos. CO176-CO178 (3)			6.10	6.10

22nd Summer Olympic Games, Moscow, July 19-Aug. 3.

Tents and Rotary Emblem — OA19

1980, Sept. 30   **Litho.**
CO179	OA19	25s multicolored	.70	.70
CO180	OA19	2pa multicolored	5.75	5.75

Boy Scout Jamboree; Rotary Intl., 75th anniv. Peelable backing shows map of Tonga. For surcharges see Nos. 502-503.

No. CO111 Surcharged

1980, Dec. 3   **Litho.**
CO181	OA13	2pa on 65s multi	4.75	4.75

OFFICIAL STAMPS

Types of Postage Issue of 1892 Overprinted in Carmine

Perf. 12x11½
1893, Feb. 13   **Wmk. 62**
O1	A4	1p ultra	11.50	55.00
a.		Half used as ½p on cover		
O2	A5	2p ultra	30.00	62.50
O3	A4	4p ultra	55.00	100.00
O4	A5	8p ultra	100.00	200.00
O5	A5	1sh ultra	110.00	210.00
		Nos. O1-O5 (5)	306.50	637.50

Values are for copies of good color. Faded and discolored copies sell for much less.
The overprinted initials stand for "Gaue Faka Buleaga" (On Government Service).

Nos. O1-O5 with Additional Surcharge Handstamped in Black

1893
O6	A4	½p on 1p ultra	20.00	57.50
O7	A5	2½p on 2p ultra	27.50	50.00
O8	A4	5p on 4p ultra	27.50	50.00
O9	A5	7½p on 8p ultra	27.50	92.50
O10	A5	10p on 1sh ultra	32.50	95.00
		Nos. O6-O10 (5)	135.00	345.00

Catalogue values for unused stamps in this section, from this point to the end of the section, are for Never Hinged items.

Redrawn Banana and Coconut Types of Regular Issue, 1970, Inscribed "Official Post"

1970, June 9   **Typo.**   *Die Cut*
Self-adhesive
O11	A39	1s yel, blk & dp car	.55	.55
O12	A39	2s yel, blk & blue	.70	.70
O13	A39	3s yel, blk & brn	.70	.70
O14	A39	4s yel, blk & emer	.70	.70
O15	A39	5s yel, blk & org	.80	.80

Litho.; Embossed on Gilt Foil
O16	A44	6s brown & multi	.95	.95
O17	A44	7s brown & multi	1.00	1.00
O18	A44	8s brown & multi	1.10	1.10
O19	A44	9s brown & multi	1.50	1.50
O20	A44	10s brown & multi	1.75	1.75
		Nos. O11-O20 (10)	9.75	9.75

Nos. O13, O17-O18 and O20 have self-adhesive control numbers in lower left corner of paper backing.

Types of Regular Issue 1970-72

1972, Sept. 30   **Typo.**
Self-adhesive
O21	A51	1s yel, red & brn	.20	.20
O22	A51	2s yel, grn & brn	.25	.20
O23	A51	3s yel, emer & brn	.35	.20
O24	A51	4s yel, blk & brn	.35	.25
O25	A51	5s yellow & brn	.35	.25
O26	A44	6s brown & green	.40	.25
O27	A44	7s brown & green	.45	.30
O28	A44	8s brown & green	.45	.30
O29	A44	9s brown & green	.45	.30
O30	A44	10s brown & green	.55	.35
O31	A52	15s green & ultra	.90	.50
O32	A52	20s green & ver	1.10	.70
O33	A52	25s green & dk brn	1.25	.80
O34	A52	40s green & org	2.50	1.75
O35	A52	50s green & vio bl	2.75	2.00
		Nos. O21-O35 (15)	12.30	8.35

Paper backing is brown on Nos. O26-O35. Nos. O30-O35 have self-adhesive control number in lower left corner, Nos. O21-O29 lower right corner.

Types of Regular Issue 1978

Designs: 1s-5s, Bananas (similar to type A75). 6s-10s, Coconuts. 15s-1pa, Pineapples.

1978, Sept. 29   **Typo.**
O36	A75	1s yellow & lilac	.25	.25
O37	A75	2s yellow & brown	.25	.25
O38	A75	3s multicolored	.35	.35
O39	A75	4s multicolored	.35	.35
O40	A75	5s multicolored	.35	.35
O41	A76	6s multicolored	.50	.50
O42	A76	7s multicolored	.50	.50
O43	A76	8s multicolored	.50	.50
O44	A76	9s multicolored	.50	.50
O45	A76	10s multicolored	.50	.50
O46	A76	15s multicolored	1.25	1.25
O47	A76	20s multicolored	1.40	1.40
O48	A76	30s multicolored	1.50	1.50
O49	A76	50s multicolored	2.00	2.00
O50	A76	1pa multicolored	3.00	3.00
		Nos. O36-O50 (15)	13.20	13.20

Nos. O36-O50 issued in coils; self-adhesive control numbers on paper backing except on 1s. See note after No. 226.

Type of 1984 Overprinted "OFFICIAL"

1984-85   **Litho.**   *Die Cut*
O52	A103	1s multicolored	.50	.50
O53	A103	2s multicolored	.50	.50
O54	A103	3s multicolored	.50	.50
O55	A103	5s multicolored	.50	.50
O56	A103	6s multicolored	.50	.50
O57	A103	9s multicolored	.75	.75
a.		Perf. 14½ ('85)	.75	.75
O58	A103	10s multicolored	.75	.75
O59	A103	13s multicolored	1.25	1.25
O60	A103	15s multicolored	1.25	1.25
O61	A103	20s multicolored	1.50	1.50
O62	A103	29s multicolored	1.75	1.75
O63	A103	32s multicolored	1.75	1.75
O64	A103	47s multicolored	2.00	2.00
O65	A103	1pa multicolored	4.00	4.00
O66	A103	2pa multicolored	7.00	7.00
O67	A103	5pa multicolored ('85)	12.00	12.00
		Nos. O52-O67 (16)	36.50	36.50

Nos. 532-534 Ovptd. "OFFICIAL"

1983, Feb. 22   **Litho.**   *Die Cut*
O68	A96a	29s multicolored	4.75	4.75
O69	A96a	32s multicolored	4.75	4.75
O70	A96a	47s multicolored	10.00	10.00
		Nos. O68-O70 (3)	19.50	19.50

O68-O70 handstamped.

Nos. 564-565, 567-568, 570, 572 and 577 Surcharged "OFFICIAL"

1986, Apr. 16   **Litho.**   *Die Cut*
Self-adhesive
O71	A103	4s on 2s, #564	1.00	1.00
O72	A103	4s on 13s, #570	1.00	1.00
O73	A103	42s on 3s, #565	3.25	3.25
O74	A103	42s on 9s, #568	3.25	3.25
O75	A103	57s on 6s, #567	3.50	3.50
O76	A103	57s on 20s, #572	3.50	3.50
O77	A103	2.50pa on 2pa, #577	12.00	12.00
		Nos. O71-O77 (7)	27.50	27.50

Marine Type Inscribed "POSTAGE & REVENUE" and "OFFICIAL"

1995-96   **Litho.**   *Perf. 14*
O78	A155a	10s multicolored	.60	.60
O79	A155a	20s multicolored	.90	.40
O80	A155a	45s multicolored	1.10	.70
O81	A155a	60s multicolored	1.40	.95
O82	A155a	80s multicolored	1.75	1.25
O83	A155a	1pa multicolored	2.25	1.75
O84	A155a	2pa multicolored	4.00	4.00
O85	A155a	3pa multicolored	5.00	5.00

O86	A155a	5pa multicolored	9.75	9.75
O87	A155a	10pa multicolored	14.00	14.00
		Nos. O78-O87 (10)	40.75	38.40

Issued: 10s-80s, 9/25/95; 1pa-10pa, 5/31/96.

NIUAFO'OU

Tin Can Island

Catalogue values for all unused stamps in this country are for Never Hinged items.

Nos. 1-63 are self-adhesive stamps on peelable inscribed backing paper and imperforate.

Niuafo'ou Airport Type of Tonga

1983, May 11   **Litho.**   *Die Cut*
1	A97	29s multicolored	1.75	1.75
2	A97	1pa multicolored	4.75	4.75

Map of Niuafo'ou — A1

1983, May 11
3	A1	1s buff, blk & red	.35	.35
4	A1	2s buff, blk & brt green	.35	.35
5	A1	3s buff, blk & brt blue	.35	.35
6	A1	4s buff, blk & brn org	.35	.35
7	A1	5s buff, blk & deep rose lil	.35	.35
8	A1	6s buff, blk & grnsh blue	.35	.35
9	A1	9s buff, blk & lt ol grn	.35	.35
10	A1	10s buff, blk & brt bl	.35	.35
11	A1	13s buff, blk & brt grn	.40	.40
12	A1	15s buff, blk & brn org	.50	.50
13	A1	20s buff, blk & grnsh blue	.65	.65
14	A1	29s buff, blk & deep rose lil	1.00	1.00
15	A1	32s buff, blk & lt ol grn	1.10	1.10
16	A1	47s buff, blk & org	1.60	1.60
		Nos. 3-16 (14)	8.05	8.05

See Nos. 19-22.

Tonga No. 520 Surcharged or Ovptd. in Purple or Gold "NIUAFO'OU / Kingdom of Tonga"

1983, May 11
17	A93	1pa on 2pa multi (P)	3.25	3.25
18	A93	2pa multicolored (G)	6.75	6.75

Nos. 17-18 each exist se-tenant with label.

Map Type of 1983
Value Typo. in Violet Blue

1983, May 30
19	A1	3s buff & black	.30	.30
20	A1	5s buff & black	.30	.30
21	A1	32s buff & black	1.50	1.50
22	A1	2pa buff & black	8.00	8.00
		Nos. 19-22 (4)	10.10	10.10

The denomination on Nos. 19-22 added like a surcharge and is larger than on Nos. 5-7, 15, covering part of the design.
Nos. 19-22 each exist se-tenant with label.

Eruption of Niuafo'ou, Sept. 9, 1946 A2

1983, Sept. 29
23	A2	5s shown	.50	.35
24	A2	29s Lava flow	1.90	1.25
25	A2	32s Moving to high ground	2.10	1.25
26	A2	1.50pa Evacuation to Eua	6.50	6.50
		Nos. 23-26 (4)	11.00	9.35

Birds — A3

1983, Nov. 15
27	A3	1s Purple swamphen	1.00	1.00
28	A3	2s White-collared king-fisher	1.00	1.00
29	A3	3s Red-headed par-rotfinch	1.00	1.00
30	A3	5s Banded rail	1.25	1.25
31	A3	6s Niuafo'ou megapode	1.60	1.60
32	A3	9s Giant forest honey-eater	2.50	2.50
33	A3	10s Purple swamphen, drinking	2.50	2.50
34	A3	13s Banded rail, diff.	2.75	2.75
35	A3	15s Niuafo'ou megapode, diff.	2.75	2.75

Size: 25x39mm
36	A3	20s like #34	3.25	3.25
37	A3	29s Red-headed par-rotfinch, diff.	3.50	3.50
38	A3	32s White-collared king-fisher, diff.	3.50	3.50
39	A3	47s like #35	4.25	4.25

Size: 32x42mm
40	A3	1pa like #33	8.00	9.75
41	A3	2pa like #35	11.00	14.00
		Nos. 27-41 (15)	49.85	54.60

Nos. 34-36, 39 and 41 horiz.
For surcharges see Nos. 66-73.

Wildlife A4

1984, Mar. 7
42	A4	29s Green turtle	.90	.90
43	A4	32s Flying fox, vert.	.90	.90
44	A4	47s Humpback whale	3.25	2.10
45	A4	1.50pa Niuafo'ou megapode, vert.	6.00	8.25
		Nos. 42-45 (4)	11.05	12.15

Map A5

1984, Aug. 20
46	A5	47s Intl. Date Line, Cent.	1.00	1.00
47	A5	2pa shown	3.50	3.50

AUSIPEX '84 — A6   A7

1984, Sept. 17
48	A6	32s Australia No. 15	.90	.90
49	A6	1.50pa No. 10	4.50	4.50

Souvenir Sheet
50		Sheet of 2	4.50	4.50

No. 50 contains two imperf. stamps similar to Nos. 48-49, but with denomination replacing logo. No. 50 without denominations was not valid for postage.

1985, Feb. 20

Jacob Le Maire, 400th Birth Anniv.: 13s, Dutch band entertaining natives. 32s, Natives preparing kava. 47s, Native outrigger canoes. 1.50pa, Le Maire's ship at anchor.

51	A7	13s multicolored	.50	.50
52	A7	32s multicolored	1.10	1.10
53	A7	47s multicolored	1.50	1.50
54	A7	1.50pa multicolor	4.50	5.50
		Nos. 51-54 (4)	7.60	8.60

Souvenir Sheet

55	A7	1.50pa multicolored	4.00	4.00

Mail Ships A8

1985, May 22 — Die Cut

56	A8	9s Ysabel, 1902	.60	.60
a.		Perf. 14	.90	.90
57	A8	13s Tofua I, 1908	1.25	1.25
a.		Perf. 14	1.90	1.90
58	A8	47s Mariposa, 1934	1.90	1.90
a.		Perf. 14	2.75	2.75
59	A8	1.50pa Matua, 1936	4.25	6.00
a.		Perf. 14	6.50	9.00
		Nos. 56-59 (4)	8.00	9.75
		Nos. 56a-59a (4)	12.05	14.55

Rocket Mail — A9

Designs: 32s, Preparing to fire rocket. 42s, Rocket airborne. 57s, Captain watching rocket's progress. 1.50pa, Islanders reading mail.

1985, Nov. 5

60	A9	32s multicolored	1.50	.90
61	A9	42s multicolored	2.00	1.10
62	A9	57s multicolored	2.75	1.60
63	A9	1.50pa multicolored	5.75	6.50
		Nos. 60-63 (4)	12.00	10.10

Self-adhesive stamps discontinued.

Halley's Comet — A10

Nos. 64, 65: a, Drawing of Comet in 684. b, Comet shown in Bayeux Tapestry, 1066. c, Edmond Halley. d, Comet, 1910. e, Infrared photography, 1986.

1986, Mar. 26 — Perf. 14

64	A10	42s Strip of #a.-e.	36.00	32.50
65	A10	57s Strip of #a.-e.	36.00	32.50

Nos. 32-39 Surcharged in Blue

1986, Apr. 16 — Die Cut

Self-Adhesive

66	A3	4s on 9s #32	1.50	2.75
67	A3	4s on 10s #33	1.50	2.75
68	A3	42s on 13s #34	3.75	2.75
69	A3	42s on 15s #35	3.75	2.75
70	A3	57s on 29s #37	4.75	3.25
71	A3	57s on 32s #38	4.75	3.25
72	A3	2.50pa on 20s #36	13.00	14.00
73	A3	2.50pa on 47s #39	13.00	14.00
		Nos. 66-73 (8)	46.00	45.50

Placement of surcharge varies.

AMERIPEX '86 Type of Tonga

1986, May 22 — Perf. 14

74	A117	57s Surveying	3.00	3.00
75	A117	1.50pa Agriculture	5.50	5.50
a.		Souv. sheet of 2, #74-75, imperf.	10.00	10.00

Peace Corps in Tonga, 25th anniv.

First Tongan Postage Stamps, Cent. A11

1986, Aug. 27

76	A11	42s Swimmers with mail	1.60	1.60
77	A11	57s Loading tin can mail into canoe	2.10	2.10
78	A11	1pa Rocket mail	3.75	3.75
79	A11	2.50pa Outrigger canoe	6.50	6.50
		Nos. 76-79 (4)	13.95	13.95

Souvenir Sheet

80	A11	2.50pa Outrigger canoe, diff.	14.00	14.00

Red Cross — A12

1987, Mar. 11 — Perf. 14x14½

81	A12	15s Balanced diet	1.25	1.25
82	A12	42s Post-natal care	3.25	3.25
83	A12	1pa Insects spread disease	4.75	4.75
84	A12	2.50pa Fight against drugs, alcohol, smoking	7.50	7.50
		Nos. 81-84 (4)	16.75	16.75

Sharks A13

1987, Apr. 29 — Perf. 14

85	A13	29s Hammerhead	3.00	2.75
86	A13	32s Tiger	3.00	2.75
87	A13	47s Gray nurse	3.50	3.00
88	A13	1pa Great white	6.00	8.25
		Nos. 85-88 (4)	15.50	16.75

Souvenir Sheet

89	A13	2pa Shark attack	18.00	18.00

Aviators and Aircraft A14

Designs: 42s, Capt. E. C. Musick and Sikorsky S-42. 57s, Capt. J.W. Burgess and Shorts S-30. 1.50pa, Sir Charles Kingsford Smith and Fokker F.VIIb-3m. 2pa, Amelia Earhart and Lockheed Electra 10A.

1987, Sept. 2

90	A14	42s multicolored	2.50	1.75
91	A14	57s multicolored	3.00	2.00
92	A14	1.50pa multicolored	4.50	4.50
93	A14	2pa multicolored	5.25	5.25
		Nos. 90-93 (4)	15.25	13.50

First Niuafo'ou Postage Stamps, 5th Anniv. A15

Designs: 42s, 57s, Niuafo'ou megapode, No. 15. 1pa, 2pa, Concorde, No. 1.

1988, May 18

94	A15	42s multicolored	1.50	1.00
95	A15	57s multicolored	1.50	1.10
96	A15	1pa multicolored	5.00	3.75
97	A15	2pa multicolored	6.00	4.75
		Nos. 94-97 (4)	14.00	10.60

#96-97, Niuafo'ou Airport Inauguration, 5th anniv.

Settlement of Australia, Bicent.
Type of Tonga
Miniature Sheet

Designs: a, Arrival of First Fleet, Sydney Cove, Jan. 1788. b, Aborigines. c, Early settlement. d, Soldier on guard. e, Herd of sheep. f, Horseman. g, Locomotive, kangaroos. h, Train, kangaroos. i, Flying doctor service. j, Cricket players. k, Stadium, batsman guarding wicket. l, Sydney Harbor Bridge, Opera House.

1988, July 11 — Perf. 13½

98	A128	42s Sheet of 12, #98a-98 l	50.00	50.00

Polynesian Islands — A16

Birds and landmarks: 42s, Audubon's shearwater, blowholes at Houma, Tonga. 57s, Kiwi, Akaroa Harbor, New Zealand. 90s, Red-tailed tropicbird, Rainmaker Mountain, Samoa. 2.50pa, Laysan albatross, Kapoho Volcano, Hawaii.

1988, Aug. 18 — Perf. 14

99	A16	42s multicolored	1.50	1.00
100	A16	57s multicolored	2.50	1.60
101	A16	90s multicolored	2.75	2.75
102	A16	2.50pa multicolored	5.25	5.25
		Nos. 99-102 (4)	12.00	10.60

Miniature Sheet

Mutiny on the Bounty, Bicent. — A17

Designs: a, Sextant. b, William Bligh. c, Royal Navy lieutenant. d, Midshipman. e, Contemporary newspaper, Tahitian girl. f, Breadfruit. g, *Mutiny on the Bounty* excerpt, pistol grip. h, Pistol barrel, illustration of Bounty castaways. i, Tahitian girl, newsprint. j, Bligh's and Fletcher Christian's signatures. k, Christian, Pitcairn Island. l, Tombstone of John Adams.

1989, Apr. 28 — Perf. 13½

103	A17	42s Sheet of 12, #a.-l.	30.00	30.00

Marine Conservation — A18

1989, June 2 — Perf. 14

104	A18	32s Hatchet fish	1.40	1.40
105	A18	42s Snipe eel	1.60	1.60
106	A18	57s Viper fish	2.00	2.00
107	A18	1.50pa Angler fish	5.00	5.00
		Nos. 104-107 (4)	10.00	10.00

Evolution of the Earth — A19

A20

Designs: 1s, Formation of the crust. 2s, Cross-section of crust. 5s, Volcanism. 10s, Surface cools. 13s, Gem stones. 15s, Oceans form. 20s, Mountains develop. 32s, River valley. 42s, Silurian Era plant life. 45s, Early marine life. 50s, Trilobites, Cambrian Era marine life. 57s, Carboniferous Era forest, coal seams. 60s, Dinosaurs feeding. 80s, Dinosaurs fighting. 1pa, Carboniferous Era insect, amphibians. 1.50pa, Stegosaurus, Jurassic Era. 2pa, Birds and mammals, Jurassic Era. 5pa, Hominid family, Pleistocene Era. 10pa, Mammoth, saber tooth tiger.

1989-93 — Perf. 14½

108	A19	1s multicolored	.70	.70
109	A19	2s multicolored	.70	.70
110	A19	5s multicolored	.90	.90
111	A19	10s multicolored	.90	.90
111A	A19	13s multicolored	1.10	1.10
112	A19	15s multicolored	.90	.90
113	A19	20s multicolored	.90	.90
114	A19	32s multicolored	1.10	1.10
115	A19	42s multicolored	1.50	1.50
115A	A19	45s multicolored	1.50	1.50
116	A19	50s multicolored	1.60	1.60
117	A19	57s multicolored	1.60	1.60
117A	A19	60s multicolored	1.75	1.75
117B	A19	80s multicolored	2.10	2.10

Size: 26x40mm
Perf. 14

118	A19	1pa multicolored	3.00	3.00
119	A19	1.50pa multicolored	4.75	4.75
120	A19	2pa multicolored	4.75	4.75
121	A19	5pa multicolored	9.25	9.25

Perf. 14

121A	A19	10pa multicolored	16.00	16.00
		Nos. 108-121A (19)	55.00	55.00

Issued: 1s-10s, 15s-42s, 50s-57s, 6/6/89; 13s, 45s, 60s, 80s, 5/3/93; 10pa, 9/14/93; others, 8/1/89.

1989, Nov. 17 — Perf. 14

122	A20	57s multicolored	1.90	1.90

Miniature Sheet

Nos. 108-121 with UPU emblem: Nos. 123a-123e, #108-112. Nos. 123f-123j, #113-117, Nos. 123k-123n, #118-121.

123		Sheet of 15, #a.-n., 122	27.50	27.50
a.-e.		A19 32s any single, perf. 14½	1.00	1.00
f.-j.		A19 42s any single, perf. 14½	1.50	1.50
k.-n.		A19 57s any single, perf. 14	2.00	2.00

Miniature Sheet

Lake Vai Lahi, Niuafo'ou A21

a, d, Left part of lake. b, e, Small islands in center of lake. c, f, Small islet in right side of lake.

1990, Apr. 4 — Perf. 14

124		Sheet of 6	11.00	11.00
a.-c.		A21 42s any single	1.00	1.00
d.-f.		A21 1pa any single	2.25	2.25

Nos. 124a-124c and 124d-124f printed in continuous designs.

Penny Black, 150th Anniv. A22

Tin Can Mail and: 42s, Penny Black. 57s, US #2. 75s, Western Australia #1. 2.50pa, Cape of Good Hope #178.

1990, May 1
125	A22	42s multicolored	1.75	1.40
126	A22	57s multicolored	1.90	1.60
127	A22	75s multicolored	2.10	2.10
128	A22	2.50pa multicolored	7.25	7.00
		Nos. 125-128 (4)	13.00	12.10

Polynesian Whaling — A23

Designs: 15s, Whale surfacing. 42s, Whale diving beneath outrigger canoe. 57s, Tail flukes. 1pa, 2pa, Old man, two whales.

1990　　　　　　　　　　　**Perf. 11½**
129	A23	15s multicolored	2.50	2.50
130	A23	42s multicolored	3.50	3.50
131	A23	57s multicolored	3.75	3.75
132	A23	2pa multicolored	9.75	9.75
		Nos. 129-132 (4)	19.50	19.50

Souvenir Sheet
Perf. 14x14½
133	A23	1pa multicolored	20.00	20.00

Issue dates: #133, Sept. 4, others, June 6.
The entire souvenir sheet, No. 133, shows a modified No. 132. The 37½x30½mm stamp shows the two whales.
For surcharges see Nos. 139, 174-178.

UN Development Program, 40th Anniv. — A24

Designs: No. 134a, Agriculture and fisheries. No. 134b, Education. No. 135a, Health care. No. 135b, Communications.

1990, Oct. 25　　　　　　　**Perf. 14**
134	A24	57s Pair, #a.-b.	3.00	3.00
135	A24	2.50pa Pair, #a.-b.	12.00	12.00

Charting of Niuafo'ou, Bicent. — A24a

Designs: No. 136a, 32s, The Bounty. b, 42s, Chart showing location of Niuafo'ou and Tonga. c, 57s, The Pandora.
No. 137a, 2pa, Capt. Edwards of the Pandora. b, 3pa, Capt. Bligh of the Bounty.

1991, July 25　　　　　**Litho.**　　**Perf. 14½**
136	A24a	Strip of 3, #a.-c.	6.00	6.00

Souvenir Sheet
137	A24a	Sheet of 2, #a.-b.	18.00	18.00

No. 133 Surcharged in Dark Blue Violet

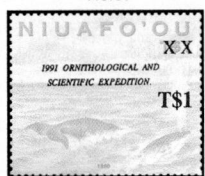

1991, July 31　　**Litho.**　　**Perf. 14x14½**
139	A23	1pa on 1pa #133	13.00	13.00

"1991 Ornithological and Scientic Expedition" overprint appears on souvenir sheet at top center.

Ceresium Unicolor — A25

1991, Sept. 11　　　　　　**Perf. 14½x14**
140	A25	42s Larva stage	1.25	1.25
141	A25	57s Mature beetle	1.50	1.50
142	A25	1.50pa Larva stage, diff.	3.75	3.75
143	A25	2.50pa Mature beetle on tree limb	6.50	6.50
		Nos. 140-143 (4)	13.00	13.00

For surcharges, see Tonga Nos. 1127, 1129.

Christmas A26

Legend of the origin of the coconut tree: 15s, No. 146a, Heina bathing in lake being watched by eel. 42s, No. 146b, Heina weeping over plant growing from eel's grave. No. 146c, 1.50pa, Heina's boy climbing coconut tree. No. 146d, 3pa, "Eel's face" on coconut.

1991, Nov. 12　　**Litho.**　　**Perf. 14½**
144	A26	15s multicolored	.75	.75
145	A26	42s multicolored	2.00	2.00
146	A26	Sheet of 4, #a.-d.	17.50	17.50
		Nos. 144-146 (3)	20.25	20.25

For surcharge, see Tonga No. 1128.

Nos. 144-145 inscribed "Christmas Greetings 1991." No. 146 contains Nos. 144-145, 146a-146d inscribed "A Love Story."

Miniature Sheet

Discovery of America, 500th Anniv. — A27

Designs: a, Columbus. b, Queen Isabella, King Ferdinand. c, Columbus being blessed by Abbot of Palos. d, Men in boat, 15th century compass. e, Wooden traverse, wind rose, Nina. f, Bow of Santa Maria. g, Stern of Santa Maria. h, Pinta. i, Two men raising cross. j, Explorers, natives. k, Columbus kneeling before King and Queen. l, Columbus' second coat of arms.

1992, Apr. 28　　**Litho.**　　**Perf. 13½**
147	A27	57s Sheet of 12, #a.-l.	35.00	35.00

Miniature Sheet

World War II in Pacific, 50th Anniv. A28

Newspaper headline and: a, Battleship ablaze at Pearl Harbor. b, Destroyed aircraft. c, Japanese A6M Zero fighter. d, Declaration of war, Pres. Franklin D. Roosevelt. e, Japanese T95 tank, Gen. MacArthur, Japanese naval ensign. f, Douglas SBD Dauntless dive bomber, Admiral Nimitz. g, Bren gun, Gen. Sir Thomas Blamey. h, Australian mortar crew, Kokoda Trail. i, US battleship, Maj. Gen. Julian C. Smith. j, Aircraft carrier USS Enterprise. k, American soldier, flag, Maj. Gen. Curtis Lemay. l, B-29 bomber, surrender ceremony on USS Missouri in Tokyo bay.

1992, May 12　　**Litho.**　　**Perf. 14**
148	A28	42s Sheet of 12, #a.-l.	27.50	27.50

King Taufa'ahau IV, 25th Anniv. of Coronation A29

45s, 2pa, King, Queen Halaevalu during coronation. No. 150a, King, Tongan national anthem. b, Extract from investiture ceremony. c, Tongan national anthem, singers.

1992, July 4　　　　**Perf. 13½x13**
149	A29	45s multicolored	1.10	1.10

Size: 51x38mm
Perf. 12½x12
150	A29	80s Strip of 3, #a.-c.	6.00	6.00
151	A29	2pa multicolored	5.00	5.00
		Nos. 149-151 (3)	12.10	12.10

Megapodius Pritchardii — A30

1992, Sept. 15　　**Litho.**　　**Perf. 14**
152	A30	45s Female & male	2.00	2.00
153	A30	60s Female with egg	2.50	2.50
154	A30	80s Chick	3.50	3.50
155	A30	1.50pa Head of male	6.00	6.00
		Nos. 152-155 (4)	14.00	14.00

World Wildlife Fund.

First Niuafo'ou Postage Stamps, 10th Anniv. A31

1993, May 3　　**Litho.**　　**Perf. 14x14½**
156	A31	60s Nos. 4, 117A	1.75	1.75
157	A31	80s Nos. 7, 117B	2.25	2.25

Aviation in Niuafo'ou, 10th Anniv. — A32

Airplanes of: 1pa, South Pacific Island Airways. 2.50pa, Friendly Islands Airways.

1993, May 3
158	A32	1pa multicolored	3.50	3.50
159	A32	2.50pa multicolored	7.50	7.50

King's 75th Birthday Type of Tonga
King and: 45s, 2pa, Patrol boat Pangai.

No. 161a, Sporting events. b, Aircraft and communications. c, Musical instruments.

1993, July 1　　　　　**Perf. 13x13½**
160	A167	45s multicolored	1.00	1.00

Perf. 12x12½
Size: 37x48mm
161	A167	80s Strip of 3, #a.- c.	5.50	5.50
162	A167	2pa multicolored	4.25	4.25
		Nos. 160-162 (3)	10.75	10.75

Wildlife — A33

Designs: a, Two parrots. b, Bird with fish. c, Butterfly, beetle. d, Birds, dragonfly, butterfly. e, Bird in flight, two on ground.

1993, Aug. 10　　**Litho.**　　**Perf. 14**
163	A33	60s Strip of 5, #a.-e.	7.50	7.50

No. 163 is a continuous design.

Winners of Children's Painting Competition — A34

Designs: Nos. 164a, 165a, Ofato Beetle Grubbs of Niuafo'ou, by Peni Finau. Nos. 164b, 165b, Crater Lake Megapode, Volcano, by Paea Puletau.

1993, Dec. 1　　**Litho.**　　**Perf. 14**
164	A34	10s Pair, #a.-b.	1.00	1.00
165	A34	1pa Pair, #a.-b.	7.50	7.50

Beetles A35

1994, Mar. 15　　**Litho.**　　**Perf. 14**
168	A35	60s Scarabaeidea	1.75	1.75
169	A35	80s Coccinellidea	2.10	2.10
170	A35	1.50pa Cerambycidea	3.75	3.75
171	A35	2.50pa Pentatomidae	6.75	6.75
		Nos. 168-171 (4)	14.35	14.35

A36　　　　　　　　A37

Sailing Ships: a, Stern of HMS Bounty. b, Bow of HMS Bounty. c, HMS Pandora. d, Whaling ship. e, Trading schooner.

1994, June 21　　**Litho.**　　**Perf. 14**
172	A36	80s Strip of 5, #a.-e.	17.50	17.50

No. 172 is a continuous design.

1994, Sept. 21　　**Litho.**　　**Perf. 14½**

1946 Volcanic Eruption: a, Blue-crowned lorikeet, lava flow. b, Black Pacific ducks, lava flow. c, Megapodes, palm trees (b). d, White-tailed tropic birds, people evacuating island (c). e, People wading out to sailboats, Pacific reef heron.

173 A37 80s Strip of 5, #a.-e.   9.50 9.50

No. 173 is a continuous design.

Nos. 129-133 Surcharged in Blue

1995, June 30   Litho.   Perf. 11½
174 A23 60s on 42s #130   2.50 2.50
175 A23 80s on 15s #129   3.25 3.25
176 A23 80s on 57s #131   3.50 3.50
177 A23 2pa on #132   8.75 8.75
  Nos. 174-177 (4)   18.00 18.00

Souvenir Sheet
178 A23 1.50pa on 1pa #133   9.00 9.00

Size and location of surcharge varies. Surcharge on No. 178 includes "COME WHALE WATCHING / IN THE SOUTH PACIFIC."

Victory in the Pacific Type of Tonga

Nos. 179, 180: a, Soldier holding rifle. b, Soldier aiming rifle, tank. c, Front of tank. d, Troops coming off boat, firing weapons. e, Troops on beach.

1995, Aug. 1   Litho.   Perf. 14x14½
179 A177 60s Strip of 5, #a.-e. 13.00 13.00
180 A177 80s Strip of 5, #a.-e. 17.00 17.00

Nos. 179-180 are continuous designs and were issued together in sheets containing 10 stamps.

Singapore '95 Type of Tonga

Designs, vert: No. 181a, 45s, like #117A. b, 60s, like #117B.
2pa, Plesiosaurus.

1995, Sept. 1   Litho.   Perf. 12
181 A178 Pair, #a.-b.   4.00 4.00
Souvenir Sheet
182 A178 2pa multicolored   5.50 5.50

Beijing Intl. Coin & Stamp Show '95 Type of Tonga
Souvenir Sheet

Design: 1.40pa, The Great Wall of China.

1995, Sept. 14   Perf. 14½
183 A179 1.40pa multicolored   5.50 5.50

End of World War II, UN, 50th Anniv. Type of Tonga

No. 184: a, London blitz. b, UN emblem, "50." c, Concorde.
No. 185: a, Building of Siam-Burma Railway by Allied prisoners of war. b, Like #184b. c, Japanese bullet train.

1995, Oct. 20   Litho.   Perf. 14
184 A180 60s Strip of 3, #a.-c.   5.50 5.50
185 A180 80s Strip of 3, #a.-c.   7.50 7.50

Nos. 184b, 185b are 23x31mm.

Mailmen of Niuafo'ou A38

Portrait, illustration of postal history: 45s, Charles Stuart Ramsey, companions, floating with poles. 60s, Ramsey with can of mail encountering shark. 1pa, Walter George Quensell, mail being lowered from ship to canoes. 3pa, Quensell, original "tin can" mail cancels.

1996, Aug. 21   Litho.   Perf. 14
186 A38 45s multicolored   1.25 1.25
187 A38 60s multicolored   1.75 1.75
188 A38 1pa multicolored   3.00 3.00
189 A38 3pa multicolored   9.00 9.00
  Nos. 186-189 (4)   15.00 15.00

Congress of Preshistoric and Protohistoric Sciences Type of Tonga

a, Prehistoric man making drawings, fire, living in huts, animals. b, Ancient Egyptians, Romans.

1996, Sept. 5   Perf. 12
190 A185 1pa Pair, #a.-b.   7.00 7.00

Evacuation of Niuafo'ou, 50th Anniv. — A39

a, Island, two canoes. b, Volcano, four canoes. c, Edge of island, canoe. d, Canoe. e, People boarding MV Matua.

1996, Dec. 2   Perf. 14
191 A39 45s Strip of 5, #a.-e.   6.00 6.00
192 A39 60s Strip of 5, #a.-e.   9.00 9.00

Nos. 191-192 are continuous designs and were issued together in sheet containing 10 stamps.

UNICEF, 50th Anniv. Type of Tonga

Children's toys on checkerboard: a, Dolls, truck, balls on pegs. b, Tricycle, car, balls on pegs, teddy bear, train. c, Car, helicopter, ice skates, books, blocks.

1996, Oct. 29   Litho.   Perf. 14
193 A187 80s Strip of 3, #a.-c.   6.50 6.50

No. 193 is a continuous design.

Ocean Environment — A40

Various zooplankton and phytoplankton.

1997, May 19   Litho.   Perf. 14
194 A40 60s red & multi   1.50 1.50
195 A40 80s brown & multi   2.00 2.00
196 A40 1.50pa blue & multi   4.00 4.00
197 A40 2.50pa green & multi   7.00 7.00
  Nos. 194-197 (4)   14.50 14.50

Pacific '97 Type of Tonga
Souvenir Sheet

Design: Oakland Bay Bridge, back-naped tern.

1997, May 30
198 A191 2pa multicolored   7.00 7.00

1997 Wedding Anniv., Coronation Anniv. Type of Tonga

No. 199: a, King Taufa'ahau, Queen Halaevalu Mata'aho on wedding day. b, King in coronation regalia.
5pa, King in coronation procession, horiz.

1997, June 30   Litho.   Perf. 12
Size: 34x47mm
199 A193 80s vert. pair, #a.-b.   5.00 5.00
Souvenir Sheet
200 A193 5pa multicolored   13.00 13.00

No. 199 was issued in sheets of 6 stamps.

Diana, Princess of Wales (1961-97)
Common Design Type

Various portraits: a, 10s. b, 80s, c, 1pa. d, 2.50pa.

Perf. 13½x14
201 CD355 Sheet of 4, #a.-d.   7.75 7.75

No. 201 sold for 4.40pa + 50s with surtax from international sales going to the Princess Diana Memorial Fund and surtax from local sales going to designated local charity.

Blue Crowned Lorikeet — A41

World Wildlife Fund: 10s, Young birds in nest. 55s, Adult on branch of flower. 80s, Adult on branch of bush. 3pa, Two adults on tree branch.

1998, May 15   Litho.   Perf. 14½x15
202 A41 10s multicolored   1.00 1.00
203 A41 55s multicolored   2.00 2.00
204 A41 80s multicolored   2.50 2.50
205 A41 3pa multicolored   7.75 7.75
  a. Sheet, 2 each #202-205   26.50 26.50
  Nos. 202-205 (4)   13.25 13.25

King Taufa'ahau Tupou IV Type of Tonga

1998, July 4   Litho.   Perf. 14
207 A196 2.70pa multicolored   4.50 4.50

See Tonga #985a for souvenir sheet containing one #207.

Fish A43

a, 10s, Amphiprion melanopus. b, 55s, Amphipiron perideraion. c, 80s, Amphipiron chrysopterus.

1998, Sept. 23   Litho.   Perf. 14
208 A43 Strip of 3, #a.-c.   2.50 2.50

Intl. Year of the Ocean. No. 208 was issued in sheets of 9 stamps.

Year of the Tiger Type of Tonga

Designs: a, 55s, Head of tiger with mouth open. b, 80s, Two tigers standing. c, 1pa, Two tigers lying down. 1pa, Head of tiger.

1998, July 23   Litho.   Perf. 14
209 A183 Sheet of 4, #a.-d.   5.00 5.00

No. 209 is a continuous design. Singpex '98.

Christmas A44

Designs: 20s, Angel playing mandolin. 55s, Angel playing violin. 1pa, Children singing, bells. 1.60pa, Children singing, candles.

1998, Nov. 12   Perf. 14x14½
210 A44 20s multicolored   .40 .40
211 A44 55s multicolored   1.10 1.10
212 A44 80s multicolored   2.00 2.00
213 A44 1.60pa multicolored   3.00 3.00
  Nos. 210-213 (4)   6.50 6.50

New Year 1999 (Year of the Rabbit) A45

Stylized rabbits: a, 10s. b, 55s. c, 80s. d, 1pa.

1999, Feb. 16   Perf. 14
214 A45 Sheet of 4, #a.-d.   4.25 4.25

Jakob le Maire (1585-1616), Explorer — A46

1999, Mar. 19   Litho.   Perf. 14
215 A46 80s shown   1.25 1.25
216 A46 2.70pa Tongiaki canoe   4.00 4.00
  a. Souvenir sheet, #215-216   5.25 5.25

Australia '99 World Stamp Expo (#216a).

Flowers A47

55s, Cananga odorata. 80s, Gardenia tannaensis, vert. 1pa, Coleus amboinicus, vert. 2.50pa, Hernandia moerenhoutiana.

Perf. 13x13¼, 13¼x13
1999, Sept. 29   Litho.
217 A47 55s multicolored   .75 .75
218 A47 80s multicolored   1.25 1.25
219 A47 1pa multicolored   1.50 1.50
220 A47 2.50pa multicolored   4.00 4.00
  Nos. 217-220 (4)   7.50 7.50

Souvenir Sheet

Millennium — A48

a, 1pa, Dove. b, 2.50pa, Native boat.

2000, Jan. 1   Litho.   Perf. 14½x15
221 A48 Sheet of 2, #a.-b.   5.00 5.00

Souvenir Sheet

New Year 2000 (Year of the Dragon) — A49

Illustration reduced.
Various dragons; a, 10s. b, 55s. c, 80s. d, 1pa.

Litho. with Foil Application
2000, Feb. 4   Perf. 14½
222 A49 Sheet of 4, #a.-d.   4.50 4.50

Souvenir Sheet

The Stamp Show 2000, London — A50

Illustration reduced.

Litho. with Foil Application

			2000, May 22		**Perf. 13x13¼**
223	A50	Sheet of 2		6.25	6.25
a.		$1.50 Queen Mother		2.00	2.00
b.		$2.50 Queen Salote Tupou III		3.25	3.25

Souvenir Sheet

World Stamp Expo 2001, Anaheim — A51

No. 224: a, 10s, Man and woman. b, 2.50pa, Satellite dish. c, 2.70pa, Intelsat.

2000, July 7   Litho.   Perf. 13x13¼
224 A51 Sheet of 3, #a-c   8.25 8.25

Butterflies — A52

Designs: 55s, Jamides bochus. 80s, Blue moon. 1pa, Eurema hecabe aprica. 2.70pa, Monarch.

2000, Oct. 25   Perf. 14
225-228 A52 Set of 4   8.00 8.00

Souvenir Sheet

New Year 2001 (Year of the Snake) — A53

No. 229 — Various snakes: a, 10s. b, 55s, c, 80s, d, 1pa.

Litho. with Foil Application

2001, Feb. 1   Perf. 14¼
229 A53 Sheet of 4, #a-d   4.25 4.25

Hong Kong 2001 Stamp Exhibition.

Fish — A54

Designs: 80s, Prognichthys sealei. 1pa, Xiphias gladius. 2.50pa, Katsuwonus pelamis.

2001, June 5   Litho.   Perf. 13¾
230-232 A54 Set of 3   7.00 7.00
232a   Souvenir sheet, #230-232 7.00 7.00

Souvenir Sheet

Fruit — A55

No. 233: a, 55s, Papaya. b, 80s, Limes. c, 1pa, Mangos. d, 2.50pa, Bananas.

Perf. 14¼x14

2001, Sept. 19   Litho.   Unwmk.
233 A55 Sheet of 4, #a-d   8.50 8.50

Barn Owl A56

Designs: Nos. 234, 238a, 10s, Owl in flight. Nos. 235, 238b, 55s, Adult feeding young. Nos. 236, 238c, 2.50pa, Four owls. Nos. 237, 238d, 2.70pa, Owl's head.

2001, Nov. 21   Perf. 12¾x13¼
Without Vertical Bister Line
Separating Panels
234-237 A56 Set of 4   10.00 10.00

Souvenir Sheet

With Vertical Bister Line Separating Panels

238 A56 Sheet of 4, #a-d   10.00 10.00

Reign Of Queen Elizabeth II, 50th Anniv. Issue
Common Design Type
Souvenir Sheet

No. 239: a, 15s, Princess Elizabeth with Queen Mother. b, 90s, Wearing purple hat. c, 1.20pa, As young woman. d, 1.40pa, Wearing red hat. e, 2.25pa, 1955 portrait by Annigoni (38x50mm).

Perf. 14¼x14½, 13¾ (2.25pa)
2002, Feb. 6   Litho.   Wmk. 373
239 CD360 Sheet of 5, #a-e   7.00 7.00

Souvenir Sheet

New Year 2002 (Year of the Horse) — A517

Various horses: a, 65s. b, 80s. c, 1pa. d, 2.50pa.

Litho. With Foil Application
2002, Feb. 12   Unwmk.   Perf. 14
240 A57 Sheet of 4, #a-d   8.00 8.00

Megapodius Pritchardii A58

Designs: 15s, Bird, eggs. 70s, Two birds. 90s, Bird, vert. 2.50pa, Two birds, vert.

Perf. 14x13½, 13½x14
2002, Apr. 9   Litho.
241-244 A58 Set of 4   6.00 6.00
244a   Souvenir sheet, #243-244 5.00 5.00

Nos. 243-244 lack white frame around stamp.

Cephalopods A59

Designs: 80s, Octopus vulgaris. 1pa, Sepioteuthis lessoniana. 2.50pa, Nautilus belauensis.

2002, July 25   Litho.   Perf. 13¾
245-247 A59 Set of 3   6.50 6.50
247a   Souvenir sheet, #245-247 6.50 6.50

Souvenir Sheet

Mail Planes — A60

No. 248: a, 80c, Casa C-212 Aviocar. b, 1.40pa, Britten-Norman Islander. c, 2.50pa, DHC 6-300 Twin Otter.

2002, Nov. 27   Litho.   Perf. 12¾
248 A60 Sheet of 3, #a-c   7.00 7.00

New Year 2003 (Year of the Ram) Type of Tonga

No. 249: a, 65s, One ram. 80s, Three sheep. 1pa, Three sheep, diff. 2.50pa, Two sheep.

2003, Apr. 14   Litho.   Perf. 13¼
249 A223 Sheet of 4, #a-d   4.75 4.75

Coronation of Queen Elizabeth II, 50th Anniv. Type of Tonga

Designs: 90s, Queen Elizabeth II. 1.20pa, Queen Elizabeth II seated. 1.40pa, Queen Salote of Tonga in coach. 2.50pa, Queen Salote.

2003, June 2   Litho.
250-253 A224 Set of 4   10.00 10.00

New Year (Year of the Monkey) Type of Tonga

No. 254: a, 60s, Spider monkey. b, 80s, Ring-tailed lemur. c, 1pa, Cotton-top tamarin. d, 2.50pa, White-cheeked gibbon.

2004, Feb. 12   Litho.   Perf. 13¼
254 A228 Sheet of 4, #a-d   5.75 5.75

Trees Type of Tonga

Designs: 45s, Pawpaw (papaya). 60s, Banana. 80s, Coconut. 1.80pa, Lime.

2004   Litho.   Perf. 14¼x14
255-258 A229 Set of 4   3.75 3.75

Christmas Type of Tonga

Designs: 15s, Madonna and Child. 90s, Journey to Bethlehem. 1.20pa, Annunciation to the Shepherds. 2.60pa, Magi.

2004, Dec.   Perf. 14
259-262 A230 Set of 4   5.25 5.25

Royalty Type of Tonga

Designs: 30s, King George Tupou I. 65s, King George Tupou II. 80s, Queen Salote Tupou III. 3.05pa, King Taufa'ahau Tupou IV.

2004, July 7   Litho.   Perf. 14
263-266 A231 Set of 4   5.75 5.75
266a   Souvenir sheet, #263-266 5.75 5.75

New Year 2005 (Year of the Rooster) Type of Tonga
Souvenir Sheet

No. 267 — Various roosters with panel color of: a, 65s, Gray. b, 80s, Grayish tan. c, 1pa, Gray. d, 2.50pa, Yellow green.

2005, Feb. 12
267 A232 Sheet of 4, #a-d   5.25 5.25

TRANSCAUCASIAN FEDERATED REPUBLICS

ˌtranˌt̯s-ko-'kā-zhən 'fe-də-rāted ri-'pə-bliks

LOCATION — In southeastern Europe, south of the Caucasus Mountains between the Black and Caspian Seas
GOVT. — Former republic
AREA — 71,255 sq. mi.
POP. — 5,851,000 (approx.)
CAPITAL — Tiflis

The Transcaucasian Federation was made up of the former autonomies of Armenia, Georgia and Azerbaijan. Its stamps were replaced by those of Russia.

100 Kopecks = 1 Ruble

Russian Stamps of 1909-17 Overprinted in Black or Red

1923   Unwmk.   Perf. 14½x15

1	A15	10k dark blue	3.00	5.00
2	A14	10k on 7k lt bl	3.00	5.00
3	A11	25k grn & gray vio	3.00	5.00
4	A11	35k red brn & grn (R)	3.00	5.00
a.		Double overprint	40.00	40.00
5	A8	50k brn red & grn	3.00	5.00
6	A9	1r pale brn, brn & org	8.25	10.00
7	A12	3½r mar & lt grn	35.00	

Imperf

8	A9	1r pale brn, brn & red org	5.00	6.00
		Nos. 1-8 (8)	63.25	
		Nos. 1-6,8 (7)		41.00

No. 7 was prepared but not issued.

Overprinted on Stamps of Armenia Previously Handstamped:

   a   c

Perf. 14½x15

9	A11(c)	25k grn & gray vio	250.00	250.00
10	A8(c)	50k vio & grn	250.00	150.00

Perf. 13½

11	A9(a)	1r pale brn, brn & org	100.00	50.00
12	A9(c)	1r pale, brn, brn & org	100.00	50.00

Imperf

13	A9(c)	1r pale brn, brn & red org	35.00	35.00
		Nos. 9-13 (5)	735.00	535.00

Counterfeit overprints exist.

Oil Fields — A1

Soviet
Symbols — A2

1923 **Perf. 11½**
14	A1	40,000r red violet	2.00	*4.00*
15	A1	75,000r dark grn	2.00	*4.00*
16	A1	100,000r blk vio	2.00	*4.00*
17	A1	150,000r red	2.00	*4.00*
18	A2	200,000r dull grn	2.00	*4.00*
19	A2	300,000r blue	2.00	*4.00*
20	A2	350,000r dark brn	2.00	*4.00*
21	A2	500,000r rose	2.00	*4.00*
		Nos. 14-21 (8)	16.00	*32.00*

Nos. 14-15 Surcharged in Brown

1923
22	A1	700,000r on 40,000r	3.00	*5.00*
a.		Imperf., pair	15.00	
23	A1	700,000r on 75,000r	3.00	*5.00*
a.		Imperf., pair	15.00	

Types of Preceding Issue with Values
in Gold Kopecks

1923, Oct. 24
25	A2	1k orange	2.25	*5.00*
26	A2	2k blue green	2.25	*5.00*
27	A2	3k rose	3.00	*5.00*
28	A2	4k gray brown	2.00	*5.00*
29	A1	5k dark violet	2.00	*5.00*
30	A1	9k deep blue	2.00	*5.00*
31	A1	18k slate	2.00	*5.00*
		Nos. 25-31 (7)	15.50	*35.00*

Nos. 14-21, 25-31 exist imperf. but are not
known to have been issued in that condition.
Value, $14 each.

TRANSVAAL

tran̲t̲s-'väl

(South African Republic)

LOCATION — Southern Africa
GOVT. — A former British Colony
AREA — 110,450 sq. mi.
POP. — 1,261,734 (1904)
CAPITAL — Pretoria

Transvaal was known as the South
African Republic until 1877 when it was
occupied by the British. The republic
was restored in 1884 and continued
until 1900 when it was annexed to Great
Britain and named "The Transvaal."

12 Pence = 1 Shilling
20 Shillings = 1 Pound

Most unused stamps between Nos.
1-96, 119-122 and 136-137 were
issued with gum, but do not expect gum
on scarcer stamps as few examples
retain their original gum. In many cases
removal of the remaining gum may
enhance the preservation of the
stamps. Otherwise, values for unused
stamps are for examples with original
gum as defined in the catalogue introduction.

Very fine imperforate stamps will
have adequate to large margins. However, rouletted stamps are valued as
partly rouletted, with straight edges,
and rouletted just into the design, as the
rouletting methods were quite
inaccurate.

First Republic

Coat of Arms
A1   A2

Mecklenburg Printings
By Adolph Otto, Gustrow
Fine Impressions
Thin Paper

A1 has spread wings on eagle.

1869 **Unwmk.** **Imperf.**
1	A1	1p brown lake	475.00
a.		1p red	625.00 *625.00*
2	A1	6p ultra	200.00 *200.00*
3	A1	1sh dark green	750.00 *750.00*
a.		Tete beche pair	

Rouletted 15½, 16
4	A1	1p red	110.00
a.		1p brown lake	150.00
5	A1	6p ultra	100.00 *100.00*
6	A1	1sh blue green	125.00 *125.00*
a.		1sh yellow green	175.00 *160.00*
b.		1sh deep green	210.00 *225.00*

Nos. 1-6 were printed from 2 sets of plates,
differing in the spacing between the stamps.
The only known example of No. 3a is in a
museum.
See Nos. 9-24, 26-33, 35-36, 38-39, 41-42,
43-49, 119, 122. For overprints see Nos. 53-
61, 63-66, 68-72, 75-78, 81-83, 86-87, 90-91,
94.

1871-74
7	A2	3p lilac	90.00 *100.00*
a.		3p violet	100.00 *110.00*
8	A2	6p brt ultra ('74)	67.50 *27.50*
a.		Half used as 3p on cover	*1,600.*

Many forgeries exist in colors duller or
lighter than the genuine stamps.
In forgeries of type A1, all values, the "D" of
"EENDRAGT" is not noticeably larger than the
other letters and does not touch the top of the
ribbon. In type A1 genuine stamps, the "D" is
large and touches the ribbon top. The eagle's
eye is a dot and its face white on the genuine
stamps; the eye is a loop or blob attached to
the beak, and the beak is strongly hooked, on
the forgeries. Many forgeries of the 1sh have
the top line of the ribbon broken above
"EENDRAGT."
Forgeries of type A2 usually can be
detected only by color.
A sharply struck cancellation of a numeral in
three rings is found on many of these forgeries. The similar genuine cancellation is always
roughly or heavily struck.
See Nos. 25, 34, 4337, 40, 42B, 120-121. For
overprints see Nos. 50-52, 62, 67, 73-74, 79-
80, 84-85, 88-89, 92-93, 95-96.

Local Printings
(A) By M. J. Viljoen, Pretoria
Poor Impressions,
Overinked and Spotted
Thin Soft Paper

1870 **Imperf.**
9	A1	1p pink	100.00
a.		1p rose red	77.50
b.		1p carmine	80.00 *72.50*
10	A1	6p dull ultra	350.00 *80.00*
a.		Tete beche pair	

The only known examples of No. 10a are in
museums.

Rouletted 15½, 16
11	A1	1p carmine	775.00 *300.00*
a.		Rouletted 6½	*1,100.*
12	A1	6p dull ultra	225.00 *110.00*

Hard Paper, Thick to Medium
Imperf
13	A1	1p carmine	80.00 *90.00*
14	A1	6p ultra	95.00
15	A1	1sh gray green	125.00 *110.00*
a.		1sh dark green	*650.00 300.00*
b.		Tete beche pair	*23,000.*
c.		Half used as 6p on cover	*2,000.*

The existence of No. 14 is questionable.

Rouletted 15½, 16
16	A1	1p light carmine	80.00 *97.50*
a.		1p carmine	57.50 *62.50*
17	A1	6p ultra	100.00 *95.00*
a.		Tete beche pair	*20,000. 15,000.*
18	A1	1sh dark green	140.00 *85.00*
a.		1sh gray green	575.00 *175.00*

Copies of Nos. 16 to 18 are sometimes so
heavily inked as to be little more than blots of
color.

(B) By J. P. Borrius, Potchefstroom
Clearer Impressions Though Often
Overinked
Thick Porous Paper

1870 **Imperf.**
19	A1	1p black	150.00 *125.00*
20	A1	6p indigo	250.00

Rouletted 15½, 16
21	A1	1p black	20.00 *30.00*
22	A1	6p gray blue	160.00 *70.00*
a.		6p indigo	100.00 *90.00*
b.		6p bright ultra	

Thin Transparent Paper
23	A1	1p carmine	225.00 *750.00*
24	A1	1p brt carmine	175.00 *62.50*
a.		1p deep carmine	75.00 *45.00*
25	A2	3p gray lilac	110.00 *57.50*
26	A1	6p ultra	75.00 *35.00*
27	A1	1sh yellow green	92.50 *47.50*
a.		1sh deep green	92.50 *47.50*
b.		Half used as 6p on cover	—

Thick Soft Paper
28	A1	1p dull rose	450.00 *85.00*
a.		1p brown rose	575.00 *140.00*
b.		Printed on both sides	
29	A1	6p dull blue	100.00 *50.00*
a.		6p bright blue	225.00 *75.00*
b.		6p ultramarine	210.00 *75.00*
c.		Rouletted 6½	
30	A1	1sh yellow green	950.00 *750.00*

The paper of Nos. 28 to 30 varies considerably in thickness.

(C) By P. Davis & Son, Natal
Thin to Medium Paper

1874 **Perf. 12½**
31	A1	1p red	110.00 *45.00*
a.		1p brownish red	110.00 *45.00*
32	A1	6p deep blue	160.00 *70.00*
a.		6p blue	150.00 *62.50*
b.		Horiz. pair, imperf. between	

(D) By the Stamp Commission,
Pretoria
Pelure Paper

1875-76 **Imperf.**
33	A1	1p pale red	57.50 *57.50*
a.		1p orange red	50.00 *27.50*
b.		1p brown red	62.50 *35.00*
c.		Pin perf.	*400.00*
34	A2	3p gray lilac	57.50 *47.50*
a.		3p dull violet	60.00 *45.00*
b.		3p violet	70.00 *47.50*
35	A1	6p blue	57.50 *47.50*
a.		6p pale blue	57.50 *57.50*
b.		6p dark blue	62.50 *50.00*
c.		Tete beche pair	
d.		Pin perf.	— *400.00*

The only known examples of No. 35c are in
museums.

Rouletted 15½, 16
36	A1	1p orange red	400.00 *140.00*
a.		Rouletted 6½	*1,100. 225.00*
37	A2	3p dull violet	450.00 *150.00*
a.		Rouletted 6½	*1,000. 275.00*
38	A1	6p blue	175.00 *110.00*
a.		Rouletted 6½	*1,100. 125.00*

The paper of this group varies slightly in
thickness and is sometimes divided into pelure
and semipelure. We believe there was only
one lot of the paper and that the separation is
not warranted.

Thick Hard Paper
Imperf
39	A1	1p orange red ('76)	27.50 *20.00*
40	A2	3p dull violet	425.00 *125.00*
41	A1	6p deep blue	70.00 *22.50*
a.		6p blue	110.00 *27.50*
b.		Tete beche pair	*19,000.*

Rouletted 15½, 16
42	A1	1p orange red ('76)	450.00 *175.00*
a.		Rouletted 6½ ('75)	*700.00 175.00*
42B	A2	3p lilac	400.00
43	A1	6p deep blue	675.00 *300.00*
a.		6p blue	*850.00 125.00*
b.		Rouletted 6½ ('75)	*750.00 275.00*

Soft Porous Paper
Imperf
44	A1	1p orange red	150.00 *62.50*
45	A1	6p deep blue	225.00 *60.00*
a.		6p dull blue	400.00 *100.00*
46	A1	1sh yellow green	400.00 *125.00*
a.		Half used as 6p on cover	*1,800.*

Rouletted 15½, 16
47	A1	1p orange red	425.00
a.		Rouletted 6½	*500.00*
48	A1	6p deep blue	175.00
a.		Rouletted 6½	*1,250.*
49	A1	1sh yellow grn	800.00 *400.00*
a.		Rouletted 6½	*1,400.*
b.		Rouletted 15½-16x16½	*500.00 325.00*

First British Occupation

Stamps and Types of
1875 Overprinted

Red Overprint
Pelure Paper
1877 **Unwmk.** **Imperf.**
50	A2	3p lilac	1,500.	*210.00*
a.		Overprinted on back	3,750.	*3,750*
b.		Double ovpt., red and black		
			7,000.	

Rouletted 15½, 16
51	A2	3p lilac		*1,800.*
a.		Rouletted 6½		*1,500.*

Thin Hard Paper
Imperf
52	A2	3p lilac	1,500.	*350.00*

Soft Porous Paper
53	A1	6p deep blue	1,800.	*200.00*
a.		6p deep blue		*275.00*
b.		Inverted overprint		*6,250.*
c.		Double overprint	5,100.	*1,100.*
54	A1	1sh yellow grn	700.00	*210.00*
a.		Inverted overprint		*5,100.*
b.		Half used as 6p on cover		*2,000.*

Rouletted 15½, 16
55	A1	6p blue		*1,900.*
a.		Rouletted 6½		*1,400.*
56	A1	1sh yellow grn	1,800.	*850.00*
a.		Rouletted 6½	3,500.	*1,200.*

Black Overprint
Pelure Paper
Imperf
57	A1	1p red	300.00	*110.00*

Rouletted 15½, 16
58	A1	1p red		*1,200.*

Thick Hard Paper
Imperf
59	A1	1p red	27.50	*25.00*
a.		Inverted overprint	625.00	*575.00*

Rouletted 15½, 16
60	A1	1p red	175.00	*57.50*
a.		Rouletted 6½	750.00	*225.00*
b.		Inverted overprint		
c.		Double overprint	—	*1,250.*

Soft Porous Paper
Imperf
61	A1	1p red	29.00	*25.00*
a.		Double overprint		*1,300.*
62	A2	3p lilac	92.50	*47.50*
a.		3p deep lilac	200.00	*97.50*
b.		Inverted overprint		
63	A1	6p dull blue	100.00	*35.00*
a.		6p bright blue	175.00	*35.00*
b.		6p dark blue	175.00	*35.00*
c.		Inverted overprint		*850.00*
d.		Double overprint	4,000.	
64	A1	6p blue, *rose*	92.50	*47.50*
a.		Tete beche pair		
b.		Inverted overprint	110.00	*55.00*
c.		Overprint omitted	4,000.	*2,900.*
d.		Half used as 3p on cover		
65	A1	1sh yellow grn	110.00	*57.50*
a.		Tete beche pair	*22,500.*	*22,500.*
b.		Inverted overprint	1,250.	*500.00*
c.		Half used as 6p on cover		*1,250.*

The only known examples of No. 64a are in
museums.

Rouletted 15½, 16
66	A1	1p red	85.00	*85.00*
a.		Rouletted 6½	750.00	*175.00*
67	A2	3p lilac	200.00	*75.00*
a.		Rouletted 6½		*850.00*
68	A1	6p dull blue	225.00	*62.50*
a.		Inverted overprint	—	*850.00*
b.		Rouletted 6½		*1,350.*
c.		As "a," rouletted 6½		*4,500.*
69	A1	6p blue, *rose*	200.00	*80.00*
a.		Inverted overprint	625.00	*80.00*
b.		Rouletted 6½		
c.		Tete beche pair		
d.		Overprint omitted		
e.		As "a," rouletted 6½		*750.00*
f.		As "d," rouletted 6½		
70	A1	1sh yellow grn	225.00	*100.00*
a.		Inverted overprint	1,250.	*575.00*
b.		Rouletted 6½	525.00	*150.00*
c.		As "a," rouletted 6½	1,750.	*700.00*

In this issue the space between "V. R." and
"TRANSVAAL" is normally 8½mm but in position 11 it is 12mm. In this and the following
issues there are numerous minor varieties of
the overprint, missing periods, etc.
The only known examples of No. 69c are in
museums.

Types A1 and A2 Overprinted

1877-79 Imperf.

71	A1 1p red, *blue*		62.50	35.00
a.	"Transvral"		6,250.	2,900.
b.	Inverted overprint		900.00	450.00
c.	Double overprint		4,500.	
d.	Overprint omitted			
72	A1 1p red, *org* ('78)		22.50	22.50
a.	Printed on both sides			
b.	Pin perf.			
73	A2 3p lilac, *buff*		57.50	30.00
a.	Inverted overprint			850.00
b.	Pin perf.			
74	A2 3p lilac, *grn* ('79)		175.00	50.00
a.	Inverted overprint			2,250.
b.	Double overprint			
c.	Pin perf.			
75	A1 6p blue, *grn*		97.50	42.50
a.	Tete beche pair			20,000.
b.	Inverted overprint			1,250.
c.	Half used as 3p on cover			
d.	Pin perf.			
76	A1 6p blue, *bl* ('78)		62.50	30.00
b.	Tete beche pair			2,500.
b.	Overprint omitted			1,100.
c.	Inverted overprint			900.00
d.	Half used as 3p on cover			3,750.
f.	Pin perf.			
	Nos. 71-76 (6)		477.50	210.00

The only known examples of No. 76a are in museums.

Rouletted 15½, 16

77	A1 1p red, *blue*		100.00	42.50
a.	"Transvral"			3,500.
b.	Inverted overprint			
c.	Double overprint			
78	A1 1p red, *org* ('78)		35.00	30.00
a.	Horiz. pair, imperf. vert.		700.00	
b.	Rouletted 6½		275.00	125.00
79	A2 3p lilac, *buff*		110.00	30.00
a.	Inverted overprint			3,500.
b.	Vert. pair, imperf. horiz.			
c.	Rouletted 6½			125.00
80	A2 3p lilac, *grn* ('79)		700.00	175.00
a.	Inverted overprint			
b.	Rouletted 6½		750.00	300.00
81	A1 6p blue, *green*		97.50	32.50
a.	Inverted overprint			75.00
b.	Overprint omitted			4,500.
c.	Tete beche pair			800.00
d.	Half used at 3p on cover		—	1,100.
e.	Rouletted 6½			
82	A1 6p blue, *bl* ('78)		250.00	62.50
a.	Inverted overprint			1,000.
b.	Overprint omitted		—	4,000.
c.	Tete beche pair			
d.	Horiz. pair, imperf. vert.			
e.	Half used as 3p on cover			850.00
f.	Double overprint			
g.	Rouletted 6½			350.00
h.	As "a," rouletted 6½			
	Nos. 77-82 (6)		1,292.	372.50

The only known examples of No. 81c are in museums. The existence of No. 82c is questioned.

Types A1 and A2 Overprinted

Imperf

83	A1 1p red, *org* ('78)		62.50	50.00
84	A2 3p lilac, *buff* ('78)		75.00	40.00
a.	Pin perf.		850.00	850.00
85	A2 3p lilac, *grn* ('79)		125.00	40.00
a.	Inverted overprint			2,250.
b.	Overprint omitted			4,000.
c.	Printed on both sides			1,100.
86	A1 6p blue, *bl* ('78)		125.00	35.00
a.	Tete beche pair		17,500.	
b.	Inverted overprint			700.00
	Nos. 83-86 (4)		387.50	165.00

Rouletted 15½, 16

87	A1 1p red, *org* ('78)		160.00	140.00
a.	Rouletted 6½			350.00
88	A2 3p lilac, *buff* ('78)		175.00	125.00
a.	Vert. pair, imperf. horiz.			
b.	Rouletted 6½			400.00
89	A2 3p lilac, *grn* ('79)		700.00	175.00
a.	Inverted overprint			
b.	Overprint omitted			350.00
c.	Rouletted 6½ ('97)			
90	A1 6p blue, *bl* ('78)		425.00	175.00
a.	Tete beche pair		—	1,250.
b.	Inverted overprint			
d.	Rouletted 6½			400.00
e.	As "b," rouletted 6½			

Types A1 and A2 Overprinted

1879 Imperf.

91	A1 1p red, *orange*		45.00	35.00
a.	1p red, *yellow*		50.00	42.50
b.	Small capital "T"		350.00	225.00
92	A2 3p lilac, *green*		45.00	29.00
a.	Small capital "T"		250.00	125.00
93	A2 3p lilac, *blue*		50.00	35.00
a.	Small capital "T"		275.00	100.00
	Nos. 91-93 (3)		140.00	99.00

Rouletted 15½, 16

94	A1 1p red, *yellow*		400.00	225.00
a.	1p red, *orange*		850.00	425.00
b.	Small capital "T"		1,100.	750.00
c.	Rouletted 6½		750.00	750.00
d.	Pin perf.			850.00
95	A2 3p lilac, *green*		850.00	275.00
a.	Small capital "T"			
b.	Rouletted 6½			
96	A2 3p lilac, *blue*			200.00
a.	Small capital "T"			800.00
b.	Rouletted 6½			950.00
c.	Pin perf.			

Queen Victoria — A3

1878-80 Engr. Perf. 14, 14½

97	A3	½p vermilion ('80)	25.00	90.00
98	A3	1p red brown	14.00	4.50
99	A3	3p claret	17.50	5.00
100	A3	4p olive green	24.00	6.25
101	A3	6p slate	12.50	4.50
a.		Half used as 3p on cover		
102	A3	1sh green	140.00	42.50
103	A3	2sh blue	175.00	85.00
		Nos. 97-103 (7)	408.00	237.75

For surcharges see Nos. 104-118, 138-139.

No. 101 Surcharged in Red or Black:

(a) Surcharged

1879

104	A3 1p on 6p slate (R)		82.50	65.00
105	A3 1p on 6p slate (Bk)		35.00	24.00

(b) Surcharged 1 Penny

106	A3 1p on 6p slate (R)		350.00	275.00
107	A3 1p on 6p slate (Bk)		160.00	85.00

(c) Surcharged

108	A3 1p on 6p slate (R)		200.00	115.00
109	A3 1p on 6p slate (Bk)		65.00	32.50

(d) Surcharged

110	A3 1p on 6p slate (R)		210.00	125.00
111	A3 1p on 6p slate (Bk)		55.00	50.00
a.	Pair, one without surcharge			

(e) Surcharged

112	A3 1p on 6p slate (R)		350.00	225.00
113	A3 1p on 6p slate (Bk)		150.00	75.00

(f) Surcharged

114	A3 1p on 6p slate (R)		325.00	150.00
115	A3 1p on 6p slate (Bk)		90.00	55.00

(g) Surcharged 1 Penny

116	A3 1p on 6p slate (R)		—	3,000.
117	A3 1p on 6p slate (Bk)		550.00	175.00

Surcharge distinctions: a, "PENNY" in gothic capitals. b, "1" has heavy serif at base; "P," thin serif at base. c, No serif at base of "1." d, Heavy serifs at base of "1" and "p." e, Italics. f, "1" has long, sloping serif at top, thin serif at base. g, Tail of "y" missing.

Second Republic

No. 100 Surcharged

1882		Unwmk.	Perf. 14, 14½	
118	A3 1p on 4p olive grn		15.00	5.00
a.	Inverted surcharge		350.00	250.00

1883			Perf. 12	
119	A1 1p black		5.75	2.00
b.	Imperf.			
b.	Vert. pair, imperf. horiz.		625.00	400.00
c.	Horiz. pair, imperf. vert.		275.00	
120	A2 3p red		11.00	2.50
a.	Horiz. pair, imperf. vert.		700.00	
b.	Half used as 1p on cover			700.00
121	A2 3p black, *rose*		26.00	5.75
a.	Half used as 1p on cover			750.00
122	A1 1sh green		62.50	4.50
a.	Tete beche pair		950.00	175.00
b.	Half used as 6p on cover			500.00
	Nos. 119-122 (4)		105.25	14.75

The so-called reprints of this issue are forgeries. They were made from the counterfeit plates described in the note following No. 8, plus a new false plate for the 3p. The false 3p plate has many small flaws and defects.

Forgeries of No. 120 are in dull orange red, clearly printed on whitish paper, and those of No. 121 in brownish or grayish black on bright rose. Genuine copies of No. 120 lack the orange tint and the paper is yellowish; genuine copies of No. 121 are in black without gray or brown shade, on dull lilac rose paper.

A 6p in slate on white, apparently of this issue, is a late print from the counterfeit plate.

A4

Perf. 13½, 11½x12, 12½, 12½x12

1885-93			Typo.	
123	A4	½p gray	.80	.20
124	A4	1p rose	.80	.20
125	A4	2p brown	2.00	2.75
126	A4	2p olive bis ('87)	1.40	.20
127	A4	2½p purple ('93)	2.50	.55
128	A4	3p violet	2.75	1.40
129	A4	4p bronze green	4.25	.90
130	A4	6p blue	4.25	2.25
a.		Imperf.		
131	A4	1sh green	2.75	.70
132	A4	2sh6p yellow	9.00	2.50
133	A4	5sh steel blue	9.00	4.50
134	A4	10sh pale brown	35.00	9.00
135	A4	£5 dark green ('92)	3,750.	210.00
		Nos. 123-134 (12)	74.50	25.15

Reprints of Nos. 123-137, 140-163, 166-174 closely resemble the originals. Paper is whiter; perf. 12½, large holes.

Excellent counterfeits of No. 135 exist.

For overprint and surcharges see Nos. 140-147, 163, 213.

Nos. 120, 122 Surcharged

1885			Perf. 12	
136	A2	½p on 3p red	5.75	11.00
a.		Surcharge reading down	5.75	11.00
137	A1	½p on 1sh green	25.00	57.50
a.		Surcharge reading down	25.00	57.50
b.		Tete beche pair	850.00	400.00

Almost all copies of No. 137b have telegraph cancellations. Postally used examples are rare.

Nos. 101, 128 Surcharged in Red or Black

		Perf. 14		
138	A3	½p on 6p slate	62.50	97.50
139	A3	2p on 6p slate	6.25	12.50
		Perf. 11½x12, 12½x12		
140	A4	½p on 3p vio (Bk)	4.50	4.50
a.		"PRNNY"	45.00	70.00
b.		2nd "N" of "PENNY" invtd	97.50	110.00

No. 128 Surcharged

No. 141	No. 142

1887				
141	A4 2p on 3p violet		1.75	3.75
a.	Double surcharge		200.00	200.00
142	A4 2p on 3p violet		8.50	8.50
a.	Double surcharge			300.00

Nos. 126, 130, 131 Surcharged

Nos. 143-144	Nos. 145-146

No. 147

Red Surcharge

1893				
143	A4 ½p on 2p olive bis		.90	2.00
a.	Inverted surcharge		2.75	2.75
b.	Bars 14mm apart		1.75	2.75
c.	As "b," inverted		5.75	11.00

Black Surcharge

144	A4 ½p on 2p olive bis		.95	2.00
a.	Inverted surcharge		5.00	5.75
b.	Bars 14mm apart		1.25	2.25
c.	As "b," inverted		22.50	17.50
145	A4 1p on 6p blue		.80	.85
a.	Inverted surcharge		1.75	2.25
b.	Double surcharge		62.50	50.00
c.	Pair, one without surcharge		250.00	
d.	Bars 14mm apart		1.10	1.10
e.	As "d," inverted		5.75	4.50
f.	As "d," double			90.00
146	A4 2½p on 1sh green		1.40	4.25
a.	Inverted surcharge		7.50	8.50
b.	Fraction line misplaced "²/₁₂"		35.00	70.00
c.	As "b," inverted		400.00	350.00
d.	Bars 14mm apart		1.75	4.25
e.	As "d," inverted		8.50	18.00
147	A4 2½p on 1sh green		5.50	4.75
a.	Inverted surcharge		8.50	8.50
b.	Bars 14mm apart		9.00	9.50
c.	As "b," inverted		22.50	22.50
d.	Double surcharge		85.00	95.00
	Nos. 143-147 (5)		9.55	13.85

A13

Wagon with Two Shafts

		1894	Typo.	Perf. 12½	
148	A13	½p gray		.50	.40
149	A13	1p rose		1.00	.20
150	A13	2p olive bister		1.00	.20
151	A13	6p blue		1.75	.40
152	A13	1sh yellow grn		10.00	12.00
		Nos. 148-152 (5)		14.25	13.20

Counterfeits of #148-152 are plentiful.
See note following No. 135 for reprints.

		1895-96	Wagon with Pole	
153	A13	½p gray	.75	.20
154	A13	1p rose	.75	.20
155	A13	2p olive bister	.80	.20
156	A13	3p violet	1.50	.20
157	A13	4p slate	2.00	.45
158	A13	6p blue	2.00	.30
159	A13	1sh green	3.00	.90
160	A13	5sh slate blue ('96)	13.00	20.00
161	A13	10sh red brown ('96)	13.00	3.50
		Nos. 153-161 (9)	36.80	25.95

Most of the unused specimens of Nos. 153-161 now on the market are reprints.
See Nos. 166-174. For surcharge and overprints see Nos. 162, 214-220, 232-235.
See note following No. 135 for reprints.

Nos. 159, 127 Surcharged in Red or Green

		1895		
162	A13	½p on 1sh green (R)	.30	.20
a.		Inverted surcharge	5.25	5.25
b.		"Pennij" instead of "Penny"	60.00	60.00
c.		Double surcharge	60.00	60.00
163	A4	1p on 2½p pur (G)	.60	.20
a.		Inverted surcharge	20.00	20.00
b.		Surcharge sideways		
c.		Surcharge on back		
d.		Space between "1" and "d"	1.25	1.25

A16

		1895		Perf. 11½	
164	A16	6p rose (G)		.80	.80
a.		Vertical pair, imperf. between			

Counterfeits of No. 164 are on the 6p dark red revenue stamp of 1898, and have a shiny green ink for the overprint. The false overprint is also found on other revenue denominations, though only the 6p rose was converted to postal use.

Coat of Arms, Wheat Field and Railroad Train — A17

		1895, Sept. 6		Litho.	
165	A17	1p red		1.00	1.00
a.		Imperf.			
b.		Vertical pair, imperf. between		80.00	85.00

Penny Postage in Transvaal. Horiz. pair, imperf. between also exists.
For overprint see No. 245.

With Pole

		1896	Typo.	Perf. 12½	
166	A13	½p green		.25	.20
167	A13	1p rose & grn		.25	.20
168	A13	2p brown & grn		.25	.20
169	A13	2½p ultra & grn		.40	.20
170	A13	3p red vio & grn		1.00	.75

171	A13	4p olive & grn	1.00	.75
172	A13	6p violet & grn	.50	.40
173	A13	1sh bister & grn	.75	.20
174	A13	2sh6p lilac & grn	1.10	1.00
		Nos. 166-174 (9)	5.50	3.90

See note following No. 135 for reprints.
For overprints and surcharges see Nos. 202-212, 214-235, 237-244, 246-251, Cape of Good Hope Nos. N5-N8.

Pietersburg Issue

Date large; "P" in Postzegel large — A18

Date small; "P" in Postzegel large — A19

Date small; "P" in Postzegel small — A20

		1901	Typeset	Imperf.
		Initials in Red		
175	A18	½p black, *green*		37.50
a.		Initials omitted		125.00
b.		Initials in black		45.00
176	A19	½p black, *green*		50.00
a.		Initials omitted		125.00
b.		Initials in black		45.00
177	A20	½p black, *green*		50.00
a.		Initials omitted		125.00
b.		Initials in black		45.00
		Initials in Black		
178	A18	1p black, *rose*		10.00
179	A19	1p black, *rose*		13.00
180	A20	1p black, *rose*		16.00
181	A18	2p black, *orange*		15.00
182	A19	2p black, *orange*		20.00
183	A20	2p black, *orange*		22.50
184	A18	4p black, *dull blue*		25.00
185	A19	4p black, *dull blue*		30.00
186	A20	4p black, *dull blue*		40.00
187	A18	6p black, *green*		32.50
188	A19	6p black, *green*		47.50
189	A20	6p black, *green*		65.00
190	A18	1sh black, *yellow*		75.00
191	A19	1sh black, *yellow*		55.00
192	A20	1sh black, *yellow*		140.00
		Perf. 11½		
		Initials in Red		
193	A18	½p black, *green*		13.00
194	A19	½p black, *green*		15.00
195	A20	½p black, *green*		20.00
		Initials in Black		
196	A18	1p black, *rose*		10.00
a.		Horiz. pair, imperf. vert.		125.00
197	A19	1p black, *rose*		13.00
a.		Horiz. pair, imperf. vert.		150.00
198	A20	1p black, *rose*		13.00
a.		Horiz. pair, imperf. vert.		150.00
199	A18	2p black, *orange*		15.00
200	A19	2p black, *orange*		17.00
201	A20	2p black, *orange*		17.00

Nos. 193 to 201 inclusive are always imperforate on one side.
The setting consisted of 12 stamps of type A18, 6 of type A19, and 6 of type A20. Numerous type-setting varieties exist. The perforated stamps are from the first printing and were put into use first. Used copies are not valued as all seen show evidence of having been canceled to order.

Second British Occupation
Issued under Military Authority

Nos. 166-174, 160-161, 135 Overprinted

		1900	Unwmk.	Perf. 12½	
202	A13	½p green		.20	.20
a.		"V.I.R."		650.00	

203	A13	1p rose & grn	.20	.20
204	A13	2p brown & grn	1.40	.40
a.		"V.I.R."	650.00	
205	A13	2½p ultra & grn	.50	.40
206	A13	3p red vio & grn	.50	.20
207	A13	4p olive & grn	1.10	.20
a.		"V.I.R."	650.00	
208	A13	6p violet & grn	1.10	.40
209	A13	1sh bister & grn	1.10	.80
210	A13	2sh6p hel & grn	1.75	2.25
211	A13	5sh slate blue	3.50	4.00
212	A13	10sh red brown	5.25	4.50
213	A4	£5 dark green		
		Nos. 202-212 (11)	16.60	13.55

Nos. 202 to 213 have been extensively counterfeited. The overprint on the forgeries is clear and clean, with small periods and letters showing completely. In the genuine, letters are worn and lack many or all serifs; the periods are large and oval.
The genuine overprint exists inverted; double; with period missing after "V," after "R," after "I," etc.

Issued in Lydenburg

Overprinted in Black

		1900		
214	A13	½p green	110.00	110.00
215	A13	1p rose & grn	100.00	80.00
216	A13	2p brown & grn	800.00	700.00
217	A13	2½p ultra & grn		800.00
218	A13	4p olive & grn	2,250.	650.00
219	A13	6p violet & grn	2,250.	575.00
220	A13	1sh bister & grn	2,500.	

Beware of counterfeits.

No. 167 Surcharged

221	A13	3p on 1p rose & green	80.00	70.00

Issued in Rustenburg

Nos. 166-170, 172-174 Handstamped in Violet

		1900		Perf. 12½	
223	A13	½p green		100.00	100.00
224	A13	1p rose & grn		95.00	60.00
225	A13	2p brown & grn		200.00	190.00
226	A13	2½p ultra & grn		120.00	80.00
227	A13	3p red vio & grn		190.00	110.00
229	A13	6p violet & grn		650.00	500.00
230	A13	1sh bister & grn		1,300.	650.00
231	A13	2sh6p hel & grn		4,250.	

Issued in Schweizer Reneke
Nos. 166-168 and 172 Handstamped "BESIEGED" in Black

		1900	Typo.	Perf. 12½
232	A13	½p green		250.00
233	A13	1p rose & green		275.00
234	A13	2p brown & green		450.00
235	A13	6p violet & green		900.00
		Nos. 232-235 (4)		1,875.

Same Overprint on Cape of Good Hope No. 59 and Type of 1893
Perf. 14

236	A15	½p green	650.00
236A	A15	1p carmine	650.00

In 1902 five revenue stamps overprinted "V.R.I." are said to have been used postally in Volksrust. There seems to be some doubt that this issue was properly authorized for postal use.

Issued in Wolmaransstad

Nos. 166-173 Handstamped in Blue or Red

		1900		
237	A13	½p green	175.00	
238	A13	1p rose & grn	160.00	175.00
239	A13	2p brown & grn	1,400.	1,400.
240	A13	2½p ultra & grn (R)	2,000.	2,000.
241	A13	3p red vio & grn	2,500.	
242	A13	4p olive & grn	3,000.	3,750.
243	A13	6p violet & grn	2,750.	4,250.
244	A13	1sh bister & grn		

No. 165 Overprinted in Blue

245	A17	1p red	160.00	150.00

Regular Issues
No. 166-168, 170-171, 174
Surcharged or Overprinted

		1901-02		
246	A13	½p on 2p brn & grn	.80	.65
247	A13	½p green	.40	.80
248	A13	1p rose & grn	.40	.20
a.		Overprint "E" omitted	65.00	
249	A13	3p red vio & grn	2.00	1.50
250	A13	4p olive & grn	2.25	1.50
251	A13	2sh6p hel & grn	7.75	10.00
		Nos. 246-251 (6)	13.60	14.65

Excellent counterfeits of Nos. 246 to 251 are plentiful. See note after No. 213 for the recognition marks of the counterfeits.

Edward VII — A27

Nos. 260, 262 to 267 and 275 to 280 have "POSTAGE" at each side; the other stamps of type A27 have "REVENUE" at the right.

Wmk. Crown and C A (2)

		1902-03	Typo.	Perf. 14	
252	A27	½p gray grn & blk		1.40	.20
253	A27	1p rose & blk		1.25	.20
254	A27	2p violet & blk		3.25	.30
255	A27	2½p ultra & blk		5.75	.80
256	A27	3p ol grn & blk		6.00	.30
257	A27	4p choc & blk		4.75	.35
258	A27	6p brn org & blk		3.50	.50
259	A27	1sh ol grn & blk		12.00	6.00
260	A27	1sh red brn & blk		11.00	1.25
261	A27	2sh brown & blk		37.50	37.50
262	A27	2sh yel & blk		15.00	9.00
263	A27	2sh6p black & vio		13.00	10.00
264	A27	5sh vio & blk, yel		20.00	20.00
265	A27	10sh vio & blk, red		47.50	22.50
266	A27	£1 violet & grn		175.00	100.00
267	A27	£5 violet & org		1,300.	575.00
		Nos. 252-266 (15)		356.90	208.90

Issue dates: 3p, 4p, Nos. 260, 262, £1, £5, 1903. Others, Apr. 1, 1902.

		1904-09		Wmk. 3	
268	A27	½p gray grn & blk		4.00	1.75
269	A27	1p rose & blk		2.75	.20
270	A27	2p violet & blk		5.50	.40
271	A27	2½p ultra & blk		7.50	2.25
272	A27	3p ol grn & blk		2.50	.20
273	A27	4p choc & blk		3.00	.50
274	A27	6p brn org & blk		2.25	.30
275	A27	1sh red brn & blk		4.50	.30
276	A27	2sh yellow & blk		15.00	4.00
277	A27	2sh6p blk & red vio		35.00	3.00
278	A27	5sh vio & blk, *yel*		16.00	1.25

279	A27	10sh vio & blk, *red*	37.50	2.00
280	A27	£1 violet & grn	160.00	17.50
		Nos. 268-280 (13)	295.50	33.75

The 2p and 3p are on chalky paper, the 2½p, 4p, 6p and £1 on both chalky and ordinary, and the other values on ordinary paper only.

Issue years: ½p, 1p, 5sh, 1904. 2½p, 6p, 1sh, 1905. 2p, 3p, 4p, 2sh, 1906. 10sh, 1907. £1, 1908. 2sh6p, 1909.

1905-10

281	A27	½p green		1.50	.20
a.		Booklet pane of 6			
282	A27	1p carmine		1.00	.20
a.		Wmk. 16 (anchor) ('07)			275.00
b.		Booklet pane of 6			
283	A27	2p dull vio ('10)		3.00	.40
284	A27	2½p ultra ('10)		11.00	4.00
		Nos. 281-284 (4)		16.50	4.80

Wmk. 16 is illustrated in the Cape of Good Hope.

Some of the above stamps are found with the overprint "C. S. A. R." for use by the Central South African Railway, the control mark being applied after the stamps had left the post office.

POSTAGE DUE STAMPS

D1

Wmk. Multiple Crown and C A (3)
1907		Typo.	Perf. 14	
J1	D1	½p green & blk	3.50	1.10
J2	D1	1p carmine & blk	4.25	.65
J3	D1	2p brown org	4.25	1.00
J4	D1	3p blue & blk	7.50	2.75
J5	D1	5p violet & blk	2.25	10.00
J6	D1	6p red brown & blk	4.50	11.00
J7	D1	1sh black & car	10.00	7.00
		Nos. J1-J7 (7)	36.25	33.50

Most canceled copies of #J1-J7 were used outside the Transvaal under the Union of South Africa administration in 1910-16.

The stamps of Transvaal were replaced by those of South Africa.

TRINIDAD

'tri-nə-ˌdad

LOCATION — West Indies, off the Venezuelan coast
GOVT. — British Colony which became part of the Colony of Trinidad and Tobago in 1889
AREA — 1,864 sq. mi.
POP. — 387,000
CAPITAL — Port of Spain

12 Pence = 1 Shilling
20 Shillings = 1 Pound

In 1847 David Bryce, owner of the "Lady McLeod," issued a blue, lithographed, imperf. stamp to prepay his 5-cent rate for carrying letters on his sail-equipped steamer between Port of Spain and San Fernando, another Trinidad port. The stamp pictures the "Lady McLeod" above the monogram "LMcL," expressing no denomination. Value, unused, $50,000, used (pen canceled), $12,500. Used stamps canceled by having a corner skinned off are worth less.

Values for unused stamps are for examples with original gum as defined in the catalogue introduction. However, Nos. 9-12 are seldom found with gum, and these are valued without gum.
Values for Nos. 18-26 are for stamps with pin perforations on two or three sides. Stamps with pin perforations on all four sides are not often seen and command large premiums.
Very fine examples of Nos. 27-47 will have perforations touching the design on one or more sides due to the narrow spacing of the stamps on the plates and imperfect perforating methods. These stamps with perfs clear of the design on all four sides are scarce and command substantially higher prices.

"Britannia"
A1   A2

1851-53   Unwmk.   Engr.   Imperf.
Blued Paper

1	A1	(1p) brick red ('56)	200.00	85.00
a.		(1p) brown red ('53)	360.00	77.50
2	A1	(1p) purple brown	18.00	90.00
3	A1	(1p) blue	18.00	72.50
a.		(1p) deep blue, deeply blued paper	175.00	95.00
4	A1	(1p) gray brn ('53)	57.50	90.00
a.		(1p) gray ('52)	90.00	77.50
		Nos. 1-4 (4)	293.50	337.50

1854-57
White Paper

6	A1	(1p) brown red ('57)	3,250.	77.50
7	A1	(1p) gray	50.00	95.00
8	A1	(1p) black violet	30.00	100.00

See Nos. 14, 18, 22, 27, 33, 39, 43, 45, 48, 58. For surcharges see Nos. 62-64.

1852   Litho.
Fine Impressions
Yellowish Paper

9	A2	(1p) blue	11,500.	1,950.
a.		(1p) deep blue	11,500.	1,950.
b.		White paper		1,950.

1853
Bluish Paper

10	A2	(1p) blue	10,000.	2,400.

Same, Lines of Background More or Less Worn

1855-60
Thin Paper

11	A2	(1p) slate blue	5,500.	800.00
12	A2	(1p) blue	5,000.	500.00
a.		(1p) greenish blue		800.00
13	A2	(1p) rose	17.50	750.00
a.		(1p) dull red	17.50	725.00

A3

1859   Engr.   Imperf.
White Paper

14	A1	(1p) dull rose	—	—
15	A3	4p gray lilac	125.00	400.00
a.		4p dull lilac		
16	A3	6p green	15,000.	525.00
17	A3	1sh slate blue	125.00	425.00

Pin-perf. 12½

18	A1	(1p) dull rose red	2,000.	70.00
a.		(1p) lake	2,250.	70.00
19	A3	4p brown lilac		1,250.
a.		4p dull purple	7,500.	1,250.
20	A3	6p deep green	3,500.	250.00
a.		6p yellow green	3,500.	250.00
21	A3	1sh black violet	9,000.	1,750.

Pin-perf. 14

22	A1	(1p) rose red	275.00	35.00
a.		(1p) carmine	2,500.	37.50
23	A3	4p brown lilac	250.00	150.00
a.		4p violet	600.00	160.00
b.		4p dull violet	1,650.	125.00
24	A3	6p deep green	800.00	100.00
25	A3	6p yellow green	200.00	160.00
a.		Vert. pair, imperf. between	8,000.	
26	A3	1sh black violet	9,000.	1,150.

1860   Clean-cut Perf. 14 to 15½

27	A1	(1p) dull rose	175.00	67.50
a.		(1p) lake	100.00	40.00
b.		Horiz. pair, imperf. vert.	3,000.	
29	A3	4p violet brown	200.00	95.00
a.		4p dull violet		375.00
30	A3	6p deep green	300.00	175.00
31	A3	6p yellow green	475.00	100.00
32	A3	1sh black violet		

1861   Rough Perf. 14 to 16½

33	A1	(1p) dull rose	160.00	32.50
34	A3	4p gray lilac	750.00	100.00
35	A3	4p brown lilac	325.00	85.00
a.		4p dull violet	750.00	115.00
36	A3	6p green	475.00	85.00
a.		6p blue green	325.00	95.00
37	A3	1sh indigo	1,000.	350.00
a.		1sh purplish blue	1,675.	550.00

1863   Perf. 11½ to 12
Thick Paper

39	A1	(1p) carmine	160.00	24.00
a.		Perf. 11½-12x11	2,000.	600.00
40	A3	4p dull violet	225.00	72.50
41	A3	6p dp blue green	1,350.	100.00
a.		Perf. 11½-12x11		8,000.

42	A3	1sh indigo	2,750.	110.00

Perf. 12½

43	A1	(1p) lake	57.50	24.00

Perf. 13

45	A1	(1p) lake	27.50	15.00
46	A3	6p emerald	300.00	42.50
47	A3	1sh brt violet	4,000.	225.00

1864-72   Wmk. 1   Perf. 12½

48	A1	(1p) red	65.00	3.00
a.		(1p) lake	65.00	7.25
b.		(1p) rose	65.00	3.00
c.		(1p) carmine	65.00	3.25
d.		Imperf., pair	800.00	800.00
49	A3	4p brt violet	140.00	14.50
a.		4p pale violet	250.00	20.00
b.		Imperf.	600.00	
50	A3	4p lilac	200.00	20.00
a.		4p gray lilac		
51	A3	4p gray ('72)	160.00	6.75
52	A3	6p blue green	160.00	9.00
a.		6p emerald	110.00	17.50
53	A3	6p yellow grn	100.00	5.50
a.		6p dp grn	500.00	9.00
b.		Imperf., pair	800.00	
54	A3	1sh purple	200.00	10.00
a.		1sh lilac	150.00	10.00
b.		1sh violet	150.00	10.00
c.		1sh red lilac	160.00	10.00
d.		Imperf.	750.00	
55	A3	1sh orange yel ('72)	175.00	1.75
		Nos. 48-55 (8)	1,200.	70.50

See Nos. 59-61A, 65. For surcharge see No. 67.

Queen
Victoria — A4

1869-94   Typo.   Perf. 12½

56	A4	5sh dull lake	200.00	90.00
a.		Imperf., pair	1,250.	

Perf. 14

57	A4	5sh claret ('94)	67.50	100.00

For overprint see No. O7.

1876   Engr.   Perf. 14

58	A1	(1p) carmine	32.50	1.75
a.		(1p) red	57.50	1.75
b.		(1p) lake	32.50	1.75
c.		Half used as ½p on cover		750.00
59	A3	4p gray	140.00	.85
60	A3	6p yellow green	115.00	2.25
a.		6p deep green	150.00	2.10
61	A3	1sh orange yellow	150.00	4.00
		Nos. 58-61 (4)	437.50	8.85

Perf. 14x12½

61A	A3	6p yellow green		6,750.

Value for No. 61A is for stamp with perfs barely touching the design.

Type A1 Surcharged in Black

HALFPENNY

1879   Wmk. 1   Perf. 14

62	A1	½p lilac	14.50	10.00

Same Surcharge

1882   Wmk. Crown and C A (2)

63	A1	½p lilac	250.00	90.00
64	A1	1p carmine	42.50	1.75
a.		Half used as ½p on cover		675.00

Type of 1859

1882   Wmk. 2

65	A3	4p gray	215.00	10.00

No. 60 Surcharged by pen and ink in Black or Red

1882   Wmk. 1

67	A3	1p on 6p green (R)	11.00	6.75
a.		Half used as ½p on cover		400.00
b.		Black surcharge		1,900.

Counterfeits of No. 67b are plentiful. Various handwriting exists on both 60 and 60a.

A7   A8

A9

1883-84   Typo.   Wmk. 2

68	A7	½p green	6.00	1.50
69	A7	1p rose	12.00	.60
a.		Half used as ½p on cover		950.00
70	A7	2½p ultra	15.00	.70
a.		2½p blue	15.00	.75
71	A7	4p slate	3.00	.70
72	A7	6p olive brn ('84)	4.75	5.50
73	A7	1sh orange brn ('84)	5.75	3.50
		Nos. 68-73 (6)	46.50	12.50

For overprints see Nos. O1-O6.

1896-1904   Perf. 14

ONE PENNY:
Type I — Round "O" in "ONE."
Type II — Oval "O" in "ONE."

74	A8	½p lilac & green	4.00	.35
75	A8	½p gray grn ('02)	.75	2.40
76	A8	1p lil & car, type I	4.25	.20
77	A8	1p lil & car, type II ('00)	400.00	4.75
78	A8	1p blk, red, type II ('01)	1.50	.20
a.		Value omitted	36,000.	
79	A8	2½p lilac & ultra	7.25	.25
80	A8	2½p vio & bl, bl ('02)	20.00	.75
81	A8	4p lilac & orange	7.75	21.00
82	A8	4p grn & ultra, buff ('02)	2.00	20.00
83	A8	5p lilac & violet	9.50	16.00
84	A8	6p lilac & black	9.00	6.50
85	A8	1sh grn & org brn	8.25	7.75
86	A8	1sh blk & bl, yel ('04)	22.50	6.50

Wmk. C A over Crown (46)

87	A9	5sh green & org	55.00	90.00
88	A9	5sh lil & red vio ('02)	60.00	77.50
89	A9	10sh grn & ultra	210.00	400.00
		Revenue cancel		25.00
90	A9	£1 grn & car	175.00	240.00
		Nos. 74-90 (17)	996.75	894.15

No. 82 also exists on chalky paper. Nos. 88 and 90 exist on both ordinary and chalky paper.

Circular "Registrar General" cancels are revenue usage and of minimal value.

See Nos. 92-104.

Landing of Columbus — A10

1898　　　Engr.　　　Wmk. 1

91	A10	2p gray vio & yel brn	2.50	1.25

400th anniv. of the discovery of the island of Trinidad by Columbus, July 31, 1498.

1904-09　　　　　　　Wmk. 3
Chalky Paper

92	A8	½p gray green	4.25	2.75
93	A8	1p blk, red, type II	6.00	.20
94	A8	2½p vio & bl, bl	27.50	1.10
95	A8	4p blk & car, yel ('06)	2.00	10.00
96	A8	6p lilac & blk ('05)	19.00	18.00
97	A8	6p vio & dp vio ('06)	8.50	12.00
98	A8	1sh blk & bl, yel	24.00	9.50
99	A8	1sh vio & bl, yel	13.00	19.00
100	A8	1sh blk, grn ('06)	2.00	1.50
101	A9	5sh lil & red vio ('07)	55.00	110.00
102	A9	£1 grn & car ('07)	175.00	300.00
		Nos. 92-102 (11)	336.25	484.05

The ½p and 1p also exist on ordinary paper. For overprints see Nos. O8-O9.

1906-07

103	A8	1p carmine ('07)	1.75	.20
104	A8	2½p ultramarine	4.50	.20

A11　　　　　　　A12

1909
Ordinary Paper

105	A11	½p gray green	5.00	.20
106	A12	1p carmine	5.00	.20
107	A11	2½p ultramarine	16.00	3.75
		Nos. 105-107 (3)	26.00	4.15

For overprint see No. O10.

POSTAGE DUE STAMPS

D1

Wmk. Crown and C A (2)
1885, Jan. 1　Typo.　Perf. 14

J1	D1	½p black	22.50	55.00
J2	D1	1p black	7.75	.25
J3	D1	2p black	35.00	.25
J4	D1	3p black	60.00	.50
J5	D1	4p black	42.50	4.75
J6	D1	5p black	27.50	.70
J7	D1	6p black	45.00	6.50
J8	D1	8p black	65.00	4.00
J9	D1	1sh black	77.50	9.00
		Nos. J1-J9 (9)	382.75	80.95

1906-07　　　　　　Wmk. 3

J10	D1	1p black	5.50	.25
J11	D1	2p black	32.50	.25
J12	D1	3p black	15.00	3.25
J13	D1	4p black	15.00	16.00
J14	D1	5p black	15.00	16.00
J15	D1	6p black	7.25	12.00
J16	D1	8p black	14.50	16.00
J17	D1	1sh black	15.00	42.50
		Nos. J10-J17 (8)	119.75	106.25

See Trinidad and Tobago Nos. J1-J16.

OFFICIAL STAMPS

Postage Stamps of 1869-84 Overprinted in Black

1893-94　　Wmk. 2　　Perf. 14

O1	A7	½p green	42.50	65.00
O2	A7	1p rose	45.00	72.50
O3	A7	2½p ultra	55.00	110.00
O4	A7	4p slate	57.50	115.00
O5	A7	6p olive brown	57.50	115.00
O6	A7	1sh orange brown	77.50	150.00

Wmk. Crown and C C (1)
Perf. 12½

O7	A4	5sh dull lake	190.00	575.00
		Nos. O1-O7 (7)	525.00	1,202.

Nos. 92 and 103 Overprinted

1909-10　　Wmk. 3　　Perf. 14

O8	A8	½p gray green	1.25	9.00
O9	A8	1p carmine	1.25	9.00
a.		Double overprint		375.00
b.		Inverted overprint	900.00	275.00
c.		Vertical overprint	125.00	150.00

Same Overprint on No. 105

1910

O10	A11	½p gray green	6.50	9.00

Stamps of Trinidad have been superseded by those inscribed "Trinidad and Tobago."

TRINIDAD AND TOBAGO

ˈtri-nə-ˌdad and tə-ˈbā-ˌgō

LOCATION — West Indies off the coast of Venezuela
GOVT. — Republic
AREA — 1,980 sq. mi.
POP. — 1,102,096 (1999 est.)
CAPITAL — Port-of-Spain

The two British colonies of Trinidad and Tobago were united from 1889 until 1899, when Tobago became a ward of the united colony. From 1899 until 1913 postage stamps of Trinidad were used. The two islands became a state in August 1962, and the independent Republic of Trinidad and Tobago on August 1, 1976.

12 Pence = 1 Shilling
20 Shillings = 1 Pound
100 Cents = 1 Dollar (1935)

> **Catalogue values for unused stamps in this country are for Never Hinged items, beginning with Scott 62 in the regular postage section and Scott J9 in the postage due section.**

A1

"Britannia" — A2

1913　Typo.　Wmk. 3　Perf. 14
Ordinary Paper

1	A1	½p green	3.50	.20
2	A1	1p scarlet	1.75	.20
a.		1p carmine	2.75	.20
4	A1	2½p ultra	8.00	.50

Chalky Paper

5	A1	4p scar & blk, yel	.80	7.00
6	A1	6p red vio & dull vio	11.00	5.00
7	A1	1sh black, emerald	1.75	3.50
a.		1sh black, green	2.00	5.00
b.		1sh black, bl grn, ol back	9.50	10.00
		Nos. 1-2,4-7 (6)	26.80	16.40

1914
Surface-colored Paper

8	A1	4p scar & blk, yel	2.00	11.00
9	A1	1sh black, green	1.60	3.50

Chalky Paper

10	A2	5sh dull vio & red vio	70.00	110.00
11	A2	£1 green & car	160.00	210.00
		Nos. 8-11 (4)	233.60	334.50

1921-22　　　　　　Wmk. 4
Ordinary Paper

12	A1	½p green	3.25	2.75
13	A1	1p scarlet	.75	.40
14	A1	1p brown ('22)	.75	1.90
15	A1	2p gray ('22)	1.25	1.50
16	A1	2½p ultra	1.00	19.00
17	A1	3p ultra ('22)	4.50	4.00

Chalky Paper

18	A1	6p red vio & dull vio	2.50	19.00
19	A2	5sh dull vio & red vio	62.50	62.50
20	A2	£1 green & car	125.00	325.00
		Nos. 12-20 (9)	201.50	436.05

For overprints see #B2-B3, MR1-MR13, O1-O5.

"Britannia" and King George V — A3

1922-28
Ordinary Paper

21	A3	½p green	.55	.20
22	A3	1p brown	.55	.20
23	A3	1½p rose red	2.50	2.00
24	A3	2p gray	.55	1.40
25	A3	3p ultra	.55	1.40

Chalky Paper

26	A3	4p red & blk, yel ('28)	3.75	3.75
27	A3	6p red vio & dl vio	2.50	29.00
28	A3	6p red & grn, emer ('24)	1.40	.70
29	A3	1sh blk, emer ('25)	6.25	2.00
30	A3	5sh vio & dull vio	25.00	42.50
31	A3	£1 rose & green	140.00	250.00

Wmk. Multiple Crown and C A (3)
Chalky Paper

32	A3	4p red & blk, yel	3.75	11.00
33	A3	1sh blk, emerald	4.00	11.00
		Nos. 21-33 (13)	191.35	355.15

First Boca — A4

Designs: 2c, Agricultural College. 3c, Mt. Irvine Bay, Tobago. 6c, Discovery of Lake Asphalt. 8c, Queen's Park, Savannah. 12c, Town Hall, San Fernando. 24c, Government House. 48c, Memorial Park. 72c, Blue Basin.

1935-37　Engr.　Wmk. 4　Perf. 12

34	A4	1c emer & bl, perf. 12½ ('36)	.40	.20
a.		Perf. 12	.50	1.10

35	A4	2c lt brn & ultra, perf. 12	1.00	1.25
a.		Perf. 12½ ('36)	1.25	.20
36	A4	3c red & black, perf. 12½ ('36)	3.25	.40
a.		Perf. 12	.40	.40
37	A4	6c bl & brn, perf. 12	5.00	3.00
a.		Perf. 12½ ('37)	10.00	5.50
38	A4	8c red org & yel grn	4.50	4.25
39	A4	12c dk violet & blk	4.00	2.25
a.		Perf. 12½ ('37)	10.00	7.50
40	A4	24c ol grn & blk	4.00	2.00
a.		Perf. 12½ ('37)	16.00	12.00
41	A4	48c slate green	11.00	19.00
42	A4	72c mag & sl grn	35.00	40.00
		Nos. 34-42 (9)	68.15	72.35

Common Design Types pictured following the introduction.

Silver Jubilee Issue
Common Design Type

1935, May 6　　　　Perf. 11x12

43	CD301	2c black & ultra	.40	1.00
44	CD301	3c car & blue	.40	1.75
45	CD301	6c ultra & brn	2.00	3.50
46	CD301	24c brn vio & ind	8.00	21.00
		Nos. 43-46 (4)	10.80	27.25
		Set, never hinged	20.00	

Coronation Issue
Common Design Type

1937, May 12　　　Perf. 13½x14

47	CD302	1c deep green	.20	.20
48	CD302	2c yellow brown	.20	.20
49	CD302	8c deep orange	.50	.50
		Nos. 47-49 (3)	.90	.90
		Set, never hinged	1.50	

First Boca — A13

George VI — A14

Various Frames and: 2c, Agricultural College. 3c, Mt. Irvine Bay, Tobago. 4c, Memorial Park. 5c, General Post Office and Treasury. 6c, Discovery of Lake Asphalt. 8c, Queen's Park, Savannah. 12c, Town Hall, San Fernando. 24c, Government House. 60c, Blue Basin.

Perf. 11½x11

1938-41　Wmk. 4　　Engr.

50	A13	1c emer & blue	.25	.20
51	A13	2c lt brn & ultra	.25	.20
52	A13	3c dk car & blk	8.50	1.50
52A	A13	3c vio brn & bl grn ('41)	.20	.20
53	A13	4c brown	22.50	1.50
53A	A13	4c red ('41)	.25	.25
54	A13	5c mag ('41)	.20	.20
55	A13	6c brt bl & sep	1.10	.75
56	A13	8c red org & yel grn	.95	.85
57	A13	12c dk vio & blk	2.00	.20
58	A13	24c dk ol grn & blk	.50	.20
59	A13	60c mag & sl grn	6.50	1.75

Perf. 12

60	A14	$1.20 dk grn ('40)	8.00	1.50
61	A14	$4.80 rose pink ('40)	16.00	30.00
		Nos. 50-61 (14)	67.20	39.30
		Set, never hinged	110.00	

Watermark sideways on Nos. 50-59.

> **Catalogue values for unused stamps in this section, from this point to the end of the section, are for Never Hinged items.**

Peace Issue
Common Design Type

Perf. 13½x14

1946, Oct. 1　Engr.　Wmk. 4

62	CD303	3c brown	.20	.20
63	CD303	6c deep blue	.25	.25

Silver Wedding Issue
Common Design Types
1948, Nov. 22 Photo. Perf. 14x14½
64 CD304 3c red brown .20 .20

Engr. Perf. 11½x11
65 CD305 $4.80 rose car 22.50 32.50

UPU Issue
Common Design Types
Engr.; Name Typo. on 6c, 12c
Perf. 13½, 11x11½
1949, Oct. 10 Wmk. 4
66 CD306 5c red violet .40 .40
67 CD307 6c indigo 2.00 2.00
68 CD308 12c rose violet .50 .50
69 CD309 24c olive .50 .50
Nos. 66-69 (4) 3.40 3.40

University Issue
Common Design Types
Inscribed: "Trinidad"
1951, Feb. 16 Engr. Perf. 14x14½
70 CD310 3c chocolate & grn .25 .20
71 CD311 12c purple & blk .60 .50

Types of 1938 with Portrait of Queen Elizabeth II
1953, Apr. 20 Perf. 11½x11
72 A13 1c yel grn & dp blue .20 .20
73 A13 2c org brn & sl blue .20 .20
74 A13 3c vio brn & blue grn .20 .20
75 A13 4c red .20 .20
76 A13 5c magenta .20 .20
77 A13 6c blue & brown .55 .35
78 A13 8c red org & dp grn 2.50 .35
79 A13 12c dk violet & blk .35 .20
80 A13 24c dk ol grn & blk 2.50 .35
81 A13 60c rose car & grnsh blk 25.00 1.25

Perf. 11½
82 A14 $1.20 dark green 1.40 .65
a. Perf. 12 3.50 2.20
83 A14 $4.80 rose pink 10.00 16.00
a. Perf. 12 15.00 17.50
Nos. 72-83 (12) 43.30 20.15

For surcharge see No. 85.

Coronation Issue
Common Design Type
1953, June 3 Perf. 13½x13
84 CD312 3c dark green & blk .25 .20

No. 73 Surcharged "ONE CENT"
Perf. 11½x11
1956, Dec. 20 Wmk. 4
85 A13 1c on 2c org brn & sl blue 1.75 2.00

West Indies Federation
Common Design Type
Perf. 11½x11
1958, Apr. 22 Engr. Wmk. 314
86 CD313 5c green .20 .20
87 CD313 6c blue .20 .40
88 CD313 12c carmine rose .30 .25
Nos. 86-88 (3) .70 .85

Cipriani Memorial, Port-of-Spain A27

Queen's Hall, Port-of-Spain A28

Designs: 5c, Whitehall. 6c, Treasury Building. 8c, Governor General's House. 10c, General Hospital, San Fernando. 12c, Oil refinery. 15c, Crest of colony. 25c, Scarlet ibis. 35c, Lake Asphalt (Pitch). 50c, Jinnah Memorial Mosque. 60c, Anthurium lilies. $1.20, Copperrumped hummingbird and hibiscus. $4.80, Map.

Perf. 13½x14, 14x13½
1960, Sept. 24 Photo. Wmk. 314
Size: 22½x25mm, 25x22½mm
89 A27 1c dark gray & buff .20 .20
a. Wmkd. sideways ('66) .50 .50
90 A28 2c ultra .20 .20
91 A28 5c dark blue .20 .20
92 A28 6c lt red brown .20 .20
93 A28 8c yellow green .20 .35
94 A28 10c light purple .20 .20
95 A28 12c bright red .20 .20

96 A28 15c orange 1.10 .55
97 A28 25c dk blue & crim .90 .20
98 A28 35c green & black 4.00 .20
99 A28 50c blue, yel & olive .40 .45
100 A27 60c multicolored .60 .20
a. Perf. 14 ('65) 160.00 24.00

Size: 48x25mm
101 A28 $1.20 multicolored 16.00 3.00
102 A28 $4.80 lt bl & lt yel 25.00 15.00
grn
Nos. 89-102 (14) 49.40 21.15

See #116. For overprints see #123-124, 126.

Scouts and Map of Trinidad and Tobago — A29

1961, Apr. 4 Perf. 13½x14
103 A29 8c multicolored .20 .20
104 A29 25c multicolored .35 .35

2nd Caribbean Scout Jamboree, Valsayn Park, Trinidad, Apr. 4-14.

Independent State

Underwater Scene from Painting by Carlisle Chang — A30

Designs: 8c, Elizabeth II and new Terminal Building, Piarco Airport. 25c, Elizabeth II and Hilton Hotel. 35c, Map and greater bird of paradise. 60c, Map and scarlet ibis.

1962, Aug. 31 Photo. Perf. 14½
105 A30 5c blue green .30 .20
106 A30 8c slate .50 .20
107 A30 25c purple .30 .20
108 A30 35c emer, yel, brn & blk 2.75 .20
109 A30 60c ultra, black & ver 3.25 3.00
Nos. 105-109 (5) 7.10 3.80

Issued to mark Trinidad and Tobago's independence, Aug. 31, 1962.

Freedom from Hunger Issue

Protein Food — A31

1963, June 1 Perf. 14x13½
110 A31 5c henna brown .20 .20
111 A31 8c citron .20 .20
112 A31 25c violet blue .60 .60
Nos. 110-112 (3) 1.00 1.00

See note in Common Design section.

Girl Guide Emblem A32

Perf. 14½x14
1964, Sept. 15 Wmk. 314
113 A32 6c red, dk blue & yel .20 .20
114 A32 25c brt blue, dk bl & yel .20 .20
115 A32 35c lt green, dk bl & yel .30 .30
Nos. 113-115 (3) .70 .70

50th anniv. of the Trinidad and Tobago Girl Guide Association.

Arms of Independent State — A33

1964, Sept. 15 Perf. 14x13½
116 A33 15c orange .40 .40

For overprint see No. 125.

ICY Emblem A34

Unwmk.
1965, Nov. 15 Litho. Perf. 12
Granite Paper
117 A34 35c dull yel, red brn & grn .70 .70

International Cooperation Year, 1965.

Eleanor Roosevelt — A35

Perf. 13½x14
1965, Dec. 10 Wmk. 314
118 A35 25c vio blue, red & blk .40 .40

Issued to honor Eleanor Roosevelt and to publicize the Eleanor Roosevelt Memorial Foundation.

"Redhouse," Parliament Building — A36

8c, Map of Trinidad & Tobago, royal yacht "Britannia," arms of State. 25c, Flag, map. 35c, Flag, Trinity Hills, General Post Office, sugar cane, coconut palms, derricks.

1966, Feb. 8 Photo. Wmk. 314
119 A36 5c ultra, red, blk & grn .55 .20
120 A36 8c ultra, sil, blk & yel brn 2.50 .30
121 A36 25c red, blk & emerald 2.50 1.40
122 A36 35c ultra, red, blk & grn 2.50 1.90
Nos. 119-122 (4) 8.05 3.80

Visit of Elizabeth II and Prince Philip.

Nos. 93, 94, 116 and 100 Overprinted:
"FIFTH YEAR OF / INDEPENDENCE / 31st AUGUST 1967"
Perf. 14x13½, 13½x14
1967, Aug. 31 Photo. Wmk. 314
123 A28 8c yellow green .20 .20
124 A28 10c lt purple .20 .20
125 A33 15c orange .20 .20
126 A27 60c multicolored .30 .30
Nos. 123-126 (4) .90 .90

On 60c, the overprint is arranged in 5 lines.

Carnival Symbols A37

Designs: 10c, Calypso King, vert. 15c, Steel band. 25c, Chinese masks. 35c, Carnival King, vert. 60c, Carnival Queen, vert.

Unwmk.
1968, Feb. 16 Litho. Perf. 12
127 A37 5c pink & multi .25 .25
128 A37 10c vio blue & multi .25 .25
129 A37 15c multicolored .25 .25
130 A37 25c multicolored .25 .25
131 A37 35c dk purple & multi .25 .25
132 A37 60c brown ol & multi .45 .45
Nos. 127-132 (6) 1.70 1.70

Issued to publicize the Trinidad Carnival.

WHO Emblem and Eye Examination A38

Dancing Children and Human Rights Flame A39

Wmk. 314
1968, May 7 Photo. Perf. 14
133 A38 5c rose red, gold & blk .20 .20
134 A38 25c orange, gold & blk .30 .30
135 A38 35c brt blue, gold & blk .40 .40
Nos. 133-135 (3) .90 .90

1968, Aug. 5 Perf. 14
136 A39 5c carmine, yel & blk .20 .20
137 A39 10c red, yel & blk .20 .20
138 A39 25c yel grn, yel & blk .25 .25
Nos. 136-138 (3) .65 .65

International Human Rights Year.

Bicycling and Map A40

Designs (Olympic Rings, Map of Trinidad and Tobago and): 15c, Weight lifting. 25c, Relay race. 35c, Running. $1.20, Map of Mexico and flags of Mexico and Trinidad and Tobago.

Photo.; Gold Impressed (except $1.20)
1968, Oct. 12 Perf. 14
139 A40 5c vio, gold & multi .20 .20
140 A40 15c red, gold & multi .20 .20
141 A40 25c org, gold & multi .20 .20
142 A40 35c brt grn, gold & multi .35 .20
143 A40 $1.20 blue, gold & multi 1.25 .80
Nos. 139-143 (5) 2.20 1.60

19th Olympic Games, Mexico City, 10/12-27.

Cacao A41

Designs: 3c, Sugar refinery. 5c, Redtailed chachalaca. 6c, Oil refinery. 8c, Fertilizer plant. 10c, Green hermit (hummingbird) vert. 12c, Citrus fruit, vert. 15c, Coat of arms, vert. 20c, 25c, Flag and map of islands, vert. 30c, Wild poinsettia, vert. 40c, Scarlet ibis. 50c, Maracas Bay. $1, Blooming tabebuia (tree) vert. $2.50, Fishermen hauling in net. $5, Red House, Port-of-Spain.

Photo.; Silver or Gold Impressed
1969, Apr. 1 Wmk. 314 Perf. 14
144 A41 1c silver & multi .20 .25
145 A41 3c gold & multi .20 .25
a. Wmk. upright ('74) .60 .60
146 A41 5c gold & multi .20 .25
a. Wmk. upright ('73) 8.00 4.50
147 A41 6c gold & multi .20 .25
a. Wmk. upright ('74) .30 .25
148 A41 8c silver & multi .20 .25
149 A41 10c gold & multi .20 .25
b. Wmk. 373 ('76) .30 .25
150 A41 12c silver & multi .20 .25
151 A41 15c silver & multi .20 .25
152 A41 20c gold & multi .20 .25

153	A41	25c silver & multi	.30	.25
154	A41	30c silver & multi	.35	.25
155	A41	40c gold & multi	.55	.35
156	A41	50c silver & multi	.70	.50
157	A41	$1 gold & multi	1.75	1.25
158	A41	$2.50 gold & multi	4.25	5.00
159	A41	$5 gold & multi	8.75	9.00
		Nos. 144-159 (16)	18.45	18.85

For overprint see No. 187.

Capt. A. A.
Cipriani,
ILO
Emblem
and Gate
A42

ILO, 50th Anniv.: 15c, Industrial Court's & ILO emblems, & Woodford Square gate.

Unwmk.

1969, May 1　　Photo.　　Perf. 12

160	A42	6c dp car, gold & blk	.20	.20
161	A42	15c brt blue, gold & blk	.20	.20

Union Jack
and Flags
of CARIFTA
Members
A43

Designs: 6c, Cornucopia, vert. 30c, Map of Caribbean, vert. 40c, Jet plane and "Strength through Unity" emblem.

1969, Aug. 1　　Perf. 14x13½, 13½x14

162	A43	6c lilac, gold & multi	.20	.20
163	A43	10c multicolored	.20	.20
164	A43	30c red, emer, blk & gold	.25	.25
165	A43	40c blue, blk, grn & gold	.35	.35
		Nos. 162-165 (4)	1.00	1.00

Caribbean Free Trade Area (CARIFTA).

Moon Landing and Earth — A44

40c, Lunar landing module & astronauts on moon. $1, Astronauts Aldrin at control panel, Armstrong collecting rocks.

1969, Sept. 1　　Litho.　　Perf. 14

166	A44	6c multi	.20	.20
167	A44	40c multi, vert.	.30	.30
168	A44	$1 multi	.75	.75
		Nos. 166-168 (3)	1.25	1.25

See note after US No. C76.

Maces of Senate and House of
Representatives — A45

10c, Chamber of Parliament. 15c, View of Kennedy Complex, University of the West Indies at St. Augustine. 40c, Cannon & view of Scarborough from Fort King George.

Perf. 14x13½

1969, Oct. 23　　Photo.　　Wmk. 314

169	A45	10c multicolored	.20	.20
170	A45	15c multicolored	.20	.20
171	A45	30c lt blue & multi	.25	.25
172	A45	40c multicolored	.25	.25
		Nos. 169-172 (4)	.90	.90

15th Conf. of the Commonwealth Parliamentary Assoc., Port-of-Spain, Oct. 4-19.

Congress
Emblem and
Landscape
A46

Carnival King as
"Man in the Moon"
A47

6c, Congress emblem (steel drum and bird). 30c, Palms, landscape and emblem, horiz.

Perf. 14x13½, 13½x14

1969, Nov. 2　　Litho.　　Unwmk.

173	A46	6c red, black & gold	.20	.20
174	A46	30c lt blue, plum & gold	.25	.25
175	A46	40c ultra, black & gold	.25	.25
		Nos. 173-175 (3)	.70	.70

24th Cong. of the Intl. Junior Chamber of Commerce.

1970, Feb. 2　　Wmk. 314　　Perf. 14

Designs: 6c, Carnival Queen as "City Beneath the Sea." 15c, Bambara god (antelope) from the Band of the Year. 30c, Pheasant Queen (Chanticleer) of Malaya. 40c, Steel Band of the Year with 1969 Calypso and Road March Kings, horiz.

176	A47	5c dk brown & multi	.20	.20
177	A47	6c dk blue & multi	.20	.20
178	A47	15c violet bl & multi	.20	.20
179	A47	30c dk green & multi	.25	.25
180	A47	40c green & multi	.25	.25
		Nos. 176-180 (5)	1.10	1.10

Issued to publicize the Trinidad Carnival.

Mahatma
Gandhi and
Indian
Flag — A48

Design: 10c, Gandhi monument, vert.

Unwmk.

1970, Mar. 2　　Photo.　　Perf. 12

181	A48	10c ultra & multi	.60	.50
182	A48	30c crimson & multi	1.40	1.10

Mohandas K. Gandhi (1869-1948), leader in India's fight for independence.

"Culture,
Science,
Arts and
Technology"
A49

UN, 25th Anniv.: 10c, Children of various races, map of Trinidad and Tobago and "UNICEF." 20c, Noah's ark, rainbow, dove and UN emblem.

1970, June 26　　Photo.　　Perf. 13½

183	A49	5c multicolored	.20	.20
184	A49	10c multicolored	.50	.50
185	A49	20c multicolored	.75	.75
		Nos. 183-185 (3)	1.45	1.45

UPU Headquarters, Bern — A50

1970, June 26　　Unwmk.　　Perf. 12

186	A50	30c ultra & multi	.50	.50

Opening of new UPU Headquarters in Bern.

No. 146 Overprinted:
"NATIONAL / COMMERCIAL / BANK
/ ESTABLISHED / 1.7.70"
Photo.; Gold Embossed

1970, July 1　　Wmk. 314　　Perf. 14

187	A41	5c gold & multi	.30	.20

San Fernando Town Hall — A51

Designs: 3c, East Indian Immigrants, 1820, after painting by Cazabon, vert. 40c, Ships in San Fernando Harbor, 1860, after painting by Michel J. Cazabon.

Perf. 14x13½, 13½x14

1970, Nov.　　Litho.　　Wmk. 314

188	A51	3c bister & multi	.20	.20
189	A51	5c lemon & multi	.20	.20
190	A51	40c lemon & multi	.75	.75
		Nos. 188-190 (3)	1.15	1.15

Municipality of San Fernando, 125th anniv.

Madonna
and Child,
by
Titian — A52

Paintings: 3c, Adoration of the Shepherds, School of Saville. 30c, Adoration of the Shepherds, by Louis Le Nain. 40c, Virgin and Child with St. John and Angel, by Morando. $1, Adoration of the Magi, by Paolo Veronese.

Perf. 13½

1970, Dec. 8　　Unwmk.　　Litho.

191	A52	3c dull org & multi	.20	.20
a.		Booklet pane of 2		.20
192	A52	5c brt pink & multi	.20	.20
a.		Booklet pane of 2		.25
193	A52	30c lt ultra & multi	.25	.25
a.		Booklet pane of 2		.60
194	A52	40c yellow grn & multi	.25	.25
a.		Booklet pane of 2		.75
b.		Souvenir sheet of 4, #191-194	2.75	2.75
195	A52	$1 pale lilac & multi	.60	.60
		Nos. 191-195 (5)	1.50	1.50

Brocket Deer — A53

Perf. 14x13½

1971, Aug. 9　　Litho.　　Wmk. 314

196	A53	3c shown	.40	.25
197	A53	5c Collared peccary	.50	.20
198	A53	6c Paca	.60	.40
199	A53	30c Agouti	1.75	3.25
200	A53	40c Ocelot	1.75	2.40
		Nos. 196-200 (5)	5.00	6.50

Capt. A. A.
Cipriani
A54

Virgin and Child
with St. John, by
Bartolommeo
A55

Design: 30c, Chaconia medal (for distinction in social field).

1971, Aug. 31　　Perf. 14

201	A54	5c multicolored	.20	.20
202	A54	30c multicolored	.30	.30

9th anniversary of independence. Capt. Arthur Andrew Cipriani (died 1945) was mayor of Port of Spain and member of First Executive Council.

1971, Oct. 25　　Litho.　　Perf. 14x14½

Christmas: 5c, Local creche. 10c, Virgin and Child with Sts. Jerome and Dominic, by Filippino Lippi. 15c, Virgin and Child with St. Anne, by Gerolamo dai Libri.

203	A55	3c yellow & multi	.20	.20
204	A55	5c dull blue & multi	.20	.20
205	A55	10c red & multi	.25	.25
206	A55	15c orange & multi	.35	.35
		Nos. 203-206 (4)	1.00	1.00

Satellite
Earth
Station,
Matura
A56

Dish
Antenna
A57

Design: 40c, Satellite over earth (Africa).

1971, Nov. 18　　Perf. 14

207	A56	10c ultra & multi	.20	.20
208	A57	30c green & multi	.25	.25
209	A57	40c black & multi	.35	.35
a.		Souvenir sheet of 3	2.25	2.25
		Nos. 207-209 (3)	.80	.80

Opening of Satellite Earth Station at Matura. No. 209a contains 3 imperf. stamps with simulated perforations similar to Nos. 207-209.

Morpho
Hybrid
A58

Butterflies: 5c, Purple mort bleu. 6c, Jaune d'abricot. 10c, Purple king shoemaker. 20c, Southern white pape. 30c, Little jaune.

1972, Feb. 18　　Photo.　　Wmk. 314

210	A58	3c olive & multi	1.00	.80
211	A58	5c ocher & multi	1.50	.20
212	A58	6c yellow & multi	1.75	.80
213	A58	10c yel grn & multi	2.00	.30
214	A58	20c lilac & multi	3.00	2.40
215	A58	30c dull grn & multi	4.50	3.00
		Nos. 210-215 (6)	13.75	7.50

S.S. Lady McLeod and Stamp A59

10c, Map of Trinidad and Tobago. 30c, Commemorative inscription.

1972, Apr. 12   Litho.   Perf. 14½x14
216 A59 5c blue & multi .20 .20
217 A59 10c blue & multi .25 .25
218 A59 30c blue & multi .65 .65
a. Souvenir sheet of 3, #216-218 1.50 1.50
Nos. 216-218 (3) 1.10 1.10

125th anniv. of the Lady McLeod stamp.

Trinity Cross — A60

Medals: 10c, Chaconia medal. 20c, Hummingbird medal. 30c, Medal of Merit.

1972, Aug. 28   Photo.   Perf. 13½x13
219 A60 5c blue & multi .20 .20
220 A60 10c multicolored .20 .20
221 A60 20c yellow grn & multi .25 .25
222 A60 30c brt rose & multi .25 .40
a. Souvenir sheet of 4, #219-222 1.25 1.25
Nos. 219-222 (4) .90 1.10

10th anniversary of independence. See Nos. 235-238.

Olympic Rings, Relay Race Medal, 1964 A61

Olympic Rings and: 20c, Bronze medal, 200-meters, 1964. 30c, Bronze medals, weight lifting, 1952. 40c, Silver medal, 400-meters, 1964. 50c, Silver medal, weight lifting, 1948.

1972, Sept. 7   Litho.   Perf. 14
223 A61 10c yellow & multi .20 .20
224 A61 20c multicolored .30 .30
225 A61 30c lilac & multi .40 .40
226 A61 40c lt blue & multi .50 .50
227 A61 50c orange & multi .60 .60
a. Souv. sheet of #223-227 + label 2.50 2.50
Nos. 223-227 (5) 2.00 2.00

20th Olympic Games, Munich, 8/26-9/11.

Holy Family, by Titian A62

Christmas: 3c, Adoration of the Kings, by Dosso Dossi. 30c, Like 5c.

1972, Nov. 9   Photo.   Wmk. 314
228 A62 3c blue & multi .20 .20
229 A62 5c rose lilac & multi .20 .20
230 A62 30c lt green & multi .50 .50
a. Souvenir sheet of 3, #228-230 2.25 2.25
Nos. 228-230 (3) .90 .90

ECLA Headquarters, Santiago, Chile — A63

Designs: 20c, INTERPOL emblem. 30c, WHO emblem. 40c, University of West Indies Administration Building.

1973, Aug. 15   Litho.   Wmk. 314
231 A63 10c orange & multi .20 .20
232 A63 20c multicolored .25 .25
233 A63 30c ultra & multi .35 .35
234 A63 40c lilac & multi .45 .45
a. Souvenir sheet of 4, #231-234 1.40 1.40
Nos. 231-234 (4) 1.25 1.25

Economic Commission for Latin America, 25th anniv. (10c); Intl. Criminal Police Organization, 50th anniv. (20c); Intl. Meteorological cooperation, cent. (30c); Admission of 1st students to the University of West Indies, 25th anniv. (40c).

Medal Type of 1972 Redrawn

Medals: 10c, Trinity Cross. 20c, Medal of Merit. 30c, Chaconia medal. 40c, Hummingbird medal.

1973, Aug. 30   Photo.   Perf. 14½x14
235 A60 10c dark green & multi .20 .20
236 A60 20c dark brown & multi .20 .20
237 A60 30c dark blue & multi .20 .20
238 A60 40c deep violet & multi .40 .40
a. Souv. sheet, #235-238, perf. 14 1.50 1.50
Nos. 235-238 (4) 1.00 1.00

11th anniv. of independence. "Trinidad and Tobago" in one line on #235-238.

General Post Office, Port of Spain A64

40c, Conference Hall & flags, Chagaramas.

1973, Oct. 8   Photo.   Perf. 14
239 A64 30c multicolored .25 .25
240 A64 40c multicolored .40 .40
a. Souvenir sheet of 2, #239-240 1.25 1.25

2nd Commonwealth Conf. of Postal Administrations, Trinidad, Oct. 8-20. On #240a the perforations extend through margin and divide map.

Virgin and Child, by Murillo — A65

1973, Oct. 22   Perf. 14½x14
241 A65 5c pink & multi .20 .20
242 A65 $1 lt blue & multi .80 .80
a. Souv. sheet, #241-242, perf. 14 1.25 1.25

Christmas 1973.

Post Office and UPU Emblem — A66

UPU, Cent.: 50c, Map of Islands, UPU emblem, means of transportation.

1974, Nov. 18   Photo.   Perf. 13½x14
243 A66 40c brt purple & multi .50 .50
244 A66 50c blue gray & multi .75 .75
a. Souvenir sheet of 2, #243-244 27.50 30.00

Humming Bird I, Transatlantic Crossing, 1960 — A67

Design: 50c, Globe, Humming Bird II, Harold and Kwailan La Borde.

1974, Dec. 2   Perf. 14½
245 A67 40c multicolored .50 .50
246 A67 50c multicolored .70 .70
a. Souvenir sheet of 2, #245-246 3.50 3.50

First anniversary of the voyage around the world by Harold and Kwailan La Borde aboard Humming Bird II, 1969-1973.

"Equality" and IWY Emblem A68

1975, June 23   Litho.   Wmk. 314
247 A68 15c multicolored .20 .20
248 A68 30c multicolored .50 .50

International Women's Year 1975.

Dr. Pawan and Laboratory Equipment — A69

25c, Vampire bat, microscope, syringe, bat's head.

Perf. 14x14½
1975, Sept. 23   Photo.   Wmk. 373
249 A69 25c yellow & multi .50 .50
250 A69 30c lt blue & multi .60 .60

Isolation of rabies virus by Dr. Joseph Lennox Pawan (1887-1957).

Boeing 707, BWIA Emblem, Air Routes A70

Designs: 30c, Boeing 707 on ground. 40c, Boeing 707 in the air.

Wmk. 373
1975, Nov. 27   Litho.   Perf. 14½
251 A70 20c dark blue & multi .50 .50
252 A70 30c deep ultra & multi .70 .70
253 A70 40c dull green & multi .90 .90
a. Souvenir sheet of 3, #251-253 2.75 2.75
Nos. 251-253 (3) 2.10 2.10

British West Indian Airways, 35th anniv.

Land of the Hummingbird Costume — A71

Carnival 1976: $1, Carib Prince riding pink ibis. Designs show prize-winning costumes from 1974 carnival.

1976, Jan. 12   Photo.   Perf. 14½
254 A71 30c multicolored .40 .40
255 A71 $1 multicolored 1.10 1.10
a. Souvenir sheet of 2, #254-255 1.75 1.75

Angostura Building, Port of Spain A72

Designs (Exposition Medals, obverse and reverse): 35c, New Orleans, 1885-86. 45c, Sydney, 1879. 50c, Brussels, 1897.

1976, July 14   Litho.   Perf. 13
256 A72 5c bister & multi .20 .20
257 A72 35c yellow grn & multi .20 .20
258 A72 45c blue & multi .30 .30
259 A72 50c violet & multi .30 .30
a. Souv. sheet, #256-259, perf. 14 1.25 1.25
Nos. 256-259 (4) 1.00 1.00

Sesquicentennial of the manufacture of Angostura Bitters.

Map of West Indies, Bats, Wicket and Ball A72a

Prudential Cup — A72b

1976, Oct. 4   Unwmk.   Perf. 14
260 A72a 35c lt blue & multi .55 .55
261 A72b 45c lilac rose & blk .75 .75
a. Souvenir sheet of 2, #260-261 2.75 2.75

World Cricket Cup, won by West Indies Team, 1975.

Columbus Sailing through the Bocas, by A. Camps-Campins — A73

Paintings: 10c, View, by Jean Michael Cazabon. 20c, Landscape, by Cazabon. 35c, Los Gallos Point, by Cazabon. 45c, Corbeaux Town, by Cazabon.

1976, Nov. 1   Litho.   Wmk. 373
262 A73 5c ocher & multi .55 .55
263 A73 10c lilac & multi .55 .55
264 A73 20c green & multi .55 .55
265 A73 35c red orange & multi .55 .55
266 A73 45c blue & multi .65 .65
a. Souvenir sheet of 5, #262-266 3.00 3.00
Nos. 262-266 (5) 2.85 2.85

For overprints see Nos. 325, 327.

Hasely Crawford and Gold Medal A74

1977, Jan. 4   Litho.   Perf. 12½
267 A74 25c multicolored .50 .45
a. Souvenir sheet of 1 .70 .60

Hasely Crawford, winner of 100-meter dash at Montreal Olympic Games.

Sikorsky S-38 (Lindbergh's Plane) — A75

Designs: 35c, Charles Lindbergh delivering first airmail to Port of Spain, 1927. 45c, Boeing 707, British West Indies Airways. 50c, Boeing 747, British Airways.

1977, Apr.　Wmk. 373　Perf. 13

268	A75	20c lt blue & multi	.30 .30
269	A75	35c lt blue & multi	.50 .50
270	A75	45c lt blue & multi	.60 .60
271	A75	50c lt blue & multi	1.10 .75
a.		Souv. sheet, #268-271, perf. 14	5.25 5.25
		Nos. 268-271 (4)	2.50 2.15

Airmail to Trinidad & Tobago, 50th anniv.

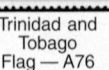

Trinidad and Tobago Flag — A76

White Poinsettia — A77

35c, Coat of arms. 45c, Government House.

1977, July 26　Litho.　Perf. 13½x13

272	A76	20c yellow & multi	.40 .40
273	A76	35c red & multi	.70 .70
274	A76	45c lt blue & multi	.90 .90
a.		Souv. sheet #272-274, perf. 14	2.25 2.25
		Nos. 272-274 (3)	2.00 2.00

Inauguration of the Republic, Aug. 1, 1976.

1977, Oct. 11　Litho.　Perf. 14½

Christmas: 45c, 50c, Red poinsettia.

275	A77	10c multicolored	.20 .20
276	A77	35c multicolored	.40 .40
277	A77	45c multicolored	.55 .55
278	A77	50c multicolored	.60 .60
a.		Souvenir sheet of 4, #275-278	1.75 1.75
		Nos. 275-278 (4)	1.75 1.75

Robinson Crusoe Hotel, Tobago A78

15c, Turtle Beach Hotel, Tobago. 25c, Mount Irvine Hotel, Tobago. 70c, Mount Irvine beach, Tobago. $5, Holiday Inn, Trinidad.

Wmk. 373
1978, Jan. 17　Litho.　Perf. 14

279	A78	6c multicolored	.20 .20
280	A78	15c multicolored	.20 .20
281	A78	25c multicolored	.20 .20
282	A78	70c multicolored	.45 .45
283	A78	$5 multicolored	3.25 3.25
a.		Souvenir sheet of 5, #279-283	4.50 4.50
		Nos. 279-283 (5)	4.30 4.30

For overprint see No. 326.

Paphinia Cristata A79

Orchids: 30c, Caularthron bicornutum. 40c, Miltassia. 50c, Oncidium ampiliatum. $2.50, Oncidium papilio.

1978, June 7　Wmk. 373　Perf. 14

284	A79	12c multicolored	.75 .75
285	A79	30c multicolored	.85 .85
286	A79	40c multicolored	1.10 1.10
287	A79	50c multicolored	1.50 1.50
288	A79	$2.50 multicolored	6.75 6.75
a.		Souvenir sheet of 5, #284-288	11.50 11.50
		Nos. 284-288 (5)	10.95 10.95

Miss Universe and Trophy — A80

Designs: 35c, Portrait with crown. 45c, Miss Universe in evening dress.

1978, Aug. 2　Litho.　Perf. 14½

289	A80	10c multicolored	.55 .55
290	A80	35c multicolored	.75 .75
291	A80	45c multicolored	.95 .95
a.		Souvenir sheet of 3, #289-291	2.50 2.50
		Nos. 289-291 (3)	2.25 2.25

Janelle (Penny) Commissiong, Miss Universe, 1977.

Tayra A81

1978, Nov. 7　Perf. 13½x14

292	A81	15c shown	.20 .20
293	A81	25c Ocelot	.35 .30
294	A81	40c Porcupine	.55 .50
295	A81	70c Yellow anteater	1.10 .95
a.		Souvenir sheet of 4, #292-295	2.75 2.75
		Nos. 292-295 (4)	2.20 1.75

"Burst of Beauty" — A82

Day Care Center — A83

Costumes: 10c, Rain worshipper. 35c, Zodiac. 45c, Praying mantis. 50c, Eye of the hurricane. $1, Steel orchestra.

1979, Feb. 1　Litho.　Perf. 13½

296	A82	5c multicolored	.20 .20
297	A82	10c multicolored	.20 .20
298	A82	35c multicolored	.25 .25
299	A82	45c multicolored	.30 .30
300	A82	50c multicolored	.35 .35
301	A82	$1 multicolored	.70 .70
		Nos. 296-301 (6)	2.00 2.00

Unwmk.
1979, June 5　Litho.　Perf. 13

IYC Emblem and: 10c, School lunch program. 35c, Dental care. 45c, Nursery school. 50c, Free school bus. $1, Medical care.

302	A83	5c multicolored	.20 .20
303	A83	10c multicolored	.20 .20
304	A83	35c multicolored	.25 .25
305	A83	45c multicolored	.30 .30
306	A83	50c multicolored	.30 .30
307	A83	$1 multicolored	.65 .65
a.		Souvenir sheet of 6, #302-307	1.90 1.90
		Nos. 302-307 (6)	1.90 1.90

International Year of the Child.

Geothermal Exploration A84

Designs: 35c, Hydrogeology. 45c, Petroleum exploration. 70c, Preservation of the environment.

1979, July 3　Wmk. 373

308	A84	10c multicolored	.20 .20
309	A84	35c multicolored	.30 .30
310	A84	45c multicolored	.35 .35
311	A84	70c multicolored	.55 .55
a.		Souvenir sheet of 4, #308-311	2.50 2.50
		Nos. 308-311 (4)	1.40 1.40

4th Latin American Geological Cong., July 7-15.

Map of Tobago and Tobago No. 1 — A85

15c, Tobago #2, 7. 35c, Tobago #28, 11. 45c, Tobago #25, 4. 70c, Great Britain #28 used in Scarborough and Tobago #5. $1, General Post Office, Scarborough and Tobago #6.

Perf. 13½x14
1979, Aug. 1　Litho.　Wmk. 373

312	A85	10c multicolored	.20 .20
313	A85	15c multicolored	.20 .20
314	A85	35c multicolored	.25 .25
315	A85	45c multicolored	.30 .30
316	A85	70c multicolored	.45 .45
317	A85	$1 multicolored	.65 .65
a.		Souvenir sheet of 6, #312-317	2.50 2.50
		Nos. 312-317 (6)	2.05 2.05

Centenary of Tobago's postage stamps.

Rowland Hill, Trinidad and Tobago No. 109 — A86

Hill and: 45c, Trinidad and Tobago #273. $1, Trinidad #62, Tobago #10.

1979, Oct. 4　Perf. 13

318	A86	25c multicolored	.25 .25
319	A86	45c multicolored	.40 .40
320	A86	$1 multicolored	.80 .80
a.		Souvenir sheet of 3, #318-320	2.25 2.25
		Nos. 318-320 (3)	1.45 1.45

Sir Rowland Hill (1795-1879), originator of penny postage.

Poui Tree A87

Designs: 10c, Court House. 50c, Royal Train locomotive. $1.50, Bacchante freighter.

Wmk. 373
1980, Jan. 21　Litho.　Perf. 14½

321	A87	5c multicolored	.20 .20
322	A87	10c multicolored	.20 .20
323	A87	50c multicolored	.45 .45
324	A87	$1.50 multicolored	1.40 1.40
a.		Souvenir sheet of 4, #321-324	2.75 2.75
		Nos. 321-324 (4)	2.25 2.25

Princes Town centenary.

Nos. 262, 279, 263 Overprinted in 3 or 5 Lines:
"1844-1980 POPULATION CENSUS 12th MAY 1980"

1980, Apr. 8　Litho.　Perf. 14

325	A73	5c multicolored	.20 .20
326	A78	6c multicolored	.20 .20
327	A73	10c multicolored	.20 .20
		Nos. 325-327 (3)	.60 .60

Scarlet Ibis Hen and Nest — A88

Scarlet Ibis: b, Nest and eggs. c, Chick in nest. d, Male. e, Male and female.

Wmk. 373
1980, May 6　Litho.　Perf. 14½

328		Strip of 5, multi	5.75 5.75
a.-e.		A88 single stamp	.90 .90

Bronze and Silver Medals, 1948, 1952 A89

Wmk. 373
1980, July 22　Litho.　Perf. 14

329	A89	10c shown	.20 .20
330	A89	15c Hasely Crawford, 1976 gold medal	.20 .20
331	A89	70c 1964 silver, bronze medals	.65 .65
		Nos. 329-331 (3)	1.05 1.05

Souvenir Sheet
332	A89	$2.50 Moscow '80 emblem, vert.	1.90 1.90

22nd Summer Olympic Games, Moscow, July 19-Aug. 3.

Charcoal Production — A90

Wmk. 373
1980, Sept. 8　Litho.　Perf. 14

333	A90	10c shown	.20 .20
334	A90	55c Logging	.30 .30
335	A90	70c Teak plantation	.40 .40
336	A90	$2.50 Watershed management	1.50 1.50
a.		Souvenir sheet of 4, #333-336	3.00 3.00
		Nos. 333-336 (4)	2.40 2.40

11th Commonwealth Forestry Conference.

Elizabeth Bourne, Judiciary and Isabella Tesbier, Government — A91

Decade for Women: No. 338, Beryl McBurnie, dance and culture; Audrey Jeffers, social work. No. 339, Dr. Stella Abidh, public health; Louise Horne, nutrition.

1980, Sept. 29

337	A91	$1 multicolored	.70 .70
338	A91	$1 multicolored	.70 .70
339	A91	$1 multicolored	.70 .70
		Nos. 337-339 (3)	2.10 2.10

Stadium and Netball League Emblem — A92

1980, Oct. 21
340 A92 70c multicolored   .55 .55

1979 World Netball Tournament, Port-of-Spain.

Athlete, Man in Wheelchair, IYD Emblem — A93

Wmk. 373
1981, Apr. 6   Litho.   Perf. 14½
341 A93 10c shown   .20 .20
342 A93 70c Amputee with
            crutch   .35 .35
343 A93 $1.50 Blind people   .85 .85
344 A93 $2 IYD emblem   1.10 1.10
    Nos. 341-344 (4)   2.50 2.50

International Year of the Disabled.

Marine Preservation — A94

1981, July 7   Litho.   Perf. 13x13½
345 A94 10c Land   .20 .20
346 A94 55c shown   .40 .40
347 A94 $3 Sky   2.50 2.50
  a. Souvenir sheet of 3, #345-347 5.00 5.00
    Nos. 345-347 (3)   3.10 3.10

World Food Day — A95

1981, Oct. 16   Litho.   Perf. 14½x14
348 A95 10c Produce   .20 .20
349 A95 15c Rice threshing,
            mill   .20 .20
350 A95 45c Bigeye   .40 .40
351 A95 55c Cow, pig, goats   .50 .50
352 A95 $1.50 Poultry   1.25 1.25
353 A95 $2 Smallmouth grunt 1.75 1.75
  a. Souvenir sheet of 6, #348-353 5.00 5.00
    Nos. 348-353 (6)   4.30 4.30

President Awards — A96

1981, Nov. 30   Perf. 14
354 A96 10c First aid   .20 .20
355 A96 70c Motor mechanics   .55 .55
356 A96 $1 Hiking   .75 .75
357 A96 $2 President giving
            award   1.50 1.50
    Nos. 354-357 (4)   3.00 3.00

Commonwealth Pharmaceutical Conference A97

1982, Feb. 12   Litho.   Perf. 14½x14
358 A97 10c Pharmacist   .75 .75
359 A97 $1 Pluchea symphitfolia 3.00 3.00
360 A97 $2 Nopalea
            cocheniifera   5.25 5.25
    Nos. 358-360 (3)   9.00 9.00

Scouting Year — A98

1982, June 28   Litho.   Perf. 14
361 A98 15c Production   .20 .20
362 A98 55c Tolerance   .75 .75
363 A98 $5 Discipline   6.50 6.50
    Nos. 361-363 (3)   7.45 7.45

25th Anniv. of Tourist Board — A99

Perf. 13½x14
1982, Oct. 18   Litho.   Wmk. 373
364 A99 55c Charlotteville   .45 .45
365 A99 $1 Boating   .85 .85
366 A99 $3 Fort George   2.50 2.50
    Nos. 364-366 (3)   3.80 3.80

Pa Pa Bois — A100

Designs: Various folklore characters.

1982, Nov. 8
367 A100 10c multicolored   .20 .20
368 A100 15c multicolored   .20 .20
369 A100 65c multicolored   .55 .55
370 A100 $5 multicolored   4.25 4.25
  a. Souvenir sheet of 4, #367-370 7.50 7.50
    Nos. 367-370 (4)   5.20 5.20

Canefarmers' Centenary — A101

1982, Dec. 13   Litho.   Perf. 14
371 A101 30c Harvest   .40 .40
372 A101 70c Loading bullock
            cart   .95 .95
373 A101 $1.50 Field   2.00 2.00
  a. Souvenir sheet of 3, #371-373,
        perf. 14½   4.00 4.00
    Nos. 371-373 (3)   3.35 3.35

20th Anniv. of Independence — A102

1982, Dec. 28   Perf. 13½x14
374 A102 10c Natl. Stadium   .20 .20
375 A102 35c Caroni Arena
            Water Treatment
            Plant   .30 .30
376 A102 50c Mount Hope Ma-
            ternity Hospital .55 .55
377 A102 $2 Natl. Insurance
            Board Mall, Toba-
            go   1.90 1.90
    Nos. 374-377 (4)   2.95 2.95

Commonwealth Day — A103

1983, Mar. 14   Perf. 14
378 A103 10c Flags   .20 .20
379 A103 55c Satellite view   .40 .40
380 A103 $1 Oil industry, vert. .75 .75
381 A103 $2 Maps, vert.   1.50 1.50
    Nos. 378-381 (4)   2.85 2.85

10th Anniv. of CARICOM — A104

1983, July 11   Litho.   Perf. 14
382 A104 35c Jet, map   .75 .75

World Communications Year — A105

1983, Aug. 5   Perf. 14½
383 A105 15c Operator   .25 .25
384 A105 55c Scarborough PO,
            Tobago   .70 .70
385 A105 $1 Textel Building 1.25 1.25
386 A105 $3 Morne Bleu Re-
            ceiving Station 3.75 3.75
    Nos. 383-386 (4)   5.95 5.95

Commonwealth Finance Ministers Conference — A106

Wmk. 373
1983, Sept. 19   Litho.   Perf. 14
387 A106 $2 multicolored   1.50 1.50

World Food Day — A107

1983, Oct. 17   Perf. 14x13½
388 A107 10c Kingfish   .55 .55
389 A107 55c Flying fish   1.10 1.10
390 A107 70c Queen conch   1.50 1.50
391 A107 $4 Red shrimp   7.50 7.50
    Nos. 388-391 (4)   10.65 10.65

Flowers — A108

1983, Dec. 14   Wmk. 373   Perf. 14
392 A108 5c Bois pois   .20 .20
393 A108 10c Maraval Lily   .20 .20
394 A108 15c Star grass   .20 .20
395 A108 20c Bois caco   .20 .20
396 A108 25c Strangling fig   .20 .20
397 A108 30c Cassia mos-
            chata   .20 .20
398 A108 50c Chalice flower   .60 .65
399 A108 65c Black stick   .70 .85
400 A108 80c Columnea
            scandens   .90 1.00
401 A108 95c Cats Claws   1.00 1.25
402 A108 $1 Bois l'agli   1.10 1.25
403 A108 $1.50 Eustoma ex-
            eltatum   1.60 2.00

Size: 38½x26mm
404 A108 $2 Chaconia,
            horiz.   2.25 2.50
405 A108 $2.50 Chysothemis
            pulchella,
            horiz.   3.00 3.25
406 A108 $5 Centratherum
            punctatum,
            horiz.   6.00 6.75
407 A108 $10 Savanna flow-
            er, horiz.   11.50 13.00
    Nos. 392-407 (16)   29.85 33.70

"1984" imprint: #392, 393, 394, 396. Value $15.
"1986": #393.
"1989": #392.

1985-89   Wmk. 384
392a A108 5c   .55 .55
393a A108 10c   .55 .55
395a A108 20c ('89)   .55 .55
396a A108 25c ('89)   .55 .55
397a A108 30c ('87)   .55 .55
399a A108 65c ('87)   1.10 1.10
400a A108 80c ('87)   1.25 1.25
401a A108 95c   1.90 1.90
402a A108 $1   2.10 2.10
403a A108 $1.50 ('87)   2.40 2.40
404a A108 $2 ('89)   3.25 3.25
405a A108 $2.50 ('89)   4.25 4.25
406a A108 $5   10.00 10.00
407a A108 $10   21.00 21.00
    Nos. 392a-407a (14)   50.00 50.00

"1985" imprint: #392a, 393a, 401a, 402a, 406a, 407a.
"1987:" #393a, 397a, 399a, 400a-404a, 406a-407a.
"1988:" #393a, 395a-397a, 399a-402a, 406a-407a.
"1989:" #393a, 395a-397a, 399a, 402a-407a.

Castles on Chess Board A109

1984 Summer Olympics A110

World Chess Federationn, 60th Anniv.: Various chess pieces.

Wmk. 373
1984, Sept. 12   Litho.   Perf. 14
408 A109 50c multicolored   1.75 1.75
409 A109 70c multicolored   2.50 2.50
410 A109 $1.50 multicolored 5.25 5.25
411 A109 $2 multicolored   7.25 7.25
    Nos. 408-411 (4)   16.75 16.75

1984, Sept. 21   Perf. 14x14½
412 A110 15c Swimming   .25 .25
413 A110 55c Running   .65 .65
414 A110 $1.50 Yachting   1.60 1.60

415 A110 $4 Bicycling   4.25 4.25
a.   Souvenir sheet of 4, #412-415   8.00 8.00
       Nos. 412-415 (4)   6.75 6.75

St. Mary's Children's Home, 125th
Anniv. — A111

1984, Nov. 13   Litho.   Perf. 13½
416 A111   10c Children's band   .20   .20
417 A111   70c St. Mary's Home   .90   .90
418 A111 $3 Group scene   3.50 3.50
       Nos. 416-418 (3)   4.60 4.60

Christmas
1984
A112

1984, Nov.   Litho.   Perf. 14
419 A112   10c Parang Band   .35   .35
420 A112   30c Musical notes,
               Poinsettia   .40   .40
421 A112 $1 Bandola, Cuatro,
               Bandolin   1.50 1.50
422 A112 $3 Fiddle, Guitar,
               Double Bass   4.50 4.50
       Nos. 419-422 (4)   6.75 6.75

Emancipation, 150th
Anniv. — A113

1984, Oct. 22   Litho.   Perf. 13½x13
423 A113   35c Slave ship   .75   .75
424 A113   55c Map, Slave Tri-
               angle   1.25 1.25
425 A113 $1 Book by Eric
               Williams   2.25 2.25
426 A113 $2 Toussaint
               L'Ouverture   4.75 4.75
a.   Souvenir sheet of 4, #423-
       426   10.50 10.50
       Nos. 423-426 (4)   9.00 9.00

Labor
Day — A114

Labor leaders: No. 427, A.A. Cipriani and
T.U.B. Butler. No. 428, A. Cola Rienzi and
C.T.W.E. Worrell. No. 429, C.P. Alexander
and Q. O'Connor.

Wmk. 373
1985, June 17   Litho.   Perf. 14
427 A114   55c dull rose & blk   1.25 1.25
428 A114   55c brt green & blk   1.25 1.25
429 A114   55c lt orange & blk   1.25 1.25
       Nos. 427-429 (3)   3.75 3.75

Ships
A115

Wmk. 373
1985, Aug 20   Litho.   Perf. 14½
430 A115   30c Lady Nelson   .60   .60
431 A115   95c Lady Drake   1.75 1.75
432 A115 $1.50 Federal Palm   2.75 2.75
433 A115 $2 Federal Maple   3.50 3.50
       Nos. 430-433 (4)   8.60 8.60

UN
Decade
for
Women
A116

Women in the arts, public service and education: No. 434, Sybill Atteck, Marjorie Pad-
more. No. 435, May Cherrie, Evelyn Tracey.
No. 436, Jessica Smith-Phillips, Irene Omilta
McShine.

1985, Oct. 30   Wmk. 384   Perf. 14
434 A116 $1.50 multicolored   1.75 1.75
435 A116 $1.50 multicolored   1.75 1.75
436 A116 $1.50 multicolored   1.75 1.75
       Nos. 434-436 (3)   5.25 5.25

Intl. Youth
Year — A117

Anniversaries and events: 10c, Natl. Cadet
Force, 75th anniv. 65c, Girl Guides, 75th
anniv.

1985, Nov. 27   Perf. 14x14½
437 A117   10c Cadet emblem   1.00 1.00
438 A117   65c Badges, anniv.
               emblem   2.40 2.40
439 A117   95c shown   3.25 3.25
       Nos. 437-439 (3)   6.65 6.65

A118   A119

Sisters of St. Joseph de Cluny in Trinidad,
150th Anniv.: 10c, Sister Anne-Marie
Javouhey, founder. 65c, St. Joseph's Convent,
Port-of-Spain. 95c, Statue of Sr. Anne-Marie.

Perf. 14x14½
1986, Mar. 19   Litho.   Wmk. 384
440 A118   10c multicolored   .20   .20
441 A118   65c multicolored   .60   .60
442 A118   95c multicolored   1.00 1.00
       Nos. 440-442 (3)   1.80 1.80

Wmk. 384
1986, Apr. 21   Litho.   Perf. 14½
443 A119   10c At the Cenotaph   .30   .30
444 A119   15c Aboard HMY Bri-
               tannia   .30   .30
445 A119   30c With Pres. Clarke   .30   .30
446 A119 $5 Receiving bouquet   4.25 4.25
       Nos. 443-446 (4)   5.15 5.15

Queen Elizabeth II, 60th birthday.

Locomotives, AMERIPEX '86 — A120

Perf. 14½x14
1986, May 26   Wmk. 373
447 A120   65c Arma tank loco-
               motive   .40   .40
448 A120   95c Canadian-built
               No. 22   .65   .65
449 A120 $1.10 Tender engine   .75   .75
450 A120 $1.50 Saddle tank   1.00 1.00
a.   Souvenir sheet of 4, #447-450   3.00 3.00
       Nos. 447-450 (4)   2.80 2.80

Boy Scouts,
75th Anniv.
A121

1986, July 21   Wmk. 384   Perf. 14
451 A121 $1.70 Campsite   1.50 1.50
452 A121 $2 Uniforms, 1911,
               1986   2.00 2.00

Dr. Eric Williams (1911-1981), First
Prime Minister — A122

Wmk. 373
1986, Sept. 25   Litho.   Perf. 14
453 A122   10c Graduating col-
               lege, 1935   .35   .35
454 A122   30c Wearing red tie   .35   .35
a.   Black tie   .45   .45
455 A122   95c Pro-Chancellor of
               UWI   1.00 1.00
456 A122 $5 Williams, prime
               minister's resi-
               dence   5.25 5.25
a.   Souvenir sheet of 4, #453-456   7.75 7.75
       Nos. 453-456 (4)   6.95 6.95

       Nos. 453-454 vert.

Intl. Peace
Year
A123

1986, Oct. 30   Wmk. 384
457 A123   95c shown   .60   .60
458 A123 $3 Dove   2.40 2.40

Giselle LaRonde,
Miss World
1986 — A124

Wmk. 384
1987, July 27   Litho.   Perf. 14
459 A124   10c Wearing folk
               costume   .70   .70
460 A124   30c Bathing suit   1.50 1.50
461 A124   95c Crown   3.25 3.25
462 A124 $1.65 Crown and
               sash   5.25 5.25
       Nos. 459-462 (4)   10.70 10.70

Republic
Bank,
150th
Anniv.
A125

Designs: 10c, Colonial Bank, Port of Spain.
65c, Cocoa plantation. 95c, Oil fields. $1.10,
Tramcar, Belmont Tramway Co.

Wmk. 373
1987, Dec. 21   Litho.   Perf. 14
463 A125   10c buff, red brn &
               blk   .55   .55
464 A125   65c buff, red brn &
               blk   .80   .80
465 A125   95c buff, red brn &
               blk   1.40 1.40
466 A125 $1.10 buff, red brn &
               blk   1.60 1.60
       Nos. 463-466 (4)   4.35 4.35

Defense Force,
25th
Anniv. — A126

Various army, coast guard and navy
uniforms.

Wmk. 384
1988, Feb. 29   Litho.   Perf. 14
467 A126   10c Army   .75   .35
468 A126   30c Army (women)   2.00   .45
469 A126 $1.10 Navy, army,
               coast guard   3.75 3.25
470 A126 $1.50 Navy   4.75 4.75
       Nos. 467-470 (4)   11.25 8.80

Cricket
A127

Bat, wicket posts, ball, 18th cent. belt buckle
and batters: 30c, George John. 65c, Learie
Constantine. 95c, Sonny Ramadhin. $1.50,
Gerry Gomez. $2.50, Jeffrey Stollmeyer.

Wmk. 373
1988, June 6   Litho.   Perf. 14
471 A127   30c multicolored   1.60   .55
472 A127   65c multicolored   3.00 1.40
473 A127   95c multicolored   3.25 2.25
474 A127 $1.50 multicolored   4.00 4.00
475 A127 $2.50 multicolored   5.25 5.75
       Nos. 471-475 (5)   17.10 13.95

Oilfield Workers'
Trade Union, 50th
Anniv. — A128

50, Star, oil well and: 10c, Uriah Buzz Butler, labor leader. 30c, Adrian C. Rienzi, pres.
from 1937-42. 65c, John Rojas, pres. from
1943-62. $5, George Weekes, pres. from
1962-87.

Wmk. 384
1988, July 11   Litho.   Perf. 14½
476 A128   10c multicolored   .20   .20
477 A128   30c multicolored   .20   .20
478 A128   65c multicolored   .55   .55
479 A128 $5 multicolored   2.50 2.50
       Nos. 476-479 (4)   3.45 3.45

Borough of
Arima, Cent.
A129

20c, Mary Werges, Santa Rosa Church.
30c, Gov. W. Robinson, royal charter. $1.10,
Mayor C.P. Lopez greeting Gov. Robinson at
train station. $1.50, Mayor J.F. Wallen, centen-
nial emblem.

Wmk. 384
1988, Aug. 22   Litho.   Perf. 14½
480 A129   20c multicolored   .30   .30
481 A129   30c multicolored   .30   .30
482 A129 $1.10 multicolored   1.10 1.10
483 A129 $1.50 multicolored   1.50 1.50
       Nos. 480-483 (4)   3.20 3.20

Lloyds of London, 300th Anniv.
Common Design Type

Designs: 30c, Queen Mother at the "Topping
Out" ceremony of new Lloyds's building, 1984.
$1.10, BWIA Tristar 500, horiz. $1.55, ISCOTT

iron and steel mill, horiz. $2, *Atlantic Empress* on fire off Tobago.

1988, Nov. 21   Litho.   Perf. 14

484	CD341	30c multicolored	.85	.35
485	CD341	$1.10 multicolored	3.00	1.75
486	CD341	$1.55 multicolored	2.75	2.40
487	CD341	$2 multicolored	5.25	3.50
		Nos. 484-487 (4)	11.85	8.00

Unification of the Islands, Cent. — A130

Torch and: 40c, Natl. arms, 1889, and 1p Type A1. $1, Badge from Tobago flag and Tobago No. 31. $1.50, Badge from Trinidad flag and Trinidad No. 71. $2.25, Natl. arms, 1989, and No. 274.

Wmk. 384

1989, Mar. 20   Litho.   Perf. 14½

488	A130	40c multicolored	.70	.70
489	A130	$1 multicolored	1.90	1.00
490	A130	$1.50 multicolored	2.50	2.50
491	A130	$2.25 multicolored	3.25	3.50
		Nos. 488-491 (4)	8.35	7.30

Rare Species A131

Designs: a, *Pipile pipile.* b, *Phyllodytes auratus.* c, *Cebus albifrons trinitatis.* d, *Tamandua tetradactyla.* e, *Lutra longicaudis.* Printed in a continuous design.

Perf. 14x14½

1989, July 31   Wmk. 373

492		Strip of 5	22.50	22.50
a.-e.	A131	$1 any single	2.40	2.40

A132

1989, Oct. 2   Perf. 14½

493	A132	10c Men using walking sticks	.90	.50
494	A132	40c City Hall	.80	.50
495	A132	$1 Guides and leader	2.50	1.25
496	A132	$2.25 Volunteers, anniv. emblem	3.75	3.75
		Nos. 493-496 (4)	7.95	6.00

Blind Welfare, 75th anniv. (10c), Port-of-Spain City Hall, 75th anniv. (40c), Girl Guides, 75th anniv. ($1), and Red Cross, 50th anniv. ($2.25).

Perf. 14½x14

1989, Nov. 30   Wmk. 384

Drum instruments played in a steel band.

497	A133	10c Tenor	.40	.40
498	A133	40c Guitar	.40	.40
499	A133	$1 Cello	.70	.80
500	A133	$2.25 Bass	1.75	2.00
		Nos. 497-500 (4)	3.25	3.60

Mushrooms A134

1990, May 3   Perf. 14x13½

501	A134	10c *Xeromphalina tenuipes*	.60	.60
502	A134	40c *Dictyophora indusiata*	1.00	1.00
503	A134	$1 *Leucocoprinus birnbaumii*	2.40	2.40
504	A134	$2.25 *Crinipellis perniciosa*	5.00	5.00
		Nos. 501-504 (4)	9.00	9.00

Stamp World London '90.

Scarlet Ibis A135

1990, Sept. 7   Perf. 14

505	A135	40c Immature bird	2.50	.50
506	A135	80c Mating display	2.75	2.00
507	A135	$1 Adult male	3.25	2.00
508	A135	$2.25 Adult, egg & young	5.50	5.00
		Nos. 505-508 (4)	14.00	9.50

World Wildlife Fund.

Yellow Oriole — A136

1990, Dec. 17   Litho.   Wmk. 384

509	A136	20c shown	.30	.30
510	A136	25c Green rumped parrotlet	.65	.40
511	A136	40c Fork-tailed flycatcher	.30	.30
512	A136	50c Copper rumped hummingbird	.70	.55
513	A136	$1 Bananaquit	.85	.55
514	A136	$2 Semp	1.25	1.25
515	A136	$2.25 Channel-billed toucan	.65	.65
516	A136	$2.50 Bay headed tanager	.70	.70
517	A136	$5 Green honeycreeper	4.50	4.50
a.		Souvenir sheet of 1, wmk. 373	4.50	4.50
518	A136	$10 Cattle egret	3.25	3.25
519	A136	$20 Golden olive woodpecker	9.50	9.50
520	A136	$50 Peregrine falcon	24.00	24.00
		Nos. 509-520 (12)	46.65	45.95

No. 517a issued 2/3/97 for Hong Kong '97. For overprints & surcharge see #565-568, 597A.

1994-98   Wmk. 373

510a	A136	25c	.90	.90
512a	A136	50c	.60	.60
513a	A136	$1	.90	.90
514a	A136	$2	2.00	2.00
516a	A136	$2.50	2.40	2.40
517b	A136	$5	4.75	4.75
518a	A136	$10	9.75	9.75
519a	A136	$20	20.00	20.00
		Nos. 510a-519a (8)	41.30	41.30

Issued: #510a, 8/94; #512a, 4/95; #510a, 8/94; #513a, 3/3/97; #516a, 518a, 519a, 10/14/98; #517b, 6/1996.
#510a, 513a, 514a, 517b dated 1990; #517a dated 1997.

University of the West Indies A137

Chancellors and Campus Buildings: 40c, HRH Princess Alice, Administration Building. 80c, Sir Hugh Wooding, Main Library. $1, Sir Allen Lewis, Faculty of Engineering. $2.25, Sir Shridath Ramphal, Faculty of Medical Studies.

Perf. 13½x14

1990, Oct. 15   Litho.   Wmk. 373

521	A137	40c multicolored	.60	.60
522	A137	80c multicolored	1.10	1.10
523	A137	$1 multicolored	1.60	1.60
524	A137	$2.25 multicolored	3.50	3.50
		Nos. 521-524 (4)	6.80	6.80

Britsh West Indies Airways, 50th Anniv. A138

Airplanes: 40c, Lockheed Lodestar. 80c, Vickers Viking 1A. $1, Vickers Viscount 702. $2.25, Boeing 707. $5, Lockheed TriStar 500.

1990, Nov. 27   Perf. 14

525	A138	40c multicolored	1.90	.65
526	A138	80c multicolored	2.75	1.90
527	A138	$1 multicolored	3.00	1.90
528	A138	$2.25 multicolored	5.50	7.00
		Nos. 525-528 (4)	13.15	11.45

Souvenir Sheet

529	A138	$5 multicolored	8.75	8.75

Ferns A139

1991, July 1   Perf. 13½

530	A139	40c *Lygodium volubile*	.65	.65
531	A139	80c *Blechnum occidentale*	1.25	1.25
532	A139	$1 *Gleichenia bifida*	1.60	1.60
533	A139	$2.25 *Polypodium lycopodiodes*	3.50	3.50
		Nos. 530-533 (4)	7.00	7.00

Trinidad & Tobago in World War II — A140

Designs: 40c, Firing practice by Trinidad & Tobago regiment. 80c, Fairey Barracuda surprises U-boat. $1, Avro Lancaster returns from bombing raid. $2.25, River class frigate on convoy duty. No. 538a, Supermarine Spitfire. b, Vickers Wellington.

Perf. 13½x14

1991, Dec. 7   Litho.   Wmk. 384

534	A140	40c multicolored	1.40	1.40
535	A140	80c multicolored	2.75	2.75
536	A140	$1 multicolored	3.50	3.50
537	A140	$2.25 multicolored	7.50	7.50
		Nos. 534-537 (4)	15.15	15.15

Souvenir Sheet of 2

538	A140	$2.50 #a.-b.	22.50	22.50

H. E. Rapsey — A141

Inca Clathrata Quesneli — A142

Holy Name Convent — A143

Religions of Trinidad and Tobago — A145

1992, Mar. 30   Wmk. 373   Perf. 14

539	A141	40c multicolored	.80	.80
540	A142	80c multicolored	1.60	1.60
541	A143	$1 multicolored	2.10	2.10
		Nos. 539-541 (3)	4.50	4.50

#539, Building and Loan Assoc., cent. #540, Trinidad & Tobago Field Naturalists' Club. #541, Holy Name Convent, cent.

1992, Apr. 21   Litho.   Perf. 14

#544, Baptist, baptism by immersion. #545, Muslim, minaret. #546, Hindu, Brahman..the source of all. #547, Christianity, cross. #548, Baha'i, slogan.

544	A145	40c multicolored	1.25	1.25
545	A145	40c multicolored	1.25	1.25
546	A145	40c multicolored	1.25	1.25
547	A145	40c multicolored	1.25	1.25
548	A145	40c multicolored	1.25	1.25
		Nos. 544-548 (5)	6.25	6.25

BWIA Aircraft A146

Wmk. 373

1992, Aug. 6   Litho.   Perf. 14

549	A146	$2.25 MD83	4.50	4.50
550	A146	$2.25 L1011	4.50	4.50

Natl. Museum and Art Gallery, Cent. A147

Wmk. 384

1992, Dec. 7 **Litho.** *Perf. 14½*
551 A147 $1 multicolored .75 .75

Christmas — A148

1992, Dec. 21
552 A148 40c multicolored .50 .50

Trinidad Guardian, 75th Anniv. — A149

1992, Dec. 23
553 A149 40c multicolored .50 .50

Philatelic Society of Trinidad & Tobago, 50th Anniv. A150

1992, Dec. 30
554 A150 $2.25 multicolored 1.75 1.75

CARICOM (Caribbean Economic Community), 20th Anniv. — A151

Map of CARICOM nations, portraits of West Indian men: 50c, $1.50, $2.75, $3, Derek Walcott, Sir Shridath Ramphal, William Demas.
$6, Order of the Caribbean Community. Illustration reduced.

Perf. 13x13½

1994, Jan. 31 **Litho.** **Wmk. 373**
555 A151 50c pink & multi .30 .30
556 A151 $1.50 green & multi .90 .90
557 A151 $2.75 gray & multi 1.90 1.90
558 A151 $3 violet & multi 1.90 1.90
  Nos. 555-558 (4) 5.00 5.00

Souvenir Sheet
Perf. 13½x13

559 A151 $6 multicolored 4.50 4.50

No. 559 contains one 34x56mm stamp.

Drum Instruments Played in a Steel Band — A152

1994, Feb. 11 *Perf. 14x15*
560 A152 50c Quadrophonic
  pan .35 .35
561 A152 $1 Tenor base pan .75 .75
562 A152 $2.25 Six pan 1.60 1.60
563 A152 $2.50 Rocket pan 1.75 1.75
  Nos. 560-563 (4) 4.45 4.45

Alwyn Roberts Kitchener, Calypso Singer — A153

1994, Feb. 11 *Perf. 14*
564 A153 50c multicolored 2.50 2.50

Nos. 510-511, 514, 518 Ovptd. with Hong Kong '94 Exhibition Emblem

Wmk. 384

1994, Feb. 18 **Litho.** *Perf. 14*
565 A136 25c multicolored .40 .40
566 A136 40c multicolored .40 .40
567 A136 $2 multicolored 1.50 1.50
568 A136 $10 multicolored 7.75 7.75
  Nos. 565-568 (4) 10.05 10.05

Hotels & Lodges A154

#569, Trinidad Hilton. #570, Sandy Point Village, Tobago. #571, Asa Wright Nature Center and Lodge. #572, ML's Bed and Breakfast.

Wmk. 373

1994, Aug. 10 **Litho.** *Perf. 14*
569 A154 $3 multicolored 1.75 1.75
570 A154 $3 multicolored 1.75 1.75
571 A154 $3 multicolored 1.75 1.75
572 A154 $3 multicolored 1.75 1.75
  Nos. 569-572 (4) 7.00 7.00

Snakes A155

50c, Boa constrictor. $1.25, Horse whip or vine snake. $2.50, Bushmaster. $3, Large coral snake.

Wmk. 373

1994, Sept. 19 *Perf. 14*
573 A155 50c multicolored .40 .40
574 A155 $1.25 multicolored 1.10 1.10
575 A155 $2.50 multicolored 2.10 2.10
576 A155 $3 multicolored 2.40 2.40
  Nos. 573-576 (4) 6.00 6.00

Trinidad Art Society, 50th Anniv. — A156

Artworks: No. 577, Copper sculpture, by Ken Morris. No. 578, Fisherman, by Sybil Atteck. No. 579, Snowballman, by Mahmoud P. Alladin.

1995, Mar. 6 **Wmk. 384**
577 A156 50c multicolored 1.10 1.10
578 A156 50c multicolored 1.10 1.10
579 A156 50c multicolored 1.10 1.10
  Nos. 577-579 (3) 3.30 3.30

Conservation — A157

Designs: $1.25, Leatherback turtle. $2.50, POS Lighthouse, vert. $3, "Knowsley" Ministry of Foreign Affairs.

1995, Aug. 7
580 A157 $1.25 multicolored .85 .85
581 A157 $2.50 multicolored 1.75 1.75
582 A157 $3 multicolored 2.10 2.10
  Nos. 580-582 (3) 4.70 4.70

Brian Lara, Cricket Hero — A158

Designs: $1.25, Batting. $2.50, In batting stance. $3, Batting, diff.
No. 587: a, $3.75, With arms raised at crowd. b, $5.01, Down on one knee with bat.

Perf. 13x13½

1996, May 15 **Litho.** **Wmk. 373**
583 A158 50c multicolored .40 .40
584 A158 $1.25 multicolored .95 .95
585 A158 $2.50 multicolored 1.75 1.75
586 A158 $3 multicolored 2.10 2.10
  Nos. 583-586 (4) 5.20 5.20

Souvenir Sheet
587 A158 Sheet of 2, #a.-b. 6.00 6.00

Trinidad & Tobago Remembers World War II — A159

50c, Red Cross Economy Label. $1.25, Battleship USS Missouri. $2.50, US servicemen playing baseball, Queen's Park, Savannah, 1942. $3, Fulmar 1, Royal Naval Air Station.
No. 592: a, Grumman Goose seaplane. b, US Navy Airship.

Wmk. 373

1996, June 7 **Litho.** *Perf. 14*
588 A159 50c multicolored .60 .60
589 A159 $1.25 multicolored 1.40 1.40
590 A159 $2.50 multicolored 2.75 2.75
591 A159 $3 multicolored 3.25 3.25
  Nos. 588-591 (4) 8.00 8.00

Souvenir Sheet of 2
592 A159 $3 #a.-b. 12.00 12.00

A160   A161

Wendy Fitzwilliam, 1998 Miss Universe: $1.25, Lying on beach. $2.50, In traditional costume. $3, Wearing evening gown. $5, After coronation.

1999, May 3 **Litho.** *Perf. 14*
593 A160 50c multicolored .60 .60
594 A160 $1.25 multicolored 1.25 1.25
595 A160 $2.50 multicolored 2.40 2.40
596 A160 $3 multicolored 2.75 2.75
  Nos. 593-596 (4) 7.00 7.00

Souvenir Sheet
597 A160 $5 multicolored 7.00 7.00

No. 511 Surcharged **75c**

1999 Method and Perf. as Before
597A A136 75c on 40c multi

Serpentine Die Cut
2000, Jan. 27 **Litho.**
Angostura Bitters, 175th Anniv.: 75c, Angostura Bitters bottle. $3, Distillery. $4.50, Bitters bottle, cocktails.

Self-Adhesive
598 A161 75c multi .60 .60
599 A161 $3 multi 2.40 2.40
600 A161 $4.50 multi 3.50 3.50
  a. Souvenir sheet, #598-600 6.50 6.50

Tourism A162

Shoreline scenes: 75c, Maracas Bay. $1, Pirates Bay. $3.75, Pigeon Point. $5, Toco, North Coast.

2000, July 25 Litho. *Perf. 14¼x14½*
601 A162 75c multi .40 .40
602 A162 $1 multi .60 .60
603 A162 $3.75 multi 2.75 2.75
604 A162 $5 multi 3.25 3.25

Christmas A163

Design: 75c, Caroni landscape. $3.75, Pastelles, sorrel and ginger beer. $4.50, Musicians under palm trees. $5.25, Angels with steel drums.

Perf. 14¼x14½
2000, Nov. 14 **Litho.**
605 A163 75c multi .40 .40
606 A163 $3.75 multi 2.75 2.75
607 A163 $4.50 multi 3.00 3.00
608 A163 $5.25 multi 3.75 3.75

No. 515 Surcharged

Method and Perf. as Before
2001?
609 A136 75c on $2.25 multi

National Mail Center A164

Designs: $3, Building entrance. $10, Side of building.

Perf. 14¼x14½
2000, Nov. 20 **Litho.**
610-611 A164 Set of 2 7.00 7.00

Endangered Fauna A165

Designs: 25c, Pacca, 50c, Prehensile-tailed porcupine. 75c, Iguana. $1, Leatherback turtle. $2, Golden tegu. $2, Red howler monkey. $4, Weeping capuchin monkey, vert. $5, River otter. $10, Ocelot. $20, Trinidad piping guan, vert.

Perf. 14¼x14½, 14½x14¼
2001, Feb. 6 **Litho.**
612 A165 25c multi .20 .20
613 A165 50c multi .20 .20
614 A165 75c multi .35 .35
615 A165 $1 multi .50 .50
616 A165 $2 multi 1.10 1.10
617 A165 $3 multi 1.50 1.50
618 A165 $4 multi 2.10 2.10
619 A165 $5 multi 2.75 2.75
620 A165 $10 multi 5.75 5.75
621 A165 $20 multi 11.50 11.50
Nos. 612-621 (10) 25.95 25.95

Salvation Army in Trinidad & Tobago, Cent. — A166

Designs: 75c, Emblem. $2, William Booth Memorial Hall.

2001, Aug. 9 **Perf. 14½x14¼**
622-623 A166 Set of 2 2.00 2.00
623a Souvenir sheet, #622-623, perf. 13¾x14¼ 2.00 2.00

Natl. Library, 150th Anniv. A167

Designs: 75c, Port of Spain Public Library, Carnegie Free Library. $3.25, New National Library building.

2001, Aug. 9 **Perf. 14¼x14½**
624-625 A167 Set of 2 3.00 3.00
625a Souvenir sheet, #624-625 3.00 3.00

Under 17 World Soccer Championships — A168

Designs: $2, Emblem of Soca Warriors. $3.25, National flag. $4.50, Lion holding flag. $5.25, Stadiums.

2001, Sept. 6 **Perf. 14½x14**
626-629 A168 Set of 4 9.00 9.00
629a Souvenir sheet, #626-629 9.00 9.00

Flowers — A169

Designs: $1, Pachystachys coccinea. $2.50, Heliconia psittacorum. $3.25, Brownea latifolia, horiz. $3.75, Oncidium papilio.

2001 **Perf. 14½x14¼, 14¼x14½**
630-633 A169 Set of 4 7.25 7.25

Christmas — A170

People and: $1, Boats, church. $3.75, Flowers. $4.50, House, flowers. $5.25, Church, post office.

2001 **Perf. 14½x14¼**
634-637 A170 Set of 4 8.00 8.00
637a Souvenir sheet, #634-637 9.00 9.00

Butterflies A171

Designs: $1, Cracker. $3.75, Tiger. $4.50, Four continent. $5.25, "89."

2002, June 19 Litho. Perf. 13¼x13
638-641 A171 Set of 4 10.00 10.00

Hummingbirds A172

Designs: $1, Rufous-breasted hermit. $2.50, Black-throated mango. $3.25, Tufted coquette. $3.75, White-chested emerald.

2002 ? **Perf. 13x13¼**
642-645 A172 Set of 4 8.00 8.00

Historic Forts — A173

Designs: $1, Fort Picton. $3.75, Fort George. $4.50, Fort King George. $5.25, Fort James.

2002 ? **Perf. 13¼x13**
646-649 A173 Set of 4 9.00 9.00
649a Souvenir sheet, #646-649 9.00 9.00

Reign of Queen Elizabeth II, 50th Anniv. A174

Queen: $3.75, At Governor General's House. $4.50, With Mayor E. Taylor of Port of Spain. $5.25, At Red House, addressing Parliament, #119, and former personal flag of the Queen.
$10, In limousine, waving to crowd.

2002 **Litho.** **Perf. 13¾**
650-652 A174 Set of 3 9.00 9.00
Souvenir Sheet
653 A174 $10 multi 6.50 6.50

Independence, 40th Anniv. — A175

2002
654 A175 $1 multi 1.00 1.00

Christmas A176

Designs: $1, Child opening gift of steel drum, vert. $2.50, People, musicians, house. $3.75, Houses. $5.25, Santa Claus on horse-drawn cart, vert.

Perf. 14½x14¼, 14¼x14½
2002, Nov. 20 A176 Set of 4 **Litho.**
655-658 6.00 6.00

Pan-American Health Organization, Cent. — A177

Designs: $1, Emblem. $2.50, National headquarters, Port of Spain. $3.25, Steel drum with symbols. $4.50, Joseph L. Pawan (1887-1957), discoverer of vampire bat rabies.

2002, Dec. 2 **Perf. 14½x14¼**
659-662 A177 Set of 4 7.00 7.00

Cricket Players — A178

Designs: $1, Ian Raphael Bishop. $2.50, Deryck Lance Murray. $4.50, Augustine Lawrence Logie. $5.25, Ann Browne John.

2003, Feb. 7 **Perf. 13**
663-666 A178 Set of 4 7.50 7.50

Carnival A179

Various costumed participants: $1, $2.50, $3.75, vert. $4.50, vert., $5.25, vert.

Perf. 14¼x14½, 14½x14¼
2003, Feb. 25 **Litho.**
667-671 A179 Set of 5 8.00 8.00
671a Souvenir sheet of 1 5.00 5.00

Inauguration of Intl. Criminal Court — A180

Designs: $1, Trinidad & Tobago Pres. Arthur N. R. Robinson and UN Secretary General Kofi Annan. $2.50, Robinson, Prof. Benjamin Ferencz, Prof. Cherif Bassiouni, Philippe Kirsch, UN Undersecretary for Legal Affairs Hans Corell. $3.75, Robinson and Corell. $4.50, Robinson, Emma Bonino, and Italian Pres. Carlo Ciampi.
$6, Robinson, vert.

Perf. 14¾x14½, 14½x14¾
2003, Feb. 25
672-675 A180 Set of 4 7.00 7.00
Souvenir Sheet
676 A180 $6 multi 5.00 5.00

Rainforest Flora & Fauna — A181

No. 677: a, Mountain immortelle. b, Blue-crowned motmot. c, Red howler monkey. d, Butterfly orchid. e, Channel-billed toucan. f, Ocelot. g, Bromeliads. h, Lineated woodpecker. i, Tamandua. j, Emperor butterfly.

Serpentine Die Cut 12½
2003, Feb. 24 **Litho.**
Self-Adhesive
677 Booklet pane of 10 9.00
a.-j. A181 $1 Any single .85 .85

Lighthouses A182

Designs: $1, Port-of-Spain. $3.75, Chacachacare. $4.50, Port-of-Spain, diff. $5.25, Chacachacare, diff.
No. 681B, Like No. 679, spelled "Chacacharie." No. 681C, Like No. 681, spelled "Chacacharie."

2002-03 **Perf. 14½x14¼**
678-681 A182 Set of 4 9.50 9.50
681a Souvenir sheet, #678-681 9.50 9.50
681B A182 $3.75 multi — —
681C A182 $5.25 multi — —

Nos. 678, 680, 681B and 681C were issued on 11/6/02 and all were withdrawn from sale later that day when the incorrect spelling of the lighthouse was discovered. Nos. 678 and 680 were put back on sale, along with new stamps with the corrected spelling of the lighthouse, Nos. 679 and 681, and the souvenir sheet with the stamps with the corrected spelling, No. 681a, on 5/26/03. The editors would like to examine any examples of the souvenir sheet with stamps with the incorrect spelling.

Scenes of Village Life — A183

Designs: $1, Dancing the cocoa. $2.50, Dirt oven. $3.75, River washing. $4.50, Box cart racing. $5.25, Pitching marbles.

2003, Oct. 28
682-686 A183 Set of 5 7.00 7.00

Marine Life — A184

Designs: $1, Boulder brain coral. $2.50, Hawksbill turtle. $3.75, Green moray eel. $4.50, Creole wrasse. $5.25, Black-spotted sea goddess.
$10, Queen angelfish.

2003, Oct. 28   **Perf. 14¼x14½**
687-691 A184   Set of 5   10.00 10.00
Souvenir Sheet
692 A184 $10 multi   10.00 10.00

Christmas — A185

Paintings by Jean Michel Cazabon (1813-88): $1, View of Port-of-Spain from Laventille Hill. $2.50, View of Diego Martin from Fort George. $3.75, Corbeaux Town, Trinidad. $4.50, Rain Clouds over Cedros. $5.25, Los Galos, Icacos Bay.
No. 698: a, $5, River at St. Ann's. b, $6.50, House in Trinidad.

2003, Nov. 17   **Perf. 13¾**
693-697 A185   Set of 5   8.00 8.00
Souvenir Sheet
698 A185   Sheet of 2, #a-b   8.00 8.00

World AIDS Day A186

Designs: $1, Unite against AIDS. $2.50, Stigma isolates. $3.75, Care stops AIDS, vert. $4.50, Family protects, vert.
$10, People and AIDS ribbon.

2003, Nov. 21
699-702 A186   Set of 4   6.00 6.00
Souvenir Sheet
703 A186 $10 multi   6.00 6.00

2004 Carnival — A187

Calypso musicians: $1, Aldric Farrel, "The Lord Pretender." $2.50, Roy Lewis, "The Mystic Prowler." $3.75, Lord Kitchener, The Mighty Sparrow and The Roaring Lion. $4.50, McArthur Linda Sandy-Rose, "Calypso Rose." $5.25, Nap Hepburne, Lord Brynner and The Mighty Sparrow.
$10, McArthur Linda Sandy-Rose, diff.

2004, Feb. 18
704-708 A187   Set of 5   8.00 8.00
Souvenir Sheet
709 A187 $10 multi   6.00 6.00

2004 Summer Olympics, Athens — A188

Designs: $1, Track and field. $2.50, Boxing. $3.75, Taekwondo. $4.50, Swimming.

2004, July 19   **Litho.**   **Perf. 13**
710-713 A188   Set of 4   6.00 6.00

Intl. Year Commemorating the Struggle Against Slavery and Its Abolition — A189

Designs: $1, Slave ship. $2.50, Rada community, Belmont. $3.75, Daaga, Prince of Popo. $4.50, Slaves singing freedom songs, horiz. $5.25, Providence Estate Aqueduct, Tobago, horiz.
$15, Sandy's escape, horiz.

2004, Sept. 23   **Litho.**   **Perf. 13**
714-718 A189   Set of 5   8.00 8.00
Souvenir Sheet
719 A189 $15 multi   8.00 8.00

Christmas A190

Paintings by Arthur Aldwin "Boscoe" Holder: $1, Lady with Ginger Lilies. $2.50, View from Maracas Lookout. $3.75, Lady in Peacock Chair. $4.50, Caribbean Beauty in White, horiz. $5.25, Teteron Bay, Chaguaramas, horiz.
$10, Creole Ladies in Straw Hats, horiz.

2004, Nov. 22
720-724 A190   Set of 5   7.00 7.00
Souvenir Sheet
725 A190 $10 multi   5.00 5.00

Fruits — A191

Designs: $1, Mango. $2.50, Lime. $3.75, Pineapple. $4.50, Coconut, horiz. $5.25, Orange, horiz.
$10, Guava, horiz.

2004, June 7
726-730 A191   Set of 5   7.00 7.00
Souvenir Sheet
731 A191 $10 multi   6.00 6.00

Carnival — A192

Designs: $1, Dame Lorraine. $2.50, Jab Jab. $3.25, Burrokeet, horiz. $3.75, Midnight Robber. $4.50, Fancy Indian.
$15, Fancy Sailor.

2005, Jan. 18   **Litho.**   **Perf. 13**
732-736 A192   Set of 5   7.00 7.00
Souvenir Sheet
737 A192 $15 multi   7.00 7.00

Brian Lara, Cricket Player — A193

Various photos of Lara in action: $1, $2.50, $3.75, $4.50, $5.25.
$15, Lara walking under raised cricket bats.

2005, Apr. 12   **Litho.**   **Perf. 13**
738-742 A193   Set of 5   7.50 7.50
Souvenir Sheet
743 A193 $15 multi   7.50 7.50

Tobago Heritage Festival — A194

Designs: $1, Belé. $2.50, Dancing the jig. $3.75, Goat race, horiz. $4.50, Harvest Festival, horiz. $5.25, Drumming Festival, horiz.
$15, Traditional Tobago wedding.

Perf. 13½x13¼, 13¼x13½
2005, Aug. 15
744-748 A194   Set of 5   7.50 7.50
Souvenir Sheet
Perf. 13¼
749 A194 $15 multi   7.50 7.50

Medicinal Herbs A195

Designs: 25c, Rachet. 50c, Chandelier. 75c, Worm grass. $1, Black sage. $3, Wonder of the world. $3.25, Vervine. $4, Aloe vera. $5, Senna. $10, Bois bande. $20, Herbal garden.

2005, May 18   **Perf. 13¼x13**
750 A195   25c multi   .20   .20
751 A195   50c multi   .20   .20
752 A195   75c multi   .30   .30
753 A195 $1 multi   .35   .35
754 A195 $3 multi   1.00   1.00
755 A195 $3.25 multi   1.10   1.10
756 A195 $4 multi   1.40   1.40
757 A195 $5 multi   1.75   1.75
758 A195 $10 multi   3.50   3.50
759 A195 $20 multi   7.00   7.00
        Nos. 750-759 (10)   16.80 16.80

Fish and Marine Life — A196

No. 760: a, Foureye butterfly fish. b, Caribbean reef squid. c, Hawksbill turtle. d, Southern sting ray. e, Queen angelfish. f, Giant anemone. g, Peppermint shrimp. h, Rough file clam. i, White-speckled hermit crab. j, Christmas tree worm.

2005, May 1   **Litho.**
Self-Adhesive
760   Booklet of 10   7.00
  a.-j. A196 $1 Any single   .65   .65

Sir Solomon Hochoy (1905-83), First Governor-General — A197

Hochoy and: $1, Prime Minister Dr. Eric E. Williams. $2.50, Haile Selassie. $3.75, His wife, Thelma. $4.50, Queen Elizabeth II. $5.25, Honor Guard.
$15, Hochoy in uniform.

2005, Aug. 22   **Perf. 13½x13**
761-765 A197   Set of 5   7.50 7.50
Souvenir Sheet
Perf. 13½x13¼
766 A197 $15 multi   7.00 7.00

Introduction of Women Police, 50th Anniv. — A198

2005, Sept. 30   **Perf. 12¾**
767 A198 $15 black   6.50 6.50

Souvenir Sheet

Children Against Cancer — A199

2005, Nov. 7   **Perf. 13½x13¼**
768 A199 $15 multi   9.50 9.50
No. 768 sold for $20.

Anansi and the Cricket Match — A200

Anansi: $1, And friends reading cricket brochure. $2.50, And friends hiding in bathroom. $3.75, And friends under umbrella. $4.50, Holding bag, talking to woman. $5.25, Laughing at friends paying woman.
$15, Anansi rubbing stomach.

2005, Dec. 12   *Perf. 13½x13*
769-773 A200   Set of 5   7.00 7.00

Souvenir Sheet

774 A200 $15 multi   6.00 6.00

Pope John Paul
II (1920-2005)
A201

Scenes from Pope's 1985 visit to Trinidad &
Tobago: $1, Leaving airplane. $2.50, Kissing
ground. $3.75, Shaking hands with priest.
$4.50, With bishop, waving. $5.25, Celebrating
mass.
$15, Waving to crowd from police vehicle.

2006, Apr. 10 Litho.   *Perf. 13½x13¼*
775-779 A201   Set of 5   7.00 7.00

Souvenir Sheet

780 A201 $15 multi   6.00 6.00

2006 World Cup Soccer
Championships, Germany — A202

Various images of Trinidad & Tobago soccer
players in action: $1, $2.50, $3.75, $4.50.

Perf. 13¼x13½
2006, June 28   **Litho.**
781-784 A202   Set of 4   9.00 9.00

Initial reports said this set was available only
with the purchase of a first day cover for $50,
but the stamps have been made available individually at face value.

CARICOM Single
Market and
Economy
A203

Designs: $1, Cables, palm tree. $2.50,
Lighthouse, check. $3.75, Cell phone, diver.
$4.50, Sprinter's hands, beach, horiz. $5.25,
Hands on computer keyboard, globe, horiz.
$15, Map of Caribbean, horiz.

Perf. 13½x13¼, 13¼x13½
2006, July 3
785-789 A203   Set of 5   6.50 6.50

Souvenir Sheet

790 A203 $15 multi   6.50 6.50

Souvenir Sheet

Orchid Society, 50th Anniv. — A204

2006, Sept. 5   *Perf. 13½x13¼*
791 A204 $15 multi   6.00 6.00

Arrival of
Chinese to
Trinidad and
Tobago,
Bicent.
A205

Art: $1, Guayaguayare Beach, by Ou Hing
Wan. $2.50, Hosay, by Carlisle Chang. $3.75,
Saddle Road, by Amy Leong Pang, vert.
$4.50, Mother & Child, sculpture by Patrick
Chu Foon, vert. $5.25, Still Life, by Sybil
Atteck, vert.
$15, Inherent Nobility of Man, by Chang,
vert.

Perf. 14¼x14½, 14½x14¼
2006, Oct. 11
792-796 A205   Set of 5   7.00 7.00

Souvenir Sheet
Perf. 13x13¼

797 A205 $15 multi   6.50 6.50

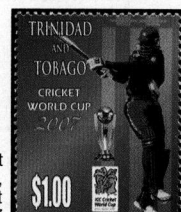

Children's
Games — A206

Designs: $1, Rim driving. $2.50, Top spinning. $3.75, Playing 3A. $4.50, Farmer in the
Den.
$15, Tire swing.

2006, Nov. 29   *Perf. 13¼*
798-801 A206   Set of 4   5.00 5.00

Souvenir Sheet

802 A206 $15 multi   6.00 6.00

2007 Cricket
World Cup,
West
Indies — A207

2007 Cricket World Cup emblem, Cricket
World Cup and: $1, Batsman. $2, Bowler.
$2.50, Bowler, diff. $3.75, Batsman, diff.
$4.50, Wicketkeeper.
$15, Cricket World Cup.

2007, Mar. 15   **Litho.**   *Perf. 13*
803-807 A207   Set of 5   4.50 4.50

Souvenir Sheet
Perf. 13½

808 A207 $15 multi   4.75 4.75

No. 808 contains one 27x45mm stamp.

Reopening of
Red House,
Cent. — A208

Designs: $1, Red House, c. 1907. $2.50,
Parliament Chamber. $3.75, Cenotaph and
Eternal Flame. $5.25, Rotunda and fountain.
$15, Dome.

2007, Sept. 14   *Perf. 13½x13¼*
809-812 A208   Set of 4   4.00 4.00

Souvenir Sheet

813 A208 $15 multi   4.75 4.75

St. Mary's
Children's Home,
150th
Anniv. — A209

Designs: $1, Main entrance, c. 1930. $2.50,
Fountain. $3.75, St. Mary's Anglican Church.
$4.50, St. Mary's Children's Home Cub Scout
pack.

2007, Sept. 21
814-817 A209   Set of 4   3.75 3.75

Historic
Buildings
A210

Designs: $1, Roomor. $2, Killarney. $2.50,
Queen's Royal College. $3.25, Hayes Court.
$3.75, Knowsley. $4.50, Mille Fleurs. $10,
Boissiere House. $20, Archbishop's House.
$50, White Hall.

2007, Dec. 14   **Litho.**   *Perf. 13*
818 A210 $1 multi   .35 .35
819 A210 $2 multi   .65 .65
820 A210 $2.50 multi   .80 .80
821 A210 $3.25 multi   1.10 1.10
822 A210 $3.75 multi   1.25 1.25
823 A210 $4.50 multi   1.50 1.50
824 A210 $10 multi   3.25 3.25
825 A210 $20 multi   6.50 6.50
826 A210 $50 multi   16.00 16.00
Nos. 818-826 (9)   31.40 31.40

SEMI-POSTAL STAMPS

Emblem of
Red Cross
SP1

Perf. 11, 12
1914, Sept. 18   **Typo.**   **Unwmk.**
B1   SP1 (½p) red (on cover)   250.00

This stamp was allowed to pay ½p postage
on one day, Sept. 18, 1914, on circulars distributed by the Red Cross. Value on cover is
for proper Red Cross usage. Value unused,
$15.

**No. 2 Overprinted in Red (Cross) and
Black (Date):**

a	b

1915, Oct. 21   **Wmk. 3**   *Perf. 14*
B2   A1 (a)   1p scarlet   2.25 2.25

1916, Oct. 19
B3   A1 (b)   1p scarlet   .80 *3.25*
   a.   Date omitted

POSTAGE DUE STAMPS

D1	D2

1923-45   **Typo.**   **Wmk. 4**   *Perf. 14*
J1   D1   1p black   .95   *1.90*
J2   D1   2p black   1.90   1.90
J3   D1   3p black ('25)   1.90   *2.75*
J4   D1   4p black ('29)   3.50   *25.00*
J5   D1   5p black ('45)   42.50 *110.00*
J6   D1   6p black ('45)   67.50 *42.50*
J7   D1   8p black ('45)   52.50 *200.00*
J8   D1   1sh black ('45)   90.00 *140.00*
   Nos. J1-J8 (8)   260.75 524.05

**Catalogue values for unused
stamps in this section, from this
point to the end of the section, are
for Never Hinged items.**

Denominations in Cents
1947, Sept. 1
J9   D1   2c black   2.50   3.25
J10   D1   4c black   1.50   4.50
J11   D1   6c black   1.90   9.00
J12   D1   8c black   1.90   *27.50*
J13   D1   10c black   1.90   *4.00*
J14   D1   12c black   1.90   *22.50*
J15   D1   16c black   3.50   *52.50*
J16   D1   24c black   12.50   *11.00*
   Nos. J9-J16 (8)   27.60 134.25

Nos. J9-J16 also exist on chalky paper.

Wmk. 4a (error)
J9a   D1   2c   60.00
J11a   D1   6c   125.00
J14a   D1   12c   150.00

1970 Unwmk. Litho.   *Perf. 14x13½*
Size: 18x23mm
J17   D2   2c green   .20   2.75
J18   D2   4c carmine rose   .20   4.25
J19   D2   6c brown   .55   5.50
J20   D2   8c lt violet   .70   6.25
J21   D2   10c brick red   .70   6.25
J22   D2   12c dull orange   .90   6.25
J23   D2   16c brt yellow grn   .90   4.25
J24   D2   24c gray   .90   4.50
J25   D2   50c blue   .90   5.00
J26   D2   60c olive green   .90   5.00
   Nos. J17-J26 (10)   6.85 50.00

Perf. 13½x14
1976-77   **Litho.**   **Unwmk.**
Size: 17x21mm
J27   D2   2c green   .20   1.75
J28   D2   4c carmine rose   .25   1.75
J29   D2   6c brown   .25   2.40
J30   D2   8c lt violet   .30   2.40
J31   D2   10c brick red   .30   2.40
J32   D2   12c dull orange   .45   3.25
   Nos. J27-J32 (6)   1.75 13.95

Issued: 4c, 12c, 4/1/76; 2c, 6c, 8c, 10, 1977.
The letters in the top label on Nos. J27-J32
are larger than the D's and O's more squarish than
the oval letters on Nos. J17-J26. "Postage
Due" is 13mm long and is composed of finer
letters than on Nos. J17-J26, which have a
14mm inscription.

WAR TAX STAMPS

Nos. 1-2 Overprinted

1917   **Wmk. 3**   *Perf. 14*
MR1   A1   1p scarlet   3.50   *4.25*
   a.   Invtd. overprint   200.00 *250.00*

Overprinted

MR2 A1 ½p green .30 .30
  a. Overprinted on face and
    back 425.00
  b. Pair, one without overprint 275.00
MR3 A1 1p scarlet .80 2.25
  a. Pair, one without overprint 425.00 800.00
  b. Double overprint 125.00

Overprinted

MR4 A1 ½p green .30 6.50
MR5 A1 1p scarlet .30 1.00

Overprinted

MR6 A1 ½p green .30 3.25
MR7 A1 1p scarlet 3.50 1.25

Overprinted

MR8 A1 ½p green .30 3.25
MR9 A1 1p scarlet 35.00 27.50

Overprinted

MR10 A1 1p scarlet .80 1.40
  a. Inverted overprint 100.00 100.00

Overprinted

MR11 A1 1p scarlet 1.75 .30
  a. Double overprint 200.00 200.00
  b. Inverted overprint 125.00 125.00

Overprinted

1918
MR12 A1 ½p green .30 2.00
MR13 A1 1p scarlet .90 1.75
  a. Double overprint 125.00
  b. Horiz. pair, one without
    overprint 1,000.

The War Tax Stamps show considerable variations in the colors, thickness of the paper, distinctness of the watermark, and the gum. Counterfeits exist of the errors of Nos. MR1-MR13.

OFFICIAL STAMPS

Regular Issue of 1913
Overprinted

1913 **Wmk. 3** **Perf. 14**
O1 A1 ½p green 1.25 7.50

Same Overprinted

1914
O2 A1 ½p green 2.25 15.00

Same Overprinted

1916
O3 A1 ½p green 1.50 3.50
  a. Double overprint 27.50

Same Overprint without Period

1917
O4 A1 ½p green 1.00 7.50

Same Overprinted

1917, Aug. 22
O5 A1 ½p green 1.75 20.00

The official stamps are found in several shades of green and on paper of varying thickness.

TRIPOLITANIA

tri-ˌpä-lə-'tā-nyə

LOCATION — In northern Africa, bordering on Mediterranean Sea
GOVT. — A former Italian Colony
AREA — 350,000 sq. mi. (approx.)
POP. — 570,716 (1921)
CAPITAL — Tripoli

Formerly a Turkish province, Tripolitania became part of Italian Libya. See Libya.

100 Centesimi = 1 Lira

Used values in italics are for postally used stamps. CTO's or stamps with fake cancels sell for about the same as unused, hinged stamps.

Watermark

Wmk. 140 — Crowns

Propaganda of the Faith Issue

Italian Stamps Overprinted

1923, Oct. 24 **Wmk. 140** **Perf. 14**
1 A68 20c ol grn & brn org 8.00 40.00
2 A68 30c claret & brn org 8.00 40.00
3 A68 50c vio & brn org 4.75 47.50
4 A68 1 l blue & brn org 4.75 60.00
  Nos. 1-4 (4) 25.50 187.50
  Set, never hinged 64.00

Fascisti Issue

Italian Stamps Overprinted in Red or Black

1923, Oct. 29 **Unwmk.**
5 A69 10c dk green (R) 9.50 14.50
6 A69 30c dk violet (R) 9.50 14.50
7 A69 50c brown car 9.50 16.00
  Wmk. 140
8 A70 1 l blue 9.50 40.00
9 A70 2 l brown 9.50 47.50
10 A71 5 l blk & bl (R) 9.50 65.00
  Nos. 5-10 (6) 57.00 197.50
  Set, never hinged 145.00

Manzoni Issue

Stamps of Italy, 1923, Overprinted in Red

1924, Apr. 1 **Wmk. 140** **Perf. 14**
11 A72 10c brown red &
    blk 12.50 40.00
12 A72 15c blue grn &
    blk 12.50 40.00
13 A72 30c black & slate 12.50 40.00
14 A72 50c org brn &
    blk 12.50 40.00
15 A72 1 l blue & blk 80.00 275.00
16 A72 5 l violet & blk 525.00 2,100.
  Nos. 11-16 (6) 655.00 2,535.
  Set, never hinged 1,630.

On Nos. 15 and 16 the overprint is placed vertically at the left side.

Victor Emmanuel Issue

Italy Nos. 175-177
Overprinted

1925-26 **Unwmk.** **Perf. 11**
17 A78 60c brown car .80 8.00
18 A78 1 l dark blue 1.60 8.00
  a. Perf. 13½ 4.75 27.50
  Perf. 13½
19 A78 1.25 l dk blue
    ('26) 2.40 25.00
  a. Perf. 11 1,250. 1,600.
  Nos. 17-19 (3) 4.80 41.00
  Set, #17-19, 18a, 19a,
    never hinged 2,600.

Saint Francis of Assisi Issue

Italy Nos. 178-180 Overprinted

1926, Apr. 12 **Wmk. 140** **Perf. 14**
20 A79 20c gray green 2.40 11.00
21 A80 40c dark violet 2.40 11.00
22 A81 60c red brown 2.40 20.00

Italy No. 182 and Type of A83
Overprinted in Red

Unwmk.
23 A82 1.25 l dark blue 2.40 27.50
24 A83 5 l + 2.50 l ol grn 6.50 55.00
  Nos. 20-24 (5) 16.10 124.50
  Set, never hinged 40.00

Volta Issue

Type of Italy
Overprinted

1927, Oct. 10 **Wmk. 140** **Perf. 14**
25 A84 20c purple 4.75 32.50
26 A84 50c deep orange 8.00 20.00
  a. Double overprint 175.00
27 A84 1.25 l brt blue 11.00 52.50
  Nos. 25-27 (3) 23.75 105.00
  Set, never hinged 60.00

Monte Cassino Issue
Types of Italy Overprinted in Red or Blue

1929, Oct. 14
28 A96 20c dk green (R) 4.75 17.50
29 A96 25c red org (Bl) 4.75 17.50
30 A98 50c + 10c crim (Bl) 4.75 20.00
31 A98 75c + 15c ol brn
    (R) 4.75 20.00
32 A96 1.25 l + 25c dk vio
    (R) 11.00 35.00
33 A98 5 l + 1 l saph (R) 11.00 40.00

Overprinted in Red

Unwmk.
34 A100 10 l + 2 l gray brn 11.00 55.00
  Nos. 28-34 (7) 52.00 205.00
  Set, never hinged 130.00

Royal Wedding Issue

Type of
Italy
Overprinted

1930, Mar. 17 — Wmk. 140

35	A101	20c yellow green	1.60	4.75
36	A101	50c + 10c dp org	1.20	8.00
37	A101	1.25 l + 25c rose red	1.20	16.00
		Nos. 35-37 (3)	4.00	28.75
		Set, never hinged	10.00	

Ferrucci Issue

Types of Italy Overprinted in Red or Blue

1930, July 26

38	A102	20c violet (R)	4.75	4.75
39	A103	25c dk green (R)	4.75	4.75
40	A103	50c black (R)	4.75	9.50
41	A103	1.25 l deep blue (R)	4.75	17.50
42	A104	5 l + 2 l dp car (Bl)	9.50	32.50
		Nos. 38-42,C1-C3 (8)	52.50	144.00
		Set, never hinged	130.00	

Virgil Issue

Types of Italy Overprinted in Red or Blue

1930, Dec. 4 — Photo.

43	A106	15c violet black	1.20	8.00
44	A106	20c orange brown	1.20	3.25
45	A106	25c dark green	1.20	3.25
46	A106	30c lt brown	1.20	3.25
47	A106	50c dull violet	1.20	3.25
48	A106	75c rose red	1.20	6.50
49	A106	1.25 l gray blue	1.20	8.00

Unwmk. Engr.

50	A106	5 l + 1.50 l dk vio	3.50	40.00
51	A106	10 l + 2.50 l ol brn	3.50	60.00
		Nos. 43-51,C4-C7 (13)	33.20	249.50
		Set, never hinged	82.50	

Saint Anthony of Padua Issue

Types of Italy Overprinted in Blue or Red

1931, May 7 — Photo. — Wmk. 140

52	A116	20c brown (Bl)	1.60	17.50
53	A116	25c green (R)	1.60	6.50
54	A118	30c gray brn (Bl)	1.60	6.50
55	A118	50c dull vio (Bl)	1.60	6.50
56	A120	1.25 l slate bl (R)	1.60	32.50

Overprinted in Red or Black

Unwmk. — Engr.

57	A121	75c black (R)	1.60	17.50
58	A122	5 l + 2.50 l dk brn (Bk)	6.50	67.50
		Nos. 52-58 (7)	16.10	154.50
		Set, never hinged	40.00	

Native Village Scene A14

1934, Oct. 16 — Wmk. 140

73	A14	5c ol grn & brn	4.00	20.00
74	A14	10c brown & black	4.00	20.00
75	A14	20c scar & indigo	4.00	16.00
76	A14	50c purple & brown	4.00	16.00
77	A14	60c org brn & ind	4.00	24.00
78	A14	1.25 l dk bl & grn	4.00	40.00
		Nos. 73-78,C43-C48 (12)	48.00	272.00
		Set, never hinged	120.00	

2nd Colonial Arts Exhibition, Naples.

SEMI-POSTAL STAMPS

Many issues of Italy and Italian Colonies include one or more semipostal denominations. To avoid splitting sets, these issues are generally listed as regular postage, airmail, etc., unless all values carry a surtax.

Holy Year Issue

Italian Stamps of 1924 Overprinted in Black or Red

1925 — Wmk. 140 — Perf. 12

B1	SP4	20c + 10c dk grn & brn	3.25	20.00
B2	SP4	30c + 15c dk brn & brn	3.25	22.50
B3	SP4	50c + 25c vio & brn	3.25	20.00
B4	SP4	60c + 30c dp rose & brn	3.25	25.00
B5	SP8	1 l + 50c dp bl & vio (R)	3.25	32.50
B6	SP8	5 l + 2 l org brn & vio (R)	3.25	47.50
		Nos. B1-B6 (6)	19.50	167.50
		Set, never hinged	42.50	

Colonial Institute Issue

Peace Substituting Spade for Sword — SP1

1926, June 1 — Typo. — Perf. 14

B7	SP1	5c + 5c brown	.95	8.00
B8	SP1	10c + 5c ol brn	.95	8.00
B9	SP1	20c + 5c bl grn	.95	8.00
B10	SP1	40c + 5c brn red	.95	8.00
B11	SP1	60c + 5c orange	.95	8.00
B12	SP1	1 l + 5c blue	.95	17.50
		Nos. B7-B12 (6)	5.70	57.50
		Set, never hinged	14.50	

The surtax was for the Italian Colonial Institute.

Fiera Campionaria Tripoli
See Libya for stamps with this inscription.

Types of Italian Semi-Postal Stamps of 1926 Overprinted like Nos. 17-19

1927, Apr. 21 — Unwmk. — Perf. 11

B19	SP10	40c + 20c dk brn & blk	2.40	32.50
B20	SP10	60c + 30c brn red & ol brn	2.40	32.50
B21	SP10	1.25 l + 60c dp bl & blk	2.40	52.50
B22	SP10	5 l + 2.50 l dk grn & blk	4.00	72.50
		Nos. B19-B22 (4)	11.20	190.00
		Set, never hinged	27.50	

The surtax was for the charitable work of the Voluntary Militia for Italian National Defense.

Allegory of Fascism and Victory — SP2

1928, Oct. 15 — Wmk. 140

B29	SP2	20c + 5c bl grn	2.40	12.00
B30	SP2	30c + 5c red	2.40	12.00
B31	SP2	50c + 10c pur	2.40	20.00
B32	SP2	1.25 l + 20c dk bl	3.25	24.00
		Nos. B29-B32 (4)	10.45	68.00
		Set, never hinged	26.00	

46th anniv. of the Societa Africana d'Italia. The surtax aided that society.

Types of Italian Semi-Postal Stamps of 1928 Overprinted

1929, Mar. 4 — Unwmk. — Perf. 11

B33	SP10	30c + 10c red & blk	4.00	20.00
B34	SP10	50c + 20c vio & blk	4.00	24.00
B35	SP10	1.25 l + 50c brn & bl	4.75	40.00
B36	SP10	5 l + 2 l ol grn & blk	4.75	72.50
		Nos. B33-B36 (4)	17.50	156.50
		Set, never hinged	45.00	

The surtax on these stamps was for the charitable work of the Voluntary Militia for Italian National Defense.

Types of Italian Semi-Postal Stamps of 1926, Overprinted in Black or Red Like Nos. B33-B36

1930, Oct. 20

B50	SP10	30c + 10c dp grn & bl grn (Bk)	21.00	32.50
B51	SP10	50c + 10c dk grn & vio (R)	21.00	45.00
B52	SP10	1.25 l + 30c blk brn & red brn (R)	21.00	55.00
B53	SP10	5 l + 1.50 l ind & grn (R)	65.00	160.00
		Nos. B50-B53 (4)	128.00	292.50
		Set, never hinged	315.00	

Ancient Arch — SP3

1930, Nov. 27 — Photo. — Wmk. 140

B54	SP3	50c + 20c ol brn	4.00	20.00
B55	SP3	1.25 l + 20c dp bl	4.00	20.00
B56	SP3	1.75 l + 20c green	4.00	22.50
B57	SP3	2.55 l + 50c purple	6.50	35.00
B58	SP3	5 l + 1 l deep car	6.50	52.50
		Nos. B54-B58 (5)	25.00	150.00
		Set, never hinged	62.50	

25th anniv. of the Italian Colonial Agricultural Institute. The surtax was for the benefit of that institution.

AIR POST STAMPS

Ferrucci Issue

Type of Italian Air Post Stamps Overprinted in Blue or Red like #38-42

1930, July 26 — Wmk. 140 — Perf. 14

C1	AP7	50c brown vio (Bl)	4.00	8.00
C2	AP7	1 l dk blue (R)	4.00	14.50
C3	AP7	5 l + 2 l dp car (Bl)	16.00	52.50
		Nos. C1-C3 (3)	24.00	75.00
		Set, never hinged	60.00	

Virgil Issue

Types of Italian Air Post Stamps Overprinted in Red or Blue like #43-51

1930, Dec. 4 — Photo.

C4	AP8	50c deep green	2.40	9.50
C5	AP8	1 l rose red	2.40	9.50

Unwmk. Engr.

C6	AP8	7.70 l + 1.30 l dk brn	6.50	47.50
C7	AP8	9 l + 2 l gray	6.50	47.50
		Nos. C4-C7 (4)	17.80	114.00
		Set, never hinged	44.00	

Airplane over Columns of the Basilica, Leptis — AP1

Arab Horseman Pointing at Airplane AP2

1931-32 — Photo. — Wmk. 140

C8	AP1	50c rose car	.80	.20
C9	AP1	60c red org	2.40	8.00
C10	AP1	75c dp bl ('32)	2.40	6.50
C11	AP1	80c dull violet	8.00	14.50
C12	AP2	1 l deep blue	1.60	.20
C13	AP2	1.20 l dk brown	24.00	17.50
C14	AP2	1.50 l org red	9.50	17.50
C15	AP2	5 l green	27.50	27.50
		Nos. C8-C15 (8)	76.20	91.90
		Set, never hinged	150.00	

For surcharges and overprint see Nos. C29-C32.

Agricultural Institute, 25th Anniv. AP3

1931, Dec. 7

C16	AP3	50c dp blue	3.25	20.00
C17	AP3	80c violet	3.25	20.00
C18	AP3	1 l gray black	3.25	27.50
C19	AP3	2 l deep green	6.50	40.00
C20	AP3	5 l + 2 l rose red	9.50	72.50
		Nos. C16-C20 (5)	25.75	180.00
		Set, never hinged	64.00	

Graf Zeppelin Issue

Mercury, by Giovanni da Bologna, and Zeppelin AP4

Designs: 3 l, 12 l, Mercury. 10 l, 20 l, Guido Reni's "Aurora." 5 l, 15 l, Arch of Marcus Aurelius.

1933, May 5

C21	AP4	3 l dark brown	8.00	120.00
C22	AP4	5 l purple	8.00	120.00
C23	AP4	10 l deep green	8.00	225.00
C24	AP4	12 l deep blue	8.00	240.00
C25	AP4	15 l carmine	8.00	240.00
C26	AP4	20 l gray black	8.00	325.00
	Nos. C21-C26 (6)		48.00	1,270.
	Set, never hinged		120.00	

For overprints and surcharges see Nos. C38-C42.

North Atlantic Flight Issue

Airplane, Lion of St. Mark AP7

1933, June 1

C27	AP7	19.75 l blk & ol brn	16.00	600.00
C28	AP7	44.75 l dk bl & lt grn	16.00	600.00
	Set, never hinged		80.00	

Type of 1931 Overprinted or Surcharged

1934, Jan. 20

C29	AP2	2 l on 5 l org brn	3.25	72.50
C30	AP2	3 l on 5 l grn	3.25	72.50
C31	AP2	5 l ocher	3.25	80.00
C32	AP2	10 l on 5 l rose	4.75	80.00
	Nos. C29-C32 (4)		14.50	305.00
	Set, never hinged		36.00	

For use on mail to be carried on a special flight from Rome to Buenos Aires.

Types of Libya Airmail Issue Overprinted in Black or Red

1934, May 1   Wmk. 140

C38	AP4	50c rose red	9.50	115.00
C39	AP4	75c lemon	9.50	115.00
C40	AP4	5 l + 1 l brn	9.50	115.00
C41	AP4	10 l + 2 l dk bl	200.00	650.00
C42	AP5	25 l + 3 l pur	200.00	650.00
	Nos. C38-C42,CE1-CE2 (7)		447.50	1,875.
	Set, never hinged		1,070.	

"Circuit of the Oases."

Plane Shadow on Desert AP11

Designs: 25c, 50c, 75c, Plane shadow on desert. 80c, 1 l, 2 l, Camel corps.

1934, Oct. 16   Photo.

C43	AP11	25c sl bl & org red	4.00	20.00
C44	AP11	50c dk grn & ind	4.00	16.00
C45	AP11	75c dk brn & org red	4.00	16.00

C46	AP11	80c org brn & ol grn	4.00	20.00
C47	AP11	1 l scar & ol grn	4.00	24.00
C48	AP11	2 l dk bl & brn	4.00	40.00
	Nos. C43-C48 (6)		24.00	136.00
	Set, never hinged		60.00	

Second Colonial Arts Exhibition, Naples.

AIR POST SEMI-POSTAL STAMPS

King Victor Emmanuel III SPAP1

1934, Nov. 5   Wmk. 140   Perf. 14

CB1	SPAP1	25c + 10c gray grn	6.50	14.50
CB2	SPAP1	50c + 10c brn	6.50	14.50
CB3	SPAP1	75c + 15c rose red	6.50	14.50
CB4	SPAP1	80c + 15c brn	6.50	14.50
CB5	SPAP1	1 l + 20c red brn	6.50	14.50
CB6	SPAP1	2 l + 20c brt bl	6.50	14.50
CB7	SPAP1	3 l + 25c pur	22.50	72.50
CB8	SPAP1	5 l + 25c org	22.50	72.50
CB9	SPAP1	10 l + 30c rose vio	22.50	72.50
CB10	SPAP1	25 l + 2 l dp grn	22.50	72.50
	Nos. CB1-CB10 (10)		129.00	377.00
	Set, never hinged		320.00	

65th birthday of King Victor Emmanuel III; non-stop flight from Rome to Mogadiscio. For overprint see No. CBO1.

AIR POST SEMI-POSTAL OFFICIAL STAMP

Type of Air Post Semi-Postal Stamps Overprinted Crown and "SERVIZIO DI STATO" in Black

1934   Wmk. 140   Perf. 14

CBO1	SPAP1	25 l + 2 l cop red	2,750. 4,400.
	Never hinged		4,250.

AIR POST SPECIAL DELIVERY STAMPS

Type of Libya Overprinted in Black Like Nos. C38-c42

1934, May 1   Wmk. 140   Perf. 14

CE1	APSD1	2.25 l red orange	9.50	115.00
CE2	APSD1	4.50 l + 1 l dp rose	9.50	115.00
	Set, never hinged		48.00	

AUTHORIZED DELIVERY STAMP

Authorized Delivery Stamp of Italy 1930, Overprinted like Nos. 38-42

1931, Mar.   Wmk. 140   Perf. 14

EY1	AD2	10c dark brown	9.50	24.00
	Never hinged		24.00	

TRISTAN DA CUNHA

ˌtris-tən-də-ˈkü-nə

LOCATION — Group of islands in the south Atlantic Ocean midway between the Cape of Good Hope and South America

GOVT. — A dependency of St. Helena

AREA — 40 sq. mi.

POP. — 313 (1988)

12 Pence = 1 Shilling
100 Cents = 1 Rand (1961)
12 Pence = 1 Shilling (1963)
20 Shillings = 1 Pound
100 Pence = 1 Pound (1971)

> **Catalogue values for all unused stamps in this country are for Never Hinged items.**

Stamps of St. Helena, 1938-49, Overprinted in Black

1952, Jan. 1   Wmk. 4   Perf. 12½

1	A24	½p purple	.20	2.10
2	A24	1p blue grn & blk	.80	1.90
3	A24	1½p car rose & blk	.80	1.90
4	A24	2p carmine & blk	.80	1.90
5	A24	3p gray	1.10	1.90
6	A24	4p ultra	4.25	3.00
7	A24	6p gray blue	5.00	3.00
8	A24	8p olive	4.50	6.50
9	A24	1sh sepia	5.00	2.50
10	A24	2sh6p deep claret	24.00	17.50
11	A24	5sh brown	26.00	27.50
12	A24	10sh violet	50.00	37.50
	Nos. 1-12 (12)		122.45	107.20
	Set, hinged		85.00	

Common Design Types pictured following the introduction.

Coronation Issue
Common Design Type

1953, June 2   Engr.   Perf. 13½x13

13	CD312	3p dk green & black	.85 1.40

Tristan Crayfish — A1

Carting Flax — A2

Designs: 1½p, Rockhopper penguin. 2p, Factory. 2½p, Mollymauk. 3p, Island boat. 4p, View of Tristan. 5p, Potato patches. 6p, Inaccessible Island. 9p, Nightingale Island. 1sh, St. Mary's Church. 2sh 6p, Elephant seal. 5sh, Flightless rail. 10sh, Island spinning wheel.

1954-58   Perf. 12½

14	A1	½p choc & red	.20	.20
a.	Bklt. pane of 4 ('58)		2.50	
15	A2	1p green & choc	.20	.60
a.	Bklt. pane of 4 ('58)		4.00	
16	A1	1½p dp plum & blk	2.00	1.40
a.	Bklt. pane of 4 ('58)		7.00	
17	A2	2p org & vio blue	.35	.20
18	A2	2½p carmine & blk	1.75	.70
19	A1	3p ol grn & ultra	.80	1.40
a.	Bklt. pane of 4 ('58)		10.50	
20	A2	4p dp bl & aqua	.80	.75
a.	Bklt. pane of 4 ('58)		13.00	
21	A2	5p gray & bl grn	.80	.75
22	A2	6p vio & dk ol grn	.80	.75
23	A2	9p henna brn & rose lil	.80	.55
24	A2	1sh choc & ol grn	.80	.55
25	A2	2sh6p blue & choc	27.50	12.50
26	A2	5sh red org & blk	60.00	16.00
27	A2	10sh red vio & org	29.00	19.00
	Nos. 14-27 (14)		125.80	55.35
	Set, hinged		70.00	

Starfish — A3

Fish: 1p, Concha. 1½p, Klipfish. 2p, Heron fish (saury). 2½p, Snipefish ("swordfish"). 3d, Tristan crawfish. 4p, Soldier fish. 5p, Five finger fish. 6p, Mackeral scad. 9p, Stumpnose. 1sh, Bluefish. 2sh6p, Snoek (snake mackerel). 5sh, Shark. 10sh, Atlantic night whale.

Perf. 12½x13

1960, Feb. 1   Engr.   Wmk. 314

28	A3	½p orange & black	.20	.20
a.	Booklet pane of 4		1.50	
29	A3	1p rose lilac & blk	.25	.20
a.	Booklet pane of 4		2.50	
30	A3	1½p grnsh bl & blk	.35	.25
a.	Booklet pane of 4		2.75	
31	A3	2p green & black	.45	.35
32	A3	2½p brown & black	.50	.35
33	A3	3p rose red & blk	1.40	1.40
a.	Booklet pane of 4		8.00	
34	A3	4p gray ol & blk	1.25	.65
a.	Booklet pane of 4		7.00	
35	A3	5p org yel & blk	1.60	.70
36	A3	6p blue & black	1.60	.80
37	A3	9p rose car & blk	1.90	.70
38	A3	1sh brn org & blk	2.75	.60
39	A3	2sh6p vio blue & blk	12.50	12.50
40	A3	5sh emerald & blk	15.00	16.00
41	A3	10sh violet & blk	50.00	50.00
	Nos. 28-41 (14)		89.75	84.70

1961, Apr. 15   Perf. 12½x13

42	A3	½c like No. 28	.20	.20
43	A3	1c like No. 29	.20	.20
44	A3	1½c like No. 30	.40	.40
45	A3	2c like No. 32	.75	.75
46	A3	2½c like No. 33	1.10	1.10
47	A3	3c like No. 34	1.10	1.10
48	A3	4c like No. 35	1.40	1.40
49	A3	5c like No. 36	1.40	1.40
50	A3	7½c like No. 37	1.40	1.40
51	A3	10c like No. 38	2.25	1.60
52	A3	25c like No. 39	9.00	9.00
53	A3	50c like No. 40	22.50	17.50
54	A3	1r like No. 41	45.00	40.00
	Nos. 42-54 (13)		86.70	76.50

Nos. 46, 49-51 surcharged for "Tristan Relief" are listed as St. Helena Nos. B1-B4.

Types of St. Helena, 1961 Overprinted

Perf. 11½x12, 12x11½

1963, Apr. 12   Photo.   Wmk. 4

55	A29	1p rose, ultra, yel & grn	.20	1.00
56	A29	1½p bis, sep, yel & grn	.20	.40
57	A29	2p gray & red	.25	1.00
58	A30	3p dk bl, rose & grnsh bl	.30	1.00
a.	Double overprint			
59	A29	4½p slate, brn & grn	.55	.70
60	A29	6p cit, brn & dp car	.80	.40
61	A29	7p vio, blk & red brn	.55	.40
62	A29	10p bl & dp claret	.55	.40
63	A29	1sh red brn, grn & yel	.55	.40
64	A29	1sh6p gray bl & blk	5.50	1.10
65	A29	2sh6p grnsh bl, yel & red	1.75	.75
66	A29	5sh grn, brn & yel	7.00	1.75
67	A29	10sh gray bl, blk & sal	7.00	1.75
	Nos. 55-67 (13)		25.20	11.05

Freedom from Hunger Issue
Common Design Type

Perf. 14x14½

1963, Oct. 2   Photo.   Wmk. 314

68	CD314	1sh6p rose carmine	1.00 .40

Red Cross Centenary Issue
Common Design Type

1964, Jan. 2   Litho.   Perf. 13

69	CD315	3p black & red	.75	.40
70	CD315	1sh6p ultra & red	1.25	.60

Flagship of Tristáo da Cunha, 1506 — A4

Queen Elizabeth II — A5

½p, Map of South Atlantic Ocean. 1 ½p, Dutch ship Heemstede, first landing, 1643. 2p, New England whaler. 3p, Confederate ship Shenandoah. 4½p, H.M.S. Galatea, 1867. 6p, H.M.S. Cilicia, 1942. 7p, H.M. Royal Yacht Britannia, 1957. 10p, H.M.S. Leopard, Evacuation, 1961. 1sh, Dutch ship Tjisadane, 1961. 1sh6p, M.V. Tristania. 2sh6p, M.V. Boissevain, returning islanders, 1963. 5sh, M.S. Bornholm, returning islanders, 1963.

Perf. 11x11½
1965, Feb. 17		**Engr.**		**Wmk. 314**
71	A4	½p black & dk blue	.20	.20
a.	Booklet pane of 4			.25
72	A4	1p black & emerald	.85	.20
a.	Booklet pane of 4			4.25
73	A4	1 ½p black & ultra	.85	.20
a.	Booklet pane of 4			4.25
74	A4	2p black & lilac	.85	.20
75	A4	3p blk & grnsh bl	.85	.20
a.	Booklet pane of 4			4.25
76	A4	4 ½p black & brown	.85	.20
77	A4	6p black & green	.70	.30
a.	Booklet pane of 4			4.25
78	A4	7p black & ver	.85	.40
79	A4	10p black & dk brn	.85	.40
80	A4	1sh black & lil rose	.85	.50
81	A4	1sh6p black & olive	4.50	2.75
82	A4	2sh6p black & brn org	3.00	3.00
83	A4	5sh black & violet	6.00	4.00

Perf. 11½x11
84	A5	10sh lil rose & dk bl	2.00	1.50
		Nos. 71-84 (14)	23.20	14.05

See Nos. 113-115. For surcharges see Nos. 108, 141-152. For overprints see Nos. 132.

ITU Issue
Common Design Type
1965, May 11	**Litho.**		**Perf. 11x11½**	
85	CD317	3p vermilion & gray	.55	.25
86	CD317	6p purple & orange	.85	.40

Intl. Cooperation Year Issue
Common Design Type
1965, Oct. 25	**Wmk. 314**		**Perf. 14½**	
87	CD318	1p blue grn & claret	.20	.30
88	CD318	6p lt violet & green	1.25	.45

Churchill Memorial Issue
Common Design Type
Wmk. 314
1966, Jan. 24	**Photo.**		**Perf. 14**	

Design in Black, Gold and Carmine Rose
89	CD319	1p bright blue	.20	.20
90	CD319	3p green	.30	.20
91	CD319	6p brown	1.40	.70
92	CD319	1sh6p violet	4.25	1.50
		Nos. 89-92 (4)	6.15	2.60

World Cup Soccer Issue
Common Design Type
1966	**Litho.**		**Perf. 14**	
93	CD320	3p multicolored	.25	.20
94	CD321	2sh6p multicolored	1.25	.55

Nos. 93-94 were issued Oct. 1 in Tristan da Cunha, but on July 1 in St. Helena.

Light Dragoon of 19th Century and Sailing Ship — A6

Wmk. 314
1966, Aug. 15	**Litho.**		**Perf. 14½**	
95	A6	3p pale green & multi	.20	.20
96	A6	6p tan & multi	.20	.20
97	A6	1sh6p gray & multi	.50	.30
98	A6	2sh6p multicolored	.85	.45
		Nos. 95-98 (4)	1.75	1.15

150th anniv. of the establishment of a garrison on Tristan da Cunha.

WHO Headquarters Issue
Common Design Type
1966, Oct. 1	**Litho.**		**Perf. 14**	
99	CD322	6p multicolored	.35	.25
100	CD322	5sh multicolored	1.90	1.00

UNESCO Anniversary Issue
Common Design Type
1966, Dec. 1	**Litho.**		**Perf. 14**	
101	CD323	10p "Education"	.35	.20
102	CD323	1sh6p "Science"	.75	.40
103	CD323	2sh6p "Culture"	1.40	.75
		Nos. 101-103 (3)	2.50	1.35

Calshot Harbor A7

Perf. 14x14½
1967, Jan. 2	**Litho.**		**Unwmk.**	
104	A7	6p dull green & multi	.20	.20
105	A7	10p brown & multi	.20	.20
106	A7	1sh6p dull blue & multi	.20	.20
107	A7	2sh6p orange brn & multi	.25	.30
		Nos. 104-107 (4)	.85	.90

Opening of the artificial Calshot Harbor.

No. 76 Surcharged with New Value and Three Bars
Perf. 11x11½
1967, May 10	**Engr.**		**Wmk. 314**	
108	A4	4p on 4½p blk & brn	.30	.30

Tristan da Cunha, Prince Alfred, Queen Elizabeth II and Prince Philip — A8

1967, July 10	**Litho.**		**Perf. 14x14½**	
109	A8	3p blue grn, dk grn & blk	.20	.20
110	A8	6p dk carmine & blk	.20	.20
111	A8	1sh6p brt grn, gray grn & blk	.20	.20
112	A8	2sh6p dull ultra, sep & blk	.25	.30
		Nos. 109-112 (4)	.85	.90

Cent. of the visit of Prince Alfred, First Duke of Edinburgh, to Tristan da Cunha.

Types of 1965
Designs: 4p, H.M.S. Challenger, 1870. 10sh, South African research vessel, R.S.A. £1, Queen Elizabeth II.

Perf. 11x11½
1967, Sept. 1	**Engr.**		**Wmk. 314**	
113	A4	4p black & orange	5.25	3.75
114	A4	10sh black & dull grn	16.00	14.00

Perf. 11½x11
115	A5	£1 brn org & dk blue	16.00	17.50
		Nos. 113-115 (3)	37.25	35.25

Wandering Albatross Nest — A9

Birds: 1sh, Big-billed buntings. 1sh6p, Tristan thrushes. 2sh6p, Great shearwaters.

Perf. 14x14½
1968, May 15	**Photo.**		**Wmk. 314**	
116	A9	4p multicolored	.20	.20
117	A9	1sh multicolored	.50	.30
118	A9	1sh6p multicolored	.85	.50
119	A9	2sh6p multicolored	1.25	.85
		Nos. 116-119 (4)	2.80	1.85

Union Jack and St. Helena Flag — A10

Design: 9p, 2sh6p, Map showing locations of St. Helena and Tristan da Cunha.

1968, Nov. 1	**Litho.**		**Wmk. 314**	
120	A10	6p violet & multi	.20	.20
121	A10	9p brn, bl grn & vio bl	.20	.20
122	A10	1sh6p green & multi	.25	.25
123	A10	2sh6p dp car, bl grn & vio bl	.35	.35
		Nos. 120-123 (4)	1.00	1.00

30th anniv. of Tristan da Cunha as a Dependency of St. Helena.

Frigate A11

Designs: 1sh, Cape Horner. 1sh6p, Barque. 2sh6p, Tea Clipper.

Perf. 11x11½
1969, June 1	**Engr.**		**Wmk. 314**	
124	A11	4p brt blue	.20	.20
125	A11	1sh rose carmine	.45	.40
126	A11	1sh6p green	.65	.50
127	A11	2sh6p sepia	1.10	.90
		Nos. 124-127 (4)	2.40	2.00

Islanders Going to First Religious Service, 1851 — A12

Designs: 4p, Tristan da Cunha, birds and ship. 1sh6p, Landing at the beach. 2sh6p, St. Mary's Church, 1969, and procession.

Perf. 14½x14
1969, Nov. 1	**Litho.**		**Wmk. 314**	
128	A12	4p multicolored	.20	.40
129	A12	9p multicolored	.20	.40
130	A12	1sh6p multicolored	.35	.55
131	A12	2sh6p multicolored	.50	.55
		Nos. 128-131 (4)	1.25	1.90

Issued to honor the work of the United Society for the Propagation of the Faith.

No. 77 Overprinted in Deep Orange: "NATIONAL / SAVINGS"
Perf. 11x11½
1970, May 15	**Engr.**		**Wmk. 314**	
132	A4	6p black & green	.30	.25

Issued to promote national savings. No. 132 also used as savings stamp.
In 1971, No. 132 was locally surcharged "2 ½p" and 3 short bars by means of a rubber handstamp. Value $7.

Globe and Red Cross A13

1sh9p, 2sh6p, British & Red Cross flags, vert.

Perf. 13½x13, 13x13½
1970, June 1			**Litho.**	
133	A13	4p emer, red & grnsh bl	.30	.20
134	A13	4p bister, red & grnsh bl	.45	.20
135	A13	1sh9p gray, vio bl & red	.75	.35
136	A13	2sh6p rose cl, vio bl & red	1.00	.60
		Nos. 133-136 (4)	2.50	1.35

Centenary of the British Red Cross Society.

Rock Lobster and Lobster Men Placing Trap — A14

10p, 2sh6p, Workers in processing plant and side view of rock lobster (jasus tristani).

Perf. 12½x13
1970, Nov. 1	**Litho.**		**Wmk. 314**	
137	A14	4p lilac rose & multi	.20	.30
138	A14	10p dull yel & multi	.25	.35
139	A14	1sh6p brown org & multi	.75	.60
140	A14	2sh6p olive & multi	1.10	.75
		Nos. 137-140 (4)	2.30	2.00

Tristan da Cunha rock lobster (crawfish) industry.

Nos. 72-74, 77-83, 113-114 Surcharged with New Value and Three Bars
Perf. 11x11½
1971, Feb. 15	**Engr.**		**Wmk. 314**	
141	A4	½p on 1p	.20	.20
142	A4	1p on 2p	.20	.20
143	A4	1 ½p on 4p	.35	.20
144	A4	2 ½p on 6p	.35	.20
145	A4	3p on 7p	.35	.20
146	A4	4p on 10p	.35	.20
147	A4	5p on 1sh	.35	.20
148	A4	7 ½p on 1sh6p	2.10	2.10
149	A4	12 ½p on 2sh6p	3.00	3.00
150	A4	15p on 1 ½p	3.00	3.50
151	A4	25p on 5sh	3.00	6.25
152	A4	50p on 10sh	4.25	12.50
		Nos. 141-152 (12)	17.50	28.75

"Quest" — A15

4p, Presentation of Scout Troop flag in front of Tristan school. 7½p, Great Britain #167a with Tristan da Cunha cancellation. 12 ½p, Sir Ernest Henry Shackleton, boat & expedition cancellations.

Perf. 13½x14
1971, June 1	**Litho.**		**Wmk. 314**	
153	A15	1 ½p lt blue & multi	1.10	.20
154	A15	4p buff, yel grn & blk	1.10	.45
155	A15	7 ½p pale grn, rose lil & blk	1.10	1.00
156	A15	12 ½p buff & multi	1.90	2.00
		Nos. 153-156 (4)	5.20	3.65

50th anniversary of the Shackleton-Rowett South Atlantic expedition.

"Victory" at Trafalgar and Thomas
Swain Catching Nelson — A16

Ships and Island Families: 2½p, "Emily of
Stonington" and inscribed P. W. Green, 1836.
4p, "Italia" and inscribed Gaetano Lavarello,
1892, and Andrea Repetto. 7½p, "Falmouth"
and Corp. William Glass, 1816. 12½p, American Whaler and inscribed 1836 Joshua Rogers, 1849, Capt. Andrew Hangan.

1971, Nov. 1

157	A16	1½p bister & multi	.20	.20
158	A16	2½p multicolored	.25	.25
159	A16	4p gray & multi	.50	.55
160	A16	7½p multicolored	.80	.85
161	A16	12½p blue & multi	1.25	1.40
		Nos. 157-161 (5)	3.00	3.25

Cow
Pudding — A17　　　Coxswain — A18

Native Flora: 1p, Peak berry and crater lake.
1½p, Sand flower, horiz. 2½p, New Zealand
flax, horiz. 3p, Island tree. 4p, Bog fern and
snow-capped mountain. 5p, Dog catcher and
albatrosses. 7½p, Celery and terns. 12½p,
Pepper tree and waterfall. 25p, Foul berry,
horiz. 50p, Tussock and penguins. £1, Tussac
and islands, horiz.

Perf. 13½x13, 13x13½

1972, Feb. 26　　　　　　Wmk. 314

162	A17	½p gray & multi	.20	.20
163	A17	1p salmon & multi	.20	.20
164	A17	1½p green & multi	.25	.25
165	A17	2½p multicolored	.25	.25
166	A17	3p multicolored	.25	.25
167	A17	4p lemon & multi	.35	.30
168	A17	5p yel grn & multi	.50	.30
169	A17	7½p dull yel & multi	2.10	1.75
170	A17	12½p multicolored	1.40	1.00
171	A17	25p gray & multi	2.75	2.40

Litho. and Engr.

172	A17	50p multicolored	6.75	4.50
173	A17	£1 lt blue & multi	12.00	4.50
		Nos. 162-173 (12)	27.00	15.90

1972, June 1　　Litho.　　Perf. 14

2½p, Launching longboat. 4p, Men rowing
longboat. 12½p, Longboat under sail.

174	A18	2½p multi, horiz.	.20	.20
175	A18	4p multi, horiz.	.20	.20
176	A18	7½p multi	.60	.40
177	A18	12½p multi	1.00	.50
		Nos. 174-177 (4)	2.00	1.30

Silver Wedding Issue, 1972
Common Design Type

Design: Queen Elizabeth II, Prince Philip,
thrush and wandering albatrosses.

Perf. 14x14½

1972, Nov. 20　　Photo.　　Wmk. 314

178	CD324	2½p multicolored	.20	.20
179	CD324	7½p ultra & multi	.50	.45

Altar, St. Mary's Church — A19

1973, July 8　　Litho.　　Perf. 13½

180	A19	25p dk blue & multi	1.40	1.40

St. Mary's Church, Tristan da Cunha, 50th
anniv.

"Challenger" off Tristan, Steil's
Sounding Instrument — A20

Designs: 4p, Challenger's laboratory. 7½p,
Challenger off Nightingale Island. 12½p, Map
of Challenger's voyage. Each stamp shows an
instrument for deep sea soundings.

Perf. 13½x14

1973, Oct. 15　　　　　　Wmk. 314

181	A20	4p multicolored	.20	.20
182	A20	5p multicolored	.30	.30
183	A20	7½p multicolored	.50	.50
184	A20	12½p multicolored	1.00	1.00
a.		Souv. sheet, #181-184, perf. 13½	2.25	2.25
		Nos. 181-184 (4)	2.00	2.00

Centenary of "Challenger's" visit to Tristan
da Cunha during oceanographic exploration
world trip, 1872-76.

View of English Port from
Shipboard — A21

5p, Inspectors at volcano rim. 7½p, Islanders disembarking from "Bornholm." 12½p,
Islanders on board ship approaching Tristan
da Cunha.

1973, Nov. 10　　　　　　Perf. 14½

185	A21	4p yellow, blk & gold	.20	.20
186	A21	5p multicolored	.25	.20
187	A21	7½p multicolored	.40	.30
188	A21	12½p multicolored	.55	.40
		Nos. 185-188 (4)	1.40	1.10

10th anniversary of return of islanders to
Tristan da Cunha.

Princess Anne's Wedding Issue
Common Design Type

1973, Nov. 14　　Wmk. 314　　Perf. 14

189	CD325	7½p multicolored	.20	.20
190	CD325	12½p bl grn & multi	.25	.20

Rockhopper Penguin — A22

Designs: Rockhopper penguins.

1974, May 1　　　　　　　Litho.

191	A22	2½p shown	2.50	1.25
192	A22	5p Colony	2.75	1.65
193	A22	7½p Penguins fishing	3.25	2.00
194	A22	25p Penguin and fledgling	7.50	5.00
		Nos. 191-194 (4)	16.00	9.90

Souvenir Sheet

Map of Tristan da Cunha, Penguin and
Sea Gull — A23

1974, Oct. 1　　Wmk. 314　　Perf. 13½

195	A23	35p multicolored	6.00	5.25

Blenheim
Palace
A24

25p, Churchill and Queen Elizabeth II.

Wmk. 373

1974, Nov. 30　　Litho.　　Perf. 14

196	A24	7½p black & yellow	.20	.20
197	A24	25p black & brown	.50	.40
a.		Souvenir sheet of 2, #196-197	1.10	1.10

Sir Winston Churchill (1874-1965).

Plocamium Fuscorubrum — A25

Aquatic Plants: 5p, Ulva lactuca. 10p,
Epymenia flabellata. 20p, Macrocystis pyrifera.

Perf. 13x14

1975, Apr. 16　　　　　　Wmk. 314

198	A25	4p lilac & multi	.20	.20
199	A25	5p ultra & multi	.20	.20
200	A25	10p yellow & multi	.40	.30
201	A25	20p lt green & multi	.75	.65
		Nos. 198-201 (4)	1.55	1.35

Killer Whales — A26

Wmk. 314

1975, Nov. 1　　Litho.　　Perf. 13½

202	A26	2p shown	.35	.20
203	A26	3p Rough-toothed dolphins	.65	.20
204	A26	5p Atlantic right whale	1.75	.85
205	A26	20p Finback whales	4.25	1.90
		Nos. 202-205 (4)	7.00	3.15

Tristan
da
Cunha
No. 1
A27

Designs: 9p, Tristan da Cunha #13, vert.
25p, Freighter Tristania II.

Perf. 13½x14, 14x13½

1976, May 6　　Litho.　　Wmk. 373

206	A27	5p lilac, vio & blk	.20	.20
207	A27	9p bluish gray, grn & blk	.25	.25

208	A27	25p multicolored	.85	.85
a.		Souvenir sheet of 3	3.00	3.00
		Nos. 206-208 (3)	1.30	1.30

Festival of Stamps 1976. #208a contains
one each of Ascension #214, St. Helena #297
and Tristan da Cunha #208.

The
Patches
A28

Views, by Roland Svensson: 3p, Tristan
house, vert. 10p, Tristan Settlement and Cliffs.
20p, Huts at Nightingale, vert.

1976, Oct. 4　　Litho.　　Perf. 14

209	A28	3p multicolored	.20	.20
210	A28	5p multicolored	.20	.20
211	A28	10p multicolored	.25	.25
212	A28	20p multicolored	.45	.45
a.		Souvenir sheet of 4, #209-211	1.50	1.25
		Nos. 209-212 (4)	1.10	1.10

An artist's view of Tristan da Cunha.
See Nos. 234-237, 268-271.

Royal Yacht Britannia — A29

15p, Royal standard. 25p, Royal family.

1977, Feb. 7　　Wmk. 373　　Perf. 13

213	A29	10p multicolored	.20	.20
214	A29	15p multicolored	.20	.20
215	A29	25p multicolored	.25	.25
		Nos. 213-215 (3)	.65	.65

25th anniv. of the reign of Elizabeth II.
For surcharges see Nos. 220-221.

H.M.S.
Eskimo,
Sept.
1970
A30

Royal Naval Ships and Arms: 10p, Naiad,
Nov. 1968. 15p, Jaguar, Mar. 1964. 20p,
London, Dec. 1964. Dates of visits to island.

1977, Oct. 1　　Litho.　　Perf. 14½

216	A30	5p multicolored	.20	.20
217	A30	10p multicolored	.20	.20
218	A30	15p multicolored	.25	.25
219	A30	20p multicolored	.35	.35
a.		Souvenir sheet of 4, #216-219	1.75	1.75
		Nos. 216-219 (4)	1.00	1.00

Nos. 214-215 Surcharged with New
Value and Bar

1977, Oct. 13　　Wmk. 373　　Perf. 13

220	A29	4p on 15p multi	2.25	4.50
221	A29	7½p on 25p multi	2.25	4.50

Giant Fulmars — A31

Perf. 13½x14, 14x13½

1977, Dec. 1　　　　　　　Litho.

222	A31	1p Pterodroma macroptera, horiz.	.20	.45
223	A31	2p Fregetta marina, horiz.	.20	.75
224	A31	3p Macronectes giganteus	.20	.75
225	A31	4p Pterodroma mollis	.20	.85

226	A31	5p Diomedea exulans	.20	.85
227	A31	10p Pterodroma brevirostris	.30	.85
228	A31	15p Sterna vittata	.55	1.25
229	A31	20p Puffinus gravis	.75	1.25
230	A31	25p Pachyptila vittata	.90	1.25
231	A31	50p Catharacta skua	2.00	1.25
232	A31	£1 Pelecanoides urinatrix	2.75	2.25
233	A31	£2 Diomedea chlororynchos	5.75	3.00
		Nos. 222-233 (12)	14.00	14.75

Nos. 224-233 are vertical. For overprints see Nos. 318-319.

Painting Type of 1976

Views by Roland Svensson: 5p, St. Mary's Church. 10p, Longboats. 15p, A Tristan home. 20p, Harbor, 1970.

Wmk. 373

1978, Mar. 1   Litho.   Perf. 14½

234	A28	5p multicolored	.20	.20
235	A28	10p multicolored	.20	.20
236	A28	15p multicolored	.25	.25
237	A28	20p multicolored	.35	.35
a.		Souvenir sheet of 4, #234-237	1.50	1.50
		Nos. 234-237 (4)	1.00	1.00

An artist's view of Tristan da Cunha.

Elizabeth II Coronation Anniversary
Common Design Types
Souvenir Sheet

1978, Apr. 21   Unwmk.   Perf. 15

238	Sheet of 6	1.40	1.40
a.	CD326 25p King's Bull	.25	.25
b.	CD327 25p Elizabeth II	.25	.25
c.	CD328 25p Tristan crawfish	.25	.25

No. 238 contains 2 se-tenant strips of Nos. 238a-238c, separated by horizontal gutter with commemorative and descriptive inscriptions and showing central part of coronation procession with coach.

Sodalite — A32

Local Minerals: 5p, Aragonite. 10p, Sulphur. 20p, Lava containing pyroxene crystal.

Perf. 13½x14

1978, June 9   Litho.   Wmk. 373

239	A32	3p multicolored	.40	.40
240	A32	5p multicolored	.45	.45
241	A32	10p multicolored	.70	.70
242	A32	20p multicolored	1.00	1.00
		Nos. 239-242 (4)	2.55	2.55

Fish A33

1978, Sept. 29   Litho.   Perf. 14

243	A33	5p Klipfish	.20	.20
244	A33	10p Fivefinger	.20	.20
245	A33	15p Concha	.30	.30
246	A33	20p Soldier	.40	.40
		Nos. 243-246 (4)	1.10	1.10

Orangeleaf and Navy Flag — A34

Royal Fleet Auxiliary Vessels: 10p, Tarbatness. 20p, Tidereach. 25p, Reliant.

1978, Nov. 24   Litho.   Perf. 12½

247	A34	5p multicolored	.25	.25
248	A34	10p multicolored	.25	.25
249	A34	20p multicolored	.35	.35
250	A34	25p multicolored	.40	.40
a.		Souvenir sheet of 4, #247-250	1.50	2.75
		Nos. 247-250 (4)	1.25	1.25

Fur Seals — A35

Wildlife conservation: 5p, Elephant seal. 15p, Tristan thrush. 20p, Tristan buntings.

Wmk. 373

1979, Jan. 3   Litho.   Perf. 14

251	A35	5p multicolored	.20	.20
252	A35	10p multicolored	.20	.20
253	A35	15p multicolored	.25	.25
254	A35	20p multicolored	.35	.35
		Nos. 251-254 (4)	1.00	1.00

Tristan Longboat — A36

Ships: 10p, Queen Mary. 15p, Queen Elizabeth. 20p, QE II. 25p, QE II, longboat, view of Tristan.

1979, Feb. 8   Perf. 14½

255	A36	5p multicolored	.20	.20
256	A36	10p multicolored	.20	.20
257	A36	15p multicolored	.25	.25
258	A36	20p multicolored	.35	.35
		Nos. 255-258 (4)	1.00	1.00

Souvenir Sheet

259	A36	25p multicolored	1.00	1.50

Visit of cruise ship QE II, Feb. 8.

Tristan da Cunha No. 12 A37

Tristan da Cunha Stamps: 10p, No. 26. 25p, No. 58, vert. 50p, 1p-local "potatoe" stamp.

Perf. 14½x14, 14x14½

1979, Aug. 27   Litho.   Wmk. 373

260	A37	5p multicolored	.20	.20
261	A37	10p multicolored	.20	.20
262	A37	25p multicolored	.40	.40
		Nos. 260-262 (3)	.80	.80

Souvenir Sheet

263	A37	50p multicolored	.75	.75

Sir Rowland Hill (1795-1879), originator of penny postage.

The Padre's House, IYC Emblem A38

IYC Emblem, Children's Drawings: 10p, "Houses in the Village." 15p, "St. Mary's Church." 20p, "Rockhopper Penguins."

1979, Nov. 26   Litho.   Perf. 14

264	A38	5p multicolored	.20	.20
265	A38	10p multicolored	.20	.20
266	A38	15p multicolored	.20	.20
267	A38	25p multicolored	.25	.25
		Nos. 264-267 (4)	.85	.85

International Year of the Child.

Painting Type of 1976

Views (Sketches by Roland Svensson): 5p, Stoltenhoff Island. 10p, Nightingale from the East. 15p, The Administrator's abode, vert. 20p, "Ridge where the goat jumped off," vert.

1980, Feb.   Litho.   Perf. 14

268	A28	5p multicolored	.20	.20
269	A28	10p multicolored	.20	.20
270	A28	15p multicolored	.20	.20
271	A28	20p multicolored	.25	.25
a.		Souvenir sheet of 4, #268-271	.90	.90
		Nos. 268-271 (4)	.85	.85

Mail Pickup Boat — A40

Golden Hinde — A41

1980, May 6   Litho.   Perf. 14

272	A40	5p shown	.20	.20
273	A40	10p Unloading mail	.20	.20
274	A40	15p Truck transport	.20	.20
275	A40	20p Delivery bell	.20	.20
276	A40	25p Distribution	.30	.30
		Nos. 272-276 (5)	1.10	1.10

London 80 Intl. Stamp Exhib., May 6-14.

Queen Mother Elizabeth Birthday
Common Design Type

1980, Aug. 11   Litho.   Perf. 14

277	CD330	14p multicolored	.30	.30

1980, Sept. 6   Perf. 14½

278	A41	5p shown	.20	.20
279	A41	10p Drake's route	.20	.20
280	A41	20p Sir Francis Drake	.25	.25
281	A41	25p Queen Elizabeth I	.35	.35
		Nos. 278-281 (4)	1.00	1.00

Sir Francis Drake's circumnavigation, 400th anniversary.

Humpty Dumpty A42

Wmk. 373

1980, Oct. 31   Litho.   Perf. 13½

282	Sheet of 9	2.10	2.10
a.	A42 15p shown	.20	.20
b.	A42 15p Mary had a Little Lamb	.20	.20
c.	A42 15p Little Jack Horner	.20	.20
d.	A42 15p Hey Diddle Diddle	.20	.20
e.	A42 15p London Bridge	.20	.20
f.	A42 15p Old King Cole	.20	.20
g.	A42 15p Sing a Song of Sixpence	.20	.20
h.	A42 15p Tom Tom the Piper's Son	.20	.20
i.	A42 25p Owl and the Pussy Cat	.20	.20

Christmas 1980.

Islands on Mid-Atlantic Ridge, Society Emblem — A43

Royal Geographical Soc., 150th Anniv. (Maps and Expeditions): 10p, Tristan da Cunha, Francis Beaufort, 1806. 15p, Tristan Island, Norwegian expedition, 1937-1938. 20p, Gough Island, scientific survey, 1955-1956.

1980, Dec. 15

283	A43	5p multicolored	.20	.20
284	A43	10p multicolored	.20	.20
285	A43	15p multicolored	.25	.25
286	A43	20p multicolored	.35	.35
		Nos. 283-286 (4)	1.00	1.00

Rev. Edwin Dodgson A44

Wmk. 373

1981, Mar. 23   Litho.   Perf. 14

287	A44	10p portrait, vert.	.20	.20
288	A44	20p shown	.35	.35
289	A44	30p Dodgson preaching, vert.	.45	.45
a.		Souvenir sheet of 3, #287-289	1.00	1.00
		Nos. 287-289 (3)	1.00	1.00

Centenary of arrival of Rev. Edwin H. Dodgson, who saved population from starvation.

Map of Tristan da Cunha showing L'heure du Berger Route, 1767 (Dalrymple's Map, 1781) — A45

Early Maps and Charts By: 5p, 21p, Capt. Denham, 1853 (diff.). 35p, Ivan Keulen, 1700.

1981, May 22

290	A45	5p multicolored	.20	.20
291	A45	14p multicolored	.40	.30
292	A45	21p multicolored	.50	.50
		Nos. 290-292 (3)	1.10	1.00

Souvenir Sheet

293	A45	35p multicolored	.60	.75

Royal Wedding Issue
Common Design Type

Wmk. 373

1981, July 22   Litho.   Perf. 14

294	CD331	5p Bouquet	.20	.20
295	CD331	20p Charles	.20	.20
296	CD331	50p Couple	.35	.35
		Nos. 294-296 (3)	.75	.75

Hiking — A46

1981, Sept. 14

297	A46	5p shown	.20	.20
298	A46	10p Camping	.20	.20
299	A46	20p Map reading	.25	.25
300	A46	25p Prince Philip	.35	.25
		Nos. 297-300 (4)	1.00	.90

Duke of Edinburgh's Awards, 25th anniv.

Inaccessible Island Rail — A47

1981, Nov. 1   Litho.   Perf. 13½x14

301	Strip of 4	1.40	1.40
a.	A47 10p Nest	.30	.30
b.	A47 10p Eggs	.30	.30
c.	A47 10p Chicks	.30	.30
d.	A47 10p Adult rail	.30	.30

Six-gilled
Shark
A48

1982, Feb. 8   Litho.   Perf. 13½x14
302 A48 5p shown   .20   .20
303 A48 14p Porbeagle shark   .40   .25
304 A48 21p Blue shark   .65   .50
305 A48 35p Hammerhead shark .95   .75
        Nos. 302-305 (4)   2.20 1.70

Marcella — A49

1982, Apr. 5   Litho.   Perf. 14
306 A49 5p shown   .35   .35
307 A49 15p Eliza Adams   .35   .55
308 A49 30p Corinthian   .50   .75
309 A49 50p Samuel & Thomas   .80 1.00
        Nos. 306-309 (4)   2.00 2.65

        See Nos. 324-327.

Princess Diana Issue
Common Design Type
Perf. 14½x14

1982, July 1   Litho.   Wmk. 373
310 CD333 5p Arms   .25   .20
311 CD333 15p Diana   .75   .20
312 CD333 30p Wedding   1.50   .35
313 CD333 50p Portrait   2.25   .60
        Nos. 310-313 (4)   4.75 1.35

Scouting
Year — A50

Perf. 13½x13, 13x13½
1982, Aug. 23   Litho.
314 A50 5p Baden-Powell, vert. .20 .20
315 A50 20p Brownsea Isld.
              camp, 1907, vert.   .35 .35
316 A50 50p Saluting   .95 .95
        Nos. 314-316 (3)   1.50 1.50

Souvenir Sheet
Perf. 14
317 A50 50p Tree illustration,
              vert.   1.25 1.10

Nos. 226, 230 Overprinted: "1st
PARTICIPATION / COMMONWEALTH
/ GAMES 1982"
Perf. 13½x14
1982, Sept. 28   Litho.   Wmk. 373
318 A31 5p multicolored   .20   .20
319 A31 25p multicolored   .40   .40

12th Commonwealth Games, Brisbane,
Australia, Sept. 30-Oct. 9.

Formation of
Volcanic
Island
A51

1982, Nov. 1   Perf. 14x14½
320 A51 5p shown   .25   .25
321 A51 15p Surface cinder
              cones   .40   .40
322 A51 25p Eruption   .50   .50
323 A51 35p 1961 eruption   .60   .60
        Nos. 320-323 (4)   1.75 1.75

Ship Type of 1982
1983, Feb. 1   Litho.   Perf. 14
324 A49 5p Islander, vert.   .20   .20
325 A49 20p Roscoe   .50   .50
326 A49 35p Columbia   .90   .75
327 A49 50p Emeline, vert.   1.25 1.10
        Nos. 324-327 (4)   2.85 2.55

Tractor
Pulling
Trailer
A52

1983, May 2   Litho.   Perf. 14
328 A52 5p shown   .20   .20
329 A52 15p Pack mules   .25   .20
330 A52 30p Oxen pulling cart .50   .40
331 A52 50p Jeep   .80   .60
        Nos. 328-331 (4)   1.75 1.40

Map of
South
Atlantic
A53

Island History.

Wmk. 373
1983, Aug. 1   Litho.   Perf. 14
332 A53 1p shown   .20   .20
333 A53 3p Tristao
              d'Acunha's flag-
              ship   .20   .20
334 A53 4p Landing, 1643   .20   .20
335 A53 5p 17th cent. views   .20   .20
336 A53 10p Landing party,
              1815   .25   .20
337 A53 15p Settlement   .35   .45
338 A53 18p Governor Glass's
              house   .45   .50
339 A53 20p Rev. W.F. Taylor,
              Peter Green   .50   .60
340 A53 25p Three-master
              John and Eliza-
              beth   .75   .90
341 A53 50p Dependency dec-
              laration of St.
              Helena, 1938   1.40 1.75
342 A53 £1 Commissioning
              ceremony   2.75 3.50
343 A53 £2 Evacuation, 1961 5.75 7.25
        Nos. 332-343 (12)   13.00 15.95

Raphael, 500th
Birth Anniv. — A54

1983, Oct. 27   Litho.   Perf. 14½
344 A54 10p multicolored   .25   .20
345 A54 25p multicolored   .65   .50
346 A54 40p multicolored   1.10   .90
        Nos. 344-346 (3)   2.00 1.60

Souvenir Sheet
347 A54 50p multi, horiz.   1.50 1.25
Details from Christ's Charge to St. Peter.

St. Helena Colony
Sesquicentenary — A55

1984, Jan. 3   Litho.   Perf. 14
348 A55 10p No. 7   .20   .20
349 A55 15p No. 9   .30   .25
350 A55 25p No. 10   .50   .40
351 A55 60p No. 12   1.25 1.00
        Nos. 348-351 (4)   2.25 1.85

Local
Fungi
A56

1984, Mar. 26
352 A56 10p Agrocybe praecox,
              vert.   .65   .75
353 A56 20p Laccaria tetraspora,
              vert.   1.10 1.10
354 A56 30p Agrocybe cylin-
              dracea   1.75 1.75
355 A56 50p Sarcoscypha coc-
              cinea   2.75 2.75
        Nos. 352-355 (4)   6.25 6.35

Constellations
A57

1984, July 30   Perf. 14½
356 A57 10p Orion   .25   .20
357 A57 20p Scorpius   .55   .45
358 A57 25p Canis Major   .65   .55
359 A57 50p Crux   1.40 1.10
        Nos. 356-359 (4)   2.85 2.30

Sheep
Shearing — A58

1984, Oct. 1
360 A58 9p shown   .25   .20
361 A58 17p Carding wool   .40   .35
362 A58 29p Spinning   .70   .60
363 A58 45p Knitting   1.10 1.00
  a.   Souvenir sheet of 4, #360-363 2.60 2.25
        Nos. 360-363 (4)   2.45 2.15

Stamps from No. 363a do not have white
border around the design.

Christmas
1984
A59

1984, Dec. 3   Perf. 14
364 A59 10p Three angels,
              Christmas dinner .25   .20
365 A59 20p Two angels, cart .50   .45
366 A59 30p Candles, sailboat .80   .70
367 A59 50p Trees, Nativity 1.25 1.10
        Nos. 364-367 (4)   2.80 2.45

Shipwrecks — A60

1985, Feb. 4   Perf. 14x13½, 13½x14
368 A60 10p HMS Julia, 1817,
              vert.   .90   .45
369 A60 25p Bell from Mabel
              Clark, 1878, vert. 1.40 1.10
370 A60 35p Barque Glenhuntley,
              1898   2.00 1.50
        Nos. 368-370 (3)   4.30 3.05

Souvenir Sheet
371 A60 60p Map of shipwreck
              sites   2.40 1.90

No. 371 contains one 48x32mm stamp.
See Nos. 393-396, 412-415.

Queen Mother 85th Birthday
Common Design Type
Perf. 14½x14

1985, June 7   Litho.   Wmk. 384
372 CD336 10p With Prince
              Charles, 1954   .30   .30
373 CD336 20p With Margaret at
              Ascot   .55   .55
374 CD336 30p Queen Mother   .80   .80
375 CD336 50p Holding Prince
              Henry   1.00 1.00
        Nos. 372-375 (4)   2.65 2.65

Souvenir Sheet
376 CD336 80p With Anne   2.50 2.50

Flags
A61

10p, Jonathan Lambert & flag of 1811, Isles
of Refreshment. 15p, Cannon & flag of 21st
Light Dragoons, 1816-17, Fort Malcolm. 25p,
HMS Falmouth, 1816, & flag of HMS Atlantic
Isle, HMS JOB 9, 1942-46. 60p, View of Tris-
tan & Union Jack, 1816 to date.

1985, Sept. 30   Wmk. 373   Perf. 14
377 A61 10p multicolored   .55   .45
378 A61 15p multicolored   .70   .60
379 A61 25p multicolored   1.25 1.10
380 A61 60p multicolored   3.25 2.40
        Nos. 377-380 (4)   5.75 4.55

Nos. 378-380 vert.

Loss of The
Lifeboat,
Cent. — A62

1985, Nov. 28
381 A62 10p Lifeboat, barque
              West Riding   .30   .30
382 A62 30p Map   .90   .90
383 A62 50p Death toll   1.50 1.50
        Nos. 381-383 (3)   2.70 2.70

Halley's
Comet
A63

1986, Mar. 3   Wmk. 384
384 A63 10p Bayeux Tapestry,
              c. 1092   .50   .50
385 A63 20p Trajectory around
              Earth   .90   .90
386 A63 30p Comet over Inac-
              cessible Is.   1.25 1.25
387 A63 50p Ship Paramour   2.00 2.00
        Nos. 384-387 (4)   4.65 4.65

Queen Elizabeth II 60th Birthday
Common Design Type

Designs: 10p, With Prince Charles, 1950.
15p, Birthday Parade, wearing uniform of
Scots Guards, 1976. 25p, At Westminster
Abbey, London, 1972, wearing mantle and
robes of the Most Noble Order of Bath. 45p,
Silver Jubilee Tour, Canada, 1977. 65p, Visiting Crown Agents' offices, 1983.

1986, Apr. 21   Perf. 14½
388 CD337 10p scarlet, blk & sil .25 .25
389 CD337 15p ultra & multi   .35   .35
390 CD337 25p green & multi   .60   .60

391	CD337	45p violet & multi	1.00	1.00
392	CD337	65p rose vio & multi	1.40	1.40
		Nos. 388-392 (5)	3.60	3.60

For overprints see Nos. 429-433.

Shipwrecks Type of 1985

1986, June 2   **Perf. 13½**

393	A60	9p SV Allanshaw, 1893	.35	.35
394	A60	20p Church font from Edward Vittery, 1881	.80	.75
395	A60	40p Figurehead, 1940	1.75	1.60
		Nos. 393-395 (3)	2.90	2.70

Souvenir Sheet
Perf. 13½x13

396	A60	65p Barque Italia, 1892	2.75	2.75
		Nos. 394-395 vert.		

Royal Wedding Issue, 1986
Common Design Type

Designs: 10p, Informal portrait. 40p, Andrew operating helicopter.

1986, July 23   **Perf. 14**

397	CD338	10p multicolored	.25	.25
398	CD338	40p multicolored	1.25	1.25

A64   A65

1986, Sept. 30

399	A64	5p Wandering albatross	.20	.20
400	A64	10p Daisy	.60	.60
401	A64	20p Vanessa butterfly	1.25	1.00
402	A64	25p Wilkins's bunting	1.50	1.25
403	A64	50p Ring-eye	2.75	2.50
		Nos. 399-403 (5)	6.30	5.45

Flora & fauna of Inaccessible Island.

1987, Jan. 23   **Perf. 14½**

Indigenous Flightless Species and Habitats: 10p, Flightless moth, Edinburgh Settlement. 25p, Strap-winged fly, Crater Lake. 35p, Flightless rail, Inaccessible Island. 50p, Gough Island moorhen, Gough Island.

404	A65	10p multicolored	.50	.50
405	A65	25p multicolored	1.25	1.25
406	A65	35p multicolored	1.75	1.75
407	A65	50p multicolored	2.50	2.50
		Nos. 404-407 (4)	6.00	6.00

Rockhopper Penguins A66

1987, June 22

408	A66	10p Swimming	.65	.65
409	A66	20p Nesting	1.40	1.40
410	A66	30p Adult and young	2.10	2.10
411	A66	50p Adult's head	3.75	3.75
		Nos. 408-411 (4)	7.90	7.90

Shipwrecks Type of 1985

Designs: 11p, Castaways attacking sea elephant, vert. 17p, Henry A. Paull, 1879, Sandy Point. 45p, Gustav Stoltenhoff, Stoltenhoff Is., vert. 70p, Map of wrecks off Inaccessible Is.

1987, Apr. 2   **Perf. 14**

412	A60	11p olive gray & blk	.60	.60
413	A60	17p dark violet & blk	1.00	1.00
414	A60	45p myrtle green & blk	3.00	3.00
		Nos. 412-414 (3)	4.60	4.60

Souvenir Sheet

415	A60	70p light blue, royal blue & apple grn	4.50	4.50

Norwegian Scientific Expedition, 50th Anniv. — A67

10p, Microscope and textbooks symbolic of expedition results. 20p, Scientists tagging a mollymawk. 30p, Expedition headquarters on the island. 50p, S.S. Thorshammer.

1987, Dec. 7   **Wmk. 384**   Litho.   **Perf. 14**

416	A67	10p multicolored	1.00	.90
417	A67	20p multicolored	2.10	1.50

Wmk. 373

418	A67	30p multicolored	3.00	2.10
419	A67	50p multicolored	4.50	3.50
		Nos. 416-419 (4)	10.60	8.00

Fauna of Nightingale Island — A68

1988, Mar. 21   **Wmk. 384**   **Perf. 14**

420	A68	5p Tristan bunting	.30	.30
421	A68	10p Tristan thrush	.55	.55
422	A68	20p Yellow-nosed albatross	1.00	1.00
423	A68	25p Great shearwater	1.25	1.25
424	A68	50p Elephant seal	2.75	2.75
		Nos. 420-424 (5)	5.85	5.85

Handicrafts A69

1988, May 30   **Perf. 14½**

425	A69	10p Painted penguin eggs	.40	.40
426	A69	15p Moccasins	.55	.55
427	A69	35p Woolen clothing	1.40	1.40
428	A69	50p Model canvas boats	1.90	1.90
		Nos. 425-428 (4)	4.25	4.25

Nos. 388-392 Ovptd. "40TH WEDDING ANNIVERSARY" in Silver

1988, Mar. 9

429	CD337	10p scar, blk & sil	.25	.25
430	CD337	15p ultra & multi	.40	.40
431	CD337	25p green & multi	.65	.65
432	CD337	45p violet & multi	1.10	1.10
433	CD337	65p rose vio & multi	1.60	1.60
		Nos. 429-433 (5)	4.00	4.00

19th Cent. Whaling A70

1988, Oct. 6   **Perf. 14x14½**

434	A70	10p "Trying out" blubber	.70	.70
435	A70	20p Harpoon guns	1.25	1.25
436	A70	30p Scrimshaw	2.10	2.10
437	A70	50p Ships	3.50	3.50
		Nos. 434-437 (4)	7.55	7.55

Souvenir Sheet

438	A70	£1 Right whale	5.50	5.50

Lloyds of London, 300th Anniv.
Common Design Type

10p, Lloyds's new building, 1988. 25p, Cargo ship *Tristania II*, horiz. 35p, Supply ship *St. Helena*, horiz. 50p, Square-rigger *Kobenhavn*, lost at sea.

1988, Nov. 7   **Perf. 14**

439	CD341	10p multicolored	.50	.50
440	CD341	25p multicolored	1.50	1.50
441	CD341	35p multicolored	2.00	2.00
442	CD341	50p multicolored	2.75	2.75
		Nos. 439-442 (4)	6.75	6.75

Paintings of the Island, 1824, by Augustus Earle (1793-1838) — A71

Designs: 1p, Government House. 3p, Squall off Tristan. 4p, Rafting Blubber. 5p, Tristan. 10p, Man Killing an Albatross. 15p, View on the Summit. 20p, Nightingale Island. 25p, Tristan, diff. 35p, "Solitude," Watching the Horizon. 50p, North Eastern. £1, Tristan, diff. £2, Governor Glass and His Companions.

1988, Dec. 10

443	A71	1p multicolored	.20	.20
444	A71	3p multicolored	.20	.20
445	A71	4p multicolored	.20	.20
446	A71	5p multicolored	.20	.20
447	A71	10p multicolored	.35	.35
448	A71	15p multicolored	.50	.60
449	A71	20p multicolored	.65	1.10
450	A71	25p multicolored	.85	1.25
451	A71	35p multicolored	1.25	2.00
452	A71	50p multicolored	1.60	2.75
453	A71	£1 multicolored	3.25	5.50
454	A71	£2 multicolored	6.50	10.50
		Nos. 443-454 (12)	15.75	24.85

Gough Is. Fauna — A72

Ferns — A73

1989, Feb. 6   Litho.   **Wmk. 384**

455	A72	5p Giant petrel	.45	.45
456	A72	10p Gough moorhen	.80	.80
457	A72	20p Gough bunting	1.50	1.50
458	A72	25p Sooty albatross	1.75	1.75
459	A72	50p Amsterdam fur seal	3.50	3.50
		Nos. 455-459 (5)	8.00	8.00

1989, May 22   **Wmk. 373**   **Perf. 14**

460	A73	10p Eriosorus cheilanthoides	.60	.60
461	A73	25p Asplenium alvarezense	1.50	1.50
462	A73	35p Elaphoglossum hybridum	2.25	2.25
463	A73	50p Ophioglossum opacum	3.00	3.00
		Nos. 460-463 (4)	7.35	7.35

A74

1989, Nov. 20   **Wmk. 384**

464	A74	10p Cattle egret	1.40	1.10
465	A74	25p Spotted sandpiper	3.00	2.50
466	A74	35p Purple gallinule	4.50	3.50
467	A74	50p Barn swallow	5.75	4.75
		Nos. 464-467 (4)	14.65	11.85

Artifacts on Exhibit in the Nautical Museum A75

1989, Sept. 25

468	A75	10p Surgeon's mortar	.60	.60
469	A75	20p Parts of a harpoon	1.25	1.25
470	A75	30p Compass with binnacle hood	1.90	1.90
471	A75	60p Rope-twisting device	3.75	3.75
		Nos. 468-471 (4)	7.50	7.50

Moths A76

1990, Feb. 1   **Perf. 14**

472	A76	10p Peridroma saucia	.75	.75
473	A76	15p Ascalapha odorata	1.25	1.25
474	A76	35p Agrius cingulata	3.00	3.00
475	A76	60p Eumorpha labruscae	5.50	5.50
		Nos. 472-475 (4)	10.50	10.50

Starfish (Echinoderms) A77

1990, June 12   **Perf. 14x13½**

476	A77	10p shown	.85	.85
477	A77	20p multi, diff.	1.60	1.50
478	A77	30p multi, diff.	2.75	2.25
479	A77	60p multi, diff.	4.75	4.50
		Nos. 476-479 (4)	9.95	9.10

Queen Mother, 90th Birthday
Common Design Types

1990, Aug. 4   **Wmk. 384**   **Perf. 14x15**

480	CD343	25p Queen Mother at the Coliseum	1.25	1.10

Perf. 14½

481	CD344	£1 Broadcasting to women of the empire, 1939	5.00	4.50

Dunnottar Castle, 1942 — A78

Designs: 15p, RMS St. Helena, 1977-1990. 35p, Launching new RMS St. Helena, 1989. 60p, Duke of York launching new RMS St. Helena. £1, New RMS St. Helena.

1990, Sept. 13   **Wmk. 373**   **Perf. 14½**

482	A78	10p multicolored	.95	.95
483	A78	15p multicolored	1.50	1.50
484	A78	35p multicolored	4.00	3.25
485	A78	60p multicolored	6.25	5.50
		Nos. 482-485 (4)	12.70	11.20

Souvenir Sheet

486	A78	£1 multicolored	9.00	9.00

See Ascension Nos. 493-497, St. Helena Nos. 535-539.

Royal Navy Warships A79

Perf. 14½x14

1990, Nov. 30   Litho.   Wmk. 373
487	A79	10p Pyramus, 1829	1.25	1.25
488	A79	25p Penguin, 1815	3.25	3.00
489	A79	35p Thalia, 1886	4.50	4.25
490	A79	50p Sidon, 1858	6.50	6.00
		Nos. 487-490 (4)	15.50	14.50

See Nos. 547-550.

1991, Feb. 4
491	A79	10p Milford, 1938	2.25	1.60
492	A79	25p Dublin, 1923	3.50	2.75
493	A79	35p Yarmouth, 1919	4.75	4.00
494	A79	50p Carlisle, 1938	5.25	6.00
		Nos. 491-494 (4)	15.75	14.35

Souvenir Sheet

Royal Viking Sun — A80

Wmk. 384
1991, Apr. 1   Litho.   Perf. 14
495	A80	£1 multicolored	11.00	11.00

Prince Philip, 70th Birthday A81

Designs: 10p, HMS Galatea, Prince Alfred. 25p, Royal Visit, 1957. 30p, HMY Britannia, Prince Philip. 50p, Settlement of Edinburgh, Prince Philip.

1991, June 10   Wmk. 373
496	A81	10p multicolored	1.50	1.25
497	A81	25p multicolored	3.25	3.00
498	A81	30p multicolored	4.25	3.50
499	A81	50p multicolored	6.50	6.00
		Nos. 496-499 (4)	15.50	13.75

Birds A82

1991, Oct. 1
500	A82	8p Gough moorhens	2.75	1.60
501	A82	10p Gough bunting	2.75	1.90
502	A82	12p Gough moorhen in nest	3.00	1.90
503	A82	15p Gough bunting with chicks	3.25	2.25
		Nos. 500-503 (4)	11.75	7.65

World Wildlife Fund.

Discovery of America, 500th Anniv. — A83

1992, Jan. 23
504	A83	10p STV Eye of the Wind	.95	.75
505	A83	15p STV Soren Larsen	1.25	1.10
506	A83	35p STV Pinta, Nina, Santa Maria	3.00	2.75
507	A83	60p Columbus, Santa Maria	5.75	4.75
		Nos. 504-507 (4)	10.95	9.35

World Columbian Stamp Expo '92, Chicago and Genoa '92 Intl. Philatelic Exhibitions.

Queen Elizabeth II's Accession to the Throne, 40th Anniv.
Common Design Type

1992, Feb. 6
508	CD349	10p multicolored	.60	.55
509	CD349	20p multicolored	1.25	1.10
510	CD349	25p multicolored	1.50	1.25
511	CD349	35p multicolored	2.10	1.90
512	CD349	65p multicolored	4.00	3.50
		Nos. 508-512 (5)	9.45	8.30

Fish — A84

Designs: 10p, Caesioperca coatsii. 15p, Mendosoma lineatum. 35p, Physiculus karrerae. 60p, Decapterus longimanus.

1992, June 1
513	A84	10p multicolored	.80	.55
514	A84	15p multicolored	1.50	1.10
515	A84	35p multicolored	3.00	2.40
516	A84	60p multicolored	5.50	4.25
		Nos. 513-516 (4)	10.80	8.30

Wreck of the Italia, Cent. — A85

Designs: 10p, Italia leaving Greenock. 45p, In mid-Atlantic. 65p, Driving ashore on Stony Beach. £1, Italia in peaceful waters.

1992, Sept. 18   Perf. 13½x14
517	A85	10p multicolored	.95	.80
518	A85	45p multicolored	3.75	3.50
519	A85	65p multicolored	5.75	5.25
		Nos. 517-519 (3)	10.45	9.55

Souvenir Sheet
520	A85	£1 multicolored	10.50	10.50

Genoa '92 Intl. Philatelic Exhibition (#520).

Insects — A86

15p, Stenoscelis hylastoides. 45p, Troglocaptomyza brevilamellata. 60p, Senilites tristanicola.

Perf. 14x13½
1993, Feb. 2   Litho.   Wmk. 384
521	A86	15p multicolored	1.25	1.25
522	A86	45p multicolored	3.50	3.50
523	A86	60p multicolored	4.50	4.00
		Nos. 521-523 (3)	9.25	8.75

Coronation of Queen Elizabeth II, 40th Anniv. — A87

Designs: 10p, Ampulla, spoon. 15p, Orb. 35p, Imperial State Crown. 60p, St. Edward's Crown.

1993, June 14   Perf. 14½
524	A87	10p green & black	.85	.70
525	A87	15p red vio & black	1.25	1.10
526	A87	35p purple & black	2.75	2.40
527	A87	60p blue & black	4.50	4.25
		Nos. 524-527 (4)	9.35	8.45

Resettlement to Tristan, 30th Anniv. — A88

Ships: No. 528, Tristania, Frances Repetto. No. 529, Boissevain. 50p, Bornholm.

1993, Nov. 10   Perf. 13½x14
528	A88	35p multicolored	2.75	2.50
529	A88	35p multicolored	2.75	2.50
a.		Pair, #528-529	6.50	6.00
530	A88	50p multicolored	4.50	4.25
		Nos. 528-530 (3)	10.00	9.25

Christmas — A89

Entire paintings or details: 5p, Madonna with Child, School of Botticelli. 15p, The Holy Family, by Daniel Gran. 35p, The Holy Virgin and Child, by Rubens. 65p, The Mystical Marriage of St. Catherine with the Holy Child, by Jan Van Balen.

1993, Nov. 30   Wmk. 373   Perf. 13
531	A89	10p multicolored	.65	.65
532	A89	15p multicolored	2.00	1.50
533	A89	35p multicolored	4.25	3.25
534	A89	65p multicolored	6.75	6.00
		Nos. 531-534 (4)	13.65	11.40

Ships A90

Designs: 1p, Duchess of Atholl, 1929. 3p, Empress of Australia, 1935. 5p, Anatolia, 1937. 8p, Viceroy of India, 1939. 10p, Rangitata, 1943. 15p, Caronia, 1950. 20p, Rotterdam, 1960. 25p, Leonardo da Vinci, 1972. 35p, Vistafjord, 1974. £1, World Discoverer, 1984. £2, Astor, 1984. £5, RMS St. Helena, 1992.

1994, Feb. 3   Wmk. 384   Perf. 14
535	A90	1p multicolored	.30	.35
536	A90	3p multicolored	.30	.35
537	A90	5p multicolored	.30	.35
538	A90	8p multicolored	.30	.35
539	A90	10p multicolored	.40	.50
540	A90	15p multicolored	.60	.70
541	A90	20p multicolored	.80	.90
542	A90	25p multicolored	1.00	1.10
543	A90	35p multicolored	1.50	1.75
544	A90	£1 multicolored	3.75	4.50
545	A90	£2 multicolored	7.75	9.00
546	A90	£5 multicolored	20.00	17.00
		Nos. 535-546 (12)	37.00	36.85

Royal Navy Warships Type of 1990
1994, May 2   Wmk. 373
547	A79	10p HMS Nigeria, 1948	1.10	1.10
548	A79	25p HMS Phoebe, 1949	2.75	2.75
549	A79	35p HMS Liverpool, 1949	3.50	3.50
550	A79	50p HMS Magpie, 1955	5.50	5.50
		Nos. 547-550 (4)	12.85	12.85

Sharks A91

1994, Aug.   Wmk. 384
551	A91	10p Blue shark	.95	.95
552	A91	45p Seven-gill shark	4.25	4.25
553	A91	65p Mako shark	5.75	5.75
		Nos. 551-553 (3)	10.95	10.95

Farm Animals — A92

1994, Nov.   Wmk. 373
554	A92	10p Donkeys	.85	.85
555	A92	20p Cattle	1.90	1.90
556	A92	35p Ducks, geese	3.50	3.50
557	A92	60p Girl feeding lamb	6.25	6.25
		Nos. 554-557 (4)	12.50	12.50

Local Transport A93

Designs: 15p, Pick-up truck. 20p, Leyland Daf Sherpa van. 45p, Yamaha motorcycle, scooter. 60p, Administrator's Landrover.

Wmk. 384
1995, Feb. 27   Litho.   Perf. 14
558	A93	15p multicolored	1.25	1.25
559	A93	20p multicolored	1.50	1.50
560	A93	45p multicolored	3.50	3.50
561	A93	60p multicolored	5.00	5.00
		Nos. 558-561 (4)	11.25	11.25

End of World War II, 50th Anniv.
Common Design Types

Designs: 15p, Lewis gun instruction, 1943. 20p, Tristan defense volunteers, 1943-46. 45p, Radio, weather stations. 60p, HNS Birmingham, 1942. £1, Reverse of War Medal, 1939-45.

Perf. 13x13½
1995, June 19   Litho.   Wmk. 373
562	CD351	15p multicolored	1.60	1.60
563	CD351	20p multicolored	2.25	2.25
564	CD351	45p multicolored	4.50	4.50
565	CD351	60p multicolored	6.50	6.50
		Nos. 562-565 (4)	14.85	14.85

Souvenir Sheet
Perf. 14
566	CD352	£1 multicolored	8.00	8.00

Souvenir Sheet

Queen Mother, 95th Birthday — A94

1995, Aug. 4   Litho.   Perf. 14½x14
567 A94 £1.50 multicolored   9.00 9.00

UN, 50th Anniv.
Common Design Type

20p, Bedford 4-ton truck. 30p, Saxon armored personnel carrier. 45p, Mi26 heavy lift helicopter. 50p, RFA Sir Tristram transporting UN vehicles.

1995, Oct. 24   Perf. 13½x13
568 CD353 20p multicolored   1.90 1.90
569 CD353 30p multicolored   3.25 3.25
570 CD353 45p multicolored   4.50 4.50
571 CD353 50p multicolored   5.25 5.25
      Nos. 568-571 (4)   14.90 14.90

Seals
A95

Sub Antarctic fur seal: 10p, On rock. 35p, Coming out of water with young.
Southern elephant seal: 45p, On beach with young. 50p, In water.

1995, Nov. 3   Perf. 13½
572 A95 10p multicolored   .75   .75
573 A95 35p multicolored   3.00 3.00
574 A95 45p multicolored   4.50 4.50
575 A95 50p multicolored   4.75 4.75
      Nos. 572-575 (4)   13.00 13.00

Queen Elizabeth II, 70th Birthday
Common Design Type

Various portraits of Queen, island scenes: 15p, Tristan from sea. 20p, Traditional cottage. 45p, The Residency. 60p, With Prince Philip.

1996, Apr. 22   Litho.   Perf. 13½
576 CD354 15p multicolored   1.00 1.00
577 CD354 20p multicolored   1.40 1.40
578 CD354 45p multicolored   3.00 3.00
579 CD354 60p multicolored   3.75 3.75
      Nos. 576-579 (4)   9.15 9.15

New Harbor — A96

15p, View of Old Harbor. 20p, Earthmoving, New Harbor construction. 45p, Crane, new construction. 60p, View of New Harbor. Nos. 581-582 are 45x28mm.

1996, July 5   Wmk. 373   Perf. 13
580 A96 15p multicolored   1.90 1.90
581 A96 20p multicolored   3.00 3.00
582 A96 45p multicolored   4.00 4.00
583 A96 60p multicolored   5.00 5.00
      Nos. 580-583 (4)   13.90 13.90

Nos. 581-582 are 45x28mm.

A97

A98

Gough Island Birds: 15p, Gough moorhen. 20p, Wandering albatross. 45p, Sooty albatross. 60p, Gough bunting.

1996, Oct. 1   Perf. 14
584 A97 15p multicolored   1.00 1.00
585 A97 20p multicolored   1.50 1.50
586 A97 45p multicolored   3.50 3.50
587 A97 60p multicolored   5.00 5.00
   a.   Souvenir sheet of 1   6.00 6.00
      Nos. 584-587 (4)   11.00 11.00

No. 587a for return of Hong Kong to China, July 1, 1997. Issued 6/20/97.

1996, Dec. 18   Perf. 13½
Presentation of Portrait of Queen Victoria, Cent.: 20p, 19th cent. map of Trista da Cunha. 30p, HMS Magpie. 45p, Peter Green, former governor. 50p, Detail of portrait of Queen Victoria, by Heinrich Von Angell.
588 A98 20p multicolored   1.60 1.60
589 A98 30p multicolored   2.50 2.50
590 A98 45p multicolored   3.50 3.50
591 A98 50p multicolored   4.00 4.00
      Nos. 588-591 (4)   11.60 11.60

Atlantic Marine Fauna of the Cretaceous — A99

Designs: a, Archelon. b, Trinacromerum. c, Platecarpus. d, Clidastes.

1997, Feb. 10   Wmk. 384   Perf. 14
592 A99 35p Sheet of 4, #a.-d.   12.00 12.00
      See No. 619.

Visual Communications — A100

Designs: No. 593, Smoke signals. No. 594, HMS Eurydice. No. 595, HMS Challenger. No. 596, Flag hoists. No. 597, Semaphore. No. 598, HMS Carlisle. No. 599, Light signals. No. 600, HMS Cilicia.

1997   Litho.   Wmk. 384   Perf. 14½
593   10p multicolored   .50   .50
594   10p multicolored   .50   .50
   a.   A100 Pair, #593-594   1.25 1.25

595   15p multicolored   .70   .70
596   15p multicolored   .70   .70
   a.   A100 Pair, #595-596   2.00 2.00
597   20p multicolored   .85   .85
598   20p multicolored   .85   .85
   a.   A100 Pair, #597-598   2.50 2.50
599   35p multicolored   1.50 1.50
600   35p multicolored   1.50 1.50
   a.   Pair, #599-600   4.25 4.25
      Nos. 593-600 (8)   7.10 7.10

Farm Animals Type of 1994
1997, Aug. 26   Litho.   Perf. 14
601 A92 20p Chickens   1.40 1.40
602 A92 30p Cattle   2.40 2.40
603 A92 45p Sheep   3.50 3.50
604 A92 50p Dogs   3.75 3.75
      Nos. 601-604 (4)   11.05 11.05

Queen Elizabeth II and Prince Philip, 50th Wedding Anniv. — A101

Designs: No. 605, Queen up close. No. 606, Prince riding polo pony. No. 607, Queen with horse. No. 608, Prince up close. No. 609, Prince in military attire, Queen in green coat. No. 610, Princess Anne riding horse. £1.50, Queen, Prince riding in open carriage, horiz.

1997, Nov. 20   Wmk. 373   Perf. 14
605   15p multicolored   .70   .70
606   15p multicolored   .70   .70
   a.   A101 Pair, #605-606   2.00 2.00
607   20p multicolored   1.00 1.00
608   20p multicolored   1.00 1.00
   a.   A101 Pair, #607-608   3.25 3.25
609   45p multicolored   2.10 2.10
610   45p multicolored   2.10 2.10
   a.   A101 Pair, #609-610   6.75 6.75
      Nos. 605-610 (6)   7.60 7.60

Souvenir Sheet
611 A101 £1.50 multicolored   14.00 14.00

First Lobster Survey, 50th Anniv. — A102

Ships: 15p, Hilary, Melodie. 20p, Tristania II, Hekla. 30p, Pequena, Frances Repetto. 45p, Tristania, Gillian Gaggins. 50p, MFV. Kelso, MV. Edinburgh. £1.20, Fr. C.P. Lawrence, lobster.

1998, Feb. 6   Perf. 14½
612 A102 15p multicolored   .85   .85
613 A102 20p multicolored   1.25 1.25
614 A102 30p multicolored   1.90 1.90
615 A102 45p multicolored   3.00 3.00
616 A102 50p multicolored   3.00 3.00
      Nos. 612-616 (5)   10.00 10.00

Souvenir Sheet
617 A102 £1.20 multicolored   12.00 12.00

Diana, Princess of Wales (1961-97)
Common Design Type

a, In beige dress. b, In white top with black collar. c, In striped top. d, In lilac & white print dress.

1998, May 15   Perf. 14½x14
618 CD355 35p Strip of 4, #a.-d.   6.00 6.00

No. 618 sold for £1.40 + 20p with surtax from international sales going to the Princess Diana Memorial Fund and surtax from local sales going to a designated local charity.

Atlantic Marine Fauna Type of 1997

Fauna of the Miocene Epoch: a, Carcharodon. b, Orycterocetus. c, Eurhinodelphis. d, Hexanchus (six gilled shark), myliobatis.

1998, July 8   Perf. 14
619 A99 45p Sheet of 4, #a.-d. 15.00 15.00

Visiting Cruise Ships
A103

1998, Sept. 15   Perf. 14
620 A103 15p Livonia   1.50 1.50
621 A103 20p Professor
              Molchanov   2.00 2.00
622 A103 45p Explorer   4.50 4.50
623 A103 60p Hanseatic   6.00 6.00
      Nos. 620-623 (4)   14.00 14.00

Sailing Ships
A104

1998, Nov. 23   Wmk. 373   Perf. 14½
624 A104 15p H.G. Johnson,
              1892   1.50 1.50
625 A104 35p Theodore, 1893   3.25 3.25
626 A104 45p Hesperides,
              1893   4.50 4.50
627 A104 50p Bessfield, 1894   4.75 4.75
      Nos. 624-627 (4)   14.00 14.00

1999, Mar. 19
628 A104 20p Derwent, 1895   2.00 2.00
629 A104 30p Strathgryffe,
              1898   2.75 2.75
630 A104 50p Celestial Em-
              pire, 1898   4.50 4.50
631 A104 60p Lamorna, 1902   4.75 4.75
      Nos. 628-631 (4)   14.00 14.00
      Nos. 624-631 (8)   28.00 28.00

Wandering Albatross — A105

World Wildlife Fund: 5p, Two adults. 8p, Adult, juvenile in nest. 12p, Adult spreading wings. 15p, Two in flight.

1999, Apr. 27   Wmk. 373   Perf. 14
632 A105 5p multicolored   .65   .65
633 A105 8p multicolored   .70   .70
634 A105 12p multicolored   .75   .75
635 A105 15p multicolored   .85   .85
   a.   Strip of 4, #632-635   3.25 3.25
      Nos. 632-635 (4)   2.95 2.95

Issued in sheets of 16.

Wedding of Prince Edward and Sophie Rhys-Jones
Common Design Type
Perf. 13¾x14
1999, June 18   Litho.   Wmk. 384
636 CD356 45c Separate por-
              traits   2.25 2.25
637 CD356 £1.20 Couple   5.75 5.75

Queen Mother's Century
Common Design Type

Queen Mother: 20p, With Princess Elizabeth on her 18th birthday. 30p, With King George VI at Balmoral. 50p, With Royal Family, 94th birthday. 60p, As colonel-in-chief of Black Watch.
£1.50, Age 5 photo, airplanes from Battle of Britain, 1940.

1999, Aug. 18   Wmk. 384   Perf. 13½
638 CD358 20p mul-
              ticolored   1.25 1.25
639 CD358 30p mul-
              ticolored   2.00 2.00
640 CD358 50p mul-
              ticolored   3.00 3.00
641 CD358 60p mul-
              ticolored   3.75 3.75
      Nos. 638-641 (4)   10.00 10.00

Souvenir Sheet
642 CD358 £1.50 black   10.00 10.00

Millennium — A106

Various birds.

2000, Jan. 1   Wmk. 373   *Perf. 14*
Color of Queen's Head
643 A106 20p bister   1.00   1.00
644 A106 30p green   1.75   1.75
645 A106 50p blue   3.25   3.25
646 A106 60p brown   4.00   4.00
    Nos. 643-646 (4)   10.00 10.00

Royalty — A107

British monarchs on 8p-£5: 1p, King Manuel I of Portugal. 3p, Frederick Henry, Prince of Orange. 5p, Empress Maria Theresa of Austria. 8p, King George III. 10p, King George IV. 15p, King Willian IV. 20p, Queen Victoria. 25p, Edward VII. 35p, George V. £1, Edward VIII. £2, George VI. £5, Elizabeth II.

2000, Feb. 1   Wmk. 384   *Perf. 14*
647 A107 1p multi   .20   .20
648 A107 3p multi   .20   .20
649 A107 5p multi   .20   .20
650 A107 8p multi   .30   .30
651 A107 10p multi   .40   .40
652 A107 15p multi   .60   .80
653 A107 20p multi   .75   1.00
654 A107 25p multi   1.00   1.10
655 A107 35p multi   1.60   1.90
656 A107 £1 multi   3.75   5.25
657 A107 £2 multi   8.25   10.00
658 A107 £5 multi   20.00 24.50
    Nos. 647-658 (12)   37.25 45.85

The Stamp Show 2000, London
A108

Designs: 15p, Longboat under oars. 45p, Longboat under sail. 50p, Cutty Sark, 1876. 60p, Cutty Sark, 2000. £1.50, Cutty Sark visiting Tristan da Cunha, 1876.

Wmk. 373
2000, May 22   Litho.   *Perf. 14*
659 A108 15p multi   1.50   1.50
660 A108 45p multi   3.75   3.75
661 A108 50p multi   4.00   4.00
662 A108 60p multi   4.75   4.75
    Nos. 659-662 (4)   14.00 14.00

Souvenir Sheet
663 A108 £1.50 multi   11.00 11.00

Prince William, 18th Birthday
Common Design Type

William: Nos. 664, 668a, As toddler, with Princes Charles and Harry, vert. Nos. 665, 668b, Holding paper, vert. Nos. 666, 668c, Wearing scarf. Nos. 667, 668d, Wearing suit and wearing sweater. No. 668e, As child, with Shetland pony.

Perf. 13¾x14¼, 14¼x13¾
2000, June 21   Litho.   Wmk. 373
Stamps With White Border
664 CD359 45p multi   2.40   2.40
665 CD359 45p multi   2.40   2.40
666 CD359 45p multi   2.40   2.40
667 CD359 45p multi   2.40   2.40
    Nos. 664-667 (4)   9.60   9.60

Souvenir Sheet
Stamps Without White Border
Perf. 14¼
668 CD359 45p Sheet of 5,
    #a-e   13.00 13.00

Ships and Helicopters — A109

No. 669, 10p: a, SA Agulhas. b, SA 330J Puma, 1999.
No. 670, 15p: a, HMS London. b, Westland Wessex HAS 1, 1964.
No. 671, 20p: a, HMS Endurance. b, Westland Lynx HAS 3, 1996.
No. 672, 50p: a, USS Spiegel Grove. b, Sikorsky UH-19F, 1963.
Illustration reduced.

Wmk. 373
2000, Sept. 4   Litho.   *Perf. 14*
Pairs, #a-b
669-672 A109 Set of 4   15.00 15.00

First Election of Winston Churchill to Parliament, Cent. — A110

Designs: 20p, During siege of Sidney Street, 1911. 30p, With Franklin D. Roosevelt, 1941. 50p, VE Day broadcast, 1945. 60p, Greeting Queen Elizabeth, 1955.

Perf. 13¾x14
2000, Oct. 2   Wmk. 373
673-676 A110 Set of 4   12.00 12.00

Souvenir Sheet

New Year 2001 (Year of the Snake) — A111

No. 677: a, 30p, Inaccessible Island rail. b, 45p, Black-faced spoonbill.
Illustration reduced.

Wmk. 373
2001, Feb. 1   Litho.   *Perf. 14½*
677 A111   Sheet of 2, #a-b   10.00 10.00
    Hong Kong 2001 Stamp Exhibition.

Age of Victoria
A112

Designs: 15p, Letter, 1846. 20p, Prince Alfred, Duke of Edinburgh, vert. 30p, HMS Galatea. 35p, Queen Victoria, vert. 50p, Charles Dickens, vert. 60p, Resupplying ships.
£1.50, Jubilee celebrations.

Wmk. 373
2001, May 24   Litho.   *Perf. 14*
678-683 A112   Set of 6   12.00 12.00

Souvenir Sheet
684 A112 £1.50 multi   9.00   9.00

Longboats — A113

No. 685: a, Boat with dark and light blue striped sails, island in distance. b, Boat with red and blue striped and white sails, boat with blue, red and yellow striped and blue and white striped sails. c, Prow and sail of boat, two boats in distance. d, Boat with blue and red and yellow striped and blue and white striped sails. e, Boat with dark and light blue sails near shore. f, Boat with red and blue striped and white sails. g, Boat with gray, red and white sails. h, Boat with sails down.

2001, July 12
685 A113 30p Sheet of 8, #a-h   11.00 11.00

Nos. 669-672 Overprinted in Blue Violet

Illustration reduced.

Wmk. 373
2001, Sept. 17   Litho.   *Perf. 14*
686 A109 10p Pair, #a-b   1.75   1.75
687 A109 15p Pair, #a-b   2.50   2.50
688 A109 20p Pair, #a-b   3.25   3.25
689 A109 50p Pair, #a-b   8.50   8.50
    Nos. 686-689 (4)   16.00 16.00

Souvenir Sheet

Birdlife International World Bird Festival — A114

Spectacled petrel: a, Head. b, Diving (island in background). c, In flight with legs extended. d, Diving (sea in background). e, Chick.

Wmk. 373
2001, Oct. 1   Litho.   *Perf. 14½*
690 A114 35p Sheet of 5, #a-e   15.00 15.00

Royal Navy Ships
A115

Designs: No. 691, 20p, HMS Penguin, 1815. No. 692, 20p, HMS Julia, 1817. No. 693, 35p, HMS Beagle, 1901. No. 694, 35p, HMS Puma, 1962. No. 695, 60p, HMS Monmouth, 1997. No. 696, 60p, HMS Somerset, 1999.

Wmk. 373
2001, Oct. 31   Litho.   *Perf. 14*
691-696 A115   Set of 6   12.00 12.00

Churches
A116

Designs: No. 697, 35p, Exterior, St. Joseph's Catholic Church. No. 698, 35p, Exterior, St. Mary's Anglican Church. No. 699, 60p, Stained glass window, St. Joseph's. No. 700, 60p, Altar, St. Mary's.

Perf. 13¼x13½, 13½x13¼
2001, Nov. 27
697-700 A116   Set of 4   13.00 13.00
    Christmas, Arrival of first USPG missionary, 150th anniv.

Tristan da Cunha Postage Stamps, 50th Anniv.
A117

Designs: Nos. 701, 45p, 705a, 45p, #5, 6, 9, 10 canceled. Nos. 702, 20p, 705, 45p, #7, 8, 11, 12 canceled. Nos. 703, 50p, 705c, 45p, #1-4 canceled. Nos. 704, 60p, 705d, 45p, Men at post office, 1952.

2002, Jan. 1   *Perf. 13½*
Without "Tristan da Cunha" in Script
701-704 A117   Set of 4   10.50 10.50

Souvenir Sheet
With "Tristan da Cunha" in Script at Top or Bottom of Stamps
705 A117 45p Sheet of 4, #a-d   11.50 11.50

Reign Of Queen Elizabeth II, 50th Anniv. Issue
Common Design Type

Designs: Nos. 706, 710a, 15p, Princess Elizabeth, 1947. Nos. 707, 710b, 30p, Wearing tiara, 1991. Nos. 708, 710c, 45p, Wearing red coat. Nos. 709, 710d, 50p, Wearing purple hat, 1997. No. 710e, 60p, 1955 portrait by Annigoni (38x50mm).

Perf. 14¼x14½, 13¾ (#710e)
2002, Feb. 6   Litho.   Wmk. 373
With Gold Frames
706-709 CD360   Set of 4   10.00 10.00

Souvenir Sheet
Without Gold Frames
710 CD360   Sheet of 5, #a-e   13.00 13.00

Fishing Industry
A118

Designs: 20p, Pelagic armorhead. 35p, Yellowtail. 50p, Splendid alfonsino. 60p, Ship San Liberatore.

Wmk. 373
2002, May   Litho.   *Perf. 14*
711-713 A118   Set of 3   6.75   6.75
714   Souvenir sheet, #711-713,
    714a   8.50   8.50
    a. A118 60p multi   1.75   1.75

Queen Mother Elizabeth (1900-2002)
Common Design Type

Designs: 20p, Wearing hat (black and white photograph). £1.50, Wearing blue green hat.
No. 717: a, 75p, Holding baby (black and white photograph). b, 75p, Wearing dark blue hat.

Wmk. 373
2002, Aug. 5   Litho.   *Perf. 14¼*
With Purple Frames
715-716 CD361   Set of 2   8.00   8.00
Souvenir Sheet
Without Purple Frames
Perf. 14½x14¼
717 CD361   Sheet of 2, #a-b   8.00   8.00

Marine Mammals — A119

No. 718: a, Gray's beaked whale. b, Dusky dolphin. c, False killer whale. d, Long-finned pilot whale. e, Sperm whale. f, Shepherd's beaked whale.
£2, Humpback whale.

Wmk. 373
2002, Sept. 24   Litho.   Perf. 13¼
718 A119 30p Sheet of 6, #a-f   15.00 15.00
Souvenir Sheet
719 A119 £2 multi   14.00 14.00

HMS Herald Survey, 150th
Anniv. — A120

Designs: 20p, Captain Denham and officers. 35p, HMS Herald in Bay of Biscay. 50p, Surveying, Oct. 30, 1852. 60p, HMS Herald and Torch at sunset, 1852.

2002, Nov. 11   Perf. 14x14¾
720-723 A120 Set of 4   8.00 8.00

Guinness Book of World
Records — A121

No. 724: a, Great Barrier Reef (longest reef). b, Greenland (biggest island). c, Sahara Desert (biggest desert). d, Amazon and Nile Rivers (longest rivers). e, Mt. Everest (biggest mountain). f, Tristan da Cunha (most remote inhabited island).
£2, Like No. 724f.

Wmk. 373
2003, Jan. 10   Litho.   Perf. 13¾
724 A121 30p Sheet of 6, #a-f   9.50 9.50
Souvenir Sheet
725 A121 £2 multi   12.00 12.00

Atlantic Yellow-
nosed
Albatross
A122

Designs: Nos. 726, 730a, 15p, Heads of two birds. Nos. 727, 730b, 30p, Bird on nest, vert. Nos. 728, 730c, 45p, Bird in flight, vert. Nos. 729, 730d, Two birds in flight. No. 730e, £1, Two birds in flight, diff.

Perf. 14¼x13¾, 13¾x14¼
2003, May 7   Litho.
Stamps With White Frames
726-729 A122 Set of 4   7.00 7.00
Souvenir Sheet
Stamps Without Frames
Perf. 14¼x14½
730 A122 Sheet of 5, #a-e   12.00 12.00
Birdlife International.

Head of Queen Elizabeth II
Common Design Type
Wmk. 373
2003, June 2   Litho.   Perf. 13¾
731 CD362 £2.80 multi   11.00 11.00

Coronation of Queen Elizabeth II,
50th Anniv.
Common Design Type

Designs: Nos. 732, 20p, 734a, Queen and extended family. Nos. 733, £1.50, 734b, Bishops paying homage to Queen at coronation.

Perf. 14¼x14½
2003, June 2   Wmk. 373
Vignettes Framed, Red Background
732-733 CD363 Set of 2   8.00 8.00
Souvenir Sheet
Vignettes Without Frame, Purple
Panel
734 CD363 75p Sheet of 2, #a-b 8.00 8.00

Prince William, 21st Birthday
Common Design Type

No. 735: a, William in polo uniform at right. b, In sweater at left.

Wmk. 373
2003, June 21   Litho.   Perf. 14¼
735   Horiz. pair   7.00 7.00
a.-b.   CD364 50p Either single   3.00 3.00

William Glass (1787-1853),
Governor — A123

No. 736: a, Arrival of Glass on HMS Falmouth, 1816. b, As corporal, stationed on Tristan da Cunha. c, Glass and family onshore, 1817. d, Glass family with dog. e, Gov. Glass conducting daughter's marriage ceremony, 1833. f, Glass as old man.

Perf. 14¼x14½
2003, Nov. 24   Litho.   Wmk. 373
736 A123 30p Sheet of 6, #a-f, +
6 labels   7.00 7.00

Royal Navy Ships — A124

No. 737, 20p: a, RFA Tideflow. b, RFA Tidespring.
No. 738, 35p: a, RFA Gold Rover. b, RFA Diligence.
No. 739, 60p: a, RFA Wave Chief. b, HMY Britannia.
Illustration reduced.

Wmk. 373
2003, Dec. 8   Litho.   Perf. 14
Horiz. pairs, #a-b
737-739 A124 Set of 3   9.50 9.50

History of Writing Implements — A125

Designs: 15p, Cave paintings and pigment blocks. 20p, Clay tablet. 35p, Egyptian writing palette. 45p, Goose quill pen. 50p, Fountain pen. 60p, Ballpoint pen. £1.50, Word processing.

2004, Jan. 8   Perf. 13¾
740-745 A125 Set of 6   8.50 8.50
Souvenir Sheet
Litho. with Margin Embossed
746 A125 £1.50 multi   8.00 8.00

Worldwide Fund for Nature
(WWF) — A126

Subantarctic fur seal: No. 747, 35p, Underwater. No. 748, 35p, Pair on rocks. No. 749, 35p, Seal on rock. No. 750, 35p, Head.

Wmk. 373
2004, July 12   Litho.   Perf. 14
747-750 A126 Set of 4   6.50 6.50
750a   Sheet, 4 each #747-750   26.00 26.00

New
Flag — A127

2004, July 27   Unwmk.   Die Cut
Self-Adhesive
Booklet Stamp
751 A127 30p multi   1.50 1.50
a.   Booklet pane of 6   9.00
Complete booklet, 2 #751a   18.00

Merchant
Ships
A128

Designs: No. 752, 20p, RMS Dunnottar Castle. No. 753, 20p, RMS Caronia. No. 754, 35p, SA Agulhas. No. 755, 35p, MV Edinburgh. No. 756, 60p, MV Explorer. No. 757, 60p, MV Hanseatic.

Wmk. 373
2004, Nov. 9   Litho.   Perf. 13¼
752-757 A128 Set of 6   12.00 12.00

Battle of
Trafalgar,
Bicent. — A129

Designs: 15p, Admiral Horatio Nelson's quadrant. 20p, HMS Royal Sovereign breaks the line, horiz. 25p, Thomas Swain aids the wounded Nelson, horiz. 35p, HMS Victory breaks the line, horiz. 50p, Nelson. 60p, HMS Victory, horiz.
No. 764: a, Capt. Thomas Masterman Hardy. b, HMS Victory.

Perf. 13¼
2005, Jan. 20   Litho.   Unwmk.
758-763 A129 Set of 6   7.75 7.75
Souvenir Sheet
764 A129 75p Sheet of 2, #a-b   5.75 5.75

No. 763 has particles of wood from the HMS Victory embedded in the areas covered by a thermographic process that produces a shiny, raised effect.

Island Flora,
Fauna and
Scenes
A130

No. 765 — Tristan da Cunha: a, Rockhopper penguins. b, Southern elephant seals. c, Tristan rock lobster. d, Crowberry. e, Tristan da Cunha island settlement and volcano.
No. 766 — Gough Island: a, Gough moorhen. b, Subantarctic fur seal. c, Bluefish. d, Gough tree fern. e, South African Weather Station.
No. 767 — Inaccessible Island: a, Inaccessible rail. b, Dusky dolphins. c, Sebastes capensis. d, Pepper tree. e, Inaccessible Island Waterfall.
No. 768 — Nightingale Island: a, Tristan thrush. b, Southern right whale. c, Fivefinger fish. d, Tussock grass. e, Nightingale Island.
No. 769 — Middle Island: a, Broad-billed prion. b, False killer whale. c, Wreckfish. d, Fern. e, Middle Island.
No. 770 - Stoltenhoff Island: a, Brown skua. b, Shepherd's beaked whales. c, Snoeks. d, Sea bind weed. e, Stoltenhoff Island.

2005   Wmk. 373   Perf. 13¾
765   Horiz. strip of 5   10.00 10.00
a.-e.   A130 50p Any single   2.00 2.00
766   Horiz. strip of 5   9.50 9.50
a.-e.   A130 50p Any single   1.90 1.90
767   Horiz. strip of 5   9.50 9.50
a.-e.   A130 50p Any single   1.90 1.90
768   Horiz. strip of 5   8.75 8.75
a.-e.   A130 50p Any single   1.75 1.75
769   Horiz. strip of 5   8.75 8.75
a.-e.   A130 50p Any single   1.75 1.75
770   Horiz. strip of 5   9.50 9.50
a.-e.   A130 50p Any single   1.90 1.90

Issued: No. 765, 2/21; No. 766, 3/28; No. 767, 4/18; No. 768, 2/7/06; No. 769, 3/30/06; No. 770, 9/27/06.
See No. 796.

Birds
A131

Designs: 1p, Kerguelen petrel. 3p, Sooty albatross. 5p, Antarctic tern. 8p, Tristan bunting. 10p, Cape petrel. 15p, Tristan moorhen. 20p, Giant fulmar. 25p, Brown skua. 35p, Great-winged petrel. £1, Broad-billed prion. £2, Soft-plumaged petrel. £5, Rockhopper penguin.

Perf. 14¼x14¾
2005, June 1   Litho.   Wmk. 373
771 A131 1p multi   .20 .20
772 A131 3p multi   .20 .20
773 A131 5p multi   .20 .20
774 A131 8p multi   .30 .30
775 A131 10p multi   .35 .35
776 A131 15p multi   .55 .55
777 A131 20p multi   .75 .75
778 A131 25p multi   .90 .90
779 A131 35p multi   1.25 1.25
780 A131 £1 multi   4.00 4.00
781 A131 £2 multi   8.00 8.00
782 A131 £5 multi   20.00 21.00
Nos. 771-782 (12)   36.70 38.45

Pope John Paul II
(1920-2005)
A132

Wmk. 373

2005, Aug. 18		**Litho.**		***Perf. 14***
783	A132	50p multi		1.90 1.90

Battle of Trafalgar, Bicent. — A133

Designs: 20p, HMS Victory. 70p, Ships in battle, horiz. £1, Admiral Horatio Nelson.

		Perf. 13¼	
2005, Oct. 18		**Litho.**	**Unwmk.**
784-786	A133	Set of 3	6.75 6.75

Discovery of Tristan da Cunha, 500th Anniv. — A134

No. 787: a, 30p, Discovery by Tristao d'Acunha, 1506. b, 30p, First survey, 1767. c, 30p, Jonathan Lambert of Salem, 1810. d, 50p, William Glass, 1816. e, 50p, Duke of Gloucester (ship), 1824. f, 80p, Wreck of the Emily, 1836.

No. 788: a, 30p, Thomas Swain (1774-1862). b, 30p, HMS Challenger, 1873. c, 30p, Rev. Edwin Dodgson arrives, 1881. d, 50p, Wreck of the Italia, 1892. e, 50p, HMS Milford, 1938. f, 80p, Norwegian Expedition, 1937-38.

		Perf. 14¼x14½	
2006		**Litho.**	**Wmk. 373**
787	A134	Sheet of 6, #a-f	9.50 9.50
788	A134	Sheet of 6, #a-f	9.50 9.50

Issued: Nos. 787-788, 2/2.

Discovery of Tristan da Cunha, 500th Anniv. Type of 2006

No. 789: a, 30p, World War II TDV training. b, 30p, HMS Atlantic Isle, 1944. c, 30p, Hands holding potatoes, 1946 potato stamp. d, 50p, Tristan da Cunha #5. e, 50p, Volcano eruption and evacuation, 1961. f, 80p, Gough Island Scientific Expedition, 1955.

No. 790: a, 30p, Royal Society Expedition, 1962. b, 30p, Resettlement, 1963. c, 30p, Denstone Expedition to Inaccessible Island, 1982. d, 50p, RMS St. Helena, 1992. e, 50p, New coat of arms, 2002. f, 80p, Hurricane disaster, 2001.

		Perf. 14¼x14¾	
2006		**Litho.**	**Wmk. 373**
789	A134	Sheet of 6, #a-f	10.50 10.50
790	A134	Sheet of 6, #a-f	10.50 10.50

Issued: Nos. 789-790, 6/1.

Queen Elizabeth II, 80th Birthday A135

Queen: No. 791, 60p, As child. No. 792, 60p, Wearing feathered hat. No. 793, 60p, Wearing red hat. No. 794, 60p, Wearing sunglasses.

No. 795: a, 50p, Like No. 792. b, 50p, Like No. 793.

2006, Apr. 21			***Perf. 14***
791-794	A135	Set of 4	9.00 9.00
		Souvenir Sheet	
795	A135	50p Sheet of 2, #a-b	3.75 3.75

Island Flora, Fauna and Scenes Type of 2005-06
Miniature Sheet

No. 796: a, Map of Tristan da Cunha, flag. b, Map of Inaccessible Island, wandering albatross. c, Map of Nightingale Island, humpback whale. d, Map of Middle Island, traditional longboats. e, Map of Stoltenhoff Island, mackerel. f, Map of Gough Island, sub-antarctic fur seal.

		Wmk. 373	
2007, Jan. 22		**Litho.**	***Perf. 13¾***
796		Sheet of 6	12.00 12.00
a.-f.	A130	50p Any single	2.00 2.00

Local Vehicles A136

Designs: 15p, Wave Dancer fishery patrol boat. 20p, Ambulance. 30p, Inshore rescue craft. 45p, Police Land Rover. 50p, Fire engine. 85p, Administrator's Land Rover.

		Perf. 12½x13	
2007, Apr. 17		**Litho.**	**Unwmk.**
797-802	A136	Set of 6	10.00 10.00

Wedding of Queen Elizabeth II and Prince Philip, 60th Anniv. — A137

Designs: No. 803, 50p, Shown. No. 804, 50p, Queen waving. No. 805, 50p, Queen and Prince (black and white photograph). No. 806, 50p, Queen and Prince (color photograph). £2, Queen in wedding gown.

2007, June 1		**Wmk. 373**		***Perf. 13¾***
803-806	A137	Set of 4		8.00 8.00
		Souvenir Sheet		
		Perf. 14		
807	A137	£2 multi		8.00 8.00

No. 807 contains one 42x57mm stamp.

Miniature Sheet

BirdLife International — A138

No. 808 — Great shearwater: a, In flight, facing right. b, In flight, facing left, showing land and sky. c, On ground, showing land and sky. d, In flight facing left, showing land and water. e, On ground, showing land only. f, Chick.

2007, July 1		**Unwmk.**	***Perf. 13¾***
808	A138	50p Sheet of 6, #a-f	12.00 12.00

Scouting, Cent. A139

Designs: 15p, Scout J. W. S. Marr and his book, *Into the Frozen South*, hands tying knot. 20p, The Quest frozen in, Marr, hands tightening rope. £1.25, Flag raising ceremony, hand with compass. £1.40, Children of Tristan da Cunha, trumpeter.

No. 813, vert.: a, Marr and Questie, the ship's cat. b, Lord Robert Baden-Powell.

2007, July 9			**Wmk. 373**
809-812	A139	Set of 4	12.50 12.50

Souvenir Sheet

813	A139	£1.50 Sheet of 2, #a-b	12.50 12.50

A140

A141

A142

A143

A144

Princess Diana (1961-97) A145

		Perf. 13x12½	
2007, Nov. 30		**Litho.**	**Unwmk.**
814	A140	50p multi	2.10 2.10
815	A141	50p multi	2.10 2.10
816	A142	50p multi	2.10 2.10
817	A143	50p multi	2.10 2.10
818	A144	50p multi	2.10 2.10
819	A145	50p multi	2.10 2.10
		Nos. 814-819 (6)	12.60 12.60

Military Uniforms — A146

Designs: No. 820, 15p, Officer, 21st Light Dragoon. No. 821, 15p, Corporal, Royal Artillery. No. 822, 20p, Privates, Royal Artillery. No. 823, 20p, Lieutenant, Royal Artillery. No. 824, £1, Soldiers from Cape Regiment. No. 825, £1, Soldiers from South Africa Army Engineering Corps.

		Unwmk.	
2007, Dec. 10		**Litho.**	***Perf. 14***
820-825	A146	Set of 6	11.00 11.00

Marine Invertebrates A147

Designs: 15p, Tristan rock lobster. 20p, Trumpet anemone. 35p, Starfish. No. 829, 60p, Tristan urchin. No. 830, 60p, Sponge. 85p, Strawberry anemone.

2007, Dec. 10		**Unwmk.**	***Perf. 13¼***
826-831	A147	Set of 6	11.00 11.00

POSTAGE DUE STAMPS

Type of Barbados 1934-47
Perf. 14

1957, Feb. 1		**Wmk. 4**		**Typo.**
		Chalky Paper		
J1	D1	1p rose red	3.00	7.00
J2	D1	2p orange yellow	3.75	9.25
J3	D1	3p green	4.00	11.50
J4	D1	4p ultramarine	4.75	13.50
J5	D1	5p deep claret	6.00	16.00
		Nos. J1-J5 (5)	21.50	57.25

Numeral — D2

		Perf. 13½x14		
1976, Sept. 3		**Litho.**	**Wmk. 373**	
J6	D2	1p lilac rose	.20	.20
J7	D2	2p grayish green	.20	.20
J8	D2	4p violet	.20	.20
J9	D2	5p light blue	.25	.40
J10	D2	10p brown	.65	.85
		Nos. J6-J10 (5)	1.50	1.85
1976, May 31			**Wmk. 314**	
J6a	D2	1p lilac rose	.20	.20
J7a	D2	2p grayish green	.20	.20
J8a	D2	4p violet	.20	.20
J9a	D2	5p light blue	.30	.30
J10a	D2	10p brown	.70	.70
		Nos. J6a-J10a (5)	1.60	1.60

Outline Map of Tristan da Cunha — D3

		Perf. 15x14		
1986, Nov. 20		**Litho.**	**Wmk. 384**	
J11	D3	1p pale yel brn & brn	.20	.25
J12	D3	2p orange & brown	.20	.25
J13	D3	5p crimson rose & brn	.20	.25
J14	D3	7p lt lilac & black	.20	.25
J15	D3	10p pale ultra & blk	.25	.30
J16	D3	25p lt green & blk	.70	.90
		Nos. J11-J16 (6)	1.60	2.20

TRUCIAL STATES

'trü-shəl 'stāts

LOCATION — Qatar Peninsula, Persian Gulf
GOVT. — Sheikdoms under British Protection
AREA — 32,300 sq. mi.
POP. — 86,000
CAPITAL — Dubai

The Trucial States are: Abu Dhabi, Ajman, Dubai, Fujeira, Ras al Khaima, Sharjah and Kalba, and Umm al Qiwain.

Stamps inscribed "Trucial States" were issued and used only in Dubai. Beginning Aug. 1972 all Trucial States used the stamps of United Arab Emirates.

100 Naye Paise = 1 Rupee

Catalogue values for all unused stamps in this country are for Never Hinged items.

7 Palm Trees — A1   Dhow — A2

Perf. 14½x14

1961, Jan. 7	**Photo.**		**Unwmk.**
1	A1	5np emerald	1.50 .20
2	A1	15np red brown	.60 .30
3	A1	20np ultra	1.50 .20
4	A1	30np orange	.60 .20
5	A1	40np purple	.60 .20
6	A1	50np brown olive	.60 .20
7	A1	75np gray	.75 .20

	Engr.		**Perf. 13x12½**
8	A2	1r emerald	6.00 3.75
9	A2	2r black	6.50 24.00
10	A2	5r rose red	8.25 26.50
11	A2	10r violet blue	14.50 27.50
		Nos. 1-11 (11)	41.40 83.25

Stamps inscribed "Trucial States" were withdrawn in June, 1963, when the individual states began issuing their own stamps.

TUNISIA

tü-'nē-zhē͜ə

LOCATION — Northern Africa, bordering on the Mediterranean Sea
GOVT. — Republic
AREA — 63,362 sq. mi.
POP. — 9,513,603 (1999 est.)
CAPITAL — Tunis

The former French protectorate became a sovereign state in 1956 and a republic in 1957.

100 Centimes = 1 Franc
1000 Millimes = 1 Dinar (1959)

Catalogue values for unused stamps in this country are for Never Hinged items, beginning with Scott 163 in the regular postage section, Scott B78 in the semipostal section, Scott C13 in the airpost section, Scott CB1 in the airpost semi-postal section, and Scott J33 in the postage due section.

Coat of Arms — A1

Perf. 14x13½

1888, July 1	**Typo.**		**Unwmk.**
1	A1	1c black, *blue*	3.00 2.25
2	A1	2c pur brn, *buff*	3.00 2.25
3	A1	5c green, *grnsh*	22.50 9.25
4	A1	15c blue, *grysh*	45.00 17.50
5	A1	25c black, *rose*	92.50 52.50
6	A1	40c red, *straw*	92.50 60.00
7	A1	75c car, *rose*	85.00 65.00
8	A1	5fr gray vio, *grysh*	425.00 300.00
		Nos. 1-8 (8)	768.50 508.75

All values exist imperforate.

Reprints were made in 1893 and some values have been reprinted twice since then. The shades usually differ from those of the originals and some reprints have white gum instead of grayish. All values except the 15c and 40c have been reprinted from retouched designs, having a background of horizontal ruled lines.

A2   A3

1888-1902			
9	A2	1c blk, *lil bl*	1.50 .85
10	A2	2c pur brn, *buff*	1.50 .85
11	A2	5c grn, *grnsh*	6.50 .85
12	A2	5c yellow grn ('99)	5.75 .85
13	A2	10c blk, *lav* ('93)	9.25 1.00
14	A2	10c red ('01)	5.75 .85
15	A2	15c blue, *grysh*	45.00 .85
16	A2	15c gray ('01)	9.25 1.25
17	A2	20c red, *grn* ('99)	17.00 1.50
18	A2	25c blk, *rose*	22.50 1.90
19	A2	25c blue ('01)	17.00 1.90
20	A2	35c brown ('02)	45.00 1.90
21	A2	40c red, *straw*	19.00 1.50
22	A2	75c car, *rose*	160.00 75.00
23	A2	75c dp vio, *org* ('93)	25.00 7.25
24	A3	1fr olive, *olive*	30.00 8.50
25	A3	2fr dull violet ('02)	160.00 140.00
26	A3	5fr red lil, *lav*	190.00 75.00
		Bar cancellation	.50

Quadrille Paper

27	A2	15c bl, *grysh* ('93)	45.00 .75
		Nos. 9-27 (19)	815.00 322.55

For surcharges see Nos. 28, 58-61.

No. 27 Surcharged in Red

1902

28	A2	25c on 15c blue	3.00 3.00

Mosque at Kairouan — A4   Plowing A5

Ruins of Hadrian's Aqueduct A6

Carthaginian Galley — A7

1906-26			**Typo.**
29	A4	1c blk, *yel*	.20 .20
30	A4	2c red brn, *straw*	.20 .20
31	A4	3c lt red ('19)	.20 .20
32	A4	5c grn, *grnsh*	.30 .20
33	A4	5c orange ('21)	.20 .20
34	A5	10c red	.30 .20
35	A5	10c green ('21)	.35 .25
36	A5	15c vio, *pnksh*	1.10 .25
a.		Imperf., pair	
37	A5	15c brn, *org* ('23)	.25 .25
38	A5	20c brn, *pnksh*	.25 .25
39	A5	25c deep blue	1.60 .60
a.		Imperf., pair	
40	A5	25c violet ('21)	.35 .25
41	A6	30c red brn & vio ('19)	.70 .60
42	A6	30c pale red ('21)	.90 .60
43	A6	35c ol grn & brn	8.75 1.75
44	A6	40c blk brn & red brn	4.25 .60
45	A6	40c blk, *pnksh* ('23)	1.10 .60
46	A6	40c gray grn ('26)	.20 .60
47	A6	50c blue ('21)	.60 .60
48	A6	60c ol grn & vio ('21)	.60 .60
49	A6	60c ver & rose ('25)	.60 .35
50	A6	75c red brn & red	.75 .60
51	A6	75c ver & dl red ('26)	.35 .35
52	A7	1fr red & dk brn	.90 .60
53	A7	1fr ind & ultra ('25)	.35 .35
54	A7	2fr brn & ol grn	5.25 1.50
55	A7	2fr grn & red, *pink* ('25)	.75 .35
56	A7	5fr violet & blue	9.50 4.50
57	A7	5fr gray vio & grn ('25)	.75 .60
		Nos. 29-57 (29)	41.60 17.80

For surcharges and overprints see Nos. 62-64, 70-73 115-116, B1-B23, B25-B27, B29-B30, B32-B36, C1-C6.

Stamps and Type of 1888-1902 Surcharged

1908, Sept.

58	A2	10c on 15c gray, *lt gray* (R)	1.40 1.40
59	A3	35c on 1fr ol, *ol* (R)	3.25 3.25
60	A3	40c on 2fr dl vio (Bl)	6.00 6.00
61	A3	75c on 5fr red lil, *lav* (Bl)	4.50 4.50
		Nos. 58-61 (4)	15.15 15.15

No. 36 Surcharged

1911

62	A5	10c on 15c vio, *pinkish*	1.50 .60

No. 34 Surcharged

1917, Mar. 16

63	A5	15c on 10c red	.75 .20
a.		"15c" omitted	37.50
b.		Double surcharge	75.00

No. 36 Surcharged

1921

64	A5	20c on 15c vio, *pinkish*	.90 .25

Arab and Ruins of Dougga — A9

1922-26		**Typo.**	**Perf. 13½x14**
65	A9	10c green	.20 .20
66	A9	10c rose ('26)	.25 .25
67	A9	30c rose	1.10 1.10
68	A9	30c lilac ('26)	.40 .40
69	A9	50c blue	.65 .65
		Nos. 65-69 (5)	2.60 2.60

For surcharges see #117, B24, B28, B31.

Stamps and Type of 1906 Surcharged in Red or Black

a   b

1923-25

70	A4(a)	10c on 5c grn, *grnsh* (R)	.35 .35
a.		Double surcharge	57.50
71	A5(b)	20c on 15c vio (Bk)	.85 .25
72	A5(b)	30c on 20c yel brn (Bk) ('25)	.35 .35
73	A5(b)	50c on 25c blue (R)	.85 .25
		Nos. 70-73 (4)	2.40 1.20

Arab Woman Carrying Water — A10   Grand Mosque at Tunis — A11

Mosque, Tunis — A12

Roman Amphitheater, El Djem (Thysdrus) — A13

1926-46		**Typo.**	**Perf. 14x13½**
74	A10	1c lt red	.20 .20
75	A10	2c olive grn	.20 .20
76	A10	3c slate blue	.20 .20
77	A10	5c yellow grn	.20 .20
78	A10	10c rose	.20 .20
78A	A12	10c brown ('46)	.20 .20
79	A11	15c gray lilac	.20 .20
80	A11	20c deep red	.25 .20
81	A11	25c gray green	.35 .25
82	A11	25c lt violet ('28)	.60 .25
83	A11	30c lt violet	.35 .35
84	A11	30c blue grn ('28)	.25 .25
84A	A12	30c dk ol grn ('46)	.20 .20
85	A11	40c deep brown	.25 .20
85A	A12	40c lil rose ('46)	.25 .25
86	A11	45c emerald ('40)	.85 .85
87	A12	50c black	.25 .20
88	A12	50c ultra ('34)	.70 .25
88B	A12	50c emerald ('40)	.20 .20
88C	A12	50c lt blue ('46)	.25 .25
89	A12	60c red org ('40)	.20 .20
89A	A12	60c ultra ('45)	.20 .20
90	A12	65c ultra ('38)	.55 .25
91	A12	70c dark red ('40)	.20 .20
92	A12	75c vermilion	.35 .35
93	A12	75c lil rose ('28)	1.00 .35
94	A12	80c blue green	1.00 .35
94A	A12	80c blk brn ('40)	.25 .25
94B	A12	80c emerald ('45)	.35 .35
95	A12	90c org red ('28)	.25 .20
96	A12	90c ultra ('39)	8.50 8.50
97	A12	1fr brown violet	.70 .35
97A	A12	1fr rose ('40)	.20 .20
98	A13	1.05fr dl bl & mag ('45)	.60 .45
98A	A12	1.20fr blk brn	.35 .25
99	A13	1.25fr gray bl & dk bl	.60 .35
100	A13	1.25fr car rose ('40)	1.00 1.00
100A	A13	1.30fr bl & vio bl ('42)	.25 .25
101	A13	1.40fr brt red vio ('40)	1.10 1.10
102	A13	1.50fr bl & dp bl ('28)	1.00 .35

102A	A13	1.50fr rose red & red org ('42)	.45	.45
102B	A12	1.50fr rose lil ('46)	.20	.20
103	A13	2fr rose & ol brn	1.40	.25
104	A13	2fr red org ('39)	.30	.30
104A	A12	2fr Prus grn ('45)	.25	.20
105	A13	2.25fr ultra ('39)	.90	.90
105A	A13	2.40fr red ('46)	.55	.35
106	A13	2.50fr green ('40)	.85	.85
107	A13	3fr dl bl & org	1.60	.60
108	A13	3fr violet ('39)	.25	.25
108A	A13	3fr blk brn ('46)	.20	.20
108B	A13	4fr ultra ('45)	.90	.55
109	A13	5fr red & grn, grnsh	2.75	.80
110	A13	5fr dp red brn ('40)	1.10	1.10
110A	A13	5fr dk green ('46)	.85	.20
110B	A13	6fr dp ultra ('45)	.60	.35
111	A13	10fr brn red & blk, *bluish*	9.50	2.75
112	A13	10fr rose pink ('40)	.60	.60
112A	A13	10fr ver ('46)	.55	.35
112B	A13	10fr ultra ('46)	.55	.25
112C	A13	15fr rose lil ('45)	.35	.20
113	A13	20fr lil & red, pnksh ('28)	1.75	.85
113A	A13	20fr dk green ('45)	.70	.35
113B	A13	25fr violet ('45)	.70	.55
113C	A13	50fr carmine ('45)	1.25	.70
113D	A13	100fr car rose ('45)	1.50	.90
		Nos. 74-113D (66)	55.50	35.55

See Nos. 152A-162, 185-189, 199-206.
For surcharges and overprints see Nos. 114, 118-121, 143-152, B74-B77, B87-B88, B91-B95, B98, C7-C12.

No. 99 Surcharged with New Value and Bars in Red

1927, Mar. 24

114	A13	1.50fr on 1.25fr	.55	.25

Stamps of 1921-26 Surcharged

1928, May 1

115	A4	3c on 5c orange	.25	.20
116	A5	10c on 15c brn, *org*	.60	.25
117	A9	25c on 30c lilac	.55	.35
118	A12	40c on 80c bl grn	.55	.35
119	A12	50c on 75c ver	.75	.55
		Nos. 115-119 (5)	2.70	1.70

No. 83 Surcharged

1929

120	A11	10c on 30c lt violet	3.50	2.00

No. 120 exists precanceled only. The value in first column is for a stamp which has not been through the post and has original gum. The value in the second column is for a postally used, gumless stamp. See No. 199a.

No. 85 Surcharged with New Value and Bars

1930

121	A11	50c on 40c dp brn	5.00	.85

A14

A15

A16

A17

Perf. 11, 12½, 12½x13

1931-34   **Engr.**

122	A14	1c deep blue	.20	.20
123	A14	2c yellow brn	.20	.20
124	A14	3c black	.35	.35
125	A14	5c yellow grn	.20	.20
126	A14	10c red	.20	.20
127	A15	15c dull violet	.60	.55
128	A15	20c dull brown	.20	.20
129	A15	25c rose red	.25	.20
130	A15	30c deep green	.55	.45
131	A15	40c red orange	.25	.25
132	A16	50c ultra	.25	.25
133	A16	75c yellow	2.10	1.90
134	A16	90c red	.60	.60
135	A16	1fr olive black	.45	.35
136	A16	1fr dk brown ('34)	.45	.35
137	A17	1.50fr brt ultra	.75	.55
138	A17	2fr deep brown	.70	.70
139	A17	3fr blue green	8.50	8.50
140	A17	5fr car rose	22.50	18.00
a.		Perf. 12½	35.00	30.00
141	A17	10fr black	40.00	30.00
142	A17	20fr dark brown	52.50	42.50
		Nos. 122-142 (21)	131.80	106.50

For surcharges see Nos. B54-B73.

Nos. 88, 102 Surcharged in Red or Black:

1937   **Perf. 14x13½**

143	A12	65c on 50c (R)	.55	.20
b.		Double surcharge	75.00	65.00
144	A13	1.75fr on 1.50fr (R)	5.00	1.25
a.		Double surcharge	70.00	70.00

1938

145	A12	65c on 50c (Bk)	.75	.25
146	A13	1.75fr on 1.50fr (R)	7.75	6.50

Stamps of 1938-39 Surcharged in Red or Carmine:

1940

147	A12	25c on 65c ultra (C)	.20	.20
148	A12	1fr on 90c ultra (R)	.35	.35

Stamps of 1938-40 Surcharged in Red or Black:

1941

149	A12	25c on 65c ultra (R)	.25	.25
150	A13	1fr on 1.25fr car rose	.55	.55
151	A13	1fr on 1.40fr brt red vio	.55	.55
152	A13	1fr on 2.25fr ultra (R)	.55	.55
		Nos. 149-152 (4)	1.90	1.90

Types of 1926 Without RF

1941-45   **Typo.**   **Perf. 14x13½**

152A	A11	30c carmine ('45)	.20	.20
152B	A12	1.20fr int blue ('45)	.20	.20
153	A12	1.50fr brn red ('42)	.40	.40
154	A13	2.40fr car & brt pink ('42)	.40	.40
155	A13	2.50fr dk bl & lt bl ('42)	.40	.40
156	A13	3fr lt violet ('42)	.25	.25
157	A13	4fr blk & bl vio ('42)	.40	.40
158	A13	4.50fr ol grn & brn ('42)	.55	.40
159	A13	5fr brown blk ('42)	.45	.45
160	A13	10fr lil & dull vio	.55	.40
161	A13	15fr henna brn ('42)	4.25	3.75
162	A13	20fr lt vio & car	2.50	1.40
		Nos. 152A-162 (12)	10.55	8.65

> **Catalogue values for unused stamps in this section, from this point to the end of the section, are for Never Hinged items.**

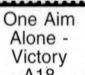

One Aim Alone - Victory A18

Mosque and Olive Tree A19

1943   **Litho.**   **Perf. 12**

163	A18	1.50fr rose	.20	.20

1944-45   **Unwmk.**   **Perf. 11½**

Size: 15½x19mm

165	A19	30c yellow ('45)	.20	.20
166	A19	40c org brn ('45)	.20	.20
168	A19	60c red org ('45)	.45	.45
169	A19	70c rose pink ('45)	.20	.20
170	A19	80c Prus grn ('45)	.30	.30
171	A19	90c violet ('45)	.30	.30
172	A19	1fr red ('45)	.30	.30
173	A19	1.50fr dp bl ('45)	.30	.30

Size: 21¼x26½mm

175	A19	2.40fr red	.40	.40
176	A19	2.50fr red brn	.45	.45
177	A19	3fr lt vio	.65	.65
178	A19	4fr brt bl vio	.45	.45
179	A19	4.50fr apple grn	.45	.45
180	A19	5fr gray	.65	.65

181	A19	6fr choc ('45)	.50	.50
182	A19	10fr brn lake ('45)	.70	.70
183	A19	15fr copper brn	.75	.75
184	A19	20fr lilac	1.00	1.00
		Nos. 165-184 (18)	8.25	8.25

For surcharge see No. B79.

Types of 1926

1946-47   **Typo.**   **Perf. 14x13½**

185	A12	2fr emerald ('47)	.60	.60
186	A12	3fr rose pink	.25	.20
187	A12	4fr violet ('47)	.60	.60
188	A13	4fr violet ('47)	.60	.60
189	A12	6fr carmine ('47)	.20	.20
		Nos. 185-189 (5)	2.25	2.20

Neptune, Bardo Museum A20

1947-49   **Engr.**   **Perf. 13**

190	A20	5fr dk grn & bluish blk	.85	.85
191	A20	10fr blk brn & bluish blk	.40	.25
192	A20	18fr dk bl gray & Prus bl ('48)	1.10	.85
193	A20	25fr dk bl & bl grn ('49)	1.50	1.50
		Nos. 190-193 (4)	3.85	2.80

For surcharge see No. B108.

Detail from Great Mosque at Kairouan A21

1948-49

194	A21	3fr dk bl grn & bl grn	.80	.55
195	A21	4fr dk red vio & red vio	.55	.40
196	A21	6fr red brn & red	.20	.20
197	A21	10fr purple ('49)	.35	.25
198	A21	12fr henna brn	.80	.55
198A	A21	12fr dk brn & org brn ('49)	.60	.35
198B	A21	15fr dk red ('49)	.55	.35
		Nos. 194-198B (7)	3.85	2.65

See No. 225. For surcharge see No. B103.

Types of 1926

1947-49   **Typo.**   **Perf. 14x13½**

199	A12	2.50fr brown orange	.55	.35
a.		2.50fr brown	1.50	.80
200	A12	4fr brown org ('49)	.85	.35
201	A12	4.50fr lt ultra	.60	.35
202	A12	5fr blue ('48)	.55	.55
203	A12	5fr lt bl grn ('49)	.50	.40
204	A12	6fr rose red	.20	.20
205	A12	15fr rose red	.60	.55
206	A13	25fr red orange	1.10	.85
		Nos. 199-206 (8)	4.95	3.60

No. 199a is known only precanceled. See note after No. 120.

Dam on the Oued Mellegue A22

1949, Sept. 1   **Engr.**   **Perf. 13**

207	A22	15fr grnsh black	2.50	.75

UPU Symbols and Tunisian Post Rider — A23

Berber Hermes at Carthage — A24

1949, Oct. 28
Bluish Paper
208	A23	5fr dark green	1.25	1.25
209	A23	15fr red brown	1.25	1.25
		Nos. 208-209,C13 (3)	4.25	4.25

UPU, 75th anniversary.
Nos. 208-209 exist imperf.

1950-51
210	A24	15fr red brown	.60	.55
211	A24	25fr indigo ('51)	.60	.55
212	A24	50fr dark green ('51)	1.90	.55
		Nos. 210-212 (3)	3.10	1.65

Horse, Carthage
Museum — A25

1950, Dec. 26   Typo.   Perf. 13½x14
Size: 21½x17½mm
213	A25	10c aquamarine	.20	.25
214	A25	50c brown	.20	.20
215	A25	1fr rose lilac	.25	.20
216	A25	2fr gray	.30	.20
217	A25	4fr vermilion	.50	.50
218	A25	5fr blue green	.30	.20
219	A25	8fr deep blue	.50	.20
220	A25	12fr red	1.25	.40
221	A25	15fr carmine rose ('50)	.50	.25
		Nos. 213-221 (9)	4.00	2.40

See Nos. 222-224, 226-228.

1951-53   Engr.   Perf. 13x14
Size: 22x18mm
222	A25	15fr carmine rose	.85	.55
223	A25	15fr ultra ('53)	1.00	.55
224	A25	30fr deep ultra	1.75	.60
		Nos. 222-224 (3)	3.60	1.70

Type of 1948-49
1951, Aug. 1   Perf. 13
225	A21	30fr dark blue	1.50	.55

Horse Type of 1950
1952   Typo.   Perf. 13½x14
226	A25	3fr brown orange	.55	.35
227	A25	12fr carmine rose	1.10	.55
228	A25	15fr ultra	.55	.20
		Nos. 226-228 (3)	2.20	1.10

Charles Nicolle — A26

Flags, Pennants and Minaret — A27

1952, Aug. 4   Engr.   Perf. 13
229	A26	15fr black brown	1.40	.75
230	A26	30fr deep blue	1.40	.75

Founding of the Society of Medical Sciences of Tunisia, 50th anniv.

1953, Oct. 18
231	A27	8fr black brn & choc	1.00	1.00
232	A27	12fr dk green & emer	1.00	1.00
233	A27	15fr indigo & ultra	1.00	1.00
234	A27	18fr dk pur & pur	1.00	1.00
235	A27	30fr dk car & car	1.00	1.00
		Nos. 231-235 (5)	5.00	5.00

First International Fair of Tunis.

Courtyard at Sousse — A28

Sidi Bou Maklouf Mosque A29

Designs: 1fr, Courtyard at Sousse. 2fr, 4fr, Citadel, Takrouna. 5fr, 8fr, View of Tatahouine. 10fr, 12fr, Ruins at Matmata. 15fr, Street Corner, Sidi Bou Said. 20fr, 25fr, Genoese fort, Tabarka. 30fr, 40fr, Bab-El-Khadra gate. 50fr, 75fr, Four-story building, Medenine.

Perf. 13½x13 (A28), 13
1954, May 29
236	A28	50c emerald	.20	.20
237	A28	1fr carmine rose	.20	.20
238	A28	2fr violet brown	.25	.25
239	A28	4fr turq blue	.35	.20
240	A28	5fr violet	.35	.20
241	A28	8fr black brown	.35	.25
242	A28	10fr dk blue grn	.35	.20
243	A28	12fr rose brown	.35	.20
244	A28	15fr dp ultra	1.75	.20
245	A29	18fr chocolate	1.50	.60
246	A29	20fr dp ultra	1.00	.25
247	A29	25fr indigo	1.00	.25
248	A29	30fr dp claret	1.00	.25
249	A29	40fr dk Prus grn	1.10	.55
250	A29	50fr dk violet	1.90	.20
251	A29	75fr carmine rose	4.25	2.00

Typo.
Perf. 14x13½
252	A28	15fr ultra	.60	.20
		Nos. 236-252 (17)	16.50	6.25

Imperforates exist. Value $50. See Nos. 271-287. For surcharge see No. B125.

Mohammed al-Amin, Bey of Tunis — A30

1954, Oct.   Perf. 13
253	A30	8fr bl & dk bl	1.00	1.00
254	A30	12fr lil gray & indigo	1.00	1.00
255	A30	15fr dp car & brn lake	1.00	1.00
256	A30	18fr red brn & blk brn	1.00	1.00
257	A30	30fr bl grn & dk bl grn	1.25	1.25
		Nos. 253-257 (5)	5.25	5.25

Theater Drapes, Dove and Sun — A31

1955
258	A31	15fr dk red brn, bl & org	1.00	1.00

Essor, Tunisian amateur theatrical society.

Rotary Emblem, Map and Symbols of Punic, Roman, Arab and French Civilizations A32

1955, May 14   Unwmk.
259	A32	12fr vio brn & blk brn	.75	.75
260	A32	15fr vio gray & dk brn	.75	.75
261	A32	18fr rose vio & dk pur	.75	.75
262	A32	25fr blue & dp ultra	.75	.75
263	A32	30fr dk Prus grn & ind	1.10	1.10
		Nos. 259-263 (5)	4.10	4.10

Rotary International, 50th anniv.

Bey of Tunis A33

Embroiderers A34

1955   Engr.   Perf. 13½x13
264	A33	15fr dark blue	.85	.20

1955, July 25   Perf. 13
15fr, 18fr, Potters. 20fr, 30fr, Florists.
265	A34	5fr rose brown	.65	.65
266	A34	12fr ultra	.65	.65
267	A34	15fr Prussian green	.65	.65
268	A34	18fr red	.65	.65
269	A34	20fr dark violet	.95	.95
270	A34	30fr violet brown	.95	.95
		Nos. 265-270 (6)	4.50	4.50

For surcharge see No. B126.

Independent Kingdom
Types of 1954 Redrawn with "RF" Omitted
1956, Mar. 1   Perf. 13½x13, 13 (A29)
271	A28	50c emerald	.20	.20
272	A28	1fr carmine rose	.20	.20
273	A28	2fr violet brown	.20	.20
274	A28	4fr turquoise blue	.20	.20
275	A28	5fr violet	.20	.20
276	A28	8fr black brown	.20	.20
277	A28	10fr dk blue grn	.20	.20
278	A28	12fr rose brown	.20	.20
279	A28	15fr deep ultra	1.25	.20
280	A29	18fr chocolate	.35	.25
281	A29	20fr deep ultra	.25	.20
282	A29	25fr indigo	.20	.20
283	A29	30fr deep claret	1.10	.20
284	A29	40fr dk Prus grn	1.10	.20
285	A29	50fr dark violet	.85	.20
286	A29	75fr carmine rose	1.60	1.10

Perf. 14x13
Typo.
287	A28	15fr ultra	.20	.20
		Nos. 271-287 (17)	8.50	4.35

Mohammed al-Amin Bey of Tunis — A35

Farhat Hached — A36

Designs: 12fr, 18fr, 30fr, Woman and Dove. 5fr, 20fr, Bey of Tunis.

1956   Unwmk.   Engr.   Perf. 13
288	A35	5fr deep blue	.25	.25
289	A35	12fr brown violet	.35	.35
290	A35	15fr red	.35	.35
291	A35	18fr dk blue gray	.50	.40
292	A35	20fr dark green	.50	.40
293	A35	30fr copper brown	1.00	.50
		Nos. 288-293 (6)	2.95	2.25

Issued to commemorate Tunisian autonomy.

1956, May 1
294	A36	15fr rose brown	.35	.35
295	A36	30fr indigo	.40	.40

Farhat Hached (1914-1952), nationalist leader.

Grapes — A37

Fruit Market A38

Designs: 15fr, Hand holding olive branch. 18fr, Wheat harvest. 20fr, Man carrying food basket ("Gifts for the wedding").

1956-57   Unwmk.   Engr.   Perf. 13
296	A37	12fr lil, vio & vio brn	.65	.25
297	A37	15fr ind, dk ol grn & red brn	.75	.25
298	A37	18fr brt violet blue	1.10	.40
299	A37	20fr brown orange	1.10	.40
300	A38	25fr chocolate	1.50	1.00
301	A38	30fr deep ultra	1.60	.65
		Nos. 296-301 (6)	6.70	2.95

Habib Bourguiba — A39

Farmers and Workers A40

Perf. 14 (A39), 11½x11 (A40)
1957, Mar. 20
302	A39	5fr dark blue	.20	.20
303	A40	12fr magenta	.20	.20
304	A39	20fr ultra	.35	.35
305	A40	25fr green	.40	.25
306	A39	30fr chocolate	.50	.40
307	A40	50fr crimson rose	.90	.60
		Nos. 302-307 (6)	2.55	2.00

First anniversary of independence.

Dove and Handclasp A41

Labor Bourse, Tunis — A42

1957, July 5   Engr.   Perf. 13
308	A41	18fr dk red violet	.35	.35
309	A42	20fr crimson	.40	.40
310	A41	25fr green	.40	.40
311	A42	30fr dark blue	.50	.50
		Nos. 308-311 (4)	1.65	1.65

5th World Congress of the Intl. Federation of Trade Unions, Tunis, July 5-13.

Republic

Officer and Soldier — A43

1957, Aug. 8   Typo.   Perf. 11
312	A43	20fr rose pink	16.00	16.00
313	A43	25fr light violet	16.00	16.00
314	A43	30fr brown orange	16.00	16.00
		Nos. 312-314 (3)	48.00	48.00

Proclamation of the Republic.

Bourguiba in Exile, Ile de la Galité A44

1958, Jan. 18   Engr.   Perf. 13
315 A44 20fr blue & dk brn   .50 .40
316 A44 25fr lt blue & vio   .50 .40

6th anniv. of Bourguiba's deportation.

Map of Tunisia — A45

25fr, Woman & child. 30fr, Hand holding flag.

1958, Mar. 20   Perf. 13
317 A45 20fr dk brown & emer   .35 .20
318 A45 25fr blue & sepia   .35 .20
319 A45 30fr red brown & red   .50 .20
  Nos. 317-319 (3)   1.20 .60

2nd anniv. of independence. See No. 321.

Andreas Vesalius and Abderrahman ibn Khaldoun — A46

1958, Apr. 17   Unwmk.
320 A46 30fr bister & slate grn   .50 .25

World's Fair, Brussels, Apr. 17-Oct. 19.

Redrawn Type of 1958

1958, June 1   Engr.   Perf. 13
321 A45 20fr brt bl & ocher   .50 .50

Date has been changed to "1 Juin 1955-1958."

3rd anniv. of the return of Pres. Habib Bourguiba.

Gardener — A47   A48

1958, May 1
322 A47 20fr multicolored   .50 .30

Labor Day, May 1.

1958, July 25   Unwmk.   Perf. 13
Blue Paper
323 A48 5fr dk vio brn & ol   .50 .25
324 A48 10fr dk grn & yel grn   .50 .25
325 A48 15fr org red & brn lake   .50 .25
326 A48 20fr vio, ol grn & yel   .50 .25
327 A48 25fr red lilac   .50 .25
  Nos. 323-327 (5)   2.50 1.25

First anniversary of the Republic.

Pres. Habib Bourguiba — A49   Fishermen Casting Net — A50

1958, Aug. 3   Unwmk.   Perf. 13
328 A49 20fr vio & brn lake   .35 .25

Pres. Bourguiba's 55th birthday.

1958, Oct. 18   Engr.   Perf. 13
329 A50 25fr dk brn, grn & red   .65 .35

6th International Fair, Tunis.

UNESCO Building, Paris A51

1958, Nov. 3
330 A51 25fr grnsh black   .60 .35

Opening of UNESCO Headquarters, Nov. 3.

Woman Opening Veil — A52   Hand Planting Symbolic Tree — A53

Habib Bourguiba at Borj le Boeuf A54

1959, Jan. 1   Engr.   Perf. 13
331 A52 20m greenish blue   .40 .25

Emancipation of Tunisian women.

1959, Mar. 2   Unwmk.   Perf. 13

10m, Shield with flag and people holding torch. 20m, Habib Bourguiba at Borj le Boeuf, Sahara.

332 A53 5m vio brn, car & sal   .25 .20
333 A53 10m multicolored   .35 .20
334 A53 20m blue   .40 .25
335 A54 30m grnsh bl, ind & org brn   .75 .50
  Nos. 332-335 (4)   1.75 1.15

25th anniv. of the founding of the Neo-Destour Party at Kasr Helal, Mar. 2, 1934.

"Independence" — A55

1959, Mar. 20
336 A55 50m olive, blk & red   .80 .40

3rd anniversary of independence.

Map of Africa and Drawings — A56

1959, Apr. 15   Litho.   Perf. 13
337 A56 40m lt bl & red brn   .65 .40

Africa Freedom Day, Apr. 15.

Camel Camp and Mosque, Kairouan A57

Horseback Rider — A58   Olive Picker — A59

Open Window A58a

Designs: ½m, Woodcock in Ain-Draham forest. 2m, Camel rider. 3m, Saddler's shop. 4m, Old houses of Medenine, gazelle and youth. 6m, Weavers. 8m, Woman of Gafsa. 10m, Unveiled woman holding fruit. 12m, Ivory craftsman. 15m, Skanes Beach, Monastir, and mermaid. 16m, Minaret of Ez-Zitouna University, Tunis. 20m, Oasis of Gabès. 25m, Oil, flowers and fish of Sfax. 30m, Modern and Roman aqueducts. 40m, Festival at Kairouan (drummer and camel). 45m, Octagonal minaret, Bizerte (boatman). 50m, Three women of Djerba island. 60m, Date palms, Djerid. 70m, Tapestry weaver. 75m, Pottery of Nabeul. 90m, Le Kef (man on horse). 100m, Road to Sidi-bou-Saïd. 200m, Old port of Sfax. ½d, Roman temple, Sbeitla. 1d, Farmer plowing with oxen, Beja.

1959-61   Unwmk.   Engr.   Perf. 13
338 A58 ½m emer, brn & bl grn ('60)   .20 .20
339 A57 1m lt bl & ocher   .20 .20
340 A58 2m multicolored   .20 .20
341 A58 3m slate green   .20 .20
342 A58 4m red brn ('60)   .25 .20
343 A58 5m gray green   .20 .20
344 A58 6m rose violet   .25 .20
345 A58 8m vio brn ('60)   .85 .35
346 A58 10m ol, dk grn & car   .20 .20
347 A58 12m vio bl & ol bis ('61)   .65 .25
348 A57 15m brt blue ('60)   .35 .20
349 A57 16m grnsh blk ('60)   .35 .25
350 A58a 20m grnsh blue   1.25 .35
351 A58 20m grnsh blk, ol & mar ('60)   2.10 .25
352 A57 25m multi ('60)   .35 .25
353 A58a 30m brn, grnsh bl & ol   .50 .20
354 A59 40m dp grn ('60)   1.90 .25
355 A58a 45m grn ('60)   .75 .35
356 A58a 50m Prus grn, dk bl & rose ('60)   1.10 .25
357 A58a 60m grn & red brn ('60)   1.10 .40
358 A59 70m multi ('60)   1.60 .60
359 A59 75m ol gray ('60)   1.50 .65
360 A58a 90m brt grn, ultra & choc ('60)   1.50 .60
361 A59 95m multicolored   2.10 1.25
362 A58a 100m dk bl, ol & brn   2.10 1.10
363 A58a 200m brt bl, bis & car   5.50 2.75
363A A59 ½d lt brn ('60)   13.50 7.50
363B A58a 1d sl grn & bis ('60)   25.00 15.00
  Nos. 338-363B (28)   65.75 34.45

UN Emblem and Clasped Hands — A60   Dancer and Coin — A61

1959, Oct. 24
364 A60 80m org brn, brn & ultra   .85 .60

UN Day, Oct. 24.

1959, Nov. 4
365 A61 50m grnsh bl & blk   .65 .65

Central Bank of Tunisia, first anniversary.

Uprooted Oak Emblem — A62

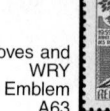

Doves and WRY Emblem A63

1960, Apr. 7   Engr.   Perf. 13
366 A62 20m blue black   .50 .35
367 A63 40m red lil & dk grn   .65 .50

World Refugee Year, 7/1/59-6/30/60.

Girl, Boy and Scout Badge — A64   Cyclist — A65

Designs: 25m, Hand giving Scout sign. 30m, Bugler and tent. 40m, Peacock and Scout emblem. 60m, Scout and campfire.

1960, Aug. 9
368 A64 10m lt blue green   .35 .35
369 A64 25m green, red & brn   .50 .40
370 A64 30m vio bl, grn & mar   .60 .40
371 A64 40m black, car & bl   .65 .50
372 A64 60m dk brn, vio blk & lake   1.40 .65
  Nos. 368-372 (5)   3.50 2.30

4th Arab Boy Scout Jamboree, Tunis, Aug.

1960, Aug. 25

Designs: 10m, Olympic rings forming flower. 15m, Girl tennis player and minaret. 25m, Runner and minaret. 50m, Handball player and minaret.

373 A65 5m dk brown & olive   .35 .35
374 A65 10m sl, red vio & emer   .35 .35
375 A65 15m rose red & rose car   .35 .35
376 A65 25m grnsh bl & gray bl   .50 .50
377 A65 50m brt green & ultra   .90 .90
  Nos. 373-377 (5)   2.45 2.45

17th Olympic Games, Rome, 8/25-9/11.

Symbolic Forest Design — A66

National Fair Emblems — A67

Designs: 15m, Man working in forest. 25m, Tree superimposed on leaf. 50m, Symbolic tree and bird.

1960, Aug. 29

378	A66	8m multicolored	.35	.25
379	A66	15m dark green	.50	.25
380	A66	25m dk pur, crim & brt grn	.65	.35
381	A66	50m Prus grn, yel grn & rose lake	1.25	.60
		Nos. 378-381 (4)	2.75	1.45

5th World Forestry Congress, Seattle, Wash., Aug. 29-Sept. 10.

1960, June 1

382	A67	100m black & green	.85	.60

5th Natl. Fair, Sousse, May 27-June 12.

Pres. Bourguiba Signing Constitution A68

Pres. Bourguiba A69

1960, June 1

383	A68	20m choc, red & emer	.50	.40
384	A69	20m grayish blk	.25	.20
385	A69	30m blue, dl red & blk	.35	.20
386	A69	40m grn, dl red & blk	.50	.25
		Nos. 383-386 (4)	1.60	1.05

Promulgation of the Constitution (No. 383).

UN Emblem and Arms — A70

Dove and "Liberated Tunisia" — A71

1960, Oct. 24   Engr.   Perf. 13

387	A70	40m mag, ultra & gray grn	.65	.60

15th anniversary of the United Nations.

1961, Mar. 20   Perf. 13

Design: 75m, Globe and arms.

388	A71	20m maroon, bis & bl	.25	.25
389	A71	30m blue, vio & brn	.35	.25
390	A71	40m yel grn & ultra	.65	.50
391	A71	75m bis, red lil & Prus bl	.85	.60
		Nos. 388-391 (4)	2.10	1.60

5th anniversary of independence.

Map of Africa, Woman and Animals — A72

Mother and Child with Flags — A73

Map of Africa: 60m, Negro woman and Arab. 100m, Arabic inscription and Guinea masque. 200m, Hands of Negro and Arab.

1961, Apr. 15   Engr.   Unwmk.

392	A72	40m bis brn, red brn & dk grn	.35	.25
393	A72	60m sl grn, blk & org brn	.40	.35
394	A72	100m sl grn, emer & vio	.85	.50
395	A72	200m dk brn & org brn	1.50	1.25
		Nos. 392-395 (4)	3.10	2.35

Africa Freedom Day, Apr. 15.

1961, June 1   Unwmk.   Perf. 13

Designs: 50m, Tunisians. 95m, Girl with wings and half-moon.

396	A73	25m pale vio, red & brn	.35	.20
397	A73	50m bl grn, sep & brn	.50	.25
398	A73	95m pale vio, rose lil & ocher	.75	.40
		Nos. 396-398 (3)	1.60	.85

National Feast Day, June 1.

Dag Hammarskjold A74

Arms of Tunisia A75

1961, Oct. 24   Photo.   Perf. 14

399	A74	40m ultramarine	.65	.35

UN Day; Dag Hammarskjold (1905-1961), Secretary General of the UN, 1953-61.

1962, Jan. 18   Perf. 11½
Arms in Original Colors

400	A75	1m black & yellow	.20	.20
401	A75	2m black & pink	.20	.20
402	A75	3m black & lt blue	.20	.20
403	A75	6m black & gray	.25	.25
		Nos. 400-403 (4)	.85	.85

Tunisia's campaign for independence, 10th anniv.

Mosquito in Spider Web and WHO Emblem — A76

Designs: 30m, Symbolic horseback rider spearing mosquito. 40m, Hands crushing mosquito, horiz.

1962, Apr. 7   Engr.   Perf. 13

404	A76	20m chocolate	.50	.35
405	A76	30m red brn & slate grn	.40	.35
406	A76	40m dk brn, mar & grn	.90	.40
		Nos. 404-406 (3)	1.80	1.10

WHO drive to eradicate malaria.

Boy and Map of Africa — A77

African Holding "Africa" — A78

1962, Apr. 15   Photo.   Perf. 14

407	A77	50m brown & orange	.60	.40
408	A78	100m blue, blk & org	.85	.60

Africa Freedom Day, Apr. 15.

Farm Worker — A79

Industrial Worker — A80

1962, May 1   Unwmk.

409	A79	40m multicolored	.50	.25
410	A80	60m dark red brown	.60	.35

Labor Day.

"Liberated Tunisia" — A81

Woman of Gabès — A82

1962, June 1   Typo.   Perf. 13½x14

411	A81	20m salmon & blk	.60	.35

National Feast Day, June 1.

1962-63   Photo.   Perf. 11½

Women in costume of various localities: 10m, 30m, Mahdia. 15m, Kairouan. 20m, 40m, Hammamet. 25m, Djerba. 55m, Ksar Hellal. 60m, Tunis.

412	A82	5m multi	.65	.25
413	A82	10m multi	.85	.40
414	A82	15m multi ('63)	1.25	.60
415	A82	20m multi	1.25	.65
416	A82	25m multi ('63)	1.25	.65
417	A82	30m multi	1.50	.85
418	A82	40m multi	1.60	.85
419	A82	50m multi	1.60	1.00
420	A82	55m multi ('63)	2.50	1.25
421	A82	60m multi ('63)	3.25	1.60
		Nos. 412-421 (10)	15.70	8.10

6 stamps issued July 25, 1962 (July 25) for the 6th anniv. of Tunisia's independence. 4 issued June 1, 1963 for Natl. Feast Day. See Nos. 470-471.

UN Emblem, Flag and Dove — A83

Aboul-Qasim Chabbi — A84

30m, Leaves, globe, horiz. 40m, Dove, globe.

1962, Oct. 24   Unwmk.

422	A83	20m gray, blk & scar	.35	.20
423	A83	30m multicolored	.50	.25
424	A83	40m claret brn, blk & bl	.75	.40
		Nos. 422-424 (3)	1.60	.85

Issued for United Nations Day, Oct. 24.

1962, Nov. 20   Engr.   Perf. 13

425	A84	15m purple	.40	.25

Aboul-Qasim Chabbi (1904-34), Arab poet.

Pres. Habib Bourguiba A85

Hached Telephone Exchange A86

1962, Dec. 7   Photo.   Perf. 12½x13½

426	A85	20m bright blue	.20	.20
427	A85	30m rose claret	.25	.20
428	A85	40m green	.25	.20
		Nos. 426-428 (3)	.70	.60

1962, Dec. 7   Litho.

Designs: 10m, Carthage Exchange. 15m, Sfax telecommunications center. 50m, Telephone operators. 100m, Symbol of automatization. 200m, Belvedere Central Exchange.

429	A86	5m multicolored	.35	.25
430	A86	10m multicolored	.85	.40
431	A86	15m multicolored	1.40	.70
432	A86	50m multicolored	1.50	.85
433	A86	100m multicolored	2.10	1.20
434	A86	200m multicolored	3.00	1.90
		Nos. 429-434 (6)	9.20	5.30

1st Afro-Asian Philatelic Exhibition; automation of the telephone system.

Dove over Globe — A87

"Hunger" — A88

1963, Mar. 21   Engr.   Perf. 13

435	A87	20m brt bl & brn	.35	.25
436	A88	40m bis brn & dk brn	.50	.25

FAO "Freedom from Hunger" campaign.

Runner and Walker — A89

Centenary Emblem — A90

1963, Feb. 17   Litho.   Perf. 13

437	A89	30m brn, blk & grn	.65	.50

Army Sports Day; 13th C.I.S.M. cross country championships.

1963, May 8   Engr.   Perf. 13

438	A90	20m brn, gray & red	.60	.35

Centenary of International Red Cross.

"Human
Rights" — A91

Hand Raising
Gateway of
Great Temple of
Philae — A92

1963, Dec. 10   Unwmk.   Perf. 13
439 A91 30m grn & dk brn   .50 .35

15th anniv. of the Universal Declaration of
Human Rights.

1964, Mar. 8   Engr.
440 A92 50m red brn, bis & bluish
                blk   .50 .35

UNESCO world campaign to save historic
monuments in Nubia.

Sunshine, Rain and
Barometer — A93

Mohammed
Ali — A94

1964, Mar. 8   Unwmk.   Perf. 13
441 A93 40m brn, red lil & slate   .50 .25

4th World Meteorological Day, Mar. 23.

1964, May 15   Engr.
442 A94 50m sepia   .50 .40

Mohammed Ali (1894-1928), labor leader.

Map of Africa and
Symbolic
Flower — A95

Pres. Habib
Bourguiba — A96

1964, May 25   Photo.   Perf. 13x14
443 A95 60m multicolored   .60 .35

Addis Ababa charter on African Unity, 1st
anniv.

1964, June 1   Engr.   Perf. 12½x13½
444 A96 20m vio bl   .20 .20
445 A96 30m black   .25 .20

"Ship and
Torch" — A97

1964, Oct. 19   Photo.   Perf. 11½x11
446 A97 50m blk & grn   .50 .35

Neo-Destour Congress, Bizerte. "Bizerte" in
Arabic forms the ship and "Neo-Destour Congress 1964" the torch of the design.

Communication Equipment and ITU
Emblem — A98

1965, May 17   Engr.   Perf. 13
447 A98 55m gray & blue   .60 .35

ITU, centenary.

Carthaginian
Coin — A99

Girl with
Book — A100

Perf. 12½x14
1965, July 9   Photo.   Unwmk.
448 A99   5m grn & blk brn   .20 .20
449 A99 10m bis & blk brn   .35 .25
450 A99 75m bl & blk brn   .85 .25
      Nos. 448-450 (3)   1.40 .70

Festival of Popular Arts, Carthage.

1965, Oct. 1   Engr.   Perf. 13
451 A100 25m brt bl, blk & red   .35 .25
452 A100 40m blk, bl & red   .40 .25
453 A100 50m red, bl & blk   .50 .35
  a.   Souvenir sheet of 3, #451-453 5.50 5.50
      Nos. 451-453 (3)   1.25 .85

Girl Students' Center; education for women.
No. 453a sold for 200m. Issued perf. and
imperf.; same value.

Links and ICY
Emblem — A101

Man Pouring
Water — A102

1965, Oct. 24
454 A101 40m blk, brt bl & rose lil .50 .25

International Cooperation Year.

1966, Jan. 18   Photo.   Perf. 13x14

Symbolic Designs: 10m, Woman and pool.
30m, Woman pouring water. 100m, Mountain
and branches.

Inscribed "Eaux Minerales"
455 A102 10m gray, ocher & dk
                red   .35 .25
456 A102 20m multicolored   .50 .40
457 A102 30m yel, bl & red   .50 .40
458 A102 100m ol, bl & yel   1.40 .75
      Nos. 455-458 (4)   2.75 1.80

Mineral waters of Tunisia.

President
Bourguiba
and Hands
A103

"Promotion of
Culture" — A104

25m, "Independence" (arms raised), flag
and doves. 40m, "Development."

1966, June 1   Engr.   Perf. 13
459 A103   5m dl pur & vio   .20 .20
460 A103 10m gray grn & sl grn   .25 .20

Perf. 11½
Photo.
461 A104 25m multi   .25 .20
462 A104 40m multi, horiz.   .65 .25
463 A104 60m multi   1.00 .40
      Nos. 459-463 (5)   2.35 1.25

10th anniversary of independence.

Map of Africa
through View
Finder, Plane and
UN
Emblem — A105

1966, Sept. 12   Engr.   Perf. 13
464 A105 15m lilac & mul-
                ticolored   .35 .25
465 A105 35m blue & multi   .40 .25
466 A105 40m multicolored   .60 .40
  a.   Souvenir sheet, #464-466   11.00 11.00
      Nos. 464-466 (3)   1.35 .90

2nd UN Regional Cartographic Conference
for Africa, held in Tunisia, Sept. 12-24.
No. 466a sold for 150m. Issued perf. and
imperf.; same value.

UNESCO
Emblem
and Nine
Muses
A106

1966, Oct. 24   Perf. 13
467 A106 100m blk & brn   1.10 .40

UNESCO, 20th anniv.

Runners and
Mediterranean
Map — A107

1967, Mar. 20   Engr.   Perf. 13
468 A107 20m dk red, brn ol & bl   .25 .25
469 A107 30m brt bl & blk   .50 .35

Mediterranean Games, Sept. 8-17.

Types of 1962-63 and 1965-66 with
EXPO '67 Emblem and Inscription and

Symbols of Various
Activities — A108

Designs: 50m, Woman of Djerba. 75m,
Woman of Gabes. 155m, Pink flamingoes.

Photo.; Engr. (A108)
1967, Apr. 28   Perf. 11½, 13 (A108)
470 A82   50m multicolored   .50 .25
471 A82   75m multicolored   .75 .35
472 A108 100m dk grn, sl bl &
                blk   1.25 .35
473 A108 110m dk brn, ultra &
                red   1.60 .65
474 AP6   155m multicolored   2.40 .85
      Nos. 470-474 (5)   6.50 2.45

EXPO '67, Intl. Exhibition, Montreal, Apr.
28-Oct. 27.

Tunisian Pavilion, Pres. Bourguiba and
Map of Tunisia — A109

Designs: 105m, 200m, Tunisian Pavilion
and bust of Pres. Bourguiba.

1967, June 13   Engr.   Perf. 13
475 A109   65m red lil & dp org   .50 .40
476 A109 105m multicolored   .60 .40
477 A109 120m brt bl   .75 .40
478 A109 200m red, lil & blk   1.25 .60
      Nos. 475-478 (4)   3.10 1.80

Tunisia Day at EXPO '67.

"Tunisia"
Holding 4-
leaf Clovers
A110

Woman Freeing
Doves — A111

1967, July 25   Litho.   Perf. 13½
479 A110 25m multicolored   .25 .20
480 A111 40m multicolored   .40 .20

10th anniversary of the Republic.

Tennis Courts, Players and Games'
Emblem — A112

10m, Games' emblem & sports emblems,
vert. 15m, Swimming pool & swimmers. 35m,
Sports Palace & athletes. 75m, Stadium &
athletes.

1967, Sept. 8   Engr.   Perf. 13
481 A112 5m sl grn & hn brn .25 .25
482 A112 10m brn red & multi .25 .25
483 A112 15m black .35 .25
484 A112 35m dk brn & Prus bl .50 .25
485 A112 75m dk car rose, vio &
          bl grn .95 .50
    Nos. 481-485 (5) 2.30 1.50
Mediterranean Games, Tunis, Sept. 8-17.

Bird, Punic Period — A113

"Mankind" and Human Rights Flame — A114

History of Tunisia: 20m, Sea horse, medallion from Kerkouane. 25m, Hannibal, bronze bust, Volubilis. 30m, Stele, Carthage. 40m, Hamilcar, coin. 60m, Mask, funereal pendant.

1967, Dec. 1   Litho.   Perf. 13½
486 A113 15m gray grn, pink &
          blk .35 .25
487 A113 20m dp bl, red & blk .35 .25
488 A113 25m dk grn & org brn .50 .25
489 A113 30m grnsh gray, pink &
          blk .50 .25
490 A113 40m red brn, yel & blk .65 .25
491 A113 60m multicolored .75 .35
    Nos. 486-491 (6) 3.10 1.60

1968, Jan. 18   Engr.   Perf. 13
492 A114 25m brick red .50 .40
493 A114 60m deep blue .50 .25
International Human Rights Year.

Computer Fantasy A115

1968, Mar. 20   Engr.   Perf. 13
494 A115 25m mag, bl vio & ol .40 .35
495 A115 40m ol grn, red brn &
          brn .40 .35
496 A115 60m ultra, slate & brn .50 .40
    Nos. 494-496 (3) 1.30 1.10
Introduction of electronic equipment for postal service.

Physician and Patient — A116   Arabian Jasmine — A117

1968, Apr. 7   Engr.   Perf. 13
497 A116 25m dp grn & brt grn .50 .40
498 A116 60m magenta & carmine .50 .40
WHO, 20th anniversary.

1968-69   Photo.   Perf. 11½
Flowers: 5m, Flax. 6m, Canna indica. 10m, Pomegranate. 15m, Rhaponticum acaule. 20m, Geranium. 25m, Madonna lily. 40m, Peach blossoms. 50m, Caper. 60m, Ariana rose. 100m, Jasmine.

Granite Paper
499 A117 5m multicolored .25 .20
500 A117 6m multicolored .25 .20
501 A117 10m multicolored .35 .20
502 A117 12m multicolored .35 .25
503 A117 15m multicolored .40 .20
504 A117 20m multicolored .50 .25
505 A117 25m multicolored .65 .30
506 A117 40m multicolored .75 .40
507 A117 50m multicolored 1.00 .40
508 A117 60m multicolored 1.40 .65
509 A117 100m multicolored 1.90 .90
    Nos. 499-509 (11) 7.80 3.90
Issued: 12, 50, 60, 100m, 4/9/68; others, 3/20/69.

Flower with Red Crescent and Globe — A118   Flutist — A119

25m, Dove with Red Crescent and globe.

1968, May 8   Engr.   Perf. 13
510 A118 15m Prus bl, grn & red .40 .35
511 A118 25m brt rose lil & red .50 .35
Red Crescent Society.

1968, June 1   Litho.   Perf. 13
512 A119 20m vio & multi .40 .25
513 A119 50m multicolored .50 .40
Stamp Day.

Jackal A120

Animals: 8m, Porcupine. 10m, Dromedary. 15m, Dorcas gazelle. 20m, Desert fox (fennec). 25m, Desert hedgehog. 40m, Arabian horse. 60m, Boar.

1968-69   Photo.   Perf. 11½
514 A120 5m dk brn, lt bl & bis .35 .25
515 A120 8m dk vio brn & yel
          grn .50 .25
516 A120 10m dk brn, lt bl &
          ocher .65 .25
517 A120 15m dk brn, ocher &
          yel grn .75 .25
518 A120 20m dl yel & dk brn 1.25 .50
519 A120 25m blk, tan & brt grn 1.60 .65
520 A120 40m blk, lil & pale grn 2.00 1.00
521 A120 60m dk brn, buff & yel
          grn 3.00 1.40
    Nos. 514-521 (8) 10.10 4.55
Issued: 5, 8, 20, 60m, 9/15/68; others, 1/18/69.

Worker and ILO Emblem — A121

60m, Young man & woman holding banner.

1969, May 1   Engr.   Perf. 13
522 A121 25m Prus bl, blk & bis .40 .35
523 A121 60m rose car, bl & yel .60 .40
ILO, 50th anniversary.

Veiled Women and Musicians with Flute and Drum A122

1969, June 20   Litho.   Perf. 14x13½
524 A122 100m dp yel grn & multi .95 .40
Stamp Day.

Tunisian Coat of Arms — A123   Symbols of Industry — A124

1969, July 25   Photo.   Perf. 11½
525 A123 15m yel & multi .25 .25
526 A123 25m pink & multi .35 .25
527 A123 40m gray & multi .40 .25
528 A123 60m lt bl & multi .50 .25
    Nos. 525-528 (4) 1.50 1.00

1969, Sept. 10   Perf. 13x12
529 A124 60m blk, red & yel .50 .30
African Development Bank, 5th anniv.

Lute — A125   Nurse and Maghrib Flags — A126

Musical Instruments: 50m, Zither, horiz. 70m, Rebab (2-strings). 90m, Drums and flute, horiz.

1970, Mar. 20   Photo.   Perf. 11½
Granite Paper
530 A125 25m multicolored .50 .40
531 A125 50m multicolored .65 .40
532 A125 70m multicolored .95 .40
533 A125 90m multicolored 1.25 .40
    Nos. 530-533 (4) 3.35 1.60

1970, May 4   Photo.   Perf. 11½
534 A126 25m lilac & multi .20 .20
6th Medical Seminar of Maghrib Countries (Morocco, Algeria, Tunisia and Libya), Tunis, May 4-10.

Common Design Types pictured following the introduction.

UPU Headquarters Issue
Common Design Type
1970, May 20   Engr.   Perf. 13
535 CD133 25m dl red & dk ol bis .50 .25

Mail Service Symbol A127

35m, Mailmen of yesterday and today, vert.

1970, Oct. 15   Litho.   Perf. 12½x13
Size: 37x31½mm
536 A127 25m pink & multi .30 .25
Size: 22x37½mm
Perf. 13x12½
537 A127 35m blk & multi .40 .25
United Nations, 25th anniversary.

Dove, Laurel and UN Emblem A128

1970, Oct. 24   Photo.   Perf. 13x12½
538 A128 40m multicolored .50 .25
United Nations, 25th anniversary.

Jasmine Vendor and Veiled Woman — A129   Lenin, after N.N. Joukov — A130

Scenes from Tunisian Life: 25m, "The 3rd Day of the Wedding." 35m, Perfume vendor. 40m, Fish vendor. 85m, Waiter in coffeehouse.

1970, Nov. 9   Photo.   Perf. 14
539 A129 20m dk grn & multi .25 .20
540 A129 25m multicolored .30 .25
541 A129 35m multicolored .50 .40
542 A129 40m dp car & multi .60 .40
543 A129 85m brt bl & multi .95 .40
a.   Souvenir sheet of 5, #539-543 7.50 7.50
    Nos. 539-543 (5) 2.60 1.65
No. 543a sold for 500m. Issued perf. and imperf.; same value.

1970, Dec. 28   Engr.   Perf. 13
544 A130 60m dk car rose 1.25 .30
Lenin (1870-1924), Russian communist leader.

Radar, Flags and Carrier Pigeon — A131

1971, May 17   Litho.   Perf. 13x12½
545 A131 25m lt bl & multi .50 .40
Coordinating Committee for Post and Telecommunications Administrations of Maghrib Countries.

UN Headquarters, Symbolic Flower — A132

1971, May 10   Photo.   Perf. 12½x13
546 A132 80m brt rose lil, blk & yel .50 .30
Intl. year against racial discrimination.

"Telecommunications" — A133

1971, May 17   *Perf. 13x12½*
547 A133 70m sil, blk & lt grn   .50 .25
3rd World Telecommunications Day.

Earth, Moon, Satellites A134

Design: 90m, Abstract composition.

1971, June 21 Photo.   *Perf. 13x12½*
548 A134 15m brt bl & blk   .40 .25
549 A134 90m scar & blk   .75 .30
Conquest of space.

"Pottery Merchant" A135

Life in Tunisia (stylized drawings): 30m, Esparto weaver selling hats and mats. 40m, Poultry man. 50m, Dyer.

1971, July 24 Photo.   *Perf. 14x13½*
550 A135 25m gold & multi   .40 .25
551 A135 30m gold & multi   .40 .25
552 A135 40m gold & multi   .50 .25
553 A135 50m gold & multi   .65 .25
   a.   Sheet of 4, #550-553, perf. 13½   7.50 7.50
     Nos. 550-553 (4)   1.95 1.00

No. 553a sold for 500m. Issued perf. and imperf.; same value.

Pres. Bourguiba Sick in 1938 A136

Designs: 25m, Bourguiba and "8," vert. 50m, Bourguiba carried in triumph, vert. 80m, Bourguiba and irrigation dam.

1971, Oct. 11   *Perf. 13½x13, 13x13½*
554 A136 25m multicolored   .25 .25
555 A136 30m multicolored   .25 .25
556 A136 50m multicolored   .40 .35
557 A136 80m blk, ultra & grn   .60 .35
     Nos. 554-557 (4)   1.50 1.20

8th Congress of the Neo-Destour Party.

Shah Mohammed Riza Pahlavi and Stone Head 6th Century B.C. — A137

50m, King Bahram-Gur hunting, 4th cent. 100m, Coronation, from Persian miniature, 1614.

1971, Oct. 17   *Perf. 11½*
Granite Paper
558 A137 25m multicolored   .35 .35
559 A137 50m multicolored   .40 .25
560 A137 100m multicolored   .75 .30
   a.   Souvenir sheet of 3, #558-560   4.50 4.50
     Nos. 558-560 (3)   1.50 .90

2500th anniv. of the founding of the Persian empire by Cyrus the Great. No. 560a sold for 500m. Issued perf. and imperf.; same value.

Pimento and Warrior A138

2m, Mint & farmer. 5m, Pear & 2 men under pear tree. 25m, Oleander & girl. 60m, Pear & sheep. 100m, Grapefruit & fruit vendor.

1971, Nov. 15   **Litho.**   *Perf. 13*
561 A138 1m lt bl & multi   .25 .20
562 A138 2m gray & multi   .30 .30
563 A138 5m citron & multi   .40 .30
564 A138 25m lilac & multi   .65 .40
565 A138 60m multicolored   1.25 .30
566 A138 100m buff & multi   1.90 .50
   a.   Souvenir sheet of 6, #561-566   8.50 8.50
     Nos. 561-566 (6)   4.75 2.00

Fruit, flowers and folklore. No. 566a sold for 500m. Exists imperf.; same value.

Dancer and Musician — A139

1971, Nov. 22   **Photo.**   *Perf. 11½*
567 A139 50m blue & multi   .50 .25
Stamp Day.

Map of Africa, Communica-tion Symbols A139a

UNICEF Emblem, Mother and Child A140

Perf. 13½x12½
1971, Nov. 30   **Litho.**
568 A139a 95m multicolored   .60 .50
Pan-African telecommunications system.

1971, Dec. 6   **Photo.**   *Perf. 11½*
569 A140 110m multicolored   .60 .40
UNICEF, 25th anniv.

Symbolic Olive Tree and Oil Vat — A141

Gondolier in Flood Waters A142

1972, Jan. 9   **Litho.**   *Perf. 13½*
570 A141 60m multicolored   .50 .25
International Olive Year.

1972, Feb. 7   **Photo.**   *Perf. 11½*
Designs: 30m, Young man and Doge's Palace. 50m, Gondola's prow and flood. 80m, Rialto Bridge and hand holding gondolier's hat, horiz.
571 A142 25m lt bl & multi   .30 .25
572 A142 30m blk & multi   .50 .25
573 A142 50m yel grn, gray & blk   .50 .40
574 A142 80m bl & multi   .95 .40
     Nos. 571-574 (4)   2.25 1.30

UNESCO campaign to save Venice.

Man Reading and Book Year Emblem — A143

"Your Heart is Your Health" — A144

1972, Mar. 27   **Photo.**   *Perf. 11½*
Granite Paper
575 A143 90m brn & multi   .60 .50
International Book Year.

1972, Apr. 7   *Perf. 13x13½*
World Health Day: 60m, Smiling man pointing to heart.
576 A144 25m grn & multi   .40 .25
577 A144 60m red & multi   .65 .40

"Only one Earth" Environment Emblem — A145

1972, June 5   **Engr.**   *Perf. 13*
578 A145 60m lemon & slate green   .60 .25
UN Conference on Human Environment, Stockholm, June 5-16.

Hurdler, Olympic Emblems A146

1972, Aug. 26   **Photo.**   *Perf. 11½*
579 A146 5m Volleyball   .25 .20
580 A146 15m shown   .30 .20
581 A146 20m Athletes   .30 .20
582 A146 25m Soccer   .30 .25
583 A146 60m Swimming, women's   .50 .25

---

584 A146 80m Running   .65 .30
   a.   Souv. sheet of 6   4.50 4.50
     Nos. 579-584 (6)   2.30 1.40

20th Olympic Games, Munich, Aug. 26-Sept. 11. No. 584a contains 6 imperf. stamps similar to Nos. 579-584. Sold for 500m.

Chessboard and Pieces — A147

Fisherman A148

1972, Sept. 25   **Photo.**   *Perf. 11½*
585 A147 60m grn & multi   2.25 1.00
20th Men's Chess Olympiad, Skopje, Yugoslavia, Sept.-Oct.

1972, Oct. 23   **Litho.**   *Perf. 13½*
586 A148 5m shown   .25 .20
587 A148 10m Basket maker   .25 .25
588 A148 25m Musician   .35 .25
589 A148 50m Married Berber woman   .85 .25
590 A148 60m Flower merchant   1.10 .35
591 A148 80m Festival   1.40 .50
   a.   Souvenir sheet of 6, #586-591   5.00 5.00
     Nos. 586-591 (6)   4.20 1.80

Life in Tunisia. No. 591a sold for 500m; exists imperf.

Post Office, Tunis A149

Litho. & Engr.
1972, Dec. 8   *Perf. 13*
592 A149 25m ver, org & blk   .30 .25
Stamp Day.

Dome of the Rock, Jerusalem A150

1973, Jan. 22   **Photo.**   *Perf. 13½*
593 A150 25m multicolored   .65 .35

Globe, Pen and Quill — A151

Family — A152

Design: 60m, Lyre and minaret.

1973, Mar. 19 Photo.   *Perf. 14x13½*
594 A151 25m gold, brt mag & brn   .25 .25
595 A151 60m bl & multi   .40 .25
9th Congress of Arab Writers.

1973, Apr. 2   *Perf. 11½*
Family Planning: 25m, profiles and dove.
596 A152 20m grn & multi   .25 .25
597 A152 25m lil & multi   .40 .35

"10" and Bird Feeding Young A153

Design: 60m, "10" made of grain and bread, and hand holding spoon.

1973, Apr. 26   Photo.   Perf. 11½
598 A153 25m multicolored   .65 .25
599 A153 60m multicolored   .65 .25
World Food Program, 10th anniversary.

Roman Head and Ship A154

Drawings of Tools and: 25m, Mosaic with ostriches and camel. 30m, Mosaic with 4 heads and 4 emblems. 40m, Punic stele to the sun, vert. 60m, Outstretched hand & arm of Christian preacher; symbols of 4 Evangelists. 75m, 17th cent. potsherd with Arabic inscription, vert.

1973, May 6
600 A154 5m multicolored   .35 .25
601 A154 25m multicolored   .50 .40
602 A154 30m multicolored   .50 .40
603 A154 40m multicolored   .75 .40
604 A154 60m multicolored   .95 .40
605 A154 75m multicolored   1.00 .50
  a.   Souvenir sheet of 6   9.25 9.25
    Nos. 600-605 (6)   4.05 2.35
UNESCO campaign to save Carthage. No. 605a contains 6 imperf. stamps similar to Nos. 600-605. Sold for 500m.

Overlapping Circles — A155   Map of Africa as Festival Emblem — A156

Design: 75m, Printed circuit board.

1973, May 17   Photo.   Perf. 14x13½
606 A155 60m yel & multi   .40 .25
607 A155 75m vio & multi   .50 .25
5th Intl. Telecommunications Day.

1973, July 15   Photo.   Perf. 13½x13
40m, African heads, festival emblem in eye.
608 A156 25m multicolored   .40 .35
609 A156 40m multicolored   .50 .35
Pan-African Youth Festival, Tunis.

Scout Emblem and Pennants — A157

1973, July 23   Litho.   Perf. 13½x13
610 A157 25m multicolored   .40 .35
International Boy Scout Organization.

Crescent-shaped Racing Cars — A158

1973, July 30   *Perf. 13x13½*
611 A158 60m multicolored   .50 .40
2nd Pan-Arab auto race.

Highway Cloverleaf A159

Traffic Lights and Signs — A160   Stylized Camel — A161

Perf. 12½x13, 13x12½
1973, Sept. 28   Litho.
612 A159 25m lt bl & multi   .65 .40
613 A160 30m multicolored   .75 .35
Highway safety campaign.

1973, Oct. 8   Photo.   Perf. 13½
Stamp Day: 10m, Stylized bird and philatelic symbols, horiz.
614 A161 10m multicolored   .40 .25
615 A161 65m multicolored   .50 .40

Copernicus A162   African Unity A163

Lithographed and Engraved
1973, Oct. 16   *Perf. 13x12½*
616 A162 60m blk & multi   1.25 .30

1973, Nov. 4   Photo.   Perf. 14x13½
617 A163 25m blk & multi   .50 .25
10th anniv. of the OAU.

Handshake and Emblems A164   Globe, Hand Holding Carnation A165

1973, Nov. 15   Litho.   Perf. 14½x14
618 A164 65m yel & multi   .50 .40
25th anniv. of Intl. Criminal Police Org.

1973, Dec. 10   Photo.   Perf. 11½
619 A165 60m blk & multi   .65 .35
25th anniv. of Universal Declaration of Human Rights.

WMO Headquarters and Emblem — A166

Design: 60m, Globe and emblem.

1973, Dec. 24   Litho.   Perf. 14x14½
620 A166 25m multicolored   .50 .25
621 A166 60m multicolored   .65 .30
Intl. meteorological cooperation, cent.

Bourguiba in the Desert, 1945 — A167

Scientist with Microscope A168

Portraits of Pres. Habib Bourguiba: 25m, Exile transfer from Galite Island to Ile de la Groix, France, 1954. 60m, Addressing crowd, 1974. 75m, In Victory Parade, 1955. 100m, In 1934.

1974, Mar. 2   Photo.   Perf. 11½
622 A167 15m plum & multi   .25 .25
623 A167 25m multicolored   .25 .25
624 A167 60m multicolored   .30 .25
625 A167 75m multicolored   .40 .25
626 A167 100m multicolored   .50 .40
  a.   Souvenir sheet of 5, #622-626   2.75 2.75
    Nos. 622-626 (5)   1.70 1.40
40th anniv. of the Neo-Destour Party. No. 626a sold for 500m. Issued perf. and imperf.; same value.

1974, Mar. 21   *Perf. 14*
627 A168 60m multicolored   1.00 .50
6th African Congress of Micropaleontology, Mar. 21-Apr. 3.

Woman with Telephones and Globe — A169   Pres. Bourguiba and Sun Flower Emblem — A171

WPY Emblem and Symbolic Design A170

60m, Telephone dial, telephones, wires.

1974, July 1   Photo.   Perf. 11½
628 A169 15m multicolored   .40 .40
629 A169 60m multicolored   .50 .50
Introduction of international automatic telephone dialing system.

1974, Aug. 19   Photo.   Perf. 11½
630 A170 110m multicolored   .65 .40
World Population Year.

1974, Sept. 12   Photo.   Perf. 11½
60m, Bourguiba and cactus flower, horiz. 200m, Bourguiba and verbena, horiz.
631 A171 25m blk, ultra & grnsh bl   .25 .25
632 A171 60m red, car & yel   .30 .25
633 A171 200m blk, brt lil & grn   1.10 .60
  a.   Souv. sheet, #631-633, imperf.   3.25 3.25
    Nos. 631-633 (3)   1.65 1.10
Congress of the Socialist Destour Party.

Jets Flying over Old World Map A172

1974, Sept. 23   Litho.   Perf. 12½
634 A172 60m brn & multi   .60 .40
25th anniversary of Tunisian aviation.

Symbolic Carrier Pigeons — A173

Handshake, Letter, UPU Emblem — A174

1974, Oct. 9   Photo.   Perf. 13
635 A173 25m multicolored   .40 .25
636 A174 60m multicolored   .50 .35
Centenary of Universal Postal Union.

Le Bardo, National
Assembly — A175

Pres. Bourguiba
Ballot — A176

1974, Nov. 3   Photo.   Perf. 11½
637 A175   25m grn, bl & blk   .40   .30
638 A176   100m org & blk   .60   .40
    Legislative (25m) and presidential elections
(100m), Nov. 1974.

Mailman with   Water
Letters and   Carrier — A178
Bird — A177

1974, Dec. 5   Litho.   Perf. 14½x14
639 A177   75m lt vio & multi   .50   .25
    Stamp Day.

1975, Feb. 17   Photo.   Perf. 13½
640 A178   5m shown   .25   .20
641 A178   15m perfume vendor   .25   .25
642 A178   25m Laundresses   .25   .25
643 A178   60m Potter   .50   .25
644 A178   110m Fruit vendor   1.00 .65
 a.   Souvenir sheet of 5, #640-644 5.00 5.00
        Nos. 640-644 (5)   2.25 1.60
    Life in Tunisia. No. 644a sold for 500m.
Issued perf. and imperf.; same value.

Steel Tower,
Skyscraper — A179

Geometric
Designs
and Arrow
A180

Perf. 14x13½, 13½x14
1975, Mar. 17   Photo.
645 A179   25m yel, org & blk   .25   .25
646 A180   65m ultra & multi   .75   .35
    Union of Arab Engineers, 13th Conference,
Tunis, Mar. 17-21.

Brass Coffeepot and Plate — A181

    15m, Horse and rider. 25m, Still life. 30m,
Bird cage. 40m, Woman with earrings. 60m,
Design patterns.

1975, Apr. 14   Perf. 13x14, 14x13
647 A181   10m blk & multi   .25   .25
648 A181   15m blk & multi   .25   .25
649 A181   25m blk & multi   .35   .25
650 A181   30m blk & multi, vert.   .40   .25
651 A181   40m blk & multi, vert.   .40   .25
652 A181   60m blk & multi   .65   .30
        Nos. 647-652 (6)   2.30 1.55
    Artisans and their works.

Communications and Weather
Symbols — A182

1975, May 17   Photo.   Perf. 11½
653 A182   50m lt bl & multi   .30   .25
    World Telecommunications Day (communi-
cations serving meteorology).

Youth and   Tunisian Woman,
Hope — A183   IWY
                    Emblem — A184

    65m, Bourguiba arriving at La Goulette,
Tunis.

1975, June 1   Photo.   Perf. 11½
654 A183   25m multi   .25   .25
655 A183   65m multi, horiz.   .40   .25
    Victory (independence), 20th anniversary.

1975, June 19   Litho.   Perf. 14x13½
656 A184   110m multicolored   .75   .35
    International Women's Year.

Children
Crossing
Street
A185

1975, July 5   Photo.   Perf. 13½x14
657 A185   25m multicolored   .25   .25
    Highway safety campaign, July 1-Sept. 30.

Djerbian
Minaret,
Hotel
and
Marina,
Jerba
A186

    Old & new Tunisia: 15m, 17th cent. minaret
& modern hotel, Tunis. 20m, Fortress, earring
& hotel, Monastir. 65m, View of Sousse, hotel
& pendant. 500m, Town wall, mosque &

palms, Tozeur. 1d, Mosques & Arab ornaments, Kairouan.

1975, July 12   Litho.   Perf. 14x14½
658 A186   10m multicolored   .25   .25
659 A186   15m multicolored   .25   .25
660 A186   20m multicolored   .25   .25
661 A186   65m multicolored   .60   .40
662 A186   500m multicolored   4.00 1.75
663 A186   1d multicolored   6.50 2.50
        Nos. 658-663 (6)   11.85 5.40

Victors — A187

Symbolic
Ship
A188

1975, Aug. 23   Photo.   Perf. 13½
664 A187   25m olive & multi   .25   .25
665 A188   50m blue & multi   .40   .25
    7th Mediterranean Games, Algiers, 8/23-9/6.

Flowers in Vase,
Birds Holding
Letters — A189

1975, Sept. 29   Litho.   Perf. 13½x13
666 A189   100m blue & multi   .50   .25
    Stamp Day.

Sadiki College, Young
Bourguiba — A190

Engr. & Litho.
1975, Nov. 17   Perf. 13
667 A190   25m sepia, orange & ol-
            ive   .30   .25
    Sadiki College, centenary.

Duck — A191

Vergil — A192

Mosaics: 10m, Fish. 25m, Lioness, horiz.
60m, Head of Medusa, horiz. 75m, Circus
spectators.

1976, Feb. 16   Photo.   Perf. 13
668 A191   5m multicolored   .30   .25
669 A191   10m multicolored   .30   .25
670 A192   25m multicolored   .75   .50
671 A192   60m multicolored   .75   .50
672 A192   75m multicolored   .90   .50
673 A192   100m multicolored   1.40 .50
 a.   Souvenir sheet of 6, #668-673 7.00 7.00
        Nos. 668-673 (6)   4.40 2.50
    Tunisian mosaics, 2nd-5th centuries.
    No. 673a sold for 500m. Issued perf. and
imperf.; same value.

Telephone
A193

1976, Mar. 10   Litho.   Perf. 14x13½
674 A193   150m blue & multi   .65   .35
    Centenary of first telephone call by Alexan-
der Graham Bell, Mar. 10, 1876.

Pres.
Bourguiba
and
"20" — A194

    Pres. Bourguiba and: 100m, "20" and sym-
bolic Tunisian flag. 150m, "Tunisia" rising from
darkness, and 20 flowers.

1976, Mar. 20   Photo.   Perf. 11½
675 A194   40m multicolored   .25   .25
676 A194   100m multicolored   .50   .25
677 A194   150m multicolored   .75   .35
        Nos. 675-677 (3)   1.50 .85

Souvenir Sheets
Perf. 11½, Imperf.
678   Sheet of 3   3.50 3.50
 a.   A194 50m like 40m   .50   .50
 b.   A194 200m like 100m   1.00 1.00
 c.   A194 250m like 150m   1.50 1.50
    20th anniversary of independence.

Blind Man with   Procession and
Cane   Buildings
A195   A196

1976, Apr. 7   Engr.   Perf. 13
679 A195   100m black & red   .50   .25
    World Health Day: "Foresight prevents
blindness."

1976, May 31   Photo.   Perf. 12x11½
680 A196   40m multicolored   .40   .25
    Habitat, UN Conf. on Human Settlements,
Vancouver, Canada, May 31-June 11.

Face and Hands Decorated with Henna — A197

Old and new Tunisia: 50m, Sponge fishing at Jerba. 65m, Textile industry. 110m, Pottery of Guellala.

1976, June 15   Photo.   Perf. 13x13½
681 A197 40m multicolored   .25   .25
682 A197 50m multicolored   .50   .25
683 A197 65m multicolored   .50   .25
684 A197 110m multicolored   .65   .50
      Nos. 681-684 (4)   1.90 1.25

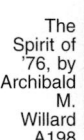

The Spirit of '76, by Archibald M. Willard A198

1976, July 4   Perf. 13x14
685 A198 200m multicolored   1.75   .85

Souvenir Sheets
Perf. 13x14, Imperf.
686 A198 500m multicolored   5.00 5.00

American Bicentennial.

Running A199

Montreal Olympic Games Emblem and: 75m, Bicycling. 120m, Peace dove.

1976, July 17   Photo.   Perf. 11½
687 A199 50m gray, red & blk   .25   .25
688 A199 75m red, yel & blk   .40   .25
689 A199 120m orange & multi   .65   .35
      Nos. 687-689 (3)   1.30   .85

21st Olympic Games, Montreal, Canada, July 17-Aug. 1.

Child Reading — A200   Heads and Bird — A201

1976, Aug. 23   Litho.   Perf. 13
690 A200 100m brown & multi   .50   .25
      Books for children.

1976, Sept. 30   Litho.   Perf. 13
691 A201 150m orange & multi   .75   .25

Non-aligned Countries, 15th anniv. of 1st Conference.

Mouradite Mausoleum, 17th Century — A202

Electronic Tree and ITU Emblem — A204

Globe and Emblem A203

Cultural Heritage: 100m, Minaret, Kairawan Great Mosque and psalmodist. 150m, Monastir Ribat monastery and Alboracq (sphinx). 200m, Barber's Mosque, Kairawan andman's bust.

1976, Oct. 25   Photo.   Perf. 14
692 A202 85m multicolored   .40   .25
693 A202 100m multicolored   .50   .25
694 A202 150m multicolored   .75   .25
695 A202 200m multicolored   1.10   .40
      Nos. 692-695 (4)   2.75 1.15

1976, Dec. 24   Photo.   Perf. 13x14
696 A203 150m multicolored   .85   .35

25th anniv. of UN Postal Administration.

1977, May 17   Photo.   Perf. 14x13½
697 A204 150m multicolored   .85   .50

9th World Telecommunications Day.

"Communication," Sassenage Castle, Grenoble — A205

1977, May 19   Litho.   Perf. 13½x13
698 A205 100m multicolored   .90   .40

10th anniv. of Intl. French Language Council.

Soccer A206

1977, June 27   Photo.   Perf. 13½
699 A206 150m multicolored   1.00   .50

Junior World Soccer Tournament, Tunisia, June 27-July 10.

Gold Coin, 10th Century — A207

Cultural Heritage: 15m, Stele, Gorjani Cemetery, Tunis, 13th century. 20m, Floral design, 17th century illumination. 30m, Bird and flowers, glass painting, 1922. 40m, Antelope, from 11th century clay pot. 50m, Gate, Sidi Bou Said, 20th century.

1977, July 9   Photo.   Perf. 13
700 A207 10m multicolored   .20   .20
701 A207 15m multicolored   .20   .20
702 A207 20m multicolored   .25   .20
703 A207 30m multicolored   .40   .25
704 A207 40m multicolored   .50   .25
705 A207 50m multicolored   .50   .25
  a.   Miniature sheet of 6, #700-705 3.75 3.75
      Nos. 700-705 (6)   2.05 1.35

"The Young Republic" and Bourguiba — A208   Diseased Knee, Gears and Globe — A210

Symbolic Cancellation, APU Emblem — A209

Habib Bourguiba and: 100m, "The Confident Republic" and 20 doves. 150m, "The Determined Republic" and 20 roses.

1977, July 25   Photo.   Perf. 13x13½
706 A208 40m multicolored   .40   .25
707 A208 100m multicolored   .50   .25
708 A208 150m multicolored   .85   .35
  a.   Souvenir sheet of 3, #706-708 2.75 2.75
      Nos. 706-708 (3)   1.75   .85

20th anniv. of the Republic. No. 708a sold for 500m. Exists imperf., same value.

1977, Aug. 16   Litho.   Perf. 13x12½
709 A209 40m multicolored   .25   .25

Arab Postal Union, 25th anniversary.

1977, Sept. 26 Photo.   Perf. 14x13½
710 A210 120m multicolored   .75   .35

World Rheumatism Year.

Farmer, Road, Water and Electricity — A211

1977, Dec. 15   Photo.   Perf. 13½
711 A211 40m multicolored   .20   .20

Rural development.

Factory Workers — A212   Pres. Bourguiba, Torch and "9" — A213

Designs: 20m, Bus driver and trains, horiz. 40m, Farmer driving tractor, horiz.

1978, Mar. 6   Perf. 13x14, 14x13
712 A212 20m rose red & multi   .25   .20
713 A212 40m black & green   .25   .25
714 A212 100m multicolored   .50   .35
      Nos. 712-714 (3)   1.00   .80

5th development plan, creation of new jobs.

1978, Apr. 9   Engr.   Perf. 13
715 A213 40m shown   .25   .25
716 A213 60m Bourguiba and "9"   .25   .25

40th anniv. of 1st fight for independence, 4/9/38.

A214

1978, May 2   Photo.   Perf. 13x13½
717 A214 150m Policeman   .90   .35

6th Regional African Interpol Conference, Tunis, May 2-5.

A215

1978, June 1   Photo.   Perf. 13x14

Designs: 40m, Tunisian Goalkeeper. 150m., Soccer player, maps of South America and Africa, flags.

718 A215 40m multicolored   .35   .25
719 A215 150m multicolored   1.00   .40

11th World Cup Soccer Championship, Argentina, June 1-25.

Destruction of Apartheid, Map of South Africa — A216

Fight Against Apartheid: 100m, White and black doves flying in unison.

1978, Aug. 30   Litho.   Perf. 13½x14
720 A216 50m multicolored   .25   .25
721 A216 100m multicolored   .50   .35

"Pollution is a Plague" A217   "Eradication of Smallpox" A218

Designs: 50m, "The Sea, mankind's patrimony." 120m, "Greening of the desert."

1978, Sept. 11 Photo.   Perf. 14x13
722 A217 10m multicolored   .25   .25
723 A217 50m multicolored   .50   .25
724 A217 120m multicolored   1.20   .35
      Nos. 722-724 (3)   1.95   .85

Protection of the environment.

1978, Oct. 16   Litho.   Perf. 12½
725 A218 150m multicolored   .75   .40

Global eradication of smallpox.

Jerba Wedding A219

5m, Horseman from Zlass. 75m, Women potters from the Mogods. 100m, Dove over Marabout Sidi Mahrez cupolas, Tunis. 500m, Plowing in Jenduba. 1d, Spring Festival in Tozeur (man on swing).

1978, Nov. 1　Photo.　Perf. 13
726 A219　5m multi, vert.　.20　.20
727 A219　60m multi　.35　.20
728 A219　75m multi　.50　.20
729 A219　100m multi　.50　.25
730 A219　500m multi　3.75　1.25
731 A219　1d multi　6.00　2.50
　　Nos. 726-731 (6)　11.30　4.60
　Traditional Arab calligraphy.

Lenin and Red Banner over Kremlin — A220

Farhat Hached, Union Emblem — A221

1978, Nov. 7　　　　Perf. 13½
732 A220 150m multicolored　1.20　.50
　Russian October Revolution, 60th anniv.

1978, Dec. 5　Photo.　Perf. 14
733 A221 50m multicolored　　.40　.20
　Farhat Hached (1914-1952), founder of General Union of Tunisian Workers.

Family — A222　　Sun with Man's Face — A223

1978, Dec. 15　Photo.　Perf. 13½
734 A222 50m multicolored　　.50　.25
Tunisian Family Planning Assoc., 10th anniv.

1978, Dec. 25　　　Perf. 14
735 A223 100m multicolored　　.75　.25
　Sun as a source of light and energy.

Plane, Weather Map and Instruments — A224

1978, Dec. 29
736 A224 50m multicolored　　.40　.25
Tunisian civil aviation and meteorology, 20th anniv.

Habib Bourguiba and Constitution — A225

1979, May 31　Photo.　Perf. 14x13½
737 A225 50m multicolored　　.50　.35
　20th anniversary of Constitution.

El Kantaoui Port A226

1979, June 3　　　Perf. 13½x14
738 A226 150m multicolored　　.75　.35
Development of El Kantaoui as a resort area.

Landscapes — A227

1979, July 14　　　Perf. 12½x13½
739 A227　50m Korbous　.25　.20
740 A227　100m Mides　.40　.20

Bow Net Weaving — A228　Pres. Bourguiba, "10" and Hands — A229

1979, Aug. 15　Photo.　Perf. 11½
741 A228 10m shown　　.35　.20
742 A228 20m Beekeeping　.85　.25

1979, Sept. 5
743 A229 50m multicolored　　.35　.20
　Socialist Destour Party, 10th Congress.

Modes of Communication, ITU Emblem — A230

1979, Sept. 20　Litho.　Perf. 11½
744 A230 150m multicolored　.90　.50
　3rd World Telecommunications Exhibition, Geneva, Sept. 20-26.

Arab Achievements — A231

1979, Oct. 1　　　Perf. 14½
745 A231 50m multicolored　　.25　.20

Children Crossing Street, IYC Emblem — A232

1979, Oct. 16　　　Perf. 14x13½
746 A232　50m shown　.25　.20
747 A232　100m Child and birds　.60　.25
　International Year of the Child.

Dove, Olive Tree, Map of Tunisia — A233　Woman Wearing Crown — A234

1979, Nov. 1　Litho.　Perf. 12
748 A233 150m multicolored　.90　.40
　2nd International Olive Oil Year.

1979, Nov. 3　　　Perf. 14½
749 A234 50m multicolored　.25　.20
　Central Bank of Tunisia, 20th anniversary.

Children and Jujube Tree — A235

1979, Dec. 25　Litho.　Perf. 15x14½
750 A235 20m shown　　.30　.20
751 A235 30m Peacocks　.60　.25
752 A235 70m Goats　1.10　.35
753 A235 85m Girl, date palm　1.10　.40
　　Nos. 750-753 (4)　3.10　1.20

Postal Code Introduction — A236

1980, Mar. 20　Photo.　Perf. 14
754 A236 50m multicolored　.40　.25

Fight Against Cigarette Smoking A237

1980, Apr. 7
755 A237 150m multicolored　　.75　.25

Pres. Bourguiba in Flower, Open Book — A238

1980, June 1　Photo.　Perf. 11½
756 A238　50m shown　.25　.25
757 A238　100m Dove, Bourguiba, mosque　.90　.40
　Victory (independence), 25th anniversary.

Butterfly and Gymnast A239

1980, June 3　Photo.　Perf. 12x11½
Granite Paper
758 A239 100m multicolored　　.50　.25
　Turin Gymnastic Games, June 1-7.

Artisans
A240　　　　A241

1980, July 21　Photo.　Perf. 13½
759 A240 30m multicolored　.30　.25
760 A241 75m multicolored　.50　.25

ibn-Khaldun (1332-1406), Historian — A242

Avicenna (Arab Physician), Birth Millenium — A243

1980, July 28   *Perf. 14*
761 A242 50m multicolored   .25 .25

1980, Aug. 18   **Engr.**   *Perf. 12½x13*
762 A243 100m redsh brn & sepia   .90 .35

Arab Achievements — A244

1980, Aug. 25   **Photo.**   *Perf. 13½x14*
763 A244 50m multicolored   .40 .25

Port Sidi bou Said A245

1980, Sept. 4   *Perf. 14*
764 A245 100m multicolored   .75 .35

World Tourism Conference, Manila, Sept. 27 — A246

1980, Sept. 27   **Photo.**   *Perf. 14*
765 A246 150m multicolored   .65 .25

Wedding in Jerba, by Yahia (1903-1969) — A247

1980, Oct. 1   *Perf. 12*
766 A247 50m multicolored   .60 .40

Tozeur-Nefta International Airport Opening — A248

1980, Oct. 13   **Photo.**   *Perf. 13x13½*
767 A248 85m multicolored   .40 .25

Eye and Text A249

1980, Oct. 26   **Litho.**   *Perf. 13½x14*
768 A249 100m multicolored   1.10 .50

7th Afro-Asian Ophthalmologic Congress.

Hegira, 1500th Anniv. A250

1980, Nov. 9
769 A250 50m Spiderweb   .25 .25
770 A250 80m City skyline   .40 .25

Film Strip and Woman's Head — A251

1980, Nov. 15   **Photo.**   *Perf. 14x13½*
771 A251 100m multicolored   .50 .35

Carthage Film Festival.

Orchid A252

1980, Nov. 17   *Perf. 13½x14*
772 A252 20m shown   .65 .35
773 A252 25m Wild cyclamen   .85 .35

Size: 39x27mm
Perf. 14
774 A252 50m Mouflon   1.60 .35
775 A252 100m Golden eagle   3.50 .40
   Nos. 772-775 (4)   6.60 1.45

Campaign to Save Kairouan Mosque A253

1980, Dec. 29   **Photo.**   *Perf. 12*
Granite Paper
776 A253 85m multicolored   .40 .25

Heinrich von Stephan (1831-1897), Founder of UPU — A254

Blood Donors' Assoc., 20th Anniv. — A255

1981, Jan. 7
777 A254 150m multicolored   .75 .40

1981, Mar. 5   **Litho.**   *Perf. 14x13½*
778 A255 75m multicolored   .75 .50

Pres. Bourguiba and Flag — A256

1981, Mar. 20   **Photo.**   *Perf. 12x11½*
Granite Paper
779 A256 50m shown   .25 .25
780 A256 60m Dove, "25"   .40 .25
781 A256 85m Doves   .65 .40
782 A256 120m Victory on winged horse   .65 .40
  a.   Souvenir sheet of 4, #779-782   3.25 3.25
   Nos. 779-782 (4)   1.95 1.30

25th anniversary of independence. No. 782 sold for 500m. Exists imperf., same value.

Pres. Bourguiba and Flower A257

1981, Apr. 10   **Photo.**   *Perf. 12x11½*
783 A257 50m shown   .25 .20
784 A257 75m Bourguiba, flower, diff.   .40 .25

Destourien Socialist Party Congress.

Mosque Entrance, Mahdia A258

1981, Apr. 20   *Perf. 13½*
785 A258 50m shown   .40 .25
786 A258 85m Tozeur Great Mosque, vert.   .40 .35
787 A258 100m Needle Rocks, Tabarka   .55 .25
   Nos. 785-787 (3)   1.35 .85

A259

Youth Festival — A260

1981, May 17   **Litho.**   *Perf. 14x15*
788 A259 150m multicolored   .40 .35

13th World Telecommunications Day.

1981, June 2   **Photo.**   *Perf. 11½*
Granite Paper
789 A260 100m multicolored   .50 .25

A261   A262

1981, June 15   **Photo.**   *Perf. 14*
790 A261 150m multicolored   .85 .35

Kemal Ataturk (1881-1938), 1st president of Turkey.

1981, July 15   **Photo.**   *Perf. 11½x12*
791 A262 150m Skifa, Mahdia   .85 .40

Mohammed Tahar Ben Achour (1879-1973), Scholar — A263

1981, Aug. 6   *Perf. 13*
792 A263 200m multicolored   1.10 .50

25th Anniv. of Personal Status Code (Women's Liberation) — A264

1981, Aug. 13
793 A264 50m Woman   .25 .25
794 A264 100m shown   .50 .35

Intl. Year of the Disabled — A265

1981, Sept. 21   **Photo.**   *Perf. 13½*
795 A265 250m multicolored   1.25 .65

Pilgrimage to
Mecca — A266

World Food
Day — A267

1981, Oct. 7   Photo.   Perf. 13½
796 A266 50m multicolored   .40 .25

1981, Oct. 16   Litho.   Perf. 12
Granite Paper
797 A267 200m multicolored   1.10 .65

Traditional
Jewelry
A268

150m, Mneguech silver earrings. 180m
Mahfdha (silver medallion worn by married
women). 200m, Essalta gold headdress.

1981, Dec. 7   Photo.   Perf. 14
798 A268 150m multi, vert.   .75 .35
799 A268 180m multi   .90 .40
800 A268 200m multi, vert.   1.10 .50
    Nos. 798-800 (3)   2.75 1.25

Bizerta
Bridge
A269

1981, Dec. 14   Litho.   Perf. 12x11½
Granite Paper
801 A269 230m multicolored   1.00 .50

A270

A271

Chemist compounding honey mixture, manuscript miniature, 1224.

1982, Apr. 3   Photo.   Perf. 13
802 A270 80m multicolored   .65 .35
    Arab Chemists' Union, 16th anniv.

1982, May 12   Photo.   Perf. 13½
803 A271 150m multicolored   1.00 .60
    Oceanic Enterprise Symposium, Tunis,
5/12-14.

A272

A273

1982, June 26   Perf. 12½
Granite Paper
804 A272 80m multicolored   .40 .25
    The Productive Family Employment
campaign.

1982, July 25   Litho.   Perf. 14x13½
    25th Anniv. of Republic: Pres. Bourguiba
and Various Women.
805 A273 80m multicolored   .35 .25
806 A273 100m multicolored   .50 .35
807 A273 200m multicolored   .85 .40
    Nos. 805-807 (3)   1.70 1.00

Scouting
Year — A274

Tunisian
Fossils — A274a

Perf. 14½x14, 14x14½
1982, Aug. 23
808 A274 80m multicolored   .40 .25
809 A274 200m multicolored   .85 .25
    75th anniv. of scouting and 50th anniv. of
scouting in Tunisia (80m, horiz.).

1982, Sept. 20   Photo.   Perf. 11½x12
    Designs: 80m, Pseudophillipsia azzouzi,
vert. 200m, Mediterraneotrigonia cherahilen-
sis, vert. 280m, Numidiopleura enigmatica.
300m, Micreschara tunisiensis, vert. 500m,
Mantelliceras pervinquieri, vert. 1000m,
Elephas africanavus.

809A A274a 80m multi   1.00   .40
809B A274a 200m multi   2.00   .60
809C A274a 280m multi   2.40   .75
809D A274a 300m multi   3.00 1.00
809E A274a 500m multi   6.00 1.60
809F A274a 1000m multi   12.00 3.00
    Nos. 809A-809F (6)   26.40 7.35

A275

A276

1982, Sept. 29   Perf. 14x13½
810 A275 80m shown   .50 .25
    Size: 23x40mm
811 A275 200m Woman, buildings   .85 .50
    30th Anniv. of Arab Postal Union.

1982, Oct. 1   Photo.   Perf. 12
Granite Paper
812 A276 200m multicolored   .85 .25
    ITU Plenipotentiaries Conf., Nairobi

World Food
Day
A277

Tahar Haddad
(1899-1935),
Social Reformer
A278

1982, Oct. 16   Litho.   Perf. 13
813 A277 200m multicolored   .90 .35

1982, Oct. 25   Engr.
814 A278 200m dark brown   .75 .25

TB Bacillus
Centenary
A279

Folk Songs and
Stories — A280

1982, Nov. 16   Litho.   Perf. 13½
815 A279 100m multicolored   .75 .25

1982, Nov. 22   Photo.   Perf. 14
816 A280 20m Dancing in the
            Rain   .25 .25
817 A280 30m Woman Sweep-
            ing   .25 .25
818 A280 70m Fisherman and
            the Child   .25 .25
819 A280 80m Rooster and the
            Oranges, horiz.   .30 .25
820 A280 100m Woman and the
            Mirror, horiz.   .50 .25
821 A280 120m The Two Girls,
            horiz.   .65 .30
    Nos. 816-821 (6)   2.20 1.55

Intl. Palestinian Solidarity Day — A281

1982, Nov. 30   Litho.   Perf. 13x12
822 A281 80m multicolored   .40 .25

Farhat Hached
(1914-1952)
A282

Bourguiba Dam
Opening
A283

1982, Dec. 6   Engr.   Perf. 13
823 A282 80m brown red   .40 .25

1982, Dec. 20   Litho.   Perf. 13½
824 A283 80m multicolored   .50 .25

Environmental Training
College
Opening — A284

1982, Dec. 29   Photo.   Perf. 11½
Granite Paper
825 A284 80m multicolored   .40 .20

World Communications Year — A285

1983, May 17   Litho.   Perf. 13½x14
826 A285 200m multicolored   .60 .35

20th Anniv. of Org.
of African
Unity — A286

Aly Ben Ayed
(1930-1972),
Actor — A288

30th Anniv. of Customs Cooperation
Council — A287

1983, May 25   Photo.   Perf. 12
Granite Paper
827 A286 230m ultra & grnsh bl   .85 .50

1983, May 30   Litho.   Perf. 13½
828 A287 100m multicolored   .40 .25

1983, Aug. 15   Engr.   Perf. 13
829 A288 80m dk car, dl red & gray   .35 .35

Stone-carved
Face, El-
Mekta — A289

Pre-historic artifacts: 20m, Neolithic neck-
lace, Kel el-Agab. 30m, Mill and grindstone,
Redeyef. 40m, Orynx head rock carving,
Gafsa. 80m, Dolmen Mactar. 100m, Acheulian
Bi-face flint, El-Mekta.

1983, Aug. 20 Photo. Perf. 11½x12
830 A289 15m multicolored   .25 .25
831 A289 20m multicolored   .40 .25
832 A289 30m multicolored   .40 .25
833 A289 40m multicolored   .40 .25
834 A289 80m multicolored   .50 .40
835 A289 100m multicolored   .65 .40
    Nos. 830-835 (6)   2.60 1.80

Sports
for All
A290

1983, Sept. 27 Litho. Perf. 12½
836 A290 40m multicolored   .25 .20

World
Fishing
Day
A291

1983, Oct. 17 Perf. 14½
837 A291 200m multicolored   1.00 .25

Evacuation of
French Troops,
20th
Anniv. — A292

1983, Oct. 17 Litho. Perf. 14x13½
838 A292 80m multicolored   .40 .25

Tapestry Weaver, by Hedi Khayachi
(1882-1948) — A293

1983, Nov. 22 Photo. Perf. 11½
Granite Paper
839 A293 80m multicolored   .65 .40

Natl. Allegiance
A294

1983, Nov. 30 Litho. Perf. 14½
840 A294 100m Children, flag   .40 .25

Jet, Woman's
Head, Emblem
A295

1983, Dec. 21 Perf. 13½
841 A295 150m multicolored   .65 .25

Pres.
Bourguiba
A296

4th Molecular
Biology
Symposium
A297

Destourien Socialist Party, 50th Anniv.: Portraits of Bourguiba. 200m, 230m horiz.

Perf. 12½x12, 12x12½
1984, Mar. 2 Photo.
Granite Paper
842 A296 40m multicolored   .25 .20
843 A296 70m multicolored   .25 .20
844 A296 80m multicolored   .40 .25
  a.   Pair, #843-844   .75 .75
845 A296 150m multicolored   .65 .40
  a.   Pair, #842, 845   1.00 1.00
846 A296 200m multicolored   .85 .40
847 A296 230m multicolored   .90 .60
  a.   Pair, #846-847   2.00 2.00
    Nos. 842-847 (6)   3.30 2.05

Nos. 844a, 845a and 847a were printed
checkerwise in sheets of ten.

1984, Apr. 3 Perf. 13½x13
848 A297 100m Map, diagram   .60 .35

Ibn El Jazzar,
Physician — A298

Economic
Development
Program, 20th
Anniv. — A299

1984, May 15 Photo. Perf. 14x13
849 A298 80m multicolored   .50 .40

1984, June 15 Perf. 11½
Granite Paper
850 A299 230m Merchant, worker   .90 .40

Coquette,
The
Sorceress
and the
Fairy
Carabosse
A300

Perf. 13½x14, 14x13½
1984, Aug. 27 Photo.
851 A300 20m shown   .20 .20
852 A300 80m Counting with fin-
             gers   .40 .25
853 A300 100m Boy riding horse,
             vert.   .50 .25
    Nos. 851-853 (3)   1.10 .70

Legends and folk tales.

Family and Education Org., 20th
Anniv. — A301

1984, Sept. 4 Perf. 13x14
854 A301 80m Family looking into
             future   .40 .25

Natl. Heritage
Protection
A302

Aboul-Qasim
Chabbi, Poet
(1909-1934)
A303

1984, Sept. 13 Perf. 14
855 A302 100m Medina Mosque
             Minaret, hand   .50 .35

1984, Oct. 9 Engr. Perf. 12½x13
856 A303 100m multicolored   .40 .25

40th
Anniv.,
ICAO
A304

1984, Oct. 25 Photo. Perf. 13
857 A304 200m Aircraft tail, bird .90 .60

Sahara
Festival
A305

1984, Dec. 3 Litho. Perf. 14½
858 A305 20m Musicians   .65 .25

20th
Anniv.,
Intelsat
A306

Perf. 13½x14½
1984, Dec. 25 Photo.
859 A306 100m Tunisian Earth Sta-
             tion   .40 .25

Mediterranean Landscape, by Jilani
Abdelwaheb (Abdul) — A307

1984, Dec. 31 Photo. Perf. 14½
860 A307 100m multicolored   .65 .40

EXPO '85,
Tsukuba,
Japan
A308

1985, Mar. 20 Photo. Perf. 12
861 A308 200m multicolored   .85 .50

Civil Protection
Week — A309

1985, May 13 Litho. Perf. 14
862 A309 100m Hands, water and
             fire   .50 .40

Pres. Habib Bourguiba, Crowded
Pier — A310

Pres. Bourguiba: 75m, On horseback, vert.
200m, Wearing hat, vert. 230m, Waving to
crowd.

1985, June 1 Perf. 12½
863 A310 75m multicolored   .25 .20
864 A310 100m multicolored   .40 .25
865 A310 200m multicolored   .85 .50
866 A310 230m multicolored   .90 .65
    Nos. 863-866 (4)   2.40 1.60

Natl. independence, 30th anniv.

Head of a
Statue,
Carthage
and Pres.
Bourguiba
A311

1985, June 4 Perf. 14
867 A311 250m multicolored   1.00 .65
    EXPO '85.

Intl. Amateur Film
Festival,
Kelibia — A312

Natl. Folk
Tales — A313

1985, July 20   *Perf. 14½x13*
868 A312 250m multicolored   1.20 .65

1985, July 29   *Perf. 14*
869 A313 25m Sun, Sun Shine
           Again, horiz.   .20 .20
870 A313 50m I Met a Man With
           Seven Wives   .25 .20
871 A313 100m Uncle Shisbene   .40 .25
       Nos. 869-871 (3)   .85 .65

Intl. Youth
Year — A314

1985, Sept. 30   *Perf. 14½x13½*
872 A314 250m multicolored   .90 .60

The Perfumers' Courtyard, 1912, by
Hedi Larnaout — A315

1985, Oct. 4   *Perf. 14*
873 A315 100m multicolored   .50 .25

Regional Bridal
Costumes
A316

UN, 40th Anniv.
A317

1985, Oct. 22   *Perf. 12*
874 A316 20m Matmata   .20 .20
875 A316 50m Moknine   .25 .20
876 A316 100m Tunis   .40 .25
       Nos. 874-876 (3)   .85 .65

1985, Oct. 24   *Perf. 14x13½*
877 A317 250m multicolored   .90 .60

Self-Sufficiency in Food
Production — A318

Perf. 13½x14½
1985, Nov. 26   Photo.
878 A318 100m Makhtar stele of
           feast   .40 .25

League of
Arab
States,
40th Anniv.
A319

1985, Nov. 29 Litho. *Perf. 13½x14*
879 A319 100m multicolored   .50 .25

Aziza Othmana
(d.
1669) — A320

Land Law,
Cent. — A321

1985, Dec. 16 Engr. *Perf. 12½x13*
880 A320 100m dk grn, hn brn &
           brn   .50 .25

1985, Dec. 25 Litho. *Perf. 13½*
881 A321 100m multicolored   .40 .20

Natl. Independence, 30th
Anniv. — A322

Perf. 13x13½, 13½x13
1986, Mar. 20   Photo.
882 A322 100m Dove, vert.   .35 .25
883 A322 120m Rocket   .40 .25
884 A322 280m Horse and rider   1.10 .65
885 A322 300m Balloons, vert.   1.20 .75
  a. Souvenir sheet of 4, #882-885 3.50 3.50
       Nos. 882-885 (4)   3.05 1.90

No. 885a exists imperf. Same value.

A323   A324

1986, Apr. 30 Litho. *Perf. 14x13½*
886 A323 300m multicolored   1.50 .40
887 A324 380m multicolored   1.90 .50

Prof. Hulusi Behcet (1889-1948), discovered virus causing Behcet's Disease affecting
eyes and joints. 3rd Mediterranean Rheumatology Day (#886). Intl. Geographical
Ophtalmological Soc. Cong. (#887).

12th
Destourian
Socialist Party
Congress
A325

1986, June 19 Photo. *Perf. 12*
888 A325 120m shown   .40 .25
889 A325 300m Torchbearer   1.10 .75

A326

Regional bridal costumes.

1986, Aug. 25 Litho. *Perf. 14*
890 A326 40m Homi-Souk   .20 .20
891 A326 280m Mahdia   .90 .60
892 A326 300m Nabeul   1.20 .65
       Nos. 890-892 (3)   2.30 1.45

A327

1986, Sept. 20 Engr. *Perf. 13*
893 A327 160m dark red   .65 .25

Hassen Husni Abdul-Wahab (1883-1968),
historian, archaeologist

Founding of Carthage, 2800th
Anniv. — A328

1986, Oct. 18 Engr. *Perf. 13*
894 A328 2d dark violet   8.00 4.00

Protohistoric
Artifacts — A329

Bedouins, by
Ammar
Farhat — A330

Design: 10m, Flint arrowhead, El Borma, c.
3000 B.C. 20m, Rock cut-out dwelling,
Sejnane, c. 1000 B.C. 50m, Lintel bas-relief
from a cult site in Tunis, c. 1000 B.C., horiz.
120m, Base of a Neolithic vase, Kesra. 160m,
Phoenician trireme, petroglyph, c. 800 B.C.,
horiz. 250m, Ceramic pot, c. 700 B.C., found
at Sejnane, vert.

1986, Oct. 30 Litho. *Perf. 13½*
895 A329 10m multicolored   .25 .25
896 A329 20m multicolored   .25 .25
897 A329 50m multicolored   .40 .25
898 A329 100m multicolored   .65 .25

---

899 A329 160m multicolored   .85 .40
900 A329 250m multicolored   1.60 .60
       Nos. 895-900 (6)   4.00 2.00

1986, Nov. 20 Photo. *Perf. 13½*
901 A330 250m multicolored   1.40 .40

Intl.
Peace
Year
A331

1986, Nov. 24   *Perf. 13½x13*
902 A331 300m multicolored   1.10 .40

FAO, 40th
Anniv. — A332

Computer
Education
Inauguration
A333

1986, Nov. 27   *Perf. 13x13½*
903 A332 280m multicolored   .90 .60

1986, Dec. 8   *Perf. 13½*
904 A333 2d multicolored   7.50 2.75

Breast-feeding for
Child
Survival — A334

Wildlife, Natl.
Parks — A335

1986, Dec. 22 Photo. *Perf. 14*
905 A334 120m multicolored   .50 .25

1986, Dec. 29   *Perf. 12*
Designs: 60m, Mountain gazelle, Chambi
Natl. Park. 120m, Addax, Bou. Hedma.
350m, Seal, Zembretta. 380m, Greylag
goose, Ichkeul.

Granite Paper
906 A335 60m multicolored   .25 .20
907 A335 120m multicolored   .50 .35
908 A335 350m multicolored   1.40 1.00
909 A335 380m multicolored   1.75 1.10
       Nos. 906-909 (4)   3.90 2.65

City of
Monastir,
Cent. — A336

1987, Jan. 24 Litho. *Perf. 12x11½*
Granite Paper
910 A336 120m Pres. Bourguiba,
           city arms   .40 .25

Invention of the Telegraph by Samuel F.B. Morse, 150th Anniv.
A337

1987, June 15 Litho. Perf. 13½x14
911 A337 500m multicolored 1.75 1.00

30th Anniv. of the Republic
A338

Pres. Bourguiba and women of various sects.

1987, July 25 Photo. Perf. 13½
912 A338 150m multi .60 .30
913 A338 250m multi 1.00 .50
914 A338 350m multi, diff. 1.40 .70
915 A338 500m multi, diff. 2.00 1.00
　a. Souvenir sheet of 4, #912-915 6.00 3.00
　Nos. 912-915 (4) 5.00 2.50

No. 915a sold for 1.50d. Exists imperf.

UN Universal Vaccination by 1990 Campaign — A339

1987, Sept. 14 Perf. 12
Granite Paper
916 A339 250m multicolored 1.00 .50

The Street, by Azouz ben Raiz (1902-1962)
A340

1987, Sept. 22 Granite Paper
917 A340 250m multicolored 1.00 .50

Arab Day for Shelter of the Homeless
A341

1987, Oct. 5 Photo. Perf. 12x11½
Granite Paper
918 A341 150m multicolored .50 .25

Advisory Council for Postal Research, 30th Anniv.
A342

1987, Oct. 9 Perf. 14
919 A342 150m Express mail .50 .25
920 A342 350m Use postal code 1.10 .60

The Arabs, by Ibn-Mandhour (1233-1312), Lexicographer
A343

1987, Oct. 26 Engr. Perf. 13
921 A343 250m plum 1.00 .50

Pasteur Institute, Tunis
A344

1987, Nov. 21 Perf. 13x12½
922 A344 250m blk, grn & rose lake 1.00 .50

Pasteur Institute, Paris, cent.

Intl. Year of the Vine (Wine) — A345

6th Volleyball Championships of African Nations — A346

1987, Nov. 27 Photo. Perf. 14
923 A345 250m multicolored 1.00 .50

1987, Dec. 2 Litho. Perf. 14x13½
924 A346 350m multicolored 1.40 .70

African Basketball Championships A347　Folk Costumes A348

1987, Dec. 15
925 A347 350m multicolored 1.50 .70

1987, Dec. 25 Photo.
926 A348 20m Midoun .25 .20
927 A348 30m Tozeur .25 .20
928 A348 150m Sfax .85 .40
　Nos. 926-928 (3) 1.35 .80

Flowering Plants — A349

1987, Dec. 29 Perf. 14½
929 A349 30m Narcissus tazetta .20 .20
930 A349 150m Gladiolus communis .60 .30
931 A349 400m Iris xiphium 1.60 .80
932 A349 500m Tulipa sylvestris 2.10 1.00
　Nos. 929-932 (4) 4.50 2.30

Declaration of Nov. 7, 1987
A350

Cameo portrait of Pres. Zine el Abidine Ben Ali and: 150m, Scales of Justice. 200m, Girl with flowers (party badges) in her hair, vert. 350m, Mermaid, doves, natl. coat of arms. 370m, "CMA," emblem of the Maghreb states (Tunisia, Mauritania, Morocco, Algeria and Libya), vert.

1988, Mar. 21 Photo. Perf. 12
Granite Paper
933 A350 150m multicolored .50 .25
934 A350 200m multicolored .60 .30
935 A350 350m multicolored 1.10 .55
936 A350 370m multicolored 1.10 .60
　Nos. 933-936 (4) 3.30 1.70

Youth and Change
A351

1988, Mar. 22 Litho. Perf. 14x14½
937 A351 75m shown .25 .20
938 A351 150m Happy family .50 .25

Martyr's Day, 50th Anniv.
A352

Perf. 13x13½, 13½x13
1988, Apr. 9 Photo.
939 A352 150m shown .45 .25
940 A352 500m Monument, vert. 1.50 .75

Opening Conference of the Constitutional Democratic Assembly — A353

1988, July 30 Perf. 12x11½
Granite Paper
941 A353 150m Flag, Pres. Ben Ali .50 .25

1988 Summer Olympics, Seoul
A354

1988, Sept. 20 Photo. Perf. 13½
942 A354 150m shown .50 .25
943 A354 430m Running, boxing, weight lifting, wrestling 1.40 1.00

A355

A356

1988, Sept. 21
944 A355 200m multicolored .60 .35

Restoration of the City of San'a, Yemen.

1988, Nov. 7 Photo. Perf. 14
945 A356 150m multicolored .70 .35

Appointment of Pres. Zine El Abidine Ben Ali, 1st anniv.

Amilcar Beach, 1942, by A. Debbeche — A357

1988, Nov. 21 Photo. Perf. 13½x13
946 A357 100m multicolored .50 .25

Tunis Air, 40th Anniv.
A358

1988, Nov. 28 Photo. Perf. 12x11½
Granite Paper
947 A358 500m multicolored 1.60 .80

UN Declaration of Human Rights, 40th Anniv. — A359

1988, Dec. 10 Perf. 12
Granite Paper
948 A359 370m black 1.25 .65

Tunisian Postage Stamp Cent. — A360

1988, Dec. 16 Perf. 12½
Granite Paper
949 A360 150m multicolored .65 .40

A361   A362

Decorative doorways.

1988, Dec. 26   *Perf. 14x13½*
950 A361 50m multi   .20 .20
951 A361 70m multi, diff.   .25 .20
952 A361 100m multi, diff.   .25 .20
953 A361 150m multi, diff.   .40 .25
954 A361 370m multi, diff.   .90 .40
955 A361 400m multi, diff.   1.10 .40
    Nos. 950-955 (6)   3.10 1.65

1989, Mar. 7   **Engr.**   *Perf. 13½x13*
956 A362 1000m dark blue   2.75 1.60

Ali Douagi (1909-49).

Natl. Day for the
Handicapped
A363

1989, May 30   **Photo.**   *Perf. 13½*
957 A363 150m multicolored   .50 .25

Education
A364

1989, July 10   *Perf. 14*
958 A364 180m multicolored   .50 .25

Family Planning
Assoc., 20th
Anniv. — A365

1989, Aug. 14   **Litho.**   *Perf. 14*
959 A365 150m multicolored   .40 .25

Family
Care
A366

1989, Aug. 14   **Litho.**   *Perf. 14*
960 A366 150m multicolored   .40 .25

Fauna
A367

1989, Aug. 28   **Photo.**   *Perf. 13½x14*
961 A367 250m Tortoise   1.00 .50
962 A367 350m Oryx   1.40 .65

Intl. Fair, Tunis   Mohamed
A368   Beyram V (1840-
        1889)
        A369

1989, Oct. 16   **Photo.**   *Perf. 14*
963 A368 150m shown   .40 .20
964 A368 370m Pavilion, horiz.   .90 .60

1989, Oct. 28   **Engr.**   *Perf. 13*
965 A369 150m blk & dp rose lil   .40 .20

Theater, Carthage   Monument
A370   A371

1989, Nov. 3   **Photo.**   *Perf. 14*
966 A370 300m multicolored   .85 .40

1989, Nov. 7   *Perf. 11½x12*
    Granite Paper
967 A371 150m multicolored   .40 .20

    Appointment of Pres. Zine El Abidine Ben
Ali, 2nd Anniv.

Nehru — A372   Flags — A373

1989, Nov. 29   **Engr.**   *Perf. 13*
968 A372 300m dark brown   .90 .35

    Jawaharlal Nehru, 1st prime minister of
independent India.

1990, Jan. 15   **Photo.**   *Perf. 12x11½*
    Granite Paper
969 A373 200m multicolored   .60 .35

    Maghreb Union summit, Tunis.

Museum
of Bardo,
Cent.
A374

1990, Feb. 20   **Litho.**   *Perf. 13½*
970 A374 300m multicolored   .90 .50

Pottery
A375

1990, Mar. 22   *Perf. 14*
971 A375 75m multicolored   .35 .20
972 A375 100m multi, diff.   .50 .35

Sheep Museum — A376

1990, Apr. 13   **Litho.**   *Perf. 13½*
973 A376 400m Sheep   1.25 .75
974 A376 450m Ram's head   1.60 .85
  a.   Souvenir sheet of 2, #973-974   3.75 3.75

    No. 974a sold for 1000m, exists imperf. Nos.
973-974 inscribed 1989.

Tunisian Olympic Movement — A377

1990, May 27
975 A377 150m multicolored   .40 .25

Child's
Drawing
A378

1990, June 5   *Perf. 14*
976 A378 150m multicolored   .40 .25

A379

1990, July 13   **Photo.**   *Perf. 14x14½*
977 A379 150m Sbiba   .50 .35
978 A379 500m Bou Omrane   1.60 .85

    Traditional costumes.

A380

1990, Aug. 1   **Litho.**   *Perf. 14*
    Relic from Punic city of Dougga.
979 A380 300m multicolored   .85 .50

Intl.
Literacy
Year
A381

1990, Sept. 8   **Photo.**   *Perf. 12x11½*
    Granite Paper
980 A381 120m multicolored   .40 .25

A382   A383

1990, Oct. 15   *Perf. 11½x12*
    Granite Paper
981 A382 150m multicolored   .50 .25

    Importance of water.

1990, Nov. 7
    Granite Paper
982 A383 150m shown   .40 .25
983 A383 150m Clock tower   .40 .25

    Appointment of Pres. Zine El Abidine Ben
Ali, 3rd anniv.

A384   A385

1990, Nov. 16   **Engr.**   *Perf. 13½x13*
984 A384 150m green   .50 .25

    Kheireddine Et-Tounsi (1822-1889), politician.

1990, Dec. 17   **Photo.**   *Perf. 13½*
    Fauna and flora.
985 A385 150m Cervus elaphus
              barbarus   .40 .20
986 A385 200m Cynara
              cardenculus   .65 .35
987 A385 300m Bubalus bubalis   1.00 .40
988 A385 600m Ophris lutea   2.10 .85
    Nos. 985-988 (4)   4.15 1.80

Maghreb Arab
Union, 2nd
Anniv. — A386

Harbor of
Tabarka — A387

1991, Jan. 21   Photo.   Perf. 13½
989 A386 180m multicolored   .50   .25

1991, Mar. 17
990 A387 450m multicolored   1.25   .50

Fish — A388

1991, Sept. 10   Photo.   Perf. 14x13
991 A388 180m Pagre   .60   .25
992 A388 350m Rouget de roche   1.25   .40
993 A388 450m Maquereau   1.25   .60
994 A388 550m Pageot commun   2.10   .90
      Nos. 991-994 (4)   5.20   2.15

Child
Welfare — A389

1991, Sept. 29   Perf. 14
995 A389 450m multicolored   1.60   .85

A390

1991, Oct. 9   Perf. 13½x14
996 A390 400m multicolored   1.25   .50

A391   A392

Jewelry.

Perf. 14x13, 13x14
1991, Oct. 22   Litho.
997   A391 120m Ring, bracelets,
                  horiz.   .40   .25
998   A391 180m Necklace   .50   .25
999   A391 220m Earrings   .65   .35
1000 A391 730m shown   2.50   1.10
      Nos. 997-1000 (4)   4.05   1.95

1991, Nov. 7   Perf. 11½
1001 A392 180m multicolored

Appointment of Pres. Zine El Abidine Ben
Ali, 4th anniv.

Tunis-Carthage Center — A393

1991, Nov. 22   Engr.   Perf. 13
1002 A393 80m red, blue &
                  green   7.00   2.50

A394

A395

1991, Dec. 12   Photo.   Perf. 14
1003 A394 450m bright blue   1.40   .55

World Day of the Rights of Man.

1991, Dec. 26   Engr.   Perf. 12½x13
1004 A395 200m blue   .50   .35

Mahmoud Bayram Et Tounsi (1893-1960),
poet.

Expo '92,
Seville — A396

General Post
Office, Tunis,
Cent. — A397

1992, Apr. 20   Photo.   Perf. 13½
1005 A396 180m multicolored   .50   .25

Perf. 13x12½, 12½x13
1992, June 15   Engr.
1006 A397 180m red brn, horiz.   .50   .25
1007 A397 450m dark brown   1.40   .45

"When the
Subconscious
Awakes," by
Moncef ben
Amor — A398

1992, July 21   Litho.   Perf. 13½
1008 A398 500m multicolored   1.50   .50

1992
Summer
Olympics,
Barcelona
A399

1992, Aug. 4
1009 A399 180m Running   .85   .40
1010 A399 450m Judo, vert.   1.90   .65

Birds — A400   A401

1992, Sept. 22   Photo.   Perf. 11½
Granite Paper
1011 A400 100m Merops
                  apiaster   .60   .25
1012 A400 180m Carduelis
                  carduelis   1.10   .40
1013 A400 200m Serinus serinus 1.25   .50
1014 A400 500m Carduelis
                  chloris   2.50   1.00
      Nos. 1011-1014 (4)   5.45

1992, Oct. 21   Perf. 11½x12
Granite Paper
1015 A401 180m multicolored   .65   .40

UN Conference on Rights of the Child.

African Human
Rights Conference,
Tunis — A402

1992, Nov. 2   Photo.   Perf. 11½
Granite Paper
1016 A402 480m multicolored   1.60   .85

A403   A404

1992, Nov. 7
Granite Paper
1017 A403 180m multicolored   .65   .40
1018 A404 730m multicolored   2.10   1.10

Appointment of Pres. Zine El Abidine Ben
Ali, 5th anniv.

Arbor Day
A405

1992, Nov. 8   Perf. 11½x12
Granite Paper
1019 A405 180m Acacia tortilis   .75   .50

Intl. Conference on Nutrition,
Rome — A406

1992, Dec. 15   Litho.   Perf. 13½
1020 A406 450m multicolored   1.60   .65

Traditional
Costumes — A407

1992, Dec. 23
1021 A407 100m Chemesse   .40   .25
1022 A407 350m Hanifites   1.10   .50

Mosaics
A408

1992, Dec. 29
1023 A408 100m Goat   .40   .25
1024 A408 180m Duck   .85   .35
1025 A408 350m Horse   1.40   .50
1026 A408 450m Gazelle   1.50   .90
      Nos. 1023-1026 (4)   4.15   2.00

Arab-African Fair
of Tunisia — A410

1993, July 10   Litho.   Perf. 13½x14
1028 A410 450m multicolored   1.40   .50

Relaxation in the Patio, by Ali Guermassi
A411

Reassembly of the Democratic Congress
A412

1993, July 20   **Litho.**   *Perf. 13½*
1029 A411 450m multicolored   1.40 .50

1993, July 29   *Perf. 13½*
1030 A412 180m multicolored   .50 .25

A413

A414

1993   *Perf. 13*
1031 A413 20m Wolf   .90 .25
1032 A414 60m Hoya carnosa   .60 .25

Appointment of Pres. Zine El Abidine, 6th Anniv.

A414A   A415

1993, Nov. 7   *Perf. 13½*
1033 A414A 180m multicolored   .50 .25
1034 A415 450m multicolored   1.40 .50

Kairouan Tapestries — A416

Designs: Various ornate patterns.

1993, Dec. 13   *Perf. 13½*
1035 A416 100m multicolored   .25 .20
1036 A416 120m multicolored   .35 .25
1037 A416 180m multicolored   .60 .35
1038 A416 350m multicolored   1.40 .75
   Nos. 1035-1038 (4)   2.60 1.55

Pasteur Institute of Tunis, Cent.
A417

Design: 450m, Charles Nicolle (1866-1936), bacteriologist, 1928 Nobel medal.

1993, Oct. 12   **Litho.**   *Perf. 13½*
1039 A417 450m multicolored   1.40 .65

A418

School Activities
A419

1993, Dec. 30   **Litho.**   *Perf. 13½*
1040 A418 180m Music   .50 .25
1041 A419 180m Art, reading   .50 .25

19th African Cup of Nations Soccer Tournament — A420

1994, Mar. 26
1042 A420 180m shown   .50 .25
1043 A420 350m Two players, diff.   1.00 .35
1044 A420 450m Map, player   1.40 .65
   Nos. 1042-1044 (3)   2.90 1.25

Presidential and Legislative Elections — A421

1994, Mar. 20
1045 A421 180m multicolored   .50 .25

Election of Pres. Zine El Abidine ben Ali — A422

1994, May 15   **Photo.**   *Perf. 11½*
Granite Paper
1046 A422 180m multicolored   .50 .35
1047 A422 350m multicolored   1.00 .75
   a.   Souvenir sheet, #1046-1047   2.50 2.50

No. 1047a exists imperf.

ILO, 75th Anniv. — A423

1994, May 12   *Perf. 13½x14*
1048 A423 350m multicolored   1.20 .35

Intl. Year of the Family — A424   Plants — A425

1994, May 15   **Litho.**   *Perf. 14x13½*
1049 A424 180m multicolored   .85 .50

1994, June 2
1050 A425 50m Prunus spinosa   .20 .20
1051 A425 100m Xeranthemum inapertum   .25 .20
1052 A425 200m Orchis simia   .65 .30
1053 A425 1d Scilla peruviana   3.00 1.50
   Nos. 1050-1053 (4)   4.10 2.20

Organization of African Unity Summit Meeting, Tunis — A426

1994, June 3   *Perf. 13½*
1054 A426 480m multicolored   1.50 .75

Intl. Olympic Committee, Cent. A427

1994, July 7   **Litho.**   *Perf. 13½*
1055 A427 450m multicolored   1.50 .65

Philakorea '94 — A428

1994, Aug 18   **Litho.**   *Perf. 13¼x13½*
1056 A428 450m multi   1.50 .65

A429   A430

Butterflies: 100m, Colias croceus, horiz. 180m, Vanessa atalanta, horiz. 300m, Papilio podalirius. 350m, Danaus chrysippus, horiz. 450m, Vanessa cardui. 500m, Papilio machaon.

Perf. 13½x14, 14x13½
1994, Oct. 13   **Litho.**
1057 A429 100m multicolored   .40 .25
1058 A429 180m multicolored   .65 .35
1059 A429 300m multicolored   .90 .50
1060 A429 350m multicolored   1.25 .65
1061 A429 450m multicolored   1.60 .85
1062 A429 500m multicolored   1.90 .90
   Nos. 1057-1062 (6)   6.70 3.50

1994, Nov. 16   *Perf. 13½*
1063 A430 350m Pres. Ali, "7," horiz.   1.00 .50
1064 A430 730m "7," Emblem   2.00 1.00

Pres. Zine El Abidine, 7th anniv. of taking office.

41st Military Boxing World Championships
A431

1994, Nov. 18   **Litho.**   *Perf. 13½x14*
1065 A431 450m multicolored   1.40 .70

Intl. Civil Aviation Organization, 50th Anniv. — A432

1994, Dec. 7   **Litho.**   *Perf. 13¾x14*
1066 A432 450m multi   1.00 .50

Wildlife — A433

1994, Dec. 27   **Litho.**   *Perf. 13½*
1067 A433 180m Anser anser   .65 .40
1068 A433 350m Aythya ferina, Aythya fuligula   1.10 .85
1069 A433 500m Bubalus bubalis   1.60 1.25
1070 A433 1d Lutra lutra, horiz.   3.00 2.75
   Nos. 1067-1070 (4)   6.35 5.25

"Composition," by Ridha Bettaieb — A434

1994, Dec. 29   **Litho.**   *Perf. 13*
1071 A434 500m multicolored   1.40 .85

Arab League, 50th Anniv. — A435

Art of Glass Blowing — A436

1995, May 29 Litho. Perf. 13½
1072 A435 180m multicolored .55 .40

1995, June 29
1073 A436 450m Water bottle 1.40 1.00
1074 A436 730m Incense burner 2.25 1.60

Aboulkacem Chebbi (1909-34), Poet — A437

1995, Aug. 12 Litho. Perf. 13½
1075 A437 180m multicolored .55 .40

4th World Conference on Women, Beijing A438

1995, Sept. 6 Litho. Perf. 13½
1076 A438 180m multicolored .55 .40

FAO, 50th Anniv. A439

1995, Oct. 2 Litho. Perf. 13½x13
1077 A439 350m multicolored .90 .65

Hannibal (247-183BC), Carthaginian General — A440

1995, Nov. 14 Engr. Perf. 14x13½
1078 A440 180m maroon .65 .40
 a. Souvenir sheet of 1 2.50 2.50

No. 1078a sold for 1d and exists imperf.

United Nations, 50th Anniv. A441

1995, Oct. 24 Litho. Perf. 14x13½
1079 A441 350m multicolored .90 .65

A442

A443

1995, Nov. 7 Litho. Perf. 13x13½
1080 A442 180m multicolored .50 .35
1081 A443 350m multicolored .95 .65

Appointment of Pres. Zine El Abidine ben Ali, 8th anniv.

Campaign Against Desertification — A444

1995, Oct. 31 Litho. Perf. 13¼
1082 A444 180m multi .35 .35

Human Rights Day — A445

1995, Dec. 10 Litho. Perf. 13x13½
1083 A445 350m multicolored .95 .65

Pedestrian Security A446

1995, Dec. 19 Perf. 13½x13
1084 A446 350m multicolored .95 .65

Flora and Fauna A447

Traditional Costumes A448

Designs: 50m, Ophrys lapethica. 180m, Gazella dorcas. 300m, Scupellaria cypria. 350m, Chlamydotis undulata.

1995, Dec. 28 Perf. 13½
1085 A447 50m multicolored .20 .20
1086 A447 180m multicolored .50 .25
1087 A447 300m multicolored .80 .55
1088 A447 350m multicolored .95 .75
 Nos. 1085-1088 (4) 2.45 1.75

1996, Mar.16 Perf. 14x13½
1089 A448 170m Jebra, Khamri .50 .40
1090 A448 200m Kaftan brode, Hammamet .50 .40

A449

A450

Independence, 40th Anniv.: 390m, Dove, rainbow, "20, 40."

1996, Mar. 20 Perf. 13x13½
1091 A449 200m multicolored .55 .30
1092 A449 390m multicolored 1.00 .75

1996, Jan. 20 Litho. Perf. 13x13½
1093 A450 440m multicolored 1.50 .85

Natl. Trade Union, 50th anniv.

Painting, "Hannana," by Noureddine Khayachi (1917-87) — A451

1996, Apr. 25 Litho. Perf. 13½
1094 A451 810m multicolored 1.90 1.60

A451a

A452

1996, June 5 Litho. Perf. 13x13½
1094A A451a 390m multicolored .90 .75

Environment Day.

1996, June 8 Litho. Perf. 13x13½
1095 A452 200m multicolored .65 .35

CAPEX '96.

Insects A453

1996, May 23 Litho. Perf. 14x13½
1096 A453 200m Coccinella septempunctata .60 .40
1097 A453 810m Apis mellifica 2.75 2.00

1996 Summer Olympic Games, Atlanta A455

Olympic emblem, and: 20m, Flags, Olympic rings, athletic field. 200m, Torch bearer, fireworks, "100," globe, vert. 390m, Early Olympic wrestlers.

1996, July 19 Litho. Perf. 13
1099 A455 20m multicolored .20 .20
1100 A455 200m multicolored .50 .35
1101 A455 390m multicolored 1.00 .85
 Nos. 1099-1101 (3) 1.70 1.40

Code of Personal Status (Women's Liberation), 40th Anniv. — A456

1996, Aug. 13 Perf. 14
1102 A456 200m multicolored .50 .35

Landmarks A457

Intl. Year to Fight Poverty A458

Designs: 20m, Ramparts of Sousse, horiz. 200m, Numidian Mausoleum, Dougga. 390m, Arch of Trajan, Makthar, horiz.

1996, Sept. 16 Photo. Perf. 11½
Granite Paper
1103 A457 20m multicolored .20 .20
1104 A457 200m multicolored .45 .35
1105 A457 390m multicolored 1.00 .85
 Nos. 1103-1105 (3) 1.65 1.40

1996, Oct. 17 Litho. Perf. 13x13½
1106 A458 390m multicolored .85 .65

Appointment of Pres. Zine El Abidine, 9th Anniv.
A459 A460

1996, Nov. 7
1107 A459 200m multicolored .45 .35
1108 A460 390m multicolored .75 .75

National Day of Saharan Tourism — A461

Designs: No. 1109, Camels, oasis, balloon. No. 1110, Decorative designs. Illustration reduced.

1996, Nov. 12 Litho. Perf. 13¼x13
1109 200m multi .40 .35
1110 200m multi .40 .35
 a. A461 Horiz. pair, #1109-1110 1.00 1.00

Ezzitouna Mosque, 1300th Anniv. — A462

1996, Nov. 25 Litho. Perf. 14x13½
1111 A462 250m multicolored .55 .40

Natl. Solidarity Day
A463   A464

1996, Dec. 8   **Perf. 13x13½**
1112 A463 500m multicolored   .95   .95
1113 A464 500m multicolored   .95   .95

World Human   UNICEF, 50th
Rights   Anniv. — A466
Day — A465

1996, Dec. 10
1114 A465 500m multicolored   1.10   .90

1996, Dec. 11
1115 A466 810m multicolored   1.75 1.50

Musical Instruments — A467

1996, Dec. 26   **Litho.**   **Perf. 13½**
1116 A467 250m Mezoued   .60   .50
1117 A467 300m Gombri   .75   .60
1118 A467 360m Tabla   .85   .65
1119 A467 500m Tar Tounsi (Riq) 1.25   .90
    Nos. 1116-1119 (4)   3.45 2.65

World
Book and
Copyright
Day
A468

1997, Apr. 23   **Litho.**   **Perf. 13½**
1120 A468 1d multicolored   2.40 1.75

Marine
Life
A469

Designs: 50m, Mytilus galloprovincialis.
70m, Tapes decussatus. 350m, Octopus vulgaris. 500m, Sepia officinalis.

1997, May 13
1121 A469   50m multicolored   .20   .20
1122 A469   70m multicolored   .20   .20
1123 A469 350m multicolored   .85   .65
1124 A469 500m multicolored   1.40 1.25
    Nos. 1121-1124 (4)   2.65 2.30

PACIFIC 97, Intl.
Stamp Exhibition,
San
Francisco — A470

1997, May 29   **Photo.**   **Perf. 11½x12**
          Granite Paper
1125 A470 250m multicolored   .70   .40

A471   A472

1997, June 16   **Litho.**   **Perf. 13½**
1126 A471 350m multicolored   1.10   .65
   Mediterranean Games, Bari.

1997, July 15
1127 A472 250m multicolored   .70   .40
   Tunis, 1997 Cultural Capital.

A473

Republic,
40th
Anniv.
A474

1997, July 25
1128 A473 130m multicolored   .35   .25
1129 A474 500m multicolored   1.25 1.00

Reptiles
A475

   100m, Uromastix acanthinurus. 350m,
Chamaeleo chamaeleon, vert. 500m, Varanus
griseus.

1997, Sept. 9   **Litho.**   **Perf. 13½**
1130 A475 100m multicolored   .25   .20
1131 A475 350m multicolored   1.00   .65
1132 A475 500m multicolored   1.25 1.10
    Nos. 1130-1132 (3)   2.50 1.95

Rosa Gallica Flore Pleno — A476

1997, Sept. 23   **Litho.**   **Perf. 13½**
1134 A476 350m multicolored   .90   .85

Intl. Day
for
Protection
of the
Elderly
A477

1997, Oct. 1   **Litho.**   **Perf. 13½**
1135 A477 250m multicolored   .60   .40

Tunisian Works of Art — A478

   #1136, "L'Automne," by Ammar Farhat.
#1137, Sculpture, "Pecheur D'Hommes," by
Hedi Selmi. #1138, "Au Cafe-Maure," by Farhat. #1139, "Le Viellard au Kanoun," by Farhat. #1140, "Cafe Des Nattes-Sidi Bou Said,"
by Hedi Khayachi. #1141, "Le Kouttab," by
Yahia Turki. 1000d, "La Fileuse," by Farhat.

1997, Nov. 5
1136 A478   250m multi, vert.   .55   .55
1137 A478   250m multi, vert.   .55   .55
1138 A478   250m multi, vert.   .55   .55
1139 A478   250m multi, vert.   .55   .55
1140 A478   500m multi   1.10 1.10
1141 A478   500m multi   1.10 1.10
1142 A478 1000m multi, vert.   2.25 2.25
   a.   Sheet of 7, #1136-1142, + 3 labels   7.25 7.25
    Nos. 1136-1142 (7)   6.65 6.65

   No. 1142a issued 11/7.

A479

A480

1997, Nov. 7
1143 A479 250m multicolored   .60   .40
1144 A480 500m multicolored   1.10 1.10
   Pres. Zine El Abdine, 10th anniv. of taking
office.

Desert
Rose — A481

1997, Nov. 29
1145 A481 250m multicolored   .60   .40

Intl. Human Rights Day — A482

1997, Dec. 10   **Litho.**   **Perf. 13½**
1146 A482 500m multicolored   .90   .90

Horses
A483

   Designs: 50m, Arabian. 70m, Barb. 250m,
Arabian barb, vert. 500m, Arabian, vert.

1997, Dec. 18   **Perf. 12½x13**
1147 A483   50m multicolored   .20   .20
1148 A483   70m multicolored   .20   .20
1149 A483 250m multicolored   .75   .40
1150 A483 500m multicolored   1.50   .75
    Nos. 1147-1150 (4)   2.65 1.55

Bombing
of Sakiet
Sidi
Yoncef,
40th
Anniv.
A484

1998, Feb. 8
1151 A484 250m multicolored   .60   .30

School
Health
Week
A485

1998, Feb. 16   **Litho.**   **Perf. 12½x13**
1152 A485 250m multicolored   .60   .30

Bar Assoc. of
Tunisia,
Cent. — A486

1998, Mar. 27   **Perf. 13x12½**
1153 A486 250m multicolored   .60   .30

Martyr's Day, 60th Anniv.
A487   A488

1998, Apr. 9
1154 A487 250m multicolored   .60   .30
1155 A488 520m multicolored   1.25   .60

Okba Ibn Nafaa Mosque,
Kairouan — A489

1998, May 28   Litho.   Perf. 13
1156 A489 500m multicolored   1.40   .70

1998 World Cup Soccer
Championships, France — A490

250m, Tunisian team. 500m Player, trophy.

1998, June 10   Litho.   Perf. 13
1157 A490 250m multi   .60   .30
1158 A490 500m multi, vert.   1.25   .60

Crustaceans — A491

1998, July 8   Perf. 12½x13
1159 A491 110m Crab   .25   .20
1160 A491 250m Shrimp   .60   .30
1161 A491 1000m Lobster   2.25 1.10
    Nos. 1159-1161 (3)   3.10 1.60

21st Reassembly of the Democratic
Congress (RCD) — A492

#1162, Pres. Zine El Abidine ben Ali, flag,
emblems. #1163, People holding torches, flag,
dove.

1998, July 30   Perf. 13
1162 A492 250m multi   .60   .30
1163 A492 250m multi, vert.   .60   .30

36th Intl. Congress on the History of
Medicine — A493

1998, Sept. 6   Litho.   Perf. 13
1164 A493 500m multicolored   1.25   .60

Paintings — A494

#1165, "The Weaver," by Ali Guermassi
(1923-92). #1166, "Woman Musician," by
Noureddine Khayachi (1917-87). 500m, Still
life by Ali Khouja (1947-91).

1998, Oct. 8
1165 A494 250m multi   .60   .30
1166 A494 250m multi, vert.   .60   .30
1167 A494 500m multi, vert.   1.25   .60
    Nos. 1165-1167 (3)   2.45 1.20

Central
Bank of
Tunisia,
40th Anniv.
A495

1998, Nov. 10   Litho.   Perf. 13
1168 A495 250m multicolored   .60   .30

A496

1998, Nov. 7
1169 A496 250m multicolored   .60   .30
    Appointment of Pres. Zine El Abidine ben
Ali, 11th anniv.

Universal
Declaration
of Human
Rights,
50th Anniv.
A497

1998, Dec. 10   Litho.   Perf. 12½x13
1170 A497 250m multicolored   .65   .35

Averroes (Ibn Rushd) (1126-1198),
Philosopher — A498

1998, Dec. 12
1171 A498 500m multicolored   1.25   .60

Musicians
A499

1998, Dec. 21   Perf. 12½x13, 13x12½
1172 A499 250m Kaddour Srarfi   .60   .30
1173 A499 250m Saliha, vert.   .60   .30
1174 A499 500m Ali Riahi, vert.   1.25   .60
    Nos. 1172-1174 (3)   2.45 1.20

Boukornine Natl. Park — A500

1998, Dec. 29   Litho.   Perf. 13
1175 A500 70m Gazelles   .20   .20
1176 A500 110m Rabbit   .25   .20
1177 A500 250m Eagles   .60   .30
1178 A500 500m Cyclamens   1.25   .60
    Nos. 1175-1178 (4)   2.30 1.30

Fruit Trees
A501

1999, Feb. 27   Litho.   Perf. 13
1179 A501 250m Orange   .65   .30
1180 A501 250m Date, vert.   .65   .30
1181 A501 500m Olive   1.25   .60
    Nos. 1179-1181 (3)   2.55 1.20

Archaeological Sites — A502

50m, Gate, Thuburbo Majus. 250m, Thermal baths, Bulla Regia. 500m, Zaghouan
Aqueduct.

1999, Mar. 31   Litho.   Perf. 13
1182 A502 50m multi, vert.   .20   .20
1183 A502 250m multi   .55   .30
1184 A502 500m multi   1.25   .60
    Nos. 1182-1184 (3)   2.00 1.10

Paintings by
Tunisian
Artists
A503

Designs: No. 1185, "L'Intemporel," by
Moncef Ben Amor. No. 1186, "Fiancailles," by
Ali Guermassi. No. 1187, "La Poterie," by
Ammar Farhat. No. 1188, "Vendeur
d'ombrelles et d'eventails," by Yahia Turki.

1999, May 6   Litho.   Perf. 13
1185 A503 250m multicolored   .55   .30
1186 A503 250m multicolored   .55   .30
1187 A503 500m multicolored   1.10   .55
1188 A503 500m multicolored   1.10   .55
    Nos. 1185-1188 (4)   3.30 1.70

Constitution, 40th Anniv. — A504

1999, June 1   Litho.   Perf. 13
1189 A504 250m multicolored   .85   .40

Flowers — A505

70m, Acacia cyanophilla. #1191, Bouganvil-
lea spectabilis. #1192, Papaver rhoeas. 500m,
Dianthus caryophylius.

1999, June 25   Litho.   Perf. 12¾
1190 A505 70m multicolored   .20   .20
1191 A505 250m multicolored   .55   .25
1192 A505 250m multicolored   .55   .25
1193 A505 500m multicolored   1.10   .55
 a.   Souvenir sheet, #1190-1193,
      imperf.   4.00 4.00
    Nos. 1190-1193 (4)   2.40 1.25
    No. 1193a sold for 1.50d.

Philex France 99 — A506

1999, July 2   Perf. 13x12¾
1194 A506 500m multicolored   1.10   .55

Tahar Haddad (b. 1899), Women's
Rights Advocate — A507

1999, Aug. 13   Litho.
1195 A507 500m multicolored   1.10   .50

Marine Life
A508

1999, Sept. 22   Perf. 12¾
1196 A508 250m Caretta caretta   .55   .25
1197 A508 500m Epinephelus
            marginatus   1.10   .55

National Organ Donation Day — A509

1999, Oct. 2   **Perf. 13x12¾**
1198 A509 250m multicolored   .55   .25

UPU, 125th Anniv. — A510   Elections — A511

1999, Oct. 9   **Perf. 12¾**
1199 A510 500m multicolored   1.10   .55

1999, Oct. 10   **Litho.**
1200 A511 500m multicolored   1.10   .55

Tamarisk A512

1999, Oct. 28   **Litho.**   **Perf. 12¾x13**
1201 A512 250m shown   .55   .25
1202 A512 500m Dromedary   1.10   .55

Appointment of Pres. Zine El Abidine Ben Ali, 12th Anniv. — A513

1999, Nov. 7   **Perf. 13x12¾**
1203 A513 250m multi   .60   .30

Human Rights Day — A514   Famous Tunisians — A515

1999, Dec. 10   **Litho.**   **Perf. 13x12¾**
1204 A514 250m multi   .60   .30

1999, Dec. 28   **Perf. 13x12¾, 12¾x13**
  #1205, Ahmed Ibn Abi Dhiaf (1802-74), historian. #1206, Abdelaziz Thaalbi (1876-1944), anti-colonial leader. 500m, Khemaies Tarnane (1894-1964), musician.
1205 A515 250m multi   .60   .30
1206 A515 250m multi   .60   .30
1207 A515 500m multi, horiz.   1.25   .60
   Nos. 1205-1207 (3)   2.45 1.20

Millennium — A516

1999, Dec. 31   **Perf. 13**
1208 A516 250m multi   .60   .30

A517

A518

Archaeology A519

Design: 100m, Methred cup. 110m, Aghlabide plate. 250m, Zaghouan water temple. 500m, Ulysses and the Sirens mosaic. Illustration A517 reduced.

2000, Apr. 22   **Litho.**   **Perf. 13x13¼**
1209 A517 100m multi   .20   .20
1210 A517 110m multi   .20   .20
       Perf. 13¼
1211 A518 250m multi   .45   .25
1212 A519 500m multi   .90   .45
   Nos. 1209-1212 (4)   1.75 1.10

Ferry Carthage — A520

2000, Apr. 29   **Perf. 13¼x13**
1213 A520 500m multi   .90   .45
  a.   Souvenir sheet, imperf.   3.75 1.90
   No. 1213a sold for 2d.

Expo 2000, Hanover — A521

2000, June 1   **Perf. 13¼x13**
1214 A521 1d multi   2.10 1.10

Trees A522

Designs: 50m, Carob. 100m, Apricot. 250m, Avocado, vert. 400m, Apple.

2000, July 5   **Litho.**   **Perf. 12¾**
1215-1218 A522 Set of 4   1.60   .80

2001 Mediterranean Games, Tunis — A523

2000, Sept. 2   **Litho.**   **Perf. 13**
1219 A523 500m multi   .90   .45
  a.   Souvenir sheet of 1, imperf.   2.60 1.40
   No. 1219a sold for 1500m.

2000 Summer Olympics, Sydney — A524

2000, Sept. 22   **Perf. 12¾**
1220 A524 500m multi   .90   .45
     Souvenir Sheet
     Imperf
1221 A524 1500m multi   2.60 1.40

Flowers — A525

Designs: 110m, Freesias. 200m, Chrysanthemums. No. 1224, 250m, "Golden Times" roses. No. 1225, 250m, Vase with flowers (33x49mm). 500m, "Calibra" roses.

2000, Oct. 21   **Perf. 12¾, 13 (#1225)**
1222-1226 A525 Set of 5   2.25 1.10

Appointment of Pres. Zine El Abidine Ben Ali, 13th Anniv. A526

2000, Nov. 7   **Perf. 13**
1227 A526 250m multi   .60   .30

Art — A527

Designs: 100m, Still Life, by Hédi Khayachi. No. 1229, 250m, Landscape, by Abdelaziz Berraies. No. 1230, 250m, The Knife Sharpener, by Ali Guermassi. 400m, Date and Milk Seller, by Yahia Turki, vert.

2000, Nov. 18   Set of 4   2.00 1.00
1228-1231 A527

Intl. Human Rights Day — A528

2000, Dec. 10
1232 A528 500m multi   .90   .45

Shells — A529

Designs: 50m, Neverita josephinia. No. 1234, 250m, Phyllonotus trunculus. No. 1235, 250m, Columbella rustica. 1d, Arca noe. Illustration reduced.

2000, Dec. 29   **Perf. 13x13¼**
1233-1236 A529 Set of 4   3.00 1.50

A530

Famous Tunisians A531

Designs: No. 1237, 250m, Imam Sahnoun. No. 1238, 250m, Imam Ibn Arafa. No. 1239, 250m, Ali Belhaouane (1909-58), vert. 1d, Mohamed Jamoussi (1910-82), musician.

2000, Dec. 30   **Perf. 12¾**
1237 A530 250m shown   .45   .25
1238 A530 250m multi   .45   .25
1239 A531 250m multi   .45   .25
1240 A531 1d shown   1.90   .95
   Nos. 1237-1240 (4)   3.25 1.70

Tunisian Presidency of UN Security Council — A532

2001, Feb. 19   Litho.   Perf. 13
1241 A532 250m multi .45 .25

World Fund of Solidarity A533

2001, Mar. 29
1242 A533 500m multi .90 .45

Year of Digital Culture — A534

2001, May 17   Perf. 12¾
1243 A534 250m multi .45 .25

Mohamed Dorra, Child Killed in Israeli-Palestinian Violence — A535

2001, May 30
1244 A535 600m multi 1.10 .55

A536   A537

Designs: No. 1245, 19th cent. ceramic tile, Qallaline. No. 1246, Gigthis, horiz. No. 1247, Tunis City Hall, horiz. 500m, Needles of Tabarka.

2001, Aug. 24
1245 A536 250m multi .45 .25
1246 A537 250m multi .45 .25
1247 A537 250m multi .45 .25
1248 A537 500m multi .90 .45
Nos. 1245-1248 (4) 2.25 1.20

2001 Mediterranean Games, Tunis — A538

Designs: No. 1249, 250m, No. 1251b, Track, stadium. No. 1250, 500m, No. 1251a, Runners, medal.

2001, Sept. 2   Perf. 12¾
1249-1250 A538 Set of 2 1.40 .70
Souvenir Sheet
Imperf
1251 A538 750m Sheet of 2, #a-b 2.75 1.40

Paintings — A539

Designs: No. 1252, 250m, Sidi Bou Said, by Pierre Boucherle. No. 1253, 250m, Still Life, by Boucherle. No. 1254, 250m, Dream in Traditional Space, by Aly Ben Salem, vert. 500m, Traditional Open-air Marriage, by Ben Salem.

2001, Sept. 29   Litho.   Perf. 13
1252-1255 A539 Set of 4 2.25 1.20

Year of Dialogue Among Civilizations A540

2001, Oct. 9   Perf. 12¾x13
1256 A540 500m multi .90 .45

National Employment Fund — A541

2001, Oct. 10
1257 A541 250m multi .45 .25

Appointment of Pres. Zine El Abidine Ben Ali, 14th Anniv. — A542

2001, Nov. 7   Perf. 13x12¾
1258 A542 250m multi .45 .25

Butterflies — A543

Designs: Nos. 1259, 1263a, 250m, Ariane. No. 1260, 250m, No. 1263c, 500m, Pacha à deux queues. Nos. 1261, 1263b, 250m, Demi-deuil. Nos. 1262, 1263d, 500m, Grand paon de nuit.
Illustration reduced.

2001, Nov. 15   Perf. 13x13¼
1259-1262 A543 Set of 4 2.25 1.10
Souvenir Sheet
Imperf
1263 A543 Sheet of 4, #a-d 2.75 1.40

Birds — A544

Designs: No. 1264, 250m, No. 1268a, 300m, Bec-croise des sapins. 500m, Mesange charbonnière. No. 1266, 600m, Cigogne blanche. No. 1267, 600m, Geai des chenes.

2001, Nov. 22   Perf. 13
1264-1267 A544 Set of 4 3.25 1.75
Souvenir Sheet
1268 A544 Sheet, #1265-1267, 1268a 3.50 1.75

Intl. Human Rights Day — A545

2001, Dec. 10   Perf. 13x12¾
1269 A545 250m multi .45 .25

Famous Men A546

Designs: No. 1270, 250m, Ibrahim ibn al-Aghlab (757-812), founder of Aghlabid dynasty. No. 1271, 250m, Ibn Rachiq al Kairaouani (1000-71). 350m, Abdelaziz Laroui (1898-1971). 650m, Assad ibn al-Fourat (759-828).

2001, Dec. 29   Perf. 12¾x13
1270-1273 A546 Set of 4 2.75 1.40

Arabic Calligraphy A547

Designs: No. 1274, 350m, Shown. No. 1275, 350m, Calligraphy, vert.

2001, Dec. 31   Perf. 12¾x13, 13x12¾
1274-1275 A547 Set of 2 1.25 .65

Archaeology
A548   A549

Designs: 250m, Kef casbah. 390m, Amphitheater, Oudhna, horiz. No. 1278, Baron d'Erlanger Palace. No. 1279, Mosaic of Virgil.

Perf. 13x12¾, 12¾x13
2002, Mar. 26   Litho.
1276 A548 250m multi .35 .20
1277 A548 390m multi .55 .25
1278 A549 600m multi .80 .40
1279 A549 600m multi .80 .40
Nos. 1276-1279 (4) 2.50 1.25

Animals of Zembra and Zembretta Natl. Park — A550

Designs: No. 1280, 250m, No. 1284a, 400m, Ovis musimon. No. 1281, 250m, No. 1284b, Oryctolagus cuniculus. No. 1282, 600m, Falco peregrinus brookei. No. 1283, 600m, Larus audouinii.

2002, Apr. 10   Perf. 13
1280-1283 A550 Set of 4 2.25 1.10
Souvenir Sheet
1284 A550 Sheet, #1282-1283, 1284a-1284b 2.75 1.40

Sahara Desert Tourism A551

Designs: No. 1285, 250m, No. 1289a, 400m, Gazella leptoceros. No. 1286, 390m, No. 1289b, 400m, Sahara village. No. 1287, 600m, Horseman. No. 1288, 600m, Tamaghza.

2002, May 22   Perf. 13¼
1285-1288 A551 Set of 4 2.60 1.25
Souvenir Sheet
1289 A551 Sheet, #1287-1288, 1289a-1289b, imperf. 2.75 1.40

2002 World Cup Soccer Championships, Japan and Korea — A552

World Cup, Emblem of Tunisia and World Cup tournament and: No. 1290, 390m, No. 1292a, 500m, Player, map of Japan and Korea. No. 1291, 600m, 1292b, 1000m, Ball in goal net.

2002, May 29   Perf. 13
1290-1291 A552 Set of 2 1.40 .70
Souvenir Sheet
1292 A552 Sheet of 2, #a-b 2.10 1.10

Famous Men — A553

Designs: 100m, Sheikh Mohamed Senoussi (1851-1900). No. 1294, 250m, Mosbah Jarbou (1914-58). No. 1295, 250m, Mohamed Daghbaji (1885-1924). 1.10d, Abou al-Hassen al-Housri (1029-95).

2002, July 18   Perf. 12¾
1293-1296 A553 Set of 4 2.50 1.25

World Handicapped Games — A554

Tunisian flag and: 100m, Wheelchair racer. 700m, Discus thrower, vert.

2002, July 20
1297-1298 A554 Set of 2   1.25 .60

27th World Veterinary Congress, Tunis A555

2002, Sept. 25   Litho.   Perf. 12¾
1299 A555 600m multi   .90 .45

Travel International Club, 20th Anniv. — A556

2002, Oct. 25   Litho.   Perf. 13x13¼
1300 A556 600m multi   .90 .45

Appointment of Pres. Zine El Abidine Ben Ali, 15th Anniv. — A557

2002, Nov. 7   Perf. 13x12¾
1301 A557 390m multi   .60 .30

Assassination of Farhat Hached (1914-52) — A558

2002, Dec. 3   Litho.   Perf. 13x12¾
1302 A558 390m multi   .60 .30

Intl. Human Rights Day — A559

2002, Dec. 10
1303 A559 700m multi   1.00 .50

Art Type of 2001

Designs: No. 1304, 250m, Space for Gazelles, by Aly Ben Salem. No. 1305, 250m, Popular Arts, by Ammar Farhat, vert. No. 1306, 250m, Marriage, by Habib Bouabana, vert. 900m, Still Life, by Pierre Boucherle, vert.

2002, Dec. 28   Perf. 13
1304-1307 A539 Set of 4   2.50 1.25

Mosaics A560

Designs: 390m, Spinner. 600m, Africa.

2003, Feb. 28
1308-1309 A560 Set of 2   1.50 .75

Scouting in Tunisia, 70th Anniv. — A561

"70" and scouts: 250m, Reading map, at computer, planting tree. 600m, Saluting flag, at computer, vert.

2003, Mar. 29   Litho.   Perf. 13
1310-1311 A561 Set of 2   1.25 .60

National Book Year — A562

2003, Apr. 23
1312 A562 390m multi   .65 .30

The Washerwoman, by Yahia Turki — A563

2003, June 13
1313 A563 1d multi   1.60 .80

National Tourism Day — A564

2003, June 28   Perf. 13¼
1314 A564 600m multi   .95 .45

Parks — A565

Designs: 200m, Farhat Hached Park, Rades. 250m, Friguia Animal Park. 390m, La Marsa Park. 1d, Ennahli Park.

2003, June 28   Perf. 13
1315-1318 A565 Set of 4   3.00 1.50

A566   A567

2003, July 28   Litho.   Perf. 13x12¾
1319 A566 250m multi   .45 .25
Congress of Ambition.

2003, Aug. 3
1320 A567 390m multi   .65 .30
Pres. Habib Bourguiba (1903-2000).

A568

Flora and Fauna — A569

Designs: Nos. 1321a, 50m, 1326, 600m, Oryx dammah. Nos. 1321b, 50m, 1324, 250m, Nyctanthes sambac. Nos. 1321c, 100m, 1323, 250m, Aries. Nos. 1321d, 100m, 1327, 1d, Myrtus communis. Nos. 1321e, 200m, 1325, 390m, Struthio camelus. Nos. 1321f, 200m, 1322, 100m, Rosa canina.

2003, Sept. 25   Perf. 12¾
1321   Strip of 6   1.25 .65
  a.-b. A568 50m Either single   .20 .20
  c.-d. A568 100m Either single   .20 .20
  e.-f. A568 200m Either single   .35 .20
1322-1327 A569 Set of 6   4.50 2.25
No. 1321 was issued in a sheet of 6 strips that sold for 4500m.

Appointment of Pres. Zine El Abidine Ben Ali, 16th Anniv. — A570

2003, Nov. 7   Litho.   Perf. 13x12¾
1328 A570 250m multi   .40 .20

First 5+5 Dialogue Summit, Tunis — A571

2003, Dec. 5   Perf. 13¼
1329 A571 600m multi   1.00 .50

Universal Declaration of Human Rights — A572

2003, Dec. 10   Perf. 13x12¾
1330 A572 350m multi   .60 .30

Silver Items A573

Designs: No. 1331, 600m, Machmoum. No. 1332, 600m, Jewelry.

2003, Dec. 18   Perf. 12¾x13
1331-1332 A573 Set of 2   2.00 1.00
  1332a   Souvenir sheet, #1331-1332   2.50 2.50
No. 1332a sold for 1.50d.

African Soccer Championships — A574

Designs: 250m, Stylized soccer players, African cup, map. 600m, Map of Africa as soccer player.

2004, Jan. 24   Perf. 13
1333-1334 A574 Set of 2   1.40 .70
Values are for stamps with surrounding selvage.

Ksar Helal Congress, 70th Anniv. — A575

2004, Mar. 2   Litho.   Perf. 13x12¾
1335 A575 250m multi   .40 .20

Arab League
Conference,
Tunis
A576

2004, May 22   *Perf. 13*
1336 A576 600m multi   .95 .50

Copper Handicrafts — A577

Designs: 100m, Water jar, 18th cent. 200m,
Ewer, 18th cent. 250m, Bucket, 19th cent.
600m, Brazier, 18th cent. 700m, Amphora,
18th cent. 1000m, Ewer, 19th cent.
Illustration reduced.

2004, June 5   *Perf. 13x13¼*
1337-1342 A577 Set of 6   4.50 2.25
1343   Sheet, 3 each #1337,
           1338, 1343a-1343d   5.50 2.75
  a. A577 50m Like #1340   .20   .20
  b. A577 150m Like #1342   .25   .20
  c. A577 250m Like #1341   .40   .20
  d. A577 300m Like #1339   .50   .25

No. 1343 sold for 3500m.

Coins and
Banknotes
A578

Designs: No. 1344, 250m, Gold coin, 706.
No. 1345, 250m, Gold coin, 1767. No. 1346,
600m, Punic silver coin, 300 B.C. No. 1347,
600m, Punic gold coin, 310-290 B.C. 1000m,
Banknote, 1847 (65x30mm).

2004, July 23   *Perf. 13¼*
1344-1348 A578 Set of 5   4.25 2.10
1348a   Souvenir sheet, #1344-
           1348 + label   4.75 2.40

No. 1348a sold for 3000m.

African
Development
Bank, 40th
Anniv.
A579

2004, Sept. 10   Litho.   Perf. 13
1349 A579 700m multi   1.10 .55

Children's Art — A580

2004, Oct. 20
1350 A580 250m multi   .40 .20

Presidential
and
Legislative
Elections
A581

2004, Oct. 24
1351 A581 250m multi   .40 .20

Appointment
of Pres. Zine
El Abidine
Ben Ali, 17th
Anniv.
A582

2004, Nov. 7
1352 A582 250m multi   .40 .20

El Abidine Mosque, Carthage — A583

2004, Nov. 11
1353 A583 250m multi   .40 .40

Birds — A584

Designs: 100m, Oxyura leucocephala. No.
1355, 600m, Phoenicurus moussieri. No.
1356, 600m, Aythya nyroca. 1000m,
Marmaronetta angustirostris.

2004, Nov. 20   *Perf. 13¼*
1354-1357 A584 Set of 4   4.00 2.00

Universal
Declaration of
Human
Rights — A585

2004, Dec. 10   *Perf. 13x12¾*
1358 A585 350m multi   .60 .30

Famous
People
A586

Designs: 250m, Ibn Chabbat (1221-85),
writer. 500m, Ibn Charaf (1000-67), writer. No.
1361, 600m, Princess Elyssa. No. 1362,
600m, Hatem El Mekki (1918-2003), stamp
designer, and #580, 619. No. 1363, 600m, Dr.
Mongi Ben Hmida (1928-2002), neurologist.

2004, Dec. 18   *Perf. 12¾x13*
1359-1363 A586 Set of 5   4.25 2.10

World Handball
Championships — A587

2005, Jan. 23   *Perf. 13*
1364 A587 600m multi   1.00 .50

Native
Costumes — A588

Designs: 250m, Takhlila, Hammam Sousse.
No. 1366, 390m, Tarf-Ras ceremonial costume, Kerkennah. No. 1367, 390m, Karmas-
soud jebba. 600m, Traditional bridal costume,
Matmata.

2005, Mar. 16   *Perf. 13x12¾*
1365-1368 A588 Set of 4   2.60 1.25

World
Summit on
the
Information
Society,
Tunis
A589

2005, Apr. 7   Litho.   Perf. 13
1369 A589 600m multi   1.00 .50

Sculptures of
the Punic
and Roman
Eras — A590

Designs: No. 1370, 250m, Victory, 2nd cent.
No. 1371, 250m, Aesculapius, 2nd-3rd cent.
600m, Pottery mask of a woman's face, 4th-
5th cent. B.C. 1000m, Baal Ammon, 1st cent.

2005, May 18   *Perf. 13¼*
1370-1373 A590 Set of 4   3.25 1.60

World No Tobacco Day — A591

2005, May 31   *Perf. 13¼x13*
1374 A591 250m multi   .40 .20

Rotary
International,
Cent. — A592

2005, June 22   *Perf. 13x12¾*
1375 A592 600m multi   .90 .45

Intl. Year of Sport
and Physical
Education — A593

2005, July 1
1376 A593 600m multi   .90 .45

World Scout
Conference
A594

2005, Sept. 5
1377 A594 600m multi   .95 .45

Intl. Year of
Physics
A595

2005, Oct. 15   Litho.   Perf. 13
1378 A595 2d multi   3.00 1.50

Appointment
of Pres. Zine
El Abidine
Ben Ali, 18th
Anniv.
A596

2005, Nov. 8
1379 A596 250m multi   .40 .20

Universal
Declaration
of the Rights
of Man, 57th
Anniv.
A598

2005, Dec. 10   Litho.   Perf. 13
1381 A598 350m multi   .55 .25

Medicinal
Plants — A599

Designs: 250m, Foeniculum. No. 1383,
600m, Mentha aquatica. No. 1384, 600m,
Lavandula angustifloia. 1000m, Origanum
majorana.

2005, Dec. 22
1382-1385 A599   Set of 4   3.75 1.90
1386   Booklet pane, 2 each
        #1383-1384, 1386a,
        1386b   7.25   —
  a. A599 600m Like #1382   .90 .45
  b. A599 600m Like #1385   .90 .45
      Complete booklet, #1386   7.25

Ibn Khaldun (1332-
1406), Philosopher
A600

2006, Mar. 15   Litho.   Perf. 13x12¾
1387 A600 390m multi   .60 .30

A601

Independence, 50th Anniv. — A602

Designs: No. 1390, Stylized map and flag,
doctor examining child. No. 1391, Bridge and
ship. No. 1392, Stylized woman holding torch.
No. 1393, Woman and book. No. 1394, Computer, man, woman, "@," and stylized dove.

2006, Mar. 18   Perf. 13x12¾, 12¾x13
1388 A601 250m shown   .40 .20
1389 A602 250m shown   .40 .20
1390 A601 250m multi   .40 .20
1391 A601 250m multi   .40 .20
1392 A601 390m multi   .60 .30
1393 A601 390m multi   .60 .30
1394 A601 390m multi   .60 .30
  a.   Souvenir sheet, #1388-1394, +
       2 labels   3.75 3.75
       Nos. 1388-1394 (7)   3.40 1.70

No. 1394a sold for 2.50d.

Dialogue
Among
Civilizations
and Religions
A603

2006, Apr. 26   Litho.   Perf. 13½
1395 A603 1.35d multi   2.10 1.10

Punic and
Roman Era
Jewelry
A604

Designs: No. 1396, 250m, Gold and garnet
vestment clasps. No. 1397, 250m, Gold-plated
bronze earrings. No. 1398, 600m, Ring depicting god Baal Hammon. No. 1399, 600m, Gold
and amethyst pendants.

2006, May 18   Litho.   Perf. 13¼
1396-1399 A604   Set of 4   2.60 1.40

Special Handicapped Employment
Program — A605

2006, May 29   Perf. 13
1400 A605 2.35d multi   3.75 1.90

National Cleanliness and
Environmental Protection
Program — A606

2006, June 11
1401 A606 250m multi   .40 .20

2006 World Cup Soccer
Championships, Germany — A607

Map, flags of Germany and Tunisia and:
250m, Feet of soccer players. 600m, Soccer
player.

2006, June 14
1402-1403 A607   Set of 2   1.40 .70

Tunisian
Army, 50th
Anniv.
A608

2006, June 24
1404 A608 250m multi   .40 .20

Diplomatic
Relations
Between
Tunisia and
Japan, 50th
Anniv.
A609

2006, July 7
1405 A609 700m multi   1.10 .55

Vacation Safety Program — A610

2006, July 31
1406 A610 250m multi   .40 .20

Personal
Status Code,
50th Anniv.
A611

2006, Aug. 8
1407 A611 2.35d multi   3.75 1.90

Appointment
of Pres. Zine
El Abidine
Ben Ali, 19th
Anniv.
A612

2006, Nov. 7
1408 A612 250m multi   .40 .20

Universal Declaration of Human
Rights — A613

2006, Dec. 10
1409 A613 700m multi   1.10 .55

Traditional
Clothing and
Textiles
A614

Designs: No. 1410, 250m, Jelwa (wedding
dress). No. 1411, 250m, Silk jebba. 1.10d,
Klim. 1.35d, Woolen blanket from Gafsa.

2007, Mar. 16   Litho.   Perf. 13
1410-1413 A614   Set of 4   4.50 2.25

Independence, 51st Anniv. — A615

2007, Mar. 20
1414 A615 250m multi   .40 .20

Youth and Digital Culture
A616

2007, Mar. 21
1415 A616 250m multi .40 .20

Natl. Energy Conservation Program
A617

2007, Apr. 7
1416 A617 1d multi 1.60 .80

Dialogue Between Cultures, Civilizations and Religions
A618

2007, May 7 Litho. *Perf. 13*
1417 A618 600m multi .95 .45

Archaeological Sites — A619

Designs: No. 1418, 250m, Baths of Caracalla, Dougga. No. 1419, 250m, Punic city of Kerkouane. No. 1420, 600m, Baths, Makthar. No. 1421, 600m, Capitol, Sbeitla.

2007, May 18 *Perf. 13½*
1418-1421 A619 Set of 4 2.60 1.40

Carthage Investment Forum — A620

2007, June 21 *Perf. 13*
1422 A620 600m multi .95 .45

National Tourism Day — A621

Designs: No. 1423, 250m, Sahara tourism. No. 1424, 250m, Beach tourism. No. 1425, 600m, Tabarka Jazz Festival. No. 1426, 600m, Golf tourism.

2007, June 28
1423-1426 A621 Set of 4 2.60 1.40

A622

Republic of Tunisia, 50th Anniv.
A623

2007, July 25 Litho. *Perf. 13*
1427 A622 250m multi .40 .20
1428 A623 250m multi .40 .20

Appointment of Pres. Zine El Abidine Ben Ali, 20th Anniv.
A624

2007, Nov. 7 Litho. *Perf. 13*
1429 A624 250m multi .40 .20

Friendship Between Germany and Tunisia, 50th Anniv.
A625

2007, Dec. 17
1430 A625 600m multi 1.00 .50

Intl. Human Solidarity Day — A626

2007, Dec. 20
1431 A626 1.35d multi 2.25 1.10

French Air Raid on Sakiet Sidi Youssef, 50th Anniv.
A627

2008, Feb. 8 Litho. *Perf. 13*
1432 A627 250m multi .45 .20

SEMI-POSTAL STAMPS

No. 36 Overprinted in Red

1915, Feb. Unwmk. *Perf. 14x13½*
B1 A5 15c vio, *pnksh* 1.00 1.00

No. 32 Overprinted in Red

1916, Feb. 15
B2 A4 5c grn, *grnsh* 1.25 1.25

Types of Regular Issue of 1906 in New Colors and Surcharged

1916, Aug.
B3 A5 10c on 15c brn vio, bl 1.00 1.00
B4 A5 10c on 20c brn, *org* 1.00 1.00
B5 A5 10c on 25c bl, *grn* 3.25 3.25
B6 A6 10c on 35c ol grn & vio 6.50 6.50
B7 A6 10c on 40c bis & blk 3.00 3.00
B8 A6 10c on 75c vio brn & grn 8.50 8.50
B9 A7 10c on 1fr red & grn 3.50 3.50
B10 A7 10c on 2fr bis & bl 75.00 75.00
B11 A7 10c on 5fr vio & red 100.00 100.00
Nos. B3-B11 (9) 201.75 201.75

Nos. B3 to B11 were sold at their face value but had a postal value of 10c only. The excess was applied to the relief of prisoners of war in Germany.

Types of Regular Issue of 1906 in New Colors and Surcharged in Carmine

1918
B12 A5 15c on 20c blk, *grn* 1.90 1.90
B13 A5 15c on 25c dk bl, buff 1.90 1.90
B14 A6 15c on 35c gray grn & red 1.90 1.90
B15 A6 15c on 40c brn & lt bl 4.25 4.25
B16 A6 15c on 75c red brn & blk 7.50 7.50
B17 A7 15c on 1fr red & vio 22.50 22.50
B18 A7 15c on 2fr bis brn & red 70.00 70.00
B19 A7 15c on 5fr vio & blk 125.00 125.00
Nos. B12-B19 (8) 234.95 234.95

The different parts of the surcharge are more widely spaced on the stamps of types A6 and A7. These stamps were sold at their face value but had a postal value of 15c only. The excess was intended for the relief of prisoners of war in Germany.

Types of 1906-22 Surcharged

1923
B20 A4 0c on 1c blue .75 .75
B21 A4 0c on 2c ol brn .75 .75
B22 A4 1c on 3c green .75 .75
B23 A4 2c on 5c red vio .75 .75
B24 A9 3c on 10c vio, *bluish* .75 .75
B25 A5 5c on 15c ol grn .75 .75
B26 A5 5c on 20c bl, *pink* 1.50 1.50
B27 A5 5c on 25c vio, *bluish* 1.50 1.50
B28 A9 5c on 30c orange 1.60 1.60
B29 A6 5c on 35c bl & vio 2.25 2.25
B30 A6 5c on 40c bl & brn 2.25 2.25
B31 A9 10c on 50c blk, *bluish* 3.00 3.00
B32 A6 10c on 60c ol brn & bl 3.00 3.00
B33 A6 10c on 75c vio & lt grn 5.00 5.00
B34 A7 25c on 1fr mar & vio 5.00 5.00
B35 A7 25c on 2fr bl & rose 16.00 16.00
B36 A7 25c on 5fr grn & ol brn 57.50 57.50
Nos. B20-B36 (17) 103.10 103.10

These stamps were sold at their original values but had postal franking values only to the amounts surcharged on them. The difference was intended to be used for the benefit of wounded soldiers.

This issue was entirely speculative. Before the announced date of sale most of the stamps were taken by postal employees and practically none of them were offered to the public.

Mail Delivery — SP1

Type of Parcel Post Stamps, 1906, with Surcharge in Black

1925, June 7 *Perf. 13½x14*
B37 SP1 1c on 5c brn & red, pink .55 .55
a. Surcharge omitted 110.00 110.00
B38 SP1 2c on 10c brn & bl, yel .55 .55
B39 SP1 3c on 20c red vio & rose, lav 1.00 1.00
B40 SP1 5c on 25c sl grn & rose, bluish 1.00 1.00
B41 SP1 5c on 40c rose & grn, yel 1.00 1.00
B42 SP1 10c on 50c vio & bl, lav 2.00 2.00
B43 SP1 10c on 75c grn & ol, grnsh 1.50 1.50
B44 SP1 25c on 1fr bl & grn, bluish 1.50 1.50
B45 SP1 25c on 2fr rose & vio, pnksh 7.50 7.50
B46 SP1 25c on 5fr red & brn, lem 35.00 35.00
Nos. B37-B46 (10) 51.60 51.60

These stamps were sold at their original values but paid postage only to the amount of the surcharged values. The difference was given to Child Welfare societies.

Tunis-Chad Motor Caravan SP2

1928, Feb.	Engr.	Perf. 13½	
B47	SP2	40c + 40c org brn	1.00 1.00
B48	SP2	50c + 50c dp vio	1.40 1.40
B49	SP2	75c + 75c dk bl	1.40 1.40
B50	SP2	1fr + 1fr carmine	1.40 1.40
B51	SP2	1.50fr + 1.50fr brt bl	1.40 1.40
B52	SP2	2fr + 2fr dk grn	1.50 1.50
B53	SP2	5fr + 5fr red brn	1.90 1.90
	Nos. B47-B53 (7)		10.00 10.00

The surtax on these stamps was for the benefit of Child Welfare societies.

Nos. 122-135, 137-142 Surcharged in Black

a

b

1938		Perf. 11, 12½, 12½x13	
B54	A14(a)	1c + 1c	1.50 1.50
B55	A14(a)	2c + 2c	1.50 1.50
B56	A14(a)	3c + 3c	1.50 1.50
B57	A14(a)	5c + 5c	1.50 1.50
B58	A14(a)	10c + 10c	1.50 1.50
B59	A15(a)	15c + 15c	1.50 1.50
B60	A15(a)	20c + 20c	1.50 1.50
B61	A15(a)	25c + 25c	1.50 1.50
B62	A15(a)	30c + 30c	1.50 1.50
B63	A15(a)	40c + 40c	1.50 1.50
B64	A16(a)	50c + 50c	1.50 1.50
B65	A16(a)	75c + 75c	1.50 1.50
B66	A16(a)	90c + 90c	1.50 1.50
B67	A16(a)	1fr + 1fr	1.50 1.50
B68	A17(b)	1.50fr + 1fr	1.50 1.50
B69	A17(b)	2fr + 1.50fr	3.00 3.00
B70	A17(b)	3fr + 2fr	3.75 3.75
B71	A17(b)	5fr + 3fr	18.00 18.00
	a.	Perf. 12½	92.50 92.50
B72	A17(b)	10fr + 5fr	35.00 35.00
B73	A17(b)	20fr + 10fr	60.00 60.00
	Nos. B54-B73 (20)		142.25 142.25

50th anniversary of the post office.

Nos. 86, 100-101, 105 Surcharged in Black, Blue or Red

1941		Perf. 14x13½	
B74	A11	1fr on 45c (Bk)	.55 .55
B75	A13	1.30fr on 1.25fr (Bl)	.55 .55
B76	A13	1.50fr on 1.40fr (Bk)	.55 .55
B77	A13	2fr on 2.25fr (R)	.60 .60
	Nos. B74-B77 (4)		2.25 2.25

The surcharge measures 11x14mm on #B74.

> Catalogue values for unused stamps in this section, from this point to the end of the section, are for Never Hinged items.

British, French and American Soldiers SP3

1943	Litho.	Perf. 12	
B78	SP3	1.50fr + 8.50fr crimson	.40 .20

Liberation of Tunisia.

Children — SP3a

1944	Engr.	Perf. 13½	
B78A	SP3a	1.20fr + 1.30fr brown	.60
B78B	SP3a	1.50fr + 2fr black brown	.60
B78C	SP3a	2fr + 3fr dark green	.60
B78D	SP3a	3fr + 4fr red orange	.60
	Nos. B78A-B78D (4)		2.40

National welfare fund.
Nos. B78A-B78D were issued by the Vichy government in France, but were not issued in Tunisia.

Native Scene — SP4

Surcharged in Black: "+ 48frcs / pour nos / Combattants"

1944		Perf. 11½	
B79	SP4	2fr + 48fr red	.90 .90

The surtax was for soldiers.

Sidi Mahrez Mosque — SP5

Ramparts of Sfax — SP6

Fort Saint — SP7

Sidi-bou-Said — SP8

1945	Unwmk.	Litho.	Perf. 11½	
B80	SP5	1.50fr + 8.50fr choc & red	.85 .85
B81	SP6	3fr + 12fr dk bl grn & red	.85 .85
B82	SP7	4fr + 21fr brn org & red	.90 .90
B83	SP8	10fr + 40fr red & blk	.90 .90
	Nos. B80-B83 (4)		3.50 3.50

The surtax was for soldiers.

France No. B193 Overprinted in Black

c **TUNISIE**

1945		Perf. 14x13½	
B84	SP147	2fr + 1fr red org	.40 .40

The surtax was for the aid of tuberculosis victims.

Same Overprint on Type of France, 1945

1945	Engr.	Perf. 13	
B85	SP150	2fr + 3fr dk grn	.55 .40

Stamp Day.

Same Overprint on France No. B192

1945			
B86	SP146	4fr + 6fr dk vio brn	.40 .40

The surtax was for war victims of the P.T.T.

Types of 1926 Surcharged in Carmine

1945	Typo.	Perf. 14x13½	
B87	A10	4fr + 6fr on 10c ultra	.40 .40
B88	A12	10fr + 30fr on 80c dk grn	.40 .40

The design of type A12 is redrawn, omitting "RF." The surtax was for war veterans.

Tunisian Soldier — SP9

1946	Unwmk.	Engr.	Perf. 13	
B89	SP9	20fr + 30fr grn, red & blk	1.25 1.25

The surtax aided Tunisian soldiers in Indo-China.

Type of France Overprinted Type "c" in Carmine

1946			
B90	SP160	3fr + 2fr dk bl	.90 .90

Stamp Day.

Stamps and Types of 1926-46 Surcharged in Carmine and Black

1946		Perf. 14x13½	
B91	A12	80c + 50c emerald	.90 .90
B92	A12	1.50fr + 1.50fr rose lil	.90 .90
B93	A12	2fr + 2fr Prus grn	.90 .90
B94	A13	2.40fr + 2fr sal pink	.90 .90
B95	A13	4fr + 4fr ultra	.90 .90
	Nos. B91-B95 (5)		4.50 4.50

The two parts of the surcharge are more widely spaced on stamps of type A13.

Type of France Overprinted Type "c" in Carmine

1947		Perf. 13	
B96	SP172	4.50fr + 5.50fr sepia	.90 .90

On Type of France Surcharged in Carmine with New Value and Bars

B97	SP158	10fr + 15fr on 2fr + 3fr brt ultra	1.00 1.00

Type of 1926 Surcharged in Carmine

1947	Typo.	Perf. 14x13½	
B98	A13	10fr + 40fr black	1.00 1.00

Feeding Young Bird — SP10

1947	Engr.	Perf. 13	
B99	SP10	4.50fr + 5.50fr dk bl grn	1.25 1.25
B100	SP10	6fr + 9fr brt ultra	1.25 1.25
B101	SP10	8fr + 17fr dp car	1.25 1.25
B102	SP10	10fr + 40fr dk pur	1.25 1.25
	Nos. B99-B102 (4)		5.00 5.00

The surtax was for child welfare.

Type of Regular Issue of 1948 Surcharged in Blue

1948			
B103	A21	4fr + 10fr ol grn & org	.85 .85

The surtax was for anti-tuberculosis work.

Arch of Triumph, Sbeitla SP11

1948			
B104	SP11	10fr + 40fr ol grn & olive	1.25 1.25
B105	SP11	18fr + 42fr dk bl & indigo	1.25 1.25

Surtax for charitable works of the army.

Arago Type of France Overprinted in Carmine

1948			
B106	SP176	6fr + 4fr brt car	1.00 1.00

Stamp Day, Mar. 6-7.

Sleeping Child SP12

1949, June 1			
B107	SP12	25fr + 50fr dk grn	1.90 1.90

The surtax was for child welfare.

Neptune Type of 1947 Surcharged in Black with Lorraine Cross and "FFL+15F"

1949, Dec. 8
B108 A20 10fr + 15fr dp ultra & car ... 1.25 1.25

The surtax was for the Tunisian section of the Association of Free French.

Type of France Overprinted in Carmine

e

1949, Mar. 26
B109 SP180 15fr + 5fr indigo ... 1.25 1.25

Stamp Days, Mar. 26-27.

Type of France, 1950, Ovptd. Like No. B106 in Ultramarine

1950, Mar. 11   Unwmk.   Perf. 13
B110 SP183 12fr + 3fr dk grn ... 1.75 1.75

Stamp Days, Mar. 11-12.

Tunisian and French Woman Shaking Hands SP13

1950, June 5
B111 SP13 15fr + 35fr red ... 1.40 1.40
B112 SP13 25fr + 45fr dp ultra ... 1.40 1.40

The surtax was for Franco-Tunisian Mutual Assistance.

Arab Soldier — SP14

1950, Aug. 21   Engr.
B113 SP14 25fr + 25fr dp bl ... 2.00 2.00

The surtax was for old soldiers.

Type of France Overprinted Type "c" in Black

1951, Mar. 10
B114 SP186 12fr + 3fr brnsh gray 1.50 1.40

Stamp Days, Mar. 10-11.

Mother Carrying Child SP15

1951, June 19   Engr.   Perf. 13
B115 SP15 30fr + 15fr dp ultra ... 2.40 2.40

The surtax was for child welfare.

National Cemetery of Gammarth SP16

1952, June 15
B116 SP16 30fr + 10fr blue ... 1.90 1.90

Surtax aided orphans of the military services.

Type of France Overprinted Type "e" in Lilac

1952, Mar. 8   Unwmk.
B117 SP190 12fr + 3fr purple ... 1.40 1.40

Stamp Day, Mar. 8.

Stucco Work, Bardo SP17

Boy Campers SP18

1952, May 5   Engr.   Perf. 13
B118 SP17 15fr + 1fr ultra & indigo ... 1.00 1.00

Surtax for charitable works of the army.

1952, June 15
B119 SP18 30fr + 10fr dk grn ... 2.00 2.00

The surtax was for the Educational League vacation camps.

Type of France Surcharged Type "c" and Surtax

1952, Oct. 15
B120 A226 15fr + 5fr bl grn ... 2.00 2.00

Creation of the French Military Medal, cent.

Type of France Overprinted Type "c"

1953, Mar. 14
B121 SP193 12fr + 3fr vermilion 1.60 1.60

"Day of the Stamp."

Type of France Overprinted Type "c"

1954, Mar. 20
B122 SP196 12fr + 3fr indigo ... 1.60 1.60

Stamp Day.

Balloon Post, 1870 SP19

1955, Mar. 19
B123 SP19 12fr + 3fr red brown 1.60 1.60

Stamp Days, Mar. 19-20.

Independent Kingdom

Franz von Taxis SP20

1956, Mar. 17
B124 SP20 12fr + 3fr dark green 1.25 1.25

Stamp Days, Mar. 17-18.

Republic

No. 246 Surcharged in Red

1957, Aug. 8   Engr.
B125 A29 20fr + 10fr dp ultra ... .75 .75

15th anniversary of the army.

Florist Type of 1955 with Added Inscriptions, Surcharged in Red

1957, Oct. 19   Perf. 13
B126 A34 20fr + 10fr dk vio ... .60 .60

No. B126 is inscribed "5e. Foire Internationale" at bottom and lines of Arabic at either side.

Mailman Delivering Mail — SP21

Ornamental Cock — SP22

1959, May 1   Engr.   Perf. 13
B127 SP21 20fr + 5fr dk brn & org brn ... .50 .50

Day of the Stamp. The surtax was for the Post Office Mutual Fund.

1959, Oct. 24   Litho.   Perf. 13
B128 SP22 10m + 5m yel, lt bl & red ... .35 .35

Surtax for the Red Crescent Society.

Mailman on Camel Phoning — SP23

Dancer of Kerkennah Holding Stamp — SP24

1960, Apr. 16   Engr.   Perf. 13
B129 SP23 60m + 5m ol, org & ultra ... .75 .75

Day of the Stamp.

1961, May 6   Unwmk.   Perf. 13

Stamp Day: 15m+5m, Mail truck, horiz. 20m+6m, Hand holding magnifying glass and stamps. 50m+5m, Running boy, symbols of mail.

B130 SP24 12m + 4m multi ... .60 .60
B131 SP24 15m + 5m multi ... .75 .75
B132 SP24 20m + 5m multi ... .85 .85
B133 SP24 50m + 5m multi ... .95 .95
    Nos. B130-B133 (4) ... 3.15 3.15

Nos. B130-B133 Overprinted

1963, Oct. 24
B134 SP24 12m + 4m cl, vio & ol ... .35 .35
B135 SP24 15m + 5m ol, cl & vio bl ... .40 .40
B136 SP24 20m + 6m multi ... .50 .50
B137 SP24 50m + 5m multi ... .85 .85
    Nos. B134-B137 (4) ... 2.10 2.10

United Nations Day.

Old Man, Red Crescent SP25

Nurse Holding Bottle of Blood SP26

Tunisian Red Crescent: 75m+10m, Mother, child and Red Crescent.

1972, May 8   Engr.   Perf. 13
B138 SP25 10m + 10m pur & dk red ... .40 .35
B139 SP25 75m + 10m bis brn & dl red ... .60 .40

1973, May 10   Engr.   Perf. 13

Design: 60m+10m, Red Crescent and blood donors' arms, horiz.

B140 SP26 25m + 10m multi ... .50 .40
B141 SP26 60m + 10m gray & car ... .85 .40

Red Crescent appeal for blood donors.

Blood Donors — SP27

Man Holding Scales with Balanced Diet — SP28

Red Crescent Society: 75m+10m, Blood transfusion, symbolic design.

1974, May 8   Photo.   Perf. 14x13
B142 SP27 25m + 10m multi ... .40 .40
B143 SP27 75m + 10m multi ... .50 .50

1975, May 8   Photo.   Perf. 11½
B144 SP28 50m + 10m multi ... .50 .40

Tunisian Red Crescent fighting malnutrition.

Blood Donation, Woman and Man — SP29

1976, May 8   Photo.   Perf. 11½
B145 SP29 40m + 10m multi ... .50 .35

Tunisian Red Crescent Society.

Litter
Bearers
and Red
Crescent
SP30

1977, May 8   Photo.   Perf. 13½x14
B146 SP30 50m + 10m multi   .50   .40

Tunisian Red Crescent Society.

Blood Donors
SP31

Hand and Red
Crescent
SP32

1978, May 8   Photo.   Perf. 13x14
B147 SP31 50m + 10m multi   .50   .40

Blood drive of Tunisian Red Crescent
Society.

1979, May 8   Photo.   Perf. 13½
B148 SP32 50m + 10m multi   .50   .40

Tunisian Red Crescent Society.

Red Crescent Society
SP33   SP34

1980, May 8   Photo.   Perf. 13½
B149 SP33 50m + 10m multi   .50   .40

1981, May 8   Perf. 14½x13½
B150 SP34 50m + 10m multi   .40   .35

Dome of
the Rock,
Jerusalem
SP35

1981, Nov. 29   Photo.   Perf. 13½
B151 SP35 50m + 5m multi   .55   .35
B152 SP35 150m + 5m multi   1.00   .60
B153 SP35 200m + 5m multi   1.60   .70
    Nos. B151-B153 (3)   3.15   1.65

Intl. Palestinian Solidarity Day.

Red
Crescent
Society
SP36

1982, May 8   Photo.   Perf. 13½
B154 SP36 80m + 10m multi   .50   .40

Red Crescent
Society — SP37

1983, May 8   Litho.   Perf. 14x13½
B155 SP37 80m + 10m multi   .60   .35

Sabra and Chatilla Massacre — SP38

1983, Sept. 20   Photo.   Perf. 13
B156 SP38 80m + 5m multi   .50   .50

Red Crescent Society — SP39

1984, May 8   Litho.   Perf. 12½
B157 SP39 80m + 10m First aid   .50   .40

Red Crescent Society
SP40   SP41

1985, May 8   Litho.   Perf. 14
B158 SP40 100m + 10m multi   .40   .25

1986, May 9   Litho.   Perf. 14½x13½
B159 SP41 120m + 10m Map of Tu-
    nisia   .50   .40

Red
Crescent
Society
SP42

1987, May 8   Litho.   Perf. 13x13½
B160 SP42 150m + 10m multi   .60   .45

Intl. Red Cross and Red Crescent
Organizations, 125th Annivs. — SP43

1988, May 9   Photo.   Perf. 14
B161 SP43 150m + 10m multi   .60   .40

Red Crescent
Society
SP44

1989, May 8   Photo.   Perf. 11½
            Granite Paper
B162 SP44 150m +10m multi   .45   .30

Red Crescent Society
SP45   SP46

1990, May 8   Litho.   Perf. 14x13½
B163 SP45 150m +10m multi   .45   .25

1991, May 8   Litho.   Perf. 13½
B164 SP46 180m +10m multi   .60   .45

Red Crescent
Society — SP47

1993, Aug. 17   Litho.   Perf. 14x13½
B165 SP47 120m +30m multi   .60   .30

AIR POST STAMPS

No. 43 Surcharged in Red

1919, Apr.   Unwmk.   Perf. 14x13½
C1 A6 30c on 35c ol grn &
        brn   1.25   1.25
  a. Inverted surcharge   130.00 130.00
  b. Double surcharge   130.00 130.00
  c. Double inverted surcharge   150.00 150.00
  d. Double surcharge, one in-
        verted   130.00 130.00

Type A6, Overprinted in Rose

1920, Apr.
C2 A6 30c ol grn, bl & rose   .40   .40

Nos. 53 and 55 Overprinted in Red

1927, Mar. 24
C3 A7 1fr indigo & ultra   .90   .65
C4 A7 2fr grn & red, pink   3.00   1.90

Nos. 51 and 57 Surcharged in Black
or Red

C5 A6 1.75fr on 75c (Bk)   1.00   .55
C6 A7 1.75fr on 5fr (R)   3.00   2.00

Type A13 Ovptd. like #C3-C4 in Blue
1928, Feb.
C7 A13 1.30fr org & lt vio   3.50   1.40
C8 A13 1.80fr gray grn & red   4.25   .85
C9 A13 2.55fr lil & ol brn   1.90   .95
    Nos. C7-C9 (3)   9.65   3.20

Type A13 Surcharged like #C5-C6 in
Blue
1930, Aug.
C10 A13 1.50fr on 1.30fr org &
        lt vio   2.40   .75
C11 A13 1.50fr on 1.80fr gray
        grn & red   4.25   .60
C12 A13 1.50fr on 2.55fr lil & ol
        brn   7.75   1.75
    Nos. C10-C12 (3)   14.40   3.10

┌─────────────────────────────────┐
│ **Catalogue values for unused   │
│ stamps in this section, from this│
│ point to the end of the section, are│
│ for Never Hinged items.**   │
└─────────────────────────────────┘

UPU Type of Regular Issue
1949, Oct. 28   Engr.   Perf. 13
C13 A23 25fr dk bl, bluish   1.75   1.75

UPU, 75th anniv. Exists imperf.; value $35.

Bird from
Antique
Mosaic,
Museum of
Sousse
AP2

(Arabic on
one
line) — AP3

1949   Unwmk.
C14 AP2 200fr dk bl & indigo   5.50   1.90

1950-51
C15 AP3 100fr bl grn & brn   3.00   1.40
C16 AP3 200fr dk bl & ind ('51)   6.00   3.00

Monastir
AP4

Coast at
Korbous
AP5

Design: 1000fr, Air view of Tozeur mosque.

1953-54
C17 AP4 100fr dk bl, ind & dk
        grn ('54)   3.50   .75
C18 AP4 200fr cl, blk brn &
        red brn ('54)   4.75   1.75
C19 AP5 500fr dk brn & ultra   25.00 12.50
C20 AP5 1000fr dk green   42.50 25.00
    Nos. C17-C20 (4)   75.75 40.00

Imperforates exist.

Independent Kingdom
Types of 1953-54 Redrawn with "RF" Omitted

1956, Mar. 1
C21	AP4	100fr slate bl, indigo & dk grn	1.75	.75
C22	AP4	200fr multi	3.25	1.50
C23	AP5	500fr dk brn & ultra	6.75	4.00
C24	AP5	1000fr dk green	13.50	11.00
		Nos. C21-C24 (4)	25.25	19.25

Republic

Desert Swallows — AP6

Birds: #C26, Butcherbird. #C27, Cream-colored courser. 100m, European chaffinch. 150m, Pink flamingoes. 200m, Barbary partridges. 300m, European roller. 500m, Bustard.

1965-66   **Photo.**   **Perf. 12½**
Size: 23x31mm
C25	AP6	25m multi	.85	.35
C26	AP6	55m blk & lt bl	1.25	.85
C27	AP6	55m multi ('66)	1.25	.65

Size: 22½x33mm
Perf. 11½
C28	AP6	100m multi	1.75	1.00
C29	AP6	150m multi ('66)	5.75	2.50
C30	AP6	200m multi ('66)	6.25	2.75
C31	AP6	300m multi ('66)	9.00	5.50
C32	AP6	500m multi	13.00	6.75
		Nos. C25-C32 (8)	39.10	20.35

See No. 474.

AIR POST SEMI-POSTAL STAMP

Catalogue value for the unused stamp in this section is for a Never Hinged item.

Window, Great Mosque of Kairouan — SPAP1

Unwmk.
1952, May 5   **Engr.**   **Perf. 13**
CB1	SPAP1	50fr + 10fr blk & gray grn	3.25 3.25

Surtax for charitable works of the army.

POSTAGE DUE STAMPS

Regular postage stamps perforated with holes in the form of a "T," the holes varying in size and number, were used as postage due stamps from 1888 to 1901. For listings, see the

D1   D2

Perf. 14x13½
1901-03   **Unwmk.**   **Typo.**
J1	D1	1c black	.40	.40
J2	D1	2c orange	.85	.55
J3	D1	5c blue	.60	.40
J4	D1	10c brown	.60	.55
J5	D1	20c blue green	3.50	.75
J6	D1	30c carmine	3.00	.75

J7	D1	50c brown violet	1.75	.85
J8	D1	1fr olive green	1.25	.85
J9	D1	2fr carmine, grn	3.50	1.50
J10	D1	5fr blk, yellow	45.00	35.00
		Nos. J1-J10 (10)	60.45	41.60

No. J10 Surcharged in Blue

1914, Nov.
J11	D1	2fr on 5fr blk, yellow	1.00 1.00

In Jan. 1917 regular 5c postage stamps were overprinted "T" in an inverted triangle and used as postage due stamps.

1922-49
J12	D2	1c black	.25	.25
J13	D2	2c black, yellow	.25	.25
J14	D2	5c violet brown	.55	.25
J15	D2	10c blue	.40	.25
J16	D2	10c yel green ('45)	.20	.20
J17	D2	20c orange, yel	.40	.40
J18	D2	30c brown ('23)	.40	.25
J19	D2	50c rose red	.75	.40
J20	D2	50c blue vio ('45)	.20	.20
J21	D2	60c violet ('28)	.75	.40
J22	D2	80c bister ('28)	.60	.30
J23	D2	90c orange red ('28)	.85	.55
J24	D2	1fr green	.55	.25
J25	D2	2fr olive grn, straw	1.00	.40
J26	D2	2fr car rose ('45)	.25	.40
J27	D2	3fr vio, pink ('29)	.40	.25
J28	D2	4fr grnsh bl ('45)	.40	.40
J29	D2	5fr violet	.60	.40
J30	D2	10fr cerise ('49)	.40	.40
J31	D2	20fr olive gray ('49)	1.10	.90
		Nos. J12-J31 (20)	10.30	6.95

Inscribed: "Timbre Taxe"

1950   **Unwmk.**   **Perf. 14x13½**
J32	D2	30fr blue	1.40 1.25

Catalogue values for unused stamps in this section, from this point to the end of the section, are for Never Hinged items.

Independent Kingdom

Grain and Fruit — D3

1957, Apr. 1   **Engr.**   **Perf. 14x13**
J33	D3	1fr bright green	.25	.25
J34	D3	2fr orange brown	.25	.25
J35	D3	3fr bluish green	.50	.50
J36	D3	4fr indigo	.50	.50
J37	D3	5fr lilac	.50	.50
J38	D3	10fr carmine	.50	.50
J39	D3	20fr chocolate	1.60	1.60
J40	D3	30fr blue	2.10	2.10
		Nos. J33-J40 (8)	6.20	6.20

Republic
Inscribed "Republique Tunisienne"

1960-77
J41	D3	1m emerald	.20	.20
J42	D3	2m red brown	.20	.20
J43	D3	3m bluish green	.20	.20
J44	D3	4m indigo	.20	.20
J45	D3	5m lilac	.25	.25
J46	D3	10m carmine rose	.50	.50
J47	D3	20m violet brown	.75	.75
J48	D3	30m blue	.90	.90
J49	D3	40m lake ('77)	.25	.25
J50	D3	100m blue green ('77)	.50	.50
		Nos. J41-J50 (10)	3.95	3.95

PARCEL POST STAMPS

Mail Delivery — PP1   Gathering Dates — PP2

1906   **Unwmk. Typo.**   **Perf. 13½x14**
Q1	PP1	5c grn & vio brn	.60	.40
Q2	PP1	10c org & red	.75	.40
Q3	PP1	20c dk brn & org	1.10	.40
Q4	PP1	25c blue & brn	1.90	.40
Q5	PP1	40c gray & rose	2.40	.40
Q6	PP1	50c vio brn & vio	1.90	.40
Q7	PP1	75c bis brn & bl	3.00	.40
Q8	PP1	1fr red brn & red	2.90	.25
Q9	PP1	2fr carmine & bl	6.75	.60
Q10	PP1	5fr vio & vio brn	20.00	1.25
		Nos. Q1-Q10 (10)	41.30	4.90

1926
Q11	PP2	5c pale brn & dk bl	.40	.40
Q12	PP2	10c rose & vio	.40	.40
Q13	PP2	20c yel grn & blk	.40	.40
Q14	PP2	25c org brn & blk	.40	.40
Q15	PP2	40c dp rose & dp grn	1.50	.65
Q16	PP2	50c lt vio & blk	1.50	.65
Q17	PP2	60c ol & brn red	1.50	.65
Q18	PP2	75c gray vio & bl grn	1.50	.65
Q19	PP2	80c ver & ol brn	1.50	.65
Q20	PP2	1fr Prus bl & dp rose	1.50	.65
Q21	PP2	2fr vio & mag	3.75	.65
Q22	PP2	4fr red & blk	4.50	.65
Q23	PP2	5fr red brn & dp vio	6.00	.65
Q24	PP2	10fr dl red & grn, grnsh	12.50	.65
Q25	PP2	20fr yel grn & dp vio, lav	24.00	1.25
		Nos. Q11-Q25 (15)	61.35	9.35

Parcel post stamps were discontinued July 1, 1940.

TURKEY

'tər-kē

LOCATION — Southeastern Europe and Asia Minor, between the Mediterranean and Black Seas
GOVT. — Republic
AREA — 300,947 sq. mi.
POP. — 65,599,206 (1999 est.)
CAPITAL — Ankara

The Ottoman Empire ceased to exist in 1922, and the Republic of Turkey was inaugurated in 1923.

40 Paras = 1 Piaster
40 Paras = 1 Ghurush (1926)
40 Paras = 1 Kurush (1926)
100 Kurush = 1 Lira

Catalogue values for unused stamps in this country are for Never Hinged items, beginning with Scott 817 in the regular postage section, Scott B69 in the semipostal section, Scott C1 in the airpost section, Scott J97 in the postage due section, Scott O1 in the official section, Scott P175 in the newspaper section, and Scott RA139 in the postal tax section.

Watermarks

Wmk. 394 — "PTT," Crescent and Star

Wmk. 405

Turkish (Arabic) Numerals

١	٢	٣	٤	٥
1	2	3	4	5

٦	٧	٨	٩	٠
6	7	8	9	0

"Tughra," Monogram of Sultan Abdul-Aziz
A1   A2

A3   A4

1863   Unwmk.   Litho.   *Imperf.*
Red Band: 20pa, 1pi, 2pi
Blue Band: 5pi

Thin Paper

1	A1	20pa blk, *yellow*	75.00	20.00
a.		Tête bêche pair	250.00	200.00
b.		Without band	100.00	
c.		Green band		
2	A2	1pi blk, *dl vio*	125.00	20.00
		1pi black, *gray*	125.00	20.00
a.		Tête bêche pair	400.00	300.00
b.		Without band	140.00	
d.		Design reversed		175.00
e.		1pi blk, *yel* (error)	250.00	150.00
4	A3	2pi blk, *grnsh bl*	110.00	20.00
a.		2pi black, *ind*	110.00	20.00
b.		Tête bêche pair	400.00	300.00
c.		Without band	140.00	
5	A4	5pi blk, *rose*	225.00	45.00
a.		Tête bêche pair	500.00	400.00
b.		Without band	250.00	
c.		Green band	275.00	
d.		Red band	275.00	

Thick, Surface Colored Paper

6	A1	20pa blk, *yellow*	250.00	37.50
a.		Tête bêche pair	450.00	450.00
b.		Design reversed	325.00	325.00
c.		Without band	225.00	225.00
d.		Paper colored through	225.00	225.00
7	A2	1pi blk, *gray*	275.00	35.00
a.		Tête bêche pair	900.00	900.00
b.		Design reversed		
c.		Without band		
d.		Paper colored through	300.00	225.00
		Nos. 1-7 (6)	1,060.	177.50

The 2pi and 5pi had two printings. In the common printing, the stamps are more widely spaced and alternate horizontal rows of 12 are inverted. In the first and rare printing, the stamps are more closely spaced and no rows are tête bêche.
See Nos. J1-J4.

Crescent and Star, Symbols of Turkish Caliphate — A5

Surcharged

The bottom characters of this and the following surcharges denote the denomination. The characters at top and sides translate, "Ottoman Empire Posts."

1865   Typo.   Perf. 12½

8	A5	10pa deep green	11.00	35.00
c.		"1" instead of "10" in each corner	300.00	300.00

9	A5	20pa yellow	6.00	3.00
a.		Star without rays	6.00	*3.00*
10	A5	1pi lilac	12.50	4.00
a.		Star without rays	17.50	3.00
11	A5	2pi blue	6.50	4.00
12	A5	5pi carmine	5.50	4.50
d.		Inverted surcharge		
13	A5	25pi red orange	325.00	250.00

Imperf., Pairs

8b	A5	10pa	125.00	125.00
9b	A5	20pa	125.00	125.00
10b	A5	1pi	100.00	90.00
11a	A5	2pi	100.00	90.00
12b	A5	5pi	110.00	110.00
13a	A5	25pi	750.00	750.00

See Nos. J6-J35. For overprints and surcharges see Nos. 14-52, 64-65, 446-461, 467-468, J71-J77, Eastern Rumelia 1.

Surcharged

1867

14	A5	10pa gray green	9.50	
a.		Imperf., pair	55.00	
15	A5	20pa yellow	15.00	
a.		Imperf., pair	75.00	
16	A5	1pi lilac	20.00	
a.		Imperf., pair	110.00	
b.		Imperf., with surcharge of 5pi	25.00	
17	A5	2pi blue	5.50	40.00
a.		Imperf.		
18	A5	5pi rose	4.50	40.00
a.		Imperf.		
19	A5	25pi orange	3,500.	
		Nos. 14-18 (5)	54.50	

Nos. 14, 15, 16 and 19 were never placed in use.

Surcharged

1869   Perf. 13½

20	A5	10pa dull violet	100.00	12.00
a.		Printed on both sides		
b.		Imperf., pair	90.00	80.00
c.		Inverted surcharge		90.00
d.		Double surcharge		
e.		10pa yellow (error)		300.00
21	A5	20pa pale green	400.00	7.00
a.		Printed on both sides	450.00	275.00
22	A5	1pi yellow	10.00	2.50
c.		Inverted surcharge	100.00	
d.		Double surcharge		
e.		Surcharged on both sides		
f.		Printed on both sides		
23	A5	2pi orange red	200.00	9.00
b.		Imperf., pair	125.00	125.00
c.		Printed on both sides		125.00
d.		Inverted surcharge	70.00	70.00
e.		Surcharged on both sides		140.00
24	A5	5pi gray	3.75	10.00
25	A5	5pi gray	25.00	37.50
26	A5	25pi dull rose	37.50	125.00
		Nos. 20-26 (7)	776.25	203.00

Pin-perf., Perf. 5 to 11 and Compound

1870-71

27	A5	10pa lilac	550.00	25.00
28	A5	10pa brown	500.00	15.00
29	A5	20pa gray green	75.00	5.00
a.		Printed on both sides		
30	A5	1pi yellow	550.00	2.50
a.		Inverted surcharge	500.00	80.00
b.		Without surcharge		
31	A5	2pi red	5.00	5.00
a.		Imperf.	20.00	20.00
b.		Printed on both sides		40.00
c.		Surcharged on both sides		
32	A5	5pi blue	3.75	12.50
a.		5pi greenish blue	4.00	8.00

33	A5	5pi slate	40.00	50.00
a.		Printed on both sides		
b.		Surcharged on both sides		40.00
34	A5	25pi dull rose	40.00	75.00
		Nos. 27-34 (8)	1,763.	190.00

1873   Perf. 12, 12½

35	A5	10pa dark lilac	90.00	25.00
a.		Inverted surcharge		90.00
36	A5	10pa olive brown	110.00	17.50
a.		10pa bister	110.00	11.00
37	A5	2pi vermilion	3.50	*4.50*
a.		Surcharged on both sides	22.50	22.50
		Nos. 35-37 (3)	203.50	47.00

Surcharged

1874-75   Perf. 13½

38	A5	10pa red violet	35.00	7.50
a.		Imperf., pair	70.00	50.00
39	A5	20pa yellow green	15.00	4.00
b.		Inverted surcharge	30.00	13.00
c.		Double surcharge		
40	A5	1pi yellow	45.00	15.00
a.		Imperf., pair	100.00	80.00

Perf. 12, 12½

41	A5	10pa red violet	25.00	10.00
a.		Inverted surcharge	45.00	60.00
		Nos. 38-41 (4)	120.00	36.50

Surcharged

1876, Apr.   Perf. 13½

42	A5	10pa red lilac	1.50	.50
a.		Inverted surcharge	70.00	
b.		Imperf., pair	15.00	15.00
43	A5	20pa pale green	1.50	.50
b.		Inverted surcharge	70.00	
c.		Imperf., pair	15.00	15.00
44	A5	1pi yellow	1.50	.50
a.		Imperf., pair	27.50	27.50
46	A5	5pi gray blue	950.00	
47	A5	25pi dull rose	950.00	
		Nos. 42-44 (3)	4.50	

Nos. 46 and 47 were never placed in use.
See Nos. 64-65.

Surcharged

1876, Jan.

48	A5	¼pi on 10pa violet	2.50	2.50
49	A5	½pi on 20pa yel grn	6.25	2.50
50	A5	1¼pi on 50pa rose	1.50	2.50
a.		Imperf., pair	60.00	
51	A5	2pi on 2pi redsh brn	40.00	7.50
52	A5	5pi on 5pi gray blue	3.00	50.00
		Nos. 48-52 (5)	53.25	65.00

The surcharge on Nos. 48-52 restates in French the value originally expressed in Turkish characters.

A7

1876, Sept. Typo. Perf. 13½

53	A7	10pa black & rose lil	2.00	6.00
54	A7	20pa red vio & grn	62.50	1.50
55	A7	50pa blue & yellow	1.00	10.00
56	A7	2pi black & redsh brn	1.25	5.00
57	A7	5pi red & blue	3.00	10.00
b.		Cliché of 25pi in plate of 5pi	400.00	375.00
58	A7	25pi claret & rose	15.00	75.00
a.		Imperf.	160.00	
		Nos. 53-58 (6)	84.75	111.00

Nos. 56-58 exist perf. 11½, but were not regularly issued.

See Nos. 59-63, 66-91, J36-J38. For overprints see Nos. 462-466, 469-476, J78-J79, P10-P14, Eastern Rumelia 2-40.

1880-84   Perf. 13½

59	A7	5pa black & ol ('81)	2.50	6.50
a.		Imperf.	30.00	
60	A7	10pa black & grn ('84)	2.00	3.50
61	A7	20pa black & rose	55.00	1.00
62	A7	1pi blk & bl (piastres)	75.00	2.00
a.		1pi black & gray blue	75.00	
b.		Imperf.	40.00	
63	A7	1pi blk & bl (piastre) ('81)	110.00	3.00
		Nos. 59-63 (5)	244.50	16.00

A cliché of No. 63 was inserted in a plate of the Eastern Rumelia 1pi (No. 13). This was found in the remainder stock.

Nos. 60-61 and 63 exist perf. 11½, but were not regularly issued.

1881-82
Surcharged like Apr., 1876 Issue

64	A5	20pa gray	4.00	1.00
a.		Inverted surcharge	13.50	
b.		Imperf., pair	25.00	
65	A5	2pi pale salmon	3.00	1.00
a.		Inverted surcharge	22.50	

1884-86   Perf. 11½, 13½

66	A7	5pa lil & pale lil ('86)	200.00	150.00
67	A7	10pa grn & pale grn	1.25	1.25
68	A7	20pa rose & pale rose	1.25	1.25
69	A7	1pi blue & lt blue	1.25	1.25

Perf. 11½

70	A7	2pi och & pale och	2.00	1.25
71	A7	5pi red brn & pale brn	20.00	9.00
c.		5pi och & pale och (error)	12.00	12.00

Perf. 11½, 13½

73	A7	25pi blk & pale gray ('86)	300.00	425.00
		Nos. 66-73 (7)	525.75	589.00

Imperf

66a	A7	5pa	60.00
67a	A7	10pa	20.00
68b	A7	20pa	20.00
69b	A7	1pi	20.00
73a	A7	25pi	150.00

1886   Perf. 13½

74	A7	5pa black & pale gray	2.00	2.50
75	A7	2pi orange & lt bl	2.00	2.00
76	A7	5pi grn & pale grn	3.00	25.00
77	A7	25pi bis & pale bis	45.00	150.00
		Nos. 74-77 (4)	52.00	179.50

Imperf

74a	A7	5pa	20.00
75b	A7	2pi	20.00
76b	A7	5pi	20.00
77a	A7	25pi	35.00

Stamps of 1884-86, bisected and surcharged as above, 10pa, 20pa, 1pi and 2pi or surcharged "2" in red are stated to have been made privately and without authority. With the aid of employees of the post office, copies were passed through the mails.

1888   Perf. 13½

83	A7	5pa green & yellow	2.50	5.00
84	A7	2pi red lilac & bl	1.50	1.50
85	A7	5pi dk brown & gray	5.00	20.00
86	A7	25pi red & yellow	30.00	150.00
		Nos. 83-86 (4)	39.00	176.50

Imperf

83a	A7	5pa	20.00
84a	A7	2pi	20.00
85a	A7	5pi	20.00
86a	A7	25pi	25.00

Nos. 74-86 exist perf. 11½, but were not regularly issued.

1890   Perf. 11½, 13½

87	A7	10pa green & gray	5.00	1.00
88	A7	20pa rose & gray	1.25	1.00
89	A7	1pi blue & gray	75.00	1.00
90	A7	2pi yellow & gray	70.00	7.50
91	A7	5pi buff & gray	5.00	22.50
		Nos. 87-91 (5)	156.25	33.00

Imperf

87a	A7	10pa	20.00
88a	A7	20pa	20.00
89a	A7	1pi	100.00
90b	A7	2pi	100.00
91a	A7	5pi	25.00

Arms and Tughra of "El Gazi" (The Conqueror) Sultan Abdul Hamid

A10   A11

A12   A13

A14   No. 100

1892-98 Typo. Perf. 13½

95	A10	10pa gray green	1.50	.50
96	A11	20pa violet brn ('98)	1.25	.50
a.		20pa dark pink	7.50	.30
b.		20pa pink	10.00	.30
97	A12	1pi pale blue	110.00	4.00
98	A13	2pi brown org	3.00	1.00
a.		Tête bêche pair	30.00	30.00
99	A14	5pi dull violet	5.00	15.00
a.		Turkish numeral in upper right corner reads "50" instead of "5"	30.00	15.00
		Nos. 95-99 (5)	120.75	21.00

See Nos. J39-J42. For surcharges and overprints see Nos. 100, 288-291, 350, 355-359, 477-478, B38, B41, J80-J82, P25-P34, P36, P121-P122, P134-P137, P153-P154.

Red Surcharge

1897

100	A10	5pa on 10pa gray grn	3.00	1.25
a.		"Cniq" instead of "Cinq"	10.00	10.00

Turkish stamps of types A11, A17-A18, A21-A24, A26, A28-A39, A41 with or without Turkish overprints and English surcharges with "Baghdad" or "Iraq" are listed under Mesopotamia in Vol. 4.

Turkish stamps of types A19 and A21 with Double-headed Eagle and "Shqipenia" handstamp are listed under Albania in Vol. 1.

A16   A17

1901 Typo. Perf. 13½
For Foreign Postage

102	A16	5pa bister	1.25	.60
103	A16	10pa yellow green	1.25	.60
104	A16	20pa magenta	1.25	.60
a.		Perf. 12	2.50	1.00
105	A16	1pi violet blue	1.50	1.00
106	A16	2pi gray blue	2.50	1.00
107	A16	5pi ocher	7.50	3.00
108	A16	25pi dark green	100.00	30.00
109	A16	50pi violet	250.00	100.00
		Nos. 102-109 (8)	365.25	136.80

For Domestic Postage
Perf. 12, 13½

110	A17	5pa purple	1.25	.50
111	A17	10pa green	1.25	.50
112	A17	20pa carmine	1.25	.50
113	A17	1pi blue	1.25	.50
a.		Imperf.	20.00	
114	A17	2pi orange	2.00	.50
115	A17	5pi lilac rose	5.75	1.00

Perf. 13½

116	A17	25pi brown	10.00	2.00
a.		Perf. 12	12.50	5.25
117	A17	50pi yellow brown	32.50	3.50
a.		Perf. 12	45.00	15.00
		Nos. 110-117 (8)	55.25	9.00

Nos. 110-113 exist perf. 12x13½.
See Nos. J43-J46.
For overprints and surcharges see Nos. 165-180, 292-303, 340-341, 361-377, 479-493, B19-B20, B37, P37-P48, P69-P80, P123-P126, P138-P146, P155-P164.

A18   A19

1905 Perf. 12, 13½ and Compound

118	A18	5pa ocher	1.00	.50
119	A18	10pa dull green	1.00	.50
a.		Imperf.	4.00	3.50
120	A18	20pa carmine	1.00	.50
a.		Imperf.	4.00	3.50
121	A18	1pi blue	1.00	.50
122	A18	2pi slate	1.50	.50
123	A18	2½pi red violet	1.50	.50
a.		Imperf.	11.00	9.00
124	A18	5pi brown	2.00	.50
125	A18	10pi orange brn	3.75	.50
126	A18	25pi olive green	12.50	15.00
127	A18	50pi deep violet	50.00	30.00

See Nos. J47-J48. For overprints and surcharges see Nos. 128-131, 181-182, 304-314, 351-354, 378-389, 494-508, B1-B3, B21-B23, B39-B40, P49-P54, P127-P129, P150, P165-P171.

Overprinted in Carmine or Blue

1906

128	A18	10pa dull green (C)	3.00	1.00
129	A18	20pa carmine (Bl)	3.00	1.00
130	A18	1pi blue (C)	3.00	1.00
131	A18	2pi slate (C)	17.50	5.00
		Nos. 118-131 (14)	101.75	57.00

Stamps bearing this overprint were sold to merchants at a discount from face value to encourage the use of Turkish stamps on foreign correspondence, instead of those of the various European powers which maintained post offices in Turkey. The overprint is the Arab "B," for "Béhié," meaning "discount."

1908

132	A19	5pa ocher	1.25	.50
133	A19	10pa blue green	1.75	.50
134	A19	20pa carmine	40.00	.50
135	A19	1pi bright blue	15.00	.50
a.		1pi ultramarine	50.00	10.00
136	A19	2pi blue black	10.00	.50
137	A19	2½pi violet brown		

138	A19	5pi dark violet	80.00	.50
139	A19	10pi red	70.00	2.50
140	A19	25pi dark green	10.00	.50
141	A19	50pi red brown	50.00	35.00

See Nos. J49-J50. For overprints and surcharges see Nos. 142-145, 314B-316B, 390-396, 509-516A, B4-B6, B17, B24-B27, P55-P60, P130-P131, P151, P172, Thrace 15.

Overprinted in Carmine or Blue

142	A19	10pa blue green (C)	7.50	2.50
143	A19	20pa carmine (Bl)	7.50	2.50
144	A19	1pi brt blue (C)	15.00	5.00
145	A19	2pi blue black (C)	25.00	12.50
		Nos. 132-145 (14)	336.00	66.00

A20

Perf. 12, 13½ & Compound

1908, Dec. 17

146	A20	5pa ocher	.75	.50
147	A20	10pa blue green	1.50	.50
148	A20	20pa carmine	2.00	1.00
149	A20	1pi ultra	3.00	1.00
150	A20	2pi gray black	12.50	15.00
		Nos. 146-150 (5)	19.75	18.00

Imperf

146a	A20	5pa	3.00	3.00
147a	A20	10pa	4.00	4.00
148a	A20	20pa	5.50	5.50
149a	A20	1pi	3.00	3.00

Granting of a Constitution, the date of which is inscribed on the banderol: "324 Temuz 10" (July 24, 1908).

For overprints see Nos. 397, 517.

Tughra and "Reshad"
of Sultan
Mohammed V — A21

1909, Dec.

151	A21	5pa ocher	1.00	.50
152	A21	10pa blue green	1.00	.50
a.		Imperf.	3.00	3.00
153	A21	20pa carmine rose	1.00	.50
154	A21	1pi ultra	3.00	.50
155	A21	2pi blue black	3.00	.50
156	A21	2½pi dark brown	90.00	20.00
157	A21	5pi dark violet	3.00	1.00
158	A21	10pi dull red	37.50	1.00
159	A21	25pi dark green	350.00	100.00
160	A21	50pi red brown	125.00	80.00

The 2pa olive green, type A21, is a newspaper stamp, No. P68.

Two types exist for the 10pa, 20pa and 1pi. In the second type, the damaged crescent is restored.

See Nos. J51-J52. For overprints and surcharges see Nos. 161-164, 317-327, 342-343, 398-406, 518-528, 567, B7-B14, B18, B28-B32, P61-P68, P81, P132-P133, P152, P173, Turkey in Asia 67, 72, Thrace 1-4, 13, 13A, 14.

Overprinted in Carmine
or Blue

161	A21	10pa blue grn (C)	1.75	.75
a.		Imperf.		
162	A21	20pa car rose (Bl)	1.75	.75
a.		Imperf.		
163	A21	1pi ultra (C)	3.50	2.00
a.		Imperf.	4.00	
b.		1pi bright blue	6.50	3.00
164	A21	2pi blue black (C)	75.00	30.00
a.		Imperf.		
		Nos. 151-164 (14)	696.50	238.00

Stamps of 1901-05
Overprinted in
Carmine or Blue

The overprint was applied to 18 denominations in four settings with change of city name, producing individual sets for each city: "MONASTIR," "PRISTINA," "SALONIKA" and "USKUB."

1911, June 26   Perf. 12, 13½

165	A16	5pa bister	3.50	3.75
166	A16	10pa yellow green	3.50	3.75
167	A16	20pa magenta	6.00	7.50
168	A16	1pi violet blue	6.00	7.50
169	A16	2pi gray blue	6.00	7.50
170	A16	5pi ocher	40.00	60.00
171	A16	25pi dark green	60.00	75.00
172	A16	50pi yellow	100.00	125.00
173	A17	5pa purple	3.50	3.75
174	A17	10pa green	3.50	3.75
175	A17	20pa carmine	6.00	7.50
176	A17	1pi blue	6.00	7.50
177	A17	2pi orange	6.00	7.50
178	A17	5pi lilac rose	40.00	60.00
179	A17	25pi chocolate	85.00	125.00
180	A17	50pi yellow brown	100.00	125.00
181	A18	2½pi red violet	65.00	100.00
182	A18	10pi orange brown	60.00	60.00
		Nos. 165-182 (18)	600.00	790.00

Sultan's visit to Macedonia. The Arabic overprint reads: "Souvenir of the Sultan's Journey, 1329." Values same for all cities. See Nos. P69-P81.

General Post
Office,
Constantinople
A22

1913, Mar. 14   Perf. 12

237	A22	2pa olive green	1.00	.50
238	A22	5pa ocher	1.00	.50
239	A22	10pa blue green	1.00	.50
240	A22	20pa carmine rose	1.00	.50
241	A22	1pi ultra	1.00	.50
242	A22	2pi indigo	2.00	.50
243	A22	5pi dull violet	3.50	.50
244	A22	10pi dull red	6.00	1.00
245	A22	25pi gray green	22.50	22.50
246	A22	50pi orange brown	85.00	125.00

See Nos. J53-J58. For overprints and surcharges see Nos. 247-250, 328-339, 344, 407-414, 529-538, 568, B15-B16, B33-B36, Turkey in Asia 68, Thrace 10, 10A, 11, 11A, 12, N82.

Overprinted in
Carmine or Blue

247	A22	10pa blue green (C)	1.00	.50
248	A22	20pa car rose (Bl)	1.00	.50
249	A22	1pi ultra (C)	1.00	.50
250	A22	2pi indigo (C)	17.50	7.50
		Nos. 237-250 (14)	144.50	161.00

Mosque of Selim, Adrianople — A23

1913, Oct. 23   Engr.

251	A23	10pa green	1.50	1.00
252	A23	20pa red	2.50	2.00
253	A23	40pa blue	6.00	3.00
		Nos. 251-253 (3)	10.00	6.00

Recapture of Adrianople (Edirne) by the Turks.

See Nos. 592, J59-J62. For overprints and surcharge see Nos. 415-417, 539-540, J59-J62, J67-J70, J83-J86, Thrace N84.

Obelisk of
Theodosius in
the
Hippodrome
A24

Column of
Constantine
A25

Leander's
Tower — A26

One of the Seven
Towers — A27

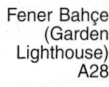

Fener Bahçe
(Garden
Lighthouse)
A28

The Castle of
Europe on the
Bosporus
A29

Mosque of
Sultan
Ahmed — A30

Monument
to the
Martyrs of
Liberty
A31

Fountains
of Suleiman
A32

Cruiser
"Hamidie"
A33

View of
Kandili on
the
Bosporus
A34

War
Ministry
(Later
Istanbul
University)
A35

Sweet
Waters of
Europe
Park
A36

Mosque
of
Suleiman
A37

The
Bosporus
A38

Sultan
Ahmed's
Fountain
A39

Sultan Mohammed V — A40

Designs A24-A39: Views of Constantinople.

1914, Jan. 14   Litho.

254	A24	2pa red lilac	.50	.40
255	A25	4pa dark brown	.50	.40
256	A26	5pa violet brown	.50	.40
257	A27	6pa dark blue	.50	.40

Engr.

258	A28	10pa green	2.00	.40
259	A29	20pa red	1.75	.40
260	A30	1pi blue	.50	.40
b.		Booklet pane of 2+2 labels		
261	A31	1½pi car & blk	1.00	.40
262	A32	1¾pi sl & red brn	1.00	.40
263	A33	2pi green & blk	2.00	.40
264	A34	2½pi org & ol grn	1.50	.40
265	A35	5pi dull violet	3.00	.40
266	A36	10pi red brown	7.00	.40
267	A37	25pi olive green	125.00	5.50
268	A38	50pi carmine	6.00	2.25
269	A39	100pi deep blue	75.00	27.50
		Cut cancellation		12.00
270	A40	200pi green & blk	550.00	400.00
		Cut cancellation		25.00
		Nos. 254-270 (17)	777.75	440.45

See Nos. 590-591, 593-598.

For overprints and surcharges see Nos. 271-287, 419, 541, 552-553, 574A, 601, 603-604, P174, Turkey in Asia 1-3, 5-9, 73-74, Thrace N77, N78.

Stamps of Preceding Issue
Overprinted in Red or Blue

271	A28	10pa green (R)	3.00	.75
272	A29	20pa green (Bl)	10.00	.75
273	A30	1pi blue (R)	3.00	.75
275	A32	1¾pi sl & red brn (Bl)	3.00	1.25
276	A33	2pi green & blk (R)	50.00	3.25
		Nos. 271-276 (5)	69.00	6.75

No. 261
Surcharged

1914, July 23

277	A31	1pi on 1½pi car & blk	3.25	2.50
a.		"1330" omitted	2.50	1.50
b.		Double surcharge		
c.		Triple surcharge	5.00	5.00

7th anniv. of the Constitution. The surcharge reads "10 July, 1330, National fête" and has also the numeral "1" at each side, over the original value of the stamp.

Stamps of
1914
Overprinted
in Black or
Red

278	A26	5pa violet brn (Bk)	1.75	.50
279	A28	10pa green (R)	3.25	.50
280	A29	20pa red (Bk)	4.00	.50
281	A30	1pi blue (R)	10.00	1.50
282	A33	2pi grn & blk (R)	15.00	1.50
283	A35	5pi dull violet (R)	50.00	4.25
284	A36	10pi red brown (R)	190.00	65.00
		Nos. 278-284 (7)	274.00	73.75

This overprint reads "Abolition of the Capitulations, 1330".

No. 269 Surcharged

1915

286	A39	10pi on 100pi	62.50	22.50
a.		Inverted surcharge	—	—

No. 270 Surcharged

287	A40	25pi on 200pi	25.00	8.00

Preceding Issues Overprinted in Carmine or Black

1915

On Stamps of 1892

288	A10	10pa gray green	1.00	.50
a.		Inverted overprint	7.50	7.50
289	A13	2pi brown orange	1.50	.50
a.		Inverted overprint	7.50	7.50
290	A14	5pi dull violet	4.00	.50
a.		On No. 99a	17.00	17.00

On Stamp of 1897

291	A10	5pa on 10pa gray grn	1.00	.50
a.		On No. 100a	5.00	5.00
b.		On No. 100a	10.00	10.00

On Stamps of 1901

292	A16	5pa bister	1.00	.50
293	A16	1pi violet blue	3.00	.50
294	A16	2pi gray blue	2.50	.50
295	A16	5pi ocher	20.00	.50
296	A16	25pi dark green	50.00	20.00
297	A17	5pa purple	1.00	.50
298	A17	10pa green	1.50	.50
299	A17	20pa carmine	1.50	.50
a.		Inverted overprint	7.50	7.50
300	A17	1pi blue	1.50	.50
a.		Inverted overprint	5.00	5.00
301	A17	2pi orange	2.00	.50
a.		Inverted overprint	7.50	7.50
b.		Double ovpt. (R and Bk)	5.00	5.00
302	A17	5pi lilac rose	2.50	.50
303	A17	25pi brown	12.50	2.00

On Stamps of 1905

304	A18	5pa ocher	1.00	.50
305	A18	10pa dull green	1.00	.50
a.		Inverted overprint	5.00	5.00
306	A18	20pa carmine	1.00	.50
a.		Inverted overprint	5.00	5.00
307	A18	1pi brt blue	1.50	.50
a.		Inverted overprint	5.00	5.00
308	A18	2pi slate	2.50	.50
a.		Inverted overprint	10.00	10.00
309	A18	2½pi red violet	1.50	.50
310	A18	5pi brown	2.00	.50
a.		Inverted overprint	10.00	10.00
311	A18	10pi orange brown	12.50	.50
312	A18	25pi olive green	50.00	8.00

On Stamps of 1906

313	A18	10pa dull green	2.00	.50
314	A18	2pi slate	5.00	.50
a.		Inverted overprint	5.00	5.00

On Stamps of 1908

314B	A19	2pi blue black	225.00	50.00
315	A19	2½pi violet brown	3.00	.50
315A	A19	5pi dark violet	100.00	35.00
315B	A19	10pi red	15.00	7.50
316	A19	25pi dark green	30.00	5.00
a.		Inverted overprint	17.00	17.00

With Additional Overprint

316B	A19	2pi blue black	15.00	5.00

On Stamps of 1909

317	A21	5pa ocher	1.00	.50
a.		Inverted overprint	10.00	10.00
b.		Double overprint	10.00	5.00
318	A21	20pa car rose	1.00	.50
a.		Inverted overprint	5.00	5.00
319	A21	1pi ultra	2.00	.50
a.		Inverted overprint	5.00	5.00
320	A21	2pi blue black	2.00	.50
a.		Inverted overprint	5.00	5.00
321	A21	2½pi dark brown	67.50	25.00
322	A21	5pi dark violet	.30	.20
a.		Inverted overprint	6.50	6.50
323	A21	10pi dull red	10.00	.50
324	A21	25pi dark green	1,750.	1,200.

With Additional Overprint

325	A21	20pa carmine rose	2.00	.50
a.		Inverted overprint	5.00	5.00
326	A21	1pi ultra	2.00	.50
327	A21	2pi blue black	3.50	.50

On Stamps of 1913

328	A22	5pa ocher	1.00	.50
a.		Inverted overprint	7.50	7.50
329	A22	10pa blue green	1.00	.50
a.		Inverted overprint	10.00	10.00
330	A22	20pa carmine rose	1.00	.50
a.		Inverted overprint	7.50	7.50
331	A22	1pi ultra	1.00	.50
a.		Inverted overprint	5.00	5.00
332	A22	2pi indigo	1.50	.50
a.		Inverted overprint	5.00	5.00
333	A22	5pi dull violet	3.00	.50
334	A22	10pi dull red	10.00	.50
a.		Inverted overprint	10.00	10.00
335	A22	25pi gray green	30.00	20.00

With Additional Overprint

336	A22	10pa blue green	1.00	.50
337	A22	20pa carmine rose	1.00	.50
338	A22	1pi ultra	2.00	.50
339	A22	2pi indigo	7.50	3.00
a.		Inverted overprint	10.00	10.00

See Nos. P121-P133.

Stamps of 1901-13 Overprinted

1916

340	A17	5pa purple	1.00	.50
a.		5pa purple, #P43	80.00	80.00
341	A17	10pa green	1.00	.50
a.		Double overprint	6.50	6.50
b.		10pa yellow green, #103	80.00	80.00
342	A21	20pa car rose, #153	2.00	.50
a.		20pa carmine rose, #162	110.00	110.00
343	A21	1pi ultra	5.50	1.00
344	A22	5pi dull violet	10.00	3.00
		Nos. 340-344 (5)	19.50	5.50

Occupation of the Sinai Peninsula.

Old General Post Office of Constantinople A41

1916, May 29 Litho. *Perf. 12½, 13½*

345	A41	5pa green	.75	.50
346	A41	10pa carmine	.75	.50
347	A41	20pa ultra	.75	.50
348	A41	1pi violet & blk	1.50	.50
349	A41	5pi yel brn & blk	20.00	2.50
		Nos. 345-349 (5)	23.75	4.50

Introduction of postage in Turkey, 50th anniv.
For overprints see Nos. 418, B42-B45.

Stamps of 1892-1905 Overprinted

1916

350	A10	10pa gray grn (R)	2.00	2.00
351	A18	20pa carmine (Bl)	3.75	2.50
352	A18	1pi blue (R)	10.00	5.00
353	A18	2pi slate (Bk)	12.50	1.00
354	A18	2½pi red violet (Bk)	20.00	1.50
		Nos. 350-354 (5)	48.25	12.00

National Fête Day. Overprint reads "10 Temuz 1332" (July 23, 1916).

Preceding Issues Overprinted or Surcharged in Red or Black:

a	b

1916

On Stamps of 1892-98

355	A10(a)	10pa gray green	1.00	.50
355A	A11(a)	20pa violet brown	.75	.50
b.		Inverted overprint	10.00	10.00
356	A12(a)	1pi gray blue	50.00	50.00
357	A13(a)	2pi brown org	5.00	1.50
358	A14(a)	5pi dull violet	50.00	50.00

On Stamp of 1897

359	A10(b)	5pa on 10pa gray grn	.75	.50

On Stamps of 1901

361	A16(a)	5pa bister	.75	.50
a.		Double overprint	7.50	7.50
362	A16(a)	10pa yel grn	1.00	.50
363	A16(a)	20pa magenta	.75	.50
364	A16(a)	1pi violet blue	1.00	.50
a.		Inverted overprint	7.50	7.50
365	A16(a)	2pi gray blue	5.00	.50
366	A16(b)	5pi on 25pi dk grn	55.00	55.00
367	A16(b)	10pi on 25pi dk grn	55.00	55.00
368	A16(a)	25pi dark green	55.00	55.00
369	A17(a)	5pa purple	75.00	50.00
370	A17(a)	10pa green	1.50	1.50
371	A17(a)	20pa carmine	.75	.50
a.		Inverted overprint	7.50	7.50
372	A17(a)	1pi blue	.75	.50
a.		Inverted overprint	7.50	7.50
373	A17(a)	2pi orange	1.50	.50
374	A17(b)	10pi on 25pi brown	5.00	1.50
375	A17(b)	10pi on 50pi yel brn	7.50	1.50
376	A17(a)	25pi brown	7.50	1.50
377	A17(a)	50pi yel brn	10.00	2.50

On Stamps of 1905

378	A18(a)	5pa ocher	.75	.50
379	A18(a)	20pa carmine	.75	.50
a.		Inverted overprint	10.00	5.00
380	A18(a)	1pi brt blue	2.00	.50
a.		Inverted overprint	10.00	5.00
381	A18(a)	2pi slate	1.00	.50
382	A18(a)	2½pi red violet	7.50	1.50
383	A18(b)	10pi on 25pi ol grn	7.50	2.50
384	A18(b)	10pi on 50pi dp vio	7.50	2.00
385	A18(a)	25pi olive green	7.50	3.00
386	A18(a)	50pi deep violet	6.00	3.00

On Stamps of 1906

387	A18(a)	10pa dull green	1.00	.60
388	A18(a)	20pa carmine	1.00	.60
389	A18(a)	1pi brt blue	1.00	.60

On Stamps of 1908

390	A19(a)	2½pi violet brown	67.50	67.50
391	A19(b)	10pi on 25pi dk grn	20.00	12.50
392	A19(b)	10pi on 50pi red brn	67.50	67.50
393	A19(b)	25pi on 50pi red brn	67.50	67.50
394	A19(a)	25pi dark green	7.50	2.50
395	A19(a)	50pi red brown	50.00	50.00

With Additional Overprint

396	A19(a)	2pi blue black	67.50	67.50

On Stamps of 1908-09

397	A20(a)	5pa ocher	67.50	67.50
398	A21(a)	5pa ocher	.75	2.50
399	A21(a)	10pa blue green	50.00	50.00
400	A21(a)	20pa carmine rose	50.00	50.00
401	A21(a)	1pi ultra	1.00	.50
402	A21(a)	2pi blue black	3.00	1.50
403	A21(a)	2½pi dark brown	50.00	50.00
404	A21(a)	5pi dark violet	50.00	50.00

With Additional Overprint

405	A21(a)	1pi ultra	67.50	67.50
406	A21(a)	2pi blue black	50.00	50.00

On Stamps of 1913

407	A22(a)	5pa ocher	1.00	.75
408	A22(a)	20pa carmine rose	1.50	.50
409	A22(a)	1pi ultra	1.50	.50
410	A22(a)	2pi indigo	3.00	1.00
411	A22(b)	10pi on 50pi org brn	12.50	10.00
412	A22(a)	25pi gray green	7.50	5.00
413	A22(a)	50pi orange brown	15.00	12.50

With Additional Overprint

414	A22(a)	1pi ultra	1.00	1.00

On Commemorative Stamps of 1913

415	A23(a)	10pa green	1.25	.50
416	A23(a)	20pa red	2.00	.50
417	A23(a)	40pa blue	6.00	2.50

On Commemorative Stamp of 1916

418	A41(a)	5pi yel brn & blk	1.00	.50

No. 277 Surcharged in Blue

419	A31	60pa on 1pi on 1½pi	2.50	3.50
a.		"1330" omitted	40.00	40.00

See Nos. P134-P152, J67-J70.

Turkish Artillery A42

Mosque at Orta Köy, Constantinople — A43

Lighthouse on Bosporus — A44

Monument to Martyrs of Liberty — A45

Map of the Dardanelles; Sultan Mohammed V — A46

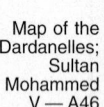
Map of the Dardanelles A47

Istanbul Across the Golden Horn A48

Pyramids of Egypt A49

Dolma Bahçe Palace and Mohammed V — A50

Sentry and Shell — A51

Sultan Mohammed V — A52

1916-18　　Typo.　　Perf. 11½, 12½

420	A42	2pa violet	1.50 .75
421	A43	5pa orange	1.00 .75
424	A44	10pa green	1.00 1.00

Engr.

425	A45	20pa deep rose	1.00 .75
426	A46	1pi dull violet	3.00 .50

Typo.

428	A47	50pa ultra	1.50 .50
429	A48	2pi org brn & ind	3.00 .50
430	A49	5pi pale blue & blk	17.50 1.00

Engr.

431	A50	10pi dark green	8.75 5.00
432	A50	10pi dark violet	32.50 2.50
433	A50	10pi dark brown	14.00 2.50
434	A51	25pi carmine, *straw*	2.25 1.50
437	A52	50pi carmine	5.00 5.00
438	A52	50pi indigo	2.00 2.50
439	A52	50pi green, *straw*	2.50 10.00
		Nos. 420-439 (15)	96.50 34.75

For overprints and surcharges see Nos. 541B-541E, 554-560, 565-566, 569-574, 575, 577-578, 579A-580, Turkey in Asia 4, 10, 64-66, Thrace N76, N80, N81. Compare designs A42-A43 with A53-A54.

Forgeries of Nos. 446-545 abound.

Preceding Issues Overprinted or Surcharged in Red, Black or Blue:

d

e

f

g

1917

On Stamps of 1865

446	A5(d)	20pa yellow (R)	45.00 67.50
a.		Star without rays (R)	50.00 57.50
447	A5(d)	1pi pearl gray (R)	45.00 67.50
a.		Star without rays (R)	50.00 57.50
448	A5(d)	2pi blue (R)	45.00 67.50
449	A5(d)	5pi carmine (Bk)	45.00 67.50

On Stamp of 1867

450	A5(d)	5pi rose (Bk)	45.00 67.50

On Stamps of 1870-71

451	A5(d)	2pi red (Bl)	45.00 67.50
452	A5(d)	5pi blue (Bl)	45.00 67.50
453	A5(d)	25pi dull rose (R)	45.00 67.50

On Stamp of 1874-75

454	A5(d)	10pa red violet (Bl)	45.00 67.50

On Stamps of April, 1876

455	A5(d)	10pa red lilac (Bl)	45.00 67.50
a.		10pa red violet (Bl)	50.00 67.50
457	A5(d)	20pa pale green (R)	45.00 67.50
458	A5(d)	1pi yellow (Bl)	45.00 67.50

On Stamps of January, 1876

459	A5(d)	¼pi on 10pa rose lil (Bl)	45.00 67.50
460	A5(d)	½pi on 20pa yel grn (R)	45.00 67.50
461	A5(d)	1¼pi on 50pa rose (Bl)	45.00 67.50

On Stamps of September, 1876

462	A7(d)	50pa blue & yel (R)	45.00 67.50
463	A7(d)	2pi blk & redsh brn (R)	45.00 67.50
464	A7(d)	25pi claret & rose (Bk)	45.00 67.50

On Stamps of 1880-84

465	A7(d)	5pa black & ol (R)	45.00 67.50
466	A7(d)	10pa black & grn (R)	45.00 67.50

On Stamps of 1881-82

467	A5(d)	20pa gray (Bl)	45.00 67.50
468	A5(d)	2pi pale sal (Bl)	45.00 67.50

On Stamps of 1884-86

469	A7(d)	10pa grn & pale grn (Bk)	45.00 67.50
470	A7(d)	20pa ocher & pale ocher (R)	45.00 67.50
471	A7(d)	5pi red brn & pale brn (Bk)	45.00 67.50

On Stamps of 1886

472	A7(d)	5pa blk & pale gray (R)	2.00 1.75
a.		Inverted overprint	30.00 30.00
473	A7(d)	2pi org & bl (Bk)	3.00 2.50
a.		Inverted overprint	35.00 35.00
474	A7(d)	5pi grn & pale grn (R)	45.00 67.50
475	A7(d)	25pi bis & pale bis (R)	45.00 67.50

On Stamp of 1888

476	A7(d)	5pi dk brn & gray (Bk)	45.00 67.50

On Stamps of 1892-98

477	A11(d)	20pa vio brn (R)	4.00 3.00
478	A13(d)	2pi brn org (R)	4.00 3.50
a.		Tête bêche pair	13.50 13.50

On Stamps of 1901

479	A16(d)	5pa bister (R)	3.00 3.00
a.		Inverted overprint	20.00 20.00
480	A16(d)	20pa mag (Bk)	2.00 1.50
a.		Inverted overprint	25.00 25.00
481	A16(d)	1pi vio bl (R)	3.00 3.00
a.		Inverted overprint	20.00 20.00

482	A16(d)	2pi gray bl (R)	5.00 5.00
483	A16(d)	5pi ocher (R)	32.50 50.00
484	A16(e)	10pi on 50pi yel (R)	32.50 50.00
485	A16(d)	25pi dk grn (R)	100.00 50.00
486	A17(d)	5pa purple (Bk)	32.50 50.00
487	A17(d)	10pa green (R)	5.00 5.00
488	A17(d)	20pa car (Bk)	2.00 1.50
a.		Inverted overprint	20.00 20.00
489	A17(d)	1pi blue (R)	1.00 .90
490	A17(d)	2pi org (Bk)	3.00 3.00
a.		Inverted overprint	20.00 20.00
491	A17(d)	5pi lil rose (R)	32.50 50.00
492	A17(e)	10pi on 50pi yel brn (R)	32.50 50.00
493	A17(d)	25pi brown (R)	5.00 5.00

On Stamps of 1905

494	A18(d)	5pa ocher (R)	2.00 1.00
a.		Inverted overprint	20.00 20.00
495	A18(d)	10pa dl grn (R)	32.50 50.00
496	A18(d)	20pa car (Bk)	1.00 1.00
a.		Double ovpt., one invtd.	35.00 35.00
b.		Inverted overprint	35.00 35.00
497	A18(d)	1pi blue (R)	1.50 1.00
a.		Inverted overprint	35.00 35.00
498	A18(d)	2pi slate (R)	5.00 5.00
499	A18(d)	2½pi red vio (Bk)	5.00 5.00
a.		Inverted overprint	20.00 20.00
500	A18(d)	5pi brown (R)	35.00 45.00
501	A18(d)	10pi orange brn (R)	35.00 50.00
502	A18(e)	10pi on 50pi dp vio (R)	35.00 50.00
503	A18(d)	25pi ol grn (R)	35.00 50.00

On Nos. 128-131

504	A18(d)	10pa dl grn (R)	1.50 1.00
a.		Inverted overprint	20.00 20.00
505	A18(d)	20pa car (Bk)	1.00 .75
a.		Double ovpt., one invtd.	20.00 20.00
b.		Inverted overprint	20.00 20.00
506	A18(d)	1pi brt bl (Bk)	1.00 .75
a.		Inverted overprint	20.00 20.00
507	A18(d)	1pi brt bl (R)	1.50 1.25
a.		Inverted overprint	20.00 20.00
508	A18(d)	2pi slate (Bk)	35.00 50.00
		Nos. 494-508 (15)	227.00 311.75

On Stamps of 1908

509	A19(d)	5pa ocher (R)	1.50 1.25
510	A19(d)	10pa bl grn (R)	20.00 20.00
510A	A19(d)	1pi brt blue (R)	125.00 140.00
511	A19(d)	2pi bl blk (R)	35.00 50.00
512	A19(d)	2½pi violet brn (Bk)	35.00 35.00
512A	A19(d)	10pi red (R)	150.00 225.00
513	A19(e)	10pi on 50pi red brn (R)	35.00 50.00
514	A19(d)	25pi dark green (R)	35.00 50.00

With Additional Overprint

514A	A19(d)	10pa bl grn (Bk)	150.00 225.00
515	A19(d)	1pi brt bl (Bk)	35.00 50.00
516	A19(d)	2pi bl blk (R)	5.00 5.00
516A	A19(d)	2pi bl blk (Bk)	35.00 67.50

On Stamps of 1908-09

517	A20(d)	5pa ocher (R)	3.00 3.00
518	A21(d)	5pa ocher (R)	2.00 1.50
a.		Double overprint	20.00 20.00
b.		Dbl. ovpt., one inverted	20.00 20.00
519	A21(d)	10pa bl grn (R)	2.00 1.50
520	A21(d)	20pa carmine rose (Bk)	2.00 1.50
a.		Double overprint	35.00 35.00
521	A21(d)	1pi ultra (R)	1.00 .75
a.		1p bright blue (R)	30.00 30.00
522	A21(d)	2pi bl blk (R)	5.00 5.00
523	A21(d)	2½pi dk brn (Bk)	35.00 50.00
524	A21(d)	5pi dk vio (R)	35.00 50.00
525	A21(d)	10pi dull red (R)	35.00 50.00

With Additional Overprint

525A	A21(d)	10pa bl grn (Bk)	175.00 225.00
526	A21(d)	1pi ultra (Bk)	125.00 90.00
527	A21(d)	1pi ultra (R)	2.50 2.50
a.		1pi bright blue (R)	125.00 140.00
528	A21(d)	2pi bl blk (Bk)	35.00 50.00

On Stamps of 1913

529	A22(d)	5pa ocher (R)	1.25 1.25
530	A22(d)	10pa bl grn (R)	35.00 50.00
531	A22(d)	20pa car rose (Bk)	1.50 2.50
532	A22(d)	1pi ultra (R)	1.50 3.50
533	A22(d)	2pi indigo (R)	3.50 3.50
534	A22(d)	5pi dl vio (R)	35.00 50.00
535	A22(d)	10pi dl red (Bk)	45.00 50.00

With Additional Overprint

536	A22(d)	10pa bl grn (Bk)	1.50 1.50
a.		Inverted overprint	20.00 20.00
537	A22(d)	1pi ultra (Bk)	3.00 3.00
a.		Inverted overprint	20.00 20.00
538	A22(d)	2pi indigo (Bk)	35.00 100.00

On Commemorative Stamps of 1913

539	A23(d)	10pa green (R)	5.00 5.00
a.		Inverted overprint	20.00 20.00
540	A23(d)	40pa blue (R)	7.00 7.00
a.		Inverted overprint	20.00 20.00

On No. 277, with Addition of New Value

541	A31	60pa on 1pi on 1½pi red vio	1.50 1.50
a.		"1330" omitted	45.00 45.00

On Stamps of 1916-18

541B	A51(f)	25pi car, *straw*	5.00 5.00
541C	A52(g)	50pi carmine	17.50 17.50
541D	A52(g)	50pi indigo	35.00 50.00
541E	A52(g)	50pi green, *straw*	17.50 27.50

Ovptd. on Eastern Rumelia No. 12

542	A4(d)	20pa blk & rose (Bl)	35.00 35.00

Ovptd. in Black on Eastern Rumelia #15-17

543	A4(d)	5pa lilac & pale lilac	45.00 45.00
544	A4(d)	10pa green & pale green	45.00 45.00
545	A4(d)	20pa carmine & pale rose	45.00 45.00

Some experts question the status of Nos. 510A, 512A and 525A.
See Nos. J71-J86, P153-P172.

Surcharged

1917

545A	A52a	5pa on 1pi red	1.00 .75

It is stated that No. 545A was never issued without surcharge.
See Nos. 548f, 545A, 602.

Turkish Artillery A53

1917　　Typo.　　Perf. 11½, 12½

546	A53	2pa Prussian blue	150.00

In type A42 the Turkish inscription at the top is in one group, in type A53 it is in two groups. It is stated that No. 546 was never placed in use. Examples were distributed through the Universal Postal Union at Bern.

For surcharges see Nos. 547-548, Turkey in Asia 69-70.

Surcharged

547	A53	5pi on 2pa Prus bl		15.00	1.75
a.		Inverted surcharge		20.00	9.00
b.		Turkish "5" omitted at lower left			

Surcharged

1918

548	A53	5pi on 2pa Prus blue		15.00	2.00
g.		Inverted surcharge		20.00	10.00

Top line of surcharge on Nos. 547-548 reads "Ottoman Posts."
For surcharge see Thrace No. N79.

No. 545A Surcharged

1918

548A	A52a	2pa on 5pa on 1pi red	2.00	1.75
b.		Double surcharge	10.00	10.00
c.		Inverted surcharge	10.00	10.00
d.		Double surcharge inverted	10.00	10.00
e.		Dbl. surch., one inverted	10.00	10.00
f.		In pair with No. 545A	17.50	17.50

Enver Pasha and Kaiser Wilhelm II on Battlefield A54

St. Sophia and Obelisk of the Hippodrome A55

1918   Typo.   Perf. 12, 12½

549	A54	5pa brown red	100.00
550	A55	10pa gray green	100.00

The stamps, of which very few saw postal use, were converted into paper money by pasting on thick yellow paper and reperforating.

Values are for copies with original gum. Stamps removed from the yellow paper are worth $8 each.

Armistice Issue

Overprinted in Black or Red

1919, Nov. 30
On Stamps of 1913

552	A34	2½pi org & ol grn	125.00	300.00
553	A38	50pi carmine	125.00	300.00

On Stamps of 1916-18

554	A46	1pi dull violet (R)	7.50	10.00
555	A47	50pa ultra (R)	1.00	1.50
556	A48	2pi org brn & ind	1.00	1.00

557	A49	5pi pale bl & blk (R)		1.00	1.50
558	A50	10pi dark green		6.25	10.00
559	A51	25pi carmine, *straw*		6.25	10.00
560	A52	50pi grn, *straw* (R)		6.25	10.00

Fountain in Desert near Sinai — A56

Sentry at Beersheba — A57

Turkish Troops at Sinai A58

Typo.

562	A56	20pa claret	.75	1.50
563	A57	1pi blue (R)	125.00	150.00
564	A58	25pi slate blue (R)	125.00	150.00
		Nos. 552-564 (12)	530.00	946.00

The overprint reads: "Souvenir of the Armistice, 30th October 1334." Nos. 562 to 564 are not known to have been regularly issued without overprint.

See No. J87. For overprints and surcharges see Nos. 576, 579, 582, 583-584, 586, Turkey in Asia 71, Thrace N83.

Stamps of 1911-19 Overprinted in Turkish
"Accession to the Throne of His Majesty, 3rd July 1334-1918," the Tughra of Sultan Mohammed VI and sometimes Ornaments and New Values

Dome of the Rock, Jerusalem A59

1919

565	A42	2pa violet		1.00	2.50
566	A43	5pa orange		.75	.50
567	A21	5pa on 2pa ol grn		.75	.50
a.		Inverted surcharge		10.00	10.00
568	A22	10pa on 2pa ol grn		1.00	.50
569	A44	10pa green		1.25	1.50
a.		Inverted overprint		25.00	25.00
570	A45	20pa deep rose		1.25	.50
a.		Inverted overprint		12.00	12.00
571	A46	1pi dull violet		1.25	1.00
572	A47	60pa on 50pa ultra		1.25	1.00
573	A48	60pa on 2pi org brn & ind		1.00	.50
574	A48	2pi orange brn & ind		1.00	1.00
574A	A34	2½pi orange & ol grn		25.00	37.50
575	A49	5pi pale blue & blk		1.00	1.00
576	A56	10pi on 20pa cl		1.00	1.00
577	A50	10pi dark brown		2.50	2.50
578	A48	25pi carmine, *straw*		2.00	2.00
579	A57	35pi on 1pi blue		1.50	2.00
579A	A52	50pi carmine		25.00	37.50
580	A52	50pi green, *straw*		6.00	5.00
581	A59	100pi on 10pa green		6.00	6.00
582	A58	250pi on 25pi sl bl		6.00	6.00
		Nos. 565-582 (20)		86.50	108.50

See note after #586. See #J88-J91.
For overprint and surcharge see Nos. 585, Thrace N82.

Surcharged with Ornaments, New Values and

Perf. 11½, 12½

583	A56	20pa claret	1.75	10.00
584	A57	1pi deep blue	2.50	17.50
585	A59	60pa on 10pa green	1.50	7.50
586	A58	25pi slate blue	7.50	50.00
a.		Inverted overprint		100.00
		Nos. 583-586 (4)	13.25	85.00

#576, 579, 581, 582, 583-586 were prepared in anticipation of the invasion and conquest of Egypt by the Turks. They were not issued at that time but subsequently received various overprints in commemoration of Sultan Mehmet Sadi's accession to the throne (#565-582) and of the 1st anniv. of this event (#583-586).
For surcharge see Thrace No. N83.

Designs of 1913 Modified

1920   Litho.   Perf. 11, 12

590	A26	5pa brown orange	1.00	.50

Engr.

591	A28	10pa green	1.00	.50
592	A23	20pa rose	1.00	.50
593	A30	1pi blue green	3.75	.50
594	A32	3pi blue	1.00	.50
595	A34	5pi gray	50.00	.50
596	A36	10pi gray violet	12.50	.50
597	A37	25pi dull violet	5.00	2.50
598	A38	50pi brown	5.00	10.00
		Nos. 590-598 (9)	80.25	16.00

On most stamps of this issue the designs have been modified by removing the small Turkish word at right of the tughra of the Sultan. In the 3pi and 5pi the values have been altered, while for the 25pi the color has been changed.
For surcharges see Thrace Nos. N77, N78, N84.

30 PARAS

PARAS 60

4½ PIASTRES

PIASTRES 7¼

Black Surcharge

1921-22

600	SP1	30pa on 10pa red vio	1.25	.50
a.		Double surcharge	37.50	37.50
b.		Imperf.		
601	A28	60pa on 10pa green	1.25	.50
a.		Double surcharge	22.50	22.50
602	A52a	4½pi on 1pi red	4.50	1.50
a.		Inverted surcharge	20.00	20.00
603	A32	7½pi on 3pi blue	12.50	1.00
604	A32	7½pi on 3pi bl (R) ('22)	20.00	2.50
a.		Double surcharge	30.00	30.00
		Nos. 600-604 (5)	39.50	6.00

ΕΛΛΗΝΙΚΗ ΚΑΤΟΧΗ ΛΕΠΤΑ·50

Turkish Stamps of 1916-21 with Greek surcharge as above in blue or black are of private origin.

Issues of the Republic

Crescent and Star — A64

TWO PIASTERS:
Type I — "2" measures 3¼x1¾mm
Type II — "2" measures 2¾x1½mm

FIVE PIASTERS:
Type I — "5" measures 3½x2¼mm
Type II — "5" measures 3x1¾mm

Perf. 11, 12, 13½, 13½x12

1923-25   Litho.

605	A64	10pa gray black	.25	.25
606	A64	20pa citron	.25	.25
607	A64	1pi deep violet	.25	.25
a.		Slanting numeral in lower left corner	.50	.25
608	A64	1½pi emerald	.25	1.50
609	A64	2pi bluish grn (I)	2.00	.50
a.		2pi deep green (II)	.75	.25
610	A64	3pi yel brn	1.00	.50
611	A64	3¾pi lilac brown	2.50	2.50
612	A64	4½pi carmine	.75	1.00
613	A64	5pi purple (I)	3.50	1.50
a.		5pi violet (II)	12.50	1.00
614	A64	7½pi blue	2.50	.50
615	A64	10pi slate	7.50	1.00
a.		10pi blue	7.50	1.00
616	A64	11¼pi dull rose	2.50	2.00
617	A64	15pi brown	10.00	1.00
618	A64	18¾pi myrtle green	4.50	3.00
619	A64	22½pi orange	6.00	2.00
620	A64	25pi black brown	30.00	2.50
621	A64	50pi gray	75.00	4.00
622	A64	100pi dark violet	150.00	8.50
624	A64	500pi deep green	500.00	160.00
		Cut cancellation		1.60
		Nos. 605-624 (19)	798.75	192.75
		Set, never hinged	3,000.	

#605-610, 612-617 exist imperf. & part perf.

Bridge of Sakarya and Mustafa Kemal — A65

1924, Jan. 1   Perf. 12

625	A65	1½pi emerald	.50	.30
626	A65	3pi purple	.60	.50
627	A65	4½pi pale rose	2.00	1.60
628	A65	5pi yellow brown	2.00	1.60
629	A65	7½pi deep blue	2.00	1.60
630	A65	50pi orange	22.50	10.00
631	A65	100pi brown violet	52.50	20.00
632	A65	200pi olive brown	52.50	35.00
		Nos. 625-632 (8)	154.60	70.60
		Set, never hinged	750.00	

Signing of Treaty of Peace at Lausanne.

The Legendary Blacksmith and his Gray Wolf — A66

Sakarya Gorge — A67

Fortress of
Ankara — A68

Mustafa Kemal
Pasha — A69

1926

				Engr.
634	A66	10pa slate	.50	.20
635	A66	20pa orange	.50	.20
636	A66	1g brt rose	.50	.20
637	A67	2g green	1.50	.25
638	A67	2½g gray black	2.00	.50
639	A67	3g copper red	2.50	.50
640	A68	5g lilac gray	3.00	.50
641	A68	6g red	1.00	.25
642	A68	10g deep blue	7.50	.50
643	A68	15g deep orange	10.00	1.25
644	A69	25g dk green & blk	15.00	1.25
645	A69	50g carmine & blk	20.00	1.50
646	A69	100g olive grn & blk	35.00	2.00
647	A69	200g brown & blk	90.00	5.50
		Nos. 634-647 (14)	189.00	14.60
		Set, never hinged	800.00	

Stamps of 1926
Overprinted in
Black, Silver or Gold

1927, Sept. 9

648	A66	1g brt rose	.50	.50
649	A67	2g green	.50	1.00
650	A67	2½g gray black	1.50	2.00
651	A67	3g copper red	2.00	2.50
652	A68	5g lilac gray	2.50	4.00
653	A68	6g red	1.50	1.00
654	A68	10g deep blue	3.50	3.50
655	A68	15g deep orange	5.00	5.00
656	A69	25g dk green & blk (S)	15.00	20.00
657	A69	50g car & blk (S)	27.50	37.50
658	A69	100g ol grn & blk (G)	60.00	75.00
		Nos. 648-658 (11)	119.50	152.50
		Set, never hinged	425.00	

Agricultural and industrial exhibition at Izmir, Sept. 9-20, 1927.

The overprint reads: "1927" and the initials of "Izmir Dokuz Eylul Sergisi" (Izmir Exhibition, September 9).

Second Izmir Exhibition Issue
Nos. 634-647 Overprinted in Red or Black

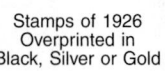

On A66-A68

On A69

1928, Sept. 9

659	A66	10pa slate (R)	.50	.40
660	A66	20pa orange	.50	.40
661	A66	1g brt rose	1.00	.50
662	A67	2g green (R)	1.50	1.50
663	A67	2½g gray blk (R)	1.50	1.50
664	A67	3g copper red	1.50	1.50
665	A68	5g lilac gray (R)	2.00	3.00
666	A68	6g red	1.00	1.00
667	A68	10g deep blue	3.50	3.00
668	A68	15g deep orange	5.00	2.00
669	A69	25g dk grn & blk (R)	15.00	6.25
670	A69	50g car & blk	17.50	20.00
671	A69	100g ol grn & blk (R)	40.00	50.00
672	A69	200g brn & blk (R)	62.50	62.50
		Nos. 659-672 (14)	152.50	153.05
		Set, never hinged	650.00	

The overprint reads "Izmir, September 9, 1928."

Nos. 636, 652, 654
Surcharged in Black
(#673) or Red (#674-675)

1929

673	A66	20pa on 1g brt rose	.50	.25
a.		Inverted surcharge	3.50	3.50
674	A68	2½k on 5g lilac gray	1.00	.50
a.		Inverted surcharge	7.50	7.50
675	A68	6k on 10g deep blue	6.00	.75
		Nos. 673-675 (3)	7.50	1.50
		Set, never hinged	40.00	

Railroad Bridge
over Kizil
Irmak — A70

A71

A72

A73

Latin Inscriptions
Without umlaut over first "U" of
"CUMHURIYETI"

1929

				Engr.
676	A70	2k gray black	5.00	1.00
677	A70	2½k green	3.00	1.00
678	A70	3k violet brown	4.00	1.50
679	A71	6k dark violet	25.00	1.00
680	A72	12½k deep blue	35.00	3.75
681	A73	50k carmine & blk	60.00	8.75
		Nos. 676-681 (6)	132.00	17.00
		Set, never hinged	400.00	

See Nos. 682-691, 694-695, 697, 699. For surcharges & overprints see #705-714, 716-717, 719, 721, 727, 765-766, 770-771, 777, C2, C7.

Sakarya
Gorge — A74

Mustafa Kemal
Pasha — A75

With umlaut over first "U" of
"CUMHURIYETI"

1930

682	A71	10pa green	.25	.25
683	A70	20pa gray violet	.25	.25
684	A70	1k olive green	.50	.50
685	A70	1½k olive black	.50	.40
686	A70	2k dull violet	3.00	.50
687	A70	2½k deep green	2.00	.50
688	A70	3k brown orange	20.00	1.50
689	A71	4k deep rose	7.50	.50
690	A72	5k rose lake	11.50	.50
691	A71	6k indigo	7.50	.50
692	A74	7½k red brown	.25	.25
694	A72	12½k deep ultra	.75	.50
695	A72	15k deep orange	.75	.50
696	A74	17½k dark gray	.75	.50
697	A72	20k black brown	50.00	2.00
698	A72	25k olive brown	1.00	1.00
699	A72	30k yellow brown	1.75	.50
700	A74	40k red violet	1.50	1.00
701	A75	50k red & black	3.50	1.25
702	A75	100k olive grn & blk	3.50	1.25
703	A75	200k dk green & blk	3.75	1.50
704	A75	500k chocolate & blk	17.50	22.50
		Nos. 682-704 (22)	138.00	38.40
		Set, never hinged	400.00	

For surcharges and overprints see Nos. 715, 718, 720, 722-726, 767-769, 772-773,

---

775-776, 778-780, 823-828, 848-850, C1, C3-C6, C8-C11.

Nos. 682-704 Surcharged in Red or Black:

Sivas	D. Y. Sivas
D. Y.	30 ag. 930
30 ag. 930	10 P.
1 K.	b
a	

Sivas	
c	D. Y.
	30 ag. 930
	40 K.

1930, Aug. 30

705	A71(a)	10pa on 10pa (R)	.50	1.25
706	A70(b)	10pa on 20pa	.50	1.50
707	A70(b)	20pa on 1ku	1.00	1.25
708	A71(a)	1k on 1½k (R)	.50	1.25
709	A70(b)	1½k on 2k	1.00	1.50
710	A70(b)	2k on 2½k (R)	2.50	2.00
711	A70(b)	2½k on 3k	2.00	1.50
712	A71(a)	3k on 4k	2.00	2.00
713	A72(a)	4k on 5k	2.50	4.00
714	A71(a)	5k on 6k (R)	3.50	3.00
715	A74(a)	6k on 7½k	.75	.50
716	A72(a)	7½k on 12½k (R)	1.25	1.00
717	A72(a)	12½k on 15k	1.25	4.00
718	A74(b)	15k on 17½k (R)	5.00	4.00
719	A72(b)	17½k on 20k (R)	5.00	2.00
720	A74(b)	20k on 25k (R)	7.50	2.50
721	A72(b)	25k on 30k	5.00	2.50
722	A74(b)	30k on 40k	7.50	7.50
723	A75(c)	40k on 50k	15.00	7.50
724	A75(c)	50k on 100k (R)	70.00	16.00
725	A75(c)	100k on 200k (R)	85.00	27.50
726	A75(c)	250k on 500k (R)	75.00	35.00
		Nos. 705-726 (22)	294.25	129.25
		Set, never hinged	800.00	

Inauguration of the railroad between Ankara and Sivas.

There are numerous varieties in these settings as: "309," "390," "930" inverted, no period after "D," no period after "Y" and raised period before "Y."

No. 685 Surcharged
in Red

1931, Apr. 1

727	A71	1k on 1½k olive blk	.60	.20

Olive Tree with Roots
Extending to All
Balkan
Capitals — A76

1931, Oct. 20

			Engr.	Perf. 12
728	A76	2½k dark green	.40	.20
729	A76	4k carmine	.50	.20
730	A76	6k steel blue	.50	.20
731	A76	7½k dull red	.50	.20
732	A76	12k deep orange	1.00	.25
733	A76	12½k dark blue	1.00	.20
734	A76	30k dark violet	1.75	1.50
735	A76	50k dark brown	3.00	.75
736	A76	100k brown violet	6.25	1.00
		Nos. 728-736 (9)	14.90	5.05
		Set, never hinged	20.00	

Second Balkan Conference.

A77

A78

Mustafa Kemal Pasha
(Kemal Atatürk) — A79

1931-42   Typo.   Perf. 11½, 12

737	A77	10pa blue green	.20	.20
738	A77	20pa deep orange	.20	.20
739	A77	30pa brt violet ('38)	.25	.20
740	A78	1k dk slate green	.20	.20
740A	A77	1½k magenta ('42)	.55	.20
741	A78	2k dark violet	.50	.20
741A	A78	2k yel grn ('40)	.25	.25
742	A77	2½k green	.50	.20
743	A78	3k brn org ('38)	1.50	.20
744	A78	4k slate	2.50	.20
745	A78	5k rose red	.25	.25
745A	A78	5k brown blk ('40)	2.00	.50
746	A78	6k deep blue	3.00	.20
746A	A78	6k rose ('40)	.80	.30
747	A77	7½k deep rose ('32)	.50	.20
747A	A78	8k brt blue ('38)	3.50	.20
b.		8k dark blue ('36)	3.50	
748	A77	10k black brn ('32)	1.00	.20
748A	A77	10k deep blue ('40)	7.00	.60
749	A77	12k bister ('32)	1.00	.20
750	A79	12½k indigo ('32)	1.00	.20
751	A77	15k org yel ('32)	1.00	.20
752	A77	20k olive grn ('32)	1.00	.20
753	A77	25k Prus blue ('32)	2.50	1.00
754	A77	30k magenta ('32)	7.50	.50
755	A79	100k maroon ('32)	200.00	5.50
756	A79	200k purple ('32)	3.75	2.00
757	A79	250k chocolate ('32)	100.00	11.50
		Nos. 737-757 (27)	342.45	25.80
		Set, never hinged	750.00	

See Nos. 1015-1033, 1117B-1126. For overprints see Nos. 811-816.

Symbolizing 10th
Anniversary of
Republic — A80

President Atatürk — A81

1933, Oct. 29   Perf. 10

758	A80	1½k blue green	1.25	1.00
759	A80	2k olive brown	1.25	1.00
760	A81	3k red brown	1.25	1.00
761	A81	6k deep blue	1.25	1.00
762	A80	12½k dark green	3.25	2.50
763	A80	25k dark brown	8.00	5.00
764	A81	50k orange brown	20.00	15.00
		Nos. 758-764 (7)	36.25	26.50
		Set, never hinged	55.00	

10th year of the Turkish Republic. The stamps were in use for three days only.

TURKEY

649

Nos. 682, 685, 692, 694, 696-698, 702
Overprinted or Surcharged in Red:

1934, Aug. 26 — Perf. 12

765	A71	10pa green	.50	1.00
766	A71	1k on 1½k	1.00	.75
767	A74	2k on 25k	1.50	1.25
768	A74	5k on 7½k	5.00	5.00
769	A74	6k on 17½k	2.50	2.00
770	A72	12½k deep ultra	7.50	5.00
771	A72	15k on 20k	50.00	45.00
772	A74	20k on 25k	35.00	37.50
773	A75	50k on 100k	40.00	37.50
	Nos. 765-773 (9)	143.00	135.00
	Set, never hinged	600.00	

Izmir Fair, 1934.

Nos. 696, 698, 701-704 Surcharged in Black

1936, Oct. 26

775	A74	4k on 17½k	1.00	.50
776	A74	5k on 25k	1.00	.50
777	A73	6k on 50k	1.00	.50
778	A75	10k on 100k	1.75	1.00
779	A75	20k on 200k	5.50	2.00
780	A75	50k on 500k	10.00	3.25
	Nos. 775-780 (6)	20.25	7.75
	Set, never hinged	67.50	

"1926" in Overprint

775a	A74	4k on 17½k	6.50	3.75
776a	A74	5k on 25k	7.00	3.75
777a	A73	6k on 50k	7.00	3.75
778a	A75	10k on 100k	9.00	4.50
779a	A75	20k on 200k	20.00	10.00
780a	A75	50k on 500k	55.00	27.50
	Nos. 775a-780a (6)	104.50	53.25
	Set, never hinged	250.00	

Re-militarization of the Dardanelles.

Hittite Bronze Stag — A82

Thorak's Bust of Kemal Atatürk — A83

1937, Sept. 20 — Litho. — Perf. 12

781	A82	3k light violet	1.75	1.25
782	A83	6k blue	3.00	2.00
783	A82	7½k bright pink	4.75	3.75
784	A83	12½k indigo	10.00	7.50
	Nos. 781-784 (4)	19.50	14.50
	Set, never hinged	32.50	

2nd Turkish Historical Congress, Istanbul, Sept. 20-30.

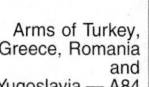

Arms of Turkey, Greece, Romania and Yugoslavia — A84

1937, Oct. 29 — Perf. 11½

785	A84	8k carmine	6.75	3.50
786	A84	12½k dark blue	15.00	4.75

The Balkan Entente.

Street in Izmir A85

Fig Tree — A87

30pa, View of Fair Buildings. 3k, Tower, Government Square. 5k, Olive branch. 6k, Woman with grapes. 7½k, Woman picking grapes. 8k, Izmir Harbor through arch. 12k, Statue of Pres. Ataturk. 12½k, Pres. Ataturk.

1938, Aug. 20 — Photo. — Perf. 11½
Inscribed: "Izmir Enternasyonal Fuari 1938"

789	A85	10pa dark brown	.50	.60
790	A85	30pa purple	.75	.50
791	A87	2½k brt green	1.25	1.00
792	A87	3k brown orange	1.25	1.00
793	A87	5k olive green	2.25	.75
794	A85	6k brown	5.00	.40
795	A87	7½k scarlet	5.00	2.50
796	A87	8k brown lake	3.50	1.50
797	A87	12k rose violet	6.25	3.50
798	A87	12½k deep blue	10.00	8.50
	Nos. 789-798 (10)	35.75	19.75
	Set, never hinged	70.00	

Izmir International Fair.

President Atatürk Teaching Reformed Turkish Alphabet A95

1938, Nov. 2

799	A95	2½k brt green	1.00	.55
800	A95	3k orange	1.25	.55
801	A95	6k rose violet	1.50	.65
802	A95	7½k deep rose	1.75	1.00
803	A95	8k red brown	2.00	1.10
804	A95	12½k brt ultra	2.50	1.25
	Nos. 799-804 (6)	10.00	5.10
	Set, never hinged	18.00	

Reform of the Turkish alphabet, 10th anniv.

Army and Air Force A96

Atatürk Driving Tractor — A98

3k, View of Kayseri. 7½k, Railway bridge. 8k, Scout buglers. 12½k, President Ataturk.

1938, Oct. 29
Inscribed: "Cumhuriyetin 15 inc yil donumu hatirasi"

805	A96	2½k dark green	.45	.35
806	A96	3k red brown	.45	.35
807	A98	6k bister	.75	.35
808	A96	7½k red	1.25	.90
809	A96	8k rose violet	4.00	2.50
810	A98	12½k deep blue	2.25	1.75
	Nos. 805-810 (6)	9.15	6.20
	Set, never hinged	20.00	

15th anniversary of the Republic.

Stamps of 1931-38 Overprinted in Black

1938, Nov. 21 — Perf. 11½x12

811	A78	3k brown orange	.50	.35
812	A78	5k rose red	.50	.35
813	A78	6k deep blue	.75	.50
814	A77	7½k deep rose	.80	.55
815	A78	8k dark blue	2.00	.75
a.		8k bright blue	225.00	150.00
816	A79	12½k indigo	3.75	1.75
	Nos. 811-816 (6)	8.30	4.25
	Set, never hinged	15.00	

President Kemal Atatürk (1881-1938). The date is that of his funeral.

> **Catalogue values for unused stamps in this section, from this point to the end of the section, are for Never Hinged items.**

Turkish and American Flags — A102

Presidents Inönü and F. D. Roosevelt and Map of North America A103

Designs: 3k, 8k, Inonu and Roosevelt. 7½k, 12½k, Kemal Ataturk and Washington.

1939, July 15 — Photo. — Perf. 14

817	A102	2½k ol grn, red & bl	.25	.20
818	A103	3k dk brn & bl grn	.50	.20
819	A102	6k purple, red & bl	.50	.20
820	A103	7½k org ver & bl grn	1.00	.40
821	A103	8k dp cl & bl grn	.75	.40
822	A103	12½k brt bl & bl grn	2.00	.85
	Nos. 817-822 (6)	5.00	2.25

US constitution, 150th anniversary.

Nos. 698, 702-704 Surcharged in Black

1939, July 23 — Unwmk. — Perf. 13

823	A74	3k on 25k	.40	.25
824	A75	6k on 200k	.65	.50
825	A74	7½k on 25k	.75	.50
826	A75	12k on 100k	1.00	.50
827	A75	12½k on 200k	2.00	.50
828	A75	17½k on 500k	3.00	1.00
	Nos. 823-828 (6)	7.80	3.25

Annexation of Hatay.

Railroad Bridge A105

Locomotive A106

Track Through Mountain Pass A107

Design: 12½k, Railroad tunnel, Atma Pass.

1939, Oct. 20 — Typo. — Perf. 11½

829	A105	3k lt orange red	3.25	3.25
830	A106	6k chestnut	3.75	3.75
831	A107	7½k rose pink	5.25	5.25
832	A107	12½k dark blue	8.75	8.75
	Nos. 829-832 (4)	21.00	21.00

Completion of the Sivas to Erzerum link of the Ankara-Erzerum Railroad.

Atatürk Residence in Ankara — A109

Kemal Atatürk — A110

A111

Designs: 5k, 6k, 7½k, 8k, 12½k, 17½k, Various portraits of Ataturk, "1880-1938."

1939-40 — Photo.

833	A109	2½k brt green	1.00	.50
834	A110	3k dk blue gray	1.00	.50
835	A110	5k chocolate	1.25	.75
836	A110	6k chestnut	1.25	.75
837	A110	7½k rose red	3.75	1.00
838	A110	8k gray green	1.75	1.00
839	A110	12½k brt blue	2.00	1.50
840	A110	17½k brt rose	6.50	2.00
	Nos. 833-840 (8)	18.50	8.00

Souvenir Sheet

841	A111	100k blue black	70.00	100.00

Death of Kemal Ataturk, first anniversary. Size of No. 841: 90x120mm.
Issued: 2½k, 6k, 12½k, 11/11/39; others, 1/3/40.

Namik Kemal A118

Arms of Turkey, Greece, Romania and Yugoslavia A119

1940, Jan. 3

842	A118	6k chestnut	1.25	.60
843	A118	8k dk olive grn	3.00	1.50
844	A118	12k brt rose red	3.50	2.00
845	A118	12½k brt blue	7.50	3.00
	Nos. 842-845 (4)	15.25	7.10

Birth cent. of Namik Kemal, poet and patriot.

Perf. 11½
1940, Jan. 1 — Typo. — Unwmk.

846	A119	8k light blue	3.50	1.00
847	A119	10k deep blue	7.00	2.25

The Balkan Entente.

Nos. 703-704
Surcharged in Red or
Black

1940, Aug. 20   Perf. 12
848 A75 6k on 200k dk grn &
           blk (R)   .75 1.00
849 A75 10k on 200k dk grn &
           blk   1.25 1.50
850 A75 12k on 500k choc &
           blk   2.00 2.50
     Nos. 848-850 (3)   4.00 5.00
13th International Izmir Fair.

Map of
Turkey
and
Census
Figures
A120

1940, Oct. 1   Typo.   Perf. 11½
851 A120 10pa dark blue green   .25   .25
852 A120 3k orange   1.25 1.25
853 A120 6k carmine rose   1.50 1.50
854 A120 10k dark blue   2.50 2.50
     Nos. 851-854 (4)   5.50 5.50
Census of Oct. 20, 1940.

Runner — A121   Pole
                       Vaulter — A122

Hurdler
A123

Discus
Thrower — A124

1940, Oct. 5
855 A121 3k olive green   2.50 2.50
856 A122 6k rose   7.50 3.50
857 A123 8k chestnut brown   3.50 4.00
858 A124 10k dark blue   5.50 10.00
     Nos. 855-858 (4)   19.00 20.00
11th Balkan Olympics.

Mail
Carriers on
Horseback
A125

Postman of 1840   Old Sailing
and   Vessel and
1940 — A126   Modern
                     Mailboat — A127

Design: 12k, Post Office, Istanbul.

1940, Dec. 31   Typo.   Perf. 10
859 A125 3k gray green   .50   .50
860 A126 6k rose   .75   .75
861 A127 10k dark blue   1.00 1.00
862 A127 12k olive brown   1.50 1.50
     Nos. 859-862 (4)   3.75 3.75
Centenary of the Turkish post.

Harbor
Scene
A129

Statue of
Atatürk — A132

Designs: 3k, 6k, 17½k, Various Izmir Fair
buildings. 12k, Girl picking grapes.

1941, Aug. 20   Litho.   Perf. 11½
**Inscribed: "Izmir Enternasyonal
Fuari 1941"**
863 A129 30pa dull green   .25   .20
864 A129 3k olive gray   .35   .20
865 A129 6k salmon rose   .50   .20
866 A129 10k blue   .75   .30
867 A129 12k dull brown vio   .95   .45
868 A129 17½k dull brown   1.50 1.25
     Nos. 863-868 (6)   4.30 2.60
Izmir International Fair, 1941.

Tomb of
Barbarossa
II — A135

Barbarossa II
(Khair ed-
Din) — A137

Barbarossa's Fleet in Battle — A136

1941
869 A135 20pa dark violet   .20   .20
870 A136 3k light blue   .75   .75
871 A136 6k rose red   1.25 1.25
872 A136 10k deep ultra   1.50 1.50
873 A136 12k dull brn & bis   1.75 1.75
874 A137 17½k multicolored   2.25 2.25
     Nos. 869-874 (6)   7.70 7.70
400th death anniv. of Barbarossa II.

President Inönü
A138   A138a

1942-45   Perf. 11½x11, 11
875   A138   0.25k yellow bis   .20   .20
876   A138   0.50k lt yellow grn   .20   .20
877   A138   1k gray green   .20   .20
877A A138   1½k brt vio ('45)   .20   .20
878   A138   2k bluish green   .30   .20
879   A138   4k fawn   .30   .30
880   A138   4½k slate   .30   .30
881   A138   5k light blue   .35   .20
882   A138   6k salmon
                   rose   .30   .20
883   A138   6¾k ultra   .20   .20
884   A138   9k blue violet   .80   .20
885   A138   10k dark blue   .30   .20
886   A138   13½k brt pink   .30   .20
887   A138   16k Prus green   .50   .20
888   A138   17½k rose lake   .30   .20
889   A138   20k brown violet   .50   .50
890   A138   27½k orange   .50   .50
891   A138   37k buff   .50   .50
892   A138   50k purple   1.60   .25
893   A138   100k olive bister   .50 3.00
894   A138a 200k brown   17.50 2.50
      Nos. 875-894 (21)   30.35 10.45

Ankara — A139   Antioch — A141

0.50k, Mohair goats. 1½k, Ankara Dam. 2k,
Oranges. 4k, Merino sheep. 4½k, Train. 5k,
Tile decorating. 6k, Atatürk statue, Ankara.
6¾k, 10k, Pres. Ismet Inonu. 13½k, Grand
National Assembly. 16k, Arnavutkoy, Istanbul.
17½k, Republic monument, Istanbul. 20k,
Safety monument, Ankara. 27½k, Post Office,
Istanbul. 37k, Monument at Afyon. 50k, "Peo-
ple's House," Ankara. 100k, Atatürk & Inonu.
200k, Pres. Inonu.

1943, Apr. 1   Perf. 11
896 A139 0.25k citron   .20   .20
897 A139 0.50k brt green   .40   .20
898 A141 1k yellow olive   .20   .20
899 A141 1½k deep violet   .20   .20
900 A139 2k brt blue green   .40   .20
901 A139 4k copper red   2.00   .50
902 A139 4½k black   2.00   .20
903 A141 5k sapphire   1.25   .50
904 A139 6k carmine rose   .20   .20
905 A139 6¾k brt ultra   .20   .20
906 A139 10k dark blue   .20   .20
907 A141 13½k brt red violet   .30   .20
908 A141 16k myrtle green   3.50   .20
909 A139 17½k brown orange   1.00   .20
910 A139 20k sepia   1.25   .20
911 A139 27½k dk orange   1.50 1.00
912 A139 37k lt yellow brn   1.25   .40
913 A141 50k purple   10.00   .20
914 A139 100k dk olive grn   12.50 2.50
915 A139 200k dark brown   9.00   .20
  a. Souvenir sheet   70.00 100.00
     Nos. 896-915 (20)   47.55 9.70
No. 915a contains one stamp similar to No.
915, perf. 13½ and printed in sepia. Issued
Apr. 20.
For surcharge see No. 928.

Girl with
Grapes — A158

Entrance
to Izmir
Fair
A159

Fair
Building
A160

1943, Aug. 20   Litho.   Perf. 11½
916 A158 4½k dull olive   .25   .25
917 A159 6k carmine rose   .25   .25
918 A160 6¾k blue   .25   .25
919 A159 10k dark blue   .50   .25
920 A158 13½k sepia   1.00 1.00
921 A160 27½k dull gray   1.50 1.75
     Nos. 916-921 (6)   3.75 3.75
Izmir International Fair.

Soccer
Team on
Parade
A161

Turkish Flag and
Soldier — A162

Designs: 6¾k, Bridge. 10k, Hospital. 13½k,
View of Ankara. 27½k, President Inonu.

1943, Oct. 29   Perf. 11x11½, 11½x11
**Inscribed: "Cumhuriyetin 20 nci
Yildonomu Hatirasi"**
922 A161 4½k lt olive grn   1.50 1.75
923 A162 6k rose red   .50   .20
924 A161 6¾k ultra   .50   .20
925 A161 10k violet blue   .50   .20
926 A161 13½k olive   .75   .20
927 A162 27½k lt brown   .95   .75
     Nos. 922-927 (6)   4.70 3.30
Republic, 20th anniv. Nos. 922-927 exist
imperf.

No. 905 Surcharged with New Value in
Red

1945   Perf. 11
928 A139 4½k on 6¾k brt ultra   1.00   .45

Recording Census   President Ismet
Data — A167   Inönü — A169

1945, Oct. 21   **Litho.**   **Perf. 11½**
929 A167 4½k olive black .55 .20
930 A167 9k violet .60 .20
931 A167 10k violet blue .60 .20
932 A167 18k dark red 1.25 .50
   Nos. 929-932 (4) 3.00 1.10

Souvenir Sheet
Imperf
933 A167 1 l chocolate 75.00 100.00
Census of 1945.

Perf. 11½ to 12½
1946, Apr. 1   **Unwmk.**
934 A169 0.25k brown red .20 .20
935 A169 1k slate grn .20 .20
936 A169 1½k plum .50 .20
937 A169 9k purple 1.00 .20
938 A169 10k deep blue 1.50 .20
939 A169 50k chocolate 5.00 .20
   Nos. 934-939 (6) 8.40 1.20

U.S.S. Missouri A170

1946, Apr. 5   **Perf. 11½**
940 A170 9k dark purple .40 .20
941 A170 10k dk chalky blue .60 .20
942 A170 27½k olive green 1.50 2.00
   a. Imperf., pair 30.00
   Nos. 940-942 (3) 2.50 2.40
Visit of the USS Missouri to Istanbul, 4/5.

Sower A171   Dove and Flag-Decorated Banderol A172

1946, June 16   **Perf. 11½ to 12½**
943 A171 9k violet .25 .20
944 A171 10k dark blue .40 .20
945 A171 18k olive green .65 1.00
946 A171 27½k red orange 1.25 2.50
   Nos. 943-946 (4) 2.55 3.90
Passing of legislation to distribute state lands to poor farmers.

1947, Aug. 20   **Photo.**   **Perf. 12**
947 A172 15k violet & dk bl .40 .25
948 A172 20k blue & dk blue 1.00 .50
949 A172 30k brown & gray blk .40 .25
950 A172 1 l ol grn & dk grn .50 .50
   Nos. 947-950 (4) 2.30 1.50
Izmir International Fair.

Victory Monument, Afyon Karahisar A173   Ismet Inönü as General A174

Kemal Atatürk as General — A175

1947, Aug. 30
951 A173 10k dk brn & pale brn .50 .30
952 A174 15k brt violet & gray .35 .20
953 A175 20k dp blue & gray .55 .20
954 A173 30k grnsh blk & gray 1.00 .30

---

955 A174 60k ol gray & pale brn 1.50 .65
956 A175 1 l dk green & gray 2.50 1.25
   Nos. 951-956 (6) 6.40 2.90
25th anniv. of the Battle of Dumlupinar, Aug. 30, 1922.

Grapes and Istanbul Skyline A176

1947, Sept. 22
957 A176 15k rose violet .40 .25
958 A176 20k deep blue .75 .50
959 A176 60k dark brown 1.25 .75
   Nos. 957-959 (3) 2.40 1.50
International Vintners' Congress, Istanbul.

Approaching Train, Istanbul Skyline and Sirkeci Terminus — A177

1947, Oct. 9
960 A177 15k rose violet .40 .25
961 A177 20k brt blue .60 .20
962 A177 60k olive green 1.50 1.25
   Nos. 960-962 (3) 2.50 1.70
International Railroad Congress, Istanbul.

President Ismet Inönü
A178   A179

1948   **Unwmk.**   **Engr.**   **Perf. 12, 14**
963 A178 0.25k dark red .20 .20
964 A178 1k olive black .20 .20
965 A178 2k brt rose lilac .20 .20
966 A178 3k red orange .20 .20
967 A178 4k dark green .20 .20
968 A178 5k blue .20 .20
969 A178 10k chocolate .20 .20
970 A178 12k deep red 1.00 .30
971 A178 15k violet .20 .20
972 A178 20k deep blue .30 .20
973 A178 30k brown 1.50 .30
974 A178 60k black 4.00 .50
975 A179 1 l olive green 8.00 .50
976 A179 2 l dark brown 30.00 5.00
977 A179 5 l deep plum 17.50 27.50
   Nos. 963-977 (15) 63.90 35.90
For overprints see Nos. O13-O42.

President Ismet Inönü and Lausanne Conference — A180

Conference Building A180a

1948, July 23   **Photo.**   **Perf. 11½**
978 A180 15k rose lilac .70 .70
979 A180a 20k blue .90 .90
980 A180a 40k gray green 1.10 1.10
981 A180 1 l brown 1.75 1.75
   Nos. 978-981 (4) 4.45 4.45
25th anniversary of Lausanne Treaty.

Statue of Kemal Atatürk, Ankara — A181

1948, Oct. 29
982 A181 15k violet .40 .40
983 A181 20k blue .50 .50
984 A181 40k gray green 1.10 1.10
985 A181 1 l brown 2.25 2.25
   Nos. 982-985 (4) 4.25 4.25
25th anniv. of the proclamation of the republic.

A182   A183

A184

Wrestlers A185

1949, June 3
986 A182 15k rose lilac 2.00 .50
987 A183 20k blue 2.50 1.00
988 A184 30k brown 2.50 .50
989 A185 60k green 3.50 3.00
   Nos. 986-989 (4) 10.50 5.00
5th European Wrestling Championships, Istanbul, June 3-5, 1949.

Ancient Galley A186

Galleon Mahmudiye A187   Monument to Khizr Barbarossa A188

Designs: 15k, Cruiser Hamidiye. 20k, Submarine Sakarya. 30k, Cruiser Yavuz.

1949, July 1
990 A186 5k violet .75 .50
991 A187 10k brown .75 .50
992 A186 15k lilac rose .75 .50
993 A186 20k gray blue 1.75 .90
994 A186 30k gray 1.00 .50
995 A188 40k olive green 3.50 1.75
   Nos. 990-995 (6) 8.50 4.65
Fleet Day, July 1, 1949.

A189

UPU Monument, Bern A190

Perf. 11½
1949, Oct. 9   **Unwmk.**   **Photo.**
996 A189 15k violet .50 .25
997 A189 20k blue .50 .25
998 A190 30k dull rose .50 .25
999 A190 40k green 1.00 .50
   Nos. 996-999 (4) 2.50 1.25
UPU, 75th anniversary.

Istanbul Fair Building A191

1949, Oct. 1   **Litho.**   **Perf. 10**
1000 A191 15k brown .50 .25
1001 A191 20k blue .50 .25
1002 A191 30k olive .60 .50
   Nos. 1000-1002 (3) 1.60 1.00
Istanbul Fair, Oct. 1-31.

Boy and Girl and Globe — A192   Aged Woman Casting Ballot — A193

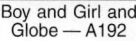
Kemal Atatürk and Map A194

1950, Aug. 13   **Perf. 11½**
1003 A192 15k purple .20 .20
1004 A192 20k deep blue .30 .30
2nd World Youth Council Meeting, 1950. No. 1004 exists imperf. Value $3.

1950, Aug. 30
1005 A193 15k dark brown .25 .25
1006 A193 20k dark blue .25 .25
1007 A194 30k dk blue & gray .50 .50
   Nos. 1005-1007 (3) 1.00 1.00
Election of May 14, 1950.

Hazel
Nuts — A195

Symbolical of
1950
Census — A196

Designs: 12k, Acorns. 15k, Cotton. 20k,
Symbolical of the fair. 30k, Tobacco.

1950, Sept. 9
1008	A195	8k gray grn & buff	.50	.50
1009	A195	12k magenta	1.00	1.00
1010	A195	15k brn blk & lt brn	.50	.50
1011	A195	20k dk blue & aqua	1.50	1.50
1012	A195	30k brn blk & dull org	1.50	1.50
		Nos. 1008-1012 (5)	5.00	5.00

Izmir International Fair, Aug. 20-Sept. 20.

1950, Oct. 9   Litho.   Perf. 11½
1013	A196	15k dark brown	.20	.20
1014	A196	20k violet blue	.30	.20

General census of 1950.

Atatürk Types of 1931-42
Perf. 10x11½, 11½x12
1950-51				**Typo.**
1015	A77	10p dull red brn	.20	.20
1016	A77	10p vermilion ('51)	.35	.50
1017	A77	20p blue green	1.00	.25
1018	A78	1k olive green	.25	.20
1019	A78	2k plum	.25	.20
1020	A78	2k dp yellow ('51)	.75	.30
1021	A78	3k yellow orange	.55	.20
1022	A78	3k gray ('51)	.75	.20
1023	A78	4k green ('51)	.75	.20
1024	A78	5k blue	.50	.20
1025	A78	5k plum ('51)	3.50	.30
1026	A77	10k brown orange	1.00	.20
1027	A77	15k purple	1.25	.20
1028	A77	15k brown carmine	12.00	.25
1029	A77	20k dark blue	20.00	.25
1030	A77	30k pink ('51)	17.00	.50
1031	A79	100k red brown ('51)	2.50	.50
1032	A79	200k dark brown	10.00	1.00
1033	A79	200k rose violet ('51)	10.00	1.50
		Nos. 1015-1033 (19)	83.10	7.15

16th Century Flight
of Hezarfen Ahmet
Celebi — A197

Plane over
Istanbul
A198

40k, Biplane over Taurus Mountains.

1950, Oct. 17   Litho.   Perf. 11
1034	A197	20k dk green & blue	.50	.35
1035	A197	40k dk brown & blue	.75	.75
1036	A198	60k purple & blue	1.25	.90
		Nos. 1034-1036 (3)	2.50	2.00

Regional meeting of the ICAO, Istanbul,
Oct. 17.

Farabi
A199

1950, Dec. 1   Unwmk.   Perf. 11½
Multicolored Center
1037	A199	15k blue	.50	.50
1038	A199	20k blue violet	.50	.50
1039	A199	60k red brown	3.00	2.00
1040	A199	1 l gold & bl vio	3.50	3.00
		Nos. 1037-1040 (4)	7.50	6.00

Death millenary of Farabi, Arab philosopher.

Mithat Pasha and Security Bank
Building — A200

Design: 20k, Agricultural Bank.

1950, Dec. 21   Photo.
1041	A200	15k rose violet	1.00	1.00
1042	A200	20k blue	1.00	1.00

3rd Congress of Turkish Cooperatives,
Istanbul, Dec. 25, 1950.

Floating a
Ship
A201

Lighthouse — A202

1951, July 1
1043	A201	15k shown	.50	.50
1044	A201	20k Steamship	.50	.50
1045	A201	30k Diver rising	1.00	1.00
1046	A202	1 l shown	2.00	2.00
		Nos. 1043-1046 (4)	4.00	4.00

25th anniv. of the recognition of coastal
rights in Turkish waters to ships under the
Turkish flag.

Mosque of
Sultan
Ahmed
A203

Henry Carton de
Wiart — A204

Designs: 20k, Dolma Bahce Palace. 60k,
Rumeli Hisari Fortress.

1951, Aug. 31   Photo.   Perf. 13½
1047	A203	15k dark green	.25	.25
1048	A203	20k deep ultra	.30	.30
1049	A204	30k brown	.35	.35
1050	A203	60k purple brown	1.75	1.75
		Nos. 1047-1050 (4)	2.65	2.65

40th Interparliamentary Conf., Istanbul.

Allegory of
Food and
Agriculture
A205

Designs: 20k, Dam. 30k, United Nations
Building. 60k, University, Ankara.

1952, Jan. 3   Unwmk.   Perf. 14
**Inscribed: "Akdeniz Yetistirme
Merkezi. Ankara 1951."**
1051	A205	15k green	.75	.50
1052	A205	20k blue violet	.90	.60
1053	A205	30k blue	2.00	1.50
1054	A205	60k red	3.00	2.50
a.		Souvenir sheet of 4	75.00	75.00
		Nos. 1051-1054 (4)	6.65	5.10

UN Mediterranean Economic Instruction
Center.
No. 1054a contains one each of Nos. 1051-
1054, imperf., with inscriptions in dark blue
gray.

Abdulhak Hamid
Tarhan, Poet,
Birth
Cent. — A206

1952, Feb. 5   Photo.   Perf. 13½
1055	A206	15k dark purple	.50	.50
1056	A206	20k dark blue	.50	.50
1057	A206	30k brown	.50	.50
1058	A206	60k dark olive grn	1.75	1.75
		Nos. 1055-1058 (4)	3.25	3.25

Ruins, Bergama
A207

Tarsus Cataract
A208

Designs: 2k, Ruins, Milas. 3k, Karatay Gate,
Konya. 4k, Kozak plateau. 5k, Urgup. 10k,
12k, 15k, 20k, Kemal Ataturk. 30k, Mosque,
Bursa. 40k, Mosque, Istanbul. 75k, Rocks,
Urgup. 1 l, Palace, Istanbul. 2 l, Pavilion, Istan-
bul. 5 l, Museum interior, Istanbul.

1952, Mar. 15   Perf. 13½
1059	A207	1k brown orange	.20	.20
1060	A207	2k olive green	.20	.20
1061	A207	3k rose brown	.20	.20
1062	A207	4k blue green	.50	.50
1063	A207	5k brown	.20	.20
1064	A207	10k dark brown	.50	.50
1065	A207	12k brt rose car	.50	.50
1066	A207	15k purple	.25	.20
1067	A207	20k chalky blue	.75	.20
1068	A207	30k grnsh gray	.50	.20
1069	A207	40k slate blue	3.50	.20
1070	A208	50k olive	.50	.20
1071	A208	75k slate	.50	.25
1072	A208	1 l deep purple	.50	.20
1073	A208	2 l brt ultra	2.00	.30
1074	A208	5 l sepia	30.00	7.50
		Nos. 1059-1074 (16)	40.50	11.25

Imperfs, value, set $75.
For surcharge & overprint see #1075, 1255.

No. 1059 Surcharged with New Value
in Black

1952, June 1
1075	A207	0.50k on 1k brn org	.25	.20

Technical
Faculty
Building
A209

1952, Aug. 20   Perf. 12x12½
1076	A209	15k violet	.50	.50
1077	A209	20k blue	.75	.75
1078	A209	60k brown	1.25	1.25
		Nos. 1076-1078 (3)	2.50	2.50

8th Intl. Congress of Theoretic and Applied
Mechanics.

Turkish
Soldier — A210

Pigeons
Bandaging
Wounded
Hand — A212

20k, Soldier with Turkish flag. 30k, Soldier &
child with comic book. 60k, Raising Turkish
flag.

1952, Sept. 25   Perf. 14
1079	A210	15k Prus blue	.30	.30
1080	A210	20k deep blue	.40	.40
1081	A210	30k brown	.60	.60
1082	A210	60k olive blk & car	1.25	1.25
		Nos. 1079-1082 (4)	2.55	2.55

Turkey's participation in the Korean war.

1952, Oct. 29   Perf. 12½x12

20k, Flag, rainbow and ruined homes.

Dated "1877-1952"
1085	A212	15k dk green & red	.55	.25
1086	A212	20k blue & red	1.25	.45

Turkish Red Crescent Society, 75th anniv.

Relief From Panel
of Aziziye
Monument — A213

Aziziye
Monument
A214

Design: 40k, View of Erzerum.

1952, Nov. 9   Perf. 11
1087	A213	15k purple	.30	.30
1088	A214	20k blue	.50	.50
1089	A214	40k olive gray	.70	.70
		Nos. 1087-1089 (3)	1.50	1.50

75th anniv. of the Battle of Aziziye at
Erzerum.

Rumeli Hisari Fortress A215

Troops Entering Constantinople — A216

Sultan Mohammed II — A217

Designs: 8k, Soldiers moving cannon. 10k, Mohammed II riding into sea, and Turkish armada. 12k, Landing of Turkish army. 15k, Ancient wall, Constantinople. 30k, Mosque of Faith. 40k, Presenting mace to Patriarch Yenadios. 60k, Map of Constantinople, c. 1574. 1 l, Tomb of Mohammed II. 2.50 l, Portrait of Mohammed II.

1953, May 29   Photo.   Perf. 11½
Inscribed: "Istanbulun Fethi 1453-1953"

1090	A215	5k brt blue	1.00	.50
1091	A215	8k gray	1.50	.50
1092	A215	10k blue	.50	.50
1093	A215	12k rose lilac	1.00	.50
1094	A215	15k brown	.75	.25
1095	A216	20k vermilion	1.00	.25
1096	A216	30k dull green	2.00	1.00
1097	A215	40k violet blue	3.50	1.25
1098	A215	60k chocolate	2.50	1.25
1099	A215	1 l blue green	6.00	1.75

Perf. 12

1100	A217	2 l multi	12.50	5.00
1101	A217	2.50 l multi	7.50	7.50
a.		Souvenir sheet	150.00	75.00
		Nos. 1090-1101 (12)	39.75	20.25

Conquest of Constantinople by Sultan Mohammed II, 500th anniv.

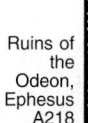

Ruins of the Odeon, Ephesus A218

15k, Church of St. John the Apostle. 20k, Shrine of Virgin Mary, Panaya Kapulu. 40k, Ruins of the Double Church. 60k, Shrine of the Seven Sleepers. 1 l, Restored house of the Virgin Mary.

1953, Aug. 16   Litho.   Perf. 13½
Multicolored Center

1102	A218	12k sage green	.25	.25
1103	A218	15k lilac	.20	.20
1104	A218	20k dk slate blue	.25	.25
1105	A218	40k light green	.55	.55
1106	A218	60k violet blue	.75	.75
1107	A218	1 l brown red	2.25	2.25
		Nos. 1102-1107 (6)	4.25	4.25

Pres. Celal Bayar, Mithat Pasha. Herman Schulze-Delitzsch and People's Bank — A219

Design: 20k, Pres. Bayar, Mithat Pasha and University of Ankara.

1953, Sept. 2   Photo.   Perf. 10½

1108	A219	15k orange brown	.50	.50
1109	A219	20k Prus green	.50	.50

5th Intl. People's Circuit Congress, Istanbul, Sept.

Combined Harvester A220

Kemal Atatürk — A221

Designs: 15k, Berdan dam. 20k, Military parade. 30k, Diesel train. 35k, Yesilkoy airport.

1953, Oct. 29   Perf. 14

1110	A220	10k olive bister	.20	.20
1111	A220	15k dark gray	.20	.20
1112	A220	20k rose red	.35	.35
1113	A220	30k olive green	.75	.75
1114	A220	35k dull blue	.35	.35
1115	A221	55k dull purple	1.10	1.10
		Nos. 1110-1115 (6)	2.95	2.95

Turkish Republic, 30th anniv.

Kemal Atatürk and Mausoleum at Ankara — A222

1953, Nov. 10

1116	A222	15k gray black	.50	.25
1117	A222	20k violet brown	.75	.40

15th death anniv. of Kemal Atatürk.

Type of 1931-42
Without umlaut over first "U" of "CUMHURIYETI"
Perf. 11½x12, 10x11½

1953-56   Typo.   Unwmk.

1117B	A77	20p yellow	.30	.20
1118	A78	1k brown orange	.30	.20
1119	A78	2k rose pink ('53)	.25	.20
1120	A78	3k yellow brn ('53)	.25	.20
1120A	A78	4k slate ('56)	1.50	.40
1121	A78	5k blue	2.00	.20
1121A	A78	8k violet ('56)	.25	.20
1122	A77	10k dark olive ('53)	.25	.20
1123	A77	12k brt car rose ('53)	.25	.20
1124	A77	15k fawn	.60	.20
1125	A77	20k rose lilac	3.50	.40
1126	A77	30k lt blue grn ('54)	1.25	.20
		Nos. 1117B-1126 (12)	10.70	2.80

Compass and Map A223

Designs: 20k, Globe, crescent and stars. 40k, Tree symbolical of 14 NATO members.

1954, Apr. 4   Photo.   Perf. 14

1127	A223	15k brown	1.50	1.10
1128	A223	20k violet blue	2.00	1.50
1129	A223	40k dark green	14.00	12.00
		Nos. 1127-1129 (3)	17.50	14.60

NATO, 5th anniv.

Industry, Engineering and Agriculture — A224

Justice and Council of Europe Flag — A225

1954, Aug. 8   Litho.   Perf. 10½

1130	A224	10k brown	2.75	2.00
1131	A225	15k dark green	2.50	1.00
1132	A225	20k blue	2.75	1.00
1133	A224	30k brt violet	12.00	8.50
		Nos. 1130-1133 (4)	20.00	12.50

Council of Europe, 5th anniv.

Flag Signals to Plane — A226

Amaury de La Grange and Plane A227

Design: 45k, Kemal Ataturk and air fleet.

1954, Sept. 20   Perf. 12½

1134	A226	20k black brown	.20	.20
1135	A227	35k dull violet	.25	.20
1136	A227	45k deep blue	.45	.30
		Nos. 1134-1136 (3)	.90	.70

47th Congress of the Intl. Aeronautical Federation, Istanbul, 1954.

Souvenir Sheet

A228

1954, Oct. 18   Imperf.

1137	A228	Sheet of 3	12.50	5.50
a.		20k aquamarine	.65	.65
b.		30k violet blue	.65	.65
c.		1 l red violet	1.40	1.40

First anniv. of Law of Oct. 17, 1953, reorganizing the Department of Post, Telephone and Telegraph.

Ziya Gokalp A229

Kemal Atatürk A230

1954, Oct. 25   Perf. 11

1138	A229	15k rose lilac	.25	.20
1139	A229	20k dark green	.35	.20
1140	A229	30k crimson	.60	.35
		Nos. 1138-1140 (3)	1.20	.75

30th death anniv. of Ziya Gokalp, author and historian.

1955, Mar. 1   Perf. 12½

1141	A230	15k carmine rose	.20	.20
1142	A230	20k blue	.20	.20
1143	A230	40k dark gray	.30	.20
1144	A230	50k blue green	.55	.20
1145	A230	75k orange brown	.65	.20
		Nos. 1141-1145 (5)	1.90	1.00

Relief Map of Dardanelles — A231

Artillery Loaders — A232

30k, Minelayer Nusrat. 60k, Col. Kemal Atatürk.

1955, Mar. 18   Perf. 10½

1146	A231	15k green	.20	.20
1147	A232	20k orange brown	.20	.20
1148	A231	30k ultra	.25	.20
1149	A232	60k olive gray	.80	.40
		Nos. 1146-1149 (4)	1.45	1.00

Battle of Gallipoli, 40th anniversary.

Aerial Map A233

1955, Apr. 14   Perf. 11

1150	A233	15k gray	.30	.20
1151	A233	20k aquamarine	.30	.20
1152	A233	50k brown	.50	.20
1153	A233	1 l purple	.95	.40
		Nos. 1150-1153 (4)	2.05	1.00

City Planning Congress, Ankara, 1955.

Carnation — A234

1955, May 19   Litho.   Perf. 10
1154 A234 10k shown   .50   .50
1155 A234 15k Tulip   .50   .50
1156 A234 20k Rose   .75   .50
1157 A234 50k Lily   1.75 1.00
      Nos. 1154-1157 (4)   3.50 2.50
National Flower Show, Istanbul, May 20-
Aug. 20.

Battle First
Aid Station
A235

30k, Gulhane Military Hospital, Ankara.

1955, Aug. 28   Unwmk.   Perf. 12
1158 A235 20k red, lake & gray   .40   .20
1159 A235 30k dp grn & yel grn   .60   .25
XVIII Intl. Congress of Military Medicine,
Aug. 8-Sept. 1, Istanbul.

Soccer
Game
A236

Emblem and Soccer
Ball — A237

1 l, Emblem with oak & olive branches.

1955, Aug. 30   Perf. 10
1160 A236 15k light ultra   .50   .20
1161 A237 20k crimson rose   .60   .20
1162 A236   1 l light green   1.25   .75
      Nos. 1160-1162 (3)   2.35 1.15
Intl. Military Soccer Championship games,
Istanbul, Aug. 30.

Sureté
Monument,
Ankara
A238

20k, Dolma Bahce Palace. 30k, Police College, Ankara. 45k, Police Martyrs' Monument,
Istanbul.

1955, Sept. 5   Perf. 10
Inscribed: "Enterpol Istanbul 1955"
1163 A238 15k blue green   .25   .25
1164 A238 20k brt violet   .35   .35
1165 A238 30k gray black   .40   .30
1166 A238 45k lt brown   .80   .50
      Nos. 1163-1166 (4)   1.80 1.40
24th general assembly of the Intl. Criminal
Police, Istanbul, Sept. 5-9.

Early
Telegraph
Transmitter
A239

Modern
Transmitter
A240

Perf. 13½x14, 14x13½
1955, Sept. 10   Photo.
1167 A239 15k olive   .20   .20
1168 A240 20k crimson rose   .20   .20
1169 A239 45k fawn   .40   .20
1170 A240 60k ultra   .40   .40
      Nos. 1167-1170 (4)   1.20 1.00
Centenary of telecommunication.

Academy of
Science,
Istanbul
A241

Designs: 20k, University. 60k, Hilton Hotel.
1 l, Kiz Kulesi (Leander's Tower).

1955, Sept. 12   Perf. 13½x14
1171 A241 15k yellow orange   .25   .25
1172 A241 20k crimson rose   .25   .25
1173 A241 60k purple   .35   .25
1174 A241   1 l deep blue   .65   .45
      Nos. 1171-1174 (4)   1.50 1.20
10th meeting of the governors of the Intl.
Bank of Reconstruction and Development and
the Intl. Monetary Fund, Istanbul, Sept. 12-16.

Surlari,
Istanbul
A242

Mosque of   Congress
Sultan   Emblem — A244
Ahmed — A243

Designs: 30k, Haghia Sophia. 75k, Map of
Constantinople, by Christoforo Buondel-
monti, 1422.

1955, Sept. 15   Litho.   Perf. 11½
1175 A242 15k grnsh blk & Prus
                 grn   .35   .20
1176 A243 20k vermilion & org   .25   .20
1177 A242 30k sepia & vio brn   .25   .20
1178 A243 75k ultramarine   .70   .50
      Nos. 1175-1178 (4)   1.55 1.10
10th Intl. Congress of Byzantine Research,
Istanbul, Sept. 15-21, 1955.

1955, Sept. 26   Perf. 10½x11
30k, Chalet in Istanbul. 55k, Bridges.
**Inscribed: "Beynelmiel X. Vol
Kongresi Istanbul 1955"**
1179 A244 20k red violet   .20   .20
1180 A244 30k dk grn & yel grn   .20   .20
1181 A244 55k dp bl & brt bl   .75   .40
      Nos. 1179-1181 (3)   1.15   .80
10th International Transportation Congress.

Map of
Turkey,
Showing
Population
Increase
A245

1955, Oct. 22   Unwmk.   Perf. 10
Map in Rose
1182 A245 15k lt & dk gray & red   .35   .25
1183 A245 20k lt & dk vio & red   .25   .25
1184 A245 30k lt & dk ultra & red   .30   .25
1185 A245 60k lt & dk bl grn &
                 red   .70   .30
      Nos. 1182-1185 (4)   1.60 1.05
Census of 1955.

Waterfall,
Antalya — A246

Alanya and
Seljukide
Dockyards
A247

Designs: 30k, Theater at Aspendos. 45k,
Ruins at Side. 50k, View of Antalya. 65k, St.
Nicholas Church at Myra (Demre) and St.
Nicholas.

Perf. 14x13½, 13½x14
1955, Dec. 10   Photo.   Unwmk.
1186 A246 18k bl, ol grn & ultra   .25   .25
1187 A247 20k blue, ultra & brn   .25   .25
1188 A247 30k dl grn, ol bis &
                 grn   .25   .25
1189 A246 45k yel grn & brn   2.25 1.00
1190 A246 50k Prus grn & ol bis   .40   .30
1191 A247 65k orange ver & blk   .50   .40
      Nos. 1186-1191 (6)   3.90 2.45

Kemal Atatürk — A248

1955-56   Litho.   Perf. 12½
1192 A248 0.50k carmine   .20   .20
1193 A248   1k yellow orange   .20   .20
1194 A248   2k brt blue   .20   .20
1195 A248   3k scarlet   .20   .20
1196 A248   5k lt brown   .20   .20
1197 A248   6k lt blue grn   .20   .20
1198 A248 10k blue green   .20   .20
1199 A248 18k rose violet   .20   .20
1200 A248 20k lt violet bl   .25   .20
1201 A248 25k olive green   .30   .20
1202 A248 30k violet   .35   .20
1203 A248 40k fawn   .45   .20
1204 A248 75k slate blue   1.25   .20
      Nos. 1192-1204 (13)   4.20 2.60
Issue dates: 3k, 1955. Others, 1956.

Tomb at   Zubeyde
Nigde — A249   Hanum — A250

1956, Apr. 12   Perf. 10½
1205 A249 40k violet bl & bl   .20   .20
25th anniv. of the Turkish History Society.
The tomb of Hüdavent Hatun, a sultan's
daughter, exemplifies Seljukian architecture of
the 14th century.

1956, May 13   Perf. 11
1206 A250 20k pale brn & dk brn   .25   .25
Imperf
1207 A250 20k lt grn & dk grn   .75 1.50
Mother's Day; Zubeyde Hanum, mother of
Kemal Ataturk.

Shah
and
Queen
of Iran
A251

1956, May 15   Unwmk.   Perf. 11
1208 A251 100k grn & pale grn   1.00 1.00
Imperf
1209 A251 100k red & pale grn   8.50 6.00
Visit of the Shah and Queen of Iran to Turkey, May 15.

Erenkoy
Sanitarium
A252

1956, July 31   Perf. 11
1210 A252 50k dk bl grn & pink   .40   .20
Anti-Tuberculosis work among PTT
employees.

Symbol of Izmir
Fair — A253

A254

1956, Aug. 20   Perf. 11
1211 A253 45k brt green   .20   .20
Souvenir Sheet
Imperf
1212 A254 Sheet of 2   3.00 3.00
  a.   50k rose red   .75   .40
  b.   50k bright ultramarine   .75   .40
25th Intl. Fair, Izmir, 8/20-9/20. See #C28.

Hands Holding
Bottled
Serpent — A255

1956, Sept. 10   Litho.   Perf. 10½
1213 A255 25k multicolored   .30   .30
  a.   Tete beche pair   1.25
25th Intl. Anti-Alcoholism Congress, Istanbul
Sept. 10-15.
Printed both in regular sheets and in sheets
with alternate vertical rows inverted.

Medical Center at Kayseri — A256

Sariyar Dam — A257

1956, Nov. 1   **Perf. 12½x12**
1214 A256 60k violet & yel   .20 .20

750th anniv. of the first medical school and clinic in Anatolia.

1956, Dec. 2   **Litho.**   **Perf. 10½**
1215 A257 20k vermilion   .20 .20
1216 A257 20k bright blue   .20 .20

Inauguration of Sariyar Dam.

Freestyle Wrestling A258

Mehmet Akif Ersoy — A259

Design: 65k, Greco-Roman wrestling.

1956, Dec. 8   **Unwmk.**   **Perf. 10½**
1217 A258 40k brt yel grn & brn   .50 .35
1218 A258 65k lt bluish gray & dp car   .50 .35

16th Olympic Games, Melbourne, Nov. 22-Dec. 8, 1956.

1956, Dec. 26
1219 A259 20k brn & brt yel grn   .25 .20
1220 A259 20k rose car & lt gray   .25 .20
1221 A259 20k vio bl & brt pink   .25 .20
    Nos. 1219-1221 (3)   .75 .60

20th death anniv. of Mehmet Akif Ersoy, author of the Turkish National Anthem. Each value bears a different verse of the anthem.

Theater in Troy — A260

Trojan Vase — A261

Design: 30k, Trojan Horse.

    Perf. 13½x14, 14x13½
1956, Dec. 31   **Photo.**   **Unwmk.**
1222 A260 15k green   1.00 .60
1223 A261 20k red violet   1.00 .60
1224 A260 30k chestnut   1.50 .60
    Nos. 1222-1224 (3)   3.50 1.80

Excavations at Troy.

Mobile Chest X-Ray Unit A262

Kemal Atatürk — A263

1957, Jan. 1   **Litho.**   **Perf. 12**
1225 A262 25k ol brn & red   .20 .20

Fight against tuberculsois.

1956-57   **Perf. 12½**
1226 A263 ½k blue green   .20 .20
1227 A263 1k yellow orange   .20 .20
1228 A263 3k gray olive   .20 .20
1229 A263 5k violet   .20 .20
1230 A263 6k rose car ('57)   .35 .20
1231 A263 10k rose violet   .20 .20
1232 A263 12k fawn ('57)   .30 .20
1233 A263 15k lt violet bl   .20 .20
1234 A263 18k carmine ('57)   .30 .20
1235 A263 20k lt brown   .20 .20
1236 A263 25k lt blue green   .20 .20
1237 A263 30k slate blue   .20 .20
1238 A263 40k olive ('57)   .40 .20
1239 A263 50k orange   .35 .20
1240 A263 60k brt blue ('57)   .50 .20
1241 A263 70k Prus green ('57)   1.75 .20
1242 A263 75k brown   1.00 .25
    Nos. 1226-1242 (17)   6.75 3.50

Pres. Heuss of Germany — A264

1957, May 5   **Unwmk.**   **Perf. 10½**
1243 A264 40k yellow & brown   .20 .20

Visit of Pres. Theodor Heuss of Germany to Turkey, May 5. See No. C29.

View of Bergama and Ruin A265

40k, Dancers in kermis at Bergama.

1957, May 24
1244 A265 30k brown   .20 .20
1245 A265 40k green   .20 .20

20th anniv. of the kermis at Bergama (Pergamus).

Symbols of Industry and Flags A266

1957, July 1   **Photo.**   **Perf. 13½x14**
1246 A266 25k violet   .20 .20
1247 A266 40k gray blue   .20 .20

Turkish-American collaboration, 10th anniv.

Osman Hamdi Bey A267

Hittite Sun Course from Alaça Höyük — A268

1957, July 6   **Perf. 10½**
1248 A267 20k beige, pale brn & blk   .30 .20
1249 A268 30k Prussian green   .35 .20

75th anniv. of the Academy of Art. The 20k exists with "cancellation" omitted.

King of Afghanistan — A269

1957, Sept. 1   **Litho.**   **Perf. 10½**
1250 A269 45k car lake & pink   .20 .20

Visit of Mohammed Zahir Shah, King of Afghanistan, to Turkey. See No. C30.

Medical Center, Amasya A270

Design: 65k, Suleiman Medical Center.

1957, Sept. 29   **Unwmk.**   **Perf. 10½**
1251 A270 25k vermilion & yellow   .20 .20
1252 A270 65k brt grnsh bl & citron   .30 .20

11th general meeting of the World Medical Assoc.

Mosque of Suleiman A271

Architect Mimar Koca Sinan (1489-1587) A272

1957, Oct. 18   **Perf. 11**
1253 A271 20k gray green   .20 .20
1254 A272 100k brown   .30 .25

400th anniv. of the opening of the Mosque of Suleiman, Istanbul.

No. 1073 Surcharged with New Value and "ISTANBUL Filatelik n. Sergisi 1957"

1957, Nov. 11   **Photo.**   **Perf. 13½**
1255 A208 50k on 2 l brt ultra   .25 .20

1957 Istanbul Philatelic Exhibition.

Forestation Map of Turkey — A273

25k, Forest & hand planting tree, vert.

1957, Nov. 18   **Litho.**   **Perf. 10½**
1256 A273 20k green & brown   .20 .20
1257 A273 25k emerald & bl grn   .20 .20

Centenary of forestry in Turkey. Nos. 1256-1257 each come with two different tabs attached (four tabs in all) bearing various quotations.

A274

A275

1957, Nov. 23
1258 A274 50k pink, vio, red & yel   .50 .25

400th death anniv. of Fuzuli (Mehmet Suleiman Ogiou), poet.

1957, Nov. 28   **Photo.**   **Perf. 14x13½**
1259 A275 65k dk Prus blue   .20 .20
1260 A275 65k rose violet   .20 .20

Benjamin Franklin (1706-1790).

Green Dome, Tomb of Mevlana, at Konya — A276

Mevlana — A278

Konya Museum A277

    Perf. 11x10½, 10½x11
1957, Dec. 17   **Litho.**   **Unwmk.**
1261 A276 50k green, bl & vio   .20 .20
1262 A277 100k dark blue   .30 .20

Miniature Sheet
Imperf

1263 A278 100k multicolored   1.25 1.00

Jalal-udin Mevlana (1207-1273), Persian poet and founder of the Mevlevie dervish order. No. 1263 contains one stamp 32x42mm.

Kemal Atatürk (Double Frame; Serifs) — A279

1957   Unwmk.   Perf. 11½
Size: 18x22mm

1264	A279	½k lt brown	.20	.20
1265	A279	1k lt violet bl	.20	.20
1266	A279	2k black violet	.20	.20
1267	A279	3k orange	.20	.20
1268	A279	5k blue green	.20	.20
1269	A279	6k dk slate grn	.20	.20
1270	A279	10k violet	.20	.20
1271	A279	12k brt green	.20	.20
1272	A279	15k dk blue grn	.20	.20
1273	A279	18k rose carmine	.20	.20
1274	A279	20k brown	.20	.20
1275	A279	25k brown red	.20	.20
1276	A279	30k brt blue	.20	.20
1277	A279	40k slate blue	.20	.20
1278	A279	50k yellow orange	.20	.20
1279	A279	60k black	.25	.20
1280	A279	70k rose violet	.25	.20
1281	A279	75k gray olive	.30	.20

Size: 21x29mm

1282	A279	100k carmine	.65	.20
1283	A279	250k olive	1.75	.20
		Nos. 1264-1283 (20)	6.20	4.00

College Emblem — A280   View of Adana — A281

1958, Jan. 16   Litho.   Perf. 10½x11
1288	A280	20k bister, ind & org	.20	.20
1289	A280	25k dk blue, bis & org	.20	.20

"Turkiye" on top of 25k. 75th anniv. of the College of Economics and Commerce, Istanbul.

1958   Photo.   Perf. 11½
Size: 26x20½mm

1290	A281	5k Adana	.20	.20
1291	A281	5k Adapazari	.20	.20
1292	A281	5k Adiyaman	.20	.20
1293	A281	5k Afyon	.20	.20
1294	A281	5k Amasya	.20	.20
1295	A281	5k Ankara	.20	.20
1296	A281	5k Antakya	.20	.20
1297	A281	5k Antalya	.20	.20
1298	A281	5k Artvin	.20	.20
1299	A281	5k Aydin	.20	.20
1300	A281	5k Balikesir	.20	.20
1301	A281	5k Bilecik	.20	.20
1302	A281	5k Bingol	.20	.20
1303	A281	5k Bitlis	.20	.20
1304	A281	5k Bolu	.20	.20
1305	A281	5k Burdur	.20	.20
1306	A281	5k Bursa	.20	.20
1307	A281	5k Canakkale	.20	.20
1308	A281	5k Cankiri	.20	.20
1309	A281	5k Corum	.20	.20
1310	A281	5k Denizli	.20	.20
1311	A281	5k Diyarbakir	.20	.20

Size: 32½x22mm

1312	A281	20k Adana	.20	.20
1313	A281	20k Adapazari	.20	.20
1314	A281	20k Adiyaman	.20	.20
1315	A281	20k Afyon	.20	.20
1316	A281	20k Amasya	.20	.20
1317	A281	20k Ankara	.20	.20
1318	A281	20k Antakya	.20	.20
1319	A281	20k Antalya	.20	.20
1320	A281	20k Artvin	.20	.20
1321	A281	20k Aydin	.20	.20
1322	A281	20k Balikesir	.20	.20
1323	A281	20k Bilecik	.20	.20
1324	A281	20k Bingol	.20	.20
1325	A281	20k Bitlis	.20	.20
1326	A281	20k Bolu	.20	.20
1327	A281	20k Burdur	.20	.20
1328	A281	20k Bursa	.20	.20
1329	A281	20k Canakkale	.20	.20
1330	A281	20k Cankiri	.20	.20
1331	A281	20k Corum	.20	.20
1332	A281	20k Denizli	.20	.20
1333	A281	20k Diyarbakir	.20	.20
		Nos. 1290-1333 (44)	8.80	8.80

1959
Size: 26x20½mm

1334	A281	5k Edirne	.20	.20
1335	A281	5k Elazig	.20	.20
1336	A281	5k Erzincan	.20	.20
1337	A281	5k Erzurum	.20	.20
1338	A281	5k Eskisehir	.20	.20
1339	A281	5k Gaziantep	.20	.20
1340	A281	5k Giresun	.20	.20
1341	A281	5k Gumusane	.20	.20
1342	A281	5k Hakkari	.20	.20
1343	A281	5k Isparta	.20	.20
1344	A281	5k Istanbul	.20	.20
1345	A281	5k Izmir	.20	.20
1346	A281	5k Izmit	.20	.20
1347	A281	5k Karakose	.20	.20
1348	A281	5k Kars	.20	.20
1349	A281	5k Kastamonu	.20	.20
1350	A281	5k Kayseri	.20	.20
1351	A281	5k Kirklareli	.20	.20
1352	A281	5k Kirsehir	.20	.20
1353	A281	5k Konya	.20	.20
1354	A281	5k Kutahya	.20	.20
1355	A281	5k Malatya	.20	.20

Size: 32½x22mm

1356	A281	20k Edirne	.20	.20
1357	A281	20k Elazig	.20	.20
1358	A281	20k Erzincan	.20	.20
1359	A281	20k Erzurum	.20	.20
1360	A281	20k Eskisehir	.20	.20
1361	A281	20k Gaziantep	.20	.20
1362	A281	20k Giresun	.20	.20
1363	A281	20k Gumusane	.20	.20
1364	A281	20k Hakkari	.20	.20
1365	A281	20k Isparta	.20	.20
1366	A281	20k Istanbul	.20	.20
1367	A281	20k Izmir	.20	.20
1368	A281	20k Izmit	.20	.20
1369	A281	20k Karakose	.20	.20
1370	A281	20k Kars	.20	.20
1371	A281	20k Kastamonu	.20	.20
1372	A281	20k Kayseri	.20	.20
1373	A281	20k Kirklareli	.20	.20
1374	A281	20k Kirsehir	.20	.20
1375	A281	20k Konya	.20	.20
1376	A281	20k Kutahya	.20	.20
1377	A281	20k Malatya	.20	.20
		Nos. 1334-1377 (44)	8.80	8.80

1960
Size: 26x20½mm

1378	A281	5k Manisa	.20	.20
1379	A281	5k Maras	.20	.20
1380	A281	5k Mardin	.20	.20
1381	A281	5k Mersin	.20	.20
1382	A281	5k Mugla	.20	.20
1383	A281	5k Mus	.20	.20
1384	A281	5k Nevsehir	.20	.20
1385	A281	5k Nigde	.20	.20
1386	A281	5k Ordu	.20	.20
1387	A281	5k Rize	.20	.20
1388	A281	5k Samsun	.20	.20
1389	A281	5k Siirt	.20	.20
1390	A281	5k Sinop	.20	.20
1391	A281	5k Sivas	.20	.20
1392	A281	5k Tekirdag	.20	.20
1393	A281	5k Tokat	.20	.20
1394	A281	5k Trabzon	.20	.20
1395	A281	5k Tunceli	.20	.20
1396	A281	5k Urfa	.20	.20
1397	A281	5k Usak	.20	.20
1398	A281	5k Van	.20	.20
1399	A281	5k Yozgat	.20	.20
1400	A281	5k Zonguldak	.20	.20

Size: 32½x22mm

1401	A281	20k Manisa	.20	.20
1402	A281	20k Maras	.20	.20
1403	A281	20k Mardin	.20	.20
1404	A281	20k Mersin	.20	.20
1405	A281	20k Mugla	.20	.20
1406	A281	20k Mus	.20	.20
1407	A281	20k Nevsehir	.20	.20
1408	A281	20k Nigde	.20	.20
1409	A281	20k Ordu	.20	.20
1410	A281	20k Rize	.20	.20
1411	A281	20k Samsun	.20	.20
1412	A281	20k Siirt	.20	.20
1413	A281	20k Sinop	.20	.20
1414	A281	20k Sivas	.20	.20
1415	A281	20k Tekirdag	.20	.20
1416	A281	20k Tokat	.20	.20
1417	A281	20k Trabzon	.20	.20
1418	A281	20k Tunceli	.20	.20
1419	A281	20k Urfa	.20	.20
1420	A281	20k Usak	.20	.20
1421	A281	20k Van	.20	.20
1422	A281	20k Yozgat	.20	.20
1423	A281	20k Zonguldak	.20	.20
		Nos. 1378-1423 (46)	9.20	9.20
		Nos. 1290-1423 (134)	26.80	26.80

Ruins at Pamukkale A282

Designs: 25k, Travertines at Pamukkale.

1958, May 18   Litho.   Perf. 12
1424	A282	20k brown	.20	.20
1425	A282	25k blue	.20	.20

"Industry" A283   Symbolizing New Europe A284

1958, Oct. 10   Unwmk.   Perf. 10½
1426	A283	40k slate blue	.20	.20

National Industry Exhibition.

Europa Issue
1958, Oct. 10
1427	A284	25k vio & dull pink	.50	.25
1428	A284	40k brt ultra	.50	.25

Letters A285

1958, Oct. 5
1429	A285	20k orange & blk	.20	.20

Intl. Letter Writing Week, Oct. 5-11.

Atatürk 20th Anniv. Death — A286

1958, Nov. 10   Perf. 12
1430	A286	25k Flame and mausoleum	.20	.20
1431	A286	75k Atatürk	.25	.20
a.	A286	Pair, #1430-1431	.45	.25

20th death anniv. of Kemal Ataturk.

Emblem — A288

1959, Jan. 10   Litho.   Perf. 10
1432	A288	25k dk violet & yel	.20	.20

25th anniv. of the Agricultural Faculty of Ankara University.

Blackboard and School Emblem — A289

1959, Jan. 15   Perf. 10½
1433	A289	75k black & yellow	.20	.20

75th anniv. of the establishment of a secondary boys' school in Istanbul.

State Theater, Ankara A290

Design: 25k, Portrait of Sinasi.

1959, Mar. 30   Unwmk.   Perf. 10½
1434	A290	20k red brn & emer	.20	.20
1435	A290	25k Prus grn & org	.20	.20

Centenary of the Turkish theater; Sinasi, writer of the first Turkish play in 1859.

Globe and Stars A291

1959, Apr. 4   Perf. 10
1436	A291	105k red	.20	.20
1437	A291	195k green	.40	.25

10th anniversary of NATO.

Aspendos Theater A292

1959, May 1   Litho.   Perf. 10½
1438	A292	20k bis brn & vio	.20	.20
1439	A292	20k grn & ol bis	.20	.20

Aspendos (Belkins) Festival.

No. B70 Surcharged in Ultramarine

1959, May 5
1440	SP25	105k on 15k + 5k org	.35	.20

Council of Europe, 10th anniversary.

Basketball — A293

1959, May 21   Perf. 10
1441	A293	25k red org & dk bl	.25	.20

11th European and Mediterranean Basketball Championship.

"Karadeniz"
A294

Telegraph
Mast — A295

Kemal
Atatürk — A296

Designs: 1k, Turkish Airlines' SES plane. 10k, Grain elevator, Ankara. 15k, Iron and Steel Works, Karabück. 20k, Euphrates Bridge, Birecik. 25k, Zonguldak Harbor. 30k, Gasoline refinery, Batman. 40k, Rumeli Hisari Fortress. 45k, Sugar factory, Konya. 55k, Coal mine, Zonguldak. 75k, Railway. 90k, Crane loading ships. 100k, Cement factory, Ankara. 120k, Highway. 150k, Harvester. 200k, Electric transformer.

Perf. 10½, 11, 11½, 12½, 13½
1959-60   Litho.   Unwmk.

1442	A294	1k indigo	.20	.20
1443	A294	5k brt blue ('59)	.20	.20
1444	A294	10k blue	.20	.20
1445	A294	15k brown	.50	.20
1446	A294	20k slate green	.20	.20
1447	A294	25k violet	.20	.20
1448	A294	30k lilac	.30	.25
1449	A294	40k blue	.50	.20
1450	A294	45k dull violet	.50	.20
1451	A294	55k olive brown	.50	.20
1452	A295	60k green	.65	.20
1453	A295	75k gray olive	2.50	.20
1454	A295	90k dark blue	5.50	.20
1455	A295	100k gray	7.50	.20
1456	A295	120k magenta	2.50	.25
1457	A295	150k orange	2.50	.30
1458	A295	200k yellow green	3.00	.30
1459	A296	250k black brown	3.00	.40
1460	A296	500k dark blue	5.00	.60
	Nos. 1442-1460 (19)		35.45	4.70

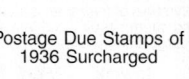

Postage Due Stamps of 1936 Surcharged

1959, June 1   Perf. 11½

1461	D6	20k on 20pa brown	.85	.20
1462	D6	20k on 2k lt blue	.25	.20
1463	D6	20k on 3k brt vio	.25	.20
1464	D6	20k on 5k Prus bl	.25	.20
1465	D6	20k on 12k brt rose	.25	.20
	Nos. 1461-1465 (5)		1.85	1.00

Anchor
Emblem — A297

Design: 40k, Sea Horse emblem.

1959, July 4   Perf. 11

1466	A297	30k multicolored	.20	.20
1467	A297	40k multicolored	.20	.20

50th anniv. of the Merchant Marine College.

11th Century Warrior A298

1959, Aug. 26   Litho.   Perf. 11

1468	A298	2½ l rose lil & lt bl	.70	.50

Battle of Malazkirt, 888th anniversary.

A299

Ornament — A300

Design: 40k, Mosque.

1959, Oct. 19   Unwmk.   Perf. 12½

1469	A299	30k black & red	.20	.20
1470	A299	40k lt blue, blk & ocher	.20	.20
1471	A300	75k dp blue, yel & red	.30	.20
	Nos. 1469-1471 (3)		.70	.60

Turkish Artists Congress, Ankara.

Kemal
Atatürk — A301

Litho.; Center Embossed
1959, Nov. 10   Perf. 14

1472	A301	500k dark blue	2.00	1.00
a.	Min. sheet of 1, red, imperf.		3.00	2.00

School of Political Science, Ankara A302

Emblem — A303

Crossed Swords Emblem — A304

1959, Dec. 4   Photo.   Perf. 13½

1473	A302	40k green & brown	.20	.20
1474	A302	40k red brown & bl	.20	.20
1475	A303	1 l lt & dk vio & buff	.30	.20
	Nos. 1473-1475 (3)		.70	.60

Political Science School, Ankara, cent.

Inscribed: "Kara Harbokulunum 125 Yili"

Design: 40k, Bayonet and flame.

1960, Feb. 28   Litho.   Perf. 10½

1476	A304	30k vermilion & org	.20	.20
1477	A304	40k brown, car & yel	.20	.20

125th anniv. of the Territorial War College.

Window on World and WRY Emblem A305

Spring Flower Festival — A306

150k, Symbolic shanties & uprooted oak emblem.

1960, Apr. 7

1478	A305	90k brt grnsh bl & blk	.20	.20
1479	A305	105k yellow & blk	.30	.20

World Refugee Year, 7/1/59-6/30/60.

1960, June 4   Photo.   Perf. 11½
Granite Paper

1480	A306	30k Carnations	.35	.20
1481	A306	40k Jasmine	.40	.20
1482	A306	75k Rose	.60	.20
1483	A306	105k Tulip	.80	.30
	Nos. 1480-1483 (4)		2.15	.90

Atatürk Square, Nicosia A307

Design: 105k, Map of Cyprus.

1960, Aug. 16   Litho.   Perf. 10½

1484	A307	40k blue & pink	.20	.20
1485	A307	105k blue & yellow	.25	.20

Independence of the Republic of Cyprus.

Women and Nest A308

Design: 30k, Globe and emblem.

1960, Aug. 22   Photo.   Perf. 11½

1486	A308	30k lt vio & yel	.20	.20
1487	A308	75k grnsh bl & gray	.25	.20

16th meeting of the Women's Intl. Council.

Soccer A309

#1489, Basketball. #1490, Wrestling. #1491, Hurdling. #1492, Steeplechase.

1960, Aug. 25

1488	A309	30k yellow green	.50	.40
1489	A309	30k black	.50	.40
1490	A309	30k slate blue	.50	.40
1491	A309	30k purple	.50	.40
1492	A309	30k brown	.50	.40
a.	Sheet of 25, #1488-1492		17.50	10.00
	Nos. 1488-1492 (5)		2.50	2.00

17th Olympic Games, Rome, 8/25-9/11. Printed in sheets of 25 (5x5) with every horizontal and every vertical row containing one of each design. Also printed in normal sheets of 100.

Common Design Types pictured following the introduction.

Europa Issue, 1960
Common Design Type
1960, Sept. 19
Size: 33x22mm

1493	CD3	75k green & bl grn	.85	.50
1494	CD3	105k dp bl & lt bl	1.25	.85

Aga and di Page Turcan Ahval —

UN Emblem and Torch — A311

1960, Oct. 21   Photo.   Perf. 11½

1495	A310	40k brown blk & sl	.20	.20
1496	A310	60k brn blk & bis brn	.20	.20

Centenary of Turkish journalism.

1960, Oct. 24   Unwmk.

Design: 105k, UN headquarters building and UN emblem forming "15," horiz.

1497	A311	90k brt bl & dk bl	.20	.20
1498	A311	105k lt bl grn & brn	.25	.20

15th anniversary of the United Nations.

Army Emblem A312

Tribunal A313

Design: 195k, "Justice," vert.

1960, Oct. 14   Litho.   Perf. 13

1499	A312	40k violet & bister	.20	.20
1500	A313	105k red, gray & brn	.25	.20
1501	A313	195k grn, rose red & brn	.45	.20
	Nos. 1499-1501 (3)		.90	.60

Trial of ex-President Celal Bayar and ex-Premier Adnan Menderes.

Revolutionaries and Statue — A314

Prancing Horse, Broken Chain — A315

Designs: 30k, Ataturk and hand holding torch. 105k, Youth, soldier and broken chain.

1960, Dec. 1   Photo.   Perf. 14½

1502	A314	10k gray & blk	.20	.20
1503	A314	30k purple	.20	.20
1504	A315	40k brt red & blk	.20	.20
1505	A314	105k blue blk & red	.40	.20
	Nos. 1502-1505 (4)		1.00	.80

Revolution of May 27, 1960.

65

Faculty
Building
A316

Sculptured Head of
Atatürk — A317

Designs: 40k, Map of Turkey and sun disk.

1961, Jan. 9   Litho.   Perf. 13
1506 A316 30k slate grn & gray   .30 .20
1507 A316 40k brn blk & bis brn   .40 .20
1508 A317 60k dk green & buff   .50 .20
    Nos. 1506-1508 (3)   1.20 .60

25th anniv. of the Faculty of Languages, History and Geography, University of Ankara.

Communication and
Transportation — A318

40k, Highway construction, telephone & telegraph. 75k, New parliament building, Ankara.

1961, Apr. 27   Unwmk.   Perf. 13
1509 A318 30k dull vio & blk   .20 .20
1510 A318 40k green & black   .35 .20
1511 A318 75k dull blue & blk   .45 .20
    Nos. 1509-1511 (3)   1.00 .60

9th conference of ministers of the Central Treaty Org. (CENTO), Ankara.

Flag and
People — A319

Legendary
Wolf and
Osman
Warriors
A320

Design: 60k, "Progress" (Atatürk showing youth the way).

1961, May 27   Litho.
1512 A319 30k multicolored   .20 .20
1513 A320 40k sl grn & yel   .20 .20
1514 A319 60k grn, pink & dk red   .25 .20
    Nos. 1512-1514 (3)   .65 .60

First anniversary of May 27 revolution.

Rockets
A321

Designs: 40k, Crescent and star emblem, "50" and Jet. 75k, Atatürk, eagle and jets, vert.

1961, June 1
1515 A321 30k brn, org yel & blk   .20 .20
1516 A321 40k violet & red   .25 .20
1517 A321 75k slate blk & bis   .55 .25
    Nos. 1515-1517 (3)   1.00 .65

50th anniversary of Turkey's air force.

Europa Issue, 1961
Common Design Type
1961, Sept. 18   Perf. 13
    Size: 32x22mm
1518 CD4 30k dk violet bl   .55 .35
1519 CD4 40k gray   .65 .35
1520 CD4 75k vermilion   1.25 .60
    Nos. 1518-1520 (3)   2.45 1.30

Tulip and
Cogwheel
A322

Open Book and
Olive Branch
A324

Torch,
Hand and
Cogwheel
A323

1961, Oct. 21   Unwmk.   Litho.
1521 A322 30k slate, pink & sil   .20 .20
1522 A323 75k ultra, org & blk   .35 .20

Technical and professional schools, cent.

1961, Oct. 29
1523 A324 30k red, blk & olive   .20 .20
1524 A324 75k brt blue, blk & grn   .30 .20

Inauguration of the new Parliament.

Kemal Atatürk
A325   A326

1961-62   Litho.   Perf. 10x10½
    Size: 20x25mm
1525 A325 1k brown org ('62)   .75 .20
1526 A325 5k blue   1.25 .20
1527 A325 10k sepia   2.00 .20
1528 A326 10k car rose   2.00 .20
1529 A325 30k dull grn ('62)   5.75 .25
    Size: 21½x31mm
1530 A325 10 l violet ('62)   12.00 1.50
    Nos. 1525-1530 (6)   23.75 2.55

NATO Emblem and
Dove — A327

Scouts at
Campfire
A328

Design: 105k, NATO emblem, horiz.

1962, Feb. 18   Unwmk.   Perf. 13
1545 A327 75k dl bl, blk & sil   .20 .20
1546 A327 105k crimson, blk & sil   .30 .20

10th anniv. of Turkey's admission to NATO.

1962, July 22   Litho.
60k, Scouts with flag. 105k, Scouts saluting.
1547 A328 30k lt grn, blk & red   .20 .20
1548 A328 60k gray, blk & red   .25 .20
1549 A328 105k tan, blk & red   .35 .20
    Nos. 1547-1549 (3)   .80 .60

Turkish Boy Scouts, 50th anniversary.

Soldier
Statue — A329

Oxcart from
Victory
Monument,
Ankara
A330

Design: 75k, Atatürk.

1962, Aug. 30   Unwmk.   Perf. 13
1550 A329 30k slate green   .20 .20
1551 A330 40k gray & sepia   .20 .20
1552 A329 75k gray blk & lt gray   .30 .20
    Nos. 1550-1552 (3)   .70 .60

40th anniv. of Battle of Dumlupinar.

Europa Issue, 1962
Common Design Type
1962, Sept. 17
    Size: 37x23mm
1553 CD5 75k emerald & blk   .65 .40
1554 CD5 105k red & blk   .85 .50
1555 CD5 195k blue & blk   1.50 .65
    Nos. 1553-1555 (3)   3.00 1.55

Brown imprint.

Virgin Mary's   20pa Stamp of
House, Ephesus   1863
A331   A332

40k, Inside view after restoration, horiz. 75k, Outside view, horiz. 105k, Statue of Virgin Mary.

1962, Dec. 8   Photo.   Perf. 13½
1556 A331 30k multicolored   .20 .20
1557 A331 40k multicolored   .20 .20
1558 A331 75k multicolored   .25 .20
1559 A331 105k multicolored   .35 .20
    Nos. 1556-1559 (4)   1.00 .80

1963, Jan. 13   Perf. 13x13½
Issue of 1863: 30k, 1pi. 40k, 2pi. 75k, 5pi.
1560 A332 10k yellow, brn & blk   .20 .20
1561 A332 30k rose, lil & blk   .20 .20
1562 A332 40k lt bl, bluish grn &
              blk   .25 .20
1563 A332 75k red brn, rose &
              blk   .45 .20
    Nos. 1560-1563 (4)   1.10 .80
Centenary of Turkish postage stamps. See No. 1601, souvenir sheet.

Starving
People
A333

Designs: 40k, Sowers. 75k, Hands protecting Wheat Emblem, and globe.

1963, Mar. 21   Unwmk.   Perf. 13
1564 A333 30k dp bl & dk bl   .20 .20
1565 A333 40k brn org & brn   .20 .20
1566 A333 75k grn & dk grn   .25 .20
    Nos. 1564-1566 (3)   .65 .60
FAO "Freedom from Hunger" campaign.

Julian's Column,
Ankara — A334

Ethnographic
Museum
A335

10k, Ankara Citadel. 30k, Gazi Institute of Education. 50k, Atatürk's mausoleum. 60k, President's residence. 100k, Ataturk's home, Cankaya. 150k, Parliament building.

1963   Litho.   Perf. 13
1568 A334 1k sl grn & yel grn   .20 .20
1569 A334 1k purple   .20 .20
1570 A335 5k sepia & buff   .20 .20
1571 A335 10k lil rose & pale
              bl   .40 .20
1573 A335 30k black & violet   .90 .20
1574 A335 50k blue & yellow   1.90 .20
1575 A335 60k dk blue gray   2.50 .40
1576 A335 100k olive brown   1.75 .40
1577 A335 150k dull green   8.00 1.10
    Nos. 1568-1577 (9)   16.05 3.10

Map of
Turkey and
Atom
Symbol
A336

Designs: 60k, Symbols of medicine, agriculture, industry and atom. 100k, Emblem of Turkish Atomic Energy Commission.

1963, May 27   Unwmk.   Perf. 13
1584 A336 50k red brn & blk   .20 .20
1585 A336 60k grn, dk grn, yel
              & red   .25 .20
1586 A336 100k violet bl & bl   .55 .30
    Nos. 1584-1586 (3)   1.00 .70

Turkish nuclear research center, 1st anniv.

Meric Bridge
A337

Sultan
Murad I — A338

Designs: 10k, Üçserefeli Mosque. 60k, Summerhouse, Edirne Palace.

1963, June 17
1587 A338 10k dp bl & yel grn   .20 .20
1588 A337 30k red org & ultra   .20 .20
1589 A337 60k dk bl, red & brn   .20 .20
1590 A338 100k multicolored   .65 .25
    Nos. 1587-1590 (4)   1.25 .85

600th anniv. of the conquest of Edirne (Adrianople).

Soldier and Rising Sun A339

1963, June 28
1591 A339 50k red, blk & gray .20 .20
1592 A339 100k red, blk & ol .30 .20

600th anniversary of the Turkish army.

Plowing A340

Mithat Pasha — A341

Design: 50k, Agriculture Bank, Ankara.

Perf. 13x13½, 13½x13
1963, Aug. 27 Photo. Unwmk.
1593 A340 30k brt yel grn, red brn & grn .20 .20
1594 A340 50k pale vio & Prus bl .20 .20
1595 A341 60k gray & green .30 .20
Nos. 1593-1595 (3) .70 .60

Centenary of Agriculture Bank, Ankara.

Sports and Exhibition Palace, Istanbul and #5 — A342

Designs: 50k, Sultan Ahmed Mosque & Turkey in Asia #22. 60k, View of Istanbul & Turkey in Asia #87. 100k, Rumeli Hisari Fortress & #679. 130k, Ankara Fortress & #C2.

1963, Sept. 7 Litho. Perf. 13
1596 A342 10k blk, yel & rose .20 .20
a. Rose omitted 37.50 37.50
1597 A342 50k blk, grn & rose lil .30 .20
1598 A342 60k dk brn, dk bl & blk .35 .20
1599 A342 100k dk vio & lil rose .50 .20
1600 A342 130k brn, tan & dp org .75 .20
Nos. 1596-1600 (5) 2.10 1.00

"Istanbul 63" Intl. Stamp Exhibition.

Type of 1963 Inscribed: "F.I.P. GÜNÜ" Souvenir Sheet

Issues of 1863: 10k, 20pa. 50k, 1pi. 60k, 2pi. 130k, 5pi.

Unwmk.
1963, Sept. 13 Litho. Imperf.
1601 Sheet of 4 2.00 1.50
a. A332 10k yel, brown & blk .25 .25
b. A332 50k lilac, pink & blk .25 .25
c. A332 60k bluish grn, lt bl & blk .40 .25
d. A332 130k red brn, pink & blk .50 .25

Intl. Philatelic Federation.

Europa Issue, 1963
Common Design Type
1963, Sept. 16
Size: 32x24mm
1602 CD6 50k red & black .60 .25
1603 CD6 130k bl grn, blk & bl .80 .35

Atatürk and First Parliament Building A343

Atatürk and: 50k, Turkish flag. 60k, New Parliament building.

1963, Oct. 29 Photo. Perf. 13½
1604 A343 30k blk, gold, yel & mar .20 .20
1605 A343 50k dk grn, gold, yel & red .30 .20
1606 A343 60k dk brn, gold & yel .40 .20
Nos. 1604-1606 (3) .90 .60

40th anniversary of Turkish Republic.

Atatürk, 25th Death Anniv. — A344

1963, Nov. 10
1607 A344 50k red, gold, grn & brn .25 .20
1608 A344 60k red, gold, bl & brn .35 .20

NATO, 15th Anniv. A346

130k, NATO emblem and olive branch.

1964, Apr. 4 Litho. Perf. 13
1610 A346 50k grnsh bl, vio bl & red .25 .20
1611 A346 130k red & black .45 .40

12 Stars and Europa with Torch A347

Design: 130k, Torch and stars.

1964, May 5 Litho. Perf. 12
1612 A347 50k red brn, yel & vio bl .35 .20
1613 A347 130k vio bl, lt bl & org .60 .40

15th anniversary of Council of Europe.

Recaizade Mahmut Ekrem, Writer — A348

Portraits: 1k, Hüseyin Rahmi Gürpinar, novelist. 5k, Ismail Hakki Izmirli, scientist. 10k, Sevket Dag, painter. 60k, Gazi Ahmet Muhtar Pasha, commander. 100k, Ahmet Rasim, writer. 130k, Salih Zeki, mathematician.

1964 Litho. Perf. 13½x13
1614 A348 1k red & blk .20 .20
1615 A348 5k dull grn & blk .20 .20
1616 A348 10k tan & blk .20 .20
1617 A348 50k ultra & dk bl .70 .20
1618 A348 60k gray & blk .80 .20
1619 A348 100k grnsh bl & dk bl .90 .20
1620 A348 130k brt grn & dk grn 4.00 .40
Nos. 1614-1620 (7) 7.00 1.60

Mosque of Sultan Ahmed A349

Kiz Kulesi, Mersin — A350

Designs: No. 1622, Zeus Temple, Silifke. No. 1623, View of Amasra. No. 1625, Augustus' Gate and minaret, Ankara.

1964, June 11 Unwmk. Perf. 13
1621 A349 50k gray ol & yel grn .20 .20
1622 A349 50k claret & car .20 .20
1623 A349 50k dk bl & vio bl .20 .20
1624 A350 60k sl grn & dk gray .30 .20
1625 A350 60k dk brn & org brn .30 .20
Nos. 1621-1625 (5) 1.20 1.00

Kars Castle — A351   **Alp Arslan, Conqueror of Kars, 1064 — A352**

1964, Aug. 16 Unwmk. Perf. 13
1626 A351 50k blk & pale vio .40 .40
1627 A352 130k blk, gold, sal & pale vio 1.25 .60

900th anniversary of conquest of Kars.

Europa Issue, 1964
Common Design Type
1964, Sept. 14 Litho. Perf. 13
Size: 22x33mm
1628 CD7 50k org, ind & sil .90 .50
1629 CD7 130k lt bl, mag & cit 1.75 .85

Fuat, Resit and Ali Pashas — A353

Design: 60k, Mustafa Resit Pasha, vert.

1964, Nov. 3 Perf. 13
Sizes: 48x33mm (50k, 100k); 22x33mm (60k)
1630 A353 50k multicolored .30 .20
1631 A353 60k multicolored .40 .20
1632 A353 100k multicolored .60 .30
Nos. 1630-1632 (3) 1.30 .70

125th anniversary of reform decrees.

Parachutist — A354

Designs: 90k, Glider, horiz. 130k, Ataturk watching squadron in flight.

1965, Feb. 16 Litho. Perf. 13
1633 A354 60k lt bl, blk, red & yel .20 .20
1634 A354 90k bister & multi .30 .20
1635 A354 130k lt blue & multi .50 .20
Nos. 1633-1635 (3) 1.00 .60

Turkish Aviation League, 40th anniv.

Emblem A355

Designs: 50k, Radio mast and waves, vert. 75k, Hand pressing button.

1965, Feb. 24 Unwmk. Perf. 13
1636 A355 30k multicolored .20 .20
1637 A355 50k multicolored .20 .20
1638 A355 75k multicolored .35 .20
Nos. 1636-1638 (3) .75 .60

Telecommunications meeting of the Central Treaty Org., CENTO.

Coast of Ordu — A356

50k, Manavgat Waterfall, Antalya. 60k, Sultan Ahmed Mosque, Istanbul. 100k, Hali Rahman Mosque, Urfa. 130k, Red Tower, Alanya.

1965, Apr. 5 Litho.
1639 A356 30k multicolored .20 .20
1640 A356 50k multicolored .25 .20
1641 A356 60k multicolored .25 .20
1642 A356 100k multicolored .45 .20
1643 A356 130k multicolored .65 .20
Nos. 1639-1643 (5) 1.80 1.00

ITU Emblem, Old and New Communication Equipment — A357

1965, May 17 Perf. 13
1644 A357 50k multicolored .35 .20
1645 A357 130k multicolored .65 .25

ITU, centenary.

ICY Emblem A358

1965, June 26 Litho. Unwmk.
1646 A358 100k red org, red brn & brt grn .30 .20
1647 A358 130k gray, lil & ol grn .45 .25

International Cooperation Year.

Hands Holding Book A358a

Map and Flags of Turkey, Iran and Pakistan A358b

1965, July 21 Unwmk. Perf. 13

1648	A358a	50k org brn, yel & dk brn	.30	.20
1649	A358b	75k dl bl, red, grn blk & org	.45	.20

1st anniv. of the signing of the Regional Cooperation Development Pact by Turkey, Iran and Pakistan.

Kemal Ataturk — A359

1965 Litho. Perf. 12½

1650	A359	1k brt green	.20	.20
1651	A359	5k violet blue	.20	.20
1652	A359	10k blue	.60	.20
1653	A359	25k gray	1.50	.20
1654	A359	30k magenta	2.00	.20
1655	A359	50k brown	3.00	.25
1656	A359	150k orange	7.50	.20
		Nos. 1650-1656 (7)	15.00	1.75

Europa Issue, 1965
Common Design Type

1965, Sept. 27 Perf. 13
Size: 32x23mm

1665	CD8	50k gray, ultra & grn	1.25	.70
1666	CD8	130k tan, blk & grn	2.25	1.40

Map of Turkey and People A360

Designs: 50k, "1965." 100k, "1965," symbolic eye and man, vert.

1965, Oct. 24 Unwmk. Litho. Perf. 13

1667	A360	10k multicolored	.20	.20
1668	A360	50k grn, blk & lt yel grn	.20	.20
1669	A360	100k orange, sl & blk	.40	.20
		Nos. 1667-1669 (3)	.80	.60

Issued to publicize the 1965 census.

Plane over Ankara Castle A361

Designs: 30k, Archer and Ankara castle. 50k, Horsemen with spears (ancient game). 100k, Three stamps and medal. 150k, Hands holding book, vert.

1965, Oct. 25

1670	A361	10k brt vio, yel & red	.20	.20
1671	A361	30k multicolored	.20	.20
1672	A361	50k lt gray ol, ind & red	.20	.20
1673	A361	100k gray & multi	.40	.25
		Nos. 1670-1673 (4)	1.00	.85

Souvenir Sheet
Imperf

1674	A361	150k multicolored	1.10	1.00

1st Natl. Postage Stamp Exhibition "Ankara 65."

Resat Nuri Guntekin, Novelist — A362

Portraits: 5k, Besim Omer Akalin, M.D. 10k, Tevfik Fikret, poet. 25k, Tanburi Cemil, composer. 30k, Ahmet Vifik Pasha, playwright. 50k, Omer Seyfettin, novelist. 60k, Kemalettin Mimaroglu, architect. 150k, Halit Ziya Usakligil, novelist. 220k, Yahya Kemal Beyatli, poet.

1965 Litho. Perf. 13½x13
Black Portrait and Inscriptions

1675	A362	1k rose	.20	.20
1676	A362	5k blue	.30	.20
1677	A362	10k buff	.30	.20
1678	A362	25k dull red brn	.50	.20
1679	A362	30k gray	.50	.20
1680	A362	50k orange	.75	.20
1681	A362	60k red lilac	.85	.20
1682	A362	150k lt green	1.10	.20
1683	A362	220k tan	2.00	.30
		Nos. 1675-1683 (9)	6.50	1.90

Training Ship Savarona A363

Designs: 60k, Submarine "Piri Reis." 100k, Cruiser "Alpaslan." 130k, Destroyer "Gelibolu." 220k, Destroyer "Gemlik."

1965, Dec. 6 Photo. Perf. 11½

1684	A363	50k blue & brown	.35	.20
1685	A363	60k blue & black	.50	.20
1686	A363	100k blue & black	.80	.25
1687	A363	130k blue & vio blk	1.25	.40
1688	A363	220k blue & indigo	1.75	.65
		Nos. 1684-1688 (5)	4.65	1.70

First Congress of Turkish Naval Society.

Kemal Ataturk — A364   Halide Edip Adivar, Writer — A365

1965 Litho. Perf. 13½
Imprint: "Apa Ofset Basimevi"
Black Portrait and Inscriptions

1689	A364	1k rose lilac	.50	.20
1690	A364	5k lt green	.70	.20
1691	A364	10k blue gray	.90	.20
1692	A364	50k olive bister	1.10	.30
1693	A364	150k silver	1.75	.70
		Nos. 1689-1693 (5)	4.95	1.60

See Nos. 1724-1728.

1966 Litho. Perf. 13½

Portraits: 25k, Huseyin Sadettin Arel, writer and composer. 30k, Kamil Akdik, graphic artist. 60k, Abdurrahman Seref, historian. 130k, Naima, historian.

1694	A365	25k gray & brn blk	.50	.20
1695	A365	30k rose vio & blk brn	.50	.20
1696	A365	50k blue & black	.55	.20
1697	A365	60k lt grn & blk brn	.55	.20
1698	A365	130k lt vio bl & blk	1.10	.20
		Nos. 1694-1698 (5)	3.10	1.00

Tiles, Green Mausoleum, Bursa — A366

Tiles: 60k, Spring flowers, Hurrem Sultan Mausoleum, Istanbul. 130k, Stylized flowers, 16th century.

1966, May 15 Litho. Perf. 13½x13

1699	A366	50k multicolored	.50	.20
1700	A366	60k multicolored	.80	.30
1701	A366	130k multicolored	1.25	.35
		Nos. 1699-1701 (3)	2.55	.85

On No. 1700 the black ink was applied by a thermographic process and varnished, producing a shiny, raised effect to imitate the embossed tiles of the design source.

Volleyball A367   View of Bodrum A368

1966, May 20 Perf. 13x13½

1702	A367	50k tan & multi	.35	.20

4th Intl. Military Volleyball Championship.

1966, May 25 Perf. 13x13½, 13½x13

Views: 30k, Kusadasi. 50k, Anadolu Hisari, Istanbul. 90k, Marmaris. 100k, Izmir.

1703	A368	10k multi	.20	.20
1704	A368	30k multi	.60	.20
1705	A368	50k multi, horiz.	.30	.20
1706	A368	90k multi	.30	.20
1707	A368	100k multi, horiz.	.40	.20
		Nos. 1703-1707 (5)	1.80	1.00

Inauguration of Keban Dam — A369

Design: 60k, View of Keban Dam area.

1966, June 10 Perf. 13½

1708	A369	50k multicolored	.30	.20
1709	A369	60k multicolored	.50	.20

Visit of King Faisal of Saudi Arabia A370

1966, Aug. 29 Litho. Perf. 13½x13

1710	A370	100k car rose & dk car	.75	.30

Symbolic Postmark and Stamp A371

Designs: 60k, Flower made of stamps. 75k, Stamps forming display frames. 100k, Map of Balkan states, magnifying glass and stamp.

1966, Sept. 3 Perf. 13½x13

1711	A371	50k multicolored	.20	.20
1712	A371	60k multicolored	.20	.20
1713	A371	75k multicolored	.40	.20
		Nos. 1711-1713 (3)	.80	.60

Souvenir Sheet
Imperf

1714	A371	100k multicolored	1.50	1.25

2nd "Balkanfila" stamp exhibition, Istanbul.

Sultan Suleiman on Horseback A372

90k, Mausoleum, Istanbul. 130k, Suleiman.

1966, Sept. 6 Perf. 13½x13

1715	A372	60k multicolored	.40	.20
1716	A372	90k multicolored	.70	.25
1717	A372	130k multicolored	1.40	.40
		Nos. 1715-1717 (3)	2.50	.85

Sultan Suleiman the Magnificent (1496?-1566). On No. 1717 a gold frame was applied by raised thermographic process.

Europa Issue, 1966
Common Design Type

1966, Sept. 26 Litho. Perf. 13x13½
Size: 22x33mm

1718	CD9	50k lt bl, vio bl & blk	1.10	.65
a.		Black (inscriptions & imprint) omitted	65.00	
1719	CD9	130k lil, dk red lil & blk	2.25	1.10

Symbols of Education, Science and Culture A373

1966, Nov. 4 Litho. Perf. 13

1720	A373	130k brn, bis brn & yel	.45	.20

UNESCO, 20th anniversary.

Middle East University of Technology A374

Designs: 100k, Atom symbol. 130k, design symbolizing sciences.

1966, Nov. 15

1721	A374	50k multicolored	.20	.20
1722	A374	100k multicolored	.30	.20
1723	A374	130k multicolored	.50	.30
		Nos. 1721-1723 (3)	1.00	.70

10th anniv. of the Middle East University of Technology.

Ataturk Type of 1965
Imprint: "Kiral Matbaasi — Ist"

1966 Litho. Perf. 12½
Black Portrait and Inscriptions

1724	A364	25k yellow	.25	.20
1725	A364	30k pink	.30	.20
1726	A364	50k rose lilac	1.25	.20
1727	A364	90k pale brown	.70	.20
1728	A364	100k gray	1.00	.20
		Nos. 1724-1728 (5)	3.50	1.00

Statue of Ataturk, Ankara — A375

Equestrian Statues of Ataturk: No. 1729A, Statue in Izmir. No. 1729B, Statue in Samsun.

Without Imprint

1967 Litho. Perf. 13x12½
Size: 23x16mm

1729	A375	10k black & yellow	.30	.20

Inscribed "1967"
Imprint: Kiral Matbaasi
Size: 22x15mm

1729A	A375	10k black & salmon	.30	.20
1729B	A375	10k black & lt grn	.30	.20
		Nos. 1729-1729B (3)	.90	.60

Issued for use on greeting cards. See Nos. 1790-1791A, 1911.

Puppets Karagöz and Hacivat — A376

Intl. Tourist Year Emblem and: 60k, Sword and shield game. 90k, Traditional military band. 100k, raised effect.

Perf. 13x13½, 13½x13

1967, Mar. 30				Litho.
1730	A376	50k multicolored	.50	.20
1731	A376	60k multicolored	.70	.20
1732	A376	90k multicolored	.90	.25
1733	A376	100k multicolored	1.40	.35
		Nos. 1730-1733 (4)	3.50	1.00

Intl. Tourist Year. On No. 1733 the black ink was applied by a thermographic process and varnished, producing a shiny, raised effect.

Woman Vaccinating Child, Knife and Lancet — A377

Fallow Deer — A378

1967, Apr. 1 — Perf. 13x13½
1734	A377	100k multicolored	.60	.25

250th anniv. of smallpox vaccination (variolation) in Turkey. The gold was applied by a thermographic process and varnished, producing a shiny, raised effect.

1967, Apr. 23   Litho.   Perf. 13x13½
1735	A378	50k shown	.30	.20
1736	A378	60k Wild goat	.40	.20
1737	A378	100k Brown bear	.55	.20
1738	A378	130k Wild boar	.80	.25
		Nos. 1735-1738 (4)	2.05	.85

Soccer Players and Emblem with Map of Europe A379

130k, Players at left, smaller emblem.

1967, May 1 — Perf. 13
1739	A379	50k multicolored	.65	.20
1740	A379	130k yellow & multi	.85	.30

20th Intl. Youth Soccer Championships.

Sivas Hospital A380

1967, July 1   Litho.   Perf. 13
1741	A380	50k multicolored	.40	.20

750th anniversary of Sivas Hospital.

Selim Sirri Tarcan A381

60k, Olympic Rings, Baron Pierre de Coubertin.

1967, July 20
1742	A381	50k lt blue & multi	.25	.20
1743	A381	60k lilac & multi	.25	.20
a.		Pair, #1742-1743	.50	.40

1st Turkish Olympic competitions.

Ahmed Mithat, Writer — A382

Portraits: 5k, Admiral Turgut Reis. 50k, Sokullu Mehmet, statesman. 100k, Nedim, poet. 150k, Osman Hamdi, painter.

1967   Litho.   Perf. 12½
1744	A382	1k green & blk	.50	.20
1745	A382	5k dp bister & blk	.75	.20
1746	A382	50k brt violet & blk	1.00	.20
1747	A382	100k citron & blk	2.00	.30
1748	A382	150k yellow & blk	3.00	.30
		Nos. 1744-1748 (5)	7.25	1.20

Ruins of St. John's Church, Ephesus A383

Design: 130k, Inside view of Virgin Mary's House, Ephesus.

1967, July 26 — Perf. 13
1749	A383	130k multicolored	.25	.20
1750	A383	220k multicolored	.55	.30

Visit of Pope Paul VI to the House of the Virgin Mary in Ephesus, July 26.

Plate on Firing Grid and Ornaments A384

1967, Sept. 1
1751	A384	50k pale lil, blk, ind & bl	.30	.20

5th International Ceramics Exhibition.

View of Istanbul and Emblem A385

1967, Sept. 4   Litho.   Perf. 13
1752	A385	130k dk blue & gray	.30	.20

9th Congress of the Intl. Commission of Large Dams.

Stamps, Ornament and Map of Turkey A386

Kemal Ataturk A387

Design: 60k, Grapes and stamps.

1967
1753	A386	50k multicolored	.20	.20
1754	A386	60k multicolored	.25	.20
a.		Souvenir sheet, #1753-1754	1.25	1.25

Intl. Trade Fair, Izmir.

1967   Litho.   Perf. 11½x12
Booklet Stamps
1755	A387	10k black & lt grn	1.25	.30
a.		Booklet pane of 10	100.00	
b.		Booklet pane of 25	250.00	
1756	A387	50k black & pale rose	1.25	.30
a.		Booklet pane of 2	40.00	
b.		Bklt. pane, 5 #1755, 4 #1756 + label	35.00	

Symbolic Water Cycle — A388

Human Rights Flame — A390

Child and Angora Cat, Man with Microscope — A389

1967, Dec. 1   Litho.   Perf. 13
1757	A388	90k lt grn, blk & org	.25	.20
1758	A388	130k lilac, blk & org	.30	.25

Hydrological Decade (UNESCO), 1965-74.

1967, Dec. 23 — Perf. 13

60k, Horse and man with microscope.

1759	A389	50k multicolored	.35	.20
1760	A389	60k multicolored	.45	.25

125th anniv. of Turkish veterinary medicine.

1968, Jan. 1 — Perf. 13x13½
1761	A390	50k rose lil, dk bl & org	.20	.20
1762	A390	130k lt bl, dk bl & red org	.35	.20

International Human Rights Year.

Archer on Horseback — A391

Miniatures, 16th Century: 50k, Investiture. 60k, Sultan Suleiman the Magnificent receiving an ambassador, vert. 100k, Musicians.

Perf. 13x13½, 13½x13
1968, Mar. 1				Litho.
1763	A391	50k multicolored	.50	.50
1764	A391	60k multicolored	1.00	1.00
1765	A391	90k multicolored	1.25	1.25
1766	A391	100k multicolored	1.50	1.50
		Nos. 1763-1766 (4)	4.25	4.25

Kemal Ataturk — A392

1968   Litho.   Perf. 12½
1767	A392	1k dk & lt blue	.20	.20
1768	A392	5k dk & lt green	.20	.20
1769	A392	50k org brn & yel	1.50	.20
1770	A392	200k dk brown & pink	5.00	.25
		Nos. 1767-1770 (4)	6.90	.85

Law Book and Oak Branch A393

Mithat Pasha and Scroll A394

1968, Apr. 1 — Perf. 13
1771	A393	50k multicolored	.35	.35
1772	A394	60k multicolored	.40	.40

Centenary of the Court of Appeal.

1968, Apr. 1

Designs: 50k, Scales of Justice. 60k, Ahmet Cevdet Pasha and scroll.

1773	A393	50k multicolored	.25	.20
1774	A394	60k multicolored	.35	.20

Centenary of the Supreme Court.

Europa Issue, 1968
Common Design Type
1968, May 6		Litho.	Perf. 13
		Size: 31½x23mm	
1775	CD11	100k pck bl, yel & red	1.75	.75
1776	CD11	130k green, yel & red	3.25	1.25

Yacht Kismet — A395

"Fight Usury" A396

1968, June 15   Litho.   Perf. 13
1777	A395	50k lt ultra & multi	.50	.50

Round-the-world trip of the yacht Kismet, Aug. 22, 1965-June 14, 1968.

1968, June 19
1778	A396	50k multicolored	.35	.35

Centenary of the Pawn Office, Istanbul.

Sakarya Battle and Independence Medal — A397

130k, Natl. anthem & reverse of medal.

1968, Aug. 30   *Perf. 13x13½*
1779 A397   50k gold & multi   .40 .40
1780 A397   130k gold & multi   .60 .60

Turkish Independence medal. The gold on Nos. 1779-1780 was applied by a thermographic process and varnished, producing a shiny, raised effect.

Ataturk and Galatasaray High School — A398

50k, "100" and old and new school emblems. 60k, Portraits of Beyazit II and Gulbaba.

1968, Sept. 1   **Litho.**
1781 A398   50k gray & multi   .25 .25
1782 A398   60k tan & multi   .50 .50
1783 A398   100k lt blue & multi   .75 .75
    Nos. 1781-1783 (3)   1.50 1.50

Centenary of Galatasaray High School.

Charles de Gaulle — A399

1968, Oct. 25   **Litho.**   *Perf. 13*
1784 A399   130k multicolored   .90 .50

Visit of President Charles de Gaulle of France to Turkey.

Kemal Ataturk — A400

Ataturk and his Speech to Youth — A401

50k, Ataturk's tomb and Citadel of Ankara. 60k, Ataturk looking out a train window. 250k, Framed portrait of Ataturk in military uniform.

1968, Nov. 10
1785 A400   30k orange & blk   .30 .20
1786 A400   50k brt grn & sl grn   .30 .20
1787 A400   60k bl grn & blk   .35 .20
1788 A401   100k blk, gray & brt grn   .70 .20
1789 A401   250k multicolored   1.25 .40
    Nos. 1785-1789 (5)   2.90 1.20

30th death anniv. of Kemal Ataturk.

Ataturk Statue Type of 1967

Equestrian Statues of Ataturk: No. 1790, Statue in Zonguldak. No. 1791, Statue in Antakya. No. 1791A, Statue in Bursa.

Imprint: Kiral Matbaasi 1968
1968-69   **Litho.**   *Perf. 13x12½*
        Size: 22x15mm
1790 A375   10k black & lt blue   .25 .20
1791 A375   10k blk & brt rose lil   .25 .20
         Perf. 13½
Imprint: Tifdruk Matbaacilik Sanayii A. S. 1969
        Size: 21x16½mm
1791A A375   10k dk grn & tan ('69)   .30 .20
    Nos. 1790-1791A (3)   .80 .60

Ince Minare Mosque, Konya — A402

ILO Emblem A403

Historic Buildings: 10k, Doner Kumbet (tomb), Kayseri. 50k, Karatay Medresse (University Gate), Konya. 100k, Ortakoy Mosque, Istanbul. 200k, Ulu Mosque, Divriki.

1968-69   **Photo.**   *Perf. 13x13½*
1792 A402   1k dk brn & buff ('69)   .20 .20
1793 A402   10k plum & dl rose ('69)   .30 .20
1794 A402   50k dk ol grn & gray   .40 .20
1795 A402   100k dk & lt grn ('69)   1.10 .25
1796 A402   200k dp bl & lt bl ('69)   1.75 .35
    Nos. 1792-1796 (5)   3.75 1.20

1969, Apr. 15   **Litho.**   *Perf. 13*
1797 A403   130k dk red & black   .30 .20

ILO, 50th anniv.

Sultana Hafsa, Medical Pioneer A404

1969, Apr. 26   **Litho.**   *Perf. 13½x13*
1798 A404   60k multicolored   .75 .75

Europa Issue, 1969
Common Design Type

1969, Apr. 28   *Perf. 13*
        Size: 32x23mm
1799 CD12   100k dull vio & multi   *1.60* .65
1800 CD12   130k gray grn & multi   *2.25* 1.60

Kemal Ataturk — A405

Map of Istanbul — A407

Ataturk and S.S. Bandirma A406

1969, May 19   **Litho.**   *Perf. 13*
1801 A405   50k multicolored   .25 .25
1802 A406   60k multicolored   .35 .35

50th anniv. of the landing of Kemal Ataturk at Samsun.

1969, May 31
1803 A407   130k vio bl, lt bl, gold & red   .35 .20

22nd Congress of the Intl. Chamber of Commerce, Istanbul.

Educational Progress A408

Agricultural Progress A409

Designs: 90k, Pouring ladle and industrial symbols. 100k, Road sign (highway construction). 180k, Oil industry chart and symbols.

1969   **Litho.**   *Perf. 13½x13*
1804 A408   1k black & gray   .20 .20
1805 A408   1k black & bis brn   .20 .20
1806 A408   1k black & lt grn   .20 .20
1807 A408   1k black & lt vio   .20 .20
1808 A408   1k black & org red   .20 .20
1809 A409   50k brown & ocher   .40 .20
1810 A409   90k blk & grnsh gray   .65 .20
1811 A408   100k black & org red   .90 .20
1812 A408   180k violet & orange   1.60 .20
    Nos. 1804-1812 (9)   4.55 1.80

Issued: 1, 100k, 4/8; 50k, 6/11; 90, 180k, 8/15.

Sultan Suleiman Receiving Sheik Abdul Latif — A410

Kemal Ataturk — A411

Designs: 80k, Lady Serving Wine, Safavi miniature, Iran. 130k, Lady on Balcony, Mogul miniature, Pakistan.

1969, July 21   **Litho.**   *Perf. 13*
1813 A410   50k yellow & multi   .30 .20
1814 A410   80k yellow & multi   .50 .20
1815 A410   130k yellow & multi   .85 .35
    Nos. 1813-1815 (3)   1.65 .75

5th anniv. of the signing of the Regional Cooperation for Development Pact by Turkey, Iran and Pakistan.

1969, July 23

Design: 60k, Ataturk monument and bas-relief showing congress.
1816 A411   50k black & gray   .25 .25
1817 A411   60k black & grnsh gray   .35 .35

50th anniversary, Congress of Erzerum.

Sivas Congress Delegates A412

Design: 50k, Congress Hall.

1969, Sept. 4   **Litho.**   *Perf. 13*
1818 A412   50k dk brn & dp rose   .25 .25
1819 A412   60k olive blk & yel   .35 .35

50th anniv. of the Congress of Sivas (preparation for the Turkish war of independence).

Bar Dance — A413

Folk Dances: 50k, Candle dance (çaydaçira). 60k, Scarf dance (halay). 100k, Sword dance (kiliç-kalkan). 130k, Two male dancers (zeybek), vert.

1969, Sept. 9
1820 A413   30k brown & multi   .40 .20
1821 A413   50k multicolored   .50 .20
1822 A413   60k multicolored   .80 .20
1823 A413   100k yellow & multi   .90 .90
1824 A413   130k multicolored   1.50 .50
    Nos. 1820-1824 (5)   4.10 2.00

1914 Airplane "Prince Celaleddin" A414

75k, First Turkish letter carried by air.

1969, Oct. 18   **Litho.**   *Perf. 13*
1825 A414   60k dk blue & blue   .25 .20
1826 A414   75k black & bister   .35 .20

55th anniv. of the first Turkish mail transported by air.

"Kutadgu Bilig" A415

1969, Nov. 20   **Litho.**   *Perf. 13*
1827 A415   130k ol bis, brn & gold   .35 .20

900th anniv. of "Kutadgu Bilig," a book about the function of the state, compiled by Jusuf of Balasagun in Tashkent, 1069.

Ataturk's Arrival in Ankara, after a Painting — A416

Design: 60k, Ataturk and his coworkers in automobiles arriving in Ankara, after a photograph.

1969, Dec. 27 **Litho.** *Perf. 13*
1828 A416 50k multicolored .60 .20
1829 A416 60k multicolored 1.00 .30

50th anniv. of Kemal Ataturk's arrival in Ankara, Dec. 27, 1919.

Bosporus Bridge, Map of Europe and Asia — A417

Design: 60k, View of proposed Bosporus Bridge and shore lines.

1970, Feb. 20 **Litho.** *Perf. 13*
1830 A417 60k gold & multi .75 .30
1831 A417 130k gold & multi 1.50 .65

Foundation ceremonies for the bridge across the Bosporus linking Europe and Asia.

Kemal Ataturk and Signature A418

Kemal Ataturk A419

1970 **Litho.** *Perf. 13*
1832 A418 1k dp orange & brn .20 .20
1833 A419 5k silver & blk .20 .20
1834 A419 30k citron & blk .35 .20
1835 A418 50k lt olive & blk .45 .20
1836 A419 50k pink & blk .50 .20
1837 A419 75k lilac & blk .75 .20
1838 A419 100k blue & blk 1.00 .20
 Nos. 1832-1838 (7) 3.45 1.40

Education Year Emblem — A420

Turkish EXPO '70 Emblem — A421

1970, Mar. 16
1839 A420 130k ultra, pink & rose lil .45 .20

International Education Year.

1970, Mar. 27
100k, EXPO '70 emblem & Turkish pavilion.
1840 A421 50k gold & multi .20 .20
1841 A421 100k gold & multi .30 .20

EXPO '70 International Exhibition, Osaka, Japan, Mar. 15-Sept. 13.

Opening of Grand National Assembly A422

Design: 60k, Session of First Grand National Assembly, 1920.

1970, Apr. 23
1842 A422 50k multicolored .20 .20
1843 A422 100k multicolored .30 .20

Turkish Grand National Assembly, 50th anniv.

Emblem of Cartographic Service A423

Map of Turkey and Gen. Mehmet Sevki Pasha — A424

Designs: 60k, Plane and aerial mapping survey diagram. 100k, Triangulation point in mountainous landscape.

Perf. 13½x13 (A423), 13x13½ (A424)
1970, May 2 **Litho.**
1844 A423 50k blue & multi .40 .20
1845 A424 60k blk, gray grn & brick red .40 .20
1846 A423 100k multicolored .60 .35
1847 A424 130k multicolored 1.00 .50
 Nos. 1844-1847 (4) 2.40 1.25

Turkish Cartographic Service, 75th anniv.

Europa Issue, 1970
Common Design Type

1970, May 4 *Perf. 13*
Size: 37x23mm
1848 CD13 100k ver, blk & org *1.50* .75
1849 CD13 130k dk bl grn, blk & org *3.50* 1.50

Inauguration of UPU Headquarters, Bern — A425

1970, May 20
1850 A425 60k blk & dull blue .25 .20
1851 A425 130k blk & dl ol grn .45 .20

Lady with Mimosa, by Osman Hamdi (1842-1910) A426

Paintings: No. 1853, Deer, by Seker Ahmet (1841-1907). No. 1854, Portrait of Fevzi Cakmak, by Avni Lifij (d. 1927). No. 1855, Sailboats, by Nazmi Ziya (1881-1937); horiz.

1970 **Litho.** *Perf. 13*
Size: 29x49mm
1852 A426 250k multicolored 1.10 .35
1853 A426 250k multicolored 1.10 .35
Size: 32x49mm
1854 A426 250k multicolored 1.10 .35
Size: 73½x33mm
1855 A426 250k multicolored 1.10 .35
 Nos. 1852-1855 (4) 4.40 1.40

Issued: #1852-1853, 6/15; #1854-1855, 12/15.

Turkish Folk Art — A427

1970, June 15
1856 A427 50k multicolored .40 .20

3rd National Stamp Exhibition, ANKARA 70, Oct. 28-Nov. 4. Pane of 50, each stamp setenant with label. This 50k, in pane of 50 without labels, was re-issued Oct. 28 with Nos. 1867-1869.

View of Fethiye A428

80k, Seeyo-Se-Pol Bridge, Esfahan, Iran. 130k, Saiful Malook Lake, Pakistan.

1970, July 21 **Litho.** *Perf. 13*
1857 A428 60k multicolored .25 .20
1858 A428 80k multicolored .30 .20
1859 A428 130k multicolored .45 .25
 Nos. 1857-1859 (3) 1.00 .65

6th anniv. of the signing of the Regional Cooperation for Development Pact by Turkey, Iran and Pakistan.

Sultan Balim's Tomb — A429

Haci Bektas Veli — A430

30k, Tomb of Haci Bektas Veli, horiz.

1970, Aug. 16 **Litho.** *Perf. 13*
1860 A429 30k multicolored .20 .20
1861 A429 100k multicolored .40 .20
1862 A430 130k multicolored .80 .20
 Nos. 1860-1862 (3) 1.40 .60

700th death anniv. of Haci Bektas Veli, mystic.

Hittite Sun Disk and "ISO" A431

1970, Sept. 15
1863 A431 110k car rose, gold & blk .20 .20
1864 A431 150k ultra, gold & blk .30 .20

8th General Council Meeting of the Intl. Standardization Org., Ankara.

UN Emblem, People and Globe — A432

Stamp "Flower" and Book — A433

100k, UN emblem and propeller, horiz.

1970, Oct. 24 **Litho.** *Perf. 13*
1865 A432 100k gray & multi .30 .20
1866 A432 220k multicolored .55 .25

25th anniversary of the United Nations.

1970, Oct. 28
Designs: 60k, Ataturk monument and stamps, horiz. 130k, Abstract flower.
1867 A433 10k multicolored .20 .20
1868 A433 60k blue & multi .20 .20
Souvenir Sheet
1869 A433 130k dk green & org 2.00 1.50

3rd National Stamp Exhibition, ANKARA 70, Oct. 28-Nov. 4. See note below No. 1856.

Inönü Battle Scene — A434

Design: No. 1871, Second Battle of Inönü.

1971 **Litho.** *Perf. 13*
1870 A434 100k multicolored .50 .20
1871 A434 100k multicolored .50 .20

1st and 2nd Battles of Inönü, 50th anniv. Issue dates: #1870, Jan. 10; #1871, Apr. 1.

Village on River Bank, by Ahmet Sekür — A435

Painting: No. 1872, Landscape, Yildiz Palace Garden, by Ahmet Ragip Bicakcilar.

1971, Mar. 15 **Litho.** *Perf. 13*
1872 A435 250k multicolored 1.25 .40
1873 A435 250k multicolored 1.25 .40

See #1901-1902, 1909-1910, 1937-1938.

Campaign Against Discrimination A436

1971, Mar. 21 **Litho.** *Perf. 13*
1874 A436 100k multicolored .20 .20
1875 A436 250k gray & multi .45 .25

Intl. Year against Racial Discrimination.

Europa Issue, 1971
Common Design Type

1971, May 3 **Litho.** *Perf. 13*
Size: 31½x22½mm
1876 CD14 100k lt bl, cl & mag *2.10* 1.00
1877 CD14 150k dp org, grn & red *3.50* 1.50

Kemal Ataturk
A437   A438

1971

1878	A437	5k gray & ultra	.50	.20
1879	A437	25k gray & dk red	.75	.20
1880	A438	25k brown & pink	.50	.25
1881	A437	100k gray & violet	1.00	.20
1882	A438	100k green & salmon	1.00	.30
1883	A438	250k blue & gray	2.50	.50
1884	A437	400k tan & olive grn	4.00	.60
	Nos. 1878-1884 (7)		10.25	2.25

Pres. Kemal   Mosque of
Gürsel — A439   Selim,
              Edirne — A440

1971, May 27   Litho.   *Perf. 13*

1885	A439	100k multicolored	.35	.20

Revolution of May 27, 1960; Kemal Gürsel (1895-1966), president.

1971, July 21   Litho.   *Perf. 13*

150k, Religious School, Chaharbagh, Iran. 200k, Badshahi Mosque, Pakistan.

1886	A440	100k multi	.25	.20
1887	A440	150k multi	.35	.20
1888	A440	200k multi, horiz.	.50	.20
	Nos. 1886-1888 (3)		1.10	.60

Regional Cooperation by Turkey, Iran and Pakistan, 7th anniversary.

Alp Arslan and Battle of
Malazkirt — A441

Design: 250k, Archers on horseback.

1971, Aug. 26   Litho.   *Perf. 13x13½*

1889	A441	100k multicolored	.75	.20
1890	A441	250k red, org & blk	1.20	.40

900th anniversary of the Battle of Malazkirt, which established the Seljuk Dynasty in Asia Minor.

Battle of Sakarya — A442

1971, Sept. 13

1891	A442	100k violet & multi	1.00	.45

50th anniversary of the victory of Sakarya.

Turkey-Bulgaria Railroad — A443

Designs: 110k, Ferry and map of Lake Van. 250k, Turkey-Iran railroad.

1971

1892	A443	100k multicolored	.75	.20
1893	A443	110k multicolored	.75	.20
1894	A443	250k yellow & multi	1.75	.60
	Nos. 1892-1894 (3)		3.25	1.00

Turkish railroad connections with Bulgaria &Iran. Issued: 110, 250k, 9/27; 100k, 10/4.

Netball and
Map of
Mediterranean
A444

200k, Runner and stadium, vert. 250k, Shot put and map of Mediterranean, vert.

1971, Oct. 6

1895	A444	100k dull vio & blk	.35	.20
1896	A444	200k brn, blk & emer	.55	.25

Souvenir Sheet

Imperf

1897	A444	250k ol bis & slate grn	.95	.85

Mediterranean Games, Izmir.

Tomb of Cyrus the Great — A445

Designs: 100k, Harpist, Persian mosaic, vert. 150k, Ataturk and Riza Shah Pahlavi.

1971, Oct. 13

1898	A445	25k lt blue & multi	.25	.20
1899	A445	100k multicolored	.65	.20
1900	A445	150k dk brown & buff	1.10	.25
	Nos. 1898-1900 (3)		2.00	.65

2500th anniversary of the founding of the Persian empire by Cyrus the Great.

Painting Type of 1971

No. 1901, Sultan Mohammed I and his Staff. No. 1902, Palace with tiled walls.

1971, Nov. 15   *Perf. 13*

1901	A435	250k multicolored	1.25	.40
1902	A435	250k multicolored	1.25	.40

Yunus
Emre — A446

1971, Dec. 27   Litho.   *Perf. 13*

1903	A446	100k brown & multi	.65	.20

650th death anniv. of Yunus Emre, Turkish folk poet.

First Turkish World Map and Book
Year Emblem — A447

1972, Jan. 3   *Perf. 13*

1904	A447	100k buff & multi	.50	.20

International Book Year.

Doves and NATO
Emblem — A448

Fisherman, by
Cevat
Dereli — A449

1972, Feb. 18   Litho.   *Perf. 13*

1905	A448	100k dull grn, blk & gray	.80	.25
1906	A448	250k dull bl, blk & gray	1.00	.60

Turkey's membership in NATO, 20th anniv.

Europa Issue 1972
Common Design Type

1972, May 2   *Perf. 13*

Size: 22x33mm

1907	CD15	110k blue & multi	3.00	1.00
1908	CD15	250k brown & multi	4.50	2.00

Painting Type of 1971

No. 1909, Forest, Seker Ahmet. No. 1910, View of Gebze, Anatolia, by Osman Hamdi.

1972, May 15   Litho.

1909	A435	250k multicolored	1.25	.35
1910	A435	250k multicolored	1.25	.35

Ataturk Statue Type of 1967

Design: 25k, Ataturk Statue in front of Ethnographic Museum, Ankara.

Imprint: Ajans - Turk/Ankara 1972

Perf. 12½x11½

1972, June 12   Litho.

Size: 22x15½mm

1911	A375	25k black & buff	.20	.20

1972, July 21   Litho.   *Perf. 13*

Paintings: 125k, Young Man, by Abdur Rehman Chughtai (Pakistan). 150k, Persian Woman, by Behzad.

1912	A449	100k gold & multi	.60	.20
1913	A449	125k gold & multi	.90	.25
1914	A449	150k gold & multi	1.00	.35
	Nos. 1912-1914 (3)		2.50	.80

Regional Cooperation for Development Pact among Turkey, Iran and Pakistan, 8th anniv.

Ataturk and Commanders at Mt.
Koca — A450

Designs: No. 1916, Battle of the Commander-in-chief. No. 1917, Turkish army entering Izmir. 110k, Artillery and cavalry.

1972   Litho.   *Perf. 13x13½*

1915	A450	100k lt ultra & blk	1.00	.20
1916	A450	100k pink & multi	1.00	.20
1917	A450	100k yellow & multi	1.00	.20
1918	A450	110k orange & multi	1.00	.25
	Nos. 1915-1918 (4)		4.00	.85

50th anniv. of fight for establishment of independent Turkish republic. Issued: #1915, 1918, 8/26; #1916, 8/30; #1917, 9/9.

"Cancer is
Curable"
A451

International
Railroad Union
Emblem — A452

1972, Oct. 10   Litho.   *Perf. 12½x13*

1919	A451	100k blk, brt bl & red	.35	.20

Fight against cancer.

1972, Dec. 31   Litho.   *Perf. 13*

1920	A452	100k sl grn, ocher & red	.30	.20

Intl. Railroad Union, 50th anniv.

Kemal
Ataturk — A453

1972-76   Litho.   *Perf. 13½x13*

Size: 21x26mm

1921	A453	5k gray & blue	.20	.20
1922	A453	25k orange ('75)	.25	.20
1923	A453	100k buff & red brn ('73)	1.00	.20
1924	A453	100k lt gray & gray ('75)	.35	.20
1925	A453	110k lt bl & vio bl	.75	.25
1926	A453	125k dull grn ('73)	1.25	.20
1927	A453	150k tan & brown	1.00	.20
1928	A453	150k lt grn & grn ('75)	.25	.20
1929	A453	175k yel & lil ('73)	1.75	.25
1930	A453	200k buff & red	1.25	.20
1931	A453	250k pink & pur ('75)	.30	.20
1931A	A453	400k gray & Prus bl ('76)	.35	.20
1932	A453	500k pink & violet	2.00	.50
1933	A453	500k gray & ultra ('75)	.75	.30

Size: 22x33mm

Perf. 13

1934	A453	10 l pink & car rose ('75)	1.75	.30
	Nos. 1921-1934 (15)		13.20	3.60

See Nos. 2060-2061.

Europa Issue 1973
Common Design Type
1973, Apr. 4   Litho.   Perf. 13
Size: 32x23mm

1935	CD16	110k gray & multi	3.25	1.75
1936	CD16	250k multicolored	6.75	2.75

Painting Type of 1971
Paintings: No. 1937, Beyazit Almshouse, Istanbul, by Ahmet Ziya Akbulut. No. 1938, Flowers, by Suleyman Seyyit, vert.

1973, June 15   Litho.   Perf. 13

1937	A435	250k multicolored	.85	.35
1938	A435	250k multicolored	.85	.35

Helmet, Sword and Oak Leaves — A454

Mausoleum of Antiochus I — A455

Design: 100k, Helmet, sword and laurel.

1973, June 28   Perf. 13x12½

1939	A454	90k brown, gray & grn	.25	.20
1940	A454	100k brown, lem & grn	.25	.20

Army Day.

1973, July 21   Litho.   Perf. 13
Designs: 100k, Colossal heads, mausoleum of Antiochus I (69-34 B.C.), Commagene, Turkey. 150k, Statue, Shahdad Kerman, Persia, 3000 B.C. 200k, Street, Mohenjo-daro, Pakistan.

1941	A455	100k lt blue & multi	.25	.20
1942	A455	150k olive & multi	.30	.20
1943	A455	200k brown & multi	.45	.60
		Nos. 1941-1943 (3)	1.00	1.00

Regional Cooperation for Development Pact among Turkey, Iran and Pakistan, 9th anniv.

Minelayer Nusret A456

Designs: 25k, Destroyer Istanbul. 100k, Speedboat Simsek and Naval College. 250k, Two-masted training ship Nuvid-i Futuh.

1973, Aug. 1
Size: 31½x22mm

1944	A456	5k Prus bl & multi	.20	.20
1945	A456	25k Prus bl & multi	.20	.20
1946	A456	100k Prus bl & multi	.60	.20

Size: 48x32mm

1947	A456	250k blue & multi	1.50	.25
		Nos. 1944-1947 (4)	2.50	.85

abu-al-Rayhan al-Biruni A457

Emblem of Darussafaka Foundation A458

1973, Sept. 4   Litho.   Perf. 13x12½

1948	A457	250k multicolored	.70	.70

abu-al-Rayhan al-Biruni (973-1048), philosopher and mathematician.

1973, Sept. 15   Perf. 13

1949	A458	100k silver & multi	.30	.20

Centenary of the educational and philanthropic Darussafaka Foundation.

BALKANFILA IV Emblem — A459

Designs: 110k, Symbolic view and stamps. 250k, "Balkanfila 4."

1973   Litho.   Perf. 13

1950	A459	100k gray & multi	.35	.20
1951	A459	110k multicolored	.20	.20
1952	A459	250k multicolored	.45	.20
		Nos. 1950-1952 (3)	1.00	.60

BALKANFILA IV, Philatelic Exhibition of Balkan Countries, Izmir, Oct. 26-Nov. 5. Issued: 100k, Sept. 26; 110k, 250k, Oct. 26.

Sivas Shepherd Dog — A460

Kemal Ataturk — A461

1973, Oct. 4

1953	A460	25k shown	.20	.20
1954	A460	100k Angora cat	.60	.20

1973, Oct. 10   Litho.   Perf. 13

1955	A461	100k gold & blk brn	.40	.20

35th death anniv. of Kemal Ataturk.

Flower and "50" — A462

Ataturk — A463

250k, Torch & "50." 475k, Grain & cogwheel.

1973, Oct. 29

1956	A462	100k purple, red & bl	.20	.20
1957	A462	250k multicolored	.45	.20
1958	A462	475k brt blue & org	.70	.35
		Nos. 1956-1958 (3)	1.35	.75

Souvenir Sheet
Imperf

1959	A463	500k multicolored	1.75	1.00

50th anniv. of the Turkish Republic. #1959 contains one stamp with simulated perforations.

Bosporus Bridge A464

150k, Istanbul & Bosporus Bridge. 200k, Bosporus Bridge, children & UNICEF emblem, vert.

1973, Oct. 30   Perf. 13

1960	A464	100k multicolored	.30	.20
1961	A464	150k multicolored	.50	.30
1962	A464	200k multicolored	.55	.30
		Nos. 1960-1962 (3)	1.35	.80

Inauguration of the Bosporus Bridge from Istanbul to Üsküdar, Oct. 30, 1973; UNICEF; children from East and West brought closer through Bosporus Bridge (No. 1962).

Mevlana's Tomb and Dancers — A465

Jalal-udin Mevlana — A466

1973, Dec. 1   Perf. 13x12½

1963	A465	100k blk, lt ultra & grn	.30	.20
1964	A466	250k blue & multi	.55	.25

Jalal-udin Mevlana (1207-1273), poet and founder of the Mevlevie dervish order.

Cotton and Ship — A467

Export Products: 90k, Grapes. 100k, Figs. 250k, Citrus fruits. 325k, Tobacco. 475k, Hazelnuts.

1973, Dec. 10   Litho.   Perf. 13

1965	A467	75k black, gray & bl	.20	.20
1966	A467	90k black, olive & bl	.30	.20
1967	A467	100k black, emer & bl	.40	.20
1968	A467	250k blk, brt yel & bl	1.10	.25
1969	A467	325k blk, yel & bl	1.10	.25
1970	A467	475k blk, org brn & bl	1.60	.40
		Nos. 1965-1970 (6)	4.70	1.50

Pres. Inönü — A468

Hittite King, 8th Century B.C. — A469

1973, Dec. 25   Litho.   Perf. 13

1971	A468	100k sepia & buff	.50	.20

Ismet Inönü, (1884-1973), first Prime Minister and second President of Turkey.

1974, Apr. 29   Litho.   Perf. 13
Europa: 250k, Statuette of a Boy, (2nd millenium B.C.).

1972	A469	110k multicolored	5.50	1.50
1973	A469	250k lt blue & multi	9.50	3.50

Silver and Gold Figure, 3000 B.C. — A470

Child Care — A471

Archaeological Finds: 175k, Painted jar, 5000 B.C., horiz. 200k, Vessels in bull form, 1700-1600 B.C., horiz. 250k, Pitcher, 700 B.C.

1974, May 24   Litho.   Perf. 13

1974	A470	125k multicolored	.35	.20
1975	A470	175k multicolored	.60	.20
1976	A470	200k multicolored	.75	.20
1977	A470	250k multicolored	1.10	.40
		Nos. 1974-1977 (4)	2.80	1.00

1974, May 24

1978	A471	110k gray blue & blk	.30	.20

Sisli Children's Hospital, Istanbul, 75th anniv.

Anatolian Rug, 15th Century A472

Designs: 150k, Persian rug, late 16th century. 200k, Kashan rug, Lahore.

1974, July 21   Litho.   Perf. 12½x13

1979	A472	100k blue & multi	1.00	.20
1980	A472	150k brown & multi	1.50	.20
1981	A472	200k red & multi	3.00	.25
		Nos. 1979-1981 (3)	5.50	.65

10th anniversary of the Regional Cooperation for Development Pact among Turkey, Iran and Pakistan.

Dove with Turkish Flag over Cyprus A473

1974, Aug. 26   Litho.   Perf. 13

1982	A473	250k multicolored	.80	.40

Cyprus Peace Operation.

Wrestling A474

Arrows Circling Globe A475

90k, 250k, various wrestling holds, horiz.

1974, Aug. 29

1983	A474	90k multicolored	.25	.20
1984	A474	100k multicolored	.40	.20
1985	A474	250k multicolored	.70	.25
		Nos. 1983-1985 (3)	1.35	.65

World Freestyle Wrestling Championships.

1974, Oct. 9   Litho.   Perf. 13

UPU Emblem and: 110k, "UPU" in form of dove. 200k, Dove.

1986	A475	110k bl, gold & dk bl	.25	.20
1987	A475	200k green & brown	.30	.20
1988	A475	250k multicolored	.55	.30
		Nos. 1986-1988 (3)	1.10	.70

Centenary of Universal Postal Union.

"Law Reforms" A476

"National Economy" A477

"Education" A478

1974, Oct. 29

1989	A476	50k blue & black	.20	.20
1990	A477	150k red & multi	.25	.20
1991	A478	400k multicolored	.65	.30
		Nos. 1989-1991 (3)	1.10	.70

Works and reforms of Kemal Ataturk.

Arrows Pointing Up — A479

Cogwheel and Map of Turkey A480

1974, Nov. 29   Litho.   Perf. 13

| 1992 | A479 | 25k brown & black | .20 | .20 |
| 1993 | A480 | 100k brown & gray | .35 | .20 |

3rd 5-year Development Program (#1992), and industrialization progress (#1993).

Volleyball — A481

1974, Dec. 30

1994	A481	125k shown	.25	.20
1995	A481	175k Basketball	.45	.20
1996	A481	250k Soccer	.80	.20
		Nos. 1994-1996 (3)	1.50	.60

Automatic Telex Network A482

Postal Check A483

Radio Transmitter and Waves A484

1975, Feb. 5   Litho.   Perf. 13

1997	A482	5k black & yellow	.20	.20
1998	A483	50k ol grn & org	.20	.20
1999	A484	100k blue & black	.30	.20
		Nos. 1997-1999 (3)	.70	.60

Post and telecommunications.

Child Entering Classroom A485

Children's paintings: 50k, View of village. 100k, Dancing children.

1975, Apr. 23   Litho.   Perf. 13

2000	A485	25k multicolored	.20	.20
2001	A485	50k multicolored	.20	.20
2002	A485	100k multicolored	.30	.20
		Nos. 2000-2002 (3)	.70	.60

Karacaoglan Monument in Mut, by Huseyin Gezer — A486

1975, Apr. 25

| 2003 | A486 | 110k dk grn, bis & red | .45 | .25 |

Karacaoglan (1606-1697), musician.

Orange Harvest in Hatay, by Cemal Tollu — A487

Europa: 250k, Yoruk Family on Plateau, by Turgut Zaim.

1975, Apr. 28

| 2004 | A487 | 110k bister & multi | 2.75 | 1.10 |
| 2005 | A487 | 250k bister & multi | 4.25 | 2.00 |

Porcelain Vase, Turkey A488

Designs: 200k, Ceramic plate, Iran, horiz. 250k, Camel leather vase, Pakistan.

Perf. 13½x13, 13x13½

1975, July 21   Litho.

2006	A488	110k multicolored	1.00	.30
2007	A488	200k multicolored	1.50	.50
2008	A488	250k ultra & multi	1.50	.80
		Nos. 2006-2008 (3)	4.00	1.60

Regional Cooperation for Development Pact among Turkey, Iran and Pakistan.

Horon Folk Dance — A489

Regional Folk Dances: 125k, Kasik. 175k, Bengi. 250k, Kasap. 325k, Kafkas, vert.

1975, Aug. 30   Litho.   Perf. 13

2009	A489	100k blue & multi	.55	.20
2010	A489	125k green & multi	.75	.20
2011	A489	175k rose & multi	.90	.20
2012	A489	250k multicolored	1.10	.25
2013	A489	325k orange & multi	1.75	.40
		Nos. 2009-2013 (5)	5.05	1.25

Knight Slaying Dragon — A490

The Plunder of Salur Kazan's House — A491

Design: 175k, Two Wanderers, horiz.

1975, Oct. 15   Litho.   Perf. 13

2014	A490	90k multicolored	.25	.20
2015	A490	175k multicolored	.40	.20
2016	A491	200k multicolored	.60	.40
		Nos. 2014-2016 (3)	1.25	.90

Illustrations for tales by Dede Korkut.

Common Carp A492

1975, Nov. 27   Litho.   Perf. 12½x13

2017	A492	75k Turbot	.75	.50
2018	A492	90k shown	1.00	.60
2019	A492	175k Trout	1.50	.75
2020	A492	250k Red mullet	3.00	.85
2021	A492	475k Red bream	3.75	1.25
		Nos. 2017-2021 (5)	10.00	3.95

Women's Participation A493

Insurance Nationaliza-tion — A494

Fine Arts — A495

1975, Dec. 5   Perf. 12½x13, 13x12½

2022	A493	100k bis, blk & red	.20	.20
2023	A494	110k violet & multi	.30	.20
2024	A495	250k multicolored	.40	.20
		Nos. 2022-2024 (3)	.90	.60

Works and reforms of Ataturk.

Ceramic Plate — A496

Europa: 400k, Decorated pitcher.

1976, May 3   Litho.   Perf. 13

| 2025 | A496 | 200k purple & multi | 5.00 | 2.00 |
| 2026 | A496 | 400k multicolored | 10.00 | 3.00 |

Sultan Ahmed Mosque A497

1976, May 10

| 2027 | A497 | 500k gray & multi | .80 | .40 |

7th Islamic Conference, Istanbul.

Lunch in the Field A498

Children's Drawings: 200k, Boats on the Bosporus, vert. 400k, Winter landscape.

1976, May 19   Litho.   Perf. 13

2028	A498	50k multicolored	.20	.20
2029	A498	200k multicolored	.25	.20
2030	A498	400k multicolored	.45	.20
		Nos. 2028-2030 (3)	.90	.60

Samsun 76, First National Junior Philatelic Exhibition, Samsun.

Storks, Sultan Marsh A499

Conservation Emblem and: 200k, Horses, Manyas Lake. 250k, Borabay Lake. 400k, Manavgat Waterfall.

1976, June 5

2031	A499	150k multicolored	2.00	.60
2032	A499	200k multicolored	.65	.20
2033	A499	250k multicolored	1.10	.20
2034	A499	400k multicolored	1.25	.25
		Nos. 2031-2034 (4)	5.00	1.25

European Wetland Conservation Year.

Nasreddin Hodja Carrying Liver — A500

Montreal Olympic Emblem and Flame — A501

Turkish Folklore: 250k, Friend giving recipe for cooking liver. 600k, Hawk carrying off liver and Hodja telling hawk he cannot enjoy liver without recipe.

1976, July 5   Litho.   Perf. 13
2035	A500	150k multicolored	.25 .20
2036	A500	250k multicolored	.40 .20
2037	A500	600k multicolored	.95 .35
	Nos. 2035-2037 (3)		1.60 .75

1976, July 17

Designs: 400k, "76," Montreal Olympic emblem, horiz. 600k, Montreal Olympic emblem and ribbons.

2038	A501	100k red & multi	.20 .20
2039	A501	400k red & multi	.50 .20
2040	A501	600k red & multi	.90 .40
	Nos. 2038-2040 (3)		1.60 .85

21st Olympic Games, Montreal, Canada, 7/17-8/1.

Kemal Ataturk A502

Designs: 200k, Riza Shah Pahlavi. 250k, Mohammed Ali Jinnah.

1976, July 21   Litho.   Perf. 13½
2041	A502	100k multicolored	.25 .20
2042	A502	200k multicolored	.35 .20
2043	A502	250k multicolored	.50 .25
	Nos. 2041-2043 (3)		1.10 .65

Regional Cooperation for Development Pact among Turkey, Pakistan and Iran, 12th anniversary.

"Ataturk's Army" A503

Ataturk's Speeches A504

"Peace at Home and in the World" A505

1976, Oct. 29   Litho.   Perf. 13
2044	A503	100k black & red	.20 .20
2045	A504	200k gray grn & multi	.25 .20
2046	A505	400k blue & multi	.55 .25
	Nos. 2044-2046 (3)		1.00 .65

Works and reforms of Ataturk.

Hora A506

1977, Jan. 19   Litho.   Perf. 13
2047	A506	400k multicolored	.70 .25

MTA Sismik 1 "Hora" geophysical exploration ship.

Keyboard and Violin Sound Hole — A507

1977, Feb. 24   Litho.   Perf. 13x13½
2048	A507	200k multicolored	.40 .20

Turkish State Symphony Orchestra, sesquicentennial.

Ataturk and "100" — A508

Design: 400k, Hand holding ballot.

1977, Mar. 21   Litho.   Perf. 13
2049	A508	200k black & red	.25 .20
2050	A508	400k black & brown	.50 .25

Centenary of Turkish Parliament.

Hierapolis (Pamukkale) A509

Europa: 400k, Zelve (mountains and poppies).

1977, May 2   Litho.   Perf. 13½x13
2051	A509	200k multicolored	6.00 2.00
2052	A509	400k multicolored	10.00 3.00

Terra Cotta Pot, Turkey A510

Designs: 225k, Terra cotta jug, Iran. 675k, Terra cotta bullock cart, Pakistan.

1977, July 21   Litho.   Perf. 13
2053	A510	100k multicolored	.25 .20
2054	A510	225k multicolored	.75 .25
2055	A510	675k multicolored	1.50 .55
a.	Souv. sheet, #2053-2055		8.00 8.00
	Nos. 2053-2055 (3)		2.50 1.00

Regional Cooperation for Development Pact among Turkey, Iran and Pakistan, 13th anniv.

Finn-class Yacht A511

Kemal Ataturk A512

200k, Three yachts. 250k, Symbolic yacht.

1977, July 28
2056	A511	150k lt bl, bl & blk	.25 .20
2057	A511	200k ultra & blue	.40 .20
2058	A511	250k ultra & black	.55 .20
	Nos. 2056-2058 (3)		1.20 .60

European Finn Class Sailing Championships, Istanbul, July 28.

Ataturk Type of 1972

1977, June 13   Litho.   Perf. 13½x13
2060	A453	100k olive	.50 .20
2061	A453	200k brown	.75 .25

Imprint: "GUZEL SANATLAR MATBAASI A.S. 1977"

1977, Sept. 23   Litho.   Perf. 13
Size: 20½x22mm
2062	A512	200k blue	.50 .20
2063	A512	250k Prussian blue	.75 .25

Imprint: "TIFDRUK-ISTANBUL 1978"

1978, June 28   Photo.   Perf. 13
Size: 20x25mm
2065	A512	10k brown	.45 .20
2066	A512	50k grnsh gray	.50 .20
2067	A512	1 l fawn	.60 .20
2068	A512	2½ l purple	.75 .20
2069	A512	5 l blue	1.00 .20
2072	A512	25 l dl grn & lt bl	2.50 .30
2073	A512	50 l dp org & tan	3.50 .70
	Nos. 2065-2073 (7)		9.30 2.00

No. 1832 Surcharged with New Value and Wavy Lines

1977, Aug. 17
2078	A418	10k on 1k dp org & brn	.30 .20

"Rationalism" A513

"National Sovereignty" A514

"Liberation of Nations" — A515

1977, Oct. 29   Litho.   Perf. 13
2079	A513	100k multicolored	.20 .20
2080	A514	200k multicolored	.20 .20
2081	A515	400k multicolored	.40 .20
	Nos. 2079-2081 (3)		.80 .60

Works and reforms of Ataturk.

Mohammad Allama Iqbal — A516

Trees and Burning Match — A517

1977, Nov. 9   Perf. 13x12½
2082	A516	400k multicolored	.45 .20

Mohammad Allama Iqbal (1877-1938), Pakistani poet and philosopher.

1977, Dec. 15   Litho.   Perf. 13

Design: 250k, Sign showing growing tree.
2083	A517	50k green, blk & red	.20 .20
2084	A517	250k gray, grn & blk	.25 .20

Forest conservation. See type A542.

Wrecked Car — A518

Passing on Wrong Side — A519

Traffic Sign, "Slow!" — A520

Two types of 50k:
I — Number on license plate.
II — No number on plate.

Traffic Safety: 250k, Tractor drawing overloaded farm cart. 800k, Accident caused by incorrect passing. 10 l, "Use striped crossings."

1977-78   Perf. 13½x13, 13x13½
2085	A518	50k ultra, blk & red, II	.60 .55
a.	Type I		.70 .55
2086	A519	150k red, gray & blk	.25 .20
2087	A518	250k ocher, blk & red	.50 .20
2088	A520	500k gray, red & blk	.50 .20
2089	A520	800k multicolored	1.10 .20
2090	A520	10 l dl grn, blk & brn	1.75 .35
	Nos. 2085-2090 (6)		4.70 1.75

Issued: 500k, 1977; others, 1978.

Ishak Palace, Dogubeyazit — A521

Europa: 5 l, Anamur Castle.

1978, May 2   Litho.   Perf. 13
2091	A521	2½ l multicolored	7.00 2.50
2092	A521	5 l multicolored	12.00 3.50

Riza Shah Pahlavi — A522

1978, June 16   Litho.   Perf. 13x13½
2093 A522 5 l multicolored   .50   .50

Riza Shah Pahlavi (1877-1944) of Iran, birth centenary.

Yellow Rose, Turkey A523

3½ l, Pink roses, Iran. 8 l, Red roses, Pakistan.

1978, July 21   Litho.   Perf. 13
2094 A523 2½ l multi   .25   .20
2095 A523 3½ l multi   .40   .20
2096 A523 8 l multi   1.00   .30
    Nos. 2094-2096 (3)   1.65   .70

Regional Cooperation for Development Pact among Turkey, Iran and Pakistan.

Anti-Apartheid Emblem — A524

1978, Aug. 14   Litho.   Perf. 13½x13
2097 A524 10 l multicolored   .85   .25

Anti-Apartheid Year.

View of Ankara — A525

Design: 5 l, View of Tripoli, horiz.

Perf. 13x12½, 12½x13
1978, Aug. 17
2098 A525 2½ l multi   .30   .20
2099 A525 5 l multi   .75   .20

Turkish-Libyan friendship.

Souvenir Sheet

Bridge and Mosque — A526

1978, Oct. 25   Imperf.
2100 A526 15 l multicolored   1.50 1.00

Edirne '78, 2nd Natl. Phil. Youth Exhib.

Independence Medal A527

Latin Alphabet A529

Speech Reform A528

1978, Oct. 29   Perf. 13x13½, 13½x13
2101 A527 2½ l multi   .20   .20
2102 A528 3½ l multi   .25   .20
2103 A529 5 l multi   .35   .20
    Nos. 2101-2103 (3)   .80   .60

Ataturk's works and reforms.

House on Bosporus, 1699 — A530

Turkish Houses: 2½ l, Izmit, 1774, vert. 3½ l, Kula, 17th cent., vert. 5 l, Milas, 18th-19th cent., vert. 8 l, Safranbolu, 18th-19th cent.

Perf. 13x12½, 12½x13
1978, Nov. 22
2104 A530 1 l multi   .30   .20
2105 A530 2½ l multi   .50   .20
2106 A530 3½ l multi   .50   .30
2107 A530 5 l multi   .75   .30
2108 A530 8 l multi   1.25   .35
    Nos. 2104-2108 (5)   3.30 1.35

Carrier Pigeon, Plane, Horseback Rider, Train A531

Europa: 5 l, Morse key, telegraph and Telex machine. 7½ l, Telephone dial and satellite.

1979, Apr. 30   Litho.   Perf. 13
2109 A531 2½ l multicolored   3.00 1.00
2110 A531 5 l org brn & blk   5.00 1.00
2111 A531 7½ l brt blue & blk   5.75 1.50
    Nos. 2109-2111 (3)   13.75 3.50

Plowing, by Namik Ismail A532

Paintings: 7½ l, Potters, by Kamalel Molk, Iran. 10 l, At the Well, by Allah Baksh, Pakistan.

1979, Sept. 5   Litho.   Perf. 13½x13
2112 A532 5 l multi   .20   .20
2113 A532 7½ l multi   .35   .20
2114 A532 10 l multi   .55   .25
    Nos. 2112-2114 (3)   1.10   .65

Regional Cooperation for Development Pact among Turkey, Pakistan and Iran, 15th anniversary.

A533

A534

1979, Sept. 17   Perf. 13
2115 A533 5 l Colemanite   .35   .20
2116 A533 7½ l Chromite   .50   .20
2117 A533 10 l Antimonite   .80   .20
2118 A533 15 l Sulphur   1.00   .30
    Nos. 2115-2118 (4)   2.65   .90

10th World Mining Congress.

1979, Sept. 24
2119 A534 5 l multicolored   .30   .20

8-shaped road, train tunnel, plane and emblem.

European Ministers of Communications, 8th Symposium.

Youth — A535

Secularization A536

Design: 5 l, National oath.

1979, Oct. 29   Perf. 13x12½, 12½x13
2120 A535 2½ l multi   .20   .20
2121 A536 3½ l multi   .20   .20
2122 A535 5 l black & orange   .30   .20
    Nos. 2120-2122 (3)   .70   .60

Ataturk's works and reforms.

Poppies — A537

1979, Nov. 26   Litho.   Perf. 13x13½
2123 A537 5 l shown   .25   .20
2124 A537 7½ l Oleander   .45   .20
2125 A537 10 l Late spider orchid   .70   .20
2126 A537 15 l Mandrake   1.10   .25
    Nos. 2123-2126 (4)   2.50   .85

See Nos. 2154-2157.

Kemal Ataturk A538   A538a

Perf. 12½x11½, 13x12½(No. 2131)
1979-81   Litho.
2127 A538 50k olive ('80)   .20   .20
2128 A538 1 l grn & lt grn   .30   .20
2129 A538 2½ l purple   .50   .20
2130 A538 2½ l bl grn & lt bl ('80)   .30   .20
2131 A538 2½ l orange ('81)   .40   .20
2132 A538 5 l ultra & gray   .70   .20
    a. Sheet of 8   6.00 6.00

2133 A538 7½ l brown   .75   .30
2134 A538 7½ l red ('80)   1.00   .30
2135 A538 10 l rose carmine   1.25   .40
2136 A538 20 l gray ('80)   1.75   .50
    Nos. 2127-2136 (10)   7.15 2.70

No. 2132a for Ankara '79 Philatelic Exhibition, Oct. 14-20.
For surcharge see No. 2261.

1980-82   Photo.   Perf. 13½
2137 A538a 7½ l red brown   .30   .20
    c. Sheet of 4   4.00 2.50
2137A A538a 10 l brown   .75   .20
2138 A538a 20 l lilac   .75   .20
2138A A538a 30 l gray   1.00   .30
2139 A538a 50 l orange red   2.00   .30
2140 A538a 75 l brt green   2.75   .60
2141 A538a 100 l blue   3.00   .75
    Nos. 2137-2141 (7)   10.55 2.55

No. 2137c for ANTALYA '82 4th Natl. Junior Stamp Show. Exists both perf 13½ and imperf. Same value.
    Issued: #2137, 7/15/81; #2137c, 10/3/82; 30 l, 9/23/81; others, 12/10/80.
See Nos. 2164-2169.

Turkish Printing, 250th Anniversary — A539

1979, Nov. 30   Litho.   Perf. 13
2142 A539 10 l multicolored   .60   .45

2nd International Olive Oil Year — A540

Perf. 12½x13, 13x12½
1979, Dec. 20   Litho.
2143 A540 5 l shown   .20   .20
2144 A540 10 l Globe, oil drop, vert.   .45   .20

Uskudarli Hoca Ali Riza Bey (1857-1930), Painter — A541

Europa: 15 l, Ali Sami Boyar (1880-1967), painter. 20 l, Dr. Hulusi Behcet (1889-1948), physician, discovered Behcet skin disease.

1980, Apr. 28   Perf. 13
2145 A541 7½ l multi   1.75 1.00
2146 A541 15 l multi   2.50 1.25
2147 A541 20 l multi   3.25 1.25
    Nos. 2145-2147 (3)   7.50 3.50

Forest Conservation A542   Earthquake Destruction A543

1980, July 3   Perf. 13½x13
2148 A542 50k ol grn & red org   .30   .20

See type A517. For surcharge see No. 2262.

1980, Sept. 8   *Perf. 13*
2149 A543 7½ l shown   .30 .25
2150 A543 20 l Seismograph   .70 .50
7th World Conference on Earthquake Engineering, Istanbul.

Games' Emblem, Sports — A544   Hegira — A545

1980, Sept. 26   *Perf. 13x13½*
2151 A544 7½ l shown   .25 .20
2152 A544 20 l Emblem, sports, diff.   .70 .20
First Islamic Games, Izmir.

1980, Nov. 9
2153 A545 20 l multicolored   .80 .40

Plant Type of 1979
1980, Nov. 26   *Perf. 13*
2154 A537 2½ l Manisa tulip   .20 .20
2155 A537 7½ l Ephesian bellflower   .50 .20
2156 A537 15 l Angora crocus   .75 .20
2157 A537 20 l Anatolian orchid   1.25 .20
   Nos. 2154-2157 (4)   2.70 .80

Avicenna Treating Patient A546

Avicenna (Arab Physician), Birth Millenium: 20 l, Portrait, vert.

1980, Dec. 15
2158 A546 7½ l multi   .40 .20
2159 A546 20 l multi   .70 .30

Balkanfila VIII Stamp Exhibition, Ankara A547

1981, Jan. 1   Litho.   *Perf. 13*
2160 A547 10 l red & black   .75 .25

Kemal Ataturk — A548

1981, Feb. 4   *Perf. 13*
2163 A548 10 l lilac rose   .50 .20

Ataturk Type of 1980
1983-84   *Perf. 13x13½*
2164 A538a 15 l grnsh blue   .25 .20
2165 A538a 20 l orange ('84)   .30 .20
2167 A538a 65 l bluish grn   .95 .20
2169 A538a 90 l lilac rose   1.25 .20
   Nos. 2164-2169 (4)   2.75 .80

Issued: #2164, 2167, 2169, 11/30; #2165, 7/25.

Sultan Mehmet the Conqueror (1432-1481) — A549

1981, May 3   Litho.   *Perf. 13x12½*
2173 A549 10 l multicolored   .30 .25
2174 A549 20 l multicolored   .65 .50

Gaziantep (Folk Dance) A550

Antalya A551

1981, May 4   Litho.   *Perf. 13*
2175 A550 7½ l shown   .25 .20
2176 A550 10 l Balikesir   .35 .20
2177 A550 15 l Kahramanmaras   .55 .25
2178 A551 35 l shown   4.00 1.10
2179 A551 70 l Burdur   5.00 2.25
   Nos. 2175-2179 (5)   10.15 4.00
Nos. 2178-2179 show CEPT (Europa) emblem.

Nos. C40, 1925, 1931A, 2089 Surcharged in Black with New Value and Wavy Lines

1981, June 3   *Perf. 13½x13*
2179A AP7 10 l on 60k   .40 .20
2180 A453 10 l on 110k   .40 .20
2181 A453 10 l on 400k   .40 .20
2182 A520 10 l on 800k   .40 .20
   Nos. 2179A-2182 (4)   1.60 .80

A552

Kemal Ataturk A553

1981, June 22   *Perf. 13x12½*
2183 A552 7½ l Rug, Bilecik   .20 .20
2184 A552 10 l Embroidery   .25 .20
2185 A552 15 l Drum, zurna players   .40 .20
2186 A552 20 l Embroidered napkin   .40 .20
2187 A552 30 l Rug, diff.   .75 .20
   Nos. 2183-2187 (5)   2.00 1.00
22nd Intl. Turkish Folklore Congress.

1981, May 19   Litho.   *Perf. 14x15*
2188 A553 2½ l No. 1801   .20 .20
2189 A553 7½ l No. 1816   .20 .20
2190 A553 10 l No. 1604   .20 .20
2191 A553 20 l No. 804   .50 .20
2192 A553 25 l No. 777   .60 .20
2193 A553 35 l No. 1959   .75 .20
   Nos. 2188-2193 (6)   2.45 1.20

Souvenir Sheet
2194   Sheet of 6   11.00 5.50
   a.   A553 2½ l like 2½ l   .20 .20
   b.   A553 37½ l like 7½ l   .40 .20
   c.   A553 50 l like 10 l   .60 .20

   d.   A553 100 l like 20 l   1.25 .40
   e.   A553 125 l like 25 l   1.50 .50
   f.   A553 175 l like 35 l   2.25 .65

Souvenir Sheet

Balkanfila VIII Stamp Exhibition, Ankara — A554

1981, Aug. 8   Litho.   *Perf. 13*
2195 A554   Sheet of 2   6.00 5.00
   a.   50 l No. B68   2.75 2.50
   b.   50 l No. 733   2.75 2.50

5th General Congress of European Physics Society A555

1981, Sept. 7   *Perf. 12½x13*
2196 A555 10 l red & multi   .50 .20
2197 A555 30 l blue & multi   .80 .30

World Food Day A556

1981, Oct. 16
2198 A556 10 l multicolored   .25 .20
2199 A556 30 l multicolored   .60 .20

Constituent Assembly Inauguration — A557

1981, Oct. 23   *Perf. 13*
2200 A557 10 l multicolored   .25 .20
2201 A557 30 l multicolored   .60 .20

Ataturk — A558

Portraits of Ataturk.

1981-82   *Perf. 11½x12½, 13 (#2204)*
2202 A558 1 l green   .20 .20
2203 A558 2½ l purple   .20 .20
2204 A558 2½ l gray & org   .50 .20
2205 A558 5 l blue   .20 .20
2206 A558 10 l orange   .20 .20
2207 A558 35 l brown   .70 .20
   Nos. 2202-2207 (6)   2.00 1.20

Issued: #2204, 12/10/81; others, 1/27/82.

Literacy Campaign A559   Energy Conservation A560

1981, Dec. 24   *Perf. 13½*
2217 A559 2½ l Procession   .35 .20

1982, Jan. 11   *Perf. 13*
2218 A560 10 l multicolored   .45 .20

Magnolias, by Ibrahim Calli (b. 1882) A561   Sultanhan Caravanserai A562

1982, Mar. 17   *Perf. 13x13½, 13½x13*
2219 A561 10 l shown   .25 .20
2220 A561 20 l Fishermen, horiz.   .50 .20
2221 A561 30 l Sewing Woman   .65 .20
   Nos. 2219-2221 (3)   1.40 .60

Europa Issue
1982, Apr. 26   *Perf. 13x12½*
2222 A562 30 l shown   .75 .25
2223 A562 70 l Silk Route   1.60 .50
   a.   Min. sheet, 2 each #2222-2223   7.00 7.00
   b.   Pair, #2222-2223   2.50 1.00

1250th Anniv. of Kul-Tigin Monument, Kosu Saydam, Mongolia — A563

1982, June 9   *Perf. 13*
2224 A563 10 l Monument   .20 .20
2225 A563 30 l Kul-Tigin (685-732), Gok-Turkish commander   .40 .20

Pendik Shipyard Opening A564

1982, July 1   *Perf. 12½x13*
2226 A564 30 l Ship, emblem   .40 .20

Mountains of Anatolia A565

1982, July 17   *Perf. 13*
2227 A565 7½ l Agri Dagi, vert.   .20 .20
2228 A565 10 l Buzul Dagi   .30 .20
2229 A565 15 l Demirkazik, vert.   .50 .20
2230 A565 20 l Erciyes   .70 .20
2231 A565 30 l Kackar Dagi, vert.   .90 .20
2232 A565 35 l Uludag   1.25 .20
   Nos. 2227-2232 (6)   3.85 1.20

Beyazit State Library Centenary A566

1982, Sept. 27
2233 A566 30 l multicolored   .50 .25

Musical Instruments of Anatolia — A567

1982, Oct. 13
2234 A567 7½ l Davul   .30 .20
2235 A567 10 l Baglama   .40 .20
2236 A567 15 l shown   .60 .20
2237 A567 20 l Kemence   .90 .20
2238 A567 30 l Ney   1.10 .20
    Nos. 2234-2238 (5)   3.30 1.00

Roman Temple Columns, Sart A568

1982, Nov. 3
2239 A568 30 l multi   1.25 .40

Family Planning and Mother-Child Health — A569

1983, Jan. 12   Litho.   Perf. 13
2240 A569 10 l Family on map   .25 .20
2241 A569 35 l Mother and child   .75 .20

30th Anniv. of Customs Cooperation Council — A570

1983, Jan. 26
2242 A570 45 l multi   .75 .20

1982 Constitution — A571

1983, Jan. 27
2243 A571 10 l Ballot box   .50 .20
2244 A571 30 l Open book, scale   .75 .30

Manastirli Bey A572

1983, Mar. 16   Litho.
2245 A572 35 l multi   .45 .20

Manastirli Hamdi Bey (1890-1945), telegrapher of news of Istanbul's occupation to Ataturk, 1920.

Europa Issue

Piri Reis, Geographer A573

1983, May 5   Litho.   Perf. 12½x13
2246 A573 50 l shown   15.00 2.50
2247 A573 100 l Ulug Bey
              (1394-1449),
              astronomer   35.00 7.50

Youth Week A574

1983, May 16
2248 A574 15 l multi   .25 .20

World Communications Year — A575

1983, May 16   Perf. 13
2249 A575 15 l Carrier pigeon,
              vert.   .30 .20
2250 A575 50 l Phone lines   .60 .20
2251 A575 70 l Emblem, vert.   1.10 .20
    Nos. 2249-2251 (3)   2.00 .60

50th Anniv. of State Civil Aviation A576

1983, May 20   Litho.   Perf. 13
2252 A576 50 l Plane, jet   .75 .20
2253 A576 70 l Airport   1.00 .30

18th Council of Europe Art Exhibition A577

15 l, Eros, 2nd cent. BC, vert. 35 l, Two-headed duck, Hittite, 14th cent BC. 50 l, Zinc jugs, plate, 16th cent., vert. 70 l, Marcus Aurelius and his wife Faustina the Young, 2nd cent.

1983, May 22   Perf. 13
2254 A577 15 l multi   .40 .20
2255 A577 35 l multi   .90 .20
2256 A577 50 l multi   1.00 .20
2257 A577 70 l multi   1.10 .20
    Nos. 2254-2257 (4)   3.40 .80

Council of Europe's "The Water's Edge" Campaign — A578

Coastal Views.

1983, June 1   Litho.   Perf. 13x12½
2258 A578 10 l Olodeniz   .40 .25
2259 A578 25 l Olympus   .40 .25
2260 A578 35 l Kekova   .90 .50
    Nos. 2258-2260 (3)   1.70 1.00

Nos. 2127, 2148 Surcharged
Perf. 12½x11½, 13½x13

1983, June 8
2261 A538 5 l on 50k olive   .20 .20
2262 A542 5 l on 50k ol grn &
              red org   .20 .20

Kemal Ataturk A579   Aga Khan Architecture Award A580

1983, June 22   Perf. 13
2263 A579 15 l bl grn & bl   .25 .20
  a.   Sheet of 5 + label   1.75 1.25
2264 A579 50 l green & blue   .80 .20
2265 A579 100 l orange & blue   1.75 .30
    Nos. 2263-2265 (3)   2.80 .70

For surcharge see No. 2432.

1983, Sept. 4   Photo.   Perf. 11½
2266 A580 50 l View of Istanbul   .75 .20

60th Anniv. of the Republic A582

1983, Oct. 29   Perf. 13½x13
2268 A582 15 l multi   .25 .20
2269 A582 50 l multi   .75 .20

Columns, Aphrodisias — A583

1983, Nov. 2   Perf. 13
2270 A583 50 l multi   1.00 .75

UNESCO Campaign for Istanbul and Goreme — A584

1984, Feb. 15   Litho.   Perf. 13
2271 A584 25 l St. Sophia Basili-
              ca   .30 .20
2272 A584 35 l Goreme   .45 .20
2273 A584 50 l Istanbul   .60 .20
    Nos. 2271-2273 (3)   1.35 .60

Natl. Police Org. Emblem A585

1984, Apr. 10   Litho.   Perf. 13
2274 A585 15 l multi   .50 .30

Europa (1959-84) A586

1984, Apr. 30   Perf. 13½x13
2275 A586 50 l blue & multi   15.00 2.50
2276 A586 100 l gray & multi   26.00 5.00

Mete Khan, Hun Ruler, 204 BC, Flag A587

Sixteen States (Hun Rulers and Flags): 20 l, Panu, Western Hun empire (48-216). 50 l, Attila, 375-454. 70 l, Aksunvar, Ak Hun empire, 420-562.

1984, June 20   Litho.   Perf. 13
2277 A587 10 l multi   .75 .20
2278 A587 20 l multi   1.00 .40
2279 A587 50 l multi   2.00 .50
2280 A587 70 l multi   3.50 .50
    Nos. 2277-2280 (4)   7.25 1.60

See Nos. 2315-2318, 2349-2352, 2382-2385.

Occupation of Cyprus, 10th Anniv. A588

1984, July 20   Litho.   Perf. 13
2281 A588 70 l Dove, olive
              branch   1.10 .50

Wild Flowers A589   Armed Forces Day A590

1984, Aug. 1   Perf. 11½x12½
2282 A589 10 l Marshmallow
              flower   .20 .20
2283 A589 20 l Red poppy   .25 .20
2284 A589 70 l Sowbread   .85 .20
2285 A589 200 l Snowdrop   2.50 .30
2286 A589 300 l Tulip   4.00 .40
    Nos. 2282-2286 (5)   7.80 1.30

See Nos. 2301-2308. For surcharges see Nos. 2465, 2467, 2479-2480.

1984, Aug. 26   Perf. 13½x13
2287 A590 20 l Soldier, dove,
              flag   .30 .20
2288 A590 50 l Sword   .50 .20
2289 A590 70 l Arms, soldier,
              flag   .75 .20
2290 A590 90 l Map, soldier   1.00 .20
    Nos. 2287-2290 (4)   2.55 .80

Trees and Wood Products A591   Pres. Ismet Inonu (1884-1973), A592

Seed, Tree and Product: 10 l, Liquidambar, liquidambar grease. 20 l, Oriental spruce, stringed instrument. 70 l, Oriental beech, chair. 90 l, Cedar of Lebanon, ship.

1984, Sept. 19 Litho. Perf. 13x12½
2291 A591 10 l multi .50 .20
2292 A591 20 l multi .50 .20
2293 A591 70 l multi 1.00 .20
2294 A591 90 l multi 1.50 .20
    Nos. 2291-2294 (4) 3.50 .80

1984, Sept. 24 Perf. 13
2295 A592 20 l Portrait .30 .20

First Intl. Turkish Carpet Congress — A593

1984, Oct. 7 Perf. 13x13½
2296 A593 70 l Seljukian carpet, 13th cent. .75 .50

Ruins of Ancient City of Harran A594

1984, Nov. 7 Perf. 13½x13
2297 A594 70 l Columns, arch 1.75 1.25

Turkish Women's Suffrage, 50th Anniv. A595

1984, Dec. 5 Litho. Perf. 13
2298 A595 20 l Women voting .25 .20

40th Anniv., ICAO — A596

1984, Dec. 7 Litho. Perf. 13
2299 A596 100 l Icarus, ICAO emblem 1.25 1.00

Souvenir Sheet

No. 1047 — A597

1985, Jan. 13 Litho. Imperf.
2300 A597 Sheet of 4, 2 each #a.-b. 4.00 3.00
 a.-b. 70 l, any single .50 .50
 Istanbul '87. No. 2300b has denomination in lower right.

Flower Type of 1984
1985 Perf. 11½x12½
2301 A589 5 l Narcissus .50 .30
    Perf. 12½x13
2308 A589 100 l Daisy 1.10 .20
 Issue dates: #2301, Feb. 6; #2308, July 31.

Turkish Aviation League, 60th Anniv. A598

1985, Feb. 16 Perf. 13
2310 A598 10 l Parachutist, glider .30 .25
2311 A598 20 l Hot air balloon, vert. .70 .50

INTELSAT, 20th Anniv. — A599

1985, Apr. 3
2312 A599 100 l multi 1.50 .75

Europa Issue

Ulvi Cemal Erkin (1906-1972) and Kosekce — A600

 Composers and music: 200 l, Mithat Fenmen (1916-1982) and Concertina.

1985, Apr. 29 Perf. 13½x13
2313 A600 100 l multi 25.00 3.50
2314 A600 200 l multi 35.00 5.00

Turkish States Type of 1984
 Sixteen States (Kagan rulers and flags): 10 l, Bilge, Gokturk Empire (552-743) and Orhon-Turkish alphabet. 20 l, Bayan, Avar Empire (565-803). 70 l, Hazar, Hazar Empire (651-983). 100 l, Kutlug Kul Bilge, Uygur State (774-1335).

1985, June 20
2315 A587 10 l multi .40 .20
2316 A587 20 l multi .75 .20
2317 A587 70 l multi 1.40 .20
2318 A587 100 l multi 2.75 .20
    Nos. 2315-2318 (4) 5.30 .80

Intl. Youth Year A601

1985, Aug. 8
2319 A601 100 l multi 1.10 .75
2320 A601 120 l multi 1.50 1.25

Postal Code Inauguration A602

1985, Sept. 4 Perf. 13
Background Color
2321 A602 10 l pale yel brn .25 .20
2322 A602 20 l fawn .40 .20
2323 A602 20 l gray green .40 .20
2324 A602 20 l brt blue .40 .20
2325 A602 70 l rose lilac .90 .20
2326 A602 100 l gray 1.25 .30
    Nos. 2321-2326 (6) 3.60 1.30

Symposium of Natl. Palaces — A603

1985, Sept. 25 Perf. 13½x13
2327 A603 20 l Aynalikavak, c. 1703 .35 .20
2328 A603 100 l Beylerbeyi, 1865 1.40 .20

UN, 40th Anniv. A604

1985, Oct. 24
2329 A604 100 l multi 1.25 1.00

Alanya Fortress and City A605

1985, Nov. 7
2330 A605 100 l multi 1.50 .75

A606   A607

1985, Nov. 12 Perf. 13x13½
2331 A606 100 l multi 1.25 .75
 Turkish Meteorological Service, 60th anniv.

1985, Dec. 14
2332 A607 20 l multi .50 .25
 Isik Lyceum, Istanbul, cent.

Ataturk — A608

Perf. 11½x12½
1985, Dec. 18 Litho.
2334 A608 10 l pale bl & ultra .20 .20
2335 A608 20 l beige & brn .25 .20
2336 A608 100 l lt pink & claret 1.25 .20
    Nos. 2334-2336 (3) 1.70 .60

7th Intl. Children's Festival, Ankara A609

 Various children's drawings.

1986, Apr. 23 Litho. Perf. 12½x13
2342 A609 20 l multi .30 .25
2343 A609 100 l multi .85 .25
2344 A609 100 l multi 1.00 1.00
    Nos. 2342-2344 (3) 2.15 1.50

Europa Issue

Pollution A610

1986, Apr. 28 Perf. 13
2345 A610 100 l shown 12.00 2.50
2346 A610 200 l Bandaged leaf 17.50 5.00

1st Ataturk Intl. Peace Prize — A611
Kirkpinar Wrestling Matches, Edirne — A613

1st Turkish Submarine, Cent. — A612

1986, May 19 Litho. Perf. 13
2347 A611 20 l gold & multi .50 .50
2348 A611 100 l silver & multi 1.25 .75

States Type of 1984
 Sixteen States (Devleti rulers and flags): 10 l, Bilge Kul Kadir Khan, Kara Khanids State (840-1212). 20 l, Alp-Tekin, Ghaznavids State (963-1183). 100 l, Seldjuk Bey, Seldjuks State (1040-1157). 120 l, Muhammed Harezmsah, Khwarizm-Shahs State (1157-1231).

1986, June 20
2349 A587 10 l multi .50 .20
2350 A587 20 l multi 1.00 .30
2351 A587 100 l multi 1.50 .50
2352 A587 120 l multi 3.50 1.00
    Nos. 2349-2352 (4) 6.50 2.00

1986, June 16 Litho. Perf. 13
2353 A612 20 l Torpedo sub Abdulhamid 1.00 .50

1986, June 30
2354 A613 10 l Oiling bodies .50 .50
2355 A613 20 l Five wrestlers .50 .50
2356 A613 100 l Two wrestlers 1.50 1.00
    Nos. 2354-2356 (3) 2.50 2.00

Organization for Economic Cooperation and Development, 25th Anniv. — A614

1986, Sept. 30 Litho. Perf. 13½x13
2357 A614 100 l multi 1.00 .30

Automobile, Cent. — A615

1986, Oct. 15
2358 A615 10 l Benz Veloci-pede, 1886 .75 .50
2359 A615 20 l Rolls-Royce Silver Ghost, 1906 1.00 .50

2360 A615 100 l Mercedes Touring Car, 1928   2.00 1.00
2361 A615 200 l Abstract speed-
ing car   2.75 1.50
Nos. 2358-2361 (4)   6.50 3.50

Paintings
A616

Celal Bayar (1883-
1986), 3rd
President — A617

Designs: 100 l, Bouquet with Tulip, by
Feyhaman Duran (1886-1970). 120 l, Landscape with Fountain, by H. Avni Lifij (1886-
1927), horiz.

1986, Oct. 22   Perf. 13½x13, 13x13½
2362 A616 100 l multi   .70 .40
2363 A616 120 l multi   2.00 .55

1986, Oct. 27   Perf. 13
2364 A617 20 l shown   .50 .20
2365 A617 100 l Profile   .75 .20

Kubad-Abad Ruins, Beysehir
Lake — A618

1986, Nov. 7   Perf. 13½x13
2366 A618 100 l multi   1.10 .40

Mehmet Akif Ersoy (1873-1936),
Composer of the Turkish National
Anthem — A619

1986, Dec. 27 Litho. Perf. 13½x13
2367 A619 20 l multi   .50 .25

Road Safety   Intl. Year of
A620   Shelter for the
                     Homeless
                     A622

Butterflies
A621

1987, Feb. 4   Litho.   Perf. 13x13½
2368 A620 10 l Use seatbelts   .20 .20
2369 A620 20 l Don't drink alco-
                   hol and drive   .25 .20
2370 A620 150 l Observe speed
                   limit   1.10 .20
Nos. 2368-2370 (3)   1.55 .60

For surcharges see Nos. 2466, 2477-2478.

1987, Feb. 25   Perf. 13½x13
2371 A621 10 l Celerio
               euphorbiae   .50 .25
2372 A621 20 l Vanessa ata-
               lanta   1.00 .50
2373 A621 100 l Euplagia
               quadripunctaria 4.00 1.75
2374 A621 120 l Colias crocea 4.50 2.50
Nos. 2371-2374 (4)   10.00 5.00

1987, Mar. 18 Litho. Perf. 13x13½
2375 A622 200 l multi   1.25 .75

Karabuk
Iron and
Steel
Works,
50th
Anniv.
A623

1987, Apr. 3   Litho.   Perf. 13½x13
2376 A623 50 l Interior   .30 .20
2377 A623 200 l Exterior   .80 .20

Natl. Sovereignty — A624

1987, Apr. 23   Perf. 13½x13
2378 A624 50 l multi   .35 .20

Founding of the Turkish state, 67th anniv.

Architecture — A625

Europa: 50 l, Turkish History Institute,
1951-67, designed by Turgut Cansever with
Ertur Yener. 200 l, Social Insurance Institute,
1963, designed by Sedad Hakki Eldem.

1987, Apr. 28   Perf. 13
2379 A625 50 l multi   10.00 2.00
2380 A625 200 l multi   25.00 4.00

92nd Session, Intl.
Olympic Committee,
Istanbul, May 9-
12 — A626

1987, May 9   Litho.   Perf. 13x13½
2381 A626 200 l multi   1.25 .75

Turkish States Type of 1984

Sixteen states (Devleti and Imparatorlugu
rulers and flags): 10 l, Batu Khan, Golden
Horde State (1227-1502). 20 l, Kutlug Timur
Khan, Great Timur Empire (1368-1507). 50 l,
Babur Shah, Babur Empire (1526-1858).
200 l, Osman Bey Gasi, Ottoman Empire
(1299-1923).

1987, June 20   Perf. 12½x13
2382 A587 10 l multi   .50 .25
2383 A587 20 l multi   1.00 .30
2384 A587 50 l multi   1.50 .30
2385 A587 200 l multi   3.25 1.00
Nos. 2382-2385 (4)   6.25 1.85

Album of the Conqueror, Mehmet II,
15th Cent., Topkapi Palace
Museum — A627

Untitled paintings by Mehmet Siyah Kalem:
10 l, Two warriors, vert. 20 l, Three men, donkey. 50 l, Blackamoor whipping horse. 200 l,
Demon, vert.

Perf. 13½x13, 13x13½
1987, July 1   Litho.
2386 A627 10 l multi   .75 .40
2387 A627 20 l multi   1.00 .40
2388 A627 50 l multi   1.25 .40
2389 A627 200 l multi   2.00 1.00
Nos. 2386-2389 (4)   5.00 2.20

Natl.
Palaces
A628

1987, Sept. 25   Perf. 13½x13
2390 A628 50 l Ihlamur, c. 1850 1.00 .60
2391 A628 200 l Kucuksu Pavil-
               ion, 1857   2.00 .75
See Nos. 2425-2426.

"Tughra," Suleiman's Calligraphic
Signature — A629

Designs: 30 l, Portrait, vert. 200 l, Suleiman
Receiving a Foreign Minister, contemporary
miniature, vert. 270 l, Bust, detail of bas-relief,
The Twenty-Three Law-Givers, entrance to the
gallery of the US House of Representatives.

Litho., Litho. & Engr. (270 l)
1987, Oct. 1   Perf. 13½x13, 13x13½
2392 A629 30 l multi   .50 .35
2393 A629 50 l shown   .75 .45
2394 A629 200 l multi   2.00 .80
2395 A629 270 l multi   2.50 1.10
Nos. 2392-2395 (4)   5.75 2.70

Suleiman the Magnificent (1494-1566), sultan of the Turkish Empire (1520-1566). On No.
2395, the gold ink was applied by a thermographic process producing a shiny, raised
effect.

A630

Presidents: a, Cemal Gursel (1961-1966). b,
Cevdet Sunay (1966-1973). c, Fahri S.

Koruturk (1973-1980). d, Kenan Evren (1982-
). e, Ismet Inonu (1938-1950). f, Celal Bayar
(1950-1960). g, Mustafa Kemal Ataturk (1923-
1938).

1987, Oct. 29   Litho.   Imperf.
Souvenir Sheet
2396 A630 Sheet of 7   6.00 6.00
a.-f.   50 l any single   .60 .60
g.   100 l multi, 26x37mm   .75 .75

A631

1988, Apr. 9   Litho.   Perf. 13
2397 A631 50 l shown   .75 .50
2398 A631 200 l Mosque, archi-
               tectural ele-
               ments   2.25 1.00

Joseph (Mimar) Sinan (1489-1588), architect.

Health — A632

1988, May 4
2399 A632 50 l Immunization,
               horiz.   .20 .20
2400 A632 200 l Fight drug abuse .35 .20
2401 A632 300 l Safe work condi-
               tions, horiz.   .50 .20
2402 A632 600 l Organ donation 1.10 .30
Nos. 2399-2402 (4)   2.15 .90

Europa Issue

Telecommunications — A633

Transport and communication: 200 l, Modes
of transportation, vert.

1988, May 2   Litho.   Perf. 13, 12½
2403 A633 200 l multi   5.00 2.00
2404 A633 600 l multi   15.00 3.00

Steam,
Electric and
Diesel
Locomotives
A634

50 l, American Standard steam engine, c.
1850. 100 l, Steam engine produced in
Esslingen for Turkish railways, 1913. 200 l,
Henschel Krupp steam engine, 1926. 300 l, E
43001 Toshiba electric engine produced in
Japan, 1987. 600 l, MTE-Tulomsas #24361
diesel-electric high-speed engine, 1984.

1988, May 24   Perf. 13
2405 A634 50 l buff, brn & blk 1.00 .50
2406 A634 100 l buff, brn & blk 2.00 1.00
2407 A634 200 l buff, brn & blk 3.00 1.75
2408 A634 300 l buff, brn & blk 3.50 2.00
2409 A634 600 l buff, brn & blk 5.50 3.25
Nos. 2405-2409 (5)   15.00 8.50

Court of
Cassation
(Supreme
Court),
120th
Anniv.
A635

1988, July 1   Litho.   Perf. 13½x13
2410 A635 50 l multi   .50 .30

Bridge Openings — A636

Designs: 200 l, Fatih Sultan Mehmet Bridge, Kavacik-Hisarustu. 300 l, Seto Ohashi (Friendship) Bridges, the Minami and Kita.

1988, July 3   Litho.   Perf. 13x13½
2411 A636 200 l multi   1.25 .75
2412 A636 300 l multi   2.00 1.00

Telephone System A637

1988, Aug. 24   Litho.   Perf. 13½x13
2413 A637 100 l multi   .45 .20

1988 Summer Olympics, Seoul A638

Perf. 12½x13, 13x12½
1988, Sept. 17   Litho.
2414 A638 100 l Running   .50 .20
2415 A638 200 l Archery   .75 .20
2416 A638 400 l Weight lifting   1.00 .25
2417 A638 600 l Gymnastics, vert.   1.50 .35
   Nos. 2414-2417 (4)   3.75 1.00

Naim Suleymanoglu, 1988 Olympic Gold Medalist, Weight Lifting — A639

1988, Oct. 5   Litho.   Perf. 13x12½
2418 A639 1000 l multi   5.00 2.50

Aerospace Industries A640

1988, Oct. 28   Perf. 13½x13, 13x13½
2419 A640 50 l Gear, aircraft, vert.   .20 .20
2420 A640 200 l shown   .60 .20

Butterflies A641

1988, Oct. 28   Perf. 13½x13
2421 A641 100 l Goneptery rhamni   1.50 .75
2422 A641 200 l Chazara briseis   3.50 1.25
2423 A641 400 l Allancastria cerisyi godart   5.00 2.25

2424 A641 600 l Nymphalis antiopa   7.50 3.50
a. Souvenir sheet of 4, #2421-2424   35.00 35.00
   Nos. 2421-2424 (4)   17.50 7.75
ANTALYA '88.

Natl. Palaces Type of 1987
1988, Nov. 3   Litho.   Perf. 13
2425 A628 100 l Maslak Royal Lodge, c. 1890   .50 .50
2426 A628 400 l Yildiz Sale Pavilion, 1889   1.00 1.00

Souvenir Sheet

Kemal Ataturk — A642

1988, Nov. 10   Perf. 13x13½
2427 A642 400 l multi   1.75 1.75

Medicinal Plants of Anatolia A643

1988, Dec. 14   Litho.   Perf. 13
2428 A643 150 l Tilia rubra   .45 .20
2429 A643 300 l Malva silvestris   .65 .20
2430 A643 600 l Hyoscyamus niger   1.25 .20
2431 A643 900 l Atropa belladonna   2.50 .30
   Nos. 2428-2431 (4)   4.85 .90

Stamps of 1983-85 Surcharged

Perf. 13, 11½x12½
1989, Feb. 8   Litho.
2432 A579 50 l on 15 l No. 2263   .20 .20
2433 A608 75 l on 30 l No. 2334   .30 .20
2434 A608 150 l on 20 l No. 2336   .75 .20
   Nos. 2432-2434 (3)   1.25 .60
Surcharge on No. 2432 is slightly different.

Artifacts in the Museum of Anatolian Civilizations, Ankara — A644

Designs: 150 l, Seated Goddess with Child, neolithic bisque figurine, Hacilar, 6th millennium B.C. 300 l, Lead figurine, Alisar Huyuk, Assyrian Trading Colonies Era, c. 19th cent. B.C. 600 l, Human-shaped vase, Kultepe, Assyrian Trading Colonies Era, 18th cent. B.C. 1000 l, Ivory mountain god, Bogazkoy, Hittite Empire, 14th cent. B.C.

1989, Feb. 8   Litho.   Perf. 13½x13
2435 A644 150 l multi   .50 .20
2436 A644 300 l multi   .75 .50
2437 A644 600 l multi   1.25 1.00
2438 A644 1000 l multi   2.50 1.50
   Nos. 2435-2438 (4)   5.00 3.20
See Nos. 2458-2461, 2495-2498, 2520-2523, 2617-2620.

NATO, 40th Anniv. A645

Wmk. 394
1989, Apr. 4   Litho.   Perf. 13½
2439 A645 600 l multi   .90 .20

Europa Issue

Children's Games — A646

Perf. 13x12½
1989, Apr. 23   Wmk. 394
2440 A646 600 l Leapfrog   20.00 3.50
2441 A646 1000 l Open the door, Headbezirgan   30.00 5.00

Steamships — A647

Perf. 13½x13
1989, July 1   Litho.   Wmk. 394
2442 A647 150 l Sahilbent   2.50 1.50
2443 A647 300 l Ragbet   3.75 2.00
2444 A647 500 l Tari   5.00 2.50
2445 A647 1000 l Guzelhisar   7.50 3.75
   Nos. 2442-2445 (4)   18.75 9.75

French Revolution, Bicent. — A648   Kemal Ataturk — A649

Wmk. 394
1989, July 14   Litho.   Perf. 14
2446 A648 600 l multi   1.25 .20

1989, Aug. 16   Perf. 13x13½
2447 A649 2000 l gray & bluish gray   2.00 .50
2448 A649 5000 l gray & deep red brn   5.00 1.25
See Nos. 2485-2486, 2538-2541. For surcharges see Nos. 2655-2656.

No. 2336 Surcharged in Bright Blue
Perf. 11½x12½
1989, Aug. 31   Litho.   Unwmk.
2449 A608 500 l on 20 l   .70 .20

Photography, 150th Anniv. — A650

1989, Oct. 17   Perf. 13½x13
2450 A650 175 l Camera   .25 .20
2451 A650 700 l Shutter   .85 .20

State Exhibition of Paintings and Sculpture A651

Designs: 200 l, Manzara, by Hikmet Onat. 700 l, Sari Saz, by Bedri Rahmi Eyuboglu. 1000 l, Kadin, by Zuhtu Muridoglu.

Perf. 13½x13
1989, Oct. 30   Litho.   Wmk. 394
2452 A651 200 l multicolored   .25 .20
2453 A651 700 l multicolored   .80 .20
2454 A651 1000 l multicolored   1.10 .30
   Nos. 2452-2454 (3)   2.15 .70

Jawaharlal Nehru, 1st Prime Minister of Independent India — A652

1989, Nov. 14   Perf. 13½x12½
2455 A652 700 l multicolored   .80 .20

Sea Turtles A653

1989, Nov. 16   Perf. 13½x13
2456 A653 700 l Caretta caretta   2.00 1.25
2457 A653 1000 l Chelonia mydas   4.50 2.50
a. Souv. sheet of 2, #2456-2457   12.00 12.00

Artifacts Type of 1989
Perf. 13x12½, 12½x13
1990, Feb. 8   Litho.   Wmk. 394
2458 A644 100 l Ivory female deity   .25 .25
2459 A644 200 l Ceremonial vessel   .40 .40
2460 A644 500 l Seated goddess pendant   .90 .65
2461 A644 700 l Carved lion   1.50 1.10
   Nos. 2458-2461 (4)   3.05 2.40
Nos. 2458 and 2460 vert.

Wars of Dardanelles, 1915 — A654

1990, Mar. 18   Perf. 13
2462 A654 1000 l multicolored   .85 .20

EXPO '90 Intl. Garden and Greenery Exposition, Osaka — A655

Illustration reduced.

Perf. 12½x13
1990, Apr. 1   Litho.   Wmk. 394
2463 1000 l Bridge at left   1.00 .25
2464 1000 l Pavilion at left   1.00 .25
a. A655 Pair, #2463-2464   2.00 .75

Nos. 2301, 2368 and 2284
Surcharged
Perfs. as Before

1990, Apr. 4				Litho.	
2465	A589	50 l on 5 l	#2301	.60	.20
2466	A620	100 l on 10 l	#2368	1.50	.20
2467	A589	200 l on 70 l	#2284	3.50	.25
		Nos. 2465-2467 (3)		5.60	.65

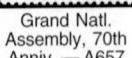

Grand Natl.
Assembly, 70th
Anniv. — A657

Europa
1990 — A658

1990, Apr. 23			Perf. 13	
2468	A657	300 l multicolored	.50	.50

1990, May 2

Post offices.

2469	A658	700 l Ulus, Ankara	7.50	2.75
2470	A658	1000 l Sirkeci, Istanbul, horiz.	10.00	3.00

8th
European
Supreme
Courts
Conf.
A659

1990, May 7			Litho.	Perf. 12½x13	
2471	A659	1000 l multicolored		1.50	.75

Salamandra Salamandra — A660

World Environment Day: No. 2473, Triturus vittatus. No. 2474, Bombina bombina. No. 2475, Hyla arborea, vert.

1990, June 5			Perf. 13½x13	
2472	A660	300 l multicolored	.50	.50
2473	A660	500 l multicolored	.50	.50
2474	A660	1000 l multicolored	1.00	1.00
2475	A660	1500 l multicolored	1.75	1.75
		Nos. 2472-2475 (4)	3.75	3.75

Turkey-Japan Relations, Cent. — A661

1990, June 13			Perf. 12½x13	
2476	A661	1000 l multicolored	1.50	1.00

**Traffic Types of 1987 and Nos.
2283-2284 Surcharged**

1990, June 20			Perf. 14	
2477	A620	150 l on 10 l	2.00	.50
2478	A620	300 l on 20 l	3.00	.50

			Perf. 11½x12½	
2479	A589	300 l on 70 l	#2284	3.00	.75
2480	A589	1500 l on 20 l	#2283	8.75	.75
		Nos. 2477-2480 (4)		16.75	2.50

Boats in Saintes Marines — A662

Paintings by Vincent Van Gogh (1853-1890): 300 l, Self-portrait, vert. 1000 l, Vase with Sunflowers, vert. 1500 l, Road of Cypress and Stars.

Wmk. 394

1990, July 29			Litho.	Perf. 13	
2481	A662	300 l multicolored		1.50	1.00
2482	A662	700 l multicolored		2.75	1.50
2483	A662	1000 l multicolored		3.25	2.25
2484	A662	1500 l multicolored		3.50	3.00
		Nos. 2481-2484 (4)		11.00	7.75

Ataturk Type of 1989

1990, Aug. 1		Unwmk.	Perf. 14	
2485	A649	500 l gray & olive grn	.75	.20
2486	A649	1000 l gray & rose vio	1.00	.40

A664   A665

			Perf. 13x13½	
1990, Aug. 22			Wmk. 394	
2487	A664	300 l multicolored	.50	.50

Intl. Literacy Year.

1990, Oct. 17   Litho.   Perf. 13x13½

State exhibition of paintings and sculpture by: 300 l, Nurullah Berk. 700 l, Cevat Dereli. 1000 l, Nijad Sirel.

2488	A665	300 l multicolored	.30	.20
2489	A665	700 l multicolored	.60	.25
2490	A665	1000 l multicolored	.90	.35
		Nos. 2488-2490 (3)	1.80	.80

PTT, 150th
Anniv.
A666

Past and present communication methods: 200 l, Post rider, truck, train, airplane, ship. 250 l, Telegraph key, computer terminal. 400 l, Telephone switchboard, computerized telephone exchange. 1500 l, Power lines, satellite.

1990, Oct. 23			Perf. 14	
2491	A666	200 l multicolored	.20	.20
2492	A666	250 l multicolored	.20	.20
2493	A666	400 l multicolored	.30	.20
2494	A666	1500 l multicolored	1.10	2.25
a.		Souv. sheet of 4, #2491-2494	3.00	2.25
		Nos. 2491-2494 (4)	1.80	2.85

For surcharges see Nos. 2657-2659.

Artifacts Type of 1989

300 l, Figurine of a woman, c. 5000-4500 BC. 500 l, Sistrum, c. 2100-2000 BC. 1000 l, Spouted vessel with 3-footed pedestal, c. 2000-1750 BC. 1500 l, Ceremonial vessel, 1900-1700 BC.

1991, Feb. 8			Litho.	Perf. 13x12½	
2495	A644	300 l multi		.25	.20
2496	A644	500 l multi		.50	.30
2497	A644	1000 l multi		.75	.50
2498	A644	1500 l multi		1.50	.75
		Nos. 2495-2498 (4)		3.00	1.75

Nos. 2495-2498 are vert.

Lakes of
Turkey
A667

Wmk. 394

1991, Apr. 24		Litho.	Perf. 13	
2499	A667	250 l Abant	.20	.20
2500	A667	500 l Egridir	.40	.20
2501	A667	1500 l Van	1.10	.60
		Nos. 2499-2501 (3)	1.70	1.00

Europa — A668

Unwmk.

1991, May 6		Litho.	Perf. 13	
2502	A668	1000 l multicolored	15.00	3.50
2503	A668	1500 l multi, diff.	22.50	4.00

Natl. Statistics
Day — A669

1991, May 9			Perf. 13½x13	
2504	A669	500 l multicolored	.40	.20

Eastern Mediterranean Fiber Optic
Cable System — A670

1991, May 13

2505	A670	500 l multicolored	.40	.20

European Conf. of
Transportation
Ministers — A671

1991, May 22			Perf. 13	
2506	A671	500 l multicolored	.60	.40

Caricature
Art
A672

500 l, "Amcabey" by Cemal Nadir Guler. 1000 l, "Abdulcanbaz" by Turhan Selcuk, vert.

Wmk. 394

1991, Sept. 11		Litho.	Perf. 13	
2507	A672	500 l multicolored	.60	.20
2508	A672	1000 l multicolored	1.00	.50

Ceramics
A673

Wall facings: 500 l, 13th cent. Seljuk bird. 1500 l, 16th cent. Ottoman floral pattern.

1991, Sept. 23			Perf. 13½x13	
2509	A673	500 l multicolored	.40	.20
2510	A673	1500 l multicolored	1.25	.60

Symposium on Intl.
Protection of Human
Rights,
Antalya — A674

1991, Oct. 4			Perf. 13x12½	
2511	A674	500 l multicolored	.40	.20

Southeastern
Anatolia
Irrigation and
Power Project
A675

1991, Oct. 6		Unwmk.	Perf. 13½x13	
2512	A675	500 l multicolored	.40	.20

Turkish Fairy
Tales — A676

Baldboy: 500 l, With genie. 1000 l, At party. 1500 l, Plowing field.

1991, Oct. 9			Perf. 13x13½	
2513	A676	500 l multicolored	.40	.20
2514	A676	1000 l multicolored	.80	.40
2515	A676	1500 l multicolored	1.25	.60
		Nos. 2513-2515 (3)	2.45	1.20

Snakes
A677

			Perf. 12½x13	
1991, Oct. 23			Wmk. 394	
2516	A677	250 l Eryx jaculus	2.00	.50
2517	A677	500 l Elaphe quatuorlineata	3.00	1.00
2518	A677	1000 l Vipera xanthina	6.00	2.00
2519	A677	1500 l Vipera kaznakovi	8.00	3.50
		Nos. 2516-2519 (4)	19.00	7.00

World Environment Day.

Antiquities Type of 1989

300 l, Statuette of Mother Goddess, Neolithic, 6000 B.C., vert. 500 l, Hasanoglan statuette, Early Bronze Age, 3000 B.C., vert. 1000 l, Inandik vase, Old Hittite, 18th cent. B.C., vert. 1500 l, Lion statuette, Urartian, 8th cent. B.C., vert.

Wmk. 394

1992, Feb. 12		Litho.	Perf. 13	
2520	A644	300 l multicolored	.25	.20
2521	A644	500 l multicolored	.40	.20
2522	A644	1000 l multicolored	.80	.40
2523	A644	1500 l multicolored	1.25	.60
		Nos. 2520-2523 (4)	2.70	1.40

Discovery
of
America,
500th
Anniv.
A678

Wmk. 394

1992, May 4		**Litho.**		***Perf. 13***	
2524	A678	1500 l	shown	7.00	2.00
2525	A678	2000 l	Balloons, vert.	12.50	3.00

Europa.

Settlement
of Jews in
Turkey,
500th
Anniv.
A679

1992, May 15			***Perf. 12½x13***	
2526	A679	1500 l multicolored	1.00	1.00

A681   A682

Wmk. 394

1992, June 1		**Litho.**	***Perf. 13***	
2529	A681	500 l multicolored	.40	.40

Turkish Court of Accounts, 130th anniv.

1992, June 4

2530	A682	1500 l multicolored	.75	.75

Economics Congress, Izmir.

World Environment Day — A683

1992, June 5		**Litho.**		***Perf. 13***	
2531	A683	500 l	Vanellus vanellus	.50	.50
2532	A683	1000 l	Oriolus oriolus	.75	.50
2533	A683	1500 l	Tadorna tadorna	1.00	.50
2534	A683	2000 l	Halcyon smyrnensis, vert.	1.50	1.00
		Nos. 2531-2534 (4)		3.75	2.50

Ataturk Type of 1989 and:

Kemal   A683b
Ataturk — A683a

10,000 l, Full face. 100,000 l, Facing left.

Perf. 13, 14 (#2539, 2541, 2543-2544A)

1992-96		**Litho.**	**Unwmk.**	
2538	A649	250 l gold, brn & org	1.25	.20
2539	A649	5000 l gold & vio	1.50	.40
2540	A649	10,000 l gold & blue	3.75	1.90

2541	A649	20,000 l gold & lil rose	6.50	1.60
2542	A683a	50,000 l multi	3.50	1.75
2543	A683b	50,000 l lake & pink	2.00	.90
2544	A683b	100,000 l grn bl & yel org	3.50	1.75
		Nos. 2538-2544 (7)	22.00	8.50

Issued: 250 l, 10,000 l, 5/28/92; 5000 l, 20,000 l, 9/29/93; #2542, 11/10/94; #2543, 100,000 l, 6/1/96.
For surcharges see Nos. 2655, 2732.

Black Sea
Economic
Cooperation
Summit — A684

Wmk. 394

1992, June 25		**Litho.**	***Perf. 13***	
2545	A684	1500 l multicolored	.60	.30

1992
Summer
Olympics,
Barcelona
A685

1992, July 25			**Wmk. 394**		
2546	A685	500 l	Doves	.30	.20
2547	A685	1000 l	Boxing	.40	.25
2548	A685	1500 l	Weight lifting	.75	.30
2549	A685	2000 l	Wrestling	1.50	.45
		Nos. 2546-2549 (4)		2.95	1.20

Anatolian
Folktales — A686

Scenes: 500 l, Woman carrying milk to soldiers. 1000 l, Pouring milk into trough. 1500 l, Soldiers dipping into trough.

Perf. 13x12½

1992, Sept. 23		**Litho.**	**Wmk. 394**	
2550	A686	500 l multicolored	.20	.20
2551	A686	1000 l multicolored	.30	.20
2552	A686	1500 l multicolored	.50	.25
		Nos. 2550-2552 (3)	1.00	.65

Turkish Handicrafts — A687

500 l, Embroidered flowers. 1000 l, Dolls in traditional costumes, vert. 3000 l, Saddlebags.

1992, Oct. 21		***Perf. 13½x13, 13x13½***		
2553	A687	500 l multicolored	.20	.20
2554	A687	1000 l multicolored	.35	.20
2555	A687	3000 l multicolored	.95	.50
		Nos. 2553-2555 (3)	1.50	.90

See Nos. 2585-2588, 2611-2612.

Fruits — A688

Wmk. 394

1992, Nov. 25		**Litho.**		***Perf. 13***	
2556	A688	500 l	Cherries	.25	.20
2557	A688	1000 l	Peaches	.50	.20
2558	A688	3000 l	Grapes	1.00	.45
2559	A688	5000 l	Apples	2.00	.75
		Nos. 2556-2559 (4)		3.75	1.60

See Nos. 2565-2568.

Famous
Men — A689

Designs: No. 2560, Sait Faik Abasiyanik (1906-54), writer. No. 2561, Fikret Mualla Saygi (1904-67), artist. No. 2562, Cevat Sakir Kabaagacli (1886-1973), author. No. 2563, Muhsin Ertugrul (1892-1979), actor and producer. No. 2564, Asik Veysel Satiroglu (1894-1973), composer.

Perf. 14, 13½x13 (#2561, 2564)

1992, Dec. 30			**Litho.**	
2560	A689	T multicolored	.65	.20
2561	A689	T multicolored	.65	.20
2562	A689	M multicolored	.90	.20
2563	A689	M multicolored	.90	.20
2564	A689	M multicolored	.90	.20
		Nos. 2560-2564 (5)	4.00	1.00

Value on day of issue: Nos. 2560-2561, 500 l. Nos. 2562-2564, 1000 l.
See Nos. 2577-2581.

Fruit Type of 1992
Wmk. 394

1993, Apr. 28		**Litho.**		***Perf. 13***	
2565	A688	500 l	Bananas	.50	.30
2566	A688	1000 l	Oranges	.50	.50
2567	A688	3000 l	Pears	1.00	.75
2568	A688	5000 l	Pomegranates	2.00	1.40
		Nos. 2565-2568 (4)		4.00	2.95

Europa — A690

Sculptures by: 1000 l, Hadi Bara. 3000 l, Zuhtu Muridoglu.

1993, May 3

2569	A690	1000 l multicolored	1.25	.60
2570	A690	3000 l multicolored	2.25	1.00

A691

Wmk. 394

1993, July 6		**Litho.**	***Perf. 13***	
2571	A691	2500 l lt bl, dk bl & gold	.75	.50

Economic Cooperation Organization Meeting, Istanbul.

Houses — A692

1993, July 7

Various houses from Black Sea region.

2572	A692	1000 l	multicolored	.50	.20
2573	A692	2500 l	multi, horiz.	.50	.40
2574	A692	3000 l	multicolored	1.00	.60
2575	A692	5000 l	multi, horiz.	1.00	.80
		Nos. 2572-2575 (4)		3.00	2.00

See Nos. 2604-2607, 2631-2634, 2647-2650, 2676-2679.

Hodja Ahmet Yesevi (1093-1166),
Poet — A693

1993, July 28

2576	A693	3000 l lt bl, dk bl & gold	1.00	.40

Famous Men Type of 1992

Designs: No. 2577, Haci Arif Bey (1831-84), composer. No. 2578, Neyzen Tevfik Kolayli (1878-1953), poet. No. 2579, Munir Nurettin Selcuk (1900-81), composer, musician. No. 2580, Cahit Sitki Taranci (1910-56), poet. No. 2581, Orhan Veli Kanik (1914-50), writer.

Perf. 14, 13½x13 (2578-2580)

1993, Aug. 4		**Litho.**	**Unwmk.**	
2577	A689	T brown & red brown	.65	.20
2578	A689	T brown & red brown	.65	.20
2579	A689	M brown & red brown	.90	.20
2580	A689	M brown & red brown	.90	.20
2581	A689	M brown & red brown	.90	.20
		Nos. 2577-2581 (5)	4.00	1.00

Value on day of issue: Nos. 2577-2578, 500 l. Nos. 2579-2581, 1000 l.

Istanbul,
Proposed
Site for
2000
Olympics
A694

1993, Aug. 11			***Perf. 12½x13***	
2582	A694	2500 l multicolored	.80	.40

Protection of Mediterranean Sea
Against Pollution — A695

Unwmk.

1993, Oct. 12		**Litho.**	***Perf. 13***	
2583	A695	1000 l	Amphora on sea floor	.20	.20
2584	A695	3000 l	Dolphin jumping	.50	.25

Handicrafts Type of 1992
Perf. 12½x13, 13x12½

1993, Oct. 21				**Wmk. 394**	
2585	A687	1000 l	Painted rug	.20	.20
2586	A687	2500 l	Earrings	.40	.20
2587	A687	5000 l	Money purse, vert.	.80	.40
		Nos. 2585-2587 (3)		1.40	.80

Republic, 70th Anniv. — A696

1993, Oct. 29   Wmk. 394   Perf. 13
2588 A696 1000 l multicolored .40 .40

Civil Defence Organization — A697

Perf. 12½x13
1993, Nov. 25   Unwmk.
2589 A697 1000 l multicolored .40 .40

Turksat Satellite — A698   Natl. Water Project — A699

Designs: 1500 l, Satellite, globe, map of Turkey. 5000 l, Satellite transmissions to areas in Europe and Asia.

Perf. 13x13½
1994, Jan. 21   Litho.   Wmk. 394
2590 A698 1500 l multicolored .20 .20
2591 A698 5000 l multicolored .55 .20

1994, Feb. 28   Perf. 13x12½
2592 A699 1500 l multicolored .40 .30

Native Cuisine A700

Perf. 12½x13
1994, Mar. 23   Litho.   Wmk. 394
2593 A700 1000 l Ezogel in corbasi .50 .50
2594 A700 1500 l Mixed dolma .50 .50
2595 A700 3500 l Shish kebabs .50 .50
2596 A700 5000 l Baklava 1.00 .50
    Nos. 2593-2596 (4) 2.50 2.00

Europa A701

1500 l, Marie Curie (1867-1934), chemist, vert. 5000 l, Albert Einstein (1879-1955), physicist.

Unwmk.
1994, May 2   Litho.   Perf. 13
2597 A701 1500 l multicolored .50 .50
2598 A701 5000 l multicolored 1.50 1.50

World Environment Day — A703

Views of: 6000 l, Antalya. 8500 l, Mugla, vert.

Wmk. 394
1994, June 5   Litho.   Perf. 13
2602 A703 6000 l multicolored 1.00 .75
2603 A703 8500 l multicolored 1.60 1.00

Houses Type of 1993
2500 l, 2-story housing complex. 3500 l, 3-story home with balconies. 6000 l, Tri-level country home. 8500 l, 2-story home.

1994, July 7
2604 A692 2500 l multi, horiz. .40 .40
2605 A692 3500 l multi, horiz. .40 .40
2606 A692 6000 l multi, horiz. .40 .40
2607 A692 8500 l multi, horiz. 1.25 .40
    Nos. 2604-2607 (4) 2.45 1.60

Tourism A704

1994, Aug. 3
2608 A704 5000 l Hiking .50 .30
2609 A704 10,000 l Rafting 1.00 .50

Project of the Year 2001 A705

1994, Aug. 27
2610 A705 2500 l multicolored .50 .50

Handicrafts Type of 1992
Designs: 7500 l, Kusak pattern used on 18th cent. clothing, vert. 12,000 l, Pacalik pattern used on 19th cent. clothing.

1994, Oct. 21
2611 A687 7500 l multicolored 1.00 .50
2612 A687 12,500 l multicolored 1.50 1.50

Mushrooms — A706

1994, Nov. 16
2613 A706 2500 l Morchella conica .50 .50
2614 A706 5000 l Agaricus bernardii .75 .75
2615 A706 7500 l Lactarius deliciosus 1.25 1.25
2616 A706 12,500 l Macrolepiota procera 2.50 2.50
    Nos. 2613-2616 (4) 5.00 5.00
    See Nos. 2637-2640.

Antiquities Type of 1989
Lydian Treasures, 6th cent. B.C.: 2500 l, Silver pitcher, vert. 5000 l, Silver incense burner, vert. 7500 l, Gold, glass necklace. 12,500 l, Gold brooch.

1994, Dec. 7
2617 A644 2500 l multicolored .50 .35
2618 A644 5000 l multicolored .70 .40
2619 A644 7500 l multicolored 1.10 .60
2620 A644 12,500 l multicolored 2.00 .80
    Nos. 2617-2620 (4) 4.30 2.15

Nevruz, New Day A707

1995, Mar. 21
2621 A707 3500 l multicolored .40 .40

Europa — A708

1995, May 5
2622 A708 3500 l Flowers 1.00 1.00
2623 A708 15,000 l Olive branch 2.00 2.00

Istanbul '96 World Stamp Exhibition — A709

a, 7000 l, Buildings. b, 25,000 l, Tower, buildings. c, 7000 l, Mosque, city along harbor. c, 25,000 l, Residential area, mosque, harbor.

1995, May 24
2624 A709 Block of 4, #a.-d. 5.00 2.50
    Nos. 2624a-2624b and 2624c-2624d are each continuous designs.

European Nature Conservation Year — A710

1995, June 5
2625 A710 5000 l Field of poppies .30 .20
2626 A710 15,000 l Trees .85 .40
2627 A710 25,000 l Mountain valley 1.40 .70
    Nos. 2625-2627 (3) 2.55 1.30

A711   A712

1995, Feb. 1
2628 A711 15,000 l red & blue 1.25 1.25
    Motion Pictures, cent.

1995, Apr. 23
2629 A712 5000 l multicolored .40 .40
    1sh Conference of the Moslem Women Parliamentaries, Pakistan.

Houses Type of 1993
5000 l, 2-story block house. 10,000 l, Tower of part-stone house. 15,000 l, Interior view of 2-story house, horiz. 20,000 l, Three unit-connecting apartment, horiz.

1995, July 7
2631 A692 5000 l multicolored .75 .35
2632 A692 10,000 l multicolored 1.00 .35
2633 A692 15,000 l multicolored 1.10 .50
2634 A692 20,000 l multicolored 1.25 1.00
    Nos. 2631-2634 (4) 4.10 2.20

UN, 50th Anniv. — A713

1995, Oct. 24
2635 A713 15,000 l shown .80 .40
2636 A713 30,000 l UN emblem, "50" 1.60 .80

Mushroom Type of 1994
Designs: 5000 l, Amanita phalloides. 10,000 l, Lepiota helveola. 20,000 l, Gyromitra esculenta. 30,000 l, Amanita gemmata.

1995, Nov. 16
2637 A706 5000 l multicolored .50 .50
2638 A706 10,000 l multicolored .80 .80
2639 A706 20,000 l multicolored 1.75 1.75
2640 A706 30,000 l multicolored 2.00 2.00
    Nos. 2637-2640 (4) 5.05 5.05

Children's Rights A714

6,000 l, Rainbow, hearts, flower, sun in sky. 10,000 l, Child's hand drawing letter "A."

1996, Mar. 13
2641 A714 6,000 l multicolored .40 .40
2642 A714 10,000 l multicolored 1.10 1.00

Fauna — A715

Designs: a, 5,000 l, Bee. b, 10,000 l, Dog. c, 15,000 l, Rooster. d, 30,000 l, Fish.

1996, Apr. 10   Unwmk.
2643 A715 Sheet of 4, #a.-d. 5.00 5.00
    Instanbul '96.

Famous Women A716

Perf. 12½x13
1996, May 5   Litho.   Unwmk.
2644 A716 10,000 l Nene Hatun 1.50 1.50
2645 A716 40,000 l Halide Edip Adivar 3.00 3.00
    Europa.

World Environment Day — A717

Unwmk.
1996, June 3   **Litho.**   *Perf. 13*
2646 A717 50,000 l multicolored   1.75   .90

Houses Type of 1993
Designs: 10,000 l, Tri-level block house, horiz. 15,000 l, Two story with bay window, gate at entrance to side courtyard, horiz. 25,000 l, Two story townhouse, double wooden doors at bottom. 50,000 l, Flat-roofed, two-story townhouse.

1996, July 7   *Perf. 13*
2647 A692 10,000 l multicolored   .35   .20
2648 A692 15,000 l multicolored   .60   .30
2649 A692 25,000 l multicolored   .90   .45
2650 A692 50,000 l multicolored   1.75   .90
    Nos. 2647-2650 (4)   3.60 1.85

1996 Summer Olympic Games, Atlanta — A718

a, 10,000 l, Archery. b, 15,000 l, Wrestling. c, 25,000 l, Weight lifting. d, 50,000 l, Hurdles.

1996, July 19
2651 A718   Sheet of 4, #a.-d.   6.50 6.50
    ISTANBUL '96. Exists imperf.

Turkish Press, 50th Anniv. A719

1996, July 24   *Perf. 12½x13*
2652 A719 15,000 l multicolored   .60   .30

Euro '96, European Soccer Championships, Great Britain — A720

1996, June 8   *Perf. 13*
2653 A720 15,000 l Player, vert.   .60   .30
2654 A720 50,000 l Soccer ball, flags   1.75   .90

Nos. 2447, 2491, 2493-2494, 2538 Surcharged in Orange or Deep Violet Blue

or

Perfs., Printing Methods as Before
1996, July 22
2655 A649   T on 250 l #2538
       (O)   .75   .20
2656 A649   T on 2000 l #2447   .75   .20

2657 A666   M on 200 l #2491   1.10   .20
2658 A666   M on 400 l #2493   1.10   .20
2659 A666   M on 1500 l #2494   1.10   .20
    Nos. 2655-2659 (5)   4.80 1.00

Nos. 2655-2656 and 2657-2659 had face values of 10,000 l and 15,000 l on day of issue.
See No. 2732.

Methods of Transportation — A721

a, 25,000 l, Airplane (b). b, 50,000 l, Helicopter, ship (d). c, 75,000 l, Train. d, 100,000 l, Bus (c).

Unwmk.
1996, Sept. 27   **Litho.**   *Perf. 13*
2660 A721   Sheet of 4, #a.-d.   10.00 10.00
    Istanbul '96.

New Year A722

Unwmk.
1996, Oct. 23   **Litho.**   *Perf. 13*
2661 A722 15,000 l multicolored   .55   .30

Social and Cultural Heritage A723

10,000 l, Public Library, Bayezit, Amasya. 15,000 l, Mosque and hospital, Divrigi.

1996, Dec. 17   **Litho.**   *Perf. 13*
2662 A723 10,000 l multicolored   .30   .30
2663 A723 15,000 l multicolored   .50   .50

Stories and Legends — A724

Europa: 25,000 l, Little children dressed in flowers and leaves riding a giant peacock. 70,000 l, Genie, man being riding a giant bird.

1997, May 5   **Litho.**   *Perf. 13*
2664 A724 25,000 l multicolored   *1.25 1.25*
2665 A724 70,000 l multicolored   *2.50 2.50*

White Cat — A725

Designs: a, 25,000 l, Tail, hindquarters. b, 50,000 l, Back legs. c, 75,000 l, Front legs. d, 150,000 l, Face.

1997, Apr. 23
2666 A725   Sheet of 4, #a.-d.   9.00 7.50

Language Day — A726

1997, May 13   **Litho.**   *Perf. 13*
2667 A726 25,000 l multicolored   .50   .50

World Environment Day — A727

1997, June 5
2668 A727 35,000 l multicolored   .60   .60

Orchids — A728

Designs: 25,000 l, Ophrys tenthredinifera. 70,000 l, Ophrys apifera.

1997, May 28
2669 A728 25,000 l multicolored   .60   .20
2670 A728 70,000 l multicolored   1.40   .45

25th Intl. Istanbul Festival A729

1997, June 13   *Perf. 13½*
Background Color
2671 A729   15,000 l blue   .20   .20
2672 A729   25,000 l pink   .50   .50
2673 A729   70,000 l blue green   1.25 1.25
2674 A729   75,000 l purple   1.50 1.50
2675 A729   100,000 l green blue   2.00 2.00
    Nos. 2671-2675 (5)   5.45 5.45

House Type of 1993
Inscribed: 25,000 l, Bir Urfa Evi, vert. 40,000 l, Bir Mardin Evi. 80,000 l, Bir Diyarbakir Evi. 100,000 l, Kemaliye'de Bir Ev, vert.

1997, July 7   **Litho.**   *Perf. 13*
2676 A692   25,000 l multicolored   .40   .40
2677 A692   40,000 l multicolored   .80   .80
2678 A692   80,000 l multicolored   1.50 1.50
2679 A692   100,000 l multicolored   2.00 2.00
    Nos. 2676-2679 (4)   4.70 4.70

A730   A731

Flowers: 40,000 l, Lilium candidum. 100,000 l, Euphorbia pulcherima.

1997, Sept. 8   **Litho.**   *Perf. 13*
2680 A730   40,000 l multicolored   .85   .20
2681 A730 100,000 l multicolored   1.90   .50

1997, Sept. 13
World Air Games: No. 2682, Hang gliding. No. 2683, Sailplane. No. 2684, Man pointing up at biplanes. No. 2685, Hot air balloon.
2682 A731   40,000 l multicolored   .80   .80
2683 A731   40,000 l multicolored   .80   .80
2684 A731 100,000 l multicolored   2.25 2.25
2685 A731 100,000 l multicolored   3.00 3.00
    Nos. 2682-2685 (4)   6.85 6.85

Forestry Congress A732

1997, Oct. 13   **Litho.**   *Perf. 13*
2686 A732 50,000 l multicolored   1.00 1.00

15th European Gymnastics Congress — A733

1997, Oct. 13
2687 A733 100,000 l multicolored   2.00 2.00

Traditional Women's Headcovers A734

1997, Nov. 19   **Litho.**   *Perf. 13*
2688 A734   50,000 l Gaziantep   1.00   .50
2689 A734   50,000 l Canakkale   1.00   .50
2690 A734 100,000 l Isparta   1.75 1.00
2691 A734 100,000 l Bursa   1.75 1.00
    Nos. 2688-2691 (4)   5.50 3.00

See Nos. 2711-2714, 2748-2751, 2765-2768.

1998 Winter Olympic Games, Nagano — A735

Slalom skiers: No. 2692, #1 on bib. No. 2693, #119 on bib.

1998, Feb. 7   **Litho.**   *Perf. 13*
2692   125,000 l multicolored   2.00 2.00
2693   125,000 l multicolored   2.00 2.00
   a. A735 Pair, #2692-2693   4.25 4.25

Intl. Year of the Ocean — A736

Designs: a, 50,000 l, Turtle, jellyfish. b, 75,000 l, Fish, octopus. c, 125,000 l, Coral, crab. d, 125,000 l, Fish, coral, starfish.

1998, Apr. 18   **Litho.**   *Perf. 13*
2694 A736   Sheet of 4, #a.-d.   6.00 6.00

Dardenelles Campaign — A737

Memorial Statues: #2695, "Mother with Children," Natl. War Memorial, Wellington. #2696, "With Great Respect to the Mehmetcik, Gallipoli" (Turkish soldier carrying wounded ANZAC).

1998, Mar. 18   Litho.   Perf. 13
2695 A737 125,000 l multicolored 1.10 1.10
2696 A737 125,000 l multicolored 1.10 1.10

See New Zealand Nos. 1490-1491.

A738

A739

Europa (National Festivals and Holidays): 100,000 l, Kemal Ataturk, natl. flag, people celebrating. 150,000 l, Ataturk, natl. flag, children of different races celebrating together.

1998, May 5
2697 A738 100,000 l multicolored 1.25 1.25
2698 A738 150,000 l multicolored 2.25 2.25

1998, May 1   Litho.   Perf. 13

Tulips: 50,000 l, Sylvestris. 75,000 l, Armena (pink). 100,000 l, Armena (violet). 125,000 l, Saxatilis.

2699 A739 50,000 l multicolored .65 .65
2700 A739 75,000 l multicolored 1.10 1.10
2701 A739 100,000 l multicolored 1.25 1.25
2702 A739 125,000 l multicolored 2.00 2.00
    Nos. 2699-2702 (4)   5.00 5.00

Souvenir Sheet

World Environment Day — A740

Owls: a, Two on branches. b, One flying, one standing.

1998, June 5   Litho.   Perf. 13½
2703 A740 150,000 l Sheet of 2,
        #a.-b.   4.00 4.00

Contemporary Arts — A741

75,000 l, Couple dancing. 100,000 l, Man playing cello. 150,000 l, Ballerina.

1998, Aug. 14   Litho.   Perf. 13
2704 A741 75,000 l multi   .70 .35
2705 A741 100,000 l multi, vert.   .90 .45
2706 A741 150,000 l multi, vert.   1.40 .70
    Nos. 2704-2706 (3)   3.00 1.50

Kemal Ataturk — A742

1998, Aug. 20   Litho.   Perf. 13
2707 A742 150,000 l cl & brn   1.25 .50
2708 A742 175,000 l bl & rose
        brn   1.75 .65
2709 A742 250,000 l brn & cl   2.25 .95
2710 A742 500,000 l brn & dk
        bl   5.00 1.90
    Nos. 2707-2710 (4)   10.25 4.00

Traditional Headcovers Type of 1997

1998, Nov. 24   Litho.   Perf. 13
2711 A734 75,000 l Afyon   .70 .35
2712 A734 75,000 l Ankara   .70 .35
2713 A734 175,000 l Mus   1.60 .80
2714 A734 175,000 l Mugla   1.60 .80
    Nos. 2711-2714 (4)   4.60 2.30

Turkish Republic, 75th Anniv. — A743

275,000 l, Flag, silhouette of Ataturk.

1998, Oct. 29   Litho.   Perf. 13
2715 A743 175,000 l shown   1.75 .90
    a.   Souvenir sheet of 1, imperf.   1.75 1.25
2716 A743 275,000 l red & blk   2.75 1.40
    a.   Souvenir sheet of 1, imperf.   2.75 2.00

Nos. 2715a, 2716a have simulated perforations.

Famous People A744

#2717, Ihap Hulusi Görey (1898-1986). #2718, Bedia Muvahht (1897-1993). No. 2719, Feza Gürsey (1921-92). #2720, Haldun Taner (1915-86). #2721, Vasfi Riza Zobu (1902-92).

1998, Dec. 31   Photo.   Perf. 13
2717 A744 M gray bl, bl & plum   1.25 .25
2718 A744 M lil, dp lil & plum   1.25 .25
2719 A744 T org, brn & plum   1.50 .40
2720 A744 T gray vio, vio &
        plum   1.50 .40
2721 A744 T grn, blk & plum   1.50 .40
    Nos. 2717-2721 (5)   7.00 1.70

On day of issue, Nos. 2717-2718 were valued at 50,000 l each, and Nos. 2719-2721 were valued at 75,000 l each.

NATO, 50th Anniv. A745

1999, Apr. 4   Litho.   Perf. 13
2722 A745 200,000 l multicolored 2.00 1.50

Ottoman Empire, 700th Anniv. A746

Designs: No. 2723, Man on horse surrounded by people in buildings. No. 2724, Man on horse, three men in foreground. No. 2725, Men seated.
    No. 2726, Man on white horse, castle. No. 2727, Group of women, horiz.

1999, Apr. 12
2723 A746 175,000 l multicolored 1.50 1.10
2724 A746 175,000 l multicolored 1.50 1.10
2725 A746 175,000 l multicolored 1.50 1.10
    Nos. 2723-2725 (3)   4.50 3.30
Size: 79x119mm, 119x79mm
Imperf
2726 A746 200,000 l multicolored 1.50 1.50
2727 A746 200,000 l multicolored 1.50 1.50

Europa A747

Natl. Parks: 175,000 l, Köprülü Canyon, vert. 200,000 l, Kackarlar.

Perf. 13¼x13, 13x13¼
1999, May 5   Litho.
2728 A747 175,000 l multicolored 2.00 2.00
2729 A747 200,000 l multicolored 2.00 2.00

World Environment Day — A748

No. 2730: a, 100,000 l, Tetrax tetrax. 200,000 l, Hoplopterus spinosus.
    No. 2731: a, 100,000 l, Marbled duck. b, 200,000 l, Sitta kruperi.

1999, June 3   Litho.   Perf. 13¼
2730 A748 Sheet of 2, #a.-b.   2.50 2.50
2731 A748 Sheet of 2, #a.-b.   2.50 2.50

See Nos. 2763-2764.

No. 2538 Surcharged in Violet Blue

1999   Litho.   Perf. 13
2732 A649 T on 250 l #2537   .75 .40

No. 2732 sold for 50,000 l on day of issue.

Souvenir Sheet

National Congress During the War for Independence — A749

Designs: a, 100,000 l, Ataturk, two other men, building. b, 100,000 l, Ataturk, two other men seated. c, 200,000 l, Two men standing in front of building. d, 200,000 l, Ataturk standing in front of building.

Perf. 13¼x13
1999, June 22   Litho.   Unwmk
2733 A749 Sheet of 4, #a.-d.   5.00 5.00

Art — A750

1999, July 8   Litho.   Perf. 13¼
2734 A750 250,000 l shown   1.50 .75
2735 A750 250,000 l multi, diff.   1.50 .75

Tourism — A751

Perf. 13x13¼, 13¼x13
1999, Sept. 19   Litho.

No. 2736, Temple to Zeus. No. 2737, Antakya Archaelogical Museum, horiz. No. 2738, Golf course, Antalya. No. 2739, Sailboat off Bodrum.

2736 A751 125,000 l multi   1.00 1.00
2737 A751 125,000 l multi   1.00 1.00
2738 A751 225,000 l multi   1.50 1.50
2739 A751 225,000 l multi   1.50 1.50
    Nos. 2736-2739 (4)   5.00 5.00

Dams A752

225,000 l, Cubuk 1. 250,000 l, Atatürk.

1999, Sept. 19   Litho.   Perf. 13¼x13
2740 A752 225,000 l multi   1.50 1.50
2741 A752 250,000 l multi   1.50 1.50

Kemal Atatürk — A753

1999, Sept. 27   Litho.   Perf. 13¾
2742 A753 225,000 l grn &
        brn   2.50 .55
2743 A753 250,000 l brn & lil   2.50 .65
2744 A753 500,000 l pink &
        grn   3.75 1.40
2745 A753 1,000,000 l bl & red   6.25 2.75
    Nos. 2742-2745 (4)   15.00 5.35

Thanks for Earthquake Rescue
Efforts — A754

Designs: 225,000 l, Hands holding wreckage, flowers, vert. 250,000 l, Rescuers, handclasp.

Perf. 13¼x13, 13x13¼
1999, Oct. 15   **Litho.**
2746 A754 225,000 l multi   1.10   .55
2747 A754 250,000 l multi   1.40   .65

Women's Headcovers Type of 1997
1999, Nov. 24   Litho.   Perf. 13¼
2748 A734 150,000 l Manisa   .80   .40
2749 A734 150,000 l Nigde   .80   .40
2750 A734 250,000 l Antalya   1.40   .65
2751 A734 250,000 l Amasya   1.40   .65
      Nos. 2748-2751 (4)   4.40 2.10

Caravansaries — A755

1999, Dec. 24 Litho. Perf. 13¼x13
2752 A755 150,000 l Sarapsa   .65   .25
2753 A755 250,000 l Obruk   1.00   .45

Millennium
A756

Designs: 275,000 l, Earth, brain, satellite. 300,000 l, Monachus monachus.

2000, Feb. 1   Litho.   Perf. 13¼
2754 A756 275,000 l multi   2.00 2.00
2755 A756 300,000 l multi   2.00 2.00

Merchant
Ships
A757

125,000 l, Bug. 150,000 l, Gülcemal. 275,000 l, Nusret. 300,000 l, Bandirma.

2000, Mar. 16
2756 A757 125,000 l multi   .55   .55
2757 A757 150,000 l multi   .65   .65
2758 A757 250,000 l multi   1.75 1.75
2759 A757 300,000 l multi   2.00 2.00
      Nos. 2756-2759 (4)   4.95 4.95

Grand National
Assembly, 80th
Anniv. — A758

Perf. 13x13¼, 13¼x13
2000, Apr. 23   **Litho.**
2760 A758 275,000 l shown   1.00 1.00
2761 A758 300,000 l Sprouts,
                       horiz.   1.10 1.10

Europa, 2000
Common Design Type
2000, May 9   Perf. 13x13¼
2762 CD17 300,000 l multi   2.00 2.00

World Environment Day Type of 1999
Souvenir Sheets
No. 2763, 275,000 l: a, Aquila heliaca. b, Picus viridis.
No. 2764, 275,000 l: a, Oxyura leucocephala. b, Recurvirostra avosetta.

2000, June 5   Litho.   Perf. 13¼
Sheets of 2, #a-b
2763-2764 A748 Set of 2   5.00 5.00

Women's Headcover Type of 1997
Designs: No. 2765, 275,000 l, Trabzon. No. 2766, 275,000 l, Tunceli. No. 2767, 275,000 l, Corum. No. 2768, 275,000 l, Izmir.

2000, July 15 Set of 4
2765-2768 A734 Set of 4   5.00 5.00

Souvenir Sheet

Nomadic
Life
A759

a, Woman at loom, woman seated. b, Women & containers. c, Women, 2 goats, carpet on tent rope. d, Woman, children, 6 goats, carpet on rope.

2000
2769   Sheet of 4   5.50 5.50
a.-d. A759 300,000 l Any single 1.00 1.00

Military
Leaders — A760

Designs: 100,000 l, Gen. Yakup Sevki Subasi. 200,000 l, Lt. Gen. Musa Kazim Karabekir (c. 1882-1948). 275,000 l, Marshal Mustafa Fevzi Cakmak (1876-1950). 300,000 l, Gen. Cevat Cobanli (1871-1938).

2000
2770-2773 A760 Set of 4   4.50 4.50

2000
Summer
Olympics,
Sydney
A761

Designs: 125,000 l, Rhythmic gymnastics. 150,000 l, Swimming. 275,000 l, High jump. 300,000 l, Archery.

2000
2774-2777 A761 Set of 4   4.00 4.00

Crocuses — A762

Designs: 250,000 l, Crocus chrysanthus. 275,000 l, Crocus olivieri. 300,000 l, Crocus biflorus. 1,250,000 l, Crocus sativus.

2000, Oct. 9   Litho.   Perf. 13¾x14
2778-2781 A762 Set of 4   8.25 3.75

Architecture — A763

Designs: 200,000 l, Arslan Baba. 275,000 l, Karasaç Ana. 300,000 l, Hoca Ahmet Yesevi.

2000, Oct. 19   Litho.   Perf. 13¼x13
2782-2784 A763 Set of 3   4.00 4.00

Turksat   Women's
2A — A764   Clothing — A765

2001, Jan. 25   Litho.   Perf. 13x13¾
2785 A764 200,000 l multi   1.25 1.25

2001, Mar. 19
Designs: No. 2786, 200,000 l, Afyon. No. 2787, 200,000 l, Balikesir. No. 2788, 325,000 l, Kars. No. 2789, 325,000 l, Tokat.
2786-2789 A765 Set of 4   3.00 3.00

Women's Headcovers Type of 1997
Designs: 200,000 l, Mersin-Silifke. 250,000 l, Sivas. 425,000 l, Aydin. 450,000 l, Hakkari.

2001, Apr. 16   Litho.   Perf. 13¼
2790-2793 A734 Set of 4   3.50 3.50

Europa — A766

Waterfalls: 450,000 l, Düdenbasi. 500,000 l, Yerköprü.

2001, May 5   Perf. 13
2794-2795 A766 Set of 2   3.00 3.00

Aviators
A767

Designs: 250,000 l, Capt. Ismail Hakki Bey. 300,000 l, Lieut. Nuri Bey. 450,000 l, Lieut. Sadik Bey. 500,000 l, Capt. Fethi Bey.

2001, May 15
2796-2799 A767 Set of 4   5.00 5.00

World Environment Day Type of 1999
No. 2800, 300,000 l: a, Turdus pilaris. b, Carduelis carduelis.
No. 2801, 450,000 l: a, Merops apiaster. b, Upupa epops.

2001, June 5   Perf. 13¼
Sheets of 2, #a-b
2800-2801 A748 Set of 2   5.00 5.00

Kemal   Medicinal
Ataturk — A768   Plants — A769

Ataturk (1881-1938) and: 300,000 l, Turkish flag. 450,000 l, Birthplace.

2001, May 19   Litho.   Perf. 13
2802-2803 A768 Set of 2   2.00 2.00

2001, June 27   Perf. 13¾
Designs: 250,000 l, Myrtus communis. 300,000 l, Achillea millefolium. 450,000 l, Hypericum perforatum. 1,750,000 l, Rosa moyesii. 1,750,000 l, Crataegus oxyacantha.
2804-2808 A769 Set of 5   10.00 2.25

Horses
A770

Designs: 300,000 l, Horse and foal. No. 2810, 450,000 l, Three horses. No. 2811, 450,000 l, Two horses galloping. 500,000 l, Horse, vert.

2001, July 16   Perf. 13
2809-2812 A770 Set of 4   4.50 4.50

Merchant Ships Type of 2000
Designs: 250,000 l, Resitpasa. No. 2814, 300,000 l, Mithatpasa. No. 2815, 300,000 l, Gülnihal, 500,000 l, Aydin.

2001, Sept. 3   Perf. 13¼
2813-2816 A757 Set of 4   3.75 3.75

Architecture
A771

Designs: No. 2817, 300,000 l, Sirvansahlar Palace, Baku, Azerbaijan. No. 2818, 300,000 l, Sultan Tekes Mausoleum, Urgench, Uzbekistan. 450,000 l, Timur Mausoleum, Samarkand, Uzbekistan. 500,000 l, While Tlightning Mausoleum, Bursa.

2001, Oct. 15
2817-2820 A771 Set of 4   4.00 4.00

Sultan Nevruz
A772

2002, Mar. 21   Litho.   Perf. 13¼
2821 A772 400,000 l multi   1.10 1.10

Women's Clothing Type of 2001
Designs: 350,000 l, Kastamonu. 400,000 l, Canakkale. 500,000 l, Amasya-Ilisu. 600,000 l, Elazig.

2002, Apr. 16   Perf. 13x13¼
2822-2825 A765 Set of 4   4.50 4.50

Europa — A773

2002, May 5   Litho.   Perf. 13x13¼
2826   A773   500,000 l   multi   1.50 1.50

2002 World Cup Soccer
Championships, Japan and
Korea — A774

Designs: 400,000 l, Players, referee.
600,000 l, Crowd, player making scissors kick.

2002, May 31   Litho.   Perf. 13¼x13
2827-2828   A774   Set of 2   2.50 2.50

Famous
Men — A775

Designs: 100,000 l, Muzaffer Sarisözen
(1898-1963), musician. 400,000 l, Arif Nihat
Asya (1904-75), writer. 500,000 l, Vedat Tek
(1873-1942), architect. 600,000 l, Hilmi Ziya
Ulken (1901-74), philosopher. 2,500,000 l,
Ibrahim Calli (1882-1960), painter.

2002, June 3   Perf. 13¾x14
2829-2833   A775   Set of 5   11.00 3.75

Souvenir Sheet

Wild Cats — A776

No. 2834: a, Panthera pardus tulliana. b,
Lynx lynx. c, Panthera tigris. d, Caracal
caracal.

2002, June 20   Perf. 13¼x13
2834   A776   400,000 l   Sheet of 4,
                    #a-d   4.50 4.50

Souvenir Sheet

Shells — A777

Various shells: a, 400,000 l. b, 500,000 l. c,
600,000 l. d, 750,000 l.

2002, June 25
2835   A777   Sheet of 4, #a-d   6.00 6.00

Third Place Finish of Turkish Team in
World Cup Soccer
Championships — A778

Designs: 400,000 l, Players in action.
700,000 l, Team photo.

2002, July 29   Perf. 13x13¼
2836-2837   A778   Set of 2   2.75 2.75

String
Instruments
A779

Designs: 450,000 l, Violin. 700,000 l, Bass.

2002, Oct. 10   Perf. 13¼x13
2838-2839   A779   Set of 2   3.00 3.00

Merchant Ships Type of 2000
Designs: 450,000 l, Ege. 500,000 l, Ayvalik.
No. 2842, 700,000 l, Karadeniz. No. 2843,
700,000 l, Marakaz.

2002, Nov. 4   Litho.   Perf. 13
2840-2843   A757   Set of 4   5.00 5.00

Souvenir Sheet

Turkish and Hungarian
Buildings — A780

No. 2844: a, 450,000 l, Gazi Kassim Pasha
Mosque, Pécs, Hungary. b, 700,000 l, Rakoczi
House, Tekirdag, Turkey.

2002, Dec. 2   Litho.   Perf. 13¼
2844   A780   Sheet of 2, #a-b   3.00 3.00
       See Hungary Nos. 3819-3820.

BJK Soccer Team, Cent. — A781

Team emblem and: 500,000 l, Eagle, Turkish and team flags. 700,000 l, Eagle, stadium.
750,000 l, Soccer players. 1,000,000 l, Eagle's
head.

2003, Mar. 3   Perf. 13x13¼
2845-2848   A781   Set of 4   6.50 6.50

A782   A783

Europa: 500,000 l, Travel poster. 700,000 l,
Ankara State Theater poster.

2003, May 9   Litho.   Perf. 13
2849-2850   A782   Set of 2   3.00 3.00

2003, May 29

Conquest of Constantinople, 550th Anniv.:
No. 2851, 500,000 l, Leaders at table. No.
2852, 500,000 l, Sultan Mehmet II seated.
700,000 l, Robe. 1,500,000 l, Sultan Mehmet II
and cartouche.

2851-2854   A783   Set of 4   6.00 6.00

Souvenir Sheet

World Environment Day — A784

No. 2855: a, Gazella subgutturosa. b,
Cervus elaphus. c, Capreolus capreolus. d,
Cervus dama.

2003, June 5
2855   A784   500,000 l   Sheet of 4,
                    #a-d   4.50 4.50

Zodiac
A785

2003, June 19   Perf. 13¼
2856   A785   500,000 l   multi   1.00 1.00

Women's Clothing Type of 2001
Designs: No. 2857, 500,000 l, Sivas. No.
2858, 500,000 l, Gaziantep. No. 2859,
700,000 l, Erzincan. No. 2860, 700,000 l,
Ankara-Beypazari.

2003, July 8   Perf. 13
2857-2860   A765   Set of 4   5.50 5.50

Fruit
Blossoms — A786

Blossoms: 500,000 l, Ayva cicegi (quince).
700,000 l, Erik cicegi (plum). 750,000 l, Kiraz
cicegi (cherry) . 1,000,000 l, Nar cicegi (pomegranate). 3,000,000 l, Portakal cicegi (orange).

2003, July 25   Perf. 13¾x14
2861-2865   A786   Set of 5   12.00 6.50

Brass
Instruments
A787

Designs: 600,000 l, French horn. 800,000 l,
Trumpet.

2003, Sept. 23   Litho.   Perf. 13¼x13
2866-2867   A787   Set of 2   3.00 3.00

Republic
of Turkey,
80th
Anniv.
A788

Kemal Ataturk, flag and: No. 2868,
600,000 l, Cavalry. No. 2869, 600,000 l,
Buildings.

2003, Oct. 29   Litho.   Perf. 13¼x13
2868-2869   A788   Set of 2   2.50 2.50

Navy
Ships
A789

Designs: No. 2870, 600,000 l, Karadeniz.
No. 2871, 600,000 l, Gediz. No. 2872,
700,000 l, Salihreis. No. 2873, 700,000 l,
Kocatepe.

2003, Nov. 14
2870-2873   A789   Set of 4   6.00 6.00

Agriculture Bank, 140th Anniv. — A790

2003, Nov. 20   Perf. 13x13¼
2874   A790   600,000 l   multi   1.25 1.25

Buildings
Associated with
Kemal
Ataturk — A791

Designs: 600,000 l, House, Trabzon.
700,000 l, Museum, Sakarya. 800,000 l,
House, Selanik. 1,000,000 l, Museum, Ankara.

2003, Dec. 12
2875-2878   A791   Set of 4   5.50 5.50

PTT
Bank — A792

2004, Mar. 3   **Perf. 14**
2879 A792 600,000 l multi   .95   .45

Women's Clothing Type of 2001

Designs: 600,000 l, Edirne. No. 2881, 700,000 l, Tunceli. No. 2882, 700,000 l, Burdur. 800,000 l, Trabzon.

2004, Apr. 30   **Perf. 13x13¼**
2880-2883 A765   Set of 4   5.00 5.00

Europa — A793

Designs: 700,000 l, Skier, windsurfer. 800,000 l, Tourist at archaeological ruins, ships.

2004, May 9
2884-2885 A793   Set of 2   3.00 3.00

Souvenir Sheet

World Environment Day — A794

No. 2886: a, Falco tinnunculus. b, Buteo buteo. c, Aquila chrysaetos. d, Milvus migrans.

2004, June 5   **Perf. 13¼x13**
2886 A794 700,000 l Sheet of 4,
         #a-d   5.00 5.00

Caravansaries — A795

Designs: 600,000 l, Mamahatun Caravansary, Erzincan. 700,000 l, Cardak Caravasary, Denizli.

2004, June 7
2887-2888 A795   Set of 2   2.50 2.50

Gendarmerie, 165th
Anniv. — A796

2004, June 14   **Perf. 13¼x13¼**
2889 A796 600,000 l multi   .80   .40

Birds — A797

Designs: 100,000 l, Regulus regulus. 250,000 l, Sylvia rueppelli. 600,000 l, Hippolais polyglotta. 700,000 l, Passer domesticus. 800,000 l, Emberiza bruniceps. 1,000,000 l, Fringilla coelebs. 1,500,000 l, Phoenicurus phoenicurus. 3,500,000 l, Erithacus rubecula.

20004, July 23   **Perf. 14**
2890 A797   100,000 l multi   .20   .20
2891 A797   250,000 l multi   .35   .20
2892 A797   600,000 l multi   .80   .40
2893 A797   700,000 l multi   .95   .50
2894 A797   800,000 l multi   1.10   .55
2895 A797 1,000,000 l multi   1.40   .70
2896 A797 1,500,000 l multi   2.10 1.00
2897 A797 3,500,000 l multi   4.75 2.40
    Nos. 2890-2897 (8)   11.65 5.95

2004
Summer
Olympics,
Athens
A798

Designs: 600,000 l, Wrestling. No. 2899, 700,000 l, Weight lifting. No. 2900, 700,000 l, Women's track and field, vert. 800,000 l, Wrestling, diff.

     Perf. 13¼x13, 13x13¼
2004, Aug. 13
2898-2901 A798   Set of 4   5.00 5.00

Souvenir Sheet

Navy Submarines — A799

No. 2902: a, 600,000 l, 18 Mart. b, 700,000 l, Preveze. c, 700,000 l, Anafartalar. d, 800,000 l, Atilay.

2004, Sept. 14   **Perf. 13x13¼**
2902 A799   Sheet of 4, #a-d   5.00 5.00

Piri Reis (1465-1554), Admiral and
Map Compiler — A800

2004, Sept. 20
2903 A800 600,000 l multi   1.00 1.00

Waterfalls
A801

Designs: 600,000 l, Kapuzbasi Waterfall. 700,000 l, Sudüsen Waterfall, vert.

2004, Oct. 19   **Perf. 13x13¼, 13¼x13**
2904-2905 A801   Set of 2   3.00 3.00

Buildings Associated With Kemal
Ataturk — A802

Designs: 600,000 l, Ataturk Summer House, Bursa. No. 2907, 700,000 l, Ataturk House Museum, Erzurum. No. 2908, 700,000 l, Ataturk House, Havza. 800,000 l, State Railways Director's Building, Ankara.

2004, Nov. 8   Litho.   Perf. 13¼x13
2906-2909 A802   Set of 4   5.00 5.00

Souvenir Sheet

Turkish Stars Aerobatics Team — A803

No. 2910: a, 600,000 l, Two airplanes. b, 700,000 l, Five airplanes. c, 800,000 l, Seven airplanes flying upwards. d, 900,000 l, Seven airplanes flying left.

2004, Dec. 7   Litho.   Perf. 13¼x13
2910 A803   Sheet of 4, #a-d   6.00 6.00

Provinces
A804

2005, Jan. 1   **Litho.**   **Perf. 14**
2914 A804   1k   Adana   .20   .20
2915 A804   5k   Adiyaman   .20   .20
2916 A804   10k   Afyon   .20   .20
2917 A804   25k   Agri   .35   .20
2918 A804   50k   Amasya   .70   .35
2919 A804   60k   Ankara   .85   .40
2920 A804   60k   Bitlis   .85   .40
2921 A804   70k   Antalya   1.00   .50
2922 A804   70k   Bolu   1.00   .50
2923 A804   80k   Artvin   1.10   .55
2924 A804   80k   Burdur   1.10   .55
2925 A804   90k   Aydin   1.25   .60
2926 A804   1 l   Balikesir   1.50   .75
2927 A804   1.50   Bilecik   2.25 1.10
2928 A804   3.50 l   Bingol   5.00 2.50
2929 A804   3.50 l   Bursa   5.00 2.50
   Nos. 2914-2929 (16)   22.55 11.50

A805   A806

Designs: 60k, Batiburnu Lighthouse, Canakkale. 70k, Zonguldak Lighthouse, Zonguldak.

2005, Mar. 18   Litho.   Perf. 13x13¼
2930-2931 A805   Set of 2   2.00 1.00

2005, Apr. 1

Marmaris Intl. Maritime Festival: 70k, Sailboat. 80k, Sailboat, sun on horizon.

2932-2933 A806   Set of 2   2.25 1.10

A807   A808

2005, Apr. 10
2934 A807 70k multi   1.10   .55

Turkish Police, 160th anniv.

2005, Apr. 23

Grand National Assembly, 85th anniv.: 60k, Torch, star and crescent. 70k, Crescent and fireworks over Grand National Assembly.

2935-2936 A808   Set of 2   1.90   .95

Europa — A809

2005, May 9
2937 A809 70k multi   1.10   .55

Caftans of
Sultans — A810

Caftan of Sultan: No. 2938, 70k, Ahmed I (shown). No. 2939, 70k, Ahmed I, diff. No. 2940, 70k, Murad III. No. 2941, 70k, Selim.

2005, May 20
2938-2941 A810   Set of 4   4.25 2.10

Souvenir Sheet

World Environment Day — A811

No. 2942: a, 60k, Pagellus bogaraveo. b, 70k, Epinephelus guaza. c, 70k, Merlanyus euxinus. d, 80k, Maena smaris.

2005, June 5   Litho.   Perf. 13¼x13
2942 A811   Sheet of 4, #a-d   4.25 2.10

Tapestries & Carpets — A812

Designs: 60k, Carpet from Hereke region, Turkey. 70k, L'humanité Assaillie par les Sept Pechés Capitaux tapestry, Belgium.

2005, June 22   Litho.   Perf. 13x13¼
2943-2944 A812   Set of 2   2.00 1.00
See Belgium Nos. 2098-2099.

World Architecture Congress, Istanbul — A813

2005, July 3
2945 A813 70k multi   1.10 .55

Mosaics A814

Designs: 60k, Akelos. No. 2947, 70k, Oceanos and Tethys. No. 2948, 70k, Achilles. 80k, Menad.

2005, July 5   Perf. 13¼x13
2946-2949 A814   Set of 4   4.25 2.10

Clocks — A815

Designs: 60k, Musical clock, 1770. 70k, Clock, 1867.

2005, July 20   Perf. 13x13¼
2950-2951 A815   Set of 2   2.00 1.00

Turkish Grand Prix, Istanbul — A816

2005, Aug. 19   Litho.   Perf. 13x13¼
2952 A816 70k multi   1.10 .55

Philanthropic Businessmen — A817

Designs: 60k, Sakip Sabanci (1933-2004). 70k, Vehbi Koç (1901-96).

2005, Sept. 21   Litho.   Perf. 13¼x13
2953-2954 A817   Set of 2   2.00 1.00

Provinces A818

2005, Sept. 28   Perf. 13¾
2955 A818   50k Canakkale   .75   .35
2956 A818   60k Cankiri   .90   .45
2957 A818   60k Corum   .90   .45
2958 A818   60k Denizli   .90   .45
2959 A818   60k Diyarbakir   .90   .45
2960 A818   60k Edirne   .90   .45
2961 A818   60k Elazig   .90   .45
2962 A818   70k Erzincan   1.10   .55
2963 A818   70k Erzurum   1.10   .55
2964 A818   70k Eskisehir   1.10   .55
2965 A818   70k Gaziantep   1.10   .55
2966 A818   70k Giresun   1.10   .55
2967 A818   70k Gumushane   1.10   .55
2968 A818   1 l Hakkari   1.50   .75
2969 A818 1.50 l Hatay   2.25 1.10
2970 A818 2.50 l Isparta   3.75 1.90
  Nos. 2955-2970 (16)   20.25 10.10

Mevlana Jalal ad-Din ar-Rumi (1207-73), Islamic Philosopher A819

2005, Sept. 30   Perf. 13x13¼
2971 A819 70k multi   1.10 .55
See Iran No. 2911 and Syria No. 1574.

Galatasaray Sports Club, Cent. — A820

Club emblem and: No. 2972, 60k, Soccer stadium crowd, lion and "100." No. 2973, 70k, Soccer stadium, trophy.
  No. 2974: a, 60k, Man, lion and "100." b, 70k, Club emblem, building. c, 80k, Soccer players. d, 1 l, Soccer players with trophy.

2005, Oct. 11   Perf. 13x13¼
2972-2973 A820   Set of 2   1.90 .95
             Souvenir Sheet
                  Perf. 13¼x13
2974 A820   Sheet of 4, #a-d   4.50 2.25
No. 2974 contains four 41x26mm stamps.

Start of Negotiations for Turkish Admission to European Union — A821

2005, Nov. 3   Perf. 13¼x13
2975 A821 70k multi   1.10 .55

Vegetables — A824

Designs, 60k, Allium porrum (leeks). 70k, Allium sativum (garlic). 80k, Allium cepa (onions).

2005, Nov. 21   Litho.   Perf. 13x13¼
2978-2980 A824   Set of 3   3.25 1.60

Europa Stamps, 50th Anniv. (in 2006) — A825

Designs: No. 2981, 60k, Vignette of #1907. No. 2982, 70k, Vignette of #1628. 80k, Vignette of #B120. 1 l, Vignette of #1719.
  No. 2985, horiz.: a, 10k, #1520. b, 25k, #1800. c, 60k, #1553. d, 70k, #1775.
  No. 2986, horiz.: a, 10k, #1493. b, 25k, #1936. c, 60k, #1602. d, 70k, #1876.

2005, Dec. 15   Litho.   Perf. 13x13¼
2981-2984 A825   Set of 4   4.75 2.40
              Souvenir Sheets
                  Perf. 13¼x13
2985 A825   Sheet of 4, #a-d   2.50 1.25
                   Imperf
2986 A825   Sheet of 4, #a-d   2.50 1.25

2006 Winter Olympics, Turin A826

Designs: 60k, Speed skating. 70k, Skiing.

2006, Feb. 10   Perf. 13¼x13
2987-2988 A826   Set of 2   2.00 1.00

March 29 Total Solar Eclipse A827

2006, Mar. 29   Litho.   Perf. 13¼x13
2989 A827 70k multi   1.10 .55

Support for Education A828

2006, Apr. 10
2990 A828 60k multi   .95 .45

Karaoglan, Cartoon Hero — A829

Karaoglan: 60k, With bow and arrow. No. 2992, 70k, Attacking swordsman. No. 2993, 70k, On horseback. 80k, On horseback, diff.

2006, Apr. 20   Perf. 13x13¼
2991-2994 A829   Set of 4   4.25 2.10

Izzet Baysal (1907-2000), Architect — A830

2006, May 11   Litho.   Perf. 13¼x13
2995 A830 60k multi   .85 .45

A831

A832

A833

A834

A835

A836

A837

A838

A839

Kemal Ataturk (1881-1938) — A840

2006, May 19

2996		Block of 10	7.50	3.75
a.	A831	60k multi	.75	.35
b.	A832	60k multi	.75	.35
c.	A833	60k multi	.75	.35
d.	A834	60k multi	.75	.35
e.	A835	60k multi	.75	.35
f.	A836	60k multi	.75	.35
g.	A837	60k multi	.75	.35
h.	A838	60k multi	.75	.35
i.	A839	60k multi	.75	.35
j.	A840	60k multi	.75	.35

Europa — A841

2006, May 30   **Perf. 13x13¼**
2997 A841 70k multi   .90 .45

Miniature Sheet

World Environment Day — A842

No. 2998: a, 25k, Parched earth. b, 50k, Tree. c, 60k, Tree, diff. d, 70k, Forest.

2006, June 5
2998 A842   Sheet of 4, #a-d   2.75 1.40

Intl. Year of Deserts and Desertification.

2006 World Cup Soccer Championships, Germany — A843

Designs: No. 2999, 70k, Player dribbling ball. No. 3000, 70k, Player kicking ball, horiz.

2006, June 9   **Perf. 13x13¼, 13¼x13**
2999-3000 A843   Set of 2   1.90 .95

Airplanes
A844

Designs: 60k, Deperdussin monoplane. No. 3002, 70k, Bleriot monoplane. No. 3003, 70k, R. E. P. monoplane.

2006, June 22   **Perf. 13¼x13**
3001-3003 A844   Set of 3   2.60 1.40

Treasures of Karun — A845

Designs: No. 3004, 70k, Bracelet and coins. No. 3005, 70k, Winged sun disc pectoral and bracelet. 80k, Lion's head bracelets.

2006, July 10   **Perf. 13x13¼**
3004-3006 A845   Set of 3   2.75 1.40

Provinces
A846

2006, Sept. 11   **Perf. 13¼x13**

3007	A846	10k	Kahramanmaras	.20	.20
3008	A846	10k	Manisa	.20	.20
3009	A846	50k	Kirsehir	.70	.35
3010	A846	50k	Kocaeli	.70	.35
3011	A846	60k	Izmir	.80	.40
3012	A846	60k	Konya	.80	.40
3013	A846	60k	Mardin	.80	.40
3014	A846	60k	Mugla	.80	.40
3015	A846	70k	Istanbul	.95	.50
3016	A846	70k	Mersin	.95	.50
3017	A846	1 l	Kastamonu	1.40	.70
3018	A846	1 l	Kirklareli	1.40	.70
3019	A846	1.60 l	Kayseri	2.25	1.10
3020	A846	2 l	Malatya	2.75	1.40
3021	A846	4 l	Kars	5.50	2.75
3022	A846	4 l	Kutahya	5.50	2.75
		Nos. 3007-3022 (16)		25.70	13.10

Scenes From Movie, "Selvi Boylum Al Yazmalim" — A847

Various scenes: 60k, 70k.

2006, Sept. 16   **Perf. 13x13¼**
3023-3024 A847   Set of 2   1.75 .85

Turkish Railroads, 150th Anniv. A848

Designs: 60k, Steam locomotive. 70k, Electric train.

2006, Sept. 23   **Perf. 13¼x13**
3025-3026 A848   Set of 2   1.75 .85

Central Bank, 75th Anniv. A849

2006, Oct. 3
3027 A849 60k multi   .80 .40

Intl. Telecommunications Union Conference, Antalya — A850

Conference emblem and: 60k, Globe with spotlight on Turkey. 70k, Map with lines drawn to Turkey.

2006, Nov. 6   **Perf. 13¼x13¼**
3028-3029 A850   Set of 2   1.90 .95

Middle East Technical University, Ankara, 50th Anniv. — A851

2006, Nov. 15   **Litho.**   **Perf. 13x13¼**
3030 A851 60k multi   .85 .40

Turkish Atomic Energy Authority, 50th Anniv. A852

2006, Nov. 22   **Litho.**   **Perf. 13¼x13**
3031 A852 60k multi   .85 .40

Geothermal Resources — A853

Designs: 60k, Four steam clouds. 70k, Steam leaving smokestack.

2006, Dec. 11
3032-3033 A853   Set of 2   1.90 .95

Airplanes Type of 2006

Designs: 60k, Breguet XIV B-2. No. 3035, 70k, Albatros C-XV. No. 3036, 70k, Fiat R2.

2007, Mar. 15   **Litho.**   **Perf. 13¼x13**
3034-3036 A844   Set of 3   3.00 1.50

A854

A855

A856

Hittite Artifacts A857

2007, Mar. 30

3037	A854	60k multi	.90	.45
3038	A855	60k multi	.90	.45
3039	A856	60k multi	.90	.45
3040	A857	60k multi	.90	.45
		Nos. 3037-3040 (4)	3.60	1.80

Third Meeting of Economic Cooperation Organization Postal Authorities, Tehran — A858

2007, Apr. 5   **Perf. 13x13¼**
3041 A858 60k multi   .90 .45

Tekirdag as Part of Turkey, 650th Anniv. A859

2007, Apr. 14   **Perf. 13¼x13**
3042 A859 60k multi   .90   .45

Fenerbahce Sports Club, Cent. — A860

Club emblem and: No. 3043, 60k, Men witnessing signing ceremony. No. 3044, 70k, Quotation and Arabic text.
No. 3045 — Club emblem and: a, 60k, Lighthouse. b, 70k, Three men seated at table. c, 80k, Building, stadium interior. d, 90k, Stadium exterior.

2007, May 3   **Perf. 13x13¼**
3043-3044 A860   Set of 2   2.00 1.00

Souvenir Sheet
Perf. 13¼x13
3045 A860   Sheet of 4, #a-d   4.50 4.50

No. 3045 contains four 38x23mm stamps. No. 3045 exists affixed to a booklet cover which was only sold in a set with an imperforate sheet of eight 41x31mm stamps depicting various athletes, two first day covers, and a folder, for 25 l.

Souvenir Sheet

Mevlana Jalal ad-Din ar-Rumi (1207-73), Islamic Philosopher — A861

No. 3046: a, 25k, Portrait. b, 50k, Arabic calligraphy. c, 60k, Dervishes. d, 70k, Mausoleum.

2007, May 8   **Perf. 13x13¼**
3046 A861   Sheet of 4, #a-d   3.25 1.60

Europa A862

Designs: 60k, Turkish Scouting emblem, Scout at campfire. 70k, Scouts saluting.

2007, May 9   **Perf. 13¼**
3047-3048 A862   Set of 2   2.00 1.00

Scouting, cent.

Mehmetcik Foundation, 25th Anniv. — A863

2007, May 17   **Litho.**   **Perf. 13¼x13**
3049 A863 60k multi   .95   .45

Souvenir Sheet

World Environment Day — A864

No. 3050: a, 25k, Goats. b, 50k, Cattle. c, 60k, Sheep. d, 70k, Chickens.

2007, June 5   **Litho.**   **Perf. 13¼x13**
3050 A864   Sheet of 4, #a-d   3.00 1.50

Turkish Cuisine — A865

Designs: No. 3051, 1 l, Nohutlu Bulgur Pilavi (chick pea and bulgur pilaf). No. 3052, 1 l, Yüksük Corbasi (soup). 2 l, Asure (vegetables).

2007, June 20   **Litho.**   **Perf. 13x13¼**
3051-3053 A865   Set of 3   6.25 3.25

Black Sea Economic Cooperation Organization, 15th Anniversary Summit A866

2007, June 25   **Perf. 13¼**
3054 A866 60k multi   .95   .95

Provinces Type of 2006
2007, July 10   **Perf. 13¼x13**
3055	A846	10k	Siirt	.20 .20
3056	A846	50k	Ordu	.80 .40
3057	A846	60k	Rize	.95 .45
3058	A846	1 l	Nigde	1.60 .80
3059	A846	2 l	Nevsehir	3.25 1.60
3060	A846	2 l	Samsun	3.25 1.60
3061	A846	4 l	Mus	6.25 3.25
3062	A846	4 l	Sakarya	6.25 3.25
			Nos. 3055-3062 (8)	22.55 11.55

Turkish Language Association, 75th Anniv. — A867

2007, July 12   **Perf. 13x13¼**
3063 A867 70k multi   1.10   .55

Roses A869

Color of rose: No. 3065, 60k, White. No. 3066, 60k, Red. No. 3067, 60k, Yellow.

2007, Aug. 16   **Litho.**   **Perf. 13¼**
3065-3067 A869   Set of 3   2.75 1.40

Shadow Play Characters A870

Designs: 60k, Tuzsuz Deli Bekir and Efe. 70k, Hacivat and Karagöz. 80k, Tiryaki and Celebi.

2007, Sept. 13   **Litho.**   **Perf. 13¼x13**
3068-3070 A870   Set of 3   3.75 1.90

Miniature Sheet

Balkanfila XIV Intl. Philatelic Exhibition, Istanbul — A871

No. 3071: a, 60k, Blue Mosque, Galata Tower. b, 70k, Hagia Sophia. c, 80k, City walls and painting. d, 1 l, Bosporus Bridge.

2007, Oct. 28
3071 A871   Sheet of 4, #a-d   5.25 2.60

Mimar Sinan (1489-1588), Architect A873

Sinan and: 60k, Büyükcekmece Bridge. No. 3074, 70k, Bath of Roxelana (Haseki Hürrem Sultan Hamami Ayasofya). No. 3075, 70k, Selimye Mosque, Edirne. 80k, Suleiman Mosque, Istanbul.

2007, Nov. 14   **Perf. 13¼**
3073-3076 A873   Set of 4   4.75 2.40

World Philosophy Day — A874

2007, Nov. 22   **Perf. 13x13¼**
3077 A874 60k multi   1.00   .50

Cartoon Character "Keloglan" — A875

Designs: 60k, Keloglan in giant's hand. No. 3079, 70k, Keloglan leaving house. No. 3080, 70k, Keloglan on horse. 80k, Keloglan with carpet and birds.

2007, Nov. 28
3078-3081 A875   Set of 4   4.75 2.40

Provinces Type of 2006
2007, Dec. 4   **Perf. 13¼x13**
3082	A846	5k	Tunceli	.20 .20
3083	A846	10k	Tokat	.20 .20
3084	A846	65k	Sanliurfa	1.10 .55
3085	A846	65k	Trabzon	1.10 .55
3086	A846	80k	Sivas	1.40 .70
3087	A846	85k	Usak	1.50 .75
3088	A846	1 l	Tekirdag	1.75 .90
3089	A846	4.50 l	Sinop	7.75 4.00
			Nos. 3082-3089 (8)	15.00 7.85

SEMI-POSTAL STAMPS

Regular Issues Overprinted in Carmine or Black

Overprint reads: "For War Orphans"
Perf. 12, 13½ and Compound
1915   **Unwmk.**
On Stamps of 1905
B1	A18	10pa dull grn (#119)	.75	.50
B2	A18	10pi orange brown	12.50	.80

On Stamp of 1906
B3	A18	10pa dull grn (#128)	40.00	25.00

On Stamps of 1908
B4	A19	10pa blue green	1.50	.75
B5	A19	5pi dark violet	75.00	12.50
		Nos. B1-B5 (5)	129.75	39.55

With Additional Overprint

B6	A19	10pa blue green	240.00	175.00

On Stamps of 1909
B7	A21	10pa blue green	1.00	.75
a.		Inverted overprint	22.50	22.50
b.		Double overprint, one invtd.	30.00	30.00
B8	A21	20pa carmine rose	1.00	.75
a.		Inverted overprint	27.50	27.50
B9	A21	1pi ultra	1.00	.75
B10	A21	5pi dark violet	8.75	1.50
		Nos. B7-B10 (4)	11.75	3.75

With Additional Overprint

B11	A21	10pa blue green	1.00	.75
b.		Double overprint, one inverted	5.00	5.00
B12	A21	20pa carmine rose	1.50	.75
B13	A21	1pi ultra	2.00	.75

On Stamps of 1913
B14	A22	10pa blue green	1.00	.75
a.		Inverted overprint	22.50	22.50
B15	A22	1pi ultra	1.00	.75
a.		Double overprint	5.00	5.00
		Nos. B11-B15 (5)	6.50	3.75

With Additional Overprint

B16 A22 10pa blue green   1.25   .75
  a. Inverted overprint   27.50   27.50
On Newspaper Stamp of 1908
B17 A19 10pa blue green   360.00 175.00
On Newspaper Stamp of 1909
B18 A21 10pa blue green   1.25   1.00

Regular Issues Overprinted in Carmine or Black

1916
On Stamps of 1901
B19 A17 1pi blue   1.00   .50
B20 A17 5pi lilac rose   10.00   1.50
On Stamps of 1905
B21 A18 1pi brt blue   7.50   2.00
B22 A18 5pi brown   7.50   5.00
On Stamp of 1906
B23 A18 1pi brt blue   1.00   .75
On Stamps of 1908
B24 A19 20pa carmine (Bk)   *300.00*
B25 A19 10pi red   500.00 200.00

With Additional Overprint

B26 A19 20pa carmine   2.00   1.50
B27 A19 1pi brt blue (C)   20.00   5.00
On Stamps of 1909
B28 A21 20pa carmine rose   2.00   1.25
B29 A21 1pi ultra   1.00   .75
B30 A21 10pi dull red   175.00 100.00

With Additional Overprint

B31 A21 20pa carmine rose   1.50   .75
B32 A21 1pi ultra   2.00   1.00
On Stamps of 1913
B33 A22 20pa carmine rose   2.00   1.50
B34 A22 1pi ultra   2.00   1.00
  a. Inverted overprint   5.00   5.00
B35 A22 10pi dull red   22.50   15.00

With Additional Overprint

B36 A22 20pa carmine rose   2.00   1.25
On Newspaper Stamps of 1901
B37 A16 5pi ocher   11.50   6.00
  a. 5pa bister, No. P37   150.00 150.00

Regular Issues Surcharged in Black

On Stamp of 1899
B38 A11 10pa on 20pa vio brn   2.00   1.50
On Stamp of 1905
B39 A18 10pa on 20pa carmine   2.00   1.50
On Stamp of 1906
B40 A18 10pa on 20pa carmine   1.50   1.25

On Newspaper Stamp of 1893-99
B41 A11 10pa on 20pa violet brn   2.00   1.50
  Nos. B38-B41 (4)   7.50   5.75

Nos. 346-349 Overprinted

B42 A41 10pa carmine   1.00   .75
  a. Inverted overprint   6.75   6.75
B43 A41 20pa ultra   1.00   .75
  a. Inverted overprint   6.75   6.75
B44 A41 1pi violet & blk   1.00   .90
  a. Inverted overprint   6.75   6.75
B45 A41 5pi yel brn & blk   1.00   .75
  a. Inverted overprint   11.00   11.00
  Nos. B42-B45 (4)   4.00   3.15

Nos. B42-B45 formed part of the Postage Commemoration issue of 1916.

A Soldier's Farewell — SP1

1917, Feb. 20   Engr.   Perf. 12½
B46 SP1 10pa red violet   1.25   .50

For surcharges see Nos. 600, B47.

Stamp of Same Design Surcharged

B47 SP1 10pa on 20pa car rose   2.00   .50

Badge of the Society — SP9

School Teacher — SP10

Marie Sklodowska Curie — SP16

Kemal Atatürk — SP23

Designs: 2k+2k, Woman farmer. 2½k+2½k, Typist. 4k+4k, Aviatrix and policewoman. 5k+5k, Women voters. 7½k+7½k, Yildiz Palace, Istanbul. 10k+10k, Carrie Chapman Catt. 12½k+12½k, Jane Addams. 15k+15k, Grazia Deledda. 20k+20k, Selma Lagerlof. 25k+25k, Bertha von Suttner. 30k+30k, Sigrid Undset.

1935, Apr. 17   Photo.   Perf. 11½
Inscribed: "XII Congres Suffragiste International"

B54 SP9 20pa + 20pa brn   .50   .50
B55 SP10 1k + 1k rose
  car   .75   .50
B56 SP10 2k + 2k sl bl   1.00   .75

B57 SP10 2½k + 2½k yel
  grn   1.00   .75
B58 SP10 4k + 4k blue   1.50   1.00
B59 SP10 5k + 5k dl vio   2.50   2.00
B60 SP10 7½k + 7½k org
  red   2.50   2.00
B61 SP16 10k + 10k org   2.50   2.50
B62 SP16 12½k + 12½k dk
  bl   2.50   2.50
B63 SP16 15k + 15k violet   5.00   5.00
B64 SP16 20k + 20k red
  org   7.50   6.25
B65 SP16 25k + 25k grn   15.00   14.00
B66 SP16 30k + 30k ultra   90.00 100.00
B67 SP16 50k + 50k dk sl
  grn   175.00 150.00
B68 SP23 100k + 100k brn
  car   125.00 140.00
  Nos. B54-B68 (15)   432.25 427.75
Set, never hinged   675.00

12th Congress of the Women's Intl. Alliance.

> **Catalogue values for unused stamps in this section, from this point to the end of the section, are for Never Hinged items.**

Katip Chelebi — SP24

Perf. 10½
1958, Sept. 24   Litho.   Unwmk.
B69 SP24 50k + 10k gray   .25   .20

Mustafa ibn 'Abdallah Katip Chelebi Hajji Khalifa (1608-1657), Turkish author.

Road Building Machine SP25

Kemal Atatürk — SP26

Ruins, Göreme SP27

Design: 25k+5k, Tanks and planes.

1958, Oct. 29
B70 SP25 15k + 5k orange   .20   .20
B71 SP26 20k + 5k lt red brn   .20   .20
B72 SP25 25k + 5k brt grn   .20   .20
  Nos. B70-B72 (3)   .60   .60

The surtax went to the Red Crescent Society and to the Society for the Protection of Children.

For surcharge see No. 1440.

1959, July 8   Litho.   Perf. 10
B73 SP27 105k + 10k pur & buff   .30   .20

Issued for tourist publicity.

Istanbul SP28

1959, Sept. 11
B74 SP28 105k + 10k lt bl & red   .30   .20

15th International Tuberculosis Congress.

Manisa Asylum SP29

Merkez Muslihiddin SP30

Kermis at Manisa: 90k+5k, Sultan Camil Mosque, Manisa, vert.

1960, Apr. 17   Unwmk.   Perf. 13
B75 SP29 40k + 5k grn & lt bl   .25   .20
B76 SP29 40k + 5k vio & rose lil .25   .20
B77 SP29 90k + 5k dp cl & car
  rose   .60   .20
B78 SP30 105k + 10k multi   .80   .20
  Nos. B75-B78 (4)   1.90   .80

Census Chart SP31

Census Symbol — SP32

1960, Sept. 23   Photo.   Perf. 11½
Granite Paper
B79 SP31 30k + 5k bl & rose pink   .20   .20
B80 SP32 50k + 5k grn, dk bl & ul-
  tra   .25   .20

Issued for the 1960 Census.

Old Observatory SP33

Fatin Gökmen — SP34

Designs: 30k+5k, Observatory emblem. 75k+5k, Building housing telescope.

1961, July 1   Litho.   Perf. 13
B81 SP33 10k + 5k grnsh bl &
  grn   .25   .25
B82 SP33 30k + 5k vio & blk   .75   .75

B83 SP34 40k + 5k brown .25 .25
B84 SP33 75k + 5k olive grn .75 .75
Nos. B81-B84 (4) 2.00 2.00

Kandili Observatory, 50th anniversary.

Anti-Malaria Work — SP35

UNICEF, 10th anniv.: 30k+5k, Mother and infant, horiz. 75k+5k, Woman distributing pasteurized milk.

1961, Dec. 11   Unwmk.   Perf. 13
B85 SP35 10k + 5k Prus green .20 .20
B86 SP35 30k + 5k dull violet .30 .20
B87 SP35 75k + 5k dk olive bis .60 .20
Nos. B85-B87 (3) 1.10 .60

Malaria Eradication Emblem, Map and Mosquito SP36

1962, Apr. 7   Litho.
B88 SP36 30k + 5k dk & lt brn .30 .20
B89 SP36 75k + 5k blk & lil .35 .20

WHO drive to eradicate malaria.

Poinsettia SP37

Wheat and Census Chart SP38

Flowers: 40k+10k, Bird of paradise flower. 75k+10k, Water lily.

1962, May 19   Perf. 12½x13½
Flowers in Natural Colors
B90 SP37 30k + 10k lt bl & blk .20 .20
B91 SP37 40k + 10k lt bl & blk .30 .20
B92 SP37 75k + 10k lt bl & blk .80 .30
Nos. B90-B92 (3) 1.30 .70

Inscribed: "Umumi Ziraat Sayimi"
1963, Apr. 14   Photo.   Perf. 11½
Design: 60k+5k, Wheat and chart, horiz.
B93 SP38 30k + 5k gray grn & yel .20 .20
B94 SP38 60k + 5k org yel & blk .20 .20

1961 agricultural census. Two black bars obliterate "Kasim 1960" inscription.

Red Lion and Sun, Red Crescent, Red Cross and Globe SP39

Designs: 60k+10k, Emblems in flowers, vert. 100k+10k, Emblems on flags.

1963, Aug. 1   Perf. 13
B95 SP39 50k + 10k multi .20 .20
B96 SP39 60k + 10k multi .25 .20
B97 SP39 100k + 10k multi .40 .30
Nos. B95-B97 (3) .85 .70

Centenary of International Red Cross.

Angora Goat — SP40

Olympic Torch Bearer — SP41

Animals: 10k+5k, Steppe cattle, horiz. 50k+5k. Arabian horses, horiz. 60k+5k, Three Angora goats. 100k+5k, Montofon cattle, horiz.

1964, Oct. 4   Litho.   Perf. 13
B98 SP40 10k + 5k multi .30 .20
B99 SP40 30k + 5k multi .30 .20
B100 SP40 50k + 5k multi .50 .20
B101 SP40 60k + 5k multi .70 .20
B102 SP40 100k + 5k multi .90 .20
Nos. B98-B102 (5) 2.70 1.00

Issued for Animal Protection Day.

1964, Oct. 10   Unwmk.
Designs: 10k+5k, Running, horiz. 60k+5k, Wrestling. 100k+5k, Discus.
B103 SP41 10k + 5k org brn, blk & red .30 .20
B104 SP41 50k + 5k ol, blk & red .30 .20
B105 SP41 60k + 5k bl, blk & red .70 .20
B106 SP41 100k + 5k vio, blk, red & sil 1.00 .30
Nos. B103-B106 (4) 2.30 .90

18th Olympic Games, Tokyo, Oct. 10-25.

Map of Dardanelles and Laurel SP42

Designs: 90k+10k, Soldiers and war memorial, Canakkale. 130k+10k, Turkish flag and arch, vert.

1965, Mar. 18   Litho.   Perf. 13
B107 SP42 50k + 10k vio, yel & gold .20 .20
B108 SP42 90k + 10k vio bl, bl, yel & grn .25 .20
B109 SP42 130k + 10k dk brn, red & yel .45 .40
Nos. B107-B109 (3) .90 .80

50th anniversary of Battle of Gallipoli.

Tobacco Plant — SP43

Goddess, Basalt Carving — SP44

50k+5k, Tobacco leaves and Leander's tower, horiz. 100k+5k, Tobacco leaf.

1965, Sept. 16   Unwmk.   Perf. 13
B110 SP43 30k + 5k brn, lt brn & grn .20 .20
B111 SP43 50k + 5k vio bl, ocher & pur .30 .20
B112 SP43 100k + 5k blk, ol grn & ocher .50 .25
Nos. B110-B112 (3) 1.00 .65

Second International Tobacco Congress.

Perf. 13½x13, 13x13½
1966, June 6   Litho.
Archaeological Museum, Ankara: 30k+5k, Eagle and rabbit, ivory carving, horiz. 60k+5k, Bronze bull. 90k+5k, Gold pitcher.
B113 SP44 30k + 5k multi .20 .20
B114 SP44 50k + 5k multi .30 .20
B115 SP44 60k + 5k multi .45 .25
B116 SP44 90k + 5k multi .60 .35
Nos. B113-B116 (4) 1.55 1.00

Grand Hotel Ephesus SP45

Designs: 60k+5k, Konak Square, Izmir, vert. 130k+5k, Izmir Fair Grounds.

1966, Oct. 18   Litho.   Perf. 12
B117 SP45 50k + 5k multi .20 .20
B118 SP45 60k + 5k multi .25 .20
B119 SP45 130k + 5k multi .55 .35
Nos. B117-B119 (3) 1.00 .75

33rd Congress of the Intl. Fair Assoc.

Europa Issue, 1967
Common Design Type
1967, May 2   Litho.   Perf. 13x13½
Size: 22x33mm
B120 CD10 100k + 10k multi 1.00 1.00
  a.   Dark blue ("Europa") omitted
B121 CD10 130k + 10k multi 2.50 1.75

Cloverleaf Crossing, Map of Turkey SP46

130k+5k, Highway E5 & map of Turkey.

1967, June 30   Litho.   Perf. 13
B122 SP46 60k + 5k multi .30 .20
B123 SP46 130k + 5k multi, vert. .60 .30

Inter-European Express Highway, E5.

WHO Emblem SP47

1968, Apr. 7   Litho.   Perf. 13
B124 SP47 130k + 10k lt ultra, blk & yel .35 .20

WHO, 20th anniversary.

Efem Pasha, Dr. Marko Pasha and View of Istanbul — SP48

60k+10k, Omer Pasha, Dr. Abdullah Bey & wounded soldiers. 100k+10k, Ataturk & Dr. Refik Say in front of Red Crescent headquarters, vert.

1968, June 11   Litho.   Perf. 13
B125 SP48 50k + 10k multi .40 .20
B126 SP48 60k + 10k multi .50 .25
B127 SP48 100k + 10k multi .80 .40
Nos. B125-B127 (3) 1.70 .85

Centenary of Turkish Red Crescent Society.

NATO Emblem and Dove SP49

NATO, 20th anniv.: 130k+10k, NATO emblem and globe surrounded by 15 stars, symbols of the 15 NATO members.

1969, Apr. 4   Litho.   Perf. 13
B128 SP49 50k + 10k brt grn, blk & lt bl .25 .20
B129 SP49 130k + 10k bluish blk, bl & gold .45 .30

Red Cross, Crescent, Lion and Sun Emblems SP50

Design: 130k+10k, Conference emblem and Istanbul skyline.

1969, Aug. 29   Litho.   Perf. 13
B130 SP50 100k + 10k dk & lt bl & red .50 .30
B131 SP50 130k + 10k red, lt bl & blk .80 .45

21st Intl. Red Cross Conf., Istanbul.

Erosion Control SP51

60k+10k, Protection of flora (dead tree). 130k+10k, Protection of wildlife (bird of prey).

1970, Feb. 9   Litho.   Perf. 13
B132 SP51 50k + 10k multi .25 .25
B133 SP51 60k + 10k multi .40 .40
B134 SP51 130k + 10k multi .95 .95
Nos. B132-B134 (3) 1.60 1.60

1970 European Nature Conservation Year.

Globe and Fencer SP52

Design: 130k+10k, Globe, fencer and folk dancer with sword and shield.

1970, Sept. 13   Litho.   Perf. 13
B135 SP52 90k + 10k bl & blk .30 .20
B136 SP52 130k + 10k ultra, lt bl, blk & org .40 .20

International Fencing Championships.

"Children's Protection" SP53

Designs: 100k+15k, Hand supporting child, vert. 110k+15k, Mother and child.

1971, June 30   Litho.   Perf. 13
Star and Crescent Emblem in Red
B137 SP53 50k + 10k lil rose & blk .20 .20
B138 SP53 100k + 15k brn, rose & blk .25 .20
B139 SP53 110k + 15k org brn, bis & blk .30 .20
Nos. B137-B139 (3) .75 .60

50th anniv. of the Child Protection Assoc.

UNICEF, 25th Anniv. — SP54

"Your Heart is your Health" — SP55

1971, Dec. 11
B140 SP54 100k + 10k multi .25 .20
B141 SP54 250k + 15k multi .60 .40

1972, Apr. 7   Litho.   Perf. 13
B142 SP55 250k + 25k gray, blk & red   .55 .40

World Health Day.

Olympic Emblems, Runners
SP56

100k+15k, Olympic rings & motion emblem. 250k+25k, Olympic rings & symbolic track ('72).

1972, Aug. 26
B143 SP56 100k + 15k multi   .25 .20
B144 SP56 110k + 25k multi   .35 .20
B145 SP56 250k + 25k multi   .50 .30
  Nos. B143-B145 (3)   1.10 .70

20th Olympic Games, Munich, 8/26-9/11.

Emblem of Istanbul Technical University
SP57

1973, Apr. 21   Litho.   Perf. 13
B146 SP57 100k + 25k multi   .50 .25

Istanbul Technical University, 200th anniv.

Dove and "50"
SP58

1973, July 24   Litho.   Perf. 12½x13
B147 SP58 100k + 25k multi   .35 .20

Peace Treaty of Lausanne, 50th anniversary.

World Population Year — SP59

1974, June 15   Litho.   Perf. 13
B148 SP59 250k + 25k multi   .75 .35

Guglielmo Marconi (1874-1937), Italian Electrical Engineer and Inventor
SP60

1974, Nov. 15   Litho.   Perf. 13½
B149 SP60 250k + 25k multi   .75 .35

Dr. Albert Schweitzer
SP61

Africa with South-West Africa
SP62

1975, Jan 14   Litho.   Perf. 13
B150 SP61 250k + 50k multi   .90 .45
  Dr. Albert Schweitzer (1875-1965), medical missionary and music scholar.

1975, Aug. 26   Litho.   Perf. 13x12½
B151 SP62 250k + 50k multi   .70 .35
  Namibia Day (independence for South-West Africa).

Ziya Gökalp
SP63

Spoonbill
SP64

1976, Mar. 23   Litho.   Perf. 13
B152 SP63 200k + 25k multi   .35 .20
  Ziya Gökalp (1876-1924), philosopher.

1976, Nov. 19   Litho.   Perf. 13
  Birds: 150k+25k, European roller. 200k+25k, Flamingo. 400k+25k, Hermit ibis, horiz.
B153 SP64 100k + 25k multi   .40 .20
B154 SP64 150k + 25k multi   .45 .20
B155 SP64 200k + 25k multi   .85 .25
B156 SP64 400k + 25k multi   1.50 .35
  Nos. B153-B156 (4)   3.20 1.00

Decree by Mehmet Bey, and Ongun Holy Bird — SP65

1977, May 13   Litho.   Perf. 13
B157 SP65 200k + 25k grn & blk   .50 .25

700th anniv. of Turkish as official language.

10th World Energy Conference
SP66

Design: 600k+50k, Conference emblem and globe with circles.

1977, Sept. 19   Litho.   Perf. 12½
B158 SP66 100k + 25k multi   .40 .20
B159 SP66 600k + 25k multi   1.25 .50

Running
SP67

Designs: 2½ l+50k, Gymnastics. 5 l+ 50k, Table tennis. 8 l+50k, Swimming.

1978, July 18   Litho.   Perf. 13
B160 SP67 1 l + 50k multi   .30 .20
B161 SP67 2½ l + 50k multi   .40 .30
B162 SP67 5 l + 50k multi   .80 .30
B163 SP67 8 l + 50k multi   1.50 .35
  Nos. B160-B163 (4)   3.00 1.15

GYMNASIADE '78, World School Games, Izmir.

Ribbon and Chain
SP68

Design: 5 l+50k, Ribbon and flower, vert.

Perf. 12½x13, 13x12½

1978, Sept. 3   Litho.
B164 SP68 2½ l + 50k multi   .75 .20
B165 SP68 5 l + 50k multi   1.00 .20

European Declaration of Human Rights, 25th anniversary.

Children, Head of Ataturk
SP69

Black Francolin
SP70

IYC Emblem and: 5 l+50k, Children with globe as balloon. 8 l+50k, Kneeling person and child, globe.

1979, Apr. 23   Litho.   Perf. 13x13½
B166 SP69 2½ l + 50k multi   .25 .20
B167 SP69 5 l + 50k multi   .40 .20
B168 SP69 8 l + 50k multi   .60 .25
  Nos. B166-B168 (3)   1.25 .65

International Year of the Child.

1979, Dec. 3   Litho.   Perf. 13x13½
  #B170, Great bustard. #B171, Crane. #B172, Gazelle. #B173, Mouflon muffelwild.
B169 SP70 5 l + 1 l multi   .80 .20
B170 SP70 5 l + 1 l multi   .80 .20
B171 SP70 5 l + 1 l multi   .80 .20
B172 SP70 5 l + 1 l multi   .80 .20
B173 SP70 5 l + 1 l multi   .80 .20
  a.   Strip of 5, #B169-B173   6.00 6.00

European Wildlife Conservation Year. No. B173a has continuous design.

Flowers, Trees and Sun
SP71

Rodolia Cardinalis
SP72

Environment Protection: 7½ l+ 1 l Sun, water. 15 l+1 l, Industrial pollution, globe. 20 l+1 l, Flower in oil puddle.

1980, June 4   Litho.   Perf. 13
B174 SP71 2½ l + 1 l multi   .20 .20
B175 SP71 7½ l + 1 l multi   .25 .20
B176 SP71 15 l + 1 l multi   .45 .25
B177 SP71 20 l + 1 l multi   .50 .35
  Nos. B174-B177 (4)   1.40 1.00

1980, Dec. 3   Litho.   Perf. 13
  Useful Insects: 7½ l+1 l, Bracon hebetor; 15 l+1 l, Calosoma sycophanta; 20 l+1 l, Deraeocoris rutilus.
B178 SP72 2½ l + 1 l multi   .25 .20
B179 SP72 7½ l + 1 l multi   .45 .20
B180 SP72 15 l + 1 l multi   .80 .20
B181 SP72 20 l + 1 l multi   1.00 .20
  Nos. B178-B181 (4)   2.50 .80

Intl. Year of the Disabled
SP73

TB Bacillus Centenary
SP75

Insects
SP74

1981, Mar. 25   Litho.   Perf. 13
B182 SP73 10 l + 2½ l multi   .30 .20
B183 SP73 20 l + 2½ l multi   .45 .20

1981, Dec. 16   Litho.   Perf. 13
  Useful Insects: No. B184, Cicindela campestris. No. B185, Syrphus vitripennis. No. B186, Ascalaphus macaronius. No. B187, Empusa fasciata.
B184 SP74 10 l + 2½ l multi   .30 .20
B185 SP74 20 l + 2½ l multi   .50 .20
B186 SP74 30 l + 2½ l multi   .75 .25
B187 SP74 40 l + 2½ l multi   1.00 .35
  Nos. B184-B187 (4)   2.55 1.00

See Nos. B190-B194, B196-B200.

1982, Mar. 24   Perf. 13x12½
  Portraits: #B188, Dr. Tevfik Saglam (1882-1963). #B189, Robert Koch.
B188 SP75 10 l + 2½ l multi   .50 .25
B189 SP75 30 l + 2½ l multi   1.25 .25

Insect Type of 1981

  Useful Insects: 10 l+2½ l, Eurydema spectabile. 15 l+2½ l, Dacus oleae. 20 l+2½ l, Klapperichicen viridissima. 30 l+2½ l, Leptinotarsa decemlineata. 35 l+2½ l, Rhynchites auratus.

1982, Aug. 18   Litho.   Perf. 13
B190 SP74 10 l + 2½ l multi   .55 .20
B191 SP74 15 l + 2½ l multi   .75 .20
B192 SP74 20 l + 2½ l multi   .75 .20
B193 SP74 30 l + 2½ l multi   .95 .20
B194 SP74 35 l + 2½ l multi   1.00 .20
  Nos. B190-B194 (5)   4.00 1.00

Richard Wagner (1813-1883), Composer — SP76

1983, Feb. 13
B195 SP76 30 l + 5 l multi   1.10 1.00

Insect Type of 1981

  Harmful Insects: 15 l+5 l, Eurygaster Intergriceps Put. 25 l+5 l, Phyllobius nigrofasciatus Pes. 35 l+5 l, Cercopis intermedia Kbm. 50 l+10 l, Graphosoma lineatum (L). 75 l+10 l, Capnodis miliaris (King).

1983, Sept. 14   Litho.   Perf. 13
B196 SP74 15 l + 5 l multi   .50 .20
B197 SP74 25 l + 5 l multi   .65 .20
B198 SP74 35 l + 5 l multi   .85 .20
B199 SP74 50 l + 10 l multi   1.25 .25
B200 SP74 75 l + 10 l multi   1.75 .40
  Nos. B196-B200 (5)   5.00 1.25

Topkapi Museum Artifacts SP77

1984 Summer Olympics SP78

1984, May 30   Litho.   Perf. 13
B201 SP77 20 l + 5 l Kaftan,
               16th cent.   .30   .20
B202 SP77 70 l + 15 l Ewer   .95   .40
B203 SP77 90 l + 20 l Swords   1.60   .45
B204 SP77 100 l + 25 l Lock, key   1.90   .55
        Nos. B201-B204 (4)   4.75   1.60

Surtax was for museum. See Nos. B208-B211, B213-B216, B218-B221.

1984, July 28

Designs: 20 l+5 l, Banners, horiz. 70 l+15 l, Medalist Oyunları. 100 l+20 l, Running, horiz.
B205 SP78 20 l + 5 l multi   .75   .50
B206 SP78 70 l + 15 l multi   .90   .75
B207 SP78 100 l + 20 l multi   1.50   1.00
        Nos. B205-B207 (3)   3.15   2.25

Artifacts Type of 1984

Ceramicware: 10 l+5 l, Iznik plate. 20 l+10 l, Iznik boza pitcher and mug, 16th cent. 100 l+15 l, Du Paquier ewer and basin, 1730. 120 l+20 l, Ching dynasty plate, 1522-1566.

1985, May 30   Litho.   Perf. 13
B208 SP77 10 l + 5 l multi   .50   .20
B209 SP77 20 l + 10 l multi   .80   .40
B210 SP77 100 l + 15 l multi   1.75   1.10
B211 SP77 120 l + 20 l multi   2.50   1.40
        Nos. B208-B211 (4)   5.55   3.10

Rabies Vaccine, Cent. — SP79

1985, July 16   Perf. 13x13½
B212 SP79 100 l + 15 l Pasteur   1.50   1.00

Artifacts Type of 1984

20 l+5 l, Metal and ceramic incense burner, c. 17th cent. 100 l+10 l, Jade lidded mug decorated with precious gems, 16th cent. 120 l+15 l, Dagger designed by Mahmut I, 1714. 200 l+30 l, Willow buckler, defensive shield, undated.

1986, May 30   Litho.   Perf. 13x12½
B213 SP77 20 l + 5 l multi   .50   .25
B214 SP77 100 l + 10 l multi   1.00   .40
B215 SP77 120 l + 15 l multi   1.10   .50
B216 SP77 200 l + 30 l multi   2.25   .75
        Nos. B213-B216 (4)   4.85   1.90

General Assembly of NATO SP80

1986, Nov. 13   Litho.   Perf. 13½x13
B217 SP80 100 l + 20 l multi   1.25   .40

Artifacts Type of 1984

Designs: 20 l+5 l, Crystal and gold ewer, 16th cent., vert. 50 l+10 l, Emerald and gold pendant, 17th cent. 200 l+15 l, Sherbet jug, 19th cent., vert. 250 l+30 l, Crystal and gold pen box, 16th cent.

1987, May 30   Litho.   Perf. 13
B218 SP77 20 l + 5 l multi   .75   .20
B219 SP77 50 l + 10 l multi   1.00   .40
B220 SP77 200 l + 15 l multi   1.25   1.00
B221 SP77 250 l + 30 l multi   2.00   1.25
        Nos. B218-B221 (4)   5.00   2.85

15th Intl. Chemotherapy Congress, Istanbul — SP81

1987, July 19   Litho.   Perf. 13
B222 SP81 200 l + 25 l multi   .85   .20

Intl. Road Transport Union (IRU) 21st World Congress SP82

1988, June 13   Litho.   Perf. 12½x13
B223 SP82 200 l + 25 l multi   .55   .20

European Environmental Campaign Balancing Nature and Development — SP83

Designs: 100 l+25 l, Hands, desert reclamation. 400 l+50 l, Eye, road, planted field.

1988, Oct. 19   Litho.   Perf. 12½x13
B224 SP83 100 l + 25 l multi   .35   .20
B225 SP83 400 l + 50 l multi   1.25   .30

Silkworm Industry SP84

Perf. 13½x13
1989, Apr. 15   Litho.   Wmk. 394
B226 SP84 150 l + 50 l Silkworm   .30   .20
B227 SP84 600 l + 100 l Cocoon,
               strands   1.10   .25

Council of Europe, 40th Anniv. SP85

1989, May 5   Litho.   Perf. 13
B228 SP85 600 l + 100 l multi   .90   .25

European Tourism Year SP86

1990, Apr. 26   Wmk. 394
B229 SP86 300 l + 50 l Antalya   .35   .20
B230 SP86 1000 l + 100 l Istan-
               bul   1.10   .30

Fight Against Addictions — SP87

Fight Against: No. B231, Smoking. No. B232, Drugs, horiz.

1990, June 26   Litho.   Perf. 13
B231 SP87 300 l + 50 l multi   .30   .20
B232 SP87 1000 l + 100 l multi   .90   .45

Yunus Emre (died c.1321), Poet
SP88   SP89

1991, June 26   Litho.   Perf. 13
B233 SP88 500 l + 100 l multi   .50   .25
B234 SP89 1500 l + 100 l multi   1.25   .65

Wolfgang Amadeus Mozart (1756-1791), Composer — SP90

1991, July 24
B235 SP90 1500 l + 100 l multi   1.25   .65

Turkish Supreme Court, 30th Anniv. SP91

1992, Apr. 25
B236 SP91 500 l + 100 l multi   .50   .25

Scouts Planting Tree SP92

#B238 Mountain climber on rope, vert.

1992, Dec. 18
B237 SP92 1000 l + 200 l multi   .50   .30
B238 SP92 3000 l + 200 l multi   .90   .50

Travertine, Pamukkale — SP93

Different views of rock formations.

1993, June 6
B239 SP93 1000 l + 200 l multi   .30   .20
B240 SP93 3000 l + 500 l multi   .80   .40

Intl. Day for Natural Disaster Reduction SP94

1993, Oct. 13   Perf. 12½x13
B241 SP94 3000 l + 500 l multi   .90   .50

Intl. Olympic Committee, Cent. — SP95

1994, Aug. 17   Perf. 13
B242 SP95 12,500 l + 500 l multi   1.50 1.00

Trees SP96

Designs: No. B243, Platanus orientalis. No. B244, Cupressus sempervirens, vert.

1994, Nov. 30
B243 SP96 7500 l + 500 l multi   1.00   .80
B244 SP96 12,500 l + 500 l multi   2.00   1.50

TBMM (Great Natl. Assembly), 75th Anniv. SP97

1995, Apr. 23
B245 SP97 3500 l + 500 l multi   .25   .20

The Epic of Manas SP98

Designs: No. B246, Lancers charging. No. B247, Abay Kunanbay (1845-1904), poet, vert.

1995, June 28
B246 SP98 3500 l + 500 l multi   .25   .20
B247 SP98 3500 l + 500 l multi   .25   .20

For the People of Bosnia-Herzegovina — SP99

1996, Feb. 28
B248 SP99 10,000 l + 2500 l multi   .75   .75

Ankara University, 50th Anniv. SP100

Unwmk.
1996, Nov. 20   Litho.   Perf. 13
B249 15,000 l + 2500 l multi   .65   .30

Fight Against Cancer, 50th Anniv. SP101

1997, Feb. 18   Litho.   Perf. 12½x13
B250 SP101 25,000 l + 5000 l
               multi   .65   .30

Pakistan Independence, 50th Anniv. — SP102

Mohammed Ali Jinnah (1876-1948).

1997, Mar. 23   Litho.   Perf. 13
B251 SP102 25,000 l +5000 l
                          multi   .60   .30

Universal Declaration of Human Rights SP103

Stylized designs: 75,000 l, Puzzle piece with outlines of people's faces. 175,000 l, Heart-shaped kite with people as tail.

1998, Dec. 10   Litho.   Perf. 13½
B252 SP103 75,000 l +25,000 l   1.00   .50
B253 SP103 175,000 l +25,000 l   2.00 1.00

GATA 100, Yilinda SP104

1998, Dec. 30   Litho.   Perf. 13
B254 SP104 75,000 l +10,000 l
                          multi   .60   .30

Kemal Ataturk's Entry Into War College, Cent. — SP105

1999, Mar. 13   Litho.   Perf. 13
B255 SP105 75,000 l +5,000 l
                          multi   .40   .20

Council of Europe, 50th Anniv. SP106

1999, Apr. 30   Litho.   Perf. 13¼
B256 SP106 175,000 l +10,000 l   2.00 1.25

Church, Mosque and Synagogue — SP107

Dancers SP108

2000, May 25   Litho.   Perf. 13¼
B257 SP107 275,000 l +10,000 l   1.50 1.50
B258 SP108 300,000 l +10,000 l   1.50 1.50

Tombs and Mausoleums — SP109

150,000 l+25,000 l, Usta Sagirt Kumbeti Ahlat, vert. 200,000 l+25,000 l, Kocbasli Mezar Tasi Tunceli. 275,000 l+25,000 l, Isabey Turbesi, Uskup, vert. 300,000 l+25,000 l, Yusuf bin Kuseyr Turbesi, Nahcivan, vert.

2000
B259-B262 SP109 Set of 4   5.00 5.00

Coins SP110

Various coins with background colors of: No. B263, 300,000 l + 25,000 l, Red. No. B264, 300,000 l + 25,000 l, Blue green. 450,000 l + 25,000 l, Dark carmine. 500,000 l + 25,000 l, Blue violet.

2001, Oct. 1   Litho.   Perf. 13
B263-B266 SP110 Set of 4   5.50 5.50

Caravansaries — SP111

Designs: 300,000 l + 25,000 l, Ashab i Kehf Han, Afsin. 500,000 l + 25,000 l, Horozlu Han, Konya.

2001, Nov. 19   Litho.   Perf. 13
B267-B268 SP111 Set of 2   2.75 2.75

Turkey's Admission to NATO, 50th Anniv. SP112

2002, Feb. 18
B269 SP112 400,000 l + 25,000 l 1.10 1.10

Trains SP113

Designs: 500,000 l + 25,000 l, Steam locomotive. 700,000 l + 25,000 l, Electric locomotive.

2002, Sept. 16   Litho.   Perf. 13¼x13
B270-B271 SP113 Set of 2   3.25 3.25

Trains SP114

Designs: 600,000 l+50,000 l, Trolley. 800,000 l+50,000 l, Subway.

2003, Sept. 9   Litho.   Perf. 13¼x13
B272-B273 SP114 Set of 2   2.75 2.75

Ibrahim Hakki Erzurumlu (1703-72), Writer — SP115

2003, Dec. 24   Litho.   Perf. 13x13¼
B274 SP115 600,000 l +50,000 l
                          multi   .95   .95

Lighthouses SP116

Designs: 600,000 l + 50,000 l, Kerempe Lighthouse, Kastamonu. 700,000 l + 50,000 l, Taslikburnu Lighthouse, Antalya.

2004, Apr. 5
B275-B276 SP116 Set of 2   3.00 3.00

Scouting — SP117

Designs: 600,000 l + 50,000 l, Girl Scout in foreground. 700,000 l + 50,000 l, Boy Scout in foreground.

2004, Sept. 30
B277-B278 SP117 Set of 2   2.25 2.25

Rotary International, Cent. — SP118

2005, Feb. 23   Litho.   Perf. 13x13¼
B279 SP118 80k +10k multi   1.50 1.50

Intl. Year of Physics SP119

2005, Sept. 13   Litho.   Perf. 13¼x13
B280 SP119 70k +10k multi   1.25 1.25

World Forests Day SP120

2006, Mar. 21   Litho.   Perf. 13¼x13
B281 SP120 60k +10k multi   1.10 1.10

Mehmet Akif Ersoy (1873-1936), Poet — SP121

Ersoy at: 60k+10k, Left. 70k+10k, Right.

2006, Oct. 13   Litho.   Perf. 13¼x13
B282-B283 SP121 Set of 2   2.10 2.10

Coast Guard Command, 25th Anniv. — SP122

2007, July 13   Litho.   Perf. 13x13¼
B284 SP122 60k + 10k multi   1.10 1.10

Marbled Art — SP123

Designs: 60k+10k, White flowers. 70k+10k, Red tulips.

2007, Dec. 6   Perf. 13¼x13
B285-B286 SP123 Set of 2   2.60 2.60

AIR POST STAMPS

Catalogue values for unused stamps in this section are for Never Hinged items.

Nos. 692, 695, 698, 700 Overprinted or Surcharged in Brown or Blue

1934, July 15   Unwmk.   Perf. 12
C1 A74 7½k (Br)   .75   .20
C2 A72 12½k on 15k (Br)   .75   .25
C3 A74 20k on 25k (Br)   .75   .25
C4 A74 25k (Bl)   1.00   .40
C5 A74 40k (Br)   2.25 1.25
        Nos. C1-C5 (5)   5.50 2.35

Regular Stamps of
1930 Surcharged in
Brown

1937
C6	A74	4½k on 7½k red brn	5.00	1.00
C7	A72	9k on 15k dp org	40.00	20.00
C8	A74	35k on 40k red vio	4.25	
		Nos. C6-C8 (3)	55.00	25.25

Nos. 698, 703-704
Surcharged in Black

1941, Dec. 18
C9	A74	4½k on 25k	2.00	1.50
C10	A75	9k on 200k	9.75	8.25
C11	A75	35k on 500k	6.25	5.25
		Nos. C9-C11 (3)	18.00	15.00

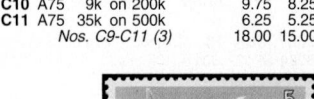

Plane over
Izmir
AP1

Planes over: 5k, 40k, Izmir. 20k, 50k,
Ankara. 30k, 1 l, Istanbul.

1949, Jan. 1   Photo.   Perf. 11½
C12	AP1	5k gray & vio	.25	.25
C13	AP1	20k bl gray & brn	.25	.25
C14	AP1	30k bl gray & ol brn	1.00	.25
C15	AP1	40k bl & dp ultra	1.00	1.00
C16	AP1	50k gray vio & red brn	1.00	.25
C17	AP1	1 l gray bl & dk grn	3.00	.65
		Nos. C12-C17 (6)	6.50	2.65

For overprints see Nos. C19-C21.

Plane Over
Rumeli
Hisari
Fortress
AP2

1950, May 19   Unwmk.
C18	AP2	2½ l gray bl & dk grn	22.50	14.00

Nos. C12, C14 and C16 Overprinted
in Red

1951, Apr. 9   Perf. 11½
C19	AP1	5k gray & vio	1.50	.50
C20	AP1	30k bl gray & ol brn	2.00	.60
C21	AP1	50k gray vio & red brn	2.50	.70
		Nos. C19-C21 (3)	6.00	1.80

Industrial Congress, Ankara, Apr. 9.

Yesilkoy
Airport and
Plane
AP3

Designs: 20k, 45k, Yesilkoy Airport and
plane in flight. 35k, 55k, Ankara Airport and
plane. 40k, as No. C22.

1954, Nov. 1   Perf. 14
C22	AP3	5k red brn & bl	1.00	.25
C23	AP3	20k brn org & bl	.65	.25
C24	AP3	35k dk grn & bl	.65	.25
C25	AP3	40k dp car & bl	.65	.25
C26	AP3	45k violet & bl	1.50	.25
C27	AP3	55k black & bl	4.00	.50
		Nos. C22-C27 (6)	8.45	1.75

Symbol of Izmir
Fair — AP4

1956, Aug. 20   Litho.   Perf. 10½
C28	AP4	25k reddish brown	.25	.20

25th Intl. Fair at Izmir, Aug. 20-Sept. 20.

Heuss Type of Regular Issue, 1957

1957, May 5
C29	A264	40k sal pink & magenta	.25	.20

Zahir Shah Type of Regular Issue,
1957

1957, Sept. 1
C30	A269	25k grn & lt grn	.25	.20

Hawk — AP5

Crane — AP6

Birds: 40k, 125k, Swallows. 65k, Cranes.
85k, 195k, Gulls. 245k, Hawk.

1959, Aug. 13   Litho.   Perf. 10½
C31	AP5	40k bright lilac	.50	.20
C32	AP5	65k blue green	3.00	.40
C33	AP5	85k bright blue	1.00	.40
C34	AP5	105k yel & sepia	.75	.40
C35	AP6	125k brt violet	1.00	.40
C36	AP6	155k yel green	1.25	.40
C37	AP6	195k violet blue	1.50	.40
C38	AP6	245k brn & brn org	3.50	1.00
		Nos. C31-C38 (8)	12.50	3.60

De Havilland
Rapide
Biplane
AP7

Kestrel — AP8

Designs: 60k, Fokker Friendship transport
plane. 130k, DC9-30. 220k, DC-3. 270k, Viscount 794.

1967, July 13   Litho.   Perf. 13½x13
C39	AP7	10k pink & blk	.25	.20
C40	AP7	60k lt grn, red & blk	.30	.20
C41	AP7	130k bl, blk & red	.65	.20

C42	AP7	220k lt brn, blk & red	.95	.30
C43	AP7	270k org, blk & red	1.40	.35
		Nos. C39-C43 (5)	3.55	1.25

For surcharge see No. 2179A.

1967, Oct. 10   Litho.   Perf. 13

Birds: 60k, Golden eagle. 130k, Falcon.
220k, Sparrow hawk. 270k, Buzzard.

C44	AP8	10k brown & salmon	.60	.20
C45	AP8	60k brown & yellow	.45	.20
C46	AP8	130k brown & lt bl	1.10	.20
C47	AP8	220k brown & lt grn	1.75	.25
C48	AP8	270k org brn & gray	2.50	.35
		Nos. C44-C48 (5)	6.40	1.20

F-104 Jet
Plane — AP9

Turkish Air
Force
Emblem
and Jets
AP10

Designs: 200k, Victory monument, Afyon,
and Jets. 325k, F-104 jets and pilot. 400k, Bleriot XI plane with Turkish flag. 475k, Flight of
Hezarfen Ahmet Celebi from Galata Tower to
Usküdar.

1971, June 1   Litho.   Perf. 13
C49	AP9	110k multi	.50	.20
C50	AP9	200k multi	1.10	.20
C51	AP10	250k multi	1.10	.25
C52	AP10	325k multi	1.75	.25
C53	AP10	400k brown & lt grn	1.90	.30
C54	AP10	475k multi	2.50	.35
		Nos. C49-C54 (6)	8.85	1.55

The gold ink on No. C51 is applied by a
thermographic process which gives a raised
and shiny effect.

F-28
Plane — AP11

1973, Dec. 11   Litho.   Perf. 13
C55	AP11	110k shown	.45	.25
C56	AP11	250k DC-10	.90	.30

POSTAGE DUE STAMPS

Same Types as Regular Issues of
Corresponding Dates

1863   Unwmk.   Imperf.
Blue Band
J1	A1	20pa blk, *red brn*	100.00	32.50
a.		Tête bêche pair	225.00	225.00
b.		Without band	50.00	
c.		Red band	90.00	45.00
J2	A2	1pi blk, *red brn*	150.00	22.50
a.		Tête bêche pair	225.00	225.00
b.		Without band	50.00	
J3	A3	2pi blk, *red brn*	500.00	70.00
a.		Tête bêche pair	650.00	450.00
J4	A4	5pi blk, *red brn*	300.00	80.00
a.		Tête bêche pair	425.00	425.00
b.		Without band	100.00	
c.		Red band	150.00	
		Nos. J1-J4 (4)	1,050.	205.00

1865   Perf. 12½
J6	A5	20pa brown	4.00	5.00
J7	A5	1pi brown	4.00	5.00
b.		Half used as 20pa on cover		
c.		Printed on both sides	25.00	
J8	A5	2pi brown	12.50	25.00
a.		Half used as 1pi on cover		
J9	A5	5pi brown	5.00	30.00
a.		Half used as 2½pi on cover		
J10	A5	25pi brown	45.00	100.00
		Nos. J6-J10 (5)	70.50	165.00

Exist imperf. Values, $60 to $100 each.
The 10pa brown is an essay. Value about
$2,750.

1867
J11	A5	20pa bister brn	7.50	100.00
J12	A5	1pi bister brn	7.50	
a.		With surcharge of 5pi	13.50	
b.		Imperf., pair	65.00	
J13	A5	2pi fawn	75.00	
J14	A5	5pi fawn	17.50	
J15	A5	25pi bister brn	21,250.	
		Nos. J11-J14 (4)	107.50	

Nos. J12-J15 were not placed in use.

1869   Perf. 13½
With Yellow-Brown Border
J16	A5	20pa bister brn	10.00	10.00
a.		Without surcharge		
J17	A5	1pi bister brn	550.00	5.00
a.		Without surcharge		
J18	A5	2pi bister brn	800.00	5.00
J19	A5	5pi bister brn	1.50	12.50
b.		Without border		
c.		Printed on both sides	15.00	
J20	A5	25pi bister brn	—	—
		Nos. J16-J20 (4)	1,361.	32.50

With Brown Border
Color of border ranges from brown to reddish
brown and black brown.
J21	A5	20pa bister brn	125.00	20.00
a.		Inverted surcharge		
b.		Without border		
J22	A5	1pi bister brn	550.00	12.50
a.		Without surcharge		
J23	A5	2pi bister brn	450.00	12.50
b.		Inverted surcharge		
J24	A5	5pi bister brn	2.50	15.00
a.		Without surcharge		
J25	A5	25pi bister brn	37.50	100.00
		Nos. J21-J25 (5)	1,165.	160.00

**Pin-perf., Perf. 5 to 11½ and
Compound**

1871
With Brick Red Border
J26	A5	20pa brick brn	875.00	50.00
J27	A5	1pi brick brn		5,000.
J28	A5	2pi brick brn	110.00	140.00
J29	A5	5pi brick brn	7.50	25.00

With Black Brown Border
J31	A5	20pa bister brn	150.00	2.50
a.		Half used as 10pa on cover		
b.		Imperf., pair		16.50
c.		Printed on both sides	40.00	40.00
J32	A5	1pi bister brn	225.00	2.50
a.		Half used as 20pa on cover		
c.		Inverted surcharge	50.00	35.00
d.		Printed on both sides		
J33	A5	2pi bister brn	6.00	9.00
a.		Half used as 1pi on cover		
c.		Imperf., pair		16.50
J34	A5	5pi bister brn	2.50	20.00
a.		Half used as 2½pi on cover		
c.		Printed on both sides		
J35	A5	25pi bister brn	40.00	125.00
a.		Inverted surcharge		
		Nos. J31-J35 (5)	423.50	159.00

1888   Perf. 11½ and 13½
J36	A7	20pa black	3.00	12.50
J37	A7	1pi black	3.00	12.50
J38	A7	2pi black	3.00	15.00
b.		Diagonal half used as 1pi		
		Nos. J36-J38 (3)	9.00	40.00

Imperf
J36a	A7	20pa		11.00
J37a	A7	1pi		11.00
J38a	A7	2pi		11.00

1892   Perf. 13½
J39	A11	20pa black	7.00	12.50
J40	A12	1pi black	22.50	12.50
a.		Printed on both sides		
J41	A13	2pi black	17.50	12.50
		Nos. J39-J41 (3)	47.00	37.50

1901
J42	A11	20pa black, *deep rose*	2.50	20.00

1901
J43	A17	10pa blk, *deep rose*	4.00	6.00
J44	A17	20pa blk, *deep rose*	3.75	8.75
J45	A17	1pi blk, *deep rose*	3.00	10.00
J46	A17	2pi blk, *deep rose*	1.75	15.00
		Nos. J43-J46 (4)	12.50	39.75

1905   Perf. 12
J47	A18	1pi black, *deep rose*	3.00	10.00
J48	A18	2pi black, *deep rose*	4.50	20.00

1908,   Perf. 12, 13½ and Compound
J49	A19	1pi black, *deep rose*	80.00	7.50
J50	A19	2pi black, *deep rose*	12.50	45.00

1909
J51	A21	1pi black, *deep rose*	15.00	50.00
J52	A21	2pi black, *deep rose*	150.00	175.00
a.		Imperf.	65.00	

1913   **Perf. 12**

J53	A22	2pa blk, *deep rose*	1.00	.50
J54	A22	5pa blk, *deep rose*	1.00	.50
J55	A22	10pa blk, *deep rose*	1.00	.50
J56	A22	20pa blk, *deep rose*	1.00	.50
J57	A22	1pi blk, *deep rose*	4.50	10.00
J58	A22	2pi blk, *deep rose*	8.00	17.50
		Nos. J53-J58 (6)	16.50	29.50

Adrianople Issue

Nos. 251-253 Surcharged in Black, Blue or Red

1913

J59	A23	2pa on 10pa green (Bk)	3.25	.35
J60	A23	5pa on 20pa red (Bl)	3.25	.35
J61	A23	10pa on 40pa bl (R)	10.00	.80
J62	A23	20pa on 40pa bl (Bk)	32.50	11.00
		Nos. J59-J62 (4)	49.00	12.50

For surcharges see Nos. J67-J70, J83-J86.

D1   D2

D3   D4

1914   **Engr.**

J63	D1	5pa claret	1.25	10.00
J64	D2	20pa red	1.25	10.00
J65	D3	1pi dark blue	1.25	10.00
J66	D4	2pi slate	1.25	10.00
		Nos. J63-J66 (4)	5.00	40.00

For surcharges and overprints see Nos. J87-J91.

Nos. J59 to J62 Surcharged in Red or Black

1916

J67	A23	10pa on 2pa on 10pa (R)	55.00	55.00
J68	A23	20pa on 5pa on 20pa	55.00	55.00
J69	A23	40pa on 10pa on 40pa	55.00	55.00
J70	A23	40pa on 20pa on 40pa (R)	55.00	55.00
		Nos. J67-J70 (4)	220.00	220.00

Preceding Issues Overprinted in Red, Black or Blue

1917

On Stamps of 1865

J71	A5	20pa red brn (Bl)	45.00	67.50
J72	A5	1pi red brn (Bl)	45.00	67.50
J73	A5	2pi bis brn (Bl)	45.00	67.50
J74	A5	5pi bis brn (Bl)	45.00	67.50
J75	A5	25pi dk brn (Bl)	45.00	67.50
		Nos. J71-J75 (5)	225.00	337.50

On Stamp of 1869
Red Brown Border

J76	A5	5pi bis brn (R)	45.00	67.50

On Stamp of 1871
Black Brown Border

J77	A5	5pi bis brn	75.00	50.00

On Stamps of 1888

J78	A7	1pi black (R)	45.00	67.50
J79	A7	2pi black (R)	45.00	67.50

On Stamps of 1892

J80	A11	20pa black (R)	2.50	2.50
J81	A12	1pi black (R)	2.50	2.50
J82	A13	2pi black (R)	2.50	2.50
		Nos. J80-J82 (3)	7.50	7.50

Adrianople Issue
On Nos. J59 to J62 with Addition of New Value

J83	A23	10pa on 2pa on 10pa (R)	1.25	1.00
J84	A23	20pa on 5pa on 20pa (Bk)	1.50	1.00
J85	A23	40pa on 10pa on 40pa (Bk)	2.00	1.50
a.		"40pa" double		
J86	A23	40pa on 20pa on 40pa (R)	3.75	3.50
		Nos. J83-J86 (4)	8.50	7.00

Nos. J71-J86 were used as regular postage stamps.

Armistice Issue

No. J65 Overprinted

1919, Nov. 30

J87	D3	1pi dark blue	125.00	150.00

Accession to the Throne Issue
Postage Due Stamps of 1914 Overprinted in Turkish "Accession to the Throne of His Majesty. 3rd July, 1334-1918"

1919

J88	D1	10pa on 5pa claret	25.00	37.50
J89	D2	20pa red	25.00	37.50
J90	D3	1pi dark blue	25.00	37.50
J91	D4	2pi slate	25.00	37.50
		Nos. J88-J91 (4)	100.00	150.00

Railroad Bridge over Kizil Irmak — D5   Kemal Atatürk — D6

1926   **Engr.**

J92	D5	20pa ocher	1.25	2.50
J93	D5	1g red	2.00	5.00
J94	D5	2g blue green	3.00	5.00
J95	D5	3g lilac brown	3.50	12.50
J96	D5	5g lilac	6.00	20.00
		Nos. J92-J96 (5)	15.75	45.00
		Set, never hinged	30.00	

Catalogue values for unused stamps in this section, from this point to the end of the section, are for Never Hinged items.

1936   **Litho.**   **Perf. 11½**

J97	D6	20pa brown	.20	.20
J98	D6	2k light blue	.20	.20
J99	D6	3k bright violet	.20	.20
J100	D6	5k Prussian blue	.20	.20
J101	D6	12k bright rose	.35	.20
		Nos. J97-J101 (5)	1.15	1.00

For surcharges see Nos. 1461-1465.

Local Issues

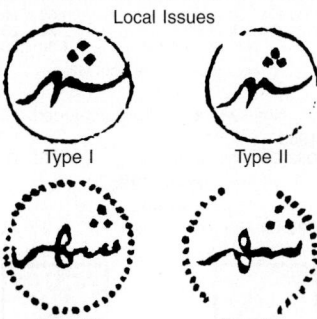

Type I   Type II

Type III   Type IV

Type V   Type VI

During 1873//1882 Turkish stamps with the above overprints were used for local postage in Constantinople (types 1-5) and Mount Athos (type 6).

MILITARY STAMPS

For the Army in Thessaly

Tughra and Bridge at Larissa — M1

1898, Apr. 21   **Unwmk.**   **Perf. 13**

M1	M1	10pa yellow green	10.00	7.50
M2	M1	20pa rose	10.00	7.50
M3	M1	1pi dark blue	10.00	7.50
M4	M1	2pi orange	10.00	7.50
M5	M1	5pi violet	10.00	7.50
		Nos. M1-M5 (5)	50.00	37.50

Issued for Turkish occupation forces to use in Thessaly during the Greco-Turkish War of 1897-98.

Forgeries of Nos. M1-M5 are perf. 11½.

OFFICIAL STAMPS

Catalogue values for unused stamps in this section are for Never Hinged items.

O1

Perf. 10 to 12 and Compound

1948   **Typo.**   **Unwmk.**

O1	O1	10pa rose brown	.50	.20
O2	O1	1k gray green	.50	.20
O3	O1	2k rose violet	.50	.20
O4	O1	3k orange	.50	.20
O5	O1	5k blue	25.00	.90
O6	O1	10k brown org	7.50	.20
O7	O1	15k violet	2.50	.20
O8	O1	20k dk blue	3.00	.20
O9	O1	30k olive bister	5.00	.80
O10	O1	50k black	5.00	.80
O11	O1	1 l bluish grn	5.00	.80
O12	O1	2 l lilac rose	10.00	1.00
		Nos. O1-O12 (12)	65.00	5.70

Regular Issue of 1948 Overprinted Type "a" in Black

1951

O13	A178	5k blue	.20	.20
O14	A178	10k chocolate	.30	.20
O15	A178	20k deep blue	.60	.20
O16	A178	30k brown	.90	.20
		Nos. O13-O16 (4)	2.00	.80

Overprint "a" is 15½mm wide. Points of crescent do not touch star. The 0.25k (No. 963) exists with overprint "a" but its status is questionable.

b   c

Overprinted Type "b" in Dark Brown

1953

O17	A178	0.25k dk red	.20	.20
O18	A178	5k blue	.30	.20
O19	A178	10k chocolate	.40	.20
O20	A178	15k violet	1.00	.20
O21	A178	20k deep blue	6.00	1.00
O22	A178	30k brown	1.25	.20
O23	A178	60k black	1.40	.20
		Nos. O17-O23 (7)	10.55	2.30

Overprint "b" is 14mm wide. Lettering thin with sharp, clean corners.

Overprinted Type "c" in Black or Green Black

1953-54

O23A	A178	0.25k dk red (G Bk)	.25	.20
f.		Black overprint	4.00	4.00
g.		Violet overprint ('53)	4.00	4.00
O23B	A178	10k chocolate	12.50	.65
O23C	A178	15k violet	15.00	1.00
O23D	A178	30k brown	6.50	.65
O23E	A178	60k black	8.00	1.00
		Nos. O23A-O23E (5)	42.25	3.50

Lettering of type "c" heavy with rounded corners.

Small Star — d   Large Star — e

Overprinted or Surcharged Type "d" in Black

1955

O24	A178	0.25k dark red	.30	.20
O25	A178	1k olive black	.30	.20
O26	A178	2k brt rose lil	.30	.20
O27	A178	3k red orange	.40	.20
O28	A178	4k dk green	.50	.25
O29	A178	5k on 15k vio	.50	.25
O31	A178	10k on 15k vio	.60	.25
O32	A178	15k violet	.60	.25
O33	A178	20k deep blue	.70	.25
O35	A179	40k on 1 l ol grn	.80	.35
O36	A179	75k on 2 l dk brn	1.10	.80
O37	A179	75k on 5 l dp plum	8.00	8.00
		Nos. O24-O37 (12)	14.10	11.20

Type "d" measures 15x16mm. Overprint on Nos. O35-O37 measures 19x22mm. Nos. O29, O31, O35-O37 have two bars and new value added.

Overprinted or Surcharged Type "e" in Black

1955

O25a	A178	1k olive black	.40	.20
O29a	A178	5k on 15k violet	1.10	.20
O30	A178	5k blue	1.50	.25
O31a	A178	10k on 15k violet	2.50	1.00
c.		"10" without serif	.50	.30
O33a	A178	20k deep blue	.80	.30
O34	A178	30k brown	.50	.30

Heavy crescent — f

Thin crescent — g

Overprinted or Surcharged Type "f" in Black

1957

O24b	A178	0.25k dark red	.50	.20
O38b	A178	½k on 1k ol blk	.40	.20
O25b	A178	1k olive black	.40	.30
O31b	A178	10k on 15k violet	.80	.30
O35b	A179	75k on 1 l olive grn	1.50	.50
		Nos. O24b-O35b (5)	3.60	1.50

Type "f" crescent is larger and does not touch wavy line. The surcharged "10" on No. O31b exists only without serifs. The overprint on O35b measures 17x22 ½mm.

Overprinted or Surcharged Type "g" in Black

1957

O38	A178	½k on 1k ol blk	.40	.30
O39	A178	1k ol blk	.40	.30
O40	A178	2k on 4k dk grn	.40	.30
O41	A178	3k on 4k dk grn	.40	.30
O42	A178	10k on 12k dp red	.40	.30
		Nos. O38-O42 (5)	2.00	1.50

The shape of crescent and star on type "g" varies on each value. Overprint measures 14x18mm. The surcharged stamps have two bars and new value added.

O2   O3

O4

1957   **Litho.**   **Perf. 10½**

O43	O2	5k blue	.25	.20
O44	O2	10k orange brn	.25	.20
O45	O2	15k lt violet	.25	.20
O46	O2	20k red	.25	.20
O47	O2	30k gray olive	.25	.20
O48	O2	40k brown vio	.25	.20
O49	O2	50k grnsh blk	.25	.20
O50	O2	60k lt yel grn	.30	.20
O51	O2	75k yellow org	.50	.25
O52	O2	100k green	.75	.25
O53	O2	200k deep rose	1.25	.50
		Nos. O43-O53 (11)	4.55	2.60

1959   **Unwmk.**   **Perf. 10**

O54	O2	5k rose	.20	.20
O55	O2	10k ol grn	.20	.20
O56	O2	15k car rose	.20	.20
O57	O2	20k lilac	.20	.20
O58	O2	40k blue	.20	.20
O59	O2	60k orange	.25	.20
O60	O2	75k gray	.50	.20
O61	O2	100k violet	.65	.20
O62	O2	200k red brn	1.10	.65
		Nos. O54-O62 (9)	3.50	2.25

1960   **Litho.**   **Perf. 10½**

O63	O3	1k orange	.20	.20
O64	O3	5k vermilion	.20	.20
O65	O3	10k gray grn	.35	.20
O67	O3	30k red brn	.20	.20
O70	O3	60k green	.25	.20
O71	O3	1 l rose lilac	.30	.20
O72	O3	1½ l brt ultra	.95	.20
O74	O3	2½ l violet	1.50	.35
O75	O3	5 l blue	3.50	.85
		Nos. O63-O75 (9)	7.45	2.60

For surcharge see No. O83.

1962   **Typo.**   **Perf. 13**

O76	O4	1k olive bister	.30	.20
O77	O4	5k brt green	.30	.20
O78	O4	10k red brown	.30	.20
O79	O4	15k dk blue	.30	.20

O80	O4	25k carmine	.30	.20
O81	O4	30k ultra	.30	.20
		Nos. O76-O81 (6)	1.80	1.20

For surcharge see No. O82.

Nos. O81 and O70 Surcharged

1963

O82	O4	50k on 30k ultra	.35	.20

         Perf. 10½

Litho.

O83	O3	100k on 60k green	.50	.20

O5   O6

O7

1963   **Litho.**   **Perf. 12½**

O84	O5	1k gray	.50	.20
O85	O5	5k salmon	.50	.20
O86	O5	10k green	.50	.20
O87	O5	50k car rose	.50	.20
O88	O5	100k ultra	1.00	.50
		Nos. O84-O88 (5)	3.00	1.30

For surcharge see No. O139.

1964   **Unwmk.**   **Perf. 12½**

O89	O6	1k gray	.20	.20
O90	O6	5k blue	.20	.20
O91	O6	10k yellow	.20	.20
O92	O6	30k red	.40	.20
O93	O6	50k lt green	.50	.20
O94	O6	60k brown	1.50	.20
O95	O6	80k pale grnsh bl	3.50	.40
O96	O6	130k indigo	3.00	.60
O97	O6	200k lilac	7.50	.80
		Nos. O89-O97 (9)	17.00	3.00

For surcharge see No. O140.

1965   **Litho.**   **Perf. 13**

O98	O7	1k emerald	.20	.20
O99	O7	10k ultra	.25	.20
O100	O7	50k orange	.35	.20
		Nos. O98-O100 (3)	.80	.60

For surcharge see No. O141.

Carpet Designs   Seljuk Tile, 13th Century
O8   O9

1k, Usak. 50k, Bergama. 100k, Ladik. 150k, Seljuk. 200k, Nomad. 500k, Anatolia.

1966   **Litho.**   **Perf. 13**

O101	O8	1k orange	.20	.20
O102	O8	50k green	.20	.20
O103	O8	100k brt pink	.30	.20
O104	O8	150k violet blue	.65	.20
O105	O8	200k olive bister	.80	.20
O106	O8	500k lilac	3.00	.40
		Nos. O101-O106 (6)	5.15	1.40

For surcharge see No. O142.

1967   **Litho.**   **Perf. 11½x12**

O107	O9	1k dk bl & lt bl	.30	.20
O108	O9	50k org & dk bl	.30	.20
O109	O9	100k lil & dk bl	.30	.20
		Nos. O107-O109 (3)	.90	.60

For surcharge see No. O143.

Leaf Design — O10

1968   **Litho.**   **Perf. 13**

O110	O10	50k brn & lt grn	.20	.20
O111	O10	150k blk & dl yel	.50	.20
O112	O10	500k red brn & lt bl	1.60	.20
		Nos. O110-O112 (3)	2.30	.60

O11   O12

O13

1969, Aug. 25   **Litho.**   **Perf. 13**

O113	O11	1k lt grn & red	.20	.20
O114	O11	10k lt grn & bl	.20	.20
O115	O11	50k lt grn & brn	.20	.20
O116	O11	100k lt grn & red vio	.40	.20
		Nos. O113-O116 (4)	1.00	.80

1971, Mar. 1   **Litho.**   **Perf. 11½x12**

O117	O12	5k brown & blue	.20	.20
O118	O12	10k vio bl & ver	.20	.20
O119	O12	30k org & vio bl	.20	.20
O120	O12	50k Prus bl & sepia	.35	.20
O121	O12	75k yellow & green	.60	.20
		Nos. O117-O121 (5)	1.55	1.00

1971, Nov. 15   **Litho.**   **Perf. 11½x12**

O122	O13	5k lt bl & gray	.20	.20
O123	O13	25k cit & lt brn	.20	.20
O124	O13	100k org & olive	.20	.20
O125	O13	200k dk brn & bis	.40	.20
O126	O13	250k rose lil & vio	.60	.20
O127	O13	500k dk bl & brt bl	.95	.45
		Nos. O122-O127 (6)	2.55	1.45

O14   O15

O16

1972, Apr. 7   **Litho.**   **Perf. 13**

O128	O14	5k buff & blue	.20	.20
O129	O14	100k buff & olive	.25	.20
O130	O14	200k buff & carmine	.55	.20
		Nos. O128-O130 (3)	1.00	.60

1973, Sept 20   **Litho.**   **Perf. 13**

O131	O15	100k violet & buff	.65	.20

1974, June 17   **Litho.**   **Perf. 13½x13**

O132	O16	10k sal pink & brn	.20	.20
O133	O16	25k blue & dk brn	.20	.20
O134	O16	50k brt pink & brn	.20	.20
O135	O16	150k lt grn & brn	.40	.20
O136	O16	250k rose & brn	.65	.20
O137	O16	500k yellow & brn	1.25	.25
		Nos. O132-O137 (6)	2.90	1.25

O17   O18

O19

1975, Nov. 5   **Litho.**   **Perf. 12½x13**

O138	O17	100k lt blue & maroon	.20	.20

Nos. O84, O89, O98, O101, O107 Surcharged in Red or Black

Perf. 12½, 13, 11½x12

1977, Aug. 17   **Litho.**

O139	O5	5k on 1k gray	.20	.20
O140	O6	5k on 1k gray	.20	.20
O141	O7	5k on 1k emer	.20	.20
O142	O8	5k on 1k org (B)	.20	.20
O143	O9	5k on 1k dk & lt bl	.20	.20
		Nos. O139-O143 (5)	1.00	1.00

1977, Dec. 29   **Litho.**   **Perf. 13½x13**

O144	O18	250k lt bl & grn	.35	.20

1978   **Photo.**   **Perf. 13½**

O145	O19	50k pink & rose	.20	.20
O146	O19	2½ l buff & grnsh blk	.25	.20
O147	O19	4½ l lil rose & sl grn	.40	.20
O148	O19	5 l lt blue & pur	.40	.20
O149	O19	10 l lt grn & grn	.85	.20
O150	O19	25 l yellow & red	2.25	.20
		Nos. O145-O150 (6)	4.35	1.20

O20   O21

O22

1979   **Litho.**   **Perf. 13½**

O151	O20	50k dp org & brn	.20	.20
O152	O20	2½ l bl & dk bl	.25	.20

1979, Dec. 20   **Litho.**   **Perf. 13½**

O153	O21	50k sal & dk bl	.20	.20
O154	O21	1 l lt grn & red	.20	.20
O155	O21	2½ l lil rose & red	.30	.20
O156	O21	5 l lt bl & mag	.30	.20
O157	O21	7½ l lt lil & dk bl	.30	.20
O158	O21	10 l yel & dk bl	.40	.20
O159	O21	35 l gray & rose ('81)	1.25	.20
O160	O21	50 l pnksh & dk bl ('81)	1.50	.20
		Nos. O153-O160 (8)	4.45	1.60

1981, Oct. 23   **Litho.**   **Perf. 13½**

O161	O22	5 l yel & red	2.00	.20
O162	O22	10 l salmon & red	2.50	.20
O163	O22	35 l gray & rose	3.00	.20
O164	O22	50 l pink & dk bl	3.50	.20
O165	O22	75 l pale grn & grn	6.00	.25
O166	O22	100 l lt bl & dk bl	8.00	.45
		Nos. O161-O166 (6)	25.00	1.50

O23   O24

1983-84   **Litho.**   **Perf. 12½x13**
Background Color

O167	O23	5 l yellow	1.00	.20
O168	O23	15 l yellow bister	1.25	.20
O169	O23	20 l gray ('84)	.50	.20
O170	O23	50 l sky blue	3.00	.20
O171	O23	65 l pink	3.75	.20
O172	O23	70 l pale rose ('84)	.75	.20
O173	O23	90 l bister brn	5.50	.20
O174	O23	90 l bl gray ('84)	1.10	.20
O175	O23	100 l lt green ('84)	1.75	.20
O176	O23	125 l lt green	6.00	.20
O177	O23	230 l pale salmon ('84)	3.00	.40
		Nos. O167-O177 (11)	27.60	2.70

For surcharges see Nos. O184, O186-O190.

1986-87

O178	O24	5 l yel & vio		.40	.20
O179	O24	10 l org & vio		.40	.20
O180	O24	20 l gray & vio		.40	.20
O180A	O24	50 l pale blue & dp			
		ultra ('87)		.50	.20
O181	O24	100 l lt yel grn & vio		2.00	.20
O182	O24	300 l pale vio &			
		blue ('87)		2.50	.20
		Nos. O178-O182 (6)		6.20	1.20

For surcharges see Nos. O183, O185.

Nos. O179, O168, O180, O172, O173, O177 Surcharged in Dark Orange

1989

O183	O24	500 l on 10 l	2.00	.20
O184	O23	500 l on 15 l	2.00	.20
O185	O23	500 l on 20 l	2.00	.20
O186	O23	1000 l on 70 l	3.00	.25
O187	O23	1000 l on 90 l	3.00	.25
O188	O23	1250 l on 230 l	4.00	.50
		Nos. O183-O188 (6)	16.00	1.60

Issued: #O183, O185-O188, 8/9; #O184, 6/7.

Nos. O171, O173 & O174 Surcharged in Black

1991, Mar. 27

O189	O23	100 l on 65 l	.40	.20
O189A	O23	250 l on 90l (#O173)	—	
O190	O23	250 l on 90 l(#O174)	.80	.20

O25   O26

O27

Perf. 11½x12½

1992, Mar. 24   Litho.

O191	O25	3000 l lt brn & dk brn	2.00	.30
O192	O25	5000 l lt grn & dk grn	6.00	.50

1992, Dec. 2   Litho.   Perf. 12½x13

O193	O26	1000 l bl grn & vio	.50	.20
O194	O26	10,000 l vio bl & bl		
		grn	4.50	.50

1993, Sept. 27   Litho.   Perf. 12½x13

O195	O27	1000 l brown & green	1.00	.20
O196	O27	1500 l brown & green	1.50	.20
O197	O27	5000 l green & claret	4.00	.40
		Nos. O195-O197 (3)	6.50	.80

O28   O29

O30

1994, May 9   Litho.   Perf. 11½x12

O198	O28	2500 l pink & violet	1.00	.20
O199	O28	25,000 l yel & brn	2.75	.50

1995, Jan. 25

O200	O29	3500 l violet & lt vio	1.00	.20
O201	O29	17,500 l bl grn & lt grn	4.00	.45

1995, May 17

O202	O30	50,000 l ol & apple		
		grn	3.25	1.60

O31

1995, Nov. 8   Litho.   Perf. 12½x13

O203	O31	5000 l salmon & org	.75	.20

O32   O32a

O32b   O32c

1996, July 10   Litho.   Perf. 11½x12¼

O204	O32	15,000 l bl & red	1.00	.20
O205	O32a	20,000 l grn & pur	1.50	.25
O206	O32b	50,000 l pur & grn	2.00	.40
O207	O32c	100,000 l red & bl	3.00	.75
		Nos. O204-O207 (4)	7.50	1.60

O33   O34

O35

1997, Feb. 5   Litho.   Perf. 12½x13

O208	O33	25,000 l red & blue	.55	.30

1997, Aug. 4   Litho.   Perf. 12½x13

O209	O34	40,000 l multicolored	.55	.30
O210	O35	250,000 l multicolored	3.50	1.75

O36   O37

O38   O39

1998, June 10   Litho.   Perf. 12½x13

O211	O36	40,000 l dk bl & lt bl	.40	.20
O212	O37	100,000 l purple	1.00	.50
O213	O38	200,000 l brn & pale		
		bl grn	1.90	1.00
O214	O39	500,000 l brn & pale		
		bl grn	4.75	2.50
		Nos. O211-O214 (4)	8.05	4.20

O40   O41

O42

1998, July 29   Litho.   Perf. 12½x13

O215	O40	75,000 l multicolored	.75	.30

1999   Litho.   Perf. 11½x12¼

O216	O41	(R) vio & blue grn	2.50	.45
O217	O42	(RT) black & pink	4.50	.45

O43   O44

O45   O46

2000, Apr. 3   Litho.   Perf. 11½x12¼

O218	O43	50,000 l blue &		
		pink	.40	.20
O219	O44	75,000 l brn &		
		gray	.50	.20
O220	O45	500,000 l red brn &		
		lt bl	3.00	.40
O221	O46	1,250,000 l dk bl &		
		buff	6.00	1.00
		Nos. O218-O221 (4)	9.90	1.80

O46a

Perf. 11½x12¼

2000, Nov. 20   Litho.

O221B	O46a	RT dk bl & lt bl	—	

No. O221B sold for 500,000 l on day of issue. An additional stamp was released in this set. The editors would like to examine any examples.

O47

Perf. 11½x12¼

2001, Dec. 13   Litho.

O222	O47	R blue & yel org	1.00	.20

Sold for 300,000 l on day of issue.

O48   O49

O50   O51

O52

Perf. 11½x12¼

2002, Dec. 10   Litho.

O223	O48	50,000 l multi	.20	.20
O224	O49	100,000 l multi	.25	.20
O225	O50	250,000 l multi	.50	.30
O226	O51	500,000 l multi	1.00	.60
O227	O52	1,500,000 l multi	3.75	1.75
		Nos. O223-O227 (5)	5.70	3.05

O53   O54

O55   O56

Perf. 11½x12¼

2003, Aug. 18   Litho.

O228	O53	500,000 l bl & red	1.00	.70
O229	O54	750,000 l bl & yel	1.50	.80
O230	O55	1,000,000 l bl & grn	1.50	1.00
O231	O56	3,000,000 l bl & yel	5.00	2.10
		Nos. O228-O231 (4)	9.00	4.60

O57

2003, Oct. 13   Litho.   Perf. 11½x12¼

O232	O57	R pink & purple	1.25	.85

Sold for 600,000 l on day of issue.

Buildings
O58

Designs: 100,000 l, Hamidiye Etfal Children's Sanitorium. 500,000 l, Heating Plant, Silahtaraga. 600,000 l, PTT Headquarters, Ankara, vert. 1,000,000 l, Finance Ministry building, Ankara, vert. 3,500,000 l, Old Post and Telegraph Ministry building, Istanbul.

2004, Oct. 15   Perf. 13¼x13, 13x13¼

O233	O58	100,000 l multi	.20	.20
O234	O58	500,000 l multi	.75	.50
O235	O58	600,000 l multi	.80	.60
O236	O58	1,000,000 l multi	1.50	1.00
O237	O58	3,500,000 l multi	5.50	2.00
		Nos. O233-O237 (5)	8.75	4.30

Building Type of 2004

Design: 60k, Prime Minister's Building, Ankara.

2005, Jan. 1   Litho.   Perf. 14
O238 O58 60k multi   .90   .90

Buildings
O59

Designs: 10k, Museum of the Republic, Ankara. 25k, Culture and Tourism Ministry, Ankara. 50k, State Guest House, Ankara. 60k, Sculpture Museum, Ankara. 1 l, Ethnographic Museum, Ankara. 3.50 l, National Library, Ankara.

2005, July 4   Litho.   Perf. 13¼x13
Frame Color
O239 O59   10k orange   .20   .20
O240 O59   25k orange   .35   .35
O241 O59   50k yel green   .75   .75
O242 O59   60k blue   .90   .90
O243 O59   1 l yellow   1.50 1.50
O244 O59   3.50 l dull org   5.25 5.25
      Nos. O239-O244 (6)   8.95 8.95

Kemal
Ataturk — O60

Various portraits.

2006, Apr. 21   Litho.   Perf. 13x13¼
Background Color
O245 O60   10k blue   .20   .20
O246 O60   50k brown   .75   .75
O247 O60   60k dark red   .95   .95
O248 O60   1 l blue green   1.50 1.50
O249 O60   3.50 l red   5.50 5.50
      Nos. O245-O249 (5)   8.90 8.90

Kemal
Ataturk — O61

Various portraits.

**   Perf. 13x13½**
2007, Feb. 26   Litho.   Wmk. 405
O250 O61   10k multi   .20   .20
O251 O61   50k multi   .70   .70
O252 O61   60k multi   .85   .85
O253 O61   1 l multi   1.40 1.40
O254 O61   4 l multi   5.75 5.75
      Nos. O250-O254 (5)   8.90 8.90

Kemal
Ataturk — O62

**   Perf. 13x13½**
2007, Dec. 4   Litho.   Wmk. 405
O255 O62 65k multi   1.10 1.10

NEWSPAPER STAMPS

N1

Black Overprint

1879   Unwmk.   Perf. 11½ and 13½
P1   N1 10pa blk & rose lilac 225.00 225.00
Other stamps found with this "IMPRIMES" overprint were prepared on private order and have no official status as newspaper stamps. Counterfeits exist of No. P1.

The 10pa surcharge, on half of 20pa rose and pale rose was made privately. See note after No. 77.

Regular Issue of 1890 Handstamped in Black

There are two types of this handstamp, varying slightly in size.

1891   Perf. 13½, 11½
P10 A7 10pa grn & gray   40.00 12.50
  a.   Imperf.   22.50 12.50
P11 A7 20pa rose &
              gray   75.00 15.00
P12 A7   1pi blue & gray 200.00 150.00
P13 A7   2pi yel & gray 500.00 400.00
P14 A7   5pi buff & gray 1,000. 750.00
      Nos. P10-P14 (5)   1,815. 1,327.

Blue Handstamp

P10b A7 10pa green & gray 200.00 125.00
P11a A7 20pa rose & gray   300.00 250.00
P12a A7   1pi blue & gray   400.00 375.00
      Nos. P10b-P12a (3)   900.00 750.00

This overprint in red and on 2pi and 5pi in blue is considered bogus.

Same Handstamp on Regular Issue of 1892

1892   Perf. 13½
P25 A10 10pa gray green   400.00 100.00
P26 A11 20pa rose   1,250. 375.00
P27 A12   1pi pale blue   110.00 150.00
P28 A13   2pi brown org   200.00 175.00
P29 A14   5pi pale violet 1,800. 1,250.
  a.   On No. 99a   500.00
      Nos. P25-P29 (5)   3,760. 2,050.

The handstamps on Nos. P10-P29 are found double, inverted and sideways. Counterfeit overprints comprise most of the copies offered for sale in the marketplace.

Regular Issues of 1892-98 Overprinted in Black

1893-98
P30 A10 10pa gray grn   3.75   2.50
P31 A11 20pa vio brn ('98) 3.00   1.50
  a.   20pa dark pink   .60   .60
  b.   20pa pink   225.00 15.00
P32 A12   1pi pale blue   3.00   1.50
P33 A13   2pi brown org   27.50 12.50
  a.   Tete beche pair   22.50
P34 A14   5pi pale violet 85.00 75.00
  a.   On No. 99a   140.00 65.00
      Nos. P30-P34 (5)   122.25 93.00

For surcharge and overprints see Nos. B41, P134-P136, P153-P154.

No. 95 Surcharged

1897
P36 A10 5pa on 10pa gray grn 5.00   3.00
  a.   "Cinq" instead of "Cinq" 15.00 15.00
For overprint see No. P137.

Nos. 102-107 Overprinted in Black

1901   Perf. 12, 13½ and Compound
P37 A16   5pa bister   1.00   1.00
  a.   Inverted overprint
P38 A16 10pa yellow grn   6.25   6.25
P39 A16 20pa magenta   32.50   7.50
P40 A16   1pi violet blue   60.00 22.50
P41 A16   2pi gray blue   42.50 37.50
P42 A16   5pi ocher   300.00 90.00
      Nos. P37-P42 (6)   442.25 164.75

For overprints see Nos. B37, P69-P74, P123, P138-P141, P155-P158.

Same Overprint on Nos. 110-115

1901
P43 A17   5pa purple   8.75   2.00
P44 A17 10pa green   32.50   2.50
P45 A17 20pa carmine   8.75   1.50
  a.   Overprinted on back
P46 A17   1pi blue   25.00   2.00
P47 A17   2pi orange   87.50   4.00
  a.   Inverted overprint
P48 A17   5pi lilac rose   160.00 27.50
      Nos. P43-P48 (6)   322.50 39.50

For overprints see Nos. P75-P80, P124-P126, P142-P146, P159-P164.

Same Overprint on Regular Issue of 1905

1905
P49 A18   5pa ocher   2.50   1.00
P50 A18 10pa dull green   30.00   1.50
P51 A18 20pa carmine   2.50   1.25
P52 A18   1pi pale blue   2.50   1.25
P53 A18   2pi slate   70.00 10.00
P54 A18   5pi brown   175.00 20.00
      Nos. P49-P54 (6)   282.50 35.00

For overprints see Nos. P127-P129, P147-P150, P165-P171.

Regular Issue of 1908 Overprinted in Carmine or Blue

1908
P55 A19   5pa ocher (Bl)   10.00   .50
P56 A19 10pa blue grn (C) 17.50   .50
P57 A19 20pa carmine (Bl) 22.50   1.00
P58 A19   1pi brt blue (C) 100.00   2.50
P59 A19   2pi blue blk (C) 150.00   7.50
P60 A19   5pi dk violet (C)200.00 17.50
      Nos. P55-P60 (6)   500.00 29.50

For overprints see Nos. B17, P130-P131, P151, P172.

Same Overprint on Regular Issue of 1909

1909
P61 A21   5pa ocher (Bl)   3.50   1.25
  a.   Imperf.
P62 A21 10pa blue grn (C)   8.75   1.50
P63 A21 20pa car rose (Bl) 60.00   1.75
  a.   Imperf.
P64 A21   1pi brt blue (C) 100.00   5.00
P65 A21   2pi blue blk (C) 250.00 30.00
P66 A21   5pi dk violet (C)500.00 65.00
      Nos. P61-P66 (6)   922.25 104.50

For surcharge and overprints see Nos. B18, P67-P68, P81, P132-P133, P152.

No. 151 Surcharged in Blue

1910   Perf. 12, 13½ and Compound
P67 A21   2pa on 5pa ocher   .75   .75

1911   Perf. 12
P68 A21   2pa olive green   1.00   .50

Preceding Newspaper Issues with additional Overprint in Carmine or Blue

The overprint was applied to 13 denominations in four settings with change of city name, producing individual sets for each city: "MONASTIR," "PRISTINA," "SALONIKA" and "USKUB."

1911, June 26   Perf. 12, 13½
P69 A16   5pa bister   15.00 22.50
P70 A16 10pa yellow grn   15.00 22.50
P71 A16 20pa magenta   15.00 22.50
P72 A16   1pi violet blue   15.00 22.50
P73 A16   2pi gray blue   20.00 30.00
P74 A16   5pi ocher   40.00 60.00
P75 A17   5pa purple   7.50 12.50
P76 A17 10pa green   7.50 12.50
P77 A17 20pa carmine   7.50 12.50
P78 A17   1pi blue   7.50 12.50
P79 A17   2pi orange   10.00 15.00
P80 A17   5pi lilac rose   20.00 30.00
P81 A21   2pa olive green   2.50   3.75
      Nos. P69-P81 (13)   182.50 278.75

Values for each of the 4 city sets of 13 are the same.

The note after No. 182 will also apply to Nos. P69-P81.

Newspaper Stamps of 1901-11 Overprinted in Carmine or Black

1915
**   On Stamps of 1893-98**
P121 A10 10pa gray green   6.00   .50
  a.   Inverted overprint   10.00 10.00
P122 A13   2pi yellow brn   1.50   1.00
  a.   Inverted overprint   10.00 10.00
**   On Stamps of 1901**
P123 A16 10pa yellow grn   1.00   .50
P124 A17   5pa purple   1.00   1.00
P125 A17 20pa carmine   2.00   1.00
P126 A17   5pi lilac rose   20.00   5.00
**   On Stamps of 1905**
P127 A18   5pa ocher   2.00   1.00
  a.   Inverted overprint   7.50   7.50
P128 A18   2pi slate   17.50   5.00
P129 A18   5pi brown   10.00   .60
**   On Stamps of 1908**
P130 A19   2pi blue blk   1,375. 550.00
P131 A19   5pi dk violet   10.00   1.25
**   On Stamps of 1909**
P132 A21   5pa ocher   1.00   .50
P133 A21   5pi dk violet   100.00 35.00
  Nos. P121-P129,P131-P133
      (12)   172.00 52.35

Preceding Newspaper Issues with additional Overprint in Red or Black

1916
**   On Stamps of 1893-98**
P134 A10 10pa gray green   2.00   .75
P135 A11 20pa violet brn   1.00   .75
P136 A14   5pi dull violet 50.00 50.00

On Stamp of 1897

P137	A10	5pa on 10pa gray grn	.60	.50

On Stamps of 1901

P138	A16	5pa bister	.50	.30
P139	A16	10pa yellow grn	.90	.90
P140	A16	20pa magenta	1.00	.90
a.		Inverted overprint	10.00	10.00
P141	A16	1pi violet blue	1.00	1.00
P142	A17	5pa purple	50.00	50.00
P143	A17	10pa green	50.00	50.00
P144	A17	20pa carmine	1.50	.90
P145	A17	1pi blue	1.50	.90
P146	A17	2pi orange	1.50	.90

On Stamps of 1905

P147	A18	5pa ocher	1.00	.75
P148	A18	10pa dull green	50.00	50.00
P149	A18	20pa carmine	50.00	50.00
P150	A18	1pi pale blue	1.75	1.00

On Stamp of 1908

P151	A19	5pa ocher	62.50	62.50

On Stamp of 1909

P152	A21	5pa ocher	62.50	62.50
		Nos. P134-P152 (19)	389.25	384.55

Preceding Newspaper Issues with additional Overprint in Red or Black

1917

On Stamps of 1893-98

P153	A12	1pi gray (R)	2.50	2.00
P154	A11	20pa vio brn (R)	3.75	3.75

On Stamps of 1901

P155	A16	5pa bister (Bk)	1.50	1.25
a.		Inverted overprint	20.00	20.00
P156	A16	10pa yel grn (R)	1.50	1.25
P157	A16	20pa mag (Bk)	1.50	1.25
P158	A16	2pi gray bl (R)	40.00	30.00
P159	A17	5pa purple (Bk)	2.25	2.25
a.		Inverted overprint	20.00	20.00
b.		Double overprint	20.00	20.00
c.		Double ovpt., one inverted	25.00	25.00
P160	A17	10pa green (R)	22.50	35.00
P161	A17	20pa car (Bk)	1.50	1.25
P162	A17	1pi blue (R)	3.00	3.00
P163	A17	2pi orange (Bk)	2.50	2.50
P164	A17	5pi lil rose (R)	32.50	50.00

On Stamps of 1905

P165	A18	5pa ocher (R)	2.50	2.00
a.		Inverted overprint	10.00	10.00
P166	A18	5pa ocher (Bk)	3.00	2.50
a.		Inverted overprint	10.00	10.00
P167	A18	10pa dull grn (R)	2.50	2.00
P168	A18	20pa car (Bk)	2.50	2.00
a.		Double overprint	15.00	15.00
P169	A18	1pi blue (R)	2.50	2.00
a.		Inverted overprint	25.00	25.00
P170	A18	2pi slate (R)	32.50	50.00
P171	A18	5pi brown (R)	32.50	50.00

On Stamps of 1908

P172	A19	5pa ocher (R)	32.50	50.00
		Nos. P153-P172 (20)	225.50	294.00

Nos. P153-P172 were used as regular postage stamps.

#P173

#P174

1919

Blue Surcharge and Red Overprint

P173	A21	5pa on 2pa ol grn	1.25	1.00
a.		Red overprint double	12.50	5.00
b.		Blue surcharge double	12.50	5.00

1920   Red Surcharge

P174	A25	5pa on 4pa brn	1.25	.50

Catalogue values for unused stamps in this section, from this point to the end of the section, are for Never Hinged items.

Dove and Citadel of Ankara — N6

1952-55   Litho.   Perf. 12½

P175	N6	0.50k grnsh gray	.20	.20
P176	N6	0.50k violet ('53)	.20	.20

Perf. 10½, 10

P177	N6	0.50k red org ('54)	.20	.20
P178	N6	0.50k brown ('55)	.20	.20
		Nos. P175-P178 (4)	.80	.80

POSTAL TAX STAMPS

Map of Turkey and Red Crescent PT1

1928   Unwmk.   Typo.   Perf. 14

Crescent in Red

RA1	PT1	½pi lt brown	.30	.20
RA2	PT1	1pi red violet	.30	.20
RA3	PT1	2½pi orange	.30	.20

Engr.
Various Frames

RA4	PT1	5pi dk brown	.60	.45
RA5	PT1	5pi yellow green	.75	.55
RA6	PT1	20pi slate	1.25	.60
RA7	PT1	50pi dark violet	3.75	1.40
		Nos. RA1-RA7 (7)	7.25	3.60
		Set, never hinged	13.00	

The use of these stamps on letters, parcels, etc. in addition to the regular postage, was obligatory on certain days in each year.

For surcharges see Nos. RA16, RA21-RA22.

Cherubs Upholding Star — PT2

1932

RA8	PT2	1k ol bis & red	.50	.20
RA9	PT2	2½k dk brn & red	.65	.20
RA10	PT2	5k green & red	.85	.20
RA11	PT2	25k black & red	2.75	.90
		Nos. RA8-RA11 (4)	4.75	1.50
		Set, never hinged	7.50	

For surcharges and overprints see Nos. RA12-RA15, RA28-RA29, RA36-RA38.

No. RA8 Surcharged

20 para

RA12	PT2	20pa on 1k	.50	.30
RA13	PT2	3k on 1k	1.50	.70
a.		3 "kruus"	2.50	2.50

By a law of Parliament the use of these stamps on letters and telegraph forms, in addition to the regular fees, was obligatory from Apr. 20-30 of each year. The inscription in the tablet at the bottom of the design states that the money derived from the sale of the stamps is devoted to child welfare work.

No. RA8 Surcharged

20 para

1933

RA14	PT2	20pa on 1k ol bis & red	.25	.20
RA15	PT2	3k on 1k ol bis & red	1.00	.60

No. RA5 Surcharged

5 Beş Kuruş

RA16	PT1	5k on 10pi yel grn & red	1.50	.75
		Nos. RA14-RA16 (3)	2.75	1.55

PT3   PT4

1933   Perf. 11, 11½

RA17	PT3	20pa gray vio & red	.65	.20
RA18	PT4	1k violet & red	.80	.20
RA19	PT4	5k dk brown & red	2.50	.50
RA20	PT3	15k green & red	3.50	.50
		Nos. RA17-RA20 (4)	7.45	1.40
		Set, never hinged	11.00	

Nos. RA17 and RA20 were issued in Ankara; Nos. RA18 and RA19 in Izmir.
For overprint see No. RA27.

Nos. RA3, RA1 Surcharged in Black

5 Beş kuruş

1933-34

RA21	PT1	1k on 2½pi orange	.50	.30
RA22	PT1	5k on ½pi lt brown	1.50	.50

Map of Turkey PT5

1934-35   Crescent in Red   Perf. 12

RA23	PT5	½k blue ('35)	.20	.20
RA24	PT5	1k red brown	.20	.20
RA25	PT5	2½k brown ('35)	.50	.20
RA26	PT5	5k blue green ('35)	1.25	.20
		Nos. RA23-RA26 (4)	2.15	.80
		Set, never hinged	5.00	

Frame differs on No. RA26.
See Nos. RA30-RA35B. For surcharge see No. RA63.

Nos. RA17, RA8-RA9 Overprinted "P.Y.S." in Roman Capitals

1936   Perf. 11, 14

RA27	PT3	20pa gray vio & red	.40	.20
RA28	PT2	1k ol bis & red	.40	.20
RA29	PT2	3k on 2½k dk brn & red	.75	.20
		Nos. RA27-RA29 (3)	1.55	
		Set, never hinged	12.00	

Type of 1934-35, Inscribed "Türkiye Kizilay Cemiyeti"

1938-46   Perf. 8½-11½

Type I — Imprint, "Devlet Basimevi." Crescent red.

Type II — Imprint, "Alaeddin Kiral Basimevi." Crescent carmine.
Type III — Imprint, "Damga Matbaasi." Crescent red.

Crescent in Red or Carmine

RA30	PT5	½k blue (I)	.50	.20
a.		Type II	4.00	1.00
b.		Type III	.50	.20
RA31	PT5	1k red vio (I)	.40	.20
a.		Type II	6.50	2.00
b.		Type III	.50	.20
RA32	PT5	2½k orange (I)	.30	.20
a.		Type III	2.00	1.00
RA33	PT5	5k blue grn (I)	.50	.20
RA33A	PT5	5k choc (III) ('42)	1.00	1.00
RA34	PT5	10k pale grn (I)	1.50	.30
a.		Type III	2.00	1.00
RA35	PT5	20k black (I)	2.50	1.00
RA35A	PT5	50k pur (III) ('46)	7.50	1.00
RA35B	PT5	1 l blue (III) ('44)	30.00	2.50
		Nos. RA30-RA35B (9)	44.20	5.80
		Set, never hinged	75.00	

No. RA9 Surcharged in Black

20 Para P.Y.S.

1938   Perf. 14

RA36	PT2	20pa on 2½k	.40	.20
RA37	PT2	1k on 2½k	.60	.20

No. RA9 Surcharged in Black

P.Y.S 20 Para

1938   Unwmk.   Perf. 14

RA37A	PT2	20pa on 2½k	.90	.50
RA37B	PT2	1k on 2½k	1.10	.65

No. RA9 Surcharged "1 Kurus" in Black

1939   Perf. 14

RA38	PT2	1k on 2½k dk brn & red	.50	.50

Child — PT6   Nurse with Child — PT7

1940   Typo.   Perf. 12

Star in Carmine

RA39	PT6	20pa bluish grn	.30	.20
RA40	PT6	1k violet	.30	.20
RA41	PT7	1k lt blue	.30	.20
RA42	PT7	2½k pale red lil	.30	.20
RA43	PT6	3k black	.35	.20
RA44	PT7	5k pale violet	.30	.20
RA45	PT7	10k blue green	1.00	.40
RA46	PT7	15k dark blue	.75	.30
RA47	PT7	25k olive bister	2.50	1.25
RA48	PT7	50k olive gray	6.00	2.50
		Nos. RA39-RA48 (10)	12.10	5.65
		Set, never hinged	30.00	

Soldier and Map of Turkey — PT8

1941-44   Perf. 11½

RA49	PT8	1k purple	.40	.20
RA50	PT8	2k light blue	2.50	.20
RA51	PT8	3k chestnut	2.75	.50
RA51A	PT8	4k mag ('44)	9.50	.35

RA52 PT8 5k brt rose   7.75   2.50
RA53 PT8 10k dk blue   11.00   4.00
  Nos. RA49-RA53 (6)   33.90   7.75
Set, never hinged   75.00

The tax was used for national defense.

Baby — PT9   Nurse and
                       Baby — PT13

Nurse and
Children
PT10

Nurse
Feeding
Child
PT11

Nurse and
Child PT12

President Inonu
Holding
Child — PT15

Nurse and
Child — PT14

Children
PT16

1942   Unwmk.   Typo.   Perf. 11½
Star in Red

RA54 PT9   20pa brt violet   .40   .20
RA55 PT9   20pa chocolate   .40   .20
RA56 PT10 1k dk slate grn   .40   .20
RA57 PT11 2½k yellow grn   .40   .30
RA58 PT12 3k dark blue   .40   .30
RA59 PT13 5k brt pink   .40   .30
RA60 PT14 10k lt blue   .70   .40
RA61 PT15 15k dk red brn   1.10   .50
RA62 PT16 25k brown   1.75 1.00
  Nos. RA54-RA62 (9)   5.95 3.60

See Nos. RA175, RA179-RA180.

No. RA32 Surcharged with New Value
in Brown

1942   Perf. 10
RA63 PT5 1k on 2½k org & red (I)   .20 .20

Child
Eating — PT17

Nurse and
Child — PT18

Nurse
and Child
PT19

Child and Red   President Inönü
Star — PT20   and Child — PT21

Inscribed: "Sefcat Pullari 23 Nisan 1943
Cocuk Esirgeme Kurumu."

1943   Star in Red   Perf. 11
RA64 PT17 50pa lilac   .20   .20
RA65 PT17 50pa gray green   .25   .20
RA66 PT18 1k lt ultra   .25   .20
RA67 PT19 3k dark red   .30   .20
RA68 PT20 15k cream & blk   1.50   .40
RA69 PT21 100k brt violet blue 2.50 1.60
  a.   Souvenir sheet, #RA64-RA69,
       imperf.   5.50 5.50
  Nos. RA64-RA69 (6)   5.00 2.80

Star and   Hospital
Crescent   PT24
PT23

Nurse and   Baby
Children   PT26
PT25

Nurse Bathing   Nurse Feeding
Baby — PT27   Child — PT28

Baby with   Child — PT30
Bottle — PT29

Hospital — PT31

Perf. 10 to 12 and Compound
1943-44
Star in Red

RA71 PT23 20pa deep blue   .40   .30
RA72 PT24 1k gray green   .40   .20
RA73 PT25 3k pale gray   .40   .20
RA74 PT26 5k yellow or-
                ange   .70   .30
RA75 PT26 5k violet brn   .30   .20
RA76 PT27 10k red   .40   .30
RA77 PT28 15k red violet   .60   .40
RA78 PT29 25k pale violet   .90   .50
RA79 PT30 50k lt blue   2.00 1.00
RA80 PT31 100k lt green   5.00 4.00
  Nos. RA71-RA80 (10)   11.10 7.40
Set, never hinged   22.00

For surcharge see No. RA156.

Nurse Holding   Nurse Feeding
Baby — PT32   Child — PT33

Child — PT34

Star and
Crescent
PT35

1945-47   Unwmk.   Litho.   Perf. 11½
Star in Red

RA81 PT32 1k lilac brn   .40   .20
  a.   1k rose violet   .50   .20
RA82 PT33 5k yellow grn   .70   .20
  a.   5k green   .70   .20
RA83 PT34 10k red brown   .50   .20
RA84 PT35 250k gray black   9.50 3.50
RA84A PT35 500k dull vio
                ('47)   37.50 12.50
  Nos. RA81-RA84A (5)   48.60 16.60
Set, never hinged   90.00

Imprint on No. RA82: "Kagit ve Basim isleri
A.S. ist." On No. RA82a: "Guzel Sanatlar
Matbaasi — Ankara."

Nurse and   President Inönü
Wounded Soldier   and Victim of
PT36   Earthquake
                     PT37

Removing
Wounded from
Hospital
Ship — PT38

Nurse and   Feeding the
Soldier — PT39   Poor — PT40

Wounded   Symbolical of
Soldiers on   Red Crescent
Landing   Relief — PT42
Raft — PT41

1945   Perf. 12x10, 10x12
Crescent in Red

RA85 PT36 20pa dp bl & brn
                org   .50   .20
RA86 PT37 1k ol grn & ol
                bis   .50   .20
RA87 PT38 2½k dp bl & red   1.00   .50
RA88 PT39 5k dp bl & red   2.00 1.00
RA89 PT40 10k dp bl & lt
                grn   2.00 1.00
RA90 PT41 50k blk & gray
                grn   4.50 2.00
RA91 PT42 1 l black & yel   15.00 7.50
  Nos. RA85-RA91 (7)   25.50 12.40
Set, never hinged   45.00

See Nos. RA181-RA182.

Ankara
Sanatorium
PT43

1946   Perf. 12
RA92 PT43 20k red & lt bl   .65   .30
See No. RA210. For surcharge see No.
RA186.

Covering Sleeping
Child — PT44

Designs: 1k, Mother and child. 2½k, Nurse
at playground. 5k, Doctor examining infant.
15k, Feeding child. 25k, Bathing child. 50k,
Weighing baby. 150k, Feeding baby.

1946   Litho.   Perf. 12½
Inscribed: "25ci Yil Hatirasi 1946"
Star in Carmine

RA93	PT44	20pa brown	.35	.20
RA94	PT44	1k blue	.35	.20
RA95	PT44	2½k carmine	.35	.20
RA96	PT44	5k vio brn	.60	.20
RA97	PT44	15k violet	.90	.50
RA98	PT44	25k gray grn	1.25	.60
RA99	PT44	50k bl grn	1.75	1.50
RA100	PT44	150k gray brn	3.25	1.75
	Nos. RA93-RA100 (8)		8.80	5.15
	Set, never hinged		15.00	

For surcharge see No. RA155.

Hospital Ship — PT52

Ambulance Plane — PT53

Hospital Train — PT54

Ambulance PT55

Boy Scout and Red Crescent Flag — PT56

Stretcher Bearers and Wounded Soldier PT57

Nurse and Hospital — PT58

Sanatorium PT59

1946   Perf. 11½

RA101	PT52	1k multi	1.25	1.25
RA102	PT53	4k multi	1.25	1.25
RA103	PT54	10k multi	3.50	3.50
RA104	PT55	25k multi	4.50	4.50
RA105	PT56	40k multi	8.50	8.50
RA106	PT57	70k multi	6.00	6.00
RA107	PT58	1 l multi	5.50	5.50
RA108	PT59	2½ l multi	12.50	12.50
	Nos. RA101-RA108 (8)		43.00	43.00

For overprints see Nos. RA139-RA146.

Souvenir Sheet

Pres. Inönü and Child — PT60

1946   Unwmk.   Typo.   *Imperf.*
Without Gum

RA109 PT60 250k slate blk, pink & red   20.00   17.50

Turkish Society for the Prevention of Cruelty to Children, 25th anniv.

Nurse and Wounded Soldier PT61

Pres. Inönü and Victim of Earthquake PT62

Nurse and Soldier — PT64

Symbolical of Red Crescent Relief — PT67

1946-47   Litho.   Perf. 11½
Crescent in Red

RA113	PT61	20pa dk bl vio & ol ('47)	.20	.20
RA114	PT62	1k dk brn & yel	.45	.20
RA115	PT64	5k dp bl & red	.45	.25
RA116	PT67	1 l brn blk & yel	1.90	1.25
	Nos. RA113-RA116 (4)		3.00	1.90

PT68

Nurse and Wounded Soldier — PT69

Victory and Soldier — PT70

1947
Crescent in Red

RA117	PT68	250k brn blk & grn	5.25	2.00
RA118	PT69	5 l sl gray & org	8.75	3.50

Booklet Pane of One
Perf. 11½ (top) x Imperf.

RA119 PT70 10 l deep blue   22.50

Black numerals above No. RA119 indicate position in booklet.

President Inönü and Victim of Earthquake PT71

Nurse and Child PT72

1947   Perf. 11½

RA120	PT71	1k dk brn, pale bl & red	.20	.20
RA121	PT72	2½k bl vio & car	.20	.20

See Nos. RA221-RA223. For surcharge see No. RA154.

Nurse Offering Encouragement PT73

Plant with Broken Stem PT74

Perf. 8½, 11½x10, 11x10½
1948-49   Typo.   Unwmk.
Crescent in Red

RA122	PT73	½k ultra ('49)	.55	.20
RA123	PT73	1k indigo	.20	.20
RA124	PT73	2k lilac rose	.20	.20
RA125	PT73	2½k org ('49)	.20	.20
RA126	PT73	3k bl grn	.20	.20
RA127	PT73	4k gray ('49)	.35	.20
RA128	PT73	5k blue	.70	.20
RA129	PT73	10k pink	1.25	.20
RA130	PT73	25k chocolate	1.60	.25

Perf. 10

RA130A	PT74	50k ultra & bl gray ('49)	2.25	.75
RA130B	PT74	100k grn & pale grn ('49)	5.25	1.00
	Nos. RA122-RA130B (11)		12.75	3.60
	Set, never hinged		30.00	

For surcharges see Nos. RA151-RA153, RA187.

Nurse and Children — PT75

Various Scenes with Children.
Inscribed: "1948 Cocuk Yili Hatirasi"

1948   Litho.   Perf. 11
Star in Red

RA131	PT75	20pa dp ultra	.30	.20
RA132	PT75	20pa rose lilac	.30	.20
RA133	PT75	1k dp Prus bl	.50	.30
RA134	PT75	3k dk brn vio	.75	.50
RA135	PT75	15k slate black	1.50	1.25
RA136	PT75	30k orange	3.50	3.00

RA137	PT75	150k yellow grn	4.50	4.00
RA138	PT75	300k brown red	7.00	6.50
	Nos. RA131-RA138 (8)		18.35	15.95
	Set, never hinged		30.00	

No. RA136 is arranged horizontally. For overprints and surcharges see Nos. RA199-RA206.

> **Catalogue values for unused stamps in this section, from this point to the end of the section, are for Never Hinged items.**

Nos. RA101 to RA108 Overprinted in Carmine

1949   Perf. 11½

RA139	PT52	1k multi	10.00	10.00
RA140	PT53	4k multi	10.00	10.00
RA141	PT54	10k multi	10.00	10.00
RA142	PT55	25k multi	10.00	10.00
RA143	PT56	40k multi	20.00	20.00
RA144	PT57	70k multi	10.00	10.00
RA145	PT58	1 l multi	10.00	10.00
RA146	PT59	2½ l multi	10.00	10.00
	Nos. RA139-RA146 (8)		90.00	90.00

Ruins and Tent PT76

"Protection" PT77

Booklet Panes of One
1949   *Perf. 10 (top) x Imperf.*

RA149	PT76	5k gray, vio gray & red	3.00	2.00
RA150	PT76	10k red vio, sal & red	3.00	2.00

Black numerals above each stamp indicate its position in the booklet.

No. RA124 Surcharged in Black
1950   Unwmk.   Perf. 8½

RA151 PT73 20pa on 2k   1.25   1.00

Postal Tax Stamps of 1944-48 Surcharged with New Value in Black or Carmine

Perf. 8½ to 12½ and Compound
1952

RA152	PT73	20pa on 3k bl grn	.50	.25
RA153	PT73	20pa on 4k gray	.75	.25
RA154	PT72	1k on 2½k bl vio & car (C)	1.00	1.50
RA155	PT44	1k on 2½k car	2.00	1.00
RA156	PT25	1k on 3k pale gray brn	2.00	1.00
	Nos. RA152-RA156 (5)		6.25	4.00

Various Symbolical Designs Inscribed "75 iNCi" etc.

1952   Typo.   Perf. 10
Crescent in Carmine

RA157	PT77	5k bl grn & bl	2.00	1.50
RA158	PT77	15k yel grn, bl & cr	2.00	1.50
RA159	PT77	30k bl, grn & brn	2.00	1.50
RA160	PT77	1 l blk, bl & cr	2.00	1.50
	a.	Souvenir sheet, #RA157-RA160, imperf.	30.00	30.00
	Nos. RA157-RA160 (4)		8.00	6.00

Printed in sheets of 20 containing one horizontal row of each value.

Nurse and Children PT78

Design: 1k, Nurse and baby.

1954 Litho. Perf. 10½
Star in Red
RA161 PT78 20pa aqua .60 .35
RA162 PT78 20pa yellow .90 .35
RA163 PT12 1k deep blue 1.50 .80
Nos. RA161-RA163 (3) 3.00 1.50

Globe and Flag — PT79

Designs: 5k, Winged nurse in clouds. 10k, Protecting arm of Red Crescent.

1954
RA164 PT79 1k multi .20 .20
RA165 PT79 5k multi .50 .20
RA166 PT79 10k car, grn & gray 1.00 .20
Nos. RA164-RA166 (3) 1.70 .60

See Nos. RA208, RA211-RA213. For surcharges see Nos. RA187A-RA187B.

Florence Nightingale — PT80

Selimiye Barracks PT81

30k, Florence Nightingale, full-face.

1954, Nov. 4
Crescent in Carmine
RA167 PT80 20k gray grn & dk brn .50 .50
RA168 PT80 30k dl brn & blk .75 .50
RA169 PT81 50k buff & blk 1.25 .50
Nos. RA167-RA169 (3) 2.50 1.50

Arrival of Florence Nightingale at Scutari, cent.

Type of 1942 and

Children Kissing — PT82

Nurse Holding Baby — PT83

1955, Apr. 23
Star in Red
RA170 PT82 20pa chalky bl .20
RA171 PT82 20pa org brn .20 .20
RA172 PT82 1k lilac .20 .20
RA173 PT82 3k gray bis .20 .20
RA174 PT82 5k orange .20 .20
RA175 PT12 10k green 2.50 .75
RA176 PT83 15k dk blue .25 .20
RA177 PT83 25k brn car 1.50 1.40
RA178 PT83 50k dk gray grn 2.00 1.50
RA179 PT12 2½ l dull brn 375.00 125.00
RA180 PT12 10 l rose lil 875.00 250.00
Nos. RA170-RA180 (11) 1,257. 379.85

Types of 1945
Inscribed: "Turkiye Kizilay Dernegi"
1955 Litho. Perf. 10½x11½, 10½
Crescent in Red
RA181 PT36 20pa vio brn & lem .25 .25
RA182 PT41 1k blk & gray grn .25 .25

Nurse — PT85

Nurses on Parade PT86

Design: 100k, Two nurses under Red Cross and Red Crescent flags and UN emblem.

Perf. 10½
1955, Sept. 5 Unwmk. Litho.
Crescent and Cross in Red
RA183 PT85 10k blk & pale brn .75 .35
RA184 PT86 15k dk grn & pale yel .75 .45
RA185 PT85 100k lt ultra 3.50 1.75
Nos. RA183-RA185 (3) 5.00 2.55

Meeting of the board of directors of the Intl. Council of Nurses, Istanbul, Aug. 29-Sept. 5, 1955.

Nos. RA92 and RA130B Surcharged "20 Para"
1955
RA186 PT43 20p on 20k .50 .40
Typo.
RA187 PT74 20p on 100k (surch. 11½x2mm) .60 .40
   c. Surcharge 13½x2½mm 1.00 .75

No. RA164 Surcharged with New Value and Two Bars
1956 Litho. Perf. 10½
RA187A PT79 20p on 1k multi .25 .25
RA187B PT79 2.50k on 1k multi .25 .25

Woman and Children — PT87

Designs: 10k, 25k, 50k, Flag and building. 250k, 5 l, 10 l, Mother nursing baby.

1956 Litho. Perf. 10½
Star in Red
RA188 PT87 20pa red org .50 .50
RA189 PT87 20pa gray grn .50 .50
RA190 PT87 1k purple .50 .50
RA191 PT87 1k grnsh bl .50 .50
RA192 PT87 3k lt red brn 1.00 .50
RA193 PT87 10k rose car 2.00 2.00
RA194 PT87 25k brt grn 4.00 2.00
RA195 PT87 50k brt ultra 6.00 2.50
RA196 PT87 250k red lilac 15.00 5.00
RA197 PT87 5 l sepia 35.00 15.00
RA198 PT87 10 l dk sal grn 57.50 30.00
Nos. RA188-RA198 (11) 122.50 59.00

Nos. RA131-RA138 Overprinted and Surcharged in Black or Red: "IV. DUNYA Cocuk Gunu 1 Ekim 1956"
1956, Oct. 1 Unwmk. Perf. 11
RA199 PT75 20pa (R) 10.00 10.00
RA200 PT75 20pa 10.00 10.00
RA201 PT75 1k (R) 10.00 10.00
RA202 PT75 3k (R) 10.00 10.00
RA203 PT75 15k (R) 10.00 10.00
RA204 PT75 25k on 30k 10.00 10.00
RA205 PT75 100k on 150k (R) 12.00 12.00
RA206 PT75 250k on 300k 14.00 14.00
Nos. RA199-RA206 (8) 86.00 86.00

The tax was for child welfare.

Type of 1954, Redrawn Type of 1946, and

Flower PT88

Children PT89

1957 Unwmk. Perf. 10½
Crescent in Red
RA207 PT88 ½k lt ol gray & brn .50 .20
RA208 PT79 1k ol bis, blk & grn .50 .20
RA209 PT88 2½k yel grn & bl grn .50 .20
RA210 PT43 20k red & lt bl 2.75 1.25
RA211 PT79 25k lt gray, blk & grn 2.75 1.25
RA212 PT79 50k bl, dk grn & grn 8.00 1.50
RA213 PT79 100k vio, blk & grn 8.75 3.00
Nos. RA207-RA213 (7) 23.75 7.60

No. RA210 inscribed "Turkiye Kizilay Cemiyeti." No. RA92 inscribed ". . . . Dernegi."

1957 Unwmk. Perf. 10½
RA214 PT89 20pa car & red .20 .20
RA215 PT89 20pa grn & red .20 .20
RA216 PT89 1k ultra & car .20 .20
RA217 PT89 3k red org & car 1.50 1.50
Nos. RA214-RA217 (4) 2.10 2.10

"Blood Donor and Recipient" PT90

Child and Butterfly PT91

Designs: 75k, Figure showing blood circulation. 150k, Blood transfusion symbolism.

1957, May 22
Size: 24x40mm
RA218 PT90 25k gray, blk & red .25 .20
Size: 22½x37½mm
RA219 PT90 75k grn, blk & red .50 .30
RA220 PT90 150k yel grn & red 1.25 .60
Nos. RA218-RA220 (3) 2.00 1.10

Redrawn Type of 1947
Inscribed: "V Dunya Cocuk Gunu"
1957 Star in Red Perf. 10½
RA221 PT72 100k blk & bis brn 1.25 .75
RA222 PT72 150k blk & yel grn 1.25 .75
RA223 PT72 250k blk & vio 2.50 1.00
Nos. RA221-RA223 (3) 5.00 2.50

The tax was for child welfare.

1958 Litho. Unwmk.
Various Butterflies. 50k, 75k horiz.
RA224 PT91 20k gray & red .75 .75
RA225 PT91 25k multi .75 .75
RA226 PT91 50k multi 1.50 1.50
RA227 PT91 75k grn, yel & blk 2.00 2.00
RA228 PT91 150k multi 2.50 2.50
Nos. RA224-RA228 (5) 7.50 7.50

Florence Nightingale — PT92

1958
Crescent in Red
RA229 PT92 1 l bluish green .40 .25
RA230 PT92 1½ l gray .60 .50
RA231 PT92 2½ l red .80 .60
Nos. RA229-RA231 (3) 1.80 1.35

Turkey stopped issuing postal tax stamps in June, 1958. Similar stamps of later date are private charity stamps issued by the Red Crescent Society and the Society for the Protection of Children.

POSTAL TAX AIR POST STAMPS
Air Fund Issues

These stamps were obligatory on all air mail for 21 days a year. Tax for the Turkish Aviation Society: 20pa for a postcard, 1k for a regular letter, 2 1/2k for a registered letter, 3k for a telegram, 5k-50k for a package, higher values for air freight. Postal tax air post stamps were withdrawn Aug. 21, 1934 and remainders destroyed later that year.

Biplane PTAP1

Perf. 11, Pin Perf.
1926 Unwmk. Litho.
Type PTAP1
Size: 35x25mm
RAC1 20pa brn & pale grn 3.00 .30
RAC2 1g blue grn & buff 2.00 .30
Size: 40x29mm
RAC3 5g vio & pale grn 8.00 1.00
RAC4 5g car lake & pale grn 35.00 15.00
Nos. RAC1-RAC4 (4) 48.00 16.60
Set, never hinged 275.00

PTAP2

PTAP3

1927-29
Type PTAP2
RAC5 20pa dl red & pale grn 1.00 .20
RAC6 1k green & yel .90 .20
Type PTAP3
Perf. 11½
RAC7 2k dp cl & yel grn 1.00 .35
RAC8 2½k red & yel grn 6.00 1.60
RAC9 5k dk bl gray & org .80 .45
RAC10 10k dk grn & rose 3.75 1.25
RAC11 15k green & yel 3.75 1.00
RAC12 20k ol brn & yel 5.00 2.00
RAC13 50k dk bl & cob bl 8.00 4.50
RAC14 100k car & lt bl 110.00 80.00
Nos. RAC5-RAC14 (10) 140.20 91.55
Set, never hinged 825.00

#RAC1, RAC5, RAC7 and RAC11
Surcharged in Black (RAC15-RAC16,
RAC18-RAC19) or Red (Others)

1930-31

RAC15	1k ("Bir kurus") on RAC1		200.00	75.00
RAC16	1k ("Bir Kurus") on RAC5		1.00	.50
RAC17	100pa ("Yuz Para") on RAC7		1.75	.75
RAC18	5k ("Bes Kurus") on RAC5		6.50	1.50
RAC19	5k ("5 Kurus") on RAC5		2.00	.75
RAC20	10k ("On kurus") on RAC7		3.00	1.25
RAC21	50k ("Elli kurus") on RAC7		11.00	4.00
RAC22	1 l ("Bir lira") on RAC7		37.50	9.00
RAC23	5 l ("Bes lira") on RAC11		2,000.	400.00
	Nos. RAC15-RAC23 (9)		2,262.	492.75
	Set, never hinged		5,000.	

PTAP4

PTAP5

1931-32   Litho.   Perf. 11½

RAC24	PTAP4 20pa black	5.00	1.75

Typo.

RAC25	PTAP5 1k brown car ('32)	2.00	.50
RAC26	PTAP5 5k red ('32)	4.00	.75
RAC27	PTAP5 10k green ('32)	6.00	1.50
	Nos. RAC24-RAC27 (4)	17.00	4.50

PTAP6

1933

Type PTAP6

RAC28	10pa ("On Para") grn	3.50	2.00
RAC29	1k ("Bir Kurus") red	8.00	2.75
RAC30	5k ("Bes Kurus") lil	12.00	3.00
	Nos. RAC28-RAC30 (3)	23.50	7.75

TURKEY IN ASIA

ˈtər-kē in ˈā-zhə

(Anatolia)

40 Paras = 1 Piaster

This designation, which includes all of Turkey in Asia Minor, came into existence during the uprising of 1919, led by Mustafa Kemal Pasha. Actually there was no separation of territory, the Sultan's sovereignty being almost immediately reduced to a small area surrounding Constantinople. The formation of the Turkish Republic and the expulsion of the Sultan followed in 1923. Subsequent issues of postage stamps are listed under Turkey (Republic).

Issues of the Nationalist Government

Turkish Stamps of 1913-18 Surcharged in Black or Red

(The Surcharge reads "Angora 3 Piastres")

1920   Unwmk.   Perf. 12

On Stamps of 1913

1	A24	3pi on 2pa red lilac	4.00	4.25
2	A25	3pi on 4pa dk brn	37.50	37.50
3	A27	3pi on 6pa dk bl	250.00	150.00

On Stamp of 1916-18

4	A42	3pi on 2pa vio (Bk)	15.00	10.00
		Nos. 1-4 (4)	306.50	201.75

Turkish Stamps of 1913-18
Handstamped in Black or Red

(The Surch. reads "Post, Piastre 3")

1921   Perf. 12

On Stamps of 1913

5	A24	3pi on 2pa red lilac	25.00	25.00
a.		On No. 1	45.00	67.50
6	A25	3pi on 4pa dk brown	30.00	30.00
a.		On No. 2	150.00	160.00
7	A25	3pi on 4pa dk brn (R)	150.00	175.00
a.		On No. 2	150.00	160.00
8	A27	3pi on 6pa dk blue	125.00	150.00
a.		On No. 3	275.00	300.00
9	A27	3pi on 6pa bl (R)	62.50	75.00
a.		On No. 3	100.00	125.00

On Stamps of 1916-18

10	A42	3pi on 2pa vio (R)	62.50	75.00
a.		On No. 4	90.00	110.00
		Nos. 5-10 (6)	455.00	530.00

Turkish Revenue Stamps Handstamped in Turkish "Osmanli Postalari, 1336" (Ottoman Post, 1920).

Dash at upper left is set high. Bottom (date) line is 8½mm long.

Dash at upper left is set lower. Bottom (date) line is 10mm long.

Dash at upper left is set lower. Bottom (date) line is 9mm long.

Religious Tribunals Revenue — R1

12	R1	1pi green (a, b, c)	750.00	300.00
13	R1	5pi ultra (a, b)	16,000.	15,500.
14	R1	50pi gray grn (a, b, c)	25.00	35.00
		Cut cancellation		1.50
15	R1	100pi buff (a)	140.00	90.00
a.		100pi yellow (a)	90.00	67.50
		Cut cancellation		7.50
16	R1	500pi orange (a)	225.00	150.00
		Cut cancellation		19.00
17	R1	1000pi brown (a)	3,000.	1,750.
		Cut cancellation		175.00
		See Nos. 29-32.		

Court Costs Revenue — R2

Black Overprint

18	R2	10pa green (b, c)	110.00	100.00
19	R2	1pi ultra (a, c)		15,000.
20	R2	5pi rose (c)	15,000.	—
21	R2	50pi ocher (a, b,	50.00	50.00
a.		50pi yellow (a, b, c)	12.00	16.00
		Cut cancellation, #21, 21a		2.00
22	R2	100pi brown (a)	150.00	100.00
		Cut cancellation		20.00
23	R2	500pi slate (a)	325.00	325.00
		Cut cancellation		20.00
		See Nos. 24, 33-39.		

Notary Public Revenue R3

Design R2 Overprinted "Katibi Adliye Masus dur" in Red

24	R3	50pi ocher (a)	1,250.	150.00
		Cut cancellation		20.00

Laborer's Passport Tax Stamp — R4

Notary Public Revenue — R5

Black Overprint

25	R4	2pi emerald (a, c)	—	20,000.
26	R5	100pi yellow brn (a)	1,250.	150.00
		Cut cancellation		20.00
		See Nos. 46-48.		

Theater Tax Stamp — R6

Land Registry Revenue — R7

27	R6	20pa black	5,000.	5,000.
28	R7	2pi blue black	6,250.	6,250.
		See Nos. 40, 45.		

Hejaz Railway Tax Stamp — R8

Perf. 11½

28A	R8	2pi dk red & bl (b)	1,750.	1,750.

Turkish Revenue Stamps Overprinted in Turkish "Osmanli Postalari, 1337" (Ottoman Post, 1921)

On #29-63

Perf. 12

29	R1	10pa slate	16.00	13.50
a.		Handstamped overprint	100.00	50.00
b.		Double overprint		
30	R1	1pi green	27.50	18.00
a.		Inverted overprint	35.00	22.50
b.		Handstamped overprint	3,250.	3,250.
31	R1	5pi ultra	27.50	13.50
a.		"1337" inverted	100.00	90.00
b.		Half used as 2½pi on cover		
c.		Handstamped overprint	875.00	875.00
		Nos. 29-31 (3)	71.00	45.00

Handstamped Overprint

32	R1	50pi green	6,250.	6,250.

Design R2 Overprinted

33	R2	10pa green	22.50	22.50
a.		Handstamped overprint	3,500.	3,500.
34	R2	1pi ultra	45.00	22.50
a.		Handstamped overprint	875.00	875.00
35	R2	5pi red	22.50	22.50
a.		Inverted overprint		
b.		"1337" inverted	100.00	100.00
c.		Half used as 2½pi on cover		
d.		Handstamped overprint	6,750.	6,750.
36	R2	50pi ocher, handstamped ovpt.	500.00	100.00
		Cut cancellation		10.00
		Nos. 33-36 (4)	590.00	167.50

Design R3 Overprinted
Additional Turkish Overprint in Red or Black

37	R3	10pa green (R)	90.00	57.50
38	R3	1pi ultra (R)	67.50	45.00
39	R3	5pi rose (Bk)	67.50	45.00
a.		"1337" inverted	200.00	200.00
b.		Handstamped overprint	6,250.	6,250.
		Nos. 37-39 (3)	225.00	147.50

Design R7 Overprinted

40	R7	2pi blue black	110.00	100.00
a.		Handstamped overprint	5,000.	5,000.

R12

1921　　　　　　　　　　Perf. 12
Overprinted in Black
41	R12	5pi green	150.00 125.00
		Cut cancellation	15.00
a.		Handstamped overprint	5,000. 5,000.

Museum
Tax Stamp
R13

Overprinted in Black
42	R13	1pi ultra	400.00 400.00
a.		Handstamped overprint	5,000. 5,000.
43	R13	5pi deep green	450.00 450.00
a.		Handstamped overprint	5,000.

Handstamped Overprint
44	R13	5pi dark vio	6,250. 6,250.

The overprint variety "337" for "1337" exists on Nos. 42-43.

Design R6 Overprinted
Perf. 12, 12½
45	R6	20pa black	12.50 4.25
a.		Date 4½mm high	15.00
b.		"337" for "1337"	25.00

Design R5 Overprinted
46	R5	10pa green	25.00 25.00
a.		Overprint 21mm long	
b.		"131" for "1337"	
47	R5	1pi ultra	37.50 25.00
a.		"13" for "1337"	50.00
b.		"131" for "1337"	50.00 50.00
c.		Inverted overprint	90.00 90.00
d.		Handstamped overprint	4,000. 4,000.
48	R5	5pi red	62.50 25.00
a.		Inverted overprint	90.00 90.00
b.		"131" for "1337"	85.00 85.00
c.		Handstamped overprint	4,000. 4,000.
		Nos. 46-48 (3)	125.00 75.00

R16

Perf. 11½, 11½x11
Overprinted in Black
49	R16	10pa pink	4.00 1.50
a.		Imperf.	
b.		Date "1237"	5.00 2.00
d.		Inverted overprint	
e.		Handstamped overprint	1,750. 1,750.
50	R16	1pi yellow	10.00 5.00
a.		Overprint 18mm long	10.00 5.00
b.		Date "1332"	12.00
c.		Date "1317"	
d.		Inverted overprint	
e.		Handstamped overprint	1,750. 1,750.
51	R16	2pi yellow grn	12.50 5.00
a.		Date "1237"	15.00
b.		Date "1317"	
c.		Imperf.	
d.		Inverted overprint	40.00 9.00
e.		Handstamped overprint	—
52	R16	5pi red	20.00 1.00
a.		Horiz. pair, imperf. vert.	
b.		Inverted overprint	25.00 7.50
c.		Double overprint	30.00 12.50
d.		Date "1332"	45.00
e.		Half used as 2½pi on cover	
f.		Overprint 18mm long	20.00 7.50
g.		Handstamped overprint	1,750. 1,750.
		Nos. 49-52 (4)	46.50 12.50

Design R8 Overprinted
TURKISH INSCRIPTIONS:

20 Paras

1 Piaster

---

2 Piasters

5 Piasters

1921　　　　　　　　　Perf. 11½
Dark Red & Blue
53	R8	20pa on 1pi	75.00 75.00
54	R8	1pi on 1pi	5.00 3.00
55	R8	2pi on 1pi	5.00 3.00
a.		Inverted surcharge	
56	R8	5pi on 1pi	8.00 5.00
		Nos. 53-56 (4)	93.00 86.00

See No. 57.

No. 54 Overprinted

57	R8	1pi on 1pi dk red & bl	45.00 45.00

Hejaz Railway Tax
Stamp — R19

Overprinted in Black
58	R19	1pi grn & brn red	5.00 4.00
a.		Double overprint	
b.		Handstamped overprint	

The errors "1307," "1331" and "2337" occur once in each sheet of Nos. 53-58.

Naval League
Labels — R20

1921　　　　　　　Perf. 12x11½
Overprinted in Black
59	R20	1pa orange	10.00 15.00
a.		Date "1327"	15.00 3.50
60	R20	2pa indigo	10.00 15.00
61	R20	5pa green	12.50 17.50
62	R20	10pa brown	25.00 30.00
63	R20	40pa red brown	175.00 190.00
		Nos. 59-63 (5)	232.50 267.50

The error "2337" occurs on all values of this issue.

The Naval League stamps have pictures of three Turkish warships. They were sold for the benefit of sailors of the fleet but did not pay postage until they were overprinted in 1921.

Turkish Stamps of 1915-20
Overprinted

a　　　　　　　b

The overprints on Nos. 64-77 read "Adana December 1st, 1921." This issue commemorated the withdrawal of the French from Cilicia.
On No. 71 the lines of the overprint are further apart than on Nos. 68-70 and 73-74.

1921　　　　　　　　　Perf. 12
64	A44 (a)	10pa grn (424)	8.00 6.00
65	A45 (a)	20pa deep rose (425)	8.00 6.00
a.		Inverted overprint	20.00

66	A51 (a)	25pi car, *straw* (434)	15.00 20.00
a.		Double overprint	
b.		Inverted overprint	37.50 37.50
		Nos. 64-66 (3)	31.00 32.00

On Newspaper Stamp of 1915
67	A21 (a)	5pa och (P132)	90.00 150.00

On Stamp of 1915
68	A22 (b)	5pa och (328)	350.00 400.00

On Stamps of 1917-18
69	A53 (b)	5pi on 2pa (547)	12.50 15.00
70	A53 (b)	5pi on 2pa (548)	12.50 15.00

On Stamp of 1919
71	A57 (b)	35pi on 1pi bl (Bk; 579)	40.00 45.00
a.		Inverted surcharge	

On Newspaper Stamp of 1915
72	A21 (b)	5pa och (P132)	200.00 200.00

On No. 72 the overprint is vertical, half reading up and half reading down.

On Stamps of 1920
73	A32 (b)	3pi blue (594)	12.50 10.00
74	A36 (b)	10pi gray vio (596)	15.00 15.00

On Postage Due Stamps of 1914
75	D1 (a)	5pa claret (J63)	350.00 350.00
76	D2 (a)	20pa red (J64)	350.00 400.00
a.		Inverted overprint	
77	D3 (b)	1pi dk bl (J65)	350.00 350.00
a.		Inverted overprint	750.00 750.00
		Nos. 75-77 (3)	1,050. 1,150.

Withdrawal of the French from Cilicia. Forged overprints exist.

Pact of Revenge,
Burning Village at
Top — A21

Izmir
Harbor — A22

Mosque of
Selim,
Adrianople
A23

Mosque of
Selim,
Konya — A24

Soldier — A25

Legendary
Gray
Wolf — A26

Snake Castle
and Seyhan
River,
Adana — A27

Parliament
Building at
Sivas — A28

A29

Mosque at
Urfa — A30

Map of
Anatolia
A31

Declaration of Faith
from the Koran — A32

1922　　　Litho.　　　Perf. 11½
78	A21	10pa violet brn	1.00 .25
79	A22	20pa blue grn	1.00 .25
80	A23	1pi dp blue	1.50 .35
81	A24	2pi red brown	3.00 .50
82	A25	5pi dk blue	3.00 .50
83	A26	10pi dk brown	12.50 .75
84	A27	25pi rose	15.00 1.00
85	A28	50pi indigo	1.00 15.00
86	A29	50pi dk gray	1.00 1.25
87	A30	100pi violet	75.00 5.00
		Cut cancellation	1.25
88	A31	200pi slate	200.00 62.50
		Cut cancellation	3.00
89	A32	500pi green	125.00 27.50
		Cut cancellation	5.00
		Nos. 78-89 (12)	439.00 114.85
		Set, never hinged	2,000.

Imperf
79a	A22	20pa	25.00 30.00
80a	A23	1pi	15.00 20.00
82a	A25	5pi	15.00 20.00
84a	A27	25pi	35.00 30.00
85a	A28	50pi	27.50 30.00

Stamps of
Type A23
Overprinted

1922
90	A23	1pi deep blue	7.00 15.00
91	A23	5pi deep blue	7.00 20.00
92	A23	10pi brown	7.00 20.00
93	A23	25pi rose	10.00 25.00
94	A23	50pi slate	12.50 25.00
95	A23	100pi violet	17.50 37.50
96	A23	200pi black vio	17.50 50.00
97	A23	500pi blue green	25.00 75.00
		Nos. 90-97 (8)	103.50
		Set, never hinged	200.00

Withdrawal of the French from Cilicia and the return of the Kemalist Natl. army. The overprint reads: "Adana, Jan. 5, 1922."
No. 90-97 without overprint were presented to some high government officials.

First
Parliament
House,
Ankara — A33

1922   Litho.

98	A33	5pa violet	.50	2.50
99	A33	10pa green	1.50	2.50
100	A33	20pa pale red	2.00	2.00
101	A33	1pi brown org	10.00	1.50
102	A33	2pi red brown	20.00	4.25
103	A33	3pi rose	3.50	.50
a.		Arabic "13" in right corner	10.00	7.50
b.		Thin grayish paper	55.00	7.50
		Nos. 98-103 (6)	37.50	13.25
		Set, never hinged	130.00	

Nos. 98-103, 103b exist imperf. In 1923 several stamps of Turkey and Turkey in Asia were overprinted in Turkish for advertising purposes. The overprint reads: "Izmir Economic Congress, 17 Feb., 1339."

POSTAGE DUE STAMPS

D1

1922   Litho.   Perf. 11½

J1	D1	20pa dull green	.50	5.00
a.		Imperf.		
J2	D1	1pi gray green	.50	5.00
J3	D1	2pi red brown	1.50	17.50
J4	D1	3pi rose	3.50	25.00
J5	D1	5pi dark blue	4.50	55.00
		Nos. J1-J5 (5)	10.50	
		Set, never hinged	55.00	

TURKISH REPUBLIC OF NORTHERN CYPRUS

ˈtər-kish ri-ˈpə-blik of ˈnor-thə̲ȑn ˈsī-prəs

LOCATION — Northern 40% of the Island of Cyprus in the Mediterranean Sea off the coast of Turkey.

Established following Turkish invasion of Cyprus in 1974. On Nov. 15, 1983 Turkey declared the Turkish Republic of Northern Cyprus to be independent. No other country has recognized this country.

1000 Milliemes = 1 Pound
100 Kurus = 1 Turkish Lira (1978)

Catalogue values for all unused stamps in this country are for Never Hinged items.

Letters bearing these stamps enter international mail via the Turkish Post Office.

Watermark

Wmk. 390

Republic of Turkey, 50th Anniv.
A1   A2

Designs: 3m, Woman sentry. 5m, Military parade. 10m, Flag bearers. 15m, Anniversary

---

emblem. 20m, Ataturk statue. 50m, Painting, "The Fallen." 70m, Turkish flag, map of Cyprus.

Perf. 12x11½, 11½x12

1974, July 27   Litho.   Unwmk.

1	A1	3m multicolored	45.00	37.50
2	A2	5m multicolored	.50	.20
3	A1	10m multicolored	.75	.20
4	A1	15m multicolored	1.00	.50
5	A1	20m multicolored	1.25	.20
6	A1	50m multicolored	4.00	2.75
7	A2	70m multicolored	35.00	15.00
		Nos. 1-7 (7)	87.50	56.85

First day covers are dated 1/29/73.

Nos. 5, 3 Surcharged

1975, Mar. 3   Perf. 12x11½

8	A1	30m on 20m, #5	1.25	1.00
9	A1	100m on 10m, #3	3.00	2.25

Surcharge appears in different positions.

Historical Sites and Landmarks A3

Designs: 3m, Namik Kemal's bust, Famagusta. 5m, 30m, Kyrenia Harbor. 10m, Ataturk Statue, Nicosia. 15m, St. Hilarion Castle. 20m, Ataturk Square, Nicosia. 25m, Coastline, Famagusta. 50m, Lala Mustafa Pasha Mosque, Famagusta vert. 100m, Kyrenia Castle. 250m, Kyrenia Castle, exterior walls. 500m, Othello Tower, Famagusta vert.

1975-76   Perf. 13

10	A3	3m pink & multi	.40	.30
11	A3	5m bl & multi	.40	.30
12	A3	10m pink & multi	.45	.40
13	A3	15m pink & multi	.50	.40
14	A3	15m bl & multi	.50	.40
15	A3	20m pink & multi	3.00	.40
16	A3	20m bl & multi	.40	.40
17	A3	25m pink & multi	.60	.50
18	A3	30m pink & multi	.90	.75
19	A3	50m pink & multi	1.50	1.00
20	A3	100m pink & multi	1.75	1.25
21	A3	250m pink & multi	2.50	1.75
22	A3	500m pink & multi	3.50	3.00
		Nos. 10-22 (13)	16.40	10.85

Issued: #10, 12-13, 15, 17-22, 4/21; #11, 14, 16, 8/2/76. #1, 14, 16 have different inscriptions and "1976."
For surcharges see Nos. 28-29.

Peace in Cyprus — A4

Designs: 50m, Map, olive branch, severed chain. 150m, Map, globe, olive branch, vert.

1975, July 20   Perf. 13½x13, 13x13½

23	A4	30m multicolored	.40	.25
24	A4	50m multicolored	.50	.35
25	A4	150m multicolored	1.10	1.00
		Nos. 23-25 (3)	2.00	1.60

Europa — A5

Paintings: 90m, Pomegranates by I.V. Guney. 100m, Harvest Time by F. Direkoglu.

1975, Dec. 29   Perf. 13

26	A5	90m multicolored	2.00	1.00
27	A5	100m multicolored	3.00	1.50

Nos. 19, 20 Surcharged

1976, Apr. 28   Perf. 13

28	A3	10m on 50m, #19	.50	.50
29	A3	30m on 100m, #20	1.25	1.25

Europa — A6   Olympic Games, Montreal — A8

Fruits — A7

1976, May 3

30	A6	60m Expectation	.75	.30
31	A6	120m Man in Meditation	1.50	.65

1976, June 28

32	A7	10m Ceratonia siliqua	.20	.20
33	A7	25m Citrus nobilis	.30	.20
34	A7	40m Fragaria vesca	.40	.20
35	A7	60m Citrus sinensis	.50	.30
36	A7	80m Citrus limon	.75	.45
		Nos. 32-36 (5)	2.15	1.35

For surcharges see Nos. 66-69.

1976, July 17

Design: 100m, Olympic rings, doves, horiz.

37	A8	60m multicolored	.75	.20
38	A8	100m multicolored	1.00	.35

Liberation Monument — A9

1976, Nov. 1   Perf. 13x13½

39	A9	30m multi	.50	.20
40	A9	150m multi, diff.	.90	.45

Europa — A10

1977, May 2   Perf. 13

41	A10	80m Salamis Bay	2.00	.75
42	A10	100m Kyrenia Port	3.00	1.25

Handicrafts A11

1977, June 27

43	A11	15m Pottery	.25	.20
44	A11	30m Gourds, vert.	.40	.20
45	A11	125m Baskets	.60	.30
		Nos. 43-45 (3)	1.25	.70

Landmarks A12

Designs: 20m, Arap Ahmet Pasha Mosque, Nicosia, vert. 40m, Paphos Castle. 70m, Bekir Pasha aqueduct, Larnaca. 80m, Sultan Mahmut library, Nicosia.

1977, Dec. 2   Perf. 13x13½, 13½x13

46	A12	20m multicolored	.20	.20
47	A12	40m multicolored	.30	.20
48	A12	70m multicolored	.40	.25
49	A12	80m multicolored	.60	.40
		Nos. 46-49 (4)	1.50	1.05

Namik Kemal (1840-1888), Writer — A13

1977, Dec. 21   Perf. 13

50	A13	30m Bust, home	.30	.20
51	A13	140m Portrait, vert.	.90	.50

Social Security — A14   Europa — A15

Designs: 275k, Man with sling, crutch. 375k, Woman with children.

1978, Apr. 17   Perf. 13x13½

52	A14	150k blk, bl & yel	.30	.20
53	A14	275k blk, grn & red org	.40	.20
54	A14	375k blk, red org & bl	.70	.25
		Nos. 52-54 (3)	1.40	.65

1978, May 2   Perf. 13x13½, 13½x13

225k, Oratory in Buyuk Han, Nicosia. 450k, Reservoir, Selimiye Mosque, Nicosia.

55	A15	225k multi	3.25	1.00
56	A15	450k multi, horiz.	6.50	1.50

Transportation A16

1978, July 10   Perf. 13½x13

57	A16	75k Roadway	.30	.20
58	A16	100k Hydrofoil	.40	.20
59	A16	650k Airplane	.70	.70
		Nos. 57-59 (3)	1.40	1.10

National Oath — A17

Kemal
Ataturk — A18

1978, Sept. 13
60 A17 150k Dove, olive branch .35 .20
61 A17 225k Stylized pen, vert. .50 .20
62 A17 725k Stylized dove .90 .65
　　　Nos. 60-62 (3) 1.75 1.05

1978, Nov. 10
63 A18 75k bl grn & lt grn .20 .20
64 A18 450k brn & buff .20 .20
65 A18 650k Prus bl & lt bl .30 .30
　　　Nos. 63-65 (3) .70 .70

Nos. 33-36
Surcharged

1979, June 4
66 A7 50k on 25m .25 .20
67 A7 1 l on 40m .30 .20
68 A7 3 l on 60m .25 .20
69 A7 5 l on 80m .50 .25
　　　Nos. 66-69 (4) 1.30 .85

Souvenir Sheet

Turkish Invasion of Cyprus, 5th
Anniv. — A19

Illustration reduced.

1979, July 2 *Imperf.*
70 A19 15 l multicolored 3.50 3.25

Europa
A20

Communications: 3 l, Stamps, building,
map. 8 l, Early and modern telephones, globe,
satellite.

1979, Aug. 20 **Litho.** *Perf. 13*
71 A20 2 l multicolored 1.50 .40
72 A20 3 l multicolored 2.00 .65
73 A20 8 l multicolored 4.25 1.00
　　　Nos. 71-73 (3) 7.75 2.05

Intl. Consultative
Radio Committee. — A21

1979, Sept. 24
74 A21 2 l blue & multi .20 .20
75 A21 5 l gray & multi .25 .20
76 A21 6 l green & multi .35 .30
　　　Nos. 74-76 (3) .80 .70

Intl. Year
of the
Child
A22

Childrens' drawings of children.

1979, Oct. 29
77 A22 1½ l multi, vert. .20 .20
78 A22 4½ l multicolored .35 .30
79 A22 6 l multi, vert. .45 .40
　　　Nos. 77-79 (3) 1.00 .90

Press reports in Jan. 1980 state that
the 1979 UPU Congress declared Turkish Cyprus stamps invalid for international mail.

A23　　　Europa — A24

Anniv. and events: 2½ l, Lala Mustafa Pasha
Mosque, Famagusta. 10 l, Arap Ahmet Pasha
Mosque, Lefkosa. 20 l, Holy Kaaba, Mosque.

1980, Mar. 23
80 A23 2½ l multicolored .25 .20
81 A23 10 l multicolored .45 .25
82 A23 20 l multicolored .70 .70
　　　Nos. 80-82 (3) 1.40 1.15

1st Islamic Conference in Turkish Cyprus
(2½ l). General Assembly of World Islam Congress (10 l). Moslem year 1400 AH (20 l).

1980, May 23
83 A24 5 l Ebu-Suud Efendi *.75 .40*
84 A24 30 l Sultan Selim II *2.50 .80*

Historic
Landmarks
A25

Designs: 2½ l, Omer's Shrine, Kyrenia. 3½ l,
Entrance gate, Famagusta. 5 l, Funerary mon-
uments, Famagusta. 10 l, Bella Paise Abbey,
Kyrenia. 20 l, Selimiye Mosque, Nicosia.

1980, June 25
　　　　　Blue Paper
85 A25 2½ l buff & Prus bl .20 .20
86 A25 3½ l pale pink & dk grn .20 .20
87 A25 5 l pale bl grn & dk
　　　　car .20 .20
88 A25 10 l lt grn & red lil .25 .20
89 A25 20 l buff & dk bl .40 .35
　　　Nos. 85-89 (5) 1.25 1.15

For overprints and surcharges see Nos.
198-200.

Cyprus
Postage
Stamps,
Cent.
A26

1980, Aug. 16
90 A26 7½ l No. 5, vert. .25 .20
91 A26 15 l No. 199 .35 .20
92 A26 50 l Social welfare,
　　　　vert. .90 .80
　　　Nos. 90-92 (3) 1.50 1.20

Palestinian
Solidarity
A27

15 l, Dome of the Rock, entrance, vert.

1980, Mar. 24
93 A27 15 l multicolored .30 .25
94 A27 35 l multicolored .75 .60

World Muslim
Congress
Statement — A28

1981, Mar. 24
95 A28 1 l In Turkish .20 .20
96 A28 35 l In English .75 .65

Ataturk by Feyhamam Duran — A29

1981, May 19
97 A29 20 l multicolored 1.00 .65

Printed with se-tenant label promoting Ataturk Stamp Exhibition.

Europa
A30

Folk dances.

1981, June 29
98 A30 10 l multicolored *.75 .40*
99 A30 30 l multi, diff. *2.00 1.00*

Souvenir Sheet

Ataturk, Birth Cent. — A31

Illustration reduced.

1981, July 23 *Imperf.*
100 A31 150 l multicolored 2.25 1.75

No. 100 has simulated perfs.

Flowers
A32

Designs: 1 l, Convolvulus althaeoides, vert.
5 l, Cyclamen persicum. 10 l, Mandragara
officinarum. 25 l, Papaver rhoeas, vert. 30 l,
Arum dioscoridis, vert. 50 l, Chrysanthemum
segetum. 100 l, Cistus salyiaefolius, vert.
150 l, Ferula communis.

1981-82 *Perf. 13*
101 A32 1 l multicolored .20 .20
102 A32 5 l multicolored .20 .20
103 A32 10 l multicolored .25 .25
104 A32 25 l multicolored .40 .40
105 A32 30 l multicolored .45 .45
106 A32 50 l multicolored .75 .75
107 A32 100 l multicolored 1.50 1.50
108 A32 150 l multicolored 2.25 2.25
　　　Nos. 101-108 (8) 6.00 6.00

Issue dates: 1 l, 10 l, 25 l, 150 l, Sept. 28; 5
l, 30 l, 50 l, 100 l, Jan. 22, 1982.
For surcharge & overprints see #138-141,
201.

Intl. Year
for
Disabled
Persons
A33

Fight Against　　World Food
Apartheid — A34　　Day — A35

1981, Oct. 16
109 A33 7½ l multicolored .20 .20
110 A34 10 l multicolored .35 .30
111 A35 20 l multicolored .65 .50
　　　Nos. 109-111 (3) 1.20 1.00

Palestinian
Solidarity
A36

1981, Nov. 29
112 A36 10 l multicolored .25 .25

Royal Wedding of
Prince Charles and
Lady Diana
Spencer — A37

1981, Nov. 30
113 A37 50 l multicolored 1.00 .70

Souvenir Sheet

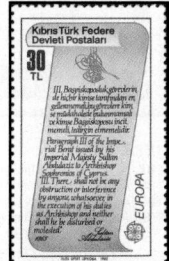

Charter of
Cyprus,
1865 — A38

Turkish Forces
Landing in
Tuzla — A39

1982, July 30
114   Sheet of 4   5.00 5.00
  a. A38 30 I multicolored   1.00 1.00
  b. A39 70 I multicolored   1.00 1.00

Europa. #114 contains 2 each #114a, 114b.

Buffavento
Castle — A40

Windsurfing — A41

Kantara
Castle
A42

Tourism: 30 I, Shipwreck museum.

Perf. 12½x12, 12x12½
1982, Aug. 20
116   A40   5 I multicolored   .25   .20
117   A41 10 I multicolored   .30   .25
118   A42 15 I multicolored   .35   .30
119   A42 30 I multicolored   .60   .40
  Nos. 116-119 (4)   1.50 1.15

Art Treasures — A43

Designs: 30 I, The Wedding by Aylin Orek.
50 I, Carob Pickers by Ozden Nazim, vert.

1982, Dec. 3   *Perf. 13x13½, 13½x13*
120   A43 30 I multicolored   .30   .30
121   A43 50 I multicolored   .50   .50

Robert
Koch, TB
Bacillus
A44

World Cup Soccer Championships,
Spain — A45

Scouting, 75th
Anniv. — A46

1982, Dec. 15   *Perf. 12½*
122   A44 10 I multicolored   .25   .20
123   A45 30 I multicolored   .75   .60
124   A46 70 I multicolored   2.00 1.50
  Nos. 122-124 (3)   3.00 2.30

Paintings
A47

30 I, Calloused Hands by Salih Oral. 35 I,
Malya-Limassol Bus by Emin Cizenel.

1983, May 16   *Perf. 13½x13*
125   A47 30 I multicolored   .90   .75
126   A47 35 I multicolored   1.25 1.00

Miniature Sheet

Europa — A48

a, Map by Piri Reis. b, Cyprus seen from
Skylab.

1983, June 30   *Perf. 13*
127   A48   Sheet of 2   60.00 60.00
  a.-b. 100 I any single   15.00 15.00

25th Anniv.
of Turkish
Resistance
A49

Designs: 15 I, No. 3. 20 I, Exploitation, Suppression & Resurrection by Aziz Hasan. 25 I,
Resistance by Guner Pir.

1983, Aug. 1   *Perf. 13*
129   A49 15 I multi, vert.   .30   .30
130   A49 20 I multi   .45   .45
131   A49 25 I multi, vert.   .50   .50
  Nos. 129-131 (3)   1.25 1.25

World Communications Year — A50

1983, Aug. 1
132   A50 30 I shown   .60   .60
133   A50 50 I Letters   1.00 1.00

Birds
A51

1983, Oct. 10
134   A51 10 I Merops apiaster   .25   .20
135   A51 15 I Carduelis cardue-
              lis   .35   .20
136   A51 50 I Erithacus rubecu-
              la   1.00   .70
137   A51 65 I Oriolus oriolus   1.40 1.00
  a.   Block of 4, #134-137   3.50 3.00
  Nos. 134-137 (4)   3.00 2.10

Nos. 103, 108
Ovptd.

Nos. 101, 104 Ovptd. or Surcharged

1983, Dec. 7
138   A32 10 I multicolored   .20   .20
139   A32 15 I on 1 I multi   .20   .20
140   A32 25 I multicolored   .35   .35
141   A32 150 I multicolored   2.00 2.00
  Nos. 138-141 (4)   2.75 2.75

Europa,
25th Anniv.
A52

1984, May 30   *Perf. 12x12½*
142   A52 50 I blk, yel & brn   1.00   .50
143   A52 100 I blk, bl & ultra   2.00 1.00
  a.   Pair, #142-143   3.25 2.75

Olympics,
Los
Angeles
A53

Perf. 12½x12, 12x12½
1984, June 19
144   A53 10 I Olympic flame, vert.   .20   .20
145   A53 20 I Olympic rings   .20   .20
146   A53 70 I Judo   .60   .60
  Nos. 144-146 (3)   1.00 1.00

Ataturk
Cultural
Center
A54

Perf. 12x12½
1984, July 20   Wmk. 390
147   A54 120 I blk, yel & brn   .90   .90

Turkish
Invasion of
Cyprus,
10th
Anniv.
A55

1984, July 20
148   A55 20 I shown   .40   .40
149   A55 70 I Map, flag, olive
              branch   .70   .70

Forest Conservation — A56

1984, Aug. 20
150   A56 90 I multicolored   1.25   .75

Paintings — A57

20 I, Old Turkish Houses in Nicosia by
Cevdet Cagdas. 70 I, Scenery by Olga Rauf.

1984, Sept. 21   *Perf. 13*
151   A57 20 I multicolored   .40   .40
152   A57 70 I multicolored   1.10 1.10

Proclamation of
Turkish Republic of
Northern
Cyprus — A58

Unanimous Vote by Legislative
Assembly — A59

Perf. 12½x12, 12x12½
1984, Nov. 15
153   A58 20 I multicolored   .40   .30
154   A59 70 I multicolored   .80   .70

Independence, 1st Anniv.

European Taekwondo Championship,
Kyrenia — A60

1984, Dec. 10
155	A60	10 l	Competitors	.30 .20
156	A60	70 l	Flags	.60 .55

Balance of the Spirit — A61

Paintings by Saulo Mercader: 20 l, The Look, vert.

1984, Dec. 10　　Perf. 12½x13, 13x12½
157	A61	20 l	multicolored	.20 .20
158	A61	70 l	multicolored	.50 .50

Visit by Nuremburg Chamber Orchestra A62

1984, Dec. 10　　Perf. 12½
159	A62	70 l	multicolored	1.00 .50

Dr. Fazil Kucuk (1906-1984), Politician — A63

70 l, Kucuk reading newspaper, c. 1970.

1985, Jan.
160	A63	20 l	multicolored	.20 .20
161	A63	70 l	multicolored	.50 .50

Domestic Animals A64

1985, May 29　　Perf. 12x12½
162	A64	100 l	Capra	.55 .55
163	A64	200 l	Bos taurus	1.10 1.10
164	A64	300 l	Ovis aries	1.60 1.60
165	A64	500 l	Equus asinus	2.75 2.75
		Nos. 162-165 (4)		6.00 6.00

Europa — A65　　Paintings — A66

Composers: No. 166, George Frideric Handel (1685-1759). No. 167, Domenico Scarlatti (1685-1757). No. 168, Johann Sebastian Bach (1685-1750). No. 169, Buhurizade Mustafa Itri (1640-1712).

1985, June 26　　Perf. 12½x12
166	A65	20 l	grn & multi	*.30 .25*
167	A65	20 l	brn lake & multi	*.30 .25*
168	A65	100 l	bl & multi	1.25 .80
169	A65	100 l	brn & multi	1.25 .80
a.		Block of 4, #166-169		3.75 3.75

Printed in sheets of 16, containing 4 No. 169a.

1985, Aug.　　Perf. 12½x13

Paintings: 20 l, Pastoral Life by Ali Atakan. 50 l, Woman Carrying Water by Ismet V. Guney.
170	A66	20 l	multicolored	.35 .35
171	A66	50 l	multicolored	.55 .55

Intl. Youth Year A67

Wmk. 390
1985, Oct. 29　　Litho.　　Perf. 12½
172	A67	20 l	shown	.20 .20
173	A67	100 l	Globe, dove	.60 .60

Northern Cyprus Air League — A68　　Development of Rabies Vaccine, Cent. — A69

Ismet Inonu (1884-1973), Turkish Pres. — A70

UN, 40th Anniv. A71

Blood Donor Services A72

1985, Nov. 29
174	A68	20 l	multicolored	.20 .20
175	A69	50 l	Pasteur	.30 .30
176	A70	70 l	brown	.60 .60
177	A71	100 l	multicolored	.60 .60
178	A72	100 l	multicolored	.60 .60
		Nos. 174-178 (5)		2.30 2.30

Paintings — A73

20 l, House with Arches by Gonen Atakol. 100 l, Ataturk Square by Yalkin Muhtaroglu.

1986, June 20　　Perf. 13
179	A73	20 l	multicolored	.20 .20
180	A73	100 l	multicolored	.40 .40

Miniature Sheet

Europa — A74

1986, June 20　　Perf. 12x12½
181	A74		Sheet of 2	16.00 16.00
a.		100 l	Gyps fulvus	4.00 2.00
b.		200 l	Roadside litter	8.00 4.00

Karagoz Puppets — A75

1986, July 25　　Perf. 12½x13
182	A75	100 l	multicolored	.90 .40

Anatolian Artifacts A76

Designs: 10 l, Ring-shaped composite pottery, Kernos, Old Bronze Age (2300-1050 B.C.). 20 l, Bird-shaped lidded pot, Skuru Hill tomb, Morphou, late Bronze Age (1600-1500 B.C.), vert. 50 l, Earthenware jug, Vryse, Kyrenia, Neolithic Age (4000 B.C.). 100 l, Terra sigillata statue of Artemis, Sea of Salamis, Roman Period (200 B.C.), vert.

1986, Sept. 15　　Perf. 12½
183	A76	10 l	multicolored	.20 .20
184	A76	20 l	multicolored	.20 .20
185	A76	50 l	multicolored	.25 .25
186	A76	100 l	multicolored	.50 .50
		Nos. 183-186 (4)		1.15 1.15

For surcharge see No. 295A.

Defense Forces, 10th Anniv. — A77　　World Food Day — A78

World Cup Soccer Championships, Mexico — A79

Halley's Comet A80

1986, Oct. 13
187	A77	20 l	multicolored	.20 .20
188	A78	50 l	multicolored	.30 .30
189	A79	100 l	multicolored	.35 .35
190	A80	100 l	multicolored	.40 .40
		Nos. 187-190 (4)		1.25 1.25

Development Projects — A81

1986, Nov. 17
191	A81	20 l	Water resources	.20 .20
192	A81	50 l	Housing	.20 .20
193	A81	100 l	Airport	.45 .45
		Nos. 191-193 (3)		.85 .85

Royal Wedding of Prince Andrew and Sarah Ferguson — A82

Anniv. and events: No. 195, Queen Elizabeth II, 60th birthday.

Perf. 12½x13
1986, Nov. 20　　Wmk. 390
194	A82	100 l	multicolored	.50 .35
195	A82	100 l	multicolored	.50 .35
a.		Pair, #194-195		1.00 .70

Trakhoni Station, 1904 A83

1986, Dec. 31
196	A83	50 l	shown	.35 .25
197	A83	100 l	Locomotive #1, 1904	.90 .60

Rail transport, 1904-1951.

Nos. 86, 88-89, 105 Overprinted or Surcharged

a

b

1987, May 18　　Unwmk.　　Perf. 13
198	A25(a)	10 l	on #89	.40 .20
199	A25(a)	15 l	on 3½ l, #86	.40 .20
200	A25(a)	20 l	on #88	.50 .25
201	A32(b)	30 l	on #105	.80 .35
		Nos. 198-201 (4)		2.10 1.00

Paintings — A84

Folk Dancers — A86

Europa A85

Designs: 50 l, Shepherd by Feridun Isiman. 125 l, Pear Woman by Mehmet Uluhan.

Perf. 12½x13

1987, May 27 **Wmk. 390**
202 A84 50 l multicolored .35 .20
203 A84 125 l multicolored .85 .40

1987, June 30 **Perf. 12½**
Modern architecture: 50 l, Bauhaus-style house, designed by A. Vural Behaeddin, 1973. 200 l, House, designed by Necdet Turgay, 1979.

204 A85 50 l multicolored 1.50 .40
205 A85 200 l multicolored 4.00 1.75
a. Bklt. pane, 2 each #204-205 12.00

No. 205a contains two copies each of Nos. 204-205, printed alternately, with unprinted selvage at each end of the pane, perf between stamps and selvage and imperf on outside edges. Thus, singles from the pane gauge 12½ by imperf.

1987, Aug. 20
206 A86 20 l multicolored .20 .20
207 A86 50 l multi, diff. .20 .20
208 A86 200 l multi, diff. .50 .50
209 A86 1000 l multi, diff. 2.50 2.50
Nos. 206-209 (4) 3.40 3.40

For surcharge see No. 295B.

Infantry Regiment, 1st Anniv. — A87

5th Islamic Summit Conf., Kuwait — A88

Pharmaceutical Federation — A89

1987, Sept. 30
210 A87 50 l multicolored .20 .20
211 A88 200 l multicolored .50 .50
212 A89 200 l multicolored .50 .50
Nos. 210-212 (3) 1.20 1.20

Ahmet Belig Pasha (1851-1924), Egyptian Judge — A90

Mehmet Emin Pasha (1813-1871), Turkish Grand Vizier — A91

Famous men: 125 l, Mehmet Kamil Pasha (1832-1913), grand vizier.

1987, Oct. 22
213 A90 50 l brn & yel .20 .20
214 A91 50 l multicolored .20 .20
215 A91 125 l multicolored .35 .30
Nos. 213-215 (3) .75 .70

Pres. Rauf Denktash, Turkish Prime Minister Turgut Ozal A92

1987, Nov. 2
216 A92 50 l multi .20 .20

New Kyrenia Harbor A93

Wmk. 390
1987, Nov. 20 **Litho.** **Perf. 12½**
217 A93 150 l shown .40 .40
218 A93 200 l Eastern Mediterranean University .55 .55

Chair Weaver, by Osman Guvenir — A94

Paintings: 20 l, Woman Making Pastry, by Ayhan Mentes, vert. 150 l, Woman Weaving a Rug, by Zekai Yesiladali, vert.

Wmk. 390
1988, May 2 **Litho.** **Perf. 13**
219 A94 20 l multi .20 .20
220 A94 50 l multi .20 .20
221 A94 150 l multi .45 .35
Nos. 219-221 (3) .85 .75

Europa A95

1988, May 31 **Perf. 12½**
222 A95 200 l Tugboat Piyale Pasha 2.75 1.00
223 A95 500 l Satellite dish, broadcast tower, vert. 4.00 1.25

Bayrak Radio and Television Corporation, 25th anniv. (500 l).

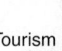

Tourism A96

Photographs: 150 l, Nicosia, by Aysel Erduran. 200 l, Famagusta, by Sonia Halliday and Laura Lushington. 300 l, Kyrenia, by Halliday and Lushington.

1988, June 17
224 A96 150 l multi .25 .25
225 A96 200 l multi .35 .35
226 A96 300 l multi .50 .50
Nos. 224-226 (3) 1.10 1.10

Turkish Prime Ministers — A97

No. 227, Bulent Ecevit, 1970's. No. 228, Bulent Ulusu, Sept. 21, 1980-Dec. 13, 1983. No. 229, Turgut Ozal, from Dec. 13, 1983.

1988, July 20
227 A97 50 l shown .20 .20
228 A97 50 l multi .20 .20
229 A97 50 l multi .20 .20
Nos. 227-229 (3) .60 .60

Civil Defense A98

1988, Aug. 8 **Perf. 12x12½**
230 A98 150 l multicolored .35 .35

Summer Olympics, Seoul A99

1988, Sept. 17 **Perf. 12½**
231 A99 200 l shown .30 .30
232 A99 250 l Women's running .40 .40
233 A99 400 l Seoul .65 .65
Nos. 231-233 (3) 1.35 1.35

Sedat Simavi (1896-1953), Turkish Journalist — A100

Intl. Conferences, Kyrenia — A101

North Cyprus Intl. Industrial Fair — A102

Intl. Red. Cross and Red Crescent Organizations, 125th Anniv. — A103

US-USSR Summit Meeting on Nuclear Arms Reduction A104

WHO, 40th Anniv. — A105

1988, Oct. 17 **Perf. 12½x12, 12x12½**
234 A100 50 l olive grn .20 .20
235 A101 100 l multi .25 .25
236 A102 300 l multi .55 .55
237 A103 400 l multi .85 .85
238 A104 400 l Gorbachev and Reagan .85 .85
239 A105 600 l multi 1.10 1.10
Nos. 234-239 (6) 3.80 3.80

Miniature Sheet

Portraits and Photographs of Kemal Ataturk — A106

b, Holding canteen. c, In uniform. d, Facing left.

1988, Nov. 10 **Perf. 12½**
240 A106 Sheet of 4 2.25 2.00
a.-d. 250 l any single .35 .25

Souvenir Sheet

Turkish Republic of Northern Cyprus,
5th Anniv. — A107

1988, Nov. 15   *Imperf.*
241 A107 500 l multicolored   2.00 1.50

Dervis Pasha Mansion, 19th Cent.,
Nicosia — A108

Designs: 400 l, Gamblers' Inn, 17th cent.,
Asmaalti Meydani. 600 l, Camii Cedit Mosque,
1902, Paphos, vert.

1989, Apr. 28   *Perf. 13*
242 A108 150 l shown   .30   .30
243 A108 400 l multi   .80   .80
244 A108 600 l multi   1.25 1.25
        Nos. 242-244 (3)   2.35 2.35

Europa — A109

1989, May 31   *Perf. 12½x12*
245 A109 600 l Girl, doll   2.25 1.00
246 A109 1000 l Flying kite   3.25 1.25
  a.   Bklt. pane, 2 each #245-246,
        perf. 12½   10.50

Geneva
Peace
Summit,
Aug. 24,
1988
A110

1989, June 30   *Perf. 12½*
247 A110 500 l blk & dark red   1.00 1.00

Wildlife
A111

1989, July 31
248 A111 100 l Alectoris chukar   .20   .20
249 A111 200 l Lepus cyprius   .40   .40
250 A111 700 l Francolinus
                        francolinus   1.40 1.40
251 A111 2000 l Vulpes vulpes   4.00 4.00
        Nos. 248-251 (4)   6.00 6.00

Natl. Development Projects — A112

Perf. 12½x12, 12x12½
1989, Sept. 29
252 A112 100 l Road construc-
                        tion   .20   .20
253 A112 150 l Sanitary water
                        supply   .30   .30
254 A112 200 l Afforestation   .40   .40
255 A112 450 l Telecommunica-
                        tions   .90   .90
256 A112 650 l Power station   1.25 1.25
257 A112 700 l Irrigation ponds   1.40 1.40
        Nos. 252-257 (6)   4.45 4.45

        Nos. 253-256 vert.

Free Port, Famagusta, 15th
Anniv. — A113

Turkish Cypriot
Post, 25th
Anniv. — A114

Saded Newspaper, Cent. — A115

Intl. Marine Organization, 30th
Anniv. — A116

Erenkoy
Uprising,
25th
Anniv.
A117

Perf. 12x12½, 12½x13 (450 l)
1989, Nov. 17
258 A113 100 l multicolored   .20   .20
259 A114 450 l multicolored   .90   .90
260 A115 500 l multicolored   1.00 1.00
261 A116 600 l multicolored   1.25 1.25
262 A117 1000 l multicolored   2.00 2.00
        Nos. 258-262 (5)   5.35 5.35

Erdal Inonu   Agriculture
A118   A119

1989, Dec. 15   *Perf. 12½x12*
263 A118 700 l multicolored   1.40 1.40

Visit of Inonu, Turkish politician, to northern
Cyprus.

1989, Dec. 25 *Perf. 12x12½, 12½x12*
264 A119 150 l Mule drawn   .30   .30
265 A119 450 l Ox drawn   .90   .90
266 A119 550 l Millstone, olive
                        press   1.10 1.10
        Nos. 264-266 (3)   2.30 2.30

        Nos. 264-265 horiz.

World
Health
Day
A120

Perf. 12x12½
1990, Apr. 19 Litho. Wmk. 390
267 A120 200 l shown   .40   .20
268 A120 700 l Cigarette, heart   1.50   .40

Europa
A121

Post offices.

Perf. 12x12½
1990, May 31 Litho. Wmk. 390
269 A121 1000 l Yenierenkoy   3.00 1.50
270 A121 1500 l Ataturk
                        Meydani   4.50 2.00
  a.   Souv. sheet, 2 #269, 2 #270   18.00 16.00

World Cup Soccer Championships,
Italy — A122

1990, June 8
271 A122 300 l Turkish Cypriot
                        team   .65   .65
272 A122 1000 l Ball, emblem,
                        globe   2.00 2.00

A123   A126

A125

World Environment Day: Birds.

1990, June 5   *Perf. 12*
273 A123 150 l Turdus
                        philomelos   4.00   .75
274 A123 300 l Sylvia atri-
                        capilla   5.75 1.25
275 A123 900 l Phoenicurus
                        ochruros   12.00 2.75
276 A123 1000 l Phyllosopus
                        collybita   15.00 5.00
        Nos. 273-276 (4)   36.75 9.75

For surcharge see No. 386.

1990, July 31 *Perf. 13x12½, 12½x13*

Designs: 300 l, Painting by Filiz Ankac. 1000
l , Sculpture by Sinasi Tekman, vert.

279 A125 300 l multicolored   .65   .65
280 A125 1000 l multicolored   2.00 2.00

Wmk. 390
1990, Aug. 24 Litho. *Perf. 12½*
281 A126 150 l Amphitheater,
                        Soli   .35   .35
282 A126 1000 l Mosaic, Soli   2.00 2.00

        European Tourism Year.

Visit by
Turkish
President
Kenan
Evren
A127

1990, Sept. 19
283 A127 500 l multicolored   1.00 1.00

Traffic
Safety
A128

1990, Sept. 21
284 A128 150 l Wear seat belts   .35   .35
285 A128 300 l Obey the speed
                        limit   .65   .65
286 A128 1000 l Obey traffic sig-
                        nals   2.00 2.00
        Nos. 284-286 (3)   3.00 3.00

A129   Flowers — A130

1990, Oct. 1
287 A129 1000 l multicolored   2.00 2.00

Visit by Turkish Prime Minister Yildirim
Akbulut.

Perf. 12½x12
1990, Oct. 31 Litho. Wmk. 390
288 A130 150 l Rosularia cypria   .35   .20
289 A130 200 l Silene fraudra-
                        trix   .40   .20
290 A130 300 l Scutellaria
                        sibthorpii   .65   .20
291 A130 600 l Sedum
                        lampusae   1.25   .30
292 A130 1000 l Onosma caes-
                        pitosum   2.00   .50
293 A130 1500 l Arabis cypria   3.25   .80
        Nos. 288-293 (6)   7.90 2.00

For surcharges see Nos. 295C, 387.

Intl.
Literacy
Year
A131

1990, Nov. 24   *Perf. 12x12½*
294 A131 300 l Ataturk as teach-
                        er   .65   .20
295 A131 750 l A, b, c, books,
                        map   1.60   .40

Nos. 183, 206, 288 Surcharged

1991, June 3
Perfs. & Printing Methods as Before

295A	A76	250 l on 10 l #183		.20	.20
295B	A86	250 l on 20 l #206		.20	.20
295C	A130	500 l on 150 l #288		.35	.25
		Nos. 295A-295C (3)		.75	.65

Shape of obliterator varies.

Orchids — A132

Wmk. 390
1991, July 8   Litho.   Perf. 14

296	A132	250 l Ophrys lapethica	.55	.55
297	A132	500 l Ophrys kotschyi	1.60	1.60

See Nos. 303-306.

A133

Perf. 12½x12
1991, July 29   Litho.   Wmk. 390

Europa: a, Hermes space shuttle. b, Ulysses probe.

Miniature Sheet

298	A133	2000 l Sheet of 2, #a.-b.	8.00	8.00

Public Fountains A134

Wmk. 390
1991, Sept. 9   Litho.   Perf. 12

299	A134	250 l Kuchuk Medrese	.20	.20
300	A134	500 l Djafer Pasha	.35	.35
301	A134	1500 l Sarayonu Square	1.10	1.10
302	A134	5000 l Arabahmet Mosque	3.50	3.50
		Nos. 299-302 (4)	5.15	5.15

Orchid Type of 1991
1991, Oct. 10   Perf. 14

303	A132	100 l Serapias levan-tina	.20	.20
304	A132	500 l Dactylorhiza romana	.40	.40
305	A132	2000 l Orchis simia	1.40	1.40
306	A132	3000 l Orchis sancta	2.00	2.00
		Nos. 303-306 (4)	4.00	4.00

Hindiler by Salih M. Cizel — A135

Painting: 500 l, Dusme by Asik Mene.

Wmk. 390
1991, Nov. 5   Litho.   Perf. 13

307	A135	250 l multicolored	.20	.20
308	A135	500 l multicolored	.25	.25

See type A143. For surcharge see No. 381.

World Food Day A136

Basbakan Mustafa Cagatay (1937-1989) A137

Eastern Mediterranean University — A138

Wolfgang Amadeus Mozart, Death Bicent. A139

1991, Nov. 20   Perf. 12

309	A136	250 l multicolored	.20	.20
310	A137	500 l multicolored	.30	.30
311	A138	500 l multicolored	.30	.30
312	A139	1500 l multicolored	.85	.85
		Nos. 309-312 (4)	1.65	1.65

For surcharge see No. 380.

World AIDS Day A140

1991, Dec. 13   Perf. 12

313	A140	1000 l multicolored	.55	.55

Lighthouses — A141

1991, Dec. 16   Perf. 12x12½

314	A141	250 l Canbulat Burcu, Famagusta	.20	.20
315	A141	500 l Yat Limani, Kyrenia	.30	.30
316	A141	1500 l Turizm Limani, Kyrenia	.85	.85
		Nos. 314-316 (3)	1.35	1.35

Tourism A142

Designs: 250 l, Elephant and hippopotamus fossils, Kyrenia. 500 l, Roman fish ponds, Lambusa (58 BC-398 AD). 1500 l, Roman tomb and church, Lambusa (58 BC-1192 AD).

1991, Dec. 27

317	A142	250 l multicolored	.20	.20
318	A142	500 l multicolored	.30	.30
319	A142	1500 l multicolored	.85	.85
		Nos. 317-319 (3)	1.35	1.35

Paintings A143

Designs: 500 l, Ebru, by Arife Kandulu. 3500 l, Nicosia, by Ismet Tartar.

Wmk. 390
1992, Mar. 31   Litho.   Perf. 14

320	A143	500 l multicolored	.25	.25
321	A143	3500 l multicolored	1.75	1.75

See type A135.

Tourism A144

No. 322, Ancient building, Famagusta. No. 323, Trap shooting range, Nicosia. 1000 l, Salamis Bay resort, Famagusta. 1500 l, Casino, Kyrenia.

1992, Apr. 21   Perf. 13½x14, 14x13½

322	A144	500 l multi	.25	.25
323	A144	500 l multi	.25	.25
324	A144	1000 l multi	.50	.50
325	A144	1500 l multi, vert.	.75	.75
		Nos. 322-325 (4)	1.75	1.75

Souvenir Sheet

Discovery of America, 500th Anniv. — A145

Europa: a, 1500 l, Santa Maria, Nina and Pinta. b, 3500 l, Columbus.

1992, May 29   Perf. 13½x14

326	A145	Sheet of 2, #a.-b.	10.00	10.00

Sea Turtles A146

Perf. 13½x14
1992, June 30   Litho.   Wmk. 390

327	A146	1000 l Green turtle	3.00	3.00
328	A146	1500 l Loggerhead turtle	3.50	3.50
a.		Souv. sheet, 2 ea #327-328	14.00	14.00

World Wildlife Fund.

1992 Summer Olympics, Barcelona A147

#329: a, Women's gymnastics, vert. b, Tennis, vert. 1000 l, High jump. 1500 l, Cycling.

1992, July 25   Perf. 14x13½

329	A147	500 l Pair, #a-b.	.75	.75

Perf. 13½x14

330	A147	1000 l multicolored	.50	.50
331	A147	1500 l multicolored	.75	.75
		Nos. 329-331 (3)	2.00	2.00

Electric Power Plant, Kyrenia A148

Social Insurance, 15th Anniv. A149

Intl. Federation of Women Artists A150

Veterinary Services A151

Perf. 13½x14
1992, Sept. 30   Litho.   Wmk. 390

332	A148	500 l multicolored	.25	.25
333	A149	500 l multicolored	.25	.25
334	A150	1500 l multicolored	.75	.75
335	A151	1500 l multicolored	.75	.75
		Nos. 332-335 (4)	2.00	2.00

Civil Aviation Office, 17th Anniv. A152

Meteorology Office, 18th Anniv. — A153

Mapping, 14th Anniv. A154

Perf. 13½x14
1992, Nov. 20   Litho.   Wmk. 390

336	A152	1000 l multicolored	.50	.50
337	A153	1000 l multicolored	.50	.50
338	A154	1200 l multicolored	.60	.60
		Nos. 336-338 (3)	1.60	1.60

Native
Cuisine
A155

Food: 2000 l, Zulbiye (pastry). 2500 l, Cicek Dolmasi (stuffed squash flowers). 3000 l, Tatar Boregi (flaky pastry dish). 4000 l, Seftali kebab (meat dish).

1992, Dec. 14
339	A155	2000 l multicolored	1.00	1.00
340	A155	2500 l multicolored	1.25	1.25
341	A155	3000 l multicolored	1.50	1.50
342	A155	4000 l multicolored	2.00	2.00
		Nos. 339-342 (4)	5.75	5.75

Intl. Conference on Nutrition, Rome.
See Nos. 388-390.

Tourism
A156

Designs: 500 l, Church and Monastery of St. Barnabas. 10,000 l, Bowl.

Perf. 13½x14
1993, Apr. 1　　Litho.　　Wmk. 390
343	A156	500 l multi	.25	.25
344	A156	10,000 l multi	5.00	5.00

Souvenir Sheet

Europa — A157

Contemporary paintings by: a, 2000 l, Turksal Ince. b, 3000 l, Ilkay Onsoy.

Perf. 14x13½
1993, May 5　　Litho.　　Wmk. 390
345	A157	Sheet of 2, #a.-b.	2.00	2.00

Trees — A158

1993, June 11　　　　Perf. 14x13½
346	A158	500 l Olea europea	.25	.20
347	A158	1000 l Eucalyptus camaldulensis	.50	.50
348	A158	3000 l Platanus orientalis	1.50	1.50
349	A158	4000 l Pinus brutia tenore	2.00	2.00
		Nos. 346-349 (4)	4.25	4.20

Arabahmet Rehabilitation
Project — A159

Perf. 13½x14
1993, Sept. 20　　Litho.　　Wmk. 390
350	A159	1000 l shown	.20	.20
351	A159	3000 l Homes, diff.	.50	.50

Creation of Turkish Republic of
Northern Cyprus, 10th Anniv.
A160

Designs: No. 353, Flags changing to dove, vert. 1000 l, Dove flying from flag. 5000 l, Flowers forming "10," map.

Perf. 13½x14, 14x13½
1993, Nov. 15　　Litho.　　Wmk. 390
352	A160	500 l multicolored	.20	.20
353	A160	500 l multicolored	.20	.20
354	A160	1000 l multicolored	.20	.20
355	A160	5000 l multicolored	.80	.80
		Nos. 352-355 (4)	1.40	1.40

Ataturk, 55th Death
Anniv. — A161

State
Theaters,
30th Anniv.
A162

Turkish Resistance Organization, 35th
Anniv. — A163

Turkish
News
Agency,
20th
Anniv.
A164

Tchaikovsky, Death Cent. — A165

Perf. 14x13½, 13½x14
1993, Dec. 27　　Litho.　　Wmk. 390
356	A161	500 l multicolored	.20	.20
357	A162	500 l multicolored	.20	.20
358	A163	1500 l multicolored	.30	.30
359	A164	2000 l multicolored	.40	.40
360	A165	5000 l multicolored	1.10	1.10
		Nos. 356-360 (5)	2.20	2.20

Soyle Falci,
by Goral
Ozkan
A166

Design: 6500 l, Sculpture, IV Hareket, by Senol Özdevrim.

1994, Mar. 31　　　　Perf. 14
361	A166	1000 l multicolored	.20	.20
362	A166	6500 l multicolored	1.40	1.40

Fazil Kucuk (1906-84), Physician and
Political Leader — A167

1994, Apr. 1
363	A167	1500 l multicolored	.30	.30

Souvenir Sheet

Archaeological Discoveries — A168

Europa: a, Neolithic village, Ayios Epectitos Vrysi. b, Neolithic man, early tools found in excavation.

1994, May 16　　　　Perf. 13½
364	A168	8500 l Sheet of 2, #a.-b.	3.00	3.00

1994 World Cup Soccer
Championships, US — A169

1994, June 30
365	A169	2500 l Trophy, vert.	.20	.20
366	A169	10,000 l US map	.80	.80

Turkish
Postal
Service in
Northern
Cyprus,
30th Anniv.
A170

1994, June 30
367	A170	50,000 l multicolored	4.00	4.00

A171

A172

Turkish
Peace
Operation,
20th
Anniv.
A173

1994, July 20　　　　Perf. 14
368	A171	2500 l shown	.20	.20
369	A172	5000 l Monument	.40	.40
370	A172	7000 l Monument, diff.	.50	.50
371	A173	8500 l shown	.65	.65
		Nos. 368-371 (4)	1.75	1.75

First Rural Postal Cancellations,
Cent. — A174

Postmarks, stamps: 1500 l, Karpas, Cyprus #131. 2500 l, Gazi Magusa (Famagusta), #71. 5000 l, Bey Keuy, Cyprus #150. 7000 l, Aloa, Cyprus, #179. 8500 l, Pyla, Cyprus #152.

1994, Aug. 15　　　　Perf. 13½
372	A174	1500 l multicolored	.20	.20
373	A174	2500 l multicolored	.20	.20
374	A174	5000 l multicolored	.35	.35
375	A174	7000 l multicolored	.55	.55
376	A174	8500 l multicolored	.70	.70
		Nos. 372-376 (5)	2.00	2.00

Sea Shells — A175

1994, Nov. 15　　　　Perf. 14
377	A175	2500 l Charonia tritonis	.20	.20
378	A175	12,500 l Tonna galea	.70	.35
379	A175	12,500 l Cypraea talpa	.70	.35
		Nos. 377-379 (3)	1.60	.90

Nos. 307, 309
Surcharged

1994, Dec. 12　　Perfs., etc. as Before
380	A136	1500 l on 250 l multi	.20	.20
381	A135	2500 l on 250 l multi	.20	.20

Size and location of surcharge varies.

European Nature Conservation
Year — A176

Designs: 2000 l, Donkeys on mountain top.
3500 l, Shoreline. 15,000 l, Donkeys in field.

1995, Feb. 10   Wmk. 390   Perf. 14
382 A176 2000 l multicolored   .20   .20
383 A176 3500 l multicolored   .20   .20
384 A176 15,000 l multicolored 1.00 1.00
        Nos. 382-384 (3)   1.40 1.40

Souvenir Sheet

Peace and Freedom — A177

Europa: a, Globe, dove. b, Doves over
Europe.
Illustration reduced.

1995, Apr. 20   Perf. 13½x14
385 A177 15,000 l Sheet of 2,
                        #a.-b.   2.50 2.50

Nos. 275 & 290 Surcharged

1995, Apr. 21   Perfs., etc. as Before
386 A123 2000 l on 900 l #275   1.75 1.50
387 A130 3500 l on 300 l #290   3.50 3.50

Size and location of surcharge varies.

Native Cusine Type of 1992

Food: 3500 l, Sini katmeri. 10,000 l, Kolokas
musakka, Bullez kizartma. 14,000 l, Enginar
dolmasi.

Perf. 13½x14
1995, May 29   Litho.   Wmk. 390
388 A155 3500 l multicolored   .20   .20
389 A155 10,000 l multicolored .55   .55
390 A155 14,000 l multicolored .80   .80
        Nos. 388-390 (3)   1.55 1.55

Butterflies
A178

1995, June 30
391 A178 3500 l Papilio
                      machaon   .20   .20
392 A178 4500 l Charaxes jasi-
                      us   .20   .20
393 A178 15,000 l Cynthia cardui .70 .70
394 A178 30,000 l Vanessa ata-
                      lanta   1.40 1.40
        Nos. 391-394 (4)   2.50 2.50

Visit by
Turkish
Pres.
Suleyman
Demirel
A179

1995, Aug. 21   Perf. 13½
395 A179 5000 l multicolored   .25   .25

Tourism
A180

Designs: 3500 l, Beach scene, Kyrenia.
7500 l, Sailboats. 15,000 l, Ruins, Famagusta,
vert. 20,000 l, St. George Cathedral,
Famagusta, vert.

1995, Aug. 21
396 A180 3500 l multicolored   .20   .20
397 A180 7500 l multicolored   .40   .40
398 A180 15,000 l multicolored .80   .80
399 A180 20,000 l multicolored 1.00 1.00
        Nos. 396-399 (4)   2.40 2.40

State
Printing
Office,
20th Anniv.
A181

Turkish
Natl.
Assembly,
75th
Anniv.
A182

Louis
Pasteur
(1822-95)
A183

UN, 50th
Anniv.
A184

G. Marconi (1874-1937), Radio,
Cent. — A185

Motion Pictures,
Cent. — A186

Perf. 13½x14, 14x13½
1995, Nov. 7   Litho.   Wmk. 390
400 A181 3000 l multicolored   .20   .20
401 A182 3000 l multicolored   .20   .20
402 A183 5000 l multicolored   .25   .25
403 A184 22,000 l multicolored 1.25 1.25
404 A185 30,000 l multicolored 1.60 1.60
405 A186 30,000 l multicolored 1.60 1.60
        Nos. 400-405 (6)   5.10 5.10

A187   A188

Tombstone inscriptions, Orhon and Yenisey
river region: 5000 l, Kültigin Heykelinin Basi.
10,000 l, Kültigin Yaziti.

1995, Dec. 28   Perf. 14x13½
406 A187 5000 l multicolored   .25   .25
407 A187 10,000 l multicolored .55   .55
     Reading of Orhon Epitaphs, cent.

1996, Jan. 31
408 A188 10,000 l multicolored .55   .55
     Bosnia-Herzegovina.

Fish
A189

Designs: 60,000 l, Mullus surmuletus.
10,000 l, Thalassoma pavo. 28,000 l, Diplodus
vulgaris. 40,000 l, Epinephelus guaza.

1996, Mar. 29   Perf. 14
409 A189 6,000 l multicolored   .20   .20
410 A189 10,000 l multicolored .30   .30
411 A189 28,000 l multicolored .80   .80
412 A189 40,000 l multicolored 1.10 1.10
        Nos. 409-412 (4)   2.40 2.40

Tourism
A190

Designs: 100,000 l, Pomegranate tree, vert.
150,000 l, Pomegranate fruit, vert. 250,000 l,
Bellapais Monastery. 500,000 l, Folk dancing.

Perf. 14x13½, 13½x14
1996, Apr. 26   Litho.   Wmk. 390
413 A190 100,000 l multi   2.50   2.50
414 A190 150,000 l multi   3.75   3.75
415 A190 250,000 l multi   6.25   6.25
416 A190 500,000 l multi   12.50 12.50
        Nos. 413-416 (4)   25.00 25.00

Famous
Women
A191

Europa: 15,000 l, Beria Remzi Ozoran.
50,000 l, Kadriye Hulusi Hacibulgur.

1996, May 31   Perf. 13½x14
417 A191 15,000 l multicolored .50   .50
418 A191 50,000 l multicolored 2.00 2.00

World Environment Day — A192

Designs: a, Older, dying trees in mountainous area. b, Newly-planted trees.

1996, June 28   Perf. 13½
419 A192 50,000 l Sheet of 2,
                        #a.-b.   1.10 1.10

1996 Summer Olympic Games,
Atlanta — A193

a, 15,000 l, Basketball. b, 50,000 l, Javelin.
c, 15,000 l, Discus. d, 50,000 l, Volleyball.

1996, July 31
420 A193 Sheet of 4, #a.-d.   3.00 3.00

Euro '96, European Soccer
Championship, Great Britain — A194

1996, Oct. 31   Perf. 13½x14
421 A194 15,000 l shown   .40   .40
422 A194 35,000 l Flags, soccer
                        ball   1.40 1.40
a.   Pair, #421-422   2.00 2.00

Civil
Defense
A195

Security
Forces — A196

Nasreddin
Hodja
A197

Children's Rights A198

Perf. 13½x14, 14x13½
1996, Dec. 23   Litho.   Wmk. 390
423 A195 10,000 l multicolored .25 .25
424 A196 20,000 l multicolored .50 .50
425 A197 50,000 l multicolored 1.25 1.25
426 A198 75,000 l multicolored 1.90 1.90
  Nos. 423-426 (4) 3.90 3.90

Paintings — A199

Designs: 25,000 l, Buildings, people, by Lebibe Sonuc. 70,000 l, Woman seated beside plant, by Ruzen Atakan.

1997, Jan. 31   Perf. 14
427 A199 25,000 l multicolored .65 .65
428 A199 70,000 l multicolored 1.75 1.75

Mushrooms A200

Natl. Flag on Mountainside A201

Designs: 15,000 l, Amanita phallioides. No. 430, Morchella esculenta. No. 431, Pleurotus eryngii. 70,0000 l, Amanita muscaria.

1997, Mar. 31
429 A200 15,000 l multicolored .45 .45
430 A200 25,000 l multicolored .65 .65
431 A200 25,000 l multicolored .65 .65
432 A200 70,000 l multicolored 1.75 1.75
  Nos. 429-432 (4) 3.50 3.50

1997, Apr. 23
433 A201 60,000 l multicolored 1.50 1.50

Stories and Legends A202

Europa: 25,000 l, Woman with broom, children playing, man with donkey. 70,000 l, Well, apple tree, man behind bushes.

1997, May 30   Perf. 13½x14
434 A202 25,000 l multicolored .75 .75
435 A202 70,000 l multicolored 1.75 1.75

Visit by Turkish Leaders A203

Designs: 15,000 l, Prime Minister Necmeddin Erbakan, vert. 80,000 l, Pres. Süleyman Demirel.

Perf. 14x13½, 13½x14
1997, June 20
436 A203 15,000 l multicolored .30 .30
437 A203 80,000 l multicolored 1.50 1.50

A204

A205

Raptors: No. 438, Aquila chrysaetos. No. 439, Falco eleanorae. 75,000 l, Falco tinnunculus. 100,000 l, Pernis apivorus.

1997, July 31   Perf. 14x13½
438 A204 40,000 l multicolored .55 .55
439 A204 40,000 l multicolored .55 .55
440 A204 75,000 l multicolored 1.00 1.00
441 A204 100,000 l multicolored 1.40 1.40
  Nos. 438-441 (4) 3.50 3.50

1997, Oct. 28
Old Coins Used in Cyprus: 25,000 l, 1861 Abdül Aziz gold lira. 40,000 l, 1808 Mahmud II gold rumi. 75,000 l, 1566 Selim II gold lira. 100,000 l, 1909 Mehmed V gold besibirlik.

442 A205 25,000 l multicolored .35 .35
443 A205 40,000 l multicolored .55 .55
444 A205 75,000 l multicolored 1.00 1.00
445 A205 100,000 l multicolored 1.40 1.40
  Nos. 442-445 (4) 3.30 3.30

Turk Lisesi, Cent. A206

Scouting, 90th Anniv. A207

Fight Against AIDS — A208

Diesel Engine, Cent. A209

Perf. 13½x14, 14x13½
1997, Dec. 22   Litho.   Wmk. 390
446 A206 25,000 l multicolored .30 .30
447 A207 40,000 l multicolored .50 .50
448 A208 100,000 l multicolored 1.25 1.25
449 A209 150,000 l multicolored 1.75 1.75
  Nos. 446-449 (4) 3.80 3.80

Ismet Sevki (1884-1957) and Ahmet Sevki (1874-1959), Photographers — A210

1998, Jan. 28   Perf. 13½x14
450 A210 40,000 l shown .50 .50
451 A210 105,000 l Ahmet Sevki, vert. 1.25 1.25

Turkish Pres. Süleyman Demirel — A216

1998 World Cup Soccer Championships, France — A217

Design: 175,000 l, Pres. Demirel, Pres. Rauf R. Denktash, view of ocean, horiz.

Insects A211

Designs: 40,000 l, Agrion splendens. 65,000 l, Ascalaphus macaronius. 125,000 l, Podalonia hirsuta. 150,000 l, Rhyssa persuasoria.

1998, Mar. 30
452 A211 40,000 l multicolored .40 .40
453 A211 65,000 l multicolored .65 .65
454 A211 125,000 l multicolored 1.25 1.25
455 A211 150,000 l multicolored 1.50 1.50
  Nos. 452-455 (4) 3.80 3.80

Doors — A212

1998, Apr. 30   Perf. 14x13½
456 A212 115,000 l shown 1.10 1.10
457 A212 140,000 l Door, steps 1.40 1.40

Natl. Festival A213

Europa: 150,000 l, Globe, map of Cyprus, flags, vert.

1998, May 30   Perf. 13½x14, 14x13½
458 A213 40,000 l multicolored .65 .65
459 A213 150,000 l multicolored 2.10 2.10

Intl. Year of the Ocean A214

Various marine life.

1998, June 30   Perf. 13½x14
460 A214 40,000 l multicolored .30 .30
461 A214 90,000 l multicolored .65 .65

Visit by Turkish Prime Minister Mesut Yilmaz A215

1998, July 20
462 A215 75,000 l multicolored .55 .55

1998, July 25   Perf. 13½x14, 14x13½
463 A216 75,000 l multicolored .55 .55
464 A216 175,000 l multicolored 1.25 1.25

Establishment of Yaylacik water program.

1998, July 31   Perf. 13½x14, 13x13½
75,000 l, Team coming across field, fans in stadium. 175,000 l, Holding up World Cup trophy.
465 A217 75,000 l multi, horiz. .55 .55
466 A217 175,000 l multi 1.25 1.25

Visit of Turkish Deputy Prime Minister Bülent Ecevit — A218

Traditional Crafts — A219

1998, Sept. 5   Perf. 14
467 A218 200,000 l multicolored 1.50 1.50

1998, Oct. 26   Perf. 13½x14, 14x13½
468 A219 50,000 l Kalayci, horiz. .40 .40
469 A219 75,000 l Sepetci .60 .60
470 A219 130,000 l Bileyici 1.00 1.00
471 A219 400,000 l Oymaci, horiz. 3.00 3.00
  Nos. 468-471 (4) 5.00 5.00

Bayrak Radio & Television, 35th Anniv. A220

Turkish Cyprus, 15th Anniv. A221

Turkish Republic, 75th Anniv. A222

Universal Declaration of Human Rights, 50th Anniv. — A223

No. 476a, 75,000 l, Natl. flag, map of Turkish Cyprus.

1998, Nov. 15
472 A220 50,000 l multicolored .40 .40
473 A221 75,000 l multicolored .55 .55
474 A222 75,000 l multicolored .55 .55
475 A223 175,000 l multicolored 1.25 .65
  Nos. 472-475 (4) 2.75 2.15
    Souvenir Sheet
476 Sheet of 2, #473, #476a 1.10 1.10

A224

1999, Jan. 15 *Perf. 14*
477 A224 75,000 l multicolored .55 .55
Dr. Fazil Kücük (1906-84), politician.

A225

1999, Jan. 30
Scene from "Othello," by Verdi: a, Singers standing. b, Singer on floor.
478 A225 200,000 l Sheet of 2, #a.-b. 2.00 2.00

Snakes
A226

Designs: 50,000 l, Malpolon monspessulanus insignitus. 75,000 l, Hierophis jugularis. 195,000 l, Vipera lebetina. 220,000 l, Natrix natrix.

1999, Mar. 26 *Perf. 13½x14*
479 A226 50,000 l multicolored .40 .40
480 A226 75,000 l multicolored .60 .60
481 A226 195,000 l multicolored 1.60 1.60
482 A226 220,000 l multicolored 1.75 1.75
Nos. 479-482 (4) 4.35 4.35

Europa
A227

1999, May 17 *Perf. 14*
483 A227 75,000 l Sütunlu Cave .75 .75
484 A227 200,000 l Incirli Cave, vert. 1.75 1.75

Turkish Peace Operation, 25th Anniv. A228

Wmk. 390
1999, July 20 **Litho.** *Perf. 13¾*
485 A228 150,000 l shown 1.25 1.25
486 A228 250,000 l Dove, map, sun 2.00 2.00

Turkish Postal Administration in Cyprus, 35th Anniv. — A229

1999, Nov. 12 **Litho.** *Perf. 13¾*
487 A229 75,000 l multicolored .25 .25

UPU, 125th Anniv. A230

1999, Nov. 12
488 A230 225,000 l multicolored .80 .80

Total Solar Eclipse, Aug. 11 — A231

1999, Nov. 12
489 A231 250,000 l multicolored .90 .90

Destruction of Turkish Heritage in Southern Cyprus — A232

Photos of: 75,000 l, Building, Limassol. 150,000 l, Mosque, Evdim. 210,000 l, Bayraktar Mosque, Nicosia (Lefkosa). 1,000,000 l, Cami-i Kebir Mosque, Paphos (Baf), vert.

1999, Dec. 3
490 A232 75,000 l multi .20 .20
491 A232 150,000 l multi .55 .55
492 A232 210,000 l multi .75 .75
493 A232 1,000,000 l multi 3.75 3.75
Nos. 490-493 (4) 5.25 5.25

Millennium A233

Designs: 75,000 l, Cellular phone. 150,000 l, "Welcome 2000." 275,000 l, Computer. 300,000 l, Satellite.

2000, Mar. 3 **Litho.** *Perf. 13¾*
494 A233 75,000 l multi .25 .25
495 A233 150,000 l multi .50 .50
496 A233 275,000 l multi .95 .95
497 A233 300,000 l multi 1.00 1.00
Nos. 494-497 (4) 2.70 2.70

Beach Scenes A234

Designs: 300,000 l, Umbrella, pail, shovel, beach ball, sailboats. 340,000 l, Beach chair.

2000, Apr. 29 **Litho.** *Perf. 13¾*
498 A234 300,000 l multi 1.00 1.00
499 A234 340,000 l multi 1.10 1.10

Europa, 2000
Souvenir Sheet
Common Design Type and

A235

2000, May 31 **Wmk. 390** *Perf. 14*
500 Sheet of 2 1.90 1.90
a. CD17 300,000 l multi .95 .95
b. A235 300,000 l multi .95 .95

4th Intl. Music Festival, Bellpais Abbey A236

Designs: 150,000 l, Bellapais Abbey. 350,000 l, Blended colors, vert.

2000, June 21 *Perf. 13¾*
501 A236 150,000 l multi .45 .45
502 A236 350,000 l multi 1.10 1.10

Visit of Turkish Pres. Ahmet N. Sezer — A237

2000, June 22
503 A237 150,000 l multi .45 .45

2000 Summer Olympics, Sydney A238

125,000 l, Torch and Olympic rings, vert. 200,000 l, Runner.

2000, July 25
504-505 A238 Set of 2 .90 .90

No. 409 Surcharged

Method & Perf. as Before
2000, Sept. 28 **Wmk. 390**
506 A189 50,000 l on 6000 l .20 .20

Flora and Fauna — A239

Designs: 125,000 l, Praying mantis on flower. 200,000 l, Butterfly on flower. 275,000 l, Bee on flower. 600,000 l, Snail on flower stem.

Wmk. 390
2000, Oct. 16 **Litho.** *Perf. 13¾*
507-510 A239 Set of 4 3.75 3.75

Kerchief Borders A240

Background colors: 125,000 l, Yellow. 200,000 l, Lilac. 265,000 l, Green. 350,000 l, Brown.

2000, Nov. 28
511-514 A240 Set of 4 3.00 3.00

Restored Buildings, Lefkosa A241

Designs: 125,000 l, Lusignan House. 200,000 l, Eaved House.

Wmk. 390
2001, Mar. 28 **Litho.** *Perf. 13¾*
515-516 A241 Set of 2 .75 .75

Art — A242

Works by: 125,000 l, Inci Kansu. 200,000 l, Emel Samioglu. 350,000 l, Ozden Selenge, vert. 400,000 l, Ayhatun Atesin.

2001, Mar. 30
517-520 A242 Set of 4 2.50 2.50

Europa — A243   World Environment Day — A244

Designs: 200,000 l, Degirmenlik Reservoir. 500,000 l, Waterfall, Sinar.

2001, May 31
521-522 A243 Set of 2 1.60 1.60

2001, June 22
Designs: 125,000 l, Atomic model, x-ray images. 450,000 l, X-ray images, radiation symbol.
523-524 A244 Set of 2 1.10 1.10

Police Uniforms — A245

Uniforms from: 125,000 l, 1885. 200,000 l, 1933. 500,000 l, 1934. 750,000 l, 1983.

2001, Aug. 24
525-528 A245 Set of 4 2.75 2.75

Automobiles — A246

Designs: 175,000 l, 1954 MG TF. 300,000 l, 1948 Vauxhall 14. 475,000 l, 1922 Bentley. 600,000 l, 1955 Jaguar XK 120.

Wmk. 390
2001, Nov. 2   Litho.   Perf. 13¾
529-532 A246   Set of 4   1.90 1.90

Publication of The Genocide Files, by Harry Scott Gibbons — A247

2001, Dec. 24
533 A247   200,000 l multi   .30 .30

July 20th Technical School, Cent. A248

2001, Dec. 24
534 A248   200,000 l multi   .30 .30

Cartoon Art — A249

Designs: 250,000 l, Chef with grinder and book, by Utku Karsu, vert. 300,000 l, People singing "We Are the World," malnourished Africans, by Musa Kayra. 475,000 l, Can of diet cola airdropped for a malnourished African, by Serhan Gazi, vert. 850,000 l, Child viewing city and painting a country scene, by Mustafa Tozaki, vert.

Wmk. 390
2002, Feb. 28   Litho.   Perf. 13¾
535-538 A249   Set of 4   2.60 2.60

Tourism A250

Underwater photographs: 250,000 l, Turtle swimming. 300,000 l, Starfish on coral. 500,000 l, Fish. 750,000 l, Shipwreck.

2002, Mar. 27
539-542 A250   Set of 4   2.50 2.50

Souvenir Sheet

Europa — A251

No. 543: a, Man on stilts. b, Tightrope walker.

Wmk. 390
2002, May 27   Litho.   Perf. 13¾
543 A251   600,000 l Sheet of 2,
                    #a-b   1.50 1.50

2002 World Cup Soccer Championships, Japan and Korea — A252

Designs: 300,000 l, Soccer team. 1,000,000 l, "Lift Embargo on Sports."

2002, June 24
544-545 A252   Set of 2   1.60 1.60

Native Costumes — A253

Designs: 250,000 l, Woman. 300,000 l, Man. 425,000 l, Man, diff. 700,000 l, Woman, diff.

2002, Aug. 8
546-549 A253   Set of 4   2.00 2.00

Children's Art — A254

Art by: 300,000 l, M. A. Alpdogan. 600,000 l, S. Avci, vert.

Wmk. 390
2002, Sept. 30   Litho.   Perf. 13¾
550-551 A254   Set of 2   .90 .90

Sports Personalities A255   Famous Men A256

Designs: 300,000 l, Sureyya Ayhan, winner of women's 1500m race at 2002 European Track and Field Championships. 1,000,000 l, Park Jung-tae (1944-2002), father of modern taekwondo.

2002, Oct. 28
552-553 A255   Set of 2   1.60 1.60

2002, Dec. 3
Designs: 100,000 l, Oguz Karayel (1933-96), soccer player. 175,000 l, Mete Adanir (1961-89), soccer player. 300,000 l, M. Necati Ozkan (1899-1970). 575,000 l, Osman Turkay (1927-2001), poet, horiz.

554-557 A256   Set of 4   1.40 1.40

Art — A257

Paintings by: 250,000 l, S. Bayraktar. 1,000,000 l, F. Sükan.

Wmk. 390
2003, Feb. 21   Litho.   Perf. 13¾
558-559 A257   Set of 2   1.50 1.50

Souvenir Sheet

Europa — A258

Poster art: a, Tree. b, Question mark.

2003, May 8
560 A258   600,000 l Sheet of 2,
                    #a-b   1.60 1.60

Birds A259

Designs: 100,000 l, Oenanthe cypriaca. 300,000 l, Sylvia melanothorax. 500,000 l, Phalacrocorax pygmeus, vert. 600,000 l, Phoenicopterus ruber, vert.

2003, June 3
561-564 A259   Set of 4   2.10 2.10

Chests A260

Chest from: 250,000 l, Seher. 300,000 l, Lapta. 525,000 l, Baf. 1,000,000 l, Karpaz ve Akatu.

Perf. 13¾x14
2003, July 25   Litho.   Wmk. 390
565-568 A260   Set of 4   3.00 3.00

Flowers — A261

Designs: 150,000 l, Gladiolus triphyllus. 175,000 l, Tulipa cypria. 500,000 l, Ranunculus asiaticus. 525,000 l, Narcissus tazetta.

2003, Oct. 21   Perf. 14x13¾
569-572 A261   Set of 4   1.75 1.75

National Anniversaries — A262

No. 573 — Kemal Ataturk and flag of: a, Turkey. b, Turkish Republic of Northern Cyprus.

2003, Nov. 14   Perf. 13¾x14
573 A262   3,000,000 l Horiz. pair,
                    #a-b   8.50 8.50

Republic of Turkey, 80th anniv. (#573a), Turkish Republic of Northern Cyprus, 20th anniv. (#573b).

Federation of Agricultural Producers, 60th Anniv. A263

2003, Dec. 12
574 A263   300,000 l multi   .45 .45

Lions International in Turkish Republic of Northern Cyprus, 40th Anniv. — A263a

2003, Dec. 12
575 A264   500,000 l multi   .70 .70

Turkish Postal Service in Northern Cyprus, 40th Anniv. A264

Emblem and: 250,000 l, Mailbox and Nicosia Post Office. 1,500,000 l, Globe, winged envelopes.

Perf. 13¾x14
2004, Apr. 30   Litho.   Wmk. 390
576-577 A264   Set of 2   2.40 2.40

Souvenir Sheet

Europa — A265

No. 578: a, Beach, sailboat. b, Woman holding drink, beach.

2004, May 25
578 A265   600,000 l Sheet of 2,
                    #a-b   1.60 1.60

Exists imperf.

Eurasia
Postal
Union
A266

2004, June 7
579 A266 300,000 l multi   .40   .40

Flowers — A267

Designs: 250,000 l, Salvia veneris.
300,000 l, Phlomis cypria. 500,000 l,
Pimpinella cypria. 600,000 l, Rosularia cypria.

2004, July 9   **Perf. 14x13¾**
580-583 A267   Set of 4   2.40 2.40

Soccer
Stadiums
A268

Stadium and: 300,000 l, European Soccer
Championships emblem. 1,000,000 l, UEFA
(European Football Union) 50th anniv.
emblem.

2004, Aug. 20   **Perf. 13¾x14**
584-585 A268   Set of 2   1.75 1.75

2004 Summer Olympics,
Athens — A269

No. 586, 300,000 l: a, Sailing, handball. b,
Boxing, equestrian.
No. 587, 500,000 l: a, Weight lifting, gym-
nastics. b, Canoeing, tennis.

2004, Sept. 24   **Perf. 14x13¾**
Horiz. pairs, #a-b
586-587 A269   Set of 2   2.25 2.25

Eastern Mediterranean University, 25th
Anniv. (in 2004) — A270

2005, Feb. 15   Litho.   Perf. 13¾x14
588 A270 15k multi   .25   .25

Cyprus Turkish Philatelic Association,
25th Anniv. (in 2004) — A271

2005, Feb. 15
589 A271 30k multi   .50   .50

Website for Universities in Turkish
Republic of Northern Cyprus — A272

2005, Feb. 15
590 A272 50k multi   .80   .80

A273

Tourism
A274

2005, Mar. 9
591 A273 10k multi   .20   .20
592 A274 1 l multi   1.60 1.60

Children's
Drawings — A275

Drawings of men and women by: 25k, E.
Demirci. 50k, E. Oztemiz.

2005, Apr. 22   **Perf. 14x13¾**
593-594 A275   Set of 2   1.10 1.10

Europa — A276

No. 595: a, Woman at left, round table. b,
Oven, square table, woman at right.
Illustration reduced.

2005, May 30   **Perf. 13¾x14**
595 A276 60k Pair, #a-b   1.75 1.75
   c.   Souvenir sheet, 2 #595   3.50 3.50

Flowers — A277

Designs: 15k, Fianthus cyprius. 25k, Del-
phinium caseyi. 30k, Brassica hilarionis. 50k,
Limonium albidum.

2005, July 8   **Perf. 14x13¾**
596-599 A277   Set of 4   1.90 1.90

Arts in
Towns
A278

Designs, 10k, Beach, umbrellas, musical
symbols, artist's palette, olive branches,
Kyrenia (Girne). 25k, Musical symbols,
mosque, Famagusta (Gazimagusa). 50k,
Dancers, building, Nicosia (Lefkosa). 1 l, Theater and masks, Kyrenia, Famagusta and
Nicosia.

Perf. 13½x13¾
2005, Sept. 9   Litho.   Wmk. 390
600-603 A278   Set of 4   2.75 2.75

Ercan
Airport — A279

2005, Nov. 23   **Perf. 13¾x13½**
604 A279 50k multi   .75   .75

University
of
Northern
Cyprus
A280

2005, Nov. 23   **Perf. 13½x13¾**
605 A280 1 l multi   1.50 1.50

Europa
Stamps,
50th
Anniv.
A281

Designs: No. 606, 1.40 l, Map of Cyprus.
No. 607, 1.40 l, Photo of Cyprus from space,
satellite.

2006, Jan. 6
606-607 A281   Set of 2   4.25 4.25
   607a   Souvenir sheet, #606-607   4.25 4.25

No. 607a exists imperf.

Flowers Type of 2005

Designs: 15k, Helianthemum obtusifolium.
25k, Iris sisyrhinchium, horiz. 40k, Ranunculus
asiaticus, horiz. 50k, Crocus veneris, horiz.
60k, Anemone coronaria, horiz. 70k, Cyclamen persicum.

Perf. 14x13¾, 13¾x14
2006   Litho.   Wmk. 390
608-613 A277   Set of 6   3.75 3.75

Art — A282

Design: 55k, Sculpture by S. Oztan. 60k,
Painting by M. Hastürk.

Perf. 13¾x13½
2006, Apr. 7   Litho.   Wmk. 390
614-615 A282   Set of 2   1.75 1.75

Dr. Fazil Kucuk
(1906-84),
Politician — A283

2006, May 18
616 A283 40k multi   .50   .50

Kemal Ataturk
(1881-1938)
A284

2006, May 18
617 A284 1 l multi   1.25 1.25

Europa — A286

Designs: No. 618, 70k, Birds and stars. No.
619, 70k, Pregnant woman, fetus, flags of
European countries.

2006, May 18
618-619 A286   Set of 2   1.75 1.75
   619a   Souvenir sheet, #618-619   1.75 1.75

No. 619a exists imperf.

2006 World Cup Soccer
Championships, Germany — A287

No. 620: a, 50k, World Cup trophy, map of
Germany, mascots, soccer ball and field. b,
1 l, Soccer ball, player, Brandenburg Gate.

2006, July 7   **Perf. 13¾x13½**
620 A287 Pair, #a-b   2.00 2.00

Birds
A288

Forest Fire
Prevention
A289

Designs: 40k, Vanellus vanellus. 50k, Anas platyrhynchos. 60k, Alcedo atthis. 1 l, Himantopus himantopus.

2006, Sept. 22
621-624 A288 Set of 4   3.50 3.50

2006, Oct. 10   *Perf. 14x13¾*
625 A289 50k multi   .70   .70

Naci Talat (1945-91), Politician A290

2006, Oct. 10   *Perf. 14*
626 A290 70k multi   .95   .95

Eastern Mediterranean Intl. Regatta — A291

2006, Oct. 10   *Perf. 14x13¾*
627 A291 1.50 l multi   2.10 2.10

Environmental Conference — A292

Designs: 50k, Leaf. 80k, Globe, plant and drought-stricken ground.

                    Wmk. 390
2007, Feb. 19   **Litho.**   *Perf. 14*
628-629 A292 Set of 2   1.90 1.90

Antique Household Items A293

Designs: 70k, Pitcher. 80k, Iron. 1.50 l, Oil lamp, vert. 2 l, Gas burner and pot, vert.

2007, Apr. 6   *Perf. 13¾x14, 14x13¾*
630-633 A293 Set of 4   7.50 7.50

Europa — A294

Emblems, tent, campfire, hand giving Scout sign, dove and: No. 634, 80k, One Scout. No. 635, 80k, Three Scouts playing musical instruments.

2007, May 4   *Perf. 14x13¾*
634-635 A294 Set of 2   2.40 2.40
635a   Souvenir sheet, #634-635,
             imperf.   2.40 2.40
       Scouting, cent.

Painting by O. Keten — A295

Painting by S. Cavusoglu A296

2007, July 12 *Perf. 14x13¾, 13¾x14*
636 A295 50k multi   .80   .80
637 A296 70k multi   1.10 1.10

Occupations of the Past — A297

Designs: 40k, Rattan weaver. 65k, Fruit peddler. 70k, Shoemaker. 1 l, Shoeshiner.

2007, Sept. 14   *Perf. 13¾x14*
638-641 A297 Set of 4   4.75 4.75

Methods of Postal Transport — A298

Designs: 50k, Carrier pigeons. 60k, Mounted postman, coach, automobile. 1 l, Postman on bicycle, horiz. 1.25 l, Postman on motor scooter, horiz.

          Perf. 14x13¾, 13¾x14
2007, Nov. 16
642-645 A298 Set of 4   5.75 5.75

POSTAL TAX STAMP

Trees — PT1

1995, July 24 **Litho.**   *Perf. 14*
RA1 PT1 1000 l black & green 1.50 1.25

TURKMENISTAN

ˌtərk-ˌme-nə-ˈstan

LOCATION — Southern Asia, bounded by Kazakhstan, Uzbekistan, Iran and Afghanistan
GOVT. — Independent republic, member of the Commonwealth of Independent States
AREA — 188,417 sq. mi.
POP. — 4,366,383 (1999 est.)
CAPITAL — Ashgabat

With the breakup of the Soviet Union on Dec. 26, 1991, Turkmenistan and ten former Soviet republics established

---

the Commonwealth of Independent States.

100 Kopecks = 1 Ruble
Manat (1994)

> **Catalogue values for all unused stamps in this country are for Never Hinged items.**

Dagdan Necklace, 19th Century — A1

Designs: No. 3, Girl in traditional costume, horiz. No. 4, Akhaltekin horse and rider in native riding dress. No. 5, Mollanepes Theater, horiz. 15r, National arms. No. 7, Pres. Saparmurad Niyazov at left, national flag, horiz. No. 8, Niyazov at right, flag, horiz. No. 9, Map of Turkmenistan.

1992   **Litho.**   *Perf. 12x12½*
1   A1 50k multicolored   .25   .25
              Perf. 12½
2   A1 10r multicolored   .35   .35
3   A1 10r multicolored   .40   .40
4   A1 10r multicolored   .40   .40
5   A1 10r multicolored   .40   .40
6   A1 15r multicolored   .70   .70
7   A1 25r multicolored   1.00 1.00
8   A1 25r multicolored   2.40 2.40
       Nos. 1-8 (8)   5.90 5.90
         Size: 112x79mm
              Imperf
9   A1 10r multicolored   7.00 7.00
Issued: 50k, 1992; #8, 12/8; others, 8/27. Nos. 2-8 exist imperf.

Nos. 4, 6 Ovptd. with Horse's Head
1992, Dec. 12
         Color of Overprint
10   A1 10r black   4.00 4.00
11   A1 10r brown   4.00 4.00
12   A1 10r red   4.00 4.00
13   A1 10r vermilion   —
14   A1 10r carmine   4.00 4.00
15   A1 10r green   4.00 4.00
16   A1 15r black   4.00 4.00
17   A1 15r brown   4.00 4.00
18   A1 15r red   —
19   A1 15r pink   —
20   A1 15r blue   4.00 4.00
21   A1 15r yellow   —
       Nos. 10-21 (9)   36.00 36.00

1992 Summer Olympics, Barcelona A2

Designs: a, 1r, Weight lifting. b, 3r, Equestrian. c, 5r, Wrestling. d, 10r, Rowing. e, 15r, Emblem of Turkmenistan Olympic Committee. No. 23, Flags, symbols for modern pentathalon, weight lifting, rowing, gymnastics.

1992, Dec. 15 **Photo.** *Perf. 10½x10*
22   A2   Strip of 5, #a.-e.   6.25 6.25
              Imperf
         Size: 108x82mm
23   A2 15r multicolored   6.50 6.50
       For surcharge see No. 33.

Musical Instruments — A3

               Photo. & Engr.
1992, Sept. 13   *Perf. 12x11½*
28   A3 35k buff, red brn, gold & black   .30   .30

Horse A4

1992, Aug. 9   **Photo.** *Perf. 12*
29   A4 20k shown   .20   .20
30   A4 40k Snake, vert.   .25   .25

A5

1992, Nov. 29 **Litho.** *Perf. 12x11½*
31   A5 1r multicolored   .30   .30

US Pres. Bill Clinton, Pres. Saparmurad Niyazov — A6

Designs dated: a. 21.30.93. b. 22.03.93. c, 23.03.93. d, 24.03.93. e, 25.03.93.

1993, Mar. 21 **Litho.** *Perf. 10½*
32   A6 100r Strip of 5, #a.-e. 10.00 10.00
Pres. Niyazov's visit to New York City & Washington DC.
Exists imperf.

         No. 22 Surcharged

1993, Apr. 1   **Photo.** *Perf. 10½x10*
33   A2   Strip of 5   7.00 7.00
a.   25r on 1r   1.40 1.40
b.   10r on 3r   .65   .65
c.   15r on 5r   .75   .75
d.   15r on 10r   .75   .75
e.   50r on 15r   2.40 2.40
       Size of surcharge varies.

Phoca Caspica — A7

World Wildlife Fund A8

Phoca caspica: #34a, 25r, Facing right. #34b, 500r, Facing left. 15r, Lying in snow. 50r, On rocks. 100r, Mother and young. 150r, Swimming.

1993, Oct. 11   Litho.   Perf. 13½

34	A7	Pair #a.-b.	3.75	3.75
35	A8	15r multicolored	.60	.60
36	A8	50r multicolored	.95	.95
37	A8	100r multicolored	1.60	1.60
38	A8	150r multicolored	3.25	3.25
a.		Bklt. pane, 2 ea #34-38	24.00	24.00
		Booklet, #38a	27.50	
		Nos. 34-38 (5)	10.15	10.15

Formation of Tovarishch Society for
Exploitation of Turkmen Oil Fields,
115th Anniv. — A9

Designs: 1m, Two men viewing oil field.
1.5m, Early tanker Turkmen. 2m, Oil well. 3m,
Alfred Nobel, Ludwig Nobel, Robert Nobel,
Petr Bilderling, vert. 5m, Early oil field.

1994, June 26   Litho.   Perf. 13

39	A9	1m multicolored	.50	.50
40	A9	1.5m multicolored	.75	.75
41	A9	2m multicolored	1.00	1.00
42	A9	3m multicolored	1.25	1.25
a.		Miniature sheet of 8 + label	10.00	10.00
		Nos. 39-42 (4)	3.50	3.50

Souvenir Sheet

43	A9	5m multicolored	2.50	2.50

See Azerbaijan Nos. 416-418a.

Repetek
Natl. Park
A10

Designs: 3m, Repetek Institute. No. 45,
Desert, camels. No. 46, Echus carinatus. No.
47, Varanus griseus. 20m, Testudo horsfieldi.
No. 49, Haloxylon ammodendron.

1994, Dec. 11   Litho.   Perf. 13

44	A10	3m multicolored	.50	.50
45	A10	5m multicolored	.55	.55
46	A10	5m multicolored	.55	.55
a.		Miniature sheet of 8 + label	10.00	10.00
47	A10	10m multicolored	1.10	1.10
48	A10	20m multicolored	2.00	2.00
		Nos. 44-48 (5)	4.70	4.70

Souvenir Sheet

49	A10	10m multicolored	2.50	2.50

Intl. Olympic Committee, Cent. — A11

1994, Dec. 30   Litho.   Perf. 14

50	A11	11.25m multicolored	2.00	2.00

Souvenir Sheet

51	A11	20m multicolored	4.00	4.00

Miniature Sheet

Save the Aral Sea — A12

Designs: a, Feis caracal. b, Salmo trutta
aralensis. c, Hyaena hyaena. d, Pseudoscaphirhynchus kaufmanni. e, Aspiolucius
esocinus.

1996, Apr. 29   Litho.   Perf. 14

52	A12	100m Sheet of 5, #a.-e.	8.50	8.50

Independence, 5th Anniv. — A13

#53, Map of Turkmenistan on globe, vert.
#54, Train pulling into station. #55, Natl. Air-
port, vert. #56, Iranian Pres. Rafsanjani, Turkmenistan Pres. Saparmurad Niyazov, Turkish
Pres. Demirel. 500m, UN Secretary-General
Boutros Boutros-Gali, Pres. Niyazov, vert.
1000m, Natl. flag, arms.

1996, Oct. 27   Litho.   Perf. 14

53	A13	100m multicolored	.25	.25
54	A13	100m multicolored	.40	.40
55	A13	300m multicolored	.75	.75
56	A13	300m multicolored	1.00	1.00
57	A13	500m multicolored	1.50	1.50
58	A13	1000m multicolored	2.75	2.75
		Nos. 53-58 (6)	6.65	6.65

1996
Summer
Olympic
Games,
Atlanta
A14

1997, May 5   Litho.   Perf. 14x14½

59	A14	100m Judo	.60	.60
60	A14	300m Boxing	1.50	1.50
61	A14	300m Track & field	1.50	1.50
62	A14	300m Wrestling	1.50	1.50
63	A14	500m Shooting	3.00	3.00
		Nos. 59-63 (5)	8.10	8.10

Souvenir Sheet

64	A14	1000m Olympic torch	6.25	6.25

Women's
Traditional
Clothing — A15

Various costumes.

1999, July 5   Litho.   Perf. 14

65	A15	500m multi	.75	.75
66	A15	1000m multi	1.25	1.25
67	A15	1200m multi	1.75	1.75
68	A15	2500m multi	2.25	2.25
69	A15	3000m multi	3.00	3.00
		Nos. 65-69 (5)	9.00	9.00

Items inscribed "Turkmenistan" that
were not authorized by Turkmenistan
postal officials but which have appeared
on the market include:

Single stamps of 100m depicting
Princess Diana (3 different stamps),
Mother Teresa, Pope John Paul II and
Mother Teresa, 50th Anniv. of India, and
50th Anniv. of Pakistan.

Sheets of 4 stamps with denominations of 100m depicting JAPEX 98 /
Cats.

Sheets of 9 stamps with denominations of 100m depicting the Titanic,
Trains, Golfers, Japanese Armor, Japanese Paper Dolls, and Japanese Art.

Sheets of 6 stamps with denominations of 120m depicting Millennium (8
different sheets).

Sheets of 6 stamps with denominations of 120m depicting Pokémon, and
Brad Pitt.

Sheets of 4 stamps with denominations of 195m depicting Greenpeace,
Elvis Presley, Birds, Orchids, and Japanese Fashion.

Sheets of 6 stamps with denominations of 195m depicting Marilyn
Monroe.

Sheets of 9 stamps with denominations of 195m depicting Cacti, and Minerals.

Sheets of 4 stamps with denominations of 250m depicting Akira
Kurosawa.

Sheets of 2 stamps with denominations of 390m depicting Brazilian soccer
players from 1998 World Cup.

Sheets of 9 stamps with denominations of 1000m depicting IBRA / Mushrooms (2 different sheets).

Souvenir sheets of 1 stamp with vari-
ous denominations depicting Hokusai
Artwork (2 different sheets), Pope John
Paul II (2 different sheets), the Titanic (2
different sheets), 1998 Winter Olympics
(2 sheets), Year of the Tiger (2 sheets),
50th Anniv. of Israel, Princess Diana,
Queen Mother, Che Guevara, Frank
Sinatra, Marilyn Monroe, Elvis Presley,
International Year of Older Persons /
Bob Hope, 1998 World Cup Soccer
Championships, Severiano Ballasteros,
Jacques Villeneuve, Leaders of the
World / Automobiles, and Maria de
Medici / Millennium.

Falcons — A16

a, 1000m, Falco tinnunculus. b, 1000m,
Falco peregrinus, looking left. c, 1000m, Falco
peregrinus, looking right. d, 2500m, Falco tinnunculus, diff. e, 3000m, Falco peregrinus,
diff.

2000, Mar. 30   Litho.   Perf. 14

70	A16	Sheet of 5, #a-e	12.00	12.00

Horn — A17

2000, Oct.   Litho.   Imperf.
Self-Adhesive

71	A17	A multi	1.50	1.50

Sold for 5000m on day of issue.

UN Resolution on the Permanent
Neutrality of Turkmenistan, 5th
Anniv. — A18

UN emblem, "5," and flags of Turkmenistan
and resolution co-sponsors: a, Afghanistan. b,
Armenia. c, Azerbaijan. d, Bangladesh. e,
Belarus. f, Colombia. g, Czech Republic. h,
Egypt. i, France. j, Georgia. k, India. l, Indone-
sia. m, Iran. n, Kenya. o, Kyrgyzstan. p, Malay-
sia. q, Mauritius. r, Pakistan. s, Moldova. t,
Russia. u, Senegal. v, Tajikistan. w, Turkey. x,
Ukraine.

2000, Dec.   Litho.   Perf. 14

72		Sheet of 24 + label	50.00	50.00
a.-x.	A18	3000m Any single	2.00	2.00

Trade Center
Building
A19

Flag and
Arms
A20

2001, Apr. 24   Litho.   Imperf.
Self-Adhesive

73	A19	B multi	.90	.90
74	A20	U multi	1.75	1.75

No. 73 sold for 1,200m, No. 74 sold for
3,000m on day of issue.

Horses — A21

No. 75, horiz.: a, Perenli. b, Garader. c, Pyyada. d, Tyllanur. e, Arkadas. f, Yanardag.
No. 76, 5000m, Yanardag, diff., horiz. (denomination at LR). No. 77, 5000m, Yanardag, diff., horiz. (denomination at UR).
No. 78: a, Bitarap. b, Yanardag, diff.

2001, Aug. 20   Litho.   Perf. 14½x14
75   A21 3000m Sheet of 6,
     #a-f   11.00 11.00
Size: 116x90mm
Imperf
76-77 A21 Set of 2   6.00 6.00
Souvenir Sheet
Perf. 14x14½
78   A21 5000m Sheet of 2, #a-b   6.00 6.00

Items inscribed "Turkmenistan" that were not authorized by Turkmenistan postal officials but which have appeared on the market include:
Sheets of 9 stamps with denominations of 50m depicting Kim Basinger, Matt Damon, and Pope John Paul II.
Sheets of 9 stamps with denominations of 100m depicting Leading Personalities of the 20th Century.
Sheets of 6 stamps with denominations of 120m depicting Leonardo DiCaprio, and Princess Diana.
Sheets of 8 stamps with denominations of 120m and one label depicting scenes and people from the 20th Century (3 different sheets).
Sheets of 9 stamps with denominations of 120m depicting Princess Diana, Musical group V.I.P., Television show "Xena, Warrior Princess," Elizabeth Taylor, Bruce Lee, Jackie Chan, Tiger Woods, Muhammad Ali, Monaco Grand Prix race cars, Auto racer David Coulthard, Soccer player David Beckham, Euro 2000 European Football Championships, Rugby players, Tennis Stars of the Millennium, Sportsmen of the Millennium, Elephants, Cats, Butterflies, and Pokémon.
Sheets of 2 stamps with denominations of 390m depicting Soccer players from the 1998 World Cup (2 different sheets depicting French and Japanese players).
Souvenir sheets of 1 with denominations of 975m depicting the Mona Lisa, Marilyn Monroe, and Lucille Ball.

A22

Independence, 10th Anniv. — A23

No. 79 — 500m coins with reverses showing: a, Building with domed roof, coin denomination at right. b, Building with domed roof and tower, coin denomination at left. c, Building with pointed, conical roof. d, Building with archway. e, Building with domed roof on cubic base. f, Statue.
No. 80 — Archaeological sites: a, Soltan Sanjar. b, Nusay. c, Gyz Gala. d, Urgenç. e, Anew. f, Köne Urgenç.
No. 81 — Items in National museum: a, Horn. b, 19th cent. carpet. c, Musical instrument. d, Statue of nude woman. e, Vase. f, 20th cent. decoration.
No. 82, horiz. — Hotels: a, Ahal. b, Gara Altyn. c, Demiryolçy. d, Altyn Suw. e, Köpetdag. f, Aziya.
No. 83 — Buildings: a, Altyn Asyryn Yasayys Jaylary. b, Bitaraplyk Binasy (Arch of Neutrality). c, Türkmendöwletätiyaçlandyrys. d, Random Tower. e, Türkmenbasy Bank. f, Altyn Asyr Söwda Merkezi (Trade Center Building).
No. 84 — Monuments to: a, Oguz Han. b, Seljuk Bay. c, Bayram Han. d, Soltan Sanjar. e, Gorkut Ata. f, Görogly Beg.
No. 85 — Monuments to: a, Sahyrlary Bayram Han. b, Sahyrlary Kemine. c, Sahyrlary Zelili. d, Sahyrlary Seydi. e, Sahyrlary Mollanepes. f, Sahyrlary Mätäji.

2001   Litho.   Imperf.
79   A22 500m Sheet of 6, #a-f   3.00 3.00
80   A23 1000m Sheet of 6, #a-f   5.00 5.00
81   A23 1200m Sheet of 6, #a-f   7.00 7.00
82   A23 1250m Sheet of 6, #a-f   8.00 8.00
83   A23 1250m Sheet of 6, #a-f   8.00 8.00
84   A23 3000m Sheet of 6, #a-f   15.00 15.00
85   A23 3000m Sheet of 6, #a-f   15.00 15.00
     Nos. 79-85 (7)   61.00 61.00

Issued: Nos. 79-80, 10/17; No. 81, 10/19; Nos. 82-83, 10/23; Nos. 84-85, 10/21.

Mohammed Ali Jinnah (1876-1948), First Governor General of Pakistan — A24

2001, Dec. 25   Litho.   Perf. 13
86   A24 500m multi   1.00 1.00

Birds — A25

No. 87, 3000m: a, Motacilla flava. b, Lanius isabellinus. c, Oenanthe oenanthe. d, Corvus monedula. e, Corvus cornix. f, Upupa pyrrhocorax.
No. 88, 3000m: a, Sylvia communis. b, Cuculus canorus. c, Sylvia curruca. d, Corvus pica. e, Corvus frugilegus. f, Corvus corax.
No. 89, 5000m, Anas crecca. No. 90, 5000m, Riparia riparia.

2002, Dec. 1   Litho.   Perf. 14
Sheets of 6, #a-f
87-88 A25 Set of 2   19.00 19.00
Souvenir Sheets
89-90 A25 Set of 2   6.00 6.00

Butterflies — A26

No. 91, 3000m, vert.: a, Vanessa indica. b, Cynthia cardui. c, Pararge aegeria. d, Pieris rapae. e, Lysandra bellargus. f, Anthocharis cardamines.
No. 92, 3000m, vert.: a, Pandoriana pandora. b, Chazara briseis. c, Aphantopus hyperantus. d, Iolana iolas. e, Pararge schakra. f, Maniola jurtina.
No. 93, 5000m, Hamearis lucina. No. 94, 5000m, Quercusia quercus.

2002, Dec. 1
Sheets of 6, #a-f
91-92 A26 Set of 2   19.00 19.00
Souvenir Sheets
93-94 A26 Set of 2   6.00 6.00

Souvenir Sheet

Permanent Neutrality of Turkmenistan, 10th Anniv. — A32

No. 100: a, UN Secretary General Kofi Annan and Turkmenistan Pres. Saparmurad Niyazov. b, Sculpture on building, UN emblem.

2005, Dec. 1   Litho.   Perf. 11½
100 A32 5000m Sheet of 2,
     #a-b   15.00 15.00

Souvenir Sheets

A33

A34

A35

Akhal-Teke Horses — A36

No. 101: a, Horse's head. b, Horse rearing up.
No. 102: a, Pony nursing. b, Horse walking left.
No. 103: a, Horse facing right. b, Horse facing left.
No. 104: a, Gray horse and mountain. b, Brown horse and mountain.

2005, Dec. 1
101 A33 2500m Sheet of 2,
     #a-b   6.25 6.25
102 A34 2500m Sheet of 2,
     #a-b   6.25 6.25
103 A35 2500m Sheet of 2,
     #a-b   6.25 6.25
104 A36 2500m Sheet of 2,
     #a-b   6.25 6.25
     Nos. 101-104 (4)   25.00 25.00

Miniature Sheet

Ashgabat Architecture — A37

No. 105: a, 3000m, Building with dome, fountain at left. b, 3000m, Rukhiyet Palace (building with three green domes, automobiles). c, 3000m, Building with three golden domes and fountain. d, 3000m, Goktepe Mosque (green domes). e, 3000m, Mosque with golden domes. f, 3000m, Statue of Akhal-Teke horses. g, 3000m, Domed building with fence. h, 3000m, Central Bank and flags. i, 5000m, Neutrality Arch at night, vert. j, 5000m, Oil and Gas Ministry Building with flagpoles at right, vert. k, 5000m, President Hotel with flagpoles at left, vert. l, Independence Monument with statues at left and right, vert. Sizes: Nos.

105a-105h, 40x30mm; Nos. 105i-105l, 40x60mm.

2006	Litho.		Perf. 13x12¾
105 A37	Sheet of 12, #a-l, + label		
		25.00	25.00

TURKS AND CAICOS ISLANDS

'tərks ən̩d̪, ' kā-kəs 'ī-ləndz

LOCATION — A group of islands in the West Indies, at the southern extremity of the Bahamas
GOVT. — British colony; a dependency of Jamaica until 1959
AREA — 192 sq. mi.
POP. — 16,863 (1999 est.)
CAPITAL — Grand Turk

12 Pence = 1 Shilling
20 Shillings = 1 Pound
100 Cents = 1 US Dollar (1969)

Catalogue values for unused stamps in this country are for Never Hinged items, beginning with Scott 90.

Dependency's Badge
A6　　A7

1900-04	Engr.	Wmk. 2	Perf. 14	
1	A6	½p green	3.00	4.50
2	A6	1p rose	4.00	.85
3	A6	2p black brown	1.10	1.40
4	A6	2p gray blue ('04)	2.00	1.10
a.		2½p blue ('00)	8.50	17.50
5	A6	4p orange	4.25	8.00
6	A6	6p violet	2.75	7.50
7	A6	1sh purple brn	3.75	20.00

		Wmk. 1		
8	A7	2sh violet	45.00	67.50
9	A7	3sh brown lake	62.50	85.00
		Nos. 1-9 (9)	128.35	195.85

1905-08		Wmk. 3		
10	A6	½p green	5.75	.20
11	A6	1p carmine	18.00	.55
12	A6	3p violet, yel ('08)	2.50	7.00
		Nos. 10-12 (3)	26.25	7.75

King Edward VII — A8

1909, Sept. 2			Perf. 14	
13	A8	½p yellow green	.85	.45
14	A8	1p carmine	1.40	.45
15	A8	2p gray	3.50	1.60
16	A8	2½p ultra	4.25	4.25
17	A8	3p violet, yel	2.75	2.25
18	A8	4p red, yel	3.75	8.00
19	A8	6p violet	8.00	7.00
20	A8	1sh black, green	8.00	9.50
21	A8	2sh red, grn	40.00	55.00
22	A8	3sh black, red	40.00	45.00
		Nos. 13-22 (10)	112.50	133.50

Turk's-Head Cactus
A9

George V
A10

1910-11		Wmk. 3		
23	A9	¼p claret	2.00	1.10
24	A9	¼p red ('11)	.70	.50

See Nos. 36, 44.

1913-16				
25	A10	½p yellow green	.55	2.00
26	A10	1p carmine	1.10	2.50
27	A10	2p gray	2.50	4.00
28	A10	2½p ultra	2.50	3.50
29	A10	3p violet, yel	2.50	12.50

30	A10	4p scarlet, yel	1.10	11.00
31	A10	5p olive grn ('16)	7.50	25.00
32	A10	6p dull violet	2.75	4.00
33	A10	1sh orange	1.75	5.75
34	A10	2sh red, bl grn	8.50	30.00
a.		2sh red, grnsh white ('19)	30.00	80.00
b.		2sh red, emerald ('21)	55.00	80.00
35	A10	3sh black, red	17.50	30.00
		Nos. 25-35 (11)	48.25	130.25

Issued: 5p, 5/18/16; others, 4/1/13.
For overprints see Nos. MR1-MR13.

1921, Apr. 23			Wmk. 4	
36	A9	¼p red	2.75	17.50
37	A10	½p green	3.00	6.25
38	A10	1p scarlet	1.10	6.25
39	A10	2p gray	1.10	21.00
40	A10	2½p ultra	2.00	8.50
41	A10	5p olive green	9.00	57.50
42	A10	6p dull violet	7.50	57.50
43	A10	1sh brown orange	7.50	32.50
		Nos. 36-43 (8)	33.95	207.00

A11　　A12

Inscribed "Postage"

1922-26				
44	A9	¼p gray black ('26)	1.10	1.25
45	A11	½p green	3.00	4.50
46	A11	1p brown	.65	3.75
47	A11	1½p rose red ('25)	9.00	21.00
48	A11	2p gray	.65	7.00
49	A11	2½p violet, yel	.65	2.40
50	A11	3p ultra	.65	7.00
51	A11	4p red, yel	1.60	21.00
52	A11	5p yellow grn	1.25	30.00
53	A11	6p dull violet	.95	8.50
54	A11	1sh orange	1.10	25.00
55	A11	2sh red, green	2.75	12.50

		Wmk. 3		
56	A11	2sh red, green ('25)	35.00	95.00
57	A11	3sh black, red ('25)	7.00	37.50
		Nos. 44-57 (14)	65.35	276.40

Issued: #47, 56-57, 11/24; #44, 10/11; others, 11/20.

Inscribed "Postage and Revenue"

1928, Mar. 1			Wmk. 4	
60	A12	½p green	.95	.60
61	A12	1p brown	.95	.90
62	A12	1½p red	.95	4.00
63	A12	2p dk gray	.95	.60
64	A12	2½p vio, yel	.95	6.25
65	A12	3p ultra	.95	8.75
66	A12	6p brown vio	.95	9.25
67	A12	1sh brown org	4.50	9.25
68	A12	2sh red, grn	7.75	45.00
69	A12	5sh green, yel	13.50	45.00
70	A12	10sh violet, bl	62.50	125.00
		Nos. 60-70 (11)	94.90	254.60

Common Design Types pictured following the introduction.

Silver Jubilee Issue
Common Design Type

1935, May 6			Perf. 11x12	
71	CD301	½p green & blk	.40	.80
72	CD301	3p ultra & brn	2.10	5.25
73	CD301	6p ol grn & lt bl	2.10	6.00
74	CD301	1sh brn vio & ind	4.00	4.00
		Nos. 71-74 (4)	8.60	16.05
		Set, never hinged	16.00	

Coronation Issue
Common Design Type

1937, May 12			Perf. 13½x14	
75	CD302	½p deep green	.20	.20
76	CD302	2p gray	.45	.40
77	CD302	3p brt ultra	.60	.45
		Nos. 75-77 (3)	1.25	1.05
		Set, never hinged	1.75	

Raking Salt — A13

Salt Industry — A14

1938-45		Wmk. 4	Perf. 12½	
78	A13	¼p black	.20	.20
79	A13	½p green	2.40	.20
80	A13	1p brown	.45	.20
81	A13	1½p carmine	.45	.20
82	A13	2p gray	.70	.30
83	A13	2½p orange	2.50	1.10
84	A13	3p ultra	.30	.30
85	A13	6p rose violet	6.00	1.75
85A	A13	6p blk brn ('45)	.20	.20
86	A13	1sh bister	2.40	10.00
86A	A13	1sh dk ol grn ('45)	.20	.20
87	A14	2sh rose car	25.00	17.00
88	A14	5sh green	30.00	19.00
89	A14	10sh dp violet	7.50	8.50
		Nos. 78-89 (14)	78.30	59.15
		Set, never hinged	125.00	

Catalogue values for unused stamps in this section, from this point to the end of the section, are for Never Hinged items.

Peace Issue
Common Design Type

1946, Nov. 4	Engr.	Perf. 13½x14	
90	CD303	2p gray black	.20	.20
91	CD303	3p deep blue	.25	.20

Silver Wedding Issue
Common Design Types

1948, Sept. 13	Photo.	Perf. 14x14½	
92	CD304	1p red brown	.20	.30

Perf. 11½x11

Engr.; Name Typo.

| 93 | CD305 | 10sh purple | 11.00 | 15.00 |

Dependency's Badge — A17

Flag and Merchant Ship — A18

Map of the Islands A19

Victoria and George VI A20

1948, Dec. 14	Engr.	Perf. 12½	
94	A17	½p green	.20	.20
95	A17	2p carmine	.45	.20
96	A18	3p deep blue	.70	.55
97	A19	6p violet	.90	.65
98	A20	2sh ultra & blk	1.40	1.10
99	A20	5sh blue grn & blk	4.00	2.75
100	A20	10sh chocolate & blk	6.25	7.00
		Nos. 94-100 (7)	13.90	12.45

Cent. of political separation from the Bahamas.

UPU Issue
Common Design Types
Engr.; Name Typo. on 3p, 6p
Perf. 13½, 11x11½

1949, Oct. 10			Wmk. 4	
101	CD306	2½p red orange	.20	.20
102	CD307	3p indigo	1.90	1.90
103	CD308	6p chocolate	.75	.75
104	CD309	1sh olive	.75	.75
		Nos. 101-104 (4)	3.60	3.60

Loading Bulk Salt — A21

Dependency's Badge — A22

Designs: 1p, Salt Cay. 1½p, Caicos mail. 2p, Grand Turk. 2½p, Sponge diving. 3p, South Creek. 4p, Map. 6p, Grand Turk Light. 1sh, Government House. 1sh6p, Cockburn Harbor. 2sh, Government offices. 5sh, Salt Loading.

1950, Aug. 2	Engr.	Perf. 12½	
105	A21	½p deep green	.85	.60
106	A21	1p chocolate	.70	1.25
107	A21	1½p carmine	1.25	.90
108	A21	2p red orange	.60	.60
109	A21	2½p olive green	1.10	.60
110	A21	3p ultra	.30	.60
111	A21	4p rose car & blk	3.50	1.25
112	A21	6p ultra & blk	2.75	.80
113	A21	1sh bl gray & blk	1.25	.80
114	A21	1sh6p red & blk	11.00	5.25
115	A21	2sh ultra & emer	4.00	5.75
116	A21	5sh black & ultra	24.00	11.50
117	A22	10sh purple & blk	24.00	27.50
		Nos. 105-117 (13)	75.30	57.40

Coronation Issue
Common Design Type

1953, June 2		Perf. 13½x13	
118	CD312	2p red orange & blk	.40	.85

M. S. Kirksons A23

Design: 8p, Flamingos in flight.

1955, Feb. 1		Wmk. 4	Perf. 12½	
119	A23	5p emerald & blk	.80	.80
120	A23	8p yellow brn & blk	3.25	.80

Queen Elizabeth II — A24

Bonefish A25

Pelican and Salinas A26

Designs: 2p, Red grouper. 2½p, Spiny lobster. 3p, Albacore. 4p, Muttonfish snapper. 5p,

Permit. 6p, Conch. 8p, Flamingos. 1sh, Spanish mackerel. 1sh6p, Salt Cay. 2sh, Caicos sloop. 5sh, Cable office. 10sh, Dependency's badge.

Perf. 13½x14 (1p), 13½x13
1957-60   Engr.   Wmk. 314
121	A24	1p lil rose & dk bl	.20	.20
122	A25	1½p orange & slate	.20	.20
123	A25	2p ol & brn red	.20	.20
124	A25	2½p brt grn & car	.20	.20
125	A25	3p purple & blue	.20	.20
126	A25	4p blk & dp rose	.70	.20
127	A25	5p brown & grn	.95	.75
128	A25	6p ultra & car	1.90	.85
129	A25	8p black & ver	3.25	.20
130	A25	1sh blk & dk blue	.80	.20
131	A25	1sh6p vio bl & dk brn	12.00	2.10
132	A25	2sh lt brn & vio bl	12.00	4.00
133	A25	5sh brt car & blk	1.90	3.00

Perf. 14
134	A26	10sh purple & blk	12.50	13.00

Perf. 14x14½
Photo.
135	A26	£1 dk red & brn	55.00	26.00
	Nos. 121-135 (15)		102.00	51.30

Issued: £1, 11/1/60; others, 11/25/57.

Map of Islands A27

Perf. 13½x14
1959, July 4   Wmk. 4   Photo.
136	A27	6p ol grn & salmon	.70	.70
137	A27	8p violet & salmon	.80	.80

Granting of a new constitution.

Freedom from Hunger Issue
Common Design Type
Perf. 14x14½
1963, June 4   Wmk. 314
138	CD314	8p carmine rose	.50	.50

Red Cross Centenary Issue
Common Design Type
1963, Sept. 2   Litho.   Perf. 13
139	CD315	2p black & red	.20	.20
140	CD315	8p ultra & red	.70	.70

Shakespeare Issue
Common Design Type
1964, Apr. 23   Photo.   Perf. 14x14½
141	CD316	8p green	.40	.40

ITU Issue
Common Design Type
Perf. 11x11½
1965, May 17   Litho.   Wmk. 314
142	CD317	1p ver & brown	.20	.20
143	CD317	2sh emer & lt blue	.80	.80

Intl. Cooperation Year Issue
Common Design Type
1965, Oct. 25   Wmk. 314   Perf. 14½
144	CD318	1p blue grn & claret	.20	.20
145	CD318	8p lt violet & green	.60	.60

Churchill Memorial Issue
Common Design Type
1966, Jan. 24   Photo.   Perf. 14
Design in Black, Gold and Carmine Rose
146	CD319	1p bright blue	.20	.20
147	CD319	2p green	.20	.20
148	CD319	3p brown	.40	.40
a.		Gold impression double	200.00	
149	CD319	1sh6p violet	.90	.90
	Nos. 146-149 (4)		1.70	1.70

Royal Visit Issue
Common Design Type
1966, Feb. 4   Litho.   Perf. 11x12
Portraits in Black
150	CD320	8p violet blue	.45	.45
151	CD320	1sh6p dk car rose	.85	.85

Andrew Symmers Landing with Union Jack — A28

Designs: 8p, Andrew Symmers, his signature, Royal Warrant and Union Jack. 1sh6p, New coat of arms, Royal Cypher and St. Edward's crown.

Perf. 13½
1966, Oct. 1   Unwmk.   Photo.
152	A28	1p dk blue & dp org	.20	.20
153	A28	8p dk blue, dl yel & car	.20	.20
154	A28	1sh6p multicolored	.35	.35
	Nos. 152-154 (3)		.75	.75

200th anniv. of the landing of Andrew Symmers, British agent, establishing the ties with Great Britain.

UNESCO Anniversary Issue
Common Design Type
Wmk. 314
1966, Dec. 1   Litho.   Perf. 14
155	CD323	1p "Education"	.20	.20
156	CD323	8p "Science"	.30	.30
157	CD323	1sh6p "Culture"	.50	.50
	Nos. 155-157 (3)		1.00	1.00

Turk's-head Cactus — A29

Boat Building A30

Designs: 2p, Donkey cart. 3p, Sisal industry. 4p, Conch industry. 6p, Salt industry. 8p, Skin diving. 1sh, Fishing. 1sh6p, Water skiing. 2sh, Crawfish industry. 3sh, Map of Islands. 5sh, Fishing industry. 10sh, Coat of arms. £1, Queen Elizabeth II.

Perf. 14½x14, 14x14½
1967, Feb. 1   Photo.   Wmk. 314
158	A29	1p vio, red & yel	.20	.35
159	A30	1½p choc & org yel	.20	.35
160	A29	2p gray, red & sl	.20	.35
161	A30	3p green & dk brn	.20	.35
162	A30	4p grnsh bl, blk & pink	.20	.35
163	A29	6p blue & dk brn	.20	.35
164	A29	8p aqua, dk bl & yel	.20	.35
165	A30	1sh grnsh bl & red brn	.20	.35
166	A29	1sh6p brt grnsh bl, yel & brn	.40	.60
167	A30	2sh multicolored	.55	.85
168	A30	3sh grnsh bl & mar	.75	1.10
169	A30	5sh sky bl, dk bl & yel	1.25	1.90
170	A30	10sh multicolored	2.75	4.00
171	A29	£1 dk car rose, sil & dk bl	5.50	8.50
	Nos. 158-171 (14)		12.80	19.75

See #181, 217-230. For surcharges see #182-195.

Turks Islands No. 1 A31

Designs: 6p, Turks Islands No. 2 and portrait of Queen Elizabeth on simulated stamp. 1sh, Turks Islands No. 3 (like 1p).

1967, May 1   Photo.   Perf. 14½
172	A31	1p lilac rose & blk	.20	.20
173	A31	6p gray & black	.20	.20
174	A31	1sh Prus blue & blk	.45	.45
	Nos. 172-174 (3)		.85	.85

Centenary of Turks Islands stamps.

Human Rights Flame A32

1968, Apr. 1   Perf. 14x14½
175	A32	1p lt green & multi	.20	.20
176	A32	8p lt blue & multi	.20	.20
177	A32	1sh6p multicolored	.45	.45
	Nos. 175-177 (3)		.85	.85

International Human Rights Year.

Martin Luther King, Jr. and Protest March of 1968 A33

1968, Oct. 1   Photo.   Wmk. 314
178	A33	2p dk blue, dk & lt brn	.20	.20
179	A33	8p dk car rose, dk & lt brn	.20	.20
180	A33	1sh6p dp vio, dk & lt brn	.30	.30
	Nos. 178-180 (3)		.70	.70

Martin Luther King, Jr. (1929-68), American civil rights leader.

Nos. 158-171 Surcharged

Designs as before and: ¼c, Coat of arms like 10sh.

Perf. 14x14½, 14½x14
1969, Sept. 8   Photo.   Wmk. 314
181	A30	¼c lt gray & multi	.20	.20
182	A30	1c on 1p multi	.20	.20
183	A29	2c on 2p multi	.20	.20
184	A29	3c on 3p multi	.20	.20
185	A30	4c on 4p multi	.20	.20
186	A29	5c on 6p multi	.20	.20
187	A29	7c on 8p multi	.20	.20
188	A30	8c on 1 ½p multi	.20	.20
189	A30	10c on 1sh multi	.20	.20
190	A29	15c on 1sh6p multi	.20	.20
191	A30	20c on 2sh multi	.30	.50
192	A30	30c on 3sh multi	.40	.65
193	A30	50c on 5sh multi	.60	.95
194	A30	$1 on 10sh multi	1.40	2.25
195	A29	$2 on £1 multi	6.00	9.50
	Nos. 181-195 (15)		10.70	15.85

The surcharge is differently arranged on each denomination to fit the design; the old denomination is obliterated with a rectangle on the 8c and 15c.

See Nos. 217-230.

1969   Wmk. 314 Sideways
182a	A29	1c on 1p	.20	.30
183a	A29	2c on 2p	.20	.30
184a	A29	3c on 3p	.20	.30
186a	A29	5c on 6p	.20	.30
187a	A29	7c on 8p	.20	.30
190a	A29	15c on 1sh6p	.30	.50
195a	A29	$2 on £1	3.00	4.75
	Nos. 182a-195a (7)		4.30	6.75

Nativity with John the Baptist — A34

Designs from the Book of Hours of Eleanora, Duchess of Tuscany: 3c, 30c, Flight into Egypt.

Perf. 13x12½
1969, Oct. 20   Litho.   Wmk. 314
196	A34	1c plum & multi	.20	.20
197	A34	3c dk blue & multi	.20	.20
198	A34	15c olive & multi	.25	.25
199	A34	30c yellow brn & multi	.45	.45
	Nos. 196-199 (4)		1.10	1.10

Christmas.

Coat of Arms — A35

1970, Feb. 2   Litho.   Perf. 13x12½
200	A35	7c brown & multi	.20	.20
201	A35	35c violet blue & multi	.75	.75

New Constitution, inaugurated 6/16/69. See No. 769.

Christ Bearing the Cross, by Dürer — A36

Albrecht Dürer Engravings: 7c, Christ on the Cross. 50c, The Lamentation for Christ.

Perf. 13½x14
1970, Mar. 17   Engr.   Wmk. 314
202	A36	5c dp blue & blk	.20	.20
203	A36	7c vermilion & blk	.20	.20
204	A36	50c dk brown & multi	.75	.75
	Nos. 202-204 (3)		1.15	1.15

Easter.

Dickens and "Oliver Twist" Scene A37

Charles Dickens and Scene from: 3c, "A Christmas Carol." 15c, "Pickwick Papers." 30c, "The Old Curiosity Shop."

Litho. & Engr.
1970, June 17   Perf. 13½x13
205	A37	1c yel, red brn & blk	.20	.20
206	A37	3c sal pink, sl & blk	.20	.20
207	A37	15c salmon, bl & blk	.25	.25
208	A37	30c lt blue, ol & blk	.55	.55
	Nos. 205-208 (4)		1.20	1.20

Charles Dickens (1812-70), English novelist.

Red Cross Ambulance, 1870 — A38

5c, 30c, Red Cross ambulance, 1970.

1970, Aug. 4   Litho.   Perf. 13½x14
209	A38	1c orange & multi	.20	.20
210	A38	5c ocher & multi	.20	.20
211	A38	15c brt pink & multi	.30	.30
212	A38	30c multicolored	.55	.55
		Nos. 209-212 (4)	1.25	1.25

Centenary of British Red Cross Society.

Gen. George Monck, Duke of Albemarle, and his Coat of Arms — A39

Designs: 8c, 35c, Coats of arms of Charles II and Queen Elizabeth II.

1970, Dec. 1   Litho.   Perf. 12½x13½
213	A39	1c multicolored	.20	.20
214	A39	8c multicolored	.20	.20
215	A39	10c multicolored	.30	.30
216	A39	35c multicolored	1.00	.95
		Nos. 213-216 (4)	1.70	1.65

Tercentenary of the issue of Letters Patent to the Six Lords Proprietors.

Types of 1967
Values in Cents and Dollars

Designs: 1c, Turk's-head cactus. 2c, Donkey cart. 3c, Sisal industry. 4c, Conch industry. 5c, Salt industry. 7c, Skin diving. 8c, Boat building. 10c, Fishing. 15c, Water skiing. 20c, Crawfish industry. 30c, Map of Islands. 50c, Fishing industry. $1, Arms of Colony. $2, Queen Elizabeth II.

Perf. 14x14½, 14½x14
1971, Feb. 2   Photo.   Wmk. 314
217	A29	1c violet, red & yel	.20	.30
218	A29	2c gray, yel & slate	.20	.30
219	A29	3c green & dk brn	.20	.30
220	A30	4c grnsh bl, blk & pink	.20	.30
221	A29	5c blue & dk brown	.20	.30
222	A29	7c aqua, dk bl & yel	.20	.30
223	A30	8c choc & org yel	.20	.30
224	A30	10c grnsh bl & red brn	.30	.40
225	A29	15c brt grnsh bl, yel & brn	.60	.70
226	A30	20c multicolored	.85	1.10
227	A30	30c grnsh bl & mar	1.25	1.60
228	A30	50c sky bl, dk bl & yel	2.00	2.50
229	A30	$1 blue & multi	4.00	4.75
230	A29	$2 dk car rose, sil & dk blue	7.50	9.50
		Nos. 217-230 (14)	17.90	22.65

The ¼c, released with this set is a shade of No. 181, the background being a greenish, slightly darker gray.

Queen Conch and Emblem A40

Tourist publicity (Sun, Sea and Sand Emblem and): 1c, Seahorse, vert. 15c, American oyster catcher. 30c, Blue Marlin.

Perf. 14½x14, 14x14½
1971, May 2   Litho.   Wmk. 314
232	A40	1c multicolored	.20	.20
233	A40	3c multicolored	.20	.20
234	A40	15c multicolored	.40	.40
235	A40	30c multicolored	.75	.75
		Nos. 232-235 (4)	1.55	1.55

Pirate Sloop A41

Designs: 3c, Pirates burying treasure. 15c, Marooned pirate. 30c, Buccaneers.

1971, July 17   Perf. 14½x14
236	A41	2c multicolored	.20	.20
237	A41	3c multicolored	.20	.20
238	A41	15c multicolored	.70	.70
239	A41	30c multicolored	1.40	1.40
		Nos. 236-239 (4)	2.50	2.50

A42

Adoration of the Virgin and Child, from Wilton Diptych, French School, c. 1395 — A43

1971, Oct. 12   Litho.   Perf. 14x13½
240	A42	2c dull brn & multi	.20	.20
241	A43	2c dull brn & multi	.20	.20
242	A42	8c green & multi	.20	.20
243	A43	8c green & multi	.20	.20
244	A42	15c dk blue gray & multi	.30	.30
245	A43	15c dk blue gray & multi	.30	.30
		Nos. 240-245 (6)	1.40	1.40

Christmas.

Rocket Launch, Cape Canaveral — A44

10c, Space capsule in orbit around earth. 15c, Map of Turks & Caicos Islands & splashdown. 20c, Distinguished Service Medal, vert.

1972, Feb. 21   Perf. 13½
246	A44	5c lt blue & blk	.20	.20
247	A44	10c multicolored	.20	.20
248	A44	15c lt green & multi	.30	.30
249	A44	20c blue & multi	.40	.40
		Nos. 246-249 (4)	1.10	1.10

First orbital flight by US astronaut Lt. Col. John H. Glenn, Jr., and splashdown off Turks and Caicos Islands, 10th anniversary.

The Three Crosses, by Rembrandt — A45

Details from Etchings by Rembrandt: 2c, Christ Before Pilate, vert. 30c, Descent from the Cross, vert.

1972, Mar. 17   Perf. 14x13½, 13½x14
250	A45	2c lilac & black	.20	.20
251	A45	15c pink & black	.30	.30
252	A45	30c yellow & black	.60	.60
		Nos. 250-252 (3)	1.10	1.10

Easter.

Richard Grenville and "Revenge" — A46

Discoverers and explorers of the Americas: ¼c, Christopher Columbus, Niña, Pinta and Santa Maria, vert. 10c, Capt. John Smith and three-master, vert. 30c, Juan Ponce de León and three-master.

1972, July 4
253	A46	¼c multicolored	.20	.20
254	A46	8c multicolored	1.40	.20
255	A46	10c multicolored	1.40	.30
256	A46	30c multicolored	3.00	1.00
		Nos. 253-256 (4)	6.00	1.75

Silver Wedding Issue, 1972
Common Design Type

Design: Queen Elizabeth II, Prince Philip, turk's-head cactus and spiny lobster.

Perf. 14x14½
1972, Nov. 20   Photo.   Wmk. 314
257	CD324	10c ultra & multi	.20	.20
258	CD324	20c multicolored	.40	.40

Treasure Hunting, c. 1700 — A47

Designs: 5c, Replica of silver bank medallion, 1687, obverse. 10c, Same, reverse. 30c, Scuba diver, 1973.

Perf. 14x14½
1973, Jan. 18   Litho.   Wmk. 314
259	A47	3c Prus blue & multi	.20	.20
260	A47	5c plum, silver & blk	.20	.20
261	A47	10c brt rose, silver & blk	.20	.20
262	A47	30c violet blue & multi	.90	.90
a.		Souvenir sheet of 4, #259-262	2.25	2.25
		Nos. 259-262 (4)	1.50	1.50

Treasure hunting.

Arms of Jamaica, Turks and Caicos Islands — A48

1973, Apr. 16   Litho.   Perf. 13½x14
263	A48	15c buff & multi	.35	.35
264	A48	35c lt green & multi	.75	.75

Centenary of annexation to Jamaica.

Sooty Tern — A49

Birds: 1c, Magnificent frigate bird. 2c, Noddy tern. 3c, Blue gray gnatcatcher. 4c, Little blue heron. 5c, Catbird. 7c, Black-whiskered vireo. 8c, Osprey. 10c, Flamingo. 15c, Brown pelican. 20c, Parula warbler. 30c, Northern mockingbird. 50c, Ruby-throated hummingbird. $1, Bahama bananaquit. $2, Cedar waxwing. $5, Painted bunting.

Wmk. 314 Sideways
1973, Aug. 1   Litho.   Perf. 14
265	A49	¼c yellow & multi	.20	.20
266	A49	1c pink & multi	.20	.20
267	A49	2c orange & multi	.55	.50
268	A49	3c lilac rose & multi	.55	.50
269	A49	4c lt blue & multi	.20	.20
270	A49	5c lt green & multi	.40	.20
271	A49	7c salmon & multi	.45	.20
272	A49	8c blue & multi	.55	.50
273	A49	10c brt blue & multi	.65	.65
274	A49	15c tan & multi	1.00	.90
275	A49	20c brt yel & multi	2.75	2.50
276	A49	30c yellow & multi	2.25	2.10
277	A49	50c yellow & multi	3.50	3.25
278	A49	$1 blue & multi	6.75	6.75
279	A49	$2 gray & multi	15.00	13.50
		Nos. 265-279 (15)	34.65	31.95

1974-75   Wmk. 314 Upright
266a	A49	1c pink & multi ('75)	.60	.80
267a	A49	2c orange & multi	1.25	1.60
268a	A49	3c lil rose & multi ('75)	2.00	2.50
275a	A49	20c brt yel & multi ('75)	6.25	8.00
		Nos. 266a-275a (4)	10.10	12.90

1976-77   Wmk. 373
265a	A49	¼c yellow & multi ('77)	.20	.20
266b	A49	1c pink & multi ('77)	.20	.20
267b	A49	2c orange & multi ('77)	.20	.20
268b	A49	3c lilac rose & multi	.20	.20
269a	A49	4c lt bl & multi ('77)	.20	.20
270a	A49	5c lt green & multi ('77)	.20	.20
273a	A49	10c brt bl & multi ('77)	.25	.20
274a	A49	15c tan & multi ('77)	.40	.65
275b	A49	20c brt yel & multi	.50	.60
276a	A49	30c yel & multi ('77)	.75	1.25
277a	A49	50c yel & multi ('77)	1.25	2.00
278a	A49	$1 blue & multi ('77)	2.50	4.00
279b	A49	$2 gray & multi ('77)	5.25	8.00
279A	A49	$5 yel grn & multi	13.50	21.00
		Nos. 265a-279A (14)	25.60	39.15

Bermuda Sloop — A50

Old Sailing Ships: 5c, HMS Blanche. 8c, US privateer Grand Turk and packet Hinchinbrooke. 10c, HMS Endymion. 15c, RMS Medina. 20c, HMS Daring.

1973, July 19   Litho.   Perf. 13½
280	A50	2c multicolored	.20	.20
281	A50	5c multicolored	.20	.20
282	A50	8c multicolored	.40	.40
283	A50	10c multicolored	.55	.55
284	A50	15c multicolored	.85	.85
285	A50	20c multicolored	1.10	1.10
a.		Souvenir sheet of 6, #280-285	3.75	3.75
		Nos. 280-285 (6)	3.30	3.30

Princess Anne's Wedding Issue
Common Design Type

1973, Nov. 14   Wmk. 314   Perf. 14
286	CD325	12c blue grn & multi	.20	.20
287	CD325	18c slate & multi	.25	.25

Lucayan Stool A51

Designs: Lucayan artifacts.

1974, July 17   Litho.   Perf. 14½
288	A51	6c shown	.20	.20
289	A51	10c Broken wood bowl	.20	.20
290	A51	12c Greenstone axe	.20	.20
291	A51	18c Wood bowl	.25	.25
292	A51	35c Animal head, fragment of stool	.50	.50
a.		Souvenir sheet of 5, #288-292	2.50	2.50
		Nos. 288-292 (5)	1.35	1.15

Carvings made by Lucayan Indians, first inhabitants of the islands.

Grand Turk G.P.O. A52

UPU Emblem and: 12c, Map of Turks and Caicos Islands and local mail sloop. 18c, "United Service" (globe and "UPU"). 55c, Design symbolic of the Islands joining the UPU in 1881.

1974, Oct. 9   Wmk. 314   Perf. 14

293	A52	4c yellow & multi	.20	.20
294	A52	12c blue & multi	.20	.20
295	A52	18c violet & multi	.25	.25
296	A52	55c lt blue & multi	.75	.75
		Nos. 293-296 (4)	1.40	1.40

Centenary of Universal Postal Union.

"His Finest Hour" A53

12c, Churchill and Franklin D. Roosevelt.

1974, Nov. 30   Wmk. 373

297	A53	12c multicolored	.20	.20
298	A53	18c multicolored	.35	.35
a.		Souvenir sheet of 2, #297-298	.70	.70

Sir Winston Churchill (1874-1965).

Spanish Captain, c. 1492 — A54   Old Windmill, Salt Cay — A55

Uniforms: 20c, Officer, Royal Artillery, 1783. 25c, Officer, 67th Foot, 1798. 35c, Private, First West India Regiment, 1833.

1975, Mar. 26   Wmk. 314   Perf. 14½

299	A54	5c blue & multi	.20	.20
300	A54	20c blue & multi	.30	.30
301	A54	25c blue & multi	.40	.40
302	A54	35c blue & multi	.55	.55
a.		Souvenir sheet of 4, #299-302	1.75	1.75
		Nos. 299-302 (4)	1.45	1.45

1975, Oct. 16   Litho.   Wmk. 373

Salt industry: 10c, Pink salt pans, horiz. 20c, Salt raking at Salt Cay, horiz. 25c, Unprocessed salt ready for shipment.

303	A55	6c violet & multi	.20	.20
304	A55	10c lt brown & multi	.20	.20
305	A55	20c red & multi	.30	.30
306	A55	25c magenta & multi	.40	.40
		Nos. 303-306 (4)	1.10	1.10

Star Coral A56

1975, Dec. 4   Litho.   Wmk. 373

307	A56	6c shown	.20	.20
308	A56	10c Elkhorn coral	.30	.25
309	A56	20c Brain coral	.60	.50
310	A56	25c Staghorn coral	.75	.60
		Nos. 307-310 (4)	1.85	1.55

Schooner A57

American Bicentennial: 20c, Ship of the line. 25c, Frigate Grand Turk. 55c, Ketch.

1976, May 28   Perf. 14x13½

311	A57	6c orange & multi	.20	.20
312	A57	20c violet blue & multi	.40	.30
313	A57	25c brown & multi	.50	.35
314	A57	55c multicolored	.90	.80
a.		Souvenir sheet of 4, #311-314	2.75	2.75
		Nos. 311-314 (4)	2.00	1.65

Turks and Caicos Islands No. 151 A58

25c, Turks and Caicos Islands No. 150.

1976, July 14   Wmk. 373   Perf. 14½

315	A58	20c carmine & multi	.50	.45
316	A58	25c violet blue & multi	.60	.55

Visit of Queen Elizabeth II and Prince Philip to the Caribbean, 10th anniversary.

Virgin and Child, by Carlo Dolci — A59

Christmas: 10c, Virgin and Child with St. John, by Botticelli. 20c, Adoration of the Kings, from Retable by the Master of Paradise. 25c, Adoration of the Kings, illuminated page, French, 15th century.

1976, Nov. 10   Litho.   Perf. 14x13½

317	A59	6c multicolored	.20	.20
318	A59	10c orange & multi	.20	.20
319	A59	20c red lilac & multi	.30	.30
320	A59	25c multicolored	.35	.35
		Nos. 317-320 (4)	1.05	1.05

Queen with Regalia — A60

Designs: 6c, Queen presenting Order of British Empire to E. T. Wood, Grand Turk, 1966. 55c, Royal family on balcony of Buckingham Palace. $5, Portrait of Queen from photograph taken during her 1966 visit to Grand Turk.

1977   Litho.   Perf. 14x13½

321	A60	6c multicolored	.20	.20
322	A60	25c multicolored	.35	.35
323	A60	55c multicolored	.75	.75
		Nos. 321-323 (3)	1.30	1.30

Souvenir Sheet
Perf. 14

324	A60	$5 multicolored	3.25	3.25

25th anniv. of the reign of Elizabeth II.

Friendship 7 Capsule — A61

Designs: 3c, Lunar rover, vert. 6c, Tracking Station on Grand Turk. 20c, Moon landing craft, vert. 25c, Col. Glenn's rocket leaving launching pad, vert. 50c, Telstar 1 satellite.

1977, June 20   Litho.   Perf. 13½

325	A61	1c multicolored	.20	.20
326	A61	3c multicolored	.20	.20
327	A61	6c multicolored	.20	.20
328	A61	20c multicolored	.25	.25
329	A61	25c multicolored	.35	.35
330	A61	50c multicolored	.75	.75
		Nos. 325-330 (6)	1.95	1.95

US Tracking Station on Grand Turk, 25th anniversary.

Adoration of the Kings, 1634 by Rubens — A63

Rubens Paintings: ¼c, Flight into Egypt. 1c, Adoration of the Kings, 1624. 6c, Madonna with Garland. 20c, $1, Virgin and Child Adored by Angels. $2, Adoration of the Kings, 1618.

1977, Dec. 23

331	A63	¼c multicolored	.20	.20
332	A63	½c multicolored	.20	.20
333	A63	1c multicolored	.20	.20
334	A63	6c multicolored	.20	.20
335	A63	20c multicolored	.25	.25
336	A63	$2 multicolored	2.10	2.10
		Nos. 331-336 (6)	3.15	3.15

Souvenir Sheet

337	A63	$1 multicolored	1.90	1.90

Christmas and 400th birth anniversary of Peter Paul Rubens (1577-1640).

Map of Turks Island Passage A64

Designs: 20c, Grand Turk lighthouse and sailboat (LUG cargo vessel). 25c, Deepsea fishing yacht. 55c, S.S. Jamaica Planter.

Wmk. 373, Unwmkd.
1978, Feb. 2   Litho.   Perf. 13½

338	A64	6c multicolored	.20	.20
339	A64	20c multicolored	.40	.40
340	A64	25c multicolored	.50	.45
341	A64	55c multicolored	1.10	1.10
a.		Souv. sheet of 4, #338-341, unwmkd.	2.50	2.50
		Nos. 338-341 (4)	2.20	2.10

Turks Island Passage, a major Caribbean shipping route.
No. 341a exists watermarked. Value $50.

Queen Victoria in Coronation Regalia — A65

Nos. 322 and 323 were also issued in booklet panes of 2.
Issued: #321-323, Feb. 7; #324, Dec. 6.

British Monarchs in Coronation Regalia: 10c, Edward VII. 25c, George V. $2, George VI. $2.50, Elizabeth II.

1978, June 2   Litho.   Perf. 14

342	A65	6c multicolored	.20	.20
343	A65	10c multicolored	.20	.20
344	A65	25c multicolored	.30	.30
345	A65	$2 multicolored	1.50	1.50
		Nos. 342-345 (4)	2.20	2.20

Souvenir Sheet

346	A65	$2.50 multicolored	2.00	2.00

25th anniversary of coronation of Queen Elizabeth II. Nos. 342-345 also issued in sheets of 3 plus label, perf. 12.

Wilbur Wright and Flyer 3 A66

Aviation Progress: 6c, Cessna 337 and Wright brothers. 10c, Southeast Airlines' Electra and Orville Wright. 15c, C47 cargo plane on South Caicos runway. 35c, Norman-Britten Islander at Grand Turk airport. $1, Orville Wright and Flyer, 1902. $2, Wilbur Wright and Flyer.

1978, June 29   Litho.   Perf. 14½

347	A66	1c multicolored	.20	.20
348	A66	6c multicolored	.20	.20
349	A66	10c multicolored	.20	.20
350	A66	15c multicolored	.20	.20
351	A66	35c multicolored	.60	.60
352	A66	$2 multicolored	2.10	2.10
		Nos. 347-352 (6)	3.50	3.50

Souvenir Sheet

353	A66	$1 multicolored	.85	.85

Queen Elizabeth II — A67

Designs: 15c, Ampulla and anointing spoon. 25c, St. Edward's crown.

Imperf. x Roulette 5
1978, July 24   Litho.
Self-adhesive

354		Souvenir booklet	3.00
a.		A67 Bklt. pane of 3, 15c, 25c, $2	1.90
b.		A67 Bklt. pane, 3 each, 15c, 25c	1.10

25th anniv. of coronation of Queen Elizabeth II. #354 contains #354a-354b printed on peelable paper backing with music and text of hymns.

11th Commonwealth Games, Edmonton, Canada, Aug. 3-12 — A68

1978, Aug. 3   Litho.   Perf. 15

355	A68	6c shown	.20	.20
356	A68	20c Weight lifting	.25	.25
357	A68	55c Boxing	.70	.70
358	A68	$2 Bicycling	1.50	1.50
		Nos. 355-358 (4)	2.65	2.65

Souvenir Sheet

359	A68	$1 Sprinting	1.40	1.40

Fish A69

1978-79		Litho.	Perf. 14	
360	A69	1c Indigo hamlet	.20	.20
361	A69	2c Tobacco fish	.20	.20
362	A69	3c Passing Jack	.20	.20
363	A69	4c Porkfish	.20	.20
364	A69	5c Spanish grunt	.20	.20
365	A69	7c Yellowtail snapper	.20	.20
366	A69	8c Foureye butter- lyfish	.20	.20
367	A69	10c Yellow fin grouper	.20	.20
368	A69	15c Beau Gregory	.30	.30
369	A69	20c Queen angelfish	.40	.40
370	A69	30c Hogfish	.60	.60
371	A69	50c Fairy Basslet	1.00	1.00
372	A69	$1 Clown wrasse	1.90	1.90
373	A69	$2 Stoplight par- rotfish	4.25	4.25
374	A69	$5 Queen triggerfish	10.00	10.00
		Nos. 360-374 (15)	20.05	20.05

Issue dates: 1c, 3c, 5c, 10c, 15c, 20c, Nov. 17, 1978; others Feb. 6, 1979.
Nos. 368-369, 372-374 exist dated 1983. Value $22.50.

1981, Dec. 15			Perf. 12½x12	
360a	A69	1c	.20	.20
364a	A69	5c	.20	.20
367a	A69	10c	.20	.20
369a	A69	20c	.55	.55
371a	A69	50c	1.25	1.25
372a	A69	$1	2.50	2.50
373a	A69	$2	5.50	5.50
374a	A69	$5	13.00	13.00
		Nos. 360a-374a (8)	23.40	23.40

Virgin with the Goldfinch, by Dürer — A70

Dürer Paintings: 20c, Virgin and Child with St. Anne. 35c, Nativity, horiz. $1, Adoration of the Kings, horiz. $2, Praying Hands.

1978, Dec. 11		Litho.	Perf. 14	
375	A70	6c multicolored	.20	.20
376	A70	20c multicolored	.20	.20
377	A70	35c multicolored	.45	.45
378	A70	$2 multicolored	1.75	1.75
		Nos. 375-378 (4)	2.60	2.60

Souvenir Sheet

379	A70	$1 multicolored	2.40	2.40

Christmas and 450th death anniversary of Albrecht Dürer (1471-1528), German painter.

Ospreys A71

Endangered Species: 20c, Green turtle. 25c, Queen conch. 55c, Rough-toothed dolphin. $1, Humpback whale. $2, Iguana.

1979, May 17		Litho.	Perf. 14	
380	A71	6c multicolored	.25	.20
381	A71	10c multicolored	.70	.50
382	A71	25c multicolored	.90	.40
383	A71	55c multicolored	1.90	.90
384	A71	$1 multicolored	3.50	1.75
		Nos. 380-384 (5)	7.25	3.60

Souvenir Sheet

385	A71	$2 multicolored	4.25	3.75

The Beloved, by Dante Gabriel Rossetti A72

Paintings and IYC Emblem: 25c, Tahitian Girl, by Paul Gauguin. 55c, Calmady Children, by Sir Thomas Lawrence. $1, Mother and Daughter (detail), by Gauguin. $2, Marchesa Elena Grimaldi, by Van Dyck.

1979, July 2		Litho.	Perf. 14	
386	A72	6c multicolored	.20	.20
387	A72	25c multicolored	.20	.20
388	A72	55c multicolored	.40	.40
389	A72	$1 multicolored	.80	.80
		Nos. 386-389 (4)	1.60	1.60

Souvenir Sheet

390	A72	$2 multicolored	1.50	1.50

International Year of the Child.

Stampless Cover and "Medina" — A73

Designs: 20c, Map of Islands and Rowland Hill. 45c, Stamped envelope and "Orinoco." 75c, Paddlewheeler "Shannon" and letter. $1, Royal Packet "Trent," map of Islands. $2, New and old seals.

1979, Sep. 10		Litho.	Perf. 14	
391	A73	6c multicolored	.20	.20
392	A73	20c multicolored	.25	.25
393	A73	45c multicolored	.60	.60
394	A73	75c multicolored	1.00	1.00
395	A73	$1 multicolored	1.20	1.20

			Perf. 12	
396	A73	$2 multicolored ('80)	3.25	3.25
a.		Souv. sheet of 1, perf. 14 ('79)	2.00	2.00
		Nos. 391-396 (6)	6.50	6.50

Nos. 391-395 were issued in sheets of 40, and in sheets of 5 stamps plus label, in changed colors, perf. 12.
No. 396 issued May 6, 1980 in sheet of 5 plus label picturing signal flags and map.

No. 396a overprinted: "BRASILIANA 79"
Souvenir Sheet

1979, Sept. 10		Litho.	Perf. 14	
397	A73	$2 multicolored	1.75	1.75

Brasiliana 79 Intl. Philatelic Exhibition, Rio de Janeiro, Sept. 15-23.

Cuneiform Script — A74

Designs: 5c, Egyptian papyrus; Chinese writing. 15c, Greek runner; Roman post horse; Roman ship. 25c, Pigeon post; railway post; steamship postal packet. 40c, Balloon post; first airmail plane; supersonic airmail jet. $1, Original stamp press (3 designs each of 5c, 15c, 25c, 40).

Imperf. x Roulette 5, Imperf. ($1)

1979, Sept. 27			Litho.	
		Self-adhesive		
398		Souvenir booklet	6.00	
a.		A74 Bklt. pane of 1 ($1)		
b.		A74 Bklt. pane, 3 each 5c, 15c		
c.		A74 Bklt. pane, 3 each 25c, 40c		

Sir Rowland Hill (1795-1879), originator of penny postage. No. 398 contains 3 booklet panes on peelable paper backing with descriptions of stamp designs.

International Year of the Child A74a

Designs: Aquatic scenes.

1979, Nov. 2		Litho.	Perf. 11	
399	A74a	¼c Pluto and starfish	.20	.20
400	A74a	½c Minnie Mouse	.20	.20
401	A74a	1c Mickey Mouse skin-diving	.20	.20
402	A74a	2c Goofy riding turtle	.20	.20
403	A74a	3c Donald and dolphin	.20	.20
404	A74a	4c Mickey Mouse and fish	.20	.20
405	A74a	5c Goofy surfing	.20	.20
406	A74a	25c Pluto and lobster	.60	.25
407	A74a	$1 Daisy Duck water- skiing	2.50	1.00
		Nos. 399-407 (9)	4.50	2.65

Souvenir Sheet
Perf. 13½x14

408	A74a	$1.50 Goofy	1.90	1.50

St. Nicholas, Icon, 17th Century — A75

Icons or Illuminations: 3c, Emperor Otto II, 10th century. 6c, St. John, Book of Lindisfarne. 15c, Christ and angels. 20c, Christ attended by angels, Book of Kells, 9th century. 25c, St. John the Evangelist. 65c, Christ enthroned, 17th century. $1, St. John, 8th century. $2, St. Matthew, Book of Lindisfarne.

1979, Nov. 26				
409	A75	1c multicolored	.20	.20
410	A75	3c multicolored	.20	.20
411	A75	6c multicolored	.20	.20
412	A75	15c multicolored	.20	.20
413	A75	20c multicolored	.20	.20
414	A75	25c multicolored	.35	.35
415	A75	65c multicolored	.80	.80
416	A75	$1 multicolored	1.20	1.20
		Nos. 409-416 (8)	3.35	3.35

Souvenir Sheet

417	A75	$2 multicolored	2.00	2.00

Christina's World, by Andrew Wyeth — A76

Art Treasures: 10c, Ivory leopards, Benin, 19th century. 20c, The Kiss, by Gustav Klimt, vert. 25c, Portrait of a Lady, by Rogier van der Weyden, vert. 80c, Sumerian bull's head harp, 2600 B.C., vert. $1, The Wave, by Hokusai. $2, Holy Family, by Rembrandt, vert.

1979, Dec. 19			Perf. 13½	
418	A76	6c multicolored	.20	.20
419	A76	10c multicolored	.20	.20
420	A76	20c multicolored	.25	.25
421	A76	25c multicolored	.35	.35
422	A76	80c multicolored	1.00	1.00
423	A76	$1 multicolored	1.20	1.20
		Nos. 418-423 (6)	3.20	3.20

Souvenir Sheet

424	A76	$2 multicolored	2.00	2.00

Pied-billed Grebe — A77

1980, Feb. 20		Litho.	Perf. 14	
425	A77	20c shown	.75	.40
426	A77	25c Ovenbirds	.90	.45
427	A77	35c Marsh hawks	1.25	.65

428	A77	55c Yellow-bellied sap- sucker	2.00	.90
429	A77	$1 Blue-winged teals	3.50	1.75
		Nos. 425-429 (5)	8.40	4.15

Souvenir Sheet

430	A77	$2 Glossy ibis	4.25	4.25

Stamp Under Magnifier, Perforation Gauge, London 1980 Emblem A78

1980, May 6		Litho.	Perf. 14x14½	
431	A78	25c shown	.35	.35
432	A78	40c Stamp in tongs, gauge	.50	.50

Souvenir Sheet

433	A78	$2 Exhibition Hall	1.75	1.75

London 1980 International Stamp Exhibition, May 6-14.

Trumpet Triton A79

1980, June 26		Litho.	Perf. 14	
434	A79	15c shown	.30	.30
435	A79	20c Measled cowry	.40	.40
436	A79	30c True tulip	.55	.55
437	A79	45c Lion's paw	.85	.85
438	A79	55c Sunrise tellin	1.00	1.00
439	A79	70c Grown cone	1.40	1.40
		Nos. 434-439 (6)	4.50	4.50

Queen Mother Elizabeth, 80th Birthday — A80

1980, Aug. 4		Litho.	Perf. 14	
440	A80	80c multicolored	1.00	1.00

Souvenir Sheet
Perf. 12

441	A80	$1.50 multicolored	1.75	1.75

Pinocchio — A81

Christmas: Scenes from Walt Disney's Pinocchio.

1980, Sept. 25			Perf. 11	
442	A81	¼c multicolored	.20	.20
443	A81	½c multicolored	.20	.20
444	A81	1c multicolored	.20	.20
445	A81	2c multicolored	.20	.20
446	A81	3c multicolored	.20	.20
447	A81	4c multicolored	.20	.20
448	A81	5c multicolored	.20	.20
449	A81	75c multicolored	1.10	1.10
450	A81	$1 multicolored	1.50	1.50
		Nos. 442-450 (9)	4.00	4.00

Souvenir Sheet

451	A81	$2 multi, vert.	4.50	4.50

Medical Examination, Lions — A82

1980, Oct. 8   Litho.   Perf. 14
452 A82 10c shown   .20 .20
453 A82 15c Scholarships,
              Kiwanis   .20 .20
454 A82 45c Education, Soropti-
              mists   .70 .70
455 A82 $1 Lobster boat, Rota-
              ry   1.25 1.25
      Nos. 452-455 (4)   2.35 2.35
Souvenir Sheet
456 A82 $2 Funds for schools,
              Rotary   2.25 2.25
Lions, Rotary, Kiwanis and Soroptimists service organizations; 75th anniv. of Rotary Intl.

Martin Luther King, Jr. (1929-
68) — A83

Human Rights Leaders: 30c, John F. Kennedy. 45c, Roberto Clemente (1934-72),
baseball player. 70c, Frank Worrel (1927-67),
cricket player. $1, Harriet Tubman (1823-
1913), born slave, helped others escape to
freedom. $2, Marcus Garvey (1887-1940),
Jamaican black nationalist leader.

1980, Dec. 22   Litho.   Perf. 14
457 A83 20c multicolored   .25 .25
458 A83 30c multicolored   .35 .35
459 A83 45c multicolored   .55 .55
460 A83 70c multicolored   .90 .90
461 A83 $1 multicolored   1.25 1.25
      Nos. 457-461 (5)   3.30 3.30
Souvenir Sheet
462 A83 $2 multicolored   2.00 2.00

Racing
Yachts
A84

Designs: Racing yachts.

1981, Jan. 29   Litho.   Perf. 14
463 A84 6c multicolored   .20 .20
464 A84 15c multicolored   .20 .20
465 A84 35c multicolored   .50 .50
466 A84 $1 multicolored   1.20 1.20
      Nos. 463-466 (4)   2.10 2.10
Souvenir Sheet
467 A84 $2 multicolored   2.00 2.00
South Caicos Regatta. No. 467 contains
one 28x42mm stamp.

Pluto
Listening to
Sea
Shell — A85

1981, Feb. 16   Perf. 13½x14
468 A85 10c shown   .20 .20
469 A85 75c Pluto on raft,
              dolphin   1.00 1.00
Souvenir Sheet
470 A85 $1.50 Pluto   2.75 2.75
50th anniversary of Walt Disney's Pluto.

Night Queen
Cactus — A86

1981, Feb. 10   Perf. 14
471 A86 25c shown   .30 .30
472 A86 35c Ripsaw cactus   .40 .40
473 A86 55c Royal strawberry
              cactus   .65 .65
474 A86 80c Caicos cactus   1.00 1.00
      Nos. 471-474 (4)   2.35 2.35
Souvenir Sheet
475 A86 $2 Turks head cactus   2.00 2.00

Donald Duck
and Louie
with Easter
Egg — A87

Easter: Various Disney characters with
Easter eggs.

1981, Mar. 20   Litho.   Perf. 11
476 A87 10c multicolored   .20 .20
477 A87 25c multicolored   .45 .45
478 A87 60c multicolored   1.25 1.25
479 A87 80c multicolored   1.50 1.50
      Nos. 476-479 (4)   3.40 3.40
Souvenir Sheet
480 A87 $4 multicolored   7.00 7.00

Woman with Fan,
1909 — A88

1981, May 28   Litho.   Perf. 14
481 A88 20c shown   .20 .20
482 A88 45c Woman with Pears,
              1909   .60 .60
483 A88 80c The Accordionist,
              1911   1.00 1.00
484 A88 $1 The Aficionado,
              1912   1.25 1.25
      Nos. 481-484 (4)   3.05 3.05
Souvenir Sheet
485 A88 $2 Girl with a Mando-
              lin, 1910   2.75 2.75
Pablo Picasso (1881-1973).

Royal Wedding Issue
Common Design Type and

A88a

1981, June 23   Litho.   Perf. 14
486 CD331a 35c Couple   .20 .20
487 CD331a 65c Kensington
                Palace   .30 .30
488 CD331a 90c Charles   .40 .40
      Nos. 486-488 (3)   .90 .90
Souvenir Sheet
489 CD331 $2 Glass coach   1.75 1.75

Self-adhesive
Imperf. x Roulette 5 (20c, $1),
Imperf. ($2)
1981, July 7
490   Booklet   4.00
   a. A88a Pane of 6 (3x20c, Lady Di-
              ana, 3x$1, Charles)   2.25
   b. A88a Pane of 1, $2, Couple   1.75
Nos. 486-488 also printed in sheets of 5
plus label, perf. 12, in changed colors.

Underwater Marine Biology
Observation — A89

1981, Aug. 21   Litho.   Perf. 14
491 A89 15c shown   .20 .20
492 A89 40c Underwater photog-
              raphy   .55 .55
493 A89 75c Diving for wreckage   1.00 1.00
494 A89 $1 Diver, dolphins   1.25 1.25
      Nos. 491-494 (4)   3.00 3.00
Souvenir Sheet
495 A89 $2 Diving flag   2.50 2.50

Br'er Rabbit Barricading his
Door — A90

Christmas: Scenes from Walt Disney's
Uncle Remus.

1981, Nov. 2   Litho.   Perf. 14x13½
496 A90 ¼c multicolored   .20 .20
497 A90 ½c multicolored   .20 .20
498 A90 1c multicolored   .20 .20
499 A90 2c multicolored   .20 .20
500 A90 3c multicolored   .20 .20
501 A90 4c multicolored   .20 .20
502 A90 5c multicolored   .20 .20
503 A90 75c multicolored   1.25 1.25
504 A90 $1 multicolored   1.75 1.75
      Nos. 496-504 (9)   4.40 4.40
Souvenir Sheet
505 A90 $2 multicolored   3.50 3.50

Flags of
Turks and
Caicos
Islands
A91

Maps of Various Islands: a, Grand Turk. b,
Salt Cay. c, South Caicos. d, East Caicos. e,
Middle Caicos. f, North Caicos. g, Caicos
Cays. h, Providenciales. i, West Caicos.

1981, Dec. 1   Perf. 14
506   Strip of 10   5.00 5.00
   a.-j. A91 20c any single   .50 .50

Caribbean
Buckeyes — A92

Scouting
Year — A93

1982, Jan. 21   Litho.   Perf. 14
507 A92 20c shown   .40 .40
508 A92 35c Clench's hairstreaks   .75 .75
509 A92 65c Gulf fritillarys   1.25 1.25
510 A92 $1 Bush sulphurs   2.10 2.10
      Nos. 507-510 (4)   4.50 4.50
Souvenir Sheet
511 A92 $2 Turk Isld. leaf but-
              terfly   5.75 5.75

1982, Feb. 17   Litho.   Perf. 14
512 A93 40c Flag ceremony   .90 .90
513 A93 50c Building raft   1.10 1.10
514 A93 75c Cricket match   1.50 1.50
515 A93 $1 Nature study   2.00 2.00
      Nos. 512-515 (4)   5.50 5.50
Souvenir Sheet
516 A93 $2 Baden-Powell, sa-
              lute   3.50 3.50

1982 World Cup
Soccer — A94

Designs: Various soccer players.

1982, Apr. 30   Litho.   Perf. 14
517 A94 10c multicolored   .20 .20
518 A94 25c multicolored   .35 .35
519 A94 45c multicolored   .60 .60
520 A94 $1 multicolored   1.25 1.25
      Nos. 517-520 (4)   2.40 2.40
Souvenir Sheet
521 A94 $2 multi, horiz.   2.00 2.00
#517-520 issued in sheets of 5 + label.

Phillis Wheatley (1753-1784), Poet,
and Washington Crossing
Delaware — A95

Washington's 250th Birth Anniv. and F.D.
Roosevelt's Birth Centenary: 35c, Washing-
ton, Benjamin Banneker (1731-1806), astrono-
mer and mathematician, map. 65c, FDR,
George Washington Carver (1864-1943). 80c,
FDR with stamp collection. $2, FDR examining
Washington stamp.

1982, May 3   Litho.   Perf. 14
522 A95 20c multicolored   .30 .30
523 A95 35c multicolored   .60 .60
524 A95 65c multicolored   1.10 1.10
525 A95 80c multicolored   1.50 1.50
      Nos. 522-525 (4)   3.50 3.50
Souvenir Sheet
526 A95 $2 multicolored   3.00 3.00

Second Thoughts, by Norman Rockwell — A96

1982, June 23 Litho. Perf. 14x13½
527	A96	8c shown	.20	.20
528	A96	15c The Proper Gratuity	.25	.25
529	A96	20c Before the Shot	.30	.30
530	A96	25c The Three Umpires	.40	.40
		Nos. 527-530 (4)	1.15	1.15

Princess Diana Issue
Common Design Type

1982 Litho. Perf. 14½x14
530A	CD332	8c Sandringham	.30	.20
530B	CD332	35c Wedding	1.40	.55
530C	CD332	$1.10 Diana	4.50	1.75
		Nos. 530A-530C (3)	6.20	2.50

1982, July 1 Perf. 14½x14
531	CD332	55c Sandringham	1.60	1.00
532	CD332	70c Wedding	1.60	1.00
533	CD332	$1 Diana	3.00	1.75
		Nos. 531-533 (3)	6.20	3.75

Also issued in sheetlets of 5 + label.

Souvenir Sheet
534	CD332	$2 Diana, diff.	6.00	4.00

Skymaster over Caicos Cays — A97

1982, Aug. 26 Litho. Perf. 14
535	A97	8c shown	.20	.20
536	A97	15c Jetstar, Grand Turk	.35	.35
537	A97	65c Helicopter, South Caicos	1.00	1.00
538	A97	$1.10 Seaplane, Providenciales	1.90	1.90
		Nos. 535-538 (4)	3.45	3.45

Souvenir Sheet
539	A97	$2 Boeing 727	3.00	3.00

Christmas — A98

Christmas: Scenes from Walt Disney's Mickey's Christmas Carol.

1982, Dec. 1 Litho. Perf. 13½
540	A98	1c multicolored	.20	.20
541	A98	1c multicolored	.20	.20
542	A98	2c multicolored	.20	.20
543	A98	2c multicolored	.20	.20
544	A98	3c multicolored	.20	.20
545	A98	3c multicolored	.20	.20
546	A98	4c multicolored	.20	.20
547	A98	65c multicolored	1.10	1.10
548	A98	$1.10 multicolored	2.50	1.50
		Nos. 540-548 (9)	5.00	4.00

Souvenir Sheet
549	A98	$2 multicolored	4.50	4.50

Trams and Locomotives — A99

1983, Jan. 18 Litho. Perf. 14
550	A99	15c West Caicos trolley tram	.30	.30
551	A99	55c West Caicos steam locomotive	1.10	1.10
552	A99	90c Mule-drawn tram, East Caicos	1.60	1.60
553	A99	$1.60 Sisal locomotive, East Caicos	3.00	3.00
		Nos. 550-553 (4)	6.00	6.00

Souvenir Sheet
554	A99	$2.50 Steam engine	4.50	4.50

A99a

1983, Mar. 14
555	A99a	1c Woman crossing guard	.20	.20
556	A99a	8c Wind and solar energy sources	.20	.20
557	A99a	65c Sailing	1.10	1.10
558	A99a	$1 Cricket game	1.75	1.75
a.		Block or strip of 4, #555-558	4.00	4.00

Commonwealth Day.

Easter — A100

Crucifixion, by Raphael. $2.50 shows entire painting.

1983, Apr. 7 Litho. Perf. 14
559	A100	35c Mary Magdalene, St. John	.50	.50
560	A100	50c Mary	.70	.70
561	A100	95c Angel looking to heaven	1.10	1.10
562	A100	$1.10 Angel looking to earth	1.25	1.25
		Nos. 559-562 (4)	3.55	3.55

Souvenir Sheet
563	A100	$2.50 multicolored	5.00	5.00

Piked Whale A101

1983 Litho. Perf. 14
564	A101	50c shown	1.40	1.40
565	A101	65c Right whale	1.90	1.90
566	A101	70c Killer whale	2.10	2.10
567	A101	95c Sperm whale	3.00	3.00
568	A101	$1.10 Gooseback whale	3.25	3.25
569	A101	$2 Blue whale	5.75	5.75
570	A101	$2.20 Humpback whale	6.75	6.75
571	A101	$3 Longfin pilot whale	8.75	8.75
		Nos. 564-571 (8)	32.90	32.90

Souvenir Sheet
572	A101	$3 Fin whale	11.50	11.50

Issued: 50c, $2.20, #571, 5/16; 70c, 95c, $2, 6/13; others 7/11. Issued in sheets of 4.
For overprints see Nos. 637-639.

Manned Flight Bicentenary A102

1983, Aug. 30 Litho. Perf. 14
573	A102	25c 1st hydrogen balloon, 1783	.35	.35
574	A102	35c Friendship 7, 1962	.50	.50
575	A102	70c Montgolfiere, 1783	.90	.90
576	A102	95c Columbia space shuttle	1.25	1.25
		Nos. 573-576 (4)	3.00	3.00

Souvenir Sheet
577	A102	$2 Montgolfiere, Columbia	3.00	3.00

Ships A103

1985 Litho. Perf. 12½x12
578	A103	4c Dug-out canoe	.20	.20
579	A103	5c Santa Maria	.20	.20
580	A103	8c Spanish treasure galleons	.20	.20
581	A103	10c Bermuda sloop	.35	.20
582	A103	20c Privateer Grand Turk	.90	1.10
583	A103	25c Nelson's Frigate Boreas	1.00	1.40
584	A103	30c Warship Endymion	1.50	2.00
585	A103	35c Bark Caesar	1.75	2.40
586	A103	50c Schooner Grapeshot	2.50	3.00
587	A103	65c Invincible	3.25	4.25
588	A103	95c Magicienne	4.50	6.00
589	A103	$1.10 Durban	5.50	7.00
590	A103	$2 Sentinel	9.00	12.00
591	A103	$3 Minerva	14.00	19.00
592	A103	$5 Caicos sloop	22.50	29.00
		Nos. 578-592 (15)	67.35	87.95

Issued: 4c, 8c, 10c, 30c, 65c, $1.10, $5, Mar.; 5c, 20c, 25c, 35c, 50c, 95c, $2, Aug. 12; $3, Dec.

1983-84 Perf. 14
578a	A103	4c	.20	.20
579a	A103	5c	.20	.20
580a	A103	8c	.20	.20
581a	A103	10c	.30	.20
582a	A103	20c	.90	.95
583a	A103	25c	1.10	1.25
584a	A103	30c	2.00	1.25
585a	A103	35c	1.75	1.60
586a	A103	50c	2.25	2.25
587a	A103	65c	3.25	3.00
588a	A103	95c	4.50	4.00
589a	A103	$1.10	5.25	4.75
590a	A103	$2	9.00	8.75
591a	A103	$3	14.50	13.50
592a	A103	$5	21.00	22.50
		Nos. 578a-592a (15)	66.40	64.60

Issued: 10c, 30c, 65c, $1.10-$3, 10/5/83; 8c, 25c, 50c, 95c, 12/16/83; 4c, 5c, 20c, 35c, $5, 1/9/84.
For overprints see Nos. 744-746.

Christmas A104

Designs: Scenes from Walt Disney's *Oh Christmas Tree*.

1983, Nov. Perf. 11
593	A104	1c Fifer Pig	.20	.20
594	A104	1c Fiddler Pig	.20	.20
595	A104	2c Practical Pig	.20	.20
596	A104	2c Pluto	.20	.20
597	A104	3c Goofy	.20	.20
598	A104	3c Mickey Mouse	.20	.20
599	A104	35c Gyro Gearloose	.60	.60
600	A104	50c Ludwig Von Drake	.80	.80
601	A104	$1.10 Huey, Dewey and Louie	1.90	1.90
		Nos. 593-601 (9)	4.50	4.50

Souvenir Sheet
Perf. 13½
602	A104	$2.50 Around the tree	6.50	6.50

John F. Kennedy (1917-1963), 20th Death Anniv. — A105

1983, Dec. 22 Litho. Perf. 14
603	A105	20c multicolored	.30	.30
604	A105	$1 multicolored	1.60	1.60

Classic Cars A106

1984, Mar. 15 Litho. Perf. 14
605	A106	4c Cadillac V-16, 1933 + label	.20	.20
606	A106	8c Rolls Royce Phantom III, 1937 + label	.20	.20
607	A106	10c Saab 99, 1969 + label	.20	.20
608	A106	25c Maserati Bora, 1973 + label	.75	.75
609	A106	40c Datsun 260Z, 1970 + label	1.25	1.25
610	A106	55c Porsche 917, 1971 + label	1.75	1.75
611	A106	80c Lincoln Continental, 1939 + label	2.50	2.50
612	A106	$1 Triumph TR3A, 1957 + label	3.00	3.00
		Nos. 605-612 (8)	9.85	9.85

Souvenir Sheet
613	A106	$2 Daimler, 1886	3.75	3.75

125th anniv. of first commercially productive oil well, Drake's Rig, Titusville, Pa. Nos. 605-612 se-tenant with labels showing flags and auto museum names. No. 613 for 150th birth anniv. of Gotlieb Daimler, inventor of high-speed internal combustion engine.

Easter — A107

450th death anniv. of Antonio Allegri Correggio (Various cameo portraits of Correggio, paintings): 15c, Rest on the Flight to Egypt with St. Francis. 40c, St. Luke and St. Ambrose. 60c, Diana and her Chariot. 95c, Deposition of Christ. $2, Nativity with St. Elizabeth and the Infant St. John.

1984, Apr. 9
614	A107	15c multicolored	.20	.20
615	A107	40c multicolored	.85	.85
616	A107	60c multicolored	1.10	1.10
617	A107	95c multicolored	1.60	1.60
		Nos. 614-617 (4)	3.75	3.75

Souvenir Sheet
618	A107	$2 multi, horiz.	3.00	3.00

1984 Los Angeles Olympics — A108

Various Disney characters participating in Olympic sports.

1984, Feb. 21   Litho.   Perf. 14
619	A108	1c 500-meter	.30	.30
620	A108	1c Diving	.30	.30
621	A108	2c Single kayak	.30	.30
622	A108	2c 1000-meter kayak	.30	.30
623	A108	3c Highboard diving	.30	.30
624	A108	3c Kayak slalom	.30	.30
625	A108	25c Freestyle swimming	.80	.80
626	A108	75c Water polo	2.25	2.25
627	A108	$1 Yachting	3.00	3.00
		Nos. 619-627 (9)	7.85	7.85

Souvenir Sheet
628	A108	$2 Platform diving	6.00	6.00

1984, Apr.   Perf. 12½x12
Same Designs
619a	A108	1c	.25	.25
620a	A108	1c	.25	.25
621a	A108	2c	.25	.25
622a	A108	2c	.25	.25
623a	A108	3c	.25	.25
624a	A108	3c	.25	.25
625a	A108	25c	.65	.65
626a	A108	75c	1.90	1.90
627a	A108	$1	2.50	2.50
		Nos. 619a-627a (9)	6.55	6.55

Souvenir Sheet
628a	A108	$2	6.00	6.00

Nos. 619a-628a inscribed with Olympic rings emblem. Printed in sheets of 5.

Sir Arthur Conan Doyle (1859-1930) — A109

Scenes from the Adventures of Sherlock Holmes.

1984, July 16   Litho.   Perf. 14
629	A109	25c Second Stain	3.50	2.10
630	A109	45c Final Problem	4.75	3.50
631	A109	70c Empty House	6.75	5.25
632	A109	85c Greek Interpreter	8.25	6.75
		Nos. 629-632 (4)	23.25	17.60

Souvenir Sheet
633	A109	$2 Doyle, vert.	16.00	19.00

Nos. 567-568, 572 Overprinted with UPU Emblem and: "19TH UPU CONGRESS / HAMBURG, WEST GERMANY./ 1874-1984"

1984   Litho.   Perf. 14
637	A101	95c multicolored	3.50	2.50
638	A101	$1.10 multicolored	3.50	3.00

Souvenir Sheet
639	A101	$3 multicolored	6.75	6.75

AUSIPEX '84 A110

Darwin, Ship, Map of Australia, Fauna.

1984, Aug. 22   Perf. 14x13½
640	A110	5c Clown fish	.95	.75
641	A110	35c Monitor lizard	3.25	3.00
642	A110	50c Rainbow lorikeets	4.25	3.50
643	A110	$1.10 Koalas	5.50	4.75
		Nos. 640-643 (4)	13.95	12.00

Souvenir Sheet
644	A110	$2 Grey kangaroo	5.25	5.25

Christmas — A111

Scenes from Walt Disney's The Toy Tinkers.

1984   Litho.   Perf. 14
645	A111	20c multicolored	1.00	.50
646	A111	35c multicolored	1.40	.70
647	A111	50c multicolored	2.00	1.00
648	A111	75c multicolored	2.75	1.75
649	A111	$1.10 multicolored	3.25	2.50
		Nos. 645-649 (5)	10.40	6.45

Souvenir Sheet
650	A111	$2 multicolored	4.75	4.75

No. 648 issued in sheets of 8. Issue dates: 75c, Nov. 26, others, Oct. 8.

Audubon Birth Bicentenary A112

Cameo portrait of Audubon, signature and illustrations from Birds of North America.

1985, Jan. 28   Litho.   Perf. 14
651	A112	25c Dendroica magnoliae	2.25	1.10
652	A112	45c Asio flammeus	3.50	2.25
653	A112	70c Zenaida macroura	4.25	4.25
654	A112	85c Progne subis	4.25	4.75
		Nos. 651-654 (4)	14.25	12.35

Souvenir Sheet
655	A112	$2 Haematopus ostralegus	6.75	6.00

Intl. Civil Aviation Org., 40th Anniv. A113

Pioneers & inventions: 8c, Leonardo da Vinci, 15th century glider wing. 25c, Sir Alliott Verdon Roe, 1949 C. 102 Jet. 65c, Robert H. Goddard, first liquid fuel rocket launch, 1926. $1, Igor Sikorsky, 1939 Sikorsky VS300. $2, Aviator Amelia Earhart, 1937 Lockheed 10E Electra.

1985, Feb. 21
656	A113	8c multicolored	.85	.45
657	A113	25c multicolored	2.50	.60
658	A113	65c multicolored	4.25	2.25
659	A113	$1 multicolored	6.50	5.25
		Nos. 656-659 (4)	14.10	8.55

Souvenir Sheet
660	A113	$2 multicolored	4.50	4.50

Arrival of the Statue of Liberty in New York, Cent. A114

Designs: 20c, Flags of US, France, Franklin, Lafayette. 30c, Designer Frederic A. Bartholdi, engineer Gustave Eiffel, Statue, Eiffel Tower. 65c, Isere, arriving in New York with Statue, 1885. $1.10, Fund raisers Louis Agassiz, H. W. Longfellow, Charles Sumner, Joseph Pulitzer. $2, Dedication day, Oct. 28, 1886.

1985, Mar. 28
661	A114	20c multicolored	1.10	.80
662	A114	30c multicolored	1.60	.95
663	A114	65c multicolored	3.50	2.10
664	A114	$1.10 multicolored	3.75	2.50
		Nos. 661-664 (4)	9.95	6.35

Souvenir Sheet
665	A114	$2 multicolored	5.50	5.50

Royal Navy A115

Designs: 20c, Sir Edward Hawke, Royal George. 30c, Lord Nelson, H.M.S. Victory. 65c, Adm. Sir George Cockburn, H.M.S. Albion. 95c, Adm. Sir David Beatty, H.M.S. Indefatigable. $2, 18th century naval gunner, cannons.

1985, Apr. 17
666	A115	20c multicolored	3.25	2.25
667	A115	30c multicolored	3.50	3.25
668	A115	65c multicolored	5.25	4.50
669	A115	95c multicolored	6.50	7.00
		Nos. 666-669 (4)	18.50	17.00

Souvenir Sheet
670	A115	$2 multicolored	6.00	6.00

Intl. Youth Year A116

Anniversaries: 25c, Return of Halley's Comet, 1986. 35c, Mark Twain (1835-1910), Mississippi river boat. 50c, Jakob Grimm (1785-1863), Hansel & Gretel, vert. 95c, Grimm, Rumpelstiltskin, vert. $2, Twain, Grimm, portraits.

1985, May 17
671	A116	25c multicolored	1.75	.55
672	A116	35c multicolored	2.75	.70
673	A116	50c multicolored	3.25	1.00
674	A116	95c multicolored	4.50	2.25
		Nos. 671-674 (4)	12.25	4.50

Souvenir Sheet
675	A116	$2 multicolored	6.00	6.00

Queen Mother, 85th Birthday — A117

Designs: 30c, Queen Mother outside Clarence House, vert. 50c, Visiting Biggin Hill Airfield by helicopter. $1.10, 80th birthday portrait, vert. $2, With Prince Charles at the 1968 Garter Ceremony, Windsor Castle, vert.

1985, July 15
676	A117	30c multicolored	1.00	1.00
677	A117	50c multicolored	1.50	1.50
678	A117	$1.10 multicolored	3.50	3.50
		Nos. 676-678 (3)	6.00	6.00

Souvenir Sheet
679	A117	$2 multicolored	5.00	5.00

George Frideric Handel — A118   Johann Sebastian Bach — A119

Handel or Bach and: 4c, King George II, Zadok the Priest music, 1727. 10c, Queen Caroline, Funeral Anthem, 1737. 15c, Bassoon, Invention No. 3 in D Major. 40c, Natural horn, Invention No. 3 in D Major. 50c, King George I, Water Music, 1714. 60c, Viola d'amore, Invention No. 3 . . . 95c, Clavichord, Invention No. 3 . . . $1.10, Queen Anne, Or la Tromba from Rinaldo. No. 688, Handel, portrait. No. 689, Bach, portrait.

1985, July 17   Perf. 15
680	A118	4c multicolored	.70	.55
681	A118	10c multicolored	1.10	.55
682	A119	15c multicolored	1.10	.50
683	A119	40c multicolored	2.25	1.00
684	A118	50c multicolored	3.00	2.50
685	A119	60c multicolored	2.75	1.25
686	A119	95c multicolored	3.25	2.50
687	A118	$1.10 multicolored	5.25	5.00
		Nos. 680-687 (8)	19.40	13.85

Souvenir Sheets
688	A118	$2 multicolored	6.75	6.75
689	A119	$2 multicolored	5.00	4.75

Motorcycle Centenary — A120

Flag of US, UK, Fed. Rep. of Germany or Japan and: 8c, 1915 dual cylinder Harley-Davidson. 25c, 1950 Thunderbird Triumph. 55c, 1985 BMW K100RS. $1.20, 1985 Honda 1100 Shadow. $2, 1885 Daimler Single Track, vert.

1985, Sept. 4   Perf. 14
690	A120	8c multicolored	1.00	.40
691	A120	25c multicolored	2.10	1.00
692	A120	55c multicolored	3.25	2.50
693	A120	$1.20 multicolored	5.00	7.75
		Nos. 690-693 (4)	11.35	11.65

Souvenir Sheet
694	A120	$2 multicolored	6.00	6.00

Pirates of the Caribbean — A121

Disneyland, 30th Anniv.: No. 695, Fate of Capt. Kidd. No. 696, Pirates imprisoned. No. 697, Bartholomew Roberts, church-going pirate. No. 698, Buccaneers in battle. No. 699, Bride auction. No. 700, Plunder. No. 701, Singing pirates. No. 702, Blackbeard. No. 703, Henry Morgan. No. 704, Mary Read, Anne Bonney.

1985, Oct. 4   Litho.   Perf. 14
695	A121	1c multicolored	.35	.35
696	A121	1c multicolored	.35	.35
697	A121	2c multicolored	.35	.35
698	A121	2c multicolored	.35	.35
699	A121	3c multicolored	.35	.35
700	A121	3c multicolored	.35	.35
701	A121	35c multicolored	2.25	.90
702	A121	75c multicolored	4.25	4.75
703	A121	$1.10 multicolored	4.75	5.50
		Nos. 695-703 (9)	13.35	13.25

Souvenir Sheet
704	A121	$2.50 multicolored	8.75	8.75

Girl Guides, 75th Anniv. A122

Uniforms of Turks and Caicos and: 10c, Papua New Guinea and China brownies. 40c, Surinam and Korea brownies. 70c, Australia and Canada girl guides. 80c, West Germany and Israel girl guides.

1985, Nov. 4

705	A122	10c multicolored	1.10	.75
706	A122	40c multicolored	2.75	2.10
707	A122	70c multicolored	3.75	4.50
708	A122	80c multicolored	3.75	4.75
		Nos. 705-708 (4)	11.35	12.10

Souvenir Sheet

709	A122	$2 Anniv. emblem	5.00	5.00

Grand Turk Chapter, 35th anniv.

World Wildlife Fund A123

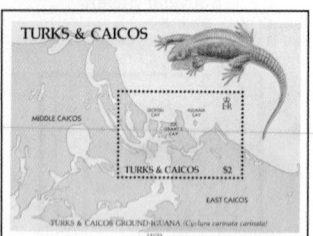

Map of the Islands — A124

Turks & Caicos ground iguanas.

1986, Nov. 20   **Perf. 14**

710	A123	8c multicolored	2.50	1.25
711	A123	10c multicolored	2.50	1.25
712	A123	20c multicolored	4.25	2.50
713	A123	35c multicolored	9.75	8.50
		Nos. 710-713 (4)	19.00	13.50

Souvenir Sheet

714	A124	$2 multicolored	18.50	19.00

A125

Christmas — A126

Wedding pictures.

1986, Dec. 19   **Litho.**   **Perf. 14**

715	A125	35c Couple	1.25	1.25
716	A125	65c Sarah in coach	2.25	2.25
717	A125	$1.10 Couple, close-up	4.00	4.00
		Nos. 715-717 (3)	7.50	7.50

Souvenir Sheet

718	A125	$2 In Westminster Abbey	7.00	7.00

Wedding of Prince Andrew and Sarah Ferguson.

1987, Dec. 9   **Litho.**   **Perf. 14**

Illuminations by miniaturist Giorgio Giulio Clovio (1498-1578) from the Farnese Book of Hours: 35c, Prophecy of the Birth of Christ to King Achaz. 50c, The Annunciation. 65c, The Circumcision. 95c, Adoration of the Kings. $2, The Nativity, from the Townley Lectionary.

719	A126	35c multicolored	1.50	.85
720	A126	50c multicolored	2.25	2.10
721	A126	65c multicolored	2.75	2.75
722	A126	95c multicolored	4.00	4.50
		Nos. 719-722 (4)	10.50	10.20

Souvenir Sheet

723	A126	$2 multicolored	8.00	9.25

Accession of Queen Victoria to the Throne of England, 150th Anniv. A127

Ships and memorials: 8c, HMS Victoria, Victoria Cross. 35c, SS Victoria, coin. 55c, Victoria & Albert I, Great Britain No. 1. 95c, Victoria & Albert II, Victoria Public Library, Turks & Caicos. $2, Bark Victoria.

1987, Dec. 24

724	A127	8c multicolored	3.75	1.60
725	A127	35c multicolored	3.75	3.25
726	A127	55c multicolored	4.25	4.25
727	A127	95c multicolored	5.25	7.00
		Nos. 724-727 (4)	17.00	16.10

Souvenir Sheet

728	A127	$2 multicolored	11.00	11.00

US Constitution Bicentennial — A128

Designs: 10c, NJ state flag. 35c, Freedom of Worship, vert. 65c, US Supreme Court, vert. 80c, John Adams, vert. $2, George Mason, vert.

1987, Dec. 31

729	A128	10c multicolored	.25	.25
730	A128	35c multicolored	.75	.75
731	A128	65c multicolored	2.00	2.00
732	A128	80c multicolored	3.00	3.00
		Nos. 729-732 (4)	6.00	6.00

Souvenir Sheet

733	A128	$2 multicolored	3.75	4.25

Discovery of America, 500th Anniv. (in 1992) A129

4c, Caravel, first sighting of land, Oct. 12, 1492. 25c, Columbus meets with Indians, Oct. 14. 70c, Fleet anchored in harbor, Oct. 15. $1, Landing, Oct. 16. $2, Nina, Pinta and Santa Maria.

1988, Jan. 20

734	A129	4c multicolored	.80	.50
735	A129	25c multicolored	1.50	.95
736	A129	70c multicolored	4.50	5.00
737	A129	$1 multicolored	4.50	5.00
		Nos. 734-737 (4)	11.30	11.45

Souvenir Sheet

738	A129	$2 multicolored	8.00	8.00

Sea Scouts Salute Jamboree and Australia A130

Australia Bicent.: 8c, Arawak artifact, scouts exploring cave on Middle Caicos, vert. 35c,

---

Santa Maria, scouts rowing to Hawks Nest. 65c, Scouts diving to explore a sunken Spanish galleon, vert. 95c, Plantation worker cutting sisal, scouts exploring plantation ruins. $2, Splashdown of Friendship 7, piloted by John Glenn, Feb. 20, 1962, vert.

1988, Feb. 12   **Litho.**   **Perf. 14**

739	A130	8c multicolored	.35	.35
740	A130	35c shown	1.00	1.00
741	A130	65c multicolored	1.90	1.90
742	A130	95c multicolored	2.75	2.75
		Nos. 739-742 (4)	6.00	6.00

Souvenir Sheet

743	A130	$2 multicolored	5.25	5.75

Nos. 581, 583 and 590 Ovptd. "40th WEDDING ANNIVERSARY / H.M. QUEEN ELIZABETH II / H.R.H. THE DUKE OF EDINBURGH"

1988, Mar. 14   **Litho.**   **Perf. 14**

744	A103	10c multicolored	.25	.25
745	A103	25c multicolored	.75	.75
746	A103	$2 multicolored	6.00	6.00
		Nos. 744-746 (3)	7.00	7.00

A131

A132

1988, Aug. 29   **Litho.**

747	A131	8c Soccer	.70	.35
748	A131	30c Yachting	1.25	1.25
749	A131	70c Cycling	4.50	3.75
750	A131	$1 Running	3.50	4.50
		Nos. 747-750 (4)	9.95	9.85

Souvenir Sheet

751	A131	$2 Swimming	5.00	5.00

1988 Summer Olympics, Seoul.

1988, Sept. 5   **Litho.**

Billfish Tournament: 8c, Passenger jet, fishing boat and fisherman reeling-in giant swordfish. 10c, Photographing prize catch. 70c, Fishing boat, lighthouse. $1, Blue marlin. $2, Sailfish.

752	A132	8c multicolored	1.25	.30
753	A132	10c multicolored	.65	.30
754	A132	70c multicolored	2.75	3.00
755	A132	$1 multicolored	3.25	3.75
		Nos. 752-755 (4)	7.90	7.35

Souvenir Sheet

756	A132	$2 multicolored	6.00	6.00

Christmas A133

Paintings by Titian: 15c, Madonna and Child with St. Catherine and the Infant John the Baptist, c. 1530. 25c, Madonna with a Rabbit, c. 1526. 35c, Virgin and Child with Sts. Stephen, Jerome and Mauritius, c. 1520. 40c, The Gypsy Madonna, c. 1510. 50c, The Holy Family and a Shepherd, c. 1510. 65c, Madonna and Child, c. 1510. $3, Madonna and Child with St. John the Baptist and St. Catherine, c.

1530. No. 764, Adoration of the Magi, c. 1560. No. 765, The Annunciation, c. 1560.

1988, Oct. 24   **Litho.**

757	A133	15c multicolored	.40	.40
758	A133	25c multicolored	.60	.60
759	A133	35c multicolored	.85	.85
760	A133	40c multicolored	.95	.95
761	A133	50c multicolored	1.25	1.25
762	A133	65c multicolored	1.50	1.50
763	A133	$3 multicolored	7.00	7.00
		Nos. 757-763 (7)	12.55	12.55

Souvenir Sheets

764	A133	$2 multicolored	5.00	5.00
765	A133	$2 multicolored	5.00	5.00

Visit of Princess Alexandra, 1st Cousin of Queen Elizabeth II — A134

Various portraits and: 70c, Government House. $1.40, Map. $2, Flora, vert.

1988, Nov. 14   **Litho.**   **Perf. 14**

766	A134	70c multicolored	4.50	3.75
767	A134	$1.40 multicolored	10.00	10.50

Souvenir Sheet

768	A134	$2 multicolored	16.00	16.00

Arms Type of 1970 Without Inscription
Perf. 14½x15

1988, Dec. 15   **Litho.**   **Unwmk.**

769	A35	$10 multicolored	20.00	20.00

Pre-Columbian Societies and Their Customs — A135

UPAE and discovery of America anniv. emblems and: 10c, Hollowing-out tree to make a canoe, vert. 50c, Body painting and statue. 65c, Three islanders with body paint. $1, Canoeing, vert. $2, Petroglyph.

1989, May 15   **Litho.**   **Perf. 14**

770	A135	10c multicolored	.40	.40
771	A135	50c multicolored	1.60	1.60
772	A135	65c multicolored	2.00	2.00
773	A135	$1 multicolored	3.00	3.00
		Nos. 770-773 (4)	7.00	7.00

Souvenir Sheet

774	A135	$2 multicolored	8.00	8.25

Discovery of America 500th anniv. (in 1992)

Souvenir Sheet

Lincoln Memorial, Washington, D.C. — A136

1989, Nov. 17   **Litho.**   **Perf. 14**

775	A136	$1.50 multicolored	4.25	4.25

World Stamp Expo '89.

Miniature Sheets

American Presidential Office, 200th Anniv. — A137

US presidents, historic events and monuments.

No. 776: a, Jackson, early train. b, Van Buren, origins of baseball and Moses Fleetwood Walker, 1st black to play professional baseball. c, Harrison, Harrison's "Keep the Ball Rollin'" slogan and parade. d, Tyler, annexation of Texas, 1845. e, Polk, 1st US postage stamps (#2), 1847, and discovery of gold in California, 1849. f, Taylor, Mexican-American War, 1847.

No. 777: a, Hayes, end of Civil War reconstruction. b, Garfield, Garfield leading Union soldiers in the Battle of Shiloh. c, Arthur, opening of the Brooklyn Bridge, 1883. d, Cleveland, Columbian Exposition, 1893 (US #245). e, Benjamin Harrison, Pan-American Union building, map. f, McKinley, Spanish-American War (Rough Riders Monument, by Solon Borglum).

No. 778: a, Hoover, 1933 Olympic Games, Los Angeles and Lake Placid (American sprinter Ralph Metcalf and Norwegian figure skater Sonja Henie). b, Franklin Delano Roosevelt, Roosevelt's support of the March of Dimes (dime, 1946). c, 150th anniv. of inauguration of Washington, New York World's Fair, 1939. d, Truman, founding of the U.N., 1945. e, Eisenhower, invasion of Normandy, 1944. f, Kennedy, Apollo 11 mission, 1969.

1989, Nov. 19   *Perf. 14*
776		Sheet of 6	10.00	10.00
a.-f.	A137	50c any single	1.60	1.60
777		Sheet of 6	10.00	10.00
a.-f.	A137	50c any single	1.60	1.60
778		Sheet of 6	10.00	10.00
a.-f.	A137	50c any single	1.60	1.60

Fraser is incorrectly spelled "Frazer" on No. 778c.

Christmas — A138

Religious paintings by Giovanni Bellini: 15c, Madonna and Child. 25c, The Madonna of the Shrubs. 35c, The Virgin and Child. 40c, The Virgin and Child with a Greek Inscription. 50c, The Madonna of the Meadow. 65c, The Madonna of the Pear. 70c, The Virgin and Child, diff. $1, Madonna and Child, diff. No. 787, The Madonna with John the Baptist and Another Saint. No. 788, The Virgin and Child Enthroned.

1989, Dec. 18
779	A138	15c multicolored	.50	.50
780	A138	25c multicolored	.80	.80
781	A138	35c multicolored	1.10	1.10
782	A138	40c multicolored	1.40	1.40
783	A138	50c multicolored	1.60	1.60
784	A138	65c multicolored	2.00	2.00
785	A138	70c multicolored	2.25	2.25
786	A138	$1 multicolored	6.50	6.50
		Nos. 779-786 (8)	16.15	16.15

Souvenir Sheets
787	A138	$2 multicolored	8.00	8.00
788	A138	$2 multicolored	8.00	8.00

Souvenir Sheet

 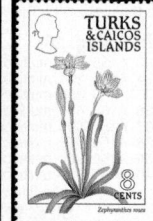

1st Moon Landing, 20th Anniv. — A139   Flowers — A140

Designs: a, Liftoff. b, Eagle lunar module on Moon's surface. c, Aldrin obtaining soil samples. d, Neil Armstrong walking on Moon. e, Columbia and Eagle in space.

1990, Jan. 8
789		Sheet of 5	7.50	7.50
a.-e.	A139	50c any single	1.40	1.40

1990, Jan. 11   *Litho.*   *Perf. 14*
790	A140	8c Zephyranthes rosea	.20	.20
791	A140	10c Sophora tomentosa	.20	.20
792	A140	15c Coccoloba uvifera	.35	.35
793	A140	20c Encyclia gracilis	.50	.50
794	A140	25c Tillandsia streptophylla	.60	.60
795	A140	30c Maurandella antirrhiniflora	.70	.70
796	A140	35c Tillandsia balbisiana	.85	.85
797	A140	50c Encyclia rufa	1.25	1.25
798	A140	65c Aechmea lingulata	1.50	1.50
799	A140	80c Asclepias curassavica	1.90	1.90
800	A140	$1 Caesalpinia bahamensis	2.40	2.40
801	A140	$1.10 Capparis cynophallophora	2.75	2.75
802	A140	$1.25 Stachytarpheta jamaicensis	3.00	3.00
803	A140	$2 Cassia biflora	4.75	4.75
804	A140	$5 Clusia rosea	12.00	12.00
805	A140	$10 Opuntia bahamana	24.00	24.00
		Nos. 790-805 (16)	56.95	56.95

1994   *Perf. 12*
790a	A140	8c	.20	.20
791a	A140	10c	.20	.20
792a	A140	15c	.35	.35
793a	A140	20c	.50	.50
794a	A140	25c	.60	.60
795a	A140	30c	.70	.70
796a	A140	35c	.85	.85
797a	A140	50c	1.25	1.25
798a	A140	65c	1.50	1.50
799a	A140	80c	1.90	1.90
800a	A140	$1	2.40	2.40
801a	A140	$1.10	2.75	2.75
802a	A140	$1.25	3.00	3.00
803a	A140	$2	4.75	4.75
804a	A140	$5	12.00	12.00
805a	A140	$10 ('95)	24.00	24.00
		Nos. 790a-805a (16)	56.95	56.95

Birds A141

1990, Feb. 19
806	A141	10c Yellow-billed cuckoo	1.25	.80
807	A141	15c White-tailed tropic bird	1.40	.80
808	A141	20c Kirtland's warbler	1.75	1.10
809	A141	30c Yellow-crowned night heron	2.25	1.10
810	A141	50c West Indian tree duck	3.25	1.60
811	A141	80c Yellow-bellied sapsucker	4.00	3.50
812	A141	$1 American kestrel	5.50	6.50
813	A141	$1.40 Mockingbird	5.25	4.25
		Nos. 806-813 (8)	24.65	19.65

Souvenir Sheets
814	A141	$2 Osprey	12.50	12.50
815	A141	$2 Yellow warbler	12.50	12.50

Fish A142

1990, Feb. 12   *Litho.*   *Perf. 14*
816	A142	8c Queen parrotfish	.30	.30
817	A142	10c Queen triggerfish	.30	.30
818	A142	25c Sergeant major	.70	.70
819	A142	40c Spotted goatfish	1.10	1.10
820	A142	50c Neon goby	1.40	1.40
821	A142	75c Nassau grouper	2.10	2.10
822	A142	80c Jawfish	2.25	2.25
823	A142	$1 Blue tang	2.75	2.75
		Nos. 816-823 (8)	10.90	10.90

Souvenir Sheets
824	A142	$2 Butter hamlet	8.00	8.00
825	A142	$2 Queen angelfish	8.00	8.00

Butterflies A143

1990, Mar. 19
826	A143	15c White peacock	1.00	.70
827	A143	25c Cloudless sulphur	1.25	.90
828	A143	35c Mexican fritillary	1.60	1.10
829	A143	40c Fiery skipper	1.75	1.25
830	A143	50c Chamberlain's sulphur	1.75	1.50
831	A143	60c Pygmy blue	2.10	2.10
832	A143	90c Dusky swallowtail	3.50	4.25
833	A143	$1 Antillean dagger wing	3.50	4.25
		Nos. 826-833 (8)	16.45	16.05

Souvenir Sheets
834	A143	$2 Thomas's blue	9.00	9.00
835	A143	$2 9 Queen species	9.00	9.00

Nos. 826, 831 and 833 vert.

America Issue A144

Fish, UPAE and discovery of America 500th anniv. emblems.

1990, Apr. 2
836	A144	10c Rock beauty	.80	.50
837	A144	15c Coney	.90	.65
838	A144	25c Red hind	1.25	.85
839	A144	50c Banded butterflyfish	1.75	1.75
840	A144	60c French angelfish	2.40	2.10
841	A144	75c Blackbar soldierfish	2.50	2.75
842	A144	90c Stoplight parrotfish	2.75	3.25
843	A144	$1 French grunt	3.00	3.50
		Nos. 836-843 (8)	15.35	15.35

Souvenir Sheets
844	A144	$2 Gray angelfish	5.00	5.00
845	A144	$2 Blue chromis	5.00	5.00

Penny Black, 150th Anniv. — A145

British Pillar Boxes — A146

25c, 1p essay in blue, without letters. 35c, Letter Box #1, 1855. 50c, Penfold Box, 1866. 75c, Great Britain #3, essay. $1, 2p blue essay. $1.25, Air mail box, 1935. #852, Great Britain #1. #853, K type box, 1979.

1990, May 3   *Litho.*   *Perf. 14*
846	A145	25c bluish blk	1.40	.90
847	A146	35c gray & pale brn	1.00	1.00
848	A145	50c gray & dk blue	1.40	1.40
849	A145	75c red brown	3.00	2.25
850	A145	$1 dk blue	3.75	3.75
851	A146	$1.25 gray & blue	3.00	4.50
		Nos. 846-851 (6)	13.55	13.80

Souvenir Sheets
852	A145	$2 black	6.00	6.00
853	A146	$2 blk & red brn	7.50	7.50

Stamp World London '90.

Queen Mother, 90th Birthday — A147

1990, Aug. 20   *Litho.*   *Perf. 14*
854	A147	10c multicolored	.55	.50
855	A147	25c multi, diff.	1.10	.80
856	A147	75c multi, diff.	2.00	2.00
857	A147	$1.25 multi, diff.	3.25	3.75
		Nos. 854-857 (4)	6.90	7.05

Souvenir Sheet
858	A147	$2 multi, diff.	7.00	7.00

Birds A148

1990, Sept. 24   *Litho.*   *Perf. 14*
859	A148	8c Stripe-headed tanager, vert.	1.25	.90
860	A148	10c Black-whiskered vireo	1.25	.90
861	A148	25c Blue-grey gnatcatcher	1.60	.90
862	A148	40c Lesser scaup	3.25	1.90
863	A148	50c White-cheeked pintail	3.25	1.90
864	A148	75c Common stilt	3.75	3.75
865	A148	80c Common oystercatcher, vert.	3.75	4.50
866	A148	$1 Tricolored heron	4.50	5.25
		Nos. 859-866 (8)	22.60	20.00

Souvenir Sheets
867	A148	$2 Bahama woodstar	6.25	6.25
868	A148	$2 American coot	6.25	6.25

Christmas A149

Different details from paintings by Rubens: 10c, 50c, 75c, No. 876, Triumph of Christ over Sin and Death. 35c, 45c, 65c, $1.25, No. 877,

St. Theresa Praying for the Souls in Purgatory. Nos. 876-877 show entire painting.

1990, Dec. 17			Litho.	Perf. 14	
869	A149	10c	multicolored	.45	.20
870	A149	35c	multicolored	1.50	1.25
871	A149	45c	multicolored	1.60	1.50
872	A149	50c	multicolored	1.90	1.60
873	A149	65c	multicolored	2.75	2.10
874	A149	75c	multicolored	3.00	2.75
875	A149	$1.25	multicolored	4.50	4.50
		Nos. 869-875 (7)		15.70	13.90

Souvenir Sheets

876	A149	$2	multicolored	9.00	9.00
877	A149	$2	multicolored	9.00	9.00

1992 Summer Olympics, Barcelona — A150

1991, Jan. 17					
878	A150	10c	Kayaking	.20	.20
879	A150	25c	Track	.80	.80
880	A150	75c	Pole vault	2.25	2.25
881	A150	$1.25	Javelin	3.75	3.75
		Nos. 878-881 (4)		7.00	7.00

Souvenir Sheet

882	A150	$2	Baseball	9.00	10.00

No. 878 inscribed Canoeing.

Voyages of Discovery A151

Designs: 5c, Henry Hudson, 1611. 10c, Roald Amundsen (airship), 1926. 15c, Amundsen (ship), 1906. 50c, USS Nautilus, 1958. 75c, Robert Scott, 1911. $1, Richard Byrd, Floyd Bennett, 1926. $1.25, Lincoln Ellsworth, 1935. $1.50, Cook, 1772-75. No. 891, The Nina. No. 892, The search for land.

1991, Apr. 15			Litho.	Perf. 14	
883	A151	5c	multicolored	1.00	.70
884	A151	10c	multicolored	1.00	.70
885	A151	15c	multicolored	1.50	1.00
886	A151	50c	multicolored	2.00	1.50
887	A151	75c	multicolored	3.50	2.75
888	A151	$1	multicolored	3.75	3.50
889	A151	$1.25	multicolored	5.50	6.75
890	A151	$1.50	multicolored	5.75	7.75
		Nos. 883-890 (8)		24.00	24.65

Souvenir Sheets

891	A151	$2	multicolored	8.00	8.00
892	A151	$2	multicolored	8.00	8.00

Discovery of America, 500th anniv. (in 1992).

Butterflies A152

1991, May 13			Litho.	Perf. 14	
893	A152	5c	White peacock	.30	.30
894	A152	25c	Orion	.90	.90
895	A152	35c	Gulf fritillary	1.25	1.25
896	A152	45c	Caribbean buckeye	1.60	1.60
897	A152	55c	Flambeau	1.90	1.90
898	A152	65c	Malachite	2.25	2.25
899	A152	70c	Florida white	2.50	2.50
900	A152	$1	Great southern white	3.50	3.50
		Nos. 893-900 (8)		14.20	14.20

Souvenir Sheets

901	A152	$2	Giant hairstreak	7.50	7.50
902	A152	$2	Orange-barred sulphur	7.50	7.50

Extinct Animals A153

1991, June 3					
903	A153	5c	Protohydrochoerus	.35	.35
904	A153	10c	Phororhacos	.35	.35
905	A153	15c	Prothylacynus	.55	.55
906	A153	50c	Borhyaena	1.75	1.75
907	A153	75c	Smilodon	2.75	2.75
908	A153	$1	Thoatherium	3.50	3.50
909	A153	$1.25	Cuvieronius	4.50	4.50
910	A153	$1.50	Toxodon	5.50	5.50
		Nos. 903-910 (8)		19.25	19.25

Souvenir Sheets

911	A153	$2	Mesosaurus	8.50	8.50
912	A153	$2	Astrapotherium	8.50	8.50

Royal Family Birthday, Anniversary
Common Design Type

1991			Litho.	Perf. 14	
913	CD347	10c	multicolored	.70	.35
914	CD347	25c	multicolored	.95	.80
915	CD347	35c	multicolored	1.25	.95
916	CD347	45c	multicolored	2.75	1.50
917	CD347	50c	multicolored	3.00	1.90
918	CD347	65c	multicolored	2.25	2.25
919	CD347	80c	multicolored	2.75	3.00
920	CD347	$1	multicolored	3.50	4.25
		Nos. 913-920 (8)		17.15	15.00

Souvenir Sheets

921	CD347	$2	Elizabeth, Philip	6.25	6.75
922	CD347	$2	Diana, sons, Charles	8.50	8.50

10c, 45c, 50c, $1, No. 922, Charles and Diana, 10th wedding anniv., issued: July 29. Others, Queen Elizabeth II, 65th birthday, issued: June 8.
For overprints see Nos. 1020-1022.

Mushrooms — A154

10c, Pluteus chrysophlebius. 15c, Leucopaxillus gracillimus. 20c, Marasmius haematocephalus. 35c, Collybia subpruinosa. 50c, Marasmius atrorubens, vert. 65c, Leucocoprinus birnbaumii, vert. $1.10, Trogia cantharelloides, vert. $1.25, Boletellus cubensis, vert. No. 931, Gerronema citrinum. No. 932, Pyrrhoglossum pyrrhum, vert.

1991, June 24			Litho.	Perf. 14	
923	A154	10c	multicolored	.35	.35
924	A154	15c	multicolored	.55	.55
925	A154	20c	multicolored	.70	.70
926	A154	35c	multicolored	1.25	1.25
927	A154	50c	multicolored	1.75	1.75
928	A154	65c	multicolored	2.25	2.25
929	A154	$1.10	multicolored	4.00	4.00
930	A154	$1.25	multicolored	4.50	4.50
		Nos. 923-930 (8)		15.35	15.35

Miniature Sheets

931	A154	$2	multicolored	7.50	7.75
932	A154	$2	multicolored	7.50	7.75

Paintings by Vincent Van Gogh — A155

Paintings: 15c, Weaver Facing Left, with Spinning Wheel. 25c, Head of a Young Peasant with Pipe, vert. 35c, The Old Cemetery Tower at Nuenen, vert. 45c, Cottage at Nightfall. 50c, Still Life with Open Bible. 65c, Lane at the Jardin du Luxembourg. 80c, The Pont du Carrousel and the Louvre. $1, Vase with

Poppies, Cornflowers, Peonies and Chrysanthemums, vert. No. 941, Entrance to the Public Park. No. 942, Plowed Field.

1991, Aug. 26				Perf. 13	
933	A155	15c	multicolored	.65	.65
934	A155	25c	multicolored	1.10	1.10
935	A155	35c	multicolored	1.40	1.40
936	A155	45c	multicolored	2.00	2.00
937	A155	50c	multicolored	2.25	2.25
938	A155	65c	multicolored	2.75	2.75
939	A155	80c	multicolored	3.50	3.50
940	A155	$1	multicolored	4.25	4.25
		Nos. 933-940 (8)		17.90	17.90

Size: 107x80mm
Imperf

941	A155	$2	multicolored	8.50	8.50
942	A155	$2	multicolored	8.50	8.50

Phila Nippon '91 A156

Japanese steam locomotives.

1991, Nov. 4			Litho.	Perf. 14	
943	A156	8c	Series 8550	.60	.60
944	A156	10c	C 57	.60	.60
945	A156	45c	Series 4110	1.90	1.25
946	A156	50c	C 55	1.90	1.25
947	A156	65c	Series 6250	2.75	2.75
948	A156	80c	E 10	3.00	3.00
949	A156	$1	Series 4500	3.25	3.50
950	A156	$1.25	C 11	4.25	4.25
		Nos. 943-950 (8)		18.25	17.20

Souvenir Sheets

951	A156	$2	C 62	5.75	5.75
952	A156	$2	C 58	5.75	5.75

Christmas A157

Details or entire paintings by Gerard David: 8c, Adoration of the Shepherds. 15c, Virgin and Child Enthroned with Two Angels. 35c, The Annunciation (outside wings). 45c, The Rest on the Flight into Egypt. 50c, The Rest on the Flight into Egypt, diff. 65c, Virgin and Child with Angels. 80c, The Adoration of the Shepherds, diff. $1.25, The Perussis Altarpiece. No. 961, The Adoration of the Kings. No. 962, The Nativity.

1991, Dec. 23				Perf. 12	
953	A157	8c	multicolored	.40	.40
954	A157	15c	multicolored	.65	.65
955	A157	35c	multicolored	1.40	1.40
956	A157	45c	multicolored	1.75	1.75
957	A157	50c	multicolored	2.10	2.10
958	A157	65c	multicolored	3.50	2.50
959	A157	80c	multicolored	3.25	3.25
960	A157	$1.25	multicolored	5.00	5.00
		Nos. 953-960 (8)		18.05	17.05

Souvenir Sheets
Perf. 14½

961	A157	$2	multicolored	6.75	6.75
962	A157	$2	multicolored	6.75	6.75

Boy Scouts A160

No. 968, Member of Boy Scout Service Corps at New York World's Fair, 1964-65. No. 969, Lord Robert Baden-Powell, vert. $2, Silver Buffalo Award.

1992, July 6			Litho.	Perf. 14	
968	A160	$1	multicolored	4.50	4.50

969	A160	$1	multicolored	4.50	4.50

Souvenir Sheet

970	A160	$2	multicolored	8.50	8.50

17th World Scout Jamboree, Korea.

Anniversaries and Events — A161

Designs: 25c, Astronaut releasing communications satellite. 50c, Tree with dead side, healthy side. 65c, Emblems, globe, food products. 80c, Fish in polluted, clean water. $1, Runners, Lions Intl. emblem. $1.25, Orbiting quarantine facility modules. No. 977, Planned orbital transfer vehicle for Mars. No. 977A, Industrial pollution, clean beach.

1992-93			Litho.	Perf. 14	
971	A161	25c	multicolored	1.50	1.50
972	A161	50c	multicolored	1.75	1.75
973	A161	65c	multicolored	4.25	4.25
974	A161	80c	multicolored	2.50	2.50
975	A161	$1	multicolored	5.00	5.00
976	A161	$1.25	multicolored	7.00	7.00
		Nos. 971-976 (6)		22.00	22.00

Souvenir Sheets

977	A161	$2	multicolored	10.00	10.00
977A	A161	$2	multicolored	10.00	10.00

Intl. Space Year (#971, 976-977). Earth Summit, Rio de Janeiro (#972, 974, 977A). Intl. Conf. on Nutrition, Rome (#973). Lions Intl., 75th anniv. (#975).
Issued: #972, 974, 977A, 1/93; others, 12/92.

Queen Elizabeth II's Accession to the Throne, 40th Anniv.
Common Design Type

1992, Feb. 6			Litho.	Perf. 14	
978	CD348	10c	multicolored	.70	.70
979	CD348	20c	multicolored	1.40	1.40
980	CD348	25c	multicolored	1.50	1.50
981	CD348	35c	multicolored	1.50	1.50
982	CD348	50c	multicolored	2.25	2.25
983	CD348	65c	multicolored	2.75	2.75
984	CD348	80c	multicolored	2.75	2.75
985	CD348	$1.10	multicolored	3.25	3.25
		Nos. 978-985 (8)		16.10	16.10

Souvenir Sheets

986	CD348	$2	Queen at left, boat dock	7.50	7.50
987	CD348	$2	Queen at right, shoreline	7.50	7.50

Spanish Art — A162

Paintings: 8c, St. Monica, by Luis Tristan. 20c, 45c, The Vision of Ezekiel: The Resurrection of the Flesh (different details) by Francisco Collantes. 50c, The Martyrdom of St. Philip, by Jose de Ribera. 65c, St. John the Evangelist, by Juan Ribalta. 80c, Archimedes by Jose de Ribera. $1, St. John the Baptist in the Desert by de Ribera. $1.25, The Martyrdom of St. Philip (detail), by de Ribera. No. 996, The Baptism of Christ by Juan Fernandez Navarrete. No. 997, Battle between Christians and Moors at El Sotillo, by Francisco de Zurbaran.

1992, May 26			Litho.	Perf. 13	
988	A162	8c	multicolored	.20	.20
989	A162	20c	multicolored	.70	.70
990	A162	45c	multicolored	1.75	1.75
991	A162	50c	multicolored	1.75	1.75
992	A162	65c	multicolored	2.10	2.10
993	A162	80c	multicolored	2.75	2.75
994	A162	$1	multicolored	3.50	3.50
995	A162	$1.25	multicolored	4.25	4.25
		Nos. 988-995 (8)		17.00	17.00

Size: 95x120mm

Imperf

996	A162	$2 multicolored	8.50	8.50
997	A162	$2 multicolored	8.50	8.50

Granada '92.

Discovery of America, 500th Anniv. A163

Commemorative coins, scenes of first voyage: 10c, Nina, ship. 15c, Pinta, ship. 20c, Santa Maria, Columbus' second coat of arms. 25c, Fleet at sea, ships. 30c, Landfall, sailing ship. 35c, Setting sail, Columbus departing. 50c, Columbus sighting New World, Columbus. 65c, Columbus exploring Caribbean, ship. 80c, Claiming land for Spain, Columbus, priest and cross. $1.10, Columbus exchanging gifts with native, Columbus, native.
No. 1008, Coins like #998-1000. No. 1009, Coins like #1004, 1006-1007.

1992, Oct.   Litho.   Perf. 14

998	A163	10c multicolored	.70	.70
999	A164	15c multicolored	1.10	1.10
1000	A164	20c multicolored	1.10	1.10
1001	A164	25c multicolored	1.50	1.50
1002	A164	30c multicolored	1.50	1.50
1003	A164	35c multicolored	1.75	1.75
1004	A164	50c multicolored	2.00	2.00
1005	A164	65c multicolored	3.00	3.00
1006	A164	80c multicolored	3.00	3.00
1007	A164	$1.10 multicolored	3.25	3.25
		Nos. 998-1007 (10)	18.90	18.90

Souvenir Sheets

1008	A164	$2 multicolored	8.50	8.50
1009	A164	$2 multicolored	8.50	8.50

Christmas A164

Details or entire paintings by Simon Bening: 8c, Nativity. 15c, Circumcision. 35c, Flight to Egypt. 50c, Massacre of the Innocents.
By Dirk Bouts: 65c, The Annunciation. 80c, The Visitation. $1.10, The Adoration of the Angels. $1.25, The Adoration of the Wise Men. No. 1018, The Virgin and Child. No. 1019, The Virgin Seated with the Child.

1992, Nov.   Litho.   Perf. 13½x14

1010	A164	8c multicolored	.55	.55
1011	A164	15c multicolored	1.10	1.10
1012	A164	35c multicolored	1.60	1.60
1013	A164	50c multicolored	2.00	2.00
1014	A164	65c multicolored	2.75	2.75
1015	A164	80c multicolored	3.25	3.25
1016	A164	$1.10 multicolored	3.75	3.75
1017	A164	$1.25 multicolored	3.75	3.75
		Nos. 1010-1017 (8)	18.75	18.75

Souvenir Sheets

1018	A164	$2 multicolored	8.50	8.50
1019	A164	$2 multicolored	8.50	8.50

Nos. 915, 918 & 921 Ovptd. in Red or Black

1993, Mar. 20   Litho.   Perf. 14

1020	CD347	35c on #915	2.75	2.75
1021	CD347	65c on #918	5.75	5.75

Souvenir Sheet

1022	CD347	$2 on #921 (Bk)	10.00	10.00

Miniature Sheet

Coronation of Queen Elizabeth II, 40th Anniv. — A165

Designs: a, 15c, Chalice and paten from royal collection. b, 50c, Official coronation photograph. c, $1, Coronation ceremony. d, $1.25, Queen, Prince Philip.
$2, New Portrait.

1993, June 2   Litho.   Perf. 13½x14

1023	A165	Sheet, 2 ea #a.-d.	16.00	16.00

Souvenir Sheet

Perf. 14

1024	A165	$2 multicolored	10.00	10.00

No. 1024 contains one 28x42mm stamp.

Christmas A166

Details or entire woodcut, Mary, Queen of the Angels, by Durer: 8c, 20c, 35c, $1.25.
Details or entire paintings by Raphael: 50c, $1, Virgin and Child with St. John the Baptist. 65c, The Canagiani Holy Family. 80c, The Holy Family with the Lamb.
Each $2: No. 1033, Mary, Queen of the Angels, by Durer. No. 1034, The Canagiani Holy Family, diff., by Raphael.

Perf. 13½x14, 14x13½

1993, Dec.   Litho.

1025-1032	A166	Set of 8	18.00	18.00

Souvenir Sheets

1033-1034	A166	Set of 2	13.00	13.00

Dinosaurs A167

8c, Omphalosaurus. 15c, Coelophysis. 20c, $2 (#1043), Triceratops. 35c, $2 (#1044), Dilophosaurus. 50c, Pterodactylus. 65c, Elasmosaurus. 80c, Stegosaurus. $1.25, Euoplocephalus.

1993, Nov. 15   Litho.   Perf. 14

1035-1042	A167	Set of 8	10.00	10.00

Souvenir Sheets

1043-1044	A167	Set of 2	17.00	17.00

Birds A168

Designs: 10c, Killdeer. 15c, Yellow-crowned night heron, vert. 35c, Northern mockingbird. 50c, Eastern kingbird, vert. 65c, Magnolia warbler. 80c, Cedar waxwing, vert. $1.10, Ruby-throated hummingbird. $1.25, Painted bunting, vert. No. 1053, American kestrel. No. 1054, Ruddy duck.

1993, Dec.

1045	A168	10c multicolored	.50	.50
1046	A168	15c multicolored	.75	.75
1047	A168	35c multicolored	1.90	1.90
1048	A168	50c multicolored	2.50	2.50
1049	A168	65c multicolored	3.50	3.50
1050	A168	80c multicolored	4.00	4.00
1051	A168	$1.10 multicolored	5.50	5.50
1052	A168	$1.25 multicolored	6.25	6.25
		Nos. 1045-1052 (8)	24.90	24.90

Souvenir Sheets

1053	A168	$2 multicolored	8.50	8.50
1054	A168	$2 multicolored	8.50	8.50

Fish A169

Designs: 10c, Bluehead wrasse. 20c, Honeycomb cowfish. 25c, Glasseye snapper. 35c, Spotted drum. 50c, Jolthead porgy. 65, Smallmouth grunt. 80c, Peppermint bass. $1.10, Indigo hamlet.
Each $2: No. 1063, Bonnethead shark. No. 1064, Sharpnose shark.

1993, Dec. 15

1055-1062	A169	Set of 8	11.50	11.50

Souvenir Sheets

1063-1064	A169	Set of 2	12.00	12.00

1994 World Cup Soccer Championships, US — A170

Designs: 8c, Segio Goycoechea, Argentina. 10c, Bado Illgner, Germany. 50c, Nico Claesen, Belgium. 65c, West German team. 80c, Cameroun team. $1, Santin, Francescoli, Uruguay; Cuciuffo, Argentina. $1.10, Sanchez, Mexico.
Each $2: No. 1072, Imre Garaba, Hungary, vert. No. 1073, Pontiac Silverdome.

1994, Sept. 26   Litho.   Perf. 14

1065-1071	A170	Set of 7	13.50	13.50

Souvenir Sheets

1072-1073	A170	Set of 2	10.00	10.00

Mushrooms — A171

Designs: 5c, Xerocomus guadelupae, vert. 10c, Volvariella volvacea, vert. 35c, Hygrocybe atrosquamosa. 50c, Pleurotus ostreatus. 65c, Marasmius pallescens. 80c, Coprinus plicatilis, vert. $1.10, Bolbitius vitellinus. $1.50, Pyroglossum lilaceipes, vert.
Each $2: No. 1082, Lentinus edodes. No. 1083, Russula cremeolilacina, vert.

1994, Oct. 10

1074-1081	A171	Set of 8	12.00	12.00

Souvenir Sheets

1082-1083	A171	Set of 2	11.50	11.50

Christmas A172

Illustrations from French Book of Hours: 25c, The Annunciation. 50c, The Visitation. 65c, Annunciation to the Shepherds. 80c, The Nativity. $1, Flight into Egypt.
$2, The Adoration of the Magi.

1994, Dec. 5   Litho.   Perf. 14

1084-1088	A172	Set of 5	14.00	14.00

Souvenir Sheet

1089	A172	$2 multicolored	8.00	8.00

Butterflies A173

Designs: 15c, Dryas julia. 20c, Urbanus proteus. 25c, Colobura dirce. 50c, Papilio homerus. 65c, Chiodes catillus. 80c, Eurytides zonaria. $1, Hypolymnas misippus. $1.25, Phoebis avellaneda.
Each $2: No. 1098, Eurema adamsi. No. 1099, Morpho peleides.

1994, Dec. 12

1090-1097	A173	Set of 8	13.00	13.00

Souvenir Sheets

1098-1099	A173	Set of 2	9.50	9.50

D-Day, 50th Anniv. A174

Designs: 10c, Gen. Montgomery, British landing on Juno Beach. 15c, Adm. Sir Bertram Ramsay, British commandos at Sword Beach. 35c, Gun crew aboard HMS Belfast. 50c, Montgomery, Eisenhower, Tedder review battle scene. 65c, Gen. Eisenhower, 101st Airborne Div. paratroopers. 80c, Gen. Omar Bradley, US landings on Omaha Beach. $1.10, Second wave of US troops on D-Day. $1.25, Supreme Commander Eisenhower presents Operation Overload.
Each $2: No. 1108, Eisenhower, Montgomery seated at table. No. 1109, Beachhead secured.

1994, Dec. 19

1100-1107	A174	Set of 8	12.00	12.00

Souvenir Sheets

1108-1109	A174	Set of 2	9.00	9.00

Orchids A175

Designs: 8c, Cattleya deckeri. 20c, Epidendrum carpophorum. 25c, Epidendrum ciliare. 50c, Encyclia phoenicea. 65c, Bletia patula. 80c, Brassia caudata. $1, Brassavola nodosa. $1.25, Bletia purpurea.
Each $2: No. 1118, Ionopsis utricularioides. No. 1119, Vanilla planifolia.

1995, Jan. 5

1110-1117	A175	Set of 8	12.00	12.00

Souvenir Sheets

1118-1119	A175	Set of 2	10.00	10.00

Miniature Sheet of 12

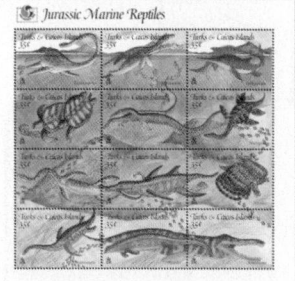

PHILAKOREA '94 — A176

Jurassic marine reptiles: a, Elasmosaurus. b, Plesiosaurus. c, Ichthyosaurus. d, Arcfielon. e, Askeptosaurus. f, Macroplata. g, Ceresiosaurus. h, Lipoleurodon. i, Henodus. j, Muraenosaurus. k, Placodus. l, Kronosaurus.

1995, Jan. 23

1120	A176	35c #1120a-1120 l	10.50	10.50

First Manned Moon Landing, 25th Anniv. A177

Designs: 10c, Apollo XI in flight. 20c, Simulated moon landing. 25c, Painting, Astronauts on the Moon, by Kovales. 35c, First foot, footprint on moon. 50c, Aldrin, solar wind experiment. 65c, Armstrong, Aldrin setting up flag on moon. 80c, Command module Columbia in Lunar orbit. $1.10, Recovery of Apollo XI in Pacific.

Each $2: No. 1129, Lift-off at Cape Canaveral, vert. No. 1130, Moon rock on display in Houston.

1995, Jan. 9   Litho.   Perf. 14

1121-1128	A177	Set of 8	9.00	9.00

Souvenir Sheets

1129-1130	A177	Set of 2	9.00	9.00

Intl. Olympic Committee, Cent. — A178

Summer, Winter Olympic events: 8c, Fencing. 10c, Speed skating. 15c, Diving. 20c, Cycling. 25c, Ice hockey. 35c, Figure skating. 50c, Soccer. 65c, Bobsled. 80c, Super giant slalom. $1.25, Equestrian.

Each $2: #1141, Gymnastics. #1142, Downhill skiing.

1995, Feb. 6

1131-1140	A178	Set of 10	17.00	17.00

Souvenir Sheets

1141-1142	A178	Set of 2	11.50	11.50

Domestic Cats A179

Various cats, kittens: 15c, 20c, 35c, 50c, 65c, 80c, $1, $1.25.

Each $2: No. 1151, Two sleeping. No. 1152, Kitten, ladybugs in flowers.

1995, July 3   Litho.   Perf. 14

1143-1150	A179	Set of 8	17.00	17.00

Souvenir Sheets

1151-1152	A179	Set of 2	12.00	12.00

Birds — A180

A180a

10c, Belted kingfisher. 15c, Clapper rail. 20c, American redstart. 25c, Roseate tern. 35c, Purple gallinule. 45c, Ruddy turnstone. 50c, Barn owl. 60c, Brown booby. 80c, Great blue heron. $1, Antillean nighthawk. $1.25, Thick-billed vireo. $1.40, American flamingo. $2, Wilson's plover. $5, Blue-winged teal. $10, Reddish egret.

1995, Aug. 2   Litho.   Perf. 13

1153	A180	10c multi	.20	.20
1154	A180	15c multi	.40	.40
1155	A180	20c multi	.55	.55
1156	A180	25c multi	.70	.70
1157	A180	35c multi	.95	.95
1158	A180	45c multi	1.25	1.25
1159	A180	50c multi	1.40	1.40
1160	A180	60c multi	1.75	1.75
1161	A180	80c multi	2.25	2.25
1162	A180	$1 multi	2.75	2.75
1163	A180	$1.25 multi	3.50	3.50
1164	A180	$1.40 multi	3.75	3.75
1165	A180	$2 multi	5.50	5.50
1166	A180	$5 multi	13.50	13.50
1166A	A180a	$10 multi	27.50	27.50
		Nos. 1153-1166A (15)	65.95	65.95

Queen Mother, 95th Birthday A181

No. 1167: a, Drawing. b, Wearing crown jewels. c, Formal portrait. d, Blue dress with pearls.

$2, Green blue outfit.

1995, Aug. 4   Perf. 13½x14

1167	A181	50c Block or strip of 4, #a.-d.	9.00	9.00

Souvenir Sheet

1168	A181	$2 multicolored	9.00	9.00

No. 1167 was issued in sheets of 8 stamps.

VE Day, 50th Anniv. A182

Designs: 10c, "Big Three" meet at Yalta. 15c, Allied war prisoners released. 20c, American, Soviets meet at Elbe River. 25c, Death of Franklin D. Roosevelt. 60c, US 9th Army confirms cease fire. 80c, New York City celebrates VE Day. $1, Nuremberg War Crimes trials begin.

$2, Big Ben, US Capitol, St. Basil's Cathedral.

1995, Aug. 14   Litho.   Perf. 14

1169-1175	A182	Set of 7	11.00	11.00

Souvenir Sheet

1176	A182	$2 multicolored	6.00	6.00

Miniature Sheet of 9

Singapore '95 — A183

Diving equipment, each 60c: No. 1177a, Wm. James, scuba, 1825. b, Rouquayrol apparatus, 1864. c, Fluess oxygen rebreathing apparatus, 1878. d, Armored diving suit, 1900. e, Jim Janett explores sunken Lusitania in Peress armored diving suit, 1935. f, Cousteau-Gagnan aqualung, 1943. g, Underwater camera, 1955. h, Sylvia Earle dives to 1,520 ft. in Jim suit, 1979. i, Spider propeller-driven rigid suit, 1984.

Each $2: No. 1178, Helmet diver, 1935. No. 1179, Jacques-Yves Cousteau.

1995, Sept. 1   Perf. 14½

1177	A183	Sheet of 9, #a.-i.	15.00	15.00

Souvenir Sheets

1178-1179	A183	Set of 2	10.00	10.00

Christmas A184

Details or entire paintings, by Piero di Cosimo (1462-1521): 20c, Madonna and Child with Young St. John. 25c, Adoration of the Child. 60c, Madonna and Child with Young St. John, St. Margaret, and An Angel. $1, Madonna and Child with An Angel.

$2, Madonna and Child with Angels and Saints.

1995, Dec. 29   Litho.   Perf. 14

1180-1183	A184	Set of 4	9.00	9.00

Souvenir Sheet

1184	A184	$2 multicolored	10.50	10.50

UN, 50th Anniv. — A185

Designs: 15c, Rights of women and children. 60c, Peace. 80c, Human rights. $1, Education.

Each $2: No. 1189, Flags of nations forming "50." No. 1190, Tractor, portions of UN, FAO emblems.

1996, Feb. 26   Litho.   Perf. 14

1185-1188	A185	Set of 4	6.25	6.25

Souvenir Sheets

1189-1190	A185	Set of 2	10.00	10.00

Queen Elizabeth II, 70th Birthday A186

No. 1191: a, Portrait. b, Wearing blue hat. c, In uniform, on horseback.

$2, As younger woman wearing white and yellow hat.

1996, Apr. 21   Litho.   Perf. 13½x14

1191	A186	80c Strip of 3, #a.-c.	5.50	5.50

Souvenir Sheet

1192	A186	$2 multicolored	4.75	4.75

No. 1191 was issued in sheets of 9 stamps.

History of Underwater Exploration A187

No. 1193, each 55c: a, Glaucus, God of Divers, 2500BC. b, Alexander the Great decends to ocean bottom, 332BC. c, Salvage

diver, 1430. d, Borelli's rebreathing device, 1680. e, Edmond Halley's diving bell, 1690. f, John Lethbridge's diving machine, 1715. g, Klingert's diving apparatus, 1789. h, Drieberg's triton, 1808. i, Seibe's diving helmet, 1819.

No. 1194, each 60c: a, Jim Jarrat in "Iron Man" armored diving suit explores Lusitania, 1935. b, Cousteau, team excavate first shipwreck using scuba gear, 1952. c, Oldest shipwreck ever found, coast of Turkey, 1959. d, Swedish warship Vasa raised, 1961. e, Mel Fisher discovers Spanish galleon Atocha, 1971. f, Whydah, first pirate ship found, is discovered by Barry Clifford, 1984. g, Dr. Robert Ballard, using robot sub Argo finds battleship Bismarck, 1989. h, Radeau "Land Tortoise" scuttled in 1758 during French and Indian War found in Lake George, NY, 1991. i, Deep-diving nuclear submarine recovers ancient Roman shipwreck cargo, 1994.

Each $2: No. 1195, Arab diver Issa, 12th cent. No. 1196, Pearl diver in Caribbean, 1498. No. 1197, Diver in Newtsuit investigates Edmund Fitzgerald. No. 1198, Submarine Alvin explores Titanic, 1985.

1996, May 13   Litho.   Perf. 14

1193	A187	Sheet of 9, #a.-i.	16.00	16.00
1194	A187	Sheet of 9, #a.-i.	12.00	12.00

Souvenir Sheets

1195-1198	A187	Set of 4	20.00	20.00

CHINA '96 (Nos. 1193, 1195-1196). CAPEX '96 (Nos. 1194, 1197-1198).

1996 Summer Olympics, Atlanta A188

Olympic gold medals for: No. 1199, Equestrian. No. 1200, Cycling. No. 1201, Fencing. No. 1202, Gymnastics. No. 1203, Hurdles. No. 1204, Pole vault. No. 1205, Sprints. No. 1206, Swimming. No. 1207, Diving. No. 1208, Running.

1996, May 27   Perf. 13½

1199-1208	A188	55c Set of 10	11.00	11.00
1208a		Sheet of 10, #1199-1208	11.00	

Nos. 1199-1208 issued in sheets as well as in No. 1208a.

A189   A190

James A.G.S. McCartney (1945-80), 1st Chief Minister of Turks & Caicos Islands,

1996, July 3   Litho.   Perf. 14

1209	A189	60c multicolored	1.25	1.25

Ministerial Government, 20th anniv.
No. 1209 was issued in sheets of 9.

1996, Sept. 8   Litho.   Perf. 14

Working Dogs: No. 1210: a, Space research. b, Racing. c, Rescue. d, Military. e, Sporting. f, Companion. g, Hearing ear. h, Sled. i, Police. j, Guarding. k, Watch. l, Security.

Each $2: No. 1211, Guide. No. 1212, Sheep dog.

1210	A190	25c Sheet of 12, #a.-l.	12.00	12.00

Souvenir Sheets

1211-1212	A190	Set of 2	13.00	13.00

Winnie the Pooh, Christmas A191

Designs: 15c, Pooh trying to stay awake. 20c, Piglet, star. 35c, Ribbons and bows. 50c, Jingle bells. 60c, "Pooh loves Christmas." 80c, "Big hearts come in bouncy packages." $1, Santa Pooh. $1.25, "My most favorite."
No. 1221, Piglet, cookie. No. 1222, Piglet placing star atop tree.

1996, Nov. 25   Litho.   Perf. 13½x14
| 1213-1220 | A191 | Set of 8 | 17.00 | 17.00 |

Souvenir Sheets
| 1221 | A191 | $2 multicolored | 7.50 | 7.50 |
| 1222 | A191 | $2.60 multicolored | 9.50 | 9.50 |

Flowers — A192

A193

No. 1223: a, Giant milkweed. b, Geiger tree. c, Passion flower. d, Hibiscus.
No. 1224: a, Yellow elder. b, Prickly poppy. c, Frangipani. d, Seaside mahoe.
Each $2: No. 1225, Chain of love. No. 1226, Firecracker.

1997, Feb. 10   Litho.   Perf. 14
| 1223 | A192 | 20c Strip or block of 4, #a.-d. | 3.25 | 3.25 |
| 1224 | A192 | 60c Strip or block of 4, #a.-d. | 4.75 | 4.75 |

Souvenir Sheets
| 1225-1226 | A192 | Set of 2 | 9.00 | 9.00 |

Nos. 1223-1224 were each issued in sheets of 8 stamps.

1997, Mar. 24   Litho.   Perf. 14
UNICEF, 50th Anniv.: a, Dove flying right. b, Three children. c, Dove flying left. d, Boy with dog, girl holding cat.
| 1227 | A193 | 60c Sheet of 4, #a.-d. | 6.00 | 6.00 |

Souvenir Sheets

UNESCO, 50th Anniv. — A194

Canterbury Cathedral: No. 1228, View from rear. No. 1229, Interior view. Illustration reduced.

1997, Mar. 24   Litho.   Perf. 14
| 1228 | A194 | $2 multicolored | 4.50 | 4.50 |
| 1229 | A194 | $2 multicolored | 4.50 | 4.50 |

Queen Elizabeth II, Prince Philip, 50th Wedding Anniv. A195

Designs: a, Queen waving. b, Royal arms. c, Queen, Prince riding in car. d, Prince, Queen seated. e, Windsor Castle. f, Prince Philip. $2, Wedding portrait.

1997, Apr. 21   Litho.   Perf. 14
| 1230 | A195 | 60c Sheet of 6, #a.-f. | 12.50 | 12.50 |

Souvenir Sheet
| 1231 | A195 | $2 multicolored | 9.00 | 9.00 |

Heinrich von Stephan (1831-97), Founder of UPU A196

Portrait of Von Stephan and: No. 1232: a, British mail coach, 1700's. b, UPU emblem. c, Space shuttle, future transport.
$2, Von Stephan, Hemerodrome, messenger of ancient Greece.

1997, July 1   Litho.   Perf. 14
| 1232 | A196 | 50c Sheet of 3, #a.-c. | 6.00 | 6.00 |

Souvenir Sheet
| 1233 | A196 | $2 multicolored | 5.50 | 5.50 |

PACIFIC 97.

Underwater Exploration A197

No. 1234: a, Edgerton camera taking photos at 6,000 ft., 1954. b, Conshelf Habitat, 1963. c, Sealab II, 1965. d, Research Habitat, Tektite, 1970. e, Discovery of Galapagos Volcanic Rift, 1974. f, Epaulard, robot survey craft, 1979. g, Sea life discovered thriving in undersea oil field, 1995. h, Deep flight, 1996, one-man research vessel. i, Sea ice is studied from above, under sea, Okhotsk Tower, off Japan, 1996.
Each $2: No. 1235, Coelacanth. No. 1236, John Williamson makes first underwater movies, 1914.

1997, Aug. 21   Litho.   Perf. 14
| 1234 | A197 | 20c Sheet of 9, #a.-i. | 8.00 | 8.00 |

Souvenir Sheets
| 1235-1236 | A197 | Set of 2 | 10.00 | 10.00 |

Stampshow 97.

Christmas A198

Entire paintings or details: 15c, Adoration of an Angel, by Studio of Fra Angelico. 20c, Scenes from the Life of St. John the Baptist, by Master of Saint Severin. 35c, Archangel Gabriel, by Masolino de Panicale. 50c, 60c, Jeremiah with Two Angels, by Gherardo Starnina (diff. angels). 80c, The Annunciation, by Giovanni di Palo di Grazia. $1, The Annunciation, by Carlo di Bracceso. $1.25, The Nativity, by Benvenuto di Giovanni Guasta.

Each $2: No. 1245, The Wilton Diptych (right panel), by unknown English or French artist, c. 1395. No. 1246, Adoring Angels, from The Journey of the Magi, by Benozzo Gozzoli.

1997, Dec. 8   Litho.   Perf. 14
| 1237-1244 | A198 | Set of 8 | 11.50 | 11.50 |

Souvenir Sheets
| 1245-1246 | A198 | Set of 2 | 10.00 | 10.00 |

World Wildlife Fund — A199

Snapper: a, Blackfin. b, Dog. c, Cubera. d, Mahogany.

1998, Feb. 24   Litho.   Perf. 14
| 1247 | A199 | 25c Block of 4, #a.-d. | 3.00 | 3.00 |

No. 1247 was issued in sheets of 16 stamps. Intl. Year of the Reef.

Marine Life — A200

Underwater photographs: 20c, Spotted flamingo tongue. 50c, Feather duster. 60c, Squirrel fish. 80c, Queen angelfish. $1, Barracuda. $1.25, Fairy basslet.
Each $2: No. 1254, Rough file clam. No. 1255, Spotted cleaning shrimp.

1998, May 1   Litho.   Perf. 14
| 1248-1253 | A200 | Set of 6 | 13.00 | 13.00 |

Souvenir Sheets
| 1254-1255 | A200 | Set of 2 | 9.50 | 9.50 |

A201   A202

Stylized designs showing symbol for earth, water, and — No. 1256: a, Dove. b, Crab. c, Fish. d, Clover leaf.
$2, Symbol for earth and water.

1998, July 30   Litho.   Perf. 14
| 1256 | A201 | 50c Sheet of 4, #a.-d. | 7.00 | 7.00 |

Souvenir Sheet
| 1257 | A201 | $2 multicolored | 6.50 | 6.50 |

Intl. Year of the Ocean.

Royal Air Force, 80th Anniv.
Common Design Type Re-Inscribed

Designs: 20c, SE 5A. 50c, Sopwith Camel. 60c, Supermarine Spitfire. 80c, Avro Lancaster. $1, Panavia Tornado. $1.25, Hawker Hurricane.
Each $2: No. 1264, Hawker Siddeley Harrier. No. 1265, Avro Vulcan.

1998, Aug. 18   Litho.   Perf. 14
| 1258-1263 | CD350 | Set of 6 | 16.00 | 16.00 |

Souvenir Sheets
| 1264-1265 | CD350 | Set of 2 | 16.00 | 16.00 |

1998, July 30   Litho.   Perf. 14
Anniversaries and Events: 20c, University of the West Indies, 50th anniv. 60c, UNESCO,

World Summit Program. 80c, Universal Declaration of Human Rights. $1, John Glenn's return to space.
$2, NASA Space Shuttle leaving launching pad.

| 1266-1269 | A202 | Set of 4 | 6.25 | 6.25 |

Souvenir Sheet
| 1270 | A202 | $2 multicolored | 5.50 | 5.50 |

A203

A204

1998, Aug. 31
| 1271 | A203 | 60c multicolored | 2.25 | 2.25 |

Diana, Princess of Wales (1961-97). No. 1271 was issued in sheets of 6.

1998, Nov. 30   Litho.   Perf. 14
Paintings by Sister Thomasita Fessler — #1272: a, Magi's Visit. b, Flight Into Egypt. c, Wedding Feast. d, Maria. e, Annunciation & Visitation. f, Nativity. $2, Queen of Mothers.
| 1272 | A204 | 50c Sheet of 6, #a.-f. | 10.50 | 10.50 |

Souvenir Sheet
| 1273 | A204 | $2 multicolored | 5.50 | 5.50 |

Christmas. Nos. 1272e-1272f are each 58x48mm.

Coral Gardens A205

No. 1274: a, Flamingos in flight. b, Sailboats. c, Seagulls, lighthouse. d, House along shore, seagulls. e, Pillar coral, yellowtail snapper (f). f, Eliptical star coral. g, Porkfish. h, Spotted eagle ray. i, Large ivory coral. j, Mustard hill coral, shy hamlet. k, Blue crust coral. l, Fused staghorn coral, massive starlet coral. m, Queen angelfish, massive starlet coral. n, Pinnate spiny sea fan. o, Knobby star coral, squirrelfish. p, Lowridge cactus coral, juvenile porkfish. q, Orange telesto coral. r, Spanish hogfish (q), Knobby ten-ray star coral. s, Boulder brain coral, clown wrasse. t, Rainbow parrotfish, regal sea fan. u, Great star coral, bluestriped grunt. v, Stinging coral, blue tang. w, Lavender thin finger coral. x, Juvenile french grunt (w), brilliant sea fingers.
Each $2: No. 1275, Sea fan. No. 1276, Elkhorn coral.

1999, June 7   Litho.   Perf. 14¼x14½
| 1274 | A205 | 20c Sheet of 24, #a.-x. | 24.00 | 24.00 |

Souvenir Sheets
| 1275-1276 | A205 | Set of 2 | 19.00 | 19.00 |

Wedding of Prince Edward and Sophie Rhys-Jones — A206

Portraits — #1277: a, Couple facing forward. b, Edward. c, Sophie. d, Couple walking arm in arm.
Each $2: No. 1278, Couple facing forward. No. 1279, Couple facing each other.

1999, June 19   Litho.   Perf. 14
1277 A206 60c Sheet of 4,
               #a.-d.   7.50   7.50
Souvenir Sheets
1278-1279 A206 Set of 2   12.00 12.00

Queen Mother (b. 1900) A207

Designs: a, At age 7. b, At age 19. c, At wedding. d, With daughters. e, With King George VI during World War II. f, In 1958. g, At age 60. h, In 1970. i, With Princes Charles and William, 1983. j, Current photograph.

1999, Aug. 4   Litho.   Perf. 13½x13¾
1280 A207 50c Sheet of 10,
               #a.-j.   19.00 19.00
Stamp inscription on No. 1280f is incorrect.
No. 1280 was reissued in 2002 with added inscription in margin, "Good Health and Happiness to her Majesty The Queen Mother on her 101st Birthday." Value, $19.

2nd World Underwater Photography Competition Winners A208

No. 1281: a, 10c, Painted tunicates (8th place). b, 20c, Peacock flounder (7th). c, 50c, Squirt anemone shrimps (6th). d, 60c, Juvenile drum (5th). e, 80c, Batwing coral crab (4th). f, $1, Moon jellyfish (3rd).
Each $2: No. 1282, Christmas tree worms (2nd). No. 1283, Longhorn nudibranch (1st).

1999, Oct. 11   Litho.   Perf. 14¼x13¾
1281 A208 Sheet of 6, #a.-f.   11.00 11.00
   g.   As No. 1281, with corrected
           pictures   6.50   6.50
Issued: No. 1281g, 11/6/00.
On No. 1281, the illustrations for the 10c and 20c stamps are incorrect, with the 10c stamp inscribed "Painted tunicates," but depicting a peacock flounder, and the 20c stamp inscribed "Peacock flounder," but depicting painted tunicates. The pictures were switched on No. 1281g, making the inscriptions match the pictures.

Souvenir Sheets
Perf. 13¾
1282-1283 A208 Set of 2   16.00 16.00
Nos. 1282-1283 each contain one 50x38mm stamp.

Christmas A209

Paintings by Anthony Van Dyck: 20c, The Mystic Marriage of Saint Catherine. 50c, Rest on the Flight into Egypt. No. 1286, $2, Holy Family with Saints John and Elizabeth.
No. 1287, The Madonna of the Rosary.

1999, Dec. 7   Perf. 13¾
1284-1286 A209 Set of 3   10.50 10.50
Souvenir Sheet
1287 A209 $2 multicolored   10.50 10.50

Millennium A210

Perf. 14½x14¼
1999, Nov. 15   Litho.
1288 A210 20c silver & multi   .80   .80
1289 A210 $1 gold & multi   4.00   4.00

Millennium A211

Globe, clock and: No. 1290: a, London. b, Turks & Caicos Islands. c, New York. d, Rome. e, Jerusalem. f, Paris.
Each $2: No. 1291, Flag of Islands. No. 1292, Arms of Islands.

2000, Jan. 18   Litho.   Perf. 14x13¾
1290 A211 50c Sheet of 6,
               #a.-f.   12.00 12.00
Souvenir Sheets
1291-1292 A211 Set of 2   18.00 18.00

Mushrooms — A212

No. 1293, vert.: a, Pholiota squarroides. b, Psilocybe squamosa. c, Spathularia velutipes. d, Russula. e, Clitocybe clavipes. f, Boletus frostii.
No. 1294, Strobilurus conigenoides. No. 1295, Stereum ostrea.
Illustration reduced.

2000, July 6   Litho.   Perf. 14
1293 A212 50c Sheet of 6, #a-
               f   10.00 10.00
Souvenir Sheets
1294-1295 A212 $2 Set of 2   13.00 13.00

Souvenir Sheet

2000 Summer Olympics, Sydney — A213

No. 1296: a, Johan Gabriel Oxenstierna. b, Javelin. c, Aztec Stadium, Mexico City and Mexican flag. d, Ancient Greek runners.

2000, Sept. 25
1296 A213 50c Sheet of 4, #a-d   8.00   8.00

Birds A214

Designs: No. 1297, Chickadee. No. 1298, Scrub turkey. No. 1299, Sickle-bill gull.
No. 1300: a, Egret. b, Tern. c, Osprey. d, Great blue heron. e, Pelican. f, Bahama pintail.
No. 1301, Flamingo, vert. No. 1302, Macaw, vert.

2000, Oct. 2
1297-1299 A214 50c Set of 3   5.50   5.50
1300 A214 60c Sheet of 6, #a-
               f   12.50 12.50
Souvenir Sheets
1301-1302 A214 $2 Set of 2   15.00 15.00

Dogs and Cats — A215

No. 1303, 60c: a, Airedale terrier. b, Beagle. c, Dalmatian. d, Chow chow. e, Chihuahua. f, Pug.
No. 1304, 80c: a, Egyptian mau. b, Manx. c, Burmese. d, Korat. e, Maine coon cat. f, American shorthair.
No. 1305, $2, Collie. No. 1306, $2, Devon rex.

2000, Nov. 13   Litho.   Perf. 14
Sheets of 6, #a-f
1303-1304 A215 Set of 2   24.00 24.00
Souvenir Sheets
1305-1306 A215 Set of 2   12.00 12.00

Battle of Britain, 60th Anniv. A216

Designs: No. 1307, 50c, Douglas Robert Stewart Bader. No. 1308, 50c, Alan Christopher "Al" Deere. No. 1309, 50c, James Edgar "Johnny" Johnson. No. 1310, 50c, Edgar James "Cobber" Kain. No. 1311, 50c, James Harry "Ginger" Lacey. No. 1312, 50c, Air Vice-marshal Trafford Leigh. No. 1313, 50c, Adolph Gysbert "Sailor" Malan. No. 1314, Air Vice-marshal Keith Park.
No. 1315, each 50c: a, Winston Churchill. b, Barrage balloon. c, Heinkel He-111 Casa 2 111E. d, Soldier's farewell kiss to son. e, Hawker Hurricane. f, Dr, Jocelyn Henry Temple Peakins, clergyman in Home Guard. g, RAF fighter pilots scramble after an alert. h, Civilian volunteers scan the skies.
No. 1316, $2, Churchill, British flag. No. 1317, $2, London children.

2000, Dec. 4   Perf. 14
Stamps + labels
1307-1314 A216 Set of 8   14.00 14.00
1315 A216 Sheet of 8, #a-h   14.00 14.00
Souvenir Sheets
1316-1317 A216 Set of 2   13.00 13.00

Butterflies — A217

No. 1318, 50c: a, Clorinde. b, Blue night. c, Small lace-wing. d, Mosaic. e, Monarch. f, Grecian shoemaker.
No. 1319, 50c: a, Giant swallowtail. b, Common morpho. c, Tiger pierid. d, Banded king shoemaker. e, Figure-of-eight. f, Polydamas swallowtail.
No. 1320, $2, Orange-barred sulphur. No. 1321, $2, White peacock.

2000, Dec. 11   Litho.
Sheets of 6, #a-f
1318-1319 A217 Set of 2   22.50 22.50
Souvenir Sheets
1320-1321 A217 Set of 2   14.00 14.00

Ships A218

Designs: No. 1322, 60c, Neptune. No. 1323, 60c, Eagle. No. 1324, 60c, Gloria. No. 1325, 60c, Clipper ship, vert.
No. 1326, 60c: a, Viking long ship. b, Henri Grace à Dieu. c, Golden Hind. d, Endeavor. e, Anglo-Norman. f, Libertad.
No. 1327, 60c: a, Northern European cog. b, Carrack. c, Mayflower. d, Queen Anne's Revenge. e, Holkar. f, Amerigo Vespucci.
No. 1328, $2, USS Constitution, vert. No. 1329, $2, Denmark, vert.

2001, May 15   Litho.   Perf. 14
1322-1325 A218 Set of 4   9.25   9.25

Sheets of 6, #a-f
1326-1327 A218 Set of 2   27.50 27.50
Souvenir Sheets
1328-1329 A218 Set of 2   18.00 18.00

Whales
A219

Designs: No. 1330, 50c, Beluga. No. 1331, 50c, Killer. No. 1332, 50c, Dwarf sperm. No. 1333, 50c, Shortfin pilot.
No. 1334, 50c: a, Bowhead. b, Two killer. c, Pygmy sperm. d, Right. e, Sperm. f, California gray.
No. 1335, 50c: a, Narwhal. b, One killer (in air). c, Bryde's. d, Belugas. e, Sperm (and starfish). f, Pilot.
No. 1336, $2, Cuvier's beaked. No. 1337, $2, Humpback (with calf).

2001, May 15
1330-1333 A219 Set of 4   9.00 9.00
Sheets of 6, #a-f
1334-1335 A219 Set of 2   26.00 26.00
Souvenir Sheets
1336-1337 A219 Set of 2   18.00 18.00

UN Women's
Human Rights
Campaign — A220

Designs: 60c, Woman. 80c, Woman, bird, torch.

2001, June 18   Litho.   Perf. 14
1338-1339 A220 Set of 2   7.00 7.00

Phila Nippon
'01 — A221

Designs: No. 1340, 60c, Autumn Moon in Mirror, by Suzuki Harunobu. No. 1341, 60c, Rikaku II as a Fisherman, by Hirosada. No. 1342, 60c, Musical Party, by Hishikawa Moronobu. No. 1343, 60c, Kannon and Four Farmers, by H. Gatto. No. 1344, 60c, Rain in Fifth Month, by Kunisada I. No. 1345, 60c, The Lives of Women, by Kuniyoshi Utagawa.

2001, July 30   Perf. 12x12¼
1340-1345 A221 Set of 6   12.00 12.00

Queen Victoria (1819-1901) — A222

No. 1346, 60c, oval frames: a, Wearing white headcovering. b, Wearing crown as young woman. c, Wearing black hat. d, Wearing crown as old woman.
No. 1347, 60c, rectangular frames: a, Wearing white headcovering. b, Holding flowers. c, Wearing white dress. d, Wearing crown, white dress with blue sash.
No. 1348, $2, Brown orange background. No. 1349, $2, Holding umbrella.

2001, July 2   Perf. 14
Sheets of 4, #a-d
1346-1347 A222 Set of 2   19.00 19.00
Souvenir Sheets
1348-1349 A222 Set of 2   14.00 14.00

Queen Elizabeth II, 75th
Birthday — A223

No. 1350: a, In pink hat. b, With crown looking left. c, In green hat. d, With crown looking forward. e, In red orange hat. f, With crown and veil.
$2, Wearing robe.

2001, July 2
1350 A223 60c Sheet of 6, #a-
f   14.50 14.50
Souvenir Sheet
1351 A223 $2 multi   8.00 8.00

Butterflies — A224

Designs: 10c, Cuban mimic. 15c, Gundlach's swallowtail, vert. 20c, Graphium androcles. 25c, Eastern black swallowtail. 35c, Papilio velvois, vert. 45c, Schaus swallowtail, vert. 50c, Pipevine swallowtail, vert. 60c, Euploea mniszecki, vert. 80c, Poey's black swallowtail, vert. $1, Graphium encelades, vert. $1.25, Jamaican ringlet. $1.40, Eastern

tiger swallowtail. $2, Graphium milon, vert. $5, Palamedes swallowtail. $10, Zebra swallowtail.

Perf. 14x14¾, 14¾x14
2001, Sept. 27
1352 A224 10c multi   .20 .20
1353 A224 15c multi   .30 .30
1354 A224 20c multi   .40 .40
1355 A224 25c multi   .50 .50
1356 A224 35c multi   .70 .70
1357 A224 45c multi   .90 .90
1358 A224 50c multi   1.00 1.00
1359 A224 60c multi   1.25 1.25
1360 A224 80c multi   1.60 1.60
1361 A224 $1 multi   2.00 2.00
1362 A224 $1.25 multi   2.50 2.50
1363 A224 $1.40 multi   3.00 3.00
1364 A224 $2 multi   4.25 4.25
1365 A224 $5 multi   11.00 11.00
1366 A224 $10 multi   22.50 22.50
Nos. 1352-1366 (15)   52.10 52.10
25c, 35c, $5, $10 exist dated "2003." Value, set $32.50.

Reign of Queen
Elizabeth II, 50th
Anniv. — A225

No. 1367: a, Crossing Place Trail, Middle Caicos. b, Wades Green Plantation, North Caicos. c, Underwater scenery, Grand Turk. d, St. Thomas Anglican Church, Grand Turk. e, Ripsaw band, Grand Turk. f, Basketweaving.
No. 1368: a, Visit of Princess Royal, 1960. b, Visit of Queen Elizabeth II, 1966. c, Visit of Princess Alexandra, 1988. d, Visit of Duke of Edinburgh, 1993. e, Visit of Prince Andrew, 2000.
No. 1369: a, Salt Industry, 1952-62. b, Space splashdown, 1962-72. c, Ministerial government system, 1972-82. d, Quincentennial of Columbus' landfall, 1982-92. e, National Museum, 1992-2002.

2002, June 1   Litho.   Perf. 14¼
1367   Sheet of 6   4.25 4.25
a.-f. A225 25c Any single   .70 .70
Perf. 13¾
1368   Sheet of 5   8.75 8.75
a.-e. A225 60c Any single   1.75 1.75
Perf. 13¾x14¼
1369   Sheet of 5   11.00 11.00
a.-e A225 80c Any single   2.10 2.10
No. 1368 contains five 31x31mm stamps; No. 1369 contains five 30x34mm stamps.

20th World Scout Jamboree,
Thailand — A226

No. 1370: a, Scout with mallet and chisel. b, Scout with rifle. c, Scout hanging on rope above water. d, Scouts and lantern.
$2, Handicapped Scouts.

2002, July 15   Perf. 14
1370 A226 80c Sheet of 4, #a-d   9.50 9.50
Souvenir Sheet
1371 A226 $2 multi   6.00 6.00

Intl. Year of Ecotourism — A227

No. 1372, vert.: a, Humpback whale. b, Water sports. c, Regattas. d, Queen angelfish. e, Manta ray. f, Turtle.
$2, Jojo dolphin.

2002, July 15
1372 A227 60c Sheet of 6, #a-f   12.50 12.50
Souvenir Sheet
1373 A227 $2 multi   6.25 6.25
No. 1372 contains six 28x42mm stamps.

Intl. Year of Mountains — A228

No. 1374: a, Devil's Peak, South Africa. b, Mt. Drakensburg, South Africa. c, Mt. Blanc, France. d, Roan Mountain, US. e, Mt. Sefton, New Zealand. f, Mt. Cook, New Zealand.
$2, Northwest Highlands, Scotland.

2002, July 22
1374 A228 80c Sheet of 6, #a-
f   14.00 14.00
Souvenir Sheet
1375 A228 $2 multi   6.25 6.25

United We
Stand — A229

2002, Aug. 5
1376 A229 50c multi   1.50 1.50
Printed in sheets of 4.

Insects and Birds — A230

No. 1377, 60c: a, Hawk moth. b, Burnet moth. c, Mammoth wasp. d, Branch-boring

beetle. e, Flower mantid, Pseudocrebotra species. f, Flower mantid, Creobroter species.
No. 1378, 60c: a, Sooty tern. b, Magnificent frigatebird. c, American white pelican. d, Northern shoveler. e, Baltimore oriole. f, Roseate spoonbill.
No. 1379, $2, Tiphiid wasp. No. 1380, $2, Greater flamingo, vert.

2002, Aug. 12   **Perf. 14**
Sheets of 6, #a-f
1377-1378 A230   Set of 2   22.50 22.50
Souvenir Sheets
1379-1380 A230   Set of 2   12.00 12.00

Queen Mother Elizabeth (1900-2002) — A231

No. 1381: a, Without hat. b, With hat.

2002, Oct. 21
1381 A231 80c Sheet, 2 each
    #a-b   10.00 10.00

First Nonstop Solo Transatlantic Flight, 75th Anniv. — A232

No. 1382: a, Charles Lindbergh's early exploits as a barnstormer. b, Lindbergh standing in front of Spirit of St. Louis. c, Spirit of St. Louis. d, Take-off from Roosevelt Field. e, Crossing the Atlantic. f, Arrival and welcome in Paris.

2002, Nov. 18   **Litho.**   **Perf. 14**
1382 A232 60c Sheet of 6, #a-
    f   11.50 11.50

Pres. John F. Kennedy (1917-63) — A233

No. 1383 — Portrait color: a, Orange brown. b, Red violet. c, Greenish gray. d, Blue violet. e, Purple. f, Dull brown.

2002, Nov. 18
1383 A233 60c multi   11.50 11.50

Christmas
A234

Designs: 20c, Madonna and Child, by Giovanni Bellini, vert. 25c, Adoration of the Magi, by Correggio. 60c, Transfiguration of Christ, by Bellini, vert. 80c, Polyptych of St. Vincent Ferrer, by Bellini, vert. $1, Miraculous Mass, by Simone Martini, vert.
$2, Christ in Heaven with Four Saints, by Domenico Ghirlandaio.

2002, Nov. 25
1384-1388 A234   Set of 5   8.00 8.00
Souvenir Sheet
1389 A234 $2 multi   6.00 6.00

Japanese Art — A235

Designs: 25c, Nagata no Taro Nagamune, by Kuniyoshi Utagawa. 35c, Danjuro Ichikawa VII, by Kunisada Utagawa. 60c, Nagata no Taro Nagamune, by Kuniyoshi Utagawa, diff. $1, Nagata no Taro Nagamune, by Kuniyoshi Utagawa, diff.
No. 1394 — Scroll of Actors, by Chikanobu Toyohara and others: a, Smiling man holding fan. b, Man holding sword at mouth. c, Man holding sword vertically. d, Man with tree branch above head.
$2, Two Women by a River, by Chikanobu Hashimoto.

2003, June 17   **Litho.**   **Perf. 14¼**
1390-1393 A235   Set of 4   4.50 4.50
1394 A235 80c Sheet of 4, #a-d   6.50 6.50
Souvenir Sheet
1395 A235 $2 multi   4.00 4.00

Rembrandt Paintings
A236

Designs: 25c, Portrait of a Young Man Resting His Chin on His Hand. 50c, A Woman at an Open Door. No. 1398, $1, The Return of the Prodigal Son. No. 1399, $1, Portrait of an Elderly Man.
No. 1400: a, Nicolaas van Bambeeck. b, Agatha Bas, Wife of Nicolaas van Bambeeck. c, Portrait of a Man Holding His Hat. d, Saskia in a Red Hat.
$2, Christ Driving the Money Changers from the Temple.

Perf. 14¼, 13¼ (#1400)
2003, June 17
1396-1399 A236   Set of 4   5.50 5.50
1400 A236 60c Sheet of 4, #a-d   5.00 5.00
Souvenir Sheet
1401 A236 $2 multi   4.00 4.00

Paintings by Joan Miró — A237

Designs: 25c, Portrait of a Young Girl. 50c, Table with Glove. 60c, Self-portrait, 1917. $1, The Farmer's Wife.
No. 1406: a, Portrait of Ramon Sunyer. b, Self-portrait, 1919. c, Portrait of a Spanish Dancer. d, Portrait of Joana Obrador.
No. 1407, Flowers and Butterfly. No. 1408, Still Life of the Coffee Grinder, horiz.

2003, June 17   **Perf. 14¼**
1402-1405 A237   Set of 4   4.75 4.75
1406 A237 80c Sheet of 4, #a-d   6.50 6.50
Imperf
Size: 104x83mm
1407 A237 $2 multi   4.00 4.00
Size: 83x104mm
1408 A237 $2 multi   4.00 4.00

Caribbean Community, 30th Anniv. — A238

2003, July 4   **Perf. 14**
1409 A238 60c multi   1.25 1.25

Tanya Streeter, World Champion Freediver — A239

No. 1410: a, Wearing wetsuit in water. b, Diving underwater, portrait. c, Wearing bathing suit at shore. d, Standing in front of map. e, Holding on to diving apparatus.

2003, July 15
1410 A239 20c Sheet of 5, #a-e   2.00 2.00

Coronation of Queen Elizabeth II, 50th Anniv. — A240

No. 1411: a, Wearing crown and white robe. b, Wearing lilac dress. c, Wearing tiara and red dress.
$2, Wearing hat and blue cape. $5, Profile portrait.

2003, Aug. 25
1411 A240 80c Sheet of 3, #a-
     c   5.00 5.00
Souvenir Sheets
1412-1413 A240   Set of 2   14.00 14.00

Prince William, 21st Birthday — A241

No. 1414: a, Portrait in blue. b, Pink background. c, Purple background.
$2, Dark blue background.

2003, Aug. 25
1414 A241 $1 Sheet of 3, #a-c   6.00 6.00
Souvenir Sheet
1415 A241 $2 multi   4.00 4.00

Tour de France Bicycle Race, Cent. — A242

No. 1416: a, Eddy Merckx, 1974. b, Bernard Thévenet, 1975. c, Lucien Van Impe, 1976. d, Thévenet, 1977.
$2, Bernard Hinault, 1979.

2003, Aug. 25   **Perf. 13¾x14¼**
1416 A242 $1 Sheet of 4, #a-d   8.00 8.00
Souvenir Sheet
1417 A242 $2 multi   4.00 4.00

100 Years of Aviation

Powered Flight, Cent. — A243

No. 1418: a, Vought F4U Corsair. b, Messerschmidt Me 262. c, A6M. d, Hawker Hurricane.
$2, Supermarine Spitfire Mk IX.

2003, Aug. 25   **Perf. 14**
1418 A243 60c Sheet of 4, #a-d   5.00 5.00
Souvenir Sheet
1419 A243 $2 multi   4.00 4.00

German Teddy Bears — A244

No. 1420, vert.: a, Bear with red and yellow uniform. b, Bear with dress. c, Bear with violin case. d, Bear with sword.
$2, Bear on beer mug.

2003, Aug. 25   **Perf. 12x12¼**
1420 A244 50c Sheet of 4, #a-d   4.00 4.00
Souvenir Sheet
Perf. 12¼x12
1421 A244 $2 multi   4.00 4.00

Butterflies
A245

Designs: 50c, Papilio thersites. 60c, Papilio andraemon. 80c, Papilio pelaus. $1, Consul hippona.
$2, Papilio pelaus, diff.

2003, Nov. 17   **Perf. 14**
1422-1425 A245 Set of 4   6.00 6.00
Souvenir Sheet
1426 A245 $2 multi   4.00 4.00

Orchids
A246

Designs: 50c, Laelia anceps. 60c, Laelia briegeri. 80c, Laelia fidelensis. $1, Laelia cinnabarina.
$2, Laelia rubescens.

2003, Nov. 17
1427-1430 A246 Set of 4   6.00 6.00
Souvenir Sheet
1431 A246 $2 multi   4.00 4.00

Dogs
A247

Designs: 50c, Beagle. 60c, Sabueso Español, vert. 80c, Basset hound, vert. $1, Jack Russell terrier, vert.
$2, Dachshund.

2003, Nov. 17
1432-1435 A247 Set of 4   6.00 6.00
Souvenir Sheet
1436 A247 $2 multi   4.00 4.00

Cats
A248

Designs: 50c, Persian. 60c, Cymric. 80c, Main Coon, vert. $1, Tiffany.
$2, Kurile Island bobtail.

2003, Nov. 17
1437-1440 A248 Set of 4   6.00 6.00
Souvenir Sheet
1441 A248 $2 multi   4.00 4.00

Christmas
A249

Paintings: 25c, Madonna of the Harpies, by Andrea del Sarto. 60c, Madonna and Child with St. John, by del Sarto. 80c, Madonna and Child with St. Joseph and St. Peter Martyr, by del Sarto. $1, Madonna and Child with the Angels, by del Sarto.
$2, Montefeltro Altarpiece, by Piero della Francesca.

2003, Nov. 24   **Perf. 14¼**
1442-1445 A249 Set of 4   5.50 5.50
Souvenir Sheet
1446 A249 $2 multi   4.00 4.00

Marine Life — A250

Photographs from underwater photography contest: Nos. 1447, 1452a, 25c, Golden Rough Head Blennie, by Rand McMeins. Nos. 1448, 1452b, 50c, Octopus at Night, by Marc Van Driessche. Nos. 1449, 1452c, 60c, Sea Turtle, by Mike Nebel. Nos. 1450, 1452d, 80c, Juvenile Octopus, by Amber Blecker. Nos. 1451, 1452e, $1, School of Horse Eye Jacks, by Blecker.
$2, Coral Reef, by Keith Kaplan, vert.

Perf. 12, 12¾ (#1452)
2006, June 1   **Litho.**
Stamps With Thin "Shadow" Frame
1447-1451 A250 Set of 5   6.50 6.50

Miniature Sheet
Stamps With Thick "Shadow" Frame
1452 A250 Sheet of 5, #a-e   6.50 6.50
Souvenir Sheet
1453 A250 $2 multi   4.00 4.00

Washington 2006 World Philatelic Exhibition. (Nos. 1452-1453). The perforation tips at the tops of the stamps on Nos. 1452a-1452e are all white, gradiating to blue on the lower halves of the stamps, while the perforation tips on Nos. 1447-1451 show other colors. The shadow frames at the bottom of Nos 1452a-1452e are 1mm thick and about ½mm thick on Nos. 1447-1451. The distances between the bottom of the denomination and the top of the country name differ on Nos. 1452a-1452e from those found on Nos. 1447-1451. No. 1447 has incorrect spelling, "Ruogh," in inscription, while No. 1452a has word correctly spelled as "Rough."

Queen Elizabeth II, 80th Birthday — A251

No. 1454 — Various depictions of Queen Elizabeth II: a, 50c. b, 60c. c, 80c. d, $1.
$6, Wearing crown.

2006, Sept. 12   **Litho.**   **Perf. 13½**
1454 A251 Sheet of 4, #a-d   6.00 6.00
Souvenir Sheet
1455 A251 $6 multi   12.00 12.00

Christmas — A252

The Birth of Christ and Adoration of the Shepherds, by Peter Paul Rubens: Nos. 1456, 1460a, 25c, Praying shepherd. Nos. 1457, 1460b, 60c, Infant Jesus. Nos. 1458, 1460c, 80c, Heads of two shepherds. Nos. 1459, 1460d, $1, Virgin Mary.
$6, Our Lady, The Christ Child and Saints, by Rubens, vert.

2006, Dec. 27   **Perf. 13¼x13½**
Stamps With Painting Title
1456-1459 A252 Set of 4   5.50 5.50
Stamps Without Painting Title
1460 A252 Sheet of 4, #a-d   5.50 5.50
Souvenir Sheet
Perf. 13½x13¼
1461 A252 $6 multi   12.00 12.00

Shells
A253

Christmas
A254

Designs: 10c, Cymatium muricinum. 15c, Tellina radiata. 20c, Tonna maculosa. 25c, Leucozonia nassa. 35c, Trachycardium magnum. 45c, Papyridea soleniformis. 50c, Epitonium lamellosum. 60c, Astraea brevispina. 80c, Bulla striata. $1, Murex margaritensis. $1.25, Chama macerophylla. $1.40,

Vasum capitellum. $2, Coralliophila abbreviata. $5, Trachycardium isocardia. $10, Oliva reticularis.

2007, June 11   **Litho.**   **Perf. 12¾**
1462 A253 10c multi   .20 .20
1463 A253 15c multi   .30 .30
1464 A253 20c multi   .40 .40
1465 A253 25c multi   .50 .50
1466 A253 35c multi   .70 .70
1467 A253 45c multi   .90 .90
1468 A253 50c multi   1.00 1.00
1469 A253 60c multi   1.25 1.25
1470 A253 80c multi   1.60 1.60
1471 A253 $1 multi   2.00 2.00
1472 A253 $1.25 multi   2.50 2.50
1473 A253 $1.40 multi   3.00 3.00
1474 A253 $2 multi   4.00 4.00
1475 A253 $5 multi   10.00 10.00
1476 A253 $10 multi   20.00 20.00
Nos. 1462-1476 (15)   48.35 48.35

Perf. 14¼x14¾, 14¾x14¼
2007, Dec. 10
Paintings: 25c, The Virgin and Child, by Carlo Maratta. 60c, The Adoration of the Magi, by Vincent Malo, horiz. 80c, The Annunciation, by Robert Campin, horiz. $1, The Adoration of the Magi, by Giovanni di Paolo, horiz.
$6, The Adoration of the Magi, by Quentin Massys.

1477-1480 A254 Set of 4   5.50 5.50
Souvenir Sheet
Perf. 14
1481 A254 $6 multi   12.00 12.00
No. 1481 contains one 28x42mm stamp.

Worldwide Fund for Nature (WWF) — A255

No. 1482 — Red-tailed hawk: a, Pair on fenceposts. b, Adults and chicks at nest. c, Adults on hill and in flight. d, Head of hawk.

2007, Dec. 24   **Perf. 13¼**
1482   Horiz. strip of 4   4.00 4.00
   a.-d A255 50c Any single   1.00 1.00
   e. Souvenir sheet, 2 each #a-d   8.00 8.00

Wedding of Queen Elizabeth II and Prince Philip, 60th Anniv. — A256

No. 1483, vert.: a, Couple, country name in purple. b, Queen, country name in purple. c, Queen, country name in blue. d, Couple, country name in blue. e, Couple, country name in black. f, Queen, country name in black.
$6, Couple on balcony.

2007, Dec. 28   **Perf. 13¼**
1483 A256 $1 Sheet of 6, #a-f   12.00 12.00
Souvenir Sheet
1484 A256 $6 multi   12.00 12.00

Princess Diana (1961-97) — A257

No. 1485 — Various photographs as shown.
$6, Princess Diana wearing hat.

2007, Dec. 28
1485 A257 $1 Sheet of 4, #a-d   8.00   8.00

Souvenir Sheet

1486 A257 $6 multi   12.00 12.00

WAR TAX STAMPS

Regular Issue of 1913-16 Overprinted

1917		**Wmk. 3**		**Perf. 14**

Black Overprint at Bottom of Stamp

MR1	A10	1p carmine	.20	1.75
a.	Double overprint		200.00	275.00
b.	"TAX" omitted		110.00	
c.	Pair, one without ovpt.			
MR2	A10	3p violet, yel	1.40	5.75
a.	Double overprint		110.00	

Black Overprint at Top or Middle of Stamp

1917

MR3	A10	1p carmine	.20	1.40
a.	Inverted overprint		55.00	
b.	Double overprint		50.00	62.50
c.	Pair, one without overprint		625.00	
MR4	A10	3p violet, yel	.70	2.00
a.	Double overprint		50.00	
b.	Dbl. ovpt., one inverted		375.00	

Same Overprint in Violet or Red

1918-19

MR5	A10	1p car (V) ('19)	.20	1.10
a.	Double overprint		24.00	
b.	"WAR" omitted		175.00	
MR6	A10	3p violet, yel (R)	11.00	30.00
a.	Double overprint		375.00	

Regular Issue of 1913-16 Overprinted in Black

1918

MR7	A10	1p carmine	.20	1.40
MR8	A10	3p violet, yel	2.75	4.25

Same Overprint in Red

1919

MR9	A10	3p violet, yel	.20	2.75

Regular Issue of 1913-16 Overprinted in Black

MR10	A10	1p carmine	.20	1.10
a.	Double overprint		160.00	190.00
MR11	A10	3p violet, yel	.35	3.00

Regular Issue of 1913-16 Overprinted

MR12	A10	1p carmine	.20	2.75
a.	Double overprint		100.00	
MR13	A10	3p violet, yel	.55	3.00

CAICOS

Catalogue values for all unused stamps in this country are for Never Hinged items.

Turks & Caicos Nos. 360, 364, 366, 369, 371-373 Ovptd. with Black Bar and "CAICOS ISLANDS"

Unwmk.

1981, July 24		**Litho.**		**Perf. 14**
1	A69	1c Indigo hamlet	.20	.20
2	A69	5c Spanish grunt	.20	.20
3	A69	8c Foureye butterflyfish	.20	.20
4	A69	20c Queen angelfish	.40	.40
5	A69	50c Fairy basslet	.95	.95
6	A69	$1 Clown wrasse	1.90	1.90
7	A69	$2 Stoplight parrotfish	3.75	3.75
		Nos. 1-7 (7)	7.60	7.60

Common Design Types pictured following the introduction.

Royal Wedding Issue
Common Design Type
Turks & Caicos Nos. 486-489 Ovptd. with Black Bar and "Caicos Islands"

1981, July 24

8	CD331a	35c Charles & Diana	.35	.35
9	CD331a	65c Kensington Palace	.65	.65
10	CD331a	90c Prince Charles	.90	.90
		Nos. 8-10 (3)	1.90	1.90

Souvenir Sheet

11	CD331	$2 Glass coach	5.00	5.00

Roulette x Imperf. (#12a), Imperf. (#12b)

1981, Oct. 29

Self-Adhesive

12		Souvenir booklet	27.50
a.	A88a Pane, 3 each 20c, Diana, $1, Charles)		15.00
b.	A88a Pane of 1 $2, Couple		10.00

Nos. 8-11 exist with overprint in all capital letters, values about the same. Nos. 8-10, in both overprint types, also exist in sheets of 5 plus label in changed colors, perf. 12.

Hawksbill turtle C1

1983-84				**Perf. 14**
13	C1	8c Diver with lobster and conch shell	.35	.35
14	C1	10c shown	.35	.35
15	C1	20c Stone idol, Arawak Indians	.80	.80
16	C1	35c Sloop construction	1.25	1.25
17	C1	50c Marine biology	1.90	1.90
18	C1	95c 707 Jetliner	4.00	4.00
19	C1	$1.10 15th cent. Spanish ship	4.50	4.50
20	C1	$2 British soldier, Fort St. George	8.00	8.00
21	C1	$3 Pirates Anne Bonny, Calico Jack	12.00	12.00
		Nos. 13-21 (9)	33.15	33.15

Issued: #13-19, 6/6/83; #20-21, 5/18/84.
For overprints see Nos. 47-49.

Christmas Type of Turks and Caicos
Walt Disney characters in Santa Claus is Coming to Town.

1983, Nov. 7				**Perf. 11**
22	A104	1c Chip 'n Dale	.50	.50
23	A104	1c Goofy & Patch	.50	.50
24	A104	2c Morty, Ferdie & Pluto	.50	.50
25	A104	2c Morty	.50	.50
26	A104	3c Donald, Huey, Dewey & Louie	.50	.50
27	A104	3c Goofy & Louie	.50	.50
28	A104	50c Uncle Scrooge	3.25	3.25
29	A104	70c Mickey Mouse & Ferdie	4.50	4.50
30	A104	$1.10 Pinocchio, Jiminy Cricket and Figaro	6.25	6.25
		Nos. 22-30 (9)	17.00	17.00

Souvenir Sheet

Perf. 13½x14

31	A104	$2 Morty & Ferdie, fireplace	11.00	11.00

Drawings by Raphael — C2   1984 Summer Olympics, Los Angeles — C3

Designs: 35c, Leda and the Swan. 50c, Study of Apollo for Parnassus. 95c, Study of two figures for The Battle of Ostia. $1.10, Study for the Madonna of the Goldfinch. $2.50, The Garvagh Madonna.

1983, Dec. 15				**Perf. 14**
32	C2	35c multicolored	1.25	1.25
33	C2	50c multicolored	1.75	1.75
34	C2	95c multicolored	3.25	3.25
35	C2	$1.10 multicolored	3.75	3.75
		Nos. 32-35 (4)	10.00	10.00

Souvenir Sheet

36	C2	$2.50 multicolored	8.00	8.00

500th birth anniv. of Raphael.

1984, Mar. 1				
37	C3	4c High jump	.20	.20
38	C3	25c Archery	.50	.50
39	C3	65c Cycling	1.40	1.40
40	C3	$1.10 Soccer	2.40	2.40
		Nos. 37-40 (4)	4.50	4.50

Souvenir Sheet

41	C3	$2 Show jumping, horiz.	4.75	4.75

Easter — C4

Walt Disney characters: 35c, Horace Horsecollar, Clarabelle Cow. 45c, Mickey, Minnie & Chip. 75c, Gyro Gearloose, Chip 'n Dale. 85c, Mickey, Chip 'n Dale. $2.20, Donald sailing with nephews.

1984, Apr. 15				**Perf. 14x13½**
42	C4	35c multicolored	1.50	1.50
43	C4	45c multicolored	1.75	1.75
44	C4	75c multicolored	3.00	3.00
45	C4	85c multicolored	3.75	3.75
		Nos. 42-45 (4)	10.00	10.00

Souvenir Sheet

46	C4	$2.20 mulitcolored	10.00	10.00

Nos. 18-19 Ovptd. with emblem and "Universal Postal Union 1874-1984"

1984, June 19				**Perf. 14**
47	C1	95c multicolored	2.00	2.00
48	C1	$1.10 multicolored	2.50	2.50

No. 20 Ovptd. "AUSIPEX 1984"

1984, Aug. 22				
49	C1	$2 multicolored	6.00	6.00

Columbus' First Landfall — C5

1984, Sept. 21				
50	C5	10c Sighting manatees	1.00	1.00
51	C5	70c Fleet	4.50	4.50
52	C5	$1 West Indies landing	6.50	6.50
		Nos. 50-52 (3)	12.00	12.00

Souvenir Sheet

53	C5	$2 Fleet, map	5.00	5.00

Columbus' first landing, 492nd anniv.

Christmas C6

Walt Disney characters: 20c, Santa Claus. 35c, Donald at refrigerator. 50c, Donald, Micky riding toy train. 75c, Donald carrying presents. $1.10, Huey, Louie, Dewey and Donald singing carols. $2, Donald as Christmas tree.

Perf. 13½x14, 12x12½ (75c)

1984, Nov. 26				
54	C6	20c multicolored	1.10	1.10
55	C6	35c multicolored	2.00	2.00
56	C6	50c multicolored	2.75	2.75
57	C6	75c multicolored	4.25	4.25
58	C6	$1.10 multicolored	6.25	6.25
		Nos. 54-58 (5)	16.35	16.35

Souvenir Sheet

Perf. 13½x14

59	C6	$2 multicolored	6.25	6.25

No. 57 printed in sheets of 8.

Audubon Birth Bicentenary — C7

1985, Feb. 12				**Perf. 14**
60	C7	20c Thick-billed vireo	1.10	1.10
61	C7	35c Black-faced grassquit	2.00	2.00
62	C7	50c Pearly-eyed thrasher	2.75	2.75
63	C7	$1 Greater Antillean bullfinch	5.50	5.50
		Nos. 60-63 (4)	11.35	11.35

Souvenir Sheet

64	C7	$2 Stripe-headed tanagers	6.00	6.00

No. 64 exists imperf.

Intl. Youth Year — C8

1985, May 8				
65	C8	16c Education	.30	.30
66	C8	35c Health	.70	.70
67	C8	70c Love	1.40	1.40
68	C8	90c Peace	1.75	1.75
		Nos. 65-68 (4)	4.15	4.15

Souvenir Sheet

69	C8	$2 Peace dove, child	5.25	5.25

UN 40th anniv.

Intl. Civil Aviation Org., 40th Anniv. C9

1985, May 26

70	C9	35c DC-3	2.50	2.50
71	C9	75c Convair 440	5.00	5.00
72	C9	90c TCNA Islander	6.00	6.00
		Nos. 70-72 (3)	13.50	13.50

Souvenir Sheet

73	C9	$2.20 Hang glider	8.00	8.00

Queen Mother, 85th Birthday Type of Turks & Caicos

1985, July 7

74	A117	35c Wearing green hat	1.25	1.25
75	A117	65c With Princess Anne, horiz.	2.00	2.00
76	A117	95c Wearing white hat	3.25	3.25
		Nos. 74-76 (3)	6.50	6.50

Souvenir Sheet

77	A117	$2 Inspecting guards-men	6.50	6.50

Mark Twain, 150th Birth Anniv. — C10

Walt Disney characters in Tom Sawyer, Detective (Intl. Youth Year): 8c, Mickey and Goofy as Tom and Huck reading reward poster. 35c, Meeting Jake Dunlap. 95c, Spying on Jubiter Dunlap. $1.10, With Pluto finding body. No. 86, Unmasking Jubiter Dunlap.

Walt Disney characters portraying Six Soldiers of Fortune (The Brothers Grimm, Bicent.): 16c, Donald receiving his meager pay. 25c, Donald meets Horace Horsecollar as strong man. 65c, Donald meets Mickey the marksman. $1.35, Goofy wins footrace against Princess Daisy. No. 87, Soldiers with sack of gold.

1985, Dec. 5			**Perf. 14x13½**	
78	C10	8c multicolored	.50	.50
79	C10	16c multicolored	.80	.80
80	C10	25c multicolored	1.25	1.25
81	C10	35c multicolored	1.75	1.75
82	C10	65c multicolored	3.00	3.00
83	C10	95c multicolored	4.75	4.75
84	C10	$1.10 multicolored	5.75	5.75
85	C10	$1.35 multicolored	7.00	7.00
		Nos. 78-85 (8)	24.80	24.80

Souvenir Sheet

86	C10	$2 multicolored	7.50	7.50
87	C10	$2 multicolored	7.50	7.50

Stamps are no longer being produced for Caicos.

TURKS ISLANDS

ˈtərks ˈī-lənds

LOCATION — West Indies, at the southern extremity of the Bahamas
GOVT. — Former dependency of Jamaica
POP. — 2,000 (approx.)
CAPITAL — Grand Turk

In 1848 the Turks Islands together with the Caicos group, lying to the northwest, were made a British colony. In 1873 the Colony became a dependency under the government of Jamaica although separate stamp issues were continued. Postage stamps inscribed Turks and Caicos Islands have been used since 1900.

12 Pence = 1 Shilling

Values for unused stamps are for examples with original gum as defined in the catalogue introduction. Very fine examples of Nos. 1-42 will have generally rough perforations that cut into the design on one or more sides due to the narrow spacing of the stamps on the plates and imperfect perforating methods. Stamps with perfs clear of the design on all four sides are extremely scarce and will command substantially higher prices.

Because of the printing and imperfect perforating methods, stamps are often found scissor separated. Prices will not be adversely affected on those stamps where the scissor cut does not remove the perforations.

Watermark

Wmk. 5 — Small Star

Queen Victoria — A1

1867		Unwmk.		**Engr.**
1	A1	1p rose	67.50	67.50
2	A1	6p gray black	110.00	140.00
3	A1	1sh slate blue	105.00	67.50
		Nos. 1-3 (3)	282.50	275.00

Perf. 11 to 13x14 to 15

1873-79				**Wmk. 5**
4	A1	1p lake	57.50	57.50
5	A1	1p dull red ('79)	62.50	67.50
a.		Horiz. pair, imperf. btwn.	21,000.	
b.		Perf. 11-12	1,100.	
6	A1	1sh violet	5,750.	2,250.

Stamps offered as No. 6 are often copies from which the surcharge has been removed.

Stamps of 1867-79 Surcharged in Black:

a   b

c

d   e

12 settings of the ½p, 9 of 2½p, and 6 of 4p.

1881		Unwmk.	**Perf. 11 to 13**	
7	(a)	½p on 6p gray blk	85.00	140.00
7A	(b)	½p on 6p gray blk	80.00	120.00
8	(b)	½p on 1sh slate bl	110.00	180.00
a.		Double surcharge	5,750.	
8B	(c)	½p on 1sh slate bl	11,000.	
c.		Without fraction bar		

Perf. 11 to 13x14 to 15
Wmk. 5

9	(a)	½p on 1p dull red	150.00	200.00
a.		Double surcharge		
10	(b)	½p on 1p dull red	55.00	90.00
11	(c)	½p on 1p dull red	210.00	275.00
a.		Double surcharge	4,250.	

12	(d)	½p on 1p dull red	260.00	
a.		Without fraction bar	1,150.	
b.		Double surcharge		
13	(e)	½p on 1p dull red	600.00	
14	(a)	½p on 1sh violet	175.00	225.00
a.		Double surcharge	4,000.	
15	(b)	½p on 1sh violet	140.00	225.00
a.		Without fraction bar	625.00	
16	(c)	½p on 1sh violet	105.00	190.00

f   g   h

Perf. 11 to 13
Unwmk.

17	(f)	2½p on 6p gray blk	9,500.	
18	(g)	2½p on 6p gray blk	375.00	450.00
a.		Horiz. pair, imperf. between	19,000.	
b.		Double surcharge	9,500.	
19	(h)	2½p on 6p gray blk	175.00	325.00
a.		Double surcharge	9,500.	

i   j

Perf. 11 to 13x14 to 15
Wmk. 5

20	(i)	2½p on 1sh violet	2,600.	
21	(h)	2½p on 1sh violet	625.	950.
22	(j)	2½p on 1sh violet	9,500.	

k   l

m   n

Perf. 11 to 13
Unwmk.

24	(k)	2½p on 6p gray blk	8,500.	
25	(k)	2½p on 1sh slate bl	15,000.	
26	(l)	2½p on 1sh slate bl	1,500.	
27	(m)	2½p on 1sh slate bl	2,200.	
a.		Without fraction bar	8,000.	
28	(n)	2½p on 1sh slate bl	6,500.	

o

Perf. 11 to 13x14 to 15
Wmk. 5

29	(l)	2½p on 1p dull red	600.00	
30	(o)	2½p on 1p dull red	1,350.	
31	(l)	2½p on 1sh violet	850.00	
a.		Double surcharge of "½"	4,000.	
32	(o)	2½p on 1sh violet	1,350.	
b.		Double surcharge of "½"	5,750.	

p   q

r

Perf. 11 to 13
Unwmk.

33	(p)	4p on 6p gray black	85.00	120.00
34	(q)	4p on 6p gray black	375.00	475.00
35	(r)	4p on 6p gray black	475.00	350.00

Copies of No. 33 with top of "4" painted in are sometimes offered as No. 35.

Perf. 11 to 13x14 to 15
Wmk. 5

36	(r)	4p on 1p dull red	950.00	625.00
a.		Inverted surcharge	3,250.	
37	(p)	4p on 1p dull red	850.00	550.00
a.		Inverted surcharge		
38	(p)	4p on 1sh violet	450.00	625.00
39	(q)	4p on 1sh violet	2,750.	

Wmk. Crown and C C (1)

1881		**Engr.**	**Perf. 14**	
40	A1	1p brown red	77.50	105.00
a.		Diagonal half used as ½p on cover		
41	A1	6p olive brown	120.00	175.00
42	A1	1sh slate green	190.00	140.00
		Nos. 40-42 (3)	387.50	420.00

A2   A3

1881			**Typo.**	
43	A2	4p ultramarine	155.00	67.50

1882-95		**Engr.**	**Wmk. 2**	
44	A1	1p orange brn ('83)	77.50	35.00
a.		Half used as ½p on cover	4,750.	
45	A1	1p car lake ('89)	3.50	2.25
46	A1	6p yellow brn ('89)	4.00	3.00
47	A1	1sh black brn ('87)	5.50	4.00
a.		1sh deep brown	5.50	4.00

Typo.
Die A

48	A2	½p dull green ('85)	3.50	4.00
a.		½p blue green ('82)	10.50	25.00
49	A2	2½p red brown ('82)	21.00	15.00
50	A2	4p gray ('84)	20.00	2.75
a.		Half used as 2p on cover	4,750.	

Die B

51	A2	½p gray green ('94)	3.50	2.00
52	A2	2½p ultra ('93)	3.50	2.75
53	A2	4p dk vio & bl ('95)	11.00	15.00

For explanation of dies A and B see back of this volume.

1887		**Engr.**	**Perf. 12**	
54	A1	1p carmine lake	14.00	3.25

No. 49 Surcharged in Black

1889				
55	A2	1p on 2½p red brown	11.00	13.50
a.		Double surcharge		
b.		Double surcharge, one inverted		
c.		"One" omitted	1,800.	
d.		Half used as ½p on cover	5,500.	

No. 55c caused by the misplacement of the surcharge. Stamps also exist from the same sheet reading "Penny One."

No. 50 Surcharged in Black

Two types of surcharge:
Type I — Upper bar continuous across sheet.
Type II — Upper bar breaks between stamps.

1893				
56	A2	½p on 4p gray (I)	165.00	155.00
a.		Type II	3,250.	1,450.

This surcharge exists in five settings.

1894   **Typo.**
57 A3 5p olive grn & car-
        mine   6.75   17.50
  a. Diag. half used as 2½p on
        cover   5,000.

TUVALU

tü-'vä-ˌü

LOCATION — A group of islands in the
  Pacific Ocean northeast of Australia.
GOVT. — Independent state in the
  British Commonwealth
AREA — 9½ sq. mi.
POP. — 10,588 (1999 est.)
CAPITAL — Funafuti

Tuvalu, formerly Ellice Islands, consists of nine islands.

Australian dollar

> Catalogue values for all unused
> stamps in this country are for
> Never Hinged items.

Watermark

Wmk. 380 — "POST OFFICE"

Gilbert and Ellice Islands Types of
1971
Overprinted "TUVALU" and Bar
in Violet Blue or Silver (35c)
Wmk. 373

1976, Jan. 1   Litho.   Perf. 14
1   A18 1c   1.25   .60
2   A19 2c   1.60   .85
  a. Wmk. 314 sideways   240.00 25.00
  b. Wmk. 314 upright   1,500. 140.00
3   A19 3c Wmk. 314   2.50   1.25
  a. Wmk. 373   .80   .55
4   A19 4c   1.60   .90
5   A19 5c Wmk. 314   1.60   1.25
6   A19 6c   1.60   .85
7   A18 8c Wmk. 314   1.60   1.25
8   A19 10c Wmk. 314   1.60   1.60
9   A18 15c   2.50   1.00
10 A19 20c   1.60   1.25
11 A19 25c Wmk. 314   10.50   3.50
  a. Wmk. 373   .90   .75
12 A18 35c   2.50   1.40
13 A18 50c   1.60   1.25
  a. Wmk. 314   47.50 22.50
14 A18 $1   1.60   1.60
  a. Wmk. 314   110.00 70.00
15 A18 $2   2.10   1.60
    Nos. 1-15 (15)   35.75 20.15

Men from Gilbert and Ellice — A1

Designs: 10c, Map of Gilbert and Ellice
Islands, vert. 35c, Gilbert and Ellice canoes.

1976, Jan. 1   Wmk. 373
16 A1 4c multicolored   .60   .75
17 A1 10c multicolored   .80   .90
18 A1 35c multicolored   1.10   1.25
    Nos. 16-18 (3)   2.50   2.90

Separation of the Gilbert and Ellice Islands.

50c Coin and
Octopus — A2

New coinage: 10c, 10c-coin and red-dyed
crab. 15c, 20c-coin and flyingfish. 35c, $1-coin
and green turtle.

Wmk. 373
1976, Apr. 21   Litho.   Perf. 14
19 A2 5c bister & multi   .30   .30
20 A2 10c ultra & multi   .85   .65
21 A2 15c blue & multi   1.25   .80
22 A2 35c lt green & multi 2.25   1.40
    Nos. 19-22 (4)   4.65   3.15

Map of Niulakita,
Leathery
Turtle — A3

Te
Ano
Game
A4

2c, Map of Nukulaelae and sleeping mat.
4c, Map of Nui and talo vegetable. 5c, Map of
Nanumanga and grass dancing skirt. 6c, Map
of Nukufetau and coconut crab. 8c, Map of
Funafuti and banana tree. 10c, Map of Tuvalu
Islands. 15c, Map of Niutao and flyingfish. 20c,
Map of Vaitupu and maneapa (house). 25c,
Map of Nanumea and palu fish hook. 50c,
Canoe pole fishing. $1, Reef fishing by flare.
$2, House. $5, Colony Ship M.V. Nivanga.

1976   Wmk. 373   Litho.   Perf. 13½
23-37   A3   Set of 15   65.00 18.00

Issue dates: $5, Sept. 1; others July 1.
See #58-70. For overprints see #85-91.

New
Testament
A5

Designs: 20c, Lotolelei Church, Nanumea.
25c, Kelupi Church, Nui. 30c, Mataloa o
Tuvalu Church, Vaitupu. 35c, Palataiso o
Keliso Church, Nanumanga.

Perf. 14x14½
1976, Oct. 6   Litho.   Wmk. 373
38-42   A5   Set of 5   7.50   6.00

Christmas 1976. Printed in sheets of 10
stamps and 2 labels.

Prince Philip Carried Ashore at
Vaitupu — A6

Designs: 15c, Queen and Prince Philip on
Buckingham Palace balcony. 50c, Queen
Leaving Buckingham Palace for coronation.

1977, Feb. 9   Litho.   Perf. 13½x14
43 A6 15c multicolored   1.75   1.50
44 A6 35c multicolored   2.25   2.50
45 A6 50c multicolored   3.50   3.50
  a. Souv. sheet, #43-45, perf. 15 8.00 6.50
    Nos. 43-45 (3)   7.50   7.50

25th anniv. of the reign of Elizabeth II.

Health (Microscope) — A7

20c, Education (blackboard). 30c, Fruit
growing (palm). 35c, Map of South Pacific
Territory.

1977, May 4   Litho.   Perf. 13½x14
46 A7 5c lilac & multi   .65   .50
47 A7 20c orange & multi   .65   .50
48 A7 30c yellow grn & multi .65   .50
49 A7 35c lt blue & multi   .95   .65
    Nos. 46-49 (4)   2.90   2.15

South Pacific Commission, 30th anniv.

Swearing-in Ceremony and Scout
Emblem — A8

Designs (Scout Emblem and): 20c, Scouts
in outrigger canoe. 30c, Scouts under sun
shelter. 35c, Lord Baden-Powell.

Perf. 13½x14
1977, Aug. 10 Litho.   Wmk. 373
50 A8 5c multicolored   .55   .55
51 A8 20c multicolored   .55   .55
52 A8 30c multicolored   .85   .85
53 A8 35c multicolored   .85   .85
    Nos. 50-53 (4)   2.80   2.80

Scouting in Tuvalu (Ellice Islands), 50th
anniv.

Hurricane Beach and Coral — A9

Designs: 20c, Boring apparatus on "Porpoise," vert. 30c, Map of islands showing line
of dredgings to prove Darwin's theory, vert.
35c, Charles Darwin and "Beagle."

Perf. 13½
1977, Nov. 2   Unwmk.   Litho.
54 A9 5c multicolored   .75   .75
55 A9 20c multicolored   .75   .75
56 A9 30c multicolored   1.10   .90
57 A9 35c multicolored   1.10   .90
    Nos. 54-57 (4)   3.70   3.30

1896-97 Royal Soc. of London Expeditions
to explore coral reefs by dredging and boring.

Types of 1976
Designs: 30c, Fatele, local dance. 40c,
Screw pine. Others as before.

1977-78   Unwmk.   Perf. 13½
58 A3 1c multicolored   .35   .35
59 A3 2c multicolored   .35   .35
60 A3 4c multicolored   .35   .35
61 A3 5c multicolored   .35   .35
62 A3 6c multicolored   .35   .35
63 A3 8c multicolored   .35   .35
64 A3 10c multicolored   .35   .35
66 A3 20c multicolored   2.50   1.75
67 A3 25c multicolored   1.75   .60
68 A4 30c multicolored   .70   .70

---

69 A4 40c multicolored   .95   1.00
70 A4 $5 multicolored   7.00   7.00
    Nos. 58-70 (12)   15.35 13.50

Issued: #58, 61, 63-64, 67, 1977; others,
1978.

Pacific
Pigeon — A10

Wild Birds of Tuvalu: 20c, Reef heron. 30c,
Fairy tern. 40c, Lesser frigate bird.

Perf. 14x13½
1978, Jan. 25   Litho.   Unwmk.
73 A10 8c lilac & multi   1.60   .90
74 A10 20c ocher & multi   2.00   1.25
75 A10 30c dull green & multi 2.50 1.75
76 A10 40c brt green & multi 2.50 2.00
    Nos. 73-76 (4)   8.60   5.90

Lawedua — A11

Ships: 20c, Tug Wallacia. 30c, Freighter
Cenpac Rounder. 40c, Pacific Explorer.

1978, Apr. 5   Unwmk.   Perf. 13½x14
77 A11 8c multicolored   .20   .20
78 A11 20c multicolored   .35   .35
79 A11 30c multicolored   .55   .45
80 A11 40c multicolored   .70   .65
    Nos. 77-80 (4)   1.80   1.65

Canterbury Cathedral — A12

Designs: 30c, Salisbury Cathedral. 40c,
Wells Cathedral. $1, Hereford Cathedral.

1978, June 2   Litho.   Perf. 13½x14
81 A12 8c multicolored   .25   .25
82 A12 30c multicolored   .25   .25
83 A12 40c multicolored   .25   .25
84 A12 $1 multicolored   .65   .65
  a. Souv. sheet, #81-84, perf. 15 1.25 1.25
    Nos. 81-84 (4)   1.40   1.40

25th anniv. of coronation of Elizabeth II.
#81-84 were also issued in bklt. panes of 2.

Types of 1976 Overprinted:
"INDEPENDENCE 1ST OCTOBER
1978"

1978, Oct. 1   Litho.   Perf. 13½
85 A3 8c multicolored   .25   .25
86 A3 10c multicolored   .25   .25
87 A3 15c multicolored   .25   .25
88 A3 20c multicolored   .25   .25
89 A4 30c multicolored   .25   .25
90 A4 35c multicolored   .25   .25
91 A4 40c multicolored   .30   .30
    Nos. 85-91 (7)   1.80   1.80

Independence, Oct. 1, 1978. Overprint in 3
lines on vert. stamps, 1 line on horiz.

White
Frangipani — A13

Wild Flowers: 20c, Zephyrantes rosea. 30c, Gardenia taitensis. 40c, Clerodendron inerme.

1978, Oct. 4   Unwmk.   Perf. 14
92	A13	8c multicolored	.25	.25
93	A13	20c multicolored	.25	.30
94	A13	30c multicolored	.35	.40
95	A13	40c multicolored	.50	.70
		Nos. 92-95 (4)	1.35	1.65

Squirrelfish — A14

Fish: 2c, Yellow-banded goatfish. 4c, Imperial angelfish. 5c, Rainbow butterfly. 6c, Blue angelfish. 8c, Blue striped snapper. 10c, Orange clownfish. 15c, Chevroned coralfish. 20c, Fairy cod. 25c, Clown triggerfish. 30c, Long-nosed butterfly. 35c, Yellowfin tuna. 40c, Spotted eagle ray. 45c, Black-tipped rock cod. 50c, Hammerhead shark. 70c, Lionfish, vert. $1, White-barred triggerfish, vert. $2, Beaked coralfish, vert. $5, Tiger shark, vert.

1979, Jan. 24   Litho.   Perf. 14
96	A14	1c multicolored	.20	.20
97	A14	2c multicolored	.20	.20
98	A14	4c multicolored	.20	.20
99	A14	5c multicolored	.20	.20
100	A14	6c multicolored	.20	.20
101	A14	8c multicolored	.20	.20
102	A14	10c multicolored	.20	.20
103	A14	15c multicolored	.20	.20
104	A14	20c multicolored	.20	.20
105	A14	25c multicolored	.20	.20
106	A14	30c multicolored	.25	.25
107	A14	35c multicolored	.30	.30
108	A14	40c multicolored	.35	.35
108A	A14	45c multicolored	1.90	1.25
109	A14	50c multicolored	.55	.55
110	A14	70c multicolored	.60	.60
111	A14	$1 multicolored	.80	.80
112	A14	$2 multicolored	1.90	1.90
113	A14	$5 multicolored	4.50	4.50
		Nos. 96-113 (19)	13.15	12.50

No. 108A issued June 16, 1981.
#101, 104, 106, 108 and #102, 105, 107, 108A were also issued in booklet panes of 4. For surcharge & overprints see #150, O1-O19.

Capt. Cook
A15

Designs: 30c, Flag raising on new island. 40c, Observation of transit of Venus. $1, Death of Capt. Cook.

1979, Feb. 14   Perf. 14x14½
114	A15	8c multicolored	.20	.20
115	A15	30c multicolored	.20	.20
116	A15	40c multicolored	.20	.20
117	A15	$1 multicolored	.40	.40
a.		Strip of 4, #114-117	2.75	2.75

Bicentenary of death of Capt. James Cook (1728-1779). Nos. 114-117 printed se-tenant horizontally in sheets of 12 (4x3) with gutters between horizontal rows.

Grumman Goose over
Nukulaelae — A16

Grumman Goose over: 20c, Vaitupu. 30c, Nui. 40c, Funafuti.

1979, May 16   Litho.   Perf. 14x13½
118	A16	8c multicolored	.35	.35
119	A16	20c multicolored	.35	.35
120	A16	30c multicolored	.45	.55
121	A16	40c multicolored	.65	.65
		Nos. 118-121 (4)	1.80	1.90

Inauguration of internal air service.

Hill, Tuvalu No. 16, Letterbox, London,
1855 — A17

Hill, Stamps of Tuvalu and: 40c, No. 17, Penny Black. $1, No. 18, mail coach.

1979, Aug. 20   Litho.   Perf. 13½x14
122	A17	30c multicolored	.30	.30
123	A17	40c multicolored	.30	.30
124	A17	$1 multicolored	.75	.75
a.		Souvenir sheet of 3, #122-124	1.75	1.75
		Nos. 122-124 (3)	1.35	1.35

Sir Rowland Hill (1795-1879), originator of penny postage.

Boy — A18

Designs: Children of Tuvalu.

1979, Oct. 20   Litho.   Perf. 14
125	A18	8c multicolored	.25	.25
126	A18	20c multicolored	.25	.25
127	A18	30c multicolored	.30	.30
128	A18	40c multicolored	.35	.35
		Nos. 125-128 (4)	1.15	1.15

International Year of the Child.

Cowry
Shells
A19

1980, Feb.   Litho.   Perf. 14
129	A19	8c Cypraea Argus	.25	.25
130	A19	20c Cypraea scurra	.25	.25
131	A19	30c Cypraea carneola	.35	.35
132	A19	40c Cypraea aurantium	.50	.50
		Nos. 129-132 (4)	1.35	1.35

Philatelic Bureau, Funafuti, Tuvalu No.
28, Arms, London 1980
Emblem — A20

Coat of Arms, London 1980 Emblem and: 20c, Gilbert and Ellice #41, Nukulaelae cancel, Tuvalu #24. 30c, US airmail cover. $1, Map of Tuvalu.

1980, Apr. 30   Litho.   Perf. 13½x14
133	A20	10c multicolored	.30	.30
134	A20	20c multicolored	.30	.30
135	A20	30c multicolored	.35	.35
136	A20	$1 multicolored	.95	.95
a.		Souvenir sheet of 4, #133-136	2.00	2.00
		Nos. 133-136 (4)	1.90	1.90

London 80 Intl. Stamp Exhib., May 6-14.

Queen Mother
Elizabeth, 80th
Birthday — A21

1980, Aug. 14   Litho.   Perf. 14
| 137 | A21 | 50c multicolored | .50 | .50 |

Issued in sheets of 10 plus 2 labels.

Aethaloessa Calidalis — A22

1980, Aug. 20   Litho.   Perf. 14
138	A22	8c shown	.20	.20
139	A22	20c Parotis suralis	.20	.20
140	A22	30c Dudua aprobola	.30	.30
141	A22	40c Decadarchis simulans	.40	.40
		Nos. 138-141 (4)	1.10	1.10

Air Pacific Heron (First Regular Air
Service to Tuvalu, 1964) — A23

Aviation Anniversaries: 20c, Hawker Siddeley 748 (air service to Tuvalu). 30c, Sunderland Flying Boat (War time service to Funafuti, 1945. 40c, Orville Wright and Flyer (Wright brothers' first flight, 1903).

1980, Nov. 5   Litho.   Perf. 14
142	A23	8c multicolored	.25	.25
143	A23	20c multicolored	.25	.25
144	A23	30c multicolored	.35	.25
145	A23	40c multicolored	.50	.45
		Nos. 142-145 (4)	1.35	1.20

Hypolimnas Bolina Elliciana — A24

1981, Feb. 3   Litho.   Perf. 14½
146	A24	8c shown	.30	.30
147	A24	20c Hypolimnas, diff.	.35	.35
148	A24	30c Hypolimnas, diff.	.45	.45
149	A24	40c Junonia vallida	.75	.75
		Nos. 146-149 (4)	1.85	1.85

No. 109 Surcharged

1981, Feb. 24   Litho.   Perf. 14
| 150 | A14 | 45c on 50c multicolored | .60 | .60 |

Elizabeth,
1809
A25

Wmk. 373
1981, May 13   Litho.   Perf. 14
151	A25	10c shown	.25	.25
152	A25	25c Rebecca, 1819	.25	.25
153	A25	35c Independence II, 1821	.35	.35
154	A25	40c Basilisk, 1872	.45	.45
155	A25	45c Royalist, 1890	.50	.50
156	A25	50c Olivebank, 1920	.65	.65
		Nos. 151-156 (6)	2.45	2.45

See Nos. 216-221, 353-356, 410-413.

Prince
Charles,
Lady
Diana,
Royal
Yacht
Charlotte
A25a

Prince Charles and Lady
Diana — A25b

Illustration A25b is reduced.

Wmk. 380
1981, July 10   Litho.   Perf. 14
157	A25a	10c Couple, Carolina	.20	.20
a.		Blkt. pane of 4, perf. 12, unwmkd.		.30
158	A25b	10c Couple	.40	.40
159	A25a	45c Victoria and Albert III	.25	.25
160	A25b	45c like #158	.50	.50
a.		Blkt. pane of 2, perf. 12, unwmkd.		.50
161	A25a	$2 Britannia	1.00	1.00
162	A25b	$2 like #158	2.75	2.75
		Nos. 157-162 (6)	5.10	5.10

Royal wedding. Issued in sheets of 7 (6 design A25a; 1 design A25b). Set of 3 $12. For surcharges see Nos. B1-B2.

Souvenir Sheet

1981, Dec.   Litho.   Perf. 12
| 163 | A25b | $1.50 Couple | .85 | .85 |

Admission to
UPU — A26

Wmk. Harrison's, London
1981, Nov. 19   Engr.   Perf. 14½x14
164	A26	70c dark blue	.50	.50
165	A26	$1 dark red brown	.75	.75
a.		Souv. sheet of 2, #164-165, unwmkd.	2.00	2.00

Amatuku Maritime School — A27

1982, Feb. 17   Litho.   Perf. 13½x14
166 A27	10c Map	.35	.35
167 A27	25c Motorboat	.35	.35
168 A27	35c School, dock	.45	.45
169 A27	45c Flag, ship	.65	.65
	Nos. 166-169 (4)	1.80	1.80

A27a

Wmk. 380
1982, May 19   Litho.   Perf. 14
170 A27a	10c Caroline of Bran- denburg-An- sbach, 1714	.20	.20
171 A27a	45c Brandenburg-An- sbach arms	.25	.25
172 A27a	$1.50 Diana	1.00	1.00
	Nos. 170-172 (3)	1.45	1.45

21st birthday of Princess Diana, July 1.

#170-172 Overprinted: "ROYAL BABY"
1982, July 14   Litho.   Perf. 14
173 A27a	10c multicolored	.30	.30
174 A27a	45c multicolored	.30	.30
175 A27a	$1.50 multicolored	.90	.90
	Nos. 173-175 (3)	1.50	1.50

Birth of Prince William of Wales, June 21.

Scouting Year — A28

1982, Aug. 18
176 A28	10c Emblems	.25	.25
177 A28	25c Campfire	.40	.35
178 A28	35c Parade	.55	.40
179 A28	45c Scout	.70	.45
	Nos. 176-179 (4)	1.90	1.45

Visit of Queen
Elizabeth II and
Prince
Philip — A29

1982, Oct. 26   Litho.   Perf. 14
180 A29	25c Arms, Duke of Edin- burgh's Personal Standard	.25	.25
181 A29	45c Flags	.50	.50
182 A29	50c Queen Elizabeth II, maps	.55	.55
a.	Souvenir sheet of 3, #180-182	1.50	1.50
	Nos. 180-182 (3)	1.30	1.30

Handicrafts — A30

1c, Fisherman's hat, lures, hooks. 2c, Cowrie shell handbags. 5c, Wedding & baby food baskets. 10c, Canoe model. 15c, Women's sun hats. 20c, Climbing rope. 25c, Pandanus baskets. 30c, Tray, coconut stands. 35c, Pandanus pillows, shell necklaces. 40c, Round baskets, fans. 45c, Reef sandals, fish trap. 50c, Rat trap, canoe bailers, vert.. 60c, Waterproof boxes, vert.. $1, Pump drill, adze, vert. $2, Fisherman's hat, canoe bailers, vert. $5, Fishing rod, lures, scoop nets, vert.

1983-84   Litho.   Perf. 14
183 A30	1c multicolored	.35	.25
184 A30	2c multicolored	.35	.25
185 A30	5c multicolored	.35	.25
186 A30	10c multicolored	.35	.25
186A A30	15c multicolored	2.50	2.75
187 A30	20c multicolored	.35	.25
188 A30	25c multicolored	.35	.25
188A A30	30c multicolored	2.25	2.25
189 A30	35c multicolored	.50	.40
190 A30	40c multicolored	.35	.55
191 A30	45c multicolored	.40	.65
192 A30	50c multicolored	.50	.70
192A A30	60c multicolored	3.25	2.25
193 A30	$1 multicolored	.50	.70
194 A30	$2 multicolored	.70	.85
195 A30	$5 multicolored	1.10	1.25
	Nos. 183-195 (16)	14.15	13.85

Issued: 15c, 1984; others, 3/14/83.
For surcharges & overprints see #207, 230,
O20-O32.

Commonwealth Day — A31

Wmk. 373
1983, Mar. 14   Litho.   Perf. 14
196 A31	20c Fishing industry	.35	.20
197 A31	35c Traditional dancing	.35	.30
198 A31	45c Satellite view	.45	.40
199 A31	50c First container ship	.60	.50
	Nos. 196-199 (4)	1.75	1.40

Dragonflies — A32

1983, May 25   Wmk. 380
200 A32	10c Pantala flavescens	.25	.25
201 A32	35c Anax guttatus	.65	.65
202 A32	40c Tholymis tillarga	.75	.75
203 A32	50c Diplacodes bipunctata	.85	.85
	Nos. 200-203 (4)	2.50	2.50

Boys Brigade Centenary — A33

1983, Aug. 10   Wmk. 373
204 A33	10c Running, emblem	.30	.30
205 A33	35c Canoeing	.75	.75
206 A33	45c Officer, boys	1.75	1.75
	Nos. 204-206 (3)	2.80	2.80

No. 193 Surcharged in Black
1983, Aug. 26   Wmk. 380
| 207 A30 | 60c on $1 multi | 1.00 | .60 |

First Manned Flight
Bicentenary — A34

1983, Sept. 21   Wmk. 373
208 A34	25c Montgolfier balloon, vert.	.40	.40
209 A34	35c McKinnon Turbo Goose	.50	.50
210 A34	45c Beechcraft Super King Air 200	.60	.60
211 A34	50c Double Eagle II Bal- loon, vert.	.70	.70
a.	Souvenir sheet of 4, #208-211	3.00	3.00
	Nos. 208-211 (4)	2.20	2.20

World Communications Year — A35

1983, Nov. 18   Wmk. 380
212 A35	25c Conch Shell Trum- pet, vert.	.25	.25
213 A35	35c Radio Operator, vert.	.40	.40
214 A35	45c Teleprinter	.55	.55
215 A35	50c Transmitting station	.60	.60
	Nos. 212-215 (4)	1.80	1.80

Ship Type of 1981
1984, Feb. 16   Wmk. 380
216 A25	10c Titus, 1897	.25	.25
217 A25	20c Malaita, 1905	.25	.25
218 A25	25c Aymeric, 1906	.30	.30
219 A25	35c Anshun, 1965	.40	.40
220 A25	45c Beaverbank, 1970	.50	.50
221 A25	50c Benjamin Bowring, 1981	.65	.65
	Nos. 216-221 (6)	2.35	2.35

Leaders of the World
Large quantities of some Leaders
of the World issues were sold at a
fraction of face value when the
printer was liquidated.

Historic Locomotives — A36

Perf. 12½x13
1984, Feb. 29   Unwmk.
Se-tenant Pairs, #a.-b.
a. — Side and front views.
b. — Action scene.
222 A36	1c Class GS-4, US, 1941	.25	.25
223 A36	15c AD-60, Australia, 1952	.30	.30
224 A36	40c C38, Australia, 1943	.90	.90
225 A36	60c Achilles England, 1892	1.25	1.25
	Nos. 222-225 (4)	2.70	2.70

See Nos. 235-246, 291-294, 320-323.

No. 191 Surcharged
Wmk. 380
1984, Feb. 1   Litho.   Perf. 14
| 230 A30 | 30c on 45c multi | .55 | .55 |

For overprint see No. O25.

Beach
Flowers
A38

1984, May 30
231 A38	25c Ipomoea pes- caprae	.50	.50
232 A38	45c Ipomoea macrantha	.75	.75
233 A38	50c Triumfetta procum- bens	.95	.95
234 A38	60c Portulaca quadrifida	1.25	1.25
	Nos. 231-234 (4)	3.45	3.45

Train Type of 1984
1984   Litho.   Perf. 12½x13
Se-tenant Pairs, #a.-b.
a. — Side and front views.
b. — Action scene.
235 A36	1c Class 9700, Ja- pan, 1897	.45	.45
236 A36	10c Casey Jones, US, 1896	.45	.45
237 A36	15c Class 2310K, France, 1909	.45	.45
238 A36	15c Triplex, US, 1914	.45	.45
239 A36	20c Class 370, Gt. Britain, 1981	.45	.45
240 A36	25c Class 4F, Gt. Britain, 1924	.60	.60
241 A36	30c Glass 640, Italy, 1907	.70	.70
242 A36	40c Tornado, Gt. Brit- ain, 1888	.90	.90
243 A36	50c Broadlands, Gt. Britain, 1967	1.25	1.25
244 A36	60c Locomotion, Gt. Britain, 1825	1.60	1.60
245 A36	$1 C57, Japan, 1937	2.40	2.40
246 A36	$1 Class 4500, France, 1906	2.40	2.40
	Nos. 235-246 (12)	12.10	12.10

Issued: #235, 237, 241, 245, 10/4; others,
6/27.

15th
South
Pacific
Forum
A38a

1984, Aug. 21   Litho.   Perf. 14
| 255 A38a | 60c National flag | .55 | .55 |
| 256 A38a | 60c Tuvalu crest | .55 | .55 |

Ausipex
'84
A38b

1984, Aug. 21   Perf. 14
| 257 A38b | 60c Exhib. emblem | .55 | .55 |
| 258 A38b | 60c Royal Exhibi. Building | .55 | .55 |

A. Shrewsbury Playing Cricket — A39

Cricket players in action or portrait.

1984, Nov. 5   Litho.   Perf. 12½
Se-tenant Pairs #a.-b.
259 A39	5c shown	.35	.35
260 A39	30c H. Verity	1.00	1.00
261 A39	50c E.H. Hendren	1.00	1.00
262 A39	60c J. Briggs	1.25	1.25
	Nos. 259-262 (4)	3.60	3.60

Drawings, Christmas 1984 — A40

1984, Nov. 14   Litho.   Perf. 14½x14
267 A40 15c By Eli Faalata   .30   .30
268 A40 40c By Toakai Niutao   .40   .40
269 A40 50c By Falesa Teuila   .50   .50
270 A40 60c By Piuani Talie   .65   .65
   Nos. 267-270 (4)   1.85 1.85

Classic Automobiles — A41

Sketch listed first followed by angled view.

1984, Dec. 7   Litho.   Perf. 12½x13
Se-tenant Pairs, #a.-b.
   a. — Side and front views.
   b. — Action scene.
271 A41 1c Morris Minor, 1949   .50   .50
272 A41 15c Studebaker Avanti,
           1963   .50   .50
273 A41 50c Chevrolet Interna-
           tional Six, 1929   1.25 1.25
274 A41 $1 Allard J2, 1950   2.50 2.50
   Nos. 271-274 (4)   4.75 4.75

See Nos. 299-302, 332-339, 396-396E, 414-425.

John J. Audubon — A42

#279a, Common flicker. #279b, Say's phoebe. #280a, Townsend's warbler. #280b, Bohemian waxwing. #281a, Prothonotary warbler. #281b, Worm-eating warbler. #282a, Broad-winged hawk. #282b, Northern harrier.

1985, Feb. 12   Litho.   Perf. 12½
279 A42 1c Pair, #a.-b.   .35   .35
280 A42 25c Pair, #a.-b.   .75   .75
281 A42 50c Pair, #a.-b.   1.50 1.50
282 A42 70c Pair, #a.-b.   1.90 1.90
   Nos. 279-282 (4)   4.50 4.50

Birds and Eggs A43

1985, Feb. 27   Perf. 14
287 A43 15c Black-naped tern   .50   .35
288 A43 40c Black noddy   1.10   .85
289 A43 50c White-tailed tropic-
           bird   1.40   .95
290 A43 60c Sooty tern   1.75 1.25
   Nos. 287-290 (4)   4.75 3.40

Train Type of 1984
1985, Mar. 19   Perf. 12½
Se-tenant Pairs, #a.-b.
   a. — Side and front views.
   b. — Action scene.
291 A36 5c Churchward, U.K.   .35   .35
292 A36 10c Class K.F., China   .35   .35
293 A36 30c Class 99.77, East
           Germany   .90   .90
294 A36 $1 Pearson, U.K.   3.00 3.00
   Nos. 291-294 (4)   4.60 4.60

Automobile Type of 1984
1985, Apr. 3
Se-tenant Pairs, #a.-b.
   a. — Side and front views.
   b. — Action scene.
299 A41 1c Rickenbacker, 1923   .50   .50
300 A41 20c Detroit-Electric,
           1914   .50   .50
301 A41 50c Packard Clipper,
           1941   1.25 1.25
302 A41 70c Audi Quattro, 1982 1.90 1.90
   Nos. 299-302 (4)   4.15 4.15

World War II Aircraft A44

1985, May 29   Litho.   Perf. 14
307 A44 15c Curtiss P-40N   2.25 1.25
308 A44 40c Consolidated B-
           24D Liberator   2.50 1.90
309 A44 50c Lockheed PV-1
           Ventura   2.50 2.75
310 A44 60c Douglas C-54
           Skymaster   2.50 2.75
   a.   Souvenir sheet of 4, #307-310 10.00 10.00
   Nos. 307-310 (4)   9.75 8.65

Queen Mother, 85th Birthday — A45

#310a, Facing right. #310b, Facing left. #311a, 317a, Facing right. #311b, 317b, Facing front. #312a, 316a, Waving to crowd. #312b, 316b, Facing front. #313a, Facing front. #313b, Facing left. #314a, As a young woman. #314b, as Queen Consort.

1985-86   Litho.   Perf. 12½
311 A45 5c Pair, #a.-b.   .45   .45
312 A45 30c Pair, #a.-b.   .70   .70
313 A45 60c Pair, #a.-b.   1.40 1.40
314 A45 $1 Pair, #a.-b.   2.10 2.10
   Nos. 311-314 (4)   4.65 4.65

Souvenir Sheets
315 A45 $1.20 #a.-b.   2.50 2.50
316 A45 $2 #a.-b.   6.25 6.25
317 A45 $3 #a.-b.   8.75 8.75

Issued: #316-317, 6/10/86; others, 7/4/85.

Train Type of 1984
1985, Sept. 18
Se-tenant Pairs, #a.-b.
   a. — Side and front views.
   b. — Action scene.
320 A36 10c 1936 Green Arrow,
           U.K.   .40   .40
321 A36 40c 1982 G.M. (EMD)
           SD-50, US   1.10 1.10
322 A36 65c 1932 DRG Flying
           Hamburger, Ger-
           many   1.50 1.50
323 A36 $1 1908 JNR Class
           1070, Japan   1.60 1.60
   Nos. 320-323 (4)   4.60 4.60

Girl Guides, 75th Anniv. — A46

1985, Aug. 28   Litho.   Perf. 15
328 A46 15c Playing guitar   .35   .25
329 A46 40c Camping   .70   .70
330 A46 50c Flag bearer   .85   .85
331 A46 60c Guides' salute   1.00 1.00
   a.   Souvenir sheet of 4, #328-331 3.25 3.25
   Nos. 328-331 (4)   2.90 2.80

Car Type of 1984
5c, 1929 Cord L-29, US. 10c, 1932 Horch 670 V-12, Germany. 15c, 1901 Lanchester, UK. 35c, 1950 Citroen 2 CV, France. 40c, 1957 MGA, UK. 55c, 1962 Ferrari 250-GTO, Italy. $1, 1932 Ford V-8, US. $1.50, 1977 Aston Martin-Lagonda, UK.

1985, Oct. 8   Perf. 12½
   a. — Side and front views.
   b. — Action scene.
332-339 A41 Set of 8 pairs   7.75 7.75

Crabs A47

1986, Jan. 7   Perf. 15
348 A47 15c Stalk-eyed ghost   .40   .40
349 A47 40c Red and white
           painted   1.10 1.10
350 A47 50c Red-spotted   1.25 1.25
351 A47 60c Red hermit   1.60 1.60
   Nos. 348-351 (4)   4.35 4.35

Souvenir Sheet of 2

Events — A48

#352a, American and Soviet flags, chess board & knight. #352b, Rotary Intl. emblem.

1986, Mar. 19   Litho.   Perf. 13x12½
352 A48 $3 #a.-b.   8.00 8.00

Fischer and Karpov, world chess champions; Rotary Intl., 80th anniv.
No. 352 exists with plain or decorated border.

Ship Type of 1981
1986, Apr. 14   Perf. 15
353 A25 15c Messenger of
           Peace   .35   .35
354 A25 40c John Wesley   .90   .90
355 A25 50c Duff   1.10 1.10
356 A25 60c Triton   1.25 1.25
   Nos. 353-356 (4)   3.60 3.60

Queen Elizabeth II, 60th Birthday — A49

Various portraits.

1986, Apr. 21   Perf. 12½
357 A49 10c multicolored   .40   .40
358 A49 90c multicolored   .60   .60
359 A49 $1.50 multicolored   1.00 1.00
360 A49 $3 multi, vert.   2.00 2.00
   Nos. 357-360 (4)   4.00 4.00

Souvenir Sheet
361 A49 $4 multicolored   5.00 5.00

Peace Corps, 25th Anniv. A50

1986, May 22   Perf. 14
362 A50 50c multicolored   1.00 1.00

For overprint see No. 374.

A51

A52

1986, May 22   Perf. 14x13½
363 A51 60c multicolored   .90   .90

AMERIPEX '86.

1986, June 30   Litho.   Perf. 15
Players and teams.
364 A52 1c So. Korea   .20   .20
365 A52 5c France   .20   .20
366 A52 10c W. Germany,
           1974   .20   .20
367 A52 40c Italy   .45   .45

Size: 60x40mm
Perf. 13x12½
368 A52 60c W. Germany vs.
           Holland, 1974   .55   .55
369 A52 $1 Canada   .95   .95
370 A52 $2 No. Ireland   2.10 2.10
371 A52 $3 England   2.75 2.75
   Nos. 364-371 (8)   7.40 7.40

Souvenir Sheets
372 A52 $1.50 like #369   2.10 2.10
373 A52 $2.50 like #370   3.50 3.50

1986 World Cup Soccer Championships. Nos. 366 and 368 picture emblem; others picture character trademark.

No. 362 Ovptd. with STAMPEX '86 Emblem
1986, Aug. 4   Litho.   Perf. 14
374 A50 50c multicolored   .70   .70

A53

Wedding of Prince Andrew and Sarah
Ferguson — A54

#381a, Andrew, vert. #381b, Couple, vert.
#382a, Andrew. #382b, Princess Diana,
Sarah.

Perf. 12½

			Litho.	Unwmk.
1986, July 18		Litho.	Unwmk.	
381	A53	60c Pair, #a.-b.	1.25	1.25
382	A53	$1 Pair, #a.-b.	2.50	2.50

Souvenir Sheet
Perf. 13x12½

383	A54	$6 Newlyweds	5.75	5.75

No. 382a pictures Westminster Abbey in LR.
For overprints see Nos. 389-390.

Geckos
A55

1986, July 30		Litho.	Perf. 14	
384	A55	15c Mourning gecko	.40	.30
385	A55	40c Oceanic stump-toed	1.40	1.10
386	A55	50c Azure-tailed skink	1.75	1.40
387	A55	60c Moth skink	2.50	1.90
		Nos. 384-387 (4)	6.05	4.70

Souvenir Sheet

South
Pacific
Forum,
15th
Anniv.
A56

Flags and maps: a, Australia. b, Cook
Islands. c, Micronesia. d, Fiji. e, Kiribati. f,
Nauru. g, New Zealand. h, Niue. i, Papua New
Guinea. j, Solomon Islands. k, Tonga. l,
Tuvalu. m, Vanuatu. n, Western Samoa.

Wmk. 380

1986, Aug. 4	Litho.	Perf. 15	
388	Sheet of 14 + label	10.00	10.00
a.-n.	A56 40c any single	.70	.70

No. 388 has center label picturing Executive
Committee headquarters, Suva, Fiji.

Nos. 381-382 Ovptd. "Congratulations
to T.R.H. The Duke & Duchess of
York" in Silver

1986		Unwmk.	Perf. 12½	
389	A53	60c Pair, #a.-b.	1.75	1.75
390	A53	$1 Pair, #a.-b.	2.75	2.75

Exist tete-beche.

Car Type of 1984

15c, 1953 Cooper, UK. 40c, 1964 Rover
2000, UK. 50c, 1930 Ruxton, US. 60c, 1950
Jowett Jupiter, UK. 90c, 1964 Cobra Daytona
Coupe, US. $1.50, 1903 Packard Model F "Old
Pacific," US.

1986, Oct.	Litho.	Perf. 12½	
Se-tenant Pairs, #a.-b.			
a. — Side and front views.			
b. — Action scene.			
391-396	A41	Set of 6 pairs	7.75 7.75

Marine
Life
A57

1986, Nov. 5		Unwmk.	Perf. 14	
397	A57	15c Sea star	1.10	1.10
398	A57	40c Pencil urchin	1.90	1.90
399	A57	50c Fragile coral	2.10	2.10
400	A57	60c Pink coral	2.40	2.40
		Nos. 397-400 (4)	7.50	7.50

See Nos. 465-468, 524-527.

Souvenir Sheets

Statue of Liberty, Cent. — A58

Various views of the statue.

1986, Nov. 24				
401	A58	$1.25 multicolored	1.10	1.10
402	A58	$1.50 multicolored	1.50	1.50
403	A58	$1.80 multicolored	1.90	1.90
404	A58	$2 multicolored	2.10	2.10
405	A58	$2.25 multicolored	2.40	2.40
406	A58	$2.50 multicolored	2.50	2.50
407	A58	$3 multicolored	3.25	3.25
408	A58	$3.25 multicolored	3.50	3.50
409	A58	$3.50 multicolored	4.00	4.00
		Nos. 401-409 (9)	22.25	22.25

Ships Type of 1981

1987, Feb. 4		Unwmk.	Perf. 14	
410	A25	15c Southern Cross IV	1.00	1.00
411	A25	40c John Williams VI	2.25	2.25
412	A25	50c John Williams IV	2.40	2.40
413	A25	60c M.S. Southern Cross	2.40	2.40
		Nos. 410-413 (4)	8.05	8.05

Car Type of 1984

1c, 1938 Talbot-Lago, France. 2c, 1930
Dupont Model G, US. 5c, 1950 Riley RM, U.K.
10c, 1915 Chevrolet Baby Grand, US. 20c,
1968 Shelby Mustang GT 500 KR, US. 30c,
1952 Ferrari 212 Export Barchetta, Italy. 40c,
1912 Peerless Model 48-Six, US. 50c, 1954
Sunbeam Alpine, U.K. 60c, 1969 Matra-Ford
MS80, France. 70c, 1934 Squire 1-Litre, U.K.
75c, 1931 Talbot 105, U.K. $1, 1928 Plymouth
Model Q, US.

Perf. 12½

1987, May 7	Litho.	Unwmk.	
Se-tenant Pairs, #a.-b.			
a. — Side and front views.			
b. — Action scene.			
414-425	A41	Set of 12 pairs, #a.-b.	8.75 8.75
425c		Souv. sheet of 2	3.75 3.75

Ferns — A59

1987, July 7		Wmk. 380	Perf. 14	
438	A59	15c Nephrolepis saligna	.20	.20
439	A59	40c Asplenium nidus	1.00	1.00
440	A59	50c Microsorum scolopendria	1.25	1.25
441	A59	60c Pteris tripartita	1.50	1.50
		Nos. 438-441 (4)	3.95	3.95

Souvenir Sheet

442	A59	$1.50 Psilotum nudum	3.75	3.75

A60

#443a, 444b, 445a, 456b, Flowers, all diff.
#443b, 444a, 445b, 456a, Woman wearing
fou, all diff.

1987, Aug. 12		Wmk. 380		
443	A60	15c Pair, #a.-b.	.50	.50
444	A60	40c Pair, #a.-b.	1.25	1.25
445	A60	50c Pair, #a.-b.	1.50	1.50
446	A60	60c Pair, #a.-b.	2.00	2.00
		Nos. 443-446 (4)	5.25	5.25

Crayfish
and
Coconut
Crabs
A61

Wmk. 380

1987, Nov. 11		Litho.	Perf. 14	
451	A61	40c Coconut crabs	1.50	1.10
452	A61	50c Painted crayfish	1.90	1.40
453	A61	60c Ocean crayfish	2.10	1.75
		Nos. 451-453 (3)	5.50	4.25

Photograph of Queen Victoria, 1897,
by Downey — A62

60c, Elizabeth and Philip on their wedding
day, 1947. 80c, Elizabeth, Charles, Philip, c.
1950. $1, Elizabeth, Anne, 1950. $2, Elizabeth, 1970. $3, Elizabeth, children, 1950.

1987, Nov. 20	Unwmk.	Perf. 15	
454-458	A62	Set of 5	6.00 6.00

Souvenir Sheet

459	A62	$3 red org & blk	5.25	5.25

Accession of Queen Victoria to the throne of
England, sesquicentennial; wedding of Queen
Elizabeth II and Prince Philip, 40th anniv.

16th World Scout Jamboree, Australia,
1987-88 — A63

Jamboree and Australia bicentennial
emblems plus: 40c, Aborigine, Ayer's Rock.
60c, Capt. Cook, by Dance, and HMS
Endeavor. $1, Scout and Scout Park Arch.
$1.50, Koala and kangaroo. $2.50, Lord and
Lady Baden-Powell.

Perf. 13x12½

1987, Dec. 2		Litho.	Unwmk.	
460	A63	40c multicolored	.55	.55
461	A63	60c multicolored	.80	.80
462	A63	$1 multicolored	1.50	1.50
463	A63	$1.50 multicolored	2.10	2.10
		Nos. 460-463 (4)	4.95	4.95

Souvenir Sheet

464	A63	$2.50 multicolored	3.75	3.75

Marine Life Type of 1986
Unwmk.

1988, Feb. 29		Litho.	Perf. 15	
465	A57	15c Spanish dancer	.65	.35
466	A57	40c Hard corals	1.60	.75
467	A57	50c Feather stars	1.90	.95
468	A57	60c Staghorn corals	2.25	1.10
		Nos. 465-468 (4)	6.40	3.15

Birds
A64

1988, Mar. 2			Perf. 15	
469	A64	5c Jungle fowl	.20	.20
470	A64	10c White tern	.20	.20
471	A64	15c Brown noddy	.20	.20
472	A64	20c Phoenix petrel	.20	.20
473	A64	25c Pacific golden plover	.25	.25
474	A64	30c Crested tern	.30	.30
475	A64	35c Sooty tern	.35	.35
476	A64	40c Bristle-thighed curlew	.40	.40
477	A64	45c Eastern bar-tailed godwit	.45	.45
478	A64	50c Reef heron	.50	.50
479	A64	55c Greater fri-gatebird	.55	.55
480	A64	60c Red-footed booby	.65	.65
481	A64	70c Red-necked stint	.75	.75
482	A64	$1 New Zealand long-tailed cuck-oo	1.25	1.25
483	A64	$2 Red-tailed tropic-bird	2.25	2.25
484	A64	$5 Banded rail	5.50	5.50
		Nos. 469-484 (16)	14.00	14.00

For overprints see Nos. 676-679, 796-799,
O33-O48.

Intl. Red Cross and Red Crescent
Organizations, 125th Annivs. — A65

Perf. 12½

1988, May 9		Litho.	Unwmk.	
485	A65	15c Jean-Henri Du-nant	.30	.30
486	A65	40c Junior Red Cross	.35	.35
487	A65	50c Care for the hand-icapped	.55	.55
488	A65	60c First aid training	.60	.60
		Nos. 485-488 (4)	1.80	1.80

Souvenir Sheet

489	A65	$1.50 Lecture	1.90	1.90

A66

Voyages of Capt. Cook — A67

Designs: 20c, HMS *Endeavour* (starboard side). 40c, *Endeavour* (stern). 50c, Landing, Tahiti, 1769, vert. 60c, Maori chief, vert. 80c, *Resolution* and native Hawaiian sail ship. $1, Cook, by Sir Nathaniel Dance-Holland (1735-1811), vert. $2.50, Antarctic icebergs surrounding the *Resolution*. Illustration A67 reduced.

1988, June 15   Litho.   Perf. 12½
490-495 A66   Set of 6   5.75   5.75

Souvenir Sheet
496   A67 $2.50 shown   16.00 16.00

Fungi — A68

1988, July 25   Litho.   Perf. 15
497 A68 40c Ganoderma applanatum   1.25 1.25
498 A68 50c Pseudoepicoccum cocos   1.50 1.50
499 A68 60c Rigidoporus zonalis   1.75 1.75
500 A68 90c Rigidoporus microporus   2.50 2.50
        Nos. 497-500 (4)   7.00 7.00
        See Nos. 520-523.

1988 Summer Olympics, Seoul — A69

Perf. 12½
1988, Aug. 19   Unwmk.
501 A69 10c Rifles, target   .40   .40
502 A69 20c Judo   .65   .65
503 A69 40c One-man kayak   1.50 1.50
504 A69 60c Swimming   2.25 2.25
505 A69 80c Yachting   2.75 2.75
506 A69 $1 Balance beam   4.00 4.00
        Nos. 501-506 (6)   11.55 11.55

Natl. Independence, 10th Anniv. — A70

Wmk. 380
1988, Sept. 28   Litho.   Perf. 14
507 A70 60c Queen Elizabeth in boat   1.10 1.10
  a.   Souvenir sheet of 1   1.10 1.10
508 A70 90c In sedan chair   1.60 1.60
  a.   Souvenir sheet of 1   1.60 1.60
509 A70 $1 shown   1.90 1.90
  a.   Souvenir sheet of 1   1.90 1.90
510 A70 $1.20 Seated at dais   2.40 2.40
  a.   Souvenir sheet of 1   2.40 2.40
        Nos. 507-510 (4)   7.00 7.00
        Nos. 507-508 and 510 vert.

Christmas — A71

Unwmk.
1988, Dec. 5   Litho.   Perf. 14
511 A71 15c Mary   .40   .40
512 A71 40c Christ child   1.00 1.00
513 A71 60c Joseph   1.50 1.50
        Nos. 511-513 (3)   2.90 2.90

Souvenir Sheet
514 A71 $1.50 Heraldic angel   2.75 2.75

Palm-frond or Pandanus-leaf Skirts — A72

1989, Mar. 31   Litho.   Perf. 14
515 A72 40c multi   1.25 1.25
516 A72 50c multi, diff.   1.50 1.50
517 A72 60c multi, diff.   1.75 1.75
518 A72 90c multi, diff.   2.50 2.50
        Nos. 515-518 (4)   7.00 7.00

Souvenir Sheet
519 A72 $1.50 multi, vert.   4.50 4.50

Fungi Type of 1988
1989, May 24   Litho.   Perf. 14
520 A68 40c Trametes muelleri   1.25 1.25
521 A68 50c Pestalotiopsis palmarum   2.50 2.50
522 A68 60c Trametes cingulata   3.00 3.00
523 A68 90c Schizophyllum commune   4.75 4.75
        Nos. 520-523 (4)   11.50 11.50

Marine Life Type of 1986
1989, July 31   Litho.   Perf. 14
524 A57 40c Pennant coralfish   1.90 1.90
525 A57 50c Anemone fish   2.40 2.40
526 A57 60c Batfish   2.75 2.75
527 A57 90c Threadfin coralfish   5.00 5.00
  a.   Miniature sheet of 4, #524-527   12.00 12.00
        Nos. 524-527 (4)   12.05 12.05

Souvenir Sheet

Maiden Voyage of M.V. *Nivaga II*, 1988 — A73

1989, Oct. 9   Litho.   Perf. 14
528 A73 $1.50 multicolored   7.00 7.00

Christmas — A74

Tropical Trees — A75

Unwmk.
1989, Nov. 29   Litho.   Perf. 14
529 A74 40c Conch shell   1.00 1.00
530 A74 50c Flower bouquet   1.40 1.40
531 A74 60c Germinated coconut   1.60 1.60
532 A74 90c Shell jewelry   2.25 2.25
        Nos. 529-532 (4)   6.25 6.25

1990, Feb. 28   Litho.   Perf. 14½
533 A75 15c *Cocus nucifera*   .65   .65
534 A75 30c *Rhizophora samoensis*   1.25 1.25
535 A75 40c *Messerschmidia argentea*   1.60 1.60
536 A75 50c *Pandanus tectorius*   2.00 2.00
537 A75 60c *Hernandia nymphaeifolia*   2.50 2.50
538 A75 90c *Pisonia grandis*   4.00 4.00
        Nos. 533-538 (6)   12.00 12.00

Penny Black, 150th Anniv. A76

1990, May 3   Litho.   Perf. 14
539 A76 15c multicolored   1.10 1.10
540 A76 40c multicolored   3.00 3.00
541 A76 90c multicolored   7.00 7.00
        Nos. 539-541 (3)   11.10 11.10

Souvenir Sheet
542 A76 $2 multicolored   9.25 9.25
        Stamp World London '90.

World War II Ships A77

Designs: 15c, Japanese merchant conversion, 1940. 30c, USS Unimak, seaplane tender, 1944. 40c, Amagari, Japanese Hubuki class, 1942. 50c, AO-24 USS Platte, Nov. 1, 1943. 60c, Japanese Shumushu Class (Type A) escort. 90c, CV-22 USS Independence.

1990
543-548 A77 Set of 6   18.00 18.00

Flowers — A78

1990, Sept. 21   Litho.   Perf. 14½
549 A78 15c Erythrina fusca   .35   .35
550 A78 30c Capparis cordifolia   .65   .65
551 A78 40c Portulaca pilosa   .90   .90
552 A78 50c Cordia subcordata   1.10 1.10
553 A78 60c Scaevola taccada   1.40 1.40
554 A78 90c Suriana maritima   2.10 2.10
        Nos. 549-554 (6)   6.50 6.50

UN Development Program, 40th Anniv. — A79

1990, Nov. 20   Litho.   Perf. 14
555 A79 40c Surveyor   1.75 1.75
556 A79 60c Communications station   2.25 2.25
557 A79 $1.20 Fishing boat *Te Tautai*   4.50 4.50
        Nos. 555-557 (3)   8.50 8.50

Christmas A80

Seashells — A81

1990, Nov. 20
558 A80 15c Mary and Joseph   .55   .55
559 A80 40c Nativity   1.60 1.60
560 A80 60c Shepherds   2.25 2.25
561 A80 90c Three Kings   3.50 3.50
        Nos. 558-561 (4)   7.90 7.90

1991, Jan. 18   Litho.   Perf. 14
562 A81 40c Murex ramosus   1.50 1.50
563 A81 50c Conus marmoreus   2.00 2.00
564 A81 60c Trochus niloticus   2.25 2.25
565 A81 $1.50 Cypraea mappa   5.00 5.00
        Nos. 562-565 (4)   10.75 10.75

Insects A82

1991, Mar. 22   Litho.   Perf. 14
566 A82 40c Cylas formicarius   1.75 1.75
567 A82 50c Heliothis armiger   2.40 2.40
568 A82 60c Spodoptera litura   2.75 2.75
569 A82 $1.50 Agrius convolvuli   6.50 6.50
        Nos. 566-569 (4)   13.40 13.40

A83

A84

Endangered marine life.

1991, May 31   Litho.   *Perf. 14*
570 A83   40c Green turtle   1.50   1.50
571 A83   50c Humpback
                 whale   1.75   1.75
572 A83   60c Hawksbill turtle   2.25   2.25
573 A83 $1.50 Sperm whale   5.25   5.25
       Nos. 570-573 (4)   10.75 10.75

1991, July 31   Litho.   *Perf. 14*
574 A84   40c Soccer   2.25   2.25
575 A84   50c Volleyball   2.75   2.75
576 A84   60c Lawn tennis   3.50   3.50
577 A84 $1.50 Cricket   8.00   8.00
       Nos. 574-577 (4)   16.50 16.50

9th South Pacific Games.

World
War II
Ships
A85

1991, Oct. 15   Litho.   *Perf. 14*
578 A85   40c USS Tennes-
                 see   3.50   2.75
579 A85   50c IJN Haguro   3.75   3.50
580 A85   60c HMS Achilles   5.00   4.00
581 A85 $1.50 USS North Car-
                 olina   10.50 10.50
       Nos. 578-581 (4)   22.75 20.75

A86

A87

Christmas: various   traditional   dance
costumes.

1991, Dec. 13
582 A86   40c multicolored   1.90   1.90
583 A86   50c multicolored   2.50   2.50
584 A86   60c multicolored   3.00   3.00
585 A86 $1.50 multicolored   7.50   7.50
       Nos. 582-585 (4)   14.90 14.90

1992, Jan. 29   Litho.   *Perf. 14*

Constellations.

586 A87   40c Southern Fish   1.75   1.75
587 A87   50c Scorpio   2.25   2.25
588 A87   60c Sagittarius   2.75   2.75
589 A87 $1.50 Southern Cross   6.50   6.50
       Nos. 586-589 (4)   13.25 13.25

British Annexation of the Gilbert &
Ellice Islands, Cent. — A88

1992, Mar. 23   Litho.   *Perf. 14*
590 A88   40c King George VI   2.25   2.25
591 A88   50c King George V   2.75   2.75
592 A88   60c King Edward
                 VII   3.50   3.50
593 A88 $1.50 Queen Victoria   9.00   9.00
       Nos. 590-593 (4)   17.50 17.50

Discovery
of
America,
500th
Anniv.
A89

Columbus and: 40c, Queen Isabella & King
Ferdinand of Spain. 50c, Polynesians. 60c,
South American Indians. $1.50, North Ameri-
can Indians.

1992, May 22   Litho.   *Perf. 14*
594 A89   40c black & dk blue   1.50   1.50
595 A89   50c black & dk
                 plum   1.75   1.75
596 A89   60c black & dk
                 green   2.00   2.00
597 A89 $1.50 black & dk pur-
                 ple   4.75   4.75
       Nos. 594-597 (4)   10.00 10.00

World Columbian Stamp Expo '92, Chicago.

Fish
A90

Designs: 15c, Bluespot butterflyfish. 20c,
Pink parrotfish. 25c, Stripe surgeonfish. 30c,
Moon wrasse, 35c, Harlequin filefish. 40c, Bird
wrasse. 45c, Black-finned pigfish. 50c, Blue-
green chromis. 60c, Hump-headed Maori
wrasse. 70c, Ornate coralfish, vert. 90c, Sad-
dled butterflyfish, vert. $1, Vagabond butterf-
lyfish, vert. $2, Longfin bannerfish, vert. $3,
Moorish idol, vert.

1992, July 15
598-611 A90 Set of 14   17.00 17.00

For overprints & surcharge see #629-632,
716.

1992 Summer
Olympics,
Barcelona — A91

1992, July 27   Litho.   *Perf. 14*
612 A91   40c Discus   1.25   1.25
613 A91   50c Javelin   1.60   1.60
614 A91   60c Shotput   2.10   2.10
615 A91 $1.50 Track & field   5.25   5.25
       Nos. 612-615 (4)   10.20 10.20

Souvenir Sheet
616 A91 $2 Olympic stadi-
                 um   6.50   6.50

Blue
Coral
A92

Various views of blue coral.

1992, Sept. 1
617 A92   10c multicolored   1.50   1.50
618 A92   25c multicolored   3.25   3.25
619 A92   30c multicolored   3.25   3.25
620 A92   35c multicolored   4.00   4.00
       Nos. 617-620 (4)   12.00 12.00

World Wildlife Fund.

Christmas — A93   Wild
                               Flowers — A94

Designs: 40c, Fishermen seeing angel. 50c,
Fishermen sailing canoes toward island. 60c,
Adoration of the fishermen. $1.50, Flowers,
shell necklaces.

1992, Dec. 25   Litho.   *Perf. 14*
621 A93   40c multicolored   .90   .90
622 A93   50c multicolored   1.10   1.10
623 A93   60c multicolored   1.25   1.25
624 A93 $1.50 multicolored   3.25   3.25
       Nos. 621-624 (4)   6.50   6.50

1993, Feb. 2   Litho.   *Perf. 14*
625 A94   40c Calophyllum in-
                 ophyllum   1.10   1.10
626 A94   50c Hibiscus tiliaceus   1.40   1.40
627 A94   60c Lantana camara   1.60   1.60
628 A94 $1.50 Plumeria rubra   3.75   3.75
       Nos. 625-628 (4)   7.85   7.85

Nos. 601,
603, &
605-606
Ovptd.

1992, Sept. 1   Litho.   *Perf. 14*
629 A90   30c on #601   1.50   1.50
630 A90   40c on #603   1.75   1.75
631 A90   50c on #605   2.50   2.50
632 A90   60c on #606   2.75   2.75
       Nos. 629-632 (4)   8.50   8.50

World
War II in
the
Pacific,
50th
Anniv.
A95

1993, Apr. 23   Litho.   *Perf. 14*
633 A95   40c Japanese
                 bombers   1.90   1.90
634 A95   50c Anti-aircraft
                 gun, vert.   2.25   2.25
635 A95   60c Using flame
                 thrower   2.75   2.75
636 A95 $1.50 Map of Funafuti
                 Atoll, vert.   7.75   7.75
       Nos. 633-636 (4)   14.65 14.65

Souvenir Sheet

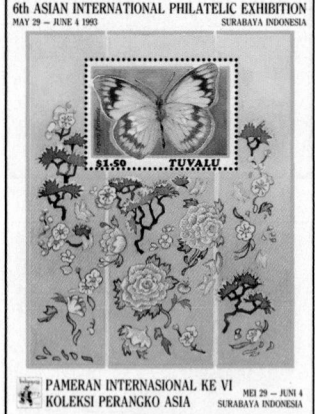

Indopex '93 — A96

1993, May 29   *Perf. 14x14½*
637 A96 $1.50 Cepora perimale   7.50   7.50

Marine
Life
A97

1993, June 29   Litho.   *Perf. 14*
638 A97   40c Giant clam   1.00   1.00
639 A97   50c Anemone crab   1.25   1.25
640 A97   60c Octopus   1.50   1.50
641 A97 $1.50 Green turtle   3.50   3.50
       Nos. 638-641 (4)   7.25   7.25

Coronation of Queen Elizabeth II, 40th
Anniv. — A98

Queen: 40c, Riding in parade with Prince
Phillip. 50c, Drinking coconut milk. 60c, Holding umbrella. $1.50, With natives. $2, Coronation ceremony.

1993, July 5
642 A98   40c multicolored   .95   .95
643 A98   50c multicolored   1.25   1.25
644 A98   60c multicolored   1.50   1.50
645 A98 $1.50 multicolored   3.50   3.50
       Nos. 642-645 (4)   7.20   7.20

Souvenir Sheet
646 A98 $2 multicolored   10.00 10.00

Souvenir Sheet

Taipei '93 — A99

Illustration reduced.

Litho. & Typo.
1993, Aug. 14   *Perf. 14½x14*
647 A99 $1.50 Geoffroyi godart   7.00   7.00

Souvenir Sheet

Bangkok '93 — A100

Illustration reduced.

1993, Oct. 1   Litho.   Perf. 14x14½
648 A100 $1.50 Paradisea staud-
inger   4.50 4.50

Greenhouse Effect — A101   Christmas — A102

Beach scene with: 40c, Sun at UR. 50c, Sun at UL. 60c, Crab on beach. $1.50, Sea gull in flight.

1993, Nov. 2   Litho.   Perf. 13½
649 A101 40c multicolored   .75   .75
650 A101 50c multicolored   1.00 1.00
651 A101 60c multicolored   1.25 1.25
652 A101 $1.50 multicolored   3.00 3.00
a. Souvenir sheet of 4, #649-
652, perf. 14½x14   7.25 7.25
Nos. 649-652 (4)   6.00 6.00

1993, Dec. 6   Litho.   Perf. 13½
653 A102 40c shown   .90   .90
654 A102 50c Candle, flowers 1.10 1.10
655 A102 60c Angel, flowers   1.40 1.40
656 A102 $1.50 Palm tree, can-
dles   3.25 3.25
Nos. 653-656 (4)   6.65 6.65

Souvenir Sheet

Hong Kong '94 — A103

Illustration reduced.

1994, Feb. 18   Perf. 14½x14
657 A103 $2 Monarch   6.25 6.25

Scenic Views A104

1994, Feb. 18   Litho.   Perf. 14
658 A104 40c shown   1.00 1.00
659 A104 50c Beach, trees,
diff.   1.10 1.10

---

660 A104 60c Boats, ocean   1.40 1.40
661 A104 $1.50 Boats, beach   3.75 3.75
Nos. 658-661 (4)   7.25 7.25

New Year 1994 (Year of the Dog) — A105

1994, Apr. 23   Litho.   Perf. 14
662 A105 40c Irish setter   1.00 1.00
663 A105 50c Golden retriever 1.10 1.10
664 A105 60c West Highland
terrier   1.40 1.40
665 A105 $1.50 German shep-
herd   3.75 3.75
Nos. 662-665 (4)   7.25 7.25

A106

1994, June 7
666 A106 40c Australia   .65   .65
667 A106 50c England   .85   .85
668 A106 60c Argentina   1.00 1.00
669 A106 $1.50 Germany   2.50 2.50
Nos. 666-669 (4)   5.00 5.00

Souvenir Sheet
670 A106 $2 US   7.25 7.25

1994 World Cup Soccer Championships, US.

A107

1994, Aug. 16   Litho.   Perf. 14
Seashells.
671 A107 40c Umbonium giganteum   1.00 1.00
672 A107 50c Turbo petholatus 1.25 1.25
673 A107 60c Planaxis savignyi 1.50 1.50
674 A107 $1.50 Hydatina physis 3.75 3.75
Nos. 671-674 (4)   7.50 7.50

Souvenir Sheet

PHILAKOREA '94 — A108

Illustration reduced.

1994, Aug. 16
675 A108 $1.50 Pekinese dog   4.75 4.75

Nos. 469-470, 476-477 Ovptd.

1994, Aug. 31   Litho.   Perf. 15
676 A64 5c multicolored   .35   .35
677 A64 10c multicolored   .35   .35
678 A64 40c multicolored   1.00 1.00
679 A64 45c multicolored   1.10 1.10
Nos. 676-679 (4)   2.80 2.80

First Manned Moon Landing, 25th Anniv. — A109

a, 40c, Saturn V. b, 50c, Apollo 11. c, 60c, Neil Armstrong. d, $1.50, Splash-down.

1994, Oct. 31   Perf. 14
680 A109 Strip of 4, #a.-d.   7.25 7.25

Christmas — A110

40c, Boys playing in water. 50c, Islanders, fish being gathered. 60c, People seated under canopy, food. $1.50, Traditional dancers.

1994, Dec. 15   Litho.   Perf. 14
681 A110 40c multicolored   .95   .95
682 A110 50c multicolored   1.10 1.10
683 A110 60c multicolored   1.40 1.40
684 A110 $1.50 multicolored   3.50 3.50
Nos. 681-684 (4)   6.95 6.95

New Year 1995 (Year of the Boar) A111

40c, One pig. 50c, Pig, piglet. 60c, Three pigs. $1.50, Sow nursing litter.

1995, Jan. 30   Litho.   Perf. 14
685-688 A111 Set of 4   5.50 5.50

FAO, 50th Anniv. A112

40c, Men with vegetables in wheelbarrow. 50c, Man with sack of vegetables. 60c, Girl cleaning vegetables. $1.50, Girl mixing food.

1995, Mar. 31   Litho.   Perf. 14
689-692 A112 Set of 4   6.75 6.75

Visit South Pacific Year A113

1995, May 26   Litho.   Perf. 14
693 A113 40c shown   .75   .75
694 A113 50c Sailboat   .95   .95
695 A113 60c Hut   1.10 1.10
696 A113 $1.50 Home, beach   2.75 2.75
Nos. 693-696 (4)   5.55 5.55

Pacific Coastal Orchids A114

40c, Dendrobium comptonii. 50c, Dendrobium aff. involutum. 60c, Dendrobium rarum. $1.50, Grammatophyllum scriptum.

1995, July 28   Litho.   Perf. 14
697-700 A114 Set of 4   7.25 7.25

Souvenir Sheet

Jakarta '95, Asian World Stamp Exhibition — A116

Illustration reduced.

1995, Aug. 19   Litho.   Perf. 12
702 A116 $1 Traditional dancer 2.50 2.50

For overprint see No. 702.

Souvenir Sheet

Singapore '95 World Stamp Exhibition — A117

Illustration reduced.

1995, Sept. 1
703 A117 $1 Phalaenopsis
amabillis   2.75 2.75

End of World War II, 50th Anniv. A118

40c, Soldier with sub-machine gun, map of Japan, Tuvalu. 50c, Soldier holding rifle, landing exercise on beach. 60c, US Marine, offshore air and sea battle. $1.50, Soldier firing rifle, atomic mushroom cloud.

1995, Aug. 19   Litho.   Perf. 14
704-707 A118 Set of 4   9.75 9.75

Souvenir Sheet

UN, 50th Anniv. — A119

a, Rowing in outrigger canoes. b, UN New York headquarters. Illustration reduced.

1995, Oct. 24		**Perf. 14½**	
708 A119	$1 Sheet of 2, #a.-b.	4.25	4.25

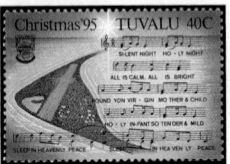

Christmas — A120

Scores and verses to Christmas carols and: 40c, Map of island, "Silent Night." 50c, Boy carolers, "O Come All Ye Faithful." 60c, Girl carolers, "The First Noel." $1.50, Angel, "Hark the Herald Angels Sing."

1995, Dec. 15	**Litho.**	**Perf. 14**	
709-712 A120	Set of 4	6.50	6.50

Miniature Sheet

Independence, First Tuvalu Postage Stamps, 20th Anniv. — A121

a, 40c, #16. b, 60c, #17. c, $1, #18.

1996, Jan. 1	**Litho.**	**Perf. 14**	
713 A121	Sheet of 3, #a.-c.	5.25	5.25

Miniature Sheet

New Year 1996 (Year of the Rat) — A122

Stylized rats: a, Looking right. b, Facing left, drinking from container.

1996, Feb. 23	**Litho.**	**Perf. 14x14½**	
714 A122	50c Sheet of 2, #a.-b.	2.50	2.50
c.	Ovptd. in sheet margin	2.50	2.50
d.	With added inscription in sheet margin	2.50	2.50

No. 714c is overprinted in sheet margin with exhibition emblem of Hongpex '96.
No. 714d is inscribed in sheet margin with two exhibition emblems of China '96. Issued: 5/18.

No. 702
Ovptd. in Gold

1996, Mar. 21	**Litho.**	**Perf. 12**	
715 A116	$1 multicolored	1.75	1.75

No. 715 also contains same overprint in sheet margin.

No. 604 Surcharged in Black, Red & Blue

1996, Oct. 21	**Litho.**	**Perf. 14**	
716 A90	$1 on 45c multi	1.60	1.60

1996 Summer Olympic Games, Atlanta A123

1996, Sept. 11	**Litho.**	**Perf. 14**	
717 A123	40c Beach volleyball	.60	.60
718 A123	50c Swimming	.75	.75
719 A123	60c Weight lifting	.90	.90
720 A123	$1.50 David Tua, boxer	2.25	2.25
	Nos. 717-720 (4)	4.50	4.50

UNICEF, 50th Anniv. A124

1996, Oct. 28			
721 A124	40c Immunization	.60	.60
722 A124	50c Education for life	.75	.75
723 A124	60c Water tank project	.90	.90
724 A124	$1.50 Hydroponic farm	2.25	2.25
	Nos. 721-724 (4)	4.50	4.50

Christmas A125

Designs: 40c, Magi following star. 50c, Shepherds seeing star. 60c, Adoration of the Magi. $1.50, Nativity scene.

1996, Nov. 25		**Perf. 14½**	
725 A125	40c multicolored	.70	.70
726 A125	50c multicolored	.85	.85
727 A125	60c multicolored	1.00	1.00
728 A125	$1.50 multicolored	2.50	2.50
	Nos. 725-728 (4)	5.05	5.05

Fish
A126

1997, Mar. 15		**Perf. 14**	
729 A126	25c Bluetail mullet	.40	.40
730 A126	30c Queen fish leatherskin	.45	.45
731 A126	40c Paddletail	.60	.60
732 A126	45c Long-nose emperor	.70	.70
	Complete bklt., 4 ea #729-732	8.75	
733 A126	50c Long-snouted unicornfish	.75	.75
734 A126	55c Brigham's snapper	.80	.80
735 A126	60c Red bass	.90	.90
736 A126	70c Red jobfish	1.00	1.00
737 A126	90c Leopard flounder	1.40	1.40
738 A126	$1 Red snapper	1.50	1.50
739 A126	$2 Longtail snapper	3.00	3.00
a.	Souv. sheet of 1, wmk. 373	3.00	3.00
740 A126	$3 Black trevally	4.50	4.50
	Nos. 729-740 (12)	16.00	16.00

No. 739a for return of Hong Kong to China, July 1, 1997.

Souvenir Sheet

New Year 1997 (Year of the Ox) — A127

1997, June 20	**Litho.**	**Perf. 14**	
741 A127	$2 multicolored	5.25	

Hong Kong '97.

Ducks and Drakes A128

1997, May 29	**Litho.**	**Perf. 14**	
742 A128	40c White pekin	.60	.60
743 A128	50c Muscovy	.75	.75
744 A128	60c Pacific black	.90	.90
745 A128	$1.50 Mandarin	2.25	2.25
	Nos. 742-745 (4)	4.50	4.50

PACIFIC 97.

Domestic Cats — A129

40c, Korat king. 50c, Long-haired ginger kitten. 60c, Shaded cameo. $1.50, American Maine coon.

1997, June 20			
746 A129	40c multicolored	.70	.70
747 A129	50c multicolored	.85	.85
748 A129	60c multicolored	1.00	1.00
749 A129	$1.50 multicolored	2.50	2.50
	Nos. 746-749 (4)	5.05	5.05

Queen Elizabeth II and Prince Philip, 50th Wedding Anniv. — A130

Designs: No. 750, Queen, Prince standing in open vehicle. No. 751, Queen in yellow hat. No. 752, Queen holding umbrella. No. 753, Queen reading, Prince up close. No. 754, Three pictures of Queen. No. 755, Prince in top hat, Queen. $2, Queen, Prince riding in open carriage, horiz.

	Wmk. 373		
1997, Oct. 1	**Litho.**	**Perf. 14½**	
750	40c multicolored	.60	.60
751	40c multicolored	.60	.60
a.	A130 Pair, #750-751	1.25	1.25
752	50c multicolored	.75	.75
753	50c multicolored	.75	.75
a.	A130 Pair, #752-753	1.50	1.50
754	60c multicolored	.85	.85
755	60c multicolored	.85	.85
a.	A130 Pair, #754-755	1.75	1.75
	Nos. 750-755 (6)	4.40	4.40

Souvenir Sheet

756 A130	$2 multicolored	3.50	3.50

No. 756 contains one 38x32mm stamp.

Traditional Activities — A131

Christmas: 40c, Turtle hunting. 50c, Pole fishing. 60c, Canoe racing. $1.50, Traditional dance.

	Perf. 13½x13		
1997, Nov. 25	**Litho.**	**Wmk. 373**	
757 A131	40c multicolored	.60	.60
758 A131	50c multicolored	.75	.75
759 A131	60c multicolored	.90	.90
760 A131	$1.50 multicolored	2.25	2.25
	Nos. 757-760 (4)	4.50	4.50

Souvenir Sheet

New Year 1998 (Year of the Tiger) — A132

Illustration reduced.

1998, Feb. 2	**Litho.**	**Perf. 13**	
761 A132	$1.40 multicolored	2.25	2.25

Diana, Princess of Wales (1961-97)
Common Design Type

Designs: a, Wearing red evening dress. b, Wearing black evening dress. c, Wearing tiara. d, With collar up on coat.

	Perf. 14½x14		
1998, Mar. 31	**Litho.**	**Wmk. 373**	
762 CD355	80c Sheet of 4, #a.-d.	4.50	4.50

No. 762 sold for $3.20 + 20c, with surtax from international sales being donated to the Princess Diana Memorial Fund and surtax from national sales being donated to designated local charity.

Royal Air Force, 80th Anniv.
Common Design Type of 1993 Reinscribed

Designs: 40c, Hawker Woodcock. 50c, Vickers Victoria. 60c, Bristol Brigand $1.50, De Haviland DHC 1 Chipmunk.

No. 767: a, Sopwith Pup. b, Armstrong Whitworth FK8. c, North American Harvard. d, Vultee Vengeance.

Wmk. 384

1998, Apr. 1		**Litho.**	**Perf. 13½**	
763	CD350	40c multicolored	.70	.70
764	CD350	50c multicolored	.80	.80
765	CD350	60c multicolored	1.00	1.00
766	CD350	$1.50 multicolored	2.50	2.50
		Nos. 763-766 (4)	5.00	5.00

Souvenir Sheet

767	CD350	$1 Sheet of 4, #a.-d.	6.00	6.00

Ships
A133

Designs: 40c, "Los Reyes," "Santiago," 1567. 50c, "Morning Star," missionary topsail schooner, 1867. 60c, "The Light," brigantine of Church of the Resurrection, 1870. $1.50, New Zealand missionary schooner, 1900.

Wmk. 373

1998, May 19		**Litho.**	**Perf. 14**	
768	A133	40c multicolored	.50	.50
769	A133	50c multicolored	.60	.60
770	A133	60c multicolored	.75	.75
771	A133	$1.50 multicolored	1.75	1.75
		Nos. 768-771 (4)	3.60	3.60

Dolphins and Porpoises — A134

40c, Bottlenose dolphin. 50c, Dall's porpoise. 60c, Harbor porpoise. $1.50, Common dolphin.

Perf. 13½x13

1998, Aug. 21		**Litho.**	**Wmk. 384**	
772	A134	40c multicolored	.55	.55
773	A134	50c multicolored	.75	.75
774	A134	60c multicolored	.90	.90
775	A134	$1.50 multicolored	2.25	2.25
		Nos. 772-775 (4)	4.45	4.45

Greenpeace, Save Our Seas
A135

Marine life: 20c, Bleached platygyra daedalea, psammocora digitata. 30c, Bleached acropora robusta. 50c, Bleached acropora hyacinthus. $1, Bleached acropora danai, montastrea curta.
$1.50, Bleached seriatopora, bleached stylophora.

Wmk. 373

1998, Nov. 6		**Litho.**	**Perf. 14½**	
776	A135	20c multicolored	.30	.30
777	A135	30c multicolored	.55	.55
778	A135	50c multicolored	.90	.90
779	A135	$1 multicolored	1.60	1.60
		Nos. 776-779 (4)	3.35	3.35

Souvenir Sheet

780	A135	$1.50 multicolored	2.25	2.25

Intl. Year of the Ocean (#780).

Christmas — A136

40c, Flight into Egypt. 50c, Angel speaking to shepherds. 60c, Nativity. $1.50, Adoration of the Magi.

1998, Nov. 20			**Perf. 14½x14**	
781	A136	40c multicolored	.55	.55
782	A136	50c multicolored	.70	.70
783	A136	60c multicolored	.80	.80
784	A136	$1.50 multicolored	2.00	2.00
		Nos. 781-784 (4)	4.05	4.05

Independence, 20th Anniv. — A137

Stamps on stamps, Prime Ministers: 40c, #722, Bikenibeu Paeniu. 60c, Kamuta Latasi. 90c, Tomasi Puapua. $1.50, Design like #166, Toaripi Lauti.

Wmk. 384

1998, Oct. 1		**Litho.**	**Perf. 14**	
785	A137	40c multicolored	.55	.55
786	A137	60c multicolored	.85	.85
787	A137	90c multicolored	1.25	1.25
788	A137	$1.50 multicolored	2.00	2.00
a.		Souvenir sheet, #785-788	4.75	4.75
		Nos. 785-788 (4)	4.65	4.65

Souvenir Sheet

New Year 1999 (Year of the Rabbit) — A138

Illustration reduced.

Perf. 14½x14

1999, Feb. 16		**Litho.**	**Wmk. 373**	
789	A138	$2 multicolored	3.25	3.25

Australia '99, World Stamp Expo A139

Maritime history: 40c, Heemskerck, 1642. 50c, HMS Endeavour, 1769. 90c, PS Sophie Jane, 1831. $1.50, P&O SS Chusan, 1852. $2, HM Brig "Supply."

1999, Mar. 19			**Perf. 14**	
790	A139	40c multicolored	.60	.60
791	A139	50c multicolored	.70	.70
792	A139	90c multicolored	1.40	1.40
793	A139	$1.50 multicolored	2.10	2.10
		Nos. 790-793 (4)	4.80	4.80

Souvenir Sheet

794	A139	$2 multicolored	2.50	2.50

Nos. 472, 475, 479, 482 Ovptd.

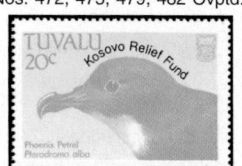

1999, June 11		**Litho.**	**Perf. 15**	
796	A64	20c on #472	.30	.30
797	A64	35c on #475	.50	.50
798	A64	55c on #479	.80	.80
799	A64	$1 on #482	1.40	1.40
		Nos. 796-799 (4)	3.00	3.00

50% of the sales of Nos. 796-799 will be donated to the Kosovo Relief Fund.

1st Manned Moon Landing, 30th Anniv.
Common Design Type

40c, Lift-off. 60c, Lunar module prepares to touchdown. 90c, Ascent stage approaches Command module. $1.50, Recovery.
$2, Looking at earth from moon.

Perf. 14x13¾

1999, July 20		**Litho.**	**Wmk. 384**	
800	CD357	40c multicolored	.60	.60
801	CD357	60c multicolored	.80	.80
802	CD357	90c multicolored	1.40	1.40
803	CD357	$1.50 multicolored	2.10	2.10
		Nos. 800-803 (4)	4.90	4.90

Souvenir Sheet
Perf. 14

804	CD357	$2 multicolored	2.50	2.50

No. 804 contains one circular stamp 40mm in diameter.

Queen Mother's Century
Common Design Type

Queen Mother: 40c, With King George VI inspecting bomb damage. 60c, With daughters at Balmoral. 90c, With Princes Harry and William, 95th birthday. $1.50, As colonel-in-chief of Queen's Dragoon Guards.
$2, Age 6 photo, photo of Yuri Gagarin.

Wmk. 384

1999, Aug. 16		**Litho.**	**Perf. 13½**	
805	CD358	40c multicolored	.60	.60
806	CD358	60c multicolored	.85	.85
807	CD358	90c multicolored	1.40	1.40
808	CD358	$1.50 multicolored	2.10	2.10
		Nos. 805-808 (4)	4.95	4.95

Souvenir Sheet

809	CD358	$2 multicolored	4.25	4.25

Flowers — A141

No. 810: a, Fetai. b, Ateate. c, Portulacacae lueta. d, Tamoloc. e, Beach pea. f, Pomegranate (red letters).
No. 811: a, Cup of gold. b, Rock rose. c, Bower plant. d, Lavender star. e, Hybrid mandevilla. f, Pomegranate (white letters).
No. 812, Scrambled eggs, vert.

Perf. 13¾

1999, Nov. 22		**Litho.**	**Unwmk.**	
810	A141	90c Sheet of 6, #a.-f.	6.75	6.75
811	A141	90c Sheet of 6, #a.-f.	6.75	6.75

Souvenir Sheet

812	A141	$3 multi	5.25	5.25

A142

Millennium — A143

No. 813, Lady of peace with frame.
No. 814: a, Like No. 813, no frame. b, Olive branch. c, Dove. d. Lion. e, Lamb. f, War crowning peace.

No. 815: Sun on horizon, clock, computer keyboard.

Perf. 14½x14¼

1999, Dec. 31			**Litho.**	
813	A142	90c multi	1.10	1.10
814	A142	90c Sheet of 6, #a.-f.	7.75	7.75

Souvenir Sheet
Perf. 14

815	A143	$2 multi	2.75	2.75

No. 813 printed in sheets of 6.

Worldwide Fund for Nature — A144

Sand tiger shark: a, 10c, Close-up of head. b, 30c, Facing left. c, 50c, Swimming above seaweed. d, 60c, Three sharks.

Perf. 13¼x13½

2000, Feb. 7		**Litho.**	**Unwmk.**	
816	A144	Strip of 4, #a.-f.	3.00	3.00
e.		Souvenir sheet, 2 #816	9.50	9.50

Souvenir Sheet
Stamps Without WWF Emblem

817	A144	Sheet of 4, #a.-d	2.75	2.75

Marine Life and Birds — A145

Illustration reduced.
No. 818, each 90c: a, Common tern. b, White-tailed tropicbird. c, Red emperor snapper. d, Clown triggerfish. e, Longfin bannerfish. f, Harlequin tuskfish.
No. 819, each 90c: a, Wilson's storm petrel. b, Common dolphin. c, Spotted seahorse. d, Threeband demoiselle. e, Coral hind. f, Palette surgeonfish.
No. 820, each 90c: a, Great frigatebird. b, Brown booby. c, Dugong. d, Red knot. e, Common starfish. f, Hawksbill turtle.
No. 821, each 90c: a, Manta ray. b, White shark. c, Hammerhead shark. d, Tiger shark. e, Great barracuda. f, Leatherback turtle.
No. 822, each 90c: a, Whale shark. b, Six-spot grouper. c, Bluestreak cleaner wrasse. d, Lemon shark. e, Spotted trunkfish. f, Long-nosed butterflyfish.
No. 823, each 90c: a, Chevroned butterflyfish. b, Mandarinfish. c, Bicolor angelfish. d, Copperbanded butterflyfish. e, Clown anemonefish. f, Lemonpeel angelfish.
Each $3: No. 824, Picassofish. No. 825, Pygmy parrotfish. No. 826, Sailfish.

2000, Mar. 8			**Perf. 14**	
		Sheets of 6, #a.-f.		
818-823	A145	Set of 6	45.00	45.00
		Souvenir Sheets		
824-826	A145	Set of 3	11.00	11.00

Butterflies — A146

Illustration reduced.

No. 827, each 90c: a, Birdwing. b, Tailed emperor. c, Orchid swallowtail. d, Union Jack. e, Long-tailed blue. f, Common Jezabel.

No. 828, each 90c: a, Caper white. b, Common Indian crow. c, Eastern flat. d, Cairns birdwing. e, Monarch. f, Meadow argus.

No. 829, each 90c, horiz.: a, Glasswing. b, Leftwing. c, Moth butterfly. d, Blue triangle. e, Beak. f, Plane.

Each $3: No. 830, Great egg-fly. No. 831, Palmfly, horiz.

2000, May 1   Sheets of 6, #a.-f.
827-829 A146   Set of 3   22.50 22.50
        Souvenir Sheets
830-831 A146   Set of 2   7.50 7.50

Birds — A147

#832, each 90c: a, Red-billed leiothrix. b, Gray shrike-thrush. c, Great frigatebird. d, Common kingfisher. e, Chestnut-breasted finch. f, White tern.

#833, each 90c: a, White-collared kingfisher. b, Scaled petrel. c, Superb blue wren. d, Osprey. e, Great cormorant. f, Peregrine falcon.

#834, each 90c: a, Rainbow lorikeet. b, White-throated tree creeper. c, White-tailed kingfisher. d, Golden whistler. e, Black-bellied plover. f, Beach thick-knee.

Each $3: #835, Morepork. #836, Broad-billed prion, horiz.
Illustration reduced.

2000, June 1   Litho.   Perf. 14
              Sheets of 6, #a-f
832-834 A147   Set of 3   22.50 22.50
        Souvenir Sheets
835-836 A147   Set of 2   7.50 7.50

Dogs and Cats — A148

No. 837: a, Fox terrier. b, Collie. c, Boston terrier. d, Pembroke Welsh corgi. e, Pointer. f, Dalmatian.

No. 838, vert.: a, Dalmatian. b, Boston terrier. c, Fox terrier. d, Pointer. e, Pembroke Welsh corgi. f, Collie.

No. 839, vert. (denominations in orange): a, Ticked taboy oriental shorthair. b, Balinese. c, Somali. d, Chinchilla Persian. e, Tonkinese. f, Japanese bobtail.

No. 840, vert. (denominations in green): a, Lilac oriental shorthair. b, Balinese. c, Somali. d, Chinchilla Persian. e, Tonkinese. f, Japanese bobtail.

No. 841, Scottish terrier. No. 842, Oriental shorthair, vert.
Illustration reduced.

2000, July 3   Litho.   Perf. 14
              Sheets of 6, #a-f
837-840 A148   90c Set of 4   22.50 22.50
        Souvenir Sheets
841-842 A148 $3 Set of 2   7.75 7.75

Birds and Animals — A149

No. 843, horiz.: a, Brown noddy. b, Great frigatebird. c, Emperor angelfish. d, Common dolphin. e, Hermit crab. f, Threadfin butterflyfish.

No. 844, horiz.: a, Red-footed booby. b, Red-tailed tropicbird. c, Black-bellied plover. d, Common tern. e, Ruddy turnstone. f, Sanderling.

$3, Great frigatebird.
Illustration reduced.

2000, Aug. 3
              Sheets of 6, #a-f
843-844 A149   90c Set of 2   14.50 14.50
        Souvenir Sheet
845   A149 $3 Great frigatebird   3.75 3.75

New Year 2000 and 2001 (Years of the Dragon and Snake) A150

Designs: 40c, Dragon. 60c, Snake. 90c, Snake, diff. $1.50, Dragon, diff.

2001, Jan. 15   Litho.   Perf. 13½x13¼
846-849 A150   Set of 4   5.25 5.25

Motofoua Secondary School Fire, 1st Anniv. A151

Fire trucks: 60c, Anglo specialist rescue uUnit. 90c, Anglo 4800 water/foam tender. $1.50, Bronto 33-2T1 combined telescopic ladder/hydralulic platform. $2, Anglo 450 LRX water tender.
$3, Wormold "Arrestor" ARFFV.

2001, Mar. 9   Litho.   Perf. 13¼
850-853 A151   Set of 4   14.50 14.50
        Souvenir Sheet
854   A151 $3 multi   7.75 7.75

.tv Corporation A152

Palm fronds, satellite dish and: 40c, Woman. 60c, Dancers. 90c, Man. $1.50, Child.
$2, Map.

2001, May 30   Litho.   Perf. 14¼x14½
855-858 A152   Set of 4   5.75 5.75
        Souvenir Sheet
859   A152 $2 multi   3.25 3.25

        Souvenir Sheet

Phila Nippon '01 — A153

2001, Aug. 1   Perf. 13
860   A153 $3 multi   4.00 4.00

No. 805 Surcharged in Gold like No. 861 and Nos. 806-808 Overprinted in Gold

Wmk. 384
2001, Aug. 4   Litho.   Perf. 13½
860A CD358   60c multi   .65   .65
860B CD358   90c multi   .95   .95
860C CD358 $1.50 multi   1.60 1.60
860D CD358 $2 on 40c multi   2.25 2.25
      Nos. 860A-860D (4)   5.45 5.45

No. 809 Surcharged in Gold

2001, Aug. 4   Wmk. 384   Perf. 13½
        Souvenir Sheet
861   CD358 $5 on $2 multi   5.50 5.50

Fauna A154

Designs: 25c, Mosquito. 30c, Giant African snail. 40c, Cockroach. 45c, Stick insect. 50c, Green stink bug. 55c, Dragonfly. 60c, Monarch caterpillar. 70c, Coconut beetle. 90c, Honeybee. $1, Monarch butterfly. 42, Common eggfly butterfly. $3, Painted lady butterfly.

Unwmk.
2001, Oct. 31   Litho.   Perf. 13
862 A154   25c multi   .25   .25
863 A154   30c multi   .30   .30
864 A154   40c multi   .40   .40
865 A154   45c multi   .45   .45
866 A154   50c multi   .50   .50
867 A154   55c multi   .55   .55
868 A154   60c multi   .60   .60
869 A154   70c multi   .70   .70
870 A154   90c multi   .90   .90
871 A154 $1 multi   1.00 1.00
872 A154 $2 multi   2.00 2.00
873 A154 $3 multi   3.00 3.00
     Nos. 862-873 (12)   10.65 10.65

United We Stand — A155

Statue of Liberty and Tuvalu flag: No. 874, $2, Blue background. No. 875, $2, Yellow background.

2002, Jan. 10   Perf. 14
874-875 A155   Set of 2   4.25 4.25

Paintings Depicting Chapter Scenes From "The Tale of Genji" — A156

No. 876, 40c — Chapter: a, 1. b, 2. c, 3. d, 4. e, 5. f, 6.
No. 877, 60c — Chapter: a, 8, b, 9. c, 10. d, 11. e, 12. f, 13.
No. 878, 90c — Chapter: a, 15. b, 16, c, 17. d, 18. e, 19, f, 20.
No. 879, $4 — Chapter 7. No. 880, $4, Chapter 14. No. 881, $4, Chapter 21.

2002, Apr. 24   Litho.   Perf. 14¼
              Sheets of 6, #a-f
876-878 A156   Set of 3   12.50 12.50
              Imperf
879-881 A156   Set of 3   13.00 13.00

Nos. 876-878 each contain six 37x50mm stamps.

UN Special Session on Children and Convention on Rights of the Child A157

Designs: 40c, Boy in wheelchair. 60c, Boy and girl sitting near fence. 90c, Nauti Primary School, Funafuti. $4, Mother and child.
No. 886: a, Taulosa Karl. b, Simalua Jacinta Enele.

2002, May 8 Litho. Perf. 13¼x13½
882-885 A157 Set of 4   6.50 6.50
Souvenir Sheet
886 A157 $1 Sheet of 2, #a-b   2.25 2.25

Reign of Queen Elizabeth II, 50th Anniv. — A158

No. 887: a, Princes William and Harry. b, Queen in blue green suit. c, Queen and Prince Philip. d, Queen wearing red hat.
$4, Queen on horseback.

2002, June 17 Perf. 14¼
887 A158 $1.50 Sheet of 4, #a-d 6.75 6.75
Souvenir Sheet
888 A158 $4 multi   4.50 4.50

2002 World Cup Soccer Championships, Japan and Korea — A159

No. 889: a, Tom Finney. b, Poster from 1974 World Cup. c, Portuguese player and flag. d, Uruguayan player and flag. e, Suwon World Cup Stadium, Seoul (56x42mm).
$4, Johann Cruyff.

2002, July 15 Perf. 14
889 A159 90c Sheet of 5, #a-e   5.00 5.00
Souvenir Sheet
890 A159 $4 multi   4.25 4.25

Queen Mother Elizabeth (1900-2002) — A160

No. 891: a, 60c, Wearing tiara (lilac shading at UL) (26x29mm). b, 60c, Wearing tiara (lilac shading at UR) (26x29mm). c, 90c, In crowd, holding bouquet of flowers (lilac shading at UL) (28x23mm). d, 90c, Receiving flowers from children (lilac shading at UR) (28x23mm). e, 90c, With teddy bear (lilac shading at UL) (28x23mm). f, With man, woman and children (lilac shading at UR) (28x23mm). g, Color photograph (40x29mm).
No. 892, $2, lilac shading at UL: a, As child, with another young girl. b, As older woman.
No. 893, $2, lilac shading at UR: a, Smelling flower. b, Wearing brooch.

Perf. Compound x14¼ (60c), 13¼x10¾ (90c), 13¼x14¼ ($1.50)
2002, Aug. 12
891 A160   Sheet of 7, #a-g   6.75 6.75
Souvenir Sheets
Perf. 14¾
892-893 A160 Set of 2   8.50 8.50

20th World Scout Jamboree, Thailand — A161

No. 894 — Merit badges: a, Citizenship in the World. b, First Aid. c, Personal Fitness. d, Environmental Science.
$5, Lord Robert Baden-Powell.

2002, Oct. 2 Perf. 14¼
894 A161 $1.50 Sheet of 4, #a-d 6.50 6.50
Souvenir Sheet
895 A161 $5 multi   5.50 5.50

Intl. Year of Mountains — A162

No. 896, horiz.: a, Mt. Fitzroy, Chile. b, Mt. Foraker, US. c, Mt. Fuji, Japan. d, Mt. Malaku, Nepal and China.
$4, Mt. Godwin Austen, Kashmir.

2002, Oct. 2
896 A162 $1.50 Sheet of 4, #a-d 6.50 6.50
Souvenir Sheet
897 A162 $4 multi   4.50 4.50

Elvis Presley (1935-77) — A163

2002, Dec. 27 Litho. Perf. 14¼
898 A163 $1 multi   1.10 1.10
No. 898 was printed in sheets of 6.

Princess Diana (1961-97) — A164

No. 899 — Diana wearing: a, Black dress, no necklace. b, Black dress, choker necklace. c, Blue dress. d, Blue green scarf. e, Pink blouse, hand at chin. f, Pink dress.
$4, Black dress, hand on chin.

2002, Dec. 27 Perf. 14
899 A164 $1 Sheet of 6, #a-f   7.00 7.00
Souvenir Sheet
900 A164 $4 multi   4.50 4.50

Year of the Horse (in 2002) — A165

Various horses: 40c, 60c, 90c, $2.
No. 905: a, Head of horse, seahorse. b, Heads of horse, three seahorses.

2003, Jan. 23 Perf. 13¼
901-904 A165 Set of 4   4.75 4.75
Souvenir Sheet
905 A165 $1.50 Sheet of 2, #a-b 3.50 3.50

New Year 2003 (Year of the Ram) — A166

No. 906: a, Green and black background. b, White background. c, Blue background.

2003, Feb. 1 Perf. 14x13¾
906 A166 75c Vert. strip of 3,
          #a-c   2.75 2.75
No. 906 printed in sheets containing two strips.

Pres. John F. Kennedy (1917-63) — A167

No. 907: a, In Solomon Islands, 1943. b, On PT 109, 1942. c, Receiving medal for gallantry, 1944. d, Campaigning for Senate, 1952.
$4, With father and brothers.

2003, Mar. 24 Perf. 14
907 A167 $1.75 Sheet of 4, #a-d 8.50 8.50
Souvenir Sheet
908 A167 $4 multi   5.00 5.00

Powered Flight, Cent. — A168

No. 909, $1.75: a, Orville Wright in early plane, 1903. b, Wilbur Wright and King Alfonso XIII of Spain, 1909. c, Wilbur Wright's plane, 1908. d, Gabriel Voisin's plane piloted by Léon Delagrange, 1907.

No. 910, $1.75: a, Voisin's motor boat powered glider, 1905. b, Trajan Vuia's single winged plane, 1906. c, Santos-Dumont's biplane, 1906. d, Orville Wright circles parade ground, 1908.

No. 911, $4, Wright Brothers biplane in flight, 1908. No. 912, $4, Glenn Curtiss pilots June Bug, 1908.

2003, May 19　　Litho.　　Perf. 14
Sheets of 4, #a-d
909-910 A168　Set of 2　　19.00 19.00
Souvenir Sheets
911-912 A168　Set of 2　　10.50 10.50

Coronation of Queen Elizabeth II, 50th Anniv. — A169

No. 913: a, Wearing gray dress. b, Wearing tiara. c, Wearing yellow hat.
$4, Wearing hat and pearl necklace.

2003, Aug. 11
913 A169　$2 Sheet of 3, #a-c　　8.00 8.00
Souvenir Sheet
914 A169　$4 multi　　5.25 5.25

Prince William, 21st Birthday — A170

No. 915: a, Wearing school cap. b, Wearing blue shirt. c, Wearing polo helmet.
$4, Wearing suit and tie.

2003, Aug. 11
915 A170　$1.50 Sheet of 3, #a-c　6.00 6.00
Souvenir Sheet
916 A170　$4 multi　　5.25 5.25

General Motors Automobiles — A171

No. 917, $1 — Corvettes: a, Yellow 1979. b, Red 1979. c, Silver 1979. d, 1980.
No. 918, $1.50 — Cadillacs: a, 1931 V-16 Sport Phaeton. b, 1959 Eldorado convertible. c, 1979 Seville Elegante. d, 1983 Seville Elegante.
No. 919, $4, 1990 Corvette. No. 920, $4, 1954 Cadillac Coupe de Ville.

2003, Sept. 8　　　　　Perf. 13¾
Sheets of 4, #a-d
917-918 A171　Set of 2　　13.50 13.50
Souvenir Sheets
919-920 A171　Set of 2　　10.50 10.50
Corvettes, 50th anniv.; Cadillacs, 100th anniv.

Tour de France Bicycle Race, Cent. — A172

No. 921: a, Gastone Nencini, 1960. b, Jacques Anquetil, 1961. c, Anquetil, 1962. d, Anquetil, 1963.
$4, Jan Janssen, 1968.

2003, Oct. 6　　　Perf. 13¾x13¼
921 A172　$1 Sheet of 4, #a-d　　5.50 5.50
Souvenir Sheet
922 A172　$4 multi　　5.50 5.50

Butterflies — A173

No. 923, horiz.: a, Malachite. b, White M hairstreak. c, Giant swallowtail. d, Bahamian swallowtail.
$3, Polydamas swallowtail.

2003, Dec. 16　　　　　Perf. 14
923 A173　$1.25 Sheet of 4, #a-d　7.75 7.75
Imperf
924 A173　$3 multi　　4.50 4.50
No. 923 contains four 42x28mm stamps.

Flowers — A174

No. 925: a, Rhododendron. b, Golden Artist tulip. c, Golden Splendor lily. d, Flamingo flower.
$3, Candy Bianca rose.

2003, Dec. 16　　　　　Perf. 14
925 A174　$1.25 Sheet of 4, #a-d　7.75 7.75
Imperf
926 A174　$3 multi　　4.50 4.50
No. 925 contains four 28x42mm stamps.

Orchids — A175

No. 927, vert.: a, Dimerandra emarginata. b, Oncidium lanceanum. c, Isochilus linearis. d, Oeceoclades maculata.
$3, Oncidium ampliatum.

2003, Dec. 16　　　　　Perf. 14
927 A175　$1.25 Sheet of 4, #a-d　7.75 7.75
Souvenir Sheet
928 A175　$3 multi　　4.50 4.50

Birds — A176

No. 929: a, Blue-gray gnatcatcher. b, White-eyed vireo. c, Clapper rail. d, Sandhill crane.
$3, Grasshopper sparrow.

2003, Dec. 16
929 A176　$1.25 Sheet of 4, #a-d　7.75 7.75
Souvenir Sheet
930 A176　$3 multi　　4.50 4.50

New Year 2004 (Year of the Monkey) A177

Paintings by Chang Dai-chen: 75c, Monkey and Old Tree. $1.50, Two Monkeys.

2004, Jan. 4　　　　　Perf. 13½
931 A177　75c multi　　1.25 1.25
Souvenir Sheet
932 A177　$1.50 multi　　2.40 2.40
No. 931 printed in sheets of 4.

Paintings by Norman Rockwell — A178

No. 933, vert.: a, 100th Year of Baseball. b, The Locker Room (The Rookie). c, The Dugout. d, Game Called Because of Rain.
$3, New Kids in the Neighborhood.

2004, Jan. 30　　　　　Perf. 14¼
933 A178　$1.25 Sheet of 4, #a-d　7.75 7.75
Souvenir Sheet
934 A178　$3 multi　　4.75 4.75
2004 AmeriStamp Expo, Norfolk, Va. (#933).

Paintings by Pablo Picasso (1881-1973) — A179

No. 935, vert.: a, Seated Woman. b, Woman in Armchair. c, Bust of Françoise. d, Head of a Woman.
$4, Françoise Gilot with Paloma and Claude.

2004, Mar. 1　　Litho.　　Perf. 14¼
935 A179　$1.50 Sheet of 4, #a-d　9.25 9.25
Imperf
936 A179　$4 multi　　6.25 6.25
No. 935 contains four 37x50mm stamps.

Paintings by Paul Gauguin (1848-1903) A180

Designs: 50c, Les Seins aux Fleurs Rouges. 60c, Famille Tahitienne. No. 939, $1, Tahitiennes sur la Plage. $2, Jeune Fille à L'Eventail.

No. 941, $1: a, Nafea Faa Ipoipo. b, Le Cheval Blanc. c, Pape Moe. d, Contes Barbares.
$4, Femmes de Tahiti, horiz.

2004, Mar. 1   **Perf. 14¼**
937-940 A180   Set of 4   6.25 6.25
941 A180 $1 Sheet of 4, #a-d   6.25 6.25
                    Imperf
                Size: 93x73mm
942 A180 $4 multi   6.25 6.25

Paintings in the Hermitage, St. Petersburg, Russia A181

Designs: 50c, Philadelphia and Elizabeth Wharton, by Anthony Van Dyck. 80c, A Glass of Lemonade, by Gerard Terborch. $1, A Mistress and Her Servant, by Pieter de Hooch. $1.20, Portrait of a Man and His Three Sons, by Bartholomaeus Bruyn the Elder.
$4, The Milkmaid's Family, by Louis le Nain, horiz.

2004, Mar. 1   **Perf. 14¼**
943-946 A181 Set of 4   5.50 5.50
                    Imperf
                Size: 80x68mm
947 A181 $4 multi   6.25 6.25

Fight Against HIV and AIDS A182

Designs: 60c, Speaker at conference. 90c, Speaker and dais. $1.50, People standing in front of banner. $2, People seated at dais.
$3, Conference participants.

2004, May 17   **Perf. 13x13½**
948-951 A182 Set of 4   7.00 7.00
            Souvenir Sheet
952 A182 $3 multi   4.25 4.25

            Souvenir Sheet

Inauguration of Republic of China President Chen Shui-bian — A183

No. 953: a, Pres. Chen Shui-bian. b, Saufatu Sopoanga, Prime Minister of Tuvalu.

2004, May 20   **Perf. 13½x13¼**
953 A183 $2 Sheet of 2, #a-b   5.50 5.50

            Souvenir Sheet

Diplomatic Relations Between Tuvalu and the Republic of China, 25th Anniv. — A183a

2004, Sept. 19 Litho.   Perf. 13¼x13
953C A183a $5 multi   7.50 7.50

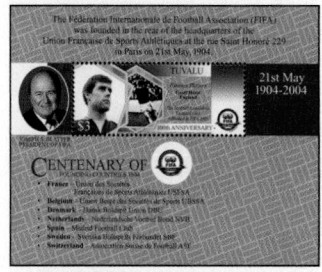

FIFA (Fédération Internationale de Football Association), Cent. — A184

No. 954: a, Sebastiano Rossi. b, Clarence Seedorf. c, Zico. d, Jack Charlton.
$3, Geoff Hurst.

            Perf. 12¾x12½
2004, Nov. 29   **Litho.**
954 A184 $1 Sheet of 4, #a-d   6.25 6.25
            Souvenir Sheet
955 A184 $3 multi   4.75 4.75

            Miniature Sheet

World Peace — A185

No. 956: a, Alfred Nobel. b, Doves. c, Nelson Mandela.

2005, Jan. 14   **Perf. 12¾**
956 A185 $1.50 Sheet of 3, #a-c 7.00 7.00

            Miniature Sheet

Election of Pope John Paul II, 25th Anniv. (in 2003) — A186

No. 957: a, With papal arms. b, At microphone. c, Wearing miter. d, Placing prayer in Wailing Wall, Jerusalem.

2005, Jan. 14
957 A186 $1.50 Sheet of 4, #a-d 9.25 9.25

D-Day, 60th Anniv. (in 2004) — A187

No. 958: a, Gen. George C. Marshall. b, Adm. Sir Ramsay Bertram Home. c, Gen. Walter Bedell Smith. d, Field Marshal Alan Francis Brooke.
$3, Gen. George S. Patton.

2005, Jan. 14
958 A187 $1.50 Sheet of 4, #a-d 9.25 9.25
            Souvenir Sheet
959 A187 $3 multi   4.75 4.75

Dogs — A188

Designs: 20c, Rat terrier. 75c, Large Spanish hound. $1, Lundehund. $2, Beagle harrier.
$3, Old Danish pointer.

2005, Apr. 26 Litho. Perf. 13¾x13¼
960-963 A188 Set of 4   6.25 6.25
            Souvenir Sheet
964 A188 $3 multi   4.75 4.75

Marine Life — A189

No. 965: a, Striped-face unicornfish. b, Great barracuda. c, Blue-ringed octopus. d, Giant clam.
$3, Humpback whale.

2005, Apr. 26   **Perf. 13¼x13¾**
965 A189 $1 Sheet of 4, #a-d   6.25 6.25
            Souvenir Sheet
966 A189 $3 multi   4.75 4.75

Medicinal Plants — A190

No. 967: a, Common toadflax. b, Pomegranate. c, Black horehound. d, Agnus castus
$3, Black henbane.

2005, Apr. 26   **Perf. 13¾x13¼**
967 A190 $1 Sheet of 4, #a-d   6.25 6.25
            Souvenir Sheet
968 A190 $3 multi   4.75 4.75

Insects — A191

No. 969, vert.: a, Louse fly. b, Predacious dung beetle. c, Ladybug. d, Mosquito.
$3, House fly.

2005, Apr. 26   **Perf. 13¾x13¼**
969 A191 $1 Sheet of 4, #a-d   6.25 6.25
            Souvenir Sheet
            Perf. 13¼x13¾
970 A191 $3 multi   4.75 4.75

Pope John Paul II (1920-2005) and Queen Elizabeth II — A192

2005, July 12   **Perf. 13½**
971 A192 $4 multi   6.25 6.25

Battle of Trafalgar, Bicent. — A193

No. 972: a, HMS Victory collides with French ship Redoubtable. b, Admiral Horatio Nelson. c, HMS Victory leads the British fleet. d, Nelson breaths his last breath.
$3, Admiral Cuthbert Collingwood.

2005, July 28   *Perf. 12*
972 A193 $1.50 Sheet of 4, #a-d   9.25 9.25
Souvenir Sheet
973 A193 $3 multi   4.75 4.75

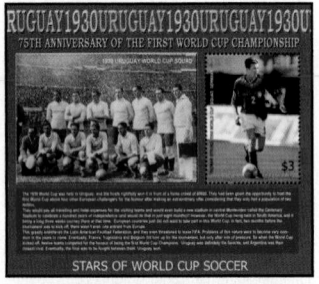

World Cup Soccer Championships, 75th Anniv. — A194

No. 974: a, Thomas Berthold. b, Bobby Charlton. c, Klaus Augenthaler.
$3, Thomas Strunz.

2005, July 28   *Perf. 13¼*
974 A194 $2 Sheet of 3, #a-c   9.25 9.25
Souvenir Sheet
Perf. 12
975 A194 $3 multi   4.75 4.75

End of World War II, 60th Anniv. — A195

No. 976, $2: a, Sir Winston Churchill. b, Gen. Charles de Gaulle. c, Newspaper report on death of Adolf Hitler.
No. 977, $2: a, Pres. Harry S. Truman. b, Newspaper report on end of war. c, Gen. Dwight D. Eisenhower.
No. 978, $3, Gen. George S. Patton. No. 979, $3, Brig. Gen. Paul W. Tibbets, Jr. and Enola Gay.

2005, Sept. 21   *Perf. 12¾*
Sheets of 3, #a-c
976-977 A195   Set of 2   18.50 18.50
Souvenir Sheets
978-979 A195   Set of 2   9.25 9.25

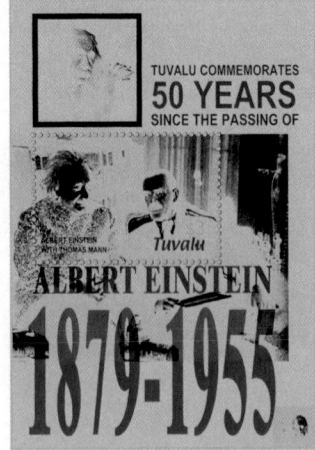

Albert Einstein (1879-1955), Physicist — A196

No. 981 — Einstein and: a, Hendrik Lorentz. b, Fritz Haber. c, David Ben-Gurion.
$3, Einstein with Thomas Mann.

2005, Sept. 21
980 A196 $2 Sheet of 3, #a-c   9.25 9.25
Souvenir Sheet
981 A196 $3 multi   4.50 4.50

Rotary International, Cent. — A197

No. 982: a, Child. b, Hand holding pills. c, Children.
$3, Paul P. Harris, founder.

2005, Nov. 28
982 A197 $2 Sheet of 3, #a-c   9.25 9.25
Souvenir Sheet
983 A197 $3 multi   4.50 4.50

Hans Christian Andersen (1805-75), Author — A198

No. 984: a, Andersen seated. b, Sculpture of Andersen. c, Head of Andersen.
$3, Statue of Andersen.

2005, Nov. 28
984 A198 $2 Sheet of 3, #a-c   9.25 9.25
Souvenir Sheet
985 A198 $3 multi   4.50 4.50

A199

Elvis Presley (1935-77) — A200

No. 987 — Presley and: a, Gable and top of column of house. b, Roofline of house. c, Bottom of column of house. d, Archway of house.

2006, Jan. 30   *Perf. 13½*
986 A199 $3 multi   4.50 4.50
987 A200 $3 Sheet of 4, #a-d   18.00 18.00
No. 986 printed in sheets of 4.

National Basketball Association Players and Team Emblems — A201

No. 988, 35c: a, Emblem of Detroit Pistons. b, Chauncey Billups.
No. 989, 35c: a, Emblem of New Jersey Nets. b, Rodney Buford.
No. 990, 35c: a, Emblem of Boston Celtics. b, Ricky Davis.
No. 991, 35c: a, Emblem of Miami Heat. b, Udonis Haslem.
No. 992, 35c: a, Emblem of Indiana Pacers, horiz. b, Stephen Jackson.
No. 993, 35c: a, Emblem of Minnesota Timberwolves. b, Wally Szczerbiak.

2006, Jan. 30   *Perf. 13¼*
Sheets of 12, 2 #a, 10 #b
988-993 A201   Set of 6   37.50 37.50

Souvenir Sheet

2006 World Cup Soccer Championships, Germany — A202

No. 994 — Player and uniform for: a, 90c, Spain. b, $1, South Korea. c, $1.50, France. d, $2, United States.

2006, June 9   **Litho.**   *Perf. 13¼*
994 A202   Sheet of 4, #a-d   8.25 8.25

Corals A203

Designs: 10c, Montipora aequituberculata. 25c, Montipora capricornis. 30c, Montipora verrucosa. 40c, Acropora caroliniana. 50c, Acropora aculeus. 60c, Acropora anthocercis. 65c, Acropora granulosa. 80c, Acropora rosaria. 90c, Acropora cerealis. $1, Acropora yongei. $2, Acropora echinata. $5, Astreopora myriophthalma.

2006, Oct. 12   *Perf. 12¾*
995 A203 10c multi   .20 .20
996 A203 25c multi   .40 .40
997 A203 30c multi   .45 .45
998 A203 40c multi   .60 .60
999 A203 50c multi   .75 .75
1000 A203 60c multi   .90 .90
1001 A203 65c multi   1.00 1.00
1002 A203 80c multi   1.25 1.25
1003 A203 90c multi   1.40 1.40
1004 A203 $1 multi   1.50 1.50
1005 A203 $2 multi   3.00 3.00
1006 A203 $5 multi   7.50 7.50
Nos. 995-1006 (12)   18.95 18.95

Miniature Sheets

Pres. John F. Kennedy (1917-63) — A204

No. 1007, $1.30: a, On PT109, 1942. b, Receiving medal for gallantry, 1944. c, Portrait with brown background. d, In Ensign's uniform, 1941.
No. 1008, $1.30: a, Wearing bow tie. b, Wearing tan suit. c, With Eleanor Roosevelt. d, Portrait and U.S. Capitol.

2006, Sept. 21   **Litho.**   *Perf. 13½*
Sheets of 4, #a-d
1007-1008 A204   Set of 2   15.50 15.50

Queen Elizabeth II, 80th Birthday — A205

No. 1009: a, As child holding dog. b, Wearing crown and holding scepter. c, Wearing jacket. d, Wearing sash and tiara.
$3, Wearing crown.

2006, Sept. 21

1009	A205	$1.30 Sheet of 4, #a-d	7.75	7.75

Souvenir Sheet

1010	A205	$3 multi	4.50	4.50

Space Achievements — A206

No. 1011 — Space Shuttle Discovery's return to space: a, Nose of Shuttle, open cargo doors, text in white reading down. b, Tail of Shuttle, stars, Earth, text in red reading across. c, Tail and wings of Shuttle, open cargo doors, text in red reading down. d, Astronaut on robotic arm. e, Head-on view of Shuttle nose, text in red reading across. f, Robotic arm, text in red and white.

No. 1012 — International Space Station: a, Top of rocket boosters. b, Space Station, text in white reading across. c, Space Shuttle. d, Space Station, text in white reading up.

$3, Calipso Satellite.

2006

1011	A206	$1 Sheet of 6, #a-f	9.50	9.50
1012	A206	$1.30 Sheet of 4, #a-d	7.75	7.75

Souvenir Sheet

1013	A206	$3 multi	4.50	4.50

Issued: No. 1011, 12/21; Nos. 1012-1013, 9/21.

Miniature Sheet

Wolfgang Amadeus Mozart (1756-91), Composer — A207

No. 1014: a, Mozart gazing out window. b, Mozart family, 1780. c, Mozart, 1763. d, Art deco illustration of the young Mozart.

2006, Oct. 26

1014	A207	$1.30 Sheet of 4, #a-d	8.00	8.00

Rembrandt (1606-69), Painter A208

Designs: 10c, Woman in Bed. 20c, The Flight into Egypt. 35c, The Suicide of Lucretia. 95c, Esther Preparing to Intercede with Ahasuerus. $1, Rembrandt's Mother. $2, Child with Dead Peacock.

$3, The Abduction of Ganymede.

2006, Nov. 9 — Perf. 14¼

1015-1020	A208	Set of 6	7.25	7.25

Imperf
Size: 76x106mm

1021	A208	$3 multi	4.75	4.75

Worldwide Fund for Nature (WWF) — A209

Various Pygmy killer whales.

2006, Nov. 9 — Perf. 13½

1022		Horiz. strip of 4		11.00	11.00
	a.	A209 40c Four whales		.65	.65
	b.	A209 60c Two whales		.95	.95
	c.	A209 90c Four whales, diff.		1.40	1.40
	d.	A209 $5 Two whales, diff.		8.00	8.00
	e.	Miniature sheet, 2 each #1022a-1022d		22.00	22.00

Butterflies — A210

No. 1023: a, Tailed jay. b, Ixias undatus. c, Hebomoia leucippe detanii. d, Rajah Brooke's birdwing.

$3, Painted lady.

2006, Nov. 23

1023	A210	$1 Sheet of 4, #a-d	6.50	6.50

Souvenir Sheet

1024	A210	$3 multi	4.75	4.75

Birds — A211

No. 1025: a, Reed warbler. b, Indian pitta. c, Gurney's pitta. d, Northern shrike.

$3, Black-backed fairy wren.

2006, Nov. 23

1025	A211	$1 Sheet of 4, #a-d	6.50	6.50

Souvenir Sheet

1026	A211	$3 multi	4.75	4.75

Miniature Sheet

Wedding of Queen Elizabeth II and Prince Philip, 60th Anniv. — A212

No. 1027: a, Photograph, denomination in pink. b, Drawing, denomination in white. c, Photograph, denomination in light green. d, Drawing, denomination in pink. e, Photograph, denomination in white. f, Drawing, denomination in light green.

2007, May 1 — Litho. — Perf. 13¼

1027	A212	$1 Sheet of 6, #a-f	10.00	10.00

Princess Diana (1961-97) — A213

No. 1028: a, Wearing black and white hat, pink frame. b, Wearing beige dress, pink frame. c, Wearing pink hat, pink frame. d, Wearing pink hat, lilac frame. e, Wearing beige dress, no frame. f, Wearing black and white hat, lilac frame.

$3, Princess Diana in Tomb of King Seti I, Egypt.

2007, May 1

1028	A213	$1 Sheet of 6, #a-f	10.00	10.00

Souvenir Sheet

1029	A213	$3 multi	5.00	5.00

Global Warming — A214

No. 1030, $1: a, Windmills. b, Smokestacks, graph of atmospheric carbon dioxide. c, Tree seedling. d, Robotic arm lifting logs, thermometer. e, Recycling emblem. f, Thermometer, graph of global temperatures.

No. 1031, $1 — Text: a, Cause - Deforestation. b, Effect - Melting ice cap. c, Cause - Industrialization. d, Effect - Warmer temperature. e, Cause - Traffic. f, Effect - Extreme weather.

No. 1032, $2 — Text: a, Effect: Habitats destroyed. b, Prevention: Use renewable energy. c, Effect: Coral reef bleaching. d, Prevention: Recycle. e, Effect: Erratic weather patterns. f, Prevention: Plant trees.

No. 1033, $3, Earth on fire, smokestacks, automobile getting fuel. No. 1034, $3, Windmills. No. 1035, $3, Plant in parched soil, vert.

2007, July 21 — Litho.

Sheets of 6, #a-f

1030-1032	A214	Set of 3	31.00	31.00

Souvenir Sheets

1033-1035	A214	Set of 3	15.50	15.50

First Helicopter Flight, Cent. — A215

Designs: 20c, BO-105. 75c, NH 90, horiz. $1, S-65/RH-53D, horiz. $2, AH 64 Apache, horiz.

No. 1040, horiz.: a, BO-105, diff. b, S-65/RH-53D, diff. c, AH 64 Apache, diff. d, NH 90, diff.

$3, HUP Retriever, horiz.

2007, July 28 — Perf. 13¼

1036-1039	A215	Set of 4	6.75	6.75
1040	A215	$1.30 Sheet of 4, #a-d	9.00	9.00

Souvenir Sheet

1041	A215	$3 multi	5.25	5.25

Scouting, Cent. A216

Scout: 20c, On bicycle. 75c, At campfire. $1, Playing cricket. $2, Shooting arrow.

$3, Dove, Scouting flag, vert.

2007, Aug. 15

1042-1045	A216	Set of 4	6.50	6.50

Souvenir Sheet

1046	A216	$3 multi	5.00	5.00

No. 1046 contains one 37x51mm stamp.

Paintings by Qi Baishi (1864-1957) — A217

No. 1047: a, A Good Wind for Thousands of Miles, top half. b, As "a," bottom half. c, The Yuxia and Lianhua Mountains, top half. d, As "c," bottom half. e, Autumn Landscape with Cormorants, top half. f, As "e," bottom half.

No. 1048: a, Grasshopper on a Branch. b, Fish and Catfish.

$3, Ink Landscape.

2007, Sept. 21

1047	A217	$1 Sheet of 6, #a-f	11.00	11.00
1048	A217	$2.50 Sheet of 2, #a-b	9.00	9.00

Souvenir Sheet

1049	A217	$3 multi	5.50	5.50

Princess Diana (1961-97) — A218

Illustration reduced.

Litho. & Embossed
2007, Oct. 1 Serpentine Die Cut
Without Gum
1050 A218 $9 gold & multi 16.50 16.50

Miniature Sheet

Elvis Presley (1935-77) — A219

No. 1051: a, Holding guitar. b, Wearing white shirt. c, Wearing suit and tie. d, Wearing Hawaiian shirt. e, Wearing blue shirt. f, Wearing Army uniform.

2007, Oct. 1 Litho. Perf. 13¼
1051 A219 90c Sheet of 6, #a-f 9.75 9.75

Miniature Sheet

Pres. John F. Kennedy (1917-63) — A220

No. 1052 — Kennedy: a, Pointing, text at left. b, Pointing, text at right. c, Not pointing, text at left. d, Not pointing, text at right.

2007, Oct. 15   Perf. 12¾
1052 A220 $1 Sheet of 4, #a-d 7.50 7.50

Miniature Sheet

Marilyn Monroe (1926-62), Actress — A221

No. 1053: a, Wearing white boa. b, Wearing black dress, denomination in white. c, Wearing black and white dress, denomination in purple. d, Wearing beige dress.

2007, Oct. 15
1053 A221 $1 Sheet of 4, #a-d 7.50 7.50

Miniature Sheet

Pope Benedict XVI — A222

No. 1054: a, Photomosaic (Pope's ear). b, Photomosaic (Pope's neck and shoulder). c, Photomosaic (Pope's chest). d, Photograph of Pope.

2007, Nov. 11   Perf. 12¼x12
1054 A222 $1.30 Sheet of 4, #a-d 9.25 9.25

Christmas — A223

Paintings: 20c, The Adoration of the Shepherds, by Francisco Zurbaran. 75c, Madonna and Child with Angels, by Hans Memling. $1, The Nativity, by Maestro Esiguo. $2, The Nativity, by Philippe de Champaigne.

2007, Dec. 14   Perf. 14
1055-1058 A223 Set of 4 7.00 7.00

SEMI-POSTAL STAMPS

Nos. 159-160 Surcharged and Overprinted: "TONGA CYCLONE / RELIEF / 1982" in 1 or 3 Lines
Wmk. 380
1982, May 20 Litho. Perf. 14
B1 A25a 45c + 20c multi .45 .45
B2 A25b 45c + 20c multi .45 .45

POSTAGE DUE STAMPS

Arms of Tuvalu — D1

1981, May 13 Litho. Perf. 14
J1 D1 1c brt rose lil & blk .30 .30
J2 D1 2c grnsh bl & blk .30 .30
J3 D1 5c yellow brn & blk .30 .30
J4 D1 10c blue grn & blk .30 .30
J5 D1 20c chocolate & blk .30 .30
J6 D1 30c orange & blk .30 .30
J7 D1 40c ultra & blk .30 .30
J8 D1 50c yellow grn & blk .40 .40
J9 D1 $1 brt lilac & blk .65 .65
  Nos. J1-J9 (9) 3.15 3.15

1982-83   Perf. 14x15
J1a D1 1c bright rose lilac & black .20 .20
J2a D1 2c greenish blue & black .20 .20
J3a D1 5c yellow brown & black .20 .20
J4a D1 10c blue green & black .20 .20
J5a D1 20c chocolate & black .25 .25
J6a D1 30c orange & black .40 .30
J7a D1 40c ultra & black .50 .35

J8a D1 50c yellow green & black .60 .45
J9a D1 $1 bright lilac & black .95 .65
  Nos. J1a-J9a (9) 3.50 2.80

Issued: 1c-20c, 11/25/82 (inscribed "1982"); 30c-$1, 5/25/83 (inscribed "1983").

OFFICIAL STAMPS

Nos. 96-113 Overprinted: "OFFICIAL"
1981 Litho. Unwmk. Perf. 14
O1 A14 1c multicolored .25 .25
O2 A14 2c multicolored .25 .25
O3 A14 4c multicolored .25 .25
O4 A14 5c multicolored .25 .25
O5 A14 6c multicolored .25 .25
O6 A14 8c multicolored .25 .25
O7 A14 10c multicolored .25 .25
O8 A14 15c multicolored .25 .25
O9 A14 20c multicolored .25 .25
O10 A14 25c multicolored .30 .30
O11 A14 30c multicolored .35 .35
O12 A14 35c multicolored .40 .40
O13 A14 40c multicolored .50 .50
O14 A14 45c multicolored .55 .55
O15 A14 50c multicolored .60 .60
O16 A14 70c multicolored .80 .80
O17 A14 $1 multicolored 1.10 1.10
O18 A14 $2 multicolored 2.40 2.40
O19 A14 $5 multicolored 5.75 5.75
  Nos. O1-O19 (19) 15.00 15.00

No. 193 Surcharged and Overprinted "OFFICIAL"
Wmk. 380
1983, Aug. Litho. Perf. 14
O20 A30 60c on $1 multi .75 .75

Nos. 185-186A, 188, 230, 188A-195 Overprinted: "OFFICIAL"
1984 Litho. Wmk. 380 Perf. 14
O21 A30 5c multicolored .20 .35
O22 A30 10c multicolored .20 .35
O23 A30 15c multicolored .20 .65
O24 A30 25c multicolored .30 .55
O25 A30 30c on 45c multi .65 .65
O25A A30 30c multicolored .40 .65
O26 A30 35c multicolored .50 .70
O27 A30 40c multicolored .55 .70
O28 A30 45c multicolored .65 .70
O29 A30 50c multicolored .65 .65
O29A A30 60c multicolored .75 .90
O30 A30 $1 multicolored .95 .90
O31 A30 $2 multicolored 1.50 1.00
O32 A30 $5 multicolored 3.50 2.25
  Nos. O21-O32 (14) 11.00 11.00

Issued: #O23, O29A, Apr. 30; others Feb. 1.

Nos. 469-484 Overprinted "OFFICIAL"
1989, Feb. 22 Litho. Perf. 15
O33 A64 5c multicolored .20 .20
O34 A64 10c multicolored .20 .20
O35 A64 15c multicolored .20 .20
O36 A64 20c multicolored .25 .25
O37 A64 25c multicolored .30 .30
O38 A64 30c multicolored .40 .40
O39 A64 35c multicolored .45 .45
O40 A64 40c multicolored .50 .50
O41 A64 45c multicolored .60 .60
O42 A64 50c multicolored .65 .65
O43 A64 55c multicolored .70 .70
O44 A64 60c multicolored .75 .75
O45 A64 70c multicolored .90 .90
O46 A64 $1 multicolored 1.25 1.25
O47 A64 $2 multicolored 2.50 2.50
O48 A64 $5 multicolored 6.50 6.50
  Nos. O33-O48 (16) 16.35 16.35

For the following islands all are types of Tuvalu unless otherwise specified.
See note following Tuvalu No. 221.

Leaders of the World
Large quantities of some Leaders of the World sets, including unissued stamps, were sold at a fraction of face value when the printer was liquidated.

FUNAFUTI

Catalogue values for all unused stamps in this country are for Never Hinged items.

Locomotive Type of 1984
Perf. 12½x13
1984-86 Litho. Unwmk.
Se-tenant Pairs, #a.-b.
a. — Side and front views.
b. — Action scene.
1 5c 1919 Class C51, Japan .50 .50
2 5c 1935 F.C.C. Andes Class, Peru .50 .50
3 15c 1934 Kolhapur Class, UK .50 .50
4 15c 1941 V.R. Class H, Australia .50 .50
5 15c 1885 S.A.R. Class Y, Australia .50 .50
6 20c 1951 Class 4, UK .50 .50
7 20c 1928 Class U, UK .50 .50
8 25c 1923 Eryri Cog, UK .60 .60
9 30c 1927 Royal Scot Class, UK .80 .80
10 35c 1828 Lancashire Witch, UK .90 .90
11 35c 1906 NY, NH & H RR Class EP-1, US .90 .90
12 40c 1942 Springbok Class B1, UK 1.00 1.00
13 40c 1827 Royal George, UK 1.00 1.00
14 40c 1926 Northern Pacific Class A5, US 1.00 1.00
15 40c 1900 Aberdare Class 2600, UK 1.00 1.00
16 50c 1829 Sans Pareil, UK 1.40 1.40
17 50c 1924 EST Class 241A, France 1.40 1.40
18 55c 1911 Class 8K, UK 1.50 1.50
19 60c 1913 Sir Gilbert Claughton, UK 1.75 1.75
20 60c 1920 Sherlock Holmes, UK 1.75 1.75
21 60c 1949 Class K1, UK 1.75 1.75
22 $1 1925 Class P1, UK 2.75 2.75
23 $1 1940 SNCF Class 232R, France 2.75 2.75
24 $1.50 1904 B&O Class DD-1 4.25 4.25
  Nos. 1-24 (24) 30.00 30.00

Issued: #3, 6, 9, 12, 16, 19, 4/16/84; 1, 4, 8, 10, 13, 18, 20, 22, 12/24/84; 2, 5, 11, 14, 17, 23, 4/29/85; 7, 15, 21, 24, 12/30/86.
1986 stamps not inscribed "Leaders of the World."

Automobile Type of 1984
1984-87
Se-tenant Pairs, #a.-b.
a. — Side and front views.
b. — Action scene.
Design A41
25 1c 1957 Triumph TR3A, UK .20 .20
26 1c 1932 Nash Special 8 Convertible, US .20 .20
27 10c 1937 Cord 812 Supercharged, US .20 .20
28 10c 1925 AC Six, UK .20 .20
29 20c 1924 Alfa Romeo P2, Italy .40 .40
30 30c 1935 Aston Martin Ulster, UK .60 .60
31 40c 1948 Morgan 4+4, UK .85 .85
32 40c 1906 Renault GP, France .85 .85
33 55c 1903 Cadillac Model A 1.10 1.10
34 60c 1971 Porsche 917K, Germany 1.25 1.25
35 60c 1913 Simplex 75HP, US 1.25 1.25
36 75c 1939 Delahaye Type 165, France 1.50 1.50
37 80c 1938 Opel Admiral, Germany 1.60 1.60
38 $1 1936 Jaguar SS 100, UK 2.00 2.00
39 $1 1965 Aston Martin DB5, UK 2.00 2.00
40 $1.50 1977 Porsche 935 3.25 3.25
  Nos. 25-40 (16) 17.45 17.45

Issued: #25, 27, 31, 38, 9/13/84; 26, 30, 33, 34, 2/8/85; 28-29, 32, 35-37, 39-40, 8/27/87.
1987 stamps not inscribed "Leaders of the World."

Queen Mother Type of 1985
Hats: #45a, White. #45b, White. #46a, 50a, Pink. #46b, 50b, Tiara. #47a, 51a, Blue. #47b, 51b, Blue with veil covering face. #48a, Blue. #48b, Tiara. #49a, Headband. #49b, Hat.

1985-86   Perf. 13x12½
45 A45 5c Pair, #a.-b. .45 .45
46 A45 25c Pair, #a.-b. .70 .70
47 A45 80c Pair, #a.-b. 2.10 2.10
48 A45 $1.05 Pair, #a.-b. 2.50 2.50
  Nos. 45-48 (4) 5.75 5.75

Souvenir Sheets of 2

49	A45	$1.05 #a.-b.	3.50	3.50
50	A45	$2 #a.-b.	3.75	3.75
51	A45	$3 #a.-b.	5.75	5.75

Issued: #45-49, 8/26; #50-51, 1/3/86.

Elizabeth II 60th Birthday Type

1986, Apr. 21   Perf. 13x12½, 12½x13

52	A49	10c Trooping the colors	.20	.20
53	A49	50c Tiara	.55	.55
54	A49	$1.50 As young woman, 1952	1.75	1.75
55	A49	$3.50 Tiara, diff., vert.	3.75	3.75
		Nos. 52-55 (4)	6.25	6.25

Souvenir Sheet

56	A49	$5 Scarf	6.25	6.25

Royal Wedding Type of 1986

#59a, Andrew holding rifle, vert. #59b, Sarah Ferguson, vert. #60a, Couple. #60b, Prince Philip and Andrew.

1986, July 23

59	A53	60c Pair, #a.-b.	1.25	1.25
60	A53	$1 Pair, #a.-b.	2.00	2.00

Souvenir Sheet

61	A56	$4 Newlyweds	5.25	5.25

Nos. 59-60 Ovptd. in Silver "Congratulations to T.R.H. The Duke & Duchess of York"

1986, July 23

62	A53	60c Pair, #a.-b.	1.40	1.40
63	A53	$1 Pair, #a.-b.	2.25	2.25

Royal Anniversaries — A1

1987   Perf. 15

66	A1	20c Queen Victoria	.20	.20
67	A1	50c George VI, Family	.55	.55
68	A1	75c Elizabeth	.85	.85
69	A1	$1.20 Elizabeth, Philip	1.40	1.40
70	A1	$1.75 Elizabeth, diff.	2.00	2.00
		Nos. 66-70 (5)	5.00	5.00

Souvenir Sheet

71	A1	$3 Elizabeth, Family	3.25	3.25

Elizabeth's 40th wedding anniv., Queen Victoria's accession to the throne, sesquicentennial.

Summer Olympics Type of 1988

1988, Aug. 19   Perf. 13x12½

72	A69	10c Hurdles	.20	.20
73	A69	20c High jump	.25	.25
74	A69	40c Running	.50	.50
75	A69	50c Discus	.60	.60
76	A69	80c Pole vault	1.00	1.00
77	A69	90c Javelin	1.10	1.10
		Nos. 72-77 (6)	3.65	3.65

NANUMAGA

Automobile Type of 1984

Perf. 12½x13

1984-87   Litho.   Unwmk.

Se-tenant Pairs, #a.-b.

a. — Side and front views.

b. — Action scene.

Design A41

1		5c 1903 De Dion-Bouton Single Cylinder	.25	.25
2		5c 1955 Ford Thunderbird	.25	.25
3		5c 1966 Lotus Elan, UK	.25	.25
4		10c 1915 Stutz Bearcat	.25	.25
5		10c 1915 Dodge 4-Cylinder Touring Car	.25	.25
6		10c 1976 Jaguar XJ-S, UK	.25	.25
7		10c 1928 Morgan Super Sports, UK	.25	.25
8		15c 1906 Spyker, Holland	.40	.40
9		20c 1957 Dual-Ghia, US	.50	.50
10		25c 1966 Lamborghini P400 Miura Coupe, Italy	.65	.65
11		25c 1947 Kaiser Traveler, US	.65	.65

12		25c 1951 Lancia Aurelia, Italy	.65	.65
13		30c 1963 Chevrolet Corvette Coupe	.80	.80
14		40c 1949 Jaguar XK 120, UK	1.10	1.10
15		40c 1930 Renault Reinastella, France	1.10	1.10
16		50c 1938 Alvis Speed 25, UK	1.25	1.25
17		60c 1956 Studebaker Golden Hawk	1.60	1.60
18		75c 1909 Alco, US	2.00	2.00
19		$1 1966 Shelby GT-350 Coupe, US	2.75	2.75
20		$1 1968 Mercedes 300 SEL, Germany	2.75	2.75
21		$1 1953 BRM V-16, UK	2.75	2.75
22		$1 1910 Lozier Briarcliff, US	2.75	2.75
		Nos. 1-22 (22)	23.45	23.45

Issued: #1, 4, 10, 14, 19, 6/11/84; #2, 5, 16, 20, 12/24/84; #6, 11, 18, 21, 7/23/85; #3, 7-9, 12, 15, 17, 22, 8/6/87.

1987 stamps not inscribed "Leaders of the World."

British Monarchs — A2

1984, Nov. 27   Perf. 13x12½

Se-tenant Pairs, #a.-b.

a. — Left stamp.

b. — Right stamp.

23	A2	10c Richard I	.40	.40
24	A2	20c Richard I, diff.	.60	.60
25	A2	30c Third Crusade	1.00	1.00
26	A2	40c Alfred the Great	1.25	1.25
27	A2	50c Alfred, diff.	1.50	1.50
28	A2	$1 Battle of Edington	3.25	3.25
		Nos. 23-28 (6)	8.00	8.00

Locomotive Type of 1984

1985, Apr. 3   Perf. 12½x13

Se-tenant Pairs, #a.-b.

a. — Side and front views.

b. — Action scene.

Design A36

29		10c 1906 NYC & HR Class S	.25	.25
30		25c 1884 T.R. Class B, Australia	.70	.70
31		50c 1902 Decapod, UK	1.25	1.25
32		60c 1846 Coppernob, UK	1.50	1.50
		Nos. 29-32 (4)	3.70	3.70

Flowers — A3

#33a, Tecophilaea cyanocrocus. #33b, Lilium pardalinum. #34a, Canarina abyssinica. #34b, Vanda coerulea. #35a, Lathyrus maritimus. #35b, Narcissus tazetta. #36a, Bauera sessiflora. #36b, Thelymitra venosa.

1985, May 3   Perf. 13x12½

33	A3	25c Pair, #a.-b.	.60	.60
34	A3	30c Pair, #a.-b.	.70	.70
35	A3	40c Pair, #a.-b.	1.00	1.00
36	A3	50c Pair, #a.-b.	1.25	1.25
		Nos. 33-36 (4)	3.55	3.55

Queen Mother Type of 1985

Hats: #45a, White. #45b, Blue feathered. #46a, 50a, Violet blue wide-brimmed. #46b, 50b, Blue green wide-brimmed. #47a, 51a, Tiara. #47b, 51b, Light blue. #48a, Dark blue. #48b, Black.

#49a, As young girl. #49b, As young woman.

1985-86

45	A45	15c Pair, #a.-b.	.50	.50
46	A45	55c Pair, #a.-b.	2.10	2.10
47	A45	65c Pair, #a.-b.	2.25	2.25
48	A45	90c Pair, #a.-b.	3.25	3.25
		Nos. 45-48 (4)	8.10	8.10

Souvenir Sheets of 2

49	A45	$1.15 #a.-b.	3.75	3.75
50	A45	$2.10 #a.-b.	4.50	4.50
51	A45	$2.50 #a.-b.	5.00	5.00

Issued: #41-49, 9/5; 50-51, 1/3/86.

Elizabeth II 60th Birthday Type

1986, Apr. 21   Perf. 13x12½, 12½x13

52	A49	5c White hat	.35	.35
53	A49	$1 As young woman	1.10	1.10
54	A49	$1.75 Tam	2.00	2.00
55	A49	$2.50 Tiara, vert.	2.75	2.75
		Nos. 52-55 (4)	6.20	6.20

Souvenir Sheet

56	A49	$4 Portrait	6.25	6.25

World Cup Soccer Championships, Mexico — A4

Players and teams from participating countries.

Perf. 12½x13, 13x12½

1986, June 30

57	A4	1c Uruguay, vert.	.25	.25
58	A4	5c Morocco, vert.	.25	.25
59	A4	5c Hungary, vert.	.25	.25
60	A4	10c Poland, vert.	.25	.25
61	A4	20c Argentina, vert.	.25	.25
62	A4	35c Bulgaria	.25	.25
63	A4	50c Portugal, vert.	.30	.30
64	A4	60c Belgium	.40	.40
65	A4	75c France	.50	.50
66	A4	$1 Canada, vert.	.75	.75
67	A4	$2 Germany	1.40	1.40
68	A4	$4 Scotland, vert.	2.75	2.75
		Nos. 57-68 (12)	7.60	7.60

Royal Wedding Type of 1986

#71a, Prince Andrew, vert. #71b, Sarah Ferguson, vert. #72a, Prince Philip, Andrew. #72b, Prince Andrew.

1986, July 23

71	A53	60c Pair, #a.-b.	1.50	1.50
72	A53	$1 Pair, #a.-b.	2.50	2.50

Souvenir Sheet

73	A56	$4 Couple	5.25	5.25

Nos. 71-72 Ovptd. in Silver "Congratulations to T.R.H. The Duke & Duchess of York"

1986, Oct. 26

74	A53	60c Pair, #a.-b.	1.40	1.40
75	A53	$1 Pair, #a.-b.	2.25	2.25

Royal Anniversaries — A5

1987, Oct. 15   Perf. 15

78	A5	15c Queen Victoria	.20	.20
79	A5	35c Princesses Margaret and Elizabeth	.40	.40
80	A5	60c Elizabeth holding Princess Anne	.65	.65
81	A62	$1.50 Elizabeth, Philip	1.75	1.75

82	A62	$1.75 Elizabeth wearing tiara	2.00	2.00
		Nos. 78-82 (5)	5.00	5.00

Souvenir Sheet

83	A5	$3 Elizabeth	3.25	3.25

Elizabeth's 40th wedding anniv.; Victoria's accession to the throne, sesquicentennial.

NANUMEA

Locomotive Type of 1984

Perf. 12½x13

1984-85   Litho.   Unwmk.

Se-tenant Pairs, #a.-b.

a. — Side and front views.

b. — Action scene.

Tuvalu Design A36

1		1c 1940 Class E94, Germany	.30	.30
2		15c 1946 Class 2251, UK	.40	.40
3		20c 1941 Bantam Cock Class V4, UK	.60	.60
4		30c 1902 Class C1, UK	.95	.95
5		35c 1952 S.N.C.F. CC 7121, France	1.10	1.10
6		40c 1903 La France Frenchmen Class, UK	1.25	1.25
7		50c 1929 5700 Class, UK	1.60	1.60
8		50c 1954 S.N.C.F. Class BB 1200, France	1.60	1.60
9		60c 1881 Fairlight Class G, UK	1.90	1.90
10		60c 1928 V.R. Class S, Australia	1.90	1.90
		Nos. 1-10 (10)	11.60	11.60

Issued: #2-4, 6-7, 9, 4/30; others, 2/8/85.

Cricket Players Type of 1984

1984, Oct. 9   Perf. 13x12½

Se-tenant Pairs, #a.-b.

Tuvalu Design A39

11		1c J.A. Snow	.40	.40
12		10c C.J. Tavare	.40	.40
13		40c G.B. Stevenson	1.10	1.10
14		$1 P. Carrick	2.50	2.50
		Nos. 11-14 (4)	4.40	4.40

Automobile Type of 1984

1985-86   Perf. 12½x13

Se-tenant Pairs, #a.-b.

a. — Side and front views.

b. — Action scene.

Tuvalu Design A41

15		5c 1965 Humber Supersnipe, UK	.25	.25
16		10c 1934 Singer 9, UK	.25	.25
17		15c 1948 Holden FX 2.1 Liter Sedan, Australia	.40	.40
18		20c 1953 Buick Skylark	.55	.55
19		20c 1951 Simca Aronde, France	.55	.55
20		35c 1967 Toyota 2000 GT, Japan	1.10	1.10
21		40c 1960 Elva Courier, UK	1.25	1.25
22		50c 1952 Bentley Continental, UK	1.60	1.60
23		50c 1938 Hispano-Suiza V12 Saoutchik Cabriolet, Spain/France	1.60	1.60
24		50c 1913 Peugeot Bebe, France	1.60	1.60
25		60c 1935 Bluebird V (LSR), UK	1.75	1.75
26		60c 1978 Mazda RX7, Japan	1.75	1.75
27		75c 1970 Lola T70, UK	2.10	2.10
28		$2 1908 Locomobile, US	6.25	6.25
		Nos. 15-28 (14)	21.00	21.00

Issued: #15, 21-22, 25, 1/14; #17-18, 23, 26, 2/22; #16, 19-20, 24, 27-28, 12/30/86.

Cats — A6

#29a, American short-hair. #29b, Turkish Angora. #30a, Korat. #30b, American Maine Coon. #31a, Himalayan. #31b, Shaded Cameo. #32a, Long-haired ginger. #32b, Siamese Seal Point.

1985, May 28　　Perf. 13x12½
29	A6	5c Pair, #a.-b.	.30	.30
30	A6	30c Pair, #a.-b.	.80	.80
31	A6	50c Pair, #a.-b.	1.25	1.25
32	A6	$1 Pair, #a.-b.	2.50	2.50
		Nos. 29-32 (4)	4.85	4.85

Queen Mother Type of 1985

Hats: #41a, 47a, Light gray. #41b, 47b, Light blue. #42a, Lavender. #42b, Blue. #43a, Purple. #43b, Pink. #44a, 46a, Blue. #44b, 46b, Blue flowered. #45a, Feathered. #45b, Veiled.

1985-86
41	A45	5c Pair, #a.-b.	.25	.25
42	A45	30c Pair, #a.-b.	.80	.80
43	A45	75c Pair, #a.-b.	2.10	2.10
44	A45	$1.05 Pair, #a.-b.	2.75	2.75
		Nos. 41-44 (4)	5.90	5.90

Souvenir Sheets of 2
45	A45	$1.20 #a.-b.	4.00	4.00
46	A45	$1 #a.-b.	2.00	2.00
47	A45	$4 #a.-b.	8.00	8.00

Issued: #41-45, 9/5; 46-47, 1/10/86.

Elizabeth II 60th Birthday Type

1986, Apr. 21　Perf. 13x12½, 12½x13
48	A49	10c As teenager	.30	.30
49	A49	80c As young woman	.80	.80
50	A49	$1.75 Red hat	1.75	1.75
51	A49	$3 Tiara, vert.	3.00	3.00
		Nos. 48-51 (4)	5.85	5.85

Souvenir Sheet
52	A49	$4 Green print hat	4.75	4.75

1986 World Cup Soccer
Championships, Mexico — A7

1986, June 10　　Perf. 13x12½
53	A7	1c Italy, 1934	.25	.25
54	A7	2c Italy, 1938	.25	.25
55	A7	5c Uruguay, 1950	.25	.25
56	A7	10c Brazil, 1958	.25	.25
57	A7	25c Argentina vs. Holland, 1978	.25	.25
58	A7	40c Brazil vs. Czechoslovakia, 1962	.30	.30
59	A7	50c Uruguay vs. Argentina, 1930	.40	.40
60	A7	75c West Germany vs. Hungary, 1954	.60	.60
61	A7	90c Brazil, 1970	.70	.70
62	A7	$1 West Germany, 1974	.80	.80
63	A7	$2.50 Italy vs. West Germany, 1982	2.00	2.00
64	A7	$4 England, 1966	3.25	3.25
		Nos. 53-64 (12)	9.30	9.30

Royal Wedding Type of 1986

1986, July 23　Perf. 13x12½, 12½x13
65	A53	60c Prince Andrew in jeep, vert.	.55	.55
66	A53	60c Sarah Ferguson, vert.	.55	.55
67	A53	$1 Couple	.85	.85
68	A53	$1 Prince Andrew, Princess Anne and parents	.85	.85
		Nos. 65-68 (4)	2.80	2.80

Souvenir Sheet
69	A56	$4 Newlyweds	5.25	5.25

Nos. 65-68 Ovptd. in Silver
"Congratulations to T.R.H. The Duke & Duchess of York"

#70a, Prince Andrew in jeep. #70b, Sarah Ferguson. #71a, Couple. #71b, Prince Andrew, Princess Anne and parents.

1986, Oct. 28
70	A53	60c Pair, #a.-b.	1.40	1.40
71	A53	$1 Pair, #a.-b.	2.25	2.25

Elizabeth 40th Wedding Anniv. Type

1987, Oct. 15　　Perf. 15
74	A62	40c Victoria	.45	.45
75	A62	60c Elizabeth & Philip, wedding portrait	.70	.70
76	A62	80c Elizabeth, Philip & Prince Charles	.90	.90

77	A62	$1 Elizabeth, Princess Anne	1.10	1.10
78	A62	$2 Elizabeth	2.25	2.25
		Nos. 74-78 (5)	5.40	5.40

Souvenir Sheet
79	A62	$3 Royal family, diff.	4.25	4.25

Queen Victoria's accession to the throne, 150th anniv.

NIUTAO

Automobile Type of 1984
Perf. 12½x13

1984-85　　Litho.　　Unwmk.
Se-tenant Pairs, #a.-b.
a. — Side and front views.
b. — Action scene.
Tuvalu Design A41
1	15c 1930 Bentley 4½ Liter Supercharged, UK	.40	.40
2	20c 1935 Wolseley Hornet Special, UK	.55	.55
3	25c 1920 Crossley 25/30HP, UK	.70	.70
4	30c 1976 Cadillac Eldorado 7-Liter V-8	.85	.85
5	40c 1968 Austin Mini Cooper, UK	1.25	1.25
6	40c 1958 BMW 507 Cabriolet, W. Germany	1.25	1.25
7	50c 1963 Porsche 365C Cabriolet, W. Germany	1.50	1.50
8	60c 1971 Tyrrell Ford 001, UK	1.75	1.75
	Nos. 1-8 (8)	8.25	8.25

Issued: #1, 4-5, 7, 4/16; #2-3, 6, 8, 5/2/85.

Locomotive Type of 1984
1984-85
Se-tenant Pairs, #a.-b.
a. — Side and front views.
b. — Action scene.
Tuvalu Design A36
9	5c 1830 Planet, UK	.25	.25
10	10c 1863 Prince, UK	.25	.25
11	10c 1943 Gordon Austerity Class, UK	.25	.25
12	20c 1830 Northumbrian, UK	.55	.55
13	30c 1879 Merddin Emrys, UK	.80	.80
14	40c 1829 Agenoria, UK	1.10	1.10
15	45c 1909 Atchison, Topeka & Santa Fe, 1301	1.25	1.25
16	50c 1897 Class 6200, Japan	1.50	1.50
17	60c 1938 F.M.S.R. Class O, Malaya	1.60	1.60
18	75c 1880 1F, UK	2.10	2.10
19	$1 1908 Class E550, Italy	3.00	3.00
20	$1.20 1914 J.N.R. Class 6760, Japan	3.50	3.50
	Nos. 9-20 (12)	16.15	16.15

Issue dates: Nos. 9-10, 12, 14, 16, 19, Sept. 17; Nos. 11, 13, 15, 18, 20, Aug. 21, 1985.

Cricket Players Type of 1984
1985, Jan. 7　　Perf. 13x12½
Se-tenant Pairs, #a.-b.
a. — Head.
b. — Action scene.
Tuvalu Design A39
21	1c S.G. Hinks	.25	.25
22	15c C. Penn	.50	.50
23	50c T.M. Alderman	1.75	1.75
24	$1 K.B.S. Jarvis	3.50	3.50
	Nos. 21-24 (4)	6.00	6.00

Audubon Bicentennial Type

#25a, Purple finch. #25b, White-throated sparrow. #26a, Anna's hummingbird. #26b, Smith's longspur. #27a, White-tailed kite. #27b, Harris' hawk. #28a, Northern oriole. #28b, Great crested flycatcher.

1985, Apr. 4
25	A42	5c Pair, #a.-b.	.20	.20
26	A42	15c Pair, #a.-b.	.40	.40
27	A42	25c Pair, #a.-b.	.65	.65
28	A42	$1 Pair, #a.-b.	2.75	2.75
		Nos. 25-28 (4)	4.00	4.00

Queen Mother Type of 1985

Hat: #37a, Light blue. #37b, Yellow. #38a, 43a, Black. #38b, 43b, Blue. #39a, Teal. #39b, Pink. #40a, 42a, White. #40b, 42b, Blue. #41a, As young woman. #41b, Feathered.

1985-86
37	A45	15c Pair, #a.-b.	.40	.40
38	A45	35c Pair, #a.-b.	1.00	1.00
39	A45	70c Pair, #a.-b.	2.00	2.00
40	A45	95c Pair, #a.-b.	2.75	2.75
		Nos. 37-40 (4)	6.15	6.15

Souvenir Sheets
41	A45	$1.05 #a.-b.	2.50	2.50
42	A45	$1.50 #a.-b.	3.50	3.50
43	A45	$4 #a.-b.	8.75	8.75

Issued: #37-41, 9/4; #42-43, 1/10/86.

Elizabeth II 60th Birthday Type
1986, Apr. 21　Perf. 13x12½, 12½x13
44	A49	5c White & gray hat	.30	.30
45	A49	60c Infant	.60	.60
46	A49	$1.50 Flowered white hat	1.50	1.50
47	A49	$3.50 Tiara, vert.	3.75	3.75
		Nos. 44-47 (4)	6.15	6.15

Souvenir Sheet
48	A49	$5 With tiara, diff.	7.75	7.75

For overprints see Nos. 58-62.

Royal Wedding Type

#51a, Couple, vert. #51b, Sarah Ferguson, vert. #52a, Prince Andrew. #52b, Sarah in evening gown.

1986, July 23　Perf. 12½x13, 13x12½
51	A53	60c Pair, #a.-b.	1.00	1.00
52	A53	$1 Pair, #a.-b.	2.00	2.00

Souvenir Sheet
53	A56	$4 Newlyweds	5.25	5.25

Nos. 51-52 Ovptd. in Silver
"Congratulations to T.R.H. The Duke & Duchess of York"

1986, Oct. 28
54	A53	60c Pair, #a.-b.	1.40	1.40
55	A53	$1 Pair, #a.-b.	2.25	1.10

Nos. 44-48 Ovptd. in Gold
"40th WEDDING ANNIVERSARY OF H.M. QUEEN ELIZABETH II"

1987, Mar.　Perf. 13x12½, 12½x13
58	A49	5c multicolored	.20	.20
59	A49	60c multicolored	.75	.75
60	A49	$1.50 multicolored	1.90	1.90
61	A49	$3.50 multicolored	4.50	4.50
		Nos. 58-61 (4)	7.35	7.35

Souvenir Sheet
62	A49	$5 multicolored	6.25	6.25

NUI

Locomotives Type of 1984
1984-88　Litho.　Perf. 12½x13
Se-tenant Pairs, #a.-b.
a. — Side and front views.
b. — Action scene.
Tuvalu Design A36
1	5c 1911 Class 8800, Japan	.20	.20
2	5c 1932 Soviet Union Railways Class SU	.20	.20
3	10c 1847 Jenny Lind Type, UK	.20	.20
4	10c 1907 Victorian Government Railways Class A2, Australia	.20	.20
5	15c same, 1950 Class R	.30	.30
6	15c 1913 Class 9600, Japan	.30	.30
7	20c 1934 LMS Stanier Tilbury Class 4P, UK	.40	.40
8	25c 1924 Jinty Class 3, UK	.55	.55
9	25c 1928 Boston & Albany Class D12	.55	.55
10	25c 1847 Iron Duke Class, UK	.55	.55
11	25c 1917 Wabash Railroad Class L	.55	.55
12	30c 1943 South Australian Government Railways 520 Class	.65	.65
13	35c 1885 Tennant Class 1463, UK	.75	.75
14	40c 1977 No. 10000, UK	.85	.85
15	40c 1848 Padarn Railway Fire Queen, UK	.85	.85
16	50c 1935 Princess Margaret Rose Class 8P, UK	1.10	1.10
17	50c 1932 Soviet Union Railways Class IS	1.10	1.10
18	60c 1973 D.B. Class ET403, W. Germany	1.25	1.25

19	60c 1916 E. Tenn. & W. N. Carolina R.R. No. 10	1.25	1.25
20	75c 1973 D.B. Class 151, W. Germany	1.60	1.60
21	75c 1909 Tasmanian Goverment Railways Class K Garratt	1.60	1.60
22	$1 1927 B&O President Class	2.25	2.25
23	$1 1832 Mohawk & Hudson Railroad Experiment	2.25	2.25
24	$1.25 1934 Union Pacific Railroad, M-10000 Streamliner	2.75	2.75
	Nos. 1-24 (24)	22.25	22.25

Issued: #5, 8, 12, 16, 3/19; #1, 6, 9, 22, 2/22/85; #3, 10, 13, 14, 18, 20, 23, 24, 8/7/87; #2, 4, 7, 11, 15, 17, 19, 21, 1/29/88.
1987 and 1988 stamps not inscribed "Leaders of the World."

British Monarchs Type of Nanumaga
1984, July 18　　Perf. 13x12½
Se-tenant Pairs, #a.-b.
25	A2	1c Queen Anne	.40	.40
26	A2	5c Henry V	.40	.40
27	A2	15c Henry V, diff.	.40	.40
28	A2	40c Queen Anne, diff.	1.00	1.00
29	A2	50c Queen Anne, diff.	1.50	1.50
30	A2	$1 Henry V, diff.	2.50	2.50
		Nos. 25-30 (6)	6.20	6.20

Automobile Type of 1984
1985　　　Perf. 12½x13
Se-tenant Pairs, #a.-b.
a. — Side and front views.
b. — Action scene.
Tuvalu Design A41
31	5c 1909 Buick	.25	.25
32	15c 1966 Oldsmobile Toronado	.35	.35
33	25c 1947 Railton Mobil Special, UK	.70	.70
34	30c 1924 Opel Laubfrosch, Germany	.75	.75
35	40c 1966 Jensen FF, UK	1.00	1.00
36	40c 1963 Lotus-Climax GP MK 25, UK	1.00	1.00
37	50c 1910 Delaunay Belleville, France	1.40	1.40
38	60c 1956 Jensen 541, UK	1.50	1.50
39	90c 1924 Hispano-Suiza H6 Boulogne, France	2.25	2.25
40	$1.10 1972 Citroen-Maserati S.M. Coupe, France	2.75	2.75
	Nos. 31-40 (10)	11.95	11.95

Issued: #33-35, 37, 4/2; #31-32, 36, 38-40, 10/9.

Cricket Players Type of 1984
1985, May 27　　Perf. 13x12½
Se-tenant Pairs, #a.-b.
Tuvalu Design A39
41		1c S.C. Goldsmith	.20	.20
42		40c S.N.V. Waterton	1.00	1.00
43		60c A. Sidebottom	1.40	1.40
44		70c A.A. Metcalfe	1.90	1.90
		Nos. 41-44 (4)	4.50	4.50

Queen Mother Type of 1985

#49a, 54a, Purple. #49b, 54b, Tiara. #50a, Light blue. #50b, Lavender. #51a, Violet. #51b, White. #52a, 55a, Light blue. #52b, 55b, Tiara. #53a, White. #53b, Black.

1985-86
49	A45	5c Pair, #a.-b.	.20	.20
50	A45	50c Pair, #a.-b.	1.25	1.25
51	A45	75c Pair, #a.-b.	2.00	2.00
52	A45	85c Pair, #a.-b.	2.25	2.25
		Nos. 49-52 (4)	5.70	5.70

Souvenir Sheets of 2
53	A45	$1.15 #a.-b.	3.50	3.50
54	A45	$1.50 #a.-b.	3.00	3.00
55	A45	$3.50 #a.-b.	7.50	7.50

Issued: #49-53, 9/4; 54-55, 1/8/86.

Elizabeth II 60th Birthday Type
1986, Apr. 21　Perf. 13x12½, 12½x13
56	A49	10c Feathered hat	.20	.20
57	A49	80c As young woman	.80	.80
58	A49	$1.75 Tiara	1.75	1.75
59	A49	$3 Tiara, diff., vert.	3.00	3.00
		Nos. 56-59 (4)	5.75	5.75

Souvenir Sheet
60	A49	$4 Portrait	6.25	6.25

Royal Wedding Type of 1986

#63a, Couple, vert. #63b, Prince Andrew, vert. #64a, Couple, Queen Elizabeth II. #64b, Andrew as young boy.

1986, July 23 *Perf. 12½x13, 13x12½*
63	A53	60c Pair, #a.-b.	1.10	1.10
64	A53	$1 Pair, #a.-b.	1.75	1.75

Souvenir Sheet
65	A56	$4 Sarah in wedding dress	6.25	6.25

Nos. 63-64 Ovptd. in Silver
"Congratulations to T.R.H. The Duke &
Duchess of York"

1986, Oct. 28
66	A53	60c Pair, #a.-b.	1.40	1.40
67	A53	$1 Pair, #a.-b.	2.25	2.25

Elizabeth 40th Wedding Anniv. Type of Funafuti

1987, Oct. 15 *Perf. 15*
70	A1	20c Queen Victoria	.20	.20
71	A1	50c George VI, Family	.60	.60
72	A1	75c Elizabeth	.85	.85
73	A1	$1.20 Elizabeth, Philip	1.40	1.40
74	A1	$1.75 Elizabeth, diff.	2.00	2.00
		Nos. 70-74 (5)	5.05	5.05

Souvenir Sheet
75	A1	$3 Elizabeth, Family	3.50	3.50

Queen Victoria's accession to the throne, sesquicentennial.

NUKUFETAU

Automobile Type of 1984
Perf. 12½x13

1984-85 Litho. Unwmk.
Se-tenant Pairs, #a.-b.
a. — Side and front views.
b. — Action scene.
Tuvalu Design A41
1	5c	1904 Mercedes 28 PS, Germany	.25	.25
2	10c	1966 Ford GT40 Mark II	.25	.25
3	10c	1911 Vauxhall Prince Henry, UK	.25	.25
4	15c	1956 Lincoln Continental Mark II	.40	.40
5	20c	1950 Bristol 400, UK	.50	.50
6	25c	1913 Morris Oxford "Bullnose," UK	.75	.75
7	30c	1923 Austin Seven Tourer	.80	.80
8	50c	1921 Bugatti Type 13 "Brescia," France	1.50	1.50
9	50c	1967 Monteverdi, Switzerland	1.50	1.50
10	60c	1925 Lancia Lambda, Italy	1.60	1.60
11	60c	1938 Panhard Dynamic, France	1.60	1.60
12	75c	1960 A.C. Ace, UK	2.00	2.00
13	$1.50	1950 Land Rover Model 80, UK	4.50	4.50
		Nos. 1-13 (13)	15.90	15.90

Issued: #2, 6-8, 10, 5/23; others, 6/26/85.

British Monarchs Type of Nanumaga
1984, Nov. 27 *Perf. 13x12½*
Se-tenant Pairs, #a.-b.
14	A2	1c Mary II	.50	.50
15	A2	10c Mary II, diff.	.50	.50
16	A2	30c Mary II, diff.	.85	.85
17	A2	50c Henry IV	1.60	1.60
18	A2	60c Henry IV, diff.	1.90	1.90
19	A2	$1 Henry IV, diff.	3.00	3.00
		Nos. 14-19 (6)	8.35	8.35

Cricket Players Type of 1984
1985, Jan. 7
Se-tenant Pairs, #a.-b.
20	A39	1c D.G. Aslett	.35	.35
21	A39	10c N.R. Taylor	.35	.35
22	A39	55c S. Oldham	1.75	1.75
23	A39	$1 C.W.J. Athey	3.75	3.75
		Nos. 20-23 (4)	6.20	6.20

Locomotive Type of 1984
1985-88
Se-tenant Pairs, #a.-b.
a. — Side and front views.
b. — Action scene.
Tuvalu Design A36
24	1c	1900 Class XV, Germany	.20	.20
25	5c	1859 ECR Class Y, UK	.20	.20
26	10c	1923 Nord Super Pacific, France	.20	.20
27	10c	1905 LNWR Experiment Class, UK	.20	.20
28	15c	1941 SR Merchant Navy Class, UK	.30	.30
29	20c	1830 S. Carolina Railroad Best Friend of Charleston	.40	.40
30	25c	1941 SR No. 1, UK	.55	.55
31	30c	1987 Class 89, UK	.65	.65
32	40c	1923 Southern Pacific Railroad Class 4300, US	.85	.85
33	50c	1956 New South Wales Government Railways Class 46	1.10	1.10
34	60c	1953 D.B. Class V200, Germany	1.25	1.25
35	60c	1900 Union Railroad Class S-7, US	1.25	1.25
36	60c	1877 Phildelphia & Reading Railroad Camelback	1.25	1.25
37	70c	1968 J.N.R. Class 381, Japan	1.50	1.50
38	$1	1933 Rio Grande Southern Railroad Galloping Goose Railcar, US	2.25	2.25
a.		Souvenir sheet of 2	2.50	2.50
39	$1.50	1935 Chicago, Milwaukee, St. Paul & Pacific Class A	3.25	3.25
		Nos. 24-39 (16)	15.40	15.40

Issued: #24, 26, 34, 37, 4/2/85; #29, 32, 35, 39, 3/20/86; #25, 27-28, 30-31, 33, 36, 38, 38a, 9/10/87.
1986 and 1987 stamps not inscribed "Leaders of the World."

Queen Mother Type of 1985
Hat: #44a, Wide-brimmed blue. #44b, Tiara. #45a, Tiara. #45b, Lavender. #46a, Blue. #46b, White stole. #47a, 50a, White. #47b, 50b, Blue. #48a, 49a, White. #48b, 49b, Wide-brimmed.

1985, Sept. 5 *Perf. 13x12½*
44	A45	10c Pair, #a.-b.	.20	.20
45	A45	45c Pair, #a.-b.	1.00	1.00
46	A45	65c Pair, #a.-b.	1.60	1.60
47	A45	$1 Pair, #a.-b.	2.50	2.50
		Nos. 44-47 (4)	5.30	5.30

Souvenir Sheets of 2
48	A45	$1.10 #a.-b.	3.75	3.75
49	A45	$1.75 #a.-b.	4.00	4.00
50	A45	$3 #a.-b.	6.75	6.75

Elizabeth II 60th Birthday Type
1986, Apr. 21 *Perf. 13x12½, 12½x13*
51	A49	5c Scarf	.35	.35
52	A49	40c Tiara	.40	.40
53	A49	$2 Bareheaded	1.90	1.90
54	A49	$4 Tiara, vert.	4.25	4.25
		Nos. 51-54 (4)	6.90	6.90

Souvenir Sheet
55	A49	$5 Blue hat	6.25	6.25

For overprints see Nos. 65-69.

Royal Wedding Type of 1986
#58a, Couple, vert. #58b, Andrew, vert. #59a, Andrew, parents. #59b, Andrew.

1986, July 22
58	A53	60c Pair, #a.-b.	1.25	1.25
59	A53	$1 Pair, #a.-b.	2.00	2.00

Souvenir Sheet
60	A56	$4 Wedding ceremony	5.25	5.25

Nos. 58-59 Ovptd. in Silver
"Congratulations to T.R.H. The Duke &
Duchess of York"

1986, Oct. 28
61	A53	60c Pair, #a.-b.	1.40	1.40
62	A53	$1 Pair, #a.-b.	2.25	2.25

Nos. 51-55 Ovptd. in Gold
"40th WEDDING ANNIVERSARY OF
H.M. QUEEN ELIZABETH II"

1987, Oct. 15
65	A49	5c multicolored	.20	.20
66	A49	40c multicolored	.50	.50
67	A49	$2 multicolored	2.50	2.50
68	A49	$5 multicolored	5.00	5.00
		Nos. 65-68 (4)	8.20	8.20

Souvenir Sheet
69	A49	$5 multicolored	6.25	6.25

NUKULAELAE

Locomotive Type of 1984
Perf. 12½x13

1984-86 Litho. Unwmk.
Se-tenant Pairs, #a.-b.
a. — Side and front views.
b. — Action scene.
Tuvalu Design A36
1	5c	1891 Calbourne Class 02, UK	.25	.25
2	5c	1912 K.P.E.V. Class T18, Germany	.25	.25
3	10c	1942 SNCF Class 141P, France	.25	.25
4	10c	1962 Class 47, UK	.25	.25
5	15c	1941 Union Pacific Big Boy, US	.25	.25
6	15c	1955 DRB 83-10, Germany	.25	.25
7	20c	1940 S.N.C.F. 160-A-1, France	.45	.45
8	25c	1901 Class AEG High Speed Railcar, Germany	.50	.50
9	25c	1839 Albion Railroad Samson, Canada	.50	.50
10	40c	1907 Saint Class, UK	.90	.90
11	40c	1900 Nord De Glehn Atlantic, France	.90	.90
12	40c	1851 Folkstone Class, UK	.90	.90
13	50c	1914 J.N.R. Class 8620, Japan	1.10	1.10
14	50c	1936 Class 8F, UK	1.10	1.10
15	80c	1857 Shannon, UK	1.90	1.90
16	$1	1948 Class A1, UK	2.40	2.40
17	$1	1955 E.A.R. Class 59, Kenya	2.40	2.40
18	$1	1897 V.R. Class Na, Australia	2.40	2.40
19	$1	1859 Undine Class, UK	2.40	2.40
20	$1.50	1935 Turbomotive, UK	3.50	3.50
		Nos. 1-20 (20)	22.85	22.85

Issued: #1, 5, 10, 16, 5/23; #2, 7, 11, 17, 12/12; #3, 8, 13, 18, 3/24/85; #4, 6, 9, 12, 14, 15, 19-20, 7/11/86.
1986 stamps not inscribed "Leaders of the World."

Cricket Players Type of 1984
1984, Aug. 8 *Perf. 13x12½*
Se-tenant Pairs, #a.-b.
21	A39	5c D.B. Close	.20	.20
22	A39	15c G. Boycott	.40	.40
23	A39	30c D.L. Bairstow	.95	.95
24	A39	$1 T.G. Evans	3.00	3.00
		Nos. 21-24 (4)	4.55	4.55

Automobile Type of 1984
1985 *Perf. 12½x13*
Se-tenant Pairs, #a.-b.
a. — Side and front views.
b. — Action scene.
Tuvalu Design A41
25	5c	1924 Bugatti Type 35, France	.30	.30
26	10c	1908 Sizaire-Naudin, France	.30	.30
27	25c	1965 Sunbeam Tiger, UK	.65	.65
28	35c	1907 Napier 60HP Touring Car, UK	.90	.90
29	35c	1975 BMW 2002 TII, Germany	.90	.90
30	50c	1910 Austro-Daimler Prince Henry, Austria	1.40	1.40
31	50c	1927 La Salle, US	1.40	1.40
32	70c	1901 Oldsmobile Curved Dash Buckboard	1.90	1.90
33	75c	1955 Rover 90, UK	2.10	2.10
34	$1	1948 Chrysler Town & Country	2.50	2.50
		Nos. 25-34 (10)	12.35	12.35

Issue dates: #25, 28, 30, 32, Feb. 8; #26-27, 29, 31, 33-34, July 23.

Dogs — A8

#35a, Hungarian vizsla. #35b, Bearded collie. #36a, Bernese mountain dog. #36b, Boxer. #37a, Labrador retriever. #37b, Shetland sheepdog. #38a, Welsh springer spaniel. #38b, Scottish terrier.

1985, Apr. 30
35	A8	5c Pair, #a.-b.	.20	.20
36	A8	20c Pair, #a.-b.	.45	.45
37	A8	50c Pair, #a.-b.	1.10	1.10
38	A8	70c Pair, #a.-b.	1.60	1.60
		Nos. 35-38 (4)	3.35	3.35

Queen Mother Type of 1985
Hat: #47a, Purple. #47b, Blue. #48a, 52a, Tiara. #48b, 52b, Lavender. #49a, 53a, Pink. #49b, 53b, Dark blue. #50a, Light purple. #50b, Light blue. #51a, As young girl. #51b, Lace.

1985-86
47	A45	5c Pair, #a.-b.	.20	.20
48	A45	25c Pair, #a.-b.	.55	.55
49	A45	85c Pair, #a.-b.	2.00	2.00
50	A45	$1 Pair, #a.-b.	2.50	2.50
		Nos. 47-50 (4)	5.25	5.25

Souvenir Sheets of 2
51	A45	$1.20 #a.-b.	3.00	3.00
52	A45	$1.20 #a.-b.	2.50	2.50
53	A45	$3.50 #a.-b.	7.25	7.25

Issued: #46-51, 9/4; #52-53, 1/8/86.

Elizabeth II 60th Birthday Type
1986, Apr. 21 *Perf. 13x12½, 12½x13*
54	A49	10c White hat	.25	.25
55	A49	$1 As young woman	1.00	1.00
56	A49	$1.50 In orange dress	1.50	1.50
57	A49	$3 Tiara, vert.	3.00	3.00
		Nos. 54-57 (4)	5.75	5.75

Souvenir Sheet
58	A49	$4 In brown dress	6.25	6.25

Royal Wedding Type of 1986
#61a, Andrew, vert. #61b, Couple, vert. #62a, Sarah Ferguson and Princess Diana. #62b, Andrew.

1986, July 23 *Perf. 12½x13, 13x12½*
61	A53	60c Pair, #a.-b.	1.25	1.25
62	A53	$1 Pair, #a.-b.	2.00	2.00

Souvenir Sheet
63	A56	$4 Sarah in wedding dress	5.25	5.25

Nos. 61-62 Ovptd. in Silver
"Congratulations to T.R.H. The Duke &
Duchess of York"

1986, Oct. 28
64	A53	60c Pair, #a.-b.	1.40	1.40
65	A53	$1 Pair, #a.-b.	2.25	2.25

Queen Elizabeth II 40th Wedding Anniv. Type of Nanumaga
1987, Oct. 15 *Perf. 15*
68	A5	15c Queen Victoria	.20	.20
69	A5	35c Princesses Margaret and Elizabeth	.40	.40
70	A5	60c Elizabeth holding Princess Anne	.65	.65
71	A5	$1.50 Elizabeth, Philip	1.75	1.75
72	A5	$1.75 Elizabeth wearing tiara	2.00	2.00
		Nos. 68-72 (5)	5.00	5.00

Souvenir Sheet
73	A5	$3 Elizabeth	3.50	3.50

Queen Victoria's accession to the throne, sesquicentennial.

VAITUPU

Automobile Type of 1984
Perf. 12½x13

1984-85   Litho.   Unwmk.
Se-tenant Pairs, #a.-b.
a. — Side and front views.
b. — Action scene.
Tuvalu Design A41

1	5c	1961 Lotus Elite, UK	.35	.35
2	15c	1950 MG TD Midget, UK	.35	.35
3	15c	1932 Hillman Minx, UK	.35	.35
4	15c	1905 White Model E Steam Car, US	.35	.35
5	25c	1935 Auburn Supercharged 851, US	.75	.75
6	25c	1981 Renault RE20, France	.75	.75
7	30c	1928 Lea-Francis Hyper	.85	.85
8	30c	1940 Packard Darrin	.85	.85
9	30c	1938 Graham, US	.85	.85
10	40c	1968 Chevrolet Camaro	1.25	1.25
11	40c	1957 Renault Dauphine-Gordini, France	1.25	1.25
12	50c	1930 Packard Eight	1.60	1.60
13	50c	1926 Miller Special, US	1.60	1.60
14	60c	1950 Healey Silverstone, UK	1.90	1.90
15	60c	1970 De Tomaso Pantera, Italy	1.90	1.90
16	$1	1927 Bentley 3-Liter, UK	3.00	3.00
		Nos. 1-16 (16)	17.95	17.95

Issued: #2, 5, 7, 12, Mar. 19; #1, 3, 6, 8, 10, 13-14, 16, Dec. 12; #4, 9, 11, 15, Apr. 4, 1985.

British Monarchs Type of Nanumaga
1984, July 18   Perf. 13x12½
Se-tenant Pairs, #a.-b.

17	A2	1c Richard III	.35	.35
18	A2	5c Charles I	.35	.35
19	A2	15c Charles I, diff.	.35	.35
20	A2	40c Richard III, diff.	1.00	1.00
21	A2	50c Richard III, diff.	1.25	1.25
22	A2	$1 Charles I, diff.	2.50	2.50
		Nos. 17-22 (6)	5.80	5.80

Locomotive Type of 1984
1985-87   Perf. 12½x13
Se-tenant Pairs, #a.-b.
a. — Side and front views.
b. — Action scene.
Tuvalu Design A36

23	5c	1929 D.R.G. V3201, Germany	.20	.20
24	10c	1841 G.W.R. Leo Class, UK	.20	.20
25	10c	1937 New York Central Railroad Class J3a	.20	.20
26	15c	1949 Richmond, Fredericksburg & Potomac Railroad Class E8	.30	.30
27	25c	1845 Columbine, UK	.55	.55
28	25c	1954 BR Class 2MT, UK	.55	.55
29	25c	1980 Amtrak Class AEM-7	.55	.55
30	35c	1981 Via Rail LRC Class MPA-27a, Canada	.75	.75
31	45c	1983 British Columbia Railway Class GF6C	.95	.95
32	50c	1888 D&H Class B, India	1.10	1.10
33	60c	1936 D.R. Class 45, Germany	1.25	1.25
34	65c	1904 Northern Pacific Railway Class W, US	1.40	1.40
35	80c	1855 W. & A. R.R. General, US	1.75	1.75
36	85c	1938 Chicago & North Western Railway Class E-4	1.90	1.90
37	$1	1911 J.N.R. Class 9020 Mallet, Japan	2.25	2.25
38	$1	1977 Chicago Regional Transportation Authority Class F40	2.25	2.25
		Nos. 23-38 (16)	16.15	16.15

Issued: #24, 27, 32-33, 3/7/85; #23, 28, 35, 37, 1/16/86; #25-26, 29-31, 34, 36, 38, 9/10/87.

1986 and 1987 stamps not inscribed "Leaders of the World."

A9

Butterfly illustrations by Roger V. Vigurs: #39a, Marpesia petreus. #39b, Pseudolycaena marsyas. #40a, Charaxes jasius. #40b, Junonia coenia. #41a, Palaeochrysophanus hippothoe. #41b, Sticopthalma camadeva. #42a, Phoebis avellaneda. #42b, Apatura iris.

1985, Mar. 12   Perf. 13x12½

39	A9	5c Pair, #a.-b.	.20	.20
40	A9	15c Pair, #a.-b.	.45	.45
41	A9	50c Pair, #a.-b.	1.50	1.50
42	A9	75c Pair, #a.-b.	2.25	2.25
		Nos. 39-42 (4)	4.40	4.40

Queen Mother Type of 1985

Hat: #51a, 57a, Light blue. #51b, 57b, White. #52a, Tiara. #52b, Lavender. #53a, 56a, Violet. #53b, 56b, Green. #54a, Blue. #54b, Pink. #55a, Looking up. #55b, Looking forward.

1985-86

51	A45	15c Pair, #a.-b.	.30	.30
52	A45	40c Pair, #a.-b.	.95	.95
53	A45	65c Pair, #a.-b.	1.50	1.50
54	A45	95c Pair, #a.-b.	2.40	2.40
		Nos. 51-54 (4)	5.15	5.15

Souvenir Sheets of 2

55	A45	$1.10 #a.-b.	3.75	3.75
56	A45	$2 #a.-b.	4.00	4.00
57	A45	$2.50 #a.-b.	5.50	5.50

Issued: #51-55, 8/28; 56-57, 1/8/86.

Elizabeth II 60th Birthday Type
1986, Apr. 21   Perf. 13x12½, 12½x13

58	A49	5c Green hat	.35	.35
59	A49	60c As young woman	.55	.55
60	A49	$2 Flowered hat	1.90	1.90
61	A49	$3.50 Tiara, vert.	3.25	3.25
		Nos. 58-61 (4)	6.05	6.05

Souvenir Sheet

62	A49	$5 Straw hat	6.25	6.25

For overprints see Nos. 72-76.

Royal Wedding Type of 1986
#65a, Andrew, vert. #65b, Sarah Ferguson, vert. #66a, Charles, Andrew. #66b, Couple.

1986, July 18   Perf. 12½x13, 13x12½

65	A53	60c Pair, #a.-b.	1.25	1.25
66	A53	$1 Pair, #a.-b.	2.00	2.00

Souvenir Sheet

67	A56	$4 Newlyweds	5.25	5.25

Nos. 65-66 Ovptd. in Silver
"Congratulations to T.R.H. The Duke & Duchess of York"
1986, Oct. 28

68	A53	60c Pair, #a.-b.	1.40	1.40
69	A53	$1 Pair, #a.-b.	2.25	2.25

Nos. 58-62 Ovptd. in Gold
"40th WEDDING ANNIVERSARY OF H.M. QUEEN ELIZABETH II"
1987, Oct. 15   Perf. 13x12½, 12½x13

72	A49	5c multicolored	.20	.20
73	A49	60c multicolored	.75	.75
74	A49	$2 multicolored	2.50	2.50
75	A49	$3 multicolored	3.75	3.75
		Nos. 72-75 (4)	7.20	7.20

Souvenir Sheet

76	A49	$5 multicolored	6.25	6.25

UBANGI-SHARI

ü-'baŋˌg͟e̅ 'shär-e̅

(Ubangi-Shari-Chad)

LOCATION — In Western Africa, north of the equator
GOVT. — French Colony
AREA — 238,767 sq. mi.
POP. — 833,916
CAPITAL — Bangui

In 1910 French Congo was divided into the three colonies of Gabon, Middle Congo and Ubangi-Shari and officially named "French Equatorial Africa." Under that name in 1934 the group, with the territory of Chad included, became a single administrative unit. See Gabon.

100 Centimes = 1 Franc

Stamps of Middle Congo Overprinted in Black

1915-22   Unwmk.   Perf. 14x13½
Chalky Paper

1	A1	1c ol gray & brn	.35	.35
a.		Double overprint	210.00	
b.		Imperf.	60.00	
2	A1	2c violet & brn	.35	.35
3	A1	4c blue & brn	.55	.55
4	A1	5c dk grn & bl	.55	.55
5	A1	5c yel & bl ('22)	.90	.90
6	A1	10c carmine & bl	1.10	1.10
7	A1	10c dp grn & bl grn ('22)	.95	.95
8	A1	15c brn vio & blue	1.60	1.60
9	A1	20c brown & blue	3.50	3.50

No. 8 is on ordinary paper.

Overprinted

10	A2	25c blue & grn	1.60	1.60
11	A2	25c bl grn & gray ('22)	1.25	1.25
12	A2	30c scarlet & grn	1.40	1.40
13	A2	30c dp rose & rose ('22)	1.10	1.10
14	A2	35c vio brn & bl	4.75	4.75
15	A2	40c dl grn & brn	6.50	6.50
16	A2	45c vio & red	6.50	6.50
17	A2	50c bl grn & red	6.00	6.00
18	A2	50c blue & grn ('22)	1.10	1.10
19	A2	75c brown & bl	14.00	14.00
20	A3	1fr dp grn & vio	14.00	14.00
21	A3	2fr vio & gray grn	16.50	16.50
22	A3	5fr blue & rose	42.50	42.50
		Nos. 1-22 (22)	127.05	127.05

For surcharges see Nos. B1-B2.

Types of Middle Congo, 1907-22, Overprinted in Black or Red

1922

23	A1	1c violet & grn	.55	.55
a.		Overprint omitted	190.00	
b.		Imperf.	42.50	
24	A1	2c grn & salmon	.85	.85
25	A1	4c ol brn & brn	1.10	1.10
a.		Overprint omitted	210.00	
26	A1	5c indigo & rose	1.10	1.10
27	A1	10c dp grn & gray grn	1.60	1.60
28	A1	15c lt red & dl bl	1.75	1.75
29	A1	20c choc & salmon	5.75	5.75

Overprinted

30	A2	25c vio & salmon	7.75	7.75
31	A2	30c rose & pale rose	3.50	3.50
32	A2	35c vio & grn	5.00	5.00
33	A2	40c ind & vio (R)	5.00	5.00
34	A2	45c choc & vio	5.00	5.00
35	A2	50c dk bl & pale bl	3.00	3.00
36	A2	60c on 75c vio, *pnksh*	3.75	3.75
37	A2	75c choc & sal	5.75	5.75
38	A3	1fr grn & dl bl (R)	9.00	9.00
a.		Overprint omitted	300.00	
39	A3	2fr grn & salmon	12.50	12.50
40	A3	5fr grn & ol brn	22.00	22.00
		Nos. 23-40 (18)	94.95	94.95

Stamps of 1922 Issue with Additional Overprint in Black, Blue or Red

1924-33

41	A1	1c vio & grn (Bl)	.35	.35
a.		"OUBANGUI CHARI" omitted	150.00	
42	A1	2c grn & sal (Bl)	.35	.35
a.		"OUBANGUI CHARI" omitted	150.00	
b.		Double overprint	150.00	
43	A1	4c ol brn & brn (Bl)	.40	.40
a.		Double overprint (Bl + Bk)	195.00	
b.		"OUBANGUI CHARI" omitted	175.00	
44	A1	5c ind & rose	.40	.40
a.		"OUBANGUI CHARI" omitted	145.00	
45	A1	10c dp grn & gray grn	.60	.60
46	A1	10c red org & dl bl ('25)	.90	.90
47	A1	15c sal & dl bl	.90	.90
48	A1	15c sal & dl bl (Bl) ('26)	.90	.90
49	A1	20c choc & salmon (Bl)	1.10	1.10

On Nos. 41-49 the color in ( ) refers to the overprint "Afrique Equatoriale Francaise."

50	A2	25c vio & salmon (Bl)	.85	.85
a.		Imperf.		
51	A2	30c rose & pale rose (Bl)	.45	.45
52	A2	30c choc & red ('25)	.85	.85
a.		"OUBANGUI CHARI" omitted	150.00	
53	A2	30c dk grn & grn ('27)	1.40	1.40
54	A2	35c vio & grn (Bl)	.85	.85
a.		"OUBANGUI CHARI" omitted		
55	A2	40c ind & vio (Bl)	.85	.55
56	A2	45c choc & vio (Bl)	.90	.40
57	A2	50c dk bl & pale bl (R)	.60	.60
58	A2	50c gray & bl vio ('25) (R)	1.60	1.60
59	A2	60c on 75c dk vio, *pnksh* (R)	.60	.60
60	A2	65c org brn & bl ('28)	1.60	1.60
61	A2	75c choc & sal (Bl) ('25) (R)	1.75	1.75
62	A2	75c dp bl & lt bl ('25) (R)	1.20	1.20
a.		"OUBANGUI CHARI" omitted	150.00	
63	A2	75c rose & dk brn ('28)	2.50	2.50
64	A2	90c brn red & pink ('30)	5.00	5.00
65	A3	1fr grn & ind (Bk + Bl)	.85	.85
66	A3	1fr grn & ind (R + Bl)	1.60	1.60
67	A3	1.10fr bister & bl ('28)	2.50	2.50
68	A3	1.25fr mag & lt grn ('33)	9.00	9.00
69	A3	1.50fr ultra & bl ('30)	6.50	6.50

70	A3	1.75fr dk brn & dp		
		buff ('33)	11.50	11.50
71	A3	2fr grn & red	1.40	1.40
a.		"OUBANGUI CHARI" omitted	1,450.	1,100.
72	A3	3fr red vio ('30)	5.75	5.75
73	A3	5fr grn & ol brn		
		(Bl)	4.50	4.50
		Nos. 41-73 (33)	70.50	69.70

On Nos. 65, 66 the first overprint color refers to OUBANGUI CHARI.
For surcharges see Nos. 74-81.

Types of 1924 Issue Surcharged with New Values in Black or Red

1925-26

74	A3	65c on 1fr vio & ol	2.00	2.00
a.		"65" omitted	150.00	
75	A3	85c on 1fr vio & ol	2.00	2.00
a.		"AFRIQUE EQUATORIALE		
		FRANCAISE" omitted	150.00	
b.		Double surcharge	165.00	
76	A3	1.25fr on 1fr dk bl &		
		ultra (R) ('26)	1.25	1.25
a.		"1f25" omitted	175.00	125.00

Bars cover old denomination on No. 76.

Types of 1924 Issue Surcharged with New Values and Bars

1927

77	A2	90c on 75c brn red &		
		rose red	2.00	2.00
78	A3	1.50fr on 1fr ultra & bl	2.00	2.00
79	A3	3fr on 5fr org brn &		
		dl red	3.25	3.25
80	A3	10fr on 5fr ver & vio	18.00	18.00
81	A3	20fr on 5fr vio & gray	26.00	26.00
		Nos. 77-81 (5)	51.25	51.25

Common Design Types pictured following the introduction.

Colonial Exposition Issue
Common Design Types

| 1931 | | Engr. | | Perf. 12½ |

Name of Country Typo. in Black

82	CD70	40c deep green	5.25	5.25
83	CD71	50c violet	5.25	5.25
84	CD72	90c red orange	5.25	5.25
a.		Imperf.	125.00	
85	CD73l	1.50fr dull blue	5.25	5.25
		Nos. 82-85 (4)	21.00	21.00

SEMI-POSTAL STAMPS

Regular Issue of 1915 Surcharged

1916 Unwmk. Perf. 14x13½
Chalky Paper

B1	A1	10c + 5c car & blue	3.25	3.25
a.		Inverted surch.	100.00	160.00
b.		Double surcharge	100.00	160.00
c.		Double surch., one invtd.	130.00	130.00
d.		Vertical surcharge	125.00	125.00
e.		No period under "C"	18.00	18.00

Regular Issue of 1915 Surcharged in Carmine

| B2 | A1 | 10c + 5c car & blue | 1.60 | 1.60 |

POSTAGE DUE STAMPS

Postage Due Stamps of France Overprinted

1928 Unwmk. Perf. 14x13½

J1	D2	5c light blue	1.50	1.50
J2	D2	10c gray brown	1.60	1.60
J3	D2	20c olive green	2.00	2.00
J4	D2	25c bright rose	2.00	2.00
J5	D2	30c light red	2.00	2.00
J6	D2	45c blue green	2.00	2.00
J7	D2	50c brown violet	2.50	2.60
J8	D2	60c yellow brown	3.00	3.00
J9	D2	1fr red brown	4.00	4.00
J10	D2	2fr orange red	5.75	6.00
J11	D2	3fr bright violet	5.75	6.00
		Nos. J1-J11 (11)	32.10	32.70

Landscape D3

Emile Gentil — D4

1930				Typo.
J12	D3	5c dp bl & olive	.85	.85
J13	D3	10c dk red & brn	1.10	1.10
J14	D3	20c green & brn	1.25	1.25
J15	D3	25c lt bl & brn	1.40	1.40
J16	D3	30c bis brn & Prus bl	2.50	2.50
J17	D3	45c Prus bl & ol	3.00	3.00
J18	D3	50c red vio & brn	5.25	5.25
J19	D3	60c gray lil & bl blk	5.75	5.75
J20	D4	1fr bis brn & bl blk	5.75	5.75
J21	D4	2fr violet & brown	6.50	6.50
J22	D4	3fr dp red & brn	7.50	7.50
		Nos. J12-J22 (11)	40.85	40.85

Stamps of Ubangi-Shari were replaced in 1936 by those of French Equatorial Africa.

UGANDA

ü-'gan-də

LOCATION — East Africa, at the Equator and separated from the Indian Ocean by Kenya and Tanzania
GOVT. — Independent state
AREA — 91,343 sq. mi.
POP. — 21,619,700 (1999 est.)
CAPITAL — Kampala

Stamps of 1898-1902 were replaced by those issued for Kenya, Tanganyika and Uganda. Uganda became independent October 9, 1962.

Cowries (50 = 4 Pence)
16 Annas = 1 Rupee (1896)
100 Cents = 1 Shilling (1962)

> Catalogue values for unused stamps in this country are for Never Hinged items, beginning with Scott 79 in the regular postage section and Scott J1 in the postage due section.

Unused values for Nos. 1-68 are for stamps without gum. Very fine examples will be evenly cut and will show at least two full typewritten framelines.

A1   A2

Nos. 1-53 were produced with a typewriter by Rev. Ernest Millar of the Church Missionary Society. They were 20-26mm wide, with nine stamps in a horizontal row. Later two more were added to each row, and the stamps became narrower, 16-18mm.

Rev. Millar got a new typewriter in 1895, and the stamps he typed on it have a different appearance. A violet ribbon in the machine, inserted late in 1895, resulted in Nos. 35-53.

Nos. 1-53 are on thin, tough, white paper, laid horizontally with traces of a few vertical lines.

Forgeries of Nos. 1-53 are known.

Without Gum
Wide Letters
Typewritten on Thin Laid Paper
Stamps 20 to 26mm wide

			Unwmk.	Imperf.
1895				
1	A1	10(c) black	5,750.	3,750.
2	A1	20(c) black	5,250.	1,600.
3	A1	30(c) black	1,800.	1,800.
4	A1	40(c) black	3,250.	1,550.
5	A1	50(c) black	1,550.	1,300.
6	A1	60(c) black	2,100.	2,100.

Surcharged with New Value in Black, Pen-written

10	A1	10 on 50(c) black	—	
11	A1	15 on 10(c) black	—	
12	A1	15 on 20(c) black	—	
13	A1	15 on 40(c) black	—	
14	A1	15 on 50(c) black	—	
15	A1	25 on 50(c) black	—	
16	A1	50 on 60(c) black	—	

Stamps 16 to 18mm wide

17	A1	5(c) black	1,750.	1,100.
18	A1	10(c) black	1,750.	1,500.
19	A1	15(c) black	1,150.	1,500.
20	A1	20(c) black	1,500.	750.
21	A1	25(c) black	1,100.	1,100.
22	A1	30(c) black	8,750.	8,750.
23	A1	40(c) black	8,000.	8,000.
24	A1	50(c) black	3,750.	5,750.
25	A1	60(c) black	7,500.	

Narrow Letters
Stamps 16 to 18mm wide

26	A2	5(c) black	1,000.	
27	A2	10(c) black	1,000.	
28	A2	15(c) black	1,000.	
29	A2	20(c) black	800.	
30	A2	25(c) black	1,000.	
31	A2	30(c) black	1,100.	
32	A2	40(c) black	1,100.	
33	A2	50(c) black	950.	
34	A2	60(c) black	1,900.	
35	A2	5(c) violet	575.	575.

36	A2	10(c) violet	550.	550.
37	A2	15(c) violet	700.	500.
38	A2	20(c) violet	425.	325.
39	A2	25(c) violet	800.	800.
40	A2	30(c) violet	1,100.	800.
41	A2	40(c) violet	925.	925.
42	A2	50(c) violet	1,000.	1,150.
43	A2	100(c) violet	3,250.	3,750.

As a favor to a philatelist, 35c and 45c denominations were made in black and violet. They were not intended for postal use and no rate called for those denominations.

A3   A4

1896

44	A3	5(c) violet	550.	950.
45	A3	10(c) violet	500.	575.
46	A3	15(c) violet	550.	950.
47	A3	20(c) violet	325.	275.
48	A3	25(c) violet	325.	
49	A3	30(c) violet	575.	1,150.
50	A3	40(c) violet	625.	1,150.
51	A3	50(c) violet	700.	900.
52	A3	60(c) violet	1,600.	
53	A3	100(c) violet	1,500.	2,250.

Overprinted "L" in Black

1896		Typeset	White Paper
54	A4	1a black (thin "1")	200.00	175.00
a.		Small "O" in "POSTAGE"	1,350.	1,000.
55	A4	2a black	110.00	140.00
a.		Small "O" in "POSTAGE"	475.00	525.00
56	A4	3a black	275.00	350.00
a.		Small "O" in "POSTAGE"	1,500.	1,800.
57	A4	4a black	110.00	175.00
a.		Small "O" in "POSTAGE"	525.00	

Yellowish Paper

58	A4	8a black	210.00	250.00
a.		Small "O" in "POSTAGE"	1,250.	1,500.
59	A4	1r black	425.00	475.00
a.		Small "O" in "POSTAGE"	1,750.	
60	A4	5r black	37,500.	37,500.

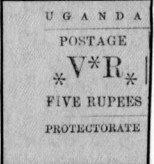

A4a

Without Overprint
White Paper

61	A4a	1a black (thin "1")	125.00	110.00
a.		Small "O" in "POSTAGE"	700.00	625.00
62	A4a	1a black (thick "1")	21.00	27.50
a.		Small "O" in "POSTAGE"	90.00	110.00
63	A4a	2a black	29.00	32.50
a.		Small "O" in "POSTAGE"	110.00	140.00
64	A4a	3a black	30.00	35.00
a.		Small "O" in "POSTAGE"	125.00	160.00
65	A4a	4a black	30.00	35.00
a.		Small "O" in "POSTAGE"	110.00	140.00

Yellowish Paper

66	A4a	8a black	32.50	35.00
a.		Small "O" in "POSTAGE"	140.00	160.00
67	A4a	1r black	87.50	110.00
a.		Small "O" in "POSTAGE"	350.00	450.00
68	A4a	5r black	250.00	400.00
a.		Small "O" in "POSTAGE"	850.00	1,050.

A5   A6

Queen Victoria

1898-1902		Engr.	Wmk. 2	Perf. 14
69	A5	1a red	2.25	2.50
70	A5	1a car rose ('02)	2.25	1.10
71	A5	2a brown	4.00	8.00
72	A5	3a gray	13.00	30.00
73	A5	4a dark green	7.00	7.50
74	A5	8a olive gray	9.00	27.50

Wmk. 1

75	A6	1r ultra	45.00	47.50
76	A6	5r brown	80.00	110.00
		Nos. 69-76 (8)	162.50	234.10

A7

1902	Wmk. 2	Black Overprint
77	A7	½a yellow green	2.25	1.60
a.		Inverted overprint	2,000.	
b.		Double overprint	2,250.	
c.		Pair, one without overprint	4,750.	

Red Overprint

78	A7	2½a dark blue	3.25	3.50
a.		Double overprint	750.00	

> Catalogue values for unused stamps in this section, from this point to the end of the section, are for Never Hinged items.

Ripon Falls and Speke Monument
A8

Wmk. 314

1962, July 28		Engr.	Perf. 14
79	A8	30c vermilion & blk	.30	.30
80	A8	50c violet & blk	.30	.30
81	A8	1.30sh green & blk	.55	.55
82	A8	2.50sh ultra & blk	2.00	2.00
		Nos. 79-82 (4)	3.15	3.15

Cent. of the discovery of the source of the Nile by John Hanning Speke.

Independent State

Murchison Falls — A9

Mulago Hospital, X-Ray Service
A10

Designs: 10c, Tobacco growing. 15c, Coffee growing. 20c, Ankole cattle. 30c, Cotton growing. 50c, Mountains of the Moon. 1.30sh, Rubaga and Namirembe Cathedrals and Kibuli Mosque. 2sh, Makerere College and students. 5sh, Copper mining. 10sh, Cement factory. 20sh, Parliament.

		Perf. 14½x14, 14x14½		
1962, Oct. 9		Photo.	Unwmk.	
83	A9	5c Prus green	.25	.25
84	A9	10c red brown	.25	.25
85	A9	15c grn, blk & car	.25	.25
86	A9	20c bister & pur	.25	.25
87	A9	30c brt blue	.25	.25
88	A9	50c bluish grn & blk	.25	.25
89	A10	1sh bl grn, sep & red	.25	.25
90	A10	1.30sh pur & ocher	.40	.25
91	A10	2sh grnsh bl, blk & dk car	.50	.30
92	A10	5sh dk green & red	1.25	.65
93	A10	10sh red brn & slate	2.50	1.30
94	A10	20sh blue & pale brn	7.00	3.50
		Nos. 83-94 (12)	13.40	7.75

Uganda's independence, Oct. 9, 1962.

Crowned Crane — A11

1965, Feb. 20		Photo.	Perf. 14½
95	A11	30c bl grn, blk, yel & red	.40	.20
96	A11	1sh30c ultra, blk, yel & red	1.10	.70

Intl. Trade Fair at Lugogo Stadium, Kampala, Feb. 20-28.

Black Bee-eater   African Jacana
A12   A13

Arms of Uganda and Birds: 15c, Orange weaver. 20c, Narina trogon. 30c, Sacred ibis. 40c, Blue-breasted kingfisher. 50c, Whale-headed stork. 65c, Black-winged red bishop. 1sh, Ruwenzori turaco. 1.30sh, African fish eagle. 2.50sh, Great blue turaco. 5sh, Lilac-breasted roller. 10sh, Black-collared lovebird. 20sh, Crowned crane.

		Perf. 14½x14, 14x14½		
1965, Oct. 9		Photo.	Unwmk.	
		Birds in Natural Colors		
		Size: 17x21mm, 21x17mm		
97	A12	5c lt vio bl & blk	.30	.30
98	A13	10c dull blue & red	.30	.30
99	A12	15c dk brown & org	.30	.30
100	A13	20c bister & brt grn	.30	.30
101	A13	30c hn brn & blk	2.00	.30
102	A12	40c lt yel grn & red	1.25	.30
103	A12	50c dp pur & gray	.35	.30
104	A13	65c gray & brick red	2.75	1.50

		Perf. 14½		
		Size: 41x25mm, 25x41mm		
105	A13	1sh lt blue & blk	.70	.30
106	A12	1.30sh yel & red brn	7.00	.30
107	A13	2.50sh brt yel grn & blk	5.50	.45
108	A12	5sh lil gray & vio bl	8.50	3.00
109	A13	10sh lt brown & blk	13.50	7.75
110	A13	20sh olive grn & blk	25.00	25.00
		Nos. 97-110 (14)	67.75	40.55

Parliament Building — A14

13th Commonwealth Parliamentary Assoc. Conf.: 30c, Animal carvings from entrance hall of Uganda Parliament. 50c, Arms of Uganda. 2.50sh, Parliament Chamber.

1967, Oct. 26		Photo.	Perf. 14½
111	A14	30c multicolored	.20	.20
112	A14	50c multicolored	.20	.20
113	A14	1.30sh multicolored	.35	.30
114	A14	2.50sh multicolored	.70	.60
		Nos. 111-114 (4)	1.45	1.30

Cordia Abyssinica A15

Black-galled Acacia A16

Flowers: 10c, Grewia similis. 15c, Cassia didymobotrya. 20c, Coleus barbatus. 30c, Ochna ovata. 40c, Ipomoea spathulata (morning glory). 50c, Spathodea nilotica (flame tree). 60c, Oncoba spinosa. 70c, Carissa edulis. 1.50sh, Clerodendrum myricoides (blue butterfly bush). 2.50sh, Acanthus arboreus. 5sh, Kigelia aethiopium (sausage tree). 10sh, Erythrina abyssinica (Uganda coral). 20sh, Monodora myristica.

Perf. 14½x14

1969, Oct. 9		Photo.	Unwmk.	
115	A15	5c multicolored	.20	.20
116	A15	10c multicolored	.20	.20
117	A15	15c multicolored	.20	.20
118	A15	20c multicolored	.20	.20
119	A15	30c multicolored	.20	.20
120	A15	40c gray & multi	.20	.20
121	A15	50c tan & multi	.20	.20
122	A15	60c multicolored	.20	.20
123	A15	70c multicolored	.20	.20

Perf. 14

124	A16	1sh multicolored	.35	.20
125	A16	1.50sh multicolored	.55	.20
126	A16	2.50sh multicolored	.70	.20
127	A16	5sh multicolored	1.25	.20
128	A16	10sh multicolored	3.00	.55
129	A16	20sh tan & multi	7.75	1.25
		Nos. 115-129 (15)	15.40	4.40

Values of Nos. 124-129 are for canceled-to-order stamps. Cancellations were printed on Nos. 128-129. Postally used examples sell for higher prices.

Nos. 125-126, 129 Surcharged

1975, Sept. 29		Photo.	Perf. 14	
130	A16	2sh on 1.50sh multi	1.25	1.25
131	A16	3sh on 2.50sh multi	25.00	25.00
132	A16	40sh on 20sh multi	10.00	10.00
		Nos. 130-132 (3)	36.25	36.25

Millet — A17

Ugandan Crops: 20c, Sugar cane. 30c, Tobacco. 40c, Onions. 50c, Tomatoes. 70c, Tea. 80c, Bananas. 1sh, Corn. 2sh, Pineapple. 3sh, Coffee. 5sh, Oranges. 10sh, Peanuts. 20sh, Cotton. 40sh, Beans.

1975, Oct. 9		Photo.	Perf. 14x14½	

Size: 21x17mm
Multicolored, Name Panel as follows

133	A17	10c lt brown	.20	.20
134	A17	20c blue	.20	.20
135	A17	30c vermilion	.20	.20
136	A17	40c lilac	.20	.20
137	A17	50c olive	.20	.20
138	A17	70c brt green	.20	.20
139	A17	80c purple	.20	.20

Perf. 14½
Size: 41x25mm

140	A17	1sh ocher	.20	.20
141	A17	2sh slate	.25	.25
142	A17	3sh blue	.40	.40
143	A17	5sh yellow green	.50	.55
144	A17	10sh brown red	1.00	1.10
145	A17	20sh rose lilac	2.10	2.25
146	A17	40sh orange	4.00	4.25
		Nos. 133-146 (14)	9.85	10.40

See #195-198. For surcharge & overprints see #175, 203-206, 227-244, 253-257.

Communications Type of Tanzania 1976

Designs: 50c, Microwave tower. 1sh, Cordless switchboard and operators, horiz. 2sh, Telephones of 1880, 1930 and 1976. 3sh, Message switching center, horiz.

1976, Apr. 15		Litho.	Perf. 14½	
147	A6a	50c blue & multi	.20	.20
148	A6a	1sh red & multi	.20	.20
149	A6a	2sh yellow & multi	.35	.25
150	A6a	3sh multicolored	.50	.40
a.		Souvenir sheet of 4	1.75	1.75
		Nos. 147-150 (4)	1.25	1.05

Telecommunications development in East Africa. No. 150a contains 4 stamps similar to Nos. 147-150 with simulated perforations.

Olympics Type of Tanzania 1976

Designs: 50c, Akii Bua, Ugandan hurdler. 1sh, Filbert Bayi, Tanzanian runner. 2sh, Steve Muchoki, Kenyan boxer. 3sh, Olympic torch, flags of Kenya, Tanzania and Uganda.

1976, July 5		Litho.	Perf. 14½	
151	A6b	50c blue & multi	.20	.20
152	A6b	1sh red & multi	.25	.20
153	A6b	2sh yellow & multi	.45	.40
154	A6b	3sh blue & multi	.70	.60
a.		Souv. sheet of 4, #151-154, perf. 13	7.00	5.00
		Nos. 151-154 (4)	1.60	1.40

21st Olympic Games, Montreal, Canada, July 17-Aug. 1.

Railway Type of Tanzania 1976

Designs: 50c, Tanzania-Zambia Railway. 1sh, Nile Bridge, Uganda. 2sh, Nakuru Station, Kenya. 3sh, Class A locomotive, 1896.

1976, Oct. 4		Litho.	Perf. 14	
155	A6c	50c lilac & multi	.20	.20
156	A6c	1sh emerald & multi	.40	.20
157	A6c	2sh brt rose & multi	.80	.45
158	A6c	3sh yellow & multi	1.25	.65
a.		Souv. sheet of 4, #155-158, perf 13	3.50	3.50
		Nos. 155-158 (4)	2.65	1.50

Rail transport in East Africa.

Fish Type of Tanzania 1977

1977, Jan. 10		Litho.	Perf. 14½	
159	A6d	50c Nile perch	.20	.20
160	A6d	1sh Tilapia	.30	.20
161	A6d	3sh Sailfish	.85	.60
162	A6d	5sh Black marlin	1.25	1.00
a.		Souvenir sheet of 4, #159-162	6.00	5.50
		Nos. 159-162 (4)	2.60	2.00

Festival Type of Tanzania 1977

Festival Emblem and: 50c, Masai tribesmen bleeding cow. 1sh, Dancers from Uganda. 2sh, Makonde sculpture, Tanzania. 3sh, Tribesmen skinning hippopotamus.

1977, Jan. 15			Perf. 13½x14	
163	A6e	50c multicolored	.20	.20
164	A6e	1sh multicolored	.25	.20
165	A6e	2sh multicolored	.45	.40
166	A6e	3sh multicolored	.70	.60
a.		Souvenir sheet of 4, #163-166	2.60	2.25
		Nos. 163-166 (4)	1.60	1.40

2nd World Black and African Festival, Lagos, Nigeria, Jan. 15-Feb. 12.

Rally Type of Tanzania 1977

Safari Rally Emblem and: 50c, Automobile passing through village. 1sh, Winner at finish line. 2sh, Car passing through washout. 5sh, Car, elephants and Mt. Kenya.

1977, Apr. 5		Litho.	Perf. 14	
167	A6f	50c multicolored	.20	.20
168	A6f	1sh multicolored	.20	.20
169	A6f	2sh multicolored	.45	.30
170	A6f	5sh multicolored	1.10	.85
a.		Souvenir sheet of 4, #167-170	2.50	2.50
		Nos. 167-170 (4)	1.95	1.55

25th Safari Rally, Apr. 7-11.

Church Type of Tanzania 1977

Designs: 50c, Rev. Canon Apolo Kivebulaya. 1sh, Uganda Cathedral. 2sh, Early grass-topped Cathedral. 5sh, Early tent congregation, Kigezi.

1977, June 30		Litho.	Perf. 14	
171	A6g	50c multicolored	.20	.20
172	A6g	1sh multicolored	.20	.20
173	A6g	2sh multicolored	.40	.30
174	A6g	5sh multicolored	1.00	.75
a.		Souvenir sheet of 4, #171-174	2.00	2.00
		Nos. 171-174 (4)	1.80	1.45

Church of Uganda, centenary.

Type of 1975 Surcharged with New Value and 2 Bars

1977, Aug. 22		Photo.	Perf. 14x14½	
175	A17	80c on 60c bananas	.50	.20

No. 175 was not issued without surcharge.

Wildlife Type of Tanzania 1977

Wildlife Fund Emblem and: 50c, Pancake tortoise. 1sh, Nile crocodile. 2sh, Hunter's hartebeest. 3sh, Red colobus monkey. 5sh, Dugong.

1977, Sept. 26		Litho.	Perf. 14x13½	
176	A6h	50c multicolored	.30	.25
177	A6h	1sh multicolored	.50	.40
178	A6h	2sh multicolored	2.25	1.00
179	A6h	3sh multicolored	3.25	1.40
180	A6h	5sh multicolored	3.25	2.50
a.		Souvenir sheet of 4, #177-180	8.50	6.00
		Nos. 176-180 (5)	9.55	5.55

Endangered species.

Soccer Type of Tanzania

Soccer Cup and: 50c, Soccer scene and Joe Kadenge. 1sh, Mohammed Chuma receiving trophy, and his portrait. 2sh, Shot on goal and Omari S. Kidevu. 5sh, Backfield defense and Polly Ouma.

1978, May 3		Litho.	Perf. 14x13½	
181	A8a	50c green & multi	.20	.20
182	A8a	1sh lt brown & multi	.20	.20
183	A8a	2sh lilac & multi	.40	.30
184	A8a	5sh dk blue & multi	1.10	.75
a.		Souvenir sheet of 4, #181-184	2.25	2.25
		Nos. 181-184 (4)	1.90	1.45

World Soccer Cup Championships, Argentina, June 1-25.
See Nos. 203-206.

Crop Type of 1975

Designs as before.

1978, June		Litho.	Perf. 14½	

Size: 41x25mm
Multicolored, Name Panel as follows

195	A17	5sh blue	.25	.25
196	A17	10sh rose lilac	.50	.50
197	A17	20sh brown	1.00	1.00
198	A17	40sh deep orange	2.10	2.10
		Nos. 195-198 (4)	3.85	3.85

Shot Put A18

1978, July 10		Litho.	Perf. 14	
199	A18	50c shown	.20	.20
200	A18	1sh Broad jump	.20	.20
201	A18	2sh Running	.40	.40
202	A18	5sh Boxing	1.00	1.00
a.		Souv. sheet of 4, #199-202, perf 12	2.75	2.75
		Nos. 199-202 (4)	1.80	1.80

Commonwealth Games, Edmonton, Canada, Aug. 3-12.
For overprints see Nos. 249-252.

Soccer Type of 1978 Inscribed: "WORLD CUP 1978"

Designs: 50c, Backfield defense and Polly Ouma. 2sh, Shot on goal and Omari S. Kidevu. 5sh, Soccer scene and Joe Kadenge. 10sh, Mohammed Chuma receiving trophy, and his portrait.

1978, Sept. 11			Perf. 14x13½	
203	A8a	50c dk blue & multi	.20	.20
204	A8a	2sh lilac & multi	.45	.35
205	A8a	5sh green & multi	1.00	.90
206	A8a	10sh lt brown & multi	2.00	1.75
a.		Souv. sheet of 4, #203-206, perf. 12	4.00	4.00
		Nos. 203-206 (4)	3.65	3.20

World Cup Soccer Championship winners.

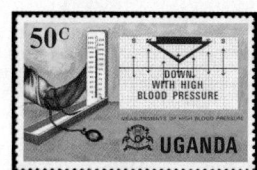

Blood Pressure Gauge and Chart — A19

1978, Sept. 25		Litho.	Perf. 14	
207	A19	50c shown	.20	.20
208	A19	1sh Heart	.20	.20
209	A19	2sh Retina	.40	.35
210	A19	5sh Kidneys	1.00	.95
a.		Souvenir sheet of 4, #207-210	2.75	2.75
		Nos. 207-210 (4)	1.80	1.70

World Health Day and Hypertension Month.

Cattle Unloaded from Plane A20

Flyer 1 and: 1.50sh, "Islander" on runway, Kampala. 2.70sh, Coffee loaded on transport jet. 10sh, Concorde.

1978, Dec. 16				
211	A20	1sh multicolored	.20	.20
212	A20	1.50sh multicolored	.25	.20
213	A20	2.70sh multicolored	.45	.40
214	A20	10sh multicolored	1.90	1.40
a.		Souvenir sheet of 4, #211-214	3.00	3.00
		Nos. 211-214 (4)	2.80	2.20

75th anniversary of 1st powered flight.
For overprints see Nos. 258-261.

Elizabeth II Leaving Owen Falls Dam — A21

Designs: 1.50sh, Coronation regalia. 2.70sh, Coronation ceremony. 10sh, Royal family on balcony of Buckingham Palace.

1979, Mar. 1		Litho.	Perf. 12½x12	
215	A21	1sh multicolored	.20	.20
216	A21	1.50sh multicolored	.20	.20
217	A21	2.70sh multicolored	.35	.30
218	A21	10sh multicolored	1.40	1.10
a.		Souvenir sheet of 4, #215-218	2.40	2.40
		Nos. 215-218 (4)	2.15	1.80

25th anniv. of coronation of Elizabeth II.
For overprints see Nos. 245-248.

Bishop Joseph Kiwanuka A22

Designs: 1.50sh, Lubaga Cathedral. 2.70sh, Ugandan pilgrims and St. Peter's, Rome. 10sh, Friar Lourdel-Mapeera, missionary.

1979, Feb. 15			Perf. 14	
219	A22	1sh multicolored	.20	.20
220	A22	1.50sh multicolored	.20	.20
221	A22	2.70sh multicolored	.35	.30
222	A22	10sh multicolored	1.40	1.10
a.		Souvenir sheet of 4, #219-222	2.40	2.40
		Nos. 219-222 (4)	2.15	1.80

Ugandan Catholic Church, centenary.
See No. 274. For overprints see Nos. 262-265.

Child Receiving Vaccination — A23

IYC Emblem and: 1.50sh, Handicapped children playing. 2.70sh, Ugandan IYC emblem. 10sh, Teacher and pupils.

1979, July 16		Litho.	Perf. 14	
223	A23	1sh multicolored	.20	.20
224	A23	1.50sh multicolored	.20	.20
225	A23	2.70sh multicolored	.25	.25
226	A23	10sh multicolored	1.10	.90
a.		Souvenir sheet of 4, #223-226	2.00	2.00
		Nos. 223-226 (4)	1.75	1.55

International Year of the Child.
For overprints see Nos. 266-269.

Nos. 133-146, 195-198, 215-218
Overprinted: "UGANDA / LIBERATED / 1979"

1979, July 12 Photo. *Perf. 14x14½*
Size: 21x17mm

227	A17	10c multicolored	.20	.20
228	A17	20c multicolored	.20	.20
229	A17	30c multicolored	.20	.20
230	A17	40c multicolored	.20	.20
231	A17	50c multicolored	.20	.20
232	A17	70c multicolored	.20	.20
233	A17	80c multicolored	.20	.20

Perf. 14½
Size: 41x25mm

234	A17	1sh multicolored	.20	.20
235	A17	2sh multicolored	.25	.20
236	A17	3sh multicolored	.40	.30
237	A17	5sh multicolored	.55	.45
238	A17	10sh multicolored	1.10	.90
239	A17	20sh multicolored	2.25	2.00
240	A17	40sh multicolored	4.50	3.75
		Nos. 227-240 (14)	10.65	9.20

1979 Litho. *Perf. 14½*
Multicolored, name panel as follows

241	A17	5sh blue	.75	.55
242	A17	10sh rose lilac	1.40	1.10
243	A17	20sh brown	2.60	2.25
244	A17	40sh deep orange	5.25	4.50
		Nos. 241-244 (4)	10.00	8.40

1979, July 12 Litho. *Perf. 12½x12*

245	A21	1sh multicolored	.20	.20
246	A21	1.50sh multicolored	.20	.20
247	A21	2.70sh multicolored	.25	.20
248	A21	15sh on 10sh multi	1.60	1.10
a.		Souvenir sheet of 4	3.00	
		Nos. 245-248 (4)	2.25	1.75

No. 248a contains Nos. 245-247 and a 15sh in design of No. 218. Issued Aug. 1.

Nos. 199-202; 203, 204-206; 211-214; 219-222, 223-226 Overprinted: "UGANDA LIBERATED 1979"

1979, Aug. 1 Litho. *Perf. 14*

249	A18	50c multicolored	.20	.20
250	A18	1sh multicolored	.20	.20
251	A18	2sh multicolored	.35	.25
252	A18	5sh multicolored	.85	.75

Type A17 of Kenya

1979, Aug. 1 *Perf. 14x13½*

253	A17	50c multi	.20	.20
255	A17	2sh multi (#204)	.30	.25
256	A17	5sh multi	.85	.70
257	A17	10sh multi	1.75	1.40

Overprint exists on No. 183.

1979, Aug. 1 *Perf. 14*

258	A20	1sh multicolored	.20	.20
259	A20	1.50sh multicolored	.30	.25
260	A20	2.70sh multicolored	.60	.50
261	A20	10sh multicolored	2.10	1.75

1979, Aug. 1

262	A22	1sh multicolored	.20	.20
263	A22	1.50sh multicolored	.25	.20
264	A22	2.70sh multicolored	.45	.40
265	A22	10sh multicolored	1.60	1.40

1979, Aug. 16

266	A23	1sh multicolored	.20	.20
267	A23	1.50sh multicolored	.25	.20
268	A23	2.70sh multicolored	.50	.45
269	A23	10sh multicolored	1.75	1.60
a.		Souvenir sheet of 4, #266-269	2.75	2.75
		Nos. 249-269 (20)	13.10	11.30

ITU Emblem, Radio Waves A24

1979, Sept. 11

270	A24	1sh lt gray & multi	.20	.20
271	A24	1.50sh orange & multi	.20	.20
272	A24	2.70sh yellow & multi	.20	.20
273	A24	10sh blue & multi	.90	.75
		Nos. 270-273 (4)	1.50	1.35

50th anniv. of Intl. Radio Consultative Committee (CCIR) of the ITU.

No. 222a Redrawn and Inscribed: FREEDOM OF WORSHIP DECLARED
Souvenir Sheet

1979, Sept. *Perf. 12*

274		Sheet of 4	2.25	2.25
a.		A22 1sh No. 219	.20	.20
b.		A22 1.50sh No. 220	.20	.20
c.		A22 2.70sh No. 221	.35	.35
d.		A22 10sh No. 222	1.40	1.25

In top panel of margin scrolls and coat of arms have been replaced by inscription.

A25

1979, Nov. 12 Litho. *Perf. 14*

275	A25	1sh #110	.20	.20
276	A25	1.50sh #112	.20	.20
277	A25	2.70sh #94	.40	.35
278	A25	10sh #69	1.50	1.25
a.		Souvenir sheet of 4, #275-278	2.25	1.25
		Nos. 275-278 (4)	2.30	2.00

Sir Rowland Hill (1795-1879), originator of penny postage.
For overprints see Nos. 293-296.

Thomson's Gazelle — A26

1979, Dec. 3 Litho. *Perf. 14*
Size: 21x17mm

279	A26	10c multicolored	.20	.20
280	A26	20c multicolored	.20	.20
281	A26	30c multicolored	.20	.20
282	A26	50c multicolored	.20	.20
283	A26	80c multicolored	.20	.20

Size: 39x25mm

284	A26	1sh multicolored	.20	.20
285	A26	1.50sh multicolored	.20	.20
286	A26	2sh multicolored	.25	.20
287	A26	2.70sh multicolored	.30	.30
288	A26	3.50sh multicolored	.40	.35
289	A26	5sh multicolored	.60	.55
290	A26	10sh multicolored	1.10	1.00
291	A26	20sh multicolored	2.50	2.10
292	A26	40sh multicolored	5.25	4.25
		Nos. 279-292 (14)	11.80	10.15

Nos. 284, 286, 289 reissued inscribed 1982. See Nos. 400-406. For surcharges see Nos. 386-392.

Designs: 10c, Impalas. 20c, Large-spotted genet. 50c, Bush babies. 80c, Wild hunting dogs. 1sh, Lions. 1.50sh, Mountain gorillas. 2sh, Zebras. 2.70sh, Leopards. 3.50sh, Black rhinoceroses. 5sh, Defassa waterbucks. 10sh, African black buffaloes. 20sh, Hippopotami. 40sh, African elephants.

Nos. 275-278a Overprinted: "LONDON 1980"

1980, May 6 Litho. *Perf. 14*

293	A25	1sh multicolored	.20	.20
294	A25	1.50sh multicolored	.20	.20
295	A25	2.70sh multicolored	.40	.35
296	A25	10sh multicolored	1.40	1.40
a.		Souvenir sheet of 4, #293-296	2.25	2.25
		Nos. 293-296 (4)	2.20	2.15

London 80 Intl. Stamp Exhib., May 6-14.

Paul Harris Wheeling Rotary Cart A27

1980, Aug. Litho. *Perf. 14*

297	A27	1sh Rotary emblem, vert.	.20	.20
298	A27	20sh shown	2.10	1.60
a.		Souvenir sheet of 2, #297-298	3.00	3.00

Rotary International, 75th anniversary.

Soccer, Flags of Olympic Participants, Flame — A28

1980, Dec. 29 Litho. *Perf. 14*

299	A28	1sh shown	.20	.20
300	A28	2sh Relay race	.20	.20
301	A28	10sh Hurdles	.80	.80
302	A28	20sh Boxing	1.60	1.60
		Nos. 299-302 (4)	2.80	2.80

Souvenir Sheet

303		Sheet of 4	3.00	3.00
a.		A28 2.70sh like #299	.20	.20
b.		A28 3sh like #300	.25	.20
c.		A28 5sh like #301	.40	.35
d.		A28 25sh like 302	2.10	1.75

22nd Summer Olympic Games, Moscow, July 19-Aug. 3.

Nos. 299-303 Overprinted with Sport, Winner and Country

1980, Dec. 29

304	A28	1sh multicolored	.20	.20
305	A28	2sh multicolored	.20	.20
306	A28	10sh multicolored	.80	.80
307	A28	20sh multicolored	1.60	1.60
		Nos. 304-307 (4)	2.80	2.80

Souvenir Sheet

308		Sheet of 4	3.00	3.00
a.		A28 2.70sh like #304	.20	.20
b.		A28 3sh like #305	.25	.20
c.		A28 5sh like #306	.40	.35
d.		A28 25sh like #307	2.10	1.75

Souvenir Sheet

Christ in the Storm on the Sea of Galilee, by Rembrandt — A29

1980, Dec. 31 *Imperf.*

309	A29	25sh multicolored	7.00	6.00

Christmas 1980.

Heinrich von Stephan and UPU Emblem A30

1981, June 2 Litho. *Perf. 14*

310	A30	1sh shown	.20	.20
311	A30	2sh UPU headquarters	.40	.30
312	A30	2.70sh Mail plane, 1935	.50	.40
313	A30	10sh Mail train, 1927	1.75	1.50
a.		Souvenir sheet of 4, #310-313	4.00	4.00
		Nos. 310-313 (4)	2.85	2.40

Von Stephan (1831-97), UPU founder.

Common Design Types pictured following the introduction.

Royal Wedding Issue
Common Design Type

1981 Litho. *Perf. 14*

314	CD331a	10sh Couple	.20	.20
a.		10sh on 1sh	.20	.20

315	CD331a	50sh Tower of London	.30	.25
a.		50sh on 5sh	.30	.25
316	CD331a	200sh Prince Charles	1.50	1.25
a.		200sh on 20sh	1.50	1.25
		Nos. 314-316 (3)	2.00	1.70
		Nos. 314a-316a (3)	2.00	1.70

Souvenir Sheet

317	CD331	250sh Royal mews	1.50	1.50
a.		250sh on 25sh, light orange	1.50	1.50

Royal wedding. Issue dates: surcharges, July 13; others, July 29. Nos. 314-316 also issued in sheets of 5 plus label, perf. 12, in changed colors.
For overprints see Nos. 342-345.

Sleeping Woman Before Green Shutters, by Picasso — A31

Picasso Birth Centenary: 20sh, Bullfight. 30sh, Nude Asleep on a Landscape. 200sh, Interior with a Girl Drawing. 250sh, Minotaur.

1981, Sept. 21 Litho. *Perf. 14*

318	A31	10sh multicolored	.20	.20
319	A31	20sh multicolored	.35	.30
320	A31	30sh multicolored	.50	.40
321	A31	200sh multicolored	3.50	2.75

Size: 120x146mm
Imperf

322	A31	250sh multicolored	5.00	4.00
		Nos. 318-322 (5)	9.55	7.65

Intl. Year of the Disabled A32

1981, Dec. *Perf. 15*

323	A32	1sh Sign language	.20	.20
324	A32	10sh Teacher in wheel-chair	.20	.20
325	A32	50sh Retarded children	.80	.65
326	A32	200sh Blind man	3.25	2.60
a.		Souvenir sheet of 4, #323-326	5.75	5.00
		Nos. 323-326 (4)	4.45	3.65

1982 World Cup Soccer A33

Designs: Various soccer players.

1982, Jan. 11 Litho. *Perf. 14*

327	A33	1sh multicolored	.20	.20
328	A33	10sh multicolored	.20	.20
329	A33	50sh multicolored	.85	.75
330	A33	200sh multicolored	3.50	3.00
		Nos. 327-330 (4)	4.75	4.15

Souvenir Sheet

331	A33	250sh World Cup	4.50	4.50

TB Bacillus Centenary — A34

1982, June 14 Litho.

332	A34	1sh Koch	.35	.30
333	A34	10sh Microscope	.60	.35
334	A34	50sh Inoculation	2.75	1.40

335 A34 100sh Virus under microscope 5.75 2.75
Nos. 332-335 (4) 9.45 4.80

Souvenir Sheet

336 A34 150sh Medical School 6.50 4.00

Peaceful
Uses of
Outer
Space
A35

1982, May 17 Litho. *Perf. 15*
337 A35 5sh Mpoma Satellite
Earth Station .35 .35
338 A35 10sh Pioneer II .35 .35
339 A35 50sh Columbia space
shuttle 1.60 1.40
340 A35 100sh Voyager II, Saturn 3.25 2.75
Nos. 337-340 (4) 5.55 4.85

Souvenir Sheet

341 A35 150sh Columbia shuttle 5.25 4.50

Nos. 314-317 Overprinted: "21st
BIRTHDAY / HRH Princess of Wales /
JULY 1 1982"

1982, July 7 *Perf. 14*
342 CD331 10sh multicolored .20 .20
343 CD331 50sh multicolored .55 .45
344 CD331 200sh multicolored 2.25 1.75
Nos. 342-344 (3) 3.00 2.40

Souvenir Sheet

345 CD331 250sh multicolored 4.50 4.00

Also issued in sheets of 5 + label in
changed colors, perf. 12x12½.

20th Anniversary of Independence
A 150sh souvenir sheet showing the
Coat of Arms was not issued.

Hornbill — A36

1982, July 12
346 A36 1sh shown .25 .25
347 A36 20sh Superb starling .70 .60
348 A36 50sh Bateleur eagle 1.60 1.40
349 A36 100sh Saddle-bill
stork 3.50 2.90
Nos. 346-349 (4) 6.05 5.15

Souvenir Sheet

350 A36 200sh Laughing dove 12.50 11.00

Scouting
Year
A37

1982, Aug. 23
351 A37 5sh Scouts .45 .45
352 A37 20sh Trophy presentation .95 .75
353 A37 50sh Helping dis-
abled 2.40 2.10
354 A37 100sh First aid instruction 4.75 4.25
Nos. 351-354 (4) 8.55 7.55

Souvenir Sheet

355 A37 150sh Baden-Powell 6.00 5.25

For overprints see Nos. 376-380.

Franklin D. Roosevelt (1882-
1945) — A38

Roosevelt and Washington: 50sh, 200sh,
Inaugurations. No. 358, Mount Vernon. No.
359, Hyde Park.

1982, Sept. Litho.
356 A38 50sh multicolored .70 .60
357 A38 200sh multicolored 2.75 2.40

Souvenir Sheets

358 A38 150sh multicolored 2.00 1.90
359 A38 150sh multicolored 2.00 1.90

Italy's
Victory
in 1982
World
Cup
A39

1982, Oct. Litho. *Perf. 14½*
359A A39 10sh Players .20 .20
359B A39 200sh Team 3.00 3.00

Souvenir Sheet

359C A39 250sh Globe 3.00 3.00

— A39a

1983, Mar. 14 Litho. *Perf. 14*
360 A39a 5sh Dancers .20 .20
361 A39a 20sh Traditional currency .30 .30
362 A39a 50sh Village .70 .70
363 A39a 100sh Drums 1.40 1.40
Nos. 360-363 (4) 2.60 2.60

Commonwealth Day.

St. George
and the
Dragon, by
Raphael
A40

1983, Apr.
364 A40 5sh shown .20 .20
365 A40 20sh St. George and
the Dragon,
1505 .35 .35
366 A40 50sh Moses Parts
the Red Sea .90 .90
367 A40 200sh Expulsion of
Heliodorus 3.25 3.25
Nos. 364-367 (4) 4.70 4.70

Souvenir Sheet

368 A40 250sh Leo the Great
and Attila,
1513 3.25 3.25

A41

7th Non-aligned Summit
Conference — A42

1983, Aug. 15 Litho. *Perf. 14½*
369 A41 5sh multicolored .20 .20
370 A42 200sh multicolored 2.00 2.00

African
Elephants
and World
Wildlife
Emblem
A43

5sh, Three adults with elephant bones.
10sh, Three adults walking. 30sh, Elephants
standing in water hole. 70sh, Adults with calf.

1983, Aug. 22 *Perf. 15*
371 A43 5sh multicolored 1.25 1.25
372 A43 10sh multicolored 2.00 2.00
373 A43 30sh multicolored 4.75 4.75
374 A43 70sh multicolored 12.00 12.00
Nos. 371-374 (4) 20.00 20.00

Nos. 371-374 were reprinted in 1990, perf
14. Value $25.

Souvenir Sheet

375 A43 300sh Zebras, vert. 8.00 7.00

No. 375 does not have the WWF emblem.
See Nos. 948-953.

Nos. 351-355 Overprinted or
Surcharged: "BOYS BRIGADE
CENTENARY 1883-1983"

1983, Sept. 19 Litho. *Perf. 14*
376 A37 5sh multicolored .20 .20
377 A37 20sh multicolored .20 .20
378 A37 50sh multicolored .55 .55
379 A37 400sh on 100sh multi 4.50 4.50
Nos. 376-379 (4) 5.45 5.45

Souvenir Sheet

380 A37 150sh multicolored 1.75 1.75

World Communications Year — A44

Designs: 20sh, Mpoma Satellite Earth Station. 50sh, Railroad, Computer Operator.
70sh, Filming Lions. 100sh, Pilots, Radio
Communications. 300sh, Communications
Satellite.

1983, Oct. 3 Litho. *Perf. 15*
381 A44 20sh multicolored .25 .25
382 A44 50sh multicolored .80 .80
383 A44 70sh multicolored 1.10 1.10
384 A44 100sh multicolored 1.60 1.60
Nos. 381-384 (4) 3.75 3.75

Souvenir Sheet

385 A44 300sh multicolored 3.50 3.50

Nos. 279, 281-285, 289 Surcharged

1983, Nov. 7 Litho. *Perf. 14*
386 A26 100sh on 10c multi
387 A26 135sh on 1sh multi
388 A26 175sh on 30c multi
389 A26 200sh on 50c multi
390 A26 400sh on 80c multi
391 A26 700sh on 1sh multi
392 A26 1000sh on 1.50sh
Nos. 386-392 (7) 18.00 18.00

World
Food Day
A45

Christmas — A46

1983, Dec. 12 Litho. *Perf. 14*
395 A46 10sh Navitity .20 .20
396 A46 50sh Sheperds and
Angel .40 .40
397 A46 175sh Flight into Egypt 1.25 1.25
398 A46 400sh Angels Blowing
Trumpets 3.00 3.00
Nos. 395-398 (4) 4.85 4.85

Souvenir Sheet

399 A46 300sh Three Kings 2.25 2.25

Animal Type of 1979

1983, Dec. 19
400 A26 100sh like No. 284 .70 .70
401 A26 135sh like No. 285 .85 .85
402 A26 175sh like No. 286 1.00 1.00
403 A26 200sh like No. 287 1.40 1.40
404 A26 400sh like No. 288 3.00 3.00
405 A26 700sh like No. 292 4.75 4.75
406 A26 1000sh like No. 291 6.50 6.50
Nos. 400-406 (7) 18.20 18.20

1984
Summer
Olympics
A48

1983 *Perf. 14½*
417 A48 5sh Ruth Kyalisiima .20 .20
418 A48 115sh Javelin .50 .50
419 A48 155sh Wrestling .65 .65
420 A48 175sh Rowing .85 .85
Nos. 417-420 (4) 2.20 2.20

Souvenir Sheet

421 A48 500sh Akii-Bua 2.40 2.40

For overprints see Nos. 458-462.

Intl. Civil
Aviation
Org., 40th
Anniv.
A49

1984, Sept.
422 A49 5sh Passenger service .55 .55
423 A49 115sh Cargo service 1.90 1.90
424 A49 155sh Police airwing 2.75 2.75
425 A49 175sh Soroti Flying
School plane 4.00 4.00
Nos. 422-425 (4) 9.20 9.20

Souvenir Sheet

426 A49 250sh Hot air balloon 5.00 5.00

Butterflies
A50

1984, Oct. Litho. *Perf. 14½*
427 A50 5sh Silver-barred
Charaxes .35 .35
428 A50 115sh Western Em-
peror Swal-
lowtail 2.75 2.75
429 A50 155sh African Giant
Swallowtail 3.75 3.75
430 A50 175sh Blue Salamis 4.50 4.50
Nos. 427-430 (4) 11.35 11.35

Souvenir Sheet

431 A50 250sh Veinted Yellow 5.50 5.00

1984, Jan. 12 Litho. *Perf. 14*
393 A45 10sh Plowing .50 .50
394 A45 200sh Banana crop 5.75 5.75

Freshwater Fish — A51

1985	Litho.		Perf. 15	
432	A51	5sh Nothobranchius taeniopygus	.55	.55
433	A51	10sh Bagrus dogmac	.80	.55
434	A51	50sh Polypterus senegalus	1.50	.45
435	A51	100sh Clarias	1.50	.45
436	A51	135sh Mormyrus kannume	2.50	1.40
437	A51	175sh Synodontis victoriae	2.50	2.40
438	A51	205sh Haplochromis brownae	2.50	2.75
439	A51	400sh Lates niloticus	2.50	3.00
440	A51	700sh Protopterus aethiopicus	2.50	3.50
441	A51	1000sh Barbus radcliffii	2.50	3.50
442	A51	2500sh Malapterus electricus	3.00	4.75
		Nos. 432-442 (11)	22.35	23.30

Issued: #432-435, 437-441, 4/1; #436, 442, 6/10.

For overprints see Nos. 490-494.

Easter
A52

1985, May 13	Litho.		Perf. 14	
443	A52	5sh The Last Supper	.55	.55
444	A52	115sh Jesus confronts doubting Thomas	1.75	1.75
445	A52	155sh Crucifixion	1.90	2.50
446	A52	175sh Pentecost	2.50	3.25
		Nos. 443-446 (4)	6.70	8.05

Souvenir Sheet

447	A52	250sh Last prayer in garden	1.25	1.25

UN Child
Survival
Campaign
A53

1985, July 1				
448	A53	5sh Mother breastfeeding	.40	.40
449	A53	115sh Growth monitorization	2.10	2.10
450	A53	155sh Immunization	2.75	2.75
451	A53	175sh Oral rehydration therapy	3.25	3.25
		Nos. 448-451 (4)	8.50	8.50

Souvenir Sheet

452	A53	500sh Expectant Mother, food	6.00	6.00

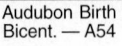

Audubon Birth
Bicent. — A54

UN Decade for
Women — A56

1985, July				
453	A54	115sh Acrocephalus schoenobaenus	2.10	1.75
454	A54	155sh Ardeola ibis	2.50	1.90
455	A54	175sh Galerida gristata	2.10	2.50

456	A54	500sh Aythya fuligula	3.50	5.00
		Nos. 453-456 (4)	10.20	11.15

Souvenir Sheet

457	A54	1000sh Strix aluco	11.50	11.50

See Nos. 469-473.

Nos. 417-421 Ovptd. or Surcharged with Winners Names, Medals and Countries in Gold

Gold medalists: 5sh, Benita Brown-Fitzgerald, US, 100-meter hurdles. 115sh, Arto Haerkoenen, Finland, javelin. 155sh, Atsuji Miyahara, Japan, 115-pound Greco-Roman wrestling. 100sh, West Germany, quadruple sculls. 1200sh, Edwin Moses, US, 400-meter hurdles.

1985, July			Perf. 15	
458	A48	5sh multicolored	.25	.25
459	A48	115sh multicolored	.35	.35
460	A48	155sh multicolored	.50	.50
461	A48	1000sh on 175sh multi	3.00	3.00
		Nos. 458-461 (4)	4.10	4.10

Souvenir Sheet

462	A48	1200sh on 500sh multi	3.50	3.50

1985	Litho.		Perf. 14	

5sh, Natl. Women's Day, Mar. 8. 115sh, Girl Guides 75th anniv., horiz. 155sh, Mother Theresa, 1979 Nobel Peace Prize laureate. 1000sh, Queen Mother. #467, Queen Mother inspecting troops. #468, like 115sh, horiz.

463	A56	5sh multicolored	.20	.20
464	A56	115sh multicolored	1.75	1.60
465	A56	155sh multicolored	2.90	2.50
466	A56	1000sh multicolored	1.40	1.75
		Nos. 463-466 (4)	6.25	6.05

Souvenir Sheets

467	A56	1500sh multicolored	3.50	3.50
468	A56	1500sh multicolored	5.00	5.00

Issued: #466-467, Aug. 21; others, Nov. 1.

Audubon Type of 1985

1985, Dec. 23			Perf. 12½x12	
469	A54	5sh Rock ptarmigan	.65	.40
470	A54	155sh Sage grouse	2.25	2.00
471	A54	175sh Lesser yellowlegs	2.25	2.50
472	A54	500sh Brown-headed cowbird	3.75	4.50
		Nos. 469-472 (4)	8.90	9.40

Souvenir Sheet
Perf. 14

473	A54	1000sh Whooping crane	9.50	9.50

UN, 40th
Anniv.
A57

Designs: 10sh, Forest resources, vert. 180sh, UN Peace-keeping Force. 200sh, Emblem, UN Development Project. 250sh, Intl. Peace Year. 2000sh, Natl., UN flags, vert. 2500sh, Flags, UN Building, New York, vert.

1986, Feb.			Perf. 15	
474	A57	10sh multicolored	.25	.25
475	A57	180sh multicolored	.35	.35
476	A57	200sh multicolored	.45	.45
477	A57	250sh multicolored	.55	.55
478	A57	2000sh multicolored	4.25	4.25
		Nos. 474-478 (5)	5.85	5.85

Souvenir Sheet

479	A57	2500sh multicolored	3.25	3.25

1986 World Cup Soccer
Championships, Mexico — A58

Various soccer plays.

1986, Mar.			Perf. 14	
480	A58	10sh multicolored	.30	.30
481	A58	180sh multicolored	1.00	.60
482	A58	250sh multicolored	1.10	.75
483	A58	2500sh multicolored	6.25	7.00
		Nos. 480-483 (4)	8.65	8.65

Souvenir Sheet

484	A58	3000sh multicolored	6.00	6.00

No. 484 contains vert. stamp.
For overprints see Nos. 514-518.

A59

Halley's Comet — A60

Designs: 50sh, Arecibo radio telescope, Puerto Rico, and Tycho Brahe (1546-1601), Danish astronomer. 100sh, Recovery of Astronaut John Glenn, US space capsule, Caribbean, 1962. 140sh, Adoration of the Magi, 1301, by Giotto (1276-1337). 2500sh, Sighting, 1835, Davy Crockett at The Alamo.

1986, Mar.	Litho.		Perf. 14	
485	A59	50sh multicolored	.30	.25
486	A59	100sh multicolored	.45	.25
487	A59	140sh multicolored	.70	.45
488	A59	2500sh multicolored	5.50	6.75
		Nos. 485-488 (4)	6.95	7.70

Souvenir Sheet

489	A60	3000sh multicolored	7.50	7.50

For overprints see Nos. 519-523.

Nos. 437, 440-442 and 468 Ovptd. "NRA LIBERATION / 1986" in Silver or Black

1986, Apr.			Perf. 15	
490	A51	175sh multi	1.50	1.25
491	A51	700sh multi	4.00	4.00
492	A51	1000sh multi (Bk)	4.50	4.50
493	A51	2500sh multi (Bk)	7.00	8.25
		Nos. 490-493 (4)	17.00	18.00

Souvenir Sheet
Perf. 14

494	A56	1500sh multi (Bk)	5.75	4.75

No. 494 ovptd. in one line in margin. A 400sh also exists with silver overprint. All stamps exist with overprint colors transposed.

Queen Elizabeth II, 60th Birthday
Common Design Type

1986, Apr. 21			Perf. 14	
495	CD339	100sh At London Zoo, c. 1938	.25	.25
496	CD339	140sh At the races, 1970	.25	.25
497	CD339	2500sh Sandringham, 1982	4.25	4.25
		Nos. 495-497 (3)	4.75	4.75

Souvenir Sheet

498	CD339	3000sh Engagement, 1947	4.75	4.75

AMERIPEX '86 — A61

1986, May 22			Perf. 15	
499	A61	50sh Niagara Falls	.30	.30
500	A61	100sh Jefferson Memorial	.30	.30
501	A61	250sh Liberty Bell	.50	.50
502	A61	1000sh The Alamo	1.90	1.90

503	A61	2500sh George Washington Bridge	4.50	4.50
		Nos. 499-503 (5)	7.50	7.50

Souvenir Sheet

504	A61	3000sh Grand Canyon	3.75	3.75

Statue of Liberty, cent.

A62

Statue of Liberty, Cent. — A63

Tall ships, Operation Sail: 50sh, Gloria, Colombia, vert. 100sh, Mircea, Romania, vert. 140sh, Sagres II, Portugal. 2500sh, Gazela Primero, US.

1986, July			Perf. 14	
505	A62	50sh multicolored	.75	.60
506	A62	100sh multicolored	1.00	.60
507	A62	140sh multicolored	1.75	1.25
508	A62	2500sh multicolored	7.75	9.25
		Nos. 505-508 (4)	11.25	11.70

Souvenir Sheet

509	A63	3000sh multicolored	4.50	4.50

Royal Wedding Issue, 1986
Common Design Type

Designs: 50sh, Prince Andrew and Sarah Ferguson. 140sh, Andrew and Princess Anne. 2500sh, At formal affair. 3000sh, Couple diff. Nos. 510-512 horiz.

1986, July 23				
510	CD340	50sh multicolored	.25	.25
511	CD340	140sh multicolored	.25	.25
512	CD340	2500sh multicolored	4.00	4.75
		Nos. 510-512 (3)	4.50	5.25

Souvenir Sheet

513	CD340	3000sh multicolored	5.00	5.00

Nos. 480-484 Ovptd. or Surcharged "WINNERS Argentina 3 W. Germany 2" in Gold in 2 or 3 Lines

1986, Sept. 15	Litho.		Perf. 14	
514	A58	50sh on 10sh multi	.20	.20
515	A58	180sh multicolored	.25	.20
516	A58	250sh multicolored	.30	.30
517	A58	2500sh multicolored	3.75	3.25
		Nos. 514-517 (4)	4.50	3.95

Souvenir Sheet

518	A58	3000sh multicolored	6.00	6.00

Nos. 485-489 Ovptd. with Halley's Comet Emblem

1986, Oct. 15	Litho.		Perf. 14	
519	A59	50sh multicolored	.35	.35
520	A59	100sh multicolored	.60	.40
521	A59	140sh multicolored	.80	.70
522	A59	2500sh multicolored	7.25	8.25
		Nos. 519-522 (4)	9.00	9.70

Souvenir Sheet

523	A60	3000sh multicolored	6.50	6.50

Christian Martyrs A64

Designs: 50sh, St. Kizito. 150sh, St. Kizito educating Ganda converts. 200sh, Execution of Bishop James Hannington. 1000sh, Mwanga's execution of converts, cent. 1500sh, King Mwanga sentencing Christians to death.

1986, Oct. 15

524	A64	50sh multicolored	.20	.20
525	A64	150sh multicolored	.20	.20
526	A64	200sh multicolored	.50	.50
527	A64	1000sh multicolored	2.00	2.00
		Nos. 524-527 (4)	2.90	2.90

Souvenir Sheet

528	A64	1500sh multicolored	2.25	2.25

A65

Christmas — A66

Paintings by Albrecht Durer and Titian: 50sh, Madonna of the Cherries. 150sh, Madonna and Child, vert. 200sh, Assumption of the Virgin, vert. 2500sh, Praying Hands, vert. No. 533, Adoration of the Magi. No. 534, Presentation of the Virgin in the Temple.

1986, Nov. 26   Litho.   Perf. 14

529	A65	50sh multicolored	.20	.20
530	A65	150sh multicolored	.55	.20
531	A65	200sh multicolored	.75	.30
532	A65	2500sh multicolored	5.50	7.00
		Nos. 529-532 (4)	7.00	7.70

Souvenir Sheets

533	A66	3000sh multicolored	5.25	5.25
534	A66	3000sh multicolored	5.25	5.25

Birds and Animals A67

1987   Perf. 15

535	A67	2sh Red-billed firefinch	.40	.35
536	A67	5sh African pygmy kingfisher	.55	.35
537	A67	10sh Scarlet-chested sunbird	.80	.35
538	A67	25sh White rhinoceros	1.25	.95
539	A67	35sh Lion	1.25	1.25
540	A67	45sh Cheetahs	1.50	1.75
541	A67	50sh Cordon bleu	1.75	2.10
542	A67	100sh Giant eland	2.75	3.50
		Nos. 535-542 (8)	10.25	10.60

Souvenir Sheets

543	A67	150sh Carmine bee-eaters	4.75	4.75
544	A67	150sh Cattle egret, zebra	4.75	4.75

Issue dates: Nos. 535-537, 541, 543, Nov. 2; Nos. 538-540, 542-544, July 22.

Transportation Innovations — A68

1987, Aug. 14

545	A68	2sh Eagle, 1987	.30	.30
546	A68	3sh Bremen, 1928	.30	.30
547	A68	5sh Winnie Mae, 1933	.35	.35
548	A68	10sh Voyager, 1986	.50	.50
549	A68	15sh Chanute bi-plane glider, 1896	.80	.80
550	A68	25sh Norge, 1926	1.10	1.10
551	A68	35sh Curtis biplane, USS Pennsylvania, 1911	1.75	1.75
552	A68	45sh Freedom 7, 1961	2.00	2.00
553	A68	100sh Concorde, 1976	5.75	6.75
		Nos. 545-553 (9)	12.85	13.85

1988 Summer Olympics, Seoul A69

Flags and athletes.

1987, Oct. 5   Perf. 14½x14

554	A69	5sh Torch bearer	.25	.25
555	A69	10sh Swimming	.30	.30
556	A69	50sh Cycling	1.40	1.40
557	A69	100sh Gymnastic rings	2.75	2.75
		Nos. 554-557 (4)	4.70	4.70

Souvenir Sheet

558	A69	150sh Boxing	4.25	4.50

A70

Natl. Independence, 25th Anniv. — A71

1987, Oct. 8

559	A70	5sh shown	.25	.25
560	A70	10sh Mulago Hospital	.45	.45
561	A70	25sh Independence Monument	1.00	1.00
562	A70	50sh High Court	1.90	1.90
		Nos. 559-562 (4)	3.60	3.60

Souvenir Sheet

563	A71	100sh shown	3.25	3.25

A72

Science and Space — A73

Birds — A74

Designs: 5sh, Hippocrates, father of modern medicine, caduceus and surgeons. 25sh, Albert Einstein and Theory of Relativity equation. 35sh, Sir Isaac Newton and Optics Theory. 45sh, Karl Benz (1844-1929), German engineer, automobile pioneer, and the Velocipede, Mercedes-Benz sports coupe and manufacturers' emblems.

1987, Nov. 2   Perf. 14½x14

564	A72	5sh multicolored	.70	.70
565	A72	25sh multicolored	2.75	2.75
566	A72	35sh multicolored	3.25	3.25
567	A72	45sh multicolored	4.00	4.00
		Nos. 564-567 (4)	10.70	10.70

Souvenir Sheet
Perf. 14x14½

568	A73	150sh shown	6.00	6.00

1987, Nov. 2   Litho.   Perf. 14

569	A74	5sh Golden-backed weaver	.65	.70
570	A74	10sh Hoopoe	1.50	1.25
571	A74	15sh Red-throated bee-eater	1.60	1.25
572	A74	25sh Lilac-breasted roller	2.10	1.75
573	A74	35sh Pygmy goose	2.25	2.00
574	A74	45sh Scarlet-chested sunbird	2.50	2.50
575	A74	50sh Crowned crane	2.50	2.50
576	A74	100sh Long-tailed fiscal shrike	4.50	4.75
		Nos. 569-576 (8)	17.60	16.70

Souvenir Sheets

577	A74	150sh African barn owl, horiz.	5.00	5.00
578	A74	150sh African fish-eagle, horiz.	5.00	5.00

14th World Boy Scout Jamboree, Australia, 1987-88 — A75

Activities: 5sh, Stamp collecting, Uganda Nos. 84 and 116. 25sh, Planting trees, Natl. flag. 35sh, Canoeing on Lake Victoria. 45sh, Hiking and camping. 150sh, Logo of 1987 jamboree and natl. Boy Scout organization emblem.

1987, Nov. 20

579	A75	5sh multicolored	.30	.30
580	A75	25sh multicolored	1.25	1.25
581	A75	35sh multicolored	1.75	1.75
582	A75	45sh multicolored	2.10	2.10
		Nos. 579-582 (4)	5.40	5.40

Souvenir Sheet

583	A75	150sh multicolored	5.00	5.00

Christmas A76

The life of Christ and the Virgin pictured on bas-reliefs, c. 1250, and a tapestry from France: 5sh, The Annunciation. 10sh, The Nativity. 50sh, Flight into Egypt. 100sh, The Adoration of the Magi. 150sh, The Mystic Wine Tapestry.

1987, Dec. 18

584	A76	5sh multicolored	.25	.25
585	A76	10sh multicolored	.25	.25
586	A76	50sh multicolored	1.60	1.75
587	A76	100sh multicolored	3.00	3.50
		Nos. 584-587 (4)	5.10	5.75

Souvenir Sheet

588	A76	150sh multicolored	5.00	5.00

Locomotives — A77

Designs: 5sh, Class 12 2-6-2T light shunter. 10sh, Class 92 1Co-Co1 diesel electric. 15sh, Class 2-8-2. 25sh, Class 2-6-2T light shunter. 35sh, Class 4-8-0. 45sh, Class 4-8-2. 50sh, Class 4-8-4+4-8-4 Garratt. 100sh, Class 87 1Co-Co1 diesel electric. No. 597, Class 59 4-8-2+2-8-4 Garratt. No. 598, Class 31 2-8-4.

1988, Jan. 18

589	A77	5sh multicolored	.25	.25
590	A77	10sh multicolored	.45	.45
591	A77	15sh multicolored	.70	.65
592	A77	25sh multicolored	1.00	1.00
593	A77	35sh multicolored	1.60	1.25
594	A77	45sh multicolored	2.00	1.75
595	A77	50sh multicolored	2.10	1.90
596	A77	100sh multicolored	5.00	3.00
		Nos. 589-596 (8)	13.10	10.25

Souvenir Sheets

597	A77	150sh multicolored	5.25	5.25
598	A77	150sh multicolored	5.25	5.25

Minerals — A78

1988, Jan. 18

599	A78	1sh Columbite-tantalite	.20	.20
600	A78	2sh Galena	.20	.20
601	A78	5sh Malachite	.20	.20
602	A78	10sh Cassiterite	.35	.35
603	A78	35sh Ferberite	1.50	1.50
604	A78	50sh Emerald	2.00	2.00
605	A78	100sh Monazite	3.75	3.75
606	A78	150sh Microcline	6.00	6.00
		Nos. 599-606 (8)	14.20	14.20

1988 Summer Olympics, Seoul A79

1988, May 16   Litho.   Perf. 14

607	A79	5sh Hurdles	.30	.30
608	A79	25sh High jump	.55	.75
609	A79	35sh Javelin	.60	.75
610	A79	45sh Long jump	.85	1.00
		Nos. 607-610 (4)	2.30	2.80

Souvenir Sheet

611	A79	150sh Medals, five-ring emblem	2.25	2.25

For overprints see Nos. 651-655.

Flowers A80

1988, July 28   Litho.   Perf. 15

612	A80	5sh	Spathodea campanulata	.60	.20
613	A80	10sh	Gloriosa simplex	.60	.20
614	A80	20sh	Thevetica peruviana, vert.	.80	.60
615	A80	25sh	Hibiscus schizopetalus	.80	.80
616	A80	35sh	Aframomum sceptrum	.80	.85
617	A80	45sh	Adenium obesum	.80	1.10
618	A80	50sh	Kigelia africana, vert.	1.00	1.40
619	A80	100sh	Clappertonia ficifolia	1.50	2.25
			Nos. 612-619 (8)	6.90	7.40

Souvenir Sheets

620	A80	150sh	Costus spectabiis	3.50	3.50
621	A80	150sh	Canarina abyssinica, vert.	3.50	3.50

Intl. Red Cross, 125th Anniv. — A81

1988, Oct. 28   Litho.   Perf. 14

622	A81	10sh	"AIDS"	.30	.30
623	A81	40sh	Immunize children	1.00	1.00
624	A81	70sh	Relief distribution	2.10	2.10
625	A81	90sh	First aid	2.75	2.75
			Nos. 622-625 (4)	6.15	6.15

Souvenir Sheet

626	A81	150sh	Jean-Henri Dunant, vert.	3.25	3.25

Paintings by Titian — A82

Designs: 10sh, Portrait of a Lady, c. 1508. 20sh, Portrait of a Man, 1507. 40sh, Portrait of Isabella d'Este, c. 1534. 50sh, Portrait of Vincenzo Mosti, 1520. 70sh, Pope Paul III Farnese, c. 1545. 90sh, Violante, 1515. 100sh, Lavinia, Titian's Daughter, c. 1565. 250sh, Portrait of Dr. Parma, c. 1515. No. 635, The Speech of Alfonso D'Avalos, c. 1540. No. 636, Cain and Abel.

1988, Oct. 31   Perf. 14

627	A82	10sh	multicolored	.25	.25
628	A82	20sh	multicolored	.40	.40
629	A82	40sh	multicolored	.60	.60
630	A82	50sh	multicolored	.75	.75
631	A82	70sh	multicolored	.85	.85
632	A82	90sh	multicolored	1.00	1.00
633	A82	100sh	multicolored	1.25	1.25
634	A82	250sh	multicolored	2.40	2.40
			Nos. 627-634 (8)	7.50	7.50

Souvenir Sheets

635	A82	250sh	multicolored	4.75	4.75
636	A82	350sh	multicolored	4.75	4.75

Game Preserves — A83

Designs: 10sh, Giraffes, Kidepo Valley Natl. Park. 25sh, Zebras, Lake Mburo Natl. Park. 100sh, African buffalo, Murchison Falls Natl. Park. 250sh, Pelicans, Queen Elizabeth Natl. Park. 350sh, Roan antelopes, Lake Mburo Natl. Park.

1988, Nov. 18   Litho.   Perf. 14

637	A83	10sh	multicolored	.45	.20
638	A83	25sh	multicolored	1.25	.50
639	A83	100sh	multicolored	2.55	2.75
640	A83	250sh	multicolored	7.00	8.50
			Nos. 637-640 (4)	11.25	11.95

Souvenir Sheet

641	A83	350sh	multicolored	4.25	4.25

WHO 40th Anniv., Alma Ata Declaration 10th Anniv. — A84

1988, Dec. 1

642	A84	10sh	Primary health care	.25	.25
643	A84	25sh	Mental health	.45	.45
644	A84	45sh	Rural health care	.75	.75
645	A84	100sh	Dental care	1.75	1.75
646	A84	200sh	Postnatal care	3.25	3.25
			Nos. 642-646 (5)	6.45	6.45

Souvenir Sheet

647	A84	350sh	Conference Hall, Alma-Ata, USSR	4.25	4.25

Miniature Sheet

Christmas, Mickey Mouse 60th Birthday — A85

Walt Disney characters: No. 648a, Santa Claus. b, Goofy. c, Mickey Mouse. d, Huey at conveyor belt. e, Dewey packing building blocks. f, Donald Duck. g, Chip-n-Dale. h, Louie at conveyor belt controls. No. 649, Preparing reindeer for Christmas eve flight. No. 650, Mickey loading sleigh with toys, horiz.

1988, Dec. 2   Perf. 13½x14, 14x13½

648			Sheet of 8	10.00	10.00
a.-h.			A85 50sh any single	.80	.80

Souvenir Sheets

649	A85	350sh	multicolored	5.75	5.75
650	A85	350sh	multicolored	5.75	5.75

Nos. 607-611 Ovptd. or Surcharged to Honor Olympic Winners

5sh: "110 M HURDLES / R. KINGDOM / USA"

25sh: "HIGH JUMP / G. AVDEENKO / USSR"

35sh: "JAVELIN / T. KORJUS / FINLAND"

300sh: "LONG JUMP / C. LEWIS / USA"

1989, Jan. 30   Litho.   Perf. 14

651	A79	5sh	multicolored	.25	.25
652	A79	25sh	multicolored	.30	.30
653	A79	35sh	multicolored	.35	.35
654	A79	300sh on 45sh multi		3.25	3.25
			Nos. 651-654 (4)	4.15	4.15

Souvenir Sheet

655	A79	350sh on 150sh multi		5.00	5.00

1990 World Cup Soccer Championships, Italy — A86

Various action scenes.

1989, Apr. 24   Litho.   Perf. 14

656	A86	10sh	multi, vert.	.35	.35
657	A86	25sh	multicolored	.55	.55
658	A86	75sh	multicolored	1.60	1.60
659	A86	200sh	multi, vert.	4.00	4.00
			Nos. 656-659 (4)	6.50	6.50

Souvenir Sheet

660	A86	300sh	multicolored	4.50	4.50

Mushrooms — A87

1989, Aug. 14   Litho.   Perf. 14

661	A87	10sh	Suillus granulatus	.60	.60
662	A87	15sh	Omphalotus olearius	.75	.75
663	A87	45sh	Oudemansiella radicata	1.50	1.50
664	A87	50sh	Clitocybe nebularis	1.50	1.50
665	A87	60sh	Macrolepiota rhacodes	1.60	1.60
666	A87	75sh	Lepista nuda	1.90	1.90
667	A87	150sh	Suillus luteus	3.50	3.50
668	A87	200sh	Agaricus campestris	3.75	3.75
			Nos. 661-668 (8)	15.10	15.10

Souvenir Sheets

669	A87	350sh	Schizophyllum commune	8.00	8.00
670	A87	350sh	Bolbitius vitellinus	8.00	8.00

"The Thirty-six Views of Mt. Fuji" — A88

Prints by Hokusai (1760-1849): 10sh, Fuji and the Great Wave off Kanagawa. 15sh, Fuji from Lake Suwa. 20sh, Fuji from Kajikazawa. 60sh, Fuji from Shichirigahama. 90sh, Fuji from Ejiri in Sunshu. 120sh, Fuji Above Lightning. 200sh, Fuji from Lower Meguro in Edo. 250sh, Fuji from Ko. No. 679, The Red Fuji from the Foot. No. 680, Fuji from Umezawa.

1989, May 15   Litho.   Perf. 14x13½

671	A88	10sh	multicolored	.35	.35
672	A88	15sh	multicolored	.35	.35
673	A88	20sh	multicolored	.35	.35
674	A88	60sh	multicolored	.90	.90
675	A88	90sh	multicolored	1.40	1.40
676	A88	120sh	multicolored	2.00	2.00
677	A88	200sh	multicolored	3.25	3.25
678	A88	250sh	multicolored	4.00	4.00
			Nos. 671-678 (8)	12.60	12.60

Souvenir Sheets

679	A88	500sh	multicolored	6.25	6.25
680	A88	500sh	multicolored	6.25	6.25

Hirohito (1901-1989), Showa emperor, and Akihito, Heisei emperor of Japan.

PHILEXFRANCE '89 — A89

1989, July 7   Litho.   Perf. 14

681	A89	20sh No. 1		.55	.55
682	A89	70sh No. 10		1.40	1.40
683	A89	100sh No. 48		1.60	1.60

684	A89	250sh No. 67		3.25	3.25
a.		Souvenir sheet of 4, #681-684		10.50	10.50
			Nos. 681-684 (4)	6.80	6.80

No. 684a sold for 500sh.

2nd All African Scout Jamboree, Aug. 3-15 — A90

1989, Aug. 3   Litho.   Perf. 14

685	A90	10sh	Fatal child ailments	.35	.35
686	A90	70sh	Raising poultry	1.75	1.75
687	A90	90sh	Immunization	2.10	2.10
688	A90	100sh	Brick-making	2.10	2.10
			Nos. 685-688 (4)	6.30	6.30

Souvenir Sheet

689	A90	500sh	Natl. emblem, vert.	5.75	5.75

Scouting, 75th anniv.
For surcharges see Nos. 1301-1304.

Miniature Sheet

Wildlife at Waterhole — A91

Designs: a, Saddle-billed stork. b, White pelican. c, Marabou stork. d, Egyptian vulture, giraffes. e, Bateleur eagle, antelope. f, African elephant. g, Giraffe. h, Goliath heron. i, Black rhinoceros, zebras. j, Zebras, oribi. k, African fish eagle. l, Hippopotamus. m, Black-backed jackal, white pelican. n, Cape buffalo. o, Olive baboon. p, Bohor reedbuck. q, Lesser flamingo, serval. r, Shoebill stork. s, Crowned crane. t, Impala. No. 691, Lion. No. 692, Long-crested eagle.

1989, Sept. 12   Perf. 14½x14

690			Sheet of 20	22.00	22.00
a.-t.		A91 30sh any single		.60	.60

Souvenir Sheets

691	A91	500sh	multicolored	5.75	5.75
692	A91	500sh	multicolored	5.75	5.75

1st Moon Landing, 20th Anniv. — A92   Butterflies — A93

Quotations and scenes from the Apollo 11 mission.

1989, Oct. 20   Litho.   Perf. 14

693	A92	10sh	Launch vehicle, Moon	.30	.30
694	A92	20sh	Eagle lower stage on Moon	.30	.30
695	A92	30sh	Columbia	.55	.55
696	A92	50sh	Eagle landing	.75	.75
697	A92	70sh	Aldrin on Moon	1.10	1.10
698	A92	250sh	Armstrong on ladder	3.75	3.75
699	A92	300sh	Eagle ascending	4.25	4.25
700	A92	350sh	Aldrin, diff.	5.00	5.00
			Nos. 693-700 (8)	16.00	16.00

Souvenir Sheets

701	A92	500sh	Liftoff	5.25	5.25
702	A92	500sh	Parachute landing	5.25	5.25

Nos. 693-697 and 699 horiz.

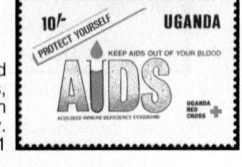

1989, Nov. 13
"UGANDA" in Black

703	A93	5sh Ioalus pallene	.65	.65
704	A93	10sh Hewitsonia boisduvali	.70	.70
705	A93	20sh Euxanthe wakefeildi	1.10	1.10
706	A93	30sh Papilio echerioides	1.25	1.25
707	A93	40sh Acraea semivitrea	1.40	1.40
708	A93	50sh Colotis antevippe	1.40	1.40
709	A93	70sh Acraea perenna	1.75	1.75
710	A93	90sh Charaxes cynthia	1.75	1.75
711	A93	100sh Euphaedra neophroa	1.75	1.75
712	A93	150sh Cymothoe beckeri	2.25	2.25
713	A93	200sh Vanessula milca	2.25	2.25
714	A93	400sh Mimacraea marshalli	3.25	3.25
715	A93	500sh Axiocerses amanga	3.50	3.50
716	A93	1000sh Precis hierta	4.50	4.50
		Nos. 703-716 (14)	27.50	27.50

See Nos. 826-839 for "UGANDA" in blue.

Explorers of Africa
A94

Designs: 10sh, John Speke (1827-64), satellite view of Lake Victoria. 25sh, Sir Richard Burton (1821-90), satellite view of Lake Tanganyika. 40sh, Richard Lander (1804-34), bronze ritual figure of the Bakota tribe. 90sh, Rene Caillie (1799-1838), mosque. 125sh, Dorcas gazelle and Sir Samuel Baker (1821-93), discoverer of Lake Albert. 150sh, Phoenician galley and Necho II (d. 595 B.C.), king of Egypt credited by Herodotus with sending an expedition to circumnavigate Africa. 250sh, Vasco da Gama (c. 1460-1524), 1st European to sail around the Cape of Good Hope, and caravel. 300sh, Sir Henry Stanley (1841-1904), discoverer of Lake Edward, and Lady Alice. No. 725, Dr. David Livingstone (1813-73), discoverer of Victoria Falls, and steam launch Ma-Robert. No. 726, Mary Kingsley (1862-1900), ethnologist, and tail-spot climbing perch.

1989, Nov. 15   Litho.   Perf. 14

717	A94	10sh multicolored	.40	.40
718	A94	25sh multicolored	.45	.45
719	A94	40sh multicolored	.75	.75
720	A94	90sh multicolored	1.60	1.60
721	A94	125sh multicolored	2.25	2.25
722	A94	150sh multicolored	2.75	2.75
723	A94	250sh multicolored	4.50	4.50
724	A94	300sh multicolored	5.50	5.50
		Nos. 717-724 (8)	18.20	18.20

Souvenir Sheets

725	A94	500sh multicolored	6.50	6.50
726	A94	500sh multicolored	6.50	6.50

Anniversaries and Events — A95

1989, Dec. 12

727	A95	10sh Bank emblem	.25	.25
728	A95	20sh Satellite dishes, arrows	.25	.25
729	A95	75sh Nehru	2.10	2.10
730	A95	90sh Pan-American Dixie Clipper	2.10	2.10
731	A95	100sh Locomotion, Stephenson	2.10	2.10
732	A95	150sh Concorde cockpit	3.50	3.50
733	A95	250sh Wapen von Hamburg, Leopoldus Primus	3.50	3.50
734	A95	300sh Concorde cockpit, crew	4.25	4.25
		Nos. 727-734 (8)	18.05	18.05

Souvenir Sheets

735	A95	500sh Storming of the Bastille	5.75	5.75
736	A95	500sh Emperor Frederick I Barbarossa, charter	5.75	5.75

African Development Bank 25th anniv. (10sh); World Telecommunications Day, May 17 (20sh); Birth cent. of Jawaharlal Nehru, 1st prime minister of independent India (75sh); 1st scheduled transatlantic airmail flight, 50th anniv. (90sh); 175th anniv. of the invention of the 1st steam locomotive by George Stephenson and opening of the Stockton & Darlington Railway in 1825 (100sh); 1st test flight of the Concorde, 20th anniv. (150sh, 300sh); Port of Hamburg, 800th anniv. (250sh, No. 736); and French revolution bicent. (No. 735).

Christmas — A96   Orchids — A97

Religious paintings by Fra Angelico: 10sh, Madonna and Child. 20sh, Adoration of the Magi. 40sh, Virgin and Child Enthroned with Saints. 75sh, The Annunciation. 100sh, St. Peter Martyr triptych center panel. 150sh, Virgin and Child Enthroned with Saints, diff. 250sh, Virgin and Child Enthroned. 350sh, Annalena Altarpiece. No. 745, Bosco ai Frati Altarpiece. No. 746, Madonna and Child with Twelve Angels.

1989, Dec. 18

737	A96	10sh multicolored	.25	.25
738	A96	20sh multicolored	.25	.25
739	A96	40sh multicolored	.55	.55
740	A96	75sh multicolored	.90	.90
741	A96	100sh multicolored	1.10	1.10
742	A96	150sh multicolored	1.50	1.50
743	A96	250sh multicolored	2.10	2.10
744	A96	350sh multicolored	2.40	2.40
		Nos. 737-744 (8)	9.05	9.05

Souvenir Sheets

745	A96	500sh multicolored	4.00	4.00
746	A96	500sh multicolored	4.00	4.00

1989, Dec. 18

747	A97	10sh Aerangis kotschyana	.25	.25
748	A97	15sh Angraecum infundibulare	.25	.25
749	A97	45sh Cyrtorchis chailluana	.60	.60
750	A97	50sh Aerangis rhodosticta	.65	.65
751	A97	100sh Eulophia speciosa	1.25	1.25
752	A97	200sh Calanthe sylvatica	2.75	2.75
753	A97	250sh Vanilla imperialis	3.25	3.25
754	A97	350sh Polystachya vulcanica	4.50	4.50
		Nos. 747-754 (8)	13.50	13.50

Souvenir Sheets

755	A97	500sh Ansellia africana	5.75	5.75
756	A97	500sh Ancistrochilus rothschildianus	5.75	5.75

For overprints see Nos. 782-786A.

EXPO '90, Osaka — A98

Flowering trees.

1990, Apr. 17   Litho.   Perf. 14

757	A98	10sh Thevetia peruviana	.30	.30
758	A98	20sh Acanthus eminens	.30	.30
759	A98	90sh Gnidia glauca	.80	.80
760	A98	150sh Oncoba spinosa	1.10	1.10
761	A98	175sh Hibiscus rosa-sinensis	1.25	1.25
762	A98	400sh Jacaranda mimosifolia	2.00	2.00
763	A98	500sh Erythrina abyssinica	2.25	2.25
764	A98	700sh Bauhinia purpurea	2.50	2.50
		Nos. 757-764 (8)	10.50	10.50

Souvenir Sheets

765	A98	1000sh Delonix regia	6.75	6.75
766	A98	1000sh Cassia didymobatrya	6.75	6.75

World War II Milestones — A99

Designs: 5sh, Allies penetrate west wall, Dec. 3, 1944. 10sh, VE Day, May 8, 1945. 20sh, US forces capture Okinawa, June 22, 1945. 75sh, DeGaulle named commander of all Free French forces, Apr. 4, 1944. 100sh, US troops invade Saipan, June 15, 1944. 150sh, Allied troops launch Operation Market Garden, Sept. 17, 1944. 200sh, Gen. MacArthur returns to Philippines, Oct. 20, 1944. 300sh, US victory at Coral Sea, May 8, 1942. 350sh, First battle of El Alamein, July 1, 1942. 500sh, Naval battle at Guadalcanal, Nov. 12, 1942. 1000sh, Battle of Britain.

1990, June 8   Litho.   Perf. 14

767	A99	5sh multicolored	.35	.35
768	A99	10sh multicolored	.35	.35
769	A99	20sh multicolored	.35	.35
770	A99	75sh multicolored	.75	.75
771	A99	100sh multicolored	1.00	1.00
772	A99	150sh multicolored	1.50	1.50
773	A99	200sh multicolored	2.00	2.00
774	A99	300sh multicolored	3.25	3.25
775	A99	350sh multicolored	3.50	3.50
776	A99	500sh multicolored	5.00	5.00
		Nos. 767-776 (10)	18.05	18.05

Souvenir Sheet

777	A99	1000sh multicolored	7.50	7.50

Queen Mother, 90th Birthday — A100

1990, July 5

778		250sh Hands clasped	1.00	1.00
779		250sh Facing left	1.00	1.00
780		250sh Holding dog	1.00	1.00
a.		A100 Strip of 3, #778-780	4.25	4.25
		Nos. 778-780 (3)	3.00	3.00

Souvenir Sheet

781	A100	1000sh like No. 778	4.25	4.25

Nos. 747-754 Ovptd. in Silver

Nos. 755-756 Ovptd. in Silver in Sheet Margin

1990   Litho.   Perf. 14

782	A97	10sh on No. 747	.85	.85
782A	A97	15sh on No. 748	.85	.85
782B	A97	45sh on No. 749	1.25	1.25
783	A97	50sh on No. 750	1.25	1.25
783A	A97	100sh on No. 751	1.60	1.60
784	A97	200sh on No. 752	2.10	2.10
785	A97	250sh on No. 753	2.10	2.10
785A	A97	350sh on No. 754	2.50	2.50
		Nos. 782-785A (8)	12.50	12.50

Souvenir Sheet

786	A97	500sh on No. 755	5.75	5.75
786A	A97	500sh on No. 756	5.75	5.75

Issue dates: 15sh, 45sh, 100sh, 350sh, No. 786A, Nov.; others, July 30.

Pan African Postal Union, 10th Anniv.
A101

Designs: 750sh, UN Conference on the least developed countries, Paris, Sept. 3-14.

1990, Aug. 3   Litho.   Perf. 14

787	A101	80sh multicolored	1.00	1.00

Souvenir Sheet

788	A101	750sh multicolored	4.50	4.50

Great Britain No. O1 — A102

Designs: 50sh, Canada #12. 100sh, Baden #4b. 150sh, Switzerland #3L1. 200sh, US #C3a. 300sh, Western Australia #1. 500sh, Uganda #29. 600sh, Great Britain #2. No. 797, Uganda #29. No. 798, Sir Rowland Hill.

1990, Aug. 6   Litho.   Perf. 14

789	A102	25sh multicolored	.30	.30
790	A102	50sh multicolored	.55	.55
791	A102	100sh multicolored	1.00	1.00
792	A102	150sh multicolored	1.25	1.25
793	A102	200sh multicolored	1.40	1.40
794	A102	300sh gray & black	1.90	1.90
795	A102	500sh multicolored	2.10	2.10
796	A102	600sh multicolored	2.10	2.10
		Nos. 789-796 (8)	10.60	10.60

Souvenir Sheets
Size: 108x77mm

797	A102	1000sh multicolored	6.00	6.00

Size: 119x85mm

798	A102	1000sh scarlet & blk	6.00	6.00

Penny Black, 150th anniversary. Nos. 797-798, Stamp World London '90.

Birds A103

1990, Sept. 3   Litho.   Perf. 14

799	A103	10sh African jacana	.90	.90
800	A103	15sh Ground hornbill	.90	.90
801	A103	45sh Kori bustard, vert.	1.10	1.10
802	A103	50sh Secretary bird	1.10	1.10
803	A103	100sh Egyptian geese	1.75	1.75
804	A103	300sh Goliath heron, vert.	3.00	3.00
805	A103	500sh Ostrich, vert.	4.00	4.00
806	A103	650sh Saddlebill stork, vert.	4.25	4.25
		Nos. 799-806 (8)	17.00	17.00

Souvenir Sheets

807	A103	1000sh	Volturine guinea fowl, vert.	5.75	5.75
808	A103	1000sh	Lesser flamingo, vert.	5.75	5.75

World Cup Soccer Championships, Italy — A104

Players from various national teams.

1990, Sept. 24

809	A104	50sh	Cameroun	.30	.30
810	A104	100sh	Egypt	.60	.60
811	A104	250sh	Ireland	1.50	1.50
812	A104	600sh	West Germany	3.75	3.75
			Nos. 809-812 (4)	6.15	6.15

Souvenir Sheets

813	A104	1000sh	Sweden	5.25	5.25
814	A104	1000sh	Scotland	5.25	5.25

WHO, Promote Better Health — A105

Walt Disney characters in scenes promoting improved health: 10sh, Mickey, Minnie Mouse having a good breakfast. 20sh, Huey, Dewey and Louie looking before crossing street. 50sh, Mickey, Donald Duck against smoking. 90sh, Mickey saving Donald from choking. 100sh, Mickey, Goofy using seat belts. 250sh, Mickey, Minnie avoiding drugs. 500sh, Donald, Daisy exercising. 600sh, Mickey showing bicycle safety. No. 823, Mickey, friends at doctor's office. No. 824, Mickey, friends walking.

1990, Oct. 19   Litho.   Perf. 13½x13

815	A105	10sh	multicolored	.30	.30
816	A105	20sh	multicolored	.30	.30
817	A105	50sh	multicolored	.45	.45
818	A105	90sh	multicolored	.75	.75
819	A105	100sh	multicolored	.85	.85
820	A105	250sh	multicolored	1.90	1.90
821	A105	500sh	multicolored	4.25	4.25
822	A105	600sh	multicolored	5.00	5.00
			Nos. 815-822 (8)	13.80	13.80

Souvenir Sheets

823	A105	1000sh	multicolored	6.00	6.00
824	A105	1000sh	multicolored	6.00	6.00

Butterfly Type of 1989
"Uganda" in Blue

1990-92   Perf. 14

826	A93	10sh	like #704	.65	.65
827	A93	20sh	like #705	.75	.75
828	A93	30sh	like #706	.75	.75
829	A93	40sh	like #707	.75	.75
830	A93	50sh	like #708	1.00	1.00
831	A93	70sh	like #709	1.00	1.00
832	A93	90sh	like #710	1.10	1.10
833	A93	100sh	like #711	1.10	1.10
834	A93	150sh	like #712	1.50	1.50
835	A93	200sh	like #713	1.90	1.90
836	A93	400sh	like #714	2.25	2.25
837	A93	500sh	like #715	2.25	2.25
838	A93	1000sh	like #716	4.50	4.50
839	A93	2000sh	like #716	11.00	11.00
839A	A93	3000sh	Euphaedra eusemoides	13.50	13.50
839B	A93	4000sh	Acraea natalica	14.50	14.50
839C	A93	5000sh	Euphaedra themis	14.50	14.50
			Nos. 826-839C (17)	73.00	73.00

Issue dates: 50sh, 400sh, 500sh, 1000sh, 1991. 3000sh, 4000sh, Jan. 2, 1992. Nos. 827, 833, 835 and 839 exist dated 1991.
This is an expanding set, numbers may change.

Christmas
A106

Details from paintings by Rubens: 10sh, 500sh, The Baptism of Christ. 20sh, 150sh, 400sh, 600sh, St. Gregory the Great and Other Saints. 100sh, Saints Nereus, Domitilla and Achilleus. 300sh, Saint Augustine. No. 853, Victory of Eucharistic Truth Over Heresy, horiz. No. 854, Triumph of Faith, horiz.

1990, Dec. 17   Litho.   Perf. 14

845	A106	10sh	multicolored	.25	.25
846	A106	20sh	multicolored	.25	.25
847	A106	100sh	multicolored	.90	.90
848	A106	150sh	multicolored	1.25	1.25
849	A106	300sh	multicolored	2.00	2.00
850	A106	400sh	multicolored	2.10	2.10
851	A106	500sh	multicolored	2.25	2.25
852	A106	600sh	multicolored	2.50	2.50
			Nos. 845-852 (8)	11.50	11.50

Souvenir Sheets

853	A106	1000sh	multicolored	6.25	6.25
854	A106	1000sh	multicolored	6.25	6.25

Natl. Census A107

Design: 1000sh, Counting on fingers, houses, people.

1990, Dec. 28   Litho.   Perf. 14

855	A107	20sh	multicolored	1.00	1.00

Souvenir Sheet

856	A107	1000sh	multicolored	7.25	7.25

Wetlands Fauna — A108

No. 857:a, Damselfly. b, Purple gallinule. c, Sitatunga. d, Purple heron. e, Bushpig. f, Vervet monkey. g, Long reed frog. h, Malachite kingfisher. i, Marsh mongoose. j, Painted reed frog. k, Jacana. l, Charaxes butterfly. m, Nile crocodile. n, Herald snake. o, Dragonfly. p, Lungfish.
No. 858, Nile monitor, horiz.

1991, Jan. 1   Litho.   Perf. 14

857	A108	70sh	Sheet of 16, #a.-p.	17.00	17.00

Souvenir Sheet

858	A108	1000sh	multi	9.50	9.50

Fish
A109

Designs: 10sh, Haplochromis limax. 20sh, Notobranchius palmqvisti. 40sh, Distichodus affinis. 90sh, Haplochromis sauvagei. 100sh, Aphyosemion calliurum. 350sh, Haplochromis johnstoni. 600sh, Haplochromis dichrourus. 800sh, Hemichromis bimaculatus. No. 867, Haplochromis sp. No. 868, Aphyosemion striatum.

1991, Jan. 18   Litho.   Perf. 14

859	A109	10sh	multicolored	.30	.30
860	A109	20sh	multicolored	.30	.30
861	A109	40sh	multicolored	.30	.30
862	A109	90sh	multicolored	.55	.55
863	A109	100sh	multicolored	.65	.65
864	A109	350sh	multicolored	1.60	1.60
865	A109	600sh	multicolored	3.25	3.25
866	A109	800sh	multicolored	4.00	4.00
			Nos. 859-866 (8)	10.95	10.95

Souvenir Sheets

867	A109	1000sh	multicolored	7.50	7.50
868	A109	1000sh	multicolored	7.50	7.50

1992 Summer Olympics, Barcelona — A110

1991, Feb. 25   Litho.   Perf. 14

869	A110	20sh	Women's hurdles	.30	.30
870	A110	40sh	Long jump	.30	.30
871	A110	125sh	Table tennis	.90	.90
872	A110	250sh	Soccer	2.00	2.00
873	A110	500sh	800-meter race	3.75	3.75
			Nos. 869-873 (5)	7.25	7.25

Souvenir Sheets

874	A110	1200sh	Women's 4x100-meter relay, horiz.	7.00	7.00
875	A110	1200sh	Opening ceremony, horiz.	7.00	7.00

Trains
A111

Designs: 10sh, 10th Class, Zimbabwe. 20sh, 12th Class, Zimbabwe. 80sh, Tribal class, Tanzania and Zambia. 200sh, 4-6-0 Type, Egypt. 300sh, Mikado, Sudan. 400sh, Mountain class Garrat, Uganda. 500sh, Mallet Type, Uganda. 1000sh, 5 F 1 Electric locomotive, South Africa. No. 884, 4-8-2 Type, Zimbabwe. No. 885, Atlantic type, Egypt. No. 886, 4-8-2 Type, Angola. No. 887, Mallet Compound Type, Natal.

1991, Apr. 2   Litho.   Perf. 14

876	A111	10sh	multicolored	.30	.30
877	A111	20sh	multicolored	.30	.30
878	A111	80sh	multicolored	.50	.50
879	A111	200sh	multicolored	1.40	1.40
880	A111	300sh	multicolored	2.10	2.10
881	A111	400sh	multicolored	2.75	2.75
882	A111	500sh	multicolored	3.25	3.25
883	A111	1000sh	multicolored	6.50	6.50
			Nos. 876-883 (8)	17.10	17.10

Souvenir Sheets

884	A111	1200sh	multicolored	5.50	5.50
885	A111	1200sh	multicolored	5.50	5.50
886	A111	1200sh	multicolored	5.50	5.50
887	A111	1200sh	multicolored	5.50	5.50

Even though Nos. 886-887 have the same issue date as Nos. 876-885, their dollar value was lower when they were released.

Phila Nippon '91 — A112

Walt Disney characters in Japan: 10sh, Scrooge McDuck celebrating Ga-No-Iwai. 20sh, Mickey removes shoes before entering Minnie's home. 70sh, Cartman Goofy leading horse. 80sh, Daisy, Minnie exchange gifts. 300sh, Minnie kneels at entrance to home. 400sh, Mickey, Donald in volcanic sand bath. 500sh, Clarabelle Cow enjoys incense burning. 1000sh, Mickey, Minnie writing New Year cards. No. 896, Mickey, Donald and Goofy in

public bath. No. 897, Mickey and friends playing Japanese music.

1991, May 29   Litho.   Perf. 14x13½

888	A112	10sh	multicolored	.25	.25
889	A112	20sh	multicolored	.25	.25
890	A112	70sh	multicolored	.45	.45
891	A112	80sh	multicolored	.50	.50
892	A112	300sh	multicolored	1.90	1.90
893	A112	400sh	multicolored	2.40	2.40
894	A112	500sh	multicolored	3.25	3.25
895	A112	1000sh	multicolored	6.00	6.00
			Nos. 888-895 (8)	15.00	15.00

Souvenir Sheets

896	A112	1200sh	multicolored	7.50	7.50
897	A112	1200sh	multicolored	7.50	7.50

17th World Scout Jamboree, Korea — A113

Designs: 20sh, Lord Baden-Powell. 80sh, Scouts collecting stamps. 100sh, Scout encampment, NY World's Fair, 1939. 150sh, Cover of 1st Scout Handbook. 300sh, Cooking over campfire. 400sh, Neil Armstrong, Edwin Aldrin, 1st scouts on moon. 500sh, Hands raised for Scout Pledge. 1000sh, Statue to Unknown Scout, Gilwell Park, England. No. 906, William D. Boyce, Lord Baden-Powell, Rev. L. Hadley. No. 907, 17th Jamboree Emblem.

1991, May 27   Perf. 14

898	A113	20sh	multicolored	.30	.30
899	A113	80sh	multicolored	.45	.45
900	A113	100sh	multicolored	.55	.55
901	A113	150sh	grn & blk	.80	.80
902	A113	300sh	multicolored	1.60	1.60
903	A113	400sh	multicolored	2.25	2.25
904	A113	500sh	multicolored	2.75	2.75
905	A113	1000sh	multicolored	5.25	5.25
			Nos. 898-905 (8)	13.95	13.95

Souvenir Sheets

906	A113	1200sh	multicolored	7.50	7.50
907	A113	1200sh	cream & blk	7.50	7.50

For surcharge see No. 1305.

Paintings by Vincent Van Gogh — A114

Paintings: 10sh, Snowy Landscape with Arles in the Background. 20sh, Peasant Woman Binding Sheaves, vert. 60sh, The Drinkers. 80sh, View of Auvers. 200sh, Mourning Man, vert. 400sh, Still Life: Vase with Roses. 800sh, The Raising of Lazarus. 1000sh, The Good Samaritan, vert. No. 916, First Steps. No. 917, Village Street and Steps in Auvers with Figures.

1991, June 26   Litho.   Perf. 13½

908	A114	10sh	multicolored	.20	.20
909	A114	20sh	multicolored	.20	.20
910	A114	60sh	multicolored	.30	.30
911	A114	80sh	multicolored	.40	.40
912	A114	200sh	multicolored	1.00	1.00
913	A114	400sh	multicolored	2.00	2.00
914	A114	800sh	multicolored	4.00	4.00
915	A114	1000sh	multicolored	5.00	5.00
			Nos. 908-915 (8)	13.10	13.10

Size: 102x76mm
Imperf

916	A114	1200sh	multicolored	7.00	7.00
917	A114	1200sh	multicolored	7.00	7.00

Royal Family Birthday, Anniversary
Common Design Type

1991, July 5   Litho.   Perf. 14

918	CD347	20sh	multi	.25	.25
919	CD347	70sh	multi	.40	.40
920	CD347	90sh	multi	.65	.65
921	CD347	100sh	multi	.70	.70
922	CD347	200sh	multi	1.25	1.25
923	CD347	500sh	multi	3.00	3.00

| 924 | CD347 | 600sh multi | 3.75 | 3.75 |
| 925 | CD347 | 1000sh multi | 6.00 | 6.00 |

Nos. 918-925 (8) 16.00 16.00

Souvenir Sheets

| 926 | CD347 | 1200sh Elizabeth, Philip | 6.00 | 6.00 |
| 927 | CD347 | 1200sh Sons, Diana, Charles | 7.50 | 7.50 |

20sh, 100sh, 200sh, 1000sh, No. 927, Charles and Diana, 10th wedding anniversary. Others, Queen Elizabeth II, 65th birthday.

Charles de Gaulle, Birth Cent. A115

Designs: 20sh, Portrait, vert. 70sh, Liberation of Paris, 1944, vert. 90sh, With King George VI, 1940, vert. 100sh, Reviewing Free French forces, 1940. 200sh, Making his appeal on BBC, 1940. 500sh, In Normandy, 1944. 600sh, At Albert Hall, 1940. 1000sh, Becoming President of France, 1959, vert. No. 936, Entering Paris, 1944, vert. No. 937, With Eisenhower, 1942.

1991, July 15   *Perf. 14*

928	A115	20sh multicolored	.20	.20
929	A115	70sh multicolored	.35	.35
930	A115	90sh multicolored	.45	.45
931	A115	100sh multicolored	.50	.50
932	A115	200sh multicolored	1.00	1.00
933	A115	500sh multicolored	2.50	2.50
934	A115	600sh multicolored	3.00	3.00
935	A115	1000sh multicolored	5.00	5.00

Nos. 928-935 (8) 13.00 13.00

Souvenir Sheets

| 936 | A115 | 1200sh multicolored | 6.00 | 6.00 |
| 937 | A115 | 1200sh multicolored | 6.00 | 6.00 |

Mushrooms A116

Designs: 20sh, Volvariella bingensis. 70sh, Agrocybe broadwayi. 90sh, Camarophyllus olidus. 140sh, Marasmius arborescens. 180sh, Marasmiellus subcinereus. 200sh, Agaricus campestris. 500sh, Chlorophyllum molybdites. 1000sh, Agaricus bingensis. No. 946, Leucocoprinus cepaestipes, horiz. No. 947, Laccaria lateritia, horiz.

1991, July 19   *Litho.*   *Perf. 14*

938	A116	20sh multicolored	.30	.30
939	A116	70sh multicolored	.50	.50
940	A116	90sh multicolored	.65	.65
941	A116	140sh multicolored	1.00	1.00
942	A116	180sh multicolored	1.25	1.25
943	A116	200sh multicolored	1.40	1.40
944	A116	500sh multicolored	4.00	4.00
945	A116	1000sh multicolored	8.00	8.00

Nos. 938-945 (8) 17.10 17.10

Souvenir Sheets

| 946 | A116 | 1200sh multicolored | 6.50 | 6.50 |
| 947 | A116 | 1200sh multicolored | 6.50 | 6.50 |

World Wildlife Type of 1983

1991, Aug. 1

948	A43	100sh as No. 371	1.00	1.00
949	A43	140sh as No. 372	1.40	1.40
950	A43	200sh as No. 373	1.90	1.90
951	A43	600sh as No. 374	5.50	5.50

Nos. 948-951 (4) 9.80 9.80

Souvenir Sheets
Perf. 13x12½

| 952 | A43 | 1200sh Giraffe | 11.00 | 11.00 |
| 953 | A43 | 1200sh Rhinoceros | 11.00 | 11.00 |

World Wildlife Fund. Nos. 952-953 do not have the WWF emblem.

Flowers in Royal Botanical Gardens, Kew — A118

No. 954: a, Cypripedium calceolus. b, Rhododendron thomsonii. c, Ginkgo biloba. d, Magnolia campbellii. e, Wisteria sinensis. f, Clerodendrum ugandense. g, Eulophia horsfallii. h, Aerangis rhodosticta. i, Abelmoschus moschatus. j, Gloriosa superba. k, Carissa edulis. l, Ochna kirkii. m, Canarina abyssinica. n, Nymphaea caerulea. o, Ceropegia succulenta. p, Strelitzia reginae. q, Strongylodon macrobotrys. r, Victoria amazonica. s, Orchis militaris. t, Sophora microphylla.

No. 955 — Royal Botanic Gardens, Melbourne, Australia: a, Anigozanthos manglesii. b, Banksia grandis. c, Clianthus formosus. d, Gossypium sturtianum. e, Callistemon lanceolatus. f, Saintpaulia ionantha. g, Calodendrum capense. h, Aloe ferox. i, Bolusanthus speciousus. j, Lithops schwantesii k, Protea repens. l, Plumbago capensis. m, Clerodendrum thomsoniae. n, Thunbergia alata. o, Schotia latifolia. p, Epacris impressa. q, Acacia pycnantha. r, Telopea speciosissima. s, Wahlenbergia gloriosa. t, Eucalyptus globulus.

No. 956, The Pagoda, Kew. No. 957, Temple of the Winds, Melbourne.

1991, Nov. 25   *Litho.*   *Perf. 14½*

| 954 | A118 | 100sh Sheet of 20, #a.-t. | 17.00 | 17.00 |
| 955 | A118 | 90sh Sheet of 20, #a.-t. | 11.00 | 11.00 |

Souvenir Sheets

| 956 | A118 | 1400sh multicolored | 9.50 | 9.50 |
| 957 | A118 | 1400sh multicolored | 7.00 | 7.00 |

No. 956 contains one 30x38mm stamp.

While Nos. 955 and 957 have the same issue date as Nos. 954 and 956, their dollar value have been lower when released. Numbers have been reserved for additional values in this set.

Christmas A120

Paintings by Piero Della Francesca: 20sh, Madonna with Child and Angels. 50sh, The Baptism of Christ. 80sh, Polyptych of Mercy. 100sh, The Madonna of Mercy. 200sh, The Legend of the True Cross: The Annunciation. 500sh, Pregnant Madonna. 1000sh, Polyptych of St. Anthony: The Annunciation. 1500sh, The Nativity. No. 968, The Brera Altarpiece. No. 969, Polyptych of St. Anthony.

1991, Dec. 18   *Litho.*   *Perf. 12*

960	A120	20sh multicolored	.20	.20
961	A120	50sh multicolored	.25	.25
962	A120	80sh multicolored	.40	.40
963	A120	100sh multicolored	.50	.50
964	A120	200sh multicolored	1.00	1.00
965	A120	500sh multicolored	2.50	2.50
966	A120	1000sh multicolored	5.00	5.00
967	A120	1500sh multicolored	7.50	7.50

Nos. 960-967 (8) 17.35 17.35

Souvenir Sheets
Perf. 14½

| 968 | A120 | 1800sh multicolored | 9.00 | 9.00 |
| 969 | A120 | 1800sh multicolored | 9.00 | 9.00 |

Boy Scouts A121

Designs: 20sh, Boy Scout Monument, Silver Bay, NY and Ernest Thompson Seton, first chief scout. 50sh, Tree house and Daniel

Beard, Boy Scout pioneer, vert. 1500sh, Boy Scout emblem.

1992, Jan. 6   *Litho.*   *Perf. 14*

| 970 | A121 | 20sh multicolored | .50 | .50 |
| 971 | A121 | 50sh multicolored | .65 | .65 |

Souvenir Sheet

| 972 | A121 | 1500sh multicolored | 7.50 | 7.50 |

YMCA-Boy Scouts partnership, Lord Robert Baden-Powell, 50th death anniv. in 1991 (#970) and 17th World Scout Jamboree, Korea (#971-972).

A number has been reserved for an additional value in this set.

Balloons A122

Balloons: a, Modern Hot Air. b, Sport. c, Pro Juventute. d, Blanchard's. e, Nadar's Le Geant. f, First trans-Pacific balloon crossing. g, Montgolfier's. h, Paris, Double Eagle II, used in first trans-Atlantic balloon crossing. i, Tethered.

1992, Jan. 6   *Litho.*   *Perf. 14*

| 974 | A122 | 200sh Sheet of 9, #a.-i. | 10.50 | 10.50 |

Japanese Attack on Pearl Harbor, 50th Anniv. (in 1991) A123

Designs: a, Japanese bombers attack USS Vestal. b, Japanese Zero fighter. c, Zeros over burning USS Arizona. d, Battleship Row, USS Nevada under way. e, Japanese Val dive bomber. f, US Dauntless dive bomber attacking Hiryu. g, Japanese planes over Midway Island. h, US Buffalo fighter plane. i, US Wildcat fighters over carrier. j, USS Yorktown and Hammann torpedoed by Japanese submarine.

1992, Jan. 6   *Litho.*   *Perf. 14½x15*

| 975 | A123 | 200sh Sheet of 10, #a.-j. | 13.50 | 13.50 |

Battle of Midway, 50th anniv. (#975f-975j). Inscription for No. 975i incorrectly describes fighters as Hellcats.

Anniversaries and Events — A124

Designs: 400sh, Glider No. 8. 500sh, Man breaking pieces from Berlin Wall. 700sh, Portrait of Mozart and scene from "The Magic Flute." 1200sh, Electric locomotive.

1992, Jan. 6   *Litho.*   *Perf. 14*

976	A124	400sh multicolored	2.00	2.00
977	A124	500sh multicolored	2.50	2.50
978	A124	700sh multicolored	3.50	3.50

Nos. 976-978 (3) 8.00 8.00

Souvenir Sheet

| 979 | A124 | 1200sh multicolored | 6.00 | 6.00 |

Otto Lillienthal, hang glider, cent. (in 1991) (#976). Brandenburg Gate, Bicent. (#977). Wolfgang Amadeus Mozart, death bicent. (#978), Trans-Siberian Railway, cent. (#979).

Walt Disney Characters on World Tour — A125

Designs: 20sh, Safari surprise in Africa. 50sh, Pluto's tail of India. 80sh, Donald's calypso beat in Caribbean. 200sh, Goofy pulling rickshaw in China. 500sh, Minnie, Mickey on camel in Egypt. 800sh, Wrestling, Japanese style. 1000sh, Goofy bullfighting in Spain. 1500sh, Mickey scoring in soccer game. No. 988, Daisy singing opera in Germany. No. 989, Mickey and Pluto as Cossack dancers in Moscow.

1992, Feb.   *Perf. 13*

980	A125	20sh multi	.30	.30
981	A125	50sh multi	.30	.30
982	A125	80sh multi	.30	.30
983	A125	200sh multi	.70	.70
984	A125	500sh multi	1.75	1.75
985	A125	800sh multi	3.00	3.00
986	A125	1000sh multi	3.50	3.50
987	A125	1500sh multi	5.25	5.25

Nos. 980-987 (8) 15.10 15.10

Souvenir Sheets

| 988 | A125 | 2000sh multi, vert. | 7.50 | 7.50 |
| 989 | A125 | 2000sh multi, vert. | 7.50 | 7.50 |

Queen Elizabeth II's Accession to the Throne, 40th Anniv.
Common Design Type

1992, Feb. 6   *Litho.*   *Perf. 14*

990	CD348	100sh multi	.50	.50
991	CD348	200sh multi	1.00	1.00
992	CD348	500sh multi	2.50	2.50
993	CD348	1000sh multi	5.00	5.00

Nos. 990-993 (4) 9.00 9.00

Souvenir Sheets

| 994 | CD348 | 1800sh Queen, waterfalls | 9.00 | 9.00 |
| 995 | CD348 | 1800sh Queen, dam | 9.00 | 9.00 |

Dinosaurs A126

1992, Apr. 8   *Litho.*   *Perf. 14*

996	A126	50sh Kentrosaurus	.35	.35
997	A126	200sh Iguanodon	.65	.65
998	A126	250sh Hypsilophodon	1.25	1.25
999	A126	300sh Brachiosaurus	1.00	1.00
1000	A126	400sh Peloneustes	1.75	1.75
1001	A126	500sh Pteranodon	1.60	1.60
1002	A126	800sh Tetralophodon	2.50	2.50
1003	A126	1000sh Megalosaurus	4.50	4.50

Nos. 996-1003 (8) 13.60 13.60

Souvenir Sheets

| 1004 | A126 | 2000sh like #1003 | 7.50 | 7.50 |
| 1005 | A126 | 2000sh like #998 | 7.50 | 7.50 |

Nos. 1004-1005 printed in continuous design.

While Nos. 997, 999, 1001-1002, 1005 have the same release date as Nos. 996, 998, 1000, 1003-1004, their value in relation to the dollar was lower when they were released.

Easter A127

Paintings: 50sh, The Entry into Jerusalem (detail), by Giotto. 100sh, Pilate and the Watch from psalter of Robert de Lisle. 200sh, The Kiss of Judas (detail), by Giotto. 250sh, Christ Washing the Feet of the Disciples, illumination from Life of Christ. 300sh, Christ Seized in the Garden from Melissande Psalter. 500sh, Doubting Thomas, illumination from Life of Christ. 1000sh, The Marys at the Tomb (detail), artist unknown. 2000sh, The Ascension, from 14th century Florentine illuminated manuscript.

Limoge enamels: No. 1014, Agony at Gethsemane. No. 1015, The Piercing of Christ's Side.

1992		Litho.	Perf. 13½x14	
1006	A127	50sh multi	.25	.25
1007	A127	100sh multi	.35	.35
1008	A127	200sh multi	.75	.75
1009	A127	250sh multi	.85	.85
1010	A127	300sh multi	1.00	1.00
1011	A127	500sh multi	1.75	1.75
1012	A127	1000sh multi	3.50	3.50
1013	A127	2000sh multi	7.00	7.00
	Nos. 1006-1013 (8)		15.45	15.45

Souvenir Sheets

1014	A127	2500sh multi	7.50	7.50
1015	A127	2500sh multi	7.50	7.50

Musical
Instruments
A128

1992, July 20		Litho.	Perf. 14	
1016	A128	50sh Adungu	.25	.25
1017	A128	100sh Endingidi	.35	.35
1018	A128	200sh Akogo	.75	.75
1019	A128	250sh Nanga	.85	.85
1020	A128	300sh Engoma	1.00	1.00
1021	A128	400sh Amakondere	1.40	1.40
1022	A128	500sh Akaky-enkye	1.75	1.75
1023	A128	1000sh Ennanga	3.50	3.50
	Nos. 1016-1023 (8)		9.85	9.85

Discovery
of
America,
500th
Anniv.
A129

Designs: 50sh, World map, 1486. 100sh, Map of Africa, 1508. 150sh, New World, 1500. 200sh, Nina, astrolabe. 600sh, Quadrant, Pinta. 800sh, Hour glass. 900sh, 15th century compass. 2000sh, World map, 1492. No. 1032, 1490 Map by Henricus Martellus, 1490. No. 1033, Sections of 1492 globe.

1992, July 24		Litho.	Perf. 14	
1024	A129	50sh multi	.30	.30
1025	A129	100sh multi	.30	.30
1026	A129	150sh multi	.30	.30
1027	A129	200sh multi	.85	.85
1028	A129	600sh multi	2.50	2.50
1029	A129	800sh multi	3.25	3.25
1030	A129	900sh multi	3.50	3.50
1031	A129	2000sh multi	2.75	2.75
	Nos. 1024-1031 (8)		13.75	13.75

Souvenir Sheets

1032	A129	2500sh multi, vert.	7.25	7.25
1033	A129	2500sh multi	5.00	5.00

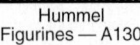

World Columbian Stamp Expo '92, Chicago. While Nos. 1024, 1026, 1031 and 1033 have the same issue date as Nos. 1027-1030 and 1032, their value in relation to the dollar was lower when they were released.

Hummel
Figurines — A130

1992 Summer
Olympics,
Barcelona — A131

No. 1042: a, Like #1034. b, Like #1035. c, Like #1036. d, Like #1037.
No. 1043: a, Like #1039. b, Like #1038. c, Like #1040. d, Like #1041.

1992, Aug. 28		Litho.	Perf. 14	
1034	A130	50sh Little Laundry Girl	.25	.25
1035	A130	200sh Scrub Girl	.80	.80
1036	A130	250sh Sweeper Girl	.90	.90
1037	A130	300sh Little Mother	1.10	1.10

1038	A130	600sh Little Mountaineer	1.60	1.60
1039	A130	900sh Little Knitter	2.25	2.25
1040	A130	1000sh Little Cowboy	2.75	2.75
1041	A130	1500sh Little Astronomer	5.50	5.50
	Nos. 1034-1041 (8)		15.15	15.15

Souvenir Sheets

1042	A130	500sh Sheet of 4, #a.-d.	7.25	7.25
1043	A130	500sh Sheet of 4, #a.-d.	7.25	7.25

While Nos. 1034, 1038-1040, 1043 have the same release date as Nos. 1035-1037, 1041-1042, their value in relation to the dollar was lower when they were released.

1992		Litho.	Perf. 14	
1044	A131	50sh Javelin	.35	.35
1045	A131	100sh High jump, horiz.	.35	.35
1046	A131	200sh Pentathlon (Fencing)	.65	.65
1047	A131	250sh Volleyball	.80	.80
1048	A131	300sh Women's platform diving	1.00	1.00
1049	A131	500sh Team cycling	1.60	1.60
1050	A131	1000sh Tennis	3.25	3.25
1051	A131	2000sh Boxing, horiz.	6.50	6.50
	Nos. 1044-1051 (8)		14.50	14.50

Souvenir Sheets

1052	A131	2500sh Baseball	7.50	7.50
1053	A131	2500sh Basketball	7.50	7.50

Wild
Animals
A132

1992, Sept. 25		Litho.	Perf. 14	
1054	A132	50sh Spotted hyena	.25	.25
1055	A132	100sh Impala	.25	.25
1056	A132	200sh Giant forest hog	.45	.45
1057	A132	250sh Pangolin	.55	.55
1058	A132	300sh Golden monkey	.70	.70
1059	A132	800sh Serval	1.75	1.75
1060	A132	1000sh Bush genet	2.25	2.25
1061	A132	3000sh Defassa waterbuck	6.75	6.75
	Nos. 1054-1061 (8)		12.95	12.95

Souvenir Sheets

1062	A132	2500sh Mountain gorilla	6.50	6.50
1063	A132	2500sh Hippopotamus	6.50	6.50

Birds — A133

Designs: 20sh, Red necked falcon. 30sh, Yellow-billed hornbill. 50sh, Purple heron. 100sh, Regal sunbird. 150sh, White-brown robin chat. 200sh, Shining-blue kingfisher. 250sh, Great blue turaco. 300sh, Emerald cuckoo. 500sh, Abyssinian roller. 800sh, Crowned crane. 1000sh, Doherty's bush shrike. 2000sh, Splendid glossy starling. 3000sh, Little bee eater. 4000sh, Red-headed lovebird.

1992, Aug.		Litho.	Perf. 15x14	
1064	A133	20sh multi	.20	.20
1065	A133	30sh multi	.20	.20
1066	A133	50sh multi	.20	.20
1067	A133	100sh multi	.20	.20
1068	A133	150sh multi	.30	.30
1069	A133	200sh multi	.40	.40
1070	A133	250sh multi	.50	.50
1071	A133	300sh multi	.55	.55
1072	A133	500sh multi	1.00	1.00
1073	A133	800sh multi	1.60	1.60
1074	A133	1000sh multi	2.00	2.00
1075	A133	2000sh multi	4.00	4.00
1076	A133	3000sh multi	6.00	6.00
1076A	A133	4000sh multi	8.00	8.00
	Nos. 1064-1076A (14)		25.15	25.15

Issued: 3000sh, Oct.; others, Aug.?

Walt Disney's Goofy, 60th
Anniv. — A134

Scenes from Disney animated films: 50sh, Hawaiian Holiday, 1937, vert. 100sh, The Nifty Nineties, 1941, vert. 200sh, Mickey's Fire Brigade, 1935, vert. 250sh, The Art of Skiing, 1941. 300sh, Mickey's Amateurs, 1937. 1000sh, Boat Builders, 1938. 1500sh, The Olympic Champ, 1942, vert. 2000sh, The Olympic Champ, 1942, vert. No. 1085, Goofy and Wilbur, 1939. No. 1086, Goofy's family tree, vert.

Perf. 13½x14, 14x13½

1992, Nov. 2			Litho.	
1077	A134	50sh multi	.25	.25
1078	A134	100sh multi	.25	.25
1079	A134	200sh multi	.50	.50
1080	A134	250sh multi	.65	.65
1081	A134	300sh multi	.80	.80
1082	A134	1000sh multi	2.50	2.50
1083	A134	1500sh multi	4.00	4.00
1084	A134	2000sh multi	5.25	5.25
	Nos. 1077-1084 (8)		14.20	14.20

Souvenir Sheets

1085	A134	3000sh multi	7.50	7.50
1086	A134	3000sh multi	7.50	7.50

Souvenir Sheet

UN Headquarters, New York
City — A135

1992, Oct. 28		Litho.	Perf. 14	
1087	A135	2500sh multi	7.50	7.50

Postage Stamp Mega Event '92, NYC.

Christmas
A136

Details or entire paintings by Zurbaran: 50sh, The Annunciation (angel at left). 200sh, The Annunciation (angel at right). 250sh, The Virgin of the Immaculate Conception. 300sh, The Virgin of the Immaculate Conception (detail). 800sh, 900sh, The Holy Family with Saints Anne, Joachim and John the Baptist (800sh, entire, 900sh, detail). 1000sh, Adoration of the Magi. No. 1096, The Virgin of the Immaculate Conception (Virgin with arms outstretched). No. 1097, The Virgin of the Immaculate Conception (Virgin with arms folded).

1992, Nov. 16		Litho.	Perf. 13½x14	
1088	A136	50sh multi	.30	.30
1089	A136	200sh multi	.50	.50
1090	A136	250sh multi	.70	.70
1091	A136	300sh multi	.85	.85
1092	A136	800sh multi	2.25	2.25
1093	A136	900sh multi	2.50	2.50
1094	A136	1000sh multi	2.75	2.75
1095	A136	2000sh multi	5.50	5.50
	Nos. 1088-1095 (8)		15.35	15.35

Souvenir Sheets

1096	A136	2500sh multi	7.50	7.50
1097	A136	2500sh multi	7.50	7.50

World Health Organization — A137

Anniversaries and Events — A138

Designs: 50sh, Improving household food security. 200sh, Continue to breastfeed. 250sh, At four months old, give breast milk and soft food. No. 1101, Drink water from a safe and protected source. No. 1102, Jupiter, Voyager 2. No. 1103, Mother holding baby. No. 1104, Impala. No. 1105, Zebra. No. 1106, Count Ferdinand von Zeppelin, zeppelin. 2000sh, Neptune, Voyager 2. 3000sh, Count Zeppelin, zeppelin, diff. No. 1109, Voyager 2, Jupiter, diff. No. 1110, Wart hog. No. 1111, Doctor examining child, Lions Intl. emblem. No. 1112, Count Zeppelin, balloon.

1992		Litho.	Perf. 14	
1098	A137	50sh multi	.20	.20
1099	A137	200sh multi	.40	.40
1100	A137	250sh multi	.50	.50
1101	A137	300sh multi	.60	.60
1102	A138	300sh multi	.60	.60
1103	A137	800sh multi	1.60	1.60
1104	A138	800sh multi	2.00	2.00
1105	A138	1000sh multi	2.50	2.50
1106	A138	1000sh multi	2.00	2.00
1107	A138	2000sh multi	4.00	4.00
1108	A138	3000sh multi	6.00	6.00
	Nos. 1098-1108 (11)		20.40	20.40

Souvenir Sheets

1109	A138	2500sh multi	5.75	5.75
1110	A138	2500sh multi	5.00	5.00
1111	A138	2500sh multi	5.00	5.00
1112	A138	2500sh multi	5.00	5.00

WHO (#1098-1101, 1103). Intl. Space Year (#1102, 1107, 1109). Earth Summit, Rio de Janeiro (#1104-1105, 1110). Count Zeppelin, 75th anniv. of death (#1106, 1108, 1112). Lions Intl., 75th anniv. (#1111).
Issue dates: Nos. 1098-1103, 1106, 1109, 1112, Nov.; others, Dec.

1993 Visit
of Pope
John Paul
II to
Uganda
A139

A139a

Designs: 50sh, Cathedral in Kampala, site of Papal Mass, Kampala, hands releasing doves. 200sh, Site of Papal Mass, Pope. 250sh, Ugandan man, Pope. 300sh, Three Ugandan Catholic leaders, Pope. 800sh, Pope waving, Ugandan map and flag. 900sh, Ugandan woman, Pope wearing mitre. 1000sh, Pope, Ugandan flag, site of Papal Mass. 2000sh, Ugandan flag, Pope waving.
No. 1121, Pope at door of airplane, vert. No. 1122, Pope delivering message at podium, vert.
No. 1123, Pope John Paul II. No. 1124, Pope with hands raised.

1993, Feb. 1   Litho.   Perf. 14

1113	A139	50sh multi	.30	.30
1114	A139	200sh multi	.50	.50
1115	A139	250sh multi	.60	.60
1116	A139	300sh multi	.70	.70
1117	A139	800sh multi	1.75	1.75
1118	A139	900sh multi	1.90	1.90
1119	A139	1000sh multi	2.25	2.25
1120	A139	2000sh multi	4.50	4.50
		Nos. 1113-1120 (8)	12.50	12.50

Souvenir Sheets

1121	A139	3000sh multi	7.25	7.25
1122	A139	3000sh multi	7.25	7.25

Embossed
Perf. 12

1123	A139a	5000sh gold	30.00	30.00

Souvenir Sheet
Imperf

1124	A139a	5000sh gold	30.00	30.00

Miniature Sheet

Louvre Museum, Bicent. A140

Details or entire paintings by Rembrandt: No. 1125a, Self-Portrait with an Easel. b, Birds of Paradise. c, The Beef Carcass. d, The Supper at Emmaus. e, Hendrickje Stoffels. f, Titus, Son of the Artist. g, The Holy Family (left). h, The Holy Family (right).
2500sh, Philosopher in Meditation, horiz.

1993, Apr. 5   Litho.   Perf. 12

1125	A140	500sh Sheet of 8, #a.-h. + label	11.25	11.25

Souvenir Sheet
Perf. 14½

1126	A140	2500sh multi	7.00	7.00

Dogs A141

1993, May 28   Litho.   Perf. 14

1127	A141	50sh Afghan hound	.45	.45
1128	A141	100sh Newfoundland	.45	.45
1129	A141	200sh Siberian huskies	.80	.80
1130	A141	250sh Briard	1.00	1.00
1131	A141	300sh Saluki	1.40	1.40
1132	A141	800sh Labrador retriever, vert.	3.50	3.50
1133	A141	1000sh Greyhound	4.00	4.00
1134	A141	1500sh Pointer	6.50	6.50
		Nos. 1127-1134 (8)	18.10	18.10

Souvenir Sheets

1135	A141	2500sh Cape hunting dog	11.00	11.00
1136	A141	2500sh Norwegian elkhound	11.00	11.00

Miniature Sheet

Coronation of Queen Elizabeth II, 40th Anniv. A142

No. 1137: a, 50sh, Official coronation photograph. b, 200sh, Orb, Rod of Equity & Mercy.

c, 500sh, Queen during coronation ceremony. d, 1500sh, Queen Elizabeth II, Princess Margaret.
2500sh, The Crown, by Grace Wheatley, 1959.

1993, June 2   Litho.   Perf. 13½x14

1137	A142	Sheet, 2 each #a.-d.	13.50	13.50

Souvenir Sheet
Perf. 14

1138	A142	2500sh multicolored	7.50	7.50

No. 1138 contains one 28x42mm stamp.

Miniature Sheet

Taipei '93 — A143

Funerary objects: No. 1139a, Tomb guardian god. b, Civil official. c, Tomb guardian god, diff. d, Civil official, diff. e, Chimera. f, Civil official, diff.
2500sh, Statue of Sacred Mother, Ceremonial Hall, Taiyuan, Shanxi.

1993, Sept. 22   Litho.   Perf. 14x13½

1139	A143	600sh Sheet of 6, #a.-f.	8.50	8.50

Souvenir Sheet

1140	A143	2500sh multicolored	8.00	8.00

With Bangkok '93 Emblem

Thai sculpture: No. 1141a, Standing Buddha, 13th-15th cent. b, Crowned Buddha, 13th cent. c, Thepanom, 15th cent. d, Crowned Buddha, 12th cent. e, Four-armed Avalokitesvara, 9th cent. f, Lop Buri standing Buddha, 13th cent.
2500sh, Buddha, interior of Wat Mahathat.

1993, Sept. 22

1141	A143	600sh Sheet of 6, #a.-f.	8.50	8.50

Souvenir Sheet

1142	A143	2500sh multicolored	8.00	8.00

With Indopex '93 Emblem
Miniature Sheet

Japanese Wayang Puppets, Indonesia: No. 1143a, Bupati karma, Prince of Wangga. b, Rahwana. c, Sondjeng Sandjata. d, Raden Damar Wulan. e, Klitik figure. f, Hanaman. 2500sh, Candi Mendut in Kedu Plain, Java, Indonesia.

1993, Sept. 22   Litho.   Perf. 13½x14

1143	A143	600sh Sheet of 6, #a.-f.	8.50	8.50

Souvenir Sheet

1144	A143	2500sh multicolored	8.00	8.00

A144   A145

1993, Oct. 1   Litho.   Perf. 14

1145	A144	50sh Gutierrez, Voeller	.35	.35
1146	A144	200sh Tomas Brolin	.60	.60
1147	A144	250sh Gary Lineker	.75	.75
1148	A144	300sh Munoz, Butragueno	.85	.85
1149	A144	800sh Carlos Valderrama	2.40	2.40
1150	A144	900sh Diego Maradona	2.55	2.55

1151	A144	1000sh Pedro Troglio	3.00	3.00
1152	A144	2000sh Enzo Scifo	6.00	6.00
		Nos. 1145-1152 (8)	16.50	16.50

Souvenir Sheets

1153	A144	2500sh Brazil coaches	7.25	7.25
1154	A144	2500sh De Napoli, Skuhravy, horiz.	7.25	7.25

1994 World Cup Soccer Championships, US.

1993, Nov. 3   Perf. 14

Cathedrals of the World: 50sh, York Minster, England. 100sh, Notre Dame, Paris. 200sh, Little Metropolis, Athens. 250sh, St. Patrick's, New York. 300sh, Ulm, Germany. 800sh, St. Basil's, Moscow. 1000sh, Roskilde, Denmark. 2000sh, Seville, Spain. No. 1163, Namirembe, Uganda. No. 1163A, St. Peter's, Vatican City.

1155	A145	50sh multi	.35	.35
1156	A145	100sh multi	.35	.35
1157	A145	200sh multi	.65	.65
1158	A145	250sh multi	.70	.70
1159	A145	300sh multi	.95	.95
1160	A145	800sh multi	2.50	2.50
1161	A145	1000sh multi	3.25	3.25
1162	A145	2000sh multi	6.25	6.25
		Nos. 1155-1162 (8)	15.00	15.00

Souvenir Sheets

1163	A145	2500sh multi	7.50	7.50
1163A	A145	2500sh multi	7.50	7.50

Christmas A146

Details or entire woodcut, The Virgin with Carthusian Monks, by Durer: 50sh, 200sh, 300sh, 2000sh.
Details or entire paintings by Raphael: 100sh, 800sh, Sacred Family. 250sh, The Virgin of the Rose. 1000sh, Holy Family (Virgin with Beardless Joseph).
No. 1172, 2500sh, The Virgin with Carthusian Monks, by Durer. No. 1173, 2500sh, Sacred Family, by Raphael.

1993, Nov. 19   Litho.   Perf. 13½x14

1164-1171	A146	Set of 8	13.50 13.50

Souvenir Sheets

1172-1173	A146	Set of 2	16.00 16.00

Mickey Mouse, Friends with Dinosaurs — A147

Disney characters depicted with: 50sh, Stegosaurus. 100sh, Pteranodon. 200sh, Mamenchisaurus. 250sh, Rock painting. 300sh, Dino "sails." 800sh, Diplodocus. 800sh, Mamenshisaurus, diff. 1000sh, Triceratops.
No. 1182, 2500sh, Tyrannosaurus rex, Mickey. No. 1183, 2500sh, Minnie, Mickey, mamenchisaurus, diff.

1993, Dec. 22   Litho.   Perf. 14x13½

1174-1181	A147	Set of 8	14.00 14.00

Souvenir Sheets

1182-1183	A147	Set of 2	13.00 13.00

Rinderpest Campaign A148   Picasso (1881-1973) A149

1993, Dec. 29   Perf. 14

1184	A148	200sh multicolored	.50	.50

1993, Dec. 29

Paintings: 100sh, Woman in Yellow, 1907. 250sh, Gertrude Stein, 1906. 2500sh, Woman by a Window, 1956.

1185-1186	A149	Set of 2	.75	.75

Souvenir Sheet

1187	A149	2500sh multicolored	8.00	8.00

Copernicus (1473-1543) — A150

Polska '93 — A151

Telescopes: 500sh, Early. 1000sh, Modern. 2500sh, Copernicus.

1993, Dec. 29

1188-1189	A150	Set of 2	2.50	2.50

Souvenir Sheet

1190	A150	2500sh multicolored	8.00	8.00

1993, Dec. 29

Paintings: 800sh, Creation of the World, by S. I. Witkiewicz par J. Gloqowski, 1921. 1000sh, For the Right to Work, by Andrezej Strumillo, 1952. 2500sh, Temptation of St. Anthony I, by S. I. Witkiewicz (1908-21), horiz.

1191-1192	A151	Set of 2	3.00	3.00

Souvenir Sheet

1193	A151	2500sh multicolored	4.25	4.25

World Meteorological Day — A152   Fruits and Crops — A153

Designs: 50sh, Weather station, horiz. 200sh, Observatory at Meteorological Training School, Entebbe. 250sh, Satellite receiver at National Meteorological Center, horiz. 300sh, Reading temperatures, National Center, Entebbe, horiz. 400sh, Automatic weather station. 800sh, Destruction by hail storm, horiz. 2500sh, Barograph, horiz.

1993, Dec. 29

1194-1199	A152	Set of 6	3.75	3.75

Souvenir Sheet

1200	A152	2500sh multicolored	4.25	4.25

1993, Dec. 29

Designs: 50sh, Passiflora edulis. 100sh, Helianthus annus. 150sh, Musa sapientum. 200sh, Vanilla fragrans. 250sh, Ananas comosus. 300sh, Artocarpus heterophyllus. 500sh, Sorghum bicolor. 800sh, Zea mays. No. 1209, 2000sh, Sesamum indicum. No. 1210, 2000sh, Coffea canephora.

1201-1208	A153	Set of 8	4.50	4.50

Souvenir Sheets

1209-1210	A153	Set of 2	8.50	8.50

Automotive Anniversaries — A154

No. 1211: a, 1903 Model A Ford, Henry Ford. b, Model T Snowmobile at 1932 Winter Olympics, Jack Shea. c, Lee Iacocca, Ford Mustang at New York World's Fair. d, Jim Clark, Lotus-Ford winning 1965 Indianapolis 500 race.
No. 1212: a, 1994 Mercedes Benz S600 Coupe. b, 1955 Mercedes Benz W196 Grand Prix Champion car, Juan Manuel Fangio. c, 1938 Mercedes Benz W125 road speed record holder, Rudolph Caracciola. d, Carl Benz, 1893 Benz Viktoria.
No. 1213, Carl Benz, vert. No. 1214, Henry Ford, vert.

1994, Jan. 18   Litho.   Perf. 14

1211	A154	700sh Strip of 4, #a.-d.	6.25	6.25
1212	A154	800sh Strip of 4, #a.-d.	7.25	7.25

Souvenir Sheets

1213	A154	2500sh multicolored	4.50	4.50
1214	A154	2500sh multicolored	4.50	4.50

First Ford motor, cent. (#1211, #1214). First Benz four-wheel car, cent. (#1212, #1213).

A155

Hong Kong '94 — A156

Stamps, religious shrines, Repulse Bay: No. 1215, Hong Kong #531. No. 1216, #1163.
Snuff boxes, Qing Dynasty: No. 1217a, Glass painted enamel with pavilion. b, Porcelain with floral design. c, Porcelain with quail design. d, Porcelain with openwork design. e, Agate with pair of dogs. f, Agate with man on donkey.

1994, Feb. 18   Litho.   Perf. 14

1215	A155	500sh multicolored	.90	.90
1216	A155	500sh multicolored	.90	.90
a.		Pair, #1215-1216	1.75	1.75

Miniature Sheet

1217	A156	200sh Sheet of 6, #a.-f.	2.25	2.25

Nos. 1215-1216 issued in sheets of 5 pairs. No. 1216a is continuous design.
New Year 1994 (Year of the Dog) (#1217e).

Miniature Sheet

1994 World Cup Soccer Championships, US — A157

Designs: No. 1218a, Georges Grun, Belgium. b, Oscar Ruggeri, Argentina. c, Frank Rijkaard, Holland. d, Magid "Tyson" Musisi, Uganda. e, Donald Keeman, Holland. f, Igor Shallmov, Russia.
No. 1219, 2500sh, RFK Stadium, Washington DC. No. 1220, 2500sh, Ruud Gullit, Holland.

1994, June 27   Litho.   Perf. 14

1218	A157	500sh Sheet of 6, #a.-f.	5.50	5.50

Souvenir Sheets

1219-1220	A157	Set of 2	9.00	9.00

Heifer Project Intl., 50th Anniv. A158

1994, June 29   Litho.   Perf. 14

1221	A158	100sh multicolored	1.50	1.50

Moths — A159   Native Crafts — A160

Designs: 100sh, Lobobunaea goodii. 200sh, Bunaeopsis hersilia. 300sh, Rufoglanis rosea. 350sh, Acherontia atropos. 400sh, Rohaniella pygmaea. 450sh, Euchloron megaera. 500sh, Epiphora rectifascia. 1000sh, Polyphychus coryndoni.
Lobobunaea goodii: No. 1230, 2500sh, Wings down. No. 1231, 2500sh, Wings extended.

1994, July 13

1222-1229	A159	Set of 8	6.75	6.75

Souvenir Sheets

1230-1231	A159	Set of 2	10.00	10.00

1994, July 18

Designs: 100sh, Wood stool. 200sh, Wood & banana fiber chair. 250sh, Raffia & palm leaves basket. 300sh, Wool tapestry showing tree planting. 450sh, Wool tapestry showing hair grooming. 500sh, Wood sculpture, drummer. 800sh, Decorated gourds. 1000sh, Lady's bag made from bark cloth.
No. 1240, 2500sh, Raffia baskets. No. 1241, 2500sh, Papyrus hats.

1232-1239	A160	Set of 8	7.00	7.00

Souvenir Sheets

1240-1241	A160	Set of 2	10.00	10.00

Cats — A161   ILO, 75th Anniv. — A162

Cat, historic landmark: 50sh, Turkish angora, Blue Mosque, Turkey, horiz. 100sh, Japanese bobtail, Mt. Fuji, Japan, horiz. 200sh, Norwegian forest cat, windmill, Holland, horiz. 300sh, Egyptian mau, pyramids, Egypt. 450sh, Rex, Stonehenge, England. 500sh, Chartreux, Eiffel Tower, France, horiz. 1000sh, Burmese, Shwe Dagon Pagoda, Burma. 1500sh, Maine coon, Pemaquid Point Lighthouse, Maine.
No. 1250, 2500sh, Russian blue, horiz. No. 1251, 2500sh, Manx, horiz.

1994, July 22

1242-1249	A161	Set of 8	12.00	12.00

Souvenir Sheets

1250-1251	A161	Set of 2	15.00	15.00

1994, July 29

1252	A162	350sh multicolored	1.00	1.00

PHILAKOREA '94 — A163

Designs: 100sh, Eight story Sari pagoda, Paekyangsa. 350sh, Ch'omsongdae (Natl. treasure). 1000sh, Pulguksa Temple exterior. 2500sh, Bronze mural, Pagoda Park, Seoul.

1994, Aug. 8

1253-1255	A163	Set of 3	3.00	3.00

Souvenir Sheet

1256	A163	2500sh multicolored	5.00	5.00

Intl. Year of the Family A164

1994, Aug. 11

1257	A164	100sh multicolored	1.00	1.00

D-Day, 50th Anniv. A165

Designs: 300sh, Mulberry Harbor pierhead moves into position. 1000sh, Mulberry Harbor floating bridge lands armor.
2500sh, Ships, Mulberry Harbor.

1994, Aug. 11

1258	A165	300sh multicolored	.60	.60
1259	A165	1000sh multicolored	2.00	2.00

Souvenir Sheet

1260	A165	2500sh multicolored	5.00	5.00

A166

Intl. Olympic Committee, Cent. — A167

Designs: 350sh, John Akii-bua, Uganda, 100-meter hurdles, 1972. 900sh, Heike Herkel, Germany, high jump, 1992.

2500sh, Aleksei Urmanov, Russia, figure skating, 1994.

1994, Aug. 11

1261	A166	350sh multicolored	.70	.70
1262	A167	900sh multicolored	1.75	1.75

Souvenir Sheet

1263	A166	2500sh multicolored	5.00	5.00

First Manned Moon Landing, 25th Anniv. A168

No. 1264 — Project Mercury astronauts: a, 50sh, Alan B. Shepard, Jr., Freedom 7. b, 100sh, M. Scott Carpenter, Aurora 7. c, 200sh, Virgil I. Grissom, Liberty Bell 7. d, 300sh, L. Gordon Cooper, Jr., Faith 7. e, 400sh, Walter M. Schirra, Jr., Sigma 7. f, 500sh, Donald K. Slayton, Apollo-Soyuz, 1975. g, John H. Glenn, Jr., Friendship 7.
3000sh, Apollo 11 anniv. emblem.

1994, Aug. 11

1264	A168	Sheet of 7, #a.-g. + 2 labels	4.25	4.25

Souvenir Sheet

1265	A168	3000sh multicolored	6.00	6.00

A169

Disney's The Lion King — A169a

No. 1266: a, Baby Simba. b, Mufasa, Simba, Sarabi. c, Young Simba, Nala. d, Timon. e, Rafiki. f, Pumbaa. g, Hyenas. h, Scar. i, Zazu.
No. 1267: a, Rafiki, Mufasa. b, Rafiki, Mufasa, Sarabi. c, Rafiki, Simba. d, Scar, Zazu. e, Rafiki seeing vision. f, Simba, Scar. g, Simba, Nala. h, Simba trying on mane. i, Simba, Nala, Zazu.
No. 1268: a, Scar plots evil plan. b, Mufasa rescues Simba. c, Destroying Mufasa. d, Simba escaping hyenas. e, Timon, Pumbaa, Simba. f, Simba, Timon, Pumbaa sing Hakuna Matata. g, Rafiki. h, Simba, Nala. i, Simba seeing reflection.
No. 1269, 2500sh, Simba, Timon. No. 1270, 2500sh, Characters of the Lion King, vert. No. 1271, 2500sh, Simba's colorful animal kingdon.
No. 1271A, Mufasa, Simba. No. 1271B, Mufasa, Simba on back, standing on rock.
Illustration A169a reduced.

Perf. 14x13½, 13½x14

1994, Sept. 30

1266	A169	100sh Sheet of 9, #a.-i.	2.75	2.75
1267	A169	200sh Sheet of 9, #a.-i.	5.75	5.75
1268	A169	250sh Sheet of 9, #a.-i.	7.50	7.50
Nos. 1266-1268 (3)			16.00	16.00

Souvenir Sheets

1269-1271	A169	Set of 3	24.00	24.00

Litho. & Embossed

Perf. 11½

1271A	A169a	5000sh gold	
1271B	A169a	5000sh gold	

Sierra Club, Cent. — A170

No. 1272, horiz.: a, 200sh, Cheetahs. b, 250sh, Cheetah kittens. c, 300sh, African wild dog. d, 500sh, African wild dog. e, 600sh, Grevy's zebra. f, 800sh, Chimpanzee. g, 1000sh, Grevy's zebra.
No. 1273: a, 100sh, Chimpanzee. b, 200sh, Chimpanzee. c, 250sh, African wild dog. d, 300sh, Cheetah. e-f, 500sh, 600sh, Gelada baboon. g, 800sh, Grevy's zebra. h, 1000sh, Gelada baboon.

1994, Nov. 9
1272 A170 Sheet of 7, #a.-g. + label   9.00 9.00
1273 A170 Sheet of 8, #a.-h.   9.25 9.25

ICAO, 50th Anniv. A171

Designs: 100sh, Entebbe Intl. Airport terminal building. 250sh, Entebbe control tower.

1994, Nov. 14   Litho.   Perf. 14
1274 A171 100sh multicolored   .50   .50
1275 A171 250sh multicolored   1.00 1.00

Environmental Protection — A172

Designs: 100sh, Stop poaching. 250sh, Waste disposals. 350sh, Overfishing is a threat. 500sh, Deforestation.

1994, Nov. 15
1276-1279 A172 Set of 4   3.50 3.50

Christmas A173

Paintings: 100sh, Adoration of the Christ Child, by Fillipino Lippi. 200sh, The Holy Family Rests on the Flight into Egypt, by Annibale Carracci. 300sh, Madonna with Christ Child ant St. John, by Piero di Cosimo. 350sh, The Conestabile Madonna, by Raphael. 450sh, Madonna and Child with Angels, after Antonio Rossellino. 500sh, Madonna and Child with St. John, by Raphael. 900sh, Madonna and Child, by Luca Signorelli. 1000sh, Madonna with the Child Jesus, St. John and an Angel, in style of Pier Francesco Fiorentino.
No. 1288, 2500sh, The Madonna of the Magnificat, by Sandro Botticelli. No. 1289, 2500sh, Adoration of the Magi, by Fra Angelico & Filippo Lippi.

1994, Dec. 5   Litho.   Perf. 13½x14
1280-1287 A173 Set of 8   10.00 10.00
Souvenir Sheets
1288-1289 A173 Set of 2   12.50 12.50

Tintoretto (1518-94) A174

Details or entire paintings: 100sh, Self-portrait. 300sh, A Philosopher. 400sh, The Creation of the Animals, horiz. 450sh, The Feast of Belshazzar, horiz. 500sh, The Raising of the Brazen Serpent. 1000sh, Elijah Fed by the Angel.
No. 1296, 2000sh, Finding of Moses. No. 1297, 2000sh, Moses Striking Water from a Rock.

1995, Feb. 7   Litho.   Perf. 13½
1290-1295 A174 Set of 6   6.50 6.50
Souvenir Sheets
1296-1297 A174 Set of 2   10.00 10.00

Birds A175

No. 1298: a, White-faced tree duck. b, European shoveler. c, Hartlaub's duck. d, Milky eagle-owl. e, Avocet. f, African fish eagle. g, Spectacled weaver. h, Black-headed gonolek. i, Great crested grebe. j, Red-knobbed coot. k, Woodland kingfisher. l, Pintail. m, Squacco heron. n, Purple gallinule. o, African darter. p, African jacana.
No. 1299, 2500sh, Fulvous tree duck. No. 1300, 2500sh, Pygmy goose.

1995, Apr. 24   Litho.   Perf. 14
1298 A175 200sh Sheet of 16, #a.-p.   8.00 8.00
Souvenir Sheets
1299-1300 A175 Set of 2   12.00 12.00

Nos. 685-688, 906 Surcharged

1995, June 1   Litho.   Perf. 14
1301 A90 100sh on #688 multi   .25   .25
1302 A90 450sh on 70sh #686   1.25 1.25
1303 A90 800sh on 90sh #687   2.00 2.00
1304 A90 1500sh on 10sh #685   3.75 3.75
     Nos. 1301-1304 (4)   7.25 7.25
Souvenir Sheet
1305 A113 2500sh on 1200sh multi   6.00 6.00

UN, 50th Anniv. — A176

Designs: 1000sh, Hands releasing butterflies, dragonfly, dove.
No. 1308, Infant's hand holding adult's finger.

1995, July 6   Litho.   Perf. 14
1306 A176 450sh shown   1.25 1.25
1307 A176 1000sh multicolored   2.75 2.75
Souvenir Sheet
1308 A176 2000sh multicolored   4.50 4.50

FAO, 50th Anniv. — A177

No. 1309 — Corn huskers: a, 350sh, Young woman. b, 500sh, Old woman, girl. c, 1000sh, Woman with baby on back.
2000sh, Boy beside bore well for livestock, irrigation.

1995, July 6
1309 A177 Strip of 3, #a.-c.   4.00 4.00
Souvenir Sheet
1310 A177 2000sh multicolored   4.50 4.50

A178

End of World War II, 50th Anniv. A179

No. 1311: a, Russian 152mm gun fires into center of Berlin. b, Soviets capture Moltke Bridge. c, Emperor William Memorial Church, now war memorial. d, Brandenburg Gate falls to Russian tanks. e, US B-17's continue to devastate industrial Germany. f, Soviet tanks enter Berlin. g, Hitler's chancellery lies in ruins. h, Reichstag burns.
Flags of countries each forming "VJ": No. 1312a, Australia. b, Great Britain. c, New Zealand. d, US. e, China. f, Canada.
No. 1313, Waving Soviet flag from atop building in Berlin. No. 1314, US flag, combat soldier.

1995, July 6
1311 A178 500sh Sheet of 8, #a.-h. + label   9.00 9.00
1312 A179 600sh Sheet of 6, #a.-f. + label   8.00 8.00
Souvenir Sheets
1313 A178 2500sh multicolored   5.50 5.50
1314 A179 2500sh multicolored   5.50 5.50

No. 1313 contains one 56x42mm stamp.

Queen Mother, 95th Anniv. A181

No. 1317: a, Drawing. b, Waving. c, Formal portrait. d, Green blue outfit.
2500sh, Pale blue outfit.

1995, July 6   Perf. 13½x14
1317 A181 500sh Block or strip of 4, #a.-d. 4.50 4.50
Souvenir Sheet
1318 A181 2500sh multicolored   5.50 5.50

No. 1317 was issued in sheets of 8 stamps.
Sheets of Nos. 1317-1318 exist with with black border and text "In Memoriam/1900-2002" in sheet margins.

Dinosaurs A182

Designs: 150sh, Veloceraptor. 200sh, Psittacosaurus. 350sh, Dilophosaurus. 400sh, Kentrosaurus. 500sh, Stegosaurus. 1500sh, Pterodaustro.
No. 1325, vert: a, Archaeopteryx. b, Quetzalcoatlus. c, Pteranodon (b, d). d, Brachiosa (g, h). e, Tsintaosaur. f, Allosaur (g-h). g, Tyranosaur (f, i-k). h, Apatosaur (l). i, Giant dragonfly. j, Dimorphodon. k, Triceratops (l). l, Compsognathus.
No. 1326, 2000sh, Parasaurolophus. No. 1327, 2000sh, Shunosaurus.

1995, July 15   Perf. 14
1319-1324 A182 Set of 6   9.00 9.00
1325 A182 300sh Sheet of 12, #a.-l. 11.00 11.00
Souvenir Sheets
1326-1327 A182 Set of 2   10.50 10.50

Reptiles — A183

1995	Litho.	Perf. 14x15	
1328	50sh Rough scaled bush viper	.20	.20
1329	100sh Pygmy python	.20	.20
1330	150sh Three horned chameleon	.30	.30
1331	200sh African rock python	.40	.40
1332	350sh Nile monitor	.70	.70
1333	400sh Savannah monitor	.85	.85
1334	450sh Bush viper	.95	.95
1335	500sh Nile crocodile	1.00	1.00

Size: 38x24mm
Perf. 14

1336	700sh Bell's hinged tortoise	1.40	1.40
1337	900sh Rhinoceros viper	1.90	1.90
1338	1000sh Gaboon viper	2.00	2.00
1339	2000sh Spitting cobra	4.00	4.00
1340	3000sh Leopard tortoise	6.25	6.25
1341	4000sh Puff adder	8.25	8.25
1341A	5000sh Common house gecko	10.00	10.00
1341B	6000sh Dwarf chameleon	12.00	12.00
1341C	10,000sh Boomslang	20.00	20.00
	Nos. 1328-1341C (17)	70.40	70.40

Issued: 5000sh, 6000sh, 10,000sh, 11/20; others, 8/21.
Compare with Nos. 1550-1552.

1995, July 6
1315 A180 2000sh multicolored   4.50 4.50
Souvenir Sheet
1316 A180 2000sh multicolored   4.50 4.50

Rotary Intl., 90th Anniv. — A180

Rotary emblem and: No. 1315, Paul Harris. No. 1316, Natl. flag.

1995, July 6   Litho.   Perf. 14

Nsambya Church A184

Designs: 450sh, Namilyango College. 500sh, Intl. Cooperative Alliance, cent. 1000sh, UN Volunteers, 25th anniv.

1995, Sept. 7   Litho.   Perf. 14
1342-1345 A184 Set of 4   4.50 4.50
Mill Hill Missionaries in Uganda, cent. (#1342-1343).

Scenic Landscapes & Waterfalls of Uganda — A185

Designs: No. 1346, 50sh, Bwindi Forest. No. 1347, 50sh, Sipi Falls, vert. No. 1348, 100sh, Karamoja. No. 1349, 100sh, Murchison Falls. No. 1350, 450sh, Sunset, Lake Mburo Natl. Park. No. 1351, 450sh, Bujagali Falls. No. 1352, 500sh, Sunset, Gulu District. No. 1353, 500sh, Two Falls, Murchison. No. 1354, 900sh, Kabale District. No. 1355, 900sh, Falls, Rwenzoris, vert. No. 1356, 1000sh, Rwenzori Mountains. No. 1357, 1000sh, Falls, Rwenzoris, diff., vert.

1995, Sept. 14
1346-1357 A185 Set of 12   12.50 12.50

1996 Summer Olympics, Atlanta A186

Athletes: 50sh, Peter Rono, runner. 350sh, Reiner Klimke, dressage. 450sh, German cycling team. 500sh, Grace Birungi, runner. 900sh, Francis Ogola, track. 1000sh, Nyakana Godfrey, welter-weight boxer.
No. 1364, 2500sh, Rolf Dannenberg, discus, vert. No. 1365, 2500sh, Sebastian Coe, runner.

1995, Sept. 21
1358-1363 A186 Set of 6   7.25 7.25
Souvenir Sheets
1364-1365 A186 Set of 2   11.00 11.00

Domestic Animals A187

No. 1366: a, Peafowl (e). b, Pouter pigeon. c, Rock dove. d, Rouen duck. e, Guinea fowl. f, Donkey. g, Shetland pony. h, Palomino. i, Pigs. j, Border collie. k, Merino sheep. l, Milch goat. m, Black dutch rabbit. n, Lop rabbit. o, Somali cat (p). p, Asian cat.
No. 1367, 2500sh, Saddle bred horses. No. 1368, 2500sh, Oxen.

1995, Oct. 2
1366 A187 200sh Sheet of 16,
              #a.-p.   9.00 9.00
Souvenir Sheets
1367-1368 A187 Set of 2   13.00 13.00

Boy Scouts at Immunization Centers — A188

Designs: 150sh, Dressing children for weighing, vert. 350sh, Helping mothers carry children, vert. 450sh, Checking health cards. 800sh, Assisting in immunization. 1000sh, Weighing children, vert.

1995, Oct. 18   Litho.   Perf. 14
1369-1373 A188 Set of 5   6.00 6.00

Establishment of Nobel Prize Fund, Cent. — A189

No. 1374, 300sh: a, Hideki Yukawa, physics, 1949. b, F.W. DeKlerk, peace, 1993. c, Nelson Mandela, peace, 1993. d, Odysseus Elytis, literature, 1979. e, Ferdinand Buisson, peace, 1927. f, Lev Landau, physics, 1962. g, Halldor Laxness, literature, 1955. h, Wole Soyinka, literature, 1986. i, Desmond Tutu, peace, 1984. j, Susumu Tonegawa, physiology or medicine, 1987. k, Louis de Broglie, physics, 1929. l, George Seferis, literature, 1963.
No. 1375, 300sh: a, Hermann Staudinger, chemistry, 1953. b, Fritz Haber, chemistry, 1918. c, Bert Sakmann, physiology or medicine, 1991. d, Adolf O.R. Windaus, chemistry, 1928. e, Wilhelm Wien, physics, 1911. f, Ernest Hemingway, literature, 1954. g, Richard M. Willstätter, chemistry, 1915. h, Stanley Cohen, physiology or medicine, 1986. i, J. Hans D. Jensen, physics, 1963. j, Otto H. Warburg, physiology or medicine, 1931. k, Heinrich O. Wieland, chemistry, 1927. l, Albrecht Kossel, physiology or medicine, 1910.
No. 1376, 2000sh, Werner Forssmann, physiology or medicine, 1956. No. 1377, 2000sh, Nelly Sachs, literature, 1966.

1995, Oct. 31
Sheets of 12, #a-l
1374-1375 A189 Set of 2   18.00 18.00
Souvenir Sheets
1376-1377 A189 Set of 2   10.00 10.00

Christmas A190

Details or entire paintings of the Madonna and Child, by: 150sh, Hans Holbein the Younger. 350sh, Procaccini. 500sh, Pisanello. 1000sh, Crivelli. 1500sh, Le Nain.
No. 1383, 2500sh, The Holy Family, by Andrea Del Sarto. No. 1384, 2500sh, Madonna and Child, by Bellini.

1995, Nov. 30   Litho.   Perf. 13½x14
1378-1382 A190 Set of 5   7.75 7.75
Souvenir Sheets
1383-1384 A190 Set of 2   10.00 10.00

Orchids — A191

Designs: 150sh, Ansellia africana. 450sh, Satyricum crassicaule. 500sh, Polystachya cultriformis. 800sh, Disa erubescens.
No. 1389: a, Aerangis iuteoalba. b, Satyrium sacculatum. c, Bolusiella maudiae. d, Habenaria attenuata. e, Cyrtorchis arcuata. f, Eulophia angolensis. g, Tridactyle bicaudata. h, Eulophia horsfallii. i, Diaphananthe fragrantissima.
No. 1390, 2500sh, Diaphananthe pulchella. No. 1391, 2500sh, Rangaeris amaniensis.

1995, Dec. 8   Perf. 14
1385-1388 A191 Set of 4   6.00 6.00
Miniature Sheet
1389 A191 350sh Sheet of 9,
              #a.-i.   14.00 14.00
Souvenir Sheets
1390-1391 A191 Set of 2   12.00 12.00

New Year 1996 (Year of the Rat) A192

Rat eating: a, Purple grapes. b, Radishes. c, Corn. d, Squash.
2000sh, Green grapes.

1996, Jan. 29   Litho.   Perf. 14
1392 A192 350sh Block of 4,
              #a.-d.   2.75 2.75
   e. Miniature sheet, No. 1392   2.75 2.75
Souvenir Sheet
1393 A192 2000sh multicolored   4.00 4.00
No. 1392 issued in sheets of 16 stamps.

Miniature Sheet

Wildlife A193

No. 1394: a, 150sh, Wild dogs. b, 200sh, Fish eagle. c, 250sh, Hippopotamus. d, 350sh, Leopard. e, 400sh, Lion. f, 450sh, Lioness. g, 500sh, Meerkat. h, 550sh, Black rhinoceros. No. 1395: a, 150sh, Gorilla. b, 200sh, Cheetah. c, 250sh, Elephant. d, 350sh, Thomson's gazelle. e, 400sh, Crowned crane. f, 450sh, Sattlebill. g, 500sh, Vulture. h, 550sh, Zebra. No. 1396, 2000sh, Giraffe, vert. No. 1397, 2000sh, Gray heron.

1996, Mar. 27   Litho.   Perf. 14
1394 A193 Sheet of 8, #a.-h.   6.25 6.25
1395 A193 Sheet of 8, #a.-h.   6.75 6.75
Souvenir Sheets
1396-1397 A193 Set of 2   9.50 9.50

Disney Characters on the Orient Express — A194

Designs: 50sh, From London to Constantinople via Calais. 100sh, From Paris to Athens. 150sh, Ticket for the Pullman. 200sh, Pullman Corridor. 250sh, Dining car. 300sh, Staff beyond reproach. 600sh, Fun in the Pullman. 700sh, 1901 Unstoppable train enters the buffet in Frankfurt station. 800sh, 1929 passage

---

detained five days by snowstorm. 900sh, Filming "Murder on the Orient Express."
No. 1408, 2500sh, Donald Duck in engine. No. 1409, 2500sh, Mickey, Goofy, Minnie waving from back of train.

1996, Apr. 15   Perf. 14x13½
1398-1407 A194 Set of 10   10.50 10.50
Souvenir Sheets
1408-1409 A194 Set of 2   13.00 13.00

Paintings by Qi Baishi (1864-1957) A195

No. 1410: a, 50sh, Autumn Pond. b, 100sh, Partridge and Smartweed. c, 150sh, Begonias and Mynah. d, 200sh, Chrysanthemums, Cocks and Hens. e, 250sh, Crabs. f, 300sh, Wisterias and Bee. g, 350sh, Smartweed and Ink-drawn Butterflies. h, 400sh, Lotus and Mandarin Ducks. i, 450sh, Lichees and Locust. j, 500sh, Millet and Preying Mantis.
No. 1411: a, Locust, flowers. b, Crustaceans.

1996, May 8   Litho.   Perf. 15x14
1410 A195 Sheet of 10, #a.-j.   8.00 8.00
Souvenir Sheet
              Perf. 14
1411 A195 800sh Sheet of 2,
              #a.-b.   5.00 5.00
No. 1411 contains two 48x34mm stamps. The captions on Nos. 1410c and 1410d are transposed.
CHINA '96, 9th Asian Intl. Philatelic Exhibition.
See Nos. 1475-1476.

Queen Elizabeth II, 70th Birthday — A196

No. 1412: a, Portrait. b, As young woman, wearing crown jewels. c, Wearing red hat, coat.
2000sh, Portrait, diff.

1996, July 10   Perf. 13½x14
1412 A196 500sh Strip of 3,
              #a.-c.   4.00 4.00
Souvenir Sheet
1413 A196 2000sh multicolored   5.00 5.00
No. 1412 was issued in sheets of 9 stamps.

Jerusalem, 3000th Anniv. — A197

No. 1414: a, 300sh, Knesset Menorah. b. 500sh, Jerusalem Theater. c, 1000sh, Israel Museum.
2000sh, Grotto of the Nativity.

1996, July 10   *Perf. 14*
1414 A197 Sheet of 3, #a.-c.   4.00 4.00
Souvenir Sheet
1415 A197 2000sh multicolored   4.50 4.50
For overprint see Nos. 1556-1557.

Radio, Cent.
A198

Entertainers: 200sh, Ella Fitzgerald. 300sh, Bob Hope. 500sh, Nat "King" Cole. 800sh, Burns & Allen.
2000sh, Jimmy Durante.

1996, July 10   *Perf. 13½x14*
1416-1419 A198 Set of 4   3.50 3.50
Souvenir Sheet
1420 A198 2000sh multicolored   4.00 4.00

Mushrooms
A199

No. 1421: a, 150sh, Coprinus disseminatus. b, 300sh, Caprinus radians. c, 350sh, Hygrophorus coccineus. d, 400sh, Marasmius siccus. e, 450sh, Cortinarius collinitus. f, 500sh, Cortinarius cinnabarinus. g, 550sh, Coltricia cinnamomea. h, 1000sh, Mutinus elegans.
No. 1422, 2500sh, Inocybe soroia. No. 1423, 2500sh, Flammulina velutipes.

1996, June 24   *Perf. 14*
1421 A199 Sheet of 8, #a.-h.   7.50 7.50
Souvenir Sheets
1422-1423 A199 Set of 2   10.00 10.00

Butterflies
A200

No. 1424: a, 50sh, Catopsilia philea. b, 100sh, Dione vanillae. c, 150sh, Metemorpha dido. d, 200sh, Papilio sesotris. e, 250sh, Papilio neophilus. f, 300sh, Papilio thoas. g, 350sh, Diorina periander. h, 400sh, Morpho cipris. i, 450sh, Catonephele numilia. j, 500sh, Heliconius doris. k, 550sh, Prepona antimache. l, 600sh, Eunica alcmena.
No. 1425, 2500sh, Caligo martia. No. 1426, 2500sh, Heliconius doris.

1996, June 26
1424 A200 Sheet of 12, #a.-l.   8.50 8.50
Souvenir Sheets
1425-1426 A200 Set of 2   10.00 10.00

UNICEF, 50th Anniv. A201

Designs: 450sh, Two children. 500sh, Two children wearing hats. 550sh, Boy in classroom.
2000sh, Mother and child, vert.

1996, July 10   *Litho.*   *Perf. 14*
1427-1429 A201 Set of 3   3.00 3.00
Souvenir Sheet
1430 A201 2000sh multicolored   4.00 4.00

UNESCO, 50th Anniv. — A202

Natl. Parks: 450sh, Darien, Panama. 500sh, Los Glaciares, Argentina. 550sh, Tubbatha Reef Marine Park, Philippines.
2500sh, Rwenzori Mountains, Uganda.

1996, July 10
1431-1433 A202 Set of 3   4.00 4.00
Souvenir Sheet
1434 A202 2500sh multicolored   6.00 6.00

Trains — A203

No. 1435: a, Loco Type B.B.B., Japan, 1968. b, Stephenson's "Rocket," 1829. c, "Austria," 1843. d, 19th cent. type. e, Loco Anglo-Indian, India, 1947. f, Type CoCo DB, Germany.
No. 1436: a, "Lady of Lynn," Great Western, England. b, Chinese type, 1930. c, Meyer-Ritson, Chile. d, Union Pacific "Centennial," US. e, "581" Japanese Natl. Railway, Japan, 1968. f, Co.Co. Series "120" DB, Germany.
No. 1437, 2500sh, Mallard, Great Britain. No. 1438, 2500sh, "99" Type 1-5-0, Germany.

1996, July 25
1435 A203 Sheet of 6,
     #a.-f.   5.50 5.50
1436 A203 550sh Sheet of 6,
     #a.-f.   6.50 6.50
Souvenir Sheets
1437-1438 A203 Set of 2   10.00 10.00

Uganda Post Office, Cent. A204

Designs: 150sh, Emblem. 450sh, Post bus service. 500sh, Modern mail transportation means. 550sh, "100," #48, #59.

1996, Aug. 30   *Litho.*   *Perf. 14*
1439-1442 A204 Set of 4   4.50 4.50

Fruits
A205

Designs: 150sh, Mango, vert. 350sh, Orange, vert. 450sh, Paw paw, vert. 500sh, Avocado, vert. 550sh, Watermelon.

1996, Oct. 8   *Litho.*   *Perf. 14*
1443-1447 A205 Set of 5   4.50 4.50

Christmas A206

Details or entire paintings: 150sh, Annunciation, by Lorenzo Di Credi. 350sh, Madonna of the Loggia (detail), by Botticelli. 400sh, Virgin in Glory with Child and Angels, by Lorenzetti P. 450sh, Adoration of the Child, by Filippino Lippi. 500sh, Madonna of the Loggia, by Botticelli. 550sh, The Strength, by Botticelli.
No. 1454, 2500sh, Holy Allegory, by Giovanni Bellini, horiz. No. 1455, 2500sh, The Virgin on the Throne with Child and Saints, by Ghirlandaio, horiz.

1996, Nov. 18   *Perf. 13½x14*
1448-1453 A206 Set of 6   5.75 5.75
Souvenir Sheets
Perf. 14x13½
1454-1455 A206 Set of 2   10.00 10.00

Sylvester Stallone in Movie, "Rocky III" — A207

1996, Nov. 21   *Litho.*   *Perf. 14*
1456 A207 800sh Sheet of 3   6.00 6.00

1996 Summer Olympic Games, Atlanta A208

Scenes from first Olympic Games in US, St. Louis, 1904: 350sh, Steamboat race, stadium. 450sh, Boxer George Finnegan. 500sh, Quadriga race (ancient games). 800sh, John Flanagan, hammer throw, vert.

1996, Dec. 8
1457-1460 A208 Set of 4   5.00 5.00

Traditional Attire — A209

Designs: 150sh, Western region, vert. 350sh, Karimo Jong women, vert. 450sh, Ganda. 500sh, Acholi.
No. 1465, vert. — Headdresses: a, Acholi. b, Alur. c, Bwola dance. d, Madi. e, Karimojong. f, Karimojong with feathers.

1997, Jan. 2
1461-1464 A209 Set of 4   4.00 4.00
1465 A209 300sh Sheet of 6,
     #a.-f.   5.00 5.00

New Year 1997 (Year of the Ox) A210

Paintings of oxen: Nos. 1466a, 1467b, Walking left. Nos. 1466b, 1467b, Calf nursing. Nos. 1466c, 1467d, Calf lying down, adult. Nos. 1466d, 1467c, Adult lying down.
1500sh, Calf, vert.

1997, Jan. 24   *Litho.*   *Perf. 14*
1466 A210 350sh Strip of 4,
     #a.-d.   3.50 3.50
1467 A210 350sh Sheet of 4,
     #a.-d.   3.50 3.50
Souvenir Sheet
1468 A210 1500sh multicolored   4.00 4.00
No. 1466 was issued in sheets of 4 vert. strips.

World Wildlife Fund — A211

No. 1469 — Rothschild's giraffe: a, Running. b, One bending neck across another's back. c, Head up close. d, Young giraffe, adult facing opposite directions.
2500sh, like #1469d, horiz.

1997, Feb. 12
1469 A211 300sh Strip of 4,
     #a.-d.   3.00 3.00
Souvenir Sheet
1470 A211 2500sh multicolored   6.50 6.50
No. 1469 was issued in sheets of 4 strips with each strip in a different order.
No. 1470 does not have the WWF emblem.

Souvenir Sheet

Mural from Tomb in Xian — A212

Illustration reduced.

1996, May 8   *Litho.*   *Perf. 14*
1471 A212 500sh multicolored   1.50 1.50
China '96. No. 1471 was not available until March 1997.

Promulgation of the Constitution, Oct. 8, 1995 — A213

Designs: 150sh, shown. 350sh, Scroll. 550sh, Closed book, vert.

1997, Feb. 25   *Perf. 14x13½*
1472-1474 A213 Set of 3   2.75 2.75

Paintings Type of 1996

No. 1475 — Paintings by Wu Changshuo (1844-1927): a, 50sh, Red Plum Blossom and Daffodil. b, 100sh, Peony. c, 150sh, Rosaceae. d, 200sh, Pomegranate. e, 250sh, Peach, Peony, and Plum Blossom. f, 300sh, Calyx canthus. g, 350sh, Chrysanthemum. h, 400sh, Calabash. i, 450sh, Chrysanthemum, diff. j, 500sh, Cypress tree.
No. 1476: a, 550sh, Litchi. b, 1000sh, Water lily.

1997, Mar. 5   *Perf. 14x15*
1475 A195 Sheet of 10, #a.-j.   6.50 6.50

Souvenir Sheet
Perf. 14

1476 A195 Sheet of 2, #a.-b.   3.50 3.50

Hong Kong '97. No. 1476 contains two 51x38mm stamps.

Summer Olympic
Winners — A214

No. 1477: a, 150sh, Sohn Kee-chung, marathon, 1936. b, 200sh, Walter Davis, high jump, 1952. c, 250sh, Roland Matthes, swimming, 1968. d, 300sh, Akii Bua, 400m hurdles, 1972. e, 350sh, Wolfgang Nordwig, pole vault, 1972. f, 400sh, Wilma Rudolph, 4x100m relay, 1960. g, 450sh, Abebe Bikila, marathon, 1964. h, 500sh, Edwin Moses, 400m hurdles, 1984. i, 550sh, Randy Williams, long jump, 1972.

No. 1478: a, 150sh, Bob Hayes, 100m, 1964. b, 200sh, Rod Milburn, 110m hurdles, 1972. c, 250sh, Filbert Bayi, running, 1976. d, 300sh, H. Kipchoge Keino, steeple chase, 1972. e, 350sh, Ron Ray, running, 1976. f, 400sh, Joe Frazier, boxing, 1976. g, 450sh, Carl Lewis, 100m race, 1984. h, 500sh, Gisela Mauermayer, discus, 1936. i, 550sh, Dietmar Mogenburg, high jump, 1984.

1997, Mar. 3   Litho.   Perf. 14
Sheets of 9, #a-i

1477-1478 A214 Set of 2   15.00 15.00

No. 1478h is inscribed shot put in error.

Disney's "Toy Story" — A215

No. 1479, vert.: a, Woody. b, Buzz Lightyear. c, Bo Peep. d, Hamm. e, Slinky. f, Rex.
No. 1480: a, Woody on Andy's bed. b, "Get this wagon train a-movin." c, Bo Peep, blocks. d, Buzz Lightyear. e, Slinky, Rex. f, Woody hides. g, Buzz, Woody. h, Rex, Slinky, Buzz. i, Buzz, Woody on bed.
No. 1481: a, Woody telling Buzz he's sheriff. b, Green Army on alert. c, Woody, Buzz compete. d, Woody sights alien. e, Buzz ponders fate. f, "The Cla-a-a-a-a-w." g, Intergalactic emergency. h, Buzz, Woody argue at gas station. i, Buzz, Woody give chase.
No. 1482, 2000sh, Woody spots an intruder, vert. No. 1483, 2000sh, Andy's toys, vert. No. 1484, 2000sh, Buzz Lightyear in space, vert.

1997, Apr. 2   Perf. 14x13½, 13½x14
1479 A215 Sheet of 6,
                #a.-f.   1.75 1.75
1480 A215 Sheet of 9,
                #a.-i.   3.75 3.75
1481 A215 Sheet of 9,
                #a.-i.   4.50 4.50
Souvenir Sheets
1482-1484 A215 Set of 3   14.00 14.00

Man in Space
A216

No. 1484A: b, Pioneer 10. c, Voyager 1. d, Viking Orbiter. e, Pioneer, Venus 1. f, Mariner 9. g, Galileo Entry Probe. h, Mariner 10. i, Voyager 2.
No. 1485: a, Sputnik 1. b, Apollo. c, Soyuz. d, Intelsat 1. e, Manned maneuvering unit. f, Skylab. g, Telstar 1. h, Hubble telescope.
No. 1486, Space shuttle Challenger. No. 1486A, Mars Viking Lander Robot.

1997, Apr. 16   Litho.   Perf. 14
1484A A216 250sh Sheet of 8,
                     #b.-i.   5.00 5.00
1485   A216 300sh Sheet of 8,
                     #a.-h.   5.50 5.50
Souvenir Sheet
1486   A216 2000sh multicolored 4.75 4.75
1486A A216 2000sh multicolored 5.00 5.00

No. 1486 contains one 34x61mm stamp, No. 1486A one 61x35mm stamp.

Deng Xiaoping (1904-97), Chinese
Leader — A217

Designs: a, 500sh. b, 550sh. c, 1000sh. 2000sh, Portrait, diff.

1997, May 9
1487 A217 Sheet of 3, #a.-c.   5.00 5.00
Souvenir Sheet
1488 A217 2000sh multicolored   5.00 5.00

Environmental
Protection — A218

No. 1489: a-d, Various water hyacinths.
No. 1490: a, Buffalo. b, Uganda kob. c, Guinea fowl. d, Malibu stork.
2500sh, Gorilla.

1997, May 14
1489 A218 500sh Sheet of 4,
                    #a.-d.   4.50 4.50
1490 A218 550sh Sheet of 4,
                    #a.-d.   5.00 5.00
Souvenir Sheet
1491 A218 2500sh multicolored   5.50 5.50

Queen
Elizabeth
II, Prince
Philip,
50th
Wedding
Anniv.
A219

No. 1492: a, Queen. b, Royal arms. c, Queen in purple outfit, Prince. d, Prince, Queen in white hat. e, Buckingham Palace. f, Prince Philip.
2000sh, Queen in wedding dress.

1997, June 2   Litho.   Perf. 14
1492 A219 200sh Sheet of 6,
                    #a.-f.   3.00 3.00
Souvenir Sheet
1493 A219 2000sh multicolored   4.50 4.50

Paul E. Harris (1868-1947), Founder
of Rotary, Intl. — A220

Designs: 1000sh, Combating hunger, Harris. 2500sh, First Rotarians, Gustavus H. Loehr, Sylvester Schiele, Hiram E. Shorey, Paul E. Harris.

1997, June 2
1494 A220 1000sh multicolored   2.00 2.00
Souvenir Sheet
1495 A220 2500sh multicolored   5.00 5.00

Heinrich
von
Stephan
(1831-97)
A221

No. 1496 — Portrait of Von Stephan and: a, Chinese post boat. b, UPU emblem. c, Russian special post.
2500sh, Von Stephan, French postman on stilts.

1997, June 2
1496 A221 800sh Sheet of 3,
                    #a.-c.   4.75 4.75
Souvenir Sheet
1497 A221 2500sh multicolored   5.00 5.00
PACIFIC 97.

Chernobyl
Disaster,
10th Anniv.
A222

Designs: 500sh,   UNESCO.   700sh, Chabad's Children of Chernobyl.

1997, May 21   Litho.   Perf. 14x13½
1498 A222 500sh multicolored   1.50 1.50
1499 A222 700sh multicolored   2.00 2.00

1998
Winter
Olympic
Games,
Nagano
A223

Designs: 350sh, Men's slalom, vert. 450sh, Two-man bobsled, vert. 800sh, Women's slalom. 2000sh, Men's speed skating.
No. 1504: a, Ski jumping. b, Giant slalom. c, Cross-country skiing. d, Ice hockey. e, Man, pairs figure skating. f, Woman, pairs figure skating.
No. 1505, 2500sh, Downhill skiing. No. 1506, 2500sh, Women's figure skating.

1997, June 23   Litho.   Perf. 14
1500-1503 A223 Set of 4   7.25 7.25
1504 A223 500sh Sheet of 6,
                    #a.-f.   6.25 6.25
Souvenir Sheets
1505-1506 A223 Set of 2   10.00 10.00

Makerere University, 75th
Anniv. — A224

Designs: 150sh, Main building, administration block. 450sh, East African School of Librarianship, vert. 500sh, Buyana stock farm. 550sh, Ceramic dish, School of Architectural and Fine Arts.

1997, July 31   Perf. 14x13½, 13½x14
1507-1510 A224 Set of 4   4.00 4.00

Mahatma Gandhi
(1869-1948)
A225

Various portraits.

1997, Oct. 5   Litho.   Perf. 14
1511 A225 600sh multicolored   2.50 2.50
1512 A225 700sh multicolored   2.75 2.75
Souvenir Sheet
1513 A225 1000sh multicolored   4.00 4.00

1998 World Cup Soccer
Championships, France — A226

No. 1514, vert.: a, 200sh, Fritz Walter, Germany. b, 300sh, Daniel Passarella, Argentina. c, 450sh, Dino Zoff, Italy. d, 500sh, Bobby Moore, England. e, 600sh, Diego Maradona, Argentina. f, 550sh, Franz Beckenbauer, West Germany.
No. 1515 — Argentina vs. West Germany, Mexico City, 1986: a, d, e, f, h, Action scenes. b, Azteca Stadium. c, Argentine player holding World Cup. g, Argentina team picture.
No. 1516 — Top tournament scorers: a, Paulo Rossi. b, Mario Kempes. c, Gerd Muller. d, Grzegorz Lato. e, Ademir. f, Eusebio Ferreica da Silva. g, Salvatore (Toto) Schillaci. h, Leonidas da Silva. i, Gary Lineker.
No. 1517, 2000sh, England, 1966. No. 1518, 2000sh, W. Germany, 1990.

1997, Oct. 3   Litho.   Perf. 14
1514 A226 Sheet of 6, #a.-f.   10.50 10.50
1515 A226 250sh Sheet of 8,
                    #a.-h.   8.00 8.00
1516 A226 250sh Sheet of 9,
                    #a.-i. + label 9.00 9.00
Souvenir Sheets
1517-1518 A226 Set of 2   8.50 8.50

Diana, Princess
of Wales (1961-
97)
A227

No. 1519 was issued in sheets of 6.

1997, Dec. 1
1519 A227 60sh multicolored   1.75 1.75

Christmas
A228

Sculpture, entire paintings or details: 200sh, Putto and Dolphin, by Andrea del Verrocchio. 300sh, The Fall of the Rebel Angels, by Pieter Bruegel the Elder. 400sh, The Immaculate

Conception, by Murillo. 500sh, Music-making Angel, by Rosso Fiorentino. 600sh, Cupid and Psyche, by Adolphe-William Bouguereau. 700sh, Cupid and Psyche, by Antonio Canova.

No. 1526, 2500sh, Virgin, Angels from The Assumption of the Virgin, by El Greco. No. 1527, 2500sh, Angel from The Assumption of the Virgin, by El Greco.

1997, Dec. 1
1520-1525 A228 Set of 6   5.50 5.50
Souvenir Sheets
1526-1527 A228 Set of 2   10.00 10.00

New Year 1998 (Year of the Tiger) A229

Various paintings of tigers: No. 1528: a, Looking backward. b, Jumping. c, Lying, looking forward. d, Lying, mouth open.
1500sh, On cliff.

1998, Jan. 16   **Litho.**   **Perf. 13½**
1528 A229   350sh Sheet of 4,
   #a.-d.   2.75 2.75
Souvenir Sheet
1529 A229 1500sh multicolored   3.00 3.00

Tourist Attractions — A230

Designs: 300sh, Namugongo Martyrs Shrine, vert. 400sh, Kasubi Tombs. 500sh, Tourist boat, Kazinga Channel. 600sh, Elephant. 700sh, Bujagali Falls, Jinja.

1998, Feb. 6   **Litho.**   **Perf. 14**
1530-1534 A230 Set of 5   6.00 6.00

Mother Teresa (1910-97) — A231

No. 1535: a-h, Various portraits. 2000sh, With Diana, Princess of Wales (1961-97).

1998, Feb. 9   **Litho.**   **Perf. 14**
1535 A231   300sh Sheet of 8,
   #a.-h.   6.75 6.75
Souvenir Sheet
1536 A231 2000sh multicolored   6.00 6.00
Nos. 1535a, 1535d-1535e, 1535h are each 22x36mm.

UNICEF in Uganda, 30th Anniv. A232

Designs: 300sh, "Support for children with disabilities." 400sh, "Safeguard children

---

against polio." 600sh, "Sanitation... responsibility for all." 700sh, "Children's right to basic education."

1998, Mar. 6   **Perf. 13½x14**
1537-1540 A232 Set of 4   5.50 5.50

Dinosaurs — A233

Designs, horiz: 300sh, Pteranodon. 400sh, Diplodocus. 500sh, Lambeosaurus. 600sh, Centrosaurus. 700sh, Parasaurolophus.
No. 1546: a, Cetiosaurus. b, Brontosaurus. c, Brachiosaurus. d, Deinonychus. e, Dimetrodon. f, Megalosaurus.
No. 1547, 2500sh, Tyrannosaurus. No. 1548, 2500sh, Iguanodon.

1998, Mar. 24   **Litho.**   **Perf. 14**
1541-1545 A233 Set of 5   5.50 5.50
1546 A233 600sh Sheet of 6,
   #a.-f.   8.00 8.00
Souvenir Sheets
1547-1548 A233 Set of 2   12.00 12.00
Nos. 1547-1548 each contain one 43x57mm stamp.

Writers — A234

No. 1549: a, Rita Dove. b, Mari Evans. c, Sterling A. Brown. d, June Jordan. e, Stephen Henderson. f, Zora Neale Hurston.

1998, Apr. 6
1549 A234 300sh Sheet of 6,
   #a.-f.   4.25 4.25

Reptiles — A235

Designs: 300sh, Armadillo girdled lizard. 600sh, Spotted sandveld lizard. 700sh, Bell's ringed tortoise.

1998, Apr. 21   **Perf. 13½**
1550 A235 300sh multicolored   .75 .75
1551 A235 600sh multicolored   1.50 1.50
1552 A235 700sh multicolored   1.75 1.75
   Nos. 1550-1552 (3)   4.00 4.00
Compare with Nos. 1328-1335.

Mickey Mouse, 70th Birthday — A236

No. 1553 — Scenes from cartoon, "Runaway Brain:" a, Mickey afraid of shadow. b, Mickey petting Pluto, newspaper. c, Mickey playing computer game, Pluto. d, Mickey, Minnie running. e, Mickey as target of experiment. f, Minnie being held captive by Pete on top of skyscraper. g, Mickey throwing lasso. h, Mickey surrounding Pete with rope. i, Mickey, Minnie holding onto rope above skyscrapers.

No. 1554, 3000sh, Mickey, Minnie embracing on top of skyscraper. No. 1555, 3000sh, Mickey, Minnie kissing on raft, vert.

1998, May 4   **Litho.**   **Perf. 14x13½**
1553 A236 400sh Sheet of 9,
   #a.-i.   8.50 8.50
Souvenir Sheets
1554-1555 A236 Set of 2   14.00 14.00

Nos. 1414-1415 Ovptd.

1998, May 13   **Litho.**   **Perf. 14**
1556 A197 Sheet of 3, #a.-c.
   (#1414)   4.00 4.00
Souvenir Sheet
1557 A197 2000sh multi (#1415)   4.50 4.50
Sheet margins of Nos. 1556-1557 each contain additional overprint, "ISRAEL 98 — WORLD STAMP EXHIBITION/TEL-AVIV 13-21 MAY 1998."

Sailing Ships A237

No. 1558, 1000sh: a, Fishing schooner. b, Chesapeake oyster boat. c, Java Sea schooner.
No. 1559, 1000sh: a, Santa Maria, 15th cent. galleon. b, Mayflower, 15th cent. galleon. c, Bark.
No. 1560, 3000sh, Boat with lateen sails. No. 1561, 3000sh, Thames River barge, vert.

1998, June 2   **Litho.**   **Perf. 13x13½**
Sheets of 3, #a-c + Label
1558-1559 A237 Set of 2   13.00 13.00
Souvenir Sheets
1560-1561 A237 Set of 2   13.00 13.00
Nos. 1560-1561 are continuous designs.

Aircraft A238

No. 1562: a, US F4F Wildcat. b, Japanese Zero. c, British Spitfire. d, British Harrier. e, S3A Viking. f, US Corsair.
No. 1563: a, Dornier Do-X transatlantic flyer, 1929. b, German Zucker mail rocket, 1930. c, X-15 Rocket Plane, 1955. d, Goddard's Rocket, 1930's. e, Wright brothers' flight, 1903. f, 160R Sikorsky helicopter, 1939.
No. 1564, 2500sh, P40 Tomahawk. No. 1565, 2500sh, SH346 Seabat.

1998, July 24   **Litho.**   **Perf. 14**
1562 A238 500sh Sheet of 6,
   #a.-f.   7.00 7.00
1563 A238 600sh Sheet of 6,
   #a.-f.   8.25 8.25
Souvenir Sheets
1564-1565 A238 Set of 2   12.00 12.00

Flowers of the Mediterranean — A239

No. 1566, vert: a, Onosma. b, Rhododendron luteum. c, Paeonia mascula. d, Geranium macorrhizum. e, Cyclamen graecum. f, Lilium

---

rhodopaedum. g, Narcissus pseudonarcissus. h, Paeonia rhodia. i, Aquilegia amaliae.
No. 1567: a, Paeonia peregrina. b, Muscari comutatum. c, Sternbergia. d, Dianthus. e, Verbascum. f, Aubrieta gracilis. g, Galanthus nivalis. h, Campanula incurva. i, Crocus sieberi.
No. 1568, 2000sh, Paeonia parnassica, vert. No. 1569, 2000sh, Pancratium maritimum, vert.

1998, Sept. 23   **Litho.**   **Perf. 14**
1566 A239 300sh Sheet of 9,
   #a.-i.   5.50 5.50
1567 A239 600sh Sheet of 9,
   #a.-i.   11.00 11.00
Souvenir Sheets
1568-1569 A239 Set of 2   9.00 9.00

Christmas A240

Birds: 300sh, Bohemian waxwing. 400sh, House sparrow. 500sh, Black-capped chickadee. 600sh, Eurasian bullfinch. 700sh, Painted bunting. 1000sh, Northern cardinal.
No. 1576, 2500sh, Winter wren, vert. No. 1577, 2500sh, Red-winged blackbird, vert.

1998, Dec. 3   **Litho.**   **Perf. 14**
1570-1575 A240 Set of 6   7.00 7.00
Souvenir Sheets
1576-1577 A240 Set of 2   11.00 11.00

Diana, Princess of Wales (1961-97) A241

1998, Dec. 28   **Litho.**   **Perf. 14½**
1578 A241 700sh multicolored   2.00 2.00

Picasso A242

Paintings: 500sh, Woman Reading, 1935, vert. 600sh, Portrait of Dora Maar, 1937, vert. 700sh, Des Moiselles D'Avignon, 1907.
2500sh, Night Fishing at Antibes, 1939, vert.

1998, Dec. 28   **Perf. 14½x13, 13x14½**
1579-1581 A242 Set of 3   3.75 3.75
Souvenir Sheet
1582 A242 2500sh multicolored   5.25 5.25

Gandhi — A243

1998, Dec. 28   **Perf. 14**
1583 A243 600sh Portrait   2.00 2.00
Souvenir Sheet
1584 A243 2500sh Family portrait, horiz.   6.00 6.00
No. 1583 was issued in sheets of 4.

1998 World Scouting Jamboree, Chile — A244

No. 1585: a, Cub Scouts greet Pres. Eisenhower, Georgia, 1956. b, Uncle Dan Beard at 90th birthday party, 1990. c, Future Vice President Hubert Humphrey leads South Dakota troop, 1934.
2000sh, Young scout, tamed beaver, vert.

1998, Dec. 28
| 1585 | A244 | 700sh | Sheet of 3, | | |
| | | | #a.-c. | 6.00 | 6.00 |

Souvenir Sheet
| 1586 | A244 | 2000sh multicolored | 4.00 | 4.00 |

New Year 1999 (Year of the Rabbit) A245

No. 1587 — Rabbits: a, White. b, With carrot. c, Brown & white. e, Black & white.

1999, Jan. 4
| 1587 | A245 | 350sh | Sheet of 4, | | |
| | | | #a.-d. | 3.00 | 3.00 |

Souvenir Sheet
| 1588 | A245 | 1500sh Rabbit, diff. | 3.00 | 3.00 |

Uganda Post Office A246

1999, Jan. 18
| 1589 | A246 | 300sh multicolored | 1.75 | 1.75 |

Traditional Hairstyles — A247

Hairstyle, region: 300sh, Iru, Bairu. 500sh, Enshunju, Bahima. 550sh, Elemungole, Karamojong. 600sh, Longo, Langi. 700sh, Ekikuura, Bahima.

1999, Feb. 1
| 1590-1594 | A247 | Set of 5 | 6.00 | 6.00 |

Marine Life A248

No. 1595: a, Wolfish. b, Equal sea star. c, Purple sea urchin. d, Mountain crab.
No. 1596: a, Blue marlin. b, Arctic tern. c, Common dolphin. d, Blacktip shark. e, Manta ray. f, Blackedge moray. g, Loggerhead turtle. h, Sailfin tang. i, Two-spotted octopus.
No. 1597, 2500sh, Sea nettle jellyfish. No. 1598, 2500sh, Decatopecten striatus.

1999, Mar. 15   Litho.   Perf. 14
| 1595 | A248 | 500sh | Sheet of 4, | | |
| | | | #a.-d. | 4.00 | 4.00 |

| 1596 | A248 | 500sh | Sheet of 9, | | |
| | | | #a.-i. | 10.00 | 10.00 |

Souvenir Sheets
| 1597-1598 | A248 | each | 9.50 | 9.50 |
Intl. Year of the Ocean.

Intl. Year of the Elderly A249

Designs: 300sh, Income generating activity. 500sh, Learning from each other. 600sh, Leisure time for the aged. 700sh, Distributing food to the aged.

1999, July 19   Litho.   Perf. 13x13½
| 1599-1602 | A249 | Set of 4 | 3.50 | 3.50 |

First Manned Moon Landing, 30th Anniv. — A250

No. 1603: a, Apollo 11 launch. b, Apollo 11 command and service modules. c, Edwin E. Aldrin, Jr. on lunar module ladder. d, Saturn V ready to launch. e, Lunar module descending. f, Aldrin on moon.
No. 1604: a, Freedom 7. b, Gemini 4. c, Apollo 11 command and service modules, diff. d, Vostok 1. e, Saturn V. f, Lunar module on moon.
No. 1605, 3000sh, Aldrin with scientific experiment. No. 1606, 3000sh, Command module re-entry.

1999, Nov. 24   Litho.   Perf. 13¾
1603	A250	600sh	Sheet of 6,		
			#a.-f.	5.75	5.75
1604	A250	700sh	Sheet of 6,		
			#a.-f.	6.50	6.50

Souvenir Sheets
| 1605-1606 | A250 | Set of 2 | 10.00 | 10.00 |

Queen Mother (b. 1900) — A251

No. 1607: a, With stole. b, At wedding. c, With tiara (black and white photo). d, With tiara (color photo).
3000sh, Visiting Cambridge, 1961.

1999, Nov. 24   Perf. 14
| 1607 | A251 | 1200sh | Sheet of 4, | | |
| | | | #a.-d. | 7.50 | 7.50 |

Souvenir Sheet
Perf. 13¾
| 1608 | A251 | 3000sh multicolored | 5.00 | 5.00 |
No. 1608 contains one 38x51mm stamp.

Hokusai Paintings A252

No. 1609: a, Dragon Flying Over Mount Fuji (dragon). b, Famous Poses From the Kabuki Theater (one figure). c, Kitsune No Yomeiri. d, Dragon Flying Over Mount Fuji (Mount Fuji). e, Famous Poses From the Kabuki Theater (two figures). f, Girl Holding Cloth.
3000sh, Japanese Spaniel.

1999, Nov. 24   Litho.   Perf. 13¾
| 1609 | A252 | 700sh | Sheet of 6, | | |
| | | | #a.-f. | 6.50 | 6.50 |

Souvenir Sheet
| 1610 | A252 | 3000sh multicolored | 5.00 | 5.00 |

Birds — A253

Designs: 300sh, African penduline tit. 1000sh, Yellow-fronted tinkerbird. 1200sh, Zebra waxbill. 1800sh, Sooty anteater chat.
No. 1615: a, Gray-headed kingfisher. b, Green-headed sunbird. c, Speckled pigeon. d, Gray parrot. e, Barn owl. f, Gray crowned crane. g, Shoebill. h, Black heron.
No. 1616: a, Scarlet-chested sunbird. b, Lesser honeyguide. c, African palm swift. d, Swamp flycatcher. e, Lizard buzzard. f, Osprey. g, Cardinal woodpecker. h, Pearl-spotted owlet.
No. 1617: a, Fox's weaver. b, Chin-spot flycatcher. c, Blue swallow. d, Purple-breasted sunbird. e, Knob-billed duck. f, Red-collared widowbird. g, Ruwenzori turaco. h, African cuckoo hawk.
No. 1618, 3000sh, Four-banded sandgrouse. No. 1619, 3000sh, Paradise whydah.

1999, Dec. 6   Perf. 14
1611-1614	A253	Set of 4	6.50	6.50
1615	A253	500sh	Sheet of 8,		
			#a.-h.	6.00	6.00
1616	A253	600sh	Sheet of 8,		
			#a.-h.	7.25	7.25
1617	A253	700sh	Sheet of 8,		
			#a.-h.	8.25	8.25

Souvenir Sheets
| 1618-1619 | A253 | Set of 2 | 9.00 | 9.00 |

Primates — A254

Designs: 300sh, L'hoesti monkey. 400sh, Blue monkey. 500sh, Patas monkey. 600sh, Red-tailed monkey. 700sh, Black and white colobus. 1000sh, Mountain gorilla.
2500sh, Olive baboon.

1999, Nov. 19   Litho.   Perf. 13½x14
| 1620-1625 | A254 | Set of 6 | 5.25 | 5.25 |

Souvenir Sheet
| 1626 | A254 | 2500sh multicolored | 4.00 | 4.00 |

Butterflies A255

Designs: 300sh, Epiphora bauhiniae, vert. 400sh, Phylloxiphia formosa. 500sh, Bunaea alcinoe, vert. 600sh, Euchloron megaera. 700sh, Argema mimosae, vert. 1800sh, Denephila nerii.
3000sh, Lobobunaea angasana.

Perf. 13½x13¼, 13¼x13½
2000, Jan. 19   Litho.
| 1627-1632 | A255 | Set of 6 | 6.75 | 6.75 |

Souvenir Sheet
| 1633 | A255 | 3000sh multi | 5.00 | 5.00 |

A256   A257

UPU, 125th anniv. (in 1999): 600sh, Postman, two women, girl. 700sh, Woman, girl, mail box. 1200sh, Postman in horse-drawn wagon.

2000, Jan. 28   Litho.   Perf. 14
| 1634-1636 | A256 | Set of 3 | 4.50 | 4.50 |

2000, Feb. 18
No. 1637, 600sh — Orchids: a, Angraecum eichcerianum. b, Angraecum leonis. c, Arophyllum giganteum. d, Bulbophyllum barbigerum. e, Angraecum ciryamae. f, Aerangis ellisii. g, Disa umiflora. h, Eulophia alta. i, Ancistrochilus stylosa.
No. 1638, 600sh: a, Eulophia paivenna. b, Ansellia gigantea. c, Anglaecopsis gracillima. d, Bonatea steudneri. e, Bulbophyllum falcatum. f, Aerangis citrata. g, Eulophiella elisabethae. h, Aerangis rhodosticta. i, Angraecum scottianum.
No. 1639, 700sh: a, Grammangis ellisii. b, Eulophia stenophylia. c, Oeoniella polystachys. d, Cymbidiella humblotti. e, Polystachya bella. f, Vanilla polycepis. g, Eulophileea roemplerana. h, Habenaria englerana. i, Ansellia frallana.
No. 1640, 700sh: a, Eulophia orthoplectra. b, Cirrhopetalum umbellatum. c, Eulophiella rolfei. d, Eulophia porphyroglossa. e, Eulopia petersii. f, Cyrtorchis arcuata. g, Eurychone rothschildiana. h, Eulophia quartiniana. i, Eulophia stenophylia (one flower).
No. 1641, 3000sh, Polystachya tayloriana, horiz. No. 1642, 3000sh, Ancistrochilus rothschildianus, horiz. No. 1643, 3000sh, Calanthe corymbosa, horiz. No. 1644, 3000sh, Cymbidiella rhodochila, horiz.

Sheets of 9, #a.-i.
| 1637-1638 | A257 | Set of 2 | 16.00 | 16.00 |
| 1639-1640 | A257 | Set of 2 | 21.00 | 21.00 |

Souvenir Sheets
| 1641-1644 | A257 | Set of 4 | 20.00 | 20.00 |

Butterflies — A258

Designs: 300sh, Short-tailed admiral. 400sh, Guineafowl. 1200sh, Club-tailed charaxes. 1800sh, Cymothoe egesta.
No. 1649: a, Charaxes anrticlea. b, Epitola posthumus. c, Beautiful monarch. d, Blue-banded nymph. e, Euxanthe crossleyi. f, African map. g, Western blue charaxes. h, Noble.
No. 1650: a, Green-veined charaxes. b, Ansorge's leaf butterfly. c, Crawshay's sapphire blue. d, Palla ussheri. e, Friar. f, Blood-red cymothoe. g, Mocker. h, Charaxes eupuale.

No. 1651: a, Aeraea pseudolycia. b, Veined yellow. c, Buxton's hairstreak. d, Iolaus isomenias. e, Veined swallowtail. f, Figtree blue. g, Scarlet tip. h, Precis octavia.
No. 1652, 3000sh, African monarch. No. 1653, 3000sh, Kigezi swordtail.

2000, May 24   Litho.   Perf. 14
1645-1648 A258 Set of 4   6.50 6.50
1649 A258 500sh Sheet of 8, #a-h   6.75 6.75
1650 A258 600sh Sheet of 8, #a-h   6.75 6.75
1651 A258 700sh Sheet of 8, #a-h   7.75 7.75

Souvenir Sheets
1652-1653 A258 Set of 2   9.00 9.00
The Stamp Show 2000, London (Nos. 1649-1653).

Popes — A259

No. 1654: a, Agapetus II (946-55). b, Alexander II (1061-73). c, Anastasius IV (1153-54). d, Benedict VIII (1012-24). e, Benedict VII (974-83). f, Calixtus II (1119-24).
No. 1655, Celestine III (1191-98).
Illustration reduced.

2000, June 28   Perf. 13¾
1654 A259 900sh Sheet of 6, #a-f   7.50 7.50

Souvenir Sheet
1655 A259 3000sh multi   4.00 4.00

Monarchs — A260

No. 1655A: b, Philip II of France (1180-1223). c, Richard I of England (1189-99). d, William I of England (1066-87).
No. 1656: a, Boris III of Bulgaria (1918-43). b, Holy Roman Emperor Charles V (1519-58). c, Pedro II of Brazil (1831-89). d, Empress Elizabeth of Austria (1854-98). e, Francis Joseph of Austria (1848-1916). f, Frederick I of Bohemia (1619-20).
No. 1657, Mutesa I of Buganda (1191-98). No. 1657A, Cwa II Kabaleega.
Illustration reduced.

2000, June 28   Perf. 13¾
1655A A260 900sh Sheet of 3, #b-d   4.00 4.00
1656 A260 900sh Sheet of 6, #a-f   7.50 7.50

Souvenir Sheets
1657 A260 3000sh multi   4.25 4.25
1657A A260 3000sh multi   4.25 4.25

Millennium — A261

No. 1658 — Highlights of 1850-1900: a, Opening of Japan. b, First safe elevator. c, Bessemer process of steel production. d, Florence Nightingale establishes nursing as a professsion. e, Louis Pasteur proposes germ theory of disease. f, First oil well drilled. g, Charles Darwin publishes *The Origin of Species*. h, Gregor Mendel discovers laws of heredity. i, Alfred Nobel invents dynamite. j, Suez Canal opens. k, Invention of the telephone. l, Invention of the electric light. m, World's time zones established. n, Invention of the electric motor. o, Motion pictures appear. p, US Civil War (57x37mm). q, Restoration of the Olympic Games.
Illustration reduced.

2000, June 28   Perf. 12¾x12½
1658 A261 300sh Sheet of 17, #a-q + label   8.00 8.00

Millennium — A262

Designs: 300sh, Education for all. 600sh, Nile River. 700sh, Non-traditional exports. 1800sh, Tourism.

2000, July 24   Perf. 14½
1659-1662 A262 Set of 4   6.00 6.00

Common Market for Eastern and Southern Africa A263

Designs: 500sh, Border checkpoint before and after COMESA treaty. 1400sh, Open border checkpoint.

2000, July 24
1663-1664 A263 Set of 2   2.50 2.50

Modern British Commonwealth, 50th Anniv. — A264

Designs: 600sh, Flags. 1200sh, Map.

2000, July 24
1665-1666 A264 Set of 2   2.25 2.25

Trains A265

Designs: 300sh, Kenya Railways A 60 Class 4-8-2+2-8-4. 400sh, Mozambique Railways Baldwin 2-8-0. 600sh, Uganda Railways 73 Class German locomotive. 700sh, South Africa Railways Baby Garratt. 1200sh, Uganda Railways 82 Class French locomotive. 1400sh, East Africa Railway Beyer Garratt 4-8-2+2-8-4. 1800sh, Rhodesian Railways 2-8-2+2-8-2 Beyer Garratt. 2000sh, East African Railways Garratt.
No. 1675, 700sh: a, Uganda Railways 36 Class German locomotive. b, South African Railways Class 19D 4-8-2. c, Algeria Railways Garratt 4-8-2+2-8-4. d, Cameroon Railways French locomotive. e, South Africa railways electric freight locomotive. f, Rhodesia Railways 14A Class 2-8-2. g, British-built Egyptian railways locomotive. h, Uganda Railways 73 Class German locomotive, diff.
No. 1676, 700sh: a, 36 Class German locomotive (no counrtry specified). b, Rhodesian Railways 12th Class locomotive. c, Rhodesian Railways Garratt. d, 62 Class German locomotive. e, South Africa Railways Beyer Garratt. f, Sudan Railways locomotive. g, Nigerian Railways locomotive. h, 4-8-0 South Africa Railways.
No. 1677, 3500sh, East African Railways locomotive. No. 1678, 3500sh, Rhodesian Railways Alco 2-8-0. No. 1679, 3500sh, Egyptian State Railways 4-8-2.

2000, Aug. 14   Perf. 14
1667-1674 A265 Set of 8   11.00 11.00

Sheets of 8, #a-h
1675-1676 A265 Set of 2   14.00 14.00

Souvenir Sheets
1677-1679 A265 Set of 3   13.50 13.50
Nos. 1677-1679 each contain one 56x42mm stamp.

Christmas — A266

Artwork by: 300sh, Drateru Fortunate Oliver, vert. 400sh, Brenda Tumwebaze. 500sh, Joseph Mukiibi, vert. 600sh, Paul Serunjogi. 700sh, Edward Maswere. 1200sh, Ndeba Harriet. 1800sh, Jude Kasagga, vert.
No. 1687, 3000sh, Nicole Kwiringira, vert. No. 1688, 3000sh, Michael Tinkamanyire, vert.

2000, Dec. 14   Litho.   Perf. 14
1680-1686 A266 Set of 7   7.00 7.00

Souvenir Sheets
1687-1688 A266 Set of 2   7.50 7.50

New Year 2001 (Year of the Snake) — A267

No. 1689: a, Snake with tongue out. b, Snake wrapped around person. c, Snake with open mouth. d, Snake hanging from branch.

2001, Jan. 5
1689 A267 600sh Sheet of 4, #a-d   3.00 3.00

Souvenir Sheet
1690 A267 2500sh shown   3.25 3.25

Wildlife — A268

No. 1691: a, Bongo, horiz. b, Black rhinoceros, horiz. c, Leopard.
No. 1692, 3000sh, Parrot. No. 1693, 3000sh, Mountain gorillas, horiz.

Perf. 13¼x13¾, 13¾x13¼
2001, Feb. 5
1691 A268 600sh Strip of 3, #a-c   2.25 2.25

Souvenir Sheets
1692-1693 A268 Set of 2   7.50 7.50

Holy Year 2000 — A269

Designs: 300sh, Holy Family. 700sh, Madonna and Child. 1200sh, Nativity, horiz.

2001, Apr. 4   Litho.   Perf. 13¼
1694-1696 A269 Set of 3   2.75 2.75

East African School of Library and Information Science, Makerere University, Kampala — A270

Nairobi University, Kenya — A271

Universities and Flags on Map — A272

Design: 1200sh, Nkrumah Hall, University of Dar es Salaam, Tanzania.

2001, Apr. 23
1697 A270 300sh multi   .40 .40
1698 A271 400sh multi   .50 .50
1699 A270 1200sh multi   1.50 1.50
1700 A272 1800sh multi   2.25 2.25
      Nos. 1697-1700 (4)   4.65 4.65

World Meteorological Organization,
50th Anniv. (in 2000) — A273

Designs: 300sh, Anemometer, vert. 2000sh,
Tropical sun recorder.

2001, May 28
1701-1702 A273 Set of 2 3.00 3.00

UN High Commissioner for
Refugees — A274

Designs: 300sh, Ensure crop production.
600sh, Ensure community participation.
700sh, Ensure improved skills. 1800sh,
Ensure improved health and water services.

2001, June 15
1703-1706 A274 Set of 4 4.25 4.25

Phila Nippon '01,
Japan — A275

Designs: 600sh, Kikunojo Segawa I and
Danjuro Ichikawa as Samurai, by Kiyonobu II.
700sh, Kamezo Tchimura as a Warrior, by
Kiyohiro. 1000sh, Danjuro Ichikawa as
Shirobei, by Kiyomitsu. 1200sh, Actor Sangoro
Arashi, by Shunsho. 1400sh, Koshiro Mat-
sumoto IV as Sukenari Juro, by Kiyonaga.
2000sh, Pheasant on Pine Branch, by
Kiyomasu II.
3500sh, Tale of Ise, by Eishi.

2001, Aug. 1 **Litho.** **Perf. 14**
1707-1712 A275 Set of 6 8.75 8.75
Souvenir Sheet
1713 A275 3500sh multi 4.50 4.50

Cats and
Dogs — A276

Designs: 400sh, Tabby British shorthair.
900sh, Turkish cat.
No. 1716, 600sh, horiz.: a, Blue and cream
shorthair. b, Manx. c, Angora. d, Red and
white British shorthair. e, Turkish cat, diff. f,
Egyptian mau.
No. 1717, 1400sh, horiz.: a, Red tabby
shorthair. b, Japanese bobtail. c, Siamese. d,
Tabby Persian. e, Black and white Persian. f,
Blue Russian.
No. 1718, 3500sh, Blue-eyed British
shorthair. No. 1719, 3500sh, Calico American
shorthair.

2001, Aug. 23
1714-1715 A276 Set of 2 1.60 1.60
Sheets of 6, #a-f
1716-1717 A276 Set of 2 15.00 15.00
Souvenir Sheets
1718-1719 A276 Set of 2 9.00 9.00

2001, Aug. 23
Designs: 1100sh, German shepherd.
1200sh, Irish setter.
No. 1722, 700sh, horiz.: a, Rottweiler. b,
Flat-coated retriever. c, Samoyed. d, Poodle.
e, Maltese. f, Irish terrier.
No. 1723, 1300sh, horiz: a, English sheepdog. b, German shepherd, diff. c, Great Dane.
d, Boston terrier. e, Bull terrier. f, Australian
terrier.
No. 1724, 3500sh, Bloodhound. No. 1725,
3500sh, Pointer, horiz.

1720-1721 A276 Set of 2 3.00 3.00
Sheets of 6, #a-f
1722-1723 A276 Set of 2 15.00 15.00
Souvenir Sheets
1724-1725 A276 Set of 2 9.00 9.00
APS Stampshow, Chicago (#1723).

Royal Navy Submarines,
Cent. — A277

No. 1726, vert.: a, HMS Tribune. b, HMS
Royal Oak. c, HMS Invincible. d, HMS Dread-
nought. e, HMS Ark Royal. f, HMS Cardiff.

2001, Aug. 27
1726 A277 1000sh Sheet of 6,
#a-f 7.50 7.50
Souvenir Sheet
1727 A277 3500sh HMS Triad 4.50 4.50

Queen Victoria (1819-1901) — A278

No. 1728: a, Wearing tiara. b, Wearing white
head covering, looking right. c, Wearing black
hat. d, Wearing red dress with blue sash. e,
Wearing white head covering, looking left. f,
With hand on chin.
3500sh, Wearing black, hat, diff.

2001, Aug. 27
1728 A278 1000sh Sheet of 6,
#a-f 7.50 7.50
Souvenir Sheet
1729 A278 3500sh multi 4.50 4.50

Queen Elizabeth II, 75th
Birthday — A279

No. 1730: a, In 1926. b, In 1931. c, In 1939.
d, In 1955. e, In 1963. f, In 1999.
3500sh, Wearing cap.

2001, Aug. 27
1730 A279 1000sh Sheet of 6,
#a-f 7.50 7.50
Souvenir Sheet
1731 A279 3500sh multi 4.50 4.50

Toulouse-Lautrec Paintings — A280

No. 1732: a, Woman Combing Her Hair. b,
The Toilette. c, The English Girl at the Star in
Le Havre.
3500sh, Ambassadeurs: Aristide Bruant.

2001, Aug. 27 **Litho.** **Perf. 13¾**
1732 A280 1500sh Sheet of 3,
#a-c 5.75 5.75
Souvenir Sheet
1733 A280 3500sh multi 4.50 4.50

Monet Paintings — A281

No. 1734, horiz.: a, Storm, Belle-Ile Coast.
b, The Manneporte, Etretat. c, The Rocks at
Pourville, Low Tide. d, The Wild Sea.
3500sh, Sunflowers.

2001, Aug. 27
1734 A281 1200sh Sheet of 4,
#a-d 6.00 6.00
Souvenir Sheet
1735 A281 3500sh multi 4.50 4.50

Year of Dialogue
Among Civilizations
A282

Perf. 13¾x13¼
2001, Nov. 16 **Litho.**
1736 A282 3000sh multi 3.75 3.75

Intl.
Volunteers
Year
A283

Designs: 300sh, Ebola outbreak. 700sh,
Save life, donate blood. 2000sh, Collective
effort for clean water.

2001, Nov. 16 **Perf. 13¼x13¾**
1737-1739 A283 Set of 3 3.75 3.75

Mushrooms — A284

Designs: 300sh, Amanita excelsa. 500sh,
Coprinus cinereus. 600sh, Scleroderma
aurantium. 700sh, Armillaria mellea. 1200sh,
Leopiota procera. 2000sh, Flammulina
velutipes.
3000sh, Amanita phalloides.

2001, Nov. 26 **Perf. 14½**
1740-1745 A284 Set of 6 6.75 6.75
Souvenir Sheets
1746   A284 3000sh multi 3.75 3.75
1746A A284 3000sh multi 3.75 3.75

Christmas — A285

Musical instruments: 400sh, Single skin
long drum. 800sh, Animal horn trumpet, horiz.
1000sh, Bugisu clay drum. 1200sh, Musical
bow. 1400sh, Pan pipes. 2000sh, Log xylo-
phones, horiz.
No. 1753, 3500sh, Eight-stringed giant bow
harp. No. 1754, Nativity scene, horiz.

2001 **Perf. 13¾x13¼, 13¼x13¾**
1747-1752 A285 Set of 6 8.50 8.50
Souvenir Sheets
1753-1754 A285 Set of 2 9.00 9.00

New Year 2002 (Year of the
Horse) — A286

No. 1755: a, White horse facing left. b, Dark
brown and gray brown horse facing right with
all feet on ground. c, Tan and brown horse
facing right, with two feet raised.
3000r, Rearing horse.

2002, May 8 **Litho.** **Perf. 14x14¼**
1755 A286 1200sh Sheet of 3,
#a-c 4.50 4.50
Souvenir Sheet
1756 A286 3000sh multi 3.75 3.75

Historic Sites of East Africa A287

Designs: 400sh, Namugongo Shrine Church, Uganda. 800sh, Maruhubi Palace Ruins, Zanzibar, Tanzania. 1200sh, Kings' Burial Grounds, Mparo, Uganda. 1400sh, Old Law Courts, Mombasa, Kenya.

2002, May 8		**Perf. 14½**	
1757-1760 A287	Set of 4	4.75	4.75

Reign of Queen Elizabeth II, 50th Anniv. — A288

No. 1761: a, Wearing blue dress. b, Wearing blue and red hat. c, Without hat. d, Wearing blue hat.
3500sh, Wearing brown hat.

2002, June 17		**Perf. 14¼**	
1761 A288	1500sh Sheet of 4, #a-d	7.50	7.50
Souvenir Sheet			
1762 A288	3500sh multi	4.50	4.50

8th Intl. Interdisciplinary Congress on Women, Kampala — A289

Designs: 400sh, Women, building. 1200sh, Makerere University arms, vert.

Perf. 13¼x13¾, 13¾x13¼			
2002, July 8			
1763-1764 A289	Set of 2	2.00	2.00

United We Stand — A290

2002, July 15		**Perf. 13¾x13¼**	
1765 A290	1500sh multi	1.90	1.90

Printed in sheets of 4.

Intl. Year of Mountains — A291

No. 1766: a, Tateyama, Japan. b, Mt. Nikko, Japan. c, Mt. Hodaka, Japan.
3500sh, Mt. Fuji, Japan.

2002, July 15		**Perf. 13¼x13¾**	
1766 A291	2000sh Sheet of 3, #a-c	7.50	7.50
Souvenir Sheet			
1767 A291	3500sh multi	4.50	4.50

2002 Winter Olympics, Salt Lake City — A292

Designs: No. 1768, 1200sh, Cross-country skiing. No. 1769, 1200sh, Ski jumping.

2002, July 15		**Perf. 13¾x13¼**	
1768-1769 A292	Set of 2	3.00	3.00
1769a	Souvenir sheet, #1768-1769	3.00	3.00

20th World Scout Jamboree, Thailand — A293

No. 1770: a, Scout in forest, 1930s. b, Scout saluting. c, Scouts hiking. d, Scout badge.
3500sh, Lord Robert Baden-Powell.

2002		**Perf. 13¼x13¾**	
1770 A293	1400sh Sheet of 4, #a-d	7.00	7.00
Souvenir Sheet			
Perf. 13¾x13¼			
1771 A293	3500sh multi	4.50	4.50

Mammals, Insects, Flowers and Mushrooms — A294

Designs: 400sh, Ceratotherium simum. 800sh, Macrotermes subhyalinus. No. 1774, 1200sh, Gloriosa superba. 1400sh, Cyptotrama asprata.
No. 1776, 1000sh, horiz. — Insects: a, Nudaurelia cytherea. b, Locusta migratoria. c,
Anacridium aegyptium. d, Sternotomis bohemanni. e, Papilio dardarus. f, Mantis polyspilota.
No. 1777, 1000sh, horiz. — Mushrooms: a, Termitomyces microcarpus. b, Agaricus trisulphuratus. c, Macrolepiota zeyheri. d, Lentinus stupeus. e, Lentinus sajor-caju. f, Lentinus velutinus.
No. 1778, 1200sh, horiz. — Flowers: a, Canarina eminii. b, Vigna unguiculata. c, Gardenia ternifolia. d, Canavalia rosea. e, Hibiscus calyphyllus. f, Nymphaea lotus.
No. 1779, 1200sh, horiz. — Mammals: a, Kobus kob. b, Alcelaphus buselaphus. c, Damaliscus lunatus. d, Papio anubis. e, Panthera leo. f, Phacochoerus africanus.
No. 1780, 4000sh, Glossina austeni, horiz.
No. 1781, 4000sh, Podoscypha parvula, horiz.
No. 1782, 4000sh, Abutilon grandiflorum, horiz. No. 1783, 4000sh, Kobus ellipsiprymnus.

2002, Nov. 6	**Litho.**	**Perf. 14**	
1772-1775 A294	Set of 4	4.75	4.75
Sheets of 6, #a-f			
1776-1779 A294	Set of 4	35.00	35.00
Souvenir Sheets			
1780-1781 A294	Set of 4	20.00	20.00

A295

Pres. John F. Kennedy (1917-63) — A296

Various photos.

2002, Dec. 30			
1784 A295	1200sh Sheet of 4, #a-d	6.00	6.00
1785 A296	1400sh Sheet of 4, #a-d	7.00	7.00

A297

Pres. Ronald Reagan — A298

Various photos.

A299

Princess Diana (1961-97) — A300

2002, Dec. 30			
1786 A297	1200sh Sheet of 4, #a-d	6.00	6.00
1787 A298	1400sh Sheet of 4, #a-d	7.00	7.00

2002, Dec. 30			
1788 A299	1200sh Sheet of 4, #a-d	6.00	6.00
1789 A300	2000sh Sheet of 4, #a-d	10.00	10.00

New Year 2003 (Year of the Ram) — A301

No. 1790: a, Ram on stage. b, Ram on hill. c, Ram on hill, six ram's heads. d, Six rams. e, Ram in field. f, Ram on mountainside.

2003, Feb. 1		**Perf. 14¼x14**	
1790 A301	1000sh Sheet of 6, #a-f	7.50	7.50

Japanese Art — A302

Designs: 400sh, Beauty Arranging Her Hair, by Eisen Keisai. 1000sh, Geishas, by Tsukimaro Kitagawa. 1200sh, Woman Behind a Screen, by Chikanobu Toyohara. 1400sh, Geishas, by Kitagawa, diff.

No. 1795: a, Scene in a Villa (basin in foreground), by Kinichika Toyohara. b, Scene in a Villa (screen at left), by Kunichika Toyohara. c, Visiting a Flower Garden (two people), by Kunisada Utagawa. d, Visiting a Flower Garden (one person), by Utagawa.
5000sh, Woman and Children, by Chikakazu.

2003, May 26   Litho.   Perf. 14¼
1791-1794 A302 Set of 4   5.00 5.00
1795 A302 1200sh Sheet of 4,
#a-d   6.00 6.00
Souvenir Sheet
1796 A302 5000sh multi   6.25 6.25

Rembrandt
Paintings
A303

Designs: 400sh, Jacob Blessing the Sons of Joseph. 1000sh, A Young Woman in Profile With Fan. 1200sh, The Apostle Peter Kneeling. 1400sh, The Painter Hendrick Martensz Sorgh.
No. 1801: a, Portrait of Margaretha de Geer. b, Portrait of a White Haired Man. c, Portrait of Nicolaes Ruts. d, Portrait of Catrina Hooghsaet.
5000sh, Joseph Accused by Potiphar's Wife.

2003, May 26
1797-1800 A303 Set of 4   5.00 5.00
1801 A303 1400sh Sheet of 4,
#a-d   7.00 7.00
Souvenir Sheet
1802 A303 5000sh multi   6.25 6.25

Paintings of Joan Miró — A304

Designs: 400sh, Group of Personages in the Forest. 800sh, Nocturne. 1200sh, The Smile of a Tear. 1400sh, Personage Before the Sun.
No. 1807, vert: a, Man's Head III. b, Catalan Peasant by Moonlight. c, Woman in the Night. d, Seated Woman.
No. 1808, 3500sh, Self-portrait II. No. 1809, 3500sh, Woman with Three Hairs, Birds and Constellations.

2003, May 26   Perf. 14¼
1803-1806 A304 Set of 4   4.75 4.75
1807 A304 1400sh Sheet of 4,
#a-d   7.00 7.00
Imperf
Size: 103x82mm
1808-1809 A304 Set of 2   8.75 8.75

Buganda Princess Katrina-Sarah
Ssangalyambogo, 2nd
Birthday — A305

Princess and: 400sh, Bulange (government office building). 1200sh, Twekobe (palace), vert. 1400sh, Drummer, vert.

Perf. 13x13¼, 13¼x13
2003, June 16
1810-1812 A305 Set of 3   3.75 3.75

Coronation of Queen Elizabeth II, 50th
Anniv. — A306

No. 1813: a, As toddler. b, As young woman, wearing flowered hat. c, Wearing robe and feathered hat.
3500sh, Wearing crown.

2003, July 15   Perf. 14
1813 A306 2000sh Sheet of 3,
#a-c   7.50 7.50
Souvenir Sheet
1814 A306 3500sh multi   4.50 4.50

Prince William, 21st Birthday — A307

No. 1815: a, Wearing cap. b, Wearing blue striped shirt. c, Wearing white shirt.
5000sh, With hand on chin.

2003, July 15
1815 A307 2000sh Sheet of 3,
#a-c   7.50 7.50
Souvenir Sheet
1816 A307 5000sh multi   6.25 6.25

General Motors Automobiles — A308

No. 1817, 1200sh — Cadillacs: a, 1979 Seville Elegante. b, 1998 Eldorado Touring Coupe. c, 2002 Escalade. d, 1983 Seville Elegante.
No. 1818, 1400sh — Corvettes: a, 1970. b, 1972. c, 1982 Collector Edition. d, 1977.
No. 1819, 3500sh, Cadillac Eldorado convertible, 1950s. No. 1820, 3500sh, 1982 Collector Edition Corvette, diff.

2003, July 15   Perf. 14¼
Sheets of 4, #a-d
1817-1818 A308 Set of 2   13.00 13.00
Souvenir Sheets
1819-1820 A308 Set of 2   8.75 8.75

Millennium Development
Goals — A309

Designs: No. 1821, 400sh, Promote gender equity and empower women. No. 1822, 400sh, Improve maternal health. 600sh, Ensure environmental sustainability. 1000sh, Reduce child mortality. No. 1825, 1200sh, Eradicate extreme poverty and hunger. No. 1826, 1200sh, Combat HIV, AIDS, malaria and other diseases. 1400sh, Achieve universal primary education. 2000sh, Develop a global partnership for development.

2003, Oct. 24   Perf. 14½
1821-1828 A309 Set of 8   10.50 10.50

Dances and
Costumes — A310

Dances: 400sh, Entogoro. 800sh, Karimojong. 1400sh, Teso.
No. 1832 — Costumes: a, Kiga. b, Acholi. c, Karimojong. d, Ganda.

2003, Nov. 10   Perf. 14
1829-1831 A310 Set of 3   3.25 3.25
1832 A310 1200sh Sheet of 4,
#a-d   6.00 6.00

Christmas — A311

Dances: 300sh, Journey to Bethlehem. 400sh, Shepherds and angels. 1200sh, Nativity. 1400sh, Adoration of the Magi.
3000sh, Holy Family.

2003, Nov. 10
1833-1836 A311 Set of 4   4.25 4.25
Souvenir Sheet
1837 A311 3000sh multi   3.75 3.75

All-Africa Conference on Assuring
Food and Nutrition Security in Africa
by 2020, Kampala — A312

Map of Africa, food basket, Intl. Food Policy Research Institute emblem and: 400sh, Boy. 1400sh, Boy, diff.

2004, Aug. 31   Litho.   Perf. 14¼
1838-1839 A312 Set of 2   2.25 2.25

Straight Talk Foundation — A313

Child and: 400sh, "Pioneers in Adolescent Health Communication." 1200sh, "Communication for Better Adolescent Health," vert.

2004, Sept. 22
1840-1841 A313 Set of 2   2.00 2.00

Campaign Against Child
Labor — A314

Inscriptions: 400sh, "Stop Child Domestic Labor." 2000sh, "Keep the Community Informed."

2004, Sept. 22
1842-1843 A314 Set of 2   3.00 3.00

Rotary International, Cent. (in
2005) — A315

Rotary emblem and: 400sh, "Celebrate Rotary." 1200sh, "A Century of Service / A New Century of Success," vert.

2004, Sept. 22
1844-1845 A315 Set of 2   2.00 2.00

New Year 2005 (Year of the
Rooster) — A316

No. 1846 — Rooster shades: a, Blue. b, Orange. c, Purple. d, Red.
5000sh, Yellow.

2005, Apr. 4   Litho.   Perf. 14
1846 A316 1200sh Sheet of 4,
#a-d   6.00 6.00
Souvenir Sheet
1847 A316 5000sh multi   6.25 6.25

Fight Against
Tuberculosis,
HIV and
Leprosy — A317

WHO emblem and: No. 1848, 400sh, Ill man in blanket. No. 1849, 400sh, Doctor holding arm of ill man. No. 1850, 400sh, Mother and infant. No. 1851, 400sh, Infant in blanket. No. 1852, 400sh, Leper with artificial leg. No. 1853, 400sh, Leper wearing crucifix.

2005, May 31   **Perf. 13x12¾**
1848-1853 A317   Set of 6   3.00 3.00

Flowering Plants — A318

Designs: 100sh, Clerodendrum sp. 400sh, Calliandra haematocephala. 600sh, Asteraceae compositae. 850sh, Angraecum sp. 900sh, Delonix regia. 1100sh, Bidens grantii. 1200sh, Musa sapientum. 1400sh, Begonia coccinea. 1600sh, Impatiens walleriana. 2000sh, Strelitzia reginae. 5000sh, Tecomaria capensis. 6000sh, Ixora hybrida. 10,000sh, Datura suaveolens. 20,000sh, Cucurbita pepo.

		Perf. 12¾x13½		
2005, June 22				**Litho.**
1854	A318	100sh multi	.20	.20
1855	A318	400sh multi	.45	.45
1856	A318	600sh multi	.70	.70
1857	A318	850sh multi	1.00	1.00
1858	A318	900sh multi	1.10	1.10
1859	A318	1100sh multi	1.25	1.25
1860	A318	1200sh multi	1.40	1.40
1861	A318	1400sh multi	1.60	1.60
1862	A318	1600sh multi	1.90	1.90
1863	A318	2000sh multi	2.40	2.40
1864	A318	5000sh multi	5.75	5.75
1865	A318	6000sh multi	7.00	7.00
1866	A318	10,000sh multi	11.50	11.50
1867	A318	20,000sh multi	23.00	23.00
		Nos. 1854-1867 (14)	59.25	59.25

Fish A319

Designs: 400sh, Synodontis afrofischeri. 600sh, Protopterus aethiopicus. 1100sh, Clarias gariepinus. 1200sh, Rastrineobola agentea. 1600sh, Bagrus docmac. 2000sh, Schilbe mystus.

No. 1874: a, Mormyrus kannume. b, Barbus jacksonni. c, Bagrus docmac, diff. d, Labeo victorianus.

2005, Oct. 6   **Litho.**   **Perf. 13¼**
1868-1873 A319   Set of 6   8.75 8.75
Souvenir Sheet
1874 A319 1000sh Sheet of 4, #a-d   5.00 5.00

Western Union in Africa, 10th Anniv. — A320

Designs: 400sh, Map of Africa, olive branches. 1600sh, Globe. 2000sh, Globe and flags, vert.

2006, July 20   **Litho.**   **Perf. 14¼**
1875-1877 A320   Set of 3   5.00 5.00

Bank of Uganda, 40th Anniv. — A321

Designs: 400sh, Bank emblem. 600sh, Bank emblem, building, wildlife. 1600sh, Bank emblem, Tilapia nilotica. 2000sh, Bank emblem, mountain gorilla.

2006, Oct. 3   **Perf. 13¼**
1878-1881 A321   Set of 4   5.75 5.75

Wetlands A322

Designs: 400sh, Cattle and herdsman at water, Ramsar Convention emblem. 1600sh, People and birds near stream. 2000sh, Fishermen at Lake George.

2006   **Perf. 13x13½**
1882-1884 A322   Set of 3   5.00 5.00

2007 Commonwealth Heads of Government Meeting, Kampala — A323

Flag of Uganda and: 400sh, Commonwealth Heads of Government Meeting emblem. 1600sh, Boniface Kiprop, runner. 2000sh, Dorcas Inzikuru, runner. 5000sh, Arms of Uganda, vert.

2007, Nov. 27   **Litho.**   **Perf. 13x13½**
1885-1888 A323   Set of 4   10.50 10.50

SEMI-POSTAL STAMPS

> Catalogue values for all unused stamps in this section are for never Hinged items.

PAPU (Pan African Postal Union), 18th Anniv. — SP1

1998, Jan. 18   **Litho.**   **Perf. 14**
B1 SP1 300sh +150sh Mountain gorilla   1.10 1.10

POSTAGE DUE STAMPS

> Catalogue values for unused stamps in this section are for Never Hinged items.

Type of Kenya, 1967
Perf. 14x13½

1967, Jan. 3		**Litho.**	**Unwmk.**	
J1	D1	5c red	.20	4.00
J2	D1	10c green	.20	4.00
J3	D1	20c dark blue	.25	5.00
J4	D1	30c reddish brown	.45	6.50
J5	D1	40c red lilac	.65	7.25
J6	D1	1sh orange	2.00	18.00
		Nos. J1-J6 (6)	3.75	44.75

1970, Mar. 31			**Perf. 14x15**	
J1a	D1	5c red	.20	1.25
J2a	D1	10c green	.20	1.25
J3a	D1	20c dark blue	.30	4.25
J4a	D1	30c reddish brown	.40	5.00
J5a	D1	40c red lilac	.60	6.00
		Nos. J1a-J5a (5)	1.70	17.75

1973			**Perf. 15**	
J1b	D1	5c red	.20	1.25
J2b	D1	10c green	.20	1.25
J3b	D1	20c dark blue	.70	3.25
J4b	D1	30c reddish brown	.95	4.75
J5b	D1	40c red lilac	1.60	7.25
J6b	D1	1sh orange	4.00	13.00
		Nos. J1b-J6b (6)	7.65	30.75

Nos. J1-J6 Overprinted in Black: "LIBERATED / 1979"

1979, Dec.		**Litho.**	**Perf. 14**	
J7	D1	5c red	.20	.70
J8	D1	10c green	.20	.70
J9	D1	20c violet blue	.20	.70
J10	D1	30c reddish brown	.20	1.00
J11	D1	40c red lilac	.25	1.00
J12	D1	1sh orange	.70	1.25
		Nos. J7-J12 (6)	1.75	5.35

Wildlife — D2

1985, Mar. 11		**Litho.**	**Perf. 15x14**	
J13	D2	5sh Lion	.20	.95
J14	D2	10sh African buffalo	.20	.95
J15	D2	20sh Kob antelope	.60	1.40
J16	D2	40sh Elephant	1.25	2.10
J17	D2	50sh Zebra	1.25	2.10
J18	D2	100sh Rhinoceros	1.75	3.50
		Nos. J13-J18 (6)	5.25	11.00

UKRAINE

yü-'krān

LOCATION — In southeastern Europe, bordering on the Black Sea
GOVT. — Republic
AREA — 231,900 sq. mi.
POP. — 48,760,474 (2001)
CAPITAL — Kyiv

Following the collapse of the Russian Empire, a national assembly met at Kyiv and declared the Ukrainian National Republic on Jan. 22, 1918. During three years of civil war, the Ukrainian army, as well as Bolshevik, White Russian, Allied and Polish armies, fought back and forth across the country. By November, 1920, Ukraine was finally occupied by Soviet forces, and Soviet stamps were used from that time, until the recreation of the independent Ukraine on Dec. 26, 1991.

200 Shahiv = 100 Kopiyok (Kopecks)
= 1 Karbovanets (Ruble)

100 Shahiv = 1 Hryvnia

100 Kopiyok = 1 Karbovanets (1992)

100 Kopiyok = 1 Hryvnia (1996)

> Catalogue values for unused stamps in this country are for Never Hinged items, beginning with Scott 100 in the regular postage section, Scott B9 in the semi-postal section, and Scott F1 in the registration section.

Watermarks

Wmk. 116 — Crosses and Circles

Wmk. 399

Republic's Trident Emblem — A1   Ukrainian Peasant — A2

Allegorical Ukraine — A3   Trident — A4

Inscription of Value — A5

1918, July		**Typo.**	**Imperf.**	
		Thin Paper		
1	A1	10sh buff	.20	.30
2	A2	20sh brown	.20	.30
3	A3	30sh ultra	.20	.30
a.		30sh blue	2.50	6.00
4	A4	40sh green	.20	.30
5	A5	50sh red	.20	.30
		Nos. 1-5 (5)	1.00	1.50

The stamps of this issue exist perforated or pin-perforated unofficially.
Forgeries of this set exist on a very thin, glossy paper.
These designs were earlier (April, 1918) utilized for money tokens, printed on thin cardboard, perforated 11½, and bearing an inscription on the reverse "Circulates on par with coins" in Ukrainian. These tokens exist favor canceled but were not postage stamps. Value uncanceled, $6 each.

Stamps of Russia Overprinted in Violet, Black, Blue, Red, Brown or Green

This trident-shaped emblem was taken from the arms of the Grand Prince Volodymyr and adopted as the device of the Ukrainian Republic.

In the early months of independence, Russian stamps were commonly used, but the influx of large quantities of stamps from Russia made it necessary to take measures to protect postal revenue. In August, 1918, local post offices were ordered to send their existing stocks of Russian stamps to regional centers, where they were overprinted with the trident arms. Unoverprinted Russian stamps were declared invalid after October 1, although they were often accepted for use.

This overprint was handstamped, typographed or lithographed. It was applied in various cities in the Ukraine and there are numerous types.

Nos. 6-47 represent the basic Russian stamps that received these overprints. Values are for the most common overprint variety.

For a more detailed listing of these overprints, see the Scott Classic Specialized Catalogue.

The basic Russian stamps to which Trident overprints were applied:

A8

A9

A11

A12

A13

A14

A15

On Stamps of 1902-03

			1918	Wmk. 168		Perf. 13½
6	A12	3½r black & gray			27.50	32.50
7	A12	7r black & yellow			22.50	27.50

On Stamps of 1909-18
Lozenges of Varnish on Face
Perf. 14, 14½x15
Unwmk.

8	A14	1k orange	.20	.25
9	A14	2k green	.20	.25
10	A14	3k red	.20	.25
11	A15	4k carmine	.20	.25
12	A14	5k claret	.20	.25
13	A14	7k light blue	.20	.25
14	A15	10k dark blue	.20	.25
15	A11	14k blue & rose	.20	.40
16	A11	15k red brn & bl	.20	.25
17	A8	20k blue & car	.20	.25
18	A11	25k grn & gray vio	.20	.25
19	A11	35k red brn & grn	.20	.25
20	A8	50k violet & grn	.20	.25
21	A11	70k brown & org	.20	.25

Perf. 13½

22	A9	1r lt brn, brn & org	.40	.65
23	A12	3½r mar & lt grn	.80	1.90
24	A13	5r dk bl, grn & pale bl	5.50	7.50
25	A12	7r dk grn & pink	6.50	8.75
26	A13	10r scar, yel & gray	7.50	11.00
		Nos. 6-26 (21)	73.50	93.45

On Stamps of 1917
Perf. 14, 14½x15

27	A14	10k on 7k light blue	.25	.30
28	A11	20k on 14k bl & rose	.20	.25

On Stamps of 1917-18
Imperf

29	A14	1k orange	.20	.25
30	A14	2k gray green	.20	.25
31	A14	3k red	.20	.25
32	A15	4k carmine	.20	.25
33	A14	5k claret	.75	1.00
34	A11	15k red brn & bl	.20	.25
35	A8	20k bl & car	.50	1.50
36	A11	25k grn & gray vio	55.00	—
37	A11	35k red brn & grn	.20	.25
38	A8	50k violet & grn	.25	.75
39	A11	70k brown & org	.20	.25
40	A9	1r pale brn, brn & red org	.30	.35
41	A12	3½r mar & lt grn	.50	1.10
42	A13	5r dk bl, grn & pale bl	.55	1.40
43	A12	7r dk grn & pink	1.60	1.90
44	A13	10r scar, yel & gray	45.00	55.00
		Nos. 29-44 (16)	105.85	64.75

On Postal Savings Bank Stamps

		Wmk. 171	Litho.		
		Perf. 14, 14½x14¾			
45		1k red, *buff*	.85	16.00
46		5k green, *buff*	7.50	75.00
47		10k brown, *buff*	1.90	240.00
		Nos. 45-47 (3)	10.25	331.00

Nos. 45-47 were used and accepted as postage stamps during stamp shortages.

The trident overprint was applied by favor to Russia Nos. 88-104, 110-111, the Romanov issue.

For surcharges see Russian Offices in the Turkish Empire Nos. 320-339.

A6

1919, Jan.   Litho.

48	A6	20hr red & green	3.50	22.50

Because of its high face value, No. 48 was used primarily on money transfer forms or parcel receipts.

Nos. 1 and 5
Surcharged

35 к.

1919   Unwmk.   Imperf.

49	A1	35k on 10sh buff	8.00	16.50
50	A5	70k on 50sh red	22.50	37.50
a.		Surcharge inverted	55.00	

Some authorities state that Nos. 49-50 were issued by the Soviets in the Ukraine in April 1919.

Excellent forged surcharges exist.

Ukrainian Soviet Socialist Republic

During 1920/1921, hyperinflation of the ruble created a desperate need for stamps to pay ever-rising postal rates. Many Russian cities and districts surcharged existing stocks of Russian stamps in needed denominations for provisional use.

In June 1920 the national government of the Soviet Ukrainian Republic authorized the Kharkiv post office to create such surcharges for use in the Kharkiv region and in adjacent oblasts. Both unoverprinted Russian stamps

and stamps bearing the regional trident overprints of Katerynoslav, Kharkiv and Kyiv were surcharged to raise their face value 100-fold. They were sold at 236 post offices in the Ukraine from June 1920 through Feb. 1921.

In Feb. 1922 three Russian postal savings stamps were surcharged for provisional use by the Kyiv post office, at the direction of the central government. As with the Kharkiv surcharges, these stamps were distributed over a wide area within the country.

KHARKIV ISSUE
Ukrainian and Russian Stamps
Handstamp Surcharged

Ukrainian trident overprinted issues and unoverprinted Russian stamps revalued 100-fold by changing denominations from kopecks to rubles.

Two types of overprint: type I, Cyrillic RUB (not including periods) 9.5mmx6.5mm; type II, 8.5mmx6.5mm.

Number of basic Ukrainian or Russian stamp shown in parentheses.

1920, June
Type I Reading Upward
On Katerynoslav Trident Ovpt. Issue of 1918

51	A11	15k red brown & blue (#16a)	75.00	75.00

On Kharkiv Trident Ovpt. Issue of 1918

No. 52

Perf. 14x14½

52	A14	1k orange (#8b)	55.00	60.00
a.		Surcharge reading downward	150.00	150.00
53	A14	2k green (#9b)	60.00	65.00
54	A14	3k red (#10b)	20.00	25.00
55	A11	15k red brn & blue (#16b)	25.00	20.00
56	A8	20k blue & car (#17b)	150.00	175.00
a.		Surcharge reading downward	300.00	300.00
57	A11	20k on 14k blue & rose (#28b)	170.00	190.00

Imperf

58	A14	1k orange (#29b)	45.00	55.00
a.		Surcharge reading downward	120.00	120.00
59	A14	2k green (#30b)	250.00	250.00
60	A14	3k red (#31b)	30.00	35.00

On Kyiv Trident Ovpt. Issue of 1918

No. 61

No. 63

On Kyiv II Overprint
Perf. 14x14½

61	A14	1k orange (#8f)	25.00	30.00

Imperf

62	A14	1k orange (#29f)	15.00	20.00
a.		Surcharge reading downward	—	

On Kyiv III Overprint

63	A14	3k red (#31g)	15.00	20.00

On Russian Arms Issue of 1909-18

No. 64

Perf. 14x14½

64	A14	1k orange (#73)	40.00	50.00
65	A14	2k green (#74)	5.00	6.00
a.		Surcharge reading downward	10.00	10.00
66	A14	3k red (#75)	6.00	6.00
67	A15	4k red (#76)	325.00	
68	A14	5k claret (#77)	7.00	6.00
a.		Surcharge reading downward	12.00	10.00

69	A15	10k dk blue (#79)	15.00	15.00
a.		Surcharge reading downward	90.00	100.00
70	A11	15k red brn & blue (#81)	7.00	6.00
a.		Surcharge reading downward	10.00	9.00
71	A8	20k blue & car (#82)	7.00	6.00
a.		Surcharge reading downward	15.00	12.00

Imperf

72	A14	1k orange (#119)	30.00	36.00
a.		Surcharge reading downward	100.00	100.00
73	A14	2k green (#120)	45.00	55.00
74	A14	3k red (#121)	30.00	36.00
75	A14	5k claret (#123)	9.00	7.00
a.		Surcharge reading downward	18.00	18.00
76	A11	15k red brn & blue (#125)	120.00	130.00
a.		Surcharge reading downward		

Type II Reading Upward

No. 79a

On Kharkiv Trident Ovpt. Issue of 1918

77	A14	3k red (#31b)	35.00	40.00

On Kyiv Trident Ovpt. Issue of 1918

78	A14	1k orange (#29f)	20.00	25.00

On Russian Arms Issue of 1919-18
Perf. 14x14½

79	A14	2k green (#74)	6.00	7.00
a.		Surcharge reading downward	12.00	12.00
80	A14	5k claret (#77)	8.00	7.00
a.		Surcharge reading downward	15.00	12.00
81	A15	10k dk blue (#79)	18.00	18.00
a.		Surcharge reading downward	100.00	115.00
82	A11	15k red brn & blue (#81)	8.00	7.00
a.		Surcharge reading downward	12.00	10.00
83	A8	20k blue & car (#82)	8.00	7.00

Imperf

84	A14	2k green (#120)	50.00	60.00

KYIV ISSUE
Russian Postal Savings Stamps
Handstamp Surcharged

1922, Feb.   Wmk. 171

85		7500 (r) on 5k, green, *buff*	45.00	35.00
a.		Surcharge reading downward	60.00	45.00
86		8000 (r) on 5k, green, *buff*	150.00	90.00
a.		Surcharge reading downward	180.00	150.00
87		15000 (r) on 10k, brown, *buff*	225.00	150.00
a.		Surcharge reading downward	450.00	250.00

Nos. 85-87 are normally found on stamps watermarked with a vertical diamond pattern (Wmk. 171) but also exist on paper watermarked sideways, with both upward and downward-reading surcharges. These are rare and are worth approximately 8 times the values shown.

Nos. 1-5 surcharged in grivni (hryven) with the Polish eagle were sold as Polish occupation issues. They are of private origin.

Nos. 1-3 and 5 overprinted diagonally as above ("South Russia") are believed to be of private origin.

A lithographed set of 14 stamps (1hr-200hr) of these types, perf. 11½, was prepared in 1920, but never placed in use. Value, set $3.

All values exist imperf., some with inverted centers. Trial printings exist on various papers, including inverted, multiple, omitted and misaligned center vignettes. These are from the printer's waste.

This set handstamped "VILNA UKRAINA / 1921" and 6 values additionally overprinted "DOPLATA" are of private origin.

In 1923 the Ukrainian government-in-exile in Warsaw prepared an 11-value set, consisting of the 10h, 20h and 40h denominations surcharged and overprinted with the Cyrillic "UPP," supposedly intended as a Field Post issue for a planned invasion of the Ukraine. The invasion never occurred, and the stamps were never issued.

For German stamps overprinted "Ukraine" see Russia Nos. N29-N48.

Catalogue values for unused stamps in this section, from this point to the end of the section, are for Never Hinged items.

Cossacks in Ukraine, 500th Anniv. — A20

Design: No. 101, Ukrainian emigrants to Canada.

1992, Mar. 1 **Litho.** *Perf. 12*
100 A20 15k multicolored .60 .60
101 A20 15k multicolored .60 .60

Ukrainian emigration to Canada, centennial (No. 101). Dated 1991.

Mykola V. Lysenko (1842-1912), Composer — A21

1992, Mar. 22 *Perf. 13*
102 A21 1r multicolored .55 .55

Numerous trident overprints on Soviet stamps exist. Many of them are legitimate local issues and were in official use. Locally produced stamps also exist.

Ukrainian Girl — A22

1992 **Litho.** *Perf. 12x12½*
118 A22 50k bright blue .20 .20
119 A22 70k bister .20 .20
121 A22 1kb yellow green .20 .20
122 A22 2kb purple .20 .20
124 A22 5kb blue .20 .20
126 A22 10kb red .50 .50
128 A22 20kb green 1.25 1.25
130 A22 50kb brown 1.75 1.75
Nos. 118-130 (8) 4.50 4.50

Issued: Nos. 124, 126, 128, 130, 5/16; 118-119, 121-122, 6/17.

Mykola I. Kostomarov (1817-1885), Writer — A23

1992, May 16 **Photo.** *Perf. 12x11½*
133 A23 20k olive green .60 .60

1992 Summer Olympics, Barcelona
A24   A25

1992, July 25 **Litho.** *Perf. 13*
134 A24 3kb yel green & multi .35 .35
135 A25 4kb multicolored .50 .50
136 A24 5kb buff & multi .65 .65
Nos. 134-136 (3) 1.50 1.50

World Forum of Ukrainians, Kyiv — A26

1992, Aug. 19 **Litho.** *Perf. 13*
137 A26 2kb multicolored .55 .55

Declaration of Independence from the Soviet Union — A27

1992, Aug. 19 *Perf. 13½x13*
138 A27 2kb multicolored .55 .55

Souvenir Sheet

Union of Ukrainian Philatelists, 25th Anniv. — A28

1992, Aug. 21 *Perf. 12*
139 A28 2kb multicolored .75 1.00

Intl. Letter Writing Week A29

1992, Oct. 4 *Perf. 13x13½*
140 A29 5kb multicolored .60 .60

World Congress of Ukrainian Lawyers, Kyiv — A30

1992, Oct. 18 **Litho.** *Perf. 13*
141 A30 15kb multicolored 1.00 1.00

Ukrainian Diaspora in Austria A31

Perf. 13½x14½
1992, Nov. 27 **Litho.**
142 A31 5kb multicolored .70 .70

Пошта України 0.50

Embroidery A32

1992, Nov. 16 **Litho.** *Perf. 11½x12*
143 A32 50k black & orange .55 .55

Mohyla Academy, Kyiv, 360th Anniv. — A33

1992, Nov. 27 **Litho.** *Perf. 12x12½*
144 A33 1.50kb multicolored .55 .55

Souvenir Sheet

Ukrainian Medal Winners, 1992 Summer Olympics, Barcelona — A34

1992, Dec. 14 **Litho.** *Perf. 14*
145 A34 10kb multicolored 4.00 4.00

Coats of Arms — A35

1993, Feb. 15 **Litho.** *Perf. 14x13½*
148 A35 3kb Lviv .70 .70
150 A35 5kb Kyiv 1.10 1.10

See No. 292.

Cardinal Joseph Slipyj (1892-1984) A36

1993, Feb. 17 **Litho.** *Perf. 14x13½*
166 A36 15kb multicolored 1.00 1.00

1st Vienna-Cracow-Lviv-Kyiv Air Mail Flight, 75th Anniv. — A37

1993, Mar. 31 *Perf. 13½x14*
167 A37 35kb Biplane .75 .75
168 A37 50kb Jet 1.10 1.00

Easter A39

1993, Apr. 8 **Litho.** *Perf. 13½*
169 A39 15kb multicolored 1.00 1.00

UN Declaration of
Human Rights,
45th
Anniv. — A40

Design: 5kb, Country Wedding in Lower
Austria, by Ferdinand Georg Waldmuller.

Perf. 14½x13½

1993, June 11   Litho.
170 A40 5kb multicolored   1.25 1.25

A41

A41a

A41b

A41c

A41d

A41e

A41f

A41g

A41h

Villagers at Work: 50kb, #177, Reaper with
scythe. 100kb, #185, Ox carts. #173A, 200kb,
500kb, Reaper with sickle. #173B, Farmer with
oxen. 150kb, 300kb, #184, Shepherd. #183,
Bee keeper. #184A, Fisherman. #186, Potter.
(Illustrations A41a-A41h help identify the Cyrillic characters, not the designs.)

Perf. 12x12½, 14 (#174, 180, 182, 184)

1993-98   Litho.
171	A41	50kb green	.20	.20
172	A41	100kb blue	.20	.20
173	A41c	(100kb) brown	.30	.30
174	A41e	(100kb) magenta	.35	.35
175	A41	150kb red	.20	.20
176	A41	200kb orange	.25	.25
177	A41d	(250kb) green	.50	.50
178	A41	300kb violet	.25	.25
179	A41	500kb brown	.30	.30
180	A41f	(1800kb) org brn	.50	.50
181	A41a	(5000kb) red	2.50	2.50
182	A41g	(5300kb) blue	1.25	1.25
183	A41b	(10,000kb) blue	.40	.20
a.		Perf. 14	2.25	2.25
184	A41h	(17,000kb) red brn	2.25	2.25
		Nos. 171-184 (14)	9.45	

Nos. 174, 181 issued for domestic letter
rate; Nos. 177, 180 for letters within the Commonwealth of Independent States; Nos. 183-
184 for mail abroad, surface and airmail.
Actual amounts sold for varied with inflation.
No. 183a sold for 30k on date of issue and
was used for the domestic rate.

Issued: 50, 100, 150, 200, 300, 500kb,
12/18/93; #181, 183a, 5/28/94; #173, 177,
7/2/94; #174, 182, 10/15/94; #180, 184,
11/12/94; #183, 12/30/98.

Famine Deaths,
60th Anniv. — A42

1993, Sept. 12   Litho.   Perf. 12
188 A42 75kb brown   .70 .70

First
Ukrainian
Postage
Stamp,
75th Anniv.
A43

1993, Oct. 9
189 A43 100kb blue & brown   .70 .70

Stamp Day.

Liberation
of Kyiv,
50th Anniv.
A44

1993, Nov. 6   Litho.   Perf. 12
190 A44 75kb multicolored   .70 .70

A45

A46

1994, Jan. 15   Litho.   Perf. 12
191 A45 200kb black & red   .70 .70

Ahapit, Kyivan Rus physician, Middle Ages.

1994, Feb. 19   Perf. 12x12½
Endangered species: No. 192, Erythronium
dens, canis. No. 193, Cypripedium calceolus.

192 A46 200kb multicolored   .60 .60
193 A46 200kb multicolored   .60 .60

Independence Day — A47

Illustration reduced.

1994, Sept. 3   Litho.   Imperf.
194 A47 5000kb multicolored   1.50 2.50

No. 194 has simulated perforations.

Kyiv
University
A47a

Litho. & Engr.
1994, Sept. 24   Perf. 13x13½
194A A47a 10,000kb mul-
                ticolored   1.00 1.00

Souvenir Sheet
Perf. 12½x13
194B A47a 25,000kb mul-
                ticolored   2.50 2.50

No. 194B contains one 40x27mm stamp.

Liberation
of Soviet
Areas,
50th
Anniv.
A48

Battle maps and: a, Katyusha rockets, liber-
ation of Russia. b, Fighter planes, liberation of
Ukraine. c, Combined offensive, liberation of
Belarus.

1994, Oct. 8   Litho.   Perf. 12½x12
195 A48 500kb Block of 3, #a.-c.,
                + label   1.25 1.25

See Russia No. 6213, Belarus No. 78.

Excavation of
Trypillia culture,
Cent. — A49

1st Books Printed
in Ukrainian, 500th
Anniv. — A50

1994, Dec. 17   Litho.   Perf. 12x12½
196 A49 4000kb multicolored   .35 .35

1994, Dec. 17   Perf. 13½
197 A50 4000kb multicolored   .35 .35

Sofiyivka
Natural
Park,
Bicent.
A51

1994, Dec. 17   Perf. 12½x12
198 A51 5000kb multicolored   .35 .35

Ilya Y. Repin
(1844-1930),
Painter — A52

1994, Dec. 17   Perf. 12x12½
199 A52 4000kb multicolored   .35 .35

City of Uzhhorod, 1100th
Anniv. — A53

1995, Jan. 28   Litho.   Perf. 12
200 A53 5000kb multicolored   .30 .30

Ivan Franko (1856-1916),
Writer — A54

Ivan Puliuj (1845-
1918),
Physicist — A55

No. 203, Lesia Ukrainka (1871-1913), poet.

1995, Feb. 2   Perf. 13½
201 A54 3000kb multicolored   .35 .35
202 A55 3000kb multicolored   .40 .40
203 A54 3000kb multicolored   .35 .35
        Nos. 201-203 (3)   1.10 1.10

Falco
Peregrinus — A56

1995, Apr. 15   Litho.   Perf. 12
204 A56 5000kb shown   .45 .45
205 A56 10,000kb Grus grus   .50 .50

Maksym T. Rylskyi (1895-1964),
Writer — A57

1995, Apr. 15   Perf. 13½x14
206 A57 50,000kb multicolored   .95 .95

End of World War
II, 50th
Anniv. — A58

1995, May 9   Litho.   Perf. 13½
207 A58 100,000kb multicolored 1.75 1.75

Artek, Intl.
Children's
Camp
A59

1995, June 16   Litho.   Perf. 13½
208 A59 5000kb multicolored   .35 .35

Famous
Writers
A60

Design: 1000kb, Ivan Kotliarevskyi (1769-1838), depiction of his poem, "Eneida." 3000kb, Taras Shevchenko (1814-61), his book, "Kobzar."

1995, July 8
209 A60 1000kb multicolored   .30 .30
210 A60 3000kb multicolored   .30 .30

Hetman Petro Konashevych-
Sahaidachny — A61

1995, July 22   Litho.   Perf. 13½
211 A61 30,000kb multicolored   .65 .65

Arms of
Luhansk — A62

1995   Litho.   Perf. 13½
212 A62 10,000kb shown   .35 .35
213 A62 10,000kb Chernihiv   .30 .30

Issued: No. 212, 9/15; No. 213, 10/22.

Hetman Bohdan Khmelnytsky
(Khmelnytskyi; 1593?-1657) — A63

1995, Sept. 23   Litho.   Perf. 12½x12
214 A63 40,000kb multi   .90 .90

Hetman Ivan Mazepa (1640?-
1709) — A64

1995, Oct. 14   Perf. 13½
215 A64 30,000kb multi   .65 .65

A65   A66

1995, Oct. 14
216 A65 50,000kb multi   1.25 1.25
European Nature Protection Year.

1995, Oct. 22
217 A66 50,000kb multi   1.25 1.25
Intl. Children's Day.

UN, 50th
Anniv.
A67

1995, Oct. 24   Perf. 12x12½
218 A67 50,000kb multi   1.25 1.25

A68   A69

1995, Dec. 9   Perf. 13½
219 A68 50,000kb multi   1.25 1.25
Ivan Karpenko-Karyi, playwright, actor.

1995, Dec. 23
220 A69 50,000kb multi   .90 .90
Mikhailo Hrushevskyi, 1st Ukrainian president.

P. Safarik (1795-1861), Writer — A70

1995, Dec. 27
221 A70 30,000kb green   .90 .90

Trolleybus   Streetcar
A71   A72

City Bus — A73

1995, Dec. 27   Litho.   Perf. 14
222 A71 (1000kb) blue violet   .20 .20
223 A72 (2000kb) green   2.75 2.75
224 A73 (3000kb) red   .20 .20
     Nos. 222-224 (3)   3.15 3.15

The postal rate that No. 223 paid was sharply increased greatly affecting the cost of the stamp at the post offices.
No. 222 also exists dated "2003" and "2006." No. 224 exists dated "2006."

Taras Shevchenko University
Astronomical Observatory, Kyiv, 150th
Anniv. — A74

a, 20,000 l, Early astronomical instruments. b, 30,000 l, Telescope. c, 50,000 l, Observatory, sun.

1996, Jan. 13   Perf. 12
225 A74 Strip of 3, #a.-c.   1.90 1.90

Souvenir Sheet

1994 Winter Olympics,
Lillehammer — A75

Medalists: a, 40,000kb, Valentina Tserbe, bronze, biathlon. b, 50,000kb, Oksana Bayul, gold, figure skating.

1996, Jan. 13
226 A75 Sheet of 2, #a.-b.   2.25 3.50

Ahatanhel   Kharkiv Zoo,
Krymskyi (1871-   Cent. — A77
1942),
Writer — A76

1996, Jan. 15   Perf. 13½
227 A76 20,000kb bister & brown .70 .70

1996, Mar. 23   Perf. 12½x12
228 A77 20,000kb multicolored   .60 .60

Ivan S. Kozlovskyi
(1900-93), Opera
Singer — A78

1996, Mar. 23   Perf. 13½
229 A78 20,000kb multicolored   .45 .45

Motion
Pictures,
Cent.
A79

Oleksandr Dovzhenko, film maker, house.

1996, Mar. 23   Perf. 12½x12
230 A79 4000kb multicolored   .75 .75
No. 230 was issued se-tenant with two labels showing scenes from films.

Chernobyl Nuclear
Disaster, 10th
Anniv. — A80

1996, Apr. 26   Litho.   Perf. 13½
231 A80 20,000kb multicolored   .60 .60

Symyrenky Family
A81

Vasyl Fedorovych (1835-1915), Volodymyr Levkovych (1891-1938), Levko Platonovych (1855-1920).

1996, May 25
232 A81 20,000kb multicolored .60 .60

Vasil Stefanyk (1871-1936), Writer — A82

1996, June 29
233 A82 20,000kb multicolored .60 .60

Mykola M. Myklukho-Maklai (1846-88), Explorer, Philologist — A83

Litho. & Engr.
1996, July 17   **Perf. 13½**
234 A83 40,000kb multicolored 1.10 1.10

1996 Summer Olympic Games, Atlanta — A84

Modern Olympic Games, Cent. A85

1996, July 19   Litho.   Perf. 13½
235 A84 20,000kb Wrestling .50 .50
236 A84 40,000kb Handball 1.00 1.00
237 A85 40,000kb Greek athletes 1.00 1.00
Nos. 235-237 (3) 2.50 2.50

Souvenir Sheet
Perf. 12
238 A84 100,000kb Gymnast 2.00 2.00

Independence, 5th Anniv. — A86

First Ukrainian Satellite, "Sich-1" — A87

1996, Aug. 24   Perf. 13½
239 A86 20,000kb multicolored .70 .70

1996, Aug. 31
240 A87 20,000kb multicolored .70 .70

Locomotives — A88

Designs: 20,000kb, Steam, class OD. 40,000kb, Diesel class 2 TE-116.

1996, Aug. 31
241 A88 20,000kb multicolored .50 .50
242 A88 40,000kb multicolored 1.00 1.00
a. Pair, #241-242 1.50 1.50

Airplanes Designed by O.K. Antonov (1906-84) A89

No. 243, Glider A-15, portrait of Antonov. No. 244, AN-2. No. 245, AN-124. No. 246, AN-225.

1996, Sept. 14
243 A89 20,000kb multicolored .60 .60
244 A89 20,000kb multicolored .60 .60
245 A89 40,000kb multicolored 1.00 1.00
246 A89 40,000kb multicolored 1.00 1.00
a. Block of 4, #243-246 3.50 3.50

Ivan Piddubnyi (1871-1949), Wrestler — A90

1996, Nov. 16
247 A90 40k multicolored .70 .70

First Ukrainian Antarctic Expedition A91

1996, Nov. 23
248 A91 20k multicolored 1.75 1.75

A92   A93

Flowers: 20k, Leontopodium alpinum. 40k, Narcissus anqustifolius.

1996, Nov. 23
249 A92 20k multicolored .60 .60
250 A92 40k multicolored .95 .95
a. Pair, #249-250 + label 1.75 1.75

1996, Dec. 7   Litho.   Perf. 13½
251 A93 20k multicolored .45 .45
UNESCO, 50th anniv.

Viktor S. Kosenko, Composer, Birth Cent. A94

1996, Dec. 21   Litho.   Perf. 13½
252 A94 20k multicolored .45 .45

St. Sophia's Cathedral, Kyiv — A95

Illinska (St. Elijah) Church, Subotiv A96

St. George Church, Drohobych A97

#256, Troitska Cathedral, Novomoskovsk.

1996, Dec. 25
253 A95 20k multicolored .40 .40
254 A96 20k multicolored .40 .40
255 A97 20k multicolored .40 .40
256 A97 20k multicolored .40 .40
a. Block of 4, #253-256 1.75 1.75

UNICEF, 50th Anniv. A98

1996, Dec. 31
257 A98 20k multicolored .45 .45

Petro Mohyla (1596-1647), Metropolitan of Kyiv — A99

1996, Dec. 31
258 A99 20k multicolored .45 .45

Wild Animals — A100

1997, Mar. 22   Litho.   Perf. 13½
259 A100 20k Lynx lynx 1.00 1.00
260 A100 20k Ursos arctos 1.00 1.00
a. Pair, #259-260 + label 2.50 2.50

Cathedral of the Exaltation of the Holy Cross, Poltava, 17th Cent. A101

Designs: No. 262, St. George's Cathedral, Lviv, 18th cent. No. 263, Protection Fortified Church, Sutkivtsi, 14-15th cent.

1997, Apr. 19   Litho.   Perf. 13½
261 A101 20k multicolored .80 .80
262 A101 20k multicolored .80 .80
263 A101 20k multicolored .80 .80
Nos. 261-263 (3) 2.40 2.40

Legendary Founders of Kyiv — A101a

Europa: a, Kyi (holding staff and shield) and Shchek (holding sword). b, Khoriv (holding sword, leaning on shield) and sister, Lybid.

1997, May 6   Litho. & Engr.   Perf. 13
264 A101a 40k Sheet of 2, #a.-b. 3.00 4.00

4th Natl. Philatelic Exhibition, Cherkasy A102

Design: Statue of Taras Shevchenko, stamps, exhibition hall.

1997, May 17   Litho.   Perf. 13½
265 A102 10k multicolored .70 .70

Yurii V. Kondratiuk (1897-1942), Space Pioneer — A103

1997, June 21   Perf. 12½x12
266 A103 20k multicolored .75 .75

Constitution, 1st Anniv. — A104

1997, June 28   Perf. 13½
267 A104 20k multicolored .60 .60

Midsummer Festival of Ivan Kupalo — A104a

1997, July 5   Litho.   Perf. 13½
268 A104a 20k multicolored .65 .65

Princess Olha
A105

Sultana
Roksoliana
A106

1997, July 12   Litho.   Perf. 13½
269 A105 40k multicolored   1.10 1.10
270 A106 40k multicolored   1.10 1.10

First
Ukrainian
Emigration
to
Argentina,
Cent.
A107

Design: Monument to poet Taras
Shevchenko, Buenos Aires.

1997, Aug. 16   Litho.   Perf. 13½
271 A107 20k multicolored   .75 .75

For Exceptional
Service — A108

Order of Yaroslav the Wise — A109

Medals for: No. 273, Military Service. 30k,
Bravery. 40k, Order of Bohdan Khmelnytsky.
No. 276, Honored Service.
No. 277: a, Medal hanging from chain. b, 8-point star.
Illustration A109 reduced.

Litho. & Engr.
1997, Aug. 20   Perf. 13½
272 A108 20k multicolored   1.25 1.25
273 A108 20k multicolored   1.25 1.25
274 A108 30k multicolored   1.90 1.90
275 A108 40k multicolored   2.50 2.50
276 A108 60k multicolored   3.75 3.75
a.   Strip of 5, #272-276   11.00 11.00

Souvenir Sheet
Perf. 13
277 A109 60k Sheet of 2, #a.-
              b.   9.00 9.00

Nos. 277a-277b are each 35x50mm.

Hetman — A110

No. 278, Dmytro "Baida" Vyshnevetskyj (?-1563), boats, archers. No. 279, Pylyp Orlyk
(1672-1742), Stockholm harbor, crowd in
Thessaloniki street.

1997, Sept. 13   Litho.   Perf. 12½x12
278 A110 20k multicolored   .60 .60
279 A110 20k multicolored   .60 .60

See Nos. 357-358, 376-377.

Solomiia
Krushelnytska
(Salomea
Krusceniski, 1872-
1952), Actress,
Singer — A111

1997, Sept. 23   Litho.   Perf. 13½
280 A111 20k multicolored   .80 .80

Airplanes
A112

Designs: 20k, Antonov An-74 TK-200. 40k,
Antonov An-38-100.

1997, Oct. 30
281 A112 20k multicolored   .55 .55
282 A112 40k multicolored   1.25 1.25

Ships
A113

1997, Dec. 6   Litho.   Perf. 13½
283 A113 20k Zavyietnyj, 1903   .55 .55
284 A113 40k Serhii Korolev,
          1970, Academi-
          cian   1.25 1.25

A114

1997, Dec. 6   Litho.   Perf. 12x12½
285 A114 40k multi + label   1.50 1.50
Participation of Ukrainian astronaut in US
space shuttle mission.

A115

1997, Dec. 20   Perf. 13½
Vasyl Krychevskyi (1872-1952), painter,
architect.
286 A115 10k multicolored   .75 .75

Christmas — A116

1997, Dec. 20
287 A116 20k multicolored   .50 .50

Traditional
Handicrafts
A117

Region: #288, Rooster, Dnipropetrovsk.
#289, Vest, Chernivtsi. #290, Ram, Poltava.
#291, Molded design, Ivano-Frankivsk.

1997, Dec. 20
288 A117 20k multicolored   .55 .55
289 A117 20k multicolored   .55 .55
290 A117 40k multicolored   .95 .95
291 A117 40k multicolored   .95 .95
         Nos. 288-291 (4)   3.00 3.00

Perf. 11½
288a   20k   .60 .60
289a   20k   .60 .60
290a   40k   1.00 1.00
291a   40k   1.00 1.00
b.   Sheet, 2 each #288a-291a   7.25 7.25
Nos. 288-291 have colored border. Nos.
288a-291a do not.

Arms Type of 1993

Arms of Transcarpathia (Zakarpattya).

1997, Dec. 30   Litho.   Perf. 13½
292 A35 20k multicolored   .90 .90

A118   A119

Wildlife: a, 20k, Skylark. b, 40k, White-tailed
eagle. c, 20k, Black stork. d, 40k, Long-eared
hedgehog. e, 20k, Garden dormouse. f, 40k,
Wild boar.

1997, Dec. 30   Litho.   Perf. 11½
293 A118 Sheet of 6, #a.-f.   5.00 5.00

Litho. & Engr.
1997, Dec. 20   Litho.   Perf. 13½
294 A119 60k multicolored   1.10 1.10
Hryhorii Skovoroda (1722-94), philosopher.

A120   A121

1998, Jan. 6   Litho.   Perf. 13½
295 A120 20k multicolored   .70 .70
Volodymyr Sosiura (1898-1965), poet.

1998, Feb. 14   Litho.   Perf. 13½
296 A121 20k Figure skating   .75 .75
297 A121 20k Biathlon   .75 .75
1998 Winter Olympic Games, Nagano.

Bilhorod Dnistrovskyi Fortress, 2500th
Anniv. — A122

1998, Apr. 21   Litho.   Perf. 13½
298 A122 20k multicolored   .75 .75

UKRFILEKS 98 Natl. Philatelic
Exhibition, Sevastopol — A123

Design: Frigate, "Hetman Sahaidachnyi."

1998, Apr. 28   Litho.   Perf. 13½
299 A123 30k multi + label   .90 .90

European Bank of Reconstruction and
Development — A124

Obverse, reverse of Ukrainian coins: a, 1k,
Gold, 11th cent. b, 1k, Silver, 11th cent. c, 60k,
500h St. Sophia Cathedral gold coin. d, 60k,
200h Taras Shevchenko gold coin. e, 30k,
1,000,000k Bohdan Khmelnytsky silver coin. f,
30k, 10h Petro Mohyla silver coin.

Litho. & Engr.
1998, May 8   Perf. 13½
300 A124 Sheet of 6, #a.-f.   10.00 10.00

Ivan Kupalo Natl.
Festival — A125

1998, May 16   Litho.   Perf. 13½
301 A125 40k multicolored   1.75 1.75
Europa.

Souvenir Sheet

Askania Nova Nature Preserve,
Cent. — A126

a, 40k, Deer. b, 60k, Przewalski horses.
Illustration reduced.

1998, May 16   Litho.   Perf. 11½
302 A126 Sheet of 2, #a.-b.   2.50 2.50

Paintings from Lviv Picture Gallery — A127

Designs: No. 303, Portrait of Maria Theresa, by J.E. Liotard. No. 304, Man with a Cello, by Gerard von Honthorst. 40k, Madonna and Child, 17th cent. Lviv School.
1.20h, Madonna and Child and Two Saints, by 16th cent. Italian school.

1998, June 20   **Perf. 13½**
303 A127 20k multicolored   .40   .40
304 A127 20k multicolored   .40   .40
305 A127 40k multicolored   .80   .80
a.   Strip of 3, #303-305   1.75   1.75
       Souvenir Sheet
306 A127 1.20h multicolored   2.00   2.00

       Souvenir Sheet

Polytechnical Institute, Kyiv, Cent. — A128

Illustration reduced.

1998, June 27   **Litho.**   **Perf. 11½**
307 A128 1h multicolored   3.00   3.00

Askold & Dyr A129

       Litho. & Engr.
1998, July 4   **Perf. 13½**
308 A129 3h multi + label   4.00   4.00

Hetman Bohdan Khmelnytsky A130

Designs: a, 30k, Battle scene, denomination LR. b, 2k, Portrait of Khmelnytsky. c, 30k, Battle scene, denomination LL. d, 40k, denomination LR. e, 60k, Battle scene. f, 40k, Battle scene, denomination LL.

1998, July 25   **Litho. & Engr.**
309 A130 Sheet of 6, #a.-f.   6.75   6.75
    Ukrainian uprising, 350th anniv.

Town of Halych, 1100th Anniv. A131

1998, Aug. 8   **Litho.**
310 A131 20k multicolored   .70   .70

Queen Anna Yaroslavna (1024?-75) A132

1998, Aug. 8
311 A132 40k multicolored   .90   .90

Yurii Lysianskyi (1773-1837), Explorer — A133

1998, Aug. 13
312 A133 40k multicolored   .90   .90

Natalia Uzhvii (1898-1986), Stage Actress — A134

1998, Sept. 8   **Litho.**   **Perf. 13½**
313 A134 40k multicolored   .90   .90

Polytechnical Institute, Kyiv, Cent. — A135

Designs: 10k, W.L. Kirpichov, first president. No. 315, E.O. Paton, bridge. No. 316, S.P. Timoschenko, mathematical formula. 30k, Igor I. Sikorsky, biplane. 40k, Sergei P. Korolev, rocket, satellite.

1998, Sept. 10   **Perf. 12½x12**
314 A135 10k multicolored   .40   .40
315 A135 20k multicolored   .40   .40
316 A135 20k multicolored   .40   .40
317 A135 30k multicolored   .75   .75
318 A135 40k multicolored   .85   .85
a.   Strip of 5, #314-318   3.00   3.00

   A136   A137

1998, Sept. 19   **Litho.**   **Perf. 13½**
319 A136 10k multicolored   .70   .70
       World Post Day.

1998, Sept.19
320 A137 20k multicolored   .50   .50
   Ukrainian book, 1000th anniv.

Church Architecture A138

Designs: No. 321, Church of the Transfiguration, Chernihiv, 11th cent. No. 322, Church of the Holy Protection, Kharkiv, 17th cent.

1998, Sept. 21
321 A138 20k multicolored   .70   .70
322 A138 20k multicolored   .70   .70

World Wildlife Fund A139

Branta ruficollis: a, f, 20k, Adults. b, g, 30k, Female on nest. c, h, 40k, Female with goslings. d, i, 60k, Adults, goslings.

1998, Oct. 10   **Litho.**   **Perf. 13½**
323   A139   Block of 4, #a.-d.   2.75   2.75
e.   Block of 4, perf. 11 ½, #f.-i.   3.25   3.25
j.   Sheet of 2, #323e   6.50   6.50

Antonov Airplanes A140

1998, Nov. 28   **Litho.**   **Perf. 13½**
324 A140 20k Antonov 140   .50   .50
325 A140 40k Antonov 70   .70   .70

     Hetman Type of 1997
   Design: Petro Doroshenko (1627-98).

1998, Nov. 28   **Litho.**   **Perf. 12½x12**
326 A141 20k multicolored   .80   .80

Borys D. Hrinchenko (1863-1910), Writer — A142

1998, Dec. 4   **Litho.**   **Perf. 13½**
327 A142 20k multicolored   .60   .60

Christmas — A143

1998, Dec. 11
328 A143 30k multicolored   .65   .65

Ukrainians in Australia, 50th Anniv. A144

1998, Dec. 20
329 A144 40k multicolored   .60   .60

Illintsi Meteor Impact Area A145

1998, Dec. 25
330 A145 40k multicolored   .90   .90

Universal Declaration of Human Rights, 50th Anniv. — A146

Paintings of various flowers by Kateryna Bilokur (1900-61): 30k, 1940. 50k, 1959.

1998, Dec. 25
331 A146 30k multicolored   .65   .65
332 A146 50k multicolored   .95   .95
a.   Pair, #331-332 +label   1.60   1.60

Serhii Paradzhanov (1924-90), Film Director — A147

1999, Feb. 27   **Litho.**   **Perf. 13½**
333 A147 40k multi + label   .75   .75

Volodymyr Ivasiuk (1949-79), Composer A148

1999, Mar. 4
334 A148 30k multicolored   .40   .40

Scythian Gold A149

1999, Mar. 20
335	A149	20k Clasp	.35	.35
336	A149	40k Boar	.60	.60
337	A149	50k Young elk	.75	.75
338	A149	1h Necklace	1.25	1.25
a.		Block of 4, #335-338	3.00	3.00

Spring Easter Dance — A150

1999, Apr. 7
339	A150	30k multicolored	.45	.45

A151

Synevyr Natl. Park: a, 50k, Wooden monuments on bank of Tereblyia River. b, 1h, Thymallus thymallus, river scene.

1999, Apr. 24
340	A151	Pair, #a.-b.	1.25	1.25

Europa.

A152

1999, May 13
341	A152	40k multicolored	.55	.55

Panas Myrnyi (1849-1920), writer.

Honoré de Balzac (1799-1850), Writer — A153

1999, May 20
342	A153	40k multicolored	.55	.55

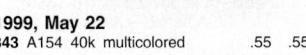

Council of Europe, 50th Anniv. A154

1999, May 22
343	A154	40k multicolored	.55	.55

Aleksandr Pushkin (1799-1837), Poet — A155

1999, June 6
344	A155	40k + label	.55	.55

Sailboats — A156

No. 345: a, Bark (Baidak), double sails, one man at tiller. b, Cossack (Chaika), single sail, rowers.

1999, June 26
345	A156	30k Pair, #a.-b.	1.00	1.00

Souvenir Sheet

Yaroslav the Wise — A157

1999, July 2   Litho.   Perf. 11½
346	A157	1.20h multicolored	1.50	2.50

Principality of Halytsko-Volynskyi, 800th Anniv. — A158

1999, July 27   Perf. 13½
347	A158	50k multicolored	.75	.75

A159   A160

Designs: a, 30k, Icon of St. George. b, 60, Girl in a Red Hat, by O.O. Murashko.

1999, July 27
348	A159	Pair, #a.-b. + label	1.50	1.50

Natl. Museum of Art, Cent.

1999, Aug. 7
349	A160	30k Bee on flower	1.00	1.00

Bee keeping in Ukraine.

A161   A162

1999, Aug. 14   Litho.   Perf. 13½
350	A161	30k multicolored	.60	.60

UPU, 125th anniv.

1999, Aug. 14
351	A162	30k multicolored	.60	.60

Poltava, 1100th anniv.

Presidential Medals — A163

Designs: 30k, Order of Princess Olga. No. 353: a, Medal with trident. b, Medal with star.

1999, Aug. 17   Litho. & Engr.
352	A163	30k multicolored	.50	.50

Souvenir Sheet of 2
353	A163	2.50h #a.-b.	5.75	5.75

No. 353 contains two 35x50mm stamps.

Polish-Ukrainian Cooperation in Nature Conservation — A164

a, Cervus elaphus. b, Felis silvestris.

1999, Sept. 22   Litho.   Perf. 13½
354	A164	1.40h Pair, #a.-b.	2.00	2.00

See Poland Nos. 3477-3478.

National Bank — A165

1999, Sept. 28   Litho. & Engr.
355	A165	3h multicolored	2.50	2.50

Souvenir Sheet
356	A165	5h multicolored	3.75	3.75

Hetman Type of 1997

Designs: No. 357, Ivan Vyhovskyi (d. 1664), cavalry in water. No. 358, Pavlo Polubotok (1660-1724), ships in water.

1999   Litho.   Perf. 12¼x12
357	A110	30k multi	.60	.60
358	A110	30k multi	.60	.60

Issued: No. 357, 11/20; No. 358, 12/22.

A166

Christmas A167

1999, Nov. 26   Wmk. 399   Perf. 13½
359	A166	30k multi	.50	.50

Unwmk.
360	A167	60k multi	.75	.75

Children's Art — A168

a, Spacecraft, alien creatures. b, Elephant in space. c, Rocket and space car on planet.

1999, Nov. 30   Unwmk.   Perf. 11½
361	A168	10k Strip of 3, #a.-c.	.70	.70

Fauna A169

Designs: a, 40k, Desmana moschata. b, 60k, Gyps fulvus. c, 40k, Lucanus cervus.

1999, Dec. 9   Perf. 13½
362	A169	Strip of 3, #a.-c.	1.50	1.50

Church of St. Andrew, Kyiv — A170

1999, Dec. 12
363	A170	60k multi + label	1.25	1.25

Mushrooms A171

Designs: a, 30k, Armillariella mellea. b, 30k, Paxillus atrotomentosus. c, 30k, Pleurotus ostratus. d, 40k, Cantharellus cibarius. e, 60k, Agaricus campester.

1999, Dec. 15   Perf. 11½
364	A171	Sheet of 5, #a.-e., + label	3.25	3.25

New Year 2000 — A172

1999, Dec. 18   **Perf. 13½**
365   A172   50k multi + label   2.00   2.00

Motor Vehicles — A173

a, Kraz-65032 truck. b, Tavriia Nova car.

1999, Dec. 18   **Litho.**
366   A173   30k Pair, #a.-b.   1.00   1.00

Works of Maria Prymachenko — A174

Denomination colors: a, Green. b, Violet.

1999, Dec. 22
367   A174   30k Pair, #a.-b., + central label   1.00   1.00

Halshka
Hulevychivna,
Philanthropist
A175

1999, Dec. 25   **Perf. 13½**
368   A175   30k multi   .50   .50

Zoogeographic Endowment
Fund — A176

Animals from: a, 10k, Carpathian Reserve. b, 30k, Polissia Reserve. c, 40k, Kaniv Reserve. d, 60k, Trakhtemyriv Reserve. e, 1h, Askaniia-Nova Reserve (ram, birds). f, 1h, Kara-Dag Reserve (birds).

1999, Dec. 28   **Perf. 11½**
369   A176   Sheet of 6, #a.-f.   3.00   4.00

Christianity, 2000th Anniv. — A177

Designs: a, Mother of God mosaic, St. Sofia Cathedral, Kyiv, 11th cent. b, Christ Pantocrator fresco, Church of the Savior's Transfiguration, Polotsk, Belarus, 12th cent. c, Volodymyr Madonna, Tretiakov Gallery, Moscow, 12th cent.

2000, Jan. 5   **Litho.**   **Perf. 11½**
370   A177   80k Sheet of 3, #a.-c.   3.50   4.25

Souvenir Sheet

Opera and Ballet Theaters — A178

No. 371: a, National Academic, Kyiv. b, Odessa State, Odessa. c, Kharkov State Academic, Kharkov. d, Ivan Franko State Academic, Lviv.
Illustration reduced.

2000, Jan. 29   **Litho.**   **Perf. 11½**
371   A178   40k Sheet of 4, #a.-d.   5.00   5.00

Kyiv Bridges — A179

No. 372: a, 10k, Moscow Bridge. b, 30k, Y. O. Paton Bridge. c, 40k, Pedestrian park bridge. d, 60k, Subway bridge.
Illustration reduced.

2000, Jan. 29   **Perf. 12¼x12**
372   A179   Block of 4, #a.-d.   3.00   3.00

Souvenir Sheet

Peresopnytsia Gospel — A180

Illustration reduced.

2000, Feb. 8   **Perf. 11½**
373   A180   1.50h multi   2.25   2.40

A181   A182

2000, Feb. 11   **Perf. 13½**
374   A181   30k multi   .50   .50
Oksana Petrusenko (1900-40), opera singer

2000, Feb. 18
375   A182   40k multi   1.00   1.00
Marusia Churai, 17th cent. singer

Hetman Type of 1997

Designs: No. 376, Danylo Apostol (1654-1734), church, burning castle. No. 377, Ivan Samoylovych (d. 1690), tent, winter scene.

2000   **Perf. 12¼x12**
376   A110   30k multi   .55   .55
377   A110   30k multi   .55   .55
Issued: No. 376, 2/22; No. 377, 3/3.

World
Meteorological
Organization, 50th
Anniv. — A183

2000, Mar. 10   **Litho.**   **Perf. 13½**
378   A183   30k multi   .55   .55

Europa, 2000
Common Design Type

2000, Mar. 29   **Litho.**   **Perf. 13½**
379   CD17   3h multi   2.50   2.50

Souvenir Sheets

Easter Eggs — A184

No. 380: a, 30k, Egg with black and red star design, Podillia region. b, 30k, Flower egg, Chernihiv region. c, 30k, Egg with leaf design, Kyiv region. d, 30k, Egg with green, white and yellow geometric design, Odesa region. e, 70k, Egg with reindeer design, Hutsulschyna region. f, 70k, Egg with cross design, Volyn region.

2000, Apr. 28   **Perf. 11½**
380   A184   Sheet of 6, #a-f   2.75   3.00

Stamp Exhibitions — A185

No. 381: a, Woman in native costume, Austria #2. b, Man in native costume, Great Britain #1.
Illustration reduced.

2000, May 20
381   A185   80k Sheet of 2, #a-b   1.25   1.25
WIPA 2000 Stamp Exhibition, Vienna; The Stamp Show 2000, London.

Donetsk Oblast — A186

City of Kyiv — A187

2000   **Perf. 12¼x12**
382   A186   30k multi   .55   .55
383   A187   30k multi   .55   .55
Regional and administrative areas.
Issued: No. 382, 5/26; No. 383, 5/28.

6th Natl. Philatelic Exhibition,
Donetsk — A188

2000, May 28   **Litho.**   **Perf. 12¼x12**
384   A188   30k multi   .60   .60

City of Ostroh,
900th
Anniv. — A189

2000, June 16   **Litho.**   **Perf. 13½**
385   A189   30k multi   .60   .60

2000 Summer
Olympics,
Sydney — A190

2000, June 26
386   A190   30k High jump   .45   .45
387   A190   30k Boxing   .45   .45
388   A190   70k Yachting   .75   .75
389   A190   1h Rhythmic gymnastics   1.40   1.40
    Nos. 386-389 (4)   3.05   3.05

Petro Prokopovych (1775-1850),
Apiarist — A191

2000, July 12   **Litho.**   **Perf. 13½**
390   A191   30k multi   .70   .70

Shipbuilding — A192

Illustration reduced.

2000, July 14
391 A192 Pair   1.50 1.50
  a. 40k Ship St. Paul   .60 .60
  b. 70k Ship St. Nicholas   .90 .90

Tetiana Pata (1884-1976),
Artist — A193

No. 392: a, Leafy Plants with Flowers, 1950s. b, Viburnum Berries and Bird, 1957. Illustration reduced.

2000, July 21
392 A193 Horiz. pair, #a-b +
      central label   1.00 1.00
  a.-b. 40k Any single   .45 .45

Dubno, 900th
Anniv. — A194

2000, July 26
393 A194 30k multi   .60 .60

Harvest
Festival — A195

2000, Aug. 4
394 A195 30k multi   .55 .55

Souvenir Sheet

Presidential Symbols — A196

Designs: a, Flag. b, Mace. c, Seal. d, Badge.

2000, Aug. 18   **Litho.**   **Perf. 11½**
395 A196 60k Sheet of 4, #a-d   3.00 3.00

Regional and Administrative Areas

Volynska Oblast — A197

Autonomous Republic of
Crimea — A198

2000   **Perf. 12¼x12**
396 A197 30k multi   .55 .55
397 A198 30k multi   .65 .65
   Issued: No. 396, 8/23; No. 397, 10/20.

Kyiv Post Office, 225th Anniv. — A199

Illustration reduced.

2000, Sept. 3   **Perf. 11½**
398 A199 30k multi   .50 .50

Endangered Amphibians — A200

No. 399: a, 30k, Triturus vulgaris. b, 70k, Salamandra salamandra.
Illustration reduced.

2000, Sept. 8   **Perf. 13½**
399 A200 Pair, #a-b   1.25 1.25

Yurij
Drohobych
(1450-94),
Writer
A201

2000, Sept. 12
400 A201 30k multi   .50 .50

Souvenir Sheet

Carpathian National Park — A202

No. 401: a, Mt. Breskul, 1911 meters. b, Mt. Hoberla, 2061 meters.

2000, Sept. 15   **Perf. 11½**
401 A202 80k Sheet of 2, #a-b   3.00 3.00

Flowers — A203

Designs: a, Marigolds. b, Chamomiles. c, Hollyhocks. d, Poppies. e, Periwinkles. f, Cornflowers. g, Morning glories. h, Martagon lilies. i, Peonies. j, Bluebells.

2000, Oct. 6
402 A203 30k Sheet of 10, #a-j   5.00 5.00

Children's Folk Tales — A204

Designs: a, "Ivasyk and Telesyk," (boy in boat, witch). b, "The Crooked Duck," (couple with duck). c, "The Cat and the Rooster."

2000, Nov. 3
403   30k Horiz. strip of 3   1.10 1.10
  a.-c. A204 Any single   .35 .35

New
Year
2001
A205

2000, Nov. 24
404 A205 30k multi   .50 .50

St. Onufius'   Church of Christ's
Church,   Birth,
Lviv — A206   Velyke — A207

Design: 70k, Church of the Resurrection, Sumy.

2000, Dec. 8   **Perf. 13½**
405 A206 30k multi   .30 .30
406 A207 30k multi   .30 .30
407 A207 70k multi   .65 .65
     Nos. 405-407 (3)   1.25 1.25

Souvenir Sheet

St. Vladimir (c. 956-1015), Kyivan
Prince — A208

2000, Dec. 15   **Perf. 11½**
408 A208 2h multi   2.25 2.25

Dmytro Rostovskyi (1651-1709),
Religious Leader — A209

2001, Jan. 16   **Litho.**   **Perf. 13½**
409 A209 75k multi   .80 .80

Love — A210

2001, Jan. 26
410 A210 30k multi   .55 .55

Souvenir Sheet

Prince Danylo Romanovych (1201-
64) — A211

2001, Feb. 1   **Perf. 11½**
411 A211 3h multi   3.00 3.00

Hetman Type of 1997

Designs: 30k, Yuryi Khmelnytski (1641-85), as monk in Turkish prison, Kamianets-Podilskyi fortifications. 50k, Mykhailo Khanenko (1620-80), leading troops, relinquishing power.

2001, Feb. 20   **Perf. 12¼x12**
412-413 A110   Set of 2   1.00 1.00

Invention of the Telephone, 125th Anniv. A212

2001, Mar. 6   *Perf. 13½*
414 A212 70k multi   .75 .75

Children's Art — A213

Art by: 10k, Alyna Nochvaj. 30k, Olyia Pynych. 40k, Dasha Chemberzhi.

2001, Mar. 7   *Perf. 11½*
415-417 A213   Set of 3   1.10 1.10

Hollyhocks A214

Marigolds A215

Sunflower A216

Viburnum Opulus Berries A217

Wheat — A218

2001, Apr. 4   **Litho.**   *Perf. 13¾*
418 A214   (10k) multi   .20 .20
419 A215   (30k) multi   .20 .20
420 A216   (71k) multi   .50 .50
421 A217 (2.66h) multi   1.75 1.75
422 A218 (3.65h) multi   2.50 2.50
    Nos. 418-422 (5)   5.15 5.15

2006, Oct. 9   *Perf. 11½,*
Dated 2006
418a A214   (10k) multi   .20 .20
419a A215   (30k) multi   .20 .20
420a A216   (71k) multi   .35 .35
421a A217 (2.66h) multi   1.25 1.25
422a A218 (3.65h) multi   1.90 1.90
    Nos. 418a-422a (5)   3.90 3.90

Nos. 420, 422 exist dated "2004." Nos. 421, 422 exist dated "2005" and "2006."
Nos. 418a-422a were issued only in No. F2b.
See Nos. 453-454.

Folktales — A219

No. 423: a, The Fox and Wolf (fox on sleigh, fish). b, The Mitten (bear, fox, wolf, rabbit mouse, frog). c, Sirko the Dog (wolf with bottle, dog).
Illustration reduced.

2001, Apr. 14   *Perf. 13½*
423 A219 30k Horiz. strip of 3,
    #a-c   .80 .80

Ships — A220

No. 424: a, 20k, Twelve Apostles. b, 30k, Three Priests.
Illustration reduced.

2001, Apr. 20
424 A220   Horiz. pair, #a-b   .65 .65

Europa — A221

Fish, jellyfish, seaweed: a, 28x40mm. b, 56x40mm.
Illustration reduced.

2001, Apr. 27
425 A221 1h Horiz. pair, #a-b   2.10 2.10

Holy Trinity A222

2001, May 15
426 A222 30k multi   .40 .40

Souvenir Sheet

Apiculture — A223

No. 427: a, Bee on flower. b, Plant cutting, jar of honey, bowl of pollen, jars. c, Worker on honeycomb. d, Queen. e, Hive. f, Drone.

2001, May 22   *Perf. 11½*
427 A223 50k Sheet of 6, #a-f   4.50 6.00

Souvenir Sheet

Kyievo-Pecherska Monastery, 950th Anniv. — A224

2001, May 25
428 A224 1.50h multi   1.50 1.50

Visit of Pope John Paul II, June 23-27 A225

2001, June 15   *Perf. 13½*
429 A225 3h multi   2.50 2.50

Regional and Administrative Areas

Zakarpatska Oblast — A226

Kharkivska Oblast — A227

2001   *Perf. 12¼x12*
430 A226 30k multi   .50 .50
431 A226 30k multi   .50 .50
    Issued: No. 430, 6/29; No. 431, 8/18.

Regional and Administrative Areas

Chernihivska Oblast — A228

Kirovohradska Oblast — A229

2001   **Litho.**   *Perf. 12¼x12*
432 A228 30k multi   .50 .50
433 A229 30k multi   .50 .50
    Issued: No. 432, 9/21; No. 433, 9/22.

Souvenir Sheet

Icons From Khanenko Art Museum — A230

No. 434: a, 20k, Virgin and Child, 28x40mm. b, 30k, St. John the Baptist, 28x40mm. c, Saints Serhyi and Bacchus, 56x40mm.

2001, July 12   **Litho.**   *Perf. 11½*
434 A230   Sheet of 3, #a-c   1.00 1.75

Endangered Species A231

No. 435: a, Milvus milvus. b, Scirtopoda telum.

2001, July 24   *Perf. 13*
435 A231 1h Vert. pair, #a-b   1.60 1.60

Dmytro Bortnianskyi (1751-1825), Composer — A232

2001, July 26
436 A232 20k multi   .30 .30

Soccer — A233

2001, Aug. 10
437 A233 50k multi   .50 .50

Souvenir Sheet

Independence, 10th Anniv. — A234

2001, Aug. 15   *Perf. 11½*
438 A234 3h multi   2.75 2.75

7th Natl. Philatelic Exhibition, Dnipropetrovsk — A235

2001, Oct. 7   **Litho.**   *Perf. 12¼x12*
439 A235 30k multi   .45 .45

Year of Dialogue Among Civilizations A236

2001, Oct. 9   *Perf. 13*
440 A236 70k multi   1.10 1.10

Souvenir Sheet

Black Sea Marine Life — A237

No. 441: a, 30k, Seahorses. b, 70k, Dolphins, birds.

2001, Oct. 19   **Perf. 11½**
441 A237   Sheet of 2, #a-b   1.50 1.50

Christmas — A238

2001, Nov. 9   **Perf. 12¼x12**
442 A238 30k multi   .45 .45

St. Nicholas A239

2001, Nov. 16   **Perf. 13**
443 A239 30k multi   .45 .45

Happy New Year — A240

2001, Nov. 23
444 A240 30k multi   .45 .45

Poets — A241

No. 445: a, Taras Shevchenko (1814-61), Ukrainian poet. b, Akakii Tsereteli (1840-1915), Georgian poet.

2001, Dec. 19
445 A241 40k Horiz. pair, #a-b   .75 .75
    See Georgia No. 276.

Regional Costumes

Kyivshchyna Region — A242

Chernihivshchyna Region — A243

Poltavshchyna Region — A244

No. 446: a, 20k, Two women. b, 50k, Man and woman.
No. 447: a, 20k, Musicians and girl. b, 50k, Bride and groom, boy.
No. 448: a, 20k, Priest and family. b, 50k, Two women.

2001, Dec. 20   **Perf. 13¼**
446 A242   Horiz. pair, #a-b   .60 .60
447 A243   Horiz. pair, #a-b   .60 .60
448 A244   Horiz. pair, #a-b   .60 .60
  c.   Souvenir sheet, #446-448, perf. 11½   2.00 2.00
    Nos. 446-448 (3)   1.80 1.80

Hetman Type of 1997

Designs: No. 449, 40k, Pavlo Teteryia (d. 1670) holding scepter, people in town, horsemen and carriage heading for town. No. 450, 40k, Demyian Mnohohrishnyi, receiving scepter, boats in river. No. 451, 40k, Ivan Briukhovetskyi (d. 1668), battle scenes.

2002, Jan. 17   **Perf. 12¼x12**
449-451 A110   Set of 3   .85 .85

Scythian Military History — A245

No. 452: a, Archer on horseback. b, Swordsman in battle. c, Commander on horseback, warrior. d, Female warrior.
Illustration reduced.

2002, Jan. 29   **Perf. 13**
452 A245 40k Block of 4, #a-d   1.10 1.10

Flower Type of 2001 and

Periwinkle — A246

2002   **Litho.**   **Perf. 13¾**
453 A246   5k multi   .30 .30
  a.   Perf. 11½, dated "2006"   .30 .30
454 A214   10k multi   .30 .30
  a.   Perf. 11½, dated "2006"   .30 .30

Issued: 5k, 2/1; 10k, 2/26; Nos. 453a-454a, 10/9/06. Nos. 453a-454a were issued only in No. F2b.
No. 453 exists dated "2004," "2005" and "2006." No. 454 exist sdated "2005."

Sporting Achievements — A247

Designs: No. 455, 40k, Zhanna Pintusevich-Block winning 100-meter dash at 2001 World Track and Field Championships. No. 456, 40k, Swimmer at 2000 Summer Olympics.

2002, Feb. 15   **Perf. 13**
455-456 A247   Set of 2   .50 .50

Regional and Administrative Areas

Kyivska Oblast — A248

2002, Feb. 18   **Perf. 12¼x12**
457 A248 40k multi   .30 .30

Shipbuilding — A249

No. 458: a, Frigate Sizopol and coast. b, Brigantine Perseus.
Illustration reduced.

2002, Feb. 22   **Perf. 13½**
458 A249 40k Horiz. pair, #a-b   .55 .55

Issuance of First Stamp After Independence, 10th Anniv. — A250

2002, Mar. 1
459 A250 40k No. 100   .45 .45

Leonid Hlibov (1827-93), Writer — A251

2002, Mar. 4   **Litho.**   **Perf. 13¼**
460 A251 40k multi   .35 .35

Ruslan Ponomariov, Winner of 16th World Chess Championships — A252

2002, Mar. 29   **Perf. 13½**
461 A252 3.50h multi   1.75 1.75

Souvenir Sheet

Europa — A253

No. 462: a, Lion. b, Tiger, horiz.

2002, Apr. 4   **Perf. 11½**
462 A253 1.75h Sheet of 2, #a-b   2.50 3.25

Palm Sunday — A254

2002, Apr. 19   **Perf. 13½**
463 A254 40k multi   .35 .35

Worldwide Fund for Nature (WWF) — A255

Various views of Elaphe situla: a, 40k. b, 70k. c, 80k. d, 2.50h.
Illustration reduced.

2002, May 25   **Perf. 13½**
464 A255   Block of 4, #a-d   2.25 2.25
  e.   Perf. 11½   2.25 2.25

Souvenir Sheet

Opera and Ballet Theaters — A256

No. 465: a, Donetsk (tree at center). b, Dnipropetrovsk (trees at side).

2002, May 31   **Perf. 11½**
465 A256 1.25h Sheet of 2, #a-b   1.25 2.00

Flower Type of 2001 and

Blue Cornflower A257   Lilac A258

2002   **Litho.**   **Perf. 13¾**
466 A215   30k multi   .30 .30
  a.   Perf. 11½, dated "2006"   .30 .30
467 A257   45k multi   .30 .30
  a.   Perf. 11½, dated "2006"   .30 .30
468 A258   (80k) multi   .60 .60
  a.   Perf. 11½, dated "2006"   .60 .60

Issued: 30k, 6/1; 45k, 9/18; (80k), 7/5.
Nos. 466-468 exist dated "2004." Nos. 466, 467 exist dated "2005" and "2006."
Nos. 466a-468a issued 10/9/06. Nos. 466a-468a were issued only in No. F2b.

Regional and Administrative Areas

Luhanska Oblast — A259

Chernivetska Oblast — A260

Odeska Oblast — A261

Cherkaska Oblast — A262

Sumska Oblast — A263

2002   **Perf. 12¼x12**
469 A259 40k multi   .30   .30
470 A260 40k multi   .30   .30
471 A261 45k multi   .35   .35
472 A262 45k multi   .35   .35
473 A263 45k multi   .35   .35
     Nos. 469-473 (5)   1.65   1.65

Issued: No. 469, 6/2; No. 470, 6/27; No.
471, 9/20. No. 472, 10/9; No. 473, 10/21.

Endangered
Species
A264

No. 474: a, Phalacrocorax aristotelis. b,
Phocoena phocoena.

2002, June 14   Litho.   Perf. 13
474 A264 70k Pair, #a-b   .90   .90

Mykola Leontovich
(1877-1921),
Composer — A265

2002, June 21   Perf. 13½
475 A265 40k multi   .35   .35

Souvenir Sheet

Black Sea Nature Reserve — A266

No. 476: a, Haematopus ostralegus
(40x28mm). b, Larus genei (40x28mm). c, Iris
pumila (22x26mm). d, Numenius arquata
(26x22mm). e, Charadrius alexandrinus
(26x22mm).

2002, July 13   Perf. 11½
476 A266 50k Sheet of 5, #a-e 1.50 2.50

Folk Tales — A267

No. 477: a, Fox and Pancake. b, Mr. Cat. c,
Speckled Chicken.
Illustration reduced.

2002, July 19   Perf. 14¼x14
477 A267 40k Horiz. strip of 3,
          #a-c   .80   .80

Art of Hanna Sobachko-
Shostak — A268

No. 478: a, Cage for Starlings, 1963 (peach
background). b, Vase with Flowers, 1964 (red
background). c, Chamomile Flowers, 1964
(yellow background).

2002, Aug. 9   Perf. 14x14¼
478   Horiz. strip of 3   .90   .90
   a.-c. A268 45k Any single   .30   .30

Space Pioneers — A269

Designs: 40k, Yurii V. Kondratiuk (1897-
1942). 45k, Mykhailo Yianhel (1911-71). 50k,
Mykola Kybalchych (1853-81). 70k, Serhii
Korolov (1907-66).

2002, Aug. 23   Perf. 12¼x12
479-482 A269 Set of 4   1.25   1.25

Marine Life — A270

No. 483: a, Phoca caspica. b, Huso huso
ponticus.
Illustration reduced.

2002, Sept. 6   Perf. 14x14¼
483 A270 75k Horiz. pair, #a-b   1.00 1.00
           See Kazakhstan No. 386.

Khotyn, 1000th Anniv. — A271

2002, Sept. 21   Perf. 12¼x12
484 A271 40k multi   .25   .25

Odesaphil 2002
Stamp Exhibition,
Odesa — A272

2002, Oct. 5   Litho.   Perf. 14¼x14
485 A272 45k multi   .30   .30

Paintings of Kyiv by Taras Shevchenko
(1814-61) — A273

Designs: 45k, Askold's Tomb. 75k, Dnieper
River Shoreline. 80k, St. Alexander's Church.

                              Perf. 13¾x14½
2002, Nov. 15   Litho.
486-488 A273 Set of 3   1.25   1.25

Happy New
Year — A274

2002, Nov. 22   Perf. 14x14¼
489 A274 45k multi   .30   .30

Regional Costumes

Vinychyna Region — A275

Cherkashchyna Region — A276

Ternopilska Region — A277

No. 490: a, Family, rainbow. b, Family, fruit
tree.
No. 491: a, Four girls holding hands. b,
Couple gathering crops.
No. 492: a, Priest blessing family. b, People
with Easter baskets.

2002, Dec. 6   Perf. 13¼
490 A275 45k Horiz. pair, #a-b   .55   .55
491 A276 45k Horiz. pair, #a-b   .55   .55
492 A277 45k Horiz. pair, #a-b   .55   .55
   c. Souvenir sheet, #490-492, perf.
       11½   1.75   1.75
       Nos. 490-492 (3)   1.65   1.65

Folk Tales — A278

No. 493: a, Koza-Dezera (cow on bridge). b,
The Straw Bull. c, The Fox and Crane.
Illustration reduced.

2003, Jan. 17 Litho. Perf. 14¼x14
493 A278 45k Horiz. strip of 3,
          #a-c   .75   .75

Speed
Skating
A279

2003, Jan. 24   Perf. 14x14¼
494 A279 65k multi   .35   .35

Military History — A280

No. 495: a, War with Goths, 4th cent. (soldier with spear and shield) b, Battles with
Huns, 5th cent. (archer). c, Balkan campaigns,
6th cent. (soldier with hatchet). d, Battles with
the Avars, 6th cent. (soldier with spears).
Illustration reduced.

2003, Feb. 7
495 A280 45k Block of 4, #a-d   1.00 1.00

Shipbuilding — A281

No. 496: a, Steamship Grozny (denomination at left. b, Steamship Odessa (denomination at right).
Illustration reduced.

2003, Feb. 14
496 A281 1h Horiz. pair, #a-b   1.10 1.10

Mikola Arkas (1853-1909),
Composer — A282

2003, Feb. 21
497 A282 45k multi   .25   .25

Souvenir Sheet

Javorivsky National Nature
Park — A283

No. 498: a, 1h, Alcede atthis (32x44mm). b, 1h, Cypripedium calceolus (36x41mm). c, 1.50h, Eudia pavonia, horiz. (44x32mm)

2003, Mar. 3   *Perf. 11½*
498 A283   Sheet of 3, #a-c   1.90 3.00

Europa — A284

Poster by Oleksiy Shtanko: a, Virgin Mary with dove. b, Guardian angel. Illustration reduced.

2003, Mar. 21   *Perf. 11½*
499 A284 1.75h Horiz. pair, #a-b   3.00 3.00
  c.   Booklet pane, 2 #499 + central
       label   5.25 —
       Complete booklet, #499c   5.25

Space Pioneers Type of 2002

Designs: 45k, Olleksandr Zasiadko (1779-1837). 65k, Kostyantin Konstantinov (1817-71). 70k, Valyntyn Hlushko (1908-89). 80k, Volodymyr Chelomei (1914-84).

2003, Apr. 11 Litho. *Perf. 13¾x14½*
500-503 A269   Set of 4   1.40 1.40

Ukrainian Red Cross Society, 85th
Anniv. — A285

2003, Apr. 18
504 A285 45k multi   .30 .30

Regional and Administrative Areas

Dnipropetrovska Oblast — A286

Lvivska Oblast — A287

Khmelnytska Oblast — A288

Mykolayivska Oblast — A289

Zaporizhiya Oblast — A290

2003
505 A286 45k multi   .30 .30
506 A287 45k multi   .30 .30
507 A288 45k multi   .30 .30
508 A289 45k multi   .30 .30
509 A290 45k multi   .30 .30
          Nos. 505-509 (5)   1.50 1.50

Issued: No. 505, 4/21; No. 506, 5/8; No. 507, 9/8; No. 508, 10/4; No. 509, 10/11.

Hetman Type of 1997

Designs: No. 510, 45k, Ivan Skoropadskiy (1646-1722) wearing robe, serfs in field, subjects bowing. No. 511, 45k, Kyrylo Rozumovskiy (1728-1803) holding scepter, attack of palace, palace ruins.

2003, May 22
510-511 A110   Set of 2   .50 .50

Souvenir Sheet

Volodymyr Monomakh (1053-1125),
Grand Prince of Kyiv — A291

2003, May 28   *Perf. 11½*
512 A291 3.50h multi   1.90 1.90

Owls — A292

No. 513: a, Bubo bubo. b, Strix uralensis. c, Strix aluco. d, Strix nebulosa. e, Glaucidium passerinum. f, Aegolius funereus. g, Otus scops. h, Athene noctua. i, Tyto alba. j, Asio otus. k, Asio flammeus. l, Surnia ulula. Size of # 513e-513h: 25x27mm; others: 25x36mm.

2003, June 14
513 A292 45k Sheet of 12, #a-l   2.75 4.50

Oleksandr
Myshuha (1853-
1922), Opera
Singer — A293

2003, June 20   *Perf. 13¼*
514 A293 45k multi   .30 .30

Sweet Pea — A294

2003, July 4   *Perf. 13¾*
515 A294 65k multi   .50 .50
  a.   Perf. 11½, dated "2006"   .35 .35

No. 515 exists dated "2004" and "2005." No. 515a issued 10/9/06. No. 515a was issued only in No. F2b.

Paintings Type of 2002

Paintings of Kyiv: No. 516, 45k, Podil, by Mykhailo Sazhyn, 1840. No. 517, 45k, Kyiv-Pecherska Monastery, by Vasyl Timm, 1857. No. 518, 45k, Ruins of St. Irene Monastery, by Sazhyn, 1846. No. 519, 45k, View of Old City from Yaroslav Embankment, by Timm, 1854.

2003, July 18   *Perf. 13¾x14½*
516-519 A273   Set of 4   1.00 1.00

Customs and Traditions — A295

No. 520: a, Celebration of the Harvest (Church, flowers and insects). b, Ascension (Church, fruit).

2003, July 25   *Perf. 14¼x14*
520 A295 45k Horiz. pair, #a-b   .50 .50

Borys
Hmyryia
(1903-69),
Composer
A296

2003, Aug. 5   *Perf. 14x14¼*
521 A296 45k multi   .30 .30

Souvenir Sheet

Manyiavskyi Monastery — A297

No. 522: a, Denomination at LL. b, Denomination at LR.

2003, Aug. 15   *Perf. 11x11½*
522 A297 1.25h Sheet of 2, #a-b 1.40 2.50

Yevpatoriya, 2500th Anniv. — A298

2003, Aug. 29   *Perf. 13¾x14½*
523 A298 45k multi   .30 .30

Ancient Trade Routes — A299

No. 524: a, Arrival of Scandinavian seamen in rowboat, coin of Danish King Svend Estridsen. b, Silver coin of Prince Volodymyr Sviatoslavovych, Slavic warship with sail.

2003, Sept. 17   *Perf. 11½*
524 A299 80k Vert. pair, #a-b, +
          central label   .90 .90
  c.   Booklet pane, #524   2.40 —
  d.   Booklet pane, #524a   1.25 —
  e.   Booklet pane, #524b   1.25 —
       Complete booklet, #524c, 524d,
       524e   5.00

Hryhoryi Kvitka-Osnovyianenko (1778-
1843), Writer — A300

2003, Nov. 14 Litho. *Perf. 14¼x14*
525 A300 45k multi   .30 .30

Famine of 1932-33 — A301

2003, Nov. 21   *Perf. 13¾x14½*
526 A301 45k multi   .30 .30

Christmas
A302

Litho. with Foil Application
2003, Nov. 25   *Perf. 13¼x13½*
527 A302 45k multi   .70 .70

New Year's
Greetings
A303

2003, Nov. 25 Litho. *Perf. 13½*
528 A303 45k multi   .70 .70

Regional Costumes

Kharkiv Region — A304

Sumy Region — A305

Donetsk Region — A306

No. 529: a, Women, religious icons. b, Family, lute.
No. 530: a, Woman, men. b, Group of women.
No. 531: a, Family, sled. b, Workers in field.

2003, Dec. 19   Perf. 13¼
529 A304 45k Horiz. pair, #a-b   1.00 1.00
530 A305 45k Horiz. pair, #a-b   1.00 1.00
531 A306 45k Horiz. pair, #a-b   1.00 1.00
  c.   Souvenir sheet, #529-531, perf.
        11½   3.00 3.00

Unification of Ukraine and Western
Ukraine, 85th Anniv. — A307

2004, Jan. 22 Litho. Perf. 13¾x14½
532 A307 45k multi   .30   .30

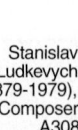

Stanislav
Ludkevych
(1879-1979),
Composer
A308

2004, Jan. 24   Perf. 13¼
533 A308 45k multi   .30   .30

Possessions of Hetman Bohdan
Khmelnytsky — A309

No. 534: a, Flag. b, Mace. c, Cap. d,
Watercup decorated with leaves. e, Tankard. f,
Sword.

Litho. With Foil Application
2004, Jan. 29   Perf. 11½
534 A309 45k Sheet of 6, #a-f   1.50 2.50

Shipbuilding — A310

No. 535: a, 1h, Oil tanker Kriti Amber
(55x26mm). b, 2.50h, Anti-submarine ship
Mikolayiv (55x29mm). c, 3.50h Aircraft carrier
Admiral Kuznetzov (55x40mm).

2004, Feb. 21   Litho.   Perf. 11½
535 A310   Sheet of 3, #a-c   4.00 6.00

Regional and Administrative Areas

Ternopilska Oblast — A311

2004, Mar. 3   Perf. 13¾x14½
536 A311 45k multi   .30   .30

Membership in
UNESCO, 50th
Anniv. — A312

2004, Mar. 19   Perf. 14¼x14
537 A312 45k multi   .30   .30

Butterflies — A313

No. 538: a, 45k, Endromis versicolora. b,
75k, Smerinthus ocellatus. c, 80k, Catocala
fraxini. d, 2.60h, Apatura ilia. e, 3.50h, Papilio
machaon.

2004, Mar. 6   Perf. 8
538 A313   Sheet of 5, #a-e   4.50 7.00

Famous
Ukrainians
A314

Designs: No. 539, 45k, Serhyi Lyfar (1904-
86), ballet dancer and choreographer. No.

540, 45k, Maria Zankovetska (1854-1934),
actress. No. 541, 45k, Mykhaylo Mak-
symovych (1804-73), historian.

2004   Litho.   Perf. 14x14¼
539-541 A314   Set of 3   .75   .75
Issued: No. 539, 4/2, Nos. 540-541, 7/23.

Zenit-1
Rocket
A315

2004, Apr. 14
542 A315 45k multi   .30   .30

European Weight Lifting
Championships, Kyiv — A316

2004, Apr. 20
543 A316 65k multi   .35   .35

Miniature Sheet

Europa — A317

No. 544: a, 45k, Lastivchyne Hnizdo
(22x33mm). b, 75k, Carpathian Mountains
(22x33mm). c, 2.61h, Khotyn Castle
(29x33mm). d, 3.52h, Pecherska Lavra
(39x28mm).

2004, Apr. 23   Perf. 11½
544 A317   Sheet of 4, #a-d   4.00 6.00

UEFA (European
Football Union),
50th
Anniv. — A318

2004, May 17   Perf. 14¼x14
545 A318 3.52h multi   2.00 2.00

FIFA (Fédération Internationale de
Football Association), Cent. — A319

No. 546: a, 45k, Player #11. b, 75k, Player
#6. c, 80k, Fan. d, 2.61h, Two women players.
Illustration reduced.

2004, May 17   Perf. 13¼
546 A319   Block of 4, #a-d   2.60 2.60

Symon Petlura
(1879-1926),
Political
Leader — A320

2004, May 21
547 A320 45k multi   .30   .30

Painting Type of 2002

Designs: No. 548, 45k, Kiev with St.
Andrew's Church, by unknown artist, 1889.
No. 549, 45k, Fountain Near the Golden Gate,
by Petro Levchenko, 1910. No. 550, 45k,
Spring in Kurenivka, by Abram Manevych,
1914-15. No. 551, 45k, St. Michael's Cathedral From the South, by Mykola Burachek,
1919.

2004, June 11   Perf. 13¾x14½
548-551 A273   Set of 4   1.00 1.00

Folktales — A321

No. 552: a, The Cat. b, Ivasyk Telesyk. c,
The Fat Man.
Illustration reduced.

2004, June 18   Perf. 14¼x14
552 A321 45k Horiz. strip of 3,
          #a-c   .75   .75

2004
Summer
Olympics,
Athens
A322

2004, June 26   Perf. 14x14¼
553 A322 2.61h multi   1.40 1.40

Regional and Administrative Areas

Rovenska Oblast — A323

Khersonska Oblast — A324

Poltavska Oblast — A325

2004   Perf. 13¾x14½
554 A323 45k multi   .30   .30
555 A324 45k multi   .30   .30
556 A325 45k multi   .30   .30
Issued: No. 554, 7/16; No. 555, 8/20; No.
556, 9/22.

Balaklava, 2500th Anniv. — A327

Perf. 13¾x14½
2004, Aug. 14   Litho.
557 A327 45k multi   .30   .30

Kharkiv, 350th
Anniv. — A328

2004, Aug. 20   **Perf. 14¼x14**
558 A328 45k multi   .30   .30

Bridges — A329

No. 559: a, Inhulskyi Bridge (open draw-bridge). b, Darnytska Bridge (three arches above roadway). c, B. M. Preobrazhenskoho Bridge (arches below roadway). d, Southern Buh Bridge (swing bridge).

2004, Aug. 25   **Perf. 13¾x14½**
559 A329 45k Block of 4, #a-d   1.00 1.00

No. 194B Surcharged

Litho. & Engr.
2004, Sept. 15   **Perf. 12½x13**
560 A47a 2.61h on 25,000kb
              multi   1.50 1.50
Taras Shevchenko University, 170th anniv.

Kirovohrad, 250th Anniv. — A330

Perf. 13¾x14¼
2004, Sept. 17   Litho.
561 A330 45k multi   .30   .30

Military History — A331

No. 562: a, Infantryman of Prince Oleg, 10th cent. b, National militia, 11th-12th cent. c, Archer on horseback, 12th cent. d, Cavalry-man for Danylo Halyts, 13th cent.
Illustration reduced.

2004, Oct. 15   **Perf. 14x14¼**
562 A331 45k Block of 4, #a-d   1.00 1.00

Miniature Sheet

Birds of the Danube Nature
Reserve — A332

No. 563: a, 45k, Cygnus olor. b, 75k, Phalacrocorax pygmaeus. c, 80k, Egretta alba. d, 2.61h, Anser anser. e, 3.52h, Platalea leucordia.

2004, Oct. 26   **Perf. 11½**
563 A332 Sheet of 5, #a-e   4.50 7.00

Intl. Space
Station,
Khartron
Systems
Emblem
A333

1516 Battle Between Cossacks and
Tartars Using Fiery Projectiles
A334

2004, Nov. 12   **Perf. 14x14¼**
564 A333 45k multi   .30   .30
565 A334 45k multi   .30   .30

Christmas
A335

No. 566: a, Magi facing right ("2" in back-ground). b, Magi facing left ("5" in back-ground). c, Nativity ("0" in background).

Litho. With Foil Application
2004, Nov. 26   **Perf. 13¼**
566   Horiz. strip of 4, #a-b,
              2 #c   1.00 1.00
  a.-c. A335 45k Any single, gold &
              multi   .25   .25
Numbers in background of strip of 4 read "2005."

New Year's
Greetings
A336

No. 567: a, Santa Claus, large trees at left ("2" in background). b, Santa Claus, large trees at right ("5" in background). c, Tree and gifts ("0" in background).

2004, Nov. 26
567   Horiz. strip of 4, #a-b,
              2 #c   1.00 1.00
  a.-c. A336 45k Any single, silver &
              multi   .25   .25
Numbers in background of strip of 4 read "2005."

Ukrainian and Iranian Aircraft — A337

No. 568: a, Antonov-140, Ukraine (denomi-nation at left). b, Iran-140, Iran (denomination at right).

2004, Nov. 30   Litho.   **Perf. 11½**
568   Horiz. pair + central la-
              bel   .90   .90
  a.-b. A337 80k Either single .45   .45
              See Iran No.

Regional Costumes

Lvivshchyna Region — A338

Ivano-Frankivshchyna Region — A339

Hutsulshchyna Region — A340

No. 569: a, Family, rooster. b, Family, pitcher.
No. 570: a, Musicians. b, Dancers at wedding.
No. 571: a, Men, child, lamb. b, Family, cradle.

2004, Dec. 10   **Perf. 13¼**
569 A338 60k Horiz. pair, #a-b   .70   .70
570 A339 60k Horiz. pair, #a-b   .70   .70
571 A340 60k Horiz. pair, #a-b   .70   .70
  c.   Miniature sheet, #569-571, perf.
              11½   2.10 2.10

Poppy — A341

2005, Jan. 14   Litho.   **Perf. 13¾**
572 A341 1h multi   .55   .55
  a.   Perf. 11½, dated "2006" .40   .40
No. 572 exists dated "2006."
No. 572a issued 10/9/06. No. 572a was issued only in No. F2b.

November - December 2004 Protests
Against Rigged Elections — A342

2005, Jan. 23   **Perf. 11½**
573 A342 45k multi   .30   .30
Printed in sheets of 7 + label.

Famous Ukrainians Type of 2004

Design: No. 574, Pavlo Virskyi (1905-75), choreographer. No. 575, Volodymyr Vyn-nychenko (1880-1951), writer and statesman.

2005   Litho.   **Perf. 14x14¼**
574 A314 45k multi   .30   .30
575 A314 45k multi   .30   .30
Issued. No. 574, 2/4; No. 575, 7/15.

Miniature Sheet

Moths — A343

No. 576: a, 45k, Acherontia atropos. b, 75k, Catocala sponsa. c, 80k, Staurophora celsia. d, 2.61h, Marumba quercus. e, Saturnia pyri.

2005, Feb. 11   **Perf. 11½**
576 A343 Sheet of 5, #a-d   4.50 4.50

Regional and Administrative Areas

Vinnytska Oblast — A344

2005, Feb. 23   **Perf. 13¾x14½**
577 A344 45k multi   .30   .30

Regional and Administrative Areas

Sevastopol City — A345

Ivano-Frankivska Oblast — A346

Zhitomyrska Oblast — A347

2005	**Litho.**	**Perf. 13¾x14½**		
578	A345	45k multi	.30	.30
579	A345	45k multi	.30	.30
580	A347	70k multi	.40	.40
	Nos. 578-580 (3)		1.00	1.00

Issued: No. 578, 6/11; No. 579, 7/16; 70k, 9/10.

Paintings by Ivan Aivazovskyi A348

No. 581: a, Sea — Koktebel, 1853. b, Towers on the Rock Near the Bosporus, 1859.

2005, Mar. 4   Litho.   Perf. 14x14¼
581		Horiz. pair, #a-b, + central label	.60	.60
a.-b.	A348	45k Either single	.30	.30

The Shepherd, by Heorhyi Yakutovych (1930-2000) — A349

Litho. & Engr.
2005, Mar. 26   Perf. 11½
582	A349	3.52h silver & gray blue	2.00	2.00

Cosmos-1 Satellite A350

Zenit-2 Rocket A351

Designs: No. 585, Dnepr rocket. No. 586, Cyclone-3 rocket.

2005, Apr. 12   Litho.   Perf. 14x14¼
583	A350	45k shown	.30	.30
584	A351	45k shown	.30	.30
585	A351	45k multi	.30	.30
586	A351	45k multi	.30	.30
	Nos. 583-586 (4)		1.20	1.20

A352

End of World War II, 60th Anniv. — A353

2005   Perf. 14x14¼
587	A352	45k multi	.30	.30

Souvenir Sheet
Perf. 11½
588	A353	80k multi	.50	.50

Issued: 45k, 4/22; 80k, 5/7. No. 587 issued in sheets of 8 + central label.

Ninth Intl. Philatelic Exhibition, Kyiv — A354

2005, May 17   Perf. 13¾x14½
589	A354	45k multi	.30	.30

Painting Type of 2002

Paintings of Kyiv: 45k, New Street, by Serhyi Shyshko, 1966. 75k, Park in Winter, by Shyshko, 1960. 80k, Sacred Sophia, by Yuryi Khymych, 1965. 1h, Khreshchatyk Boulevard, by Khymych, 1967, vert.

Perf. 13¾x14½, 14½x13¾
2005, May 18   Set of 4
590-593	A273		2.25	2.25

Ruslana, Winner of 2004 Eurovision Song Contest — A355

Logo for 2005 Eurovision Song Contest A356

2005, May 19   Perf. 11½
594	A355	45k multi	.30	.30
595	A356	2.50h multi	1.40	1.40

Europa — A357

Nos. 596 and 597: a, 2.61h, Bowl of borscht, beets, onions, garlic, tomatoes, pepper, beans, lard, parsley and dill. b, 3.52h, Lidded tureen, cabbage, carrots, onion, garlic, pepper. Illustration reduced.

2005, May 20   Perf. 11½
Stamp Size: 45x32mm
596	A357	Horiz. pair, #a-b	3.50	3.50

Booklet Stamps
Stamp Size: 40x27mm
Perf. 14x14¼
597	A357	Horiz. pair, #a-b	6.00	6.00
c.		Booklet pane, 2 #597	12.00	—
		Complete booklet, #597c	12.00	

Complete booklet sold for 19.38h.

Development of the Cyrillic Alphabet — A358

Litho. & Embossed
2005, May 21   Perf. 14¼x14
598	A358	45k multi	.30	.30

Souvenir Sheet

Flora and Fauna in Karadazkyi Nature Reserve — A359

No. 599: a, 45k, Falco cherrug (33x40mm). b, 70k, Ascalaphus macaronius (29x35mm). c, 2.50h, Tursiops truncatus ponticus (33x33mm). d, 3.50h, Martes foina (49x33mm).

2005, July 28   Litho.   Perf. 11½
599	A359	Sheet of 4, #a-d	4.25	4.25

World Summit on the Information Society, Tunis A360

2005, Aug. 12   Perf. 14x14¼
600	A360	2.50h multi	1.40	1.40

Series Ov Locomotive — A361

Series C Locomotive — A362

Series Shch Locomotive — A363

Series Ye Locomotive — A364

2005, Aug. 31
601	A361	70k multi	.40	.40
602	A362	70k multi	.40	.40
603	A363	70k multi	.40	.40
604	A364	70k multi	.40	.40
	Nos. 601-604 (4)		1.60	1.60

Nos. 601-604 were each printed in sheets of 11 + label.

Sumy, 350th Anniv. — A365

2005, Sept. 2
605	A365	45k multi	.30	.30

Nasturtium A366   Water Lily A367

Violets — A368   Wild Rose — A369

2005   Perf. 13¾
606	A366	25k multi	.20	.20
a.		Perf. 11½, dated "2006"	.20	.20
607	A367	70k multi	.40	.40
a.		Perf. 11½, dated "2006"	.30	.30
608	A368	(1.53h) multi	1.10	1.10
a.		Perf. 11½, dated "2006"	.80	.80
609	A369	(2.55h) multi	1.90	1.90
a.		Perf. 11½, dated "2006"	1.40	1.40
	Nos. 606-609 (4)		3.60	3.60

Issued: 25k, 9/8; 70k, 9/12; #608, 12/16; #609, 11/24.
Nos. 606-609 exist dated "2006."
Nos. 606a-609a issued 10/9/06. Nos. 606a-609a were issued only in No. F2b.

Horses — A370

No. 610: a, Novoolexandrivskyi heavy draft horse (brown horse facing left with four-line inscription). b, Orlov-Rostopchin (white horse). c, Ukrainian riding horse (brown horse facing left with three-line inscription). d, Thoroughbred (brown horse facing right).
Illustration reduced.

2005, Sept. 15   Perf. 11½
610	A370	70k Block of 4, #a-d	1.60	1.60

"Safety - Green Light" A371

"Give a Helping Hand" A372

"No to Drugs" A373

2005, Oct. 14   *Perf. 14x14¼*
611   Horiz. strip of 3   1.25   1.25
   a.   A371 70k multi   .40   .40
   b.   A372 70k multi   .40   .40
   c.   A373 70k multi   .40   .40

Military History — A374

No. 612: a, Commander Bobrok Volnyets at Battle of Kulikovo, 1380. b, Artillerymen and riflemen, 14th-15th cent. c, Knight Ivanko Sushyk at Grunwald, 1410. d, Prince Konstiantyn Ostrozkyi at Orsha, 1512.
Illustration reduced.

2005, Oct. 21
612   A374 70k Block of 4, #a-d   1.60   1.60

Famous Ukrainians Type of 2004

Designs: No. 613, Dmytro Yiavornytskyi (1855-1940), historian. No. 614, Oleg Antonov (1906-84), aircraft designer.

2005-06   *Litho.*
613   A314 70k multi   .45   .45
614   A314 70k multi   .45   .45
   Issued: #613, 11/7; #614, 2/7/06.

Christmas A375

Litho. With Foil Application
2005, Nov. 11   *Perf. 13¼*
615   A375 70k multi   .45   .45

New Year's Day — A376

2005, Nov. 11   *Litho.*
616   A376 70k multi   .45   .45

St. Barbara's Church, Vienna, Austria — A377

2005, Dec. 9   *Perf. 14¼x14*
617   A377 75k multi + label   .50   .50

Lviv National Museum, Cent. — A378

No. 618: a, Archangel Michael, by unknown artist (denomination at right). b, Dalmatynka, by Teofil Kopystynskyi (denomination at left).
Illustration reduced.

2005, Dec. 13   *Litho.*
618   A378 70k Horiz. pair, #a-b, +   central label   .85   .85

Regional Costumes

Zhytomyrshchyna Region — A379

Rivnenshchyna Region — A380

Volyn Region — A381

No. 619: a, Family and dog, St. Basil's Day. b, Man and woman, St. Zosyma's Day.
No. 620: a, People with animals, St. George's Day. b, Men, women and musician, Sts. Peter and Paul's Day.
No. 621: a, People with buckets, Annunciation Day. b, Family and cat, St. Nicholas's Day.

2005, Dec. 20   *Perf. 13¼*
619   A379 70k Horiz. pair, #a-b   .85   .85
620   A380 70k Horiz. pair, #a-b   .85   .85
621   A381 70k Horiz. pair, #a-b   .85   .85
   c.   Miniature sheet, #619-621, perf. 11½   3.50   3.50

Europa Stamps, 50th Anniv. — A382

Designs: Nos. 622a, 623a, 1.30h, 50th anniversary emblem. Nos. 622a, 622b, 2.50h, CEPT emblem.

2006, Jan. 5   *Litho.*   *Perf. 13¼*
With Names of Designers at Right of Stamps
622   A382   Vert. pair, #a-b   2.25   2.25

Souvenir Sheet
Without Names of Designers at Right of Stamps
Perf. 11½
623   A382   Sheet of 2, #a-b   2.25   2.25

Art by Hryhoryi Narbut (1886-1920) — A383

Litho. & Engr.
2006, Mar. 10   *Perf. 11½*
624   A383 3.33h multi   1.90   1.90
   Printed in sheets of 11 + label.

Miniature Sheet

Traditional Women's Headdresses — A384

No. 625: a, Drawing of woman wearing fur hat. b, Woman, facing left, wearing black hat with brown ribbon. c, Drawing of woman facing left, wearing undecorated head covering. d, Woman wearing large floral head covering. e, Woman wearing red kerchief. f, Woman wearing small floral head covering. g, Woman wearing white kerchief with red dots. h, Woman wearing brown kerchief with knot in front. i, Drawing of woman, facing right, wearing undecorated head covering. j, Woman wearing floral headcovering with thin black edge. k, Woman wearing kerchief with floral pattern. l, Woman wearing small floral head covering with ribbon.

2006, Mar. 30   *Litho.*   *Perf. 11½*
625   A384 70k Sheet of 12, #a-l   5.00   5.00

Coronas-1 Satellite A385

Designs: No. 627, Welding in space. No. 628, International observation of Comet Galileo.

2006, Apr. 12   *Perf. 14x14¼*
Color of Panel Denomination Panel
626   A385 85k gray   .50   .50
627   A385 85k red brown   .50   .50
628   A385 85k dull brown   .50   .50
   Nos. 626-628 (3)   1.50   1.50

Europa — A386

Designs: Nos. 629a, 630a, 2.50h, Earth and Saturn. Nos. 629b, 630b, 3.50h, Earth and Jupiter.
Illustration reduced.

2006, Apr. 28   *Perf. 11½*
Top Cyrillic Inscription in Black
629   A386   Horiz. pair, #a-b   3.50   3.50
Top Cyrillic Inscription in Red
630   A386   Booklet pane of 2,   #a-b + 2 labels   7.25   7.25
   Complete booklet, #630   7.25
   Nos. 630a-630b are 52x26mm. No. 630 sold for 11.52h.

2006 World Cup Soccer Championships, Germany — A387

Designs: 2.50k, Ukrainian soccer players. 3.50k, Soccer ball.

2006, May 4
631-632 A387   Set of 2   3.50   3.50

Georgia, Ukraine, Azerbaijan and Moldova Summit, Kiev A388

2006, May 23   *Perf. 14x14¼*
633   A388 70k multi   .45   .45

Paintings of Kiev — A389

Designs: No. 634, 70k, Zaborovskyi Gate, by Boris Tulin, 1987 (shown). No. 635, 70k, Olha Basystiuk Sings, by Tulin, 1987. No. 636, 70k, Kiev-Pecherska Lavra, by Oleksandr Hubarev, 1990. No. 637, 70k, Andrew's Alley, by Hubarev, 1983.

2006, May 24   *Perf. 13¾x14¼*
634-637 A389   Set of 4   1.60   1.60

Souvenir Sheet

Lviv, 750th Anniv. — A390

No. 638 — View of Lviv, 1618 and: a, 70k, Coat of arms (38x31mm). b, 2.50h, Coin (69x31mm).

2006, June 16   *Perf. 11½*
638 A390   Sheet of 2, #a-b   1.90 1.90

Miniature Sheet

Fauna of Shatskyi National Park — A391

No. 639: a, Lanius excubitor (28x40mm). b, Lynx lynx (33x35mm). c, Anguilla anguilla (41x29mm). d, Bufo calamita (28x29mm). e, Mustela erminea (45x29mm).

2006, July 14
639 A391   70k Sheet of 5, #a-e   2.00 2.00

Miniature Sheet

Cossack Hetmen — A392

No. 640: a, Ivan Bohun (denomination at UL). b, Ivan Honta (denomination at UR). c, Ivan Pidkova (denomination at LL). d, Ivan Sirko (denomination at LR).

Litho. & Engr. With Foil Application
2006, Aug. 18
640 A392   3.50h Sheet of 4, #a-d   7.25 7.25

Famous Ukrainians Type of 2004

Design: Ivan Franko (1856-1916), writer.

2006, Aug. 27   Litho.   *Perf. 14x14¼*
641 A314   70k multi   .45   .45

Series L Locomotive — A393

Series SO Locomotive — A394

Series YS Locomotive — A395

Series FD Locomotive — A396

2006, Sept. 15
642 A393   70k multi   .45   .45
643 A394   70k multi   .45   .45
644 A395   70k multi   .45   .45
645 A396   70k multi   .45   .45
        Nos. 642-645 (4)   1.80 1.80

Each stamp printed in sheets of 11 + label.

Tenth Natl. Philatelic Exhibition, Lviv — A397

2006, Oct. 6   Litho. & Embossed
646 A397   70k multi   .45   .45

Military History — A398

No. 647: a, Cossack-siroma, 16th-17th cent. b, Naval campaigns of 16th-18th cents. c, Khmelnychna national liberation movement (soldiers aiming guns), 17th cent. d, Haidamachnya national liberation movement (soldier with sword), 17th cent. Illustration reduced.

2006, Nov. 3   Litho.   *Perf. 14x14¼*
647 A398   70k Block of 4, #a-d   1.50 1.50

Horses in Sports — A399

No. 648: a, Dressage. b, Horse racing. c, Harness racing. d, Show jumping. Illustration reduced.

2006, Nov. 17   *Perf. 11½*
648 A399   70k Block of 4, #a-d   1.50 1.50
    Printed in sheets containing two each of Nos. 648a-648d.

St. Nicholas's Day — A400

No. 649: a, Children following angel. b, Angel and St. Nicholas.

Litho. With Foil Application
2006, Nov. 17   *Perf. 13¼*
649 A400   70k Horiz. pair, #a-b .75   .75

Christmas — A401

2006, Nov. 24   *Perf. 14¼x14*
650 A401   70k multi   .40   .40

Lviv, 750th Anniv. A402

Litho. & Engr.
2006, Dec. 1   *Perf. 14x13¾*
651 A402   3.50h multi   1.90 1.90
    Printed in sheets of 10 + 5 labels. See Austria No. 2075.

Regional Costumes

Zaporizhzha Region — A403

Khersonshchyna Region — A404

Odeshchyna Region — A405

No. 652: a, People with flags, candle, and swords, St. Michael's Day. b, People and horses, Assumption Day.
No. 653: a, Women and spinning wheel, St. Catherine's Day. b, Men and oxen, St. Elias's Day.
No. 654: a, People and pig, St. Barbara and St. Sava's Day. b, People and fish, St. Boris and St. Hlib's Day.

2006, Dec. 15   Litho.   *Perf. 13¼*
652 A403   70k Horiz. pair, #a-b .75   .75
653 A404   70k Horiz. pair, #a-b .75   .75
654 A405   70k Horiz. pair, #a-b .75   .75
  c.   Miniature sheet, #652-654, perf.
        11½   2.25 2.25

Famous Ukrainians Type of 2004

Designs: No. 655, 70k, Metropolitan Ivan Ohienko (1882-1972). No. 656, 70k, Igor Stravinsky (1882-1971), composer.

2007   Litho.   *Perf. 14x14¼*
655-656 A314   Set of 2   .75   .75

    Issued: No. 655, 1/12; No. 656, 6/8.

Conjoined Pots   Candelabra
A406   A407

Clay Bull   Inkwell
A408   A409

Mug — A410   Rag Doll — A411

Folk decorative art: 3k, Horse figurine. 5k, Whistle. 10k, Jug. 50k, Spinning wheel. 60k, Demijohn. 70k, Circular water container. 85k, Ladle. 1h, Decorated cup with handle. 2h, Pitcher with handle.

2007   Litho.   *Perf. 13¾*
657 A406   1k multi   .20   .20
658 A406   3k multi   .20   .20
659 A406   5k multi   .20   .20
660 A406   10k multi   .20   .20
661 A406   50k multi   .25   .25
662 A406   60k multi   .30   .30
663 A406   70k multi   .35   .35
664 A406   85k multi   .45   .45
665 A406   1h multi   .50   .50
666 A407 (1.52h) multi   .80   .80
667 A406   2h multi   1.00 1.00
668 A408 (2.48h) multi   1.25 1.25
669 A409 (3.33h) multi   1.75 1.75
670 A410 (3.79h) multi   2.00 2.00
671 A411 (10.10h) multi   5.25 5.25
        Nos. 657-671 (15)   14.70 14.70

    Issued: Nos. 657, 658, 660, 669, 4/14; Nos. 659, 663, 667, 670, 671, 3/16; Nos. 661, 662, 664, 1/26; Nos. 665, 666, 668, 4/6.

St. Michael's Cathedral, Adelaide, Australia — A412

2007, Feb. 9   *Perf. 13¼*
672 A412   3.35k multi + label   1.75 1.75

Souvenir Sheet

Taras Shevchenko (1814-61), Poet — A413

No. 673: a, 2.50h, Drawing of Shevchenko's house, poem (66x40mm). b, 3.35h, Shevchenko (36x40mm).

Litho. With Foil Application

2007, Feb. 23   *Perf. 11½*
673 A413   Sheet of 2, #a-b   3.00 3.00

Wedding Rings — A414

Flowers — A415

Pechersk Lavra Monastery, Kiev — A416

Oranta Monument — A417

Illustrations reduced.

2007, Mar. 1   **Litho.**   *Perf. 11½*
674 A414 70k multi + label   1.40 1.40
675 A415 70k multi + label   1.40 1.40
676 A416 70k multi + label   1.40 1.40
677 A417 70k multi + label   1.40 1.40
    Nos. 674-677 (4)   5.60 5.60

Nos. 674-676 were printed in sheets of 22 stamps + 22 labels that could be personalized, and sold for 60.60h per sheet. No. 677 was printed in sheets of 18 stamps + 18 labels that could be personalized, and sold for 54.60h per sheet. Labels shown are generic.

Space Exploration A418

Designs: No. 678, 70k, Leonid Kadeniuck, first Ukrainian cosmonaut. No. 679, 70k, Sea Launch rocket lifting off.

2007, Apr. 12   *Perf. 14x14¼*
678-679 A418 Set of 2   .75 .75

Europa — A419

Nos. 680 and 681: a, 2.50h, Scout emblem, neckerchief and "100." b, 3.35h, Scouts. Illustration reduced.

2007, Apr. 28   *Perf. 14x14¼*
    Stamp Size: 40x28mm
680 A419   Horiz. pair, #a-b   3.00 3.00
    Stamp Size: 45x33mm
    Perf. 11½
681 A419   Booklet pane of 2,
      #a-b   6.75   —
    Complete booklet, #681   6.75

Scouting, cent. No. 681 sold for 11.52h.

Paintings of Kiev — A420

Designs: No. 682, 70k, Sunny Day, Yaroslaviv Val, by Vitalii Petrovskyi, 1997. No. 683, 70k, Street of Recollections, by Tetiana Kuhai, 2004 (red panel), vert. No. 684, 70k, Kiev Walk, by Yulia Kuznietsova, 2004 (lilac panel), vert. No. 685, 70k, Snowing, by Maria Lashkevych, 2007.

    Perf. 13¾x14½, 14½x13¾
2007, May 18
682-685 A420   Set of 4   1.50 1.50

Miniature Sheets

Dogs — A421

Cats — A422

No. 686: a, Pug. b, Irish setter. c, Alaskan malamute. d, Basset hound. e, Bull mastiff. f, American cocker spaniel.
No. 687: a, American shorthair. b, Sphynx. c, Scottish fold. d, Snowshoe. e, Russian blue. f, Somali.

2007, June 15   *Perf. 11½*
686 A421 70k Sheet of 6, #a-f   2.25 2.25
687 A422 70k Sheet of 6, #a-f   2.25 2.25

Roman Shukhevych (1907-50), Military Leader — A423

2007, June 29   *Perf. 14x14¼*
688 A423 70k multi   .35 .35

Miniature Sheet

Wedding Headdresses — A428

No. 693: a, Woman facing right wearing floral headdress with gray ribbon behind head. b, Woman facing left wearing gathered fabric headdress with broad red headband. c, Woman facing left wearing floral headdress with broad red ribbon at back. d, Woman facing right wearing ribboned floral headdress. e, Woman facing forward wearing tall red headdress with black and white spots. f, Woman wearing fabric headdress. g, Woman wearing headdress with wide floral ring above smaller floral rings. h, Man wearing hat and jacket with high collar. i, Woman facing left wearing tall floral headdress covering ear. j, Man wearing tall hat and collarless shirt with decorated front. k, Woman wearing headdress with one floral ring above bropad red headband. l, Man wearing hat with chinstrap.

2007, Aug 23   **Litho.**   *Perf. 11½*
693 A428 70k Sheet of 12, #a-l   4.50 4.50

Dnieper River Fish Preservation — A429

No. 694: a, Acipenser gueldenstaedtii. b, Zingel zingel.

2007, Sept. 6
694   Horiz. pair + central label 2.10 2.10
  a. A429 1.50k multi   .80 .80
  b. A429 2.50k multi   1.25 1.25

See Moldova No. 569.

Pereyaslav Khmelnytskyi, 1100th Anniv. — A430

2007, Sept. 16   *Perf. 14x14¼*
695 A430 70k multi   .40 .40

Worldwide Fund for Nature (WWF) — A431

No. 696 — Pelecanus onocrotalus: a, 70k, In flight. b, 1.50h, In water. c, 2.50h, Two birds. d, 3.50h, One bird standing.

2007, Sept. 20   *Perf. 14x14¼*
696 A431   Block of 4, #a-d   3.50 3.50
  e.   Miniature sheet, 4 each
    #696a-696d, perf. 11½, + 4
    labels   14.00 14.00

Souvenir Sheet

Launch of Sputnik 1, 50th Anniv. — A432

2007, Oct. 4   *Perf. 11½*
697 A432 3.33h multi   1.75 1.75

Miniature Sheets

A433

Peasant Houses — A434

No. 698 — House from: a, Podillya, with ox cart in front. b, Kiev, with couple, cat and pumpkins in front. c, Lemkivshchyna, with horse and ducks in front. d, Hutsulshchyna, with horse in front. e, Volyn, with wheat sheaves in front. f, Slobozhanshchyna, with sunflowers at sides of house.
No. 699 — House from: a, Polissya, with basket weavers and horse in front. b, Khorolshchyna, with children rolling hoop in front. c, Bukovyna, with couple in doorway. d, Boikivshchyna, with dog and people carrying bundles of sticks in front. e, Poltava, people threshing grain in front. f, Lower Dnieper area, with man with fishing net in front.

2007, Oct. 24
698 A433 70k Sheet of 6, #a-f   2.25 2.25
699 A434 70k Sheet of 6, #a-f   2.25 2.25

Christmas and New Year's Day — A435

No. 700: a, Angels in sled. b, Angels with Christmas tree.

Litho. With Foil Application
2007, Nov. 16   *Perf. 13½*
700 A435 70k Horiz. pair, #a-b   .85 .85

Christmas and New Year's
Day — A436

Illustration reduced.

2007, Nov. 23   *Perf. 11½*
701 A436 1h multi + label   2.25 2.25
   Printed in sheets of 18 stamps + 18 labels
that could be personalized.

2012 European Soccer
Championships, Poland and
Ukraine — A437

Illustration reduced.

2007, Dec. 22
702 A437 3.33h multi   1.90 1.90

Regional Costumes

Khmelnytska Region — A438

Bukovyna Region — A439

Zakarpatyia Region — A440

   No. 703: a, Potter and carolers, Christmas.
b, People celebrating St. Simeon's Day,
horses.
   No. 704: a, Woman holding cross, man,
woman, fruit basket, St. Ephrosinia's Day. b,
Man holding violin, women and children,
Ascension Day.
   No. 705: a, Men and blacksmith holding
mugs, Kuzma and Demyan Day. b, People
near cross and candle, Easter.

2007, Dec. 22   **Litho.**   *Perf. 13¼*
703 A438 70k Horiz. pair, #a-b   .80 .80
704 A439 70k Horiz. pair, #a-b   .80 .80
705 A440 70k Horiz. pair, #a-b   .80 .80
   c.   Miniature sheet, #703-705, perf.
     11½   2.40 2.40

 Aries — A441   Taurus — A442

 Gemini — A443   Cancer — A444

 Leo — A445   Virgo — A446

 Libra — A447   Scorpio — A448

 Sagittarius A449   Capricorn A450

 Aquarius — A451   Pisces — A452

2008, Jan. 18   *Perf. 14¼x14*
706 A441 1h multi   .55 .55
707 A442 1h multi   .55 .55
708 A443 1h multi   .55 .55
709 A444 1h multi   .55 .55
710 A445 1h multi   .55 .55
711 A446 1h multi   .55 .55
712 A447 1h multi   .55 .55
713 A448 1h multi   .55 .55
714 A449 1h multi   .55 .55
715 A450 1h multi   .55 .55
716 A451 1h multi   .55 .55
717 A452 1h multi   .55 .55
    Nos. 706-717 (12)   6.60 6.60

2008 Summer Olympics,
Beijing — A453

   No. 718: a, 1h, Archery. b, 1.30h, Fencing.
c, 2.47h, Cycling. d, 3.33h, Rowing.
   Illustration reduced.

Litho. With Foil Application
2008, Jan. 26   *Perf. 11½*
718 A453   Block of 4, #a-d   4.50 4.50

SEMI-POSTAL STAMPS

Ukrainian Soviet Socialist Republic

 "Famine" — SP1

 Taras H. Shevchenko SP2

 "Death" Stalking Peasant — SP3

 "Ukraine" Distributing Food — SP4

Perf. 14½x13½, 13½x14½
1923, June		**Litho.**		**Unwmk.**
B1	SP1	10k + 10k gray bl &		
		blk	.85	5.50
B2	SP2	20k + 20k vio brn &		
		org brn	.85	5.50
B3	SP3	90k + 30k db & blk,		
		straw	.85	5.50
B4	SP4	150k + 50k red brn &		
		blk	.85	5.50
		Nos. B1-B4 (4)	3.40	22.00

Imperf., Pairs
B1a	SP1	10k + 10k	90.00	110.00
B2a	SP2	20k + 20k	90.00	110.00
B3a	SP3	90k + 30k	90.00	110.00
B4a	SP4	150k + 50k	90.00	110.00

   The values of these stamps are in
karbovanets, which by 1923 converted to
rubles at 100 to 1.

Wmk. 116
Same Colors
B5	SP1	10k + 10k	45.00	65.00
B6	SP2	20k + 20k	45.00	65.00
	a.	*Imperf., pair*		2,400.

B7	SP3	90k + 30k	32.50	65.00
B8	SP4	150k + 50k	32.50	65.00
		Nos. B5-B8 (4)	155.00	260.00

> Catalogue values for unused
> stamps in this section, from this
> point to the end of the section, are
> for Never Hinged items.

 Mercy and Health Fund — SP5

1994, Jan. 15   **Litho.**   *Perf. 12*
B9 SP5 150kb +20kb multi   .35

 Third Natl. Philatelic Exhibition, Lviv — SP6

1995, Sept. 23   **Litho.**   *Perf. 13½*
B10 SP6 50,000kb +5000kb multi 1.00

Souvenir Sheet

Zymnenska Icon of Madonna and
Child — SP7

Illustration reduced.

1999, Sept. 4   **Litho.**   *Perf. 11½*
B11 SP7 1.20h +10k multicolored 2.50 2.50
     Intl. Year of the Elderly.

REGISTRATION STAMP

> Catalogue values for unused
> stamps in this section are for
> Never Hinged items.

 Trident — R1

2001, Apr. 1   **Litho.**   *Perf. 13¾*
F1 R1 (10.84h) multi   7.25 7.25
   a.   Perf. 11½, dated "2006"   5.25 5.25

   No. F1a issued 10/9/06. No. F1a was issued
only in No. F2b.

Trident With
Frame — R2

2005-06   Litho.   Perf. 13¾

F2	R2 (10.10h) multi		5.75	5.75
a.	Perf. 11½, dated "2006"		4.50	4.50
b.	Sheet of 18, #418a-422a, 453a- 454a, 466a-468a, 515a, 572a, 606a-609a, F1a, F2a		18.00	18.00

Issued: No. F2, 10/28/05; No. F2a, 10/9/06.
No. F2 exists dated "2006." No. F2a was
issued only in No. F2b. No. F2b sold for
35.41h and exists imperf.

MILITARY STAMPS

COURIER FIELD POST ISSUE

Nos. 1-5, 48
Surcharged

Кур'єрсько-
польова
Пошта.
10 Гривень

1920, Aug. 26

M1	A1	10hr on 10sh buff	16.50	—
a.		Inverted surcharge	65.00	
M2	A2	10hr on 20sh brown	32.50	—
M3	A3	10hr on 30sh ul- tramarine	37.50	—
M4	A4	10hr on 40sh green	45.00	—
a.		Inverted surcharge	190.00	
M5	A5	10hr on 50sh red	37.50	—
M6	A1	20hr on 10sh buff	45.00	—
M7	A2	20hr on 20sh brown	11.00	—
a.		Inverted surcharge	45.00	
M8	A3	20hr on 30sh ul- tramarine	32.50	—
a.		Inverted surcharge	140.00	
M9	A4	20hr on 40sh green	32.50	—
M10	A5	20hr on 50sh red	32.50	—
a.		Inverted surcharge	140.00	
M11	A1	40hr on 10sh buff	175.00	—
M12	A2	40hr on 20sh brown	82.50	—
M13	A3	40hr on 30sh ul- tramarine	350.00	—
M14	A4	40hr on 40sh green	175.00	—
M15	A5	40hr on 50sh red	350.00	—
M16	A6	40hr on 20hr red & green	—	—

Nos. M1-M16 were prepared to facilitate
communications between the Ukrainian government-in-exile at Tarnow, Poland, and its
military units in the field.
Only two copies of No. M16 are known, one
unused and one used on cover.
Forged surcharges and cancellations exist.

UMM AL QIWAIN

'um-al-kī-'wīn

LOCATION — Oman Peninsula, Arabia,
on Arabian Gulf
GOVT. — Sheikdom under British
protection
AREA — 300 sq. mi.
POP. — 5,700

Umm al Qiwain is one of six Persian
Gulf sheikdoms to join the United Arab
Emirates which proclaimed indepen-
dence Dec. 2, 1971. See United Arab
Emirates.

100 Naye Paise = 1 Rupee
100 Dirham = 1 Riyal (1967)

Catalogue values for all unused
stamps in this country are for
Never Hinged items.

Sheik
Ahmed bin
Rashid al
Mulla and
Gazelles
A1

Photogravure and Lithographed

1964, June 29   Unwmk.   Perf. 14

Size: 35x22mm

1	A1	1np shown	.20	.20
2	A1	2np Snake	.20	.20
3	A1	3np Hyena	.20	.20
4	A1	4np Conspicuous trig- gerfish	.20	.20
5	A1	5np Fish	.20	.20
6	A1	10np Silver angelfish	.20	.20
7	A1	15np Palace	.20	.20
8	A1	20np Umm al Qiwain	.20	.20
9	A1	30np Tower	.20	.20

Size: 42x26mm

10	A1	40np as 1np	.20	.20
11	A1	50np as 2np	.20	.20
12	A1	70np as 3np	.65	.20
13	A1	1r as 4np	.80	.25
14	A1	1.50r as 4np	1.00	.30
15	A1	2r as 10np	1.25	.50

Size: 52x33mm

16	A1	3r as 15np	2.40	1.50
17	A1	5r as 20np	4.00	2.75
18	A1	10r as 30np	7.00	4.50
		Nos. 1-18 (18)	19.30	12.20

National Stadium, Tokyo, and
Discobolus — A2

Designs: 1r, 2r, National Stadium, Tokyo.
1.50r, Indoor swimming arena. 3r, Komazawa
Gymnasium. 4r, Stadium entrance.

1964, Nov. 25   Photo.   Perf. 14

19	A2	50np multi	.30	.20
20	A2	1r multi	.50	.20
21	A2	1.50r multi	.65	.20
22	A2	2r multi	1.00	.25
23	A2	3r multi	1.25	.45
24	A2	4r multi	2.50	.85
25	A2	5r multi	3.25	1.00
		Nos. 19-25 (7)	9.45	3.15

18th Olympic Games, Tokyo, Oct. 10-25,
1964. Perf. and imperf. souvenir sheets contain 4 stamps similar to #22-25 in changed
colors. Size: 145x115mm.

A3

A4

Designs: 10np, Pres. Kennedy's funeral cor-
tege leaving White House. 15np, Mrs. Kennedy with children, and Robert Kennedy following coffin. 50np, Horse-drawn caisson. 1r,
Presidents Truman and Eisenhower, and Margaret Truman Daniels. 2r, Pres. Charles de
Gaulle, Emperor Haile Selassie, Chancellor
Ludwig Erhart, Sir Alec Douglas-Home and
King Frederick IX. 3r, Kennedy family on steps
of St. Matthew's Cathedral. 5r, Honor guard at
tomb. 7.50r, Portrait of Pres. John F.
Kennedy.

Perf. 14½

1965, Jan. 20   Unwmk.   Photo.
Black Design with Gold Inscriptions

Size: 29x44mm

26	A3	10np pale blue	.20	.20
27	A3	15np pale yellow	.20	.20
28	A3	50np pale green	.25	.20
29	A3	1r pale pink	.40	.20
30	A3	2r pale green	.75	.30

Size: 33x51mm

31	A3	3r pale gray	1.25	.50
32	A3	5r pale blue	2.00	.75
33	A3	7.50r pale yellow	3.00	1.25
		Nos. 26-33 (8)	8.05	3.60

Pres. John F. Kennedy. A souvenir sheet
contains 2 stamps similar to Nos. 32-33 with
pale green (5r) and pale salmon (7.50r) backgrounds, size: 29x44mm. Size of sheet:
114x70mm.

1969, Nov. 19   Litho.   Perf. 14½

Designs: 10d, Astronaut on Moon. 20d,
Landing module approaching moon. 30d,
Apollo XII on launching pad. 50d, Com-
manders Charles Conrad, Jr., Alan L. Bean,
Richard F. Gordon, Jr., earth and moon, horiz.
75d, Earth and Apollo XII, horiz. 1r, Sheik
Ahmed, rocket and lunar landing module,
horiz.

34	A4	10d multi	.20
35	A4	20d multi	.20
36	A4	30d multi	.20
37	A4	50d emerald & multi	.25
38	A4	75d purple & multi	.50
39	A4	1r dk bl & multi	.70
		Nos. 34-39 (6)	2.05

US Apollo XII moon landing mission, 11/14-
24/69.
Two imperf. souvenir sheets of 3 exist, containing stamps similar to Nos. 34-36 and Nos.
37-39.

A5

A7

A6

1970, May 29   Litho.   Perf. 14

40	A5	10d James A. Lovell	.20
41	A5	30d Fred W. Haise, Jr.	.25
42	A5	50d John L. Swigert, Jr.	.50
a.		Souv. sheet of 3, #40-42	1.50
		Nos. 40-42 (3)	.95

Safe return of the crew of Apollo 13.

1970, Aug. 14   Litho.   Perf. 13½x14

Designs: 5d, 1.25r, EXPO '70 Emblem. 10d,
20d, Japanese Pavilion.

43	A6	5d yellow & multi	.20
44	A6	10d blue & multi	.20
45	A6	20d red & multi	.20
48	A6	1.25r red & multi	.50
		Nos. 43-48 (4)	1.10

EXPO '70 Intl. Exhib., Osaka, Japan, Mar.
15-Sept. 13, 1970.
A 40d and 1r, showing the Emperor and
Empress of Japan, and a souvenir sheet containing these and Nos. 43-45, 48 were prepared, but not issued.

1970, Oct. 12   Litho.   Perf. 14½x14

Uniforms: 10d, Private, North Lancashire
Regiment. 20d, Royal Navy seaman. 30d,
Officer, North Lancashire (Loyal) Regiment.
50d, Private, York and Lancaster Regiment.
75d, Royal Navy officer. 1r, Officer, York and
Lancaster Regiment.

49	A7	10d multi	.20
50	A7	20d multi	.25
51	A7	30d multi	.35
a.		Souv. sheet of 3, #49-51	2.00
52	A7	50d buff & multi	.70
53	A7	75d multi	1.00

54	A7	1r buff & multi		1.50
a.		Souv. sheet of 3, #52-54		3.75
		Nos. 49-54 (6)		4.00

British landings on the Trucial Coast, 150th
anniv.
Stamps of Umm al Qiwain were replaced in
1972 by those of United Arab Emirates.

AIR POST STAMPS

Type of Regular Issue, 1964
Photogravure and Lithographed

1965   Unwmk.   Perf. 14

Size: 42x26mm

C1	A1	15np as #1	.20	.20
C2	A1	25np as #2	.20	.20
C3	A1	35np as #3	.20	.20
C4	A1	50np as #4	.60	.20
C5	A1	75np as #5	1.10	.30
C6	A1	1r as #6	1.40	.40

Size: 52x33mm

C7	A1	2r as #7	2.25	.55
C8	A1	3r as #8	3.25	.75
C9	A1	5r as #9	4.50	1.25
		Nos. C1-C9 (9)	13.70	4.05

Issued: #C7-C9, Nov. 6; others, Oct. 18.

AIR POST OFFICIAL STAMPS

Type of Regular Issue, 1964
Photogravure and Lithographed

1965, Dec. 22   Unwmk.   Perf. 14

Size: 42x26mm

CO1	A1	75np as #6	.75	.20

Size: 52x33mm

CO2	A1	2r as #7	1.50	.45
CO3	A1	3r as #8	1.75	.75
CO4	A1	5r as #9	2.75	1.25
		Nos. CO1-CO4 (4)	6.75	2.65

OFFICIAL STAMPS

Type of Regular Issue, 1964
Photogravure and Lithographed

1965, Dec. 22   Unwmk.   Perf. 14

Size: 42x26mm

O1	A1	25np as #1	.30	.20
O2	A1	40np as #2	.40	.20
O3	A1	50np as #3	.60	.20
O4	A1	75np as #4	1.00	.20
O5	A1	1r as #5	1.25	.25
		Nos. O1-O5 (5)	3.55	1.05

UNITED ARAB EMIRATES

yu-ˌni-təd ˈar-əb i-ˈmiˌ ə r-əts

(Trucial States)

LOCATION — Arabia, on Arabian Gulf
GOVT. — Federation of sheikdoms
AREA — 32,300 sq. mi.
POP. — 2,377,453 (1995)
CAPITAL — Abu Dhabi

The UAE was formed Dec. 2, 1971, by the union of Abu Dhabi, Ajman, Dubai, Fujeira, Sharjah and Umm al Qiwain. Ras al Khaima joined in Feb. 1972.

1,000 Fils = 1 Dinar
100 Fils = 1 Dirham (1973)

Catalogue values for all unused stamps in this country are for Never Hinged items.

Abu Dhabi Nos. 56-67 Overprinted

دولة الامارات العربية المتحده

UAE

1972, Aug. Litho. Unwmk. *Perf. 14*
1	A10	5f multicolored	3.25	3.25
2	A10	10f multicolored	3.25	3.25
3	A10	25f multicolored	5.00	5.00
4	A10	35f multicolored	6.50	6.50
5	A10	50f multicolored	11.00	11.00
6	A10	60f multicolored	12.00	12.00
7	A10	70f multicolored	16.00	16.00
8	A10	90f multicolored	20.00	20.00
9	A11	125f multicolored	65.00	65.00
10	A11	150f multicolored	90.00	90.00
11	A11	500f multicolored	210.00	210.00
12	A11	1d multicolored	400.00	400.00
		Nos. 1-12 (12)	842.00	842.00

The overprint differs.
#1-12 were used in Abu Dhabi. #2-3 were placed on sale later in Dubai & Sharjah.

Map and Flag of UAE A1

Almagta Bridge, Abu Dhabi — A2

Designs: 10f, Like 5f. 15f, 35f, Coat of arms of UAE (eagle). 75f, Khor Fakkan, Sharjah. 1d, Steel Clock Tower, Dubai. 1.25d, Buthnah Fort, Fujeira. 2d, Alfalaj Fort, Umm al Qiwain. 3d, Khor Khwair, Ras al Khaima. 5d, Palace of Sheik Rashid bin Humaid al Nuaimi, Ajman. 10d, Sheik Zaid bin Sultan al Nahayan, Abu Dhabi.

1973, Jan. 1 Unwmk. *Perf. 14½*
Size: 41x25mm
13	A1	5f multicolored	.20	.20
14	A1	10f multicolored	.20	.20
15	A1	15f blue & multi	.45	.20
16	A1	35f olive & multi	.75	.30

Perf. 14x15
Size: 45x29½mm
17	A2	65f multicolored	1.25	1.25
18	A2	75f multicolored	1.50	1.25
19	A2	1d multicolored	2.00	1.25
20	A2	1.25d multicolored	4.25	2.00
21	A2	2d multicolored	47.50	12.50
22	A2	3d multicolored	8.75	6.75

23	A2	5d multicolored	10.50	7.00
24	A2	10d multicolored	22.50	15.00
		Nos. 13-24 (12)	99.85	47.90

For surcharge see No. 68.

Festival Emblem A3

1973, Mar. 27 Litho. *Perf. 13½x14*
25	A3	10f shown	8.25	.35
26	A3	1.25d Trophy	19.00	11.00

National Youth Festival, Mar. 27.

Pedestrian Crossing in Dubai — A4

35f, Traffic light school crossing sign, vert. 1.25d, Traffic policemen with car & radio, vert.

1973, Apr. 1 *Perf. 13½x14, 14x13½*
27	A4	35f green & multi	4.50	2.25
28	A4	75f blue & multi	8.75	4.50
29	A4	1.25d violet & multi	14.00	8.25
		Nos. 27-29 (3)	27.25	15.00

Traffic Week, Apr. 1-7.

Human Rights Flame and People — A5

1973, Dec. 10 Litho. *Perf. 14½x14*
30	A5	35f blue, blk & org	1.50	.95
31	A5	65f red, blk & org	7.25	2.40
32	A5	1.25d olive, blk & org	10.50	4.75
		Nos. 30-32 (3)	19.25	8.10

25th anniversary of the Universal Declaration of Human Rights.

UPU and Arab Postal Union Emblems — A6

1974, Aug. 5 Litho. *Perf. 14x14½*
33	A6	25f multicolored	2.00	1.00
34	A6	60f emerald & multi	4.00	2.00
35	A6	1.25d lt brown & multi	7.50	4.50
		Nos. 33-35 (3)	13.50	7.50

Centenary of Universal Postal Union.

Health Care — A7

Education — A8

Designs: 65f, Construction. 1.25d, UAE flag, UN and Arab League emblems.

1974, Dec. 2 Litho. *Perf. 13½*
36	A7	10f multicolored	1.10	.40
37	A8	35f multicolored	3.25	1.10
38	A8	65f blue & brown	3.00	1.50
39	A8	1.25d multicolored	7.00	3.50
		Nos. 36-39 (4)	14.35	6.50

Third National Day.

Arab Man and Woman Holding Candle over Book — A9

Man and Woman Reading Book — A10

1974, Dec. 27 *Perf. 14x14½, 14½x14*
40	A9	35f deep ultra & multi	2.75	.60
41	A10	65f orange brn & multi	3.50	1.25
42	A10	1.25d gray & multi	7.50	2.50
		Nos. 40-42 (3)	13.75	4.35

World Literacy Day.

Oil De-gassing Station — A11

50f, Off-shore drilling platform. 100f, Underwater storage tank. 125f, Oil production platform.

1975, Mar. 10 Litho. *Perf. 13x13½*
43	A11	25f multicolored	1.60	.55
44	A11	50f multicolored	3.25	1.10
45	A11	100f multicolored	8.25	2.75
46	A11	125f multicolored	12.00	4.50
a.		Souvenir sheet of 4, #43-46	45.00	30.00
		Nos. 43-46 (4)	25.10	8.90

9th Arab Petroleum Conference.

Three stamps to commemorate the 2nd Gulf Long Distance Swimming Championship were prepared in June, 1975, but not issued. Value $500.

Jabal Ali Earth Station — A12

Jabal Ali Earth Station: 35f, 65f, Communications satellite over globe.

1975, Nov. 8 Litho. *Perf. 13*
47	A12	15f multicolored	1.25	.35
48	A12	35f multicolored	4.25	.90
49	A12	65f multicolored	4.25	1.25
50	A12	2d multicolored	12.50	3.50
		Nos. 47-50 (4)	22.25	6.00

Various Scenes — A13

Sheik Hamad, Fujeira Ruler — A14

Supreme Council Members (Sheikdom rulers): 60f, Sheik Rashid bin Humaid al Naimi, Ajman. 80f, Sheik Ahmed bin Rashid al Mulla, Umm al Qiwain. 90f, Sheik Sultan bin Mohammed al Qasimi, Sharjah. 1d, Sheik Saqr bin Mohammed al Qasimi, Ras al Khaima. 140f, Sheik Rashid bin Said al Maktum, Dubai. 5d, Sheik Zaid bin Sultan al Nahayan, Abu Dhabi.

1975, Dec. 2 Litho. *Perf. 14*
51	A13	10f multicolored	.90	.20
52	A14	35f multicolored	2.40	.90
53	A14	60f multicolored	3.50	1.75
54	A14	80f multicolored	4.75	3.00
55	A14	90f multicolored	5.50	3.25
56	A14	1d multicolored	5.50	3.50
57	A14	140f multicolored	9.00	4.50
58	A14	5d multicolored	35.00	18.00
		Nos. 51-58 (8)	66.55	35.10

Fourth National Day.

Students and Lamp of Learning — A15

Arab Literacy Day: 15f, Lamp of learning.

1976, Feb. 8 Litho. *Perf. 14*
59	A15	15f orange & multi	1.40	.35
60	A15	50f ultra & multi	2.50	1.40
61	A15	3d multicolored	13.50	7.75
		Nos. 59-61 (3)	17.40	9.50

Children Crossing Street — A16

Traffic Week: 15f, Traffic lights and signals, vert. 80f, Road and traffic lights.

Perf. 14½x14, 14x14½

1976, Apr. 1 Litho.

62	A16	15f brt blue & multi	2.50	1.25
63	A16	80f blue & multi	9.50	4.50
64	A16	140f ocher & multi	21.00	12.00
		Nos. 62-64 (3)	33.00	17.75

Waves and Ear Phones, ITU Emblem, Coat of Arms — A17

1976, May 17 Litho. **Perf. 14**

65	A17	50f gray grn & multi	1.60	.65
66	A17	80f pink & multi	3.50	1.60
67	A17	2d tan & multi	7.00	3.25
		Nos. 65-67 (3)	12.10	5.50

International Telecommunications Day.

No. 18 Surcharged

1976 Litho. **Perf. 14x15**

68	A2	50f on 75f multi	75.00	24.00

Coat of Arms — A18

1976, Aug. 15 Litho. **Perf. 11½**

69	A18	5f dull rose	.40	.40
70	A18	10f golden brown	.40	.20
71	A18	15f orange	.65	.40
72	A18	35f dull red brn	1.00	.20
73	A18	50f bright lilac	1.40	.20
74	A18	60f bister	1.50	.20
75	A18	80f yellow green	2.00	.80
76	A18	90f ultra	2.25	.80
77	A18	1d blue	2.50	.80
78	A18	140f olive green	4.00	1.75
79	A18	150f rose violet	4.00	2.00
80	A18	2d slate	5.50	2.75
81	A18	5d blue green	14.50	6.75
82	A18	10d lilac rose	27.50	14.00
		Nos. 69-82 (14)	67.60	30.95

See Nos. 91-104.

Sheik Zaid — A19

1976, Dec. 12 Litho. **Perf. 13**

83	A19	15f rose & multi	6.00	.60
84	A19	140f blue & multi	12.00	5.00

5th National Day.

Symbolic Falcon and Globe — A20

1976, Dec. 15 **Perf. 14x13½**

85	A20	80f yellow & multi	6.00	1.50
86	A20	2d red & multi	11.00	6.00

International Falconry Congress, Abu Dhabi, Dec. 1976.

A21

A22

1976, Dec. 30 Litho. **Perf. 13**

87	A21	50f multicolored	5.00	1.50
88	A21	80f multicolored	10.00	3.00

Mohammed Ali Jinnah (1876-1948), 1st Governor General of Pakistan.

1977, Apr. 12 Litho. **Perf. 13½x14**

APU emblem, members' flags.

89	A22	50f multicolored	6.00	1.50
90	A22	80f multicolored	9.00	3.50

Arab Postal Union, 25th anniversary.

Arms Type of 1976

1977, July 25 Litho. **Perf. 11½**

91	A18	5f dull rose & blk	.40	.35
92	A18	10f gldn brn & blk	.40	.40
93	A18	15f dull org & blk	.55	.45
94	A18	35f lt brown & blk	1.40	.50
95	A18	50f brt lilac & blk	1.60	.55
96	A18	60f bister & blk	1.75	.60
97	A18	80f yel grn & blk	1.75	.60
98	A18	90f ultra & blk	2.75	.95
99	A18	1d blue & blk	4.00	1.40
100	A18	140f ol grn & blk	6.00	1.90
101	A18	150f rose vio & blk	6.50	2.25
102	A18	2d slate & blk	10.00	3.25
103	A18	5d bl grn & blk	22.50	8.25
104	A18	10d lil rose & bl	37.50	24.50
		Nos. 91-104 (14)	97.10	45.90

Man Reading Book, UAE Arms, UN Emblem A23

1977, Sept. 8 Litho. **Perf. 14x13½**

105	A23	50f green, brn & gold	3.50	.80
106	A23	3d blue & multi	12.50	5.50

International Literacy Day.

A set of three stamps for the 6th Natl. Day was withdrawn from sale on the day of issue, Dec. 2, 1977. Value, $850.

Post Horn and Sails — A24

1979, Apr. 14 Photo. **Perf. 12x11½**

107	A24	50f multicolored	1.25	1.00
108	A24	5d multicolored	8.50	6.00

Gulf Postal Organization, 2nd Conf., Dubai.

Arab Achievements — A25

1980, Mar. 22 Litho. **Perf. 14x14½**

109	A25	50f multicolored	.75	.50
110	A25	140f multicolored	2.25	1.25
111	A25	3d multicolored	4.50	2.75
		Nos. 109-111 (3)	7.50	4.50

9th National Day — A26

1980, Dec. 2 Litho. **Perf. 13½**

112	A26	15f multicolored	.60	.35
113	A26	50f multicolored	2.00	1.00
114	A26	80f multicolored	2.50	1.50
115	A26	150f multicolored	3.75	2.25
		Nos. 112-115 (4)	8.85	5.10

Souvenir Sheet
Perf. 13½x14

116	A26	3d multicolored	15.00	15.00

Family on Graph — A27

Hegira (Pilgrimage Year) — A28

1980, Dec. 15

117	A27	15f shown	.80	.35
118	A27	80f Symbols	2.75	1.25
119	A27	90f like #118	3.50	2.25
120	A27	2d like #117	7.25	5.00
		Nos. 117-120 (4)	14.30	8.85

1980 population census.

1980, Dec. 18 **Perf. 14x13½**

121	A28	15f multicolored	.50	.25
122	A28	80f multicolored	2.00	1.25
123	A28	90f multicolored	2.75	1.50
124	A28	140f multicolored	4.25	2.50
		Nos. 121-124 (4)	9.50	5.50

Souvenir Sheet

125	A28	2d multicolored	11.50	11.50

No. 125 contains one 36x57mm stamp.

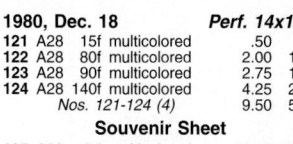

OPEC Emblem — A29

1980, Dec. 21 **Perf. 14**

126	A29	50f Men holding OPEC emblem, vert.	1.25	.50
127	A29	80f like #126	2.00	1.25
128	A29	90f shown	2.25	1.50
129	A29	140f like #128	4.00	2.25
		Nos. 126-129 (4)	9.50	5.50

Souvenir Sheet

130	A29	3d like #128	18.00	18.00

Traffic Week — A30

15f, 80f, Crossing guard, students, traffic light. 50f, 5d, Crossing guard, traffic light and signs.

1981, Mar. 26 Litho. **Perf. 14½**

131	A30	15f multicolored	.65	.30
132	A30	50f multicolored	1.25	.75
133	A30	80f multicolored	2.50	1.50
134	A30	5d multicolored	11.00	7.50
		Nos. 131-134 (4)	15.40	10.05

Size of Nos. 131 and 133: 25½x35mm.

10th Natl. Day — A31

1981, Dec. 2 Litho. **Perf. 15x14**

135	A31	25f Cogwheel	.75	.40
136	A31	150f Soldiers	5.00	2.50
137	A31	2d UN emblem	6.50	3.00
		Nos. 135-137 (3)	12.25	5.90

Intl. Year of the Disabled — A32

Perf. 14½x14, 14x14½

1981, Dec. 26 Litho.

138	A32	25f Couple	.75	.35
139	A32	45f Man in wheel-chair, vert.	1.50	1.10
140	A32	150f like #139	5.00	2.50
141	A32	2d like #138	7.50	3.25
		Nos. 138-141 (4)	14.75	7.20

Natl. Arms — A33

1982-86

142	A33	5f multicolored	.20	.20
143	A33	10f multicolored	.20	.20
144	A33	15f multicolored	.20	.20
145	A33	25f multicolored	.20	.20
145A	A33	35f multicolored	.20	.20
146	A33	50f multicolored	.40	.40
147	A33	75f multicolored	.60	.60
148	A33	100f multicolored	.90	.90
149	A33	110f multicolored	1.00	1.00
150	A33	125f multicolored	1.50	1.40
151	A33	150f multicolored	1.75	1.25
151A	A33	175f multicolored	2.00	1.25

Size: 23x27mm
Perf. 13

152	A33	2d multicolored	2.25	1.60
152A	A33	250f multicolored	2.40	1.40
153	A33	3d multicolored	3.50	1.90
154	A33	5d multicolored	6.00	3.25
155	A33	10d multicolored	13.00	8.25
156	A33	20d multicolored	24.50	13.50
157	A33	50d multicolored	50.00	24.50
		Nos. 142-157 (19)	110.80	62.20

Issued: 35f, 175f, 250f, 12/15/84; 50d, 2/6/86; others, 3/7/82.

6th Arab Gulf Soccer
Championships — A34

1982, Apr. 4   Litho.   Perf. 14

167	A34	25f Emblem, flags	1.25	.60
168	A34	75f Eagle, soccer ball, stadium, vert.	3.25	2.40
169	A34	125f Players, vert.	4.25	3.00
170	A34	3d like 75f, vert.	9.25	7.75
		Nos. 167-170 (4)	18.00	13.75

2nd
Disarmament
Meeting
A35

1982, Oct. 24   Litho.   Perf. 13x13½

171	A35	25f multicolored	.65	.30
172	A35	75f multicolored	2.00	1.25
173	A35	125f multicolored	3.50	2.40
174	A35	150f multicolored	4.00	3.00
		Nos. 171-174 (4)	10.15	7.95

11th Natl.
Day — A36

Designs: 25f, 150f, Skyscraper, communications tower, natl. crest, castle turret, open book, flag. 75f, 125f, Sun, bird, vert.

1982, Dec. 2   Litho.   Perf. 14½

175	A36	25f multicolored	.60	.40
176	A36	75f multicolored	2.40	1.60
177	A36	125f multicolored	3.25	2.25
178	A36	150f multicolored	3.75	2.75
		Nos. 175-178 (4)	10.00	7.00

A37

A38

1983, Dec. 20   Litho.   Perf. 14x14½

179	A37	25f multicolored	.80	.30
180	A37	150f multicolored	3.50	1.60
181	A37	2d multicolored	5.00	3.00
182	A37	3d multicolored	7.00	3.75
		Nos. 179-182 (4)	16.30	8.65

World Communications Year.

1983, Jan. 8   Litho.   Perf. 14½

Arab Literacy Day: 25f, 75f, Oil lamp, open Koran. 35f, 3d, Scribe.

183	A38	25f multicolored	42.50	60.00
184	A38	35f multicolored	1.50	.80
185	A38	75f multicolored	42.50	55.00
186	A38	3d multicolored	10.00	5.00

Nos. 183 and 185 withdrawn from sale on day of issue because of an error in Koranic inscription.

INTELSAT, 20th Anniv. — A39

1984, Nov. 24   Litho.   Perf. 14½

187	A39	2d multicolored	5.50	5.00
188	A39	2.50d multicolored	8.00	7.00

13th Natl.
Day
A40

Flag, portrait of an Emir and building or view from each capital.

1984, Dec. 2   Perf. 14½x13½

189	A40	1d Building, pavilion	2.50	1.50
190	A40	1d Fortress, cannon	2.50	1.50
191	A40	1d Port, boats	2.50	1.50
192	A40	1d Fortress	2.50	1.50
193	A40	1d Oil refinery	2.50	1.50
194	A40	1d Building, garden	2.50	1.50
195	A40	1d Oil well, palace	2.50	1.50
		Nos. 189-195 (7)	17.50	10.50

Tidy Week — A41

A42

1985, Mar. 15   Perf. 12½

196	A41	5d multicolored	11.50	10.00

1985, Sept. 10   Perf. 13½x14½

197	A42	2d multicolored	7.00	4.50
198	A42	250f multicolored	10.00	6.50

World Junior Chess Championships, Sharjah, Sept. 10-27.

14th Natl.
Day — A43

1985, Dec. 2   Perf. 14x13½

199	A43	50f multicolored	.75	.55
200	A43	3d multicolored	7.00	4.50

Population
Census — A44

1985, Dec. 16

201	A44	50f multicolored	1.10	.55
202	A44	1d multicolored	3.00	1.40
203	A44	3d multicolored	7.75	3.50
		Nos. 201-203 (3)	11.85	5.45

Intl.
Youth
Year
A45

1985, Dec. 23   Perf. 14½

204	A45	50f Silhouettes, sapling, vert.	1.00	.65
205	A45	175f Globe, open book	3.00	1.60
206	A45	2d Youth carrying world, vert.	3.75	2.25
		Nos. 204-206 (3)	7.75	4.50

Women and
Family
Day — A46

1986, Mar. 21   Perf. 13½

207	A46	1d multicolored	1.50	1.00
208	A46	3d multicolored	4.50	3.25

General
Postal
Authority,
1st Anniv.
A47

Designs: 50f, 250f, Posthorn, map, natl. flag, globe. 1d, 2d, Emblem, globe, vert.

1986, Apr. 1

209	A47	50f multicolored	.60	.50
210	A47	1d multicolored	1.25	.80
211	A47	2d multicolored	3.25	2.25
212	A47	250f multicolored	3.50	2.75
		Nos. 209-212 (4)	8.60	6.30

United
Arab
Shipping
Co., 10th
Anniv.
A48

1986, Aug. 20   Perf. 13x13½

213	A48	2d shown	4.50	2.75
214	A48	3d Ship's bow, vert.	5.50	3.75

A49

A51   Hawk — A50

1986, Sept. 1   Perf. 13½x13

215	A49	250f multicolored	4.25	1.65
216	A49	3d multicolored	5.25	1.90

Emirates Telecommunications Corp., Ltd., 10th anniv.

1986, Sept. 9   Photo.   Perf. 15x14
Booklet Stamps
Background Color

217	A50	50f pale green	.75	.75
218	A50	75f pink	1.25	1.25
219	A50	125f gray	2.00	2.00
a.		Bklt. pane, 75f, 125f, 2 50f	8.00	
		Nos. 217-219 (3)	4.00	4.00

1986, Oct. 25   Perf. 13½

220	A51	50f Jet, camel	1.75	1.25
221	A51	175f Jet	5.50	4.25

Emirates Airlines, 1st anniv.

State
Crests,
GCC
Emblem
A52

1986, Nov. 2   Perf. 13

222	A52	50f shown	.80	.50
222A	A52	175f like no. 223	2.75	2.25
223	A52	3d Tree, emblem	4.50	4.25
		Nos. 222-223 (3)	8.05	7.10

Gulf Cooperation Council supreme council 7th session, Abu Dhabi, Nov. 1986. No. 222A incorrectly inscribed "1.75f."

15th Natl.
Day — A53

1986, Dec. 2   Litho.   Perf. 13½
224 A53 50f shown   1.10   .55
225 A53 1d like 50f   2.50 1.60
226 A53 175f Flag, emblem   4.50 2.75
227 A53 2d like 175f   4.50 3.25
    Nos. 224-227 (4)   12.60 8.15

27th Chess Olympiad, Dubai — A54

1986, Nov. 14   Perf. 12½
228 A54 50f Skyscraper, vert.   1.40   .80
229 A54 2d shown   5.50 4.50
230 A54 250f Tapestry, diff.   7.00 5.50
  a.   Souv. sheet, #228-230, perf
       13   22.50 22.50
    Nos. 228-230 (3)   13.90 10.80

No. 230a exists imperf. Value, $35.

Arab Police
Day — A55

1986, Dec. 18   Perf. 13½
231 A55 50f multicolored   1.75 1.00
232 A55 1d multicolored   3.00 2.50

A56

A57

1987, Mar. 15
233 A56 50f multicolored   1.75 1.00
234 A56 1d multicolored   3.00 2.50

Municipalities and Environment Week.

1987, Apr. 10
235 A57 200f multicolored   3.50 3.50
236 A57 250f multicolored   4.00 4.00

UAE Flight Information Region, 1st anniv.

A58

A59

1987, May 25
237 A58 50f Water   1.00 1.00
238 A58 2d Solar energy, oil
         well   8.50 8.50

Conservation.

1987, June 23
239 A59 1d multicolored   1.75 1.75
240 A59 3d multicolored   4.50 4.50

United Arab Emirates University, 10th anniv.

1st Shipment of Crude Oil from Abu
Dhabi, 25th Anniv. — A60

1987, July 4   Perf. 13
241 A60 50f Oil rig   .80   .80
242 A60 1d Drilling well, vert.   1.90 1.90
243 A60 175f Crew, drill   3.00 3.00
244 A60 2d Oil tanker   3.25 3.25
    Nos. 241-244 (4)   8.95 8.95

Arab Palm Tree
and Date
Day — A61

1987, Sept. 15   Litho.   Perf. 14x15
245 A61 50f shown   .90   .90
246 A61 1d Tree, fruit, diff.   1.60 1.60

A62

1987, Nov. 21   Litho.   Perf. 13x13½
247 A62 2d multicolored   3.00 3.00
248 A62 250f multicolored   3.50 3.50

Intl. Year of Shelter for the Homeless.

1987, Dec. 15   Perf. 13½
249 A63 1d multicolored   2.00 2.00
250 A63 2d multicolored   4.50 4.50

Salim Bin Ali Al-Owais (b. 1887), poet.

A63

UN Child
Survival
Campaign
A64

Abu Dhabi Intl.
Airport, 6th Anniv.
A65

1987, Oct. 25   Litho.   Perf. 13
251 A64 50f Growth monitoring   .60   .50
252 A64 1d Immunization   1.25 1.00
253 A64 175f Oral rehydration
         therapy   2.00 1.75
254 A64 2d Breast feeding,
         horiz.   2.25 1.90
    Nos. 251-254 (4)   6.10 5.15

1988, Jan. 2
255 A65 50f Control tower   .85   .85
256 A65 50f Terminal interior   .85   .85
257 A65 100f Aircraft over airport 2.00 2.00
258 A65 100f Aircraft at gates   2.00 2.00
    Nos. 255-258 (4)   5.70 5.70

Natl. Arts
Festival
A66

1988, Mar. 21   Litho.   Perf. 13½
259 A66 50f multicolored   1.25 1.25
260 A66 250f multicolored   3.75 3.75

Youth
Cultural
Festival
A67

Winning children's drawings of a design
contest sponsored by the Ministry of Education and the Sharjah Cultural and Information
Department.

Perf. 13x13½, 13½x13
1988, May 25   Litho.
261 A67 50f Net fisherman   .75   .50
262 A67 1d Woman   1.40 1.25
263 A67 1.75d Youth as flower   2.25 2.00
264 A67 2d Recreation   2.75 2.50
    Nos. 261-264 (4)   7.15 6.25

Palestinian
Uprising — A68

1988, June 28   Litho.   Perf. 13½
265 A68 2d multicolored   2.75 2.25
266 A68 250f multicolored   3.50 2.75

A69

Banks — A70

1988, July 16   Litho.   Perf. 13½
267 A69 50f multicolored   2.50 2.50
268 A70 50f multicolored   2.50 2.50

Abu Dhabi Natl. Bank, Ltd., 20th anniv. (No.
267); Natl. Bank of Dubai, Ltd., 25th anniv.
(No. 268).

Port Rashid,
Dubai, 16th
Anniv. — A71

1988, Aug. 31   Litho.   Perf. 13½
269 A71 50f Ground transporta-
         tion   .60   .60
270 A71 1d Piers   1.25 1.25
271 A71 175f Ship at dock   2.50 2.50
272 A71 2d Ship, unloading
         cranes   2.75 2.75
    Nos. 269-272 (4)   7.10 7.10

1988 Summer Olympics, Seoul — A72

1988, Sept. 17   Perf. 15x14½
273   2d Swimming   3.25 3.25
274   250f Cycling   4.00 4.00
  a.   A72 Pair, #273-274   7.50 7.50

Ras Al Khaima Natl. Museum, 1st
Anniv. — A74

1988, Nov. 19   Litho.   Perf. 14
275 A74 50f Vase, vert.   .75   .55
276 A74 3d Gold crown   3.25 2.25

18th Arab Scout Conference, Nov. 29-
Dec. 3, Abu Dhabi — A75

1988, Nov. 29   Perf. 12½
277 A75 1d multicolored   1.20 1.20

10th Arbor
Day — A76

Perf. 13½x13, 13x13½
1989, Mar. 6   **Litho.**
278 A76   50f Ghaf, vert.   .60   .60
279 A76 100f Palm   1.25   1.25
280 A76 250f Dahlia blossom   2.75   2.75
   Nos. 278-280 (3)   4.60   4.60

Sharjah
Intl. Airport,
10th Anniv.
A77

1989, Apr. 21   **Litho.**   **Perf. 13½**
281 A77   50f multicolored   .90   .90
282 A77 100f multicolored   2.10   2.10

Postal
Service,
80th Anniv.
A78

1989, Aug. 19   **Litho.**   **Perf. 13x13½**
283 A78   50f Seaplane   1.00   1.00
284 A78   3d Ship   6.50   6.50

Al-Ittihad
Newspaper, 20th
Anniv. — A79

1989, Oct. 20   **Litho.**   **Perf. 13½**
285 A79   50f shown   .75   .75
286 A79   1d Al Ittihad Press   1.25   1.25

Gulf Investment Corporation, 5th
Anniv. — A80

1989, Nov. 25
287 A80   50f multicolored   .75   .75
288 A80   2d multicolored   3.25   3.25

Child on
Crutches,
Hands — A81

Bank
Building — A82

Designs: 2d, Crouched youth, cracked
earth, bread in hand, horiz.

1989, Dec. 5   **Perf. 15x14, 14x15**
289 A81   2d multicolored   2.75   2.75
290 A81 250f shown   3.25   3.25

Intl. Volunteer's Day, Red Crescent Soc.

1989, Dec. 20   **Perf. 13½**
291 A82   50f Emblem, architec-
                    ture   .75   .75
292 A82   1d shown   1.25   1.25

Commercial Bank of Dubai, Ltd., 20th Anniv.

Astrolabe,
Manuscript
Page and
Ship of Bin
Majid, 15th
Cent.
Navigator
and Writer
A83

1989, Dec. 25   **Perf. 13x13½, 13½x13**
293 A83   1d shown   1.25   1.25
294 A83   3d Ship, page, vert.   4.25   4.25

Heritage revival.

A84

Falcon — A85

1990, Jan. 17   **Perf. 13½**
295 A84   50f multicolored   .75   .75
296 A84   1d multicolored   1.90   1.90

3rd Al Ain festival.

1990, Feb. 17   **Litho.**   **Perf. 11½**
Granite Paper
297 A85   5f multicolored   .20   .20
298 A85   20f multicolored   .20   .20
299 A85   25f multicolored   .20   .20
301 A85   50f multicolored   .45   .40
302 A85 100f multicolored   2.25   1.25
303 A85 150f multicolored   3.75   1.75
304 A85 175f multicolored   4.00   2.00

Size: 21x26mm
Perf. 11½x12
306 A85   2d multicolored   5.50   3.00
307 A85 250f multicolored   6.00   3.25
309 A85   3d multicolored   7.75   3.75
310 A85   5d multicolored   11.00   6.50
311 A85   10d multicolored   22.50 13.00
312 A85   20d multicolored   37.50 22.50
313 A85   50d multicolored   100.00 60.00
   Nos. 297-313 (14)   201.30 118.00

See also Nos. 726A-726G.

A86

A87

1990, Mar. 10   **Litho.**   **Perf. 13½**
316 A86   50f multicolored   .60   .60
317 A86 250f multicolored   2.50   2.50

Children's cultural festival.

1990, Aug. 5   **Litho.**   **Perf. 14x15**
318 A87 175f shown   1.90   1.90
319 A87   2d Starving child   2.50   2.50

Red Crescent Society.

Dubai
Chamber
of
Commerce
and
Industry,
25th Anniv.
A88

1990, July 1   **Perf. 13**
320 A88   50f multicolored   .75   .75
321 A88   1d multicolored   1.50   1.50

World Cup Soccer Championships,
Italy — A89

UAE emblem, character trademark and: 1d,
Leaning Tower of Pisa, desert, vert. 2d, Soccer ball, vert. 250f, Circle of flags. 3d, Map,
vert.

1990, June 8   **Perf. 13½**
322 A89   50f multicolored   .75   .75
323 A89   1d multicolored   1.50   1.50
324 A89   2d multicolored   3.00   3.00
325 A89 250f multicolored   4.00   4.00
   Nos. 322-325 (4)   9.25   9.25

Souvenir Sheet
Perf. 12½
326 A89   3d multicolored   7.00   7.00

A90

A91

1990, Sept. 22   **Litho.**   **Perf. 13½**
327 A90   50f shown   .75   .75
328 A90   1d Emblem, 30 years   2.25   2.25
329 A90 175f Emblem, drop of oil 3.50   3.50
   Nos. 327-329 (3)   6.50   6.50

Organization of Petroleum Exporting Countries (OPEC), 30th anniv.

1990, Aug. 25   **Perf. 14x14½**
Flowers.
330 A91   50f Argyrolobeum
               roseum   .90   .90
331 A91   50f Lamranthus
               roseus   .90   .90
332 A91   50f Centavrea pseudo
               sinaica   .90   .90
333 A91   50f Calotropis procera   .90   .90
   a. Souvenir sheet of 4, #330-333 4.50 4.50
334 A91   50f Nerium oleander   .90   .90
335 A91   50f Catharanthus
               roseus   .90   .90
336 A91   50f Hibiscus rosa
               sinensis   4.00   4.00
337 A91   50f Bougainvillea
               glabra   4.00   4.00
   a. Souvenir sheet of 4, #334-337 17.00 17.00
   Nos. 330-337 (8)   13.40 13.40

A92

A93

1990, Oct. 8   **Litho.**   **Perf. 13**
338 A92   50f Water pollution   .50   .50
339 A92   3d Air pollution   3.25   3.25

Environmental pollution.

1990, Dec. 2   **Perf. 13½**
340 A93   50f shown   .50   .50
341 A93 175f Bank building,
               horiz.   3.25   3.25

Central Bank, 10th anniv.

Intl. Conference
on High Salinity
Tolerant
Plants — A94

1990, Dec. 8   **Perf. 13x13½**
342 A94   50f Tree   .50   .50
343 A94 250f Water, trees   2.75   2.75

Grand
Mosque, Abu
Dhabi — A95

2d, Al Jumeirah Mosque, Dubai, vert.

Perf. 13½x13, 13x13½
1990, Nov. 26
344 A95   1d multicolored   1.10   1.10
345 A95   2d multicolored   4.50   4.50

A96

A98

A97

1991, Jan. 16   Litho.   Perf. 13x13½
346 A96 50f multicolored   1.00 1.00
347 A96   2d multicolored   2.50 2.50

Abu Dhabi Intl. Fair.

1991, May 17   Litho.   Perf. 14x13½
348 A97   2d multicolored   3.00 3.00
349 A97   3d multicolored   4.50 4.50

World Telecommunications Day.

1991, June 18   Perf. 13½
350 A98   1d Sheikh Saqr Mosque 1.50 1.50
351 A98   2d King Faisal Mosque 3.25 3.25

Children's
Paintings
A99

Designs: 50f, Celebration. 1d, Women waving flags. 175f, Women playing blind-man's buff. 250f, Women dancing for men.

1991, July 15   Litho.   Perf. 14x13½
352 A99   50f multicolored   .60   .45
353 A99   1d multicolored   1.40 1.00
354 A99 175f multicolored   2.50 2.25
355 A99 250f multicolored   3.00 2.50
       Nos. 352-355 (4)   7.50 6.20

Fish
A100

1991, Aug. 5   Litho.   Perf. 13½x14
356 A100 50f Yellow marked butterflyfish   .60   .60
357 A100 50f Golden trevally   .60   .60
358 A100 50f Two banded porgy   .60   .60
359 A100 50f Red snapper   .60   .60
360 A100   1d Three banded grunt   1.25 1.25
361 A100   1d Rabbit fish   1.25 1.25
362 A100   1d Black bream   1.25 1.25
363 A100   1d Greasy grouper   1.25 1.25
 a.   Min. sheet of 8, #356-363 8.50 8.50
       Nos. 356-363 (8)   7.40 7.40

A101

A103

A102

Intl. Aerospace Exhibition, Dubai: 175f, Jet fighter over Dubai Intl. Airport. 2d, Fighter silhouette over airport.

1991, Nov. 3   Litho.   Perf. 13½
364 A101 175f multicolored   2.25 2.25
365 A101   2d multicolored   2.50 2.50

1991, Oct. 7   Perf. 13
Sheikh Rashid Bin Said Al Maktum (1912-90), Ruler of Dubai and: 50f, Airport, vert. 175f, City skyline, vert. 2d, Waterfront, satellite dish.

366 A102   50f multicolored   .50   .50
367 A102   1d multicolored   1.10 1.10
368 A102 175f multicolored   2.00 2.00
369 A102   2d multicolored   2.25 2.25
       Nos. 366-369 (4)   5.85 5.85

1991, Oct. 8   Litho.   Perf. 13½
370 A103   50f multicolored   .75   .75
371 A103   1d multicolored   1.75 1.75

Civil Defense Day.

A104

A105

A106

20th Natl. Day — A107

#374, Emir at left, fortress, cannon. #377, Fortress on rocky outcropping. #378, Emir at right, fortress, cannon. 3d, Sheikh Said bin Sultan al Nahayan, Defense Forces.

1991, Dec. 2   Litho.   Perf. 13
372 A104   75f multicolored   1.20 1.20
373 A105   75f multicolored   1.20 1.20
374 A105   75f multicolored   1.20 1.20
375 A106   75f multicolored   1.20 1.20
376 A107   75f multicolored   1.20 1.20
377 A107   75f multicolored   1.20 1.20
378 A107   75f multicolored   1.20 1.20

Imperf
Size: 70x90mm
378A A107   3d multicolored   8.00 8.00
       Nos. 372-378A (8)   16.40 16.40

On Nos. 372-378 portions of the design were applied by a thermographic process producing a shiny, raised effect.

A108

A109

1991, Nov. 16   Perf. 13½
379 A108 50f lt green & multi   .45   .45
380 A108   3d orange & multi   3.75 3.75

Gulf Cooperaton Council, 10th anniv.

1992, Jan. 15   Litho.   Perf. 13½
381 A109 175f pink & multi   2.20 2.20
382 A109 250f lt blue & multi 2.50 2.50

Abu Dhabi National Oil Co., 20th anniv.

Al-Jahli
Castle Al-
Ain
A110

1992, Apr. 20   Litho.   Perf. 13½
383 A110   2d multicolored   2.00 2.00
384 A110 250f multicolored   60.00 60.00

Expo '92, Seville.
No. 384 was withdrawn because of poor rendition of Arabic word for "postage."

A111

A112

Mosques: 50f, Sheikh Rashid bin Humaid al Nuaimi, Ajman. 1d, Sheikh Ahmed Bin Rashid Al Mualla, Umm Al Quwain.

1992, Mar. 26   Perf. 14x13½
385 A111 50f multicolored   .80   .80
386 A111   1d multicolored   1.60 1.60

See Nos. 417-418.

1992, Apr. 20   Perf. 13½x13
387 A112   1d shown   1.75 1.75
388 A112   3d Ear with hearing aid 4.00 4.00

Week of the deaf child.

Zayed Seaport, 20th Anniv. — A113

1992, June 28   Litho.   Perf. 13½
389 A113   50f Aerial view   .50   .50
390 A113   1d Cargo transport 1.25 1.25
391 A113 175f Ship docked   2.25 2.25
392 A113   2d Map   2.50 2.50
       Nos. 389-392 (4)   6.50 6.50

1992 Summer
Olympics,
Barcelona
A114

1992, July 25   Litho.   Perf. 14x13½
393 A114   50f Yachting   .50   .50
394 A114   1d Running   1.00 1.00
395 A114 175f Swimming   2.00 2.00
396 A114 250f Cycling   2.25 2.25
       Nos. 393-396 (4)   5.75 5.75

Souvenir Sheet
396A A114   3d Equestrian   5.75 5.75

Children's
Paintings
A115

1992, Aug. 15   Perf. 13½x14
397 A115   50f Playing soccer   .50   .50
398 A115   1d Playing in field 1.00 1.00
399 A115   2d Playground   2.25 2.25
400 A115 250f Children among trees   3.00 3.00
       Nos. 397-400 (4)   6.75 6.75

Intl. Bank of
United Arab
Emirates, 15th
Anniv. — A116

Design: 175f, Bank emblem.

Litho. & Embossed
1992, Sept. 9   *Perf. 11*
401 A116 50f gold & multi   .75   .75
     Size: 35x41mm
     Perf. 11½
402 A116 175f lake, gold & vio   2.25 2.25

Traditional Musical
Instruments — A116a

1992, Oct. 17   **Litho.**   *Perf. 13½*
402A A116a 50f Tambourah,
     vert.   .60   .60
402B A116a 50f Oud, vert.   .60   .60
402C A116a 50f Rababah,
     vert.   1.25 1.25
     g.   Sheet, #402A-402C, perf.
       12¾   3.50 3.50
402D A116a 1d Mizmar,
     shindo   2.50 2.50
402E A116a 1d Tabel, hibban   2.50 2.50
402F A116a 1d Marwas, duff   2.50 2.50
     h.   Sheet, #402D-402F, perf.
       12¾   7.25 7.25
     Nos. 402A-402F (6)   9.95 9.95

Camels
A117

Designs: 50f, Race. 1d, Used for transportation, vert. 175f, Harnessed for obtaining water
from well. 2d, Roaming free, vert.

1992, Dec. 23   **Litho.**   *Perf. 13½*
403 A117 50f multicolored   .50   .30
404 A117 1d multicolored   1.25   .70
405 A117 175f multicolored   2.50 1.25
406 A117 2d multicolored   2.75 1.50
     Nos. 403-406 (4)   7.00 3.75

A118

A119

1992, Dec. 21
407 A118 50f multicolored   1.25 1.25
408 A118 2d yellow & multi   5.50 5.50

Gulf Cooperation Council, 13th session.

1993, Jan. 28   **Litho.**   *Perf. 13½*
409 A119 2d shown   2.50 2.50
410 A119 250f Building, fishing
     boat   4.25 4.25

Dubai Creek Golf and Yacht Club.

A120

A121

1993, Jan. 16
411 A120 50f Golf, horiz.   .75   .75
412 A120 1d Fishing   1.50 1.50
413 A120 2d Boating, horiz.   3.00 3.00
414 A120 250f Motor vehicle
     touring, horiz.   3.75 3.75
     Nos. 411-414 (4)   9.00 9.00

Tourism.

1993, Mar. 27   **Litho.**   *Perf. 14x13½*
415 A121 50f violet & multi   1.00 1.00
416 A121 3d red brown & multi   4.00 4.00

Natl. Youth Festival.

Mosque Type of 1992

1993, Feb. 16   *Perf. 13½*
   50f, Thabit bin Khalid Mosque, Fujeira. 1d,
Sharq al Morabbah Mosque, Al Ain.
417 A111 50f multicolored   1.25 1.25
418 A111 1d multicolored   2.50 2.50

Shells
A122

1993, Apr. 3   **Litho.**   *Perf. 13*
419 A122 25f Conus textile   .35   .35
420 A122 50f Pinctada
     radiata   .50   .50
421 A122 100f Murex scolopax   1.00 1.00
422 A122 150f Natica pulicaris   1.50 1.50
423 A122 175f Lambis truncata
     sebae   2.25 2.25
424 A122 200f Cardita bicolor   2.50 2.50
425 A122 250f Cypraea
     grayana   3.00 3.00
426 A122 300f Cymatium
     trilineatum   4.00 4.00
     Nos. 419-426 (8)   15.10 15.10

Campaign
Against
Drugs
A123

Design: 1d, Skull, drugs, vert.

1993, Aug. 21   **Litho.**   *Perf. 13½*
427 A123 50f multicolored   1.60 1.60
428 A123 1d multicolored   2.25 2.25

A124

A125

Natl. Bank of Abu Dhabi, 25th Anniv.: 50f,
Abu Dhabi skyline, bank emblem. 1d, Bank
emblem. 175f, Bank building, emblem. 2d,
Skyline, emblem, diff.

Litho. & Typo.
1993, Sept. 15   *Perf. 11½*
429 A124 50f silver & multi   .55   .55
430 A124 1d silver & multi   1.10 1.10
431 A124 175f silver & multi   2.50 2.50
432 A124 2d silver & multi   2.75 2.75
     Nos. 429-432 (4)   6.90 6.90

1993, Nov. 10   **Litho.**   *Perf. 13½*
   Dubai Ports Authority: 50f, Aerial view of
port. 1d, Loading cargo. 2d, Aerial view, diff.
250f, Globe.
433 A125 50f purple & multi   .60   .60
434 A125 1d green & multi   1.50 1.50
435 A125 2d orange & multi   3.00 3.00
436 A125 250f pink & multi   3.75 3.75
     Nos. 433-436 (4)   8.85 8.85

Natl. Day
A126

Children's paintings: 50f, Soldiers saluting
flag. 1d, Two women sitting, one standing,
flag, vert. 175f, Flag, boat. 2d, Flags atop castle tower.

1993, Dec. 2   **Litho.**   *Perf. 13½*
437 A126 50f multicolored   .60   .60
438 A126 1d multicolored   1.50 1.50
439 A126 175f multicolored   2.75 2.75
440 A126 2d multicolored   3.00 3.00
     Nos. 437-440 (4)   7.85 7.85

Archaeological Discoveries — A127

Designs: 50f, Tomb. 1d, Rectangular artifact. 175f, Animal-shaped artifact. 250f, Bowl.

1993, Dec. 15   *Perf. 14x13½*
441 A127 50f multicolored   .60   .60
442 A127 1d multicolored   1.40 1.40
443 A127 175f multicolored   2.50 2.50
444 A127 250f multicolored   3.25 3.25
     Nos. 441-444 (4)   7.75 7.75

10th
Childrens'
Festival,
Sharjah
A128

Children's paintings: 50f, Children with balloons, flags. 1d, Children playing, three trees.
175f, Child with picture, girls with balloons. 2d,
House, children playing outdoors.

1994, Mar. 19   **Litho.**   *Perf. 13x13½*
445 A128 50f green & multi   .60   .60
446 A128 1d blue & multi   1.50 1.50
447 A128 175f red violet & multi   2.50 2.50
448 A128 2d carmine & multi   2.75 2.75
     Nos. 445-448 (4)   7.35 7.35

Arabian
Horses
A129

50f, Brown horse on hind feet, vert. 1d,
White horse. 175f, Head of brown horse, vert.
250f, Head of white and brown horse.

1994, Jan. 25   *Perf. 13x13½, 13½x13*
449 A129 50f multicolored   .60   .60
450 A129 1d multicolored   1.50 1.50
451 A129 175f multicolored   2.50 2.50
452 A129 250f multicolored   3.25 3.25
     Nos. 449-452 (4)   7.85 7.85

10th
Conference
of Arab
Towns,
Dubai
A130

Perf. 13x13½, 13½x13
1994, May 15   **Litho.**
453 A130 50f Map, city, vert.   .55   .55
454 A130 1d shown   2.25 2.25

Pilgrimage to
Mecca — A131

1994, Apr. 29   **Litho.**   *Perf. 13x13½*
455 A131 50f shown   .75   .75
456 A131 2d Holy Ka'aba   3.00 3.00

Intl. Year of
the Family
A132

Intl.
Olympic
Committee,
Cent.
A133

Arab Housing
Day — A134

Writers Assoc.,
10th
Anniv. — A135

1994, June 15   *Perf. 13x13½*
457 A132 1d multicolored   1.40 1.40
458 A133 1d multicolored   1.40 1.40

Perf. 13½x13

459	A134	1d multicolored	1.40	1.40
460	A135	1d multicolored	1.40	1.40
		Nos. 457-460 (4)	5.60	5.60

Archaeological Finds, Al Qusais,
Dubai — A136

Designs: 50f, Lidded pitcher, vert. 1d,
Pointed-handle pitcher. 175f, Pitcher, arm-
shaped handle. 250f, Short round vase.

1994, Aug. 16   Litho.   Perf. 13½

461	A136	50f multicolored	.55	.55
462	A136	1d multicolored	1.30	1.30
463	A136	175f multicolored	2.20	2.20
464	A136	250f multicolored	3.00	3.00
		Nos. 461-464 (4)	7.05	7.05

Environmental Protection — A137

Designs: 50f, Arabian leopard. 1d, Gordon's
wildcat. 2d, Caracal. 250f, Sand cat.

1994, Oct. 10   Litho.   Perf. 13½

465	A137	50f multicolored	.60	.60
466	A137	1d multicolored	1.60	1.60
467	A137	2d multicolored	3.50	3.50
468	A137	250f multicolored	4.25	4.25
		Nos. 465-468 (4)	9.95	9.95

12th Arab Gulf Soccer Championships,
Abu Dhabi — A138

1994, Nov. 3   Litho.   Perf. 13½

469	A138	50f Ball, emblem, vert.	.55	.55
470	A138	3d Soccer players	3.75	3.75

Birds
A139

50f, Merops orientalis. 175f, Halcyon
chloris. 2d, Dromas ardeola. 250f, Coracias
benghalensis. 3d, Phoenicopterus ruber.

1994, Dec. 12

471	A139	50f multicolored	.60	.60
472	A139	175f multicolored	3.25	3.25
473	A139	2d multicolored	3.50	3.50
474	A139	250f multicolored	5.50	5.50
		Nos. 471-474 (4)	12.85	12.85

Souvenir Sheet

475	A139	3d multi, vert.	8.00	8.00

Archaeological Finds, Mulaiha,
Sharjah — A140

Designs: 50f, Front of carved horse, vert.
175f, Ancient coin, vert. 2d, Inscription on
metal, vert. 250f, Inscription on stone.

1995, Jan. 25   Litho.   Perf. 13½

476	A140	50f multicolored	.55	.55
477	A140	175f multicolored	2.25	2.25
478	A140	2d multicolored	3.00	3.00
479	A140	250f multicolored	3.25	3.25
		Nos. 476-479 (4)	9.05	9.05

Natl.
Dances
A141

1995, Feb. 14

480	A141	50f Al-Naashat	.50	.50
481	A141	175f Al-Ayaalah	2.10	2.10
482	A141	2d Al-Shahhoh	2.40	2.40
		Nos. 480-482 (3)	5.00	5.00

A142

A143

1995, Mar. 19   Litho.   Perf. 13½

483	A142	50f Helicopters	.50	.50
484	A142	1d Emblem	1.50	1.50
485	A142	175f Warships, horiz.	2.75	2.75
486	A142	2d Artillery, horiz.	3.25	3.25
		Nos. 483-486 (4)	8.00	8.00

Intl. Defense Exhibition & Conf., Abu Dhabi.

1995, Mar. 22

487	A143	1d Arab League em- blem	1.25	1.25
488	A143	2d FAO emblem	2.75	2.75
489	A143	250f UN emblem	3.50	3.50
		Nos. 487-489 (3)	7.50	7.50

50th Anniv. of Arab League, FAO & UN.

General Post
Office Authority,
10th
Anniv. — A144

1995, Apr. 1

490	A144	50f multicolored	.75	.75

First Gulf Cooperation Council
Philatelic Exhibition, Abu
Dhabi — A145

1995, Apr. 11   Litho.   Perf. 13½

491	A145	50f multicolored	.75	.75

Traditional
Games, Ajman
Museum — A146

50f, Boy with hoop, stick. 175f, Girl on
swing. 2d, Boy, girl playing stick game within
marked boundary. 250f, Two girls playing
game with stones.

1995, Aug. 28   Litho.   Perf. 13½x13

492	A146	50f multicolored	.45	.45
493	A146	175f multicolored	1.90	1.90
494	A146	2d multicolored	2.25	2.25
495	A146	250f multicolored	2.50	2.50
		Nos. 492-495 (4)	7.10	7.10

A147

A148

Birds: 50f, Falco naumanni. 175f,
Phalacrocorax nigrogularis. 2d, Cursorius cur-
sor. 250f, Upupa epops.

1995, Sept. 25

496	A147	50f multicolored	.55	.55
497	A147	175f multicolored	2.10	2.10
498	A147	2d multicolored	2.50	2.50
499	A147	250f multicolored	2.75	2.75
		Nos. 496-499 (4)	7.90	7.90

See Nos. 528-532.

1995, Nov. 20

Natl. Census: 50f, Stylized family, building.
250f, Mosque, skyscrapers, stylized family.

500	A148	50f multicolored	.50	.50
501	A148	250f multicolored	2.50	2.50

National
Day
A149

Children's paintings: 50f, People wearing
feathered headdresses, palm trees, building.
175f, Girls with flags, balloons, flowers. 2d,
Trees, family in front of house holding balloons, flags. 250f, Groups of children along
street watching parade of cars.

1995, Dec. 2   Perf. 13x13½

502	A149	50f multicolored	.45	.45
503	A149	175f multicolored	1.25	1.25
504	A149	2d multicolored	1.40	1.40
505	A149	250f multicolored	1.75	1.75
		Nos. 502-505 (4)	4.85	4.85

Environmental Protection — A150

1996, Jan. 25   Litho.   Perf. 13x13½

506	A150	50f Dugong dugon	.50	.50
507	A150	2d Delphinus delphis	1.50	1.50
508	A150	3d Megaptera novae- angliae	2.25	2.25
a.		Souvenir sheet, #506-508	4.75	4.75
		Nos. 506-508 (3)	4.25	4.25

A151

A152

1996, Feb. 27   Perf. 13½

509	A151	50f shown	.50	.50
510	A151	3d Building, beach	2.75	2.75

Hobie Cat 16 World Sailing Championships.

1996, Apr. 15

Archaelogical Finds, Fujeira Museum: 50f,
Two-handled pitcher. 175f, Kettle. 250f, Bracelet. 3d, Metal ornament, horiz.

511	A152	50f multicolored	.50	.50
512	A152	175f multicolored	1.25	1.25
513	A152	250f multicolored	2.25	2.25
514	A152	3d multicolored	2.75	2.75
		Nos. 511-514 (4)	6.75	6.75

1996
Summer
Olympic
Games,
Atlanta
A153

Perf. 13½x14, 14x 13½

1996, July 19   Litho.

515	A153	50f Shooting	.50	.50
516	A153	1d Cycling, vert.	.80	.80
517	A153	250f Running, vert.	2.00	2.00
518	A153	350f Swimming	2.50	2.50
		Nos. 515-518 (4)	5.80	5.80

Women's
Union, 21st
Anniv.
A154

Perf. 14x13½, 13½x14

1996, Aug. 15

519	A154	50f Emblem, vert.	.50	.50
520	A154	3d shown	2.75	2.75

A155

A156

1996, Sept. 15　　　　Perf. 14x13½
521　A155　1d shown　　　　.75　.75
522　A155　250f Soccer player　2.00　2.00

11th Asian Soccer Cup Championship.

1996, Oct. 15　　　　Perf. 13½
UN Campaign Against Illegal Use of Drugs:
50f, World with snake around it. 3d, Half of
man's face, half of skull, hypodermic needle,
pills.
523　A156　50f multicolored　　　.75　.75
524　A156　3d multicolored　　2.75　2.75

Sheikh Saeed Al-Maktoum House,
Cent. — A157

Designs: 250f Sheikh Saeed, close-up view
of house. 350f, Overall view of house.

1996, Nov. 12　Litho.　Perf. 13x13½
525　A157　50f multicolored　　　.50　.50
526　A157　250f multicolored　1.75　1.75
527　A157　350f multicolored　2.50　2.50

Bird Type of 1995

Designs: 50f, Pterocles exustus. 150f, Otus
brucei. 250f, Hypocolus ampelinus. 3d, Irania
gutturalis. 350f, Falco concolor.

1996, Nov. 18　　　　Perf. 14x13½
528　A147　50f multicolored　　　.35　.35
529　A147　150f multicolored　1.25　1.25
530　A147　250f multicolored　2.25　2.25
531　A147　3d multicolored　　3.00　3.00
532　A147　350f multicolored　3.25　3.25

Children's
Paintings
A158

50f, Face. 1d, Boats. 250f, Flowers. 350f,
Woman in long dress, palm tree, tent.

Perf. 14x13½, 13½x14
1996, Nov. 19
533　A158　50f multi, vert.　　　.35　.35
534　A158　1d multi　　　　　.80　.80
535　A158　250f multi, vert.　2.25　2.25
536　A158　350f multi, vert.　2.75　2.75

Sheik Zaid
bin Sultan
al
Nahayan,
Accession
to the
Throne of
Abu
Dhabi,
30th
Anniv.
A158a

A159

Sheik and: 50f, 250f, Flowers. 1d, 350f,
Date palm.

1996, Dec. 2　Photo.　Perf. 12
537　A158a　50f red & multi　　.40　.40
538　A158a　1d olive & multi　.65　.65
539　A158a　250f purple & multi　1.60　1.60
540　A158a　350f gray & multi　2.25　2.25
　　Nos. 537-540 (4)　　　4.90　4.90

Photo. & Embossed
Imperf
Size: 90x70mm
541　A159　5d On horseback,
　　　　　　gazelles　　　5.00　5.00

Anniversaries
A160

Natl. Day, 25th
Anniv. — A161

Photo. & Embossed
1996, Dec. 2　　　　　Perf. 12
542　A160　50f red violet & multi　.30　.30
543　A160　1d silver & multi　　1.40　1.40

Sheik Zaid bin Sultan al Nahayan's accession to the throne of Abu Dhabi, 30th anniv.,
Creation of United Arab Emirates, 25th anniv.

1996, Dec. 2
50f, 150f, Seven rulers of United Arab Emirates. 1d, 3d, Heraldic eagle, national flag. 5d,
Score of Natl. Anthem.

Granite Paper
544　A161　50f green & multi　　.70　.70
545　A161　1d multicolored　1.25　1.25
546　A161　150f tan & multi　1.60　1.60
547　A161　3d multicolored　3.25　3.25
　　Nos. 544-547 (4)　　　6.80　6.80

Photo. & Embossed
Imperf
Size: 70x90mm
547A　A161　5d multicolored　5.50　5.50

Butterflies
A162

1997, Jan. 28　Litho.　Perf. 14x13½
548　A162　50f Agrodiaetus
　　　　　　loewii　　　　.60　.60
549　A162　1d Papilio machaon　1.25　1.25
550　A162　150f Orithya　　1.90　1.90
551　A162　250f Chrysippus　3.25　3.25
　　Nos. 548-551 (4)　　　7.00　7.00

Dubai
Shopping
Festival
A163

Perf. 13¼x13¾, 13¾x13¼
1997, Feb. 22　　　　　Litho.
552　A163　50f shown　　　　.50　.50
553　A163　250f Shopping bag,
　　　　　　vert.　　　　2.50　2.50

Intl. Defense
Exhibition &
Conference
A164

50f, Helicopter airlifting jeep. 1d, Emblem.
250f, Artillery, emblem. 350f, Ships, emblem.

1997, Mar. 16　Litho.　Perf. 13½
554　A164　50f multicolored　　.40　.40
555　A164　1d multicolored　　.75　.75
556　A164　250f multicolored　2.10　2.10
557　A164　350f multicolored　2.75　2.75
　　Nos. 554-557 (4)　　　6.00　6.00

Emirates Bank
Group, 20th
Anniv. — A165

Perf. 13¾x13¼
1997, Mar. 23　　　　　Litho.
568　A165　50f multi　　　　.55　.55
569　A165　1d buff & multi　1.20　1.20
　a.　Souv. sheet, #568-569, imperf.　6.00　6.00

No. 569a sold for 5d.

Technical
Education and
National
Development
Conference
A166

1997, Apr. 6　　　　Perf. 13¾x13¼
570　A166　50f shown　　　　.75　.75
571　A166　250f Emblem　　2.75　2.75

Sharjah
Heritage
A167

Designs: 50f, Coins. 3d, Museum.

1997, June 17　Litho.　Perf. 13½
572　A167　50f multicolored　　.75　.75
573　A167　3d multicolored　3.25　3.25

Emirates
Philatelic
Association
A168

Perf. 13¾x13¼, 13¼x13¾
1997, June 24　　　　　Litho.
574　A168　50f shown　　　　.50　.50
575　A168　250f Stamps, horiz.　2.50　2.50

Children's
Paintings
A169

50f, Cats. 1d, Children playing. 250f, Children, moon, vert. 3d, Abstract.

1997, Sept. 15　Litho.　Perf. 13½
576　A169　50f multicolored　　.50　.50
577　A169　1d multicolored　　.90　.90
578　A169　250f multicolored　2.00　2.00
579　A169　3d multicolored　2.50　2.50
　　Nos. 576-579 (4)　　　5.90　5.90

Reunion, by
Sheikha Hassan
Maktoum al
Maktoum — A170

Mindscape, by Sarah Majid al Futtaim
A170a

Blue Musings, by Maha Abdulla Al
Mazroui — A170b

The
Pause,
by
Khulood
Mattar
Rashid
A170c

The Seas I, by
Sheikha Sawsan
Abdulaziz Al
Qasimi — A170d

Still Life, by
Sheikha Bodour
Sultan Al Qasimi
A170e

The Opening, by Tina Ahmed and Others — 170f

Illustration A170f reduced.

1997, Oct. 25   Litho.   *Perf. 13¾*

580	A170	50f multi	.65	.65
581	A170a	50f multi	.65	.65
582	A170b	50f multi	.65	.65
583	A170c	50f multi	.65	.65
584	A170d	50f multi	.65	.65
585	A170e	50f multi	.65	.65
	Nos. 580-585 (6)		3.90	3.90

Imperf

586	A170f	5d multi	6.00	6.00

Intl. Aerospace Exhibition, Dubai A171

Perf. 13½x13¾

1997, Nov. 16   Litho.

587	A171	250f Jet fighter	2.50	2.50
588	A171	3d VTOL airplane	3.25	3.25

26th National Day A172

Sheikh Zaid bin Sultan al Nahayan and: 50f, Gardens. 1d, Trees and mountains. 150f, Water, trees and mountains. 250f, Roadway.

1997, Dec. 2   Litho.   *Perf. 13½x13¾*

589	A172	50f multi	.45	.45
590	A172	1d multi	.75	.75
591	A172	150f multi	1.20	1.20
592	A172	250f multi	1.75	1.75
	Nos. 589-592 (4)		4.15	4.15

3rd Afro-Arab Trade Fair A173

Perf. 13x13¼, 13¼x13

1997, Dec. 6   Litho.

593	A173	150f Emblem, vert.	1.25	1.25
594	A173	350f Handshake	2.75	2.75

Arthropods A174

50f, Blepharopsis mendica. 150f, Galeodes sp. 250f, Crocothemis arythraea. 350f, Xylocopa aestuans.

1998, Feb. 2   Litho.   *Perf. 13¼*

595	A174	50f multicolored	.50	.50
596	A174	150f multicolored	1.25	1.25
597	A174	250f multicolored	2.25	2.25
598	A174	350f multicolored	3.00	3.00
	Nos. 595-598 (4)		4.50	

ISAF World Sailing Championship — A175

Various sailboats.

Perf. 13¼x13, 13x13¼

1998, Mar. 2   Litho.

599	A175	50f multi, vert.	.45	.45
600	A175	1d multi	1.25	1.25
601	A175	250f multi	2.10	2.10
602	A175	3d multi, vert.	3.00	3.00
	Nos. 599-602 (4)		6.80	6.80

A176

A177

Triple Intl. Defense Exhibition & Conf., Abu Dhabi: 50f, Combat soldiers in protective gear, horiz. 1d, Emblem over world map, skyline of Abu Dhabi. 150f, Electronic gear. 350f, Missile battery, electronic warfare components.

1998, Mar. 15   Litho.   *Perf. 13½*

603	A176	50f multicolored	.45	.45
604	A176	1d multicolored	1.25	1.25
605	A176	150f multicolored	2.10	2.10
606	A176	350f multicolored	3.00	3.00
	Nos. 603-606 (4)		6.80	6.80

1998, Apr. 20   Litho.   *Perf. 13½*

607	A177	50f shown	.50	.50
608	A177	3d Emblem, monument	3.75	3.75

Sharjah, 1998 Arab cultural capital.

World Environment Day — A178

1998, May 17   Litho.   *Perf. 13½*

609	A178	1d Landscape, oryx	1.75	1.75
610	A178	350f multicolored	3.00	3.00

Henna A179

Various designs painted on hands.

1998, Sept. 9   Litho.   *Perf. 13½*

611	A179	50f multicolored	.60	.60
612	A179	1d multicolored	.90	.90
613	A179	150f multicolored	1.40	1.40
614	A179	2d multicolored	1.75	1.75

615	A179	250f multicolored	2.25	2.25
616	A179	3d multicolored	2.75	2.75
	Nos. 611-616 (6)		9.65	9.65

Art — A180

1998, Oct. 20   Litho.   *Perf. 13½*

617	A180	50f Fish	.50	.50
618	A180	1d shown	.95	.95
619	A180	250f Mosque, palm trees, vert.	2.25	2.25
620	A180	350f Door, jar	3.25	3.25
	Nos. 617-620 (4)		4.20	

27th National Day A181

1998, Dec. 2   Litho.   *Perf. 13x13¼*

621	A181	50f Mountain road	.45	.45
622	A181	350f Boat, city skyline	4.25	4.25

Flowers — A182

Designs: 25f, Indigofera arabica. 50f, Centaureum pulchellum. 75f, Lavandula citriodora. 1d, Taverniera glabra. 150f, Convolvulus deserti. 2d, Capparis spinosa. 250f, Rumex vesicirus. 3d, Anagallis arvensis. 350f, Tribulus arabicus. 5d, Reichardia tinitana.

1998, Dec. 8   Litho.   *Perf. 13¼x13¾*

623	A182	25f multicolored	.20	.20
624	A182	50f multicolored	.45	.45
625	A182	75f multicolored	.60	.60
626	A182	1d multicolored	.80	.80
627	A182	150f multicolored	1.25	1.25
628	A182	2d multicolored	1.60	1.60
629	A182	250f multicolored	2.10	2.10
630	A182	3d multicolored	2.50	2.50
631	A182	350f multicolored	2.75	2.75
632	A182	5d multicolored	4.00	4.00
	Nos. 623-632 (10)		16.25	16.25

Arthropods A183

50f, Anthia duodecimguttata. 150f, Daphnis nerii. 250f, Acorypha glaucopsis. 350f, Androctonus crassicauda.

1999, Mar. 15   Litho.   *Perf. 13½x14*

633	A183	50f multicolored	.60	.60
634	A183	150f multicolored	1.40	1.40
635	A183	250f multicolored	2.75	2.75
636	A183	350f multicolored	4.25	4.25
	Nos. 633-636 (4)		9.00	9.00

Intl. Day for Monuments and Sites A184

1999, Apr. 18   Litho.   *Perf. 13x13½*

637	A184	150f shown	1.50	1.50
638	A184	250f Fort	2.75	2.75

UPU, 125th Anniv. — A185

1999   Litho.   *Perf. 13½x13*

639	A185	50f shown	1.00	1.00
640	A185	350f Emblem, "125"	2.75	2.75

Imperf

Size: 90x70mm

641	A185	5d Hemispheres	6.00	6.00

Environmental Protection — A186

Marine life: 50f, Lamprometra klunzingeri. 150f, Pelagia noctiluca. 250f, Hexabranchus sanguineus. 3d, Siphonochalina siphonella.

1999, Nov. 3   Litho.   *Perf. 13½x14*

642	A186	50f multi	.60	.60
643	A186	150f multi	2.00	2.00
644	A186	250f multi	3.25	3.25
645	A186	3d multi	3.75	3.75
	Nos. 642-645 (4)		9.60	9.60

Handicrafts A187

Designs: 50f, Lacemaking. 1d, Embroidery. 250f, Woman with wickerwork. 350f, Finished wickerwork.

1999, Nov. 8   *Perf. 14x13½*

646	A187	50f multi	.60	.60
647	A187	1d multi	1.40	1.40
648	A187	250f multi	3.50	3.50
649	A187	350f multi	5.50	5.50
	Nos. 646-649 (4)		11.00	11.00

14th Pro World Ten-pin Bowling Championships A188

Designs: 50f, Emblem. 250f, Bowler, pins, Abu Dhabi skyline.

1999, Nov. 16   Litho.   *Perf. 14x13½*

650-651	A188	Set of 2	3.25	3.25

Children's Art — A189

Art by: 50f, Nooran Khaleefa. 1d, Khawla Al Hawal. 150f, Khawla Salem. 250f, Fatimah Ibrahim.

1999, Dec. 15   *Perf. 13x13½*

652-655	A189	Set of 4	5.75	5.75

Millennium
A190

Falcon and "2000" in: 50f, Gray and silver. 250f, Blue and gold.

1999, Dec. 22   *Perf. 13½x13*
656-657 A190 Set of 2   2.75 2.75

Dubai Ports and Customs, Cent. A191

50f, Old building. 3d, Modern building.

2000, Jan. 26   *Perf. 13x13½*
658-659 A191 Set of 2   3.75 3.75

Intl. Desertification Conference, Dubai — A192

2000, Feb. 12   *Perf. 13½x13*
660 A192 250f multi   2.50 2.50

Environmental Protection — A193

Designs: 50f, Palm trees, Al Gheel. 250f, Aggah Beach.

2000, Feb. 29   **Litho.**   *Perf. 13x13½*
661 A193 50f multi   .50 .50
662 A193 250f multi   2.25 2.25

2000 Summer Olympics, Sydney A194

Emblem and: 50f, Swimmer. 2d, Runner. 350f, Shooter.

2000, Sept. 16   **Litho.**   *Perf. 13x13½*
663-665 A194 Set of 3   4.25 4.25

Dubai Intl. Holy Koran Award — A195

50f, Medal on ribbon of flags. 250f, Sheikh Zaid bin Sultan al Nahayan and UAE flag.

2000, Sept. 23   *Perf. 13½x13*
666-667 A195 Set of 2   4.25 4.25

World Meteorological Organization, 50th Anniv. — A196

Designs: 50f, Barometer and modern map. 250f, Gauge's pointer and old map .

2000
668-669 A196 Set of 2   4.25 4.25

Expansion of Dubai Intl. Airport A197

Denominations: 50f, 350f.

2000, Nov. 4   **Litho.**   *Perf. 13x13½*
670-671 A197 Set of 2   5.75 5.75

Development and Environment A198

Designs: 50f, Smile. 250f, Flower. 3d, Heart as leaf. 350f, Heart as globe.

2001, Mar. 20   **Litho.**   *Perf. 13¼x13*
672-675 A198 Set of 4   10.00 10.00

Dubai Millennium, Winner of 2000 Dubai World Cup A199

Designs: 3d, Horse's head. 350f, Horse at track.

2001, Mar. 24   *Perf. 13x13¼*
676-677 A199 Set of 2   9.50 9.50

Sultan Bin Ali Al Owais (1925-2000), Poet — A200

Designs: 50f, Calligraphy. 1d, Portrait.

2001, Apr. 30   *Perf. 13¼x13*
678-679 A200 Set of 2   3.75 3.75

Arab Bank for Investment and Foreign Trade, 25th Anniv. — A201

Designs: 50f, Emblem. 1d, Emblem, diff.

2001, July 7   **Litho.**   *Perf. 13¼x13*
680-681 A201 Set of 2   2.75 2.75

7th GCC Postage Stamp Exhibition, Dubai — A202

2001, July 10
682 A202 50f multi   1.75 1.75

Traditional Boats A203

Designs: 50f, Shahoof. 250f, Bagarah. 3d, Sam'aa. 350f, Jalboot.

2001, Aug. 25   *Perf. 14x13¼*
683-686 A203 Set of 4   10.00 10.00

Year of Dialogue Among Civilizations A204

Designs: 50f, Emblem. 250f, Branch with multicolored leaves.

2001, Oct. 9   *Perf. 13¼x13*
687-688 A204 Set of 2   3.75 3.75

Emirates Post A205

Falcons and inscription: 50f, Changing. 250f, Growing. 3d, Achieving.

2001, Sept. 15   *Perf. 13x13¼*
689-691 A205 Set of 3   7.50 7.50

Children's Art — A206

Designs: 1d, Mosque. 250f, Boatbuilding. 3d, Man pouring coffee, vert. 350f, Falconry.

Perf. 14x13¼, 13¼x14
2001, Nov. 12   **Litho.**
692-695 A206 Set of 4   10.50 10.50

Unification of Armed Forces, 25th Anniv. — A207

2001, Dec. 30   *Perf. 13¼x13*
696 A207 1d multi   2.75 2.75

Intl. Water Resources and Management Conference, Dubai — A208

2002, Feb. 2
697 A208 50f multi   2.00 2.00

UAE University, 25th Anniv. — A209

Background colors: 50f, Blue. 1d, Red.

2002, Mar. 25   *Perf. 13¼x14*
698-699 A209 Set of 2   2.75 2.75

Arabian Saluki A210

Various salukis: 50f, 150f, 250f, 3d.

2002, Apr. 29   **Litho.**   *Perf. 13½x13½*
700-703 A210 Set of 4   14.00 14.00

Emirates Post, 1st Anniv. — A211

"1" and: 50f, Ring of text. 3d, Emblem.

2002, May 29   *Perf. 13¼x13*
704 A211 50f blue   2.00 2.00
     Souvenir Sheet
     Perf. 14¼
705 A211 3d multi   11.50 11.50

No. 705 contains one 45x35mm stamp.

Rashid Bin Salim Al-Suwaidi Al-Khadhar (1905-80), Poet A212

Designs: 50f, Text. 250f, Portrait.

2002, July 17   **Litho.**   *Perf. 13½x13¼*
706-707 A212 Set of 2   6.50 6.50

Children's Creativity A213

Designs: 50f, Antelope and boat, by Amna al-Bloushi. 1d, Children, by Fahd al-Habsi. 2d, Earth holding flower, by Hana Mohammed. 250f, Fish, by Hatem al-Dhaheri. 3d, Child holding Earth, by Abdulla Ridha. 350f, Stick figures, by Yousef al-Sind. 5d, Emblem of Latifa Bint Mohammed Award for Childhood Creativity (29x39mm).

Perf. 13x13¼, 13¼x13 (5d)
2002, Oct. 9
708-714 A213   Set of 7   17.50 17.50

Sheikh Hamdan Bin Rashid Al-Maktoum Award for Medical Sciences A214

Designs: 50f, Award, emblem, sand dunes. 250f, Caduceus, map.

2002, Oct. 21   **Perf. 13x13¼**
715-716 A214   Set of 2   4.75 4.75

31st National Day — A215

Landmarks in the Emirates: Nos. 717, 724a, 50f, Ajman. Nos. 718, 724b, 50f, Sharjah. Nos. 719, 724c, 50f, Dubai. Nos. 720, 724d, 50f, Abu Dhabi. Nos. 721, 724e, 50f, Ras al Khaima. Nos. 722, 724f, Fujeira. Nos. 723, 724g, Umm al Qiwain.

2002, Dec. 2   Litho.   Perf. 13¼x14
717-723 A215   Set of 7   7.50 7.50
Souvenir Sheet
Litho. & Embossed
Imperf
724   Sheet of 7   7.50 7.50
a.-g. A215 50f Any single   1.00 1.00
No. 724 sold for 5d.

Thuraya Satellite Communications A216

Denominations: 25f, 250f.

2002   Litho.   Perf. 14
725-726 A216   Set of 2   2.75 2.75
Issued: 25f, 1/27; 250f, 1/6.

Falcon Type of 1990
2003-04   Litho.   Perf. 11½
Granite Paper
726A A85 125f multi   .90   .90
Size: 21x26mm
Perf. 11½x11¾
726B A85 225f multi   1.50 1.50
726C A85 275f multi   2.00 2.00
726D A85 325f multi   2.75 2.75
726E A85 375f multi   1.90 1.90

726F A85 4d multi   2.25 2.25
726G A85 6d multi   3.00 3.00
       Nos. 726A-726G (7)   14.30 14.30
Issued: 125f, 2/23; 225f, 11/24/04; 275f, 325f, 375f, 4/13; 4d, 6d, 9/16.

Items in Al Ain National Museum A217

Designs: 50f, Jar from Hili tombs. 275f, Pottery from Umm an-Nar tombs. 4d, Bronze axe. 6d, Soapstone vessel.

2003, Feb. 25   Perf. 14x13½
727-730 A217   Set of 4   11.50 11.50

National Bank of Dubai, 40th Anniv. A218

Panel color: 50f, Blue. 4d, Orange. 6d, Red.

2003, Apr. 15   Litho.   Perf. 14x13¼
731-733 A218   Set of 3   10.50 10.50

Miniature Sheet

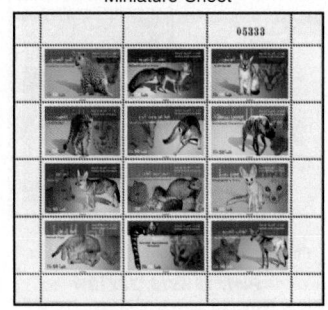

Wildlife — A218a

No. 733A: b, Arabian leopard. c, Blanford's fox. d, Caracal. e, Cheetah. f, Gordon's wild cat. g, Striped hyena. h, Jackal. i, White-tailed mongoose. j, Ruppell's fox. k, Sand cat. l, Small spotted genet. m, Arabian wolf.

2003, June 10   Litho.   Perf. 14½
733A A218a 50f Sheet of 12, #b-   8.00 8.00
               m

Coins A219

Designs: 50f, Dirham of Caliph Al Walid bin Abdul Malik. 125f, Arab Sasanian Dirham of Caliph Abdul Malik Bin Marwan. 275f, Dinar of Al Mustansir Billah Al Fatimi. 375f, Dinar of Caliph Abdul Malik bin Marwan.
5d, Dirham of Caliph Muhammed Al Ameen to mark election of Mousa Al Natiq Bilhaq.

2003, July 20   Litho.   Perf. 13¼x13¾
734-737 A219   Set of 4   7.50 7.50
Size: 106x73mm
Imperf
738 A219 5d multi   20.00 20.00

Sheikh Zaid bin Sultan al Nahayan, 37th Anniv. of Accession as Ruler of Abu Dhabi A220

Sheikh Zaid and: 50f, Camel and sand dune. 175f, Modern buildings.

2003, Aug. 6   Litho.   Perf. 13
739-740 A220   Set of 2   2.75 2.75

World Youth Soccer Championships, United Arab Emirates — A221

2003, Sept. 7   Perf. 13x13¼
741 A221 375f multi   3.75 3.75

World Bank Boards of Governors Annual Meetings, Dubai — A222

Emblem and: 50f, Emirates Tower. 175f, Falcon. 275f, Mosque domes, horiz. 375f, Dhow. 5d, English and Arabic text.

Perf. 13¼x13, 13x13¼
2003, Sept. 23   Litho.
742-745 A222   Set of 4   8.50 8.50
Imperf
Size: 118x74mm
746 A222 5d multi   6.75 6.75

Peace A223

Dove and: 50f, Zakharafs. 225f, Door and wind tower. 275f, Columns. 325f, Water taxi.

2003, Oct. 1   Perf. 13x13¼
747-750 A223   Set of 4   9.50 9.50

Traditional Housing A224

Designs: 50f, Palm frond house. 175f, Mud house. 275f, Stone house. 325f, Tent.

2003, Oct. 20   Perf. 13½x14
751-754 A224   Set of 4   10.00 10.00

Falcons — A225

Designs: 50f, Peregrine falcon. 125f, Hybrid gyr-peregrine falcon. 275f, Gyrfalcon. 375f, Saker falcon.

2003, Nov. 17   Perf. 13¼x14
755-758 A225   Set of 4   5.75 5.75

Poetry of Saeed Bin Ateej Al Hamli (1875-1919) A226

Poetry: 125f, Four short lines. 175f, Four long lines.

2003, Dec. 29   Perf. 13x13¼
759-760 A226   Set of 2   3.25 3.25

Mohammed Bin Saeed Bin Ghubash (1899-1969), Religious Scholar — A227

Designs: 50f, Portrait. 175f, Books.

2004, Apr. 5   Litho.   Perf. 13¼x14
761-762 A227   Set of 2   3.25 3.25

Fourth Family Meeting — A228

Color of hands: 375f, Orange. 4d, Purple.

2004, Apr. 19
763-764 A228   Set of 2   5.25 5.25

FIFA (Fédération Internationale de Football Association), Cent. — A229

2004, May 21   Litho.   Perf. 13x13¼
765 A229 375f multi   2.75 2.75

Handicrafts by Special Needs Persons — A230

Designs: 50f, Handcrafted vase. 125f, Painting. 275f, Framed branch. 5d, Pottery artwork.

2004, June 29   **Perf. 13¼x13**
766-769   A230   Set of 4   5.25 5.25

2004 Summer Olympics, Athens A231

Olympic rings and: 50f, Track athlete. 125f, Rifle shooter. 275f, Swimmer. 375f, 2004 Athens Olympics emblem, torch bearer.

2004, Aug. 13   **Litho.**   **Perf. 13x13¼**
770-773   A231   Set of 4   4.50 4.50

Endangered or Extinct Persian Gulf Marine Life — A232

Designs: 50f, Black finless porpoise. 175f, Serranidae. 275f, Whale shark. 375f, Dugongidae.

2004, Sept. 26   **Perf. 14**
774-777   A232   Set of 4   4.75 4.75
777a   Booklet pane, 2 each #774-777   9.50
    Complete booklet, #777a   9.50

Operation Emirates Solidarity for Mine Clearance in South Lebanon — A233

Flags and: 275f, Person clearing mines. 375f, Map, people clearing mines, horiz.

2004, Oct. 25   **Perf. 13x12¾, 12¾x13**
778-779   A233   Set of 2   3.50 3.50

Sheik Dr. Sultan bin Mohammed al-Qassimi, Ruler of Sharjah — A234

Color of denomination: 50f, Orange brown. 125f, Green. 275f, Red brown. 4d, Blue.

2004, Nov. 30   **Perf. 13½x14**
780-783   A234   Set of 4   4.75 4.75

Traditional Women's Clothing — A235

Designs: 50f, Drawers. 125f, Robe. 175f, Gown. 225f, Jalabia. 275f, Scarf. 375f, Yashmak.

2004, Dec. 29   **Litho.**   **Perf. 14**
784-789   A235   Set of 6   6.75 6.75
789a   Booklet pane, #784-789   6.75 6.75
    Complete booklet, #789a   6.75

Dubai Aluminum, 25th Anniv. A236

Designs: 50f, Smelting complex. 275f, Smelting complex, sheikhs (brown background). 375f, Like 275f, blue background.

2005, Jan. 8   **Perf. 13**
790-792   A236   Set of 3   4.00 4.00

10th Dubai Shopping Festival — A237

Designs: 50f, Emblem. 125f, Emblem, diff. 275f, Emblem and "10," green background. 375f, Emblem and "10," red background.

2005, Jan. 12   **Perf. 13¼x13**
793-796   A237   Set of 4   4.50 4.50

2nd Intl. Gathering of Scouting and Belonging, Sharjah — A238

Designs: 50f, Emblem. 375f, Scouts and truck.

2005, Apr. 1   **Litho.**   **Perf. 13¼x14**
797-798   A238   Set of 2   2.40 2.40

Shaikha Fatima Bint Mubarak, Women's Rights Activist — A239

2005, Apr. 10   **Perf. 14½**
799   A239   50f multi   .30 .30

Al Majedi Bin Dhaher, 17th Century Poet A240

Poetry and: 50f, Sand. 175f, Bricks.

2005, May 30   **Litho.**   **Perf. 14½**
800-801   A240   Set of 2   1.25 1.25

Reptiles A241

Designs: 50f, Agama. 125f, Desert monitor. 225f, Sand lizard. 275f, Dune sand gecko. 375f, Spiny-tailed lizard. 5d, Sand skink.

2005, Aug. 2   **Perf. 13¾**
802-807   A241   Set of 6   8.50 8.50
807a   Booklet pane, #802-807   8.50
    Complete booklet, #807a   8.50

Accession of Sheik Khalifa Bin Zayed Al Nahyan, 1st Anniv. — A242

Sheik Khalifa: 50f, With a child. 175f, With another sheik. 275f, With another sheik, diff. 375f, Kissing sheik.

2005, Nov. 3   **Litho.**   **Perf. 14x13¼**
808-811   A242   Set of 4   4.75 4.75
811a   Sheet of 4, #808-811   5.50 5.50

No. 811a sold for 10d.

2005 Census — A243

Emblem at: 50f, Bottom. 375f, Left, horiz.

Perf. 13¼x13, 13x13¼
2005, Nov. 10
812-813   A243   Set of 2   2.40 2.40

Desert Plants A244

Designs: 50f, Leptadenia pyrotechnica. 125f, Lycium shawii. 225f, Calotropis procera. 275f, Prosopis cineraria. 325f, Zizyphus spinachristi. 375f, Acacia tortilis.

2005, Nov. 27   **Litho.**   **Perf. 13½**
814-819   A244   Set of 6   7.50 7.50
819a   Booklet pane, #814-819   7.50
    Complete booklet, #819a   7.50

34th National Day — A245

Children's art: 50f, Flower in Arabic script, by Shaimaa Mohammed Al Halabi. 125f, Ring of children, by Muaz Jamal Ahmed Hassan, horiz. 275f, Hands, by Pithani Srinidhi. 375f,

---

Doves, flag and plants, by Lina Abu Baker Mukhtar, horiz.

2005, Dec. 2   **Perf. 14¼**
820-823   A245   Set of 4   4.50 4.50

Pearl Diving Tools A246

Designs: 50f, F'ttam (nose clip). 125f, Al Khabet (finger protectors). 175f, Al Dayeen (basket). 275f, Sea rock (diver's weight). 375f, Diver's outfit.

2005, Dec. 21   **Perf. 14**
824-828   A246   Set of 5   5.50 5.50

A souvenir sheet containing Nos. 824-828 with pearl halves affixed to each stamp sold for 100d.

Gulf Cooperation Council Day for Autistic Children — A247

2006, Apr. 4   **Litho.**   **Perf. 13**
829   A247   4d multi   2.25 2.25

Souvenir Sheet

Hamad Bin Khalifa Abu Shehab (1932-2002), Poet — A248

No. 830: a, 1d, Head. b, 2d, Hands, poetry in Arabic text.

2006, Apr. 26   **Perf. 14¼**
830   A248   Sheet of 2, #a-b   1.75 1.75

A249

Gulf Cooperation Council, 25th
Anniv. — A250

Illustration A250 reduced.

Litho. with Foil Application
2006, May 25   *Perf. 14*
831 A249 1d multi   .55   .55
Imperf
Size: 165x105mm
832 A250 5d multi   2.75 2.75
See Bahrain Nos. 628-629, Kuwait Nos.
1646-1647, Oman Nos. 477-478, Qatar Nos.
1007-1008, and Saudi Arabia No. 1378.

Dubai Police,
50th
Anniv. — A251

2006, June 1   *Perf. 13¼x13*
833 A251 1d multi   .55   .55

19th
Asian
Stamp
Exhibition,
Dubai
A252

Designs: 1d, shown. 4d, Four towers.

Litho. With Foil Application
2006, June 24   *Perf. 13¾*
834-835 A252 Set of 2   2.75 2.75

Dubai Intl.
Holy Koran
Award,
10th Anniv.
A253

2006, July 24 Litho.   *Perf. 14x13½*
836 A253 1d multi   .55   .55

Al Raha Beach Developments — A254

Designs: 1d, Khor Al Raha. 2d, Al Lissaily.
350f, Al Wateed (40x40mm). 4d, Al Bandar
(40x40mm).

2006, Sept. 18 Litho.   *Perf. 13*
837-840 A254 Set of 4   5.75 5.75

UPU Strategy Conference,
Dubai — A255

Designs: 1d, Green arrows. 4d, Blue and
green arrows.

Litho. & Embossed
2006, Sept. 27   *Perf. 14x13½*
841-842 A255 Set of 2   2.75 2.75

12th Gulf
Cooperation
Council Postage
Stamp Exhibition
A256

2006, Nov. 13 Litho.   *Perf. 13¼x13*
843 A256 1d multi   .55   .55

35th National
Day — A257

2006, Dec. 1
844 A257 1d multi   .55   .55
A souvenir sheet containing one stamp sold
for 10d.

Sheikh Mohammed bin Rashid al
Maktoum, Prime Minister — A258

Sheikh Mohammed: 1d, Wearing kaffiyeh.
4d, Wearing polo helmet (44x53mm).

**Litho. With 3-Dimensional Plastic
Affixed**
2006, Dec. 2   *Serpentine Die Cut 9*
Self-Adhesive
845-846 A258 Set of 2   2.75 2.75

Gazelles
A259

Designs: 1d, Tahr. 2d, Sand gazelle. 3d,
Mountain gazelle. 350f, Arabian oryx.

2006, Nov. 29 Litho.   *Perf. 14*
847-850 A259 Set of 4   5.25 5.25
850a   Souvenir sheet, #847-
               850   5.25 5.25

Intl.
Volunteers
Day
A260

Man giving items to: 2d, Two children. 4d,
Three children.

2006, Dec. 5   *Perf. 13x13¼*
851-852 A260 Set of 2   3.25 3.25

Women's
Jewelry
A261

Designs: 1d, Mariya um alnairat. 150f,
Mortasha. 2d, Shaghab bu shouk. 3d, Shahid
ring. 350f, Bushuq. 4d, Tassah.

2006, Dec. 31   *Perf. 13x13¼*
853-858 A261 Set of 6   8.25 8.25
858a   Booklet pane, #853-858 8.25
               Complete booklet, #858a 8.25

Falcon — A262

2007, Jan. 31   *Perf. 13¼x13*
Background Color
859 A262 1d buff   .55   .55
860 A262 150f gray   .85   .85
861 A262 2d lilac   1.10 1.10
862 A262 3d yellow   1.60 1.60
863 A262 350f yel green   1.90 1.90
864 A262 4d pink   2.25 2.25
865 A262 5d blue vio   2.75 2.75
   Nos. 859-865 (7)   11.00 11.00
Booklet Stamps
Self-Adhesive
Serpentine Die Cut 12½
Background Color
865A A262 1d buff   .55   .55
865B A262 150f gray   .85   .85
865C A262 2d lilac   1.10 1.10
865D A262 3d yellow   1.60 1.60
865E A262 350f yel green   1.90 1.90
865F A262 4d pink   2.25 2.25
865G A262 5d blue vio   2.75 2.75
   h.   Booklet pane, #865A-865G 11.00   —
         Complete booklet, #865Gh   11.00
   Nos. 865A-865G (7)   11.00 11.00

Dubai Tennis
Championships
A263

Background colors: 1d, Orange. 3d, Red
violet.

2007, Feb. 19   *Perf. 14*
866-867 A263 Set of 2   2.25 2.25

18th Arabian Gulf Soccer Cup
Championships, Abu Dhabi — A264

Arabian Gulf Cup with frame in: 1d, Red. 3d,
Green.

2007, May 9 Litho.   *Perf. 14x13¾*
868-869 A264 Set of 2   2.25 2.25
869a   Souvenir sheet, #868-869 5.50 5.50
       No. 869a sold for 10d.

Etisalat (Telecommunications
Company), 30th Anniv. — A265

Denomination color: 1d, Blue. 3d, Orange
red. 350f, Purple. 4d, Red.

2007, May 17   *Perf. 13x13¼*
870-873 A265 Set of 4   6.25 6.25
   Each stamp has a die cut opening.

Souvenir Sheet

World Blood Donor Day — A266

No. 874 — World Blood Donor Day emblem
and: a, 1d, Heart. b, 3d, Blood drop.

2007, June 14   *Perf. 13*
874 A266 Sheet of 2, #a-b 2.25 2.25

Sheikh Ahmed Mohamed Hasher Al
Maktoum, UAE's First Olympic Gold
Medalist — A267

2007, July 17   *Perf. 14x13½*
875 A267 3d multi   1.75 1.75

A268

Emirates Bank, 30th Anniv. A269

Perf. 14x13¾ (A268), 14 (A269)

2007, Aug. 28

876	A268	1d blue & multi	.55	.55
877	A268	150f blue & multi	.85	.85
878	A268	3d brn & multi	1.75	1.75
879	A269	350f brn & multi	1.90	1.90
a.		Souvenir sheet, #876-879	8.25	8.25
		Nos. 876-879 (4)	5.05	5.05

No. 879a sold for 15d.

Emirates Banks Association, 25th Anniv. — A270

2007, Oct. 4   **Perf. 13¾**

880	A270	1d red & bis brn	.55	.55

Abu Dhabi Islamic Bank, 10th Anniv. — A271

Differing backgrounds with denominations of: 1d, 150f, 2d, 3d.

2007, Nov. 8   **Litho.**   **Perf. 14¼**

881-884	A271	Set of 4	4.25	4.25
884a		Souvenir sheet, #881-884	4.25	4.25

Abu Dhabi Police, 50th Anniv. — A272

Litho. With Foil Application

2007, Nov. 14   **Perf. 13¼x14**

885	A272	1d multi	.55	.55

Children's Art — A273

Designs: Nos. 886, 892, Woman and two men in prayer. Nos. 887, 893, Woman presenting gift to another woman, vert. Nos. 888, 894, Children facing mosque. Nos. 889, 895, Hands holding child giving item to woman, vert. Nos. 890, 896, Child helping man across street. Nos. 891, 897, Child helping handicapped person, vert.

2007, Nov. 29   **Litho.**   **Perf. 14**

886	A273	1d multi	.55	.55
887	A273	150f multi	.85	.85
888	A273	2d multi	1.10	1.10
889	A273	3d multi	1.75	1.75

890	A273	350f multi	1.90	1.90
891	A273	4d multi	2.25	2.25
		Nos. 886-891 (6)	8.40	8.40

Booklet Stamps
Self-Adhesive
Die Cut Perf. 11¼x12, 12x11¼

892	A273	1d multi	.55	.55
893	A273	150f multi	.85	.85
894	A273	2d multi	1.10	1.10
895	A273	3d multi	1.75	1.75
896	A273	350f multi	1.90	1.90
897	A273	4d multi	2.25	2.25
a.		Complete booklet, #892-897	8.50	
		Nos. 892-897 (6)	8.40	8.40

Complete booklet is stapled in center with one stamp per page and with the center leaf of the booklet having stamps on both sides.

Souvenir Sheet

Sheikh Mohammed Al Khazraji (1919-2006), Chief Justice — A274

No. 898: a, 1d, Facing right. b, 3d, Facing forward.

2007, Dec. 9   **Perf. 13½x13¾**

898	A274	Sheet of 2, #a-b	2.25	2.25

Al Abbas Group, 40th Anniv. A275

Denominations: 1d, 150f, 2d, 3d.

2007, Dec. 16   **Perf. 14¼**

899-902	A275	Set of 4	4.25	4.25

Al Rostamani Group, 50th Anniv. A276

Background colors: 1d, Gray. 150f, Prussian blue.

2007, Dec. 23   **Perf. 13x13¼**

903-904	A276	Set of 2	1.40	1.40

Union Properties, 20th Anniv. A277

Designs: 1d, Emblem. 150f, F1 Theme Park, Dubai, horiz. 2d, Uptown. 3d, Green community, horiz.

Perf. 13¼x13½, 13½x13¼

2007, Dec. 27

905-908	A277	Set of 4	4.25	4.25
908a		Souvenir sheet, #905-908	8.50	8.50

No. 908a sold for 15d.

Federal National Council, 36th Anniv. A278

2008, Dec. 12   **Perf. 13¼**

909	A278	1d multi	.55	.55

National Bank of Abu Dhabi, 40th Anniv. A279

"40" and: 1d, Yellow panel at top. 150f, Yellow panel at top. 225d, White panel at top. 4d, White panel at top.

2008, Feb. 13   **Perf. 13**

910-913	A279	Set of 4	4.75	4.75
913a		Souvenir sheet, #910-913	8.25	8.25

No. 913a sold for 15d.

UPPER SENEGAL AND NIGER

ˈə-pər ˌse-nə-gäl and ˈnī-jər

LOCATION — In Northwest Africa, north of French Guinea and Ivory Coast
GOVT. — A former French Colony
AREA — 617,600 sq. mi.
POP. — 2,474,142
CAPITAL — Bamako

In 1921 the name of this colony was changed to French Sudan and postage stamps so inscribed were placed in use.

100 Centimes = 1 Franc

Gen. Louis Faidherbe A1

Oil Palms — A2

Dr. N. Eugène Ballay — A3

Perf. 14x13½

1906-07   **Unwmk.**   **Typo.**
Name of Colony in Red or Blue

1	A1	1c slate	1.60	1.60
2	A1	2c brown	1.75	1.60
3	A1	4c brn, *gray bl*	2.25	1.60
4	A1	5c green	6.25	2.75
5	A1	10c car (B)	6.25	2.75
6	A1	15c vio ('07)	5.00	5.00
7	A2	20c bluish gray	6.25	5.00
8	A2	25c bl, *pnksh*	20.00	5.00

9	A2	30c vio brn, *pnksh*	8.25	5.75
10	A2	35c blk, *yellow*	6.50	5.00
11	A2	40c car, *az* (B)	10.50	8.25
12	A2	45c brn, *grnsh*	12.50	10.50
13	A2	50c dp vio	12.50	10.50
14	A2	75c bl, *org*	12.50	12.50
15	A3	1fr blk, *azure*	29.00	29.00
16	A3	2fr bl, *pink*	52.50	52.50
17	A3	5fr car, *straw* (B)	110.00	110.00
		Nos. 1-17 (17)	303.60	269.30

Camel with Rider — A4

1914-17   **Perf. 13½x14**

18	A4	1c brn vio & vio	.35	.35
19	A4	2c gray & brn vio	.35	.35
20	A4	4c black & blue	.35	.35
21	A4	5c yel grn & bl grn	.90	.60
22	A4	10c red org & rose	2.50	2.00
23	A4	15c choc & org ('17)	2.00	1.25
24	A4	20c brn vio & blk	2.25	1.60
25	A4	25c ultra & bl	1.60	1.50
26	A4	30c ol brn & brn	1.60	1.60
27	A4	35c car rose & vio	3.00	2.00
28	A4	40c gray & car rose	2.50	1.25
29	A4	45c bl & ol brn	2.25	2.00
30	A4	50c black & green	2.50	2.50
31	A4	75c org & ol brn	2.50	2.50
32	A4	1fr brown & brn vio	2.50	2.50
33	A4	2fr green & blue	3.00	3.00
34	A4	5fr violet & black	13.00	13.00
		Nos. 18-34 (17)	43.15	38.35

See Burkina Faso for types of this issue that escaped overprinting.
For surcharge see No. B1.

SEMI-POSTAL STAMP

Regular Issue of 1914 Surcharged in Red

1915   **Unwmk.**   **Perf. 13½x14**

B1	A4	10c + 5c red orange & rose	2.00	2.00

POSTAGE DUE STAMPS

Natives — D1   D2

1906   **Unwmk.**   **Typo.**   **Perf. 14x13½**

J1	D1	5c green, *greenish*	4.00	3.75
J2	D1	10c red brown	8.25	8.00
J3	D1	15c dark blue	11.50	11.50
J4	D1	20c black, *yellow*	15.00	7.50
J5	D1	50c violet	27.50	24.00
J6	D1	60c black, *buff*	18.00	19.00
J7	D1	1fr black, *pinkish*	37.50	37.50
		Nos. J1-J7 (7)	121.75	111.25

1914

J8	D2	5c green	1.25	1.25
J9	D2	10c rose	1.25	1.25
J10	D2	15c gray	1.25	1.25
J11	D2	20c brown	1.40	1.40
J12	D2	30c blue	2.25	2.25
J13	D2	50c black	1.75	1.75
J14	D2	60c orange	6.50	6.50
J15	D2	1fr violet	6.50	6.50
		Nos. J8-J15 (8)	22.15	22.15

Stamps of Upper Senegal and Niger were superceded in 1921 by those of French Sudan.

UPPER SILESIA

ˈə-pər si̇lˈlē-zhē-ˌə

LOCATION — Formerly in eastern Germany and prior to World War I a part of Germany.

A plebiscite held under the terms of the Treaty of Versailles failed to determine the status of the country, the voting resulting about equally in favor of Germany and Poland. Accordingly, the League of Nations divided the territory between Germany and Poland.

100 Pfennig = 1 Mark
100 Fennigi = 1 Marka

Plebiscite Issues

A1

Perf. 14x13½

1920, Feb. 20   Typo.   Unwmk.

1	A1	2½pf slate	.40	.55
2	A1	3pf brown	.40	.85
3	A1	5pf green	.30	.35
4	A1	10pf dull red	.40	.90
5	A1	15pf violet	.20	.40
6	A1	20pf blue	.20	.40
a.		Imperf., pair	275.00	
b.		Half used as 10pf on cover		85.00
7	A1	50pf violet brn	3.50	6.50
8	A1	1m claret	5.00	9.25
9	A1	5m orange	4.25	9.25
		Nos. 1-9 (9)	14.65	28.45
		Set, never hinged	45.00	

Black Surcharge

5	5	5	5
Pf.	Pf.	Pf.	Pf.
I	II	III	IV

10	A1	5pf on 15pf vio (I)	13.00	42.50
		Never hinged	35.00	
a.		Type II	13.00	42.50
b.		Type III	13.00	42.50
c.		Type IV	13.00	42.50
11	A1	5pf on 20pf blue (I)	.65	2.00
		Never hinged	1.60	
a.		Type II	.80	2.25
b.		Type III	1.00	2.50
c.		Type IV	1.25	3.25

Red Surcharge

10	10	10	10
Pf.	Pf.	Pf.	Pf.
I	II	III	IV

12	A1	10pf on 20pf bl (I)	.65	1.60
		Never hinged	1.60	
a.		Type II	.65	1.60
b.		Type III	.65	1.60
c.		Type IV	.65	1.60
d.		Imperf.	50.00	

Black Surcharge

50	50	50	50	50
Pf.	Pf.	Pf.	Pf.	Pf.
I	II	III	IV	V

13	A1	50pf on 5m org (I)	14.00	42.50
		Never hinged	80.00	
a.		Type II	15.00	45.00
b.		Type III	16.00	80.00
c.		Type IV	16.00	80.00
d.		Type V	25.00	100.00

Nos. 10-13 are found with many varieties including surcharges inverted, double and double inverted.

Dove with Olive Branch Flying over Silesian Terrain — A2

A3

1920, Mar. 26   Typo.   Perf. 13½x14

15	A2	2½pf gray	.25	.40
16	A2	3pf red brown	.25	.40
17	A2	5pf green	.25	.40
18	A2	10pf dull red	.25	.40
19	A2	15pf violet	.25	.40
20	A2	20pf blue	.65	1.60
21	A2	25pf dark brown	.25	.40
22	A2	30pf orange	.25	.40
23	A2	40pf olive green	.25	1.00

Perf. 14x13½

24	A3	50pf gray	.25	.40
25	A3	60pf blue	.25	1.60
26	A3	75pf deep green	.85	2.00
27	A3	80pf red brown	.65	1.00
28	A3	1m claret	.50	.40
29	A3	2m dark brown	.50	.40
30	A3	3m violet	.70	.40
31	A3	5m orange	2.75	4.00
		Nos. 15-31 (17)	9.10	15.60
		Set, never hinged	40.00	

Nos. 18-28 Overprinted in Black or Red

1921, Mar. 20

32	A2	10pf dull red	3.25	10.00
33	A2	15pf violet	3.25	10.00
34	A2	20pf blue	4.50	14.00
35	A2	25pf dk brn (R)	12.00	32.50
36	A2	30pf orange	9.00	20.00
37	A2	40pf olive grn (R)	11.00	20.00

Overprinted

38	A3	50pf gray (R)	11.00	27.50
39	A3	60pf blue	12.00	22.50
40	A3	75pf deep green	12.00	27.50
41	A3	80pf red brown	19.00	35.00
42	A3	1m claret	22.50	65.00
		Nos. 32-42 (11)	119.50	284.00
		Set, never hinged	625.00	

Inverted or double overprints exist on Nos. 32-33, 35-40. Counterfeit overprints exist.

Type of 1920 and Surcharged

1922, Mar.

45	A3	4m on 60pf ol grn	.80	1.60
46	A3	10m on 75pf red	.80	2.50
47	A3	20m on 80pf orange	6.25	13.00
		Nos. 45-47 (3)	7.85	17.10
		Set, never hinged	25.00	

Stamps of the above design were a private issue not recognized by the Inter-Allied Commission of Government. Value, set of 7, $65.00 unused, $225.00 never hinged, $225 used.

OFFICIAL STAMPS

German Stamps of 1905-20 Handstamped in Blue

1920, Feb.   Wmk. 125   Perf. 14, 14½
On Stamps of 1906-19

O1	A22	2pf gray	1.10	1.25
O3	A22	2½pf gray	.55	.65
O4	A16	3pf brown	.55	.65
O5	A16	5pf green	.55	.65
O6	A22	7½pf orange	.55	.65
O7	A16	10pf car rose	.55	.65
O8	A16	15pf dk violet	.55	.65
O9	A16	20pf blue violet	.55	.65
O10	A16	25pf org & blk, yel	5.25	6.50
O11	A16	30pf org & blk, buff	.55	.65
O12	A22	35pf red brown	.55	.65
O13	A16	40pf lake & blk	.55	.65
O14	A16	50pf vio & blk, buff	.55	.65
O15	A16	60pf magenta	.55	.65
O16	A16	75pf green & blk	.55	.65
O17	A16	80pf lake & blk, rose	6.50	8.00
O18	A17	1m car rose	1.10	1.25
O19	A21	2m gray blue	5.25	6.50

On National Assembly Stamps of 1919-20

O25	A23	10pf car rose	.90	1.10
O26	A24	15pf choc & bl	1.60	2.00
O27	A25	25pf green & red	3.25	4.00
O28	A25	30pf red vio & red	2.50	3.00

On Semi-Postal Stamps of 1919

O30	A16	10pf + 5pf carmine	6.50	8.00
O31	A22	15pf + 5pf dk vio	6.50	8.00
		Nos. O1-O31 (24)	47.60	58.05

Red Handstamp

O5a	A16	5pf	10.00	14.00
O8a	A22	15pf	6.50	10.00
O9a	A16	20pf	6.50	10.00
O13a	A16	40pf	20.00	30.00
O16a	A16	75pf	20.00	30.00
O26a	A24	15pf	1.10	1.25
		Nos. O5a-O26a (6)	64.10	95.25

Values of Nos. O1-O31 are for reprints made with a second type of handstamp differing in minor details from the original (example: period after "S" is round instead of the earlier triangular form). Originals are scarce. Counterfeits exist.

Germany No. 65C with this handstamp is considered bogus by experts.

Local Official Stamps of Germany, 1920, Overprinted

1920, Apr.   Perf. 14

O32	LO2	5pf green	.30	.45
O33	LO3	10pf carmine	.30	.45
O34	LO4	15pf violet brn	.30	.45
O35	LO5	20pf deep ultra	.30	.45
O36	LO6	30pf orange, buff	.30	.45
O37	LO7	50pf violet, buff	.50	1.40
O38	LO8	1m red, buff	6.00	10.00
		Nos. O32-O38 (7)	8.00	13.65

Same Overprint on Official Stamps of Germany, 1920-21

1920-21

O39	O1	5pf green	1.00	2.40
O40	O2	10pf carmine	.20	.20
O41	O3	15pf violet brn	.20	.20
O42	O4	20pf deep ultra	.20	.20
O43	O5	30pf orange, buff	.20	.20
O44	O6	40pf carmine rose	.20	.20
O45	O7	50pf violet, buff	.20	.20
O46	O8	60pf red brown	.20	.20
O47	O9	1m red, buff	.20	.20
O48	O10	1.25m dk blue, yel	.20	.20
O49	O11	2m dark blue	7.00	8.00
O50	O12	5m brown, yel	.20	.20

1922, Feb.   Wmk. 126

O51	O11	2m dark blue	.20	.20
		Nos. O39-O51 (13)	10.20	12.60

This overprint is found both horizontal, reading upright or inverted, and vertical, reading up or down. These variations generally command no premium over the values above.

The overprint also exists on most values double and double, one inverted, in the above formats, as well as at a 45 degree angle, upreading and downreading, either upright or inverted. These varieties generally sell for 25-100 percent over the value of normal examples.

URUGUAY

'yur-ə-ˌgwä

LOCATION — South America, between Brazil and Argentina and bordering on the Atlantic Ocean
GOVT. — Republic
AREA — 68,037 sq. mi.
POP. — 3,137,668 (1996)
CAPITAL — Montevideo

120 Centavos = 1 Real
8 Reales = 1 Peso
100 Centesimos = 1 Peso (1859)
1000 Milesimos = 1 Peso (1898)

Watermarks

Wmk. 187 — R O in Diamond

Wmk. 188 — REPUBLICA O. DEL URUGUAY

Wmk. 189 — Caduceus

Wmk. 227 — Greek Border and REPUBLICA O. DEL URUGUAY in Alternate Curved Lines

Wmk. 327 — Coat of Arms

Wmk. 332 — Large Sun and R O U

Catalogue values for unused stamps in this country are for Never Hinged items, beginning with Scott 534 in the regular postage section, Scott B5 in the semi-postal section, Scott C113 in the airpost section, Scott CB1 in the airpost semi-postal section, Scott E9 in the special delivery section, and Scott Q64 in the parcel post section.

Carrier Issues

Issued by Atanasio Lapido, Administrator-General of Posts

"El Sol de Mayo"
A1   A1a

Unwmk.

1856, Oct. 1   **Litho.**   *Imperf.*
1	A1	60c blue	350.	—
2	A1	80c green	325.	—
3	A1	1r vermilion	300.	—

1857, Oct. 1
3B	A1a	60c blue	2,750.	—

Nos. 1-3d were spaced very closely on the stone. Very fine examples will have clear margins on three sides and touching or slightly cut into the frames on the fourth (consult the grading illustrations in the catalogue introduction). All genuinely used examples are pen canceled. Certification by a recognized authority is recommended.

Stamps with tiny faults, such as small thin spots, sell for about 75% of the values of sound examples.

See Nos. 410-413, 771A.

A2

1858, Mar.
4	A2	120c blue	250.	—
c.		Tête bêche pair		7,500.
5	A2	180c green	100.00	200.00
c.		Thick paper	450.00	
d.		Tête bêche pair		—
6	A2	240c dull ver	150.00	1,500.
c.		180c in stone of 240c		—
d.		Thick paper (dull ver)		—
e.		240c setenant with a vacant place		5,000.
		Nos. 4-6 (3)	500.00	1,700.

Government Issues

A3   A4

1859, June 26
Thin Numerals
7	A3	60c lilac	25.00	20.00
a.		60c gray lilac	25.00	20.00
8	A3	80c yellow	190.00	35.00
a.		80c orange	275.00	50.00
9	A3	100c brown lake	55.00	45.00
a.		100c brown rose	55.00	45.00
10	A3	120c blue	35.00	15.00
a.		120c slate blue	50.00	17.50
11	A3	180c green	15.00	17.50
12	A3	240c vermilion	50.00	50.00
		Nos. 7-12 (6)	370.00	182.50

1860
Thick Numerals
13	A4	60c dull lilac	15.00	8.00
a.		60c gray lilac	17.50	10.00
b.		60c brown lilac	17.50	12.00
c.		60c red lilac	17.50	12.00
d.		As "a," fine impression (1st printing)	70.00	40.00
14	A4	80c yellow	20.00	16.00
a.		80c orange	45.00	18.00
15	A4	100c rose	45.00	35.00
a.		100c carmine	45.00	35.00
16	A4	120c blue	21.00	16.00
17	A4	180c yellow grn	175.00	225.00
a.		180c deep green	225.00	250.00
		Nos. 13-17 (5)	276.00	300.00

No. 13 was first printed (1860) in sheets of 192 (16x12) containing 24 types. The impressions are very clear; paper is whitish and of better quality than that of the later printings. In the 1861-62 printings, the layout contains 12 types and the subjects are spaced farther apart.

Coat of Arms — A5

1864, Apr. 13
18	A5	6c rose	12.00	7.00
a.		6c carmine	32.50	25.00
b.		6c red	32.50	25.00
c.		6c brick red	32.50	25.00
20	A5	6c salmon	300.00	385.00
21	A5	8c green	17.00	17.00
a.		Tête bêche pair	775.00	
22	A5	10c yellow	25.00	20.00
a.		10c ocher	25.00	20.00
23	A5	12c blue	15.00	15.00
a.		12c dark blue	25.00	15.00
b.		12c slate blue	30.00	50.00

No. 20, which is on thicker paper, was never placed in use.

Stamps of 1864 Surcharged in Black

1866, Jan. 1
24	A5	5c on 12c blue	20.00	42.50
a.		5c on 12c slate blue	25.00	45.00
b.		Inverted surcharge	150.00	
c.		Double surcharge	150.00	
e.		Pair, one without surcharge		
d.		Triple surcharge	55.00	
25	A5	10c on 8c brt grn	20.00	42.50
a.		10c on 8c dl grn	20.00	42.50
b.		Tête bêche pair	300.00	
c.		Double surcharge	150.00	
26	A5	15c on 10c ocher	20.00	67.50
		15c on 10c yellow	20.00	67.50
b.		Inverted surcharge	150.00	
c.		Double surcharge	150.00	
27	A5	20c on 6c rose	27.00	67.50
		20c on 6c rose red	30.00	50.00
b.		Inverted surcharge	150.00	
c.		Double surcharge	150.00	
d.		Pair, one without surcharge		
28	A5	20c on 6c brick red	350.00	
a.		Double surcharge	400.00	
		Nos. 24-27 (4)	87.00	220.00

Many counterfeits exist.
No. 28 was not issued.

Coat of Arms and Numeral of Value — A7

A8   A8a

A8b   A8c

ONE CENTESIMO:
Type I — The wavy lines behind "CENTESIMO" are clear and distinct. Stamps 4mm apart.
Type II — The wavy lines are rough and blurred. Stamps 3mm apart.

1866, Jan. 10   *Imperf.*
29	A7	1c black (type II)	4.00	15.00
a.		1c black (type I)	4.00	15.00
30	A8	5c blue	4.00	2.00
a.		5c dull blue	4.00	2.00
b.		5c ultramarine	25.00	10.00
c.		Numeral with white flag	25.00	12.00
d.		"ENTECIMOS"	25.00	12.00
e.		"CENTECIMO"	25.00	12.00
f.		"CENTECIMOS" with small "S"	25.00	12.00
g.		Pelure paper	100.00	100.00
h.		Thick paper		
31	A8a	10c yellow green	15.00	5.00
a.		10c blue green	17.00	6.00
b.		"I" of "CENTECIMOS" omitted	27.50	14.00
c.		"CENIECIMOS"	27.50	14.00
d.		"CENTRCIMOS"	27.50	14.00
32	A8b	15c orange yel	25.00	9.00
a.		15c yellow	25.00	9.00
33	A8c	20c rose	30.00	10.00
a.		20c lilac rose	30.00	10.00
b.		Thick paper	35.00	15.00
		Nos. 29-33 (5)	78.00	41.00

See Nos. 34-38. For overprint see No. O11.
Engraved plates were prepared for Nos. 30 to 33 but were not put in use. The stamps were printed from lithographic transfers from the plate. In 1915 a few reprints of the 15c were made from the engraved plate by a California philatelic society, each sheet being numbered and signed by officers of the society; then the plate was defaced.

1866-67   *Perf. 8½ to 13½*
34	A7	1c black	5.00	20.00
35	A8	5c blue	5.00	1.00
a.		5c dark blue	5.00	1.00
b.		Numeral with white flag	15.00	8.00
c.		"ENTECIMOS"	15.00	8.00
d.		"CENTECIMO"	15.00	8.00
e.		"CENTECIMOS" with small "S"	15.00	8.00
f.		Pelure paper	90.00	20.00
36	A8a	10c green	12.00	4.00
a.		10c yellow green	14.00	4.00
b.		"CENIECIMOS"	20.00	10.00
c.		"I" of "CENTECIMOS" omitted	20.00	10.00
d.		"CENTRCIMOS"	20.00	10.00
e.		Pelure paper	90.00	20.00
37	A8b	15c orange yel	21.00	6.00
a.		15c yellow	21.00	6.00
b.		Thin paper	25.00	10.00
38	A8c	20c rose	25.00	10.00
a.		20c brown rose	25.00	10.00
b.		Thin paper	30.00	15.00
c.		Thick paper	30.00	15.00
		Nos. 34-38 (5)	68.00	41.00

A9   A10

A11   A12

1877-79   **Engr.**   *Rouletted 8*
39	A9	1c red brown	.55	.40
40	A10	5c green	.65	.40
a.		Thick paper	4.00	2.00
41	A11	10c vermilion	1.00	.65
42	A11	20c bister	1.10	.65
43	A11	50c black	7.00	3.00
43A	A12	1p blue ('79)	35.00	20.00
		Nos. 39-43A (6)	45.30	25.10

The first printing of the 1p had the coat of arms smaller with quarterings reversed. These "error" stamps were not issued, and all were ordered burned. A copy is known to have been in a celebrated Uruguayan collection and a few others exist.
See No. 44. For overprints and surcharges see Nos. 52-53, O1-O8, O10, O19.

1880, Nov. 10   **Litho.**   *Rouletted 6*
44	A9	1c brown	.40	.40
a.		Imperf., pair	10.00	
b.		Rouletted 12½	2.50	

Joaquin Suárez — A13

1881, Aug. 25 — Perf. 12½
45 A13 7c blue   1.75 1.75
a.   Imperf., pair   9.00 9.00

For overprint see No. O9.

Devices from Coat of Arms
A14   A14a

1882, May 15
46 A14 1c green   1.25 1.25
a.   1c yellow green   4.00 2.00
b.   Imperf., pair   13.00
47 A14a 2c rose   1.00   .75
a.   Imperf., pair   15.00

These stamps bear numbers from 1 to 100 according to their position on the sheet. Counterfeits of Nos. 46 and 47 are plentiful. See Nos. 1132-1133. For overprints see Nos. 54, O12-O13, O20.

Coat of Arms
A15   A16

Gen. Máximo   General José
Santos — A17   Artigas — A18

Perf. 12, 12x12½, 12x13, 13x12
1883, Mar. 1
48 A15 1c green   1.25 1.00
49 A16 2c red   1.50 1.25
50 A17 5c blue   2.50 1.75
51 A18 10c brown   3.00 2.10
     Nos. 48-51 (4)   8.25 6.10

Imperf., Pairs
48a A15   1c   7.00
49a A16   2c   7.00
50a A17   5c   6.50
51a A18   10c   11.00

For overprints see Nos. O14-O18.

No. 40 Overprinted in Black

1883, Sept. 24 — Rouletted 8
52 A10 5c green   1.00   .75
a.   Double overprint   15.00 15.00
b.   Overprint reading down   6.00 6.00
c.   "Provisorio" omitted   7.00 7.00
d.   "1883" omitted   4.50 4.50

No. 52 with overprint in red is a color essay.

No. 41 Surcharged in Black

1884, Jan. 15
53 A11 1c on 10c ver   .50   .50
a.   Small figure "1"   4.25 4.25
b.   Inverted surcharge   4.25 4.25
c.   Double surcharge   8.00 5.00

No. 47 Overprinted in Black

Perf. 12½
54 A14a 2c rose   .75   .75
a.   Double overprint   14.00
b.   Imperf., pair   40.00

A22   A23

Thick Paper
1884, Jan. 25 — Litho. Unwmk.
55 A22 5c ultra   2.00 1.00
a.   Imperf., pair   7.50 4.00

Thin Paper
Perf. 12½, 13 and Compound
56 A23 5c blue   1.50   .70
a.   Imperf., pair   14.00

For overprints see Nos. O21-O22.

A24   A24a

A24b   Artigas — A25

Santos — A26   A27

A28

1884-88 — Engr. Rouletted 8
57 A24   1c gray   .80   .50
58 A24   1c olive   .75   .40
59 A24   1c green   .65   .40
60 A24a 2c vermilion   .40   .25
60A A24a 2c rose ('88)   .40   .25
61 A24b 5c deep blue   .80   .30
61A A24b 5c blue, blue   2.00   .85
62 A24b 5c violet ('86)   .50   .20
63 A24b 5c lt bl ('88)   .50   .20
64 A25   7c dk brown   2.00   .85
65 A25   7c org ('88)   2.00   .75
66 A26   10c olive brn   .80   .35
67 A27   20c red violet   2.00 1.00
68 A27   20c bis brn ('88)   2.00 1.00
69 A28   25c gray violet   4.00 1.50
70 A28   25c ver ('88)   3.00 1.00
     Nos. 57-70 (16)   22.60 9.80

Water dissolves the blue in the paper of No. 61A. For overprints see Nos. 73, 98-99, O23-O34, O36-O39, O61.

A29   A30

1887, Oct. 17 — Litho. Rouletted 9
71 A29 10c lilac   2.50 1.25
a.   10c gray lilac   3.00 1.25

For overprint see No. O40.

1888, Jan. 1 — Engr. Rouletted 8
72 A30 10c violet   .60   .25

For overprint see No. O35.

No. 62 Overprinted in Black

1889, Oct. 14
73 A24b 5c violet   .40   .40
a.   Inverted overprint   8.00 6.00
b.   Inverted "A" for "V" in "Provisorio" 4.00 4.00

No. 73 with overprint in red is a color essay.

Coat of   Numeral of
Arms — A32   Value — A33

A34   A35

A36   A37

Justice   Mercury
A38   A39

A40

Perf. 12½ to 15½ and Compound
1889-1901   Engr.
74 A32   1c green   .50   .20
a.   Imperf., pair   13.00
75 A32   1c dull bl ('94)   .50   .20
76 A33   2c rose   .50   .20
77 A33   2c red brn ('94)   .55   .25
78 A33   2c org ('99)   .55   .25
79 A34   5c dp blue   .50   .20
80 A34   5c rose ('94)   .55   .20
81 A35   7c bister brn   1.00   .30
82 A35   7c green ('94)   4.75 2.75
83 A35   7c car ('00)   4.00 1.75
84 A36   10c blue grn   3.50   .85
a.   Printed on both sides   20.00
85 A36   10c org ('94)   3.25   .60
86 A37   20c orange   2.50   .60
87 A37   20c brown ('94)   4.75 1.75

---

88 A37   20c lt blue ('00)   2.75   .40
a.   20c greenish blue   3.00   .40
89 A38   25c red brown   3.25   .85
90 A38   25c ver ('94)   6.75 3.50
91 A38   25c bis brn ('01)   3.75   .50
92 A39   50c lt blue   7.50 5.00
93 A39   50c lilac ('94)   11.00 5.50
94 A39   50c car ('01)   6.75 1.00
95 A40   1p lilac   18.00 5.00
96 A40   1p lt blue ('94)   25.00 7.00
97 A40   1p dp grn ('01)   20.00 2.25
a.   Imperf., pair   30.00
     Nos. 74-97 (24)   132.15 41.10

For surcharges and overprints see Nos. 100-101, 142, 180, 185, C1-C3, O41-O60, O89-O91, O108-O109.

Nos. 59 and 62 Overprinted in Red

a   b

1891-92 — Rouletted 8
98 A24 (a) 1c green ('92)   .40   .40
a.   Inverted overprint   6.00 6.00
b.   Double overprint   7.75 7.75
c.   "PREVISORIO"   3.00 2.50
d.   "PREVISORIO"   4.00 4.00
99 A24b (b) 5c violet   .20   .20
a.   "1391"   4.00 2.75
b.   Double overprint   4.00 2.75
c.   Inverted overprint   4.00 2.75
d.   Double ovpt., one invtd.   5.00 3.00

Nos. 86 and 81 Surcharged in Black or Red

c   d

Perf. 12½ to 15½ and Compound
1892
100 A37 (c) 1c on 20c org (Bk)   .40   .40
a.   Inverted surcharge   3.00 3.00
101 A35 (d) 5c on 7c bis brn   .40   .40
      (R)
a.   Inverted surcharge   1.00 1.00
b.   Double surcharge, one invtd.   3.00 3.00
c.   Double surcharge   3.00 3.00
d.   Vertical surcharge   10.00
e.   "PREVISORIO"   3.00 3.00
f.   "Cinco" omitted   4.50

No. 101 with surcharge in green is a color essay.

Several surcharge errors of date and misspelling of "Centésimos" exist. Value $15.

A45   A46

Arms   Peace
A47   A48

1892   Engr.
102 A45   1c green   .50   .20
103 A46   2c rose   .50   .20
104 A47   5c blue   .50   .20
105 A48   10c orange   2.00   .85
     Nos. 102-105 (4)   3.50 1.45

Issued: 1c, 2c, 3/9; 5c, 4/19; 10c, 12/15.

Liberty
A49

Arms
A50

1894, June 2
106 A49 2p carmine   27.50 17.00
107 A50 3p dull violet   27.50 17.00

Gaucho
A51

Solis Theater
A52

Locomotive
A53

Bull's Head
A54

Ceres — A55

Sailing
Ship — A56

Liberty
A57

Mercury
A58

Coat of
Arms — A59

Montevideo
Fortress — A60

Cathedral in
Montevideo
A61

Perf. 12 to 15½ and Compound
1895-99
108 A51 1c bister   .50   .20
109 A51 1c slate bl ('97)   .50   .20
   a. Printed on both sides   14.00
110 A52 2c blue   .50   .20
111 A52 2c claret ('97)   .50   .20
112 A53 5c red   .50   .20
113 A53 5c green ('97)   .65   .20
   a. Imperf., pair   3.50
114 A53 5c grnsh bl ('99)   1.00   .40
115 A54 7c deep green   7.75 2.50
116 A54 7c orange ('97)   3.50 1.25
117 A55 10c brown   2.00   .50
118 A56 20c green & blk   7.00   .85
119 A56 20c cl & blk ('97)   4.75 1.00
120 A57 25c red brn & blk   5.50 1.50
   a. Center inverted   2,000.
121 A57 25c pink & bl ('97)   3.50   .60
122 A58 50c blue & blk   7.00 3.50
123 A58 50c grn & brn ('97)   5.00 1.25

124 A59 1p org brn & blk   14.00 5.50
125 A59 1p yel brn & bl ('97)   9.50 3.50
126 A60 2p violet & grn   32.50 20.00
127 A60 2p bis & car ('97)   9.50 2.00
128 A61 3p carmine & blue   32.50 20.00
129 A61 3p lil & car ('97)   12.50 2.50
   Nos. 108-129 (22)   160.65 67.65

All values of this issue exist imperforate but
they were not issued in that form.
For overprints and surcharges see Nos.
138-140, 143, 145, 147, O62-O78.

President Joaquin Suárez
A62   A63

Statue of President
Suárez — A64

Perf. 12½ to 15 and Compound
1896, July 18
130 A62 1c brown vio & blk   .25   .20
131 A63 5c pale bl & blk   .25   .20
132 A64 10c lake & blk   1.00   .30
   Nos. 130-132 (3)   1.50   .70

Dedication of Pres. Suárez statue.
For overprints and surcharge see Nos. 133-
135, 144, 146, 152, O79-O81.

Same Overprinted in Red:

e   f

1897, Mar. 1
133 A62 (e) 1c brn vio & blk   .40   .40
   a. Inverted overprint   6.00   6.00
134 A63 (e) 5c pale blue & blk   .50   .40
   a. Inverted overprint   9.50   6.00
135 A64 (f) 10c lake & blk   1.00   .60
   a. Inverted overprint   12.00   9.50
   b. Double overprint   7.50
   Nos. 133-135 (3)   1.90 1.40

"Electricity" — A68

1897-99   **Engr.**
136 A68 10c red   1.75   .40
137 A68 10c red lilac ('99)   .75   .50
For overprints see Nos. 141, O82-O83.

Regular Issues
Overprinted in Red or
Blue

1897, Sept. 26
138 A51 1c slate bl (R)   .80   .60
   a. Inverted overprint   4.75   4.75
139 A52 2c claret (Bl)   1.25 1.25
   a. Inverted overprint   4.75   4.75
140 A53 5c green (Bl)   1.75 1.60
   a. Inverted overprint   7.75   7.75
   b. Double overprint
141 A68 10c red (Bl)   2.75 2.75
   a. Inverted overprint   17.00 17.00
   Nos. 138-141 (4)   6.55 6.20

Commemorating the Restoration of Peace
at the end of the Civil War.
Issue for use only on the days of the
National Fête, Sept. 26-28, 1897.

Regular Issues
Surcharged in Black,
Blue or Red

1898, July 25
142 A32 ½c on 1c bl (Bk)   .40   .40
   a. Inverted surcharge   3.00   3.00
143 A51 ½c on 1c bis (Bl)   .40   .40
   a. Inverted surcharge   3.00
   b. Double surcharge   2.50
144 A62 ½c on 1c brn vio & blk
           (R)   .40   .40
145 A52 ½c on 2c blue (Bk)   .40   .40
146 A63 ½c on 5c pale bl & blk
           (R)   .40   .40
   a. Double surcharge   6.25
147 A54 ½c on 7c dp grn (R)   .40   .40
   Nos. 142-147 (6)   2.40 2.40

The 2c red brown of 1894 (#77) was also
surcharged like #142-147 but was not issued.
Value $12.

Liberty — A69

Statue of
Artigas — A70

1898-99   Litho.   Perf. 11, 11½
148 A69 5m rose   .25   .25
149 A69 5m purple ('99)   .25   .25

1899-1900   Engr.   Perf. 12½, 14, 15
150 A70 5m lt blue   .25   .25
151 A70 5m orange ('00)   .25   .25

No. 135 With
Additional Surcharge
in Black

1900, Dec. 1
152 A64 5c on 10c lake & blk   .50   .25
   a. Black bar covering "1897" omitted   15.00

Cattle — A72

Girl's
Head — A73

Shepherdess — A74

Perf. 13½ to 16 and Compound
1900-10   **Engr.**
153 A72 1c yellow green   .40   .20
154 A73 5c dull blue   .80   .20
155 A73 5c slate grn ('10)   .80   .20
156 A74 10c gray violet   1.00   .20
   Nos. 153-156 (4)   3.00   .80

For surcharges and overprints see Nos.
179, 184, O84, O86, O88, O106-O107.

Eros and
Cornucopia
A75

Basket of Fruit
A76

1901, Feb. 11
157 A75 2c vermilion   .50   .20
158 A76 7c brown orange   1.75   .25

For surcharges and overprints see Nos.
197-198, O85, O87, O105.

General
Artigas — A78

Cattle — A79

Eros — A80

Cow — A81

Shepherdess
A82

Numeral
A83

Justice — A84

1904-05   Litho.   Perf. 11½
160 A78 5m orange   .40   .20
   a. 5m yellow   .40   .20
161 A79 1c green   .50   .20
   a. Imperf., pair   3.50
162 A80 2c dp orange   .20   .20
   a. 2c orange red   .20   .20
   b. Imperf., pair   3.00
163 A81 5c blue   .80   .20
   a. Imperf., pair   3.50
164 A82 10c dk violet ('05)   .50   .20
165 A83 20c gray grn ('05)   2.50   .50
166 A84 25c olive bis ('05)   3.25   .40
   Nos. 160-166 (7)   8.15 2.30

For overprints see Nos. 167-169, O92-O98,
O101-O103.

Overprinted Diagonally
in Carmine or Black

1904, Oct. 15
167 A79 1c green (C)   .40   .40
168 A80 2c deep orange (Bk)   .65   .40
169 A81 5c dark blue (C)   1.25   .60
   Nos. 167-169 (3)   2.30 1.40

End of the Civil War of 1904. In the first
overprinting, "Paz 1904" appears at a 50-
degree angle; in the second, at a 63-degree
angle.

A85

A86

1906, Feb. 23   Litho.   Unwmk.
170 A85 5c dark blue   1.10   .20
   a. Imperf., pair   6.00

1906-07
171 A86 5c deep blue   .30   .30
172 A86 7c orange brn ('07)   .70   .50
173 A86 50c rose   5.00 1.00
   Nos. 171-173 (3)   6.00 2.05

Cruiser "Montevideo" — A87

1908, Aug. 23   Typo.   Rouletted 13

174	A87	1c car & dk grn	2.00	1.50
175	A87	2c green & dk grn	2.00	1.50
176	A87	5c org & dk grn	2.00	1.50
		Nos. 174-176 (3)	6.00	4.50

Center Inverted

174a	A87	1c	300.00	300.00
175a	A87	2c	300.00	300.00
176a	A87	5c	300.00	300.00
		Nos. 174a-176a (3)	900.00	900.00

Imperf., Pairs

174b	A87	1c		30.00
175b	A87	2c		30.00
176b	A87	5c		30.00

Independence of Uruguay, declared Aug. 25, 1825. Counterfeits exist.

For surcharges and overprints see Nos. 186, O99-O100, O104, O110.

View of the Port of Montevideo — A88

Wmk. 187

1909, Aug. 24   Engr.   Perf. 11½

| 177 | A88 | 2c lt brown & blk | 1.25 | 1.00 |
| 178 | A88 | 5c rose red & blk | 1.25 | 1.00 |

Issued to commemorate the opening of the Port of Montevideo, Aug. 25, 1909.

Nos. 156, 91
Surcharged

Perf. 14 to 16

1909, Sept. 13   Unwmk.

179	A74	8c on 10c dull vio	.75	.20
a.		"Contesimos"	4.00	2.00
180	A38	23c on 25c bis brn	1.75	.60

Centaur — A89

Wmk. 187

1910, May 22   Engr.   Perf. 11½

| 182 | A89 | 2c carmine red | .60 | .40 |
| 183 | A89 | 5c deep blue | .60 | .40 |

Cent. of Liberation Day, May 25, 1810. The 2c in deep blue and 5c in carmine red were prepared for collectors.

Stamps of 1900-06 Surcharged

g   h

---

i

Perf. 14 to 16, 11½

1910, Oct. 6   Unwmk.

Black Surcharge

| 184 | A72 (a) | 5m on 1c yel grn | .20 | .20 |
| a. | | Inverted surcharge | 4.50 | 3.75 |

Dark Blue Surcharge

| 185 | A39 (b) | 5c on 50c dull red | .40 | .20 |
| a. | | Inverted surcharge | 4.50 | 4.50 |

Blue Surcharge

186	A86 (c)	5c on 50c rose	.80	.45
a.		Double surcharge	20.00	
b.		Inverted surcharge	10.00	8.75
		Nos. 184-186 (3)	1.40	.85

Artigas   "Commercial
A90   Progress"
                 A91

1910, Nov. 21   Engr.   Perf. 14, 15

187	A90	5m dk violet	.20	.20
188	A90	1c dp green	.20	.20
189	A90	2c orange red	.20	.20
190	A90	5c dk blue	.20	.20
191	A90	8c gray blk	.40	.20
192	A90	20c brown	.60	.20
193	A91	23c dp ultra	2.75	.40
194	A91	50c orange	4.00	1.25
195	A91	1p scarlet	7.50	1.25
		Nos. 187-195 (9)	16.05	4.10

See Nos. 199-210. For overprints see Nos. 211-213, O118-O124.

Symbolical of the
Posts — A92

1911, Jan. 6   Wmk. 187   Perf. 11½

| 196 | A92 | 5c rose car & blk | .80 | .60 |

1st South American Postal Cong., at Montevideo, Jan. 1911.

No. 158 Surcharged
in Red or Dark Blue

Perf. 14 to 16

1911, May 17   Unwmk.

197	A76	2c on 7c brn org (R)	.40	.40
198	A76	5c on 7c brn org (Bl)	.40	.40
a.		Inverted surcharge	8.50	8.50

Centenary of the battle of Las Piedras, won by the forces under Gen. Jose Gervasio Artigas, May 8, 1811.

Types of 1910

FOUR AND FIVE CENTESIMOS:
Type I — Large numerals about 3mm high.
Type II — Small numerals about 2¼mm high.

1912-15   Typo.   Perf. 11½

199	A90	5m violet	.20	.20
a.		5m purple	.20	.20
200	A90	5m magenta	.20	.20
a.		5m dull rose	.20	.20
201	A90	1c green ('13)	.20	.20
202	A90	2c brown org	.20	.20
203	A90	2c rose red ('13)	.20	.20
a.		2c deep red ('14)	.20	.20

204	A90	4c org (I) ('14)	.20	.20
a.		4c orange (II) ('15)	.20	.20
b.		4c yellow (II) ('13)	.20	.20
205	A90	5c dull bl (I)	.40	.20
a.		5c blue (II)	.40	.20
206	A90	8c ultra ('13)	.50	.20
207	A90	20c brown ('13)	1.40	.20
a.		20c chocolate	1.40	
208	A91	23c dk blue ('15)	3.50	.60
209	A91	50c orange ('14)	3.50	1.50
210	A91	1p vermilion ('15)	10.50	1.25
		Nos. 199-210 (12)	21.00	5.15

Stamps of 1912-15
Overprinted

1913, Apr. 4

211	A90	2c brown orange	.85	.50
a.		Inverted overprint	5.00	4.50
212	A90	4c yellow	.85	.50
213	A90	5c blue	.85	.50
		Nos. 211-213 (3)	2.55	1.50

Cent. of the Buenos Aires Cong. of 1813.

Liberty
Extending
Peace to the
Country — A93

1918, Jan. 3   Litho.

| 214 | A93 | 2c green & red | .85 | .50 |
| 215 | A93 | 5c buff & blue | .85 | .50 |

Promulgation of the Constitution.

Statue of   Harbor of
Liberty, New   Montevideo
York Harbor   A95
A94

Perf. 14, 15, 13½

1919, July 15   Engr.

217	A94	2c carmine & brn	.55	.20
218	A94	4c orange & brn	.55	.20
219	A94	5c blue & brn	.80	.40
220	A94	8c org brn & ind	.80	.40
221	A94	20c ol bis & blk	2.00	.80
222	A94	23c green & blk	4.00	1.25
		Nos. 217-222 (6)	8.70	3.25

Peace at end of World War I.
Perf 13½ used only on 2c, 20c, 23c.

1919-20   Litho.   Perf. 11½

225	A95	5m violet & blk	.20	.20
226	A95	1c green & blk	.20	.20
227	A95	2c red & blk	.20	.20
228	A95	4c orange & blk	.35	.20
229	A95	5c ultra & slate	.40	.20
230	A95	8c gray bl & lt brn	.50	.20
231	A95	20c brown & blk	1.60	.35
232	A95	23c green & brn	2.75	.65
233	A95	50c brown & blk	5.00	2.00
234	A95	1p dull red & bl	10.00	3.00
		Nos. 225-234 (10)	21.20	7.20

For overprints see Nos. O125-O131.

José Enrique   Mercury — A97
Rodó — A96

1920, Feb. 28   Engr.   Perf. 14, 15

235	A96	2c car & blk	.55	.40
236	A96	4c org & bl	.65	.50
237	A96	5c bl & brn	.75	.55
		Nos. 235-237 (3)	1.95	1.45

Issued to honor José Enrique Rodó, author.
For surcharges see Nos. P2-P4.

1921-22   Litho.   Perf. 11½

238	A97	5m lilac	.20	.20
239	A97	5m gray blk ('22)	.20	.20
240	A97	1c lt grn	.20	.20
241	A97	1c vio ('22)	.20	.20
242	A97	2c fawn	.40	.20
243	A97	2c red ('22)	.40	.20
244	A97	3c bl grn ('22)	.60	.20
245	A97	4c orange	.40	.20
246	A97	5c ultra	.50	.20
247	A97	5c choc ('22)	.60	.20
248	A97	12c ultra ('22)	2.40	.60
249	A97	36c ol grn ('22)	7.75	2.75
		Nos. 238-249 (12)	13.85	5.35

See Nos. 254-260. For overprint and surcharge see Nos. E1, P1.

Dámaso A.
Larrañaga (1771-
1848), Bishop,
Writer, Scientist and
Physician — A98

1921, Dec. 10   Unwmk.

| 250 | A98 | 5c slate | 1.25 | 1.00 |

Mercury Type of 1921-22

1922-23   Wmk. 188

254	A97	5m gray blk	.20	.20
255	A97	1c violet ('23)	.20	.20
a.		1c red violet	.20	.20
256	A97	2c pale red	.25	.20
257	A97	2c deep rose ('23)	.30	.20
259	A97	5c yel brn ('23)	.65	.20
260	A97	8c salmon pink ('23)	1.00	.90
		Nos. 254-260 (6)	2.60	1.90

Equestrian
Statue of
Artigas — A99

Unwmk.

1923, Feb. 26   Engr.   Perf. 14

264	A99	2c car & sepia	.40	.25
265	A99	5c vio & sepia	.40	.25
266	A99	12c blue & sepia	.40	.25
		Nos. 264-266 (3)	1.20	.75

Southern   Battle Monument
Lapwing   A101
A100

Perf. 12½, 11½x12½

1923, June 25   Litho.   Wmk. 189
Size: 18x22½mm

267	A100	5m gray	.20	.20
268	A100	1c org yel	.20	.20
269	A100	2c lt vio	.20	.20
270	A100	3c gray grn	.40	.20
271	A100	5c lt bl	.40	.20
272	A100	8c rose red	.80	.50
273	A100	12c dp bl	.80	.50
274	A100	20c brn org	2.00	.50
275	A100	36c emerald	4.00	1.75
276	A100	50c orange	6.75	2.75
277	A100	1p brt rose	32.50	20.00
278	A100	2p lt grn	47.50	20.00
		Nos. 267-278 (12)	95.75	47.00

See #285-298, 309-314, 317-323, 334-339.
For surcharges and overprints see Nos. 345-348, O132-O148, P5-P7.

1923, Oct. 12   Wmk. 188   Perf. 11½

279	A101	2c dp grn	.55	.40
280	A101	5c scarlet	.55	.40
281	A101	12c dk bl	.55	.40
	Nos. 279-281 (3)		1.65	1.20

Unveiling of the Sarandí Battle Monument by José Luis Zorrilla, Oct. 12, 1923.

"Victory of Samothrace" — A102

Unwmk.

1924, July 29   Typo.   Perf. 11

282	A102	2c rose	20.00	10.00
283	A102	5c mauve	20.00	10.00
284	A102	12c brt bl	20.00	10.00
	Nos. 282-284 (3)		60.00	30.00

Olympic Games. Sheets of 20 (5x4).

Five hundred sets of these stamps were printed on yellow paper for presentation purposes. They were not on sale at post offices. Value for set, $650.

Lapwing Type of 1923
First Redrawing
Imprint: "A. BARREIRO Y RAMOS"

1924, July 26   Litho.   Perf. 12½, 11½
Size: 17¼x21½mm

285	A100	5m gray blk	.20	.20
286	A100	1c fawn	.20	.20
287	A100	2c rose lil	.30	.20
288	A100	3c gray grn	.20	.20
289	A100	5c chalky blue	.20	.20
290	A100	8c pink	.50	.20
291	A100	10c turq blue	.40	.20
292	A100	12c slate blue	.50	.25
293	A100	15c lt vio	.50	.20
294	A100	20c brown	.75	.30
295	A100	36c salmon	3.00	.70
296	A100	50c greenish gray	5.00	2.00
297	A100	1p buff	12.00	4.00
298	A100	2p dl vio	20.00	10.00
	Nos. 285-298 (14)		43.75	18.85

Landing of the 33 "Immortals" Led by Juan Antonio Lavalleja — A103

Perf. 11, 11½

1925, Apr. 19   Wmk. 188

300	A103	2c salmon pink & blk	1.40	.80
301	A103	5c lilac & blk	1.40	.80
302	A103	12c blue & blk	1.40	.80
	Nos. 300-302 (3)		4.20	2.40

Cent. of the landing of the 33 Founders of the Uruguayan Republic.

Legislative Palace — A104

Perf. 11½

1925, Aug. 24   Unwmk.   Engr.

303	A104	5c vio & blk	1.25	.80
304	A104	12c bl & blk	1.25	.80

Dedication of the Legislative Palace.

General Fructuoso Rivera — A105

Wmk. 188

1925, Sept. 24   Litho.   Perf. 11

305	A105	5c light red	.50	.40

Centenary of Battle of Rincón. See No. C9.

Battle of Sarandí A106

1925, Oct. 12   Perf. 11½

306	A106	2c bl grn	1.25	1.00
307	A106	5c dl vio	1.25	1.00
308	A106	12c dp bl	1.25	1.00
	Nos. 306-308 (3)		3.75	3.00

Centenary of the Battle of Sarandi.

Lapwing Type of 1923
Second Redrawing
Imprint: "Imprenta Nacional"

1925-26   Perf. 11, 11½, 10½
Size: 17½x21¾mm

309	A100	5m gray blk	1.00	.25
310	A100	1c dl vio	1.25	.25
311	A100	2c brt rose	1.60	.25
312	A100	3c gray grn	1.25	.40
313	A100	5c dl bl ('26)	2.00	.25
314	A100	12c slate blue	4.00	.40
	Nos. 309-314 (6)		11.10	1.80

The design differs in many small details from that of the 1923-24 issues. These stamps may be readily identified by the imprint and perforation.

Lapwing Type of 1923
Third Redrawing
Imprint: "Imp. Nacional" at center

1926-27   Perf. 11, 11½, 10½
Size: 17½x21¾mm

317	A100	5m gray	.40	.20
318	A100	1c lt vio ('27)	2.40	.55
319	A100	2c red	1.75	.40
320	A100	3c gray grn	2.40	.65
321	A100	5c lt bl	.75	.20
322	A100	8c pink ('27)	3.50	.80
323	A100	36c rose buff	8.00	4.00
	Nos. 317-323 (7)		19.20	6.80

These stamps may be distinguished from preceding stamps of the same design by the imprint.

Philatelic Exhibition Issue

Post Office at Montevideo A107

Unwmk.

1927, May 25   Engr.   Imperf.

330	A107	2c green	4.75	3.50
a.	Sheet of 4		20.00	20.00
331	A107	5c dull red	4.75	3.50
a.	Sheet of 4		20.00	20.00
332	A107	8c dark blue	4.75	3.50
a.	Sheet of 4		20.00	20.00
	Nos. 330-332 (3)		14.25	10.50

Printed in sheets of 4 and sold at the Montevideo Exhibition. Lithographed counterfeits exist.

Lapwing Type of 1923
Fourth Redrawing
Imprint: "Imp. Nacional" at right

Perf. 11, 11½

1927, May 6   Litho.   Wmk. 188
Size: 17¾x21¾mm

334	A100	1c gray vio	.40	.25
335	A100	2c vermilion	.40	.25
336	A100	3c gray grn	.80	.35
337	A100	5c blue	.40	.25
338	A100	8c rose	3.00	.80
339	A100	20c gray brn	4.00	1.60
	Nos. 334-339 (6)			

The design has been slightly retouched in various places. The imprint is in italic capitals and is placed below the right numeral of value.

Inauguración
Ferrocarril
SAN CARLOS
a ROCHA
14/1/1928

No. 292 Surcharged in Red

5 cts. 5

1928, Jan. 13   Unwmk.   Perf. 11½

345	A100	2c on 12c slate blue	2.00	2.00
346	A100	5c on 12c slate blue	2.00	2.00
347	A100	10c on 12c slate blue	2.00	2.00
348	A100	15c on 12c slate blue	2.00	2.00
	Nos. 345-348 (4)		8.00	8.00

Issued to celebrate the inauguration of the railroad between San Carlos and Rocha.

General Rivera — A108

1928, Apr. 19   Engr.   Perf. 12

349	A108	5c car rose	.50	.35

Centenary of the Battle of Las Misiones.

Artigas (7 dots in panels below portrait.) — A109

Imprint:
"Waterlow & Sons. Ltd., Londres"

Perf. 11, 12½, 13x13½, 12½x13, 13x12½

1928-43
Size: 16x19½mm

350	A109	5m black	.20	.20
350A	A109	5m org ('43)	.20	.20
351	A109	1c dk vio	.20	.20
352	A109	1c brn vio ('34)	.20	.20
352A	A109	1c vio bl ('43)	.20	.20
353	A109	2c dp grn	.20	.20
353A	A109	2c brn red ('43)	.20	.20
354	A109	3c bister	.20	.20
355	A109	3c dp grn ('32)	.20	.20
355A	A109	3c brt grn ('43)	.20	.20
356	A109	5c red	.20	.20
357	A109	5c ol grn ('33)	.20	.20
357A	A109	5c dl pur ('43)	.20	.20
358	A109	7c car ('32)	.20	.20
359	A109	8c dk bl	.20	.20
360	A109	8c brn ('33)	.20	.20
361	A109	10c orange	.25	.20
362	A109	10c red org ('32)	.60	.40
363	A109	12c dp bl ('32)	.40	.20
364	A109	15c dl bl	.40	.20
365	A109	17c dk vio ('32)	.80	.20
366	A109	20c ol brn	.65	.20
367	A109	20c red brn ('33)	1.25	.50
368	A109	24c car rose	.90	.35
369	A109	24c yel ('33)	.80	.40
370	A109	36c ol grn ('33)	1.40	.50
371	A109	50c gray	2.40	1.25
372	A109	50c blk ('33)	3.50	1.60
373	A109	50c blk brn ('33)	3.00	1.25
374	A109	1p yel grn	7.00	1.00
	Nos. 350-374 (30)		26.55	14.45

1929-33   Perf. 12½
Size: 22 to 22½x28½ to 29½mm

375	A109	1p ol brn ('33)	6.00	4.00
376	A109	2p dk grn	17.00	9.00
377	A109	2p dl red ('32)	20.00	16.00
378	A109	3p dk bl	25.00	17.00
379	A109	3p blk ('32)	23.00	20.00
380	A109	4p violet	28.00	17.00
381	A109	4p dk ol grn ('32)	23.00	20.00
382	A109	5p car brn	32.50	23.00
383	A109	5p red org ('32)	30.00	20.00
384	A109	10p lake ('33)	92.50	70.00
385	A109	10p dp ultra ('33)	92.50	70.00
	Nos. 375-385 (11)		389.50	286.00

See Nos. 420-423, 462. See type A135.

Equestrian Statue of Artigas — A110

1928, May 1

386	A110	2p Prus bl & choc	16.00	7.75
387	A110	3p dp rose & blk	23.00	12.00

Symbolical of Soccer Victory — A111

Gen. Eugenio Garzón — A112

1928, July 29

388	A111	2c brn vio	16.00	9.25
389	A111	5c dp red	16.00	9.25
390	A111	8c ultra	16.00	9.25
	Nos. 388-390 (3)		48.00	27.75

Uruguayan soccer victories in the Olympic Games of 1924 and 1928. Printed in sheets of 20, in panes of 10 (5x2).

1928, Aug. 25   Imperf.

391	A112	2c red	1.40	1.40
a.	Sheet of 4		6.50	6.50
392	A112	5c yel grn	1.40	1.40
a.	Sheet of 4		6.50	6.50
393	A112	8c dp bl	1.40	1.40
a.	Sheet of 4		6.50	6.50
	Nos. 391-393 (3)		4.20	4.20

Dedication of monument to Garzon. Issued in sheets of 4. Lithographed counterfeits exist.

Black River Bridge A113

Gauchos Breaking a Horse — A114

Peace A115

Montevideo A116

Liberty and Flag of Uruguay A117

Liberty with Torch and Caduceus A118

Statue of Artigas A124

Artigas Dictating Instructions for 1813 Congress A119

Seascape
A120

Montevideo
Harbor,
1830 — A121

Liberty and
Coat of
Arms
A122

Montevideo
Harbor,
1930 — A123

1930, June 16   *Perf. 12½, 12*

394	A113	5m gray blk	.20	.20
395	A114	1c dk brn	.20	.20
396	A116	2c brn rose	.20	.20
397	A116	3c yel grn	.20	.20
398	A117	5c dk bl	.20	.20
399	A118	8c dl red	.35	.20
400	A119	10c dk vio	.50	.35
401	A120	15c bl grn	.65	.50
402	A121	20c indigo	.80	.65
403	A122	24c red brn	1.10	.80
404	A123	50c org red	3.00	2.00
405	A124	1p black	6.00	3.00
406	A124	2p bl vio	14.00	8.50
407	A124	3p dk red	20.00	14.00
408	A124	4p red org	23.00	19.00
409	A124	5p lilac	35.00	22.50
		Nos. 394-409 (16)	105.40	72.50

Cent. of natl. independence and the promulgation of the constitution.

Type of 1856 Issue
Values in Centesimos
Wmk. 227

1931, Apr. 11   Litho.   *Imperf.*

410	A1	2c gray blue	3.00	2.00
a.		Sheet of 4	15.00	15.00
411	A1	8c dull red	3.00	2.00
a.		Sheet of 4	15.00	15.00
412	A1	15c blue black	3.00	2.00
a.		Sheet of 4	15.00	15.00

Wmk. 188

413	A1	5c light green	3.00	2.00
a.		Sheet of 4	15.00	15.00
		Nos. 410-413 (4)	12.00	8.00

Sold only at the Philatelic Exhibition, Montevideo, Apr. 11-15, 1931. Issued in sheets of 4.

Juan Zorrilla de San
Martin, Uruguayan
Poet — A125

1932, June 6   Unwmk.   *Perf. 12½*

414	A125	1½c brown violet	.20	.20
415	A125	3c green	.20	.20
416	A125	7c dk blue	.25	.20
417	A125	12c lt blue	.40	.25
418	A125	1p deep brown	20.00	13.00
		Nos. 414-418 (5)	21.05	13.85

Semi-Postal Stamp
No. B2 Surcharged

1932, Nov. 1   *Perf. 12*

419	SP1	1½c on 2c + 2c dp grn	.35	.35

Artigas Type of 1928
Imprint: "Imprenta Nacional" at center

1932-35   Litho.   *Perf. 11, 12½*
Size: 15¾x19¼mm

420	A109	5m lt brown ('35)	.20	.20
421	A109	1c pale violet ('35)	.20	.20
422	A109	15m black	.25	.20
423	A109	5c bluish grn ('35)	.50	.20
		Nos. 420-423 (4)	1.15	.80

Gen. J. A.
Lavalleja
A126

Flag of the
Race and Globe
A127

1933, July 12   Engr.   *Perf. 12½*

429	A126	15m brown lake	.20	.20

Perf. 11, 11½, 11x11½

1933, Aug. 3   Litho.

430	A127	3c blue green	.50	.25
431	A127	5c rose	.50	.25
432	A127	7c lt blue	.50	.25
433	A127	8c dull red	1.00	.55
434	A127	12c deep blue	.65	.25
435	A127	17c violet	1.75	.80
436	A127	20c red brown	3.50	1.60
437	A127	24c yellow	3.50	1.75
438	A127	36c orange	5.00	2.40
439	A127	50c olive gray	5.50	3.00
440	A127	1p bister	13.00	6.25
		Nos. 430-440 (11)	35.40	17.35

Raising of the "Flag of the Race" and of the 441st anniv. of the sailing of Columbus from Palos, Spain, on his first voyage to America.

Sower
A128

Juan Zorrilla
de San
Martin
A129

1933, Aug. 28   Unwmk.   *Perf. 11½*

441	A128	3c blue green	.25	.20
442	A128	5c dull violet	.40	.25
443	A128	7c lt blue	.40	.25
444	A128	8c deep red	.80	.50
445	A128	12c ultra	2.00	1.00
		Nos. 441-445 (5)	3.85	2.20

3rd Constituent National Assembly.

1933, Nov. 9   Engr.   *Perf. 12½*

446	A129	7c slate	.20	.20

Albatross Flying over Map of the
Americas — A130

1933, Dec. 3   Typo.   *Perf. 11½*

447	A130	3c green, blk & brn	2.75	2.00
448	A130	7c turq bl, brn & blk	1.60	.80
449	A130	12c dk bl, gray & ver	2.40	1.60
450	A130	17c ver, gray & vio	5.00	2.75
451	A130	20c yellow, bl & grn	6.00	3.50
452	A130	36c red, blk & yel	7.75	5.50
		Nos. 447-452 (6)	25.50	16.15

7th Pan-American Conf., Montevideo. Issued in sheets of 6. Value, $200. For overprints see Nos. C61-C62.

General Rivera — A131

1934, Feb.   Engr.   *Perf. 12½*

453	A131	3c green	.20	.20

Stars Representing the Three
Constitutions — A132

1934, Mar. 23   Typo.

454	A132	3c yellow grn & grn	.60	.40
455	A132	7c org red & red	.60	.40
456	A132	12c ultra & blue	2.00	.80

Perf. 11½

457	A132	17c brown & rose	2.50	1.25
458	A132	20c yellow & gray	3.50	1.60
459	A132	36c dk vio & bl grn	3.50	1.60
460	A132	50c black & blue	7.00	3.25
461	A132	1p dk car & vio	16.00	6.75
		Nos. 454-461 (8)	35.70	16.05

First Year of Third Republic.

Artigas Type of 1928
Imprint: "Barreiro & Ramos S. A."

1934, Nov. 28   Litho.

462	A109	50c brown black	6.00	2.50

"Uruguay" and
"Brazil" Holding
Scales of Justice
A133

Florencio
Sánchez
A134

1935, May 30   Unwmk.   *Perf. 11*

463	A133	5m brown	.80	.40
464	A133	15m black	.40	.20
465	A133	3c green	.40	.20
466	A133	7c orange	.40	.20
467	A133	12c ultra	.80	.60
468	A133	50c yellow green	4.00	2.50
		Nos. 463-468 (6)	6.80	4.10

Visit of President Vargas of Brazil.

1935, Nov. 7

469	A134	3c green	.20	.20
470	A134	7c brown	.20	.20
471	A134	12c blue	.55	.35
		Nos. 469-471 (3)	.95	.75

Florencio Sanchez (1875-1910), author.

Artigas (6 dots in panels
below portrait) — A135

Imprint: "Imprenta Nacional" at center

1936-44   *Perf. 11, 12½*

474	A135	5m org brn ('37)	.20	.20
475	A135	5m lt brown ('39)	.20	.20
476	A135	1c lt violet ('37)	.20	.20
477	A135	2c dk brown ('37)	.20	.20
478	A135	2c green ('39)	.20	.20
479	A135	5c brt blue ('37)	.20	.20
480	A135	5c bluish grn ('39)	.40	.20
481	A135	12c dull blue ('38)	.40	.20
482	A135	20c fawn	1.40	.35
482A	A135	20c rose ('44)	1.00	.40
483	A135	50c brown black	3.00	.80

Size: 21½x28½mm

483A	A135	1p brown	8.50	3.00
483B	A135	2p blue	14.00	12.00
483C	A135	3p gray black	20.00	16.00
		Nos. 474-483C (14)	49.90	34.15

See Nos. 488, 576. See type A109.

Power Dam on
Black
River — A136

1937-38

484	A136	1c dull violet	.20	.20
485	A136	10c blue	.50	.20
486	A136	15c rose	1.25	.65
487	A136	1p choc ('38)	6.25	2.50
		Nos. 484-487 (4)	8.20	3.55

Imprint: "Imprenta Nacional" at right
1938

488	A135	1c bright violet	.40	.20

International Law Congress,
1889 — A137

1939, July 16   Litho.   *Perf. 12½*

489	A137	1c brown orange	.20	.20
490	A137	2c dull green	.25	.20
491	A137	5c rose ver	.25	.20
492	A137	12c dull blue	.65	.40
493	A137	50c lt violet	2.50	1.50
		Nos. 489-493 (5)	3.85	2.50

50th anniversary of the Montevideo Congress of International Law.

Artigas
A138   A138a

1939-43   Litho.   Unwmk.
Size: 15¾x19mm

494	A138	5m dl brn org ('40)	.20	.20
495	A138	1c lt blue	.20	.20
496	A138	2c lt violet	.20	.20
497	A138	5c violet brn	.20	.20
498	A138	8c rose red	.25	.20
499	A138	10c green	.50	.20
500	A138	10c green	1.25	.60

Size: 24x29½mm

501	A138	1p dull brn ('41)	2.50	1.00
502	A138	2p dl rose vio ('40)	7.00	3.00
503	A138	4p orange ('43)	9.25	4.00
504	A138	5p ver ('41)	14.00	6.00
		Nos. 494-504 (11)	35.55	15.80

See No. 578.

Redrawn: Horizontal lines in portrait
background

1940-44
Size: 17x21mm

505	A138a	5m brn org ('41)	.20	.20
506	A138a	1c lt blue	.20	.20
507	A138a	2c lt violet ('41)	.20	.20
508	A138a	5c violet brn	.20	.20
509	A138a	8c sal pink ('44)	.20	.20
510	A138a	10c green ('41)	.40	.20
511	A138a	50c olive bis ('42)	6.25	1.75
511A	A138a	50c yel grn ('44)	4.75	1.75
		Nos. 505-511A (8)	12.40	4.70

See Nos. 568-575, 577, 601, 632, 660-661. For surcharges see Nos. 523, 726.

Juan Manuel
Blanes, Artist
A139

Francisco
Acuna de
Figueroa
A140

1941, Aug. 11   Engr.   Perf. 12½
512 A139 5m ocher   .25   .20
513 A139 1c henna brown   .25   .20
514 A139 2c green   .25   .20
515 A139 5c rose carmine   .60   .20
516 A139 12c deep blue   1.25   .60
517 A139 50c dark violet   4.75 3.25
   Nos. 512-517 (6)   7.35 4.65

1942, Mar. 18   Unwmk.
518 A140 1c henna brown   .20   .20
519 A140 2c deep green   .20   .20
520 A140 5c rose carmine   .25   .20
521 A140 12c deep blue   1.00   .40
522 A140 50c dark violet   3.25 2.50
   Nos. 518-522 (5)   4.90 3.50

Issued in honor of Francisco Acuna de
Figueroa, author of the National anthem.

No. 506 Surcharged in
Red

1943, Jan. 27
523 A138a 5m on 1c lt bl   .25   .20

Coat of
Arms — A141   Clio — A142

1943, Mar. 12   Litho.
524 A141 1c on 2c dl vio brn
   (R)   .20   .20
525 A141 2c on 2c dl vio brn
   (V)   .20   .20
  a. Inverted surcharge 20.00 20.00

Nos. 524-525 are unissued stamps
surcharged. See Nos. 546-555, Q67, Q69,
Q74-Q76.

1943, Aug. 24
526 A142 5m lt violet   .20   .20
527 A142 1c lt ultra   .20   .20
528 A142 2c brt rose   .50   .20
529 A142 5c buff   .50   .20
   Nos. 526-529 (4)   1.40   .80

100th anniversary of the Historic and Geo-
graphic Institute of Uruguay.

Swiss Colony
Monument
A143

YMCA Seal
A144

Overprinted "1944" and Surcharged in
Various Colors

1944, May 18
530 A143 1c on 3c dull grn (R)   .20   .20
531 A143 5c on 7c brn red (B)   .20   .20
532 A143 10c on 12c dk bl (Br)   .65   .25
   Nos. 530-532 (3)   1.05   .65

Founding of the Swiss Colony, 50th anniv.

1944, Sept. 8
533 A144 5c blue   .20   .20

100th anniv. of the YMCA.

> **Catalogue values for unused
> stamps in this section, from this
> point to the end of the section, are
> for Never Hinged items.**

"La Educación
del Pueblo"
A145

José Pedro
Varela
A146

A147

Monument
A148

Perf. 11½
1945, June 13   Unwmk.
534 A145 5m brt green   .20   .20
535 A146 1c dp brown   .20   .20

Perf. 12½
536 A147 2c rose red   .20   .20
537 A148 5c blue   .20   .20
  a. Perf. 11½   .20   .20
   Nos. 534-537 (4)   .80   .80

José Pedro Varela, author, birth cent.

Santiago
Vazquez
A149

Silvestre
Blanco
A150

Eduardo
Acevedo
A151

Bruno
Mauricio de
Zabala
A152

José Pedro
Varela — A153

José
Ellauri — A154

Gen. Luis de
Larrobla — A155

**Engraved (5m, 5c, 10c);
Lithographed**
1945-47   Perf. 10½, 11, 11½, 12½
538 A149 5m purple ('46)   .20   .20
539 A150 1c yel brn ('46)   .20   .20
540 A151 2c brown vio   .20   .20
541 A152 3c grn & dp grn ('47) .20 .20
542 A153 5c brt carmine   .20   .20
543 A154 10c ultra   .40   .20
544 A155 20c dp grn & choc
   ('47)   1.25   .50
   Nos. 538-544 (7)   2.65 1.70

No. C86A Surcharged in Blue

1946, Jan. 9   Perf. 12½
545 AP7 20c on 68c pale vio brn 1.25   .60

Inauguration of the Black River Power Dam.
See No. C120.

Type A141 Overprinted

1946-51 Unwmk. Litho. Perf. 12½
546 A141 5m orange ('49)   .20   .20
  a. Inverted overprint
547 A141 2c dl vio brn ('47)   .20   .20
548 A141 3c green   .20   .20
549 A141 5c ultra ('51)   .20   .20
550 A141 10c orange brn   .35   .20
551 A141 20c dk green   .65   .25
552 A141 50c brown   2.00 1.00
553 A141 3p lilac rose   7.00 4.50
   Nos. 546-553 (8)   10.80 6.75

Type A141 Surcharged

1947-48
554 A141 2c on 5c ultra ('48) .20   .20
555 A141 3c on 5c ultra   .20   .20

Statue of
Ariel — A158

Bas-relief
A160

Bust of José Enrique
Rodó — A159

Bas-relief
A161

Perf. 12½
**1948, Jan. 30   Unwmk.   Engr.
Center in Orange Brown**
556 A158 1c grnsh gray   .20   .20
557 A159 2c purple   .20   .20
558 A160 3c green   .20   .20
559 A161 5c red violet   .25   .20
560 A160 10c dp orange   .35   .20
561 A161 12c ultra   .40   .20
562 A158 20c rose violet   .80   .25
563 A159 50c dp carmine   2.50   .90
   Nos. 556-563 (8)   4.90 2.35

Dedication of the Rodó monument.

View of the Port,
Paysandú — A162

Arms of
Paysandú
A163

1948, Oct. 9   Litho.
564 A162 3c blue green   .25   .20
565 A163 7c ultra   .40   .25

Exposition of Industry and Agriculture,
Paysandú, October-November 1948.

Santa Lucia
River
Highway
Bridge
A164

1948, Dec. 10
566 A164 10c dark blue   .80   .20
567 A164 50c green   2.50 1.00

Redrawn Artigas Types of 1940, 1936,
1939

1948-51   Litho.   Perf. 12½
568 A138a 5m gray ('49)   .20   .20
569 A138a 1c rose vio ('50)   .20   .20
570 A138a 2c orange   .20   .20
571 A138a 2c choc ('50)   .20   .20
572 A138a 3c blue green   .20   .20
572A A138a 7c violet blue   .20   .20
573 A138a 8c rose car ('49)   .20   .20
574 A138a 10c orange brn ('51) .20   .20
575 A138a 12c blue ('51)   .20   .20
576 A135   20c violet   .30   .20
577 A138a 20c rose pink ('51) .55   .20

Size: 18x21¾mm
578 A138   1p lilac rose ('51) 1.10   .25
   Nos. 568-578 (12)   3.75 2.45

Nos. 571-572A also exist perf. 11.

Plowing
A165

Mounted
Cattle
Herder
A166

1949, Apr. 29   Unwmk.   Perf. 12½
579 A165 3c green   .20 .20
580 A166 7c blue   .40 .20
4th Regional American Conf. of Labor, 1949.

Cannon, Rural and Urban Views — A167

Symbolical of Soccer Matches — A168

1950, Oct. 11   Litho.
581 A167 1c lilac rose   .25 .20
582 A167 3c green   .25 .20
583 A167 7c deep blue   .25 .20
    Nos. 581-583 (3)   .75 .60
200th anniv. of the founding of Cordón, a district of Montevideo.

1951, Mar. 20   Perf. 12½, 11
584 A168 3c green   1.00 .25
585 A168 7c violet blue   2.25 .80
4th World Soccer Championship, Rio de Janeiro.

Gen. José Artigas — A169

Flight of the People A170

1c, 2c, 5c, Various equestrian portraits of Artigas. 7c, Dictating instructions. 8c, In congress. 10c, Artigas' flag. 14c, At the citadel. 20c, Arms of Artigas. 50c, In Paraguay. 1p, Bust.

Engraved and Photogravure
1952, Jan. 7   Unwmk.   Perf. 13½
586 A169 5m slate   .20 .20
587 A169 1c bl & blk   .20 .20
588 A170 2c pur & red brn   .20 .20
589 A170 3c aqua & dk brn   .20 .20
590 A170 5c red org & blk   .20 .20
591 A170 7c ol & blk   .25 .20
592 A170 8c car & blk   .35 .20
593 A170 10c choc, brt ultra & crim   .35 .20
594 A169 14c dp bl   .35 .20
595 A169 20c org yel, dp ultra & car   .80 .20
596 A169 50c org brn & blk   1.60 .40
597 A169 1p bl gray & cit   3.00 1.25
    Nos. 586-597 (12)   7.70 3.65
Centenary (in 1950) of the death of Gen. José Artigas.

Plane and Stagecoach A171

1952, Oct. 9   Photo.   Perf. 13½x13
598 A171 3c bl grn   .20 .20
599 A171 7c blk brn   .20 .20
600 A171 12c ultra   .30 .20
    Nos. 598-600 (3)   .70 .60
75th anniv. (in 1949) of the UPU.

Redrawn Artigas Type of 1940-44
1953, Feb. 23   Litho.   Perf. 11
    Size: 24x29½mm
601 A138a 2p fawn   11.00 8.50

Franklin D. Roosevelt — A172

1953, Apr. 9   Engr.   Perf. 13½
602 A172 3c green   .20 .20
603 A172 7c ultra   .25 .20
604 A172 12c blk brn   .40 .25
    Nos. 602-604 (3)   .85 .65
5th Postal Cong. of the Americas & Spain.

Ceibo, Natl. Flower — A173

Horse Breaking — A174

Legislature Building A175

"Island of Seals" (Southern Sea Lions) — A176

Fair Entrance — A177

Designs: 2c, 10c, 5p, Ombu tree. 3c, 50c, Passion Flower. 7c, 3p, Montevideo fortress. 12c, 2p, Outer gate, Montevideo.

Perf. 13x13½, 13½x13, 12½x12½, 13x12½
Photo. (5m, 3c, 20c, 50c); Engr.
1954, Jan. 14   Unwmk.
605 A173 5m multi   .20 .20
606 A174 1c car & blk   .20 .20
607 A174 2c brn & grn   .20 .20
608 A173 3c multi   .20 .20
609 A175 5c pur & red brn   .20 .20
610 A173 7c brn & grn   .20 .20
611 A176 8c car & ultra   .40 .20
612 A174 10c org & grn   .35 .20
613 A175 12c dp ultra & dk brn   .25 .20
614 A174 14c rose lil & blk   .25 .20
615 A173 20c grn, brn, gray & car   .70 .20
616 A175 1p car & multi   2.00 .20
617 A175 1p car & red brn   2.50 1.00
618 A175 2p car & blk brn   4.00 1.60
619 A173 3p lil & grn   4.75 2.00
620 A176 4p dp brn & dp ultra   13.00 5.00
621 A174 5p vio bl & grn   10.00 4.00
    Nos. 605-621 (17)   39.40 16.00
For surcharges see Nos. 637-639, 750, C299.

1956, Jan. 19   Litho.   Perf. 11
622 A177 3c pale olive green   .25 .20
623 A177 7c blue   .25 .20
    Nos. 622-623,C166-C168 (5)   2.00 1.30
First Exposition of National Products.

José Batlle y Ordonez, Birth Centenary A178

Design: 7c, Full length portrait.

Perf. 13½
1956, Dec. 15   Wmk. 90   Photo.
624 A178 3c rose red   .20 .20
625 A178 7c sepia   .25 .20
    Nos. 624-625,C169-C172 (6)   1.95 1.50

Same Surcharged with New Values
1957-58
626 A178 5c on 3c ('58)   .20 .20
627 A178 10c on 7c   .25 .20
    a. Surcharge inverted   20.00 20.00

Diver — A179

Eduardo Acevedo — A180

Design: 10c, Swimmer at start, horiz.

Perf. 10½, 11½
1958, Feb. 15   Litho.   Unwmk.
628 A179 5c brt bl grn   .20 .20
629 A179 10c brt bl   .35 .20
14th South American swimming meet, Montevideo.

1958, Mar. 19   Perf. 11½, 10½
630 A180 5c lt ol grn & blk   .20 .20
631 A180 10c ultra & blk   .25 .20
Eduardo Acevedo (1856-1948), lawyer, legislator, minister of foreign affairs, birth cent.

Artigas Type of 1940-44
1958, Sept. 25   Litho.   Perf. 11
632 A138a 5m blue   .25 .20

Baygorria Hydroelectric Works — A181

1958, Oct. 30   Unwmk.   Perf. 11
633 A181 5c yel grn & blk   .20 .20
634 A181 10c brn org & blk   .20 .20
635 A181 1p bl gray & blk   .65 .25
636 A181 2p rose & blk   1.25 .55
    Nos. 633-636 (4)   2.30 1.20

Nos. 608, 610 and 605 Surcharged Similarly to

Photogravure and Engraved
1958-59   Perf. 13x13½
637 A173 5c on 3c multi ('59)   .30 .20
638 A173 10c on 7c brn & grn   .30 .20
639 A173 20c on 5m multi   .30 .20
    Nos. 637-639 (3)   .90 .60

Gabriela Mistral — A182

Carlos Vaz Ferreira — A183

Wmk. 327
1959, July 6   Litho.   Perf. 11½
640 A182 5c green   .20 .20
641 A182 10c dark blue   .20 .20
642 A182 20c red   .20 .20
    Nos. 640-642 (3)   .60 .60
Gabriela Mistral, Chilean poet and educator.

1959, Sept. 3   Perf. 11
643 A183 5c blk & lt bl   .25 .20
644 A183 10c blk & ocher   .25 .20
645 A183 20c blk & ver   .25 .20
646 A183 50c blk & vio   .35 .25
647 A183 1p blk & grn   .55 .25
    Nos. 643-647 (5)   1.65 1.10
Ferreira (1872-1958), educator and author.

A184

A185

Wmk. 332
1960, May 16   Litho.   Perf. 12
648 A184 3c red lil & blk   .20 .20
649 A184 5c dp vio & blk   .20 .20
650 A184 10c brt bl & blk   .20 .20
651 A184 20c chocolate & blk   .25 .20
652 A184 1p gray & blk   .40 .20
653 A184 2p org & blk   1.00 .20
654 A184 3p olive grn & blk   1.60 .40
655 A184 4p yel brn & blk   2.00 .75
656 A184 5p brt red & blk   2.50 .75
    Nos. 648-656 (9)   8.35 3.10
Dr. Martin C. Martinez (1859-1940), statesman.

1960, June 6   Wmk. 332   Perf. 12
657 A185 10c Uprooted oak emblem   .25 .20
Issued to publicize World Refugee Year, July 1, 1959-June 30, 1960. See No. C207.

Revolutionists and Cabildo, Buenos Aires — A186

1960, Nov. 4   Litho.   Perf. 12
658 A186 5c bl & blk   .20 .20
659 A186 10c bl & ocher   .20 .20
    Nos. 658-659,C208-C210 (5)   1.10 1.00
150th anniv. of the May Revolution of 1810.

Artigas Type of 1940-44
1960-61   Wmk. 332   Perf. 11
660 A138a 2c gray   .20 .20
661 A138a 50c brn ('61)   .20 .20

Gen. Manuel Oribe
(1796?-1857),
Revolutionary
Leader, Pres. of
Uruguay (1835-
38) — A187

1961, Mar. 4   Litho.   Perf. 12
671 A187 10c brt bl & blk   .25 .20
672 A187 20c bis & blk   .25 .20
673 A187 40c grn & blk   .25 .20
  Nos. 671-673 (3)   .75 .60

Cavalry
Charge
A188

1961, June 12   Wmk. 332   Perf. 12
674 A188 20c bl & blk   .20 .20
675 A188 40c emer & blk   .30 .20

  150th anniversary of the revolution.

Welfare, Justice   Gen. José
and   Fructuoso
Education — A189   Rivera — A190

1961, Aug. 14   Wmk. 322   Perf. 12
676 A189 2c bister & lilac   .35 .20
677 A189 5c bister & orange   .35 .20
678 A189 10c bister & scarlet   .35 .20
679 A189 20c bister & yel grn   .35 .20
680 A189 50c bister & light vio   .35 .20
681 A189 1p bister & blue   .35 .20
682 A189 2p bister & citron   1.00 .20
683 A189 3p bister & gray   1.40 .65
684 A189 4p bister & light bl   2.40 .80
685 A189 5p bister & chocolate 2.50 1.25
  Nos. 676-685 (10)   9.40 4.15

  Inter-American Economic and Social Con-
ference of the Organization of American
States, Punta del Este, August, 1961. See
Nos. C233-C244.

Wmk. 332
1962, May 29   Litho.   Perf. 12
686 A190 10c brt red & blk   .20 .20
687 A190 20c bis & blk   .20 .20
688 A190 40c grn & blk   .20 .20
  Nos. 686-688 (3)   .60 .60

  Issued to honor Gen. José Fructuoso Rivera
(1790-1854), first President of Uruguay.

Spade, Grain,
Swiss "Scarf" and
Hat — A191

Bernardo
Prudencio
Berro — A192

1962, Aug. 1   Wmk. 332   Perf. 12
689 A191 10c bl, blk & car   .20 .20
690 A191 20c lt grn, blk & car   .25 .20
  Nos. 689-690,C245-C246 (4)   1.05 .90

  Swiss Settlement in Uruguay, cent.

1962, Oct. 22   Litho.   Perf. 12
691 A192 10c grnsh bl & blk   .20 .20
692 A192 20c yel brn & blk   .25 .25

  Pres. Bernardo P. Berro (1803-1868).

Damaso
Larrañaga
A193

1963, Jan. 24   Wmk. 332   Perf. 12
693 A193 20c lt bl grn & dk brn   .20 .20
694 A193 40c tan & dk brn   .25 .25

  Damaso Antonio Larranaga (1771-1848),
teacher, writer and founder of National Library.

Rufous-bellied Thrush — A194

  Birds: 50c, Rufous ovenbird. 1p, Chalk-
browed mockingbird. 2p, Rufous-collared
sparrow.

1963, Apr. 1   Wmk. 332   Perf. 12
695 A194 2c rose, brn & blk   .20 .20
696 A194 50c lt brn & blk   .65 .20
697 A194 1p tan, brn & blk   1.60 .20
698 A194 2p lt brn, blk & gray   3.00 .80
  Nos. 695-698 (4)   5.45 1.40

  Thin frame on No. 696, no frame on No.
698.

UPAE
Emblem
A195

1963, May 31   Litho.
699 A195 20c ultra & blk   .50 .20
  Nos. 699,C252-C253 (3)   .95 .60

  50th anniv. of the founding of the Postal
Union of the Americas and Spain, UPAE. For
surcharge see No. C321.

Wheat
Emblem — A196

Anchors — A197

1963, July 8   Wmk. 332   Perf. 12
700 A196 10c grn & yel   .25 .20
701 A196 20c brn & yel   .30 .20
  Nos. 700-701,C254-C255 (4)   1.15 1.00

  FAO "Freedom from Hunger" campaign.

1963, Aug. 16
702 A197 10c org & vio   .25 .20
703 A197 20c dk red & gray   .30 .20
  Nos. 702-703,C256-C257 (4)   1.35 1.00

  Voyage around the world by the Uruguayan
sailing vessel "Alferez Campora," 1960-63.

Large
Intestine,
Congress
Emblem
A198

1963, Dec. 9   Litho.
704 A198 10c lt grn, blk & dk car   .25 .20
705 A198 20c org, yel, blk & dk car .30 .20

  1st Uruguayan Proctology Cong., Montevideo, Dec. 9-15.

Red Cross
Centenary
Emblem
A199

  Imprint: "Imp. Nacional"

1964, June 5   Wmk. 332   Perf. 12
706 A199 20c blue & red   .25 .20
707 A199 40c gray & red   .30 .20

  Centenary of International Red Cross.
No. 706 exists with imprint missing. Value
$4.

Luis
Alberto de
Herrera
A200

1964, July 22   Litho.   Unwmk.
708 A200 20c dl grn, bl & blk   .20 .20
709 A200 40c lt bl, bl & blk   .20 .20
710 A200 80c yel org, bl & blk   .20 .20
711 A200 1p lt vio, bl & blk   .40 .25
712 A200 2p gray, bl & blk   .60 .50
  Nos. 708-712 (5)   1.60 1.35

  Herrera (1873-1959), leader of Herrerista
party and member of National Government
Council.

Nile Gods
Uniting
Upper and
Lower
Egypt (Abu
Simbel)
A201

1964, Oct. 30   Wmk. 332   Perf. 12
713 A201 20c multi   .25 .20
  Nos. 713,C266-C267 (3)   1.15 .90

  UNESCO world campaign to save historic
monuments in Nubia. See No. C267a.

Pres. John
F. Kennedy
A202

1965, Mar. 5   Wmk. 327   Perf. 11½
714 A202 20c gold, emer & blk   .25 .20
  a. Gold omitted

715 A202 40c gold, redsh brn &
           blk   .30 .20
  a. Gold omitted
  Nos. 714-715,C269-C270 (4)   1.15 1.00

Tete
Beche
Pair of
1864, No.
21a
A203

1965, Mar. 19   Wmk. 332   Perf. 12
716 A203 40c black & green   .25 .20

  1st Rio de la Plata Stamp Show, sponsored
jointly by the Argentine and Uruguayan philatelic associations, Montevideo, Mar. 19-28.
See No. C271.

Benito
Nardone
A204

  40c, Benito Nardone before microphone.

1965, Mar. 25   Litho.
717 A204 20c blk & emer   .25 .20
718 A204 40c blk & emer, vert.   .30 .20

  1st anniversary of the death of Benito Nardone, president of the Council of Government.

Artigas Quotation — A205

  40c, Artigas bust, quotation. 80c, José
Artigas.

Perf. 12x11½
1965, May 17   Litho.   Wmk. 327
719 A205 20c bl, yel & red   .25 .20
720 A205 20c vio bl, cit & blk   .25 .20
721 A205 80c brn, yel, red & bl   .35 .20
  Nos. 719-721,C273-C275 (6)   1.80 1.40

  José Artigas (1764-1850), leader of the
independence revolt against Spain.

Soccer
A206

  Designs: 40c, Basketball. 80c, Bicycling. 1p,
Woman swimmer.

1965, Aug. 3   Litho.   Wmk. 327
722 A206 20c grn, org & blk   .30 .20
723 A206 40c hn brn, cit & blk   .30 .20
724 A206 80c gray, red & blk   .30 .20
725 A206 1p bl, yel grn & blk   .30 .20
  Nos. 722-725,C276-C281 (10)   3.90 2.80

  18th Olympic Games, Tokyo, 10/10-25/64.

No. 572A Surcharged
in Red

1965   Unwmk.   Perf. 12½
726 A138a 10c on 7c vio bl   .25 .20

No. B5 Surcharged:

1966, Jan. 25 Wmk. 327 Perf. 11½
727 SP2 4c on 5c + 10c grn & org .25 .20
Association of Uruguayan Architects, 50th anniv.

Winston
Churchill
A207

Wmk. 332
1966, Apr. 29 Litho. Perf. 12
728 A207 40c car, dp ultra & brn .25 .20
Sir Winston Spencer Churchill, statesman and World War II leader. See No. C284.

Arms of Rio
de Janeiro
and Sugar
Loaf
Mountain
A208

1966, June 9 Litho. Wmk. 332
729 A208 40c emer & brn .25 .20
400th anniversary of the founding of Rio de Janeiro. See No. C285.

Army
Engineer — A209

Daniel Fernandez
Crespo — A210

1966, June 17 Litho.
730 A209 20c blk, red, vio bl & yel .25 .20
50th anniversary of the Army Engineers Corps.

1966, Sept. 16 Wmk. 332 Perf. 12
Portraits: No. 732, Washington Beltran. No. 733, Luis Batlle Berres.
731 A210 20c lt bl & blk .25 .20
732 A210 20c lt bl & dk brn .25 .20
733 A210 20c brick red & blk .25 .20
Nos. 731-733 (3) .75 .60
Issued to honor political leaders.

Old Printing
Press — A211

1966, Oct. 14 Photo. Perf. 12
734 A211 20c tan, grnsh gray & dk brn .25 .20
50th anniversary of State Printing Office.

Fireman
A212

1966 Litho.
735 A212 20c red & blk .40 .25
Issued to publicize fire prevention. Printed with alternating red and black labels inscribed: "Prevengase del fuego! Del pueblo y para el pueblo."

No. 716 Overprinted in Red: "Segunda Muestra y / Jornadas Rioplatenses / de Filatelia / Abril 1966 / Centenario del Sello / Escudito Resellado"
1966, Nov. 4
736 A203 40c blk & grn .25 .20
2nd Rio de la Plata Stamp Show, Buenos Aires, Apr. 1966, and cent. of Uruguay's 1st surcharged issue. See No. C298.

General Leandro
Gomez — A213

#738, Gen. Juan Antonio Lavalleja. #739, Aparicio Saravia, revolutionary, on horseback.

Wmk. 332
1966, Nov. 24 Litho. Perf. 12
737 A213 20c slate, blk & dp bl .30 .25
738 A213 20c red, blk & bl .30 .25
739 A213 20c blue & blk, horiz. .30 .25
Nos. 737-739 (3) .90 .75

Montevideo
Planetarium
A214

1967, Jan. 13 Wmk. 332 Perf. 12
740 A214 40c pink & blk .30 .20
10th anniv. of the Montevideo Municipal Planetarium. See No. C301.

Sunflower, Cow
and
Emblem — A215

Church of San
Carlos — A216

1967, Jan. 13 Litho.
741 A215 40c dk brn & yel .30 .20
Young Farmers' Movement, 20th anniv.

1967, Apr. 17 Wmk. 332 Perf. 12
742 A216 40c lt bl, blk & dk red .25 .20
Bicentenary of San Carlos.

Eduardo
Acevedo
A217

1967, Apr. 17
743 A217 20c grn & brn .20 .20
744 A217 40c org & grn .25 .20
Issued to honor Eduardo Acevedo, lawyer, legislator and Minister of Foreign Affairs.

Arms of
Carmelo
A218

José Enrique Rodó
A219

1967, Aug. 11 Litho. Perf. 12
745 A218 40c lt & dk bl & ocher .25 .20
Founding of Carmelo, 150th anniv.

1967, Oct. 6 Wmk. 332 Perf. 12
2p, Portrait of Rodó and sculpture, horiz.
746 A219 1p gray, brn & blk .25 .20
747 A219 2p rose claret, blk & tan .25 .20
50th anniversary of the death of José Enrique Rodó, author.

Senen M.
Rodriguez
and
Locomotive
A220

1967, Oct. 26 Litho. Perf. 12
748 A220 2p ocher & dk brn .35 .20
Centenary of the founding of the first national railroad company.

Child and Map
of Americas
A221

Cocoi Heron
A222

1967, Nov. 10 Wmk. 332 Perf. 12
749 A221 1p vio & red .25 .20
Inter-American Children's Institute, 40th anniv.

No. 610 Surcharged
in Red

Perf. 13x13½
1967, Nov. 10 Engr. Unwmk.
750 A173 1p on 7c brn & grn .25 .20

1968-70 Wmk. 332 Litho. Perf. 12
Birds: 1p, Great horned owl. 3p, Brown-headed gull, horiz. No. 754, White-faced tree duck, horiz. No. 754A, Black-tailed stilts. 5p, Wattled jacanas, horiz. 10p, Snowy egret, horiz.
751 A222 1p dl yel & brn 2.00 .40
752 A222 2p bl grn & blk 2.00 .40
753 A222 3p org, gray & blk ('69) 1.50 .35
754 A222 4p brn, tan & blk 3.25 .60
754A A222 4p ver & blk ('70) 1.50 .35

755 A222 5p lt red brn, blk & yel 3.75 .60
756 A222 10p lil & blk 6.75 .80
Nos. 751-756 (7) 20.75 3.50

Concord
Bridge,
Presidents
of
Uruguay,
Brazil
A223

1968, Apr. 3
757 A223 6p brown .25 .20
Opening of Concord Bridge across the Uruguay River by Presidents Jorge Pacheco Areco of Uruguay and Arthur Costa e Silva of Brazil.

Soccer Player and
Trophy — A224

1968, May 29 Litho.
758 A224 1p blk & yel .25 .20
Victory of the Penarol Athletic Club in the Intercontinental Soccer Championships of 1966.

St. John
Bosco,
Symbols of
Education
and Industry
A225

1968, July 31 Wmk. 332 Perf. 12
759 A225 2p brn & blk .25 .20
75th anniv. of the Don Bosco Workshops of the Salesian Brothers.

Sailors'
Monument,
Montevideo
A226

Designs: 6p, Lighthouse and buoy, vert. 12p, Gunboat "Suarez" (1860).

1968, Nov. 12 Litho. Perf. 12
760 A226 2p gray ol & blk .20 .20
761 A226 6p lt grn & blk .20 .20
762 A226 12p brt bl & blk .20 .20
Nos. 760-762, C340-C343 (7) 1.50 1.40
Sesquicentennial of National Navy.
For surcharge see No. Q101.

Oscar D.
Gestido
A227

1968, Dec. 6 Wmk. 332 Perf. 12
763 A227 6p brn, dp car & bl .25 .20
First anniversary of the death of President Oscar D. Gestido.

Gearwheel, Grain and Two Heads A228

1969, Mar. 17   **Litho.**   **Perf. 12**
764 A228 2p blk & ver   .25 .20
    25th anniversary of Labor University.

Bicyclists A229

1969, Mar. 21   **Wmk. 332**
765 A229 6p dk bl, org & emer   .30 .20
    1968 World Bicycle Championships. See No. C347.

Gymnasts and Club Emblem A230

1969, May 8   **Wmk. 332**   **Perf. 12**
766 A230 6p blk & ver   .30 .20
    75th anniversary of L'Avenir Athletic Club.

Baltasar Brum (1883-1933) A231

    Former presidents: No. 768, Tomas Berreta (1875-1947).

1969   **Litho.**   **Perf. 12**
767 A231 6p rose red & blk   .25 .20
768 A231 6p car rose & blk   .25 .20

Fair Emblem — A232

1969, Aug. 15   **Wmk. 332**   **Perf. 12**
769 A232 2p multi   .25 .20
    Issued to publicize the 2nd Industrial World's Fair, Montevideo, 1970.

Diesel Locomotive A233

    Design: No. 771, Old steam locomotive and modern railroad cars.

1969, Sept. 19   **Litho.**   **Wmk. 332**
770 A233 6p car, blk & ultra   .30 .25
771 A233 6p car, blk & ultra   .30 .25
   e.   Pair, #770-771   .60 .60
    Centenary of Uruguayan railroads. No. 771e has continuous design and label between pairs.
    For surcharges see Nos. Q102-Q103.

Souvenir Sheet

Diligencia Issue, 1856 — A233a

1969, Oct. 1   **Imperf.**
771A A233a   Sheet of 3   8.00 8.00
   b.   60p blue   2.00 2.00
   c.   80p green   2.50 2.50
   d.   100p red   3.00 3.00
    Stamp Day 1969. No. 771A contains stamps similar to No. 1-3, with denominations in pesos.
    No. 771A was re-issued Apr. 15, 1972, with black overprint for 15th anniv. of 1st Lufthansa flight from Uruguay to Germany and the Munich Olympic Games. Value $27.50.

"Combat" and Sculptor Belloni — A234

1969, Oct. 22   **Wmk. 332**   **Perf. 12**
772 A234 6p olive, slate grn & blk   .25 .20
    José L. Belloni (1882-), sculptor.

Reserve Officers' Training Center Emblem A235

    Design: 2p, Training Center emblem, and officer in uniform and as civilian.

1969, Nov. 5   **Litho.**
773 A235 1p yel & dk bl   .25 .20
774 A235 2p dk brn & lt bl   .25 .20
    Reserve Officers' Training Center, 25th anniv.

Map of Americas and Sun — A236   Stylized Pine — A237

1970, Apr. 20   **Wmk. 332**   **Perf. 12**
775 A236 10p dp bl & gold   .25 .20
    11th meeting of the governors of the Inter-American Development Bank, Punta del Este.

1970, May 14
776 A237 2p red, blk & brt grn   .25 .20
    2nd National Forestry and Wood Exhibition.

Artigas' Ancestral Home in Sauce A238

1970, June 18   **Wmk. 332**   **Perf. 12**
777 A238 15p ver, ultra & blk   .30 .25

Map of Uruguay, Sun and Sea A239

1970, July 8   **Litho.**
778 A239 5p greenish blue   .25 .20
    Issued for tourist publicity.

EXPO '70 Emblem, Mt. Fuji and Uruguay Coat of Arms A240

    EXPO '70 Intl. Exhibition, Osaka, Japan, 3/15-9/13: No. 780, Geisha. No. 781, Sun Tower. No. 782, Youth pole.

1970, Aug. 5   **Wmk. 332**   **Perf. 12**
779 A240 25p grn, slate bl & yel   .30 .30
780 A240 25p org, slate bl & grn   .30 .30
781 A240 25p yel, slate bl & pur   .30 .30
782 A240 25p pur, slate bl & org   .30 .30
   a.   Block of 4, #779-782   1.25 1.25

Cobbled Street in Colonia del Sacramento A241

Mother and Son by Edmundo Prati in Salto — A242

1970, Oct. 21   **Litho.**   **Perf. 12**
783 A241 5p blk & multi   .25 .20
    290th anniv. of the founding of Colonia del Sacramento, the 1st European settlement in Uruguay.

1970, Nov. 4   **Litho.**
784 A242 10p grn & blk   .35 .30
    Issued to honor mothers.

URUEXPO Emblem A243

1970, Dec. 9   **Wmk. 332**   **Perf. 12**
785 A243 15p bl, brn org & vio   .30 .30
    URUEXPO '70, National Philatelic Exposition, Montevideo, Sept. 26-Oct. 4.

Children Holding Hands, and UNESCO Emblem — A244

    Children's Drawings: No. 786, Two girls holding hands, vert. No. 788, Boy sitting at school desk, vert. No. 789, Astronaut and monster.

1970, Dec. 29   **Litho.**   **Perf. 12½**
786 A244 10p multi   .20 .20
787 A244 10p multi   .20 .20
788 A244 10p dp car & multi   .20 .20
789 A244 10p bl & multi   .20 .20
   a.   Block of 4, #786-789 + 2 labels   .80 .80
    International Education Year.

Alfonso Espinola (1845-1905), Physician, Professor and Philanthropist A245

1971, Jan. 13   **Wmk. 332**   **Perf. 12**
790 A245 5p org & blk   .25 .20

Exposition Poster — A246

1971   **Litho.**   **Perf. 12**
791 A246 15p multi   .25 .20
    Uruguay Philatelic Exposition, 1971, Montevideo, March 26-Apr. 19.

5c Coin of 1840, Obverse A247

    Design: #793, 1st coin of Uruguay, reverse.

1971, Apr. 16   **Wmk. 332**   **Perf. 12**
792 A247 25p bl, brn & blk   .55 .55
793 A247 25p bl, brn & blk   .45 .45
   a.   Pair, #792-793   1.25 1.25
    Numismatists' Day.

Domingo Arena, Lawyer and Journalist — A248

1971, May 3   **Wmk. 332**   **Perf. 12**
794 A248 5p dk car   .25 .20

National Anthem A249

1971, May 19   **Litho.**
795 A249 15p bl, blk & yel   .30 .30

José F. Arias, Physician — A250

1971, May 25   Wmk. 332   *Perf. 12*
796 A250 5p sepia   .25 .20

Eduardo Fabini, Bar from "Campo" A251

1971, June 2   **Litho.**
797 A251 5p dk car rose & blk   .30 .30
Eduardo Fabini (1882-1950), composer, and 40th anniversary of first radio concert.

José E. Rodó, UPAE Emblem A252

1971, July 15   Wmk. 332   *Perf. 12*
798 A252 15p ultra & blk   .25 .20
José Enrique Rodó (1871-1917), writer, first Uruguayan delegate to Congress of the Postal Union of the Americas and Spain.

Water Cart and Faucet A253

1971, July 17
799 A253 5p ultra & multi   .25 .20
Centenary of Montevideo's drinking water system.

Sheep and Cloth A254

Design: 15p, Sheep, cloth and bale of wool.

1971, Aug. 7
800 A254 5p grn & gray   .20 .20
801 A254 15p dk bl, grnsh bl & gray .25 .20
Wool Promotion.

José Maria Elorza and Merilin Sheep A255

1971, Aug. 10
802 A255 5p lt bl, grn & blk   .20 .20
José Maria Elorza, developer of the Merilin sheep.

Criollo Horse A256

1971, Aug. 11
803 A256 5p blk, gray bl & org   .25 .20

Bull and Ram A257

1971, Aug. 13
804 A257 20p red, grn, blk & gold   .40 .35
Centenary of Rural Association of Uruguay; 19th International Cattle Breeding Exposition, and 66th National Cattle Championships at Prado, Aug. 1971.

Symbol of Liberty and Order A258

20p, Policemen, flag of Uruguay and emblem.

1971
805 A258 10p gray, blk & bl   .25 .20
806 A258 20p dk bl, blk, lt bl &
        gold   .30 .25
To honor policemen killed on duty. Issue dates: 10p, Sept. 9; 20p, Nov. 4.

10p Banknote of 1896 — A259

Design: No. 808, Reverse of 10p note.

1971, Sept. 23
807 A259 25p dl grn, gold & blk   .40 .40
808 A259 25p dl grn, gold & blk   .40 .40
 a. Pair, #807-808 + label   1.00 1.00
75th anniversary of Bank of the Republic.

Farmer and Arms of Durazno A260

1971, Oct. 11
809 A260 20p gold, bl & blk   .25 .20
Sesquicentennial of the founding of Durazno.

Emblem and Laurel — A261

1971, Oct. 20
810 A261 10p vio bl, gold & red   .25 .20
Winners of Liberator's Cup, American Soccer Champions, 1971.
For surcharge see No. 825.

Voter Casting Ballot — A262

Design: 20p, Citizens voting, horiz.

1971, Nov. 22   Wmk. 332   *Perf. 12*
811 A262 10p bl & blk   .25 .20
812 A262 20p bl & blk   .25 .20
Universal, secret and obligatory franchise.

Map of Uruguay on Globe A263

1971, Dec. 23
813 A263 20p lt bl & vio brn   .25 .20
7th Littoral Expo., Paysandu, 3/26-4/11.

Juan Lindolfo Cuestas — A264

1971, Dec. 27
814 A264 10p shown   .20 .20
815 A264 10p Julio Herrera y
        Obes   .20 .20
816 A264 10p Claudio Williman   .20 .20
817 A264 10p José Serrato   .20 .20
818 A264 10p Andres Martinez
        Truebá   .20 .20
 a. Horiz. strip of 5, #814-818   1.25 1.25
Presidents of Uruguay.

Souvenir Sheet

Uruguay No. 4, Cathedral of Montevideo and Plaza de la Constitucion — A265

1972, Jan. 17   ***Imperf.***
819 A265 120p brn, bl & dp rose   1.00 1.00
Stamp Day 1971 (release date delayed). See Nos. 834-835, 863.

Bartolomé Hidalgo — A266

Missa Solemnis, by Beethoven — A267

1972, Feb. 28   ***Perf. 12***
820 A266 5p lt brn, blk & red   .25 .20
Bartolomé Hidalgo (1788-1822), Uruguayan-Argentine poet.

1972, Apr. 20   Litho.   Wmk. 332
822 A267 20p lil, emer & blk   .25 .20
12th Choir Festival of Eastern Uruguay.

Dove and Wounded Bird — A268

Columbus Arch, Colon — A269

1972, May 9
823 A268 10p ver & multi   .25 .20
To honor Dionision Disz (age 9), who died saving his sister.

1972, June 21
824 A269 20p red, bl & blk   .25 .20
Centenary of Colon, now suburb of Montevideo.

No. 810 Surcharged in Silver

(Surcharge 69mm wide)

1972, June 30
825 A261 50p on 10p multi   .25 .25
    Winners of the 1971 Intl. Soccer Cup.

Tree
Planting — A270

"Collective
Housing" — A271

1972, Aug. 5   Wmk. 332   Perf. 12
826 A270 20p grn & blk   .25 .20
    Afforestation program.

1972, Sept. 30   Litho.
827 A271 10p dp bl & multi   .25 .20
    Publicity for collective housing plan.

Amethyst
A272

Uruguayan Gem Stones: 9p, Agate. 15p,
Chalcedony.

1972, Oct. 7
828 A272 5p gray & multi   .25 .25
829 A272 9p gray bl & multi   .25 .25
830 A272 15p gray grn & multi   .30 .30
    Nos. 828-830 (3)   .80 .80

Uniform of
1830 — A273

Design: 20p, Lancer.

1972, Nov. 21   Litho.
831 A273 10p multi   .25 .20
832 A273 20p rose red & multi   .25 .25

Red
Cross and
Map of
Uruguay
A274

1972, Dec. 11   Wmk. 332   Perf. 12
833 A274 30p multi   .30 .25
    75th anniv. of the Uruguayan Red Cross.

Stamp Day Type of 1972
Souvenir Sheets

Designs: 200p, Coat of arms type of 1864
similar to Nos. 18, 20-21, but 60p, 60p and
80p. 220p, Similar to Nos. 22-23, but 100p and
120p.

1972, Dec. 20   Imperf.
834 A265 200p multi   1.25 .60
835 A265 220p multi   1.50 .75
    Stamp Day 1972. 1st printed cancellations,
200th anniv., #834; Decree establishing regular postal service, cent., #835.

Scales of
Justice,
Olive
Branch
A275

1972, Dec. 27   Wmk. 332   Perf. 12
836 A275 10p gold, dk & lt bl   .25 .20
    Civil Rights Law for Women, 25th anniv.

Gen. José   Hand Holding Cup;
Artigas   Grain, Map of
A276   Americas
                       A277

1972-74   Wmk. 332   Litho.   Perf. 12
837 A276 5p yel ('74)   .20 .20
838 A276 10p dk bis ('74)   .20 .20
839 A276 15p emer ('74)   .20 .20
840 A276 20p lilac ('73)   .20 .20
841 A276 30p lt bl ('73)   .20 .20
842 A276 40p dp org ('73)   .20 .20
843 A276 50p ver ('73)   .20 .20
844 A276 75p ap grn ('73)   .20 .20
845 A276 100p emerald   .20 .20
846 A276 150p choc ('73)   .20 .20
847 A276 200p dk bl ('73)   .35 .30
848 A276 250p pur ('73)   .40 .35
849 A276 500p gray ('73)   1.00 .60
849A A276 1000p blue ('73)   2.00 1.25
    Nos. 837-849A (14)   5.75 4.50

    For surcharges see Nos. 929-932.

1973, Jan. 9
850 A277 30p rose red, yel & blk   .25 .20
    Intl. Institute for Agricultural Research, 39th
anniv.

Elbio Fernández
and José P.
Varela — A278

1973, Jan. 16
851 A278 10p dl grn, gold & blk   .25 .20
    Society of Friends of Public Education, cent.

Map of
Americas,
"1972" and
Columbus
A279

1973, Jan. 30
852 A279 50p purple   .20 .20
    Tourist Year of the Americas 1972.

Carlos
Maria
Ramirez,
Scales
and
Books
A280

1973, Feb. 15
853 A280 10p shown   .20 .20
854 A280 10p Justino Jimenez
             de Arechaga   .20 .20
855 A280 10p Juan Andres Ra-
             mirez   .20 .20
856 A280 10p Justino E. Jimenez
             de Arechaga   .20 .20
    a. Horiz. strip, #853-856 + label 1.00 1.00
    Professorship of Constitutional Rights, cent.

Provincial
Map of
Uruguay
A281

1973, Feb. 27   Litho.   Perf. 12½x12
857 A281 20p bl & multi   .25 .20
    See No. 1167.

Francisco
de los
Santos
A282

1973, May 16   Wmk. 332   Perf. 12
858 A282 20p grn & blk   .25 .20
    Soldiers' Day and Battle of Piedras. Santos
was a courier who went through enemy lines.

No. C319 Surcharged with New Value
and: "HOMENAJE AL 4 CENTENARIO
DE CORDOBA . ARGENTINA . 1973"
1973, May 9   Litho.   Imperf.
    Souvenir Sheet
859 AP57 100p on 5p multi   .75 .75
    Founding of Cordoba in Argentina, 400th
anniv.

Friar, Indians,
Church — A283

1973, July 25   Perf. 12
860 A283 20p lt ultra, pur & blk   .25 .20
    Villa Santo Domingo Soriano, first Spanish
settlement in Uruguay.

Symbolic
Fish
A284

1973, Aug. 15
861 A284 100p bl & multi   .30 .25
    First station of Oceanographic and Fishery
Service, Montevideo.

A285

Herrera — A286

Sun over flower in Italian colors.

1973, Sept.
862 A285 100p multi   .20 .20
    Italian Chamber of Commerce of Uruguay.

Stamp Day Type of 1972
Souvenir Sheet

Design: 240p, Thin numeral sun type of
1859 and street scene.

            Wmk. 332
1973, Oct. 1   Litho.   Imperf.
863 A265 240p grn, org & blk   1.50 1.50
    Stamp Day 1973.

1973, Nov. 12   Perf. 12
866 A286 50p gray, brn & dk brn   .20 .20
    Centenary of the birth of Luis Alberto de
Herrera.

Emblem of
Social
Coordination
Volunteers
A287

            Wmk. 352
1973, Nov. 19   Litho.   Perf. 12
867 A287 50p bl & multi   .25 .20
    Festival of Nations, Montevideo.

Arm with
Arteries and
Heart
A288

1973, Nov. 22
868 A288 50p blk, red & pink   .20 .20
    3rd Cong. of the Pan-American Federation
of Blood Donors, Montevideo, Nov. 23-25.

Madonna, by Rafael Perez Barradas — A289

1973, Dec. 10   Litho.   Wmk. 332
869 A289 50p grn, gray & yel grn   .30 .20
Christmas 1973.

Nicolaus Copernicus — A290

1973, Dec. 26   Litho.
870 A290 50p grn & multi   .25 .20
500th anniversary of the birth of Nicolaus Copernicus (1473-1543), Polish astronomer.

Praying Hands and Andes — A291

75p, Statue of Christ on mountain, and flower.

1973, Dec. 26   Litho.
871 A291 50p blk, lt grn & ultra   .20 .20
872 A291 75p bl, blk & org   .25 .20
Survival and rescue of victims of airplane crash.

OAS Emblem and Map of Americas A292

1974, Jan. 14   Wmk. 332   Perf. 12
873 A292 250p gray & multi   .60 .40
25th anniversary of the Organization of American States (OAS).

Scout Emblems and Flame A293

1974, Jan. 21
874 A293 250p multi   .60 .40
1st Intl. Boy Scout Games, Montevideo, 1974.

Hector Suppici Sedes and Car — A294

1974, Jan. 28   Perf. 12
875 A294 50p sep, grn & blk   .30 .25
70th anniversary of the birth of Hector Suppici Sedes (1903-1948), automobile racer.

Three Gauchos — A295

1974, Mar. 20   Litho.   Wmk. 332
876 A295 50p multi   .25 .20
Centenary of the publication of "Los Tres Gauchos Orientales" by Antonio D. Lussich.

Rifle, Target and Swiss Flag A296

1974, Apr. 2
877 A296 100p multi   .25 .20
Centenary of the Swiss Rifle Association.

Map of Uruguay and Compass Rose A297

1974, Apr. 23   Litho.
878 A297 50p multi   .25 .20
Military Geographical Service.

Montevideo Stadium Tower — A298

Design: 75p, Soccer player, Games' emblem, horiz. 1000p, similar to 75p.

1974, May 7   Wmk. 332   Perf. 12
879 A298   50p multi   .20 .20
880 A298   75p multi   .20 .20
881 A298   1000p multicolored   20.00 7.75
World Cup Soccer Championship, Munich, June 13-July 7.
No. 881 had limited distribution. A souvenir sheet of one No. 881 was not valid for postage.

Tourism — A299

Wmk. 332
1974, June 6   Litho.   Perf. 12
882 A299 1000p multicolored   35.00 35.00
No. 882 had limited distribution.

Old and New School and Founders A300

1974, May 21
883 A300 75p black & bister   .25 .20
Centenary of the Osimani-Llerena Technical School at Salto, founded by Gervasio Osimani and Miguel Llerena.

Gardel and Score — A301

Volleyball and Net — A302

Wmk. 332
1974, June 24   Litho.   Perf. 12
884 A301 100p multi   .35 .25
Carlos Gardel (1887-1935), singer and motion picture actor. See No. 1173.

1974, July 11   Wmk. 332   Perf. 12
885 A302 200p lil, yel & blk   .30 .25
First anniversary of Women's Volleyball championships, Montevideo, 1973.

"Protect your Heart" — A303

Portrait and Statue — A304

1974, July 24   Litho.
886 A303 75p ol grn, yel & red   .25 .20
Heart Foundation publicity.

1974, Aug. 5
887 A304 75p dk & lt bl   .25 .20
Centenary (in 1973) of the founding of San José de Mayo by Eusebio Vidal.

A305   A306

Artigas statue, Buenos Aires, flags of Uruguay and Argentina.

1974, Aug. 13   Perf. 12½
888 A305 75p multi   .30 .20
Unveiling of Artigas monument, Buenos Aires.

1974, Sept. 24   Wmk. 332   Perf. 12
889 A306 100p Radio tower and waves   .20 .20
50th anniv. of Broadcasting in Uruguay.

URUEXPO 74 Emblem — A307

URUEXPO Emblem and Old Map of Montevideo Bay — A308

1974
890 A307 100p blk, dk bl & red   .20 .20
891 A308 300p sepia, red & grn   .50 .50
URUEXPO 74 Philatelic Exhibition, 10th anniversary of Philatelic Circle of Uruguay (100p) and 250th anniversary of fortification of Montevideo.
Issue dates: 100p, Oct. 1; 300p, Oct. 19.

Letters and UPU Emblem A309

UPU Cent.: 200p, UPU emblem, letter, and globe.

1974, Oct. 9
892 A309 100p lt bl & multi .20 .20
893 A309 200p lil, blk & gold .30 .20
   Nos. 892-893,C395-C396 (4) 2.10 2.00

A 1000p souvenir sheet was not valid for postage. Value $45.

Artigas Statue and Map of Lavalleja A310

1974, Oct. 17   **Perf. 12**
894 A310 100p ultra & multi .30 .20

Unveiling of Artigas statue in Minas, Lavalleja.

Ship in Dry Dock, Arsenal's Emblem A312

1974, Nov. 15   **Litho.**   **Wmk. 332**
896 A312 200p multi .30 .30

Centenary of Naval Arsenal, Montevideo.

Globe Hydrogen Balloon — A313

1974, Nov. 20
897 A313 100p shown .25 .20
898 A313 100p Farman biplane .25 .20
899 A313 100p Castaibert monoplane .25 .20
900 A313 100p Bleriot monoplane .25 .20
  a. Strip of 4, #897-900 1.50 1.50
901 A313 150p Military and civilian pilots' em-
   blems .25 .20
902 A313 150p Nieuport biplane .25 .20
903 A313 150p Breguet-Bidon
   fighter .25 .20
904 A313 150p Caproni bomber .25 .20
  a. Strip of 4, #901-904 1.50 1.50
   Nos. 897-904 (8) 2.00 1.60

Aviation pioneers.

Sugar Loaf Mountain and Summit Cross — A314

1974, Nov. 30
905 A314 150p multi .25 .20

Cent. of the founding of Sugar Loaf City.

Adoration of the Kings — A315

1974   **Perf. 12**
906 A315 100p shown .20 .20
907 A315 150p Three Kings .20 .20
   Nos. 906-907,C400 (3) .70 .60

Christmas 1974. See No. C401. Issue dates: 100p, Dec. 17; 150p, Dec. 19.

Nike, Fireworks, Rowers and Club Emblem — A316

1975, Jan. 27   **Litho.**   **Wmk. 332**
908 A316 150p gray & multi .20 .20

Centenary of Montevideo Rowing Club.

Treaty Signing, by José Zorilla de San Martin — A317

1975, Feb. 12   **Perf. 12**
909 A317 100p multi .30 .20

Commercial Treaty between Great Britain and Uruguay, 1817.

Rose — A318

1975, Mar. 18   **Litho.**   **Wmk. 332**
910 A318 150p multi .60 .40

Bicentenary of city of Rosario.

"The Oath of the 33," by Juan M. Blanes — A319

1975, Apr. 16   **Perf. 12**
911 A319 150p gold & multi .35 .20

Sesquicentennial of liberation movement.

Ship, Columbus and Ancient Map — A320

1975, Oct. 9   **Litho.**   **Wmk. 332**
912 A320 1p gray & multi 1.25 .80

Hispanic Stamp Day.

Leonardo Olivera and Santa Teresa Fort — A321

Artigas as Young and Old Man A322

1975   **Litho.**   **Wmk. 332**   *Perf. 12*
913 A321 10c org & multi .20 .20
914 A322 50c vio bl & multi .50 .40

Sesquicentennial of the capture of Fort Santa Teresa (10c) and of Uruguay's declaration of independence (50c).
  Issue dates: 10c, Oct. 20; 50c, Oct. 17.

Battle of Rincon, by Diogenes Hequet — A323

#916, Artigas' Home, Ibiray, Paraguay. 25c, Battle of Sarandi, by J. Manuel Blanes.

1975
915 A323 15c ol & blk .20 .20
916 A323 15c ol & multi .20 .20
917 A323 25c ol & multi .30 .30
   Nos. 915-917 (3) .70 .70

Uruguayan independence. Nos. 915 and 917, 150th anniversary of Battles of Rincon and Sarandi. No. 916, 50th anniversary of school at Artigas mansion.
  Issued: #915, 10/23; #916, 11/18; #917, 11/28.

"En Familia," by Sanchez A324

Florencio Sanchez A325

Plays by Sanchez: #919, Barranca Abajo. #920, M'Hijo el Doctor. #921, Canillita.

1975, Oct. 31   **Wmk. 332**   *Perf. 12*
918 A324 20c gray, red & blk .30 .20
919 A324 20c bl, grn & blk .30 .20
920 A324 20c red, bl & blk .30 .20
921 A324 20c grn, gray & blk .30 .20
922 A325 20c multi .30 .20
  a. Block of 5 stamps + 4 labels 2.50

Florencio Sanchez (1875-1910), dramatist, birth centenary. Nos. 918-922 printed se-tenant in sheets of 30 stamps and 20 labels.

Maria Eugenia Vaz Ferreira A326

Design: No. 924, Julio Herrera y Reissig.

1975
923 A326 15c yel, blk & brn .20 .20
924 A326 15c org, blk & maroon .20 .20

Maria Eugenia Vaz Ferreira (1875-1924), poetess, and Julio Herrera y Reissig (1875-1910), poet, birth anniversaries.
  Issue dates: #923, Dec. 9; #924, Dec. 29.

A327

Virgin and
Child — A328

Fireworks — A329

1975
925 A327 20c bl & multi .30 .30
926 A328 30c blk & multi .45 .45
927 A329 60c multi .60 .60
Nos. 925-927 (3) 1.35 1.35
Christmas 1975.
Issued: 20c, 12/16; 30c, 12/15; 60c, 12/11.

Col. Lorenzo
Latorre (1840-
1916), Pres. of
Uruguay (1876-
80)
A330

1975, Dec. 30 *Perf. 12*
928 A330 15c multi .30 .20

Nos. 840, 842-843,
849A Surcharged

1975
929 A276 10c on 20p lilac .25 .25
930 A276 15c on 40p orange .25 .25
931 A276 50c on 50p ver .45 .45
932 A276 1p on 1000p blue .95 .95
Nos. 929-932 (4) 1.90 1.90
There are two surcharge types for Nos. 929
and 930. Values are the same.

Ariel,
Stars,
Book and
Youths
A331

1976, Jan. 12 Litho. Wmk. 332
933 A331 15c grn & multi .20 .20
75th anniversary of publication of "Ariel," by
Jose Enrique Rodo (1872-1917), writer.

Water
Sports — A332

Telephone
A333

1976, Mar. 12 Litho. Wmk. 332
934 A332 30c multi .25 .20
23rd South American Swimming, Diving and
Water Polo Championships.

1976, Apr. 9 *Perf. 12*
935 A333 83c multi .45 .30
Centenary of first telephone call by Alexander Graham Bell, Mar. 10, 1876.

"Plus Ultra"
and Columbus'
Ships — A334

Wmk. 332
1976, May 10 Litho. Perf. 12
936 A334 63c gray & multi .50 .30
Flight of Dornier "Plus Ultra" from Spain to
South America, 50th anniversary.

A335 A336

Dornier "Wal" and Boeing 727, hourglass.

1976, May 24
937 A335 83c gray & multi .75 .30
Lufthansa German Airline, 50th anniv.

1976, June 3 *Perf. 11½*
Designs: 10c, Olympics. 15c, Telephone,
cent. 25c, UPU, cent., UN #2. 50c, World Cup
Soccer Championships, Argentina, 1978.
938 A336 10c shown 1.40 .50
939 A336 15c multicolored 1.40 .50
940 A336 25c multicolored 1.40 .50
941 A336 50c multicolored 1.40 .50
Nos. 938-941 (4) 5.60 2.00
Nos. 938-941 had limited distribution.
A souvenir sheet containing one each, Nos.
938-941, was not valid for postage. Value $25.

Louis
Braille
A340

1976, June 7
942 A340 60c blk & brn .75 .30
Sesquicentennial of the invention of the
Braille system of writing for the blind by Louis
Braille (1809-1852).

Signing of US
Declaration of
Independence
A341

1976, June 21
943 A341 1.50p multi 1.75 1.40
American Bicentennial.

The Candombe, by P. Figari — A342

Wmk. 332
1976, July 29 Litho. Perf. 12
944 A342 30c ultra & multi .25 .20
Abolition of slavery, sesquicentennial.

Gen.
Fructuoso
Rivera
Statue
A343

1976, Aug. 2
945 A343 5p on 10p multi 3.50 1.75
No. 945 was not issued without surcharge.

General Accounting Office — A344

Wmk. 332
1976, Aug. 24 Litho. Perf. 12
946 A344 30c bl, blk & brn .30 .20
National General Accounting Office,
sesquicentennial.

Old Pump,
Emblem and
Flame — A345

1976, Sept. 6
947 A345 20c red & blk .20 .20
First official fire fighting service, centenary.

Spearhead
A348

Figurine
A349

La Yerra, by J.
M. Blanes
A350

The Gaucho,
by Blanes
A351

Artigas — A352

Designs: 15c, Ceibo flower.

1976-79 Litho. Wmk. 332 Perf. 12
948 A346 1c violet .20 .20
949 A347 5c lt grn .20 .20
950 A347 15c car rose .20 .20
951 A348 20c gray .20 .20
952 A349 30c gray blue .20 .20
953 A352 45c brt bl ('79) .20 .20
954 A350 50c grnsh bl ('77) .20 .20
955 A351 1p dk brn ('77) .40 .20
956 A352 1p brt yel ('79) .20 .20
957 A352 1.75p bl grn ('79) .30 .30
958 A352 1.95p gray ('79) .30 .30
959 A352 2p dl grn ('77) .95 .40
960 A352 2p lil rose ('79) .40 .35
961 A352 2.65p vio ('79) .40 .40
962 A352 5p dk bl 3.00 2.00
963 A352 10p brn ('77) 5.75 2.00
Nos. 948-963 (16) 13.10 7.55

"Diligencia" Uruguay No. 1 — A353

Wmk. 332
1976, Sept. 26 Litho. Perf. 12
964 A353 30c bister, red & blue .30 .20
Philatelic Club of Uruguay, 50th anniv.

Games'
Emblem — A354

1976, Oct. 26 Litho. Perf. 12
965 A354 83c gray & multi .75 .40
5th World University Soccer Championships.

World Cup Soccer Championships,
Argentina — A355

Anniversaries and Events: 30c, 1976 Summer Olympics, Montreal. 50c, Viking spacecraft. 80c, Nobel prizes, 75th anniv.

Southern
Lapwing
A346

Mburucuya
Flower
A347

1976, Nov. 12   **Perf. 12**
966	A355	10c multicolored	1.60	.80
967	A355	30c multicolored	1.60	.80
968	A355	50c multicolored	1.60	.80
969	A355	80c multicolored	1.60	.80
	Nos. 966-969 (4)		6.40	3.20

Nos. 966-969 had limited distribution.
See Nos. C424-C425.

Eye and Spectrum
A356

1976, Nov. 24
970 A356 20c blk & multi   .30 .20

Foresight prevents blindness.

Map of Montevideo, 1748 — A357

45c, Montevideo Harbor, 1842. 70c, First settlers, 1726. 80c, Coin with Montevideo arms, vert. 1.15p, Montevideo's first coat of arms, vert.

Wmk. 332
1976, Dec. 30   **Litho.**   **Perf. 12**
971	A357	30c multi	.30	.20
972	A357	45c multi	.45	.20
973	A357	70c multi	.60	.35
974	A357	80c multi	.85	.35
975	A357	1.15p multi	1.40	.45
	Nos. 971-975 (5)		3.60	1.55

Founding of Montevideo, 250th anniversary.

Symbolic of Flight
A358

1977, May 7   **Litho.**   **Perf. 12**
976 A358 80c multi   .75 .50

50th anniversary of Varig airlines.

Artigas Mausoleum — A359

1977, June 17   **Litho.**   **Perf. 12**
977 A359 45c multi   .45 .30

A360

A361

1977, July 5   **Wmk. 332**
978 A360 45c Map of Uruguay, arch   .45 .30

Centenary of Salesian Brothers' educational system in Uruguay.

1977, July 21

Anniversaries and events: 20c, Werner Heisenberg, Nobel Prize for Physics. 30c, World Cup Soccer Championships, Uruguay Nos. 282, 390. 50c, Lindbergh's trans-Atlantic flight, 50th anniv. 1p, Rubens 400th birth anniv.

979	A361	20c shown	1.25	.80
980	A361	30c multicolored	1.25	.80
981	A361	50c multicolored	1.25	.80
982	A361	1p multicolored	1.25	.80
a.	Strip, 2 ea #979-982 + 2 labels		—	—
	Nos. 979-982 (4)		5.00	3.20

Nos. 979-982 had limited distribution.
A souvenir sheet containing Nos. 979-982, imperf., was not valid for postage. It sold for 8p. See Nos. C426-C427.

Children — A362

Windmills — A364

"El Sol de Mayo"
A363

1977, Aug. 10   **Litho.**   **Perf. 12**
983 A362 45c multi   .45 .30

Interamerican Children's Inst., 50th anniv.

1977, Oct. 1   **Litho.**   **Perf. 12**
984 A363 45c multi   .35 .35

Stamp Day 1977.

1977, Sept. 29   **Wmk. 332**
985 A364 70c yel, car & blk   .55 .35

Spanish Heritage Day.

Souvenir Sheet

View of Sans (Barcelona), by Barradas — A365

1977, Oct. 7   **Litho.**   **Perf. 12**
986	A365	Sheet of 2	6.50	6.50
a.-b.		5p, single stamp	3.00	3.00

ESPAMER '77 Philatelic Exhibition, Barcelona, Oct. 7-13.

Planes, UN Emblem, Globe
A366

1977, Oct. 17
987 A366 45c multi   .25 .20

30th anniv. of Civil Aviation Organization.

Holy Family — A367

Santa Claus — A368

1977, Dec. 1   **Wmk. 332**
988 A367 45c multi   .25 .20
989 A368 70c blk, yel & red   .25 .20

Christmas 1977.

Map of Rio Negro Province
A369

1977, Dec. 16
990 A369 45c multi   .20 .20

Rio Negro Dam; development of argiuclture, livestock and beekeeping. See Nos. 1021-1033.

Mail Collection
A370

1977, Dec. 21
991	A370	50c shown	.20	.20
992	A370	50c Mail truck	.20	.20
993	A370	50c Post office counter	.20	.20
994	A370	50c Postal boxes	.20	.20
995	A370	50c Mail sorting	.20	.20
996	A370	50c Pigeonhole sorting	.20	.20
997	A370	50c Route sorting (seated carriers)	.20	.20
998	A370	50c Home delivery	.20	.20
999	A370	50c Special delivery (motorcyclists)	.20	.20
1000	A370	50c Airport counter	.20	.20
a.		Strip of 10, #991-1000	2.40	2.40

Uruguayan postal service, 150th anniv.

Edison's Phonograph, 1877 — A371

1977, Dec. 30
1001 A371 50c vio brn & yel   .20 .20

Centenary of invention of the phonograph.

"R", Rainbow and Emblem
A372

1977, Dec. 30   **Wmk. 332**
1002 A372 50c multi   .20 .20

World Rheumatism Year.

Emblem and Diploma
A373

1978, Mar. 27   **Litho.**   **Perf. 12**
1003 A373 50c multi   .25 .25

50th anniversary of Military College.

Erhard Schon by Albrecht Durer (1471-1528) — A374

Painting: 50c, Self-Portrait by Peter Paul Rubens (1577-1640).

1978, June 13   **Perf. 12½**
1004 A374 25c blk & brn   1.00 .95
1005 A374 50c brn & blk   1.75 1.40

Nos. 1004-1005 had limited distribution.
See Nos. C430-C432.

Map and Arms of Artigas
Department — A375

Wmk. 332
1978, June 16   Litho.   *Perf.* 12
1006 A375 45c multi   .30 .20

Souvenir Sheet

Anniversaries — A376

Designs: 2p, Papilio thoas. No. 1007b,
"100." No. 1007c, Argentina '78 emblem and
globes. 5p, Model T Ford.

Wmk. 332
1978, Aug. 24   Litho.   *Perf.* 12
1007 A376 Sheet of 4   18.00 18.00
  a. 2p multi   1.75 1.75
  b. 4p multi   3.50 3.50
  c. 4p multi   3.50 3.50
  d. 5p multi   4.25 4.25

75th anniv. of 1st powered flight; URUEXPO
'78 Phil. Exhib.; Parva Domus social club,
cent.; 11th World Cup Soccer Championship,
Argentina, June 1-25; Ford motor cars, 75th
anniv.

Visiting Angels, by Solari — A377

Designs (Details from No. 1008b): No.
1008a, Second angel. No. 1008c, Third angel.

1978, Sept. 13   Unwmk.
1008 Strip of 3   1.60 1.60
  a. A377 1.50p, 19x30mm   .30 .30
  b. A377 1.50p, 38x30mm   .30 .30
  c. A377 1.50p, 19x30mm   .30 .30

Solari, Uruguayan painter.

Bernardo
O'Higgins
A378

#1010, José de San Martin and monument.

1978   Wmk. 332
1009 A378 1p multi   .25 .20
1010 A378 1p multi   .25 .20

Benardo O'Higgins (1778-1842 and José de
San Martin (1778-1850), South American
liberators.
Issued: #1009, Sept. 13; #1010, Oct. 10.

Telephone
Dials
A379

1978, Sept. 25
1011 A379 50c multi   .30 .20
Automation of telephone service.

Symbolic
Stamps
A380

Iberian Tile
Pattern — A381

1978, Oct. 31
1012 A380 50c multi   .25 .20
1013 A381 1p multi   .25 .20
Stamp Day (50c) and Spanish heritage (1p).

Boeing
727
A382

1978, Nov. 27
1014 A382 50c multi   .50 .20
Inauguration of Boeing 727 flights by
PLUNA Uruguayan airlines, Nov. 1978.

Angel Blowing Horn — A383

1978, Dec. 7
1015 A383 50c multi   .20 .20
1016 A383 1p multi   .30 .20
Christmas 1978.

A384

A385

1978, Dec. 15   *Perf.* 12½
1017 A384 1p Flag flying on Plaza
            of the Nation   .25 .20

Wmk. 332
1978, Dec. 27   Litho.   *Perf.* 12
1018 A385 1p blk, red & yel   .30 .20
Horacio Quiroga (1868-1928), short story
writer.

Arch,
Olympic
Rings,
Lake
Placid and
Moscow
Emblems
A386

7p, Olympic Rings, Lake Placid '80 emblem.

1979, Apr. 28   Litho.   *Perf.* 12
1019 A386 5p multi   1.75 1.40
1020 A386 7p multi   2.00 1.00
81st Session of Olympic Organizing Committee, Apr. 3-8 (5p), and 13th Winter Olympic
Games, Lake Placid, NY, Feb. 12-24.

Souvenir Sheets
1021   Sheet of 4   30.00 30.00
  a. A386 3p similar to #1019
  b. A386 5p Olympic rings
  c. A386 7p Rider looking back
  d. A386 10p Rider facing forward
1022   Sheet of 4   30.00 30.00
  a. A386 3p similar to #1020
  b. A386 5p Uruguay '79
  c. A386 7p World Chess Olym-
            pics '78
  d. A386 10p Sir Rowland Hill,
            Great Britain stamp

No. 1022d shows Great Britain No. 836, but
with 11p denomination. No. 1021c-1021d have
continuous design.
Nos. 1021-1022 had limited distribution.
Except for No. 1022d, singles were sold for
postal use in 1980. Nos. 1021-1022 exist
imperf.

Map and
Arms of
Paysandu
A387

Map and Arms of
Maldonado
A388

1979-81
1023 A387 45c shown   .20 .20
1024 A387 45c Salto   .20 .20
1025 A388 45c shown   .20 .20
1026 A387 45c Cerro Largo   .20 .20
1027 A387 50c Treinta y Tres   .20 .20
1028 A387 50c Durazno ('80)   .20 .20
1029 A388 2p Rocha ('81)   .35 .35
1030 A388 2p Flores   .35 .35
  Nos. 1023-1030 (8)   1.90 1.90
  See No. 990.

Sapper with
Pickax,
1837 — A389

Army Day: No. 1039, Artillery man with cannon, 1830.

1979, May 18   Litho.   *Perf.* 12
1038 A389 5p multi   1.90 1.00
1039 A389 5p multi   1.90 1.00

Madonna
and Child
by Durer
A390

Anniversaries and events: 80c, World Cup
Soccer Championships, Spain. 1.30p, Sir
Rowland Hill, Greece No. 117.

1979, June 18   *Perf.* 12
1040 A390 70c brn & gray   6.50 3.25
1041 A390 80c multicolored   5.00 2.75
1042 A390 1.30p multicolored   5.00 2.75
  Nos. 1040-1042 (3)   16.50 8.75
Nos. 1040-1042 had limited distribution.
Issued in sheets of 24 containing 6 blocks of
4 with margin around. See #C437-C438.

Salto
Dam
A391

1979, June 19
1043 A391 2p multi   .45 .30

Crandon
Institute
Emblem,
Grain
A392

1979, July 19
1044 A392 1p vio bl & bl   .30 .20
Crandon Institute (private Methodist school),
centenary.

IYC Emblem,
Smiling
Kites — A393

Cinderella
A394

1979
1045 A393 2p multi   .55 .25
1046 A394 2p multi   .55 .25
International Year of the Child. Issue dates:
No. 1045, July 23; No. 1046, Aug. 29.

Uruguay Coat of Arms 150th
Anniversary — A395

1979, Sept. 6
1047 A395 8p multi   2.75 1.40

Virgin and
Child — A396

Symbols, by
Torres-Garcia
A397

Wmk. 332
1979, Nov. 19   Litho.   Perf. 12
1048 A396 10p multi   2.75 1.60
Christmas 1979; Intl. Year of the Child.

1979, Nov. 12
1049 A397 10p yel & blk   2.75 1.60
J. Torres-Garcia (1874-1948), painter.

UPU and Brazilian Postal
Emblems — A398

1979, Oct. 11
1050 A398 5p multi   1.25 .80
18th UPU Congress, Rio, Sept.-Oct.

Dish Antenna and Sun — A400

Perf. 12x11½
1979, Nov. 26   Litho.   Wmk. 332
1052 A400 10p multi   2.75 1.25
Telecom '79, 3rd World Telecommunications
Exhibition, Geneva, Sept. 20-26.

Spanish Heritage
Day — A401

1979, Dec. 3   Perf. 12
1053 A401 10p multi   2.75 1.60

Silver
Coin
Centenary
A402

Designs: Obverse and reverse of coins in
denominations matching stamps.

1979, Dec. 26
1054 A402 10c multi   .20   .20
1055 A402 20c multi   .20   .20
1056 A402 50c multi   .20   .20
1057 A402 1p multi   .40   .20
        Nos. 1054-1057 (4)   1.00   .80

Souvenir Sheet

Security
Agent — A403

1980, Jan. 10
1058   Sheet of 4   3.50 3.50
  a. A403 1p Police emblem   .30   .30
  b. A403 2p shown   .50   .50
  c. A403 3p Policeman, 1843   .75   .75
  d. A403 4p Cadet, 1979   1.00 1.00
Police force sesquicentennial.

Light Bulb, Thomas Edison — A404

1980, Jan. 18
1059 A404 2p multi   .40   .30
Centenary of electric light (1979).

Bass and
Singer — A405

1980, Jan. 30
1060   Sheet of 4   3.00 3.00
  a. A405 2p Radio waves   .65   .65
  b. A405 2p shown   .65   .65
  c. A405 2p Ballerina   .65   .65
  d. A405 2p Television waves   .65   .65
Performing Arts Society, 50th anniversary.

Stamp
Day — A406

La Leyenda
Patria — A407

1980, Feb.
1061 A406 1p multi   .35   .20

1980, Feb. 26
1062 A407 1p multi   .30   .20

Printers'
Association,
50th
Anniversary
A408

1980, Feb.
1063 A408 1p multi   .35   .20

Lufthansa Cargo Container Service
Inauguration — A409

1980, Apr. 12   Unwmk.   Perf. 12½
1064 A409 2p multi   .60   .25

Conf. Emblem,
Banners — A410

Man, Woman and
Birds — A411

1980, Apr. 28   Wmk. 332   Perf. 12
1065 A410 2p multi   .60   .35
8th World Hereford Conf., Punta del Este
and Livestock Exhib., Prado/Montivideo.

1980   Litho.   Perf. 12
1066 A411 1p multi   .30   .20
International Year of the Child (1979).

Latin-American Lions, 9th
Forum — A412

1980, May 6   Wmk. 332   Perf. 12
1067 A412 1p multi   .30   .20

Souvenir Sheet

Rifleman,
1814 — A413

1980, May 16
1068   Sheet of 4   4.00 4.00
  a. A413 2p shown   .80   .80
  b. A413 2p Cavalry officer, 1830   .80   .80
  c. A413 2p Private Liberty Dragoons,
        1826   .80   .80
  d. A413 2p, Artigas Militia officer,
        1815   .80   .80
Army Day, May 18.

Arms of
Colonia — A414

Colonia,
1680
A415

1980, June 17   Litho.   Perf. 12
1069 A414 50c multi   1.50 .80
Souvenir Sheet
1070   Sheet of 4   1.40 1.40
  a. A415 1p shown   .25   .25
  b. A415 1p 1680, diff.   .25   .25
  c. A415 1p 1980   .25   .25
  d. A415 1p 1980, diff.   .25   .25
Colonia, 300th anniversary.

Rotary Emblem
on Globe — A416

Hand Putting Out
Cigarette — A417

1980, July 8
1071 A416 5p multi   1.50 .90
   Rotary International, 75th anniversary.

1980, Sept. 8   **Photo.**
1072 A417 1p multi   .25 .20
   World Health Day and anti-smoking
campaign.

Artigas — A418

Christmas
1980
A419

Wmk. 332
1980-85   **Litho.**   **Perf. 12½**
1073 A418   10c blue ('81)   .20 .20
1074 A418   20c orange   .20 .20
1075 A418   50c red   .20 .20
1076 A418   60c yellow   .20 .20
1077 A418   1p gray   .45 .25
1078 A418   2p brown   .85 .30
1079 A418   3p brt grn   1.50 .35
1080 A418   4p brt bl ('82)   1.75 .45
1081 A418   5p green ('82)   .95 .25
1082 A418   6p brt org ('85)   .35 .20
1083 A418   7p lil rose ('82) 4.50 .75
1084 A418   10p blue ('82)   1.75 .35
1085 A418   12p blk ('85)   .95 .25
1086 A418   15.50p emer ('85) 1.25 .30
1087 A418   20p dk vio ('82)   3.75 .75
1088 A418   30p lt brn ('82)   5.50 .75
1089 A418   50p gray bl ('82) 9.00 1.90
      Nos. 1073-1089 (17)   33.35 7.65

1980, Dec. 15   **Litho.**   **Perf. 12**
1090 A419 2p multi   .50 .25

Constitution Title Page — A420

1980, Dec. 23   **Perf. 12½**
1091 A420 4p brt bl & gold   1.25 .65
   Sesquicentennial of Constitution.

A421

A422

1980, Dec. 30   **Perf. 12**
1092 A421   5p Montevideo Sta-
              dium   1.75 1.00
1093 A421   5p Soccer gold cup 1.75 1.00
            Size: 25x79mm
1094 A421   10p Flags   1.75 1.00
   a.   Souv. sheet of 3, #1092-1094 9.00 9.00
        Nos. 1092-1094 (3)   5.25 3.00
   Soccer Gold Cup Championship,
Montevideo.

1981, Jan. 27
1095 A422 2p multi   .60 .20
   Spanish Heritage Day.

UPU Membership Centenary — A423

1981, Feb. 6
1096 A423 2p multi   .60 .20

Alexander von
Humboldt (1769-
1859), German
Explorer and
Scientist — A424

1981, Feb. 19
1097 A424 2p multi   .60 .25

Intl. Education Congress and Fair,
Montevideo (1980) — A425

1981, Mar. 31
1098 A425 2p multi   .60 .20

Hand Holding
Gold Cup — A426

Eighth Notes on
Map of
Americas — A427

1981, Apr. 8
1099 A426 2p multi   .60 .25
1100 A426 5p multi   1.40 .50
   1980 victory in Gold Cup Soccer
Championship.

1981, Apr. 28
1101 A427 2p multi   .60 .20
   Inter-American Institute of Musicology, 40th
anniv.

World Tourism Conference, Manila,
Sept. 27, 1980 — A428

Wmk. 332
1981, June 1   **Litho.**   **Perf. 12**
1102 A428 2p multi   .60 .25

Inauguration of PLUNA Flights to
Madrid — A429

1981, May 12
1103 A429   2p multi   .40 .25
1104 A429   5p multi   .95 .45
1105 A429   10p multi   1.90 .95
      Nos. 1103-1105 (3)   3.25 1.65

Army
Day — A430

Natl. Atomic
Energy
Commission, 25th
Anniv. — A431

Wmk. 332
1981, May 18   **Litho.**   **Perf. 12**
1106 A430 2p Cavalry soldier, 1843 .60 .25
1107 A430 2p Infantryman, 1843   .60 .25

1981, July 20
1108 A431 2p multi   .60 .25

Europe-South American Soccer
Cup — A432

1981, Aug. 4
1109 A432 2p multi   .80 .25

Stone Tablets, Salto Grande
Excavation — A433

1981, Sept. 10
1110 A433 2p multi   .60 .25

10th Lavalleja
Week — A434

1981, Oct. 3
1111 A434 4p multi   1.40 .45

Intl. Year
of the
Disabled
A435

Wmk. 332
1981, Oct. 26   **Litho.**   **Perf. 12**
1112 A435 2p multi   .60 .25

UN Environmental Law Meeting
Montevideo, Oct. 28-Nov. 6 — A436

1981, Oct. 28
1113 A436 5p multi   1.40 .45

A437

A439

1981, Oct. 13
1114 A437 2p multi   .60 .25

50th anniv. of ANCAP (Natl. Administration of Combustible Fuels, Alcohol and Cement).

Souvenir Sheets

Uruguay 81 Intl. Philatelic Exhibition — A438

No. 1114A: b, Copa de Oro trophy. c, Soccer player kicking ball.
No. 1115: a, Chess pieces. b, Prince Charles and Lady Diana, flags of Uruguay and Great Britain.

Wmk. 332
1981, Nov. 23   Litho.   Perf. 12
1114A A438 5p Sheet of 2, #b-
       c   23.00 23.00
1115   A438 5p Sheet of 2, #a-
       b   25.00 25.00

1982 World Cup Soccer Championships, Spain (No. 1114Ac), World Chess Championships, Atlanta (No. 1115a); Wedding of Prince Charles and Lady Diana (No. 1115b). Nos. 1114A-1115 exist imperf., which were not valid for postage.

1981, Dec. 5   Perf. 12
1116 A439 2p multi   .65 .25
Topographical Society sesqu. See No. 1407.

Bank of Uruguay, 85th Anniv. — A440

1981, Dec. 17   Perf. 12½
1117 A440 2p multi   .60 .25

Palmar Dam — A441

1981, Dec. 22   Perf. 12
1118 A441 2p multi   .65 .25

Christmas 1981 A442

1981, Dec. 23
1119 A442 2p multi   .60 .25

Pres. Joaquin Suarez Bicentenary A443

1982, Mar. 15
1120 A443 5p multi   1.60 .50

Artillery Captain, 1872, Army Day — A444

Cent. (1981) of Pinocchio, by Carlo Collodi — A445

Wmk. 332
1982, May 18   Litho.   Perf. 12
1121 A444 3p shown   1.00 .25
1122 A444 3p Florida Battalion,
            1865   1.00 .25
            See Nos. 1136-1137.

1982, June 17
1123 A445 2p multi   .60 .25

2nd UN Conference on Peaceful Uses of Outer Space, Vienna, Aug. 9-21 — A446

1982, June 3
1124 A446 3p multi   1.25 .70

World Food Day A447

1982
1125 A447 2p multi   .60 .20

25th Anniv. of Lufthansa's Uruguay-Germany Flight — A448

1982, Apr. 14   Unwmk.   Perf. 12½
1126 A448 3p Lockheed L-1049-
            G Super Constel-
            lation   1.00 .40
1127 A448 7p Boeing 747   2.25 .80

American Air Forces Cooperation System — A449

1982, Apr. 14   Wmk. 332   Perf. 12
1128 A449 10p Emblem   2.65 .80

Juan Zorilla de San Martin (1855-1931), Painter — A450

1982, Aug. 18   Perf. 12½
1129 A450 3p Self-portrait   .80 .40

165th Anniv. of Natl. Navy — A451

1982, Nov. 15   Perf. 12
1130 A451 3p Navy vessel
            Capitan Miranda   1.00 .40

Natl. Literacy Campaign — A452

Stamp Day — A453

1982, Nov. 30
1131 A452 3p multi   .80 .35

1982, Dec. 23   Perf. 12½
1132 A453 3p like #46   .30 .20
1133 A453 3p like #47   .30 .20
    a.   Pair, #1132-1133   1.10 1.10

These stamps bear numbers from 1 to 100 according to their position on the sheet.

Christmas 1982 — A454

1983, Jan. 4   Perf. 12
1134 A454 3p multi   .50 .25

Eduardo Fabini (1882-1950), Composer — A455

1983, May 10
1135 A455 3p gold & brn   .50 .20

Army Day Type of 1982
1983, May 18
1136 A444 3p Military College ca-
            det, 1885   .45 .20
1137 A444 3p 2nd Cavalry Regi-
            ment officer, 1885   .45 .20

Visit of King Juan Carlos and Queen Sofia of Spain, May — A456

1983, May 20   Unwmk.
1138 A456 3p Santa Maria, globe   .80 .40
1139 A456 7p Profiles, flags   1.75 .80
    Size of No. 1138: 29x39mm.

Brasiliana '83 Emblem — A457

80th Anniv. of First Automobile in Uruguay — A458

Opening of UPAE Building, Montevideo A459

Jose Cuneo
(1887-1977),
Painter — A460

1982
World
Cup
A461

Graf Zeppelin Flight Over Montevideo,
50th Anniv. (1984) — A462

J.W. Goethe (1749-1832), 150th
Death Anniv. — A463

First
Space
Shuttle
Flight
A464

1983   Litho.   Wmk. 332   Perf. 12
1140	A457 3p multi	1.00	1.00
1141	A458 3p multi	1.00	1.00
1142	A459 3p multi	1.00	1.00
1143	A460 3p multi	1.00	1.00
a.	Souvenir sheet of 4	6.00	6.00
1144	A461 7p multi	1.50	1.50
1145	A462 7p multi	1.50	1.50
1146	A463 7p multi	1.50	1.50
1147	A464 7p multi	1.50	1.50
a.	Souvenir sheet of 4	10.00	10.00
	Nos. 1140-1147 (8)	10.00	10.00

No. 1143a contains stamps similar to Nos.
1140-1143. No. 1147a stamps similar to Nos.
1144-1147. Nos. 1143a and 1147a for
URUEXPO '83 and World Communications
Year.
   Issued: #1142, 6/8; #1143, 1146, 9/29;
#1143a, 1147a, 6/9; #1140, 7/22; #1144,
12/13; #1146, 9/20; #1145, 12/8.

Bicentenary of
City of
Minas — A465

Wmk. 332
1983, Oct. 17   Litho.   Perf. 12
1148	A465 3p Founder	.65	.20

World Communications Year — A466

1983, Nov. 30
1149	A466 3p multi	.25	.20

Garibaldi
Death
Centenary
A467

1983, Dec. 5
1150	A467 7p multi	1.00	.40

Christmas
1983
A468

**Lithographed and Embossed
(Braille)**
1983, Dec. 21   Perf. 12½
1151	A468 4.50p multi	.55	.25

50th Anniv. of Automatic
Telephones — A469

1983, Dec. 27   Perf. 12
1152	A469 4.50p multi	.50	.20

Simon
Bolivar,
Battle
Scene
A470

Wmk. 332
1984, Mar. 28   Litho.   Perf. 12
1153	A470 4.50p brn & gldn brn	1.10	.40

Gen. Leandro
Gomez — A471

1984, Jan. 2
1154	A471 4.50p multi	.40	.25

American
Women's
Day — A472

Reunion
Emblem
A473

1984, Feb. 18
1155	A472 4.50p Flags, emblem	.40	.25

1984, Mar. 23
1156	A473 10p multi	.95	.45

Intl. Development Bank Governors, 25th
annual reunion, Punta del Este.

50th
Anniv. of
Radio
Club of
Uruguay
(1983)
A474

1984, Apr. 11
1157	A474 7p multi	.60	.30

A475

1984, Feb. 7   Litho.   Perf. 12
1158	A475 4.50p multi	.40	.25

Intl. Maritime Org., 25th anniv.

A476

1984, May 2   Litho.   Perf. 12
1159	A476 4.50p multi	.40	.25

1930 World Soccer Championships,
Montevideo.

Department of San Jose de Mayo,
200th Anniv. — A477

1984, May 9   Litho.   Perf. 12
1160	A477 4.50p multi	.40	.25

Tourism,
50th
Anniv.
A478

1984, May 15   Litho.   Perf. 12
1161	A478 4.50p multi	.40	.25

Military
Uniforms — A479

Artigas on the
Plains — A480

1984, June 19   Litho.   Perf. 12
1162	A479 4.50p Artillery Regiment, 1895		.45	.20
1163	A479 4.50p Cazadores, 2nd battalion		.45	.20

1984, July 2   Litho.   Perf. 12
1164	A480 4.50p bl & blk	.40	.25
1165	A480 8.50p bl & redsh brn	.75	.40

A.
Penarol
Soccer
Club
A481

1984, Aug. 21   Litho.   Perf. 12
1166	A481 4.50p Championship trophy	.45	.25

Provincial Map Type of 1973
1984, Sept. 21   Litho.   Perf. 12
1167	A281 4.50p multi	.40	.25

Childrens
Council,
50th
Anniv.
A482

1984, Oct. 11   Litho.   Perf. 12
1168	A482 4.50p multi	.40	.25

Christmas
A483

A484

1984 Litho. Perf. 12
1169 A483 6p multi .60 .30

1985, Feb. 13 Litho. Perf. 12
1170 A484 4.50p multi .40 .25
1st Jr. World Basketball Championships.

Don Bruno
Mauricio de
Zabala, 300th
Birth
Anniv. — A485

1985, Apr. 16 Litho. Perf. 12
1171 A485 4.50p multi .60 .20

Intl. Olympic Committee, 90th
Anniv. — A486

Design: Olympic rings, Los Angeles and
Sarajevo 1984 Games emblems.

1985, May 22 Perf. 12½
1172 A486 12p multi 1.00 .50

Carlos Gardel,
(1890-1935),
Entertainer
A487

Catholic Circle of
Workers,
Cent. — A488

1985, June 21 Perf. 12
1173 A487 6p lt gray, red brn & bl .35 .20

Wmk. 332
1985, June 21 Litho. Perf. 12
1174 A488 6p Cross, clasped
hands .20 .20

Icarus, by Hans Erni — A489

1985, July Photo. Wmk. 332
1175 A489 4.50p multi .25 .20
Intl. Civil Aviation Org., 40th anniv.

American Air
Forces
Cooperation
System, 25th
Anniv. — A490

1985, July
1176 A490 12p Emblem, flags .30 .20

FUNSA, Natl. Investment Funds Corp.,
50th Anniv. — A491

1985, July 31 Litho. Wmk. 332
1177 A491 6p multi .25 .20

Intl. Youth
Year
A492

1985, Aug. 28
1178 A492 12p mar & blk .30 .20

Installation of Democratic
Government — A493

1985, Aug. 30
1179 A493 20p brt pur, yel ocher &
dk grnsh bl .80 .35

Intl. Book
Fair — A494

1985
1180 A494 20p multi .80 .35

Military
School,
Cent.
A495

1985, Nov. 29 Litho. Perf. 12
1181 A495 10p multi .40 .20

Department of
Flores,
Cent. — A496

Day of Hispanic
Solidarity — A498

Christmas
1985
A497

1985, Dec. 9
1182 A496 6p Map, arms .20 .20

1985, Dec. 23
1183 A497 10p multi .40 .20
1184 A497 22p multi .60 .30

1985, Dec. 27
1185 A498 12p Isabel Monument .30 .20

3rd Inter-American Agricultural
Congress — A499

Wmk. 332
1986, Jan. 7 Photo. Perf. 12
1186 A499 12p blk, dl yel & red .30 .20

UPU Day
A500

1986, Jan. 14 Litho. Perf. 12
1187 A500 15.50p multi .45 .25

1985
Census
A501

1986, Jan. 21
1188 A501 10p multi .25 .25

Conaprole, 50th Anniv. — A502

1986, Jan. 25
1189 A502 10p gold, brt ultra & bl .30 .20

UN, 40th
Anniv.
A503

Wmk. 332
1986, Feb. 26 Litho. Perf. 12
1190 A503 20p multi .45 .25

Brokers and
Auctioneers
Assoc., 50th
Anniv. — A504

1986, Mar. 19
1191 A504 10p multi .20 .20

Gen. Manuel Ceferino
Oribe (1792-1857),
President — A505

Portraits: Nos. 1196, 1200, 2p, 7p, 15p, 20p,
Oribe. Nos. 1195, 1209, 1211, 3p, Lavalleja.
Nos. 1199, 1208, 1210, 30p, 100p, 200p, Arti-
gas. No. 1198, 17p, 22p, 26p, 45p, 75p,
Rivera.

1986-89 Perf. 12½
1192	A505	1p dl grn	.20	.20
1193	A505	2p scarlet	.20	.20
1194	A505	3p ultra	.20	.20
1195	A505	5p dark blue	.20	.20
1196	A505	5p violet blue	.20	.20
1197	A505	7p tan	.20	.20
1198	A505	10p lilac rose	.25	.20
1199	A505	10p brt green	.20	.20
1200	A505	10p bluish grn	.20	.20
1201	A505	15p dull blue	.20	.20
1202	A505	17p deep blue	.25	.20
1203	A505	20p light brown	.20	.20
1204	A505	22p violet	.20	.20
1205	A505	26p olive blk	.30	.20
1206	A505	30p pale org	.30	.25

1207	A505	45p dark red	.30	.20
1208	A505	50p dp bis	.55	.45
1209	A505	50p bright pink	.20	.20
1210	A505	60p dark gray	.75	.45
1211	A505	60p orange	.20	.20
1211A	A505	75p red orange	.30	.25
1211B	A505	100p dl red brn	1.10	.60
1211C	A505	200p brt yel grn	1.50	.75
	Nos. 1192-1211C (23)		8.20	6.15

The 22p is airmail.

Issued: 1p, 7p, 4/18; #1195, 30p, 6/16; #1198, 22p, 9/24; #1208, 8/5; 100p, 7/2; 2p, 6/16/87; 3p, #1210, 8/14/87; #1199, 17p, 8/4/87; 26p, 9/2/87; 15p, 9/9/88; 45p, 12/20/88; 200p, 10/19/88; #1211A, 5/19/89; #1211, 7/27/89; #1196, 1203, 8/15/89; #1209, 12/12/89; #1200, 1989.

See Nos. 1321-1329.

Italian Chamber of Commerce in Uruguay — A506

1986, May 5   *Perf. 12*
1212 A506 20p multi   .60 .20

A507

A508

1986, May 28   **Photo.**   *Perf. 12*
1213 A507 20p multi   .50 .30

1986 World Cup Soccer Championships, Mexico.

Wmk. 332
1986, May 19   **Litho.**   *Perf. 12*
1214 A508 10p multi   .20 .20

Genocide of the Armenian people, 71st anniv.

A509

A510

1986, June 16
1215 A509 10p multi   .20 .20

El Dia Newspaper, cent.

1986, July 14
1216 A510 20p Garcia, Peruvian flag   .40 .20

State visit of Pres. Alan Garcia of Peru.

Simon Bolivar, Gen. Sucre, Map A511

1986, July 24
1217 A511 20p multi   .45 .25

State visit of Pres. Jaime Lusinchi of Venezuela.

State Visit of Pres. Jose Sarney of Brazil — A512

Zelmar Michelini, Assassinated Liberal Senator — A513

1986, July 31
1218 A512 20p multi   .30 .20

1986, Aug. 21
1219 A513 10p vio bl & rose lake   .20 .20

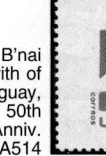

B'nai B'rith of Uruguay, 50th Anniv. A514

1986, Sept. 10
1220 A514 10p red, gold & red brn   .25 .20

General Agreement on Tariffs & Trade (GATT) Committee Meeting, Punta del Este — A515

1986, Sept. 15
1221 A515 10p multi   .20 .20

Scheduled Flights between Uruguay and Spain, 40th Anniv. — A516

1986, Sept. 22
1222 A516 20p multi   .30 .20

Fish Exports A517

1986, Oct. 1
1223 A517 20p multi   .30 .20

Wool Exports A518

1986, Oct. 15
1224 A518 20p multi   .30 .20

Pres. Blanco, Natl. and Dominican Flags A519

1986, Oct. 29
1225 A519 20p multi   .25 .20

State visit of Pres. Salvador Jorge Blanco of the Dominican Republic.

State Visit of Pres. Sandro Pertini of Italy — A520

State Visit of Pres. Raul Alfonsin of Argentina A521

1986, Oct. 31
1226 A520 20p grn & buff   .25 .25

1986, Nov. 10
1227 A521 20p multi   .30 .20

Hispanic Solidarity Day A522

Design: Felipe and Santiago, the patron saints of Montevideo, and cathedral.

Wmk. 332
1987, Jan. 12   **Litho.**   *Perf. 12*
1228 A522 10p rose lake & blk   .20 .20

JUVENTUS, 50th Anniv. (in 1986) — A523

1987, Jan. 28
1229 A523 10p brt yel, blk & ultra   .20 .20

Juventus, a Catholic sports, culture and leisure organization.

Hector Gutierrez Ruiz (1934-1976), Politician — A524

Intl. Symposium on Science and Technology A525

1987, Feb. 23
1230 A524 10p brn & deep mag   .20 .20
1231 A525 20p multi   .25 .25

Ruiz represented Uruguay at an earlier science and technology symposium.

Visit of Pope John Paul II to La Plata Region — A526

Dr. Jose F. Arias (1885-1985), Founder of the University of Crafts — A527

1987, Mar. 31
1232 A526 50p blk & deep org .75 .40

1987, Apr. 28
1233 A527 10p multi .20 .20

Jewish Community in Uruguay, 70th Anniv. — A528

1987, July 8
1234 A528 10p blk, org & brt bl .25 .20

Pluna Airlines, 50th Anniv. (in 1986) A529

1987, Sept. 16
1235 A529 10p Dragon Fly .20 .20
1236 A529 20p Douglas DC-3 .25 .20
1237 A529 25p Vickers Viscount .30 .20
1238 A529 30p Boeing 707 .40 .25
Nos. 1235-1238 (4) 1.15 .85

Artigas Antarctic Station A530

1987, Sept. 28
1239 A530 20p multi .25 .20

Uruguay Mortgage Bank, 75th Anniv. A531

1987, Oct. 14
1240 A531 26p multi .30 .25

Exports — A532

1987, Oct. 28
1241 A532 51p Beef .70 .40
1242 A532 51p Milk products .70 .40

Christmas 1987 — A533

1987, Dec. 21
1243 A533 17p Nativity, vert. .40 .20
1244 A533 66p shown .80 .50

State Visit of Jose Napoleon Duarte, President of El Salvador — A534

VARIG Airlines, 60th Anniv. (in 1987) — A535

1988, Jan. 12
1245 A534 20p brt olive grn & Prus blue .25 .20

1988, Feb. 9
1246 A535 66p blk, blue & brt yel .85 .85

Post Office Stamp Foundation A536

Wmk. 332
1988, Feb. 9 **Litho.** **Perf. 12**
1247 A536 30p on 10+5p brt blue, blk & yel .25 .20
No. 1247 not issued without surcharge.

Intl. Peace Year A537

1988, Feb. 11
1248 A537 10p multi .20 .20

Euskal Erria, 75th Anniv. (in 1987) — A538

1988, Mar. 9
1249 A538 66p multi .60 .40
Basque-Uruguayan diplomatic relations.

Air Force, 75th Anniv. A539

1988, Mar. 11
1250 A539 17p multi .25 .20

Interamerican Children's Institute, 60th Anniv. — A540

Wmk. 332
1988, Mar. 28 **Litho.** **Perf. 12**
1251 A540 30p apple grn, blk & grn .30 .20

State Hydroelectric Works (UTE), 75th Anniv. — A541

1988, Apr. 20
1252 A541 17p shown .20 .20
1253 A541 17p Baygorria Dam .20 .20
1254 A541 51p Gabriel Terra Dam .55 .25
1255 A541 51p Constitucion Dam .55 .25
1256 A541 66p Dams on map .80 .40
Nos. 1252-1256 (5) 2.30 1.30
Dated 1987.

Postal Union of America and Spain (UPAE), 75th Anniv. (in 1987) A542

1988, May 10
1257 A542 66p multi .55 .45

Israel, 40th Anniv. A543

1988, May 17
1258 A543 66p lt ultra & blk .55 .35

Postal Messenger of Peace — A544

1988, May 24
1259 A544 66p multi .55 .35

Portrait, *La Cumparsita* Tango — A545

Firemen, Cent. — A546

1988, June 7
1260 A545 17p Parade, horiz. .40 .20
1261 A545 51p Score 1.25 .55
Gerardo H. Matos Rodrigues, composer.

1988, June 21
1262 A546 17p Pablo Banales, founder .25 .20
1263 A546 26p Fireman, 1900 .30 .25
1264 A546 34p Emblem, horiz. .40 .30
1265 A546 51p Merry Weather fire engine, 1907, horiz. .60 .40
1266 A546 66p Fire pump, 1888, horiz. .95 .60
Size: 44x24½mm
1267 A546 100p Ladder truck, 1921 1.50 1.00
Nos. 1262-1267 (6) 4.00 2.75

Capitan Miranda Trans-world Voyage, Cent. — A547

1988, July 28
1268 A547 30p multi .30 .20

Exports A548

1988
1269 A548 30p Citrus fruit .25 .20
1270 A548 45p Rice .55 .25
1271 A548 55p Footwear .60 .30
1272 A548 55p Leather and furs .60 .35
Nos. 1269-1272 (4) 2.00 1.10
Issued: 30p, #1272, 9/14; 45p, #1271, 8/23.

Natl. Museum of Natural History, 150th Anniv. — A549

30p, *Usnea densirostra* fossil. 90p, *Toxodon platensis* bone, Quaternary period.

1988, Sept. 20
1273 A549 30p blk, yel & red brn .40 .25
1274 A549 90p blk, ultra & beige .95 .55
  a. Pair, #1273-1274 2.00 2.00

Battle of Carpinteria, 150th Anniv. (in 1986) — A550

1988, Nov. 23
1275 A550 30p multi .25 .20
  Horiz. row contains two stamps, label, then two more stamps.

A551

A552

1988, Dec. 21
1276 A551 115p multi .95 .95
      Christmas.

1988, Dec. 27
  Paintings: a, *Manolita Pina, 1920,* by J. Torres Garcia. b, *78 Squares and Rectangles,* by J.P. Costigliolo. c, Print publicizing an exhibition of works by Pedrero Figari, 1945. d, *Self-portrait, 1947,* by J. Torres Garcia.
1277 Block or strip of 4 + label 3.25 3.25
  a.-d. A552 115p any single .75 .50
  No. 1277 can be collected as a vert. or horiz. strip of 4, or block of 4, with label.

Spanish Heritage Day A553

1989, Jan. 9
1278 A553 90p multi .65 .40
1279 A553 115p multi .95 .50

Armenian Organization Hnchakian, Cent. — A554

Wmk. 332
1989, June 7 Litho. Perf. 12
1280 A554 210p red, yel & blue 1.40 .55

French Revolution, Bicentennial — A555

1989, July 3
1281 A555 50p Plumb line, frame .25 .20
1282 A555 50p Liberty tree .25 .20
1283 A555 210p Eye in sunburst 1.10 .45
1284 A555 210p Liberty 1.10 .45
  Nos. 1281-1284 (4) 2.70 1.30

Use Postal Codes — A556

1989, July 25
1285 A556 50p Montevideo Dept. map .25 .20
1286 A556 210p National map, vert. .95 .30

3rd Pan American Milk Congress A557

1989, Aug. 24
1287 A557 170p sky blue & ultra .95 .35

A558

A559

Wmk. 332
1989, Aug. 29 Photo. Perf. 12
1288 A558 170p multicolored .85 .30
  Joaquin Jose da Silva Xavier.

1989, Aug. 31
1289 A559 210p blk, red & bl 1.00 .35
  Inter-Parliamentary Union Conf., London.

FAO Emblem, Map, Citrus Slice — A560

1989, Sept. 11
1290 A560 180p multicolored .70 .30
  8th Conf., Intergovernmental Group on Citrus Fruits.

UN Decade for the Disabled — A561

1989, Oct. 4
1291 A561 50p shown .30 .20
1292 A561 210p Disabled people .85 .35

America Issue — A562

  Nacurutu artifact and UPAE emblem.
1989, Oct. 11 Perf. 12½
1293 A562 60p multicolored .45 .20
1294 A562 180p multicolored 1.10 .45

City of Pando, Bicentennial — A563

1989, Dec. 27 Litho. Perf. 12
1295 A563 60p multicolored .25 .20

Christmas A564

1989, Dec. 19
1296 A564 70p Virgin of Trienta y Tres .35 .20
1297 A564 210p Barradas, horiz. .95 .45

Charity Hospital, Bicent. (in 1988) — A565

1990, Jan. 23 Wmk. 332
1298 A565 60p multicolored .60 .60

Provincial Arms and Maps A566

1990
1299 A566 70p Soriano .30 .30
1300 A566 70p Florida, vert. .35 .35
1301 A566 90p Canelones .40 .40
1302 A566 90p Lavalleja, vert. .40 .40
1303 A566 90p San Jose, vert. .40 .40
1304 A566 90p Rivera .40 .40
  Nos. 1299-1304 (6) 2.25 2.25
    Dated 1989.

Writers — A567

  Designs: a, Luisa Luisi (1883-1940). b, Javier de Viana (1872-1926). c, Delmira Agustini (1886-1914). d, J. Zorrilla de San Martin (1855-1931). e, Alfonsina Storni (1892-1938). f, Julio Casal (1889-1954). g, Juana de Ibarbourou (1895-1979). h, Carlos Roxlo (1861-1926).

1990, Mar. 20
1320 Block of 8 + 2 labels 4.25 4.25
  a.-b. A567 60p any single .25 .25
  c.-d. A567 75p any single .30 .30
  e.-f. A567 170p any single .70 .70
  g.-h. A567 210p any single .95 .95
  Printed in sheets of 4 blocks of 4 separated by vert. and horiz. rows of 5 labels. Position of denomination varies to form border around each block.
    Dated 1989.

Portraits Type of 1986

  25p, 30p, Lavalleja. 60p, 90p, Rivera. 100p, 150p, 300p, 500p, 1000p, Artigas.

1990 Litho. Wmk. 332 Perf. 12½
1321 A505 25p orange .20 .20
1322 A505 30p ultra .20 .20
1323 A505 60p purple .20 .20
1324 A505 90p org red .45 .30
1325 A505 100p brown .35 .35
1326 A505 150p dk blue green .70 .50
1327 A505 300p blue 1.25 1.00
1328 A505 500p orange red 2.00 1.00
1329 A505 1000p red 4.25 3.00
  Nos. 1321-1329 (9) 9.60 6.75

  Issued: 30p, 60p, 7/17; 90p, 3/24; 150p, 6/22; 300p, 7/5; 500p, 3/22; 1000p, 7/24.

A568

A569

1990, Apr. 3   *Perf. 12*
1346 A568 70p multicolored   .35 .35
  City of Mercedes, bicent. Dated 1989.

1990, Apr. 24
1347 A569 210p multicolored   .95 .95
  Intl. Agricultural Development Fund, 10th anniv. Dated 1989.

Traffic Safety — A570

Designs: a, Bus, car. b, Don't drink and drive. c, Cross on the green light. d, Obey traffic signs.

1990, May 28
1348 A570 70p Block of 4, #a.-d.   .95 .95

General Artigas — A571

1990, June 18
1349 A571 60p red & blue   .35 .35

A572

1990, June 26
1350 A572 70p multicolored   .30 .30
  Intl. Mothers' Day. Dated 1989.

A573

1990, July 10
  Treaty of Montevideo, 1889: a, Gonzalo Ramirez. b, Ildefonso Garcia. c, Flags at left. d, Flags at right.
1351 A573 60p Block of 4, #a.-d.   1.25 1.25
  Nos. 1351c-1351d printed in continuous design. Dated 1989.

Microphone, Tower — A574

  b, Newspaper boy. c, Television camera. d, Books.

1990, Sept. 26
1352 A574 70p Block of 4, #a.-d.   1.50 1.50

Carlos Federico Saez (1878-1901) — A575

  Portraits: b, Pedro Blanes Viale (1879-1926). c, Edmundo Prati (1889-1970). d, Jose L. Zorrilla de San Martin (1891-1975).

1990, Dec. 26
1353   Block of 4   2.75 2.75
 a.-b. A575 90p any single   .40 .40
 c.-d. A575 210p any single   .90 .90

Prevent Forest Fires — A576

    Wmk. 332
1990, Oct. 26   **Litho.**   *Perf. 12*
1354 A576 70np multicolored   1.50 1.50

America Issue — A577

1990, Nov. 6
1355 A577 120p Odocoileus
     bezoarticus   .60 .60
1356 A577 360p Peltophorum
     dubium, vert.   1.75 1.75

Army Corps of Engineers, 75th Anniv. — A578

1991, Jan. 21
1357 A578 170p multicolored   .85 .85

The Nativity by Brother Juan B. Maino — A579

1990, Dec. 24
1358 A579 170p bister & multi   .85 .85
1359 A579 830p silver & multi   4.25 4.25

Organization of American States, Cent. (in 1989) A580

    Wmk. 332
1991, Mar. 21   **Litho.**   *Perf. 12*
1360 A580 830p bl, blk & yel   3.50 3.50

Prevention of AIDS — A581

1991, Mar. 8
1361 A581 170p bl & multi   .85 .85
1362 A581 830p grn & multi   4.25 4.25

Carnival — A582

1991, Feb. 19
1363 A582 170p multicolored   .85 .85

Education — A583

  Expanding youth's horizons: a, Stone ax, megalithic monument. b, Wheel, pyramids. c, Printing press, solar system. d, Satellite, diagram.

    Wmk. 332
1991, Apr. 23   **Litho.**   *Perf. 12*
1364   Block of 4   2.40 2.40
 a.-b. A583 120p any single   .30 .30
 c.-d. A583 330p any single   .95 .95

Natl. Cancer Day — A584

1991, June 17
1365 A584 360p red & black   .95 .95

A585

Exports of Uruguay — A586

    Perf. 12½x13, 13x12½
1991   **Litho.**   **Wmk. 332**
1366 A585 120p Textiles   .30 .30
1367 A586 120p Clothing   .40 .25
1368 A585 400p Semiprecious
     stones, granite   1.25 1.25
  Nos. 1366-1368 (3)   1.95 1.80
  Issued: #1366, 400p, 4/23; #1367, 6/26.

7th Pan American Maccabiah Games — A587

1991, July 4   *Perf. 12½x13*
1369 A587 1490p multicolored   4.00 4.00

Dornier Wal, Route Map — A588

1991, July 5   *Perf. 12*
1370 A588 1510p multicolored   3.50 3.50
    Espamer '91.

Entrance to Sacramento Colony A589

  Railroads and Trains: 540p, 825p, First locomotive, 1869. 600p, like 360p. 800p, Entrance to Sacramento Colony. 1510p, 2500p, Horse-drawn streetcar.

    Wmk. 332
1991-2002   **Litho.**   *Perf. 12*
1378 A589 360p ol bis & yel   .95 .60
1378A A589 540p dk bl &
     gray   1.40 .95
1379 A589 600p brn, yel &
     blk   .95 .85

1379A A589 800p grn & yel
grn .95 .95
1379B A589 825p bl, gray &
blk 1.40 1.25
1380 A589 1510p ol bis &
emer 4.25 3.00
1382 A589 2500p ol bis, emer & blk 3.50 3.00
Nos. 1378-1382 (7) 13.40 10.60

Issued: 360p, 540p, 1510p, July 19; 825p, Feb. 11, 1992; 2500p, May 29, 2002; 600p, June 18, 1992; 800p, Feb. 9, 1993.
For surcharges, see Nos. 2011B, 2059.

Sagrada
Family
College,
Cent. — A590

College of the
Immaculate
Heart of Mary,
Cent. — A591

Wmk. 332
1991, June 26 Litho. Perf. 12
1383 A590 360p multicolored .75 .75
1384 A591 1370p multicolored 3.00 3.00

Constitutional Oath — A592

1991, July 17
1385 A592 360p multicolored .80 .80

Swiss
Confederation,
700th
Anniv. — A593

1991, Aug. 1 Perf. 13x12½
1386 A593 1510p multicolored 4.25 4.25
Souvenir Sheet
Perf. 12
1387 A593 3000p multicolored 9.00 9.00

Photography, 150th Anniv. — A594

Perf. 12½x13
1991, Sept. 12 Litho. Wmk. 332
1388 A594 1370p multi 2.50 2.50

Actors Society
of Uruguay,
50th
Anniv. — A595

1991, Aug. 24 Perf. 12
1389 A595 450p blk & red .85 .85

CREA (Agriculture Association), 25th
Anniv. — A596

1991, Sept. 14 Perf. 12½x13
1390 A596 450p multicolored .85 .85

Whitbread
Around the World
Race — A597

1991, Aug. 20 Perf. 13x12½
1391 A597 1510p multicolored 3.00 3.00

Amerigo Vespucci (1454-
1512) — A598

America Issue: 450p, First landing at River
Plate, 1602, vert.

1991, Oct. 11 Perf. 12
1392 A598 450p yel & brn .85 .85
1393 A598 1740p ol & brn 3.00 3.00

Automobiles — A599

Designs: 350p, Gladiator, 1902. 1370p, E.M.F., 1909. 1490p, Renault, 1912. 1510p, Clement-Bayard, 1903, vert.

1991, Oct. 18 Perf. 12½x13, 13x12½
1394 A599 360p multicolored .85 .85
1395 A599 1370p multicolored 3.00 3.00
1396 A599 1490p multicolored 3.00 3.00
1397 A599 1510p multicolored 3.50 3.50
Nos. 1394-1397 (4) 10.35 10.35

Team Nacional Montevideo, Winners
of Toyota and Europe-South America
Soccer Cups — A600

Wmk. 332
1991, Nov. 8 Litho. Perf. 12
1398 A600 450p shown 1.00 1.00
1399 A600 450p Emblem, trophy,
vert. 1.00 1.00

Margarita Xirgu (1888-1969),
Actress — A601

1991, Oct. 4
1400 A601 360p yel & brn .65 .65

INTERPOL,
60th Congress
A602

1991, Oct. 30
1401 A602 1740p multicolored 3.00 3.00

Maria Auxiliadora Institute,
Cent. — A603

1991, Nov. 11
1402 A603 450p multicolored .85 .85

Technological Laboratory, 25th
Anniv. — A604

1991, Nov. 11
1403 A604 1570p dk bl & lt bl 2.75 2.75

The Table by Zoma Baitler — A605

1991, Oct. 18
1404 A605 360p multicolored .65 .65

World
Food Day
A606

1991,Oct. 16 Perf. 12½x13
1405 A606 1740p multicolored 3.00 3.00

Ships
A607

Designs: a, Steam yacht, Gen. Rivera. b, Coast Guard cutter, Salto. c, Cruiser, Uruguay. d, Tanker, Pte. Oribe.

Wmk. 332
1991, Oct. 4 Litho. Perf. 12
1406 Block of 4 9.00 9.00
a.-b. A607 450p any single 1.00 1.00
c.-d. A607 1570p any single 3.25 3.25

Topographical Society Type of 1981
1991, Dec. 3 Perf. 12½
1407 A439 550p multi .75 .75

Topographical Society, 160th anniv.

World AIDS
Day — A608

1991, Dec. 1
1408 A608 550p bl, blk & brt yel .95 .95
1409 A608 2040p lt grn, blk & lil 3.50 3.50

Export
Industries
A609

Wmk. 332
1991, Mar. 20 Litho. Perf. 12½
1410 A609 120p multicolored .20 .20

Christmas
A610

1991, Dec. 24   *Perf. 12*
1411 A610 550p Angel   .75 .75
1412 A610 2040p Adoration of
             the Angels   2.75 2.75

Muscians — A611

Designs: No. 1413a, Francisco Canaro. No. 1413b, Anibal Troilo. No. 1414a, Juan de Dios Filiberto. No. 1414b, Pintin Castellanos.

Wmk. 332
1992, Jan. 20   **Photo.**   *Perf. 12*
1413 A611 450p Pair, #a.-b.   1.50 1.50
1414 A611 450p Pair, #a.-b.   1.50 1.50

Patricio Aylwin, Pres. of Chile — A612

1992, Mar. 23   **Litho.**   **Unwmk.**
1415 A612 550p multicolored   .65 .65

Penarol, Winners of Liberator's Cup in Club Soccer — A612a

La Paz City, 120th Anniv. — A612b

Perf. 13x12½
1992, May 29   **Litho.**   **Wmk. 332**
1415A A612a 600p yel & blk   .70 .70
Souvenir Sheet
Perf. 12
1415B A612a 3000p yel & blk   3.75 3.75

1992, May 25   *Perf. 13x12½*
1415C A612b 550p multicolored   .65 .65

World No-Smoking Day — A613

Wmk. 332
1992, May 31   **Litho.**   *Perf. 12*
1416 A613 2500p multicolored   3.00 3.00

United Nations World Health Day A614

Wmk. 332
1992, July 28   **Litho.**   *Perf. 13*
1417 A614 2500p bl, lt bl & red   3.00 3.00

Mercosur
A615

1992, Aug. 5   **Photo.**   *Perf. 12*
1418 A615 2500p multicolored   2.75 2.75

Olymphilex '92, Barcelona — A616

Wmk. 332
1992, Aug. 8   **Photo.**   *Perf. 12*
1419 A616 2900p multicolored   3.50 3.50

Discovery of America, 500th Anniv. — A617

Perf. 11½x12, 12x11½
1992, Oct. 10   **Litho.**   **Unwmk.**
1420 A617 700p Ship, masts,
            vert.   1.00 1.00
1421 A617 2900p Globe, ship   3.50 3.50

Jose Pedro Varela Natl. Teachers College, 50th Anniv. A618

1992, Oct. 22   *Perf. 12x11½*
1422 A618 700p multicolored   .75 .75

22nd Regional FAO Conference — A619

Designs: 2500p, Emblems. 2900p, Emblems, children with food basket.

1992, Sept. 28
1423 A619 2500p multicolored   2.50 2.50
1424 A619 2900p multicolored   3.00 3.00
Intl. Conf. on Nutrition, Rome, Italy (#1424).

Cesar Vallejo (1892-1938), Poet — A620

1992, Sept. 30
1425 A620 2500p brn & dk brn   2.50 2.50

A621

A622

1992, Oct. 26   *Perf. 11½x12*
1426 A621 700p gray, red & blk   .75 .75
Assoc. of Wholesalers and Retailers, cent.

Perf. 11½x12
1992, Oct. 10   **Litho.**   **Unwmk.**
1427 A622 700p black, blue &
            grn   1.25 1.25
Monument to Columbus, cent.

A623

A624

Ruins and lighthouse, Colonia del Sacramento.

1992, Oct. 10
1428 A623 700p multicolored   1.25 1.25
Discovery of America, 500th anniv.

1992, Oct. 19
1429 A624 700p red lil, rose lil &
            blk   1.25 1.25
Columbus Philanthropic Society, cent.

A625

A626

1992, Oct. 19
1430 A625 2900p multicolored   3.00 3.00
Judaism in the Americas, 500th anniv.

1992, Oct. 30
1431 A626 2900p multicolored   3.00 3.00
Lebanon Society of Uruguay, 50th anniv.

Pan American Health Organization, 90th Anniv. — A627

Perf. 12x11½
1992, Dec. 15   **Litho.**   **Unwmk.**
1432 A627 3200p blk, bl & yel   3.00 3.00

22nd Lions Club Forum for Latin America and the Caribbean — A628

1992, Dec. 2
1433 A628 2700p multicolored   2.50 2.50

Christmas
A629

1992, Dec. 1   *Perf. 11½x12*
1434 A629 800p Nativity scene   .75   .75
1435 A629 3200p Star in sky   3.00 3.00

General
Manuel
Oribe,
Birth
Bicent.
A630

Designs: No. 1436, Oribe, Oriental College.
No. 1437, Oribe in military dress uniform, vert.

Perf. 12x11½, 11½x12
1992, Dec. 8   **Litho.**   **Unwmk.**
1436 A630 800p multicolored   .75   .75
1437 A630 800p multicolored   .75   .75

Logosofia, 60th Anniv. — A631

1992, Dec. 29   *Perf. 12x11½*
1438 A631 800p blue & yellow   .75   .75

Immigrants'
Day — A632

1992, Dec. 4   *Perf. 11½x12*
1439 A632 800p black & green   .75   .75

ANDEBU, 70th Anniv. — A633

Caritas
of
Uruguay,
30th
Anniv.
A634

1992, Dec. 22   **Photo.**   *Perf. 12x11½*
1440 A633 2700p Satellite   2.50 2.50
1441 A634 3200p Map, huts by
            water   3.00 3.00

A635

A636

1992, Dec. 18   *Perf. 11½x12*
1442 A635 800p brown & yellow   .75   .75

Jose H. Molaguero S. A., 50th anniv.

Perf. 11½x12
1993, Mar. 1   **Litho.**   **Unwmk.**
1443 A636 80c multicolored   .65   .65

Wilson Ferreira Aldunate.

Economic Science and Accountancy
College, Cent. — A637

Perf. 12x11½
1993, Apr. 15   **Photo.**   **Unwmk.**
1444 A637 1p multicolored   1.00 1.00

Souvenir Sheet

Polska '93, Intl. Philatelic
Exhibition — A638

a, Lech Walesa. b, Pope John Paul II.

1993, May 3   *Perf. 11½x12*
1445 A638 2p Sheet of 2, #a.-b.   4.50 4.50

A639

A639a

A639b

A639c

A639e

A639g

A639h

A639d

A639f

Design A639g shows the Postal Administration Tower.

ONE PESO (Letter Box — A639):
Type I — "Bugon vecinal 1879" 21½mm, letter box 23½mm high.
Type II — "Bugon vecinal 1879" 22mm, letter box 22½mm high.
Type III — "Bugon vecinal 1879" 19½mm,
letter box 21mm high.
There are other differences among the three
types.

		Wmk. 332		
1993-99		**Litho.**	**Perf. 12½**	
1446	A639	50c gray ol & yel	.20	.20
1447	A639	1p lt brn & yel	.40	.40
		(I)		
a.		Type II	.50	.50
b.		Type III, unwatermarked	.25	.25
c.		Type III, photo., unwmkd.	.25	.25
1448	A639a	1p org yel & bl	.80	.80
		Perf. 12		
1449	A639b	1p org & bl	.55	.55
1450	A639c	(1.20p) blue	.60	.60
1451	A639c	(1.40p) green	.65	.65
1452	A639d	1.40p yel & bl	.65	.65
1453	A639c	(1.60p) red	1.00	1.00
1454	A639	1.80p bl & yel	1.10	1.10
1455	A639c	(1.80p) brown	1.00	1.00
1456	A639c	(2p) gray	1.00	1.00
1457	A639c	(2.30p) lilac	1.25	1.25
1458	A639	2.60p bl, yel & grn	1.25	1.25
1459	A639e	(2.60p) blu & yel	1.25	1.25
1460	A639e	(2.90p) bl & yel	1.25	1.25
1460A	A639e	(3p) gray & brt yel grn	.85	.85
b.		Unwmkd.	.85	.85
1461	A639e	(3.10p) red & pink	.90	.90
1462	A639e	(3.20p) rose brn & lt brn	2.75	2.75
1462A	A639e	(3.50p) pur & lt bl	—	—
1462B	A639e	(3.80p) brt blue		
1463	A639e	(4p) bis & yel, litho.	.95	.95
1464	A639f	5p bl & yel, perf. 12½	2.00	2.00
1465	A639g	6p blue & blk	1.40	1.40
1465A	A639f	7p blue & yel	2.70	2.70
1465B	A639	7.50p vio & yel	3.00	3.00
1465C	A639h	8p bl & yel	3.00	3.00
		Nos. 1446-1462,1463-1465C (24)	30.50	30.50

The design of Nos. 1460A, 1462-1463 does
not include "PORTE MINIMO." There are
minor design differences between #1464 and
1465A.
Issued: #1448, 4/15/93; #1450, 8/2/93;
#1451, 12/1/93; #1452, 1/4/94; #1453, 4/4/94;
#1455, 8/1/94; #1454 8/9/94; #1449, 10/3/94;
1456, 12/1/94. #1457, 4/1/95; #1458, (2.60p),
8/10/95; 50c, #1447, 8/27/96; #1460, (3.10p),
(3.50p), 4/1/96; 7.50p, 5/21/96; 5p, 1997;
(3.80p), 5/9/97; #1463, 8/1/97; 6p, 8/13/97;
(3.50p), 7/28/98; (3p), 2/1/99. #1460Ab, 1999.

Interior Fire
Service, 50th
Anniv. — A640

15th Congress of
UPAEP — A641

Perf. 11½x12
1993, May 28   **Litho.**   **Unwmk.**
1466 A640 1p multicolored   .75   .75

1993, June 21
1467 A641 3.50p multicolored   2.50 2.50

Uruguayan Navy, 175th Anniv. — A642

Sailing ship, Pedro Campbell, first admiral.

Perf. 12x11½
1993, June 28   **Litho.**   **Wmk. 332**
1468 A642 1p multicolored   .90   .90

Intl. University Society, 25th
Anniv. — A643

1993, July 2
1469 A643 1p multicolored   .90   .90

Automobile Club of Uruguay, 75th
Anniv. — A644

1993, July 19   **Photo.**   **Unwmk.**
1470 A644 3.50p 1910
            Hupmobile   2.50 2.50

Uruguay Battalion in UN Peacekeeping
Force, Cambodia — A645

Perf. 12x11½
1993, Aug. 6   **Litho.**   **Unwmk.**
1471 A645 1p multicolored   .90   .90

Souvenir Sheet

Brasiliana '93 — A646

World Cup Soccer Champions: a, Uruguay, 1930, 1950. b, Brazil, 1958, 1962, 1970.

1993, July 28   Perf. 11½x12
1472 A646 2.50p Sheet of 2, #a.-
b.   3.75 3.75

State Television Channel 5, 30th Anniv. — A647

1993, Aug. 19   Perf. 12x11½
1473 A647 1.20p multicolored   .90 .90

ANDA, 60th Anniv. A648

Perf. 12½
1993, Sept. 24   Litho.   Unwmk.
1474 A648 1.20p multicolored   .85 .85

Natl. Police Academy, 50th Anniv. A649

1993, Sept. 24
1475 A649 1.20p multicolored   .90 .90

Newspaper Diario El Pais, 75th Anniv. — A650

Perf. 12½
1993, Sept. 30   Litho.   Unwmk.
1476 A650 1.20p multicolored   1.00 1.00

Latin American Conference on Rural Electrification — A651

1993, Oct. 11
1477 A651 3.50p multicolored   2.50 2.50

B'nai B'rith, 150th Anniv. A652

1993, Oct. 13
1478 A652 3.70p multicolored   2.75 2.75

A653   Fauna — A654

1993   Photo.   Wmk. 332   Perf. 12½
1482 A653   20c Seriema bird   .45 .20
1484 A653   30c Dragon bird   .60 .25
1486 A653   50c Anteaters,
                horiz.   1.00 .40
1492 A654 1.20p Giant armadillo   1.25 1.25
     Nos. 1482-1492 (4)   3.30 2.10

  Issued: 1.20p, 8/3/93; 20c, 30c, 50c, 10/22/93.
  This is an expanding set. Numbers may change.
  For surcharge, see No. 2011A.

America Issue A655

Perf. 12½
1993, Oct. 6   Litho.   Unwmk.
1504 A655 1.20p Caiman latiros-
                tris   .85 .85
1505 A655 3.50p Athene cunicu-
                laria, vert.   2.50 2.50

Souvenir Sheet

Whitbread Trans-Global Yacht Race — A656

1993, Oct. 22   Perf. 11½x12
1506 A656 5p multicolored   3.50 3.50

Beatification of Mother Francisca Rubatto — A657

1993, Nov. 22
1514 A661 3.70p multicolored   2.50 2.50

Intl. Year of Indigenous People — A658

1993, Oct. 29   Wmk. 332   Perf. 12
1507 A657 1.20p multicolored   1.25 1.25

Perf. 13x12½
1993, Oct. 29   Unwmk.
1508 A658 3.50p multicolored   2.50 2.50

Rotary Club of Montevideo, 75th Anniv. — A658a

Perf. 12½
1993, Nov. 10   Litho.   Unwmk.
1508A A658a 3.50p dk bl & bis   3.00 3.00

Rhea Americana A659

1993, Dec. 20   Litho.   Perf. 12
1509 A659 20c shown   .70 .35
1510 A659 20c With chicks   .80 .40
1511 A659 50c Head   1.25 .75
1512 A659 50c Two walking   1.25 .75
     Nos. 1509-1512 (4)   4.00 2.25
     World Wildlife Fund.

Children's Rights Day A660

1994, Jan. 4   Perf. 12½
1513 A660 1.40p multicolored   .95 .95

Independence of Lebanon, 50th Anniv. — A661

1993, Nov. 22
1514 A661 3.70p multicolored   2.50 2.50

Eduardo Victor Haedo — A662

1993, Nov. 24
1515 A662 1.20p multicolored   .85 .85

Christmas A663

Intl. AIDS Day — A664

1993, Dec. 7
1516 A663 1.40p shown   .90 .90
1517 A663   4p Nativity, diff.   2.75 2.75

1993, Dec. 1
1518 A664 1.40p multicolored   1.90 1.90

Souvenir Sheets of 4 & 2

Anniversaries & Events — A665

Designs: No. 1519a, Switzerland #3L1, 1913 Swiss private air mail stamp. b, Germany #C40, Uruguay #C426c. c, Uruguay #C372, US #C76. d, Uruguay #C282a, US #C104.
No. 1520a, Switzerland Types A1, A2. b, Switzerland #B541.

1993, Nov. 18
1519 A665   1p #a.-d.   8.50 8.50
1520 A665 2.50p #a.-b.   8.50 8.50

Swiss postage stamps, 150th anniv. (#1519a, 1520). Dr. Hugo Eckener, 125th anniv. of birth (#1519b). First man on moon, 25th anniv. (#1519c). 1994 World Cup Soccer Championships, US (#1519d).
Nos. 1519-1520 exist imperf. Value $25.

17th Inter-American Naval Conference — A666

1994, Mar. 21   Litho.   Perf. 12½
1521 A666 3.70p multicolored   2.50 2.50

A667

A668

1994, Mar. 11 *Perf. 12½*
1522 A667 4p multicolored 2.75 2.75
5th World Sports Congress, Punta del Este.

Unwmk.
1994, Apr. 4 **Litho.** *Perf. 12*
1523 A668 3.90p multicolored 2.50 2.50
Latin America Youth Organization, 7th conference.

A669

1994, Apr. 18
1524 A669 4.30p multicolored 2.75 2.75
4th World Congress on Merino Wool.

A670

1994, Apr. 28 *Perf. 12½*
1525 A670 4.30p multicolored 2.75 2.75
ILO, 75th anniv.

Miniature Sheet

1994 Winter Olympic Medal Winners
A671

Designs: a, Katja Seizinger. b, Markus Wasmeier. c, Vreni Schneider. d, Gustav Weder.

1994, May 6 *Perf. 12*
1526 A671 1.25p Sheet of 4, #a.-
d. 8.00 8.00
No. 1526 exists demonitized and imperf on paper with watermark 322. This item was sold with No. 1526 and has a matching serial number.

Miniature Sheet

1994 World Cup Soccer Championships, US — A672

a, Soccer ball, flags of Uruguay, Brazil. b, Ball, flags of Italy, Argentina. c, Ball, flags of Germany, Great Britain. d, Olympic Rings.

1994, May 16
1527 A672 1.25p Sheet of 4, #a.-
d. 8.00 8.00
Uruguay, Olympic soccer gold medalists, 1924-1928 (#1527d).
See note after No. 1526.

Clemente Estable (1894-1976), Biologist — A673

1994, May 23 **Litho.** *Perf. 12½*
1528 A673 1.60p olive & black 1.00 1.00

Electoral Court, 70th Anniv. — A674

1994, June 7
1529 A674 1.60p multicolored 1.00 1.00

Natl. Commission to Prevent Tapeworms — A675

Perf. 12½
1994, June 17 **Litho.** **Unwmk.**
1530 A675 1.60p multicolored .95 .95

Souvenir Sheet

Cesareo L. Berisso, First Aviator to Land at Natl. Airport, Carrasco — A676

1994, June 21 *Perf. 12*
1531 A676 5p multicolored 3.00 3.00

Intl. Cooperatives, 150th Anniv. — A677

1994, July 1 *Perf. 12½*
1532 A677 4.30p multicolored 2.50 2.50

Commission on Integration of Regional Electricity, 30th Anniv. — A678

1994, July 8
1533 A678 1.60p multicolored .95 .95

Abate Pierre
A679

Perf. 12½
1994, Aug. 5 **Litho.** **Unwmk.**
1534 A679 4.80p multicolored 2.75 2.75

Intl. Year of the Family
A680

1994, July 28
1535 A680 4.80p multicolored 2.75 2.75

The Man of Lugano, by Goffredo Sommavilla (1850-1944) — A681

Perf. 12½
1994, Aug. 15 **Litho.** **Unwmk.**
1536 A681 4.80p multicolored 2.75 2.75

First Manned Moon Landing, 25th Annvi.
A682

1994, July 20
1537 A682 3p multicolored 2.00 2.00

Intl. Olympic Committee, Cent. — A683

1994, Aug. 23
1538 A683 4.80p multicolored 3.00 3.00

Elbio Fernandez School, 125th Anniv.
A684

A685

Perf. 12½
1994, Aug. 29 **Litho.** **Unwmk.**
1539 A684 1.80p multicolored 1.00 1.00

A686

1994, Sept. 10 *Perf. 12*
1540 A685 1.80p black & blue 1.25 1.25
Gral. Aparicio Saravia, 90th Death Anniv.

1994, Sept. 30 *Perf. 12½*
1541 A686 4.80p multicolored 2.50 2.50
6th Latin American Urban Congress.

General Assoc. of Uruguayan Authors, 65th Anniv. — A687

Perf. 12½
1994, Sept. 26 **Litho.** **Unwmk.**
1542 A687 1.80p multicolored .95 .95

America Issue
A688

1994, Oct. 10
1543 A688 1.80p Stagecoach 1.25 1.25
1544 A688 4.80p Paddle steamer 3.50 3.50

A689

A690

Perf. 12½
1994, Oct. 28 Litho. Unwmk.
1545 A689 2p multicolored 1.10 1.10
Assoc. of Directors of Marketing, 50th anniv.

1994, Nov. 25
1546 A690 2p multicolored 1.10 1.10
YMCA in Uruguay, 85th anniv.

Lottery,
55th
Anniv.
A691

1994, Nov. 21
1547 A691 2p multicolored 1.10 1.10

First Intl.
Seminar
to
Promote
Roads in
Uruguay,
Punta del
Este
A692

1994, Oct. 14
1548 A692 2p multicolored 1.10 1.10

Uruguayan Press Assoc., 50th
Anniv. — A693

1994, Oct. 24
1549 A693 2p multicolored 1.10 1.10

Miniature Sheet

Natl.
Mint,
150th
Anniv.
A694

Portions of old coin press and: a, Mint building. b, 1844 Copper coin. c, 1844 Silver coin. d, Montevideo silver peso.

1994, Oct. 17 Perf. 12
1550 A694 1.50p Sheet of 4, #a.-
d. 7.00 7.00

No. 1550 exists demonetized and imperf. on paper with watermark 332. This item was sold with No. 1550 and has matching serial numbers.

Miniature Sheet

Natl.
Navy
A695

Ships: a, ROU Uruguay, ROU Artigas. b, ROU Fortuna. c, ROU Uruguay. d, ROU Cte. Pedro Campbell.

1994, Nov. 15
1551 A695 1.50p Sheet of 4, #a.-
d. 7.00 7.00

Latin American Peace Movement, 25th
Anniv. — A696

1994, Nov. 15 Perf. 12½
1552 A696 4.30p multicolored 2.40 2.40

4th Conference of the Latin American and Caribbean Organization of High Fiscal Entities, Montevideo — A697

1994, Dec. 5
1553 A697 5.50p multicolored 3.00 3.00

Christmas
A698

1994, Dec. 2
1554 A698 2p shown 1.10 1.10
1555 A698 5.50p Star, tree,
house 3.00 3.00

Uruguayan Red Cross & Red Crescent Societies, 75th Anniv. — A699

Perf. 12½
1994, Dec. 20 Litho. Unwmk.
1556 A699 5p multicolored 2.50 2.50

City Post
Office — A700

1995-97 Litho. Wmk. 332 Perf. 12
1557 A700 20c yellow green .35 .35
1565 A700 10p brown 4.75 4.75
1566 A700 10p dark brown 2.75 2.75
Unwmk.
1566A A700 10p claret &
black 2.75 2.75
Nos. 1557-1566A (4) 10.60 10.60

Issued: 20c, 1/11/95; 10p, 5/21/96; #1566, 1566A, 1997.
Denomination has no decimal places on Nos. 1566-1566A.
This is an expanding set. Number may change.

Naval
Aviation,
70th
Anniv.
A704

Perf. 12½
1995, Feb. 7 Litho. Unwmk.
1567 A704 2p multicolored 1.10 1.10

World Tourism Organization — A705

Designs: No. 1568, Ranch house, sheep herders. No. 1569, Water recreation park. No. 1570, Native wildlife. No. 1571, Beach resort.

1995, Feb. 13
1568 A705 5p multicolored 3.00 3.00
1569 A705 5p multicolored 3.00 3.00
1570 A705 5p multicolored 3.00 3.00
1571 A705 5p multicolored 3.00 3.00
Nos. 1568-1571 (4) 12.00 12.00

17th World
Conference of
Lifeguard
Services — A706

1995, Feb. 15
1572 A706 5p multicolored 2.50 2.50

Rotary
Intl., 90th
Anniv.
A707

1995, Feb. 22
1573 A707 5p multicolored 2.50 2.50

ICAO,
50th
Anniv.
A708

1995, Mar. 14
1574 A708 5p multicolored 2.50 2.50

Pietro Mascagni (1863-1945),
Composer — A709

Perf. 12½
1995, Mar. 30 Litho. Unwmk.
1575 A709 5p multicolored 2.50 2.50

Miniature Sheet

Butterflies
A710

Designs: a, Phoebis neocypris. b, Diogas erippus. c, Euryades duponcheli. d, Automeris coresus.

1995, June 15 Litho. Perf. 12½
1576 A710 5p Sheet of 4, #a.-
d. 10.00 10.00

Wild Dog
A711

1995, May 17 Litho. Perf. 12½
1577 A711 2.30p multicolored 1.25 1.25

America Cup
Soccer
Championships
A712

Game scenes, flags of participating countries, match sites: a, Paysandu. b, Rivera. c, Ball (no site). d, Montevideo. e, Maldonado.

1995, July 4
1578 A712 2.30p Strip of 5, #a.-
e. 5.25 5.25
No. 1578 is a continuous design.

FAO, 50th
Anniv. — A713

1995, July 7
1579 A713 5.50p multicolored 2.50 2.50

UN Peace-Keeping Missions — A714

1995, July 14 Litho. Perf. 12½
1580 A714 2.30p multicolored 1.25 1.25

Visit of
Italy's
Pres.
Oscar
Luigi
Scalfaro
A715

1995, July 21
1581 A715 5.50p multicolored 2.50 2.50

A716

A717

1995, July 24
1582 A716 5p multicolored   2.25 2.25
Rotary Intl., 90th anniv.

1995, Sept. 22
1583 A717 2.60p multicolored   1.25 1.25
Jose Pedro Varela, 150th birth anniv.

Miniature Sheet

Shells
A718

a, Zidona dufresnei. b, Boccinanops duartei. c, Dorsanum moniliferum. d, Olivancillaria uretai.

1995, Aug. 4
1584 A718 5p Sheet of 4, #a.-
d.   15.00 15.00

America
Issue
A719

Designs: 3p, Dicksonia selloinflorus, vert. 6p, Chrysocyon brachyurus.

Unwmk.
1995, Oct. 10   **Litho.**   **Perf. 12**
1585 A719 3p multicolored   1.40 1.40
1586 A719 6p multicolored   2.75 2.75

Carlos
Gardel,
Musician
A720

1995, Sept. 4   **Perf. 12½**
1587 A720 5.50p blue & black   2.50 2.50

Flowers — A721

Designs: a, Notocactus roseinflorus. b, Verbena chamaedryfolia. c, Bauhinia candicans. d, Tillandsia aeranthos. e, Eichhornia crassipes.

1995, Sept. 12
1588 A721 3p Strip of 5, #a.-e.   8.50 8.50

Miniature Sheet

Uruguay's
Artigas
Antarctic
Scientific
Research
Base, 10th
Anniv.
A722

Designs: a, 2.50p, Albatross. b, 4p, Fairchild FAU572. c, 4p, ROU Vanguard. d, 2.50p, PTS/M Amphibian transporter.

1995, Oct. 13
1589 A722   Sheet of 4, #a.-d.   8.00 8.00
Uruguayan Antarctic Institute, 20th anniv.
No. 1589 exists demonitized and imperf. on paper with watermark 332. This item was sold with No. 1589 and has matching serial numbers.

Holocaust
Memorial — A723

1995, Sept. 27   **Litho.**   **Perf. 13x12½**
1590 A723 6p multicolored   4.00 4.00

UN, 50th
Anniv. — A724

1995, Oct. 24   **Litho.**   **Perf. 12**
1591 A724 6p multicolored   3.25 3.25

Early Locomotives — A725

No. 1592, Beyer & Peacock, 1876. No. 1593, Criollo, 1895. No. 1594, Beyer & Peacock, 1910.

1995, Nov. 7
1592 A725 3p multicolored   1.40 1.40
1593 A725 3p multicolored   1.40 1.40
1594 A725 3p multicolored   1.40 1.40
    Nos. 1592-1594 (3)   4.20 4.20

Uruguayan Navy, 178th Anniv. — A726

No. 1595, Sailing ship, Artiguista. No. 1596, ROU Pte. Rivera. No. 1597, ROU Montevideo.

1995, Nov. 15   **Perf. 12½**
1595 A726 3p multicolored   1.40 1.40
1596 A726 3p multicolored   1.40 1.40
1597 A726 3p multicolored   1.40 1.40
    Nos. 1595-1597 (3)   4.20 4.20

Motion
Pictures,
Cent.
A727

1995, Dec. 13
1598 A727 6p Lumiere Brothers   3.25 3.25

A728

Christmas
A729

1995, Dec. 15
1599 A728 2.90p multicolored   1.25 1.25
1600 A729 6.50p multicolored   3.00 3.00

Modern
Olympic
Games,
Cent.
A730

Designs: a, Equestrian event, Atlanta 1996. b, Ski jumper, Nagano 1988. c, Torch bearer, Sydney 2000. d, Skier, Salt Lake City 2002.

1996, Jan. 30   **Litho.**   **Perf. 12½**
1601 A730 2.50p Sheet of 4, #a.-
d.   8.00 8.00
Latin America Philatelic Exposition.
No. 1601 exists demonitized and imperf. on paper with watermark 332. This item was sold with No. 1601 and has matching serial numbers.

Carnival
Personalities
A732

1996, Feb. 16   **Litho.**   **Perf. 12½**
1603 A732 2.90p Rosa Luna   1.25 1.25
1604 A732 2.90p Pepino   1.25 1.25
1605 A732 2.90p Santiago Luz   1.25 1.25
    Nos. 1603-1605 (3)   3.75 3.75

Golf in
Uruguay
A733

Designs: a, Cantegril Country Club. b, Cerro Golf Club. c, Fay Crocker. d, Lago Golf Club. e, Golf Club of Uruguay.

1996, Feb. 27
1606 A733 2.90p Strip of 5,
    #a.-e.   12.00 12.00
No. 1606 was issued in sheets of 25 stamps.

Famous
People,
Events
A734

Designs: a, Statue, Cardinal Barbieri (1892-1979). b, Yitzhak Rabin (1922-95), Nobel Peace Prize. c, Soccer players, First World Cup Soccer Championship, Grand Park Central, July 13, 1930. d, Robert Stolz (1880-1975), composer.

1996, Mar. 8
1607 A734 2.50p Sheet of 4, #a.-
d.   5.75 5.75
Philatelic Academy of Uruguay. The Stamp of Today, SODRE TV Chanel 5, 10th anniv.

Montevideo, Capital of Latin American Culture — A735

1996, Mar. 5
1608 A735 2.90p Solis Theater,
       1837   1.25 1.25
a.   Booklet pane of 3   5.00
    Complete booklet, #1608a   5.00

General
Census
A736

1996, Apr. 29
1609 A736 3.20p multicolored   1.25 1.25

1998 World Cup Soccer
Championships, France — A737

a, Player in early uniform, Olympic champions, 1924-28, world cup champions, 1930-50, older trophy. b, Trophy, player. d, Two children playing, UNICEF emblem, soccer emblems. e, Olympic rings, two players, eliminations for Atlanta '96.

1996, Apr. 10
1610 A737 2.50p Sheet of 4, #a.-
d.   6.50 6.50
Latin America Philatelic Exposition.
No. 1610 exists demonitized and imperf. on paper with watermark 332. This item was sold with No. 1610 and has matching serial numbers.

Bones from
Indian Burial
Grounds — A738

1996, Apr. 18
1611 A738 3.20p multicolored   1.25   1.25

Alfredo
Zitarrosa
(1936-89),
Guitarist
A739

1996, Mar. 15   *Perf. 12*
1612 A739 3p multicolored   1.50   1.50

Prehistoric Animals — A740

Designs: a, Glyptodon claripes. b,
Macrauchenia patachonica. c, Toxodon
platensis. d, Glossotherium robostum. e,
Titanosaurus.

1996, Apr. 18   *Perf. 12½*
1613 A740 3.20p Strip of 5, #a.-
          e.   8.00   8.00
No. 1613 was issued in sheets of 25 stamps.

Taking Care of Planet Earth,
Everyone's Responsibility, by Soraya
Campanella — A741

                          Unwmk.
1996, June 5   **Litho.**   *Perf. 12*
1614 A741 3.20p multicolored   1.50   1.50

Souvenir Sheet

Calidris Canutus — A742

1996, May 28   *Perf. 12½*
1615 A742 12p multicolored   9.00   9.00
                CAPEX '96.

Early Methods of
Transportation — A743

Designs: a, 1912 Dion-Buton omnibus. b,
1928 Ford Model A. c, 1940 Raleigh bicycle. d,
1926 Magirus firetruck. e, 1917 Hotchkiss
ambulance.

1996, May 21
1616 A743 3.20p Strip of 5, #a.-
          e.   7.50   7.50
No. 1616 was issued in sheets of 25 stamps.

Sailing
Ships
A744

Designs: a, Our Lady of Encina, 1726. b,
San Francisco. c, Ships of E. Moreau. d, Bold
Lady. e, Our Lady of the Light.

1996, June 17   **Litho.**   *Perf. 12½*
1617 A744 3.20p Strip of 5, #a.-
          e.   7.50   7.50
No. 1617 was issued in sheets of 25 stamps.

Landscape in Las Flores, by Carmelo
de Arzadun — A745

1996, July 15   **Litho.**   *Perf. 12½*
1618 A745 3.50p multicolored   1.40   1.40

Jewish Community in Uruguay, 80th
Anniv. — A746

1996, July 29
1619 A746 7.50p multicolored   3.00   3.00

A747

Scientists
from
Uruguay
A748

No. 1620, Enrique Legrand (1861-1939).
No. 1621, Victor Bertullo (1919-79). No. 1622,
Tomas Beno Hirschfeld (1939-86). No. 1623,
Miguel C. Rubino (1886-1945).

1996, July 30
1620 A747 3.50p multicolored   1.40   1.40
1621 A747 3.50p multicolored   1.40   1.40
1622 A748 3.50p multicolored   1.40   1.40
1623 A748 3.50p multicolored   1.40   1.40
          Nos. 1620-1623 (4)   5.60   5.60

Bank of Uruguay, Cent. — A749

1996, Sept. 9   *Perf. 12*
1624 A749 3.50p 10p note   1.40   1.40
  a.   Booklet pane, #1624   2.00
1625 A749 3.50p 500p note   1.40   1.40
  a.   Booklet pane, #1625   2.00
       Complete bklt., #1624a, 1625a   4.00

Souvenir Sheet

Otto Lilienthal (1848-1896) — A750

Illustration reduced.

1996, Aug. 30
1626 A750 12p multicolored   4.75   4.75
                AEROFILA '96.

Scientists
A751

No. 1627, Albert Einstein. No. 1628, Aristotle. No. 1629, Isaac Newton.

1996, Sept. 3   *Perf. 12½*
1627 A751 7.50p multicolored   3.00   3.00
1628 A751 7.50p multicolored   3.00   3.00
1629 A751 7.50p multicolored   3.00   3.00
          Nos. 1627-1629 (3)   9.00   9.00

National
Heritage — A752

Designs: No. 1630, Map of Gorriti Island
showing locations of Spanish forts, 18th cent.
No. 1631, Narbona Church, 18th cent.

              Perf. 13x12½
1996, Sept. 12   **Litho.**   **Unwmk.**
1630 A752 3.50p multicolored   1.40   1.40
1631 A752 3.50p multicolored   1.40   1.40

Rural
Assoc.,
125th
Anniv.
A753

1996, Sept. 20   *Perf. 12½x13*
1632 A753 3.50p multicolored   1.50   1.50

Marine
Life
A754

a, Carchardon carcharias. b, Alopias
vulpinus. c, Notorynchus cepedianus. d, Squatina dumerili.

1996, Sept. 23
1633 A754 3.50p Sheet of 4, #a.-
          d.   5.50   5.50
                Istanbul '96.

Sports Champions from
Uruguay — A755

Designs: a, Angel Rodriguez, boxing, 1917.
b, Leandro Noli, cycling, 1939. c, Eduardo G.
Risso, rowing, 1948. d, Estrella Puente, javelin, 1949. e, Oscar Moglia, basketball, 1956.

1996, Oct. 1
1634 A755 3.50p Strip of 5, #a.-
          e.   8.50   8.50

Traditional
Costumes
A756

America issue: 3.50p, Gaucho. 7.50p,
Woman of the campana.

1996, Oct. 11   *Perf. 13x12½*
1635 A756 3.50p multicolored   1.40   1.40
1636 A756 7.50p multicolored   3.00   3.00

3rd Space Conference of the
Americas — A757

1996, Nov. 4   **Wmk. 332**   *Perf. 12*
1637 A757 3.50p multicolored   1.75   1.75

Comic
Strips,
Cent.
A758

"Peloduro," by Julio E. Suarez.

1996, Nov. 7
1638 A758 4p multicolored   1.75 1.75

Health Institute, Cent. A759

1996, Nov. 20
1639 A759 4p multicolored   1.75 1.75

Church of the 7th Day Adventists in Uruguay, Cent. — A760

Wmk. 332
1996, Nov. 26   Litho.   Perf. 12½
1640 A760 3.50p multicolored   1.40 1.40

Felix de Azara (1746-1811), Naturalist — A761

1996, Nov. 20   Perf. 12
1641 A761 4p multicolored   1.75 1.75

Fish A762

Designs: No. 1642, Cynolebia nigripinnis. No. 1643, Cynolebia viarius.

Unwmk.
1997, Feb. 24   Litho.   Die Cut
Self-Adhesive
1642 A762 4p multicolored   1.60 1.60
1643 A762 4p multicolored   1.60 1.60

Popular Festivals A763

#1644, Natl. Folklore Festival, Durazno. #1645, Traditional Gaucho Festival, Tacuarembo.

1997   Wmk. 332   Perf. 12½
1644 A763 4p multi   1.60 1.60
1645 A763 4p multi, vert.   1.60 1.60

   Issued: #1644, 1/30; #1645, 3/10.
See Nos. 1653-1656.

Mushrooms — A764

Designs: a, Tricholoma nudum. b, Agaricus xanthodermus. c, Russula sardonia. d, Microsporum canis. e, Polyporus versicolor.

1997, Feb. 7
1646 A764 4p Strip of 5, #a.-e.   10.00 10.00
No. 1646 was issued in sheets of 25 stamps.

Ports A765

No. 1647, Colonia. No. 1648, Punta del Este. No. 1649, Santiago Vázquez. No. 1650, Buceo.

1997, Feb. 28   Litho.   Die Cut
Self-Adhesive
1647 A765 4p multicolored   1.60 1.60
1648 A765 4p multicolored   1.60 1.60
1649 A765 4p multicolored   1.60 1.60
1650 A765 4p multicolored   1.60 1.60
   Nos. 1647-1650 (4)   6.40 6.40

Artigas' Lancers, Bicent. A766

1997, Mar. 10   Wmk. 332   Perf. 12½
1651 A766 4p multicolored   1.60 1.60

Military Academy, 50th Anniv. — A767

1997, Mar. 13
1652 A767 4p multicolored   1.60 1.60

Popular Festivals Type of 1997

Coat of arms and: No. 1653, Performers under outdoor pavilion, Beer Week. No. 1654, Ruben Lena, bridge, river, Olimar River Festival, vert. No. 1655, Guitar, man on horse, Festival de Minas Y Abril. No. 1656, Family around person on horseback, Roosevelt Park.

1997   Litho.
1653 A763 5p multicolored   2.00 2.00
1654 A763 5p multicolored   2.00 2.00
1655 A763 5p multicolored   2.00 2.00

Die Cut
Unwmk.
Self-Adhesive
1656 A763 5p multicolored   2.00 2.00
   Nos. 1653-1656 (4)   8.00 8.00

   Lions Intl. (#1656). Issued: #1653, 3/23; #1654, 3/24; #1655, 4/26; #1656, 3/21.

United Mobile Coronary Unit (UCM), 20th Anniv. A768

1997, Apr. 4   Unwmk.   Die Cut
Self-Adhesive
1657 A768 5p multicolored   2.00 2.00

UNICEF, 50th Anniv. — A769

1997, Apr. 8   Die Cut
Self-Adhesive
1658 A769 5p multicolored   2.00 2.00

Lighthouses A770

Various birds and: a, Anchorena Tower, 1920. b, Farallón Lighthouse, 1870. c, José Ignacio Lighthouse, 1877. d, Santa Maria Lighthouse, 1874. e, Vigía Tower, 18th cent.

1997, Apr. 22   Die Cut
Self-Adhesive
1659 A770 5p Strip of 5, #a.-e.   13.00 13.00

Prehistoric Animals A771

Designs: a, Devincenzia gallinali. b, Smilodon populator. c, Mesosaurus tenuidens. d, Doedicurus clavicaudatus. e, Artigasia magna.

1997, May 5   Die Cut
Self-Adhesive
1660 A771 5p Strip of 5, #a.-e.   13.00 13.00

A772

Ecclesiastical Provinces — A772a

#1661, Church, diocese of Salto. #1662, Church, diocese of Melo. #1663, Bishop Jacinto Vera, 1st bishop of Montevideo. #1664, Msgr. Mariano Soler, 1st archbishop of Montevideo.

Wmk. 332
1997, May 9   Litho.   Perf. 12½
1661 A772   5p multicolored   2.00 2.00
1662 A772   5p multicolored   2.00 2.00
1663 A772a 5p multicolored   2.00 2.00
1664 A772a 5p multicolored   2.00 2.00
   Nos. 1661-1664 (4)   8.00 8.00

Youth Stamp Collecting A773

Designs: a, 2p, Boy, "Philately?" b, 2p, Boy thinking of stamps. c, 2p, Girl with soccer ball, boy. d, 1p, Boy looking at stamps in album. e, 1p, Boy with tongs and magnifying glass.

1997, May 25   Unwmk.
1665 A773   Strip of 5, #a.-e.   4.00 4.00

PACIFIC 97 — A774

1997, May 29   Perf. 12
1666 A774 10p Rynchops niger   4.00 4.00

Maccio Theater of San Jose, 85th Anniv. A775

1997, June 5   Wmk. 332   Perf. 12½
1667 A775 5p multicolored   2.00 2.00

Inter-American Institute of Children, 70th Anniv. — A776

1997, June 9   Unwmk.
1668 A776 5p multicolored   2.00 2.00

Colony of Sacramento — A777

1997, July 4
1669 A777 5p multicolored   2.00 2.00

Punta del Este, 90th Anniv. A778

1997, July 1
1670 A778 5p multicolored   2.00 2.00

Uruguayan Comics — A779

Scenes from comics by: No. 1671, Julio E. Suarez (Peloduro). No. 1672, Geoffrey Foladori.

Perf. 12½

1997, June 30	**Litho.**	**Unwmk.**	
1671	A779	5p multicolored	1.50 1.50
1672	A779	5p multicolored	1.50 1.50

Zionism, Cent. A780

Design: Theodor Herzl (1860-1904), founder of Zionist movement.

1997, July 17
1673 A780 5p multicolored   1.50 1.50

Children's Painting A781

Geranoaetus Melanoleucus A782

1997, July 21	**Litho.**	**Die Cut**	
Self-Adhesive			
1674	A781	15p multicolored	4.50 4.50
1675	A782	25p multicolored	7.75 7.75
a.		Type II ('04)	2.00 2.00

Type I stamps have printer's name at right, designer's name at left, and have an eagle's head that is rounder, with its edge making a sharper angle with the right margin than on type II. Type II stamps have the printer's name at left and the designer's name at right.
No. 1675a issued 2004. No. 1675a also exists dated "2005."
Nos. 1674, 1675 exist dated 1999.
See Nos. 1840, 1850, 1853, 1855.

Isolation of Acetylsalicylic Acid from Willow Trees, Cent. — A783

1997, Aug. 12	**Litho.**	**Perf. 12½**	
1676	A783	6p multicolored	1.40 1.40
a.		Booklet pane of 2	4.50
		Complete booklet, #1676a	4.50

Department of Salto — A784

1997, Aug. 26
1677 A784 6p multicolored   1.75 1.75

Felix Mendelssohn (1809-47) — A785

No. 1679, Johannes Brahms (1833-97).

1997, Sept. 1			
1678	A785	6p multicolored	1.60 1.60
1679	A785	6p multicolored	1.60 1.60
a.		Pair, #1678-1679	3.50 3.50

Natural History Museum of Montevideo, 160th Anniv. — A786

Designs: a, Lucas Kraguevich, paleontologist. b, Jose Arechavaleta, botantist. c, Garibaldi J. Devincenzi, zoologist. d, Antonio Taddei, archaelogist.

1997, Sept. 3
1680 A786 6p Strip of 4, #a.-d.   5.75 5.75

Mercosur (Common Market of Latin America) A787

1997, Sept. 26		**Perf. 12**	
1681	A787	11p multicolored	3.00 3.00

See Argentina, No. 1975; Bolivia No. 1019; Brazil, No. 2646; Paraguay, No. 2564.

Souvenir Sheet

Passiflora Coerulea — A788

Illustration reduced.

1997, Sept. 26		**Perf. 12½**	
1682	A788	15p multicolored	4.25 4.25

1st Philatelic Exhibition of Mercosur countries.

Heinrich von Stephan (1831-97) A789

1997, Oct. 9
1683 A789 11p multicolored   3.00 3.00

Souvenir Sheet

Spanish-Uruguayan Monument — A790

Illustration reduced.

1997, Oct. 9
1684 A790 15p Monument   4.00 4.00

Philatelic Exhibition, Spain 1997.

America Issue — A791

Designs: 6p, Woman carrying mail. 11p, Man delivering letters.

1997, Oct. 10			
1685	A791	6p multicolored	1.60 1.60
1686	A791	11p multicolored	3.00 3.00

Artigas Scientific Base, Antarctica — A792

1997, Oct. 15		**Perf. 12**	
1687	A792	6p Pygoscelis papua	1.60 1.60

Painting, by Domingo Laporte (1855-1928) — A793

1997, Oct. 21		**Perf. 12½**	
1688	A793	6p multicolored	1.75 1.75

Galicia House, 80th Anniv. A794

1997, Oct. 24
1689 A794 6p multicolored   1.75 1.75

3rd Intl. Congress of Aeronautical and Space History, Montevideo — A795

Perf. 12½

1997, Oct. 27	**Litho.**	**Unwmk.**	
1690	A795	6p Arme 2 Biplane	1.75 1.75

1st Biennial Interparliamentary Exhibition of MERCOSUR Paintings, Montevideo — A796

1997, Oct. 28
1691 A796 11p multicolored   3.00 3.00

Souvenir Sheet

Pope John Paul II, Holy Year 2000 — A797

Illustration reduced.

1997, Nov. 7
1692 A797 10p multicolored   6.50 6.50

Third Intl. Assembly Punta del Este, and of arrival of first Polish colonists at River Plate, cent.

Uruguayan Navy, 180th Anniv. — A798

1997, Nov. 14
1693 A798 6p multicolored   1.75 1.75

Shanghai '97 Intl. Stamp and Coin Exhibition A799

No. 1694: a, 3.50p, Front and back of 1 peso coin. b, 3.50p, Chinese flag, Hong Kong harbor, flower, junk. c, 4p, Michael Schumacher, Formula 1 driving champion, Ferrari. d, 4p, Sojourner on Mars, Pathfinder Mission.
No. 1695: a, 3.50p, Martina Hingis, 1997 Wimbledon Ladies' champion. b, 3.50p, Jan Ullrich, 1997 Tour de France winner. c, 4p, Soccer players, 1998 World Cup Soccer Championship, France. d, 4p, Ski jumper, 1998 Winter Olympic Games, Nagano.

1997, Nov. 19			
1694	A799	Sheet of 4, #a.-d.	4.25 4.25
1695	A799	Sheet of 4, #a.-d.	4.25 4.25

Christmas A800

1997, Nov. 20			
1696	A800	6p Magi	1.75 1.75
1697	A800	11p Madonna & Child	3.00 3.00

Uruguayan Sportsmen — A801

Designs: a, Adesio Lombardo, Olympic bronze medalist, basketball, Helsinki, 1952. b, Guillermo Douglas, Olympic bronze medalist, single sculls, Rome, 1932. c, Obdulio Varela, soccer player on 1950 World Cup championship team. d, Atilio Francois, silver medalist, 1947 World Cycling Championships, Paris. e, Juan López Testa, South American 100 meters champion, 1947.

1997, Nov. 26
1698 A801 6p Strip of 5, #a.-e.   8.50 8.50

Mevifil '97, 1st Intl. Exhibition of Philatelic Audio-Visual and Computer Systems — A802

1997, Dec. 1   *Perf. 12*
1699 A802 11p multicolored   3.00 3.00

INDEPEX '97 A803

Early vehicles, inventors: a, 1st Land Rover, 1947. b, Henry Ford (1863-1947), Model A. c, Robert Bosch (1861-1942), inventor of automotive components. d, Rudolf Diesel (1858-1913), patented first diesel engine, 1897.

1997, Dec. 8   *Perf. 12½*
1700 A803 6p Strip of 4, #a.-d.   6.50 6.50

Naval Academy of Uruguay, 90th Anniv. A804

1997, Dec. 12
1701 A804 6p multicolored   1.60 1.60

Supreme Court of Uruguay, 90th Anniv. A805

1997, Dec. 12
1702 A805 6p multicolored   1.60 1.60

Uruguayan Post Office, 170th Anniv. — A806

1997, Dec. 19
1703 A806 6p multicolored   1.60 1.60

MEVIR (Movement for Eradication of Unsanitary Rural Housing), 90th Anniv. — A807

Design: Homes, Dr. A. Gallinal, logo.

1997, Dec. 26
1704 A807 6p multicolored   1.60 1.60

Construction Projects — A808

a, Preparation. b, Planning. c, Execution.

1997, Dec. 29   *Perf. 12*
1705 A808 6p Strip of 3, #a.-c.   5.00 5.00
  d.   Booklet pane, #1705   6.00
        Complete booklet, #1705d   6.00

Souvenir Sheet

1897 Revolution, Cent. — A809

Design: Gen. Antonio "Chiquito" Saravia and Col. Diego Lamas. Illustration reduced.

1997, Dec. 30   *Perf. 12½*
1706 A809 15p multicolored   4.00 4.00

Painting by Héctor Ragni (b. 1898) — A810

1998, Feb. 6
1707 A810 6p multicolored   1.60 1.60

Naval Station, Montevideo — A811

1998, Feb. 13
1708 A811 6p multicolored   1.60 1.60

Native Trees — A812

a, Butia capitata. b, Grove of butia capitata. c, Grove of phytolacca dioica. d, Phytolacca dioica.

1998, Mar. 20   *Perf. 12*
1709 A812 6p Block of 4, #a.-d.   7.00 7.00

Museum of Humor — A813

Cartoons: No. 1710, by Oscar Abín. No. 1711, by Emilio Cortinas.

1998, Mar. 13   *Perf. 12½*
1710 A813 6p multicolored   1.60 1.60
1711 A813 6p multicolored   1.60 1.60
  a.   Pair, #1710-1711   3.25 3.25

Wilson Ferreira Aldunate (1919-88) A814

1998, Mar. 17   *Perf. 12*
1712 A814 6p multicolored   1.60 1.60

Fossilized Animals — A815

Designs: a, Testudinites sellowi. b, Proborhyaena gigantea. c, Propachyrucos schiaffinos. d, Stegomastodon platensis.

1998, Mar. 26
1713 A815 6p Block of 4, #a.-d.   7.00 7.00

Israel '98, State of Israel, 50th Anniv. — A816

1998, Mar. 31   *Perf. 12*
1714 A816 12p multicolored   3.25 3.25

Birds — A820

a, Plyborus plancus. b, Cygnus melancoryphus. c, Platalea ajaja. d, Theristicus caudatus.

1998, Apr. 30
1718 A820 6p Block of 4, #a.-d.   6.25 6.25

Organization of American States, 50th Anniv. — A821

1998, Apr. 14   Litho.   Perf. 12¾x12½
1719 A821 12p multi   3.00 3.00

61st World Congress of Sports Journalism A822

1998, Apr. 21   Litho.   Perf. 12
1720 A822 6p multicolored   1.60 1.60

Land Settlement
Institute, 50th
Anniv. — A823

1998, Apr. 22 Litho. *Perf. 12¾x12½*
1721 A823 6p multi   1.50 1.50

Souvenir Sheet

Intl.
Topical
Philatelic
Exhibition,
Nueva
Helvecia
A824

Cross and: a, 3.50p, Switzerland #5, Uruguay #1. b, 3.50p, Obverse and reverse of Euro coin. c, 4p, Olympic rings and mountain. d, 4p, Space station.

1998, May 12 *Perf. 12½x12¾*
1722 A824 Sheet of 4, #a.-d.   3.75 3.75

Swiss Republic, bicent.

Souvenir Sheet

Whales
A825

a, 3.50p, Balaenoptera physalus (b). b, 3.50p, Balaenoptera acutorostrata. c, 4p, Megaptera novaeangliae (d). d, 4p, Eubalaena australis (c).

1998, May 15 Litho. *Perf. 12½*
1723 A825 Sheet of 4, #a.-d.   3.75 3.75

Ambiente '98, Maia, Portugal; Intl. Year of the Ocean; Expo '98, Lisbon.

1983 Labor Day Democracy
Demonstrations — A826

Perf. 12¼x12¾
1998, May 27 Litho. Wmk. 332
1724 A826 6p brn & blk   1.50 1.50

See Nos. 1740, 1775.

Street Cars — A827

Historic Montevideo trams: a, English "La Comercial," 1906. b, German Transatlantica Co., 1907. c, Transatlantica, 1908. d, Transatlantica double decker, 1916.

1998, May 29 Litho. *Perf. 12*
1725 A827 6p Block of 4, #a.-d.   6.25 6.25

Juvalux '98 — A828

Wildcats: a, Felis colocola. b, Felis pardalis. c, Felis wiedil. d, Panthera onca.

Unwmk.
1998, June 18 Litho. *Perf. 12*
1726 A828 6p Block of 4, #a.-d.   6.00 6.00

Ships
A829

a, "Sirus." b, Gunboat "18 de Julio." c, Transport, "Maldonado." d, "Instituto de Pesca No. 1."

1998, June 25 Litho. *Perf. 12*
1727 A829 6p Block of 4, #a.-d.   6.00 6.00

Jesuit
Mission
Church,
Calera de
las
Huérfanas
A830

Perf. 12½x12¾
1998, July 24 Litho. Unwmk.
1728 A830 12p multi   3.00 3.00

Monument to the
Peace of 1872,
San José de
Mayo, 125th
Anniv. — A831

1998, July 31 *Perf. 12¾x12½*
1729 A831 6p multi   1.50 1.50

155mm
Artillery
Unit No.
5, Cent.
A832

1998, Aug. 7 *Perf. 12½x12¾*
1730 A832 6p multi   1.50 1.50

Butterflies — A833

1998, Aug. 14 Litho. *Perf. 12*
1731 A833 6p Eacles imperialis   1.50 1.50
1732 A833 6p Protoparce lucetius   1.50 1.50
  a. Pair, #1731-1732   3.00 3.00

First Monument
to José Artigas,
San José de
Mayo,
Cent. — A834

Perf. 12¾x12½
1998, Aug. 24 Litho.
1733 A834 6p multi   1.50 1.50

A835

1998, Aug. 28
1734 A835 6p multi   1.50 1.50

Dr. Mauricio López Lombo (1918-93), zoo founder.

A836

1998, Aug. 31
1735 A836 6p multi   1.50 1.50

Falleri-Balzo Music Conservatory, Montevideo, cent.

José Fernández
Vergara (1810-
1906), Founder of
Pueblo
Vergara — A837

1998, Sept. 8
1736 A837 6p multi   1.50 1.50

Souvenir Sheet

El Pais Newspaper, 80th
Anniv. — A838

Illustration reduced.

1998, Sept. 14 *Perf. 12½x12¾*
1737 A838 12p multi   3.00 3.00

Collective Medical
Assistance
Institute, 145th
Anniv. — A839

1998, Sept. 24 *Perf. 12¾x12½*
1738 A839 6p multi   1.50 1.50

Postal Link
Between
Montevideo and
Corunna, Spain,
230th
Anniv. — A840

1998, Sept. 24
1739 A840 12p multi   3.00 3.00

Espamer '98, Buenos Aires.

Democracy Demonstration Type

6p, March of the Social and Cultural Assoc. of Public School Students, 9/25/83.

Perf. 12½x12¾
1998, Sept. 25 Wmk. 332
1740 A826 6p brn & blk   1.50 1.50

Iberoamericana '98 Philatelic
Exhibition, Maia, Portugal — A841

Airplanes: a, Junkers J52. b, Spad VII. c, Ansaldo SVA-10. d, Neybar.

Unwmk.
1998, Oct. 2 Litho. *Perf. 12*
1741 A841 6p Block of 4, #a.-d.   6.00 6.00

Death of
Chilean
Pres.
Salvador
Allende,
25th
Anniv.
A842

Perf. 12¼x12¾
1998, Oct. 2 Litho. Unwmk.
1742 A842 12p multi   3.00 3.00

50th Anniv. of
Enrique
Rodríguez
Fabregat (1885-
1976) as UN
Commissioner for
Palestine — A843

1998, Oct. 5 *Perf. 12¾x12½*
1743 A843 6p multi   1.50 1.50

Radio Carve, 70th Anniv. A844

1998, Oct. 7   Litho.   Perf. 12½x12¾
1744   A844   6p multi   1.50   1.50

World Post Day A845

1998, Oct. 9   Litho.   Perf. 12½x12¾
1745   A845   12p multi   3.00   3.00

Ilsapex '98, Johannesburg.

America Issue — A846

Famous women: 6p, Julia Guarino (1897-1985), first woman architect in South America. 12p, Dr. Paulina Luisi (1875-1950).

1998, Oct. 9   Litho.   Perf. 12
1746   A846   6p multi   1.50   1.50
1747   A846   12p multi   3.00   3.00

Assoc. of Inland Pharmacies, 50th Anniv. — A847

1998, Oct. 10   Perf. 12½x12¾
1748   A847   6p multi   1.50   1.50

Postal Services A847a

Serpentine Die Cut 11¼
1998, Oct. 15   Litho.   Unwmk.
Self-Adhesive
1748A   A847a   25p multi   6.00   6.00

Exists dated 1999.

Classic Vehicles — A848

Designs: a, 1950 Lancia fire engine. b, 1946 Maserati San Remo. c, 1954 Alfa Romeo trolley bus. d, 1936 Fiat Topolino.

1998, Oct. 23   Litho.   Perf. 12
1749   A848   6p Block of 4, #a.-d.   6.25   6.25

Italia'98.

Artists A849

Designs: No. 1750, Sculpture, "Motherhood," and self-portrait of Nerses Ounanian (1920-57). No. 1751, Illustrations from book "Piquín y Chispita," by Serafin J. Garcia (1905-85), vert. No. 1752, Musical score by Héctor M. Artola (1903-82), vert.

Perf. 12½x12¾, 12¾x12½
1998, Oct. 27   Litho.
1750   A849   6p multi   1.50   1.50
1751   A849   6p multi   1.50   1.50
1752   A849   6p multi   1.50   1.50
   Nos. 1750-1752 (3)   4.50   4.50

Juvenalia '98 — A850

1998, Oct. 30 Litho.   Perf. 12¾x12½
1753   A850   6p multi   1.50   1.50

Souvenir Sheet

Uruguay-Germany Philatelic Exhibition, Montevideo — A851

Designs: a, 3.50p, Zeppelin cover, Zeppelin NT. b, 3.50p, Germany #1592, Germany Berlin #9N584, German Democratic Republic #2791, mail box. c, 4p, Brandenburg Gate, Volkswagen Beetle, Konrad Adenauer. d, 4p, Airplane, German mark note and coin.

1998, Nov. 6 Litho.   Perf. 12½x12¾
1754   A851   Sheet of 4, #a.-d.   3.75   3.75
   IBRA '99, 150th anniv. of German stamps (#1754a, 1754b), 50th anniv. of Federal Republic of Germany (#1754c), 50th anniv. of German mark (#1754d).

16th Congress of Expenditure Control Boards — A852

1998, Nov. 9
1755   A852   12p blue & silver   3.00   3.00

Uruguayan Chamber of Industries, Cent. — A853

1998, Nov. 9
1756   A853   6p multi   1.50   1.50

Flowers — A854

Serpentine Die Cut 11¼
1998-99   Litho.
Self-Adhesive
1757   A854   1p Oxalis pudica   .25   .25
1760   A854   4p Oxalis pudica
                  (white)   .90   .90
1761   A854   5p Oxalis pudica
                  (purple)   .70   .70
1762   A854   6p Eugenia
                  uniflora   1.50   1.50
1763   A854   7p Eugenia
                  uniflora   1.60   1.60
1765   A854   9p Eugenia
                  uniflora   5.00   5.00
1766   A854   10p Aechmea
                  recurvata   2.50   2.50
1770   A854   14p Acca sellowi-
                  ana   3.25   3.25
1771   A854   50p Acca sellowi-
                  ana   8.75   8.75
   Nos. 1757-1770 (8)   15.70 15.70

Issued: 7p, 2/4/99; 4p, 12/23/99; 14p, 8/6/99; 1p, 6p, 10p, 50p, 1998. 9p, 1999. 5p, 2/19/02.
   No. 1757 exists dated 1999, 2000, 2001, 2002. No. 1766 exists dated 1999. No. 1766 exists dated 2003.

Christmas — A855

Designs: 6p, The Virgin's Descent to Reward St. Ildefons' Writings (detail), by El Greco. 12p, St. Peter's Tears (detail), by Bartolomé Esteban Murillo.

1998, Nov. 23   Litho.   Perf. 12
1772   A855   6p multi   1.50   1.50
1773   A855   12p multi   3.00   3.00

Paso Del Molina Neighborhood of Montevideo, 250th Anniv. — A856

1998, Nov. 26   Perf. 12½x12¾
1774   A856   6p multi   1.50   1.50

Labor Day Type
6p, Proclamation at the Obelisk, 11/27/83.

Perf. 12¼x12¾
1998, Nov. 27   Litho.   Wmk. 332
1775   A826   6p brn & blk   1.50   1.50

Morosoli Cultural Awards — A857

Perf. 12¾x12½
1998, Nov. 27   Litho.   Unwmk.
1776   A857   6p multi   1.50   1.50

Universal Declaration of Human Rights, 50th Anniv. — A858

1998, Dec. 10   Perf. 12½x12¾
1777   A858   6p multi   1.50   1.50

Uruguayan Olympic Committee, 75th Anniv. — A859

1998, Dec. 15   Perf. 12
1778   A859   6p multi   1.50   1.50

Uruguayan Sportsmen A860

Designs: a, Juan Lopez (1907-83), soccer coach. b, Hector Scarone (1899-1967), soccer player. c, Leandro Gomez Harley (1902-79), basketball player, hurdler. d, Liberto Corney (1905-55), boxer.

1998, Dec. 15   Perf. 12¾x12½
1779   A860   6p Block of 4, #a.-d.   6.00   6.00

Famous Uruguayans — A861

Designs: No. 1780, Dr. Roberto Caldeyro Barcia (1921-96), physiologist. No. 1781, Dr. José Verocay (1876-1923), pathologist. No. 1782, Dr. José L. Duomarco (1905-85), medical researcher.

Perf. 12¼x12¾
1998, Dec. 18   Litho.   Unwmk.
1780   A861   6p multi   1.50   1.50
1781   A861   6p multi   1.50   1.50
1782   A861   6p multi   1.50   1.50
   Nos. 1780-1782 (3)   4.50   4.50

Emile Zola's "J'accuse" Letter, Cent. (in 1998) A862

1999, Jan. 4   Litho.   Perf. 12½x12¾
1783   A862   14p multicolored   3.50   3.50

Las Cañas Resort, Fray Bentos A863

1999, Feb. 26
1784 A863 7p multicolored   1.60 1.60

Rio de la Plata Boundary Treaty, 25th Anniv. A864

1999, Mar. 15
1785 A864 7p multicolored   1.60 1.60

Famous Uruguayans — A865

Designs: No. 1786, Joaquin Torres Garcia (1874-1949), painter. No. 1787, Luis Ernesto Aroztegui (1930-94), textile artist. No. 1788, Juan José Morosoli (1899-1957), writer.

1999, Mar. 26
1786 A865 7p multicolored   2.50 2.50
1787 A865 7p multicolored   2.50 2.50
1788 A865 7p multicolored   2.50 2.50
       Nos. 1786-1788 (3)   7.50 7.50

Birds and Flowering Trees A866

a, Psidium cattleianum, Pipraeidea melanonota. b, Tabebuia ipe, Chlorostilbon aureoventris. c, Duranta repens, Tangara preciosa. d, Citharexylum montevidense, Tachuris rubigastra.

1999, Apr. 14 Litho. Perf. 12¼x12¾
1789 A866 7p Block of 4, #a.-d.   6.00 6.00

Carriages A867

Designs: a, Break de chasse. b, Mylord. c, Coupé trois quarts. d, Break de champ.

1999, Apr. 29 Litho. Perf. 12½x12¾
1790 A867 7p Block of 4, #a.-d.   6.50 6.50

National Soccer Team, Cent. — A868

Designs: a, B. Céspedes, M. Nebel, C. Céspedes, team's first field. b, H. Castro, P. Cea, A. Ciocca, team flag. c, R. Porta, A García, S. Gambetta, team headquarters.

1999, May 5 Litho. Perf. 12
1791 A868 7p Strip of 3, #a.-c.   5.75 5.75
       Complete booklet, #1791   6.75

Children's Millennium Stamp Design Contest Winners A869

Designs: a, By Stefani Andrea Furtado. b, By Pilar Trujillo. c, By Lucia Lavie. d, By Cecilia Chopitea.

1999, May 6 Litho. Perf. 12½x12¾
1792 A869 7p Block of 4, #a.-d.   6.50 6.50

Jorge Chebataroff (1909-84), Geographer, Botanist — A870

1999, May 14
1793 A870 7p multicolored   1.60 1.60

Formation of Infantry Brigade No. 1, 60th Anniv. A871

Paintings: No. 1794, Infantry Battalion No. 2 at Battle of Montecaseros, 1852. No. 1795, Infantry Brigade No. 1 at Battle of Estero Bellaco, 1866. No. 1796, Infantry Battalion No. 1 at Battle of Boquerón, 1866.

1999, May 18
1794 A871 7p multicolored   1.75 1.75
1795 A871 7p multicolored   1.75 1.75
1796 A871 7p multicolored   1.75 1.75
       Nos. 1794-1796 (3)   5.25 5.25

Villa de la Restauracion, 150th Anniv. — A872

1999, May 24 Perf. 12¾x12½
1797 A872 7p multicolored   1.75 1.75

Souvenir Sheet

Barcelona, Spain Soccer Team, Cent. — A873

Illustration reduced.

1999, May 28 Litho. Perf. 12½x12¾
1798 A873 15p multi   3.25 3.25

1st Festival of Film Critics, Montevideo A874

1999, June 2 Perf. 12¾x12¼
Booklet Stamp
1799 A874 7p multi   1.60 1.60
  a.   Booklet pane, 2 #1799   3.25
        Complete booklet, #1799a   3.25

Philex France 99 A875

Horses: a, Arabian. b, Quarter horse. c, Thoroughbred. d, Shetland pony.

Perf. 12½x12¾
1999, June 10   Litho.
1800 A875 7p Block of 4, #a.-d.   6.25 6.25

Publication "Marcha," 60th Anniv. — A876

Perf. 12¼x12¾
1999, June 23   Litho.
1801 A876 7p multi   1.60 1.60

Permanent Home for "Espacio Ciencia" Science Exhibits — A877

1999, July 2 Perf. 12¾x12¼
1802 A877 7p multi   1.60 1.60

Artigas Antarctic Scientific Base, 25th Anniv. A878

1999, July 12 Perf. 12¼x12¾
1803 A878 7p multi   1.60 1.60

Republic of Uruguay University, 150th Anniv. A879

1999, July 19
1804 A879 7p yel & blk   1.60 1.60

UNESCO Regional Office, 50th Anniv. — A880

1999, July 20 Perf. 12¾x12¼
1805 A880 7p multi   1.60 1.60

The Last Charruas — A881

a, One seated, one standing. b, Two seated.

1999, July 22 Litho. Perf. 12¾x12½
1806 A881 7p Pair, #a.-b.   3.25 3.25

Souvenir Sheet

Millennium A882

a, 3.50p, Apollo space program. b, 3.50p, Soccer players, 2000 Olympic Games, Sydney. c, 4p, Centenary of Zeppelins. d, 4p, #C60.

1999, July 30 Litho. Perf. 12½x12¾
1807 A882 Sheet of 4, #a.-d.   5.75 5.75

UPU, 125th anniv., Bangkok 2000, Espana 2000, WIPA 2000, Hanover World's Fair.

El Galpon Theater, Montevideo, 50th Anniv. — A883

1999, Aug. 3 Perf. 12¾x12¼
1808 A883 7p multi   1.60 1.60

China 1999 World Philatelic Exhibition — A884

Sea planes: a, Piper J-3. b, Short Sunderland.

1999, Aug. 18 Perf. 12¼x12¾
1809 A884 7p Pair, #a.-b.   3.25 3.25

Dogs — A885

Designs: a, Cocker spaniel. b, German shepherd. c, Dalmatian. d, Basset hound.

Perf. 12¾x12½
1999, Aug. 24 **Litho.**
1810 A885 7p Block of 4, #a.-d. 6.00 6.00

Insects & Flowers A886

a, Halictidae, Oxalis sp. b, Apanteles sp., Epidendrum paniculosum. c, Metabolosia univita, Baccharis trimera. d, Compositae, Cantarido.

Perf. 12½x12¾
1999, Sept. 10 **Litho.**
1811 A886 7p Block of 4, #a.-d. 6.00 6.00

A887

A888

Uruguayan Artists: No. 1812, Orlando Aldama (1904-87), writer. No. 1813, Julio Martínez Oyanguren (1901-73), guitarist.

Perf. 12¾x12½
1999, Sept. 13 **Litho.**
1812 A887 7p multi 1.60 1.60
1813 A887 7p multi 1.60 1.60

Perf. 12¾x12¼
1999, Sept. 18 **Litho.**
1814 A888 7p multi 1.60 1.60
Cultural heritage of Mercosur countries.

First Uruguayan Participation in Olympics, Paris, 1924 — A889

Designs: a, Poster, medal. b, Medal, medal-winning soccer team.

1999, Sept. 30 **Perf. 12¼x12¾**
1815 A889 7p Pair, #a.-b. 3.25 3.25

Intl. Year of Older Persons A890

1999, Oct. 1 **Litho.** **Perf. 12¼x12¾**
1816 A890 7p multi 1.60 1.60

Philatelic Witches Sabbath, by Mariano Barbasán — A891

1999, Oct. 1 **Perf. 12**
1817 A891 7p multi 1.60 1.60
Stamp Day.

America Issue, A New Millennium Without Arms — A892

7p, Arms in trash can. 14p, Earth, satellites.

1999, Oct. 6 **Perf. 13¾x12¼**
1818 A892 7p multi 1.60 1.60
1819 A892 14p multi 3.25 3.25

Inter-American Development Bank, 40th Anniv. — A893

1999, Oct. 6 **Perf. 12¼x12¾**
1820 A893 7p multi 1.60 1.60

Winner of Older Person's Stamp Design Contest A894

1999, Oct. 8
1821 A894 7p multi 1.60 1.60

El Ceibo Society, 50th Anniv. A895

1999, Oct. 8
1822 A895 7p multi 1.60 1.60

Third Intl. Conference of Ministers for Sports, Punta del Este — A896

1999, Oct. 13 **Perf. 12**
1823 A896 7p multi 1.60 1.60

Souvenir Sheets

Official Service of Broadcasting, Television and Entertainment — A897

Illustration reduced.
No. 1824: a, 4p, Television cameraman. b, 4p, Building. c, 3p, Radio studio. d, 3p, Film cameraman.
No. 1825: a, 4p, Symphony orchestra. b, 4p, Chamber music group. c, 3p, Chorus. d, 3p, Ballet dancers.

1999, Oct. 22 **Perf. 12¼x12¾**
1824 A897 Sheet of 4, #a.-d. 3.25 3.25
1825 A897 Sheet of 4, #a.-d. 3.25 3.25

Uruguayan Standards Institute, 60th Anniv. — A898

1999, Nov. 3
1826 A898 7p multi 1.60 1.60

A899

A900

1999, Nov. 3 **Perf. 12¾x12¼**
1827 A899 7p multi 1.60 1.60
Vice-President Hugo Batalla (1926-98).

1999, Nov.12
Cover of 4/29/29 Mundo Uruguayo magazine.
1828 A900 7p multi 1.60 1.60
Exhibition of art and design from the 1920s, Blanes Museum, Montevideo.

Millennium — A901

Illustration reduced.
No. 1829 — Various buildings and: a, "1999." b, "2000."

1999, Nov. 23 **Litho.** **Perf. 12**
1829 A901 3.50p Pair, #a.-b. 1.60 1.60

Celmar Poumé (1924-83), Cartoonist A902

1999, Nov. 26 **Perf. 12¾x12¼**
1830 A902 7p multi 1.60 1.60

Christmas A903

9p, Tree with ornaments. 18p, Carolers.

Perf. 12¼x12¾, 12¾x12¼
1999, Dec. 3
1831 A903 9p multi 2.00 2.00
1832 A903 18p multi, vert. 4.00 4.00

Tannat Wines, 20th Anniv. — A904

1999, Dec. 9 **Perf. 12**
1833 A904 9p shown 2.00 2.00
1834 A904 9p Wine drinker 2.00 2.00

New Maldonado Department Governmental Building — A905

1999, Dec. 11 **Perf. 12¼x12¾**
1835 A905 9p multi 2.00 2.00

Types of 1997 and

Crow's Gorge Nature Reserve A907

Design: 2p, Penitente Waterfall, vert. 5p, Bird. 10p, Crow's Gorge Nature Reserve. No. 1841, Gruta del Palacio, vert. 100p, Sierra de los Caracoles.

Serpentine Die Cut 11¼, Die Cut (#1836A, 1840, 1850, 1853)

2000-04   Litho.

Self-Adhesive

1836	A907	2p multi	.30	.30
1836A	A908	5p multi	.45	.45
1837	A907	10p multi	.85	.85
1838	A907	11p multi	2.00	2.00
1840	A781	20p multi	4.50	4.50
1841	A907	20p multi	5.00	5.00
1850	A782	32p multi	7.25	7.25
1853	A782	80p multi	18.00	18.00
1854	A907	100p multi	14.00	14.00
1855	A782	100p multi	7.50	7.50
	Nos. 1836-1855 (10)		59.85	59.85

Issued: 32p, 1/20. No. 1840, 80p, 12/12. 11p, 3/16/01. No. 1841, 4/26/01. 2p, 8/1/01. No. 1854, 2/13/02. No. 1855, 10/5/04. 5p, 12/1; 10p, 10/18; No. 1855A, 9/26. This is an expanding set. Numbers may change.

No. 1855 has straight numerals in denomination.

No. 1836 exists dated "2002." No. 1841 exists dated "2006."

50th Anniv of Artistic Career of Carlos Páez Vilaró — A916

2000, Jan. 15   Litho.   **Perf. 12**
1856   A916   9p multi   2.00   2.00

Orchids — A917

No. 1857: a, 5p, Laelia purpurata. b, 4p, Cattleya corcovado. c, 4p, Cattleya sp. "hybrid." d, 5p, Laelia tenebrosa.

2000, Mar. 3
1857   A917   Block of 4, #a.-d.   4.00   4.00

Lighthouses — A918

No. 1858: a, 5p, Isla de Flores, 1828. b, 4p, Punta del Este, 1860. c, 4p, Cabo Polonio, 1881. d, 5p, Punta Brava, 1876.

2000, Mar. 14
1858   A918   Block of 4, #a.-d.   4.00   4.00

Carlos Quijano (1900-84), Economics Journalist — A919

2000, Mar. 30   **Perf. 12¼x12¾**
1859   A919   9p multi   2.00   2.00

The Gold Rush, Starring Charlie Chaplin, 75th Anniv. A920

2000, Apr. 7   Litho.   **Perf. 12¼x12¾**
1860   A920   18p multi   4.00   4.00
Lubrapex 2000 Stamp Show, Brazil.

El Cordón Neighborhood of Montevideo, 250th Anniv. — A921

2000, Apr. 10   Litho.   **Perf. 12¼x12¾**
1861   A921   9p multi   2.00   2.00

Mural "Espina de la Cruz," by Children of Mercedes — A922

a, 5p, Branches. b, 4p, Two red flowers.

2000, Apr. 26   **Perf. 12¼x12**
1862   A922   Pair, #a-b   2.00   2.00

Francisco García y Santos (1856-1921), Government Official — A923

2000, May 2   **Perf. 12¾x12¼**
1863   A923   9p multi   2.00   2.00

Uruguayan Notaries Assoc., 125th Anniv. — A924

2000, May 9   Litho.   **Perf. 12¾x12¼**
1864   A924   9p multi   2.00   2.00

Intl. Museum Day — A925

2000, May 18   Litho.   **Perf. 12¾x12¼**
1865   A925   9p multi   2.00   2.00

Stampin' the Future Children's Stamp Design Contest Winners — A926

Artwork by: a, 5p, Helena Perez. b, 4p, Maria Pia Pereyra. c, 4p, Virginia Regueiro. d, 5p, Blanca E. Lima.
Illustration reduced.

2000, June 2   Litho.   **Perf. 12**
1866   A926   Block of 4, #a-d   4.00   4.00

Club Soriano, 90th Anniv. A927

2000, June 9   Litho.   **Perf. 12¼x12¾**
1867   A927   9p multi   2.00   2.00

Antonio Rupenian, Founder of Radio Armenia — A928

2000, June 16   **Perf. 12¾x12¼**
1868   A928   18p multi   4.00   4.00

"1900 Generation" Writers, Cent. — A929

Perf. 12¾x12¼
2000, June 22   Litho.
1869   A929   9p multi   2.00   2.00

Cacti — A930

No. 1870: a, 5p, Notocactus ottonis. b, 4p, Echinopsis multiplex.

2000, July 4   **Perf. 12¼**
1870   A930   Horiz. pair, #a-b   2.00   2.00

Uruguayan Soccer Association, Cent. — A931

No. 1871: a, 5p, Players marching. b, 4p, Team photo. c, 4p, Stadium, World Cup. d, 5p, Players in action, World Cup.
Illustration reduced.

2000, July 14   Litho.   **Perf. 12¼x12**
1871   A931   Block of 4, #a-d   8.75   8.75

Opera Anniversaries — A932

No. 1872: a, 9p, Scene from Carmen, composer Georges Bizet. b, 9p, Scene from Tosca, composer Giacomo Puccini.
Illustration reduced.

2000, July 20
1872   A932   Pair, #a-b   4.00   4.00
Carmen, 125th anniv.; Tosca, cent.

Latin American Integration Association, 20th Anniv. — A933

2000, Aug. 11   **Perf. 12¾x12¼**
1873   A933   18p multi   4.00   4.00

Naval Aviation, 75th Anniv. A934

2000, Aug. 18   **Perf. 12¼x12¾**
1874 A934 9p multi   2.00 2.00

ORT, 120th Anniv. A935

2000, Aug. 28
1875 A935 9p multi   2.00 2.00

Luis de la Robla (1780-1844), First Postmaster General — A936

2000, Aug. 28   **Perf. 12¾x12¼**
1876 A936 9p multi   2.00 2.00

Gonzalo Rodriguez (1971-99), Race Car Driver — A937

a, 9p, Rodriguez, dark blue car. b, 9p, Rodriguez holding trophy, light blue car. Illustration reduced.

2000, Sept. 11   **Perf. 12x12¼**
1877 A937 Pair, #a-b   4.00 4.00

Gen. José Artigas (1764-1850) A938

2000, Sept. 22 Litho. Perf. 12¼
1878 A938 9p multi + label   1.60 1.60

España 2000 Intl. Philatelic Exhibition — A939

Birds: a, 5p, Donacospiza albifrons. b, 4p, Geositta cunicularia. c, 4p, Phacellodomus striaticollis. d, 5p, Cacicus chrysopterus.

Illustration reduced.

2000, Sept. 27   **Perf. 12**
1879 A939 Block of 4, #a-d   3.25 3.25

Soka Gakkai International, 25th Anniv. — A940

2000, Oct. 2   **Perf. 12¼x12¾**
1880 A940 18p multi   3.25 3.25

America Issue, Fight Against AIDS — A941

No. 1881: a, 9p, Tic-tac-toe game with condoms and crosses. b, 18p, Syringe and red ribbon.

2000, Oct. 10   **Perf. 12¼**
1881 A941 Horiz. pair, #a-b   4.75 4.75

Mercosur Cultural Heritage Day — A942

2000, Oct. 14   **Perf. 12¾x12¼**
1882 A942 18p multi   3.25 3.25

Dragon, by Luis Mazzey (1895-1983) — A943

2000, Oct. 19   **Perf. 12¼x12¾**
1883 A943 9p multi   1.60 1.60

Fire Fighters A944

Designs: No. 1884, 9p, At car crash. No. 1885, 9p, Searching for victims, vert.

Perf. 12¼x12¾, 12¾x12¼
2000, Oct. 26
1884-1885 A944 Set of 2   3.25 3.25

Prof. Julio Ricaldoni (1906-93), Structural Engineer A945

2000, Nov. 13   **Perf. 12¼x12¾**
1886 A945 9p multi   1.60 1.60

29th Conference on Structural Engineering, Punta del Este.

Training Ship "Capitan Miranda," 70th Anniv. A946

2000, Nov. 15
1887 A946 9p multi   1.60 1.60

Holy Roman Emperor Charles V (1500-58) A947

2000, Nov. 22   **Litho.**
1888 A947 22p multi   4.00 4.00

Christmas A948

Designs: 11p, Fireworks. 22p, Holy Family.

2000, Dec. 1
1889-1890 A948 Set of 2   5.75 5.75

Sarandi del Yi, 125th Anniv. — A949

2000, Dec. 14   **Perf. 12¾x12¼**
1891 A949 11p multi   2.00 2.00

Forest Fire Prevention Service A950

2001, Feb. 9 Litho. Perf. 12½x12¾
1892 A950 11p multi   2.00 2.00

Amphibians and Reptiles — A951

No. 1893: a, Phyllomedusa iheringii. b, Acanthochelys spixii. c, Phrynops hilarii. d, Scinax sqalirostris.

2001, Feb. 15   **Perf. 12**
1893 A951 11p Block of 4, #a-d   8.00 8.00

Paysandú Rowing Club, Cent. A952

2001, Feb. 28   **Perf. 12½x12¾**
1894 A952 11p multi   2.00 2.00

17th Congress of Latin American Confederation of Congress Organizers A953

2001, Mar. 2   **Perf. 12¾x12½**
1895 A953 11p multi   2.00 2.00

City of Belén, Bicent. — A954

2001, Mar. 14
1896 A954 11p multi   2.00 2.00

David, by Michelangelo, 500th Anniv. — A955

2001, Mar. 22
1897 A955 22p multi   4.00 4.00

Uruguayan Society of Performers, 50th Anniv. — A956

2001, Mar. 26　　　*Perf. 12½x12¾*
1898　A956　11p multi　　　　　2.00　2.00

Casal Catalá, 75th Anniv. — A957

2001, Apr. 20　　　*Perf. 12¾x12½*
1899　A957　11p multi　　　　　2.00　2.00

Universidad Mayor de la República Engineering Faculty, 85th Anniv. — A958

2001, Apr. 30
1900　A958　11p blue　　　　　　2.00　2.00

Rodolfo V. Tálice (1899-1999), Biologist — A959

2001, May 2　　　　*Perf. 12½x12¾*
1901　A959　11p multi　　　　　2.00　2.00

Montevideo Lions Club, 50th Anniv. — A960

2001, May 14　　　*Perf. 12¾x12½*
1902　A960　11p multi　　　　　2.00　2.00

Invention of the Telephone, 125th Anniv. A961

2001, May 22　　　*Perf. 12½x12¾*
1903　A961　22p multi　　　　　4.00　4.00

Snakes — A962

No. 1904: a, Philodryas olfersii. b, Bothrops alternatus.
Illustration reduced.

2001, May 28　　　　*Perf. 12*
1904　A962　11p Horiz. pair, #a-b　4.00　4.00

Juan Manuel Blanes (1830-1901), Painter — A963

**2001, June 8　Litho.　*Perf. 12½x12¾*
1905　A963　11p multi　　　　　1.75　1.75

Start of Pediatrics Teaching by Dr. Luis Morquio, Cent. — A964

2001, June 15　　　*Perf. 12¾x12½*
1906　A964　11p multi　　　　　1.75　1.75

The Ring of the Nibelung, by Richard Wagner — A965

No. 1907: a, The Rhinegold (El Oro del Rin). b, The Valkyrie (La Walquiria). c, Siegfried (Sigfrido). d, The Twilight of the Gods (El Ocaso de los Dioses).

2001, June 29　　　　*Perf. 12*
1907　A965　11p Block of 4, #a-d　6.50　6.50

Intl. Organization for Migration, 50th Anniv. — A966

2001, July 5　　　*Perf. 12¾x12½*
1908　A966　22p blue & black　　3.25　3.25

Thomas Alva Edison (1847-1931) A967

2001, July 12
1909　A967　22p multi　　　　　3.25　3.25

Laying of Foundation Stone for Montevideo Port, Cent. — A968

2001, July 18　　　*Perf. 12½x12¾*
1910　A968　11p multi　　　　　1.75　1.75

Fowl — A969

No. 1911: a, New Hampshire. b, Orpington-Buff. c, Araucanas. d, Leghorn-Light brown.
Illustration reduced.

2001, July 30　　　　*Perf. 12*
1911　A969　11p Block of 4, #a-d　6.75　6.75

Moby Dick, by Herman Melville, 150th Anniv. — A970

2001, Aug. 2　　　*Perf. 12¾x12½*
1912　A970　22p multi　　　　　3.25　3.25

Bernardo González Pecotche (1901-63), Founder of Logosophy A971

2001, Aug. 7　　　　*Perf. 12*
1913　A971　11p multi　　　　　1.75　1.75

First Concorde Flight, 25th Anniv. A972

2001, Aug. 10　　　*Perf. 12½x12¾*
1914　A972　22p multi　　　　　3.25　3.25

Rose Varieties — A973

No. 1915: a, Louis Philippe. b, Souvenir de Mme. Léonie Viennot. c, Kronenbourg. d, Lady Hillingdon.

2001, Aug. 16　　　　*Perf. 12*
1915　A973　11p Block of 4, #a-d　6.75　6.75

Apiculture — A974

No. 1916: a, Apiculturists. b, Bee on flower.
Illustration reduced.

2001, Sept. 12
1916　A974　12p Horiz. pair, #a-b　3.50　3.50

Town of Dolores, Bicent. — A975

2001, Sept. 21　　　*Perf. 12¾x12½*
1917　A975　12p multi　　　　　1.75　1.75

Uruguay Philatelic Club, 75th Anniv. A976

Sun and inscription: No. 1918, 12p, "75 Años." No. 1919, 12p, "1er Presidente / Dr. Miguel A. Paez Formoso."

2001, Sept. 26　　　*Perf. 12½x12¾*
1918-1919　A976　Set of 2　　　3.50　3.50

America Issue - UNESCO World Heritage Sites — A977

Buildings from Historic Quarter of Colonia del Sacramento: a, 12p, Basilica del Santisimo. b, 24p, San Benito de Palermo Chapel.

2001, Sept. 28　　　　*Perf. 12*
1920　A977　Horiz. pair, #a-b　5.25　5.25

Carlos
Amoretti,
50th Anniv.
as Artist
A978

2001, Oct. 2   Perf. 12½x12¾
1921 A978 12p multi   1.75 1.75

Town of Sauce,
150th
Anniv. — A979

2001, Oct. 12   Perf. 12¾x12½
1922 A979 12p multi   1.75 1.75

Uruguay -
Japan
Diplomatic
Relations,
80th Anniv.
A980

Perf. 12¼x12¾
2001, Sept. 24   Litho.
1923 A980 24p multi   3.50 3.50

Prevention
of Illegal
Drug Use
A981

2001, Oct. 16
1924 A981 12p multi   1.75 1.75

Year of Dialogue
Among
Civilizations
A982

2001, Oct. 23   Perf. 12¾x12¼
1925 A982 24p multi   3.50 3.50

Honorary
Committee for
Fighting
Cancer — A983

2001, Oct. 29
1926 A983 12p multi   1.75 1.75

Ultimas Noticias
Newspaper, 20th
Anniv. — A984

2001, Oct. 31
1927 A984 12p multi   1.75 1.75

Sauce
Basketball
Club, 50th
Anniv.
A985

2001, Nov. 9   Perf. 12¼x12¾
1928 A985 12p multi   1.75 1.75

Blood Donor's
Day — A986

2001, Nov. 12   Perf. 12¾x12¼
1929 A986 12p multi   1.75 1.75

Juan Zorilla de San Martín (1855-
1931), Writer — A987

2001, Nov. 13   Perf. 12¼x12¾
1930 A987 12p multi   1.75 1.75

Uruguayan Navy's Hydrographic Ship
"Oyarvide" — A988

2001, Nov. 14
1931 A988 12p multi   1.75 1.75

Uruguayan Visit of
Rotary Intl.
President Richard
King and Wife
Cherie — A989

2001, Nov. 20   Perf. 12¾x12¼
1932 A989 24p multi   3.50 3.50

Peñarol Athletic Club, 110th
Anniv. — A990

2001, Nov. 22   Perf. 12
1933 A990 12p multi   1.75 1.75

Julio Sosa (1926-
64), Tango
Singer — A991

2001, Nov. 26   Perf. 12¾x12¼
1934 A991 12p multi   1.75 1.75

José Nasazzi
(1901-68), Soccer
Player — A992

2001, Nov. 29
1935 A992 12p multi   1.75 1.75

Christmas — A993

Paintings of Adoration of the Shepherds, by:
12p, José Ribera. 24p, Anton Raphael Mengs.

2001, Dec. 6
1936-1937 A993   Set of 2   5.25 5.25

Church of San
Carlos,
Bicent. — A994

2001, Dec. 7
1938 A994 12p multi   1.75 1.75

National Museum of Visual Arts, 90th
Anniv. — A995

2001, Dec. 12   Perf. 12
1939 A995 12p multi   1.75 1.75

State Insurance
Bank, 90th
Anniv. — A996

2001, Dec. 20   Perf. 12¾x12¼
1940 A996 12p multi   1.75 1.75

Guettarda Uruguensis — A997

2001, Dec. 21   Perf. 12¼x12¾
1941 A997 24p multi   3.50 3.50

St. Josemaría Escrivá de Balaguer
(1902-75) — A998

Balaguer and quotes: a, "El trabajo es. . ." b,
"Quieres de verdad. . ." c, "La santidad. . ." d,
"Que busques. . ."
Illustration reduced.

2002, Jan. 9   Perf. 12
1942 A998 12p Block of 4, #a-d   7.00 7.00

Uruguayan Association of Directors of
Carnivals and Folk Festivals, 50th
Anniv. — A999

Feet of: a, Ringmaster. b, Clown. c, Acrobat.

2002, Mar. 8   Litho.   Perf. 12½
                   Self-Adhesive
1943   Booklet pane of 3   3.25 3.25
  a.-b. A999 6p Either single   .80 .80
  c.   A999 12p black   1.60 1.60
         Booklet, #1943   3.50

Christianity in
Armenia,
1700th Anniv.
A1000

2002, Apr. 23   Perf. 12
1944 A1000 12p multi   1.50 1.50

New Year 2003 (Year of the Horse) — A1001

2002, May 14   *Perf. 12¾x12¼*
1945 A1001 24p multi   3.00 3.00

2002 World Cup Soccer Championships, Japan and Korea — A1002

No. 1946: a, Flags, soccer ball, and field (38mm diameter). b, Soccer players, years of Uruguayan championships.
Illustration reduced.

2002, May 21   *Perf. 12¾*
1946 A1002 12p Horiz. pair, #a-b 2.75 2.75

See Argentina No. 2184, Brazil No. 2840, France No. 2891, Germany No. 2163 and Italy No. 2526.

Book Day — A1003

2002, May 24   *Perf. 12¾x12¼*
1947 A1003 12p multi   1.40 1.40

Inter-American Children's Institute, 75th Anniv. — A1004

2002, June 10   *Perf. 12¼x12¾*
1948 A1004 12p multi   1.40 1.40

Department of Tacuarembó, 165th Anniv. — A1005

2002, June 14
1949 A1005 12p multi   1.40 1.40

Cerro de Montevideo Lighthouse, Bicent. — A1006

Designs: 12p, Old lighthouse. 24p, New lighthouse, vert.

Perf. 12¼x12¾, 12¾x12¼
2002, June 24
1950-1951 A1006   Set of 2   3.75 3.75

Villa Constitución, 150th Anniv. — A1007

2002, July 11   *Perf. 12¼x12¾*
1952 A1007 12p multi   1.00 1.00

"We Are United" A1008

2002, July 17
1953 A1008 6p multi   .50 .50

Printed in sheets of 3 + label. Value $2.

Natural Uruguay A1009

2002, July 22   *Litho.*
1954 A1009 24p blue & orange   2.40 2.40

Montevideo Botanical Gardens, Cent. — A1010

No. 1955: a, Botanical Gardens building, Erythrina cristigalli. b, Rhodophiala bifida. c, Prof. Atilio Lombardo and Tillandsia arequitae. d, Heteropterys dumetorum.

2002, July 31   *Perf. 12*
1955   Horiz. strip of 4   4.25 4.25
a.-d.   A1010 12p Any single   1.00 1.00

Montevideo Wanderers Soccer Team, Cent. — A1011

2002, Aug. 1   *Perf. 12¾x12¼*
1956 A1011 12p black   1.10 1.10

Sportsmen — A1012

Designs: No. 1957, 12p, Lorenzo Fernández, soccer player. No. 1958, 12p, José Leandro Andrade, soccer player. No. 1959, 12p, Alvaro Gestido, soccer player. No. 1960, 12p,

---

César L. Gallardo, fencer. No. 1961, 12p, Pedro Petrone, soccer player.

2002, Aug. 16   *Perf. 12¼x12¾*
1957-1961 A1012   Set of 5   5.25 5.25

Elvis Presley (1935-77) A1013

2002, Aug. 19   *Perf. 12¾x12¼*
1962 A1013 24p multi   2.10 2.10

Agustín Bisio (1894-1952), Poet — A1014

2002, Aug. 30   *Perf. 12¾x12¼*
                            Self-Adhesive
1963 A1014 12p multi   1.10 1.10

City of Artigas, 150th Anniv. — A1015

2002, Sept. 12   *Perf. 12¾x12¼*
                            Self-Adhesive
1964 A1015 12p multi   1.10 1.10

Uruguayan Cooperative Society of Bus Services, 65th Anniv. — A1016

2002, Sept. 16   *Perf. 12¼x12¾*
1965 A1016 12p multi   1.10 1.10

Psychoanalysis, Cent. — A1017

2002, Sept. 20   *Perf. 12*
1966 A1017 12p multi   1.10 1.10

24th Latin American Psychoanalysis Congress, Montevideo.

Horacio Arredondo (1888-1967), Historical Preservationist, and San Miguel Fort — A1018

2002, Sept. 20   *Perf. 12¼x12¾*
1967 A1018 12p multi   1.10 1.10

Paso del Rey Barracks Natl. Historic Monument — A1019

2002, Sept. 23   *Perf. 12*
1968 A1019 12p multi   1.10 1.10

Intl. Year of Ecotourism — A1020

2002, Sept. 24   *Litho.*
1969 A1020 12p multi   1.10 1.10

Uruguayan Postal Services, 175th Anniv. — A1021

Designs: No. 1970, Postal Services headquarters, Montevideo. No. 1971, Letter box.

2002, Oct. 9   *Perf. 12¾x12¼*
1970 A1021 12p multi   1.10 1.10

                            Souvenir Sheet
                            Imperf
1971 A1021 12p multi   1.10 1.10

First Equestrian Statue of Brig. Gen. Juan Antonio Lavalleja, Cent. — A1022

2002, Oct. 11   *Perf. 12¾x12¼*
1972 A1022 12p multi   1.10 1.10

America Issue — Youth, Education and Literacy A1023

"ANALFABETISMO" in: 12p, Word search puzzle. 24p, Bowl of alphabet soup.

2002, Oct. 16   **Perf. 12¼x12¾**
1973-1974 A1023   Set of 2   3.25 3.25

Christmas
A1024

2002, Nov. 4   **Perf. 12¾x12¼**
1975 A1024 12p multi   1.10 1.10

Association of Uruguayan Pharmacies, 65th Anniv. — A1025

2002, Nov. 8   **Litho.**
1976 A1025 12p multi   1.10 1.10

Tannat Wine — A1026

2002, Nov. 13
1977 A1026 12p multi   1.10 1.10

Uruguayan Navy, 185th Anniv. — A1027

2002, Nov. 13   **Perf. 13½**
1978 A1027 12p multi   1.10 1.10

National Organ and Tissue Bank, 25th Anniv. A1028

2002, Nov. 15
1979 A1028 12p multi   1.10 1.10

Taxis in Uruguay, Cent. A1029

2002, Nov. 25   **Perf. 12¼x12¾**
1980 A1029 12p multi   1.10 1.10

Brig. Gen. Manuel Oribe (1792-1857) A1030

2002, Nov. 28   **Perf. 12¾x12¼**
1981 A1030 12p multi   1.10 1.10

George Harrison (1943-2001), Rock Musician A1031

2002, Nov. 29   **Perf. 13½**
1982 A1031 24p multi   3.00 3.00

Pan-American Health Organization, Cent. — A1032

2002, Dec. 2
1983 A1032 12p multi   1.10 1.10

Uruguayan Participation in U.N. Peace Keeping Missions, 50th Anniv. — A1033

2002, Dec. 6   **Perf. 12¼x12¾**
1984 A1033 12p multi   1.10 1.10

Alfredo Testoni (1919-2000), Artist — A1034

2002, Dec. 9   **Perf. 13½**
1985 A1034 12p multi   1.10 1.10

Mercosur A1035

Designs: 12p, Ship and coastline. 24p, Beach.

2002, Dec. 12
1986-1987 A1035   Set of 2   3.25 3.25

Battle of Ituzaingó, 175th Anniv. A1036

2002, Dec. 17   **Litho.**
1988 A1036 12p multi   1.10 1.10

Battle of Juncal, 175th Anniv. A1037

2002, Dec. 17
1989 A1037 12p multi   1.10 1.10

Village of Juanicó, 130th Anniv. A1038

2002, Dec. 23   **Perf. 12¼x12¾**
1990 A1038 12p multi   1.10 1.10

Uruguay on World Map A1039

2003, Jan. 17 Litho. Perf. 12¼x12¾
1991 A1039 12p multi   1.10 1.10

Busqueda Weekly, 30th Anniv. A1040

2003, Jan. 29
1992 A1040 12p multi   1.10 1.10

Water Goddess Iemanja — A1041

2003, Jan. 29   **Perf. 12¾x12¼**
1993 A1041 12p multi   1.10 1.10

Uruguay - People's Republic of China Diplomatic Relations, 15th Anniv. — A1042

2003, Jan. 31   **Perf. 12**
1994 A1042 12p multi   1.10 1.10

New Year 2003 (Year of the Ram) — A1043

2003, Feb. 7   **Perf. 12¾x12¼**
1995 A1043 5p multi   .45 .45

Explorers A1044

Explorers and maps of their voyages: a, Christopher Columbus, 4th voyage, 1502. b, Juan Díaz de Solís, 1516. c, Sebastian Cabot, 1526-30. d, Hernando Arias de Saavedra, 1597-1618.

2003, Feb. 14   **Perf. 12**
1996   Horiz. strip of 4   3.50 3.50
   a.-d. A1044 12p Any single   .85 .85

Communications Services Regulatory Union, 2nd Anniv. — A1045

2003, Feb. 21   **Perf. 12¼x12¾**
1997 A1045 12p multi   1.10 1.10

Intl. Women's Day — A1046

2003, Mar. 7   **Perf. 12¾x12¼**
1998 A1046 12p multi   1.10 1.10

City of Treinta y Tres, 150th Anniv. A1047

2003, Mar. 10   **Perf. 12¼x12¾**
1999 A1047 12p multi   1.10 1.10

Butterflies — A1048

No. 2000: a, Heliconius erato. b, Junonia evarete. c, Dryadula phaetusa. d, Parides perrhebus.

2003, Mar. 18   *Perf. 12*
2000 A1048 12p Block of 4, #a-d   5.00 5.00

First Presidency of José Batlle y Ordóñez, Cent. — A1049

No. 2001 — Batlle y Ordóñez: a, Wearing overcoat. b, Wearing presidential sash. c, With head on hand. d, Wearing white jacket.

2003, Mar. 25   *Perf. 12*
2001   Horiz. strip of 4   3.50 3.50
a.-d. A1049 12p Any single   .85 .85

Rural Women's Crafts A1050

No. 2002: a, Basket weaving. b, Knitting. c, Pottery making. d, Food canning. e, Jewelry making.

2003, Mar. 23   *Litho.*   *Perf. 12*
2002   Horiz. strip of 5   5.50 5.50
a.-e. A1050 12p Any single   1.10 1.10

Farruco's Chapel — A1051

2003, Apr. 4   *Litho.*   *Perf. 12¾x12¼*
2003 A1051 12p multi   1.10 1.10

Natural Foods A1052

2003, Apr. 9   *Perf. 12¼x12¾*
2004 A1052 12p multi   1.10 1.10

Cerros Azules Caiman Farm A1053

Serpentine Die Cut 11¼
2003, Apr. 10
Self-Adhesive
2005 A1053 12p multi   1.10 1.10

Memorial to 1972 Airplane Crash in the Andes — A1054

2003, Apr. 22   *Perf. 12¾x12¼*
2006 A1054 12p multi   1.10 1.10

Military Center — A1055

2003, May 21
2007 A1055 12p multi   1.10 1.10

May 18, 1811 Military Museum, 150th Anniv. A1056

2003, May 26   *Perf. 12*
2008 A1056 12p multi   1.10 1.10

Casa de Ximénes and Las Bóvedas, Montevideo Historical District — A1057

2003, May 30   *Perf. 12¼*
2009 A1057 14p multi   1.40 1.40

Wilson Ferreira Aldunate (1919-88), Politician — A1058

No. 2010: a, Brown background. b, Green background. c, Dark violet background, text at right. d, Light violet background, text at left. Illustration reduced.

2003, June 16   *Litho.*   *Perf. 12*
2010 A1058 14p Block of 4, #a-d   4.75 4.75

Olympic Soccer Gold Medal, 75th Anniv. A1059

2003, June 18
2011 A1059 14p multi   1.10 1.10

Nos. 1382, 1492 Overprinted in Gold

Methods, Perfs and Watermarks as Before
2003, June 18
2011A   A654 (14p) on 1.20p
     #1492   1.50 1.50
2011B   A589 (36p) on 2500p
     #1382   4.50 4.50
Compare No. 2011A with No. 2055.

Richard Anderson College, 70th Anniv. — A1060

2003, July 15
2012 A1060 14p multi   1.10 1.10

Santa Isabel del Paso de los Toros, Cent. — A1061

2003, July 17
2013 A1061 14p multi   1.10 1.10

National Association of Affiliates, 70th Anniv. — A1062

2003, July 24
2014 A1062 14p multi   1.10 1.10

Jesús María College, Carrasco, 50th Anniv. — A1063

2003, Aug. 4
2015 A1063 14p multi   1.10 1.10

Philatelic Academy of Uruguay, 25th Anniv. A1064

2003, Aug. 5
2016 A1064 14p multi   1.10 1.10

Palacio Heber A1065

2003, Aug. 14
2017 A1065 14p multi   1.10 1.10

Parva Domus Magna Quies, 125th Anniv. — A1066

2003, Aug. 15
2018 A1066 14p multi   1.10 1.10

Security Dept. Commission of Interior Ministry, 4th Anniv. — A1067

2003, Aug. 18
2019 A1067 14p multi   1.10 1.10

First International Victory of Uruguayan Soccer Team, Cent. — A1068

2003, Sept. 12   *Perf. 12½x12¾*
2020 A1068 14p multi   1.10 1.10

Lauro Ayestarán (1913-66), Musicologist — A1069

2003, Sept. 19   *Perf. 12*
2021 A1069 14p multi   1.10 1.10

Asociacion Española Primera de Socorros Mutuos Hospital, 150th Anniv. A1070

2003, Sept. 19   *Perf. 12½x12¾*
2022 A1070 14p multi   1.10 1.10

Dr. Manuel Quintela Clinical Hospital, 50th Anniv. A1071

2003, Sept. 23   *Perf. 12*
2023 A1071 14p multi   1.10 1.10

Society of Friends of Public Education, 135th Anniv. — A1072

2003, Sept. 24
2024 A1072 14p multi   1.10 1.10

Association of Uruguayan Newspaper Reporters, 45th Anniv. — A1073

2003, Sept. 29   *Perf. 12½x12¾*
2025 A1073 14p multi   1.10 1.10

Pres. Fructoso Rivera (c. 1788-1854) A1074

2003, Oct. 1   *Perf. 12*
2026 A1074 14p multi   1.60 1.60

Naval Club, 75th Anniv. A1075

2003, Oct. 1   *Perf. 12½x12¾*
2027 A1075 14p multi   1.10 1.10

Malos Pensamientos Radio Program — A1076

2003, Oct. 3
2028 A1076 14p multi   1.10 1.10

Successes in Intl. Events by Milton Wynants, Cyclist — A1077

2003, Oct. 7   *Perf. 12¾x12½*
2029 A1077 14p multi   1.10 1.10

Ente Nazionale Assistenza Sociale in Uruguay, 50th Anniv. — A1078

2003, Oct. 9   *Perf. 12½x12¾*
2030 A1078 14p multi   1.10 1.10

City of Cardona, Cent. — A1079

2003, Oct. 10   *Perf. 12*
2031 A1079 14p multi   1.10 1.10

Construction League of Uruguay, 84th Anniv. — A1080

2003, Oct. 14   *Perf. 12¾x12½*
2032 A1080 14p multi   1.10 1.10

María Tsakos Foundation, 25th Anniv. — A1081

2003, Oct. 15
2033 A1081 14p multi   1.10 1.10

America Issue — Flora and Fauna A1082

Designs: 14p, Prosopis affinis. 36p, Agouti paca paca.

2003, Oct. 22   *Perf. 12½x12¾*
2034-2035 A1082   Set of 2   3.75 3.75

Independence of Lebanon, 60th Anniv. — A1083

2003, Oct. 24
2036 A1083 14p olive grn & red   1.10 1.10

Souvenir Sheet

Masons in Uruguay, 147th Anniv. — A1084

2003, Oct. 29   *Perf. 12¾x12½*
2037 A1084 14p multi   1.10 1.10

Cacho Bochinche Television Show, 30th Anniv. A1085

2003, Oct. 29   *Perf. 12½x12¾*
2038 A1085 14p multi   1.10 1.10

Morenada, 50th Anniv. — A1086

2003, Oct. 29
2039 A1086 14p multi   1.10 1.10

Brig. Gen. Juan A. Lavalleja (c. 1786-1853) A1087

2003, Oct. 30   *Perf. 12*
2040 A1087 14p multi   1.10 1.10

Souvenir Sheet

Election of Pope John Paul II, 25th Anniv. — A1088

No. 1089 — Uruguayan flag and: a, Pope John Paul II, Vatican arms. b, Polish eagle, map of Latin America.

2003, Oct. 31
2041 A1088 12p Sheet of 2, #a-b 2.00 2.00

Union of Latin American Polish Societies and Organizations, 10th anniv. (#2041b).

Souvenir Sheet

2006 World Cup Soccer Championships, Germany — A1089

No. 2042 — World Cup trophy and: a, Uruguayan flag, J. A. Schiaffino. b, German flag, Fritz Walter.

2003, Oct. 31
2042 A1089 12p Sheet of 2, #a-b 2.00 2.00

Christmas A1090

2003, Nov. 7   *Perf. 12¾x12½*
2043 A1090 14p multi   1.10 1.10

Italian Chamber of Commerce of Uruguay, 120th Anniv. A1091

2003, Nov. 10   *Perf. 12½x12¾*
2044 A1091 14p multi   1.10 1.10

Visit of Manuel Fraga Iribarne, President of Spanish Autonomous Community of Galicia — A1092

2003, Nov. 10
2045 A1092 14p multi   1.10 1.10

San Gregorio de Polanco, 150th Anniv. A1093

2003, Nov. 14
2046 A1093 14p multi   1.10 1.10

United Biblical Society, Bicent. A1094

2003, Nov. 24
2047 A1094 14p multi   1.10 1.10

R.O.U. Paysandu A1095

2003, Nov. 25   **Perf. 12**
2048 A1095 14p multi   1.10 1.10

University Culture Foundation, 35th Anniv. — A1096

2003, Nov. 28
2049 A1096 14p multi   1.10 1.10

Uruguayan Air Force, 50th Anniv. A1097

2003, Dec. 4
2050 A1097 14p multi   1.10 1.10

Visit of Mirko Tremaglia, Italian Minister for Italians Abroad — A1098

2003, Dec. 15
2051 A1098 14p multi   1.10 1.10

Mercosur A1099

Designs: 14p, Horn. 36p, Silver stirrup.

2003, Dec. 16
2052-2053 A1099   Set of 2   5.00 5.00

Powered Flight, Cent. A1100

2003, Dec. 19
2054 A1100 14p multi   1.10 1.10

Nos. 1378, 1382, 1458 and 1492 Surcharged in Black or Blue Violet

j

k

Methods and Perfs. as Before
2004   **Wmk. 332**
2055 A654(j)   1p on 1.20p
                #1492   .25 .25
2056 A639(j)   2p on 2.60p
                #1458 (BV)   .25 .25
2057 A589(k)   5p on 2500p
                #1382   .40 .40
2058 A589(k) 10p on 360p #1378   .70 .70
2059 A589(k) 50p on 825p
                #1379B   3.50 3.50
      Nos. 2055-2059 (5)   5.10 5.10

Issued: Nos. 2055-2056, 1/19; Nos. 2057-2058, 2/16; No. 2059, 3/23. Obliterator on Nos. 2055 and 2056 covers the centesimos portion of the denomination.
Compare No. 2055 with No. 2011A.

Birds — A1101

No. 2060: a, Puffinius gravis. b, Macronectes halli. c, Daption capense. d, Diamedea melanophrys.
Illustration reduced.

Unwmk.
2004, Jan. 22   Litho.   Perf. 12
2060 A1101 14p Block of 4, #a-d   6.00 6.00

Isla de Lobos Lighthouse A1102

No. 2061: a, Isla de Flores Lighthouse. b, Farallon Lighthouse. c, La Panela Lighthouse. d, Banco Ingles Floating Lighthouse.

2004, Feb. 10   Litho.   Perf. 12
2061 A1102 10p Block of 4, #a-d   3.00 3.00
2062 A1102 14p shown   1.00 1.00

Abitab, 10th Anniv. — A1103

Unwmk.
2004, Feb. 12   Litho.   Perf. 12
2063 A1103 14p multi   1.10 1.10

National Naval Prefecture, 175th Anniv. — A1104

2004, Feb. 20   Litho.   Perf. 12
2064 A1104 14p multi   1.10 1.10

Maté Containers — A1105

No. 2065: a, Maté de Cáliz. b, Maté de Plata Colonial. c, Maté de Calabaza.
Illustration reduced.

2004, Mar. 4
2065 A1105 5p Strip of 3, #a-c   1.25 1.25

33 Orientales Mechanized Infantry Battalion No. 10, Cent. — A1106

2004, Mar. 12
2066 A1106 14p multi   1.10 1.10

Intl. Water Day A1107

2004, Mar. 25
2067 A1107 14p multi   1.10 1.10

Regional Energy Integration Commission, 40th Anniv. — A1108

2004, Mar. 25
2068 A1108 14p multi   1.10 1.10

Grenadier Guards, 80th Anniv. — A1109

2004, Apr. 1
2069 A1109 14p multi   1.10 1.10

Expansion of La Teja Refinery — A1110

2004, Apr. 2
2070 A1110 14p multi   1.10 1.10

Florida Infantry Batallion No. 1, 175th Anniv. A1111

2004, Apr. 16
2071 A1111 14p multi   1.10 1.10

Tribute to Servicemen — A1112

2004, May 26
2072 A1112 14p multi   1.10 1.10

Medicinal Plants — A1113

No. 2073: a, Malva sylvestris. b, Achyrocline satureiodes. c, Baccharis trimera. d, Mentha x piperita.

2004, June 3
2073   Strip of 4   9.75 9.75
a.-d. A1113 36p Any single   2.40 2.40

Map and Arms of Montevideo Department — A1114

2004, June 17
2074 A1114 14p multi   1.10 1.10 —
a.   Booklet pane of 2   2.40
    Complete booklet, #2074a   2.40
    No. 2074a sold for 35p.

Carlos Gardel (1890-1935), Singer — A1115

2004, June 24   Litho.   Perf. 12
2075 A1115 14p multi   1.10 1.10

Campaign Against Illegal Drugs — A1116

2004, June 25   Litho.   Perf. 12
2076 A1116 14p multi   1.10 1.10

Renán Rodríguez, Politician — A1117

2004, Aug. 10
2077 A1117 14p multi   1.10 1.10

Maimonides (1135-1204), Philosopher A1118

2004, Aug. 12
2078 A1118 16p multi   1.25 1.25

Galician Center, Montevideo, 125th Anniv. — A1119

2004, Aug. 30
2079 A1119 16p multi   1.25 1.25

1904 Battles of Gen. Aparicio Saravia — A1120

No. 2080 — Battle of: a, Illescas. b, Fray-Marcos. c, Paso del Parque. d, Masoller.

2004, Sept. 8
2080   Block of 4   3.00 3.00
a.-d. A1120 10p Any single   .75 .75

Highway Patrol, 50th Anniv. A1121

2004, Sept. 15   Perf. 12½x12¾
2081 A1121 16p multi   1.25 1.25

Joaquín Torres García (1874-1949), Painter — A1122

2004, Sept. 19
2082 A1122 16p multi   1.25 1.25

Magisterial Cooperative, 75th Anniv. — A1123

2004, Sept. 22
2083 A1123 16p multi   1.25 1.25

Army Administrative Corps, Cent. — A1124

2004, Sept. 22
2084 A1124 16p multi   1.25 1.25

FIFA (Fédération Internationale de Football Association), Cent. — A1125

2004, Oct. 5   Perf. 12
2085 A1125 37p multi   2.75 2.75

Uruguay - Republic of Korea Diplomatic Relations, 40th Anniv. — A1126

2004, Oct. 7
2086 A1126 16p multi   1.25 1.25

Montevideo Cathedral, Bicent. — A1127

2004, Oct. 19   Litho.   Perf. 12
2087 A1127 16p multi   1.25 1.25

Montevideo Council Building — A1128

2004, Oct. 22   Litho.   Perf. 12
2088 A1128 16p multi   1.25 1.25

Tomás Toribio House — A1129

2004, Oct. 22
2089 A1129 16p multi   1.25 1.25

America Issue - Environmental Protection — A1130

Dirty and clean: 16p, Water. 37p, Birds.

2004, Oct. 26
2090-2091 A1130   Set of 2   4.00 4.00

Armored Infantry Batallion No. 13, Cent. — A1131

2004, Nov. 16
2092 A1131 16p multi   1.25 1.25

Corner Store, 18th Cent. A1132

2004, Nov. 22
2093 A1132 16p multi   1.25 1.25

PriceWaterhouseCoopers in Uruguay, 85th Anniv. — A1133

2004, Dec. 7
2094 A1133 16p multi   1.25 1.25

Review of Court Clerks, Cent. — A1134

2004, Dec. 8
2095 A1134 16p multi   1.25 1.25

Christmas
A1135

2004, Dec. 14
2096 A1135 16p multi   1.25 1.25

Water
Conservation
A1136

2004, Dec. 21
2097 A1136 37p multi   3.00 3.00

Souvenir Sheet

Punta del Este — A1137

2004, Dec. 27
2098 A1137 16p multi   1.25 1.25

1912 Orenstein & Kopell
Locomotive — A1138

Serpentine Die Cut 11¼
2004, Dec. 28
Self-Adhesive
2099 A1138 30p multi   2.75 2.75

Rotary
International,
Cent. — A1139

2005, Feb. 23   Litho.   Perf. 12
2100 A1139 37p multi   4.50 4.50

Bridges — A1140

No. 2101: a, Chuy del Tacuari Bridge. b, Barra Bridge, Maldonado. c, Mauá Bridge Yaguarón River. d, Castells Bridge, Víboras. Illustration reduced.

2005, Mar. 18
2101 A1140 16p Block of 4, #a-d   6.75 6.75

Ninth Meeting of Latin American
Energy Regulators — A1141

2005, Apr. 5
2102 A1141 16p multi   1.25 1.25

"Liberating Dragoons" Ninth
Mechanized Cavalry Regiment,
Cent. — A1142

2005, Apr. 11
2103 A1142 16p multi   1.25 1.25

Armenian
Genocide, 90th
Anniv. — A1143

2005, Apr. 25
2104 A1143 16p multi   1.25 1.25

Fingerprint Analysis in Uruguay,
Cent. — A1144

2005, Apr. 26
2105 A1144 16p multi   1.25 1.25

No. 1446 Surcharged

Wmk. 332
2005, May 27   Litho.   Perf. 12½
2106 A639 2p on 50c #1446   .25 .25

Fountains
A1145

Designs: No. 2107, 10p, Constitution Plaza Fountain. No. 2108, 10p, Botanical Garden Fountain. No. 2109, 10p, Athlete's Fountain, Rodó Park. 37p, Cordier Fountain, Prado, horiz.

2005, June 8   Litho.   Perf. 12
2107-2110 A1145   Set of 4   5.75 5.75

Catholic
Circle,
120th
Anniv.
A1146

2005, June 9
2111 A1146 16p multi   1.40 1.40

SOS
Children's
Villages,
45th
Anniv.
A1147

2005, June 23
2112 A1147 16p multi   1.40 1.40

St. John
the
Baptist
College,
75th
Anniv.
A1148

2005, June 24
2113 A1148 16p multi   1.40 1.40

Souvenir Sheet

Death of Pope John Paul II and
Election of Pope Benedict
XVI — A1149

No. 2114: a, Cross and statue of Pope John Paul II, Montevideo. b, Pope Benedict XVI.

Perf. 12x11¾
2005, July 15   Litho.   Unwmk.
2114 A1149 10p Sheet of 2, #a-b   1.75 1.75

Medical
Association
Assistance
Center, 70th
Anniv. — A1150

2005   Perf. 12
2115 A1150 16p multi   1.40 1.40
**Inscribed "Correos Uruguay" at
Right**
Perf. 12¾x12½
2116 A1150 16p multi   1.40 1.40
Issued: No. 2115, 7/19; No. 2116, 8/4.

Seminary
College,
125th
Anniv.
A1151

Designs: No. 2117, 16p, St. Ignatius of Loyola, college building. No. 2118, 16p, College building.

2005, July 29   Perf. 12
2117-2118 A1151   Set of 2   2.75 2.75

General Liber Seregni (1916-
2004) — A1152

No. 2119 — Inscriptions: a, Vocacion. b, Comienzo. c, Liberacion. d, Reconocimiento. Illustration reduced.

2005
2119 A1152 16p Block of 4, #a-d   5.50 5.50
   e.   Booklet pane, #2119   5.25 —
     Complete booklet, #2119e   7.00

Issued: No. 2119, 8/1; No. 2119e, 10/11.

Pope John
Paul II (1920-
2005)
A1153

2005, Aug. 11   Perf. 13½x13¾
2120 A1153 37p multi   3.25 3.25

Europa
Stamps,
50th
Anniv.
A1154

Designs: 16p, Landscape, by C. De Arzadun, Spain #1263. 37p, The Emus, by De Arzadun, Spain, #1126, vert.

Perf. 13¾x13½, 13½x13¾
2005, Aug. 11   Litho.
2121-2122 A1154   Set of 2   4.50 4.50

Urutem 2005 Philatelic Exhibition A1155

2005, Aug. 15 Litho. Perf. 12
2123 A1155 16p multi 1.40 1.40

Legislative Palace, 80th Anniv. A1156

2005, Aug. 24 Litho. Perf. 12
2124 A1156 16p multi 1.40 1.40

Estadio Centenario, 75th Anniv. — A1157

Children's art: No. 2125, $16, Stadium, by Jonatan Belón. No. 2126, 16p, "75" made with flag and soccer field, by Sofia Arca.

2005, Aug. 30
2125-2126 A1157 Set of 2 2.75 2.75

Carlos Solé, Soccer Broadcaster — A1158

2005, Sept. 20
2127 A1158 16p multi 1.40 1.40

World Cup Soccer Championships, 75th Anniv. — A1159

Designs: No. 2128, 16p, Parade of athletes. No. 2129, 16p, Handshake before match. No. 2130, 16p, Awarding of World Cup. 37p, Flags of Germany and Uruguay, emblem of 2006 World Cup Soccer Championships, Germany.

2005, Oct. 3
2128-2131 A1159 Set of 4 7.25 7.25

44th Congress of Intl. Congress and Convention Association, Montevideo — A1160

No. 2132: a, Fish sun and buildings. b, Association emblem. Illustration reduced.

2005, Nov. 4 Litho. Perf. 12
2132 A1160 8p Horiz. pair, #a-b 1.40 1.40

Uruguay River Fish — A1161

No. 2133: a, Rhamdia sapo. b, Odontesthes bonariensis. c, Hoplias malabaricus. d, Pygocentrus nattereri. Illustration reduced.

2005, Nov. 22
2133 A1161 16p Block of 4, #a-d 5.50 5.50

El Escolar Magazine, 50th Anniv. — A1162

2005, Nov. 23
2134 A1162 16p multi 1.40 1.40

Customhouse Brokers Association, 70th Anniv. — A1163

2005, Nov. 25
2135 A1163 16p multi 1.40 1.40

Detail From Mural, *Oficios*, by Julio Alpuy — A1164

2005, Dec. 1
2136 A1164 16p multi 1.40 1.40

Writers — A1165

Designs: 16p, Juan Zorilla de San Martin (1855-1931). 37p, Constancio C. Vigil (1876-1954).

2005, Dec. 9
2137-2138 A1165 Set of 2 4.50 4.50

Commercial and Industrial Center of Salto, Cent. — A1166

2005, Dec. 12
2139 A1166 16p multi 1.40 1.40

Central Español Soccer Team, Cent. A1167

2005, Dec. 12
2140 A1167 16p multi 1.40 1.40

Christmas — A1168

2005, Dec. 12
2141 A1168 16p multi 1.40 1.40

Montevideo Atheneum, 137th Anniv. — A1169

2005, Dec. 14 Litho.
2142 A1169 16p multi 1.40 1.40

1924 Paris Olympics, 80th Anniv. (in 2004) A1170

Designs: No. 2143, 16p, Andrés Mazali, soccer gold medalist. No. 2144, 16p, Juan Pedro Cea, soccer gold medalist. No. 2145, 16p, Alfredo Ghierra, soccer gold medalist. 37p, Urn showing soccer players, vert.

2005, Dec. 20 Perf. 12
2143-2146 A1170 Set of 4 7.25 7.25

America Issue, Fight Against Poverty — A1171

Designs: 16p, Children, teacher and school. 37p, Men with shovel.

2005, Dec. 22
2147-2148 A1171 Set of 2 4.50 4.50

Capitán Miranda, 75th Anniv. — A1172

No. 2149: a, Capitán Miranda in 1930. b, Capitán Miranda in 2005. c, Capt. Francisco P. Miranda (1869-1925). d, Crests of ships Capitán Miranda, Cádiz, and Montevideo. Illustration reduced.

2005, Dec. 28
2149 A1172 16p Block of 4, #a-d 5.50 5.50

No. 1492 Surcharged in Brown

2005? Photo. Wmk. 332 Perf. 12½
2150 A654 1p on 1.20p #1492 .25 .25

Obliterator on No. 2150 covers the "20" of original denomination. Compare with Nos. 2055 and 2011A.

Maldonado, 250th Anniv. — A1173

Designs: No. 2151, 16p, San Fernando Cathedral. No. 2152, 16p, Dragoon Quarters.

2006, Feb. 22 Litho. Perf. 12
2151-2152 A1173 Set of 2 2.75 2.75

Alfredo Zitarrosa (1936-89), Singer — A1174

Zitarrosa and: No. 2153, 16p, Guitar, violin. No. 2154, 16p, Guitar, violin, vert.

2006, Mar. 10
2153-2154 A1174 Set of 2 2.75 2.75

Solís Theater, 150th Anniv. — A1175

2006, Mar. 28
2155 A1175 16p multi 1.40 1.40

Diario Español
Newspaper,
Cent. — A1176

2006, May 15
2156 A1176 16p multi   1.40 1.40

Public Enterprise Day — A1177

2006, May 19
2157 A1177 16p black   1.40 1.40

Assassinated Politicians — A1178

Designs: No. 2158, 16p, Héctor Gutiérrez
Ruiz (1934-76). No. 2159, 16p, Zelmar Miche-
lini (1924-76). No. 2160, 16p, Michelini and
Gutiérrez Ruiz.

2006, June 1
2158-2160 A1178   Set of 3   4.00 4.00

SODRE Symphonic Orchestra, 75th
Anniv. — A1179

2006, June 20
2161 A1179 16p black   1.40 1.40

Masons in
Uruguay, 150th
Anniv. — A1180

2006, Aug. 15
2162 A1180 16p multi   1.40 1.40

Horse Breeds — A1181

No. 2163: a, Appaloosa. b, Percheron. c,
Belgian Heavy Draft. d, Criollo.

Illustration reduced.

2006, Aug. 18
2163 A1181 16p Block of 4, #a-d   5.50 5.50

First Uruguayan Postage Stamps,
150th Anniv. — A1182

2006, Sept. 29
2164 A1182 16p multi   1.40 1.40

Eladio Dieste (1917-2000),
Architect — A1183

2006, Oct. 3
2165 A1183 16p multi   1.40 1.40

Syndical Unification Congress, 40th
Anniv. — A1184

No. 2166: a, Marchers with banner. b,
Marchers with flag.
Illustration reduced.

2006, Oct. 3
2166 A1184 16p Horiz. pair, #a-b   2.75 2.75

Diplomatic
Relations
Between
Uruguay and
the Sovereign
Military Order
of Malta, 40th
Anniv.
A1185

2006, Oct. 4
2167 A1185 16p multi   1.40 1.40

Paysandú, 250th Anniv. — A1186

2006, Oct. 12
2168 A1186 16p multi   1.40 1.40

Dr. Washington
Beltrán (1914-
2003), Politician
A1187

2006, Oct. 25
2169 A1187 16p multi   1.40 1.40

16th Ibero-American Summit,
Montevideo — A1188

2006, Nov. 1   Litho.   Perf. 12
2170 A1188 37p multi   3.25 3.25

Salto,
250th
Anniv.
A1189

2006, Nov. 7   Litho.   Perf. 12
2171 A1189 16p multi   1.40 1.40

Channel 10, 50th Anniv. — A1190

2006, Nov. 8   Litho.   Perf. 12
2172 A1190 16p multi   1.40 1.40

America Issue, Energy
Conservation — A1191

No. 2173: a, 16p, Screw-in fluorescent light
bulbs. b, 37p, Solar panels.
Illustration reduced.

2006, Nov. 17   Litho.   Perf. 12
2173 A1191   Horiz. pair, #a-b   4.50 4.50

Sports
A1192

Designs: No. 2174, 16p, Indoor soccer. No.
2175, 16p, Handball. No. 2176, 16p, Rugby.
No. 2177, 16p, Tennis.

2006, Nov. 30
2174-2177 A1192   Set of 4   5.25 5.25

Christmas
A1193

2006, Dec. 7
2178 A1193 37p multi   3.00 3.00

Musical
Instruments
A1194

Designs: 15p, Guitar. 37p, Drum, horiz.

2006, Dec. 11
2179-2180 A1194   Set of 2   4.25 4.25

Ocean Liners and Ports — A1195

No. 2181: a, Queen Mary 2, Montevideo. b,
Costa Fortuna, Montevideo. c, Zuiderman,
Montevideo. d, Star Princess, Punta del Este.
Illustration reduced.

2006, Dec. 18
2181 A1195 37p Block of 4,
             #a-d   12.50 12.50

Uruguayan Lottery, 150th
Anniv. — A1196

2006, Dec. 22   Litho.   Perf. 12
2182 A1196 15p multi   1.25 1.25

Optimist Class Yacht World
Championships — A1197

2006, Dec. 28   Litho.   Perf. 12
2183 A1197 37p multi   3.00 3.00

Uruguay
Post
Emblem
A1198

Serpentine Die Cut 11¼
2006, Dec. 29 Litho.
Self-Adhesive
2184 A1198 15p multi 1.25 1.25

No. 1492
Surcharged in
Golden Brown

No. 1454 Surcharged in
Black and Silver

**Methods, Perfs, and Watermarks As
Before**
2007, Jan. 24
2185 A654 1p on 1.20p #1492 .20 .20
2186 A639 2p on 1.80p #1454 .20 .20
 Compare No. 2185 with Nos. 2011A, 2055
and 2150.

Punta del Este, Cent. — A1199

Unwmk.
2007, Jan. 26 Litho. *Perf. 12*
2187 A1199 37p multi 3.25 3.25

José Nasazzi
Children's
Soccer
Cup — A1200

2007, Feb. 5 Litho. *Perf. 12*
2188 A1200 15p multi 1.25 1.25

Julia Arévalo (1898-1985),
Politician — A1201

2007, Mar. 8 Litho. *Perf. 12*
2189 A1201 15p multi 1.25 1.25

Colón
Soccer
Club,
Cent.
A1203

2007, Mar. 12 Litho. *Perf. 12*
2191 A1203 15p multi 1.25 1.25

Campaign
Against Dengue
Fever — A1204

Serpentine Die Cut 11¼
2007, Mar. 28
Self-Adhesive
2192 A1204 15p multi 1.25 1.25

National
Cadastre,
Cent.
A1205

2007, Apr. 12 *Perf. 12*
2193 A1205 15p multi 1.25 1.25

Regional Art
Meeting
A1206

2007, June 8
2194 A1206 15p multi 1.25 1.25

Shells — A1207

 No. 2195: a, 5p, Aequipecten tehuelchus. b,
5p, Trophon pelseneeri. c, 10p, Ameri-
cominella duartei. d, 10p, Conus clenchi.
Illustration reduced.

2007, June 26
2195 A1207 Block of 4, #a-d 2.50 2.50

Giuseppe Garibaldi (1807-82), Italian
Leader — A1208

 Designs: 15p, Ship, Garibaldi on horseback.
37p, Garibaldi, ship.
2007, July 4
2196-2197 A1208 Set of 2 4.50 4.50
 See Brazil Nos. 3021-3022.

Guichón,
Cent. — A1209

2007, July 13
2198 A1209 15p multi 1.40 1.40

Souvenir Sheet

La Estrella del Sur Publication,
Bicent. — A1210

2007, July 19 *Perf. 12½x12¾*
2199 A1210 15p multi 1.40 1.40

Agronomy Faculties, Cent. — A1211

2007, July 30
2200 A1211 15p multi 1.40 1.40

Scouting,
Cent. — A1212

 Children's drawings: No. 2201, 15p, Scout
emblem, by Victoria Ferrer. No. 2202, 15p,
Scouts at Flag Ceremony, by Paula Barrios.
 No. 2203, horiz.: a, Knot, Lord Robert
Baden-Powell and Duke of Connaught. b,
Knot, International Scout emblem patch.

2007, Aug. 9 *Perf. 12*
2201-2202 A1212 Set of 2 2.60 2.60
Souvenir Sheet
2203 A1212 25p Sheet of 2, #a-b 4.25 4.25

Three
Musicians
in
Primary
Colors,
by José
Gurvich
(1927-74)
A1213

2007, Aug. 17
2204 A1213 15p multi 1.25 1.25

Diplomatic Relations Between Uruguay
and Guatemala, Cent. — A1214

 No. 2205: a, 15p, Santa Catarina Arch, Anti-
gua, Guatemala. b, 37p, City gate, Colonia del
Sacramento, Uruguay.
Illustration reduced.

2007, Sept. 3 Litho. *Perf. 12½x12¾*
2205 A1214 Horiz. pair, #a-b 4.50 4.50

German
College and
High
School,
Montevideo,
150th Anniv.
A1215

 No. 2206: a, Anniversary emblem. b, Children's drawing of girl and colors of flags of
Germany and Uruguay.

2007, Sept. 5 *Perf. 12*
2206 Horiz. pair + central label 2.60 2.60
 a.-b. A1215 15p Either single 1.25 1.25

Occupations — A1216

 Designs: 1p, Peanut vendor. 7p, Knife
grinder, vert. 10p, Organ grinder, vert. 25p,
Barber, vert. 50p, Druggist, vert.

Serpentine Die Cut 11¼
2007, Oct. 6
Self-Adhesive
2207 A1216 1p multi .20 .20
2208 A1216 7p multi .65 .65
2209 A1216 10p multi .90 .90
2210 A1216 25p multi 2.25 2.25
2211 A1216 50p multi 4.50 4.50
 Nos. 2207-2211 (5) 8.50 8.50
 See No. B13.

Marine Mammal
Conservation — A1217

2007, Oct. 12 *Die Cut*
Self-Adhesive
2212 A1217 37p multi 3.50 3.50

Butterflies — A1218

No. 2213: a, 5p, Eurybia lycisca. b, 10p, Catagramma excelsior pastazza. c, 15p, Agrias claudina. d, 20p, Marpesia marcella. Illustration reduced.

			2007, Oct. 26	Perf. 12½x12¾		
2213	A1218		Block of 4, #a-d		4.75	4.75

Torrijos - Carter Panama Canal Treaties, 30th Anniv. A1219

			2007, Nov. 5		Perf. 12	
2214	A1219		37p multi		3.50	3.50

America Issue, Education For All A1220

Designs: 15p, Rectangles. 37p, Squares and rectangles.

			2007, Nov. 22			
2215-2216	A1220		Set of 2		4.75	4.75

Naval School, Cent. — A1221

			2007, Dec. 5		Perf. 12x11¾	
2217	A1221		12p multi		1.10	1.10

Diplomatic Relations Between Uruguay and Russia, 150th Anniv. — A1223

No. 2219: a, 12p, Sacred Heart of Jesus Sanctuary, Uruguay. b, 37p, St. Basil's Cathedral, Russia. Illustration reduced.

			2007, Dec. 21	Litho.	Perf. 12	
2219	A1223		Horiz. pair, #a-b + central label		4.50	4.50

Christmas A1224

			2007, Dec. 21			
2220	A1224		12p multi		1.10	1.10

Architecture A1225

Designs: 12p, House, by Julio Vilamajó. 37p, Joaquín Torres García Building, by Carlos Ott.

			2007, Dec. 28			
2221-2222	A1225		Set of 2		4.50	4.50

SEMI-POSTAL STAMPS

Indigent Old Man — SP1

Unwmk.

			1930, Nov. 13	Engr.	Perf. 12	
B1	SP1		1c + 1c dark violet		.20	.20
B2	SP1		2c + 2c deep green		.20	.20
B3	SP1		5c + 5c red		.30	.30
B4	SP1		8c + 8c gray violet		.30	.30
			Nos. B1-B4 (4)		1.00	1.00

The surtax on these stamps was for a fund to assist the aged.
For surcharge see No. 419.

> Catalogue values for unused stamps in this section, from this point to the end of the section, are for Never Hinged items.

Dam, Child and Rising Sun — SP2

Wmk. 327

			1959, Sept. 29	Litho.	Perf. 11½	
B5	SP2		5c + 10c green & org		.20	.20
B6	SP2		10c + 10c dk bl & org		.20	.20
B7	SP2		1p + 10c purple & org		.40	.40
			Nos. B5-B7,CB1-CB2 (5)		1.35	1.35

National recovery. For surcharges see Nos. 727, Q100.

Souvenir Sheet

Taipei '96, Intl. Philatelic Exhibition — SP3

Illustration reduced.

Unwmk.

			1996, Oct. 21	Litho.	Perf. 12	
B8	SP3		7p +3p multi		6.00	6.00

Gen. Artigas Central Railway Station, Montevideo, Cent. — SP4

a, Baldwin, 1889. b, Hudswell Clarke, 1895. c, Luis Andreoni, engineer. d, Hawthorn Leslie, 1914. e, General Electric, 1954.

Perf. 12½

			1997, July 15	Litho.	Unwmk.	
B9	SP4		4p +1p, Strip of 5, #a.-e.		10.00	10.00

Diana, Princess of Wales (1961-97) — SP5

Designs: No. B10, In protective clothing. No. B11, In blue blouse. No. B12, In white.

			1998, Jan. 15	Litho.	Perf. 12½	
B10	SP5		2p +1p multi		2.00	2.00
B11	SP5		2p +1p multi		2.00	2.00

Souvenir Sheet
Perf. 12

B12	SP5		12p +3p multi		10.00	10.00

No. B12 contains one 35x50mm stamp.

Occupations Type of 2008
Serpentine Die Cut 11¼

			2007, Nov. 18		Litho.	
			Self-Adhesive			
B13	A1216		5p +2p Baker		.65	.65

AIR POST STAMPS

No. 91 Overprinted in Dark Blue, Red or Green

			1921-22	Unwmk.	Perf. 14	
C1	A38		25c bister brn (Bl)		15.00	12.00
a.			Black overprint		625.00	625.00
C2	A38		25c bister brn (R)		6.50	5.00
a.			Inverted overprint		77.50	77.50

C3	A38		25c bister brn (G) ('22)		6.50	5.00
			Nos. C1-C3 (3)		28.00	22.00

This overprint also exists in light yellow green.

No. C1a was not issued. Some authorities consider it an overprint color trial.

AP2

Wmk. 188

			1924, Jan. 2	Litho.	Perf. 11½	
C4	AP2		6c dark blue		2.50	2.50
C5	AP2		10c scarlet		3.50	3.00
C6	AP2		20c deep green		5.00	5.00
			Nos. C4-C6 (3)		11.00	10.50

Heron — AP3

			1925, Aug. 24		Perf. 12½	
			Inscribed "MONTEVIDEO"			
C7	AP3		14c blue & blk		30.00	14.00
			Inscribed "FLORIDA"			
C8	AP3		14c blue & blk		30.00	14.00

These stamps were used only on Aug. 25, 1925, the cent. of the Assembly of Florida, on letters intended to be carried by airplane between Montevideo and Florida, a town 60 miles north. The stamps were not delivered to the public but were affixed to the letters and canceled by post office clerks. Later uncanceled copies came on the market.

One authority believes Nos. C7-C8 served as registration stamps on these two attempted special flights.

Gaucho Cavalryman at Rincón — AP4

			1925, Sept. 24		Perf. 11	
C9	AP4		45c blue green		15.00	

Centenary of Battle of Rincon. Used only on Sept. 24. No. C9 was affixed and canceled by post office clerks.

Albatross — AP5

			1926, Mar. 3	Wmk. 188	Imperf.	
C10	AP5		6c dark blue		1.50	1.50
C11	AP5		10c vermilion		2.00	2.00
C12	AP5		20c blue green		2.50	2.50
C13	AP5		25c violet		4.00	4.00
			Nos. C10-C13 (4)		10.00	10.00

Excellent counterfeits exist.

			1928, June 25		Perf. 11	
C14	AP5		10c green		2.50	2.00
C15	AP5		20c orange		4.00	3.00
C16	AP5		30c indigo		4.00	3.00
C17	AP5		38c green		7.00	6.00
C18	AP5		40c yellow		8.00	6.00
C19	AP5		50c violet		9.00	7.00
C20	AP5		76c orange		17.00	15.00
C21	AP5		1p red		20.00	18.00
C22	AP5		1.14p indigo		45.00	40.00
C23	AP5		1.52p yellow		70.00	65.00

C24	AP5	1.90p violet	90.00	75.00
C25	AP5	3.80p red	200.00	150.00
		Nos. C14-C25 (12)	476.50	390.00

Counterfeits of No. C25 exist.

1929, Aug. 23   **Unwmk.**

C26	AP5	4c olive brown	4.00	3.00

The design was redrawn for Nos. C14-C26. The numerals are narrower, "CENTS" is 1mm high instead of 2½mm and imprint letters touch the bottom frame line.

Pegasus
AP6

1929-43   **Engr.**   **Perf. 12½**
Size: 34x23mm

C27	AP6	1c red lilac ('30)	.40	.40
C28	AP6	1c dk blue ('32)	.40	.40
C29	AP6	2c yellow ('30)	.40	.40
C30	AP6	2c olive grn ('32)	.40	.40
C31	AP6	4c Prus bl ('30)	.70	.70
C32	AP6	4c car rose ('32)	.70	.70
C33	AP6	6c dull vio ('30)	.70	.70
C34	AP6	6c red brn ('32)	.70	.70
C35	AP6	8c red orange	3.00	2.50
C36	AP6	8c gray ('30)	4.00	3.00
C36A	AP6	8c brt grn ('43)	2.50	2.00
C37	AP6	16c indigo	.50	.50
C38	AP6	16c rose ('30)	3.25	3.00
C39	AP6	24c claret	4.25	3.50
C40	AP6	24c brt vio ('30)	3.00	2.50
C41	AP6	30c bister ('30)	3.00	2.75
C42	AP6	30c dk grn ('30)	2.00	1.50
C43	AP6	40c dk brown	5.50	5.00
C44	AP6	40c yel org ('30)	6.00	5.00
C45	AP6	60c blue green	5.00	3.25
C46	AP6	60c emer ('30)	8.50	7.00
C47	AP6	60c dp org ('31)	3.00	2.00
C48	AP6	80c dk ultra	8.00	7.00
C49	AP6	80c green ('30)	15.00	12.00
C50	AP6	90c light blue	8.00	6.00
C51	AP6	90c dk olive grn ('30)	15.00	12.00
C52	AP6	1p car rose ('30)	10.00	7.50
C53	AP6	1.20p olive grn	22.00	20.00
C54	AP6	1.20p dp car ('30)	30.00	26.00
C55	AP6	1.50p red brown	25.00	20.00
C56	AP6	1.50p blk brn ('30)	20.00	15.00
C57	AP6	3p deep red	40.00	35.00
C58	AP6	3p ultra ('30)	30.00	25.00
C59	AP6	4.50p black	75.00	55.00
C60	AP6	4.50p violet ('30)	45.00	35.00
C60A	AP6	10p dp ultra ('43)	17.00	12.00
		Nos. C27-C60A (36)	417.90	335.40

See Nos. C63-C82. For surcharges see Nos. C106-C112, C114.

Nos. 450, 452 Overprinted in Red

1934, Jan. 1   **Perf. 11½**

C61	A130	17c ver, gray & vio	20.00	15.00
a.		Sheet of 6	140.00	
b.		Gray omitted	150.00	
c.		Double overprint	150.00	
C62	A130	36c red, blk & yel	20.00	15.00
a.		Sheet of 6	140.00	

7th Pan-American Conference, Montevideo.

Pegasus Type of 1929

1935   **Engr.**   **Perf. 12½**
Size: 31½x21mm

C63	AP6	15c dull yellow	2.50	2.00
C64	AP6	22c brick red	1.50	1.40
C65	AP6	30c brown violet	2.50	2.00
C66	AP6	37c gray lilac	1.40	1.00

C67	AP6	40c rose lake	2.00	1.40
C68	AP6	47c rose	4.00	3.50
C69	AP6	50c Prus blue	1.40	.80
C70	AP6	52c dp ultra	4.00	3.50
C71	AP6	57c grnsh blue	2.00	1.75
C72	AP6	62c olive green	1.75	.80
C73	AP6	87c gray green	5.00	4.00
C74	AP6	1p olive	3.50	2.25
C75	AP6	1.12p brown red	3.50	2.25
C76	AP6	1.20p bister brn	15.00	12.00
C77	AP6	1.27p red brown	15.00	13.00
C78	AP6	1.62p rose	10.00	9.00
C79	AP6	2p brown rose	17.00	14.00
C80	AP6	2.12p dk slate grn	17.00	14.00
C81	AP6	3p dull blue	15.00	13.00
C82	AP6	5p orange	60.00	60.00
		Nos. C63-C82 (20)	184.05	161.65

Counterfeits exist.

Power Dam on Black River — AP7

Imprint: "Imp. Nacional" at center

1937-41   **Litho.**

C83	AP7	20c lt green ('38)	5.50	4.00
C84	AP7	35c red brown	8.00	6.50
C85	AP7	62c blue grn ('38)	.80	.30
C86	AP7	68c yel org ('38)	2.00	1.50
C86A	AP7	68c pale vio brn ('41)	1.75	.70
C87	AP7	75c violet	7.50	5.00
C88	AP7	1p dp pink ('38)	2.50	1.75
C89	AP7	1.38p rose ('38)	25.00	20.00
C90	AP7	3p dk blue ('40)	17.00	12.00
		Nos. C83-C90 (9)	70.05	51.75

Imprint at left

C91	AP7	8c pale green ('39)	.60	.50
C92	AP7	20c lt green ('38)	2.00	1.50

For surcharge and overprint see Nos. 545, C120.

Plane over Sculptured Oxcart — AP8

1939-44   **Perf. 12½**

C93	AP8	20c slate	.50	.40
C94	AP8	20c lt violet ('43)	.80	.80
C95	AP8	20c blue ('44)	.60	.40
C96	AP8	35c red	1.00	.80
C97	AP8	50c brown org	1.00	.30
C98	AP8	75c deep pink	1.10	.20
C99	AP8	1p dp blue ('40)	3.25	.60
C100	AP8	1.38p brt vio	5.50	2.25
C101	AP8	1.38p yel org ('44)	5.00	4.00
C102	AP8	2p blue	8.00	1.40
a.		Perf. 11	7.00	1.10
C103	AP8	5p rose lilac	10.00	2.25
C104	AP8	5p bl grn ('44)	15.00	7.00
C105	AP8	10p rose ('40)	100.00	65.00
		Nos. C93-C105 (13)	151.75	85.40

Counterfeits exist. They are perf 13, rather than 12½.
For surcharges see Nos. C116-C119.

Nos. C68, C71, C75, C73, C77-C78, C80 Surcharged in Red or Black

1944, Nov. 22

C106	AP6	40c on 47c	1.00	1.00
C107	AP6	40c on 57c (R)	1.00	1.00
C108	AP6	74c on 1.12p	1.00	1.00
C109	AP6	79c on 87c	2.00	2.00
C110	AP6	79c on 1.27p	3.00	3.00
C111	AP6	1.20p on 1.62p	2.00	2.00
C112	AP6	1.43p on 2.12p (R)	2.00	2.00
		Nos. C106-C112 (7)	12.00	12.00

Catalogue values for unused stamps in this section, from this point to the end of the section, are for Never Hinged items.

Legislature Building
AP9

Unwmk.
1945, May 11   **Engr.**   **Perf. 11**

C113	AP9	2p ultra	4.00	2.00

Type of 1929, Surcharged in Violet

1945, Aug. 14   **Perf. 12½**

C114	AP6	44c on 75c brown	1.00	.50

Allied Nations' victory in Europe.

"La Eolo"
AP10

1945, Oct. 31   **Perf. 11**

C115	AP10	8c green	2.00	1.00

Nos. C97 and C101 Surcharged in Violet, Black or Blue

1945-46   **Perf. 12½**

C116	AP8	14c on 50c (V) ('46)	1.00	.50
a.		Inverted surcharge	37.50	
C117	AP8	23c on 1.38p	1.00	.50
a.		Inverted surcharge	75.00	
C118	AP8	23c on 50c	1.00	.50
a.		Inverted surcharge	75.00	
C119	AP8	1p on 1.38p (Bl)	1.00	.50
a.		Inverted surcharge	75.00	
		Nos. C116-C119 (4)	4.00	2.00

Victory of the Allied Nations in WWII.

No. C85 Overprinted in Black

1946, Jan. 9

C120	AP7	62c blue green	2.00	1.00

Issued to commemorate the inauguration of the Black River Power Dam.

AP11

Black Overprint

1946-49   **Litho.**

C121	AP11	8c car rose	.20	.20
a.		Inverted overprint		
C122	AP11	50c brown	.40	.20
a.		Double overprint	25.00	
C123	AP11	1p lt bl	.65	.25
C124	AP11	2p ol ('49)	3.50	3.00

C125	AP11	3p lil rose	4.50	3.00
C126	AP11	5p rose car	8.50	6.00
		Nos. C121-C126 (6)	17.75	11.65

Four-Motored Plane — AP12

National Airport
AP13

1947-49   **Perf. 11½, 12½**

C129	AP12	3c org brn ('49)	.20	.20
C130	AP12	8c car rose ('49)	.20	.20
C131	AP12	14c ultra	.20	.20
C132	AP12	23c emerald	.20	.20
C133	AP13	1p car & brn ('49)	1.25	.40
C134	AP13	3p ultra & brn ('49)	2.75	1.60
C135	AP13	5p grn & brn ('49)	8.00	4.00
C136	AP13	10p lil rose & brn	12.00	6.00
		Nos. C129-C136 (8)	24.80	12.80

Counterfeits exist, perf 11¼. Design size of genuine copies is 34½x24mm, while forgeries are 33½x23½mm.
See Nos. C145-C164. For surcharges see Nos. C206, Q94.

AP14

School of Architecture, University of Uruguay
AP15

Black Overprint

1948, June 9   **Perf. 12½**

C137	AP14	12c blue	.20	.20
C138	AP14	24c Prus grn	.30	.20
C139	AP14	36c slate blue	.45	.40
		Nos. C137-C139 (3)	.95	.70

1949, Dec. 7

Designs: 27c, Medical School. 31c, Engineering School. 36c, University.

C141	AP15	15c carmine	.20	.20
C142	AP15	27c chocolate	.20	.20
C143	AP15	31c dp ultra	.40	.20
C144	AP15	36c dull green	.60	.30
		Nos. C141-C144 (4)	1.40	.90

Founding of the University of Uruguay, cent.

Plane Type of 1947-49

1952-59   **Unwmk.**   **Perf. 11, 12½**

C145	AP12	10c blk ('54)	.20	.20
C146	AP12	10c lt red ('58)	.20	.20
a.		Imperf., pair	30.00	
C147	AP12	15c org brn	.20	.20
a.		Vert. pair, imperf btwn.	42.50	
C148	AP12	20c lil rose ('54)	.25	.20
C149	AP12	21c purple	.30	.20
C150	AP12	27c yel grn ('57)	.30	.20
C151	AP12	31c chocolate	.45	.20
C152	AP12	36c ultra	.30	.20
C153	AP12	36c blk ('58)	.30	.20
C154	AP12	50c lt bl ('57)	.60	.50
C155	AP12	50c bl blk ('58)	.50	.20
C156	AP12	62c dl sl bl ('53)	.70	.50
C157	AP12	65c rose ('53)	.70	.50
C158	AP12	84c org ('59)	1.00	.70
C159	AP12	1.08p vio brn	1.60	.80
C160	AP12	2p Prus bl	2.50	1.40
C161	AP12	3p red org	3.00	1.75
C162	AP12	5p dk gray grn	6.50	4.00
C163	AP12	5p gray ('57)	3.50	2.50
C164	AP12	10p dp grn ('55)	17.00	12.50
		Nos. C145-C164 (20)	40.10	27.15

Planes and
Show
Emblem
AP16

Unwmk.

1956, Jan. 5   Litho.   Perf. 11

C166	AP16	20c ultra	.35	.35
C167	AP16	31c olive grn	.45	.25
C168	AP16	36c car rose	.70	.30
		Nos. C166-C168 (3)	1.50	.90

First Exposition of National Products.

Type of Regular Issue and

José
Batlle y
Ordonez
AP17

Designs: 10c, Full-face portrait without
hand. 36c, Portrait facing right.

Perf. 13½

1956, Dec. 15   Wmk. 90   Photo.

C169	A178	10c magenta	.30	.20
C170	A178	20c grnsh blk	.30	.20
C171	AP17	31c brown	.30	.30
C172	A178	36c bl grn	.60	.40
		Nos. C169-C172 (4)	1.50	1.10

Stamp of 1856 and
Stagecoach — AP18

1956, Dec. 15   Litho.

C173	AP18	20c grn, bl & pale yel	.45	.30
C174	AP18	31c brn, bl & lt bl	.55	.30
C175	AP18	36c dp claret & bl	.65	.30
		Nos. C173-C175 (3)	1.65	.90

1st postage stamps of Uruguay, cent.

Flags of 21   Men and Torch of
American   Freedom — AP20
Nations — AP19

Perf. 11, 11½ (No. C177)

1958, June 19   Unwmk.

C176	AP19	23c blue & blk	.30	.20
C177	AP19	34c green & blk	.45	.20
C178	AP19	44c cerise & blk	.45	.30
		Nos. C176-C178 (3)	1.20	.70

Organization of American States, 10th anniv.

1958, Dec. 10   Perf. 11

C179	AP20	23c blk & blue	.25	.20
C180	AP20	34c blk & yel grn	.35	.20
C181	AP20	44c blk & org red	.65	.35
		Nos. C179-C181 (3)	1.25	.75

10th anniversary of the signing of the Universal Declaration of Human Rights.

"Flight" from
Monument to
Fallen
Aviators — AP21

1959   Litho.   Perf. 11
Size: 22x37½mm

C182	AP21	3c bis brn & blk	.25	.20
C183	AP21	8c brt lil & blk	.25	.20
C184	AP21	38c black	.25	.20
C185	AP21	50c citron & blk	.25	.20
C186	AP21	60c vio & blk	.25	.20
C187	AP21	90c ol grn & blk	.30	.25
C188	AP21	1p blue & blk	.40	.20
C189	AP21	2p ocher & blk	1.40	.55
C190	AP21	3p grn & blk	1.50	.95
C191	AP21	5p vio brn & blk	2.00	1.50
C192	AP21	10p dp rose car & blk	6.50	4.25
		Nos. C182-C192 (11)	13.35	8.75

See Nos. C211-C222. For surcharge see
No. Q97.

Alberto Santos-Dumont — AP22

1959, Feb. 13   Wmk. 327   Perf. 11½

C193	AP22	31c multi	.25	.20
C194	AP22	36c multi	.25	.20

Airplane flight of Alberto Santos-Dumont,
Brazilian aeronaut, in 1906 in France.

Girl and
Waves
AP23

Designs: 38c, 60c, 1.05p, Compass and
map of Punta del Este.

1959, Mar. 6   Perf. 11½

C195	AP23	10c ocher & lt bl	.20	.20
C196	AP23	38c grn & bis	.20	.20
C197	AP23	60c lilac & bister	.30	.20
C198	AP23	90c red org & grn	.40	.25
C199	AP23	1.05p blue & bister	.60	.45
		Nos. C195-C199 (5)	1.70	1.30

50th anniv. of Punta del Este, seaside resort.

Torch,
YMCA
Emblem
and
Chrismon
AP24

Wmk. 327

1959, Dec. 22   Litho.   Perf. 11½

C200	AP24	38c emer, blk & gray	.30	.25
C201	AP24	50c bl, blk & gray	.35	.20
C202	AP24	60c red, blk & gray	.45	.40
		Nos. C200-C202 (3)	1.10	.85

50th anniv. of the YMCA in Uruguay.

José Artigas and   Refugees and
George   WRY Emblem
Washington   AP26
AP25

1960, Mar. 2   Perf. 11½x12

C203	AP25	38c red & blk	.20	.20
C204	AP25	50c brt bl & blk	.25	.20
C205	AP25	60c dp grn & blk	.40	.20
		Nos. C203-C205 (3)	.85	.60

Pres. Eisenhower's visit to Uruguay, Feb.
1960.
No. C204 exists imperforate, but was not
regularly issued in this form.

No. C150
Surcharged

1960, Apr. 8   Unwmk.   Perf. 11

C206	AP12	20c on 27c yel grn	.25	.20
a.		Perf. 12½	.25	.20

1960, June 6   Wmk. 332
Size: 24x35mm

C207	AP26	60c brt lil rose & blk	.35	.20

World Refugee Year, 7/1/59-6/30/60.

Type of Regular Issue, 1960
Wmk. 332

1960, Nov. 4   Litho.   Perf. 12

C208	A186	38c bl & ol grn	.20	.20
C209	A186	50c bl & ver	.20	.20
C210	A186	60c bl & pur	.30	.20
		Nos. C208-C210 (3)	.70	.60

Type of 1959 Redrawn with Silhouette
of Airplane Added

1960-61   Litho.   Perf. 12

C211	AP21	3c blk & pale vio	.30	.20
C212	AP21	20c blk & crimson	.30	.20
C213	AP21	38c blk & pale bl	.30	.20
C214	AP21	50c blk & buff	.30	.20
C215	AP21	60c blk & dp grn	.40	.20
C216	AP21	90c blk & rose	.45	.20
C217	AP21	1p blk & gray	.60	.20
C218	AP21	2p blk & yel grn	.85	.20
C219	AP21	3p blk & red lil	1.10	.25
C220	AP21	5p blk & org ver	1.60	.50
C221	AP21	10p blk & yel	3.00	1.00
C222	AP21	20p blk & dk bl ('61)	5.75	2.25
		Nos. C211-C222 (12)	14.95	5.60

Pres.
Gronchi
and Flag
Colors
AP27

1961, Apr. 17   Wmk. 332   Perf. 12

C223	AP27	90c multi	.25	.20
C224	AP27	1.20p multi	.30	.25
C225	AP27	1.40p multi	.35	.35
		Nos. C223-C225 (3)	.90	.80

Visit of President Giovanni Gronchi of Italy
to Uruguay, April, 1961.

Carrasco
National
Airport
AP28

1961, May 16   Wmk. 332   Perf. 12
Building in Gray

C226	AP28	1p lt vio	.25	.20
C227	AP28	2p ol gray	.45	.20
C228	AP28	3p orange	.75	.40
C229	AP28	4p purple	.90	.45
C230	AP28	5p aqua	1.25	.60
C231	AP28	10p lt ultra	2.40	1.00
C232	AP28	20p maroon	3.75	2.00
		Nos. C226-C232 (7)	9.75	4.85

Type of Regular "CIES" Issue, 1961

1961, Aug. 3   Litho.   Wmk. 332

C233	A189	20c blk & org	.30	.20
C234	A189	45c blk & grn	.30	.20
C235	A189	50c blk & gray	.30	.20
C236	A189	90c blk & plum	.30	.20
C237	A189	1p blk & dp rose	.40	.20
C238	A189	1.40p blk & lt vio	.50	.20
C239	A189	2p blk & bister	.55	.25
C240	A189	3p blk & lt bl	.85	.30
C241	A189	4p blk & yellow	1.25	.55
C242	A189	5p blk & blue	1.50	.85
C243	A189	10p blk & yel grn	2.75	1.50
C244	A189	20p blk & dp pink	5.75	2.75
		Nos. C233-C244 (12)	14.75	7.40

Swiss
Flag,
Plow,
Wheat
Sheaf
AP29

1962, Aug. 1   Wmk. 332   Perf. 12

C245	AP29	90c car, org & blk	.25	.20
C246	AP29	1.40p car, bl & blk	.35	.30

Cent. of the Swiss Settlement in Uruguay.

Red-crested
Cardinal — AP30

Birds: 45c, White-capped tanager, horiz.
90c, Vermilion flycatcher. 1.20p, Great kiskadee, horiz. 1.40p, Fork-tailed flycatcher.

1962, Dec. 5   Litho.   Perf. 12

C247	AP30	20c gray, blk & red	.20	.20
C248	AP30	45c multi	.35	.20
C249	AP30	90c crim rose, blk & lt brn	.75	.20
C250	AP30	1.20p lt bl, blk & yel	.60	.20
C251	AP30	1.40p blue & sepia	1.10	.20
		Nos. C247-C251 (5)	3.00	1.05

No frame on #C248, thin frame on #C251.
See #C258-C263. For surcharge see #C320.

Type of Regular UPAE Issue, 1963

1963, May 31   Wmk. 332   Perf. 12

C252	A195	45c bluish grn & blk	.20	.20
C253	A195	90c magenta & blk	.25	.20

Freedom from Hunger
Type of Regular Issue

1963, July 9   Wmk. 332   Perf. 12

C254	A196	90c red & yel	.25	.25
C255	A196	1.40p violet & yel	.35	.35

"Alferez
Campora"
AP31

1963, Aug. 16   Litho.

C256	AP31	90c dk grn & org	.30	.20
C257	AP31	1.40p ultra & yel	.50	.40

Voyage around the world by the Uruguayan
sailing vessel "Alferez Campora," 1960-63.

Bird Type of 1962

Birds: 1p, Glossy cowbird (tordo). 2p, Yellow cardinal. 3p, Hooded siskin. 5p, Sayaca tanager. 10p, Blue and yellow tanager. 20p, Scarlet-headed marsh-bird. All horizontal.

1963, Nov. 15   Wmk. 332   Perf. 12
C258	AP30	1p vio bl, blk & brn org	.45	.20
C259	AP30	2p lt brn, blk & yel	1.00	.25
C260	AP30	3p yel, brn & blk	1.50	.40
C261	AP30	5p emer, bl grn & blk	2.40	.50
C262	AP30	10p multi	5.00	1.00
C263	AP30	20p gray, org & blk	10.50	5.50
	Nos. C258-C263 (6)		20.85	7.85

Frame on Nos. C260-C263.

Pres. Charles de Gaulle AP32

2.40p, Flags of France and Uruguay.

1964, Oct. 9   Litho.   Perf. 12
C264	AP32	1.50p multi	.35	.20
C265	AP32	2.40p multi	.65	.35

Charles de Gaulle, Pres. of France, Oct. 1964.

Submerged Statue of Ramses II — AP33

Design: 2p, Head of Ramses II.

1964, Oct. 30   Litho.   Wmk. 332
C266	AP33	1.30p multi	.30	.25
C267	AP33	2p bis, red brn & brt bl	.60	.45
	a.	Souv. sheet of 3, #713, C266-C267, imperf.	1.60	1.60

UNESCO world campaign to save historic monuments in Nubia.

National Flag AP34

1965, Feb. 18   Wmk. 332   Perf. 12
C268	AP34	50p gray, dk bl & yel	6.50	4.00

Kennedy Type of Regular Issue

1965, Mar. 5   Wmk. 327   Perf. 11½
C269	A202	1.50p gold, lil & blk	.25	.25
C270	A202	2.40p gold, brt bl & blk	.35	.25

Issue of 1864, No. 23 — AP35

6c, 8c, 10c denominations of 1864 issue.

Wmk. 332
1965, Mar. 19   Litho.   Perf. 12
C271   Sheet of 10   2.25 2.25

"URUGUAY" at bottom
a.	AP35 1p blue & black		.25	.25
b.	AP35 1p brick red & black		.25	.25
c.	AP35 1p green & black		.25	.25
d.	AP35 1p ocher & black		.25	.25
e.	AP35 1p carmine & black		.25	.25

"URUGUAY" at top
f.	AP35 1p blue & black		.25	.25

g.	AP35 1p brick red & black		.25	.25
h.	AP35 1p green & black		.25	.25
i.	AP35 1p ocher & black		.25	.25
j.	AP35 1p carmine & black		.25	.25

1st Rio de la Plata Stamp Show, sponsored jointly by the Argentine and Uruguayan philatelic associations, Montevideo, Mar. 19-28. No. C271 contains two horizontal rows of stamps and two rows of labels; Nos. C271a-C271e are in first row, Nos. C271f-C271j in second row. Adjacent labels in top and bottom rows.

For overprint see No. C298.

National Arms — AP36

Artigas Monument AP37

1965, Apr. 30   Wmk. 332   Perf. 12
C272	AP36	20p multi	1.75	1.00

Type of Regular Issue and AP37.

Designs: 1.50p, Artigas and wagontrain. 2.40p, Artigas quotation.

Perf. 11½x12, 12x11½
1965, May 17   Litho.   Wmk. 327
C273	AP37	1p multi	.20	.20
C274	A205	1.50p multi	.30	.25
C275	A205	2.40p multi	.45	.35
	Nos. C273-C275 (3)		.95	.80

José Artigas (1764-1850), leader of the independence revolt against Spain.

Olympic Games Type of Regular Issue

Designs: 1p, Boxing. 1.50p, Running. 2p, Fencing. 2.40p, Sculling. 3p, Pistol shooting. 20p, Olympic rings.

1965, Aug. 3   Litho.   Perf. 12x11½
C276	A206	1p red, gray & blk	.20	.20
C277	A206	1.50p emer, bl & blk	.20	.20
C278	A206	2p dk car, bl & blk	.30	.25
C279	A206	2.40p lt ultra, org & blk	.45	.30
C280	A206	3p lil, yel & blk	.60	.35
C281	A206	20p dk vio bl, pink & lt bl	.95	.70
	Nos. C276-C281 (6)		2.70	2.00

Souvenir Sheet

Designs: 5p, Stamp of 1924, No. 284. 10p, Stamp of 1928, No. 389.

C282		Sheet of 2	1.75	1.75
	a.	5p buff, blue & black	.55	.55
	b.	10p blue, black & rose red	.80	.80

18th Olympic Games, Tokyo, 10/10-25/64.

ITU Emblem and Satellite AP38

1966, Jan. 25   Wmk. 332   Perf. 12
C283	AP38	1p bl, bluish blk & ver	.25	.20

Cent. of the ITU (in 1965).

Winston Churchill — AP39

1966, Apr. 29   Wmk. 332   Perf. 12
C284	AP39	2p car, brn & gold	.45	.20

Rio de Janeiro Type of Regular Issue

1966, June 9   Wmk. 332   Perf. 12
C285	A208	80c dp org & brn	.25	.20

International Cooperation Year Emblem AP40

1966, June 9   Litho.
C286	AP40	1p bluish grn & blk	.25	.20

UN International Cooperation Year.

President Zalman Shazar of Israel AP41

1966, June 21   Wmk. 327
C287	AP41	7p multi	.45	.25

Visit of Pres. Zalman Shazar of Israel.

Crested Screamer — AP42

1966, July 7   Wmk. 327   Perf. 12
C288	AP42	100p bl, blk, red & gray	6.00	1.75

Jules Rimet Cup, Soccer Ball and Globe AP43

1966, July 11   Litho.
C289	AP43	10p dk pur, org & lil	.60	.25

World Cup Soccer Championship, Wembley, England, July 11-30.

Bulls AP44

1966   Wmk. 327, 332 (10p)
C290	AP44	4p Hereford	.20	.20
C291	AP44	6p Holstein	.20	.20
C292	AP44	8p Shorthorn	.45	.25
C293	AP44	15p Aberdeen Angus	.75	.30
C294	AP44	20p Norman	1.40	.45

C295	AP44	30p Jersey	1.75	.75
C296	AP44	50p Charolais	3.00	1.25
	Nos. C290-C296 (7)		7.75	3.40

Issued to publicize Uruguayan cattle. Issued: 4p, 50p, 8/13; 6p, 30p, 8/29; 10p, 15p, 20p, 9/26.

Boiso Lanza, Early Plane and Space Capsule AP45

1966, Oct. 14   Litho.   Perf. 12
C297	AP45	25p ultra, blk & lt bl	.75	.45

Issued to honor Capt. Juan Manuel Boiso Lanza, pioneer of military aviation.

No. C271 Overprinted: "CENTENARIO DEL SELLO / ESCUDITO RESELLADO"

1966, Nov. 4   Wmk. 332
C298   Sheet of 10   2.25 2.25

"URUGUAY" at bottom
a.-e.	AP35 1p each		.25	.25

"URUGUAY" at top
f.-j.	AP35 1p each		.25	.25

2nd Rio de la Plata Stamp Show, Buenos Aires, Apr. 1966, sponsored by the Argentine and Uruguayan philatelic associations, and for the cent. of Uruguay's 1st surcharged issue. The addition of black numerals makes the designs resemble the surcharged issue of 1866, Nos. 24-28.

Labels in top row are overprinted "SEGUNDA MUESTRA 1966", in bottom row "SEGUNDAS JORNADAS 1966" and "CENTENARIO DEL SELLO / ESCUDITO RESELLADO" in both rows. One label each in top and bottom rows is overprinted "BUENOS AIRES / ABRIL 1966."

No. 613 Surcharged in Dark Blue

Perf. 12½x13
1966, Dec. 17   Engr.   Unwmk.
C299	A175	1p on 12c	.25	.20

Philatelic Club of Uruguay, 40th anniv.

Dante Alighieri — AP46

Planetarium Projector — AP47

Wmk. 332
1966, Dec. 27   Litho.   Perf. 12
C300	AP46	50c sepia & bister	.25	.20

Dante Alighieri (1265-1321), Italian poet.

1967, Jan. 13   Wmk. 332   Perf. 12
C301	AP47	5p dl bl & blk	.45	.25

Montevideo Municipal Planetarium, 10th anniv.

Archbishop
Makarios
and Map of
Cyprus
AP48

1967, Feb. 14   Wmk. 332   Perf. 12
C302 AP48 6.60p rose lil & blk   .25 .20
Visit of Archbishop Makarios, president of
Cyprus, Oct. 21, 1966.

Dr. Albert
Schweitzer Holding
Fawn — AP49

1967, Mar. 31   Litho.   Wmk. 332
C303 AP49 6p grn, blk, brn & sal   .50 .50
Albert Schweitzer (1875-1965), medical
missionary.

Corriedale
Ram
AP50

Various Rams: 4p, Ideal. 5p, Romney
Marsh. 10p, Australian Merino.

1967, Apr. 5
C304 AP50   3p red org, blk &
              gray   1.40 .20
C305 AP50   4p emer, blk & gray 1.40 .20
C306 AP50   5p ultra, blk & gray 1.40 .20
C307 AP50 10p yel, blk & gray   1.40 .40
       Nos. C304-C307 (4)   5.60 1.00
Uruguayan sheep raising.

Flag of
Uruguay
and Map
of the
Americas
AP51

1967, Apr. 8
C308 AP51 10p dk gray, bl & gold   .35 .20
Meeting of American Presidents, Punta del
Este, Apr. 10-12.

Numeral
Stamps of
1866, Nos.
30-31
AP52

Design: 6p, Nos. 32-33; diff. frame.

Wmk. 332
1967, May 10   Litho.   Perf. 12
C309 AP52 3p yel, yel grn & blk   .20 .20
  a.   Souvenir sheet of 4   1.00 1.00
C310 AP52 6p bis, dp rose & blk   .35 .25
  a.   Souvenir sheet of 4   1.75 1.75

Cent. of the 1866 numeral issue. Nos.
C309a-C310a each contain 4 stamps similar
to Nos. C309 and C310 respectively (the
arrangement of colors differs in the souvenir
sheets).

Ansina, Portrait by
Medardo
Latorre — AP53

1967, May 17
C311 AP53 2p gray, dk bl & red   .25 .20
Issued to honor Ansina, servant of Gen.
José Artigas.

Plane
Landing
AP54

1967, May 30
C312 AP54 10p red, bl, blk & yel   .35 .25
30th anniv. (in 1966) of PLUNA Airline.

Shooting for
Basket — AP55

Basketball Game — AP56

Basketball Players in Action: No. C314,
Driving (ball shoulder high). No. C315, About
to pass (ball head high). No. C316, Ready to
pass (ball held straight in front). No. C317,
Dribbling with right hand.

1967, June 9
C313 AP55 5p multi   .30 .25
C314 AP55 5p multi   .30 .25
C315 AP55 5p multi   .30 .25
C316 AP55 5p multi   .30 .25
C317 AP55 5p multi   .30 .25
  a.   Strip of 5, Nos. C313-C317 1.75 1.50

Souvenir Sheet
C318 AP56 10p org, brt grn & blk 1.75 1.75
5th World Basketball Championships, Montevideo, May 1967.
For overprint see No. C349.

José Artigas, Manuel Belgrano, Flags
of Uruguay and Argentina — AP57

Wmk. 332
1967, June 19   Litho.   Imperf.
C319 AP57 5p bl, grn & yel   1.00 1.00
3rd Rio de la Plata Stamp Show, Montevideo, Uruguay, June 18-25.
For surcharge see No. 859.

**Nos. C248 and C252 Surcharged in
Gold**
1967, June 22   Perf. 12
C320 AP30 5.90p on 45c multi   .25 .20
C321 A195 5.90p on 45c multi   .25 .20

Don Quixote and Sancho Panza,
Painted by Denry Torres — AP58

1967, July 10
C322 AP58 8p bister brn & brn   .30 .25
Issued in honor of Miguel de Cervantes
Saavedra (1547-1616), Spanish novelist.
For surcharge see No. C356.

Stone Axe — AP59

Railroad
Crossing
AP60

Designs: 15p, Headbreaker stones. 20p,
Spearhead. 50p, Birdstone. 75p, Clay pot.
100p, Ornitholite (ritual sculpture), Balizas,
horiz. 150p, Lasso weights (boleadores).
200p, Two spearheads.

1967-68   Wmk. 332   Perf. 12
C323 AP59 15p gray & blk   .20 .20
C324 AP59 20p gray & blk   .20 .20
C325 AP59 30p gray & lt gray   .45 .20
C326 AP59 50p gray & blk   .60 .20
C327 AP59 75p brn & blk   1.00 .35
C328 AP59 100p gray & blk   1.40 .60
C329 AP59 150p gray & blk
              ('68)   1.75 .60
C330 AP59 200p gray & blk
              ('68)   2.40 1.25
       Nos. C323-C330 (8)   8.00 3.60

1967, Dec. 4
C331 AP60 4p blk, yel & red   .25 .20
10th Pan-American Highway Congress,
Montevideo.

Lions Emblem and
Map of South
America — AP61

1967, Dec. 29
C332 AP61 5p pur, yel & emer   .30 .20
50th anniversary of Lions International.

Boy Scout
AP62

1968, Jan. 24   Litho.
C333 AP62 9p sepia & brick red   .40 .25
Issued in memory of Robert Baden-Powell,
founder of the Boy Scout organization.

Sun, UN Emblem and Transportation
Means — AP63

1968, Feb. 29   Wmk. 332   Perf. 12
C334 AP63 10p gray, yel, lt & dk bl .25 .20
Issued for International Tourist Year.

Octopus
AP64

Marine Fauna: 20p, Silversides. 25p, Chara-
cin. 30p, Catfish, vert. 50p, Squid, vert.

1968   Wmk. 332   Perf. 12
C335 AP64 15p lt grn, bl & blk   .70 .20
C336 AP64 20p brn, grn & bl   .70 .20
C337 AP64 25p multi   1.00 .20
C338 AP64 30p bl, grn & blk   1.25 .50
C339 AP64 50p dp org, grn & dk
              bl   2.00 .65
       Nos. C335-C339 (5)   5.65 1.75
Issued: 30p, 50p, 10/10; 15p, 20p, 25p, 11/5.

Navy Type of Regular Issue
Designs: 4p, Naval Air Force. 6p, Naval
arms. 10p, Signal flags, vert. 20p, Corsair
(chartered by General Artigas).

1968, Nov. 12   Litho.
C340 A226 4p bl, blk & red   .20 .20
C341 A226 6p multi   .20 .20
C342 A226 10p lt ultra, red & yel .20 .20
C343 A226 20p ultra & blk   .30 .20
       Nos. C340-C343 (4)   .90 .80

Rowing
AP65

1969, Feb. 11   Wmk. 332   Perf. 12
C344 AP65 30p shown   .35 .20
C345 AP65 50p Running   .65 .30
C346 AP65 100p Soccer   1.00 .45
       Nos. C344-C346 (3)   2.00 .95
19th Olympic Games, Mexico City, 10/12-
27/68.

Bicycling Type of Regular Issue
Designs: 20p, Bicyclist and globe, vert.

1969, Mar. 21   Wmk. 332   Perf. 12
C347 A229 20p bl, pur & yel   .30 .20

"EFIMEX
68" and
Globe
AP66

1969, Apr. 10   Wmk. 332   Perf. 12
C348 AP66 20p dk grn, red & bl   .30 .20
EFIMEX '68, International Philatelic Exhibi-
tion, Mexico City, Nov. 1-9, 1968.

No. C318 Overprinted with Names of Participating Countries, Emblem, Bars, etc. and "CAMPEONATO MUNDIAL DE VOLEIBOL"

1969, Apr. 25
Souvenir Sheet

C349 AP56 10p org, brt grn & blk .45 .45

Issued to commemorate the World Volleyball Championships, Montevideo, Apr. 1969.

Book, Quill and Emblem — AP67

Automobile Club Emblem — AP68

1969, Sept. 16   Litho.   *Perf. 12*
C350 AP67 30p grn, org & blk .45 .25

10th Congress of Latin American Notaries.

1969, Oct. 7   Wmk. 332   *Perf. 12*
C351 AP68 10p ultra & red .25 .20

50th anniv. (in 1968) of the Uruguayan Automobile Club.

ILO Emblem AP69

1969, Oct. 29   Litho.   *Perf. 12*
C352 AP69 30p dk bl grn & blk .40 .25

50th anniv. of the ILO.

Exhibition Emblem — AP70

1969, Nov. 15   Wmk. 332   *Perf. 12*
C353 AP70 20p ultra, yel & grn .30 .20

ABUEXPO 69 Philatelic Exhibition, San Pablo, Brazil, Nov. 15-23.

Rotary Emblem and Hemispheres AP71

1969, Dec. 6   *Perf. 12*
C354 AP71 20p ultra, bl & bis .50 .25

South American Regional Rotary Conference and the 50th anniv. of the Montevideo Rotary Club.

Dr. Luis Morquio — AP72

1969, Dec. 22   Litho.   Wmk. 332
C355 AP72 20p org red & brn .25 .20

Centenary of the birth of Dr. Luis Morquio, pediatrician.

No. C322 Surcharged "FELIZ AÑO 1970 / 6.00 / PESOS"

1969, Dec. 24
C356 AP58 6p on 8p bis brn & brn .25 .20

Issued for New Year 1970.

Mahatma Gandhi and UNESCO Emblem AP73

1970, Jan. 26   Wmk. 332   *Perf. 12*
C357 AP73 100p lt bl & brn 3.00 .80

Mohandas K. Gandhi (1869-1948), leader in India's fight for independence.

Evaristo C. Ciganda — AP74   Giuseppe Garibaldi — AP75

1970, Mar. 10   Litho.
C358 AP74 6p brt grn & brn .25 .20

Ciganda, author of the 1st law for teachers' pensions, birth cent.

1970, Apr. 7   Unwmk.   *Perf. 12*
C359 AP75 20p rose car & pink .25 .20

Centenary of Garibaldi's command of foreign legionnaires in the Uruguayan Civil War.

Fur Seal AP76

Designs: 20p, Rhea, vert. 30p, Common tegu (lizard). 50p, Capybara. 100p, Mulita armadillo. 150p, Puma. 200p, Nutria.

1970-71   Wmk. 332   *Perf. 12*
C361 AP76 20p pur, emer & blk .75 .20
C362 AP76 30p emer, yel & blk .75 .25
C363 AP76 50p dl yel & brn 1.50 .45
C365 AP76 100p org, sep & blk 2.00 .65
C366 AP76 150p emer & brn 1.50 .75
C367 AP76 200p brt rose, brn & blk ('71) 3.75 1.90
C368 AP76 250p gray, bl & blk 4.75 2.00
Nos. C361-C368 (7) 15.00 6.20

Soccer and Mexican Flag AP77

1970, June 2   Litho.   *Perf. 12*
C369 AP77 50p multi .60 .45

9th World Soccer Championships for the Jules Rimet Cup, Mexico City, 5/30-6/21.

"U N" and Laurel — AP78

1970, June 26   Wmk. 332   *Perf. 12*
C370 AP78 32p dk bl & gold .50 .25

25th anniversary of the United Nations.

Eisenhower and US Flag — AP79

1970, July 14   Litho.
C371 AP79 30p gray, vio bl & red .40 .25

Issued in memory of Gen. Dwight David Eisenhower, 34th Pres. of US (1890-1969).

Neil A. Armstrong Stepping onto Moon — AP80

1970, July 21
C372 AP80 200p multi 3.00 1.25

1st anniv. of man's 1st landing on the moon.

Flag of the "Immortals" — AP81

1970, Aug. 24   Wmk. 332   *Perf. 12*
C373 AP81 500p bl, blk & red 4.50 4.50

The 145th anniversary of the arrival of the 33 "Immortals," the patriots, who started the revolution for independence.

Congress Emblem with Map of South America AP82

1970, Sept. 16   Unwmk.   *Perf. 12*
C374 AP82 30p bl, dk bl & yel .30 .25

Issued to publicize the 5th Pan-American Congress of Rheumatology, Punta del Este.

Souvenir Sheet

Types of First Air Post Issue — AP83

1970, Oct. 1   Wmk. 332   *Perf. 12½*
C375 AP83 Sheet of 3 3.00 3.00
  a.   25p brown (Bl) .90 .90
  b.   25p brown (R) .90 .90
  c.   25p brown (G) .90 .90

Stamp Day. #C375 contains 3 stamps similar to #C1-C3, but with denominations in pesos.

Flags of ALALC Countries — AP84

1970, Nov. 23   Litho.   *Perf. 12*
C376 AP84 22p multi .30 .25

For the Latin-American Association for Free Trade (Asociación Latinoamericana de Libre Comercio).

Yellow Fever, by J. M. Blanes AP85

1971, June 8   Wmk. 332   *Perf. 12*
C377 AP85 50p blk, dk red brn & yel .55 .30

Juan Manuel Blanes (1830-1901), painter.

Racial Equality, UN Emblem AP86

1971, June 28   Litho.
C378 AP86 27p blk, pink & bis .35 .25

Intl. Year Against Racial Discrimination.

Congress Emblem with Maps of Americas AP87

1971, July 6   Wmk. 332   *Perf. 12*
C379 AP87 58p dl grn, blk & org .45 .35

12th Pan-American Congress of Gastroenterology, Punta del Este, Dec. 5-10, 1971.

Committee
Emblem
AP88

1971, Nov. 29
C380 AP88 30p bl, blk & yel   .30 .25
Inter-governmental Committee for European
Migration.

Llama and
Mountains
AP89

Munich Olympic
Games
Emblem — AP90

1971, Dec. 30
C381 AP89 37p multi   .45 .35
EXFILIMA '71, Third Inter-American Phila-
telic Exposition, Lima, Peru, Nov. 6-14.

1972, Feb. 1   Perf. 11½x12
Designs (Munich '72 Emblem and): 100p,
Torchbearer. 500p, Discobolus.
C382 AP90 50p blk, red & org   .30 .20
C383 AP90 100p multi   .55 .40
C384 AP90 500p multi   2.75 2.00
      Nos. C382-C384 (3)   3.60 2.60
20th Olympic Games, Munich, 8/26-9/11.

Retort and WHO
Emblem — AP91

Ship with Flags
Forming
Sails — AP92

1972, Feb. 22   Perf. 12
C385 AP91 27p multi   .25 .20
50th anniversary of the discovery of insulin
by Frederick G. Banting and Charles H. Best.

1972, Mar. 6   Wmk. 332
C386 AP92 37p multi   .30 .25
Stamp Day of the Americas.

1924 and 1928 Gold Medals,
Soccer — AP93

Design: 300p, Olympic flag, Motion and
Munich emblems, vert.

1972, June 12   Litho.   Perf. 12
C387 AP93 100p bl & multi   .45 .45
C388 AP93 300p multi   1.40 1.40
20th Olympic Games, Munich, 8/26-9/11.

Cross
AP94

1972, Aug. 10
C389 AP94 37p vio & gold   .25 .20
Dan A. Mitrione (1920-70), slain US official.

Interlocking
Squares and UN
Emblem — AP95

1972, Aug. 16
C390 AP95 30p gray & multi   .25 .20
3rd UN Conf. on Trade and Development
(UNCTAD III), Santiago, Chile, Apr.-May 1972.

Brazil's "Bull's-eye," 1843 — AP96

**   Wmk. 332**
1972, Aug. 26   Litho.   Perf. 12
C391 AP96 50p grn, yel & bl   .25 .20
4th Inter-American Philatelic Exhibition,
EXFILBRA, Rio de Janeiro, Aug. 26-Sept. 2.

Map of South
America,
Compass
Rose — AP97

1972, Sept. 28
C392 AP97 37p multi   .30 .20
Uruguay's support for extending territorial
sovereignty 200 miles into the sea.

Adoration of the Kings and Shepherds,
by Rafael Perez Barradas — AP98

1972, Oct. 12
C393 AP98 20p lemon & multi + la-
            bel   .40 .25
Christmas 1972 and first biennial exhibition
of Uruguayan painting, 1970.

WPY
Emblem
AP99

**   Wmk. 332**
1974, Aug. 20   Litho.   Perf. 12
C394 AP99 500p gray & red   .75 .60
World Population Year 1974.

Soccer, Olympics
and UPU
Emblems
AP100

Anniversaries and events: No. C398a, 17th
UPU Congress, Lausanne. No. C398b, World
Soccer Federation, 1st South American presi-
dent. No. C398c, 1976 Summer and Winter
Olympics, Innsbruck and Montreal.

1974, Aug. 30
C395 AP100 200p grn & multi   .80 .80
C396 AP100 300p org & multi   .80 .80
C397 AP100 500p multicolored   8.50 8.50
       Souvenir Sheet
C398   Sheet of 3   70.00 70.00
a.-c.   AP100 500p any single   20.00 20.00
Centenary of Universal Postal Union.
Nos. C397-C398 had limited distribution.

Mexico
No. O1
and
Mexican
Coat of
Arms
AP101

**   Wmk. 332**
1974, Oct. 15   Litho.   Perf. 12
C399 AP101 200p multi   .25 .20
EXFILMEX '74 5th Inter-American Philatelic
Exhibition, Mexico City, Oct. 26-Nov. 3.

Christmas Type of 1974
240p, Kings following star. 2500p, Virgin &
Child.

1974
C400 A315 240p multi   .30 .20
       Miniature Sheet
C401 A315 2500p multi   3.00 3.00
Issued: 240p. Dec. 27; 2500p, Dec. 31.

Spain No. 1, Colors of Spain and
Uruguay — AP102

1975, Mar. 4
C402 AP102 400p multi   .35 .25
Espana 75, International Philatelic Exhibi-
tion, Madrid, Apr. 4-13.

Souvenir Sheet

Nos. C253, 893 and C402 — AP103

**   Wmk. 332**
1975, Apr. 4   Litho.   Perf. 12
C403 AP103 Sheet of 3   5.00 5.00
a.   1000p No. C253   1.50 1.50
b.   1000p No. 893   1.50 1.50
c.   1000p No. C402   1.50 1.50
Espana 75 Intl. Phil. Exhib., Madrid, Apr. 4-
13.

1976 Summer &
Winter Olympics,
Innsbruck &
Montreal
AP104

1975, May 16   Perf. 12
C404 AP104 400p shown   .80 .60
C405 AP104 600p Flags,
             Olympic
             rings   1.10 .95

       Souvenir Sheets
C406   Sheet of 2   42.50 42.50
a.   AP104 500p Montreal emblem   12.50 12.50
b.   AP104 1000p Innsbruck em-
           blem   27.50 27.50
C407   Sheet of 2   42.50 42.50
a.   AP104 500p Emblems, horiz.   12.50 12.50
b.   AP104 1000p Flags, horiz.   27.50 27.50
Nos. C404-C407 had limited distribution.

Floor
Design for
Capitol,
Rome
AP105

1975, Aug. 15
C408 AP105 1p multi   .85 .85
500th birth anniversary of Michelangelo
Buonarroti (1475-1564), Italian sculptor,
painter and architect.

Apollo-Soyuz Space Mission, USA &
Uruguay Independence — AP106

Anniversaries and events: 15c, Apollo-
Soyuz spacecraft. 20c, Apollo-Soyuz spacecraft. 25c, Artigas monument, vert. 30c,
George Washington, Pres. Artigas. No. C412,
Early Aircraft, vert. No. C413a, Apollo spacecraft, astronauts. No. C413b, US and Uruguayan Declarations of Independence. No.
C413c, Modern aircraft. No. C413d, UN Sec-
retaries General. No. C414c, Boiso Lanza, aviation pioneer. 1p, Flags of UN and Uruguay.

1975, Sept. 29
C409	AP106 10c multicolored	1.10	.85
C410	AP106 15c multicolored	1.60	1.25
C411	AP106 25c multicolored	2.00	1.40
C412	AP106 50c multicolored	2.75	1.75
	Nos. C409-C412 (4)	7.45	5.25

Souvenir Sheets
C413	Sheet of 4	37.50	37.50
a.-d.	AP106 40c any single	8.00	8.00
C414	Sheet of 4	37.50	37.50
a.	AP106 20c multicolored	1.50	1.50
b.	AP106 30c multicolored	3.75	3.75
c.	AP106 50c multicolored	6.50	6.50
d.	AP106 1p multicolored	14.00	14.00

Nos. C409-C414 had limited distribution.

Sun, Uruguay No. C59 and other
Stamps — AP108

Wmk. 332
1975, Oct. 13   Litho.   Perf. 12
C415	AP108 1p blk, gray & yel	2.00	1.00

Uruguayan Stamp Day.

Montreal Olympic
Emblem and
Argentina
'78 — AP109

Flags of US and
Uruguay — AP110

UPU and UPAE
Emblems
AP111

Wmk. 332
1975, Oct. 14   Litho.   Perf. 11½
C416	AP109 1p multi	1.40	.60
C417	AP110 1p multi	1.40	.60
C418	AP111 1p multi	1.40	.60
a.	Souvenir sheet of 3	14.00	14.00
	Nos. C416-C418 (3)	4.20	1.80

EXFILMO '75 and ESPAMER '75 Stamp
Exhibitions, Montevideo, Oct. 10-19. No.

C418a contains 3 stamps similar to Nos.
C416-C418, 2p each.

Ocelot
AP112

Orchid: #C416, Oncidium bifolium.

1976, Jan.   Litho.   Perf. 12
C419	AP112 50c vio bl & multi	.40	.30
C420	AP112 50c emer & multi	.40	.30

Souvenir Sheets

Olympics, Soccer, Telecommunications
and UPU — AP113

1976, June 3   Perf. 11½
C422	Sheet of 3	50.00	50.00
a.	AP113 30c Soccer player	6.00	6.00
b.	AP113 70c Alexander Graham Bell	14.00	14.00
c.	AP113 1p UPU emblem, UN #5	20.00	20.00
C423	Sheet of 3	50.00	50.00
a.	AP113 40c Discus thrower	6.00	6.00
b.	AP113 60c Telephone, cent.	9.00	9.00
c.	AP113 2p UPU emblem, UN #11	25.00	25.00

Nos. C422-C423 had limited distribution.

**Anniversaries and Events Type of
1976
Souvenir Sheets**

20c, Frederick Passy, Henri Dunant. 35c,
Nobel prize, 75th anniv. 40c, Viking space-
craft. 60c, 1976 Summer Olympics, Montreal.
75c, US space missions. 90c, 1976 Summer
Olympics, diff.
World Cup Soccer Championships, Argen-
tina: 1p, Uruguay, 1930 champions. 1.50p,
Uruguay, 1950 champions.

1976, Nov. 12   Perf. 12
C424	Sheet of 4	37.50	37.50
a.	A355 20c multicolored	2.50	2.50
b.	A355 40c multicolored	4.50	4.50
c.	A355 60c multicolored	6.50	6.50
d.	A355 1.50p multicolored	16.00	16.00
C425	Sheet of 4	37.50	37.50
a.	A355 35c multicolored	5.00	5.00
b.	A355 75c multicolored	7.00	7.00
c.	A355 90c multicolored	8.00	8.00
d.	A355 1p multicolored	10.00	10.00

Nos. C424-C425 had limited distribution.

**Nobel Prize Type of 1977
Souvenir Sheets**

Anniversaries and events: 10c, World Cup
Soccer Championships. 40c, Victor Hess,
Nobel Prize in Physics. 60c, Max Plank, Nobel
Prize in Physics. 80c, Graf Zeppelin, Con-
corde. 90c, Virgin and Child by Rubens. 1.20p,
World Cup Soccer Championships, diff. 1.50p,
Eduardo Bonilla, Count von Zeppelin. 2p, The
Nativity by Rubens.

1977, July 21
C426	Sheet of 4	35.00	35.00
a.	A361 10c multicolored	1.00	1.00
b.	A361 60c multicolored	4.00	4.00
c.	A361 80c multicolored	6.00	6.00
d.	A361 2p multicolored	14.00	14.00
C427	Sheet of 4	35.00	35.00
a.	A361 40c multicolored	2.50	2.50
b.	A361 90c multicolored	6.50	6.50
c.	A361 1.20p multicolored	7.50	7.50
d.	A361 1.50p multicolored	11.00	11.00

Nos. C426-C427 had limited distribution.

Uruguay
Natl.
Postal
System,
150th
Anniv.
AP114

1977, July 27
C428	AP114 8p multicolored	10.00	10.00

Souvenir Sheet
C429	AP114 10p multicolored	15.00	15.00

No. C428, imperf., was not valid for post-
age. Souvenir sheets sold in the package with
No. C429 were not valid for postage.
For overprint see No. C435.

Paintings Type of 1978
Paintings: 1p, St. George Slaying Dragon by
Durer. 1.25p, Duke of Lerma by Rubens. No.
432a, Madonna and Child by Durer. No. 432b,
Holy Family by Rubens. No. 432c, Flight from
Egypt by Francisco de Goya (1746-1828).

1978, June 13   Perf. 12½
C430	A374 1p brn & blk	3.25	3.25
C431	A374 1.25p blk & brn	3.50	3.50

Souvenir Sheet
C432	Sheet of 3	18.00	18.00
a.-c.	A374 1p any single	5.00	5.00

Nos. C430-C432 had limited distribution.

Souvenir Sheet

ICAO, 30th Anniv. and 1st Powered
Flight, 75th Anniv. — AP115

Designs: a, Concorde, Dornier DO-x. b,
Graf Zeppelin, Wright Brothers' Flyer. c,
Space shuttle and De Pinedo's plane.

1978, June 13
C433	Sheet of 3	22.50	22.50
a.-c.	AP115 1p any single	6.00	6.00

No. C433 had limited distribution.

Souvenir Sheet

World Cup Soccer Championships,
Argentina — AP116

1978, June 13   Perf. 12
C434	Sheet of 3	45.00	45.00
a.	AP116 50c multicolored	4.00	4.00
b.	AP116 1.50p multicolored	11.00	11.00
c.	AP116 2p multicolored	16.00	16.00

No. C434 had limited distribution.

No. C428 Overprinted in Black

1978, Aug. 28
C435	AP114 8p multicolored	6.00	3.00

No. C435 had limited distribution.

Madonna and Child Type of 1979
Various Madonna and Child etchings by
Albrecht Dürer with Intl. Year of the Child
emblem at: a, UL. b, UR.

Wmk. 332
1979, June 18   Litho.   Perf. 12½
C436	A390 1.50p Sheet of 2, #a-b	22.50	22.50

No. C436 had limited distribution.

Boiso
Lanza,
Wright
Brothers
AP117

75th anniv. of powered flight.

1979, June 18   Perf. 12½
C437	AP117 1.80p multicolored	2.75	1.50

No. C437 had limited distribution.
Issued in sheet of 24 containing 6 blocks of
4r with margin around. See Nos. 1040-1042.

Souvenir Sheet

1982 World Cup Soccer
Championships, Spain — AP118

1979, June 18   Perf. 12
C438	Sheet of 3	32.50	32.50
a.	AP118 50c Jules Rimet cup	2.50	2.50
b.	AP118 2.50p Uruguay flag	10.00	10.00
c.	AP118 3p Espana '82	14.00	14.00

No. C438 had limited distribution.

AIR POST SEMI-POSTAL STAMPS

Catalogue values for unused
stamps in this section are for
Never Hinged items.

Type of Semi-Postal Stamps, 1959
Wmk. 327
1959, Dec. 29   Litho.   *Perf. 11½*
CB1 SP2 38c + 10c brown & org   .25   .25
CB2 SP2 60c + 10c gray grn & org   .30   .30

Issued for national recovery.

SPECIAL DELIVERY STAMPS

No. 242 Overprinted MENSAJERIAS

1921, Aug.   Unwmk.   *Perf. 11½*
E1 A97 2c fawn   .55   .20
  a.   Double overprint   3.25

Caduceus — SD1

Imprint: "IMP. NACIONAL."

1922, Dec. 2   Wmk. 188
Size: 21x27mm
E2 SD1 2c light red   .40   .20

1924, Oct. 1
E3 SD1 2c pale ultra   .40   .20

1928   Unwmk.   *Perf. 11*
E4 SD1 2c light blue   .40   .20

Imprint: "IMPRA. NACIONAL."
1928-36   Wmk. 188
Size: 16½x19½mm.
E5 SD1 2c black, *green*   .20   .20
Unwmk.
E6 SD1 2c blue green ('29)   .20   .20
Perf. 11½, 12½
E7 SD1 2c blue ('36)   .20   .20
  Nos. E5-E7 (3)   .60   .60

1944, Oct. 23   *Perf. 12½*
E8 SD1 2c salmon pink   .25   .20

> Catalogue values for unused stamps in this section, from this point to the end of the section, are for Never Hinged items.

1947, Nov. 19
E9 SD1 2c red brown   .20   .20

No. E9 Surcharged with New Value
1957, Oct. 30
E10 SD1 5c on 2c red brown   .20   .20

LATE FEE STAMPS

Galleon and Modern Steamship — LF1

Wmk. Crossed Keys in Sheet
1936, May 18   Litho.   *Perf. 11*
I1 LF1 3c green   .20   .20
I2 LF1 5c violet   .20   .20
I3 LF1 6c blue green   .20   .20
I4 LF1 7c brown   .25   .25
I5 LF1 8c carmine   .50   .50
I6 LF1 12c deep blue   .65   .65
  Nos. I1-I6 (6)   2.00   2.00

POSTAGE DUE STAMPS

D1

1902   Unwmk.   Engr.   *Perf. 14 to 15*
Size: 21¼x18½mm
J1 D1 1c blue green   .40   .20
J2 D1 2c carmine   .40   .20
J3 D1 4c gray violet   .65   .20
J4 D1 10c dark blue   .95   .25
J5 D1 20c ocher   1.50   .80
  Nos. J1-J5 (5)   3.90   1.65

Surcharged in Red

1904
J6 D1 1c on 10c dk bl   .80   .80
  a.   Inverted surcharge   7.75   7.75

1913-15   Litho.   *Perf. 11½*
Size: 22½x20mm
J7 D1 1c lt grn   .50   .20
J8 D1 2c rose red   .50   .25
J9 D1 4c dl vio   .65   .25
J10 D1 6c dp brn   .80   .40
Size: 21¼x19mm
J11 D1 10c dl bl   .80   .40
  Nos. J7-J11 (5)   3.25   1.50

Imprint: "Imprenta Nacional"
1922
Size: 20x17mm
J12 D1 1c bl grn   .20   .20
J13 D1 2c red   .25   .20
J14 D1 3c red brn   .40   .25
J15 D1 4c brn vio   .25   .20
J16 D1 5c blue   .40   .25
J17 D1 10c gray grn   .40   .20
  Nos. J12-J17 (6)   1.90   1.30

1926-27   Wmk. 188   *Perf. 11*
Size: 20x17mm
J18 D1 1c bl grn ('27)   .40   .20
J19 D1 3c red brn ('27)   .40   .20
J20 D1 5c slate blue   .40   .20
J21 D1 6c light brown   .40   .40
  Nos. J18-J21 (4)   1.60   1.00

1929   Unwmk.   *Perf. 10½, 11*
J22 D1 1c blue green   .20   .20
J23 D1 10c gray green   .40   .20

Figure of Value Redrawn
(Flat on sides)
1932   Wmk. 188
J24 D1 6c yel brn   .40   .25

Imprint: "Casa A. Barreiro Ramos S. A."
1935   Unwmk.   Litho.   *Perf. 12½*
Size: 20x17mm
J25 D1 4c violet   .40   .40
J26 D1 5c rose   .40   .40

Type of 1935
Imprint: "Imprenta Nacional" at right
1938
J27 D1 1c blue green   .20   .20
J28 D1 2c red brown   .20   .20
J29 D1 3c deep pink   .20   .20
J30 D1 4c light violet   .20   .20
J31 D1 5c blue   .20   .20
J32 D1 8c rose   .20   .20
  Nos. J27-J32 (6)   1.20   1.20

OFFICIAL STAMPS

Regular Issues
Handstamped in Black, Red or Blue

Many double and inverted impressions exist of the handstamped overprints on Nos. O1-O83. Prices are the same as for normal stamps or slightly more.

On Stamps of 1877-79
1880-82   Unwmk.   *Rouletted 8*
O1 A9 1c red brown   4.00   3.50
O2 A10 5c green   3.00   2.50
O3 A11 20c bister   2.50   2.00
O4 A11 50c black   18.00   15.00
O5 A12 1p blue   20.00   16.00
  Nos. O1-O5 (5)   47.50   39.00

On No. 44
Rouletted 6
O6 A9 1c brown ('81)   4.75   4.25

On Nos. 43-43A
Rouletted 8
O7 A11 50c black (R)   17.00   16.00
O8 A12 1p blue (R)   22.50   20.00

On Nos. 45, 41, 37a
Perf. 12½
O9 A13 7c blue (R) ('81)   3.25   2.50

Rouletted 8
O10 A11 10c ver (Bl)   1.75   1.50

Perf. 13½
O11 A8b 15c yellow (Bl)   5.00   4.00

On Nos. 46-47
1883   *Perf. 12½*
O12 A14 1c green   6.00   6.00
O13 A14a 2c rose   7.00   7.00

On Nos. 50-51
Perf. 12½, 12x12½, 13
O14 A17 5c blue (R)   3.00   3.00
  a.   Imperf., pair   4.50
O15 A18 10c brown (Bl)   5.00   5.00
  a.   Imperf., pair   6.00

No. 48 Handstamped

1884   *Perf. 12½*
O16 A15 1c green   29.00   25.00

Overprinted Type "a" in Black
On Nos. 48-49
1884   *Perf. 12, 12x12½, 13*
O17 A15 1c green   29.00   25.00
O18 A16 2c red   10.00   8.00

On Nos. 53-56
Rouletted 8
O19 A11 1c on 10c ver   1.50   1.25
  a.   Small "1" (No. 53a)   5.00

Perf. 12½
O20 A14a 2c rose   5.00   5.00
O21 A22 5c ultra   5.00   5.00
O22 A23 5c blue   3.75   1.75
  Nos. O17-O22 (6)   54.25   46.00

On Stamps of 1884-88
1884-89   Rouletted 8
O23 A24 1c gray   9.25   4.25
O24 A24 1c green ('88)   1.90   .95
O25 A24 1c olive grn   2.50   1.50
O26 A24a 2c vermilion   .80   .50
O27 A24a 2c rose ('88)   1.75   .95
O28 A24b 5c slate blue   1.75   .95
O29 A24b 5c slate bl, *bl*   5.00   2.50
O30 A24b 5c violet ('88)   5.00   2.50
O31 A24b 5c lt blue ('89)   5.00   2.50
O32 A25 7c dk brown   5.00   2.50
O33 A25 7c orange ('89)   2.50   1.50
O34 A26 10c olive brn   1.50   .70
O35 A30 10c violet ('89)   12.50   7.50
O36 A27 20c red violet   2.50   1.50
O37 A27 20c bister brn ('89)   12.50   5.50
O38 A28 25c gray violet   3.50   2.50
O39 A28 25c vermilion ('89)   12.50   8.00
  Nos. O23-O39 (17)   85.45   46.30

The OFICIAL handstamp, type "a," was also applied to No. 73, the 5c violet with "Provisorio" overprint, but it was not regularly issued.

On No. 71
1887   Rouletted 9
O40 A29 10c lilac   5.00

No. O40 was not regularly issued.

On Stamps of 1889-1899
Perf. 12½ to 15 and Compound
1890-1900
O41 A32 1c green   .80   .80
O43 A32 1c blue ('95)   2.00   2.00
O44 A33 2c rose   .80   .80
O45 A33 2c red brn ('95)   2.50   2.50
O46 A33 2c orange ('00)   .80   .80
O47 A34 5c deep blue   1.50   1.50
O48 A34 5c rose ('95)   2.00   2.00
O49 A35 7c bister brown   1.25   .80
O50 A35 7c green ('95)   25.00
O51 A36 10c blue green   1.25   .80
O52 A36 10c orange ('95)   25.00
O53 A37 20c orange   1.25   .80
O54 A37 20c brown ('95)   25.00
O55 A38 25c red brown   1.25   .80
O56 A38 25c ver ('95)   55.00
O57 A39 50c lt blue   4.50   4.50
O58 A39 50c lilac ('95)   5.50   5.50
O59 A40 1p lilac   7.00   5.00
O60 A40 1p lt blue ('95)   40.00   22.50

Nos. O50, O52, O54, O56 and O60 were not regularly issued.

On No. 99
1891   Rouletted 8
O61 A24b 5c violet   1.50   1.25
  a.   "1391"   9.00

On Stamps of 1895-99
Perf. 12½ to 15 and Compound
1895-1900
O62 A51 1c bister   .60   .50
O63 A51 1c slate blue ('97)   1.25   .55
O64 A52 2c blue   .25   .55
O65 A52 2c claret ('97)   1.25   .55
O66 A53 5c red   .80   .55
O67 A53 5c green ('97)   1.25   .55
O68 A53 5c grnsh blue ('00)   .95   .75
O69 A54 7c deep green   .50   .50
O70 A55 10c brown   .50   .50
O71 A56 20c green & blk   .80   .80
O72 A56 20c claret & blk ('97)   4.50   2.25
O73 A57 25c red brn & blk   .80   .80
O74 A57 25c pink & bl ('97)   4.50   2.25
O75 A58 50c blue & blk   .95   .95
O76 A58 50c grn & brn ('97)   5.75   2.75
O77 A59 1p org brn & blk   4.75   4.75
O78 A59 1p yel brn & bl ('97)   9.25   5.75
  a.   Inverted overprint
  Nos. O62-O78 (17)   38.65   25.10

On Nos. 133-135
1897, Sept.
O79 A62 1c brown vio & blk   1.25   1.00
O80 A63 5c pale bl & blk   1.75   1.00
O81 A64 5c red lake & blk   1.75   1.10
  Nos. O79-O81 (3)   4.75   3.10

On Nos. 136-137
Perf. 12½ to 15 and Compound
1897-1900
O82 A68 10c red   2.50   1.50
O83 A68 10c red lilac ('00)   1.25   1.25

Regular Issue of 1900-01 Overprinted

1901   *Perf. 14 to 16*
O84 A72 1c yellow green   .50   .20
O85 A75 2c vermilion   .60   .20
O86 A73 5c dull blue   .60   .20
O87 A76 7c brown orange   .85   .50
O88 A74 10c gray violet   .90   .55
O89 A37 20c lt blue   7.75   4.00
O90 A38 25c bister brown   1.50   .80
O91 A40 1p deep green   10.00   5.75
  a.   Inverted overprint   12.50   8.00
  Nos. O84-O91 (8)   22.70   12.20

Most of the used official stamps of 1901-1928 have been punched with holes of various shapes, in addition to the postal cancellations.

Regular Issue of 1904-05 Overprinted

1905   *Perf. 11½*
O92 A79 1c green   .50   .20
O93 A80 2c orange red   .50   .20
O94 A81 5c deep blue   .50   .20
O95 A82 10c dark violet   1.00   .40

O96	A83	20c gray green	3.00	1.00
a.		Inverted overprint		
O97	A84	25c olive bister	2.00	.80
		Nos. O92-O97 (6)	7.50	2.80

Regular Issues of 1904-07 Overprinted

1907, Mar.

O98	A79	1c green	.25	.20
O99	A86	5c deep blue	.25	.20
O100	A86	7c orange brown	.25	.20
O101	A82	10c dark violet	.25	.20
O102	A83	20c gray green	.40	.35
a.		Inverted overprint	4.00	
O103	A84	25c olive bister	.50	.40
O104	A86	50c rose	.95	.70
		Nos. O98-O104 (7)	2.85	2.25

Regular Issues of 1900-10 Overprinted

1910, July 15   Perf. 14½ to 16

O105	A75	2c vermilion	8.50	4.00
O106	A73	5c slate green	5.00	3.00
O107	A74	10c gray violet	2.50	1.25
O108	A37	20c grnsh blue	2.50	1.25
O109	A38	25c bister brown	4.25	2.40

Perf. 11½

O110	A86	50c rose	5.75	2.50
a.		Inverted overprint	20.00	15.00
		Nos. O105-O110 (6)	28.50	14.40

Peace—O1

1911, Feb. 18   Litho.

O111	O1	2c red brown	.40	.25
O112	O1	5c dark blue	.40	.40
O113	O1	8c slate	.40	.60
O114	O1	20c gray brown	.55	.95
O115	O1	23c claret	.80	.95
O116	O1	50c orange	1.50	1.25
O117	O1	1p red	4.00	1.50
		Nos. O111-O117 (7)	8.05	5.90

Regular Issue of 1912-15 Overprinted

1915, Sept. 16

O118	A90	2c carmine	.55	.40
O119	A90	5c dark blue	.55	.40
O120	A90	8c ultra	.55	.40
O121	A90	20c dark brown	1.25	.50
O122	A91	23c dark blue	4.00	3.50
O123	A91	50c orange	6.00	3.50
O124	A91	1p vermilion	8.00	4.00
		Nos. O118-O124 (7)	20.90	12.70

Regular Issue of 1919 Overprinted

1919, Dec. 25

O125	A95	2c red & black	.80	.40
a.		Inverted overprint	3.50	
O126	A95	5c ultra & blk	.95	.40
O127	A95	8c gray bl & lt brn	.95	.40
a.		Inverted overprint	3.50	
O128	A95	20c brown & blk	2.00	.80
O129	A95	23c green & brn	2.00	.80
O130	A95	50c brown & bl	4.00	2.00
O131	A95	1p dull red & bl	10.00	4.00
a.		Double overprint	15.00	
		Nos. O125-O131 (7)	20.70	8.80

Regular Issue of 1923 Overprinted

1924   Wmk. 189   Perf. 12½

O132	A100	2c violet	.20	.20
O133	A100	5c light blue	.20	.20
O134	A100	12c deep blue	.30	.20
O135	A100	20c buff	.40	.20
O136	A100	36c blue green	1.75	1.25
O137	A100	50c orange	3.50	2.50
O138	A100	1p pink	6.25	5.00
O139	A100	2p lt green	12.00	10.00
		Nos. O132-O139 (8)	24.60	19.55

Same Overprint on Regular Issue of 1924

1926-27   Unwmk.   Imperf.

O140	A100	2c rose lilac	.40	.20
O141	A100	5c pale blue	.60	.20
O142	A100	8c pink ('27)	.80	.20
O143	A100	12c slate blue	.95	.20
O144	A100	20c brown	2.00	.40
O145	A100	36c dull rose	3.00	.95
		Nos. O140-O145 (6)	7.75	2.15

Regular Issue of 1924 Overprinted

1928   Perf. 12½

O146	A100	2c rose lilac	1.50	.95
O147	A100	8c pink	1.50	.50
O148	A100	20c turq blue	2.00	.50
		Nos. O146-O148 (3)	5.00	1.95

Since 1928, instead of official stamps, Uruguay has used envelopes with "S. O." printed on them, and stamps of many issues which are punched with various designs such as star or crescent.

NEWSPAPER STAMPS

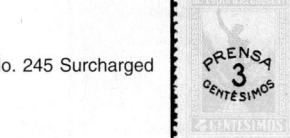

No. 245 Surcharged

1922, June 1   Unwmk.   Perf. 11½

P1	A97	3c on 4c orange	.40	.40
a.		Inverted surcharge	9.25	9.25
b.		Double surcharge	2.50	2.50

Nos. 235-237 Surcharged

1924, June 1   Perf. 14½

P2	A96	3c on 2c car & blk	.40	.40
P3	A96	6c on 4c red org & bl	.40	.40
P4	A96	9c on 5c bl & brn	.40	.40
		Nos. P2-P4 (3)	1.20	1.20

Nos. 288, 291, 293 Overprinted or Surcharged in Red:

1926   Imperf.

P5	A100	3c gray green	.80	.25
a.		Double overprint	1.00	1.00
P6	A100	9c on 10c turq bl	.95	.40
a.		Double surcharge	1.00	1.00
P7	A100	15c light violet	1.25	.50
		Nos. P5-P7 (3)	3.00	1.15

PARCEL POST STAMPS

Mercury — PP1

Imprint: "IMPRENTA NACIONAL"

Perf. 11½

1922, Jan. 15   Litho.   Unwmk.

Size: 20x29½mm

Inscribed "Exterior"

Q1	PP1	5c grn, *straw*	.20	.20
Q2	PP1	10c grn, *bl gray*	.40	.20
Q3	PP1	20c grn, *rose*	2.00	.55
Q4	PP1	30c grn, *grn*	2.00	.20
Q5	PP1	50c grn, *blue*	3.50	.40
Q6	PP1	1p grn, *org*	5.00	1.50
		Nos. Q1-Q6 (6)	13.10	3.05

Inscribed "Interior"

Q7	PP1	5c grn, *straw*	.25	.20
Q8	PP1	10c grn, *bl gray*	.25	.20
Q9	PP1	20c grn, *rose*	1.00	.25
Q10	PP1	30c grn, *grn*	1.40	.25
Q11	PP1	50c grn, *blue*	2.25	.35
Q12	PP1	1p grn, *org*	5.75	1.25
		Nos. Q7-Q12 (6)	10.90	2.50

Imprint: "IMP. NACIONAL" Inscribed "Exterior"

1926, Jan. 20   Perf. 11½

Q13	PP1	20c grn, *rose*	1.75	.50

Inscribed "Interior"

Perf. 11

Q14	PP1	5c grn, *yellow*	.40	.20
Q15	PP1	10c grn, *bl gray*	.50	.20
Q16	PP1	20c grn, *rose*	1.00	.20
Q17	PP1	30c grn, *bl grn*	1.75	.40
		Nos. Q13-Q17 (5)	5.40	1.50

Inscribed "Exterior"

1926   Perf. 11½

Q18	PP1	5c blk, *straw*	.40	.20
Q19	PP1	10c blk, *bl gray*	.50	.20
Q20	PP1	20c blk, *rose*	1.10	.20

Inscribed "Interior"

Q21	PP1	5c blk, *straw*	.40	.20
Q22	PP1	10c blk, *bl gray*	.50	.20
Q23	PP1	20c blk, *rose*	1.00	.20
Q24	PP1	30c blk, *bl grn*	1.75	.40
		Nos. Q18-Q24 (7)	5.65	1.60

PP2   PP3

Perf. 11, 11½

1927, Feb. 22   Wmk. 188

Q25	PP2	1c dp bl	.20	.20
Q26	PP2	2c lt grn	.20	.20
Q27	PP2	4c violet	.20	.20
Q28	PP2	5c red	.25	.20
Q29	PP2	10c dk brn	.40	.20
Q30	PP2	20c orange	.60	.40
		Nos. Q25-Q30 (6)	1.85	1.40

See Nos. Q35-Q38, Q51-Q54.

1928, Nov. 20   Perf. 11

Size: 15x20mm

Q31	PP3	5c blk, *straw*	.20	.20
Q32	PP3	10c blk, *gray blue*	.20	.20
Q33	PP3	20c blk, *rose*	.50	.20
Q34	PP3	30c blk, *green*	.80	.20
		Nos. Q31-Q34 (4)	1.70	.80

Type of 1927 Issue

1929-30   Unwmk.   Perf. 11, 12½

Q35	PP2	1c violet	.20	.20
Q36	PP2	1c ultra ('30)	.20	.20
Q37	PP2	2c bl grn ('30)	.20	.20
Q38	PP2	5c red ('30)	.20	.20
		Nos. Q35-Q38 (4)	.80	.80

Nos. Q35-Q38, and possibly later issues, occasionally show parts of a papermaker's watermark.

PP4

1929, July 27   Wmk. 188   Perf. 11

Q39	PP4	10c orange	.50	.50
Q40	PP4	15c slate blue	.50	.50
Q41	PP4	20c ol brn	.50	.50
Q42	PP4	25c rose red	1.00	.50
Q43	PP4	50c dark gray	2.00	1.00
Q44	PP4	75c violet	8.00	6.00
Q45	PP4	1p gray green	7.50	3.00
		Nos. Q39-Q45 (7)	20.00	12.00

For overprints see Nos. Q57-Q63.

Ship and Train — PP5   Numeral of Value — PP6

1938-39   Unwmk.   Perf. 12½

Q46	PP5	10c scarlet	.40	.20
Q47	PP5	20c dk bl	.60	.20
Q48	PP5	30c lt vio ('39)	.95	.20
Q49	PP5	50c green	1.75	.20
Q50	PP5	1p brn org	2.50	1.10
		Nos. Q46-Q50 (5)	6.20	1.90

See #Q70-Q73, Q80, Q88-Q90, Q92-Q93, Q95.

Type of 1927 Redrawn

1942-55?   Litho.   Perf. 12½

Q51	PP2	1c vio ('55)		
Q52	PP2	2c bl grn	.20	.20
Q54	PP2	5c lt red ('44)	.20	.20

The vertical and horizontal lines of the design have been strengthened, the "2" redrawn, etc. No. Q51 has oval "O" in CENTESIMO, 2¼mm from frame line at right; No. Q35 has round "O" 1¾mm from frame line.

1943, Apr. 28   Engr.

Q55	PP6	1c dk car rose	.20	.20
Q56	PP6	2c grnsh blk	.20	.20

Parcel Post Stamps of 1929 Overprinted in Black

1943, Dec. 15   Wmk. 188   Perf. 11

Q57	PP4	10c orange	1.00	.50
Q58	PP4	15c slate blue	1.00	.50
Q59	PP4	20c olive brn	1.00	.50
Q60	PP4	25c rose red	1.50	1.00
Q61	PP4	50c dk gray	2.50	2.00
Q62	PP4	75c violet	5.00	4.00
Q63	PP4	1p gray grn	8.00	4.50
		Nos. Q57-Q63 (7)	20.00	13.00

Catalogue values for unused stamps in this section, from this point to the end of the section, are for Never Hinged items.

Bank of the Republic — PP7   University — PP8

Perf. 12½

1945, Sept. 5   Litho.   Unwmk.

Q64	PP7	1c green	.20	.20
Q65	PP8	2c brt vio	.20	.20

See Nos. Q77-Q79, Q84.

Custom
House — PP9

Type A141
Overprinted

1946, Dec. 11   *Perf. 11½*
Q66 PP9 5c yel brn & bl   .20 .20

Red Overprint

1946, Dec. 27   *Perf. 12½*
Q67 A141 1p light blue   .70 .20
     See Nos. Q69, Q76.

Mail
Coach — PP11

Type A141
Overprinted

1946, Dec. 23
Q68 PP11 5p red & ol brn   12.00 5.00

Black Overprint

1947
Q69 A141 2c dull violet brn   .20 .20
     See Nos. Q74-Q76.

Type of 1938

1947-52	**Unwmk.**	*Perf. 12½*
Q70 PP5	5c brown org ('52)	.20 .20
Q71 PP5	10c violet	.20 .20
Q72 PP5	20c vermilion	.25 .20
Q73 PP5	30c blue	.50 .20
	Nos. Q70-Q73 (4)	1.15 .80

Type of 1947
Black Overprint

1948-49		
Q74 A141	1c rose lilac ('49)	.20 .20
Q75 A141	5c ultra	.20 .20
Q76 A141	5p rose carmine	4.00 1.75
	Nos. Q74-Q76 (3)	4.40 2.15

Types of 1945

1950		
Q77 PP8	1c vermilion	.20 .20
Q78 PP7	2c chalky blue	.20 .20

1952   *Perf. 11*
Q79 PP7 10c blue green   .20 .20

Type of 1938-39

1954   *Perf. 12½*
Q80 PP5 20c carmine   .20 .20

Custom
House — PP13

1p, State Railroad Administration Building.

1955   **Unwmk.**   **Litho.**   *Perf. 12½*
Q81 PP13 5c brown   .20 .20
Q82 PP13 1p light ultra   2.00 1.50
   See Nos. Q83, Q85-Q86, Q96. For
surcharge see No. Q87.

Types of 1945 and 1955

Design: 20c, Solis Theater.

1956-57		*Perf. 11*
Q83 PP13	5c gray ('57)	.30 .20
Q84 PP7	10c lt olive grn	.20 .20
Q85 PP13	20c yellow	.20 .20
Q86 PP13	20c lt red brn ('57)	.20 .20
	Nos. Q83-Q86 (4)	.90 .80

No. Q83 Surcharged with New Value
in Red

1957
Q87 PP13 30c on 5c gray   .20 .20

Type of 1938-39

1957-60   **Wmk. 327**   *Perf. 11*
Q88 PP5 20c lt blue ('59)   .20 .20
         Unwmk.
Q89 PP5 30c red lilac   .20 .20
         Perf. 12½
Q90 PP5 1p dk blue ('60)   .25 .25
    Nos. Q88-Q90 (3)   .65 .65
  Nos. Q88 and Q93 are in slightly larger for-
mat–17¼x21mm instead of 16x19½mm.

National
Printing
Works
PP14

1960, Mar. 23   **Wmk. 327**   *Perf. 11*
Q91 PP14 30c yellow green   .20 .20

Type of 1938-39

1962-63   **Wmk. 332**   *Perf. 11*
Q92 PP5 50c slate green   .20 .20
         Perf. 10½
Q93 PP5 1p blue grn ('63)   .50 .50

No. C158
Surcharged

1965   **Unwmk.**   *Perf. 11*
Q94 AP12 5p on 84c orange   .35 .20
  For use on regular and air post parcels.

Types of 1938-55

1p, State Railroad Administration Building.

1966   **Litho.**   *Perf. 10½*
Q95 PP5 10c blue green   .20 .20
         Wmk. 327
Q96 PP13 1p brown   .20 .20

No. C184
Surcharged in Red

1966   **Unwmk.**   *Perf. 11*
Q97 AP21 1p on 38c black   .20 .20

Plane and
Bus — PP15

Design: 20p, Plane facing left and bus;
"Encomiendas" on top.

         Wmk. 332
1969, July 8   **Litho.**   *Perf. 12*
Q98 PP15 10p blk, crim & bl grn   .20 .20
Q99 PP15 20p bl, blk & yel   .40 .20

No. B7
Surcharged

1971, Feb. 3   **Wmk. 327**   *Perf. 11½*
Q100 SP2 60c on 1p + 10c   1.25 .60

No. 761 Surcharged in Red

1971, Nov. 12   **Wmk. 332**   *Perf. 12*
Q101 A226 60c on 6p lt grn & blk   .45 .25

Nos. 770-771 Surcharged

1972, Nov. 6   **Litho.**   *Perf. 12*
Q102 A233 1p on 6p multi (#770)   1.00 .55
Q103 A233 1p on 6p multi (#771)   1.00 .55
   a.   Pair, #Q102-Q103   2.00 1.10
    See note after No. 771.

Parcels and
Arrows
PP16

Old Mail
Truck
PP17

Designs: Early means of mail transport.

1974	**Wmk. 332**	**Litho.**	*Perf. 12*
Q104 PP16	75p shown		.20 .20
Q105 PP17	100p shown		.40 .25
Q106 PP17	150p Steam engine		.95 .95
Q107 PP17	300p Side-wheeler		.90 .55
Q108 PP17	500p Plane		1.40 .80
	Nos. Q104-Q108 (5)		3.85 2.75

Issue dates: 75p, Feb. 13; others, Mar. 6.

UZBEKISTAN

ˌuz-ˌbe-ki-ˈstan

LOCATION — Central Asia, bounded
by Kazakhstan, Turkmenistan, Tajikistan, Afghanistan and Kyrgyzstan
GOVT. — Independent republic, member of the Commonwealth of Independent States
AREA — 172,741 sq. mi.
POP. — 25,155,064 (2001 est.)
CAPITAL — Tashkent (Toshkent)

  With the breakup of the Soviet Union
on Dec. 26, 1991, Uzbekistan and ten
former Soviet republics established the
Commonwealth of Independent States.

100 Kopecks = 1 Ruble
100 Tiyin = 1 Sum

Princess Nadira
(1792-1842) — A1

         Perf. 11½x12
1992, May 7   **Unwmk.**   **Photo.**
1   A1 20k multicolored   .30 .30

Melitaea
Acreina
A2

1992, Aug. 31   **Litho.**   *Perf. 12*
2   A2 1r multicolored   .30 .30

Independence from Soviet Union, 1st
Anniv. — A3

1992, Sept. 25   **Photo.**   *Perf. 12*
3   A3 1r multicolored   .30 .30

Khiva
Mosque,
19th
Cent. — A4

1992, Oct. 20   *Perf. 11½*
4   A4 50k multicolored   .30 .30

Samarkand — A5

1992, Oct. 28   **Litho.**   *Perf. 13x13½*
5   A5 10r multicolored   .50 .50
  Winner of 1992 Aga Khan Award for
Architecture.

Samovar,
19th
Cent. — A6

1992, Nov. 20   *Perf. 12x11½*
6   A6 50k multicolored   .35 .35

Fauna
A7

Designs: 1r, Teratoscincus scincus. No. 8,
Naja oxiana. No. 9, Ondatra zibethica, vert. 3r,

Pandion haliaetus, vert. 5r, Remiz pendulinus, vert. 10r, Dryomys nitedula, vert. 15r, Varanus griseus. 20r, Cervus elaphus baktrianus.

1993, Mar. 12   Litho.   Perf. 12

7	A7	1r multicolored	.20	.20
8	A7	2r multicolored	.20	.20
9	A7	2r multicolored	.20	.20
10	A7	3r multicolored	.20	.20
11	A7	5r multicolored	.20	.20
12	A7	10r multicolored	.35	.35
13	A7	15r multicolored	.75	.75
		Nos. 7-13 (7)	2.10	2.10

Souvenir Sheet

14	A7	20r multicolored	.75	.75

Russia Nos. 4596-4600, 5838, 5841-5843, 5984 Surcharged in Vio Bl, Brt Bl, Bl, Red, Blk and Grn

a

Methods and perfs as before

1993

15	A2765	2r on 1k (#5838, BB)	.50	.50
16	A2138	8r on 4k (#4599, Bl)	.45	.45
17	A2138	15r on 2k (#4597)	4.00	4.00
18	A2138	15r on 2k (#5984)	4.00	4.00
19	A2765	15r on 3k (#5839, R)	4.00	4.00
20	A2765	15r on 4k (#4520, V)	4.00	4.00
21	A2765	15r on 4k (#5840, R)	4.00	4.00
22	A2765	15r on 5k (#5841)	4.00	4.00
23	A2139	15r on 6k (#4600, R)	4.00	4.00
24	A2765	15r on 7k (#5985a, R)	4.00	4.00
25	A2765	15r on 10k (#5842)	4.00	4.00
26	A2765	15r on 15k (#5843, R)	4.00	4.00
27	A2138	20r on 4k (#4599, Bk)	.65	.65
28	A2139	30r on 3k (#4598, G)	.65	.65
28A	A2138	100r on 1k (#4596, R)	.80	.80
29	A2138	500r on 1k (#4596, Bl)	5.00	5.00
		Nos. 15-29 (16)	48.05	48.05

No. 18 exists imperf. Numbers have been reserved for additional stamps with uncertain status.

Flag and Coat of Arms — A8

Perf. 12x12½, 11½x12 (#33)

1993, June 10   Litho.

30	A8	8r multicolored	.25	.25
31	A8	15r multicolored	.30	.30
33	A8	50r multicolored	.80	.80
34	A8	100r multicolored	1.75	1.75
		Nos. 30-34 (4)	3.10	3.10

No. 33 is 19x26½mm.

Flowers — A9

1993, Sept. 10   Perf. 12

38	A9	20r Dianthus uzbekis-tanicus	.20	.20
39	A9	20r Colchicum kesselr-ingii	.20	.20
40	A9	25r Crocus alatavicus	.30	.30
41	A9	25r Salvia bucharica	.30	.30

42	A9	30r Tulipa kaufmanniana	.35	.35
43	A9	30r Tulipa greigii	.35	.35
		Nos. 38-43 (6)	1.70	1.70

Souvenir Sheet

44	A9	50r Tulip	1.00	1.00

Coat of Arms — A10

1994, July 2   Litho.   Perf. 12

45	A10	1t green	.20	.20

Perf. 11½x12

46	A10	75s claret	.25	.25

1995   Litho.   Perf. 14

47	A10	2s green	.80	.80

Size: 20x33mm

48	A10	3s carmine	.80	.80
49	A10	6s carmine	1.25	1.25
49A	A10	15s blue	2.00	2.00

Denomination Shown with Decimal

50	A10	3s carmine	.25	.25
51	A10	6s blue	1.25	1.25
		Nos. 45-51 (8)	6.80	6.80

Issued: 15s, 12/26; others, 4/18.
See Nos. 151A-154, 228-237.

Statue of Tamerlane, Tashkent — A10a

1994, Sept. 1   Litho.   Perf. 12½x12

52	A10a	20t multicolored	.40	.40

Bakhouddin, 675th Anniv. — A11

1994, Aug. 1   Perf. 12½x12

55	A11	100s multi + label	.50	.50

Souvenir Sheet

President's Cup Intl. Tennis Tournament, Tashkent — A12

1994, June 3   Perf. 12x12½

56	A12	500s multicolored	1.25	1.25

Ulugh Beg (1394-1449), Astronomer — A13

30t, Portals of Samarkand. 35t, Portals of Bukhara. 40t, Globe, astrolabe. 45t, Statue. 60t, Portrait.

1994, Sept. 15   Litho.   Perf. 12x12½

57	A13	30t multi + label	.20	.20
58	A13	35t multi + label	.20	.20
59	A13	40t multi + label	.20	.20
60	A13	45t multi + label	.50	.50
		Nos. 57-60 (4)	1.10	1.10

Souvenir Sheet

61	A13	60t multicolored	1.00	1.00

Russia Nos. 4596, 5113, 5839, 5840, 5843, 5984 Surcharged in Red Violet or Red

b

Methods and perfs as before

1995, Jan.

61A	A2138(a)	2s on 1k (#4596, R)	1.50	1.50
61B	A2765(a)	2s on 3k (#5839, R)	1.50	1.50
61C	A2765(b)	200s on 2k (#5984)	1.50	1.50
61D	A2765(b)	200s on 4k (#5840)	1.50	1.50
61E	A2436(b)	200s on 5k (#5113)	1.50	1.50
61F	A2765(b)	200s on 15k (#5843)	1.50	1.50
		Nos. 61A-61F (6)	9.00	9.00

No. 61C exists imperf.

Souvenir Sheet

End of World War II, 50th Anniv. — A14

1995, May 8   Litho.   Perf. 12

62	A14	20s multicolored	2.25	2.25

Souvenir Sheet

UPU — A15

1995, Sept. 21

63	A15	20s multicolored	2.00	2.00

Capra Falconeri A16

1995, Aug. 15   Perf. 12½

64	A16	6s shown	.85	.50
65	A16	10s Three on mountain	1.25	.75
66	A16	10s Up close	1.25	.75
67	A16	15s Lying down	2.10	1.25
		Nos. 64-67 (4)	5.45	3.25

World Wildlife Fund.

Intl. Tennis Tournament, Tashkent '95 — A17

1995, Aug. 25   Perf. 14

68	A17	10s multicolored	1.40	1.40

Silk Road Architecture A19

Designs: 6s, Mosque, 15th cent. No. 71, Blue-domed mosque, ruins, 15th cent. No. 72, Mosque with 4 minarets, 19th cent. No. 73, Cylindrical-style mosque, 19th cent. 20s, Map of mosque sites, camel, mosque.

1995, Aug. 28   Litho.   Perf. 12x12½

70	A19	6s multicolored	1.00	1.00
71	A19	10s multicolored	2.00	2.00
72	A19	10s multicolored	2.00	2.00
73	A19	15s multicolored	3.00	3.00
		Nos. 70-73 (4)	8.00	8.00

Souvenir Sheet

74	A19	20s multicolored	5.00	5.00

Folktales — A20

6s, Man wrestling with creature, woman spilling bowls. #76, Man looking at stork, nest of eggs. #77, Women watching man cut into watermelon full of gold coins. #78, Creature carrying woman. 15s, Man holding beads, parrot.

1995, Aug. 24

75	A20	6s multi + label	1.25	1.25
76	A20	10s multicolored	1.75	1.75
77	A20	10s multicolored	1.75	1.75
78	A20	10s multicolored	1.75	1.75
79	A20	15s multicolored	2.50	2.50
		Nos. 75-79 (5)	9.00	9.00

Moths A21

6s, Karanasa abramovi. #81, Colias roma-novi. #82, Parnassius delphius. #83, Neohip-parchia fatua. #84, Chasara staudingeri. #85, Colias wiskotti. 15s, Parnassius tianschanicus. 20s, Colias christophi.

1995, Oct. 10   Perf. 12½x12

80	A21	6s multicolored	1.25	1.25
81	A21	10s multicolored	2.00	2.00
82	A21	10s multicolored	2.00	2.00
83	A21	10s multicolored	2.00	2.00
84	A21	10s multicolored	2.00	2.00
85	A21	10s multicolored	2.00	2.00
86	A21	15s multicolored	3.00	3.00
		Nos. 80-86 (7)	14.25	14.25

Souvenir Sheet

87	A21	20s multicolored	3.00	3.00

Aircraft
A22

1995, Oct. 10
88	A22	6s JIN-2	1.25	1.25
89	A22	10s IL-76	2.00	2.00
90	A22	10s KA-22	2.00	2.00
91	A22	10s AN-8	2.00	2.00
92	A22	10s AN-22	2.00	2.00
93	A22	10s AN-12	2.00	2.00
94	A22	15s IL-114	3.25	3.25
		Nos. 88-94 (7)	14.50	14.50

Souvenir Sheet
95	A22	20s like No. 94	3.00	3.00

Wildlife from
Tashkent
Zoo — A23

Designs: 6s, Camelus ferus. No. 97, Aegupius monachus. No. 98, Ursus arctos isabellinus. No. 99, Zebra. No. 100, Macaca mulatta. No. 101, Pelecanus crispus. 15s, Loxodonta africana.
20s, Capra falconeri.

1995, Nov. 30   **Perf. 12x12½**
96	A23	6s multicolored	1.00	1.00
97	A23	10s multicolored	1.75	1.75
98	A23	10s multicolored	1.75	1.75
99	A23	10s multicolored	1.75	1.75
100	A23	10s multicolored	1.75	1.75
101	A23	10s multicolored	1.75	1.75
102	A23	15s multicolored	2.50	2.50
		Nos. 96-102 (7)	12.25	12.25

Souvenir Sheet
103	A23	20s multicolored	3.00	3.00

Wild
Animals
A24

Designs: 10s, Ovis ammon bocharensis. No. 105, Ovis ammon severtzov. No. 106, Cervus elaphus bactrianus. No. 107, Capra sibirica. No. 108, Ovis ammon karelini. No. 109, Ovis ammon cycloceros. 20s, Saiga tatarica.
25s, Gazella subgutturosa.

1996, Feb. 16   **Perf. 12½x12**
104	A24	10s multicolored	1.00	1.00
105	A24	15s multicolored	1.50	1.50
106	A24	15s multicolored	1.50	1.50
107	A24	15s multicolored	1.50	1.50
108	A24	15s multicolored	1.50	1.50
109	A24	15s multicolored	1.50	1.50
110	A24	20s multicolored	2.25	2.25
		Nos. 104-110 (7)	10.75	10.75

Souvenir Sheet
111	A24	25s multicolored	2.75	2.75

Painting
A25

1995, Oct.   Litho.   Perf. 12x12½
112	A25	15s multicolored	1.60	1.60

Souvenir Sheet

Save the Aral Sea — A26

a, 15s, Felis caracal. b, 15s, Salmo trutta aralensis. c, 20s, Hyaena hyaena. d, 20t, Pseudoscaphirynchus kaufmanni. e, 25t, Aspiolucius esocinus.

1996, May 15   **Perf. 14**
113	A26	Sheet of 5, #a.-e.	5.50	5.50

See Kazakhstan #145, Kyrgyzstan #107, Tadjikistan #91, Turkmenistan #52.

1996
Summer
Olympic
Games,
Atlanta
A27

1996, June 23   Litho.   Perf. 12½x12
114	A27	6s Soccer	.50	.50
115	A27	10s Equestrian event	1.00	1.00
116	A27	15s Boxing	1.25	1.25
117	A27	20s Cycling	2.00	2.00
		Nos. 114-117 (4)	4.75	4.75

Souvenir Sheet

Tamerlane (1336-1405) — A28

1996, Aug. 31   Litho.   Perf. 14
118	A28	20s multicolored	4.50	4.50
a.		Inscribed "1336-1404," perf 12x12½	5.50	5.50

Issued: No. 118a, 8/9/96.

Souvenir Sheet

Independence Day — A29

Illustration reduced.

1996, Aug. 27   Litho.   Perf. 12x12½
119	A29	20s multicolored	2.50	2.50

Tashkent Tennis
Cup Championship
A30

1996, Sept. 2   Litho.   Perf. 14
121	A30	12s green	7.50	7.50

A31

A32

1996, Sept. 18   **Perf. 14**
122	A31	15s Faijzulla Khodjaev	2.25	2.25

1996, Oct. 14   Litho.   Perf. 14
123	A32	15s black & buff	2.25	2.25

Abdurauf Fitrat (1886-1996).

Futuristic Space Travel — A33

9s, Shuttle-type vehicle. #126, Vehicle in front of sun. #127, Sun's rays, vehicle traveling left. #128, Large vehicle, sun in distance. #129, Saucer-shaped vehicle landing on planet. 25s, Two men in cockpit.
30s, Two different space vehicles.

1997, Mar. 17
124	A33	9s multi, vert.	.75	.75
125	A33	15s shown	1.25	1.25
126	A33	15s multi	1.25	1.25
127	A33	15s multi	1.25	1.25
128	A33	15s multi, vert.	1.25	1.25
129	A33	15s multi, vert.	1.25	1.25
130	A33	25s multi, vert.	1.50	1.50
		Nos. 124-130 (7)	8.50	8.50

Souvenir Sheet
131	A33	30s multi, vert.	5.50	5.50

Fairy Tales
A34

#132, Genie. #133, Bird. #134, Child holding mirror in front of couple. #135, Ape. #136, Face of creature, horse. #137, Large bird attacking deer. 30s, Two people kneeling before throne.
35s, Man on horse.

1997, Apr. 18
132	A34	15s multicolored	1.00	1.00
133	A34	15s multicolored	1.00	1.00
134	A34	20s multicolored	1.25	1.25
135	A34	20s multicolored	1.25	1.25
136	A34	25s multicolored	1.50	1.50
137	A34	25s multicolored	1.50	1.50
138	A34	30s multicolored	2.00	2.00
		Nos. 132-138 (7)	9.50	9.50

Souvenir Sheet
139	A34	35s multicolored	6.00	6.00

Abdulhamid
Sulaymon, Birth
Cent. — A35

1997, June 20
140	A35	6s lilac, black & gray	2.00	2.00

Pantera
Pardus
Tullianus
A36

Designs: No. 142, Yawning. No. 143, Stretching. 25s, Walking on fallen tree. 30s, With mouth open.

1997, May 28
141	A36	9s multicolored	.75	.75
142	A36	15s multicolored	1.40	1.40
143	A36	15s multicolored	1.40	1.40
144	A36	25s multicolored	2.50	2.50
		Nos. 141-144 (4)	6.05	6.05

Souvenir Sheet
145	A36	30s multicolored	3.00	3.00

No. 145 contains one 30x40mm stamp.

Sites on
Silk Road
A37

In Bukhara: No. 146, Ancient citadel. No. 147, Tomb of Ismail Samani, vert.
In Khiva: No. 148, Minaret, vert. No. 149, Fortress wall with open door.
No. 150, Mosque, Bukhara. No. 151, Minaret, Khiva, diff., vert.

1997   Litho.   Perf. 14
146	A37	15s multicolored	1.25	1.25
147	A37	15s multicolored	1.25	1.25
148	A37	15s multicolored	1.25	1.25
149	A37	15s multicolored	1.25	1.25
		Nos. 146-149 (4)	5.00	5.00

Souvenir Sheets
150	A37	30s multicolored	2.50	2.50
151	A37	30s multicolored	2.50	2.50

Issued: Nos. 146-147, 150, 10/7; Nos. 148-149, 151, 10/8.

Arms Type of 1994 Redrawn

1998   Litho.   Perf. 14
Size: 14x22mm
151A	A10	2s green	.35	.35
152	A10	3s carmine	.50	.50
153	A10	6s green	.70	.70
153A	A10	12s green	2.25	2.25
153B	A10	15s red	1.40	1.40
154	A10	45s blue	3.50	3.50
		Nos. 151A-154 (6)	8.70	8.70

Nos. 152-154 have country name "O'ZBEKISTON" at top and "POCHTA 1998" at bottom.
#152, 153 exist dated 1999.
Issued: 6s, 2/25; 12s, 15s, 45s, 3/25; 2s, 4/16; 3s, 4/17.

Intl. Tennis
Tournament,
Tashkent
A38

Emblem and: No. 155, President's Cup. No. 156, Tennis player. No. 157, Camel.

1997   Litho.   Perf. 14
155	A38	6s blue & grn	2.50	2.50
156	A38	6s blue & grn	2.50	2.50
157	A38	6s blue & grn	2.50	2.50
		Nos. 155-157 (3)	7.50	7.50

Automobiles — A39

a, 9s, Tico. b, 12s, Damas. c, 15s, Nexia.

1997, Sept. 19   Litho.   Perf. 14
158 A39 Block of 3, #a.-c. + la-
         bel   4.50 4.50

Tennis
Tournament
A40

Sharq Taronlalari
Intl. Music
Festival
A41

1998, Aug. 17   Litho.   Perf. 14
159 A40 15s multicolored   1.50 1.50

1998, July 15
160 A41 15s multicolored   1.00 1.00

Berdaq
Monument
A42

Kamoliddin
Behzod, Poet
A43

1998, Aug. 17
161 A42 15s blue & brown   1.00 1.00

1998, Aug. 17
162 A43 15s multicolored   1.00 1.00

Imam Al-Buxorily
A44

Ahmad Al-
Fargoni
A45

1998, June 26
163 A44 15s multicolored   1.00 1.00

1998, June 26
164 A45 15s multicolored   1.00 1.00

Folktales — A46

Designs: a, 8s, Woman holding baby. b,
10s, "Alpomish" over rainbow. c, 15s, Three
men seated before fire. d, 15s, Man talking to
man with sword. e, 18s, Man riding horse. f,
18s, Knight with longbow, squire with arrow. g,
20s, Swordmaker at work. h, 20s, Man fighting
lion. i, 25s, Man, woman walking arm in arm.

1998, Nov. 27   Litho.   Perf. 14
165 A46 Sheet of 9, #a.-i.   6.50 6.50

No. 165 is a continuous design.

Arms Type of 1994 Redrawn

1999-2001   Litho.   Perf. 14
Size: 14x23mm
167 A10 5s blue green   .40 .40
168 A10 6s green   .85 .85
168A A10 10s dk green   .40 .40
  d.   10s emerald, dated "2004"   .40 .40
168B A10 15s lt blue   .70 .70
168C A10 17s dk blue   .75 .75
169 A10 30s blue   .85 .85
170 A10 40s rose   .50 .50
170A A10 45s rose   1.50 1.50
  a.   45s carmine, dated 2001   1.75 1.75
171 A10 60s rose car   1.50 1.50
     Nos. 167-171 (9)   7.45 7.45

Issued: 6s, 3/22/99. 15s, 17s, 30s, 45s,
12/5/00. 5s, 60s, 1/17/01; No. 168A, 40s,
2/5/01. No. 168Ad, 6/15/04.
Nos. 167-171 have country name
"O'ZBEKISTON" at top and "POCHTA" and
year at bottom. Stamps issued in 2001 are
inscribed "2000." No. 170 exists dated "2001."
No. 167 exists dated "2004" and "2005."
No. 168 is inscribed "6 so'm." No. 153 is
inscribed "6-00."

Trains — A47

Locomotives: #172, OV steam, 1897-1917.
#173, EA steam, 1931-35. 28s, FD steam,
1931-41. 36s, SO steam, 1934-52. #176, VL-
22 electric. #177, KCh. 69s, TEP-6.

1999, May 11   Litho.   Perf. 14
172 A47 18s multicolored   .50 .50
173 A47 18s multicolored   .50 .50
174 A47 28s multicolored   .75 .75
175 A47 36s multicolored   .85 .85
176 A47 56s multicolored   1.40 1.40
177 A47 56s multicolored   1.40 1.40
178 A47 69s multicolored   1.60 1.60
     Nos. 172-178 (7)   7.00 7.00

A48

A49

Designs: 18s, Horse rearing.
No. 180, horiz.: a, 36s, Robed rider on
horse. b, 28s, White horse. c, 69s, Jockey on
race horse.
75s, Black horse, horiz.

1999, May 25
179 A48 18s multicolored   1.50 1.50
180 A48   Vert. strip of 3, #a.-
              c.   4.00 4.00
Souvenir Sheet
181 A48 75s multicolored   3.50 3.50

No. 180 printed in sheets of 8 stamps containing 2 strips and one each of Nos. 180a and
180c.

1999, June 8

Story of Badal Qorachi — #182: a, 18s,
Woman, deer. b, 18s, Two archers on horses.
c, 28s, Archer on horse. d, 36s, White giant. e,
56s, Black giant. f, 56s, Troll, cat, bones. g,
Man, woman.
75s, Woman on sofa, demon, horiz.

182 A49 Sheet of 7, #a.-g. + la-
         bel   7.00 7.00
Souvenir Sheet
183 A49 75s multicolored   3.00 3.00

A50   A51

Reptiles: No. 184, Trapelus sanguinolentus.
No. 185, horiz.: a, 18s, Eremias arguta. b,
18s, Vipera ursinii. c, 28s, Phrynocephalus
mystaceus. d, 36s, Agkistrodon halys. e, 56s,
Eumeces schneideri. f, 69s, Vipera lebetina.
75s, Two lizards, horiz.

1999, June 22
184 A50 56s multicolored   1.25 1.25
185 A50   Sheet of 6, #a.-f.   6.25 6.25
Souvenir Sheet
186 A50 75s multicolored   3.00 3.00

1999, July 7
187 A51 45s light green & black   1.40 1.40
         UPU, 125th anniv.

A52

A53

1999, July 21
188 A52 30s green & claret   1.25 1.25
Muhammadrizo Erniyozbek ogli-Ogahiy, poet.

1999, Oct. 22   Litho.   Perf. 14x13¾

Birds of Prey: No. 189, Circaetus qallicus.
No. 190, Falco tinnunculus. No. 191, Aquila
chrysaetos. No. 192, Gyps fulvus. 36s, Falco
cherrug. 56s, Gypaetus barbatus. 60s, Pandion haliaetus.
75s, Bird, hatchlings.

189 A53 15s multi   .60 .60
190 A53 15s multi   .60 .60
191 A53 18s multi   .75 .75
192 A53 18s multi   .75 .75
193 A53 36s multi   1.10 1.10
194 A53 56s multi   1.50 1.50
195 A53 60s multi   1.75 1.75
     Nos. 189-195 (7)   7.05 7.05
Souvenir Sheet
196 A53 75s multi   3.25 3.25

A54

A55

Soccer.

1999, Nov. 8
197 A54 15s Two players   .55 .55
198 A54 18s Two players, diff.   .55 .55
199 A54 28s Two players, diff.   .70 .70
200 A54 28s Player, goalie   .70 .70
201 A54 36s Player, goalie, diff. 1.25 1.25
202 A54 56s Two players, diff.   1.50 1.50
203 A54 69s Two players, diff.   1.90 1.90
     Nos. 197-203 (7)   7.15 7.15
Souvenir Sheet
Perf. 13¾x14
204 A54 75s Two players, horiz.   3.00 3.00

1999, Dec. 13   Litho.   Perf. 14x13¾

Prehistoric Animals: a, 28s, Meqaneura. b,
28s, Mesosaurus. c, 36s, Rhamphorhynchus.
d, 36s, Styracosaurus albertensis. e, 56s,
Trachodon annectens. f, 56s, Tarbosaurus
bataar. g, 69s, Arsinoitherium. h, 75s,
Phororhacos.

205 A55 Sheet of 8, #a.-h.   9.00 9.00

Uzbek
National
Circus — A56

28s, Woman and lion. # 207, 36s, Acrobat
with bow and arrow. #208, 36s, Acrobat. #209,
56s, Clown on horse. #210, 56s, Two riders on
horse. 69s, Wire walker.
100s, Woman, camels, llamas, horiz.

2000. Jan. 4   Perf. 14
206 A56 28s multi   .70 .70
207 A56 36s multi   .70 .70
208 A56 36s multi   .70 .70
209 A56 56s multi   1.40 1.40
210 A56 56s multi   1.40 1.40
211 A56 69s multi   1.75 1.75
     Nos. 206-211 (6)   6.65 6.65
Souvenir Sheet
212 A56 100s multi   2.75 2.75

Horses — A57

Designs: 69s, Horses pulling carriage.
No. 214: a, 36s, Horse in dressage competition. b, 36s, Horse jumping fences. c, 56s,

Horses in race. d, 56s, Horse jumping steeple-chase fence. e, 75s, Horse with sulky. f, 75s, Race winner.

2000, Feb. 1
213 A57 69s multi   1.25 1.25

Sheet of 6
214 A57 #a.-f.   6.75 6.75

Ajiniyoz Qo'siboy, Poet — A58

2000, Mar. 31   Litho.   Perf. 14
215 A58 28s multi   .90   .90

 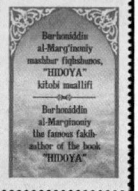

Famous Uzbek Writers — A59

Designs: No. 216, 60s, Burhoniddin al Marg'inoniy. No. 217, 60s, Imam Abu mansur al-Moturidiy, horiz.

2000, Oct. 24
Stamp + label
216-217 A59 Set of 2   2.75 2.75

UN High Commissioner for Refugees, 50th Anniv. — A60

2000, Dec. 11
218 A60 125s multi + label   2.25 2.25

Bats
A61

Designs: 15s, Tadarida teniotis. 30s, Otonycteris hemrichi. 45s, Nyctalus lasiopterus, vert. 50s, Muotis frater, vert. 60s, Rhinolophus hipposideros, vert. 90s, Barbastella leucomelas, vert. 125s, Nyctalus noctula, vert. 160s, Unidentified bat, vert.

2001, Feb. 23   Perf. 13¾x14, 14x13¾
219-225 A61 Set of 7   5.75 5.75
Souvenir Sheet
226 A61 160s multi   3.25 3.25

Dated 2000.

Native Costumes — A62

2001, Feb. 26   Perf. 14x13¾
227   Horiz. strip of 5 + label   6.00 6.00
  a. A62 45s multi   .50   .50
  b. A62 50s multi, diff.   .60   .60
  c. A62 60s multi, diff.   .70   .70
  d. A62 90s multi, diff.   1.00 1.00
  e. A62 125s multi, diff.   1.50 1.50

Dated 2000.

Arms Type of 1994 Redrawn
2001-05   Litho.   Perf. 14
Size: 14x23mm
228 A10 15s emerald   .60   .60
229 A10 17s dull green   .60   .60
230 A10 20s dull green   .60   .60
231 A10 25s bright blue   .60   .60
232 A10 30s sky blue   .60   .60
232A A10 30s green   .75   .75
  b. light green, dated "2005" .75   .75
233 A10 33s gray blue   .75   .75
234 A10 45s red   1.00 1.00
235 A10 50s rose   1.10 1.10
236 A10 60s rose pink   1.40 1.40
237 A10 100s rose   1.75 1.75
     Nos. 228-237 (11)   9.75 9.75

Issued: 15s, 17s, 25s, 33s, 50s, 60s, 100s, 4/3; 20s, 30s, 4/11; 45s, 6/22. No. 232A, 5/26/03; No. 232Ab, 3/25/05.
No. 237 exists dated "2003." No. 232A exists dated "2004."

Ali Shir Nava'i (1441-1501), Poet — A63

2001, Apr. 11
238   Horiz. strip of 5 + label   8.25 8.25
  a. A63 60s Hayrat ul-abror   1.00 1.00
  b. A63 70s Farhod va Shirin   1.00 1.00
  c. A63 85s Layli va Majnun   1.25 1.25
  d. A63 90s Sab'ai sayyora   1.25 1.25
  e. A63 125s Saddi Iskandariy 1.75 1.75

World Environment Day — A64

2001, June 20
239 A64 100s multi   1.90 1.90

Avesto, 2700th Anniv. — A65

2001, June 20
240 A65 160s multi   2.75 2.75

Souvenir Sheet

Termiz, 2500th Anniv. — A66

2001, June 20
241 A66 175s multi   3.75 3.75

Souvenir Sheet

Independence, 10th Anniv. — A67

2001, June 20
242 A67 175s multi   3.50 3.50

Souvenir Sheet

Regional Communications Cooperation — A68

2001, June 20
243 A68 175s multi   3.50 3.50

10th Anniv. of Independence Issue

Vertical Label

Horizontal Label

Tourist Hotel — A69

Monuments — A70

Inauguration of Pres. Islam Karimov — A71

Pres. Karimov at United Nations A72

Pres. Karimov at Istanbul Summit A73

Hirmon A74

Silk Cocoons A75

Fergana Refinery A76

Power Station A77

Daewoo Auto Factory A78

Securities Exchange A79

Kamchik Tunnel A80

Pres. Karimov and US Pres. Clinton A81

Pres. Karimov and Russian Pres. Vladimir Putin A82

Pres. Karimov and Japanese Emperor Akihito A83

Pres. Karimov and Chinese Pres. Jiang Zemin A84

Pres. Karimov and German Chancellor Gerhard Schröder A85

Pres. Karimov and French Pres. Jacques Chirac A86

Pres. Karimov and British Prime Minister John Major A87

Pres. Karimov and Iranian Pres. Ali Mohammad Khatami — A88

Pres. Karimov and Egyptian Pres. Hosni Mubarak A89

Pres. Karimov and Italian Pres. Carlos Ciampi A90

Pres. Karimov and Indian Pres. Kocheril Narayanan A91

Pres. Karimov and Pope John Paul II — A92

Textile Workers A93

Shurtan Gas Complex — A94

Muborak Refinery — A95

Oil Pipeline — A96

Solar Collector A97

Soldiers with Flag A98

Missiles A99

Soldiers Training A100

Kurash Sports Complex A101

New Year's Celebration — A102

Mother and Child — A103

Wedding A104

Bukhara Refinery — A105

Nuclear Power Plant — A106

A70 Designs: No. 245, Zahriddin Bobur Monument. No. 246, Amir Temur Monument. No. 247, Al-Motorudi Monument. No. 248, Al-Marginoniy Monument. No. 249, Jaloliddin Manguberdi Monument. No. 250, Al-Bukhoriy Monument. No. 273, Alisher Navoi Monument. No 274, Berdaq Monument. No. 284, Alpom-ish Monument. No. 288, Al-Fargoniy Monument.

2001   Litho.   *Perf. 14x13¾, 13¾x14*
Stamp + Label with Same Orientation

244	A69	60s multi	.40	.40
245	A70	60s multi	.40	.40
246	A70	70s multi	.40	.40
247	A70	75s multi	.40	.40
248	A70	75s multi	.40	.40
249	A70	85s multi	.60	.60
250	A70	90s multi	.60	.60
251	A71	90s multi	.60	.60
252	A72	90s multi	.60	.60
253	A73	90s multi	.60	.60
254	A74	90s multi	.60	.60
255	A75	90s multi	.60	.60
256	A76	90s multi	.60	.60
257	A77	90s multi	.60	.60
258	A78	90s multi	.60	.60
259	A79	90s multi	.60	.60
260	A80	90s multi	.60	.60
261	A81	95s multi	.70	.70
262	A82	95s multi	.70	.70
263	A83	95s multi	.70	.70
264	A84	95s multi	.70	.70
265	A85	95s multi	.70	.70
266	A86	95s multi	.70	.70
267	A87	95s multi	.70	.70
268	A88	95s multi	.70	.70
269	A89	95s multi	.70	.70
270	A90	95s multi	.70	.70
271	A91	95s multi	.70	.70
272	A92	95s multi	.70	.70
273	A70	115s multi	.85	.85
274	A70	115s multi	.85	.85
275	A93	115s multi	.85	.85
276	A94	115s multi	.85	.85
277	A95	115s multi	.85	.85
278	A96	115s multi	.85	.85
279	A97	115s multi	.85	.85
280	A98	115s multi	.85	.85
281	A99	115s multi	.85	.85
282	A100	115s multi	.85	.85
283	A101	115s multi	.85	.85
284	A70	125s multi	.85	.85
285	A102	125s multi	.85	.85
286	A103	125s multi	.85	.85
287	A104	125s multi	.85	.85
288	A70	160s multi	1.10	1.10
289	A105	160s multi	1.10	1.10
290	A106	160s multi	1.10	1.10
	Nos. 244-290 (47)		*33.65*	*33.65*

Nos. 244-290 were each printed in sheets of 2 stamps and 2 labels.

Uzbekistan Arms — A107

Uzbekistan Flag — A108

Motor Vehicles A109

Central Bank Building — A110

Bank Association Building — A111

Tashkent Khokimiyat Building A112

Central Trade Center Building
A113

Shurtan Gas Complex
A114

Shurtan Gas Complex
A115

Couple with Baby
A116

Children
A117

Farm Equipment
A118

Airplanes
A119

Constitution
A120

Majlis Hall — A121

Gold Ingots and Coins
A122

Muruntay Gold Mine
A123

Independence Day Celebrations — A124

Independence Day Celebrations — A125

A109 Designs: No. 292a, Nexia. No. 292b, Damas. No. 293a, Tico. No. 293b, Matiz.
A118 Designs: No. 298a, Case 2022 cotton picker. No. 298b, SHR-100 tractor.
A119 Designs: No. 299a, IL-76 MF cargo plane. No. 299b, IL-114-100 passenger plane.

291	Pair with central label	1.25	1.25
a.	A107 90s multi	.60	.60
b.	A108 90s multi	.60	.60
292	Pair with central label	1.25	1.25
a.-b.	A109 90s Any single	.60	.60
293	Pair with central label	1.25	1.25
a.-b.	A109 90s multi	.60	.60
294	Pair with central label	1.25	1.25
a.	A110 90s multi	.60	.60
b.	A111 90s multi	.60	.60
295	Pair with central label	1.25	1.25
a.	A112 90s multi	.60	.60
b.	A113 90s multi	.60	.60
296	Pair with central label	2.00	2.00
a.	A114 115s multi	1.00	1.00
b.	A115 115s multi	1.00	1.00
297	Pair with central label	2.00	2.00
a.	A116 125s multi	1.00	1.00
b.	A117 125s multi	1.00	1.00
298	Pair with central label	2.25	2.25
a.-b.	A118 160s Any single	1.10	1.10
299	Pair with central label	1.50	1.50
a.	A119 90s multi	.65	.65
b.	A119 115s multi	.85	.85
300	Pair with central label	1.25	1.25
a.	A120 90s multi	.80	.80
b.	A121 60s multi	.40	.40
301	Pair with central label	1.50	1.50
a.	A122 115s multi	.80	.80
b.	A123 90s multi	.50	.50
302	Pair with central label	1.50	1.50
a.	A124 125s multi	.85	.85
b.	A125 90s multi	.60	.60
	Nos. 291-302 (12)	18.25	18.25

Nos. 291-302 printed in sheets of four stamps and two labels (two pairs).

Theater A126

Theater A127

Theater A128

Medals — A129

Combine A130

Combine A131

Pres. Karimov and Farmers A132

Soldier Taking Oath Before Flag A133

Man and Soldier Embracing A134

Frontier Guards and Dog A135

Athletes — A136

Soldiers in Formation A137

Diver Training A138

Decontamination Training — A139

Modern Architecture — A140

Armed Forces — A141

Archaeology — A142

High School — A143

Uzbekistan on World Map — A144

A129 Designs: No. 304a, Dostelik. No. 304b, I Darajali "Shon-Sharaf." No. 304c, II Darajali "Shon-Sharaf." No. 305a, I Darajali Sog'lom Avlod Uchun. No. 305b, II Darajali

Sog'lom Avlod Uchun. No. 305c, Mehnat Shuhrati. No. 306a, Jaloliddin Manguberdi. No. 306b, Buyuk Xizmatlari Uchun. No. 306c, El-Yurt Hurmati. No. 307a, Oltin Yildiz. No. 307b, Mustaqillik. No. 307c, Amir Temur.

A136 Designs: No. 310a, Muhammadqodir Abdullayev. No. 310b, Lina Cheryazova. No. 310c, Artur Grigoryan. No. 312a, 160s, Armen Bagdasarov. No. 312b, 160s, Rustam Qosimjonov. No. 312c, 115s, Otabek Kosimov. No. 312d, 115s, Iroda To'laganova. No. 312e, 100s, Dilshod Muxtorov. No. 312e, 115s, Oksana Chusovitina.

No. 313: a, Temuriylar Tarixi Muzeyi (Amir Temur Museum). b, Oqsaroy. c, Oliy Majlis. d, Motamsaro Ona (Monument to Grieving Mother). e, Shahidlar Xotirasi (Respect Monument). f, Interkontinental mehmonxonasi (Intercontinental Hotel). g, Milliy Bank (National Bank). h, Yunusobod Sport Majmuasi (Yunusobod Sport Complex).

No. 314: a, 60s, Infantrymen, tank. b, 70s, Airplane and crew. c, 80s, Helicopter and crew. d, 90s, Soldier directing tank with flags. e, 90s, Minesweeper. f, 115s, Soldiers in classroom. g, 160s, Tanks. h, 60s, Artillery.

No. 315: a, 75s, Pot. b, 75s, Artifact with arch. c, 75s, Artifact with hole at top and side. d, 80s, Broken pot. e, 80s, Anthropomorphic figure with arms. f, 80s, Buddha. g, 80s, Costumed figure. h, 80s, Disk. i, 80s, Anthropomorphic figure missing arm. j, 80s, Box. k, 80s, Face.

303	Strip of 3 + label	1.75	1.75
a.	A126 90s multi	.55	.55
b.	A127 90s multi	.55	.55
c.	A128 90s multi	.55	.55
304	Strip of 3 + label	3.00	3.00
a.-c.	A129 160s Any single	.95	.95
305	Strip of 3 + label	3.00	3.00
a.-c.	A129 160s Any single	.95	.95
306	Strip of 3 + label	3.00	3.00
a.-c.	A129 160s Any single	.95	.95
307	Strip of 3 + label	3.00	3.00
a.-c.	A129 160s Any single	.95	.95
308	Strip of 3 + label	3.00	3.00
a.	A130 160s multi	.95	.95
b.	A131 160s multi	.95	.95
c.	A132 160s multi	.95	.95
309	Strip of 3 + label	2.00	2.00
a.	A133 60s multi	.40	.40
b.	A134 80s multi	.55	.55
c.	A135 90s multi	.65	.65
310	Strip of 3 + label	2.75	2.75
a.	A136 160s multi	1.10	1.10
b.-c	A136 115s Any single	.80	.80
311	Block of 3 + label	2.00	2.00
a.	A137 115s multi	.75	.75
b.	A138 80s multi	.55	.55
c.	A139 70s multi	.45	.45
	Nos. 303-311 (9)	23.50	23.50

Sheets

312	A136	Sheet of 6, #a-f, + 3 labels	5.00	5.00
313	A140	115s Sheet of 8, #a-h, + label	7.00	7.00
314	A141	Sheet of 8, #a-h, + label	5.00	5.00
315	A142	Sheet of 11, #a-k, + label	6.00	6.00

Souvenir Sheets

316	A143	160s multi	1.50	1.50
317	A144	175s multi	2.00	2.00

Labels have same orientation as stamps and are at left side of strips on Nos. 303-310, and at UR on No. 311. No. 312 contains three different labels.

Commonwealth of Independent States, 10th Anniv. — A145

2001, Nov. 8   *Perf. 13¾x14*
318 A145 60s multi   1.10 1.10

Artwork of Oral Tansiqboyev — A146

No. 319: a, 100s, Mening Qo'shig'im (My Song). b, 125s, Angren-Qo'qon Tog'yo'li (Angren-Kokand Mountain Road). Illustration reduced.

2001, Nov. 8
319 A146   Pair, #a-b, with central label   3.75 3.75

Flowers — A147

Designs: 45s, Zygophyllum bucharicum. 50s, Viola hissarica. 60s, Bergenia hissarica. 70s, Eremurus hilariae. 85s, Salvia korolkowii. 90s, Lamyropappus schakaptaricus. 145s, Punica granatum.
175s, Undescribed flowers.

2002, May 10   **Litho.**   *Perf. 14x13¾*
320-326 A147   Set of 7   6.75 6.75
Souvenir Sheet
327 A147   175s multi   2.25 2.25

Hominids — A148

No. 328: a, 40s, Dryopithecus maior. b, 45s, Homo erectus modjokertensis. c, 50s, Pithecanthropus erectus. d, 60s, Australopithecus afarensis. e, 70s, Zinjanthropus boisei. f, 85s, Homo sapiens neanderthalensis. g, 90s, Sinanthropus pekinensis. h, 125s, Protanthropus heidelbergensis. i, 160s, Homo sapiens fossilis.

2002, May 10   *Perf. 13¾x14*
328 A148   Sheet of 9, #a-i, + 3 labels   9.00 9.00

Protection of Ozone Layer — A149

2002, June 7   **Litho.**   *Perf. 13¾x14*
329 A149   40s multi   1.25 1.25
Souvenir Sheet

City of Shahrisabz, 2700th Anniv. — A150

2002, June 14   *Perf. 14*
330 A150   30s multi   1.25 1.25

Uzbek Sports A151

Designs: 45s, Chavgon. 50s, Poyga. 60s, Kamondan otish. 70s, Qiz quvmoq. 85s, Ro'molcha olish. 90s, Kurash. 145s, Uloq. 175s, Ro'molcha olish, diff.

2002, July 26   *Perf. 13¾x14*
331-337 A151   Set of 7   5.75 5.75
Souvenir Sheet
338 A151   175s multi   2.25 2.25

Ancient Coins — A152

No. 339: a, 30s, Silver tetradrachm of Eucratides I c. 171-135 BC, obverse. b, 45s, As "a," reverse. c, 60s, Silver coin of Buxoro, obverse. d, 90s, As "c," reverse. e, 125s, Silver miri of Tamerlane, 1370-1405, obverse. f, 160s, As "e," reverse.
Illustration reduced.

2002, Aug. 1
339 A152   Block of 6, #a-f   6.25 6.25

City of Nukus, 70th Anniv. — A153

2002, Oct. 2
340 A153   100s multi   1.40 1.40

Iris Varieties — A154

Designs: 15s, Qoraqum. 30s, Solnechniy zaychik. 45s, Simfoniya. 50s, Chimyon. 60s, Ikar. 90s, Babye leto. 125s, Toshkent. 160s, Askiya.

2002, Oct. 2   *Perf. 14x13¾*
341-347 A154   Set of 7   5.50 5.50
Souvenir Sheet
348 A154   160s multi   2.50 2.50

Uzbekistan postal officials have declared the following items as "illegal":
Sheets of eight stamps depicting Trains (4 different sheets with denominations of 56s, 75s, 95s and 125s);
Sheets of six stamps with various denominations depicting Birds (2 different), Animals, Year of the Snake, Chiroptera, Lizards, Chess;
Sheets of one label and five stamps with various denominations depicting Perissodactyla;
Souvenir sheets of one depicting Trains (8 different 36s sheets, 4 different 56s sheets, 2 different 75s sheets).

G'afur G'ulom (1903-66), Poet — A155

2003, May 4   **Litho.**   *Perf. 13¾x14*
349 A155   1000s brown   7.00 7.00

European Bank Annual Meeting Issue

Vertical Label

Horizontal Label

National Bank, Tashkent — A156

Kaltaminor Minaret, Khiva — A157

Aloqabank, Tashkent A158

Pres Karimov and European Bank for
Reconstruction and Development Pres.
Jean Lemierre — A159

Islamkhodja
Minaret,
Khiva — A160

East Gates,
Khiva — A161

Samanid Museum,
Bukhara — A162

Ark,
Bukhara — A163

Women's
Traditional
Dress — A164

Women's
Traditional
Dress — A165

Women's
Traditional
Dress — A166

Women's
Traditional
Dress — A167

Women's
Traditional
Dress — A168

A157 Designs: 630s, Gumbazi Sayyidon
Mausoleum, Shahrisabz. 920s, Go'ri Amir
Mausoleum, Samarqand. 970s, Chorminor
Madrasasi, Bukhara. 1330s, Registon, Samar-
qand, horiz.

2003, May 4   Perf. 14x13¾, 13¾x14
**Stamp + Label with Same
Orientation**

350	A156	520s multi	5.50	5.50
351	A157	520s multi	5.50	5.50
352	A157	630s multi	6.25	6.25
353	A157	920s multi	9.75	9.75
354	A157	970s multi	10.50	10.50
355	A158	970s multi	10.50	10.50
356	A157	1330s multi	13.00	13.00
357	A159	1330s multi	13.00	13.00
358		Horiz. pair with central label	12.00	12.00
a.	A160	580s multi	5.50	5.50
b.	A161	520s multi	5.50	5.50
359		Horiz. pair with central label	18.00	18.00
a.	A162	1170s multi	11.00	11.00
b.	A163	630s multi	6.00	6.00
360		Horiz. strip of 5 with flanking label	24.00	24.00
a.	A164	240s multi	2.40	2.40
b.	A165	320s multi	3.50	3.50
c.	A166	520s multi	5.50	5.50
d.	A167	580s multi	5.50	5.50
e.	A168	630s multi	6.25	6.25

Types of 2001-02
**Stamp + Label with Same
Orientation**

361	A110	520s multi	5.50	5.50
362	A111	580s multi	5.50	5.50
363		Horiz. pair with central label	12.00	12.00
a.	A74	170s multi	1.75	1.75
b.	A93	920s multi	9.75	9.75
364		Horiz. pair with central label	8.50	8.50
a.	A107	240s multi	2.40	2.40
b.	A108	520s multi	5.50	5.50
365		Horiz. pair with central label	9.00	9.00
a.	A114	630s multi	6.25	6.25
b.	A115	240s multi	2.40	2.40
366		Horiz. pair with central label	9.00	9.00
a.	A122	520s multi	5.50	5.50
b.	A123	320s multi	3.50	3.50
367		Horiz. pair with flanking label	12.00	12.00
a.	A152	520s Like #339a	5.50	5.50
b.	A152	520s Like #339b	5.50	5.50
368		Horiz. pair with flanking label	12.00	12.00
a.	A152	580s Like #339c	5.50	5.50
b.	A152	580s Like #339d	5.50	5.50
369		Horiz. pair with flanking label	13.00	13.00
a.	A152	630s Like #339e	6.25	6.25
b.	A152	630s Like #339f	6.25	6.25
370	A140	Sheet of 8 + central label	52.50	52.50
a.		520s Like #313a	5.50	5.50
b.		970s Like #313b	10.50	10.50
c.		580s Like #313c	5.50	5.50
d.		630s Like #313d	6.25	6.25
e.		320s Like #313e	3.50	3.50
f.		630s Like #313f	6.25	6.25
g.		920s Toshkent shahar hokimiyati (mayor's house)	9.75	9.75

h.		240s Like #313h	2.40	2.40

Type of 2001 Redrawn

371		Horiz. pair with central label	17.00	17.00
a.	A109	630s Like #292a	6.25	6.25
b.	A109	970s Like #293b	10.50	10.50
		Nos. 350-371 (22)	284.00	284.00

Famous
Men — A169

Designs: 125s, Komil Yormatov, film director. 500s, Jo'raxon Sultonov, singer.

2003, July 8   Perf. 13¾x14
372-373	A169	Set of 2	5.50 5.50

Birds — A170

Designs: No. 374, 100s, Ciconia ciconia
asiatica. No. 375, 100s, Ciconia nigra. No.
376, 125s, Platalea leucorodia. No. 377, 125s,
Phoenicopterus ruber.

2003, Sept. 17   Perf. 14x13¾
374-377	A170	Set of 4	6.50 6.50

Caps — A171

Designs: No. 378, 100s, Kula-tung. No. 379,
100s, Erkaklar do'ppisi. No. 380, 100s,
Bayram do'ppisi. No. 381, 125s, Ayollar
do'ppisi. No. 382, 125s, Ayollar taxya-do'ppisi.
No. 383, 155s, Erkaklar do'ppisi, diff. No. 384,
155s, Bolalar bayram do'ppisi.

2003, Oct. 7
378-384	A171	Set of 7	10.00 10.00

Paintings — A172

No. 385: a, Tong. Onalik, by R. Ahmedov. b,
Baxt, by S. Ayitbayev.

2003, Nov. 19
385	A172	970s Horiz. pair, #a-b	12.00	12.00

See Kazakhstan No. 434.

Abuxoliq G'ijduvoniy, Bukhara, 900th
Anniv. — A173

Illustration reduced.

2003, Nov. 28   Perf. 13¾x14
386	A173	125s multi + label	2.00 2.00

Souvenir Sheet

2004 Summer Olympics,
Athens — A174

2004, June 15 Litho.   Perf. 14x13¾
387	A174	205s multi	2.50 2.50

Ma'murjon   Abdulla Qodiriy
Uzoqov (1904-   (1894-1938),
63),   Writer — A176
Singer — A175

2004, Oct. 11   Perf. 14
388	A175	100s lt blue & blk	1.25 1.25
389	A176	125s lt blue & blk	1.50 1.50

Grapes — A177

Designs: 60s, Kaltak. No. 391, 100s, Oq
husayni. No. 392, 100s, Kattaqo'rg'on. No.
393, 125s, Echkemar. No. 394, 125s, Qizil
Xurmoni. 155s, Qora Andijon. 210s, Parkent.

2004, Oct. 11   Perf. 14x13¾
390-396	A177	Set of 7	10.00 10.00

Jewelry of 19th
and 20th
Centuries
A178

Inscriptions: 60s, Tumor, Samarqand. No.
398, 100s, Tumor, Toshkent. No. 399, 100s,
Qi'ltiqtumor, Qo'qon. No. 400, 125s, Tumor,
Buxoro. No. 401, 125s, Bo'yintumor, Toshkent.
155s, Qo'ltiqtumor, Buxoro. 210s, Tumor, Buxoro, diff.

2004, Oct. 18
397-403	A178	Set of 7	11.00 11.00

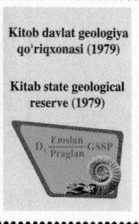

Kitab State Geological Reserve, 25th Anniv. — A179

2004, Dec. 1
404 A179 100s multi + label 1.50 1.50

Arms Type of 1994 Redrawn

2004-06	Litho.		Perf. 14
	Size: 14x23mm		
405	A10	35s green	.20	.20
406	A10	60s green	.30	.30
a.	light green, dated "2005"		.30	.30
407	A10	65s green	.35	.35
408	A10	125s dark blue	.50	.50
409	A10	200s red	.70	.70
410	A10	250s blue	.90	.90
411	A10	290s red	1.00	1.00
412	A10	350s blue	1.25	1.25
413	A10	430s red	1.50	1.50
414	A10	2500s red	8.50	8.50
415	A10	3700s blue	12.00	12.00
	Nos. 405-415 (11)		27.20	27.20

Issued: No. 406, 6/15; Nos. 406a, 408, 4/15/05; others, 1/5/06. Nos. 405, 407, 409-415 are dated "2005," though issued in 2006.

Oybek (1905-68), Writer — A180

2005, Apr. 25 Litho. Perf. 14x13¾
416 A180 125s multi 1.10 1.10

Miniature Sheet

End of World War II, 60th Anniv. — A181

No. 417: a, 60s, Veterans at war memorial. b, 60s, Child with balloon at memorial. c, 100s, Sculptures. d, 100s, Child looking at memorial. e, 125s, Veterans looking at airplane sculpture. f, 125s, Woman passing soldiers. g, 155s, Soldier and floral display. h, 155s, Man looking at scrapbook.

2005, May 6
417 A181 Sheet of 8, #a-h, + central label 8.00 8.00

Tashkent University of Information Technologies, 50th Anniv. — A182

Illustration reduced.

2005, May 25 Perf. 13¾x14
418 A182 125s multi + label 1.50 1.50

Qarshi, 2700th Anniv. — A183

2005, Aug. 1
419 A183 125s multi 1.00 1.00

Doves — A184

No. 420: a, 85s, Qopqon-chinni. b, 85s, Ruyan. c, 100s, Novvoti. d, 100s, Oq kaptar. e, 125s, Juk. f, 125s, Chelkar. g, 155s, Udi. h, 155s, Gulsor.
210s, Buxoro kaptari.

2005, Sept. 15
420 A184 Sheet of 8, #a-h 6.75 6.75
Souvenir Sheet
421 A184 210s multi 2.00 2.00

Miniature Sheet

Toreutic Art — A185

No. 422: a, 60s, Teapot with ribbed ornamentation. b, 60s, Teapot with round ornamentation. c, 100s, Teapot, diff. d, 125s, Teapot, diff. 155s, Teapot-samovar. 340s, Teapot with square lid.

2005, Oct. 25
422 A185 Sheet of 6, #a-f 7.25 7.25

Ma'mun Academy, 1000th Anniv. — A186

2005, Dec. 15 Perf. 13¾x14
423 A186 430s multi 2.75 2.75

Paintings A187

Designs: No. 424, 200s, Ko'i, by V. I. Yenin. No. 425, 200s, Osuda Kun, by B. Boboyev, vert. No. 426, 250s, Samarqand, Navro'z, by G. Abdurahmanov, vert. No. 427, 250s, Qo'qondagi Choyxona, by J. Umarbekov, vert. No. 428, 300s, Oqtosh, by R. Ahmedov, vert. No. 429, 300s, Yoz, by Y. P. Melnikov, vert. 350s, Kuz, by N. Qo'ziboyev, vert.

2006, Jan. 3 Perf. 13¾x14, 14x13¾
424-430 A187 Set of 7 9.00 9.00

Dated 2005.

Rustam Qosimjonov, Intl. Chess Federation World Champion — A188

2006, Jan. 5 Perf. 13¾x14
431 A188 200s multi 1.25 1.25

Dated 2005.

Medalists at 2004 Summer Olympics, Athens — A189

Designs: No. 432, 200s, Artur Taymazov, 120kg freestyle wrestling gold medalist. No. 433, 200s, Aleksandr Doxturushvili, 74kg Greco-Roman wrestling gold medalist. 250s, Magomed Ibragimov, 96kg freestyle wrestling silver medalist. 350s, O'tkir Haydarov and Bahodir Sultonov, 81kg and 54kg boxing bronze medalists, horiz.

2006, Jan. 5 Perf. 14x13¾, 13¾x14
432-435 A189 Set of 4 5.50 5.50

Dated 2005.

2006 Winter Olympics, Turin — A190

Designs: 1540s, Skiing. 2155s, Figure skating.

2006, May 19 Litho. Perf. 14x13¾
436-437 A190 Set of 2 12.50 12.50

Musical Instruments A191

Designs: 200s, Tanbur and Qashqar rubobi. 250s, Surnay and Tor. 290s, Surnay and Doira. 350s, Nay and Dutor. 410s, G'ijjak. 430s, Nog'om. 580s, Tanbur and Chang.

2006, May 19
438-444 A191 Set of 7 10.00 10.00

Dogs A192

Designs: 350s, Labrador retriever. 540s, Cocker spaniel. 600s, German shepherd. 780s, Asian sheepdog.
1150s, Collie and German shepherd.

2006, May 19 Perf. 13¾x14
445-448 A192 Set of 4 8.50 8.50
Souvenir Sheet
449 A192 1150s multi 3.50 3.50

Souvenir Sheet

2006 World Cup Soccer Championships, Germany — A193

2006, May 19 Perf. 14x13¾
450 A193 720s multi 3.25 3.25

Fish — A194

No. 451: a, 45s, Salmo trutta aralensis. b, 90s, Acipenser nudiventris. c, 250s, Pseudoscaphirhynchus kaufmanni. d, 300s, Barbus brachcephalus.
1010s, Aspiolucius esocinus.

2006, July 10 Perf. 13¾x14
451 A194 Sheet of 4, #a-d 3.00 3.00
Souvenir Sheet
452 A194 1010s multi 3.50 3.50

Bell Tower, Tashkent A195   Alisher Navoiy Theater A196

2006, Aug. 10 Perf. 14x13¾
453 A195 55s green .35 .35
Perf. 13¾x14
454 A196 90s emerald .45 .45

Butterflies
A197

Designs: 45s, Papilio alexanor. 90s, Parnassius mnemosyne. 200s, Parnassius apollonius. 250s, Parnassius maximinus. 300s, Parnassius honrathi. No. 460, 350s, Hypermnestra helios. No. 461, 350s, Parnassius charltonius. 1010s, Parnassius actius.

2006, Aug. 10   **Perf. 13¾x14**
455-461 A197   Set of 7   5.75   5.75
        Souvenir Sheet
462 A197 1010s multi   4.00   4.00

15th Anniv. of Independence Issue

Horizontal Label

Vertical
Label

Pres. Islam Karimov and Indian Prime
Minister Manmohan Singh — A198

School and Children, Kokand — A199

House of Children's Creativity — A200

Senate Chamber — A201

Emblem of 2005 Intl. Cotton Fair,
Tashkent, and Cotton Boll — A202

Pres. Karimov and People's Republic
of China Chairman Hu Jintao — A203

Pres. Karimov and Latvian Pres. Vaire
Vike-Fraiberg — A204

Qungirot Soda Factory — A205

Leaders at Shanghai Cooperation
Organization Summit,
Tashkent — A206

Cement
Factory
A207

Railroad Construction — A208

Pres. Karimov and Graduates of
Vaseda University — A209

Monument of Independence and
Humanism — A210

Mine — A211

Bronze Smelter — A212

Festival — A213

Daewoo Nexia DOHC — A214

Kurash
A215

Intl. Kurash
Association
Medal
A216

Pres. Karimov and Cotton
Pickers — A217

Pres. Karimov and Cotton
Pickers — A218

Pres. Karimov and Farmers — A219

Roads — A220

Textiles — A221

Military — A222

Sports — A223

A198 Designs — Pres. Karimov and: No. 466, Malaysian King Tuanku Syed Sirajuddin. No. 470, Writer Said Akhmad. No. 474, Slovenian Pres. Janez Drnovsek. No. 477, Russian Pres. Vladimir Putin. No. 480, South Korean Pres. Roh Moo-hyun. No. 483, Uzbek labor leader.

A200 Designs: No. 469, Humanism Arch. No. 478, Medical School, Margilan. No. 484, Tashkent Railway Station. No. 486, Senate Building.

A206 Design: No. 482, Leaders at Euro-Asian Economic Union meeting.

A207 Design: No. 481, Angren Coal Mine.

A213 Design: No. 489b, 90s, Festival, diff.

A214 Design: No. 490b, 200s, Daewoo Damas II.

A215 Designs: No. 491b, 90s, Kurash, diff. No. 491c, 100s, Kurash, diff.

A216 Designs: No. 492b, 580s, FILA Wrestling medal. No. 492c, 720s, National Olympic Committee medal.

No. 494: a, 90s, Winding mountain road. b, 180s, Road construction. c, 55s, Highway.

No. 495: a, 410s, Workers and textile mill machinery. b, 580s, Women holding skeins of thread. c, 250s, Textile mill machinery.

No. 496: a, 410s, Soldiers in joint Uzbekistan-Russia anti-terrorism exercises, flags. b, 100s, Graduation of cadets. c, 250s, Soldiers at desks.

No. 497: a, 580s, Pres. Karimov and student athletes. b, 45s Stadium. c, 55s, Swimming meet. d, 90s, Athletes with medals. e, 200s, Karate. f, 250s, Soccer. g, 100s, Synchronized swimming. h, 290s, Equestrian event.

Perf. 13¾x14, 14x13¾

2006, Aug. 25
Stamp + Label With Same Orientation

463	A198	45s multi	.60	.60
464	A199	45s multi	.60	.60
465	A200	45s multi	.60	.60
466	A198	55s multi	.60	.60
467	A201	90s multi	.60	.60
468	A202	90s multi	.60	.60
469	A200	95s multi	.60	.60
470	A198	100s multi	.60	.60
471	A203	200s multi	1.00	1.00
472	A204	200s multi	1.00	1.00
473	A205	200s multi	1.00	1.00
474	A198	250s multi	1.25	1.25
475	A206	250s multi	1.25	1.25
476	A207	250s multi	1.25	1.25
477	A198	290s multi	1.50	1.50
478	A200	290s multi	1.50	1.50
479	A208	290s multi	1.50	1.50
480	A198	350s multi	1.50	1.50
481	A207	350s multi	1.50	1.50
482	A206	410s multi	2.00	2.00
483	A198	430s multi	2.10	2.10
484	A198	430s multi	2.10	2.10
485	A209	580s multi	3.00	3.00
486	A200	720s multi	3.75	3.75
487	A210	1010s multi	5.25	5.25
		Nos. 463-487 (25)	37.25	37.25

Pairs

488		Horiz. pair with central label	1.20	1.20
a.	A211	45s multi	.60	.60
b.	A212	45s multi	.60	.60
489		Horiz. pair with central label	1.20	1.20
a.	A213	45s multi	.60	.60
b.	A213	45s multi	.60	.60
490		Horiz. pair with central label	2.50	2.50
a.	A214	45s multi	1.50	1.50
b.	A214	200s multi	1.00	1.00
		Nos. 488-490 (3)	4.90	4.90

Strips

491		Strip of 3 + label	3.25	3.25
a.	A215	430s multi	2.10	2.10
b.	A215	90s multi	.60	.60
c.	A215	100s multi	.60	.60
492		Strip of 3 + label	9.00	9.00
a.	A216	410s multi	2.00	2.00
b.	A216	580s multi	3.00	3.00
c.	A216	720s multi	3.75	3.75
493		Strip of 3 + label	3.00	3.00
a.	A217	200s multi	1.00	1.00
b.	A218	250s multi	1.25	1.25
c.	A219	90s multi	.60	.60
		Nos. 491-493 (3)	15.25	15.25

Sheets

494	A220	Sheet of 3, #a-c, + label	1.60	1.60
495	A221	Sheet of 3, #a-c, + label	6.00	6.00
496	A222	Sheet of 3, #a-c, + label	3.75	3.75
497	A223	Sheet of 8, #a-h, + label	8.25	8.25
		Nos. 494-497 (4)	19.60	19.60

Nos. 463-475, 477-480, 482-486 were printed in sheets of 2 stamps and 2 labels. Nos. 476, 481 and 487 were printed in sheets of 5 stamps and 5 labels. Nos. 488-490 were printed in sheets of 4 stamps and 2 labels (2 pairs).

National Flag, 15th Anniv. — A224

Illustration reduced.

2006, Nov. 1   **Perf. 13¾x14**
498   A224   600s multi + label   2.40   2.40

Miniature Sheet

Intl. Year of Deserts and Desertification — A225

No. 499: a, 45s, Oxyura leucocephala. b, 250s, Haliaeetus albicilla. c, 350s, Phalcrocorax pygmaeus. d, 350s, Marmaronetta angustirostris.

2006, Nov. 1
499   A225   Sheet of 4, #a-d   3.75   3.75

Roses — A226

Designs: 45s, Rosa divina. 90s, Rosa maracandica. 250s, Rosa persica. 350s, Rosa vassilczencoi.
600s, Rosa divina, diff.

2006, Nov. 1   **Perf. 14x13¾**
500-503   A226   Set of 4   3.75   3.75
Souvenir Sheet
504   A226   600s multi   1.75   1.75

Souvenir Sheet

Year of Charity and Medical Workers — A227

2006, Nov. 17   **Perf. 13¾x14**
505   A227   720s multi   2.75   2.75

Souvenir Sheet

Regional Communications Commonwealth, 15th Anniv. — A228

2006, Nov. 17
506   A228   1010s multi   4.25   4.25

2006 Asian Games, Doha, Qatar A229

Designs: 90s, High jump. 250s, Tennis. No. 509, 350s, Basketball. No. 510, 350s, Soccer.

2006, Dec. 27   **Litho.**   **Perf. 13¾x14**
507-510   A229   Set of 4   1.75   1.75

Diplomatic Relations Between Uzbekistan and People's Republic of China, 15th Anniv. — A230

2006, Dec. 29
511   A230   200s multi   .35   .35

Admission to the United Nations, 15th Anniv. — A231

2007, Mar. 1
512   A231   410s multi   .65   .65

Souvenir Sheet

Spring Festival — A232

2007, Mar. 1   **Perf. 14x13¾**
513   A232   1440s multi   2.40   2.40

2007 Winter Asian Games, Changchun, People's Republic of China — A233

Designs: 250s, Figure skating. 350s, Skiing.

2007, Mar. 1
514-515   A233   Set of 2   1.00   1.00

Abdulla Qahhor (1907-68), Writer — A234

No. 516: a, 350s, Scene from "Shohi So'zana." b, 420s, Qahhor.
Illustration reduced.

2007, May 31   **Perf. 13¾x14**
516   A234   Horiz. pair, #a-b   1.25   1.25

Souvenir Sheets

A235

A236

A237

Architecture — A238

No. 517: a, 200s, Norbo'tabiy Madrasasi (madrassa). b, 410s, Daxmai Shohon Maqbarasi (mausoleum). c, 430s, Xudoyorxon Saroyi (palace).

No. 518: a, 250s, Modarixon Madrasasi (madrassa). b, 420s, Mir Arab Madrasasi (madrassa). c, 430s, Chor Bakr Me'moriy Majmuasi (mausoleum).

No. 519: a, 90s, Qo'shdarvoza (city gate). b, 250s, Muhammad Rahimxon Madrasasi (madrassa). c, 1010s, Pahlavon Mahmud Maqbarasi (mausoleum).

No. 520: a, 300s, Yunusxon Maqbarasi (mausoleum). b, 350s, Baroqxon Madrasasi (madrassa). c, Abulqosim Madrasasi (madrassa).

2007, May 31   Perf. 13¾x14, 14x13¾
517 A235   Sheet of 3, #a-c, +
            label   1.75 1.75
518 A236   Sheet of 3, #a-c, +
            label   1.75 1.75
519 A237   Sheet of 3, #a-c, +
            label   2.25 2.25
520 A238   Sheet of 3, #a-c, +
            label   2.25 2.25
      Nos. 517-520 (4)   8.00 8.00

Margilan, 2000th
Anniv. — A239

2007, June 30   Perf. 14x13¾
521 A239   350s multi   .55   .55

Quddus
Muhammadiy
(1907-99),
Poet — A240

2007, July 30   Perf. 13¾x14
522 A240   410s light blue & blk   .65   .65

Berries
A241

Designs: 100s, Fragaria. 250s, Ribes nigrum. 580s, Rubus idaeus. 720s, Grossularia reclinata.

2007, July 30   Litho.
523-526 A241 Set of 4   2.60 2.60

Jewelry — A242

Designs: 300s, Yarim tirnoq. 350s, Ko'krak do'zi, horiz. 670s, Shovkala, horiz. 720s, Bodomoy.

2007, July 30   Perf. 14x13¾, 13¾x14
527-530 A242 Set of 2   3.25 3.25

Miniature Sheets

Samarqand, 2750th Anniv. — A243

No. 531: a, 45s, Registon Maydoni, Ulug'bel Madrasasi. b, 55s, Registon Maydoni, Sherdor Madrasasi. c, 100s, Registon Maydoni, Tillakori Madrasasi. d, 180s, Amir Temur Maqbarasi, Umumiy Ko'rinishi. e, 200s, Bibixonim Masjidi. f, 250s, Ruhobod Maqbarasi. g, 490s, Registon Maydoni, Umumiy Ko'rinishi. h, 720s, Shohisinda Majmuasi, Qo'shgumbazli Maqbara.

No. 532, vert.: a, 90s, Imom al-Moturidiy Maqbarasi. b, 100s, Imom Buxoriy Maqbarasi. c, 180s, Amir Temur Maqbarasi Kirish Peshtoqi. d, 200s, Amir Temur Haykali (statue). e, 410s, Bibixonim Maqbarasi. f, 680s, Shohizinda Majmuasi. g, 700s, Bibixonim Masjidi Kirish Peshtoqi. h, 1150s, Shohizinda Majmuasi, Tuman Oqo Maqbarasi.

2007, July 30   Perf. 13¾x14
531 A243   Sheet of 8, #a-h, +
            central label   3.25 3.25
            Perf. 14x13¾
532 A243   Sheet of 8, #a-h, +
            central label   5.50 5.50

Acinonyx
Jubatus
A244

Designs: 90s, Leaping. 490s, Resting. 680s, Walking. 780s, Standing.
1440s, Adult with juvenile, vert.

2007, Oct. 3   Perf. 13¾x14
533-536 A244 Set of 4   3.25 3.25
            Souvenir Sheet
            Perf. 14x13¾
537 A244   1440s multi   2.25 2.25

Souvenir Sheet

Tashkent Subway, 30th Anniv. — A245

No. 538: a, 540s, Train and system map. b, 780s, Subway emblem and station entrance.

2007, Nov. 20   Perf. 14x13¾
538 A245   Sheet of 2, #a-b   2.10 2.10

Constitution, 15th
Anniv. — A246

2007, Dec. 5   Litho.
539 A246   600s multi   .95   .95

Miniature Sheet

Zahiruddin Muhammad Babur (1483-1530), Founder of Mughal Dynasty — A247

No. 540 — Inscriptions: a, 200s, Boburning toj kiyib Farg'ona taxtiga chiqishi (Coronation). b, 250s, Boburning Samarqandliklar tomonidan tantana bilan kutib olinishi (Samarqand people welcome Babur). c, 350s, Bobur Hirotda Sulton Huseyn xonadonida (Babur at Sultan Hussein's house). d, 350s, Bengaliya elchisi Bobur qabulida (Babur receives Bengal ambassador). e, 350s, Babur. f, 410s, Qobul qal'asining qamaldan ozod etilishi (Babur freeing Kabul fortress). g, 490s, Bobur Dehli atrofidagi maqbaralami ziyorat qilmoqda (Babur views Delhi mausoleum). h, 540s, Qobul atrofidagi Xo'ja Seyoron chashmasi (Xo'ja Seyoron Spring near Kabul). i, 680s, Bobur Mon Sing va Bikramojit saroylarini tomosha qilmoqda (Babur views Man Singh and Bikramajit Palaces).

2008, Feb. 13
540 A247   Sheet of 9, #a-i   5.75 5.75

National   Alisher Navoiy
Academic Drama   Theater — A249
Theater — A248

2008, Feb. 28   Perf. 13¾x14
541 A248   45s blue   .20   .20
542 A249   90s dark green   .20   .20

No. 542 has thicker lettering than No. 454.

VANUATU

ˌvan-ˌwä-'tü

LOCATION — Island group in south Pacific Ocean northeast of New Caledonia
GOVT. — Republic
AREA — 5,700 sq. mi.
POP. — 189,036 (1999 est.)
CAPITAL — Port Vila

The Anglo-French condominium of New Hebrides (Vol. 4) became the independent state of Vanuatu July 30, 1980.

Hebrides franc Vatu (1981)

Catalogue values for all unused stamps in this country are for Never Hinged items.

Erromango Is. and
Kaori Tree — A44

Designs: 10fr, Archipelago and man making copra. 15fr, Espiritu Santo Island and cattle. 20fr, Efate Island and Post Office, Vila. 25fr, Malakula Island and headdresses. 30fr, Aoba and Maewo Islands and pig tusks. 35fr, Pentecost Island and land diving. 40fr, Tanna Island and Prophet John Frum's Red Cross. 50fr, Shepherd Island and canoe with sail. 100fr, Banks Island and dancers. 200fr, Ambrym Island and carvings. 200fr, Aneityum Island and decorated baskets. 500fr, Torres Islands and fishing with bow and arrow.

Wmk. 373
1980, July 30   Litho.   Perf. 14
280 A44   5fr multicolored   .20   .20
281 A44   10fr multicolored   .20   .20
282 A44   15fr multicolored   .35   .30
283 A44   20fr multicolored   .45   .40
284 A44   25fr multicolored   .55   .45
285 A44   30fr multicolored   .70   .60
286 A44   35fr multicolored   .80   .65
287 A44   40fr multicolored   .80   .75
288 A44   50fr multicolored   .85   .90
289 A44   70fr multicolored   1.60 1.25
290 A44   100fr multicolored   1.60 1.00
291 A44   200fr multicolored   1.75 1.75
292 A44   500fr multicolored   3.25 3.75
      Nos. 280-292 (13)   13.10 12.20

Inscribed in French
Unwmk.
280a A44   5fr multicolored   .50   .20
281a A44   10fr multicolored   .65   .20
282a A44   15fr multicolored   .75   .65
283a A44   20fr multicolored   .80   .75
284a A44   25fr multicolored   .90   .85
285a A44   30fr multicolored   .90 1.00
286a A44   35fr multicolored   1.00 1.25
287a A44   40fr multicolored   1.40 1.40
288a A44   50fr multicolored   1.60 1.60
289a A44   70fr multicolored   2.25 2.25
290a A44   100fr multicolored   2.40 2.50
291a A44   200fr multicolored   2.75 4.25
292a A44   500fr multicolored   6.25 8.25
      Nos. 280a-292a (13)   22.15 25.15

Rotary   Kiwanis
Emblem — A52   Emblem — A53

1980, Sept. 16   Wmk. 373
293	A52	10fr Emblem, horiz.	.20	.20
294	A52	40fr shown	.65	.65

Inscribed in French
Unwmk.
293a	A52	10fr multicolored	.20	.20
294a	A52	40fr multicolored	.85	.85

75th anniv. of Rotary Intl. and 8th anniv. of Port Vila Rotary Club (40fr).

1980, Sept. 16   Wmk. 373
295	A53	10fr shown	.20	.20
296	A53	40fr Emblem, horiz.	.50	.50

Inscribed in French
Unwmk.
295a	A53	10fr multicolored	.25	.20
296a	A53	40fr multicolored	1.00	.85

New Zealand District Kiwanis Convention, Port Vila, Sept. 16-18.

Christmas A54

Erythrura Trichroa — A55

Paintings: 10fr, Virgin and Child, by Michael Pacher. 15fr, Virgin and Child, by Hans Memling. 30fr, Rest on the Flight to Egypt, by Adriaen van der Werff.

1980, Nov. 12   Wmk. 373
297	A54	10fr multicolored	.20	.20
298	A54	15fr multicolored	.25	.25
299	A54	30fr multicolored	.55	.55
		Nos. 297-299 (3)	1.00	1.00

1981, Feb. 18
300	A55	10fr shown	.60	.30
301	A55	20fr Chalcophaps indica	1.10	.70
302	A55	30fr Pachycephala pectoralis	1.60	1.10
303	A55	40fr Ptilinopus tannensis	2.10	1.40
		Nos. 300-303 (4)	5.40	3.50

Duke of Edinburgh's 60th Birthday — A56

1981, June 10   Perf. 14x14½
304	A56	15fr Tribesman, portrait	.20	.20
305	A56	25fr Portrait	.30	.30
306	A56	35fr Family	.45	.45
307	A56	45fr shown	.60	.60
		Nos. 304-307 (4)	1.55	1.55

Common Design Types
pictured following the introduction.

Royal Wedding Issue
Common Design Type

1981, July 29
308	CD331	15v Bouquet	.25	.25
309	CD331	45v Charles	.55	.55
310	CD331	75v Couple	.80	.80
		Nos. 308-310 (3)	1.60	1.60

First Anniv. of Independence — A57

1981, July 19
311	A57	15v Map, flag, vert.	.20	.20
312	A57	25v Emblem	.20	.20
313	A57	45v Anthem	.60	.60
314	A57	75v Arms, vert.	.80	.80
		Nos. 311-314 (4)	1.80	1.80

Christmas A58

Designs: Children's drawings.

Wmk. 373
1981, Nov. 11   Litho.   Perf. 14
315	A58	15v Three kings	.20	.20
316	A58	25v Girl holding lamb, vert.	.35	.35
317	A58	35v Butterfly-angel	.50	.50
318	A58	45v Gift bearer, vert.	.70	.70
a.		Souvenir sheet, #315-318	2.50	2.50
		Nos. 315-318 (4)	1.75	1.75

Broadbills — A59

Orchids — A60

1982, Feb. 8   Perf. 14½x14
319	A59	15v shown	.75	.75
320	A59	20v Rainbow lorries	1.00	1.00
321	A59	25v Buff-bellied flycatchers	1.25	1.25
322	A59	45v Fantails	2.25	2.25
		Nos. 319-322 (4)	5.25	5.25

Perf. 14x13½, 13½x14
1982, June 15
323	A60	1v Flickengeria comata	.20	.70
324	A60	2v Calanthe triplicata	.30	.75
325	A60	10v Dendrobium sladei	.35	.40
326	A60	15v Dendrobium mohlianum	.50	.35
327	A60	20v Dendrobium macrophyllum	.60	.40
328	A60	25v Dendrobium purpureum	.95	.70
329	A60	30v Robiquetia mimus	1.10	1.10
330	A60	35v Dendrobium mooreanum	1.25	1.25
331	A60	45v Spathoglottis plicata	1.50	1.40
332	A60	50v Dendrobium seemannii	1.75	1.75
333	A60	75v Dendrobium conanthum	2.75	2.75
334	A60	100v Dendrobium macranthum	3.25	2.75
335	A60	200v Coelogyne lamellata	4.00	4.25
336	A60	500v Bulbophyllum longiscapum	7.75	9.25
		Nos. 323-336 (14)	26.25	27.80

Nos. 330-333, 336 horiz.
For surcharges see Nos. 383, 512, 551-554, 586-589A, B1.

Scouting Year A61

Wmk. 373
1982, Sept. 1   Litho.   Perf. 14
337	A61	15v Around campfire	.45	.45
338	A61	20v First aid	.50	.50
339	A61	25v Signal tower	.65	.65
340	A61	45v Building raft	1.40	1.40
341	A61	75v Scout sign	2.00	2.00
		Nos. 337-341 (5)	5.00	5.00

Christmas — A62

Details from Nativity painting. 35v, 45v horiz.

1982, Nov. 16
342	A62	15v multicolored	.40	.40
343	A62	25v multicolored	.65	.65
344	A62	35v multicolored	.95	.95
345	A62	45v multicolored	1.25	1.25
a.		Souvenir sheet of 4, #342-345	4.25	4.25
		Nos. 342-345 (4)	3.25	3.25

Hypolimnas Octocula A63

1983, Jan. 17   Perf. 14½
346		Pair	2.75	2.10
a.		A63 15v shown	1.25	.95
b.		A63 15v Euploea sylvester	1.25	.95
347		Pair	3.25	2.75
a.		A63 20v Polyura sacco	1.50	1.25
b.		A63 20v Papilio canopus	1.50	1.25
348		Pair	4.25	3.00
a.		A63 25v Parantica pumila	2.00	1.50
b.		A63 25v Luthrodes cleotas	2.00	1.50
		Nos. 346-348 (3)	10.25	7.85

A64

1983, Mar. 14   Perf. 13½x14
349	A64	15v Pres. Sokomanu	.20	.20
350	A64	20v Fisherman	.25	.25
351	A64	25v Herdsman, cattle	.30	.30
352	A64	75v Flags, map	.90	.90
		Nos. 349-352 (4)	1.65	1.65

Commonwealth Day. 20v, 75v inscribed in French.

Economic Zone — A65

a, Thunnus albacares. b, Map. c, Matthew Isld. d, Hunter Isld. e, Epinephelus morrhua, etelis carbunculus. f, Katsuwonus pelamis.

Perf. 14x13½
1983, May 23   Litho.   Wmk. 373
353		Sheet of 6	5.00	5.00
a.-f.		A65 25v multicolored	.80	.80

Manned Flight Bicentenary — A66

Balloons or Airships: 15v, Montgolfiere, 1783. 20v, J.A.C. Charles 1st hydrogen balloon, 1783. 25v, Blanchard & Jeffries 1st English Channel crossing, 1785. 35v, H. Giffard's 1st mechanically powered airship, 1852. 40v, Renard and Krebs' airship, 1884. 45v, Graf Zeppelin's 1st transworld flight, 1929.

1983, Aug. 4   Litho.   Perf. 14
354	A66	15v multi, vert.	.40	.40
355	A66	20v multi, vert.	.45	.45
356	A66	25v multi, vert.	.60	.60
357	A66	35v multi	.80	.80
358	A66	40v multi	.90	.90
359	A66	45v multi	1.10	1.10
		Nos. 354-359 (6)	4.25	4.25

For overprint see No. 372.

World Communications Year — A67

1983, Oct. 10   Litho.   Wmk. 373
360	A67	15v Mail transport, Bauerfield Airport	.30	.30
361	A67	20v Switchboard operator	.45	.45
362	A67	25v Telex operator	.65	.65
363	A67	45v Satellite earth station	1.10	1.10
a.		Souv. sheet of 4, #360-363 + 3 labels	6.50	6.50
		Nos. 360-363 (4)	2.50	2.50

No. 363a issued for WCY and 75th anniv. of New Hebrides stamps.

Local Fungi — A68

1984, Jan. 9   Litho.   Perf. 14
364	A68	15v Cymatoderma elegans, vert.	1.10	1.10
365	A68	25v Lignosus rhinoceros, vert.	1.25	1.25
366	A68	35v Stereum ostrea	2.00	2.00
367	A68	45v Ganoderma boninenze, vert.	2.50	2.50
		Nos. 364-367 (4)	6.85	6.85

Lloyd's List Issue
Common Design Type

1984, Apr. 30   Litho.   Perf. 14½x14
368	CD335	15v Port Vila	.40	.40
369	CD335	20v Induna	.55	.55
370	CD335	25v Air Vanuatu jet	.70	.70
371	CD335	45v Brahman Express	1.25	1.25
		Nos. 368-371 (4)	2.90	2.90

No. 359 Overprinted "UPU CONGRESS / HAMBURG"

1984, June 11   Wmk. 373   Perf. 14
372	A66	45v multicolored	.90	.90

Cattle A69

1984, July 3   Litho.   Perf. 14
373	A69	15v Charolais	.30	.30
374	A69	25v Charolais-Afrikaner	.45	.45
375	A69	45v Friesian	.85	.85
376	A69	75v Charolais-Brahman	1.40	1.40
		Nos. 373-376 (4)	3.00	3.00

Ausipex '84 — A70

Ships.

1984, Sept. 7
377	A70	25v Makambo	.90	.65
378	A70	45v Rockton	1.60	1.25
379	A70	100v Waroonga	3.00	4.75
a.		Souvenir sheet of 3, #377-379	5.50	5.75
		Nos. 377-379 (3)	5.50	6.65

Christmas A71

1984, Nov. 19　Litho.　Wmk. 373
380	A71	25v Father Christmas, child in hospital	.60	.35
381	A71	45v Nativity	1.10	.90
382	A71	75v Father Christmas, children	1.75	1.75
		Nos. 380-382 (3)	3.45	3.00

No. 323 Surcharged with 2 Black Bars

1985, Jan. 22　Litho.　Perf. 14x13½
383	A60	5v on 1v multi	2.00	1.25

Ceremonial Dance Costumes — A71a

Audubon Birth Bicent. — A72

1985, Jan. 22　　　　Perf. 14
384	A71a	20v Ambrym Island	.40	.40
385	A71a	25v Pentecost Island	.60	.60
386	A71a	45v Women's Grade Ceremony, S.W. Malakula	1.00	1.00
387	A71a	75v Same, men's	1.50	1.50
		Nos. 384-387 (4)	3.50	3.50

Wmk. 373

1985, Mar. 26　Litho.　Perf. 14

Peregrine falcons.
388	A72	20v multicolored	1.25	1.25
389	A72	35v multicolored	1.50	1.50
390	A72	45v multicolored	1.75	1.75
391	A72	100v multicolored	3.00	3.00
		Nos. 388-391 (4)	7.50	7.50

Queen Mother 85th Birthday
Common Design Type
Perf. 14½x14

1985, June 7　　　　Wmk. 384
392	CD336	5v Wedding photo	.30	.30
393	CD336	20v 80th birthday celebration	.55	.55
394	CD336	35v At Ancona, Italy	.70	.70
395	CD336	55v Holding Prince Henry	1.10	1.10
		Nos. 392-395 (4)	2.65	2.65

Souvenir Sheet
396	CD336	100v At Covent Garden Opera	3.50	3.50

EXPO '85, Tsukuba — A73

35v, Mala naval patrol boat. 45v, Japanese fishing fleet, Port Vila. 55v, Mobile Force Band. 100v, Prime Minister Walter H. Lini.

1985, July 26　Wmk. 373　Perf. 14
397	A73	35v multicolored	.80	.50
398	A73	45v multicolored	1.00	.75
399	A73	55v multicolored	1.10	.90
400	A73	100v multicolored	1.25	1.90
a.		Souvenir sheet of 4, #397-400	5.25	5.25
		Nos. 397-400 (4)	4.15	4.05

Natl. independence, 5th anniv.

Intl. Youth Year A74

Children's drawings.

1985, Sept. 16　Wmk. 373　Perf. 14
401	A74	20v Alain Lagaliu	.65	.65
402	A74	30v Peter Obed	.75	.75
403	A74	50v Mary Estelle	1.25	1.25
404	A74	100v Abel M rani	2.10	2.10
		Nos. 401-404 (4)	4.75	4.75

Natl. and UN Flags, Map A75

1985, Sept. 24　Litho.　Perf. 14
405	A75	45v multicolored	1.25	1.10

Admission of Vanuatu to UN, 4th anniv.

Sea Slugs — A76

Scuba Diving — A77

1985, Nov. 11　Wmk. 373　Perf. 14½
406	A76	20v Chromodoris elisa bethina	.50	.50
407	A76	35v Halgerda auranti-omaculata	.95	.95
408	A76	55v Chromodoris kuniei	1.40	1.40
409	A76	100v Notodoris minor	2.50	2.50
		Nos. 406-409 (4)	5.35	5.35

Nos. 407-408 horiz. See Nos. 497-500.

1986, Jan. 22　Wmk. 384　Perf. 14
410	A77	30v shown	1.10	.65
411	A77	35v Volcanic eruption	1.25	.70
412	A77	55v Land diving	1.25	1.10
413	A77	100v Wind surfing	1.60	2.50
		Nos. 410-413 (4)	5.20	4.95

See No. 479.

Queen Elizabeth II 60th Birthday
Common Design Type

Designs: 20v, With Prince Charles and Princess Anne, 1951. 35v, At christening of Prince William, the Music Room, Buckingham Palace, 1982. 45v, State visit, 1985. 55v, State visit to Mexico, 1974. 100v, Visiting Crown Agents' offices, 1983.

1987, Jan. 22
434	A82	20v Datsun 240Z, 1969	.40	.40
435	A82	45v Model A Ford, 1927	.80	.80
436	A82	55v Unic, 1924-25	.95	.95
437	A82	135v Citroen DS19, 1975	2.25	2.25
		Nos. 434-437 (4)	4.40	4.40

1986, Apr. 21　Litho.　Perf. 14x14½
414	CD337	20v scar, blk & sil	.35	.35
415	CD337	35v ultra & multi	.60	.60
416	CD337	45v green & multi	.70	.70
417	CD337	55v violet & multi	.90	.90
418	CD337	100v multicolored	1.75	1.75
		Nos. 414-418 (5)	4.30	4.30

For overprints & surcharges see #465-469, B2-B6.

AMERIPEX '86 — A78

1986, May 19　Wmk. 373　Perf. 14
419	A78	45v SS President Coolidge	1.10	.75
420	A78	55v As troop ship, 1942	1.25	.95
421	A78	135v Site of sinking, 1942	2.40	2.40
a.		Souvenir sheet of 3, #419-421	5.50	5.00
		Nos. 419-421 (3)	4.75	4.40

Halley's Comet A79

1986, June 23　Wmk. 384　Perf. 14½
422	A79	30v Comet, deity statue	1.40	1.40
423	A79	45v Family sighting comet	1.60	1.60
424	A79	55v Comet over SW Pacific	1.90	1.90
425	A79	100v Edmond Halley, manuscript	2.50	2.50
		Nos. 422-425 (4)	7.40	7.40

Coral A80

1986, Oct. 27　Wmk. 373　Perf. 14
426	A80	20v Daisy	.75	.75
427	A80	45v Organ pipe	1.75	1.75
428	A80	55v Sea fan	2.10	2.10
429	A80	135v Soft	5.25	5.25
		Nos. 426-429 (4)	9.85	9.85

Intl. Peace Year A81

1986, Nov. 3　Litho.　Perf. 14
430	A81	30v Children of the world	.75	.75
431	A81	45v Child praying	1.25	1.25
432	A81	55v UN building, negotiators	1.50	1.50
433	A81	135v Peoples working in harmony	3.75	3.75
		Nos. 430-433 (4)	7.25	7.25

Automotives A82

IRHO Coconut Research Station, 25th Anniv. A83

1987, May 13　　　　Perf. 14½x14
438	A83	35v Nursery	.65	.65
439	A83	45v Cocos nucifera tree	.95	.95
440	A83	100v Cocos nucifera fruit	1.60	1.60
441	A83	135v Station	2.00	2.00
		Nos. 438-441 (4)	5.20	5.20

Fish — A84

Perf. 14x14½

1987, July 15　　　　Wmk. 384
442	A84	1v Cirrhitichthys aprinus	.25	.25
443	A84	5v Zanclus cornutus	.25	.25
444	A84	10v Canthigaster cinctus	.25	.25
445	A84	15v Amphiprion rubrocinctus	.35	.35
446	A84	20v Acanthurus lineatus	.50	.50
447	A84	30v Thalassoma hardwicki	.65	.65
448	A84	35v Anthias tuka	.70	.70
449	A84	40v Adioryx micros-tomus	.80	.80
450	A84	45v Balistoides con-spicillum	1.00	1.00
451	A84	50v Xyrichtys taeniouris	1.10	1.10
452	A84	55v Hemitaurich-thys polyepis	1.25	1.25
453	A84	65v Pterois volitans	1.40	1.40
454	A84	100v Paracirrhites for-steri	2.50	2.50
455	A84	300v Balistapus undu-latus	6.75	6.75
456	A84	500v Chaetodon ephippium	9.25	9.25
		Nos. 442-456 (15)	27.00	27.00

Insects A85

1987, Sept. 22　Wmk. 373　Perf. 14
457	A85	45v Xylotrupes gideon	1.00	1.00
458	A85	55v Phyllodes imperialis	1.10	1.10
459	A85	65v Cyphogaster	1.50	1.50
460	A85	100v Othreis fullonia	2.25	2.25
		Nos. 457-460 (4)	5.85	5.85

Christmas Carols — A86

1987, Nov. 10　　　　Perf. 13½x14
461	A86	20v Away in a Manger	.45	.45
462	A86	45v Once in Royal David's City	1.00	1.00
463	A86	55v While Shepherds Watched Their Flocks	1.25	1.25
464	A86	65v We Three Kings of Orient Are	1.50	1.50
		Nos. 461-464 (4)	4.20	4.20

Nos. 414-418 Ovptd. in Silver:
"40TH WEDDING ANNIVERSARY"
Perf. 14x14½
1987, Dec. 9　Litho.　Wmk. 384
465	CD337	20v scar, blk & sil	.60	.60
466	CD337	35v ultra & multi	.75	.75
467	CD337	45v green & multi	1.00	1.00

468 CD337 55v violet & multi   1.10 1.10
469 CD337 100v multicolored   1.90 1.90
   Nos. 465-469 (5)   5.35 5.35

World
Wildlife
Fund — A87

Dugongs.

1988, Feb. 29   Perf. 13x13½
470 A87 5v Mother, calf   1.25   .45
471 A87 10v Adult   2.00 1.00
472 A87 20v Two adults   2.50 1.25
473 A87 45v Herd   4.50 3.25
   Nos. 470-473 (4)   10.25 5.40

Australia
Bicentennial
A88

Burns Philip emblem, bicent. emblem and steamships.

1988, May 18   Wmk. 373   Perf. 12
474 A88 20v S.S. Tambo   .40   .40
475 A88 45v S.S. Induna   .85   .85
476 A88 55v S.S. Morinda   1.00 1.00
477 A88 65v S.S. Marsina   1.10 1.10
   Nos. 474-477 (4)   3.35 3.35

Capt. James Cook
(1728-1779),
Explorer — A89

Perf. 14 on 2 or 3 Sides
1988, July 29   Wmk. 384
478 A89 45v black & red   .90   .90
SYDPEX '88. No. 478 printed in panes of 10 plus 5 center labels picturing a map of Vanuatu, HMS Resolution, exhibition emblem, HMS Endeavour or a map of Australia.

Tourism Type of 1986
Souvenir Sheet
Wmk. 373
1988, Aug. 24   Litho.   Perf. 14
479   Sheet of 2   4.50 4.50
a. A77 55v like No. 412   1.10 1.10
b. A77 100v like No. 413   2.25 2.25
EXPO '88. Nos. 479a-479b are dated 1988 and "Vanuatu" is inscribed in violet blue.

1988 Summer
Olympics,
Seoul — A90

1988, Sept. 19   Perf. 13½x14
480 A90 20v Boxing   .30   .30
481 A90 45v Track events   .85   .85
482 A90 55v Signing Olympic
        agreement   1.00 1.00
483 A90 65v Soccer   1.25 1.25
   Nos. 480-483 (4)   3.40 3.40
Souvenir Sheet
484 A90 150v Tennis   4.00 4.00
Intl. Tennis Federation, 75th anniv. (150v).

Lloyds of London, 300th Anniv.
Common Design Type

Designs: 20v, Lloyds new building, 1988. 55v, Cargo ship Shirrabank, horiz. 65v, Adela, horiz. 145v, Excursion steamer General Slocum on fire in New York Harbor, 1904.

1988, Oct. 25   Wmk. 384   Perf. 14
485 CD341 20v multicolored   .55   .55
486 CD341 55v multicolored 1.40 1.40
487 CD341 65v multicolored 1.50 1.50
488 CD341 145v multicolored 3.75 3.75
   Nos. 485-488 (4)   7.20 7.20

FAO — A91

Perf. 14½x14, 14x14½
1988, Nov. 14
489 A91 45v Tending crops   1.10 1.10
490 A91 55v Fishing, vert. 1.25 1.25
491 A91 65v Animal husbandry,
          vert.   1.25 1.25
492 A91 120v Produce market 1.60 1.60
   Nos. 489-492 (4)   5.20 5.20

Christmas
A92

Carols: 20v, Silent Night, Holy Night. 45v, Angels From the Realms of Glory. 65v, O Come All Ye Faithful. 155v, In That Poor Stable How Charming Jesus Lies.

1988, Dec. 1   Litho.   Perf. 14½x14
493 A92 20v multicolored   .50   .50
494 A92 45v multicolored   .80   .80
495 A92 65v multicolored   .90   .90
496 A92 155v multicolored 2.40 2.50
   Nos. 493-496 (4)   4.60 4.70

Marine Life Type of 1985
Shrimp.

1989, Feb. 1   Perf. 14
497 A76 20v Periclimenes brevi-
          carpalis   .50   .50
498 A76 45v Lysmata grabhami 1.25 1.25
499 A76 65v Rhynchocinetes   1.60 1.60
500 A76 150v Stenopus hispidus 3.25 3.25
   Nos. 497-500 (4)   6.60 6.60

Economic &
Social
Commission
for Asia and
the Pacific
(ESCAP)
A93

Perf. 12x12½
1989, Apr. 5   Litho.   Wmk. 373
501 A93 20v Consolidated
          Catalina   1.25 1.25
502 A93 45v Douglas DC-3   1.75 1.75
503 A93 55v Embraer
          EMB110
          Bandeirante   1.90 1.90
504 A93 200v Boeing 737-300 6.00 6.00
   Nos. 501-504 (4)   10.90 10.90
Inauguration of the Sydney-Noumea-Espiritu Santo Service, 1948 (20v).

PHILEXFRANCE '89 — A94

Exhibition emblem and: No. 505a, Porte de Versailles Hall Number 1. No. 505b, Eiffel Tower. No. 506, Revolt of French Troops, Nancy, 1790.

1989, July 5   Wmk. 373   Perf. 12
505   A94   Pair   6.50 6.50
a.-b. 100v any single   3.00 3.00
Souvenir Sheet
Perf. 14
Wmk. 384
506   A94 100v multicolored 2.75 2.75
French revolution, bicent.

Moon Landing, 20th Anniv.
Common Design Type

Apollo 17: 45v, Command module in space. 55v, Harrison Schmitt, Gene Cerman and Ron Evans. 65v, Mission emblem. 120v, Liftoff. 100v, Recovery of Apollo 11 crew after spashdown.

1989, July 20   Wmk. 384   Perf. 14
Size of Nos. 508-509: 29x29mm
507 CD342 45v multicolored 1.75 1.75
508 CD342 55v multicolored 1.75 1.75
509 CD342 65v multicolored 2.00 2.00
510 CD342 120v multicolored 3.50 3.50
   Nos. 507-510 (4)   9.00 9.00
Souvenir Sheet
511 CD342 100v multicolored 3.25 3.25

No. 324
Surcharged

Perf. 14x13½
1989, Oct. 18   Litho.   Wmk. 373
512 A60 100v on 2v multi   6.50 6.50
STAMPSHOW '89, Melbourne.

World
Stamp
Expo
'89 — A95

Perf. 14x13½
1989, Nov. 6   Litho.   Wmk. 384
513 A95 65v New Hebrides
          #256   4.50 4.50
Souvenir Sheet
514   Sheet of 2   11.50 11.50
a. A95 65v New Hebrides #254 4.00 4.00
b. A95 100v The White House
          (detail)   6.00 6.00

A96

A97

Flora.

Perf. 12½x12
1990, Jan. 5   Wmk. 373
515 A96 45v Alocasia macror-
          rhiza   1.10 1.10
516 A96 55v Acacia spirorbis 1.25 1.25
517 A96 65v Metrosideros col-
          lina   1.50 1.50
518 A96 145v Hoya australis 3.50 3.50
   Nos. 515-518 (4)   7.35 7.35

1990, Apr. 30   Perf. 13x13½
Stamp World London '90 Exhibition emblem and simulated stamps or stamps on stamps:

45v, Kava (simulated stamps). 65v, Luganville P.O. exterior, interior (simulated stamps). 100v, Propeller plane, 19th cent. packet (simulated stamps). 150v, New Hebrides #187-188, first day cancellation. 200v, Great Britain #1, Vanuatu #281.
519 A97 45v multicolored   1.10 1.10
520 A97 65v multicolored   1.75 1.75
521 A97 100v multicolored   2.50 2.50
522 A97 200v multicolored   4.50 4.50
   Nos. 519-522 (4)   9.85 9.85
Souvenir Sheet
523 A97 150v multicolored   8.50 8.50
Penny Black, 150th anniv. No. 523 margin pictures first day cancel and cachet.

Independence, 10th Anniv. — A98

25v, Natl. Council of Women Emblem. 50v, Pres. Frederick Kalomuana Timakata. 55v, Preamble to Constitution. 65v, Vanuaaku Pati flag. 80v, Reserve Bank. 150v, Prime Minister Walter H. Lini.

1990, July 30   Perf. 14
524 A98 25v multicolored   .50   .50
525 A98 50v multicolored   1.10 1.10
526 A98 55v multicolored   1.25 1.25
527 A98 65v multicolored   1.40 1.40
528 A98 80v multicolored   1.75 1.75
   Nos. 524-528 (5)   6.00 6.00
Souvenir Sheet
529 A98 150v multi   6.75 6.75

Minature Sheet

Charles De Gaulle (1890-1970) — A99

Wmk. 373
1990, Nov. 22   Litho.   Perf. 14
530   Sheet, 2 ea #530c-530f
       + 2 labels   26.50 26.50
a. A99 20v At Bayeux, after D-day
          landing   4.75 4.75
b. A99 25v Alsace, 1945   4.75 4.75
c. A99 30v Portrait   1.90 1.90
d. A99 45v Spitfire, Biggin Hill,
          1942   2.10 2.10
e. A99 55v Casablanca, 1943 2.25 2.25
f. A99 65v Day of Glory, Paris,
          1944   2.40 2.40

Christmas — A100

1990, Dec. 5   Perf. 13
531   Strip of 5   6.00 6.00
a. A100 25v Angel facing right .60 .60
b. A100 50v Shepherds   .90   .90
c. A100 65v Nativity   1.00 1.00
d. A100 70v The Three Kings 1.10 1.10
e. A100 80v Angel facing left 1.10 1.10

Butterflies
A101

Perf. 14x14½
1991, Jan. 9   Wmk. 384
532 A101 25v Parthenos sylvia .85 .85
533 A101 55v Euploea leucos-
          tictos   1.60 1.60
534 A101 80v Lampides
          boeticus   2.25 2.25
535 A101 150v Danaus plexippus 4.25 4.25
   Nos. 532-535 (4)   8.95 8.95

Art
Festival — A102

Phila Nippon
'91 — A103

Wmk. 373

1991, May 2   Litho.   Perf. 13½

536	A102	25v Dance	.60	.60
537	A102	65v Weaving	1.60	1.60
538	A102	80v Carving	2.10	2.10
539	A102	150v Music	3.75	3.75
		Nos. 536-539 (4)	8.05	8.05

Elizabeth & Philip, Birthdays
Common Design Types
Wmk. 384

1991, June 17   Litho.   Perf. 14½

540	CD345	65v multicolored	1.00	1.00
541	CD346	70v multicolored	1.10	1.10
a.		Pair, #540-541 + label	2.75	2.75

Wmk. 373

1991, Nov. 15   Litho.   Perf. 14½

Birds: 50v, White-collared kingfisher. 55v, Green palm lorikeet. 80v, Scarlet robin. 100v, Pacific swallow. 150v, Reef heron.

542	A103	50v multicolored	1.25	1.25
543	A103	55v multicolored	1.25	1.25
544	A103	80v multicolored	1.90	1.90
545	A103	100v multicolored	2.25	2.25
		Nos. 542-545 (4)	6.65	6.65

Souvenir Sheet

546	A103	150v multicolored	4.50	4.50

Fight
Against
AIDS
A104

Designs: 25v, Multiple partners, unsafe sex can spread AIDS. 65v, AIDS victim and care giver. 80v, AIDS kills, shark. 150v, Children's playground.

1991, Nov. 29   Wmk. 384   Perf. 14

547	A104	25v multicolored	.75	.75
548	A104	65v multicolored	1.40	1.40
549	A104	80v multicolored	1.75	1.75
550	A104	150v multicolored	3.25	3.25
		Nos. 547-550 (4)	7.15	7.15

Nos. 324-326 &
329 Surcharged

Perf. 14x13½

1991, June 12   Litho.   Wmk. 373

551	A60	20v on 2v #324	.75	.75
552	A60	60v on 10v #325	2.25	2.25
553	A60	70v on 15v #326	2.75	2.75
554	A60	80v on 30v #329	3.00	3.00
		Nos. 551-554 (4)	8.75	8.75

Queen Elizabeth II's Accession to the Throne, 40th Anniv.
Common Design Type

1992, Feb. 6   Wmk. 384   Perf. 14

555	CD349	20v multicolored	.40	.40
556	CD349	25v multicolored	.50	.50
557	CD349	60v multicolored	1.10	1.10
558	CD349	65v multicolored	1.25	1.25

Wmk. 373

559	CD349	70v multicolored	1.25	1.25
		Nos. 555-559 (5)	4.50	4.50

New Hebrides Participation in World
War II — A105

Designs: 50v, Grumman F4F-4 Wildcat. 55v, Douglas SBD-3 Dauntless. 65v, Consolidated PBY-5A Catalina. 80v, USS Hornet. 200v, Vought-Sikorsky OS2U-3.

Perf. 13½x14

1992, May 22   Litho.   Wmk. 373

560	A105	50v multicolored	2.75	2.75
561	A105	55v multicolored	2.75	2.75
562	A105	65v multicolored	3.00	3.00
563	A105	80v multicolored	4.25	4.25
		Nos. 560-563 (4)	12.75	12.75

Souvenir Sheet

564	A105	200v multicolored	14.00	14.00

World Columbian Stamp Expo, Chicago (No. 564).
See Nos. 590-594, 664-667.

Vanuatu's Membership in the World
Meteorological Organization, 10th
Anniv. — A106

Designs: 25v, Meteorological station, Port Vila. 60v, Cyclone near Vanuatu seen by Japanese satellite GMS 4. 80v, Weather chart showing cyclone. 105v, Cyclone warning broadcast by radio.

1992, June 20   Perf. 14

565	A106	25v multicolored	.65	.65
566	A106	60v multicolored	1.60	1.60
567	A106	80v multicolored	2.10	2.10
568	A106	105v multicolored	2.25	2.25
		Nos. 565-568 (4)	6.60	6.60

1992 Melanesian Cup — A107

1992, July 20   Perf. 13½x14

569	A107	20v Soccer team, trophy	.60	.60
570	A107	65v Soccer players	1.50	1.50
571	A107	70v Men's track	1.75	1.75
572	A107	80v Women's track	1.75	1.75
		Nos. 569-572 (4)	5.60	5.60

1992 Summer Olympics, Barcelona (#571-572).
For surcharges see Nos. 621-622.

World Food
Day — A108

Designs: 20v, "Breast is best." 70v, Central Hospital, Port Vila. 80v, "Give your children a healthy future." 150v, Nutritious food.

1992, Oct. 16   Wmk. 384   Perf. 14

573	A108	20v green & brown	.50	.50
574	A108	70v brown & green	1.25	1.25
575	A108	80v green & brown	1.50	1.50
576	A108	150v brown & green	2.75	2.75
		Nos. 573-576 (4)	6.00	6.00

Turtles
A109

1992, Dec. 15   Perf. 14x14½

577	A109	55v Leatherback turtle	1.75	1.75
578	A109	65v Loggerhead turtle	2.00	2.00
579	A109	70v Hawksbill turtle	2.75	2.75
580	A109	80v Green turtle	3.50	3.50
		Nos. 577-580 (4)	10.00	10.00

Souvenir Sheet

581	A109	200v Green turtle hatchlings	7.50	7.50

Hibiscus — A110

Designs: 25v, Light pink hibiscus rosa-sinensis. 55v, Hibiscus tiliaceus. 80v, Red hibiscus rosa-sinensis. 150v, Dark pink hibiscus rosa-sinensis.

Wmk. 384

1993, Mar. 3   Litho.   Perf. 14

582	A110	25v multicolored	.55	.55
583	A110	55v multicolored	1.25	1.25
584	A110	80v multicolored	1.60	1.60
585	A110	150v multicolored	3.00	3.00
		Nos. 582-585 (4)	6.40	6.40

Nos. 331, 333-335 Surcharged

Perf. 13½x14, 14x13½

1993, Apr. 21   Litho.   Wmk. 373

586	A60	40v on 45v #331	1.00	1.00
587	A60	55v on 75v #333	1.40	1.40
588	A60	65v on 100v #334	1.60	1.60
589	A60	150v on 200v #335	4.00	4.00
		Nos. 586-589 (4)	8.00	8.00

Size and location of surcharge varies.

No. 326 Surcharged

1993, June 1

589A	A60	20v on 35v #326	8.00	8.00

World War II Type of 1992

20v, Grumman F6F-3 Hellcat. 55v, Lockheed P-38F Lightning. 65v, GrummanTBF-1 Avenger. 80v, USS Essex. 200v, Douglas C-47 Dakota.

1993, June 30   Perf. 13½

590	A105	20v multicolored	1.10	1.10
591	A105	55v multicolored	3.00	3.00
592	A105	65v multicolored	3.75	3.75
593	A105	80v multicolored	4.50	4.50
		Nos. 590-593 (4)	12.35	12.35

Souvenir Sheet

594	A105	200v multicolored	13.00	13.00

Island
Scenes
A111

Designs: 5v, Iririki Island, Port Vila. 10v, Iririki Island, yachts. 15v, Court House, Port Vila. 20v, Two girls, Pentecost Island. 25v, Women dancers, Tanna Island. 30v, Market, Port Vila. 45v, Man with canoe, Erakor Island, vert. 50v, Coconut trees, Champagne Beach. 55v, Coconut trees, North Efate Islands. 60v, Fish (Banks Group). 70v, Sea fan, Tongoa Island, vert. 75v, Espiritu Santo Island. 80v, Sailboat at sunset, Port Vila Bay, vert. 100v, Mele Waterfall, vert. 300v, Yasur Volcano, Tanna Island, vert. 500v, Erakor Island.

1993, July 7   Perf. 14x14½, 14½x14

595	A111	5v multicolored	.20	.20
596	A111	10v multicolored	.20	.20
597	A111	15v multicolored	.30	.30
598	A111	20v multicolored	.40	.40
599	A111	25v multicolored	.45	.45
600	A111	30v multicolored	.55	.50
601	A111	45v multicolored	.80	.80
602	A111	50v multicolored	.90	.90
603	A111	55v multicolored	1.00	1.00
604	A111	60v multicolored	1.10	1.10
605	A111	70v multicolored	1.25	1.25
606	A111	75v multicolored	1.40	1.40
607	A111	80v multicolored	1.40	1.40
608	A111	100v multicolored	1.75	1.75
609	A111	300v multicolored	5.25	5.25
610	A111	500v multicolored	8.75	8.75
		Nos. 595-610 (16)	25.70	25.65

For surcharges see Nos. 619-620, 742-745A, 745D.

Shells — A112

Wmk. 373

1993, Sept. 15   Litho.   Perf. 14½

611	A112	55v Trochus niloticus	1.60	1.60
612	A112	65v Lioconcha castrensis	2.10	2.10
613	A112	80v Turbo petholatus	2.50	2.50
614	A112	150v Pleuroploca trapezium	4.75	4.75
		Nos. 611-614 (4)	10.95	10.95

See Nos. 632-635, 654-657.

Louvre
Museum,
Bicent.
A113

Paintings by De La Tour: 25v, St. Joseph the Carpenter. 55v, The Newborn. 80v, Adoration of the Shepherds (detail). 150v, Adoration of the Shepherds (entire).

Wmk. 373
1993, Nov. 10   Litho.   Perf. 14

615	A113	25v multicolored	.60	.60
616	A113	55v multicolored	1.25	1.25
617	A113	80v multicolored	1.90	1.90
618	A113	150v multicolored	4.00	4.00
		Nos. 615-618 (4)	7.75	7.75

Nos. 570, 572, 598, 600 Surcharged

1993, Dec. 6   Litho.   Wmk. 373
Perfs. as Before

619	A111	15v on 20v #598	.35	.35
620	A111	25v on 30v #600	.50	.50
621	A107	55v on 65v #570	1.25	1.25
622	A107	70v on 80v #572	1.50	1.50
		Nos. 619-622 (4)	3.60	3.60

Service Organizations A114

Intl. Year of the Family A115

Hong Kong '94: 25v, Kiwanis Intl., Charity Races, vert. 60v, Lions Intl. Twin Otter on mercy mission. 75v, Rotary Intl. fighting malaria, vert. 150v, Red Cross blood donar service. 200v, Emblems of service organizations.

Perf. 14x15, 15x14
1994, Feb. 18   Litho.   Wmk. 373

623	A114	25v multicolored	.50	.50
624	A114	60v multicolored	1.40	1.40
625	A114	75v multicolored	1.60	1.60
626	A114	150v multicolored	3.00	3.00
		Nos. 623-626 (4)	6.50	6.50

Souvenir Sheet

627	A114	200v multicolored	4.25	4.25

1994, Mar. 2   Perf. 14

628	A115	25v vio & rose brn	.50	.50
629	A115	60v ver & dk grn	1.25	1.25
630	A115	90v green & sepia	1.75	1.75
631	A115	150v brn & vio bl	3.00	3.00
		Nos. 628-631 (4)	6.50	6.50

Shell Type of 1993
1994, May 31   Litho.   Perf. 12

632	A112	60v Cyprea argus	1.60	1.60
633	A112	70v Conus marmoreus	1.90	1.90
634	A112	85v Lambis chiragra	2.50	2.50
635	A112	155v Chicoreus brunneus	4.50	4.50
		Nos. 632-635 (4)	10.50	10.50

Tourism — A116

Designs: a, 25v, Slit gong (drum), traditional hut. b, 75v, Volcano, boats. c, 90v, Sailboats, airplane, green palm lorikeet. d, 200v, Helicopter, woman with tray of fruit.

1994, July 27   Litho.   Perf. 13½

636	A116	Strip of 4, #a.-d.	9.50	9.50

Anemonefish — A117

1994, Aug. 16   Litho.   Perf. 12

637	A117	55v Pink	2.50	2.50
638	A117	70v Clark's	3.25	3.25
639	A117	80v Red & black	3.50	3.50
640	A117	140v Orange-fin	6.50	6.50
a.		Souvenir sheet of 1	6.50	6.50
		Nos. 637-640 (4)	15.75	15.75

Philakorea '94 (#640a).

ICAO, 50th Anniv. — A118

Designs: 25v, 1950 Qantas Catalina. 60v, 1956 Tai Douglas DC3. 75v, 1966 New Herbrides Airways Drover. 90v, 1994 Air Vanuatu Boeing 737.

1994, Dec. 7

641	A118	25v multicolored	.70	.70
642	A118	60v multicolored	2.00	2.00
643	A118	75v multicolored	2.25	2.25
644	A118	90v multicolored	3.00	3.00
		Nos. 641-644 (4)	7.95	7.95

Hibiscus A119

1995, Feb. 1   Litho.   Perf. 12

645	A119	25v The Path	.55	.55
646	A119	60v Old Frankie	1.40	1.40
647	A119	90v Fijian white	2.10	2.10
648	A119	200v Surf rider	4.75	4.75
		Nos. 645-648 (4)	8.80	8.80

Lizards A120

Designs: 25v, Emoia nigromarginata. 55v, Nactus multicarinatus. 70v, Lepidodactylus. 80v, Emoia caerulocauda. 140v, Emoia sanfordi.

1995, Apr. 12

649	A120	25v multicolored	.60	.60
650	A120	55v multicolored	1.40	1.40
651	A120	70v multicolored	1.75	1.75
652	A120	80v multicolored	2.00	2.00
653	A120	140v multicolored	3.50	3.50
		Nos. 649-653 (5)	9.25	9.25

Shell Type of 1993
1995, June 1

654	A112	25v Epitonium scalare	.70	.70
655	A112	55v Strombus latissimus	1.60	1.60
656	A112	90v Conus bullatus	2.50	2.50
657	A112	200v Pterynotus pinnatus	5.75	5.75
		Nos. 654-657 (4)	10.55	10.55

Anniversaries — A121

Designs: 25v, Girls wearing traditional head pieces. 55v, Stylized picture of natives dancing, vert. 60v, Children, doves, natl. flag, UN flag, vert. 75v, Embroidered tapestry of native, vert. 90v, Troops parading. 140v, Group in traditional ceremony.

Perf. 14x13½, 13½x14
1995, July 28   Litho.

658	A121	25v multicolored	.55	.55
659	A121	55v multicolored	1.25	1.25
660	A121	60v multicolored	1.25	1.25
661	A121	75v multicolored	1.75	1.75
662	A121	90v multicolored	1.90	1.90
663	A121	140v multicolored	3.00	3.00
a.		Souvenir sheet of 1	3.75	3.75
		Nos. 658-663 (6)	9.70	9.70

UN, 50th anniv. (#660). Singapore 95 (#663a). Others, independence, 15th anniv.

World War II Type of 1992
1995, Sept. 1   Litho.   Perf. 12½

664	A105	60v SB2C Helldiver	3.00	3.00
665	A105	70v Spitfire Mk VIII	3.50	3.50
666	A105	75v F4U-1A Corsair	3.50	3.50
667	A105	80v PV1 Ventura	4.00	4.00
		Nos. 664-667 (4)	14.00	14.00

Souvenir Sheet
Perf. 13½

667A	A105	140v Japanese surrender, USS Missouri	9.50	9.50

No. 667A for Singapore 95.

Artifacts — A122

Ambae money mat and: a, 25v, Rambaramp mortuary effigy, Malakula. b, 60v, Wusi pot, Espiritu Santo. c, 75v, Slit gong, Efate Island. d, 90v, Tapa cloth, Erromango Island. Nos. 668e, 668f, like No. 668d. Illustration reduced.

1995, Nov. 22   Litho.   Perf. 13½x13

668	A122	Strip of 4, #a.-d.	5.50	5.50
e.		90v Perf. 14	1.90	1.90
f.		Souvenir sheet, #668e	3.00	3.00

No. 668f, 9th Asian Intl. Philatelic Exhibition, Beijing.
Issued: Nos. 668e, 668f, Dec. 1995.
See No. 720.

Fishing A123

1996, Feb. 1   Litho.   Perf. 14

669	A123	55v Cast net	1.25	1.25
670	A123	75v Reef	1.50	1.50
671	A123	80v Deep water, vert.	1.60	1.60
672	A123	140v Game, vert.	3.00	3.00
		Nos. 669-672 (4)	7.35	7.35

Flying Foxes A124

No. 673, Notopteris macdonaldi, facing left. No. 674, Pteropus anetianus, green leaves on tree, vert. No. 675, Pteropus anetianus, diff., vert. No. 676, Notopteris macdonaldi, diff. No. 677, vert: a, 90v, Pteropus tonganus. b, 140v, Pteropus tonganus, diff.

1996, Apr. 3   Litho.   Perf. 14

673	A124	25v multicolored	.95	.75
674	A124	25v multicolored	.95	.75
675	A124	25v multicolored	.95	.75
676	A124	25v multicolored	.95	.75
		Nos. 673-676 (4)	3.80	3.00

Souvenir Sheet

677	A124	Sheet of 2, #a.-b.	6.00	6.00

World Wildlife Fund (Nos. 673-676). 9th Asian Intl. Philatelic Exhibition (No. 677).

UNICEF, 50th Anniv. A125

Unwmk.
1996, June 5   Litho.   Perf. 14

678	A125	55v Immunizations	1.40	1.40
679	A125	60v Breast feeding	1.60	1.60

Radio, Cent. A126

60v, Airplane, radio signal. 75v, Radio Vanuatu. 80v, Guglielmo Marconi. 90v, Ship, radio signal.

1996, June 5   Perf. 14½

680	A126	60v multicolored	1.10	1.10
681	A126	75v multicolored	1.25	1.25
682	A126	80v multicolored	1.40	1.40
683	A126	90v multicolored	1.60	1.60
a.		Block of 4, #680-683	6.75	6.75

Modern Olympic Games, Cent. — A127

Designs: 25v, Marie Kapalu, Tawai Keiruan, Baptiste Firiam, Tava Kalo, 1996 athletes from Vanuatu. 70v, 1996 Athletes in training. 75v, 1950's Athletes. 200v, 1896 Athletes.

1996, July 17   Perf. 14

684	A127	25v multicolored	.50	.50
685	A127	70v multicolored	1.50	1.50
686	A127	75v multicolored	1.50	1.50
687	A127	200v multicolored	4.50	4.50
		Nos. 684-687 (4)	8.00	8.00

Christmas A128

Children of various races holding candles in front of churches: a, 25v, Presbyterian, Roman Catholic. b, 60v, Church of Christ. c, 75v, 7th Day Adventist, Apostolic. d, 90v, Anglican.

1996, Sept. 11　　Litho.　　Perf. 14
688　A128　Strip of 4, #a.-d.　　5.00　5.00

No. 688 is a continuous design.

Hibiscus
A129

1996, Nov. 13　　Litho.　　Perf. 13½
689　A129　25v Lady Cilento　　　.60　.60
690　A129　60v Kinchen's Yellow　1.50　1.50
691　A129　90v D.J. O'Brien　　　2.10　2.10
692　A129　200v Cuban Variety　　4.50　4.50
　a.　　Sheet of 2, #689, #692　　6.00　6.00
　　　Nos. 689-692 (4)　　　　8.70　8.70

Hong Kong '97. No. 692a issued 2/12/97.

Diving
A130

Designs: 70v, Coral Garden. 75v, Lady of the President Coolidge. 90v, "Boris," Queensland grouper. 140v, Wreck of the President Coolidge.

1997, Jan. 15　　Litho.　　Perf. 14½x14
693　A130　70v multicolored　　1.50　1.50
694　A130　75v multicolored　　1.50　1.50
695　A130　90v multicolored　　1.90　1.90
696　A130　140v multicolored　　3.00　3.00
　a.　　Souvenir sheet, #694, 696　6.00　6.00
　b.　　Souvenir sheet, #693-696　12.00　12.00
　　　Nos. 693-696 (4)　　　　7.90　7.90

Pacific '97 (#696a).

Birds
A131

25v, Sharp-tailed sandpiper. 55v, Crested tern. 60v, Little pied cormorant. 75v, Brown booby. 80v, Reef heron. 90v, Red-tailed tropic bird.

1997, June 4　　Litho.　　Perf. 13½x14
697　A131　25v multi　　　　　.60　.60
698　A131　55v multi　　　　1.25　1.25
699　A131　60v multi　　　　1.40　1.40
700　A131　75v multi　　　　1.60　1.60
701　A131　80v multi, vert.　　1.60　1.60
702　A131　90v multi, vert.　　1.90　1.90
　　　Nos. 697-702 (6)　　　8.35　8.35

Air Vanuatu, 10th Anniv.
A132

Designs: 25v, Pilot at controls. 60v, Airplane being serviced, cargo loaded. 90v, Serving drinks to passengers. 200v, Passengers leaving plane upon arrival at Vanuatu.

1997, Apr. 2　　　　　Perf. 14½x14
703　A132　25v multicolored　　.55　.55
704　A132　60v multicolored　1.40　1.40
705　A132　90v multicolored　2.10　2.10
706　A132　200v multicolored　4.50　4.50
　　　Nos. 703-706 (4)　　　8.55　8.55

No. 704 is 81x31mm.

Thomas A. Edison (1847-1931) — A133

Designs: 60v, Light bulb, Edison. 70v, Hydro dam, Santo. 200v, Port Vila by dusk.

1997, Aug. 27　　Litho.　　Perf. 12
707　A133　60v multicolored　　1.10　1.10
708　A133　70v multicolored　　1.25　1.25
709　A133　200v multicolored　　3.50　3.50
　a.　　Block of 3, #707-709 + label　7.25　7.25

No. 709 is 80x30mm.

Fish — A134

Designs: 25v, Yellow-faced angelfish. 55v, Flame angelfish. 60v, Lemonpeel angelfish. 70v, Emperor angelfish. 140v, Multi-barred angelfish.

1997, Nov. 12　　Litho.　　Perf. 14x13½
710　A134　25v multicolored　　.45　.45
711　A134　55v multicolored　1.10　1.10
712　A134　60v multicolored　1.25　1.25
713　A134　70v multicolored　1.40　1.40
714　A134　140v multicolored　2.75　2.75
　　　Nos. 710-714 (5)　　　6.95　6.95

Architecture in Vanuatu
A135

Designs: 30v, Fale-Espiritu Santo. 65v, Natl. Cultural Center. 80v, University of the South Pacific. 200v, Chief's Nakamal.

1998, Feb. 11　　Litho.　　Perf. 14½x14
715　A135　30v multicolored　　.55　.55
716　A135　65v multicolored　1.25　1.25
717　A135　80v multicolored　1.40　1.40
718　A135　200v multicolored　3.50　3.50
　　　Nos. 715-718 (4)　　　6.70　6.70

Diana, Princess of Wales (1961-97)
Common Design Type

Various portraits: a, 75v. b, 85v. c, 145v.

1998, Mar. 31　　Litho.　　Perf. 14½x14
718A　CD355　95v multicolored　　1.75　1.75

Sheet of 4
719　CD355　#a.-c., 718A　　9.75　9.75

No. 719 sold for 400v + 50v, with surtax from international sales being donated to The Diana, Princess of Wales Memorial Fund and surtax from national sales being donated to designated local charity.

Artifacts Type of 1995

Tribal masks: a, 30v, South West Malakula. b, 65v, North Ambrym. c, 75v, Gana Island Banks. d, 85v, Uripiv Island, Malakula. e, 95v,

Vao Island, Malakula, and Central South Pentecost.

1998, June 3　　Litho.　　Perf. 14½
720　A122　Strip of 5, #a.-e.　　8.75　8.75

Butterflies — A136

30v, Danaus plexippus. 60v, Hypolimnas bolina. 65v, Eurema hecabe. 75v, Nymphalidae. 95v, Precis villida. 205v, Tirumala hamata.

1998, July 23　　Litho.　　Die Cut
Self-Adhesive
721　A136　30v multicolored　　.60　.60
722　A136　60v multicolored　1.25　1.25
723　A136　65v multicolored　1.50　1.50
724　A136　75v multicolored　1.75　1.75
725　A136　95v multicolored　2.00　2.00
726　A136　205v multicolored　3.75　3.75
　a.　　Souvenir sheet of 1　　5.50　5.50
　　　Nos. 721-726 (6)　　10.85　10.85

Singpex '98 (#726a).

Volcanoes — A137

30v, Yasur, Tanna. 60v, Marum & Benbow, Ambrym. 75v, Gaua. 80v, Lopevi. 145v, Ambae.

1998, Oct. 23　　Litho.　　Perf. 15x14
728　A137　30v multicolored　　.55　.55
729　A137　60v multicolored　1.10　1.10
730　A137　75v multicolored　1.40　1.40
731　A137　80v multicolored　1.40　1.40
732　A137　145v multicolored　2.75　2.75
　　　Nos. 728-732 (5)　　　7.20　7.20

Early Explorers — A138

Explorer, ship: 34v, Pedro Fernandez de Quiros, San Pedro y Paulo, 1606. 73v, Louis-Antoine de Bougainville, Boudeuse, 1768. 84v, Capt. James Cook, HMS Resolution, 1774. 90v, Jean-Fancois de Galaup de la Perouse, Astrolabe, 1788. 96v, Jules Sebastien-Cesar Dumont d'Urville, Astrolabe, "1788."

1999, Feb. 17　　Litho.　　Perf. 14
733　A138　34v multicolored　　.60　.60
734　A138　73v multicolored　2.00　2.00
735　A138　84v multicolored　2.25　2.25
　a.　　Souv. sheet of #733-735　4.50　4.50
736　A138　90v multicolored　2.25　2.25
737　A138　96v multicolored　2.40　2.40
　a.　　Souv. sheet of #734, 736-737　6.75　6.75
　　　Nos. 733-737 (5)　　　9.50　9.50

No. 735a was released for Australia '99 World Stamp Expo on 3/19/99; No. 737a for PhilexFrance 99.

Birds — A139

34v, Vanuatu kingfisher. 67v, Shining cuckoo. 73v, Peregrine falcon. 107v, Rainbow lorikeet.

1999, May 12　　Litho.　　Perf. 14
738　A139　34v multicolored　　.85　.85
739　A139　67v multicolored　1.50　1.50
　　　Booklet, 5 #739　　　9.00
740　A139　73v multicolored　1.75　1.75
741　A139　107v multicolored　2.50　2.50
　a.　　Sheet of 1　　　　5.50　5.50
　b.　　Sheet of 1 with China 1999 emblem in margin　　4.50　4.50
　　　Nos. 738-741 (4)　　6.60　6.60

Issued: #741b, 8/18.

Nos. 601, 603-605, 607, 608
Surcharged

Perf. 14½x14, 14x14½
1998-2000　　　　　　　　Litho.
742　A111　1v on 100v #608　　.20　.20
742A　A111　2v on 45v #601　　.20　.20
743　A111　2v on 55v #603　　.20　.20
744　A111　3v on 60v #604　　.20　.20
744A　A111　3v on 75v #606　　.20　.20
745　A111　4v on 45v #601　　.20　.20
745A　A111　5v on 70v #605
745B　A111　34v on 20v #598　　.50　.50
745C　A111　67v on 300v #609　1.00　1.00
745D　A111　73v on 80v #607　　—
　　　Nos. 742-745D (8)　　2.70　2.70

Issued: No. 742, No. 742A, 743, 744, 745, 745A, 12/18/98; No. 744A, 4/27/99; Nos. 745B, 745C, 745D, 2/17/00.

Ceremonial Dancers — A140

1v, Banks Islands. 2v, Small Nambas, Laman-Malakula. 3v, Small Nambas, Malakula. 5v, Smol Bag Theatre. 107v, South West Bay, Malakula. 200v, Big Nambas, Malakula. 500v, Pentecost.

1999, July 14　　　　　Perf. 14
746　A140　1v multicolored　　.20　.20
747　A140　2v multicolored　　.20　.20
748　A140　3v multicolored　　.20　.20
749　A140　5v multicolored　　.20　.20
750　A140　107v multicolored　1.90　1.90
751　A140　200v multicolored　3.75　3.75
752　A140　500v multicolored　9.25　9.25
　　　Nos. 746-752 (7)　　15.70　15.70

Poisonous Fish — A141

Designs: 34v, Pterois antennata. 84v, Pterois antennata, diff. 90v, Pterois volitans. 96v, Pterois volitans, diff.

1999, Oct. 13   Litho.   Perf. 14¼
753	A141	34v multi	.70	.70
754	A141	84v multi	1.60	1.60
755	A141	90v multi	1.90	1.90
756	A141	96v multi	2.10	2.10
		Nos. 753-756 (4)	6.30	6.30

Millennium
A142

Designs: a, 34v, Fish. b, 68v, Girl, land diver, vert. c, 84v, Fetish, vert. d, 90v, Bird, flowers. e, 96v, Man with conch shell.

1999, Dec. 1   Perf. 14½
| 757 | A142 | Sheet of 5, #a.-e. | 8.00 | 8.00 |

Souvenir Sheet

Queen Mother, 100th Birthday — A143

a, 107v, As child. b, 100v, As old woman. Illustration reduced.

Litho. with Foil Application
2000, May 22   Perf. 13¼
| 758 | A143 | Sheet of 2, #a-b | 6.00 | 6.00 |

The Stamp Show 2000, London.

Intelsat
A144

Designs: 10v, Launch vehicle. 34v, Port Vila ground station. 100v, Intelsat 802 over Vanuatu. 225v, Intelsat and Tam Tam drum.

Litho. with Foil Application
2000, June 21   Die Cut Perf. 10
Self-Adhesive
| 759-762 | A144 | Set of 4 | 8.00 | 8.00 |
| 762a | | Souvenir sheet, #760, 762 | 6.00 | 6.00 |

World Stamp Expo 2000, Anaheim (#762a).

Independence,
20th Anniv., UN
Peace
Year — A145

Artwork: 34v, Abstract painting by Sero Kuautonga. 67v, Tapa cloth by Moses Pita. 73v, Tapestry by Juliet Pita. 84v, Natora wood carving by Emmannuel Watt. 90v, Watercolor by Joseph John.

2000, July 29 Litho.   Perf. 13¾x13¼
| 763-767 | A145 | Set of 5 | 9.50 | 9.50 |
| | | Booklet, 5 #764 | 8.00 | |

2000 Summer Olympics,
Sydney — A146

Designs: 56v, Runner. 67v, Weight lifter. 90v, High jumper. 96v, Boxer.

2000, Sept. 15   Perf. 13¼x13
| 768-771 | A146 | Set of 4 | 6.00 | 6.00 |
| | | Booklet, 5 #769 | 6.50 | |

Dolphins — A147

34v, Common. 73v, Spotted. 84v, Spinner. 107v, Bottlenose.

2000, Nov. 30   Litho.   Perf. 12½
| 772-775 | A147 | Set of 4 | 7.00 | 7.00 |
| 775a | | Souvenir sheet, #774-775 | 6.00 | 6.00 |

Hong Kong 2001 Stamp Exhibition (#775a).

Birds — A148

Designs: 35v, Cardinal honeyeater. 60v, Vanuatu white-eye. 90v, Santo Mountain starling. 100v, Royal parrotfinch. 110v, Vanuatu Mountain honeyeater.

2001, Feb. 1   Litho.   Perf. 14
| 776-780 | A148 | Set of 5 | 12.00 | 12.00 |
| 780a | | Horiz. strip, #776-780 | 12.00 | 12.00 |

Exports — A149

Designs: 35v, Vanilla. 75v, Cacao. 90v, Coffee. 110v, Copra.

2001, Apr. 11   Perf. 13¼x13
| 781-784 | A149 | Set of 4 | 7.00 | 7.00 |

Whales
A150

Designs: 60v, Sperm. 80v, Humpback, vert. 90v, Blue.

Perf. 14½x14¾, 14¾x14½
2001, July 18   Litho.
| 785-787 | A150 | Set of 3 | 7.00 | 7.00 |
| 787a | | Souvenir sheet, #785-787, perf. 14½ | 7.00 | 7.00 |

See New Caledonia No. 874.

Ceremonial Dancers Type of 1999

Designs: 35v, Snake dance, Banks Islands, horiz. 100v, Toka Dance, Tanna, horiz. 300v, Rom Dance, Ambryn, horiz. 1000v, Brasive Dance, Futuna, horiz.

2001, Sept. 12 Litho.   Perf. 13x13¼
788	A140	35v multi	.90	.90
789	A140	100v multi	2.50	2.50
790	A140	300v multi	7.50	7.50

Litho. With Foil Application
| 791 | A140 | 1000v multi | 24.00 | 24.00 |
| | | Nos. 788-791 (4) | 34.90 | 34.90 |

Sand
Drawings — A151

Various sand drawings and: a, Four people on beach. b, Man standing in canoe in water. c, Man sitting on canoe, man rowing canoe. d, Canoe, shelter.

Perf. 12¾x13½
2001, Nov. 28   Litho.
792	A151	60v multi	1.00	1.00
792A	A151	90v multi	1.50	1.50
792B	A151	110vmulti	1.90	1.90
792C	A151	135vmulti	2.40	2.40
Cd.		Horiz. strip of 4 + central label	9.00	9.00

Intl. Year of
Ecotourism
A152

Designs: Nos. 793, 798a, 35v, Mount Yasur, Pentecost Island land diver, dancers. Nos. 794, 798b, 60v Dancers, man making kava. Nos. 795, 798c, 75v, Siri Falls, flowers, birds, vert. Nos. 796, 798d, 110v, Kayakers, scuba diver, vert. Nos. 797, 798e, 135v, Beach bungalows, tourists.

2002, Jan. 30   Litho.   Perf. 14
Stamps + Label
| 793-797 | A152 | Set of 5 | 10.50 | 10.50 |

Souvenir Sheet
Without Labels
Perf. 14½x14¾
| 798 | A152 | Sheet of 5, #a-e | 10.50 | 10.50 |

Nos. 793, 794, and 797 are 38x26mm and Nos. 795-796 are 26x38mm, while Nos. 798a, 798b, and 798e are 37x25mm and Nos. 798c-798d are 25x37mm.

Horses
A153

Designs: 35v, Working horses. 60v, Cattle roundup. 75v, Horse racing. 80v, Tourism and horses. 200v, Wild Tanna horse.

2002, Mar. 27   Perf. 14¾x14
799-803	A153	Set of 5	10.00	10.00
803a		Souvenir sheet of 1	5.00	5.00
803b		Souvenir sheet of 1 with Philakorea 2002 emblem	5.00	5.00

Issued: No. 803b, 7/31/02.

Soccer
A154

Designs: 35v, Children's soccer. 80v, Under 17 soccer. 110v, Women's soccer. 135v, International soccer.

2002, May 31   Litho.   Perf. 13¾
| 804-807 | A154 | Set of 4 | 8.50 | 8.50 |

Value is for stamps with surrounding selvage.

Reforestation — A155

No. 808: a, Girl with seedling of Artocarpus atilis. b, Boy and man planting seedling of Endospermum medullosum. c, Canoe carver with Gyrocarpus americanus log. d, Mother and child with Dracontomelon vitiense fruit.

Serpentine Die Cut
2002, July 31   Litho.
Self-Adhesive
808		Horiz. strip of 4	8.00	
a.	A155	35v multi	.95	.95
b.	A155	60v multi	1.60	1.60
c.	A155	90v multi	2.25	2.25
d.	A155	110v multi	3.00	3.00

Dugongs
A156

Designs: 35v, Pair nuzzling. 75v, Pair swimming. 80v, One swimming. 135v, One on ocean floor.

2002, Sept. 25 Litho.   Perf. 13¾
| 812-815 | A156 | Set of 4 | 7.50 | 7.50 |
| 815a | | Souvenir sheet, #814-815 | 8.50 | 8.50 |

Orchids — A157

Designs: 35v, Dendrobium gouldii. 60v, Dendrobium polysema. 90v, Dendrobium spectabile. 110v, Flickingeria comata.

2002, Nov. 27   Litho.   Perf. 13¼
| 816-819 | A157 | Set of 4 | 7.50 | 7.50 |

Year of Cattle — A158

Cattle Breeds: 35v, Limousin. 80v, Charolais. 110v, Simmental. 135v, Red Brahman.

2003, Jan. 29   **Perf. 13**
820-823 A158   Set of 4   8.25 8.25

Pentecost Island Land Divers — A159

Designs: 35v, Diver on platform. 80v, Diver in air. 110v, Dancers, platform. 200v, Diver and platform (35x90mm).

2003, Mar. 26   **Perf. 13¾x13¼**
824-827 A159   Set of 4   11.50 11.50
827a   Souvenir sheet of 1   6.25 6.25

Snorkeling A160

Various people snorkeling: 35v, 80v, 90v, 110v, 135v. 80v and 90v are vert.

2003, May 28   **Litho.**   **Perf. 13¾**
828-832 A160   Set of 5   8.50 8.50
832a   Souvenir sheet, #828-832, perf. 13¼   9.50 9.50

Natanggura Palm — A161

Half of palm nut and: 35v, Man planting palm tree, carved dolphins. 80v, Man weaving thatch for roof, carved turtle. 90v, Carver, carved lizard. 135v, Carvers, carved fish.

2003, July 23   **Perf. 13¾x13¼**
833-836 A161   Set of 4   6.50 6.50

Opening of Underwater Post Office in May 2003 — A162

2003, Sept. 24   **Perf. 13¾**
837 A162   90v multi   1.60 1.60

Sea Horses — A163

Designs: 60v, Hippocampus kuda. 90v, Hippocampus histrix. 200v, Hippocampus bargibanti.

2003, Sept. 24
838-840 A163   Set of 3   6.00 6.00
840a   Souvenir sheet of 1   3.50 3.50

Moths A164

Designs: 35v, Daphnis hypothous. 90v, Hippotion celerio. 110v, Euchromia creusa. 135v, Eudocima salaminia.

2003, Nov. 26   **Perf. 13½**
841-844 A164   Set of 4   6.50 6.50

Activities at Underwater Post Office — A165

Designs: 35v, Workers placing mail in bag. 80v, Swimmer placing mail in mail box. 110v, Swimmer at counter. 220v, Clerk at counter, swimmer near mail box.

2004, Jan. 30   **Perf. 13¾x13½**
845-848 A165   Set of 4   8.25 8.25
848a   Souvenir sheet of 1   4.75 4.75

2004 Hong Kong Stamp Expo (#848a).

Starfish A166

Designs: 35v, Protoreaster nodulosus. 60v, Linckia laevigata. 90v, Fromia monilis. 250v, Echinaster callosus.

Serpentine Die Cut
2004, Apr. 28   **Litho.**
Self-Adhesive
849-852 A166   Set of 4   9.50 9.50

Red-tailed Tropicbird A167

Designs: 35v, Adult and juvenile. 50v, Adult and chick, vert. 75v, Adult flying above juvenile, vert. 135v, Adult in flight. 200v, Adult pair.

2004, July 14   **Litho.**   **Perf. 13¾**
853-857 A167   Set of 5   12.50 12.50
857a   Souvenir sheet, #853-857, perf. 13½   12.50 12.50

Musket Cove to Port Vila Yacht Race, 25th Anniv. — A168

Various yachts: 35v, 80v, 90v, 200v. 80v and 200v are vert.

2004, Sept. 18   **Perf. 14¼**
858-861 A168   Set of 4   12.00 12.00
861a   Souvenir sheet of 1   6.25 6.25

See Fiji Nos. 1024-1027.

Miniature Sheet

Marine Life — A169

No. 862: a, Red and black anemonefish. b, Longfin bannerfish. c, Goldman's sweetlips. d, Green turtle. e, Clark's anemonefish. f, Harlequin sweetlips. g, Yellowtail coris. h, Emperor angelfish. i, Hairy red hermit crab, leaf oyster. j, Spotfin lionfish. k, Yellow-lipped sea krait. l, Clam.

Serpentine Die Cut 13¼
2004, Nov. 24   **Litho.**
Self-Adhesive
862 A169 35v Sheet of 12, #a-l 12.00 12.00

Christmas A170

Serpentine Die Cut 13
2004, Nov. 24
Self-Adhesive
863 A170 80v multi   2.50 2.50

Sunsets A171

Designs: 60v, Sailboat. 80v, Man with raised arm, vert. 90v, Sailboats, vert. 135v, Man blowing conch shell.

2005, Jan. 19   **Perf. 14x14½, 14½x14**
864-867 A171   Set of 4   11.00 11.00

Miniature Sheet

Lapita People — A172

No. 868: a, 50v, Man holding tool, vert. b, 70v, People cleaning fish. c, 110v, People tending fire and carrying animal to fire. d, 200v, Women making baskets, mother and child, vert.

2005, Mar. 2   **Perf. 13¼**
868 A172   Sheet of 4, #a-d   12.50 12.50

Pacific Explorer 2005 World Stamp Expo, Sydney.

Volcano Post A173

Mail box on Mount Yasur and: 35v, Five tourists. 80v, Native woman. 100v, Three postal workers. 250v, Postal worker removing mail.

2005, May 31   **Litho.**   **Perf. 14x14¼**
869-872 A173   Set of 4   13.00 13.00
872a   Souvenir sheet of 1   7.50 7.50

Souvenir Sheet

Independence, 25th Anniv. — A174

No. 873: a, 35v, Vanuatu natives celebrating. b, 50v, Soldiers raising Vanuatu flag, 1980. c, 400v, Children and statue of family.

2005, July 30   **Litho.**   **Perf. 13**
873 A174   Sheet of 3, #a-c   15.00 15.00

Miniature Sheet

Corals — A175

No. 874: a, Lace coral. b, Star coral. c, Red coral (Tubastraea sp.). d, Plate coral. e, Brown anthelia. f, Bubble coral. g, Flowerpot coral. h, Cup coral. i, Daisy coral. j, Sun coral (Tubastraea diaphana). k, Mushroom-feather coral. l, Sun coral (Tubastraea micrantha).

Serpentine Die Cut 13½x13¼
2005, Sept. 7   **Litho.**
Self-Adhesive
874 A175 35v Sheet of 12, #a-l 13.00 13.00

Landscapes — A176

Designs: 80v, Horse and rider on beach. 90v, Palm trees. 110v, Waterfall. 135v, Harbor.

2005, Nov. 16   **Litho.**   **Perf. 14¼x14**
875-878 A176   Set of 4   13.00 13.00

Miniature Sheet

Reef Shells — A177

No. 879: a, Crocus clam. b, Pearl oyster. c, Gold-ringer cowrie. d, Cock-a-comb oyster. e, Tiger cowrie. f, Textile cone. g, Marlinspike. h, Vibex bonnet. i, Erosa cowrie. j, Scorpion conch. k, Honey cowrie. l, Umbilical ovula.

Serpentine Die Cut 13½
2006, Feb. 8   Self-Adhesive

879 A177 35v Sheet of 12, #a-l 13.00 13.00

Queen Elizabeth II, 80th Birthday A178

Queen: 50v, As young woman in Army uniform. 100v, Without hat. No. 882, 110v, With blue hat. No. 883, 200v, With yellow hat.
No. 884: a, 110v, Like 100v. b, 200v, Like No. 882.

2006, Apr. 21   Litho.   Perf. 14
With White Frames

880-883 A178 Set of 4   8.25 8.25

Souvenir Sheet
Without White Frames

884 A178 Sheet of 2, #a-b   5.75 5.75

Souvenir Sheet

Arrival in Vanuatu of Pedro Fernandez de Quiros, 400th Anniv. — A179

2006, May 10   Perf. 13¼

885 A179 350v multi   6.50 6.50

2006 World Cup Soccer Championships, Germany — A180

Various soccer players, 2006 World Cup emblem on soccer jersey: 35v, 80v, 110v, 135v.

2006, June 9   Litho.   Die Cut
Self-Adhesive

886-889 A180 Set of 4   6.50 6.50
889a   Souvenir sheet, #886-889 6.50 6.50

Flowers A181

Designs: 5v, Passiflora foetida. 10v, Hibiscus rosa-sinensis. 20v, Cereus undatus. 40v, Strelitzia reginae. 50v, Spathodea campanulata. 70v, Delonix regia. 90v, Hibiscus hilaceus. 100v, Nymphaea sp. 150v, Plumeria

obtusa. 500v, Allamanda cathartica. 1000v, Thunbergia grandiflora.

Serpentine Die Cut 11¾
2006, July 1   Self-Adhesive

890 A181 5v multi   .20 .20
891 A181 10v multi   .20 .20
892 A181 20v multi   .35 .35
893 A181 40v multi   .70 .70
894 A181 50v multi   .90 .90
895 A181 70v multi   1.25 1.25
896 A181 100v multi   1.75 1.75
897 A181 150v multi   2.75 2.75
898 A181 500v multi   9.00 9.00
899 A181 1000v multi 18.00 18.00

Inscribed "International Post" at Left

900 A181 5v multi   .20 .20
901 A181 10v multi   .20 .20
902 A181 20v multi   .35 .35
903 A181 50v multi   .90 .90
904 A181 90v multi   1.60 1.60
905 A181 100v multi   1.75 1.75
906 A181 500v multi   9.00 9.00
907 A181 1000v multi 18.00 18.00
      Nos. 890-907 (18)   67.10 67.10

Miniature Sheet

Worldwide Fund for Nature (WWF) — A182

No. 908: a, 70v, Giant grouper and coral. b, 90v, Giant grouper and smaller fish. c, 100v, Juvenile giant groupers. d, 150v, Giant grouper, smaller fish, diff.

2006, Oct. 4   Litho.   Perf. 13¼

908 A182 Sheet, 2 each #a-
              d   15.00 15.00

Shipwreck of the SS President Coolidge — A183

Designs: 90v, Diver, corals. 100v, Divers, fish. 130v, Shipwreck, fish. 150v, Ship sinking, sailors leaving ship (85x30mm).

2006, Nov. 29   Litho.   Perf. 13¼

909-912 A183 Set of 4   9.00 9.00

Shipwreck Type of 2006
Souvenir Sheet

No. 913: a, 90v, Like #909. b, 100v, Like #910. c, 130v, Like #911. d, 150v, Like #912.

2006, Nov. 29   Litho.   Perf. 13¼
Stamps Without "International Post"

913 A183 Sheet of 4, #a-d   9.00 9.00

Reef Heron A184

Reef heron: 10v, With wings extended. 20v, Standing on land, vert. 50v, With fish in bill, vert. 70v, Head. 250v, Chicks.

2007, Feb. 9   Litho.   Perf. 14½

914-918 A184 Set of 5   7.50 7.50
918a   Souvenir sheet, #914-918 7.50 7.50

Diving at Million Dollar Point A185

Designs: Nos. 919, 923a, 90v, Divers near submerged jeep. Nos. 920, 923b, 100v, Divers near submerged truck, vert. (42x60mm). Nos. 921, 923c, 130v, Diver, diff. Nos. 922, 923d, 150v, Diver, lionfish.

2007, Apr. 18   Perf. 13¼
Stamps Inscribed "International Post"

919-922 A185 Set of 4   9.25 9.25

Souvenir Sheet
Stamps Without "International Post" Inscription

923 A185 Sheet of 4, #a-d   9.25 9.25

Fruit — A186

Designs: 30v, Bananas. 40v, Watermelon. 70v, Limes. 100v, Papayas. 250v, Coconuts.

2007, June 27   Serpentine Die Cut
Self-Adhesive

924-928 A186 Set of 5   9.75 9.75

James A. Michener (1907-97), Writer A187

Michener: 40v, With pen. 90v, At typewriter. 130v, With island natives. 350v, Holding book.

2007, Aug. 22   Perf. 14½

929-932 A187 Set of 4   12.00 12.00

Banded Iguana — A188

Designs: 50v, Two iguanas, two flowers. 70v, Iguana on branch. 100v, Iguana. 250v, Iguana on flower bud.

Serpentine Die Cut 15
2007, Nov. 7   Litho.
Self-Adhesive

933-936 A188 Set of 4   10.00 10.00
936a   Souvenir sheet, #935-936 7.50 7.50

Air Vanuatu, 20th Anniv. — A189

Designs: 40v, Three airplanes at airport. 90v, Boeing 737-800. 130v, Boeing 737-300. 180v, Twin Otter. 250v, ATR 42.

2007-08   Serpentine Die Cut 15

937 A189 40v multi   .85 .85
938 A189 90v multi   1.90 1.90
939 A189 130v multi   2.75 2.75
940 A189 180v multi   3.75 3.75
941 A189 250v multi   5.25 5.25
      Nos. 937-941 (5)   14.50 14.50

First flight of Boeing 737-800 (#938). Issued: 40v, 130v, 180v, 250v, 11/23; 90v, 1/17/08.

Coconut Crabs A190

Crab on: 60v, Beach. 500v, Tree, vert.

Perf. 13½x13¼, 13¼x13½
2008, Feb. 20   Litho.

942-943 A190 Set of 2   12.50 12.50
943a   Souvenir sheet, #942-943 12.50 12.50

SEMI POSTAL STAMPS

Nos. 324 and 414-418 Surcharged "Hurricane Relief Fund"
Wmk. 373 (No. B1), 384
Perf. 14x13½, 14x14½
1987, May 12   Litho.

B1 A60   20v +10v on 2v   1.40 1.40
B2 CD337 20v +10v   1.40 1.40
B3 CD337 35v +15v   2.40 2.40
B4 CD337 45v +20v   2.75 2.75
B5 CD337 55v +25v   5.25 5.25
B6 CD337 100v +50v   5.75 5.75
      Nos. B1-B6 (6)   18.95 18.95

Old value of #B1 obliterated by 2 horizontal bars. Surcharge indicated by text "Surcharge +10."

VATICAN CITY

ˈva-ti-kən ˈsi-tē

LOCATION — Western Italy, directly outside the western boundary of Rome

GOVT. — Independent state subject to certain political restrictions under a treaty with Italy

AREA — 108.7 acres

POP. — 870 (1999 est.)

100 Centesimi = 1 Lira
100 Cents = 1 Euro (2002)

Catalogue values for unused stamps in this country are for Never Hinged items, beginning with Scott 68 in the regular postage section, Scott C1 in the airpost section, Scott E3 in the special delivery section, and Scott J7 in the postage due section.

Watermarks

Wmk. 235 —
Crossed Keys

Wmk. 277 —
Winged Wheel

Papal
Arms — A1

 (Pope Pius XI — A2 image — placed below)

Pope Pius
XI — A2

Unwmk.

1929, Aug. 1   Engr.   Perf. 14
Surface-Colored Paper

1	A1	5c dk brn & pink	.20	.25
2	A1	10c dk grn & lt grn	.25	.30
3	A1	20c violet & lilac	.55	.40
4	A1	25c dk bl & lt bl	.70	.45
5	A1	30c indigo & yellow	.80	.60
6	A1	50c ind & sal buff	1.25	.65
7	A1	75c brn car & gray	1.60	1.00

Photo.
White Paper

8	A2	80c carmine rose	1.25	.40
9	A2	1.25 l dark blue	2.00	.75
10	A2	2 l olive brown	3.75	1.40
11	A2	2.50 l red orange	3.25	2.50
12	A2	5 l dk green	3.75	8.50
13	A2	10 l olive blk	8.00	11.50
		Nos. 1-13,E1-E2 (15)	53.35	52.20
		Set, never hinged	170.00	

The stamps of Type A1 have, in this and subsequent issues, the words "POSTE VATICANE" in rows of colorless letters in the background.

For surcharges and overprints see Nos. 14, 35-40, 61-67, J1-J6, Q1-Q13.

No. 5 Surcharged in Red

1931, Oct. 1

14	A1	25c on 30c ind & yel	2.10	1.40
		Never hinged	6.75	

Arms of Pope
Pius XI — A5

Vatican Palace
and
Obelisk — A6

Vatican
Gardens — A7

Pope
Pius XI
A8

St.
Peter's
Basilica
A9

1933, May 31   Engr.   Wmk. 235

19	A5	5c copper red	.20	.20
a.		Imperf., pair	250.00	275.00
20	A6	10c dk brn & blk	.20	.20
21	A6	12½c dp grn & blk	.20	.20
22	A6	20c orange & blk	.20	.20
a.		Vertical pair imperf. between and at bottom	250.00	250.00
23	A6	25c dk olive & blk	.20	.20
a.		Imperf., pair	150.00	175.00
24	A7	30c blk & dk brn	.20	.20
25	A7	50c viot & dk brn	.20	.20
26	A7	75c brn red & dk brn	.20	.20
27	A7	80c rose & dk brn	.20	.20
28	A8	1 l violet & blk	3.25	2.75
29	A8	1.25 l dk bl & blk	11.00	5.00
30	A8	2 l dk brn & blk	27.50	20.00
31	A8	2.75 l dk vio & blk	32.50	40.00
32	A9	5 l blk brn & dk grn	.20	.25
33	A9	10 l dk blue & dk grn	.20	.30
34	A9	20 l blk & dp grn	.25	.35
		Nos. 19-34,E3-E4 (18)	77.40	71.35
		Set, never hinged	235.00	

Nos. 8-13 Surcharged in
Black

1934, June 16   Unwmk.

35	A2	40c on 80c	3.25	1.90
36	A2	1.30 l on 1.25 l	57.50	37.50
a.		Small figures "30" in "1.30"	10,000.	7,250.
		Never hinged	12,500.	
37	A2	2.05 l on 2 l	125.00	14.00
a.		No comma btwn. 2 & 0	275.00	20.00
		Never hinged	850.00	
38	A2	2.55 l on 2.50 l	82.50	150.00
a.		No comma btwn. 2 & 5	150.00	275.00
		Never hinged	475.00	
39	A2	3.05 l on 5 l	275.00	275.00
40	A2	3.70 l on 10 l	250.00	400.00
a.		No comma btwn. 3 & 7		
		Nos. 35-40 (6)	793.25	878.40
		Set, never hinged	2,500.	

A second printing of Nos. 36-40 was made in 1937. The 2.55 l and 3.05 l of the first printing and 1.30 l of the second printing sell for more.

The status of No. 40a has been questioned. The editors would like to examine an authenticated copy of this variety.

Forged surcharges of Nos. 35-40 are plentiful.

Tribonian
Presenting
Pandects to
Justinian I
A10

Pope
Gregory IX
Promulgating
Decretals
A11

1935, Feb. 1   Photo.

41	A10	5c red orange	1.25	.75
42	A10	10c purple	1.25	.75
43	A10	25c green	12.50	12.50
44	A11	75c rose red	45.00	27.50
45	A11	80c dark brown	35.00	21.00
46	A11	1.25 l dark blue	45.00	20.00
		Nos. 41-46 (6)	140.00	82.50
		Set, never hinged	550.00	

Intl. Juridical Congress, Rome, 1934.

Doves and
Bell — A12

Allegory of
Church and
Bible — A13

St. John
Bosco — A14

St. Francis de
Sales — A15

1936, June 22

47	A12	5c blue green	.75	1.00
48	A13	10c black	.75	1.00
49	A14	25c yellow green	40.00	8.50
50	A12	50c rose violet	.75	1.00
51	A13	75c rose red	40.00	40.00
52	A14	80c orange brn	1.50	2.00
53	A15	1.25 l dark blue	2.00	2.00
54	A15	5 l dark brown	2.00	6.25
		Nos. 47-54 (8)	87.75	61.75
		Set, never hinged	325.00	

Catholic Press Conference, 1936.

Crypt of St.
Cecilia in
Catacombs
of St.
Calixtus
A16

Basilica of Sts. Nereus and Achilleus
in Catacombs of St. Domitilla
A17

1938, Oct. 12   Perf. 14

55	A16	5c bister brown	.20	.20
56	A16	10c deep orange	.20	.20
57	A16	25c deep green	.25	.25
58	A17	75c deep rose	5.50	5.50
59	A17	80c violet	17.00	17.00
60	A17	1.25 l blue	22.50	22.50
		Nos. 55-60 (6)	45.65	45.65
		Set, never hinged	140.00	

Intl. Christian Archaeological Congress, Rome, 1938.

Interregnum Issue

Nos. 1-7 Overprinted
in Black

1939, Feb. 20   Perf. 14

61	A1	5c dk brn & pink	27.50	6.00
62	A1	10c dk grn & lt grn	.30	.20
63	A1	20c violet & lilac	.30	.20
64	A1	25c dk bl & lt bl	3.00	3.50
65	A1	30c indigo & yellow	.60	.20
a.		Pair, one without ovpt.	1,300.	
66	A1	50c indigo & sal buff	.60	.20
67	A1	75c brn car & gray	.60	.20
		Nos. 61-67 (7)	32.90	10.50
		Set, never hinged	100.00	

Catalogue values for unused stamps in this section, from this point to the end of the section, are for Never Hinged items.

Coronation of Pope
Pius XII — A18

1939, June 2   **Photo.**

68	A18	25c green	2.25	.30
69	A18	75c rose red	.50	.45
70	A18	80c violet	6.25	3.00
71	A18	1.25 l deep blue	.50	.45
		Nos. 68-71 (4)	9.50	4.20

Coronation of Pope Pius XII, Mar. 12, 1939.

Arms of Pope
Pius XII — A19

Pope Pius XII
A20   A21

Wmk. 235

1940, Mar. 12   **Engr.**   **Perf. 14**

72	A19	5c dark carmine	.20	.20
73	A20	1 l purple & blk	.20	.20
74	A21	1.25 l slate bl & blk	.20	.20
a.		Imperf., pair	450.00	500.00
75	A20	2 l dk brn & blk	1.40	.85
76	A21	2.75 l dk rose vio & blk	2.00	1.75
		Nos. 72-76 (5)	4.00	3.20

See #91-98. For surcharges see #102-109.

A22

Picture of Jesus inscribed "I have Compassion on the Multitude."

1942, Sept. 1   **Photo.**   **Unwmk.**

77	A22	25c dk blue green	.20	.20
78	A22	80c chestnut brown	.20	.20
79	A22	1.25 l deep blue	.20	.20
		Nos. 77-79 (3)	.60	.60

See Nos. 84-86, 99-101.

A23

1942, Jan. 16

Consecration of Archbishop Pacelli by Pope Benedict XV.

80	A23	25c myr grn & gray grn	.20	.20
81	A23	80c dk brn & yel grn	.20	.20
82	A23	1.25 l sapphire & vio bl	.20	.20
a.		Name and value panel omitted		
83	A23	5 l vio blk & gray blk	.20	.25
		Nos. 80-83 (4)	.80	.85

25th anniv. of the consecration of Msgr. Eugenio Pacelli (later Pope Pius XII) as Archbishop of Sardes.

Type of 1942
Inscribed MCMXLIII

1944, Jan. 31

84	A22	25c dk blue green	.20	.20
85	A22	80c chestnut brown	.20	.20
86	A22	1.25 l deep blue	.20	.20
		Nos. 84-86 (3)	.60	.60

Raphael
Sanzio — A24

Designs: 80c, Antonio da Sangallo. 1.25 l, Carlo Maratti. 10 l, Antonio Canova.

1944, Nov. 21   **Wmk. 235**   **Photo.**

87	A24	25c olive & green	.30	.20
88	A24	80c cl & rose vio	.60	.25
a.		Dbl. impression of center	750.00	
89	A24	1.25 l bl vio & dp bl	.60	.25
a.		Imperf., pair	650.00	900.
90	A24	10 l bister & ol brn	1.25	.75
		Nos. 87-90 (4)	2.75	1.45

400th anniv. of the Pontifical Academy of the Virtuosi of the Pantheon.

Types of 1940

1945, Mar. 5   **Engr.**   **Unwmk.**

91	A19	5c gray	.20	.20
a.		Imperf., pair	200.00	
92	A19	30c brown	.20	.20
a.		Imperf., pair	120.00	
93	A19	50c dark green	.20	.20
94	A21	1 l brown & blk	.20	.20
95	A21	1.50 l rose car & blk	.20	.20
a.		Imperf., pair	325.00	
96	A21	2.50 l dp ultra & blk	.20	.20
97	A20	5 l rose vio & blk	.20	.25
98	A20	20 l gray grn & blk	.25	.30
		Nos. 91-98,E5-E6 (10)	2.25	2.35

Nos. 91-96 exist in pairs imperf. between, some vertical, some horizontal. Value, each $150.
Pair imperf. vertically exist of 30c and 50c (value $50), and of 5 lire (value $90).

Type of 1942
Inscribed MCMXLIV
Wmk. 277

1945, Sept. 12   **Photo.**   **Perf. 14**

99	A22	1 l dk blue green	.20	.20
100	A22	3 l dk carmine	.20	.20
a.		Jesus image omitted	100.00	100.00
101	A22	5 l deep ultra	.20	.20
		Nos. 99-101 (3)	.60	.60

Nos. 99-101 exist in pairs imperf. between, both horizontal and vertical. Value, each $140. Pairs imperf. horizontally exist of 3 lire (value $50) and 5 lire (value $60).

Nos. 91 to 98 Surcharged with New Values and Bars in Black or Blue

Two types of 25c on 30c:
I — Surcharge 16mm wide.
II — Surcharge 19mm wide.

Two types of 1 l on 50c:
I — Surcharge bars 5mm wide.
II — Bars 4mm wide.

1946, Jan. 9   **Unwmk.**   **Perf. 14**

102	A19	20c on 5c	.20	.20
103	A19	25c on 30c (I)	.20	.20
a.		Type II	.40	.20
b.		Inverted surcharge (II)	350.00	350.00
104	A19	1 l on 50c (I)	.20	.20
a.		Type II	5.00	3.50
105	A21	1.50 l on 1 l (BI)	.20	.20
a.		Double surcharge	175.00	
106	A21	3 l on 1.50 l	.20	.20
107	A21	5 l on 2.50 l	.40	.20
108	A20	10 l on 5 l	1.10	.55
109	A20	30 l on 20 l	3.25	1.50
		Nos. 102-109,E7-E8 (10)	14.25	6.75

Nos. 102, 105-109 exist in horizontal pairs, imperf. between. Value, each $150.
Vertical pairs imperf. between exist of Nos. 102, 106-107 (value, each $150) and of No. 104a (value $250).
Nos. 102, 104-108 exist in pairs imperf. vertically or horizontally, or both. Value $40 to $60.
Nos. 102-108 exist in pairs, one without surcharge. Value, Nos. 102-105, each $150; Nos. 106-108, each $200.

St. Vigilio
Cathedral,
Trent — A28

St. Angela
Merici — A29

Designs: 50c, St. Anthony Zaccaria. 75c, St. Ignatius of Loyola. 1 l, St. Cajetan Thiene. 1.50 l, St. John Fisher. 2 l, Christoforo Cardinal Madruzzi. 2.50 l, Reginald Cardinal Pole. 3 l, Marello Cardinal Cervini. 4 l, Giovanni Cardinal del Monte. 5 l, Emperor Charles V. 1 l, Pope Paul III.

Perf. 14, 14x13½

1946, Feb. 21   **Photo.**   **Unwmk.**
Centers in Dark Brown

110	A28	5c olive bister	.20	.20
111	A29	25c purple	.20	.20
112	A29	50c brown orange	.20	.20
113	A29	75c black	.20	.20
114	A29	1 l dk violet	.20	.20
115	A29	1.50 l red orange	.20	.20
116	A29	2 l yellow green	.20	.20
117	A29	2.50 l deep blue	.20	.20
118	A29	3 l brt carmine	.20	.20
119	A29	4 l ocher	.20	.20
120	A29	5 l brt ultra	.20	.20
121	A29	10 l dp rose car	.20	.20
		Nos. 110-121,E9-E10 (14)	2.80	2.80

Council of Trent (1545-63), 400th anniv.
Vertical pairs imperf. between exist of Nos. 110-111, 114, 116-117 (value, each $150); Nos. 113, 119 (value, each $100); Nos. 115, 118 (value, each $75).
Horizontal pairs imperf. between exist of #121 (value $200); #113, 117 (value $150).

Basilica of St.
Agnes — A40

Basilica of
the Holy
Cross in
Jerusalem
A41

Pope
Pius XII
A42

Basilicas: 3 l, St. Clement, 5 l, St. Prassede. 8 l, St. Mary in Cosmedin. 16 l, St. Sebastian. 25 l, St. Lawrence. 35 l, St. Paul 40 l, St. Mary Major.

Perf. 14, 14x13½

1949, Mar. 7　Photo.　Wmk. 235

122	A40	1 l dark brown	.20	.20
123	A40	3 l violet	.20	.20
124	A40	5 l deep orange	.20	.20
a.		Perf. 14x13½	15.00	4.50
125	A40	8 l dp blue grn	.20	.20

Perf. 14, 13½x14

126	A41	13 l dull green	6.00	5.00
127	A41	16 l dk olive brn	.20	.20
a.		Perf. 14	.75	.25
128	A41	25 l car rose	4.75	.65
129	A41	35 l red violet	26.00	12.00
a.		Perf. 13½x14	55.00	8.25
130	A41	40 l blue	.20	.20
a.		Perf. 13½x14	.25	.25

Engr.
Perf. 14

131	A42	100 l sepia	3.00	3.00
		Nos. 122-131,E11-E12 (12)	88.95	45.10

All values come in two perfs except the 100 l.

Jesus Giving St. Peter the Keys to Heaven — A43

Cathedrals of St. Peter, St. Paul, St. John Lateran and St. Mary Major — A44

Pope Boniface VIII Proclaiming Holy Year in 1300 — A45

Pope Pius XII in Ceremony of Opening the Holy Door — A46

Wmk. 277

1949, Dec 21　Photo.　Perf. 14

132	A43	5 l red brn & brn	.20	.20
133	A44	6 l ind & yel brn	.20	.20
134	A45	8 l ultra & dk grn	.75	.35
135	A43	10 l green & slate	.25	.25
136	A43	20 l dk grn & red brn	1.25	.25
137	A44	25 l sepia & dp blue	.60	.25
138	A45	30 l grnsh blk & rose lil	1.50	1.00
139	A46	60 l blk brn & brn rose	1.00	1.00
		Nos. 132-139 (8)	5.75	3.50

Holy Year, 1950.

Palatine Guard and Statue of St. Peter — A47

1950, Sept. 12

140	A47	25 l sepia	8.25	2.50
141	A47	35 l dark green	3.25	2.50
142	A47	55 l red brown	1.90	2.50
		Nos. 140-142 (3)	13.40	7.50

Centenary of the Palatine Guard.

Pope Pius XII Making Proclamation A48

Crowd at St. Peter's Basilica — A49

1951, May 8　　　　Unwmk.

143	A48	25 l chocolate	8.50	.75
144	A49	55 l bright blue	3.50	10.50

Proclamation of the Roman Catholic dogma of the Assumption of the Virgin Mary, Nov. 1, 1950.

A50

Pope Pius X — A51

Perf. 14x13½

1951, June 3　Photo.　Wmk. 235
Background of Medallion in Gold

145	A50	6 l purple	.20	.20
146	A50	10 l Prus green	.20	.20
147	A51	60 l blue	5.50	5.50
148	A51	115 l brown	15.00	15.00
		Nos. 145-148 (4)	20.90	20.90

Council of Chalcedon A52

Pope Leo I Remonstrating with Attila the Hun — A53

1951, Oct. 31　Engr.　Perf. 14x13½

149	A52	5 l dk gray green	.50	.25
a.		Pair, imperf. horiz.	350.00	
150	A53	25 l red brown	3.00	1.75
a.		Horiz. pair, imperf. btwn.	700.00	700.00
151	A53	35 l carmine rose	8.00	3.00
152	A53	60 l deep blue	22.50	10.00
153	A52	100 l dark brown	30.00	25.00
		Nos. 149-153 (5)	64.00	40.00

Council of Chalcedon, 1500th anniv.

No. 126 Surcharged with New Value and Bars in Carmine

1952, Mar. 15　　　　Perf. 14

154	A41	12 l on 13 l dull grn	1.75	1.00
a.		Perf. 13½x14	1.75	1.00
b.		Pair, one without surcharge	300.00	300.00

Roman States Stamp and Stagecoach — A54

1952, June 9　Engr.　Perf. 13

155	A54	50 l sep & dp bl, cr	5.00	3.25
a.		Souvenir sheet	140.00	100.00

1st stamp of the Papal States, cent. #155a contains 4 stamps similar to #155, with papal insignia and inscription in purple. Singles from the souvenir sheet differ slightly from #155. The colors are closer to black and blue, and the cream tone of the paper is visible on the back.

St. Maria Goretti — A55

St. Peter — A56

Perf. 13½x14

1953, Feb. 12　Photo.　Wmk. 235

156	A55	15 l dp brown & vio	4.25	2.00
157	A55	35 l dp rose & brn	3.25	2.00

Martyrdom of St. Maria Goretti, 50th anniv.

Perf. 13½x13, 14

1953, Apr. 23　　　　Engr.

Designs: 5 l, Pius XII and Roman sepulcher. 10 l, St. Peter and Tomb of the Apostle. 12 l, Sylvester I and Constantine Basilica. 20 l, Julius II and Bramante's plans. 25 l, Paul III and the Apse. 35 l, Sixtus V and dome. 45 l, Paul V and facade. 60 l, Urban VIII and the canopy. 65 l, Alexander VII and colonnade. 100 l, Pius VI and the sacristy.

158	A56	3 l dk red brn & blk	.20	.20
159	A56	5 l slate & blk	.20	.20
160	A56	10 l dk green & blk	.20	.20
161	A56	12 l chestnut & blk	.20	.20
162	A56	20 l violet & blk	.20	.20
163	A56	25 l dk brown & blk	.20	.20
164	A56	35 l dk carmine & blk	.20	.20
165	A56	45 l olive brn & blk	.20	.20
166	A56	60 l dk blue & blk	.20	.20
167	A56	65 l car rose & blk	.20	.20
168	A56	100 l rose vio & blk	.20	.20
		Nos. 158-168,E13-E14 (13)	2.75	2.65

St. Clare of Assisi — A57

Peter Lombard Medal — A59

Virgin Mary and St. Bernard A58

Unwmk.

1953, Aug. 12　Photo.　Perf. 13

169	A57	25 l aqua, yel brn & vio brn	2.00	1.00
170	A57	35 l brn red, yel brn & vio brn	14.00	9.00

Death of St. Clare of Assisi, 700th anniv.

1953, Nov. 10

171	A58	20 l ol grn & dk vio brn	.75	.50
172	A58	60 l brt bl & ol grn	7.25	4.00

Death of St. Bernard of Clairvaux, 800th anniv.

1953, Dec. 29

173	A59	100 l lil rose, bl, dk grn & yel	32.50	20.00

Peter Lombard, Bishop of Paris 1159.

Pope Pius XI and Vatican City — A60

1954, Feb. 12　　　　Wmk. 235

174	A60	25 l bl, red brn & cr	1.25	1.00
175	A60	60 l yel brn & dp bl	3.00	2.50

Signing of the Lateran Pacts, 25th anniv.

Pope Pius IX A61

Portraits: (At left) - 6 l, 20 l, Pope Pius IX. (At right) — 4 l, 12 l, 35 l, Pope Pius XII.

1954, May 26　Engr.　Perf. 13

176	A61	3 l violet	.20	.20
177	A61	4 l carmine	.20	.20
178	A61	6 l plum	.20	.20
179	A61	12 l blue green	1.00	.20
180	A61	20 l red brown	.90	.85
181	A61	35 l ultra	2.25	2.25
		Nos. 176-181 (6)	4.75	3.90

Marian Year; centenary of the dogma of the Immaculate Conception.

St. Pius X — A62

1954, May 29   Photo.
Colors (except background): Yellow and Plum

182	A62	10 l dark brown	.25	.25
183	A62	25 l violet	2.50	1.25
184	A62	35 l dk slate gray	4.25	2.50
		Nos. 182-184 (3)	7.00	4.00

Canonization of Pope Pius X, May 20, 1954. #182-184 exist imperf. Value, each pair $800.

Basilica of St. Francis of Assisi A63

1954, Oct. 1   Photo.   Perf. 14

185	A63	20 l dk vio gray & cr	2.00	1.75
186	A63	35 l dk brown & cream	1.50	1.40

Consecration of the Basilica of St. Francis of Assisi, 200th anniv.

St. Augustine A64

1954, Nov. 13

187	A64	35 l blue green	1.00	.90
188	A64	50 l redsh brown	1.90	1.75

1600th birth anniv. of St. Augustine.

Madonna of the Gate of Dawn, Vilnius — A65

1954, Dec. 7

189	A65	20 l pink & multi	1.00	.75
190	A65	35 l blue & multi	7.50	3.75
191	A65	60 l multicolored	12.50	5.75
		Nos. 189-191 (3)	21.00	10.25

Issued to mark the end of the Marian Year.

St. Boniface and Fulda Abbey A66

1955, Apr. 28   Engr.   Perf. 13

192	A66	10 l grnsh gray	.20	.20
193	A66	35 l violet	.60	.60
a.		Imperf., pair	100.00	
194	A66	60 l brt blue green	.70	.70
		Nos. 192-194 (3)	1.50	1.50

1200th death anniv. of St. Boniface.

Pope Sixtus II and St. Lawrence A67

Pope Nicholas V A68

1955, June 27   Wmk. 235
Photo.   Perf. 14

195	A67	50 l carmine	3.75	2.00
196	A67	100 l deep blue	2.50	2.00

Fra Angelico (1387-1455), painter. Design is from a Fra Angelico fresco.

1955, Nov. 28

197	A68	20 l grnsh bl & ol brn	.20	.20
198	A68	35 l rose car & ol brn	.35	.25
199	A68	60 l yel grn & ol brn	.70	.35
		Nos. 197-199 (3)	1.25	.80

Death of Pope Nicholas V, 500th anniv.

St. Bartholomew and Church of Grottaferrata A69

Capt. Gaspar Roust A70

1955, Dec. 29

200	A69	10 l brown & gray	.20	.20
201	A69	25 l car rose & gray	.80	.30
202	A69	100 l dk green & gray	2.00	1.50
		Nos. 200-202 (3)	3.00	2.00

900th death anniv. of St. Bartholomew, abbot of Grottaferrata.

1956, Apr. 27   Engr.   Perf. 13
6 l, 50 l, Guardsman. 10 l, 60 l, Two drummers.

203	A70	4 l dk carmine rose	.20	.20
204	A70	6 l deep orange	.20	.20
205	A70	10 l deep ultra	.20	.20
206	A70	35 l brown	.55	.40
207	A70	50 l violet	.75	.60
208	A70	60 l blue green	.85	.65
		Nos. 203-208 (6)	2.75	2.25

450th anniv. of the Swiss Papal Guard.

St. Rita of Cascia — A71

Pope Paul III Confirming Society of Jesus — A72

1956, May 19   Photo.   Perf. 14

209	A71	10 l gray green	.20	.20
210	A71	25 l olive brown	.60	.60
211	A71	35 l ultra	.45	.45
		Nos. 209-211 (3)	1.25	1.25

500th death anniv. of St. Rita of Cascia.

1956, July 31   Engr.   Perf. 13

212	A72	35 l dk red brown	.55	.55
213	A72	60 l blue gray	1.10	1.00

400th death anniv. of St. Ignatius of Loyola, founder of the Society of Jesus.

St. John of Capistrano A73

1956, Oct. 30   Perf. 14

214	A73	25 l slate blk & grn	2.25	1.25
215	A73	35 l dk brn car & brn	1.00	.75

5th cent. of the death of St. John of Capistrano, leader in the war against the Turks.

Black Madonna of Czestochowa — A74

St. Domenico Savio — A75

1956, Dec. 20

216	A74	35 l dk blue & blk	.25	.25
217	A74	60 l green & ultra	.60	.55
218	A74	100 l brn & dk car rose	1.00	.85
		Nos. 216-218 (3)	1.85	1.65

300th anniv. of the proclamation of the Madonna of Czestochowa as "Queen of Poland."

1957, Mar. 21   Wmk. 235   Perf. 13½
6 l, 60 l, Sts. Domenico Savio and John Bosco.

219	A75	4 l red brown	.20	.20
220	A75	6 l brt carmine	.20	.20
221	A75	25 l green	.20	.20
222	A75	60 l ultra	1.40	1.10
		Nos. 219-222 (4)	2.00	1.70

Death cent. of St. Domenico Savio.

Cardinal Capranica and College A76

Design: 10 l, 100 l, Pope Pius XII.

1957, June 27   Engr.   Perf. 13

223	A76	5 l dk carmine rose	.20	.20
224	A76	10 l pale brown	.20	.20
225	A76	35 l grnsh black	.20	.20
226	A76	100 l ultra	.50	.50
		Nos. 223-226 (4)	1.10	1.10

500th anniv. of Capranica College, oldest seminary in the world.

Pontifical Academy of Science A77

1957, Oct. 9   Photo.   Perf. 14

227	A77	35 l dk blue & green	.55	.55
228	A77	60 l brown & ultra	.80	.55

Pontifical Academy of Science, 20th anniv.

Mariazell A78

High Altar — A79

1957, Nov. 14   Engr.   Perf. 13½

229	A78	5 l green	.20	.20
230	A79	15 l slate	.20	.20
231	A78	60 l ultra	.70	.25
232	A79	100 l ultra	.90	.85
		Nos. 229-232 (4)	2.00	1.50

Mariazell shrine, Austria, 800th anniv.

Apparition of the Virgin Mary — A80

Designs: 10 l, 35 l, Sick man and basilica. 15 l, 100 l, St. Bernadette.

Perf. 13x14
1958, Feb. 21   Wmk. 235

233	A80	5 l dark blue	.20	.20
234	A80	10 l blue green	.20	.20
235	A80	15 l reddish brown	.20	.20
236	A80	25 l rose carmine	.20	.20
237	A80	35 l gray brown	.20	.20
238	A80	100 l violet	.20	.20
		Nos. 233-238 (6)	1.20	1.20

Centenary of apparition of the Virgin Mary at Lourdes and the establishment of the shrine.

Pope Pius XII — A81

Statue of Pope Clement XIII by Canova — A82

60 l, 100 l, Vatican pavilion at Brussels fair.

1958, June 19   Engr.   Perf. 13

239	A81	35 l claret	.30	.25

Perf. 13x14

240	A81	60 l fawn	.55	.55
241	A81	100 l violet	1.75	1.25
242	A81	300 l ultra	1.40	1.10
a.		Souvenir sheet of 4, #239-242	20.00	15.00
		Nos. 239-242 (4)	4.00	3.15

Universal and Intl. Exposition, Brussels.

1958, July 2   Perf. 14
Statues: 10 l, Clement XIV. 35 l, Pius VI. 100 l, Pius VII.

243	A82	5 l brown	.20	.20
244	A82	10 l carmine rose	.20	.20
245	A82	35 l blue gray	.25	.25
246	A82	100 l dark blue	.85	.85
		Nos. 243-246 (4)	1.50	1.50

Antonio Canova (1757-1822), sculptor.

Interregnum Issue

St. Peter's Keys and Papal Chamberlain's Insignia — A83

Wmk. 235
1958, Oct. 21   Photo.   Perf. 14

247	A83	15 l brn blk, yel	1.40	1.00
248	A83	25 l brown black	.20	.20
249	A83	60 l brn blk, pale vio	.20	.20
		Nos. 247-249 (3)	1.80	1.40

Pope John XXIII — A84

Pope
Pius XI — A85

Design: 35 l, 100 l, Coat of Arms.

1959, Apr. 2   Photo.   Perf. 14
250	A84	25 l car rose, bl & buff	.20	.20
251	A84	35 l multicolored	.20	.20
252	A84	60 l rose car, bl & ocher	.20	.20
253	A84	100 l multicolored	.20	.20
		Nos. 250-253 (4)	.80	.80

Coronation of Pope John XXIII, 11/4/58.

1959, May 25   Wmk. 235   Perf. 14
254	A85	30 l brown	.20	.20
255	A85	100 l violet blue	.20	.20

Lateran Pacts, 30th anniversary.

St. Lawrence
A86

Radio Tower and
Archangel Gabriel
A87

Portraits of Saints: 25 l, Pope Sixtus II. 50 l, Agapitus. 60 l, Filicissimus. 100 l, Cyprianus. 300 l, Fructuosus.

1959, May 25
256	A86	15 l red, brn & yel	.25	.20
257	A86	25 l lilac, brn & yel	.25	.20
258	A86	50 l Prus bl, blk & yel	.25	.20
259	A86	60 l ol grn, brn & bis	.25	.20
260	A86	100 l maroon, brn & yel	.25	.20
261	A86	300 l bis brn & dk brn	.50	.35
		Nos. 256-261 (6)	1.75	1.35

Martyrs of Emperor Valerian's persecutions.

1959, Oct. 27   Photo.   Perf. 14
262	A87	25 l rose, org yel & dk brn	.20	.20
263	A87	60 l multicolored	.20	.20

2nd anniv. of the papal radio station, St. Maria di Galeria.

St. Casimir,
Palace and
Cathedral,
Vilnius
A88

1959, Dec. 14   Engr.   Wmk. 235
264	A88	50 l brown	.20	.20
265	A88	100 l dull green	.25	.20

500th anniv. (in 1958) of the birth of St. Casimir, patron saint of Lithuania.

Nativity by
Raphael — A89

1959, Dec. 14   Engr.   Perf. 13½
266	A89	15 l dark gray	.20	.20
267	A89	25 l magenta	.20	.20
268	A89	60 l bright brown	.20	.20
		Nos. 266-268 (3)	.60	.60

St.
Antoninus — A90

Transept of Lateran
Basilica — A91

25 l, 110 l, St. Antoninus preaching.

Perf. 13x14
1960, Feb. 29   Wmk. 235
269	A90	15 l ultra	.20	.20
270	A90	25 l turquoise	.20	.20
271	A90	60 l brown	.30	.25
272	A90	110 l rose claret	.60	.35
		Nos. 269-272 (4)	1.30	1.00

5th cent. of death of St. Antoninus, bishop of Florence.

1960, Feb. 29   Photo.   Perf. 14
273	A91	15 l brown	.20	.20
274	A91	60 l black	.40	.20

Roman Diocesan Synod, February, 1960.

Flight into Egypt
by Fra
Angelico — A92

Cardinal Sarto's
Departure from
Venice — A93

Designs: 10 l, 100 l, St. Peter Giving Alms to the Poor, by Masaccio. 25 l, 300 l, Madonna of Mercy, by Piero della Francesca.

1960, Apr. 7   Wmk. 235   Perf. 14
275	A92	5 l green	.20	.20
276	A92	10 l gray brown	.20	.20
277	A92	25 l deep carmine	.25	.20
278	A92	60 l lilac	.20	.20
279	A92	100 l ultra	1.90	1.50
280	A92	300 l Prus green	.65	.40
		Nos. 275-280 (6)	3.35	2.70

World Refugee Year, 7/1/59-6/30/60.

1960, Apr. 11   Engr.   Perf. 13½
35 l, Pope John XXIII praying at coffin of Pope Pius X. 60 l, Body of Pope Pius X returning to Venice.
281	A93	15 l brown	.25	.25
282	A93	35 l rose carmine	.60	.60
283	A93	60 l Prus green	1.25	.85
		Nos. 281-283 (3)	2.10	1.70

Return of the body of Pope Pius X to Venice.

Feeding the
Hungry
A94

"Acts of Mercy," by Della Robbia: 10 l, Giving drink to the thirsty. 15 l, Clothing the naked. 20 l, Sheltering the homeless. 30 l, Visiting the sick. 35 l, Visiting prisoners. 40 l, Burying the dead. 70 l, Pope John XXIII.

1960, Nov. 8   Photo.   Perf. 14
Centers in Brown
284	A94	5 l red brown	.20	.20
285	A94	10 l green	.20	.20
286	A94	15 l slate	.20	.20
287	A94	20 l rose carmine	.20	.20
288	A94	30 l violet blue	.20	.20
289	A94	35 l violet brown	.20	.20
290	A94	40 l red orange	.20	.20
291	A94	70 l ocher	.20	.20
		Nos. 284-291,E15-E16 (10)	2.00	2.00

Holy
Family by
Gerard van
Honthorst
A95

1960, Dec. 6   Wmk. 235   Perf. 14
292	A95	10 l slate grn & slate blk	.20	.20
293	A95	15 l sepia & ol blk	.20	.20
294	A95	70 l grnsh bl & dp bl	.30	.20
		Nos. 292-294 (3)	.70	.60

St. Vincent de
Paul — A96

St.
Meinrad — A97

Designs: 70 l, St. Louisa de Marillac. 100 l, St. Louisa and St. Vincent.

1960, Dec. 6
295	A96	40 l dull violet	.20	.20
296	A96	70 l dark gray	.30	.20
297	A96	100 l dk red brown	.70	.30
		Nos. 295-297 (3)	1.20	.70

Death of St. Vincent de Paul, 300th anniv.

1961, Feb. 28   Perf. 14
Designs: 40 l, Statue of Our Lady of Einsiedeln. 100 l, Einsiedeln monastery, horiz.
298	A97	30 l dark gray	.45	.20
299	A97	40 l lt violet	1.50	.40
300	A97	100 l brown	1.50	.85
		Nos. 298-300 (3)	3.45	1.45

Death of St. Meinrad, 1,100th anniv.; Einsiedeln Abbey, Switzerland.

Pope Leo the
Great Defying
Attila — A98

Wmk. 235
1961, Apr. 6   Photo.   Perf. 14
301	A98	15 l rose brown	.20	.20
302	A98	70 l Prus green	.25	.25
303	A98	300 l brown black	1.75	.55
		Nos. 301-303 (3)	2.20	1.00

Death of Pope Leo the Great (St. Leo Magnus), 1,500th anniv. The design is from a marble bas-relief in St. Peter's Basilica.

St. Paul
Arriving in
Rome, 61
A.D. — A99

10 l, 30 l, Map showing St. Paul's journey to Rome. 20 l, 200 l, First Basilica of St. Paul, Rome.

1961, June 13   Wmk. 235   Perf. 14
304	A99	10 l Prus green	.20	.20
305	A99	15 l dl red brn & gray	.20	.20
306	A99	20 l red org & gray	.20	.20
307	A99	30 l blue	.20	.20
308	A99	75 l org brn & gray	.30	.30
309	A99	200 l blue & gray	1.60	1.10
		Nos. 304-309 (6)	2.70	2.20

Arrival of St. Paul in Rome, 1,900th anniv.

1861 and
1961
Mastheads
A100

70 l, Editorial offices. 250 l, Rotary press.

1961, July 4
310	A100	40 l red brn & blk	.20	.20
311	A100	70 l blue & blk	.40	.30
312	A100	250 l yellow & blk	1.90	1.10
		Nos. 310-312 (3)	2.50	1.60

Centenary of L'Osservatore Romano, Vatican's newspaper.

St. Patrick's
Purgatory, Lough
Derg — A101

Arms of Roncalli
Family — A102

10 l, 40 l, St. Patrick, marble sculpture.

Wmk. 235
1961, Oct. 6   Photo.   Perf. 14
313	A101	10 l buff & slate grn	.20	.20
314	A101	15 l blue & sepia	.20	.20
315	A101	40 l yellow & bl grn	.25	.20
316	A101	150 l Prus bl & red brn	.70	.50
		Nos. 313-316 (4)	1.35	1.10

Death of St. Patrick, 1,500th anniv.

1961, Nov. 25
Designs: 25 l, Church at Sotto il Monte. 30 l, Santa Maria in Monte Santo, Rome. 40 l, Church of San Carlo al Corso, Rome (erroneously inscribed with name of Basilica of Sts. Ambrosius and Charles, Milan). 70 l, Altar, St. Peter's, Rome. 115 l, Pope John XXIII.
317	A102	10 l gray & red brn	.20	.20
318	A102	25 l ol bis & sl grn	.20	.20
319	A102	30 l vio bl & pale pur	.20	.20
320	A102	40 l lilac & dk blue	.20	.20
321	A102	70 l gray grn & org brn	.30	.20
322	A102	115 l choc & slate	.70	.45
		Nos. 317-322 (6)	1.80	1.45

80th birthday of Pope John XXIII.

"The Adoration"
by Lucas
Chen — A103

Draining of
Pontine Marshes
Medal by Pope
Sixtus V,
1588 — A104

1961, Nov. 25
Center Multicolored
323 A103 15 l bluish green .20 .20
324 A103 40 l gray .20 .20
325 A103 70 l pale lilac .30 .20
    Nos. 323-325 (3) .70 .60
Christmas.

1962, Apr. 7   Wmk. 235   Perf. 14
40 l, 300 l, Map of Pontine Marshes showing 18th cent. drainage under Pope Pius VI.
326 A104 15 l dark violet .20 .20
327 A104 40 l rose carmine .20 .20
328 A104 70 l brown .20 .20
329 A104 300 l dull green .65 .40
    Nos. 326-329 (4) 1.25 1.00
WHO drive to eradicate malaria.

"The Good
Shepherd"
A105

Wheatfield (Luke
10:2) — A106

1962, June 2   Photo.
330 A105 10 l lilac & black .20 .20
331 A106 15 l blue & ocher .20 .20
332 A105 70 l lt green & blk .25 .30
333 A106 115 l fawn & ocher 1.25 1.10
334 A105 200 l brown & black 2.00 1.40
    Nos. 330-334 (5) 3.90 3.20

Issued to honor the priesthood and to stress its importance as a vocation.
"The Good Shepherd" is a fourth-century statue in the Lateran Museum, Rome.

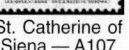

St. Catherine of
Siena — A107

Paulina M.
Jaricot — A108

1962, June 12
335 A107 15 l brown .20 .20
336 A107 60 l brt violet .30 .25
337 A107 100 l blue .60 .40
    Nos. 335-337 (3) 1.10 .85
Canonization of St. Catherine of Siena, 500th anniv. The portrait is from a fresco by Il Sodoma, Church of St. Dominic, Siena.

1962, July 5
Portrait Multicolored
338 A108 10 l pale violet .20 .20
339 A108 50 l dull green .20 .20
340 A108 150 l gray .80 .50
    Nos. 338-340 (3) 1.20 .90
Paulina M. Jaricot (1799-1862), founder of the Society for the Propagation of the Faith.

Sts. Peter
and Paul
A109

Design: 40 l, 100 l, "The Invincible Cross," relief from sarcophagus.

Wmk. 235
1962, Sept. 25   Photo.   Perf. 14
341 A109 20 l lilac & brown .20 .20
342 A109 40 l lt brown & blk .20 .20
343 A109 70 l bluish grn & brn .20 .20
344 A109 100 l sal pink & blk .20 .20
    Nos. 341-344 (4) .80 .80
6th Congress of Christian Archeology, Ravenna, Sept. 23-28.

"Faith" by
Raphael — A110

Designs: 10 l, "Hope." 15 l, "Charity." 25 l, Arms of Pope John XXIII and emblems of the Four Evangelists. 30 l, Ecumenical Congress meeting in St. Peter's. 40 l, Pope John XXIII on throne. 60 l, Statue of St. Peter. 115 l, The Holy Ghost as a dove (symbolic design).

Photo.; Center Engr. on 30 l
1962, Oct. 30
345 A110 5 l brt blue & blk .20 .20
346 A110 10 l green & blk .20 .20
347 A110 15 l ver & sepia .20 .20
348 A110 25 l ver & slate .20 .20
349 A110 30 l lilac & blk .20 .20
350 A110 40 l dk carmine & blk .20 .20
351 A110 60 l dk grn & dp org .20 .20
352 A110 115 l crimson .20 .20
    Nos. 345-352 (8) 1.60 1.60
Vatican II, the 21st Ecumenical Council of the Roman Catholic Church, which opened Oct. 11, 1962. Nos. 345-347 show "the Three Theological Virtues" by Raphael.

Nativity
Scene
A111

Set in India, following a design by Marcus Toano.

1962, Dec. 4
Center Multicolored
353 A111 10 l gray .20 .20
354 A111 15 l brown .20 .20
355 A111 90 l dull green .30 .20
    Nos. 353-355 (3) .70 .60

Miracle of the
Loaves and Fishes
by Murillo — A112

Pope John
XXIII — A113

Design: 40 l, 200 l, "The Miraculous Catch of Fishes" by Raphael.

Wmk. 235
1963, Mar. 21   Photo.   Perf. 14
356 A112 15 l brn & dk brn .20 .20
357 A112 40 l rose red & blk .20 .20
358 A112 100 l blue & dk brn .20 .20
359 A112 200 l bl grn & blk .20 .20
    Nos. 356-359 (4) .80 .80
FAO "Freedom from Hunger" campaign.

1963, May 8
360 A113 15 l red brown .20 .20
361 A113 160 l black .40 .20
Awarding of the Balzan Peace Prize to Pope John XXIII.

Interregnum Issue

Keys of St. Peter
and Papal
Chamberlain's
Insignia — A114

1963, June 15   Wmk. 235   Perf. 14
362 A114 10 l dk brown .20 .20
363 A114 40 l dk brown, yel .20 .20
364 A114 100 l dk brown, vio .20 .20
    Nos. 362-364 (3) .60 .60

Pope
Paul VI — A115

St. Cyril — A116

Design: 40 l, 200 l, Arms of Pope Paul VI.

1963, Oct. 16   Engr.   Perf. 13x14
365 A115 15 l black .20 .20
366 A115 40 l carmine .20 .20
367 A115 115 l redsh brown .20 .20
368 A115 200 l slate blue .40 .25
    Nos. 365-368 (4) 1.00 .85
Coronation of Pope Paul VI, June 30, 1963.

Wmk. 235
1963, Nov. 22   Photo.   Perf. 14
Designs: 70 l, Map of Hungary, Moravia and Poland, 16th century. 150 l, St. Methodius.
369 A116 30 l violet black .20 .20
370 A116 70 l brown .30 .20
371 A116 150 l rose claret .40 .20
    Nos. 369-371 (3) .90 .60
1100th anniv. of the beginning of missionary work among the Slavs by Sts. Cyril and Methodius. The pictures of the saints are from

16th century frescoes in St. Clement's Basilica, Rome.

African Nativity
Scene — A117

Church of the
Holy Sepulcher,
Jerusalem
A118

1963, Nov. 22
372 A117 10 l brn & pale brn .20 .20
373 A117 40 l ultra & brown .20 .20
374 A117 100 l gray olive & brn .25 .20
    Nos. 372-374 (3) .65 .60
The design is after a sculpture by the Burundi artist Andreas Bukuru.

1964, Jan. 4   Wmk. 235   Perf. 14
15 l, Pope Paul VI. 25 l, Nativity Church, Bethlehem. 160 l, Well of the Virgin Mary, Nazareth.
375 A118 15 l black .20 .20
376 A118 25 l rose brown .20 .20
377 A118 70 l brown .20 .20
378 A118 160 l ultra .20 .20
    Nos. 375-378 (4) .80 .80
Visit of Pope Paul VI to the Holy Land, Jan. 4-6.

St. Peter from
Coptic Church at
Wadi-es-Sebua,
Sudan — A119

Design: 20 l, 200 l, Trajan's Kiosk, Philae.

1964, Mar. 10   Photo.
379 A119 10 l ultra & red brn .20 .20
380 A119 20 l multicolored .20 .20
381 A119 70 l gray & red brn .20 .20
382 A119 200 l gray & multi .20 .20
    Nos. 379-382 (4) .80 .80
UNESCO world campaign to save historic monuments in Nubia.

Pietà by
Michelangelo
A120

Isaiah by
Michelangelo
A121

Designs: 15 l, 100 l, Pope Paul VI. 250 l, Head of Mary from Pietà.

1964, Apr. 22   Wmk. 235   Perf. 14
383 A120 15 l violet blue   .20 .20
384 A120 50 l dark brown   .20 .20
385 A120 100 l slate blue   .20 .20
386 A120 250 l chestnut   .20 .20
    Nos. 383-386 (4)   .80 .80
New York World's Fair, 1964-65.

1964, June 16 Engr.   Perf. 13½x14
387 A121 10 l Michelangelo, af-
          ter Jacopino del
          Conte   .20 .20
388 A121 25 l Isaiah   .20 .20
389 A121 30 l Delphie Sibyl   .20 .20
390 A121 40 l Jeremiah   .20 .20
391 A121 150 l Joel   .20 .20
    Nos. 387-391 (5)   1.00 1.00
Michelangelo Buonarroti (1475-1564). Designs are from the Sistine Chapel.

The Good Samaritan A122

Perf. 14x13½
1964, Sept. 22 Engr.   Wmk. 235
392 A122 10 l red brown & red   .20 .20
393 A122 30 l dark blue & red   .20 .20
394 A122 300 l gray & red   .25 .20
    Nos. 392-394 (3)   .65 .60
Cent. (in 1963) of the founding of the Intl. Red Cross.

Birthplace of Cardinal Nicolaus Cusanus A123

Design: 200 l, Cardinal's sepulcher, Church of San Pietro in Vincoli, Rome.

1964, Nov. 16   Wmk. 235
395 A123 40 l dull blue grn   .20 .20
396 A123 200 l rose red   .30 .20
German cardinal Nicolaus Cusanus (Nicolaus Krebs of Kues) (1401-1464).

Japanese Nativity Scene by Kimiko Koseki — A124

Pope Paul VI and Map of India and Southeast Asia — A125

1964, Nov. 16   Photo.   Perf. 14
397 A124 10 l multicolored   .20 .20
  a.   Yellow omitted
398 A124 15 l black & multi   .20 .20
399 A124 135 l bister & multi   .25 .20
    Nos. 397-399 (3)   .65 .60

1964, Dec. 2
Designs: 15 l, Pope Paul VI at prayer. 25 l, Eucharistic Congress altar, Bombay, horiz. 60 l, Gateway of India, Bombay, horiz.

400 A125 15 l dull violet   .20 .20
401 A125 25 l green   .20 .20
402 A125 60 l brown   .20 .20
403 A125 200 l dull violet   .20 .20
    Nos. 400-403 (4)   .80 .80
Trip of Pope Paul VI to India, Dec. 2-5, 1964.

Uganda Martyrs — A126

Dante by Raphael — A127

Various groups of Martyrs of Uganda.

Perf. 13½x14
1965, Mar. 16   Engr.   Wmk. 235
404 A126 15 l Prus green   .20 .20
405 A126 20 l brown   .20 .20
406 A126 30 l ultra   .20 .20
407 A126 75 l black   .20 .20
408 A126 100 l rose red   .20 .20
409 A126 160 l violet   .20 .20
    Nos. 404-409 (6)   1.20 1.20
Canonization of 22 African martyrs, 10/18/64.

Photogravure and Engraved
1965, May 18   Perf. 13½x14
Designs: 40 l, Dante and the 3 beasts at entrance to the Inferno. 70 l, Dante and Virgil at entrance to Purgatory. 200 l, Dante and Beatrice in Paradise. (40 l, 70 l, 200 l, by Botticelli.)
410 A127 10 l bis brn & dk brn   .20 .20
411 A127 40 l rose & dk brn   .20 .20
412 A127 70 l lt grn & dk brn   .20 .20
413 A127 200 l pale bl & dk brn   .20 .20
    Nos. 410-413 (4)   .80 .80
Birth of Dante Alighieri, 700th anniv.

St. Benedict by Perugino A128

Pope Paul VI Addressing UN Assembly A129

Design: 300 l, View of Monte Cassino.

1965, July 2   Photo.   Perf. 14
414 A128 40 l brown   .20 .20
415 A128 300 l dark green   .30 .20
Conferring of the title Patron Saint of Europe upon St. Benedict by Pope Paul VI; restoring of the Abbey of Monte Cassino.

1965, Oct. 4   Wmk. 235   Perf. 14
30 l, 150 l, UN Headquarters and olive branch.
416 A129 20 l brown   .20 .20
417 A129 30 l sapphire   .20 .20
418 A129 150 l olive green   .20 .20
419 A129 300 l rose violet   .25 .20
    Nos. 416-419 (4)   .85 .80
Visit of Pope Paul VI to the UN, NYC, Oct. 4.

Peruvian Nativity Scene A130   Cartographer A131

1965, Nov. 25   Engr.   Perf. 13½x14
420 A130 20 l rose claret   .20 .20
421 A130 40 l red brown   .20 .20
422 A130 200 l gray green   .20 .20
    Nos. 420-422 (3)   .60 .60

1966, Mar. 8   Photo.   Perf. 14
Designs: 5 l, Pope Paul VI. 10 l, Organist. 20 l, Painter. 30 l, Sculptor. 40 l, Bricklayer. 55 l, Printer. 75 l, Plowing farmer. 90 l, Blacksmith. 130 l, Scholar.
423 A131   5 l sepia   .20 .20
424 A131 10 l violet   .20 .20
425 A131 15 l brown   .20 .20
426 A131 20 l gray green   .20 .20
427 A131 30 l brown red   .20 .20
428 A131 40 l Prus green   .20 .20
429 A131 55 l dark blue   .20 .20
430 A131 75 l dk rose brown   .20 .20
431 A131 90 l carmine rose   .20 .20
432 A131 130 l black   .20 .20
    Nos. 423-432,E17-E18 (12)   2.40 2.40
The Pope's portrait is from a bas-relief by Enrico Manfrini; the arts and crafts designs are bas-reliefs by Mario Rudelli from the chair in the Pope's private chapel.

King Mieszko I and Queen Dabrowka A132

Designs: 25 l, St. Adalbert (Wojciech) and Cathedrals of Wroclaw and Gniezno. 40 l, St. Stanislas, Skalka Church, Wawel Cathedral and Castle, Cracow. 50 l, Queen Jadwiga (Hedwig), Holy Gate with Our Lady of Mercy, Vilnius, and Jagellon University Library, Cracow. 150 l, Black Madonna of Czestochowa, cloister and church of Bright Mountain, Czestochowa, and St. John's Cathedral, Warsaw. 220 l, Pope Paul VI blessing students and farmers.

Perf. 14x13½
1966, May 3   Engr.   Wmk. 235
433 A132 15 l black   .20 .20
434 A132 25 l violet   .20 .20
435 A132 40 l brick red   .20 .20
436 A132 50 l claret   .20 .20
437 A132 150 l slate blue   .20 .20
438 A132 220 l brown   .20 .20
    Nos. 433-438 (6)   1.20 1.20
Millenium of Christianization of Poland.

Pope John XXIII Opening Vatican II Council A133   Nativity, Sculpture by Scorzelli A134

Designs: 15 l, Ancient Bible on ornate display stand. 55 l, Bishops celebrating Mass. 90 l, Pope Paul VI greeting Patriarch Athenagoras I. 100 l, Gold ring given to participating bishops. 130 l, Pope Paul VI carried in front of St. Peter's.

1966, Oct. 11   Photo.   Perf. 14
439 A133 10 l red & black   .20 .20
440 A133 15 l brown & green   .20 .20
441 A133 55 l blk & brt rose   .20 .20
442 A133 90 l slate grn & blk   .20 .20

443 A133 100 l green & ocher   .20 .20
444 A133 130 l orange brn & brn   .20 .20
    Nos. 439-444 (6)   1.20 1.20
Conclusion of Vatican II, the 21st Ecumenical Council of the Roman Catholic Church, Dec. 8, 1965.

1966, Nov. 24   Wmk. 235   Perf. 14
445 A134 20 l plum   .20 .20
446 A134 55 l slate green   .20 .20
447 A134 225 l yellow brown   .20 .20
    Nos. 445-447 (3)   .60 .60

St. Peter, Fresco, Catacombs, Rome — A135   Cross, People and Globe — A136

Designs: 20 l, St. Paul, fresco from Catacombs, Rome. 55 l, Sts. Peter and Paul, glass painting, Vatican Library. 90 l, Baldachin by Bernini, St. Peter's, Rome. 220 l, Interior of St. Paul's, Rome.

Perf. 13½x14
1967, June 15   Photo.   Unwmk.
448 A135 15 l multi   .20 .20
449 A135 20 l multi   .20 .20
450 A135 55 l multi   .20 .20
451 A135 90 l multi   .20 .20
452 A135 220 l multi   .20 .20
    Nos. 448-452 (5)   1.00 1.00
Martyrdom of the Apostles Peter and Paul, 1,900th anniv.

1967, Oct. 13   Wmk. 235   Perf. 14
453 A136 40 l carmine rose   .20 .20
454 A136 130 l brt blue   .20 .20
3rd Congress of Catholic Laymen, Rome, Oct. 11-18.

Sculpture of Shepherd Children of Fatima — A137

Nativity, 9th Century Painting on Wood — A138

Designs: 50 l, Basilica at Fatima. 200 l, Pope Paul VI praying before statue of Virgin of Fatima.

1967, Oct. 13   Perf. 13½x14
455 A137 30 l multi   .20 .20
456 A137 50 l multi   .20 .20
457 A137 200 l multi   .20 .20
    Nos. 455-457 (3)   .60 .60
Apparition of the Virgin Mary to 3 shepherd children at Fatima, 50th anniv.

Christmas Issue
1967, Nov. 28   Photo.   Unwmk.
458 A138 25 l purple & multi   .20 .20
459 A138 55 l gray & multi   .20 .20
460 A138 180 l green & multi   .20 .20
    Nos. 458-460 (3)   .60 .60

Pope
Paul VI — A139

Holy Infant of
Prague — A140

Designs: 55 l, Monstrance from fresco by Raphael. 220 l, Map of South America.

1968, Aug. 22 Wmk. 235 Perf. 14
461 A139 25 l blk & dk red brn .20 .20
462 A139 55 l blk, gray & ocher .20 .20
463 A139 220 l blk, lt bl & sep .20 .20
       Nos. 461-463 (3) .60 .60

Visit of Pope Paul VI to the 39th Eucharistic Congress in Bogotá, Colombia, Aug. 22-25.

Engraved and Photogravure
1968, Nov. 28 Perf. 13½x14
464 A140 20 l plum & pink .20 .20
465 A140 50 l vio & pale vio .20 .20
466 A140 250 l dk bl & lt bluish
                gray .20 .20
       Nos. 464-466 (3) .60 .60

The Resurrection,
by Fra Angelico
de
Fiesole — A141

Pope Paul VI with
African
Children — A142

Easter Issue
Perf. 13½x14
1969, Mar. 6 Engr. Wmk. 235
467 A141 20 l dk carmine & buff .20 .20
468 A141 90 l green & buff .20 .20
469 A141 180 l ultra & buff .20 .20
       Nos. 467-469 (3) .60 .60

Common Design Types pictured following the introduction.

Europa Issue
Common Design Type
Perf. 13½x14
1969, Apr. 28 Photo. Wmk. 235
Size: 36½x27mm
470 CD12 50 l gray & lt brn .20 .20
471 CD12 90 l vermilion & lt brn .20 .20
472 CD12 130 l olive & lt brn .20 .20
       Nos. 470-472 (3) .60 .60

Perf. 13½x14
1969, July 31 Photo. Wmk. 235
Designs: 55 l, Pope Paul VI and African bishops. 250 l, Map of Africa with Kampala, olive branch and compass rose.
473 A142 25 l bister & brown .20 .20
474 A142 55 l dk red & brown .20 .20
475 A142 250 l multicolored .20 .20
       Nos. 473-475 (3) .60 .60

Visit of Pope Paul VI to Uganda, 7/31-8/2.

Pope
Pius IX — A143

Mt. Fuji and
EXPO '70
Emblem — A144

Designs: 50 l, Chrismon, emblem of St. Peter's Circle. 220 l, Pope Paul VI.

Perf. 13½x14
1969, Nov. 18 Engr. Wmk. 235
476 A143 30 l red brown .20 .20
477 A143 50 l dark gray .20 .20
478 A143 220 l deep plum .20 .20
       Nos. 476-478 (3) .60 .60

Centenary of St. Peter's Circle, a lay society dedicated to prayer, action and sacrifice.

1970, Mar. 16 Photo. Unwmk.
EXPO '70 Emblem and: 25 l, EXPO '70 emblem. 40 l, Osaka Castle. 55 l, Japanese Virgin and Child, by Domoto in Osaka Cathedral. 90 l, Christian Pavilion.
479 A144 25 l gold, red & blk .20 .20
480 A144 40 l red & multi .20 .20
481 A144 55 l brown & multi .20 .20
482 A144 90 l gold & multi .20 .20
483 A144 110 l blue & multi .20 .20
       Nos. 479-483 (5) 1.00 1.00

EXPO '70 Intl. Exhibition, Osaka, Japan, Mar. 15-Sept. 13.

Centenary Medal,
Jesus Giving St.
Peter the
Keys — A145

Designs: 50 l, Coat of arms of Pope Pius IX. 180 l, Vatican I Council meeting in St. Peter's, obverse of centenary medal.

Engr. & Photo.; Photo. (50 l)
1970, Apr. 29 Perf. 13x14
484 A145 20 l orange & brown .20 .20
485 A145 50 l multicolored .20 .20
486 A145 180 l ver & brn .30 .25
       Nos. 484-486 (3) .70 .65

Centenary of the Vatican I Council.

Christ, by
Simone
Martini
A146

25 l, Christ with Crown of Thorns, by Rogier van der Weyden. 50 l, Christ, by Albrecht Dürer. 90 l, Christ, by El Greco. 180 l, Pope Paul VI.

1970, May 29 Photo. Perf. 14x13
487 A146 15 l gold & multi .20 .20
488 A146 25 l gold & multi .20 .20
489 A146 50 l gold & multi .20 .20
490 A146 90 l gold & multi .20 .20
491 A146 180 l gold & multi .25 .20
       Nos. 487-491 (5) 1.05 1.00

Ordination of Pope Paul VI, 50th anniv.

Adam, by
Michelangelo; UN
Emblem — A147

Pope
Paul VI — A148

UN Emblem and: 90 l, Eve, by Michelangelo. 220 l, Olive branch.

1970, Oct. 8 Photo. Perf. 13x14
492 A147 20 l multi .20 .20
493 A147 90 l multi .20 .20
494 A147 220 l multi .25 .20
       Nos. 492-494 (3) .65 .60

25th anniversary of the United Nations.

1970, Nov. 26 Photo. Unwmk.
Designs: 55 l, Holy Child of Cebu, Philippines. 100 l, Madonna and Child, by Georg Hamori, Darwin Cathedral, Australia. 130 l, Cathedral of Manila. 220 l, Cathedral of Sydney.
495 A148 25 l multi .20 .20
496 A148 55 l multi .20 .20
497 A148 100 l multi .20 .20
498 A148 130 l multi .20 .20
499 A148 220 l multi .25 .20
       Nos. 495-499 (5) 1.05 1.00

Visit of Pope Paul VI to the Far East, Oceania and Australia, Nov. 26-Dec. 5.

Angel Holding
Lectern — A149

Madonna and
Child by
Francesco
Ghissi — A150

Sculptures by Corrado Ruffini: 40 l, 130 l, Crucified Christ surrounded by doves. 50 l, like 20 l.

1971, Feb. 2 Perf. 13x14
500 A149 20 l multicolored .20 .20
501 A149 40 l dp orange & multi .20 .20
502 A149 50 l purple & multi .20 .20
503 A149 130 l multicolored .25 .20
       Nos. 500-503 (4) .85 .80

Intl. year against racial discrimination.

1971, Mar. 26 Photo. Perf. 14
Paintings: Madonna and Child, 40 l, by Sassetta (Stefano di Giovanni); 55 l, Carlo Crivelli; 90 l, by Carlo Maratta. 180 l, Holy Family, by Ghisberto Ceracchini.
504 A150 25 l gray & multi .20 .20
505 A150 40 l gray & multi .20 .20
506 A150 55 l gray & multi .20 .20
507 A150 90 l gray & multi .20 .20
508 A150 180 l gray & multi .20 .20
       Nos. 504-508 (5) 1.00 1.00

St. Dominic,
Sienese
School — A151

St. Stephen, from
Chasuble,
1031 — A152

Portraits of St. Dominic: 55 l, by Fra Angelico. 90 l, by Titian. 180 l, by El Greco.

1971, May 25 Unwmk. Perf. 13x14
509 A151 25 l multi .20 .20
510 A151 55 l multi .20 .20
511 A151 90 l multi .20 .20
512 A151 180 l multi .25 .20
       Nos. 509-512 (4) .85 .80

St. Dominic de Guzman (1170-1221), founder of the Dominican Order.

1971, Nov. 25
180 l, Madonna as Patroness of Hungary, 1511.
513 A152 50 l multi .20 .20
514 A152 180 l black & yellow .30 .20

Millenium of the birth of St. Stephen (975?-1038), king of Hungary.

Bramante
A153

Designs: 25 l, Bramante's design for dome of St. Peter's. 130 l, Design for spiral staircase.

1972, Feb. 22 Engr. Perf. 13½x14
515 A153 25 l dull yellow & blk .20 .20
516 A153 90 l dull yellow & blk .20 .20
517 A153 130 l dull yellow & blk .25 .20
       Nos. 515-517 (3) .65 .60

Bramante (real name Donato d'Agnolo; 1444-1514), architect.

St. Mark in Storm, 12th Century
Mosaic — A154

Map of Venice, 1581 — A155

Design: 180 l, St. Mark's Basilica, Painting by Emilio Vangelli.

Unwmk.

			Perf. 14	
1972, June 6		**Photo.**		
518	A154	25 l lt brown & multi	.20	.20
519	A155	Block of 4	1.00	.60
a.-d.		50 l, UL, UR, LL, LR, each	.25	
520	A154	180 l lt blue & multi	1.10	.65
a.		Souvenir sheet, #518-520	2.50	2.50
		Nos. 518-520 (3)	2.30	1.45

UNESCO campaign to save Venice.

Gospel of St. Matthew, 13th Century, French A156

Illuminated Initials from: 50 l, St. Luke's Gospel, Biblia dell'Aracoeli 13th century, French. 90 l, Second Epistle of St. John, 14th century, Bologna. 100 l, Apocalypse of St. John, 14th century, Bologna. 130 l, Book of Romans, 14th century, Central Italy.

			Perf. 14x13½
1972, Oct. 11			
521	A156	30 l multi	.20 .20
522	A156	50 l multi	.20 .20
523	A156	90 l multi	.20 .20
524	A156	100 l multi	.20 .20
525	A156	130 l multi	.35 .25
		Nos. 521-525 (5)	1.15 1.05

Intl. Book Year. Illustrations are from illuminated medieval manuscripts.

Luigi Orione A157

Design: 180 l, Lorenzo Perosi and music from "Hallelujah."

			Perf. 14x13½
1972, Nov. 28		**Photo.**	
526	A157	50 l rose, lilac & blk	.20 .20
527	A157	180 l orange, grn & blk	.30 .20

Secular priests Luigi Orione (1872-1940), founder of CARITAS, Catholic welfare organization; and Lorenzo Perosi (1872-1956), composer.

Cardinal Bessarion A158

Eucharistic Congress Emblem — A159

40 l, Reading Bull of Union between the Greek and Latin Churches, 1439, from bronze door of St. Peter's. 130 l, Coat of arms from tomb, Basilica of Holy Apostles, Rome.

			Perf. 13x14	
1972, Nov. 28		**Wmk. 235**		**Engr.**
528	A158	40 l dull green	.20	.20
529	A158	90 l carmine	.25	.20
530	A158	130 l black	.20	.20
		Nos. 528-530 (3)	.65	.60

Johannes Cardinal Bessarion (1403?-1472), Latin Patriarch of Constantinople, who worked for union of the Greek and Latin Churches. Portrait by Cosimo Rosselli in Sistine Chapel.

1973, Feb. 27		**Photo.**	**Unwmk.**	

Designs: 75 l, Head of Mary (Pietá), by Michelangelo. 300 l, Melbourne Cathedral.

531	A159	25 l violet & multi	.20	.20
532	A159	75 l olive & multi	.20	.20
533	A159	300 l multicolored	.50	.40
		Nos. 531-533 (3)	.90	.80

40th Intl. Eucharistic Congress, Melbourne, Australia, Feb. 18-25.

St. Teresa — A160

Copernicus A161

Designs: 25 l, St. Teresa's birthplace, Alençon. 220 l, Lisieux Basilica.

			Engr. & Photo.	
1973, May 23				
534	A160	25 l black & pink	.20	.20
535	A160	55 l black & yellow	.20	.20
536	A160	220 l black & lt blue	.40	.25
		Nos. 534-536 (3)	.80	.65

St. Teresa of Lisieux and of the Infant Jesus (1873-1897), Carmelite nun.

				Perf. 14
1973, June 19		**Engr.**		

Designs: 20 l, 100 l, View of Torun.

537	A161	20 l dull green	.20 .20
538	A161	50 l brown	.20 .20
539	A161	100 l lilac	.20 .20
540	A161	130 l dark blue	.30 .20
		Nos. 537-540 (4)	.90 .80

Nicolaus Copernicus (1473-1543), Polish astronomer.

St. Wenceslas A162

				Perf. 14
1973, Sept. 25		**Photo.**		
541	A162	20 l shown		.20 .20
542	A162	90 l Arms of Prague Diocese		.20 .20
543	A162	150 l Spire of Prague Cathedral		.25 .20
544	A162	220 l St. Adalbert		.35 .20
		Nos. 541-544 (4)		1.00 .80

Millenium of Prague Latin Episcopal See.

St. Nerses Shnorali — A163

25 l, Church of St. Hripsime. 90 l, Armenian khatchkar, a stele with cross and inscription.

		Engr. & Litho.		
1973, Nov. 27				Perf. 13x14
545	A163	25 l tan & dk brown	.20	.20
546	A163	90 l lt violet & blk	.20	.20
547	A163	180 l lt green & sepia	.35	.20
		Nos. 545-547 (3)	.75	.60

Armenian Patriarch St. Nerses Shnorali (1102-1173).

Noah's Ark, Rainbow and Dove (Mosaic) — A164

Design: 90 l, Lamb drinking from stream, and Tablets of the Law (mosaic).

			Litho.	Perf. 13x14
1974, Apr. 23				
548	A164	90 l gold & multi		.20 .20
549	A164	90 l gold & multi		.30 .20

Centenary of the Universal Postal Union.

"And There was Light" — A165

St. Thomas Aquinas Teaching — A166

Designs: 25 l, Noah's Ark, horiz. 50 l, The Annunciation. 90 l, Nativity (African). 180 l, Hands holding grain (Spanish inscription: The Lord feeds his people), horiz. Designs chosen through worldwide youth competition in connection with 1972 Intl. Book Year.

		Perf. 13x14, 14x13		
1974, Apr. 23				**Photo.**
550	A165	15 l brown & multi	.20	.20
551	A165	25 l yellow & multi	.20	.20
552	A165	50 l blue & multi	.20	.20
553	A165	90 l green & multi	.20	.20
554	A165	180 l rose & multi	.25	.20
		Nos. 550-554 (5)	1.05	1.00

"The Bible: the Book of Books."

		Engr. & Litho.		
1974, June 18		**Unwmk.**		**Perf. 13x14**

Designs: 50 l, Students (left panel). 220 l, Students (right panel). Designs from a painting in the Convent of St. Mark in Florence, by an artist from the School of Fra Angelico.

Sizes: 50 l, 220 l, 20x36mm, 90 l, 26x36mm

555	A166	50 l dk brown & gold	.20	.20
556	A166	90 l dk brown & gold	.20	.20
557	A166	220 l dk brown & gold	.40	.25
a.		Strip of 3, #555-557	.70	.55

St. Thomas Aquinas (1225-1274), scholastic philosopher.

St. Bonaventure A167

Woodcuts: 40 l, Civita Bagnoregio. 90 l, Tree of Life (13th century).

				Perf. 13x14
1974, Sept. 26		**Photo.**		
558	A167	40 l gold & multi		.20 .20
559	A167	90 l gold & multi		.25 .20
560	A167	220 l gold & multi		.30 .20
		Nos. 558-560 (3)		.75 .60

St. Bonaventure (Giovanni di Fidanza; 1221-1274), scholastic philosopher.

Christ, St. Peter's Basilica — A168

Pope Paul VI Giving his Blessing — A169

Holy Year 1975: 10 l, Christus Victor, Sts. Peter and Paul. 30 l, Christ. 40 l, Cross surmounted by dove. 50 l, Christ enthroned. 55 l, St. Peter. 90 l, St. Paul. 100 l, St. Peter. 130 l, St. Paul. 220 l, Arms of Pope Paul VI. Designs of 10 l, 25 l, are from St. Peter's; 30 l, 40 l, from St. John Lateran; 50 l, 55 l, 90 l, from St. Mary Major; 100 l, 130 l, from St. Paul outside the Walls.

				Perf. 13x14
1974, Dec. 19		**Photo.**		
561	A168	10 l multi		.20 .20
562	A168	25 l multi		.20 .20
563	A168	30 l multi		.20 .20
564	A168	40 l multi		.20 .20
565	A168	50 l multi		.20 .20
566	A168	55 l multi		.20 .20
567	A168	90 l multi		.20 .20
568	A168	100 l multi		.20 .20
569	A168	130 l multi		.20 .20
570	A168	220 l multi		.25 .20
571	A169	250 l multi		.30 .25
		Nos. 561-571 (11)		2.35 2.25

Pentecost, by El Greco — A170

				Perf. 13x14
1975, May 22		**Engr.**		
572	A170	300 l car rose & orange		.60 .40

Fountain, St. Peter's Square — A171

Fountains of Rome: 40 l, Piazza St. Martha, Apse of St. Peter's. 50 l, Borgia Tower and St. Peter's. 90 l, Belvedere Courtyard. 100 l, Academy of Sciences. 200 l, Galleon.

Litho. & Engr.

1975, May 22		Perf. 14	
573 A171	20 l buff & blk	.20	.20
574 A171	40 l pale violet & blk	.20	.20
575 A171	50 l salmon & blk	.20	.20
576 A171	90 l pale citron & blk	.20	.20
577 A171	100 l pale green & blk	.20	.20
578 A171	200 l pale blue & blk	.30	.25
Nos. 573-578 (6)		1.30	1.25

European Architectural Heritage Year.

Miracle of Loaves and Fishes, Gilt Glass A172

Designs: 150 l, Painting of Christ, from Comodilla Catacomb. 200 l, Raising of Lazarus. All works from 4th century.

Perf. 14x13½			
1975, Sept. 25	Photo.	Unwmk.	
579 A172	30 l multi	.20	.20
580 A172	150 l brown & multi	.25	.20
581 A172	200 l green & multi	.45	.30
Nos. 579-581 (3)		.90	.70

9th Intl. Congress of Christian Archaeology.

Investiture of First Librarian Bartolomeo Sacchi by Pope Sixtus IV A173

Designs: 100 l, Pope Sixtus IV and books in old wooden press, from Latin Vatican Codex 2044, vert. 250 l, Pope Sixtus IV visiting Library, fresco in Hospital of the Holy Spirit. Design of 70 l is from fresco by Melozzo di Forli in Vatican Gallery.

Perf. 14x13½, 13½x14			
1975, Sept. 25	Litho. & Engr.		
582 A173	70 l gray & lilac	.20	.20
583 A173	100 l lt yellow & grn	.25	.20
584 A173	250 l gray & red	.55	.30
Nos. 582-584 (3)		1.00	.70

Founding of the Vatican Apostolic Library, 500th anniv.

Mt. Argentario Monastery A174

St. Paul of the Cross, by Giovanni Della Porta — A175

Design: 300 l, Basilica of Sts. John and Paul and burial chapel of Saint.

1975, Nov. 27	Photo.	Perf. 14x13½	
585 A174	50 l multi	.20	.20
586 A174	150 l multi	.25	.20
587 A174	300 l multi	.45	.25
Nos. 585-587 (3)		.90	.65

Bicentenary of death of St. Paul of the Cross, founder of the Passionist religious order in 1737.

Praying Women, by Fra Angelico — A176

International Women's Year: 200 l, Seated women, by Fra Angelico.

1975, Nov. 27		Perf. 13½x14	
588 A176	100 l multi	.20	.20
589 A176	200 l multi	.40	.25

Virgin and Child in Glory, by Titian A177

Design: 300 l, The Six Saints, by Titian. Designs from "The Madonna in Glory with the Child Jesus and Six Saints."

Perf. 14x13½			
1976, May 13	Engr.		
590 A177	100 l rose magenta	.25	.20
591 A177	300 l rose magenta	.50	.40
a.	Pair, #590-591	.75	.60

Titian (1477-1576), painter.

A178

A179

Designs: 150 l, Eucharist, wheat and globe. 200 l, Hands Holding Eucharist. 400 l, Hungry mankind reaching for the Eucharist.

1976, July 2	Photo.	Perf. 13½x14	
592 A178	150 l gold, red & bl	.20	.20
593 A178	200 l gold & blue	.25	.25
594 A178	400 l gold, grn & brn	.40	.40
Nos. 592-594 (3)		.85	.85

41st Intl. Eucharistic Congress, Philadelphia, PA, Aug. 1-8.

1976, Sept. 30	Photo.	Perf. 13½x14	

Details from Transfiguration by Raphael: 30 l, Moses Holding Tablets. 40 l, Transfigured Christ. 50 l, Prophet Elijah with book. 100 l, Apostles John and Peter. 150 l, Group of women. 200 l, Landscape.

595 A179	30 l ocher & multi	.20	.20
596 A179	40 l red & multi	.20	.20
597 A179	50 l violet & multi	.20	.20
598 A179	100 l multicolored	.20	.20
599 A179	150 l green & multi	.25	.20
600 A179	200 l ocher & multi	.35	.25
Nos. 595-600 (6)		1.40	1.25

St. John's Tower A180

Roman Views: 100 l, Fountain of the Sacrament. 120 l, Fountain at entrance to the gardens. 180 l, Basilica, Cupola of St. Peter's and Sacristy. 250 l, Borgia Tower and Sistine Chapel. 300 l, Apostolic Palace and Courtyard of St. Damasius.

Litho. & Engr.

1976, Nov. 23		Perf. 14	
601 A180	50 l gray & black	.20	.20
602 A180	100 l salmon & dk brn	.20	.20
603 A180	120 l citron & dk grn	.20	.20
604 A180	180 l pale gray & blk	.20	.20
605 A180	250 l yellow & brn	.25	.20
606 A180	300 l pale lilac & mag	.30	.25
Nos. 601-606 (6)		1.35	1.25

The Lord's Creatures A181

70 l, Brother Sun. 100 l, Sister Moon and Stars. 130 l, Sister Water. 170 l, Praise in infirmities and tribulations. 200 l, Praise for bodily death. Designs are illustrations by Duilio Cambellotti for "The Canticle of Brother Sun," by St. Francis.

1977, Mar. 10	Photo.	Perf. 14x13½	
607 A181	50 l multi	.20	.20
608 A181	70 l multi	.20	.20
609 A181	100 l multi	.20	.20
610 A181	130 l multi	.20	.20
611 A181	170 l multi	.20	.20
612 A181	200 l multi	.25	.20
Nos. 607-612 (6)		1.25	1.20

St. Francis of Assisi, 750th death anniv.

Sts. Peter and Paul A182

Design: 350 l, Pope Gregory XI and St. Catherine of Siena. Designs are after fresco by Giorgio Vasari.

1977, May 20	Engr.	Perf. 14	
613	170 l black	.30	.20
614	350 l black	.50	.30
a.	A182 Pair, #613-614	.85	.60

Return of Pope Gregory XI from Avignon, 600th anniv.

Dormition of the Virgin — A183

1977, July 5	Photo.	Perf. 13½x14	

Design: 400 l, Virgin Mary in Heaven. Both designs after miniatures in Latin manuscripts, Vatican Library.

| 615 A183 | 200 l multi | .30 | .20 |
| 616 A183 | 400 l multi | .55 | .30 |

Feast of the Assumption.

The Nile Deity, Roman Sculpture — A184

Sculptures: 120 l, Head of Pericles. 130 l, Roman Couple Joining Hands. 150 l, Apollo Belvedere, head. 170 l, Laocoön, head. 350 l, Apollo Belvedere, torso.

1977, Sept. 29		Perf. 14x13½	
617 A184	50 l multi	.20	.20
618 A184	120 l multi	.20	.20
619 A184	130 l multi	.20	.20
620 A184	150 l multi	.20	.20
621 A184	170 l multi	.20	.20
622 A184	350 l multi	.30	.30
Nos. 617-622 (6)		1.30	1.30

Classical sculptures in Vatican Museums.

Creation of Man and Woman — A185

Designs: 70 l, Three youths in the furnace. 100 l, Adoration of the Kings. 130 l, Raising of Lazarus. 200 l, The Good Shepherd. 400 l, Chrismon, Cross, sleeping soldiers (Resurrection). Designs are bas-reliefs from Christian sarcophagi, 250-350 A.D., found in Roman excavations.

1977, Dec. 9	Photo.	Perf. 14x13½	
623 A185	50 l multi	.20	.20
624 A185	70 l multi	.20	.20
625 A185	100 l multi	.20	.20
626 A185	130 l multi	.20	.20
627 A185	200 l multi	.20	.20
628 A185	400 l multi	.35	.25
Nos. 623-628 (6)		1.35	1.25

Madonna with the Parrot and Rubens Self-portrait A186

1977, Dec. 9		Perf. 13½x14	
629 A186	350 l multi	.50	.50

Peter Paul Rubens (1577-1640).

Pope Paul VI, by Lino Bianchi Barriviera A187

Design: 350 l, Christ's Face, by Pericle Fazzini and arms of Pope Paul VI.

1978, Mar. 9	Photo.	Perf. 14	
630 A187	350 l multi	.50	.30
631 A187	400 l multi	.50	.40

80th birthday of Pope Paul VI.

Pope Pius IX
(1792-1878)
A188

Designs: 130 l, Arms of Pope Pius IX. 170 l, Seal of Pius IX, used to sign definition of Dogma of Immaculate Conception.

Litho. & Engr.

1978, May 9   Perf. 13x14
632 A188 130 l multi   .20 .20
633 A188 170 l multi   .30 .20
634 A188 200 l multi   .35 .20
     Nos. 632-634 (3)   .85 .60

Interregnum Issues

Keys of St. Peter and Papal Chamberlain's Insignia
A189   A190

1978, Aug. 23   Photo.   Perf. 14
635 A189 120 l purple & lt green   .30 .20
636 A189 150 l purple & salmon   .35 .20
637 A189 250 l purple & yellow   .35 .20
     Nos. 635-637 (3)   1.00 .60

1978, Oct. 12   Photo.   Perf. 14
638 A190 170 l black & multi   .25 .20
639 A190 200 l black & multi   .25 .20
640 A190 250 l black & multi   .25 .20
     Nos. 638-640 (3)   .75 .60

Pope John Paul I,
Pope from Aug. 26 to Sept. 28, 1978 — A191

Pope John Paul I: 70 l, Sitting on his throne. 250 l, Walking in Vatican garden. 350 l, Giving blessing, horiz.

1978, Dec. 11   Perf. 13x14, 14x13
641 A191 70 l multi   .20 .20
642 A191 120 l multi   .25 .25
643 A191 250 l multi   .30 .30
644 A191 350 l multi   .40 .40
     Nos. 641-644 (4)   1.15 1.15

Arms of Pope John Paul II
A192

Designs: 250 l, Pope John Paul II raising hand in blessing. 400 l, Jesus giving keys to St. Peter.

Litho. & Engr.

1979, Mar. 22   Perf. 14x13
645 A192 170 l black & multi   .25 .25
646 A192 250 l black & multi   .30 .30
647 A192 400 l black & multi   .55 .45
     Nos. 645-647 (3)   1.10 1.00

Inauguration of pontificate of Pope John Paul II.

Martyrdom of St. Stanislas
A193   St. Basil the Great Instructing Monk
A194

Designs: 150 l, St. Stanislas appearing to the people. 250 l, Gold reliquary, 1504, containing saint's head. 500 l, View of Cracow Cathedral.

1979, May 18   Photo.   Perf. 14
648 A193 120 l multi   .20 .20
649 A193 150 l multi   .20 .20
650 A193 250 l multi   .35 .30
651 A193 500 l multi   .75 .65
     Nos. 648-651 (4)   1.50 1.35

900th anniversary of martyrdom of St. Stanislas (1030-1079), patron saint of Poland.

Engr. & Photo.

1979, June 25   Perf. 13½x14
St. Basil the Great, 16th cent. of death: 520 l, St. Basil the Great visiting the sick.
652 A194 150 l multi   .20 .20
653 A194 520 l multi   .85 .70

Father Secchi, Solar Protuberance, Spectrum and Meteorograph — A195

Father Angelo Secchi (1818-1878), astronomer, solar protuberance, spectrum and: 220 l, Spectroscope. 300 l, Telescope.

Litho. & Engr.

1979, June 25   Perf. 14x13½
654 A195 180 l multi   .25 .25
655 A195 220 l multi   .35 .30
656 A195 300 l multi   .40 .30
     Nos. 654-656 (3)   1.00 .85

Vatican City
A196

Papal Arms and Portraits: 70 l, Pius XI. 120 l, Pius XII. 150 l, John XXIII. 170 l, Paul VI. 250 l, John Paul I. 450 l, John Paul II.

1979, Oct. 11   Photo.   Perf. 14x13½
657 A196 50 l multi   .20 .20
658 A196 70 l multi   .20 .20
659 A196 120 l multi   .20 .20
660 A196 150 l multi   .20 .20
661 A196 170 l multi   .25 .25
662 A196 250 l multi   .30 .30
663 A196 450 l multi   .65 .50
     Nos. 657-663 (7)   2.00 1.85

Vatican City State, 50th anniversary.

Infant, by Andrea Della Robbia, IYC Emblem — A197

IYC Emblem and Della Robbia Bas Reliefs, Hospital of the Innocents, Florence.

Engr. & Photo.

1979, Nov. 27   Perf. 13½x14
664 A197 50 l multi   .20 .20
665 A197 120 l multi   .20 .20
666 A197 200 l multi   .30 .20
667 A197 350 l multi   .50 .40
     Nos. 664-667 (4)   1.20 1.00

International Year of the Child.

Abbot Desiderius Giving Codex to St. Benedict — A198

Illuminated Letters and Illustrations, Codices, Vatican Apostolic Library: 100 l, St. Benedict writing the Rule. 150 l, Page from the Rule. 220 l, Death of St. Benedict. 450 l, Montecassino (after painting by Paul Bril).

1980, Mar. 21   Photo.   Perf. 14x13½
668 A198 80 l multi   .20 .20
669 A198 100 l multi   .20 .20
670 A198 150 l multi   .25 .25
671 A198 220 l multi   .30 .30
672 A198 450 l multi   .60 .55
     Nos. 668-672 (5)   1.55 1.50

St. Benedict of Nursia (patron saint of Europe), 1500th birth anniversary.

Bernini, Medallion Showing Baldacchino in St. Peter's — A199

Gian Lorenzo Bernini (1598-1680), Architect (Self-portrait and Medallion): 170 l, St. Peter's Square with third wing (never built). 250 l, Bronze chair, Doctors of the Church. 350 l, Apostolic Palace stairway.

1980, Oct. 16   Litho.   Perf. 14x13½
673 A199 80 l multicolored   .20 .20
674 A199 170 l multicolored   .25 .25
675 A199 250 l multicolored   .35 .30
676 A199 350 l multicolored   .55 .35
     Nos. 673-676 (4)   1.35 1.10

St. Albertus Magnus on Mission of Peace — A200

1980, Nov. 18   Litho.   Perf. 13½x14
677 A200 300 l shown   .40 .30
678 A200 400 l As bishop   .55 .40

St. Albertus Magnus, 700th death anniv.

Communion of the Saints — A201

1980, Nov. 18   Perf. 14x13½
679 A201 250 l shown   .35 .25
680 A201 500 l Christ and saints   .65 .60

Feast of All Saints.

Guglielmo Marconi and Pope Pius XI, Vatican Radio Emblem, Vatican Arms
A202

Designs: 150 l, Microphone, Bible text. 200 l, St. Maria di Galeria Radio Center antenna, Archangel Gabriel statue. 600 l, Pope John Paul II.

1981, Feb. 12   Photo.   Perf. 14x13½
681 A202 100 l shown   .20 .20
682 A202 150 l multicolored   .25 .20
683 A202 200 l multicolored   .30 .25
684 A202 600 l multicolored   .80 .65
     Nos. 681-684 (4)   1.55 1.30

Vatican Radio, 50th anniversary.

Virgil Seated at Podium, Vergilius Romanus — A203

1981, Apr. 23   Litho.   Perf. 14
685 A203 350 l multicolored   .75 .65
686 A203 600 l multicolored   1.40 1.10

2000th birth anniversary of Virgil. Issued in sheets of 16 stamps plus 9 labels.

Congress Emblem
A204

Congress Emblem and: 150 l, Virgin appearing to St. Bernadette. 200 l, Pilgrims going to Lourdes. 500 l, Bishop and pilgrims.

1981, June 22   Photo.
687 A204 80 l multicolored   .20 .20
688 A204 150 l multicolored   .20 .20
689 A204 200 l multicolored   .30 .30
690 A204 500 l multicolored   .60 .60
     Nos. 687-690 (4)   1.30 1.30

42nd Intl. Eucharistic Congress, Lourdes, France, July 16-23.

Intl. Year of the Disabled
A205

1981, Sept. 29   Photo.   Perf. 14x13½
691 A205 600 l multicolored   .90 .80

Jan van Ruusbroec, Flemish Mystic, 500th Birth Anniv. — A206

Litho. & Engr.

1981, Sept. 29   Perf. 13½x14
692 A206 200 l shown   .35 .35
693 A206 300 l Portrait   .45 .45

1980 Journeys of Pope John Paul II — A207

1981, Dec. 3   Photo.   Perf. 13½x14½
694	A207	50 l	Papal arms	.20	.20
695	A207	100 l	Map of Africa	.20	.20
696	A207	120 l	Crucifix	.20	.20
697	A207	150 l	Communion	.20	.20
698	A207	200 l	African bishop	.20	.20
699	A207	250 l	Visiting sick	.30	.30
700	A207	300 l	Notre Dame, France	.40	.40
701	A207	400 l	UNESCO speech	.50	.50
702	A207	600 l	Christ of the Andes, Brazil	.90	.90
703	A207	700 l	Cologne Cathedral, Germany	1.00	1.00
704	A207	900 l	John Paul II	1.10	1.10
		Nos. 694-704 (11)		5.20	5.20

700th Death Anniv. of St. Agnes of Prague — A208

Designs: 700 l, Handing order to Grand Master of the Crosiers of the Red Star. 900 l, Receiving letter from St. Clare.

1982, Feb. 16   Photo.   Perf. 13½x14
705	A208	700 l	multicolored	1.00	1.00
706	A208	900 l	multicolored	1.10	1.10

Pueri Cantores
A209

St. Teresa of Avila (1515-1582)
A210

Luca Della Robbia (1400-1482), Sculptor: No. 708, Pueri Cantores, diff. No. 709, Virgin in Prayer (44x36mm).

Photo. & Engr.
1982, May 21   Perf. 14
707	A209	1000 l	multicolored	1.25	1.10
708	A209	1000 l	multicolored	1.25	1.10
709	A209	1000 l	multicolored	1.25	1.10
a.		Strip of 3, #707-709		4.00	3.50

1982, Sept. 23   Photo.

Sketches of St. Teresa by Riccardo Tommasi-Ferroni.
710	A210	200 l	multicolored	.25	.25
711	A210	600 l	multicolored	.80	.80
712	A210	1000 l	multicolored	1.25	1.25
		Nos. 710-712 (3)		2.30	2.30

Christmas
A211

Nativity Bas-Reliefs: 300 l, Wit Stwosz, Church of the Virgin Mary, Cracow. 450 l, Enrico Manfrini.

Photo. & Engr.
1982, Nov. 23   Perf. 14
713	A211	300 l	multicolored	.45	.45
714	A211	450 l	multicolored	.65	.65

400th Anniv. of Gregorian Calendar — A212

Sculpture Details, Tomb of Pope Gregory XIII, St. Peter's Basilica.

1982, Nov. 23   Engr.   Perf. 13½x14
715	A212	200 l	Surveying the globe	.25	.25
716	A212	300 l	Receiving Edict of Reform	.40	.40
717	A212	700 l	Presenting edict	.90	.90
a.		Souvenir sheet of 3, #715-717		2.50	2.50
		Nos. 715-717 (3)		1.55	1.55

Souvenir Sheets

Greek Vase — A213

1983, Mar. 10   Litho.   Perf. 13½x14
718		Sheet of 6		3.25	2.00
a.	A213	100 l	shown	.20	.20
b.	A213	200 l	Italian vase	.35	.25
c.	A213	250 l	Female terra-cotta bust	.50	.30
d.	A213	300 l	Marcus Aurelius bust	.55	.35
e.	A213	350 l	Bird fresco	.65	.45
f.	A213	400 l	Pope Clement VIII vestment	.75	.45

1983, June 14   Litho.   Perf. 13½x14
719		Sheet of 6		3.50	3.50
a.	A213	100 l	Horse's head, Etruscan terra cotta	.20	.20
b.	A213	200 l	Horseman, Greek fragment	.25	.20
c.	A213	300 l	Male head, Etruscan	.30	.20
d.	A213	400 l	Apollo Belvedere head	.50	.25
e.	A213	500 l	Moses, Roman fresco	.55	.35
f.	A213	1000 l	Madonna and Child, by Bernardo Daddi	1.25	.70

1983, Nov. 10   Litho.   Perf. 13½x14
720		Sheet of 6		4.00	4.00
a.	A213	150 l	Greek cup, Oedipus and the Sphinx	.25	.20
b.	A213	200 l	Etruscan bronze statue of a child	.30	.20
c.	A213	350 l	Emperor Augustus marble statue	.40	.25
d.	A213	400 l	Good Shepherd marble statue	.55	.30
e.	A213	500 l	St. Nicholas Saving a ship by G. da Fabriano	.70	.40
f.	A213	1200 l	The Holy face by G. Rouault	1.50	1.00

Vatican Collection: The Papacy and Art - US 1983 exhibition, New York, Chicago, San Francisco.

Extraordinary Holy Year, 1983-84 (1950th Anniv. of Redemption) A214

Sketches by Giovanni Hajnal.

1983, Mar. 10   Photo. & Engr.
721	A214	300 l	Crucifixion	.45	.30
722	A214	350 l	Christ the Redeemer	.55	.40
723	A214	400 l	Pope	.45	.45
724	A214	2000 l	Holy Spirit	2.75	2.75
		Nos. 721-724 (4)		4.20	3.90

Theology, by Raphael (1483-1517)
A215

St. Casimir of Lithuania (1458-1484)
A217

Gregor Johann Mendel (1822-1884), Biologist — A216

Allegories, Room of the Segnatura.

1983, June 14
725	A215	50 l	shown	.20	.20
726	A215	400 l	Poetry	.60	.60
727	A215	500 l	Justice	.70	.70
728	A215	1200 l	Philosphy	1.75	1.75
		Nos. 725-728 (4)		3.25	3.25

Photo. & Engr.
1984, Feb. 28   Perf. 14x13½

Phases of pea plant hybridization.
729	A216	450 l	multicolored	.60	.45
730	A216	1500 l	multicolored	2.00	1.50

1984, Feb. 28   Perf. 14
731	A217	550 l	multicolored	.90	.55
732	A217	1200 l	multicolored	2.00	1.25

Pontifical Academy of Sciences — A218

1984, June 18   Litho. & Engr.
733	A218	150 l	shown	.25	.20
734	A218	450 l	Secret Archives	.65	.55
735	A218	500 l	Apostolic Library	.85	.65
736	A218	1500 l	Observatory	2.25	1.75
		Nos. 733-736 (4)		4.00	3.15

Papal Journeys
A218a

1984-85   Photo.   Perf. 13½x14½
737	A218a	50 l	Pakistan	.20	.20
738	A218a	100 l	Philippines	.20	.20
739	A218a	150 l	Guam	.30	.20
740	A218a	250 l	Japan	.45	.30
741	A218a	300 l	Alaska	.55	.50
742	A218a	400 l	Africa	.80	.50
743	A218a	450 l	Portugal	.90	.60
a.		Bklt. pane, 4 ea #738, 741-743 + 4 labels ('85)		12.00	
744	A218a	550 l	Grt. Britain	1.10	.70
745	A218a	1000 l	Argentina	2.00	1.40
746	A218a	1500 l	Switzerland	3.00	1.90
747	A218a	2500 l	San Marino	4.00	3.25
748	A218a	4000 l	Spain	8.00	5.25
		Nos. 737-748 (12)		21.50	15.00

Issued: Nos. 737-748, 10/2/84; No. 743a, 3/14/85.

St. Damasus I (b. 304)
A219

St. Damasus I and: 200 l, Sepulchre of Sts. Marcellinus and Peter. 500 l, Epigraph of St. Januarius. 2000 l, Basilica, Church of the Martyrs Simplicius, Faustinus and Beatrice.

1984, Nov. 27   Photo.   Perf. 14x13½
749	A219	200 l	multicolored	.35	.25
750	A219	500 l	multicolored	.90	.60
751	A219	2000 l	multicolored	3.75	2.25
		Nos. 749-751 (3)		5.00	3.10

St. Methodius (d. 885) — A220

St. Methodius and: 500 l, Madonna and Christ. 600 l, St. Cyril, carrying the body of St. Clement I. 1700 l, Sts. Benedict and Cyril, patrons of Europe.

Photo. & Engr.
1985, May 7   Perf. 13½x14
752	A220	500 l	multicolored	.90	.50
753	A220	600 l	multicolored	1.10	.60
754	A220	1700 l	multicolored	3.25	1.60
		Nos. 752-754 (3)		5.25	2.70

St. Thomas More (1477-1535) — A221

St. Thomas More (from a portrait by Hans Holbein) and: 250 l, map of British Isles. 400 l, Frontispiece of Utopia. 2000 l, Frontispiece of Domenico Regi's biography of More.

Litho. & Engr.
1985, May 7   Perf. 14x13½
755	A221	250 l	multicolored	.45	.25
756	A221	400 l	multicolored	.80	.40
757	A221	2000 l	multicolored	3.75	2.00
		Nos. 755-757 (3)		5.00	2.65

St. Gregory VII (c. 1020-85)
A222

Designs: 150 l, Eagle from Byzantine door, St. Paul's Basilica, Rome. 450 l, St. Gregory blessing. 2500 l, Sarcophagus.

Perf. 13½x14, 14x13½
1985, June 18   Photo.
758	A222	150 l	multi, vert.	.25	.20
759	A222	450 l	multi, vert.	.75	.45
760	A222	2500 l	multicolored	4.00	2.50
		Nos. 758-760 (3)		5.00	3.15

43rd Intl. Eucharistic Congress — A223

Emblem, host, cross and: 100 l, Outline map of Africa. 400 l, Altar and Assembly of Bishops. 600 l, African chalice. 2300 l, African Christian family.

Photo. & Engr.

1985, June 18   *Perf. 13½x14*
761	A223	100 l multicolored	.20	.20
762	A223	400 l multicolored	.60	.40
763	A223	600 l multicolored	.90	.55
764	A223	2300 l multicolored	3.50	2.00
		Nos. 761-764 (4)	5.20	3.15

Concordat Agreement Ratification
A224

1985, Oct. 15   Photo.   Perf. 14x13½
765	A224	400 l Papal arms, map of Italy	.65	.35

Coaches
A225

1985, Oct. 15   *Litho. & Engr.*
766	A225	450 l dp lil rose & int bl	.75	.35
767	A225	1500 l brt bl & dp lil rose	2.00	1.40
a.		Souvenir sheet of 2, #766-767, perf. 13½x12½	3.25	3.25

Italia '85.

Intl. Peace Year
1986 — A226

Biblical and gospel texts: 50 l, Isaiah 2:4. 350 l, Isaiah 52:7. 450 l, Matthew 5:9. 650 l, Luke 2:14. 2000 l, Message for World Peace, speech of Pope John Paul II, Jan. 1, 1986.

1986, Apr. 14   Photo.   Perf. 14
768	A226	50 l multicolored	.20	.20
769	A226	350 l multicolored	.55	.30
770	A226	450 l multicolored	.80	.40
771	A226	650 l multicolored	1.10	.60
772	A226	2000 l multicolored	3.50	2.00
		Nos. 768-772 (5)	6.15	3.50

Vatican City — A227

1986, Apr. 14   *Perf. 13½x14*
773	A227	Block of 6	6.75	3.00
a.-f.		550 l, any single	1.10	.50

UNESCO World Heritage Campaign. No. 773 has continuous design.

Patron Saints of the Sick — A228

Conversion of St. Augustine (354-430) in 387 — A230

Pontifical Academy of Sciences, 50th Anniv. A229

Designs: No. 774, St. Camillus de Lellis rescuing invalid during Tiber flood, by Pierre Subleyras (1699-1749). No. 775, St. John of God with invalids, by Gomez Moreno (1834-1918). 2000 l, Pope John Paul II visiting the sick.

Litho. & Engr.

1986, June 12   *Perf. 13½x14*
774	A228	700 l multicolored	1.25	.60
775	A228	700 l multicolored	1.25	.60
776	A228	2000 l multicolored	3.50	1.90
		Nos. 774-776 (3)	6.00	3.10

Litho. & Engr.

1986, Oct. 2   *Perf. 14x13½*

School of Athens (details), by Raphael: 1500 l, Scribes. 2500 l, Students learning math.
777	A229	1500 l multicolored	2.75	1.50
778	A229	2500 l multicolored	4.25	2.50

1987, Apr. 7   Photo.   Perf. 13½x14

Religious art: 300 l, St. Augustine reading St. Paul's Epistles, fresco by Benozzo Gozzoli (1420-1498), Church of St. Augustine, San Gimignano. 400 l, Baptism of St. Augustine, painting by Bartolomeo di Gentile (1470-1534), Vatican Art Gallery. 500 l, Ecstasy of St. Augustine, fresco by Benozzo Gozzoli, Church of St. Augustine. 2200 l, St. Augustine, detail of Disputa del Sacramento, fresco by Raphael (1483-1520), Room of the Segnatura, Apostolic Palace.
779	A230	300 l multicolored	.50	.30
780	A230	400 l multicolored	.70	.45
781	A230	500 l multicolored	.85	.50
782	A230	2200 l multicolored	3.75	2.25
		Nos. 779-782 (4)	5.80	3.50

A231

Christianization Anniversaries A232

Seals: 700 l, Church of Riga, 1234-1269. 2400 l, Marian Basilica of the Assumption, Aglona, 1780.

1987, June 2   Photo.   Perf. 13½x14
783	A231	700 l multicolored	1.40	.95
784	A231	2400 l multicolored	4.75	3.25

Christianization of Latvia, 800th anniv.

1987, June 2   *Perf. 13½x14*

Designs: 200 l, Christ, statue in the Lithuanian Chapel, Vatican Crypt. 700 l, Two Angels and Our Lady Holding the Body of Christ, by a Lithuanian artist. 3000 l, Lithuanian shrine.
785	A232	200 l multicolored	.30	.25
786	A232	700 l multicolored	1.10	.75
787	A232	3000 l multicolored	4.50	3.00
		Nos. 785-787 (3)	5.90	4.00

Christianization of Lithuania, 600th anniv.

OLYMPHILEX '87, Rome, Aug. 29-Sept. 9 — A233

Details of mosaic from the Baths of Caracalla: 400 l, Judge. 500 l, Athlete. 600 l, Athlete, diff. 2000 l, Athlete, diff.

Litho. & Engr.

1987, Aug. 29   *Perf. 14*
788	A233	400 l multicolored	.65	.45
789	A233	500 l multicolored	.85	.55
790	A233	600 l multicolored	1.00	.65
791	A233	2000 l multicolored	3.25	2.25
		Nos. 788-791 (4)	5.75	3.90

Souvenir Sheet
792		Sheet of 4 + 4 labels	5.75	5.75
a.	A233	400 l like No. 788	.65	.65
b.	A233	500 l like No. 789	.80	.80
c.	A233	600 l like No. 780	1.00	1.00
d.	A233	2000 l like No. 791	3.25	3.25

Stamps from souvenir sheet have a Greek border in blue surrounding vignettes (pictured). Nos. 788-791 have single line border in blue. No. 792 has 4 labels picturing the papal arms, a goblet, a crown and the exhibition emblem.

Inauguration of the Philatelic and Numismatic Museum — A235

Designs: 400 l, Philatelic department, Vatican City, No. 1. 3500 l, Numismatic department, 1000-lire coin of 1986.

1987, Sept. 29   Photo.   Perf. 14x13½
793	A235	400 l multicolored	.60	.45
794	A235	3500 l multicolored	5.50	3.75

Journeys of Pope John Paul II, 1985-86 A236

Designs: 50 l, Venezuela, Peru, Ecuador and Trinidad & Tobago, 1985. 250 l, The Netherlands, Luxembourg, Belgium, 1985. 400 l, Togo, Ivory Coast, Cameroun, Central Africa, Zaire, Kenya and Morocco, 1985. 500 l, Liechtenstein, 1986. 4000 l, Bangladesh, Singapore, Fiji, New Zealand, Australia and Seychelles, 1986.

1987, Oct. 27   Photo.   Perf. 14x13½
795	A236	50 l multicolored	.20	.20
796	A236	250 l multicolored	.65	.45
797	A236	400 l multicolored	1.10	.70
798	A236	500 l multicolored	1.25	.85
799	A236	600 l multicolored	1.60	1.00
800	A236	700 l multicolored	1.90	1.25
801	A236	2500 l multicolored	6.75	4.50
802	A236	4000 l multicolored	11.00	7.25
		Nos. 795-802 (8)	24.45	16.20

A237

A238

Transfer of St. Nicholas Relics from Myra to Bari, 900th anniv.: 500 l, Arrival of relics at Bari. 700 l, Act of charity, three improverished women. 3000 l, Miraculous rescue of ship.

1987, Dec. 3   *Perf. 13½x14*
803	A237	500 l multicolored	2.00	1.25
804	A237	700 l multicolored	3.00	2.00
805	A237	3000 l multicolored	12.50	8.00
		Nos. 803-805 (3)	17.50	11.25

St. Nicholas of Bari (c. 270-352), bishop of Myra. Legend of Santa Claus originated because of his charitable works. Printed in sheets of 8 + 16 se-tenant labels picturing Santa Claus.

1988, Apr. 19   *Photo.*

Children and: 500 l, Sister of the Institute of the Daughters of Mary Help of Christians. 1000 l, St. John Bosco. 2000 l, Salesian lay brother. Printed in a continuous design.
806		Strip of 3	5.25	4.00
a.	A238	500 l multicolored	.70	.50
b.	A238	1000 l multicolored	1.50	1.00
c.	A238	2000 l multicolored	3.00	2.00

St. John Bosco (1815-1888), educator.

A239

A240

1988, June 16   Photo.   Perf. 13½x14
807	A239	50 l	Annunciation	.20	.20
808	A239	300 l	Nativity	.40	.25
809	A239	500 l	Pentecost	.65	.40
810	A239	750 l	Assumption	1.10	.60
811	A239	1000 l	Mother of the Church	1.40	.80
812	A239	2400 l	Refuge of Sinners	3.25	1.90
			Nos. 807-812 (6)	7.00	4.15

Marian Year, 1987-88.

1988, June 16

Baptism of the Rus' of Kiev, Millennium: 450 l, "Prince St. Vladimir the Great," from a 15th cent. icon. 650 l, Cathedral of St. Sophia, Kiev. 2500 l, "Mother of God in Prayer," from a mosaic at the cathedral.
813	A240	450 l multicolored	.75	.45
814	A240	650 l multicolored	1.00	.65
815	A240	2500 l multicolored	3.75	2.25
		Nos. 813-815 (3)	5.50	3.35

Paintings by Paolo Veronese (1528-1588) — A241

Designs: 550 l, Marriage of Cana (Madonna and Christ) the Louvre, Paris. 650 l, Self-portrait of the Artist, Villa Barbaro of Maser, Treviso. 3000 l, Marriage of Cana (woman and two men).

Perf. 13½x14, 14x13½

1988, Sept. 29   Photo. & Engr.
816	A241	550 l	multicolored	.80 .45
817	A241	650 l	multi, horiz.	.95 .55
818	A241	3000 l	multicolored	4.25 2.50
		Nos. 816-818 (3)		6.00 3.50

Christmas
A242

Luke 2:14 and: 50 l, Angel facing LR. 400 l, Angel facing UR. 500 l, Angel facing LL. 550 l, Shepherds. 850 l, Nativity. 1500 l, Magi.

1988, Dec. 12   Photo.   Perf. 13½x14
819	A242	50 l	multicolored	.20 .20
820	A242	400 l	multicolored	.60 .30
821	A242	500 l	multicolored	.70 .35
822	A242	550 l	multicolored	.80 .40
823	A242	850 l	multicolored	1.25 .60
824	A242	1500 l	multicolored	2.25 1.00
		Nos. 819-824 (6)		5.80 2.85

Souvenir Sheet
825	Sheet of 6		5.75 5.75
a.	A242 50 l	gold & multi	.20 .20
b.	A242 400 l	gold & multi	.60 .30
c.	A242 500 l	gold & multi	.70 .35
d.	A242 550 l	gold & multi	.80 .40
e.	A242 850 l	gold & multi	1.25 .60
f.	A242 1500 l	gold & multi	2.25 1.00

No. 825 has continuous design.

Feast of the Visitation, 600th Anniv. — A243

Illuminations: 550 l, The Annunciation. 750 l, The Visitation (Virgin and St. Elizabeth). 2500 l, Mary, Elizabeth and infants.

1989, May 5   Photo.   Perf. 13½x14
826	A243	550 l	multicolored	.80 .40
827	A243	750 l	multicolored	1.10 .70
828	A243	2500 l	multicolored	3.75 1.90
		Nos. 826-828 (3)		5.65 2.85

Souvenir Sheet

Gregorian Egyptian Museum, 150th Anniv. — A244

Designs: 400 l, Apis. 650 l, Isis and Apis dicephalous bust. 750 l, Statue of the physician Ugiahorresne. 2400 l, Pharaoh Mentuhotep.

Litho. & Engr.
1989, May 5   Perf. 14x13½
829	Sheet of 4		6.00 6.00
a.	A244 400 l	multicolored	.55 .30
b.	A244 650 l	multicolored	.90 .50
c.	A244 750 l	multicolored	1.10 .55
d.	A244 2400 l	multicolored	3.25 1.75

A245

A246

Birds from engravings by Eleazar Albin in *Histoire Naturelle des Oiseaux*, 1750.

1989, June 13   Photo.   Perf. 12
Granite Paper
830	A245	100 l	Parrot	.20 .20
831	A245	150 l	Green woodpecker	.20 .20
832	A245	200 l	Crested and common wrens	.25 .20
833	A245	350 l	Kingfisher	.45 .25
834	A245	500 l	Red grosbeak of Virginia	.65 .30
835	A245	700 l	Bullfinch	.90 .45
836	A245	1500 l	Lapwing plover	2.00 1.00
837	A245	3000 l	French teal	4.00 2.00
		Nos. 830-837 (8)		8.65 4.60

Photo. & Engr.
1989, Sept. 29   Perf. 13½x14

Symbols of the Eucharist.
838	A246	550 l	shown	.80 .40
839	A246	850 l	multi, diff.	1.25 .65
840	A246	1000 l	multi, diff.	1.50 .75
841	A246	2500 l	multi, diff.	3.75 1.90
		Nos. 838-841 (4)		7.30 3.70

44th Intl. Eucharistic Cong., Seoul, Oct. 5-8.

Ecclesiastical Hierarchy in the US, Bicent. — A247

Designs: 450 l, Basilica of the Assumption of the Blessed Virgin Mary, Baltimore. 1350 l, John Carroll (1735-1815), 1st bishop of Baltimore and the US. 2400 l, Cathedral of Mary Our Queen, Baltimore.

1989, Nov. 9   Photo.   Perf. 12
842	A247	450 l	multicolored	.65 .40
843	A247	1350 l	multicolored	2.00 1.25
844	A247	2400 l	multicolored	3.50 2.00
		Nos. 842-844 (3)		6.15 3.65

Papal Journeys 1988 A248

Papal arms, Pope John Paul II and maps: 50 l, Uruguay, Bolivia, Peru and Paraguay, May 7-19. 550 l, Austria, June 23-27. 800 l, Zimbabwe, Botswana, Lesotho, Swaziland and Mozambique, Sept. 10-19. 1000 l, France, Oct. 8-11. 4000 l, Pastoral visits in Italy, 1978-1988.

1989, Nov. 9   Perf. 14x13½
845	A248	50 l	multicolored	.20 .20
846	A248	550 l	multicolored	.80 .50
847	A248	800 l	multicolored	1.10 .70
848	A248	1000 l	multicolored	1.50 .90
849	A248	4000 l	multicolored	5.75 3.50
		Nos. 845-849 (5)		9.35 5.80

St. Angela Merici (c. 1474-1540) A249

Designs: 700 l, The vision of the mystical stair, Prophecy of the Ursulines. 800 l, Evangelical counsel. 2800 l, Ursulines mission continued.

1990, Apr. 5   Photo.   Perf. 13½x14
850	A249	700 l	multicolored	1.25 .80
851	A249	800 l	multicolored	1.40 .95
852	A249	2800 l	multicolored	4.75 3.25
		Nos. 850-852 (3)		7.40 5.00

Caritas Intl., 40th Anniv. A250

Designs: 450 l, Abraham. 650 l, Three visitors. 800 l, Abraham and Sarah. 2000 l, Three visitors at Abraham's table.

1990, June 5   Photo.   Perf. 12x11½
Granite Paper
853	A250	450 l	multicolored	.75 .45
854	A250	650 l	multicolored	1.10 .70
855	A250	800 l	multicolored	1.25 .85
856	A250	2000 l	multicolored	3.25 2.00
		Nos. 853-856 (4)		6.35 4.00

Souvenir Sheet
857	Sheet of 4		6.00 6.00
a.	A250 450 l	like #853	.65 .50
b.	A250 650 l	like #854	1.00 .65
c.	A250 800 l	like #855	1.25 .85
d.	A250 2000 l	like #856	3.00 2.00

Nos. 853-856 have a single line border in gold. Nos. 857a-857d have no border line.
No. 857 with "Pro Terremotati 1997" overprinted in sheet margin exists in limited quantities, sold for 8000 l to assist earthquake victims in Umbria and Marche, but was not officially issued by Vatican postal authorities. Value $25.

A251

A252

1990, June 5   Perf. 13½x14
858	A251	300 l	Ordination of St. Willibrord	.50 .30
859	A251	700 l	Stay in Antwerp	1.10 .70
860	A251	3000 l	Leaving belongings, death	4.75 3.25
		Nos. 858-860 (3)		6.35 4.25

1300th anniv. of ministry of St. Willibrord.

1990, Oct. 2

Diocese of Beijing-Nanking, 300th Anniv.: 500 l, Lake Beijing. 750 l, Church of the Immaculate Conception, Beijing, 1650. 1500 l, Lake Beijing, diff. 2000 l, Church of the Redeemer, Beijing, 1703.
861	A252	500 l	multicolored	.70 .45
862	A252	750 l	multicolored	1.10 .70
863	A252	1500 l	multicolored	2.25 1.40
864	A252	2000 l	multicolored	2.75 1.90
		Nos. 861-864 (4)		6.80 4.45

Christmas A253

Details from painting by Sebastiano Mainardi.

1990, Nov. 27   Photo.   Perf. 13
865	A253	50 l	Choir of Angels	.20 .20
866	A253	200 l	St. Joseph	.30 .30
867	A253	650 l	Holy Child	1.10 1.10
868	A253	750 l	Madonna	1.25 1.25
869	A253	2500 l	Nativity scene, vert.	4.00 4.00
		Nos. 865-869 (5)		6.85 6.85

Paintings of the Sistine Chapel — A254

Different details from lunettes: 50 l, 100 l, Eleazar. 150 l, 250 l, Jacob. 350 l, 400 l, Josiah. 500 l, 650 l, Asa. 800 l, 1000 l, Zerubbabel. 2000 l, 3000 l, Azor.

1991, Apr. 9   Photo.   Perf. 11½
Granite Paper
870	A254	50 l	multicolored	.20 .20
871	A254	100 l	multicolored	.20 .20
a.		Booklet pane of 6		.75
872	A254	150 l	multicolored	.20 .20
a.		Booklet pane of 6		1.25
873	A254	250 l	multicolored	.35 .35
874	A254	350 l	multicolored	.45 .45
875	A254	400 l	multicolored	.50 .50
876	A254	500 l	multicolored	.70 .70
877	A254	650 l	multicolored	.90 .90
a.		Booklet pane of 6		5.50
878	A254	800 l	multicolored	1.00 1.00
879	A254	1000 l	multicolored	1.40 1.40
880	A254	2000 l	multicolored	2.75 2.75
881	A254	3000 l	multicolored	4.00 4.00
		Nos. 870-881 (12)		12.65 12.65

Encyclical Rerum Novarum, Cent. A255

Arms of Pope Leo XIII and: 600 l, Title page of Encyclical. 750 l, Allegory of Church's interest in workers, employers. 3500 l, Pope Leo XIII (1878-1903).

1991, May 23   Engr.   Perf. 14x13½
882	A255	600 l	blue & dk grn	.90 .90
883	A255	750 l	sage grn & rose car	1.10 1.10
884	A255	3500 l	brt pur & dk bl	5.25 5.25
		Nos. 882-884 (3)		7.25 7.25

Vatican Observatory, Cent. — A256

Canonization of
St. Bridget, 600th
Anniv. — A257

Designs: 750 l, Astrograph for making photographic sky map, 1891. 1000 l, Zeiss Double
Astrograph, Lake Castelgandolfo, 1935, horiz.
3000 l, New telescope, Vatican Observatory,
Mt. Graham, Arizona, 1991.

Perf. 11½x12, 12x11½

**1991, Oct. 1					Photo.**

Granite Paper

885	A256	750 l multicolored	1.10	1.10
886	A256	1000 l multicolored	1.50	1.50
887	A256	3000 l multicolored	4.50	4.50
		Nos. 885-887 (3)	7.10	7.10

**1991, Oct. 1					Perf. 12½x13**

Designs: 1500 l, Receiving Madonna's revelations. 2000 l, Receiving Christ's revelations.

888	A257	1500 l multicolored	2.25	2.25
889	A257	2000 l multicolored	3.25	3.25

Journeys of Pope
John Paul II,
1990 — A258

Pope John Paul II and: 200 l, Cathedral of
Immaculate Conception, Ouagadougou,
Burkina Faso. 550 l, St. Vitus' Cathedral,
Prague. 750 l, Our Lady of Guadaloupe's
Basilica, Mexico. 1500 l, Ta' Pinu Sanctuary,
Gozo. 3500 l, Cathedral of Christ the King,
Gitega, Burundi.

Litho. & Engr.

**1991, Nov. 11					Perf. 13½x14**

890	A258	200 l green & multi	.30	.30
891	A258	550 l org brn & multi	.85	.85
892	A258	750 l claret & multi	1.10	1.10
893	A258	1500 l dk brn & multi	2.25	2.25
894	A258	3500 l grn bl & multi	5.50	5.50
		Nos. 890-894 (5)	10.00	10.00

West Africa, Jan. 25-Feb. 1 (200 l); Czecho-
slovakia, Apr. 21-22 (550 l); Mexico, Curacao,
May 6-14 (750 l); Malta, May 25-27 (1500 l);
Tanzania, Burundi, Rwanda, Ivory Coast,
Sept. 1-10 (3500 l).

A259

A260

Special Assembly for Europe of Synod of
Bishops: 300 l, Colonnade of St. Peter's Basilica. 500 l, St. Peter's Basilica and Square.
4000 l, Colonnade of St. Peter's Basilica,
Apostolic Palace.

**1991, Nov. 11					Engr.					Perf. 12½x13**

895	A259	300 l olive & blk	.45	.45
896	A259	500 l olive & blk	.80	.80
897	A259	4000 l olive & blk	6.00	6.00
a.		Strip of 3, #895-897	8.00	8.00

No. 897a has continous design.

**1992, Mar. 24					Photo.					Perf. 11½x12**

Discovery and Evangelization of America,
500th Anniv.: 500 l, Christopher Columbus.
600 l, Saint Peter Claver. 850 l, La Virgen de
los Reyes Catolicos. 1000 l, Bishop Bartolome
de las Casas. 2000 l, Father Junipero Serra.
Charts: 1500 l, New World. 2500 l, Old
World.

Granite Paper

898	A260	500 l multicolored	.75	.75
899	A260	600 l multicolored	.90	.90
900	A260	850 l multicolored	1.25	1.25
901	A260	1000 l multicolored	1.50	1.50
902	A260	2000 l multicolored	3.00	3.00
		Nos. 898-902 (5)	7.40	7.40

Souvenir Sheet

Perf. 12

903	A260	Sheet of 2	6.00	6.00
a.		1500 l multicolored	2.25	2.25
b.		2500 l multicolored	3.75	3.75

Piero Della
Francesca (d.
1492),
Painter — A261

Frescoes: 300 l, 750 l (detail), Our Lady of
Childbirth. 1000 l, 3000 l (detail), Resurrection.

**1992, May 15					Photo.					Perf. 13½x14**

904	A261	300 l multicolored	.40	.40
905	A261	750 l multicolored	1.10	1.10
906	A261	1000 l multicolored	1.40	1.40
907	A261	3000 l multicolored	4.25	4.25
		Nos. 904-907 (4)	7.15	7.15

**1992, May 15					Perf. 11½x12**

St. Giuseppe Benedetto Cottolengo: 650 l,
Comforting the sick. 850 l, With Little House of
Divine Providence.

Granite Paper

908	A262	650 l multicolored	1.00	1.00
909	A262	850 l multicolored	1.40	1.40

St. Giuseppe
Benedetto
Cottolengo (1786-
1842)
A262

A263

A264

Plants of the New World: a, Frumentum
indicum. b, Solanum pomiferum. c, Opuntia. d,
Cacaos, cacavifera. e, Solanum tuberosum,
capsicum, mordens. f, Ananas sagitae folio.

**1992, Sept. 15					Photo.					Perf. 11½x12**

Granite Paper

910		Block of 6	7.50	7.50
a.-f.	A263	850 l any single	1.25	1.25

**1992, Oct. 12					Perf. 12½x13**

911	A264	700 l multicolored	1.00	1.00

4th General Conference of the Latin American Episcopacy.

Christmas
A265

Mosaics from Basilica of St. Maria Mag-
giore, Rome: 600 l, The Annunciation. 700 l,
Nativity. 1000 l, Adoration of the Magi. 1500 l,
Presentation to the Temple.

**1992, Nov. 24					Photo.					Perf. 11½**

Granite Paper

912	A265	600 l multicolored	.90	.90
913	A265	700 l multicolored	1.00	1.00
914	A265	1000 l multicolored	1.40	1.40
915	A265	1500 l multicolored	2.10	2.10
		Nos. 912-915 (4)	5.40	5.40

St. Francis Healing Man from Ilerda,
by Giotto di Bondone (1266-
1337) — A266

**1993, Jan. 9					Litho.					Perf. 13½x14**

916	A266	1000 l multi + label	1.25	1.25

Prayer Meeting for Peace in Europe, Assisi.

Architecture
of Vatican
City and
Rome — A267

Buildings: 200 l, St. Peter's Basilica, Vatican
City. 300 l, St. John Lateran Basilica, Rome.
350 l, St. Mary Major's Basilica, Rome. 500 l,
St. Paul's Basilica, Rome. 600 l, Apostolic Palace, Vatican. 700 l, Lateran Apostolic Palace,
Rome. 850 l, Papal Palace, Castel Gandolfo.
1000 l, Chancery Palace, Rome. 2000 l, Palace of the Propagation of the Faith, Rome.
3000 l, St. Calixtus Palace, Rome.

**1993, Mar. 23					Photo.					Perf. 12x11½**

Granite Paper

917	A267	200 l multicolored	.25	.25
a.		Booklet pane of 4	1.10	
918	A267	300 l multicolored	.40	.40
a.		Booklet pane of 4	1.60	
919	A267	350 l multicolored	.50	.50
a.		Booklet pane of 4	2.00	
920	A267	500 l multicolored	.65	.65
a.		Booklet pane of 4	2.75	
921	A267	600 l multicolored	.80	.80
922	A267	700 l multicolored	.95	.95
923	A267	850 l multicolored	1.10	1.10
924	A267	1000 l multicolored	1.40	1.40
925	A267	2000 l multicolored	2.75	2.75
926	A267	3000 l multicolored	4.00	4.00
		Nos. 917-926 (10)	12.80	12.80

A268

Congress emblem, Vatican arms and: 500 l,
Cross, grape vines. 700 l, Cross, hands break-
ing bread. 1500 l, Hands lifting chalice. 2500 l,
Wheat, banner.

**1993, May 22					Litho.					Perf. 14x13½**

927	A268	500 l multicolored	.60	.60
928	A268	700 l multicolored	.90	.90
929	A268	1500 l multicolored	1.90	1.90
930	A268	2500 l multicolored	3.00	3.00
		Nos. 927-930 (4)	6.40	6.40

45th Intl. Eucharistic Congress, Seville.

A269

**1993, May 22					Engr.					Perf. 13½x14**

Traditio Legis Sarcophagus, St. Peter's
Basilica: a, 200 l, Sacrifice of Isaac. b, 750 l,
Apostle Peter receiving law from Jesus, Apostle Paul. c, 3000 l, Christ watching servant
pouring water on Pilate's hands.

931	A269	Triptych, #a.-c.	5.00	5.00

Ascension Day, May 20.

Contemporary Art — A270

Europa: 750 l, Crucifixion, by Felice
Casorati (1886-1963). 850 l, Rouen Cathedral,
by Maurice Utrillo (1883-1955).

**1993, Sept. 29					Photo.					Perf. 13**

932	A270	750 l multicolored	.95	.95
933	A270	850 l multicolored	1.00	1.00

Death of St. John
of Nepomuk,
600th
Anniv. — A271

2000 l, Buildings in Prague, Charles Bridge.

**1993, Sept. 29					Litho.					Perf. 13½x14**

934	A271	1000 l multicolored	1.25	1.25
935	A271	2000 l multicolored	2.50	2.50

Travels of
Pope John
Paul
II — A272

Visits to: 600 l, Senegal, Gambia, Guinea. 1000 l, Angola, St. Thomas and Prince. 5000 l, Dominican Republic.

1993, Nov. 23 Photo. *Perf. 12x11½*
Granite Paper
936 A272 600 l multicolored .70 .70
937 A272 1000 l multicolored 1.25 1.25
938 A272 5000 l multicolored 5.75 5.75
  Nos. 936-938 (3) 7.70 7.70

Hans Holbein the Younger (1497?-1543), Painter — A273

Details or entire paintings: 700 l, 1000 l, Madonna of Solothurn. 1500 l, Self-portrait.

Litho. & Engr.
1993, Nov. 23 *Perf. 13½x14*
939 A273 700 l multicolored .85 .85
940 A273 1000 l multicolored 1.25 1.25
941 A273 1500 l multicolored 1.75 1.75
  Nos. 939-941 (3) 3.85 3.85

Synod of Bishops, Special Assembly for Africa — A274

Designs: 850 l, Stylized crosier, dome with cross, vert. 1000 l, Crucifix, dome of St. Peter's Basilica, crosiers, African landscape.

Perf. 12½x13, 13x12½
1994, Apr. 8 Photo.
942 A274 850 l multicolored 1.10 1.10
943 A274 1000 l multicolored 1.25 1.25

The Restored Sistine Chapel — A275

Frescoes, by Michelangelo: Creation of the Sun and Moon: No. 944, Sun. No. 945, God pointing toward moon. Creation of Man: No. 946, Adam, No. 947, God. Original Sin: No. 948, Adam, Eve taking apple from serpent. No. 949, Adam, Eve forced from Garden of Eden. The Flood: No. 950, People on dry ground. No. 951, People on stone outcropping.
4000 l, Detail of Last Judgment, Christ and the Virgin.

1994, Apr. 8 Photo. *Perf. 11½*
944 A275 350 l multicolored .40 .40
945 A275 350 l multicolored .40 .40
 a. A275 Pair, #944-945 .80 .80
946 A275 500 l multicolored .60 .60
947 A275 500 l multicolored .60 .60
 a. A275 Pair, #946-947 1.25 1.25
948 A275 1000 l multicolored 1.25 1.25
949 A275 1000 l multicolored 1.25 1.25
 a. A275 Pair, #948-949 2.50 2.50
950 A275 2000 l multicolored 2.50 2.50
951 A275 2000 l multicolored 2.50 2.50
 a. A275 Pair, 950-951 5.00 5.00
  Nos. 944-951 (8) 9.50 9.50

Souvenir Sheet
Perf. 12
952 A275 4000 l multicolored 5.00 5.00
No. 952 contains one 36x54mm stamp.

European Inventions, Discoveries — A276

Europa: 750 l, Progress from wheel to atom traced by white thread. 850 l, Galileo in center of solar system, scientific instruments.

1994, May 31 Litho. *Perf. 13x13½*
953 A276 750 l multicolored .95 .95
954 A276 850 l multicolored 1.10 1.10

Intl. Year of the Family — A277

Stained glass: 400 l, God creating man and woman. 750 l, Family under names of four Evangelists. 1000 l, Parents teaching son. 2000 l, Young man comforting elderly couple.

1994, May 31 Photo. *Perf. 13x14*
955 A277 400 l multicolored .50 .50
956 A277 750 l multicolored .95 .95
957 A277 1000 l multicolored 1.25 1.25
958 A277 2000 l multicolored 2.50 2.50
  Nos. 955-958 (4) 5.20 5.20

Giovanni da Montecorvino (1247-1328), Missionary — A278

1994, Sept. 27 Litho. *Perf. 14*
959 A278 1000 l multicolored 1.40 1.40
Evangelization of China, 700th anniv.

13th Intl. Convention of Christian Archaeology, Split, Croatia — A279

Mosaics from Euphrasian Basilica, Parentium, Croatia, 6th Cent.: 700 l, Bishop Euphrasius, Archdeacon Claudius, Claudius' son. 1500 l, Madonna and Child, two angels. 3000 l, Christ, Apostles Peter & Paul.

1994, Sept. 27 *Perf. 13x14*
960 A279 700 l multicolored 1.00 1.00
961 A279 1500 l multicolored 2.00 2.00
962 A279 3000 l multicolored 4.25 4.25
  Nos. 960-962 (3) 7.25 7.25

Travels of Pope John Paul II — A280

Designs: 600 l, Benin, Uganda, Sudan. 700 l, Albania. 1000 l, Spain. 2000 l, Jamaica, Mexico, US. 3000 l, Lithuania, Latvia, Estonia.

1994, Nov. 18 Engr. *Perf. 13*
963 A280 600 l multicolored .85 .85
964 A280 700 l multicolored 1.00 1.00
965 A280 1000 l multicolored 1.40 1.40
966 A280 2000 l multicolored 2.75 2.75
967 A280 3000 l multicolored 4.25 4.25
  Nos. 963-967 (5) 10.25 10.25

Christmas A281

The Nativity, by Il Tintoretto: 700 l, The Holy Family. No. 969, The Holy Family, two women. No. 970, Adoration of the shepherds.

1994, Nov. 18 Photo. *Perf. 11½*
Granite Paper
968 A281 700 l multicolored 1.00 1.00
Size: 45x27mm
969 A281 1000 l multicolored 1.40 1.40
970 A281 1000 l multicolored 1.40 1.40
 a. Pair, #969-970 2.80 2.80
  Nos. 968-970 (3) 3.80 3.80

Peace and Freedom A282

1995, Mar. 25 Photo. *Perf. 14x13*
971 A282 750 l shown .90 .90
972 A282 850 l Hands clasp, dove 1.00 1.00
Europa.

Shrine of Loreto, 700th Anniv. — A283

Details of artworks from vaults of Sacristy: 600 l, St. Mark's, Angel with chalice, by Melozzo da Forli. 700 l, St. Mark's, Angel with lamb, by da Forli. 1500 l, 2500 l, St. John's, Music making angels, by Luca Signorelli.
No. 977, Marble carving showing Holy House of Loreto.

1995, Mar. 25 *Perf. 11½*
973 A283 600 l multicolored .70 .70
974 A283 700 l multicolored .80 .80
975 A283 1500 l multicolored 1.75 1.75
976 A283 2500 l multicolored 3.00 3.00
  Nos. 973-976 (4) 6.25 6.25

Souvenir Sheet
977 A283 3000 l multicolored 3.50 3.50
No. 977 contains one 36x36mm stamp.

Radio, Cent. A284

Designs: 850 l, Guglielmo Marconi, transmitting equipment. 1000 l, Archangel Gabriel, Pope John Paul II, Marconi broadcasting station, Vatican City.

1995, June 8 Photo. *Perf. 14*
978 A284 850 l multicolored 1.00 1.00
979 A284 1000 l multicolored 1.25 1.25
See Germany No. 1990, Ireland Nos. 973-974, Italy Nos. 2038-2039, San Marino Nos. 1336-1337.

A285

A286

European Nature Conservation Year (Scenes in Vatican Gardens & Castel Gandolfo: 200 l, Fountain of the Triton, arches of rhyncospernum jasminoides. 300 l, Avenue of roses, Palazzo Barberini. 400 l, Statue of Apollo Citaredo. 550 l, Ruins of Domitian's Villa, Avenue of roses. 750 l, Acer negundo, Viale dell'Osservatorio. 1500 l, Belvedere garden. 2000 l, Fountain of the Eagle, Quercus ilex. 3000 l, Avenue of cypresses, equestrian statue.

1995, June 8 *Perf. 12*
Granite Paper
980 A285 200 l multicolored .25 .25
981 A285 300 l multicolored .35 .35
 a. Booklet pane of 3 1.00
982 A285 400 l multicolored .50 .50
 a. Booklet pane of 3 1.50
983 A285 550 l multicolored .70 .70
 a. Booklet pane of 3 2.25
984 A285 750 l multicolored .90 .90
 a. Booklet pane of 3 2.75
  Complete booklet, #981a, 982a, 983a, 984a 7.50
985 A285 1500 l multicolored 1.90 1.90
986 A285 2000 l multicolored 2.50 2.50
987 A285 3000 l multicolored 3.75 3.75
  Nos. 980-987 (8) 10.85 10.85

1995, Oct. 3 Photo. *Perf. 13½x13*
Paintings of peace, by Paolo Guiotto: 550 l, Small hearts flying from large heart. 750 l, Stylized faces. 850 l, Doves in flight. 1250 l, Lymph reaching to smallest branches. 2000 l, Explosion of colors, people.
988 A286 550 l multicolored .70 .70
989 A286 750 l multicolored .95 .95
990 A286 850 l multicolored 1.10 1.10
991 A286 1250 l multicolored 1.50 1.50
992 A286 2000 l multicolored 2.50 2.50
  Nos. 988-992 (5) 6.75 6.75

UN, 50th anniv.

A287

A288

St. Anthony of Padua (1195-1231): 750 l, St. John of God (1495-1550). 3000 l, St. Philip Neri (1515-95).

Litho. & Engr.
1995, Oct. 3   *Perf. 13½x14*
993	A287	500 l green & brown	.65	.65
994	A287	750 l violet & green	.95	.95
995	A287	3000 l magenta & black	3.75	3.75
		Nos. 993-995 (3)	5.35	5.35

1995, Nov. 20 Photo.   *Perf. 12x11½*

Scenes depicting life of Jesus Christ from illuminated manuscripts: 400 l, The Annunciation. 850 l, Nativity. 1250 l, Flight into Egypt. 2000 l, Jesus among the teachers.

Granite Paper
996	A288	400 l multicolored	.50	.50
997	A288	850 l multicolored	1.10	1.10
998	A288	1250 l multicolored	1.60	1.60
999	A288	2000 l multicolored	2.50	2.50
		Nos. 996-999 (4)	5.70	5.70

Towards the Holy Year 2000.

Travels of Pope John Paul II
A289

Designs: 1000 l, Giving greeting in Croatia, statue of Blessed Lady, Zagreb Cathedral. 2000 l, In Italy, lighthouse in Genoa, Orvieto Cathedral, Valley of Temples in Agrigento.

1995, Nov. 20 Litho.   *Perf. 14½x14*
1000	A289	1000 l multicolored	1.25	1.25
1001	A289	2000 l multicolored	2.50	2.50

Religious Anniversaries
A290

Designs: 1250 l, Angel holding crosses, Union of Brest-Litovsk, 400th anniv. 2000 l, Cross with branches, Latin episcopal mitre, Byzantine mitre, Union of Uzhorod, 350th anniv.

1996, Mar. 16 Photo.   *Perf. 13½x14*
1002	A290	1250 l multicolored	1.60	1.60
1003	A290	2000 l multicolored	2.50	2.50

A291

Marco Polo's Return from China, 700th Anniv. — A292

Designs from miniatures, Bodleian Library, Oxford: 350 l, Marco Polo delivering Pope Gregory X's letter to Great Khan. 850 l, Great Khan dispensing alms to poor in Cambaluc. 1250 l, Marco Polo receiving golden book from Great Khan. 2500 l, Marco Polo in Persia listening to story of three Kings who go to Bethlehem to adore Jesus.

2000 l, Stylized portrait of Marco Polo drawn from first printed edition of "Il Milione." Illustration reduced.

1996, Mar. 15   *Perf. 11½*
Granite Paper
1004	A291	350 l multicolored	.45	.45
1005	A291	850 l multicolored	1.10	1.10
1006	A291	1250 l multicolored	1.60	1.60
1007	A291	2500 l multicolored	3.25	3.25
		Nos. 1004-1007 (4)	6.40	6.40

Souvenir Sheet
Perf. 12x11½
1008	A292	2000 l black	2.50	2.50

A293

A294

Famous Women: 750 l, Gianna Baretta Molla (1922-62), physician. 850 l, Sister Edith Stein (1891-1942).

1996, May 7 Engr.   *Perf. 13x14*
1009	A293	750 l blue	1.00	1.00
1010	A293	850 l brown	1.10	1.10

1996, May 7 Photo.   *Perf. 13*

Modern Olympic Games, Cent.: a, Statue of athlete. b, Athlete's torso. c, Hand. d, Statue of athlete reaching upward. e, Hercules.
1011		Strip of 5	8.00	8.00
a.-e.	A294	1250 l any single	1.60	1.60

Ordination of Pope John Paul II, 50th Anniv.
A295

Designs: 500 l, Wawel Cathedral, Krakow. 750 l, Pope John Paul II giving blessing. 1250 l, Basilica of St. John Lateran, Rome.

1996, Oct. 12 Litho.   *Perf. 14*
1012	A295	500 l multicolored	.65	.65
1013	A295	750 l multicolored	1.00	1.00
1014	A295	1250 l multicolored	1.60	1.60
		Nos. 1012-1014 (3)	3.25	3.25

Life of Jesus Christ from Illuminated Manuscripts
A296

Designs: 550 l, Baptism of Jesus at River Jordan. 850 l, Temptation in the desert. 1500 l, Cure of the leper. 2500 l, Jesus the teacher.

1996, Oct. 12 Photo.   *Perf. 12x11½*
1015	A296	550 l multicolored	.75	.75
1016	A296	850 l multicolored	1.10	1.10
1017	A296	1500 l multicolored	2.00	2.00
1018	A296	2500 l multicolored	3.25	3.25
		Nos. 1015-1018 (4)	7.10	7.10

Christmas — A297

Nativity, by Murillo (1618-82).

1996, Nov. 20 Litho.   *Perf. 13½*
1019	A297	750 l multicolored	1.00	1.00

St. Celestine V (1215-96)
A298

#1021, St. Alfonso Maria De'Liguori (1696-1787).

1996, Nov. 20   *Perf. 13½x14*
1020	A298	1250 l multicolored	1.60	1.60
1021	A298	1250 l multicolored	1.60	1.60

Travels of Pope John Paul II, 1995
A299

Designs: 250 l, Jan. 11-21, Philippines, Papua New Guinea, Australia, Sri Lanka. 500 l, May 20-22, Czech Republic, Poland. 750 l, June 3-4, Belgium. 1000 l, June 30-July 3, Slovakia. 2000 l, Sept. 14-20, Cameroun, South Africa, Kenya. 5000 l, Oct. 4-9, UN headquarters, NY, US.

1996, Nov. 20   *Perf. 14x13½*
1022	A299	250 l blue & multi	.35	.35
1023	A299	500 l blue green & multi	.65	.65
1024	A299	750 l green & multi	1.00	1.00
1025	A299	1000 l brown & multi	1.25	1.25
1026	A299	2000 l gray & multi	2.50	2.50
1027	A299	5000 l pink & multi	6.75	6.75
		Nos. 1022-1027 (6)	12.50	12.50

Papal Carriages and Automobiles
A300

Designs: 50 l, Touring carriage. 100 l, Graham Paige. 300 l, Festive traveling carriage. 500 l, Citroen Lictoria VI. 750 l, Grand touring carriage. 850 l, Mercedes Benz. 1000 l, Festive half carriage. 1250 l, Mercedes Benz 300SEL. 2000 l, Touring carriage, diff. 4000 l, Fiat "Pope mobile."

1997, Mar. 20 Photo.   *Perf. 12*
Granite Paper
1028	A300	50 l multicolored	.20	.20
1029	A300	100 l multicolored	.20	.20
1030	A300	300 l multicolored	.35	.35
1031	A300	500 l multicolored	.60	.60
1032	A300	750 l multicolored	.90	.90
1033	A300	850 l multicolored	1.00	1.00
1034	A300	1000 l multicolored	1.10	1.10
1035	A300	1250 l multicolored	1.50	1.50
1036	A300	2000 l multicolored	2.25	2.25
1037	A300	4000 l multicolored	4.75	4.75
		Nos. 1028-1037 (10)	12.85	12.85

A301

A302

Swiss Guard: 750 l, Guard in traditional attire. 850 l, Guard in armor with sword in front of iron gate.

1997, Mar. 20 Litho.   *Perf. 13½*
1038	A301	750 l multicolored	.90	.90
1039	A301	850 l multicolored	1.00	1.00
a.		Strip of 2 + 2 labels	1.90	1.90

Europa.

1997, Apr. 23 Engr.   *Perf. 14*
1040	A302	850 l deep violet	1.00	1.00

St. Adalbert (956-997). See Germany No. 1964, Poland No. 3337, Czech Republic No. 3012, Hungary No. 3569.

A303

"Looking at the Classics," Museum Exhibition — A304

Pictures from texts of Latin and Greek classics: 500 l, Aristotle observing and describing various species from man to insect, from his "De Historia Animalium." 750 l, Bacchus riding dragon, from "Metamorphoses" by Ovid. 1250 l, General haranguing his soldiers, from "Iliad" by Homer. 2000 l, Hannibal leaving Canne, two horsemen, foot soldier, from "Ab Urbe Condita" by Titus Livius.

Masks from "Comedies," by Terrence: No. 1045: a, Man, woman. b, Two women. c, Two men.

1997, Apr. 23 Photo.   *Perf. 14*
1041	A303	500 l multicolored	.60	.60
1042	A303	750 l multicolored	.90	.90
1043	A303	1250 l multicolored	1.50	1.50
1044	A303	2000 l multicolored	2.40	2.40
		Nos. 1041-1044 (4)	5.40	5.40

Perf. 13½
1045	A304	1000 l Sheet of 3, #a.-c.	3.50	3.50

A305

A306

46th Intl. Eucharistic Congress, Wroclaw, Poland: 650 l, Elements of the Eucharist, chalice, consecrated Host, arms of Wroclaw. 1000 l, The Last Supper, fish, Congress emblem. 1250 l, Wroclaw Cathedral, sheaf of wheat, holy spirit descending on church. 2500 l, "IHS" symbol of Christ on cross, doves, world with two hands on it.

1997, May 27   **Photo.**   **Perf. 13**
1046	A305	650 l	multicolored	.75	.75
1047	A305	1000 l	multicolored	1.10	1.10
1048	A305	1250 l	multicolored	1.40	1.40
1049	A305	2500 l	multicolored	2.75	2.75
		Nos. 1046-1049 (4)		6.00	6.00

1997, Sept. 15   **Litho.**   **Perf. 13x14**
1050	A306	900 l	multicolored	1.00	1.00

Pope Paul VI (1897-1978).

No. 1050 was printed se-tenant with 4 labels.

St. Ambrose (d. 397) — A307

Towards the Holy Year 2000 — A308

1997, Sept. 15   **Photo.**   **Perf. 13x14**
1051	A307	800 l	multicolored	.90	.90

1997, Sept. 15   **Perf. 12**

Illustrations of Christ's miracles: 400 l, Healing of paralyzed man. 800 l, Calming of the tempest. 1300 l, Multiplication of bread and fish. 3600 l, Peter's confession and conferment of primacy.

Granite Paper
1052	A308	400 l	multicolored	.45	.45
1053	A308	800 l	multicolored	.90	.90
1054	A308	1300 l	multicolored	1.90	1.90
1055	A308	3600 l	multicolored	4.25	4.25
		Nos. 1052-1055 (4)		7.50	7.50

1996 Travels of Pope John Paul II — A309

Designs: 400 l, Central & South America, Feb. 5-12. 900 l, Tunisia, Apr. 14. 1000 l, Slovenia , May 17-19. 1300 l, Germany, June 21-23. 2000 l, Hungary, Sept. 6-7. 4000 l, France, Sept. 19-22.

1997, Nov. 11   **Litho.**   **Perf. 14x13½**
1056	A309	400 l	multicolored	.50	.50
1057	A309	900 l	multicolored	1.00	1.00
1058	A309	1000 l	multicolored	1.25	1.25
1059	A309	1300 l	multicolored	1.50	1.50
1060	A309	2000 l	multicolored	2.25	2.25
1061	A309	4000 l	multicolored	4.75	4.75
		Nos. 1056-1061 (6)		11.25	11.25

Christmas — A310

Detail from "The Nativity," by Benozzo Gozzoli (1420-97).

1997, Nov. 11   **Photo.**   **Perf. 14**
1062	A310	800 l	multicolored	.95	.95

Feasts of Sts. Peter and Paul, June 29th — A311

1998, Mar. 24   **Photo.**   **Perf. 13**
1063	A311	800 l	St. Peter	.90	.90
1064	A311	900 l	St. Paul	1.00	1.00

Europa.

The Popes of the Holy Years 1300-1525 A312

Designs: 200 l, Boniface VIII, 1300. 400 l, Clement VI, 1350. 500 l, Boniface IX, 1390, 1400. 700 l, Martin V, 1423. 800 l, Nicholas V, 1450. 900 l, Sixtus IV, 1475. 1300 l, Alexander VI, 1500. 3000 , Clement VII, 1525.

1998, Mar. 24   **Litho.**   **Perf. 14**
1065	A312	200 l	multicolored	.25	.25
1066	A312	400 l	multicolored	.45	.45
1067	A312	500 l	multicolored	.60	.60
1068	A312	700 l	multicolored	.80	.80
1069	A312	800 l	multicolored	.90	.90
1070	A312	900 l	multicolored	1.00	1.00
1071	A312	1300 l	multicolored	1.50	1.50
1072	A312	3000 l	multicolored	3.50	3.50
		Nos. 1065-1072 (8)		9.00	9.00

Nos. 1065-1072 were each printed se-tenant with a label picturing the respective papal arms.

See Nos. 1095-1102, 1141-1150.

A313

A314

Litho. & Engr.

1998, May 19   **Perf. 13½x14**
1073	A313	900 l	Face on Shroud	1.00	1.00
1074	A313	2500 l	Cathedral of Turin	2.75	2.75

Exposition of the Shroud of Turin.

1998, May 19   **Photo.**   **Perf. 12**

Frescoes of Angels, by Melozzo da Forli (1438-94), Basilica of Sts. Apostles, Rome: Angels playing various musical instruments.

Granite Paper
1075	A314	450 l	multicolored	.60	.60
1076	A314	650 l	multicolored	.75	.75
1077	A314	800 l	multicolored	.90	.90
1078	A314	1000 l	multicolored	1.10	1.10
1079	A314	1300 l	multicolored	1.50	1.50
1080	A314	2000 l	multicolored	2.25	2.25
		Nos. 1075-1080 (6)		7.10	7.10

Towards Holy Year 2000 A315

Episodes from the Life of Christ: 500 l, Triumphal entry into Jerusalem. 800 l, Washing of the feet. 1300 l, The Last Supper. 3000 l, Crucifixion.

1998, May 19   **Perf. 12**

Granite Paper
1081	A315	500 l	multicolored	.60	.60
1082	A315	800 l	multicolored	.90	.90
1083	A315	1300 l	multicolored	1.50	1.50
1084	A315	3000 l	multicolored	3.25	3.25
		Nos. 1081-1084 (4)		6.25	6.25

Italia '98 A316

1998, Oct. 23   **Photo.**   **Perf. 14**
1085	A316	800 l	Pope John Paul II	1.00	1.00

See Italy No. 2259 and San Marino No. 1430.

The Good Shepherd — A317

Christian Sculptures — A318

1998, Oct. 25   **Perf. 12 Vert.**

Granite Paper

Booklet Stamp
1086	A317	900 l	multicolored	1.10	1.10
a.		Booklet pane of 5		5.50	
		Complete booklet, #1086a		5.50	

Italia '98.

1998, Oct. 25   **Perf. 12**

Designs: a, 600 l, Peter's denial. b, 900 l, Praying woman. c, 1000 l, Christ and the Cyrenean. 2000 l, Christ with the Cross and Two Apostles.

Granite Paper
1087	A318	Sheet of 4, #a.-d.		5.50	5.50

Italia '98. Margin is embossed.

Christmas — A319

1998, Dec. 1   **Litho.**   **Perf. 14x13½**
1088	A319	800 l	multicolored	1.00	1.00

See Croatia No. 381.

1997 Travels of Pope John Paul II — A320

Designs: 300 l, Sarajevo, 4/12-13/97. 600 l, Prague, 4/25-27/97. 800 l, Beirut, 5/10-11/97. 900 l, Poland, 5/21-6/10/97. 1300 l, Paris, 8/21-24/97. 5000 l, Rio de Janeiro, 10/2-6/97.

1998, Dec. 1   **Perf. 12½**
1089	A320	300 l	brown	.35	.35
1090	A320	600 l	green	.70	.70
1091	A320	800 l	brown	1.00	1.00
1092	A320	900 l	violet blue	1.10	1.10
1093	A320	1300 l	org brn	1.60	1.60
1094	A320	5000 l	org brn	6.00	6.00
		Nos. 1089-1094 (6)		10.75	10.75

Popes of the Holy Years Type of 1998

Popes: 300 l, Julius III, 1550. 600 l, Gregory XIII, 1575. 800 l, Clement VIII, 1600. 900 l, Urban VIII, 1625. 1000 l, Innocent X, 1650. 1300 l, Clement X, 1675. 1500 l, Innocent XII, 1700. 2000 l, Benedict XIII, 1725.

1999, Mar. 23   **Litho.**   **Perf. 14**
1095	A312	300 l	multicolored	.35	.35
1096	A312	600 l	multicolored	.65	.65
1097	A312	800 l	multicolored	.90	.90
1098	A312	900 l	multicolored	1.00	1.00
1099	A312	1000 l	multicolored	1.10	1.10
1100	A312	1300 l	multicolored	1.40	1.40
1101	A312	1500 l	multicolored	1.60	1.60
1102	A312	2000 l	multicolored	2.25	2.25
		Nos. 1095-1102 (8)		9.25	9.25

Nos. 1095-1102 were each printed se-tenant with a label picturing the respective papal arms.

Flowers from Vatican Gardens and Papal Villa, Castelgandolfo A321

Europa: 800 l, John Paul II Rose. 900 l, Water lilies.

1999, Mar. 23   **Litho.**   **Perf. 12½x13**
1103	A321	800 l	multicolored	.90	.90
1104	A321	900 l	multicolored	1.00	1.00
a.		Pair, #1103-1104 + label		1.90	1.90

Padre Pio de Pietrelcina (1887-1968) — A322

#1106: a, 1st church, San Giovanni Rotondo. b, New church, San Giovanni Rotondo. c, Like #1105.

1999, Apr. 27   Litho.   Perf. 14x13
1105 A322 800 l multicolored   .90   .90
Souvenir Sheet
Perf. 13x13½
1106 A322 Sheet of 3   2.10 2.10
  a.   300 l multi, vert.   .35   .35
  b.   600 l multi, vert.   .70   .70
  c.   900 l multi   1.00 1.00

Nos. 1106a-1106b are 30x40mm, No. 1106c is 60x40mm.

A323

Holy Places in Palestine — A324

Nos. 1107-1111: 19th cent. watercolors, Pontifical Lateran University Library.
Map of Holy Land from "Geographia Blaviana," 17th cent - #1112: a, Mediterranean Sea, denomination, LL. b, Mediterranean Sea, denomination LR. c, Red Sea, Holy Land. d, Inscription indentifying map.

1999, May 25   Photo.   Perf. 11½
Granite Paper
1107 A323 200 l Bethlehem   .20   .20
1108 A323 500 l Nazareth   .55   .55
1109 A323 800 l Lake of Tiber-
            ias   .85   .85
1110 A323 900 l Jerusalem   1.00 1.00
1111 A323 1300 l Mount Tabor   1.40 1.40
      Nos. 1107-1111 (5)   4.00 4.00

Perf. 12x11¾
1112 A324 1000 l Sheet of 4,
            #a.-d.   4.25 4.25

Towards
Holy Year
2000
A325

Events from life of Christ: 400 l, Deposition from the Cross. 700 l, Resurrection. 1300 l, Pentecost. 3000 l, Last Judgement.

1999, May 25   Perf. 12x11¾
Granite Paper
1113 A325 400 l multicolored   .45   .45
1114 A325 700 l multicolored   .75   .75
1115 A325 1300 l multicolored   1.40 1.40
1116 A325 3000 l multicolored   3.25 3.25
      Nos. 1113-1116 (4)   5.85 5.85

Kosovo 1999 — A326

1999, May 25   Perf. 12¼
Granite Paper
1117 A326 3600 l black   4.00 4.00

Proceeds from sale of stamp benefits victims of the fighting in Kosovo.

1998 Travels of
Pope John Paul
II — A327

600 l, Cuba, June 21-26. 800 l, Nigeria, Mar. 21-23. 900 l, Austria, June 19-21. 1300 l, Croatia, Oct. 2-4. 2000 l, Italy, Oct. 20.

1999, Oct. 12   Litho.   Perf. 14x13½
1118 A327 600 l multicolored   .70   .70
1119 A327 800 l multicolored   .90   .90
1120 A327 900 l multicolored   1.00 1.00
1121 A327 1300 l multicolored   1.50 1.50
1122 A327 2000 l multicolored   2.25 2.25
      Nos. 1118-1122 (5)   6.35 6.35

Council of
Europe, 50th
Anniv. — A328

1999, Oct. 12   Photo.   Perf. 11¾
Granite Paper
1123 A328 1200 l multicolored   1.40 1.40

Christmas
A329

The Birth of Christ, by Giovanni di Pietro: 500 l, Joseph (detail). 800 l, Christ (detail). 900 l, Mary (detail). 1200 l, Entire painting.

Perf. 13¼x12½
1999, Nov. 24   Litho.
1124 A329 500 l multi   .50   .50
1125 A329 800 l multi   .80   .80
1126 A329 900 l multi   .90   .90
1127 A329 1200 l multi   1.25 1.25
      Nos. 1124-1127 (4)   3.45 3.45

Opening of
the Holy
Door for
Holy Year
2000
A330

Various panels of Holy Door. Stamps on No. 1136 lack white border.

1999, Nov. 24   Photo.   Perf. 11¾x12
Granite Paper
1128 A330 200 l multi   .20   .20
1129 A330 300 l multi   .30   .30
1130 A330 400 l multi   .40   .40
1131 A330 500 l multi   .50   .50
1132 A330 600 l multi   .60   .60
1133 A330 800 l multi   .75   .75
1134 A330 1000 l multi   1.00 1.00
1135 A330 1200 l multi   1.25 1.25
      Nos. 1128-1135 (8)   5.00 5.00
Souvenir Sheet
1136   Sheet of 8, #a.-h.   5.25 5.25
  a. A330 200 l Like #1128   .20   .20
  b. A330 300 l Like #1129   .30   .30
  c. A330 400 l Like #1130   .40   .40
  d. A330 500 l Like #1131   .50   .50
  e. A330 600 l Like #1132   .60   .60
  f. A330 800 l Like #1133   .80   .80
  g. A330 1000 l Like #1134   1.00 1.00
  h. A330 1200 l Like #1135   1.25 1.25

Holy Year
2000 — A331

Designs: 800 l, St. Peter's Basilica. 1000 l, Basilica of St. John Lateran. 1200 l, Basilica of St. Mary Major. 2000 l, Basilica of St. Paul.

2000, Feb. 4   Photo.   Perf. 11¾
Granite Paper
1137 A331 800 l multi   .75   .75
1138 A331 1000 l multi   1.00 1.00
1139 A331 1200 l multi   1.25 1.25
1140 A331 2000 l multi   2.00 2.00
      Nos. 1137-1140 (4)   5.00 5.00

Popes of the Holy Year Type of 1998
Designs: 300 l, Benedict XIV, 1750. 400 l, Pius VI, 1775. 500 l, Leo XII, 1825. 600 l, Pius IX, 1875. 700 l, Leo XIII, 1900. 800 l, Pius XI, 1925. 1200 l, Pius XII, 1950. 1500 l, Paul VI, 1975. No. 1149, John Paul II with miter, 2000. No. 1150, John Paul II with hand on chin, 2000.

2000, Feb. 4   Litho.   Perf. 13¾
1141 A312 300 l multi + label   .30   .30
1142 A312 400 l multi + label   .40   .40
1143 A312 500 l multi + label   .50   .50
1144 A312 600 l multi + label   .60   .60
1145 A312 700 l multi + label   .70   .70
1146 A312 800 l multi + label   .75   .75
1147 A312 1200 l multi + label   1.25 1.25
1148 A312 1500 l multi + label   1.50 1.50
1149 A312 2000 l multi + label   2.00 2.00
      Nos. 1141-1149 (9)   8.00 8.00
Souvenir Sheet
1150 A312 2000 l multi   2.00 2.00

No. 1150 contains one label.

Christianity
in Iceland,
1000th
Anniv.
A332

2000, Feb. 4   Perf. 13¼x13¾
1151 A332 1500 l multi   1.50 1.50

See Iceland Nos. 900-901.

Europa, 2000
Common Design Type
2000, May 9   Litho.   Perf. 13¼x13
1152 CD17 1200 l multi   1.25 1.25

Printed in sheets of 10, with left and right side selvage of Priority Mail etiquettes.

Pope John Paul
II, 80th
Birthday — A333

800 l, Pope. 1200 l, Black Madonna of Jasna Gora. 2000 l, Pope's silver cross.

2000, May 9   Engr.   Perf. 13x12¾
1153 A333 800 l purple   .75   .75
1154 A333 1200 l dark blue   1.25 1.25
1155 A333 2000 l green   2.00 2.00
      Nos. 1153-1155 (3)   4.00 4.00

See Poland Nos. 3520-3522.

Restored Sistine Chapel
Frescoes — A334

Designs: 500 l, The Calling of St. Peter and St. Andrew, by Domenico Ghirlandaio. 1000 l, The Trials of Moses, by Sandro Botticelli. 1500 l, The Donation of the Keys, by Pietro Perugino. 3000 l, The Worship of the Golden Calf, by Cosimo Rosselli.

Perf. 11½x11¾
2000, May 9   Photo.   Blue Frame
Granite Paper
1156 A334 500 l multi   .50   .50
1157 A334 1000 l multi   1.00 1.00
1158 A334 1500 l multi   1.50 1.50
1159 A334 3000 l multi   3.00 3.00
      Nos. 1156-1159 (4)   6.00 6.00

20th World Youth
Day — A335

Various photos of Pope John Paul II and youth.

Perf. 13¾x13¼
2000, June 19   Litho.
Color of Cross
1160 A335 800 l red   .80   .80
1161 A335 1000 l green   1.00 1.00
1162 A335 1200 l violet   1.10 1.10
1163 A335 1500 l orange   1.50 1.50
Booklet Stamp
Self-Adhesive
Serpentine Die Cut 12
1164 A335 1000 l green   1.00 1.00
  a.   Booklet of 4 + 4 labels   4.00
      Nos. 1160-1164 (5)   5.40 5.40

47th Intl.
Eucharistic
Congress
A336

2000, June 19   Perf. 13x12½
1165 A336 1200 l multi   1.10 1.10

Beatification of
Pope John
XXIII — A337

2000, Sept. 1   Photo.   Perf. 13¼x14
1166 A337 1200 l multi   1.10 1.10

1999 Travels of Pope John Paul II — A338

#1167: a, Mexico, 1/22-28. b, Romania, 5/7-9. c, Poland, 6/17. d, Slovenia, 9/19. e, India and Georgia, 11/5-9.

2000, Sept. 1   *Perf. 11¾*
Granite Paper
1167   Horiz. strip of 5   4.50 4.50
  a.-e. A338 1000 l Any single   .90 .90

Christmas A339

Frescoes in Basilica of St. Francis, Assisi, by Giotto: 800 l, Nativity. 1200 l, Infant Jesus. 1500 l, Mary. 2000 l, Joseph.

2000, Nov. 7 Photo. *Perf. 11¾x11½*
Granite Paper
1168-1171 A339   Set of 4   5.00 5.00

Sistine Chapel Restoration Type of 2000

Paintings: 800 l, The Baptism of Christ, by Pietro Perugino. 1200 l, The Passage of the Red Sea, by Biagio d'Antonio. 1500 l, The Punishment of Core, Datan and Abiron, by Sandro Botticelli. 4000 l, The Sermon on the Mount, by Cosimo Rosselli.

Perf. 11½x11¾
2001, Feb. 15   Photo.
Granite Paper
Red Frame
1172-1175 A334   Set of 4   7.00 7.00

Christian Conversion of Armenia, 1700th Anniv. — A340

Scenes from illuminated code of 1569: 1200 l, St. Gregory prepares to give King Tiridates human features. 1500 l, St. Gregory makes Agatangel write history of Armenians. 2000 l, St. Gregory and King Tiridates meet Emperor Constantine and Pope Sylvester I.

2001, Feb. 15   *Perf. 11¾*
Granite Paper
1176-1178 A340   Set of 3   4.50 4.50

Year of Dialogue Among Civilizations A341

2001, May 22 Litho. *Perf. 14¼x14*
1179 A341 1500 l multi   1.40 1.40

Europa — A342

Designs: 800 l, Hands holding water above earth. 1200 l, Hand catching water.

2001, May 22   *Perf. 13½x13¼*
1180-1181 A342   Set of 2   1.75 1.75

Giuseppe Verdi (1813-1901), Composer A343

Verdi and: 800 l, Score from Nabucco. 1500 l, Costumes from Aida. 2000 l, Scenery from Othello.

2001, May 22   *Perf. 13¼x14¼*
1182-1184 A343   Set of 3   3.75 3.75

2000 Travels of Pope John Paul II — A344

Designs: 500 l, Mount Sinai, Feb. 26. 800 l, Mount Nebo, Mar. 20. 1200 l, The Last Supper, Mar. 23. 1500 l, Holy Sepulchre, Mar. 26. 5000 l, Fatima, May 12. 3000 l, Western Wall.

2001, Sept. 25 Litho. *Perf. 13¼*
1185-1189 A344   Set of 5   8.50 8.50
Souvenir Sheet
Perf. 13¼x14
1190 A344 3000 l multi   2.75 2.75
No. 1190 contains one 35x26mm stamp.

Remission of Debts of Poor Countries A345

Various panels by Carlo di Camerino: 200 l, 400 l, 800 l, 1000 l, 1500 l.

2001, Sept. 25 Photo. *Perf. 13*
1191-1195 A345   Set of 5   3.75 3.75

Giuseppe Toniolo Institute for Higher Studies, 80th Anniv. — A346

Litho. & Embossed
2001, Nov. 22   *Perf. 12¾*
1196 A346 1200 l red & blue   1.10 1.10

Etruscan Museum Gold Objects — A347

Designs: 800 l, Parade fibula. 1200 l, Earrings. 1500 l, Vulci fibula. 2000 l, Head of Medusa.

2001, Nov. 22 Photo. *Perf. 13½*
1197-1200 A347   Set of 4   5.25 5.25

Christmas A348

Artwork by Egino G. Weinert: 800 l, The Annunciation. 1200 l, The Nativity. 1500 l, Adoration of the Magi.

2001, Nov. 22 Litho. *Perf. 13x13¼*
1201-1203 A348   Set of 3   3.25 3.25
1202a   Booklet pane of 4 + 4 etiquettes   4.50
  Booklet, #1202a   4.50

100 Cents = 1 Euro (€)

Depictions of Virgin Mary in Vatican Basilica — A349

Designs: 8c, Our Lady of Women in Labor. 15c, Our Lady with People Praying. 23c, Our Lady at the Tomb of Pius XII. 31c, Our Lady of the Fever. 41c, Our Lady of the Slap. 52c, Mary Immaculate. 62c, Our Lady Help of Christians. 77c, Virgin of the Deesis. €1.03, L'Addolorata. €1.55, Presentation of Mary at the Temple.

2002, Mar. 12 Litho. *Perf. 13¼x13*
1204 A349 8c multi   .20 .20
1205 A349 15c multi   .35 .35
1206 A349 23c multi   .55 .55
1207 A349 31c multi   .75 .75
1208 A349 41c multi   1.00 1.00
1209 A349 52c multi   1.20 1.20
1210 A349 62c multi   1.50 1.50
1211 A349 77c multi   1.80 1.80
1212 A349 €1.03 multi   2.40 2.40
1213 A349 €1.55 multi   3.50 3.50
Nos. 1204-1213 (10)   13.25 13.25

Pontifical Ecclesiastical Academy, 300th Anniv. — A350

No. 1214: a, Pope Clement XI. b, Academy building (46x33mm). c, Pope John Paul II.

2002, Mar. 12 Engr. *Perf. 13¼x13*
1214 A350 Horiz. strip of 3   5.50 5.50
  a.-c. 77c Any single   1.80 1.80

Sistine Chapel Restoration Type of 2000

Designs: 26c, The Temptation of Christ, by Sandro Botticelli. 41c, The Last Supper, by Cosimo Rosselli. 77c, Moses' Journey in Egypt, by Pietro Perugino. €1.55, The Last Days of Moses, by Luca Signorelli.

Perf. 11½x11¾
2002, June 13   Photo.
Granite Paper
1215-1218 A334   Set of 4   7.00 7.00

Europa — A351

Christ and the Circus, by Aldo Carpi: 41c, Entire painting. 62c, Detail.

2002, June 13   *Perf. 13¼*
1219-1220 A351   Set of 2   2.40 2.40

Roman States Postage Stamps, 150th Anniv. — A352

Designs: 41c, Regina Viarum, Roman States #11. 52c, Cassian Way, Roman States #25. €1.03, Vatican walls, Vatican City #2. €1.55, St. Peter's Basilica.

2002, June 13   *Perf. 13x13¼*
1221-1223 A352   Set of 3   4.50 4.50
Souvenir Sheet
Perf.
1224 A352 €1.55 multi   3.60 3.60
No. 1224 contains one 31mm diameter stamp.

St. Leo IX (1002-54), Pope A353

Designs: 41c, Portrait. 62c, In procession, receiving papal miter. €1.29, Reading from scroll, as prisoner of Normans.

2002, Sept. 26 Litho. *Perf. 13x13¼*
1225-1227 A353   Set of 3   5.50 5.50

Cimabue (1240-1302), Artist — A354

Designs: 26c, Crucifix. 62c, Jesus Christ. 77c, Virgin Mary. €1.03, St. John.

2002, Sept. 26 Photo. *Perf. 13¼x14*
1228-1231 A354   Set of 4   6.25 6.25

Nativity, by Pseudo Ambrogio di Baldese — A355

2002, Nov. 21 Photo. *Perf. 13*
1232 A355 41c multi   .95 .95
See New Zealand No. 1834.

2001
Travels of
Pope John
Paul
II — A356

Designs: 41c, Greece, Syria and Malta, May 4-9. 62c, Ukraine, June 23-27. €1.55, Armenia and Kazakhstan, Sept. 22-27.

2002, Nov. 21   Litho.   Perf. 13x13¼
1233-1235 A356   Set of 3   6.00 6.00
1234a   Booklet pane, 4 #1234 + 4
            etiquettes   5.75
            Booklet, #1234a   5.75

A357

Pontificate of John
Paul II, 25th
Anniv. — A358

No. 1236: a, Election as Pope, 1978. b, In Poland, 1979. c, In France, 1980. d, Assassination attempt, 1981. e, At Fatima, Portugal, 1982. f, Extraordinary Holy Year, 1983. g, At Quirinale Palace, Rome, 1984. h, World Youth Day, 1985. i, At synagogue, Rome, 1986. j, Pentecost vigil, 1987. k, At European Parliament, Strasbourg, France, 1988. l, Meeting with Mikhail Gorbachev, 1989. m, At Guinea-Bissau leper colony, 1990. n, At European Bishops' Synod, 1991. o, Publication of Catechism of the Catholic Church, 1992. p, Praying for the Balkans in Assisi, 1993. q, At Sistine Chapel, 1994. r, At UN Headquarters for 50th anniv. celebrations, 1995. s, In Germany, 1996. t, In Sarajevo, Bosnia & Herzegovina, 1997. u, In Cuba, 1998. v, Opening Holy Doors, 1999. w, World Youth Day, 2000. x, Closing Holy Doors, 2001. y, Addressing Italian Parliament, 2002.

2003, Mar. 20   Litho.   Perf. 13x13¼
1236   Sheet of 25   24.00 24.00
a.-y.   A357 41c Any single   .95   .95

Etched on Silver Foil
Die Cut Perf. 12½x13
Self-Adhesive
1237 A358 €2.58 Pope John
            Paul II   6.00 6.00

Cancels can be easily removed from No. 1237.
See Poland Nos. 3668-3669.

Martyrdom of
St. George,
1700th Anniv.
A359

2003, May 6   Litho. & Engr.   Perf. 13
1238 A359 62c multi   1.50 1.50

Europa — A360

Poster art for: 41c, 1975 Holy Year. 62c, Exhibition of Slav codices, incunabula and rare books at Sistine Hall, 1985.

2003, May 6   Litho.   Perf. 13¼x13
1239-1240 A360   Set of 2   2.40 2.40

Masterpieces by Beato Angelico in
Niccolina Chapel — A361

Designs: 41c, Diaconal Consecration of St. Lawrence. 62c, St. Stephen Preaching. 77c, Trial of St. Lawrence. €1.03, Stoning of St. Stephen.

2003, May 6   Photo.   Perf. 13¼
1241-1244 A361   Set of 4   6.50 6.50

Beatification of Mother Teresa of
Calcutta — A362

Perf. 13½x13¼
2003, Sept. 23   **Litho.**
1245 A362 41c multi + label   .95   .95
Printed in sheets of 5 + 5 different labels.

19th Century
Artists — A363

Designs: 41c, Blessed Are the Pure at Heart, by Paul Gauguin. 62c, The Pietà, by Vincent van Gogh.

Perf. 13¼x13½
2003, Sept. 23   **Photo.**
1246 A363 41c multi   .95   .95
1247 A363 62c multi   1.50 1.50
a.   Booklet pane of 4 + 4 eti-
         quettes   6.00   —
         Complete booklet, #1247a   6.00

Animals in
Vatican
Basilica
Art
A364

Designs: 21c, Dragon. 31c, Camel. 77c, Horse. €1.03, Leopard.

2003, Sept. 23
1248-1251 A364   Set of 4   5.50 5.50

Canonization of Josemaría Escrivá de
Balaguer, Oct. 6, 2003 — A365

2003, Nov. 18   Litho.   Perf. 14x13¼
1252 A365 41c multi   1.00 1.00

2002
Travels of
Pope John
Paul
II — A366

Designs: 62c, Bulgaria and Azerbaijan, May 22-26. 77c, Canada, Guatemala and Mexico, July 23-Aug. 2. €2.07, Poland, Aug. 16-19.

2003, Nov. 18   Perf. 13x13¼
1253-1255 A366   Set of 3   8.50 8.50

Christmas
A367

2003, Nov. 18
Stamp With White Border
1256 A367 41c multi   1.00 1.00
Souvenir Sheet
Stamp Without White Border
1257 A367 41c multi   1.00 1.00
Death of Pope Paul VI, 25th anniv. (#1257).

St. Pius V (1504-
72)
A368

Altarpiece by Grazio Cossoli in Chapel of the Rosary, Santa Croce di Bosco Marengo: 4c, Detail depicting St. Pius V and flag. €2, Entire altarpiece.

Litho. & Silk Screened
2004, Mar. 18   Perf. 13¼x13
1258-1259 A368   Set of 2   5.00 5.00

2003
Travels of
Pope John
Paul
II — A369

Designs: 60c, Spain, May 3-4. 62c, Bosnia & Herzegovina, June 22. 80c, Croatia, June 5-9. €1.40, Slovakia, Sept. 11-14.

2004, Mar. 18   **Litho.**
1260-1263 A369   Set of 4   8.50 8.50

Papal Visits to Poland — A370

No. 1264, 45c: a, Pope with hand on chin. b, Pope praying. c, Pope carrying crucifix. d, Pope with crucifix against head.
No. 1265, 62c: a, Pope holding crucifix, diff. b, Pope with arm raised. c, Pope, wearing white, seated. d, Pope, wearing red cape, seated.

Litho. (Labels Litho. & Embossed)
2004, Mar. 18
Sheets of 4, #a-d, + 8 Labels
1264-1265 A370   Set of 2   10.50 10.50

Children AIDS
Victims — A371

2004, June 3   Photo.   Perf. 13¼x13
1266 A371 45c multi + label   1.10 1.10
Printed in sheets of 6 + 6 stamp-sized labels (with different text) and 1 large central label.

Europa — A372

Paintings of: 45c, Men on horses. 62c, People in garden.

2004, June 3   Litho.   Perf. 12¾x13¼
1267-1268 A372   Set of 2   2.60 2.60

Flags and
One-Euro
Coins — A373

2004, June 3   **Litho.**   **Perf. 13½**

1269	A373	4c Austria	.20	.20
1270	A373	8c Belgium	.20	.20
1271	A373	15c Finland	.35	.35
1272	A373	25c France	.60	.60
1273	A373	30c Germany	.70	.70
1274	A373	40c Greece	.95	.95
1275	A373	45c Vatican City	1.10	1.10
1276	A373	60c Ireland	1.40	1.40
1277	A373	62c Italy	1.50	1.50
1278	A373	70c Luxembourg	1.75	1.75
1279	A373	80c Monaco	1.90	1.90
1280	A373	€1 Netherlands	2.40	2.40
1281	A373	€1.40 Portugal	3.50	3.50
1282	A373	€2 San Marino	4.75	4.75
1283	A373	€2.80 Spain	6.75	6.75
		Nos. 1269-1283 (15)	28.05	28.05

48th Intl. Eucharistic Congress A374

Designs: 45c, Hands breaking bread over chalice. 65c, Hand raising eucharist.

2004, Sept. 16   **Litho.**   **Perf. 13x13¼**
1284-1285   A374   Set of 2   2.75   2.75

Contemporary Religious Art in Vatican Museum Collection — A375

Designs: 45c, Still Life with Bottles, by Giorgio Morandi. 60c, The Fall of an Angel, by Marino Marini. 80c, Landscape with Houses, by Ezio Pastorio. 85c, Tuscan Countryside, by Giulio Cesare Vinzio.

2004, Sept. 16   **Photo.**   **Perf. 14x13¼**

1286	A375	45c multi	1.10	1.10
1287	A375	60c multi	1.50	1.50
a.			1.50	1.50
b.	Booklet pane of 4 #1287a + 4 etiquettes		6.00	
	Complete booklet, #1287b		6.00	
1288	A375	80c multi	2.00	2.00
1289	A375	85c multi	2.10	2.10
		Nos. 1286-1289 (4)	6.70	6.70

Petrarch (1304-74), Poet A376

2004, Nov. 18   **Photo.**   **Perf. 13¼x13**
1290   A376   60c multi   1.60   1.60

Christmas A377

2004, Nov. 18   **Litho.**   **Perf. 13¼**
1291   A377   80c multi   2.25   2.25

Interregnum Issue

Arms of St. Peter and Papal Chamberlain's Insignia — A378

Inscription colors: 60c, Blue. 62c, Red. 80c, Green.

2005, Apr. 12   **Litho.**   **Perf. 13½x13**
1292-1294   A378   Set of 3   5.25   5.25

Pope Benedict XVI — A379

Pope Benedict XVI wearing: 45c, Stole. 62c, White vestments. 80c, Miter.

2005, June 2   **Litho.**   **Perf. 13¼x13**
1295-1297   A379   Set of 3   4.75   4.75

Coronation of Pope Benedict XVI, Apr. 19, 2005.

20th World Youth Day A380

2005, June 2
1298   A380   62c multi   1.50   1.50

See Germany No. 2343.

Europa A381

Ceramic plates depicting fish painted by Pablo Picasso with background colors of: 62c, Orange. 80c, Blue.

2005, June 2   **Perf. 12½**
1299-1300   A381   Set of 2   3.50   3.50

Ratification of Modifications to Italy-Vatican Concordat, 20th Anniv. — A382

Arms of Vatican City and Italy and: 45c, Pen. €2.80, Map.

2005, June 9   **Photo.**   **Perf. 13¼**
1301-1302   A382   Set of 2   8.00   8.00

See Italy Nos. 2677-2678.

Resurrection of Christ, by Perugino — A383

Various painting details: 60c, 62c, 80c, €1. €2.80, Jesus Christ.

2005, June 9   **Perf. 14x13¼**
1303-1306   A383   Set of 4   7.50   7.50

Souvenir Sheet
Perf. 13¼x13¾
1307   A383   €2.80 multi   6.75   6.75

No. 1307 contains one 29x60mm stamp.

Dinner at Emmaus, by Primo Conti A384

2005, Nov. 10   **Litho.**   **Perf. 13x13¼**
1308   A384   62c multi   1.50   1.50

Eleventh General Assembly of the Synod of Bishops.

2004 Journeys of Pope John Paul II — A385

Designs: 45c, Bern, Switzerland, June 5-6. 80c, Lourdes, France, Aug. 14-15. €2, Loreto, Italy, Sept. 5.

2005, Nov. 10
1309-1311   A385   Set of 3   7.75   7.75

The Annunciation, by Raphael — A386

Designs: Nos. 1312, 1314a, Drawing of Angel, Painting of Virgin Mary. Nos. 1313, 1314b, Painting of Angel, drawing of Virgin Mary.

Litho. & Engr.
2005, Nov. 10   **Perf. 13x13¼**

1312	A386	62c multi	1.50	1.50
1313	A386	€1 multi	2.40	2.40

Souvenir Sheet
1314   A386   €1.40 Sheet of 2, #a-b   6.75   6.75

See France No. 3153.

Swiss Papal Guards, 500th Anniv. A387

Designs: 62c, Guard and drummers. 80c, Guards and St. Peter's Basilica.

2005, Nov. 22   **Litho.**   **Perf. 14x14¼**
1315-1316   A387   Set of 2   3.50   3.50

Nos. 1315-1316 each issued in sheets of 6. See Switzerland Nos. 1224-1225.

Christmas A388

Details from Adoration of the Shepherds, by François Le Moyne: 45c, Shepherds and sheep. 62c, Angel. 80c, Madonna and Child.

2005, Nov. 22   **Perf. 13¼x13**

1317-1319	A388	Set of 3	4.50	4.50
1319a		Booklet pane of 4 #1319	7.50	
		Complete booklet, #1319a	7.50	

Europa A389

Designs: 62c, Praying hands, church, mosque and synagogue. 80c, Handshake, classroom.

2006, Mar. 16   **Litho.**   **Perf. 13x13¼**
1320-1321   A389   Set of 2   3.50   3.50

Jesuits A390

Designs: 45c, Blessed Peter Faber (1506-46). 60c, St. Ignatius of Loyola (1491-1556). €2, St. Francis Xavier (1506-52).

2006, Mar. 16
1322-1324   A390   Set of 3   7.50   7.50

Andrea Mantegna (c. 1430-1506), Painter A391

Designs: 60c, Madonna and Child. 85c, Saints Gregory and John the Baptist. €1, Saints Peter and Paul.

No. 1328 — San Zeno Polyptych: a, Country name at right. b, Country name at left.

2006, Mar. 16   **Photo.**   **Perf. 12¾**
1325-1327   A391   Set of 3   6.00   6.00

Souvenir Sheet
Perf. 13¼x13
1328   A391   €1.40 Sheet of 2, #a-b   6.75   6.75

No. 1328 contains two 21x37mm stamps.

Wolfgang Amadeus Mozart (1756-91), Composer A392

Litho. & Engr.
2006, June 22   **Perf. 14x14¼**
1329   A392   80c multi   2.10   2.10

2005 Travels of Pope Benedict XVI — A393

Designs: 62c, National Eucharistic Congress, Bari, Italy, May 21-29. €1.40, World Youth Day, Cologne, Germany, Aug. 16-21.

2006, June 22   Litho.   Perf. 13¼x13
1330-1331 A393   Set of 2   5.25 5.25

St. Peter's Basilica, 500th Anniv. — A394

No. 1332, 45c — 1506 medallion depicting: a, Allegory of architecture (denomination at LL). b, Architect Donato Bramante (denomination at UR).
No. 1333, 60c — 1506 medallion depicting: a, Pope Julius II (denomination at LL). b, Bramante's plan for St. Peter's Basilica (denomination at UR).

Litho. & Embossed
2006, June 22   Perf. 14
Horiz. Pairs, #a-b
1332-1333 A394   Set of 2   5.50 5.50

Intl. Year of Deserts and Desertification — A395

Designs: 62c, Flowers, child on parched earth. €1, Trees, child and cattle.

2006, Oct. 12   Litho.   Perf. 13½x13¼
1334-1335 A395   Set of 2   4.25 4.25

Diplomatic Relations Between Vatican City and Singapore, 25th Anniv. — A396

Designs: 85c, Merlion and St. Peter's Basilica. €2, Flags of Singapore and Vatican City.

2006, Oct. 12   Perf. 13½x13
1336-1337 A396   Set of 2   7.25 7.25
See Singapore Nos. 1232-1233.

Vatican Musum, 500th Anniv. A397

Heads from Laocoon sculpture: 60c, Son of Laocoon. 65c, Laocoon. €1.40, Son of Laocoon, diff.
€2.80, Laocoon, horiz.

Litho. & Embossed
2006, Oct. 12   Perf. 13x13¼
1338-1340 A397   Set of 3   6.75 6.75
Souvenir Sheet
Perf. 13 Horiz.
1341 A397 €2.80 multi   7.00 7.00
No. 1341 contains one 80x30mm stamp.

Christmas A398

Stained glass from Pope's private chapel: 60c, Shepherds. 65c, Holy Family. 85c, Magi and Star of Bethlehem.

2006, Oct. 12   Litho.   Perf. 13¼x13
1342-1344 A398   Set of 3   5.25 5.25
1343a   Booklet pane of 4 #1343   6.50   —
           Complete booklet, #1343a   6.50

St. Francis of Paola (1416-1507) — A399

Details from sculpture: 60c, Head of St. Francis. €1, Angel.

2007, Mar. 16   Litho.   Perf. 13x13¼
1345-1346 A399   Set of 2   4.25 4.25

Pope Benedict XVI, 80th Birthday — A400

Pope Benedict XVI: 60c, Wearing zucchetto. 65c, Without head covering. 85c, Wearing miter.

2007, Mar. 16   Perf. 13¼x13
Stamp + Label
1347-1349 A400   Set of 3   5.75 5.75

Europa A401

Designs: 60c, Scouts reading map, Scout holding chick. 65c, Scouts around campfire.

2007, June 12   Perf. 13x13¼
1350-1351 A401   Set of 2   3.50 3.50
Scouting, cent.

Christian Museum, 250th Anniv. A402

Designs: 85c, Gilded glass depicting Saints Peter and Paul, silver vase. €2, Bronze lamp with monogram of Christ, silver bottle.

2007, June 12
1352-1353 A402   Set of 2   7.75 7.75

Carlo Goldoni (1707-93), Playwright A403

Goldoni and: 60c, Bridge, man, harlequin. 85c, Church, man, woman.
€2.80, Goldoni holding book.

2007, June 12   Perf. 13x13¼
1354-1355 A403   Set of 2   4.00 4.00
Souvenir Sheet
Perf. 13
1356 A403 €2.80 multi   7.75 7.75
No. 1356 contains one 45x33mm stamp and was sold with side portions of the sheet folded to produce an effect like a theater curtain.

New Philatelic and Numismatic Museum — A404

No. 1357: a, Vatican City #37, 576, 1013, 1296. b, Four Vatican City coins. Illustration reduced.

Litho. & Embossed
2007, Sept. 20   Perf. 14
1357 A404 60c Horiz. pair, #a-b   3.50 3.50

Treaty of Rome, 50th Anniv. A405

Stars and: 15c, Atomium, Brussels. 30c, Eiffel Tower, Paris. 60c, Brandenburg Gate, Berlin. 65c, Plaza, Rome. €1, Castle, Luxembourg. €4, Buildings and bridges, Amsterdam. €2.80, Mother and child.

2007, Sept. 20   Litho.   Perf. 13x13¼
1358-1363 A405   Set of 6   19.00 19.00
Souvenir Sheet
Perf. 13x13¼ on 2 Sides
1364 A405 €2.80 multi   8.00 8.00
No. 1364 contains one 40x37mm stamp.

St. Elizabeth of Hungary (1207-31) A406

2007, Nov. 20   Perf. 13¾
1365 A406 65c multi   1.90 1.90

2006 Travels of Pope Benedict XVI — A407

Travels: 60c, Poland, May 25-28. 65c, Valencia, Spain, July 8-9. 85c, Germany, Sept. 9-14. €1.40, Turkey, Nov. 28-Dec. 1.

2007, Nov. 20   Perf. 13¼x13
1366-1369 A407   Set of 4   10.50 10.50

Christmas A408

Vatican arms and nave paintings in St. Andrew's Church, Luqa, Malta, by Giuseppe Cali: 60c, Madonna and Child. 65c, Holy Family with Women and Young Girl. 85c, Infant Jesus and Young Girl.

2007, Nov. 20
1370-1372 A408   Set of 3   6.25 6.25
See Malta Nos. 1319-1321.

Europa A409

Designs: 60c, Envelope with cachet and cancels. 85c, Handwritten letter, Pope Benedict XVI.

2008, Mar. 6   Litho.   Perf. 13¾
1374-1375 A409 Set of 2   4.50 4.50

Sistine Chapel Paintings by
Michelangelo, 500th Anniv. — A410

Designs: 5c, Libyan. 10c, Eritrean. 25c, Delphic Sibyl. 60c, Sibyl Cumana. 65c, Daniel. 85c, Jonah. €2, Ezekiel. €5, Zaccharias.

2008, Mar. 6   Perf. 13x13¼
1376	A410	5c multi	.20	.20
1377	A410	10c multi	.30	.30
1378	A410	25c multi	.75	.75
1379	A410	60c multi	1.90	1.90
1380	A410	65c multi	2.00	2.00
1381	A410	85c multi	2.60	2.60
1382	A410	€2 multi	6.25	6.25
1383	A410	€5 multi	15.50	15.50
		Nos. 1376-1383 (8)	29.50	29.50

SEMI-POSTAL STAMPS

Holy Year Issue

Cross and Orb
SP1   SP2

Perf. 13x13½

1933, Apr. 1   Unwmk.   Engr.
B1	SP1	25c + 10c green	3.50	*3.50*
B2	SP1	75c + 15c scarlet	6.25	*11.50*
B3	SP2	80c + 20c red brown	22.50	16.00
B4	SP2	1.25 l + 25c ultra	7.00	*12.00*
		Nos. B1-B4 (4)	39.25	*43.00*
		Set, never hinged	100.00	

AIR POST STAMPS

Catalogue values for unused stamps in this section are for Never Hinged items.

Statue of St.   Dove of
Peter   Peace over
AP1   Vatican
                        AP2

Elijah's   Our Lady of
Ascent into   Loreto and
Heaven   Angels
AP3   Moving the
                        Holy House
                        AP4

Wmk. 235
1938, June 22   Engr.   Perf. 14
C1	AP1	25c brown	.20	.20
C2	AP2	50c green	.20	.20
C3	AP3	75c lake	.20	.20
C4	AP4	80c dark blue	.20	.20
C5	AP1	1 l violet	.45	.45

C6	AP2	2 l ultra	1.00	.60
C7	AP3	5 l slate blk	2.25	1.50
C8	AP4	10 l dk brown vio	2.25	1.90
		Nos. C1-C8 (8)	6.75	5.25

Dove of Peace   House of Our
Above St.   Lady of
Peter's   Loreto — AP6
Basilica — AP5

Birds Circling
Cross — AP7

1947, Nov. 10   Photo.
C9	AP5	1 l rose red	.20	.20
C10	AP6	4 l dark brown	.20	.20
C11	AP5	5 l brt ultra	.20	.20
C12	AP7	15 l brt purple	.90	.50
C13	AP7	25 l dk blue green	3.50	.40
C14	AP7	50 l dk gray	5.00	1.50
C15	AP7	100 l red orange	25.00	2.00
		Nos. C9-C15 (7)	35.00	5.00

Nos. C13-C15 exist imperf. Value, each pair $1,000.

Archangel
Raphael
and Young
Tobias
AP8

1948, Dec. 28   Engr.   Perf. 14
C16	AP8	250 l sepia	25.00	10.00
C17	AP8	500 l ultra	450.00	275.00
		Set, hinged	300.00	

Angels and
Globe
AP9

1949, Dec. 3
C18	AP9	300 l ultra	20.00	5.00
C19	AP9	1000 l green	100.00	47.50
		Set, hinged	75.00	

UPU, 75th anniversary.

Franciscus   Dome of St. Peter's
Gratianus   Basilica
AP10   AP11

1951, Dec. 20   Perf. 14x13
C20	AP10	300 l deep plum	240.00	150.00
C21	AP10	500 l deep blue	35.00	17.50
		Set, hinged	175.00	

Publication of unified canon laws, 800th anniv.

1953, Aug. 10   Perf. 13
C22	AP11	500 l chocolate	21.00	2.50
C23	AP11	1000 l deep ultra	62.50	12.50
		Set, hinged	40.00	

See Nos. C33-C34.

Archangel Gabriel   Obelisk of St.
by Melozzo da   John
Forli — AP12   Lateran — AP13

Archangel Gabriel: 10 l, 35 l, 100 l, Annunciation by Pietro Cavallini. 15 l, 50 l, 300 l, Annunciation by Leonardo da Vinci.

1956, Feb. 12   Wmk. 235
C24	AP12	5 l gray black	.20	.20
C25	AP12	10 l blue green	.20	.20
C26	AP12	15 l deep orange	.20	.20
C27	AP12	25 l dk car rose	.20	.20
C28	AP12	35 l carmine	.25	.20
C29	AP12	50 l olive brown	.20	.20
C30	AP12	60 l ultra	2.75	2.25
C31	AP12	100 l orange brown	.20	.20
C32	AP12	300 l deep violet	.50	.20
		Nos. C24-C32 (9)	4.70	3.85

Type of 1953

1958   Perf. 13½
C33	AP11	500 l grn & bl grn	7.50	4.00
a.		Perf. 14	1,200.	700.00
C34	AP11	1000 l dp mag	.75	.75
a.		Perf. 14	.75	.75

1959, Oct. 27   Engr.   Perf. 13½x14

Obelisks, Rome: 10 l, 60 l, St. Mary Major. 15 l, 100 l, St. Peter. 25 l, 200 l, Piazza del Popolo. 35 l, 500 l, Trinita dei Monti.

C35	AP13	5 l dull violet	.20	.20
C36	AP13	10 l blue green	.20	.20
C37	AP13	15 l dk brown	.20	.20
C38	AP13	25 l slate grn	.20	.20
C39	AP13	35 l ultra	.20	.20
C40	AP13	50 l yellow grn	.20	.20
C41	AP13	60 l rose carmine	.20	.20
C42	AP13	100 l bluish black	.20	.20
C43	AP13	200 l brown	.20	.20
C44	AP13	500 l orange brn	.30	.20
		Nos. C35-C44 (10)	2.10	2.00

Archangel Gabriel
by Filippo
Valle — AP14

Jet over St.
Peter's Cathedral
AP15

1962, Mar. 13   Wmk. 235
C45	AP14	1000 l brown	1.25	.75
C46	AP14	1500 l dark blue	1.75	1.25

1967, Mar. 7   Photo.   Perf. 14

Designs: 40 l, 200 l, Radio tower and statue of Archangel Gabriel (like A87). 90 l, 500 l, Aerial view of St. Peter's Square and Vatican City.

C47	AP15	20 l brt violet	.20	.20
C48	AP15	40 l black & pink	.20	.20
C49	AP15	90 l sl bl & dk gray	.20	.20
C50	AP15	100 l black & salmon	.20	.20
C51	AP15	200 l vio blk & gray	.20	.20
C52	AP15	500 l dk brn & lt brn	.25	.20
		Nos. C47-C52 (6)	1.25	1.20

Archangel Gabriel
by Fra
Angelico — AP16

1968, Mar. 12   Engr.   Perf. 13½x14
C53	AP16	1000 l dk car rose, *cr*	1.00	.75
C54	AP16	1500 l black, *cr*	1.75	1.50

St.
Matthew,
by Fra
Angelico
AP17

The Evangelists, by Fra Angelico from Niccolina Chapel: 300 l, St. Mark. 500 l, St. Luke. 1000 l, St. John.

Engr. & Photo.
Perf. 14x13½
1971, Sept. 30   Unwmk.
C55	AP17	200 l blk & pale grn	.20	.20
C56	AP17	300 l black & bister	.20	.20
C57	AP17	500 l black & salmon	.85	.60
C58	AP17	1000 l black & pale lil	1.00	.75
		Nos. C55-C58 (4)	2.25	1.75

AP18

AP19

Seraph, mosaic from St. Mark's Basilica, Venice.

Litho. & Engr.
1974, Feb. 21   Perf. 13x14
C59	AP18	2500 l multicolored	2.50	2.00

Litho. & Engr.
1976, Feb. 19   Perf. 13x14

Last Judgment, by Michelangelo: 500 l, Angel with Trumpet. 1000 l, Ascending figures. 2500 l, Angels with trumpets.

C60	AP19	500 l sal, bl & brn	1.25	1.10
C61	AP19	1000 l sal, bl & brn	1.50	1.10
C62	AP19	2500 l sal, bl & brn	2.00	1.50
		Nos. C60-C62 (3)	4.75	3.70

Radio
Waves,
Antenna,
Papal
Arms
AP20

1978, July 11   Engr.   Perf. 14x13
C63	AP20	1000 l multicolored	1.00	.70
C64	AP20	2000 l multicolored	2.00	1.40
C65	AP20	3000 l multicolored	3.00	1.90
		Nos. C63-C65 (3)	6.00	4.00

10th World Telecommunications Day.

Pope John Paul II Shaking Hands, Arms of Dominican Republic AP21

1980　Litho. & Engr.　Perf. 14x13½

C66	AP21	200 l shown	.25	.25
C67	AP21	300 l Mexico	.30	.30
C68	AP21	500 l Poland	.60	.60
C69	AP21	1000 l Ireland	1.10	1.10
C70	AP21	1500 l US	1.75	1.75
C71	AP21	2000 l UN	2.00	2.00
C72	AP21	3000 l with Dimitrios I, Turkey	3.50	3.50
		Nos. C66-C72 (7)	9.50	9.50

Issued: 3000 l, Sept. 18; others June 24.

World Communications Year — AP22

Designs: 2000 l, Moses Explaining The Law to the People by Luca Signarelli. 5000 l, Paul Preaching in Athens, Tapestry of Raphael design.

1983, Nov. 10　　　　Perf. 14

C73	AP22	2000 l multicolored	3.00	3.00
C74	AP22	5000 l multicolored	6.75	6.75

Journeys of Pope John Paul II, 1983-84 AP23

Designs: 350 l, Central America, the Caribbean, 1983. 450 l, Warsaw Cathedral, Our Lady of Czestochowa, Poland, 1983. 700 l, Statue of Our Lady, Lourdes, France, 1983. 1000 l, Mariazell Sanctuary, St. Stephen's Cathedral, Austria, 1983. 1500 l, Asia, the Pacific, 1984. 2000 l, Einsiedeln Basilica, St. Nicholas of Flue, Switzerland, 1984. 2500 l, Quebec's Notre Dame Cathedral, five crosses of the Jesuit martyrs, Canada, 1984. 5000 l, Saragossa, Spain, Dominican Republic and Puerto Rico, 1984.

1986, Nov. 20　Photo.　Perf. 14x13½

C75	AP23	350 l multicolored	.50	.50
C76	AP23	450 l multicolored	.65	.65
C77	AP23	700 l multicolored	1.00	1.00
C78	AP23	1000 l multicolored	1.50	1.50
C79	AP23	1500 l multicolored	2.25	2.25
C80	AP23	2000 l multicolored	3.25	3.25
C81	AP23	2500 l multicolored	4.00	4.00
C82	AP23	5000 l multicolored	8.00	8.00
		Nos. C75-C82 (8)	21.15	21.15

Papal Journeys Type of 1986

Designs: 450 l, Horseman, shepherdess, St. Peter's Basilica, Cathedral of Santiago in Chile, and the Sanctuary of Our Lady of Lujan, Argentina. 650 l, Youths and the Cathedral of Speyer, Federal Republic of Germany. 1000 l, St. Peter's Basilica, Altar of Gdansk, flowers and thorns. 2500 l, Crowd and American skyscrapers. 5000 l, Tepee at Fort Simpson, Canada, and American Indians.

1988, Oct. 27　Photo.　Perf. 14x13½

C83	AP23	450 l multicolored	.65	.65
C84	AP23	650 l multicolored	.95	.95
C85	AP23	1000 l multicolored	1.50	1.50
C86	AP23	2500 l multicolored	3.50	3.50
C87	AP23	5000 l multicolored	7.25	7.25
		Nos. C83-C87 (5)	13.85	13.85

Uruguay, Chile and Argentina, Mar. 30-Apr. 14, 1987 (450 l); Federal Republic of Germany, Apr. 30-May 4, 1987 (650 l); Poland, June 8-14, 1987 (1000 l); US, Sept. 10-19, 1987 (2500 l); and Canada, Sept. 20, 1987 (5000 l).

Journeys of Pope John Paul II, 1989 AP24

1990, Nov. 27　Photo.　Perf. 12
Granite Paper

C88	AP24	500 l Africa	.80	.80
C89	AP24	1000 l Scandinavia	1.60	1.60
C90	AP24	3000 l Santiago de Compostela, Spain	5.00	5.00
C91	AP24	5000 l Asia	8.00	8.00
		Nos. C88-C91 (4)	15.40	15.40

Madagascar, Reunion, Zambia and Malawi, Apr. 28-May 6 (500 l); Norway, Iceland, Finland, Denmark and Sweden, June 1-10 (1000 l); Korea, Indonesia and Mauritius, Oct. 6-16 (5000 l).

Travels of Pope John Paul II, 1991 AP25

1992, Nov. 24　Photo.　Perf. 14

C92	AP25	500 l multicolored	.65	.65
C93	AP25	1000 l multicolored	1.40	1.40
C94	AP25	4000 l multicolored	5.25	5.25
C95	AP25	6000 l multicolored	8.00	8.00
		Nos. C92-C95 (4)	15.30	15.30

Portugal, May 10-13 (500 l); Poland, June 1-9 (1000 l); Poland, Hungary, Aug. 13-20 (4000 l); Brazil, Oct. 12-21 (6000 l).

SPECIAL DELIVERY STAMPS

Pius XI SD1

Unwmk.
1929, Aug. 1　Photo.　Perf. 14

E1	SD1	2 l carmine rose	14.00	11.50
E2	SD1	2.50 l dark blue	12.00	12.00

For overprints see Nos. Q14-Q15.

Catalogue values for unused stamps in this section, from this point to the end of the section, are for Never Hinged items.

Aerial View of Vatican City SD2

1933　　　Wmk. 235　　Engr.

E3	SD2	2 l rose red & brn	.35	.35
E4	SD2	2.50 l dp blue & brn	.35	.55

1945　　　　　　　Unwmk.

E5	SD2	3.50 l dk car & ultra	.30	.30
E6	SD2	5 l ultra & green	.30	.30

Nos. E5 and E6 Surcharged with New Values and Bars in Black

1946, Jan. 9

E7	SD2	6 l on 3.50 l dk car & ultra	4.25	1.75
E8	SD2	12 l on 5 l ultra & grn	4.25	1.75

Vertical pairs imperf. between exist of No. E7 (value $150) and No. E8 (value $200).

Bishop Matteo Giberti SD3

Design: 12 l, Gaspar Cardinal Contarini.

1946, Feb. 21　　　　　　Photo.
Centers in Dark Brown

E9	SD3	6 l dark green	.20	.20
E10	SD3	12 l copper brown	.20	.20

See note after No. 121.
#E9-E10 exist imperf and part perf.

St. Peter's Basilica SD5

Design: 80 l, Basilica of St. John.

1949, Mar. 7　Wmk. 235　Perf. 14

E11	SD5	40 l slate gray	10.50	3.25
a.		Perf. 13½x14	21.00	7.50
E12	SD5	80 l chestnut brown	37.50	20.00
a.		Perf. 13½x14	40.00	22.50

St. Peter and His Tomb — SD6

85 l, Pius XII and Roman sepulcher.

Perf. 13½x13, 14
1953, Apr. 23　　　　　　Engr.

E13	SD6	50 l blue grn & dk brn	.20	.20
E14	SD6	85 l dp orange & dk brn	.35	.25

Arms of Pope John XXIII SD7

1960　　　Photo.　　Perf. 14

E15	SD7	75 l red & brown	.20	.20
E16	SD7	100 l dk blue & brown	.20	.20

Pope Paul VI by Enrico Manfrini — SD8

Design: 150 l, Papal arms.

1966, Mar. 8　Wmk. 235　Perf. 14

E17	SD8	150 l black brown	.20	.20
E18	SD8	180 l brown	.20	.20

POSTAGE DUE STAMPS

Regular Issue of 1929 Overprinted in Black and Brown

1931, Sept. 15　Unwmk.　Perf. 14

J1	A1	5c dk brown & pink	.20	.20
a.		Double frame		
J2	A1	10c dk grn & lt grn	.20	.20
a.		Frame omitted	675.00	
J3	A1	20c violet & lilac	5.75	2.00

Surcharged

J4	A1	40c on 30c indigo & yel	1.50	4.00

Surcharged

J5	A2	60c on 2 l olive brn	27.50	18.00
J6	A2	1.10 l on 2.50 l red org	3.75	16.00
		Nos. J1-J6 (6)	38.90	40.40
		Set, never hinged	100.00	

In addition to the surcharges, #J4-J6 are overprinted with ornamental frame as on #J1-J3.

Catalogue values for unused stamps in this section, from this point to the end of the section, are for Never Hinged items.

Papal Arms
D1　　　　　　D2

1945, Aug. 16　Typo.　Perf. 14

J7	D1	5c black & yellow	.20	.20
J8	D1	20c black & lilac	.20	.20
J9	D1	80c black & salmon	.20	.20
J10	D1	1 l black & green	.20	.20
J11	D1	2 l black & blue	.20	.20
J12	D1	5 l black & gray	.20	.20
a.		Imperf., pair	125.00	125.00
		Nos. J7-J12 (6)	1.20	1.20

A second type of Nos. J7-J12 exists, in which the colored lines of the background are thicker.

The 20c and 5 lire exist in horizontal pairs imperf. vertically. Value, each $100.

The 20c exists in horizontal pairs imperf. between. Value $275.

Perf. 13½x13
1954, Apr. 30　Wmk. 235　Engr.

J13	D2	4 l black & rose	.20	.20
J14	D2	6 l black & green	.30	.30
J15	D2	10 l black & yellow	.20	.20
J16	D2	20 l black & blue	.45	.30
J17	D2	50 l black & ol brn	.20	.20
J18	D2	70 l black & red brn	.20	.20
		Nos. J13-J18 (6)	1.55	1.40

Papal Arms — D3

Photo. & Engr.
1968, May 28　Wmk. 235　Perf. 14

J19	D3	10 l black, grysh bl	.20	.20
J20	D3	20 l black, pale bl	.20	.20
J21	D3	50 l black, pale lil rose	.20	.20
J22	D3	60 l black, gray	.20	.20
J23	D3	100 l black, dull yel	.20	.20
J24	D3	180 l black, bluish lil	.20	.20
		Nos. J19-J24 (6)	1.20	1.20

PARCEL POST STAMPS

Regular Issue of 1929 Overprinted

1931		**Unwmk.**	**Perf. 14**	
Q1	A1	5c dk brown & pink	.40	.30
Q2	A1	10c dk grn & lt grn	.40	.30
Q3	A1	20c violet & lilac	4.75	5.50
Q4	A1	25c dk bl & lt bl	6.25	4.25
Q5	A1	30c indigo & yel	9.25	4.25
Q6	A1	50c indigo & sal buff	9.25	4.25
Q7	A1	75c brn car & gray	2.75	2.75

Overprinted

Q8	A2	80c carmine rose	1.60	1.90
Q9	A2	1.25 l dark green	2.75	2.00
Q10	A2	2 l olive brown	.55	.85
a.		Inverted overprint	325.00	475.00
Q11	A2	2.50 l red orange	.55	.85
a.		Double overprint	225.00	
b.		Inverted overprint	500.00	
Q12	A2	5 l dark green	.55	.85
Q13	A2	10 l olive black	.55	.85
a.		Double overprint	325.00	

Special Delivery Stamps of 1929 Overprinted Vertically

Q14	SD1	2 l carmine rose	.55	.85
Q15	SD1	2.50 l dark blue	.55	.85
		Nos. Q1-Q15 (15)	40.70	30.60
		Set, never hinged	95.00	

VENEZUELA

ˌve-nə-ˈzwā-lə

LOCATION — Northern coast of South America, bordering on the Caribbean Sea
GOVT. — Republic
AREA — 352,143 sq. mi.
POP. — 23,203,466 (1999 est.)
CAPITAL — Caracas

100 Centavos = 8 Reales = 1 Peso
100 Centesimos = 1 Venezolano (1879)
100 Centimos = 1 Bolivar (1880)

Watermark

Wmk. 346

Catalogue values for unused stamps in this country are for Never Hinged items, beginning with Scott 743 in the regular postage section, Scott B2 in the semipostal section, Scott C709 in the airpost section, and Scott E1 in the special delivery section.

Coat of Arms — A1

Fine Impression
No Dividing Line Between Stamps
Unwmk.

1859, Jan. 1		**Litho.**	**Imperf.**	
1	A1	½r yellow	23.00	9.25
a.		½r orange	27.00	11.00
b.		Greenish paper	225.00	

2	A1	1r blue	325.00	20.00
a.		Half used as ½r on cover		400.00
3	A1	2r red	42.50	15.00
a.		2r dull rose red	55.00	17.00
b.		Half used as 1r on cover		450.00
c.		Greenish paper	225.00	140.00
		Nos. 1-3 (3)	390.50	44.25

Coarse Impression

1859-62
Thick Paper

4	A1	½r orange ('61)	12.00	4.00
a.		½r yellow ('59)	500.00	30.00
b.		½r olive yellow	750.00	35.00
c.		Bluish paper	575.00	
d.		½r dull rose (error)		
5	A1	1r blue ('62)	20.00	12.50
a.		1r pale blue	35.00	15.00
b.		1r dark blue	35.00	15.00
c.		Half used as ½r on cover		400.00
d.		Bluish paper	200.00	
6	A1	2r red ('62)	30.00	20.00
a.		2r dull rose	42.50	20.00
b.		Tête bêche pair	5,000.	3,500.
c.		Half used as 1r on cover		400.00
d.		Bluish paper	225.00	
		Nos. 4-6 (3)	62.00	36.50

In the fine impression, the background lines of the shield are more sharply drawn. In the coarse impression, the shading lines at each end of the scroll inscribed "LIBERTAD" are usually very heavy. Stamps of the coarse impression are closer together, and there is usually a dividing line between them.

Nos. 1-3 exist on thick paper and on bluish paper. Nos. 1-6 exist on pelure paper.

The greenish paper varieties (Nos. 1b and 3c) and the bluish paper varieties were not regularly issued.

Arms — A2   Eagle — A3

1862				**Litho.**
7	A2	¼c green	20.00	110.00
8	A2	½c dull lilac	30.00	190.00
a.		½c violet	40.00	210.00
9	A2	1c gray brown	42.50	225.00
		Nos. 7-9 (3)	92.50	525.00

Counterfeits are plentiful. Forged cancellations abound on Nos. 7-17.

1863-64				
10	A3	½c pale red ('64)	55.00	125.00
a.		½c red	60.00	125.00
11	A3	1c slate ('64)	62.50	160.00
12	A3	½r orange	7.75	3.50
13	A3	1r blue	17.00	8.50
a.		1r pale blue	30.00	13.00
b.		Half used as ½r on cover		400.00
14	A3	2r green	23.00	20.00
a.		2r deep yellow green	30.00	20.00
b.		Quarter used as ½r on cover		1,000.
c.		Half used as 1r on cover		450.00

Counterfeits exist.

Redrawn

1865				
15	A3	½r orange	4.00	2.50
a.		½r yellow	4.00	2.50

The redrawn stamp has a broad "N" in "FEDERACION." "MEDIO REAL" and "FEDERACION" are in thin letters. There are 52 instead of 49 pearls in the circle.
The status of No. 15 has been questioned.

A4   Simón Bolívar — A5

1865-70				
16	A4	½c yel grn ('67)	200.00	300.00
17	A4	1c bl grn ('67)	200.00	250.00
18	A4	½r brn vio (thin paper)	9.25	2.00
19	A4	½r lil rose ('70)	9.25	2.50
a.		½r brownish rose	9.25	3.00
b.		Tête bêche pair	110.00	150.00
20	A4	1r vermilion	42.50	15.00
a.		Half used on cover		200.00
21	A4	2r yellow	160.00	77.50
a.		Half used as 1r on cover		750.00
b.		Quarter used as ½r on cover		1,000.
		Nos. 16-21 (6)	621.00	647.00

This issue is known unofficially rouletted.
Postal forgeries exist of the ½r.

For overprints see Nos. 37-48.

Overprinted in Very Small Upright Letters "Bolivar Sucre Miranda dash> Decreto de 27 de Abril de 1870", or "Decreto de 27 de Junio 1870" in Slanting Letters

(The "Junio" overprint is continuously repeated, in four lines arranged in two pairs, with the second line of each pair inverted.)

Un	1	Siete	7
Dos	2	Nueve	9
Tres	3	Quince	15
Cuatro	4	Veinte	20
Cinco	5	Cincuenta	50

1871-76				**Litho.**
22	A5	1c yellow	1.50	.40
a.		1c orange	2.10	.45
b.		1c brown orange ('76)	2.10	.30
c.		1c pale buff ('76)	2.10	.45
d.		Laid paper	1.00	.75
23	A5	2c yellow	2.00	.45
a.		2c orange	4.00	.45
b.		2c brown orange	3.50	.75
c.		2c pale buff ('76)	3.50	.45
d.		Laid paper	3.50	.55
e.		Frame inverted	4,000.	3,000.
24	A5	3c yellow	3.00	.75
a.		3c orange	3.00	1.40
b.		3c pale buff ('76)	5.50	1.75
25	A5	4c yellow	4.00	.75
a.		4c orange	4.50	1.25
b.		4c brown orange ('76)	4.50	1.25
c.		4c buff ('76)	4.50	1.25
26	A5	5c yellow	4.00	.75
a.		5c orange	4.00	.90
b.		5c pale buff ('76)	4.00	.90
c.		Laid paper	7.50	.90
27	A5	1r rose	4.00	2.00
a.		1r pale red	4.00	2.00
b.		Laid paper	6.00	2.50
c.		Half used as ½r on cover		1,800.
28	A5	2r rose	4.50	2.00
a.		2r pale red	4.50	2.00
b.		Laid paper	12.00	2.50
29	A5	3r rose	6.00	2.00
a.		3r pale red	6.00	2.00
30	A5	5r rose	5.75	1.00
a.		5r pale red	5.75	1.00
31	A5	7r rose	22.50	4.00
a.		7r pale red	22.50	4.00
32	A5	9r green	22.50	4.25
a.		9r olive green	22.50	6.00
33	A5	15r green	55.00	8.50
a.		15r gray green ('76)	55.00	8.50
b.		Frame inverted	8,000.	6,500.
34	A5	20r green	77.50	20.00
a.		Laid paper	110.00	35.00
35	A5	30r green	375.00	110.00
a.		30r gray green ('76)	600.00	160.00
b.		Double overprint		
36	A5	50r green	1,200.	300.00
a.		50r gray green ('76)		
		Nos. 22-34 (13)	212.25	46.85
		Nos. 22-35 (14)	587.25	156.85

These stamps were made available for postage and revenue by official decree, and were the only stamps sold for postage in Venezuela from Mar., 1871 to Aug., 1873.

Due to lack of canceling stamps, the majority of specimens were canceled with pen marks. Fiscal cancellations were also made with the pen. The values quoted are for pen-canceled copies.

Different settings were used for the different overprints. Stamps with the upright letters were issued in 1871. Those with the slanting letters in one double line were issued in 1872-73. Those with the slanting overprint in two double lines were issued starting in 1874 from several different settings, those of 1877-78 showing much coarser impressions of the design than the earlier issues. The 7r and 9r are not known with this overprint. Stamps on laid paper (1875) are from a separate setting.

Stamps and Types of 1866-67 Overprinted in Two Lines of Very Small Letters Repeated Continuously Overprinted "Estampillas de Correo - Contrasena"

1873, July 1				
37	A4	½r pale rose	70.00	13.00
a.		½r rose	70.00	13.00
b.		Inverted overprint	125.00	50.00
c.		Tête bêche pair	2,750.	2,000.
38	A4	1r vermilion	85.00	25.00
a.		Inverted overprint	400.00	175.00
b.		Half used as ½r on cover		550.00
39	A4	2r yellow	300.00	125.00
a.		Inverted overprint	400.00	175.00
b.		Half used as 1r on cover		12,000.
		Nos. 37-39 (3)	455.00	163.00

Overprinted "Contrasena — Estampillas de Correo"

1873, Nov.				
40	A4	1c gray lilac	30.00	32.50
a.		Inverted overprint	6.50	17.00
41	A4	2c green	125.00	90.00
a.		Inverted overprint	40.00	50.00
42	A4	½r rose	72.50	13.00
a.		Inverted overprint	30.00	4.00
b.		1r pale	60.00	11.00
43	A4	1r vermilion	85.00	23.00
a.		Inverted overprint	35.00	9.00
b.		Inverted overprint on cover		300.00

44	A4	2r yellow	325.00	160.00
a.		Inverted overprint	110.00	50.00
b.		Half used as 1r on cover		1,500.
		Nos. 40-44 (5)	637.50	318.50

Overprinted "Contrasena — Estampilla de Correos"

1875				
45	A4	½r rose	85.00	10.00
a.		Inverted overprint	125.00	25.00
b.		Double overprint	160.00	90.00
46	A4	1r vermilion	160.00	15.00
a.		Inverted overprint	200.00	80.00
b.		Tête bêche pair	3,500.	3,000.
c.		Half used as ½r on cover		250.00

Overprinted "Estampillas de correo — Contrasena"

1876-77				
47	A4	½r rose	77.50	9.25
a.		½r pink	65.00	7.50
b.		Inverted overprint	65.00	7.50
c.		Both lines of overprint read "Contrasena"	75.00	17.50
d.		Both lines of overprint read "Estampillas de correo"	75.00	17.50
e.		Double overprint	125.00	35.00
48	A4	1r vermilion ('77)	92.50	23.00
a.		Inverted overprint	85.00	24.00
b.		Tête bêche pair	2,250.	2,500.
c.		Half used as ½r on cover		250.00

On Nos. 47 and 48 "correo" has a small "c" instead of a capital. Nos. 45 and 46 have the overprint in slightly larger letters than the other stamps of the 1873-76 issues.

Simón Bolívar
A6   A7

Overprinted "Decreto de 27 Junio 1870" Twice, One Line Inverted

1879				**Imperf.**
49	A6	1c yellow	4.00	1.00
a.		1c orange	5.00	1.50
b.		1c olive yellow	5.50	1.75
50	A6	5c yellow	3.50	.50
a.		5c orange	2.50	.75
b.		Double overprint	20.00	10.00
51	A6	10c blue	5.00	.50
52	A6	30c blue	7.75	1.00
53	A6	50c blue	7.75	1.00
54	A6	90c blue	40.00	12.00
55	A7	1v rose red	77.50	18.00
56	A7	3v rose red	130.00	55.00
57	A7	5v rose red	225.00	77.50
		Nos. 49-57 (9)	500.50	166.50

In 1879 and the early part of 1880 there were no regular postage stamps in Venezuela and the stamps inscribed "Escuelas" were permitted to serve for postal as well as revenue purposes. Postally canceled copies are extremely scarce. Values quoted are for stamps with cancellations of banks or business houses or with pen cancellations. Copies with pen marks removed are sometimes offered as unused stamps, or may have fraudulent postal cancellations added.

Nos. 49-57 exist without overprint. These probably are revenue stamps.

A8   A9

1880				**Perf. 11**
58	A8	5c yellow	1.50	.50
a.		5c orange	1.50	.50
b.		Printed on both sides	150.00	85.00
59	A8	10c yellow	2.50	.60
a.		10c orange	2.50	.60
60	A8	25c yellow	2.50	.60
a.		25c orange	2.75	.70
b.		Printed on both sides	110.00	52.50
c.		Impression of 5c on back	175.00	90.00
61	A8	50c yellow	4.75	.80
a.		50c orange	5.25	.85
b.		Half used as 25c on cover		400.00
c.		Printed on both sides	150.00	90.00
d.		Impression of 25c on back	150.00	90.00
62	A9	1b pale blue	12.00	1.40
63	A9	2b pale blue	17.00	1.75
64	A9	5b pale blue	40.00	5.75
a.		Half used as 2½b on cover		—

65	A9	10b rose red	200.00	70.00
66	A9	20b rose red	1,200.	200.00
67	A9	25b rose red	5,000.	500.00
		Nos. 58-65 (8)	280.25	81.40

See note on used values below No. 57.

Bolívar — A10

1880   Litho.   Perf. 11
Thick or Thin Paper

68	A10	5c blue	15.00	7.25
a.		Printed on both sides	225.00	140.00
69	A10	10c rose	20.00	12.00
a.		10c carmine	20.00	12.00
b.		Double impression	90.00	75.00
c.		Horiz. pair, imperf. btwn.	75.00	75.00
70	A10	10c scarlet	20.00	12.00
a.		Horiz. pair, imperf. btwn.	75.00	75.00
71	A10	25c yellow	15.00	7.25
b.		Thick paper	20.00	10.00
72	A10	50c brown	92.50	40.00
a.		50c deep brown	92.50	40.00
b.		Printed on both sides	225.00	140.00
73	A10	1b green	140.00	50.00
a.		Horiz. pair, imperf. btwn.	300.00	300.00
		Nos. 68-73 (6)	302.50	128.50

Nos. 68 to 73 were used for the payment of postage on letters to be sent abroad and the Escuelas stamps were then restricted to internal use.

Counterfeits of this issue exist in a great variety of shades as well as in wrong colors. They are on thick and thin paper, white or toned, and imperf. or perforated 11, 12 and compound. They are also found tête bêche. Counterfeits of Nos. 68 to 72 inclusive often have a diagonal line across the "S" of "CENTS" and a short line from the bottom of that letter to the frame below it. Originals of No. 73 show parts of a frame around "BOLIVAR."

Simón Bolívar
A11   A12

A13   A14

A15

1882, Aug. 1   Engr.   Perf. 12

74	A11	5c blue	.70	.35
75	A12	10c red brown	.70	.35
76	A13	25c yellow brown	1.00	.40
a.		Printed on both sides	50.00	27.50
77	A14	50c green	2.40	.70
78	A15	1b violet	3.25	1.75
		Nos. 74-78 (5)	8.05	3.55

Nos. 75-78 exist imperf. Value, set $32.50.
See Nos. 88, 92-95. For surcharges and overprints see Nos. 100-103, 108-112.

A16   A17

A18   A19

A20   A21

A22   A23

1882-88

79	A16	5c blue green	.20	.20
80	A17	10c brown	.20	.20
81	A18	25c orange	.20	.20
82	A19	50c blue	.20	.20
83	A20	1b vermilion	.25	.20
84	A21	3b dull vio ('88)	.25	.20
85	A22	10b dark brn ('88)	1.25	.80
86	A23	20b plum ('88)	1.50	.95
		Nos. 79-86 (8)	4.05	2.95

By official decree, dated Apr. 14, 1882, stamps of types A11 to A15 were to be used for foreign postage and those of types A16 to A23 for inland correspondence and fiscal use.
Issue date: Nos. 79-83, Aug. 1.
See Nos. 87, 89-91, 96-99. For surcharges and overprints see Nos. 104-107, 114-122.

1887-88   Litho.   Perf. 11

87	A16	5c gray green	.25	.20
88	A13	25c yellow brown	42.50	15.00
89	A18	25c orange	.40	.35
90	A20	1b orange red ('88)	3.50	.75
		Nos. 87-90 (4)	46.65	16.30

Perf. 14

91	A16	5c gray green	70.00	22.50

Stamps of type A16, perf. 11 and 14, are from a new die with "ESCUELAS" in smaller letters. Stamps of the 1887-88 issue, perf. 12, and a 50c dark blue, perf. 11 or 12, are believed by experts to be from printer's waste.
Counterfeits of No. 91 have been made by perforating printers waste of No. 96.

Rouletted 8

92	A11	5c blue	40.00	17.00
93	A13	25c yel brown	15.00	10.00
94	A14	50c green	15.00	10.00
95	A15	1b purple	30.00	20.00
		Nos. 92-95 (4)	100.00	57.00

1887-88

96	A16	5c green	.20	.20
97	A18	25c orange	.20	.20
98	A19	50c dark blue	.70	.70
99	A21	3b purple ('88)	3.00	3.00
		Nos. 96-99 (4)	4.10	4.10

The so-called imperforate varieties of Nos. 92 to 99, and the pin perforated 50c dark blue, type A19, are believed to be from printer's waste.

Stamps of 1882-88
Handstamp Surcharged in Violet

1892   Perf. 12

100	A11	25c on 5c blue	40.00	40.00
101	A12	25c on 10c red brn	16.00	16.00
102	A13	1b on 25c yel brn	16.00	16.00
103	A14	1b on 50c green	20.00	20.00
		Nos. 100-103 (4)	92.00	92.00

See note after No. 107.

1892

104	A16	25c on 5c bl grn	10.00	6.00
105	A17	25c on 10c brown	10.00	6.00
106	A18	1b on 25c orange	15.00	12.00
107	A19	1b on 50c blue	23.00	12.00
		Nos. 104-107 (4)	58.00	36.00

Counterfeits of this surcharge abound.

Stamps of 1882-88 Overprinted in Red or Black:

1893

108	A11	5c blue (R)	.55	.25
a.		Inverted overprint	3.25	3.25
b.		Double overprint	16.00	16.00
109	A12	10c red brn (Bk)	.90	.90
a.		Inverted overprint	4.00	4.00
b.		Double overprint	16.00	16.00
110	A13	25c yel brn (R)	.80	.50
a.		Inverted overprint	5.25	5.25
b.		Double overprint	16.00	16.00
c.		25c yel brn (Bk)	500.00	500.00
111	A14	50c green (R)	1.25	.80
a.		Inverted overprint	5.25	5.25
b.		Double overprint	27.50	27.50
112	A15	1b pur (R)	3.00	1.20
a.		Inverted overprint	10.00	10.00
		Nos. 108-112 (5)	6.50	3.65

1893

114	A16	5c bl grn (R)	.20	.20
a.		Inverted overprint	3.25	3.25
b.		Double overprint	5.25	5.25
115	A17	10c brn (R)	.20	.20
a.		Inverted overprint	3.25	3.25
116	A18	25c org (R)	.20	.20
a.		Inverted overprint	3.25	3.25
117	A18	25c org (Bk)	5.75	2.75
a.		Inverted overprint	8.25	5.00
118	A19	50c blue (R)	.20	.20
a.		Inverted overprint	3.25	3.25
119	A20	1b ver (Bk)	.60	.40
a.		Inverted overprint	4.00	4.00
120	A21	3b dl vio (R)	.90	.40
a.		Double overprint	8.25	8.25
121	A22	10b dk brn (R)	3.50	2.25
a.		Double overprint	10.00	10.00
b.		Inverted overprint	20.00	20.00
122	A23	20b plum (Bk)	3.00	3.00
a.		Double overprint	10.00	10.00
b.		Inverted overprint		
		Nos. 114-122 (9)	14.55	9.60

Counterfeits exist.

Simón Bolívar
A24   A25

1893   Engr.

123	A24	5c red brn	.90	.25
124	A24	10c blue	3.25	1.25
125	A24	25c magenta	15.00	.50
126	A24	50c brn vio	4.25	.55
127	A24	1b green	5.75	1.25
		Nos. 123-127 (5)	29.15	3.80

Many shades exist in this issue, but their values do not vary.

1893

128	A25	5c gray	.20	.20
129	A25	10c green	.20	.20
130	A25	25c blue	.20	.20
131	A25	50c orange	.20	.20
132	A25	1b red vio	.20	.20
133	A25	3b red	.55	.20
134	A25	10b dl vio	.90	.80
135	A25	20b red brn	4.25	2.75
		Nos. 128-135 (8)	6.70	4.75

By decree of Nov. 28, 1892, the stamps inscribed "Correos" were to be used for external postage and those inscribed "Instruccion" were for internal postage and revenue purposes.
For surcharge see No. 230.

After July 1, 1895, stamps inscribed "Escuelas" or "Instruccion" were no longer available for postage. Stamps of design A25 in shades different than those listed were printed after 1895.

Landing of Columbus
A26

1893   Perf. 12

136	A26	25c magenta	11.00	.60

4th cent. of the discovery of the mainland of South America, also participation of Venezuela in the Intl. Exhib. at Chicago in 1893.

Map of Venezuela
A27

1896   Litho.

137	A27	5c yel grn	3.00	2.75
a.		5c apple green	3.00	2.75
138	A27	10c blue	4.00	3.00
139	A27	25c yellow	4.00	5.50
a.		25c orange	4.00	5.50
b.		Tête bêche pair	125.00	125.00
140	A27	50c rose red	52.50	27.00
a.		50c red	52.50	52.50
b.		Tête bêche pair	375.00	375.00
141	A27	1b violet	40.00	27.00
		Nos. 137-141 (5)	103.50	65.25

Gen. Francisco Antonio Gabriel de Miranda (1752-1816).
These stamps were in use from July 4 to Nov. 4, 1896. Later usage is known.
There are many forgeries of this issue. They include faked errors, imperforate stamps and many tête bêche. The paper of the originals is thin, white and semi-transparent. The gum is shiny and crackled. The paper of the reprints is often thick and opaque. The gum is usually dull, smooth, thin and only slightly adhesive.

Bolívar — A28

1899-1901   Engr.

142	A28	5c dk grn	1.00	.25
143	A28	10c red	1.25	.40
144	A28	25c blue	1.50	.55
145	A28	50c gray blk	2.00	1.00
146	A28	50c org ('01)	1.75	.50
147	A28	1b yel grn	32.50	15.00
149	A28	2b orange	375.00	225.00
		Nos. 142-147,149 (7)	415.00	242.70

Stamps of 1899
Overprinted in Black

1900

150	A28	5c dk grn	1.25	.40
a.		Inverted overprint	4.75	4.75
151	A28	10c red	1.25	.40
a.		Inverted overprint	6.50	6.50
b.		Double overprint	10.50	10.50
152	A28	25c blue	7.75	1.25
a.		Inverted overprint	13.00	13.00
153	A28	50c gray blk	4.00	.55
a.		Inverted overprint	12.00	12.00
154	A28	1b yel grn	1.75	.80
a.		Double overprint	13.00	13.00
b.		Inverted overprint	12.00	12.00
155	A28	2b orange	2.75	2.25
a.		Inverted overprint	35.00	35.00
b.		Double overprint	32.50	32.50
		Nos. 150-155 (6)	18.75	5.65

Initials are those of R. T. Mendoza.
Counterfeit overprints exist, especially of inverted and doubled varieties.

Bolivar Type of 1899-1903 Overprinted

1900

156	A28	5c dk grn	200.00	200.00
157	A28	10c red	200.00	200.00
158	A28	25c blue	350.00	175.00
159	A28	50c yel orange	23.00	1.60
160	A28	1b slate	1.25	1.00
a.		Without overprint	4,000.	—
		Nos. 156-160 (5)	774.25	577.60

Overprinted

1900, Aug. 14

161	A28	5c green	7.75	.55
162	A28	10c red	7.00	1.00
163	A28	25c blue	7.75	1.00
		Nos. 161-163 (3)	22.50	2.55

Inverted Overprint

161a	A28	5c	9.25	6.50
162a	A28	10c	9.25	6.50
163a	A28	25c	12.00	7.25
		Nos. 161a-163a (3)	30.50	20.25

Overprint exists on each value without "Castro" or without "1900."

Type of 1893
Surcharged

1904, Jan.   Perf. 12

230	A25	5c on 50c green	.80	.60
a.		"Vele"	23.00	23.00
b.		Surcharge reading up	1.00	.50
c.		Double surcharge	18.00	18.00

Gen. José de Sucre — A35   Pres. Cipriano Castro — A37

1904-09   Engr.

231	A35	5c bl grn	.50	.20
232	A35	10c carmine	.55	.20
233	A35	15c violet	.90	.40
234	A35	25c dp ultra	6.50	.40
235	A35	50c plum	1.00	.50
236	A35	1b plum	1.10	.50
		Nos. 231-236 (6)	10.55	2.20

Issued: 15c, Dec. 1909; others, July 1, 1904.

1905, July 5   Litho.   Perf. 11½

245	A37	5c vermilion	3.25	3.25
a.		5c carmine	5.00	5.00
246	A37	10c dark blue	5.50	4.25
247	A37	25c yellow	2.00	1.50
		Nos. 245-247 (3)	10.75	9.00

National Congress. Issued for interior postage only. Valid only for 90 days.
Various part-perforate varieties of Nos. 245-247 exist. Value, $15-$30.

Liberty — A38

1910, Apr. 19   Engr.   Perf. 12

249	A38	25c dark blue	13.00	.60

Centenary of national independence.

Francisco de Miranda A39   Rafael Urdaneta A40

Bolívar — A41

1911   Litho.   Perf. 11½x12

250	A39	5c dp grn	.50	.20
251	A39	10c carmine	.50	.20
252	A40	15c gray	5.75	.40
253	A40	25c dp bl	3.25	.60
a.		Imperf., pair	40.00	50.00
254	A41	50c purple	3.50	.40
255	A41	1b yellow	3.50	1.50
		Nos. 250-255 (6)	17.00	3.30

The 50c with center in blue was never issued although copies were postmarked by favor.
The centers of Nos. 250-255 were separately printed and often vary in shade from the rest of the design. In a second printing of the 5c and 10c, the entire design was printed at one time.

Redrawn

1913

255A	A40	15c gray	3.50	2.25
255B	A40	25c deep blue	2.00	.65
255C	A41	50c purple	2.00	.65
		Nos. 255A-255C (3)	7.50	3.55

The redrawn stamps have two berries instead of one at top of the left spray; a berry has been added over the "C" and "S" of "Centimos"; and the lowest leaf at the right is cut by the corner square.

Simón Bolívar
A42   A43

1914, July   Engr.   Perf. 13½, 14, 15

256	A42	5c yel grn	37.50	.55
257	A42	10c scarlet	35.00	.50
258	A42	25c dark blue	5.75	.25
		Nos. 256-258 (3)	78.25	1.30

Printed by the American Bank Note Co.

Different frames.

1915-23   Perf. 12

259	A43	5c green	4.25	.25
260	A43	10c vermilion	10.00	.60
261	A43	10c claret ('22)	10.00	.90
262	A43	15c dull ol grn	9.25	.40
263	A43	25c ultra	6.50	.25
a.		25c blue	13.00	.60
264	A43	40c dull green	23.00	11.50
265	A43	50c dp violet	6.50	.80
266	A43	50c ultra ('23)	17.00	4.75
267	A43	75c lt blue	57.50	23.00
a.		75c greenish blue	57.50	23.00
268	A43	1b dark gray	35.00	5.25
		Nos. 259-268 (10)	179.00	47.90

See Nos. 269-285. For surcharges see Nos. 307, 309-310.

Type of 1915-23 Issue
Printed by Waterlow & Sons, Ltd.
Re-engraved

1924-39   Perf. 12½

269	A43	5c orange brn	.55	.20
a.		5c yellow brown	.55	.20
b.		Horiz. pair, imperf. btwn.	25.00	40.00
270	A43	5c green ('39)	12.00	1.00
271	A43	7½c yel grn ('39)	1.25	.40
272	A43	10c dk green	.25	.20
273	A43	10c dk car ('39)	4.00	.20
274	A43	15c olive grn	2.25	.50
275	A43	15c brown ('27)	.30	.20
276	A43	25c ultra	2.25	.25
277	A43	25c red ('28)	.25	.20
a.		Horiz. pair, imperf. btwn.	50.00	85.00

278	A43	40c dp blue ('25)	.55	.25
279	A43	40c slate bl ('39)	7.75	1.25
280	A43	50c dk blue	.55	.25
281	A43	50c dk pur ('39)	7.75	.85
282	A43	1b black	.55	.25
283	A43	3b yel org ('25)	1.75	.95
284	A43	3b red org ('39)	12.00	4.25
285	A43	5b dull vio ('25)	16.00	8.50
		Nos. 269-285 (17)	70.00	19.75

Perf. 14

269c	A43	5c	7.00	2.00
272a	A43	10c	7.00	2.00
274a	A43	15c	8.25	2.75
276a	A43	25c	12.00	4.75
280a	A43	50c	35.00	14.00
282a	A43	1b	42.50	27.00
		Nos. 269c-282a (6)	111.75	52.50

The re-engraved stamps may be distinguished from the 1915 issue by the perforation and sometimes by the colors. The designs differ in many minor details which are too minute for illustration or description.

Bolívar and Sucre A44

Perf. 11½x12, 12

1924, Dec. 1   Litho.

286	A44	25c grayish blue	2.75	.55

Redrawn

286A	A44	25c ultra	3.50	.85

Centenary of the Battle of Ayacucho.
The redrawn stamp has a whiter effect with less shading in the faces. Bolívar's ear is clearly visible and the outline of his aquiline nose is broken.

A45   A46

Revenue Stamps Surcharged in Black or Red

1926   Perf. 12, 12½

287	A45	5c on 1b ol grn	.65	.40
a.		Double surcharge	8.00	8.00
b.		Pair, one without surcharge	12.00	12.00
c.		Inverted surcharge	8.00	8.00
288	A46	25c on 5c dk brn (R)	.65	.40
a.		Inverted surcharge	8.00	8.00
b.		Double surcharge	8.00	8.00

View of Ciudad Bolívar and General J.V. Gómez — A47

1928, July 21   Litho.   Perf. 12

289	A47	10c deep green	1.00	.65
a.		Imperf., pair	40.00	

25th anniversary of the Battle of Ciudad Bolívar and the foundation of peace in Venezuela.

Simón Bolívar
A48   A49

1930, Dec. 9

290	A48	5c yellow	1.00	.35
291	A48	10c dark blue	1.00	.25
292	A48	25c rose red	1.00	.25
		Nos. 290-292 (3)	3.00	.85

Imperf., Pairs

290a	A48	5c	5.25	5.25
291a	A48	10c	6.50	6.50
292a	A48	25c	10.50	10.50

Death centenary of Simón Bolívar (1783-1830), South American liberator.
Nos. 290-292 exist part-perforate, including pairs imperf. between, imperf. horiz., imperf. vert. Value range, $6-12.

Various Frames
Bluish Winchester Security Paper

1932-38   Engr.   Perf. 12½

293	A49	5c violet	.50	.20
294	A49	7½c dk green ('37)	1.00	.40
295	A49	10c green	.60	.20
296	A49	15c yellow	1.50	.25
297	A49	22½c dp car ('38)	3.50	.50
298	A49	25c red	1.25	.20
299	A49	37½c ultra ('36)	4.50	2.00
300	A49	40c indigo	4.50	.25
301	A49	50c olive grn	4.50	.40
302	A49	1b lt blue	6.00	.70
303	A49	3b brown	40.00	13.00
304	A49	5b yellow brn	8.00	1.75
		Nos. 293-304 (12)	117.85	35.10

For surcharges see Nos. 308, 318-319, C223.

Arms of Bolívar — A50

1933, July 24   Litho.   Perf. 11

306	A50	25c brown red	3.00	2.40
a.		Imperf., pair	32.50	32.50

150th anniv. of the birth of Simón Bolívar. Valid only to Aug. 21.

Stamps of 1924-32 Surcharged in Black: (Blocks of Surcharge in Color of stamps)

1933

307	A43	7½c on 10c grn	.50	.25
a.		Double surcharge	2.50	2.50
b.		Inverted surcharge	4.25	4.25
308	A49	22½c on 25c (#298)	2.00	.85
309	A43	22½c on 25c (#277)	1.50	1.50
a.		Double surcharge	10.00	10.00
310	A43	37½c on 40c dp bl	2.00	.95
a.		Double surcharge	11.50	11.50
b.		Inverted surcharge	10.00	10.00
		Nos. 307-310 (4)	6.00	3.55

Nurse and Child — A51   River Scene — A52

Gathering Cacao Pods — A53

Cattle
Raising
A54

Plowing
A55

Perf. 11, 11½ or Compound
1937, July 1   **Litho.**
311 A51 5c deep violet   .55   .35
312 A52 10c dk slate grn   .55   .20
313 A53 15c yellow brn   1.00   .55
314 A51 25c cerise   1.00   .35
315 A54 50c yellow grn   6.50   4.25
316 A55 3b red orange   12.00   7.75
317 A51 5b lt brown   23.00 15.00
         Nos. 311-317 (7)   44.60 28.45

Nos. 311-317 exist imperforate. Value for set $75. Nos. 311-315 exist in pairs, imperf. between; value range, $20-$30.

For overprints and surcharges see Nos. 321-324, 345, 376-377, 380-384.

No. 300
Surcharged in
Black

1937, July   **Perf. 12½**
318 A49 25c on 40c indigo   7.75   .95
  a. Double surcharge   16.00 16.00
  b. Inverted surcharge   13.00 13.00
  c. Triple surcharge   32.50 32.50

Surcharged

319 A49 25c on 40c indigo   400.00 325.00
  a. Double surcharge

A56

1937, Oct. 28   **Litho.**   **Perf. 10½**
320 A56 25c blue   1.25   .45

Acquisition of the Port of La Guaira by the Government from the British Corporation, June 3, 1937. Exists imperf. See Nos. C64-C65.

A redrawn printing of No. 320, with top inscription beginning "Nacionalización . . ." was prepared but not issued. Value, $40.
For surcharge see No. 385.

Stamps of 1937
Overprinted in Black

1937, Dec. 17   **Perf. 11, 11½**
321 A51 5c deep violet   5.75   3.25
322 A52 10c dk slate grn   1.75   .75
  a. Inverted overprint   13.00 13.00
323 A51 25c cerise   1.50   .55
  a. Inverted overprint   16.00 16.00
324 A55 3b red orange   375.00 225.00
         Nos. 321-324 (4)   384.00 229.55

Part-perforate pairs exist of Nos. 321-322 and 324. Value range, $12.50 to $125.
See Nos. C66-C78.

Gathering Coffee
Beans — A57

Simón
Bolívar — A58

Post Office,
Caracas — A59

1938   **Engr.**   **Perf. 12**
325 A57 5c green   .40   .20
326 A57 5c deep green   .40   .20
327 A58 10c car rose   .70   .20
328 A58 10c dp rose   .70   .20
329 A59 15c dk violet   1.40   .25
330 A59 15c olive grn   .85   .25
331 A58 25c lt blue   .40   .20
332 A58 25c dk blue   .40   .20
333 A58 37½c dk blue   8.50   4.00
334 A58 37½c lt blue   2.75   .85
335 A59 40c sepia   20.00   7.75
336 A59 40c black   17.00   7.75
337 A57 50c olive grn   27.50   7.75
338 A57 50c dull violet   9.25   .85
339 A58 1b dp brown   12.00   5.50
340 A58 1b black brown   17.00   1.50
341 A57 3b orange   92.50 50.00
342 A59 5b black   15.00   7.75
         Nos. 325-342 (18)   226.75 95.40

See Nos. 400 and 412.

Teresa
Carreño — A60

Bolívar
Statue — A61

1938, June 12   **Perf. 11½x12**
343 A60 25c blue   5.75   .60

Teresa Carreno, Venezuelan pianist, whose remains were repatriated Feb. 14, 1938.
For surcharge see No. 386.

1938, July 24   **Perf. 12**
344 A61 25c dark blue   6.50   .60

"The Day of the Worker."
For surcharge see No. 387.

V A L E

Type of 1937
Surcharged in Black

Bs. 0,40

1938

1938   **Litho.**   **Perf. 11, 11½**
345 A51 40c on 5b lt brn   8.50   4.50
  a. Inverted surcharge   21.00 21.00

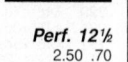

Gen. José I. Paz
Castillo, Postmaster of
Venezuela, 1859 — A62

1939, Apr. 19   **Engr.**   **Perf. 12½**
348 A62 10c carmine   2.50   .70

80th anniv. of the first Venezuelan stamp.

View of
Ojeda
A63

1939, June 24   **Photo.**
349 A63 25c dull blue   9.25   .75

Founding of city of Ojeda.

Cristóbal
Mendoza
A64

Diego
Urbaneja
A65

1939, Oct. 14   **Engr.**   **Perf. 13**
350 A64 5c green   .40   .20
351 A64 10c dk car rose   .40   .20
352 A64 15c dull lilac   1.00   .25
353 A64 25c brt ultra   .80   .20
354 A64 37½c dark blue   15.00   6.25
355 A64 50c lt olive grn   16.00   4.00
356 A64 1b dark brown   6.50   3.50
         Nos. 350-356 (7)   40.10 14.60

Mendoza (1772-1839), postmaster general.

1940-43   **Perf. 12**
357 A65 5c Prus green   .45   .20
357A A65 7½c dk bl grn ('43)   .65   .25
358 A65 15c olive   .80   .25
359 A65 37½c deep blue   1.25   .60
360 A65 40c violet blue   .95   .30
361 A65 50c violet   5.50   1.40
362 A65 1b dk violet brn   2.75   .75
363 A65 3b scarlet   8.00   3.25
         Nos. 357-363 (8)   20.35   7.00

See Nos. 399, 408, 410 and 411. For surcharges see Nos. 396, C226.

Battle of
Carabobo,
1821 — A67

1940, June 13
365 A67 25c blue   6.00   .70

Birth of General José Antonio Páez, 150th anniv.

"Crossing the
Andes" by Tito
Salas — A68

1940, June 13
366 A68 25c dark blue   6.00   .70

Death cent. of General Francisco Santander.

Monument and
Urn containing
Ashes of Simón
Bolívar — A69

Bed where Simón
Bolívar was
Born — A70

Designs: 15c, "Christening of Bolivar" by Tito Salas. 20c, Bolivar's birthplace, Caracas. 25c, "Bolivar on Horseback" by Salas. 30c, Patio of Bolivar House, Caracas. 37½c, Patio of Bolivar's Birthplace. 50c, "Rebellion of 1812" by Salas.

1940-41
367 A69 5c turq green   .25   .20
368 A70 10c rose pink   .25   .20
369 A69 15c olive   .60   .20
370 A70 20c blue ('41)   1.00   .20
371 A69 25c lt blue   .60   .20
372 A70 30c plum ('41)   1.50   .25
373 A70 37½c dk blue   3.00   1.00
374 A70 50c purple   2.00   .50
         Nos. 367-374 (8)   9.20   2.75

110th anniv. of the death of Simón Bolívar. See #397, 398, 403, 405-407, 409. For surcharges see #375, 401-402, C224, C237-C238.

No. 371 Surcharged
In Black

1941
375 A69 20c on 25c lt blue   .60   .20
  a. Inverted surcharge   10.00 10.00

Nos. 311-312
Overprinted in Black

1941   **Perf. 11½**
376 A51 5c deep violet   2.00   .50
  a. Double overprint   10.00   8.25
  b. Vert. pair, imperf. btwn. 14.00 14.00
  c. Inverted overprint   20.00 16.00
377 A52 10c dk slate grn   1.00   .30
  a. Double overprint   13.00 13.00

Symbols of
Industry
A77

Caracas
Cathedral
A78

1942, Dec. 17   **Litho.**   **Perf. 12**
378 A77 10c scarlet   1.00   .25
  a. Imperf., pair   22.50 22.50

Grand Industrial Exposition, Caracas.

1943   **Engr.**
379 A78 10c rose carmine   .75   .20

See No. 404.

Stamps of 1937
Overprinted in Black

1943   **Perf. 11, 11½**
380 A51 5c deep violet   16.00   9.50
381 A52 10c dk slate grn   6.00   4.00
382 A54 50c yellow green   8.00   4.50
383 A55 3b red orange   45.00 22.00
         Nos. 380-383 (4)   75.00 40.00

Issued for sale to philatelists & sold only in sets.

Stamps of 1937-38
Surcharged in Black

1943   *Perf. 11½, 10½, 12*
384	A51	20c on 25c cerise	27.50	27.50
385	A56	20c on 25c blue	70.00	70.00
386	A60	20c on 25c dk blue	13.50	13.50
387	A61	20c on 25c dk blue	13.50	13.50
a.		Inverted surcharge	42.50	42.50
		Nos. 384-387 (4)	124.50	124.50

Issued for sale to philatelists & sold only in sets.

Souvenir Sheet

A79

1944, Aug. 22   **Litho.**   *Perf. 12*
Flags in Red, Yellow, Blue & Black
388	A79	Sheet of 4	35.00	35.00
a.		5c Prussian green	3.00	.80
b.		10c rose	4.50	.80
c.		20c ultramarine	4.50	1.75
d.		1b rose lake	6.00	2.25

80th anniv. of Intl. Red Cross and 37th anniv. of Venezuela's joining.
No. 388 exists imperf. Value $60.

Antonio José de
Sucre — A80

1945, Mar. 3   **Engr.**   **Unwmk.**
389	A80	5c orange yellow	1.00	.50
390	A80	10c dark blue	1.50	.80
391	A80	20c rose pink	2.00	.80
		Nos. 389-391,C206-C215 (13)	16.30	10.90

Birth of Antonio de Sucre, 150th anniv.

Andrés
Bello — A81

Gen. Rafael
Urdaneta — A82

1946, Aug. 24
392	A81	20c deep blue	.65	.35
393	A82	20c deep blue	.65	.35
		Nos. 392-393,C216-C217 (4)	3.50	1.10

80th anniversary of the death of Andrés Bello (1780?-1865), educator and writer, and the centenary of the death of Gen. Rafael Urdaneta.

Allegory of the
Republic — A83

1946, Oct. 18   **Litho.**   *Perf. 11½*
394	A83	20c greenish blue	.70	.30
		Nos. 394,C218-C221 (5)	5.10	3.50

Anniversary of Revolution of October, 1945. Exists imperf.

Anti-tuberculosis Institute,
Maracaibo — A84

1947, Jan. 12
395	A84	20c ultra & yellow	.70	.30
		Nos. 395,C228-C231 (5)	6.15	4.70

12th Pan-American Health Conf., Caracas, Jan. 1947. Exists imperf. and part perf.

No. 362 Surcharged in
Green

396	A65	15c on 1b dk vio brn	.70	.30
a.		Inverted surcharge	6.00	5.00
		Nos. 396,C223-C227 (6)	30.50	23.95

Types of 1938-40

1947   **Engr.**
397	A69	5c green	.20	.20
398	A70	30c black	1.00	.50
399	A65	40c red violet	.95	.25
400	A59	5b deep orange	40.00	18.00
		Nos. 397-400 (4)	42.15	18.95

In 1947 a decree authorized the use of 5c and 10c revenue stamps of the above type for franking correspondence. Other denominations were also used unofficially.
For surcharges see Nos. 876-883.

Nos. 398 and 373
Surcharged in Red

1947   **Unwmk.**   *Perf. 12*
401	A70	5c on 30c black	.40	.20
a.		Inverted surcharge	5.00	5.00
402	A70	5c on 37½c dk bl	.45	.20
a.		Inverted surcharge	5.00	5.00

Types of 1938-43

1947-48
403	A69	5c brt ultra	.20	.20
404	A78	10c red	.20	.20
405	A69	15c rose car	.50	.20
406	A69	25c violet	.40	.20
407	A70	30c dk vio brn ('48)	.50	.20
408	A65	40c orange ('48)	.50	.20
409	A70	50c olive green	.95	.20
410	A65	1b deep blue	1.75	.20
411	A65	3b gray	3.50	.90
412	A59	5b chocolate	13.00	.60
		Nos. 403-412 (10)	21.50	7.50

M. S.
Republica
de
Venezuela
A85

Imprint: "American Bank Note Company"

1948-50   **Engr.**   *Perf. 12*
413	A85	5c blue	.20	.20
414	A85	7½c red org ('49)	.50	.30
a.		Booklet pane of 20		
415	A85	10c car rose	.40	.20
a.		Booklet pane of 10		
416	A85	15c gray ('50)	.40	.20
417	A85	20c sepia	.30	.20
418	A85	25c violet ('49)	.40	.20
419	A85	30c orange ('50)	2.75	1.60
420	A85	37½c brown ('49)	1.25	1.00
421	A85	40c olive ('50)	1.75	1.25
422	A85	50c red violet ('49)	.50	.20
423	A85	1b gray green	1.25	.40
		Nos. 413-423 (11)	9.70	5.75

Grand Colombian Merchant Fleet. See Nos. 632-634, C256-C271, C554-C556. For surcharges see Nos. 450-451.

Santos
Michelena — A86

Christopher
Columbus — A87

1949, Apr. 25   *Perf. 12½*
424	A86	5c ultra	.20	.20
425	A86	10c carmine	.40	.20
426	A86	20c sepia	1.60	.60
427	A86	1b green	5.25	2.75
		Nos. 424-427,C272-C277 (10)	15.45	9.00

Centenary of the death of Santos Michelena, Finance Minister, and the 110th anniversary of the Postal Convention of Bogota.

1949-50   **Engr.**
428	A87	5c deep ultra	.35	.20
429	A87	10c carmine	1.25	.40
430	A87	20c dark brown	1.50	.50
431	A87	1b green	4.00	1.75
		Nos. 428-431,C278-C283 (10)	15.40	7.15

450th anniversary (in 1948) of Columbus' discovery of the American mainland.
Issued: 5c, 10c, 1949; 20c, 1b, Jan. 1950.

Arms of
Venezuela
A88

1948
432	A88	5c blue	1.25	.65
433	A88	10c red	1.50	.75

The 20c and 1b, type A88, and six similar air post stamps were prepared but not issued. Value, set of 8, about $125.

Gen. Francisco de
Miranda — A89

1950, Mar. 28   **Unwmk.**   *Perf. 12*
434	A89	5c blue	.20	.20
435	A89	10c green	.35	.20
436	A89	20c sepia	.70	.30
437	A89	1b rose carmine	3.25	1.50
		Nos. 434-437 (4)	4.50	2.20

Bicentenary of birth of General Francisco de Miranda.

Map and
Population
Chart — A90

Alonso de
Ojeda — A91

1950, Sept. 1
438	A90	5c blue	.20	.20
439	A90	10c gray	.20	.20
440	A90	15c sepia	.20	.20
441	A90	25c green	.30	.20
442	A90	30c red	.40	.20
443	A90	50c violet	.80	.30
444	A90	1b red brown	2.00	1.00
		Nos. 438-444,C302-C310 (16)	8.90	5.70

8th National Census of the Americas.

1950, Dec. 18   **Photo.**   *Perf. 11½*
445	A91	5c deep blue	.20	.20
446	A91	10c deep red	.25	.20
447	A91	15c slate gray	.30	.20
448	A91	20c ultra	1.25	.50
449	A91	1b blue green	5.00	2.50
		Nos. 445-449 (5)	7.00	3.60
		Nos. 445-449,C316-C321 (11)	13.90	7.15

450th anniversary (in 1949) of the discovery of the Gulf of Maracaibo.

Nos. 414 and 420 Surcharged in Black

1951   **Unwmk.**   *Perf. 12*
450	A85	5c on 7½c red org	.30	.20
451	A85	10c on 37½c brn	.30	.20
a.		Inverted surcharge	16.00	16.00

Telegraph Stamps
Surcharged in
Black or Red

1951, June   **Engr.**
Grayish Security Paper
452		5c on 5c brown	.20	.20
453		10c on 10c green	.25	.20
454		20c on 1b blk (R)	.50	.20
455		25c on 25c carmine	.65	.25
456		30c on 2b ol grn (R)	.85	.65
		Nos. 452-456 (5)	2.45	1.50

The 5c and 10c surcharges include quotation marks on each line and values are expressed "Bs. 0.05" etc.

Bolivar
Statue, New
York — A92

1951, July 13   *Perf. 12*
457	A92	5c green	.20	.20
458	A92	10c car rose	.40	.20
459	A92	20c ultra	.40	.20
460	A92	30c slate gray	.50	.25
461	A92	40c deep green	.70	.25

462	A92 50c red brown	1.50	.50
463	A92 1b gray black	4.75	2.50
	Nos. 457-463 (7)	8.45	4.10
	Nos. 457-463,C322-C329 (15)	15.65	7.45

Relocation of the equestrian statue of Simon Bolivar in NYC, Apr. 19, 1951.

Arms of Carabobo
and
"Industry" — A93

1951   Unwmk.   Photo.   Perf. 11½

464	A93 5c green	.20	.20
465	A93 10c red	.20	.20
466	A93 15c brown	.25	.20
467	A93 20c ultra	.35	.20
468	A93 25c orange brn	.40	.20
469	A93 30c blue	.85	.35
470	A93 35c purple	3.25	2.75
	Nos. 464-470 (7)	5.50	4.10

Issue dates: 5c, 10c, Oct. 8; others, Oct. 29.

Arms of Zulia and "Industry"

471	A93 5c green	.20	.20
472	A93 10c red	.30	.20
473	A93 15c brown	.65	.30
474	A93 20c ultra	.85	.40
475	A93 50c brown org	5.25	3.75
476	A93 1b dp gray grn	1.75	.65
477	A93 5b rose violet	3.75	2.50
	Nos. 471-477 (7)	12.75	8.00

Issued: 5c, 10c, Sept. 8; others, Sept. 20.

Arms of Anzoategui and Globe

478	A93 5c green	.20	.20
479	A93 10c red	.20	.20
480	A93 15c brown	.65	.30
481	A93 20c ultra	1.10	.20
482	A93 40c red orange	2.25	1.10
483	A93 45c rose violet	6.75	3.75
484	A93 3b blue gray	2.50	1.25
	Nos. 478-484 (7)	13.65	7.00

Issue date: Nov. 9.

Arms of Caracas and Buildings

485	A93 5c green	.40	.20
486	A93 10c red	.50	.20
487	A93 15c brown	1.25	.30
488	A93 20c ultra	2.50	.30
489	A93 25c orange brn	3.75	.65
490	A93 30c blue	3.25	.75
491	A93 35c purple	32.50	19.00
	Nos. 485-491 (7)	44.15	21.40

Issued: 5c, 10c, June 20; others, Aug. 6.

Arms of Tachira and Agricultural Products

492	A93 5c green	.20	.20
493	A93 10c red	.40	.20
494	A93 15c brown	.75	.25
495	A93 20c ultra	1.75	.45
496	A93 50c brown org	110.00	14.00
497	A93 1b dp gray grn	1.75	.65
498	A93 5b dull purple	4.50	2.50
	Nos. 492-498 (7)	119.35	18.25

Issue date: Aug. 9.

Arms of Venezuela and Statue of Simon Bolivar

499	A93 5c green	.30	.20
500	A93 10c red	.25	.20
501	A93 15c brown	2.25	.45
502	A93 20c ultra	2.25	.30
503	A93 25c orange brn	3.75	.85
504	A93 30c blue	3.75	.85
505	A93 35c purple	20.00	15.00
	Nos. 499-505 (7)	32.55	17.85

Issue date: Aug. 6.

1952

Arms of Miranda and Agricultural Products

506	A93 5c green	.20	.20
507	A93 10c red	.20	.20
508	A93 15c brown	.45	.20
509	A93 20c ultra	.50	.20
510	A93 25c orange brn	.65	.30
511	A93 30c blue	1.10	.50
512	A93 35c purple	6.50	4.50
	Nos. 506-512 (7)	9.60	6.10

Arms of Aragua and Stylized Farm

513	A93 5c green	.20	.20
514	A93 10c red	.20	.20
515	A93 15c brown	.40	.20
516	A93 20c ultra	.40	.20
517	A93 25c orange brn	.90	.25

518	A93 30c blue	.90	.40
519	A93 35c purple	5.00	3.75
	Nos. 513-519 (7)	8.00	5.20

Issue date: 20c, 30c, Mar. 24.

Arms of Lara, Agricultural Products and Rope

520	A93 5c green	.20	.20
521	A93 10c red	.20	.20
522	A93 15c brown	.30	.20
523	A93 20c ultra	.70	.20
524	A93 25c orange brn	.80	.50
525	A93 30c blue	1.50	.40
526	A93 35c purple	6.25	3.75
	Nos. 520-526 (7)	9.95	5.45

Issue date: 20c, 30c, Mar. 24.

Arms of Bolivar and Stylized Design

527	A93 5c green	.20	.20
528	A93 10c red	.20	.20
529	A93 15c brown	.30	.20
530	A93 20c ultra	.65	.20
531	A93 40c red orange	2.50	.85
532	A93 45c rose violet	6.50	4.50
533	A93 3b blue gray	3.00	2.00
	Nos. 527-533 (7)	13.35	8.15

Issue date: 20c, Mar. 24.

Arms of Sucre, Palms and Seascape

534	A93 5c green	.20	.20
535	A93 10c red	.20	.20
536	A93 15c brown	.75	.20
537	A93 20c ultra	.75	.20
538	A93 40c red orange	2.50	.65
539	A93 45c rose violet	9.00	5.50
540	A93 3b blue gray	2.25	1.50
	Nos. 534-540 (7)	15.65	8.45

Arms of Trujillo Surrounded by Stylized Tree

541	A93 5c green	.20	.20
542	A93 10c red	.20	.20
543	A93 15c brown	1.10	.20
544	A93 20c ultra	1.10	.25
545	A93 50c brown orange	6.25	3.00
546	A93 1b dp gray green	1.50	.55
547	A93 5b dull purple	3.75	1.90
	Nos. 541-547 (7)	14.10	6.30

1953-54

Map of Delta Amacuro and Ship

548	A93 5c green	.20	.20
549	A93 10c red	.20	.20
550	A93 15c brown	.30	.20
551	A93 20c ultra	.50	.20
552	A93 40c red orange	1.60	1.00
553	A93 45c rose violet	7.50	4.50
554	A93 3b blue gray	2.00	1.50
	Nos. 548-554 (7)	12.30	7.80

Issue date: 20c, Feb. 13.

Arms of Falcon and Stylized Oil Refinery

555	A93 5c green	.20	.20
556	A93 10c red	.20	.20
557	A93 15c brown	.40	.20
558	A93 20c ultra	.40	.20
559	A93 50c brown orange	2.00	1.00
560	A93 1b dp gray grn	1.25	.80
561	A93 5b dull purple	3.75	2.00
	Nos. 555-561 (7)	8.20	4.60

Issue date: 20c, Feb. 13.

Arms of Guarico and Factory

562	A93 5c green	.20	.20
563	A93 10c red	.20	.20
564	A93 15c brown	.40	.20
565	A93 20c ultra	.45	.20
566	A93 40c red orange	2.25	1.40
567	A93 45c rose violet	5.50	2.75
568	A93 3b blue gray	2.25	1.25
	Nos. 562-568 (7)	11.25	6.20

Issue date: 20c, Feb. 13.

Arms of Merida and Church

569	A93 5c green	.20	.20
570	A93 10c red	.20	.20
571	A93 15c brown	.25	.20
572	A93 20c ultra	.65	.20
573	A93 50c brown orange	3.00	1.25
574	A93 1b dp gray green	.80	.55
575	A93 5b dull purple	3.00	1.60
	Nos. 569-575 (7)	8.10	4.20

Issue date: 20c, Feb. 2.

Arms of Monagas and Horses

576	A93 5c green	.20	.20
577	A93 10c red	.20	.20
578	A93 15c brown	.30	.20
579	A93 20c ultra	.45	.25
580	A93 40c red orange	2.00	.75
581	A93 45c rose violet	6.25	3.75
582	A93 3b blue gray	2.00	2.00
	Nos. 576-582 (7)	11.90	7.35

Arms of Portuguesa and Forest

583	A93 5c green	.20	.20
584	A93 10c red	.20	.20
585	A93 15c brown	.25	.20
586	A93 20c ultra	.50	.20
587	A93 50c brown org	2.75	1.75

588	A93 1b dp gray grn	.70	.30
589	A93 5b dull purple	3.00	2.00
	Nos. 583-589 (7)	7.60	4.85

Issue date: 5c, 10c, Feb. 2.

Map of Amazonas and Orchid

590	A93 5c green	.50	.20
591	A93 10c red	.50	.20
592	A93 15c brown	1.10	.20
593	A93 20c ultra	3.00	.30
594	A93 40c red orange	3.50	1.00
595	A93 45c rose violet	5.50	2.75
596	A93 3b blue gray	8.00	3.00
	Nos. 590-596 (7)	22.10	7.65

Issue date: Jan. 1954.

Arms of Apure, Horse and Bird

597	A93 5c green	.20	.20
598	A93 10c red	.20	.20
599	A93 15c brown	.35	.20
600	A93 20c ultra	1.75	.20
601	A93 50c brown org	2.25	1.75
602	A93 1b dp gray grn	.75	.65
603	A93 5b dull purple	4.50	2.50
	Nos. 597-603 (7)	10.00	5.70

Issue date: Jan. 1954.

Arms of Barinas, Cow and Horse

604	A93 5c green	.20	.20
605	A93 10c red	.20	.20
606	A93 15c brown	.25	.20
607	A93 20c ultra	1.75	.25
608	A93 50c brown org	2.00	1.25
609	A93 1b dp gray grn	.50	.25
610	A93 5b dull purple	4.50	2.25
	Nos. 604-610 (7)	9.40	4.60

Issue date: Jan. 1954.

Arms of Cojedes and Cattle

611	A93 5c green	.20	.20
612	A93 10c red	.20	.20
613	A93 15c brown	.20	.20
614	A93 20c ultra	.20	.20
615	A93 25c orange brown	.90	.25
616	A93 30c blue	1.40	.40
617	A93 35c purple	1.75	1.10
	Nos. 611-617 (7)	4.85	2.55

Issue date: Dec, 17, 1953.

Arms of Nueva Esparta and Fish

618	A93 5c green	.20	.20
619	A93 10c red	.20	.20
620	A93 15c brown	.45	.20
621	A93 20c ultra	.50	.20
622	A93 40c red orange	2.25	.85
623	A93 45c rose vio	5.50	3.25
624	A93 3b blue gray	2.50	1.75
	Nos. 618-624 (7)	11.60	6.65

Issue date: Jan. 1954.

Arms of Yaracuy and Tropical Foliage

625	A93 5c green	.40	.20
626	A93 10c red	.20	.20
627	A93 15c brown	.30	.20
628	A93 20c ultra	.45	.20
629	A93 25c orange brn	.65	.30
630	A93 30c blue	.75	.25
631	A93 35c purple	1.75	1.10
	Nos. 625-631 (7)	4.50	2.45
	Nos. 464-631 (168)	420.40	180.85

Issue date: Jan. 1954.

See Nos. C338-C553.

Ship Type of 1948-50, Redrawn Coil Stamps
Imprint: "Courvoisier S.A."

1952 Unwmk. Photo. Perf. 11½x12

632	A85 5c green	.65	.20
633	A85 10c car rose	1.10	.20
634	A85 15c gray	3.75	.20
	Nos. 632-634,C554-C556 (6)	9.50	1.20

Juan de Villegas
and Cross of
Father
Yepez — A94

Virgin of
Coromoto
and
Child — A95

1952, Sept. 14   Perf. 11½

635	A94 5c green	.20	.20
636	A94 10c red	.50	.20
637	A94 20c dk gray bl	.80	.25
638	A94 40c dp org	3.75	1.50

639	A94 50c brown	2.00	.85
640	A94 1b violet	3.75	1.00
	Nos. 635-640 (6)	11.00	4.00
	Nos. 635-640,C557-C564 (14)	22.90	8.90

Founding of the city of Barquisimeto by Juan de Villegas, 400th anniv.

1952-53   Perf. 11½x12
Size: 17x26mm

| 641 | A95 1b rose pink | 6.00 | 1.00 |

Size: 26½x41mm

| 642 | A95 1b rose pink ('53) | 4.50 | 1.00 |

Size: 36x55mm

| 643 | A95 1b rose pink ('53) | 2.00 | .75 |
| | Nos. 641-643 (3) | 12.50 | 2.75 |

300th anniv. of the appearance of the Virgin Mary to a chief of the Coromoto Indians.
Issue date: No. 641, Oct. 6.

Telegraph Stamps
Surcharged in
Black or Red

1952, Nov. 24   Engr.   Perf. 12
Grayish Security Paper

| 644 | 5c on 25c car | .25 | .20 |
| 645 | 10c on 1b blk (R) | .25 | .20 |

Surcharged

1952, Dec.

646	20c on 25c car	.30	.20
647	30c on 2b ol grn	1.90	1.25
648	40c on 1b blk (R)	.75	.40
649	50c on 3b red org	2.50	1.50
	Nos. 646-649 (4)	5.45	3.35

Post Office,
Caracas — A96

**   Perf. 13x12½**

1953-54   Unwmk.   Photo.

650	A96 5c green	.20	.20
a.	Bklt. pane of 10		
651	A96 7½c brt green	.35	.25
652	A96 10c rose carmine	.25	.20
a.	Bklt. pane of 10		
653	A96 15c gray	.40	.20
654	A96 20c ultra	.25	.20
655	A96 25c magenta	.40	.20
656	A96 30c blue	1.90	.25
657	A96 35c brt red vio	.85	.25
658	A96 40c orange	1.25	.40
659	A96 45c violet	1.90	.65
660	A96 50c red orange	1.25	.40
	Nos. 650-660 (11)	9.00	3.20

Issued: 20c, 30c, 45c, 3/11; 7½c, 25c, 50c, 6/53; 5c, 10c, 2/54; 15c, 1954.
See Nos. C565-C575, C587-C589.

Type of 1953-54 Inscribed "Republica de Venezuela"

A96a

1955

661	A96a 5c green	.20	.20
662	A96a 10c rose car	.20	.20
663	A96a 15c gray	.20	.20
664	A96a 20c ultra	.25	.20
665	A96a 30c blue	.65	.40
666	A96a 35c brt red vio	.65	.40

667 A96a40c orange 1.00 .25
668 A96a45c violet 1.25 .50
Nos. 661-668 (8) 4.40 2.15
Nos. 661-668,C597-C606 (18) 10.80 5.40

Arms of Valencia and Industrial Scene — A97

Coat of Arms — A98

1955, Mar. 26 Engr. Perf. 12
669 A97 5c brt grn .20 .20
670 A97 20c ultra .40 .20
671 A97 25c reddish brn .65 .20
672 A97 50c vermilion 1.00 .25
Nos. 669-672,C590-C596 (11) 4.85 2.40

Founding of Valencia del Rey, 400th anniv.

1955, Dec. 9 Unwmk. Perf. 11½
673 A98 5c green .30 .20
674 A98 20c ultra 1.00 .20
675 A98 25c rose car .80 .20
676 A98 50c orange 1.00 .20
Nos. 673-676,C607-C612 (10) 5.85 2.15

1st Postal Convention, Caracas, 2/9-15/54.

Book and Map of the Americas — A99

Simon Bolivar — A100

1956 Photo. Perf. 11½
Granite Paper
677 A99 5c lt grn & bluish grn .20 .20
678 A99 10c lil rose & rose vio .20 .20
679 A99 20c ultra & dk bl .20 .20
680 A99 25c gray & lil gray .25 .20
681 A99 30c lt bl & bl .25 .20
682 A99 40c bis brn & brn .30 .20
683 A99 50c ver & red brn .65 .30
684 A99 1b lt pur & vio 1.00 .50
Nos. 677-684 (8) 3.05 2.00
Nos. 677-684,C629-C635 (15) 5.55 3.65

Book Festival of the Americas, 11/15-30/56.

Engraved, Center Embossed
1957-58 Unwmk. Perf. 13½
685 A100 5c brt bl grn .20 .20
686 A100 10c red .20 .20
687 A100 20c lt slate bl .40 .20
688 A100 25c rose lake .40 .20
689 A100 30c vio blue .50 .20
690 A100 40c red orange .75 .20
691 A100 50c orange yel 1.00 .50
Nos. 685-691 (7) 3.45 1.70
Nos. 685-691,C636-C642 (14) 7.30 3.40

150th anniv. of the Oath of Monte Sacro and the 125th anniv. of the death of Simon Bolivar (1783-1830).
Issued: 10c, 50c, 1958; others, 11/15/57.

Hotel Tamanaco, Caracas A101

1957-58 Engr. Perf. 13
692 A101 5c green .20 .20
693 A101 10c carmine .20 .20
694 A101 15c black .25 .20
695 A101 20c dark blue .30 .20
696 A101 25c dp claret .30 .20
697 A101 30c dp ultra .50 .20
698 A101 35c purple .30 .20
699 A101 40c orange .40 .20
700 A101 45c rose violet .50 .20

701 A101 50c yellow .70 .25
702 A101 1b dk slate grn 1.00 .40
Nos. 692-702 (11) 4.65 2.45
Nos. 692-702,C643-C657 (26) 13.95 7.00

Issued: 5c, 10c, Oct. 10, 1957; others, 1958.
For surcharge see No. 878.

Main Post Office, Caracas — A102

1958, May 14 Litho. Perf. 14
703 A102 5c emerald .20 .20
704 A102 10c rose red .20 .20
705 A102 15c gray .20 .20
706 A102 20c lt bl .20 .20
707 A102 35c red lilac .20 .20
708 A102 45c brt vio 1.25 .85
709 A102 50c yellow .30 .20
710 A102 1b lt ol grn .75 .40
Nos. 703-710 (8) 3.30 2.45
Nos. 703-710,C658-C670 (21) 12.30 8.60

See Nos. 748-750, C658-C670, C786-C792.
For surcharges see Nos. 865, C807, C856-C861.

Main Post Office, Caracas A103

1958, Nov. 17 Engr. Perf. 11½x12
711 A103 5c green .25 .20
712 A103 10c rose red .40 .20
713 A103 15c black .50 .20
Nos. 711-713,C671-C673 (6) 2.25 1.20

Arms of Merida — A104

1958, Oct. 9 Photo. Perf. 14x13½
714 A104 5c green .20 .20
715 A104 10c bright red .20 .20
716 A104 15c greenish gray .20 .20
717 A104 20c blue .20 .20
718 A104 25c magenta .40 .20
719 A104 30c violet .20 .20
720 A104 35c light purple .25 .20
721 A104 40c orange .60 .20
722 A104 45c deep rose lilac .30 .20
723 A104 50c bright yellow .50 .20
724 A104 1b gray green 1.50 .50
Nos. 714-724 (11) 4.55 2.50
Nos. 714-724,C674-C689 (27) 12.85 7.15

400th anniversary of the founding of the city of Merida. For surcharge see No. 873.

Arms of Trujillo, Bolivar Monument and Trujillo Hotel — A105

1959, Nov. 17 Unwmk. Perf. 14
725 A105 5c emerald .20 .20
726 A105 10c rose .20 .20
727 A105 15c gray .20 .20
728 A105 20c blue .20 .20
729 A105 25c brt pink .25 .20
730 A105 30c lt ultra .40 .20
731 A105 35c lt pur .40 .20
732 A105 45c rose lilac .50 .25
733 A105 50c yellow .50 .20
734 A105 1b lt ol grn 1.25 .65
Nos. 725-734 (10) 4.10 2.50
Nos. 725-734,C690-C700 (21) 8.75 5.25

Founding of the city of Trujillo, 400th anniv.

Stadium A106

1959, Mar. 10 Litho. Perf. 13½
735 A106 5c brt grn .25 .20
736 A106 10c rose pink .25 .20
737 A106 20c blue .45 .20
738 A106 30c dk bl .55 .20
739 A106 50c red lilac .85 .20
Nos. 735-739 (5) 2.35 1.00
Nos. 735-739,C701-C705 (10) 4.20 2.25

8th Central American and Caribbean Games, Caracas, Nov. 29-Dec. 14, 1958.
#735-739 exist imperf. Value, pair $25.

Stamp of 1859, Mailman and José Ignacio Paz Castillo A107

Stamp of 1859 and: 50c, Mailman on horseback and Jacinto Gutierrez. 1b, Plane, train and Miguel Herrera.

1959, Sept. 15 Engr. Perf. 13½x14
740 A107 25c org yel .50 .25
741 A107 50c blue .50 .25
742 A107 1b rose red 1.25 .45
Nos. 740-742,C706-C708 (6) 3.90 1.85

Centenary of Venezuelan postage stamps.

| Catalogue values for unused stamps in this section, from this point to the end of the section, are for Never Hinged items. |

Alexander von Humboldt — A108

Newspaper, 1808, and View of Caracas, 1958 — A109

1960, Feb. 9 Unwmk. Perf. 13½
743 A108 5c grn & yel grn .35 .25
744 A108 30c vio bl & vio .95 .25
745 A108 40c org & brn org 5.25 1.65
Nos. 743-745,C709-C711 (6) 5.25 1.65

Centenary of the death of Alexander von Humboldt, German naturalist and geographer.

Post Office Type of 1958
1960, July Litho. Perf. 14
748 A102 25c yellow .20 .20
749 A102 30c light blue .25 .20
750 A102 40c fawn .55 .20
Nos. 748-750 (3) 1.00 .60

1960, June 6 Litho. Perf. 14
751 A109 10c rose & blk .40 .20
752 A109 20c lt blue & blk .65 .20
753 A109 35c lilac & blk 1.00 .70
Nos. 751-753,C712-C714 (6) 6.45 2.75

150th anniv. (in 1958) of the 1st Venezuelan newspaper, Gazeta de Caracas.

Agustin Codazzi A110

National Pantheon — A111

1960, June 15 Engr. Unwmk.
754 A110 5c brt green .20 .20
755 A110 15c gray .65 .20
756 A110 20c blue .50 .20
757 A110 45c purple .65 .30
Nos. 754-757,C715-C720 (10) 5.65 2.55

Centenary (in 1959) of the death of Agustin Codazzi, geographer.
For surcharges see Nos. 869, C884.

1960, May 9 Litho.
Pantheon in Bister
758 A111 5c emerald .20 .20
759 A111 20c brt blue .50 .20
760 A111 25c light olive .80 .20
761 A111 30c dull blue .95 .20
762 A111 40c fawn 1.40 .45
763 A111 45c lilac 1.25 .45
Nos. 758-763 (6) 5.10 1.75
Nos. 758-763,C721-C734 (20) 23.20 6.75

For surcharges see Nos. C894-C895.

Andres Eloy Blanco, Poet (1896-1955) A112

1960, May 21 Unwmk. Perf. 14
Portrait in Black
764 A112 5c emerald .25 .20
765 A112 30c dull blue .30 .20
766 A112 50c yellow .65 .25
Nos. 764-766,C735-C737 (6) 4.10 1.45

For surcharge see No. C874.

Independence Meeting of April 19, 1810, Led by Miranda — A113

1960, Aug. 19 Litho. Perf. 13½
Center Multicolored
767 A113 5c brt green .50 .20
768 A113 20c blue 1.00 .25
769 A113 30c violet blue 1.40 .35
Nos. 767-769,C738-C740 (6) 6.40 1.80

150th anniversary of Venezuela's Independence.
See Nos. 812-814, C804-C806. For surcharge see No. C893.

Drilling for Oil — A114

1960, Aug. 26 Engr. Perf. 14
770 A114 5c grn & slate grn 1.75 .65
771 A114 10c dk car & brn .65 .25
772 A114 15c gray & dull pur .85 .30
Nos. 770-772,C741-C743 (6) 5.60 2.10

Issued to publicize Venezuela's oil industry.

Luisa Cáceres
de Arismendi
A115

Unwmk.
1960, Oct. 21   Litho.   *Perf. 14*
Center Multicolored
773 A115 20c light blue   1.25   .35
774 A115 25c citron   1.00   .40
775 A115 30c dull blue   1.40   .50
   Nos. 773-774,C744-C746 (5)   6.70 2.35

Death of Luisa Càceres de Arismendi, 94th
anniv.

José Antonio
Anzoategui — A116

1960, Oct. 29   Engr.
776 A116 5c emerald & gray ol   .30   .20
777 A116 15c ol gray & dl vio   .45   .20
778 A116 20c blue & gray vio   .60   .20
   Nos. 776-778,C747-C749 (6)   3.20 1.50

140th anniversary (in 1959) of the death of
General José Antonio Anzoategui.

Antonio José
de
Sucre — A117

Unwmk.
1960, Nov. 18   Litho.   *Perf. 14*
Center Multicolored
779 A117 10c deep rose   .40   .20
780 A117 15c gray brown   .50   .25
781 A117 20c blue & gray vio   .70   .35
   Nos. 779-781,C750-C752 (6)   4.85 2.05

130th anniversary of the death of General
Antonio José de Sucre.

Bolivar Peak,
Merida — A118

Designs: 15c, Caroni Falls, Bolivar. 35c,
Cuacharo caves, Monagas.

1960, Mar. 22   *Perf. 14*
782 A118 5c emerald & grn   1.00 1.00
783 A118 15c gray & dk gray   3.25 3.25
784 A118 35c rose lil & lil   2.75 2.75
   Nos. 782-784,C753-C755 (6)   12.70 12.70

Buildings and
People — A119

1961   Litho.   Unwmk.
Building in Orange
785 A119 5c emerald   .20   .20
786 A119 10c carmine   .20   .20
787 A119 15c gray   .20   .20
788 A119 20c blue   .20   .20
789 A119 25c lt red brown   .25   .20
790 A119 30c dull blue   .25   .20
791 A119 35c red lilac   .35   .20
792 A119 40c fawn   .55   .25
793 A119 45c brt violet   .70   .30
794 A119 50c yellow   .55   .20
   Nos. 785-794 (10)   3.45 2.15

1960 national census. See #C756-C770.
For surcharge see No. 866.

Rafael Maria
Baralt — A120

Yellow-headed
Parrot — A121

1961, Mar. 11   Engr.   *Perf. 14*
795 A120 5c grn & slate grn   .20   .20
796 A120 15c gray & dull red brn .40   .20
797 A120 35c rose lilac & lt vio .60   .20
   Nos. 795-797,C771-C773 (6)   3.55 1.60

Rafael Maria Baralt, statesman, death cent.

1961, Sept. 6   Litho.   *Perf. 14½*
798 A121 30c shown   1.00   .40
799 A121 40c Snowy egret   1.40   .40
800 A121 50c Scarlet ibis   2.25   .70
   Nos. 798-800,C776-C778 (6)   7.30 3.30

Juan J. Aguerrevere — A122

1961, Oct. 21   Unwmk.   *Perf. 14*
801 A122 25c dark blue   .25   .20
a.   Souvenir sheet, imperf.   1.40 1.40

Centenary of the founding of the Engineering Society of Venezuela, Oct. 28, 1861.
No. 801a sold for 1b.
No. 801a exists with "Valor: Bs 1,00" omitted at lower left corner. Value, $7.

Battle of Carabobo, 1821 — A123

1961, Dec. 1   *Perf. 14*
Center Multicolored
802 A123 5c emerald & blk   .20   .20
803 A123 40c brown & blk   .60   .25
   Nos. 802-803,C779-C784 (8)   15.05 4.90

140th anniversary of Battle of Carabobo.

Oncidium Papilio
Lindl. — A124

Orchids: 10c, Caularthron bilamellatum.
20c, Stanhopea Wardii Lodd. 25c, Catasetum
pileatum. 30c, Masdevallia tovarensis. 35c,
Epidendrum Stamfordianum Batem, horiz.
50c, Epidendrum atropurpureum Willd. 3b,
Oncidium falcipetalum Lindl.

Perf. 14x13½, 13½x14
1962, May 30   Litho.   Unwmk.
Orchids in Natural Colors
804 A124 5c black & orange   .20   .20
805 A124 10c blk & brt grnsh
           bl   .20   .20
806 A124 20c black & yel grn   .50   .20
807 A124 25c black & lt blue   .70   .20
808 A124 30c black & olive   .80   .20
809 A124 35c black & yellow   .90   .25
810 A124 50c black & gray   1.00   .30
811 A124 3b black & vio   6.00 2.50
   Nos. 804-811 (8)   10.30 4.05
   Nos. 804-811,C794-C803 (18) 25.30 9.30

For surcharges see Nos. 872, C885-C887.

Independence Type of 1960
Signing Declaration of Independence.

1962, June 11   *Perf. 13½*
Center Multicolored
812 A113 5c emerald   .30   .20
813 A113 20c blue   .50   .20
814 A113 25c yellow   .75   .30
a.   Souv. sheet, #812-814, imperf 3.25 3.25
   Nos. 812-814,C804-C806 (6)   5.85 1.95

150th anniv. of the Venezuelan Declaration
of Independence, July 5, 1811.
No. 814a sold for 1.50b.

Shot
Put
A125

1962, Nov. 30   Litho.   *Perf. 13x14*
815 A125 5c shown   .25   .20
816 A125 10c Soccer   .25   .20
817 A125 25c Swimming   .35   .20
a.   Souv. sheet, #815-817, imperf 2.75 2.75
   Nos. 815-817,C808-C810 (6)   3.35 1.80

1st Natl. Games, Caracas, 1961. The
stamps are arranged so that two pale colored
edges of each stamp join to make a border
around blocks of four.
No. 817a sold for 1.40b.
For surcharge see No. C899.

Vermilion
Cardinal — A126

Malaria
Eradication
Emblem,
Mosquito and
Map — A127

Birds: 10c, Great kiskadee. 20c, Glossy
black thrush. 25c, Collared trogons. 30c, Swallow tanager. 40c, Long-tailed sylph. 3b, Black-
necked stilt.

1962, Dec. 14   *Perf. 14x13½*
Birds in Natural Colors, Black
Inscription
818 A126 5c brt yellow grn   .25   .20
819 A126 10c violet blue   .25   .20
820 A126 20c lilac rose   .50   .20
821 A126 25c dull brown   .60   .20
822 A126 30c lemon   .75   .20
823 A126 40c lilac   1.00   .30
824 A126 3b fawn   7.00 3.00
   Nos. 818-824 (7)   10.35 4.30
   Nos. 818-824,C811-C818 (15) 25.05 10.60

For surcharges see Nos. 868, C880-C882.

Lithographed and Embossed
Perf. 13½x14
1962, Dec. 20   Wmk. 346
825 A127 50c brown & black   .65   .25

WHO drive to eradicate malaria. See Nos.
C819-C819a.

White-tailed
Deer
A128

Designs: 10c, Collared peccary. 35c, Collared titi (monkey). 50c, Giant Brazilian otter.
1b, Puma. 3b, Capybara.

Perf. 13½x14
1963, Mar. 13   Litho.   Unwmk.
Multicolored Center; Black
Inscriptions
826 A128 5c green   .20   .20
827 A128 10c orange   .20   .20
828 A128 35c red lilac   .25   .20
829 A128 50c blue   .55   .25
830 A128 1b rose brown   2.75 1.40
831 A128 3b yellow   5.50 3.50
   Nos. 826-831 (6)   9.45 5.75
   Nos. 826-831,C820-C825 (12) 23.75 11.00

For surcharges see #870-871, C888-C889.

Fisherman and   Cathedral of
Map of Venezuela   Bocono
A129   A130

1963, Mar. 21
832 A129 25c pink & ultra   .25   .20
   Nos. 832,C826-C827 (3)   1.30   .90

FAO "Freedom from Hunger" campaign.

1963, May 30   Wmk. 346
833 A130 50c brn, red & grn, *buff* .55   .20

400th anniversary of the founding of
Bocono. See No. C828.

St. Peter's
Basilica,
Rome
A131

1963, June 11   *Perf. 14x13½*
834 A131 35c dk bl, brn & buff   .45   .20
835 A131 45c dk grn, red brn &
           buff   .50   .20
   Nos. 834-835,C829-C830 (4)   3.15 1.10

Vatican II, the 21st Ecumenical Council of
the Roman Catholic Church.

National Flag — A132

1963, July 29   Unwmk.   Perf. 14
836 A132 30c gray, red, yel & bl   1.00 .20
Centenary of Venezuela's flag and coat of arms. See No. C831.

Lake Maracaibo Bridge — A133

Map, Soldier and Emblem — A134

Perf. 13½x14
1963, Aug. 24   Wmk. 346
837 A133 30c blue & brown   .35 .20
838 A133 35c bluish grn & brn   .40 .20
839 A133 80c blue grn & brn   .85 .35
Nos. 837-839,C832-C834 (6)   5.10 2.00
Opening of bridge over Lake Maracaibo. For surcharge see No. 875.

1963, Sept. 10   Unwmk.
840 A134 50c red, bl & grn, buff   .50 .20
25th anniversary of the armed forces. See No. C835. For surcharge see No. C862.

Dag Hammarskjold and World Map — A135

Perf. 14x13½
1963, Sept. 25   Unwmk.
841 A135 25c dk bl, bl grn & ocher   .25 .20
842 A135 55c grn, grnsh bl & ocher   1.00 .30
Nos. 841-842,C836-C837 (4)   3.45 1.45
"1st" anniv. of the death of Dag Hammarskjold, Secretary General of the UN, 1953-61.
See #C837a. For surcharges see #867, C875-C876.

Dr. Luis Razetti — A136

Dr. Francisco A. Risquez — A137

1963, Oct. 10   Litho.
843 A136 35c blue, ocher & brn   .45 .20
844 A136 45c mag, ocher & brn   .65 .20
Nos. 843-844,C838-C839 (4)   4.00 1.75
Dr. Luis Razetti, physician, birth cent.

1963, Dec. 31   Perf. 11½x12
Design: 20c, Dr. Carlos J. Bello.
845 A137 15c multicolored   .20 .20
846 A137 20c multicolored   .30 .20
Nos. 845-846,C840-C841 (4)   2.00 1.10
Cent. of the Intl. Red Cross.

Oil Field Workers — A138

Pedro Gual — A139

10c, Oil refinery. 15c Crane & building construction. 30c, Cactus, train & truck. 40c, Tractor.

1964, Feb. 5   Litho.   Perf. 14x13½
847 A138 5c multi   .25 .20
848 A138 10c multi   .25 .20
849 A138 15c multi   .30 .20
850 A138 30c multi   .50 .25
851 A138 40c multi   .55 .25
Nos. 847-851 (5)   1.85 1.10
Nos. 847-851,C842-C846 (10)   3.35 2.10
Department of Industrial Development, cent.

1964, Mar. 20   Unwmk.   Perf. 14
852 A139 40c lt olive green   .55 .20
853 A139 50c lt red brown   .70 .25
Nos. 852-853,C847-C848 (4)   3.00 1.05
Pedro Gual (1784-1862), statesman.

Carlos Arvelo — A140

1964, Apr. 17   Engr.   Perf. 14x13½
854 A140 1b dull bl & gray   1.40 .45
Centenary of the death of Dr. Carlos Arvelo (1784-1862), chief physician of Bolivar's revolutionary army, director of Caracas Hospital, rector of Central University and professor of pathology.
For surcharge see No. 874.

Foundry Ladle and Molds A141

1964, May 22   Perf. 14x13½
855 A141 20c multicolored   .30 .20
856 A141 50c multicolored   .55 .20
Nos. 855-856,C849-C850 (4)   3.00 1.15
Orinoco Steel Mills.

Romulo Gallegos, Novelist, 80th Birthday — A142

Unwmk.
1964, Aug. 3   Litho.   Perf. 12
857 A142 5c dk & lt green   .20 .20
858 A142 10c bl & pale bl   .20 .20
859 A142 15c dk & lt red lil   .30 .20
Nos. 857-859,C852-C854 (6)   2.35 1.25

Angel Falls, Bolivar State A143

Tourist Publicity: 10c, Tropical landscape, Sucre State. 15c, San Juan Peaks, Guarico. 30c, Net fishermen, Anzoategui. 40c, Mountaineer, Merida.

1964, Oct. 22   Perf. 13½x14
860 A143 5c multi   .20 .20
861 A143 10c multi   .20 .20
862 A143 15c multi   .20 .20
863 A143 30c multi   .40 .20
864 A143 40c multi   .60 .20
Nos. 860-864 (5)   1.60 1.00

Issues of 1958-64 Surcharged in Black, Dark Blue or Lilac

1965
865 A102 5c on 1b (#710)   .40 .20
866 A119 10c on 45c (#793)   .20 .20
867 A135 15c on 55c (#842)   .20 .20
868 A126 20c on 3b (#824)   .20 .20
869 A110 25c on 45c (#757) (DB)   .20 .20
870 A128 25c on 1b (#830)   .25 .20
871 A128 25c on 3b (#831)   .30 .20
872 A124 25c on 3b (#811) (L)   .20 .20
873 A104 30c on 1b (#724)   .25 .20
874 A140 40c on 1b (#854)   .60 .20
875 A133 60c on 80c (#839)   .75 .25
Nos. 865-875 (11)   3.55 2.25
Lines of surcharge arranged variously; old denomination obliterated with bars on Nos. 867, 870-872. See Nos. C856-C899.

Revenue Stamps of 1947 Surcharged in Red or Black

Imprint: "American Bank Note Co."
1965   Engr.   Perf. 12, 13½ (No. 882)
876 R1 5c on 5c emerald   .20 .20
877 R1 5c on 20c red brn   .20 .20
878 R1 10c on 10c brn ol   .20 .20
879 R1 15c on 40c grn   .20 .20
880 R1 20c on 3b dk bl (R)   .30 .20
881 R1 25c on 5b vio bl (R)   .60 .25
882 R1 25c on 5b vio bl (R) (Imprint: "Bundesdruckerei Berlin")   .30 .20
883 R1 60c on 3b dk bl (R)   .75 .25
Nos. 876-883 (8)   2.75 1.70
Type R1 is illustrated above No. 401.

John F. Kennedy and Alliance for Progress Emblem A144

1965, Aug. 20   Photo.   Perf. 12x11½
884 A144 20c gray   .35 .20
885 A144 40c bright lilac   .55 .20
Nos. 884-885,C900-C901 (4)   2.55 1.05

Map of Venezuela and Guiana by Codazzi, 1840 — A145

Protesilaus Leucones — A146

Maps of Venezuela and Guiana: 15c, by Juan M. Restrepo, 1827, horiz. 40c, by L. de Surville, 1778.

1965, Nov. 5   Litho.   Perf. 13½
886 A145 5c multi   .20 .20
887 A145 15c multi   .30 .20
888 A145 40c multi   .55 .20
a.   Souv. sheet, #886-888, imperf   6.00 6.00
Nos. 886-888,C905-C907 (6)   2.70 1.30
Issued to publicize Venezuela's claim to part of British Guiana.
No. 888a sold for 85c.

1966, Jan. 25   Litho.   Perf. 13½x14
Various Butterflies in Natural Colors
Black Inscriptions
889 A146 20c lt olive grn   1.25 .25
890 A146 30c lt yellow grn   2.50 .25
891 A146 50c yellow   3.75 .30
Nos. 889-891,C915-C917 (6)   14.50 2.30

Ship and Map of Atlantic Ocean A147

1966, Mar. 10   Litho.   Perf. 13½x14
892 A147 60c brown, bl & blk   1.40 .45
Bicentenary of the first maritime mail.

"El Carite" Dance — A148

Various Folk Dances

Perf. 14x13½
1966, Apr. 5   Litho.   Unwmk.
893 A148 5c gray & multi   .20 .20
894 A148 10c orange & multi   .20 .20
895 A148 15c lemon & multi   .30 .20
896 A148 20c lilac & multi   .40 .20
897 A148 25c brt pink & multi   .55 .25
898 A148 35c yel grn & multi   .60 .30
Nos. 893-898,C919-C924 (12)   9.00 3.60

Type of Air Post Stamps and

Arturo
Michelena,
Self-portrait
A149

Paintings: 1b, Penthesileia, battle scene.
1.05b, The Red Cloak.

Perf. 12½x12, 12x12½

1966, May 12   Litho.   Unwmk.
899 A149 95c sepia & buff   .80   .60
900 AP74 1b multi   1.00   .60
901 AP74 1.05b multi   1.25   .60
     Nos. 899-901,C927-C929 (6) 6.30 3.30

Arturo Michelena (1863-1898), painter.
Miniature sheets of 12 exist.

Construction
Worker and Map
of
Americas — A150

Designs: 20c, as 10c. 30c, 65c, Labor
monument. 35c, Machinery worker and map
of Venezuela. 50c, Automobile assembly line.

1966, July 6   Litho.   Perf. 14x13½
902 A150 10c yellow & blk   .20   .20
903 A150 20c lt grnsh bl & blk .25   .20
904 A150 30c lt blue & vio   .25   .20
905 A150 35c lemon & olive   .35   .20
906 A150 50c brt rose & claret .50   .25
907 A150 65c salmon pink & brn .65   .30
     Nos. 902-907 (6)   2.20 1.35

2nd Conference of Ministers of Labor of the
Organization of American States.

Velvet
Cichlid
A151

1966, Aug. 31   Litho.   Perf. 13½x14
908 A151 15c shown   .25   .20
909 A151 25c Perch cichlid   .35   .20
910 A151 45c Piranha   .95   .30
     Nos. 908-910,C933-C935 (6) 5.75 1.90

Nativity — A152   Rubén
                         Dario — A154

Satellite,
Radar,
Globe,
Plane and
Ship
A153

1966, Dec. 9   Litho.   Perf. 13½x14
911 A152 65c violet & blk   .80   .30

Christmas 1966.

1966, Dec. 28   Perf. 13½x14
912 A153 45c multi   .65   .25

Ministry of Communications, 30th anniv.

1967   Litho.
913 A154 70c gray bl & dk bl 1.00   .45

Rubén Dario (pen name of Felix Rubén Garcia Sarmiento, 1867-1916), Nicaraguan poet,
newspaper correspondent and diplomat.

Old Building
and Arms,
University of
Zulia
A155

Perf. 13½x14
1967, Apr. 21   Litho.   Unwmk.
914 A155 80c gold, blk & car 1.00   .45

University of Zulia founding, 75th anniv.

Front Page and
Printing
Press — A156

1968, June 27 Photo. Perf. 14x13½
915 A156 1.50b emer, blk & brn 1.50 .60
Newspaper Correo del Orinoco, 150th anniv.

Boll
Weevil
A157

Insect Pests: 20c, Corn borer, vert. 90c,
Tobacco caterpillar.

Perf. 14x13½, 13½x14
1968, Aug. 30   Litho.
916 A157 20c multicolored   .50   .20
917 A157 75c olive & multi   1.50   .25
918 A157 90c multicolored   2.10   .35
     Nos. 916-918,C989-C991 (6) 7.10 1.40

Guayana
Substation
A158

Designs: 45c, Guaira River Dam, horiz. 50c,
Macagua Dam and power plant, horiz. 80c,
Guri River Dam and power plant.

1968, Nov. 8   Litho.
919 A158 15c fawn & multi   .20   .20
920 A158 45c dl yel & multi   .50   .20
921 A158 50c bl grn & multi   .75   .25
922 A158 80c blue & multi   1.10   .50
     Nos. 919-922 (4)   2.55 1.15

Electrification program.

House and
Piggy Bank
A159

1968, Dec. 6   Litho.   Perf. 13½x14
923 A159 45c blue & multi   .60   .25

National Savings System.

Nursery
and Child
Planting
Tree
A160

Designs: 15c, Child planting tree (vert.; this
design used as emblem on entire issue). 30c,
Waterfall, vert. 45c, Logging. 55c, Fields and
village, vert. 75c, Palambra (fish).

Perf. 14x13½, 13½x14
1968, Dec. 19   Litho.
924 A160 15c multicolored   .30   .20
925 A160 30c multicolored   .30   .20
926 A160 30c multicolored   .35   .20
927 A160 45c multicolored   .50   .20
928 A160 55c multicolored   1.10   .30
929 A160 75c multicolored   .75   .20
     Nos. 924-929 (6)   3.30 1.30
     Nos. 924-929,C1000-C1005 (12) 9.50 3.70

Issued to publicize nature conservation.

Colorada
Beach,
Sucre
A161

Designs: 45c, Church of St. Francis of Yare,
Miranda. 90c, Stilt houses, Zulia.

1969, Jan. 24   Perf. 13½x14
930 A161 15c multicolored   .20   .20
931 A161 45c multicolored   .55   .20
932 A161 90c multicolored   .80   .50
     Nos. 930-932,C1006-C1008 (6) 2.55 1.50

Tourist publicity. For souvenir sheet see No.
C1007a.

Bolivar Addressing Congress of
Angostura — A162

1969, Feb. 15   Litho.   Perf. 11
933 A162 45c multicolored   .60   .25

Sesquicentennial of the Congress of Angostura (Ciudad Bolivar).

Martin Luther
King,
Jr. — A163

1969, Apr. 1   Litho.   Perf. 13½
934 A163 1b bl, red & dk brn 1.00   .30

Rev. Dr. Martin Luther King, Jr. (1929-
1968), American civil rights leader and recipient of the Nobel Peace Prize, 1964.

Tabebuia
A164

Trees: 65c, Erythrina poeppigiana. 90c,
Platymiscium.

1969, May 30   Litho.   Perf. 13½x14
935 A164 50c multicolored   .75   .20
936 A164 65c gray & multi   1.00   .30
937 A164 90c pink & multi   1.50   .40
     Nos. 935-937,C1009-C1011 (6) 5.35 1.45

Issued to publicize nature conservation.

Still Life with Pheasant, by
Rojas — A165

Paintings by Cristobal Rojas (1858-1890):
25c, On the Balcony, vert. 45c, The Christening. 50c, The Empty Place (family). 60c, The
Tavern. 1b, Man's Arm, vert.

Perf. 14x13½, 13½x14
1969, June 27   Litho.   Unwmk.
Size: 32x42mm, 42x32mm
938 A165 25c gold & multi   .25   .20
939 A165 35c gold & multi   .45   .20
940 A165 45c gold & multi   .75   .25
941 A165 50c gold & multi   .85   .30
942 A165 60c gold & multi   1.10   .35
Perf. 11
Size: 26x53mm
943 A165 1b gold & multi   1.60   .60
     Nos. 938-943 (6)   5.00 1.90

ILO
Emblem
A166

1969, July 28   Perf. 13½
944 A166 2.50b fawn & blk   2.00 1.25

50th anniv. of the ILO.

Charter
and Coat
of Arms
A167

Industrial Complex A168

1969, Aug. 26   Litho.   *Perf. 13½*
945 A167 45c ultra & multi   .65 .25
946 A168 1b multicolored   1.00 .35

Industrial development.

House with Arcade, Carora — A169

Designs: 25c, Ruins of Pastora Church. 55c, Chapel of the Cross. 65c, House of Culture.

1969, Sept. 8   *Perf. 13x14½*
947 A169 20c multicolored   .20 .20
948 A169 25c multicolored   .30 .20
949 A169 55c multicolored   .75 .25
950 A169 65c multicolored   1.00 .35
    Nos. 947-950 (4)   2.25 1.00

400th anniversary of city of Carora.

Simon Bolivar in Madrid — A170

Designs: 10c, Bolivar's wedding, Madrid, 1802, horiz. 35c, Bolivar monument. Madrid.

Perf. 13½x14, 14x13½
1969, Oct. 28   Litho.
951 A170 10c multicolored   .20 .20
952 A170 15c brn red & blk   .30 .20
953 A170 35c multicolored   .40 .20
    a.   Souvenir sheet of 2   2.00 2.00
    Nos. 951-953 (3)   .90 .60

Bolivar's sojourn in Spain. No. 953a contains 2 imperf. stamps similar to Nos. 952-953 with simulated perforation. Sold for 75c.

"Birds in the Woods" — A171

Design: 45c, "Children in Summer Camp." Both designs are after children's paintings.

1969, Dec. 12   *Perf. 12½*
954 A171 5c emerald & multi   .20 .20
955 A171 45c red & multi   .65 .30

Issued for Children's Day.

Map of Great Colombia A172

1969, Dec. 16   Litho.   *Perf. 11½*
956 A172 45c multicolored   .55 .20

150th anniversary of the founding of the State of Great Colombia.

St. Anthony's, Clarines A173

Churches: 30c, Church of the Conception, Caroní. 40c, St. Michael's, Burbusay. 45c, St. Anthony's, Maturín. 75c, St. Nicholas, Moruy. 1b, Coro Cathedral.

1970, Jan. 15   *Perf. 14*
957 A173 10c pink & multi   .20 .20
958 A173 30c emerald & multi   .25 .20
959 A173 40c yellow & multi   .55 .20
960 A173 45c gray bl & multi   .75 .25
    a.   Souvenir sheet of 1, imperf. 1.50 1.50
961 A173 75c yellow & multi   1.00 .35
962 A173 1b orange & multi   1.25 .45
    Nos. 957-962 (6)   4.00 1.65

Colonial architecture.
No. 960a sold for 75c.

A174

1970, Feb. 13   Litho.   *Perf. 13x14½*
963 A174 95c multicolored   1.10 .35

Sesquicentennial of the city of Valera.

A175

Design: Seven Hills of Valera.

1970, July 29   Litho.   *Perf. 14x13½*

Flowers: 20c, Monochaetum Humboldtianum. 25c, Symbolanthus vasculosis. 45c, Cavedishia splendens. 1b, Befaria glauca.

964 A175 20c multicolored   .50 .20
965 A175 25c multicolored   .80 .20
966 A175 45c multicolored   1.10 .40
967 A175 1b multicolored   1.60 .55
    Nos. 964-967,C1049-C1052 (8)   8.50 2.55

Battle of Boyaca, by Martin Tovar y Tovar A176

1970, Aug. 7   *Perf. 13½x14*
968 A176 30c multicolored   .35 .20

150th anniversary of Battle of Boyaca.

Our Lady of Belén de San Mateo — A177

Designs: 35c, Pastoral Cross of Archbishop Silvestre Guevera y Lira, 1867. 40c, Our Lady of Valle. 90c, Virgin of Chiquinquira. 1b, Our Lady of Socorro de Valencia.

1970, Sept. 1   *Perf. 14x13½*
969 A177 35c gray & multi   .45 .20
970 A177 40c gray & multi   .55 .20
971 A177 60c gray & multi   .80 .30
    a.   Souvenir sheet of 1, imperf. 1.40 1.40
972 A177 90c gray & multi   .95 .40
973 A177 1b gray & multi   1.25 .50
    Nos. 969-973 (5)   4.00 1.60

The designs are from sculptures and paintings in various Venezuelan churches.
No. 971a sold for 75c.

Venezuela No. 22 and EXFILCA Emblem — A178

Designs: 20c, EXFILCA emblem and flags of participating nations, vert. 70c, Venezuela No. C13 and EXFILCA emblem, vert.

1970, Nov. 28   Litho.   *Perf. 11*
974 A178 20c yellow & multi   .30 .20
975 A178 25c dk blue & multi   .35 .20
976 A178 70c brown & multi   .75 .30
    a.   Souvenir sheet of 1, imperf. 1.40 1.40
    Nos. 974-976 (3)   1.40 .70

EXFILCA 70, 2nd Interamerican Philatelic Exhibition, Caracas, Nov. 27-Dec. 6. No. 976a is a hexagon with each side 50mm long. Sold for 85c.

Guardian Angel, by Juan Pedro Lopez — A179

1970, Dec. 1   Litho.   *Perf. 14½x13½*
977 A179 45c dull yellow & multi   .55 .25

Christmas 1970.

Jet and 1920 Plane A180

1970, Dec. 10   *Perf. 13x14*
978 A180 5c blue & multi   .25 .20

Venezuelan Air Force, 50th anniversary.

Question Mark Full of Citizens — A181

1971, Apr. 30   Litho.   *Perf. 14x13½*
Light Green, Red & Black
979   Block of 4   3.50 2.00
    a.   A181 30c frame L & T   .85 .40
    b.   A181 30c frame T & R   .85 .40
    c.   A181 30c frame L & B   .85 .40
    d.   A181 30c frame B & R   .85 .40

National Census, 1971. Sheet of 20 contains 5 No. 979 and 5 blocks of 4 labels. See No. C1054.

Battle of Carabobo A182

1971, June 21   *Perf. 13½x14*
980 A182 2b blue & multi   1.75 1.00

Sesquicentennial of Battle of Carabobo.

Map of Federal District — A183

State maps. 25c, 55c, 85c, 90c, vert.

1971   Litho.   *Perf. 13½x14, 14x13½*
981 A183 5c shown   .40 .20
982 A183 15c Monagas   .40 .20
983 A183 20c Nueva Esparta   .40 .20
984 A183 25c Portuguesa   .40 .20
985 A183 45c Sucre   .45 .20
986 A183 55c Tachira   .55 .20
987 A183 65c Trujillo   .65 .20
988 A183 75c Yaracuy   .75 .30
989 A183 85c Zulia   .95 .30
990 A183 90c Amazonas   1.50 .30
991 A183 1b Federal Dependencies 1.60 .55
    Nos. 981-991 (11)   8.05 2.85
    Nos. 981-991,C1035-C1048 (25) 19.20 6.85

Issued: 5c, 7/15; 15c, 20c, 8/16; 25c, 45c, 9/15; 55c, 65c, 10/15; 75c, 85c, 11/15; 90c, 1b, 12/15.

Madonna and Child A184   Luis Daniel Beauperthuy A185

Design: #993, Madonna & Jesus in manger.

1971, Dec. 1   *Perf. 11*
992 A184 25c multicolored   .50 .20
993 A184 25c multicolored   .50 .20
    a.   Pair, #992-993   1.00 .50

Christmas 1971. Printed checkerwise.

1971, Dec. 10   *Perf. 14x13½*
994 A185 1b vio bl & multi   1.00 .50

Dr. Luis Daniel Beauperthuy, scientist.

Globe in Heart Shape — A186

Flags of Americas and Arms of Venezuela A187

1972, Apr. 7   Litho.   Perf. 14x13½
995 A186 1b red, ultra & blk   .75   .45

"Your heart is your health," World Health Day 1972.

1972, May 16   Litho.   Perf. 14x13½

Designs: 4b, Venezuelan flag. 5b, National anthem. 10b, Araguaney, national tree. 15b, Map, North and South America. All show flags of American nations in background.

996	A187	3b multicolored	4.00	1.00
997	A187	4b multicolored	4.25	1.75
998	A187	5b multicolored	4.75	2.25
999	A187	10b multicolored	9.00	3.00
1000	A187	15b multicolored	13.00	4.25
		Nos. 996-1000 (5)	35.00	12.25

"Venezuela in America."

Parque Central Complex A188

#1002, Front view ("Parque Central" on top). #1003, Side view ("Parque Central" at right).

1972, July 25   Perf. 11½
1001	A188	30c yellow & multi	.25	.20
1002	A188	30c blue & multi	.25	.20
1003	A188	30c red & multi	.25	.20
a.		Strip of 3, #1001-1003	1.40	1.40

Completion of "Parque Central" middle-income housing project, Caracas.

Mahatma Gandhi — A189

1972, Oct. 2   Litho.   Perf. 13½x14
1004 A189 60c multicolored   .75   .40

103rd birthday of Mohandas K. Gandhi (1869-1948), leader in India's fight for independence, advocate of non-violence.

Children Playing Music — A190

Christmas: #1006, Children roller skating.

1972, Dec. 5   Litho.   Perf. 13½x14
1005	30c multicolored	.25 .20
1006	30c multicolored	.25 .20
a.	A190 Pair, #1005-1006	.70 .70

Indigo Snake A191

Snake: 15c, South American chicken snake. 25c, Venezuelan lance-head. 30c, Coral snake. 60c, Casabel rattlesnake. 1b, Boa constrictor.

1972, Dec. 15   Litho.   Perf. 13½x14
1007	A191	10c black & multi	.50	.35
1008	A191	15c black & multi	.50	.35
1009	A191	25c black & multi	.70	.35
1010	A191	30c black & multi	.80	.35
1011	A191	60c black & multi	1.50	.40
1012	A191	1b black & multi	2.25	.60
		Nos. 1007-1012 (6)	6.25	2.40

Copernicus — A192

Sun — A193

Designs: 5c, Model of solarcentric system. 15c, Copernicus' book "De Revolutionibus."

1973, Feb. 19   Litho.   Perf. 13½x14
1013	5c multicolored	.20	.20
1014	10c multicolored	.35	.20
1015	15c multicolored	.50	.20
a.	A192 Strip of 3, #1013-1015	1.10	.90

1973   Litho.   Perf. 13½

Designs: Planetary system.

Size: 26½x29mm
1016	A193	5c shown	.25	.25
1017	A193	5c Earth	.25	.25
1018	A193	20c Mars	.55	.25
1019	A193	20c Saturn	.40	.25
1020	A193	30c Asteroids	.45	.25
1021	A193	40c Neptune	.55	.25
1022	A193	50c Venus	.80	.40
1023	A193	60c Jupiter	.95	.45
1024	A193	75c Uranus	1.10	.55
1025	A193	90c Pluto	1.40	.80
1026	A193	90c Moon	2.00	.80
1027	A193	1b Mercury	2.25	.95

Size: 27x55mm
Perf. 12
1028	A193	10c Orbits and Saturn	.25	.25
1029	A193	15c Sun, Mercury, Venus, Earth	.40	.25
1030	A193	15c Jupiter, Uranus, Neptune, Pluto	.45	.25
a.		Strip of 3, #1028-1030	1.10	1.10
		Nos. 1016-1030 (15)	12.05	6.20

10th anniversary of Humboldt Planetarium. No. 1030a has continuous design showing solar system.
Issue dates: Nos. 1016, 1018, 1021, 1023-1025, Mar. 15; others Mar. 30.

OAS Emblem, Map of Americas — A194

1973, Apr. 30   Litho.   Perf. 13½x14
1031 A194 60c multicolored   .45   .25

Organization of American States, 25th anniv.

José Antonio Paez — A195

Street of the Lancers, Puerto Cabello — A196

Designs: 10c, Paez in uniform. 30c, Paez and horse, from old print. 2b, Paez at Battle of Centauro, horiz. 10c, 2b are after contemporary paintings.

1973   Perf. 14x13½, 13½x14
1032	A195	10c gold & multi	.20	.20
1033	A195	30c red, blk & gold	.25	.20
1034	A195	50c bl, vio bl & dk brn	.45	.25
1035	A196	1b multicolored	.90	.45
1036	A195	2b gold & multi	1.50	.90
		Nos. 1032-1036 (5)	3.30	2.00

Gen. José Antonio Paez (1790-1873), leader in War of Independence, President of Venezuela. The 1b for the sesquicentenary of the fall of Puerto Cabello.
Issue dates: Nos. 1033-1034, May 6; Nos. 1032, 1036, June 13; No. 1035, Nov. 8.

José P. Padilla, Mariano Montilla, Manuel Manrique — A197

1b, Naval battle. 2b, Line-up for naval battle.

1973, July 27   Litho.   Perf. 12½
1037	A197	50c multicolored	.35	.20
1038	A197	1b multicolored	.75	.35
1039	A197	2b multicolored	1.50	.75
		Nos. 1037-1039 (3)	2.60	1.30

150th anniv. of the Battle of Maracaibo.

Bishop Ramos de Lora — A198

1973, Aug. 1   Photo.   Perf. 14x13½
1040 A198 75c gold & dk brn   .60   .25

Sesquicentennial of the birth of Ramos de Lora (1722-1790), first Bishop of Merida de

Plane, Ship, Margarita Island — A199

Maracaibo and founder of the Colegio Seminario, the forerunner of the University of the Andes.

1973, Sept. 8   Litho.   Perf. 14x13½
1041 A199 5c multicolored   .20   .20

Establishment of Margarita Island as a free port.

Map of Golden Road and Waterfall — A200

Designs (Road Map and): 10c, Scarlet macaw. 20c, Church ruins. 50c, 60c, Indian mountain sanctuary. 90c, Colonial church. 1b, Flags of Venezuela and Brazil.

1973, Oct. 1   Litho.   Perf. 13
1042	A200	5c black & multi	.25	.25
1043	A200	10c black & multi	.25	.25
1044	A200	20c black & multi	.80	.25
1045	A200	50c black & multi	.85	.35
1046	A200	60c black & multi	.85	.35
1047	A200	90c black & multi	1.30	.40
1048	A200	1b black & multi	1.60	.55
		Nos. 1042-1048 (7)	5.90	2.40

Completion of the Golden Road from Santa Elena de Uairen, Brazil, to El Dorado, Venezuela.
Issued: 50c, 60c, Oct. 30; others Oct. 1.

Gen. Paez Dam and Power Station — A201

1973, Oct. 14   Perf. 14x13½
1049 A201 30c multicolored   .30   .20

Opening of the Gen. José Antonio Paez Dam and Power Station.

Child on Slide — A202

Designs: No. 1051, Fairytale animals. No. 1052, Children's book. No. 1053, Children disembarking from plane for vacation.

1973, Dec. 4   Litho.   Perf. 12
1050	A202	10c multicolored	.25	.20
1051	A202	10c multicolored	.25	.20
1052	A202	10c multicolored	.25	.20
1053	A202	10c multicolored	.25	.20
		Nos. 1050-1053 (4)	1.00	.80

Children's Foundation Festival.

King Following Star — A203

Christmas: No. 1055, Two Kings.

1973, Dec. 5   **Litho.**   **Perf. 14x13½**
1054   30c multicolored   .45   .20
1055   30c multicolored   .45   .20
   a. A203 Pair, #1054-1055   1.00   1.00

Regional
Map of
Venezuela
A204

1973, Dec. 13   **Perf. 13½x14**
1056 A204 25c multicolored   .40   .20
   Introduction of regionalization.

Handicraft
A205

Designs: 35c, Industrial park. 45c, Cog wheels and chimney.

1973, Dec. 18   **Perf. 14x13½**
1057 A205 15c blue & multi   .20   .20
1058 A205 35c multicolored   .30   .20
1059 A205 45c yellow & multi   .50   .20
   Nos. 1057-1059 (3)   1.00   .60

Progress in Venezuela and jobs for the handicapped.

Map of Carupano and
Revelers — A206

1974, Feb. 22   **Perf. 13½x14**
1060 A206 5c multicolored   .25   .20
   10th anniversary of Carupano Carnival.

Congress
Emblem — A207

1974, May 20   **Litho.**   **Perf. 13½**
1061 A207 50c multicolored   .50   .20

9th Venezuelan Engineering Congress, Maracaibo, May 19-25.

Waves
and
"M"
A208

Designs: Under-water photographs of deep-sea fish and marine life.

1974, June 20   **Litho.**   **Perf. 12½**
1062 A208 15c multicolored   .40   .20
1063 A208 35c multicolored   .60   .20
1064 A208 75c multicolored   .75   .20
1065 A208 80c multicolored   .75   .35
   Nos. 1062-1065 (4)   2.50   1.00

3rd UN Conference on the Law of the Sea, Caracas, June 20-Aug. 29.

Pupil and New School — A209

"Pay your Taxes" Campaign: 10c, 15c, 20c, like 5c. 25c, 30c, 35c, 40c, Suburban housing development. 45c, 50c, 55c, 60c, Highway and overpass. 65c, 70c, 75c, 80c, Playing field (sport). 85c, 90c, 95c, 1b, Operating room. All designs include Venezuelan coat of arms, coins and banknotes.

1974   **Perf. 13½**
1066 A209   5c blue & multi   .25   .25
1067 A209 10c ultra & multi   .25   .25
1068 A209 15c violet & multi   .25   .25
1069 A209 20c lilac & multi   .25   .25
1070 A209 25c multicolored   .25   .25
1071 A209 30c multicolored   .50   .25
1072 A209 35c multicolored   .25   .25
1073 A209 40c olive & multi   .40   .25
1074 A209 45c multicolored   .40   .25
1075 A209 50c green & multi   .40   .25
1076 A209 55c multicolored   .70   .40
1077 A209 60c multicolored   .55   .30
1078 A209 65c bister & multi   1.30   .60
1079 A209 70c multicolored   .60   .25
1080 A209 75c multicolored   .70   .30
1081 A209 80c brown & multi   .70   .30
1082 A209 85c ver & multi   .70   .30
1083 A209 90c multicolored   .85   .30
1084 A209 95c multicolored   1.50   .95
1085 A209   1b multicolored   .85   .40
   Nos. 1066-1085 (20)   11.65   6.60

Bolivar
at
Battle
of
Junin
A210

1974, Aug. 6   **Litho.**   **Perf. 13½x14**
1086 A210 2b multicolored   1.50   .75
   Sesquicentennial of the Battle of Junin.

Globe and UPU Emblem — A211

50c, Postrider, sailing ship, steamer and jet.

1974, Oct. 9   **Perf. 12**
1087 A211 45c dk blue & multi   .35   .20
1088 A211 50c black & multi   .45   .20
   Centenary of Universal Postal Union.

Rufino Blanco-Fombona — A212

Portraits of Blanco-Fombona and his books.

1974, Oct. 16   **Litho.**   **Perf. 12½**
1089 A212 10c gray & multi   .20   .20
1090 A212 30c yellow & multi   .20   .20
1091 A212 45c multicolored   .30   .20
1092 A212 90c buff & multi   .50   .25
   Nos. 1089-1092 (4)   1.20   .85

Centenary of the birth of Rufino Blanco-Fombona (1874-1944), writer.

Children
A213

1974, Nov. 29   **Litho.**   **Perf. 13½**
1093 A213 70c blue & multi   .60   .25
   Children's Foundation Festival.

General
Sucre — A214

Globe with
South American
Map and
Flags — A215

Battle of Ayacucho — A216

1b, Map of South America with battles marked.

1974, Dec. 9   **Perf. 14x13½, 13½x14**
1094 A214 30c multicolored   .20   .20
1095 A215 50c multicolored   .30   .25
1096 A215   1b multicolored   .65   .30
1097 A216   2b multicolored   1.25   .65
   Nos. 1094-1097 (4)   2.40   1.40

Sesquicentennial of the Battle of Ayacucho.

Adoration of the Shepherds, by J. B. Mayno — A217

1974, Dec. 16   **Photo.**   **Perf. 14x13½**
1098   30c Shepherd   .30   .25
1099   30c Madonna & Child   .30   .25
   a. A217 Pair, #1098-1099   .90   .90

   Christmas 1974.

Road Building, 1905 and El Ciempies
Overpass, 1972 — A219

Designs: 20c, 1b, Jesus Muñoz Tebar, first Minister of Public Works. 25c, Bridges on Caracas-La Guaira Road, 1912 and 1953. 40c, View of Caracas, 1874 and 1974. 70c, Tucacas Railroad Station, 1911, and projected terminal, 1974. 80c, Anatomical Institute, Caracas, 1911, and Social Security Hospital, 1969. 85c, Quininari River Bridge, 1804, and Orinoco River Bridge, 1967.

1974, Dec. 18   **Litho.**   **Perf. 12½**
1100 A219   5c ultra & multi   .20   .20
1101 A219 20c ocher & blk   .25   .20
1102 A219 25c blue & multi   .30   .20
1103 A219 40c yellow & multi   .30   .20
1104 A219 70c green & multi   1.40   .25
1105 A219 80c multicolored   1.10   .30
1106 A219 85c orange & multi   1.50   .30
1107 A219   1b red & black   1.60   .50
   Nos. 1100-1107 (8)   6.65   2.15

Centenary of the Ministry of Public Works.

Women and IWY
Emblem — A220

1975, Oct. 8   **Litho.**   **Perf. 13½x14**
1108 A220 90c multicolored   .60   .35

   International Women's Year.

Scout Emblem and Tents — A221

1975, Nov. 11   **Litho.**   **Perf. 13½x14**
1109 A221 20c multicolored   .20   .20
1110 A221 50c multicolored   .50   .25

14th World Boy Scout Jamboree, Lille-hammer, Norway, July 29-Aug. 7.

Adoration of the Shepherds — A222

1975, Dec. 5   **Litho.**   **Perf. 13½x14**
1111   30c multicolored   .25   .25
1112   30c multicolored   .25   .25
   a. A222 Pair, #1111-1112   .85   .85

   Christmas 1975.

Bolivar's
Tomb — A224

Design: 1.05b, National Pantheon.

1976, Feb. 2　Engr.　Perf. 14x13½
1113 A224　30c gray & ultra　.20　.20
1114 A224　1.05b sepia & car　.50　.25
Centenary of National Pantheon.

Bolivia Flag
Colors
A225

1976, Mar. 22　Litho.　Perf. 13½
1115 A225 60c multicolored　.35　.20
Sesquicentennial of Bolivia's independence.

Aerial Map
Survey — A226

1976, Apr. 8　　　Perf. 13½x12½
1116 A226 1b black & vio bl　.50　.25
Natl. Cartographic Institute, 40th anniv.

Gen. Ribas'
Signature
A227

José
Felix
Ribas
A228

1976, Apr. 26　Photo.　Perf. 12½x13
1117 A227 40c red & green　.30　.20
Perf. 13½
1118 A228 55c multicolored　.40　.20
Gen. José Felix Ribas (1775-1815), independence hero, birth bicentenary.

Musicians of the Chacao School, by
Armandio Barrios — A229

Lamas's
Colophon
A230

1976, May 13　Litho.　Perf. 13½
1119 A229 75c multicolored　.40　.25

Photo.　Perf. 12½x13
1120 A230 1.25b buff, red & gray　.70　.35
José Angel Lamas (1775-1814), composer,
birth bicentenary.

Bolivar, by José Maria
Espinoza — A231

1976　　　Engr.　　　Perf. 12
Size: 18x22½mm
1121 A231　5c green　.20　.20
1122 A231　10c lilac rose　.20　.20
1123 A231　15c brown　.20　.20
1124 A231　20c black　.20　.20
1125 A231　25c yellow　.20　.20
1126 A231　30c violet bl　.20　.20
1127 A231　45c dk purple　.20　.20
1128 A231　50c orange　.20　.20
1129 A231　65c blue　.25　.20
1130 A231　1b vermilion　.30　.25
Size: 26x32mm
Perf. 12x11½
1131 A231　2b gray　.65　.25
1132 A231　3b violet blue　.95　.40
1133 A231　4b purple　1.25　.55
1134 A231　5b orange　1.50　.75
1135 A231　10b dull purple　3.50　1.40
1136 A231　15b blue　5.25　2.00
1137 A231　20b vermilion　6.50　2.75
　Nos. 1121-1137 (17)　21.75　10.15
Issued: 5c-1b, May 17; 2b-20b, July 15.

Coil Stamps
1978, May 22　　　Perf. 13½ Horiz.
Size: 18x22½mm
1138 A231　5c green　.20　.20
1139 A231　10c lilac rose　.20　.20
1140 A231　15c brown　.20　.20
1141 A231　20c black　.20　.20
1142 A231　25c yellow　.20　.20
1143 A231　30c violet blue　.20　.20
1144 A231　45c dk purple　.20　.20
1144A A231　50c orange　.25　.20
1144B A231　65c blue　.25　.20
1144C A231　1b vermilion　.40　.20
　Nos. 1138-1144C (10)　2.30　2.00

Black control number on back of every fifth
stamp.
　See Nos. 1305-1307, 1362-1366, 1401-
1409, 1482, 1484, 1487, 1490. Compare with
designs A405-A406.

Maze
A232

Central
University
A233

Faculty
Emblems
A234

1976, June 1　Litho.　Perf. 12½x13
1145 A232 30c multicolored　.20　.20
1146 A233 50c yel, org & blk　.25　.20
1147 A234 90c black & yellow　.55　.35
　Nos. 1145-1147 (3)　1.00　.75
Central University of Venezuela, 250th anniv.

"Unity" — A235

Washington,
US Bicent.
Emblem
A236

Designs: 45c, 1.25b, similar to 15c.

1976, June 29　Litho.　Perf. 12½
1148 A235　15c multicolored　.20　.20
1149 A235　45c multicolored　.25　.20
1150 A235　1.25b multicolored　.55　.35
　Nos. 1148-1150 (3)　1.00　.75
Amphictyonic Cong. of Panama, Sesqui.

1976, July 4　Engr.　Perf. 14
US Bicentennial Emblem and: No. 1152,
Jefferson. No. 1153, Lincoln. No. 1154, F. D.
Roosevelt. No. 1155, J. F. Kennedy.
1151 A236 1b red brn & blk　.60　.30
1152 A236 1b green & blk　.60　.30
1153 A236 1b purple & blk　.60　.30
1154 A236 1b blue & blk　.60　.30
1155 A236 1b olive & blk　.60　.30
　Nos. 1151-1155 (5)　3.00　1.50
American Bicentennial.

Valve — A237

Ornament
A239

Nativity, by
Barbaro
Rivas — A238

Computer drawings of valves & pipelines.

1976, Nov. 8　Photo.　Perf. 123½x14
1156 A237 10c multicolored　.20　.20
1157 A237 30c multicolored　.20　.20
1158 A237 35c multicolored　.20　.20
1159 A237 40c multicolored　.20　.20
1160 A237 55c multicolored　.25　.20
1161 A237 90c multicolored　.45　.25
　Nos. 1156-1161 (6)　1.50　1.25
Nationalization of the oil industry.

1976, Dec. 1　Litho.　Perf. 13x14
1162 A238 30c multicolored　.40　.25
Christmas 1976.

Lithographed and Embossed
1976, Dec. 15　　　Perf. 14x13½
1163 A239 60c yellow & black　.35　.20
Declaration of Bogota (economic agreements of Andean countries), 10th anniv.

Coat of Arms of Barinas — A240

1977, May 25　Photo.　Perf. 12½x13
1164 A240 50c multicolored　.35　.20
400th anniv. of the founding of Barinas.

Crucified Christ,
Patron Saint of
La Grita — A241

1977, Aug. 6　Litho.　Perf. 13
1165 A241 30c multicolored　.30　.25
Founding of La Grita, 400th anniv. (in 1976).

Symbolic
City — A242

1977, Aug. 26　Litho.　Perf. 13½
1166 A242 1b multicolored　.50　.25
450th anniversary of the founding of Coro.

Communications Symbols — A243

1977, Sept. 30　Litho.　Perf. 13½x14
1167 A243 85c multicolored　.50　.20
9th Interamerican Postal and Telecommunications Staff Congress, Caracas, Sept. 26-30.

Cable Connecting
with TV, Telephone
and Circuit
Box — A244

1977, Oct. 12　Litho.　Perf. 14
1168 A244 95c multicolored　.50　.20
Inauguration of Columbus underwater cable
linking Venezuela and the Canary Islands.

"Venezuela"
A245

Designs: "Venezuela" horizontal on 50c,
1.05b; reading up on 80c, 1.25b; reading down
on 1.50b.

1977, Nov. 26   Photo.   *Perf. 13½x13*

1169	A245	30c brt yel & blk	.20	.20
1170	A245	50c dp org & blk	.25	.20
1171	A245	80c gray & blk	.45	.20
1172	A245	1.05b red & blk	.50	.20
1173	A245	1.25b yel & blk	.60	.20
1174	A245	1.50b gray & blk	.75	.25
	Nos. 1169-1174 (6)		2.75	1.25

Iron industry nationalization, 1st anniv.

Juan Pablo Duarte — A246   Nativity, Colonial Sculpture — A247

1977, Dec. 8   Engr.   *Perf. 11x13*

1175	A246	75c black & lilac	.50	.20

Duarte (1813-76), leader in liberation struggle.

1977, Dec. 15   Litho.   *Perf. 13*

1176	A247	30c green & multi	.25	.20

Christmas 1977.

OPEC Emblem — A248

1977, Dec. 20

1177	A248	1.05b brt & lt bl & blk	.60	.20

50th Conference of Oil Producing and Exporting Countries, Caracas.

Bicyclist A249

1978, Jan. 16   Litho.   *Perf. 13½x13*

1178	A249	5c Racing bicyclists	.20	.20
1179	A249	1.25b shown	.60	.20

World Bicycling Championships, San Cristobal, Tachira, Aug. 22-Sept. 4.

Profiles A250

1978, Apr. 21   Litho.   *Perf. 13½x14*

1180	A250	70c blk, gray & lil	.35	.20

Language Day.
Issued in tete-beche pairs. Value $2.75.

Magnetic Computer Tape and Satellite A251

1978, May 17   Litho.   *Perf. 14*

1184	A251	75c violet blue	.40	.20

10th World Telecommunications Day.

"1777-1977" — A252

Goya's Carlos III as Computer Print — A253

1978, June 23   Litho.   *Perf. 12*

1185	A252	30c multicolored	.20	.20
1186	A253	1b multicolored	.55	.20

200th anniversary of Venezuelan unification.

Bolivar Bicentenary

Juan Vicente Bolivar y Ponte, Father of Simon Bolivar — A254

The Oath on Monte Sacro, Rome, by Tito Salas — A255

1978, July 24   Engr.   *Perf. 12½*

1187	A254	30c emerald & blk	.20	.20
1188	A254	1b multicolored	.55	.25

Souvenir Sheet
Litho.
Perf. 14

1189	A255	Sheet of 5	32.50	32.50
a.		50c, single stamp	1.25	1.25

1978, Dec. 17   Engr.   *Perf. 12½*

Designs: 30c, Bolivar at 25. 1b, Simon Rodriguez. No. 1192, shown. (Bolivar's tutor).

1190	A254	30c multicolored	.20	.20
1191	A254	1b rose red & blk	.30	.20

Souvenir Sheet
Litho.
Perf. 14

1192	A255	Sheet of 5	16.00	16.00
a.		50c, single stamp	.75	.75

Size of souvenir sheet stamps: 20x24mm. Size of #1189: 154x130mm; #1192: 130x155mm.

1979, July 24   Engr.   *Perf. 12½*

Designs: 30c, Alexander Sabes Petion, president of Haiti. 1b, Bolivar's signature.
No. 1195: a, Partial map of Jamaica, horiz. b, Partial map of Jamaica, vert. c, Bolivar, 1816. d, Luis Brion. e, Petion.

1193	A254	30c org, vio & blk	.30	.20
1194	A254	1b red org & blk	.45	.20

Souvenir Sheet
Litho.
Perf. 14

1195	A255	Sheet of 5	3.25	3.25
a.-e.		50c, any single	.30	.30

Size of souvenir sheet stamps: 26x20, 20x26mm.

1979, Dec. 17   Engr.   *Perf. 12½*

Designs: 30c, Bolivar. 1b, Slave. No. 1198, Freeing of the Slaves, by Tito Salas. (30c, 1b, details from design of No. 1198.)

1196	A254	30c multicolored	.20	.20
1197	A254	1b multicolored	.30	.20

Souvenir Sheet
Litho.
Perf. 14

1198	A255	Sheet of 5	5.00	5.00
a.		50c, single stamp	.90	.90

Simon Bolivar, birth centenary. Size of souvenir sheet stamps: 22x28mm.
See Nos. 1228-1230, 1264-1266, 1276-1284, 1294-1296, 1317-1322.

"T" and "CTV" — A256   Symbolic Design — A257

Designs: Different arrangement of letters "T" and "CTV" for "Confederacion de Trabajeros Venezolanos."

1978, Sept. 27   Photo.   *Perf. 13x13½*

1199		Strip of 5	.75	.75
a.-e.	A256	30c, single stamp	.20	.20
1200		Strip of 5	1.60	1.60
a.-e.	A256	95c, single stamp	.25	.20

Workers' Day.

1978, Oct. 3   Litho.   *Perf. 14*

1201	A257	50c dark brown	.50	.25

Rafael Rangel, physician and scientist, birth cententary.

Drill Head, Tachira Oil Field Map — A258

"P" as Pipeline A259

1978, Nov. 2   Litho.   *Perf. 13½*

1202	A258	30c multicolored	.25	.20
1203	A259	1.05b multicolored	.55	.25

Centenary of oil industry.

Star — A260

1978, Dec. 6   Litho.   *Perf. 14*

1204	A260	30c multicolored	.25	.20

Christmas 1978.

"P T" — A261

1979, Feb. 8   Litho.   *Perf. 12½*

1205	A261	75c black & red	.25	.20

Creation of Postal and Telegraph Institute.

"Dam Holding Back Water" A262

1979, Feb. 15   Photo.   *Perf. 13½*

1206	A262	2b silver, gray & blk	.65	.35

Guri Dam, 10th anniversary.

San Martin, by E. J. Maury — A263

60c, San Martin, by Mercedes. 70c, Monument, Guayaquil. 75c, San Martin's signature.

1979, Feb. 25   *Perf. 12½x13*

1207	A263	40c blue, blk & yel	.20	.20
1208	A263	60c blue, blk & yel	.25	.20
1209	A263	70c blue, blk & yel	.35	.20
1210	A263	75c blue, blk & yel	.35	.25
	Nos. 1207-1210 (4)		1.15	.85

José de San Martin (1778-1850), South American liberator.

"Rotary" — A264

1979, Aug. 7   Litho.   *Perf. 14x13½*

1211	A264	85c gold & blk	.30	.20

Rotary Club of Caracas, 50th anniversary.

Our Lady of Coromoto Appearing to Children A265

Engraved and Lithographed
1979, Aug. 23   *Perf. 13*

1212	A265	55c black & dp org	.25	.20

Canonization of Our Lady of Coromoto, 25th anniv.

London Residence, Coat of Arms,
Miranda — A266

1979, Oct. 23 Litho. Perf. 14½x14
1213 A266 50c multicolored   .25 .20
Francisco de Miranda (1750-1816), Venezuelan independence fighter.

O'Leary,
Maps of
South
America
and
United
Kingdom
A267

1979, Nov. 6
1214 A267 30c multicolored   .25 .20
Daniel O'Leary (1801-1854), writer.

A268   A269

IYC Emblem and: 79c, Boy holding nest.
80c, Boys in water, bridge.

1979, Nov. 20 Litho. Perf. 14½x14
1215 A268 70c lt blue & blk   .25 .20
1216 A268 80c multicolored   .30 .20
International Year of the Child.

1979, Dec. 1 Litho. Perf. 13
1217 A269 30c multicolored   .25 .20
Christmas 1979.

Caudron
Bomber,
EXFILVE
Emblem
A270

EXFILVE Emblem and: No. 1219, Stearman biplane. No. 1220, UH-1H helicopter. No. 1221, CF-5 jet fighter.

1979, Dec. 15 Perf. 11x11½
1218 A270 75c multicolored   .25 .20
1219 A270 75c multicolored   .25 .20
1220 A270 75c multicolored   .25 .20
1221 A270 75c multicolored   .25 .20
  a.   Block of 4, #1218-1221   1.25 .60
Venezuelan Air Force, 59th anniv.; EXFILVE 79, 3rd Natl. Philatelic Exhibition, Dec. 7-17.

IPOSTEL
Emblem,
World Map
A271

1979, Dec. 27 Perf. 11½
1222 A271 75c multicolored   .30 .20
Postal and Telegraph Institute, introduction of new logo.

Queen Victoria, Hill — A272

1980, Feb. 13 Litho. Perf. 12½
1223 A272 55c multicolored   .25 .20
Sir Rowland Hill (1795-1879), originator of penny postage.

Dr. Augusto Pi Suner, Physiologist,
Birth Centenary — A273

1980, Mar. 14 Litho. Perf. 11½
1224 A273 80c multicolored   .30 .20

Spanish Seed   Juan Lovera
Leaf — A274   (1778-1841),
                     Artist — A275

Lithographed and Engraved
1980, Mar. 27 Perf. 13
1225 A274 50c multicolored   .50 .20
Pedro Loefling (1729-56), Swedish botanist.

1980, May 25 Litho. Perf. 13½
1226 A275 60c blue & dp org   .25 .20
1227 A275 75c violet & org   .30 .20

Bolivar Bicentenary Type of 1978
30c, Signing of document. 1b, House of Congress. #1230, Angostura Congress, by Tito Salas.

1980, July 24 Engr. Perf. 12½
1228 A254 30c multicolored   .20 .20
1229 A254 1b multicolored   .40 .20
Souvenir Sheet
Litho.
Perf. 14
1230 A255 Sheet of 5   3.25 3.25
  a.   50c, single stamp   .20 .20
Simon Bolivar (1783-1830), revolutionary. Size of souvenir sheet stamps: 25x20mm, 20x25mm.

Dancing Girls, by
Armando
Reveron — A276

Bernardo
O'Higgins — A277

1980, Aug. 17 Litho. Perf. 13
1231 A276 50c shown   .20 .20
Size: 25x40mm
1232 A276 65c Portrait   .45 .25
Armando Reveron (1889-1955), artist.

Lithographed and Engraved
1980, Aug. 22 Perf. 13x14
1233 A277 85c multicolored   .60 .25
Bernardo O'Higgins (1776-1842), Chilean soldier and statesman.

School Ship
Simon
Bolivar
A278

Frigate
Mariscal
Sucre
A279

Perf. 11½ (#1234), 11x11½
1980, Sept. 13 Litho.
1234 A278 1.50b shown   1.25 .40
1235 A279 1.50b shown   1.25 .40
1236 A279 1.50b Submarine
                  Picua   1.25 .40
1237 A279 1.50b Naval Academy 1.25 .40
      Nos. 1234-1237 (4)   5.00 1.60
"Picuda" is misspelled on stamp.

Workers
Holding
OPEC
Emblem
A280

20th Anniv. of OPEC (Organization of Petroleum Exporting Countries): #1239, Emblem.

1980, Sept. 14 Litho. Perf. 12x11½
1238 A280 1.50b multicolored   .50 .25
1239 A280 1.50b multicolored   .50 .25

Death of
Simon
Bolivar
A281

1980, Dec. 17 Litho. Perf. 11x11½
1240 A281 2b multicolored   1.25 .40
Simon Bolivar, 150th anniversary of death.

A282

A283

Lithographed and Engraved
1980, Dec. 17 Perf. 13x12½
1241 A282 2b multicolored   .75 .35
Gen. José Antonio Sucre, 150th anniv. of death.

1980, Dec. 19 Litho. Perf. 14x13½
1242 A283 1b Nativity by Rubens   .35 .25
Christmas 1980.

Helen Keller's Initials (Written and
Braille) — A284

Lithographed and Embossed
1981, Feb. 12 Perf. 12½
1243 A284 1.50b multicolored   .45 .25
Helen Keller (1880-1968), blind and deaf writer and lecturer.

John Baptiste de   San Felipe City,
la Salle — A285   250th
                         Anniv. — A286

1981, May 15 Litho. Perf. 11½x11
1244 A285 1.25b multicolored   .40 .20
Christian Brothers' 300th anniv.

1981, May 1 Perf. 11½
1245 A286 3b multicolored   .75 .35

Municipal
Theater of
Caracas
Centenary
A287

1981, June 28 Litho. Perf. 12
1246 A287 1.25b multicolored   1.40 .25

A288

A290

A289

1981, Sept. 15   Litho.   Perf. 11½
1247 A288 2b multicolored .60 .20
UPU membership centenary.

1981, Oct. 14   Litho.
1248 A289 1b multicolored .30 .20
11th natl. population and housing census.

1981, Dec. 3   Litho.   Perf. 11½
1249 A290 95c multicolored .35 .20
9th Bolivar Games, Barquismeto.

19th Cent. Bicycle A291

1981, Dec. 5   Photo.   Perf. 13x14
1250 A291 1b shown .55 .35
1251 A291 1.05b Locomotive, 1926 .55 .35
1252 A291 1.25b Buick, 1937 .80 .40
1253 A291 1.50b Coach 1.00 .50
Nos. 1250-1253 (4) 2.90 1.60
See Nos. 1289-1292, 1308-1311.

Christmas 1981 A292

1981, Dec. 21   Litho.   Perf. 11½
1254 A292 1b multicolored .30 .20

50th Anniv. of Natural Science Society — A293

1982, Jan. 21   Perf. 11½
1255 A293 1b Mt. Autana .30 .20
1256 A293 1.50b Sarisarinama .45 .25
1257 A293 2b Guacharo Cave .60 .30
Nos. 1255-1257 (3) 1.35 .75

20th Anniv. of Constitution A294

1982, Jan. 28   Photo.   Perf. 13x13½
1258 A294 1.85b gold & blk .60 .25

A295

A296

1982, Feb. 19   Litho.   Perf. 13½
1259 A295 3b multicolored .90 .40
20th anniv. of agricultural reform.

1982, Mar. 12   Litho.   Perf. 13½
1260 A296 1b blue & dk blue .30 .20
Jules Verne (1828-1905), science fiction writer.

Natl. Anthem Centenary (1981) A297

1982, Mar. 26   Perf. 11½
1261 A297 1b multicolored .30 .20

1300th Anniv. of Bulgaria A298

6th Natl. 5-Year Plan, 1981-85 A299

1982, June 2   Litho.   Perf. 13½
1262 A298 65c multicolored .20 .20

1982, June 11
1263 A299 2b multicolored .40 .20

Bolivar Types of 1978
1982, July 24   Engr.   Perf. 12½
1264 A254 30c Juan José Rondon .20 .20
1265 A254 1b José Antonio Anzoategui .20 .20
Souvenir Sheet
Litho.
Perf. 14
1266 A255 Sheet of 5 3.00 3.00
a.-e. 50c, any single .20 .20
Single stamps of No. 1266 show details from Battle of Boyaca, by Martin Tovar y Tovar. Size of souvenir sheet stamps: 19x26mm, 26x19mm.

Cecilio Acosta (1818-1881), Writer — A299a

1982, Aug. 13   Litho.   Perf. 11½
1266F A299a 3b multicolored .45 .25

Aloe A300

1982, Oct. 14   Photo.   Perf. 13
1267 A300 1.05b shown .65 .35
1268 A300 2.55b Tortoise 1.75 .35
1269 A300 2.75b Tara amarilla tree 2.00 .35
1270 A300 3b Guacharo bird 2.25 .40
Nos. 1267-1270 (4) 6.65 1.45

Andres Bello (1781-1865), Statesman and Reformer — A301

1982, Nov. 20   Litho.   Perf. 12
1271 A301 1.05b multicolored .45 .20
1272 A301 2.55b multicolored .95 .30
1273 A301 2.75b multicolored .95 .30
1274 A301 3b multicolored 1.25 .35
Nos. 1271-1274 (4) 3.60 1.15

Christmas 1982 — A302

Design: Holy Family creche figures by Francisco J. Cardozo, 18th cent.

Photogravure and Engraved
1982, Dec. 7   Perf. 13½
1275 A302 1b multicolored .20 .20

Bolivar Types of 1978
1982-83   Engr.   Perf. 12½
1276 A254 30c Victory Monument, Carabobo .20 .20
1277 A254 30c Monument to the Meeting plaque .20 .20
1278 A254 30c Antonio de Sucre .20 .20
1279 A254 1b Jose Antonio Paez .35 .20
1280 A254 1b Sword hilt, 1824 .35 .20
1281 A254 1b Guayaquil Monument .35 .20
Nos. 1276-1281 (6) 1.65 1.20
Souvenir Sheets
Litho.
Perf. 14
1282 A255 Sheet of 5 3.25 3.25
a.-e. 50c, any single .20 .20
1283 A255 Sheet of 5 3.25 3.25
a.-e. 50c, any single .20 .20
1284 A255 Sheet of 5 3.25 3.25
a.-e. 50c, any single .20 .20
No. 1282: Battle of Carabobo by Martin Tovar y Tovar; No. 1283, Monument to the Meeting; No. 1284, Battle of Ayacucho, by Martin Tovar y Tovar.
Issue dates: Nos. 1276-1277, 1279, 1281-1283, Dec. 17; others, Apr. 18, 1983.

Gen. Jose Francisco Bermudez — A303

Antonio Nicolas Briceno, Liberation Hero A304

Perf. 13x13½, 15x14
1982, Dec. 23   Litho.
1285 A303 3b multicolored 1.10 .30
1286 A304 3b multicolored 1.10 .30

25th Anniv. of 1958 Reforms A305

1983, Jan. 23   Perf. 10½x10
1287 A305 3b multicolored .65 .30

A306

A307

1983, Mar. 20   Photo.   Perf. 13½x13
1288 A306 4b olive & red .65 .30
25th anniv. of Judicial Police Technical Dept.

Transportation Type of 1981
Perf. 13½x14½
1983, Mar. 28   Photo.
1289 A291 75c Lincoln, 1923 .75 .30
1290 A291 80c Locomotive, 1889 .75 .30
1291 A291 85c Willys truck, 1927 .90 .30
1292 A291 95c Cleveland motorcycle, 1920 .90 .30
Nos. 1289-1292 (4) 3.30 1.20

1983, May 17   Photo.   Perf. 13x12½
1293 A307 2.85b multicolored .45 .30
World Communications Year.

Bolivar Type of 1978
Designs: 30c; Flags of Colombia, Peru, Chile, Venezuela, and Buenos Aires. 1b; Equestrian Statue of Bolivar.

Photo. & Engr. (#1294), Engr. (#1295)
1983, July 25   Perf. 12½
1294 A254 30c multicolored .35 .20
1295 A254 1b multicolored .40 .20
Souvenir Sheet
Litho.
Perf. 14
1296 A255 Sheet of 5 3.50 3.25
a.-e. 50c, any single .20 .20
Single stamps of No. 1296 show details of "The Liberator on the Silver Mountain of Potosi" Size of souvenir sheet stamps, 20x25mm.

9th Pan-American Games A308 A309

Designs: #1303a, baseball. b, cycle wheel. c, boxing glove. d, soccer ball. e, target.

Lithographed and Engraved

1983, Aug. 25   **Perf. 13**
1297	A308	2b shown	.40	.20
1298	A308	2b Swimming	.40	.20
1299	A308	2.70b Cycling	.50	.40
1300	A308	2.70b Fencing	.50	.40
1301	A308	2.85b Runners	.55	.50
1302	A308	2.85b Weightlifting	.55	.50
	Nos. 1297-1302 (6)		2.90	2.20

Souvenir Sheet

1303		Sheet of 5	11.00 11.00
a.-e.	A309	1b, any single	11.00 11.00

#1303 for Copan '83. Size: 167x121mm.

25th Anniv. of Cadafe (State Electricity Authority) — A310

1983, Oct. 27   **Litho.**   **Perf. 14**
1304	A310	3b multicolored	1.00	.45

Bolivar Type of 1976

1983, Sept. 29   **Engr.**   **Perf. 12**
Size: 26x32mm
1305	A231	25b blue green	6.25	3.00
1306	A231	30b brown	7.50	3.75
1307	A231	50b brt rose lilac	11.50	6.25
	Nos. 1305-1307 (3)		25.25	13.00

Transportation Type of 1981

Various views of Caracas Metro.

1983, Dec.   **Photo.**   **Perf. 13½x14½**
1308	A291	55c multicolored	.50	.30
1309	A291	75c multicolored	.50	.30
1310	A291	95c multicolored	.50	.30
1311	A291	2b multicolored	1.10	.45
	Nos. 1308-1311 (4)		2.60	1.35

Christmas 1983 A311

1983, Dec. 1   **Litho.**   **Perf. 13x14**
1312	A311	1b Nativity	.25	.25

Scouting Year (1982) A312

Lithographed and Engraved

1983, Dec. 14   **Perf. 12½x13**
1313	A312	2.25p Pitching tent	.40	.25
1314	A312	2.55b Planting tree	.40	.25
1315	A312	2.75b Mountain climbing	.45	.25
1316	A312	3b Camp site	.45	.25
	Nos. 1313-1316 (4)		1.70	1.00

Bolivar Type of 1976

Designs: No. 1317, Title page of "Opere de Raimondo Montecuccoli" (most valuable book in Caracas University Library). No. 1318, Pedro Gual, Congress of Panama delegate, 1826. No. 1319, Jose Maria Vargas (b. 1786), University of Caracas pres. No. 1320, José Faustino Sanchez Carrion, Congress of Panama delegate, 1826.

1984   **Engr.**   **Perf. 12½**
1317	A254	30c multicolored	.25	.20
1318	A254	30c multicolored	.25	.20
1319	A254	1b multicolored	.25	.20
1320	A254	1b multicolored	.25	.20
	Nos. 1317-1320 (4)		1.00	.80

Souvenir Sheets
Litho.
Perf. 14

1321	A255	Sheet of 5	3.00 2.75
a.-e.		50c, any single	.20 .20
1322	A255	Sheet of 5	3.25 3.25
a.-e.		50c, any single	.20 .20

Single stamps of No. 1321 show details of Arts, Science and Education, fresco by Hector Poleo; 1322, Map of South America, 1829. Size of souvenir sheet stamps: 20x30mm; 27x20mm.
Issued: #1317, 1319, 1321, 1/19; others, 1/20.

Radio Waves — A313

Intelligentsia for Peace — A314

1984, Jan. 30   **Litho.**   **Perf. 14x13**
1323	A313	2.70b multicolored	.40	.20

Radio Club of Venezuela, 50th anniv.

1984, Jan. 31
1324	A314	1b Doves	.20	.20
1325	A314	2.70b Profile	.40	.20
1326	A314	2.85b Flower, head	.40	.20
	Nos. 1324-1326 (3)		1.00	.60

President Romulo Gallegos (1884-1969) A315

Gallegos: No. 1327, Portrait as a young man in formal dress. No. 1328, Portrait, 1948.

1984-85   **Litho.**   **Perf. 11½**
1327	A315	1.70b royal bl, dl bl, beige & blk	.40	.25
1328	A315	1.70b ocher, org brn & buff	.40	.25

Issued: #1327, 10/12/84; #1328, 1/18/85.
See Nos. 1335-1336.

Pan-American Union of Engineering Associations, 18th Convention A316

1984, Oct. 28
1329	A316	2.55b pale buff, dk bl	.65	.20

Christmas 1984 A317

1984, Dec. 3
1330	A317	1b multicolored	.30	.20

Pope John Paul II, Statue of the Virgin of Caracas A318

1985, Jan. 26   **Litho.**   **Perf. 12**
1331	A318	1b multicolored	.80	.25

Papal visit, 1985.

Pascua City Bicent. A319

1985, Feb. 10
1332	A319	1.50b multicolored	.40	.25

Dr. Mario Briceno-Iragory (b. 1897), Historian — A320

1985, Oct.   **Litho.**   **Perf. 12**
1333	A320	1.25b silver & ver	.30	.20

Natl. St. Vincent de Paul Soc., Cent. — A321

1985, July
1334	A321	1b dk ol bis, ver & buff	.40	.20

Gallegos Memorial Type of 1984-85

Designs: Gallegos, diff.

1985, Aug. 8
1335	A315	1.70b gray grn, dk gray grn & dl gray grn	.30	.20
1336	A315	1.70b grn, sage grn & dl grn	.30	.20

Dated 1984.

Latin American Economic System, 10th Anniv. A322

1985, Aug. 15
1337	A322	4b black & red	1.40	.60

Miniature Sheet

Virgin Mary, Birth Bimillennium A323

Statues: a, Virgin of the Divine Shepherd. b, Chiquinquira Madonna. c, Coromoto Madonna. d, Valley Madonna. e, Virgin of Perpetual Succor. f, Virgin of Peace. g, Immaculate Conception Virgin. h, Soledad Madonna. i, Virgin of Consolation. j, Nieves Madonna.

1985, Sept. 9
1338		Sheet of 10	6.00 6.00
a.-j.	A323	1b, any single	.40 .20

OPEC, 25th Anniv. A324

1985, Sept. 13
1339	A324	6b multicolored	1.10	.60

Opening of the Museum of Contemporary Art, Caracas — A325

1985, Oct. 24   **Perf. 13½**
1340	A325	3b multicolored	.55	.30

Dated 1983.

UN, 40th Anniv. A326

1985, Nov. 15   **Perf. 12**
1341	A326	10b brt blue & ver	1.50	.90

Intl. Youth Year A327

1985, Nov. 26
1342	A327	1.50b multicolored	.30	.20

Christmas 1985 — A328

Nativity: a, Sheperds. b, Holy Family, Magi. Se-tenant in a continuous design.

1985, Dec. 2
1343	A328	Pair	1.25 1.25
a.-b.		2b, any single	.60 .20

Dr. Luis Maria Drago (b. 1859), Politician A329

1985, Dec. 20   **Perf. 13½**
1344 A329 2.70b tan, ver & sepia   .50 .35

Dated 1984.

Miniature Sheet

Natl. Oil Industry, 10th Anniv. A330

Designs: a, Industry emblem. b, Isla Oil Refinery. c, Bariven oil terminal. d, Pequiven refinery. e, Corpoven drilling rig. f, Maraven offshore rig. g, Intevep labs. h, Meneven refinery. i, Lagoven refinery. j, Emblem, early drilling rig.

1985, Dec. 13   **Perf. 12**
1345   Sheet of 10   12.00 12.00
a.-b.   A330 1b multi   .25 .25
c.-d.   A330 2b multi   .55 .25
e.-f.   A330 3b multi   1.00 .35
g.-h.   A330 4b multi   1.25 .40
i.-j.   A330 5b multi   1.50 .50

Simon Bolivar Memorial Coins — A331

1985, Dec. 18
1346 A331   2b multicolored   .35 .25
1347 A331   2.70b multicolored   .50 .30
1348 A331   3b multicolored   .55 .35
  Nos. 1346-1348 (3)   1.40 .90

Dated 1984.

Guayana Development Corp., 25th Anniv. — A332

1985, Dec. 27
1349 A332 2b Guayana City   .35 .25
1350 A332 3b Orinoco Steel Mill   .55 .35
1351 A332 5b Raul Leoni-Guri Hydro-electric Dam   .90 .60
  Nos. 1349-1351 (3)   1.80 1.20

Miniature Sheet

A333

Dr. Jose Vargas (1786-1854) — A334

Designs: No. 1352a, Handwriting and signature. b, Portrait, 1874, by Martin Tovar y Tovar. c, Statue, Palace of the Academies. d, Flags, EXFILBO '86 emblem. e, Vargas do Caracas Hospital. f, Frontispiece of lectures manual, 1842. g, Portrait, 1986, by Alirio Palacios. h, Gesneria vargasii. i, Bolivar-Vargas commemorative medal, 1955, 6th Natl. Medical Sciences Cong. j, Portrait, anonymous, 19th cent.
No. 1353a, Portrait, facing front. b, Portrait, facing left, Nos. 1352a, 1352d, 1352e, 1352h and 1352i have horizontal vignettes.

1986, Mar. 10   **Litho.**   **Perf. 12**
1352   Sheet of 10   7.75 7.75
a.-j.   A333 3b, any single   .65 .30

Souvenir Sheet
Imperf
1353   Sheet of 2   10.00 10.00
a.-b.   A334 15b, any single   4.50 .75

EXFILBO '86, Mar. 10-17, Caracas, 1st Bolivarian exhibition.

Youths Painting School Wall A335

1986, May 12   **Perf. 12**
1354 A335 3b shown   .50 .25
1355 A335 5b Repairing desk   .90 .25

Founding and maintenance of educational institutions.

Francisco Miranda's Work for American Liberation, Bicent. (1981) A336

Lithographed and Engraved
1986, Apr. 18   **Perf. 13**
1356 A336 1.05b multicolored   .20 .20

Dated 1983.

INDULAC, 45th Anniv. A337

1986, June 27   **Litho.**   **Perf. 12**
1357 A337 2.55b Milk trucks, vert.   .30 .20
1358 A337 2.70b Map, vert.   .35 .20
1359 A337 3.70b Milk processing plant   .40 .20
  Nos. 1357-1359 (3)   1.05 .60

Industria Lactea (INDULAC), Venezuelan milk processing company.

Miniature Sheet

Viasa Venezuelan Airlines, 25th Anniv. A338

a, Commemorative coin. b, Douglas DC-8 ascending. c, DC-8 taxiing. d, Boeing 747 in flight. e, DC-10 tails. f, Map of hemispheres. g, DC-10 taking off. h, Rear of DC-10 & DC8 on runway. i, DC-9 over mountains. j, Crew in cockpit.

1986, Aug. 11   **Litho.**   **Perf. 12**
1360   Sheet of 10   8.00 8.00
a.-e.   A338 3b, any single   .50 .35
f.-j.   A338 3.25b, any single   .55 .35

Miniature Sheet

Romulo Betancourt (1908-1981), President — A339

a, i, Portrait with natl. flag. b, j, Seated in armchair, smoking pipe. c, h, Wearing hat, text. d, f, Wearing sash of office. e, g, Reading.

1986, Sept. 28
1361   Sheet of 10   10.00 10.00
a.-e.   A339 2.70b, any single   .50 .20
f.-j.   A339 3b, any single   .60 .25

Redrawn Bolivar Type of 1976
1986, Sept. 29   **Litho.**   **Perf. 12½**
1362 A231 25c red   .35 .25
1363 A231 50c blue   .35 .25
1364 A231 75c pink   .35 .25
1365 A231 1b orange   .35 .25
1366 A231 2b brt yellow grn   .40 .25
  Nos. 1362-1366 (5)   1.80 1.25

Nos. 1362-1366 inscribed Armitano. For surcharges see Nos. 1453-1464.

Re-opening of Zulia University, 40th Anniv. — A340

1986, Sept. 29
1367 A340 2.70b shown   .30 .25
1368 A340 2.70b Library entrance   .30 .25
a.   Pair, #1367-1368   .60 .60

11th Congress of Architects, Engineers and Affiliated Professionals — A341

1986, Oct. 3
1369 A341 1.40b multicolored   .20 .20
1370 A341 1.55b multicolored   .20 .20
a.   Pair, #1369-1370   1.50 1.50

Fauna and Flora A342

1986, Sept. 12   **Photo.**   **Perf. 13½**
1371 A342 70c Priodontes maximus   .65 .55
1372 A342 85c Espeletia angustifolia   .65 .55
1373 A342 2.70b Crocodylus intermedius   .65 .55
1374 A342 3b Brownea grandiceps   .80 .60
  Nos. 1371-1374 (4)   2.75 2.25

Miniature Sheet

State Visit of Pope John Paul II — A343

1986, Oct. 22   **Perf. 12**
1375   Sheet of 10   6.00 6.00
a.   A343 1b Pope, mountains   .20 .20
b.   A343 2b Bridge   .30 .20
c.   A343 3b Kissing the ground   .40 .20
d.   A343 3b Statue of Our Lady   .40 .20
e.   A343 4b Crosier, buildings   .60 .20
f.   A343 5.25b Waterfall   .80 .25

#1375 contains 2 each #1375a-1375b, 1375e-1375f and one each #1375c-1375d.

Miniature Sheet

Children's Foundation, 20th Anniv. A344

Children's drawings: a, Three children. b, Hearts, children, birds. c, Child, animals. d, Animals, house. e, Landscape. f, Child, flowers on table. g, Child holding ball. h, Children, birds. i, Lighthouse, port. j, Butterfly in flight.

1986, Nov. 10
1376   Sheet of 10   4.75 4.75
a.-e.   A344 2.55b, any single   .35 .20
f.-j.   A344 2.70b, any single   .35 .20

Christmas — A345

Creche figures carved by Eliecer Alvarez.

1986, Nov. 10
1377   2b shown   .25 .20
1378   2b Virgin and child   .25 .20
a.   A345 Pair, #1377-1378   .50 .50

City Police, 25th Anniv. A346

Emblem and: a, Emergency medical aid, helicopter. b, Security at sporting event. c, Bar code. d, Cadets in front of police academy. e, Motorcycle police.

1986, Dec. 10
1379   Strip of 5   4.00 4.00
a.-e.   A346 2.70b, any single   .50 .25

Folk Art A347

Lithographed and Engraved
1987, Jan. 31   **Perf. 13**
1380 A347 2b Musical instrument   .30 .20
1381 A347 2b Fabric   .30 .20
1382 A347 3b Ceramic pot   .40 .20
1383 A347 3b Basket work   .40 .20
  Nos. 1380-1383 (4)   1.40 .80

Dated 1983. Nos. 1380, 1382 show Pre-Hispanic art.

Discovery of the Tubercle Bacillus by Robert Koch, Cent. (in 1982) A348

Lithographed and Engraved
1987, Feb. 27   *Perf. 14x14½*
1384 A348 2.55b multicolored   .55 .20

Dated 1983.

Miniature Sheet

Easter 1987 A349

Paintings and sculpture: a, Arrival of Jesus in Jerusalem. b, Christ at the Column. c, Jesus of Nazareth. d, The Descent. e, The Solitude. f, The Last Supper. g, Christ Suffering. h, The Crucifixion. i, Christ Entombed. j, The Resurrection.

1987, Apr. 2   **Litho.**   *Perf. 12*
1385   Sheet of 10   17.50 17.50
a.-e.   A349 2b, any single   1.00 .25
f.-j.   A349 2.25b, any single   1.10 .25

World Neurochemistry Congress — A350

3b, Bolivar and Bello, outdoor sculpture by Marisol Escobar. 4.25b, Retinal neurons.

1987, May 8   **Litho.**   *Perf. 12*
1386 A350   3b multicolored   .50 .20
1387 A350   4.25b multicolored   .60 .20
a.   Pair, #1386-1387   3.00 3.00

Miniature Sheet

Tourism A351

Hotels: a, f, Barquisimeto Hilton. b, g, Lake Hotel Intercontinental, Maracaibo. c, h, Macuto Sheraton, Caraballeda. d, i, Melia Caribe, Caraballeda. e, j, Melia, Puerto la Cruz.

1987, May 29   **Litho.**   *Perf. 12*
1388   Sheet of 10   15.00 15.00
a.-e.   A351 6b, any single   .65 .25
f.-j.   A351 6.50b, any single, diff.   .65 .25

Natl. Institute of Canalization, 35th Anniv. — A352

1987, June 25   **Litho.**   *Perf. 12*
1389 A352   2b Map of Amazon territory waterways   .20 .20

1390 A352 4.25b Apure and Bolivar states waterways   .35 .25
g.   Pair, #1389-1390   1.00 1.00

Vincente Emilion Sojo (1887-1974), Composer — A352a

2b, Academy of Fine Arts, Caracas. 4b, Sojos directing choir. 5b, Hymn to Bolivar score. 6b, Sojo, score on blackboard. 7b, Portrait, signature.

1987, July 1   **Litho.**   *Perf. 12*
1390A   Strip of 5   37.50 37.50
b.   A352a 2b tan & sepia   1.25 1.25
c.   A352a 4b tan & sepia   2.00 1.40
d.   A352a 5b tan & sepia   2.00 1.40
e.   A352a 6b tan & sepia   3.25 2.00
f.   A352a 7b tan & sepia   4.00 2.00

Printed in sheets of 10 containing two strips of five, black control number (UR).

Simon Bolivar University, 20th Anniv. A353

Designs: a, Bolivar statue by Roca Rey, 1973. b, Outdoor sculpture of solar panels by Alejandro Otero, 1972. c, Rectory, 1716. d, Laser. e, Owl, sculpture, 1973.

1987, July 9   **Litho.**   *Perf. 12*
1391   Strip of 5   15.00 15.00
a.   A353 2b multicolored   1.00 .50
b.   A353 3b multicolored   1.50 .50
c.   A353 4b multicolored   2.00 .60
d.   A353 5b multicolored   2.50 1.00
e.   A353 6b multicolored   3.00 1.00

Miniature Sheet

Ministry of Transportation and Communication — A354

Designs: a, Automobiles. b, Ship. c, Train, Cathedral. d, Letters, telegraph key. e, Communication towers. f, Highway. g, Airplane. h, Locomotive, rail caution signs. i, Satellite dish. j, Satellite in orbit.

1987, July 16
1392   Sheet of 10   7.50 7.50
a.-e.   A354 2b any single   .20 .20
f.-j.   A354 2.25b any single   .20 .20

Nos. 1392a and 1392f, 1392b and 1392g, 1392c and 1392h, 1392d and 1392i, 1392e and 1392j have continuous designs.

Miniature Sheet

Venezuela Navigation Company, 70th Anniv. A355

Designs: a, Corporate headquarters. b, Fork lift. c, Ship's Superstructure. d, Engine room. e, The Zulia. f, The Guarico. g, Ship's officer on the bridge. h, Bow of supertanker. i, Loading dock. j, Map of sea routes.

1987, July 31   **Litho.**   *Perf. 12*
1393   Sheet of 10   6.25 6.25
a.-b.   A355 2b, any single   .20 .20
c.-d.   A355 3b, any single   .25 .20

---

e.-f.   A355 4b, any single   .30 .20
g.-h.   A355 5b, any single   .40 .20
i.-j.   A355 6b, any single   .45 .25

Nos. 1393a, 1393c, 1393e, 1393g and 1393i in vertical strip; No. 1393b, 1393d, 1393f, 1393h and 1393j in vertical strip.

Miniature Sheet

Natl. Guard, 50th Anniv. A356

a, f, Air-sea rescue. b, g, Traffic control. c, h, Environment and nature protection. d, i, Border control. e, j, Industrial security.

1987, Aug. 6
1394   Sheet of 10   40.00 40.00
a.-e.   A356 2b, any single   1.25 .25
f.-j.   A356 4b, any single   3.00 .50

Discovery of America, 500th Anniv. (in 1992) A357

20th cent. paintings (details): 2b, Departure from Port of Palos, by Jacobo Borges. 7b, Discovery of America, by Tito Salas. 11.50b, El Padre de las Casas, Protector of the Indians, by Salas. 12b, Trading in Venezuela at the Time of the Conquest, by Salas. 12.50b, Defeat of Guaicaipuro, by Borges.

1987, Oct.   **Litho.**   *Perf. 12*
1395   Strip of 5   8.00 8.00
a.   A357 2b multi   .20 .20
b.   A357 7b multi   .60 .30
c.   A357 11.50b multi   1.00 .45
d.   A357 12b multi   1.10 .55
e.   A357 12.50b multi   1.25 .55

Christmas 1987 — A358

Paintings and sculpture representing the Spanish Colonial School, 18th cent.: 2b, *The Annunciation*, by Juan Pedro Lopez (1724-1787). 3b, *Nativity*, by Jose Francisco Rodriguez (1767-1818). 5.50b, *Adoration of the Magi*, anonymous. 6b, *Flight into Egypt*, by Lopez.

1987, Nov. 17   **Litho.**   *Perf. 12*
1396   Block of 4   6.75 6.75
a.   A358 2b multi   .25 .25
b.   A358 3b multi   .30 .25
c.   A358 5.50b multi   .50 .30
d.   A358 6b multi   .60 .30

Miniature Sheet

Sidor Mills, 25th Anniv. — A359

Natl. steel production: a-d, Exterior view of steel plant (in a continuous design). e, Tower bearing the SIDOR emblem. f, Furnaces and molten steel flowing down gutters. g, Pooring steel rods. h, Slab mill. i, Steel rod production, diff. j, Anniv. emblem.

1987, Nov. 23
1397   Sheet of 10   7.75 7.75
a.   A359 2b multi   .20 .20
b.   A359 6b multi   .60 .30
c.   A359 7b multi   .70 .35
d.   A359 11.50b multi   1.10 .55
e.   A359 12b black   1.25 .60
f.   A359 2b multi   .20 .20
g.   A359 6b multi   .60 .30
h.   A359 7b multi   .70 .35
i.   A359 11.50b multi   1.10 .55
j.   A359 12b multi   1.25 .60

Meeting of 8 Latin American Presidents, 1st Anniv. — A360

1987, Nov. 26
1398 A360 6b multi   .60 .30

Pequiven Petrochemical Co., 10th Anniv. — A361

1987, Dec. 1
1399   Strip of 5   7.75 7.75
a.   A361 2b Plastics   .20 .20
b.   A361 6b Refined oil products   .60 .30
c.   A361 7b Fertilizers   .70 .30
d.   A361 11.50b Installations   1.10 .55
e.   A361 12b Expansion   1.25 .60

St. John Bosco (1815-88) A362

Portrait of Bosco and: 2b, Map, children. 3b, National Church, Caracas. 4b, Vocational training (printer's apprentice). 5b, Church of Mary Auxiliadora. 6b, Missionary school (nun teaching children).

1987, Dec. 8
1400   Strip of 5   4.00 4.00
a.   A362 2b multi   .20 .20
b.   A362 3b multi   .30 .20
c.   A362 4b multi   .40 .20
d.   A362 5b multi   .45 .25
e.   A362 6b multi   .60 .30

Redrawn Bolivar Type of 1976

1987, Dec. 31   **Litho.**   *Perf. 12½*
1401 A231   3b emerald grn   .35 .20
1402 A231   4b gray   .50 .20
1403 A231   5b vermilion   .65 .25
1404 A231   10b dark olive bister   1.50 .50
1405 A231   15b rose claret   2.25 .80
1406 A231   20b bright blue   2.75 1.00
1407 A231   25b olive bister   3.50 1.50
1408 A231   30b dark violet   4.25 1.75
1409 A231   50b carmine   7.00 2.75
    Nos. 1401-1409 (9)   22.75 8.95

Nos. 1401-1409 inscribed Armitano.

29th Assembly of Inter-American Development Bank Governors — A363

1988, Mar. 18   **Litho.**   *Perf. 12*
1410 A363 11.50b multi   1.00 .55

Miniature Sheet

Republic Bank, 30th Anniv. A364

Bank functions and finance projects: a, Personal banking at branch. b, Capital for labor. c, Industrial projects. d, Financing technology. e, Exports and imports. f, Financing agriculture. g, Fishery credits. h, Dairy farming development. i, Construction projects. j, Tourism trade development.

1988, Apr. 11
1411	Sheet of 10	10.00	10.00
a.-e.	A364 2b any single	.35	.20
f.-j.	A364 6b any single	.50	.25

No. 1411 contains two strips of five.

Anti-Polio Campaign Day of Victory, May 25 — A365

Design: Polio victims pictured on bronze relief, Rotary and campaign emblems.

1988, May 20 Litho. *Perf. 12*
1412	A365 11.50b multi	1.00	.45

Carlos Eduardo Frias (1906-1986), Founder of the Natl. Publicity Industry — A366

1988, May 27 *Perf. 12*
1414	A366 Pair	4.00	4.00
a.	4b multi	.35	.25
b.	10b multi	.75	.45

Publicity Industry, 50th anniv.

Venalum Natl. Aluminum Corp., 10th Anniv. — A367

Designs: 2b, Factory interior. 6b, Electric smelter. 7b, Aluminum pipes. 11.50b, Aluminum blocks moved by crane. 12b, Soccer team, aluminum equipment on playing field.

1988, June 10
1415	Strip of 5	9.00	9.00
a.	A367 2b multi	.30	.20
b.	A367 6b multi	.80	.25
c.	A367 7b multi	.90	.25
d.	A367 11.50b multi	1.50	.55
e.	A367 12b multi	1.50	.55

Nature Conservation — A368

Birds: 2b, Carduelis cucullata. 6b, Eudocimus ruber. 11.50b, Harpia harpyja.

12b, Phoenicopterus ruber ruber. 12.50b, Pauxi pauxi.

1988, June 17 Litho. *Perf. 12*
1416	Strip of 5	6.00	6.00
a.	A368 2b multi	.25	.20
b.	A368 6b multi	.60	.25
c.	A368 11.50b multi	1.10	.45
d.	A368 12b multi	1.25	.40
e.	A368 12.50b multi	1.25	.45

Army Day — A369

Military uniforms: a, Simon Bolivar in dress uniform, 1828. b, Gen.-in-Chief Jose Antonio Paez in dress uniform, 1821. c, Liberation Army division gen., 1810. d, Brig. gen., 1820. e, Artillery corpsman, 1836. f, Alferez Regiment parade uniform, 1988. g, Division Gen. No. 1 dress uniform, 1988. h, Line Infantry Regiment, 1820. i, Promenade Infantry, 1820. j, Light Cavalry, 1820.

1988, June 20
1417	Sheet of 10	15.00	15.00
a., f.	A369 2b multi	.30	.20
b., g.	A369 6b multi	.75	.25
c., h.	A369 7b multi	.90	.25
d., i.	A369 11.50b multi	1.50	.45
e., j.	A369 12b multi	1.60	.45

Scabbard, Sword and Signature A370

Paintings by Tito Salas: 4.75b, *The General's Wedding.* 6b, Portrait. 7b, *Battle of Valencia.* 12b, *Retreat from San Carlos.*

1988, July 1 Litho. *Perf. 12*
1418	Strip of 5	7.50	7.50
a.	A370 2b shown	.35	.25
b.	A370 4.75b multi	.65	.25
c.	A370 6b multi	.75	.25
d.	A370 7b multi	1.25	.30
e.	A370 12b multi	2.75	.45

General Rafael Urdaneta (b. 1788).

General Santiago Marino (b. 1788), by Martin Tovar y Tovar — A371

1988, July
1419	A371 4.75b multi	.45	.25

1988 Summer Olympics, Seoul — A372

1988, Aug. 2
1420	A372 12b multi	.90	.45

Electric Industry, Cent. A373

Buildings, 1888: 2b, 1st Office. 4.75b, Jaime Carrillo and electrical plant. 10b, Bolivar Plaza. 11.50b, Baralt Theater. 12.50b, Central Thermoelectric Plant, Ramon Lagoon, 1988.

1988, Oct. 25 Litho. *Perf. 12*
1421	Strip of 5	6.50	6.50
a.	A373 2b multi	.20	.20
b.	A373 4.75b multi	.40	.20
c.	A373 10b multi	.80	.35
d.	A373 11.50b multi	.90	.45
e.	A373 12.50b multi	1.00	.45

Christmas — A374

Designs: 4b, Nativity (left side), by Tito Salas, 1936. 6b, Christ child, anonymous, 17th cent. 15b, Nativity (right side).

1988, Dec. 9
1422	4b multi	.30	.20
1423	6b multi	.45	.25
1424	15b multi	1.25	.60
a.	A374 Strip, #1423, 2 ea #1422, 1424	7.00	7.00

Miniature Sheet

Marian Year — A375

Icons: a, Our Lady of Copacabana, Bolivia. b, Our Lady of Chiquinquira, Colombia. c, Our Lady of Coromoto, Venezuela. d, Our Lady of the Clouds, Ecuador. e, Our Lady of Antigua, Panama. f, Our Lady of the Evangelization, Peru. g, Our Lady of Lujan, Argentina. h, Our Lady of Altagracia, Dominican Republic. i, Our Lady of Aparecida, Brazil. j, Our Lady of Guadalupe, Mexico.

1988, Aug. 15 Litho. *Perf. 12*
1425	Sheet of 10	8.75	8.75
a.-e.	A375 4.75b any single	.35	.20
f.-j.	A375 6b any single	.40	.25

Juan Manuel Cagigal Observatory, Cent. — A376

Designs: 2b, Bardou refracting telescope. 4.75b, Universal theodolite AUZ-27. 6b, Bust of Cagigal. 11.50b, Boulton cupola and night sky over Caracas in September. 12b, Satellite photographing Hurricane Allen.

1989, Sept. 5
1426	Strip of 5	6.75	6.75
a.	A376 2b multicolored	.25	.25
b.	A376 4.75b multicolored	.45	.25
c.	A376 6b multicolored	.60	.30
d.	A376 11.50b multicolored	1.00	.50
e.	A376 12b multicolored	1.10	.60

Comptroller-General's Office, 50th Anniv. — A377

1988, Oct. 14 Litho. *Perf. 12*
1427	A377 10b multi	.75	.40

Portrait of Founder Juan Pablo Rojas Paul, by Cristobal Rojas, 1890 — A378

1989, Oct. 21 Litho. *Perf. 12*
1428	A378	6b Commemorative medal	.40	.25
1429	A378	6.50b shown	.45	.25
a.		Pair, #1428-1429	1.00	1.00

Natl. History Academy, cent.

Portrait of Ricardo A379

Paintings: No. 1430, Simon Bolivar and Dr. Mordechay Ricardo. No. 1430A, The Octagon. Nos. 1430-1430A printed in continuous design completing the painting *The Liberator in Curacao*, by John de Pool.

1989, Jan. 27 Litho. *Perf. 12*
1430	A379	10b multi	.75	.40
1430A	A379	10b multi	.75	.40
1430B	A379	11.50b shown	1.10	.50
c.		Strip of 5, #1430B, 2 ea #1430-1430A	9.25	9.25

Convention with Holy See, 25th Anniv. — A380

Designs: a, Raul Leoni, constitutional president, 1964-69. b, Cardinal Quintero, archbishop of Caracas, 1960-80. c, Arms of Cardinal Lebrun, archbishop of Caracas since 1980. d, Arms of Luciano Storero, titular archbishop of Tigimma. e, Pope Paul VI.

1989, May 4 Litho. *Perf. 12*
1431	Strip of 5	4.00	4.00
a.-b.	A380 4b any single	.30	.20
c.-d.	A380 12b any single	.85	.55
e.	A380 16b any single	1.10	.75

Bank of Venezuela, Cent. A381

Designs: a, *Cocoa Harvest*, by Tito Salas, 1946. b, *Teaching a Boy How to Grow Coffee,* by Salas, 1946. c, Bank headquarters, Caracas. d, Archive of the Liberator, Caracas. e, Aforestation campaign (seedling). f, Aforestation campaign (five youths planting seedlings). g, 50-Bolivar bank note (left side). h, 50-Bolivar bank note (right side). i, 500-Bolivar bank note (left side). j, 500-Bolivar bank note (right side).

1989, Aug. 1
1432	Sheet of 10	8.50	8.50
a.-f.	A381 4b any single	.25	.20
g.-j.	A381 8b any single	.60	.35

Nos. 1432g-1432h and 1432i-1432j printed in continuous designs.

America
Issue — A382

UPAE emblem and pre-Columbian votive bisque artifacts: 6b, Vessel. 24b, Statue of a man.

1989
1433	A382 6b multicolored	.80	.25
1434	A382 24b multicolored	3.50	1.75
a.	Pair, #1433-1434	5.00	5.00

Christmas
A383

a, Shepherds, sheep. b, Angel appears to 3 shepherds. c, Holy Family. 12b, Two witnesses. 15b, Adoration of the kings.

1989   **Litho.**   **Perf. 12**
1435	Strip of 5	11.50	11.50
a.	A383 5b shown	.40	.25
b.-c.	A383 6b any single	.45	.25
d.	A383 12b multicolored	1.00	.45
e.	A383 15b multicolored	1.10	.60

Miniature Sheets

Bank of
Venezuela,
20th
Anniv. — A384

Tree and arms: No. 1436: a, Tabebuia chrysantha, national. b, Ceiba pentandra, Federal District. c, Myrospermum frutescens, Anzoategui. d, Pithecellobium saman, Aragua. e, Cedrela odorata, Barinas. f, Diptenyx punctata, Bolivar. g, Licania pyrofolia, Apure. h, Sterculia apetala, Carabobo.
No. 1437: a, Tabebuia rosea, Cojedes. b, Prosopis juliflora, Falcon. c, Copernicia tectorum, Guarico. d, Erythrina poeppigiana, Merida. e, Brawnea leucantha, Miranda. f, Mauritia flexuosa, Monagas. g, Malpighia glabra, Lara. h, Guaicum officinale, Nueva Esparta.
No. 1438: a, Swietenia macrophylla, Portuguesa. b, Platymiscium diadelphum, Sucre. c, Prumnopitys montana de Laub, Tachira. d, Roystonea venezuelana, Yaracuy. e, Cocos nucifera, Zulia. f, Hevea benthamiana, Federal Territory of Amazonas. g, Erythrina fusca, Trujillo. h, Rhizophora mangle, Territory of the Amacuro Delta.

1990, June 27   **Litho.**   **Perf. 12**
1436	Sheet of 8 + 2 labels	17.00	17.00
a.-f.	A384 10b any single	.50	.25
g.	A384 40b multicolored	2.00	1.00
h.	A384 50b multicolored	2.50	1.25
1437	Sheet of 8 + 2 labels	17.00	17.00
a.-f.	A384 10b any single	.50	.25
g.	A384 40b multicolored	2.00	1.00
h.	A384 50b multicolored	2.50	1.25

1438	Sheet of 8 + 2 labels	17.00	17.00
a.-f.	A384 10b any single	.50	.25
g.	A384 40b multicolored	2.00	1.00
h.	A384 50b multicolored	2.50	1.25

Central
Bank of
Venezuela,
50th Anniv.
A385

Designs: a, Santa Capilla Headquarters, 1943. b, Headquarters, 1967. c, Left half of 500b Bank Note, 1940. d, Right half of 500b Bank Note, 1940. e, Sun of Peru decoration, 1825. f, Medals Ayacucho, 1824, Boyaca, 1820 and Liberators of Quito, 1822. g, Swords of Peru, 1825. h, Cross pendant, Bucaramanga, 1830. i, Medallion of George Washington, 1826. j, Portrait of Gen. O'Leary.

1990, Oct. 15
1439	Sheet of 10	10.50	10.50
a.-f.	A385 10b any single	.50	.30
g.-h.	A385 15b any single	.75	.35
i.	A385 40b multicolored	2.00	1.00
j.	A385 50b multicolored	2.50	1.25

University
of Zulia,
Cent.
A386

Designs: a, Dr. Francisco Ochoa, founder. b, Dr. Jesus E. Lossada, President, 1946-47. c, Soil conservation. d, Developing alternative automotive fuels. e, Organ transplants.

1990, Sept. 18   **Litho.**   **Perf. 12**
1440	Strip of 5	8.00	8.00
a.-b.	A386 10b any single	.50	.30
c.-d.	A386 15b any single	.75	.35
e.	A386 20b multicolored	1.10	.55

Christmas
A387

Paintings: a, St. Joseph and Child by Juan Pedro Lopez. b, The Nativity by Lopez. c, The Return from Egypt by Matheo Moreno. d, The Holy Family by unknown artist. e, The Nativity (oval painting) by Lopez.

1990, Nov. 25
1441	Strip of 5	7.50	7.50
a.-c.	A387 10b any single	.50	.30
d.-e.	A387 20b any single	1.10	.55

OPEC, 30th
Anniv. — A388

a, Globe. b, Square emblem. c, Circular emblem. d, Diamond emblem. e, Flags.

1990, Dec. 21   **Litho.**   **Perf. 12**
1442	Strip of 5	5.50	5.50
a.-b.	A388 10b any single	.50	.30
c.	A388 20b multicolored	1.10	.55
d.	A388 30b multicolored	1.50	.75
e.	A388 40b multicolored	2.00	1.10

America
Issue — A389

1990, Dec. 12   **Litho.**   **Perf. 12**
1443	A389 10b Lake dwelling	.50	.30
1444	A389 40b Coastline	2.00	1.00
a.	Pair, #1443-1444	4.00	4.00

Exfilve '90, Caracas — A389a

Designs: 40b, Bank of Venezuela 1000b note. 50b, Bank of Caracas 100b note.

1990, Nov. 16   **Litho.**   **Imperf.**
1444B	A389a 40b multicolored	2.25	2.25
1444C	A389a 50b multicolored	2.75	2.75

No. 1444B, Bank of Venezuela, cent. No. 1444C, Bank of Caracas, cent.

St. Ignatius of
Loyola (1491-
1556)
A390

Designs: a, Jesuit quarters, Caracas. b, Death mask. c, Statue by Francisco de Vergara, 18th century. d, Statue of Our Lady of Montserrat, 11th century.

1991, Apr. 12   **Litho.**   **Perf. 12**
1445	Strip of 4 + label	12.50	12.50
a.-b.	A390 12b any single	.55	.30
c.	A390 40b multicolored	2.00	.90
d.	A390 50b multicolored	2.25	1.10

Venezuelan-American Cultural Center,
50th Anniv. — A391

Designs: a, Elisa Elvira Zuloaga (1900-1980), painter & engraver. b, Gloria Stolk (1912-1979), writer. c, Caroline Lloyd (1924-1980), composer. d, Jules Waldman (1912-1990), publisher. e, William Coles (1908-1978), attorney.

1991, July 4   **Litho.**   **Perf. 12**
1446	Strip of 5	12.50	12.50
a.-c.	A391 12b any single	.55	.30
d.	A391 40b multicolored	2.00	1.00
e.	A391 50b multicolored	2.25	1.10

Miniature Sheet

Orchids — A392

Designs: No. 1447a, 12b, Acineta alticola. b, 12b, Brassavola nodosa. c, 12b, Brachionidium brevicaudatum. d, 12b, Bifrenaria maguirei. e, 12b, Odontoglossum spectatissimum. f, 12b, Catasetum macrocarpum. g, 40b, Mendocella jorisiana. h, 40b, Cochleanthes discolor. i, 50b, Maxillaria splendens. j, 50b, Pleurothallis dunstervillei. No. 1448, Cattleya violacea.

1991, Aug. 22   **Litho.**   **Perf. 12**
1447	A392 Sheet of 10,		
	#a.-j.	15.00	15.00

Souvenir Sheet
1448	A392 50b multicolored	12.00	12.00

No. 1448 contains one 42x37mm stamp. No. 1447 exists imperf. Value $45.
See Nos. 1499-1500, 1508-1509.

Democratic Action Party, 50th
Anniv. — A393

Designs: a, People voting. b, Agricultural reform. c, Students and teachers. d, Nationalization of the petroleum industry.

1991, Sept. 13   **Litho.**   **Perf. 12**
1449	A393 12b Block of 4, #a.-d.	2.00	2.00

America
Issue
A394

1991, Oct. 24
1450	A394 12b Terepaima Chief	.45	.25
1451	A394 40b Paramaconi Chief	2.00	1.25
a.	Pair, #1450-1451	2.75	2.75

Children's Foundation, 25th Anniv. — A395

Children's drawings: a, 12b, Children in house. b, 12b, Playground. c, 12b, Carnival. d, 12b, Woman and girl walking by pond. e, 12b, Boy in hospital. f, 12b, Five children around tree. g, 12b, Two girls in colorful room. h, 40b, Classroom. i, 50b, Three children. j, 50b, Four children dancing.

1991, Oct. 31   Litho.   Perf. 12
1452 A395 Sheet of 10, #a.-j.   12.00 12.00

Nos. 1362-1364 Surcharged

1991   Litho.   Perf. 12½
1453 A231 5b on 25c red   .25 .20
1454 A231 5b on 75c pink   .25 .20
1455 A231 10b on 25c red   .50 .25
1456 A231 10b on 75c pink   .50 .25
1457 A231 12b on 50c blue   .65 .35
1458 A231 12b on 75c pink   .65 .35
1459 A231 20b on 50c blue   1.00 .50
1460 A231 20b on 75c pink   1.00 .50
1461 A231 40b on 50c blue   2.00 1.00
1462 A231 40b on 75c pink   2.00 1.00
1463 A231 50b on 50c blue   2.50 1.25
1464 A231 50b on 75c pink   2.50 1.25
    Nos. 1453-1464 (12)   13.80 7.10

Christmas A396

Children's art work: a, 10b, Wise men. b, 12b, Holy Family. c, 20b, Statues of Holy Family. d, 25b, Shepherds. e, 30b, Holy Family, cow, donkey.

1991, Nov. 14   Litho.   Perf. 12
1465 A396 Strip of 5, #a.-e.   6.75 6.75

Souvenir Sheet

Exfilve '91, Caracas — A397

1991, Nov. 29   Litho.   Perf. 12
1466 A397 50b No. 136   2.10 2.10

Discovery of America, 500th Anniv. (in 1992) A398

a, 12b, Coat of arms of Columbus. b, 12b, Santa Maria. c, 12b, Map by Juan de la Cosa. d, 40b, Sighting land. e, 50b, Columbus with Queen Isabella and King Ferdinand II.

1991, Dec. 12   Litho.   Perf. 12
1468 A398 Strip of 5, #a.-e.   4.75 4.75

1992, Mar. 15

Designs: No. 1469a, 12b, Emblem for discovery of America Commission. b, 12b, Venezuelan pavillion, Expo '92. c, 12b, 15th century map of Spain. d, 12b, Portrait of Columbus, by Susy Dembo. e, 12b, Encounter, by Ivan Jose Rojas. f, 12b, 0x500 America, by Annella Armas. g, 40b, Imago-Mundi, by Alessandro Grechi. h, 40b, Long Journey, by Gloria Fiallo. i, 50b, Playa Dorado, by Carlos Riera. j, 50b, Irminaoro, by Erasmo Sanches Cedeno. No. 1470, Untitled work, by Muaricio Sanchez.

1469 A398 Sheet of 10,
    #a.-j.   12.00 12.00
1470 A398 50b multicolored   2.25 2.25

Expo '92, Seville. No. 1470 contains one 38x42mm stamp.

Protection of Nature — A399

Turtles: No. 1471a, Geochelone carbonaria, facing left. b, Geochelone carbonaria, facing right. c, Podocnemis expansa, facing left. d, Podocnemis expansa, swimming.

1992, June 12   Litho.   Perf. 12
1471 A399 12b Block of 4, #a.-
    d.   10.00 6.00
    World Wildlife Fund.

Miniature Sheet

Beatification of Josemaria Escriva — A400

Designs: a, 18b, Teaching in Venezuela, 1975. b, 18b, Celebrating mass. c, 18b, Parents, Jose Escriva and Dolores Albas. d, 18b, Text with autograph. e, 18b, Kissing feet of Madonna. f, 18b, Commemorative medallion.

g, 60b, With Pope Paul VI. h, 60b, At desk, writing. i, 75b, Portrait. j, 75b, Portrait in St. Peter's Square, 1992.

1992, Oct. 2   Litho.   Perf. 12
1472 A400 Sheet of 10, #a.-j.   12.00 12.00

Electrification of Southern Regions A401

Designs: a, 12b, Roof of native hut. b, 12b, Transmission lines and towers. c, 12b, Horses running through pond. d, 40b, Workmen under tower. e, 50b, Baskets, crafts.

1992, July 15   Litho.   Perf. 12
1473 A401 Strip of 5, #a.-e.   4.50 4.50

Miniature Sheet

Artwork, by Mateo Manaure — A402

Color of background: a, 12b, Red. b, 12b, Red violet. c, 12b, Gray. d, 12b, Violet brown. e, 40b, Brown. f, 40b, Blue. g, 50b, Blue violet. h, 50b, Black.

1993, July 23
1474 A402 Sheet of 8, #a.-h. +
    2 labels   6.00 6.00

    Bank of Maracaibo, 110th anniv.

Discovery of America, 500th Anniv. — A403

Paintings: a, 18b, The Third Trip, by Elio Caldera. b, 60b, Descontextura, by Juan Pablo Nascimiento.

1992, Nov. 20   Litho.   Perf. 12
1476 A403 Pair, #a.-b.   2.40 2.40

Christmas A404

Artwork by Lucio Rivas: a, 18b, Adoration of the Shepherds. b, 75b, Adoration of the Magi. 100b, Flight into Egypt.

1992, Dec. 3   Litho.   Perf. 12
1477 A404 Pair, #a.-b.   2.75 2.75

Souvenir Sheet

1478 A404 100b multicolored   2.75 2.75

    No. 1478 contains one 42x38mm stamp.

Redrawn Bolivar Type of 1976 and

A405   A406

Designs: 5b, Natl. Pantheon. 10b, Victory Monument, Carabobo. 20b, Jose Antonio Paez. 25b, Luisa Caceres de Arismendi. 35b, Ezequiel Zamora. 40b, Cristobal Mendoza. #1490, Central University. #1491, Jose Felix Ribas. #1494, Manuel Piar. 200b, Simon Bolivar.

1993-94   Litho.   Perf. 12½
    Size: 18x22mm
1479 A405   1b silver   .25 .20
1480 A405   2b greenish
        blue   .25 .20
1482 A231   5b red   .25 .20
1484 A231 10b violet   .25 .20
1487 A231 20b olive green   .55 .25
1488 A405 25b red brown   .40 .30
1488A A405 35b brt yel grn   .60 .40
1489 A405 40b lt blue   .65 .45
1490 A231 50b orange   1.40 .60
1491 A405 50b lilac rose   .90 .65
1493 A406 100b brown   2.75 1.40
1494 A405 100b dark blue   1.75 1.00
1496 A405 200b brown   3.50 2.00
    Nos. 1479-1496 (13)   13.50 7.85

    Nos. 1479-1493 inscribed Armitano.
    See Nos. 1548-1562.

Orchid Type of 1991
Miniature Sheet

Designs: a, 20b, Cattleya percivaliana. b, 20b, Anguloa ruckeri. c, 20b, Chondrorhyncha flaveola. d, 20b, Stenia pallida. e, 20b, Zygosepalum lindeniae. f, 20b, Maxillaria triloris. g, 80b, Stanhopea wardii. h, 80b, Oncidium papilio. i, 100b, Oncidium hasti-labium. j, 100b, Sobralia cattleya. 150b, Polycycnis muscifera.

1993, Apr. 1   Litho.   Perf. 12
1499 A392 Sheet of 10, #a.-j.   14.00 14.00

Souvenir Sheet

1500 A392 150b multicolored   6.00 6.00

Miniature Sheet

Settlement of Tovar Colony, 150th Anniv. — A408

Designs: a, 24b, Woman. b, 24b, Children. c, 24b, Catholic Church, 1862. d, 24b, Statue of St. Martin of Tours, 1843. e, 24b, Fruits and vegetables. f, 24b, School, 1916. g, 80b, Home of founder, Augustin Codazzi, 1845. h, 80b, House of colony director, Alexander

Benitz, 1845. i, 100b, Breidenbach Mill, 1860. j, 100b, Parade.

1993, Apr. 12   Litho.   Perf. 12
1501 A408   Sheet of 10, #a.-j.   12.50 12.50

Miniature Sheet

19th Pan-American Railways Conference — A409

Designs: a, 24b, Tucacas steam locomotive. b, 24b, Halcon steam locomotive on Las Mostazas Bridge, 1894. c, 24b, Maracaibo locomotive. d, 24b, Tender, rail cars, Palo Grande Station. e, 24b, Fiat diesel locomotive, 1957. f, 24b, GP-9-L diesel locomotive, 1957. g, 80b, GP-15-L diesel locomotive, 1982. h, 80b, Metro subway train, Caracas. i, 100b, Electric locomotive. j, 100b, Passenger cars of electric train.

1993, May 25   Litho.   Perf. 12
1502 A409   Sheet of 10, #a.-j.   18.00 18.00

Nos. 1502c-1502d, 1502i-1502j are continuous designs.

A410   A411

World Day to Stop Smoking: a, 24b, Shown. b, 80b, "No smoking" emblem.

1993, May 27   Litho.   Perf. 12½x12
1503 A410   Pair, #a.-b.   2.75 2.75

1993, Oct. 7   Litho.   Perf. 12

America Issue: a, 24b, Amazona barbadensis. b, 80b, Ara macao.

1504 A411   Pair, #a.-b.   4.75 4.75

Miniature Sheets

Native Indians — A412   Christmas — A413

Designs: No. 1505a, 1b, Two Yanomami children with painted bodies, spear. b, 1b, Yanomami woman preparing food. c, 40b, Two Panare children performing in Katyayinto ceremony. d, 40b, Panare man with nose flute. e, 40b, Taurepan man in canoe. f, 40b, Taurepan girl weaving. g, 40b, Piaroa woman with infant. h, 40b, Piaroa dancers wearing war masks. i, 100b, Hoti man blowing flute. j, 100b, Hoti woman carrying baby, basket over back.
150b, Child blowing traditional whistle.

1993, Nov. 25   Litho.   Perf. 12
1505 A412   Sheet of 10, #a.-j.   9.25 9.25

Souvenir Sheet
1506 A412   150b multicolored   3.25 3.25

1993, Nov. 30

Nativity scene: a, f, 24b, Joseph. b, g, 24b, Madonna and Child. c, h, 24b, Shepherd boy, wise man holding gift, lambs. d, i, 80b, Wise man with hands folded, boy. e, j, 100b, Wise man presenting gift, boy with hands folded.

1507 A413   Sheet of 10, #a.-j.   10.50 10.50

Nos. 1507f-1507j are black, magenta & buff.

Orchid Type of 1991
Miniature Sheet

Designs: a, 35b, Chrysocycnis schlimii. b, 35b, Galeandra minax. c, 35b, Oncidium falcipetalum. d, 35b, Oncidium lanceanum. e, 40b, Sobralia violacea linden. f, 40b, Sobralia infundibuligera. g, 80b, Mendoncella burkei. h, 80b, Phragmipedium caudatum. i, 100b, Phragmipedium kaieteurum. j, 200b, Stanhopea grandiflora.
150b, Epidendrum elongatum.

1994, May 19   Litho.   Perf. 12
1508 A392   Sheet of 10, #a.-j.   16.00 16.00

Souvenir Sheet
1509 A392   150b multicolored   3.25 3.25

No. 1509 contains one 42x37mm stamp.

Miniature Sheet of 10

FEDECAMARAS (Federal Council of Production & Commerce Associations), 50th Anniv. — A414

a, 35b; f, 80b, Anniversary emblem. b, 35b; e, 80b, Luis Gonzalo Marturet (1914-64), 1st president. c, 35b; d, 80b, FEDECAMARAS emblem.

1994, July 17   Litho.   Perf. 12
1510 A414   #c, f, 2 ea #a-b, d-e   9.75 9.75

Judicial Service A415

1994, Sept. 13   Litho.   Perf. 12
1511 A415   100b multicolored   1.75 1.75

Miniature Sheet

Christmas A416

Paintings: a, 35b, g, 80b, The Nativity, by follower of Jose Lorenzo de Alvarado. b, 35b, h, 80b, Birth of Christ, 19th cent. c, 35b, i, 80b, The Nativity, diff., by follower of Jose Lorenzo de Alvarado. d, 35b, j, 80b, Adoration of the Magi, 17th cent. e, 35b, f, 80b, Birth of Christ, by School of Tocuyo.

1994, Dec. 1
1512 A416   Sheet of 10, #a.-j.   9.75 9.75

Miniature Sheet

Antonio Jose de Sucre (1795-1830) — A417

Designs: No. 1513a, 25b, Portrait. b, 25b, Dona Mariana Carcelen Y Larrea Marquesa de Solanda. c, 35b, Top of equestrian monument. d, 35b, Bottom of monument. e, 40b, Painting of Battle of Pichincha, mountains at top. f, 40b, Painting of Battle of Pichincha, battle scent. g, 80b, Painting of Battle of Ayacucho, soldiers on horseback. h, 80b, Painting of Battle of Ayacucho, dead soldiers. i, 100b, Painting of Surrender at Ayachucho, general signing document. j, 100b, Painting of Surrender at Ayachucho, seated general at right.
150b, Portion of mural, Carabobo, by Pedro Centeno Vallenilla.

1995, Feb. 2
1513 A417   Sheet of 10, #a.-j.   9.50 9.50

Souvenir Sheet
1514 A417   150b multicolored   2.50 2.50

Postal Transportation — A418

a, 35b, Post office van. b, 80b, Airplane.

1995, Mar. 22   Litho.   Perf. 12
1515 A418   Pair, #a.-b.   2.10 2.10

No. 1515 issued in sheets of 10 stamps.

Miniature Sheet

St. Jean-Baptiste de La Salle (1651-1719), Educator — A419

Denomination LR: a, 100b, Portrait. b, 35b, Students with microscope, academic education. c, 35b, Soccer players, sports education. d, 35b, Scouts at camp, citizenship education. e, 35b, La Salle College, Caracas.
Denomination LL: f, like #1516e. g, like #1516d. h, like #1516b. i, like #1516c. j, like #1516a.

1995, May 15
1516 A419   Sheet of 10, #a.-j.   7.75 7.75

Miniature Sheet

Founding of Salesian Order, Cent. A420

Designs: a, 35b, St. John Bosco (1815-88), priest with child. b, 35b, Lonely child, Madonna and Child. c, 35b, Man running machine tool. d, 35b, Young men working with electronic instruments. e, 35b, Baseball game. f, 35b, Basketball game. g, 80b, People working in fields. h, 80b, Man looking at chili peppers. i, 100b, Young tribal natives receiving religious training. j, 100b, Tribal native.

1995, Apr. 26
1517 A420   Sheet of 10, #a.-j.   8.75 8.75

Miniature Sheet

Orchids A421

Designs: a, 35b, Maxillaria guareimensis. b, 35b, Paphinia lindeniana. c, 50b, Catasetum longifolium. d, 50b, Anguloa clowesii. e, 35b, Coryanthes biflora. f, 35b, Catasetum pileatum. g, 80b, Maxillaria histrionica. h, 80b, Sobralia ruckeri. i, 35b, Mormodes convolutum. j, 35b, Huntleya lucida.
150b, Catasetum barbatum.

1995, May 31   Litho.   Perf. 12
1518 A421   Sheet of 10, #a.-j.   8.00 8.00
Souvenir Sheet
1519 A421   150b multicolored   2.25 2.25

No. 1519 contains one 42x36mm stamp. See #1534-1535, 1563-1564, 1587-1588.

CAF (Andes Development Corporation), 25th Anniv. — A422

1995, June 7
1520 A422   80b multicolored   1.25 1.25

Miniature Sheet

Beatification of Mother Maria of San Jose A423

Designs: a, 35b, In formal habit. b, 35b, Pope John Paul II. c, 35b, As young woman distributing Bibles. d, 35b, Doing embroidery work. e, 35b, Statue of Madonna, altar. f, 35b, Kneeling in devotions. g, 80b, Walking with Sisters in hospital. h, 80b, With patient in hospital. i, 100b, Working with children. j, 100b, Helping person seated along road.

1995, July 2
1521 A423   Sheet of 10, #a.-j.   9.25 9.25

Nos. 1521a-1521b, 1521c-1521d, 1521e-1521f, 1521g-1521h, 1521i-1521j are each continuous designs.

UN, 50th Anniv. — A424

Designs: a, People from different countries unfurling UN flag. b, Emblem on UN flag.

1995, June 26
1522 A424 50b Pair, #a.-b.   3.25 3.25

Gen. José Gregorio Monagas (1795-1858), President, Liberator of the Slaves — A425

a, Portrait. b, Slave family with opened chains.

1995, July 26   Litho.   Perf. 12
1523 A425 50b Pair, #a.-b.   1.40 1.40

Slave Rebellion, Bicent. — A426

Jose Leonardo Chirino and: a, Liberty leading the people (after Delacroix). b, Revolutionaries with weapons.

1995, Aug. 16
1524 A426 50b Pair, #a.-b.   1.50 1.50

Venezuelan Red Cross, Cent. A427

Designs: a, 100b, Red Cross flag. b, 80b, Carlos J. Bello Hospital. c, 35b, Surgery scene. d, 35b, Rescue workers carrying victim. e, 35b, Care givers with child.

1995, Aug. 30
1525 A427 Strip of 5, #a.-e.   4.50 4.50

America Issue A428

Environmental protection: a, 35b, Trees, lake. b, 80b, Flowers, hillside.

1995, Sept. 13   Perf. 12
1526 A428 Pair, #a.-b.   2.00 2.00

No. 1526 was issued in sheets of 10 stamps.
No. 1526 exists in two types: the heavy border at top is above "America" only: the heavy line extends over the denomination. Values the same.

Miniature Sheet

Native Aboriginals A429

No. 1527: a, 25b, Kuana man seated on post. b, 25b, Kuana woman using stones to do laundry. c, 35b, Guahibo people, one playing flute. d, 35b, Guahibo shaman with child. e, 50b, Uruak man with tree branch. f, 50b, Uruak woman cooking. g, 80b, Warao woman spinning twine. h, 80b, Warao man, woman in boat. i, 100b, Bari men with bows, arrows. j, 100b, Bari man rubbing sticks to make fire. 150b, Young boy with bird.

1995, Oct. 18
1527 A429   Sheet of 10,
                      #a.-j.   8.75 8.75
          Souvenir Sheet
1528 A429 150b multicolored   2.40 2.40
          See Nos. 1541-1542.

Miniature Sheet

Electricity in Caracas, Cent. A430

Designs: a, 35b, Ricardo Zuloaga, early pioneer. b, 35b, Early electric plant. c, 35b, Substation. d, 35b, 1908 Electric trams. e, 35b, Electric lampposts mandated by Congress, 1908. f, 35b, Lampposts, Bolivar Plaza. g, 80b, Electrical repairman. h, 80b, Lighted cross, Avila. i, 100b, Teresa Carreño Cultural Complex. j, 100b, Ricardo Zuloaga main generator plant.

1995, Nov. 6
1529 A430 Sheet of 10, #a.-j.   9.00 9.00

Miniature Sheet

Christmas A431

Designs: a, 35b, The Annunciation. b, 35b, Being turned away at the inn. c, 100b, Birth of Christ in the stable. d, 35b, Angel appearing to shepherds. e, 35b, Three Magi. f, 40b, Christmas pageant. g, 40b, Children skating. h, 100b, Christmas presents. i, 40b, Women preparing food for holidays. j, 40b, Children, mother preparing food for holidays.

1995, Nov. 15
1530 A431 Sheet of 10, #a.-j.   8.50 8.50
  Nos. 1530f-1530g, and 1530i-1530j are each continuous designs.

Miniature Sheet

Petroleum Industries of South America (PDVSA), 20th Anniv. A432

a, 35b, PDVSA emblem, 7 petroleum company emblems. b, PDVSA emblem, 6 petroleum company emblems. c, 80b, Oil derrick. d, 80b, Refinery. e, 35b, Oil tanker crossing under bridge. f, 35b, Worker, orimulsion tanks. g, 35b, Two people examining carbon. h, 35b, Semi truck hauling petrochemicals. i, 35b, Filling station. j, 35b, Gas storage tanks.

1995, Dec. 13   Litho.   Perf. 12
1531 A432 Sheet of 10, #a.-j.   9.00 9.00

Miniature Sheet

Town of El Tocuyo, 450th Anniv. A433

Designs: a, 35b, City arms. b, 35b, Workers in sugar cane field. c, Church of Our Lady of Immaculate Conception. d, Statue of Madonna inside church. e, 35b, Ruins of Temple of Santa Domingo. f. 35b, House of Culture. g, 80b, Cactus, vegetation. h, 80b, Cactus up close. i, 100b, Dancers with swords. j, 100b, Man playing guitar.

1995, Dec. 5
1532 A433 Sheet of 10, #a.-j.   9.00 9.00

Miniature Sheet

Vist of Pope John Paul II — A434

Statues of various saints, Pope and: a, 25b, Children. b, 25b, Man, woman. c, 40b, Man, woman, baby. d, 40b, Elderly man. e, 50b, Woman, boy. f, 50b, Sick person. g, 60b, Man in prison. h, 60b, Working man. i, 100b, People of various career fields. j, 100b, Priests, nuns.
  200b, Pope John Paul II holding crucifix.

1996, Jan. 26
1533 A434   Sheet of 10,
                      #a.-j.   10.00 10.00
          Souvenir Sheet
1533K A434 200b multicolored   2.50 2.50

Orchid Type of 1995

Designs: a, Epidendrum fimbriatum. b, Myoxanthus reymondii. c, Catasetum pileatum. d, Ponthieva maculata. e, Maxillaria triloris. f, Scaphosepalum breve. g, Cleistes rosea. h, Maxillaria sophronitis. i, Catasetum discolor. j, Oncidium ampliatum.
  200b, Odontoglossum naevium.

1996, May 31   Litho.   Perf. 12
1534 A421   60b Sheet of 10,
                      #a.-j.   7.25 7.25
          Souvenir Sheet
1535 A421 200b multicolored   2.50 2.50

1996 Summer Olympic Games, Atlanta A435

Designs: a, Emblem of Olympic Committee. b, Swimmer. c, Boxer. d, Cyclist. e, Medal winners.

1996, June 28   Litho.   Perf. 12
1536 A435 130b Strip of 5, #a.-e. 6.50 6.50
  No. 1536 was issued in a sheet of 10 stamps.

Use of Automation at Maiquetia Intl. Airport, 25th Anniv. A436

Designs: a, Symbol of automation. b, Map of airport flight routes. c, La Guaira Airdrome, 1929. d, Maiqueitia Airport, 1944. e, Simon Bolivar Airport, 1972. f, Interior view of terminal. g, Airport police, control tower. h, Airport firetruck. i, Airplane at terminal, Simon Bolivar Airport. j, Airplane on taxiway, Simon Bolivar Airport.

1996, Aug. 4
1537 A436 80b Sheet of 10, #a-j 8.50 8.50

America Issue A437

Traditional costumes: a, 60b, Women's. b, 130b, Men's.

1996, Sept. 10
1538 A437 Pair, #a.-b.   2.00 2.00

No. 1538 was issued in sheets of 10 stamps.

Mario Briceño-Iragorry (1897-1958) — A438

Portraits: a, As young man, Trujillo, 1913. b, At University of Mérida, 1919. c, As politician, 1944. d, As writer, 1947. e, As older man, Caracas, 1952.

1996, Sept. 24
1539 A438 80b Strip of 5, #a.-e.   4.25 4.25

No. 1539 was issued in sheets of 10 stamps.

Caracas Rotary Club, 70th Anniv. — A439

1996, Oct. 3
1540 A439 50b multicolored   .55   .55

No. 1540 was issued in sheets of 10.

Native Aboriginal Type of 1995

Designs: a, 80b, Yukpa boy working in garden. b, 80b, Paraujanos girl carrying fruit. c, 80b, Kinaroes man, woman bundling cattails. d, 80b, Motilon man with bananas. e, 80b, Chaque mother carrying infant on back. f, 100b, Guajiros man, young woman fixing hair. g, 100b, Mucuchi man carrying pack on back. h, 100b, Mape man with bow and arrow. i, 100b, Macoa woman with grain, painted faces. j, 100b, Yaruros man weaving.
  200b, Woman breastfeeding infant.

1996, Oct. 11
1541 A429 Sheet of 10, #a.-j.   9.75 9.75
          Souvenir Sheet
1542 A429 200b multicolored   2.10 2.10

Souvenir Sheet

Taipei '96, Intl. Philatelic Exhibition — A440

1996, Oct. 21   Litho.   Perf. 12
1543 A440 200b Ara chloroptera   5.50 5.50

José Gregorio Hernández (1864-1908), Physician — A441

a, As young boy. b, As student, anatomy drawing. c, Praying, Madonna statue. d, Thinking of the needy. e, In research study. f, As professor of university. g, Comforting sick patient. h, Empty chair at academy. i, Vargas Hospital, statue, portrait of Hernández. j, Hospital named after Hernández, statue.
200b, Portrait of Hernández.

1996, Oct. 26   **Litho.**   **Perf. 12**
1544 A441   60b Sheet of 10,
   #a.-j.   4.50   4.50

Souvenir Sheet
1545 A441 200b multicolored   1.50   1.50
No. 1545 contains one 42x36mm stamp.

Christmas
A442

Designs: a, 60b, Child setting up Nativity scene. b, 60b, Three men with guitars, woman. c, 60b, Rooster, people making music. d, 60b, People with painted faces dancing, singing. e, 60b, Men, woman playing drums, instruments. f, 80b, Exchanging gifts of food. g, 80b, Family at table, looking at gift of food. h, 80b, Child in hammock, presents. i, 80b, Parading replica of infant Jesus. j, 80b, Kissing feet of Christ Child.

1996, Nov. 7
1546 A442   Sheet of 10, #a.-j.   5.25   5.25

Andrés Eloy Blanco (1896-1955), Politician, Writer
A443

Designs: a, As adolescent. b, As Caracas city official, government building. c, With family. d, With democratic founders. e, As politician, building. f, As President of Constituent Assembly, building. g, As "Poet of Pueblo." h, Lincoln Memorial, as Chancellor of the Republic. i, Author of writings on Spain, sailing ship. j, Map of Spain, sailing ships, conquistador on horseback.

1997, Feb. 17   **Litho.**   **Perf. 12**
1547 A443 100b Sheet of 10,
   #a.-j.   6.25   6.25

Simon Bolivar (1783-1830) — A444

1997, Mar. 7   **Litho.**   **Perf. 13½x13**
1548	A444	15b olive	.20	.20
1549	A444	20b brown org	.20	.20
1550	A444	40b dark brown	.25	.25
1551	A444	50b rose claret	.40	.40
1552	A444	70b deep violet	.55	.55
1553	A444	90b deep blue	.80	.80
1554	A444	200b dp grn bl	1.50	1.50
1555	A444	300b dp bl grn	2.00	2.00
1556	A444	400b gray	3.00	3.00
1557	A444	500b pale sepia	3.50	3.50
1558	A444	600b pale brown	3.75	3.75
1559	A444	800b pale vio brn	4.75	4.75
1560	A444	900b slate blue	5.00	5.00

1561	A444	1000b dk org brn	5.25	5.25
1562	A444	2000b olive bister	10.00	10.00
		Nos. 1548-1562 (15)	41.15	41.15

Orchid Type of 1995
Designs: a, Phragmipedium lindleyanum. b, Zygosepalum labiosum. c, Acacallis cyanea. d, Maxillaria camaridii. e, Scuticaria steelei. f, Aspasia variegata. g, Comparettia falcata. h, Scapyglottis stellata. i, Maxillaria ruffescens. j, Vanilla pompona.
250b, Rodriguezia lanceolata.

1997, May 30   **Perf. 12**
1563 A421 165b Sheet of 10,
   #a.-j.   10.00   10.00

Souvenir Sheet
1564 A421 250b multicolored   1.00   1.00
No. 1564 contains one 42x37mm stamp.

Independence Conspiracy of Gual and España, Bicent. — A445

#1565, José María España, proclamation for independence being read. #1566, España under arrest. #1567, Manuel Gual, soldiers. #1568, Gual fleeing through door, sailing ship, standing on Trinidad. #1569, Revolutionary flag, sailing ship.

1997, July 16
1565	A445	165b multicolored	.70	.70
1566	A445	165b multicolored	.70	.70
	a.	Pair, #1565-1566	1.40	1.40
1567	A445	165b multicolored	.70	.70
	a.	Pair, #1566-1567	1.40	1.40
1568	A445	165b multicolored	.70	.70
	a.	Pair, #1567-1568	1.40	1.40
1569	A445	165b multicolored	.70	.70
	a.	Pair, #1565, 1569	1.40	1.40
	b.	Pair, #1568-1569	1.40	1.40

Printed in sheet of 10 containing one each #1566a, 1567a, 1568a, 1569a-1569b.

Treaty of Tlatelolco Banning Use of Nuclear Weapons in Latin America, 30th Anniv.
A446

Various stylized designs representing devastation resulting from use of nuclear weapons: a.-e., White inscriptions. f.-j., Black inscriptions.

1997, July 31
1570 A446 140b Sheet of 10,
   #a.-j.   6.50   6.50

Stories for Children
A447

"The Rabbit and the Tiger:" a, Rabbit, tiger carrying satchel. b, Watching rat figure digging. c, Watching turtle on his back. d, Rabbit. e. Rat in net, rabbit. f, Tiger, house, rat. g, Bird, rat, rabbit, bee, beehive. h, Rabbit, turtle. i, Tiger with stick over shoulder. j, Tiger with mouth open, bees.
250b, Rabbit, tiger.

1997, Aug. 7
1571 A447   55b Sheet of 10,
   #a.-j.   2.75   2.75

Souvenir Sheet
1572 A447 250b multicolored   1.25   1.25
No. 1572 contains one 42x37mm stamp.
The reverse of Nos. 1571a-1571j are each inscribed with parts of the childrens' story.

Unexpected Adventures of a Postman
A448

America Issue: 110p, Giving letter to woman with dog. 280p, With motor scooter in rain.

1997, Aug. 29   **Litho.**   **Perf. 12**
1573	A448	110p multicolored	.90	.90
1574	A448	280p multicolored	2.00	2.00
	a.	Pair, #1573-1574	5.00	5.00

No. 1574a was issued in sheets of 10 stamps.

Villa of Anauco Villa, Bicent.
A449

Designs: a, Inscription. b, Main entrance. c, Entrance corridor. d, Interior patio. e, Exterior corridor leading to kitchen. f, Kitchen. g, Stairs leading to balcony. h, Coach house. i, Stable. j, Outside stable, water trough.

1997, Sept. 23
1575 A449 110b Sheet of 10,
   #a.-j.   5.00   5.00

Independence in India, 50th Anniv. — A450

Designs: a, 165b, Jawaharlal Nehru. b, 200b, Sardar Patel, flag. c, 165b, Congressional building. d, 200b, Gandhi. e, 165b, Purification at the Ganges. f, 200b, Rabindranath Tagore. g, 165b, Motion picture industry. h, 200b, Traditional music. i, 165b, Insat-1B meteorological satellite. j, 200b, Use of modern technology.
250b, Minarets of Taj Majal.

1997, Oct. 2
1576 A450   Sheet of 10, #a.-j.   8.50   8.50

Souvenir Sheet
1577 A450 250b multicolored   1.60   1.60

Heinrich von Stephan (1831-97)
A451

a, 110b, Portrait. b, 280b, UPU emblem.

1997, Oct. 9   **Litho.**   **Perf. 12**
1578 A451   Pair, #a.-b.   1.10   1.10

Wicker-work A452

No. 1579: a, Red basket, Ye'Kuana. b, With handles, Ye'Kuana. c, Round, Ye'Kuana. d, Tray, Panare. e, Backpack, Pemon. f, With carrying strap, Yanomami. g, Round (dk brown), diff., Ye'Kuana. h, Tray, Ye'Kuana. i, Oval tray, Panare. j, Wide mouth, Warao.
250b, Square box with lid, Ye'Kuana.

1997, Oct. 24   **Perf. 12**
1579 A452 140b Sheet of 10,
   #a.-j.   8.00   8.00

Souvenir Sheet
1580 A452 250b multicolored   2.75   2.75
No. 1580 contains one 42x37mm stamp.

Christmas A453

a, Annunciation. b, Mary, St. Elizabeth. c, No room at the inn. d, Nativity. e, Annunciation to shepherds. f, Adoration of the shepherds. g, Magi following star. h, Adoration of the Magi. i, Presentation of Christ child in temple. j, Flight into Egypt.

1997, Oct. 31
1581 A453 110b Sheet of 10,
   #a.-j.   5.00   5.00

7th Summit of Latin American Chiefs of State and Government, Isla de Margarita
A454

a, 165b, j, 200b, Social justice. b, 165b, e, 165b, h, 200b, Summit emblem. d, 165b, g, 200b, Truthful information. e, 165b, f, 200b, Human rights.

1997, Nov. 5
1582 A454   Sheet of 10, #a.-j.   5.00   5.00

Diocese of Zulia, Cent.
A455

Churches: a, Convent. b, Church of St. Ann. c, Reliquary, Chiquinquira. d, Basilica of Chiquinquira and St. John of God. e, Church, Aranza. f, Cathedral, Maracaibo. g, Cathedral, Machiques. h, Archbishop's seal. i, Cathedral, Cabimas. j, Cathedral of the Virgin, San Carlos.

1997, Dec. 16
1583 A455 110b Sheet of 10,
   #a.-j.   3.00   3.00

Democracy in Venezuela, 40th Anniv. — A456

Designs: a, Commemorative emblem. b, Popular decision. c, Public education. d, Social development. e, Freedom of expression. f, Capital, constitution. g, Popular culture. h, Civil rights. i, Environmental protection. j, Social and civic participation.

1998, Feb. 19   **Litho.**   *Perf. 12*
1584 A456 110b Sheet of 10,
    #a.-j.   4.25 4.25

Discovery of Margarita Island, 500th Anniv. — A457

Map of Margarita Islands and: a, 200b, Angel Rock. b, 265b, Christopher Columbus, ship. c, 200b, Simon Bolivar. d, 200b, Pearl diver. e, 265b, Statue of the Virgin del Valle, church. f, 100b, Mending fish net, fishermen in boats. g, 200b, Gen. Santiago Marino. h, 100b, Petronila Mata, cannon. i, 200b, Gen. Juan Bautista Arismendi. j, 100b, Parrot.

250b, Women weeping at the Lagoon of Martyrs, horiz.

1998, Mar. 26   **Litho.**   *Perf. 12*
1585 A457 Sheet of 10, #a.-j.   6.25 6.25

Souvenir Sheet
1586 A457 250b multicolored   1.00 1.00

No. 1586 contains one 42x37mm stamp.

Orchid Type of 1995

a, Oncidium orthostates. b, Epidendrum praetervisum. c, Odontoglossum schilleranum. d, Bletia lansbergii. e, Caularthron bicornutum. f, Darwiniera bergoldii. g, Houlletia tigrina. h, Pleurothallis acuminata. i, Elleanthus lupulinus. j, Epidendrum ferrugineum.

250b, Pleurothallis immersa.

1998, May 29
1587 A421 185b Sheet of 10,
    #a.-j.   6.50 6.50

Souvenir Sheet
1588 A421 250b multicolored   1.00 1.00

No. 1588 contains one 42x37mm stamp.

Henri Pittier Natl. Park, 60th Anniv. — A458

Fauna: a, 140b, Crax pauxi. b, 150b, Spizaetus ornatus. c, 200b, Touit collaris. d, 200b, Trogon collaris. e, 350b, Cyanocorax yncas. f, 140b, Tersina viridis. g, 150b, Phyllomedusa trinitatis. h, 200b, Morpho peleides. i, 200b, Acrocinus longimanus. j, 350b, Dynastes hercules.

1998, July 17
1589 A453 Sheet of 10, #a.-j.   7.25 7.25

Comptroller General of the Republic, 60th Anniv. — A459

Designs: a, 140b, Gumersindo Torres Millet, founding Comptroller. b, 140b, Luis Antonio Pietri Yépez, first Comptroller of the democracy. c, 140b, View of capitol dome. d, 140b, Colors of flag (service to society). e, 200b, Simon Bolivar, coins. f, 200b, Various numbers on green background. g, 350b, Newspaper headlines (inform the public). h, 350b, Statue of justice (uphold law). i, 350b, Text of duties of the Comptroller General. j, 350b, Emblem, the 6th Assembly of the Latin American and Caribbean States Comptrollers.

1998, July 29
1590 A459 Sheet of 10, #a.-j.   8.25 8.25

Organization of the American States (OAS), 50th Anniv. — A460

a, 140b, Logo of the anniversary. b, 140b, OAS emblem. c, 350b, Flags forming double helix, US flag at center left. d, 150b, Deactivating land mine. e, 150b, Defending human rights. f, 200b, Simon Bolivar. g, 200b, Scroll, quill pen, inkwell. h, 350b, Flags forming double helix, Venezuelan flag at center right. i, 200b, Road sign with map of Americas. j, 200b, Mountain climbers.

1998, July 30
1591 A460 Sheet of 10, #a.-j.   7.25 7.25

Expo '98, Lisbon A461

Designs: a, 140b, Bird, turtle, crab. b, 140b, Fishermen throwing net from boat. c, 150b, Seashells, turtle. d, 150b, Fish. e, 200b, Marine life, denomination, UR. f, 200b, Marine life, denomination LR. g, 200b, Man riding through river on horse. h, 200b, Cattle in river, monkey. i, 350b, Two sea birds. j, 350b, Monkey, waterfall, flower.

1998, July 31
1592 A461 Sheet of 10, #a.-j.   8.00 8.00

18th Central American and Caribbean Games, Maracaibo A462

Figures: a, 150b, Running. b, 200b, Playing basketball. c, 150b, Bowling. d, 200b, Boxing. e, 150b, Cycling. f, 200b, Fencing. g, 150b, Performing gymnastics. h, 200b, Weight lifting. i, 150b, Swimming. j, 200b, Playing tennis.

1998, Aug. 4
1593 A462 Sheet of 10, #a.-j.   6.00 6.00

Discovery of Venezuela, 500th Anniv. — A463

Designs: a, 350b, Christopher Columbus. b, 200b, Juan de la Cosa (1460?-1510), map. c, 200b, Huts built on stilts in water. d, 150b, Women of three different races. e, 140b, 13th cent. artifact. f, 350b, Alonso de Ojeda (1465-1515), map. g, 200b, Detail of map of Jodocus Hondius. h, 200b, Modern city. i, 150b, Various people of modern Venezuela. j, 140b, Statues of Catholic king and queen.

1998, Aug. 10
1594 A463 Sheet of 10, #a.-j.   7.25 7.25

Landing of Christoper Columbus, and Exploration of Amerigo Vespucci, 500th Anniv. A464

1998, Aug. 12
1595 A464 400b multicolored   3.00 3.00

See Italy No. 2252.

Treaty of Amazon Cooperation, 20th Anniv. A465

Designs: a, Casiquiare River, denomination LR. b, Casiquiare River, denomination LL. c, Bactris gasipaes. d, Neblinaria celiae. e, Paracheidon axelrodi. f, Dendrobates leucomelas. g, Nocthocrax urumatum. h, Speothos venaticus. i, Cocuy mountain. j. Neblina Mountains.

1998, Aug. 20
1596 A465 200b Sheet of 10,
    #a.-j.   8.00 8.00

Children's Story — A466

Cockroach Martinez and Perez Rat: a, Cockroach. b, Burro. c, Parrot. d, Insects with camera, pad. e, Cat. f, Cockroach, pig. g, Goat. h, Cockroach, rat. i, Rat. j, Cockroach, bird.

350b, Cockroach.

1998, Aug. 21   **Litho.**   *Perf. 12*
1597 A466 130b Sheet of 10,
    #a.-j.   5.00 5.00

Souvenir Sheet
1598 A466 350b multicolored   1.25 1.25

State of Israel, 50th Anniv. — A467

a, 350b, Menorah. b, 350b, Moses, Ten Commandments. c, 200b, Theodore Herzl. d, 200b, King David. e, 140b, Blowing of Shofar. f, 350b, Torah. g, 350b, Praying at Wailing Wall. h, 200b, David Ben Gurion. i, 200b, Knesset. j, 140b, Book Museum.

1998, Sept. 15
1599 A467 Sheet of 10, #a.-j.   6.00 6.00

Souvenir Sheet

Comptroller General, 60th Anniv. — A468

1998, Sept.
1600 A468 480b multicolored   1.75 1.75

UPU, 125th Anniv. A469

a, 100b, Customer at window, clerks at left. b, 100b, Scanning bar code, woman at right. c, 100b, Electronic mail. d, 100b, Hybrid mail. e, 100b, Business mail. f, 300b, Like "a," clerks at right. g, 300b, Like "b," woman at left. h, 300b, Like "c," large monitor at right. i, 300b, Like "d," woman at right. j, 300b, Like "e," building with stacks at left.

1998, Sept. 29
1601 A469 Sheet of 10, #a.-j.   7.00 7.00

Legendary Caciques A470

a, Caruao. b, Manaure. c, Guacamayo. d, Tapiaracay. e, Mamacuri. f, Maniacuare. g, Mara. h, Chacao. i, Tamanaco. j, Tiuna.

500b, Indian.

1998, Oct. 9
1602 A470 420b Sheet of 10,
    #a.-j.   15.00 15.00

Souvenir Sheet
1603 A470 500b multicolored   1.75 1.75

Evangelism in Venezuela, 500th Anniv. A471

No. 1604: a, 100b, Fr. Francisco de Córdoba, Fr. Juan Garcés. b, 100b, Fr. Matías Ruíz Blanco. c, 100b, Fr. Vincente de Requejada. d, 100b, Fr. José Gumilla. e, 100b, Fr. Antonio Gonzáles de Acuña. f, 300b, Fr. Pedro de Córdoba. g, 300b, Fr. Francisco de

Pamplona. h, 300b, Fr. Bartolomé Díaz. i, 300b, Fr. Filipe Salvador Gilij. j, 300b, Don Mariano Martí.
350b, Emblem of Papal Nuncio.

1998, Oct. 24　　Litho.　　Perf. 12
1604 A471　Sheet of 10, #a.-j.　5.50 5.50
Souvenir Sheet
1605 A471　350b multicolored　1.00 1.00
No. 1605 contains one 42x37mm stamp.

Special Olympics, 30th Anniv.
A472

180b: a, Carrying torch. b, Giving hug. c, Soccer players. d, Girl holding small flag. e, Girl performing gymnastics.
420b: f, Swimmer. g, Coach walking with athletes. h, Hitting volleyball. i, Particpants cheering. j, Coach instructing girl in softball.

1998, Oct. 30　　Litho.　　Perf. 12
1606 A472　Sheet of 10, #a.-j.　10.50 10.50

Christmas
A473

Children standing in front of windows — 180b: a, Girl holding sparkler. b, Boy holding artist's brush, ornament. c, Girl with kite. d, Boy with pinwheel. e, Girls playing musical instruments.
420b: f, Boy on wagon. g, Girl with yo-yo, doll. h, Boy with bell. i, Girl with spool and thread. j, Boy on skateboard.

1998, Nov. 4
1607 A473　Sheet of 10, #a.-j.　10.50 10.50

America Issue — A474

Famous women: a, 180b, Teresa de la Parra (1889-1936), writer. b, 420b, Teresa Carreño (1853-1917), pianist.

1998, Nov. 23
1608 A474　Pair, #a.-b.　2.25 2.25

William H. Phelps (1875-1965), Ornithologist
A475

Portrait of Phelps and — 200b: a, Cephalopterus ornatus. b, Topaza pella. c, Grallaria excelsa phelpsi. d, Chrysolampis mosquitus. e, Tangara xanthogastra phelpsi.
300b: f, Radio transmitter. g, Mt. Phelps. h, Baseball and glove. i, Phelps Library. j, Cash register.

1998, Dec. 4
1609 A475　Sheet of 10, #a.-j.　12.00 12.00

Msgr. Jesús Manuel Jáuregui Moreno (1848-1905)
A476

Designs: a, Portrait as younger man. b, Christ on the cross. c, Our Mother of Angels Church. d, Madonna and Child. e, Portrait as older man.

1999, Jan. 30　　Litho.　　Perf. 12
1610 A476　500b Strip of 5, #a.-e.　8.75 8.75

Holy Sacrament for the Consecration of the Republic of Venezuela, Cent.
A477

No. 1612: a, Man, elderly woman. b, Priest. c, Ostensorium (top). d, Boy with basketball, girl. e, Man, woman holding baby. f, Lady doctor. g, Woman. h, Ostensorium (base). i, Soldier. j, Native man holding spear.
500b, Hands of priest holding the Host.

1999, June 16　　Litho.　　Perf. 12
1611 A477　250b Sheet of 10, #a.-j.　8.25 8.25
Souvenir Sheet
1612 A477　500b multicolored　1.60 1.60
No. 1612 contains one 42x37mm stamp.

Souvenir Sheet

Andino Parliament, 20th Anniv. — A478

1999　　Litho.　　Perf. 12
1613 A478　500b multi　1.50 1.50

Christmas
A479

a, 500b, Betrothal of Joseph, Mary. b, 500b, Annunciation. c, 500b, Elizabeth, Mary. d, 500b, The search for lodging in Bethlehem. e, 500b, Birth of Jesus. f, 300b, Vision of the shepherds. g, 300b, Magi following star. h, 300b, Adoration of the Magi. i, 300b, Flight into Egypt. j, 300b, Slaughter of the innocents.

1999, Nov. 5　　　　Perf. 12x12¼
1614 A479　Sheet of 10, #a.-j.　12.00 12.00

Souvenir Sheet

Expo 2000, Hanover — A480

Illustration reduced.

2000, July 8　　Litho.　　Perf. 12
1615 A480　650b multi　2.10 2.10

2nd Summit of Heads of State and Government of OPEC Countries — A481

No. 1616 — Sites in Venezuela: a, 300b, Angel Falls. b, 300b, Llanos, Cojedes. c, 300b, Quebrada Jaspe. d, 300b, Morichal Largo. e, 300b, Auyantepuy, Carrao River. f, 400b, Lake Maracaibo. g, 400b, Humboldt Peak. h, 400b, Mochima. i, 400b, Morichal Largo River. j, 400b, Auyantepuy, from Uruyen.
No. 1617, 550b: a, Saudi Arabia. b, Algeria. c, United Arab Emirates. d, Indonesia. e, Iraq. f, Iran. g, Kuwait. h, Libya. i, Nigeria. j, Qatar.

2000, Sept. 26　　Litho.　　Perf. 12
Sheets of 10, #a-j
1616-1617 A481　Set of 2　27.50 27.50

Christmas — A482

No. 1618: a, 300b, Angel and "Gloria." b, 300b, Angel and "a." c, 650b, Angel and "Dios." d, 300b, Angel and "en los." e, 300b, Angel and "Cielos." f, 300b, Shepherd and lamb. g, 550b, Joseph. h, 650b, Jesus. i, 550b, Mary. j, 300b, Woman with water jar.

2000, Nov. 29
1618 A482　Sheet of 10, #a-j　12.00 12.00

America Issue, A New Millennium Without Arms — A483

No. 1619: a, 300b, Finger in gun barrel. b, 650b, Man in heaven.

2000, Dec. 14
1619 A483　Vert. pair, #a-b　2.75 2.75

Educational Building and Endowment Foundation, 25th Anniv. — A484

No. 1620 — School buildings in: a, Caracas. b, Vargas State. c, Portuguesa State. d, Mérida State. e, Yaracuy State.

2001, May 9　　Litho.　　Perf. 12
1620 A484　Horiz. strip of 5　4.75 4.75
a.-c. A484 300b Any single　.85 .85
d.-e. A484 400b Any single　1.10 1.10

Orchids — A485

No. 1621: a, 200b, Galeottia jorisiana. b, 200b, Lycaste longipetala. c, 300b, Coryanthes albertinae. d, 300b, Hexisea bidentata. e, 400b, Lycaste macrophylla. f, 400b, Masdevallia maculata. g, 550b, Ada aurantiaca. h, 550f, Kefersteinia graminea. i, 550b, Sobralia liliastrum. j, 550b, Gongora maculata.
650b, Masdevallia tovarensis.

2001, May 25
1621 A485　Sheet of 10, #a-j　20.00 20.00
Souvenir Sheet
1622 A485　650b multi　3.25 3.25

Blessed Josemaría Escrivá de Balaguer (1902-75), Founder of Opus Dei — A486

No. 1623: a, 300b, Portrait. b, 300b, Bell of Nuestra Senora de los Angeles Church. c, 300b, Figure of Infant Jesus. d, 300b, Escrivá with men. e, 550b, Escrivá with women. f, 550f, Escrivá receiving doctorate, 1972. g, 550b, Escrivá with children, 1975. h, 300b, Commemorative plaque, Caracas Cathedral. i, 550b, Color portrait. j, 300b, Beatification ceremony, St. Peter's Square, Vatican City.

2001, June 8
1623 A486　Sheet of 10, #a-j　20.00 20.00

Battle of Carabobo, 180th Anniv.
A487

No. 1624: a, Thomas I. Ferriar. b, Bolívar in Buenavista, by Martín Tovar y Tovar. c, Quote by Simón Bolívar. d, Commemorative column. e, Pedro Camejo. f, José Antonio Páez, by Tovar y Tovar. g, Santiago Mariño, by Tovar y

Tovar. h, Simón Bolívar, by M. Eberstein. i, Manuel Cedeño, by Tito Salas. j, Ambrosio Plaza, by Salas.

2001, June 22

1624		Sheet of 10	23.00	23.00
a.-e.	A487	400b Any single	1.10	1.10
f.-j.	A487	600b Any single	1.60	1.60

Christmas — A488

Holy Family and angel with: a, 200b, Clarinet. b, 200b, Guitar. c, 220b, Lute. d, 220b, Trumpet. e, 280b, Violin. f, 280b, Harp. g, 400b, Bagpipes. h, 400b, Pan pipes. i, 500b, Drum. j, 500b, Stringed instrument.

2001, Nov. 30   Litho.   Perf. 12

1625	A488	Sheet of 10, #a-j	15.00	15.00

Navigational
Signaling,
160th
Anniv. — A489

Navigational aids: a, Margarita Aqueduct buoy. b, BNFA buoy. c, Punta Brava lighthouse. d, Punta Macolla lighthouse. e, Los Roques lighthouse. f, Isla Redonda lighthouse. g, Punta Faragoza lighthouse. h, Punta Ballena lighthouse. i, Punta Tigre lighthouse. j, Recalada de Güiria lighthouse.

2002, May 10   Litho.   Perf. 12

1626		Sheet of 10	12.00	12.00
a.-b.	A489	300b Either single	.60	.60
c.-f.	A489	450b Any single	.90	.90
g.-j.	A489	500b Any single	1.00	1.00

Symbolic Incorporation of Guacaipuro
into National Pantheon — A490

No. 1627: a, Tiaora and Caycape, sisters of Guacaipuro. b, Guacaipuro defeats Pedro de Miranda. c, Guacaipuro defeated by Juan Rodriguez Suárez. d, Killing in the gold mines. e, Death of Juan Rodriguez Suárez. f, Guacaipuro's escape from cabin fire. g, Death of Guacaipuro. h, Urquía, companion of Guacaipuro. i, Baruta, first son of Guacaipuro. j, Guacaipuro, Cacique of the Teques and Caracas people.

2002, Oct. 29   Litho.   Perf. 12

1627		Sheet of 10	7.75	7.75
a.	A490	200b multi	.30	.30
b.-g.	A490	300b any single	.45	.45
h.	A490	350b multi	.55	.55
i.	A490	400b multi	.60	.60
j.	A490	500b multi	.75	.75

Mission Robinson — A491

No. 1628: a, Toddler. b, Boy reading. c, Simón Bolívar and torch. d, Simón "Robinson" Rodriguez, Bolívar's teacher. e, Rodriguez and Eiffel Tower. f, Bolívar and flag. g, Bolívar and Rodriguez reading. h, Bolívar standing and Rodriguez seated. i, Rodriguez, men and women reading. j, Indians reading.

2003, Sept. 19   Litho.   Perf. 12x12¼

1628	A491	Sheet of 10	7.50	7.50
a.-d.		300b Any single	.35	.35
e.-f.		400b Either single	.50	.50
g.-j.		500b Any single	.65	.65

Agricultural, Fishery and Forestry
Fund (FONDAFA) — A492

No. 1629: a, Cattle drive. b, Farmer plowing field. c, Row of tractors. d, Farmer tending crops. e, Corn in field. f, Boats. g, Ear of corn. h, Farmer in tractor in field. i, Cacao pods. j, Cacao beans.

2003, Nov. 7   Perf. 12

1629	A492	Sheet of 10	7.00	7.00
a.-f.		300b Any single	.35	.35
g.-h.		400b Either single	.50	.50
i.-j.		500b Any single	.65	.65

National Urban Development Fund
(FONDUR), 28th Anniv. — A493

No. 1630: a, Barinas. b, Portuguesa. c, Carabobo. d, Miranda. e, Sucre. f, Trujillo. g, Táchira. h, Vargas. i, FONDUR emblem. j, Lara.

2003, Dec. 16   Litho.   Perf. 14¼

1630	A493	Sheet of 10	4.50	4.50
a.-f.		300b Any single	.35	.35
g.-h.		400b Either single	.50	.50
i.-j.		500b Either single	.65	.65

Natl. Urban Transportation Fund
(FONTUR), 12th Anniv. — A494

No. 1631: a, Av. Uruguay, Lara. b, Carretera del Páramo, Merida. c, Av. Cumanan-Cumanacoa, Sucre. d, Carratera Santa Lucia, Barinas. e, Francissco Fajardo Expressway, Caracas. f, Students. g, Paraiso Tunnel, Caracas. h, VIVEX Module. i, Row of buses. j, Av. Cruz Paredes, Barinas.

2003, Dec. 18   Litho.   Perf. 14¼

1631	A494	Sheet of 10	5.25	5.25
a.-c.		300b Any single	.35	.35
d.-f.		400b Either single	.50	.50
g.-j.		500b Any single	.65	.65

Natl. Telecommunications Commission
(CONATEL) — A495

No. 1632: a, Three Amazonian children, two dogs and hammock. b, Caracas and mountain. c, Amazonian children with spears. d, Snow-covered Bolivar Peak. e, Amazonian child in canoe aiming arrow. f, Medina Beach. g, Amazonian children aiming arrows skyward.

h, Angel Falls. i, Amazonian children making baskets. j, Coro Dunes.

2003, Dec. 23   Litho.   Perf. 12

1632	A495	Sheet of 10	5.25	5.25
a.-d.		300b Any single	.35	.35
e.-f.		400b Either single	.50	.50
g.-h.		500b Either single	.65	.65
i.-j.		600b Either single	.75	.75

Foundation for the Development of
Community and Municipal
Reconstruction (FUNDACOMUN),
42nd Anniv. — A496

No. 1633: a, Miranda. b, Trujillo. c, Mérida. d, Falcón. e, Vargas. f, Esparta. g, Caracas, denomination at left. h, Caracas, denomination at right. i, Barinas. j, Lara.

2004, Mar. 10   Litho.   Perf. 12

1633	A496	Sheet of 10	4.50	4.50
a.-c.		300b Any single	.30	.30
d.-f.		400b Any single	.45	.45
g.-j.		500b Any single	.50	.50

Barrio Adentro Mission — A497

No. 1634: a, Houses on hillside, people in doorway. b, Woman, house, ladder, people in alley. c, Woman, mother and child. d, Family, children. e, Boys playing baseball, boat. f, People near fence, man with cap. g, Man, sand dunes. h, Man with guitar, cows. i, Mountain, woman, cross and statue. j, Indians, river.

2004, Mar. 24   Perf. 12

1634	A497	Sheet of 10	10.50	10.50
a.-b.		300b Either single	.30	.30
c.-f.		500b Any single	.50	.50
g.		750b multi	.80	.80
h.-i.		1500b Either single	1.60	1.60
j.		1700b multi	1.75	1.75

Souvenir Sheet

Design: 1000b, Man pushing wheelbarrow, horiz.

1634K	A497	1000b multi	1.40	1.40

No. 1634K contains one 41x36mm stamp.

National Housing Institute
(INAVI) — A498

No. 1635: a, Apartment block 6, El Silencio. b, El Pilar. c, Central section of apartment block 1, El Silencio. d, La Quiboreña. e, Apartment block 7, El Silencio. f, Santa Ana. g, Apartment block 144, El Silencio. h, La Quiracha. i, Architectural drawings of Caracas buildings. j, Los Peregrinos.

2004, May 28   Litho.   Perf. 12

1635	A498	Sheet of 10	4.50	4.50
a.-c.		300b Any single	.30	.30
d.-f.		400b Any single	.45	.45
g.-j.		500b Any single	.55	.55

National Aquatic Areas and Islands
Institute (INEA) — A499

No. 1636: a, INEA emblem. b, INEA emblem and headquarters. c, Marine firefighters, boats. d, Firetruck, marine firefighter moving drum. e, Sunken tugboat Gran Roque. f, Underwater view of Gran Roque. g, Tugboats. h, Large ships at port. i, Starfish, religious statue. j, Boats and birds.

2004, June 15

1636	A499	Sheet of 10	7.75	7.75
a.-b.		300b Either single	.30	.30
c.-f.		500b Any single	.55	.55
g.		600b multi	.60	.60
h.		1000b multi	1.00	1.00
i.		1500b multi	1.60	1.60
j.		1700b multi	1.75	1.75

A500

Latin American Parliament, 40th
Anniv. — A501

No. 1637: a, Latin American Parliament emblem, 40th anniversary emblem. b, 40th anniversary emblem. c, Latin American Parliament flag and 40th anniversary emblem. d, Flags of member nations. e, Flags and Andrés Townsend Ezcurra. f, Flags and Luis Beltrán Prieto Figueroa. g, Flags and Nelson Carneiro. h, Plenary meeting room, Venezuela. i, Assembly hall, Sao Paolo. j, Latin American Parliament Building, Sao Paolo.

No. 1638: a, Latin American Parliament emblem. b, 40th Anniversary emblem. c, Mérida Session emblem. d, Charter of Social Rights. e, Flags and map of Latin America. f, Flag and map of Panama. g, Táchira Session emblem. h, Bird with ball and chain (social debt). i, Simón Bolivar. j, Constitutional Hypothesis.

2004, July 12

1637	A500	Sheet of 10	8.00	8.00
a.-c.		300b Any single	.30	.30
d.-e.		450b Either single	.45	.45
f.-g.		500b Either single	.55	.55
h.-i.		1500b Either single	1.60	1.60
j.		1700b multi	1.75	1.75
1638	A501	Sheet of 10	8.00	8.00
a.-c.		300b Any single	.30	.30
d.-e.		450b Either single	.45	.45
f.-g.		500b Either single	.55	.55
h.-i.		1500b Either single	1.60	1.60
j.		1700b multi	1.75	1.75

CVG Edelca, 40th Anniv. — A502

No. 1639: a, Macagua Hydroelectric Station and Dam,, Ciudad Guayana. b, Electric transmission towers and lines. c, Electrical power equipment. d, Room, Guri. e, Native people. f, Guri Hydroelectric Station and Dam. g, Streetlights near Macagua Hydroelectric Station and Dam. h, Solar tower, by Alejandro Otero. i, Dam, Ecomuseum, Caroní. j, Gran Sabana.
No. 1640, Guri Hydroelectric Station and Dam.

2004, July 29

1639	A502	Sheet of 10	6.50	6.50
a.-b.		300b Either single	.30	.30
c.		400b multi	.45	.45
d.-g.		500b Any single	.55	.55
h.		600b multi	.60	.60
i.		1000b multi	1.00	1.00
j.		1500b multi	1.60	1.60

Souvenir Sheet

1640	A502	1000b multi	1.00	1.00

No. 1640 contains one 41x36mm stamp.

United Nations Population
Fund — A503

No. 1641 — Inscriptions: a, Los y las adolescentes . . . b, El comporttmiento . . . c, Las niñas tienen . . . d, Los seres humanos . . . e, Promovamos el empoderamiento . . . f, Los derechjos reproductivos . . . g, Por una maternidad sin riesgo. h, El derecho al desarrollo . . . i, Eliminemos la violencia . . . j, El condón protege vidas.

2004, Sept. 15

1641	A503	Sheet of 10	8.25	8.25
a.-d.		500b Any single	.55	.55
e.-j.		1000b Any single	1.00	1.00

National Parks Institute
(INPARQUES) — A504

No. 1642 — Parks and: a, Food. b, Education. c, Recreation. d, Water. e, Landscapes. f, Biodiversity. g, Conservation. h, Electricity. i, Tourism. j, Ethnic people.

2004, Oct. 11   Litho.   Perf. 14¼x14½

1642	A504	Sheet of 10	6.50	6.50
a.-b.		300b Either single	.30	.30
c.		400b multi	.40	.40
d.-g.		500b Any single	.55	.55

h.		600b multi	.60	.60
i.		1000b multi	1.10	1.10
j.		1500b multi	1.60	1.60

National Tax and Customs
Administration (SENIAT) — A505

No. 1643 — Inscriptions: a, Aporte a la educación, cultura y deporte (children). b, Aporte a la salud. c, Dile no al contrabando. d, Con tus tributos . . . e, Aporte a la educación, cultura y deporte (baseball players). f, Construcción de futuras . . . g, Aporte a la vialidad. h, Bienvenidos a un país . . . i, Aporte a la educación, cultura y deporte (building and palm tree). j, Aporte a la educación, cultura y deporte (modern building and sculpture).

2004, Oct. 15   Litho.   Perf. 12

1643	A505	Sheet of 10	8.25	8.25
a.-d.		500b Any single	.55	.55
e.-j.		1000b Any single	1.00	1.00

A506

Banco Federal — A507

No. 1644: a, Cerro El Avila, Caracas, 1945. b, Nuevo Circo, Caracas, 1970. c, Plaza Venezuela, Caracas, 1943. d, Sculpture by Francisco Narváez, Caracas, 1940. e, Baralt Theater, Maracaibo, 1883. f, Los Próceres, Caracas, 1956. g, El Paraíso Horse Track, Caracas, 1908. h, Bullfighter Luis Sánchez Olivares, Caracas, 1950. i, Funicular, Mérida, 1954. j, Angel Falls, Bolivar State, 1937. k, Banco Federal emblem, gold star. l, Banco Federal Building (sepia). m, Lake Bridge,

Maracaibo, 1962. n, Virgin of Coromoto (sepia). o, El Silencio, Caracas, 1945.

No. 1645: a, San Fernando de Apure Church. b, Caracas Cathedral. c, Coro Cathedral. d, Santa Inés de Cumaná Cathedral. e, Our Lady of Chiquinquirá Basilica. f, Our Lady of Coromoto Basilica. g, St. Rose of Lima Church, Ortíz. h, Mérida Cathedral. i, Our Lady of the Assumption Cathedral. j, San Cristóbal Cathedral. k, Banco Federal emblem, silver star. l, Banco Federal Building (full color). m, Barquisimeto Cathedral. n, Virgin of Coromoto (full color). o, Valencia Cathedral.

2005, Jan. 20 Litho. Perf. 14¼x14½

1644	A506	Sheet of 15	9.50	9.50
a.-e.		300b Any single	.30	.30
f.-h.		400b Any single	.40	.40
i.-j.		600b Either single	.60	.60
k.-l.		750b Either single	.80	.80
m.-n.		1000b Either single	1.10	1.10
o.		1700b multi	1.75	1.75
1645	A507	Sheet of 15	9.50	9.50
a.-e.		300b Any single	.30	.30
f.-h.		400b Any single	.40	.40
i.-j.		600b Either single	.60	.60
k.-l.		750b Either single	.80	.80
m.-n.		1000b Either single	1.10	1.10
o.		1700b multi	1.75	1.75

Christmas — A508

No. 1646 — Creche figures from various states: a, Bolívar. b, Falcón. c, Mérida. d, Aragua. e, Miranda. f, Miranda, diff. g, Falcón, diff. h, Zulia. i, Bolívar, diff. j, Trujillo.

2004, Dec. 23 Perf. 12

1646	A508	Sheet of 10	7.50	7.50
a.-b.		300b Either single	.30	.30
c.-d.		400b Either single	.40	.40
e.		600b multi	.60	.60
f.-g.		750b Either single	.75	.75
h.-i.		1000b Either single	1.10	1.10
j.		1700b multi	1.75	1.75

Souvenir Sheet

Incan and Modern Mail Deliverers — A509

2004 Perf. 12

1647	A509	1000b multi	1.10	1.10

Petróleos de Venezuela, S. A. — A510

No. 1648: a, Crane above turbines, Puerto La Cruz Refinery. b, Night view of tower Puerto La Cruz Refinery. c, Aerial view of Puerto La Cruz refinery. d, Man inspecting pipes. e, Crane and Venezuelan flag. f, Storage tanks. g, Oil wells. h, Refinery towers. i, Oil tanker and pipes. j, Tankers at Guaraguao Marine Terminal.

2004, Nov. 24 Litho. Perf. 14¼

1648	A510	Sheet of 10	5.75	5.75
a.-b.		300b Either single	.30	.30
c.-d.		450b Either single	.45	.45
e.-f.		500b Either single	.50	.50
g.-h.		600b Either single	.65	.65
i.		750b multi	.80	.80
j.		1000b multi	1.10	1.10

Mountains — A511

Designs: No. 1649, Bolivar Peak, Venezuela. No. 1650, Mt. Damavand, Iran.

2004 Litho. Perf. 13

1649	A511	1700b multi	1.90	1.90
1650	A511	1700b multi	1.90	1.90
a.		Horiz. pair, #1649-1650	3.80	3.80

No. 1650 has "Republica Bolivariana de Venezuela" overprinted in black over vignette. No. 1650 exists without overprint.

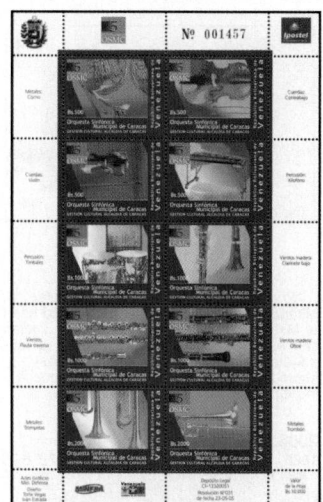

Caracas Municipal Symphony Orchestra, 25th Anniv. — A512

No. 1651: a, French horns. b, Bass (in blue) and bow. c, Violin and bow. d, Marimba. e, Timpani. f, Clarinets. g, Flutes. h, Oboes. i, Trumpets. j, Trombone.

2005 Perf. 12

1651	A512	Sheet of 10	9.50	9.50
a.-d.		500b Any single	.45	.45
e.-h.		1000b Any single	.95	.95
i.-j.		2000b Either single	1.90	1.90

16th World Youth and Student Festival — A513

No. 1652: a, Festival emblems from 1947-59. b, Festival emblems from 1962-2005. c, Festival emblem and joined arms. d, Festival emblem and text of Simón Bolívar's Vow of Monte Sacro. e, Festival emblem and Bolívar with outstretched arm, signature of Bolívar. f, Festival emblem and broken chain. g, Festival emblem, Bolívar. h, Festival emblem, dove. i, Festival emblem, dove, globe and hands. j, Festival emblem and hands.

1000b, Festival emblem and Bolívar with outstretched arm, horiz.

2005, Aug. 5 Litho. Perf. 12

1652	A513	Sheet of 10	5.00	5.00
a.-d.		300b Any single	.30	.30
e.-i.		500b Any single	.45	.45
j.		1500b multi	1.40	1.40

Souvenir Sheet
Perf. 12x11¾

1653	A513	1000b multi	1.10	1.10

No. 1653 contains one 41x36mm stamp.

IPOSTEL — A514

No. 1654: a, IPOSTEL emblem, flag, Caracas Post Office. b, Postal vans. c, IPOSTEL emblem on envelope, Caracas Post Office. d, Postal motorcycles. e, Carmelitas Post Office. f, Airplane, postal bicycles. g, Falcón Post Office. h, Mail carriers. i, Zulia Post Office. j, Postal workers in San Martín.

No. 1655: a, Man, IPOSTEL emblem, letters. b, Postal worker, mail sacks. c, Mail on conveyor belt. d, Mail carriers with parcels. e, Postal workers sorting mail. f, Postal workers at Ribas Mission. g, Mail sacks. h, Doctor, medical equipment at Barrio Adentro Mission. i, Postal worker and postal machinery. j, Forklift and Mercal emblem.

2005, Oct. 10 Perf. 12

1654	A514	Sheet of 10	9.25	9.25
a.-b.		300b Either single	.30	.30
c.-d.		400b Either single	.35	.35
e.-f.		600b Either single	.55	.55
g.-i.		1700b Any single	1.60	1.60
j.		2000b multi	1.90	1.90
1655	A514	Sheet of 10	9.25	9.25
a.-b.		300b Either single	.30	.30
c.-d.		400b Either single	.35	.35
e.-f.		600b Either single	.55	.55
g.-i.		1700b Any single	1.60	1.60
j.		2000b multi	1.90	1.90

Central Bank of Venezuela, 65th Anniv. — A515

No. 1656: a, Bank emblem. b, Caracas branch. c, Maracaibo branch. d, Venezuela Mint. e, Children's economic educational program. f, Numismatic Museum. g, Plaza Juan Pedro López. h, Gold bars. i, Bank notes and printing plates. j, Coins.

2005, Oct. 20 Perf. 12½x13½

1656	A515	Sheet of 10	8.50	8.50
a.-b.		300b Either single	.30	.30
c.-d.		400b Either single	.35	.35
e.-f.		600b Either single	.55	.55
g.-h.		1500b Either single	1.40	1.40
i.-j.		1700b Either single	1.60	1.60

Christmas — A516

No. 1657 — Angel with: a, h, Long-necked stringed instrument with bow. b, j, Lute. c, Harp. d, g, Maracas. e, i, Stringed instrument with bow. f, Horn.

2005, Dec. 1 Perf. 12

1657	A516	Sheet of 10	8.00	8.00
a.-c.		400b Any single	.35	.35
d.-f.		600b Any single	.55	.55
g.-h.		1000b Either single	.95	.95
i.		1500b multi	1.40	1.40
j.		2000b multi	1.90	1.90

National Guard — A517

No. 1658: a, Villa Zoila. b, Troops and building with ornate roof. c, Troops and automobiles. d, Troops saluting. e, Helicopter. f, Troops in inflatable raft. g, Three guardsmen at industrial site. h, Two guardsmen inspecting boxes. i, Guardsman with drug-sniffing dog. j, Guardsman, children.

2006, Feb. 23

1658	A517	Sheet of 10	8.50	8.50
a.-d.		300b Any single	.30	.30
e.-f.		400b Either single	.35	.35
g.-h.		1500b Either single	1.40	1.40
i.-j.		2000b Either single	1.90	1.90

Banco Guayana, 50th Anniv. — A518

No. 1659 — Shimaraña people: a, People with painted faces. b, Archer and man with spear. c, Canoes on water. d, Women near dock. e, Man in canoe, woman's face. f, Children. g, Bow fishermen. h, Men, child, waterfall. i, Child. j, Women, dancer and river.

2006, Mar. 16

1659	A518	Sheet of 10	9.50	9.50
a.-b.		300b Either single	.30	.30
c.-f.		500b Any single	.45	.45
g.-h.		1700b Either single	1.60	1.60
i.-j.		2000b Either single	1.90	1.90

National Tax and Customs Administration (SENIAT) — A519

No. 1660 — Customs buildings in: a, Valencia. b, Puerto Cabello. c, Paraguachón. d, Santa Elena de Uairén. e, Maiquetia (in day). f, Maiquetia (at night). g, Ureña. h, Táchira. i, Barcelona. j, La Guaira.

2006, Mar. 22

1660	A519	Sheet of 10	8.75	8.75
a.-b.		400b Either single	.35	.35
c.-d.		500b Either single	.45	.45
e.-f.		700b Either single	.65	.65
g.-h.		1000b Either single	.95	.95
i.-j.		2000b Either single	1.90	1.90

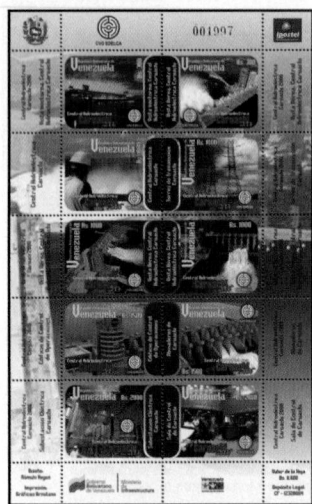

Carauchi Hydroelectric Dam Project — A520

No. 1661: a, Dam at night. b, Aerial view of dam. c, Worker at dam. d, Power lines. e, Aerial view of dam, water flowing to right. f, Aerial view of dam, water flowing straight ahead, descriptive text at left. g, Control tower. h, Spillway. i, Electrical substation. j, Control room.
No. 1662 — Rescued animals: a, Iguana iguana. b, Caluromys philander. c, Paleosuchus palpebrosus. d, Geochelone carbonaria. e, Cebus olivaceus. f, Choloepus didactylus. g, Tupinambis teguixin. h, Lora bejuca. i, Coendou prehensilis. j, Tamandua tetradactyla.
No. 1663, Aerial view of dam, water flowing straight ahead, descriptive text at top.

2006, Apr. 6

1661	A520	Sheet of 10	11.00	11.00
a.-b.		300b Either single	.30	.30
c.-f.		1000b Any single	.95	.95
g.-h.		1500b Either single	1.40	1.40
i.-j.		2000b Either single	1.90	1.90
1662	A520	Sheet of 10	11.00	11.00
a.-b.		300b Either single	.30	.30
c.-f.		1000b Any single	.95	.95
g.-h.		1500b Either single	1.40	1.40
i.-j.		2000b Either single	1.90	1.90

Souvenir Sheet

1663	A520	1000b multi	.95	.95

No. 1663 contains one 42x37mm stamp.

141st Extraordinary Meeting of OPEC A521

No. 1664 — Petroleum facilities, meeting emblem and: a, "OPEP". b, Flag of United Arab Emirates flag. c, Flag of Libya. d, Flag of Iraq. e, Flag of Saudi Arabia. f, Flag of Indonesia. g, Flag of Nigeria. h, Flag of Algeria. i, Flag of Iran. j, Flag of Qatar. k, Flag of Venezuela. l, Flag of Kuwait.

2006, June 1

1664		Sheet of 12	10.00	10.00
a.-b.	A521	300b Either single	.30	.30
c.-h.	A521	500b Any single	.45	.45
i.-j.	A521	1500b Either single	1.40	1.40
k.-l.	A521	2000b Either single	1.90	1.90

Caracas Mass Transit — A522

No. 1665: a, Train on Yellow line. b, Yellow line station. c, Plaza Venezuela Station. d, Three trains. e, Train switches. f, Line 4 Tunnel. g, Metro bus. h, Control room. i, Construction of Line 4 Nuevo Circo Station. j, Art by Jesús Soto, Chacaíto Station.

2006, July 2

1665	A522	Sheet of 10	12.00	12.00
a.-b.		300b Either single	.30	.30
c.-d.		500b Either single	.45	.45
e.-f.		1500b Either single	1.40	1.40
g.-j.		2000b Any single	1.90	1.90

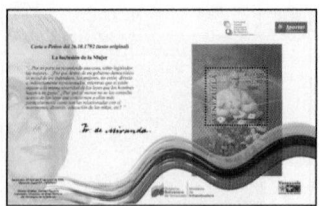

Francisco de Miranda University — A523

No. 1666, vert.: a, Miranda on horse. b, Miranda facing left. c, Nose, mouth and hand of Miranda. d, Statue of Miranda, Venezuelan flag. e, Miranda holding flag. f, Miranda at Venezuelan independence ceremonies. g, Miranda. h, Statues of Miranda. i, Miranda facing right. j, Miranda writing letter, ship.
No. 1667, Like #1666j.

2006, July 28

1666	A523	Sheet of 10	8.75	8.75
a.-d.		300b Any single	.30	.30
e.-f.		500b Either single	.45	.45
g.-h.		1500b Either single	1.40	1.40
i.-j.		2000b Either single	1.90	1.90

Souvenir Sheet

1667	A523	1500b multi	1.40	1.40

No. 1666 contains ten 35x45mm stamps.

Children's Art — A524

No. 1668: a, Flag of Liberty, by Elimar Sanchez. b, Miranda (Miranda and broken chain), by Gabriel Solano. c, Miranda and Catalina, by Elikarina Sánchez. d, Musical Aspects of Miranda (G clef), by Josmelys Díaz. e, Miranda Playing, by Nasser Sultan. f, Miranda and His Dreams, by Cynthia Urbina. g, Flag of Miranda, by Janem Sultan. h, Miranda Thinking, by Luis Miguel Martínez. i, Miranda and His Family, by Vianny Gonella. j, Diary of Miranda, by José A. Martínez.

2006

1668	A524	Sheet of 10	8.75	8.75
a.-d.		300b Any single	.30	.30
e.-f.		500b Either single	.45	.45
g.-h.		1500b Either single	1.40	1.40
i.-j.		2000b Either single	1.90	1.90

Souvenir Sheet

CVG EDELCA, 43rd Anniv. — A525

2006

1669	A525	3500b multi	3.25	3.25

Central University, Caracas — A526

No. 1670: a, Exterior of Engineering Library. b, Interior of Engineering Library. c, Electrical Engineering Building. d, School of Engineering, Metallurgy and Material Sciences, Sculpture by Harry Abend. e, School of Civil Engineering. f, School of Chemical Engineering, Petroleum and Geology, Mines and Geophysics. g, Mural by Alejandro Otero at School of Engineering. h, Machinery at Institute of Materials and Structural Models. i, Fluid Mechanics Institute. j, Aulas Auditorium.

2006

1670	A526	Sheet of 10	17.50	17.50
a.-d.		400b Any single	.35	.35
e.-f.		600b Either single	.55	.55
g.-h.		3000b Either single	2.75	2.75
i.-j.		5000b Either single	4.75	4.75

Modern Art — A527

No. 1671: a, Esfera Japón. b, Biface Naranja. c, Repetición y Progresión. d, Repetición Optica No. 2. e, Composición Dinámica. f, Muro Optico. g, Pardelas Interferentes. h, Espiral. i, Ambivalencia Dicembre. j, Estructura Cinética.
1500b, Espiral, diff.

2006

1671	A527	Sheet of 10	6.25	6.25
a.-b.		300b Either single	.30	.30
c.-f.		500b Any single	.45	.45
g.-j.		1000b Any single	.95	.95

Souvenir Sheet

1672	A527	1500b multi	1.40	1.40

No. 1671 contains ten 45x35mm stamps.

Transportation — A528

No. 1673: a, Airplane in flight. b, Simón Bolívar Intl. Airport, Maiquetía. c, Highway, Ayacucho. d, Highway, Barquisimeto. e, José Antonio Páez Highway. f, Caracas — La Guaira Viaduct. g, Line 3, Caracas Metro. h, Line 4, Caracas Metro. i, Maracaibo Metro. j, Teques Metro. k, Valencia Metro. l, Caracas — Tuy Medio tram.

2006

1673	A528	Sheet of 12	13.50	13.50
a.-g.		300b Any single	.30	.30
h.-j.		2000b Any single	1.90	1.90
k.-l.		3000b Either single	2.75	2.75

A529

Christmas — A530

No. 1674: a, Musicians. b, Toy. c, Top. d, Holiday table setting. e, Food. f, Letter to Baby Jesus. g, Illuminated cross. h, Yo-yo. i, Yo-yo, top and toy. j, Envelope with Holy Family.
No. 1675: a, Nativity. b, Food. c, Letter to Baby Jesus. d, IPOSTEL emblem with Holy Family.

2006

1674	A529	Sheet of 10	9.00	9.00
a.-b.		300b Either single	.30	.30
c.-d.		450b Either single	.40	.40
e.-f.		550b Either single	.50	.50
g.-h.		1000b Either single	.95	.95
i.		2000b multi	1.90	1.90
j.		3000b multi	2.75	2.75
1675	A530	Sheet of 4	3.50	3.50
a.-b.		300b Either single	.30	.30
c.		1000b multi	.95	.95
d.		2000b multi	1.90	1.90

Miniature Sheets

A531

A532

2007 Copa America Soccer Tournament, Venezuela — A533

No. 1676: a, Mascot Guaky and soccer ball. b, City University Olympic Stadium, Caracas. c, José E. Pachencho Stadium, Maracaibo. d, Metropolitan Stadium, Lara. e, Agustín Tovar "La Carolina" Stadium, Barinas. f, General J. A. Anzoátegui Stadium, Puerto La Cruz. g, Cachamay Total Entertainment Center, Ciudad Guayana. h, Mertopolitan Stadium, Mérida. i, Monumental Stadium, Maturin. j, Multisport Stadium, Pueblo Nuevo San Cristóbal.
No. 1677 — Mascots: a, Guaky Jugador. b, Guaky Inspector. c, Guaky Bombero. d, Guaky Doctor. e, Guaky Futbolista. f, Guaky Obrero. g, Guaky Sembrador. h, Guaky Militar. i, Guaky Policia. j, Guaky Jugador, diff.
No. 1678 — Mascot Guaky and emblem of soccer governing body of: a, Venezuela. b, Brazil. c, Argentina. d, Mexico. e, Colombia. f, Chile. g, Peru. h, Uruguay. i, Ecuador. j, Bolivia. k, Paraguay. l, United States.

2007, June 18 Litho. Perf. 12

1676	A531	Sheet of 10	13.50	13.50
a.-b.		300b Either single	.30	.30
c.-f.		400b Any single	.40	.40
g.-h.		2000b Either single	1.90	1.90
i.		3000b multi	2.75	2.75
j.		5000b multi	4.75	4.75
1677	A532	Sheet of 10	13.50	13.50
a.-b.		300b Either single	.30	.30
c.-f.		400b Any single	.40	.40
g.-h.		2000b Either single	1.90	1.90
i.		3000b multi	2.75	2.75
j.		5000b multi	4.75	4.75
1678	A533	Sheet of 12	14.50	14.50
a.-d.		300b Any single	.30	.30
e.-h.		400b Any single	.40	.40
i.-j.		2000b Either single	1.90	1.90
k.		3000b multi	2.75	2.75
l.		5000b multi	4.75	4.75
		Nos. 1676-1678 (3)	41.50	41.50

Intelligence and Prevention Service (DISIP), 38th Anniv. — A534

No. 1679 — DISIP emblem and: a, El Helicoide (Headquarters Building), denomination in red, "Venezuela" in dark blue. b, Model of El Helicoide, denomination in dark blue, "Venezuela" in orange. c, Model of El Helicoide, denomination in yellow. d, El Helicoide being built, denomination in red, "Venezuela" in green. e, Cupola of El Helicoide, denomination in orange. f, Auditorium of El Helicoide, denomination in light blue, "Venezuela" in red. g, El Helicoide, denomination in green. h, El Helicoide, denomination in red. i, Garden outside El Helicoide. j, Plaza Bolívar.
3500b, El Helicoide, denomination in yellow.

2007, June 21

1679	A534	Sheet of 10	13.50	13.50
a.-f.		300b Any single	.30	.30
g.-h.		2000b Either single	1.90	1.90
i.		3000b multi	2.75	2.75
j.		5000b multi	4.75	4.75

Souvenir Sheet

1680	A534	3500b multi	3.25	3.25

No. 1680 contains one 42x37mm stamp.

Miniature Sheet

Simón Bolívar Center, Caracas — A535

No. 1681: a, Muses de los Niños. b, Juan Pablo II buildings. c, Torres del Silencio. d, Palacio de Justicia. e, Parque Central building. f, Museo de Arte Contemporaneo de Caracas. g, Avenida Bolívar. h, Paseo Vargas. i, Teresa Carreño Theater. j, Cristobal Rojas.

2007, July 19

1681	A535	Sheet of 10	13.50	13.50
a.-d.		300b Any single	.30	.30
e.-f.		450b Either single	.40	.40
g.-h.		2000b Either single	1.90	1.90
i.		3000b multi	2.75	2.75
j.		5000b multi	4.75	4.75

Miniature Sheet

Christmas — A536

No. 1682 — Art: a, Resplendent God, by Hugo Rivero. b, Creole Christmas, by Vidalia González. c, Christmas Door, by Soccoro Peraza. d, Christmas, wood carvings by Orlando Campos. e, Christmas, wood carving by Tomás Flores. f, Christmas Wish, by Alberto Allup. g, St. Joseph, Virgin and Child, by Baldomero Higuera. h, Christmas, by Edgar Vegas. i, Holy Family, by Margarita Pérez de Lamanna. j, Merry Christmas, by Ana Teresa Pesce.

2007, Dec. 10

1682	A536	Sheet of 10	8.50	8.50
a.-d.		500b Any single	.45	.45
e.-h.		1000b Any single	.95	.95
i.-j.		1500b Either single	1.40	1.40

Miniature Sheet

Venezuelan Institute for Scientific Investigations (IVIC) — A537

No. 1683 — IVIC emblem and: a, Quimbiotec Blood Products Plant. b, Beatriz Roche Children's Band. c, Academic medal. d, Cubagua gargoyle. e, Advance Studies Center graduates. f, Bolívar and Bello Plaza. g, Molecular model. h, Investigative laboratory. i, Marcel Roche Library. j, Samuel Robinson Apartments.

2007, Dec. 14

1683	A537	Sheet of 10	9.50	9.50
a.-d.		500b Any single	.45	.45
e.-h.		1000b Any single	.95	.95
i.-j.		2000b Either single	1.90	1.90

SEMI-POSTAL STAMPS

A 5c green stamp of the Cruzada Venezolana Sanitaria Social portraying Simon Bolivar was overprinted "EE. UU. DE VENEZUELA CORREOS" in 1937.

It is stated that 50,000 copies without control numbers on back were sold by post offices and 147,700 with control numbers on back were offered for sale by the Society at eight times face value.

Bolívar Funeral Carriage SP1

Unwmk.

1942, Dec. 17　　Engr.　　Perf. 12

B1	SP1	20c + 5c blue	4.50	.50

Cent. of the arrival of Simón Bolívar's remains in Caracas. The surtax was used to erect a monument to his memory. See Nos. CB1-CB2.

> Catalogue values for unused stamps in this section, from this point to the end of the section, are for Never Hinged items.

Red Cross Nurse — SP2

1975, Dec. 15　　Litho.　　Perf. 14

B2	SP2	30c + 15c multi	.30	.20
B3	SP2	50c + 25c multi	.45	.30

Surtax for Venezuelan Red Cross.

Carmen América Fernandez de Leoni — SP3

Children in Home — SP4

1976, June 7　　Litho.　　Perf. 13½

B4	SP3	30c + 15c multi	.25	.20
B5	SP4	50c + 25c multi	.45	.30

Surtax was for the Children's Foundation, founded by Carmen América Fernandez de Leoni in 1966.

Patient — SP5

1976, Dec. 8　　Litho.　　Perf. 14

B6	SP5	10c + 5c multi	.20	.20
B7	SP5	30c + 10c multi	.25	.20

Surtax was for Anti-tuberculosis Society.

AIR POST STAMPS

Air post stamps of 1930-42 perforated "GN" (Gobierno Nacional) were for official use.

Airplane and Map of Venezuela
AP1　　　　　　AP2

1930　　Unwmk.　　Litho.　　Perf. 12

C1	AP1	5c bister brn	.20	.20
C2	AP1	10c yellow	.20	.20
a.		10c salmon	32.50	32.50
C3	AP1	15c gray	.20	.20
C4	AP1	25c lilac	.20	.20
C5	AP1	40c olive grn	.20	.20
a.		40c slate blue	40.00	
b.		40c slate green	40.00	
C6	AP1	75c dp red	.25	.20
C7	AP1	1b indigo	.40	.20
C8	AP1	1.20b blue grn	.60	.30
C9	AP1	1.70b dk blue	.75	.40
C10	AP1	1.90b blue grn	.75	.45
C11	AP1	2.10b dk blue	1.50	.60
C12	AP1	2.30b vermilion	1.50	.45
C13	AP1	2.50b dk blue	1.50	.45
C14	AP1	3.70b blue grn	1.50	1.00
C15	AP1	10b dull vio	4.50	2.25
C16	AP1	20b gray dm	7.00	4.25
		Nos. C1-C16 (16)	21.25	11.55

Nos. C1-C16 exist imperforate or partly perforated. See Nos. C119-C126.

Issued: 10b, June 8; 20b, June 16; others, Apr. 5.

Bluish Winchester Security Paper

1932, July 12　　Engr.　　Perf. 12½

C17	AP2	5c brown	.40	.20
C18	AP2	10c org yel	.40	.20
C19	AP2	15c gray lilac	.40	.20
C20	AP2	25c violet	.40	.20
C21	AP2	40c ol grn	.80	.20
C22	AP2	70c rose	.55	.20
C23	AP2	75c red org	1.00	.20
C24	AP2	1b dk bl	1.10	.20
C25	AP2	1.20b green	2.25	.85
C26	AP2	1.70b red brn	4.50	.55
C27	AP2	1.80b ultra	2.25	.35
C28	AP2	1.90b green	5.50	3.50
C29	AP2	1.95b blue	6.50	2.75
C30	AP2	2b blk brn	4.00	2.25
C31	AP2	2.10b blue	9.25	5.50
C32	AP2	2.30b red	4.00	2.25
C33	AP2	2.50b dk bl	5.50	1.40
C34	AP2	3b dk vio	5.50	.85
C35	AP2	3.70b emerald	7.75	5.50
C36	AP2	4b red org	5.50	1.40
C37	AP2	5b black	6.50	2.25
C38	AP2	8b dk car	13.00	4.50
C39	AP2	10b dk vio	25.00	7.75
C40	AP2	20b grnsh slate	55.00	20.00
		Nos. C17-C40 (24)	167.05	63.25

Pairs imperf. between exist of the 1b (value $150); the 25c and 4b (value $300 each).

Air Post Stamps of 1932 Surcharged in Black

1937, June 4

C41	AP2	5c on 1.70b red brn	11.00	7.00
C42	AP2	10c on 3.70b emer	11.00	7.00
C43	AP2	15c on 4b red org	5.00	3.50
C44	AP2	25c on 5b blk	5.00	3.50
C45	AP2	1b on 8b dk car	4.00	3.50
C46	AP2	2b on 2.10b bl	30.00	23.00
		Nos. C41-C46 (6)	66.00	47.50

Various varieties of surcharge exist, including double and triple impressions. No. C43 exists in pair imperf. between; value $30 unused, $50 used.

Allegory of Flight AP3

Allegory of Flight AP4

National Pantheon at Caracas AP5

Airplane — AP6　　　　AP7

Perf. 11, 11½ and Compound

1937, July 1　　　　　　Litho.

C47	AP3	5c brn org	.30	.40
C48	AP4	10c org red	.25	.20
C49	AP5	15c gray blk	.60	.40
C50	AP6	25c dk vio	.60	.40
C51	AP4	40c yel grn	1.10	.55
C52	AP3	70c red	1.10	.40
C53	AP5	75c bister	2.50	1.30
C54	AP3	1b dk gray	1.50	.55
C55	AP4	1.20b pck grn	6.50	4.25
C56	AP3	1.80b dk ultra	3.25	2.00

C57	AP5	1.95b lt ultra	10.00	7.75
C58	AP6	2b chocolate	4.25	2.75
C59	AP6	2.50b gray bl	11.50	11.50
C60	AP4	3b lt vio	6.50	4.50
C61	AP6	3.70b rose red	11.50	15.00
C62	AP5	10b red vio	25.00	15.00
C63	AP3	20b gray	30.00	23.00
		Nos. C47-C63 (17)	116.45	89.95

All values exist imperf., and all except the 3.70b part-perf.
Counterfeits exist.
For overprints & surcharges see #C66-C78, C114-C118, C164-C167, C169-C172, C174-C180.

1937, Oct. 28　　　　　　Perf. 11

C64	AP7	70c emerald	1.40	.55
C65	AP7	1.80b ultra	2.25	1.00

Acquisition of the Port of La Guaira by the Government from the British Corporation, June 3, 1937. Exist imperf.

A redrawn printing of Nos. C64-C65, with lower inscription beginning "Nacionalización . . ." was prepared but not issued. Price, $40 each.

For overprints see Nos. C168, C173.

Air Post Stamps of 1937 Overprinted in Black

1937, Dec. 17　　　　　　Perf. 11, 11½

C66	AP4	10c org red	1.00	.70
a.		Inverted overprint	15.00	12.00
C67	AP6	25c dk vio	2.00	1.00
C68	AP4	40c yel grn	2.00	1.40
C69	AP3	70c red	1.50	1.00
a.		Inverted overprint	15.00	14.00
b.		Double overprint	20.00	16.00
C70	AP3	1b dk gray	2.00	1.40
a.		Inverted overprint	16.00	13.00
b.		Double overprint	13.00	
C71	AP4	1.20b pck grn	30.00	20.00
a.		Inverted overprint	77.50	
C72	AP3	1.80b dk ultra	5.75	2.40
C73	AP5	1.95b lt ultra	7.75	4.25
a.		Inverted overprint	60.00	40.00
C74	AP6	2b chocolate	50.00	23.00
a.		Inverted overprint	100.00	90.00
b.		Double overprint	82.50	82.50
C75	AP6	2.50b gray bl	50.00	19.00
a.		Inverted overprint	70.00	
b.		Double overprint	100.00	82.50
C76	AP4	3b lt vio	30.00	12.00
C77	AP5	10b red vio	72.50	40.00
C78	AP3	20b gray	77.50	47.50
a.		Double overprint	150.00	150.00
		Nos. C66-C78 (13)	332.00	173.65

Counterfeit overprints exist on #C77-C78.

View of La Guaira AP8

National Pantheon AP9

Oil Wells AP10

1938-39　　Engr.　　Perf. 12

C79	AP8	5c green	1.00	.50
C80	AP8	5c dk grn	.20	.20
C81	AP9	10c car rose	1.40	.80
C82	AP9	10c scarlet	.20	.20
C83	AP8	12½c dull vio	.60	.55
C84	AP10	15c slate vio	3.00	1.25
C85	AP10	15c dk bl	.85	.20
C86	AP8	25c dk bl	3.00	1.25
C87	AP8	25c bis brn	.25	.20
C88	AP10	30c vio ('39)	2.00	.20
C89	AP9	40c dk vio	3.50	1.25
C90	AP9	40c redsh brn	2.50	.20
C91	AP8	45c Prus grn ('39)	1.00	1.00

C92	AP9	50c blue		
		('39)	1.25	.20
C93	AP10	70c car rose	.85	.25
C94	AP8	75c bis brn	6.00	2.00
C95	AP8	75c ol bis	1.40	.20
C96	AP10	90c red org		
		('39)	1.00	.20
C97	AP9	1b ol & bis	7.00	2.75
C98	AP9	1b dk vio	1.25	.20
C99	AP10	1.20b orange	20.00	5.75
C100	AP10	1.20b green	2.00	.55
C101	AP8	1.80b ultra	2.00	.55
C102	AP9	1.90b black	5.50	2.75
C103	AP10	1.95b lt bl	4.25	2.50
C104	AP8	2b ol gray	45.00	15.00
C105	AP8	2b car rose	1.75	.70
C106	AP9	2.50b red brn	45.00	20.00
C107	AP9	2.50b orange	10.00	2.75
C108	AP10	3b bl grn	20.00	4.75
C109	AP10	3b ol gray	5.50	2.00
C110	AP8	3.70b gray blk	7.75	5.50
C111	AP10	5b red brn		
		('39)	7.75	2.00
C112	AP9	10b vio brn	20.00	2.40
C113	AP10	20b red org	57.50	25.00
		Nos. C79-C113 (35)	292.25	105.00

See Nos. C227a, C235-C236, C254-C255.
For surcharge see No. C227.

Nos. C51, C56, C58-C59, C61
Surcharged

1938, Apr. 15   **Perf. 11, 11½**

C114	AP3	5c on 1.80b	.85	.60
a.		Inverted surcharge	12.50	7.50
C115	AP6	10c on 2.50b	3.00	1.40
a.		Inverted surcharge	10.00	7.50
C116	AP6	15c on 2b	1.40	1.10
C117	AP4	25c on 40c	1.75	1.40
C118	AP6	40c on 3.70b	3.50	3.25
		Nos. C114-C118 (5)	10.50	7.75

Plane & Map Type of 1930
White Paper; No Imprint

1938-39   **Engr.**   **Perf. 12½**

C119	AP1	5c dk grn ('39)	.25	.20
C120	AP1	10c org yel ('39)	.55	.20
C121	AP1	12½c rose vio ('39)	1.10	.85
C122	AP1	15c dp bl	.95	.20
C123	AP1	25c brown	1.10	.20
C124	AP1	40c olive ('39)	2.75	.40
C125	AP1	70c rose car ('39)	20.00	7.75
C126	AP1	1b blk ('39)	7.75	3.00
		Nos. C119-C126 (8)	34.45	12.80

Monument to
Sucre — AP11

Monuments at Carabobo
AP12   AP13

1938, Dec. 23   **Perf. 13½**

C127	AP11	20c brn blk	.80	.30
C128	AP12	30c purple	1.20	.30
C129	AP13	45c dk bl	1.75	.25
C130	AP13	50c lt ultra	1.50	.25
C131	AP13	70c dk car	26.00	7.50
C132	AP12	90c red org	2.50	.75
C133	AP13	1.35b gray blk	3.00	1.00
C134	AP11	1.40b slate gray	12.00	2.75
C135	AP12	2.25b green	6.00	2.00
		Nos. C127-C135 (9)	54.75	15.10

For surcharge see No. C198.

Simón
Bolívar
and
Carabobo
Monument
AP14

1940, Mar. 30   **Perf. 12**

C136	AP14	15c blue	.75	.20
C137	AP14	20c olive bis	.75	.20
C138	AP14	25c red brn	2.75	.40
C139	AP14	40c blk brn	2.25	.20
C140	AP14	1b red lilac	5.00	.55
C141	AP14	2b rose car	11.00	1.40
		Nos. C136-C141 (6)	22.50	2.95

"The
Founding
of Grand
Colombia"
AP15

1940, June 13

C142	AP15	15c copper brown	1.25	.45

Founding of the Pan American Union, 50th
anni.

Statue of Simón
Bolívar,
Caracas — AP16

1940-44

C143	AP16	5c dk grn ('42)	.20	.20
C144	AP16	10c scar ('42)	.20	.20
C145	AP16	12½c dull purple	.60	.25
C146	AP16	15c blue ('43)	.40	.20
C147	AP16	20c bis brn ('44)	.40	.20
C148	AP16	25c bis brn ('42)	.40	.20
C149	AP16	30c dp vio ('43)	.40	.20
C150	AP16	40c blk brn ('43)	.50	.20
C151	AP16	45c turq grn		
		('43)	.50	.20
C152	AP16	50c blue ('44)	.50	.25
C153	AP16	70c rose pink	1.50	.25
C154	AP16	75c ol bis ('43)	6.00	1.25
C155	AP16	90c red org ('43)	1.00	.25
C156	AP16	1b dp red lil		
		('42)	.50	.20
C157	AP16	1.20b dp yel grn		
		('43)	1.90	.60
C158	AP16	1.35b gray blk		
		('42)	8.00	3.75
C159	AP16	2b rose pink		
		('43)	1.50	.20
C160	AP16	3b blk blk ('43)	2.50	.60
C161	AP16	4b black	2.00	.60
C162	AP16	5b red brn ('44)	16.00	6.25
		Nos. C143-162 (20)	45.00	16.00

See #C232-C234, C239-C253. For
surcharges see #C225, C873.

Resellado
1943

Nos. C48, C50-C65 Overprinted

Perf. 11, 11½ & Compound
1943, Dec. 21

C164	AP4	10c orange red	2.00	.90
C165	AP6	25c dk violet	2.00	.90
C166	AP4	40c yellow grn	2.00	.90
C167	AP3	70c red	2.00	.90
C168	AP7	70c emerald	2.00	.90
C169	AP5	75c bister	2.00	.90
C170	AP4	1b dk gray	2.00	.90
C171	AP4	1.20b peacock		
		grn	5.00	1.60
C172	AP3	1.80b dk ultra	5.00	1.60
C173	AP7	1.80b dk ultra	5.00	2.50
C174	AP5	1.95b lt ultra	6.00	3.25
C175	AP6	2b chocolate	6.00	3.25
C176	AP6	2.50b gray blue	5.00	3.25
C177	AP4	3b lt violet	6.00	3.25
C178	AP6	3.70b rose red	52.50	45.00
C179	AP5	10b red violet	12.00	10.00
C180	AP3	20b gray	27.50	20.00
		Nos. C164-C180 (17)	144.00	100.00
		Set, never hinged	175.00	

Issued for sale to philatelists. Nos. C164-
C169 were sold only in sets.
Nearly all are known with invtd. ovpt.

 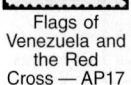

Flags of
Venezuela and
the Red
Cross — AP17

Baseball
Players — AP18

1944, Aug. 22   **Litho.**   **Perf. 12**
Flags in red, yellow, blue and black

C181	AP17	5c gray green	.20	.20
C182	AP17	10c magenta	.20	.20
C183	AP17	20c brt blue	.25	.20
C184	AP17	30c violet bl	.30	.20
C185	AP17	40c chocolate	.40	.20
C186	AP17	45c apple green	1.25	.40
C187	AP17	90c orange	1.00	.40
C188	AP17	1b gray black	2.00	.40
		Nos. C181-C188 (8)	5.60	2.20
		Set, never hinged	6.25	

80th anniv. of the Intl. Red Cross and 37th
anniv. of Venezuela's joining the organization.
Nos. C181-C188 exist imperf. and part perf.

1944, Oct. 12
"AEREO" in dark carmine

C189	AP18	5c dull vio brn	.30	.20
C190	AP18	10c gray green	.50	.20
C191	AP18	20c ultra	.50	.25
C192	AP18	30c dull rose	1.00	.40
C193	AP18	45c rose violet	2.00	.70
C194	AP18	90c red orange	3.50	1.40
C195	AP18	1b dark gray	4.00	1.40
C196	AP18	1.20b yellow grn	9.25	7.25
C197	AP18	1.80b ocher	12.00	9.25
		Nos. C189-C197 (9)	33.05	21.05
		Set, never hinged	42.50	

7th World Amateur Baseball Championship
Games, Caracas.
Nos. C189-C197 exist imperf, and all but 1b
exist part perf. Various errors of "AEREO"
overprint exist.

Habilitado
1944
VALE
Bs. 0.30

No. C134 Surcharged
in Black

1944, Nov. 17   **Perf. 13½**

C198	AP11	30c on 1.40b	.45	.45
a.		Double surcharge	32.50	32.50
b.		Inverted surcharge	12.50	12.50

Charles
Howarth — AP19

Antonio José
de
Sucre — AP20

1944, Dec. 21   **Unwmk.**   **Perf. 12**

C199	AP19	5c black	.20	.20
C200	AP19	10c purple	.20	.20
C201	AP19	20c sepia	.30	.30
C202	AP19	30c dull green	.35	.30
C203	AP19	1.20b bister	1.75	1.50
C204	AP19	1.80b deep ultra	4.00	3.00
C205	AP19	3.70b rose	3.00	3.00
		Nos. C199-C205 (7)	9.80	8.50
		Set, never hinged	12.50	

Cent. of founding of 1st cooperative shop in
Rochdale, England, by Charles Howarth.
Nos. C199-C205 exist imperf. and part perf.

1945, Mar. 3   **Engr.**

C206	AP20	5c orange	.20	.20
C207	AP20	10c violet	.20	.20
C208	AP20	20c grnsh blk	.20	.20

C209	AP20	30c brt green	.20	.20
C210	AP20	40c olive	.50	.50
C211	AP20	45c black brn	.75	.50
C212	AP20	90c redsh brn	1.00	.50
C213	AP20	1b dp red lil	1.00	.50
C214	AP20	1.20b black	3.00	2.50
C215	AP20	2b yellow	4.75	3.50
		Nos. C206-C215 (10)	11.80	8.80
		Set, never hinged	14.50	

150th birth anniv. of Antonio Jose de Sucre,
Grand Marshal of Ayacucho.

Type of 1946

1946, Aug. 24   **Perf. 12**

C216	A81	30c Bello	1.10	.20
C217	A82	30c Urdaneta	1.10	.20
		Set, never hinged	2.75	

Allegory of
Republic — AP23

Perf. 11½
1946, Oct. 18   **Litho.**   **Unwmk.**

C218	AP23	15c dp violet bl	.35	.20
C219	AP23	20c bister brn	.35	.20
C220	AP23	30c dp violet	.45	.30
C221	AP23	1b brt rose	3.25	2.50
		Nos. C218-C221 (4)	4.40	3.20
		Set, never hinged	4.75	

Anniversary of the Revolution of October,
1945. Exist imperf. and part perf.

J. R. G.
AEREO
Vale Bs. 0.15
1946

Nos. 297, 371, C152
and 362 Surcharged
in Black

1947, Jan.   **Perf. 12**

C223	A49	10c on 22½c dp car	.25	.20
a.		Inverted surcharge	4.00	4.00
C224	A69	15c on 25c lt bl	.40	.25
C225	AP16	20c on 50c blue	.40	.40
a.		Inverted surcharge	5.00	5.00
C226	A65	70c on 1b dk vio brn	.75	.45
a.		Inverted surcharge	4.00	4.00

J. R. G.
AEREO
Vale Bs. 20
1946

Type of 1938 Surcharged in Black

C227	AP10	20b on 20b org		
		red	28.00	22.50
a.		Surcharge omitted	92.50	40.00
		Nos. C223-C227 (5)	29.80	23.65
		Set, never hinged	40.00	

"J. R. G." are the initials of "Junta Revolu-
cionaria de Gobierno."
Also exist: 20c on #C143, 10c on #371.

Anti-tuberculosis
Institute,
Maracaibo — AP24

1947, Jan. 12   **Litho.**
Venezuela Shown on Map in Yellow

C228	AP24	15c dark blue	.40	.30
C229	AP24	20c dark brown	.40	.30
C230	AP24	30c dark violet	.40	.30
C231	AP24	1b carmine	4.25	3.50
		Nos. C228-C231 (4)	5.45	4.40
		Set, never hinged	6.25	

12th Pan-American Health Conf., Caracas,
Jan. 1947.
Nos. C228-C231 exist imperf., part perf. and
with yellow omitted.

Types of 1938-40

				Engr.
1947, Mar. 17				
C232	AP16	75c orange	7.50	4.50
C233	AP16	1b brt ultra	.70	.25
C234	AP16	3b red brown	17.50	8.00
C235	AP10	5b scarlet	15.00	5.00
C236	AP9	10b violet	20.00	7.50
		Nos. C232-C236 (5)	60.70	25.25
		Set, never hinged	85.00	

On Nos. C235 and C236 the numerals of value are in color on a white table.

No. 370
Surcharged in
Black

1947, June 20
C237	A70	5c on 20c blue	.40	.20
C238	A70	10c on 20c blue	.40	.20
a.		Inverted surcharge	5.00	5.00
		Set, never hinged	1.00	

Types of 1938-44

				Engr.
1947-48				
C239	AP16	5c orange	.20	.20
C240	AP16	10c dk green	.20	.20
C241	AP16	12½ bister brn	.45	.45
C242	AP16	15c gray	.20	.20
C243	AP16	20c violet	.20	.20
C244	AP16	25c dull green	.20	.20
C245	AP16	30c brt ultra	.45	.20
C246	AP16	40c green ('48)	.20	.20
C247	AP16	45c vermilion	.45	.20
C248	AP16	50c red violet	.25	.20
C249	AP16	70c dk car	1.00	.45
C250	AP16	75c purple ('48)	.65	.25
C251	AP16	90c black	1.00	.30
C252	AP16	1.20b red brn ('48)	1.25	.50
C253	AP16	3b dp blue	1.75	.50
C254	AP10	5b olive grn	9.25	5.00
C255	AP9	10b yellow	8.25	4.75
		Nos. C239-C255 (17)	25.95	14.00
		Set, never hinged	35.00	

On Nos. C254 and C255 the numerals of value are in color on a white tablet.

Issue dates: 5c, 10c, Oct. 8. 15c, Dec. 2, 40c, 75c, 1.20b, May 10, 1948. Others, Oct. 27, 1947.

M. S. Republica de
Venezuela — AP25

Santos
Michelena
AP26

Imprint: "American Bank Note Company"

				Perf. 12
1948-50		**Unwmk.**		
C256	AP25	5c red brown	.20	.20
C257	AP25	10c deep green	.20	.20
C258	AP25	15c brown	.20	.20
C259	AP25	20c violet brn	.25	.20
C260	AP25	25c brown black	.25	.20
C261	AP25	30c olive green	.25	.20
C262	AP25	45c blue green	.45	.25
C263	AP25	50c gray black	.75	.40
C264	AP25	70c orange	1.25	.40
C265	AP25	75c brt ultra	2.25	.55
C266	AP25	90c car lake	1.25	1.25
C267	AP25	1b purple	1.75	.80
C268	AP25	2b gray	1.90	1.25
C269	AP25	3b emerald	7.00	4.00
C270	AP25	4b deep blue	3.25	6.00
C271	AP25	5b orange red	13.00	6.00
		Nos. C256-C271 (16)	34.20	20.10

Issued to honor the Grand-Colombian Merchant Fleet. See Nos. C554-C556.
Issued: 5c, 10c, 15c, 25c, 30c, 1b, 7/9/48; 45c, 75c, 5b, 5/11/50; others, 3/9/49.
For surcharges see Nos. C863-C864.

1949, Apr. 25
C272	AP26	5c orange brn	.25	.20
C273	AP26	10c gray	.25	.20
C274	AP26	15c red orange	.50	.50

C275	AP26	25c dull green	1.00	.80
C276	AP26	30c plum	1.00	.80
C277	AP26	1b violet	5.00	2.75
		Nos. C272-C277 (6)	8.00	5.25

See note after No. 427.

Christopher
Columbus
AP27

				Perf. 12½
1948-49		**Unwmk.**		
C278	AP27	5c brown ('49)	.25	.20
C279	AP27	10c gray	.25	.25
C280	AP27	15c dull grn	.55	.25
C281	AP27	25c green ('49)	1.00	.55
C282	AP27	30c red vio ('49)	1.25	.80
C283	AP27	1b violet ('49)	5.00	2.25
		Nos. C278-C283 (6)	8.30	4.30

See note after No. 431.

AP28   AP29

Symbols of global air mail.

				Perf. 12
1950				
C284	AP28	5c red brown	.25	.20
C285	AP28	10c dk green	.25	.20
C286	AP28	15c olive brn	.25	.20
C287	AP28	25c olive gray	.40	.30
C288	AP28	30c olive grn	.55	.30
C289	AP28	50c black	.40	.25
C290	AP28	60c brt ultra	1.10	.60
C291	AP28	90c carmine	1.40	.75
C292	AP28	1b purple	1.90	.50
		Nos. C284-C292 (9)	6.50	3.30
		Set, never hinged	7.50	

75th anniv. of the UPU.
Issue dates: 5c, Jan. 28. Others, Feb. 19.

1950, Aug. 25   Photo.   Perf. 11½

Araguaney, Venezuelan national tree.

Foliage in Yellow
C293	AP29	5c orange brn	.25	.20
C294	AP29	10c blue grn	.25	.20
C295	AP29	15c deep plum	.50	.20
C296	AP29	25c dk gray grn	4.50	1.25
C297	AP29	30c red orange	4.75	1.60
C298	AP29	50c dark gray	2.75	.40
C299	AP29	60c deep blue	4.50	.80
C300	AP29	90c red	7.00	1.60
C301	AP29	1b rose violet	8.00	2.00
		Nos. C293-C301 (9)	32.50	8.25
		Set, never hinged	45.00	

Issued to publicize Forest Week, 1950.

Census Type of 1950

			Engr.	Perf. 12
1950, Sept. 1				
C302	A90	5c olive gray	.20	.20
C303	A90	10c green	.20	.20
C304	A90	15c olive green	.20	.20
C305	A90	25c gray	.30	.30
C306	A90	30c orange	.45	.25
C307	A90	50c lt brown	.30	.20
C308	A90	60c ultra	.30	.20
C309	A90	90c rose carmine	1.10	.45
C310	A90	1b violet	1.75	1.40
		Nos. C302-C310 (9)	4.80	3.40

Signing Act of Independence — AP31

1950, Nov. 17
C311	AP31	5c vermilion	.35	.20
C312	AP31	10c red brown	.35	.20
C313	AP31	15c violet	.50	.20

C314	AP31	30c brt blue	.70	.25
C315	AP31	1b green	3.25	1.40
		Nos. C311-C315 (5)	5.15	2.25

200th anniversary of the birth of Gen. Francisco de Miranda.

Alonso de Ojeda Type of 1950

				Perf. 11½
1950, Dec. 18		**Photo.**		
C316	A91	5c orange brn	.20	.20
C317	A91	10c cerise	.25	.20
C318	A91	15c black brn	.30	.20
C319	A91	25c violet	.55	.25
C320	A91	30c orange	1.10	.45
C321	A91	1b emerald	4.50	2.25
		Nos. C316-321 (6)	6.90	3.55

Bolivar Statue Type of 1951

			Engr.	Perf. 12
1951, July 13				
C322	A92	5c purple	.40	.20
C323	A92	10c dull green	.45	.20
C324	A92	20c olive gray	.45	.20
C325	A92	25c olive green	.50	.20
C326	A92	30c vermilion	.65	.20
C327	A92	40c lt brown	.65	.30
C328	A92	50c gray	1.60	.55
C329	A92	70c orange	2.50	1.40
		Nos. C322-C329 (8)	7.20	3.35

Queen Isabella
I — AP34

				Perf. 11½
1951, Oct. 12		**Photo.**		
C330	AP34	5c dk green & buff	.30	.20
C331	AP34	10c dk red & cream	.30	.20
C332	AP34	20c dp blue & gray	.50	.20
C333	AP34	30c dk blue & gray	.50	.20
a.		Souv. sheet of 4, #C330-C333	3.00	2.75
		Nos. C330-C333 (4)	1.60	.80
		Set, never hinged	2.25	

500th anniv. of the birth of Queen Isabella I of Spain.

Bicycle Racecourse — AP35

			Engr.	Perf. 12
1951, Dec. 18				
C334	AP35	5c green	.75	.20
C335	AP35	10c rose carmine	.85	.20
C336	AP35	20c redsh brown	.95	.25
C337	AP35	30c blue	1.25	.35
a.		Souv. sheet, #C334-C337	11.00	11.00
		Nos. C334-C337 (4)	3.80	1.00
		Set, never hinged	4.00	

3rd Bolivarian Games, Caracas, Dec. 1951.

Arms of Carabobo
and
"Industry" — AP36

				Perf. 11½
1951		**Photo.**		
C338	AP36	5c blue green	.40	.20
C339	AP36	7½c gray green	.50	.30
C340	AP36	10c car rose	.40	.20
C341	AP36	15c dark brown	.50	.20
C342	AP36	20c gray blue	.55	.20
C343	AP36	30c deep blue	1.50	.25
C344	AP36	45c magenta	.75	.25
C345	AP36	60c olive brown	1.40	.55
C346	AP36	90c rose brown	3.25	1.75
		Nos. C338-C346 (9)	9.25	3.90

Issue date: Oct. 29.

Arms of Zulia and "Industry"

C347	AP36	5c blue green	.40	.20
C348	AP36	10c car rose	.40	.20
C349	AP36	15c dark brown	.60	.20
C350	AP36	30c deep blue	4.00	1.25
C351	AP36	60c olive brown	2.40	.40
C352	AP36	1.20b brown car	8.00	5.00
C353	AP36	3b blue gray	2.75	.75

C354	AP36	5b purple brn	4.00	2.00
C355	AP36	10b violet	6.25	4.00
		Nos. C347-C355 (9)	28.80	14.00

Issued: 5b, 9/8; 5c, 3b, 10b, 10/8; others, 10/29.

Arms of Anzoategui

C356	AP36	5c blue green	.35	.20
C357	AP36	10c car rose	.35	.20
C358	AP36	15c dk brown	.45	.20
C359	AP36	25c sepia	.55	.20
C360	AP36	30c deep blue	1.40	.80
C361	AP36	50c henna brn	1.40	.40
C362	AP36	60c olive brn	2.00	.25
C363	AP36	1b purple	2.50	.80
C364	AP36	2b violet gray	4.25	1.75
		Nos. C356-C364 (9)	13.25	4.80

Issue date: Nov. 9.

Arms of Caracas and Buildings

C365	AP36	5c blue green	.70	.20
C366	AP36	7½c gray green	2.10	.95
C367	AP36	10c car rose	.50	.30
C368	AP36	15c dk brown	5.00	.65
C369	AP36	20c gray blue	3.25	.65
C370	AP36	30c deep blue	5.50	1.25
C371	AP36	45c magenta	3.25	.75
C372	AP36	60c olive brn	11.50	1.50
C373	AP36	90c rose brn	6.50	5.25
		Nos. C365-C373 (9)	38.30	11.60

Issue date: Aug. 6.

Arms of Tachira and Agricultural Products

C374	AP36	5c blue green	.30	.30
C375	AP36	10c car rose	.30	.30
C376	AP36	15c dk brown	.85	.30
C377	AP36	30c deep blue	11.00	1.25
C378	AP36	60c olive brn	8.50	1.25
C379	AP36	1.20b brown car	8.50	6.00
C380	AP36	3b blue gray	2.75	1.25
C381	AP36	5b purple brn	5.00	2.50
C382	AP36	10b violet	6.75	5.00
		Nos. C374-C382 (9)	43.95	18.15

Issue date: Aug. 9.

Arms of Venezuela and Bolivar Statue

C383	AP36	5c blue green	.40	.20
C384	AP36	7½c gray grn	1.00	.65
C385	AP36	10c car rose	.30	.20
C386	AP36	15c dk brown	2.25	.65
C387	AP36	20c gray blue	3.00	.50
C388	AP36	30c deep blue	5.50	1.10
C389	AP36	45c magenta	2.50	.45
C390	AP36	60c olive brn	11.50	2.25
C391	AP36	90c rose brn	7.25	5.00
		Nos. C383-C391 (9)	33.70	11.00

Issue date: Aug. 6.

1952
Arms of Miranda and Agricultural Products

C392	AP36	5c blue green	.30	.20
C393	AP36	7½c gray grn	.50	.30
C394	AP36	10c car rose	.30	.20
C395	AP36	15c dark brown	.60	.20
C396	AP36	20c gray blue	.90	.25
C397	AP36	30c deep blue	1.75	.40
C398	AP36	45c magenta	1.60	.20
C399	AP36	60c olive brn	3.00	.55
C400	AP36	90c rose brn	13.50	8.00
		Nos. C392-C400 (9)	22.45	10.30

Issue date: 7½c, 15c, 20c, 30c, Mar. 15.

Arms of Aragua and Stylized Farm

C401	AP36	5c blue green	.60	.20
C402	AP36	7½c gray grn	.50	.30
C403	AP36	10c car rose	.30	.20
C404	AP36	15c dk brown	1.75	.25
C405	AP36	20c gray blue	.85	.25
C406	AP36	30c deep blue	2.50	.30
C407	AP36	45c magenta	1.90	.25
C408	AP36	60c olive brn	4.00	.40
C409	AP36	90c rose brn	15.00	8.00
		Nos. C401-C409 (9)	27.40	10.15

Issue date: 7½c, 15c, 20c, 30c, Mar. 24.

Arms of Lara, Agricultural Products and Rope

C410	AP36	5c blue green	.60	.20
C411	AP36	7½c gray grn	.50	.30
C412	AP36	10c car rose	.30	.20
C413	AP36	15c dk brown	.90	.20
C414	AP36	20c gray blue	1.40	.20
C415	AP36	30c deep blue	2.75	.40
C416	AP36	45c magenta	1.40	.35
C417	AP36	60c olive brn	2.75	.65
C418	AP36	90c rose brn	15.00	10.00
		Nos. C410-C418 (9)	25.60	12.50

Issue date: 7½c, 15c, 20c, Mar. 24.

Arms of Bolivar and Stylized Design

C419	AP36	5c blue green	3.25	.35
C420	AP36	10c car rose	.30	.20
C421	AP36	15c dark brown	.50	.20
C422	AP36	25c sepia	.40	.20
C423	AP36	30c deep blue	2.25	.95
C424	AP36	50c henna brn	1.50	.40
C425	AP36	60c olive brn	2.50	.55

C426	AP36	1b purple	2.25	.40
C427	AP36	2b violet gray	5.25	1.75
		Nos. C419-C427 (9)	18.20	5.00

Issue date: 15c, 30c, Mar. 24.

Arms of Sucre, Palms and Seascape

C428	AP36	5c blue green	.30	.20
C429	AP36	10c car rose	.20	.20
C430	AP36	15c dk brown	.40	.20
C431	AP36	25c sepia	8.50	.20
C432	AP36	30c deep blue	2.75	.85
C433	AP36	50c henna brn	1.25	.30
C434	AP36	60c olive brn	1.60	.65
C435	AP36	1b purple	2.00	.50
C436	AP36	2b violet gray	4.50	2.25
		Nos. C428-C436 (9)	21.50	5.35

Issue date: 15c, 30c, Mar. 24.

Arms of Trujillo Surrounded by Stylized Tree

C437	AP36	5c blue green	5.25	.35
C438	AP36	10c car rose	.40	.20
C439	AP36	15c dk brown	1.50	.20
C440	AP36	30c deep blue	6.50	1.10
C441	AP36	60c olive brn	4.75	1.00
C442	AP36	1.20b rose red	4.25	2.40
C443	AP36	3b blue gray	2.00	1.00
C444	AP36	5b purple brn	4.50	1.75
C445	AP36	10b violet	7.75	4.00
		Nos. C437-C445 (9)	36.90	12.00

Issue date: 5c, 30c, Mar. 24.

1953-54

Map of Delta Amacuro and Ship

C446	AP36	5c bl grn	.30	.20
C447	AP36	10c car rose	.20	.20
C448	AP36	15c dk brn	.45	.20
C449	AP36	25c sepia	.65	.30
C450	AP36	30c dp bl	2.50	.75
C451	AP36	50c hn brn	1.25	.30
C452	AP36	60c ol brn	1.90	.60
C453	AP36	1b purple	2.40	.85
C454	AP36	2b vio gray	4.00	3.00
		Nos. C446-C454 (9)	13.65	6.40

Issue date: 15c, 30c, Feb. 13.

Arms of Falcon and Stylized Oil Refinery

C455	AP36	5c bl grn	.50	.25
C456	AP36	10c car rose	.25	.25
C457	AP36	15c dk brn	.50	.25
C458	AP36	30c dp bl	4.00	1.10
C459	AP36	60c ol brn	3.00	.85
C460	AP36	1.20b rose red	3.75	3.50
C461	AP36	3b bl gray	4.00	2.25
C462	AP36	5b pur brn	6.50	4.50
C463	AP36	10b violet	6.50	5.00
		Nos. C455-C463 (9)	29.00	17.95

Issue date: 10c, 15c, 30c, Feb. 13.

Arms of Guarico and Factory

C464	AP36	5c blue grn	.30	.20
C465	AP36	10c car rose	.20	.20
C466	AP36	15c dk brn	.45	.20
C467	AP36	25c sepia	.65	.30
C468	AP36	30c dp bl	2.75	1.10
C469	AP36	50c hn brn	1.40	.45
C470	AP36	60c ol brn	1.60	.65
C471	AP36	1b purple	2.75	.65
C472	AP36	2b vio gray	4.00	2.10
		Nos. C464-C472 (9)	14.10	5.85

Issue date: 15c, 30c, Feb. 13.

Arms of Merida and Church

C473	AP36	5c bl grn	.30	.25
C474	AP36	10c car rose	.25	.25
C475	AP36	15c dk brn	.50	.25
C476	AP36	30c dp bl	4.50	1.00
C477	AP36	60c ol brn	2.25	.60
C478	AP36	1.20b rose red	3.75	2.25
C479	AP36	3b bl gray	2.25	1.00
C480	AP36	5b pur brn	4.25	2.25
C481	AP36	10b violet	6.00	3.75
		Nos. C473-C481 (9)	24.05	11.60

Issue date: 10c, Feb. 2.

Arms of Monagas and Horses

C482	AP36	5c bl grn	.25	.20
C483	AP36	10c car rose	.20	.20
C484	AP36	15c dk brn	.40	.20
C485	AP36	25c sepia	.30	.20
C486	AP36	30c dp bl	3.75	1.00
C487	AP36	50c hn brn	1.50	.50
C488	AP36	60c ol brn	1.75	.50
C489	AP36	1b purple	2.50	.65
C490	AP36	2b vio gray	3.50	1.75
		Nos. C482-C490 (9)	14.15	5.20

Issue date: 10c, Feb. 2.

Arms of Portuguesa and Forest

C491	AP36	5c bl grn	1.25	.40
C492	AP36	10c car rose	.30	.30
C493	AP36	15c dk brn	.75	.30
C494	AP36	30c dp bl	3.75	1.75
C495	AP36	60c ol brn	2.75	.70
C496	AP36	1.20b rose red	6.50	3.75
C497	AP36	3b bl gray	2.25	1.25
C498	AP36	5b pur brn	4.00	2.25
C499	AP36	10b violet	5.75	4.75
		Nos. C491-C499 (9)	27.30	15.45

Issue date: 5c, 10c, 30c, Feb. 2.

Map of Amazonas and Orchid

C500	AP36	5c bl grn	.85	.20
C501	AP36	10c car rose	.20	.20
C502	AP36	15c dk brn	.85	.20
C503	AP36	25c sepia	1.75	.20
C504	AP36	30c dp bl	4.50	.45
C505	AP36	50c hn brn	3.50	.75
C506	AP36	60c ol brn	4.50	.75
C507	AP36	1b purple	17.50	2.50
C508	AP36	2b vio gray	7.00	3.00
		Nos. C500-C508 (9)	40.65	8.25

Issue date: Jan. 1954.

Arms of Apure, Horse and Bird

C509	AP36	5c bl grn	.60	.30
C510	AP36	10c car rose	.30	.30
C511	AP36	15c dk brn	.60	.30
C512	AP36	30c dp bl	2.25	1.00
C513	AP36	60c ol brn	2.10	.50
C514	AP36	1.20b brn car	3.50	2.50
C515	AP36	3b bl gray	2.10	1.10
C516	AP36	5b pur brn	4.25	2.00
C517	AP36	10b violet	6.00	4.25
		Nos. C509-C517 (9)	21.70	12.25

Issue date: Jan. 1954.

Arms of Barinas, Cow and Horse

C518	AP36	5c bl grn	.20	.20
C519	AP36	10c car rose	.20	.20
C520	AP36	15c dk brn	.75	.20
C521	AP36	30c dp blue	2.50	1.00
C522	AP36	60c ol brn	2.50	.50
C523	AP36	1.20b brn car	3.50	1.90
C524	AP36	3b bl gray	2.25	1.00
C525	AP36	5b pur brn	3.75	1.25
C526	AP36	10b violet	5.50	4.00
		Nos. C518-C526 (9)	21.15	10.25

Issue date: Jan. 1954.

Arms of Cojedes and Cattle

C527	AP36	5c bl grn	2.50	.40
C528	AP36	7½c gray grn	.65	.40
C529	AP36	10c car rose	.20	.20
C530	AP36	15c dk brn	.20	.20
C531	AP36	20c gray bl	.50	.20
C532	AP36	30c dp blue	3.50	.50
C533	AP36	45c mag	1.25	.30
C534	AP36	60c ol brn	2.50	.45
C535	AP36	90c rose brn	3.00	1.75
		Nos. C527-C535 (9)	14.30	4.40

Issue date: Dec.

Arms of Nueva Esparta and Fish

C536	AP36	5c bl grn	.40	.20
C537	AP36	10c car rose	.20	.20
C538	AP36	15c dk brn	.65	.20
C539	AP36	25c sepia	1.10	.25
C540	AP36	30c dp bl	2.25	.50
C541	AP36	50c hn brn	2.25	.50
C542	AP36	60c ol brn	2.25	.30
C543	AP36	1b purple	3.25	.75
C544	AP36	2b vio gray	4.50	2.25
		Nos. C536-C544 (9)	16.85	5.15

Issue date: Jan. 1954.

Arms of Yaracuy and Tropical Foliage

C545	AP36	5c bl grn	.55	.20
C546	AP36	7½c gray grn	6.50	6.00
C547	AP36	10c car rose	.30	.20
C548	AP36	15c dk brn	.60	.20
C549	AP36	20c gray bl	1.00	.20
C550	AP36	30c dp bl	2.00	.20
C551	AP36	45c mag	1.40	.30
C552	AP36	60c ol brn	1.40	.50
C553	AP36	90c rose brn	3.75	2.50
		Nos. C545-C553 (9)	17.50	10.60
		Nos. C338-C553 (216)	573.70	232.10

Issue date: Jan. 1954.

Ship Type of 1948-50 Redrawn Coil Stamps

Imprint: "Courvoisier S.A."

1952		**Unwmk.**	*Perf. 12x11½*	
C554	AP25	5c rose brn	.85	.20
C555	AP25	10c org red	1.40	.20
C556	AP25	15c ol brn	1.75	.20
		Nos. C554-C556 (3)	4.00	.60

Barquisimeto Type of 1952

1952, Sept. 14		**Photo.**	*Perf. 11½*	
C557	A94	5c blue green	.25	.20
C558	A94	10c car rose	.25	.20
C559	A94	20c dk blue	.40	.20
C560	A94	25c black brn	.60	.20
C561	A94	30c ultra	.75	.20
C562	A94	40c brown org	3.50	1.50
C563	A94	50c dk ol grn	1.40	.40
C564	A94	1b purple	4.75	2.00
		Nos. C557-C564 (8)	11.90	4.90

Caracas Post Office Type of 1953-54

1953, Mar. 11			*Perf. 12½*	
C565	A96	7½c yellow grn	.20	.20
C566	A96	15c dp plum	.20	.20
C567	A96	20c slate	.20	.20
C568	A96	25c sepia	.35	.20
C569	A96	40c plum	.35	.20
C570	A96	45c rose vio	.35	.20
C571	A96	50c red orange	.55	.20
C572	A96	70c dk sl grn	1.10	.55

C573	A96	75c dp ultra	3.75	.80
C574	A96	90c brown org	.90	.45
C575	A96	1b violet blue	.90	.45
		Nos. C565-C575 (11)	8.85	3.65

See Nos. C587-C589, C597-C606.

Simon Rodriguez AP39

Quotation from Bolivar's Manifesto of 1824 AP40

1954, Feb. 28			*Perf. 11½*	
C576	AP39	5c blue green	.25	.20
C577	AP39	10c car rose	.35	.20
C578	AP39	20c gray blue	.45	.20
C579	AP39	45c magenta	.70	.20
C580	AP39	65c gray green	2.25	1.00
		Nos. C576-C580 (5)	4.00	1.85

Centenary of the death of Simon Rodriguez, scholar and tutor of Bolivar.

1954, Mar. 1			**Unwmk.**	
C581	AP40	15c blk & brn buff	.20	.20
C582	AP40	25c dk red brn & gray	.65	.20
C583	AP40	40c dk red brn & red org	.45	.20
C584	AP40	65c black & blue	1.10	.60
C585	AP40	80c dk red brn & rose	.85	.45
C586	AP40	1b pur & rose lil	1.75	.35
		Nos. C581-C586 (6)	5.00	2.00

10th Inter-American Conf., Caracas, Mar. 1954.

P.O. Type of 1953

1954, Feb.		**Photo.**	*Perf. 12½*	
C587	A96	5c orange	.20	.20
C588	A96	30c red brown	1.90	1.00
C589	A96	60c bright red	1.90	1.25
		Nos. C587-C589 (3)	4.00	2.45

Valencia Arms Type of 1955

1955, Mar. 26		**Engr.**	*Perf. 12*	
C590	A97	5c blue green	.20	.20
C591	A97	10c rose pink	.20	.20
C592	A97	20c ultra	.20	.20
C593	A97	25c gray	.20	.20
C594	A97	40c violet	.45	.20
C595	A97	50c vermilion	.45	.25
C596	A97	60c olive green	.90	.25
		Nos. C590-C596 (7)	2.60	1.55

P.O. Type of 1953 Inscribed: "Republica de Venezuela"

1955		**Photo.**	*Perf. 12½*	
C597	A96a	5c orange	.20	.20
C598	A96a	10c olive brn	.20	.20
C599	A96a	15c deep plum	.20	.20
C600	A96a	20c slate	.25	.20
C601	A96a	30c red brn	.25	.20
C602	A96a	40c plum	.75	.20
C603	A96a	45c rose violet	.75	.40
C604	A96a	70c dk slate grn	1.90	.85
C605	A96a	75c deep ultra	1.25	.50
C606	A96a	90c brown org	.65	.25
		Nos. C597-C606 (10)	6.40	3.25

Caracas Arms Type of 1955

1955, Dec. 9		**Unwmk.**	*Perf. 11½*	
C607	A98	5c yellow org	.25	.20
C608	A98	15c claret brn	.25	.20
C609	A98	25c violet blk	.25	.20
C610	A98	40c red	.50	.20
C611	A98	50c red orange	.50	.20
C612	A98	60c car rose	1.00	.35
		Nos. C607-C612 (6)	2.75	1.35

University Hospital, Caracas AP43

5c, 10c, 15c, 70c, O'Leary School, Barinas. 25c, 30c, 80c, University Hospital, Caracas.

40c, 45c, 50c, 1b, Caracas-La Guaira Highway. 60c, 65c, 75c, 2b, Towers of Simon Bolivar Center.

1956-57		**Unwmk.**	*Perf. 11½*	
C613	AP43	5c orange	.25	.20
C614	AP43	10c sepia	.25	.20
C615	AP43	15c claret brown	.25	.20
C616	AP43	20c dark blue	.25	.20
C617	AP43	25c gray black	.25	.20
C618	AP43	30c henna brown	.30	.20
C619	AP43	40c bright crimson	.45	.20
C620	AP43	45c brown violet	.30	.20
C621	AP43	50c deep orange	.55	.20
C622	AP43	60c olive green	.55	.20
C623	AP43	65c bright blue	.90	.20
C624	AP43	70c blue green	.95	.25
C625	AP43	75c unity	1.00	.35
C626	AP43	80c carmine rose	1.10	.20
C627	AP43	1b plum	.70	.25
C628	AP43	2b dark car rose	1.40	.75
		Nos. C613-C628 (16)	9.45	4.00

Issued: 20c, 40c, 45c, 50c, 1b, 11/5/56; others, 1957.

Book and Flags of American Nations — AP44

1956-57

		Granite Paper		
C629	AP44	5c orange & brn	.20	.20
C630	AP44	10c brn & pale brn	.20	.20
C631	AP44	20c blue & sapphire	.20	.20
C632	AP44	25c gray vio & gray	.25	.20
C633	AP44	40c rose red & pale pur	.35	.20
C634	AP44	45c vio brn & gray brn	.45	.20
C635	AP44	60c olive & gray ol	.85	.45
		Nos. C629-C635 (7)	2.50	1.65

Book Festival of the Americas, 11/15-30/56. Issued: 5c, 40c, 11/15; others, 2/7/57.

Bolivar Type of 1957-58

		Engraved; Center Embossed		
1957-58		**Unwmk.**	*Perf. 13½*	
C636	A100	5c orange	.20	.20
C637	A100	10c olive gray	.20	.20
C638	A100	20c blue	.55	.20
C639	A100	25c gray black	.60	.20
C640	A100	40c rose red	.55	.20
C641	A100	45c rose lilac	.65	.25
C642	A100	65c yellow brn	1.10	.45
		Nos. C636-C642 (7)	3.85	1.70

Issued: 45c, 1958; others, Nov. 15, 1957.

Tamanaco Hotel Type of 1957-58

1957-58		**Engr.**	*Perf. 13*	
C643	A101	5c dull yellow	.25	.20
C644	A101	10c brown	.25	.20
C645	A101	15c chocolate	.25	.20
C646	A101	20c gray blue	.25	.20
C647	A101	25c sepia	.25	.20
C648	A101	30c violet bl	.25	.20
C649	A101	40c car rose	.30	.20
C650	A101	45c claret	.35	.20
C651	A101	50c red org	.35	.20
C652	A101	60c yellow grn	.70	.20
C653	A101	65c orange brn	1.60	.75
C654	A101	70c slate	.90	.35
C655	A101	75c grnsh blue	1.00	.45
C656	A101	1b dk claret	1.00	.45
C657	A101	2b dk gray	1.60	.55
		Nos. C643-C657 (15)	9.30	4.55

Issue dates: 5c, 10c, Oct. 10; others, 1958. For surcharge see No. C878.

Post Office Type of 1958

1958, May 14		**Litho.**	*Perf. 14*	
C658	A102	5c dp yellow	.20	.20
C659	A102	10c brown	.20	.20
C660	A102	15c red brn	.20	.20
C661	A102	20c lt blue	.20	.20
C662	A102	25c lt gray	.20	.20
C663	A102	30c lt ultra	.20	.20
C664	A102	40c brt yel grn	.20	.20
C665	A102	50c red orange	.20	.20
C666	A102	60c rose pink	.20	.20
C667	A102	65c red	.30	.20
C668	A102	90c violet	.40	.20
C669	A102	1b lilac	.50	.20
C670	A102	1.20b bister brn	6.00	3.75
		Nos. C658-C670 (13)	9.00	6.15

See Nos. C786-C792. For surcharges see Nos. C856-C861.

Post Office Type of 1958
Coil Stamps

1958		**Engr.**	*Perf. 11½x12*	
C671	A103	5c deep yellow	.25	.20
C672	A103	10c brown	.35	.20
C673	A103	15c dark brown	.50	.20
		Nos. C671-C673 (3)	1.10	.60

Merida Type of 1958

1958, Oct. 9		**Photo.**	*Perf. 13½*	
C674	A104	5c orange yellow	.20	.20
C675	A104	10c gray brown	.20	.20
C676	A104	15c dull red brn	.20	.20
C677	A104	20c chalky blue	.20	.20
C678	A104	25c brown gray	.25	.20
C679	A104	30c violet bl	.25	.20
C680	A104	40c rose car	.35	.20
C681	A104	45c brt lilac	.35	.20
C682	A104	50c red orange	.45	.25
C683	A104	60c lt olive grn	.35	.20
C684	A104	65c hennna brn	1.10	.45
C685	A104	70c gray black	.65	.35
C686	A104	75c brt grnsh bl	1.25	.65
C687	A104	80c lt vio bl	.80	.35
C688	A104	90c blue green	.80	.35
C689	A104	1b lilac	.90	.45
		Nos. C674-C689 (16)	8.30	4.65

Trujillo Type of 1959

1958, Nov. 17		**Photo.**	*Perf. 14*	
C690	A105	5c orange yel	.20	.20
C691	A105	10c lt brown	.20	.20
C692	A105	15c redsh brown	.20	.20
C693	A105	20c lt blue	.20	.20
C694	A105	25c pale gray	.25	.20
C695	A105	30c lt vio blue	.25	.20
C696	A105	40c brt yel grn	.30	.20
C697	A105	50c red orange	.30	.20
C698	A105	60c lilac rose	.45	.25
C699	A105	65c vermilion	1.40	.65
C700	A105	1b lilac	.90	.25
		Nos. C690-C700 (11)	4.65	2.75

Emblem — AP45

1959, Mar. 10		**Litho.**	*Perf. 13½*	
C701	AP45	5c yellow	.25	.20
C702	AP45	10c red brown	.25	.20
C703	AP45	15c orange	.30	.20
C704	AP45	30c gray	.50	.30
C705	AP45	50c green	.55	.35
		Nos. C701-C705 (5)	1.85	1.25

8th Central American and Caribbean Games, Caracas, Nov. 29-Dec. 14, 1958. Exist imperf. Value, pair $25.

Stamp Centenary Type of 1959

Stamp of 1859 and: 25c, Mailman and José Ignacio Paz Castillo. 50c, Mailman on horseback and Jacinto Gutierrez. 1b, Plane, train and Miguel Herrera.

1959, Sept. 15		**Engr.**	*Perf. 13½*	
C706	A107	25c orange yel	.30	.20
C707	A107	50c blue	.45	.25
C708	A107	1b rose red	.90	.45
		Nos. C706-C708 (3)	1.65	.90

> **Catalogue values for unused stamps in this section, from this point to the end of the section, are for Never Hinged items.**

Alexander von Humboldt Type of 1960

1960, Feb. 9			**Unwmk.**	
C709	A108	5c ocher & brn	.35	.20
C710	A108	20c brt bl & turq bl	.95	.20
C711	A108	40c ol & ol grn	1.40	.35
		Nos. C709-C711 (3)	2.70	.75

Newspaper Type of 1960

1960, June 11		**Litho.**	*Perf. 14*	
C712	A109	5c yellow & blk	1.90	.80
C713	A109	15c lt red brn & blk	1.00	.30
C714	A109	65c salmon & blk	1.50	.55
		Nos. C712-C714 (3)	4.40	1.65

Agustin Codazzi Type of 1960

1960, June 15			**Engr.**	
C715	A110	5c yel org & brn	.20	.20
C716	A110	10c brn & dk brn	.20	.20
C717	A110	25c gray & blk	.40	.20
C718	A110	30c vio bl & sl	.55	.20

C719	A110	50c org brn & brn	.90	.30
C720	A110	70c gray ol & ol gray	1.40	.55
		Nos. C715-720 (6)	3.65	1.65

For surcharge see No. C884.

National Pantheon Type of 1960

1960, May 9			**Litho.**	
Pantheon in Bister				
C721	A111	5c dp bister	.20	.20
C722	A111	10c red brown	.25	.20
C723	A111	15c fawn	.30	.20
C724	A111	20c lt blue	.45	.20
C725	A111	25c gray	2.40	.25
C726	A111	30c lt vio bl	2.40	.40
C727	A111	40c brt yel grn	.45	.20
C728	A111	45c lt violet	.70	.20
C729	A111	60c deep pink	.90	.30
C730	A111	65c salmon	1.25	.40
C731	A111	70c gray	1.25	.40
C732	A111	75c chalky blue	3.75	.70
C733	A111	80c lt ultra	1.90	.60
C734	A111	1.20b bister brn	2.25	.85
		Nos. C721-C734 (14)	18.10	5.00

For surcharges see Nos. C894-C895.

Andres Eloy Blanco Type of 1960

1960, May 21			*Perf. 14*	
Portrait in Black				
C735	A112	20c blue	.40	.20
C736	A112	75c grnsh blue	1.25	.30
C737	A112	90c brt violet	1.25	.30
		Nos. C735-C737 (3)	2.90	.80

For surcharge see No. C874.

Independence Type of 1960

1960, Aug. 19		**Litho.**	*Perf. 13½*	
Center Multicolored				
C738	A113	50c orange	.85	.25
C739	A113	75c brt grnsh blue	1.25	.40
C740	A113	90c purple	1.40	.35
		Nos. C738-C740 (3)	3.50	1.00

Oil Refinery AP46

			Unwmk.	
1960, Aug. 26		**Engr.**	*Perf. 14*	
C741	AP46	30c dk bl & sl bl	.50	.20
C742	AP46	40c yel grn & ol	.85	.30
C743	AP46	50c org & red brn	1.00	.40
		Nos. C741-C743 (3)	2.35	.90

Issued to publicize Venezuela's oil industry.

Luisa Cáceres de Arismendi Type of 1960

1960, Oct. 21		**Litho.**	*Perf. 14*	
Center Multicolored				
C744	A115	5c bister	.95	.35
C745	A115	10c redsh brown	1.25	.55
C746	A115	60c rose carmine	2.25	.70
		Nos. C744-C746 (3)	4.45	1.60

José Antonio Anzoategui Type of 1960

1960, Oct. 29			**Engr.**	
C747	A116	25c gray & brown	.55	.20
C748	A116	40c yel grn & ol gray	.55	.40
C749	A116	45c rose cl & dl pur	.75	.30
		Nos. C747-C749 (3)	1.85	.90

Antonio José de Sucre Type of 1960

			Unwmk.	
1960, Nov. 18		**Litho.**	*Perf. 14*	
Center Multicolored				
C750	A117	25c gray	.75	.30
C751	A117	30c violet blue	1.10	.40
C752	A117	50c brown orange	1.40	.55
		Nos. C750-C752 (3)	3.25	1.25

Type of Regular Issue, 1960

Designs: 30c, Bolivar Peak. 50c, Caroni Falls. 65c, Cuacharo caves.

1960, Mar. 22			*Perf. 14*	
C753	A118	30c vio bl & blk bl	1.90	1.90
C754	A118	50c brn org & brn	1.90	1.90
C755	A118	65c red org & red brn	1.90	1.90
		Nos. C753-C755 (3)	5.70	5.70

Cow's Head, Grain, Man and Child
AP47

Arms of San Cristobal
AP48

1961, Feb. 6		**Litho.**	**Unwmk.**	
Cow and Inscription in Black				
C756	AP47	5c yellow	.20	.20
C757	AP47	10c brown	.20	.20
C758	AP47	15c redsh brn	.20	.20
C759	AP47	20c dull blue	.20	.20
C760	AP47	25c gray	.20	.20
C761	AP47	30c violet bl	.25	.20
C762	AP47	40c yellow grn	.30	.20
C763	AP47	45c lilac	.35	.20
C764	AP47	50c orange	.40	.20
C765	AP47	60c cerise	.45	.20
C766	AP47	65c red orange	.60	.20
C767	AP47	70c gray	.90	.30
C768	AP47	75c brt grnsh bl	.85	.25
C769	AP47	80c brt violet	.85	.30
C770	AP47	90c violet	1.25	.40
		Nos. C756-C770 (15)	7.20	3.35

9th general census & 3rd agricultural census. Issued: 5-15c; 30c, 60-65c; 75-80c, 2/6; others, 4/6.
For surcharges see Nos. C865-C866.

Rafael Maria Baralt Type of 1961

1961, Mar. 11		**Litho.**	*Perf. 14*	
C771	A120	25c gray & sepia	.65	.30
C772	A120	30c dk blue & vio	.75	.30
C773	A120	40c yel grn & ol grn	.95	.40
		Nos. C771-C773 (3)	2.35	1.00

1961, Apr. 10			**Litho.**	
Arms in Original Colors				
C774	AP48	5c orange & blk	.20	.20
C775	AP48	55c yel grn & blk	.65	.25

400th anniversary of San Cristobal.
For surcharge see No. C879.

Bird Type of 1961

Birds: 5c, Troupial. 10c, Golden cock of the rock. 15c, Tropical mockingbird.

1961, Sept. 6		**Unwmk.**	*Perf. 14½*	
C776	A121	5c multicolored	1.25	.85
C777	A121	10c multicolored	.60	.45
C778	A121	15c multicolored	.80	.50
		Nos. C776-C778 (3)	2.65	1.80

Charge, Battle of Carabobo — AP49

1961, Dec. 1		**Litho.**	*Perf. 14*	
Center Multicolored				
C779	AP49	50c black & ultra	.75	.20
C780	AP49	1.05b black & org	1.75	.50
C781	AP49	1.50b blk & lil rose	2.00	.50
C782	AP49	1.90b black & lilac	2.50	1.00
C783	AP49	2b black & gray	4.00	1.25
C784	AP49	3b black & grnsh bl	4.00	1.25
		Nos. C779-C784 (6)	14.25	4.45

140th anniversary of Battle of Carabobo.
For surcharges see Nos. C867-C870.

Arms of Cardinal Quintero AP50

Archbishop Rafael Arias Blanco — AP51

1962, Mar. 1			**Unwmk.**	
C785	AP50	5c lilac rose	.25	.20
a.		Souv. sheet of 1, imperf.	2.10	1.90

1st Venezuelan Cardinal, José Humberto Quintero.
No. C785a, issued Mar. 23, sold for 1b.

Post Office Type of 1958

1962, Apr. 12		**Litho.**	*Perf. 13½x14*	
C786	A102	35c citron	.25	.20
C787	A102	55c gray olive	.40	.20
C788	A102	70c bluish green	.65	.25
C789	A102	75c brown orange	.80	.20
C790	A102	80c fawn	.80	.30
C791	A102	85c deep rose	1.25	.45
C792	A102	95c lilac rose	.85	.40
		Nos. C786-C792 (7)	5.00	2.00

For surcharges see Nos. C856-C861.

1962, May 10			*Perf. 10½*	
C793	AP51	75c red lilac	.80	.30

4th anniversary (in 1961) of the anti-communist pastoral letter of the Archbishop of Caracas, Rafael Arias Blanco.

Orchid Type of 1962

Orchids: 5c, Oncidium volvox. 20c, Cycnoches chlorochilon. 25c, Cattleya Gaskelliana. 30c, Epidendrum difforme, horiz. 40c, Catasetum callosum Lindl, horiz. 50c, Oncidium bicolor Lindl, horiz. 1b, Brassavola nodosa Lindl, horiz. 1.05b, Epidendrum lividum Lindl. 1.50b, Schomburgkia undulata Lindl. 2b, Oncidium zebrinum.

Perf. 14x13½, 13½x14

1962, May 30		**Litho.**	**Unwmk.**	
Orchids in Natural Colors				
C794	A124	5c blk & lt grn	.20	.20
C795	A124	20c black	.20	.20
C796	A124	25c black & fawn	.55	.20
C797	A124	30c black & pink	.50	.20
C798	A124	40c black & yel	.55	.20
C799	A124	50c black & lil	.75	.20
C800	A124	1b blk & pale rose	1.00	.35
C801	A124	1.05b blk & dp org	3.25	1.00
C802	A124	1.50b blk & pale vio	3.50	1.10
C803	A124	2b blk & org brn	4.50	1.60
		Nos. C794-C803 (10)	15.00	5.25

For surcharges see Nos. C885-C887.

Independence Type of 1960

Signing Declaration of Independence.

1962, June 11			*Perf. 13½*	
Center Multicolored				
C804	A113	55c olive	.60	.20
C805	A113	1.05b brt rose	2.10	.55
C806	A113	1.50b purple	1.60	.50
a.		Souv. sheet of 3, #C804-C806, imperf.	5.00	5.00
		Nos. C804-C806 (3)	4.30	1.25

No. C806a, issued Oct. 13, sold for 4.10b.
A buff cardboard folder exists with impressions of Nos. 812-814, C804-C806. Perforation is simulated. Sold for 5.60b. Value $10.
For surcharge see No. C893.

No. 710 Surcharged in Rose Carmine: "BICENTENARIO DE UPATA 1762-1962 RESELLADO AEREO VALOR Bs. 2,00"

1962, July 7			*Perf. 13½x14*	
C807	A102	2b on 1b lt ol grn	2.00	.90

Upata, a village in the state of Bolivar, 200th anniv.

National Games Type of 1962

Perf. 13x14

1962, Nov. 30		**Unwmk.**	**Litho.**	
C808	A125	40c Bicycling	.40	.25
C809	A125	75c Baseball	.60	.30
C810	A125	85c Woman athlete	1.50	.65
a.		Souv. sheet of 3, #C808-C810, imperf.	4.00	3.50
		Nos. C808-C810 (3)	2.50	1.20

See note after No. 817.
No. C810a sold for 3b.
For surcharge see No. C899.

Bird Type of 1962

Birds: 5c, American kestrel. 20c, Black-bellied tree duck, horiz. 25c, Amazon kingfisher. 30c, Rufous-tailed chachalaca. 50c, Black-and-yellow troupial. 55c, White-naped nightjar. 2.30b, Red-crowned woodpecker. 2.50b, Black-moustached quail-dove.

1962, Dec. 14 Perf. 14x13½, 13½x14
Birds in Natural Colors;
Black Inscription

C811	A126	5c car rose	.20	.20
C812	A126	20c brt blue	.50	.20
C813	A126	25c lt gray	.60	.20
C814	A126	30c lt olive	.65	.20
C815	A126	50c violet	1.00	.30
C816	A126	55c dp orange	1.75	.45
C817	A126	2.30b dl red brn	5.00	2.25
C818	A126	2.50b orange yel	5.00	2.50
	Nos. C811-C818 (8)		14.70	6.30

For surcharges see Nos. C880-C882.

Malaria
Eradication
Emblem, Mosquito
and Map — AP52

Lithographed and Embossed
Perf. 13½x14
1962, Dec. 20 Wmk. 346
C819 AP52 30c green & blk .55 .25
  a. Souv. sheet of 2, #825, C819,
      imperf. 3.00 3.00

WHO drive to eradicate malaria. No. C819a sold for 2b.

Animal Type of Regular Issue

5c, Spectacle bear, vert. 40c, Paca. 50c, Three-toed sloths. 55c, Great anteater. 1.50b, South American tapirs. 2b, Jaguar.

Perf. 14x13½, 13½x14
1963, Mar. 13 Litho. Unwmk.
Multicolored Center; Black
Inscriptions

C820	A128	5c yellow	.25	.20
C821	A128	40c brt green	.80	.25
C822	A128	50c lt violet	1.10	.30
C823	A128	55c brown olive	1.40	.40
C824	A128	1.50b gray	4.00	1.60
C825	A128	2b ultra	6.75	2.50
	Nos. C820-C825 (6)		14.30	5.25

For surcharges see Nos. C888-C889.

Freedom from Hunger Type of 1963

40c, Map, shepherd. 75c, Map, farmer.

1963, Mar. 21
C826 A129 40c lt yel grn & dl red .45 .30
C827 A129 75c yellow & brown .60 .40

Arms of
Bocono — AP53

1963, May 30 Wmk. 346
C828 AP53 1b multicolored 1.40 .40

400th anniversary of the founding of Bocono.
For surcharge see No. C892.

Papal and
Venezuelan
Arms
AP54

1963, June 11 Perf. 14x13½
Arms Multicolored
C829 AP54 80c light green 1.10 .30
C830 AP54 90c gray 1.10 .40

Vatican II, the 21st Ecumenical Council of the Roman Catholic Church.
For surcharges see Nos. C871-C872.

Arms of
Venezuela — AP55

1963, July 29 Unwmk. Perf. 14
C831 AP55 70c gray, red, yel & bl .95 .40

Cent. of Venezuela's flag and coat of arms.
For surcharge see No. C883.

Lake
Maracaibo
Bridge
AP56

Wmk. 346
1963, Aug. 24 Litho. Perf. 14
C832 AP56 90c grn, brn & ocher 1.25 .40
C833 AP56 95c blue, brn & och 1.25 .45
C834 AP56 1b ultra, brn & och 1.00 .40
  Nos. C832-C834 (3) 3.50 1.25

Opening of bridge over Lake Maracaibo.
For surcharges see Nos. C897-C898.

Armed Forces Type of 1963

1963, Sept. 10 Unwmk.
C835 A134 1b red & bl, buff 1.75 .75

For surcharge see No. 862.

Hammarskjold Type of 1963

1963, Sept. 25 Unwmk. Perf. 14
C836 A135 80c dk bl, lt ultra &
      ocher .95 .40
C837 A135 90c dk bl, bl & ocher 1.25 .55
  a. Souv. sheet of 4, #841-842,
      C836-C837, imperf. 4.50 4.50

No. C837a sold for 3b.
For surcharges see Nos. C875-C876.

Dr. Luis Razetti,
Physician, Birth
Cent. — AP57

1963, Oct. 10 Engr.
C838 AP57 95c dk blue & mag 1.40 .60
C839 AP57 1.05b dk brn & grn 1.50 .75

For surcharges see Nos. C890-C891.

Red Cross Type of 1963

Designs: 40c, Sir Vincent K. Barrington. 75c, Red Cross nurse and child.

1963, Dec. 31 Litho. Perf. 11½x12
C840 A137 40c multicolored .55 .30
C841 A137 75c multicolored .95 .40

Development Type of 1964

Designs: 5c, Loading cargo. 10c, Tractor and corn. 15c, Oil field workers. 20c, Oil refinery. 50c, Crane and building construction.

1964, Feb. 5 Unwmk. Perf. 14x13½
C842 A138 5c multicolored .25 .20
C843 A138 10c multicolored .25 .20
C844 A138 15c multicolored .25 .20
C845 A138 20c multicolored .25 .20
C846 A138 50c multicolored .50 .20
  Nos. 842-846 (5) 1.50 1.00

Cent. of the Dept. of Industrial Development and to publicize the Natl. Industrial Expo.

Pedro Gual Type of 1964

1964, Mar. 20 Perf. 14x13½
C847 A139 75c dull blue green .75 .25
C848 A139 1b bright pink 1.00 .35

Blast Furnace and
Map of
Venezuela — AP58

Arms of Ciudad
Bolivar — AP59

1964, May 22 Litho. Perf. 13½x14
C849 AP58 80c multi .90 .35
C850 AP58 1b multi 1.25 .40

Issued to publicize the Orinoco steel mills.

1964, May 22 Perf. 10½
C851 AP59 1b multi 1.25 .70

Bicentenary of Ciudad Bolivar.

AP60

AP61

1964, Aug. 3 Unwmk. Perf. 11½
C852 AP60 30c bister brn & yel .35 .20
C853 AP60 40c plum & pink .55 .20
C854 AP60 50c brn & tan .75 .25
  Nos. C852-C854 (3) 1.65 .65

80th birthday of novelist Romulo Gallegos.

1964, Nov. 11 Litho. Perf. 14x13½
C855 AP61 1b orange & dk vio 1.10 .50

Eleanor Roosevelt and 15th anniv. (in 1963) of the Universal Declaration of Human Rights.
For surcharge see No. C896.

Issues of 1947-64 Surcharged
in Black, Dark Blue, Red, Carmine or Lilac with New Value and:
"RESELLADO / VALOR"

1965
C856	A102	5c on 55c (#C787)	.40	.20
C857	A102	5c on 70c (#C788)	.40	.20
C858	A102	5c on 80c (#C790)	.40	.20
C859	A102	5c on 85c (#C791)	.40	.20
C860	A102	5c on 90c (#C668)	.40	.20
C861	A102	5c on 95c (#C792)	.40	.20
C862	A134	5c on 1b (#C835)	.55	.20
C863	AP25	10c on 3b (#C269)
(C)		.40	.20
C864	AP25	10c on 4b (#C270)
(C)		.70	.20
C865	AP47	10c on 70c (#C767)
(C)		.45	.20
C866	AP47	10c on 90c (#C770)
(C)		.40	.20
C867	AP49	10c on 1.05b
(#C780)		.60	.20
C868	AP49	10c on 1.90b
(#C782)		.40	.20
C869	AP49	10c on 2b (#C783)	.45	.20
C870	AP49	10c on 3b (#C784)	.45	.20
C871	AP54	10c on 80c (#C829)	.40	.20
C872	AP54	10c on 90c (#C830)	.40	.20
C873	AP16	15c on 3b (#C253)	.45	.20
C874	A112	15c on 90c (#C737)	.40	.20
C875	A135	15c on 80c (#C836)	.40	.20
C876	A135	15c on 90c (#C837)	.40	.20
C877	AP59	15c on 1b (#C851)	.45	.20
C878	A101	20c on 2b (#C657)
(R)		.55	.20
C879	AP48	20c on 55c (#C775)
(DB)		.45	.20

C880	A126	20c on 55c (#C816)	.60	.20
a.		25c on 55c (#C816)		
C881	A126	20c on 2.30b
(#C817)		.45	.20
C882	A126	20c on 2.50b
(#C818)		.60	.20
C883	AP55	20c on 70c (#C831)	.60	.20
C884	A110	25c on 70c (#C720)
(DB)		.65	.20
C885	A124	25c on 1.05b
(#C801) (L)		.45	.20
C886	A124	25c on 1.50b
(#C802) (L)		.45	.20
C887	A124	25c on 2b (#C803)
(L)		.60	.20
C888	A128	25c on 1.50b
(#C824)		.60	.20
C889	A128	25c on 2b (#C825)	.60	.20
C890	AP57	25c on 95c (#C838)	.55	.20
C891	AP57	25c on 1.05b
(#C839)		.60	.20
C892	AP53	30c on 1b (#C828)	.75	.20
C893	A113	40c on 1.05b
(#C805) (DB)		.60	.20
C894	A111	50c on 65c (#C730)
(DB)		.40	.20
C895	A111	50c on 1.20b
(#C734) (DB)		.75	.20
C896	AP61	50c on 1b (#C855)	.45	.20
C897	AP56	60c on 90c (#C832)	1.10	.30
C898	AP56	60c on 95c (#C833)	.85	.20
C899	A125	75c on 85c (#C810)	.95	.30
	Nos. C856-C899 (44)		23.30	9.00

Lines of surcharge arranged variously on Nos. C856-C899. Old denominations obliterated with bars on Nos. C862, C871-C873, C875-C877, C883, C885-C887, C889, C892, C896-C898. Vertical surcharge on Nos. C865-C866, C871-C872, C874, C878, C896.

Kennedy Type of 1965
1965, Aug. 20 Photo. Perf. 12x11½
C900 A144 60c lt grnsh bl .75 .30
C901 A144 80c red brn .90 .35

Medical Federation
Emblem — AP62

1965, Aug. 24 Litho. Perf. 13½x14
C902 AP62 65c red org & blk 1.10 .55

20th anniversary of the founding of the Medical Federation of Venezuela.

Unisphere
and
Venezuela
Pavilion
AP63

1965, Aug. 31 Perf. 14x13½
C903 AP63 1b multi 1.00 .30

New York World's Fair, 1964-65.

Andrés Bello
(1780?-1865),
Educator and
Writer — AP64

Perf. 14x13½
1965, Oct. 15 Litho. Unwmk.
C904 AP64 80c dk brn & org 1.10 .55

Map Type of 1965

Maps of Venezuela and Guiana: 25c, Map of Venezuela and Guiana by J. Cruz Cano, 1775. 40c, Map stamp of 1896 (No. 140). 75c, Map by the Ministry of the Exterior, 1965 (all horiz.).

1965, Nov. 5   *Perf. 13½*
C905	A145	25c multi	.35	.20
C906	A145	40c multi	.50	.20
C907	A145	75c multi	.80	.30
a.	Souv. sheet of 3, #C905-C907, imperf.		11.00	11.00
	Nos. C905-C907 (3)		1.65	.70

#C907a, issued June 7, 1966, sold for 1.65b.

ITU Emblem and Telegraph Poles AP65

1965, Nov. 19   Litho.   *Perf. 13½x14*
C908   AP65   75c blk & ol grn   .75   .30

Cent. of the ITU.

Simon Bolivar and Quotation AP66

1965, Dec. 9   *Perf. 14x13½*
C909   AP66   75c lt bl & dk brn   .75   .30

Sesquicentennial of Bolivar's Jamaica letter, Sept. 6, 1815.

Children Riding Magic Carpet and Three Kings on Camels — AP67

Fermin Toro — AP68

1965, Dec. 16   *Perf. 13½x14*
C910   AP67   70c yel & vio bl   1.10   .55

Children's Festival, 1965 (Christmas).

1965, Dec. 22   *Perf. 14x13½*
C911   AP68   1b blk & org   .90   .30

Death centenary of Fermin Toro (1808-1865), statesman and writer.

Winston Churchill — AP69

1965, Dec. 29   *Perf. 14½x13*
C912   AP69   1b lilac & blk   1.10   .40

Sir Winston Spencer Churchill (1874-1965), statesman and World War II leader.

ICY Emblem, Arms of Venezuela and UN Emblem AP70

1965, Dec. 30   *Perf. 13½x14*
C913   AP70   85c gold & vio blk   1.10   .40

International Cooperation Year, 1965.

OAS Emblem and Map of America — AP71

Farms of 1936 and 1966 — AP72

1965, Dec. 31   *Perf. 14x13½*
C914   AP71   50c bl, blk & gold   .90   .30

Organization of American States, 75th anniv.

Butterfly Type of 1966
1966, Jan. 25   Litho.   *Perf. 13½x14*
Various Butterflies in Natural Colors; Black Inscriptions
C915	A146	65c lilac	1.75	.40
C916	A146	85c blue	2.50	.50
C917	A146	1b salmon pink	2.75	.60
	Nos. C915-C917 (3)		7.00	1.50

1966, Mar. 1   *Perf. 14x13½*
C918   AP72   55c blk, yel & emer   .80   .30

30th anniversary of the Ministry for Agriculture and Husbandry.

Dance Type of 1966
Various folk dances.

1966, Apr. 5   Litho.   *Perf. 14*
C919	A148	40c bl & multi	.75	.25
C920	A148	50c multi	.90	.30
C921	A148	60c vio & multi	.60	.20
C922	A148	70c multi	1.40	.40
C923	A148	80c red & multi	1.50	.50
C924	A148	90c ocher & multi	1.60	.60
	Nos. C919-C924 (6)		6.75	2.25

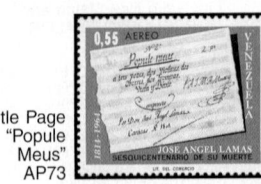

Title Page "Popule Meus" AP73

1966, Apr. 15   *Perf. 13½x14*
C925	AP73	55c yel grn, blk & bis	.55	.30
C926	AP73	95c dp mag, blk & bis	.75	.40

150th anniv. (in 1964) of the death of José Angel Lamas, composer of natl. anthem.

Circus Scene, by Michelena — AP74

Paintings by Michelena: 1b, Miranda in La Carraca. 1.05b, Charlotte Corday.

Perf. 12x12½
1966, May 12   Litho.   Unwmk.
C927	AP74	95c multi	.90	.50
C928	AP74	1b multi	1.10	.50
C929	AP74	1.05b multi	1.25	.50
	Nos. C927-C929 (3)		3.25	1.50

Cent. of the birth of Arturo Michelena (1863-1898), painter. Miniature sheets of 12 exist. See Nos. 900-901.

Abraham Lincoln — AP75

1966, May 31   *Perf. 13½x14*
C930   AP75   1b gray & blk   .90   .55

Dr. José Gregorio Hernandez AP76

1966, July 29   Litho.   *Perf. 14x13½*
C931   AP76   1b brt bl & vio bl   1.25   .50

Centenary (in 1964) of the birth of Dr. José Gregorio Hernandez, physician.

Dr. Manuel Dagnino and Hospital AP77

1966, Aug. 16   Litho.   *Perf. 13½x14*
C932   AP77   1b sl grn & yel grn   1.10   .40

Founding of Chiquinquira Hospital, cent.

Fish Type of 1966
Fish: 75c, Pearl headstander, vert. 90c, Swordtail characine. 1b, Ramirez's dwarf cichlid.

Perf. 14x13½, 13½x14
1966, Aug. 31
C933	A151	75c multi	1.40	.40
C934	A151	90c grn & multi	1.40	.40
C935	A151	1b multi	1.40	.40
	Nos. C933-C935 (3)		4.20	1.20

Rafael Arevalo Gonzalez — AP78   Simon Bolivar, 1816 — AP79

1966, Sept. 13   Litho.   *Perf. 13½x14*
C936   AP78   75c yel bis & blk   1.00   .40

Centenary of the birth of Rafael Arevalo Gonzalez, journalist.

Imprint: "Bundesdruckerei Berlin 1966"

Bolivar Portraits: 25c, 30c, 35c, by José Gil de Castro, 1825. 40c, 50c, 60c, Anonymous painter, 1825. 80c, 1.20b, 4b, Anonymous painter, c. 1829.

1966
Multicolored Center
C937	AP79	5c lem & blk	.20	.20
C938	AP79	10c lt ol grn & blk	.20	.20
C939	AP79	20c grn & blk	.20	.20
C940	AP79	25c salmon & blk	.20	.20
C941	AP79	30c pink & blk	.20	.20

C942	AP79	35c dl rose & blk	.25	.20
C943	AP79	40c bis brn & blk	.20	.20
C944	AP79	50c org brn & blk	.35	.20
C945	AP79	60c brn red & blk	.35	.20
C946	AP79	80c brt bl & blk	.75	.30
C947	AP79	1.20b dl bl & blk	1.10	.55
C948	AP79	4b vio bl & blk	3.75	2.25
	Nos. C937-C948 (12)		7.75	4.90

Issued to honor Simon Bolivar.
Issue dates: Nos. C937-C939, Aug. 15; Nos. C940-C942, Sept. 29; others, Oct. 14.
See Nos. C961-C972.

"Justice" — AP80

1966, Nov. 3   Litho.   *Perf. 14x13½*
C949   AP80   50c pale lil & red lil   .75   .30

50th anniversary of the Academy of Political and Social Sciences.

Angostura Bridge, Orinoco River — AP81

1967, Jan. 6   Litho.   *Perf. 13½x14*
C950   AP81   40c multi   .50   .20

Issued to commemorate the opening of the Angostura Bridge over the Orinoco River.

Pavilion of Venezuela AP82

1967, Apr. 28   Litho.   *Perf. 11x13½*
C951   AP82   1b multi   .90   .30

EXPO '67, International Exhibition, Montreal, Apr. 28-Oct. 27, 1967.

Statue of Chief Guaicaipuro AP83

Constellations over Caracas, 1567 and 1967 — AP84

Designs: 45c, Captain Francisco Fajardo. 55c, Diego de Losada, the Founder. 65c, Arms of Caracas. 90c, Map of Caracas, 1578. 1b, Market on Plaza Mayor, 1800.

1967   Litho.   *Perf. 14x13½, 13½x14*
C952	AP83	15c multi	.20	.20
C953	AP83	45c gold, car & brn	.35	.20
C954	AP83	55c multi	.45	.20

C955	AP84	60c blk, ultra & sil	.50 .20
C956	AP83	65c multi	.65 .25
C957	AP84	90c multi	.80 .30
C958	AP84	1b multi	.90 .35
	Nos. C952-C958 (7)		3.85 1.70

400th anniv. of the founding of Caracas (1st issue). See Nos. C977-C982 (2nd issue).

Two souvenir sheets each contain single stamps similar to Nos. C952-C953, but with simulated perforation. Sold for 1b each. Size: 80x119mm. Value $45 each.

Issued: 55c, 65c, July 28; others, July 12.

Gen. Francisco Esteban Gomez — AP85

Juan Vicente González — AP86

1967, July 31   Litho.   Perf. 14x13½

C959 AP85 90c multi   .90 .40

150th anniversary, Battle of Matasiete.

1967, Oct. 18   Litho.   Perf. 14x13½

C960 AP86 80c ocher & blk   .90 .30

Centenary of the death (in 1866) of Juan Vicente González, journalist.

Bolivar Type of 1966
Imprint: "Druck Bruder Rosenbaum. Wien"

1967-68   Litho.   Perf. 13½x14
Multicolored Center

C961	AP79	5c lemon & blk	.20 .20
C962	AP79	10c lemon & blk	.20 .20
C963	AP79	20c grn & blk	.30 .20
C964	AP79	25c salmon & blk	.25 .20
C965	AP79	30c pink & blk	.30 .20
C966	AP79	35c dl rose & blk	.30 .20
C967	AP79	40c bis brn & blk	.50 .20
C968	AP79	50c org brn & blk	4.00 .30
C969	AP79	60c brn red & blk	1.75 .80
C970	AP79	80c brt bl & blk	1.00 .40
C971	AP79	1.20b dl bl & blk	1.50 .30
C972	AP79	4b vio bl & blk	4.00 1.60
	Nos. C961-C972 (12)		14.30 4.80

Issue dates: 20c, 30c, 50c, Nov. 24; 5c, 25c, 40c, Feb. 5, 1968; others, Aug. 28, 1967.

Child with Pinwheel AP87

1967, Dec. 15   Litho.   Perf. 14x13½

C973	AP87	45c multi	.50 .20
C974	AP87	75c multi	.65 .25
C975	AP87	90c multi	.85 .30
	Nos. C973-C975 (3)		2.00 .75

Children's Festival.

Madonna with the Rosebush, by Stephan Lochner AP88

1967, Dec. 19

C976 AP88 1b multi   1.25 .55

Christmas 1967.

Palace of the Academies, Caracas — AP89

Views of Caracas: 50c, St. Theresa's Church, vert. 70c, Federal Legislature. 75c, University City. 85c, El Pulpo highways crossing. 2b, Avenida Libertador.

1967, Dec. 28   Perf. 13½x14, 14x13½

C977	AP89	10c multi	.20 .20
C978	AP89	50c lil & multi	.35 .20
C979	AP89	70c multi	.65 .20
C980	AP89	75c multi	.75 .25
C981	AP89	85c multi	.80 .30
C982	AP89	2b multi	2.25 .85
	Nos. C977-C982 (6)		5.00 2.00

400th anniv. of Caracas (2nd issue).

Dr. José Manuel Nuñez Ponte (1870-1965), Educator — AP90

1968, Mar. 8   Litho.   Perf. 14

C983 AP90 65c multi   .55 .25

De Miranda and Printing Press AP91

Designs (Miranda Portraits and): 35c, Parliament, London. 45c, Arc de Triomphe, Paris. 70c, Portrait, vert. 80c, Portrait bust and Venezuelan flags, vert.

Perf. 13½x14, 14x13½
1968, June 20   Litho.

C984	AP91	20c yel brn, grn & brn	.25 .20
C985	AP91	35c multi	.40 .20
C986	AP91	45c lt bl & multi	.75 .30
C987	AP91	70c multi	.90 .25
C988	AP91	80c multi	1.10 .40
	Nos. C984-C988 (5)		3.40 1.35

General Francisco de Miranda (1750?-1816), revolutionist, dictator of Venezuela.

Insect Type of 1968

Insect Pests: 5c, Red leaf-cutting ant, vert. 15c, Sugar cane beetle, vert. 20c, Leaf beetle.

Perf. 14x13½, 13½x14
1968, Aug. 30   Litho.

C989	A157	5c multi	.50 .20
C990	A157	15c multi	1.00 .20
C991	A157	20c gray & multi	1.50 .20
	Nos. C989-C991 (3)		3.00 .60

Three Keys — AP92

1968, Oct. 17   Litho.   Perf. 14x13½

C992 AP92 95c yel, vio & dk grn   .95 .35

Natl. Comptroller's Office, 30th anniv.

Fencing — AP93

Designs: 5c, Pistol shooting, vert. 15c, Running. 75c, Boxing. 5b, Sailing, vert.

Perf. 14x13½, 13½x14
1968, Nov. 6   Litho.   Unwmk.

C993	AP93	5c vio, bl & blk	.45 .25
C994	AP93	15c multi	.55 .25
C995	AP93	30c yel grn, dk grn & blk	.70 .25
C996	AP93	75c multi	1.25 .35
C997	AP93	5b multi	4.75 1.75
	Nos. C993-C997 (5)		7.70 2.85

19th Olympic Games, Mexico City, 10/12-27.

Holy Family, by Francisco José de Lerma — AP94

1968, Dec. 4   Litho.   Perf. 14x13½

C998 AP94 40c multi   .55 .20

Christmas 1968.

Dancing Children and Stars — AP95

1968, Dec. 13   Litho.   Perf. 14x13½

C999 AP95 80c vio & org   .75 .30

Issued for the 5th Children's Festival.

Conservation Type of 1968

Designs: 15c, Marbled wood-quail, vert. 20c, Water birds, vert. 30c, Woodcarvings and tools, vert. 90c, Brown trout. 95c, Valley and road. 1b, Red-eyed vireo feeding young bronzed cowbird.

Perf. 13½x14, 14x13½
1968, Dec. 19   Litho.

C1000	A160	15c multi	.40 .30
C1001	A160	20c multi	.40 .30
C1002	A160	30c multi	.50 .30
C1003	A160	90c multi	1.40 .40
C1004	A160	95c multi	2.00 .60
C1005	A160	1b multi	1.50 .50
	Nos. C1000-C1005 (6)		6.20 2.40

Tourist Type of 1969

Designs: 15c, Giant cactus and desert, Falcon. 30c, Hotel Humboldt, Federal District. 40c, Cable car and mountain peaks, Merida.

1969, Jan. 24   Perf. 13½x14

C1006	A161	15c multi	.25 .20
C1007	A161	30c multi	.25 .20
a.	Souv. sheet of 2, #931, C1007, imperf.		1.40 1.40
C1008	A161	40c multi	.50 .20
	Nos. C1006-C1008 (3)		1.00 .60

Tree Type of 1969

Trees: 5c, Cassia grandis. 20c, Triplaris caracasana. 25c, Samanea saman.

1969, May 30   Litho.   Perf. 13½x14

C1009	A164	5c lt grn & multi	.50 .20
C1010	A164	20c org & multi	.75 .20
C1011	A164	25c lt vio & multi	.85 .20
	Nos. C1009-C1011 (3)		2.10 .60

Alexander von Humboldt, by Joseph Stieler — AP96

Map of Maracaibo, 1562 — AP97

1969, Sept. 12   Photo.   Perf. 14

C1012 AP96 50c multi   .60 .20

Alexander von Humboldt (1769-1859), naturalist and explorer.

Perf. 13½x13, 13x13½
1969, Sept. 30   Litho.

20c, Ambrosio Alfinger, Alfonso Pacheco, Pedro Maldonado, horiz. 40c, Maracaibo coat of arms. 70c, University Hospital. 75c, Monument to the Indian Mara. 1b, Baralt Square, horiz.

C1013	AP97	20c lil & multi	.25 .20
C1014	AP97	25c org & multi	.30 .20
C1015	AP97	40c multi	.35 .20
C1016	AP97	70c grn & multi	.75 .25
C1017	AP97	75c brn & multi	.90 .30
C1018	AP97	1b multi	1.10 .40
	Nos. C1013-C1018 (6)		3.65 1.55

400th anniversary of Maracaibo.

Astronauts Neil A. Armstrong, Edwin E. Aldrin, Jr., Michael Collins and Moonscape AP98

1969, Nov. 18   Litho.   Perf. 12½

C1019	AP98	90c multi	1.25 .50
a.	Souv. sheet of 1, imperf.		1.90 1.90

See note after US No. C76.

Virgin with the Rosary, 17th Century AP99

Christmas: 80c, Holy Family, Caracas, 18th Cent.

1969, Dec. 1   Litho.   Perf. 12½

C1020	AP99	75c gold & multi	.75	.30
C1021	AP99	80c gold & multi	.90	.35
a.		Pair, #C1020-C1021	1.85	1.85

Simon Bolivar, 1819, by M. N. Bate — AP100

Bolivar Portraits: 45c, 55c, like 15c. 65c, 70c, 75c Drawing by Francois Roulin, 1828. 85c, 90c, 95c, Charcoal drawing by José Maria Espinoza, 1828. 1b, 1.50b, 2b, Drawing by Espinoza, 1830.

1970, Mar. 16   Litho.   Perf. 14x13½

C1022	AP100	15c multi	.20	.20
C1023	AP100	45c bl & multi	.40	.20
C1024	AP100	55c org & multi	.55	.20
C1025	AP100	65c multi	.55	.25
C1026	AP100	70c bl & multi	.65	.35
C1027	AP100	75c org & multi	.85	.35
C1028	AP100	85c multi	.95	.35
C1029	AP100	90c bl & multi	1.00	.40
C1030	AP100	95c org & multi	1.10	.45
C1031	AP100	1b multi	1.10	.45
C1032	AP100	1.50b bl & multi	1.25	.50
C1033	AP100	2b multi	2.75	1.60
		Nos. C1022-C1033 (12)	11.35	5.30

Issued to honor Simon Bolivar (1783-1830), liberator and father of his country.

General Antonio Guzmán Blanco and Dr. Martin J. Sanabria AP101

1970, June 26   Litho.   Perf. 13

C1034	AP101	75c brt grn & multi	.65	.30

Free obligatory elementary education, cent.

Map of Venezuela with Claim to Part of Guyana — AP102

State map and arms. 55c, 90c, vert.

Perf. 13½x14, 14x13½

1970-71   Litho.

C1035	AP102	5c shown	.35	.20
C1036	AP102	15c Apure	.35	.20
C1037	AP102	20c Aragua	.40	.20
C1038	AP102	20c Anzoategui	.45	.20
C1039	AP102	25c Barinas	.45	.20
C1040	AP102	25c Bolivar	.45	.20
C1041	AP102	45c Carabobo	.65	.20
C1042	AP102	55c Cojedes	.70	.20
C1043	AP102	65c Falcon	.75	.20
C1044	AP102	75c Guárico	.90	.25
C1045	AP102	85c Lara	1.10	.30
C1046	AP102	90c Mérida	1.10	.30
C1047	AP102	1b Miranda	1.10	.40
C1048	AP102	2b Delta Amacuro Territory	2.40	.95
		Nos. C1035-C1048 (14)	11.15	4.00

Issued: 5c, 7/15; 15c, #C1037, 1/18; #C1038-C1039, 2/15/71; 45c, 3/15/71; 55c, 65c, 4/15; 75c, 85c, 5/15/71; 90c, 1b, 6/15/71; 2b, 7/15/71.

Flower Type of 1970

Flowers: 20c, Epidendrum secundum. 25c, Oyedaea verbesinoides. 45c, Heliconia villosa. 1b, Macleania nitida.

1970, July 29   Litho.   Perf. 14x13½

C1049	A175	20c multi	.50	.20
C1050	A175	25c multi	.60	.20
C1051	A175	45c multi	1.50	.35
C1052	A175	1b multi	1.90	.45
		Nos. C1049-C1052 (4)	4.50	1.20

Caracciolo Parra Olmedo AP104

1970, Nov. 16   Photo.   Perf. 12½

C1053	AP104	20c bl & multi	.30	.20

Sesquicentennial of birth of Caracciolo Parra Olmedo (1819-1900), professor of law, rector of University of Merida.

Census Chart — AP105

1971, Apr. 30   Litho.   Perf. 13½x14

C1054		Block of 4	4.50	2.25
a.		AP105 70c, frame L & T	.80	.30
b.		AP105 70c, frame T & R	.80	.30
c.		AP105 70c, frame L & B	.80	.30
d.		AP105 70c, frame B & R	.80	.30

See note after No. 979.

Cattleya Gaskelliana — AP106

Orchids: 20c, Cattleya percivaliana, vert. 75c, Cattleya mossiae, vert. 90c, Cattleya violacea. 1b, Cattleya lawrenciana.

Perf. 14x13½, 13½x14

1971, Aug. 25

C1055	AP106	20c blk & multi	.55	.25
C1056	AP106	25c blk & multi	.80	.25
C1057	AP106	75c blk & multi	1.50	.50
C1058	AP106	90c blk & multi	2.10	.80
C1059	AP106	1b blk & multi	2.25	.90
		Nos. C1055-C1059 (5)	7.20	2.70

40th anniversary of Venezuelan Society of Natural History. Issued in sheets of 5 stamps and one label with Society emblem in blue. Value $37.50.

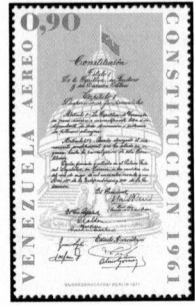

Draft of Constitution Superimposed on Capitol AP107

1971, Dec. 29   Litho.   Perf. 13½

C1060	AP107	90c multi	.80	.40

Anniversary of 1961 Constitution.

AIR POST SEMI-POSTAL STAMPS

King Vulture SPAP1

Unwmk.

1942, Dec. 17   Engr.   Perf. 12

CB1	SPAP1	15c + 10c org brn	2.25	.60
CB2	SPAP1	30c + 5c violet	2.25	.75
		Set, never hinged	7.50	

See note after No. B1.

SPECIAL DELIVERY STAMPS

> Catalogue values for unused stamps in this section are for Never Hinged items.

SD1   SD2

Perf. 12½

1949, Mar. 9   Unwmk.   Engr.

E1	SD1	30c red	.60	.30

Wmk. 116

1961, Apr. 7   Litho.   Perf. 13½

E2	SD2	30c orange	.55	.25

REGISTRATION STAMPS

Bolívar — R1

1899, May Unwmk. Engr.   Perf. 12

F1	R1	25c yellow brown	3.00	2.50

No. F1 Overprinted like Nos. 150-155

1900

F2	R1	25c yellow brown	1.50	1.50
a.		Inverted overprint	22.50	22.50
b.		Double overprint	30.00	30.00

Counterfeit overprints exist, especially of the varieties.

OFFICIAL STAMPS

Coat of Arms

O1   O3

Lithographed, Center Engraved

1898, May 1   Unwmk.   Perf. 12

O1	O1	5c bl grn & blk	.80	.55
O2	O1	10c rose & blk	.95	.85
O3	O1	25c bl & blk	1.50	1.40
O4	O1	50c yel & blk	2.50	2.25
O5	O1	1b vio & blk	2.75	2.50
		Nos. O1-O5 (5)	8.50	7.55

Nos. O4 and O5 Handstamp Surcharged in Magenta or Violet

1899, Nov.

O6	O1	5c on 50c yel & blk	4.75	4.50
O7	O1	5c on 1b vio & blk	20.00	18.00
O8	O1	25c on 50c yel & blk	20.00	18.00
O9	O1	25c on 1b vio & blk	12.00	11.00
		Nos. O6-O9 (4)	56.75	51.50

Inverted Surcharge

O6a	O1	5c on 50c	15.00	15.00
O7a	O1	5c on 1b	40.00	40.00
O8a	O1	25c on 50c	32.50	32.50
O9a	O1	25c on 1b	32.50	32.50
		Nos. O6a-O9a (4)	120.00	120.00

Nos. O6-O9 exist with double surcharge. Value each $18.50-$37.50.

Many of the magenta overprints have become violet. There are intermediate shades.

Counterfeit overprints exist.

1900   Litho., Center Engr.

O14	O3	5c bl grn & blk	.40	.40
O15	O3	10c rose & blk	.55	.55
O16	O3	25c bl & blk	.55	.55
O17	O3	50c yel & blk	.55	.55
O18	O3	1b dl vio & blk	.65	.65
		Nos. O14-O18 (5)	2.70	2.70

O4   No Stars Above Shield — O5

Imprint: "American Bank Note Co., N.Y."

1904, July   Engr.

O19	O4	5c emerald & blk	.25	.25
O20	O4	10c rose & blk	.65	.65
O21	O4	25c blue & blk	.65	.65
O22	O4	50c red brn & blk	4.25	4.25
a.		50c claret & black	4.25	4.25
O23	O4	1b red brn & blk	2.00	2.00
a.		1b claret & black	2.00	2.00
		Nos. O19-O23 (5)	7.80	7.80

1912   Lithographed in Caracas

O24	O5	5c grn & blk	.55	.30
O25	O5	10c car & blk	.55	.30
O26	O5	25c dk bl & blk	.55	.30
O27	O5	50c pur & blk	.55	.40
a.		Center double	19.00	
O28	O5	1b yel & blk	1.30	.80
		Nos. O24-O28 (5)	3.50	2.10

Perforated Initials

After 1925, Venezuela's official stamps consisted of regular postage stamps, some commemoratives and air post stamps of 1930-42 punched with "GN" (Gobierno Nacional) in large perforated initials.

LOCAL STAMPS FOR THE PORT OF CARUPANO

In 1902 Great Britain, Germany and Italy, seeking compensation for revolutionary damages, established a blockade of La Guaira and seized the custom house. Carúpano, a port near Trinidad, was isolated and issued the following provisionals. A treaty effected May 7, 1903, referred the dispute to the Hague Tribunal.

A1

A2

1902 Typeset Imperf.

1	A1	5c purple, *orange*	27.00
2	A2	10c black, *orange*	40.00
a.		Tête bêche pair	82.50
3	A1	25c purple, *green*	32.50
4	A1	50c green, *yellow*	80.00
5	A1	1b blue, *rose*	100.00
		Nos. 1-5 (5)	279.50

A3

1902

6	A3	1b black, *yellow*	200.00
a.		Tête bêche pair	

A4

1903 Handstamped

7	A4	5c carmine, *yellow*	40.00	40.00
8	A4	10c green, *yellow*	92.50	92.50
9	A4	25c green, *orange*	45.00	45.00
10	A4	50c blue, *rose*	45.00	45.00
11	A4	1b violet, *gray*	45.00	45.00
12	A4	2b carmine, *green*	45.00	45.00
13	A4	5b violet, *blue*	45.00	45.00
		Nos. 7-13 (7)	357.50	357.50

Dangerous counterfeits exist of Nos. 1-13.

LOCAL STAMPS FOR THE STATE OF GUAYANA

Revolutionary
Steamship
"Banrigh" — A1

Control Mark

1903 Typo. Perf. 12

1	A1	5c black, *gray*	19.00	19.00
2	A1	10c black, *orange*	47.50	47.50
3	A1	25c black, *pink*	19.00	19.00
4	A1	50c black, *blue*	30.00	30.00
5	A1	1b black, *straw*	25.00	25.00
		Nos. 1-5 (5)	140.50	140.50

Nos. 1-5 can be found with or without the illustrated control mark which covers four stamps.

Counterfeits include the 10c and 50c in red and are from different settings from the originals. They are on papers differing in colors from the originals. All 5c on granite paper are bogus.

Coat of
Arms
A2

1903

11	A2	5c black, *pink*	40.00
12	A2	10c black, *orange*	50.00
13	A2	25c black, *gray blue*	40.00
a.		25c black, *blue*	40.00
14	A2	50c black, *straw*	40.00
15	A2	1b black, *gray*	30.00
		Nos. 11-15 (5)	200.00

Postally used examples are very scarce, and are specimens having 9 ornaments in horizontal borders. Nos. 11-15 pen canceled sell for same values as unused.

See note on controls after No. 5.

Counterfeits exist of Nos. 11-15. Stamps with 10 ornaments in horizontal borders are counterfeits.

Nos. 1-5, 11-15 were issued by a group of revolutionists and had a limited local use. The dates on the stamps commemorate the declaration of Venezuelan independence and a compact with Spain against Joseph Bonaparte.

VIET NAM

vẽ-'ẹt-'năm

LOCATION — In eastern Indo-China
GOVT. — Kingdom
AREA — 123,949 sq. mi.
POP. — 77,311,210 (1999 est.)
CAPITAL — Hanoi

Viet Nam, which included the former French territories of Tonkin, Annam and Cochin China, became an Associated State of the French Union in 1949. The Communist Viet Minh obtained control of Northern Viet Nam in 1954, and the republic of South Viet Nam was established in October, 1955.

100 Cents (Xu) = 1 Piaster (Dong)

Catalogue values for unused stamps in this country are for Never Hinged items, beginning with Scott 27 in the regular postage section, Scott B2 in the semipostal section, Scott C1 in the airpost section, Scott J1 in the postage due section, and Scott M1 in the military section..

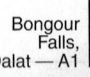

Bongour Falls, Dalat — A1

Emperor Bao-Dai — A2

Designs: 20c, 2pi, 10pi, Imperial palace, Hué. 30c, 15pi, Lake, Hanoi. 50c, 1pi, Temple, Saigon.

Perf. 13x13½, 13½x13
Unwmk.

1951, June 6-Oct. 23			Photo.	
1	A1	10c olive green	.20	.20
2	A1	20c deep plum	.20	.20
3	A1	30c blue	.30	.40
4	A1	50c red	.50	.20
5	A1	60c brown	.40	.20
6	A1	1pi chestnut brn	.40	.20
7	A2	1.20pi yellow brn	4.00	5.00
8	A1	2pi purple	1.50	.20
9	A2	3pi dull blue	4.00	.20
10	A1	5pi green	5.00	.70
11	A1	10pi crimson	13.50	.90
12	A1	15pi red brown	75.00	6.00
13	A2	30pi blue green	45.00	7.00
Nos. 1-13 (13)			150.00	21.40
Set, never hinged			250.00	

Souvenir booklets exist comprising five gummed sheets of 1 containing Nos. 1, 2, 6, 9, 12, together with commemorative inscriptions. Value, $150.

Empress Nam-Phuong A3

Globe and Lightning Bolt A4

1952, Aug. 15			Perf. 12½	
14	A3	30c dk pur, yel & brn	.60	.35
15	A3	50c blue, yel & brn	1.25	.65
16	A3	1.50pi ol grn, yel & brn	2.40	.30
Nos. 14-16 (3)			4.25	1.30
Set, never hinged			8.00	

For surcharge see No. B1.

1952, Aug. 24		Engr.	Perf. 13	
17	A4	1pi greenish blue	2.50	1.75
		Never hinged	9.00	

Viet Nam's admission to the ITU, 1st anniv.

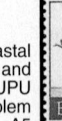

Coastal Scene and UPU Emblem A5

1952, Sept. 12				
18	A5	5pi red brown	2.75	1.25
		Never hinged	4.75	

Viet Nam's admission to the UPU, 1st anniv.

Bao-Dai and Pagoda of Literature, Hanoi — A6

1952, Nov. 10			Perf. 12	
19	A6	1.50pi rose violet	2.50	.50
		Never hinged	4.50	

39th birthday of Emperor Bao-Dai.

Crown Prince Bao-Long in Annamite Costume — A7

70c, 80c, 100pi, Prince in Annamite costume. 90c, 20pi, 50pi, Prince in Western uniform.

1954, June 15			Perf. 13	
20	A7	40c aqua	.20	.20
21	A7	70c claret	.20	.20
22	A7	80c black brown	.20	.30
23	A7	90c dark green	.40	.80
24	A7	20pi rose pink	1.25	2.25
25	A7	50pi violet	3.75	6.25
26	A7	100pi blue violet	6.00	10.00
Nos. 20-26 (7)			12.00	20.00
Set, never hinged, brown gum			20.00	
Set, never hinged, white gum			35.00	

SOUTH VIET NAM

(Republic of Viet Nam)

(Viet Nam Cong Hoa)

GOVT. — Republic
AREA — 66,280 sq. mi.
POP. — 19,600,000 (est. 1973)
CAPITAL — Saigon

Catalogue values for unused stamps in this section, from this point to the end of the section, are for Never Hinged items. Because of the tropical conditions, never hinged stamps must also be free of wrinkles, toning, and any other disturbance.

Mythological Turtle — A8

Unwmk.

1955, July 20		Engr.	Perf. 13	
27	A8	30c claret	2.50	.20
28	A8	50c dark green	6.25	1.50
29	A8	1.50pi bright blue	5.75	.60
Nos. 27-29 (3)			14.50	2.30

Refugees on Raft — A9

1955, Oct. 11				
30	A9	70c crimson rose	1.00	.20
31	A9	80c brown violet	2.75	.40
32	A9	10pi indigo	5.75	.55
33	A9	20pi vio, red brn & org	17.50	.80
34	A9	35pi dk bl, blk brn & yel	35.00	4.00
35	A9	100pi dk grn, brn vio & org	80.00	7.25
Nos. 30-35 (6)			142.00	13.20

1st anniv. of the flight of the North Vietnamese.

No. 34 is inscribed "Chiên-Dich-Huynh-Dê" (Operation Brotherhood) below design. See No. 54.

Post Office, Saigon — A10

Pres. Ngo Dinh Diem — A11

1956, Jan. 10			Perf. 12	
36	A10	60c bluish green	1.90	.25
37	A10	90c violet	3.50	.40
38	A10	3pi red brown	6.75	.60
Nos. 36-38 (3)			12.15	1.25

5th anniv. of independent postal service.

1956		Engr.	Perf. 13x13½	
39	A11	20c orange ver	.40	.20
40	A11	30c rose lilac	.75	.20
41	A11	50c brt carmine	.40	.20
42	A11	1pi violet	.80	.20
43	A11	1.50pi violet	1.60	.20
44	A11	3pi black brown	1.60	.20
45	A11	4pi dark blue	2.40	.20
46	A11	5pi red brown	3.25	.20
47	A11	10pi blue	3.75	.30
48	A11	20pi gray black	10.00	.65
49	A11	35pi green	27.50	1.40
50	A11	100pi brown	57.50	5.50
Nos. 39-50 (12)			109.95	9.45

Nos. 36-38 Overprinted

1956, Aug. 6			Perf. 12	
51	A10	60c bluish green	1.10	.45
52	A10	90c violet	2.50	.45
53	A10	3pi red brown	3.25	.90
Nos. 51-53 (3)			6.85	1.80

The overprint reads: "Government Post Office Building."

No. 34 with Black Bar over Inscription below Design

1956, Aug. 6				
54	A9	35pi dk bl, blk brn & yel	12.00	6.00

Bamboo — A12

Children — A13

1956, Oct. 26		Litho.	Perf. 13x13½	
55	A12	50c scarlet	.95	.20
56	A12	1.50pi rose violet	1.25	.20
57	A12	2pi brt green	1.60	.30
58	A12	4pi deep blue	4.25	.45
Nos. 55-58 (4)			8.05	1.15

1st anniv. of the Republic.

1956, Nov. 7		Engr.	Perf. 13½x14	
59	A13	1pi lilac rose	.80	.20
60	A13	2pi blue green	1.25	.20
61	A13	6pi purple	2.00	.20
62	A13	35pi violet blue	11.00	2.00
Nos. 59-62 (4)			15.05	2.60

"Operation Brotherhood."

Hunters on Elephants A14

Loading Cargo A15

Design: 90c, 2pi, 3pi, Mountain dwelling.

1957, July 7		Photo.	Perf. 13	
63	A14	20c yellow grn & pur	1.25	.20
64	A14	30c bister & dp mag	1.50	.20
65	A14	90c yel grn & dk brn	1.75	.20
66	A14	2pi green & ultra	2.40	.20
67	A14	3pi blue vio & brn	3.00	.75
Nos. 63-67 (5)			9.90	1.55

1957, Oct. 21			Perf. 13½x13	
68	A15	20c rose violet	.20	.20
69	A15	40c lt olive grn	.20	.20
70	A15	50c lt carmine rose	.50	.20
71	A15	2pi ultra	1.60	.20
72	A15	3pi brt green	2.25	.20
Nos. 68-72 (5)			4.75	1.00

9th Colombo Plan Conference, Saigon.

Torch, Map and Constitution A16

Farmers, Tractor and Village A17

1957, Oct. 26		Litho.	Perf. 13x13½	
73	A16	50c black, green & sal	.20	.20
74	A16	80c black, brt bl & mag	.20	.20
75	A16	1pi black, bl grn & brt car	.50	.20
76	A16	4pi blk, ol grn & fawn	.70	.20
77	A16	5pi blk, grnsh bl & cit	1.00	.35
78	A16	10pi black, ultra & rose	2.10	.55
Nos. 73-78 (6)			4.70	1.70

Republic of South Viet Nam, 2nd anniv.

1958, July 7		Engr.	Perf. 13½	
79	A17	50c yellow green	.40	.20
80	A17	1pi deep violet	.60	.20
81	A17	2pi ultra	1.25	.20
82	A17	10pi brick red	2.50	.90
Nos. 79-82 (4)			4.75	1.50

4th anniv. of the government of Ngo Dinh Diem.

Girl and Lantern — A18

A19

1958, Sept. 27

83	A18	30c yellow	.45 .20
84	A18	50c dk carmine rose	.50 .20
85	A18	2pi dp carmine	.60 .20
86	A18	3pi blue green	1.25 .20
87	A18	4pi lt olive green	2.10 .20
		Nos. 83-87 (5)	4.90 1.00

Children's Festival.

1958, Oct. 26   **Perf. 13½**

88	A19	1pi dull red brown	.60 .20
89	A19	2pi bluish green	.75 .20
90	A19	4pi rose carmine	1.10 .20
91	A19	5pi rose lilac	2.40 .75
		Nos. 88-91 (4)	4.85 1.35

Issued for United Nations Day.

> Most South Viet Nam stamps from 1958 onward exist imperforate in issued and trial colors, and also in small presentation sheets in issued colors.

UNESCO Building, Paris — A20

Torch and UN Emblem — A21

1958, Nov. 3   **Perf. 12½x13**

92	A20	50c ultra	.55 .20
93	A20	2pi bright red	.70 .20
94	A20	3pi lilac rose	1.40 .20
95	A20	6pi violet	2.25 1.00
		Nos. 92-95 (4)	4.90 1.15

UNESCO Headquarters in Paris opening, 11/3.

1958, Dec. 10   **Engr.**   **Perf. 13½**

96	A21	50c dark blue	.20 .20
97	A21	1pi brown carmine	.45 .20
98	A21	2pi yellow green	.75 .20
99	A21	6pi rose violet	1.60 .65
		Nos. 96-99 (4)	3.00 1.25

Signing of the Universal Declaration of Human Rights, 10th anniv.

Cathedral of Hué — A22

Thien Mu Pagoda, Hué — A23

National Museum A24

50c, 2pi, Palace of Independence, Saigon.

1958-59   **Perf. 13½**

100	A22	10c dk blue gray	.20 .20
101	A23	30c green ('59)	.60 .20
102	A24	40c dk green ('59)	.85 .20
103	A24	50c green ('59)	.85 .20
104	A24	2pi grnsh blue ('59)	2.50 .20
105	A23	4pi dull purple ('59)	2.75 .40
106	A24	5pi dk carmine ('59)	3.00 .40
107	A22	6pi orange brown	4.25 .50
		Nos. 100-107 (8)	15.00 2.30

Trung Sisters on Elephants A25

1959, Mar. 14   **Photo.**   **Perf. 13**

108	A25	50c multicolored	1.25 .20
109	A25	2pi ocher, grn & bl	2.50 .20
110	A25	3pi emerald, vio & bis	3.75 .20
111	A25	6pi multicolored	7.50 .80
		Nos. 108-111 (4)	15.00 1.40

Sisters Trung Trac and Trung Nhi who resisted a Chinese invasion in 40-44 A.D.

Symbols of Agrarian Reforms A26

1959, July 7   **Engr.**   **Perf. 13**

112	A26	70c lilac rose	.60 .20
113	A26	2pi dk grn & Prus bl	.70 .20
114	A26	3pi olive	1.25 .20
115	A26	6pi dark red & red	2.50 .70
		Nos. 112-115 (4)	5.05 1.30

5th anniv. of Ngo Dinh Diem's presidency.

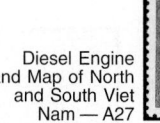

Diesel Engine and Map of North and South Viet Nam — A27

1959, Aug. 7

116	A27	1pi lt violet & grn	1.25 .20
117	A27	2pi gray & green	1.40 .20
118	A27	3pi grnsh bl & grn	1.90 .20
119	A27	4pi maroon & grn	3.25 .45
		Nos. 116-119 (4)	7.80 1.05

Re-opening of the Saigon-Dongha Railroad.

Volunteer Road Workers A28

1959, Oct. 26

120	A28	1pi org brn, ultra & grn	.95 .20
121	A28	2pi violet, org & grn	1.25 .20
122	A28	4pi dk bl, bl & bis	2.75 .45
123	A28	5pi bister, brn & ocher	3.00 .65
		Nos. 120-123 (4)	7.95 1.50

4th anniv. of the constitution, stressing communal development.

Boy Scout — A29

1959, Dec.   **Engr.**   **Perf. 13**

124	A29	3pi brt yellow grn	.50 .20
125	A29	4pi deep lilac rose	1.25 .20
126	A29	8pi dk brn & lil rose	2.25 .50
127	A29	20pi Prus bl & bl grn	5.50 1.00
		Nos. 124-127 (4)	9.50 1.90

National Boy Scout Jamboree.

Symbols of Family and Justice A30

1960

128	A30	20c emerald	.40 .20
129	A30	30c brt grnsh blue	.50 .20
130	A30	2pi orange & maroon	1.10 .20
131	A30	6pi car & rose vio	4.20 .75
		Nos. 128-131 (4)	6.20 1.35

Issued to commemorate the family code.

Refugee Family and WRY Emblem A31

1960, Apr. 7   **Engr.**   **Perf. 13**

132	A31	50c brt lilac rose	.40 .20
133	A31	3pi brt green	.70 .20
134	A31	4pi scarlet	.85 .40
135	A31	5pi dp violet blue	1.25 .55
		Nos. 132-135 (4)	3.20 1.35

World Refugee Year, 7/1/59-6/30/60.

Henri Dunant — A32

1960, May 8   **Cross in Carmine**

136	A32	1pi dark blue	.70 .20
137	A32	3pi green	2.25 .20
138	A32	4pi crimson rose	2.25 .50
139	A32	6pi dp lilac rose	2.75 .70
		Nos. 136-139 (4)	7.95 1.60

Centenary (in 1959) of the Red Cross idea.

Model Farm A33

1960, July 7   **Perf. 13**

140	A33	50c ultra	.50 .20
141	A33	1pi dark green	.60 .20
142	A33	3pi orange	1.25 .35
143	A33	7pi bright pink	2.40 .50
		Nos. 140-143 (4)	4.75 1.25

Establishment of communal rice farming.

Girl With Basket of Rice and Rice Plant A34

1960, Nov. 21

144	A34	2pi emerald & green	1.00 .20
145	A34	4pi blue & ultra	2.25 .65

Conf. of the UN FAO, Saigon, Nov. 1960.

Map and Flag of Viet Nam — A35

1960, Oct. 26   **Engr.**   **Perf. 13**

146	A35	50c grnsh bl, car & yel	.55 .20
147	A35	1pi ultra, car & yel	.75 .20
148	A35	3pi purple, car & yel	1.25 .20
149	A35	7pi yel grn, car & yel	2.25 .40
		Nos. 146-149 (4)	4.80 1.00

Fifth anniversary of the Republic.

Agricultural Development Center, Tractor and Plow — A36

1961, Jan. 3   **Perf. 13**

150	A36	50c red brown	.45 .20
151	A36	70c rose lilac	.85 .20
152	A36	80c rose red	.95 .20
153	A36	10pi bright pink	4.75 .60
		Nos. 150-153 (4)	7.00 1.20

Plant and Child — A37

Pres. Ngo Dinh Diem — A38

1961, Mar. 23   **Perf. 13**

154	A37	70c light blue	.45 .20
155	A37	80c ultra	.55 .20
156	A37	4pi olive bister	.75 .20
157	A37	7pi grnsh bl & yel grn	2.00 .50
		Nos. 154-157 (4)	3.75 1.10

Child protection.

1961, Apr. 29   **Perf. 13**

158	A38	50c brt ultra	.60 .20
159	A38	1pi red	1.00 .20
160	A38	2pi lilac rose	2.00 .20
161	A38	4pi brt violet	4.00 .20
		Nos. 158-161 (4)	7.60 .80

Second term of Pres. Ngo Dinh Diem.

Boy, Girl and Flaming Torch A39

1961, July 7   **Engr.**   **Perf. 13**

162	A39	50c red	.20 .20
163	A39	70c bright pink	.65 .20
164	A39	80c ver & maroon	.80 .20
165	A39	8pi dp claret & mag	2.25 .70
		Nos. 162-165 (4)	3.90 1.30

Issued for Youth Day.

Saigon-Bien Hoa Highway Bridge — A40

1961, July 28
166	A40	50c yellow green	.55	.20
167	A40	1pi orange brown	.80	.20
168	A40	2pi dark blue	1.25	.20
169	A40	5pi brt red lilac	2.40	.20
		Nos. 166-169 (4)	5.00	.80

Opening of Saigon-Bien Hoa Highway.

Alexandre de Rhodes A41

1961, Sept. 5
170	A41	50c rose carmine	.35	.20
171	A41	1pi claret	.50	.20
172	A41	3pi bister brown	.55	.20
173	A41	6pi emerald	1.60	.30
		Nos. 170-173 (4)	3.00	.90

Alexandre de Rhodes (1591-1660), Jesuit missionary who introduced Roman characters to express the Viet Nam language.

Young Man with Torch, Sage, Pagoda — A42

Temple Dedicated to Confucius — A43

1961, Oct. 26 *Perf. 13*
174	A42	50c orange ver	.40	.20
175	A42	1pi brt green	.85	.20
176	A42	3pi rose red	1.00	.20
177	A42	8pi rose lilac & brn	3.25	.40
		Nos. 174-177 (4)	5.50	1.00

Moral Rearmament of Youth Movement.

1961, Nov. 4 *Engr.*
178	A43	1pi brt green	.60	.20
179	A43	2pi rose red	.90	.20
180	A43	5pi olive	2.50	.50
		Nos. 178-180 (3)	4.00	.90

15th anniversary of UNESCO.

Earth Scraper Preparing Ground for Model Village — A44

Man Fighting Mosquito and Emblem — A45

1961, Dec. 11 *Perf. 13*
181	A44	50c dark green	1.00	.20
182	A44	1pi Prus bl & car lake	1.25	.20
183	A44	2pi olive grn & brn	1.75	.20
184	A44	10pi Prus blue	6.00	.35
		Nos. 181-184 (4)	10.00	.95

Agrarian reform program.

1962, Apr. 7 *Perf. 13*
185	A45	50c brt lilac rose	.45	.20
186	A45	1pi orange	.65	.20
187	A45	2pi emerald	.85	.20
188	A45	6pi ultra	2.00	.65
		Nos. 185-188 (4)	3.95	1.25

WHO drive to eradicate malaria.

Postal Check Center, Saigon — A46

Madonna of Vang — A47

1962, May 15 *Engr.* *Perf. 13*
189	A46	70c dull green	.20	.20
190	A46	80c chocolate	.40	.20
191	A46	4pi lilac rose	1.25	.20
192	A46	7pi rose red	3.00	.55
		Nos. 189-192 (4)	4.85	1.15

Inauguration of postal checking service.

1962, July 7
193	A47	50c violet & rose red	.40	.20
194	A47	1pi red brn & indigo	.55	.20
195	A47	2pi brown & rose car	1.00	.20
196	A47	8pi green & dk blue	5.25	.40
		Nos. 193-196 (4)	7.20	1.00

Catholic shrine of the Madonna of Vang.

Armed Guards and Village A48

1962, Oct. 26
197	A48	50c bright red	.55	.20
198	A48	1pi yellow green	.85	.20
199	A48	1.50pi lilac rose	1.10	.20
200	A48	7pi ultra	3.00	.65
		Nos. 197-200 (4)	5.50	1.25

"Strategic village" defense system.

Gougah Waterfall, Dalat — A49

Trung Sisters' Monument and Vietnamese Women — A50

1963, Jan. 3
201	A49	60c orange red	1.25	.20
202	A49	1pi bluish black	2.00	.20

62nd birthday of Pres. Ngo Dinh Diem; Spring Festival.

1963, Mar. 1 *Engr.*
203	A50	50c green	.20	.20
204	A50	1pi dk carmine rose	.50	.20
205	A50	3pi lilac rose	.60	.20
206	A50	8pi violet blue	1.75	.60
		Nos. 203-206 (4)	3.05	1.20

Issued for Women's Day.

Farm Woman with Grain A51

1963, Mar. 21 *Perf. 13*
207	A51	50c red	.50	.20
208	A51	1pi dk car rose	.55	.20
209	A51	3pi lilac rose	.80	.20
210	A51	5pi violet	1.40	.50
		Nos. 207-210 (4)	3.25	1.10

FAO "Freedom from Hunger" campaign.

Common Defense Emblem — A52

Emblem — A53

1963, July 7 *Engr.* *Perf. 13*
211	A52	30c bister	.65	.20
212	A52	50c lilac rose	.80	.20
213	A52	3pi brt green	1.25	.20
214	A52	7pi rose red	2.10	.35
		Nos. 211-214 (4)	4.80	.95

Common defense effort. The inscription says: "Personalism-Common Progress."

1963, Oct. 26 *Perf. 13*
215	A53	50c rose red	.40	.20
216	A53	1pi emerald	.65	.20
217	A53	4pi purple	1.40	.25
218	A53	5pi orange	2.50	.95
		Nos. 215-218 (4)	4.95	1.60

The fighting soldiers of the Republic.

Centenary Emblem and Map — A54

1963, Nov. 17 *Engr.*
Cross in Deep Carmine
219	A54	50c Prus blue	.50	.20
220	A54	1pi deep carmine	1.00	.20
221	A54	3pi orange yellow	1.40	.20
222	A54	6pi brown	3.25	.55
		Nos. 219-222 (4)	6.15	1.15

Centenary of International Red Cross.

Constitution and Scales — A55

1963, Dec. 10 *Perf. 13*
223	A55	70c orange	.20	.20
224	A55	1pi brt rose	.50	.20
225	A55	3pi green	.65	.20
226	A55	8pi ocher	1.75	.50
		Nos. 223-226 (4)	3.10	1.10

15th anniv. of the Universal Declaration of Human Rights.

Danhim Hydroelectric Station — A56

1964, Jan. 15 *Engr.*
227	A56	40c rose red	.65	.20
228	A56	1pi bister brown	.65	.20
229	A56	3pi violet blue	.95	.20
230	A56	8pi olive green	1.75	.70
		Nos. 227-230 (4)	4.00	1.30

Inauguration of the Danhim Hydroelectric Station.

Atomic Reactor A57

1964, Feb. 3 *Perf. 13*
231	A57	80c olive	.60	.20
232	A57	1.50pi brown orange	.60	.20
233	A57	3pi chocolate	1.25	.20
234	A57	7pi brt blue	1.60	.60
		Nos. 231-234 (4)	4.05	1.60

Peaceful uses of atomic energy.

Compass Rose, Barograph and UN Emblem — A58

South Vietnamese Gesturing to North Vietnamese; Map — A59

1964, Mar. 23 *Engr.*
235	A58	50c bister	.20	.20
236	A58	1pi vermilion	.40	.20
237	A58	1.50pi rose claret	.60	.20
238	A58	10pi emerald	1.90	.70
		Nos. 235-238 (4)	3.10	1.30

4th World Meteorological Day, Mar. 23.

1964, July 20 *Perf. 13*
239	A59	30c dk grn, ultra & mar	1.60	.20
240	A59	50c dk car rose, yel & blk	1.60	.20
241	A59	1.50pi dk bl, dp org & blk	1.60	.50
		Nos. 239-241 (3)	4.80	.90

10th anniv. of the Day of National Grief, July 20, 1954, when the nation was divided into South and North Viet Nam.

Hatien Beach — A60

1964, Sept. 7 *Engr.* *Perf. 13½*
242	A60	20c bright ultra	.50	.50
243	A60	3pi emerald	1.75	.55

Revolutionists and "Nov. 1" — A61

Designs: 80c, Soldier breaking chain. 3pi, Broken chain and date: "1-11 1963," vert.

1964, Nov. 1 *Engr.* *Perf. 13*
244	A61	50c red lilac & indigo	.65	.20
245	A61	80c violet & red brn	.70	.20
246	A61	3pi dk blue & red	1.10	.70
		Nos. 244-246 (3)	2.45	1.10

Anniv. of November 1963 revolution.

Temple, Saigon A62

Designs: 1pi, Royal tombs, Hué. 1.50pi, Fishermen and sailboats at Phan-Thiet beach. 3pi, Temple, Gia-Dhin.

1964-66 *Perf. 13*
Size: 35½x26mm
247	A62	50c fawn, grn & dl vio	.70	.20
248	A62	1pi olive bis & ind	1.10	.20

249 A62 1.50pi ol gray & dk sl
              grn   1.00 .20
250 A62 3pi vio, dk sl grn &
              cl   2.00 .50
   Nos. 247-250 (4)   4.80 1.10

Coil Stamp
Size: 23x17mm

250A A62 1pi ol bis & ind
              ('66)   6.00 3.50

Issue date: Nos. 247-250, Dec. 2, 1964.

Hung
Vuong and
Au Co with
their
Children
A63

1965, Apr.   Engr.   *Perf. 13*
251 A63 3pi car lake & org
              red   1.50 .45
252 A63 100pi brown vio & vio 17.50 3.50
Mythological founders of Viet Nam, c. 2000
B.C.

ITU Emblem,
Insulator and TV
Mast — A64

Buddhist Wheel
of Life and
Flames — A65

1965, May 17   Engr.
253 A64 1pi olive, dp car & bister .75 .20
254 A64 3pi henna brn, car & lil   1.75 .45
        ITU, centenary.

1965, May 15   *Perf. 13*
1.50pi, Wheel, lotus blossom and world
map, horiz. 3pi, Wheel and Buddhist flag.

Inscribed: "Phat-Giao" (Buddhism)
255 A65 50c dark carmine   1.50 .20
256 A65 1.50pi dk blue & ocher 1.50 .20
257 A65 3pi org brn & dk brn 2.25 .35
   Nos. 255-257 (3)   5.25 .75
    Anniversary of Buddha's birth.

ICY Emblem and
Women of
Various
Races — A66

Ixora — A67

1965, June 26
258 A66 50c bluish blk & bis 1.00 .20
259 A66 1pi dk brn & brn   1.00 .20
260 A66 1.50pi dark red & gray 1.60 .45
   Nos. 258-260 (3)   3.60 .85
    International Cooperation Year.

1965, Sept. 10   Engr.   *Perf. 13*
Flowers: 80c, Orchid. 1pi, Chrysanthemum.
1.50pi, Lotus, horiz. 3pi, Plum blossoms.
261 A67 70c grn, slate grn &
              red   .40 .20
262 A67 80c dk brn, lil & sl grn .55 .20
263 A67 1pi dk blue & yellow .70 .20
264 A67 1.50pi sl grn, dl grn &
              gray   1.00 .20
265 A67 3pi slate grn & org 2.10 .55
   Nos. 261-265 (5)   4.75 1.35

Student,
Dormitory and
Map of Thu
Duc — A68

1965, Oct. 15   *Perf. 13*
266 A68 50c dark brown   .20 .20
267 A68 1pi bright green   .20 .20
268 A68 3pi crimson   .75 .20
269 A68 7pi dark blue violet 2.00 .65
   Nos. 266-269 (4)   3.15 1.25
    Issued to publicize higher education.

Farm Boy
and Girl,
Pig and 4-T
Emblem
A69

4pi, Farm boy with chicken, village and 4-T
flag.

1965, Nov. 25   Engr.   *Perf. 13*
270 A69 3pi emerald & dk red 1.50 .20
271 A69 4pi dull violet & plum 2.50 .50
10th anniv. of the 4-T Clubs and the
National Congress of Young Farmers.

Basketball
A70

Designs: 1pi, Javelin. 1.50pi, Hand holding
torch, athletic couple. 10pi, Pole vault.

1965, Dec. 14   Engr.   *Perf. 13*
272 A70 50c dk car & brn org .60 .20
273 A70 1pi brn org & red brn .75 .20
274 A70 1.50pi brt green   1.10 .20
275 A70 10pi red lil & brn org 3.00 .75
   Nos. 272-275 (4)   5.45 1.35

Radio
Tower — A71

Loading Hook
and Globe — A72

Radio tower, telephone dial, map of Viet
Nam.

1966, Apr. 24   *Perf. 13*
276 A71 3pi brt blue & brn   .45 .20
277 A71 4pi purple, red & blk .55 .25
    Saigon microwave station.

1966, June 22   Engr.   *Perf. 13*
278 A72 3pi gray & dk car rose .40 .20
279 A72 4pi olive & dk purple .60 .20
280 A72 6pi brt grn & dk blue 1.00 .35
   Nos. 278-280 (3)   2.00 .75
    Appreciation of the help given by the free
world.

Hands
Reaching
for
Persecuted
Refugees
A73

1966, July 20
281 A73 3pi brn, vio brn & olive .50 .20
282 A73 7pi claret, vio brn & dk
              pur   1.25 .20
    Refugees from communist oppression.

Paper
Soldiers,
Votive
Offering
A74

Designs: 1.50pi, Man and woman making
offerings. 3pi, Floating candles in paper boats.
5pi, Woman burning paper offerings.

1966, Aug. 30   Engr.   *Perf. 13*
283 A74 50c red, blk & bis brn .75 .20
284 A74 1.50pi brown, emer &
              grn   1.25 .20
285 A74 3pi rose red & lake 1.75 .20
286 A74 5pi org brn, bis & dk
              brn   2.50 .40
   Nos. 283-286 (4)   6.25 1.00
        Wandering Souls Festival.

Oriental
Two-string
Violin
A75

Vietnamese Instruments: 3pi, Woman playing 16-string guitar. 4pi, Musicians playing
two-string guitars. 7pi, Woman and boy playing flutes.

1966   Engr.   *Perf. 13*
Size: 35½x26mm
287 A75 1pi brown red & brn   .95 .20
288 A75 3pi rose lilac & pur .95 .20
289 A75 4pi rose brown & brn 1.60 .30
290 A75 7pi dp blue & vio bl 3.50 .50
   Nos. 287-290 (4)   7.00 1.20

Coil Stamp
Size: 23x17mm
290A A75 3pi rose lil & pur 50.00 3.50
  b. Booklet pane of 5
Nos. 287-290 were issued Sept. 28.
No. 290Ab contains two vertical strip of 5
with selvage at either end. These strips were
also sold loose without booklet cover.

WHO Building,
Geneva, and
Flag — A76

Designs: 50c, WHO Building and emblem,
horiz. 8pi, WHO flag and building.

1966, Oct. 12
291 A76 50c purple & carmine .20 .20
292 A76 1.50pi red brn, vio bl &
              blk   .20 .20
293 A76 8pi grnsh bl, vio bl &
              brn   2.50 1.10
   Nos. 291-293 (3)   2.90 1.50
    Opening of WHO Headquarters, Geneva.

Hand
Holding
Spade,
and
Soldiers
A77

Soldier and
Workers — A78

Designs: 1.50pi, Flag, workers. 4pi, Soldier
and cavalryman.

1966, Nov. 1   Engr.   *Perf. 13*
294 A77 80c dull brn & red brn .40 .20
295 A77 1.50pi car rose, yel &
              brn   .85 .20
296 A78 3pi brown & slate grn .85 .20
297 A78 4pi lilac, black & brn 3.00 .35
   Nos. 294-297 (4)   5.10 .95
3rd anniv. of the revolution against the government of Pres. Ngo Dinh Diem.

Symbolic Tree
and UNESCO
Emblem — A79

Designs: 3pi, Globe and olive branches. 7pi,
Symbolic temple, horiz.

1966, Dec. 15   Engr.   *Perf. 13*
298 A79 1pi pink, brn & dk car 1.10 .20
299 A79 3pi dp bl, grn & brn org 1.10 .20
300 A79 7pi grnsh bl, dk bl & red 2.75 .65
   Nos. 298-300 (3)   4.95 1.05
        20th anniv. of UNESCO.

Bitter
Melon
A80

1967, Jan. 12   Engr.   *Perf. 13*
301 A80 50c Cashew, vert.   1.40 .20
302 A80 1.50pi shown   2.10 .20
303 A80 3pi Sweetsop   2.40 .20
304 A80 20pi Areca nuts   6.00 .55
   Nos. 301-304 (4)   11.90 1.15

Phan-Boi-Chau — A81

Designs: 20pi, Phan-Chau-Trinh portrait and
addressing crowd.

1967, Mar. 24   Engr.   Perf. 13
305 A81 1pi mar, red brn & dk brn .75 .20
306 A81 20pi vio, slate grn & blk 3.25 1.25
Issued to honor Vietnamese patriots.

Woman Carrying Produce A82

Labor Day: 1pi, Market scene. 3pi, Two-wheeled horse cart. 8pi, Farm scene with water buffalo.

1967, May 1   Engr.   Perf. 13
307 A82 50c vio bl, dk bl & ultra .20 .20
308 A82 1pi sl grn & dull pur .20 .20
309 A82 3pi dk carmine .60 .20
310 A82 8pi brt car rose & pur 1.25 .60
Nos. 307-310 (4) 2.25 1.20

Potter, Vases and Lamp — A83

Weavers and Potters A84

Designs: 1.50pi, Vase and basket. 35d, Bag and lacquerware.

1967, July 22   Engr.   Perf. 13
311 A83 50c red brn, grn & ultra .20 .20
312 A83 1.50pi grnsh bl, car & blk .55 .20
313 A84 3pi red, vio & org brn 1.40 .20
314 A83 35pi bis brn, blk & dk red 4.25 .85
Nos. 311-314 (4) 6.40 1.45
Issued to publicize Vietnamese handicrafts.

Wedding Procession A85

1967, Sept. 18   Engr.   Perf. 13
315 A85 3pi rose cl, dk vio & red 2.00 .35

Symbols of Stage, Music and Art — A86

Litho. & Engr.
1967, Oct. 27   Perf. 13
316 A86 10pi bl gray, blk & red 2.50 .20
Issued to publicize the Cultural Institute.

"Freedom and Justice" A87

Balloting A88

"Establishment of Democracy" — A89

1967, Nov. 1   Photo.
317 A87 4pi mag, brn & ocher .95 .20
318 A88 5pi brown, yel & blk 1.25 .20
319 A89 30pi dl lil, indigo & red 3.50 .65
Nos. 317-319 (3) 5.70 1.05
National Day; general elections.

Pagoda and Lions Emblem A90

1967, Dec. 5   Photo.   Perf. 13½x13
320 A90 3pi multicolored 2.50 1.25
50th anniversary of Lions International.

Teacher with Pupils and Globe — A91

1967, Dec. 10   Perf. 13x13½
321 A91 3pi tan, blk, yel & car 2.50 .40
International Literacy Day, Sept. 8, 1967.

Tractor and Village — A92

Rural Construction Program: 9pi, Bulldozer and home building. 10pi, Wheelbarrow, tractor and new building. 20pi, Vietnamese and Americans working together.

1968, Jan. 26   Photo.   Perf. 13½
322 A92 1pi multicolored .20 .20
323 A92 9pi lt blue & multi 1.00 .20
324 A92 10pi multicolored 1.60 .30
325 A92 20pi yel, red lil & blk 2.10 .45
Nos. 322-325 (4) 4.90 1.15

WHO Emblem — A93

1968, Apr. 7   Photo.   Perf. 13½
326 A93 10pi gray grn, blk & yel 2.00 1.00
WHO, 20th anniversary.

Flags of Viet Nam's Allies — A94

Designs: 1.50pi, Flags surrounding SEATO emblem. 3pi, Flags, handclasp, globe and map of Viet Nam. 50pi, Flags and handclasp.

1968, June 22   Photo.   Perf. 13½
327 A94 1pi multicolored .60 .20
328 A94 1.50pi multicolored 1.25 .20
329 A94 3pi multicolored 2.40 .20
330 A94 50pi multicolored 7.75 .95
Nos. 327-330 (4) 12.00 1.55
Issued to honor Viet Nam's allies.

Three-wheeled Truck and Tractor — A95

Private Property Ownership: 80c, Farmer, city man and symbols of property. 2pi, Three-wheeled cart, taxi and farmers. 30pi, Taxi, three-wheeled cart and tractor in field.

Inscribed: "HUU-SAN-HOA CONG-NHAN VA NONG-DAN"

1968, Nov. 1   Photo.   Perf. 13½
331 A95 80c multicolored .20 .20
332 A95 2pi steel blue & multi .20 .20
333 A95 10pi orange brn & multi 1.10 .45
334 A95 30pi gray blue & multi 3.50 1.25
Nos. 331-334 (4) 5.00 2.10

Human Rights Flame — A96

Men of Various Races — A97

1968, Dec. 10   Photo.   Perf. 13½
335 A96 10pi multicolored .90 .30
336 A97 16pi purple & multi 1.75 .35
International Human Rights Year.

UNICEF Emblem, Mother and Child — A98

6pi, Children flying kite with UNICEF emblem.

1968, Dec. 11
337 A98 6pi multicolored 1.50 .60
338 A98 16pi multicolored 3.00 .95

Workers and Train — A99

1.50pi, 3pi, Crane, train, map of Viet Nam.

1968, Dec. 15
339 A99 1.50pi multicolored 1.00 .20
340 A99 3pi org, vio bl & grn 1.10 .20
341 A99 9pi multicolored 1.50 .20
342 A99 20pi multicolored 2.75 .50
Nos. 339-342 (4) 6.35 1.10
Reopening of Trans-Viet Nam Railroad.

Farm Woman — A100

Vietnamese Women: 1pi, Merchant. 3pi, Nurses, horiz. 20pi, Three ladies.

1969, Mar. 23   Engr.   Perf. 13
343 A100 50c vio bl, lil & ocher .20 .20
344 A100 1pi grn, bis & dk brn .20 .20
345 A100 3pi brown, blk & bl .55 .20
346 A100 20pi lilac & multi 2.50 1.00
Nos. 343-346 (4) 3.45 1.60

Soldiers and Civilians A101

Family Welcoming Soldier A102

1969, June 1   Photo.   Perf. 13
347 A101 2pi multicolored .20 .20
348 A102 50pi multicolored 3.25 .75
Pacification campaign.

Man Reading Constitution, Scales of Justice A103

Voters, Torch and Scales A104

1969, June 9
349 A103 1pi yel org, yel & blk .20 .20
350 A104 20pi multicolored 4.00 .45
Constitutional democracy. Phrase on both stamps: "Democratic and Governed by Law."

Mobile Post Office — A105

Mobile Post Office: 3pi, Window service. 4pi, Child with letter. 20pi, Crowd at window and postmark: "15, 12, 67."

1969, July 10
351 A105 1pi multicolored .20 .20
352 A105 3pi multicolored .60 .20
353 A105 4pi multicolored .75 .20
354 A105 20pi ocher & multi 1.50 .50
  Nos. 351-354 (4) 3.05 1.10
Installation of the first mobile post office in Viet Nam.

Mnong-gar Woman A106

1pi, Djarai woman. 50pi, Bahnar man.

1969, Aug. 29   **Photo.**   **Perf. 13**
355 A106 1pi brt pink & multi .90 .20
356 A106 6pi sky blue & multi 2.10 .20
357 A106 50pi gray & multi 9.00 .50
  Nos. 355-357 (3) 12.00 .90
Ethnic minorities in Viet Nam.

Civilians Becoming Soldiers A107

General Mobilization: 3pi, Bayonet training. 5pi, Guard duty. 10pi, Farewell.

1969, Sept. 20
Inscribed: "TONG BONG VIEN"
358 A107 1.50pi orange & multi .75 .20
359 A107 3pi purple & multi 1.60 .20
360 A107 5pi blk, red & ocher 2.40 .20
361 A107 10pi pink & multi 3.25 .35
  Nos. 358-361 (4) 8.00 .95

ILO Emblem and Globe — A108

1969, Oct. 29   **Photo.**   **Perf. 13**
362 A108 6pi blue grn, blk & gray .60 .20
363 A108 20pi red, blk & gray 1.90 .20
ILO, 50th anniversary.

Pegu House Sparrow — A109

Birds: 6pi, Moluccan munia. 7pi, Great hornbill. 30pi, Old world tree sparrow.

1970, Jan. 15 Photo. Perf. 12½x14
364 A109 2pi blue & multi 1.25 .35
365 A109 6pi orange & multi 2.75 .70
366 A109 7pi org brn & multi 4.25 .70
367 A109 30pi blue & multi 16.00 2.10
  Nos. 364-367 (4) 24.25 3.85

Burning House and Family — A110

Design: 20pi, Family fleeing burning house and physician examining child.

1970, Jan. 31   **Photo.**   **Perf. 13**
368 A110 10pi multicolored 1.50 .20
369 A110 20pi multicolored 2.50 .30
Mau Than disaster, 1968.

Vietnamese Costumes — A111

Traditional Costumes: 1pi, Man, woman and priest, vert. 2pi, Seated woman with fan. 100pi, Man and woman.

Inscribed: "Y-PHUC CO TRUYEN"

1970, Mar. 13   **Photo.**   **Perf. 13**
370 A111 1pi lt brown & multi .20 .20
371 A111 2pi pink & multi .20 .20
372 A111 3pi ultra & multi .20 .20
373 A111 100pi multicolored 7.25 2.00
  Nos. 370-373 (4) 7.85 2.60
Issued for the Trung Sisters' Festival.

Building Workers, Pagodas and Bridge A112

Rebuilding of Hué: 20pi, Concrete mixers and scaffolds.

1970, June 10   **Litho. & Engr.**
374 A112 6pi multicolored 1.25 .20
375 A112 20pi rose lil, brn & bis 1.75 .50

Plower in Rice Field — A113

1970, Aug. 29   **Perf. 13**
376 A113 6pi multicolored 1.75 .45
"Land to the Tiller" agricultural reform program.

New Building and Scaffold A114

Construction Work — A115

1970, Sept. 15   **Engr.**   **Perf. 13**
377 A114 8pi pale ol & brn org 1.25 .20
378 A115 16pi brn, indigo & yel 2.75 .90
Reconstruction after 1968 Tet Offensive.

Productivity Year Emblem A116

1970, Oct. 3
379 A116 10pi multicolored 1.75 .45
Asian Productivity Year.

Nguyen-Dinh-Chieu — A117

Education Year Emblem — A118

1970, Nov. 16   **Engr.**   **Perf. 13½**
380 A117 6pi dull vio, red & brn 1.25 .20
381 A117 10pi grn, red & dk brn 2.00 .20
Nguyen-Dinh-Chieu (1822-1888), poet.

Litho. & Engr.
1970, Nov. 30   **Perf. 13**
382 A118 10pi pale brn, yel & blk 1.75 .65
International Education Year.

Parliament Building A119

Dancers — A120

Design: 6pi, Senate Building.

1970, Dec.
383 A119 6pi lt bl, cit & dk brn .75 .20
384 A119 10pi multicolored 1.50 .20
6pi issued Dec. 8 for the 6th Cong.; 10pi issued Dec. 9 for the 9th General Assembly of the Asian Interparliamentary Union.

1971, Jan. 12
Designs: Various Vietnamese dancers and musicians. 6pi and 7pi horizontal.
385 A120 2pi ultra & multi .85 .20
386 A120 6pi pale green & multi 2.40 .20
387 A120 7pi pink & multi 2.75 .20
388 A120 10pi brown org & multi 3.00 .45
  Nos. 385-388 (4) 9.00 1.05
For surcharge see No. 500.

Farmers and Law — A121

Agrarian Reform Law: 3pi, Tractor and law, dated 26.3.1970. 16pi, Farmers, people rejoicing and law book.

1971, Mar. 26   **Engr.**   **Perf. 13**
389 A121 2pi vio bl, dk brn & dl org .20 .20
  a. Dated "1970" 50.00
390 A121 3pi pale grn, brn & dk bl .80 .20
391 A121 16pi multicolored 3.50 .20
  Nos. 389-391 (3) 4.50 .60
No. 389 is dated "1971."
For surcharge see No. 482.

Courier on Horseback A122

Design: 6pi, Mounted courier with flag.

Engr. & Photo.
1971, June 6   **Perf. 13**
392 A122 2pi violet & multi 1.00 .20
393 A122 6pi tan & multi 3.50 .20
Postal history.

Military and Naval Operations on Vietnamese Coast — A123

1971, June 19
394 A123 3pi multi + label 1.00 .25
395 A123 40pi multi + label 5.00 .65
Armed Forces Day.

Deer — A124

Rice Harvest A125

1971, Aug. 20   **Engr.**
396 A124 9pi shown 1.75 .20
397 A124 30pi Tiger 5.75 .70

Litho. & Engr.
1971, Sept. 28   **Perf. 13**
30pi, Threshing and winnowing rice and rice plants. 40pi, Bundling and carrying rice.
398 A125 1pi multicolored .20 .20
399 A125 30pi sal pink, dk pur & blk 3.50 .25
400 A125 40pi sepia, yel & grn 4.25 .30
  Nos. 398-400 (3) 7.95 .75
For surcharge see No. 496.

Inauguration of UPU Building, Bern — A126

1971, Nov. 9   **Engr.**   **Perf. 13**
401 A126 20pi green & multi 3.25 .75

Fish — A127

Various Fish; 2pi vertical.

1971, Nov. 16   **Photo. & Engr.**
402 A127 2pi multicolored 1.75 .20
403 A127 10pi violet & multi 3.25 .20
404 A127 100pi lilac & multi 24.50 2.40
  Nos. 402-404 (3) 29.50 2.80

Mailman and Woman on Water Buffalo
A128

Rural Mail: 10pi, Bird carrying letter. 20pi, Mailman with bicycle delivering mail to villagers.

1971, Dec. 20   Engr.   Perf. 13
Inscribed: "PHAT TRIEN BUU-CHINH NONG THON"
405 A128 5pi multicolored   1.25 .20
406 A128 10pi multicolored   2.25 .20
407 A128 20pi multicolored   4.00 1.25
      Nos. 405-407 (3)   7.50 1.65

Trawler Fishermen, and Fish — A129

Publicity for Fishing Industry: 7pi, Net fishing from boat. 50d, Trawler with seine.

1972, Jan. 2   Engr.   Perf. 13
408 A129 4pi pink, blk & blue   1.00 .20
409 A129 7pi lt blue, blk & red   1.50 .20
410 A129 50pi multicolored   7.50 1.60
      Nos. 408-410 (3)   10.00 2.00

King Quang Trung (1752-1792) — A130

1972, Jan. 28   Perf. 13½
411 A130 6pi red & multi   1.10 —
a.   Booklet pane of 10
412 A130 20pi black & multi   3.50 .50
      No. 411a is imperf. horizontally.

Road Workers A131

1972, Feb. 4
413 A131 3pi multicolored   .50 .20
414 A131 8pi multicolored   1.75 .20
      Community development.

Rice Farming A132

1972, Mar. 26   Engr.   Perf. 13½
415 A132 1pi shown   .20 .20
416 A132 10pi Wheat farming   2.25 .20
      Farmers' Day.

Plane over Dalat — A133

1972, Apr. 18   Engr. & Photo.
417 A133 10pi shown   1.25 .25
418 A133 10pi over Ha-tien   1.25 .25
419 A133 10pi over Hue   1.25 .25
420 A133 10pi over Saigon   1.25 .25
a.   Block of 4, #417-420   10.00 2.00
421 A133 25pi like No. 417   2.75 .25
422 A133 25pi like No. 418   2.75 .25

---

423 A133 25pi like No. 419   2.75 .25
424 A133 25pi like No. 420   2.75 .25
a.   Block of 4, #421-424   21.00 3.50
      Nos. 417-424 (8)   16.00 2.00
      20 years Air Viet Nam.

Scholar A134

20pi, Teacher, pupils. 50pi, Scholar, scroll.

1972, May 5   Engr. & Litho.
425 A134 5pi multicolored   .60 .20
Engr.
426 A134 20pi lt green & multi   2.50 .70
427 A134 50pi pink & multi   6.75 1.00
      Nos. 425-427 (3)   9.85 1.90
      Ancient letter writing art.

Armed Farmer — A135

6pi, Civilian rifleman & Self-defense Forces emblem, horiz. 20pi, Man, woman training with rifles.

Engr. & Litho.
1972, June 15   Perf. 13
428 A135 2pi brt rose & multi   1.25 .25
429 A135 6pi multicolored   2.00 .25
430 A135 20pi lt violet & multi   2.75 .25
      Nos. 428-430 (3)   6.00 .75
      Civilian Self-defense Forces.

Hands Holding Safe — A136

1972, July 10
431 A136 10pi lt blue & multi   1.75 .20
432 A136 25pi lt green & multi   3.25 .40
      Treasury Bonds campaign.

Frontier Guard — A137   Soldier Helping Wounded Man — A138

Designs: 10pi, 3 guards and horse, horiz. 40pi, Marching guards, horiz.

1972, Aug. 14   Perf. 13
433 A137 10pi olive & multi   .70 .20
434 A137 30pi buff & multi   1.75 .30
435 A137 40pi lt blue & multi   2.40 .55
      Nos. 433-435 (3)   4.85 1.05
      Historic frontier guards.

1972, Sept. 1
Designs: 16pi, Soldier on crutches and flowers. 100pi, Veterans' memorial, map and flag.
436 A138 9pi olive & multi   1.00 .35
437 A138 16pi yellow & multi   1.40 .35
438 A138 100pi lt blue & multi   7.50 1.40
      Nos. 436-438 (3)   9.90 2.10
      For surcharge see No. 483.

Tank, Memorial, Flag and Map — A139

Soldiers and Map of Viet Nam — A140

1972, Nov. 25   Litho.   Perf. 13
439 A139 5pi multicolored   8.00 .20
440 A140 10pi ultra & multi   12.00 .20
      Victory at Binh-Long.

Book Year Emblem and Globe — A141

Designs: 4pi, Emblem, books circling globe. 5pi, Emblem, books and globe.

1972, Nov. 30
441 A141 2pi dp carmine & multi   .60 .20
442 A141 4pi blue & multi   1.00 .20
443 A141 5pi yellow bister & multi   1.50 .20
      Nos. 441-443 (3)   3.10 .60
      International Book Year.

Liberated Vietnamese Family — A142   Soldiers Raising Vietnamese Flag — A143

1973, Feb. 18   Litho.   Perf. 13
444 A142 10pi yellow & multi   2.50 .20
      To celebrate the 200,000th returnee.

1973, Feb. 24   Litho.   Perf. 13
Design: 10pi, Victorious soldiers and map of demilitarized zone, horiz.
445 A143 3pi lilac & multi   1.25 .20
446 A143 10pi yellow grn & multi   1.75 .20
      Victory at Quang Tri.

Satellite, Storm over Viet Nam — A144

1973, Mar. 23   Litho.   Perf. 12½x12
447 A144 1pi lt blue & multi   1.25 .20
      World Meteorological Day.
      For surcharge see No. 497.

Farmers with Tractor, Symbol of Law — A145

Farmer Plowing with Water Buffalos A146

Pres. Thieu Holding Agrarian Reform Law A147

1973, Mar. 26   Litho.   Perf. 12½x12
448 A145 2pi lt green & multi   5.00 .60
449 A146 5pi orange & multi   5.00 .60
      Perf. 11
450 A147 10pi blue & multi   150.00 25.00
      Nos. 448-450 (3)   160.00 26.20

3rd anniv. of the agrarian reform law; 5-year plan for rural development.
Value for No. 450 is for stamp with first day cancel. Commercially used copies are worth substantially more.
See No. 475.

INTERPOL Emblem and Headquarters — A148

2pi, INTERPOL emblem. 25pi, INTERPOL emblem, side view of Headquarters.

1973, Apr. 8   Litho.   Perf. 12½x12
451 A148 1pi olive & multi   .20 .20
452 A148 2pi yellow & multi   .20 .20
453 A148 25pi ocher, lilac & brn   4.75 .20
      Nos. 451-453 (3)   5.15 .60
      Intl. Criminal Police Org., 50th anniv.
      For surcharge see No. 498.

ITU Emblem and Waves A149

2pi, Globe and waves. 3pi, ITU emblem.

1973, May 17
454 A149 1pi dull blue & multi   .40 .20
455 A149 2pi brt blue & multi   .85 .20
456 A149 3pi orange & multi   1.25 .20
      Nos. 454-456 (3)   2.50 .60

World Telecommunications Day.
For surcharge see No. 499.

Globe, Hand Holding House — A150   Men Building Pylon — A151

Design: 10pi, Fish in net, symbols of agriculture, industry and transportation.

1973, Nov. 6   Litho.   Perf. 12x12½
457 A150 8pi gray & multi   1.10   .20
458 A150 10pi vio bl, blk & gray   1.50   .20
459 A151 15pi blk, org & lil rose   2.40   .40
     Nos. 457-459 (3)   5.00   .80
National development.
For surcharge see No. 514.

Water Buffalos
A152

1973, Dec. 20   Litho.   Perf. 12½x12
460 A152 5pi shown   2.75   .20
461 A152 10pi Water buffalo   3.75   .20

Human Rights
Flame, Three
Races
A153

Design: 100pi, Human Rights flame, scales
and people, vert.

1973, Dec. 29   Perf. 12½x12, 12x12½
462 A153 15pi ultra & multi   1.25   .20
463 A153 100pi green & multi   3.75   .50
25th anniv. of Universal Declaration of
Human Rights.

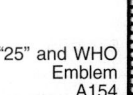

"25" and WHO
Emblem
A154

Design: 15pi, WHO emblem, diff.

1973, Dec. 31   Perf. 12½x12
464 A154 8pi orange, bl & brn   1.00   .20
465 A154 15pi lt brn, bl & brt
           pink   1.50   .20
25th anniversary of WHO.
For surcharge see No. 515.

Sampan
Ferry
A155

Design: 10pi, Sampan ferry (different).

1974, Jan. 13   Litho.   Perf. 14x13½
466 A155 5pi lt blue & multi   2.00   .20
467 A155 10pi yellow grn & multi   3.00   .70
Sampan ferry women.

Soldiers of 7
Nations
A156

American War
Memorial
A157

Map of South Viet
Nam and Allied
Flags — A158

Design: No. 469, Soldiers and flags of South
Viet Nam, Korea, US, Australia New Zealand,
Thailand and Philippines. Same flags shown
on 8pi and 60pi.

1974, Jan. 28   Perf. 12½x12, 12x12½
468 A156 8pi multicolored   .55   .20
469 A156 15pi lt brown & multi   1.10   .20
470 A157 15pi multicolored   1.10   .20
471 A158 60pi multicolored   3.50   .20
     Nos. 468-471 (4)   6.25   .80
In honor of South Viet Nam's allies.
For surcharge see No. 516.

Trung Sisters
on Elephants
Fighting
Chinese
A159

1974, Feb. 27   Litho.   Perf. 12½x12
472 A159 8pi green, citron & blk   1.50   .20
473 A159 15pi dp orange & multi   2.00   .20
474 A159 80pi ultra, pink & blk   3.75   .20
     Nos. 472-474 (3)   7.25   .60
Trung Trac and Trung Nhi, queens of Viet
Nam, 39-43 A.D. Day of Vietnamese Women.

Pres. Thieu Type of 1973 and

Farmers
Going to
Work — A160

Woman Farmer
Holding
Rice — A161

1974, Mar. 26   Litho.   Perf. 14
475 A147 10pi blue & multi   1.50   .20
   Perf. 12½x12, 12x12½
476 A160 20pi yellow & multi   1.50   .20
477 A161 70pi blue & multi   16.00 1.50
     Nos. 475-477 (3)   19.00 1.90
Agriculture Day. Size of No. 475 is
31x50mm, No. 450 is 34x54mm and printed
on thick paper. No. 475 has been extensively
redrawn and first line of inscription in bottom
panel changed to "26 THANG BA."
Value for No. 477 is for stamp with first day
cancel. Commercially used copies are worth
substantially more.

Hung
Vuong with
Bamboo
Tallies
A162

Flag
Inscribed:
Hung
Vuong,
Founder of
Kingdom
A163

1974, Apr. 2   Perf. 14x13½
478 A162 20pi yellow & multi   1.60   .45
479 A163 100pi olive & multi   5.50   .80
Hung Vuong, founder of Vietnamese nation
and of Hông-Bang Dynasty (2879-258 B.C.).

National
Library
A164

New National Library Building: 15pi, Library,
right facade and Phoenix.

1974, Apr. 14
480 A164 10pi orange, brn & blk   3.25 1.40
481 A164 15pi multicolored   4.00 1.90

Nos. 391 and 437 Surcharged with
New Value and Two Bars in Red
1974   Perf. 13
482 A121 25pi on 16pi multi   15.00 2.75
483 A138 25pi on 16pi multi   10.00 2.25

Memorial Tower,   Globe, Crane
Saigon — A165   Lifting
                        Crate — A167

Crane with
Flags, Globe
and Map of
Viet
Nam — A166

Perf. 12x12½, 12½x12
1974, June 22   Litho.
484 A165 10pi blue & multi   .60   .25
485 A166 20pi multicolored   1.40   .30
486 A167 60pi yellow & multi   4.50   .35
     Nos. 484-486 (3)   6.50   .90
International Aid Day.

Sun and
Views of
Saigon,
Dalat Hué
A168

Cau-Bong
Bridge,
Nha Trang
A169

Thien-Mu
Pagoda,
Hué — A170

1974, July 12   Perf. 14x13½, 13½x14
487 A168 5pi blue & multi   1.40   .45
488 A169 10pi blue & multi   1.40   .45
489 A170 15pi yellow & multi   2.25   .45
     Nos. 487-489 (3)   5.05 1.35
Tourist publicity.

Rhynchostylis Gigantea — A171

Orchids: 20pi, Cypripedium caliosum, vert.
200pi, Dendrobium nobile.

1974, Aug. 18
490 A171 10pi blue & multi   .35   .20
491 A171 20pi yellow & multi   .40   .25
492 A171 200pi bister & multi   6.50 1.25
     Nos. 490-492 (3)   7.25 1.70

Hands Passing
Letter, UPU
Emblem
A172

UPU Emblem and
Woman — A173

UPU Cent.: 30pi, World map, bird, UPU
emblem.

Perf. 12½x12, 12x12½
1974, Oct. 9   Litho.
493 A172 20pi ultra & multi   .30   .20
494 A172 30pi orange & multi   .65   .30
495 A173 300pi gray & multi   4.25 1.25
     Nos. 493-495 (3)   5.20 1.75

Nos. 398, 447, 451, 454, 387
Surcharged with New Value and Two
Bars in Red
1974-75
496 A125 25pi on 1pi multi   12.50
497 A144 25pi on 1pi multi   12.50
498 A148 25pi on 1pi multi   12.50
499 A149 25pi on 1pi multi   18.00
500 A120 25pi on 7pi multi   15.00
     Nos. 496-500 (5)   70.50
Issued: #496, 498, 1/1/75; others, 11/18/74.

Hien Lam
Pavilion,
Hué
A174

Throne,
Imperial
Palace,
Hué
A175

Water
Pavilion,
Hué
A176

1975, Jan. 5   Litho.   Perf. 14x13½
501 A174 25pi multicolored   1.50   .25
502 A175 30pi multicolored   2.25   .25
503 A176 60pi multicolored   2.75   .50
     Nos. 501-503 (3)   6.50 1.00
Historic sites.

Symbol of Youth, Children Holding Flower — A177

Family and Emblem A178

1975, Jan. 14   *Perf. 11½*
504 A177 20pi blue & multi   3.50 .30
Perf. 12½x12
505 A178 70pi yellow & multi   3.50 .35
Intl. Conf. on Children & Natl. Development.

Unicorn Dance A179

Boy Lighting Firecracker A180

Bringing New Year Gifts and Wishes — A181

Perf. 14x13½, 13½x14
1975, Jan. 26   Litho.
506 A179 20pi multicolored   2.50 .25
507 A180 30pi blue & multi   3.00 .30
508 A181 100pi bister & multi   7.00 .50
Nos. 506-508 (3)   12.50 1.05
Lunar New Year, Tet.

A182

A183

A184

Designs: 25pi, Military chief from play "San Hau." 40pi, Scene from "Tam Ha Nam Duong." 100pi, Warrior Luu-Kim-Dinn.

1975, Feb. 23
509 A182 25pi rose & multi   1.90 .45
510 A183 40pi lt green & multi   3.00 .45
511 A184 100pi violet & multi   10.00 .75
Nos. 509-511 (3)   14.90 1.65
National theater.

Produce, Map of Viet Nam, Ship — A185

Irrigation Project A186

1975, Mar. 26   Litho.   *Perf. 12½x12*
512 A185 10pi multicolored   1.75 .20
513 A186 50pi multicolored   5.25 .30
Agriculture Day; 5th anniv. of Agrarian Reform Law.

Nos. 457, 464, 468 Surcharged with New Value and Two Bars in Red

1975
514 A150 10pi on 8pi multi   50.00 8.25
515 A154 10pi on 8pi multi   32.50 4.00
516 A156 25pi on 8pi multi   15.00 2.75
Nos. 514-516 (3)   97.50 15.00

In the 1980's a number of South Viet Nam stamps appeared on the market. These apparently had been printed before the collapse of the Republic but saw no postal use. These include, but are not limited to, sets of two for western electric and for rural electric, one each for history, library, New Year and cows, a set of three for transportation and a set of four for economic development.

SEMI-POSTAL STAMPS

Type of 1952 Surcharged in Carmine

Perf. 12x12½
1952, Nov. 10   Unwmk.
B1 A3 1.50pi + 50c bl, yel & brn   4.00 3.25
Never hinged   10.00
The surtax was for the Red Cross.

Catalogue values for unused stamps in this section, from this point to the end of the section, are for Never Hinged items. Because of the tropical conditions, never hinged stamps must also be free wrinkles, toning, and any other disturbance.

Sabers and Flag — SP1

1952, Dec. 21   Engr.   *Perf. 13*
B2 SP1 3.30pi + 1.70pi dp claret   3.25 1.10
The surtax was for the Wounded Soldiers' Aid Organization.

X-ray Camera and Patient SP2

1960, Aug. 1   *Perf. 13*
B3 SP2 3pi + 50c bl grn & red   1.50 .90
The surtax was for the Anti-Tuberculosis Foundation.

AIR POST STAMPS

Catalogue values for unused stamps in this section, from this point to the end of the section, are for Never Hinged items. Because of the tropical conditions, never hinged stamps must also be free wrinkles, toning, and any other disturbance.

AP1

AP2

Perf. 13½x12½
1952-53   Unwmk.   Photo.
C1 AP1 3.30pi dk brn red & pale yel grn   1.00 .50
C2 AP1 4pi brown & yellow   1.50 .25
C3 AP1 5.10pi dk vio bl & sal pink   1.50 .40
C4 AP2 6.30pi yellow & car   1.50 .50
Nos. C1-C4 (4)   5.50 1.65
Issued: #C2, 11/24/53; others, 3/8/52.

Dragon AP3

Fish — AP4

1952, Sept. 3   Engr.   *Perf. 13*
C5 AP3 40c red   1.40 .35
C6 AP3 70c green   2.40 .50
C7 AP3 80c ultra   2.40 .50
C8 AP3 90c brown   2.40 .50
C9 AP4 3.70pi deep magenta   5.25 .75
Nos. C5-C9 (5)   13.85 2.60
Nos. C5-C9 exist imperforate in a souvenir booklet. Value, $175.

South Viet Nam

Phoenix — AP5

1955, Sept. 7
C10 AP5 4pi violet & lil rose   3.25 .60

Crane Carrying Letter AP6

1960, Dec. 20.   *Perf. 13*
C11 AP6 1pi olive   .90 .35
C12 AP6 4pi green & dk blue   2.10 .35
C13 AP6 5pi ocher & purple   2.50 .50
C14 AP6 10pi deep magenta   4.50 1.10
Nos. C11-C14 (4)   10.00 2.30

POSTAGE DUE STAMPS

Catalogue values for unused stamps in this section, from this point to the end of the section, are for Never Hinged items. Because of the tropical conditions, never hinged stamps must also be free wrinkles, toning, and any other disturbance.

Temple Lion D1

Dragon D2

Perf. 13x13½
1952, June 16   Typo.   Unwmk.
J1 D1 10c red & green   .85 .20
J2 D1 20c green & yellow   1.10 .20
J3 D1 30c purple & orange   1.40 .20
J4 D1 40c dk grn & sal rose   1.90 .25
J5 D1 50c dp carmine & gray   2.50 .30
J6 D1 1pi blue & silver   4.25 .20
Nos. J1-J6 (6)   12.00 1.35

South Viet Nam

1955-56
J7 D2 2pi red vio & org   .40 .20
J8 D2 3pi violet & grnsh bl   .55 .20
J9 D2 5pi violet & yellow   .60 .20
J10 D2 10pi dk green & car   .90 .20
J11 D2 20pi red & brt grn ('56)   2.00 .50
J12 D2 30pi brt grn & yel ('56)   3.00 .75
J13 D2 50pi dk red brn & yel ('56)   6.00 1.50
J14 D2 100pi pur & yel ('56)   12.00 3.50
Nos. J7-J14 (8)   25.45 7.05
Nos. J11-J14 inscribed "BUU-CHINH" instead of "TIMBRE-TAXE."

Atlas Moth — D3

Design: 3pi, 5pi, 10pi, Three butterflies.

1968, Aug. 20 Photo. Perf. 13½x13

J15	D3	50c multicolored	2.25 .50
J16	D3	1pi multicolored	2.75 .50
J17	D3	2pi multicolored	5.50 .50
J18	D3	3pi multicolored	8.00 .50
J19	D3	5pi multicolored	13.50 .50
J20	D3	10pi multicolored	18.00 .50
		Nos. J15-J20 (6)	50.00 3.00

Nos. J15-J18 Surcharged with New
Value and Two Bars in Red

1974, Oct. 1

J21	D3	5pi on 3pi multi	.75
J22	D3	10pi on 50c multi	.75
J23	D3	50pi on 1pi multi	2.75
J24	D3	60pi on 2pi multi	3.25
		Nos. J21-J24 (4)	7.50

MILITARY STAMPS

Catalogue values for unused stamps in this section, from this point to the end of the section, are for Never Hinged items. Because of the tropical conditions, never hinged stamps must also be free wrinkles, toning, and any other disturbance.

Soldier
Guarding
Village
M1

Rouletted 7½

1961, June   Unwmk.   Litho.

M1	M1	och, brn, dk grn & blk	4.00 1.00

1961, Sept.   Typo.

M2	M1	org yel, dk grn & brn	3.50 1.00

Bottom inscription on No. M1 is black, brown on No. M2.

Battle and
Refugees
M2

1969, Feb. 22 Litho.   Imperf.

M3	M2	red & green	60.00
a.		Booklet pane of 10	600.00

NORTH VIET NAM

(Democratic Republic of Viet Nam)

LOCATION — In eastern Indo-China.
GOVT. — Republic
AREA — 61,293 sq. mi.
POP. — 18,800,000 (1968 est.)
CAPITAL — Hanoi

Beginning in 1946, the Communist Viet Minh fought the French in a guerrilla war that ended with the French defeat at Dien Bien Phu in 1954. In an agreement signed in Geneva on July 21, 1954, Viet Nam was partitioned at the 17th parallel. The government in Hanoi controlled the north, and engaged in another protracted military campaign against American and South Vietnamese forces that led to the official

reunification of the country under Communist control on July 2, 1976.

100 Cents = 1 Dong
100 Xu = 1 Dong (1959)

All stamps are without gum unless otherwise indicated. Values for stamps with gum are for Never Hinged items.

Watermark

Wmk. 376 — "R de C"

VIET MINH ISSUES
Stamps and Types of Indo-China
Overprinted or Surcharged
Printing Methods and Perfs as Before

1945-46   Without Gum
No. 236 Overprinted
"VIET-NAM DAN-CHU CONG-HOA"

1L1	A41	1pi yel grn (Yersin)	8.00

Nos. 238-239 (Rhodes) Overprinted
"VIET-NAM DAN-CHU CONG-HOA"
with **"VN" & "IXIXIXIXIX"**
Obliterators
Perf. 11½

1L2	A43	15c dk vio brn, perf. 11½	1.25
a.		Perf. 12	1.25
b.		Perf. 11½, green overprint	2.50
1L3	A43	30c org brn, perf. 11½	1.00
a.		Perf. 13½	2.00
b.		Perf. 12	15.00

No. 242 Overprinted
"VIET-NAM DAN-CHU CONG-HOA"
with **"VN" & "VN.VN"** Obliterators

1L4	A44	50c dl red (Athlete)	7.00

No. 241 Overprinted
"VIET-NAM DAN-CHU CONG-HOA"
with **"VN" & "XXXX"** Obliterators

1L5	A44	10c dk vio brn & yel (Athlete)	18.00

Nos. 218-222 (Petain) Overprinted
"VIET-NAM DAN-CHU CONG-HOA"
with **"Buu-Chinh"** and
Wavy Line Obliterators

1L6	A32	3c olive brn, perf. 11½	1.75
a.		Perf. 12x14	5.00
b.		Perf. 14	15.00
1L7	A32	6c rose red	1.00
1L8	A32	10c dull grn (R)	5.00
1L9	A32	40c dk bl (R)	3.00
1L10	A32	40c slate bl (R)	3.00
		Nos. 1L6-1L10 (5)	13.75

Nos. 245-246 and Type (Pavie)
Overprinted **"VIET-NAM DAN-CHU CONG-HOA"** with **"BUU-CHINH"** and
Wavy Line & "VN" Obliterators

1L11	A46	4c org yel	1.50
1L12	A46	10c dl grn	1.50
1L13	A46	20c dark red	1.25
		Nos. 1L11-1L13 (3)	4.25

No. 165A Overprinted
"VIET-NAM DAN-CHU CONG-HOA"
with **"BUU CHINH"** and
Slanted Lines Obliterator

1L14	A22	25c dk bl (Planting Rice, R), top line 18 mm wide	60.00
a.		Top line 20 mm wide	80.00

Nos. 1L14-1L14a issued with gum.

No. 232 (Courbet) Overprinted
"VIET-NAM DAN-CHU CONG-HOA DOC-LAP TU-DO HANH-PHUC"

1L15	A39	3c lt brn	1.00
1L16	A39	6c car rose	2.00

No. 261 (Lagree) Overprinted
Vertically **"VIET-NAM DAN-CHU CONG-HOA DOC-LAP TU-DO HANH-PHUC"** with
"BUU-CHINH" & "III" Obliterator

1L17	A52	40c brt bl	1.50

Nos. 253-255 (Doumer) Overprinted
"VIET-NAM DOC-LAP TU-DO HANH-PHUC BUU-CHINH"
with Wavy Line Obliterators

1L18	A50	2c red vio	1.50
1L19	A50	4c lt brn	1.25
1L20	A50	10c yel grn	1.50
		Nos. 1L18-1L20 (3)	4.25

Nos. 217, 256-258 (Petain, Charner)
Overprinted **"VIET-NAM DOC-LAP TU-DO HANH-PHUC BUU-CHINH"**
with **"VN"** and
Wavy Line Obliterators

1L21	A32	1c blk brn	2.00
1L22	A51	10c green	1.75
1L23	A51	20c brn red	1.75
1L24	A51	1pi pale yel grn	7.50
		Nos. 1L21-1L24 (4)	13.00

No. 230 and Type (Genouilly)
Overprinted **"VIET-NAM DOC-LAP TU-DO HANH-PHUC BUU-CHINH"**
with **"X" Obliterator**

1L25	A37	5c dull brown	1.50
1L26	A37	6c carmine rose	5.00

Nos. 210-212 (Sihanouk) Surcharged
with New Value & **"X"** Obliterators

1L27	A28	5d on 1c red org (Bl)	12.50
1L28	A28	10d on 6c violet (R)	15.00
1L29	A28	15d on 25c dp ultra (R)	15.00
		Nos. 1L27-1L29 (3)	42.50

Nos. 225-226 (Sihanouk) Surcharged
with New Value with Wavy Line
and Straight Line Obliterators

1L30	A34	50xu on 1c brown	3.00
1L31	A35	2d on 6c car rose	20.00

Nos. 213-214 (Elephant) Surcharged
with New Value, **"VIET-NAM DAN-CHU CONG-HOA,"** Wavy Line and
Straight Line Obliterators

1L32	A29	2d on 3c reddish brn (G)	12.50
1L33	A29	4d on 6c crim (G)	12.50

Nos. 247-248 (Pasquier) Surcharged
Vertically with New Value,
"VIET NAM DAN CHU CONG HOA,"
Wavy Line & **"X"** Obliterators

1L34	A47	1d on 5c brn vio	4.00
1L35	A47	2d on 10c dl grn	6.50

No. B30 Surcharged with New Value,
"VIET-NAM DAN-CHU CONG-HOA,"
"Binh-si Bi-nan,"
Wavy Line Obliterator

1L36	SP7	5d on 15c+60c brn vio (Cathedral)	25.00

Nos. 259-260 (Lagree) Surcharged
Vertically with New Value,
"VIET-NAM DAN CHU CONG HOA BUU-CHINH,"
Wavy Line & **"VN"** Obliterators

1L37	A52	30xu on 1c dl gray brn (R)	1.75
1L38	A52	3d on 15c dl rose vio	3.00

Nos. 243-244 (La Grandiere) Surcharged
with New Value, **"VIET-NAM DAN CHU CONG HOA BUU CHINH,"**
Wavy Line Obliterator

1L39	A45	1d on 5c dk brn (Bl)	12.50
1L40	A45	4d on 1c dull brn	3.00

Surcharged with New Value,
"VIET-NAM Dan-chu Cong-hoa BUU-CHINH,"
Wavy & Straight Line Obliterators

1L41	A42	30xu on 15c brn vio (Garnier, R)	2.50

No. 242 (Garnier) Surcharged
with New Value, **"VIET-NAM DAN CHU CONG HOA BUU-CHINH,"**
Wavy & Straight Line Obliterators

1L42	A42	5d on 1c dull ol bis	5.00

Nos. 249-252 (De Lanessan, Van Vollenhoven) Surcharged with New Value,
"VIET-NAM DAN CHU CONG HOA BUU CHINH,"
Straight Line Obliterators

1L43	A49	50xu on 1c dl gray brn	3.00
1L44	A48	60xu on 1c lt brn	4.50
1L45	A48	1.60d on 10c green	14.00
1L46	A49	3d on 15c dl rose vio (Bl)	4.50
		Nos. 1L43-1L46 (4)	26.00

Nos. B30-B31 (Cathedral)
Surcharged with New Value,
"VIET-NAM DAN-CHU CONG-HOA CUU-DOI,"
Wavy Line Obliterators

1L47	SP7	2d on 15c+60c brn vio	22.50
1L48	SP7	3d on 40c+1.10pi blue	22.50

No. 234 (Yersin) Surcharged
with Added Value,
"VIET-NAM DAN-CHU CONGHOA Bao Anh,"
and Straight Line obliterators

1L49	A41	+2d on 6c car rose	9.00

No. 233 (Behaine) Surcharged
with Added Value, **"VIET-NAM DAN-CHU CONG-HOA Binh si bi nan,"**
Wavy Line, **"V" & "N"** Obliterators

1L50	A40	+3d on 20c dull red	5.00

No. 215 (Saigon Fair) Surcharged
with Added Value, **"VIET-NAM DAN CHU CONG HOA Chong nan mu chu"** & Wavy Line

1L51	A30	+4d on 6c car rose	9.00

No. 229 (Natl. Revolution)
Surcharged with Added Value, **"VIET-NAM DAN-CHU CONGHOA Doi song moi,"**
and **"X"** Obliterator

1L52	A36	+4d on 6c car rose	6.50

Nos. 213-214 Surcharged
with Added Value, **"VIET-NAM DAN-CHU CONG-HOA Quoc-Phong"**
and Wavy Line in Blue

1L53	A29	+5d on 3c reddish brown	17.50
1L54	A29	+10d on 6c crimson	17.50

Nos. 216, 224 Surcharged with
"VIET-NAM DAN-CHU CONG-HOA DAN-SINH" & Straight Lines

1L55	A31	30xu +3d on 6c (Nam-Phuong)	3.75

Perf. 13½

1L56	A33	30xu +3d on 6c (Bao-Dai)	3.75
a.		Perf. 12	50.00

Ho Chi Minh
VM1   VM2

1946 Litho. Unwmk. Perf. 11½
Without Gum
1L57	VM1	1h green	.50
1L58	VM1	3h rose	.50
1L59	VM1	9h yellow bister	.50

With Added Inscription "+PHU THU CUU-QUOC"
1L60	VM1	4h +6h Prussian blue	1.50
1L61	VM1	6h +9h brown violet	1.50
		Nos. 1L57-1L61 (5)	4.50

1948 Typo. Perf. 7 Rough
Thin, Rough, Brown Paper
1L62	VM2	2d brown	22.50
1L63	VM2	5d red	22.50

For surcharge and overprints see Nos. 50, O6-O7.

REPUBLIC OF NORTH VIET NAM

From 1945-2002, all stamps are without gum unless otherwise indicated. Values for stamps with gum are for Never Hinged items.

Many North Vietnamese stamps are roughly perforated, especially issues before 1958.

Ho Chi Minh, Map of Vietnam A1

1951-55 Unwmk. Litho. Imperf.
1	A1	100d brown	26.00	8.25
a.		Perf. 11¼ ('55)	35.00	6.75
2	A1	100d green	21.00	8.25
a.		Perf. 11¼ ('55)	35.00	6.75

Perf. 11¼
3	A1	200d red	30.00	8.25
a.		Imperf. ('55)	20.00	6.75
		Nos. 1-3 (3)	77.00	24.75

Nos. 1-3 printed on thin semi-transparent paper.
Nos. 1-3 used values are for cto. Postally used copies are worth about 5 times these values.
Counterfeits exist.
For surcharges, see Nos. 9-14, 36-38, and note before No. J1.

Blacksmith — A2

1953-55 Perf. 11¼
4	A2	100d violet	7.00	5.25
5	A2	500d brown	10.50	14.00

Issued: 100d, 6/53. 500d, 2/55.

Georgi Malenkov, Ho Chi Minh, Mao Tse-tung and Flags — A3

1954-55 Perf. 11¼
6	A3	50d brown & red, brnish	25.00	30.00
7	A3	100d red	20.00	25.00
8	A3	100d yellow & red, brnish	30.00	30.00
		Nos. 6-8 (3)	75.00	85.00

Issued: 50d, 10/54; #7, 1/54; #8, 4/55.
No. 7 printed on thin, white paper.

Nos. 1-3 Surcharged in Red or Blue

1954, Oct. Imperf.
9	A1	10d on 100d brown	22.50	32.50
10	A1	10d on 100d green	22.50	32.50

Perf. 11
11	A1	20d on 200d red (Bl)	22.50	42.50
		Nos. 9-11 (3)	67.50	107.50

Nos. 1-3 Surcharged in Black, Red or Blue

1954, Oct. Imperf.
12	A1	10d on 100d brown (Bk, R or Bl)	26.00	35.00
13	A1	10d on 100d green (Bk, R or Bl)	26.00	35.00

Perf. 11
14	A1	20d on 200d red (Bk or Bl)	60.00	75.00
		Nos. 12-14 (3)	112.00	145.00

Nos. 9-14 exist with counterfeit surcharges, counterfeit surcharges on counterfeit stamps, and with fantasy surcharges.

Victory at Dien Bien Phu A4

1954-56 Perf. 11¼
17	A4	10d red brn & yel brn	20.00	30.00
a.		Imperf	90.00	100.00
18	A4	50d red & org yel	20.00	30.00
a.		Imperf	20.00	40.00
19	A4	150d brown & blue	20.00	35.00
a.		Imperf	20.00	40.00
		Nos. 17-19 (3)	60.00	95.00

Issued: Imperfs, 10/54; others, 1956. See #O5.
Used values for Nos. 17-19 are for postally used copies. The 10d exists cto, perf or imperf. Value about 1/10 those shown above.

Liberation of Hanoi — A5

1955, Jan. 1 Perf. 11½
20	A5	10d lt blue & bl	7.50	8.00
21	A5	50d dk grn & grn	7.50	8.00
22	A5	150d rose & brn red	15.00	12.00
		Nos. 20-22 (3)	30.00	28.00

Nos. 20-22 used values are for postally used copies. Cto copies are worth about $1 each.

Land Reform A6

1955-56 Perf. 11¼
23	A6	5d lt green	18.00	8.50
24	A6	10d gray	18.00	8.50
25	A6	20d orange	18.00	8.50
26	A6	50d rose	18.00	8.50
27	A6	100d lt brown	37.50	32.50
		Nos. 23-27 (5)	109.50	66.50

Issued: 100d, 12/55; 20d, 50d, 2/56; others, 6/56. See Nos. O8-O9.

Return of Government to Hanoi — A7

1956, Mar. 1 Perf. 11¼
28	A7	1000d violet	32.50	25.00
29	A7	1500d dk blue	32.50	25.00
30	A7	2000d turquoise	85.00	67.50
31	A7	3000d blue green	160.00	210.00
		Nos. 28-31 (4)	310.00	327.50

Counterfeits exist, often imperf and offered as proofs.

Re-opening of Hanoi-China Railroad — A8

1956, Mar. 1
32	A8	100d dark blue	40.00	16.00
33	A8	200d blue green	40.00	16.00
34	A8	300d violet	40.00	32.50
35	A8	400d lilac brown	40.00	65.00
		Nos. 32-35 (4)	160.00	129.50

Counterfeits exist, often imperf and offered as proofs.

Nos. 1-3 Surcharged

1954, Oct. Imperf.
36	A1	10d on 100d brown	35.00	50.00
37	A1	10d on 100d green	35.00	50.00

Perf. 11
38	A1	20d on 200d red	35.00	50.00
		Nos. 36-38 (3)	105.00	150.00

Nos. 36-38 exist with counterfeit surcharges, counterfeit surcharges on counterfeit stamps, and with fantasy surcharges.

Tran Dang Ninh (1910-55), Guerrilla Leader A9

1956, July Litho. Perf. 11¼
39	A9	5d bl grn & pale grn	5.00	2.40
40	A9	10d lilac & rose	5.00	2.40
41	A9	20d gr brn & dk gray	7.75	3.00
42	A9	100d dk blue pale bl	7.75	3.00
		Nos. 39-42 (4)	25.50	10.80

Nos. 39-42 used values are for cto. Postally used value, set $14.

Mac Thi Buoi (1927-51), Guerrilla Leader A10

1956, Nov. 3 Perf. 11¼
43	A10	1000d rose & lilac rose	100.00	100.00
44	A10	2000d brown & bister	100.00	100.00
45	A10	4000d bl grn & green	150.00	100.00
46	A10	5000d ultra & lt blue	300.00	400.00
		Nos. 43-46 (4)	650.00	700.00

Nos. 43-46 used values are for postally used. Cto value, set $100.
Counterfeits exist, often imperf and offered as proofs.

Bai Thuong Dam — A11

1956-58 Perf. 11¼
47	A11	100d vio bl & lil brn	10.00	1.90
a.		Perf 13	10.00	1.60
48	A11	200d lilac & gr grn	10.00	2.25
a.		Perf 13	10.00	1.90
49	A11	300d rose & lil brn	20.00	3.25
a.		Perf 13	20.00	2.75
		Nos. 47-49 (3)	40.00	7.40

Nos. 47-49 used values are for cto. Postally used copies are worth about 10 times these values.
Issued: #47-49, 12/15/56; #47a-49a, 1958.

No. 1L63 Surcharged

1956, Dec. Typo. Perf. 7 Rough
50	VM2	5d on 5d dp red, brnish	80.00	90.00

Reprints and counterfeits exist.

Nam Dinh Textile Mill — A13

1957, Mar. Litho. Perf. 12½
51-53	A13	100d, 200d, 300d, set of 3	27.50	3.75
51a		Perf. 11½	7.50	7.50

Nos. 51-53 used values are for cto. Postally used value, set $15.
No. 51 also exists perf 11½x12½, imperf and imperf by perf 11½.

Ho Chi Minh — A14

1957 Perf. 12½
54-57	A14	20d, 60d, 100d, 300d, set of 4	24.00 21.00

Issued: 20d, 60d, 12/13; others, 5/19.

Fourth World Trade Union Congress, Leipzig
A15

1957, Aug. 1 *Perf. 12½*
58 A15 300d red violet 10.00 3.00
See Nos. O17-O20.

Democratic Republic, 12th Anniv.
A16

1957, Sept. 2 *Perf. 13*
59-60 A16 20d, 100d, set of 2 9.00 5.00

Presidents Voroshilov, Ho Chi Minh — A17

1957, Nov. 7 *Perf. 12½*
61-63 A17 100d, 500d, set of 1000d, 3 47.50 37.50

Russian revolution, 40th anniv.

Anti-illiteracy Campaign — A18

1958, Jan. 6 *Perf. 12½*
64-66 A18 50d, 150d, 1000d, set of 3 40.00 29.00

A19   A20

1958, Mar. 8
67-68 A19 150d, 500d, set of 2 40.00 32.50
Physical education.

1958, May 1
69-70 A20 50d, 150d, set of 2 13.00 8.00
May Day.

Fourth Intl. Congress of Democratic Women, Vienna
A21

1958, May *Typo.*
71 A21 150d blue 10.00 9.00

A22

A22a

#72, 150d, #75, 2000d, Basket, lace & cup, vert. #73, 150d & #74, 1000d, Potter.

1958 *Litho.*
72-75 A22, A22a Set of 4 29.00 22.50
Arts & Crafts Fair, Hanoi.
Issued: Nos. 72, 75, 6/26; others, 8/19.

Building the Reunification Railway — A23

1958, July 20
76-77 A23 50d, 150d, set of 2 10.00 4.00

August Revolution, 13th Anniv.
A24

1958, Aug. 19
78-79 A24 150d, 500d, set of 2 8.00 6.50

Resistance Movement in South Viet Nam, 13th Anniv.
A25

1958, Sept. 23
80-81 A25 50d, 150d, set of 2 10.50 5.00

A26

1958, Oct.
82 A26 150d grnsh blue & blk 3.00 1.50
Tran Hung Dao (1253-1300),

A27

1958, Nov. 7 *Engr.* *Perf. 11½*
Hanoi Engineering Plant.
83 A27 150d brown 3.50 1.40

Mutual Aid Teams — A28

1958, Nov. 7
84-85 A28 150d, 500d, set of 2 12.00 4.50

Ngoc Son Temple (Temple of Jade) — A29

1958, Dec. 1 *Photo.* *Perf. 12*
86-87 A29 150d, 2000d, set of 2 32.50 11.00

Rattanware Cooperative
A30

1958, Dec. 31
88 A30 150d greenish blue 3.50 1.25

Ha Long Bay — A31

1959, Feb. 8
89-90 A31 150d, 350d, set of 2 8.00 3.75

Cam Pha Coal Mines — A32

1959, Mar. 3 *Engr.* *Perf. 11½*
91 A32 150d blue 7.50 .75

Trung Sisters — A33

1959, Mar. 14 *Litho.* *Perf. 11*
92-93 A33 5xu, 8xu, set of 2 9.00 6.25

World Peace Movement, 10th Anniv. — A34

1959, Apr. 15
94 A34 12xu purple, *rose* 2.50 .60

Xuan Quang Dam
A35

1959, May 1
95-96 A35 6xu, 12xu, set of 2 8.50 1.50

Phu Loi Massacre
A36

1959, May 15
97-98 A36 12xu, 20xu, set of 2 7.00 1.75

Hien Luong Bridge — A37

1959, July 20
99 A37 12xu black & carmine 3.00 1.50

Me Tri Radio Station — A38

1959, Aug. 10
100-101 A38 3xu, 12xu, set of 2 5.00 1.40

Sports
A39

Designs: 1xu, Shooting. 6xu, Swimming. 12xu, Wrestling.

1959, Sept. 2
102-104 A39 Set of 3 8.00 3.00
Size of No. 103 is 43x31mm.

People's Republic of China, 10th Anniv. — A40

1959, Oct. 1
105 A40 12xu multicolored 5.00 .70

Fruits — A41

Designs: 3xu, Coconuts. 12xu, Bananas. 30xu, Pineapple.

1959, Nov. 20
106-108 A41 Set of 3   8.00 3.50

People's Army, 15th Anniv. A42

1959, Dec. 22
109 A42 12xu multicolored   3.00 1.60

A43   A44

1960, Jan. 6
110-111 A43 2xu, 12xu, set of 2   5.50 3.00
Vietnamese Workers' Party, 30th Anniv.

1960, Jan. 6
Ethnic costumes: 2xu, Ede. 10xu, Meo. No. 114, 12xu, Tay. No. 115, 12xu, Thai.
112-115 A44 Set of 4   9.00 7.00

Census A45

Designs: 1xu, People. 12xu, Transmitting tower, dam, buildings, workers.

1960, Feb. 20
116-117 A45 Set of 2   4.00 2.75
No. 117 is 37x26mm.

Intl. Women's Day, 50th Anniv. A46

1960, Mar. 8
118 A46 12xu multicolored   2.00 1.75

A47   A48

1960, Apr. 5
119-120 A47 4xu, 12xu, set of 2   62.50 30.00
Hung Vuong Temple.

1960, Apr. 22
121-122 A48 5xu, 12xu, set of 2   5.50
121a   Souv. sheet of 1, olive brown & blue, imperf.   75.00
Lenin. No. 121a exists on brownish paper.

Election of National Assembly Delegates — A49

1960, May 3   **Perf. 11**
123 A49 12xu multicolored, *rose*   2.00 1.60

A50   A51

1960, May 8
124-125 A50 8xu, 12xu, set of 2   5.00 .95
Viet Nam Red Cross.

1960, May 19
Ho Chi Minh, 70th Birthday: Nos. 128, 130, Ho with children.
126 A51   4xu green & purple
127 A51 12xu pink & brown
128 A51 12xu multicolored
        Nos. 126-128 (3)   8.00 3.00
Souvenir Sheets
Imperf
129 A51 10xu yel bis & brn, *rose*   13.50
130 A51 10xu multicolored   12.00
No. 128 is 25x39mm.

New Constitution A52

1960, July 7
131 A52 12xu lemon & gray   3.00 1.50

National Day, 15th Anniv. A53

1960, Sept. 2
132-133 A53 4xu, 12xu, set of 2   7.50 7.00

Development — A54

Designs: No. 134, Classroom. No. 135, Plowing. No. 136, Factory.

1960, Sept. 2
134-136 A54 12xu Set of 3   13.50

3rd Vietnamese Communist Party Congress — A55

1960, Sept. 4
137-138 A55 1xu, 12xu, set of 2   6.50 3.00

World Federation of Trade Unions, 15th Anniv. — A56

1960, Oct. 3
139 A56 12xu black & vermilion   6.00 5.25

Hanoi, 950th Anniv. A57

1960, Oct. 10   **Litho.**   **Perf. 11**
140-141 A57 8xu, 12xu, set of 2   7.50 3.00
141a   Souv. sheet of 1, imperf. 15.00 14.00
No. 141a exists on brownish paper.

15 Years' Achievements Exhibition — A58

1960, Oct. 20
142-143 A58 2xu, 12xu, set of 2   4.00 2.10

World Federation of Democratic Youth, 15th Anniv. — A59

1960, Nov. 10
144 A59 12xu multicolored   3.50 3.00

Trade Unions, 2nd Natl. Congress A60

1961, Feb. 10
145 A60 12xu multicolored, *rose*   2.50 1.25

Vietnamese Women's Union, 3rd Natl. Congress — A61

1961, Mar. 8   **Tinted Paper**
146-147 A61 6xu, 12xu, set of 2   7.00 2.40

Animals — A62   Ly Tu Trong — A63

Designs: 12xu, Rusa unicolor. 20xu, Helarctos malynus. 50xu, Elephas maximus. 1d, Hylobates leucogenys.

1961, Mar. 8
148-151 A62 Set of 4   30.00 13.00
        Imperf., #148-151   *60.00 60.00*

1961, Mar. 18
152-153 A63 2xu, 12xu, set of 2   3.75 2.10
Youth Labor Union, 3rd Congress.

Young Pioneers, 20th Anniv. — A64

1961, May 2
154-155 A64 1xu, 12xu, set of 2   4.75 2.50

Intl. Red Cross — A65

1961, May 8
156-157 A65 6xu, 12xu, set of 2   8.00 3.50

Intl. Children's Day — A66

1961, June 1   **Perf. 11**
158-159 A66 4xu, 12xu, set of 2   6.00 3.00

Yuri Gagarin's Space Flight A67

1961, June 15
160-161 A67 6xu, 12xu, set of
2   24.00 10.50
Imperf., #160-161   27.50

Hanoi, Hue
and Saigon
A68

1961, July 20
162-163 A68 12xu, 3d, set of 2 22.50 17.00

A69   A70

1961, July 20
164-165 A69 12xu, 2d, set of 2 10.00 2.75
Imperf., #164-165   —

Reunification campaign.

1961, Aug. 21
166-167 A70 2xu, 12xu, set of 2 6.00 2.40
Geological exploration.

Savings
Campaign
A71

1961, Aug. 21
168-169 A71 3xu, 12xu, set of 2 5.00 1.50

Ancient
Towers — A72

Gherman Titov's
Space
Flight — A73

Designs: 6xu, Thien Mu, Hue. 10xu, Pen
Brush, Bac Ninh. No. 172, 12xu, Binh Son,
Vinh Phuc. No. 173, 12xu, Cham, Phan Rang.

1961, Sept. 12
170-173 A72 Set of 4   10.00 3.75
Imperf., #170-173   12.00

1961, Oct. 17
174-175 A73 6xu, 12xu, set of 2 8.00 3.75
Imperf., #174-175   12.00

A74   A76

Port of Haiphong — A75

1961, Oct. 17
176 A74 12xu vermilion & black 3.50 2.40
22nd Communist Party Congress, Moscow.

1961, Nov. 7
177-178 A75 5xu, 12xu, set of 2 9.50 3.00

1961, Nov. 18   *Perf. 13½*
Musicians: No. 179, 12xu, Flutist. No. 180,
12xu, Cymbalist. 30xu, Dancer with fan. 50xu,
Guitarist.

179-182 A76 Set of 4   16.00 14.00
Imperf., #179-182   20.00
182a   Souvenir sheet, #179-182   60.00

Stamps on No. 182a are se-tenant and
perfed on outside edges of the strip of 4.

5th World
Trade
Union
Congress,
Moscow
A77

1961, Dec. 4   *Perf. 11*
183 A77 12xu dp red lil & gray 2.00 .80

Natl.
Resistance,
15th Anniv.
A78

1961, Dec. 4
184-185 A78 4xu, 12xu, set of 2 2.25 2.00

Tet
Holiday — A79

Designs: 6xu, Sow, piglets. 12xu, Poultry.

1962, Jan. 16   *Litho.*
186-187 A79 Set of 2   9.00 6.00

Tet Tree-Planting
Festival — A80

1962, Jan. 16
188-189 A80 12xu, 40xu, set of 2 7.00

Crops — A81

Designs: 2xu, Camellia sinensis. 6xu,
Illicium verum. No. 192, 12xu, Coffea arabica.
No. 193, 12xu, Ricinus communis. 30xu, Rhus
succedanea.

1962, Mar. 1
190-194 A81 Set of 5   24.00 9.50

Folk
Dances — A82

Designs: No. 195, 12xu, Rong Chieng. No.
196, 12xu, Bamboo. 30xu, Hat. 50xu, Parasol.

1962, Mar. 20 Photo.   *Perf. 11½x12*
195-198 A82 Set of 4   20.00 6.00
Imperf., #195-198   20.00
Souvenir Sheet
199 A82 30xu like #195   20.00

First Five
Year
Plan — A83

Designs: 1xu, Kim Lien Apartments, Hanoi.
3xu, State farm. 8xu, Natl. Institute of
Hydraulics.

1962, Apr. 10   *Litho.*   *Perf. 11*
200-202 A83 Set of 3   3.50 3.50

A84   A85

Flowers: No. 203, 12xu, Hibiscus rosa
sinensis. No. 204, 12xu, Plumeria acutifolia.
20xu, Chrysanthemum indicum. 30xu,
Nelumbium nuciferum. 50xu, Ipomoea
pulchella.

Perf. 12½x11½
1962, Apr. 10   *Photo.*
203-207 A84 Set of 5   25.00 11.00
Imperf., #203-207   30.00
206a   Souvenir sheet of 1   15.00

1962, May 4   *Litho.*   *Perf. 11*
208 A85 12xu multicolored 3.00 3.00
3rd Natl. Heroes of Labor Congress.

Harrow
A86

Dai Lai
Lake
A87

1962, May 25
209-210 A86-A87 6xu, 12xu, set
of 2   4.00 4.00

Visit by
Gherman
Titov
A88

Titov: 12xu, Waving at children. 20xu,
Receiving medal from Ho Chi Minh. 30xu,
Wearing space suit.

1962, June 12
211-213 A88 Set of 3   8.00 6.50
Imperf., #211-213   12.00

Anti-Malaria
Campaign
A89

1962, July 9
214-216 A89 8xu, 12xu, 20xu,
set of 3   7.50 3.00

War for
Reunification — A90

1962, July 20
217 A90 12xu multicolored 3.00 1.50

Ba Be
Lake — A91

Design: No. 219, Ban Gioc Falls, vert.

1962, Aug. 14
218-219 A91 12xu Set of 2   4.00 3.25

A stamp picturing a weight lifter
exists, but was not released. Value
$100.

King Quang Trung   Nguyen Trai
(1752-92)   (1380-1442)
A92   A93

1962, Sept. 16
220-221 A92 3xu, 12xu, set of 2 3.50 2.50

1962, Sept. 19
222-223 A93 3xu, 12xu, set of 2 3.50

Food Crops
A94

Designs: 1xu, Peanuts. 4xu, Beans. 6xu,
Sweet potatoes. 12xu, Corn. 30xu, Cassava.

1962, Oct. 10
224-228 A94　Set of 5　　　　　12.00　5.00
　　　Imperf., #224-228

Animal
Husbandry
A95

Designs: 2xu, Feeding poultry. No. 230,
12xu, Feeding pigs. No. 231, 12xu, Cattle
grazing. No. 232, 12xu, Tending water buffalo.

1962, Nov. 28
229-232 A95　Set of 4　　　　　7.00　3.50

A stamp commemorating the 45th
anniversary of the Russian Revolution
exists, but was not issued. Value $200.

First Five
Year Plan
A96

#233, Evening classes. #234, Clearing land.

1962, Dec. 28
233-234 A96　12xu Set of 2　　　5.00　2.00

Flights of
Vostok 3 and
4 — A97

12xu, Pavel Popovich, Vostok 4. 20xu, And-
rian Nikolayev, Vostok 3. 30xu, Rockets lifting-
off, vert.

1962, Dec. 28　　　　　　　**Perf. 11**
235-237 A97　Set of 3　　　　6.00　2.75
　　　Imperf., #235-237　　　　12.00

Guerrilla
A98

Hoang Hoa Tham
(1846-1913)
A99

1963, Jan. 15
238-239 A98　5xu, 12xu, set of 2　2.75　1.50

1963, Feb. 10
240-241 A99　6xu, 12xu, set of 2　3.00　1.40

A100

First Five
Year Plan
A100a

Designs: No. 242, Fertilizing rice paddy. No.
243, Lam Thao superphosphate plant.

1963, Feb. 25
242-243 A100-A100a 12xu Set of
　　　　　　　　　2　3.50　1.50

Karl Marx — A101

1963, Mar. 14
244-245 A101 3xu, 12xu, set of 2 3.25 1.50
　　　Nos. 244-245 are printed on greenish and
rose toned paper respectively.

Fidel Castro,
Vietnamese
Soldiers
A102

1963, Apr. 17
246 A102 12xu multicolored　　2.00　1.00

May
Day
A103

1963, May 8
247 A103 12xu multicolored　　2.00　1.00

A104

Intl. Red Cross,
Cent. — A105

Design: No. 249, Child, syringe.

1963, May 8
248 A104 12xu grn, blk & red
249 A104 12xu grn, red & blk
250 A105 20xu multicolored
　　　Nos. 248-250 (3)　7.00

Mars 1 Spacecraft — A106

6xu, 12xu (#252), Mars 1 approaching
Mars. 12xu (#253), 20xu, Mars 1 entering
orbit, vert.

1963, May 21
251-254 A106　Set of 4　　　　7.00　5.00
　　　Imperf., #251-254　　　　15.00

Fishing
Industry
A107

Designs: No. 255, Trawler, offshore fish. No.
256, Freshwater fish.

1963, July 3
255-256 A107 12xu Set of 2　　10.50　6.00

Ho Chi Minh,
Nguyen Van
Hien — A108

1963, July 20
257 A108 12xu multicolored　　2.50　1.75

Flights
of
Vostok
3, 4
A109

Designs: 12xu, Rockets in orbit. 20xu, Nikolayev. 30xu, Popovich.

1963, Aug. 11
258-260 A109　Set of 3　　　　7.00　6.00
　　　Imperf., #258-260　　　　13.00

First Five
Year Plan
for
Chemical
Industry
A110

Designs: 3xu, Viet Tri Insecticide Factory.
12xu, Viet Tri Chemical Factory.

1963, Aug. 11
261-262 A110　Set of 2　　　　3.00　2.00

Fish
A111

Designs: No. 263, 12xu, Cyprinus carpio.
No. 264, 12xu, Myloharyngodon piceus. No.
265, 12xu, Hypophthalmichthys molitrix. 20xu,
Ophiocephalus caqua. 30xu, Tilapia
mossambica.

1963, Sept. 10
263-267 A111　Set of 5　　　17.00　7.75
　　　Imperf., #263-267　　　17.00
　　a.　Souvenir Sheet 0f 1, #266　67.50

A112

A113

Birds: #268, 12xu, Francolinus stephenson.
#269, 12xu, Acridotheres cristatellus. #270,
12xu, Halcyon smyrneusis. 20xu, Diardigallus
diardi, horiz. 30xu, Egretta. 40xu, Psittacula
alexandri.

Perf. 11½x12, 12x11½
1963, Oct. 15　　　　　　　**Photo.**
268-273 A112　Set of 6　　　35.00　15.00
　　　Imperf., #268-273　　　45.00
　　　Souvenir Sheet
274 A112 50xu Sheet of 1, like
　　　　　　#272　　　　　85.00

1963, Oct. 20　　**Litho.**　**Perf. 11**
275 A113 12xu multicolored　　2.00　1.00
　World Federation of Trade Unions Congress
for Viet Nam.

GANEFO
Games
A114

#276, 12xu, Swimming. #277, 12xu, Volley-
ball, vert. #278, 12xu, Soccer, vert. 30xu, High
jump.

1963, Nov. 10
276-279 A114　Set of 4　　　　5.00　5.00
　　　Imperf., #276-279　　　6.00

A115　　　　　A116

Flowers: 6xu, Rauwolfia verticillata. No. 281,
12xu, Sophora japonica. No. 282, 12xu,
Fibraurea tinctoria. No. 283, 12xu, Cheno-
podium ambrosioides. 20xu, Momordica
cochinchinensis.

1963, Dec. 3
280-284 A115　Set of 5　　　　7.50　3.75
　　　Imperf., #280-284　　　10.00

1963, Dec. 20
285 A116 12xu multicolored　　2.50　1.00
　　　World Day for Viet Nam.

A117

First Five-Year
Plan — A118

6xu, Molten cast iron. #287, 12xu, Thai Nguyen Steel & Iron Works. #288, 12xu, Power lines.

1964, Jan. 25 **Litho.**
286-288 A117-A118 Set of 3 4.50 1.75

Intl. Quiet Sun Year — A119

1964, Jan. 25
289-290 A119 12xu, 50xu, set of 2 5.00 3.00
        Imperf., #289-290 20.00

Flights of Vostok 5 and 6 A120

#291, 12xu, Rockets in orbit. #292, 12xu, Valery Bykovsky. 30xu, Valentina Tereshkova.

1964, Mar. 25
291-293 A120 Set of 3 6.00 5.00
        Imperf., #291-293 12.00

A stamp commemorating the anniversary of the founding of the People's Democratic Republic of Korea was printed but not issued.

A121   A122

Flowers: No. 294, 12xu, Persica vulgaris. No. 295, 12xu, Hibiscus mutabilis. No. 296, 12xu, Passiflora hispida. No. 297, 12xu, Saraca dives. 20xu, Michelia champaca. 30xu, Camellia amplexicaulis.

1964, Apr. 10 **Perf. 11½x12**
294-299 A121 Set of 6 13.00 5.00
        Imperf., #294-299 15.00

1964, Apr. 27 **Perf. 11**
Costumes: 6xu, Peasant, 19th cent. No. 301, 12xu, Woman wearing large hat, 19th cent. No. 302, 12xu, Woman carrying hat.
300-302 A122 Set of 3 5.00 3.00

Battle of Dien Bien Phu, 10th Anniv. A123

Designs: 3xu, Artillery. 6xu, Machine gun emplacement. Nos. 305, 307c, Bomb disposal. Nos. 306, 307d, Farmer on tractor.

1964, May 7
303 A123 3xu red & black
304 A123 6xu blue & black
305 A123 12xu yel org & blk
306 A123 12xu red lilac & black
        Nos. 303-306 (4) 7.50 6.00
        Imperf., #303-306 11.00

Souvenir Sheet
Imperf
307 Sheet of 4 12.50
  a. A123 3xu orange & black
  b. A123 6xu yellow green & black
  c. A123 12xu red, black & orange
  d. A123 12xu blue & black

Ham Rong Bridge — A124

1964, May 17
308 A124 12xu multicolored 2.50 1.00

Wild Animals A125

Designs: No. 309, 12xu, Panthera tigris, vert. No. 310, 12xu, Pseudaxis axis, vert. No. 311, 12xu, Tapirus indicus. 20xu, Bubalus bubalis. 30xu, Rhinoceros bicornis. 40xu, Bibos banteng.

1964, June 2 **Perf. 10½**
309-314 A125 Set of 6 16.00 13.00
        Imperf., #309-314 14.00

Geneva Agreement on Viet Nam, 10th Anniv. A126

Intl. Labor Federation Committee United with People of South Viet Nam — A127

1964, July 20 **Perf. 11**
315-316 A126-A127 12xu Set of 2 3.00 1.50

Nam Bac Ninh Pumping Station A128

1964, Aug. 25
317 A128 12xu blue gray & black 1.75 .80

Liberation of Hanoi, 10th Anniv. — A129

6xu, People cheering soldiers in truck. 12xu, Construction, hammerhead crane.

1964, Oct. 10
318-319 A129 Set of 2 3.50 2.50

Natl. Defense Games — A130

Designs: 5xu, Rowing. No. 321, 12xu, Parachuting, vert. No. 322, 12xu, Gliders, vert. No. 323, 12xu, Shooting.

1964, Oct. 18
320-323 A130 Set of 4 6.50 2.50

Fruits — A131

Designs: No. 324, 12xu, Mangifera indica. No. 325, 12xu, Guarcinia mangostana. No. 326, 12xu, Nephelium litchi. 20xu, Anona squamosa. 50xu, Citrus medica.

1964, Oct. 31 Photo. Perf. 11½x12
324-328 A131 Set of 5 12.50 4.75
        Imperf., #324-328 15.00

World Solidarity Conference — A132

Designs: a, Ba Dinh Hall. b, Vietnamese soldier shaking hands with foreign people. c, Fist, planes, submarine.

1964, Nov. 25 Litho. Perf. 11
329 A132 12xu Strip of 3, #a.-c. 4.50 3.00

People's Army, 20th Anniv. A133

Designs: No. 330, Soldiers, flag. No. 331a, Coast guards. No. 331b, Mounted border guards, vert.

1964, Dec. 22
330 A133 12xu multicolored
331 A133 12xu Pair, #a.-b.
        Nos. 330-331 (2) 5.00 1.25

Cuban Revolution, 6th Anniv. — A134

Designs: a, Vietnamese, Cuban flags. b, Cuban revolutionaries.

1965, Jan. 1
332 A134 12xu Pair, #a.-b. 4.50 3.00

Economic & Cultural Development of Mountain Region — A135

Designs: 2xu, 3xu, Women pollinating corn. 12xu, Girls walking to school.

1965, Jan. 1
333-335 A135 Set of 3 3.00 2.50
        Imperf., #333-335

A136

Vietnamese Worker's Party, 35th Anniv. — A137

Politicians: No. 336a, Le Hong Phong. b, Tran Phu. c, Hoang Van Thu. d, Ngo Gia Tu. e, Nguyen Van Cu.
No. 337a, Party flag. b, Worker, soldier.

1965 **Litho.** **Perf. 11**
336 A136 6xu Strip of 5, #a.-e.
337 A137 12xu Pair, #a.-b.
        Nos. 336-337 (2) 5.00 4.75
        Issued: No. 336, 2/3; No. 337, 1/30.

Transportation Ministers Conference, Hanoi — A138

12xu, 30xu, Nguyen Van Troi, locomotive.

1965, Mar. 23
338-339 A138 Set of 2 7.00 2.00
        Imperf., #338-339

Vignette on No. 339 is mirror image of No. 338.

Flight of Voskhod 1 — A139

20xu, Cosmonauts Komarov, Feoktistov, Yegorov, rocket, globe. 1d, Cosmonauts, rocket.

1965, Mar. 30
340-341 A139 Set of 2 9.00 9.00
        Imperf., #340-341 11.00

Lenin, 95th
Birth Anniv.
A140

1965, Apr. 22   **Litho.**
342-343 A140 8xu, 12xu, set of 2   4.00

A141

A142

1965, May 19
344-345 A141 6xu, 12xu, set of 2   2.50 1.90
    Ho Chi Minh, 75th birthday.

1965, May 19
346 A142 12xu multicolored   2.50 2.00
    Afro-Asian Conference, 10th anniv.

Trade Union Conference,
Hanoi — A143

    Designs: No. 347, Workers solidarity. No. 348, Soldiers, vert. No. 349, Naval battle.

1965, June 2
347-349 A143 12xu Set of 3   4.50

Wild Animals — A144

    Designs: No. 350, 12xu, Martes flavigula. No. 351, 12xu, Chrotogale owstoni. No. 352, 12xu, Manis pentadactyla. No. 353, 12xu, Presbytis delacouri, vert. 20xu, Petaurista lylei, vert. 50xu, Nycticebus pygmaeus, vert.

1965, June 24   **Photo.**   **Perf. 12**
350-355 A144   Set of 6   17.00 5.50
    Imperf., #350-355   25.00

A145

A146

1965, July 1   **Perf. 11½x11**
356 A145 12xu multicolored   3.50 .40
    6th Socialist Postal Ministers Conference.

1965, July 20   **Litho.**   **Perf. 11**
    Nguyen Van Troi (1940-64). Denominations: 12xu, 50xu, 4d.
357-359 A146   Set of 3   9.00 6.00

A147

Insects — A148

    Designs: No. 360, 12xu, Tessaratoma papillosa. No. 361, 12xu, Rhynchocoris humeralis. No. 362, 12xu, Poeciliocoris latus.
    No. 363, 12xu, Tosena melanoptera. 20xu, Cicada. 30xu, Fulgora candelaria.

1965, July 24   **Photo.**
360-362 A147   Set of 3
363-365 A148   Set of 3
    Nos. 360-365 (6)   12.00 7.00
    Imperf., #360-365   18.00

August
Revolution,
20th Anniv.
A149

1965, Aug. 19   **Litho.**
366-367 A149 6xu, 12xu, set of 2   3.00 1.75

Crustaceans — A150

    Designs: No. 368, 12xu, Penaeus indicus. No. 369, 12xu, Scylla serrata. No. 370, 12xu, Metapenaeus joyneri. No. 371, 12xu, Neptunus. 20xu, Palinurus japonicus. 50xu, Uca marionis.

1965, Aug. 19
368-373 A150   Set of 6   20.00 8.00
    Imperf., #368-373   20.00

500th US
Warplane Shot
Down — A151

1965, Aug. 30
374 A151 12xu gray green & lilac   7.00 5.50

A152

Completion of 1st
Five-Year
Plan — A153

    #375, Foundry worker. #376, Electricity, irrigation. #377, Public health, education. #377, Students, children playing. #378, Factory worker. #379, Agricultural workers.

1965
375-377 A152 12xu Set of 3   3.50 1.75
378-380 A153 12xu Set of 3   3.50 1.75
    Imperf., #375-380
    Issued: #375-377, 9/2; #378-380, 12/25.

Nghe An, Ha Tinh Uprising, 35th
Anniv. — A154

1965, Sept. 12
381-382 A154 10xu, 12xu, set of 2   2.50 1.65
    Imperf., #381-382

Friendship Between Viet Nam,
People's Republic of China, 16th
Anniv. — A155

    Designs: No. 383, Youth holding flags, Friendship Gate. No. 384, Children waving flags, walking through Gate, vert.

1965, Oct. 1
383-384 A155 12xu Set of 2   10.00 1.75

Flight of Voskhod 2 — A156

    #385, 12xu, Konstantin Tsiolkovsky, Sputnik I. #386, 12xu, Voskhod 2, A. Leonov, P.

Belyayev. #387, 50xu, Yuri Gagarin. #388, 50xu, Leonov walking in space.

1965, Oct. 5
385-388 A156 Set of 4   8.00 3.25
    Imperf., #385-388

A157

A158

    Norman R. Morrison, US anti-war demonstration.

1965, Nov. 22
389 A157 12xu black & red   2.50 1.25

1965, Nov. 25
    Nguyen Du (1765-1820), poet: No. 390, 12xu, Birthplace. No. 391, 12xu, Museum. 20xu, Volume of poems entitled Kieu. 1d, Scene from Kieu.
390-393 A158 Set of 4   6.00 5.00

A159

    Designs: No. 394, 12xu, Ho Chi Minh. No. 395, 12xu, Karl Marx. No. 396, 12xu, Lenin. 50xu, Frederich Engels.

Litho. & Engr. (#394), Litho.
1965, Nov. 28   **Perf. 11½**
394-397 A159 Set of 4   6.00 6.00
    Nos. 395-397 have white border.

Butterflies
A160

    #398, 12xu, Cethosia cyane. #399, 12xu, Zelides sarpedon. #400, 12xu, Cethosia. #401, 12xu, Apatura ambica. 20xu, Papilio paris. 30xu, Tros aristolochiae.

1965, Nov. 28   **Litho.**   **Perf. 11**
398-403 A160 Set of 6   21.00 6.50
    Imperf., #398-403   55.00

South Viet Nam Natl. Liberation Front, 5th Anniv. — A161

1965, Dec. 20
404 A161 12xu lilac 2.50 1.25
Imperf.

1st General Elections, 20th Anniv. — A162

1966, Jan. 6
405 A162 12xu black & red 2.50 1.25

A163 A164

Orchids: No. 406, 12xu, Vanda teres. No. 407, 12xu, Dendrobium meschatum. No. 408, 12xu, Dendrobium nobile. No. 409, 12xu, Dendrobium crystallinum. 20xu, Vandopsis gigantea. 30xu, Dendrobium.

1966, Jan. 10 *Perf. 12*
406-411 A163 Set of 6 12.00 5.50
Imperf., #406-411 20.00

1966, Jan. 18 *Perf. 11*
412 A164 12xu multicolored 2.50 1.00
Imperf.

New Year 1966 (Year of the Horse).

Reptiles A165

#413, 12xu, Physignathus cocincinus. #414, 12xu, Gekko gecko. #415, 12xu, Trionyx sinensis. #416, 12xu, Testudo elongata. 20xu, Varanus salvator. 40xu, Eretmochelys imbricata.

1966, Feb. 25 *Perf. 12x11½*
413-418 A165 Set of 6 12.00 6.00
Imperf., #413-418 20.00

Natl. Sports A166

Designs: No. 419, Archery. No. 420, Wrestling. No. 421, Spear fighting.

1966, Mar. 25 *Perf. 11*
419-421 A166 12xu Set of 3 5.00 2.75

6xu, 12xu, 1d stamps for running, swimming and shooting were printed but not issued.

Youth Labor Union, 35th Anniv. — A167

1966, Mar. 26
422 A167 12xu multicolored 2.00 2.00

1000th US Warplane Shot Down — A168

1966, Apr. 29
423 A168 12xu multicolored 7.50 4.00

May Day — A169

1966, May 1
424 A169 6xu multicolored 2.00 .65

Defending Con Co Island — A170

1966, June 1
425 A170 12xu multicolored 2.50 1.50

A171

A172

1966, June 1
426 A171 12xu red & black 1.75 1.00
Young Pioneers, 25th anniv.

1966, July 1
Designs: 3xu, View of Yenan. 12xu, Ho Chi Minh, Mao Tse-Tung.
427-428 A172 Set of 2 4.00 .75
Imperf., #427-428

Chinese Communist Party, 45th anniv.

A173

A174

Luna 9: 12xu, Flight path to moon. 50xu, In lunar orbit.

1966, Aug. 5
429-430 A173 Set of 2 7.50 3.00
Imperf., #429-430 10.00

1966, Oct. 10
431 A174 12xu multicolored 10.00 3.00
With Additional Inscription: "NGAY 14.10.1966"
431A A174 12xu multicolored 15.00 3.75
Imperf., #431-431A

1500th US warplane shot down.

Victory in Dry Season Campaign — A175

Designs: 1xu, 12xu (No. 433), Woman guerrilla carrying guns. 12xu (No. 434), Soldier escorting prisoners of war.

1966, Oct. 15
432-434 A175 Set of 3 5.00 2.25
Imperf., #432-434

Vietnamese Women's Union, 20th Anniv. — A176

1966, Oct. 20
435 A176 12xu orange & black 1.00 .70
Imperf.

Birds A177

Designs: No. 436, 12xu, Pitta moluccensis. No. 437, 12xu, Psarisomus dolhousiae. Nos. 438, 12xu, Alcedo atthis, vert. No. 439, 12xu, Oriolus chinensis, vert. 20xu, Upupa epops, vert. 30xu, Oriolus traillii.

1966, Oct. 31 *Perf. 12x12½, 12½x12*
436-441 A177 Set of 6 10.00 5.00
Imperf., #436-441 25.00

GANEFO Asian Games — A178

Designs: No. 442, Soccer. No. 443, Shooting. No. 444, Swimming. No. 445, Running.

1966, Nov. 25 *Perf. 11*
442-445 Set of 4 6.00 4.00
Imperf., #442-445 9.00
443a A178 12xu Pair, #442-443
445a A178 30xu Pair, #444-445
Nos. 443a, 445a
(4) 8.50

Ho Chi Minh's Appeal for Natl. Resistance, 20th Anniv. — A179

Designs: No. 446, Flags, workers. No. 447, Soldiers, workers, ships.

1967, Jan. 30
446-447 A179 12xu Set of 2 2.00 1.75
See Nos. 501-504.

Rice Harvest A180

1967, Jan. 30
448 A180 12xu multicolored 1.50 1.40

Bamboo
A181

#449, 12xu, Bambusa arundinaceu. #450, 12xu, Arundinaria rolleana. #451, 12xu, Arundinaria racemosa. #452, 12xu, Bambusa bingami. 30xu, Bambusa nutans. 50xu, Dendrocalamus petellaris.

1967, Feb. 2   *Perf. 12x11½*
449-454 A181 Set of 6   9.00 7.25
   Imperf., #449-454   12.00

Wild Animals — A182

Designs: No. 455, 12xu, Cuon rutilans. No. 456, 12xu, Arctictis binturong. No. 457, 12xu, Arctonyx collaris. 20xu, Viverra zibetha. 40xu, Macaca speciosa. 50xu, Neofelis nebulosa.

1967, Mar. 26   Litho.   *Perf. 12*
455-460 A182 Set of 6   11.00 6.00
   Imperf., #455-460   13.00

2000th US
Aircraft Shot
Down — A183

1967, June 7   *Perf. 11*
461-462 A183 6xu, 12xu, set
              of 2 10.00   8.00

Fish
A184

#463, 12xu, Saurida filamentosa. #464, 12xu, Scomberomorus niphonius. #465, 12xu, Haplogenys mucronatus. 20xu, Lethrinus haematopterus. 30xu, Formio niger. 50xu, Lutianus erythropterus.

1967, July 25   *Perf. 12*
463-468 A184 Set of 6   11.00 9.75
   Imperf., #463-468   13.00

A185   A186

Launch of 1st Chinese ballistic missile: 12xu, Missile, flag, agricultural scene. 30xu, Missile, Gate of Heavenly Peace.

1967, July 25   *Perf. 11*
469-470 A185 Set of 2   7.50 3.00
   Imperf., #469-470

1967, Oct. 15

Russian October Revolution, 50th anniv.: 6xu, Lenin, revolutionary soldiers. No. 472a, 12xu, Lenin, armed mob. No. 472b, 12xu, Lenin, Marx, Vietnamese soldiers. 20xu, Cruiser Aurora.

471-473 A186 Set of 4   4.00 3.00

No. 472 is printed se-tenant.

2500th US Warplane Shot
Down — A187

Design: No. 475, Plane in flames, vert.

1967, Nov. 6
474-475 A187 12xu Set of 2   9.00 8.00

1st Chinese Hydrogen Bomb
Test — A188

Designs: 12xu, Atomic symbol, Gate of Heavenly Peace. 20xu, Chinese lantern, atomic symbol, dove.

1967, Nov. 20
476-477 A188 Set of 2   5.00 3.00
   Imperf., #476-477   32.50

No. 477 is 30x35mm.

A189

#478, 12xu, Rifle fire from trenches. #479, 12xu, Militia with captured US pilot. #480, 12xu, Factory anti-aircraft unit. #481, 12xu, Naval anti-aircraft unit. 20xu, Aerial dog-fight. 30xu, Heavy anti-aircraft battery.

1967, Dec. 19   *Perf. 12*
478-483 A189 Set of 6   6.00 4.75

Chickens — A190

Designs: No. 484, 12xu, White spotted cock, hen. No. 485, 12xu, Black hens. No. 486, 12xu, Bantam cock, hen. No. 487, 12xu, Bantam cock. 20xu, Fighting cocks. 30xu, Exotic hen. 40xu, Hen, chicks from Ho region. 50xu, Dong Cao's cock, hen.

1968, Feb. 29
484-491 A190 Set of 8   11.00 5.00
   Imperf., #484-491   17.50

Victories of 1966-67 — A191

No. 492: a, Soldier attacking US tank. b, Gunner firing on US ships. c, Burning village. d, Soldier firing mortar.
No. 493: a, Attacking US artillery. b, Escorting US prisoners. c, Interrogating refugees. d, Civilian demonstration.

1968, Mar. 5   *Perf. 11*
492-493 A191 12xu, 2 blocks of 4 6.00 6.00
   Imperf., #492-493

Maxim Gorki (1868-1936) — A192

1968, Mar. 5
494 A192 12xu brown & black   1.50 .80
   Imperf.

Roses — A193

Designs: No. 495, 12xu, Pale red. No. 496, 12xu, Orange. No. 497, 12xu, Pink. 20xu, Yellow, 30xu, Dark red. 40xu, Lilac.

1968, Apr. 25   Photo.   *Perf. 11½x12*
495-500 A193 Set of 6   12.00 12.00
   Imperf., #495-500   16.00

Ho Chi Minh's Appeal for Resistance
Type

Values and colors: No. 501, 6xu, greenish blue and yellow. No. 502, 12xu, vermilion. No. 503, 12xu, bright blue. No. 504, 12xu, brownish lilac.

1968, Apr. 25   Litho.   *Perf. 11*
           Size: 25x17mm
501-504 A179 6xu, 12xu Set of 4 6.00 3.00
   Imperf., #501-504

Ho Chi
Minh, Flag
A195

1968, May 19
505 A195 12xu brown & red   2.00 .50
   Imperf.

Karl
Marx — A196

1968, May 19
506 A196 12xu olive grn & blk   1.75 .25

3000th
US
Warplane
Shot
Down
A197

#507: a, 12xu, Anti-aircraft machine gunners. b, 12xu, Women firing anti-aircraft gun. #508: a, 40xu, Vietnamese plane shooting down US plane. b, 40xu, Anti-aircraft missile.

1968, May 19
507-508 A197 Set of 2 pairs   14.00 10.00
   Imperf., #507-508

Handicrafts — A198

6xu, Rattan products. #510, 12xu, Ceramics. #511, 12xu, Bamboo products. 20xu, Ivory carving. 30xu, Lacquerware. 40xu, Silverware.

1968, July 5   *Perf. 12*
509-514 A198 Set of 6   6.50 6.00
   Imperf., #509-514   15.00

Martial Arts
A199

Designs: No. 515, 12xu, Saber fencing. No. 516, 12xu, Stick fighting. No. 517, 12xu, Dagger fighting. 30xu, Unarmed combat. 40xu, Chinese war sword fighting. 50xu, Duel with swords, shields.

1968, Nov. 1
515-520 A199 Set of 6 10.00 9.00
Imperf., #515-520 16.00

Architecture — A200

Designs: No. 521, 12xu, Khue Van tower, vert. No. 522, 12xu, Bell tower, Keo pagoda, vert. 20xu, Covered bridge, Thay pagoda. 30xu, One-pillar pagoda, Hanoi, vert. 40xu, Gateway, Ninh Phuc pagoda. 50xu, Tay Phuong pagoda.

1968, Nov. 5
521-526 A200 Set of 6 6.00 5.75
Imperf., #521-526 10.00

Foreign Solidarity with Viet Nam — A201

#527, 12xu, Latin American guerrilla, vert. #528, 12xu, Cuban, Vietnamese militia. 20xu, Asian, African, Latin American soldiers, vert.

**1968, Dec. 15 Wmk. 376 Perf. 12½
With Gum**
527-529 A201 Set of 3 4.00 3.00

Scenes of War
A202

Artworks: No. 530, 12xu, Defending the mines. No. 531, 12xu, Plowman with rifle, vert. 30xu, Repairing railway track. 40xu, Wreckage of US aircraft.

**1968, Dec. 15 Wmk. 376 Perf. 12½
With Gum**
530-533 A202 Set of 4 4.00 3.75

Victories in South Viet Nam — A203

#534, 12xu, Tay Nguyen throwing grenade. #535, 12xu, Gun crews, Tri Thien. #536, 12xu, Nam Ngai shooting down US aircraft. 40xu, Insurgents, Tay Ninh, destroyed US armor. 50xu, Guerrillas preparing bamboo spike booby traps.

1969, Feb. 16 Unwmk. Perf. 11½
534-538 A203 Set of 5 6.00 6.00

Timber Industry
A204

Designs: 6xu, Loading timber trucks. No. 540, 12xu, Log raft running rapids. No. 541,

12xu, Launch towing log raft. No. 542, 12xu, Elephant hauling timber. No. 543, 12xu, Forest protection. 20xu, Water buffalo hauling log. 30xu, Hauling logs by overhead cable.

1969, Apr. 10
539-545 A204 Set of 7 9.00 8.75
Imperf., #539-545 15.00

Scenes of War — A205

Designs: No. 546, 12xu, Young guerrilla. No. 547, 12xu, Scout on patrol. 20xu, Female guerrilla, vert. 30xu, Halt at way station. 40xu, After a skirmish. 50xu, Liberated hamlet.

Perf. 12½x11½, 11½x12½
1969, July 20
546-551 A205 Set of 6 8.00 5.50
Imperf., #546-551 15.00

Tet Offensive Battles — A206

Designs: 8xu, 12xu (No. 553), Ben Tre. No. 554, 12xu, Mortar crew, Khe Sanh, vert. No. 555, 12xu, Two soldiers, flag, Hue, vert. No. 556, 12xu, Soldier running toward US Embassy, Saigon, vert.

1969, July 31 Perf. 11
552-556 A206 Set of 5 3.50 2.25
Imperf., #552-556

Liberation of Hanoi, 15th Anniv.
A207

#557, Soldier with flamethrower. #558, Children constructing toy buildings.

1969, Oct. 10
557-558 A207 12xu Set of 2 3.50 1.75
Imperf., #557-558

A208

A209

1969, Oct. 10
559 A208 12xu brn, blk & red 2.50 .80
Imperf.

Bertrand Russell Intl. War Crimes Tribunal, Stockholm and Roskilde.

1969, Nov. 20 Perf. 12
Fruits: No. 560, 12xu, Papaya. No. 561, 12xu, Grapefruit. 20xu, Tangerines. 30xu, Oranges. 40xu, Lychee nuts. 50xu, Persimmons.
560-565 A209 Set of 6 5.50 2.75
Imperf., #560-565 8.50

Viet Nam Labor Party, 40th Anniv. — A210

Designs: No. 566, Nguyen Ai Quoc. No. 567, Ho Chi Minh. No. 568, Le Hong Phong. No. 569, Tran Phu. No. 570, Nguyen Van Cu.

1970, Feb. 3 Perf. 11
566-570 A210 12xu Set of 5 5.00 4.00
Imperf., #566-570

Nos. 568-570 are 40x25mm. Nos. 566-567 issued in vert. or horiz. se-tenant pairs. Nos. 568-570 issued in horizontal strips of 3.

Children's Activities — A211

Designs: No. 571, 12xu, Playing with toys. No. 572, 12xu, Three boys at kindergarten. No. 573, 20xu, Tending a garden. No. 574, 20xu, Tending water buffaloes. 30xu, Feeding chickens. 40xu, Piano, violin duet. 50xu, Flying model airplane. 60xu, Walking to school.

1970, Mar. 8 Perf. 12
571-578 A211 Set of 8 6.50 6.50
For overprints see Nos. 2181-2188.

Lenin, Birth Centenary
A212

Designs: 12xu, Making speech. 1d, Portrait.

1970, Apr. 22 Perf. 11
579-580 A212 Set of 2 4.00 3.75
Imperf., #579-580

Shells
A213

No. 581, 12xu, On con lon. No. 582, 12xu, Oc xa cu. 20xu, Oc tien. 1d, Oc tu va.

1970, Apr. 26 Perf. 12½x12
581-584 A213 Set of 4 6.50 6.00
Imperf., #581-584 10.00

Ho Chi Minh — A214

12xu (#585, 588c, 588g), In 1930 (full face, no beard). 12xu (#586, 588b, 588f), In 1945 (facing right, beard). 2d, 6xu, (#587, 588a, 588e), In 1969 (full face, beard).

1970, May 19 Perf. 11
585-587 A214 Set of 3 4.75 4.50
Imperf., #585-587
**Souvenir Sheets of 3
Imperf**
588 Types of #585-587, #a.-c.,
  orange background 7.00
588D Types of #585-587, #e.-g.,
  pale lilac background 7.50

Stamps in souvenir sheets have white backgrounds. The 6xu stamp is larger than the 2d stamp. Nos. 588a and 588e, 588c and 588g are different colors.

Vietcong Flag
A215

1970, June 6
589 A215 12xu multicolored 1.50 .75
Formation of Revolutionary Provisional Government of South Viet Nam, 1st anniv.

Fruits and Vegetables
A216

#590, 12xu, Watermelon. #591, 12xu, Pumpkin. 20xu, Cucumber. 50xu, Zucchini. 1d, Melon.

1970, July 15 Perf. 12
590-594 A216 Set of 5 6.00 6.00
Imperf., #590-594 13.00

Consumer Industries — A217

#595, Coal miners, truck. #596, Power linesman, vert. #597, Textile worker, soldier, vert. #598, Stoker, power plant, vert.

Perf. 12x11½, 11½x12
1970, Aug. 25 Litho. & Engr.
595-598 A217 12xu Set of 4 3.25 3.25

Agriculture
A218

1970, Aug. 25   **Litho.**   *Perf. 11*
599 A218 12xu multicolored   2.00 .75

Democratic Republic of Viet Nam, 25th
Anniv. — A219

Famous people: #600, 12xu, Vo Thi Sau facing firing squad. #601, 12xu, Nguyen Van Troi, captors. #602, 12xu, Phan Din Giot attacking pillbox. #603, 12xu, Ho Chi Minh. 20xu, Nguyen Viet Xuan, troops in battle. 1d, Nguyen Van Be attacking tank with mine.

1970, Sept. 2
600-605 A219 Set of 6   4.00 3.75
   Imperf., #600-605

No. 603 is 41x28mm.

Indo-Chinese People's Summit
Conf. — A220

1970, Oct. 25
606 A220 12xu multicolored   2.50 .70
   Imperf.

Bananas
A221

Designs: No. 607, 12xu, Tay. No. 608, 12xu, Tieu. 50xu, Ngu. 1d, Mat.

1970, Oct. 25   *Perf. 12*
607-610 A221 Set of 4   7.00 4.00
   Imperf., #607-610   10.00

Friedrich Engels — A222

1970, Nov. 28   *Perf. 11*
611-612 A222 12xu, 1d, set of 2   3.25 3.00

Snakes
A223

Designs: 12xu, Akistrodon ciatus. 20xu, Calliophis macclellandii. 50xu, Bungarus faciatus. 1d, Trimeresurus gramineus.

1970, Nov. 30   **Photo.**   *Perf. 12x11½*
613-616 A223 Set of 4   6.00 5.00
   Imperf., #613-616   20.00

Natl. Liberation Front of South Viet
Nam, 10th Anniv. — A224

Design: 6xu, Mother and child, flag, vert.

1970, Dec. 20   **Litho.**   *Perf. 11*
617-618 A224 Set of 2   2.50 1.65
   Imperf., #617-618

Launching of 1st Chinese Satellite, 1st
Anniv. — A225

1971, Apr. 10
619-620 A225 12xu, 50xu Set of 2   5.00 2.00
   Imperf., #619-620

Ho Chi
Minh
A226

Denominations: 1xu, 3xu, 10xu, 12xu.

1971, May 19
621-624 A226 Set of 4   2.00 1.75
   Imperf., #621-624
624a   Souvenir sheet of 1, imperf.   6.00
No. 624a contains one 52x52mm stamp.

Tay Son Uprising, Bicent. — A227

1971, June 1
625-626 A227 6xu, 12xu, set of 2 2.50 1.65
   Imperf., #625-626

Marx, Music for The
Internationale — A228

1971, June 20   *Perf. 12½*
627 A228 12xu org, blk & red   1.00 .75
   Imperf.

Paris Commune, cent.

Hai
Thuong
Lan Ong,
Physician,
250th Birth
Anniv.
A229

1971, July 1
628-629 A229 12xu, 50xu Set of 2   3.50 2.00
   Imperf., #628-629

Statues from
Tay Phuong
Pagoda
A230

Designs: No. 630, 12xu, Vasumitri. No. 631, 12xu, Kapimala. No. 632, 12xu, Dhikaca. No. 633, 12xu, Sangkayasheta. 30xu, Bouddha Nandi. 40xu, Rahulata. 50xu, Sangha Nandi. 1d, Cakyamuni.

1971, July 30   **Photo.**   *Perf. 12*
630-637 A230 Set of 8   11.00 11.00
   Imperf., #630-637   15.00

Ho Chi Minh
Working Youth
Union, 40th
Anniv.
A231

1971, Sept. 7   **Litho.**   *Perf. 11*
638 A231 12xu multicolored   1.50 .75
   Imperf.

Flight of Luna
16 — A232

Luna 16: No. 639a, 12xu, Return from Moon. No. 639b, 12xu, Flight to Moon. 1d, On Moon.

1971, Sept. 17
639-640 A232 Set of 3   4.00 3.50
   Imperf., #639-640   12.00

No. 639 is setenant.

Flight
of
Luna
17
A233

Designs: No. 641, 12xu, Landing on Moon, vert. No. 642 12xu, On Moon. 1d, Lunakhod 1 crossing lunar crevasse.

1971, Oct. 15
641-643 A233 Set of 3   5.00 5.00
   Imperf., #641-643   16.00

Five Tigers
A234

Folk paintings: No. 644, 12xu, White tiger. No. 645, 12xu, Red tiger. No. 646, 12xu, Yellow tiger. 40xu, Green tiger. 50xu, Black tiger. 1d, Five tigers.

1971, Nov. 25   *Perf. 12*
644-649 A234 Set of 6   10.00 6.00
   Imperf., #644-649   15.00

Size: 90x119mm

Imperf
650 A234 1d multicolored   12.00

Chinese
Communist
Party, 50th
Anniv.
A235

1971, Dec. 1   *Perf. 11*
651 A235 12xu multicolored   1.50 .40

Mongolian
People's Republic,
50th
Anniv. — A236

1971, Dec. 25
652 A236 12xu multicolored   1.50 .40

Folk Engravings from Dong
Ho — A237

#653a, 12xu, Traditional wrestling. #653b, 12xu, Drum procession. #654a, 12xu, Gathering coconuts, vert. #654b, 12xu, Jealousy, vert. 40xu, Wedding of mice. 50xu, Frog school.

1972, Jan. 30
653-656 A237 Set of 6   10.00 9.00
   Imperf., #653-656   10.00

No. 653 is tete-beche.
The 30xu in design of #654a is a proof.

3rd Natl. Trade Unions Congress
A238

Designs: 1xu, Workers facing right. 12xu, Workers facing left.

1972, May 1
657-658 A238 Set of 2   2.00 1.25
Imperf., #657-658

Natl. Resistance, 25th Anniv. — A239

Designs: No. 659, Munitions worker. No. 660, Soldier in battle. No. 661, Woman in paddy field. No. 662, Text of Ho Chi Minh's appeal.

1972, May 5
659-662 A239 12xu Set of 4   3.50 1.75
Imperf., #659-662   20.00

Ho Chi Minh's Birthplace
A240

Design: No. 664, Home in Hanoi.

1972, May 19
663-664 A240 12xu Set of 2   2.50 1.75
Imperf., #663-664   5.00

A241

A242

1972, June 20
665-666 A241 12xu Set of 2   5.00 2.50
Imperf., #665-666

3500th US warplane shot down. Added inscription on No. 666 reads "NGAY 20.4.1972."

1972, Aug. 15
Georgi Dimitrov (1882-1949), Bulgarian politician: No. 668, Dimitrov at Leipzig Court, 1933.

667-668 A242 12xu Set of 2   2.50 1.50
Imperf., #667-668   5.00

Birds — A243

Designs: No. 669, 12xu, Lobivanellus indicus. No. 670, 12xu, Anas falcata. 30xu, Bubulcus ibis. 40xu, Gallicrex cinerea. 50xu, Prophyria porphyrio. 1d, Leptoptilos dubius.

1972, Oct. 12   *Perf. 12*
669-674 A243 Set of 6   10.00 8.00
Imperf., #669-674   20.00

A244

A245

4000th US warplane shot down: No. 676, Gunner holding rocket.

1972, Oct. 19   *Perf. 11*
675-676 A244 12xu Set of 2   7.00 1.75
Imperf., #675-676   8.00

1972, Dec. 1   *Perf. 12*
Tay Nguyen folk dances: #677, 12xu, Drum. #678, 12xu, Umbrella. #679, 12xu, Shield. 20xu, Horse. 30xu, Ca Dong. 40xu, Rice pounding. 50xu, Khaen. 1d, Cham rong.

677-684 A245 Set of 8   9.00 8.00
Imperf., #677-684   10.00

Flight of Soyuz 11
A246

Designs: 12xu, Soyuz 11 docking with Salyut laboratory. 1d, Soyuz 11 cosmonauts.

1972, Dec. 30   *Perf. 11*
685-686 A246 Set of 2   3.00 2.75
Imperf., #685-686   7.00

Wild Animals — A247

Designs: 12xu, Cuon alpinus. 30xu, Panthera pardus. 50xu, Felis bengalensis. 1d, Lutra lutra.

1973, Feb. 15   *Perf. 12½*
687-690 A247 Set of 4   7.00 5.00
Imperf., #687-690   17.00

Copernicus
A248

Copernicus and: No. 691a, 12xu, Armillary sphere. No. 691b, 12xu, Sun. 30xu, Signature, vert.

1973, Feb. 17   *Perf. 11*
691-692 A248 Set of 3   3.50 3.00
Imperf., #691-692

Engravings on Ngoc Lu Bronze Drums — A249

Designs: No. 693, Drummers (Nha Danh Trong). No. 694, Pounding rice (Nha Gia Gao). No. 695, Dancers (Mua). No. 696, War canoe (Thuyen). No. 697, Birds (Chim, Thu).

1973, Apr. 12
693-697 A249 12xu Set of 5   4.00 4.00
Imperf., #693-697

Wild Animals — A250

Designs: 12xu, Tragulus javanicus. 30xu, Capricornis sumatraensis. 50xu, Sus scrofa. 1d, Moschus moschiferus.

1973, May 25   *Perf. 12x12½*
698-701 A250 Set of 4   5.00 5.00
Imperf., #698-701   12.00

Birds
A251

#702, 12xu, Pycnonotus jocosus. #703, 12xu, Megalurus palustris. 20xu, Capsychus saularis. 40xu, Rhipidura albicollis. 50xu, Parus major. 1d, Zosterops japonica.

1973, July 15   *Perf. 12*
702-707 A251 Set of 6   7.00 4.00
Imperf., 702-707   15.00

Disabled Soldiers
A252   A252a

1973, July 27   *Perf. 11*
708-709 A252, A252a 12xu Set
                                 of 2 2.50
Imperf., #708-709

Three Readiness Youth Movement
A253

Designs: No. 710, Road building. No. 711, Open-air class. No. 712, On the march.

1973, Sept. 2
710-712 A253 12xu Set of 3   2.50 1.25
Imperf., #710-712

Democratic People's Republic of Korea, 25th Anniv. — A254

1973, Sept. 9
713 A254 12xu multicolored   1.50 .40
Imperf.

4181st US Warplane Shot Down
A255

Designs: No. 714, 12xu, US B-52 hit by air attack. No. 715, 12xu, US B-52, fighter crashing over Haiphong Harbor. No. 716, 12xu, Anti-aircraft battery. 1d, Aircraft wreckage caught in fishing net.

1973, Oct. 10
714-717 A255 Set of 4   7.50 3.75
Imperf., #714-717

Flowers — A256

6xu, 12xu (#719), Chrysanthemum (Cuc). #720, 12xu, Rose. #721, 12xu, Dahlia. #722, 12xu, Chrysanthemum (Bach mi). #723, 12xu, Chrysanthemum (Dai doa).

1974, Jan. 15
718-723 A256 Set of 6   40.00
Imperf., #718-723   70.00

No. 718 may not have been officially released.

Elephants
A257

#724, 12xu, Hauling logs. #725, 12xu, War elephant. 40xu, Setting logs in place. 50xu, Circus elephant. 1d, Carrying war supplies.

1974, Feb. 10   *Perf. 11½*
724-728 A257 Set of 5   7.50 7.00
Imperf., #724-728   12.00

Victory at Dien Bien Phu, 20th Anniv. — A258

Designs: a, Dien Bien Phu soldier's badge. b, Soldier waving victory flag.

1974, May 7   **Perf. 11**
729 A258 12xu Pair, #a.-b.   2.50   .70
     Imperf.   5.00

Three Responsibilities Women's Movement — A259

Designs: a, Armed worker, peasant. b, Female textile worker.

1974, June 1
730 A259 12xu Pair, #a.-b.   2.50 1.50
     Imperf.

A260

A261

Chrysanthemums: No. 731, 12xu, Brown. No. 732, 12xu, Yellow (Vang). 20xu, Ngoc Khong Tuoc. 30xu, White. 40xu, Kim. 50xu, Hong mi. 60xu, Gam. 1d, Lilac.

1974, June 20   **Perf. 12x12½**
731-738 A260   Set of 8   7.00 4.00
     Imperf., #731-738   11.00

1974, Aug. 15   **Perf. 11**
Industrial plants: No. 739, 12xu, Corchorus capsularis. No. 740, 12xu, Cyperus tojet jormis. 30xu, Morus alba.

739-741 A261   Set of 3   4.50 2.75
     Imperf., #739-741   10.00

Liberation of Hanoi, 20th Anniv. — A262

Designs: a, Woman laying bricks. b, Soldier holding child waving flag.

1974, Oct. 10
742 A262 12xu Pair, #a.-b.   2.50   .80

Solidarity with Chilean Revolution A263

Designs: No. 743, Pres. Salvador Allende, flag. No. 744, Pablo Neruda, poet.

1974, Oct. 15
743-744 A263 12xu Set of 2   2.50   .70
     Imperf., #743-744   5.00

Marine Life — A264

Designs: No. 745, 12xu, Rhizostoma. No. 746, 12xu, Loligo. 30xu, Haleotis. 40xu, Pteria martensii. 50xu, Sepia officinalis. 1d, Palinurus japonicus.

1974, Oct. 25   **Perf. 12½**
745-750 A264   Set of 6   7.00 2.50
     Imperf., #745-750   12.00

People's Republic of Albania, 30th Anniv. — A265

Designs: a, Natl. arms. b, Albanian, Vietnamese flags, women.

1974, Nov. 29   **Perf. 11**
752 A265 12xu Pair, #a.-b.   2.25   .75
     Imperf.

Paris Agreement on Vietnam, 2nd Anniv. — A266

Designs: No. 753, Intl. Conference on Viet Nam in session, 5-line inscription. No. 754, Signing of Paris Agreement, 4-line inscription.

1975, Jan. 27
753-754 A266 12xu Set of 2   2.50   .75
     Imperf.

Medicinal Plants — A267

Designs: No. 755, 12xu, Costus speciosus. No. 756, 12xu, Curcuma zedoaria. No. 757,

---

12xu, Rosa laevigata. 30xu, Erythrina indica. 40xu, Lilium brownii. 50xu, Hibiscus sagittifolius. 60xu, Papaver somniferum. 1d, Belamcanda chinensis.

1975, Feb. 2   **Perf. 11½x12**
755-762 A267   Set of 8   8.00 8.00
     Imperf., #755-762   12.50

Vietnamese Labor Party, 45th Anniv. — A268

Designs: No. 763, 12xu, Tran Phu. No. 764, 12xu, Le Hong Phong. No. 765, 12xu, Nguyen Van Cu. No. 766, 12xu, Ngo Gia Tu. 60xu, Ho Chi Minh in 1924, vert.

1975, Feb. 3   **Perf. 11**
763-767 A268   Set of 5   2.75 2.00
     Imperf., #763-767   10.00

A269

A270

Fruit: No. 768, 12xu, Achras sapota. No. 769, 12xu, Persica vulgaris. 20xu, Eugenia jambos. 30xu, Chrysophyllum cainito. 40xu, Lucuma mamosa. 50xu, Prunica granitum. 60xu, Durio ziberthinus. 1d, Prunus salicina.

1975, Apr. 25   **Perf. 12x12½**
768-775 A269   Set of 8   7.50 6.00
     Imperf., 768-775   12.00

1975, May 19   **Perf. 11**
776-777 A270 12xu, 60xu, set of 2   3.50 1.25
     Imperf., #776-777   10.00

Ho Chi Minh, 85th birthday.

People's Republic of Poland, 30th Anniv. A271

1975, July 5
778-781 A271   1xu, 2xu, 3xu, 12xu, set of 4   3.00
     Imperf., #778-781

Flags A272

Natl. Arms — A273

Flag of North Viet Nam and: No. 782, Draped flag. No. 783, Flag with star & cresent. No. 784, DDR flag and handshake.

1975
782-785 A272-A273 12xu Set of 4   6.00
     Imperf., #782-784

People's Republic of China, 25th anniv. (#782), Republic of Algeria, 20th anniv. (#783), German Democratic Republic, 25th anniv. (#784), liberation of Hungary, 30th anniv. (#785).
     Issued: No. 782, 7/5. Nos. 783-785, 8/15.

Independence, 30th Anniv. — A274

#786, Flag. #787, Natl. arms. #788-789, Ho Chi Minh proclaiming independence.

1975, Sept. 2
786-788 A274 12xu Set of 3   3.50 1.25

Souvenir Sheet
Imperf
789   A274 20xu multicolored 15.00

No. 789 contains one 45x30mm stamp.

Reptiles A275

#790, 12xu, Dermochelys coriacea. #791, 12xu, Physignathus cocincinus. 20xu, Hydrophis brookii. 30xu, Platysternon megacephalum. 40xu, Leiolepis belliana. 50xu, Python molurus. 60xu, Naja hannah. 1d, Draco maculatus.

1975, Nov. 25   **Perf. 12**
790-797 A275   Set of 8   8.00 7.00
     Imperf., #790-797   16.00

Butterflies — A276

#798, 12xu, Pathysa antiphates. #799, 12xu, Danaus plexippus. 20xu, Cynautocera papilionaria. 30xu, Maenas salaminia. 40xu, Papilio machaon. 50xu, Ixias pyrene. 60xu, Eusemia vetula. 1d, Eriboea.

1976, Jan. 6
798-805 A276   Set of 8   9.00 9.00
     Imperf., #798-805   25.00

No. 799 misspelled "Danais."

Lan Hoang Thao Orchid
A277

1976, Jan. 25 *Perf. 11*
806-807 A277 6xu, 12xu, set of 2 4.00 1.75
See Nos. 854-855.

Wild Animals
A278

#808, 12xu, Callosciurus erythraeus. #809, 12xu, Paguma larvata. 20xu, Macaca mulatta. 30xu, Hystrix hodgsoni. 40xu, Nyctereutes procyonoides. 50xu, Selenarctos thibetanus. 60xu, Panthera pardus. 1d, Cynocephalus variegatus.

1976, Mar. 20 *Perf. 12*
808-815 A278 Set of 8 7.00 2.50
Imperf., #808-815 15.00

1st Elections to Unified Natl. Assembly
A279

6xu (#816), Map, hand placing ballot in ballot box. 6xu (#817), 12xu, Map, voters.

1976, Apr. 10 *Perf. 11*
816-818 A279 Set of 3 3.50 1.25
Imperf., #816-818

Size of Nos. 817-818 is 35x22mm. Identical stamps inscribed "Mien Nam Viet Nam" are National Front issues. Same values.

Unified Natl. Assembly, 1st Session
A280

Design: 12xu, Inscribed "Doc Lap Thong Nhat Chu Nghia Xa Hoi."

1976, June 24
819-820 A280 6xu, 12xu, set of 2 2.50 .80

Identical stamps inscribed "Mien Nam Viet Nam" are National Front issues. Same values.

A281

A282

1976, June 24 *Perf. 12x12½*
821 A281 12xu multicolored 1.50 .40
Reunification of Viet Nam.

1976, June 24 *Perf. 12*
Orchids: No. 822, 12xu, Habenaria rhodocheila. No. 823, 12xu, Dendrobium devonianum. 20xu, Dendrobium tortile. 30xu, Doritis pulcherrima. 40xu, Dendrobium farmeri. 50xu, Dendrobium aggregatum. 60xu, Eria pannea. 1d, Paphiopedilum concolor.

822-829 A282 Set of 8 8.00 2.00
Imperf., #822-829 10.00

Socialist Republic of Viet Nam
AREA — 128,000 sq. mi.
POP. — 77,311,210 (1999 est.0
CAPITAL — Hanoi

Vietnamese Red Cross, 30th Anniv. — A283

1976, July 27 *Perf. 11*
830 A283 12xu multicolored 2.50 .80
Imperf.

Fish — A284

#831, 12xu, Lutjanus sebae. #832, 12xu, Dampieria melanotaenia. 20xu, Therapon theraps. 30xu, Amphiprion bifasciatus. 40xu, Abudefduf sexfasciatus. 50xu, Heniochus acuminatus. 60xu, Amphiprion macrostoma. 1d, Symphorus spilurus.

1976, Aug. 15 *Perf. 12*
831-838 A284 Set of 8 6.00 4.75
Imperf., #831-838 9.00

Viet Nam Worker's Party, 4th Natl. Congress
A285

1976, Nov. 12 *Perf. 11*
839-844 A285 2, 3, 5, 10, 12, 20xu, set of 6 3.50 2.50

Viet Nam Communist Party, 4th Natl. Congress — A286

Designs: a, Agriculture, industry. b, Ho Chi Minh, worker, farmer, soldier, scientist.

Design size 24.5mmx35mm

1976, Dec. 10
845 A286 12xu Pair, #a.-b. 2.50 .80
Imperf.

See Nos. 951-954.

Unification of Viet Nam — A287

1976, Dec. 14
846-847 A287 6xu, 12xu, set of 2 2.50 .80
Imperf., #846-847 4.50

General Offensive, 1975 — A288

Designs: 2xu, 50xu, Liberation of Buon Me Thuot. 3xu, 1d, Tanks liberating Da Nang. 6xu, 2d, Tank, soldiers liberating Presidential palace, Saigon.

1976, Dec. 14
848-853 A288 Set of 6 4.50 4.50

Lan Hoang Thao Orchid Type of 1976 Inscribed "VIET NAM" and "1976"

1976, Dec. *Litho.* *Perf. 11*
854-855 A277 6xu, 12xu, Set of 2 45.00 15.00

Dragonflies — A289

#856, 12xu, Ho. #857, 12xu, Bao. 20xu, Canh dom. 30xu, Nuong. 40xu, Suoi. 50xu, Canh vang. 60xu, Canh khoang. 1d, Canh den.

1977, Jan. 25 *Perf. 12*
856-863 A289 Set of 8 7.00 1.50
Imperf., #856-863 16.00

A290

A291

Rare Birds: 12xu (#864), 60xu, Buceros bicornis. 12xu (#865), Ptilolaemus tickelli. 20xu, Berenicornis comatus. 30xu, Aceros undulatus. 40xu, Anthracoceros malabaricus. 50xu, Anthracoceros malayanus. 1d, Aceros nipalensis.

1977, Apr. 15
864-871 A290 Set of 8 7.25 3.25
Imperf., #864-871 9.00

1977, Apr. 25 *Perf. 11*
Bronze drum and: 4xu, Thang Long Tower. 5xu, Map. 12xu, Lotus blossom. 50xu, Flag.

872-875 A291 Set of 4 4.50 2.00
Imperf., #872-875

Natl. Assembly general elections, 1st anniv.

Beetles
A292

#876, 12xu, Black-spotted (Dom den). #877, 12xu, Yellow-spotted (Lang vang). 20xu, Veined (Van gach). 30xu, Green (Nhung xanh). 40xu, Green-spotted (Hoa xanh). 50xu, Black (Van den). 60xu, Leopard skin (Da bao). 1d, Nine-spotted (Chin cham).

1977, June 15 *Perf. 12½x12*
876-883 A292 Set of 8 7.00 1.75
Imperf., #876-883 11.00

Wildflowers
A293

Designs: No. 884, 12xu, Thevetia peruviana. No. 885, 12xu, Broussonetia papyrifera. 20xu, Aleurites montana. 30xu, Cerbera manghes. 40xu, Cassia multijuga. 50xu, Cassia nodosa. 60xu, Hibiscus schizopetalus. 1d, Lagerstroesnia speciosa.

1977, Aug. 19 *Perf. 12x12½*
884-891 A293 Set of 8 5.00 1.75
Imperf., #884-891 10.00

A294   A295

Dahlias: 6xu (#892), 12xu (#894), Pink. 6xu (#893), 12xu (#895), Orange.

1977, Sept. 10 *Perf. 11*
892-895 A294 Set of 4 3.75 1.75
See Nos. 921-924.

1977, Sept. 10

Children drawing map of unified Viet Nam. Denominations: 4xu, 5xu, 10xu, 12xu, 30xu each have different colored border.

896-900   A295   Set of 5   3.75 3.75

Goldfish
A296

Designs: No. 901, 12xu, Dong nai. No. 902, 12xu, Velvet (Hoa nhung). 20xu, Blue Chinese (Tau xanh). 30xu, Dragon-eyed (Mat bong). 40xu, Cam trang. 50xu, Five-colored (Ngu sac). 60xu, Dong nai. 1d, Thap cam.

1977, Oct. 20   *Perf. 12*
901-908   A296   Set of 8   7.50 2.00
    Imperf., #901-908   10.00

A297

A298

Russian October Revolution, 60th anniv.: 12xu (No. 909, olive background), 12xu (No. 910, blue background), Ho Chi Minh, Lenin banner. 50xu, Mother holding child with flag. 1d, Workers, farmers, Moscow Kremlin, cruiser Aurora.

1977, Nov. 7
909-912   A297   Set of 4   3.00 2.50

1978, Jan. 25

Songbirds: 12xu, Gracula religiosa. No. 914, 20xu, Garrulax canorus. No. 915, 20xu, Streptopelia chinensis. 30xu, Linius schach. 40xu, Garrulax formosus. 50xu, Garrulax chinensis. 60xu, Acridotheres cristatellus. 1d, Garrulax yersini.

913-920   A298   Set of 8   6.00 1.75
    Imperf., #913-920   12.00

Cultivated Flower Type of 1977

5xu, 10xu, Sunflower. 6xu, 12xu, Pansy.

1978, Mar. 20   *Perf. 11*
921-924   A294   Set of 4   4.25 2.40

Intl. Children's Day (June 1977) — A299

1978, Mar. 20
925   A299   12xu multicolored   1.75 .40

Sports
A300

#926, 12xu, Discus. #927, 12xu, Long jump. 20xu, Hurdles. 30xu, Hammer throw. 40xu, Shot put. 50xu, Javelin. 60xu, Running. 1d, High jump.

1978, Apr. 10   *Perf. 11½*
926-933   A300   Set of 8   4.50 2.00
    Imperf., #926-933   10.00

A301

A302

4th Viet Nam Trade Union Cong.: #934, Trade Union emblem. #935, Ho Chi Minh, workers.

1978, May 1   *Perf. 11*
934-935   A301   10xu Set of 2   2.50 .80

1978, May 15

10xu, Ho Chi Minh conducting orchestra. 12xu, Ho Chi Minh's mausoleum, horiz.

936-937   A302   Set of 2   2.00 .80
    No. 937 is 39x23mm.

Young Pioneers' Cultural Palace, Hanoi — A303

1978, May 29
938   A303   10xu multicolored   1.50 .40
    Intl. Children's Day.

Sculptures from Tay Phuong Pagoda — A304

Designs: No. 939, 12xu, Sanakavasa. No. 940, 12xu, Parsva. No. 941, 12xu, Punyasas. No. 942, 20xu, Kumarata. No. 943, 20xu, Nagarjuna. 30xu, Yayata. 40xu, Cadiep. 50xu, Ananda. 60xu, Buddhamitra. 1d, Asvagmosa.

1978, July 1   *Perf. 12*
939-948   A304   Set of 10   7.00 3.00
    Imperf., #939-948   20.00

Cuban Revolution, 25th Anniv. — A305

1978, July 20   *Perf. 11*
949-950   A305   6xu, 12xu Set of 2   2.50 .80

Types of 1976

6xu (No. 951), 12xu (No. 953), like #845a. 6xu (No. 952), 12xu (No. 952), like #845b.

Design size 18.5mmx23mm

1978, Aug. 15
951-954   A286   Set of 4   4.00 2.00

Space Exploration, 20th Anniv. — A306

#955, 12xu, Sputnik. #956, 12xu, Venus 1. 30xu, Spacecraft docking. 40xu, Molniya 1. 60xu, Soyuz. 2d, Cosmonauts Gubarev, Grechko.

1978, Aug. 28   *Perf. 12½x12*
955-960   A306   Set of 6   5.00 1.75
    Imperf., #955-960   10.00

World Telecommunications Day — A307

Designs: a, Printed circuit. b, ITU emblem.

1978, Sept. 25   *Perf. 11*
962   A307   12xu Pair, #a.-b.   2.50 .80
    Imperf.   15.00

20th Congress of Socialist Postal Ministers — A308

1978, Sept. 25
963   A308   12xu multicolored   1.50 .40

Chrysanthemums — A309

No. 964, 12xu, Tim. No. 965, 12xu, Kim tien. 20xu, Hong. 30xu, Van tho. 40xu, Vang. 50xu, Thuy tim. 60xu, Vang mo. 1d, Nau do.

1978, Oct. 1   *Perf. 12*
964-971   A309   Set of 8   5.50 2.00
    Imperf., #964-971   12.00

Dinosaurs
A310

Designs: No. 972, 12xu, Plesiosaurus. No. 973, 12xu, Brontosaurus. 20xu, Iguanodon. 30xu, Tyrannosaurus rex. 40xu, Stegosaurus. 50xu, Mosasaurus. 60xu, Triceratops. 1d, Pteranodon.

1979, Jan. 1   Litho.   *Perf. 11½*
972-979   A310   Set of 8   9.00 2.00
    Imperf., #972-979   17.00

No. 977 misspelled "Mozasaurus."

A311

A312

1979, Jan. 1   *Perf. 11*
980   A311   12xu multicolored   1.50 .40
    Imperf.   5.00

Socialist Republic of Cuba, 20th anniv.

1979, Feb. 1

Quang Trung's victory over the Chinese, 190th Anniv.: #981, Battle plan. #982, Quang Trung.

981-982   A312   12xu Set of 2   2.50 .80
   a.   Perf 12, #981-982   20.00

Albert Einstein, Physicist
A313

Designs: No. 983, 12xu, Einstein. No. 984, 60xu, Equation, sun, planets.

1979, Mar. 14
983-984   A313   12xu, 60xu, set of 2   3.00 1.50

Domestic Animals — A314

10xu, Ram. 12xu, Ox. 20xu, Ewe, lamb. 30xu, White water buffalo, vert. 40xu, Cow. 50xu, Goat. 60xu, Water buffalo, calf. 1d, Young goat, vert.

1979, Mar. 20 *Perf. 12*
985-992 A314 Set of 8 5.00 1.50
Imperf., #985-992 7.00

Five Year Plan (1976-80) — A315

#993, 998, Map, emblem. #994, 999, Factory worker. #995, 1000, Peasant woman, tractor. #996, 1001, Soldier. #997, 1002, Man, atom, compass.

1979 *Perf. 11*
993-997 A315 6xu Set of 5
998-1002 A315 12xu Set of 5
1000a Perf. 12
Nos. 993-1002 (10) 10.00

Issued: Nos. 993-997, 5/1. Nos. 998-1002, 6/1. Nos. 993, 996-1002 on toned paper.

Philaserdica '79, Intl. Stamp Exhibition, Sofia, Bulgaria A316

1979, May 27 *Perf. 12*
1003-1004 12xu, 30xu, set of 2 2.50 .80

Intl. Year of the Child — A317

2xu, Ho Chi Minh, children. 20xu, Nurse, mother, child. 50xu, Children with glider, painting supplies. 1d, Girls of different races.

1979, June 1 *Perf. 11*
1005-1008 A317 Set of 4 4.00 3.00

Ornamental Birds — A318

#1009, 12xu, Lophura diardi. #1010, 12xu, Tragopan temminckii. 20xu, Phasianus colchicus. 30xu, Lophura edwardsi. 40xu, Lophura nycthemera, vert. 50xu, Polyplectron germaini, vert. 60xu, Rheinartia ocellata, vert. 1d, Pavo muticus, vert.

1979, June 16 *Perf. 12*
1009-1016 A318 Set of 8 6.00 2.10
Imperf., #1009-1016 10.00

Orchids A319

Designs: No. 1017, 12xu, Dendrobium heterocacpum. No. 1018, 12xu, Cymbidium hybridum. 20xu, Rhynchostylis gigantea. 30xu, Dendrobium mobile. 40xu, Aerides falcatum. 50xu, Paphiopedilum callosum. 60xu, Vanda teres. 1d, Dendrobium phalaenopsis.

1979, Aug. 10 *Perf. 12*
1017-1024 A319 Set of 8 6.50 1.75
Imperf., #1017-1024 10.00

Cats A320

Designs: No. 1025, 12xu, Meo tam the. No. 1026, 12xu, Meo muop, vert. 20xu, Meo khoang, vert. 30xu, Meo dom van. 40xu, Meo muop dom, vert. 50xu, Meo vang, vert. 60xu, Meo xiem. 1d, Meo van am.

1979, Nov. 10
1025-1032 A320 Set of 8 5.00 3.00
Imperf., #1025-1032 10.00

Vietnamese People's Army, 25th Anniv. — A321

a, People greeting soldiers. b, Frontier guards.

1979, Dec. 22 *Perf. 11*
1033 A321 12xu Pair, #a.-b. .80 .80

Roses — A322

Designs: 1xu, 12xu (No. 1036), Red, pink roses. 2xu, 12xu (No. 1037), Single pink rose.

1980, Jan. 1
1034-1037 A322 Set of 4 5.00 2.00
See Nos. 1084-1085.

Aquatic Flowers A323

#1038, 12xu, Nelumbium nuciferum. #1039, 12xu, Nymphala stellata. 20xu, Ipomola reptans. 30xu, Nymphoides indicum. 40xu, Jussiala repens. 50xu, Eichhornia crassipes. 60xu, Monochoria voginalis. 1d, Nelumbo nucifera.

1980, Jan. 15 *Perf. 12½*
1038-1045 A323 Set of 8 6.25 3.00
Imperf., #1038-1045 9.00

Vietnamese Communist Party, 50th Anniv. — A324

Designs: No. 1046a, Ho Chi Minh proclaiming independence, 1945. No. 1046b, Peasants with banner, improvised weapons. No. 1047a, Map, soldiers, tanks storming palace. No. 1047b, Soldiers waving flag at Dien Bien Phu. 2d, Ho Chi Minh, soldiers and workers.

1980, Feb. 3 *Perf. 11*
1046 A324 12xu Pair, #a.-b.
1047 A324 20xu Pair, #a.-b.
1048 A324 2d multicolored
Nos. 1046-1048 (5) 4.00 4.00

Lenin, 110th Anniv. of Birth A325

1980, Apr. 22 *Perf. 12*
1049-1051 A325 6xu, 12xu, 1d, set of 3 3.25 2.00

1980 Summer Olympics, Moscow A326

#1052, 12xu, Hurdles. #1053, 12xu, Running. 20xu, Team handball. 30xu, Soccer. 40xu, Wrestling. 50xu, Gymnastics, horiz. 60xu, Swimming, horiz. 1d, Sailing, horiz.

1980, May 1 *Perf. 12x12½, 12½x12*
1052-1059 A326 Set of 8 6.00 1.75
Imperf., #1052-1059 10.00

A327

A328

Ho Chi Minh, 90th anniv. of birth: 12xu, In 1924. 40xu, As president.

1980, May 19 *Perf. 11*
1060-1061 A327 Set of 2 2.00 1.25

1980, June 15
1062 A328 5xu multicolored 1.00 .40

Intl. Children's Day.

Intercosmos '80, Soviet-Vietnamese Space Mission — A329

Designs: No. 1063, 12xu, Cosmonauts. No. 1064, 12xu, Soyuz 37 atop booster. 20xu, Soyuz 37. 40xu, Soyuz docking with Salyut space station. 1d, Soyuz firing retro-rockets. 2d, Parachute landing. 3d, Cosmonauts, Soyuz-Salyut station.

1980, July 24 *Perf. 12x12½*
1063-1068 A329 Set of 6 7.00 1.25
Imperf., #1063-1068 10.00
Souvenir Sheet
1069 A329 3d multicolored 6.00
Imperf. 6.75

Saltwater Fish — A330

Designs: No. 1070, 12xu, Rhincodon typus. No. 1071, 12xu, Galeocerdo cuvier. 20xu, Orectolobus japonicus. 30xu, Heterodontus zebra. 40xu, Dasyatis uarnak. 50xu, Pristis microdon. 60xu, Sphyrna lewini. 1d, Myliobatis tobijei.

1980, Aug. 1 *Perf. 12*
1070-1077 A330 Set of 8 5.00 1.75
Imperf., #1070-1077 10.00

A331 A332

Post and Telecommunications Office, 35th Anniv.: 12xu, Ho Chi Minh reading newspaper. 20xu, Ho Chi Minh talking on telephone. 50xu, Kim Dong carrying bird in cage. 1d, Dish antenna.

1980, Aug. 15 *Litho. Perf. 12½*
1078-1081 A331 Set of 4 3.50 3.00

1980, Aug. 25 *Perf. 11, 12 (#1083)*

Natl. Telecommunications Day: No. 1082, Telephone switchboard operator. No. 1083, Train, map.

1082-1083 A332 12xu Set of 2 2.00 1.60

Rose Type of 1980

No. 1084, Pink. No. 1085, Red and pink.

1980, Aug. 25   *Perf. 11*
Size: 20x24mm
1084-1085 A322 12xu Set of 2   2.00 1.40
For surcharge see No. 1385.

Republic of
Vietnam, 35th
Anniv. — A333

Designs: No. 1086, 12xu, Ho Chi Minh. No. 1087, 12xu, Natl. arms. 40xu, Pac Bo Cave. 1d, Source of Lenin River, horiz.

1980, Sept. 2   *Perf. 12½*
1086-1089 A333 Set of 4   4.00 4.00

A334

A335

Natl. emblems: 6xu, Arms. No. 1091, 12xu, Flag, horiz. No. 1092, 12xu, Anthem.

1980, Sept. 20   *Perf. 12*
1090-1092 A334 Set of 3   5.00

1980, Oct. 6   *Perf. 11*
Nguyen Trai, 600th birth anniv.: 12xu, Nguyen Trai. 50xu, Books, horiz. 1d, Ho Chi Minh reading commemorative stele, Con Son.
1093-1095 A335 Set of 3   5.00 5.00
For surcharge see No. 1386.

A336

A337

Natl. Women's Union, 50th Anniv.: #1096, Ho Chi Minh, women. #1097, Group of 4 women.

1980, Oct. 20
1096-1097 A336 12xu Set of 2   1.50 .80

1980, Nov. 20   *Perf. 12½*
Flowers: No. 1098, 12xu, Ipomoea pulchella. No. 1099, 12xu, Biguoniaceae venusta. 20xu, Petunia hybrida. 30xu, Trapaeolum majus. 40xu, Thunbergia grandiflora. 50xu, Anlamanda cathartica. 60xu, Campsis radicans. 1d, Bougainivillaea spectabilis.
1098-1105 A337 Set of 8   6.25 1.50
Imperf., #1098-1105   10.00

Ornamental Fish — A338

Designs: No. 1106, 12xu, Betta splendens. No. 1107, 12xu, Symphysodon aequifasciata. 20xu, Poecilobrycon eques. 30xu, Gyrinocheilus aymonieri. 40xu, Barbus tetrazona. 50xu, Pterophyllum eimekei. 60xu, Xiphophorus helleri. 1d, Trichopterus sumatranus.

1981, Jan. 15   *Perf. 12*
1106-1113 A338 Set of 8   6.25 6.25
Imperf., #1106-1113   10.00

26th Soviet
Communist
Party Congress
A339

20xu, Rocket, book. 50xu, Young people, flag.

1981, Feb. 23   *Perf. 11*
1114-1115 A339 Set of 2   2.50 2.00

Animals from Cuc Phuona Natl.
Forest — A340

#1116, 12xu, Hylobates concolor. #1117, 12xu, Macaca speciosa. 20xu, Selenarctos thibetanus. 30xu, Cuon alpinus. 40xu, Sus scrofa. 50xu, Cervus unicolor. 60xu, Panthera pardus. 1d, Panthera tigris.

1981, Apr. 10   *Perf. 12½x12*
1116-1123 A340 Set of 8   8.00 1.75
Imperf., #1116-1123   10.00

Doves
A341

#1124, 12xu, Treron sieboldi. #1125, 12xu, Ducula aenea, vert. 20xu, Streptopelia tranquebarica, vert. 30xu, Macropygia unchall, vert. 40xu, Ducula badia, vert. 50xu, Treron apicauda, vert. 60xu, Chalcophaps indica. 1d, Seimun treron seimundi.

1981, June 5   *Perf. 12*
1124-1131 A341 Set of 8   5.00 4.00
Imperf., #1124-1131   9.00

Nectar-sucking Birds — A342

Designs: No. 1132, 20xu, Aethopyga siparaja. No. 1133, 20xu, Anthreptes singalensis. 30xu, Aethopyga saturata. 40xu, Aethopyga gouldiae. No. 1136, 50xu, Nectarinia chalcostetha. No. 1137, 50xu, Nectarinia hypogrammica. 60xu, Nectarinia sperata. 1d, Aethopyga nipalensis.

1981, Aug. 5   *Perf. 12½x12*
1132-1139 A342 Set of 8   5.00 1.75
Imperf., #1132-1139   10.00

A343   A343a

1981, Aug. 5   *Perf. 11*
1140 A343 12xu Lotus flower   1.00

1981, Aug. 5
Design: Factory militiawoman.
1140A A343a 12xu yel & multi   20.00
See Nos. M30-M31.

A344   A345

Fruit: No. 1141, 20xu, Elaeagnus latifolia. No. 1142, 20xu, Fortunella japonica. 30xu, Nephelium lappaceum. 40xu, Averrhoa bilimbi. No. 1145, 50xu, Ziziphus mauritiana. No. 1146, 50xu, Fragaria vesca. 60xu, Bouea oppositifolia. 1d, Syzygium aqueum.

1981, Oct. 12   *Perf. 12*
1141-1148 A344 Set of 8   5.75 1.75
Imperf., #1141-1148   10.00

1981, Nov. 15   *Perf. 11*
Planting trees: No. 1149, Ho Chi Minh. No. 1150, Three people.
1149-1150 A345 30xu Set of 2   1.75 1.00
Tree planting festival.

Bulgaria,
1300th
Anniv.
A346

1981, Dec. 9   *Perf. 11*
1151-1153 A346 30xu, 50xu, 2d, set of 3   5.50 5.50

Wild Animals — A347

Designs: No. 1154, 30xu, Orangutan. No. 1155, 30xu, Bison bonasus. No. 1156, 40xu, Kangaroo. No. 1157, 40xu, Hippopotamus. No. 1158, 50xu, Rhinoceros sondaicus. No. 1159, 50xu, Giraffe. 60xu, Zebra. 1d, Lion.

1981, Dec. 9   *Perf. 12½x12*
1154-1161 A347 Set of 8   5.00 2.00
Imperf., #1154-1161   9.00

A348

A349

World Food Day: 30xu, 50xu, Woman holding sheaf of rice. 2d, FAO emblem, horiz.

1982, Jan. 26   *Perf. 11*
1162-1164 A348 Set of 3   3.50

1982, Feb. 19
1165-1166 A349 50xu, 5d, set of 2   4.75 4.75
10th World Trade Unions Congress, Havana, Cuba.

5th Vietnamese Communist Party
Congress — A350

Designs: No. 1167, 30xu, Ho Chi Minh. No. 1168, 30xu, Hammer, sickle. No. 1169, 30xu, Worker, dam. 50xu, Women harvesting rice. 1d, Ho Chi Minh.

1982, Feb. 15
1167-1170 A350 Set of 4   4.00 2.00
Imperf
Size: 99x61 mm
1171 A350 1d multicolored   50.00

Bees &
Wasps
A351

Designs: No. 1172, 20xu, Ong bove. No. 1173, 20xu, Ong van xanh. 30xu, To vo nau. 40xu, Ong vang. No. 1176, 50xu, Ong dau nau. No. 1177, 50xu, To vo xanh. 60xu, Ong bau. 1d, Ong mat.

1982, Feb. 25   *Perf. 12*
1172-1179 A351 Set of 8   5.00 2.00
Imperf., #1172-1179   10.00

Soccer
A352

#1180, 30xu, 3 players. #1181, 30xu, 2 players. #1182, 40xu, Striped background. #1183, 40xu, grass background. #1184, 50xu, Vertically striped background. #1185, 50xu, Horizonally striped background. 60xu, 1d, Various soccer scenes.

1982, Apr. 15
1180-1187 A352 Set of 8   5.00 2.00
   Imperf., #1180-1187   10.00

For overprints see Nos. 2142-2149.

A353   A354

Vietnamese Red Cross, 35th Anniv.: 1d, Red Cross emblem.

1982, May 15   **Perf. 11**
1188-1189 A353 Set of 2   2.50

1982, May 19   **Perf. 12**
5th Natl. Women's Congress: No. 1191, Congress emblem, three women.
1190-1191 A354 12xu Set of 2   2.00

A355

A356

Birds of Prey: No. 1192, 30xu, Microhierax melanoleucos. No. 1193, 30xu, Falco tinnunculus. 40xu, Aviceda leuphotes. No. 1195, 50xu, Icthyophaga nana. No. 1196, 60xu, Milvus korschun. 2xu, Neohierax harmandi, horiz. No. 1198, 1d, Elanus caeruleus, horiz. No. 1199, 1d, Circaetus gallicus.

1982, June 1
1192-1199 A355 Set of 8   8.00 2.25
   Imperf., #1192-1199   12.00

1982, June 1   **Perf. 11**
1200-1201 A356 30xu, 3d, set of 2   5.00

Georgi Dimitrov (1882-1949), Bulgarian Communist leader.

Dahlias
A357

Designs (last word or two of Vietnamese inscription): No. 1202, 30xu, Da cam. No. 1203, 30xu, Do. 40xu, Canh se. No. 1205, 50xu, Do nhung. No. 1206, 50xu, Vang. 60xu, Do tuoi. No. 1208, 1d, Bien. No. 1209, 1d, Trang. Various flowers.

1982, July 15   **Perf. 12x12½**
1202-1209 A357 Set of 8   7.00 2.25
   Imperf., #1202-1209   12.00

1982 World Cup Soccer Championships, Spain — A358

#1210, 50xu, Ball at bottom right. #1211, 50xu, Ball at right in air. #1212, 50xu, Ball at bottom center. #1213, 1d, 1 player. #1214, 1d, 3 players. 2d, 2 players.

1982, July 15   **Perf. 12x12½**
1210-1215 A358 Set of 6   8.00 8.00
   Imperf., #1210-1215   10.00

A359

A360

1982, July 25   **Perf. 11**
1216 A359 30xu Natl. defense   1.50 .80
   See No. M32.

1982, Aug. 15
1217 A360 30xu multicolored   1.50
Cuban victory at Giron (Bay of Pigs), 20th anniv.

World Environment Day — A361

#1219, Ho Chi Minh, children planting tree.

1982, Aug. 15
1218-1219 A361 30xu Set of 2   2.00

A362

A363

1982, Sept. 20
1220 A362 30xu multicolored   1.50 .80
Rabindranath Tagore (1861-1941), poet.

1982, Sept. 25   **Perf. 12x12½**
Insects: No. 1221, 30xu, Catacanthus incarnatus. No. 1222, 30xu, Sycanus falleni. 40xu, Nezara viridula. No. 1224, 50xu, Lohita grandis. No. 1225, 50xu, Helcomeria spinosa. 60xu, Chrysocoris stollii. No. 1227, 1d, Pterygamia srayi. No. 1228, 1d, Tiarodes ostentans.

1221-1228 A363 Set of 8   6.75 2.25
   Imperf., #1221-1228   11.50

Russian Revolution, 65th Anniv. — A364

Design: No. 1230, Lenin, workers.

1982, Nov. 7   **Perf. 11**
1229-1230 A364 30xu Set of 2   1.75

9th South East Asian Games, New Delhi, India A365

#1231, 30xu, Table tennis. #1232, 30xu, Swimming. 1d, Wrestling. 2d, Shooting.

1982, Nov. 19
1231-1234 A365 Set of 4   5.50

Fish
A366

Designs: No. 1235, 30xu, Samaris cristatus. No. 1236, 30xu, Tephrinectes sinensis. No. 1237, 40xu, Psettodes erumei. No. 1238, 40xu, Zebrias zebra. No. 1239, 50xu, Cynoglossus puncticeps. No. 1240, 50xu, Pardachirus pavoninus. 60xu, Brachirus orientalis. 1d, Psettina iijimae.

1982, Dec. 15   **Perf. 12**
1235-1242 A366 Set of 8   6.00 1.75
   Imperf., #1235-1242   10.00

Socialist Ideals — A367

#1243, 30xu, Agriculture. #1244, 30xu, Industry. 1d, Natl. defense. 2d, Health & education.

1982, Dec. 25   **Perf. 11**
1243-1246 A367 Set of 4   5.50

Founding of Soviet Union, 60th Anniv. A368

1982, Dec. 30
1247 A368 30xu multicolored   2.50 .80

Sampans
A369

Designs: 30xu, Docked. 50xu, With striped sails. 1d, Sampans on Red River. 3d, With white sails. 5d, With patched sail. 10d, Fast sampan, horiz.

1983, Jan. 10   **Perf. 12½**
1248-1253 A369 Set of 6   7.50
   Imperf., #1248-1253   12.50

Locomotives — A370

30xu, Class 231-300. 50xu, Class 230-000. 1d, Class 140-601. 2d, Class 241-000. 3d, Class 141-500. 5d, Class 150-000. 8d, Class 40-300.

1983, Feb. 20   **Perf. 13**
1254-1260 A370 Set of 7   7.50
   Imperf., #1254-1260   12.50

1st Manned Balloon Flight, Bicent. A371

Balloons: 30xu, Montgolfier. 50xu, Yellow. 1d, CA-11. 2d, Hot-air. 3d, Over harbor. 5d, Le Geant. 8d, Ascending. 10d, Montgolfier, diff.

1983, Mar. 25　　Litho.　　Perf. 12½
1261-1267　A371　Set of 7　　　　8.00
　　Imperf., #1261-1267　　　　　15.00
Souvenir Sheet
Perf. 13
1268　A371　10d　Sheet of 1　　　5.50
　　No. 1268 contains one 32x40mm stamp.

Discovery of Tubercle Bacillus,
Cent. — A372

1983, Mar. 25　　　　　　Perf. 11
1269　A372　5d　multicolored　　　3.00

Laos-Cambodia-Viet Nam
Summit — A373

1983, Mar. 25
1270-1271　A373　50xu, 5d Set of
　　　　　　　　　　　　2　　2.75

Cosmonauts — A374

Designs: 30xu, Gubarev, Remek. No. 1273,
50xu, Klimuk, Hermaszewski. No. 1274, 50xu,
Bykovsky, Jahn. No. 1275, 1d, Rukavishnikov,
Ivanov. No. 1276, 1d, Farcas, Kubasov. No.
1277, 2d, Mendez, Romanenko. No. 1278, 2d,
Gorbatko, Tuan. 5d, Dzhanibekov, Gurragcha.
8d, Popov, Prunariu. No. 1281, Gagarin.

1983, Apr. 1　　　　　Perf. 12½x12
1272-1280　A374　Set of 9　　　9.00
　　Imperf., #1272-1280　　　　14.00
Souvenir Sheet
1281　A374　10d　multicolored　　5.00
　　No. 1281 contains one 36x28mm stamp.

Reptiles
A375

Designs: No. 1282, 30xu, Teratolepis fasciata. No. 1283, 30xu, Chamaeleo jacksoni.
No. 1284, 50xu, Uromastyx acanthinurus. No.
1285, 80xu, Heloderma suspectum. 1d,
Cameleo menle. 2d, Amphibolurus barbatus.
5d, Chlamydosaurus kingi. 10d, Phrynosoma
coronatum.

1983, Apr. 5　　　　　　　　Perf.
1282-1289　A375　Set of 8　　　7.50
　　Imperf., #1282-1289　　　　13.00

Raphael (1483-
1520),
Painter — A375a

Designs: 30xu, Virgin Mother Seated on
Chair. 50xu, Granduca, the Virgin Mother. 1d,
Sistine Madonna. 2d, Marriage of Maria. 3d,
The Gardener. 5d, Woman with Veil. 8d, 10d,
Self-Portrait.

1983, Apr. 30　　　　　　Perf. 12½
1289A-1289G　A375a　Set of 7　　7.50
Souvenir Sheet
Perf. 13
1289H　A375a　10d　multicolored　6.50

Chess
Pieces — A376

Designs: 30xu, Vietnamese pawns. 50xu,
Indian elephant. 1d, Scottish knight, bishop.
2d, Indian elephant, diff. 3d, Knight. 5d, Sailing
ship. 8d, Jester, elephant. 10d, Modern
pawns.

1983, May 9　　　　　　　Perf. 13
1290-1296　A376　Set of 7　　　7.00
　　Imperf., #1290-1296　　　　12.00
Souvenir Sheet
1297　A376　10d　multicolored　　7.25
　　No. 1297 contains one 28x36mm stamp.

Souvenir Sheet

TEMBAL '83 World Stamp Exhibition,
Basel — A377

1983, May 21　　　　　　　Perf. 13
1298　A377　10d　multicolored　5.00 5.00

1984 Summer
Olympics, Los
Angeles
A378

Designs: 30xu, Long jump. 50xu, Running.
1d, Javelin. 2d, High jump, horiz. 3d, Hurdles,
horiz. 5d, Shot put. 8d, Pole vault. 10d,
Discus.

1983, June 13　　Litho.　　Perf. 13
1299-1305　A378　Set of 7　　　7.50
Souvenir Sheet
1306　A378　10d　Sheet of 1　　6.25
　　No. 1306 contains one 32x40mm stamp.
　　The issuance of this set has been
questioned.

Souvenir Sheet

Brasiliana '83, Rio de Janeiro — A379

1983, July 20　　　　　　Perf. 13
1307　A379　10d　Rhamphastos
　　　　　toco　　　　　6.00 5.00

Butterflies
A380

Designs: No. 1308, 30xu, Leptocircus
meges. No. 1309, 30xu, Terias hecabe. No.
1310, 40xu, Zetides agamemnon. No. 1311,
40xu, Nyctalemon patroclus. No. 1312, 50xu,
Papilio chaon. No. 1313, 50xu, Precis almana.
60xu, Thauria lathyi. 1d, Kallima inachus.

1983, July 30　　Litho.　　Perf. 12
1308-1315　A380　Set of 8　　　6.25
　　Imperf., #1308-1315　　　　10.00

Souvenir Sheet

Bangkok '83 — A381

1983, Aug. 4　　　　　　　Perf. 13
1316　A381　10d　multicolored　10.00 10.00

Karl Marx
(1818-1883)
A382

1983, Oct. 10　　　　　　Perf. 11
1317-1318　A382　50xu, 10d, set
　　　　　　　　　　of 2　　5.00
　　Imperf., #1317-1318　　　　50.00

Phu Dong Sports Festival — A383

1983, Oct. 10
1319-1320　A383　30xu, 1d, set of
　　　　　　　　　　2　　2.00

World
Food Day
A384

Design: 50xu, Infant, fish. 4d, Family.

1983, Oct. 10　　　　　　Perf. 12½
1321-1322　A384　Set of 2　　　2.50
　　Imperf., #1321-1322　　　　5.00

Mushrooms
A385

#1323, 50xu, Flammulina velutipes. #1324,
50xu, Pleurotus ostreatus. #1325, 50xu,
Cantharellus cibarius. #1326, 50xu, Coprinus
atramentarius. 1d, Volvariella volvacea. 2d,
Agaricus silvaticus. 5d, Morchella esculenta.
10d, Amanita caesarea.

1983, Oct. 10　　　　　Perf. 12x12½
1323-1330　A385　Set of 8　　11.00 8.00
　　Imperf., #1323-1330　　　　11.00
　　For overprints see Nos. 2150-2157.

World Communications Year — A386

50xu, Letter carrier. 2d, Mail sorting room.
8d, Switchboard operators. #1334, 10d, Radio
operator, antenna. #1335, 10d, Telephone, letter, dish antenna, ship.

1983, Oct. 30　　　　　　Perf. 12½
1331-1334　A386　Set of 4　　　4.50
Souvenir Sheet
Perf. 13
1335　A386　10d　Sheet of 1　　3.00

5th Natl. Trade Unions
Congress — A387

50xu, Woman with flowers, Vietnam-Soviet
Union Friendship Cultural Building. 2d, 30d,
Welder.

1983, Nov. 16　　　　　　Perf. 11
1336-1338　A387　Set of 3　　　7.50

Water Birds
A388

Designs: No. 1339, 50xu, Ciconia nigra. No. 1340, 50xu, Ardea cinerea. No. 1341, 50xu, Ardea purpurea. No. 1342, 50xu, Ibis leucocephalus. 1d, Grus grus. 2d, Platalea minor. 5d, Nycticorax nycticorax. 10d, Anastomus oscitans.

1983, Nov. 20   **Perf. 12x12½**
1339-1346 A388 Set of 8   9.00   5.00
    Imperf. #1339-1346   14.00

No. 1343 inscribed "Grus grue."

World Peace
Conference,
Prague — A389

Designs: 50xu, Shown. 3d, 5d, 20d, Hands, globe, dove.

1984, Jan. 15   **Perf. 11**
1347-1350 A389 Set of 4   9.00

1984 Winter Olympics, Sarajevo,
Yugoslavia — A390

#1351, 50xu, Cross-country skiing, vert. #1352, 50xu, Biathlon, vert. 1d, Speed skating, vert. 2d, Bobsled, vert. 3d, Hockey. 5d, Ski jumping. 6d, Slalom skiing. 10d, Pairs figure skating.

1984, Jan. 30   **Perf. 12½**
1351-1357 A390 Set of 7   7.50
    Imperf., #1351-1357   12.00
Souvenir Sheet
1358 A390 10d multicolored   4.50

No. 1358 contains one 40x32mm stamp.

Soviet Union-Vietnamese Projects,
1978-83 — A391

Designs: 20xu (No. 1359), 4d, Hoa Binh Hydro-electric project. 20xu (No. 1360), Vietnamese-Soviet Cultural Palace. 50xu, Thang Long Bridge.

1984, Jan. 31   **Perf. 11**
With Gum
1359-1362 A391 Set of 4   55.00

Endangered Animals — A392

Designs: No. 1363, 50xu, Felis marmorata. No. 1364, 50xu, Panthera tigris. No. 1365, 50xu, Panthera pardus. No. 1366, 1d, Hylobates lar. No. 1367, 1d, Nycticebus coucang. No. 1368, 2d, Elephas indidus. No. 1369, 2d, Bos gaurus.

1984, Feb. 26   **Perf. 12½x12**
1363-1369 A392 Set of 7   5.00
    Imperf. #1363-1369   14.00

A393

A394

Wildflowers: No. 1370, 50xu, Banhinia variegata. No. 1371, 50xu, Caesalpinia pulcherrima. 1d, Cassia fistula. 2d, Delonix regia. 3d, Artagotrys uncinatus. 5d, Corchorus olitorius. 8d, Banhinia grandiflora.

1984, Mar. 15   **Perf. 12x12½**
1370-1376 A393 Set of 7   7.50
    Imperf. #1370-1376   12.50
Souvenir Sheet
1377 A393 10d Delonix regia   4.50

Location of inscriptions differs on Nos. 1373, 1377.

1984, Mar. 28   **Perf. 13**
Orchids: No. 1378, 50xu, Cymbidium. No. 1379, 50xu, Brasse cattleya. 1d, Cattleya Dianx. 2d, Cymbidium, diff. 3d, Cymbidium hybridum. 5d, Phoenix winged orchids. 8d, Yellow Queen orchids.

1378-1384 A394 Set of 7   7.00
    Imperf., #1378-1384   10.00

Nos. 1085, 1093 Surcharged

a

b

1984, Apr. 25   **Perfs. as before**
1385 A322(a)   50xu on 12xu
    #1085   2.00
1386 A335(b)   50xu on 12xu
    #1093   2.00

Souvenir Sheet

Espana '84, Madrid — A395

1984, Apr. 27   **Perf. 12½**
1387 A395 10d Ciconia ciconia   5.50

Victory at Dien Bien Phu, 30th Anniv. A396

#1388, 50xu; #1395, 10d, Ho Chi Minh, generals, battle map. #1389, 50xu, Troops, truck. 1d, Civilians carrying provisions. 2d, Man-hauling artillery. 3d, Anti-aircraft battery. 5d, Troops attacking enemy base. 8d, Troops waving flag.

1984, May 7   **Perf. 12½**
1388-1394 A396 Set of 7   6.25
Souvenir Sheet
1395 A396 10d multicolored   4.50

Souvenir Sheet

UPU Congress, Hamburg '84 — A397

1984, June 19   **Perf. 13**
1396 A397 10d Junkers JU-52
    3M   5.00

Fish
A398

Designs: No. 1397, 30xu, Cypselurus spilopterus. No. 1398, 30xu, Ostracion cornutus. 50xu, Diodon hystrix. 80xu, Chelmon rostratus. 1d, Antennarius tridens. 2d, Pterois russelli. 5d, Mola mola. 10d, Minous monodactylus.

1984, June 25   **Litho.**   **Perf. 12**
1397-1404 A398 Set of 8   7.25
    Imperf., #1397-1404   10.00

Ornamental Fish — A399

Designs: No. 1405, 50xu, Trichogaster trichopterus. No. 1406, 50xu, Brachydanio rerio. 1d, Macropodus opercularis. 2d, Gymnocorymbus ternetzi. 3d, Hyphessobrycon serpae. 5d, Labeo bicolor. 8d, Batta splendens.

1984, June 29   **Perf. 12½**
1405-1411 A399 Set of 7   6.00
    Imperf. #1405-1411   10.00

Vietnamese Trade Union Movement,
55th Anniv. — A400

Designs: No. 1412a, 50xu, House at 15 Hang Non St., Hanoi, vert. No. 1412b, 50xu, Nguyen Duc Canh, vert. 1d, Striking workers. 2d, Ho Chi Minh visiting factory. 3d, Hanoi Mechanical Engineering plant. 5d, Intl. trade union movement.

1984, July 20   **Perf. 11**
1412-1416 A400 Set of 6   5.00
Souvenir Sheet
Imperf
1417   A400 2d like #1414   10.00

No. 1412 printed se-tenant. No. 1417 contains one 45x38mm stamp.

Rock Formations, Ha Long
Bay — A401

#1418, 50xu, Hang-Bo Nau. #1419, 50xu, Nui Yen Ngua. #1420, 50xu, Hon Dua. #1421, 50xu, Hang Con Gai. #1422, 1d, Hon Coc. #1423, 1d, Hon Ga Choi. 2d, Hon Dinh Huong. 3d, Hon Su Tu. 5d, Hon Am. 8d, Nui Bai Tho.

1984, July 30   **Perf. 12½x12**
1418-1427 A401 Set of 10   7.00
    Imperf. #1418-1427   12.50

Dinosaurs — A402

#1428, 50xu, Styracosaurus. #1429, 50xu, Diplodocus. #1430, 1d, Corythosaurus. #1431, 1d, Rhamphyorhynchus. 2d, Seymouria. 3d, Allosaurus. 5d, Dimetrodon. 8d, Brachiosaurus.

1984, Aug. 30
1428-1435 A402 Set of 8   13.50
    Imperf. #1428-1435   15.00

Viet Nam-Laos-Cambodia
Friendship — A403

1984, Aug. 30   **Perf. 11**
1436-1437 A403 50xu, 10d, set
    of 2 5.00

Souvenir Sheet

Ausipex '84, Melbourne,
Australia — A404

1984, Sept. 20   **Perf. 13**
1438　A404　10d Koala　　　　10.00

Viet Nam-
Cambodia
Friendship
Agreement, 5th
Anniv. — A405

50xu, 3d, People, pagoda, statue. 50d, Dancers.

1984, Sept. 30   **Perf. 11**
1439-1441　A405　Set of 3　　10.00

Liberation
of Hanoi,
30th
Anniv.
A406

Designs: 50xu, Thang Long Bridge. 1d, Khue Van Gateway. 2d, Ho Chi Minh mausoleum.

1984, Oct. 5
1442-1444　A406　Set of 3　　4.00

Vintage Automobiles — A407

#1445, 50xu, Vis-a-Vis, vert. #1446, 50xu, Duc. 1d, Tonneau. 2d, Double phaeton. 3d, Landaulet. 5d, Torpedo. 6d, Coupe de Ville.

1984, Oct. 30   **Perf. 12½x13, 13x12½**
1445-1451　A407　Set of 7　　5.00
　　　　　Imperf., #1445-1451　11.50

Lenin (1870-
1924)
A408

Paintings of Lenin: 50xu, At his desk. 1d, Standing with revolutionaries. 3d, Speaking at factory. 5d, Meeting with farmers.

1984, Nov. 15   **Perf. 12x12½**
1452-1455　A408　Set of 4　　3.50
　　　　　Imperf., #1452-1455　8.00

UNICEF
A409

Paintings: 30xu, Woman, soldiers. 50xu, Mother, children. 1d, Miner, family. 3d, Young girl, vert. 5d, Children playing on ground. 10d, Women, child, vert.

1984, Dec. 7   **Perf. 12**
1456-1461　A409　Set of 6　　5.50
　　　　　Imperf., #1456-1461　10.00

A410　　　　　　　　A411

50xu, 30d. Frontier Forces, 25th anniv.

1984, Dec. 15   **Perf. 11**
1462-1463　A410　Set of 2　　11.00
　　　　　Imperf., #1462-1463
　　　　See No. M39.

1984, Dec.   **Perf. 12½x12**
Flora and Fauna: 20xu, Bubalus bubalis. 30xu, Felis marmorata. No. 1466, 50xu, Hibiscus rosa-sinensis. No. 1467, 50xu, Ailurus fulgens. No. 1468, 50xu, Rosa centifolia. No. 1469, 50xu, Betta splendens. No. 1470, 1d, Chrysanthemum sinense. No. 1471, 1d, Nymphaea ampla. No. 1472, 1d, Pelecanus onocrotalus. No. 1473, 1d, Panthera tigris. No. 1474, 2d, Nycticebus coucang. No. 1475, 2d, Macaca fascicularis. No. 1476, 2d, Dalia coccinea. 5d, Gekko gecko. 10d, Rhytidoceros bicornis.

1464-1478　A411　Set of 15　　12.50
　　　　　Imperf., #1464-1478　15.00

No. 1466 inscribed "Hybiscus." No. 1470 inscribed "Chrysanthemun."

A412　　　　　　　　A413

1985   **Perf. 11**
1479-1480　A412　3d, 5d, set of 2　2.75
　　　　　Imperf., #1479-1480　30.00
New Year 1985 (Year of the Buffalo). Issued: 3d, 1/21; 5d, 4/30.

1985, Apr. 26   **Perf. 11**
1481　A413　2d Ho Chi Minh　.90
Vietnamese Communist Party, 55th anniv.

Military
Victory in
South Viet
Nam, 10th
Anniv.
A414

Designs: 1d, Soldiers advancing forward. 2d, 10d, Ho Chi Minh, tank, soldiers. 4d, Construction worker. 5d, Map, women.

1985, Apr. 30   **Perf. 12½**
1482-1485　A414　Set of 4　　4.50
Souvenir Sheet
Perf. 13
1486　A414　10d multicolored　3.75

Cactus
A415

Designs: No. 1487, 50xu, Echinocereus knippelianus. No. 1488, 50xu, Lemaireocereus thurberi. 1d, Notocactus haselbergii. 2d, Parodia chrysacanthion. 3d, Pelecyphora pseudopectinata. 5d, Rebutia frebrighii. 8d, Lobivia aurea.

1985, Apr. 30   **Perf. 11½**
1487-1493　A415　Set of 7　　7.25
　　　　　Imperf., #1487-1493　15.00

Vietnamese People's Army, 40th
Anniv. — A416

Designs: No. 1494, 50xu, Ho Chi Minh. No. 1495, 50xu, Taking oath on flag. 1d, Anti-aircraft missile. 2d, Soldiers, civilians working together. 3d, Tank entering grounds of presidential palace, Saigon. 5d, Soldier demonstrating use of rifle. 8d, Officers, soldiers, map. 10d, Four soldiers representing branches of military.

1985, May 6   **Perf. 12½**
1494-1500　A416　Set of 7　　5.50
Souvenir Sheet
1501　A416　10d multicolored　3.50

A417

A418

End of World War II, 40th Anniv.: 1d, 10d, Victory Monument. 2d, Vietnamese soldier. 4d, Dove, falling American eagle. 5d, Child, doves.

1985, May 7   **Perf. 12x12½**
1502-1505　A417　Set of 4　　4.50
　　　　　Imperf., #1502-1505　12.50
Souvenir Sheet
1506　A417　10d multicolored　3.25

1985, May 13   **Perf. 11**
Liberation of Haiphong, 30th anniv.: 2d, Long Chau Lighthouse. 5d, An Duong Bridge, horiz. 10d, To Hieu (1912-44), vert.
1507-1508　A418　Set of 2　　2.25

Souvenir Sheet
Imperf
1509　A418　10d multicolored　　2.75

Ho Chi Minh, 95th Birth
Anniv. — A419

Ho Chi Minh: 1d, At battlefield. 2d, Reading. 4d, 10d, Portrait, vert. 5d, Writing.

1985, May 19   **Perf. 12½**
1510-1513　A419　Set of 4　　3.25
Souvenir Sheet
Perf. 13
1514　A419　10d multicolored　3.50
No. 1514 contains one 30x36mm stamp.

Motorcycles, Cent. — A420

Designs: No. 1515, 1d, 1895, Germany. No. 1516, 1d, 1898 tricycle, France. No. 1517, 2d, 1913 Harley-Davidson, US. No. 1518, 2d, 1918 Cleveland, US. 3d, 1935 Simplex, US. 4d, 1984 Minarelli, Italy. 6d, 1984 Honda, Japan. 10d, 1984 Honda racing bike.

1985, June 28   **Perf. 13**
1515-1521　A420　Set of 7　　5.50
　　　　　Imperf., #1515-1521　14.00
Souvenir Sheet
1522　A420　10d multicolored　3.25
No. 1522 contains one 32x40mm stamp.

Argentina '85, Buenos Aires — A421

Wild animals: No. 1523, 1d, Aptenodytes pennati, vert. No. 1524, 1d, Dolichotis patagonum, vert. No. 1525, 2d, Panthera onca. No. 1526, 2d, Hydrochoerys capibara. 3d, Peterocnemia pennata, vert. 4d, Priodontes giganteus. 6d, Voltur gryphus. 10d, Lama glama, horiz.

1985, July 5   **Perf. 12½**
1523-1529　A421　Set of 7　　8.00
　　　　　Imperf., #1523-1529　16.00
Souvenir Sheet
With Gum
Perf. 13
1530　A421　10d multicolored　4.25
No. 1530 contains one 40x32mm stamp.

12th World
Youth and
Students
Festival,
Moscow
A422

No. 1531, 2d, Youth carrying flags, globe. No. 1532, 2d, Workers, power transmission lines. 4d, Lighthouse, coastal defense. 5d, Intl. festival.

1985, July 27   *Perf. 12½*
1531-1534   A422   Set of 4   5.00
    Imperf., #1531-1534   17.50

Souvenir Sheet
With Gum
Perf. 13

1535   A422   10d like #1531   3.25

Marine Life
A423

#1536, 30xu, Nadoa tuberculata. #1537, 30xu, Luidia maculata. #1538, 30xu, Stichopus chloronotus. #1539, 30xu, Holothuria monacaria. #1540, 40xu, Astropyga radiata. #1541, 40xu, Astropecten scoparius. #1542, 40xu, Linckia laevigata.

1985, July 30   *Perf. 12*
1536-1542   A423   Set of 7   7.00
    Imperf., #1536-1542   19.00

Socialist
Republic of Viet
Nam, 40th
Anniv. — A424

Designs: 2d, Construction. 3d, Hands shaking, doves. 5d, Flag, military forces. No. 1567, 10d, Flag, Ho Chi Minh.

1985, Aug. 28   *Perf. 12½*
1543-1546   A424   Set of 4   4.50
    Imperf., #1543-1546   17.50

Souvenir Sheet
Perf. 13

1547   A424   10d like #1543   4.00
No. 1547 contains one 32x40mm stamp.

Vietnamese Police Force, 40th
Anniv. — A425

1985, Aug. 30   *Perf. 11*
1548   A425   10d multicolored   4.00
See No. M41.

1st Natl.
Sports
Festival
A426

Designs: 5d, Gymnastics. 10d, Gymnastics, running, swimming.

1985, Aug. 30
1549-1550   A426   Set of 2   4.50

German Railways, 150th
Anniv. — A427

Various locomotives: #1551, 1d, Facing left. #1552, 1d, Facing right. #1553, 2d, Facing left. #1554, 2d, Facing right. 3d, 4d, 6d.

1985, Sept. 13   *Perf. 12½*
1551-1557   A427   Set of 7   6.25
    Imperf., #1551-1557   10.00

Souvenir Sheet
With Gum
Perf. 13

1558   A427   10d multicolored   4.50
No. 1558 contains one 32x40mm stamp.

Vietnamese Geological Survey, 30th
Anniv. — A428

#1559, Drilling rigs. #1560, Aerial survey.

1985, Oct. 5   *Perf. 11*
1559-1560   A428   1d   Set of 2   2.00

Italia '85
A429

Vintage Italian cars: No. 1561, 1d, 1922 Alfa Romeo. No. 1562, 1d, 1932 Bianchi Berlina. No. 1565, 3d, 1912 Itala. No. 1563, 2d, 1928 Isotta Fraschini. No. 1564, 2d, 1930 Bugatti. 4d, 1934 Lancia Augusta. 6d, 1927 Fiat Convertable (top up). 10d, 1927 Fiat Convertable (top down).

1985, Oct. 25   *Perf. 13*
1561-1567   A429   Set of 7   5.50
    Imperf., #1561-1567   11.00

Souvenir Sheet
With Gum

1568   A429   10d multicolored   3.50
No. 1568 contains one 40x32mm stamp.

Whales
A430

Designs: No. 1569, 1d, Balaenoptera musculus. No. 1570, 1d, Balaena borealis. No. 1571, 2d, Orcinus orca. No. 1572, 2d, Delphinus. 3d, Megaptera boops. 4d, Balaenoptera physalus. 6d, Eubalaena glacialis.

1985, Nov. 15
1569-1575   A430   Set of 7   8.50
    Imperf., #1569-1575   15.00

1986 World Cup Soccer
Championships, Mexico City — A431

Various soccer plays: No. 1576, 1d, From behind goal. No. 1577, 1d, Goalie from side. No. 1578, 2d, From behind goal. No. 1579, 2d, From in front of goal, vert. 3d, vert. 4d, vert. 6d, vert.

1985, Nov. 30
1576-1582   A431   Set of 7   5.00
    Imperf., #1576-1582   10.00

Souvenir Sheet
Perf. 13

1583   A431   10d multicolored   3.50
No. 1583 contains one 40x32mm stamp.

People's
Democratic
Republic of
Laos, 10th
Anniv. — A432

a, Woman, dove. b, Woman dancing, natl. arms.

1985, Dec. 2   *Perf. 11*
1584   A432   1d   Pair, #a.-b.   1.40

Traditional Musical
Instruments — A433

#1585, 1d, Stone chimes. #1586, 1d, Large bronze drum. #1587, 2d, Flutes. #1588, 2d, Large red drum. 3d, Monochord. 4d, Moonshaped lute. 6d, Vietnamese two-string violin.

1985, Dec. 5   *Perf. 12½x12*
1585-1591   A433   Set of 7   5.00

A434

A435

Socialist Republic of Viet Nam, 40th Anniv.: No. 1592, 10d, Industry. No. 1593, 10d, Agriculture. 20d, Public health. 30d, Education.

1985, Dec. 15   *Perf. 11*
1592-1595   A434   Set of 4   30.00

1986, Jan. 6   *Litho. Perf. 11*
1596-1597   A435   50xu, 1d   Set of
               2   1.25
1st Natl. Elections, 40th anniv.

A436

A437

1986, Jan. 6
1598   A436   1d multicolored   .80
UN 40th anniv.

1986, Feb. 24   *Perf. 12½*
Halley's Comet: No. 1599, 2d, Edmond Halley. No. 1600, 2d, Isaac Newton. 3d, Rocket, flags. 5d, Comet.

1599-1602   A437   Set of 4   3.50
    Imperf., #1599-1602   9.00

A438

A439

Soviet Communist Party, 27th Congress: 50xu, Kremlin, map. 1d, Lenin banner.

1986, Feb. 25   *Perf. 11*
1603-1604   A438   Set of 2   1.25

1986, Mar. 1
1605   A439   1d   Map of Battle of
          Xuong Giang   .90
Le Loi, 600th birth anniv.

1986 World
Cup Soccer
Championships,
Mexico
City — A440

Various soccer players in action: No. 1606, 1d, Viet Nam at left. No. 1607, 1d, Viet Nam at right. 2d, Viet Nam at left. No. 1609, 3d, Viet Nam at left. No. 1610, 3d, Viet Nam at right. No. 1611, 5d, Viet Nam at left. No. 1612, 5d, Viet Nam at right.

1986, Mar. 3   *Perf. 12½*
1606-1612   A440   Set of 7   5.50
    Imperf., #1606-1612   9.00

Souvenir Sheet
Perf. 13

1613   A440   10d multicolored   3.50
No. 1613 contains one 40x32mm stamp.

1st Manned Space Flight, 25th Anniv. A441

#1614, 1d, Konstantin Tsiolkovsky. #1615, 1d, Rocket on transporter. 2d, Yuri Gagarin. #1617, 3d, Valentina Tereshkova, vert. #1618, 3d, Alexei Leonov. #1619, 5d, Apollo-Soyuz, crews. #1620, 5d, Soyuz, Salut space station. 10d, Cosmonauts, vert.

1986, Apr. 12   **Perf. 13**
1614-1620 A441 Set of 7   5.50
    Imperf., #1614-1620   10.00
Souvenir Sheet
1621 A441 10d multicolored   3.50
No. 1621 contains one 32x40mm stamp.

Ernst Thalmann (1886-1944), German Politician — A442

1986, Apr. 16   **Perf. 11**
1622 A442 2d red & black   .90

May Day — A443

1986, May 1
1623-1624 A443 1d, 5d, set of 2   2.00

Vancouver Expo '86 — A444

Airplanes: No. 1625, 1d, Hawker Hart. No. 1626, 1d, Curtiss Jenny. 2d, PZL-P23. No. 1628, 3d, Yakovlev Yak-11. No. 1629, 3d, Fokker Dr.1. No. 1630, 5d, Boeing P-12 (1920). No. 1631, 5d, Nieuport-Delage NiD.29C1 (1929).

1986, May 12   **Perf. 13**
1625-1631 A444 Set of 7   5.50
    Imperf., #1625-1631   8.00

Dam-Strengthening Committee, 40th Anniv. — A445

1986, May 22   **Perf. 11**
1632 A445 1d carmine   .60

Bonsai — A446

Designs: No. 1633, 1d, Ficus glomerata. No. 1634, 1d, Ficus benjamina. 2d, Ulmus tonkinensis. No. 1636, 3d, Persica vulgaris. No. 1637, 3d, Streblus asper. No. 1638, 5d, Pinus khasya. No. 1639, 5d, Podocarpus macrophyllus. 10d, Serissa foetida, horiz.

1986, June 16   **Perf. 12x12½**
1633-1639 A446 Set of 7   5.00
    Imperf., #1633-1639   14.00
Souvenir Sheet
     Perf. 12½x12
1640 A446 10d multicolored   3.50

Domestic Cats — A447

Various cats (Background colors): No. 1641, 1d, blue green. No. 1642, 1d, red. 2d, blue. No. 1644, 3d, brown. No. 1645, 3d, blue. No. 1646, 5d, violet. No. 1647, 5d, red, vert.

     Perf. 13x12½, 12½x13
1986, June 16
1641-1647 A447 Set of 7   5.00
    Imperf., #1641-1647   11.00

Traditional Houses A448

Designs: No. 1648, 1d, Thai den. No. 1649, 1d, Nung. 2d, Thai trang. No. 1651, 3d, Tay. No. 1652, 3d, Hmong. No. 1653, 5d, Dao. No. 1654, 5d, Tay nguyen, vert.

     Perf. 12½x12, 12x12½
1986, June 20
1648-1654 A448 Set of 7   5.00
    Imperf., #1648-1654   12.50
Souvenir Sheet
     Perf. 12x12½
1655 A448 10d like #1654   3.50

Postal Service, 40th Anniv. — A449

Designs: No. 1656, 2d, Telecommunications. No. 1657, 2d, Map, letter carrier. 4d, Soldiers, Nguyen Thi Nghia. 5d, Dish antenna.

1986, Aug. 15   **Perf. 13**
1656-1659 A449 Set of 4   3.25
    Imperf., #1656-1659   15.00

A450

Birds: No. 1660, 1d, Merops apiaster. No. 1661, 1d, Cissa chinensis. 2d, Pteruthius erythropterus. No. 1663, 3d, Garrulax leucolophus. No. 1664, 3d, Psarisomus dalhousiae, horiz. No. 1665, 5d, Cyanopica cyanus, horiz. No. 1666, 5d, Motacilla alba. 10d, Copsychus malabaricus.

1986, Aug. 28   **Perf. 13**
1660-1666 A450 Set of 7   5.00
    Imperf. #1660-1666   11.50
Souvenir Sheet
     Perf. 12½
1667 A450 10d multicolored   4.25
No. 1667 contains one 32x40mm stamp. Stockholmia '86.

A451

1986, Sept. 15   **Perf. 12x12½**
Domestic fowl: No. 1668, 1d, Plymouth Rock. No. 1669, 1d, Maleagris gallopavo. No. 1670, 2d, Ri. No. 1671, 2d, White Plymouth rock. No. 1672, 3d, Leghorn. No. 1673, 3d, Rhode Island red. No. 1674, 3d, Rhode ri. 5d, Gray Plymouth rock hen.

1668-1675 A451 Set of 8   5.50
    Imperf., #1668-1675   12.50

11th Intl. Trade Unions Congress — A452

1986, Sept. 16   **Perf. 12½**
1676 A452 1d blue & red   .80

Artifacts, Hung-Vuong Period — A453

Designs: No. 1677, 1d, Seated figure, vert. No. 1678, 1d, Knife hilt in form of female figure, vert. 2d, Bronze axe. No. 1680, 3d, Bronze axe, diff. No. 1681, 3d, Bronze bowl. No. 1682, 5d, Bronze pot (round). No. 1683, 5d, Bronze vase (open top).

1986, Oct. 15   **Perf. 12x12½, 12½x12**
1677-1683 A453 Set of 7   5.00
    Imperf., #1677-1683   11.00
Souvenir Sheet
     Perf. 12x12½
1684 A453 10d like #1677   3.50

Vietnamese Red Cross, 40th Anniv. — A454

1986, Oct. 20   **Perf. 12½**
1685 A454 3d rose & greenish blue   .85

Sailing Ships — A455

Various sail and oar-powered ships (sail colors): #1686, 1d, bl, grn, yel. #1687, 1d, org. 2d, yel. #1689, 3d, pur & red. #1690, 3d, bl. #1691, 5d, bl, brn, org. #1692, 5d, org.

     Perf. 12½x12, 12½x13 (#1688)
1986, Oct. 20
1686-1692 A455 Set of 7   5.50
No. 1688 is 38x47mm.

Butterflies — A456

Designs: No. 1693, 1d, Catopsilia scylla. No. 1694, 1d, Euploea midamus. 2d, Appias nero. No. 1696, 3d, Danaus chrysippus. No. 1697, 3d, Papilio polytes stichius. No. 1698, 5d, Euploea diocletiana. No. 1699, 5d, Charaxes polyxena.

1986, Nov. 11   **Perf. 12½**
1693-1699 A456 Set of 7   5.50
    Imperf., #1693-1699   11.00
No. 1696 misspelled "Danais."

Vietnamese Communist Party, 6th Congress — A457

1d, Construction projects. 2d, Natl. defense. 4d, Ho Chi Minh. 5d, Intl. cooperation.

1986, Nov. 20   **Perf. 11**
1700-1703   A457   Set of 4   5.50
1700a-1703a   Perf. 12½   50.00
1702b   Perf. 11x12½   27.50
Souvenir Sheet
     Imperf
1704 A457 10d like #1700   3.50

Insects A458

Designs: No. 1705, 1d, Poecilocoris nepalensis. No. 1706, 1d, Bombus americanorum. 2d, Romalea microptera. No. 1708, 3d, Chalcocoris rutilans. No. 1709, 3d, Chrysocoris sellatus. No. 1710, 5d, Paranthrene palmi. No. 1711, 5d, Crocisa crucifera. 10d, Anabrus simplex.

1986, Nov. 30   **Perf. 12½**
1705-1711 A458 Set of 7   5.50
    Imperf., #1705-1711   12.50
Souvenir Sheet
1712 A458 10d multicolored   4.00
No. 1712 contains one 32x40mm stamp.

Intl. Peace
Year — A459

1986, Dec. 7   **Perf. 11**
1713-1714 A459 1d, 3d, set of 2   1.75

Handicrafts — A460

Designs: No. 1715, 1d, Round dish. No. 1716, 1d, Rattan handbag. 2d, Rattan foot stool. No. 1718, 3d, Bamboo hand basket. No. 1719, 3d, Muong pannier. No. 1720, 5d, Rattan basket with shoulder straps. No. 1721, 5d, Rattan basket with lid. 10d, Tall rattan basket.

1986, Dec. 10   **Perf. 11½**
1715-1721 A460 Set of 7   5.00
    Imperf., #1715-1721   9.00
Souvenir Sheet
1722 A460 10d multicolored   3.50

A461

A462

1986, Dec. 18   **Perf. 11**
1723 A461 2d blue green & fawn   .90
Natl. Resistance, 40th anniv.

1986, Dec. 26   **Perf. 12x12½**
Endangered flora: No. 1724, 1d, Fokienia hodginsii. No. 1725, 1d, Amentotaxus yunnanensis. 2d, Pinus kwangtungensis. No. 1727, 3d, Taxus chinensis. No. 1728, 3d, Cupressus torulosa. No. 1729, 5d,

Ducampopinus krempfii. No. 1730, 5d, Tsuga yunnanensis. 10d, Abies nukiangensis.

1724-1730 A462 Set of 7   5.00
    Imperf., #1724-1730   12.00
Souvenir Sheet
1731 A462 10d multicolored   3.50

Elephants — A463

#1732, 1d, Two elephants. #1733, 1d, Female, calf. #1734, 3d, Elephant. #1735, 1d, Elephant facing, vert. #1736, 5d, Man riding elephant, vert. #1737, 5d, Four elephants.

1986, Dec. 30   **Perf. 12½**
1732-1737 A463 Set of 6   5.00
    Imperf., #1732-1737   13.50
No. 1737 is 68x27mm.

Vietnamese
Legends
A464

Designs: a, Son Tinh. b, My Nuong. c-e, Battle between Mountain Genie and Water Genie. f-h, Celebration.

1987, Jan. 20   **Perf. 12**
1738 A464 3d Strip of 8, #a.-h. 7.00
    Imperf.   13.50

New Year 1987
(Year of the
Cat) — A465

1987, Jan. 25   **Perf. 11**
1739 A465 3d red lilac   .80

Natl.
Events
A466

Ho Chi Minh and: 10d, August revolution, Aug. 19, 1945. 20d, Proclaiming independence, Sept. 9, 1945. 30d, Victory at Dien Bien Phu, July 7, 1954. 50d, Capture of Saigon, Apr. 30, 1975.

1987, Apr. 10   **Perf. 11**
1740-1743 A466 Set of 4   6.25

A467

A468

Champa art: 3d, Temple, Da Nang. 10d, Tower, Na Trang. 15d, Temple, Da Nang (side view). 20d, Dancing girl. 25d, Bust of woman. 30d, Girl playing flute. 40d, Dancing girl, diff.

1987, June 30   **Perf. 12x12½**
1744-1750 A467 Set of 7   7.25
    Imperf., #1744-1750   9.50
Souvenir Sheet
1751 A467 50d like #1749   4.00

1987, July 10   **Perf. 12½**
Various flowering cacti: 5d, 10d, 15d, 20d, 25d, 30d, 40d.
1752-1758 A468 Set of 7   5.00
Souvenir Sheet
                                   Perf. 13
1759 A468 50d multicolored   3.50

Global Population Reaches 5
Billion — A469

1987, July 11   **Perf. 13**
1760 A469 5d multicolored   .50

World Wildlife
Fund — A470

Designs: No. 1761, 5d, Concolor gibbon. No. 1762, 5d, Douc monkeys. 15d, Black concolor gibbon. 40d, Douc monkey.

1987, July 15   **Perf. 12½**
1761-1764 A470 Set of 4   10.00 3.50
    Imperf., #1761-1764   35.00

A471

A472

Western high plateau costumes: 5d, Male Bana. No. 1766, 20d, Female Bana. No. 1767, 20d, Female Gia Rai. No. 1768, 30d, Male Gia Rai. No. 1769, 30d, Male Ede. 40d, Female Ede.

1987, July 25   **Perf. 12x12½**
1765-1770 A471 Set of 6   6.25
    Imperf., #1765-1770   10.00

1987, July 27   **Perf. 13**
1771 A472 5d multicolored   .75
Day of the Invalids, 40th anniv.

Postal
Trade
Union,
40th
Anniv.
A473

Designs: 5d, Letter carrier, jet, truck, train. 30d, Switchboard operator.

1987, Aug. 30
1772-1773 A473 Set of 2   1.75

A474

Paintings by Picasso: No. 1774, 3d, The Three Musicians. No. 1775, 20d, War. No. 1776, 20d, Peace. No. 1777, 30d, Child with Dove, vert. No. 1778, 30d, Portrait of Gertrude Stein, vert. 40d, Guernica. 50d, Child as Harlequin.

1987, Oct. 1   **Perf. 12½**
1774-1779 A474 Set of 6   5.50
    Imperf., #1774-1779   10.00
Souvenir Sheet
1780 A474 50d multicolored   4.50
No. 1779 is 44x27mm. No. 1780 contains one 40x32mm stamp.

Coral — A475

Designs: 5d, Epanouis. 10d, Acropora. 15d, Rhizopsammia. 20d, Acropora, diff. 25d, Alcyone, 30d, Corollum. 40d, Cristatella.

1987, Oct. 3   **Perf. 12x12½**
1781-1787 A475 Set of 7   7.50
    Imperf., #1781-1787   12.50

Intl. Year
for
Housing
for the
Homeless
A476

1987, Oct. 5   **Perf. 13**
1788 A476 5d greenish bl & blk   .75

Russian Revolution, 70th Anniv. — A477

Designs: 5d, 65d, Industry, agriculture. 20d, Lenin. 30d, Construction. 50d, Ho Chi Minh.

1987, Oct. 6   **Perf. 13**
1789-1792 A477 Set of 4   3.50
Souvenir Sheet
1793 A477 65d multicolored   3.25

Hafnia '87 A478

Seaplanes: 5d, PBY-5. 10d, LeO H-246. 15d, Dornier DO-18. 20d, Short Sunderland. 25d, Rohrbach Rostra. 30d, Chetverikov ARK-3. 40d, CANT Z-509. 50d, Curtiss H-16.

1987, Oct. 12   **Perf. 13**
1794-1800 A478 Set of 7   5.00
Souvenir Sheet
1801 A478 50d multicolored   3.25

No. 1801 contains one 40x32mm stamp.

Czechoslovakia-Viet Nam Friendship Agreement, 10th Anniv. — A479

10d, Handshake. 50d, Flags, buildings.

1987, Oct. 31
1802-1803 A479 Set of 2   3.25
   Imperf., 1802-1803   17.50

Viet Nam-Soviet Union Cooperation — A480

Designs: 5d, Industry. 50d, Buildings.

1987, Nov. 3
1804-1805 A480 Set of 2   2.75

Mushrooms A481

Designs: 5d, Polyporellus squamosus. 10d, Clitocybe geotropa. 15d, Tricholoma terreum. 20d, Russula aurata. 25d, Collybia fusipes. 30d, Cortinarius violaceus. 40d, Boletus aereus.

1987, Nov. 10   **Perf. 12½**
1806-1812 A481 Set of 7   5.00
   Imperf., #1806-1812   10.00

Peace A482

1987, Nov. 30   **Perf. 13**
1813 A482 10d multicolored   1.00

Afro-Asian Solidarity Committee (AAPSO), 30th Anniv. — A483

10d, Hands, dove. 30d, Map, hands, vert.

1987, Nov. 30
1814-1815 A483 Set of 2   1.75
   Imperf., #1814-1815   20.00

Victory Over US Bombing Campaign, 15th Anniv. — A484

Designs: 10d, B-52 wreckage. 30d, Children with flowers, wreckage.

1987, Dec. 26
1816-1817 A484 Set of 2   1.75
   Imperf., #1816-1817   15.00

Productivity A485

Designs: 5d, Consumer goods. 20d, Agriculture. 30d, Export products.

1987, Dec. 30
1818-1820 A485 Set of 3   2.50

Hoang Sa, Truong Sa Islands A486

Designs: 10d, Ship, sailor. 100d, Maps.

1988, Jan. 19
1821-1822 A486 Set of 2   3.25

Roses — A487

Various roses: 5d, 10d, 15d, 20d, 25d, 30d, 40d.

1988, Jan. 20   **Perf. 12½**
1823-1829 A487 Set of 7   4.50
   Imperf., #1823-1829   10.00
Souvenir Sheet
Perf. 13
1830 A487 50d multicolored   3.50

Tropical Fish A488

Designs: 5d, Red betta splendens. 10d, Labeo bicolor. 15d, Puntis tetrazona. 20d, Brachydania albolineatus. 25d, Puntis conchonius. 30d, Betta splendens, diff. 40d, Botia lecontei.

1988, Jan. 20   **Perf. 13**
1831-1837 A488 Set of 7   5.00
   Imperf., #1831-1837   12.00

Intl. Red Cross, Red Crescent, 125th Anniv. — A489

1988, Feb. 17
1838 A489 10d multicolored   1.10

Battle of Bach Dang, 700th Anniv. A490

80d, Fleet of ships. 200d, Battle scene.

1988, Apr. 8
1839-1840 A490 Set of 2   3.75

Tourism A491

5d, One-pillar pagoda. 10d, Bach Dang River. 15d, Thien Mu Tower, Hue. 20d, Hgu Hanh Mountain, Da Nang. 25d, Nha Trang beach. 30d, Pren Waterfalls. 40d, Market, Ben Thanh. 50d, Cleft Rocks, Quang Ninh.

1988, Apr. 20   **Perf. 12½x12**
1841-1847 A491 Set of 7   5.50 5.50
   Imperf., #1841-1847   10.00
Souvenir Sheet
1848 A491 50d multicolored   3.50

Water Lilies — A492

Designs: 5d, Nymphaea lotus. No. 1850, 10d, Nymphaea pubescens. No. 1851, 10d, Nymphaea nouchali. No. 1852, 20d, Nymphaea rubra. No. 1853, 20d, Nymphaea gigantea. 30d, Nymphaea laydekeri. 50d, Nymphaea capensis.

1988, Apr. 20   **Perf. 12x12½**
1849-1855 A492 Set of 7   5.25
   Imperf., #1849-1855   12.50

Offshore Oil Drilling — A493

1988, Apr. 28   **Perf. 13**
1856 A493 1000d multicolored   9.00

A494

Parrots: No. 1857, 10d, Ara araruna. No. 1858, 10d, Psittacula himalayana. No. 1859, 20d, Aprosmictus erythropterus. No. 1860, 20d, Ara chloroptera. No. 1861, 30d, Ara militaris. No. 1862, 30d, Psittacula alexandri. 50d, Loriculus vernalis. 80d, Ara chloroptera, diff.

1988, May 5   **Perf. 12x12½**
1857-1863 A494 Set of 7   5.00
   Imperf., #1857-1863   11.00
Souvenir Sheet
1864 A494 80d multicolored   4.00

A495   A496

Membership in Council of Mutual Economic Assistance, 10th Anniv.: 200d, Map. 300d, Headquarters building.

1988, May 29   **Perf. 13**
1865-1866 A495 Set of 2   4.50

1988, June 1
1867 A496 60d multicolored   1.00

Vaccinations against disease.

Problems of Peace and Socialism Magazine, 30th Anniv. — A497

1988, July 20
1868 A497 20d multicolored   .90

A498

A499

1988, Aug. 20
1869 A498 150d multicolored 1.50
Pres. Ton Duc Thang, birth cent.

1988, Aug. 28
6th Vietnamese Trade Union Congress: 50d, Emblem. 100d, Workers.
1870-1871 A499 Set of 2 1.75

Children's Paintings A500

#1872, 10d, My Family. #1873, 10d, My House. #1874, 20d, Fishing. #1875, 20d, Flying Kites. #1876, 30d, Girl playing guitar, animals. #1877, 30d, Children in rain, vert. 50d, Girl holding dove, vert. 80d, Family, diff., vert.

Perf. 12½x12, 12x12½
1988, Sept. 25
1872-1878 A500 Set of 7 5.50 1.60
Imperf., #1872-1878 7.00
Souvenir Sheet
Perf. 12x12½
1879 A500 80d multicolored 3.75

Hydroelectric Plants — A501

Designs: 2000d, Tri An. 3000d, Hoa Binh.

1988, Sept. 27 **Perf. 13**
1880-1881 A501 Set of 2 11.00

A502

A503

1988, Nov. 3 **Perf. 13½x13**
1882 A502 50d multicolored .70
Viet Nam-USSR Friendship Agreement, 10th anniv.

1988, Dec. 27
Designs: 100d, Fidel Castro. 300d, Flags, Vietnamese, Cuban people.
1883-1884 A503 Set of 2 1.75
Cuban revolution, 30th anniv.

Wild Animals A504

Designs: No. 1885, 10d, Bos banteng. No. 1886, 10d, Bos gaurus. No. 1887, 20d, Axis porcinus. No. 1888, 20d, Tapirus indicus. No. 1889, 30d, Capricornis sumatrensis. No. 1890, 30d, Sus scrofa. 50d, Bubalus bubalus. 80d, Rhinoceros sodaicus.

1988, Dec. 30 **Perf. 12½**
1885-1891 A504 Set of 7 5.00
Imperf., #1885-1891 12.50
Souvenir Sheet
1892 A504 80d multicolored 3.50
Imperf. 13.00

Locomotives — A505

Designs: No. 1893, 20d, Kiha 80, Japan. No. 1894, 20d, LRC, Canada. No. 1895, 20d, Hitachi, Japan. No. 1896, 20d, BL-85, USSR. No. 1897, 30d, RC-1, Sweden. No. 1898, 30d, DR-1A, USSR. 50d, T3-136, USSR. 80d, SCNF Z6400.

1988, Dec. 30 **Perf. 13**
1893-1899 A505 Set of 7 5.00
Imperf., #1893-1899 12.50
Souvenir Sheet
1900 A505 80d multicolored 3.50
Imperf. 5.00
No. 1900 contains one 40x32mm stamp.

A506

A507

Fruits, vegetables: No. 1901, 10d, Lagenaria siceraria. No. 1902, 10d, Momordica charantia. No. 1903, 20d, Solanum melongena. No. 1904, 20d, Cucurbita moschata. No. 1905, 30d, Luffa cylindrica. No. 1906, 30d, Benincasa hispida. 50d, Lycopercicon esculentum.

1988, Dec. 30 **Perf. 12x12½**
1901-1907 A506 Set of 7 5.00
Imperf., #1901-1907 8.50

1988, Dec. 30 **Perf. 13**
Various project spacecraft: No. 1908, 10d, Mars. No. 1909, 10d, Moon. No. 1910, 20d, Saturn. No. 1911, 20d, Inter-planetary. No. 1912, 30d, Venus. No. 1913, 30d, Earth orbital

space station. 50d, Cosmos house. 80d, Lander docking with orbiter.
1908-1914 A507 Set of 7 3.50
Souvenir Sheet
1915 A507 80d multicolored 3.50
Cosmos Day.
No. 1915 contains one 32x40mm stamp.

Shells A508

Designs: No. 1916, 10d, Conus miles. No. 1917, 10d, Strombus lentiginosus. No. 1918, 20d, Nautilus. No. 1919, 20d, Bursa rana. No. 1920, 30d, Turbo petholatus. No. 1921, 30d, Oliva erythros. 50d, Mitra eriscopalis. 80d, Tonna tessellata.

1988, Dec. 30 **Perf. 12½x12**
1916-1922 A508 Set of 7 4.50
Imperf., #1916-1922 13.50
Souvenir Sheet
1923 A508 80d multicolored 3.50

India '89 — A509

Butterflies: No. 1924, 50d, Anaea echemus. No. 1925, 50d, Ascia monuste. No. 1926, 50d, Juniona evarete. No. 1927, 100d, Phoebis avellaneda. No. 1928, 100d, Eurema proterpia. 200d, Papilio palamedes. 300d, Danaus plexippus. 400d, Parides gundlachiamus.

1989, Jan. 7 **Perf. 12½**
1924-1930 A509 Set of 7 4.50
Imperf., #1924-1930 9.00
Souvenir Sheet
1931 A509 400d multicolored 3.00
No. 1931 contains one 40x32mm stamp. Nos. 1924-1930 printed with se-tenant label.

Natl. Day of Cambodia, 10th Anniv. — A510

Designs: 100d, Soldiers, women working in field. 500d, Viet Nam-Cambodia friendship.

1989, Jan. 7 **Perf. 13x13½**
1932-1933 A510 Set of 2 2.75
Imperf., #1932-1933 20.00

India '89 — A511

Designs: No. 1934, 100d, Science, technology. No. 1935, 100d, Agriculture, industry. 300d, Asoka pillar. 600d, Nehru (1889-1964).

1989, Jan. 20 **Perf. 13**
1934-1937 A511 Set of 4 4.00

Battle of Dong Da, Bicent. — A512

Designs: 100d, Festival. 1000d, Quang Trung defeating Qing invaders.

1989, Feb. 10 **Perf. 13**
1938-1939 A512 Set of 2 3.00

Inter-Parliamentary Union, Cent. — A513

Designs: 100d, Vietnamese membership, 10th anniv. 200d, Centennial emblem.

1989, Mar. 1
1940-1941 A513 Set of 2 1.75

Fishing Boats — A513a

Boats from: No. 1942, 10d, Quang Nam. No. 1943, 10d, Quang Tri. No. 1944, 20d, Thua Thien. No. 1945, 20d, Da Nang (sail furled). No. 1946, 30d, Da Nang (under sail). No. 1947, 30d, Quang Tri (under sail). 50d, Hue.

1989, Mar. 20 **Perf. 12½x12**
1942-1948 A513a Set of 7 5.00
Imperf., #1942-1948 10.00

Helicopters — A514

#1949, 10d, Kamov KA-26. #1950, 10d, Boeing Vertol 234. #1951, 20d, Mil MI-10(V10). #1952, 20d, MBB BO 105. #1953, 30d, Kawasaki Hughes 369HS. #1954, 30d, Bell 206B Jet Ranger. 50d, Mil MI-8. 80d, Puma SA330.

1989, Apr. 12 **Perf. 12½**
1949-1955 A514 Set of 7 4.00
Imperf., #1949-1955 10.00
Souvenir Sheet
1956 A514 80d multicolored 3.00
Imperf. 10.00
No. 1956 contains one 40x32mm stamp.

Bicycles A515

#1957, 10d, Bowden Spacelander. #1958, 10d, Rabasa Derbi. #1959, 20d, Huffy. #1960, 20d, Rabasa Derbi. #1961, 30d, VMX-PL. #1962, 30d, Premier. 50d, Columbia RX5.

1989, May 1   *Perf. 13*
1957-1963 A515 Set of 7   4.00
   Imperf., #1957-1963   10.00

Turtles — A516

No. 1964, 10d, Cuora trifasciata. No. 1965, 10d, Testudo elegans. No. 1966, 20d, Eretmochelys imbricata. No. 1967, 20d, Platysternon megacephalum. No. 1968, 30d, Dermochelys coriacea. No. 1969, 30d, Chelonia mydas. 50d, Caretta caretta. 80d, Caretta caretta, diff.

1989, May 1   *Perf. 12½*
1964-1970 A516 Set of 7   6.00
   Imperf., #1964-1970   11.50
Souvenir Sheet
1971 A516 80d multicolored   3.25
   Imperf.   10.00

Finlandia '88 (#1971).

Poisonous Snakes — A517

Designs: No. 1972, 10d, Trimeresurus popeorum. No. 1973, 10d, Trimeresurus mucrosquamatus. No. 1974, 20d, Bungarus fasciatus. No. 1975, 20d, Bungarus candidus. No. 1976, 30d, Calliophis maclellandii. No. 1977, 30d, Ancistrodon acutus. 50d, Ophiophagus hannah, vert.

1989, May 1
1972-1978 A517 Set of 7   5.75
   Imperf., #1972-1978   13.50

Pairs Figure Skating — A518

Various figure skaters: No. 1979, 10d, "Viet Nam" at left. No. 1980, 10d, "Viet Nam" at right. No. 1981, 20d, "Viet Nam" at left. No. 1982, 20d, "Viet Nam" at right, horiz. No. 1983, 30d, "Viet Nam" at left. No. 1984, 30d, "Viet Nam" at right, horiz. 50d, "Viet Nam" at left, horiz.

1989, May 29   *Perf. 13*
1979-1985 A518 Set of 7   4.00
   Imperf., #1979-1985   10.00
Souvenir Sheet
With Gum
1986 A518 80d multi, horiz.   3.50

No. 1986 contains one 40x32mm stamp.

A519   A520

1989, June 5   *Perf. 13*
1987 A519 100d buff   .75

Post & Telecommunications.

1989, July 1   *Perf. 12*
Ceramics, Li-Tran Period: 50d, Pitcher. No. 1989, 100d, Bowl. No. 1990, 100d, Jug. 200d, Jug, diff. 300d, Vase.

1988-1992 A520 Set of 5   3.75
   Imperf., #1988-1992   6.00

Legend of Giong A521

Designs: 50d, Mother nursing infant. No. 1994, 100d, Giong meets imperial messenger. No. 1995, 100d, Giong riding iron horse, people following. 200d, Giong pulling up bamboo trees. 300d, Giong flying into sky.

1989, July 1   *Perf. 12½x12*
1993-1997 A521 Set of 5   3.50
   Imperf., #1993-1997   5.50

French Revolution, Bicent. — A522

Designs: 100d, Emblem. 500d, Liberty leading the people, after Delacroix.

1989, July 14   *Perf. 13½x13*
1998-1999 A522 Set of 2   1.75

PHILEXFRANCE '89 — A523

Paintings: No. 2000, 50d, Oath of the Tennis Court, by David. No. 2001, 50d, Capture of Louis XVI, horiz. No. 2002, 50d, Liberty, Equality, Fraternity, horiz. No. 2003, 100d, Storming the Bastille. No. 2004, 100d, Death of Marat, by David. 200d, Child and Rabbit, by Prud'hon. 300d, Slave Market, by Gerome, horiz. 400d, Liberty Leading the People, by Delacroix.

1989, July 14   *Perf. 13*
2000-2006 A523 Set of 7   5.00
   Imperf., #2000-2006   10.00
Souvenir Sheet
2007 A523 400d multicolored   3.25

No. 2007 contains one 33x44mm stamp.

1989 World Cup Soccer Championships, Italy — A524

Soccer plays: No. 2008, 50d, Dribbling. No. 2009, 50d, Tackling. No. 2010, 50d, Goalie. No. 2011, 100d, Dribbling, diff. No. 2012, 100d, Dribbling, diff., vert. 200d, Preparing to kick, vert. 300d, Heading ball, vert. 400d, Heading ball, diff., vert.

Perf. 13x12½, 12½x13
1989, Aug. 27
2008-2014 A524 Set of 7   4.50
   Imperf., #2008-2014   11.00
Souvenir Sheet
Perf. 13
2015 A524 400d multicolored   3.50

No. 2015 contains one 32x40mm stamp.

Dogs A525

#2016, 50d, Dachshund. #2017, 50d, Beagle. #2018, 50d, English setter, vert. #2019, 100d, German short-haired pointer, vert. #2020, 100d, Basset hounds. 200d, German sheperd, vert. 300d, Beagle, diff.

1989, Aug. 20   *Perf. 12½*
2016-2022 A525 Set of 7   4.50
   Imperf., #2016-2022   10.00

No. 2020 is 68x28mm.

Horses A526

#2023, 50d, Tennessee Walking. #2024, 50d, Appaloosa. #2025, 50d, Tersky. #2026, 100d, Kladruber. #2026, 100d, Welsh cob. 200d, Pinto. 300d, Pony and bridle.

1989, Sept. 23   *Perf. 13*
2023-2029 A526 Set of 7   4.50
   Imperf., #2023-2029   12.50

No. 2029 is 68x28mm.

Flowers — A527

No. 2030, 50d, Paphiopedilum siamense. No. 2031, 50d, Fuchsia fulgens. No. 2032, 100d, Hemerocallis fulva. No. 2033, 100d, Gloriosa superba. 200d, Strelitzia reginae. 300d, Iris.

1989, Sept. 23   *Perf. 12½*
2030-2035 A527 Set of 6   4.50 2.00
   Imperf., #2030-2035   9.00

German Democratic Republic, 40th Anniv. — A528

1989, Oct. 7   *Perf. 13*
2036 A528 200d multicolored   .90

Immunization Campaign — A529

#2037, Woman receiving vaccination. #2038, Child receiving oral vaccine. #2039, Clinic.

1989, Oct. 20
2037-2039 A529 100d Set of 3   1.25

Drawings of Everyday Life, 19th Cent. — A530

Designs: 50d, Assembling plow. No. 2041, 100d, Harrowing. No. 2042, 100d, Irrigating. 200d, Fertilizing. 300d, Harvesting.

1989, Oct. 28   *Perf. 12x12½*
2040-2044 A530 Set of 5   3.75 2.40
   Imperf., #2040-2044   5.50

Horse Paintings, by Xu Beihong (1895-1953) A531

Various horses: 100d, 200d, 300d, 500d horiz., 800d, 1000d, 1500d.

1989, Dec. 22   *Perf. 13*
2045-2051 A531 Set of 7   5.75
   Imperf., #2045-2051   9.00
Imperf
Size: 117x72mm
2052 A531 2000d multicolored   5.50
   Imperf.   11.00

Vietnamese Communist Party, 60th Anniv. — A532

Designs: 100d, Ho Chi Minh, tank. 500d, Workers, refinery, field.

1990, Feb. 3   *Litho.*   *Perf. 13*
2053-2054 A532 Set of 2   2.75
   Imperf., #2053-2054   4.50

Ducks — A533

a, 100d, Anas platyrhynchos hybrid. b, 300d, Anas penelope. c, 500d, Anas platyrhynchos. d, 1000d, Anas erythrorhyncha. e, 2000d, Anas platyrhynchos, diff. f, 3000d, Anas undulata.

1990, Feb. 15
2055 A533 Block of 6, #a.-f. 4.50

Trucks
A534

100d, Mack. 200d, Volvo F89. 300d, Tatra 915 S1. 500d, Hino KZ30000. 1000d, Iveco. 2000d, Leyland DAF Super Comet. 3000d, Kamaz 53212.

1990, Feb. 20
2056-2062 A534 Set of 7 4.00 1.50
   Imperf., #2056-2062 5.50

Architectural Sites, Hue — A535

#2063, 100d, Tu Duc's Mausoleum. #2064, 100d, Hien Nhon Arch. 200d, Ngo Mon Gate. 300d, Thien Mu Temple. 400d, Palace, gateway.

1990, Feb. 20   **Perf. 12½x12**
2063-2066 A535 Set of 4 2.75
   Souvenir Sheet
2067 A535 400d multicolored 2.25

Goldfish — A536

Paintings
A537

100d, Bulging-eyed, horiz. 300d, Telescopic-eyed, horiz. 500d, Red-headed, horiz. 1000d, Double-tailed. 2000d, Rainbow. 3000d, Comet.

1990, Mar. 20   **Perf. 13**
2068-2073 A536 Set of 6 4.50 1.25
   Imperf., #2068-2073 7.00

1990, Apr. 10
London '90: 100d, Antonia Zarate, by Goya. 200d, Girl Holding a Paper Fan, by Renoir.

300d, Janet Grizel, by John Russell. 500d, Love Untieing the Belt of Beauty, by Sir Joshua Reynolds. 1000d, Portrait of a Woman, by George Romney. 2000d, Portrait of Madame Ginoux, by Van Gogh. 3000d, Woman in Blue, by Gainsborough. 3500d, Woman in a Straw Hat, by Van Gogh.

2074-2080 A537 Set of 7 4.50 1.50
   Imperf., #2074-2080 7.50
   Souvenir Sheet
2081 A537 3500d multicolored 3.50 1.60

1990 World Cup Soccer
Championships, Italy — A538

Various soccer players in action: 100d, 200d, 300d, 500d, 1000d, 2000d, 3000d.

1990, Apr. 19
2082-2088 A538 Set of 7 4.00
   Souvenir Sheet
2089 A538 3500d multicolored 2.75
No. 2089 contains one 32x40mm stamp.
For overprints see Nos. 2189-2196.

Cats — A539

Dogs — A540

Various cats: 100d, horiz., 200d, 300d, horiz., 500d, 1000d, horiz., 2000d, 3000d.

1990, May 5
2090-2096 A539 Set of 7 4.00
   Souvenir Sheet
2097 A539 3500d multicolored 3.25
No. 2097 contains one 44x33mm stamp.
Belgica '90 (#2097).

1990, May 15
Various dogs: 100d, 200d, 300d, 500d, 1000d, 2000d, 3000d.
2098-2104 A540 Set of 7 4.00
   Souvenir Sheet
2105 A540 3500d Collies 3.25
New Zealand '90.

Ho Chi Minh
(1890-1969)
A541

Ho Chi Minh and: 100d, Lenin. 300d, Soldiers waving flag. 500d, Hand holding rifle, dove. 1000d, Map. 2000d, Child, dove. 3000d, Stylized globe. 3500d, Flag.

1990, May 17   **Perf. 13**
2106-2111 A541 Set of 6 3.50
   Imperf., #2106-2111 5.00
   Souvenir Sheet
   Perf. 12½x13
2112 A541 3500d multicolored 2.50
No. 2112 contains one 33x44mm stamp.

Dinosaurs — A542

100d, Gorgosaurus. 500d, Ceratosaurus. 1000d, Ankylosaurus. 2000d, Ankylosaurus, diff. 3000d, Edaphosaurus.

1990, June 1   **Perf. 13**
2113-2117 A542 Set of 5 5.25 2.25

Columbus' Discovery of America,
500th Anniv. — A543

Designs: 50d, Fleet. No. 2119, 100d, Columbus presenting gifts to natives. No. 2120, 100d, Columbus, priest at Rabida. No. 2121, 100d, Columbus at Court of Ferdinand, Isabella. No. 2122, 200d, Map of Caribbean. No. 2123, 200d, Columbus, arms. 300d, Map of Atlantic. 500d, Teotihuacan pot.

1990, June 10   **Perf. 12½**
2118-2124 A543 Set of 7 5.75
   Souvenir Sheet
2125 A543 500d multicolored 2.00
No. 2125 contains one 40x32mm stamp.
For overprints see Nos. 2313-2320.

Sailing
Ships
A544

Designs: 100d, Viking longship. 500d, Caravel. No. 2128, 1000d, Carrack, 14th-15th cent. No. 2129, 1000d, Flit. No. 2130, 1000d, Carrack, 15th cent., vert. 2000d, Galleon, vert. 3000d, Galleon, diff. 4200d, Egyptian barge.

1990, June 10   **Perf. 13**
2126-2132 A544 Set of 7 5.75
   Imperf., #2126-2132 9.00
   Souvenir Sheet
   Perf. 13x12½
2133 A544 4200d multicolored 3.25
No. 2133 contains one 44x33mm stamp.

11th Asian
Games,
Beijing — A545

Designs: 100d, High jump. 200d, Basketball. 300d, Table tennis. 500d, Volleyball. 1000d, Rhythmic gymnastics. 2000d, Tennis. 3000d, Judo. 3500d, Hurdles.

1990, June 20   **Perf. 13**
2134-2140 A545 Set of 7 5.00 3.25
   Imperf., #2134-2140 6.50
   Souvenir Sheet
   Perf. 12½x13
2141 A545 3500d multicolored 2.50
No. 2141 contains one 33x44mm stamp.

Nos. 1180-1187 Ovptd. in Red, Green
and Black

1990, June 22   **Perf. 12**
2142-2149 A352 Set of 8 5.00
1990 World Cup Soccer Championships, Italy.

Nos. 1323-1330 Ovptd. in Black and
Red

1990, June 22   **Perf. 12x12½**
2150-2157 A385 Set of 8 7.25
Tourism.

Modern
Ships
A546

100d, Freighter. 300d, Container ship. 500d, Cruise ship. 1000d, Liquified natural gas tanker. 2000d, Ro-Ro ship. 3000d, Ferry.

1990, July 20   **Perf. 13**
2158-2163 A546 Set of 6 5.00
   Imperf., #2158-2163 7.50

Post & Telecommunications Dept.,
45th Anniv. — A547

Designs: 100d, Dove, ship, plane. 1000d, Satellite antenna.

1990, Aug. 15   **Perf. 13x13½**
2164-2165 A547 Set of 2 .80
   Imperf., #2164-2165 2.75

Socialist Republic of
Viet Nam, 45th
Anniv. — A548

Designs: 100d, Flag, construction projects. 500d, Map, tank, soldiers. 1000d, "VI," ship, communications network. 3000d, Workers, oil rigs. 3500d, Ho Chi Minh.

1990, Sept. 1   *Perf. 13*
2166-2169   A548   Set of 4   3.25
    Imperf., #2166-2169   4.00
Souvenir Sheet
Perf. 12½x13
2170   A548   3500d multicolored   2.50

No. 2170 contains one 33x44mm stamp. Sixth Vietnamese Communist Party Congress (#2168).

Airships
A549

Designs: 100d, Henry Gifford, 1871. 200d, Lebandy, 1910. 300d, Graf Zeppelin. 500d, R-101, 1930. 1000d, Soviet, 1936. 2000d, Tissandier, 1883. 3000d, US Navy. 3500d, "Zodiac," 1931.

1990, Sept. 10   *Perf. 12½*
2171-2177   A549   Set of 7   5.00
Souvenir Sheet
2178   A549   3500d multicolored   2.50   1.00

No. 2178 contains one 40x32mm stamp. Helvetia '90, Stamp World London '90.

Fable of Thach
Sanh — A550

Designs: a, 100d, Thach Sanh carrying bundles of wood. b, 300d, Ly Thong. c, 500d, Thach Sanh killing python. d, 1000d, Thach Sanh shooting arrow at eagle. e, 2000d, Thach Sanh in prison. f, 3000d, Thach Sanh, princess.

1990, Sept. 20   *Perf. 13*
2179   A550   Block of 6, #a.-f.   5.00
    Imperf.   6.00

Asian-Pacific Postal Training Center,
20th Anniv. — A551

1990, Sept. 25
2180   A551   150d multicolored   .45

Nos. 571-578 Ovptd. with
Red Cross in Red and
"FOR THE FUTURE GENERATION" in
various Languages in Black

Language: No. 2181, 12xu, Japanese. No. 2182, 12xu, Italian. No. 2183, 20xu, German. No. 2184, 20xu, Vietnamese. 30xu, English. 40xu, Russian. 50xu, French. 60xu, Spanish.

1990, Sept. 25   *Perf. 12*
2181-2188   A211   Set of 8   5.50

Position of overprint varies.
Use of these stamps at stated face value is unlikely.

Nos. 2082-2089 Ovptd.

1990, Sept. 25   *Perf. 13*
2189-2195   A538   Set of 7   5.00
Souvenir Sheet
2196   A538   3500d multicolored   3.25

Vietnamese Women's Federation, 60th
Anniv. — A552

Designs: 100d, Woman carrying rifle. 500d, Women working in field, laboratory.

1990, Oct. 10
2197-2198   A552   Set of 2   .50
    Imperf., #2197-2198   3.00

Correggio
(1494-1534),
Painter — A553

Various paintings of the Madonna and Child: No. 2199, 50xu, shown. No. 2200, 50xu, diff. 1d, 2d, 3d, 5d, 6d.

1990, Nov. 13   *Perf. 12½*
2199-2205   A553   Set of 7   5.50
Souvenir Sheet
2206   A553   10d multicolored   5.50

No. 2206 contains one 32x40mm stamp. Dated "1984." Use of these stamps at stated face value is unlikely.

Protection of Forests — A554

Designs: 200d, Water conservation, healthy forest. 1000d, SOS, prevent forest fires.

1990, Nov. 15   *Perf. 13*
2207-2208   A554   Set of 2   1.25

A555

A555a

Poisonous mushrooms: 200d, Amanita pantherina. 300d, Amanita phalloides. 1000d,

Amanita virosa. 1500d, Amanita muscaria. 2000d, Russula emetica. 3000d, Boletus satanas.

1991, Jan. 21
2209-2214   A555   Set of 6   5.50
    Imperf., #2209-2214   7.00

1991, Jan. 31
1992 Summer Olympics, Barcelona: 200d, Sailing. 300d, Boxing. 400d, Cycling. 1000d, High jump. 2000d, Equestrian. No. 2220, 3000d, Judo. No. 2221, 3000d, Wrestling, horiz. 5000d, Soccer, horiz.
2215-2221   A555a   Set of 7   6.25
    Imperf., #2215-2221   7.00
Souvenir Sheet
2222   A555a   5000d multicolored   3.25
    Imperf., #2222   5.00

No. 2222 contains one 44x33mm stamp.

Nguyen Binh Khiem (1491-1585),
Writer — A556

1991, Feb. 15
2223   A556   200d multicolored   .50
    Imperf.   2.00

Discovery of America, 500th
Anniv. — A557

Sailing ships: 200d, Marisiliana. No. 2225, 400d, Venetian. No. 2226, 400d, Cromster, vert. No. 2227, 2000d, Nina. No. 2228, 2000d, Pinta. 3000d, Howker, vert. 5000d, Santa Maria.
6500d, Portrait of Columbus.

1991, Feb. 22
2224-2230   A557   Set of 7   7.25
    Imperf., #2224-2230   6.00
Souvenir Sheet
2231   A557   6500d multicolored   4.00
    Imperf.   6.00

Golden Heart
Charity — A558

Women wearing traditional costumes: 200d, 500d, 1000d, 5000d.

1991, Feb. 26
2232-2235   A558   Set of 4   3.75
    Imperf., #2232-2235   5.00

Sharks
A559

Designs: 200d, Carcharhinus melanopterus. 300d, Carcharhinus amblyrhynchos. 400d, Triakis semifasciata. 1000d, Sphyrna mokarran. 2000d, Triaenodon abesus. No. 2241, 3000d, Carcharias laurus. No. 2242, 3000d, Carcharhinus leucas.

1991, Apr. 6
2236-2242   A559   Set of 7   5.50
    Imperf., #2236-2242   7.50

Endangered Birds — A560

World Wildlife Fund: 200d, Grus vipio. 300d, Grus antigone chick, vert. 400d, Grus japonensis, vert. 1000d, Grus antigone, adults, vert. 2000d, Grus nigricollis, vert. No. 2248, 3000d, Balearica regulorum, vert. No. 2249, 3000d, Bugeranus leucogerranus.

1991, Apr. 20
2243-2249   A560   Set of 7   10.00   3.50
    Imperf., #2243-2249   20.00

Shellfish
A561

Designs: 200d, 1000d, 2000d, Palinurus, all diff. 300d, Alpheus bellulus. 400d, Periclemenes brevicarpalis. No. 2255, 3000d, Astacus. No. 2256, 3000d, Palinurus, diff.

1991, Apr. 20
2250-2256   A561   Set of 7   10.00   3.50
    Imperf., #2250-2256   20.00

Young Pioneers,
50th
Anniv. — A562

Designs: 200d, shown. 400d, UN Convention on Children's Rights.

1991, May 15
2257-2258   A562   Set of 2   .50
    Imperf., #2257-2258   4.00

Rally
Cars
A563

#2259, 400d, Lada. #2260, 400d, Nissan. 500d, Ford Sierra RS Cosworth. 1000d, Suzuki. 2000d, Mazda 323 4WD. #2264, 3000d, Lancia. #2265, 3000d, Peugeot. 5000d, Peugeot 405.

1991, May 24
2259-2265   A563   Set of 7   5.50
    Imperf., #2259-2265   5.00
Souvenir Sheet
2266   A563   5000d multicolored   4.00
    Imperf.   5.00

No. 2266 contains one 44x33mm stamp.

Locomotives — A564

#2267, 400d, Puffing Billy, 1811, vert.
#2268, 400d, Fusee, 1829, vert. 500d, Stevens, 1825. 1000d, Crampton #80, 1852. 2000d, Locomotion, 1825. #2272, 3000d, Saint-Lo, 1844. #2273, 3000d, Coutances, 1855. 5000d, Atlantic, 1843.

1991, May 25
2267-2273 A564 Set of 7   5.50
   Imperf., #2267-2273   8.00
Souvenir Sheet
2274 A564 5000d multicolored   3.25
   Imperf.   6.00

No. 2274 contains one 33x44mm stamp.

Frogs
A565

World Wildlife Fund: 200d, Dendrobates leucomelas. 400d, Rana esculenta. 500d, Mantella aurantiaca. 1000d, Dendrobates tinctorius. 2000d, Hyla halowelli. No. 2280, 3000d, Agalychnis callidryas. No. 2281, 3000d, Hyla aurea.

1991, June 12
2275-2281 A565 Set of 7   10.00 3.50
   Imperf., #2275-2281   22.00

7th Vietnamese
Communist
Party Congress
A566

Designs: 200d, Ho Chi Minh, buildings. 300d, Workers. 400d, Mother, children.

1991, June
2282-2284 A566 Set of 3   1.50
   Imperf., #2282-2284   4.50

Vietnamese
Communist
Party, 60th
Anniv. — A566a

1991, June 24   Litho.   Perf. 13
2284A A566a 100d red   .75

1992
Winter
Olympics,
Albertville
A567

Designs: 200d, Speed skating, vert. 300d, Free-style skiing, vert. 400d, Bobsled. 1000d, Biathlon. 2000d, Slalom skiing. No. 2290, 3000d, Cross-country skiing, vert. No. 2291, 3000d, Ice dancing, vert. 5000d, Hockey, vert.

1991, July 15
2285-2291 A567 Set of 7   5.50
   Imperf., #2285-2291   4.00
Souvenir Sheet
2292 A567 5000d multicolored   3.25
   Imperf.   4.00

No. 2292 contains one 33x44mm stamp.

Prehistoric Animals — A568

Designs: a, 200d, Arsinoitherium zitteli. b, 500d, Elephas primigenius. c, 1000d, Baluchitherium. d, 2000d, Deinotherium giganteum. e, 3000d, Brontops. f, 3000d, Uinatherium.

1991, July 26
2293 A568 Block of 6, #a.-f.   6.25

A569

Golden Heart Charity: 200d, Eye, folded hands. 3000d, Tennis player in wheelchair.

1991, July 27
2294-2295 A569 Set of 2   1.75

1991, Aug. 20
Chess pieces: 200d, Pawn. 300d, Knight. 1000d, Rook. 2000d, Queen. No. 2300, 3000d, Bishop. No. 2301, 3000d, King. 5000d, Pawn, Knight, King.

A570

2296-2301 A570 Set of 6   5.50
   Imperf., #2296-2301   5.00
Souvenir Sheet
2302 A570 5000d multicolored   3.25
   Imperf.   5.00

No. 2302 contains one 33x44mm stamp.

PHILANIPPON '91 — A571

Butterflies: 200d, Attacus atlas. 400d, Morpho cypris. 500d, Troides rotschildi. No. 2306, 1000d, Papilio demetrius. No. 2307, 1000d, Vanessa atalanta. 3000d, Papilio weiskei. 5000d, Apatura ilia substituta. 5500d, Heliconius melpomene.

1991, Aug. 29
2303-2309 A571 Set of 7   5.75
   Imperf., #2303-2309   5.00
Souvenir Sheet
2310 A571 5500d multicolored   3.25
   Imperf.   5.00

No. 2310 contains one 44x33mm stamp.

Post and Telecommunications
Research Institute, 25th
Anniv. — A572

1991, Aug.
2311 A572 200d multicolored   .50
   Imperf.   2.00
Souvenir Sheet
2312 A572 3500d Communica-
    tions network,
    horiz.   2.50
   Imperf.   5.00

No. 2312 contains one 44x33mm stamp.

Nos. 2118-2125 Ovptd. in Red

1992, Jan. 15   Perf. 12½
2313-2319 A543 Set of 7   6.50
Souvenir Sheet
2320 A543 500d multicolored   4.00

7th Vietnamese
Communist Party
Congress
A574

200d, Workers, industry, agriculture, atomic energy symbol. 2000d, Map of Asia, hands clasped.

1992, Feb. 3   Litho.   Perf. 13
2322-2323 A574 Set of 2   2.25

1992 Winter Olympics,
Albertville — A575

Designs: 200d, Biathlon. 2000d, Hockey. 4000d, Slalom skiing. 5000d, Pairs figure skating. 6000d, Downhill skiing.

1992, Feb. 5
2324-2328 A575 Set of 5   5.50

Miniature Sheet

Columbus' Discovery of America,
500th Anniv. — A576

Designs: a, 4000d, Columbus, flag. b, 6000d, Columbus, natives. c, 8000d, Aboard ship. d, 3000d, Two sailing ships. e, 400d, Columbus' fleet setting sail.
11,000d, Columbus with Ferdinand and Isabella.

1992, Feb. 12
2329 A576 #a.-f. + label   6.25
         Imperf
      Size: 102x70mm
2330 A576 11,000d multicolored   5.00

Airplanes — A577

Designs: 400d, Tupelov TU-154M. 500d, Concorde. 1000d, Airbus A-320. 3000d, Airbus A340-300. 4000d, Boeing Dash 8-400. 5000d, Boeing 747-200. 6000d, McDonnell-Douglas MD-11CF.

1992, Mar. 6   Perf. 13
2331-2337 A577 Set of 7   5.50

A578

Intl. Decade for Natural Disaster Reduction: 400d, Storm system, weather forecasting equipment. 4000d, Man taking water depth readings.

1992, Mar. 23
2338-2339 A578 Set of 2   1.25

A579

1992, Mar. 28
1992 Summer Olympics, Barcelona: 400d, Archery. 600d, Volleyball. 1000d, Wrestling. 3000d, Fencing. 4000d, Running. 5000d, Weight lifting. 6000d, Field hockey. 10,000d, Basketball.

2340-2346 A579 Set of 7   5.50
Souvenir Sheet
2347 A579 10,000d multicolored   3.50

No. 2347 contains one 32x43mm stamp.

Motorcycles — A580

Designs: 400d, 5000d, Suzuki 500F. 500d, Honda CBR 600F. 1000d, Honda HRC 500F. 3000d, Kawasaki 250F, vert. 4000d, Suzuki RM 250F, vert. 6000d, BMW 1000F. 10,000d, Suzuki RM 250F, diff.

1992, Apr. 8
2348-2354 A580 Set of 7   5.50
Souvenir Sheet
2355 A580 10,000d multicolored   4.50

No. 2355 contains one 33x44mm stamp.

Intl. Space Year A581

400d, Space shuttle launch, vert. 500d, Launch of shuttle Columbia, vert. 3000d, Columbia in space. 4000d, Space station, shuttle Hermes. 5000d, Shuttle Hermes. 6000d, Astronauts, Hubble space telescope, vert.

1992, Apr. 12
2356-2361 A581 Set of 6   5.50

Saigon Post Office, Cent. A582

200d, Main entrance. 10,000d, Facade.

1992, Apr. 30   **Perf. 13**
2362 A582 200d multicolored   1.00
Souvenir Sheet
Perf. 13½
2363 A582 10,000d multicolored   2.50

No. 2363 contains one 43x32mm stamp.

European Cup Soccer Championships A583

Various soccer players in action: 200d, 2000d, 4000d, 5000d, 6000d.

1992, May 14   **Perf. 13**
2364-2368 A583 Set of 5   5.00
Souvenir Sheet
2369 A583 9000d multicolored   4.00

No. 2369 contains one 44x33mm stamp.

Spanish Paintings A584

Designs: 400d, Portrait of a Girl, by Zurbaran. 500d, Woman with a Jug, by Murillo. 1000d, Portrait of Maria Aptrickaia, by Velazquez. 3000d, Holy Family with St. Katherine, by de Ribera. 4000d, Madonna and Child with Saints Agnes and Thekla, by El Greco. 5000d, Woman with a Jug, by Goya, horiz. 6000d, The Naked Maja, by Goya, horiz. 10,000d, Three Women, by Picasso, horiz.

1992, May 30
2370-2376 A584 Set of 7   5.50
Souvenir Sheet
2377 A584 10,000d multicolored   4.00

No. 2377 contains one 44x33mm stamp. Expo '92, Seville (#2377).

UN Conference on Environmental Protection, 20th Anniv. — A585

Designs: 200d, Clean, polluted water. 4000d, Graph comparing current development pattern with environmentally safe pattern.

1992, June 1
2378-2379 A585 Set of 2   1.25

A586   Flowers — A587

Lighthouses: 200d, Cu Lao Xanh. 3000d, Can Gio. 5000d, Vung Tau. 6000d, Long Chau.

1992, June 14   **Perf. 13½x13**
2380-2383 A586 Set of 4   4.50

Genoa '92.

1992, June 28   **Perf. 13**
Designs: 200d, Citrus maxima. 2000d, Nerium indicum. 4000d, Ixora coccinea. 5000d, Cananga oborata. 6000d, Cassia surattensis.
2384-2388 A587 Set of 5   4.50

Birds — A588

Rodents — A589

Designs: 200d, Ducula spilorrhoa. 2000d, Petrophassa ferruginea. 4000d, Columba livia. 5000d, Lopholaimus antareticus. 6000d, Streptopelia senegalensis, horiz.

1992, July 3
2389-2393 A588 Set of 5   4.50

1992, July 26
Designs: 200d, 500d, Cavia porcellus, horiz. 3000d, Hystrix indica, horiz. 4000d, Gerbillus gerbillus. 5000d, Petaurista petaurista. 6000d, Oryctolagus cuniculus.
2394-2399 A589 Set of 6   5.50

Disabled Soldiers Day, 45th Anniv. A590

1992, July 27
2400 A590 200d multicolored   .50

3rd Phu Dong Games A591

1992, Aug. 1
2401 A591 200d multicolored   .50

Betta Splendens — A592

Various fish: 200d, 500d, 3000d, 4000d, 5000d, 6000d.

1992, Aug. 15
2402-2407 A592 Set of 6   5.50

1984 Summer Olympics, Los Angeles A592a

Designs: No. 2407A, 50xu, Gymnastics. No. 2407B, 50xu, Soccer, vert. 1d, Wrestling. 2d, Volleyball, vert. 3d, Hurdles. 5d, Basketball, vert. 8d, Weight lifting. 10d, Running, vert.

1992, Sept. 1   **Litho.**   **Perf. 12½**
2407A-2407G A592a Set of 7   4.50 4.50
Souvenir Sheet
2407H A592a 10d multi   4.50 4.50

Nos. 2407A-2407G were prepared in 1984 but were not released because of Viet Nam's boycott of the 1984 Summer Olympics.

Intl. Planned Parenthood Federation, 40th Anniv. — A593

Designs: 200d, Map showing member's locations, vert. 4000d, Anniv. emblem, map.

1992, Oct. 1
2408-2409 A593 Set of 2   1.25

Hanoi Medical School, 90th Anniv. A594

Designs: 200d, Medical students. 5000d, Alexandre Yersin, school.

1992, Nov. 20
2410-2411 A594 Set of 2   1.50

SOS Children's Villages — A595

Designs: 200d, Adult sheltering child. 5000d, Women, children inside house.

1992, Dec. 22
2412-2413 A595 Set of 2   1.50

17th Southeast Asian Games, Singapore — A596

1993, Jan. 1
2414 A596 200d multicolored   .50

Bees A597

Designs: 200d, Apis dorsata. 800d, Apis koschevnikovi. 1000d, Apis laboriosa. 2000d, Apis cerana japonica. 5000d, Apis cerana cerana. 10,000d, Apis mellifera, vert.

1993, Jan. 15
2415-2420 A597 Set of 6   5.50

Fable of Tam Cam — A598

Designs: 200d, Returning from river. 800d, Vision of old man by goldfish pool. 1000d, With unsold rice at market. 3000d, Trying on slipper for prince. 4000d, Rising from lotus flower. 10,000d, Royal couple.

1993, Jan. 18
2421-2426 A598 Set of 6   5.50

New Year 1993 (Year of the Rooster) A599

200d, 5000d, Rooster, hen and chicks.

1993, Jan. 20
2427-2428 A599 Set of 2   1.50

Medicinal Plants A600

Designs: 200d, Atractylodes macrocephala. No. 2430, 1000d, Lonicera japonica. No. 2431, 1000d, Quisqualis indica. 3000d, Rehmannia glutinosa. 12,000d, Gardenia jasminoides.

1993, Feb. 27
2429-2433 A600 Set of 5   5.50

Communications A601

200d, Map, communications equipment. 2500d, Map, Hong Kong-Sri Racha Cable route.

1993, Mar. 1
2434-2435 A601 Set of 2   .75

Asian Animals A602

200d, Ailuropoda melanoleuca. 800d, Panthera tigris. 1000d, Elephas maximus. 3000d, Rhinoceros unicornis. 4000d, Hylobates leucogenys. #2441, 10,000d, Neofelis nebulosa. #2442, 10,000d, Bos sauveli.

1993, Mar. 10
2436-2441 A602 Set of 6   5.00
Souvenir Sheet
Perf. 13½
2442 A602 10,000d multicolored   3.25

1994 World Cup Soccer Championships, U.S. — A603

Various soccer players in action.

1993, Mar. 30   *Perf. 13*
2443-2445 A603 200d, 1500d,
                 7000d, set of
                 3   2.25

Transportation — A604

Designs: 200d, Wheelbarrow. 800d, Buffalo cart. 1000d, Rickshaw, top up. 2000d, Rickshaw with passenger. 5000d, Rickshaw, top down. 10,000d, Horse-drawn carriage.

1993, Apr. 6
2446-2451 A604 Set of 6   5.00

500Kv Electricity Lines — A605

1993, May 1
2452-2453 300d, 400d, set of 2   .75

Polska '93 — A606

Paintings: 200d, Sunflowers, by Van Gogh. No. 2455, 1000d, Young Woman, by Modigliani. No. 2456, 1000d, Couple in Forest, by Rousseau. 5000d, Harlequin with Family, by Picasso. No. 2458, 10,000d, Female Model, by Matisse, horiz. No. 2459, 10,000d, Portrait of Dr. Gachet, by Van Gogh.

1993, May 7   *Perf. 13*
2454-2458 A606 Set of 5   5.00
Souvenir Sheet
Perf. 12½
2459 A606 10,000d multicolored   3.25
No. 2459 contains one 32x43mm stamp.

Da Lat, Cent. A607

Orchids: 400d, Paphiopedilum hirsutissimum. No. 2461, 1000d, Paphiopedilum malipoense. No. 2462, 1000d, Paphiopedilum gratrixianum. 12,000d, Paphiopedilum hennisianum.

1993, June 15   *Perf. 13*
2460-2463 A607 Set of 4   4.00

Asian Architecture — A608

Landmark buildings from: 400d, Thailand, vert. 800d, Indonesia, vert. 1000d, Singapore, vert. No. 2467, 2000d, Malaysia. No. 2468, 2000d, Cambodia. 6000d, Laos. 8000d, Brunei.
10,000d, Thai Binh, Viet Nam, vert.

1993, July 10   *Litho.*
2464-2470 A608 Set of 7   4.75
Souvenir Sheet
Perf. 14x13½
2471 A608 10,000d multicolored   3.25 3.25

7th Trade Union Congress — A608a

Designs: 400d, Industry, communications. 5000d, Hand holding hammer, doves, flowers.

1993, July 28 *Litho.*   *Perf. 13*
2471A-   A608a Set of 2
2471B   1.25

Crabs A609

Designs: 400d, Scylla serrata. 800d, Portunus sanguinotentus. 1000d, Charybdis bimaculata. 2000d, Paralithodes brevipes. 5000d, Portunus pelagicus. 10,000d, Lithodes turritus.

1993, July 30
2472-2477 A609 Set of 6   4.50

Stamp Day A610

5000d, Hand holding stamped envelope.

1993, Aug. 15
2478-2479 A610 Set of 2   1.50

Miniature Sheet

Tennis — A611

Women tennis players: a, 400d. c, 1000d. Male tennis players: b, 1000d. d, 12,000d.

1993, Sept. 20
2480 A611 #a.-d. + 2 labels   4.00

A613

A614

Costumes: 400d, Lo Lo. 800d, Thai. 1000d, Dao Do. 2000d, H'mong. 5000d, Kho Mu. No. 2488, 10,000d, Kinh.
No. 2489, 10,000d, Precious gem stones.

1993, Oct. 1   *Perf. 13*
2483-2488 A613 Set of 6   4.00
Souvenir Sheet
Perf. 13½
2489 A613 10,000d multicolored   3.25

Bangkok '93. Issued: Nos. 2483-2488, 10/1/93. No. 2489, 10/10/93.
No. 2489 contains one 43x32mm stamp.

1994, Jan. 1

New Year 1994 (Year of the Dog): Various dogs.

2490-2491 A614 400d, 6000d,
                 set of 2   1.75
                 Imperf., #2490-2491   4.00

Flowers A615

#2492, 400d, Prunus persica. #2493, 400d, Chrysanthemum morifolium. #2494, 400d, Rosa chinensis. 15,000d, Delonix regia.

1994
2492-2495 A615 Set of 4   5.50

Issued: #2492, 1/4; 15,000d, 4/3; #2493, 7/30; #2494, 10/10.

Chess A616

Designs: 400d, Anatoly Karpov. 1000d, Gary Kasparov. 2000d, Bobby Fischer. 4000d, Emanuel Lasker. No. 2500, 10,000d, Jose Capablanca.
No. 2501, 10,000d, King.

1994, Jan. 20
2496-2500 A616 Set of 5   4.50
   Imperf., #2496-2500   8.00
Souvenir Sheet
2501 A616 10,000d multicolored   3.25
   Imperf.   4.75

Hong Kong '94 — A617

Festivals: 400d, Hoi Lim. 800d, Cham. 1000d, Tay Nguyen. 12,000d, Nam Bo.

1994, Feb. 18
2502-2505 A617 Set of 4   4.00
   Imperf., #2502-2505   6.75

A618

A619

Various opera masks: 400d, 500d, 2000d, 3000d, 4000d, 7000d.

1994, Mar. 15
2506-2511 A618 Set of 6   4.75
   Imperf., #2506-2511   8.50

1994, Mar. 30
Various gladiolus hybridus: 400d, 2000d, 5000d, 8000d.
2512-2515 A619 Set of 4   3.75
   Imperf., #2512-2515   6.75

Japanese Paintings — A620

Paintings by: 400d, Utamaro. 500d, Harunobu. 1000d, Hokusai. 2000d, Hiroshige. 3000d, Hokusai, diff. 4000d, Utamaro, diff. 8000d, Choki.

1994, Apr. 9
2516-2522 A620 Set of 7   5.25
   Imperf., #2516-2522   9.25

Insects — A621

Designs: 400d, Cicindela aurulenta. 1000d, Harmonia octomaculata. 6000d, Cicindela tennipes. 7000d, Collyris.

1994, Apr. 20
2523-2526 A621 Set of 4   3.75
   Imperf., #2523-2526   5.50

Victory at Dien Bien Phu, 40th Anniv. A622

Designs: 400d, Soldiers dragging equipment. 3000d, Celebration.

1994, Apr.
2527-2528 A622 Set of 2   .90
   Imperf., #2527-2528   1.25

Newspaper "Young Pioneers," 40th Anniv. A623

1994, May 15   Perf. 13x13½
2529 A623 400d red & black   .45

Crocodiles — A625

Designs: 400d, Crocodylus porosus. 600d, Alligator mississippiensis. 2000d, Crocodylus niloticus. 3000d, Alligator sinensis. 4000d, Caiman yacare. 9000d, Crocodylus johnsoni. 10,000d, Caiman crocodilus.

1994, June 1   Perf. 13x13½
2532-2537 A625 Set of 6   5.00
   Imperf., #2532-2537   7.50
Souvenir Sheet
Perf. 13½
2538 A625 10,000d multicolored   3.25
   Imperf.   4.00
No. 2538 contains one 43x32mm stamp.

1994 World Cup Soccer Championships, US — A626

Various soccer players in action: 400d, 600d, 1000d, 2000d, 3000d, 11,000d.

1994, June 15   Perf. 13
2539-2544 A626 Set of 6   4.75
   Imperf., #2539-2544   8.25
Souvenir Sheet
Perf. 13½
2545 A626 10,000d multicolored   3.25
   Imperf.   4.75
No. 2545 contains one 32x43mm stamp.

Yersin's Discovery of Plague Bacillus, Cent. A627

1994, June   Perf. 13x13½
2546 A627 400d multicolored   .60

UPU, 120th Anniv. A629

Designs: 400d, UPU emblem, "120." 5000d, World map. 10,000d, UPU emblem, "P," vert.

1994, Aug. 1   Perf. 13
2551-2552 A629 Set of 2   1.40
Souvenir Sheet
Perf. 14x13½
2553 A629 10,000d multicolored   3.25

PHILAKOREA '94 — A630

Birds: 400d, Numenius arquata. 600d, Oceanites oceanicus. 1000d, Fregata minor. 2000d, Morus capensis. 3000d, Lunda cirrhata. 11,000d, Larus belcheri. 10,000d, Collocalia fuciphaga.

1994, Aug. 16   Perf. 13x13½
2554-2559 A630 Set of 6   4.75
Souvenir Sheet
Perf. 13½
2560 A630 10,000d multicolored   3.25
No. 2560 contains one 43x32mm stamp.

A631

A632

Bamboo: 400d, Bambusa blumeana. 1000d, Phyllostachys aurea. 2000d, Bambusa vulgaris. 4000d, Tetragonocalamus quadrangularis. 10,000d, Bambusa venticosa.

1994, Aug. 17   Perf. 13½x13
2561-2565 A631 Set of 5   5.00
Singpex '94.

1994, Sept. 20   Perf. 13x13½
Various bridges: 400d, 900d, 8000d.
2566-2568 A632 Set of 3   2.25

Children's Future A634

Designs: 400d+100d, Boy helping girl in wheelchair with kite. 2000d, Children dancing, vert.

1994, Oct. 2   Litho.   Perf. 13
2572-2573 A634 Set of 2   .80

A636

A637

People's Army, 50th Anniv.: 400d, People in formation. 1000d, Soldiers, battle map. 2000d, Ho Chi Minh, child. 4000d, Anti-aircraft battery.

1994, Dec. 22
2576-2579 A636 Set of 4   2.00

1994, June 25   Perf. 13
Intl. Olympic Committee, Cent.: 400d, Flags. 6000d, Pierre de Coubertin.
2580-2581 A637 Set of 2   2.75

ICAO, 50th Anniv. A638

Jets: 400d, In flight. 3000d, On ground.

1994, Dec. 7
2582-2583 A638 Set of 2   .90

Trams A639

Designs: 400d, With overhead conductor. 900d, Paris tram. 8000d, Philadelphia mail.

1994, Oct. 10   Litho.   Perf. 13x13½
2584-2586 A639 Set of 3   2.25

Liberation of Hanoi, 40th Anniv. A640

Designs: 400d, Greeting soldiers. 2000d, Workers, students, modern technology.

1994, Oct. 10
2587-2588 A640 Set of 2   .70

New Year 1995 (Year of the Boar) A641

Stylized boars: 400d, Adult, five young. 8000d, One eating.

1995, Jan. 2   Litho.   Perf. 13
2589-2590 A641 Set of 2   2.25

A642

A643

Birds: No. 2591, 400d, Pluvialis apricaria, horiz. No. 2592, 400d, Philetairus socius, horiz. No. 2593, 400d, Oxyruncus cristatus, horiz. No. 2594, 400d, Pandion haliaetus. No. 2595, 5000d, Cariama cristata.

1995, Jan. 20   Perf. 13x13½, 13½x13
2591-2595 A642 Set of 5   1.50

A number has been reserved for a souvenir sheet with this set.

1995, Feb. 1   Perf. 13
Traditional women's attire: 400d, Young women, bicycle. 3000d, Bride. 5000d, Girl in formal dress holding hat.

2597-2599 A643 Set of 3   1.90

Vietstampex '95 — A644

Owls — A645

1995, Feb. 18
2600 A644 5500d multicolored   1.50

1995, Mar. 1   Perf. 13½x13
Designs: 400d, Ketupa zeylonensis. 1000d, Strix aluco. 2000d, Strix nebulosa. 5000d, Strix seloputo. 10,000d, Otus leucotis. 12,500d, Tyto alba.

2601-2605 A645 Set of 5   3.75

Souvenir Sheet
Perf. 14x13½
2606 A645 12,500d multicolored   3.25
Imperf.   4.25

Fish A646

Designs: 400d, Pomacanthus arcuatus. 1000d, Rhinecanthus rectangulus. 2000d, Pygoplites diacanthus. 4000d, Pomacanthus ciliaris. 5000d, Balistes vetula. 9000d, Balistes conspicillum.

1995, Mar. 20   Perf. 13
2607-2612 A646 Set of 6   4.25

Lenin, 125th Birth Anniv. — A647

1995, Apr. 22   Litho.   Perf. 13
2613 A647 400d red & black   .25

End of World War II, 50th Anniv. A648

1995, May 2   Litho.   Perf. 13
2614 A648 400d multicolored   .35

A649

A650

1996 Summer Olympics, Atlanta: 400d, Hammer throw. 3000d, Cycling. 4000d, Running. 10,000d, Pole vault. 12,500d, Basketball.

1995, Apr. 5   Litho.   Perf. 13
2615-2618 A649 Set of 4   3.75

Souvenir Sheet
2619 A649 12,500d multicolored   3.25

1995, May 5
Various balloons: 500d, 1000d, 2000d, 3000d, 4000d, 5000d, 7000d.

2620-2626 A650 Set of 7   5.00

Finlandia '95, Intl. Philatelic Exhibition, Helsinki.

Miniature Sheets

Tapirus Indicus — A651

No. 2627a, 400d, With young. b, 1000d, Facing left. c, 2000d, Walking right. d, 4000d, Mouth open, left.
No. 2528a, 4000d, Facing right. b, 4000d, Eating leaves. c, 5000d, In water. d, 6000d, Head protruding out of water.

1995, Apr. 25
2627 A651 Sheet of 4, #a.-d.   5.00
2628 A651 Sheet of 4, #a.-d.   5.50

World Wildlife Fund (#2627).

Miniature Sheet

Parachutes — A652

No. 2629: a, 400d, One parachutist descending from sky. b, 2000d, Two descending. c, 3000d, One about to touch ground. d, 9000d, Three men on ground with open parachute.

1995, May 24
2629 A652 Sheet of 4, #a.-d.   3.25

Rhododendrons — A653

Designs: 400d, Fleuryi. 1000d, Sulphoreum. 2000d, Sinofalconeri. 3000d, Lyi. 5000d, Ovatum. 9000d, Tanastylum.

1995, June 30
2630-2635 A653 Set of 6   4.50

Miniature Sheet

Native Folktale — A654

a, 400d, Brothers and their parents. b, 1000d, Mother saying farewell to her departing

sons. c, 3000d, One brother is transformed into a statue. d, 10,000d, Both brothers transformed into statues.

1995, July 20   Litho.   Perf. 13
2636 A654 Sheet of 4, #a.-d.   3.25

A655

A656

400d, Statue of a woman holding child. 3000d, Three women of different races, emblem, horiz.

1995, Aug. 5
2637-2638 A655 Set of 2   .80

Women's Federation of Viet Nam: 65th anniv. (#2637), 1995 Intl. Women's Conf., Beijing (#2638).

1995, July 26
2639 A656 400d multicolored   .35

Admission to Assoc. of Southeast Asian Nations (ASEAN).

Natl. Day — A657

#2640, 400d, Ho Chi Minh, people waving flags, dove of peace. #2641, 400d, Ho Chi Minh holding child. #2642, 1000d, Communist symbol, bridge, electrical wire, building. #2643, 1000d, Ho Chi Minh, silhouettes of soldiers, building with flags flying. #2644, 2000d, Soldiers, natl. flag. #2645, 2000d, Antenna, satellite dish, van, olive branch, people on motorcycles.

1995, Aug. 14
2640-2645 A657 Set of 6   1.50

Viet Nam Labor Party, 65th anniv. (No. 2640). Ho Chi Minh, 105th birth anniv. (No. 2641). Evacuation of French troops from North Viet Nam, 40th anniv. (No. 2642). End of war in Viet Nam, 20th anniv. (No 2643). Natl. army, 50th anniv. (No. 2644). Post and Telecommunications Service, 50th anniv. (No. 2645).

Sir Rowland Hill (1795-1879) A658

Design: 4000d, Hill, "penny black."

1995, Aug. 15
2646 A658 4000d multicolored   .95

Natl. Sports Games — A659

1995, Aug. 30
2647 A659 400d multicolored   .25

Singapore '95 — A660

Orchids: 400d, Paphiopedilum druryi. 2000d, Dendrobium orcraceum. 3000d, Vanda. 4000d, Cattelya. 5000d, Paphiopedilum hirsutissimum. 6000d, Christenosia vietnamica haeger.
12,500d, Angraecum sesquipedale.

1995, Sept. 1
2648-2653 A660 Set of 6   5.25
Souvenir Sheet
2654 A660 12,500d multicolored   3.25
No. 2654 contains one 32x43mm stamp.

Asian Sites — A661

Designs: 400d, Buildings, monuments, tombs, Hue, Viet Nam. 3000d, Walkway over water, Trung Quoc. 4000d, Temple, Macao. 5000d, Kowloon, Hong Kong. 6000d, Pagoda, Dai Bac.

1995, Sept. 6
2655-2659 A661 Set of 5   4.25

UN, 50th Anniv. A662

1995, Oct. 10
2660 A662 2000d multicolored   .45

Total Solar Eclipse, Oct. 10, 1995 A663

1995, Dec. 23   Litho.   Perf. 13
2661 A663 400d multicolored   .35

Paintings of Women A664

Designs: 400d, Woman in white dress, flowers, by To Ngoc Van (1906-54) (4-1). 2000d, Washing hair, by Tran Van Can (1906-94) (4-2). 6000d, Standing beside vase of flowers, by To Ngoc Van (4-3). 8000d, Two women, by Tran Van Can (4-4).

1995, Nov. 15   Litho.   Perf. 13
2662-2665 A664 Set of 4   3.75

New Year 1996 (Year of the Rat) — A665

Stylized rats: 400d, One carrying fan, one riding horse. 8000d, Four carrying one in palanquin.
13,000d, Marching in parade, carrying banner.

1996, Jan. 2   Litho.   Perf. 13
2666 A665   400d multicolored   .20
2667 A665   8000d multicolored   1.75
Souvenir Sheet
2668 A665 13,000d multi, vert.   2.75
No. 2668 contains one 32x43mm stamp.

Dinosaurs — A666

Designs: 400d, Tsintaosaurus. 1000d, Archaeopteryx. 2000d, Psittacosaurus. 3000d, Hypsilophodon. 13,000d, Parasaurolophus.

1996, Mar. 6
2669-2673 A666 Set of 5   4.50

Kingfishers A667

Designs: 400d, Halcyon smyrnensis. 1000d, Megaceryle alcyon. 2000d, Alcedo Atthis. 4000d, Halcyon coromanda. 12,000d, Ceryle rudis.

1996, Mar. 11
2674-2678 A667 Set of 5   4.50

Flowers A668

Various flowers: No. 2679, 400d, brown (5-1). No. 2680, 400d, claret (5-2). No. 2681, 400d, green (5-3). No. 2682, 400d, blue (5-4). No. 2683, 5000d, red (5-5), vert.

Perf. 13x13½, 13½x13
1996, Jan. 10   Litho.
2679-2683 A668   Set of 5   1.25

8th Vietnamese Communist Party Congress — A669

Designs: 400d, Ho Chi Minh (2-1). 3000d, Stylized dove, satellite dish, electrical towers, hammer & sickle, building, olive branch (2-2).

1996, Feb. 3   Perf. 13
2684-2685 A669   Set of 2   .75

Asian Sites — A670

Monuments and statues in: 400d, Hanoi. 2000d, Thailand. 3000d, Bhubanesvar, India. 4000d, Kyoto, Japan. 10,000d, Borobudur, Java.

1996, Feb. 10   Litho.   Perf. 13
2686-2690 A670   Set of 5   4.50
See Nos. 2773-2777.

Statues — A671

Various statues of men in traditional costumes of early warriors: 400d, 600d, 1000d, 2000d, 3000d, 5000d, 6000d, 8000d.

1996   Litho.   Perf. 13½x13
2691-2698 A671   Set of 8   5.50

Central Committee, 50th Anniv. — A672

1996, May 22   Perf. 13
2699 A672 400d multicolored   .25

UNICEF, 50th Anniv. A673

Designs: 400d, Children of different races, cultures. 7000d, Plant, emblem, water droplets containing representations of education, drinking water, medicine, food.

1996, May 15
2700-2701 A673   Set of 2   1.75

Red Cross of Viet Nam, 50th Anniv. A674

1996, May 8   Perf. 13½
2702 A674 3000d Quotation, Ho   .75
                    Chi Minh

A675

Traditional Musical Instruments: a, 400d, Mandolin. b, 3000d, Bow and string instrument. c, 4000d, Square-shaped guitar-like instrument. d, 9000d, Zither.

1996, Apr. 24   Perf. 13½x13
2703 A675 Sheet of 4, #a.-d.   3.50
China '96 Intl. Philatelic Exhibition.

A676

1996, May 20   Perf. 13
Insects: 400d, Cincindela japonica. 500d, Calodema wallacei. 1000d, Mylabris oculata. 4000d, Chrysochroa buqueti. 5000d, Ophioniea nigrofasciata. 12,000d, Carabus tauricus.
2704-2709 A676   Set of 6   5.00

1996 Summer Olympic Games, Atlanta A677

Designs: 2000d, Soccer. 4000d, Sailing. 5000d, Field hockey.

1996, July 8
2710-2712 A677   Set of 3   2.75

Euro '96, European Soccer Championships, Great Britain — A678

Designs: a, 400d, Net, goalie. b, 8000d, Player making shot on goal.

1996, June 1
2713 A678 Pair, #a.-b.   2.00
No. 2713 is a continuous design.

Aircraft
A679

400d, Airbus A320. 1000d, AN-72. 2000d, MD-11F. 6000d, RJ-85. 10,000d, B747-400F. 13,000d, Space shuttle carried by Boeing 747.

1996, June 1
2714-2718 A679 Set of 5   4.50
Souvenir Sheet
Perf. 13½
2719 A679 13,000d multicolored 2.75

Stamp Day
A680

1996, Aug. 15   *Perf. 13*
2720 A680 400d No. 1L57 (1-1)   .25

Paintings by Nguyen Sáng (1923-88)
A681

400d, Woman, vase of flowers (2-1). 8000d, Soldiers returning from battle (2-2).

1996, Sept. 10   *Perf. 13*
2721-2722 A681 Set of 2   2.00

Hue School, Cent. — A682

400d, Women walking beside entrance (2-1). 3000d, View of portals, building (2-2).

1996, Sept. 5
2723-2724 A682 Set of 2   .75

Mushrooms
A683

Designs: 400d, Aleuria aurantia. 500d, Morchella conica. 1000d, Anthurus archeri. 4000d, Laetiporus serlphureus. 5000d, Filoboletus manipularis. 12,000d, Tremiscus helvelloides.

1996, Aug. 26   *Litho.*   *Perf. 13*
2725-2730 A683 Set of 6   5.25

Wild Animals — A684

Designs: a, 400d, Pygathrix nemacus. b, 2000d, Panthera tigris. c, 4000d, Rhinoceros sondaicus. d, 10,000d, Balearica regulorum.

1996, Oct. 10   *Litho.*   *Perf. 13*
2731 A684 Sheet of 4, #a.-d.   3.75
Taipei '96.

Campaign Promoting Iodized Salt — A685

1996, Nov. 2   *Litho.*   *Perf. 13*
2732 A685 400d multicolored   .40

Natl. Liberation Movement, 50th Anniv. — A686

1996, Dec. 19
2733 A686 400d multicolored   .40

Fruit — A687

Designs: No. 2734, Hylocereus undatus. No. 2735, Durio zibethinus. No. 2736, Persea americana. No. 2737, Garcinia mangostana. No. 2738, Nephelium lappaceum.

1997, Jan. 2   *Perf. 13x13½*
2734-2738 A687 400d Set of 5   .75

New Year 1997 (Year of the Ox) — A688

Stylized oxen: 400d, Adult, calf. 8000d, Adult.

1997, Jan. 8   *Litho.*   *Perf. 13*
2739-2740 A688 Set of 2   2.00

8th Vietnamese Communist Party Congress — A689

1997, Feb. 3
2741 A689 400d multicolored   .40

Goldfish
A690

Various carassius auratus: 400d, 1000d, 5000d, 7000d, 8000d.

1997, Feb. 5
2742-2746 A690 Set of 5   4.00
Souvenir Sheet
Perf. 13½x14
2747 A690 14,000d multicolored   3.00
No. 2747 contains one 43x32mm stamp. Hong Kong '97 (#2747).

Sculptures from Ly Dynasty — A691

Designs: 400d, Serpents in round figure, vert. 1000d, Dragon head, vert. 3000d, People playing instruments. 5000d, Gargoyle. 10,000d, Dragon-head bowl.

1997, Mar. 5
2748-2752 A691 Set of 5   4.50

Scenes — A692

Designs: 400d, Lake, people in park, Hà Tay. 5000d, Footbridge over river, Lai Chau. 7000d, Houses, fog, trees, Lào Cai.

1997, Mar. 20
2753-2755 A692 Set of 3   3.00

Huynh Thuc Khang (1876-1947)
A693

Disabled People in Sports — A694

1997, Apr. 21   *Litho.*   *Perf. 13½x13*
2756 A693 400d multi   .35

1997, Apr. 27   *Perf. 13*
1000d, Tennis. 6000d, Shooting.
2757-2758 A694 Set of 2   1.60

Wild Animals A695

400d, Chrotogale owstoni. 3000d, Lutra lutra. 4000d, Callosciurus erythraeus. 10,000d, Felis bangalensis.

1997, May 2
2759-2762 A695 Set of 4   3.75

A696

A697

1997, May 19
2763 A696 400d Women's Union   .35

1997, Apr. 15   *Litho.*   *Perf. 13*
Lilium longiflorum ?(Lilies): 400d, Red. 1000d, White. 5000d, Pink & white. 10,000d, Orange.
2764-2767 A697 Set of 4   3.50

PACIFIC 97 — A698

Suspension bridges: 400d, Golden Gate, San Francisco. 5000d, Raippaluoto. 10,000d, Seto.

1997, May 12
2768-2770 A698 Set of 3   3.25

Children
A699

400d, UN Convention on the Rights of the Child. 5000d, Breast milk is better.

1997, June 1   Litho.   Perf. 13
With Gum
2771-2772 A699 Set of 2   1.25 1.25

Asian Sites Type of 1996

Designs: 400d, Pagoda, Hanoi, Viet Nam. 1000d, Ruins of Persepolis, Iran. 3000d, Statue of woman, Iraq. 5000d, Sacred Rock, Kyaikto, Burma. 10,000d, Statue of Buddha lying down, Sr. Lanka.

1997, June 20   Litho.   Perf. 13
2773-2777 A670 Set of 5   4.25

Women's Costumes
A700

Various costumes: 400d, Woman holding umbrella, San Chay. 2000d, Woman sewing, wearing jacket tied with sash, Dao quain trang. 5000d, Woman pumping water from well provided by UNICEF, Phù Lá. 10,000d, Woman holding hands in air, Kho Me.

1997, July 8
2778-2781 A700 Set of 4   3.75

A701

A702

1997, July 11
2782 A701 400d multicolored   .35
Prevention of AIDS.

1997, Aug. 8   Litho.   Perf. 13
2783 A702 400d multicolored   .35
ASEAN, 30th anniv.

Monument to War Martyrs & Invalids, 50th Anniv. — A703

1997, July 25
2784 A703 400d multicolored   .35

Hibiscus — A704

a, 1000d, Hibiscus rosa sinensis. b, 3000d, Hibiscus schizopetalus. c, 5000d, Hibiscus syriacus (pink). d, 9000d, Hibiscus syriacus (yellow).

1997, Aug. 1
2785 A704 Sheet of 4, #a.-d.   3.75

A705

A706

1997, Aug. 26   Litho.   Perf. 13
2786 A705 400d multicolored   .35
Post and Telecommunications Union, 50th anniv.

1997, Sept. 4
Sea horses: 400d, 1000d, Hippocampus (diff.). 3000d, Hippocampus guttulatus. 5000d, Hippocampus kelloggi. 6000d, Hippocampus japonicus. 7000d, Hippocampus hippocampus.
2787-2792 A706 Set of 6   4.75

19th Southeast Asian Games — A707

1997, Oct. 11   Litho.   Perf. 13
2793 A707 5000d multicolored   1.25

Handicrafts
A708

Designs: No. 2794, 400d, Lamp. No. 2795, 400d, Two baskets. No. 2796, 400d, Swan-shaped basket. No. 2797, 400d, Deer-shaped basket. 2000d, Basket with handle.

1998, Jan. 1   Litho.   Perf. 13
2794-2798 A708 Set of 5   1.10

7th Francophone Summit, Hanoi — A709

1997, Sept. 24   Litho.   Perf. 13½x13
2799 A709 5000d multicolored   2.25

Birds
A710

400d, Syrmaticus ellioti. 3000d, Lophura diardi. 5000d, Phasianus cholchicus. 6000d, Chrysolophus amherstiae. 8000d, Polyplectron germaini.
14,000d, Lophura imperialis.

1997, Oct. 15   Perf. 13
2800-2804 A710 Set of 5   4.75
Souvenir Sheet
Perf. 13½
2805 A710 14,000d multicolored   2.75
No. 2805 contains one 43x30mm stamp.

New Year 1998 (Year of the Tiger)
A711

Stylized tigers: 400d, Adult with young. 8000d, Adult.

1998, Jan. 5   Perf. 13
2806-2807 A711 Set of 2   1.75

Sites in Vietnam
A712

Designs: No. 2808, 400d, Rocks, lake, Ninh Thuan. No. 2809, 400d, Lake, cavern, Quang Binh. 10,000d, Village of Quang Nam.

1998, Feb. 2
2808-2810 A712 Set of 3   2.10

Communist Manifesto, 150th Anniv. — A713

1998, Feb. 3
2811 A713 400d multicolored   .35

Bonsai
A714

#2812, 400d, Limonia acidissima. #2813, 400d, Deeringia polysperma. #2814, 400d, Pinus merkusii, vert. 4000d, Barringtonia acutangula, vert. 6000d, Ficus elastica, vert. 10,000d, Wrightia religiosa, vert.
No. 2818, Adenium obesum.

1998, Mar. 2
2812-2817 A714 Set of 6   4.25
Souvenir Sheet
Perf. 13½
2818 A714 14,000d multicolored   2.60
No. 2818 contains one 43x32mm stamp.

Tet Offensive, 30th Anniv. — A715

1998, Jan. 30   Litho.   Perf. 13
2819 A715 400d multicolored   .40

Opera — A716

Designs: a, 400d, Thi kính bi oan. b, 1000d, Thi mâu lên chúa. c, 2000d, Thi mâu-gia nô. d, 4000d, Thi me dôp-Xa trùong. e, 6000d, Thi kính bi phat va. f, 9000d, Thi kính xin sua.

1998, Apr. 20
2820 A716 Sheet of 6, #a.-f,   4.50

Raptors
A717

Designs: No. 2821, 400d, Pernis apivorus. No. 2822, 400d, Spizaetus ornatus. No. 2823, 400d, Accipter gentilis. 3000d, Buteo buteo. 5000d, Circus melanoleucas. 12,000d, Haliaeetus albicilla.

1998, May 4   Litho.   Perf. 13
2821-2826 A717 Set of 6   4.10

Ho Chi Minh City (Saigon), 300th Anniv. — A718

400d, Tank, natl. flag, Ho Chi Minh as young man, building. 5000d, Monument to Ho Chi Minh, symbols of industry, communications, and transportation.

1998, Apr. 30
2827-2828 A718 Set of 2   1.10

Orchids
A719

Designs: 400d, Paphiopedilum appletonianum. 6000d, Paphiopedilum helenae.

1998, May 18   Litho.   Perf. 13½
2829-2830 A719 Set of 2   1.40

Children's Paintings
A720

UNICEF: 400d, Children, mother in front of home. 5000d, Children on playground.

1998, June 1   Perf. 13
2831-2832 A720 Set of 2   1.25

1998 World Cup Soccer Championships, France — A721

Various soccer plays: 400d, 5000d, 7000d.

1998, June 10
2833-2835 A721 Set of 3   2.50

Sculptures of the Tran Dynasty
A722

Ornate designs: No. 2836, 400d, Serpent. No. 2837, 400d, Two people. 1000d, Shown. 8000d, Person. 9000d, Face.

1998, June 15   Litho.   Perf. 13
2836-2840 A722   Set of 5   3.50 3.50

A723

1998, July 13
2841 A723 2000d multicolored   .70 .70

Intl. Year of the Ocean
A724

1998, Aug. 1   Litho.   Perf. 13
2842 A724 400d multicolored   .35 .35

Stamp Day — A725

1998, Aug. 15
2843 A725 400d Bell's telephone   .35 .35

Ton Duc Thang (1888-1980)
A726

1998, Aug. 20
2844 A726 400d multicolored   .35 .35

Moths
A727

Designs: No. 2845, 400d, Antheraea helferi. No. 2846, 400d, Attacus atlas. 4000d, Argema mittrei, vert. 10,000d, Argema maenas, vert.

1998, Aug. 22
2845-2848 A727 Set of 4   3.25 3.25

Paintings by Te Bach Thach (Qi Baishi; 1863-1957)
A728

Various paintings: 400d, Dragonfly & Lotus. 1000d, Chrysanthemum, Cock & Hens. 2000d, Shrimps, 1948. 4000d, Crabs. 6000d, Lotus & Mandarin Ducks. 9000d, Shrimps, 1949.

1998, Sept. 16
2849-2854 A728 Set of 6   4.25 4.25

Legend of the Lake
A729

Designs: No. 2855, Turtle with sword leading boat. No. 2856, Lake.

1998, Oct. 10
2855-2856 A729 400d Set of 2   .70 .70

Le Thanh Tong (1442-1497) — A730

1998, Oct. 12
2857 A730 400d multicolored   .35 .35

Souvenir Sheet

Italia '98, Intl. Philatelic Exhibition — A731

Milan Cathedral. Illustration reduced.

1998, Oct. 6   Perf. 13½
2858 A731 16,000d multicolored   3.25 3.00

8th Trade Union Congress
A732

1998, Oct. 15   Litho.   Perf. 13
2859 A732 400d multicolored   .35 .35

Quy Nhon City, 396th Anniv., Binh Dinh Province, Cent. — A733

1998, Oct. 20
2860 A733 400d multicolored   .35 .35

Buoi-Chu Van An Secondary School, 90th Anniv. — A734

Designs: 400d, Students outside school. 5000d, Students listening to speaker.

1998, Nov. 20
2861-2862 A734 Set of 2   1.25 1.25

6th ASEAN Congress, Hanoi — A735

1998, Dec.   Litho.   Perf. 13
2863 A735 1000d multicolored   .45 .45

Cuban Revolution, 40th Anniv. (in 1999) — A736

1998, Dec.   Litho.   Perf. 13
2864 A736 400d multicolored   .30 .30

A737

Paintings: 400d, Birds, tree, flowers (Spring). 1000d, Flowers, ducks (Summer). 3000d, Flowers, rooster (Fall). 12,000d, Tree, flowers, deer & fawn (Winter).

1999, Jan. 4   Litho.   Perf. 13½x13
2865-2868 A737 Set of 4   3.00 3.00

A738

New Year 1999 (Year of the Cat): 400d, Cat holding tree branch. 8000d, Two cats. 13,000d, Kittens, ball.

1999, Jan. 6   **Perf. 13½**
2869-2870 A738 Set of 2 1.75 1.75
Souvenir Sheet
2871 A738 13,000d multicolored 2.50 2.50
No. 2871 contains one 32x43mm stamp.

Kites — A739

400d, Large bird with long tail. 5000d, Crescent-shaped. 7000d, Bird with long legs.

1999 **Litho.** **Perf. 13½x13**
2872-2874 A739 Set of 3 2.25 2.25

Australia '99, World Stamp Expo A740

Various sailing vessels: #2875, 400d, (4-1). #2876, 400d, (4-2). 7000d, (4-3). 9000d, (4-4).

1999, Mar. 10 **Litho.** **Perf. 13**
2875-2878 A740 Set of 4 3.00 3.00

Medicinal Plants A741

Designs: No. 2879, 400d, Kaempferia galanga. No. 2880, 400d, Tacca chantrieri, vert. No. 2881, Alpinia galanga, vert. 6000d, Typhonium trilobatum, vert. 13,000d, Asarum maximum, vert.

1999, Mar. 15
2879-2883 A741 Set of 5 3.75 3.75

Opera Masks A742

Various masks: 400d (6-1). 1000d (6-2). 2000d (6-3). 5000d (6-4). 6000d (6-5). 10,000d (6-6).

1999, Apr. 16   **Perf. 13½**
2884-2889 A742 Set of 6 4.25 4.25

IBRA'99, World Philatelic Exhibition, Nuremberg A743

Octopuses: No. 2890, 400d, Octopus gibertianus. No. 2891, 400d, Philonexis catenulata. 4000d, Paroctopus yendol. 12,000d, Octopus vulgaris.

1999, Apr. 20
2890-2893 A743 Set of 4 3.00 3.00

Landscape Paintings of Southern Viet Nam — A744

#2894, 400d, Sun over lake, Cà Mau. #2895, 400d, Rocks protruding out of water, Kien Giang. 12,000d, Traditional huts, Bac Lieu.

1999, May 4   **Perf. 13**
2894-2896 A744 Set of 3 2.25 2.25

Asia-Pacific Telecommunity, 20th Anniv. — A745

1999, May 10 **Litho.** **Perf. 13x13¼**
2897 A745 400d multi   .50 .50

Woodpeckers A746

Designs: 400d, Chrysocolaptes lucidus. 1000d, Picumnus innominatus. 3000d, Picus rabieri. 13,000d, Blythipicus pyrrhotis.

1999, May 18 **Litho.** **Perf. 13**
2898-2901 A746 Set of 4 3.00 3.00

UNICEF A747

Designs: 400d, Girl, hand. 5000d, Boy carrying factory.

1999, June 1 **Litho.** **Perf. 13**
2902-2903 A747 Set of 2 1.00 1.00

Architecture of Late 19th and Early 20th Centuries — A748

Designs: No. 2904, 400d, Government Office Building, Hanoi (3-1). No. 2905, 400d, History Museum, Ho Chi Minh City (3-2). 12,000d, Duc Ba Cathedral (3-3). 15,000d, Theater, Hanoi.

1999, June 10 **Perf. 13**
2904-2906 A748 Set of 3 2.25 2.25
Souvenir Sheet
Perf. 13½x14
2907 A748 15,000d multi 2.75 2.75
PhilexFrance '99 (No. 2907). No. 2907 contains one 44x32mm stamp.

Intl. Day to Stop Drug Abuse A749

1999, June 24 **Litho.** **Perf. 13**
2908 A749 400d multicolored .35 .35

Da Rang Bridge, Phu Yen A750

1999, July 1 **Litho.** **Perf. 13**
2909 A750 400d multi .40 .40

Le Dynasty Sculptures — A751

Designs: No. 2910, 1000d, Man Against Tiger (5-1). No. 2911, 1000d, Phoenix (5-2). 3000d, Playing Chess, vert. (5-3). 7000d, Hostler, vert. (5-4). 9000d, Dragon (5-5).

1999, July 1
2910-2914 A751 Set of 5 3.75 3.75

Birth of World's Six Billionth Person — A752

1999, Aug. 2
2915 A752 400d multi .35 .35

Chinese Landscapes — A753

Designs: 400d, Park, Beijing (4-1). 2000d, Scenic overlook, Anhwei (4-2). 3000d, Park, Shandong, (4-3). 10,000d, Park, Beijing, diff. (4-4).
14,000d, Great Wall of China.

1999, Aug. 16   **Perf. 13**
2916-2919 A753 Set of 4 3.00 3.00
Souvenir Sheet
Perf. 13½x14
2920 A753 14,000d multi 2.50 2.50
China 1999 World Philatelic Exhibition (No. 2920). No. 2920 contains one 43x32mm stamp.

Boat Races A754

Races from regions: 400d, North (3-1). 2000d, Central (3-2). 10,000d, South (3-3).

1999, Sept. 10   **Perf. 13**
2921-2923 A754 Set of 3 2.25 2.25

Women's Costumes A755

Various costumes. #2924, 400d (3-1). #2925, 400d (3-2). #2926, 12,000d (3-3).

1999, Sept. 10
2924-2926 A755 Set of 3 2.25 2.25

Buffalo Fighting Festivals A756

Fighting buffaloes: 400d, (2-1). 5000d, (2-2).

1999, Sept. 15
2927-2928 A756 Set of 2 1.00 1.00

Ngo Quyen (898-944), General — A757

1999, Oct. 21
2929 A757 400d multi   .35 .35

Nguyen Van Sieu (1799-1872), Teacher, Writer — A758

1999, Nov. 2 **Litho.** **Perf. 13**
2930 A758 400d multi   .35 .35

Tran Xuan Soan (1849-1923), Anti-colonial Leader — A759

1999, Nov. 24
2931 A759 400d multi .35 .35

United Nations Development Program — A760

Designs: 400d, Mother and child, farmer, fisherman. 8000d, Villagers, buildings.

1999, Dec. 3
2932-2933 A760 Set of 2 1.75 1.75

Viet Nam in the 20th Century — A761

Designs; No. 2934, 400d, Founding of Viet Nam Communist Party (6-1). No. 2935, 400d, Ho Chi Minh's declaration of country's independence (6-2). No. 2936, 1000d, Conquest of South Viet Nam (6-3). No. 2937, 1000d, People, dam, high tension wire tower, atom (6-4). 8000d, People, satellite, satellite dish, dam, high tension wire tower (6-5). 12,000d, Organizations Viet Nam belongs to (6-6).

2000, Jan. 1 **Litho.** *Perf. 13*
With Gum
2934-2939 A761 Set of 6 3.75 3.75
2939a Sheet, #2934-2939, without gum 4.00 4.00

New Year 2000 (Year of the Dragon) A762

Dragon: 400d, Facing right (2-1). 8000d, Facing right (2-2).

2000, Jan. 3 *Perf. 13½*
With Gum
2940-2941 A762 Set of 2 1.75 1.75

Intl. Year of Culture and Peace A763

2000, Jan. 18 **With Gum**
2942 A763 400d multi .35 .35

Viet Nam Communist Party, 70th Anniv. — A764

#2943, Ho Chi Minh (1890-1969), Pres. (8-1). #2944, Tran Phu (1904-31), 1st Gen. Sec. (8-2). #2945, Le Hong Phong (1902-42), Gen. Sec. (8-3). #2946, Ha Huy Tap (1902-41), Gen. Sec. (8-4). #2947, Nguyen Van Cu (1912-41), Gen. Sec. (8-5). #2948, Truong Chinh (1907-88), Gen. Sec. (8-6). #2949, Le Duan (1907-86), Gen. Sec. (8-7). #2950, Nguyen Van Linh (1915-98), Gen. Sec. (8-8).

2000, Feb. 2 *Perf. 13*
With Gum
2943-2950 A764 400d Set of 8 1.50 1.50

Cockfighting — A765

Postures: No. 2951, 400d, Song long cuoc (4-1). No. 2952, 400d, Long vu da dao (4-2). 7000d, Song long phuong hoang (4-3). 9000d, Nhan o giap chien (4-4).

2000, Feb. 8 **Litho.** *Perf. 13*
2951-2954 A765 Set of 4 3.50 3.50
Imperf., #2951-2954 5.75

Bangkok 2000 Stamp Exhibition A766

Palanquins: 400d, Imperial court roofed palanquin (3-1). 7000d, Palanquin without roof (3-2). 8000d, Roofed palanquin (3-3). 15,000d, Palanquin in procession.

2000, Mar. 10 **With Gum**
2955-2957 A766 Set of 3 3.25 3.25
Souvenir Sheet
2958 A766 15,000d multi 3.25 3.25

Legend of Lac Long Quan and Au Co — A767

Designs: No. 2959, 400d, Lang Long Quan and Au Co marry (6-1). No. 2960, 400d, Au Co, gives birth to 100 sons (6-2). 500d, Au Co takes 50 children to forest (6-3). 3000d, Lac Long Quan takes 50 children to sea (6-4). 4000d, Eldest son, Hung Vuong ascends to throne (6-5). 11,000d, Vietnamese ethnic groups as descendents (6-6).

2000, Apr. 4 *Perf. 13½*
2959-2964 A767 Set of 6 4.00 4.00

Souvenir Sheet

The Stamp Show 2000, London — A768

No. 2965 — Fire engines: a, 400d, Iveco Magirus, Germany. b, 1000d, Hino, Japan. c, 5000d, ZIL 103E, Russia. d, 12,000d, FPS.32 Camiva, France.
Illustration reduced.

2000, May 15 *Perf. 13*
2965 A768 Sheet of 4, #a-d 3.50 3.50

Worldwide Fund for Nature A769

Pseudoryx nghetinhensis: No. 2966, 400d, Head, vine (4-1). No. 2967, 400d, In grass (4-2). 5000d, Near pond (4-3). 10,000d, Head, mountains (4-4).

2000, May 18 *Perf. 13½*
With Gum
2966-2969 A769 Set of 4 4.50 4.50
2969a Sheet, 2 each #2966-2969 9.75 9.75

Ho Chi Minh (1890-1969) A770

2000, May 19 *Perf. 13*
With Gum
2970 A770 400d multi .35 .35

World Stamp Expo 2000, Anaheim A771

Water puppets: No. 2971, 400d, Chu teu (6-1). No. 2972, 400d, Fairy (6-2). No. 2973, 400d, Man plowing field (6-3). 3000d, Female peasant (6-4). 9000d, Drummer (6-5). 11,000d, Fisherman (6-6).

2000, June 28 *Perf. 13½*
2971-2976 A771 Set of 6 4.50 4.50

50th Vietnam Youth Volunteers' Day — A772

2000, July 15 *Perf. 13*
With Gum
2977 A772 400d multi .35 .35

Phu Dong Natl. Youth Sports Festival A773

2000, July 20 **With Gum**
2978 A773 400d multi .35 .35

Fish A774

Designs: No. 2979, 400d, Cephalopholis miniatus (6-1). No. 2980, 400d, Pomacanthus imperator (6-2). No. 2981, 400d, Epinephelus merra (6-3). 4000d, Zancius cornutus, vert. (6-4). 6000d, Chaetodon ephippium, vert. (6-5). 12,000d, Heniochus acuminatus, vert. (6-6). 15,000d, Chaetodon lunula.

2000, Aug. 7 *Perf. 13*
2979-2984 A774 Set of 6 4.00 4.00
Souvenir Sheet
Perf. 13½x13¾
2985 A774 15,000d multi 2.75 2.75

Post and Telegraph Dept., 55th Anniv. A775

2000, Aug. 15 *Perf. 13*
With Gum
2986 A775 400d multi .35 .35

People's Police, 50th Anniv. A776

Designs: 400d, Ho Chi Minh, five policemen. 2000d, Policeman checking documents, vert.

2000, Aug. 19 **Litho.** *Perf. 13*
With Gum
2987-2988 A776 Set of 2 .55 .55

Gen. Nguyen Tri Phuong, 200th Anniv. of Birth — A777

2000, Aug. 31 *Perf. 13½*
With Gum
2989 A777 400d multi .35 .35

UN Right of the Child Conference,
10th Anniv. — A778

Emblem and: 400d, Boy and girl. 5000d,
Five children, vert.

2000, Sept. 8   **Perf. 13**
2990-2991 A778   Set of 2   1.25 1.25

2000 Summer Olympics,
Sydney — A779

Designs: 400d, Running. 6000d, Shooting.
7000d, Taekwondo, vert.

2000, Sept. 15
2992-2994 A779   Set of 3   2.25 2.25

Gen. Tran Hung
Dao, 700th
Anniv. of
Death. — A780

2000, Sept. 17   **With Gum**
2995 A780 400d multi   .35 .35

Birds — A781

Designs: No. 2996, 400d, Leiothrix
argentauris. No. 2997, 400d, Pitta ellioti. No.
2998, 400d, Pomatorinus ferruginosus. 5000d,
Dicrurus paradiceus, vert. 7000d, Mela-
nochlora sultanea, vert. 10,000d, Stachyris
striolata, vert.

2000, Sept. 28   **Perf. 13½**
2996-3001 A781   Set of 6   4.50 4.50
      Souvenir Sheet
      Perf. 13½x13¾
3002 A781 15,000d Trena puella   2.75 2.75

No. 3002 contains one 42x31mm stamp.
España 2000 Intl. Philatelic Exhibition (No.
3002).

Vietnam Philately Association, 40th
Anniv. — A782

2000, Oct. 6   **Perf. 13**
      With Gum
3003 A782 400d No. 820   .35 .35

Farmer's Association, 70th
Anniv. — A783

2000, Oct. 14   **With Gum**
3004 A783 400d multi   .35 .35

Women's
Union,
70th
Anniv.
A784

2000, Oct. 14   **With Gum**
3005 A784 400d multi   .35 .35

Hanoi,
990th
Anniv.
A785

Designs: 400d, Building, and Ly Thai To,
founder of Hanoi. 3000d, Temple, two people,
monuments. 10,000d, Peasants with goods,
building.
   15,000d, People and doves.

2000, Oct. 15   **Perf. 13**
3006-3008 A785   Set of 3   2.25 2.25
      Souvenir Sheet
      Perf. 13½x13¾
3009 A785 15,000d multi   2.75 2.75

Bats — A786

Designs: No. 3010, 400d, Scotmanes
ornatus. No. 3011, 400d, Pteropus lylei.
2000d, Rhinolophus paradoxolophus. 6000d,
Eonycteris spelaea. 11,000d, Cynopterus
sphinx.

2000, Oct. 16   **Perf. 13**
3010-3014 A786   Set of 5   3.25 3.25

Fatherland
Front, 70th
Anniv. — A787

2000, Oct. 18   **With Gum**
3015 A787 400d multi   .35 .35

6th Natl.
Emulation
Congress
A788

Designs: 400d, People at work. 3000d,
Symbols of industry, vert.

2000, Nov. 10   **With Gum**
3016-3017 A788   Set of 2   .90 .90

Flowers
A789

Designs: 400d, Oxyspora sp. 5000d, Melan-
stoma villosa, vert.

2000, Nov. 15   **With Gum**
3018-3019 A789   Set of 2   1.25 1.25

Hon
Khoai
Uprising,
60th
Anniv.
A790

2000, Dec. 13   **Perf. 13**
      With Gum
3020 A790 400d multi   .35 .35

Advent of New
Millennium
A791

2001, Jan. 1   **With Gum**
3021 A791 400d multi   .35 .35

New Year
2001 (Year of
the Snake)
A792

Snake and: 400d, Pink flowers. 8000d, Yellow flowers.

2001, Jan. 1   **Perf. 13½**
      With Gum
3022-3023 A792   Set of 2   1.60 1.60

Hong Kong 2001 Stamp
Exhibition — A793

Fish: 400d, Toxotes microlepis. 800d, Cos-
mocheilus harmandi. 2000d, Anguilla bicolor
pacifica. 3000d, Chitala ornata. 7000d,
Megalops cyprinoides. 8000d, Probarbus
jullieni.

2001, Jan. 18   **Litho.**   **Perf. 13**
3024-3029 A793   Set of 6   3.50 3.50

Nobel Prize,
Cent.
A794

2001, Jan. 27   **Perf. 13½**
      With Gum
3030 A794 400d multi   .35 .35

Four Seasons — A795

No. 3031: a, 400d, Peach blossoms and
birds (spring). b, 800d, Cotton rose and
pheasant (summer). c, 4000d, Chrysanthemum and phoenix (autumn). d, 10,000d, Pine
tree and cranes (winter).

2001, Feb. 1   **Perf. 13¼x13**
      With Gum
3031 A795   Sheet of 4, #a-d   2.75 2.75

Wild Fruits — A796

Designs: No. 3032, 400d, Rubus
cochinchinensis. No. 3033, 400d, Rhizophora
mucronata. No. 3034, 400d, Podocarpus neri-
ifolius. No. 3035, 400d, Magnolia pumila.
15,000d, Taxus chinensis.

2001, Feb. 8   **Perf. 13½**
      With Gum
3032-3036 A796   Set of 5   2.60 2.60

Landscapes — A797

Designs: No. 3037, 400d, Co Tien Mountain
(3-1). No. 3038, 400d, Dong Pagoda, Yen Tu
Mountain (3-2). 10,000d, King Dinh Temple (3-
3).

2001, Feb. 23   **Perf. 13**
3037-3039 A797   Set of 3   2.00 2.00

Nhan Dan Newspaper, 50th
Anniv. — A798

2001, Mar. 11   **With Gum**
3040 A798 400d multi   .35 .35

Rubies Found in Tan Huong A799

Designs: 400d, 1960-gram ruby. 6000d, 2160-gram "Viet Nam Star."

2001, Mar. 20   **With Gum**
3041-3042 A799   Set of 2   1.10 1.10

Ho Chi Minh Youth Union, 70th Anniv. — A800

2001, Mar. 26   **Litho.**   **Perf. 13**
With Gum
3043 A800 400d multi   .35   .35

9th Communist Party Congress — A801

Designs: 400d, Ho Chi Minh, flag, map (2-1). 3000d, Hammer and sickle, Ngoc Lu bronze drum head, symbols of technology, vert (2-2).

2001, Apr. 18   **With Gum**
3044-3045 A801   Set of 2   .55   .55

Fauna in Cat Tien Natl. Park — A802

Designs: 400d, Arborophila davidi (4-1). 800d, Stichophthalma uemurai (4-2). 3000d, Rhinoceros sondaicus (4-3). 5000d, Crocodylus siamensis (4-4).

2001, Apr. 30   **Perf. 13½**
3046-3049 A802   Set of 4   2.25 2.25

Mushrooms A803

Designs: No. 3050, 400d, Phallus indusiatus (7-1). No. 3051, 400d, Aseroe arachnoidea (7-2). No. 3052, 400d, Phallus tenuis (7-3). 2000d, Phallus impudicus (7-4). 5000d, Phallus rugulosus (7-5). 6000d, Simblum periphragmoides (7-6). 7000d, Mutinus bambusinus (7-7).

2001, May 2
3050-3056 A803   Set of 7   4.00 4.00
A number has been reserved for a souvenir sheet for this set.

Mushrooms Type of 2001
Design: 13,000d,   Pseudocolus schellenbergiae.

2001, May 2   **Litho.**   **Perf. 13½x13¾**
3057 A803 13,000d multi   2.75 2.75
No. 3057 contains one 42x31mm stamp.

Ho Chi Minh Young Pioneer's League, 60th Anniv. — A804

2001, May 15   **Litho.**   **Perf. 13**
With Gum
3058 A804 400d multi   .35   .35

Viet Minh Front, 60th Anniv. A805

2001, May 19   **With Gum**
3059 A805 400d multi   .35   .35

Campaign Against Smoking — A806

2001, May 30   **Perf. 13¼x13½**
With Gum
3060 A806 800d multi   .45   .45

Children A807

Designs: 400d, Two children, UNICEF emblem. 5000d, Five children, UN emblem.

2001, June 1   **Perf. 13½**
3061-3062 A807   Set of 2   1.10 1.10
Children's safety day (#3061); UN Special Session on Children, Washington, DC (#3062).

Diesel Locomotives — A808

Designs: No. 3063, 400d, D18E (6-1). No. 3064, 400d, D4H (6-2). 800d, D11H (6-3). 2000d, D5H (6-4). 6000d, D9E (6-5). 7000d, D12E (6-6).

2001, June 5   **Perf. 13**
3063-3068 A808   Set of 6   3.50 3.50
Souvenir Sheet
Perf. 13½x13¾
3069 A808 13,000d D11H, diff.   2.75 2.75
No. 3069 contains one 43x32mm stamp.

Orchids A809

Designs: No. 3070, 800d, Vanda sp. (6-1). No. 3071, 800d, Dendrobium lowianum (6-2). No. 3072, 800d, Phajus wallichii (6-3). No. 3073, 800d, Habenaria medioflexa (6-4). No. 3074, 800d, Arundina graminifolia, vert. (6-5). 12,000d, Calanthe clavata, vert. (6-6).

Perf. 13½x13¼, 13¼x13½
2001, July 5
With Gum
3070-3075 A809   Set of 6   3.25 3.25

Phila Nippon '01 — A810

Butterflies: No. 3076, 800d, Troides aeacus (6-1). No. 3077, 800d, Inachis io (6-2). No. 3078, 800d, Ancyluris formosissima (6-3). 5000d, Cymothoe sanguris (6-4). 7000d, Taenaris selene (6-5). 10,000d, Trogonoptera brookiana (6-6). 13,000d, Atrophaneura horishanus, vert.

2001, July 16   **Perf. 13½x13¼**
3076-3081 A810   Set of 6   4.00 4.00
Souvenir Sheet
Perf. 13¾x13½
3082 A810 13,000d multi   2.75 2.75
No. 3082 contains one 32x42mm stamp.

2002 World Cup Soccer Championships, Japan and Korea — A811

No. 3083: a, 800d, Player with red shirt. b, 3000d, Player with white shirt.

2001, July 24   **Perf. 13**
With Gum
3083 A811   Horiz. pair, #a-b   .90   .90

Musical Instruments — A812

Designs: No. 3084, 800d, Ho gáo (6-1). No. 3085, 800d, Kenh (6-2). No. 3086, 800d, Dàn tú, vert. (6-3). 2000d, Dàn t'rung, vert. (6-4). 6000d, Trong kinang, vert . (6-5). 9000d, Tính tau, vert. (6-6).

Perf. 13x13¼, 13¼x13
2001, Aug. 4   **Litho.**
3084-3089 A812   Set of 6   3.25 3.25

Year of Dialogue Among Civilizations — A813

Tran Huy Lieu (1901-69), Writer — A814

2001, Oct. 9   **Litho.**   **Perf. 13¼x13½**
With Gum
3090 A813 800d multi   .45   .45

2001, Nov. 5   **Perf. 13x12¾**
With Gum
3091 A814 800d multi   .45   .45

Nam Cao (1917-51), Writer A815

2001, Nov. 30   **Perf. 13x13¼**
With Gum
3092 A815 800d multi   .45   .45

A816   A817

2001   **Perf. 13½**
With Gum
3093 A816 800d multi   .25   .25
3094 A817 3000d multi   .65   .65

New Year 2002 (Year of the Horse) A818

Horse facing: 800d, Right. 8000d, Left. 14,000d, Horse galloping.

2002, Jan. 2   **Perf. 13½**
With Gum
3095-3096 A818   Set of 2   1.40 1.40
Souvenir Sheet
Perf. 13½x13¼
3097 A818 14,000d multi   2.75 2.75
No. 3097 contains one 42x31mm stamp.

Opera Costumes A819

Designs: No. 3098, 1000d, Giáp Tuong Nam (6-1). No. 3099, 1000d, Giáp Tuong Nu (6-2). 2000d, Giáp Tuong Phan Dien (6-3). 3000d, Long Chan (6-4). 5000d, Giáp Tuong Phien (6-5). 9000d, Lung Xiem Quan Giáp (6-6).

2002, Jan. 15   **Perf. 13**
3098-3103 A819   Set of 6   3.25 3.25

Vo Thi Sáu, Heroine, 50th Anniv. of Death A820

2002, Jan. 23   *Perf. 13x13¼*
3104 A820 1000d multi   .45   .45

Program Implementation of 9th Communist Party Congress A821

Designs: 800d, Map, satellite, buildings, dam, power lines, bridge, computer keyboard (2-1). 3000d, Flag, building, doves, people (2-2).

2002, Feb. 1   *Perf. 13¼x13*
With Gum
3105-3106 A821 Set of 2   .90   .90

Cacti — A822

Designs: No. 3107, 1000d, Echinocereus albatus (5-1). No. 3108, 1000d, Echinocereus delaetii (5-2). No. 3109, 1000d, Cylindropuntia bigelowii (5-3). 5000d, Echinocereus triglochidatus (5-4). 10,000d, Epiphyllum truncatum (5-5).

2002, Feb. 18   *Perf. 13¼x13½*
3107-3111 A822 Set of 5   3.00 3.00

Victor Hugo (1802-85), French Writer A823

2002, Feb. 26   *Perf. 13x13¼*
With Gum
3112 A823 1000d multi   .45   .45

A824

2002   Litho.   Perf. 13x13¼
With Gum
3113 A824 800d multi   .45   .45

Birds — A825

Designs: 600d, Actinodura sodangorum (6-1). No. 3115, 800d, Garrulax ngoclinhensis (6-2). No. 3116, 800d, Garrulax pectoralis (6-3). No. 3117, 800d, Pomatorhinus hypoleucos (6-4). 5000d, Minla ignotincta (6-5). 8000d, Minla cyanouroptera (6-6).

2002, Mar. 15   Litho.   Perf. 13½
With Gum
3114-3119 A825 Set of 6   2.75 2.75

Landscapes A826

Designs: No. 3120, 800d, Ganh Son, Binh Thuan (3-1). No. 3121, 800d, Dawn over Tung Estuary, Quang Tri (3-2). 10,000d, Sa Huynh Harbor, Quang Ngai (3-3).

2002, Mar. 15   With Gum
3120-3122 A826 Set of 3   2.00 2.00

Primates — A827

Designs: 600d, Trachypithecus poliocephalus (8-1). 800d, Trachypithecus delacouri (8-2). 1000d, Rhinopithecus avunculus (8-3). 2000d, Pygathrix cinerea (8-4). 4000d, Nomascus concolor (8-5). 5000d, Trachypithecus laotum hatinhensis (8-6). 7000d, Trachypithecus phayrei (8-7). 9000d, Pygathrix nemaeus (8-8).

2002, Apr. 10
3123-3130 A827   Set of 8   4.50 4.50
3130a   Souvenir sheet, #3123-
                 3130 + label   4.50 4.50

Bui Thi Xuan, 200th Anniv. of Death — A828

2002, Apr. 13   Perf. 13
With Gum
3131 A828 1000d multi   .45   .45

Souvenir Sheet

2002 World Cup Soccer Championships, Japan and Korea — A829

Color of player or players: a, 1000d, Blue. b, 2000d, Red. c, 5000d, Red violet. d, 7000d, Green.

2002, June 1   Litho.
With Gum
3132 A829   Sheet of 4, #a-d   2.75 2.75

Flowers — A830

Designs: 600d, Paphiopedilum concolor (7-1). 800d, Sterculia lanceolata (7-2). 1000d, Schefflera alongensis (7-3). 2000d, Hibiscus tiliaceus (7-4). 3000d, Mussaenda glabra (7-5). 5000d, Boniodendron parviflorum (7-6). 9000d, Bauhinia ornata.

2002, June 5
3133-3139 A830   Set of 7   3.25 3.25

Chau Van Liem, Communist Party Leader, Cent. of Birth — A831

2002, June 28   Litho.   Perf. 13
With Gum
3140 A831 800d multi   .45   .45

Stamp Day — A832

2002, July 1   Perf. 13x12¾
With Gum
3141 A832 800d multi + label   .45   .45

Tay Nguyen Province A833

2002, July 10   Litho.   Perf. 13
With Gum
3142 A833 800d multi   .20   .20

Soft-shell Turtles A834

Designs: 800d, Pelochelys bibroni (4-1). 2000d, Pelodiscus sinensis. 5000d, Palea steindachneri. 9000d, Trionyx cartilagineus.

2002, July 15   Litho.   Perf. 13½
3143-3146 A834   Set of 4   2.60 2.60
3146a   Souvenir sheet, 2 each
                 #3143-3146   5.25 5.25

Viet Nam — Laos Diplomatic Relations, 40th Anniv. A835

2002, July 18   Perf. 13
With Gum
3147 A835 800d multi   .45   .45

Civil Aircraft A836

Designs: 800d, Super King Air B200 in air (4-1). 2000d, Fokker 70 (4-2). 3000d, ATR-72 (4-3). 8000d, Boeing 767-300 (4-4). 14,000d, Super King Air B200 on ground.

2002, Aug. 1   Perf. 13
With Gum
3148-3151 A836   Set of 4   2.25 2.25
Souvenir Sheet
Perf. 13½x13¾
3152 A836 14,000d multi   2.25 2.25

Autumn Festival Lanterns A837

Designs: No. 3153, 800d, Den Ong Sao (4-1). No. 3154, 800d, Den Ong Su (4-2). 2000d, Den Con Tho Om Trang (4-3). 7000d, Den Xep (4-4).

2002, Aug. 16   Perf. 13½
With Gum
3153-3156 A837   Set of 4   1.50 1.50

Viet Nam Posts and Telecommunications Trade Union, 55th Anniv. — A838

2002, Aug. 23   Perf. 13
With Gum
3157 A838 800d multi   .35   .35

Bridges — A839

Designs: No. 3158, 800d, Cau Long Bien (4-1). No. 3159, 800d, Cau Song Han (4-2). 2000d, Cau Truong Tien (4-3). 10,000d, Cau My Thuan (4-4).

2002, Sept. 27   **Perf. 13x13¼**
With Gum
3158-3161 A839   Set of 4   2.00 2.00

Communist Party's Ideology and Culture Commission, 72nd Anniv. — A840

2002, Oct. 10   **Perf. 13**
With Gum
3162 A840 800d multi   .35   .35

Hanoi Medical University, Cent. A841

2002, Nov. 15   **With Gum**
3163 A841 800d multi   .35   .35

Teachers' Day — A842

2002, Nov. 20   **With Gum**
3164 A842 800d multi   .35   .35

New Year 2003 (Year of the Ram) — A843

Various goats with background colors of: 800d, Rose pink (2-1). 8000d, Orange (2-2).

2002, Dec. 15   **Perf. 13½**
With Gum
3165-3166 A843   Set of 2   1.25 1.25

Viet Nam — South Korea Diplomatic Relations, 10th Anniv. — A844

Pagoda from: No. 3167, 800d, Viet Nam (2-1). No. 3168, 800d, South Korea (2-2).

2002, Dec. 21   **Perf. 13**
With Gum
3167-3168 A844   Set of 2   .65   .65

Starting with the 2003 issues, stamps are gummed unless otherwise indicated.

Landscapes — A845

Designs: 800d, Rung Cao Su, Bình Phuoc (3-1). 3000d, Ao Bà Om, Trà Vinh (3-2). 7000d, Mot nhanh song Rach Gam-Xoài Mút, Tien Giang (3-3).

2003, Feb. 1   **Litho.**   **Perf. 13**
3169-3171 A845   Set of 3   1.40 1.40

Viet Nam Culture Program, 60th Anniv. — A846

2003, Feb. 3
3172 A846 800d multi   .30   .30

Viet Nam Cinema Association, 50th Anniv. — A847

2003, Mar. 1
3173 A847 1000d multi   .30   .30

Khanh Hoa Province, 350th Anniv. A848

2003, Mar. 25
3174 A848 800d multi   .30   .30

Cycle Rickshaws A849

Cycle rickshaws from: 800d, Hanoi. 3000d, Ho Chi Minh City. 8000d, Haiphong.

2003, Apr. 1
3175-3177 A849   Set of 3   1.60 1.60

Adventures of the Cricket — A850

2003, May 1   **Perf. 13¼x13½**
3178   Horiz. strip of 6   2.60 2.60
  a. A850 800d Toi là út. . . (6-1)   .20   .20
  b. A850 1000d Chang bao. . . (6-2)   .20   .20
  c. A850 2000d Toi an han. . . (6-3) .25   .25
  d. A850 3000d Toi và Trui. . . (6-4) .40   .40
  e. A850 5000d Mot ngày. . . (6-5)   .65   .65
  f. A850 8000d Tu nay the. . . (6-6) 1.00 1.00

Animals in Ba Vi National Park — A851

Designs: No. 3179, 800d, Manis pentadactyla (4-1). No. 3180, 800d, Petaurista petaurista (4-2). 5000d, Selenarctos thibetanus (4-3). 10,000d, Capricornis sumatraensis (4-4).

2003, June 5   **Perf. 13½**
3179-3182 A851   Set of 4   2.25 2.25

22nd South East Asian Games, Viet Nam — A852

Designs: 800d, Soccer (4-1). 2000d, Hurdles (4-2). 3000d, Kayaking (4-3). 7000d, Wrestling (4-4).
  10,000d, Games emblem, mascot, stadium.

2003, July 1   **Perf. 13**
3183-3186 A852   Set of 4   1.75 1.75
Souvenir Sheet
              Perf. 13½x13¾
3187 A852 10,000d multi   1.25 1.25

Ninth Congress of Viet Nam Federation of Trade Unions — A853

2003, July 28   **Perf. 13**
3188 A853 800d multi   .30   .30

Camellias — A854

Designs: 800d, Camellia petelotii (4-1). 1000d, Camellia rubriflora (4-2). 5000d,

Camellia vietnamensis (4-3). 6000d, Camellia gilberti (4-4).

2003, Sept. 1   **Perf. 13½**
3189-3192 A854   Set of 4   1.75 1.75

Bangkok 2003 World Philatelic Exhibition.

Orchids A855

Designs: 800d, Paphiopedilum dianthum (2-1). 8000d, Pleione bulbocodioides (2-2).

2003, Oct. 1   **Perf. 13**
3193-3194 A855   Set of 2   1.10 1.10

Asian Elephants A856

Designs: 800d, Elephant with trunk extended (4-1). 1000d, Elephants and riders (4-2). 2000d, Elephant with trunk down (4-3). 8000d, Two elephants (4-4)

2003, Oct. 1   **Perf. 13½**
3195-3198 A856   Set of 4   1.50 1.50
3198a   Miniature sheet, 2 each
         #3195-3198   3.00 3.00

My Son World Heritage Site — A857

Various ruins: 800d, (3-1). 3000d, (3-2). 8000d (3-3).
  10,000d, Temple (43x32mm).
Illustration reduced.

2003, Dec. 1   **Perf. 13x13¼**
3199-3201 A857   Set of 3   1.50 1.50
Souvenir Sheet
              Perf. 13½x13¾
3202 A857 10,000d multi   1.25 1.25

New Year 2004 (Year of the Monkey) A858

Monkeys and: 800d, Apple tree (2-1). 8000d, Palm leaf (2-2).

2003, Dec. 1   **Perf. 13½**
3203-3204 A858   Set of 2   1.10 1.10

Ngo Gia Tu (1908-35), Leader of 1926 Strike — A859

2003, Dec. 30   **Perf. 13¼x13**
3205 A859 800d multi   .30   .30

Congratulations
A860

Designs: 800d, Flowers (2-1). 8000d, Bird with envelope (2-2).

2004, Jan. 1   *Perf. 13 Syncopated*
3206-3207 A860   Set of 2   1.10 1.10

Shells
A861

Designs: 800d, Murex trocheli (3-1). 3000d, Murex haustellum (3-2). 8000d, Chicoreus ramosus (3-3).

2004, Feb. 1   *Perf. 13*
3208-3210 A861   Set of 3   1.50 1.50

Bamboo
Lamps — A862

Various lamps with background colors of: 400d, Yellow (3-1). 1000d, Pale green (3-2). 7000d, Buff (3-3).

Perf. 13 Syncopated
2004, Mar. 1   Litho.
3211-3213 A862   Set of 3   1.10 1.10

Hué, UNESCO World Heritage
Site — A863

Designs: 800d, Pavilion of Edicts (3-1). 4000d, Ngo Mon Gate (3-2). No. 3216, 8000d, Hien Lam Pavilion (3-3).
No. 3217, 8000d, Thai Hoa Palace.

2004, Apr. 1   *Perf. 13*
Stamp + Label
3214-3216 A863   Set of 3   1.75 1.75
Souvenir Sheet
Perf. 13½x13¾
3217 A863 8000d multi   1.00 1.00
No. 3217 contains one 42x31mm stamp.

Tran Phu (1904-31), Communist
Leader — A864

2004, May 1   *Perf. 13*
3218 A864 800d multi   .30 .30

Battle of Dien Bien Phu, 50th Anniv. A865

Designs: 800d, Soldier, flowers (2-1). 5000d, Dancer, flowers.
8000d, Three dancers, flowers.

2004, May 4   *Perf. 13*
3219-3220 A865   Set of 2   .75 .75
Souvenir Sheet
Perf. 13½x13¾
3221 A865 8000d multi   1.00 1.00

FIFA (Fédération Internationale de
Football Association), Cent. — A866

2004, May 21   *Perf. 13*
3222 A866 800d multi   .30 .30

Thieu Nien Newspaper, 50th
Anniv. — A867

2004, June 1
3223 A867 800d multi   .30 .30

Bonsai — A868

Designs: 800d, Ficus microcarpa (4-1). 2000d, Premna serratifolia (4-2). 3000d, Ficus pilosa (4-3). 8000d, Ficus religiosa (4-4).

2004, July 1
3224-3227 A868   Set of 4   1.75 1.75
2004 World Stamp Championship, Singapore.

2004 Summer Olympics, Athens — A869

Designs: 800d, Hurdles (4-1). 1000d, Swimming, horiz. (4-2). 6000d, Shooting, horiz. (4-3). 7000d, Taekwondo (4-4).

2004, Aug. 1
3228-3231 A869   Set of 4   1.90 1.90

Naming of Country as Viet Nam, Bicent. A870

Designs: 800d, Citadel, Hué, lotus flower (2-1). 5000d, Ho Chi Minh, flag (2-2).

2004, Sept. 2
3232-3233 A870   Set of 2   .75 .75

World Summit on the Information Society, Geneva — A871

2004, Oct. 9
3234 A871 1000d multi   .30 .30

Liberation of Hanoi From French, 50th Anniv. — A872

2004, Oct. 10
3235 A872 800d multi   .30 .30

Dak Lak Province, Cent. — A873

2004, Nov. 22
3236 A873 800d multi   .30 .30

Hoi An, UNESCO World Heritage Site — A874

Designs: 800d, Chua Cau. 8000d, Hoi Quán Phúc Kien.

Perf. 13¼x13¾ Syncopated
2004, Dec. 1
3237 A874 800d multi   .30 .30
Souvenir Sheet
Perf. 13½x13¾
3238 A874 8000d multi   1.00 1.00
No. 3238 contains one 42x31mm stamp.

New Year 2005 (Year of the Rooster) A875

Designs: 800d, Rooster (2-1). 8000d, Hen and chicks.

2004, Dec. 15   *Perf. 13*
3239-3240 A875   Set of 2   1.10 1.10
3240a   Souvenir sheet, #3239-3240   1.10 1.10

Viet Nam Communist Party, 75th
Anniv. — A876

2005, Feb. 3
3241 A876 800d multi   .30 .30

Gia Lai Province A877

Perf. 13¼x13¾ Syncopated
2005, Mar. 16   Litho.
3242 A877 800d multi   .20 .20

Nha Trang Bay — A878

Designs: 800d, Boat near shore (2-1). 8000d, Road near shore (2-2).

2005, Apr. 2   *Perf. 13x12¾*
Stamp + Label
3243-3244 A878   Set of 2   1.10 1.10

Worldwide Fund for Nature (WWF) A879

Various views of Chrotogale owstoni: 800d, (4-1). 3000d, (4-2). 5000d, (4-3). 8000d, (4-4).

2005, May 2   *Perf. 13½*
3245-3248 A879   Set of 4   3.25 3.25
3248a   Souvenir sheet, #3245-3248, perf. 13x13½   3.50 3.50

Liberation of Haiphong, 50th
Anniv. — A880

Designs: 800d, Burning airplanes at Cat Bi Airport, Haiphong harbor (2-1). 5000d, Nam Trieu Port (2-2).

2005, May 6   *Perf. 13x12¾*
Stamp + Label
3249-3250 A880   Set of 2   .75 .75

People's Police, 60th Anniv. A881

Medals and: 800d, Marching police, statue of Ho Chi Minh (2-1). 10,000d, Police helping civilians (2-2).

2005, Aug. 10   *Perf. 13*
3251-3252 A881   Set of 2   1.40 1.40

Posts and Telecommunications Dept., 60th Anniv. — A882

2005, Aug. 15   *Perf. 13*
Background Color
3253 A882 800d beige   .20 .20
Souvenir Sheet
Perf. 13½x13¾
3254 A882 8000d gray   1.00 1.00

August Revolution, 60th Anniv. — A883

Crowd with flags in: 1000d, Hanoi (3-1). 2000d, Hué (3-2). 4000d, Saigon (3-3).

2005, Aug. 19   *Perf. 13*
3255-3257 A883 Set of 3   .90 .90
3257a Souvenir sheet, #3255-   .90 .90
3257

Traditional Dress and Houses of Ethnic Groups — A884

No. 3258: a, Ba-na (54-1). b, Bo Y (54-2). c, Brau (54-3). d, Bru-Van Kieu (54-4). e, Cham (54-5). f, Cho-ro (54-6). g, Chu-ru (54-7). h, Chut (54-8). i, Co (54-9). j, Cong (54-10). k, Co-ho (54-11). l, Co Lao (54-12). m, Co-tu (54-13). n, Dao (54-14). o, E-de (54-15). p, Gia-rai (54-16). q, Giay (54-17). r, Gie-Trieng (54-18). s, Ha Nhi (54-19). t, Hoa (54-20). u, Hre (54-21). v, Khang (54-22). w, Khmer (54-23). x, Kho-mu (54-24). y, Kinh (54-25). z, La Chi (54-26). aa, La Ha (54-27). ab, La Hu (54-28). ac, Lao (54-29). ad, Lo Lo (54-30). ae, Lu (54-31). af, Ma (54-32). ag, Mang (54-33). ah, Mnong (54-34). ai, Mong (54-35). aj, Muong (54-36). ak, Ngai (54-37). al, Nung (54-38). am, O Du (54-39). an, Pa Then (54-40). ao, Phu La (54-41). ap, Pu Peo (54-42). aq, Ra-glai (54-43). ar, Ro-mam (54-44). as, San Chay (54-45). at, San Diu (54-46). au, Si La (54-47). av, Ta-oi (54-48). aw, Tay (54-49). ax, Thai (54-50). ay, Tho (54-51). az, Xinh-mun (54-52). ba, Xo-dang (54-53). bb, Xtieng (54-54).

Perf. 13¾x13¼ Syncopated
2005, Aug. 30
3258 Sheet of 54 + 2 labels 5.50 5.50
a.-bb. A884 800d Any single   .20 .20
Complete booklet, #3258a-
3258bb   5.50

Thang Long (Hanoi), 1000th Anniv. A885

People reenacting battles and: 800d, Statue of Gen. Quang Trung, building (3-1). 5000d, Statue of Independence Fighters, building (3-2). No. 3261, 8000d, Statue of Victory Against B-52's, Long Bien Bridge (3-3).
No. 3262, Government officials on dais in Ba Dinh Square.

2005, Oct. 10 Litho. *Perf. 13*
3259-3261 A885 Set of 3   1.75 1.75
Souvenir Sheet
Perf. 13½x13¾
3262 A885 8000d multi   1.00 1.00

New Year 2006 (Year of the Dog) A886

Designs: 800d, Dog and puppies (2-1). 8000d, Dog (2-2).

2005, Dec. 1   *Perf. 13*
3263-3264 A886 Set of 2   1.10 1.10
3264a Souvenir sheet, #3263-   1.10 1.10
3264

National Coat of Arms, 50th Anniv. A887

2006, Jan. 14   *Perf. 13*
3265 A887 1000d multi   .20 .20

10th Vietnamese Communist Party Congress A888

2006, Feb. 3
3266 A888 800d multi   .20 .20

Prime Minister Pham Van Dong (1906-2000) — A889

2006, Mar. 1
3267 A889 800d multi   .20 .20

Wolfgang Amadeus Mozart (1756-91), Composer — A890

2006, Mar. 1
3268 A890 2000d multi   .25 .25

Léopold Senghor (1906-2001), First President of Senegal — A891

2006, Mar. 20 Litho. *Perf. 13*
3269 A891 800d multi   .20 .20

BirdLife International A892

Designs: 800d, Lophura edwardsi (5-1). 2000d, Arborophila davidi (5-2). 3000d, Lophura hatinhensis (5-3). 5000d, Polyplectron germaini (5-4, 49x23mm). 8000d, Rheinardia ocellata (5-5, 49x23mm).

Perf. 13¼x14 Syncopated, 13¼x13½ Syncopated (#3273-3274)
2006, Apr. 1
3270-3274 A892 Set of 5   2.40 2.40
3274a Souvenir sheet, #3270-   2.40 2.40
3274

2006 World Cup Soccer Championships, Germany — A893

Designs: 800d, One player (1-2). 10,000d, Two players (2-2).

2006, May 1 Litho. *Perf. 13¼x13*
3275-3276 A893 Set of 2   1.40 1.40

Phong Nha - Ke Bang National Park World Heritage Site — A894

Designs: 800d, Bi Ky Cave (3-1). 4000d, Xuyen Son Cave (3-2). 8000d, Nuoc Moc Stream (3-3).
12,000d, Tien Cave, vert.

2006, June 1   *Perf. 13x12¾*
3277-3279 A894 Set of 3   1.60 1.60
Souvenir Sheet
Perf. 13¾x13½
3280 A894 12,000d multi   1.50 1.50
No. 3280 contains one 32x43mm stamp.

Animals in Ben En Botanical Gardens A895

Designs: 800d, Nycticebus bengalensis (4-1). 1000d, Neofelis nebulosa, horiz. (4-2). 7000d, Cuon alpinus, horiz. (4-3). 10,000d, Nomascus leucogenys (4-4).
12,000d, Physignathus cocincinus, horiz.

2006, July 1 *Perf. 13¼x13, 13x13¼*
3281-3284 A895 Set of 4   2.40 2.40
Souvenir Sheet
Perf. 13½x13¾
3285 A895 12,000d multi   1.50 1.50

Flowers — A896

Designs: 800d, Momordica cochinchinensis (4-1). 3000d, Telosma cordata (4-2). 5000d, Momordica charantia (4-3). 8000d, Luffa cylindrica (4-4).

2006, Aug. 1   *Perf. 13*
3286-3289 A896 Set of 4   2.10 2.10

Asia-Pacific Economic Cooperation Summit — A897

2006, Sept. 16
3290 A897 8000d multi   1.00 1.00

Cooperation Between Viet Nam and European Union — A898

2006, Oct. 1   *Perf. 13x13¼*
3291 A898 800d multi   .20 .20

New Year 2007 (Year of the Pig) A899

Designs: 800d, Pig and piglets (2-1). 8000d, Pig (2-2).

2006, Dec. 15   *Perf. 13*
3292-3293 A899 Set of 2   1.10 1.10

Tran Te Xuong (1870-1907), Poet — A900

2007, Jan. 20 Litho. *Perf. 13x13¼*
3294 A900 1000d multi   .20 .20

Implementation of Resolutions of 10th Communist Party Congress — A901

Perf. 13½x13¼ Syncopated
2007, Feb. 3
3295   A901 800d multi   .20 .20

Truong Chinh (1907-88), General Secretary of Communist Party — A902

2007, Feb. 9   **Perf. 13x13¼**
3296   A902 800d multi   .20 .20

Le Duan (1907-86), First Secretary of Communist Party — A903

2007, Apr. 7
3297   A903 800d multi   .20 .20

Dugong Dugon — A904

Various depictions of Dugong dugon: 800d, (4-1). 1000d, (4-2). 7000d, (4-3). 9000d, (4-4).

2007, Aug. 1   **Litho.**   **Perf. 13**
3298-3301 A904 Set of 4   2.25 2.25

Association of South East Asian Nations (ASEAN), 40th Anniv. — A905

Designs: No. 3302, 800d, Secretariat Building, Bandar Seri Begawan, Brunei (10-1). No. 3303, 800d, National Museum of Cambodia (10-2). No. 3304, 800d, Fatahillah Museum, Jakarta, Indonesia (10-3). No. 3305, 800d, Typical house, Laos (10-4). No. 3306, 800d, Malayan Railway Headquarters Building, Kuala Lumpur, Malaysia (10-5). No. 3307, 800d, Yangon Post Office, Myanmar (Burma) (10-6). No. 3308, 800d, Malacañang Palace, Philippines (10-7). No. 3309, 800d, National Museum of Singapore (10-8). No. 3310, 800d, Vimanmek Mansion, Bangkok, Thailand (10-9). No. 3311, 800d, Presidential Palace, Hanoi, Viet Nam (10-10).

2007, Aug. 8   **Litho.**   **Perf. 13x13¼**
3302-3311 A905   Set of 10   1.00 1.00
3311a   Miniature sheet, #3302-3311 1.00 1.00

See Brunei Nos. , Burma No. 370, Cambodia Nos. , Indonesia Nos. , Laos Nos. , Malaysia No. 1170, Philippines Nos. 3103-3105 , Singapore No. 1265, and Thailand No. 2315.

Tay Nguyen Tribal Gongs A906

Various tribal members using gongs: 800d, (3-1). 5000d, (3-2). 8000d, (3-3). 12,000d, Man holding gong.

2007, Nov. 21 **Litho.** **Perf. 13x13¼**
3312-3314 A906   Set of 3   1.75 1.75
            Souvenir Sheet
3314A   A906 12,000d multi   1.50 1.50

New Year 2008 (Year of the Rat) — A907

Designs: 800d, Rat at left (2-1). 8000d, Rat at right (2-2).

2007, Dec. 1   **Perf. 13½**
3315-3316 A907 Set of 2   1.10 1.10

Ho Chi Minh (1890-1969) A908

Perf. 13¼x13½
2007, Dec. 31   **Litho.**
3317   A908 1000d dk red & pink   .20 .20
3318   A908 3000d dk & lt green   .40 .40
3319   A908 4000d dk & lt blue   .50 .50
       Nos. 3317-3319 (3)   1.10 1.10

Vietnamese Cuisine — A909

Designs: 800d, Nem rán (2-1). 9000d, Pho bò.

2008, Feb. 1   **Perf. 13x13¼**
3320-3321 A909 Set of 2   1.25 1.25

Orchids A910

Designs: 800d, Calanthe densiflora (4-1). 2000d, Ludisia discolor (4-2). 6000d, Spathoglottis affinis (4-3). 8000d, Calanthe argenteo-striata (4-4).

2008, Mar. 1   **Litho.**   **Perf. 13½**
3322-3325 A910 Set of 4   2.10 2.10

SEMI-POSTAL STAMPS

World Communications Year — SP1

#B1, Hands holding envelope with ITU emblem. #B2, Satellite dish antenna.

            Unwmk.
1983, Nov. 1   **Litho.**   **Perf. 11**
B1-B2   SP1 50xu +10xu Set of 2   3.75

AIR POST STAMP

AP1

            Unwmk.
1959, Nov. 20 **Litho.**   **Perf. 11**
C1   AP1 20xu blue & black   10.00 7.75

POSTAGE DUE STAMPS

Nos. 1-4 exist with handstamps of "TT" in a diamond. It is unclear to the editors if these stamps were used.

D1

D2

1955   **Typo.**   **Perf. 11½**
J14   D1   50d brown & yellow 15.00 9.00

1958, Dec. 1   **Litho.**   **Perf. 12½**
J15   D2   10d purple & red
J16   D2   20d orange & aqua
J17   D2   100d gray blue & red
J18   D2   300d olive grn & red
      Nos. J15-J18 (4)   15.00 14.00

MILITARY STAMPS

M1

        Perf. 12½
1958, May 1   **Litho.**   **Unwmk.**
M1   M1   multicolored   15.00 9.00

Invalids in Field Paddy M2

1959-60   **Litho.**   **Perf. 11**
M2   M2 org brn & brown
M3   M2 grey blue & olive
     Nos. M2-M3 (2)   11.50 4.50
Issued: No. M2, 3/14/59; No. M3, 7/27/60.

Soldier, Train — M3

1959, July 1
M4   M3 bluish green   5.00 1.90

Frontier Guard — M4

1961, Jan. 3
M5   M4 multicolored   15.00 9.75

Naval Patrol M5

1962, June 15
M6   M5 multicolored   5.75 3.25

Military Medal, Invalid's Badge — M6

1963, Sept. 10
M7   M6 12xu multicolored   4.50 3.75

Rifleman M7

1964, Aug.
M8   M7 multicolored   5.00 4.00

Rifleman Jumping Wall — M8

VIET NAM

1965
M9 M8 red & black
M10 M8 yellow green & black
   Nos. M9-M10 (2)   9.00 6.25
  Issued: No. M9, 7/1; No. M10, 12/25.

Soldier, Guerrilla Woman M9

1966-67
M11 M9 greenish blue & vio bl 9.00 7.00
Redrawn with two boats at right
M12 M9 olive & brown bl 13.50 10.50
  Issued: #M11, Sept. 25, 1966; #M12, 1967.

Badge of People's Army — M10

1967, Oct. 7
M13 M10 multicolored 2.00 .75

M11

M12

1968, Nov. 10
M14 M11 lilac 1.50 .40

1969, Nov. 15
M15 M12 red & brown red 1.50 .75

M13

1971, Apr. 27
M16 M13 yellow, brown & red 1.50 .75

Nguyen Van Be M14

Design: No. M18, Nguyen Viet Xuan.

1971, Oct. 30   *Perf. 11*
M17 M14 multicolored 1.50 .60
   Perf. 12½
M18 M14 black, pink & buff 2.25 1.10

M15

M16

1973, Dec. 20   *Perf. 11*
M20 M15 blue, black & buff
  a. Perf. 12½ 4.50
M22 M16 olive, red & black
  a. Perf. 12½ 4.50
   Nos. M20, M22 (2) 1.00 25

Disabled Veteran in Factory M17

No. M24, Invalid's Badge, open book, vert.

1976, July 27
M23-M24 M17 Set of 2 2.00 .25

Soldier, Map — M18   Pilot — M19

1976, Oct. 21
M25 M18 red & black 1.00

1978
No. M27, Tank driver. No. M28, Seaman.
M26-M28 M19 Set of 3 5.00 2.00
  Issued: No. M26, 6/3; others, 10/10.

M20

Designs: a, Pilot. b, Badge of People's Army.

1979, Dec. 22
M29 M20 Vertical pair, #a.-b. 3.00

Types A343a, A359 and

Ho Chi Minh — M21

#M30, Factory militiawoman. #M31, Soldier, woman pointing. #M32, Militiawoman.

1981, Aug. 5
M30 A343a salmon & multi
M31 A343a green & multi
M32 A359 blue & multi
M33 M21 blue & tan
   Nos. M30-M33 (4) 4.50 2.25
  Size of No. M32: 13x18mm.

M22

1982, Nov. 9
M34 M22 pink & greenish blue 1.50 1.00

M23

1983, Apr. 30
M35 M23 multicolored 2.25 1.10

Victory at Dien Bien Phu, 30th Anniv. M24

1984, May 5   *Litho.*
M37 M24 multicolored 1.25

Disabled Soldier Teaching Class — M25

1984, Nov. 10
M38 M25 tan & brown 1.25

Frontier Forces Type of 1984
1984, Dec. 15
M39 A410 multicolored 1.00

M26

1984, Dec. 22
M40 M26 multicolored 2.50

Policemen and Women M27

1985, Aug. 30
M41 M27 multicolored 1.00

M28

1986, Oct. 1
M42 M28 olive brown & black 1.50 .75

M29

1987, Sept. 23
M43 M29 carmine and tan 2.00 1.00

OFFICIAL STAMPS

Harvesting Rice — O1

Denominations in grams or kilograms of rice. Dated 1952.

   Perf. 11¼
1953, July Litho. Unwmk.
O1 O1 600g rose 5.50 2.50
O2 O1 1kg ol brown 6.00 4.00
O3 O1 2kg orange 8.50 6.50
O4 O1 5kg gray 15.00 10.00
   Nos. O1-O4 (4) 35.00 25.00

Dien Bien Phu Type of 1954
1954-56   *Perf. 11*
O5 A4 600g sepia & ocher 18.00 12.50
No. O5 exists perf 6, Value $60; and also imperf, Value $18.
  Issued: #O5, 10/54; perf 6, 12/54; imperf, 1956.

Nos. 1L62-1L63 Overprinted

1955 Typo. *Perf. 7 Rough*
O6-O7 VM2 100g on 2d, 100g on 5d, set of 2 440.00

Land Reform Type of 1955-56 Inscribed "SU VU" Above Value
1955 Litho. *Perf. 11*
O8-O9 A6 40d, 80d, set of 2 32.50 27.50

Cu Chinh Lan (1930-1952) O3

Denominations: 20d, 80d, 100d, 500d, 1000d, 2000d, 3000d.

1956, June Litho. *Perf. 11½*
O10-O16 O3 Set of 7 250.00 225.00

4th World Trade Union Congress Type
of 1957
Inscribed "SU VU" Above Value

1957, Aug. 1   *Perf. 12½*
O17-O20 A15 20d, 40d, 80d,
              100d, set of 4   20.00 16.00

One-Pillar
Pagoda — O4

1957-58
O21 O4 150d green and brown
O22 O4 150d orange and slate
         Nos. O21-O22
         (2)   26.00 11.00

Nos. O21-O22 exist with and without imprint
and designer's name. Issued: No. O21,
12/22/57; No. O22, 3/12/58.

Craft Fair,
Hanoi — O5

1958, May 30
O23-O24 O5 150d, 200d, set of
             2   8.00 6.00

1st World
Congress of
Young
Workers,
Prague —
O6

1958, June 26
O25 O6 150d lt olive green & red 3.50 1.75

Soldier,
Factory,
Crops — O7

1958, Aug. 19
O26-O28 O7 50, 150, 200d, set
             of 3   11.00 7.00

Opening of
New Hanoi
Stadium
O8

1958, Dec. 31
O29-O32 O8 10d, 20d, 80d,
             150d, set of 4 9.50 4.75

Planting Rice — O9

1962, Sept. 1   *Perf. 11*
O33-O35 O9 3, 6, 12xu, set of 3 3.00 2.50

Rural
Mail
Service
O10

1966, July 1   *Perf. 11*
O36-O37 O10 3xu, 6xu, set of 2 1.50 1.00

VIRGIN ISLANDS

'vər-jən 'i-lənds

LOCATION — West Indies, southeast of Puerto Rico
GOVT. — British colony
AREA — 59 sq. mi.
POP. — 19,107 (1997)
CAPITAL — Road Town

The British Virgin Islands constituted one of the presidencies of the former Leeward Islands colony until it became a colony itself in 1956. For many years stamps of Leeward Islands were used concurrently.

The Virgin Islands group is divided between Great Britain and the United States. See Danish West Indies.

12 Pence = 1 Shilling
20 Shillings = 1 Pound
100 Cents = 1 Dollar (1951)
100 Cents = 1 US Dollar (1962)

Catalogue values for unused stamps in this country are for Never Hinged items, beginning with Scott 88 in the regular postage section and Scott O1 in the officials section.

Values for unused stamps are for examples with original gum as defined in the catalogue introduction. However, Nos. 1-2c are valued without gum as the vast majority of examples are found thus.

Virgin and Lamps — A1

A3

A4

1866   Litho.   Unwmk.   Perf. 12
Toned or White Paper

1	A1	1p green	50.00	65.00
a.		Toned paper	52.50	65.00
c.		Perf. 15x12, toned paper	6,000.	7,750.
2	A3	6p rose	65.00	100.00
a.		Large "V" in "VIRGIN"	300.00	400.00
b.		White paper	100.00	120.00
c.		As "a," white paper	410.00	525.00

Copies offered as No. 1c frequently have forged perfs.

1867-70   Perf. 15

3	A1	1p blue grn ('70)	65.00	75.00
4	A1	1p yel grn ('68)	80.00	75.00
a.		Toned paper	92.50	85.00
5	A2	4p lake, buff	45.00	65.00
a.		4p lake, rose	55.00	75.00
6	A3	6p rose	650.00	650.00
a.		Toned paper ('68)	325.00	375.00
7	A4	1sh rose & blk	300.00	400.00
a.		Toned paper	300.00	400.00
b.		Double lined frame	300.00	400.00
c.		As "b," bluish paper	300.00	400.00

Colored Margins

8	A4	1sh rose & blk	70.00	87.50
a.		White paper	70.00	87.50
b.		Bluish paper	825.00	1,000.
c.		Central figure omitted	92,500.	
		Nos. 3-8 (6)	1,210.	1,352.

Copies of No. 8c have perfs. trimmed on one or two sides.

1878   Wmk. 1   Perf. 14

9	A1	1p green	90.00	110.00

See #16-17, 19-20. For surcharge see #18.

Queen Victoria — A5

1880   Typo.

10	A5	1p green	80.00	95.00
11	A5	2½p red brown	100.00	125.00

1883-84   Wmk. 2

12	A5	½p yellow	92.50	92.50
13	A5	½p green	6.00	11.00
a.		Imperf., pair	1,750.	
14	A5	1p rose	27.50	32.50
15	A5	2½p ultra ('84)	3.00	17.50
		Nos. 12-15 (4)	129.00	153.50

No. 13a probably is a plate proof.

1887   Litho.

16	A2	4p brick red	40.00	70.00
a.		4p brown red	50.00	80.00
17	A3	6p violet	17.50	85.00

No. 8 Handstamp Surcharged in Violet

1888   Unwmk.   Perf. 15

18	A4	4p on 1sh dp rose & blk, toned paper	140.00	175.00
a.		Double surcharge	7,500.	
b.		Inverted surcharge	47,500.	
c.		White paper	200.00	250.00

1889   Wmk. 2   Perf. 14

19	A1	1p carmine	2.75	8.25
20	A4	1sh brown	50.00	80.00
a.		1sh black brown	90.00	110.00

St. Ursula with Sheaf of Lilies A7

Edward VII A8

1899   Engr.

21	A7	½p yellow grn	2.75	.60
a.		"PFNNY"	92.50	140.00
b.		"F" without cross bar	92.50	140.00
c.		Horiz. pair, imperf. between	9,250.	
22	A7	1p red	3.25	2.75
23	A7	2½p ultra	13.00	3.00
24	A7	4p chocolate	4.50	20.00
a.		"PENCF"	825.	1,200.
25	A7	6p dark violet	5.00	3.50
26	A7	7p slate green	9.25	6.50
27	A7	1sh ocher	25.00	37.50
28	A7	5sh dark blue	80.00	95.00
		Nos. 21-28 (8)	142.75	168.85

1904   Typo.   Wmk. 3

29	A8	½p violet & bl grn	1.00	.60
30	A8	1p violet & scar	3.25	.55
31	A8	2p violet & bis	7.75	4.75
32	A8	2½p violet & ultra	2.75	2.75
33	A8	3p violet & blk	4.75	3.25
34	A8	6p violet & brn	3.50	3.25
35	A8	1sh green & scar	5.50	6.50
36	A8	2sh6p green & blk	32.50	72.50
37	A8	5sh green & ultra	62.50	87.50
		Nos. 29-37 (9)	123.50	181.65

Numerals of 2p, 3p, 1sh and 2sh6p of type A8 are in color on plain tablet.

George V A9   Colony Seal A10

Die I

For description of dies I and II see "Dies of British Colonial Stamps" in Table of Contents.

1913
Ordinary Paper

38	A9	½p green	1.90	5.00
39	A9	1p scarlet	2.75	17.50
a.		1p carmine red	57.50	32.50
40	A9	2p gray	5.00	30.00
41	A9	2½p ultra	6.50	11.00

Chalky Paper

42	A9	3p vio, yel	3.25	8.00
43	A9	6p dl vio & red vio	6.00	13.50
44	A9	1sh blk, green	3.75	11.00
45	A9	2sh6p blk & red, bl	57.50	60.00
46	A9	5sh grn & red, yel	42.50	140.00
		Nos. 38-46 (9)	129.15	296.00

Numerals of 2p, 3p, 1sh and 2sh6p of type A9 are in color on plain tablet.

1921   Wmk. 4
Die II

47	A9	½p green	5.00	35.00
48	A9	1p carmine	4.00	27.50

For overprints see Nos. MR1-MR2.

1922   Wmk. 3

49	A10	3p violet, yel	1.10	21.00
50	A10	1sh black, emerald	1.00	17.50
51	A10	2sh6p blk & red, bl	7.25	14.00
52	A10	5sh grn & red, yel	42.50	125.00
		Nos. 49-52 (4)	51.85	177.50

1922-28   Wmk. 4

53	A10	½p green	1.25	3.50
54	A10	1p rose red	.80	.80
55	A10	1p violet ('27)	1.40	4.75
56	A10	1½p rose red ('27)	2.10	3.25
57	A10	1½p fawn ('28)	2.25	1.90
58	A10	2p gray	1.40	7.75
59	A10	2½p ultra	3.00	24.00
60	A10	2½p orange ('23)	1.75	2.10
61	A10	3p dl vio, yel ('28)	3.25	15.00
62	A10	5p dl lil & ol grn	7.75	60.00
63	A10	6p dl vio & red vio	2.10	9.00
a.		6p brown lilac & red violet	2.10	9.00
64	A10	1sh blk, emer ('28)	3.50	19.00
65	A10	2sh6p blk & red, bl ('28)	27.50	62.50
66	A10	5sh grn & red, yel ('23)	27.50	95.00
		Nos. 53-66 (14)	85.55	308.55

The ½, 1, 2 and 2½p are on ordinary paper, the others on chalky.
Numerals of 1½p of type A10 are in color on plain tablet.

Common Design Types pictured following the introduction.

Silver Jubilee Issue
Common Design Type

1935, May 6   Engr.   Perf. 11x12

69	CD301	1p car & dk blue	.90	4.50
70	CD301	1½p black & ultra	.90	4.50
71	CD301	2½p ultra & brn	1.75	4.50
72	CD301	1sh brn vio & ind	11.50	19.00
		Nos. 69-72 (4)	15.05	32.50
		Set, never hinged	27.50	

Coronation Issue
Common Design Type

1937, May 12   Perf. 11x11½

73	CD302	1p dark carmine	.20	.50
74	CD302	1½p brown	.20	1.50
75	CD302	2½p deep ultra	.35	.50
		Nos. 73-75 (3)	.75	2.50
		Set, never hinged	1.40	

King George VI and Seal of the Colony — A11

1938-47   Photo.   Perf. 14

76	A11	½p green	.20	.20
77	A11	1p scarlet	.20	.20
78	A11	1½p red brown	.45	.85
79	A11	2p gray	.35	.70
80	A11	2½p ultra	.45	1.25
81	A11	3p orange	.35	.85
82	A11	6p deep violet	1.10	.70
83	A11	1sh olive bister	1.25	.75
84	A11	2sh6p sepia	9.75	6.00
85	A11	5sh rose lake	13.00	7.50

86	A11	10sh brt blue ('47)	6.50	17.00
87	A11	£1 gray blk ('47)	10.50	27.50
		Nos. 76-87 (12)	44.10	63.50
		Set, never hinged	67.50	

Catalogue values for unused stamps in this section, from this point to the end of the section, are for Never Hinged items.

Peace Issue
Common Design Type
Perf. 13½x14

1946, Nov. 1   Engr.   Wmk. 4

88	CD303	1½p red brown	.20	.20
89	CD303	3p orange	.20	.20

Silver Wedding Issue
Common Design Types

1949, Jan. 3   Photo.   Perf. 14x14½

90	CD304	2½p brt ultra	.35	.35

Engr.; Name Typo.
Perf. 11½x11

91	CD305	£1 gray black	17.50	21.00

UPU Issue
Common Design Types

Engr.; Name Typo. on Nos. 93 & 94
1949, Oct. 10   Perf. 13½, 11x11½

92	CD306	2½p ultra	.40	.40
93	CD307	3p deep orange	1.00	1.60
94	CD308	6p red lilac	.65	.40
95	CD309	1sh olive	.65	.40
		Nos. 92-95 (4)	2.70	2.80

University Issue
Common Design Types

1951   Engr.   Perf. 14x14½

96	CD310	3c red brn & gray blk	.40	.40
97	CD311	12c purple & black	1.10	1.10

Map of the Islands A12

1951, Apr. 2   Wmk. 4   Perf. 14½x14

98	A12	6c red orange	.35	.35
99	A12	12c purple	.45	.45
100	A12	24c olive grn	.65	.70
101	A12	$1.20 carmine	2.50	2.00
		Nos. 98-101 (4)	3.95	3.50

Restoration of the Legislative Council, 1950.

Sombrero Lighthouse — A13

Map of Jost van Dyke — A14

Designs: 3c, Sheep. 4c, Map, Anegada. 5c, Cattle. 8c, Map, Virgin Gorda. 12c, Map, Tortola. 24c, Badge of the Presidency. 60c, Dead Man's Chest. $1.20, Sir Francis Drake Channel. $2.40, Road Town. $4.80, Map, Virgin Islands.

1952, Apr. 15   Perf. 12½x13, 13x12½

102	A14	1c gray black	.40	1.60
103	A14	2c deep green	.85	.20
104	A14	3c choc & gray blk	.45	1.25
105	A14	4c red	.70	1.60
106	A14	5c gray blk & rose lake	1.40	1.60
107	A14	8c ultra	.85	1.25
108	A14	12c purple	1.50	1.60
109	A13	24c dk brown	1.60	.20
110	A14	60c blue & ol grn	2.75	17.00
111	A14	$1.20 ultra & blk	6.00	18.00
112	A14	$2.40 hn brn & dk grn	13.00	20.00
113	A14	$4.80 rose car & bl	21.00	21.00
		Nos. 102-113 (12)	50.50	84.40

Coronation Issue
Common Design Type
1953, June 2   **Perf. 13½x14**
114 CD312 2c dk green & blk   .40   .65

Map of Tortola — A15

Brown Pelican A16

Designs: 1c, Virgin Islands sloop. 2c, Nelthrop Red Poll bull. 3c, Road Harbor. 4c, Mountain travel. 5c, St. Ursula. 8c, Beach scene. 12c, Boat launching. 24c, White Cedar tree. 60c, Skipjack tuna. $1.20, Treasury Square. $4.80, Magnificent frigatebird.

Perf. 13x12½
1956, Nov. 1   **Engr.**   **Wmk. 4**

115	A15	½c claret & blk	.45	.20
116	A15	1c dk bl & grnsh bl	1.90	1.10
117	A15	2c black & ver	.40	.20
118	A15	3c olive & brt bl	.40	.45
119	A15	4c blue grn & brn	.45	.45
120	A15	5c gray	.50	.20
121	A15	8c dp ultra & org	.75	.65
122	A15	12c car & brt ultra	2.50	1.10
123	A15	24c dull red & grn	1.25	1.00
124	A15	60c yel org & dk bl	10.00	12.00
125	A15	$1.20 car & yel grn	2.75	11.00

Perf. 12x11½

126	A16	$2.40 vio brn & dl yel	37.50	20.00
127	A16	$4.80 grnsh bl & dk brn	40.00	20.00
		Nos. 115-127 (13)	98.85	68.35

Types of 1956 Surcharged

Perf. 13x12½
1962, Dec. 10   **Wmk. 314**

128	A15	1c on ½c	.20	.20
129	A15	2c on 1c	1.25	.20
130	A15	3c on 2c	.20	.20
131	A15	4c on 3c	.20	.20
132	A15	5c on 4c	.20	.20
133	A15	8c on 8c	.35	.35
134	A15	10c on 12c	.45	.45
135	A15	12c on 24c	.65	.65
136	A15	25c on 60c	3.25	1.25
137	A15	70c on $1.20	.70	3.25

Perf. 12x11½

138	A16	$1.40 on $2.40	12.50	21.00
139	A16	$2.80 on $4.80	12.50	16.00
		Nos. 128-139 (12)	32.45	43.95

Freedom from Hunger Issue
Common Design Type
1963, June 4   **Photo.**   **Perf. 14x14½**
140 CD314 25c lilac   .50   .50

Red Cross Centenary Issue
Common Design Type
Wmk. 314
1963, Sept. 2   **Litho.**   **Perf. 13**
141 CD315 2c black & red   .20   .20
142 CD315 25c ultra & red   .90   .90

Shakespeare Issue
Common Design Type
1964, Apr. 23   **Photo.**   **Perf. 14x14½**
143 CD316 10c ultramarine   .40   .40

Bonito — A17

Map of Tortola Island — A18

2c, Seaplane at Soper's Hole. 3c, Brown pelican. 4c, Dead Man's Chest (mountain). 5c, Road Harbor. 6c, Fallen Jerusalem Island. 8c, The Baths, Virgin Gorda. 10c, Map of Virgin Islands. 12c, Ferry service, Tortola—St. Thomas. 15c, The Towers. 25c, Plane at Beef Island Airfield. $1, Virgin Gorda Island. $1.40, Yachts, Tortola. $2.80, Badge.

Perf. 13x12½
1964, Nov. 2   **Engr.**   **Wmk. 314**

144	A17	1c gray ol & dk bl	.35	2.40
145	A17	2c rose red & ol	.35	.45
146	A17	3c grnsh bl & sep	4.25	2.40
147	A17	4c carmine & blk	1.10	2.40
148	A17	5c green & blk	.90	1.60
149	A17	6c orange & blk	.35	1.40
150	A17	8c pink & blk	.35	1.00
151	A17	10c lt violet & mar	1.60	.45
152	A17	12c vio bl & Prus grn	2.75	3.50
153	A17	15c gray & yel grn	.45	3.50
154	A17	25c pur & yel grn	15.00	3.50

Perf. 13x13½
Size: 27x30½mm

155	A18	70c bister brn & blk	5.25	8.00
156	A18	$1 red brn & yel grn	4.25	3.50
157	A18	$1.40 pink & blue	27.50	16.00

Perf. 11½x12
Size: 27x37mm

158	A18	$2.80 rose lilac & blk	27.50	16.00
		Nos. 144-158 (15)	91.95	66.10

For surcharges & overprints see Nos. 173-175, 190-191.

ITU Issue
Common Design Type
Perf. 11x11½
1965, May 17   **Litho.**   **Wmk. 314**
159 CD317 4c yellow & bl grn   .20   .20
160 CD317 25c blue & org yel   .80   .80

Intl. Cooperation Year Issue
Common Design Type
1965, Oct. 25   **Wmk. 314**   **Perf. 14½**
161 CD318 1c blue grn & cl   .20   .20
162 CD318 25c lt violet & grn   .65   .65

Churchill Memorial Issue
Common Design Type
1966, Jan. 24   **Photo.**   **Perf. 14**
Design in Black, Gold and Carmine Rose

163	CD319	1c brt blue	.20	.20
164	CD319	3c green	.20	.20
165	CD319	10c brown	.40	.40
166	CD319	25c violet	1.00	1.00
		Nos. 163-166 (4)	1.80	1.80

Royal Visit Issue
Common Design Type
1966, Feb. 22   **Litho.**   **Perf. 11x12**
167 CD320 2c violet blue   .20   .20
168 CD320 70c dk car rose   2.25   2.25

Stamps of 1866 — A19

Designs: 5c, R.M.S. Atrato, 1866. 25c, Beechcraft mail plane on Beef Island Airfield and 6p stamp (No. 2). 60c, Landing mail at Road Town, 1866, and 1p stamp (No. 1).

Perf. 12½x13
1966, Apr. 25   **Wmk. 314**

169	A19	5c grn, yel, red & blk	.20	.20
170	A19	10c yel, grn, red, blk & rose	.20	.20
171	A19	25c lt grn, bl, red, blk & rose	.85	.85
172	A19	60c bl, red, blk, & grn	1.75	1.75
		Nos. 169-172 (4)	3.00	3.00

Centenary of Virgin Islands postage stamps.

Nos. 155, 157-158 Surcharged with New Value and Two Bars
Perf. 13x12½, 11½x12
1966, Sept. 15   **Engr.**   **Wmk. 314**

173	A18	50c on 70c	2.00	2.00
174	A18	$1.50 on $1.40	4.00	4.00
175	A18	$3 on $2.80	4.00	4.00
		Nos. 173-175 (3)	10.00	10.00

UNESCO Anniversary Issue
Common Design Type
1966, Dec. 1   **Litho.**   **Perf. 14**

176	CD323	2c "Education"	.20	.20
177	CD323	12c "Science"	.25	.25
178	CD323	60c "Culture"	.70	.70
		Nos. 176-178 (3)	1.15	1.15

Map and Seal of Virgin Islands A20

Wmk. 314
1967, Apr. 18   **Photo.**   **Perf. 14½**

179	A20	2c gold, grn & org	.20	.20
180	A20	10c gold, rose red, grn & org	.25	.25
181	A20	25c gold, red brn, grn & org	.25	.25
182	A20	$1 gold, bl, grn & org	.85	.85
		Nos. 179-182 (4)	1.55	1.55

Introduction of new constitution.

Map of Virgin Islands, Bermuda and C.S. Mercury — A21

10c, Communications center, Chalwell, Virgin Islands. 50c, Cable ship Mercury.

1967, Sept. 14   **Wmk. 314**   **Perf. 14½**

183	A21	4c green & multi	.20	.20
184	A21	10c dp plum & multi	.20	.20
185	A21	50c bister & multi	.60	.60
		Nos. 183-185 (3)	1.00	1.00

Completion of the Bermuda-Tortola, Virgin Islands, telephone link.

Blue Marlin A22

Designs: 10c, Sergeant fish (cobia). 25c, Peto fish (Wahoo). 40c, Fishing boat, map of Virgin Islands and fishing records.

Perf. 12½x12
1968, Jan. 2   **Photo.**   **Wmk. 314**

186	A22	2c multicolored	.20	.20
187	A22	10c multicolored	.30	.30
188	A22	25c multicolored	.60	.60
189	A22	40c multicolored	.90	.90
		Nos. 186-189 (4)	2.00	2.00

Game fishing in Virgin Islands waters.

Nos. 151 and 154 Overprinted: "1968 / INTERNATIONAL / YEAR FOR / HUMAN RIGHTS"
1968, July 1   **Engr.**   **Perf. 13x12½**

190	A17	10c lt violet & maroon	.20	.20
191	A17	25c purple & green	.30	.30

Martin Luther King, Bible and Sword A23

1968, Oct. 15   **Litho.**   **Perf. 14**

192	A23	4c dl org, vio & blk	.35	.35
193	A23	25c dl org, gray grn & blk	.45	.60

Martin Luther King, Jr. (1929-68), American civil rights leader.

DHC-6 Twin Otter A24

Designs: 10c, Hawker Siddeley 748. 25c, Hawker Siddeley Heron. $1, Badge from cap of Royal Engineers.

1968, Dec. 16   **Unwmk.**   **Perf. 14**

194	A24	2c brn red & multi	.20	.60
195	A24	10c grnsh bl, blk & red	.20	.20
196	A24	25c ultra, lt bl, org & blk	.40	.20
197	A24	$1 green & multi	1.60	2.00
		Nos. 194-197 (4)	2.40	3.00

Opening of enlarged Beef Island Airport.

Long John Silver and Jim Hawkins — A25

Tourist and Rock Grouper — A26

Scenes from Treasure Island: 10c, Jim's escape from the pirates, horiz. 40c, The fight with Israel Hands. $1, Treasure trove, horiz.

Perf. 13½x13, 13x13½
1969, Mar. 18   **Photo.**   **Wmk. 314**

198	A25	4c dp car & multi	.40	.20
199	A25	10c multicolored	.45	.25
200	A25	40c ultra & multi	.55	.65
201	A25	$1 black & multi	1.10	2.00
		Nos. 198-201 (4)	2.50	3.10

Robert Louis Stevenson (1850-94). The Virgin Islands were used as the setting for "Treasure Island."

1969, Oct. 20   **Litho.**   **Perf. 12½**

Tourist Publicity: 10c, Yachts in Road Harbor, Tortola. 20c, Tourists on beach in Virgin Gorda National Park, horiz. $1, Pipe organ cactus and woman tourist.

202	A26	2c multicolored	.20	.55
203	A26	10c multicolored	.20	.20
204	A26	20c multicolored	.35	.25
205	A26	$1 multicolored	1.75	2.00
		Nos. 202-205 (4)	2.50	3.00

Carib
Canoe
A27

Ships: 1c, Santa Maria. 2c, H.M.S. Elizabeth Bonaventure. 3c, Dutch buccaneer, 1660.
4c, Thetis (1827 merchant ship). 5c, Henry
Morgan's ship. 6c, Frigate Boreas. 8c,
Schooner L'Eclair, 1804. 10c, H.M.S. Formidable. 12c, H.M.S. Nymph burning. 15c,
Packet Windsor Castle fighting French privateer. 25c, Frigate Astrea, 1808. 50c, H.M.S.
Rhone. $1, Tortola sloop. $2, H.M.S. Frob-
isher. $3, Booker Line Viking (cargo ship). $5,
Hydrofoil Sun Arrow.

Wmk. 314 Sideways

1970, Feb. 16			**Perf. 14½**	
206	A27	½c brn & ocher	.20	.20
207	A27	1c bl, lt grn & vio	.20	.20
208	A27	2c red brn, org & gray	.20	.20
209	A27	3c ver, bl & brn	.20	.20
210	A27	4c brn, bl & vio bl	.20	.20
211	A27	5c grn, pink & blk	.20	.20
212	A27	6c lil, grn & blk	.20	.20
213	A27	8c lt ol, yel & brn	.30	.30
214	A27	10c ocher, bl & brn	.35	.40
215	A27	12c sep, yel & dp cl	.50	.60
216	A27	15c org, grnsh bl & brn	.45	.55
217	A27	25c bl, grnsh gray & pur	.65	.85
218	A27	50c rose car, lt grn & brn	1.40	1.60
219	A27	$1 brn, sal pink & dk grn	2.75	3.25
220	A27	$2 gray & yel	5.50	6.75
221	A27	$3 brn, ol bis & dk bl	8.50	10.50
222	A27	$5 lil & gray	14.00	17.00
		Nos. 206-222 (17)	35.80	43.20

For overprints see Nos. 235-236.

1973, Oct. 17		**Wmk. 314 Upright**		
206a	A27	½c	.85	5.75
209a	A27	3c	2.00	2.25
210a	A27	4c	2.00	4.25
211a	A27	5c	2.00	2.10
214a	A27	10c	2.40	2.40
215a	A27	12c	3.25	3.25
		Nos. 206a-215a (6)	12.50	20.00

1974, Nov. 11		**Wmk. 314 Sideways**	**Perf. 13½**	
207a	A27	1c	1.25	1.90
214b	A27	10c	2.25	2.10
215b	A27	12c	2.25	3.00
216a	A27	15c	3.25	3.00
		Nos. 207a-216a (4)	9.00	10.00

"A Tale
of Two
Cities,"
by
Dickens
A28

Charles Dickens: 10c, "Oliver Twist." 25c,
"Great Expectations."

1970, May 4		**Litho.**	**Perf. 14½**	
223	A28	5c blk, gray & pink	.20	.20
224	A28	10c blk, pale yel grn & blue	.40	.35
225	A28	25c blk, yel & lt yel grn	.65	.95
		Nos. 223-225 (3)	1.25	1.50

Hospital
Visitor
A29

10c, Girl Scouts receiving 1st aid training at
lake side. 25c, Red Cross & Virgin Islands
coat of arms.

1970, Aug. 10		**Wmk. 314**	**Perf. 14**	
226	A29	4c multicolored	.20	.20
227	A29	10c multicolored	.55	.20
228	A29	25c multicolored	1.25	1.10
		Nos. 226-228 (3)	2.00	1.50

Centenary of British Red Cross.

Mary Read — A30

Pirates: 10c, George Lowther. 30c, Edward
Teach (Blackbeard). 60c, Henry Morgan.

1970, Nov. 16		**Wmk. 314**	**Perf. 14**	
229	A30	½c dp rose & multi	.20	.20
230	A30	10c blue grn & multi	.50	.50
231	A30	30c ultra & multi	1.40	1.40
232	A30	60c multicolored	1.90	1.90
		Nos. 229-232 (4)	4.00	4.00

Children
Spelling
out
"UNICEF"
A31

1971, Dec. 13				
233	A31	15c tan & multi	.20	.20
234	A31	30c lt blue & multi	.50	.50

25th anniv. of UNICEF.

Nos. 210 and 217 Dated "1972" and
Overprinted: "VISIT OF / H.R.H. / THE
/ PRINCESS MARGARET"

1972, Mar. 7			**Perf. 14½**	
235	A27	4c multicolored	.20	.20
236	A27	25c multicolored	.50	.60

Seaman,
1800 — A32

10c, Boatswain, 1787-1807. 30c, Captain,
1795-1812. 60c, Admiral in full dress uniform,
1787-95.

1972, Mar. 17			**Perf. 14x13½**	
237	A32	½c yellow & multi	.20	.20
238	A32	10c brt pink & multi	.40	.40
239	A32	30c orange & multi	1.10	1.10
240	A32	60c blue & multi	2.50	2.50
		Nos. 237-240 (4)	4.20	4.20

INTERPEX, 14th Intl. Stamp Exhib., NYC,
Mar. 17-19.

Silver Wedding Issue, 1972
Common Design Type

Design: Queen Elizabeth II, Prince Philip,
sailfish and "Sir Winston Churchill" yacht.

1972, Nov. 24		**Photo.**	**Perf. 14x14½**	
241	CD324	15c ultra & multi	.35	.35
242	CD324	25c Prus blue & multi	.35	.35

Allison
Tuna
A33

1972, Dec. 12		**Litho.**	**Perf. 13½x14**	
243	A33	½c Wahoo	.20	.20
244	A33	½c Blue marlin	.20	.20
a.		Horiz. or vert. pair, #243-244	.20	.20
245	A33	15c shown	.50	.50
246	A33	25c White marlin	.80	.80
247	A33	50c Sailfish	1.40	1.40

248	A33	$1 Dolphin	3.50	3.50
a.		Souvenir sheet of 6, #243-248	13.50	13.50
		Nos. 243-248 (6)	6.60	6.60

Game fish.

Lettsom House and Medal — A34

Themes from Quaker History: ½c, Dr. John
Coakley Lettsom, vert. 15c, Dr. William Thornton, vert. 30c, US Capitol, Washington, DC,
and Dr. Thornton who designed it. $1, Library
Hall, Philadelphia, and William Penn.

1973, Mar. 9		**Litho.**	**Perf. 13½**	
249	A34	½c rose & multi	.20	.20
250	A34	10c multicolored	.20	.20
251	A34	15c multicolored	.30	.30
252	A34	30c ultra & multi	.60	.60
253	A34	$1 multicolored	1.90	1.90
		Nos. 249-253 (5)	3.20	3.20

INTERPEX, 15th Intl. Phil. Exhib., NYC,
Mar. 9-11.

Hummingbirds on 1c Coin — A35

Coins and Beach Scenes: 5c, Zenaida
doves. 10c, Kingfisher. 25c, Mangrove cuck-
oos. 50c, Brown pelicans. $1, Magnificent frig-
ate birds.

1973, June 30		**Wmk. 314**	**Perf. 14½**	
254	A35	1c orange & multi	.20	.45
255	A35	5c lt blue & multi	.75	.20
256	A35	10c pale ultra & multi	1.10	.20
257	A35	25c yellow & multi	1.40	.20
258	A35	50c lt violet & multi	1.60	1.60
259	A35	$1 ultra & multi	2.00	3.00
		Nos. 254-259 (6)	7.05	5.65

New Virgin Islands coinage.

Princess Anne's Wedding Issue
Common Design Type

1973, Nov. 16		**Wmk. 314**	**Perf. 14**	
260	CD325	5c citron & multi	.20	.20
261	CD325	50c blue grn & multi	.80	.80

Virgin and Child, by Bernardino Pintoricchio A36	Arms of French Minesweeper Canopus A37

Christmas (Paintings of the Virgin and Child
by): 3c, Lorenzo Credi. 25c, Carlo Crivelli. 50c,
Bernardino Luini.

1973, Dec. 7			**Perf. 14x14½**	
262	A36	½c lt green & multi	.20	.20
263	A36	3c rose & multi	.20	.20
264	A36	25c ocher & multi	.50	.50
265	A36	50c lt blue & multi	.95	.95
		Nos. 262-265 (4)	1.85	1.85

1974, Mar. 22		**Wmk. 314**	**Perf. 14**	
266	A37	5c shown	.20	.20
267	A37	18c USS Saginaw	.40	.40
268	A37	25c HMS Rothesay	.50	.50
269	A37	50c HMCS Ottawa	1.00	1.00
a.		Souvenir sheet of 4, #266-269	3.00	3.00
		Nos. 266-269 (4)	2.10	2.10

INTERPEX Phil. Exhib., NYC, Mar. 22-24.

Famous
Explorers — A38

1974, Aug. 19			**Perf. 14½**	
270	A38	5c Columbus	.30	.30
271	A38	10c Sir Walter Raleigh	.40	.40
272	A38	25c Sir Martin Frobisher	.45	.45
273	A38	40c Sir Francis Drake	.85	.85
a.		Souvenir sheet of 4, #270-273	2.50	2.50
		Nos. 270-273 (4)	2.00	2.00

Sea
Shells
A39

1974, Sept. 30			**Perf. 13x13½**	
274	A39	5c Trumpet triton	.45	.45
275	A39	18c West Indian murex	1.00	1.00
276	A39	25c Bleeding tooth	1.25	1.25
277	A39	75c Virgin Island latirus	3.00	3.00
a.		Souvenir sheet of 4, #274-277	6.25	6.25
		Nos. 274-277 (4)	5.70	5.70

St. Mary, Aldermanbury,
London, — A40

Design: 50c, St. Mary, Fulton, Missouri.

1974, Nov. 30		**Wmk. 373**	**Perf. 14**	
278	A40	10c multicolored	.20	.20
279	A40	50c multicolored	.50	.50
a.		Souvenir sheet of 2, #278-279	1.00	1.00

Sir Winston Churchill (1874-1965).

Figurehead from
"Boreas" — A41

Figureheads: 18c, The Golden Hind. 40c,
Crowned lion from the "Superb." 85c, Warrior,
from the "Formidable."

		Perf. 13½x13		
1975, Mar. 14			**Wmk. 314**	
280	A41	5c multicolored	.20	.20
281	A41	18c multicolored	.55	.55
282	A41	40c multicolored	.75	.75
283	A41	85c multicolored	1.50	1.50
a.		Souv. sheet of 4, #280-283, perf. 14	3.25	3.25
		Nos. 280-283 (4)	3.00	3.00

INTERPEX, 17th Phil. Exhib., NYC, Mar.
14-16.

Rock
Beauty
A42

Designs: Fish.

1975   Wmk. 373   *Perf. 14*

284	A42	½c shown	.20	.20
285	A42	1c Squirrelfish	.55	.65
286	A42	3c Queen trigger-fish	1.50	1.75
287	A42	5c Blue angelfish	.35	.45
288	A42	8c Stoplight parrotfish	.35	.45
289	A42	10c Queen angel-fish	.35	.45
290	A42	12c Nassau grouper	.55	.65
291	A42	13c Blue tang	.55	.65
292	A42	15c Sergeant major	.55	.65
293	A42	18c Jewfish	1.25	1.50
294	A42	20c Bluehead wrasse	.75	.95
295	A42	25c Gray angelfish	1.60	1.90
296	A42	60c Glasseye snapper	1.90	2.40
297	A42	$1 Blue chromis	2.75	3.25
298	A42	$2.50 French angelfish	4.50	5.50
299	A42	$3 Queen parrotfish	6.25	7.25
300	A42	$5 Four-eye butterflyfish	6.75	8.00
		Nos. 284-300 (17)	30.70	36.65

Issue dates: $5, Aug. 15. Others, June 16. ½c, 5c, 8c, 10c, 12c, 13c, 15c, 20c reissued dated "1977." Value $6.50.

St. Georges Parish School — A43

Designs: 25c, Legislative Council Building. 40c, Mace and gavel of Legislative Council. 75c, Scroll with dates of historical events.

1975, Nov. 27   Litho.   Wmk. 373

301	A43	5c ultra & multi	.20	.20
302	A43	25c green & multi	.40	.40
303	A43	40c ocher & multi	.50	.50
304	A43	75c ultra & multi	.65	.65
		Nos. 301-304 (4)	1.75	1.75

Restoration of Legislative Council, 25th anniv.

Copper Mine Point — A44

Historic Sites: 18c, Dr. Thornton's Ruin, Pleasant Valley. 50c, Callwood distillery. 75c, The Dungeon.

1976, Mar. 12   Litho.   *Perf. 14½*

305	A44	5c red & multi	.20	.20
306	A44	18c red & multi	.35	.35
307	A44	50c red & multi	.70	.70
308	A44	75c red & multi	1.00	1.00
		Nos. 305-308 (4)	2.25	2.25

Massachusetts Brig Hazard — A45

Designs: 22c, American Privateer Spy. 40c, Continental Navy Frigate Raleigh. 75c, Frigate Alliance and HMS Trepasy.

1976, May 29   Wmk. 373   *Perf. 14*

309	A45	8c multicolored	.35	.35
310	A45	22c multicolored	.75	.55
311	A45	40c multicolored	1.40	1.10
312	A45	75c multicolored	2.75	2.00
a.		Souvenir sheet of 4, #309-312	8.50	8.50
		Nos. 309-312 (4)	5.25	3.85

American Bicentennial.

Government House, Tortola — A46

Designs: 15c, Government House, St. Croix, vert. 30c, Flags of US and British Virgin Islands, vert. 75c, Arms of British and US Virgin Islands.

1976, Oct. 29   Litho.   *Perf. 14*

313	A46	8c green & multi	.20	.20
314	A46	15c green & multi	.20	.20
315	A46	30c green & multi	.35	.35
316	A46	75c green & multi	.75	.75
		Nos. 313-316 (4)	1.50	1.50

US and British Virgin Islands Friendship Day, 5th anniversary.

Holy Bible — A47

8c, Queen visiting Agricultural Station, Tortola, 1966. 60c, Presentation of Holy Bible.

1977, Feb. 7   *Perf. 14x13½*

317	A47	8c silver & multi	.20	.20
318	A47	30c silver & multi	.30	.30
319	A47	60c silver & multi	.50	.50
		Nos. 317-319 (3)	1.00	1.00

25th anniv. of the reign of Elizabeth II. For overprints see Nos. 324-326.

Virgin Islands Chart, 1739 — A48

18th Century Maps of Virgin Islands: 22c, 1758. 30c, 1775. 75c, 1779.

1977, June 12   Wmk. 373   *Perf. 13½*

320	A48	8c multicolored	.35	.20
321	A48	22c multicolored	.70	.60
322	A48	30c multicolored	.95	.85
323	A48	75c multicolored	2.00	2.00
		Nos. 320-323 (4)	4.00	3.65

Type of 1977 Inscribed: "ROYAL VISIT"

Designs: 5c, Queen visiting Agricultural Station, Tortola, 1966. 25c, Holy Bible. 50c, Presentation of Holy Bible.

1977, Oct. 26   Litho.   *Perf. 14x13½*

324	A47	5c yel brn & multi	.20	.20
325	A47	25c dk blue & multi	.30	.30
326	A47	50c purple & multi	.50	.50
		Nos. 324-326 (3)	1.00	1.00

Caribbean visit of Queen Elizabeth II.

Divers Checking Equipment — A49

Tourist publicity: 5c, Cup coral inside bow of "Rhone." 8c, Sponge growing on superstructure of "Rhone." 22c, Sponge and cup coral.

30c, Scuba diver searching for sponges in cave. 75c, Marine life.

1977, Dec. 15   Wmk. 373   *Perf. 13½*

327	A49	½c multicolored	.20	.20
328	A49	5c multicolored	.20	.20
329	A49	8c multicolored	.20	.20
330	A49	22c multicolored	.70	.70
331	A49	30c multicolored	.95	.95
332	A49	75c multicolored	1.75	1.75
		Nos. 327-332 (6)	4.00	4.00

Corals A50

1978, Feb. 10   *Perf. 14*

333	A50	8c Fire	.35	.35
334	A50	15c Staghorn	.55	.55
335	A50	40c Brain	1.00	1.00
336	A50	75c Elkhorn	2.10	2.10
		Nos. 333-336 (4)	4.00	4.00

Elizabeth II Coronation Anniversary Issue
Common Design Types
Souvenir Sheet

1978, June 2   Unwmk.   *Perf. 15*

337		Sheet of 6	2.75	2.75
a.		CD326 50c Falcon of the Plantagenets	.40	.40
b.		CD327 50c Elizabeth II	.40	.40
c.		CD328 50c Iguana	.40	.40

No. 337 contains 2 se-tenant strips of Nos. 337a-337c, separated by horizontal gutter.

Lignum Vitae A51

Flowering Trees: 22c, Ginger thomas. 40c, Dog almond. 75c, White cedar.

1978, Sept. 4   Litho.   *Perf. 13x13½*

338	A51	8c multicolored	.35	.35
339	A51	22c multicolored	.55	.55
340	A51	40c multicolored	.75	.75
341	A51	75c multicolored	1.10	1.10
a.		Souvenir sheet of 4, #338-341	2.75	2.75
		Nos. 338-341 (4)	2.75	2.75

Eurema Lisa A52

Butterflies: 22c, Dione vanillae. 30c, Heliconius charitonius. 75c, Hemiargus hanno.

1978, Dec. 4   Wmk. 373   *Perf. 14*

342	A52	5c multicolored	.25	.25
343	A52	22c multicolored	1.10	.90
a.		Sheet of 9, 6 #342, 3 #343	4.25	4.25
344	A52	30c multicolored	1.40	1.25
345	A52	75c multicolored	3.50	3.00
		Nos. 342-345 (4)	6.25	5.40

Spiny Lobsters A53

Conservation: 15c, Iguana, vert. 22c, Hawksbill turtle. 75c, Black coral, vert.

1979, Feb. 10   Litho.

346	A53	5c multicolored	.20	.20
347	A53	15c multicolored	.45	.45
348	A53	30c multicolored	.80	.80
349	A53	75c multicolored	1.75	1.75
a.		Souvenir sheet of 4, #346-349	4.25	4.25
		Nos. 346-349 (4)	3.20	3.20

Strawberry Cactus — A54

West Indies Girl and Church — A55

Native Cacti: 5c, Snowy cactus. 13c, Barrel cactus. 22c, Tree cactus. 30c, Prickly pear. 75c, Dildo cactus.

1979, May 7   Wmk. 373   *Perf. 14*

350	A54	½c multicolored	.20	.20
351	A54	5c multicolored	.25	.25
352	A54	13c multicolored	.40	.40
353	A54	22c multicolored	.50	.50
354	A54	30c multicolored	.60	.60
355	A54	75c multicolored	.80	.80
		Nos. 350-355 (6)	2.75	2.75

1979, July 9   *Perf. 14x14½*

Children and IYC Emblem: 10c, African boy and dancers. 13c, Asian girl and children playing. $1, European girl and bicycle.

356	A55	5c multicolored	.20	.20
357	A55	10c multicolored	.20	.20
358	A55	13c multicolored	.20	.20
359	A55	$1 multicolored	.50	.50
a.		Souvenir sheet of 4, #356-359	1.40	1.40
		Nos. 356-359 (4)	1.10	1.10

International Year of the Child.

No. 118 — A56

Pencil Urchin — A57

Rowland Hill's Signature and: 13c, Virgin Islands No. 11, horiz. 75c, Unissued Great Britain 2d stamp, 1910, horiz. $1, Virgin Islands No. 8c.

1979, Oct. 1   Photo.   *Perf. 13½*

360	A56	5c multicolored	.20	.20
361	A56	13c multicolored	.20	.20
362	A56	75c multicolored	.85	.85
		Nos. 360-362 (3)	1.25	1.25

Souvenir Sheet

363	A56	$1 multicolored	1.00	1.00

Sir Rowland Hill (1795-1879), originator of penny postage.
For overprints see Nos. 389-390.

1979-80   Litho.   *Perf. 14*

364	A57	½c Calcified algae	.20	.20
365	A57	1c Purple-tipped sea anemone	.20	.20
366	A57	3c Starfish	.20	.20
367	A57	5c shown	.20	.20
368	A57	8c Triton's trumpet	.20	.20
369	A57	10c Christmas tree worms	.20	.20

370	A57	13c Flamingo tongue snails	.25	*.25*
371	A57	15c Spider crab	.35	.35
372	A57	18c Sea squirts	.35	*.35*
373	A57	20c Tree tulip	.40	.40
374	A57	25c Rooster tail conch	.50	.55
375	A57	30c Fighting conch	.70	.75
376	A57	60c Mangrove crab	1.50	*1.60*
377	A57	$1 Coral polyps	2.25	2.40
378	A57	$2.50 Peppermint shrimp	5.50	6.00
379	A57	$3 West Indian murex	6.75	7.25
380	A57	$5 Carpet anemone	11.50	12.50
		Nos. 364-380 (17)	31.25	33.60

Issued: 5, 8, 10, 15, 20, 25c, $2.50, $3, 12/17; others, 4/1/80.
Nos. 367-368, 370-371, 373, 375 reissued inscribed 1982. Value $12.
For overprints see Nos. O1-O15.

Rotary Athletic Meet, Tortola, Emblem A58

1980, Mar. 3   Litho.   Perf. 13½x14

381	A58	8c shown	.20	.20
382	A58	22c Paul P. Harris	.25	.25
383	A58	60c Mount Sage National Park	.55	.55
384	A58	$1 Anniversary emblem	1.00	1.00
a.		Souvenir sheet of 4, #381-384	2.50	2.50
		Nos. 381-384 (4)	2.00	2.00

Rotary International, 75th anniv.

Brown Booby, London 1980 Emblem A59

1980, May 6   Wmk. 373   Perf. 14

385	A59	20c shown	.35	.35
386	A59	25c Magnificent frigatebird	.45	.45
387	A59	50c White-tailed tropic bird	.70	.70
388	A59	75c Brown pelican	.95	.95
a.		Souvenir sheet of 4, #385-388	3.00	3.00
		Nos. 385-388 (4)	2.45	2.45

London 80 Intl. Stamp Exhib., May 6-14.

Nos. 361-362 Overprinted:
"CARIBBEAN COMMONWEALTH PARLIAMENTARY ASSOCIATION MEETING TORTOLA 11-19 JULY 1980"

1980, July 7   Photo.   Perf. 13½

389	A56	13c multicolored	.20	.20
390	A56	75c multicolored	.80	.80

Sir Francis Drake — A60

1980, Sept. 26   Litho.   Perf. 14½

391	A60	8c shown	.50	.50
392	A60	15c Queen Elizabeth I	.80	.80
393	A60	30c Drake knighted	.95	.95
394	A60	75c Golden Hinde	2.00	2.00
a.		Souvenir sheet of 4, #391-394	4.25	4.25
		Nos. 391-394 (4)	4.25	4.25

400th anniv. of circumnavigation of the world.

Jost Van Dyke A61

1980, Dec. 1   Wmk. 373   Perf. 14

395	A61	2c shown	.20	.20
396	A61	5c Peter Island	.20	.20
397	A61	13c Virgin Gorda	.20	.20
398	A61	22c Anegada	.35	.35
399	A61	30c Norman Island	.40	.40
400	A61	$1 Tortola	1.25	1.25
a.		Souvenir sheet of 1	1.50	1.50
		Nos. 395-400 (6)	2.60	2.60

Dancing Lady — A62

1981, Mar. 3   Litho.   Perf. 11

401	A62	5c shown	.35	.35
402	A62	20c Love in the mist	.40	.40
403	A62	22c Red pineapple	1.10	1.10
404	A62	75c Dutchman's pipe	1.40	1.40
405	A62	$1 Maiden apple	1.40	1.40
		Nos. 401-405 (5)	3.65	3.65

Royal Wedding Issue
Common Design Type

1981, July 22   Litho.   Perf. 14

406	CD331	10c Bouquet	.20	.20
407	CD331	35c Charles, Queen Mother	.45	.45
408	CD331	$1.25 Couple	1.50	1.50
		Nos. 406-408 (3)	2.15	2.15

#406-408 each se-tenant with decorative label.

Duke of Edinburgh's Awards, 25th Anniv. — A63

1981, Sept. 16   Wmk. 373   Perf. 14

409	A63	10c Stamp collecting	.20	.20
410	A63	15c Running	.25	.25
411	A63	50c Camping	.85	.85
412	A63	$1 Duke of Edinburgh	1.60	1.60
		Nos. 409-412 (4)	2.90	2.90

Intl. Year of the Disabled A64

1981, Oct. 19   Litho.   Perf. 14

413	A64	15c Children	.30	.30
414	A64	20c Fort Charlotte Children's Center	.40	.40
415	A64	30c Playing music	.60	.60
416	A64	$1 Center, diff.	2.00	2.00
		Nos. 413-416 (4)	3.30	3.30

A65   A66

Virgin and Child (Christmas): Details from Adoration of the Shepherds, by Rubens. 50c, horiz.

1981, Nov. 30   Litho.   Perf. 14

417	A65	5c multicolored	.20	.20
418	A65	15c multicolored	.25	.25
419	A65	30c multicolored	.50	.50
420	A65	$1 multicolored	2.00	2.00
		Nos. 417-420 (4)	2.95	2.95

Souvenir Sheet

421	A65	50c multicolored	2.25	2.25

1982, Apr. 15   Litho.   Perf. 14x14½

Hummingbirds on local flora.

422	A66	15c Green-throated carib, erythrina	.50	.50
423	A66	30c Same, bougainvillea	1.00	1.00
424	A66	35c Antillean crested hummingbird, granadilla passiflora	1.25	1.25
425	A66	$1.25 Same, hibiscus	3.75	3.75
		Nos. 422-425 (4)	6.50	6.50

10th Anniv. of Lions Club of Tortola — A67

1982, May 3   Perf. 13½x14

426	A67	10c Helping disabled	.20	.20
427	A67	20c Headquarters	.35	.35
428	A67	30c Map	.50	.50
429	A67	$1.50 Emblem	2.50	2.50
a.		Souvenir sheet of 4, #426-429	4.25	4.25
		Nos. 426-429 (4)	3.55	3.55

Princess Diana Issue
Common Design Type

1982, July 1   Litho.   Perf. 14

430	CD333	10c Arms	.20	.20
431	CD333	35c Diana	.55	.55
432	CD333	50c Wedding	.75	.75
433	CD333	$1.50 Portrait	2.50	2.50
		Nos. 430-433 (4)	4.00	4.00

10th Anniv. of Air BVI (Natl. Airline) A68

1982, Sept. 10   Wmk. 373   Perf. 14

434	A68	10c Douglas DC-3	.30	.30
435	A68	15c Britten-Norman Islander	.55	.55
436	A68	60c Hawker-Siddeley	2.40	2.40
437	A68	75c Planes	2.75	2.75
		Nos. 434-437 (4)	6.00	6.00

Scouting Year A69

1982, Nov. 18

438	A69	8c Emblem, Flag raising	.20	.20
439	A69	20c Cub scout, nature study	.40	.40
440	A69	50c Kayak, sea scout	1.00	1.00

441	A69	$1 Camp Brownsea Is., Baden-Powell	2.00	2.00
		Nos. 438-441 (4)	3.60	3.60

Commonwealth Day — A70

1983, Mar. 14   Perf. 13½x14

442	A70	10c Legislature in session	.20	.20
443	A70	30c Wind surfing	.50	.50
444	A70	35c Globe	.60	.60
445	A70	75c Flags	1.25	1.25
		Nos. 442-445 (4)	2.55	2.55

Nursing Week A71

1983, May 9   Litho.   Perf. 14½

446	A71	10c Florence Nightingale (1820-1910), vert.	.50	.50
447	A71	30c Nurse, assistant, vert.	1.25	1.25
448	A71	60c Public health	2.50	2.50
449	A71	75c Peebles Hospital	3.25	3.25
		Nos. 446-449 (4)	7.50	7.50

Boat Building A72

1983, July 25   Perf. 14

450	A72	15c First stage	.40	.40
451	A72	25c 2nd stage	.60	.60
452	A72	50c Launching	1.25	1.25
453	A72	$1 First voyage	2.50	2.50
a.		Souvenir sheet of 4, #450-453	5.00	5.00
		Nos. 450-453 (4)	4.75	4.75

Manned Flight Bicentenary — A73

1983, Sept. 15   Wmk. 373   Perf. 14

454	A73	10c Grumman Goose	.20	.20
455	A73	30c De Havilland Heron	.55	.55
456	A73	60c EMB Bandeirante	1.25	1.25
457	A73	$1.25 Hawker-Siddeley 748	2.25	2.25
		Nos. 454-457 (4)	4.25	4.25

Christmas — A74

Raphael Paintings.

1983, Nov. 7   Litho.   Perf. 14½

458	A74	8c Madonna & Child with Infant Baptist	.20	.20
459	A74	15c La Belle Jardiniere	.30	.30
460	A74	50c Madonna del Granduca	.95	.95
461	A74	$1 Terranuova Madonna	1.90	1.90
a.		Souvenir sheet of 4, #458-461	4.25	4.25
		Nos. 458-461 (4)	3.35	3.35

World Chess Federation, 60th
Anniv. — A75

1984, Feb. 20   Litho.   Perf. 14
462 A75 10c Local tournament .60 .60
463 A75 35c Chess pieces,
        vert. 1.90 1.90
464 A75 75c 1980 Olympiad,
        Winning board,
        vert. 4.50 4.50
465 A75 $1 Gold medal 7.00 7.00
    Nos. 462-465 (4) 14.00 14.00

Lloyd's List Issue
Common Design Type

1984, Apr. 16   Litho.   Perf. 14½x14
466 CD335 15c Port Purcell,
        Tortola .35 .35
467 CD335 25c Boeing 747 .65 .65
468 CD335 50c Shipwreck of
        RMS Rhone 1.25 1.25
469 CD335 $1 Booker Viking 2.75 2.75
    Nos. 466-469 (4) 5.00 5.00

Souvenir Sheet

UPU Congress — A76

1984, May 16   Wmk. 373   Perf. 14
470 A76 $1 Emblem, jet,
        mailboat 3.50 3.50

1984
Summer
Olympics
A77

1984, July 3
471 A77 15c Runners .40 .40
472 A77 15c Runner .40 .40
    a.   Pair, #471-472 1.25 1.25
473 A77 20c Wind surfers .50 .50
474 A77 20c Wind surfer .50 .50
    a.   Pair, #473-474 1.50 1.50
475 A77 30c Yachts .75 .75
476 A77 30c Yacht .75 .75
    a.   Pair, #475-476 2.25 2.25
    Nos. 471-476 (6) 3.30 3.30
Souvenir Sheet
477 A77 $1 Torch bearer, vert. 2.75 2.75

Festival (Slavery Abolition
Sesquicentennial) — A78

Designs: No. 478: a, Steel band. b, Calypso
dancers. c, Dancers (men). d, Woman in traditional dress. e, Parade float.
No. 479 (Sail color of boat(s) in foreground):
a, Green & white. b, Red & white, white, purple & white. c, white, yellow & white, blue &
white. d, Yellow, red & white. e, Purple &
white, white.
Nos. 478 and 479 each in continuous
design.

1984, Aug. 14   Perf. 13½x14
478   Strip of 5, Parade 1.50 1.50
    a.-e. A78 10c, any single .20 .20
479   Strip of 5, Regatta 3.75 3.75
    a.-e. A78 30c, any single .60 .60

Local
Boats
A79

1984, Nov. 15   Wmk. 373   Perf. 13
480 A79 10c Sloop .30 .30
481 A79 35c Fishing boat 1.25 1.25
482 A79 60c Schooner 2.25 2.25
483 A79 75c Cargo boat 2.75 2.75
    a.   Souvenir sheet of 4, #480-483 6.75 6.75
    Nos. 480-483 (4) 6.55 6.55

Four stamps picturing Michael Jackson were printed. The designs were not
acceptable to the Virgin Islands so they
were not issued. A number of copies
had been distributed in advance for
publicity purposes.

New
Coinage
A80

1985, Jan. 15   Litho.   Perf. 14½
484 A80 1c Hawksbill Turtle .20 .20
485 A80 5c Bonito .20 .20
486 A80 10c Great Barricuda .20 .20
487 A80 25c Blue Marlin .80 .80
488 A80 50c Dolphin 1.60 1.60
489 A80 $1 Spotfin Butterfly
        Fish 3.00 3.00
    a.   Miniature sheet of 6, #484-489 6.50 6.50
    Nos. 484-489 (6) 6.00 6.00

Birds — A81

1985, July 3   Wmk. 373   Perf. 14
490 A81 1c Boatswain bird .25 .30
491 A81 2c Night gaulin .25 .30
492 A81 5c Rain bird .25 .30
493 A81 8c Mockingbird .25 .30
494 A81 10c Chinchary .30 .40
495 A81 12c Wild pigeon .40 .50
496 A81 15c Bittlin .50 .55
497 A81 18c Blach witch .55 .65
498 A81 20c Pond shakey .65 .75
499 A81 25c Killy-killy .80 .90
500 A81 30c Thrushie 1.00 1.25
501 A81 35c Marmi dove 1.10 1.40
502 A81 40c Little gaulin 1.40 1.75
503 A81 50c Ground dove 1.60 2.00
504 A81 60c Blue gaulin 2.50 2.75
505 A81 $1 Pimleco 4.00 4.50
506 A81 $2 White booby 8.00 9.00
507 A81 $3 Cow bird 11.00 12.00
508 A81 $5 Turtle dove 18.00 21.00
    Nos. 490-508 (19) 52.80 60.60

For overprints see Nos. O16-O34.

1987, Oct. 28   Wmk. 384
494a A81 10c .50 .50
496a A81 15c .75 .75
498a A81 20c 1.10 1.10
499a A81 25c 1.25 1.25
501a A81 35c 1.75 1.75
505a A81 $1 5.25 5.25
507a A81 $3 15.00 15.00
    Nos. 494a-507a (7) 25.60 25.60

Queen Mother,
85th
Birthday — A82

Audubon Birth
Bicent. — A83

Portraits.

1985, Aug. 26   Litho.   Perf. 12½
509 A82 10c Facing right .20 .20
510 A82 10c Facing left .20 .20
511 A82 25c Facing right .45 .45
512 A82 25c Facing left .45 .45
513 A82 50c Facing forward .90 .90
514 A82 50c Facing forward .90 .90
515 A82 75c Facing right 1.25 1.25
516 A82 75c Facing forward 1.25 1.25
    Nos. 509-516 (8) 5.60 5.60

Souvenir Sheets

1985-86   Litho.   Perf. 13x12½
517   Sheet of 2 3.50 3.50
    a.-b. A82 $1 dull grn & multi 1.75 1.75
518   Sheet of 2 3.50 3.50
    a.-b. A82 $1 orange & multi 1.60 1.60
519   Sheet of 2 8.50 8.50
    a.-b. A82 $2.50 dl yel & multi 4.25 4.25

Issued: #517, 12/18/85; #518-519, 2/18/86.
For overprints see Nos. 528-531.

1985, Dec. 17   Perf. 15
520 A83 5c Seaside sparrow .20 .20
521 A83 30c Passenger pigeon .60 .60
522 A83 50c Yellow-breasted
        chat 1.00 1.00
523 A83 $1 American kestrel 2.00 2.00
    Nos. 520-523 (4) 3.80 3.80

Cruise
Ships
A84

1986, Jan. 27
524 A84 35c Flying Cloud .80 .80
525 A84 50c Newport Clipper 1.25 1.25
526 A84 75c Cunard Countess 1.90 1.90
527 A84 $1 Sea Goddess 2.75 2.75
    Nos. 524-527 (4) 6.70 6.70

Nos. 511-512, 515-516 Ovptd. "MIAMI
/ B.V.I. / INAUGURAL FLIGHT"

1986, Apr. 17   Litho.   Perf. 12½
528 A82 25c on No. 511 .50 .50
529 A82 25c on No. 512 .50 .50
530 A82 75c on No. 515 1.75 1.75
531 A82 75c on No. 516 1.75 1.75
    Nos. 528-531 (4) 4.50 4.50

Queen Elizabeth II, 60th
Birthday — A85

Perf. 13x12½, 12½x13
1986, Apr. 21   Litho.
532 A85 12c Portrait, 1958 .20 .20
533 A85 35c Maundy service .55 .55
534 A85 $1.50 Contemporary
        photograph 2.25 2.25

535 A85 $2 Canberra, 1982,
        vert. 3.00 3.00
    Nos. 532-535 (4) 6.00 6.00
Souvenir Sheet
536 A85 $3 Contemporary
        photograph, diff. 6.00 6.00

Stamps with blue ribbons and frames omitted were from stock sold when the printer was
liquidated.

Wedding of Prince Andrew and Sarah
Ferguson — A86

1986, July 23   Perf. 12½
537 A86 35c Couple, vert. .55 .55
538 A86 35c Sarah, vert. .55 .55
539 A86 $1 Andrew 1.60 1.60
540 A86 $1 Sarah, diff. 1.60 1.60
    Nos. 537-540 (4) 4.30 4.30

Stamps of the same denomination exist se-
tenant.
Nos. 537-540 Overprinted "Congratulations
to T.R.H. The Duke & Duchess of York" were
not issued.

Traditional Rum Production — A87

1986, July 30   Perf. 14
541 A87 12c Harvesting sugar
        cane .50 .50
542 A87 40c Grinding 2.00 2.00
543 A87 60c Distillery 3.25 3.25
544 A87 $1 Transport 5.25 5.25
    Nos. 541-544 (4) 11.00 11.00
Souvenir Sheet
545 A87 $2 Up Spirits cere-
        mony, 19th cent. 9.50 9.50

Souvenir Sheet

Wedding of Prince Andrew and Sarah
Ferguson — A88

1986, Oct. 15   Litho.   Perf. 13x12½
546 A88 $4 multicolored 7.50 6.00

Cable-Laying Ships — A89

1986, Oct. 15   Wmk. 380   Perf. 12½
547 A89 35c Sentinel .70 .70
548 A89 35c Retriever .70 .70
    a.   Pair, #547-548 1.40 1.40
549 A89 60c Cable Enterprise 1.25 1.25
550 A89 60c Mercury 1.25 1.25
    a.   Pair, #549-550 2.50 2.50
551 A89 75c Recorder 1.50 1.50
552 A89 75c Pacific Guardian 1.50 1.50
    a.   Pair, #551-552 3.00 3.00

553	A89	$1 Great Eastern	2.00	2.00
554	A89	$1 Cable Venture	2.00	2.00
a.		Pair, #553-554	4.00	4.00
		Nos. 547-554 (8)	10.90	10.90

Souvenir Sheets

555		Sheet of 2	1.40	1.40
a.-b.		A89 40c, like #547-548	.70	.70
556		Sheet of 2	1.75	1.75
a.-b.		A89 50c, like #549-550	.90	.90
557		Sheet of 2	2.75	2.75
a.-b.		A89 80c, like #551-552	1.40	1.40
558		Sheet of 2	5.25	5.25
a.-b.		A89 $1.50, like #553-554	2.50	2.50

Cable and wireless in the islands, 20th anniv.

Souvenir Sheets

Statue of Liberty, Cent. — A90

Various views of the statue.

1986, Dec. 15   Litho.   Perf. 14

559	A90	50c multicolored	.95	.95
560	A90	75c multicolored	1.60	1.60
561	A90	90c multicolored	1.75	1.75
562	A90	$1 multicolored	2.00	2.00
563	A90	$1.25 multicolored	2.50	2.50
564	A90	$1.50 multicolored	3.00	3.00
565	A90	$1.75 multicolored	3.50	3.50
566	A90	$2 multicolored	3.75	3.75
567	A90	$2.50 multicolored	5.00	5.00
		Nos. 559-567 (9)	24.05	24.05

A91

Shipwrecks — A92

1987, Apr. 15   Perf. 14

572	A91	12c Spanish galleon, 18th cent.	.85	.85
573	A91	35c HMS Astrea, 1808	2.40	2.40
574	A91	75c RMS Rhone, 1867	4.75	4.75
575	A91	$1.50 SS Rocus, 1929	10.00	10.00
		Nos. 572-575 (4)	18.00	18.00

Souvenir Sheet

576	A92	$2.50 Brig Volvart, 1918	19.00	19.00

Natl. Flags, Outline Maps — A93

Botanical Gardens — A94

1987, May 28

577	A93	10c Montserrat	.20	.20
578	A93	15c Grenada	.60	.60
579	A93	20c Dominica	.85	.85
580	A93	25c St. Kitts-Nevis	1.10	1.10
581	A93	35c St. Vincent and Grenadines	1.40	1.40
582	A93	50c Virgin Isls.	2.10	2.10
583	A93	75c Antigua & Barbuda	3.00	3.00
584	A93	$1 St. Lucia	4.25	4.25
		Nos. 577-584 (8)	13.50	13.50

11th Meeting of the Organization of Eastern Caribbean States.

1987, Aug. 12   Wmk. 384

585	A94	12c Spider lily	.75	.75
586	A94	35c Barrel cactus	2.25	2.25
587	A94	$1 Wild plantain	6.25	6.25
588	A94	$1.50 Little butterfly orchid	9.25	9.25
		Nos. 585-588 (4)	18.50	18.50

Souvenir Sheet

589	A94	$2.50 White cedar	6.25	6.25

Postal Service Bicent. A95

Designs: 10c, 18th Cent. packet, #7 canceled "A13." 20c, Map of the islands, #22 canceled "A91." 35c, Tortola Post Office and Customs House, and #5 canceled "Tortola De 20 61." $1.50, Mail plane and #154 canceled "Road town No 2 64 Tortola W.I." $2.50, Late 19th cent. steam packet and #10 canceled "A Tortola Ap 12 70."

1987, Dec. 17   Litho.   Perf. 14½

590	A95	10c multicolored	.75	.75
591	A95	20c multicolored	1.50	1.50
592	A95	35c multicolored	2.50	2.50
593	A95	$1.50 multicolored	10.50	10.50
		Nos. 590-593 (4)	15.25	15.25

Souvenir Sheet

594	A95	$2.50 multicolored	8.00	8.00

Paintings by Titian — A96

10c, Salome, 1512. 12c, Man with the Glove, c. 1520-22. 20c, Fabrizio Salvaresio, 1558. 25c, Daughter of Roberto Strozzi, 1542. 40c, Pope Julius II. 50c, Bishop Ludovico Beccadelli, 1552. 60c, Philip II. $1, Empress Isabella of Portugal, 1548. #603, Emperor Charles V at Muhlberg, 1548. #604, Pope Paul III & His Grandsons, 1546.

Perf. 13½x14

1988, Aug. 11   Unwmk.

595	A96	10c multicolored	.35	.35
596	A96	12c multicolored	.50	.50
597	A96	20c multicolored	.80	.80
598	A96	25c multicolored	1.00	1.00
599	A96	40c multicolored	1.75	1.75
600	A96	50c multicolored	2.10	2.10
601	A96	60c multicolored	2.75	2.75
602	A96	$1 multicolored	4.75	4.75
		Nos. 595-602 (8)	14.00	14.00

Souvenir Sheet

603	A96	$2 multicolored	8.25	8.25
604	A96	$2 multicolored	8.25	8.25

1st Annual Open Chess Tournament — A97

35c, Pawn & Transporter aircraft over Sir Francis Drake Channel. $1, King & Jose Raul Capablanca (1888-1942), Cuban chess master and world champion from 1921-27. $2, Match scene.

1988, Aug. 25   Unwmk.   Perf. 14

605	A97	35c multicolored	4.00	4.00
606	A97	$1 multicolored	11.50	11.50

Souvenir Sheet

607	A97	$2 multicolored	13.00	13.00

1988 Summer Olympics, Seoul A98

1988, Sept. 8

608	A98	12c Hurdling	.65	.65
609	A98	20c Windsurfing	1.10	1.10
610	A98	75c Basketball	4.00	4.00
611	A98	$1 Tennis	5.25	5.25
		Nos. 608-611 (4)	11.00	11.00

Souvenir Sheet

612	A98	$2 Running	5.50	5.50

Intl. Red Cross, 125th Anniv. A99

Safety warnings and steps in administering cardiopulmonary resuscitation (CPR): 12c, "Don't swim alone." 30c, "No swimming during electrical storms." 60c, "Don't eat before swimming." $1, "Proper equipment for boating." No. 617a, Turn victim on back. No. 617b, Position victim's chin so breathing passages are not blocked. No. 617c, Mouth-to-mouth resuscitation. No. 617d, Chest compressions. Nos. 617a-617d vert.

1988, Sept. 26

613	A99	12c multicolored	.65	.65
614	A99	30c multicolored	1.60	1.60
615	A99	60c multicolored	3.00	3.00
616	A99	$1 multicolored	5.25	5.25
		Nos. 613-616 (4)	10.50	10.50

Souvenir Sheet

617		Sheet of 4	8.75	8.75
a.-d.		A99 50c any single	1.10	1.10

#617a-617d has a continuous design.

Visit of Princess Alexandra — A100

World Wildlife Fund — A101

Various photographs of the princess.

1988, Nov. 9   Litho.   Perf. 14

618	A100	40c shown	2.00	2.00
619	A100	$1.50 multi, diff.	8.00	8.00

Souvenir Sheet

620	A100	$2 multi, diff.	9.00	9.00

1988, Nov. 15

Brown pelicans, *Pelecanus Occidentalis*.

621	A101	10c Pelican in flight	1.50	1.50
622	A101	12c Perched	1.75	1.75
623	A101	15c Close-up of head	2.00	2.00
624	A101	35c Swallowing fish	4.75	4.75
		Nos. 621-624 (4)	10.00	10.00

Reptiles, Marine Mammals and Birds — A102

20c, Anegada rock iguana. 40c, Virgin gorda dwarf gecko. 60c, Hawksbill turtle. $1, Humpback whale. #629, Northern shoveler, American widgeon & ring-necked ducks. #630, Trunk turtle.

1988, Nov. 15

625	A102	20c multicolored	1.50	1.50
626	A102	40c multicolored	2.75	2.75
627	A102	60c multicolored	4.25	4.25
628	A102	$1 multicolored	7.00	7.00
		Nos. 625-628 (4)	15.50	15.50

Souvenir Sheets

629	A102	$2 multicolored	11.50	11.50
630	A102	$2 multicolored	8.50	8.50

Spring Regatta A103

Various yachts.

1989, Apr. 7   Litho.   Perf. 14

631	A103	12c multi, diff., vert.	.50	.50
632	A103	40c shown	1.50	1.50
633	A103	75c multi, diff., vert.	2.50	2.50
634	A103	$1 multi, diff.	3.50	3.50
		Nos. 631-634 (4)	8.00	8.00

Souvenir Sheet

635	A103	$2 multi, diff., vert.	8.75	8.75

Pre-Columbian Societies and Their Customs — A104

1989, May 18

636	A104	10c Hammock	.45	.45
637	A104	20c Making a fire	.95	.95
638	A104	25c Carvers	1.10	1.10
639	A104	$1.50 Arawak family	7.50	7.50
		Nos. 636-639 (4)	10.00	10.00

Souvenir Sheet

640	A104	$2 Ritual	10.00	10.00

Discovery of America 500th anniv. (in 1992).

1st Moon Landing, 20th Anniv. A105

Highlights of the Apollo 11 mission: 15c, Lunar surface, mission emblem. 30c, Buzz Aldrin conducting solar wind experiment. 65c, Raising American flag. $1, Recovery of crew after splashdown. $2, Portrait of crew.

1989, Sept. 28 Litho. *Perf. 14*
641 A105 15c multicolored 1.00 1.00
642 A105 30c multicolored 1.75 1.75
643 A105 65c multicolored 3.50 3.50
644 A105 $1 multicolored 5.75 5.75
Nos. 641-644 (4) 12.00 12.00

Souvenir Sheet
Perf. 13½x14
645 A105 $2 multicolored 9.50 9.50

No. 645 contains one 37x46mm stamp.

Methodist Church, 200th Anniv. A106

Designs: 12c, Black Harry, Nathaniel Gilbert preaching. 25c, Book symbolizing role of the church in education. 35c, East End Methodist Church, 1810. $1.25, John Wesley, modern youth choir. $2, Thomas Coke.

1989, Oct. 24 *Perf. 14*
646 A106 12c multicolored .55 .55
647 A106 25c multicolored 1.25 1.25
648 A106 35c multicolored 1.75 1.75
649 A106 $1.25 multicolored 6.00 6.00
Nos. 646-649 (4) 9.55 9.55

Souvenir Sheet
650 A106 $2 multicolored 8.00 8.00

1990 World Cup Soccer Championships, Italy — A107

Various athletes.

1989, Nov. 6
651 A107 5c shown .70 .70
652 A107 10c multi, diff. .70 .70
653 A107 20c multi, diff. 1.50 1.50
654 A107 $1.75 multi, diff. 11.50 11.50
Nos. 651-654 (4) 14.40 14.40

Souvenir Sheet
655 A107 $2 Natl. team 11.00 11.00

Princess Alexandra, Sunset House — A108

Royal Yacht Britannia — A109

b, Princess Margaret, Government House. c, Hon. Angus Ogilvy, Little Dix Bay Hotel. d, Princess Diana & her children, Necker Island Resort.

1990, May 3 Litho. *Perf. 14*
656 Min. sheet of 4 11.50 11.50
a.-d. A108 50c any single 1.10 1.10

Souvenir Sheet
657 A109 $2 multicolored 8.50 8.50

Stamp World London '90.

Audubon's Shearwater — A110

1990, May 15
658 A110 5c shown .20 .20
659 A110 12c Red-necked pigeon .40 .40
660 A110 20c Common gallinule .70 .70
661 A110 25c Green heron .90 .90
662 A110 40c Yellow warbler 1.40 1.40
663 A110 60c Smooth-billed ani 2.25 2.25
664 A110 $1 Antillean crested hummingbird 3.50 3.50
665 A110 $1.25 Black-faced grassquit 4.50 4.50
Nos. 658-665 (8) 13.85 13.85

Souvenir Sheets
666 A110 $2 Egg of royal tern 5.50 5.50
667 A110 $2 Egg of red-billed tropicbird 5.50 5.50

Blue Tang A111

1990, June 18
668 A111 10c shown .50 .50
669 A111 35c Glasseye 1.90 1.90
670 A111 50c Slippery Dick 2.75 2.75
671 A111 $1 Porkfish 5.50 5.50
Nos. 668-671 (4) 10.65 10.65

Souvenir Sheet
672 A111 $2 Yellowtail snapper 8.00 8.00

A112

A113

1990, Aug. 30 Litho. *Perf. 14*
673 A112 12c multicolored .40 .40
674 A112 25c multi, diff. .85 .85
675 A112 60c multi, diff. 2.25 2.25
676 A112 $1 multi, diff. 4.00 4.00
Nos. 673-676 (4) 7.50 7.50

Souvenir Sheet
677 A112 $2 multi, diff. 6.00 6.00

Queen Mother, 90th birthday.

1990, Dec. 10 Litho. *Perf. 14*
Various soccer players.
678 A113 12c multicolored .50 .50
679 A113 20c multi, diff. .90 .90
680 A113 50c multi, diff. 2.10 2.10
681 A113 $1.25 multi, diff. 5.50 5.50
Nos. 678-681 (4) 9.00 9.00

Souvenir Sheet
682 A113 $2 multi, diff. 7.50 7.50

World Cup Soccer Championships, Italy.

1992 Summer Olympics, Barcelona A114

1990, Dec. 20 Litho. *Perf. 14*
683 A114 12c Judo .65 .65
684 A114 40c Yachting 2.10 2.10
685 A114 60c Hurdles 3.25 3.25
686 A114 $1 Show jumping 5.50 5.50
Nos. 683-686 (4) 11.50 11.50

Souvenir Sheet
687 A114 $2 Windsurfing 6.50 6.50

Copper Mine Ruins A115

1991, Mar. 1 Litho. *Perf. 14*
688 A115 10c Cyanthea arborea, vert. .40 .40
689 A115 25c shown 1.10 1.10
690 A115 35c Mt. Healthy windmill ruin, vert. 1.75 1.75
691 A115 $2 Baths, Virgin Gorda 8.75 8.75
Nos. 688-691 (4) 12.00 12.00

National Park Trust.

Flowers — A116

Butterflies — A117

1991-92 Litho. *Perf. 14*
692 A116 1c Haiti Haiti .20 .20
693 A116 2c Lobster claw .20 .20
694 A116 5c Frangipani .20 .20
695 A116 10c Autograph tree .20 .20
696 A116 12c Yellow allamanda .25 .25
697 A116 15c Lantana .40 .40
698 A116 20c Jerusalem thorn .55 .55
699 A116 25c Turk's cap .65 .65
700 A116 30c Swamp immortelle .75 .75
701 A116 35c White cedar .85 .85
702 A116 40c Mahoe tree 1.00 1.00
703 A116 45c Pinguin 1.10 1.10
704 A116 50c Christmas orchid 1.25 1.25
705 A116 70c Lignum vitae 1.75 1.75
706 A116 $1 African tulip tree 2.50 2.50
707 A116 $2 Beach morning glory 5.00 5.00
708 A116 $3 Organ pipe cactus 7.25 7.25
709 A116 $5 Tall ground orchid 12.50 12.50
710 A116 $10 Ground orchid 24.00 24.00
Nos. 692-710 (19) 60.60 60.60

Nos. 695, 701, 703 exist dated "1995." The 70c, $1 and $2 exist perf 12, the $3 perf 12½. These were issued in Aug. 1995. Issued: $10, 5/92; others, 5/1/91. For overprints see Nos. O37-O51.

1991, June 28 Litho. *Perf. 14*
711 A117 5c Cloudless sulphur .50 .50
712 A117 10c Flambeau .50 .50
713 A117 15c Caribbean buckeye .85 .85
714 A117 20c Gulf fritillary 1.25 1.25
715 A117 25c Polydamus swallowtail 1.40 1.40
716 A117 30c Little sulphur 1.75 1.75
717 A117 35c Zebra 2.10 2.10
718 A117 $1.50 Malachite 8.75 8.75
Nos. 711-718 (8) 17.10 17.10

Souvenir Sheets
719 A117 $2 Monarch, horiz. 10.00 10.00
720 A117 $2 Red rim, horiz. 10.00 10.00

Voyages of Discovery A118

Ships of explorers: 12c, Ferdinand Magellan, 1519-1521. 50c, Rene-Robert de la Salle, 1682. 75c, John Cabot, 1497-1498. $1, Jacques Cartier, 1534. $2, Columbus' ship, 1493 woodcut, vert.

1991, Sept. 20 Litho. *Perf. 14*
721 A118 12c multicolored .65 .65
722 A118 50c multicolored 2.75 2.75
723 A118 75c multicolored 4.25 4.25
724 A118 $1 multicolored 5.50 5.50
Nos. 721-724 (4) 13.15 13.15

Souvenir Sheet
725 A118 $2 multicolored 11.00 11.00

Vincent Van Gogh (1853-1890), Painter — A119

Paintings: 15c, Cottage with Decrepit Barn and Stooping Woman. 30c, Paul Gauguin's Armchair, vert. 75c, Breton Women. $1, Vase with Red Gladioli, vert. $2, The Dance Hall in Arles (detail).

1991, Nov. 1 *Perf. 13*
726 A119 15c multicolored .90 .90
727 A119 30c multicolored 1.75 1.75
728 A119 75c multicolored 4.50 4.50
729 A119 $1 multicolored 6.25 6.25
Nos. 726-729 (4) 13.40 13.40

Souvenir Sheet
730 A119 $2 multicolored 13.00 13.00

Christmas A120

Entire paintings or details by Quinten Massys: 15c, The Virgin and Child Enthroned. 30c, The Virgin and Child Enthroned, diff. 60c, The Adoration of the Magi. $1, Virgin in Adoration. No. 735, The Virgin Standing with Angels. No. 736, The Adoration of the Magi.

1991, Dec. 12 Litho. *Perf. 12*
731 A120 15c multicolored .85 .85
732 A120 30c multicolored 1.90 1.90
733 A120 60c multicolored 3.75 3.75
734 A120 $1 multicolored 6.00 6.00
Nos. 731-734 (4) 12.50 12.50

Souvenir Sheets
Perf. 14½
735 A120 $2 multicolored 6.75 6.75
736 A120 $2 multicolored 6.75 6.75

Mushrooms — A121

1992, Jan. 15 *Perf. 14*
737 A121 12c Agaricus
bisporus, vert. 1.00 1.00
738 A121 30c Lentinus edodes 2.25 2.25
739 A121 45c Hyrocybe
acutoconica,
vert. 3.50 3.50
740 A121 $1 Gymnopilus
chrysopellus 7.25 7.25
Nos. 737-740 (4) 14.00 14.00

Souvenir Sheet
741 A121 $2 Pleurotus os-
treatus 12.00 12.00

Queen Elizabeth II's Accession to the Throne, 40th Anniv.
Common Design Type
1992, Feb. 6 Litho. *Perf. 14*
742 CD348 12c multicolored .40 .40
743 CD348 45c multicolored 1.50 1.50
744 CD348 60c multicolored 2.10 2.10
745 CD348 $1 multicolored 3.50 3.50
Nos. 742-745 (4) 7.50 7.50

Souvenir Sheet
746 CD348 $2 multicolored 8.00 8.00

Discovery of America, 500th Anniv. A122

10c, Queen Isabella. 15c, Columbus' fleet. 20c, Columbus' second coat of arms. 30c, Landing Monument on Watling Island, Columbus. 45c, Columbus. 50c, Flag of Ferdinand & Isabella, Columbus landing on Watling Island. 70c, Convent at La Rabida. $1.50, Replica of Santa Maria at New York World's Fair, 1964-65. #755, Columbus' 2nd fleet. #756, Map.

1992, May 26 Litho. *Perf. 14*
747 A122 10c multi, vert. .50 .50
748 A122 15c multi .70 .70
749 A122 20c multi, vert. .95 .95
750 A122 30c multi 1.25 1.25
751 A122 45c multi, vert. 1.75 1.75
752 A122 50c multi 2.10 2.10
753 A122 70c multi, vert. 3.00 3.00
754 A122 $1.50 multi 6.75 6.75
Nos. 747-754 (8) 17.00 17.00

Souvenir Sheet
755 A122 $2 multicolored 8.00 8.00
756 A122 $2 multicolored 8.00 8.00

1992 Summer Olympics, Barcelona — A123

1992, Aug. Litho. *Perf. 14*
757 A123 15c Basketball .85 .85
758 A123 30c Tennis 1.90 1.90
759 A123 60c Volleyball 3.75 3.75
760 A123 $1 Soccer 6.00 6.00
Nos. 757-760 (4) 12.50 12.50

Souvenir Sheet
761 A123 $2 Olympic flame 11.00 11.00

Ministerial Government, 25th Anniv. — A124

Designs: 12c, Social progress and development. 15c, Map of Virgin Islands. 45c, Administration complex. $1.30, International finance.

1993, Apr. Litho. *Perf. 14*
762 A124 12c multicolored .40 .40
763 A124 15c multicolored .45 .45
764 A124 45c multicolored 1.40 1.40
765 A124 $1.30 multicolored 4.25 4.25
Nos. 762-765 (4) 6.50 6.50

Tourism A125

15c, Swimming from anchored yacht. 30c, Sailboat. 60c, Scuba diver in pink wetsuit. $1, Snorkelers, anchored boat.
#770: a, Trimaran, vert. b, Scuba diver, vert.

1993, Apr. Litho. *Perf. 14*
766 A125 15c multi .50 .50
767 A125 30c multi, vert. 1.25 1.25
768 A125 60c multi 2.75 2.75
769 A125 $1 multi, vert. 4.50 4.50
Nos. 766-769 (4) 9.00 9.00

Souvenir Sheet
770 A125 $1 Sheet of 2, #a.-
b. 9.00 9.00

Miniature Sheet

Coronation of Queen Elizabeth II, 40th Anniv. A126

No. 771: a, 12c, Official coronation photograph. b, 45c, Dove atop Rod of Equity and Mercy. c, 60c, Royal family. d, $1, Recent color photo.

1993, June 2 Litho. *Perf. 13½x14*
771 A126 Sheet, 2 each #a.-
d. 14.00 14.00
A souvenir sheet containing a $2 stamp was not an authorized issue. Value $15.

Discovery of Virgin Islands, 500th Anniv. A127

3c, Ferdinand and Isabella supporting Columbus. 12c, Departure of Columbus. 15c, Departure of second voyage. 25c, Arms, flag of British Virgin Islands. 30c, Columbus, Santa Maria. 45c, Columbus' second fleet at sea. 60c, Rowing ashore. $1, Landing of Columbus. #781, Natives watching ships. #782, Columbus, two ships of his fleet.

1993, Sept. 24 Litho. *Perf. 14*
773 A127 3c multicolored .30 .30
774 A127 12c multicolored .40 .40
775 A127 15c multicolored .55 .55
776 A127 25c multicolored .85 .85
777 A127 30c multicolored 1.10 1.10
778 A127 45c multicolored 1.50 1.50
779 A127 60c multicolored 2.10 2.10
780 A127 $1 multicolored 3.50 3.50
Nos. 773-780 (8) 10.30 10.30

Souvenir Sheets
781 A127 $2 multicolored 5.25 5.25
782 A127 $2 multicolored 5.25 5.25

Secondary Education and Library Services, 50th Anniv. — A128

Designs: 5c, Historical documents. 10c, Sporting activities. 15c, Stanley W. Nibbs, educator, vert. 20c, Bookmobile. 30c, Norwell E. Harrigan, educator, vert. 35c, Public library's annual summer program. 70c, Text. $1, High school.

1993, Dec. *Perf. 14x13½, 13½x14* Litho.
783 A128 5c multicolored .45 .45
784 A128 10c multicolored .45 .45
785 A128 15c multicolored .65 .65
786 A128 20c multicolored .95 .95
787 A128 30c multicolored 1.40 1.40
788 A128 35c multicolored 1.60 1.60
789 A128 70c multicolored 3.00 3.00
790 A128 $1 multicolored 4.50 4.50
Nos. 783-790 (8) 13.00 13.00

Anegada Ground Iguana — A129

5c, Crawling right. 10c, Head up to right. 15c, View from behind. 45c, Head up to left. $2, Head.

1994, Jan. Litho. *Perf. 14*
791 A129 5c multicolored .90 .90
792 A129 10c multicolored .90 .90
793 A129 15c multicolored 1.25 1.25
794 A129 45c multicolored 4.00 4.00
Nos. 791-794 (4) 7.05 7.05

Souvenir Sheet
795 A129 $2 multicolored 6.25 6.25

World Wildlife Fund.

Rotary Club of Virgin Islands, 25th Anniv. A130

Designs: 15c, Disaster relief airlift. 45c, Kids, Sea "Kats." 50c, Donated hospital equipment. 90c, Paul P. Harris (1868-1947), founder of Rotary Intl.

1994, June 3 Litho. *Perf. 14*
796 A130 15c multicolored .65 .65
797 A130 45c multicolored 1.75 1.75
798 A130 50c multicolored 2.10 2.10
799 A130 90c multicolored 3.50 3.50
Nos. 796-799 (4) 8.00 8.00

Miniature Sheet of 6

First Manned Moon Landing, 25th Anniv. A131

Designs: No. 800a, Anniversary emblem. b, Lunar landing training vehicle. c, Apollo 11 lift-off, July 16, 1969. d, Lunar module Eagle in flight. e, Moon landing site approached by Eagle. f, 1st step on Moon, July 20, 1969. No. 801, Mission patch, crew signatures.

1994, Sept. 30 Litho. *Perf. 14*
800 A131 50c #a.-f. 15.00 15.00

Souvenir Sheet
801 A131 $2 multicolored 10.50 10.50

A132   A133

Previous champions: 15c, Argentina, 1978. 35c, Italy, 1982. 50c, Argentina, 1986. $1.30, W. Germany, 1990. $2, US flag, World Cup trophy, horiz.

1994, Dec. 16 Litho. *Perf. 14*
802 A132 15c multicolored .90 .90
803 A132 35c multicolored 2.10 2.10
804 A132 50c multicolored 3.00 3.00
805 A132 $1.30 multicolored 7.50 7.50
Nos. 802-805 (4) 13.50 13.50

Souvenir Sheet
806 A132 $2 multicolored 11.50 11.50

1994 World Cup Soccer Championships, US.

UN, 50th Anniv.
Common Design Type
Designs: 15c, Peugeot P4 all-purpose light vehicle. 30c, Foden medium tanker. 45c, Sisu all-terrain vehicle. $2, Westland Lynx AH7 helicopter.

Wmk. 373
1995, Oct. 24 Litho. *Perf. 14*
807 CD353 15c multicolored .50 .50
808 CD353 30c multicolored 1.00 1.00
809 CD353 45c multicolored 1.75 1.75
810 CD353 $2 multicolored 6.75 6.75
Nos. 807-810 (4) 10.00 10.00

Wmk. 373
1995, Nov. 15 Litho. *Perf. 13*
Anegada Flamingos.
811 A133 15c Juveniles .50 .50
812 A133 20c Adults .75 .75
813 A133 60c Adult feeding 2.25 2.25
814 A133 $1.45 Adult feeding
chick 5.50 5.50
Nos. 811-814 (4) 9.00 9.00

Souvenir Sheet
815 A133 $2 Chicks 7.00 7.00

Christmas — A134

Children's paintings: 12c, House with palm trees. 50c, Santa in boat. 70c, Red house, Christmas tree, presents. $1.30, Dove of peace.

Wmk. 384
1995, Dec. 1 Litho. *Perf. 14*
816 A134 12c multicolored .60 .60
817 A134 50c multicolored 2.40 2.40
818 A134 70c multicolored 3.25 3.25
819 A134 $1.30 multicolored 6.25 6.25
Nos. 816-819 (4) 12.50 12.50

Island Scenes A135

Designs: 15c, Seine fishing. 35c, Sandy Spit, Jost Van Dyke. 90c, Map of Jost Van Dyke. $1.50, Foxy's wooden boat regatta.

Perf. 13½x13
1996, Feb. 14 Litho. *Wmk. 373*
820 A135 15c multicolored .60 .60
821 A135 35c multicolored 1.40 1.40
822 A135 90c multicolored 3.25 3.25
823 A135 $1.50 multicolored 5.75 5.75
Nos. 820-823 (4) 11.00 11.00

See Nos. 892-896.

Queen Elizabeth II, 70th Birthday
Common Design Type

Queen in various attire, scenes of Virgin Islands: 10c, Government House, Tortola. 30c, Legislative Council Chambers. 45c, Road Harbor. $1.50, Map of Virgin Islands.
$2, Wearing royal crown.

Perf. 13½x14

1996, Apr. 22		**Litho.**	**Wmk. 373**	
824	CD354	10c multicolored	.20	.20
825	CD354	30c multicolored	.90	.90
826	CD354	45c multicolored	1.40	1.40
827	CD354	$1.50 multicolored	4.00	4.00
	Nos. 824-827 (4)		6.50	6.50

Souvenir Sheet
Perf. 13x13½

828	CD354	$2 multicolored	5.25	5.25

Modern Olympic Games, Cent. A136

1996, May 22		**Litho.**	**Perf. 13**	
829	A136	20c Hurdles	.65	.65
830	A136	35c Volleyball	1.25	1.25
831	A136	50c Swimming	1.60	1.60
832	A136	$1 Sailing	3.50	3.50
	Nos. 829-832 (4)		7.00	7.00

CAPEX '96 A137

Vintage automobiles: 15c, 1934 Mercedes-Benz 500KA Cabriolet. 40c, 1934 Citroen 12. 60c, 1932 Cadillac V-8 Sport Phaeton. $1.35, 1934 Rolls Royce Phantom II.
$2, 1932 Fort Sport Coupe.

1996, June 8		**Litho.**	**Perf. 13½**	
833	A137	15c multicolored	.40	.40
834	A137	40c multicolored	1.10	1.10
835	A137	60c multicolored	2.00	2.00
836	A137	$1.35 multicolored	4.00	4.00
	Nos. 833-836 (4)		7.50	7.50

Souvenir Sheet

837	A137	$2 multicolored	5.00	5.00

UNICEF, 50th Anniv. A138

Goals of UNICEF for the year 2000: 10c, Educate the child. 15c, Children first. 30c, Children have rights. 45c, No more polio.

Perf. 14x14½

1996, Sept. 16		**Litho.**	**Wmk. 373**	
838	A138	10c multicolored	.50	.50
839	A138	15c multicolored	.75	.75
840	A138	30c multicolored	1.75	1.75
841	A138	45c multicolored	2.50	2.50
	Nos. 838-841 (4)		5.50	5.50

Girl Guiding in Virgin Islands, 25th Anniv. — A139

Designs: 10c, Rainbows, arts and crafts. 15c, Brownies, community service. 30c, Guides, campfire. 45c, Rangers, H.M. Queen's birthday parade. $2, Lady Baden-Powell, world chief guide.

		Wmk. 373		
1996, Dec. 30		**Litho.**	**Perf. 13½**	
842	A139	10c multicolored	.20	.20
843	A139	15c multicolored	.45	.45
844	A139	30c multicolored	.75	.75
845	A139	45c multicolored	1.10	1.10
846	A139	$2 multicolored	4.75	4.75
	Nos. 842-846 (5)		7.25	7.25

Game Fish A140

1997, Jan. 6		**Wmk. 384**	**Perf. 14**	
847	A140	1c Mackerel	.20	.20
848	A140	10c Wahoo	.20	.20
849	A140	15c Barracuda	.35	.35
850	A140	20c Tarpon	.50	.50
851	A140	25c Tiger shark	.60	.60
852	A140	35c Sailfish	.85	.85
853	A140	40c Dolphin	.95	.95
854	A140	50c Blackfin tuna	1.25	1.25
855	A140	60c Yellowfin tuna	1.50	1.50
856	A140	75c Kingfish	1.75	1.75
857	A140	$1.50 White marlin	3.50	3.50
a.		Souvenir sheet of 1, wmk. 373	4.25	4.25
858	A140	$1.85 Amberjack	4.50	4.50
859	A140	$2 Bonito	4.75	4.75
860	A140	$5 Bonefish	12.00	12.00
861	A140	$10 Blue marlin	24.00	24.00
	Nos. 847-861 (15)		56.90	56.90

No. 857a, Hong Kong '97.

Queen Elizabeth II and Prince Philip, 50th Wedding Anniv. — A141

#862, Prince with horse. #863, Queen Elizabeth II. #864, Queen riding in open carriage. #865, Prince Philip. #866, Queen holding hat down, Prince. #867, Prince Charles on polo pony.
$2, Queen, Prince riding in open carriage, horiz.

		Wmk. 373		
1997, July 10		**Litho.**	**Perf. 13**	
862		30c multicolored	.70	.70
863		30c multicolored	.70	.70
a.		A141 Pair, #862-863	1.75	1.75
864		45c multicolored	1.00	1.00
865		45c multicolored	1.00	1.00
a.		A141 Pair, #864-865	2.50	2.50
866		70c multicolored	1.50	1.50
867		70c multicolored	1.50	1.50
a.		A141 Pair, #866-867	4.00	4.00
	Nos. 862-867 (6)		6.40	6.40

Souvenir Sheet

868	A141	$2 multicolored	7.00	7.00

Crabs A142

		Wmk. 373		
1997, Sept. 11		**Litho.**	**Perf. 13**	
869	A142	12c Fiddler	.40	.40
870	A142	15c Coral	.60	.60
871	A142	35c Blue	1.50	1.50
872	A142	$1 Giant hermit	4.50	4.50
	Nos. 869-872 (4)		7.00	7.00

Souvenir Sheet

873	A142	$2 Arrow	7.00	7.00

Orchids A143

Designs: a, 20c, Psychilis macconnelliae. b, 50c, Tolumnia prionochila. c, 60c, Tetramicra canaliculata. d, 75c, Liparis elata.
$2, Dendrobium crumenatum, vert.

		Wmk. 373		
1997, Nov. 26		**Litho.**	**Perf. 14**	
874	A143	Strip of 4, #a.-d.	7.00	7.00

Souvenir Sheet

875	A143	$2 multicolored	6.00	6.00

World Voyage of Sir Francis Drake A144

Portions of map and: No. 876: a, Francis Drake. b, Drake Coat of Arms. c, Queen Elizabeth I. d, Christopher & Marigold. e, Golden Hinde. f, Swan. g, Cacafuego. h, Elizabeth. i, Maria. j, Drake's Astrolabe. k, Golden Hinde beakhead. l, 16th cent. compass rose.
$2, Modern ship named, "Sir Francis Drake."

1997, Dec. 13			**Perf. 14½**	
876	A144	40c Sheet of 12, #a.-l.	18.00	18.00

Souvenir Sheet

877	A144	$2 multicolored	7.00	7.00

Diana, Princess of Wales (1961-97)
Common Design Type

Portraits: a, 15c. b, 45c. c, 70c. d, $1.

Perf. 14½x14

1998, Mar. 31		**Litho.**	**Wmk. 373**	
878	CD355	Sheet of 4, #a.-d.	5.75	5.75

No. 878 sold for $2.30 + 20c, with surtax from international sales being donated to the Princess Diana Memorial Fund and surtax from national sales being donated to designated local charity.

Royal Air Force, 80th Anniv.
Common Design Type of 1993 Re-inscribed

Designs: 20c, Fairey IIIF. 35c, Supermarine Scapa. 50c, Westland Sea King HAR3. $1.50, BAe Harrier GR7.
No. 883: a, Curtiss H.12 Large America. b, Curtiss JN-4A. c, Bell Airacobra. d, Boulton-Paul Defiant.

Perf. 13½x14

1998, Apr. 1		**Litho.**	**Wmk. 373**	
879	CD350	20c multicolored	.50	.50
880	CD350	35c multicolored	1.00	1.00
881	CD350	50c multicolored	1.50	1.50
882	CD350	$1.50 multicolored	4.50	4.50
	Nos. 879-882 (4)		7.50	7.50

Souvenir Sheet

883	CD350	75c Sheet of 4, #a.-d.	8.75	8.75

Marine Life — A145

Designs: 15c, Fingerprint cyphoma. 30c, Long spined sea urchin. 45c, Split crown feather duster worm. $1, Upside down jelly. $2, Giant anemone.

1998, May 20		**Wmk. 384**	**Perf. 14½**	
884	A145	15c multicolored	.65	.65
885	A145	30c multicolored	1.40	1.40
886	A145	45c multicolored	2.10	2.10
887	A145	$1 multicolored	4.50	4.50
	Nos. 884-887 (4)		8.65	8.65

Souvenir Sheet

888	A145	$2 multicolored	8.00	8.00

No. 888 is a continuous design.

Childrens' Art Festival A146

		Wmk. 373		
1998, Aug. 25		**Litho.**	**Perf. 14**	
889	A146	30c Girl in yellow & red, vert.	.85	.85
890	A146	45c Dancer, vert.	1.40	1.40
891	A146	$1.30 shown	3.75	3.75
	Nos. 889-891 (3)		6.00	6.00

Island Scenes Type of 1996

Designs: 12c, Salt pond. 30c, Shipwreck, HMS Rhone. 70c, Traditional house. $1.45, Salt Island.
$2, Gathering salt.

1998, Oct. 28				
892	A135	12c multicolored	.50	.50
893	A135	30c multicolored	1.00	1.00
894	A135	70c multicolored	2.25	2.25
895	A135	$1.45 multicolored	5.25	5.25
	Nos. 892-895 (4)		9.00	9.00

Souvenir Sheet

896	A135	$2 multicolored	5.50	5.50

Anniversaries and Events — A147

5c, Classes in computer training, woodworking, electronics. 15c, Students playing musical instruments. 30c, Chapel, Mona Campus, Jamaica. 45c, Plaque on wall, university crest. 50c, Dr. John Coakley Lettsom, map of Little Jost Van Dyke island. $1, Crest of the Medical Society of London, building.

		Wmk. 384		
1998, Dec. 14		**Litho.**	**Perf. 14**	
897	A147	5c multicolored	.20	.20
898	A147	15c multicolored	.40	.40
899	A147	30c multicolored	.90	.90
900	A147	45c multicolored	1.25	1.25
901	A147	50c multicolored	1.50	1.50
902	A147	$1 multicolored	2.75	2.75
	Nos. 897-902 (6)		7.00	7.00

Comprehensive education in Virgin Islands, 30th anniv. (#897-898). University of West Indies, 50th anniv. (#899-900). Founding of the Medical Society of London by Dr. John Coakley Lettsom, 225th anniv. (#901-902).

Lizards A148

Designs: 5c, Rock iguana. 35c, Pygmy gecko. 60c, Slippery back skink. $1.50, Wood slave gecko.
No. 907: a, Doctor lizard. b, Yellow-bellied lizard. c, Man lizard. d, Ground lizard.

Perf. 14½x14

1999, Apr. 30		**Litho.**	**Wmk. 373**	
903	A148	5c multicolored	.25	.25
904	A148	35c multicolored	1.00	1.00
905	A148	60c multicolored	1.75	1.75
906	A148	$1.50 multicolored	4.25	4.25
	Nos. 903-906 (4)		7.25	7.25

Sheet of 4

907	A148	75c #a.-d.	8.50	8.50

Wedding of Prince Edward and Sophie Rhys-Jones
Common Design Type

Perf. 13¾x14

1999, June 15		**Litho.**	**Wmk. 384**	
908	CD356	20c Separate portraits	.45	.45
909	CD356	$3 Couple	7.25	7.25

1st Manned Moon Landing, 30th Anniv.
Common Design Type

Designs: 10c, Apollo 11 on launch pad. 40c, Second stage fires. 50c, Artist's rendition of Apollo 11 on moon. $2, Astronauts transfer to lunar module.
$2.50, Looking at earth from moon.

Perf. 14x13¾

1999, July 20   Litho.   Wmk. 384
910	CD357	10c multicolored	.20	.20
911	CD357	40c multicolored	.95	.95
912	CD357	50c multicolored	1.25	1.25
913	CD357	$2 multicolored	5.00	5.00
		Nos. 910-913 (4)	7.40	7.40

Souvenir Sheet
Perf. 14

914	CD357	$2.50 multicolored	6.25	6.25

No. 914 contains one 40mm circular stamp.

Shells — A149

Designs: 25c, Measle cowrie. 35c, West Indian top shell. 75c, Zigzag scallop. $1, West Indian fighting conch.

No. 919: a, 5c, Sunrise tellin. b, 10c, King helmet. c, 25c, Like No. 915. d, 35c, Like No. 916. e, 75c, Like No. 917. f, $1, Like No. 918.

Wmk. 373

1999, Nov. 1   Litho.   Perf. 14¼
915	A149	25c multi	.90	.90
916	A149	35c multi	1.50	1.50
917	A149	75c multi	3.00	3.00
918	A149	$1 multi	3.75	3.75
919	A149	Strip of 6, #a.-f.	10.00	10.00
		Nos. 915-919 (5)	19.15	19.15

Vignette extends to the top perforations on Nos. 915-918, but does not on stamps from No. 919.

Christmas A150

Churches: 20c, Zion Hill Methodist. 35c, Fat Hogs Bay Seventh Day Adventist. 50c, Ruins of Kingstown St. Philip's Anglican. $1, Road Town St. William's Catholic.

Perf. 13¼x13

1999, Dec. 16   Litho.   Wmk. 373
920	A150	20c multi	.45	.45
921	A150	35c multi	.80	.80
922	A150	50c multi	1.10	1.10
923	A150	$1 multi	2.40	2.40
		Nos. 920-923 (4)	4.75	4.75

British Monarchs — A151

Illustration reduced.
a, Henry VII. b, Lady Jane Grey. c, Charles I. d, William III. e, George III. f, Edward VII.

Wmk. 373

2000, Feb. 29   Litho.   Perf. 14
924	A151	60c Sheet of 6, #a.-f.	8.75	8.75

The Stamp Show 2000, London.

Prince William, 18th Birthday
Common Design Type

William: 20c, As toddler, on chest. 40c, As toddler, standing. 50c, With ski cap & goggles. 60c, Wearing suits & striped shirts. $1, Wearing sweater & bow tie.

Perf. 14¼x13¾, 13¾x14¼

2000, June 21   Litho.   Wmk. 373
Stamps With White Border
925	CD359	20c multi	.45	.45
926	CD359	40c multi, vert.	.90	.90
927	CD359	50c multi, vert.	1.25	1.25
928	CD359	$1 multi	2.40	2.40
		Nos. 925-928 (4)	5.00	5.00

Souvenir Sheet
Stamps Without White Border
Perf. 14¼
929		Sheet of 5	7.25	7.25
a.	CD359	20c multi	.40	.40
b.	CD359	40c multi	.80	.80
c.	CD359	50c multi	1.00	1.00
d.	CD359	60c multi	1.25	1.25
e.	CD359	$1 multi	2.00	2.00

Queen Mother, 100th Birthday — A152

Various photos. Frame color: 15c, Lilac. 35c, Light green. 70c, Pink. $1.50, Light blue.

Wmk. 373

2000, Aug. 4   Litho.   Perf. 13¾
930-933	A152	Set of 4	9.00	9.00

Flowering Plants and Trees — A153

10c, Red hibiscus. 15c, Pink oleander. 35c, Yellow bell. 50c, Yellow & white frangipani. 75c, Flamboyant. $2, Bougainvillea.

2000, Sept. 7   Perf. 13½x13¾
934-939	A153	Set of 6	9.75	9.75

Millennium — A154

Virgin Islands history: 5c, Site of Emancipation Proclamation. 20c Nurse Mary Louise Davies. 30c, Cheyney University, US, founded by Richard Humphries. 45c, Enid Leona Scatliffe, former chief education officer. 50c, H. Lavity Stoutt Community College. $1 Sir J. Olva Georges.
$2, Victoria Cross of Pvt. Samuel Hodge, vert.

Wmk. 373

2000, Nov. 16   Litho.   Perf. 14
940-945	A154	Set of 6	6.25	6.25

Souvenir Sheet
946	A154	$2 multi	5.00	5.00

Restoration of the Legislative Council, 50th Anniv. — A155

Virgin Islands Councilmen: 10c, Dr. Q. William Osbourne & Arnando Scatliffe. 15c, H. Robinson O'Neal & A. Austin Henley. 20c, Wilfred W. Smith & John C. Brudenell-Bruce. 35c, Howard R. Penn & I. G. Fonseca. 50c, Carlton L. de Castro & Theodolph H. Faulkner. 60c, Willard W. Wheatley. $1, H. Lavity Stoutt.

2000, Nov. 22
947-953	A155	Set of 7	9.00	9.00

Souvenir Sheet

New Year 2001 (Year of the Snake) — A156

No. 954: a, 50c, White-crowned dove. b, 50c, Bar-tailed cuckoo dove.
Illustration reduced.

2001, Feb. 1   Perf. 14½
954	A156	Sheet of 2, #a-b	4.50	4.50

Hong Kong 2001 Stamp Exhibition.

Visiting Royal Navy Ships A157

Designs: 35c, HMS Wistaria, 1923-30. 50c, HMS Dundee, 1934-35. 60c, HMS Eurydice, 1787. 75c, HMS Pegasus, 1787. $1, HMS Astrea, 1807. $1.50 HM Yacht Britannia, 1966.

Wmk. 373

2001, Sept. 28   Litho.   Perf. 14
955-960	A157	Set of 6	13.50	13.50

Nobel Prizes, Cent. — A158

Nobel laureates: 10c, Fridtjof Nansen, Peace, 1922. 20c, Albert Einstein, Physics, 1921. 25c, Sir Arthur Lewis, Economics, 1979. 40c, Saint-John Perse, Literature, 1960. 70c, Mother Teresa, Peace, 1979. $2, Christian Lous Lange, Peace, 1921.

2001, Oct. 5
961-966	A158	Set of 6	12.50	12.50

Reign Of Queen Elizabeth II, 50th Anniv. Issue
Common Design Type

Designs: Nos. 967, 971a, 15c, Princess Elizabeth in uniform. Nos. 968, 971b, 50c, In 1977. Nos. 969, 971c, 60c, Holding flowers. Nos. 970, 971d, 75c, In 1996. No. 971e, $1, 1955 portrait by Annigoni (38x50mm).

Perf. 14¼x14½, 13¾ (#971e)

2002, Feb. 6   Litho.   Wmk. 373
With Gold Frames
967-970	CD360	Set of 4	7.50	7.50

Souvenir Sheet
Without Gold Frames
971	CD360	Sheet of 5, #a-e	11.00	11.00

Reptiles in Guinness Book Of World Records A159

Designs: 5c, Estuarine crocodile. 20c, Reticulated python. 30c, Komodo dragon. 40c, Boa constrictor. $1, Dwarf caiman. $2, Sphaerodactylus parthenopion.
$1.50, Head of Sphaerodactylus parthenopion.

Perf. 13¼x13

2002, June 10   Litho.   Wmk. 373
972-977	A159	Set of 6	11.50	11.50

977a		Sheet of 6, #972-977	11.50	11.50

Souvenir Sheet
978	A159	$1.50 multi	7.00	7.00

Queen Mother Elizabeth (1900-2002)
Common Design Type

Designs: 20c, Wearing tiara (black and white photograph). 60c, Wearing dark blue hat. Nos. 981, 983a, $2, Wearing hat (black and white photograph). Nos. 982, 983b, $3, Wearing pink hat.

Perf. 13¾x14¼

2002, Aug. 5   Litho.   Wmk. 373
With Purple Frames
979-982	CD361	Set of 4	14.50	14.50

Souvenir Sheet
Without Purple Frames
Perf. 14½x14¼
983	CD361	Sheet of 2, #a-b	12.50	12.50

Royal Navy Ships A160

Designs: 20c, HMS Invincible and HMS Argo. 35c, HMS Boreas and HMS Solebay. 50c, HMS Coventry. $3, HMS Argyll.

Wmk. 373

2002, Aug. 30   Litho.   Perf. 14
984-987	A160	Set of 4	9.50	9.50

Island Scenes Type of 1996

Designs: 5c, Spring Bay. 40c, Devils Bay. 60c, The Baths. 75c, St. Thomas Bay. $1, Savannah and Pond Bay. $2, Trunk Bay.

2002, Sept. 13
988-993	A135	Set of 6	9.75	9.75

West Indian Whistling Duck — A161

Designs: Nos. 994, 998a, 10c, Duckling and eggs. Nos. 995, 998b, 35c, Duck standing on rock, vert. Nos. 996, 998c, 40c, Duck in water, vert. Nos. 997, 998d, 70c, Two ducks. No. 998e, $2, Duck's head.

Perf. 14¼x13¾, 13¾x14¼

2002, Dec.   Litho.   Wmk. 373
Stamps With Brown Border
994-997	A161	Set of 4	3.75	3.75

Souvenir Sheet
Stamps Without Brown Border
Perf. 14¼x14½ (Horiz. stamps), 14½ (Vert. stamps)
998	A161	Sheet of 5, #a-e	8.50	8.50

Birdlife International.

Anniversaries and Events — A162

No. 999, 10c: a, Sprinters. b, Cyclists.
No. 1000, 35c: a, Laser class sailboats. b, Women's long jump.
No. 1001, 50c: a, Bareboat class sailboats. b, Racing Cruiser class sailboats.
No. 1002, $1.35: a, Carlos and Esme Downing, founders of Island Sun newspaper. b, Island Sun newspaper and emblem.
Illustration reduced.

Wmk. 373

2003, Mar. 13   Litho.   Perf. 13½
Horiz. pairs, #a-b
999-1002	A162	Set of 4	13.00	13.00

2002 Commonwealth Games (#999); Admission to Olympic Games, 20th anniv. (#1000); Spring Regatta, 30th anniv. (#1001); Island Sun newspaper, 40th anniv. (#1002).

Head of Queen Elizabeth II
Common Design Type
Wmk. 373

2003, June 2   Litho.   *Perf. 13¾*
1003 CD362 $5 multi   10.00 10.00

Coronation of Queen Elizabeth II, 50th Anniv.
Common Design Type

Designs: Nos. 1004, 1006a, 15c, Queen in gown. Nos. 1005, 1006b, $5, Royal Family on Buckingham Palace balcony.

Perf. 14¼x14½
2003, June 2   Litho.   Wmk. 373
Vignettes Framed, Red Background
1004-1005 CD363 Set of 2   12.50 12.50

Souvenir Sheet
Vignettes Without Frame, Purple Panel
1006 CD363 Sheet of 2, #a-b   12.50 12.50

Prince William, 21st Birthday
Common Design Type

Designs: 50c, William in polo uniform at right. $2, William on polo pony at left.

Wmk. 373
2003, June 21   Litho.   *Perf. 14¼*
With Gray Frames
1007 CD364 50c multi   1.25 1.25
1008 CD364 $2 multi   4.75 4.75
Without Gray Frames
1009   Horiz. pair   6.00 6.00
 a. CD364 50c multi   1.25 1.25
 b. CD364 $2 multi   4.75 4.75
   Nos. 1007-1009 (3)   12.00 12.00

Powered Flight, Cent. — A163

Designs: 15c, Douglas DC-4. 20c, Boeing Stearman "Kaydet." 35c, B-25 J Mitchell. 40c, F-4B Phantom. 70c, CH-47 Chinook helicopter. $2, AH-64 Apache helicopter.
Illustration reduced.

Perf. 13¼x13¾
2003, Nov. 15   Litho.   Wmk. 373
Stamp + Label
1010-1015 A163 Set of 6   8.50 8.50

Christmas — A164

Details from Arrival of the English Ambassadors, by Vittore Carpaccio: 20c, Men standing near railing and pillar. 40c, Men, ships in background. $2.50, Seated man.
No. 1019a (36x36mm), Kneeling man delivering message.

Perf. 13¾x13½
2003, Dec. 15   Litho.   Wmk. 373
1016-1018 A164 Set of 3   8.00 8.00
Souvenir Sheet
1019 A164 Sheet, #1016-1018, 1019a   8.25 8.25
 a. $1 multi, perf. 13½x13¼   2.00 2.00

Game Fish Type of 1997
Serpentine Die Cut 12½ on 3 Sides
2004, July 1   Litho.   Unwmk.
Self-Adhesive
Booklet Stamps
Size: 21x17mm
1020 A140 15c Barracuda   .30   .30
 a. Booklet pane of 4   1.20
1021 A140 20c Tarpon   .40   .40
 a. Booklet pane of 4   1.60

1022 A140 35c Sailfish   .70   .70
 a. Booklet pane of 4   2.80
     Complete booklet, #1020a, 1022a   4.00
1023 A140 40c Dolphin   .80   .80
 a. Booklet pane of 3 + label   2.40
     Complete booklet, #1021a, 1023a   5.25
   Nos. 1020-1023 (4)   2.20 2.20

Fruit — A165

2004, July 20   Wmk. 373   *Perf. 13¾*
1024 A165 15c Pomegranates   .30   .30
1025 A165 20c Cashews   .40   .40
1026 A165 35c Tamarinds   .70   .70
1027 A165 40c Soursop   .80   .80
1028 A165 50c Mangos   1.00 1.00
1029 A165 $2 Guavaberries   4.00 4.00
1030 A165 $5 Mamee apples 10.00 10.00
   Nos. 1024-1030 (7)   17.20 17.20

Nos. 1025, 1026, 1028, 1029 exist dated "2007."

Virgin Islands Festival, 50th Anniv. — A166

Designs: 10c, Parade. 60c, Horse race. $1, Kayak race. $2.35, Festival Queen.

Wmk. 373
2004, Oct. 26   Litho.   *Perf. 13¼*
1031-1034 A166 Set of 4   8.25 8.25

Sports — A167

Designs: 75c, Women soccer players. $1, Runner.

2004, Dec. 30   *Perf. 14*
1035-1036 A167 Set of 2   3.50 3.50

FIFA (Fédération Internationale de Football Association), cent.; 2004 Summer Olympics, Athens.

Caribbean Endemic Bird Festival A168

Designs: 5c, Black and white warbler. 25c, Worm-eating warbler. 35c, Yellow warbler. 50c, Prothonotary warbler.
No. 1041: a, 10c, Prairie warbler. b, 15c, Yellow-rumped warbler. c, 40c, Black-throated blue warbler. d, 60c, Cape May warbler. e, 75c, Northern parula. f, $2.75, Palm warbler.

Wmk. 373
2005, July 8   Litho.   *Perf. 13¾*
1037-1040 A168 Set of 4   2.40 2.40
1041 A168 Miniature sheet, #1037-1040, 1041a-1041f   12.00 12.00

Fruit Type of 2004
2005, Aug. 25   Wmk. 373
1042 A165 1c Hog plum   .20   .20
1043 A165 10c Coco plum   .20   .20
1044 A165 25c Sugar apple   .50   .50
1045 A165 60c Papaya   1.25 1.25
1046 A165 75c Custard apple 1.50 1.50
1047 A165 $1 Otaheite gooseberry 2.00 2.00
1048 A165 $1.50 Guava   3.00 3.00
1049 A165 $10 Passion fruit 20.00 20.00
   Nos. 1042-1049 (8)   28.65 28.65

No. 1042 exists dated "2007."

Pope John Paul II (1920-2005) A169

Wmk. 373
2005, Aug. 18   Litho.   *Perf. 14*
1050 A169 75c multi   1.50 1.50

Worldwide Fund for Nature (WWF) — A170

Various depictions of Virgin Islands tree boa: 20c, 30c, 70c, $1.05.

Wmk. 373
2005, Sept. 15   Litho.   *Perf. 14*
1051-1054 A170 Set of 4   4.50 4.50
1054a   Miniature sheet, 2 each #1051-1054   9.00 9.00

Battle of Trafalgar, Bicent. — A171

Designs: 5c, HMS Colossus. 25c, HMS Boreas. 75c, HMS Victory. $3, Admiral Horatio Nelson, vert.
$2.50, HMS Colossus and French ship.

2005, Oct. 18   *Perf. 14x14¾, 14¾x14*
1055-1058 A171 Set of 4   8.25 8.25
Souvenir Sheet
Perf. 13½
1059 A171 $2.50 multi   5.00 5.00

No. 1059 contains one 44x44mm stamp.

Christmas A172

Flora: 15c, Century plant. 35c, Poinsettia, horiz. 60c, Inkberry. $2.50, Snow on the mountain, horiz.

2005, Nov. 3   *Perf. 14¾x14, 14x14¾*
1060-1063 A172 Set of 4   7.25 7.25

Anniversaries A173

Designs: 20c, Social Security, 25th anniv. 40c, ZBVI radio station, 40th anniv. 50c, Beef Island Airstrip, 50th anniv. $1, Rotary International, cent.

Wmk. 373
2005, Nov. 16   Litho.   *Perf. 13¾*
1064-1067 A173 Set of 4   4.25 4.25

Queen Elizabeth II, 80th Birthday A174

Queen: 15c, As young woman, in uniform. 75c, Wearing white hat. No. 1070, $1.50, Wearing large earrings. No. 1071, $2, Wearing gray hat with large brim.
No. 1072: a, $1.50, Like 75c. b, $2, Like #1070.

Perf. 14¼x14
2006, July 17   Litho.   Wmk. 373
Stamps With White Frames
1068-1071 A174 Set of 4   9.00 9.00
Souvenir Sheet
Stamps Without White Frames
1072 A174 Sheet of 2, #a-b   7.00 7.00

Red Cross Buildings A175

Designs: 20c, New building. $3, Previous building.

Wmk. 373
2007, Aug. 1   Litho.   *Perf. 14*
1073-1074 A175 Set of 2   6.50 6.50

WAR TAX STAMPS

Regular Issue of 1913 Overprinted

1916-17   Wmk. 3   *Perf. 14*
Die I
MR1 A9 1p scarlet   .55   8.00
 a. 1p carmine   2.50 20.00
MR2 A9 3p violet, *yellow* 3.50 20.00

OFFICIAL STAMPS

> **Catalogue values for unused stamps in this section are for Never Hinged items.**

Nos. 365-368, 370-380 Overprinted "OFFICIAL" in Silver

1985, July   Litho.   *Perf. 14*
O1 A57 1c multi   .30   1.25
O2 A57 3c multi   .45   1.25
O3 A57 5c multi   .45   .45
O4 A57 8c multi   .55   .60
O5 A57 13c multi   .80   .75
O6 A57 15c multi   .80   .75
O7 A57 18c multi   .90   1.50
O8 A57 20c multi   .90   .80

O9	A57	25c multi	1.25	2.00
O10	A57	30c multi	1.40	1.00
O11	A57	60c multi	2.00	2.50
O12	A57	$1 multi	3.25	3.75
O13	A57	$2.50 multi	5.75	8.00
O14	A57	$3 multi	8.75	10.00
O15	A57	$5 multi	11.50	11.50
		Nos. O1-O15 (15)	39.05	46.10

Nos. 364-380 overprinted in gold and Nos. 364, 369 overprinted in silver exist but were not issued by the Virgin Islands.

Nos. 490-508 Ovptd. "OFFICIAL"

1986		**Litho.**	**Perf. 14**	
O16	A81	1c multicolored	.40	.40
O17	A81	2c multicolored	.40	.40
O18	A81	5c multicolored	.40	.40
O19	A81	8c multicolored	.40	.40
O20	A81	10c multicolored	.40	.40
O21	A81	12c multicolored	.50	.50
O22	A81	15c multicolored	.60	.60
O23	A81	18c multicolored	.70	.70
O24	A81	20c multicolored	.85	.85
O25	A81	25c multicolored	1.00	1.00
O26	A81	30c multicolored	1.25	1.25
O27	A81	35c multicolored	1.40	1.40
O28	A81	40c multicolored	1.60	1.60
O29	A81	50c multicolored	1.75	1.75
O30	A81	60c multicolored	2.10	2.10
O31	A81	$1 multicolored	3.50	3.50
O32	A81	$2 multicolored	7.50	7.50
O33	A81	$3 multicolored	11.00	11.00
O34	A81	$5 multicolored	20.00	20.00
		Nos. O16-O34 (19)	55.75	55.75

Issue: 1, 5, 10, 15, 20-35c, $5, 7/3; others, 1/28.

Nos. 694-695, 698, 701-706, 708 Ovptd. "OFFICIAL"

1991, Sept.		**Litho.**	**Perf. 14**	
O37	A116	5c multicolored	.20	.20
O38	A116	10c multicolored	.20	.20
O41	A116	20c multicolored	.75	.75
O44	A116	35c multicolored	1.40	1.40
O45	A116	40c multicolored	1.50	1.50
O46	A116	45c multicolored	1.75	1.75
O47	A116	50c multicolored	1.90	1.90
O48	A116	70c multicolored	2.75	2.75
O49	A116	$1 multicolored	3.75	3.75
O51	A116	$3 multicolored	11.50	11.50
		Nos. O37-O51 (10)	25.70	25.70

Ovpt. on Nos. O37-O51 is 19mm long. Used values are for c-t-o copies.
Nos. O37-O38, O41, O44-O49, O51 were not available unused until mid-1992.
This set was never used in the Virgin Islands.

Nos. 694-695, 698, 700-706, 708 Ovptd. "OFFICIAL"

1992		**Litho.**	**Perf. 14**	
O55	A116	5c multicolored	.20	.20
O56	A116	10c multicolored	.20	.20
O59	A116	20c multicolored	.75	.75
O61	A116	30c multicolored	1.25	1.25
O62	A116	35c multicolored	1.40	1.40
O63	A116	40c multicolored	1.50	1.50
O64	A116	45c multicolored	1.75	1.75
O65	A116	50c multicolored	1.90	1.90
O66	A116	70c multicolored	2.75	2.75
O67	A116	$1 multicolored	3.75	3.75
O69	A116	$3 multicolored	11.50	11.50
		Nos. O55-O69 (11)	26.95	26.95

Ovpt. on Nos. O55-O56, O59, O61-O67, O69 is 15½mm long.

WALLIS AND FUTUNA ISLANDS

'wä-ləs and fə-'tü-nə

'ī-ləndz

LOCATION — Group of islands in the South Pacific Ocean, northeast of Fiji
GOVT. — French Overseas Territory
AREA — 106 sq. mi.
POP. — 15,129 (1999 est.)
CAPITAL — Mata-Utu, Wallis Island

100 Centimes = 1 Franc

Catalogue values for unused stamps in this country are for Never Hinged items, beginning with Scott 127 in the regular postage section, Scott B9 in the semipostal section, Scott C1 in the airpost section, and Scott J37 in the postage due section.

New Caledonia Stamps of 1905-28 Overprinted in Black or Red

1920-28		**Unwmk.**	**Perf. 14x13½**	
1	A16	1c black, *green*	.30	.30
a.		Double overprint	160.00	
2	A16	2c red brown	.30	.30
3	A16	4c blue, *org*	.40	.40
4	A16	5c green	.40	.40
5	A16	5c dull blue ('22)	.40	.40
6	A16	10c rose	.55	.55
7	A16	10c green ('22)	.70	.70
8	A16	10c red, *pink* ('25)	2.00	2.00
9	A16	15c violet	.95	.95
10	A17	20c gray brown	.95	.95
11	A17	25c blue, *grn*	1.40	1.40
12	A17	25c red, *yel* ('22)	.90	.90
13	A17	30c brown, *org*	1.50	1.50
14	A17	30c dp rose ('22)	1.40	1.40
15	A17	30c red orange ('25)	.85	.85
16	A17	30c lt green ('27)	2.25	2.25
17	A17	35c black, *yel* (R)	1.00	1.00
18	A17	40c rose, *grn*	1.00	1.00
19	A17	45c violet brn, *pnksh*	1.40	1.40
20	A17	50c red, *org*	1.50	1.50
21	A17	50c dark blue ('22)	1.90	1.90
22	A17	50c dark gray ('25)	2.60	2.60
23	A17	65c deep blue ('28)	5.50	5.50
24	A17	75c olive green	2.10	2.10

Overprinted

25	A18	1fr blue, *yel grn*	4.50	4.50
a.		Triple overprint	190.00	
26	A18	1.10fr orange brn ('28)	5.00	5.00
27	A18	2fr carmine, *bl*	6.50	6.50
28	A18	5fr black, *org* (R)	14.50	14.50
		Nos. 1-28 (28)	62.75	62.75

No. 9 Surcharged New Value and Bars in Various Colors

1922				
29	A16	0.01c on 15c violet (Bk)	.75	.75
30	A16	0.02c on 15c violet (Bl)	.75	.75
31	A16	0.04c on 15c violet (G)	.75	.75
32	A16	0.05c on 15c violet (R)	.75	.75
		Nos. 29-32 (4)	3.00	3.00

Stamps and Types of 1920 Surcharged with New Values and Bars in Black or Red

1924-27				
33	A18	25c on 2fr car, *bl*	1.00	1.00
34	A18	25c on 5fr black, *org*	1.00	1.00
35	A17	65c on 40c rose red, *grn* ('25)	1.60	1.60
36	A17	85c on 75c ol grn ('25)	1.40	1.40
37	A17	90c on 75c dp rose ('27)	2.25	2.25
38	A18	1.25fr on 1fr dp bl (R; '26)	1.10	1.10
39	A18	1.50fr on 1fr dp bl, *bl* ('27)	4.75	4.50
a.		Double surcharge	300.00	
b.		Surcharge omitted	290.00	
40	A18	3fr on 5fr red vio ('27)	7.00	7.00
a.		Surcharge omitted	225.00	
b.		Double surcharge	300.00	
41	A18	10fr on 5fr ol, *lav* ('27)	32.50	32.50
42	A18	20fr on 5fr vio rose, *yel* ('27)	42.50	42.50
		Nos. 33-42 (10)	95.10	94.85

New Caledonia Stamps and Types of 1928-40 Overprinted as in 1920

1930-40		**Perf. 13½, 14x13, 14x13½**		
43	A19	1c brn vio & indigo	.25	.25
a.		Double overprint	190.00	
44	A19	2c dk brn & yel grn	.25	.25
45	A19	3c brn vio & ind ('40)	.25	.25
46	A19	4c org & Prus grn	.25	.25
47	A19	5c Prus bl & dp ol	.30	.30

48	A19	10c gray lil & dk brn	.30	.30
49	A19	15c yel brn & dp bl	.30	.30
50	A19	20c brn red & dk brn	.60	.60
51	A19	25c dk grn & dk brn	1.10	1.10
52	A20	30c gray grn & bl grn	1.10	1.10
53	A20	35c Prus grn & dk grn ('38)	1.10	1.10
a.		Without overprint	200.00	
54	A20	40c brt red & olive	1.10	1.10
55	A20	45c dp bl & red org	1.10	1.10
56	A20	45c bl grn & dl grn ('40)	.90	.90
57	A20	50c violet & brown	1.10	1.10
58	A20	55c bl vio & rose red ('38)	2.40	2.40
59	A20	60c vio bl & car ('40)	.75	.75
60	A20	65c org brn & bl	2.00	2.00
61	A20	70c dp rose & brn ('38)	1.25	1.25
62	A20	75c Prus bl & ol gray	3.00	3.00
63	A20	80c dk cl & grn ('38)	1.25	1.25
64	A20	85c green & brown ('38)	3.50	3.50
65	A20	90c dp red & brt red	2.40	2.40
66	A20	90c ol grn & rose red ('39)	1.10	1.10
67	A21	1fr dp ol & sal	3.75	3.75
68	A21	1fr rose red & dk car ('38)	2.25	2.25
69	A21	1fr brn red & grn ('40)	.80	.80
70	A21	1.10fr dp grn & brn	32.50	32.50
71	A21	1.25fr brn red & grn ('33)	3.00	3.00
72	A21	1.25fr rose red & dk car ('39)	.90	.90
73	A21	1.40fr dk bl & red org ('40)	1.10	1.10
74	A21	1.50fr dp bl & bl	1.10	1.10
75	A21	1.60fr dp grn & grn ('40)	1.60	1.60
76	A21	1.75fr dk bl & red org ('33)	13.00	13.00
77	A21	1.75fr vio bl ('38)	2.25	2.25
78	A21	2fr red org & brn	1.60	1.60
79	A21	2.25fr vio bl ('39)	1.75	1.75
80	A21	2.50fr brn & lt brn ('40)	1.90	1.90
81	A21	3fr magenta & brn	1.60	1.60
82	A21	5fr dk bl & brn	2.25	2.25
83	A21	10fr vio & brn, *pnksh*	2.90	2.90
84	A21	20fr red & brn, *yel*	4.50	4.50
		Nos. 43-84 (42)	106.40	106.40

For overprints see Nos. 94-126.
For types A19 and A21 of New Caledonia, with "RF," overprinted as above, see Nos. 126A-126F.

Common Design Types pictured following the introduction.

Colonial Exposition Issue
Common Design Types

1931, Apr. 13		**Engr.**	**Perf. 12½**	
Name of Country Typo. in Black				
85	CD70	40c deep green	8.00	8.00
86	CD71	50c violet	8.00	8.00
87	CD72	90c red orange	8.00	8.00
88	CD73	1.50fr dull blue	8.00	8.00
		Nos. 85-88 (4)	32.00	32.00

Colonial Arts Exhibition Issue
Common Design Type
Souvenir Sheet

1937			**Imperf.**	
89	CD78	3fr red violet	27.50	37.50
		Never hinged	45.00	

New York World's Fair Issue
Common Design Type

1939, May 10		**Engr.**	**Perf. 12½x12**	
90	CD82	1.25fr carmine lake	3.00	3.00
91	CD82	2.25fr ultramarine	3.00	3.00

Petain Issue
New Caledonia Nos. 216A-216B Overprinted "WALLIS ET FUTUNA" in Lilac or Red

1941		**Engr.**	**Perf. 12½x12**	
92	A21a	1fr bluish green (L)	1.25	
93	A21a	2.25fr dark blue (R)	1.25	

Nos. 92-93 were issued by the Vichy government in France, but were not placed on sale in Wallis & Futuna.
For surcharges, see Nos. B8A-B8B.

Nos. 43-69, 71, 74, 77-78, 80-84 with Additional Overprint in Black

1941-43			**Perf. 14x13½**	
94	A19	1c	2.75	2.75
95	A19	2c	2.75	2.75
96	A19	3c	95.00	95.00
97	A19	4c	3.75	3.75
98	A19	5c	3.75	3.75
99	A19	10c	3.75	3.75
100	A19	15c	3.75	3.75
101	A19	20c	5.00	5.00
102	A19	25c	5.00	5.00
103	A20	30c	5.00	5.00
104	A20	35c	3.75	3.75
105	A20	40c	4.50	4.50
106	A20	45c #55	4.50	4.50
107	A20	45c #56	100.00	100.00
108	A20	50c	3.75	3.75
109	A20	60c	82.50	82.50
110	A20	60c	3.75	3.75
111	A20	70c	3.75	3.75
112	A20	75c	5.00	5.00
113	A20	80c	3.75	3.75
114	A20	85c	4.50	4.50
115	A20	90c #65	3.75	3.75
116	A20	90c #66	4.50	4.50
117	A21	1fr #68	4.50	4.50
118	A21	1.25fr #71	4.50	4.50
119	A21	1.25fr	3.75	3.75
120	A21	1.75fr #77	3.75	3.75
121	A21	2fr	4.50	4.50
122	A21	2.50fr	150.00	150.00
123	A21	3fr	3.75	3.75
124	A21	5fr	8.25	8.25
125	A21	10fr	55.00	55.00
126	A21	20fr	90.00	90.00
		Nos. 94-126 (33)	685.75	685.75

Types of New Caledonia Without "RF" overprinted as in 1920

1944				
126A	A19	10c gray lil & dk brn	1.10	
126B	A19	15c yel brn & dp bl	1.25	
126C	A21	1fr brn red & grn	1.90	
126D	A21	1.50fr blue	2.10	
126E	A21	10fr vio & brn, *pnksh*	2.10	
126F	A21	20fr red & brn, *yel*	2.60	
		Nos. 126A-126F (6)	11.05	

Nos. 126A-126F were issued by the Vichy government in France, but were not placed on sale in Wallis & Futuna.

Catalogue values for unused stamps in this section, from this point to the end of the section, are for Never Hinged items.

Ivi Poo, Bone Carving in Tiki Design
A1

1944	**Unwmk.**	**Photo.**	**Perf. 11½x12**	
127	A1	5c lt brown	.40	.30
128	A1	10c dp gray blue	.40	.30
129	A1	25c emerald	.40	.30
130	A1	30c dull orange	.40	.30
131	A1	40c dk slate grn	1.10	.90
132	A1	80c brown red	1.10	.90
133	A1	1fr red violet	.50	.40
134	A1	1.50fr red	.65	.40
135	A1	2fr gray black	.65	.50
136	A1	2.50fr brt ultra	.90	.65
137	A1	4fr dark purple	1.10	.90
138	A1	5fr lemon yellow	1.40	1.10
139	A1	10fr chocolate	1.80	1.40
140	A1	20fr deep blue	1.90	1.50
		Nos. 127-140 (14)	12.70	9.85

Nos. 127, 129 and 136 Surcharged with New Values and Bars in Black or Carmine

1946				
141	A1	50c on 5c lt brown	.90	.65
142	A1	60c on 5c lt brown	1.00	.75
143	A1	70c on 5c lt brown	1.00	.75
144	A1	1.20fr on 5c lt brown	1.00	.75
145	A1	2.40fr on 25c emerald	1.10	.90
146	A1	3fr on 25c emerald	1.10	.90
147	A1	4.50fr on 25c emerald	2.40	1.75
148	A1	15fr on 2.50fr (C)	2.50	1.75
		Nos. 141-148 (8)	11.00	8.20

Military Medal Issue
Common Design Type
Engraved and Typographed

1952, Dec. 1   *Perf. 13*
149 CD101 2fr multicolored   9.50 7.00

Wallis
Islander
A2

Unwmk.
1957, June 11   Engr.   *Perf. 13*
150 A2 3fr dk purple & lil rose   1.50 1.10
151 A2 9fr bl, dl lil & vio brn   2.75 2.25

Imperforates
Most Wallis and Futuna stamps from 1957 onward exist imperforate in issued and trial colors, and also in small presentation sheets in issued colors.

Flower Issue
Common Design Type
Design: 5fr, Montrouziera, horiz.

1958, Aug. 4   Photo.   *Perf. 12½x12*
152 CD104 5fr multicolored   4.50 2.50

Human Rights Issue
Common Design Type
1958, Dec. 10   Engr.   *Perf. 13*
153 CD105 17fr brt bl & dk bl   5.75 4.00

Women Making
Tapa Cloth — A3

Kava
Ceremony
A4

17fr, Dancers. 19fr, Dancers with paddles.

1960, Sept. 19   Engr.   *Perf. 13*
154 A3   5fr dk brown, grn & org
     brn   1.50 1.10
155 A4   7fr dk brown & Prus
     grn   2.25 1.90
156 A4 17fr ultra, claret & grn   3.00 2.25
157 A3 19fr claret & slate   3.25 2.50
   Nos. 154-157 (4)   10.00 7.75

For No. 157 with surcharge, see No. 174.

Map of South Pacific — A4a

1962, July 18   Photo.   *Perf. 13x12*
158 A4a 16fr multicolored   4.50 4.00
5th South Pacific Conf., Pago Pago, 1962.

Sea Shells — A5

1962-63   Engr.   *Perf. 13*
Size: 22x36mm
159 A5 25c Triton   1.10 1.10
160 A5 1fr Mitra episcopalis   1.10 1.10
161 A5 2fr Cypraecassis rufa   2.10 2.10
162 A5 4fr Murex tenuspina   3.00 3.00
163 A5 10fr Oliva erythrostoma   7.00 7.00
164 A5 20fr Cyprae tigris   10.50 10.50
   Nos. 159-164,C18 (7)   37.30 31.80

Red Cross Centenary Issue
Common Design Type
1963, Sept. 2   Unwmk.   *Perf. 13*
165 CD113 12fr red lil, gray & car 4.00 3.50

Human Rights Issue
Common Design Type
1963, Dec. 10   Engr.
166 CD117 29fr dk red & ocher   8.00 7.50

Philatec Issue
Common Design Type
1964, Apr. 15   Unwmk.   *Perf. 13*
167 CD118 9fr dk sl grn, grn &
     red   3.50 3.50

Queen
Amelia and
Ship
"Queen
Amelia"
A6

1965, Feb. 15   Photo.   *Perf. 12½x13*
168 A6 11fr multicolored   8.00 7.50

WHO Anniversary Issue
Common Design Type
1968, May 4   Engr.   *Perf. 13*
169 CD126 17fr bl grn, org & lil   6.50 4.50

Human Rights Year Issue
Common Design Type
1968, Aug. 10   Engr.   *Perf. 13*
170 CD127 19fr dk pur, org brn &
     brt mag   3.75 3.75

Outrigger
Canoe
A7

1969, Apr. 30   Photo.   *Perf. 13*
171 A7 1fr multicolored   1.10 1.10
   Nos. 171,C31-C35 (6)   40.60 18.85

ILO Issue
Common Design Type
1969, Nov. 24   Engr.   *Perf. 13*
172 CD131 9fr orange, brn & bl   3.00 2.90

UPU Headquarters Issue
Common Design Type
1970, May 20   Engr.   *Perf. 13*
173 CD133 21fr lil rose, ind & ol
     bis   4.00 4.00

No. 157 Surcharged with New Value and Two Bars

1971   Engr.   *Perf. 13*
174 A3 12fr on 19fr   1.25 1.25

Weight Lifting — A8

1971, Oct. 25
175 A8 24fr shown   6.00 5.25
176 A8 36fr Basketball   7.00 6.50
   Nos. 175-176,C37-C38 (4)   27.25 19.75

4th South Pacific Games, Papeete, French Polynesia, Sept. 8-19.

De Gaulle Issue
Common Design Type
Designs: 30fr, Gen. de Gaulle, 1940. 70fr, Pres. de Gaulle, 1970.

1971, Nov. 9   Engr.   *Perf. 13*
177 CD134 30fr blue & black   9.50 6.25
178 CD134 70fr blue & black   14.50 10.00

Child's
Outrigger
Canoe
A9

Designs: 16fr, Children's canoe race. 18fr, Outrigger racing canoe.

1972, Oct. 16   Photo.   *Perf. 13x12½*
Size: 35½x26½mm
179 A9 14fr dk green & multi   10.00 4.25
180 A9 16fr dk plum & multi   10.00 4.25
181 A9 18fr blue & multi   15.00 6.25
   Nos. 179-181,C41 (4)   80.00 39.75

Outrigger sailing canoes.

Rhinoceros
Beetle
A10

Insects: 25fr, Cosmopolites sordidus (beetle). 35fr, Ophideres fullonica (moth). 45fr, Dragonfly.

1974, July 29   Photo.   *Perf. 13*
182 A10 15fr ol & multi   3.75 2.10
183 A10 25fr ol & multi   4.50 3.00
184 A10 35fr gray bl & multi   9.00 4.00
185 A10 45fr multicolored   10.00 6.00
   Nos. 182-185 (4)   25.25 15.10

Georges Pompidou
(1911-74), Pres. of
France — A11

1975, Dec. 1   Engr.   *Perf. 13*
186 A11 50fr ultra & slate   8.00 5.50

Battle of Yorktown and George
Washington — A12

American Bicentennial: 47fr, Virginia Cape Battle and Lafayette.

1976, June 28   Engr.   *Perf. 13*
187 A12 19fr blue, red & olive   3.00 1.40
188 A12 47fr blue, red & maroon 4.50 4.00

For overprints see Nos. 205-206.

Conus Ammiralis — A13

Sea Shells: 23fr, Cyprae assellus. 43fr, Turbo petholatus. 61fr, Mitra papalis.

1976, Oct. 1   Engr.   *Perf. 13*
189 A13 20fr multicolored   2.75 2.00
190 A13 23fr multicolored   2.75 2.00
191 A13 43fr multicolored   6.00 4.00
192 A13 61fr ultra & multi   8.50 6.50
   Nos. 189-192 (4)   20.00 14.50

Father Chanel and Poi Church — A14

32fr, Father Chanel and map of islands.

1977, Apr. 28   Litho.   *Perf. 12*
193 A14 22fr multicolored   2.25 1.40
194 A14 32fr multicolored   2.50 1.50

Return of the ashes of Father Chanel, missionary.

Bowl,
Mortar and
Pestle
A15

Handicrafts: 25fr, Wooden bowls and leather bag. 33fr, Wooden comb, club, and boat model. 45fr, War clubs, Futuna. 69fr, Lances.

1977, Sept. 26   Litho.   *Perf. 12½*
195 A15 12fr multicolored   1.30 .75
196 A15 25fr multicolored   2.00 1.00
197 A15 33fr multicolored   2.25 1.25
198 A15 45fr multicolored   3.50 1.75
199 A15 69fr multicolored   4.50 3.00
   Nos. 195-199 (5)   13.55 7.75

Post Office, Mata Utu — A16

50fr, Sia Hospital, Mata Utu. 57fr, Administration Buildings, Mata Utu. 63fr, St. Joseph's Church, Sigave. 120fr, Royal Palace, Mara Utu.

1977, Dec. 12   Litho.   *Perf. 13*
200 A16 27fr multicolored   1.80 1.40
201 A16 50fr multicolored   2.50 1.80
202 A16 57fr multicolored   3.50 1.80
203 A16 63fr multicolored   4.50 2.75
204 A16 120fr multicolored   9.00 4.50
   Nos. 200-204 (5)   21.30 12.25

Nos. 187-188 Overprinted: "JAMES COOK / Bicentenaire de la / découverte des Iles / Hawaii 1778-1978"

1978, Jan. 20   Engr.   Perf. 13
205 A12 19fr multicolored   3.50 2.50
206 A12 47fr multicolored   7.00 4.00

Bicentenary of the arrival of Capt. Cook in the Hawaiian Islands.

Cruiser Triomphant — A17

Warships: 200fr, Destroyers Cap des Palmes and Chevreuil. 280fr, Cruiser Savorgnan de Brazza.

1978, June 18   Photo.   Perf. 13x12½
207 A17 150fr multicolored   10.50 6.25
208 A17 200fr multicolored   14.00 9.00
209 A17 280fr multicolored   18.00 12.50
      Nos. 207-209 (3)   42.50 27.75

Free French warships serving in the Pacific, 1940-1944.

Solanum Seaforthianum — A18

Flowers: 24fr, Cassia alata. 29fr, Gloriosa superba. 36fr, Hymenocallis littoralis.

1978, July 11   Photo.   Perf. 13
210 A18 16fr multicolored   1.50   .90
211 A18 24fr multicolored   1.75 1.00
212 A18 29fr multicolored   2.50 1.40
213 A18 36fr multicolored   3.50 1.80
      Nos. 210-213 (4)   9.25 5.10

Gray Egret — A19

Birds: 18fr, Red-footed booby. 28fr, Brown booby. 35fr, White tern.

1978, Sept. 5   Photo.   Perf. 13
214 A19 17fr multicolored   1.75   .90
215 A19 18fr multicolored   1.80 1.00
216 A19 29fr multicolored   2.50 1.40
217 A19 35fr multicolored   3.50 1.60
      Nos. 214-217 (4)   9.55 4.90

Traditional Patterns — A20

Designs: 55fr, Corpus Christi procession. 59fr, Chief's honor guard.

1978, Oct. 3
218 A20 53fr multicolored   3.00 1.80
219 A20 55fr multicolored   4.00 2.10
220 A20 59fr multicolored   3.50 2.50
      Nos. 218-220 (3)   10.50 6.40

Human Rights Flame A21

1978, Dec. 10   Litho.   Perf. 12½
221 A21 44fr multicolored   1.80 1.30
222 A21 56fr multicolored   2.75 1.80

30th anniversary of Universal Declaration of Human Rights.

Fishing Boat — A22

Designs: 30fr, Weighing young tuna. 34fr, Stocking young tunas. 38fr, Measuring tuna. 40fr, Angler catching tuna. 48fr, Adult tuna.

1979, Mar. 19   Litho.   Perf. 12
223 A22 10fr multicolored   .90   .50
224 A22 30fr multicolored   1.40   .90
225 A22 34fr multicolored   1.50 1.00
226 A22 38fr multicolored   2.40 1.40
227 A22 40fr multicolored   2.75 2.00
228 A22 48fr multicolored   3.75 2.00
  a. Souv. sheet of 6, #223-228 +
      3 labels   30.00 30.00
      Nos. 223-228 (6)   12.70 7.80

Tuna tagging by South Pacific Commission. For surcharge see No. 261.

Boy with Raft and IYC Emblem — A23

Design: 58fr, Girl on horseback.

1979, Apr. 9   Photo.   Perf. 13
229 A23 52fr multicolored   2.25 1.30
230 A23 58fr multicolored   2.25 1.70

International Year of the Child.

Bombax Ellipticum — A24

64fr, Callophyllum. 76fr, Pandanus odoratissimus.

1979, Apr. 23   Litho.   Perf. 13
231 A24 50fr multicolored   2.25 1.40
232 A24 64fr multicolored   3.00 1.80
233 A24 76fr multicolored   4.25 2.50
      Nos. 231-233 (3)   9.50 5.70

Green and Withered Landscapes — A25

1979, May 28   Photo.   Perf. 13
234 A25 22fr multicolored   1.80 1.10

Anti-alcoholism campaign.

Flowers — A26

1979, July 16   Photo.   Perf. 12½x13
235 A26 20fr Crinum   .90   .65
236 A26 42fr Passiflora   2.10 1.10
237 A26 62fr Canna indica   3.00 1.75
      Nos. 235-237 (3)   6.00 3.50

See Nos. 279-281.

Swimming — A27

1979, Aug. 27   Engr.   Perf. 13
238 A27 31fr shown   2.25 1.40
239 A27 39fr High jump   3.00 1.80

6th South Pacific Games, Suva, Fiji, Aug. 27-Sept. 8.

Flower Necklaces — A28

Design: 140fr, Coral necklaces.

1979, Aug. 27   Litho.
240 A28 110fr multicolored   4.25 2.75
241 A28 140fr multicolored   5.25 3.50

Trees and Birds, by Sutita — A29

Paintings by Local Artists: 65fr, Birds and Mountain, by M. A. Pilioko, vert. 78fr, Festival Procession, by Sutita.

1979, Oct. 8   Perf. 13x12½, 12½x13
242 A29 27fr multicolored   1.40 1.10
243 A29 65fr multicolored   2.25 1.50
244 A29 78fr multicolored   4.00 2.25
      Nos. 242-244 (3)   7.65 4.85

Marine Mantis A30

Marine Life: 23fr, Hexabranchus sanguineus. 25fr, Spondylus barbatus. 43fr, Gorgon coral. 45fr, Linckia laevigata. 63fr, Tridacna squamosa.

1979, Nov. 5   Photo.   Perf. 13x12½
245 A30 15fr multicolored   1.40   .75
246 A30 23fr multicolored   1.40   .90
247 A30 25fr multicolored   1.80 1.00
248 A30 43fr multicolored   2.25 1.10
249 A30 45fr multicolored   2.40 1.25
250 A30 63fr multicolored   4.50 2.50
      Nos. 245-250 (6)   13.75 7.50

See #294-297. For surcharge see #272.

Transportation Type of 1979

1980, Feb. 29   Litho.   Perf. 13
251 AP32 1fr like No. C87   .35   .25
252 AP32 3fr like No. C88   .35   .25
253 AP32 5fr like No. C89   .40   .35
      Nos. 251-253 (3)   1.10   .85

Radio Station and Tower — A31

1980, Apr. 21   Litho.   Perf. 13
254 A31 47fr multicolored   2.75 1.40

Radio station FR3, 1st anniversary.

Jesus Laid in the Tomb, by Maurice Denis — A32

1980, Apr. 28   Perf. 13x12½
255 A32 25fr multicolored   1.80   .90

Easter 1980.

Gnathodentex Mossambicus — A33

1980, Aug. 25   Litho.   Perf. 12½x13
256 A33 23fr shown   1.40   .90
257 A33 27fr Pristipomoides fi-
         lamentosus   1.80 1.00
258 A33 32fr Etelis carbuncu-
         lus   2.50 1.40
259 A33 51fr Cephalopholis
         wallisi   3.50 2.40
260 A33 59fr Aphareus rutilans   5.75 2.75
  a. Vert. strip of 5, Nos. 256-260 16.00 15.00

No. 228 Surcharged:

1980, Sept. 29   Litho.   Perf. 12
261 A22 50fr on 48fr multi   3.00 1.80

Sydpex 80 Philatelic Exhibition, Sydney.

13th World Telecommunications
Day — A34

1981, May 17   Litho.   Perf. 12½
262 A34 49fr multicolored   1.80 1.10

Pierre Curie and Laboratory
Equipment — A35

1981, May 25   Litho.   Perf. 13
263 A35 56fr multicolored   2.25 1.40

Pierre Curie (1859-1906), discoverer of
radioactivity.

Conus
Textile
A36

Designs: Marine life.

1981, June 22   Perf. 12½x13
264 A36 28fr Favites   1.10   .90
265 A36 30fr Cyanophycees   1.40   .90
266 A36 31fr Ceratium vultur   1.50   .90
267 A36 35fr Amphiprion
            frenatus   2.25 1.10
268 A36 40fr shown   2.25 1.40
269 A36 55fr Comatule   2.75 1.60
 a.   Vert. strip of 6, Nos. 264-269 11.50 11.00

No. 269a is from sheet of 24.

60th Anniv. of Anti-tuberculin Vaccine
(Developed by Calmette and
Guerin) — A37

1981, July 28   Litho.   Perf. 13
270 A37 27fr multicolored   1.10   .90

Intl. Year of the
Disabled — A38

1981, Aug. 17
271 A38 42fr multicolored   2.25 1.20

No. 245 Surcharged in Red
1981, Sept.   Photo.   Perf. 13x12½
272 A30 5fr on 15fr multi   .65   .35

Thomas Edison (1847-1931) and his
Phonograph, 1878 — A39

1981, Sept. 5   Engr.   Perf. 13
273 A39 59fr multicolored   2.50 1.40

Battle of Yorktown, 1781 (American
Revolution) — A40

1981, Oct. 19   Engr.   Perf. 13
274 A40 66fr Admiral de Grasse   2.75 1.80
275 A40 74fr Sea battle, vert.   3.50 2.75

200-Mile Zone Surveillance — A41

1981, Dec. 4   Litho.   Perf. 13
276 A41 60fr Patrol boat Diep-
            poise   1.80 1.40
277 A41 85fr Protet   2.75 2.10

TB Bacillus
Centenary — A42

1982, Mar. 24   Litho.   Perf. 13
278 A42 45fr multicolored   3.00 1.40

Flower Type of 1979 in Changed
Colors

1982, May 3   Photo.   Perf. 12½x13
279 A26 1fr like No. 235   .30   .25
280 A26 2fr like No. 236   .40   .25
281 A26 3fr like No. 237   .40   .30
        Nos. 279-281 (3)   1.10   .80

PHILEXFRANCE '82 Intl. Stamp
Exhibition, Paris, June 11-21 — A43

1982, May 12   Engr.   Perf. 13
282 A43 140fr No. 25   3.50 2.75

Acanthe
Phippium
A44

Orchids and rubiaceae (83fr).

1982, May 24   Litho.   Perf. 12½x13
283 A44 34fr shown   1.10   .90
284 A44 68fr Acanthe phippium,
            diff.   2.25 1.75
285 A44 70fr Spathoglottis pacifi-
            ca   2.50 1.75
286 A44 83fr Mussaenda
            raiateensis   3.00 2.25
        Nos. 283-286 (4)   8.85 6.65

Scouting
Year
A45

1982, June 21   Perf. 12½
287 A45 80fr Baden-Powell   2.25 1.75

Cypraea
Talpa
A46

Porcelaines shells.

1982, June 28   Perf. 12½x13
288 A46 10fr shown   .30   .30
289 A46 15fr Cypraea vitellus   .70   .30
290 A46 25fr Cypraea argus   .85   .65
291 A46 27fr Cypraea carneola   1.10   .75
292 A46 40fr Cypraea mappa   1.40 1.10
293 A46 50fr Cypraea tigris   1.75 1.25
        Nos. 288-293 (6)   6.10 4.35

Marine Life Type of 1979
1982, Oct. 1   Photo.   Perf. 13x12½
294 A30 32fr Gorgones milithea   1.40   .75
295 A30 35fr Linckia laevigata   1.75 1.10
296 A30 46fr Hexabranchus
            sanguineus   2.10 1.50
297 A30 63fr Spondylus barbatus   3.00 2.25
        Nos. 294-297 (4)   8.25 5.60

St. Teresa of Jesus of Avila (1515-
1582) — A48

1982, Nov. 8   Engr.   Perf. 13
298 A48 31fr multicolored   1.40   .75
        See No. 315.

Traditional
House
A49

1983, Jan. 20   Litho.   Perf. 13
299 A49 19fr multicolored   .90   .50

Gustave Eiffel (1832-1923),
Architect — A50

1983, Feb. 14   Engr.   Perf. 13
300 A50 97fr multicolored   3.50 2.75

A51

A52

1983, June 28   Engr.   Perf. 13
301 A51 92fr Thai dancer, 19th
            cent.   3.00 1.80

BANGKOK '83 Intl. Stamp Show, Aug. 4-13.

1983, Aug. 25   Litho.   Perf. 13x13½
302 A52 20fr multicolored   .70   .50

World Communications Year.

Cone Shells
A53

1983-84   Litho.   Perf. 13½x13
303 A53 10fr Conus tulipa   .50   .30
304 A53 17fr Conus
            capitaneus   .75   .50
305 A53 21fr Conus virgo   .75   .50
306 A53 22fr Strombus lentigi-
            nosus   .65   .50
307 A53 25fr Lambis chiragra   .75   .60
308 A53 35fr Strombus
            dentatus   1.40   .75
309 A53 39fr Conus vitulinus   1.40   .90
310 A53 43fr Lambis scorpius   1.75   .90
311 A53 49fr Strombus aurisdi-
            anae   2.00 1.40
312 A53 52fr Conus
            marmoreus   1.80 1.40
313 A53 65fr Conus leopardus   2.40 1.75
314 A53 76fr Lambis crocata   3.00 1.60
        Nos. 303-314 (12)   17.15 11.10

  Issued: 22, 25, 35, 43, 49, 76fr, 3/23/84;
others, 10/14/83.

No. 298 Redrawn with Espana '84
Emblem
1984, Apr. 27   Engr.   Perf. 13
315 A48 70fr multicolored   2.25 1.40

Denis Diderot (1713-1784), Philosopher A54

1984, May 11
316 A54 100fr Portrait, encyclo-
pedia title page 3.00 1.75

Nature Protection (Whale) A55

1984, June 5 Litho. Perf. 13x12½
317 A55 90fr Orcina orca 3.00 1.75

4th Pacific Arts Festival — A56

1984, Nov. 30 Litho. Perf. 13
318 A56 160fr Islanders 3.75 2.50

Lapita Pottery — A57

Ethno-Archaeological Museum: Excavation site, reconstructed ceramic bowl.

1985, Jan. 16 Litho. Perf. 13
319 A57 53fr multicolored 1.50 .90

Seashells A58

1985, Feb. 11
320 A58 2fr Nautilus pompilius .25 .25
321 A58 3fr Murex bruneus .25 .25
322 A58 41fr Casmaria erinaceus 1.40 .90
323 A58 47fr Conus vexillum 1.75 1.00
324 A58 56fr Harpa harpa 2.10 1.10
325 A58 71fr Murex ramosus 2.50 1.60
Nos. 320-325 (6) 8.25 5.10

Victor Hugo, Author (1802-1885) A59

Bat — A60

1985, Mar. 7 Engr.
326 A59 89fr multicolored 3.00 1.60

1985, Apr. 29 Litho.
327 A60 38fr multicolored 2.00 1.10

Intl. Youth Year — A61

1985, May 20 Litho. Perf. 12½x13
328 A61 64fr Children 1.75 1.10

UN, 40th Anniv. — A61a

1985, July 12 Engr. Perf. 13
328A A61a 49fr Prus grn, dk ultra
& red 1.50 .90

Pierre de Ronsard (1524-1585), Poet — A62

1985, Sept. 16 Engr. Perf. 13
329 A62 170fr brt bl, sep & brn 5.00 3.50

Dr. Albert Schweitzer — A63

1985, Nov. 22 Engr. Perf. 13
330 A63 50fr blk, dk red lil & org
brn 2.00 1.25

World Food Day — A64

1986, Jan. 23 Litho. Perf. 12½x13
331 A64 39fr Breadfruit 1.25 .75

Flamboyants — A65

1986, Feb. 13 Perf. 13x12½
332 A65 38fr multicolored 2.00 1.00

Seashells A66

1986, Apr. 24 Litho. Perf. 13½x13
333 A66 4fr Lambis truncata .35 .35
334 A66 5fr Charonia tritonis .35 .35
335 A66 10fr Oliva miniacea .50 .35
336 A66 18fr Distorsio anus .80 .70
337 A66 25fr Mitra mitra 1.20 .75
338 A66 107fr Conus distans 3.75 2.25
Nos. 333-338 (6) 6.95 4.75

Also exists in se-tenant strips of 6 from sheet of 24.

1986 World Cup Soccer Championships, Mexico — A67

1986, May 20 Perf. 13x12½
339 A67 95fr multicolored 3.25 1.80
UNICEF.

Discovery of Horn Islands, 370th Anniv. — A68

No. 340: a, 8fr, William Schouten, ship. b, 9fr, Jacob LeMaire, ship. c, 155fr, Map of Alo & Alofi.

1986, June 19 Engr. Perf. 13
340 A68 Strip of 3, #a.-c. 6.50 4.75

James Watt (1736-1819), Inventor, and Steam Engine — A69

1986, July 11
341 A69 74fr blk & dk red 2.40 1.50

La Lorientaise Patrol Boat — A70

7fr, 120fr vertical.

1986, Aug. 7
342 A70 6fr shown .70 .50
343 A70 7fr Commandant
Blaison .75 .50
344 A70 120fr Balny escort ship 4.25 2.75
Nos. 342-344 (3) 5.70 3.75

Rose Laurel — A71

1986, Oct. 2 Litho. Perf. 13x12½
345 A71 97fr multi 3.25 2.00

Virgin and Child, by Sandro Botticelli A72

1986, Dec. 12 Litho. Perf. 12½x13
346 A72 250fr multicolored 7.50 4.50

Christmas.

Butterflies — A73

1987, Apr. 2 Litho. Perf. 12½
347 A73 2fr Papilio mon-
trouzieri .50 .35
348 A73 42fr Belenois java 1.25 .70
349 A73 46fr Delias ellipsis 1.40 .75
350 A73 50fr Danaus pumila 1.60 .95
351 A73 52fr Luthrodes cleotas 2.00 1.00
352 A73 59fr Precis villida 2.40 1.50
Nos. 347-352 (6) 9.15 5.25

World Wrestling Championships — A74

1987, May 26 Litho. Perf. 12½
353 A74 97fr multi 3.25 1.90

For overprint see No. 360.

Seashells
A75

1987, June 24   Litho.   Perf. 13
354 A75 3fr Cymatium pileare   .35 .35
355 A75 4fr Conus textile   .35 .35
356 A75 28fr Cypraea mauritiana   1.25 .75
357 A75 44fr Bursa bubo   1.50 1.00
358 A75 48fr Cypraea tes-
                tudinaria   1.60 1.10
359 A75 78fr Cypraecassis rufa   2.75 1.50
         Nos. 354-359 (6)   7.80 5.05

Also exists in se-tenant strips of 6 from
sheet of 24.

No. 353
Overprinted

1987, Aug. 29   Litho.   Perf. 12½
360 A74 97fr multicolored   3.75 2.40
OLYMPHILEX '87, Rome.

Bust of a Girl, by
Auguste Rodin
(1840-1917)
A76

1987, Sept. 15   Engr.   Perf. 13
361 A76 150fr plum   4.50 2.75
See No. 390.

World Post Day — A77

1987, Oct. 9   Litho.   Perf. 13
362 A77 116fr multicolored   3.25 1.80

Birds — A78

1987, Oct. 28   Perf. 13x12½
363 A78 6fr Anas superciliosa   .35 .35
364 A78 19fr Pluvialis dominica   .70 .50
365 A78 47fr Gallicolumba stairi   1.25 .95
366 A78 56fr Arenaria interpres   1.60 1.00
367 A78 64fr Rallus philippensis   1.75 1.10
368 A78 68fr Limosa lapponica   2.25 1.30
         Nos. 363-368 (6)   7.90 5.20

Francis Carco (1886-1958),
Painter — A79

Design: Carco and views of the Moulin de la
Galette and Place du Tertre, Paris.

1988, Jan. 29   Litho.   Perf. 13
369 A79 40fr multicolored   1.40 .95

Jean-Francois de Galaup (1741-
c.1788), Comte de La Perouse,
Explorer — A80

Design: Ships *L'Astrolabe* and *La Boussole*,
portrait of La Perouse.

1988, Mar. 21   Engr.   Perf. 13
370 A80 70fr org brn, dark blue &
              olive grn   3.25 2.40

Intl. Red Cross
and Red
Crescent
Organizations,
125th
Anniv. — A81

1988, July 4   Engr.   Perf. 13
371 A81 30fr blk, dark red & brt
              blue grn   2.00 1.00

1988 Summer Olympics, Seoul — A82

1988, Sept. 1   Engr.   Perf. 13
372 A82 11fr Javelin   .70 .50
373 A82 20fr Women's volleyball   .95 .70
374 A82 60fr Windsurfing   2.00 1.50
375 A82 80fr Yachting   2.90 1.90
  a. Souv. sheet of 4, #372-375 + 2
        labels, gutter between   8.25 8.25
        Nos. 372-375 (4)   6.55 4.60

Intl. Maritime Organization Emblem
and Packet *Escorteur* F727 — A83

1989, Jan. 26   Litho.   Perf. 13
376 A83 26fr multi   1.00 .70

Jean Renoir (1894-1979), Film
Director, and Scene from *The Grand
Illusion* — A84

1989, Feb. 16   Engr.   Perf. 13
377 A84 24fr brt lil rose, dark vio
              brn & brt org   1.25 .75

Antoine Becquerel (1788-1878),
Physicist — A85

Perf. 13x12½
1988, Nov. 9   Engr.   Unwmk.
378 A85 18fr blk & dark ultra   .95 .50

Futuna Hydroelectric Plant — A86

Wmk. 385
1989, Apr. 13   Litho.   Perf. 13½
379 A86 25fr multi   .95 .50

A87

A88

Unwmk.
1988, Oct. 26   Litho.   Perf. 13
380 A87 17fr multi   .95 .50
World Post Day.

1989, May 17   Perf. 12½x13
381 A88 21fr multi   .95 .50
World Telecommunications Day.

Fresco
A89

1989, June 8   Perf. 12½
382 A89 22fr multi   .95 .50

PHILEXFRANCE '89 — A90

Declaration of Human Rights and
Citizenship, Bicent. — A91

1989, July 7   Litho.   Perf. 13
383 A90 29fr multi   1.00 .70
384 A91 900fr multi   22.00 14.00
  a. Souv. sheet of 2, #383-384 +
        label   30.00 30.00

No. 384 is airmail. No. 384a sold for 1000fr.

World Cycling Championships — A92

1989, Sept. 14   Engr.   Perf. 13
385 A92 10fr blk, red brn & emer   .60 .45

World Post Day — A93

Unwmk.
1989, Oct. 18   Litho.   Perf. 13
386 A93 27fr multicolored   .95 .50

Landscape — A94

1989, Nov. 23   Litho.   Perf. 13
387 A94 23fr multicolored   .95 .70

Star of
Bethlehem
A95

1990, Jan. 9   Litho.   Perf. 12½
388 A95 44fr multicolored   1.50 1.00

Fossilized
Tortoise
A96

1990, Feb. 15   Litho.   Perf. 12½x13
389 A96 48fr multicolored   2.75 1.40

Sculpture by
Auguste Rodin
(1840-1917)
A97

1990, Mar. 15   Engr.   Perf. 13
390 A97 200fr royal blue   6.00 4.00

1990 World Cup Soccer
Championships, Italy — A98

1990, Apr. 16   Litho.
391 A98 59fr multicolored   1.60 1.10

Orchids
A99

1990, May 17   Litho.   Perf. 12½
392 A99 78fr multicolored   2.75 1.50
Mother's Day

Phaeton — A100

1990, July 16   Perf. 13
393 A100 300fr multicolored   8.00 4.50
394 A100 600fr Island   17.50 8.50

Moana II — A101

1990, Aug. 16   Engr.   Perf. 13
395 A101 40fr shown   1.25 .95
396 A101 50fr Moana III   1.75 1.00

Native Huts
A102

1990, Sept. 17   Litho.   Perf. 13x12½
397 A102 28fr multicolored   .95 .50

Stamp Day
A103

1990, Oct. 16   Litho.   Perf. 12½
398 A103 97fr multicolored   3.25 1.90

Wallis Island
Pirogue — A104

1990, Nov. 16   Litho.   Perf. 13x12½
399 A104 46fr multicolored   1.50 .95

Best Wishes — A105

1990, Dec. 17   Litho.   Perf. 13x12½
400 A105 100fr multicolored   3.25 1.90

Patrol Boats — A106

1991   Engr.   Perf. 13
401 A106 42fr La Moqueuse   1.40 .95
402 A106 52fr La Glorieuse   1.75 1.00
Issue dates: 42fr, Jan. 7; 52fr, Mar. 4.

A107

1991, Feb. 4   Litho.   Perf. 13
403 A107 7fr Breadfruit picker   .35 .35
404 A107 54fr Taro planter   1.60 1.00
405 A107 62fr Spear fisherman   1.75 1.20
406 A107 72fr Native warrior   2.40 1.30
407 A107 90fr Kailao dancer   3.00 1.75
  a.   Souv. sheet of 5, #403-407   10.00 10.00
     Nos. 403-407 (5)   9.10 5.60

Issued: 7fr, 9/2; 54fr, 5/13; 62fr, 4/1; 72fr,
2/4; 90fr, 11/4.
No. 407a sold for 300fr.

Doctors
Without
Borders,
20th Anniv.
A108

1991, Feb. 18   Litho.   Perf. 13½
408 A108 55fr multicolored   1.60 1.00

Ultralight Aircraft — A108a

1991, June 24
409 A108a 85fr multicolored   2.75 1.80

Portrait of Jean by Auguste Renoir
(1841-1919) — A109

1991, July 8   Photo.   Perf. 12½x13
410 A109 400fr multicolored   11.00 8.00
Litho.
Die Cut
Self-Adhesive
411 A109 400fr multicolored   11.00 8.00

Overseas Territorial Status, 30th
Anniv. — A110

1991, July 29   Litho.   Perf. 13
412 A110 102fr multicolored   2.75 1.80

Feast of the Assumption — A111

1991, Aug. 15   Perf. 13x12½
413 A111 30fr multicolored   1.00 .70

Amnesty
Intl., 30th
Anniv.
A113

1991, Oct. 7   Perf. 13x12½
414 A113 140fr bl, vio & yel   4.50 2.75

Central Bank for Economic
Cooperation, 50th Anniv. — A114

1991, Dec. 2   Litho.   Perf. 13
415 A114 10fr multicolored   .50 .35

Flowers
A115

1fr, Monette allamanda cathartica. 4fr,
Hibiscus rosa sinensis. 80fr, Ninuphar.

1991, Dec. 2   Perf. 12½x13, 13x12½
416 A115 1fr multi   .50 .25
417 A115 4fr multi, vert.   .50 .35
418 A115 80fr multi   2.40 1.50
     Nos. 416-418 (3)   3.40 2.10

Christmas — A116

1991, Dec. 16   Litho.   Perf. 13
419 A116 60fr multicolored   2.00 1.20

Maritime Surveillance — A117

1992, Jan. 20   Litho.   Perf. 13
420 A117 48fr multicolored   2.00 1.00

1992 Winter Olympics,
Albertville — A118

1992, Feb. 17   Litho.   *Perf. 13*
421 A118 150fr multicolored   4.00 2.75

Canada '92, Intl. Philatelic Exposition,
Montreal — A119

Illustration reduced.

1992, Mar. 25   Engr.   *Perf. 13*
422 A119 35fr blk, violet & red   1.25 .70

1992 Summer Olympics,
Barcelona — A120

1992, Apr. 15   Engr.   *Perf. 13*
423 A120 106fr bl grn, grn & bl   3.25 2.25

Granada '92, Intl. Philatelic
Exposition — A121

Illustration reduced.

1992, Apr. 17   Engr.   *Perf. 12½x12*
424 A121 100fr multicolored   3.25 2.00

Expo '92, Seville — A122

1992, Apr. 20   *Perf. 13*
425 A122 200fr bl grn, ol & red
    brn   5.50 3.75

Chaetodon Ephippium — A123

Designs: 22fr, Chaetodon auriga. 23fr, Heniochus monoceros. 24fr, Pygoplites diacanthus. 25fr, Chaetodontoplus conspicillatus.
26fr, Chaetodon unimaculatus. 27fr, Siganus
punctatus. 35fr, Zebrasoma veliferum. 45fr,

Paracanthurus hepatus. 53fr, Siganus
vulpinus.

1992-93   Litho.   *Perf. 13*
426 A123 21fr multicolored   .70 .50
427 A123 22fr multicolored   .70 .50
428 A123 23fr multicolored   .70 .50
429 A123 24fr multicolored   .80 .70
430 A123 25fr multicolored   1.00 .70
431 A123 26fr multicolored   1.00 .70
432 A123 27fr multicolored   1.00 .80
433 A123 35fr multicolored   1.00 .80
434 A123 45fr multicolored   1.25 .95
435 A123 53fr multicolored   1.60 1.25
    Nos. 426-435 (10)   9.75 7.40

Issued: 21fr, 26fr, 5/18; 22fr, 7/27; 25fr,
7/27; 23fr, 24fr, 9/14; 35fr, 45fr, 6/21/93; 27fr,
53fr, 9/6/93.

Natives
A125

a, 3 warriors. b, 2 warriors. c, Warrior, 2
boats. d, 2 spear fisherman. e, 3 fisherman.

1992, June 15   Litho.   *Perf. 12*
436 A125 70fr Strip of 5, #a.-e. 12.50 9.00
  f.   Souvenir sheet of 5, #a.-e.   13.00 13.00

#436 has continuous design. #436f sold for
450fr.

Support
Ship, "La
Garonne"
A126

1992, Oct. 12   Litho.   *Perf. 12*
437 A126 20fr multicolored   .75 .50

L'Idylle D'Ixelles,
by Auguste
Rodin (1840-
1917)
A127

1992, Nov. 17   Engr.   *Perf. 13*
438 A127 300fr lilac & dk blue   8.50 6.00

Miribilis
Jalapa
A128

1992, Dec. 7   Litho.   *Perf. 12½*
439 A128 200fr multicolored   5.50 3.75

Maritime Forces of the Pacific — A129

1993, Jan. 27   Litho.   *Perf. 13x12½*
440 A129 130fr multicolored   3.75 2.75

School
Art — A130

1993, Feb. 22   Litho.   *Perf. 12*
441 A130 56fr multicolored   1.80 1.40

See Nos. 451-452.

Birds
A131

Designs: 50fr, Rallus philippensis swindellsi.
60fr, Porphyrio porphyrio. 110fr, Ptilinopus
greyi.

1993, Mar. 20   *Perf. 13½*
442 A131 50fr multicolored   1.60 1.00
443 A131 60fr multicolored   1.90 1.50
444 A131 110fr multicolored   3.25 1.90
    Nos. 442-444 (3)   6.75 4.40

Mother's
Day
A132

1993, May 30   Litho.   *Perf. 12½*
445 A132 95fr Hibiscus   2.75 1.75
446 A132 120fr Siale   3.50 2.75

Admiral Antoine d'Entrecasteaux
(1737-1793), French
Navigator — A133

1993, July 12   Engr.   *Perf. 13*
447 A133 170fr grn bl, red brn &
    blk   5.00 3.25

Taipei '93 — A134

1993, Aug. 14   Litho.   *Perf. 13x12½*
448 A134 435fr multicolored   12.50 10.00

Churches — A135

1993, Aug. 15   *Perf. 13*
449 A135 30fr Tepa, Wallis   1.00 .80
450 A135 30fr Vilamalia, Futuna   1.00 .80

School Art Type of 1993
1993   Litho.   *Perf. 13x13½, 13½x13*
451 A130 28fr Stylized trees   .80 .55
452 A130 52fr Family, vert.   1.60 1.00
    Issue dates: 28fr, Oct. 18. 52fr, Nov. 8.

Christmas
A136

1993, Dec, 6   *Perf. 13*
453 A136 80fr multicolored   2.40 1.60

Traditional
Arts and
Crafts
Exhibition
A137

1994, Mar. 24   Litho.   *Perf. 12½*
454 A137 80fr multicolored   2.40 1.60

Liberation of Paris, 50th
Anniv. — A138

1994, Apr. 21   Engr.   *Perf. 13*
455 A138 110fr black, blue & red 3.50 2.00

Satellite Communications — A139

1994, June 23   Litho.*
456 A139 10fr multicolored   2.40 1.75

1994 World Cup Soccer
Championships, U.S. — A140

1994, June 23
457 A140 105fr multicolored   3.25 2.00

Princesses Ouveennes, 1903 — A141

1994, July 21   Engr.   *Perf. 13*
458 A141 90fr blue grn, blk & red 2.50 1.50

Symbols of Playing Cards Suits — A142

1994, Aug. 25   Litho.   *Perf. 13*
459 A142 40fr multicolored 1.40 .70

Ultra-Light Aircraft — A143

1994, Aug. 25
460 A143 5fr multicolored .35 .35

Coconut — A144

1994, Oct. 13   Litho.   *Perf. 13*
461 A144 36fr multicolored 1.25 .70

Parrots A145

1994, Nov. 17   Litho.   *Perf. 13x13½*
462 A145 62fr multicolored 2.00 1.25

Grand Lodge of France, Cent. — A146

1994, Nov. 24   Engr.   *Perf. 13*
463 A146 250fr multicolored 6.50 4.50

Preparing Traditional Meal — A147

1995, Jan. 25   Litho.   *Perf. 13*
464 A147 80fr multicolored 2.40 1.40

Aerial View of Islands A148

1995, Feb. 21   *Perf. 13x13½, 13½x13*
465 A148 85fr Nukulaelae 2.25 1.25
466 A148 90fr Nukufetau, vert. 2.50 1.40
467 A148 100fr Nukufotu, Nukuloa 2.75 1.90
       Nos. 465-467 (3) 7.50 4.55

Mua College — A149

1995, Apr. 11   *Perf. 12*
468 A149 35fr multicolored 1.10 .70

UN, 50th Anniv. — A150

Illustration reduced.

1995, June 26   Litho.   *Perf. 13½*
469 A150 55fr multicolored 1.60 1.00

10th South Pacific Games — A151

1995, Aug. 1   Litho.   *Perf. 13*
470 A151 70fr multicolored 1.90 1.40

Local Plants — A152

1995, Oct. 24   Litho.   *Perf. 13½x13*
471 A152 20fr Breadfruit tree .70 .55
472 A152 60fr Tarot 1.60 1.00
473 A152 65fr Kava 2.00 1.40
       Nos. 471-473 (3) 4.30 2.95

See Nos. 478-481, 484-485.

Tapa — A153

1995, Dec. 12   Litho.   *Perf. 13*
474 A153 25fr Native life, vert. .80 .70
475 A153 26fr Fish, sea shells 1.00 .70

Mothers from the Islands — A154

1996, Jan. 14   Litho.   *Perf. 13½x13*
476 A154 80fr multicolored 2.25 1.50

Golf A155

1996, Jan. 24   *Perf. 13*
477 A155 95fr multicolored 3.50 2.00

Local Plant Type of 1995
1996   Litho.   *Perf. 13½x13*
478 A152 27fr Cananga odorata .80 .70
479 A152 28fr Mahoaa .90 .70
480 A152 45fr Hibiscus 1.25 .80
481 A152 52fr Ufi 1.60 1.00
       Nos. 478-481 (4) 4.55 3.20
Issued: #479, 481, 3/14; #478, 480, 6/20.

Sanglants Swamp — A156

1996, June 26   *Perf. 13*
482 A156 53fr multicolored 1.60 1.00

Chess — A157

1996, July 17
483 A157 110fr multicolored 3.25 2.00

Plant Type of 1995
Designs: 30fr, 48fr, Calladium.

1996, Sept. 17   Litho.   *Perf. 13½x13*
Background Color
484 A152 30fr blue green 1.00 .70
485 A152 48fr lilac 1.40 .90

Francoise Perroton, Missionary — A158

1996, Oct. 25   *Perf. 13*
486 A158 50fr multicolored 1.50 1.00

UNICEF, 50th Anniv. A159

1996, Dec. 4   Litho.   *Perf. 13*
487 A159 25fr multicolored .90 .70

CPS, 50th Anniv. A160

1997, Feb. 6   Litho.   *Perf. 13*
488 A160 7fr multicolored .35 .35

Royal Standards A161

1997, Feb. 14   Litho.   *Perf. 13x13½*
489 A161 56fr King Lavelua 1.40 1.00
490 A161 60fr King Tuiagaifo 1.40 1.00
491 A161 70fr King Tuisigave 1.90 1.00
       Nos. 489-491 (3) 4.70 3.00

Brasseur de Kava — A162

1997, Apr. 17   *Perf. 13½x13*
492 A162 170fr multicolored 4.00 2.75

Island Scenes A163

Designs: 10fr, Old man telling stories to children seated around campfire. 36fr, Braiding mat, vert. 40fr, Preparing "Kai'umu" (feast).

Perf. 13x13½, 13½x13
1997, May 20 **Litho.**
493 A163 10fr multicolored .35 .35
494 A163 36fr multicolored 1.00 .80
495 A163 40fr multicolored 1.10 .80
Nos. 493-495 (3) 2.45 1.95

Green
Lagoon
Turtles
A164

1997, June 18 **Perf. 13x13½**
496 A164 62fr Crawling ashore 1.75 1.00
497 A164 80fr Swimming 2.25 1.40

Festival of Avignon — A165

1997, July 31 **Litho.** **Perf. 13**
498 A165 160fr multicolored 4.40 2.40

Berlin
Handicapped
Sports
Festival — A166

1997, Aug. 12
499 A166 35fr multicolored 1.10 .70

D'Uvéa Karate Club — A167

Illustration reduced.

1997, Oct. 15 **Litho.** **Perf. 13x13½**
500 A167 24fr multicolored 1.00 .50

Fight Against
AIDS — A168

1997, Dec. 1 **Litho.** **Perf. 13**
501 A168 5fr multicolored 1.50 .35

Christmas — A169

1997, Dec, 24
502 A169 85fr Nativity 2.25 1.50

Preparation of UMU — A170

1998, Jan. 26
503 A170 800fr multicolored 16.50 11.00

Orchids — A171

70fr, Vanda T.M.A.. 85fr, Cattleya bow bells.
90fr, Arachnis. 105fr, Cattleya.

1998, Feb. 18 **Perf. 13**
504 A171 70fr multi, vert. 1.90 1.00
505 A171 85fr multi 2.25 1.25
506 A171 90fr multi, vert. 2.40 1.25
507 A171 105fr multi 2.75 1.50
Nos. 504-507 (4) 9.30 5.00

Telecom 2000 — A172

1998, Mar. 24 **Litho.** **Perf. 13**
508 A172 7fr multicolored .40 .40

Fishing — A173

Designs: 50fr, Fisherman casting net into
lagoon. 52fr, Fisherman sorting catch.

1998, May 26 **Litho.** **Perf. 13**
509 A173 50fr multicolored 1.40 .70
510 A173 52fr multicolored 1.40 .70

1998 World Cup Soccer
Championships, France — A174

1998, June 10
511 A174 80fr multicolored 2.10 1.40

Insects
A175

1998, July 21 **Litho.** **Perf. 13x13½**
512 A175 36fr Dragonfly 1.00 .50
513 A175 40fr Cicada 1.10 .70

Coral — A176

Various corals: a, 4fr. b, 5fr. c, 10fr. d, 15fr.

1998 **Litho.** **Perf. 13x13½**
514 A176 Strip of 4, #a.-d. 1.50 1.50

52nd Autumn Philatelic Salon — A177

1998, Nov. 5 **Litho.** **Perf. 13½**
515 A177 175fr multicolored 4.75 2.50

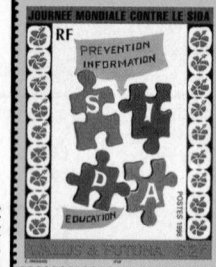

World Fight
Against
AIDS
A178

1998, Dec. 1 **Perf. 13**
516 A178 62fr multicolored 1.60 1.00

Islet of
Nuku
Taakimoa
A179

1999, Mar. 22 **Litho.** **Perf. 13**
517 A179 130fr multicolored 3.50 1.80

Souvenir Sheet

Lagoon Life — A180

a, 20fr, Various fish. b, 855fr, Fish, diver.

1999, May 17 **Litho.** **Perf. 13**
518 A180 Sheet of 2, #a.-b. 24.00 22.50

PhilexFrance '99, World Philatelic
Exhibition — A181

1999, July 2 **Litho.** **Perf. 13**
519 A181 200fr multicolored 5.50 3.25

French Senate, Bicent. — A182

1999, Sept. 20 **Engr.** **Perf. 13**
520 A182 125fr multi 3.50 2.00

Territorial Assembly Building — A183

1999, Aug. 23 **Litho.**
521 A183 17fr multi .45 .35

Pandanus
A184

1999, Oct. 18
522 A184 25fr multi .70 .45

Man
Making
Canoe
A185

1999, Nov. 8
523 A185 55fr multi 1.50 .80

French Postage Stamps, 150th
Anniv. — A186

1999, Dec. 1
524 A186 65fr Wallis & Futuna
#86 1.75 1.00

Millennium — A187

2000, Jan. 1 Litho. Perf. 13
525 A187 350fr multi 9.50 4.50

Mata'utu
Cathedral
A188

2000, Apr. 28 Photo. Perf. 13x13¼
526 A188 300fr multi 8.00 3.75

Patrol Boat "La Glorieuse" — A189

2000, June 5 Engr. Perf. 13x12¾
527 A189 155fr multi 4.25 2.40

Sosefo Papilio
Makape, First
Senator — A190

2000, June 19 Perf. 12¾x13
528 A190 115fr multi 3.00 1.50

Overseas Broadcasting
Institute — A191

2000, July 3 Perf. 13x12½
529 A191 200fr multi 5.50 2.50

Taro
Cultivation
A192

2000, July 27 Litho. Perf. 13
530 A192 275fr multi 7.50 3.50

Souvenir Sheet

2000 Summer Olympics,
Sydney — A193

Traditional games, 85fr: a, Spear throwing.
b, Sailing. c, Rowing. d, Volleyball.

2000, Sept. 15 Litho. Perf. 13
531 A193 #a-d + 2 labels 9.00 9.00

8th Pacific
Arts
Festival
A194

2000, Oct. 23 Perf. 13x13¼
532 A194 330fr multi 9.00 4.50

Fish — A195

No. 533: a, Coryphaena hippurus. b, Caranx
melanpygyus. c, Thunnus albacares.

2000, Nov. 9 Litho. Perf. 13
533 Vert. strip of 3 + 2 labels 9.25 9.25
a.-c. A195 115fr Any single 3.10 1.75

Canonization of St. Marcellin
Champagnat, 1st Anniv. — A196

2000, Nov. 13
534 A196 380fr multi 10.00 5.00

Talietumu Archaeological Site — A197

2000, Dec. 1 Perf. 13x13½
535 A197 205fr multi 5.50 2.75

Christmas
A198

2000, Dec. 25 Perf. 13
536 A198 225fr multi 6.00 2.75

Ship "Jacques Cartier" — A199

2001, Feb. 26 Engr. Perf. 13
537 A199 225fr multi 6.00 2.75

Campaign Against
Alcoholism
A200

2001, Mar. 14 Litho. Perf. 13¼x13
538 A200 75fr multi 2.00 1.00

Souvenir Sheet

Tapas — A201

Tapa with: a, Large diamond, shells, map of
islands. b, Triangles and diamonds. c, Scenes
of native life, fish, shells, boat. d, Overlapping
ovals.

2001, Apr. 14 Perf. 13
539 A201 90fr Sheet of 4, #a-d, +
2 labels 9.75 9.75

Children's Drawings of
Flowers — A202

2001, May 31
540 Horiz. strip of 4 8.25 8.25
a. A202 50fr multi 1.40 1.40
b. A202 55fr multi 1.50 1.50
c. A202 95fr multi 2.50 2.50
d. A202 100fr multi 2.75 2.75

Territorial
Status, 40th
Anniv.
A203

2001, July 29 Litho. Perf. 13
541 A203 165fr multi 4.50 2.00

Installation
of Mediator,
1st Anniv.
A204

2001, Sept. 26
542 A204 800fr multi 22.00 10.00

Year of
Dialogue
Among
Civilizations
A205

2001, Oct. 9
543 A205 390fr multi 10.50 5.00

5th Autumn
Salon — A206

Birds: a, Dacula pacifica. b, Vini australis. c, Tyto alba.

2001, Nov. 8
544   Vert. strip of 3 + 2
    labels   12.00 12.00
a.-c. A206 150fr Any single   4.00 3.00

Children's Drawings of Fruit A207

No. 545, 65fr: a, Custard apple (pomme canelle). b, Breadfruit (fruit de pain).
No. 546, 65fr: a, Pineapple. b, Mango.

2001, Aug. 22   Litho.   Perf. 13
Vert. Pairs, #a-b
545-546 A207   Set of 2 pairs   7.00 5.00

Tomb of Futuna King Fakavelikele — A208

2001, Dec. 28   Litho.   Perf. 13
547 A208 325fr multi   9.00 3.75

Finemui-Teesi College — A209

2002, Jan. 29   Perf. 13x13½
548 A209 115fr multi   3.00 1.40

Intl. Women's Day — A210

2002, Mar. 5   Litho.   Perf. 13
549 A210 800fr Queen Aloisia   22.00 10.00

Arms of Bishop Pompallier A211

2002, Apr. 19   Engr.   Perf. 13¼
550 A211 500fr multi   13.50 6.50

Uvea Firefighters A212

Serpentine Die Cut
2002, Apr. 28   Photo.
Self-Adhesive
551 A212 85fr multi   2.25 1.40

2002 World Cup Soccer Championships, Japan and Korea — A213

2002, May 31   Litho.   Perf. 13
552 A213 65fr multi   1.75 1.00

World Environment Day — A214

2002, June 5   Perf. 13x13½
553 A214 330fr multi   9.00 4.00

Traditional Buildings A215

Designs: No. 554, 50fr, Building with overhanging roof. No. 555, 50fr, Open-air shelter, vert. No. 556, 55fr, Building with two entry ways. No. 557, 55fr, Building with ladder to roof, vert.

2002, Aug. 9   Engr.   Perf. 13¼
554-557 A215   Set of 4   5.75 2.50

Discovery of the Horn Islands, 1616 A216

No. 558: a, Jacob Lemaire and compass rose. b, Map of Futuna and Alofi Islands. c, William Schouten and ship.

2002, Aug. 30   Litho.   Perf. 13x13¼
558   Horiz. strip of 3   10.00 10.00
a.-c. A216 125fr any single   3.25 3.25
d. Souvenir sheet, #558   10.00 10.00

Landscapes A217

No. 559: a, Utua Bay. b, Liku Bay. c, Kingfisher at Vele. d, Aka'Aka Bay.

2002, Sept. 20
559   Horiz. strip of 4   11.50 11.50
a. A217 95fr multi   2.50 1.50
b. A217 100fr multi   2.75 1.50
c. A217 105fr multi   2.75 1.60
d. A217 135fr multi   3.50 1.75

Enygrus Bibroni — A218

2002, Oct. 28   Litho.   Perf. 13¼x13
560 A218 75fr multi   2.00 .75

Fish A219

No. 561: a, Dendrochirus biocellatus. b, Discordipina griessingeri. c, Antennacius nummifer. d, Novaculichthys taeniourus.

2002, Nov. 7   Perf. 13x13¼
561   Vert. strip of 4 + 3
    labels   10.00 9.00
a.-d. A219 110fr Any single   3.00 1.75

Best Wishes A220

2002, Dec. 5
562 A220 140fr multi   3.75 1.40

Last Avro Lancaster Flight to Wallis, 40th Anniv. A221

2003, Jan. 26   Perf. 13
563 A221 135fr multi   3.60 1.75

St. Valentine's Day — A222

2003, Feb. 14   Perf. 13
564 A222 85fr multi   2.25 1.00

Introduction of the Euro, 1st Anniv. A223

2003, Feb. 17   Perf. 12½x12¾
565 A223 125fr multi   3.25 1.80

Values are for examples with surrounding selvage.

Alain Gerbault (1893-1941), Circumnavigator, Aboard Boat "Firecrest" — A224

2003, Mar. 6   Engr.   Perf. 13¼
566 A224 600fr grn & ol grn   16.00 8.00

Postal Art — A225

Various designs.

2003, Mar. 31   Litho.   Perf. 13
567   Horiz. strip of 5   2.40 2.40
a. A225 5fr multi   .25 .25
b. A225 10fr multi   .25 .25
c. A225 15fr multi   .40 .40
d. A225 20fr multi   .55 .25
e. A225 40fr multi   1.10 .40

Coral Reefs A226

Various views.

2003, Apr. 10   Perf. 13x13¼
568   Horiz. strip of 4   10.00 10.00
a. A226 95fr multi   1.75 1.75
b. A226 105fr multi   1.90 1.90
c. A226 110fr multi   2.00 2.00
d. A226 115fr multi   2.10 2.10

St. Pierre Chanel (1803-41), Martyred Missionary A227

2003, Apr. 28   Engr.   Perf. 12¼
569 A227 130fr multi   3.50 1.80

2003 Census — A228

2003, June 12   Litho.   Perf. 13
570 A228 55fr multi   1.50 .70

Pacific Legends
A229

Legend of the Coconut Palm: 30fr, Eel. 50fr, Coconut palms, split coconut. 60fr, Split and whole coconuts. 70fr, Coconut palms and clouds.

2003, July 28   Litho.   Perf. 13x13¼
571	Horiz. strip of 4	5.75	5.75
a.	A229 30fr multi	.80	.40
b.	A229 50fr multi	1.40	.75
c.	A229 60fr multi	1.60	.85
d.	A229 70fr multi	1.90	.95
e.	Souvenir sheet, #571a-571d	6.00	6.00

Still Life with Maori Statuette, by Paul Gauguin (1848-1903)
A230

No. 573a: Study of Heads of Tahitian Women, by Gauguin.

2003   Perf. 13
572 A230 100fr multi   2.75 1.60

Souvenir Sheet
| 573 | Sheet, #572, 573a | 5.50 | 5.50 |
| a. | A230 100fr multi | 2.75 | 2.25 |

Issued: No. 572, 7/31; No. 573, 8/20. See New Caledonia No. 929.

Futuna Waterfalls — A231

2003, Aug. 6   Perf. 13¼x13
574 A231 115fr multi   3.00 1.75

Frigate Le Nivose
A232

2003, Sept. 15   Engr.   Perf. 13¼
575 A232 325fr multi   8.75 4.00

Bishop Alexandre Poncet (1884-1973)
A233

2003, Sept. 18   Engr.   Perf. 13¼
576 A233 205fr multi   5.50 3.00

Arms of Bishop Pierre Bataillon (1810-77) — A234

2003, Oct. 1   Litho.   Perf. 13¼
577 A234 500fr multi   13.50 7.00

2003 Rugby World Cup, Australia
A235

2003, Oct. 10   Perf. 13
578 A235 65fr multi   1.75 .85

Parinari Insularum
A236

2003, Nov. 6   Litho.   Perf. 13¼x13
579 A236 250fr multi   6.75 3.50

Goddess Havea Hikule'o — A237

2004, Jan. 8
580 A237 85fr multi   2.25 1.40

People in Canoe
A238

2004, Jan. 13   Perf. 13
581 A238 75fr multi   2.00 1.25

Miniature Sheet

Campaign Against Dengue Fever — A239

No. 582: a, 5fr, Mosquito, crying man. b, 10fr, Mosquitos, man. c, 20fr, Mosquitos, trash. d, 30fr, Mosquitos, sleeping child.

Perf. 13¼x12¾
2004, Feb. 18   Litho.
582 A239 Sheet of 4, #a-d   2.25 2.25

Badminton
A240

2004, Mar. 12   Perf. 13¼x13
583 A240 55fr multi   1.50 1.25

Kava Drinkers
A241

2004, Mar. 31   Perf. 13x13¼
584 A241 205fr multi   5.50 4.25

Flora
A242

2004, Apr. 22   Perf. 13
585	Horiz. strip of 4 + central label	3.25	3.25
a.	A242 15fr Colocasia esculenta	.40	.30
b.	A242 25fr Carrica papaya	.65	.50
c.	A242 35fr Artocarpus altilus	.95	.70
d.	A242 40fr Dioscorea sp.	1.10	.80

Dispatch Boat Savorgnan de Brazza
A243

Gourdou-Leseurre GL 832 Hy No. 5 and Wallis Island — A244

2004, May 12   Engr.   Perf. 13¼
586 A243 300fr multi   8.00 6.00
587 A244 380fr multi   10.25 7.75

Souvenir Sheet
Litho.
588	Sheet of 2	18.50	18.50
a.	A243 300fr multi	8.00	6.00
b.	A244 380fr multi	9.50	7.75

First flight over Wallis Island, 68th anniv.

Seaweeds — A245

2004, June 26   Litho.   Perf. 13
589	Horiz. strip of 3 + 2 alternating labels	17.50	17.50
a.	A245 105fr Turbinaria ornata	2.90	2.90
b.	A245 155fr Padina melemele	4.25	4.25
c.	A245 175fr Tubinaria concoides	4.75	4.75

Miniature Sheet

Flowers — A246

No. 590: a, Hibiscus rosa-sinensis. b, Cananga odorata. c, Plumeria rubra. d, Ipomeapes caprae. e, Gardenia taitensis.

Serpentine Die Cut 14
2004, June 26   Photo.
Self-Adhesive
590 A246 Sheet of 5   12.50 12.50
a.-d.   85fr Any single   2.25   2.25
e.   115fr multi   3.00   3.00

Salon du Timbre 2004, Paris.

Ninth Pacific Arts Festival, Palau
A247

2004, July 22   Litho.   Perf. 13x13¼
591 A247 200fr multi   5.50 4.25

Pili'uli Lizard — A248

2004, July 26   Perf. 13
592 A248 100fr multi   2.75 2.10

Arms of Monsignor Louis Elloy (1829-78)
A249

2004, Sept. 6   Engr.   Perf. 13¼
593 A249 500fr multi   13.50 10.50

No. 517 Redrawn
2004, Nov. 10   Litho.   Perf. 13
594 A179 115fr multi   3.10 2.50

No. 594 shows a 115fr denomination below an obliterated 130fr denomination, the denomination shown on No. 517. This new denomination is not overprinted. No. 594 also has a 2004 year date, rather than an obliterated 1999 year date.

A250

Traditional Houses — A251

2004, Nov. 11　　　　**Perf. 13¼x13**
595　A250　95fr multi　　　　　2.50　2.10
596　A251　130fr multi　　　　　3.50　3.00

Nos. 595-596 were printed in sheets containing four of each stamp plus a large central label.

Miniature Sheet

Cone Shells — A252

No. 597: a, Conus eburneus. b, Conus imperialis. c, Conus generalis. d, Gastridium textile.

2005, Jan. 26　　　　**Perf. 13x13¼**
597　A252　55fr Sheet of 4, #a-d　6.00　5.00

Miniature Sheet

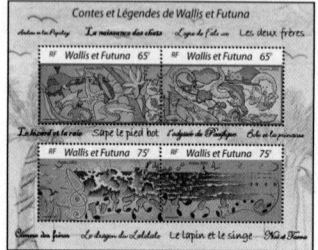

Stories and Legends — A253

No. 598: a, 65fr, Whale, bird, crab, eel, turtle. b, 65fr, Fish, octopus, dolphin, butterfly. c, 75fr, Boy, waves, G clef and musical notes. d, 75fr, Musical notes, butterflies.

2005, Jan. 31　　　　**Perf. 13**
598　A253　Sheet of 4, #a-d　　7.50　7.50

Pirogue A254

2005, Feb. 25　**Litho.**　**Perf. 13x13¼**
599　A254　330fr multi　　　　9.00　7.50

Francophone Week — A255

2005, Mar. 17
600　A255　135fr multi　　　　3.60　3.00

Printed in sheets of 10 + 5 labels. See New Caledonia No. 959.

Family Budget Inquiry A256

2005, Mar. 31　　　　**Perf. 12¾**
601　A256　205fr multi　　　　5.50　4.50

Values are for stamps with surrounding selvage.

Warriors — A257

2005, Apr. 19　　　　**Perf. 13½x13**
602　　Horiz. strip of 5　　　　3.25　3.25
　a.　A257　5fr blk, red & maroon　　.20　.20
　b.　A257　10fr blk, bl & vio blue　　.25　.20
　c.　A257　20fr blk, pur & indigo　　.55　.40
　d.　A257　30fr blk & red　　　　.80　.65
　e.　A257　50fr blk, lt grn & emerald　1.40　1.10

Traditional Cricket A258

2005, May 16　　　　**Perf. 13**
603　A258　190fr multi　　　　5.00　4.00

Butterflies — A259

No. 604: a, 40fr, Papilio montrouzieri. b, 60fr, Danaus pumila. Illustration reduced.

2005, June 30　　　　**Perf. 13x13¼**
604　A259　Horiz. pair, #a-b　　2.75　2.75

Warrior With Spear — A260

Serpentine Die Cut 11
2005, July 14
Booklet Stamp
Self-Adhesive
605　A260　115fr multi　　　　3.00　2.40
　a.　Booklet pane of 10　　　30.00

Historical Images of Wallis Island — A261

2005, July 14　**Engr.**　**Perf. 13x13¼**
606　　Horiz. pair + central label　9.00　9.00
　a.　A261　155fr Village scene　4.25　3.25
　b.　A261　175fr Family, house　4.75　3.75

First Noumea to Hihifo Flight, 58th Anniv. — A262

2005, Aug. 19
607　A262　380fr multi　　　　10.00　8.00

Souvenir Sheet

Chelomia Mydas — A263

No. 608 — Green turtle: a, Adult entering water. b, Hatchlings entering water. c, Head. d, Swimming underwater.

2005, Aug. 19　**Litho.**　**Perf. 13x13¼**
608　A263　85fr Sheet of 4, #a-d　9.25　9.25

Arms of Monsignor Jean Armand Lamaze (1833-1906) A264

2005, Oct. 5　**Engr.**　**Perf. 13¼**
609　A264　500fr multi　　　　13.50　10.00

Spattoglottis Cinguiculata — A265

2005, Oct. 30　**Litho.**　**Perf. 13**
610　A265　100fr multi　　　　2.75　2.00

Printed in sheets of 10 + 5 labels.

Design of Wallis and Futuna Islands No. 4 — A266

Design of Wallis and Futuna Islands No. 87 — A267

2005, Nov. 10　**Litho.**　**Perf. 13x13¼**
611　A266　150fr multi　　　　4.00　3.00
612　A267　150fr multi　　　　4.00　3.00

59th Autumn Philatelic Show.

Native Child A268

2006, Mar. 29　**Litho.**　**Perf. 13x13¼**
613　A268　75fr multi　　　　2.00　1.60

Monarchical Flags — A269

Designs: 55fr, Kingdom of Uvea. 65fr, Kingdom of Sigave. 85fr, Kingdom of Alo.

2006　**Litho.**　*Serpentine Die Cut 11*
Self-Adhesive
Booklet Stamps
614　A269　55fr multi　　　　1.50　1.25
　a.　Booklet pane of 10　　　15.00
615　A269　65fr multi　　　　1.75　1.40
　a.　Booklet pane of 10　　　17.50
616　A269　85fr multi　　　　2.25　1.75
　a.　Booklet pane of 10　　　22.50

Issued: 55fr, 6/17; 65fr, 4/18; 85fr, 3/29.

Haka Mai — A270

2006　　　　**Perf. 13¼x13**
617　A270　190fr multi　　　　5.00　4.25

Removal of Christ from the Cross, by Jean Soane Michon (1926-68) A271

2006, May 31　**Litho.**　**Perf. 13¼x13**
618　A271　400fr multi　　　　11.00　8.50

2006 World Cup Soccer Championships, Germany A272

2006, June 9
619　A272　100fr multi　　　　2.75　2.10

Mata Vai
A273

Mata Tai
A274

2006, June 17 *Perf. 13x13¼*
620 A273 140fr multi 3.75 3.00
621 A274 200fr multi 5.50 4.25

Historical Images From the 19th
Century — A275

2006, July 13 *Engr.* *Perf. 13x13¼*
622 Horiz. pair + central la-
bel 19.50 19.50
a. A275 330fr Girls dancing 9.00 7.00
b. A275 380fr Mua Church 10.00 8.00

Stamp
Day — A276

2006, Aug. 5 *Litho.* *Perf. 13¼x13*
623 A276 150fr multi 4.00 3.25

Twin Otter Airplane "Ville de Paris",
20th Anniv. — A277

2006, Aug. 7 *Perf. 13*
624 A277 30fr multi .80 .65

Territorial Rugby Committee — A278

2006, Sept. 9 *Perf. 12¾x13½*
625 A278 10fr multi .25 .25

Uhilamoafa
Gravesite
A279

2006, Sept. 12 *Perf. 13x13¼*
626 A279 290fr multi 7.75 6.25

Arms of
Monsignor
Joseph Félix
Blanc (1872-
1962)
A280

2006, Oct. 5 *Engr.* *Perf. 13¼*
627 A280 500fr multi 13.50 10.50

Tagaloa,
Polynesian
Deity — A281

2006, Nov. 8 *Litho.* *Perf. 13½x13*
628 A281 150fr multi 4.00 3.50

Tapas
A282

No. 629: a, Tapas design (shown). b, Mako
à Ono. c, Tauasu à Leava. d, Tapas design,
diff.

Litho. & Engr.
2006, Nov. 8 *Perf. 13x13¼*
629 Vert. strip of 4 + central label 9.25 9.25
a.-d. A282 85fr Any single 2.25 1.90

Souvenir Sheet

Christmas — A283

2006, Nov. 8 *Litho.* *Perf. 13*
630 A283 225fr multi 6.00 6.00

Pio Cardinal
Taofinu'u (1923-
2006)
A284

2007, Jan. 19 *Engr.* *Perf. 12½x13*
631 A284 800fr multi 21.50 17.50

Telemedicine
A285

2007, Feb. 28 *Litho.* *Perf. 13¼x13*
632 A285 5fr multi .20 .20

Audit
Office,
Bicent.
A286

2007, Mar. 19 *Engr.* *Perf. 13¼*
633 A286 105fr multi 2.75 2.40

Woman
A287

2007, Mar. 22 *Litho.* *Perf. 13*
634 A287 75fr multi 2.00 1.75

First Noumea-Hihifo Air Service, 50th
Anniv. — A288

2007, Apr. 30 *Engr.* *Perf. 13x12½*
635 A288 290fr multi 6.75 6.75

Fish — A289

2007, May 22 *Litho.* *Perf. 12¾x13¼*
636 Horiz. pair 2.00 2.00
a. A289 40fr Eviota .90 .90
b. A289 50fr Trimma 1.10 1.10

Secretary
General of the
Pacific
Community, 60th
Anniv. — A290

2007, June 28 *Litho.* *Perf. 13*
637 A290 155fr multi 3.50 3.50

Lolesio Tuita,
Javelin Thrower
A291

2007, July 30 *Engr.* *Perf. 12½x13*
638 A291 330fr purple & red 7.50 7.50

Buildings — A292

No. 639: a, House, Tamana. b, Sanctuary of
Pierre Chanel, Poi.

2007, July 31 *Engr.* *Perf. 13x13¼*
639 Horiz. pair with central
label 9.00 9.00
a. A292 190fr brown 4.25 4.25
b. A292 200fr brown 4.75 4.75

Discovery of
Uvea Island by
Samuel Wallis,
240th
Anniv. — A293

2007, Aug. 3 *Litho.*
640 A293 225fr multi 5.25 5.25
a. Souvenir sheet of 1 5.50 5.50
No. 640a sold for 240fr.

Legends of
Lomipeau
A294

No. 641 — People and: a, Togitapu Island.
b, Uvea Island.

2007, Aug. 3
641 Horiz. pair 1.25 1.25
a. A294 20fr multi .50 .50
b. A294 30fr multi .75 .75

Arms of
Monsignor
Armand Ölier
(1851-1911)
A295

2007, Oct. 22 *Engr.* *Perf. 13¼*
642 A295 500fr multi 12.50 12.50

Emblem of
Handisport
A296

2007, Oct. 11   Photo.   Perf. 12¾
643 A296 10fr multi   .25 .25
Values are for stamps with surrounding
selvage.

2007 Rugby World Cup
Championships, France — A297

2007, Oct. 20   Litho.   Perf. 13
644 A297 205fr multi   5.00 5.00
Printed in sheets of 10 + label.

SEMI-POSTAL STAMPS

French Revolution Issue
Common Design Type
Unwmk.

1939, July 5   Photo.   Perf. 13
Name and Value Typo. in Black
B1 CD83 45c + 25c green   19.00 19.00
B2 CD83 70c + 30c brown   19.00 19.00
B3 CD83 90c + 35c red org   19.00 19.00
B4 CD83 1.25fr + 1fr rose pink   19.00 19.00
B5 CD83 2.25fr + 2fr blue   19.00 19.00
Nos. B1-B5 (5)   95.00 95.00
Set, never hinged   160.00

New Caledonia Nos. B10 and B12
Overprinted "WALLIS ET FUTUNA" in
Blue or Red, and Common Design
Type

1941   Photo.   Perf. 13½
B6 SP2 1fr + 1fr red   2.40
B7 CD86 1.50fr + 3fr maroon   2.40
B8 SP3 2.50fr + 1fr dark blue   2.40
Nos. B6-B8 (3)   7.20
Set, never hinged   10.00

Nos. B6-B8 were issued by the Vichy government in France, but were not placed on sale in Wallis & Futuna.

Nos. 92-93
Surcharged in Black or Red

1944   Engr.   Perf. 12x12½
B8A 50c + 1.50fr on 2.50fr deep blue (R)   1.90
B8B + 2.50fr on 1fr green   1.90
Colonial Development Fund.
Nos. B8A-B8B were issued by the Vichy government in France, but were not placed on sale in Wallis & Futuna.

Catalogue values for unused stamps in this section, from this point to the end of the section, are for Never Hinged items.

Red Cross Issue
Common Design Type
1944   Photo.   Perf. 14½x14
B9 CD90 5fr + 20fr red orange   4.50 3.25
The surtax was for the French Red Cross and national relief.

AIR POST STAMPS

Catalogue values for unused stamps in this section are for Never Hinged items.

Victory Issue
Common Design Type
Perf. 12½
1946, May 8   Unwmk.   Engr.
C1 CD92 8fr dark violet   2.50 1.90

Chad to Rhine Issue
Common Design Types
1946
C2 CD93 5fr dark violet   1.40 1.10
C3 CD94 10fr dk slate grn   1.60 1.30
C4 CD95 15fr violet brn   1.60 1.30
C5 CD96 20fr brt ultra   2.40 1.75
C6 CD97 25fr brown orange   2.75 2.10
C7 CD98 50fr carmine   4.00 2.90
Nos. C2-C7 (6)   13.75 10.45

Types of New Caledonia Air Post Stamps of 1948, Overprinted in Blue:

1949, July 4   Perf. 13x12½, 12½x13
C8 AP2 50fr yel & rose red   9.50 7.00
C9 AP3 100fr yel & red brn   15.00 12.00
The overprint on No. C9 is in three lines.

UPU Issue
Common Design Type
1949, July 4   Engr.   Perf. 13
C10 CD99 10fr multicolored   12.50 8.25

Liberation Issue
Common Design Type
1954, June 6
C11 CD102 3fr sepia & vio brn   12.50 8.25

Father Louis Marie Chanel — AP1

1955, Nov. 21   Unwmk.   Perf. 13
C12 AP1 14fr dk grn, grnsh bl & ind   4.00 1.40
Issued in honor of Father Chanel, martyred missionary to the Islands.

View of Mata-Utu, Queen Amelia and Msgr. Bataillon — AP2

33fr, Map of islands and sailing ship.

1960, Sept. 19   Engr.   Perf. 13
C13 AP2 21fr blue, brn & grn   5.25 4.00
C14 AP2 33fr ultra, choc & bl grn   9.00 6.00
For No. C14 with surcharge, see No. C36.

Shell Diver — AP3

1962, Sept. 20   Unwmk.   Perf. 13
C16 AP3 100fr bl, grn & dk red brn   21.00 15.00

Telstar Issue
Common Design Type
1962, Dec. 5
C17 CD111 12fr dk pur, mar & bl   3.50 3.50

Sea Shell Type of Regular Issue
1963, Apr. 1   Engr.
Size: 26x47mm
C18 A5 50fr Harpa ventricosa   12.50 7.00

Javelin Thrower — AP4

1964, Oct. 10   Engr.   Perf. 13
C19 AP4 31fr emer, ver & vio brn   22.50 14.50
18th Olympic Games, Tokyo, Oct. 10-25.

ITU Issue
Common Design Type
1965, May 17   Unwmk.   Perf. 13
C20 CD120 50fr multicolored   21.00 15.00

Mata-Utu Wharf — AP5

1965, Nov. 26   Engr.   Perf. 13
C21 AP5 27fr brt bl, sl grn & red brn   5.25 3.50

French Satellite A-1 Issue
Common Design Type
Designs: 7fr, Diamant rocket and launching installations. 10fr, A-1 satellite.
1966, Jan. 17   Engr.   Perf. 13
C22 CD121 7fr crim, red & car lake   4.00 4.00
C23 CD121 10fr car lake, red & crim   4.50 4.50
a. Strip of 2, #C22-C23 + label   9.25 9.25

French Satellite D-1 Issue
Common Design Type
1966, June 2   Engr.   Perf. 13
C24 CD122 10fr lake, bl grn & red   3.50 3.50

WHO Headquarters, Geneva, and Emblem — AP6

1966, July 5   Photo.   Perf. 12½x13
C25 AP6 30fr org, maroon & bl   3.75 3.75
New WHO Headquarters, Geneva.

Girl and Boy Reading; UNESCO Emblem — AP7

1966, Nov. 4   Engr.   Perf. 13
C26 AP7 50fr green, org & choc   6.25 4.25
20th anniv. of UNESCO.

Athlete and Pattern AP8

Design: 38fr, Woman ballplayer and pattern.

1966, Dec. 8   Engr.   Perf. 13x12½
C27 AP8 32fr bl, dp car & blk   4.75 3.00
C28 AP8 38fr emer & brt pink   6.75 4.00
2nd South Pacific Games, Nouméa, 12/8-18.

Samuel Wallis' Ship and Coast of Wallis Island — AP9

1967, Dec. 16   Photo.   Perf. 13
C29 AP9 12fr multicolored   8.00 4.75
Bicentenary of the discovery of Wallis Island.

Concorde Issue
Common Design Type
1969, Apr. 17   Engr.   Perf. 13
C30 CD129 20fr black & plum   15.00 10.00

Man Climbing Coconut Palm — AP10

32fr, Horseback rider. 38fr, Men making wooden stools. 50fr, Spear fisherman & man holding basket with fish. 100fr, Women sorting coconuts.

1969, Apr. 30   Photo.   Perf. 13
C31 AP10 20fr multi   3.00 1.50
C32 AP10 32fr multi   5.25 2.00
C33 AP10 38fr multi   6.00 2.50
C34 AP10 50fr multi   9.25 4.50
C35 AP10 100fr multi   16.00 7.25
Nos. C31-C35 (5)   39.50 17.75

No. C14 Surcharged with New Value and Three Bars
1971   Engr.   Perf. 13
C36 AP2 21fr on 33fr multi   5.25 4.25

Pole Vault — AP11

1971, Oct. 25　Engr.　Perf. 13
C37 AP11 48fr shown　6.25 3.00
C38 AP11 54fr Archery　8.00 5.00
4th South Pacific Games, Papeete, French Polynesia, Sept. 8-19.

South Pacific Commission Headquarters, Noumea — AP12

1972, Feb. 5　Photo.　Perf. 13
C39 AP12 44fr blue & multi　7.25 4.25
South Pacific Commission, 25th anniv.

Round House and Festival Emblem — AP13

1972, May 15　Engr.　Perf. 13
C40 AP13 60fr dp car, grn & pur　9.25 5.00
South Pacific Festival of Arts, Fiji, May 6-20.

Canoe Type of Regular Issue

Design: 200fr, Outrigger sailing canoe race, and island woman.

1972, Oct. 16　Photo.　Perf. 13x12½
Size: 47½x28mm
C41 A9 200fr multicolored　45.00 25.00

La Pérouse and "La Boussole" — AP14

Explorers and their Ships: 28fr, Samuel Wallis and "Dolphin." 40fr, Dumont D'Urville and "Astrolabe." 72fr, Bougainville and "La Boudeuse."

1973, July 20　Engr.　Perf. 13
C42 AP14 22fr brn, slate & car　11.00 6.00
C43 AP14 28fr sl grn, dl red & bl　13.50 6.00
C44 AP14 40fr brn, ind & ultra　17.50 9.25
C45 AP14 72fr brown, bl & pur　25.00 12.50
　Nos. C42-C45 (4)　67.00 33.75

Charles de Gaulle — AP15

1973, Nov. 9　Engr.　Perf. 13
C46 AP15 107fr brn org & dk brn　18.00 11.00
Pres. Charles de Gaulle (1890-1970).

Red Jasmine AP16

Designs: Flowers from Wallis.

1973, Dec. 6　Photo.　Perf. 13
C47 AP16 12fr shown　1.90 1.40
C48 AP16 17fr Hibiscus tiliaceus　2.25 1.90
C49 AP16 19fr Phaeomeria magnifica　3.00 1.90
C50 AP16 21fr Hibiscus rosa sinensis　4.50 2.10
C51 AP16 23fr Allamanda cathartica　4.75 2.50
C52 AP16 27fr Barringtonia　5.50 3.00
C53 AP16 39fr Flowers in vase　8.75 6.25
　Nos. C47-C53 (7)　30.65 19.05

UPU Emblem and Symbolic Design — AP17

1974, Oct. 9　Engr.　Perf. 13
C54 AP17 51fr multicolored　8.00 4.75
Centenary of Universal Postal Union.

Holy Family, Primitive Painting AP18

1974, Dec. 9　Photo.　Perf. 13
C55 AP18 150fr multi　15.00 10.00
Christmas 1974.

Tapa Cloth — AP19

Tapa Cloth: 24fr, Village scene. 36fr, Fish & marine life. 80fr, Marine life, map of islands, village scene.

1975, Feb. 3　Photo.　Perf. 13
C56 AP19 3fr multicolored　.95 .65
C57 AP19 24fr multicolored　2.40 1.50
C58 AP19 36fr multicolored　4.00 2.25
C59 AP19 80fr multicolored　8.50 5.25
　Nos. C56-C59 (4)　15.85 9.65

DC-7 in Flight — AP20

Volleyball AP21

1975, Aug. 13　Engr.　Perf. 13
C60 AP20 100fr multicolored　7.25 5.50
First regular air service between Nouméa, New Caledonia, and Wallis.

1975, Nov. 10　Photo.　Perf. 13
C61 AP21 26fr shown　2.10 1.20
C62 AP21 44fr Soccer　3.00 1.90
C63 AP21 56fr Javelin　5.00 2.90
C64 AP21 105fr Spear fishing　10.50 6.50
　Nos. C61-C64 (4)　20.60 12.50
5th South Pacific Games, Guam, Aug. 1-10.

Lalolalo Lake, Wallis — AP22

Landscapes: 29fr, Vasavasa, Futuna. 41fr, Sigave Bay, Futuna. 68fr, Gahi Bay, Wallis.

1975, Dec. 1　Litho.　Perf. 13
C65 AP22 10fr grn & multi　1.40 .95
C66 AP22 29fr grn & multi　3.00 1.75
C67 AP22 41fr grn & multi　4.50 2.40
C68 AP22 68fr grn & multi　6.25 3.75
　Nos. C65-C68 (4)　15.15 8.85

Concorde, Eiffel Tower and Sugar Loaf Mountain — AP23

1976, Jan. 21　Engr.　Perf. 13
C69 AP23 250fr multi　27.50 20.00
1st commercial flight of supersonic jet Concorde from Paris to Rio, Jan. 21.
For overprint see No. C73.

Hammer Throw and Stadium — AP24

39fr, Diving, Stadium and maple leaf.

1976, Aug. 2　Engr.　Perf. 13
C70 AP24 31fr multi　3.00 2.25
C71 AP24 39fr multi　4.75 3.50
21st Olympic Games, Montreal, Canada, July 17-Aug. 1.

De Gaulle Memorial AP25

Photogravure and Embossed
1977, June 18　Perf. 13
C72 AP25 100fr gold & multi　10.50 7.50
5th anniversary of dedication of De Gaulle Memorial at Colombey-les-Deux-Eglises.

No. C69 Overprinted in Dark Brown:
"PARIS NEW-YORK / 22.11.77 / 1er VOL COMMERCIAL"
1977, Nov. 22　Engr.　Perf. 13
C73 AP23 250fr multicolored　27.50 17.50
Concorde, 1st commercial flight, Paris-NY.

Balistes Niger — AP26

Fish: 35fr, Amphiprion akindynos. 49fr, Pomacanthus imperator. 51fr, Zanclus cornutus.

1978, Jan. 31　Litho.　Perf. 13
C74 AP26 26fr multi　1.40 .75
C75 AP26 35fr multi　2.10 1.00
C76 AP26 49fr multi　2.40 1.25
C77 AP26 51fr multi　4.50 3.25
　Nos. C74-C77 (4)　10.40 6.25

Map of Wallis and Uvea Islands — AP27

300fr, Map of Futuna and Alofi Islands, horz.

1978, Mar. 7　Engr.
C78 AP27 300fr vio bl & grnsh bl　17.50 12.50
C79 AP27 500fr multi　23.00 19.00

Father Bataillon, Churches on Wallis
and Futuna Islands — AP28

72fr, Monsignor Pompallier, map of Wallis,
Futuna and Alofi Islands, outrigger canoe.

1978, Apr. 28   Litho.   *Perf. 13x12½*
C80 AP28 60fr multi   2.75 1.75
C81 AP28 72fr multi   3.50 2.00

First French missionaries on Wallis and
Futuna Islands.

ITU Emblem — AP29

1978, May 17   Litho.   *Perf. 13*
C82 AP29 66fr multi   3.50 2.25

10th World Telecommunications Day.

Nativity and Longhouse — AP30

1978, Dec. 4   Photo.   *Perf. 13*
C83 AP30 160fr multi   9.75 5.50

Christmas 1978.

Popes Paul VI, John Paul I, St.
Peter's, Rome — AP31

37fr, Pope Paul VI. 41fr, Pope John Paul I.

Perf. 12½x13, 13x12½
1979, Jan. 31   Litho.
C84 AP31 37fr multi, vert.   2.25 1.40
C85 AP31 41fr multi, vert.   2.40 1.75
C86 AP31 105fr multi   5.00 3.50
     Nos. C84-C86 (3)   9.65 6.65

In memory of Popes Paul VI and John Paul I.

Monoplane
of UTA
Airlines
AP32

68fr, Freighter Muana. 80fr, Hihifo Airport.

1979, Feb. 28   *Perf. 13x12½*
C87 AP32 46fr multi   1.50 .95
C88 AP32 68fr multi   2.00 1.50
C89 AP32 80fr multi   3.50 2.00
     Nos. C87-C89 (3)   7.00 4.45

Inter-Island transportation.
See Nos. 251-253.

France No. 67 and Eole Weather
Satellite — AP33

70fr, Hibiscus & stamp similar to #25. 90fr,
Rowland Hill & Penny Black. 100fr, Birds,
Kano School, Japan 17th cent. & Japan #9.

1979, May 7   Photo.   *Perf. 13*
C90 AP33 5fr multi   1.10 .65
C91 AP33 70fr multi, vert.   3.50 1.90
C92 AP33 90fr multi   4.50 2.50
C93 AP33 100fr multi   6.00 3.75
     Nos. C90-C93 (4)   15.10 8.80

Sir Rowland Hill (1795-1879), originator of
penny postage.

Cross of Lorraine and People — AP34

1979, June 18   Engr.   *Perf. 13*
C94 AP34 33fr multi   2.75 1.75

Map of
Islands,
Arms of
France
AP35

1979, July 19   Photo.   *Perf. 13*
C95 AP35 47fr multi   3.00 2.00

Visit of Pres. Valery Giscard d'Estaing of
France.

Capt. Cook, Ships and Island — AP36

1979, July 28
C96 AP36 130fr multi   7.25 4.25

Capt. James Cook (1728-1779).

Telecom Emblem, Satellite, Receiving
Station — AP37

1979, Sept. 20   Litho.   *Perf. 13*
C97 AP37 120fr multi   5.25 3.50

3rd World Telecommunications Exhibition,
Geneva, Sept. 20-26.

Virgin of
the
Crescent
Moon, by
Albrecht
Durer
AP38

1979, Dec. 17   Engr.   *Perf. 13*
C98 AP38 180fr red & blk   9.25 6.25

Christmas 1979. See No. C163.

Rotary International, 75th
Anniversary — AP39

1980, Feb. 29   Litho.   *Perf. 13*
C99 AP39 86fr multi   5.25 3.50

Rochambeau
and Troops, US
Flag,
1780 — AP40

1980, May 27   Engr.   *Perf. 13*
C100 AP40 102fr multi   5.25 3.50

Rochambeau's landing at Newport, RI
(American Revolution), bicentenary.

National Day, 10th
Anniversary — AP41

1980, July 15   Litho.   *Perf. 13*
C101 AP41 71fr multi   2.25 1.50

Transatlantic Airmail Flight, 50th
Anniversary — AP42

1980, Sept. 22   Engr.   *Perf. 13*
C102 AP42 122fr multi   4.75 3.50

Fleming,
Penicillin
Bacilli — AP43

1980, Oct. 20
C103 AP43 101fr multi   4.00 2.50

Alexander Fleming (1881-1955), discoverer
of penicillin, 25th death anniversary.

Charles De Gaulle, 10th Anniversary
of Death — AP44

1980, Nov. 9   Engr.   *Perf. 13*
C104 AP44 200fr sep & dk ol
                     grn   10.00 7.25

Virgin and Child with St. Catherine, by
Lorenzo Lotto — AP45

1980, Dec. 20   Litho.   *Perf. 13x12½*
C105 AP45 150fr multi   4.50 3.50

Christmas 1980.

Alan B. Shepard
and Spacecraft
AP46

20th Anniv. of Space Flight: 44fr, Yuri
Gagarin.

1981, May 11   Litho.   *Perf. 13*
C106 AP46 37fr multi   1.40 .95
C107 AP46 44fr multi   1.75 1.40

Vase of Flowers, by Paul Cezanne
(1839-1906) — AP47

Design: 135fr, Harlequin, by Pablo Picasso.

1981, Oct. 22   Litho.   Perf. 12½x13
C108 AP47 53fr multi   2.25 1.40
C109 AP47 135fr multi   4.50 3.00

Espana '82 World Cup
Soccer — AP48

1981-82   Engr.   Perf. 13
C110   AP48 120fr blk, brn & grn   3.75 2.25
C110A AP48 120fr lil, brn & ol
                grn   3.75 3.00
Issued: #C110, 11/16/81; #C110A,5/13/82.
For overprint see No. C115.

Christmas 1981 — AP49

1981, Dec. 21   Litho.   Perf. 12½
C111 AP49 180fr multi   6.75 4.25

Tapestry,
by Pilioho
Aloi
AP50

1982, Feb. 22   Litho.   Perf. 12½x13
C112 AP50 100fr multi   4.50 2.50

Boats at Collioure, by George Braque
(1882-1963) — AP51

1982, Apr. 13   Litho.   Perf. 12½x13
C113 AP51 300fr multi   9.25 5.25

Alberto Santos-Dumont (1873-1932),
Aviation Pioneer — AP52

1982, July 24
C114 AP52 95fr multi   3.75 2.40

No. C110 Overprinted with Winner's
Name in Blue
1982, Aug. 26   Engr.   Perf. 13
C115 AP48 120fr multi   4.00 3.00
Italy's victory in 1982 World Cup.

French Overseas Possessions Week,
Sept. 18-25 — AP53

1982, Sept. 17   Litho.
C116 AP53 105fr Beach   3.00 2.25

Day of the
Blind — AP54

1982, Oct. 18   Engr.
C117 AP54 130fr red & blue 3.75 2.00

Christmas
1982
AP55

Adoration of the Virgin, by Correggio.

1982, Dec. 20   Litho.   Perf. 12½x13
C118 AP55 170fr multi   4.50 3.00

Wind Surfing
(1984 Olympic
Event) — AP56

1983, Mar. 4   Litho.   Perf. 13
C119 AP56 270fr multi   6.50 4.75

World UPU Day — AP57

1983, Mar. 30   Litho.   Perf. 13
C120 AP57 100fr multi   2.75 1.75

Manned Flight
Bicentenary
AP58

1983, Apr. 25   Litho.   Perf. 13
C121 AP58 205fr Montgolfiere   5.75 4.00

Cat, 1926,
by Foujita
(d. 1968)
AP59

1983, May 20   Litho.   Perf. 12½x13
C122 AP59 102fr multi   3.75 2.00

Pre-Olympic
Year — AP60

1983, July 5   Engr.   Perf. 13
C123 AP60 250fr Javelin   6.50 4.50

Alfred Nobel (1833-1896) — AP61

1983, Aug. 1   Engr.   Perf. 13
C124 AP61 150fr multi   4.00 2.75

Nicephore Niepce (1765-1833),
Photography Pioneer — AP62

1983, Sept. 20   Engr.   Perf. 13
C125 AP62 75fr dk grn & rose
                vio   2.75 1.75

Raphael (1483-1520), 500th Birth
Anniv. — AP63

1983, Nov. 10   Litho.   Perf. 12½x13
C126 AP63 167fr The Triumph of
                Galatea   4.50 3.00

Pandanus
AP64

1983, Nov. 30   Litho.   Perf. 13
C127 AP64 137fr multi   4.00 3.00

Christmas
1983
AP65

1983, Dec. 22   Litho.   Perf. 12½x13
C128 AP65 200fr Sistine Madon-
                na, by
                Raphael   5.50 4.00

Steamer Commandant Bory — AP66

1984, Jan. 9   Perf. 13
C129 AP66 67fr multi   2.25 1.40

1984 Summer Olympics — AP67

1984, Feb. 3   Litho.   Perf. 13
C130 AP67 85fr Weight lifting   2.40 1.75

Frangipani
Blossoms
AP68

1984, Feb. 28   Perf. 12½
C131 AP68 130fr multi   4.00 2.25

Easter
1984
AP69

1984, Apr. 17   Litho.   Perf. 12½x13
C132 AP69 190fr Descent from
the Cross   5.00 3.25

Homage to
Jean
Cocteau
AP70

1984, June 30   Litho.   Perf. 13
C133 AP70 150fr Portrait   4.00 2.90

Soano Hoatau
Tiki Sculpture
AP71

Portrait of Alice,
by Modigliani
(1884-1920)
AP72

1984, July 26
C134 AP71 175fr multi   4.75 3.50

1984, Aug. 20
C135 AP72 140fr multi   3.75 2.50

Ausipex
'84 — AP73

1984, Sept. 21   Litho.   Perf. 12½x13
C136 AP73 180fr Pilioko Tapestry 4.00 3.00

Se-tenant with label showing exhibition
emblem.

Local Dances, by Jean
Michon — AP74

1984, Oct. 11   Photo.   Perf. 13
C137 AP74 110fr multi   3.50 2.00

Altar
AP75

1984, Nov. 5   Litho.   Perf. 13x12½
C138 AP75 52fr Mount Lulu
Chapel   1.50 1.10

Christmas 1984 — AP76

1984, Dec. 21   Litho.   Perf. 13x12½
C139 AP76 260fr Tropical Nativity 7.00 4.00

Pilioko Tapestry — AP77

1985, Apr. 3   Litho.   Perf. 13x12½
C140 AP77 500fr multi   13.50 6.50

The Post in
1926, by
Utrillo
AP78

1985, June 17   Litho.   Perf. 12½x13
C141 AP78 200fr multi   6.00 4.00

Wallis Island Pirogue — AP79

1985, Aug. 9   Perf. 13
C142 AP79 350fr multi   9.50 5.00

Ship Jacques
Cartier — AP80

1985, Oct. 2   Engr.   Perf. 13x13½
C143 AP80 51fr Prus bl, brt bl &
dk bl   1.75 1.10

Portrait of a
Young
Woman, by
Patrice
Nielly
AP81

1985, Oct. 28   Litho.   Perf. 12½x13
C144 AP81 245fr multi   6.75 4.50

Nativity, by
Jean
Michon
AP82

1985, Dec. 19   Litho.   Perf. 12½x13
C145 AP82 330fr multi   10.00 6.50

Halley's Comet — AP83

1986, Mar. 6   Litho.   Perf. 13
C146 AP83 100fr multi   3.25 1.75

Cure of Ars, Birth
Bicent. — AP84

1986, Mar. 28   Litho.   Perf. 12½x13
C147 AP84 200fr multi   5.75 4.25

French Overseas Territory Status, 25th
Anniv. — AP85

1986, July 29   Engr.   Perf. 13
C148 AP85 90fr Queen Amelia   2.75 2.25
C149 AP85 137fr July 30 Law,
Journal of the
Republic   4.50 3.25
a.   Strip of 2, #C148-C149 + label 7.25 6.00

Queen Amelia's request to France for protection, cent.

World Post Day — AP86

1986, Oct. 9   Litho.   Perf. 13
C150 AP86 270fr multi   7.25 4.00

Statue of Liberty,
Cent. — AP87

Poi Basilica, 1st
Anniv. — AP88

1986, Oct. 31   Engr.
C151 AP87 205fr multi   8.00 5.00

1987, Apr. 30   Litho.   Perf. 13
C152 AP88 230fr Fr. Chanel, basilica   7.00 3.75

Telstar Transmitting to Pleumeur-
Bodou, France — AP89

1987, May 17   Engr.   Perf. 13
C153 AP89 200fr gray, brt bl &
brn org   7.00 3.75

World Communications Day, 25th anniv. of
Telstar.

Piccard, Bathyscaphe Trieste and Stratospheric Balloon — AP90

1987, Aug. 21   Engr.   Perf. 13
C154 AP90 135fr brt ol grn, dk bl
& brt bl   4.50 3.00
Auguste Piccard (1884-1962), physicist.

Arrival of First Missionary, 150th Anniv. — AP91

Design: 260fr, Monsignor Bataillon's arrival in 1837, ship and the islands.

1987, Nov. 8   Engr.   Perf. 13
C155 AP91 260fr brt blue, blk &
blue grn   7.50 5.00

Christmas 1987 — AP92

1987, Dec. 15   Litho.   Perf. 13x12½
C156 AP92 300fr multi   8.00 5.00

Garros and Bleriot Aircraft — AP93

1988, Feb. 18   Engr.   Perf. 13
C157 AP93 600fr multi   19.00 10.50
Roland Garros (1888-1918), aviator and tennis player.

Self-portrait with Lace Cravat, by Maurice Quentin de La Tour (1704-88) AP94

1988, Apr. 8   Litho.
C158 AP94 500fr multi   15.00 9.50

World Telecommunications Day — AP95

1988, May 5   Litho.   Perf. 12½x13
C159 AP95 100fr multi   3.00 1.90

South Pacific Episcopal Conference — AP96

1988, June 1   Litho.   Perf. 13
C160 AP96 90fr Map, bishop   2.75 1.75

Christmas — AP97

Unwmk.
1988, Dec. 15   Litho.   Perf. 13
C161 AP97 400fr multi   13.00 7.00

Royal Throne — AP98

1989, Mar. 11
C162 AP98 700fr multi   19.00 10.50

The Virgin of the Crescent Moon Type of 1979

1989, Dec. 21   Engr.   Perf. 13½x13
C163 AP38 800fr plum   22.00 13.00

Christmas 1989.

Clement Ader (1841-1926), Aviation Pioneer — AP100

1990, June 9   Engr.   Perf. 13
C164 AP100 56fr multicolored   2.00 1.40
First anniversary of Wallis-Tahiti air link.

Gen. Charles de Gaulle (1890-1979) — AP101

1990, Nov. 22   Perf. 12½x13
C165 AP101 1000fr multi   27.50 19.00

Father Louis Marie Chanel, 150th Death Anniv. — AP102

1991, Apr. 28   Litho.   Perf. 13
C166 AP102 235fr multicolored   6.50 4.25

French Open Tennis Championships, Cent. — AP103

Illustration reduced.

1991, May 24   Engr.   Perf. 13x12½
C167 AP103 250fr blk, grn & org   8.00 5.50

Wolfgang Amadeus Mozart, Death Bicent. AP104

1991, Sept. 23   Engr.   Perf. 13
C168 AP104 500fr multicolored   15.00 9.50

World Columbian Stamp Expo '92, Chicago — AP105

1992, May 22   Litho.   Perf. 13x12½
C169 AP105 100fr multicolored   3.00 2.25

1992, July 15   Perf. 13
C170 AP105 800fr multicolored   22.00 13.00
Genoa '92.

First French Republic, Bicent. — AP106

1992, Aug. 17   Engr.   Perf. 13
C171 AP106 350fr blk, bl & red   9.75 7.50

Louvre Museum, Bicent. — AP107

1993, Apr. 12   Engr.   Perf. 13
C172 AP107 315fr blue, dk blue
& red   9.00 5.50

Nicolaus Copernicus, Heliocentric Solar System — AP108

1993, May 7   Engr.   Perf. 13
C173 AP108 600fr multicolored   16.00 9.25
Polska '93.

Second Year of First French Republic, Bicent. — AP109

1993, Sept. 22   Engr.   Perf. 13
C174 AP109 400fr bl, blk & red   11.00 7.50

Wallis Island Landscape — AP110

1994, Jan. 26   Litho.   Perf. 13
C175 AP110 400fr multicolored   11.00 7.50

Hong Kong '94 — AP111

1994, Feb. 18   Litho.   Perf. 14x13½
C176 AP111 700fr multicolored   19.00 12.00

South Pacific Geography
Day — AP112

1994, May 4   Litho.   *Perf. 13*
C177 AP112 85fr multicolored   2.50 1.75
See New Caledonia No. C259.

European Stamp
Salon,
Paris — AP113

1994, Sept. 22   Litho.   *Perf. 13*
C178 AP113 300fr multicolored   9.00 5.00

Antoine de Saint-Exupery (1900-44),
Aviator, Author — AP114

1994, Oct. 27   Engr.   *Perf. 13*
C179 AP114 800fr multicolored   22.00 15.00

Christmas
AP115

1994, Dec. 15   Litho.   *Perf. 13*
C180 AP115 150fr multicolored   4.00 3.00

Louis Pasteur (1822-95) — AP116

1995, Mar. 25   Litho.   *Perf. 13*
C181 AP116 350fr multicolored   9.50 4.75

AP117

AP118

1995, Apr. 19   *Perf. 13½x13*
C182 AP117 115fr multicolored   3.50 1.90
University Teacher's Training Institute of the
Pacific. See French Polynesia No. 656.

1995, May 17   *Perf. 13*
C183 AP118 200fr Painting of
Cocoa Nuts   5.50 3.00

Intl. Youth Year, 10th Anniv. — AP119

1995, July 25   Litho.   *Perf. 13*
C184 AP119 450fr multicolored   12.50 6.25

Singapore '95 — AP120

1995, Aug. 24   Litho.   *Perf. 13*
C185 AP120 500fr multicolored   13.50 6.75

Motion Pictures, Cent. — AP121

Lumiere Brothers, film strip. Illustration
reduced.

1995, Sept. 19
C186 AP121 600fr multicolored   16.00 8.50

Charles de Gaulle (1890-
1970) — AP122

1995, Nov. 14   Engr.   *Perf. 13*
C187 AP122 315fr multicolored   8.50 5.50

7th Va'a (Outrigger Canoe) World
Championship, Noumea, New
Caledonia — AP123

1996, Apr. 24   Litho.   *Perf. 13*
C188 AP123 240fr multicolored   6.50 4.25

Sisia
College — AP124

1996, May 22   Litho.   *Perf. 13½x13*
C189 AP124 235fr multicolored   6.50 4.25

Radio, Cent. — AP125

1996, July 25   Engr.   *Perf. 13*
C190 AP125 550fr multicolored   15.00 9.25

Modern Olympic Games,
Cent. — AP126

1996, Aug. 20   Engr.   *Perf. 13*
C191 AP126 1000fr blk & dk bl   27.50 17.00

50th
Autumn
Stamp
Salon
AP127

1996, Oct. 24   Litho.   *Perf. 13*
C192 AP127 175fr multicolored   4.75 3.00

Campaign
to Control
Alcoholism
AP128

1996, Nov. 19   *Perf. 13x13½*
C193 AP128 260fr multicolored   7.00 4.25

Natl. Center for
Scientific
Research
AP129

1997, Mar. 14   Litho.   *Perf. 13*
C194 AP129 400fr Lapita pot-
tery   11.00 5.50

HIHIFO Air Service — AP130

1997, July 8   Litho.   *Perf. 13*
C195 AP130 130fr multicolored   3.25 2.10

Sundown Over
the
Lagoon — AP131

1997, Sept. 22   Litho.   *Perf. 13½x13*
C196 AP131 300fr multicolored   8.00 4.25

51st Autumn Stamp Salon — AP132

350fr, #C194, 492, 497, 486, C184, C185,
475, C192, C188, 464, 493.
1000fr, Hemispheres, #486, 475, 464,
C185, C175, 493, C184, 492, C192, 497,
C188, C194, Winged Victory of Samothrace.

1997, Nov. 6   Litho.   *Perf. 13*
C197 AP132 350fr multi   9.50 4.75
      Imperf
C198 AP132 1000fr multi   27.50 24.00

Marshal Jacques Leclerc (1902-
47) — AP133

1997, Nov. 28   Litho.   *Perf. 13*
C199 AP133 800fr multicolored   22.00 11.50

Alphonse Daudet (1840-97), Writer — AP134

1997, Dec. 16   Litho.   Perf. 13
C200 AP134 710fr multi   19.00 10.00

Alofi Beach — AP135

1998, Apr. 21   Litho.   Perf. 13
C201 AP135 315fr multicolored   8.50 4.25

Cricket
AP136

1998, Sept. 22 Litho. Perf. 13x13½
C202 AP136 106fr multicolored   2.90 1.40

Paul Gauguin (1848-1903) — AP137

1998, Oct. 27   Litho.   Perf. 13
C203 AP137 700fr multicolored   19.00 9.25

Garden of Happiness — AP138

1998, Nov. 17
C204 AP138 460fr multicolored   12.50 7.25

Polynesian Dancing
AP139

1998, Dec. 15   Litho.   Perf. 13
C205 AP139 250fr multicolored   6.75 3.50

Kava Porter
AP140

1999, Jan. 18
C206 AP140 600fr multicolored   16.00 8.00

Shells
AP141

95fr, Epitonium scalare. 100fr, Cassis cornuta. 110fr, Charonia tritonis. 115fr, Lambis lambis.

1999, Feb. 15
C207 AP141 95fr multi, vert.   2.50 1.75
C208 AP141 100fr multi, vert.   2.75 1.75
C209 AP141 110fr multi   3.00 1.75
C210 AP141 115fr multi   3.10 1.75
   Nos. C207-C210 (4)   11.35 7.00

Finemui — AP142

Illustration reduced.

1999, Apr. 19   Engr.   Perf. 12¾
C211 AP142 900fr multicolored   24.00 11.50

Birds of Nuku Fotu
AP143

a, 10fr, Airgrettes. b, 20fr, Audubon's. c, 26fr, Fregates. d, 54fr, Paille en queue.

1999, June 14 Litho. Perf. 13x13¾
C212 AP143 Strip of 4, #a.-d.   3.00 2.50

Wind Song — AP144

1999, Nov. 22   Engr.   Perf. 13
C213 AP144 325fr multi   8.75 4.50

Sunrise Over a Lagoon
AP145

1999, Dec. 20   Litho.
C214 AP145 500fr multi   13.50 7.50

First Transport Flight to Futuna, 30th Anniv. — AP146

2000, Aug. 24   Litho.   Perf. 13
C215 AP146 350fr multi   9.50 4.50

AIR POST SEMI-POSTAL STAMPS

New Caledonia Nos. CB2-CB3 overprinted "ILES WALLIS ET FUTUNA"

1942, June 22   Engr.   Perf. 13
CB1 SPAP1 1.50fr + 3.50fr green 2.25
CB2 SPAP1   2fr + 6fr yellow
               brown   2.25

Native children's welfare fund.
Nos. CB1-CB2 were issued by the Vichy government in France, but were not placed on sale in Wallis & Futuna.

Colonial Education Fund
New Caledonia No. CB4 Common Design Type overprinted "ILES WALLIS ET FUTUNA"

1942, June 22
CB3 CD86a 1.20fr + 1.80fr blue
               & red   2.25

No. CB3 was issued by the Vichy government in France, but was not placed on sale in Wallis & Futuna.

POSTAGE DUE STAMPS

Postage Due Stamps of New Caledonia, 1906, Overprinted in Black or Red

1920		**Unwmk.**		**Perf. 13½x14**
J1	D2	5c ultra, *azure*	1.00	1.00
J2	D2	10c brn, *buff*	1.10	1.10
J3	D2	15c grn, *grnsh*	1.10	1.10
J4	D2	20c blk, *yel* (R)	1.50	1.50
a.		Double overprint	200.00	
J5	D2	30c carmine rose	1.50	1.50
J6	D2	50c ultra, *straw*	2.40	2.40
J7	D2	60c olive, *azure*	2.90	2.90
a.		Double overprint	200.00	
J8	D2	1fr grn, *cream*	3.75	3.75
		Nos. J1-J8 (8)	15.25	15.25

Type of 1920 Issue Surcharged

1927				
J9	D2	2fr on 1fr brt vio	17.50	17.50
J10	D2	3fr on 1fr org brn	17.50	17.50

Postage Due Stamps of New Caledonia, 1928, Overprinted as in 1920

1930				
J11	D3	2c sl bl & dp brn	.25	.25
J12	D3	4c brn red & bl grn	.25	.25
J13	D3	5c red org & bl blk	.25	.25
J14	D3	10c mag & Prus bl	.25	.25
J15	D3	15c dl grn & scar	.35	.35
J16	D3	20c maroon & ol grn	.75	.75
J17	D3	25c bis brn & sl bl	.75	.75
J18	D3	30c bl grn & ol grn	1.40	1.40
J19	D3	50c lt brn & dk red	.85	.85
J20	D3	60c mag & brt rose	1.40	1.40
J21	D3	1fr dl bl & Prus grn	1.40	1.40
J22	D3	2fr dk red & ol grn	1.40	1.40
J23	D3	3fr vio & brn	1.40	1.40
		Nos. J11-J23 (13)	10.70	10.70

Postage Due Stamps of 1930 with Additional Overprint in Black

1943				
J24	D3	2c sl bl & dp brn	37.50	37.50
J25	D3	4c brn red & bl grn	37.50	37.50
J26	D3	5c red org & bl blk	37.50	37.50
J27	D3	10c mag & Prus bl	37.50	37.50
J28	D3	15c dl grn & scar	40.00	40.00
J29	D3	20c mar & ol grn	40.00	40.00
J30	D3	25c bis brn & sl bl	40.00	40.00
J31	D3	30c bl grn & ol grn	40.00	40.00
J32	D3	50c lt brn & dk red	40.00	40.00
J33	D3	60c mag & brt rose	42.50	42.50
J34	D3	1fr dl bl & Prus grn	42.50	42.50
J35	D3	2fr dk red & ol grn	42.50	42.50
J36	D3	3fr violet & brn	42.50	42.50
		Nos. J24-J36 (13)	520.00	520.00

Catalogue values for unused stamps in this section, from this point to the end of the section, are for Never Hinged items.

Thalassoma Lunare — D1

Fish: 1fr, Zanclus cornutus, vert. 5fr, Amphirion percula.

Perf. 13x13½
1963, Apr. 1   Typo.   Unwmk.
J37 D1 1fr yel org, bl & blk   .95   .95
J38 D1 3fr red, grnsh bl & grn 1.90   *2.40*
J39 D1 5fr org, bluish grn & blk 3.00 *3.50*
   Nos. J37-J39 (3)   5.85   6.85

WESTERN UKRAINE

'wes-tərn yü-'krān

LOCATION — In Eastern Central Europe

GOVT. — A former short-lived independent State

A provisional government was established in 1918 in the eastern part of Austria-Hungary but the area later came under Polish administration.

100 Shahiv (Sotykiv) = 1 Hryvnia
100 Heller = 1 Krone

Forgeries of almost all Western Ukraine stamps are plentiful. Particularly dangerous forgeries have been noted for the Kolomyia Issue and for the First and Second Stanyslaviv Issues.

Lviv Issue

Austria Nos. 145-146, 148, 169 Overprinted

Nos. 1-4A are handstamped with an octagonal overprint that reads "ZAKHIDNO UKR. NARODNA REPUBLYKA" ("Western Ukr National Republic"), framing the image of a rearing crowned lion.

1918, Nov. 20

1	A37	3h bright violet		55.00	425.00
a.		Inverted overprint		150.00	
2	A37	5h light green		50.00	325.00
a.		Inverted overprint		150.00	
3	A37	10h magenta		50.00	325.00
a.		Inverted overprint		150.00	
4	A42	20h dark green		35.00	350.00
a.		Inverted overprint		150.00	
4A	A42	20h light green		240.00	900.00
		Nos. 1-4A (5)		430.00	2,325.

This issue was in circulation for only two days before Lviv was captured by the Poles on Nov. 22. No examples of Nos. 1-4A used in Lviv are known.

The Western Ukrainian National Republic (ZUNR) government evacuated to the city of Ternopil, which became the provisional capital. ZUNR postal operations were set up in other Western Ukrainian cities, but the Lviv Issue was used in Stanyslaviv (earliest known cancellation date, Dec. 8), Khodoriv and Kolomyia.

Nos. 1-4 exist in pairs with both normal and inverted overprints. Value $325.

Overprints in other colors (green, red and violet) are known, but these are probably proofs. Violet-black overprints are likely transitional color impressions.

Kolomyia Issue

Austria Nos. 168, 145, 147, 149 Surcharged

Kolomyia is the main town of the Pokutia region of southwestern Ukraine. Cut off from ZUNR postal officials by wartime conditions and in urgent need of basic value stamps, the Kolomyia postmaster obtained permission from the District Military Command to surcharge remaining Austrian postage stamps to either 5 or 10 sotyks, the equivalent of 5 or 10 heller. These stamps were produced on Dec. 10, under very strict security, by preparing two distinct plates (one for each value) that overprinted 25 stamps at a time (5x5 quarter sections of the Austrian 100-stamp panes). The stamps were placed on sale two days later.

1918, Dec. 12   Unwmk.   Perf. 12½

5	A42	5sot on 15h dl red		80.00	120.00
a.		Inverted overprint		600.00	725.00
b.		Double overprint		600.00	725.00

6	A37	10sot on 3h vio		87.50	120.00
7	A37	10sot on 6h dp org		1,450.	1,250.
8	A37	10sot on 12h lt bl		1,650.	1,500.
		Nos. 5-8 (4)		3,267.	2,990.

10 sotyk on 15 heller values are essays; only six were produced.

All inverted surcharges on Nos. 6-8 are forgeries. Double surcharges are forgeries.

First Stanyslaviv Issue

Austrian Stamps of 1916-18 Surcharged in Shahiv (shown) and Hryvnia Currency

At the end of December, 1918, the national government again moved, this time to the city of Stanyslaviv (present-day Ivano-Frankivsk). A shortage of qualified postal personnel resulted in a considerable delay in the creation of new ZUNR postage stamps. In the interim, remaining unoverprinted Austrian stamps were used. Finally, on March 18, 1919, 20 different available Austrian definitive stamps were typograph surcharged at the Weidenfeld Printing Shop in Stanyslaviv.

1919, Mar. 18

9	A37	3sh on 3h bright violet		16.50	22.50
10	A37	5sh on 5h light green		16.50	22.50
11	A37	6sh on 6h deep orange		32.50	55.00
12	A37	10sh on 10h mag		27.50	37.50
13	A37	12sh on 12h lt blue		27.50	37.50
a.		Double overprint		300.00	425.00
b.		Double overprint, one on reverse		82.50	210.00
14	A42	15sh on 15h dull red		27.50	37.50
15	A42	20sh on 20h deep green		27.50	37.50
16	A42	30sh on 30h dull violet		175.00	275.00
17	A39	40sh on 40h olive green		27.50	37.50
18	A39	50sh on 50h dark green		27.50	37.50
19	A39	60sh on 60h deep blue		27.50	37.50
20	A39	80sh on 80h org brn		27.50	37.50
a.		Inverted overprint		300.00	425.00
21	A39	1hr on 1k car, yel		37.50	45.00
22	A40	2hr on 2k lt blue		37.50	50.00
23	A40	3hr on 3k claret (on #161)		3,000.	3,250.
24	A40	3hr on 3k car rose (on #165)		82.50	82.50
25	A40	3hr on 3k car rose (on #173)		65.00	65.00
26	A40	4hr on 4k dk grn (on #162)		300.00	350.00
27	A40	4hr on 4k yel grn (on #166)		50.00	55.00
28	A40	10hr on 10k deep violet		650.00	900.00
a.		Double overprint		3,000.	3,500.
		Nos. 9-28 (20)		4,683.	5,472.

The 25sh on 25h, type A42, in both light and dull blue shades, never received this overprint. All such specimens are fantasies.

Second Stanyslaviv Issue

The overprinting of a second issue of postage stamps in Stanyslaviv was undertaken in early May. Stamps from several different Austrian stamp series were utilized to create four distinct sets. Most of the stamps available were Austrian postage due, charity or field post stamps.

Same Surcharge on Postage Due Stamps of Bosnia, 1904, but without Asterisks

1919, May 5

29	D1	1sh on 1h blk, red & yel		32.50	32.50
a.		Inverted overprint		65.00	65.00
b.		Double overprint		90.00	90.00
30	D1	2sh on 2h blk, red & yel		12.50	15.00
a.		Inverted overprint		85.00	150.00
31	D1	3sh on 3h blk, red & yel		12.50	15.00
a.		Inverted overprint		22.50	35.00
32	D1	4sh on 4h blk, red & yel		100.00	100.00
a.		Inverted overprint		175.00	175.00
b.		Double overprint		300.00	300.00
33	D1	5sh on 5h blk, red & yel		3,250.	3,500.
34	D1	6sh on 6h blk, red & yel		250.00	300.00
a.		Inverted overprint		600.00	600.00
b.		Double overprint		475.00	500.00
35	D1	7sh on 7h blk, red & yel		22.50	27.50
a.		Inverted overprint		37.50	42.50
36	D1	8sh on 8h blk, red & yel		17.00	22.50
a.		Inverted overprint		50.00	60.00
b.		Vertical overprint		750.00	950.00
c.		As "b," double overprint		950.00	1,100.
37	D1	10sh on 10h blk, red & yel		1,100.	1,400.
38	D1	15sh on 15h blk, red & yel		425.00	425.00
a.		Inverted overprint		550.00	600.00
39	D1	20sh on 20h blk, red & yel		6,250.	
a.		Double overprint		7,750.	17,000.
40	D1	50sh on 50h blk, red & yel		210.00	210.00
a.		Inverted overprint		350.00	300.00

Nos. 29-40 were created by overprinting Bosnian 1904 postage due stamps, which had been brought to Stanyslaviv by a Ukrainian military officer returning from the Serbian front. The same printing cliché was used as for the First Stanyslaviv Issue, but the asterisk obliterators were removed.

Most of the overprinting was made using 50-stamp panes (half of a sheet). After one half of the pane (25 positions) was overprinted, it would apparently be turned over and its second half overprinted with the same 25-position block, but as an inverted impression. After overprinting, the pane was torn into two equal 25-stamp halves.

Two types of surcharge on No. 61: Shahiv in singular (wara) and in plural (warib). Value the same.

Same Surcharge on Austrian Military Semipostal Stamps of 1918
Perf. 12½x13

41	MSP7	10sh on 10h gray green		120.00	130.00
a.		Inverted overprint		120.00	140.00
b.		Double overprint		175.00	210.00
42	MSP8	20sh on 20h magenta		110.00	100.00
a.		Inverted overprint		95.00	120.00
b.		Double overprint		140.00	175.00
43	MSP7	45sh on 45h blue		85.00	95.00
a.		Inverted overprint		72.50	100.00

Nos. 41-43 were printed in the same manner as Nos. 29-40.

Same Surcharge on Austrian Military Stamps of 1917
Perf. 12½

44	M3	1sh on 1h grnsh blue		950.00	950.00
45	M3	2sh on 2h red org		100.00	100.00
a.		Inverted overprint		125.00	125.00
b.		Double overprint		210.00	210.00
46	M3	3sh on 3h olive gray		175.00	190.00
a.		Inverted overprint		350.00	400.00
47	M3	5sh on 5h olive grn		275.00	275.00
48	M3	6sh on 6h violet		150.00	175.00
49	M3	10sh on 10h org brn		900.00	1,000.
50	M3	12sh on 12h blue		550.00	600.00
a.		Inverted overprint		650.00	725.00
51	M3	15sh on 15h brt rose		500.00	600.00
a.		Inverted overprint		625.00	725.00
52	M3	20sh on 20h red brn		16.50	20.00
a.		Inverted overprint		82.50	140.00
b.		Double overprint		47.50	55.00
53	M3	25sh on 25h ultra		3,250.	3,900.
54	M3	30sh on 30h slate		1,000.	1,200.
55	M3	40sh on 40h olive bis		850.00	850.00
56	M3	50sh on 50h deep green		9.00	9.00
a.		Inverted overprint		16.50	16.50
b.		Double overprint		55.00	55.00
57	M3	60sh on 60h car rose		950.00	950.00
58	M3	80sh on 80h dull blue		47.50	47.50
a.		Inverted overprint		80.00	85.00
59	M3	90sh on 90h dk vio		950.00	1,000.
60	M4	2hr on 2k rose, straw		13.00	17.50
a.		Inverted overprint		27.50	35.00
b.		Imperforate		3,000.	

61	M4	3hr on 3k blue, grn		22.50	25.00
a.		Inverted overprint		27.50	30.00
b.		Double overprint		60.00	65.00
62	M4	4hr on 4k rose, grn		22.50	25.00
a.		Inverted overprint		26.00	30.00
b.		Double overprint		60.00	65.00
63	M4	10hr on 10k dl violet, gray			

Two examples of No. 63 were printed, and neither was ever postally used. The "used" specimen was cut from a document prepared by the Western Ukrainian economic bureau (Ekonomat) to display the stamps that made up the First, Second and Third Stanyslaviv Issues. The specimen stamps on this document were tied with a double-ring bureau cancel that somewhat resembles a regular double-ring postal cancellation.

About half of this issue, where several sheets were available for printing, was overprinted in the manner of Nos. 29-43.

Same Surcharge on Austrian Stamps of 1916-18, but with two upper bars

64	A38	15sh on 36h vio (on #J61)		350.00	450.00
a.		Double overprint		450.00	500.00
65	A38	50sh on 42h choc (on #J63)		5,000.	5,500.
66	A37	3sh on 3h brt violet (on #145)		190.00	190.00
67	A37	5sh on 5h lt green (on #146)		190.00	190.00
a.		Inverted overprint		290.00	290.00
68	A37	6sh on 6h deep org (on #147)		725.00	725.00
69	A37	10sh on 10h magenta (on #148)		210.00	210.00
a.		Inverted overprint		250.00	250.00
70	A37	12sh on 12h lt blue (on #149)		425.00	425.00
71	A38	15sh on 15h rose red (on #150) (on #149)		190.00	190.00
a.		Inverted overprint		225.00	225.00
72	A42	15sh on 15h dull red (on #168)		210.00	210.00
73	A42	30sh on 30h dull violet (on #171)		190.00	190.00
a.		Double overprint		350.00	350.00
74	A39	40sh on 40h ol grn (on #154)		300.00	300.00
75	M3	50sh on 50h dp grn (on #M61)		475.00	475.00

The two bars in the surcharge were originally created to obliterate the "PORTO" on Nos. 64 and 65 but were subsequently retained for Nos. 66-75.

Third Stanyslaviv Issue

Austrian Stamps of 1916-18 Overprinted

1919, May

76	A37	3h brt violet		.50	1.00
77	A37	5h light green		.50	1.00
78	A37	6h deep orange		.50	1.00
79	A37	10h magenta		.50	1.00
80	A37	12h light blue		.50	1.00
81	A42	15h dull red		.50	1.00
82	A42	20h deep green		.50	1.00
83	A42	25h blue		.50	1.00
84	A42	30h dull vio		.50	1.00
85	A39	40h olive green		.75	1.25
86	A39	50h dark green		.75	1.25
87	A39	60h deep blue		.75	1.25
88	A39	80h orange brn		1.00	1.25
89	A39	90h red violet		1.00	1.60
90	A39	1k car, yel		1.25	4.00
91	A40	2k light blue		2.00	6.00
92	A40	3k carmine rose		2.50	7.50
93	A40	4k yellow grn		12.00	16.00
94	A40	10k deep violet		16.00	50.00
		Nos. 76-94 (19)		42.50	99.10

Issued: 3h-10h, 15h, 25h-40h, 60h-1k, 5/8; balance of set, 5/13.

A definitive set for Western Ukraine was ordered from the Austrian State Printing Office in March, 1919. Because of the time involved in designing and printing these stamps, Nos. 76-94 were overprinted in Vienna as a provisional issue and were delivered in two shipments. Because travel into and out of Stanyslaviv was becoming more difficult as the month wore on, it was not known whether or not the second shipment, which included the higher values, would arrive. Because of this, the Fourth Stanyslaviv Issue, Nos. 95-103, were overprinted locally.

Fourth Stanislaviv Issue

Black Surcharge on Austrian Military Stamps of 1917-18.

1919, May

95	A2	2hr on 2k rose, straw	13.00	*15.00*
96	A2	3hr on 2k rose, straw	13.00	*16.00*
97	A2	3hr on 3k grn, blue	90.00	*175.00*
a.		5" instead of "3" at left in overprint	—	
98	A2	4hr on 2k rose, straw	13.00	*16.00*
99	A2	4hr on 4k rose, grn	1,300.	*1,900.*
100	A2	5hr on 2k rose, straw	13.00	*16.00*
a.		Inverted surcharge	300.00	
101	A2	10hr on 50h dp grn (Austria type M3)	16.00	*40.00*
a.		Double surcharge	175.00	

Same Surcharge on Austrian Postage Due Stamps of 1916, but without Rosettes and Numerals

102	D5	1hr ultra	140.00	*210.00*
103	D5	5hr ultra	1,400.	*2,100.*

REGISTRATION STAMPS

Kolomyia Issue

RS1

Without Gum

1918-19 Unwmk. Typeset *Imperf.*

F1	RS1	30sot black, *rose*	210.00	175.00
F2	RS1	50sot black, *rose* ('19)	120.00	*150.00*
a.		50sot black, *deep rose* ('19)	120.00	150.00

No. F1 was printed on Dec. 10 and issued Dec. 12, 1918, along with the regular Kolomyia Issue (Nos. 5-8). On Dec. 19, the ZUNR government approved an increase in the registered letter rate to 50 sotyks, effective January 1, 1919. Because of communication disruptions, the Kolomyia post office did not learn of this decree until about January 7, when it ordered new values in the higher denomination (No. F2). F1 continued to be used, usually in combination with 20h of Austrian stamps, until supplies were exhausted, at which point No. F2 was put into use. A second printing of the 50sot value, on darker rose paper, was made in late March.

Nos. F1-F2a were typographed in vertical panes of five stamps by the Wilhelm Brauner Print Ship in Kolomyia.

Forgeries exist.

OCCUPATION STAMPS

Romanian Occupation of Pokutia

Only the stamps listed below were officially created. Soon after the Romanian occupation ended on Aug. 20, 1919, the C.M.T. handstamps fell into the hands of speculators, and some 37 other Austrian stamps were overprinted. None of these privately-created stamps are known on authentic covers.

Austrian Stamps Surcharged in Dark Violet Blue

1919, June 14   Unwmk.   Perf. 12½

On Stamps of 1916-18

N1	A37	40h on 5h lt grn	4.50	*5.50*
N2	A42	60h on 15h dl red	5.50	*6.50*
N3	A42	60h on 20h dp grn	2.25	*3.25*
a.		Inverted overprint	3,000.	
b.		Double overprint	25.00	
N4	A42	60h on 25h blue	12.00	*13.00*
a.		Inverted overprint	60.00	
b.		Double overprint	82.50	
N5	A42	60h on 30h dl vio	14.00	*15.00*
N6	A39	1k 20h on 50h dk grn	5.50	*6.50*
N7	A39	1k 20h on 60h dp bl	10.00	*12.00*
N8	A39	1k 20h on 1k car, yel	19.00	*21.00*

On Austrian Postage Due Stamps of 1910-1917

N9	D4	40h on 5h rose red	21.00	*22.50*
N10	D3	1k 20h on 25h carmine	175.00	*350.00*
N11	D4	1k 20h on 25h rose red	175.00	*350.00*
N12	D4	1k 20h on 30h rose red	1,400.	*1,400.*
N13	A38	1k 20h on 50h on 42h choc	1,500.	*1,500.*

First Vienna Issue, May 1919: Lithographed at the Austrian State Printing Office on unwatermarked white paper. Inscribed "Ukrainska Narodnia Respublika Z.O." ("Ukrainian National Republic W(estern) P(rovince)"). Design incorporates the heraldic arms of Ukraine (trident), Kiev (Archangel Michael) and Lviv (lion rampant). 10, 20 and 50 sotyk values imperf; 1 and 10 krone values perf 11½. Not issued. Value, set of 5, $6. Also exists on cream-colored paper.

Arms of Kiev   Arms of Ukraine

Arms of Lviv

Second Vienna Issue, May 1919: Lithographed at the Austrian State Printing Office on unwatermarked white paper. Inscribed "Ukrainska Narodnia Republyka Zakhidnia Oblast" ("Ukrainian National Republic Western Province"). Set of 12 values (four of each design), perf 11½ or imperf. Not issued. Value, set of 12: perf $350; imperf $550.

WEST IRIAN

(Irian Barat)

(West New Guinea)

Stamps formerly listed under West Irian now appear in Volume 1, following United Nations, and Volume 3, following Indonesia.

YEMEN

'ye-mən

LOCATION — Arabian Peninsula, south of Saudi Arabia and bordering on the Red Sea
GOVT. — Republic
AREA — 204,000 sq. mi. (est.)
POP. — 16,942,230 (1999 est.)
CAPITAL — Sana'a (San'a)

40 Bogaches = 1 Imadi
40 Bogaches = 1 Riyal (1962)
100 Fils = 1 Riyal (1978)

The Yemen Arab Republic and the People's Republic of Yemen planned a 30-month unification process scheduled for completion by November 1992. While government ministries merged, both currencies remained valid.

Catalogue values for unused stamps in this country are for Never Hinged items, beginning with Scott 44 in the regular postage section, Scott C1 in the airpost section.

Watermarks

Wmk. 127 — Quatrefoils

Wmk. 258 — Arabic Characters and Y G Multiple

Wmk. 277 — Winged Wheel

For Domestic Postage

A1

Crossed Daggers and Arabic Inscriptions — A2

1926   Unwmk.   Typo.   Imperf.
Laid Paper
Without Gum

1	A1	2½b black	40.00	40.00
2	A1	2½b black, *orange*	40.00	40.00
3	A2	5b black	40.00	40.00
		Nos. 1-3 (3)	120.00	120.00

No. 2 is known rouletted 7½ or 9.
Type A1 differs from A2 primarily in the inscription in the left dagger blade.
All come on wove paper.

For Foreign and Domestic Postage

Arabic Inscriptions
A3   A4

1930-31   Wmk. 127   Perf. 14

7	A3	½b orange ('31)	.30	.20
8	A3	1b green	.40	.30
9	A3	1b yellow grn ('31)	.35	.25
10	A3	2b olive grn	.40	.35
11	A3	2b olive brn ('31)	.35	.25
12	A3	3b dull vio ('31)	.40	.35
13	A3	4b red	.60	.50
14	A3	4b deep rose ('31)	.50	.40
15	A3	5b slate gray ('31)	.90	.50
16	A4	6b dull blue	1.25	1.00
17	A4	6b dp ultra ('31)	1.00	.75
18	A4	8b lilac rose ('31)	1.40	1.00
19	A4	10b lt brown	2.00	1.40
20	A4	10b brn org ('31)	1.75	1.00
21	A4	20b yel grn ('31)	4.50	2.50
22	A4	1i red brn & lt bl	8.00	6.00
23	A4	1i lil rose & yel grn ('31)	8.00	6.00
		Nos. 7-23 (17)	32.10	22.75

Some values exist imperforate.
For surcharges and overprints see Nos. 30, 59-62, 166-167, 169-171, 174-176.

Flags of Saudi Arabia, Yemen and Iraq — A5

1939   Litho.   Wmk. 258   Perf. 12½

24	A5	4b dl rose & ultra	.80	.50
25	A5	6b slate bl & ultra	.80	.50
26	A5	10b fawn & ultra	1.40	.75
27	A5	14b olive & ultra	2.25	1.25
28	A5	20b yel grn & ultra	3.25	1.75
29	A5	1i claret & ultra	6.50	3.50
		Nos. 24-29 (6)	15.00	8.25

2nd anniv. of the Arab Alliance. Nos. 24-29 exist imperforate. Value, set $20.
For overprints see Nos. C29-C29D.

No. 7 Handstamped in Black

Three types of surcharge:
a. 11½x16mm
b. 13-13½x15½mm
c. 12x16mm
Values of surcharged stamps are for ordinary copies. Clear, legible surcharges command a premium.

1939   Wmk. 127   Perf. 14

30	A3	4b on ½b orange	15.00	12.50

See Nos. 44-48, 59-67, 82, 86-87.

A6

A7

1940   Wmk. 258   Litho.   Perf. 12½

31	A6	½b ocher & ultra	.20	.20
32	A6	1b lt grn & rose red	.20	.20
33	A6	2b bis brn & vio	.20	.20
34	A6	3b dl vio & ultra	.25	.20
35	A6	4b rose & yel grn	.35	.30
36	A6	5b dk gray grn & bis brn	.40	.35
37	A7	6b ultra & yel org	.45	.45
38	A7	8b claret & dull bl	.55	.50
39	A7	10b brn org & yel grn	.75	.75
40	A7	14b gray grn & vio	.95	.80
41	A7	18b emerald & blk	1.10	.90
42	A7	20b yel ol & cerise	1.50	1.50
43	A7	1i vio rose, yel & brn red	2.75	2.50
		Nos. 31-43 (13)	9.65	8.85
		Set, never hinged	20.00	

No. 36 was used as a 4b stamp in 1957.
For surcharges see Nos. 44-47.

Catalogue values for unused stamps in this section, from this point to the end of the section, are for Never Hinged items.

Nos. 31-34, 36 Handstamped Type "b" in Black

1946-51   Perf. 12½

44	A6	4b on ½b ('51)	3.50	2.50
45	A6	4b on 1b ('49)	4.00	3.50
46	A6	4b on 2b ('49)	4.50	3.50
47	A6	4b on 3b ('49)	4.50	3.50

1945-48   Handstamp Type "a"

44a	A6	4b on ½b	4.00	3.00
45a	A6	4b on 1b ('48)	4.00	3.00
46a	A6	4b on 2b ('48)	4.50	3.50
47a	A6	4b on 3b ('48)	5.00	3.50
48	A6	4b on 5b ('46)	4.00	3.00

Forged surcharges exist.

A8

1946

Frames in Emerald

49	A8	4b black	1.50	.85
50	A8	6b lilac rose	2.25	1.50
51	A8	10b ultra	3.25	1.90
52	A8	14b olive green	5.50	3.25
		Nos. 49-52 (4)	12.50	7.50

Opening of Mutawakkili Hospital. Exist imperforate.
For overprints see Nos. 168, 172-173.

Mocha Coffee Tree — A9

Palace, San'a — A10

1947-58   Unwmk.   Engr.   Perf. 12½

53	A9	½b yellow brown	.25	.20
54	A9	1b purple	.70	.40
55	A9	2b ultra	1.40	.90
56	A10	4b red	2.25	1.25
57	A10	5b gray blue	2.50	1.50
58	A9	6b yellow green ('58)	3.50	2.00
		Nos. 53-58 (6)	10.60	6.25

No. 58 was printed in 1947 but not officially issued until June, 1958.

Additional values, prepared but not issued, were 10b, 20b and 1i, with views of palaces superimposed on flag, and palace square. These were looted from government storehouses during the 1948 revolution and a number of copies later reached collectors. Values, set: unused $20; used (cto) $15.
For surcharges see Nos. 63-65.

Admission of Yemen to the U.N.
10 postage, 5 airmail and 5 postage due stamps for the Admission of Yemen to the UN were not officially issued for use on domestic mail. Pictured on some of the stamps were Truman, Roosevelt, Churchill and the Statue of Liberty. Value, unused: 10v postage, $35; 5v air post, $22; 5v postage due, $14. Covers, scarce and all philatelic, exist to foreign destinations.

Nos. 9, 11, 12 and 15 Handstamped Type "a" in Black

1949   Wmk. 127   Perf. 14

59	A3	4b on 1b yellow grn	10.00	8.00
60	A3	4b on 2b olive brn	35.00	30.00
61	A3	4b on 3b dull vio	12.00	10.00
62	A3	4b on 5b slate gray	12.00	10.00

Handstamped type "b" are bogus.

Nos. 53-55 Handstamped Type "b" and "a"

1949   Unwmk.   Perf. 12½

63	A9(b)	4b on ½b yel brn	4.00	4.00
64	A9(a)	4b on 1b purple	5.00	5.00
a.		Handstamp type "b"	5.00	5.00
65	A9(a)	4b on 2b ultra	6.00	6.00
a.		Handstamp type "b"	6.00	6.00
b.		Handstamp 13x15mm		

Nos. J1-J2 Handstamped Type "b" in Black

1953   Wmk. 258

66	D1	4b on 1b org & yel grn	20.00	25.00
67	D1	4b on 2b org & yel grn	20.00	25.00
a.		Handstamp type "c"	25.00	30.00
		Nos. 59-67 (9)	124.00	123.00

Three minor types of this handstamped 4b surcharge exist. Types "a" and "b" exist inverted, double or horizontal.
Forged surcharges exist.

Parade Ground, San'a — A13

Mosque, San'a A14

Designs: 5b, Flag of Yemen. 6b, Flag & eagle. 8b, Mocha coffee branch. 14b, Walled city of San'a. 20b, 1i, Ta'iz & its citadel.

1951   Wmk. 277   Photo.   Perf. 14

68	A13	1b dark brown	.30	.20
69	A13	2b red brown	.60	.20
70	A13	3b lilac rose	.75	.35
71	A14	5b blue & red	1.25	.60
72	A13	6b dk pur & red	1.40	.65
73	A13	8b dk bl & gray grn	1.50	.75
74	A14	10b rose lilac	1.25	.85
75	A14	14b blue green	2.25	1.00
76	A14	20b rose red	3.25	1.75
77	A14	1i violet	7.50	3.00
		Nos. 68-77 (10)	20.05	9.35
		Nos. 68-77,C3-C9 (17)	44.70	17.70

No. 71 was used as a 4b stamp in 1956. For surcharges see Nos. 82, 86-87.

Palace of the Rock, Wadi Dhahr — A15

Design: 20b, Walls of Ibb.

Engraved and Photogravure
1952   Unwmk.   Perf. 14½, Imperf.
78 A15 12b choc, bl & dl grn   6.00 6.00
79 A15 20b dp car, bl & brn   9.00 9.00
   Nos. 78-79,C10-C11 (4)   35.00 35.00

Flag and View of San'a (Palace in Background) — A16

1952
80 A16 1i red brn, car & gray   12.50 12.50

4th anniv. of the accession of King Ahmed, Feb. 18, 1948. See Nos. 81, C12-C13.

Palace in Foreground
1952
81 A16 30b red brn, car & dk grn   11.00 11.00

Victory of Mar. 13, 1948. See No. C13.

No. 69 Handstamped Type "b" in Black
1951 (?)   Wmk. 277   Perf. 14
82 A13 4b on 2b red brown   5.00 5.00

Forged surcharges exist. See Nos. 86-87.

Leaning Minaret, Mosque of Ta'iz — A17

Yemen Gate, San'a — A18

1954   Photo.   Unwmk.
83 A17 4b deep orange   1.25 .40
84 A17 6b deep blue   2.00 .60
85 A17 8b deep blue green 2.50 1.50
   Nos. 83-85,C14-C16 (6)   19.50 6.65

Accession of King Ahmed I, 5th anniv.

Nos. 68 and 70 Handstamped Type "b" in Black
1955   Wmk. 277   Perf. 14
86 A13 4b on 1b dk brown   5.00 5.00
  a. Handstamp type "c"   20.00 10.00
87 A13 4b on 3b lilac rose 7.50 6.00

1956-57   Wmk. 277   Perf. 14
87A A18 1b lt brown   1.00 .75
87B A18 5b blue green   1.25 .75
87C A18 10b dark blue ('57) 1.50 .85
   Nos. 87A-87C (3)   3.75 2.35

Nos. 87A-87C were prepared for official use, but issued for regular postage. The 1b and 5b were used as 4b stamps. A 20b and 1-imadi of type A18 were not issued.

Arab Postal Union Issue

Globe — A19

Perf. 13½x13
1957-58   Wmk. 195   Photo.
88 A19 4b yellow brown   1.00 .90
89 A19 6b green ('58)   1.40 1.10
90 A19 16b violet ('58)   2.00 1.50
   Nos. 88-90 (3)   4.40 3.50

Arab Postal Union founding, July 1, 1954.

Telecommunications Issue

Globe, Radio and Telegraph A20

1959, Mar. Wmk. 318 Perf. 13x13½
91 A20 4b vermilion   1.75 1.25

Arab Union of Telecommunications. Exists imperf. Value $6.

United Arab States Issue

Flags of UAR and Yemen A21

1959, Mar. 13
92 A21 1b dl red brn & blk   .35 .25
93 A21 2b dk blue & blk   .45 .35
94 A21 4b sl grn, car & blk   .65 .50
   Nos. 92-94(6)   6.55 5.05

First anniversary of United Arab States. No. 94 exists imperf. Value $10.

Arab League Center Issue

Arab League Center, Cairo A22

Perf. 13x13½
1960, Mar. 22   Wmk. 328
95 A22 4b dull green & blk   .90 .90

Opening of the Arab League Center and the Arab Postal Museum in Cairo. Exists imperf. Value $10.

Refugees Pointing to Map of Palestine A23

1960, Apr. 7   Photo.
96 A23 4b brown   1.10 .75
97 A23 6b yellow green   1.75 1.25

World Refugee Year, 7/1/59-6/30/60. Exist imperf. Value, set $25.
In 1961 a souvenir sheet was issued containing a 4b gray and 6b sepia in type A18,

---

imperf. Black marginal inscription, "YEMEN 1960," repeated in Arabic. Size: 103x85mm. Value $50.

Torch and Olympic Rings A24

1960, Dec.   Unwmk.   Perf. 14x14½
98   A24 2b black & lil rose   .55 .35
99   A24 4b black & yellow   .85 .50
100 A24 6b black & orange   1.20 .75
101 A24 8b brn blk & bl grn 2.10 1.40
102 A24 20b dk bl, org & vio 5.00 3.00
   Nos. 98-102 (5)   9.70 6.00

17th Olympic Games, Rome, 8/25-9/11. Exist imperf. Value, set $75.
An imperf. souvenir sheet exists, containing one copy of No. 99. Size: 100x60mm. Value $90.

UN Emblem Breaking Chains — A25

1961   Unwmk.   Perf. 14x14½
103 A25 1b violet   .35 .25
104 A25 2b green   .40 .30
105 A25 3b grnsh blue   .50 .35
106 A25 4b brt ultra   .55 .40
107 A25 6b brt lilac   .70 .50
108 A25 14b rose brown 1.00 .60
109 A25 20b brown   2.00 1.60
   Nos. 103-109 (7)   5.50 4.00

15th anniversary (in 1960) of UN. Exist imperf. Value, set $14.
An imperf. souvenir sheet exists, containing one copy of No. 106. Blue marginal inscription. Size: 100x60mm. Value $25.
For overprints see Nos. 137-143.

Cranes and Ship, Hodeida A26

1961, June   Litho.   Perf. 13x13½
110 A26 4b multicolored   .85 .40
111 A26 6b multicolored   1.40 .75
112 A26 16b multicolored 2.75 1.60
   Nos. 110-112 (3)   5.00 2.75

Opening of deepwater port at Hodeida.
An imperf. souvenir sheet exists, containing one each of Nos. 110-112. Size: 160x130mm. Value $5.75.
For overprints see Nos. 177, 180.

Alabaster Funerary Mask — A27

Imam's New Palace, San'a — A28

Designs (ancient sculptures from Marib, Sheba): 2b, Horned animal's head, symbolizing Moon God (limestone). 4b, Bronze head of an Emperor 1st or 2nd century. 8b, Statue of Emperor Dhamar Ali. 10b, Statue of a child, 2nd or 3rd century (alabaster). 12b, Stairs in court of Temple of the Moon God. 20b, Alabaster relief, boy riding monster. 1i, Woman with grapes, relief.

1961, Oct. 14   Photo.   Perf. 11½
Granite Paper
113 A27 1b salmon, blk & gray   .35 .20
114 A27 2b purple & gray   .60 .20
115 A27 4b pale brn, gray & blk .80 .20
116 A27 8b brt pink & blk   1.00 .20
117 A27 10b yellow & blk   1.00 .35
118 A27 12b lt vio bl & blk   2.00 .50
119 A27 20b gray & blk   2.40 .60
120 A27 1i gray ol & blk   5.00 1.25
   Nos. 113-120,C20-C21 (10)   16.90 5.20

Exist imperf. Value, set (10), $25.
For overprints see Nos. 144-145, 147, 151, 153, 156-158, C24, C25.

1961, Nov. 15   Unwmk.
8b, Side view of Imam's palace, San'a, horiz. 10b, Palace of the Rock (Dar al-Hajar).
121 A28 4b black & lt bl grn   .35 .20
122 A28 8b blk, brt pink & grn .75 .45
123 A28 10b black, sal & grn   .85 .50
   Nos. 121-123,C22-C23 (5)   3.90 1.95

Exist imperf. Value, set (5) $6.
For overprints see #148, 152, 154, C24A, C25A.

Hodeida-San'a Road — A29

1961, Dec. 25   Litho.   Perf. 13½x13
124 A29 4b multicolored   .75 .20
125 A29 6b multicolored   .90 .40
126 A29 10b multicolored 1.50 .50
   Nos. 124-126 (3)   3.15 1.10

Opening of the Hodeida-San'a highway. A miniature sheet exists containing one each of Nos. 124-126, imperf. Size: 159x129mm. Value $7.
For overprints see Nos. 178-179.

Trajan's Kiosk, Philae, Nubia — A30

1962, Mar. 1   Photo.   Perf. 11x11½
127 A30 4b dk red brown   3.50 1.00
128 A30 6b blue green   6.25 2.00

Issued to publicize UNESCO's help in safeguarding the monuments of Nubia.
A souvenir sheet exists, containing one each of #127-128, imperf. Size: 100x88½mm. Value $12.50.

Arab League Building, Cairo, and Emblem — A31

1962, Mar. 22   Perf. 13½x13
129 A31 4b dark green   .70 .25
130 A31 6b deep ultra   .85 .40

Arab League Week, Mar. 22-28.
A souvenir sheet exists, containing one each of Nos. 129-130, imperf. Size: 94x80mm. Value $3.50.
For overprints see Nos. 164-165.

Nurses, Mother and Child — A32

Malaria Eradication
Emblem — A33

Designs: 4b, Nurse weighing child. 6b,
Vaccination. 10b, Weighing infant.

1962, June 20   Unwmk.   Perf. 11½
131	A32	2b multicolored	.60	.25
132	A32	4b multicolored	.85	.30
133	A32	6b multicolored	1.00	.40
134	A32	10b multicolored	1.75	.50
		Nos. 131-134 (4)	4.20	1.45

Issued for Child Welfare.
Exist imperf. Value, set $8.
For overprints see Nos. 146, 149-150, 155.

1962, July 20   Perf. 13½x13
135	A33	4b black & dp org	.70	.25
136	A33	6b dk brown & grn	1.00	.40

WHO drive to eradicate malaria. An imperf.
souvenir sheet contains one each of Nos. 135-
136. Size: 95x79mm. Value $15.
No. 136 has laurel leaves added and
inscription rearranged.
For overprints see Nos. 189-190.

Nos. 103-109 Overprinted

1962 Photo. Unwmk.   Perf. 14x14½
137	A25	1b violet	1.50	1.50
138	A25	2b green	1.50	1.50
139	A25	3b greenish blue	1.50	1.50
140	A25	4b brt ultra	1.50	1.50
141	A25	6b brt lilac	1.50	1.50
142	A25	14b rose brown	1.50	1.50
143	A25	20b brown	1.50	1.50
		Nos. 137-143 (7)	10.50	10.50

Nos. 113-123 and 131-134 Ovptd. in
Dark Green or Dark Red

a

b

1963, Jan. 1   Perf. 11½
144	A27 (a)	1b No. 113 (G)	.20	.20
145	A27 (a)	2b No. 114	.20	.20
146	A32 (b)	2b No. 131	.40	.40
147	A27 (a)	4b No. 115 (G)	.40	.40
148	A28 (a)	4b No. 121	.55	.55
149	A32 (b)	4b No. 132 (G)	.55	.55
150	A32 (b)	6b No. 133	.70	.70
151	A27 (a)	8b No. 116	.70	.70
152	A28 (a)	8b No. 122 (G)	1.00	1.00
153	A27 (a)	10b No. 117	1.00	1.00
154	A32 (b)	10b No. 123	1.75	1.75
155	A32 (b)	10b No. 134 (G)	1.75	1.75
156	A27 (a)	12b No. 118	1.40	1.40
157	A27 (a)	20b No. 119	2.00	2.00
158	A27 (a)	1i No. 120	5.50	5.50
		Nos. 144-158 (15)	18.10	18.10

For overprints see Nos. C24-C25A.

Proclamation of
the Republic
A34

UN Freedom
From Hunger
Campaign
A35

1963, Mar. 15   Perf. 11x11½
159	A34	4b shown	.55	.55
160	A34	6b Flag, tank	.85	.85

See Nos. C26-C28.

1963, Mar. 21   Perf. 11½x11, 11x11½
162	A35	4b Milk cow, horiz.	.90
163	A35	6b shown	1.25

An imperf. souvenir sheet of 2 exists containing one each Nos. 162-163.
For overprints see Nos. 219-220.

Nos. 129-130
Ovptd. in Dark Red

1963, Sept. 1   Perf. 13½x13
164	A31	4b dark green	7.00	7.00
165	A31	6b deep ultra	7.00	7.00

Nos. 15-16, 18-23, 50-52 Ovptd. in
Black

a

b

1963, Sept. 1
166	A3 (a)	5b No. 15	1.40	1.40
167	A4 (a)	6b No. 16	1.75	1.75
168	A8 (b)	6b No. 50	1.75	1.75
169	A4 (a)	8b No. 18	2.00	2.00
170	A4 (a)	10b No. 19	2.50	2.50
171	A4 (a)	10b No. 20	2.50	2.50
172	A8 (b)	10b No. 51	2.50	2.50
173	A8 (b)	14b No. 52	7.00	7.00
174	A4 (a)	20b No. 21	2.75	2.75
175	A4 (a)	1i No. 22	7.00	7.00
176	A4 (a)	1i No. 23	5.25	5.25
		Nos. 166-176 (11)	36.40	36.40

Nos. 111-112 and 125-126 Ovptd. in
Black

Perf. 13x13½, 13½x13
1963, Sept. 1   Litho.   Unwmk.
177	A26	6b No. 111	1.75	1.75
178	A29	6b No. 125	1.75	1.75
179	A29	10b No. 126	2.50	2.50
180	A26	16b No. 112	2.50	2.50

On Nos. 178-179 the bars eliminate old
inscription with text of overprint positioned
below and to the right of them, on Nos. 177
and 180, the text is slightly left below the bars.
Imperf. souvenir sheets of 2 exist containing
Nos. 177 and 180 or Nos. 178-179.

1st Anniv. of the Revolution — A36

Perf. 11½x11, 11x11½
1963, Sept. 26   Photo.
186	A36	2b Flag, torch, candle, vert.	.35	.30
187	A36	4b shown	.55	.45
188	A36	6b Flag, grain, chain, vert.	.90	.70

Imperf. souvenir sheets of 3 exist containing
one each Nos. 186-188.

Red Cross Centenary. Set of six. ¼,
⅓, ½, 4, 8, 20b. Imperf. souv. sheet of
two, 4, 8b. Oct. Nos. 6301-6307.

Nos. 135-136
Ovptd. in Black

1963, Nov. 25   Perf. 13½x13
189	A33	4b black & dp orange	3.00	3.00
190	A33	6b dk brown & green	4.00	4.00

UN Declaration of Human Rights, 15th
Anniv. — A37

1963, Dec. 10   Perf. 13½
191	A37	4b orange & dk brn vio	.55	.55
192	A37	6b blue grn & blk	.75	.75

An imperf. souvenir sheet of 2 exists containing one each Nos. 191-192.

1964
Olympic Sports. Set of eight, ¼, ⅓, ½,
1, 1½b, airmail 4, 20b, 1r. Imperf. souv.
sheet, 4b. Mar. 30. Nos. 6401-6409.

Bagel Spinning and Weaving Factory
Inauguration — A38

1964, Apr. 10   Perf. 11x11½, 11½x11
193	A38	2b Factory, bobbin, spool, cloth	.30	.20
194	A38	4b Loom machine	.40	.30
195	A38	6b Factory, spool, bolt of cloth	.55	.35
196	A38	16b shown	1.50	1.40

Nos. 193-195 vert. An imperf. souvenir
sheet of one exists containing No. 196.
No. 196 is air mail.

Hodeida Airport Inauguration — A39

1964, Apr. 30   Perf. 11½x11
197	A39	4b Runway	.40	.35
198	A39	6b Runway, terminal	.55	.50
199	A39	10b Aircraft, terminal, ship at sea	.75	.55

An imperf. souvenir sheet of one exists containing No. 199.

New York World's Fair. Set of seven,
¼, ⅓, ½, 1, 4b, airmail 16, 20b. Imperf.
souv. sheet, 20b. May 10. Nos. 6410-
6417.
Summer Olympics, Tokyo. Set of
nine, ¼, ⅓, ½, 1, 1½b, airmail, 4, 6, 12,
20b, Imperf. souv. sheet, 20b. June 1.
Nos. 6418-6427.
Boy Scouts. Set of nine, ¼, ⅓, ½, 1,
1½b, airmail, 4, 6, 16, 20b. Two souvenir sheets, 16b, perf.; 20b, imperf. June
20. Nos. 6428-6438.
Animals. Set of eleven, ¼, ⅓, ½, 1,
1½b, airmail, 4, 12, 20b, postage due,
4, 12, 20b. Aug. 15. Nos. 6439-6449.
Flowers. Set of eight, ¼, ⅓, ½, 1,
1½b, airmail, 4, 12, 20b. Sept. 1. Nos.
6450-6457.

San'a Intl. Airport Inauguration — A40

1964, Oct. 1
200	A40	1b shown	.35	.35
201	A40	2b Terminal, runway, air-craft	.35	.35
202	A40	4b like 2b	.35	.35
203	A40	8b like 1b	.70	.70

An imperf. souvenir sheet of two exists containing one each Nos. 202 and C30.
See No. C30.

Arab Postal
Union, 10th
Anniv.
A41

2nd Arab Summit
Conference
A42

1964, Oct. 15   Perf. 13½
204	A41	4b multicolored	.75	.65

See No. C31.

1964, Nov. 30
205	A42	4b shown	.75	.65
206	A42	6b Conference emblem, map	1.00	.80

An imperf. souvenir sheet of 2 exists containing one each Nos. 205-206.
For overprints see Nos. 221-222.

2nd Anniv. of
the Revolution
A43

Deir Yassin
Massacre
A44

1964, Dec. 30
207 A43 2b Torch, map .35 .30
208 A43 4b Revolutionary .70 .50
209 A43 6b Flag, 2 candles, map .70 .50

An imperf. souvenir sheet of one exists containing No. 209.

1965
Birds. Set of eleven, ¼, ½, ¾, 1, 1½, 4b, airmail, 6, 8, 12, 20b, 1r. Imperf. souv. sheet, 20b. Jan. 30. Nos. 6501-6512.

1965, Apr. 30 *Perf. 11x11½*
210 A44 4b red lil & deep blue .80 .60

See No. C32.

Intl. Telecommunications Union (ITU),
Cent. — A45

1965, May 17 *Perf. 11x11½, 11½x11*
211 A45 4b red & pale blue, vert. .75 .40
212 A45 6b org brn & grn 1.00 .55

A souvenir sheet of 1 exists containing #212.

Burning
of Algiers
Library,
3rd Anniv.
A46

1965, July 7 *Perf. 11½x11*
214 A46 4b sepia, red & grn .75 .50

See No. C33.

3rd Anniv. of the Revolution — A47

1965, Sept. 26
215 A47 4b Tractor, corn, grain .75 .50
216 A47 6b Tractor, tower, buildings 1.00 .55

An imperf. souvenir sheet of one exists containing No. 216.

Intl. Cooperation
Year — A48

1965, Oct. 15 *Perf. 11x11*
217 A48 4b shown .80 .60
218 A48 6b UN building, New York 1.10 .65

An imperf. souvenir sheet of one exists containing No. 218.

John F. Kennedy Memorial. Set of eight, 3x¼, ⅓, ½, 4b, airmail, 8, 12b. Two imperf. souv. sheets, 4, 8b. Nov. 29. Nos. 6513-6522.
Space Exploration. Set of eight, 3x¼, ⅓, ½b, airmail, 4, 8, 16b. Imperf. souv. sheet, 16b. Dec. 29. Nos. 6523-6531.

Nos. 162-163 Overprinted in Black

a

b

1966, Jan. 15 *Perf. 11½x11, 11x11½*
219 A35 4b sal rose & golden
   (a) brn 1.00 .75
220 A35 6b brt pur & yel
   (b) 1.75 1.00

An imperf. souvenir sheet of two exists containing Nos. 219-220.

Communications. Set of eight, 3x¼, ⅓, ½b, airmail, 4, 6, 20b. Imperf. airmail souv. sheet, 20b. Jan. 29. Nos. 6601-6609.
Animals issue of 1965 overprinted in black or red "Prevention of Cruelty to Animals" in English and Arabic. Set of eleven. Souv. sheet, 20b. Mar. 5. Nos. 6610-6621.

Nos. 205-206
Ovptd. in Red or
Black

1966, Mar. 20 *Perf. 13½*
221 A42 4b dark green (R) .75 .50
222 A42 6b orange brown .85 .55

An imperf. souvenir sheet of two exists containing Nos. 221-222 ovptd. in bright pink (4b) or black (6b) with additional inscription at bottom "CASABLANCA / 1965."

Builders of World Peace. Set of nine, 3x¼, ⅓, ½, 4b, airmail, 6, 10, 12b. Two imperf. souvenir sheets, 4, 8b. Mar. 25. Nos. 6622-6632.
Domestic Animals. Set of six, 3x¼, ⅓, ½, 4b. Imperf. souv. sheet, 22b. May 5. Nos. 6633-6639.
Space Exploration issue of 1965 overprinted "Luna IX / 3 February 1966" in English and Arabic. Set of eight. Imperf. souvenir sheet. Nos. 6640-6648.
World Cup Soccer Championship. Set of eight, 3x¼, ⅓, ½b, airmail, 4, 5, 20b. Imperf. souvenir sheet, 20b. May 29. Nos. 6649-6657.

Traffic Day — A49

1966, June 30 *Perf. 11x11½*
223 A49 4b green & ver .75 .50
224 A49 6b green & ver .85 .55

Space Exploration issue of 1965 overprinted "Surveyor 1 / 2 June 1966" in English and Arabic. Set of five, 3x1b on ¼b, 3b on ⅓b, 4b on ½b. Aug. 15. Nos. 6658-6662.
Revolution, 4th Anniv. Set of three, 2, 4, 6b. Imperf. souv. sheet of 2; 4, 6b. Sept. Nos. 6663-6666.
World's Fair issue of 1964 overprinted "1965 Sana'a." Set of seven. Imperf. souvenir sheet. Nos. 6667-6674.
WHO Headquarters Inauguration. Set of six, 3x¼b, airmail, 4, 8, 16b. Imperf. souvenir sheet, 16b. Nov. 1. Nos. 6675-6681.
Gemini 6-7. Set of eight, 3x¼, ⅓, ½, 2b, airmail, 8, 12b. Imperf. souvenir sheet, 12b. Dec. 1. Nos. 6682-6690.
Gemini 6-7 issue overprinted in red "Gemini IX / Cernan-Stafford / June 1966" in English and Arabic. Set of eight. Imperf. souvenir sheet. Dec. 25. Nos. 6691-6699.

1967
Fruit. Set of thirteen, 3x¼, ⅓, ½, 2, 4b, airmail, 6, 8, 10b, postage due, 6, 8, 10b. Feb. 10. Nos. 6701-6713.

Arab
League,
25th
Anniv.
A56

1970, Oct. 5 *Photo. Perf. 11½x11*
276 A56 5b org, grn & dark pur .35 —
277 A56 7b blue, grn & brn .75 —
278 A56 16b dark olive grn, grn & chalky blue 1.75 —

An imperf souvenir sheet of one exists containing No. 278.

UN, 25th
Anniv.
A60

1971, Apr. 4 *Photo. Perf. 11½x11*
282 A60 5b dark olive grn, grn & dark vio .55 .45
283 A60 7b blue, grn & dark blue .90 .75

Souvenir Sheet
Imperf
284 A60 16b multicolored 2.00 1.50

10th anniv. of
Revolution
A80

1972, Nov. 25 *Photo. Perf. 13*
301 A80 7b lt blue, blk & multi .65 .50
302 A80 10b gray, blk & multi 1.00 .65
Nos. 301-302,C40 (3) 6.65 4.65

For surcharge see No. 318.

25th Anniv. of
WHO — A81

1972, Dec. 1 *Litho.*
303 A81 2b lt yel grn & multi .50 .35
304 A81 21b sky blue & multi 1.40 1.20
305 A81 37b red lilac & multi 2.25 2.00
Nos. 303-305 (3) 4.15 3.55

For surcharge see No. 341A.

Burning of Al-Aqsa Mosque, 2nd
Anniv. — A82

1972, Jan. 1 *Photo. Perf. 13½*
306 A82 7b lt bl, blk & multi 1.50 .60
307 A82 18b lt bl, blk & multi 2.50 1.10
Nos. 306-307,C41 (3) 6.00 3.10

For surcharges see Nos. 319, 341.

25th Anniv. of UNICEF — A83

1973, Jan. 15 *Photo. Perf. 13*
308 A83 7b lt bl, blk & multi 1.00 .65
309 A83 10b lt bl, blk & multi 1.50 .80
Nos. 308-309,C42 (3) 4.25 2.95

For surcharge see No. C46.

UPU Cent. — A84

10th World
Hunger
Program
A85

1974, Nov. 20 *Photo. Perf. 14*
310 A84 10b multicolored .75 .40
311 A84 30b multicolored 2.25 1.50
312 A84 40b multicolored 3.25 1.90
Nos. 310-312 (3) 6.25 3.80

For surcharge see No. 341B.

1975, Feb. 5   Litho.   Perf. 13½
313 A85 10b multicolored   .25   .25
314 A85 30b multicolored   .70   .70
315 A85 63b multicolored   1.25 1.25
    Nos. 313-315 (3)   2.20 2.20

12th Anniv.
of Revolution
A86

1975, Sept. 25
316 A86 25f Janad Mosque   .50   .35
317 A86 75f Althawra Hospital   1.00   .65

Nos. 301, 306 surcharged in Black
with New Values and Bars

1975, Nov. 15   Photo.   Perf. 13½
318 A80 75f on 7b   2.00   .65
319 A82 278f on 7b   3.50 1.25
    Nos. 318-319,C46-C48 (5)   17.75 11.40

Telephone   Coffee Bean
Cent. — A87   Branch — A88

1976, Mar. 10   Litho.   Perf. 14½
320 A87 25f brt pink & blk   .65   .65
321 A87 75f lt grn & blk   2.00 2.00
322 A87 160f lt bl & blk   3.25 3.25
  a. Souvenir sheet of 1   4.00 4.00
    Nos. 320-322 (3)   5.90 5.90

No. 322a exists both perf. and imperf.

1976, Apr. 25   Perf. 14
323 A88 1f dull lilac   .20   .20
324 A88 3f pale gray   .20   .20
325 A88 5f lt bl   .20   .20
326 A88 10f bis brn   .20   .20
327 A88 25f golden brn   .25   .25
328 A88 50f brt plum   .40   .40
329 A88 75f dull pink   .70   .60

Size: 22x30mm
Perf. 14½
330 A88 1r sky blue   1.25   .70
331 A88 1.50r red lilac   1.90 1.40
332 A88 2r light grn   2.25 1.40
333 A88 5r yel org   5.00 3.00
    Nos. 323-333 (11)   12.55 8.55

For surcharges see Nos. 403-407, 592.

2nd Anniv. of
Reformation
Movement — A89

1976, June 13 Photo. Perf. 12x12½
334 A89 75f Industrial Park   1.50 1.50
335 A89 135f Forestry   2.50 2.50
Souvenir Sheet
336 A89 135f Forestry   5.00 5.00

No. 336 contains one stamp (32x47mm).

14th Anniv. of
Revolution — A90

3rd Anniv. of
Correction
Movement — A91

Designs: 25f, Natl. Institute of Public Administration. 75f, Housing and population census.
160f, Sanaa University emblem.

1976, Sept. 26 Photo. Perf. 12x12½
337 A90 25f buff & multi   .60   .60
338 A90 75f yel bis & multi   1.60 1.60
339 A90 160f pale grn & multi   3.00 3.00
    Nos. 337-339 (3)   5.20 5.20
Souvenir Sheet
340 A90 160f pale grn & multi   5.00 5.00

No. 340 contains one stamp (33x49mm).

No. 306 Surcharged in Black with New
Value and Bars

1976
341 A82 75f on 7b   1.00   .65

160F

Nos. 304, 312
Surcharged in
Black or Red

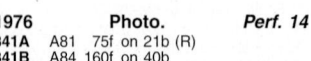

1976   Photo.   Perf. 14
341A A81 75f on 21b (R)
341B A84 160f on 40b

Size and location of surcharge varies.

1977   Photo.   Perf. 14
342 A91 25f Dish antenna   .45   .30
343 A91 75f Computer, techni-
    cian   1.25   .65
  a. Miniature sheet of 1 4.00 4.00

15th Anniv. of September
Revolution — A92

1977   Photo.   Perf. 13½
344 A92 25f Sa'ada-San'a Road   .45   .35
345 A92 75f Television, Trans-
    mitting tower   1.25   .85
346 A92 160f like 25f   2.50 2.00
  a. Souvenir sheet of 1   5.00 5.00
    Nos. 344-346 (3)   4.20 3.20

25th Anniv. of   Pres. Hamdi — A94
Arab Postal
Union — A93

1978   Perf. 14
347 A93 25f lt yel grn & multi   .90   .75
348 A93 60f bis & multi   2.25 1.60
  a. Miniature sheet of 1 5.00 4.50

1978   Perf. 11½
349 A94 25f dk grn & blk   .35   .35
350 A94 75f ultra & blk   1.25 1.10
351 A94 160f brn & blk   2.50 1.90
  a. Miniature sheet of 1 15.00 6.50
    Nos. 349-351 (3)   4.10 3.35

30th
Anniv.
of
ICAO
(1977)
A95

1979, Nov. 15   Photo.   Perf. 13½
352 A95 75f multi   1.90 1.00
353 A95 135f multi   3.00 1.60
  a. Miniature sheet of 1 5.00 4.50

Book, World Map, Arab
Achievements — A96

1979, Dec. 1   Perf. 14
354 A96 25f multi   .60   .35
355 A96 75f multi   1.50 1.00
  a. Souvenir sheet of 1 3.75 3.25

A97

A98

1980, Jan. 1
356 A97 75f multi   1.75 1.00
357 A97 135f multi, horiz.   2.75 1.60
  a. Miniature sheet of 1 5.00 4.50

12th World Telecommunications Day, May
17, 1979.

1980   Photo.   Perf. 14
Dome of the Rock.
358 A98 5f brt bl & multi   .50   .35
359 A98 10f yel & multi   1.00   .65

Palestinian fighters and their families.

Argentina World Cup — A99

World Cup emblem and various players.

1980, Mar. 30
360 A99 25f gold & multi   .40   .40
361 A99 30f gold & multi   .40   .30
362 A99 35f gold & multi   .50   .40
363 A99 50f gold & multi   .70   .50
    Nos. 360-363,C49-C52 (8) 6.55 4.80

Issued in sheets of 8.

International Year of the Child — A100

1980, Apr. 1   Perf. 13½
364 A100 25f Girl, bird   1.60   .50
365 A100 50f Girl, bird, diff. 2.25   .80
366 A100 75f Boy, butterfly,
    flower   2.40 1.25
    Nos. 364-366,C53-C55 (6) 16.75 6.80

Issued in sheets of 6.

World Scouting Jamboree — A101

1980, May 1   Perf. 13½x14
367 A101 25f Fishing   .60   .30
368 A101 35f Troup, aircraft   1.40   .50
369 A101 40f Mounted bugler,
    flag   1.40   .50
370 A101 50f Telescope, night
    sky   1.50   .65
    Nos. 367-370,C56-C58 (7) 13.05 5.35

Issued in sheets of 6.

Argentina 1978 World Cup
Winners — A102

World cup emblem and various soccer
players.

1980, June 1   Perf. 14
371 A102 25f gold & multi   .45   .25
372 A102 30f gold & multi   .60   .30
373 A102 35f gold & multi   .60   .40
374 A102 50f gold & multi   .90   .40
    Nos. 371-374,C59-C62 (8) 8.05 4.35

Hegira, 1500th Anniv. — A102A

Designs: 160f, Outside view.

1980, July 1   Perf. 13½
375 A102a 25f blk & multi   .30   .20
376 A102a 75f car rose & multi .90   .60
377 A102a 160f blk & multi   1.90   .75
  a. Miniature sheet of 1 4.00 4.00
    Nos. 375-377 (3)   3.10 1.55

17th Anniv.
of
September
Revolution
A103

A104

1980, Sept. 26   **Perf. 13½**
378 A103 25f multi   .35 .25
379 A104 75f multi   1.10 .65

Souvenir Sheet

380   100f multi   3.75 3.75

No. 380 contains one stamp combining designs A103 and A104 (42x34mm).

Al Aqsa
Mosque
A105

Mosques: 25f, Al-Rawda entrance. 100f, Al-Nabwi. 160f, Al-Haram.

1980, Nov. 6   Photo.   Perf. 13½
381 A105 25f multi   .25 .20
382 A105 75f multi   .60 .50
383 A105 100f multi   1.50 .65
384 A105 160f multi   2.00 1.00
        Nos. 381-384 (4)   4.35 2.35

Souvenir Sheet

385   160f multi   6.00 3.25

Islamic Postal Systems Week and Hegira. No. 385 contains one stamp (109x47mm) combining designs of Nos. 382-384.

Intl. Palestinian
Solidarity
Day — A106

1980, Nov. 29
386 A106 25f lt bl & multi   .40 .25
387 A106 75f ver & multi   1.10 .90

Inscribed 1979.

9th Arab Archaeological
Conference — A107

1981, Mar. 1   **Perf. 13½**
388 A107 75f Al Aamiriya
                  Mosque   1.10 .60
389 A107 125f Al Hadi Mosque   1.75 .85
   a.   Souvenir sheet of 2, #388-389 3.25 3.25

1980 World
Tourism
Conference,
Manila
A108

1981, Apr. 1
390 A108 25f shown   .20 .20
391 A108 75f Mosque, houses   .60 .30
392 A108 100f Columns, horiz.   .80 .45
393 A108 135f Bridge   1.10 .60
394 A108 160f Vuiew of San'a,
                  horiz.   1.40 .60
   a.   Miniature sheet of 1   4.50 4.50
        Nos. 390-394 (5)   4.10 2.15

Sir Rowland Hill (1795-1879), Postage
Stamp Inventor — A109

1981, Sept. 15   Litho.   Perf. 14
395 A109 25f Portrait, UPU
                  emblem   .60
396 A109 30f Emblem, stamp
                  of 1963   .70
397 A109 50f Portrait, stamps   1.00
398 A109 75f Portrait, globe,
                  jet   1.60
399 A109 100f Portrait, stamp
                  collection   2.25
400 A109 150f Jets, No. 322   4.00
        Nos. 395-400 (6)   10.15

Souvenir Sheets

401 A109 200f Portrait, vert.   7.50

Imperf

402 A109 200f Portrait, diff.   7.50

Nos. 398-402 are airmail.

Nos. 323-327 Surcharged

1981
403 A88 125f on 1f   1.00
404 A88 150f on 3f   1.25
405 A88 325f on 5f   2.75
406 A88 350f on 10f   3.25
407 A88 375f on 25f   3.50
        Nos. 403-407 (5)   11.75

20th Anniv. of Yemen Airways — A110

1983, Apr. 1   Litho.   Perf. 14
408 A110 75f yel & multi   .50 .50
409 A110 125f red & multi   .80 .80
410 A110 325f bl & multi   2.00 2.00
        Nos. 408-410 (3)   3.30 3.30

Folk Costumes — A111

1983, May 1
411 A111 50f Woman carrying
                  waterjar   2.00
412 A111 50f Women, sheep   2.00
413 A111 50f Man, donkeys   2.00
414 A111 50f Man in town
                  square   2.00
415 A111 75f Women, child,
                  well   3.00
416 A111 75f Scholar   3.00
417 A111 75f Woman on
                  beach   3.00
418 A111 75f Camel-drawn
                  plow   3.00
        Nos. 411-418 (8)   20.00

Souvenir Sheets

419 A111 200f Woman   8.00

Imperf

420 A111 200f Man   8.00

#411-414 vert. #415-420 are airmail.

Sept. 26th Revolution, 20th Anniv.
(1982) — A112

1983, Sept. 26   Litho.   Perf. 14
421 A112 100f Communications   1.00
422 A112 150f Literacy
423 A112 325f Educational develop-
                  ment
   a.   Souvenir sheet of 2, #422, 423
424 A112 400f Independence

World Communications Year — A113

1983, Dec. 15
425 A113 150f lt bl & multi
426 A113 325f lt grn & multi
   a.   Souvenir sheet of 1

Sept. 26 Revolution, 21st
Anniv. — A114

1984, Apr. 1   Litho.   Perf. 14
427 A114 100f shown
428 A114 150f Fist, statue
429 A114 325f Gate, tank
   a.   Souvenir sheet of 1

Israel
Aggression
Day — A115

1984, Sept. 7
430 A115 150f multi   1.50
431 A115 325f multi   4.00

Size: 91x120mm

Imperf

432 A115 325f multi   25.00
        Nos. 430-432 (3)   30.50

Sept. 26 Revolution, 22nd
Anniv. — A116

1985, Oct. 1
433 A116 50f Triumphal Arch
434 A116 150f San'a Castle walls
435 A116 325f Stadium, Govt. Palace,
                  San'a
   a.   Souvenir sheet of 1

Intl. Anti-
Apartheid Year
(1978) — A117

1985, Jan. 1
436 A117 150f dp ver & multi
437 A117 325f grn & multi
   a.   Souvenir sheet of 1

Intl. Civil
Aviation
Org., 40th
Anniv.
A118

1985, Sept. 20
438 A118 25f multi
439 A118 50f multi
440 A118 150f multi
441 A118 325f multi
   a.   Souvenir sheet of 1

Arabsat
Satellite,
1st Anniv.
A119

1986, Apr. 15   Litho.   Perf. 14
442 A119 150f multi   2.50
443 A119 325f multi   5.50
   a.   Souvenir sheet of 1   8.50

World Telecommunications, 120th
Anniv. — A120

1986, May 1
444 A120 150f multi   2.50
445 A120 325f multi   5.25
a.   Souvenir sheet of 1   9.00

General People's Conference, 2nd
Anniv. — A121

1986, May 1
446 A121 150f multi   2.50
447 A121 325f multi   4.50
a.   Souvenir sheet of 1   6.00

A122

A123

1986, July 1
448 A122 150f multi   2.50
449 A122 325f multi   4.50
a.   Souvenir sheet of 1   6.00

15th Islamic Foreign Ministers' Conference,
San'a, Dec. 18-22, 1984.

1986, Oct. 1
450 A123 150f multi   2.50
451 A123 325f multi   4.50
a.   Souvenir sheet of 1   6.00

UN 40th anniv.

Arab
League,
39th
Anniv.
A124

1986, Nov. 15
452 A124 150f multi   2.50
453 A124 325f multi   4.50

Natl. Arms
A125

1987, Sept. 26   Litho.   Perf. 14
454 A125 100f multi   .90
455 A125 150f multi   1.25
456 A125 425f multi   3.75
a.   Souvenir sheet of 1   4.00
457 A125 450f multi   4.00

Sept. 26th Revolution, 25th anniv.
For surcharge see No. 593.

Intl. Youth
Year (1985)
A126

1987, Oct. 15   Perf. 13x13½
458 A126 150f multi
459 A126 425f multi
a.   Souvenir sheet of 1

For surcharge see No. C150.

Drilling of
the
Republic's
First Oil
Well, 1984
A127

1987, Nov. 1   Perf. 14
460 A127 150f Oil derrick
461 A127 425f Derrick, refinery
a.   Souvenir sheet of 1

For surcharge see No. C151.

General
Population
and
Housing
Census,
1986
A128

1987, Dec. 1
462 A128 150f multi   2.50
463 A128 425f multi   4.50
a.   Souvenir sheet of 1   5.50

For surcharge see No. C152.

1986 World Cup Soccer
Championships, Mexico — A129

Designs: 100f, 150f, Match scenes, vert.
425f, Match scene and Pique, character
trademark.

1988, Jan. 1   Litho.   Perf. 14
464 A129 100f multi
465 A129 150f multi, diff.
466 A129 425f multi
a.   Souvenir sheet of 1

For surcharge see No. C153.

17th Scouting
Conference,
San'a — A130

1988, Mar. 1   Litho.   Perf. 14
467 A130 25f Skin diving
468 A130 30f Table tennis
469 A130 40f Tennis
470 A130 50f Two scouts, flag
471 A130 60f Volleyball
472 A130 100f Tug-of-war

473 A130 150f Basketball
474 A130 425f Archery
Souvenir Sheet
475 A130 425f Scout, emblem,
                hand sign
For surcharge see No. C154.

San'a Preservation — A131

1988, May 1   Litho.   Perf. 14
476 A131 25f multicolored
477 A131 50f multicolored
478 A131 100f multicolored
479 A131 150f multicolored
480 A131 425f multicolored
a.   Souvenir sheet of 1

For surcharge see No. 594.

Battle of
Hattin,
800th
Anniv. in
1987
A132

1988   Litho.   Perf. 14
482 A132 150f multicolored
483 A132 425f multicolored
a.   Souvenir sheet

For surcharge see No. C155.

Arab Telecommunication Day,
1987 — A133

1988
484 A133 100f multicolored
485 A133 150f multicolored
486 A133 425f multicolored
a.   Souvenir sheet

For surcharge see No. C156.

A134

Sept. 26
Revolution, 26th
Anniv. — A134a

1989, Sept. 30
487 A134   300f multicolored
488 A134   375f multicolored
489 A134a 850f multicolored
490 A134a 900f multicolored

A souvenir sheet containing one #488 exists.
For surcharges see Nos. 595, 605.

A135

October 14
Revolution, 25th
Anniv. — A135a

1989, Oct. 14
491 A135   300f multicolored
492 A135   375f multicolored
493 A135a 850f multicolored
494 A135a 900f multicolored

A souvenir sheet containing one #492 exists.
For surcharges see Nos. 596, 606.

1988
Summer
Olympics,
Seoul
A136

Game emblem and various events: 300f,
Table tennis, basketball, track, boxing. 375f,
Soccer game. 850f, Soccer, judo, vert. 900f,
Torch bearer.

1989, Nov. 10   Litho.   Perf. 13x13½
495 A136 300f multicolored
496 A136 375f multicolored
a.   Souvenir sheet
497 A136 850f multicolored
498 A136 900f multicolored

For surcharges see Nos. 597, 607.

Palestinian
Uprising
A137

1989, Dec. 9   Perf. 13x13½, 13½x13
499 A137 300f shown
500 A137 375f Flag raising, vert.
a.   Souvenir sheet of 1
501 A137 850f Burning barri-
                cades
502 A137 900f Man waving flag,
                vert.

For surcharges see Nos. 598, 608.

Arab Cooperation Council — A138

1990, Feb. 16   Litho.   Perf. 13x13½
504 A138 300f multicolored
505 A138 375f multicolored
a.   Souvenir sheet
506 A138 850f multicolored
507 A138 900f multicolored

For surcharges see Nos. 599, 609.

First
Exported
Oil — A139

1990, Mar. 15   *Perf. 14*
508 A139 300f multicolored
509 A139 375f multicolored
  a.   Souvenir sheet
510 A139 850f multi, diff.
511 A139 900f like 850f

For surcharges see Nos. 600, 610.

Arab Scout
Movement,
75th Anniv.
A140

1990, June 15   **Litho.**   *Perf. 13x13½*
512 A140 300f Scouts holding
            globe
513 A140 375f like No. 512
  a.   Souvenir sheet of 1
514 A140 850f Oil rig, scouts,
            globe
515 A140 900f like No. 514

For surcharges see Nos. 601, 611.

Arab Board for
Medical
Specializations,
10th
Anniv. — A141

1990, Apr. 15   **Photo.**   *Perf. 13½x13*
516 A141 300f brt grn & multi
517 A141 375f lt bl & multi
  a.   Sheet of 1, perf. 12½
518 A141 850f lt org & multi
519 A141 900f lt vio & multi

For surcharges see Nos. 602, 612.

Immunization Campaign — A142

300f, 375f, Mother feeding infant, vert.

1990, May 15   *Perf. 13½x13, 13x13½*
520 A142 300f lt bl & multi
521 A142 375f lt org & multi
  a.   Sheet of 1, perf. 12½
522 A142 850f lt bl grn & multi
523 A142 900f lt lake & multi

No. 521a contains one 26x37mm stamp.
For surcharges see Nos. 603, C157.

UN Development
Program, 40th
Anniv. — A144

1990, Oct. 24   **Litho.**   *Perf. 12*
532 A144 150f multicolored

For surcharge see No. 622.

Ducks
A145

1990, Sept. 18   **Litho.**   *Perf. 12*
533 A145 10f Pintail swimming
534 A145 20f Wigeon
535 A145 25f Ruddy shelduck
536 A145 40f Gadwall
537 A145 75f Shelduck, male
538 A145 150f Shoveler
539 A145 600f Teal

Souvenir Sheet
540 A145 460f Pintail in flight

For surcharge see No. 623.

Moths and
Butterflies
A146

1990, Nov. 3   *Perf. 12½x12*
541 A146 5f Dirphia multicolor
542 A146 20f Automeris io
543 A146 25f Papilio machaon
544 A146 40f Bhutanitis lid-
            derdalii
545 A146 55f Prepona
            demophon
            muson
546 A146 75f Agarista agricola
547 A146 700f Attacus edwardsii

Souvenir Sheet
Perf. 12x12½
548 A146 460f Daphnis nerii,
            vert.

Prehistoric
Animals
A147

Perf. 12x12½, 12½x12
1990, Nov. 27
549 A147 5f Protembolotheri-
            um, vert.
550 A147 10f Diatryma, vert.
551 A147 35f Mammuthus
552 A147 40f Edaphosaurus
553 A147 55f Dimorphodon
554 A147 75f Phororhacos
555 A147 700f Ichthyosaurus,
            vert.

Size: 61x90mm
Imperf
556 A147 460f Tyrannosaurus,
            vert.

A148

A149

Various domestic cats.

1990, Dec. 26   *Perf. 12x12½*
557 A148 5f multicolored
558 A148 15f multicolored
559 A148 35f multicolored
560 A148 55f multicolored
561 A148 60f multicolored
562 A148 150f multicolored
563 A148 600f multicolored

Size: 70x90mm
Imperf
564 A148 460f multicolored

1991, Mar. 18   **Litho.**   *Perf. 12x12½*
Mushrooms.
565 A149 50f Boletus aestivalis
566 A149 60f Suillus luteus
567 A149 80f Gyromitra es-
            culenta
568 A149 100f Leccinum
            scabrum
569 A149 130f Amanita muscaria
570 A149 200f Boletus er-
            ythropus
571 A149 300f Leccinum testace-
            oscabrum

Size: 70x90mm
Imperf
572 A149 460f Stropharia aerugi-
            nosa

Unified
Yemen
Republic,
1st Anniv.
A150

Designs: 300f, 375f, Eagle crest. 850f, 900f,
Hand holding flag, map, sun.

1991, May 22   *Perf. 13x13½*
573 A150 300f pink & multi
574 A150 375f grn bl multi
  a.   Sheet of 1, perf. 12½
575 A150 850f lt bl & multi
576 A150 900f bl grn & multi

No. 574a contains one 37x27mm stamp.
For surcharges see #604, 613, 624, 627.

Unity Agreement
Signed Nov. 30,
1989 — A151

Designs: 300f, 375f, 850f, Fist, flag, map.

1991, May 22   *Perf. 13½x13*
577 A151 225f multicolored
578 A151 300f multicolored
579 A151 375f multicolored
  a.   Sheet of 1, perf. 12½
580 A151 650f multicolored
581 A151 850f multicolored

No. 579a contains one 27x37mm stamp.
For surcharges see #614, 617-619, 625.

World Anti-Smoking Day — A153

Designs: 300f, 375f, 850f, Man facing skull
smoking cigarette.

1991, May 31   *Perf. 13x13½*
582 A153 225f multicolored
583 A153 300f multicolored
584 A153 375f multicolored
  a.   Sheet of 1, perf. 12½
585 A153 650f multicolored
586 A153 850f multicolored

No. 584a contains one 36x26mm stamp.
For surcharges see Nos. 615, 620, 626.

United
Nations,
45th Anniv.
A154

1991, June 26   *Perf. 13x13½*
587 A154 5f multicolored
588 A154 8f multicolored
589 A154 10f multicolored
590 A154 12f multicolored

Souvenir Sheet
Perf. 12½
591 A154 6f multicolored

No. 591 contains one 37x28mm stamp.

Nos. 329, 456, 480, 489-490, 493-494,
497-498, 501-502, 506-507, 510-511,
514-515, 518-519, 523, 575-576, 581
& 586 Surcharged, "Rials" Spelled Out

1993, Jan. 1   *Perfs., Etc. as Before*
592 A88   5r on 75f #329
593 A125   8r on 425f #456
594 A131   8r on 425f #480
595 A134a 10r on 900f #490
596 A135a 10r on 900f #494
597 A136   10r on 900f #498
598 A137   10r on 900f #502
599 A138   10r on 900f #507
600 A139   10r on 900f #511
601 A140   10r on 900f #515
602 A141   10r on 900f #519
603 A142   10r on 900f #523
604 A150   10r on 900f #576
605 A134a 12r on 850f #489
606 A135a 12r on 850f #493
607 A136   12r on 850f #497
608 A137   12r on 850f #501
609 A138   12r on 850f #506
610 A139   12r on 850f #510
611 A140   12r on 850f #514
612 A141   12r on 850f #518
613 A150   12r on 850f #575
614 A151   12r on 850f #581
615 A153   12r on 850f #586

Size and location of surcharge varies.

Yemen (PDR) Nos. 441, 443, 447, and
Yemen Nos. 577-578, 583 Surcharged
Type a or

c
50
R.Y

1993   *Perfs., Etc. as Before*
616   A139(a)   50r on 500f
                       #447
617   A151(a)   50r on 225f
                       #577
618   A151(c)   50r on 225f
                       #577
  a.   Pair, #617-618
619   A151(a)   100r on 300f
                       #578
620   A153(a)   100r on 300f
                       #583
621   A139(a)   200r on 5f #441
  a.   3-Line surcharge
621B   A139(a)   200r on 20f
                       #443

Size and location of surcharge varies.

Yemen Republic Nos. 532, 538, 573-
574, 579, & 584 Surcharged

a

1993, Sept. 1   *Perfs., Etc. as Before*
622 A144(a)   50r on 150f #532
623 A145(a)   50r on 150f #538
624 A150(a)   50r on 375f #574
625 A151(a)   50r on 375f #579
626 A153(a)   50r on 375f #584
627 A150(a)   100r on 300f #573

Size and location of surcharge varies.
No. 623 exists with a surcharge similar to
surcharge "c."

Yemen People's Democratic Republic
Nos. 75, 84B, 204, 208, 216, 232, 235, 244, 267, 335-336, 347, 425, 436-437, 439 & Types Surcharged
Type a and:

b

1993, Sept. 1 *Perfs., Etc. as Before*

628	A25(a)	8r on 100f #84B
629	A63(a)	8r on 110f #204
630	A64(a)	8r on 110f #208
631	A66(a)	8r on 110f #216
632	A72(a)	8r on 110f #232
633	A74(a)	8r on 110r #235
634	A76(a)	8r on 110r #244
635	A86(a)	8r on 110f #267
636	A105(a)	100r on 2d #347
637	A137(a)	100r on 300f #439
638	A24(a)	200r on 5f #75
639	(b)	200r on 15f
640	A105(b)	200r on 15f #335
641	(b)	200r on 20f
642	A105(b)	200r on 20f #336
643	A131(a)	200r on 20f #425	135.00 —
644	A134(a)	200r on 75f #436
645	A135(a)	200r on 250f #437

Size and location of surcharge varies.
No. 582 exists with a 50r type "b" surcharge.
No. 636 exists with a surcharge similar to surcharge "c."
Nos. 639, 641 without surcharge have not been listed in the Scott Catalogue.

Yemen Unity, 4th Anniv. — A155

Various views of govt. building, San'a.

1994, Sept. 27 Litho.   *Perf. 13½x14*
646	A155	3r multicolored
647	A155	5r multicolored
648	A155	8r multicolored
649	A155	20r multicolored

Souvenir Sheet
650	A155	20r multi, diff.

1994 World Cup Soccer Championships, US — A156

2r, Player in yellow shirt dribbling ball, vert. 6r, Player in striped shirt dribbling, vert. 10r, Goal keeper. No. 654, Heading ball, vert. No. 655, Tackling.

1994, Oct. 1   *Perf. 14x13½, 13½x14*
651	A156	2r multicolored
652	A156	6r multicolored
653	A156	10r multicolored
654	A156	12r multicolored

Souvenir Sheet
655	A156	12r multicolored

World Day of Environmental Protection A157

FAO, 50th Anniv. A158

Perf. 14x13½, 13½x14
1995, Oct. 15   Litho.
656	A157	15r Arabian leopard
657	A157	20r Caracal lynx
658	A157	30r Guinea fowl, horiz.

Souvenir Sheet
659	A157	50r Partridge, horiz.

1995, Oct. 16   *Perf. 14x13½*

Emblem, field, hand holding: 10r, Plant. 25r, Seed. 30r, Fish. 50r, Grain.
660	A158	10r violet & multi
661	A158	25r claret & multi
662	A158	30r light blue & multi

Souvenir Sheet
663	A158	50r dark blue & multi

A159   A160

UN, 50th anniv.: Various views of Aden Dam.

1995, Oct. 24   *Perf. 14x13½, 13½x14*
664	A159	10r multi
665	A159	15r multi
666	A159	25r multi, horiz.

Souvenir Sheet
667	A159	50r multi, horiz.

Perf. 14x13½, 13½x14
1995, Nov. 29

Naseem Hamed Kashmem, world boxing champion: 10r, With champion belts. 20r, Up close. 25r, Boxing opponent, horiz. 30r, Holding up arm as winner, trainer.
50r, Boxing opponent, diff., horiz.
668	A160	10r multicolored
669	A160	20r multicolored
670	A160	25r multicolored
671	A160	30r multicolored

Souvenir Sheet
672	A160	50r multicolored

Souvenir Sheet

CHINA '96, 9th Asian Intl. Philatelic Exhibition — A161

Illustration reduced.

1996, May 18   Litho.   *Perf. 11½*
673	A161	80r Shanghai

1996 Summer Olympic Games, Atlanta — A162

1996, July 19   *Perf. 14x13½, 13½x14*
674	A162	20r Wrestling, vert.
675	A162	50r High jump
676	A162	60r Running, vert.

677	A162	70r Gymnastics, vert.
678	A162	100r Judo, vert.

Souvenir Sheet
679	A162	150r Javelin, vert.

Landmarks A163

10r, 70r, 250r, Popular Heritage Museum, Seiyoan. 15r, 40r, 60r, 500r, Rock Palace, Wadi Dhahr, vert. 20r, 100r, 200r, Old Sana'a City. 30r, 50r, 150r, 300r, Al-Mohdhar Minaret, Tarim, vert.

Perf. 13½x14, 14x13½
1996, Sept. 26   Litho.
680	A163	10r org yel & multi
681	A163	15r grn yel & multi
682	A163	20r lt blue & multi
683	A163	30r blue & multi
684	A163	40r salmon & multi
685	A163	50r green & multi
686	A163	60r lilac & multi
687	A163	70r violet & multi
688	A163	100r yellow & multi
689	A163	150r orange & multi
690	A163	200r rose & multi
691	A163	250r gray & multi
692	A163	300r red & multi
693	A163	500r yellow & multi

Birds — A164

Designs: 20r, Tyto alba. 50r, Alectoris philbyi. 60r, Gypaetus barbatus. 70r, Alectoris melanocephala. 100r, Chlamydotis undulata. 150r, Ixobrychus minutus, vert.

1996, Oct. 14   Litho.   *Perf. 13½x14*
694	A164	20r multicolored
695	A164	50r multicolored
696	A164	60r multicolored
697	A164	70r multicolored
698	A164	100r multicolored

Souvenir Sheet
Perf. 14x13½
699	A164	150r multicolored

Rare Plants in Yemen — A165

Designs: 20r, Parodia masii. 50r, Notocatus cristata. 60r, Adenium obesum socotranum. 70r, Dracaena cinnabari. 100r, Mammillaria erythrosperma.
150r, Parodia maasii, diff.

1996, Nov. 30   *Perf. 13½x14*
700	A165	20r multicolored
701	A165	50r multicolored
702	A165	60r multicolored
703	A165	70r multicolored
704	A165	100r multicolored

Souvenir Sheet
705	A165	150r multicolored

A166

A167

Fish: 20r, Heniochus acuminatus. 50r, 150r, Cheilinus undulatus. 60r, Zebrasoma xanthurum. 70r, Pomacanthus imperator. 100r, Pomacanthus vanthometopon.

1996, Nov. 30
706	A166	20r multicolored
707	A166	20r multicolored
708	A166	60r multicolored
709	A166	70r multicolored
710	A166	100r multicolored

Souvenir Sheet
711	A166	150r multicolored

1996, Dec. 11   *Perf. 14x13½*

UNICEF, 50th Anniv.: 20r, Children with books. 50r, Girls clapping hands. 60r, Mother, child. 70r, Mother, three children.
150r, Child making jewelry, horiz.
712	A167	20r multicolored
713	A167	50r multicolored
714	A167	60r multicolored
715	A167	70r multicolored

Souvenir Sheet
Perf. 13½x14
716	A167	150r multicolored

1998 World Cup Soccer Championships, France — A168

Various soccer plays.

1998, June 10   Litho.   *Perf. 13x13½*
717	A168	10r multicolored
718	A168	15r multicolored
719	A168	35r multicolored
720	A168	65r multicolored
721	A168	75r multicolored
a.		Souvenir sheet, #717-721

Birds A169

Designs: 10r, Ardeotis arabs. 15r, Neophron percnopterus. 35r, Coracias abyssinicus. 65r, Cinnyricinclus leucogaster. 75r, Melierax metabates.

1998, Sept. 26   Litho.   *Perf. 13*
722-726	A169	Set of 5	4.25	4.25
726a		Sheet of 5, #722-726	4.25	4.25

Universal Declaration of Human Rights, 50th Anniv. A170

15r, Hands in air. 35r, Hands clasped in handshake. 100r, Hands reaching out.

1998, Oct. 12
727-729	A170	Set of 3	3.25	3.25
729a		Sheet of 3, #727-729	3.25	3.25

First General Conference of Yemeni Immigrants (in 1999) A171

Emblem &. 60r, Dhows. 90r, Fort, camel.

2000, May 16   Litho.   Perf. 14½x14
730-731 A171 Set of 2   2.00 2.00
731a   Souvenir sheet, #730-731   2.00 2.00

Tenth National Day — A172

Background colors: 30r, Light green. 50r, Rose lilac. 70r, Light blue. 150r, Orange.

2000, May 22   Perf. 14x14½
732-734 A172 Set of 3   1.60 1.60
Souvenir Sheet
735 A172 150r multi   1.60 1.60

Plants of Socotra — A173

Designs: 30r, Euphorbia abdalkuri. 70r, Dendrosicyos socotranus. 80r, Caralluma socotrana. 120r, Dracaena cinnabari. 300r, Exacum affine.

2000, July 15
736-739 A173 Set of 4   4.00 4.00
Souvenir Sheet
740 A173 300r multi   4.00 4.00

2000 Summer Olympics, Sydney — A174

Designs: 50r, Judo. 70r, Runner. 80r, Hurdler. 100r, Shooting. 300r, Tennis.

2000, Sept. 15
741-744 A174 Set of 4   4.00 4.00
Souvenir Sheet
745 A174 300r multi   4.00 4.00

Antiquities — A175

Designs: 30r, Stone idols, 3000 B.C. 70r, Statue of Ma'adi Karib, 800 B.C. 100r, Horned griffin, Royal Palace of Shabwa, 300. 120r, Statue of King of Awsan Yasduq Eil, 100 B.C. 320r, Stele with bull's head, 100 B.C., horiz.

2002, June 15   Litho.   Perf. 13x12¾
746-749 A175 Set of 4   4.25 4.25
Souvenir Sheet
Imperf
750 A175 320r multi   4.25 4.25
No. 750 contains one 41x26mm stamp.

2002 World Cup Soccer Championships, Japan and Korea — A176

Soccer players with background colors of: 30r, Bister, vert. 70r, Green. 100r, Blue, vert. 120r, Red brown, vert.
No. 755: a, Player's foot and ball. b, World Cup trophy.

2002, May 31   Perf. 13x12¾, 12¾x13
751-754 A176 Set of 4   4.25 4.25
Souvenir Sheet
Perf.
755 A176 160r Sheet of 2, #a-b   4.25 4.25
No. 755 contains two 28mm diameter stamps.

Scouting in Yemen, 75th Anniv. A177

Designs: 30r, Scout escorting man across street. 60r, Scout digging. 70r, Scouts in rowboat. 160r, Scout saluting, vert.

2002, Apr. 30   Perf. 12¾x13
756-758 A177 Set of 3   2.10 2.10
Souvenir Sheet
Perf. 13x13¼
759 A177 160r multi   2.10 2.10
No. 759 contains one 16x26mm stamp.

Palestinian Intifada — A178

Designs: 30r, Frightened child. 60r, Bleeding child. 90r, Dome of the Rock, horiz.

2002, Apr. 27   Perf. 13x12¾
760-761 A178 Set of 2   1.25 1.25
Imperf
Size: 111x78mm
762 A178 90r multi   1.25 1.25

Poets — A179

Revolution, 40th Anniv. — A180

Designs: Nos. 763, 30r, 765, 60r, 767a, 70r, Hussain Al-Muhdhar (1931-2000). Nos. 764, 30r, 766, 60r, 767b, 70r, Abdullah Al-Baradony (1929-99).

2002, June 30   Litho.   Perf. 13x12¾
763-766 A179 Set of 4   2.25 2.25

Souvenir Sheet
Perf. 13x13¼
767 A179 70r Sheet of 2, #a-b   1.75 1.75
No. 767 contains two 16x28mm stamps.

2002, Sept. 26   Perf. 13x12¾
Background colors: 30r, Dull green. 60r, Rose. 90r, Lilac.
768-769 A180 Set of 2   1.10 1.10
Imperf
Size: 110x76mm
770 A180 90r multi   1.10 1.10

World Under-17 Soccer Championships, Finland — A181

Various soccer players with background color of: 30r, Red violet. 50r, Golden brown. 70r, Blue. 100r, Green. 250r, Soccer team and stadium

2003, Aug. 13   Litho.   Perf. 12¾x13
771-774 A181 Set of 4   3.00 3.00
Imperf
Size: 109x74mm
775 A181 250r multi   3.00 3.00

Antiquities — A182

Various sculptures with background colors of: 20r, Pale yellow. 40r, Lilac. 50r, Light green. 150r, Pink. 260r, Black, horiz.

2003, Sept. 26   Perf. 13x12¾
776-779 A182 Set of 4   3.00 3.00
Souvenir Sheet
Perf. 12¾x13
780 A182 260r multi   3.00 3.00

Traditional Women's Clothing — A183

Various women with panel colors of: 30r, Purple. 60r, Yellow green. 70r, Dark green. 100r, Red violet. 150r, Brown. 410r, Purple background, horiz.

2003, Oct. 14   Perf. 13x12¾
781-785 A183 Set of 5   4.75 4.75
Souvenir Sheet
Perf. 12¾x13
786 A183 410r multi   4.75 4.75

Children's Art — A184

Designs: 20r, Girl with flower on globe, vert. 30r, Dove over buildings, vert. 40r, Dove holding swing, vert. 50r, Children in field. 60r, Animals in field. 70r, Street and park.

2003, Oct. 15   Perf. 13x12¾, 12¾x13
787-792 A184 Set of 6   3.00 3.00

Sana'a, 2004 Arabic Cultural Capital — A185

Various buildings with frame colors of: 30r, White. 50r, Purple. 70r, Black. 100r, Dark brown. 150r Red brown. 400r, Buildings, horiz.

2003, Nov. 30   Perf. 13x12¾
793-797 A185 Set of 5   4.50 4.50
Souvenir Sheet
Perf. 12¾x13
798 A185 400r multi   4.50 4.50

FIFA (Fédération Internationale de Football Association), Cent. — A186

2004, May 21   Litho.   Perf. 13x12¾
799 A186 100r multi   1.10 1.10
Dated 2005. Stamps did not appear in marketplace until 2005.

2004 Summer Olympics, Athens — A187

Designs: 70r, Running. 80r, Shooting. 100r, Swimming. 250r, Equestrian.

2004, Aug. 13
800-802 A187 Set of 3   2.75 2.75
Souvenir Sheet
803 A187 250r multi   2.75 2.75
Dated 2005. Stamps did not appear in marketplace until 2005.

Telecommunications and Technology — A188

Designs: 60r, Computer chips, "@" symbol, keyboard. 70r, Computer and stylized people, vert. 100r, Yemen Mobile emblem, vert. 400r, Like 70r, vert.

Perf. 12¾x13, 13x12¾
2004, Sept. 26
804-806 A188 Set of 3   2.50 2.50
Souvenir Sheet
807 A188 400r multi   4.50 4.50
Dated 2005. Stamps did not appear in marketplace until 2005.

Spiders
A189

No. 808: a, Tidarren argo. b, Scelidomachus socotranus. c, Habrocestum albopunctatum. d, Rafalus insignipalpis. e, Latrodectus hystrix. f, Atrophothele socotrana.
300r, Like No. 808b.

2004, Oct. 14		Perf. 12¾x13	
808	Horiz. strip of 6	3.25	3.25
a.-f.	A189 50r Any single	.50	.50

Souvenir Sheet

| 809 | A189 300r multi | 3.25 | 3.25 |

Dated 2005. Stamps did not appear in marketplace until 2005.

Traditional Men's
Clothing — A190

Men wearing various outfits with background colors of: 50r, Light yellow. 60r, Green. 70r, Pink. 100r, Blue.
360r, Orange brown.

2004, Oct. 30		Perf. 13x12¾	
810-813	A190 Set of 4	3.25	3.25

Souvenir Sheet

| 814 | A190 360r multi | 4.00 | 4.00 |

Dated 2005. Stamps did not appear in marketplace until 2005.

Handicrafts
A191

No. 815: a, Knife maker holding hammer. b, Textile worker piecing fabric. c, Jeweler. d, Weaver at loom.
3004, Like No. 815a.

2004, Nov. 30			
815	Horiz. strip of 4	3.25	3.25
a.-d.	A191 70r multi	.80	.80

Souvenir Sheet

| 816 | A191 300r multi | 3.25 | 3.25 |

Dated 2005. Stamps did not appear in marketplace until 2005.

15th National
Day — A192

Emblem and: 30r, Industrial plant. 60r, Dam and reservoir. 70r, Man holding flag.
90r, Buildings.

2005, May 22			
817-819	A192 Set of 3	1.75	1.75

Souvenir Sheet

| 820 | A192 90r multi | 1.00 | 1.00 |

United Nations,
60th
Anniv. — A193

Symbols of eight goals for a better Yemen: No. 821, 40r, Pregnant woman and doctor. No. 822, 40r, Woman, infant and doctor. No. 823, 40r, Woman reading book. No. 824, 40r, Mosquito, AIDS ribbon, medicine and bottle. No. 825, 40r, Man depositing trash in can, tree, smiling sun. 80r, Goats, hat seller and child. 100r, Woman, man and balance. 120r, Handshake.
130r, UN anniversary emblem.

2005, Oct. 24	Litho.	Perf. 13x12¾	
821-828	A193 Set of 8	5.50	5.50

Size: 111x83mm

Imperf

| 829 | A193 130r multi | 1.50 | 1.50 |

No. 829 contains one perforated label lacking a denomination.

AIR POST STAMPS

Catalogue values for unused stamps in this section are for Never Hinged items.

Plane over
San'a
AP1

1947	Unwmk.	Engr.	Perf. 12½	
C1	AP1 10b bright blue		6.00	2.00
C2	AP1 20b olive green		10.00	2.50

Views Type of Regular Issue

6b, 8b, View of San'a. 10b, Mocha coffee branch. 12b, Palace of the Rock, Wadi Dhahr. 16b, Palace, Ta'iz. 20b, 1i, Parade Ground, San'a.

1951	Wmk. 277	Photo.	Perf. 14	
C3	A14 6b blue		1.40	.50
C4	A14 8b dark brown		1.75	.60
C5	A14 10b dark green		2.25	1.40
C6	A13 12b dark blue		2.50	.80
C7	A14 16b lilac rose		3.00	.80
C8	A13 20b orange brown		3.75	1.25
C9	A13 1i dark red		10.00	3.00
	Nos. C3-C9 (7)		24.65	8.35

Nos. C3 and C4 were used provisionally in 1957 for registry and foreign ordinary mail.

Type of Regular Issue

Designs: 12b, Palace of the Rock, Wadi Dhahr. 20b, Walls of Ibb.

Engraved and Photogravure

1952	Unwmk.	Perf. 14½	
C10	A15 12b grnsh blk, bl & brn	10.00	10.00
C11	A15 20b indigo, bl & brn	10.00	10.00

Flag-and-View Type

1952
C12	A16 1i dk brn, car & brt ultra	18.00	18.00

Palace in Foreground

1952
C13	A16 30b yel grn, car & gray	11.00	11.00

Leaning Minaret,
Mosque of
Ta'iz — AP6

1954	Photo.	Perf. 14	
C14	AP6 10b scarlet	3.25	.90
C15	AP6 12b dull blue	4.00	1.25
C16	AP6 20b olive bister	6.50	2.00
	Nos. C14-C16 (3)	13.75	4.15

Accession of King Ahmed I, 5th anniv.

Type of Regular Issue

1959	Wmk. 318	Perf. 13x13½	
C17	A21 6b orange & blk	1.00	.70
C18	A21 10b red & blk	1.60	1.25
C19	A21 16b brt violet & red	2.50	2.00
	Nos. C17-C19 (3)	5.10	3.95

Antiquities of Marib Type

Designs: 6b, Columns, Temple of the Moon God. 16b, Control tower and spillway of 2,700-year-old dam of Marib.

		Perf. 11½	
1961, Oct. 14	Unwmk.	Photo.	
C20	A27 6b lt bl grn & blk	1.00	.20
C21	A27 16b lt blue & blk	2.75	1.50

For overprints see Nos. C24, C25.

Buildings Type

6b, Bab al-Yemen, main gate of San'a, horiz. 16b, Palace of the Rock (Dar al-Hajar).

1961, Nov. 15			
C22	A28 6b blk, lt bl & grn	.55	.20
C23	A28 16b blk, rose & grn	1.40	.60

For overprints see Nos. C24A, C25A.

Nos. C20-C23 Ovptd. Like Nos. 144-158 in Dark Red or Black

	Perf. 11½		
1963, Jan. 1	Photo.	Unwmk.	
C24	A27 (a) 6b No. C20	.70	.70
C24A	A28 (b) 6b No. C22	.85	.85
C25	A27 (a) 16b No. C21	1.75	1.75
C25A	A28 (a) 16b No. C23 (B)	2.75	2.75

Proclamation of the Republic Type

1963, Mar. 15	Perf. 11x11½, 11½x11		
C26	A34 8b Bayonette, torch	1.50	1.50
C27	A34 10b Jet, torch, tank	2.00	2.00
C28	A34 16b Flag, chain, torch	2.75	2.75
	Nos. C27-C28 horiz.		

Nos. 25-29
Ovptd. in Black

	Wmk. 258		
1963, Sept. 1	Litho.	Perf. 12½	
C29	A5 6b slate blue & ultra	1.50	1.50
C29A	A5 10b fawn & ultra	1.90	1.90
C29B	A5 14b olive & ultra	2.25	2.25
C29C	A5 20b yel grn & ultra	3.00	3.00
C29D	A5 1i claret & ultra	6.50	6.50
	Nos. C29-C29D (5)	15.15	15.15

Astronauts. Set of five airmail, ¼, ⅓, ½, 4, 20b. Airmail imperf. souvenir sheet, 20b. Dec. 5. Nos. 63C01-63C06. Value, set $11, souvenir $9.

1964
Astronauts issue of 1963 overprinted in black or red brown "John F. Kennedy / 1917 / 1963" in English or Arabic. Set of five airmail. May 5. Nos. 64C01-64C05.

San'a Intl. Airport Type
Perf. 11½x11

1964, Oct. 1	Photo.	Unwmk.	
C30	A40 6b Sun, buildings, aircraft	.70	.70

See note after No. 203.

APU 10th Anniv. Type

1964, Oct. 15		Perf. 13½	
C31	A41 6b blue grn & blk	1.00	.80

An imperf. souvenir sheet of one exists containing No. C31. Value $3.

Deir Yassin Massacre Type

1965, Apr. 30		Perf. 11x11½	
C32	A44 6b ver & brt org	1.00	

Library Type

1965, July 7		Perf. 11½x11	
C33	A46 6b sepia, red & int blue	.85	.55

An imperf. souvenir sheet of one exists containing No. C33. Value $2.50.

1966
Butterflies. Set of four airmail, 6, 8, 10, 16b. May 5. Nos. 66C01-66C04.

Lenin's Birth
Centenary
AP7

1970, Aug. 15	Litho.	Perf. 12x12½	
C34	AP7 6b Public speech	1.40	1.10
C35	AP7 16b Meeting with Arab delegates	3.00	1.90

8th Anniv. of the Revolution — AP8

1971, Jan. 24		Perf. 13	
C36	AP8 5b Country estate	.75	
C37	AP8 7b Workers	1.10	
C38	AP8 16b Handshake, flag, flowers, open book	1.50	
	Nos. C36-C38 (3)	3.35	

A souv. sheet of 1 exists containing No. C38. Value $5.

Revolution Type

1972, Nov. 25	Photo.	Perf. 13	
C40	A80 21b lilac, blk & multi	5.00	3.50

Al-Aqsa Mosque Type

1973, Jan. 1	Photo.	Perf. 13½	
C41	A82 24b lt bl, blk & multi	2.00	1.40
a.	Min. sheet of 1, imperf.		

UNICEF Type

1973, Jan. 15	Photo.	Perf. 13	
C42	A83 18b lt bl, blk & multi	1.75	1.50
a.	Min. sheet of 1, imperf.	3.25	3.25

For surcharge see No. C46.

11th Anniv.
of
Revolution
AP10

1973, Sept. 26 Photo. Perf. 14
C43 AP10 7b Bank .50 .35
C44 AP10 10b Cement factory .65 .55
C45 AP10 18b Hospital 1.50 1.10
Nos. C43-C45 (3) 2.65 2.00
For surcharges see Nos. C47-C48.

Nos. C42, C43, C45 Surcharged in
Black with New Value and Bars
1975, Nov. 15
C46 A83 75f on 18b lt bl, blk
& multi 2.50 2.50
C46A A80 75f on 21b #C40
(R) — —
C47 AP10 90f on 7b multi 5.50 2.75
C48 AP10 120f on 18b multi 4.25 4.25
a. Overprinted in red

Argentina 1978 World Cup Type
World cup emblem and various soccer
players.
1980, Mar. 30 Photo. Perf. 14
C49 A99 60f gold & multi .80 .60
C50 A99 75f gold & multi 1.00 .70
C51 A99 80f gold & multi 1.25 .90
C52 A99 100f gold & multi 1.50 1.00
Nos. C49-C52 (4) 4.55 3.20
Two 225f souvenir sheets exist.

IYC Type
1980, Apr. 1 Perf. 13½
C53 A100 80f Girl, bird 3.00 1.25
C54 A100 100f Boy, butterfly,
flower 3.00 1.25
C55 A100 150f Boy, butterfly,
flower, diff. 4.50 1.75
Nos. C53-C55 (3) 10.50 4.25
Two 200f souvenir sheets exist.

Scouting Type of 1980
1980, May 1 Photo. Perf. 13½x14
C56 A101 60f Bicycling 2.00 .80
C57 A101 75f Fencing 2.40 1.10
C58 A101 120f Butterfly catching 3.75 1.50
Nos. C56-C58 (3) 8.15 3.40
Two 300f souvenir sheets exist.

Argentina 1978 Winners' Type
World cup emblem and various soccer
players.
1980, June 1 Photo. Perf. 14
C59 A102 60f gold & multi 1.00 .50
C60 A102 75f gold & multi 1.40 .65
C61 A102 80f gold & multi 1.50 .75
C62 A102 100f gold & multi 1.60 1.10
Nos. C59-C62 (4) 5.50 3.00
Two 225f souvenir sheets exist.

19th Anniv. of
Sept. 26th
Revolution
(1981) — AP11

1982, Jan. 25 Litho. Perf. 14
C63 AP11 75f Map .45 .25
C64 AP11 125f Map in sunset .70 .40
C65 AP11 325f Dove in natl. col-
ors 2.00 1.25
a. Souvenir sheet of 1 5.00 5.00
C66 AP11 400f Jets 2.25 1.40
Nos. C63-C66 (4) 5.40 3.30

Al-Hasan Ibn Al-Hamadani,
Writer — AP12

1982, Feb. 1
C67 AP12 125f green & multi 1.25 .60

C68 AP12 325f blue & multi 2.75 1.40
Souvenir Sheet
C69 AP12 375f multi 3.50 3.50
No. C69 contains one stamp (36x46mm).
For surcharge see No. C138.

World Food Day — AP13

Designs: No. C76a, Eggplants. No. C76b,
Tomatoes. No. C76c, Beets, peas. No. C76d,
Cauliflower, carrots. No. C77a, Dove. No.
C77b, Water birds. No. C77c, Fish. No. C77d,
Geese.

1982, Mar. 1 Litho. Perf. 14
C70 AP13 25f Rabbits .50
C71 AP13 50f Rooster, Hens 1.00
C72 AP13 60f Turkeys 1.25
C73 AP13 75f Sheep 1.50
C74 AP13 100f Cattle 2.00
C75 AP13 125f Deer 2.50
Nos. C70-C75 (6) 8.75
Souvenir Sheets
C76 Sheet of 4 2.00
a.-d. AP13 100f, any single .50
C77 Sheet of 4 2.50
a.-d. AP13 125f, any single .60
For surcharges see Nos. C139, C144.

1980
Summer
Olympics,
Moscow
AP14

1982, Apr. 1
C78 AP14 25f Gymnastics
C79 AP14 50f Pole vault
C80 AP14 60f Javelin
C81 AP14 75f Running
C82 AP14 100f Basketball
C83 AP14 125f Soccer

Two souvenir sheets of 4 exist: 100f, picturing boxing, wrestling, canoeing, swimming,
and 125f, picturing weight lifting, discus, long
jump, fencing.
For surcharges see Nos. C140, C145.

Aviation — AP15

Various space and aircraft.

1982, May 21
C86 AP15 25f multi
C87 AP15 50f multi
C88 AP15 60f multi
C89 AP15 75f multi
C90 AP15 100f multi
C91 AP15 125f multi

Two souvenir sheets of 4 exist, 100f and
125f, picturing various aircraft and satellites.
For surcharges see Nos. C141, C146.

Intl. Year of the Disabled — AP16

Designs: Nos. C94-C99, Diff. flowers.
No. C100a, Emblem, natl. flag. b, Emblem
on globe. c, Natl. colors, UN emblems. d, Disabled man, gifts, nurse.
No. C101a, Flags, globe and nurse. b, UN
emblems, natl. flag. c, Emblem, disabled man.
d, UN emblem, nurse.

1982, June 1
C94 AP16 25f multi
C95 AP16 50f multi
C96 AP16 60f multi
C97 AP16 75f multi
C98 AP16 100f multi
C99 AP16 125f multi
Souvenir Sheets
C100 Sheet of 4
a.-d. AP16 100f, any single
C101 Sheet of 4
a.-d. AP16 125f, any single
For surcharge see No. C147.

Telecommunications Progress — AP17

Designs: 25f, FNRR communication center.
50f, Dish receivers, satellite, globe. 60f,
Broadcast towers, dish receivers. 75f, Receivers, birds over plain. 100f, Receivers, satellite,
telegraph key. No. C107, Receivers, passenger jet, Earth.
No. C108a, Receivers, Earth. b, Earth, television, flag and camera. c, Computer. d, Skyscraper, Earth, telephone.
No. C109a, Receivers, satellite, ship. b,
Communication center, bolts of energy,
receivers. c, Receivers, jet, ship, train, car,
carriage. d, Radar.

1982, July 1 Litho. Perf. 14
C102 AP17 25f multi
C103 AP17 50f multi
C104 AP17 60f multi
C105 AP17 75f multi
C106 AP17 100f multi
C107 AP17 125f multi
Souvenir Sheets
C108 Sheet of 4
a.-d. AP17 100f any single
C109 Sheet of 4
a.-d. AP17 100f any single
For surcharges see Nos. C142, C148.

TB Bacillus Centenary — AP18

1982 Litho. Perf. 14
C110 AP18 25f multi
C111 AP18 50f multi
C112 AP18 60f multi
C113 AP18 75f multi
C114 AP18 100f multi
C115 AP18 125f multi
Souvenir Sheets
C116 Sheet of 4, Fruit
a. AP18 100f, any single
C117 Sheet of 4, Flowers
a. AP18 125f, any single
For surcharges see Nos. C143, C149.

1982 World Cup Soccer
Championships, Spain — AP19

Various soccer plays.

1982, Sept. 1 Perf. 14
C118 AP19 25f multi
C119 AP19 50f multi
C120 AP19 60f multi
C121 AP19 75f multi
C122 AP19 100f multi
C123 AP19 125f multi

Palestinian Children's Day — AP20

1982, Oct. 20
C126 AP20 75f Boy
C127 AP20 125f Girl
C128 AP20 325f Boy and girl
a. Souvenir sheet of 1

Arab Postal Union, 30th
Anniv. — AP21

1982, Dec. 1
C129 AP21 75f yellow & multi
C130 AP21 125f green & multi
C131 AP21 325f magenta & multi
a. Souvenir sheet of 1

1984 Summer Olympics, Los
Angeles — AP22

1984, Nov. 15
C132 AP22 20f Wrestling
C133 AP22 30f Boxing
C134 AP22 40f Running
C135 AP22 60f Hurdling
C136 AP22 150f Pole vault
C137 AP22 325f Javelin throw

Two souvenir sheets of four 75f stamps exist
picturing water sports, gymnastics, weightlifting, shot put and discus throwing.

No. C67 Surcharged
Nos. 459, 461, 463, 466, 474, 483,
486, 522, C73, C75, C81, C83, C89,
C91, C97, C105, C107, C113 & C115
Surcharged with New Value and "AIR
MAIL"
1993, Jan. 1 Perfs, etc. as Before
C138 AP12 3r on 125f #C67
C139 AP13 3r on 125f #C75
C140 AP14 3r on 125f #C83

C141 AP15 3r on 125f #C91
C142 AP17 3r on 125f #C107
C143 AP18 3r on 125f #C115
C144 AP13 5r on 75f #C73
C145 AP14 5r on 75f #C81
C146 AP15 5r on 75f #C89
C147 AP16 5r on 75f #C97
C148 AP17 5r on 75f #C105
C149 AP18 5r on 75f #C113
C150 A126 8r on 425f #459
C151 A127 8r on 425f #461
C152 A128 8r on 425f #463
C153 A129 8r on 425f #466
C154 A130 8r on 425f #474
C155 A132 8r on 425f #483
C156 A133 8r on 425f #486
C157 A142 12r on 850f #522

Size and location of surcharge varies.

POSTAGE DUE STAMPS

D1

1942 Litho. Wmk. 258 Perf. 12½
J1 D1 1b org & yel grn   .20 .20
J2 D1 2b org & yel grn   .25 .25
J3 D1 4b org & yel grn   .45 .45
J4 D1 6b org & brt ultra   .55 .55
J5 D1 8b org & brt ultra   .80 .80
J6 D1 10b org & brt ultra 1.00 1.00
J7 D1 12b org & brt ultra 1.50 1.50
J8 D1 20b org & brt ultra 3.00 3.00
        Nos. J1-J8 (8)   7.75 7.75

Yemen had no postage due system. Nos. J1-J8 were used for regular postage. See Nos. 66-67 for surcharges.

YEMEN, PEOPLE'S DEMOCRATIC REPUBLIC OF

'pē-pəls ri-'pə-blik of 'ye-mən

LOCATION — Southern Arabia
GOVT. — Republic
AREA — 111,074 sq. mi.
POP. — 2,030,000 (est. 1981)
CAPITAL — Aden

The People's Republic of Southern Yemen was proclaimed Nov. 30, 1967, when the Federation of South Arabia achieved independence. It consisted of the former British colony of Aden and the protectorates. The name was changed to People's Democratic Republic of Yemen on Nov. 30, 1970. See South Arabia.

The Yemen Arab Republic and the People's Republic of Yemen planned a 30-month unification process scheduled for completion by November 1992. While government ministries merged, both currencies remained valid. A civil war in 1994 delayed the merger.

1,000 Fils = 1 Dinar

Catalogue values for all unused stamps in this country are for Never Hinged items.

People's Republic of Southern Yemen
South Arabia Nos. 3-16 Overprinted in Red or Blue

جمهورية اليمن الجنوبية الشعبية

Nos. 1-10

PEOPLE'S REPUBLIC OF SOUTHERN YEMEN

جمهورية اليمن الجنوبية الشعبية

PEOPLE'S REPUBLIC OF SOUTHERN YEMEN
Nos. 11-14

Perf. 14½x14
1968, Apr. 1   Photo.   Unwmk.
1   A1 5f blue   .20 .20
2   A1 10f lt vio bl   .20 .20
3   A1 15f bl grn   .20 .20
4   A1 20f green   .20 .20
5   A1 25f org brn (B) .20 .20
6   A1 30f lemon   .20 .20
7   A1 35f red brn (B) .35 .20
8   A1 50f rose red (B) .45 .35
9   A1 65f lt yel grn   .60 .40
10 A1 75f rose car (B) .80 .55
11 A2 100f multi (B)   1.25 .70
12 A2 250f multi   2.40 1.40
13 A2 500f multi (B)   4.50 2.75
14 A2 1d vio & multi   11.50 7.00
        Nos. 1-14 (14)   23.05 14.55

Globe and Flag A1

Designs: 15f, Revolutionist with broken chain and flames, vert. 50f, Aden Harbor. 100f, Cotton picking.

1968, May 25   Litho.   Perf. 13x12½
15 A1 10f multi   .20 .20
16 A1 15f multi   .20 .20
17 A1 50f multi   .75 .75
18 A1 100f multi   1.50 1.50
        Nos. 15-19 (5)   3.15 3.15

Independence Day, Nov. 30, 1967.

Girl Scouts at Campfire A2

Designs: 25f, Three Girl Scouts, vert. 50f, Three Girl Scout leaders.

Perf. 13½
1968, Sept. 21   Litho.   Unwmk.
19 A2 10f ultra & sepia   .50 .50
20 A2 25f org brn & Prus bl .70 .70
21 A2 50f yel, bl & brn   1.50 1.50
        Nos. 19-21 (3)   2.70 2.70

Girl Scout movement in Southern Yemen, established 1966 (in Aden).

Revolutionary — A3

"Freedom-Socialism-Unity" A4

King of Ausan, Alabaster Statue A5

Design: 30f, Radfan Mountains where first revolutionary fell.

1968, Oct. 14   Unwmk.   Perf. 13
22 A3 20f brn & lt bl   .30 .30
23 A3 30f grn & brn   .45 .45
24 A4 100f ver & yel   1.10 1.10
        Nos. 22-24 (3)   1.85 1.85

Revolution Day (revolution of Oct. 14, 1963).

1968, Dec. 28   Litho.   Perf. 13
Antiquities of Southern Yemen: 35f, African-type sculpture of a man. 50f, Winged bull, Assyrian-type bas-relief, horiz. 65f, Bull's head (Moon God), alabaster plaque, 230 B.C., horiz.
25 A5 5f olive & bister   .20 .20
26 A5 35f maroon & lt bl   .50 .50
27 A5 50f bister & blue   1.10 1.10
28 A5 65f lt grnsh bl & lilac 1.40 1.40
        Nos. 25-28 (4)   3.20 3.20

A6

A7

Martyr Monument, Steamer Point, Aden.

1969, Feb. 11   Litho.   Perf. 13
29 A6 15f yellow & multi   .20 .20
30 A6 35f emerald & multi .20 .20
31 A6 100f orange & multi 1.50 1.50
        Nos. 29-31 (3)   1.90 1.90

Issued for Martyr Day.

1969, June 1   Litho.   Perf. 13
Albert Thomas Monument, Geneva, and ILO emblem.
32 A7 10f brt grn, blk & lt brn .25 .25
33 A7 35f car rose, blk & lt brn .75 .75

50th anniv. of the ILO, and to honor founder Albert Thomas.

Classroom — A8

1969, Sept. 8   Litho.   Perf. 13
34 A8 35f orange & multi   .65 .65
35 A8 100f yellow & multi 1.60 1.60

International Literacy Day, Sept. 8.

Mahatma Gandhi — A9

1969, Sept. 27   Litho.   Perf. 13
36 A9 35f lt ultra & vio brn 1.75 .60

Mohandas K. Gandhi (1869-1948), leader in India's fight for independence.

Family A10

1969, Oct. 1
37 A10 25f lt grn & multi   .75 .60
38 A10 75f car rose & multi 1.50 .90

Issued for Family Day.

UN Headquarters, NYC — A11

1969, Oct. 24   Perf. 13
39 A11 20f rose red & multi .60 .20
40 A11 65f emer & multi   1.25 .60

Issued for United Nations Day.

Map and Flag of Southern Yemen — A12

40f, 50f, Tractors, flag (agricultural progress).

1969, Nov. 30   Litho.   Unwmk.
Size: 41x24½mm
41 A12 15f multi   .20 .20
42 A12 35f multi   .55 .20
Size: 37x37mm
43 A12 40f blue & multi   .60 .35
44 A12 50f brown & multi 1.00 .50
        Nos. 41-44 (4)   2.35 1.25

Second anniversary of independence.

Map of Arab League Countries, Flag and Emblem — A13

1970, Mar. 22   Unwmk.   Perf. 13
45 A13 35f lt bl & multi   .75 .25

25th anniversary of the Arab League.

Lenin — A14   Fighter — A15

1970, Apr. 22   Litho.   Perf. 13
46   A14   75f multi   1.50   .60

Lenin (1870-1924), Russian communist leader.

1970, May 15

Designs: 35f, Underground soldier and plane destroyed on ground. 50f, Fighting people hailing Arab liberation flag, horiz.

47   A15   15f grn, red & blk   .20   .20
48   A15   35f grn, bl, red & blk   .65   .55
49   A15   50f grn, blk & red   .85   .70
       Nos. 47-49 (3)   1.70   1.45

Issued for Palestine Day.

UPU Headquarters, Bern — A16

1970, May 22   Litho.   Perf. 13
50   A16   15f org & brt grn   .60   .20
51   A16   65f yel & car rose   1.40   .60

New UPU Headquarters in Bern.

Yemeni Costume — A17

Regional Costumes: 15f, 20f, Women's costumes. 50f, Three men of Aden.

1970, July 2   Litho.   Perf. 13
52   A17   10f yel & multi   .40   .20
53   A17   15f lt lil & multi   .40   .20
54   A17   20f lt bl & multi   .65   .20
55   A17   50f multi   1.25   .45
       Nos. 52-55 (4)   2.70   1.05

Camel and Calf — A18

Designs: 25f, Goats. 35f, Arabian oryx. 65f, Socotra dwarf cows.

1970, Aug. 31   Litho.   Perf. 13
56   A18   15f dk brn & multi   .40   .20
57   A18   25f car rose & multi   .70   .50
58   A18   35f ultra & multi   1.50   1.00
59   A18   65f brt grn & multi   2.40   1.50
       Nos. 56-59 (4)   5.00   3.20

A19

35f, Natl. Front Organization Headquarters. 50f, Farm worker, 1970, battle scene, 1963.

1970, Oct. 14   Litho.   Perf. 13
Size: 41½x29½mm
60   A19   25f multi   .50   .20
Size: 56½x27mm
61   A19   35f multi   .65   .45
Size: 41x24½mm
62   A19   50f multi   1.00   .60
       Nos. 60-62 (3)   2.15   1.25

7th anniversary of Oct. 14 Revolution.

UN Headquarters, Emblem — A20

1970, Oct. 24   Litho.   Perf. 13
63   A20   10f org & bl   .70   .20
64   A20   65f brt pink & bl   1.50   .80

25th anniversary of the United Nations.

People's Democratic Republic of Yemen

Temples at Philae — A21

1971, Feb. 1   Litho.   Perf. 13½x13
65   A21   5f violet & multi   .20   .20
66   A21   35f blue & multi   .65   .40
67   A21   65f green & multi   1.60   .90
       Nos. 65-67 (3)   2.45   1.50

UNESCO campaign to save the monuments in Nubia.

Scales, Book and Sword A22

1971, Mar. 1   Perf. 13x12½
68   A22   10f brt pink & multi   .20   .20
69   A22   15f brt grn & multi   .20   .20
70   A22   35f lt ultra & multi   .65   .65
71   A22   50f rose & multi   .85   .85
       Nos. 68-71 (4)   1.90   1.90

First Constitution, 1971.

Men of 3 Races, Human Rights Emblem A23

1971, Mar. 21
72   A23   20f lt bl & multi   .20   .20
73   A23   35f grn & multi   .75   .75
74   A23   65f lt vio & multi   1.10   1.10
       Nos. 72-74 (3)   2.05   2.05

Intl. year against racial discrimination.

Map and Flag — A24

"Brothers' Blood" Tree, Socotra Island — A25

1971-77   Litho.   Perf. 13½
75   A24   5f yel & multi   .20   .20
76   A24   10f grn & multi   .20   .20
77   A24   15f yel & multi   .20   .20
78   A24   20f org & multi   .20   .20
79   A24   25f bl & multi   .20   .20
80   A24   35f red org & multi   .35   .20
81   A24   40f vio & multi   .50   .20
82   A24   50f yel grn & multi   .75   .45
82A   A24   60f red & multi   1.50   .60
83   A24   65f pale vio & multi   .95   .65
84   A24   80f org brn & multi   1.10   .80
84A   A24   90f ol & multi   1.50   .75
       Perf. 13
84B   A25   110f brn & multi   2.25   .95
85   A25   125f ultra & multi   1.90   1.60
86   A25   250f org & multi   3.25   2.10
87   A25   500f multi   6.75   4.00
88   A25   1d grn & multi   15.00   9.00
       Nos. 75-88 (17)   36.80   22.30

Issued: #82A, 84A-84B, 10/17/77; others, 4/1/71.
See Nos. 332-333. For surcharges see Yemen Nos. 628, 638.

Machine Gun and Map A26   Arms with Wrench and Cogwheel A27

Designs: 45f, Woman fighter and flame, horiz. 50f, Fighter, factories and rainbow.

1971, June 9   Litho.   Perf. 12½x13
89   A26   15f multi   .20   .20
90   A26   45f green & multi   .75   .45
91   A26   50f multi   1.25   .75
       Nos. 89-91 (3)   2.20   1.40

Armed revolution in the Arabian Gulf.

1971, June 22

25f, Torch, factories, symbols. 65f, Windmill.
92   A27   15f blue & multi   .25   .25
93   A27   25f multi   .75   .55
94   A27   65f multi   1.25   .75
       Nos. 92-94 (3)   2.25   1.55

2nd anniversary of the revolution of June 22, 1969 (Corrective Move).
A 20f picturing a fighter holding rifle and flag, with flag colors transposed, was withdrawn on day of issue.

Revolutionary Emblem — A28

40f, Map of southern Arabia & flag of republic.

1971, Sept. 26
95   A28   10f yellow & multi   .20   .20
96   A28   40f lt grn & multi   .90   .55

9th anniv. of the revolution of Sept. 26.

Gamal Abdel Nasser — A29

UNICEF Emblem, Children of the World — A30

1971, Sept. 28   Litho.   Perf. 12½x13
97   A29   65f multi   1.25   .75

1st anniv. of the death of Gamal Abdel Nasser (1918-1970), President of Egypt.

1971, Dec. 11   Perf. 13x13½
98   A30   15f org, car & blk   .20   .20
99   A30   40f lt ultra, car & blk   .40   .35
100   A30   50f yel grn, car & blk   .70   .55
       Nos. 98-100 (3)   1.30   1.10

25th anniv. of UNICEF.

Pigeons A31

Birds: 40f, Partridge. 65f, Partridge and guinea fowl. 100f, European kite.

1971, Dec. 22   Perf. 13½x13
101   A31   5f bl, blk & car   .35   .25
102   A31   40f salmon & multi   1.25   .60
103   A31   65f brt grn, blk & car   3.00   1.10
104   A31   100f yel, blk & car   5.25   2.25
       Nos. 101-104 (4)   9.85   4.15

Dhow under Construction A32

Design: 80f, Dhow under sail, vert.

1972, Feb. 15   Perf. 13½x13, 13x13½
105   A32   25f bl, brn & yel   .75   .45
106   A32   80f lt bl & multi   2.40   1.60

Band — A33

Designs: 25f, 40f, 80f, Various folk dances.

1972, Apr. 8   Litho.   Perf. 13
107   A33   10f lt grn & multi   .20   .20
108   A33   25f org & multi   .40   .35
109   A33   40f red & multi   .80   .50
110   A33   80f blue & multi   1.50   1.00
       Nos. 107-110 (4)   2.90   2.05

Palestinian Fighter and Barbed Wire — A34

1972, May 15
111	A34	5f emerald & multi	.30	.20
112	A34	20f blue & multi	.60	.35
113	A34	65f org ver & multi	1.50	.85
		Nos. 111-113 (3)	2.40	1.40

Struggle for Palestine liberation.

Policemen on Parade A35

Design: 80f, Militia women on parade.

1972, June 20   Litho.   Perf. 13½
114	A35	25f lt bl & multi	.60	.20
115	A35	80f bl grn & multi	2.50	1.50
a.		Souv. sheet of 2, #114-115	9.00	9.00

Police Day. No. 115a sold for 150f.

Start of Bicycle Race A36

15f Parade of young women. 40f, Yemeni Guides & Scouts on parade. 80f, Acrobats, vert.

1972, July 20   Litho.   Perf. 13½
116	A36	10f lt bl & multi	.45	.20
117	A36	15f multi	.45	.20
118	A36	40f buff & multi	.90	.60
119	A36	80f lt ultra & multi	2.25	.90
		Nos. 116-119 (4)	4.05	1.90

Turtle A37

1972, Sept. 2   Litho.   Perf. 13
120	A37	15f Shown	.90	.20
121	A37	40f Sailfish	1.25	.70
122	A37	65f Kingfish	1.50	.90
123	A37	125f Spiny lobster	3.00	1.60
		Nos. 120-123 (4)	6.65	3.40

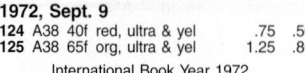

Book Year Emblem A38

1972, Sept. 9
124	A38	40f red, ultra & yel	.75	.50
125	A38	65f org, ultra & yel	1.25	.80

International Book Year 1972.

Farm Couple and Fields A39

1972, Nov. 23   Litho.   Perf. 13
126	A39	10f orange & multi	.20	.20
127	A39	25f rose lilac & multi	.70	.45
128	A39	40f red & multi	1.25	.80
		Nos. 126-128 (3)	2.15	1.45

Lands Day, publicizing land reforms.

Militia — A40

20f, Soldier guarding village. 65f, Industrial, agricultural and educational progress, vert.

1972, Dec. 2   Litho.   Perf. 13
129	A40	5f multi	.20	.20
130	A40	20f multi	.20	.20
131	A40	65f multi	1.60	1.60
a.		Souv. sheet of 3, #129-131, imperf.	4.00	4.00
		Nos. 129-131 (3)	2.00	2.00

5th anniversary of independence.

Census Chart A41

1973, Apr. 3   Litho.   Perf. 12½x13½
132	A41	25f org, emer & ol	.20	.20
133	A41	40f rose, bl & vio	1.25	1.25

Population census 1973.

WHO Emblem and "25" — A42

1973, Apr. 7   Perf. 14x12½, 12½x14
134	A42	5f "25" and WHO emblem, vert	.20	.20
135	A42	20f Shown	.20	.20
136	A42	125f "25" and WHO emblem	2.10	2.10
		Nos. 134-136 (3)	2.50	2.50

25th anniv. of the WHO.

Elephant Bay A43

Tourist Publicity: 20f, Taweels Tanks Reservoir, vert. 25f, Shibam Town. 100f, Al-Mohdar Mosque, Tarim.

1973, June 9   Litho.   Perf. 13
137	A43	20f multi	.20	.20
138	A43	25f multi	.20	.20
139	A43	40f multi	1.50	1.50
140	A43	100f multi	1.75	1.75
		Nos. 137-140 (4)	3.65	3.65

Office Buildings and Slum, Aden — A44

Design: 80f, Intersection, Aden, vert.

1973, Aug. 4   Litho.   Perf. 13
141	A44	20f multi	.20	.20
142	A44	80f multi	1.75	1.75

Nationalization of buildings.

Army Unit A45

People's Army: 20f, Four marching soldiers. 40f, Sailors on parade. 80f, Tanks.

1973, Sept. 1
143	A45	10f multi	.20	.20
144	A45	20f multi	.20	.20
145	A45	40f multi	1.00	1.00
146	A45	80f multi	1.40	1.40
		Nos. 143-146 (4)	2.80	2.80

FAO Emblem, Loading Food A46

Design: 80f, Workers and grain sacks.

1973, Dec. 19   Litho.   Perf. 13
147	A46	20f blue & multi	.20	.20
148	A46	80f blue & multi	1.75	1.75

World Food Program, 10th anniversary.

Letter and UPU Emblem A47

UPU Emblem and Yemeni Flag — A48

Map of Yemen, UPU Emblem — A49

UPU cent.: 20f, "100" formed by people, and UPU emblem.

1974, Oct. 9   Litho.   Perf. 12½x13½
149	A47	5f multi	.20	.20
150	A47	20f multi	.20	.20
151	A48	40f multi	.70	.70
152	A49	125f multi	1.25	1.25
		Nos. 149-152 (4)	2.35	2.35

Irrigation System — A50

Progress in Agriculture: 20f, Bulldozer pushing soil. 100f, Tractors plowing field.

1974   Litho.   Perf. 13
153	A50	10f multi	.20	.20
154	A50	20f multi	.20	.20
155	A50	100f multi	1.50	1.50
		Nos. 153-155 (3)	1.90	1.90

Lathe Operator — A51

Industrial progress: 40f, Printers. 80f, Women textile workers, horiz.

1975, May 1   Litho.   Perf. 13
156	A51	10f multi	.20	.20
157	A51	40f multi	.60	.60
158	A51	80f multi	1.00	1.00
		Nos. 156-158 (3)	1.80	1.80

Yemeni Woman — A52

Designs: Various women's costumes.

1975, Nov. 15   Litho.   Perf. 11½x12
159	A52	5f blk & ocher	.20	.20
160	A52	10f blk & vio	.20	.20
161	A52	15f blk & olive	.20	.20
162	A52	25f blk & rose lil	.45	.45
163	A52	40f blk & Prus bl	.75	.75
164	A52	50f blk & org brn	1.10	1.10
		Nos. 159-164 (6)	2.90	2.90

Women Factory Workers, IWY Emblem A53

1975, Dec. 30   Litho.   Perf. 12x11½
165	A53	40f blk & salmon	.60	.60
166	A53	50f blk & yel grn	1.00	1.00

International Women's Year 1975.

Soccer Player and Field — A54

Designs: Different scenes from soccer.

1976, Apr. 1   Litho.   Perf. 11½x12

167	A54	5f lt bl & brn	.20	.20
168	A54	40f yel & green	.70	.70
169	A54	80f salmon & vio	1.10	1.10
		Nos. 167-169 (3)	2.00	2.00

Rocket Take-off from Moon — A55

15f, Alexander Satalov. 40f, Lunokhod on moon, horiz. 65f, Valentina Tereshkova, rocket.

Perf. 11½x12, 12x11½

1976, Apr. 17   Litho.

170	A55	10f multi	.20	.20
171	A55	15f multi	.20	.20
172	A55	40f multi	1.00	1.00
173	A55	65f multi	1.25	1.25
		Nos. 170-173 (4)	2.65	2.65

Soviet cosmonauts and space program.

Traffic Policemen A56

1977, Apr. 16   Litho.   Perf. 14

174	A56	25f red & blk	.60	.60
175	A56	60f yel & blk	1.25	1.25
176	A56	75f grn & blk	1.50	1.50
177	A56	110f dp bl & blk	2.00	2.00
		Nos. 174-177 (4)	5.35	5.35

Traffic change to right side of road.

APU Emblem — A57

1977, Apr. 12   Litho.   Perf. 13½

178	A57	20f lt bl & multi	.20	.20
179	A57	60f gray & multi	.80	.80
180	A57	70f lt grn & multi	1.00	1.00
181	A57	90f bl grn & multi	1.10	1.10
		Nos. 178-181 (4)	3.10	3.10

Arab Postal Union, 25th anniversary.

Congress Decree and Red Star A58

Designs: 25f, Pres. Salim Rubi'a Ali, Council members Ali Nasser Muhamed and Abdul Farta Ismail. 65f, Women's militia on parade. 95f, Aerial view of textile mill.

1977, May   Photo.   Perf. 13

182	A58	25f grn, gold & dk brn	.20	.20
183	A58	35f red, gold & lt bl	.50	.50
184	A58	65f bl, gold & lil	1.00	1.00
185	A58	95f org, gold & grn	1.10	1.10
		Nos. 182-185 (4)	2.80	2.80

Unification Congress, 1st anniversary.

Afrivoluta Pringlei A59

Shells: 60f, Festilyria duponti, vert. 110f, Conus splendidulus. 180f, Cypraea 4broderipii.

1977, July 16   Litho.   Perf. 13½

186	A59	60f multi	.95	.70
187	A59	90f multi	1.40	.70
188	A59	110f multi	2.40	1.40
189	A59	180f multi	3.25	2.40
		Nos. 186-189 (4)	8.00	5.20

Emblem and Flag — A60

Designs: 20f, Man with broken chain. 90f, Pipeline, agriculture and industry. 110f, Flag, symbolic tree and hands holding tools.

1977, Nov. 30   Litho.   Perf. 13½

190	A60	5f blk & multi	.20	.20
191	A60	20f blk & multi	.20	.20
192	A60	90f blk & multi	.50	.20
193	A60	110f blk & multi	.85	.40
		Nos. 190-193 (4)	1.75	1.00

10th anniversary of independence.

Dome of the Rock A61

1978, May 15   Perf. 12

194	A61	5f multi	.70	.40

Palestinian fighters & families. See #264A.

Congress Emblem and "CUBA" — A62

Designs: 60f, Congress emblem. 90f, Festival emblem as flower. 110f, Festival emblem, dove, young man and woman.

1978, June 22   Litho.   Perf. 14

195	A62	5f multi	.20	.20
196	A62	60f multi	.65	.40
197	A62	90f multi	.85	.45
198	A62	110f multi	1.10	.70
		Nos. 195-198 (4)	2.80	1.75

11th World Youth Festival, Havana.

Silver Ornaments — A63

Designs: Various silver ornaments.

1978, July 22   Litho.   Perf. 13½

199	A63	10f blk & multi	.20	.20
200	A63	15f blk & multi	.20	.20
201	A63	20f blk & multi	.20	.20
202	A63	60f blk & multi	.20	.20
203	A63	90f blk & multi	1.00	.60
204	A63	110f blk & multi	1.50	.75
		Nos. 199-204 (6)	3.30	2.20

For surcharge see Yemen No. 629.

Yemeni Musical Instruments — A64

1978, Aug. 26   Perf. 14

205	A64	35f Almarfaai	.20	.20
206	A64	60f Almizmar	.85	.20
207	A64	90f Alqnboos	1.00	.20
208	A64	110f Simsimiya	1.75	1.00
		Nos. 205-208 (4)	3.80	1.60

For surcharge see Yemen No. 630.

"V" for Vanguard A65

1978, Oct. 11   Litho.   Perf. 14

209	A65	5f multi	.20	.20
210	A65	20f multi	.20	.20
211	A65	60f multi	.40	.20
212	A65	180f multi	.85	.50
		Nos. 209-212 (4)	1.65	1.10

1st Conf. of Vanguard Party, Oct. 11-13.

Man with Palm, Factories — A66

1978, Oct. 14

Designs: 10f, Palm branches, broken chains, horiz. 60f, Candle and "15." 110f, Woman and man with rifle, "15."

213	A66	10f multi	.20	.20
214	A66	35f multi	.20	.20
215	A66	60f multi	.45	.20
216	A66	110f multi	.75	.45
		Nos. 213-216 (4)	1.60	1.05

15th Revolution Day.
For surcharge see Yemen No. 631.

Child, Map of Arabia and IYC Emblem — A67

1979, Mar. 20   Litho.   Perf. 13½

217	A67	15f multi	.20	.20
218	A67	20f multi	.20	.20
219	A67	60f multi	.50	.20
220	A67	90f multi	.70	.20
		Nos. 217-220 (4)	1.60	.80

International Year of the Child.

Sickle, Star, Tractor, Wheat and Dove — A68

Designs: 35f, Pylon, star, compass, wheat and hammer. 60f, Students, worker and clock. 90f, Woman with raised arms, doves and star.

1979, June 22   Litho.   Perf. 14

221	A68	20f multi	.20	.20
222	A68	35f multi	.20	.20
223	A68	60f multi	.40	.20
224	A68	90f multi	.55	.20
		Nos. 221-224 (4)	1.35	.80

Corrective Move, 10th anniversary.

Yemen #52, Hill A69

Hill and: 110f, Yemen #56. 250f, Aden #12.

1979, Aug. 27   Litho.   Perf. 14

225	A69	90f multi	.60	.20
226	A69	110f multi	.75	.45

Souvenir Sheet

227	A69	250f multi	2.25	2.25

Sir Rowland Hill (1795-1879), originator of penny postage.

Book, World Map, Arab Achievements — A70

1979, Sept. 26   Litho.   Perf. 14

228	A70	60f multi	.70	.20

Party Emblem — A71   Cassia Adenesis — A72

1979, Oct. 13   Perf. 14½x14

229	A71	60f multi	.70	.20

Yemeni Socialist Party, 1st anniversary.

1979, Nov. 30   Litho.   Perf. 13½

Flowers: 90f, Nerium oleander. 110f, Calligonum comosum. 180f, Adenium obesium.

230	A72	20f multi	.20	.20
231	A72	90f multi	.90	.50
232	A72	110f multi	1.50	.75
233	A72	180f multi	1.90	.90
		Nos. 230-233 (4)	4.50	2.35

For surcharge see Yemen No. 632.

First Anniv. of
Iranian
Revolution — A73

1980, Feb. 12　　　Litho.　　　Perf. 13½
234　A73　60f multi　　　　　　　　1.10　1.10

Dido
A74

1980, Mar. 5　　　Litho.　　　Perf. 13½
235　A74　110f shown　　　　　　1.10　.50
236　A74　180f Anglia　　　　　　1.60　.70
237　A74　250f India　　　　　　　2.25　.90
　　　Nos. 235-237 (3)　　　　　4.95　2.10

For surcharge see Yemen No. 633.

Basket Maker,
London 1980
Emblem — A75

1980, May 6　　　Litho.　　　Perf. 14
238　A75　60f shown　　　　　　　.20　.20
239　A75　90f Hubble bubble pipe
　　　　　maker　　　　　　　　.65　.20
240　A75　110f Weaver　　　　　　.90　.55
241　A75　250f Potter　　　　　　2.00　1.10
　　　Nos. 238-241 (4)　　　　　3.75　2.05

London 1980 Intl. Stamp Exhib., May 6-14.

Hemprich's Skink — A76

1980, May 8　　　Litho.　　　Perf. 14
242　A76　20f shown　　　　　　　.20　.20
243　A76　35f Mole viper　　　　　.60　.20
244　A76　110f Carter's day gecko　1.50　.60
245　A76　180f Cobra　　　　　　2.50　1.25
　　　Nos. 242-245 (4)　　　　　4.80　2.25

For surcharge see Yemen No. 634.

Misha and
Olympic
Emblem — A77

Farmers
Armed — A78

1980, July 19　　　Litho.　　　Perf. 12½x12
246　A77　110f multi　　　　　　　1.10　.65

For overprint see No. 287.

1980, Oct. 17　　　　　　　　　Perf. 13½
247　A78　50f Armed farmers
　　　　　working, horiz.　　　.50　.20
248　A78　90f shown　　　　　　　.75　.50
249　A78　110f Sickle (wheat) and
　　　　　fist　　　　　　　　　1.00　.70
　　　Nos. 247-249 (3)　　　　　2.25　1.40

10th anniversary of farmers' uprising.

110th Birth
Anniversary of
Lenin — A79

1980, Nov. 7　　　Litho.　　　Perf. 12
250　A79　35f multi　　　　　　　.50　.50

Douglas DC-3 — A80

1981, Mar. 11　　　Litho.　　　Perf. 13½
251　A80　60f shown　　　　　　　.20　.20
252　A80　90f Boeing 707　　　　1.50　.20
253　A80　250f DHC Dash 7　　　3.50　1.60
　　　Nos. 251-253 (3)　　　　　5.20　2.00

Democratic Yemen Airlines, 10th anniv.

Ras
Boradli
Earth
Satellite
Station
A82

1981, June 22　　　Litho.　　　Perf. 12
257　A82　60f multi　　　　　　　.90　.65

Conocarpus
Lancifolius — A83

Supreme People's
Council, 10th
Anniv. — A84

1981, Aug. 1　　　Litho.　　　Perf. 12
258　A83　90f shown　　　　　　　.85　.20
259　A83　180f Ficus vasta　　　2.00　1.10
260　A83　250f Maerua crassifolia　3.00　1.75
　　　Nos. 258-260 (3)　　　　　5.85　3.05

1981, Aug. 18　　　Litho.　　　Perf. 15x14½
261　A84　180f multi　　　　　　1.50　.90

Desert Fox — A85

1981, Sept. 26　　　Litho.　　　Perf. 14½
262　A85　50f shown　　　　　　　.70　.20
263　A85　90f South Arabian
　　　　　leopard　　　　　　　1.40　.70
264　A85　250f Ibex　　　　　　　3.25　1.60
　　　Nos. 262-264 (3)　　　　　5.35　2.50

No. 194 Redrawn

1981, Oct. 15　　　Litho.　　　Perf. 12
　　　　　　Size: 25x27mm
264A　A61　5f multi　　　　　　　.45　.45

Denomination in upper right.

Tephrosia
Apollinea — A86

1981, Nov. 30　　　Litho.　　　Perf. 13½
265　A86　50f shown　　　　　　　.20　.20
266　A86　90f Citrullus colo-
　　　　　cynthis　　　　　　　1.00　.20
267　A86　110f Aloe sqarrosa　　1.40　.20
268　A86　250f Lawsonia inermis　3.50　2.00
　　　Nos. 265-268 (4)　　　　　6.10　2.60

For surcharge see Yemen No. 635.

Intl. Year
of the
Disabled
A87

1981, Dec. 12　　　Litho.　　　Perf. 14½
269　A87　50f multi　　　　　　　.20　.20
270　A87　100f multi　　　　　　1.00　.20
271　A87　150f multi　　　　　　1.50　1.00
　　　Nos. 269-271 (3)　　　　　2.70　1.40

TB Bacillus Centenary — A88

1982, Mar. 24　　　Litho.　　　Perf. 14½
272　A88　50f multi　　　　　　　1.10　.20

30th
Anniv. of
Arab
Postal
Union
A89

1982, Apr. 12　　　Litho.　　　Perf. 14
273　A89　100f multi　　　　　　1.25　.75

1982
World Cup
A90

Designs: Various soccer players.

1982, June 13　　　Litho.　　　Perf. 14
274　A90　50f multi　　　　　　　.70　.20
275　A90　100f multi　　　　　　1.40　.90
276　A90　150f multi　　　　　　2.00　1.25
277　A90　200f multi　　　　　　3.00　1.75
　a.　Souv. sheet of 4, #274-277　7.00　7.00
　　　Nos. 274-277 (4)　　　　　7.10　4.10

For overprints see Nos. 281-284.

60th
Anniv. of
USSR
A93

1982, Dec. 22　　　Litho.　　　Perf. 12½x12
280　A93　50f Flags, arms　　　　.65　.45

Nos. 274-277, 277a Ovptd. with
Emblem and "WORLD CUP /
WINNERS / 1982 / 1st ITALY / 2nd W-
GERMANY / 3rd POLAND / 4th
FRANCE" in Blue

1982, Dec. 30　　　Litho.　　　Perf. 14
281　A90　50f multi　　　　　　　.20　.20
282　A90　100f multi　　　　　　1.50　1.50
283　A90　150f multi　　　　　　2.25　2.25
284　A90　200f multi　　　　　　2.50　2.50
　a.　Souvenir sheet of 4, #281-284　7.00　7.00
　　　Nos. 281-284 (4)　　　　　6.45　6.45

Palestinian
Solidarity
A94

1983, Apr. 10　　　　　　　　　Perf. 13½x14½
285　A94　50f Yasser Arafat　　　.20　.20
286　A94　100f Arafat, Dome of the
　　　　　Rock　　　　　　　　3.00　3.00
　a.　Souvenir sheet of 1, imperf.　3.00　3.00

No. 246 Ovptd. with TEMBAL '83
Emblem in Yellow

1983, May 21　　　　　　　　　Perf. 12½x12
287　A77　110f multi　　　　　　4.75　4.75

World Communications Year — A95

Designs: 50f, Correspondent, postrider,
ship. 100f, Postman, coach, telegraph. No.
290, Telephones, bus. 200f, Telecommunications. No. 292, Montage.

1983, June 10　　　　　　　　　Perf. 13x13½
288　A95　50f blk & brt bl　　　　.20　.20
289　A95　100f multi　　　　　　1.50　1.50
290　A95　150f multi　　　　　　2.40　2.40
291　A95　200f multi　　　　　　2.75　2.75
　　　Nos. 288-291 (4)　　　　　6.85　6.85

Souvenir Sheet

292　A95　150f multi　　　　　　3.00　3.00

Pablo Picasso (1881-1973),
Painter — A96

Paintings: No. 293, The Poor Family, 1903.
No. 294, Woman with Crow. No. 295a, The
Gourmet. No. 295b, Woman with Child on
Beach. No. 295c, Sitting Beggar. No. 296,
The Solar Family, horiz.

1983, July 25   *Perf. 14*
293 A96 50f multi   .20   .20
294 A96 100f multi   2.00   2.00

Souvenir Sheets
295   Sheet of 3   13.50   13.50
a.   A96 50f multi   1.75   1.75
b.   A96 100f multi   4.50   4.50
c.   A96 150f multi   6.50   6.50
296 A96 150f multi   8.00   8.00

23rd Pre-Olympics Games,
1984 — A97

1983, July 30
297 A97 25f Show jumping   .20   .20
298 A97 50f Show jumping,
    diff.   .20   .20
299 A97 100f Three-day event   2.50   2.50
    Nos. 297-299 (3)   2.90   2.90

Souvenir Sheets
300   Sheet of 4   13.50   13.50
a.   A97 20f Bay, vert.   2.50   2.50
b.   A97 40f Gray, vert.   2.50   2.50
c.   A97 60f Bay, diff., vert.   3.25   3.25
d.   A97 80f Arabian   4.50   4.50
301 A97 200f Show jumping,
    diff., vert.   9.75   9.75

Locomotives — A98

1983, Aug. 24   *Perf. 14½x15*
302 A98 25f P8 steam en-
    gine, 1905   .20   .20
303 A98 50f 880 steam, 1915   .20   .20
304 A98 100f GT 2-4-4, 1923   4.00   4.00
    Nos. 302-304 (3)   4.40   4.40

Souvenir Sheets
305   Sheet of 3   20.00   20.00
a.   A98 40f D51 steam, 1936   4.75   4.75
b.   A98 60f 45 Series, 1937   4.75   4.75
c.   A98 100f PT 47, 1948   9.00   9.00
306 A98 200f P36, 1950   20.00   20.00

Natl.
Revolution,
20th Anniv.
A100

1983, Oct. 15   **Litho.**   *Perf. 13½x13*
312 A100 50f shown   .20   .20
313 A100 100f Flag, freedom
    fighter   2.75   2.75

1st Manned
Flight,
Bicent. — A101

Balloons: 100f, La Montgolfiere prototype.
No. 316a, Lunardi's. No. 316b, Charles and
Robert's. No. 316c, Wiseman's. No. 316d,
Blanchard and Jeffries's. 200f, Five-balloon
craft.

1983, Oct. 25   *Perf. 14*
314 A101 50f shown   .20   .20
315 A101 100f multi   2.50   2.50

Souvenir Sheets
316   Sheet of 4   15.00   15.00
a.   A101 20f multi   3.25   3.25
b.   A101 40f multi   3.25   3.25
c.   A101 60f multi   3.25   3.25
d.   A101 80f multi   4.75   4.75
317 A101 200f multi   13.50   13.50

1984
Winter
Olympics,
Sarajevo
A102

1983, Dec. 28   **Litho.**   *Perf. 14*
318 A102 50f Men's downhill
    skiing   .20   .20
319 A102 100f Two-man bob-
    sled   2.50   2.50

Souvenir Sheets
320   Sheet of 2   11.00   11.00
a.   A102 40f Ski jumping   3.25   3.25
b.   A102 60f Figure skating   3.25   3.25
321 A102 200f Ice hockey   11.00   11.00

1984 Summer Olympics, Los
Angeles — A103

1984, Jan. 24
322 A103 25f Fencing   .20   .20
323 A103 50f Fencing, diff.   .20   .20
324 A103 100f Fencing, diff.   1.40   1.40
    Nos. 322-324 (3)   1.80   1.80

Souvenir Sheets
325   Sheet of 4   11.00   11.00
a.   A103 20f Gymnastics   2.75   2.75
b.   A103 40f Water polo   2.75   2.75
c.   A103 60f Wrestling   2.75   2.75
d.   A103 80f Show jumping   2.75   2.75
326 A103 200f Show jumping,
    diff.   11.00   11.00

Nos. 83 and 84B Surcharged with
Black Squares

1984, May 26   **Litho.**   *Perf. 13½, 13*
332 A24 50f on 65f multi
333 A25 100f on 110f multi

Fish — A105

1984, Nov. 25   **Litho.**   *Perf. 11½*
334 A105 10f Abalistes stel-
    laris   .20   .20
335 A105 15f Caranx speci-
    ocus   .20   .20
336 A105 20f Pomadasys
    maculatus   .20   .20
337 A105 25f Chaetodon fas-
    ciatus   .20   .20
338 A105 35f Pomacanthus
    imperator   .20   .20
339 A105 50f Rastrelliger
    kanagurta   .20   .20
340 A105 100f Euthynnus af-
    finis   1.25   1.25
341 A105 150f Heniochus
    acuminatus   1.90   1.90
342 A105 200f Pomacanthus
    maculosus   2.50   2.50
343 A105 250f Pterois russellii   3.25   3.25
344 A105 400f Argyrops
    spinifer   5.00   5.00
345 A105 500f Dasyatis
    uarnak   6.25   6.25
346 A105 1d Epinephalus
    chlorostigma   12.00   12.00
347 A105 2d Drepane
    longimana   25.00   25.00
    Nos. 334-347 (14)   58.35   58.35

For surcharges see Yemen Nos. 636, 640,
642.

Natl.
Literacy
Campaign
A106

1985, Feb. 27   *Perf. 12*
350 A106 50f Girls writing   .20   .20
351 A106 100f Hand, fountain
    pen, vert.   4.25   4.25

Victory Parade,
Red Square,
Moscow,
1945 — A107

12th World Youth
and Students
Festival — A108

1985, May 9   *Perf. 12x12½*
352 A107 100f multi   1.50   1.50

Defeat of Nazi Germany, end of World War
II, 40th anniv.

1985, Aug. 3   *Perf. 12*
353 A108 50f Emblem   .20   .20
354 A108 100f Hand holding em-
    blem   4.25   4.25

UNESCO World   Natl. Socialist
Heritage   Party, 3rd Gen.
Campaign — A109   Cong. — A110

1985, Aug. 29
355 A109 50f Shibam city   .20   .20
356 A109 50f Close-up of build-
    ings   .20   .20
357 A109 100f Windows   1.90   1.90
358 A109 100f Door   1.90   1.90
    Nos. 355-358 (4)   4.20   4.20

Nos. 355-357 horiz.

1985, Oct. 10
359 A110 25f Energy   .20   .20
360 A110 50f Industry   .20   .20
361 A110 100f Agriculture   2.25   2.25
    Nos. 359-361 (3)   2.65   2.65

UN Child Survival   World Food
Campaign — A111   Day — A112

1985, Nov. 28
362 A111 50f Mother feeding
    child   .20   .20
363 A111 50f Holding child   .20   .20
364 A111 100f Feeding child, diff.   1.90   1.90
365 A111 100f Breastfeeding   1.90   1.90
    Nos. 362-365 (4)   4.20   4.20

1986, Jan. 30
366 A112 20f Almihdar Mosque,
    Aden   .20   .20
367 A112 180f Palm trees   4.00   4.00

UN Food and Agriculture Org., 40th anniv.

Lenin, Red
Square,
Moscow
A113

1986, Feb. 25   *Perf. 12x12½*
368 A113 75f multi   1.40   1.40
369 A113 250f multi   4.00   4.00

27th Soviet Communist Party Cong.,
Moscow.

Costumes Worn at
the 1984 Brides
Dance
Festival — A114

Designs: No. 370, Bride wearing red and
green costume, face markings. No. 371, Violet costume. No. 372, Veiled bride. No. 373,
Unveiled bride. No. 374, Groom holding dagger. No. 375, Groom holding rifle.

1986, Feb. 27

370	A114	50f multi	.80	.80
371	A114	50f multi	.80	.80
372	A114	50f multi	.80	.80
373	A114	100f multi	1.50	1.50
374	A114	100f multi	1.50	1.50
375	A114	100f multi	1.50	1.50
	Nos. 370-375 (6)		6.90	6.90

Revolution Martyrs — A115

1986, Oct. 15　　　Litho.　　*Perf. 12*

376	A115	75f Abdul Fattah Ismail	1.10	1.10
377	A115	75f Ali Shayaa Hadi	1.10	1.10
378	A115	75f Saleh Musleh Kasim	1.10	1.10
379	A115	75f Ali Ahmed N. Antar	1.10	1.10
	Nos. 376-379 (4)		4.40	4.40

UN Child Survival Campaign — A116

Infant Immunization Program.

1987, Apr. 7　　　Litho.　　*Perf. 12*

380	A116	20f Immunizing pregnant woman	.20	.20
381	A116	75f Immunizing infant	1.00	1.00
382	A116	140f Oral immunization	1.90	1.90
383	A116	150f Infant, girl, pregnant woman	2.00	2.00
	Nos. 380-383 (4)		5.10	5.10

1st Socialist Party General Conference — A117

1987, July 30　　　Litho.　　*Perf. 12*

384	A117	75fr multi	1.10	1.10
385	A117	150fr multi	2.10	2.10

October Revolution, Russia, 70th Anniv. — A118

Monuments, Ancient City of Shabwa — A119

1987, Nov. 7　　　Litho.　　*Perf. 12½x12*

386	A118	250f multi	4.00	4.00

1987, Nov. 18　　　　　*Perf. 12*

387	A119	25f Royal palace and court	.20	.20
388	A119	75f Palace, diff.	1.10	1.10
389	A119	140f Winged lion bas-relief on stone capital	2.00	2.00
390	A119	150f The Moon, legend on bronze tablet	2.10	2.10
	Nos. 387-390 (4)		5.40	5.40

Nos. 387-388 horiz.

Natl. Independence, 20th Anniv. — A120

Designs: 5f, Students walking to school. 75f, Family, apartments. 140f, Workers, oil derrick, thermal plant. 150f, Workers, soldier, Workers' Party headquarters.

1987, Nov. 29　　　　　*Perf. 12x12½*

391	A120	25f multi	.20	.20
392	A120	75f multi	1.00	1.00
393	A120	140f multi	1.90	1.90
394	A120	150f multi	2.00	2.00
	Nos. 391-394 (4)		5.10	5.10

September 26th Revolution, 25th Anniv. — A121

1988, Feb. 27　　　Litho.　　*Perf. 13*

395	A121	75f Revolution monument, San'a	1.10	1.10

WHO, 40th Anniv. — A122

1988, Apr. 7　　　Litho.　　*Perf. 12*

396	A122	40f Sanitary public water supply, vert.	.45	.45
397	A122	75f No smoking	.80	.80
398	A122	140f Child immunization	1.50	1.50
399	A122	250f Health care for all by the year 2000	2.75	2.75
	Nos. 396-399 (4)		5.50	5.50

1988 Summer Olympics, Seoul — A125

1988, Sept. 17　　　Litho.　　*Perf. 12x12½*

406	A125	40f Weight lifting	.25	.25
407	A125	75f Running	1.00	1.00
408	A125	140f Boxing	1.90	1.90
409	A125	150f Soccer	2.00	2.00
	Nos. 406-409 (4)		5.15	5.15

1st Freedom Fighter Killed at the Liberation Front, Radfan Mountains — A126

Perf. 12½x12, 12x12½
1988, Oct. 12　　　　　Litho.

410	A126	25f Freedom fighters, flag, vert.	.20	.20
411	A126	75f shown	.95	.95
412	A126	300f Anniv. emblem, vert.	4.00	4.00
	Nos. 410-412 (3)		5.15	5.15

October 14th Revolution, 25th anniv.

Indigenous Birds — A127

1988, Nov. 5　　*Perf. 12x12½, 12½x12*

413	A127	40f Treron waalia	.60	.60
414	A127	50f Coracias caudatus lorti, vert.	.75	.75
415	A127	75f Upupa epops, vert.	1.10	1.10
416	A127	250f Chlamydotis undulata macqueenii	3.75	3.75
	Nos. 413-416 (4)		6.20	6.20

Handicrafts — A128

Designs: 25f, Incense brazier. 75f, Cage-shaped dress form. 150f, Shell and wicker lidded basket. 250f, Wicker basket.

1988, Nov. 29　　　Litho.　　*Perf. 12½x12*

417	A128	25f multi	.20	.20
418	A128	75f multi	.90	.90
419	A128	150f multi	1.75	1.75
420	A128	250f multi	3.00	3.00
	Nos. 417-420 (4)		5.85	5.85

Aden Harbor and Yemen Port Authority, Cent. — A129

1988, Dec. 5　　　　　*Perf. 12x12½*

421	A129	75f Old harbor facility	1.40	1.40
422	A129	300f New facility	4.00	4.00

Preservation of San'a City, a Site on the UNESCO World Heritage List — A130

1988, Dec. 15　　*Perf. 12x12½, 12½x12*

423	A130	75f shown	1.00	1.00
424	A130	250f City view, diff., vert.	3.50	3.50

World Wildlife Fund — A131

1989, May 18　　　Litho.　　*Perf. 12½x12*

425	A131	20f Sand cat	1.10	.55
426	A131	25f Cat's head	1.10	.55
427	A131	50f Fennec fox	3.00	.65
428	A131	75f Fox's head	4.00	1.10
	Nos. 425-428 (4)		9.20	2.85

For surcharge see Yemen No. 643.

Military Forces — A132

Abdul Fattah Ismail — A133

Developments of the corrective movement.

1989, Aug. 15　　　　　*Perf. 12x12½*

429	A132	25f shown	.20	.20
430	A132	35f Industry	.45	.45
431	A132	40f Agriculture	.45	.45
	Nos. 429-431 (3)		1.10	1.10

June 22 Corrective Movement, 20th anniv.

1989, Aug. 28

432	A133	75f multi	.75	.75
433	A133	150f multi	1.25	1.25

50th Birthday of Abdul Fattah Ismail, 1st secretary-general of the natl. Socialist Party.

Ali Anter Yemeni Pioneer Organization, 15th Anniv. — A134

Perf. 12x12½, 12½x12
1989, Sept. 29　　　　　Litho.

434	A134	10f Drawing by Abeer Anwer	.20	.20
435	A134	25f Girl in pioneer uniform	.20	.20
436	A134	75f Parade, Aden	.70	.70
	Nos. 434-436 (3)		1.10	1.10

Nos. 434-435 vert.
For surcharge see Yemen No. 644.

Nehru and the Taj Mahal — A135

1989, Nov. 14　　　Photo.　　*Perf. 14*

437	A135	250f blk & golden brn	2.75	2.75

Jawaharlal Nehru, 1st prime minister of independent India.
For surcharge see Yemen No. 645.

Seventy-Day Siege of San'a, 1967-68 — A136

Coffee
Plant — A137

1989, Oct. 25   Litho.   Perf. 12x12½
438 A136 150f multicolored   2.00 2.00

1989, Dec. 20
439 A137 300f multicolored   4.00 4.00
For surcharge see Yemen No. 637.

Seera
Rock,
Aden, and
the Arc de
Triomphe,
Paris
A138

1989, Dec. 29   Litho.   Perf. 12½x12
440 A138 250f multicolored   3.25 3.25
French Revolution, bicent.

World Cup Soccer Championships,
Italy — A139

Character trademark, soccer plays and flags
of participants: 5f, US, Belgium, 1930. 10f,
Switzerland, Holland, 1934. 20f, Italy, France,
1938. 35f, Sweden, Spain, 1950. 50f, Federal
Republic of Germany, Austria, 1954. Brazil,
England, 1958. 500f, Russia, Uruguay, 1962.
No. 448, Soccer game.

1990, Apr. 30   Litho.   Perf. 12½x12
441 A139   5f multicolored   .20 .20
442 A139 10f multicolored   .20 .20
443 A139 20f multicolored   .20 .20
444 A139 35f multicolored   .30 .30
445 A139 50f multicolored   .35 .35
446 A139 60f multicolored   .40 .40
447 A139 500f multicolored   3.50 3.50
    Nos. 441-447 (7)   5.15 5.15
Souvenir Sheet
448 A139 340f multicolored   3.00 3.00
For surcharges see Yemen Nos. 616, 621-
621B.

YUGOSLAVIA

yü-gō-'slä-vē-ə

LOCATION — Southern Europe, bor-
dering on the Adriatic Sea
GOVT. — Republic
AREA — 39,500 sq. mi. (est)
POP. — 11,206,847 (1999 est.)
CAPITAL — Belgrade

On December 1, 1918, Bosnia and
Herzegovina, Croatia, Dalmatia, Montenegro, Serbia and Slovenia united to
form a kingdom which was later called
Yugoslavia. A republic was proclaimed

November 29, 1945. Other listings may
be found under all.
  100 Heller = 1 Krone (Bosnia &
        Herzegovina)
  100 Filler = 1 Krone (Croatia-Slavonia)
  100 Paras = 1 Dinar (General Issues)

> **Catalogue values for unused
> stamps in this country are for
> Never Hinged items, beginning
> with Scott 410 in the regular post-
> age section, Scott C50 in the air-
> post section, Scott F1 in the regis-
> tered letter section, Scott J67 in
> the postage due section, Scott
> RA1 in the postal tax section, and
> Scott RAJ1 in the postal tax due
> section.**

> Counterfeits exist of most of the
> 1918-19 overprints for Bosnia and
> Herzegovina, Croatia-Slavonia and
> Slovenia.

BOSNIA AND HERZEGOVINA

Stamps of Bosnia and Herzegovina,
1910, Overprinted or Surcharged in
Black or Red

a

b

c

1918   Unwmk.   Perf. 12½
1L1 A4(a) 3h olive green   .40 .70
1L2 A4(b) 5h dk grn (R)   .20 .20
1L3 A4(a) 10h carmine   .20 .20
1L4 A4(a) 20h dk brn (R)   .20 .20
1L5 A4(b) 25h deep blue (R)   .20 .20
1L6 A4(b) 30h green   .20 .20
1L7 A4(b) 40h orange   .20 .20
1L8 A4(b) 45h brown red   .20 .20
1L9 A4(b) 50h dull violet   .20 .20
1L10 A4(a) 60h on 50h dl vio   .20 .20
1L11 A4(b) 80h on 6h org
                brown   .20 .30
1L12 A4(a) 90h on 35h myr
                green   .20 .20
1L13 A5(c) 2k gray green   .20 .35
1L14 A4(b) 3k on 3h ol grn   .80 1.25
1L15 A5(c) 4k on 1k mar   1.40 1.90
1L16 A4(a) 10k on 2h vio   2.25 2.50
    Nos. 1L1-1L16 (16)   7.25 9.00
Inverted and double overprints and assorted
varieties exist on the stamps for Bosnia and
Herzegovina.

Bosnian Girl — A1

1918   Typo.   Perf. 11½
1L17 A1 2h ultramarine   .20 .20
1L18 A1 6h violet   .55 1.90
1L19 A1 10h rose   .20 .20
1L20 A1 20h green   .20 .20
    Nos. 1L17-1L20 (4)   1.15 2.50
Imperforate stamps of this type (A1) are
newspaper stamps of Bosnia.
See Nos. 1L21-1L22, 1L43-1L45.

Bosnia and Herzegovina Nos. P1-P2
(Nos. 1L17-1L18, Imperf.) Surcharged

1918   Imperf.
1L21 A1 3h on 2h ultra   .20 .20
  a.   Double surcharge   14.00
1L22 A1 5h on 6h violet   .20 .20
  a.   Double surcharge   14.00

Stamps of Bosnia and Herzegovina,
1906-17, Overprinted or Surcharged in
Black or Red:

d   e

f

1919   Perf. 12½
1L25 A23(d) 3h claret   .20 .50
1L26 A23(e) 5h green   .20 .20
1L27 A23(e) 10h on 6h dark
                 gray   .20 .20
1L28 A24(d) 20h on 35h myr
                 green   .20 .20
1L29 A23(e) 25h ultra   .20 .20
1L30 A23(d) 30h orange red   .45 .90
1L31 A24(d) 45h olive brn   .35 .45
1L32 A27(d) 45h on 80h org
                 brown   .20 .20
  a.   Perf. 11½   3.25 4.00
1L33 A24(d) 50h slate blue   20.00 24.00
1L34 A24(e) 50h on 72h dk
                 blue (R)   .20 .20
1L35 A24(d) 60h brown violet   .20 .20
1L36 A27(d) 80h orange brown   .20 .25
  a.   Perf. 11½   24.00 30.00
1L37 A27(d) 90h dark violet   .20 .20
  a.   Perf. 11½   2.25 2.75
1L38 A5(f)   2k gray green   .20 .25
  a.   Imperf.   27.50
  b.   Perf. 9½   4.50 5.00
1L39 A26(d) 3k car, green   .80 .90
1L40 A28(d) 4k car, green   1.75 2.50
1L41 A26(d) 5k dk vio, gray   1.75 2.75
1L42 A28(e) 10k dk vio, gray   2.00 2.75
    Nos. 1L25-1L42 (18)   29.30 36.85
Nos. 1L32, 1L36, 1L37, 1L40 and 1L42
have no bars in the overprint.
Nos. 1L25 to 1L42 exist with inverted overprint or surcharge.

Bosnia and Herzegovina Nos. P2-P4
(Nos. 1L18-1L20, Imperf.) Surcharged

1920   Imperf.
1L43 A1 2h on 6h violet   50.00 70.00
1L44 A1 2h on 10h rose   20.00 40.00
1L45 A1 2h on 20h green   1.10 2.75
    Nos. 1L43-1L45 (3)   71.10 112.75

SEMI-POSTAL STAMPS ISSUES FOR BOSNIA AND HERZEGOVINA

Leading Blind   Wounded
Soldier — SP1   Soldier — SP2

Semi-Postal Stamps of Bosnia and
Herzegovina, 1918 Overprinted

1918   Unwmk.   Perf. 12½, 13
1LB1 SP1 10h greenish bl   .65 1.00
  a.   Overprinted as No. 1LB2 27.50 37.50
1LB2 SP2 15h red brown   1.75 1.75
  a.   Overprinted as No. 1LB1 27.50 37.50
**Bosnian Semi-Postal Stamps of
1916
Overprinted like No. 1LB2**
1LB3 SP1 5h green   125.00 140.00
  a.   Overprinted as No. 1LB1 240.00 300.00
1LB4 SP2 20h magenta   75.00 95.00
    Nos. 1LB1-1LB4 (4)   202.40 237.75
Inverted and double overprints exist on Nos.
1LB1-1LB4.

Mail
Wagon
SP3

Bridge at   Srba, Hrvata i Slovenaca
Mostar
SP4

Scene near
Sarajevo — SP5

Regular Issue of Bosnia, 1906
Surcharged in Black

1919
1LB5 SP3 10h + 10h on 40h org
                 red   1.75 1.90
1LB6 SP4 20h + 10h on 20h dk
                 brown   .60 .60
1LB7 SP5 45h + 15h on 1k mar   2.50 2.75
    Nos. 1LB5-1LB7 (3)   4.85 5.25
Nos. 1LB5-1LB7 exist with surcharge
inverted. Value each $7.50.

SPECIAL DELIVERY STAMPS ISSUES FOR BOSNIA AND HERZEGOVINA

Lightning
SD1   SD2

Bosnian Special Delivery Stamps
Overprinted in Black

1918		Unwmk.		Perf. 12½, 13	
1LE1	SD1	2h vermilion		4.75	5.00
a.		Inverted overprint		32.50	
1LE2	SD2	5h deep green		1.40	1.50
a.		Inverted overprint		18.00	
b.		Overprinted as No. 1LE1		30.00	35.00

POSTAGE DUE STAMPS ISSUES FOR BOSNIA AND HERZEGOVINA

Postage Due Stamps of Bosnia and Herzegovina, 1916, Overprinted in Black or Red:

a

b

1918		Unwmk.		Perf. 12½, 13	
1LJ1	D2 (a)	2h red		.20	.20
1LJ2	D2 (b)	4h red		.25	.65
1LJ3	D2 (a)	5h red		.20	.20
1LJ4	D2 (b)	6h red		.30	.40
1LJ5	D2 (a)	10h red		.20	.20
1LJ6	D2 (b)	15h red		4.00	4.75
1LJ7	D2 (a)	20h red		.20	.20
1LJ8	D2 (b)	25h red		.25	.70
1LJ9	D2 (a)	30h red		.25	.70
1LJ10	D2 (b)	40h red		.20	.20
1LJ11	D2 (a)	50h red		.50	.80

c

d

1LJ12	D2 (c)	1k dark blue (R)		.25	.25
1LJ13	D2 (d)	3k dark blue (R)		.20	.20
		Nos. 1LJ1-1LJ13 (13)		7.00	9.45

Nos. 1LJ1-1LJ13 exist with overprint double or inverted. Value $3 to $7.
Nos. 1LJ1-1LJ11 exist with type "b" overprint instead of type "a," and vice versa. Value, each $10.

Stamps of Bosnia and Herzegovina, 1900-04, Surcharged

e

f

1919					
1LJ14	A2 (e)	2h on 35h blue		.25	1.10
1LJ15	A2 (e)	5h on 45h grnsh bl		.40	.85
1LJ16	A2 (f)	10h on 10 red		.20	.80
1LJ17	A2 (e)	15h on 40h org		.20	.80
1LJ18	A2 (f)	20h on 5h green		.20	.20
1LJ19	A2 (e)	25h on 20h pink		.20	.50
1LJ20	A2 (f)	30h on 30h bis brn		.20	.45
1LJ21	A2 (e)	1k on 50h red lil		.20	.45
1LJ22	A2 (e)	3k on 25h blue		.20	.30

Postage Due Stamps of Bosnia and Herzegovina, 1904 Surcharged:

g

h

1LJ23	D1 (g)	40h on 6h blk, red & yel		.20	.20
1LJ24	D1 (h)	50h on 8h blk, red & yel		.20	.20
1LJ25	D1 (h)	200h blk, red & grn		2.50	2.50

1LJ26	D1 (h)	4k on 7h blk, red & yel		.20	.30
		Nos. 1LJ14-1LJ26 (13)		5.15	7.80

Nos. 1LJ14-1LJ26 exist with overprint double or inverted. Value, $3 to $6.

CROATIA-SLAVONIA

Stamps of Hungary Overprinted in Blue

A1

1918		Wmk. 137		Perf. 15	
		On Stamps of 1913			
2L1	A1	6f olive green		1.10	2.00
2L2	A1	50f lake, *blue*		.85	1.75

A2

A3

On Stamps of 1916

2L3	A2	10f violet		20.00	27.50
2L4	A3	15f red		20.00	27.50

A4

On Hungary Nos. 106-107
White Numerals

2L4A	A4	10f rose		240.00	300.00
2L5	A4	15f violet		22.50	27.50
a.		Inverted overprint		125.00	

On Stamps of 1916-18
Colored Numerals

2L6	A4	2f brown orange		.20	.20
2L7	A4	3f red lilac		.20	.20
2L8	A4	5f green		.20	.20
2L9	A4	6f greenish blue		.20	.25
2L10	A4	10f rose red		1.60	2.75
2L11	A4	15f violet		.20	.20
2L12	A4	20f gray brown		.20	.30
2L13	A4	25f dull blue		.20	.20
2L14	A4	35f brown		.20	.20
2L15	A4	40f green		.20	.20

The overprints and surcharges for Croatia-Slavonia exist inverted, double, double inverted, in wrong colors, on wrong stamps, on back, in pairs with one lacking overprint, etc.

A5

A6

2L16	A5	50f red vio & lilac		.20	.20
2L17	A5	75f brt bl & pale bl		.20	.25
2L18	A5	80f grn & pale grn		.20	.20
2L19	A6	1k red brown & cl		.20	.20
2L20	A6	2k olive brn & bis		.20	.20
2L21	A6	3k dark vio & ind		.40	1.00
2L22	A6	5k dk brn & lt brn		2.00	4.00
2L23	A6	10k vio brn & vio		7.50	14.00

Stamps of Hungary Overprinted in Blue, Black or Red

A7

A8

2L24	A7	10f scarlet (Bl)		.20	.20
2L25	A7	20f dark brown (Bk)		.20	.20
2L26	A7	25f deep blue (R)		.80	2.50
2L27	A8	40f olive green (Bl)		.20	.20
		Nos. 2L6-2L27 (22)		15.70	28.10

Many other stamps of the 1913-18 issues of Hungary, the Semi-Postal Stamps of 1915-16 and Postage Due Stamps were surreptitiously overprinted but were never sold through the post office.

Freedom of Croatia-Slavonia
A9

1918		Unwmk.	Litho.	Perf. 11½	
2L28	A9	10f rose		1.00	1.00
2L29	A9	20f violet		1.25	1.25
2L30	A9	25f blue		2.50	2.50
2L31	A9	45f greenish blk		24.00	24.00
		Nos. 2L28-2L31 (4)		28.75	28.75

Independence of Croatia, Slavonia and Dalmatia.
#2L28-2L31 exist imperforate, but were not officially issued in this condition.
Excellent counterfeits of #2L28-2L31 exist.

Allegory of Freedom
A10

Youth with Standard
A11

Falcon, Symbol of Liberty — A12

1919				Perf. 11½	
2L32	A10	2f brn orange		.20	.20
2L33	A10	3f violet		.20	.20
2L34	A10	5f green		.20	.20
2L35	A11	10f red		.20	.20
2L36	A11	20f black brown		.20	.20
2L37	A11	25f deep blue		.20	.20
2L38	A11	45f dark ol grn		.20	.20
2L39	A12	1k carmine rose		.20	.20
2L40	A12	3k dark violet		.35	.35
2L41	A12	5k deep brown		.85	.70
		Nos. 2L32-2L41 (10)		2.80	2.65

				Perf. 12½	
2L32a	A10	2f		1.25	1.25
2L33a	A10	3f		1.25	1.25
2L34a	A10	5f		40.00	52.50
2L35a	A11	10f		.35	.35
2L36a	A11	20f		.30	.25
		Nos. 2L32a-2L36a (5)		43.15	55.60

#2L32-2L41 exist imperf. Value, set $25.

SEMI-POSTAL STAMPS ISSUES FOR CROATIA-SLAVONIA

SP1

SP2

SP3

1918		Wmk. 137		Perf. 15	
2LB1	SP1	10f + 2f rose red		.30	2.75
2LB2	SP2	15f + 2f dull violet		.20	.40
2LB3	SP3	40f + 2f brn carmine		.20	.85
		Nos. 2LB1-2LB3 (3)		.70	4.00

SPECIAL DELIVERY STAMP ISSUE FOR CROATIA-SLAVONIA

SD1

Hungary No. E1 Overprinted in Black

1918		Wmk. 137		Perf. 15	
2LE1	SD1	2f gray green & red		.20	.20

POSTAGE DUE STAMPS ISSUES FOR CROATIA-SLAVONIA

D1

Postage Due Stamps of Hungary Overprinted in Blue

1918		Wmk. Crown (136)		Perf. 15	
2LJ1	D1	50f green & red		175.00	175.00
		Wmk. Double Cross (137)			
2LJ2	D1	1f green & red		6.25	6.25
a.		Inverted overprint		22.50	22.50
2LJ3	D1	2f green & red		.75	.75
2LJ4	D1	10f green & red		.55	.55
2LJ5	D1	12f green & red		25.00	25.00
2LJ6	D1	15f green & red		.45	.45
2LJ7	D1	20f green & red		.45	.45
2LJ8	D1	30f green & red		1.10	1.10
2LJ9	D1	50f green & blk		7.75	7.75
		Nos. 2LJ2-2LJ9 (8)		42.30	42.30

NEWSPAPER STAMPS ISSUES FOR CROATIA-SLAVONIA

N1

N2

Hungary No. P8 Overprinted in Black

1918		Wmk. 137		Imperf.	
2LP1	N1	(2f) orange		.20	.30

1919		Litho.		Unwmk.	
2LP2	N2	2f yellow		.20	.50

SLOVENIA

Chain Breaker
A1   A2

3, 5, 10, 15f: Chain on right wrist is short, extending only about half way to the frame.

10f: Numerals are 8½mm high.

20, 25, 30, 40f: Distant mountains show faintly between legs of male figure.

40f: Numerals 7mm high. The upright strokes of the "4" extend to the same height; the "0" is 3mm wide.

1919   Unwmk.   Perf. 11½
Lithographed at Ljubljana
Fine Impression

3L1	A1	3f violet	.20	.20
3L2	A1	5f green	.20	.20
3L3	A1	10f carmine rose	.20	.20
3L4	A1	15f blue	.20	.20
3L5	A2	20f brown	.20	.20
3L6	A2	25f blue	.20	.20
3L7	A2	30f lilac rose	.20	.20
3L8	A2	40f bister	.20	.20
		Nos. 3L1-3L8 (8)	1.60	1.60

Various stamps of this series exist imperforate and part perforate. Many shades exist. See Nos. 3L9-3L17, 3L24-3L28. For surcharges see Nos. 3LJ15-3LJ32.

Allegories of Freedom
A3   A4

King Peter I — A5

3, 5, 15f: The chain on the right wrist touches the bottom tablet.

10f: Numerals are 7½mm high.

15f: Curled end of loin cloth appears above letter "H" in the bottom tablet.

20, 25, 30, 40f: The outlines of the mountains have been redrawn and they are more distinct than on the lithographed stamps.

40f: Numerals 8mm high. The left slanting stroke of the "4" extends much higher than the main vertical stroke. The "0" is 2½mm wide and encloses a much narrower space than on the lithographed stamp.

1919-20   Perf. 11½
Typographed at Ljubljana and Vienna
Coarse Impression

3L9	A1	3f violet	.20	.20
3L10	A1	5f green	.20	.20
3L11	A1	10f red	.20	.20
3L12	A1	15f blue	.20	.20
3L13	A2	20f brown	.20	.20
3L14	A2	25f blue	.20	.20
3L15	A2	30f carmine rose	.20	.20
3L16	A2	30f dp red	2.75	.90
3L17	A2	40f orange	.25	.20
3L18	A3	50f green	.30	.20
a.		50f dark green	.30	.20
b.		50f olive green	3.50	1.10
3L19	A3	60f dark blue	.50	.20
a.		60f violet blue	.85	.20
3L20	A4	1k vermilion	.30	.20
a.		1k red orange	.45	.20
3L21	A4	2k blue	.30	.20
a.		2k dull ultramarine	.90	.20

3L22	A5	5k brown lake	.45	.20
a.		5k lake	12.00	1.60
b.		5k dull red	.60	.20
3L23	A5	10k deep ultra	2.75	.90
		Nos. 3L9-3L23 (15)	9.00	4.40

Nos. 3L9-3L23 exist imperf. Value, set $90. Many of the series exist part perforate. Many shades exist of lower values. See Nos. 3L29-3L32, 3L40-3L41.

Serrate Roulette 13½

3L24	A1	5f light grn	.20	.20
3L25	A1	10f carmine	.20	.20
3L26	A1	15f slate blue	.20	.20
3L27	A2	20f dark brown	.30	.20
a.		Serrate x straight roul.	.55	.20
3L28	A2	30f car rose	.20	.20
a.		Serrate x straight roul.	.60	.20
3L29	A3	50f green	.30	.20
3L30	A3	60f dark blue	.45	.20
a.		60f violet blue	2.25	1.10
3L31	A4	1k vermilion	.65	.20
a.		1k rose red	.60	.20
3L32	A4	2k blue	13.00	1.50
		Nos. 3L24-3L32 (9)	15.50	3.10

Roulette x Perf. 11½

3L24a	A1	5f	125.00	140.00
3L25a	A1	10f	45.00	47.50
3L26a	A1	15f	140.00	150.00
3L28b	A2	30f	45.00	47.50
3L29a	A3	50f	5.25	4.00
3L30b	A3	60f	45.00	47.50
3L31b	A4	1k	45.00	47.50

Thick Wove Paper
1920   Litho.   Perf. 11½

3L40	A5	15k gray green	4.00	5.25
3L41	A5	20k dull violet	1.00	2.00

On Nos. 3L40-3L41 the horizontal lines have been removed from the value tablets. They are printed over a background of pale brown wavy lines.

Chain   Freedom
Breaker   A8
A7

King Peter I — A9

Dinar Values:
Type I — Size: 21x30½mm.
Type II — Size: 22x32½mm.

Thin to Thick Wove Paper
1920   Serrate Roulette 13½

3L42	A7	5p olive green	.20	.20
3L43	A7	10p green	.20	.20
3L44	A7	15p brown	.20	.20
3L45	A7	20p carmine	.75	1.00
3L46	A7	25p chocolate	.30	.30
3L47	A8	40p dark violet	.20	.20
3L48	A8	45p yellow	.20	.20
3L49	A8	50p dark blue	.20	.20
3L50	A8	60p red brown	.20	.20
3L51	A9	1d dark brown (I)	.20	.20

Perf. 11½

3L52	A9	2d gray vio (II)	.20	.20
3L53	A9	4d grnsh black (I)	.30	.30
3L54	A9	6d olive brn (II)	.20	.25
3L55	A9	10d brown red (II)	.30	.35
		Nos. 3L42-3L55 (14)	3.65	4.00

The 2d and 6d have a background of pale red wavy lines, the 10d of gray lines. Counterfeits exist of No. 3L45.

POSTAGE DUE STAMPS ISSUES FOR SLOVENIA

D1

1919   Litho.   Unwmk.   Perf. 11½
Ljubljana Print
Numerals 9½mm high

3LJ1	D1	5f carmine	.20	.20
3LJ2	D1	10f carmine	.20	.20
3LJ3	D1	20f carmine	.20	.20
3LJ4	D1	50f carmine	.20	.20

Nos. 3LJ1-3LJ4 were also printed in scarlet and dark red.

Numerals 8mm high

3LJ5	D1	1k dark blue	.45	.30
3LJ6	D1	5k dark blue	.65	.50
3LJ7	D1	10k dark blue	.90	.75
		Nos. 3LJ1-3LJ7 (7)	2.80	2.35

1920
Vienna Print
Numerals 11 to 12 mm high

3LJ8	D1	5f red	.20	.20
3LJ9	D1	10f red	.20	.20
3LJ10	D1	20f red	.20	.20
3LJ11	D1	50f red	1.25	.85

Numerals 7mm high

3LJ12	D1	1k Prussian blue	1.10	.70
a.		1k dark blue	5.00	4.50
3LJ13	D1	5k Prussian blue	1.60	1.25
a.		5k dark blue	8.00	6.75
3LJ14	D1	10k Prussian blue	3.75	3.25
a.		10k dark blue	14.00	15.00
		Nos. 3LJ8-3LJ14 (7)	8.30	6.65

Nos. 3LJ8-3LJ14 exist imperf. Value, set $40.

No. 3L4 Surcharged in Red

1920   Perf. 11½
On Litho. Stamps

3LJ15	A1	5p on 15f blue	.20	.20
3LJ16	A1	10p on 15f blue	.60	.60
3LJ17	A1	20p on 15f blue	.20	.20
3LJ18	A1	50p on 15f blue	.20	.20
		Nos. 3LJ15-3LJ18 (4)	1.20	1.20

Nos. 3L7, 3L12, 3L26, 3L28, 3L28a Surcharged in Dark Blue

3LJ19	A2	1d on 30f lil rose	.20	.20
3LJ20	A2	3d on 30f lil rose	.20	.20
3LJ21	A2	8d on 30f lil rose	1.10	.60
		Nos. 3LJ19-3LJ21 (3)	1.50	1.00

On Typographed Stamps
Perf. 11½

3LJ22	A1	5p on 15f pale bl	12.00	2.50
3LJ23	A1	10p on 15f pale bl	27.50	22.50
3LJ24	A1	20p on 15f pale bl	11.00	4.00
3LJ25	A1	50p on 15f pale bl	6.00	7.00
		Nos. 3LJ22-3LJ25 (4)	56.50	36.00

Serrate Roulette 13½

3LJ26	A1	5p on 15f slate bl	2.75	.50
3LJ27	A1	10p on 15f slate bl	8.50	3.25
3LJ28	A1	20p on 15f slate bl	2.75	.50
3LJ29	A1	50p on 15f slate bl	2.75	.50
3LJ30	A2	1d on 30f dp rose	2.75	.65
a.		Serrate x straight roulette	7.00	4.50
3LJ31	A2	3d on 30f dp rose	5.75	1.75
a.		Serrate x straight roulette	8.00	5.50
3LJ32	A2	8d on 30f dp rose	95.00	6.50
a.		Serrate x straight roulette	90.00	7.50
		Nos. 3LJ26-3LJ32 (7)	120.25	13.65

The para surcharges were printed in sheets of 100, ten horizontal rows of ten. There were: 5p three rows, 10p one row, 20p three rows,

---

50p three rows. The dinar surcharges were in a setting of 50, arranged in vertical rows of five. There were: 1d five rows, 3d three rows, 8d two rows.

NEWSPAPER STAMPS ISSUES FOR SLOVENIA

Eros — N1

1919   Unwmk.   Litho.   Imperf.
Ljubljana Print

3LP1	N1	2f gray	.20	.20
3LP2	N1	4f gray	.20	.20
3LP3	N1	6f gray	3.25	4.00
3LP4	N1	10f gray	.20	.20
3LP5	N1	30f gray	.20	.20
		Nos. 3LP1-3LP5 (5)	4.05	4.80

See Nos. 3LP6-3LP13. For surcharges see Nos. 3LP14-3LP23, 4LB1-4LB5.

N2

1920
Vienna Print

3LP6	N2	2f gray	.20	.20
3LP7	N2	4f gray	6.50	10.00
3LP8	N2	6f gray	1.75	2.75
3LP9	N2	10f gray	14.00	21.00
3LP10	N2	2f blue	.20	.30
3LP11	N2	4f blue	.20	.20
3LP12	N2	6f blue	90.00	110.00
3LP13	N2	10f blue	.20	.20
		Nos. 3LP6-3LP13 (8)	113.05	144.65

Nos. 3LP1, 3LP10 Surcharged:

a   b

On Ljubljana Print

3LP14	N1 (a)	2p on 2f gray	.25	.40
3LP15	N1 (a)	4p on 2f gray	.25	.40
3LP16	N1 (a)	6p on 2f gray	.40	.65
3LP17	N1 (b)	10p on 2f gray	.65	.80
3LP18	N1 (b)	30p on 2f gray	.65	.85

On Vienna Print

3LP19	N1 (a)	2p on 2f blue	.20	.20
3LP20	N1 (a)	4p on 2f blue	.20	.20
3LP21	N1 (a)	6p on 2f blue	.20	.20
3LP22	N1 (b)	10p on 2f blue	.20	.20
3LP23	N1 (b)	30p on 2f blue	.20	.25
		Nos. 3LP14-3LP23 (10)	3.20	4.15

The five surcharges were arranged in a setting of 100, in horizontal rows of ten. There were: 2p three rows, 4p three rows, 6p two rows, 10p one row and 30p one row. The sheets were perforated 11½ horizontally between the groups of the different values.

SEMI-POSTAL STAMPS ISSUE FOR CARINTHIA PLEBISCITE

SP1

Nos. 3LP2, 3LP1 Surcharged With Various Designs in Dark Red

1920

4LB1	SP1	5p on 4f gray	.20	.20
4LB2	SP1	15p on 4f gray	.20	.20
4LB3	SP1	25p on 4f gray	.20	.20
4LB4	SP1	45p on 2f gray	.20	.20
4LB5	SP1	50p on 2f gray	.20	.20
4LB6	SP1	2d on 2f gray	1.25	1.60
		Nos. 4LB1-4LB6 (6)	2.25	2.60

Nos. 4LB1 to 4LB6 have a different surcharge on each stamp but each includes the letters "K.G.C.A." which signify Carinthian Governmental Commission, Zone A.

Sold at three times face value for the benefit of the Plebiscite Propaganda Fund.

GENERAL ISSUES

For Use throughout the Kingdom

King Alexander — A1   King Peter I — A2

Unwmk.

1921, Jan. 16   **Engr.**   **Perf. 12**

1	A1	2p olive brown	.20	.20
2	A1	5p deep green	.20	.20
3	A1	10p carmine	.20	.20
4	A1	15p violet	.20	.20
5	A1	20p black	.20	.20
6	A1	25p dark blue	.20	.20
7	A1	50p olive green	.20	.20
8	A1	60p vermilion	.20	.20
9	A1	75p purple	.20	.20
10	A2	1d orange	.20	.20
11	A2	2d olive bister	.25	.20
12	A2	4d dark green	.40	.20
13	A2	5d carmine rose	2.00	.20
14	A2	10d red brown	4.00	.55
		Nos. 1-14 (14)	8.65	3.15

Exist imperf. Value, set $125.
For surcharge see No. 27.

Nos. B1-B3 Surcharged in Black, Brown, Green or Blue:

a

b

1922-24

15	SP1(a)	1d on 10p	.20	.20
16	SP2(b)	1d on 15p ('24)	.20	.20
17	SP3(a)	1d on 25p (Br)	.20	.20
18	SP2(b)	3d on 15p (G)	.80	.20
a.		Blue surcharge	1.90	.20
19	SP2(b)	8d on 15p (G)	1.40	.20
a.		Double surcharge	32.50	30.00
b.		9d on 15p (error)	150.00	
20	SP2(b)	20d on 15p	6.50	1.00
21	SP2(b)	30d on 15p (Bl)	13.50	2.50
		Nos. 15-21 (7)	22.80	4.50

A3

1923, Jan. 23   **Engr.**

22	A3	1d red brown	1.00	.20
23	A3	5d carmine	4.75	.20
24	A3	8d violet	9.25	.25
25	A3	20d green	24.00	.75
26	A3	30d red orange	62.50	2.00
		Nos. 22-26 (5)	101.50	3.40

For surcharge see No. 28.

Nos. 8 and 24 Surcharged in Black or Blue

1924, Feb. 18

| 27 | A1 | 20p on 60p ver | .25 | .20 |
| 28 | A3 | 5d on 8d violet (Bl) | 8.00 | .60 |

The color of the surcharge on No. 28 varies, including blue, blue black, greenish black and black.

A4   A5

1924, July 1   **Perf. 14**

29	A4	20p black	1.10	.20
30	A4	50p dark brown	1.10	.20
31	A4	1d carmine	.45	.20
32	A4	2d myrtle green	1.00	.20
33	A4	3d ultramarine	.80	.20
34	A4	5d orange brown	3.25	.20
35	A5	10d dark violet	11.00	.20
36	A5	15d olive green	6.50	.20
37	A5	20d vermilion	5.75	.20
38	A5	30d dark green	5.75	1.25
		Nos. 29-38 (10)	36.70	3.05

No. 33 Surcharged

1925, June 5

| 39 | A4 | 25p on 3d ultramarine | .20 | .20 |
| 40 | A4 | 50p on 3d ultramarine | .20 | .20 |

King Alexander
A6   A7

1926-27   **Typo.**   **Perf. 13**

41	A6	25p deep green	.20	.20
42	A6	50p olive brown	.20	.20
43	A6	1d scarlet	.40	.20
44	A6	2d slate black	.40	.20
45	A6	3d slate blue	.55	.20
46	A6	4d red orange	2.75	.20
47	A6	5d violet	2.10	.20
48	A6	8d black brown	5.25	.20
49	A6	10d olive brown	5.00	.20
50	A6	15d brown ('27)	9.50	.20
51	A6	20d dark vio ('27)	11.50	.20
52	A6	30d orange ('27)	35.00	.45
		Nos. 41-52 (12)	72.85	2.65

For overprints and surcharges see Nos. 53-62, 87-101, B5-B16.

Semi-Postal Stamps of 1926 Overprinted over the Red Surcharge

1928, July

53	A6	1d scarlet	2.50	.20
a.	Surcharge "0.50" inverted		
54	A6	2d black	8.00	.20
55	A6	3d deep blue	6.00	.50
56	A6	4d red orange	18.00	.60
57	A6	5d bright vio	6.00	.20
58	A6	8d black brown	9.00	.95
59	A6	10d olive brown	12.00	.20
60	A6	15d brown	70.00	3.00
61	A6	20d violet	35.00	3.00
62	A6	30d orange	80.00	6.00
		Nos. 53-62 (10)	246.50	14.85

With Imprint at Foot

1931-34   **Perf. 12½**

63	A7	25p black	.70	.20
64	A7	50p green	.60	.20
65	A7	75p slate green	.20	.20
66	A7	1d red	.65	.20
67	A7	1.50d pink	.30	.20
68	A7	1.75d dp rose ('34)	.55	.35
69	A7	3d slate blue	3.50	.20
70	A7	3.50d ultra ('34)	1.10	.25
71	A7	4d deep orange	2.00	.20
72	A7	5d purple	2.00	.20
73	A7	10d dark olive	5.50	.20
74	A7	15d deep brown	5.50	.20
75	A7	20d dark violet	9.25	.20
76	A7	30d rose	6.00	.45
		Nos. 63-76 (14)	37.85	3.25

Type of 1931 Issue
Without Imprint at Foot

1932-33

77	A7	25p black	.20	.20
78	A7	50p green	.30	.20
79	A7	1d red	.65	.20
80	A7	3d slate bl ('33)	1.60	.20
81	A7	4d deep org ('33)	3.50	.20
82	A7	5d purple ('33)	5.25	.20
83	A7	10d dk olive ('33)	17.00	.20
84	A7	15d deep brn ('33)	21.00	.20
85	A7	20d dark vio ('33)	32.50	.20
86	A7	30d rose ('33)	37.50	.35
		Nos. 77-86 (10)	119.50	2.15

See Nos. 102-115.

Nos. 41 to 52 Overprinted

1933, Sept. 5   **Perf. 13**

87	A6	25p deep green	.20	.20
88	A6	50p olive brown	.20	.20
89	A6	1d scarlet	.75	.20
90	A6	2d slate black	3.25	.70
91	A6	3d slate blue	3.00	.20
92	A6	4d red orange	2.00	.20
93	A6	5d violet	3.00	.20
94	A6	8d black brown	9.25	1.00
95	A6	10d olive brown	13.00	.20
96	A6	15d brown	16.00	1.75
97	A6	20d dark violet	29.00	.50
98	A6	30d orange	25.00	.65
		Nos. 87-98 (12)	104.65	6.00

Semi-Postal Stamps of 1926 Overprinted like Nos. 87 to 98 and Four Bars over the Red Surcharge of 1926

1933, Sept. 5

99	A6	25p green	.50	.20
100	A6	50p olive brown	.60	.20
101	A6	1d scarlet	1.25	.40
		Nos. 99-101 (3)	2.35	.80

Nos. 99-101 exist with double impression of bars. Value, each $5.50 unused, $4.50 used.

King Alexander Memorial Issue
Type of 1931-34 Issues
Borders in Black

1934, Oct. 17

102	A7	25p black	.20	.20
103	A7	50p green	.20	.20
104	A7	75p slate green	.20	.20

105	A7	1d red	.20	.20
106	A7	1.50d pink	.20	.20
107	A7	1.75d deep rose	.20	.20
108	A7	3d slate blue	.20	.20
109	A7	3.50d ultramarine	.25	.20
110	A7	4d deep orange	.40	.20
111	A7	5d purple	.45	.20
112	A7	10d dark olive	1.90	.20
113	A7	15d deep brown	3.25	.20
114	A7	20d dark violet	5.00	.20
115	A7	30d rose	3.25	.20
		Nos. 102-115 (14)	15.90	2.80

Cyrillic Characters

Latin and Cyrillic inscriptions are transposed within some sets. In some sets some stamps are inscribed in Latin, others in Cyrillic. This will be mentioned only if it is necessary to identify otherwise identical stamps.

King Peter II — A10

1935-36   **Perf. 13x12½**

116	A10	25p brown black	.20	.20
117	A10	50p yel orange	.20	.20
118	A10	75p turq green	.20	.20
119	A10	1d brown red	.20	.20
120	A10	1.50d scarlet	.20	.20
121	A10	1.75d cerise	.20	.20
122	A10	2d magenta ('36)	.20	.20
123	A10	3d brn orange	.20	.20
124	A10	3.50d ultramarine	.20	.20
125	A10	4d yellow grn	1.00	.20
126	A10	4d slate blue ('36)	.20	.20
127	A10	10d bright vio	.45	.20
128	A10	15d brown	.80	.20
129	A10	20d bright blue	3.00	.20
130	A10	30d rose pink	2.00	.20
		Nos. 116-130 (15)	9.25	3.00

For overprints see Nos. N12, 14, N29.

King Alexander — A11   Nikola Tesla — A12

1935, Oct. 9   **Perf. 12½x11½, 11½**

131	A11	75p turq green	.20	.20
132	A11	1.50d scarlet	.20	.20
133	A11	1.75d dark brown	1.00	1.60
134	A11	3.50d ultramarine	1.00	1.60
135	A11	7.50d rose carmine	1.00	1.60
		Nos. 131-135 (5)	3.40	5.20

Death of King Alexander, 1st anniv.

1936, May 28   **Litho.**   **Perf. 12½x11½**

| 136 | A12 | 75p yel grn & dk brn | .20 | .20 |
| 137 | A12 | 1.75d dull blue & indigo | .25 | .20 |

80th birthday of Nikola Tesla (1856-1943), electrical inventor.

Memorial Church, Oplenac — A13   Coats of Arms of Yugoslavia, Greece, Romania and Turkey — A14

1937, July 1

138	A13	3d Prussian grn	1.00	.50
a.	Perf. 12½		12.00	12.00
139	A13	4d dark blue	1.00	.75

"Little Entente," 16th anniversary.

Perf. 11, 11½, 12½

1937, Oct. 29   **Photo.**

| 140 | A14 | 3d peacock grn | 1.00 | .35 |
| 141 | A14 | 4d ultramarine | 1.00 | .85 |

Balkan Entente.

King Peter II — A16

1939-40		**Typo.**	**Perf. 12½**
142	A16	25p black ('40)	.20 .20
143	A16	50p orange ('40)	.20 .20
144	A16	1d yellow grn	.20 .20
145	A16	1.50d red	.20 .20
146	A16	2d dp mag ('40)	.20 .20
147	A16	3d dull red brn	.20 .20
148	A16	4d ultra	.20 .20
148A	A16	5d dk blue ('40)	.20 .20
148B	A16	5.50d dk vio brn ('40)	.50 .20
149	A16	6d slate blue	.80 .20
150	A16	8d sepia	.80 .20
151	A16	12d bright vio	1.40 .20
152	A16	16d dull violet	2.00 .20
153	A16	20d blue ('40)	2.00 .20
154	A16	30d brt pink ('40)	4.50 .30
		Nos. 142-154 (15)	13.60 3.10

For overprints and surcharges see Nos. N1-N11, N13, N15-N28, N30-N35, Croatia 1-25.

Arms of Yugoslavia, Greece, Romania and Turkey

A17   A18

1940, June 1			
155	A17	3d ultramarine	.80 .40
156	A18	3d ultramarine	.80 .40
a.		Pair, #155-156	5.00 .40
157	A17	4d dark blue	.80 .40
158	A18	4d dark blue	.80 .40
a.		Pair, #157-158	5.00 5.00
		Nos. 155-158 (4)	3.20 1.60

Balkan Entente.

Bridge at Obod — A19

1940, Sept. 29			**Litho.**
159	A19	5.50d slate grn & dull grn	1.75 2.00

Zagreb Phil. Exhib.; 500th anniv. of Johann Gutenberg's invention of printing. The first press in the Yugoslav area was located at Obod in 1493.

Issues for Federal Republic
Types of Serbia, 1942-43, Surcharged in Green or Vermilion

1944, Dec.		**Unwmk.**	**Perf. 11½**
		Overprinted with Pale Green Network	
159A	OS4	5d (3d + 2d) rose pink	.20 .25
159B	OS4	10d (7d + 3d) dk sl grn (V)	.20 .25

Similar Surcharge on Serbia Nos. 2N37-2N39

1945, Jan. 24		**Without Network**	
159C	OS4	5d (3d + 2d) rose pink	.20 .25
159D	OS4	10d (7d + 3d) dk sl grn (V)	.20 .25
159E	OS4	25d (4d + 21d) ultra (Bk)	.20 .25
		Nos. 159C-159E (3)	.60 .75

Marshal Tito (Josip Broz) — A20

Prohor Pcinski Monastery — A21

1945		**Photo.**	**Perf. 12½**
160	A20	25p bright bl grn	.25 .20
161	A20	50p deep green	.25 .20
162	A20	1d crimson rose	2.50 .20
163	A20	2d dark car rose	.25 .20
164	A20	4d deep blue	.50 .20
165	A20	5d deep green	.20 .40
166	A20	6d dark purple	.40 .20
167	A20	9d orange brown	.80 .20
168	A20	10d deep rose	.20 .40
169	A20	20d orange	4.00 1.50
170	A20	25d dark purple	.20 .20
171	A20	30d deep rose	.20 .70
		Nos. 160-171 (12)	9.75 4.60

1945, Aug. 2		**Typo.**	**Perf. 11½**
172	A21	2d red	1.00 .20

Formation of the Popular Antifascist Chamber of Deputies of Macedonia, Aug. 2, 1944.

Partisans

A22   A23

Marshal Tito — A24   City of Jajce — A25

Partisan Girl and Flag — A26

1945, Oct. 10		**Litho.**	**Perf. 12½**
173	A22	50p olive gray	.20 .20
174	A22	1d blue green	.20 .20
175	A23	1.50d orange brown	.20 .20
176	A24	2d scarlet	.20 .20
177	A25	3d red brown	1.60 .20
178	A24	4d dark blue	.30 .20
179	A25	5d dark yel grn	1.00 .20
180	A26	6d black	.45 .20
181	A26	9d deep plum	.40 .20
182	A23	12d ultramarine	.90 .20
183	A22	16d blue	.70 .20
184	A23	20d orange ver	1.60 .20
		Nos. 173-184 (12)	7.75 2.40

See Nos. 211-214. For surcharges and overprints see Nos. 202-203, 273-292, 286-289, Istria 42, 44, 46, 48, 50, Trieste 5-14.

"Labor" and "Agriculture"
A27   A28

1945, Nov. 29		**Photo.**	**Perf. 12**
185	A27	2d brn carmine	3.00 3.00
186	A28	2d brn carmine	3.00 3.00
187	A27	4d deep blue	3.00 3.00
188	A28	4d deep blue	3.00 3.00
189	A27	6d dk slate grn	3.00 3.00
190	A28	6d dk slate grn	3.00 3.00
191	A27	9d red orange	3.00 3.00
192	A28	9d red orange	3.00 3.00
193	A27	16d bright ultra	3.00 3.00
194	A28	16d bright ultra	3.00 3.00
195	A27	20d dark brown	3.00 3.00
a.		Souv. sheet of 2, #191, 195, perf. 11½	8.00 8.00
196	A28	20d dark brown	3.00 3.00
a.		Souv. sheet of 2, #192, 196, perf. 11½	8.00 8.00
		Nos. 185-196 (12)	36.00 36.00
		Se-tenant pairs, #185-196 (6)	60.00 60.00

Constitution for the Democratic Federation of Yugoslavia, Nov. 29, 1945.

Parade of Armed Forces — A31   Svetozar Markovic — A32

1946, May 9		**Unwmk.**	**Perf. 12½**
199	A31	1.50d org yel & red	.30 .20
200	A31	2.50d cerise & red	.45 .25
201	A31	5d blue & red	1.25 .90
		Nos. 199-201 (3)	2.00 1.35

Victory over fascism, 1st anniv.

Type of 1945 Surcharged with New Values in Black

1946, Apr. 1			
202	A26	2.50d on 6d bright red	.90 .20
203	A26	8d on 9d orange	.95 .20

1946, Sept. 22			
204	A32	1.50d blue green	.75 .35
205	A32	2.50d dp red lilac	.85 .50

Markovic, Serbian socialist, birth cent.

People's Theater, Sofia A33

Sigismund Monument, Warsaw — A35

Designs: 1d, Prague. 2½d, Victory Monument, Belgrade. 5d, Spassky Tower, Kremlin.

1946, Dec. 8		**Litho.**	**Perf. 11½**
206	A33	½d dk brn & yel brn	1.00 1.00
207	A33	1d grnsh blk & emer	1.00 1.00
208	A35	1½d dk car rose & rose	1.00 1.00
209	A35	2½d hn brn & brn org	1.00 1.00
210	A35	5d dark bl & blue	1.00 1.00
		Nos. 206-210 (5)	5.00 5.00

Pan-Slavic Congress, Belgrade, Dec. 1946.

Types of 1945

1947, Jan. 15		**Litho.**	**Perf. 12½**
211	A26	2.50d red orange	.35 .20
212	A25	3d dull red	.50 .20
213	A25	5d dark blue	1.10 .20
214	A26	8d orange	.90 .20
		Nos. 211-214 (4)	2.85 .80

Gorski Vijenac — A38   Peter P. Nyegosh — A39

1947, June 8			**Typo.**
215	A38	1.50d Prus grn & blk	.40 .20
216	A39	2.50d ol bis & dk car	.40 .20
217	A38	5d blue & black	.40 .20
		Nos. 215-217 (3)	1.20 .60

Centenary of the Montenegrin national epic "Gorski Vijenac" (Wreath of Mountains) by Nyegosh.

Girls' Physical Training Classes — A40

Girl Runner — A41

Physical Culture Parade A42

1947, June 15		**Litho.**	**Perf. 11**
218	A40	1.50d brown	.20 .20
219	A41	2.50d red	.25 .25
220	A42	4d violet blue	.40 .35
		Nos. 218-220 (3)	.85 .80

Natl. sports meet, Belgrade, 6/15-22/47.

Map and Star — A43

1947, Sept. 16			**Typo.**
231	A43	2.50d dp car & dark bl	.20 .20
232	A43	5d org brn & dk grn	.20 .20

Annexation of Julian Province.

Music and One-string Gusle A44

Vuk Karadzic — A45

1947, Sept. 27　　Perf. 11½x12, 12½
233 A44　1.50d green　　　　　　.25　.25
234 A45　2.50d orange red　　　　.25　.25
235 A44　　5d violet blue　　　　.25　.25
　　　Nos. 233-235 (3)　　　　　.75　.75

Centenary of Serbian literature.

Symbols of Industry
and Agriculture, Map
and Flag — A46

Danube River
Scene — A47

1948, Apr. 8　　Litho.　　Perf. 12½
236 A46　1.50d grn, bl & salmon　.20　.20
237 A46　2.50d red brn, bl & salmon　.20　.20
238 A46　　5d dk bl, bl & salmon　.20　.20
　　　Nos. 236-238 (3)　　　　　.60　.60

International Fair, Zagreb, May 8-17.

1948, July 30　　　　　Unwmk.
239 A47　2d green　　　　　　2.25　2.25
240 A47　3d carmine　　　　　2.25　2.25
241 A47　5d blue　　　　　　2.25　2.25
242 A47　10d brown orange　　2.25　2.25
　　　Nos. 239-242 (4)　　　　9.00　9.00

Danube Conference, Belgrade.

Marchers with
Party
Flag — A48

Laurent
Kosir — A49

1948, July 21　　Perf. 11½, 12½
243 A48　2d dark green　　　　.20　.20
244 A48　3d dark red　　　　　.35　.20
245 A48　10d dark blue vio　　.45　.20
　　　Nos. 243-245 (3)　　　　1.00　.60

5th Congress of the Communist Party in
Yugoslavia, July 21, 1948.

1948, Aug. 21　　　　Perf. 12½
246 A49　3d claret　　　　　　.20　.20
247 A49　5d blue　　　　　　.20　.20
248 A49　10d red orange　　　.20　.20
249 A49　12d dull green　　　.20　.20
　　　Nos. 246-249 (4)　　　　.80　.80

80th death anniv. of Laurent Kosir, recognized by Yugoslavia as inventor of the postage
stamp.

Arms of Bosnia
and
Herzegovina
A50

Arms of
Yugoslavia
A51

1948, Nov. 29　　Perf. 12½, 12x11½
**Arms of Yugoslav Peoples
Republics**
250 A50　3d green　　　　　　　　.30　.30
251 A50　3d rose lil (Macedonia)　.30　.30
252 A50　3d gray bl (Serbia)　　　.30　.30
253 A50　3d gray (Montenegro)　　.30　.30
254 A50　3d rose (Croatia)　　　　.30　.30
255 A50　3d orange (Slovenia)　　.30　.30
256 A51　10d deep carmine　　　1.40　1.40
　　　Nos. 250-256 (7)　　　　　3.20　3.20

The Cyrillic and Latin inscriptions are transposed on Nos. 252, 253 and 255.

Franc
Presern — A52

1949, Feb. 8　　Photo.　　Perf. 11½
257 A52　3d dark blue　　　　　.30　.20
258 A52　5d brown orange　　　.30　.20
259 A52　10d olive black　　　1.00　.20
　　　Nos. 257-259 (3)　　　　1.60　.60

Death cent. of Franc Presern, poet.

Ski Jump,
Planica — A53

Ski
Jumper — A54

Perf. 12½x11½
1949, Mar. 20　　　　　Litho.
260 A53　10d magenta　　　　.75　.55
261 A54　12d slate gray　　　.75　.55

Intl. Ski Championships, Planica, Mar. 13-20.

Soldiers — A55

Farmers — A56

Arms and Flags
of Macedonia
and
Yugoslavia — A57

1949, Aug. 2　　　　　Perf. 12½
262 A55　3d carmine rose　　.30　.20
263 A56　5d dull blue　　　　.40　.20
264 A57　12d red brown　　2.00　2.75
　　　Nos. 262-264 (3)　　2.70　3.15

Liberation of Macedonia, 5th anniv.
It is reported that No. 264 was not sold to
the public at post offices.
For overprints see Nos. C30-C32.

Postal
Communications
A58

UPU, 75th anniversary: 5d, Plane, locomotive and stagecoach, horiz.

1949, Sept. 8　　　　　Unwmk.
265 A58　3d red　　　　　1.50　1.50
266 A58　5d blue　　　　　.30　.30
267 A58　12d brown　　　　.30　.30
　　　Nos. 265-267 (3)　　2.10　2.10

For overprints see Trieste Nos. 15-16.

Locomotives
A60

1949, Dec. 15　　　　　Photo.
269 A60　2d Early steam　　1.00　1.00
270 A60　3d Modern steam　1.00　1.00
271 A60　5d Diesel　　　　1.00　1.00
272 A60　10d Electric　　18.00　12.00
　　　Nos. 269-272 (4)　　21.00　15.00

Centenary of Yugoslav railroads.
For overprints see Trieste Nos. 17-20.

Official Stamps
Nos. O7 and O8
Surcharged:

1949　　　　　　　　Typo.
272A O1　3d on 8d chocolate　.50　.35
272B O1　3d on 12d violet　　.50　.35

Stamps of 1945 and 1947 Overprinted
or Surcharged in Black:

a	b
c	d

1949　　　　　　　　Litho.
273 A22 (a)　50p olive gray　　.20　.20
274 A22 (a)　1d blue green　　.20　.20
275 A24 (b)　2d scarlet　　　.20　.20
276 A26 (c)　3d on 8d orange　.20　.20
277 A25 (d)　3d dull red　　　.20　.20
278 A25 (d)　5d dark blue　　.20　.20
279 A23 (a)　10d on 20d org ver　.25　.20
280 A23 (a)　12d ultramarine　.35　.20
281 A22 (a)　16d blue　　　　.60　.20
282 A23 (a)　20d orange ver　.45　.20
　　　Nos. 273-282 (10)　　2.85　2.00

On No. 279 the surcharge includes a rule
below "JUGOSLAVIJA" and "D 10" with two
bars over "20D."
See Nos. 286-289.

Surveying for
Highway
A61

Bridge, Map
and
Automobile
A62

Highway
Completion
Symbolized
A63

1950, Jan. 16　　Photo.　　Perf. 12½
283 A61　2d blue green　　.45　.45
284 A62　3d rose brown　　.45　.45
285 A63　5d violet blue　　.80　.80
　　　Nos. 283-285 (3)　　1.70　1.70

Completion of Belgrade-Zagreb highway,
Dec. 1949.

Types of 1945 Overprinted in Black

1950　　　Unwmk.　　Perf. 12½
286 A22 (a)　1d brownish org　.40　.20
287 A24 (b)　2d blue green　　.40　.20
288 A25 (d)　3d rose pink　　.60　.20
289 A25 (d)　5d blue　　　　.60　.20
　　　Nos. 286-289 (4)　　2.00　.80

Marshal
Tito — A64

Child
Eating — A65

1950, Apr. 30　　　　　Engr.
290 A64　3d red　　　　　1.00　.70
291 A64　5d dull blue　　1.00　.70
292 A64　10d brown　　10.00　10.00
293 A64　12d olive black　1.25　.70
　　　Nos. 290-293 (4)　13.25　12.10

Labor Day, May 1.

1950, June 1　　　　　Photo.
294 A65　3d brown red　　.80　.40

Issued to publicize Children's Day, June 1.

Boy and Model
Plane — A66

Map and Chess
Symbols — A67

Designs: 3d, Glider aloft. 5d, Parachutists.
10d, Aviatrix. 20d, Glider on field.

1950, July 2　　　　　Engr.
295 A66　2d dark green　　1.60　1.60
296 A66　3d brown red　　1.60　1.60
297 A66　5d violet　　　　1.60　1.60
298 A66　10d chocolate　　1.60　1.60
299 A66　20d ultramarine　12.00　12.00
　　　Nos. 295-299 (5)　18.40　18.40

Third Aviation Meet, July 2-11.

1950, Aug. 20   Photo.   Perf. 11½

3d, Rook and ribbon. 5d, Globe and chess board. 10d, Allegory of international chess. 20d, View of Dubrovnik, knight and ribbon.

300	A67	2d red brn & rose brown	.45 .35
301	A67	3d blk brn, gray brn & dl yellow	.45 .35
302	A67	5d dk grn, bl & buff	1.10 .45
303	A67	10d cl, bl & org yel	1.10 .60
304	A67	20d dk bl, bl & org yellow	22.00 14.00
		Nos. 300-304 (5)	25.10 15.75

Intl. Chess Matches, Dubrovnik, Aug. 1950.

Electrification   Coal and Logs for
A68   Export
                 A69

Designs: 50p, Metallurgy. 2d, Agriculture. 3d, Construction. 5d, Fishing. 7d, Mining. 10d, Fruitgrowing. 12d, Lumbering. 16d, Gathering sunflowers. 20d, Livestock raising. 30d, Book manufacture. 50d, Loading ship.

1950-51   Unwmk.   Engr.   Perf. 12½

305	A68	50p dk brn ('51)	.20 .20
306	A68	1d blue green	.20 .20
307	A68	2d orange	.20 .20
308	A68	3d rose red	.20 .20
309	A68	5d ultramarine	.30 .20
310	A68	7d gray	.30 .20
311	A68	10d chocolate	.50 .20
312	A68	12d vio brn ('51)	1.25 .20
313	A68	16d vio bl ('51)	1.75 .30
314	A68	20d ol grn ('51)	1.75 .25
314A	A68	30d red brn ('51)	3.50 1.00
315	A68	50d violet ('51)	21.00 12.00
		Nos. 305-315 (12)	31.15 15.15

See Nos. 343-354, 378-384A. For overprints see Trieste Nos. 68-75, 90-92.

1950, Sept. 23   Photo.

316 A69 3d red brown   .60 .20

Zagreb International Fair, 1950.

Early Sailing Vessel "Dubrovnik" A70

Partisans with Flag — A71

Designs: 3d, Partisans in boat. 5d, Loading freighter. 10d, Transatlantic ship "Zagreb." 12d, Sailboats. 20d, Naval gun and ship.

1950, Nov. 29

317	A70	2d brown violet	.20 .20
318	A70	3d orange brown	.20 .20
319	A70	5d dull green	.20 .20
320	A70	10d chalky blue	.30 .20
321	A70	12d dark blue	.80 .30
322	A70	20d red brown	8.00 2.50
		Nos. 317-322 (6)	9.70 3.60

Yugoslav navy.

1951, Mar. 27   Engr.

323 A71 3d red & red brn   3.50 2.00

Yugoslavia's resistance to Nazi Germany, 10th anniv.

Stane Rozman A72

5d, Post-boy during Slovene insurrection.

1951, Apr. 27   Photo.

325 A72 3d brown red   .35 .25
325 A72 5d dark blue   .60 .40

Slovene insurrection, 10th anniv.

Children Painting A73

1951, June 3

326 A73 3d red   .60 .20

Issued to publicize Children's Day, June 3.

Zika Jovanovich — A74

Serbian Revolutionists A75

1951, July 7

327 A74 3d brown red   .45 .25
328 A75 5d deep blue   .70 .40

Serbian insurrection, 10th anniv.

Sava Kovacevich A76

Kovacevich Leading Revolutionists A77

1951, July 13

329 A76 3d rose pink   .70 .25
330 A77 5d light blue   1.00 .40

Montenegrin insurrection, 10th anniv.

Monument to Marko Oreskovich A78

1951, July 27

331 A78 3d shown   .45 .25
332 A78 5d Monument to wounded   .70 .40

Croatian insurrection, 10th anniv.

Sium Bolaj — A79

Revolutionists A80

1951, July 27

333 A79 3d rose brown   .35 .20
334 A80 5d blue   .75 .40

Revolution in Bosnia and Herzegovina, 10th anniv.

Primoz Trubar — A81

National Handicrafts — A82

12d, Marko Marulic. 20d, Tsar Stefan Duschan.

1951, Sept. 9   Engr.

335 A81 10d slate gray   3.00 3.00
336 A81 12d brown orange   3.00 3.00
337 A81 20d violet   10.00 10.00
Nos. 335-337 (3)   16.00 16.00

Yugoslav cultural anniversaries. For overprints see Trieste Nos. 40-41.

1951, Sept. 15   Litho.   Perf. 11½

338 A82 3d multicolored   1.75 .45

Zagreb International Fair, 1951.

Mirce Acev — A83

Monument at Skopje A84

1951, Oct. 11

339 A83 3d deep plum   .55 .30
340 A84 5d indigo   1.10 .65

Macedonian insurrection, 10th anniv.

Soldier and Emblem — A85

Peter P. Nyegosh — A86

1951, Dec. 22   Photo.   Perf. 12½

341 A85 15d deep carmine   .45 .20

Army Day. See No. C54.

1951, Nov. 29   Engr.

342 A86 15d deep claret   2.00 .55

Death centenary of Nyegosh. See note after No. 217.

Types of 1950-51

1951-52   Engr.

Designs: 15d, Gathering sunflowers. 25d, Agriculture. 35d, Construction. 75d, Lumbering. 100d, Metallurgy.

343	A68	1d gray ('52)	.20 .20
344	A68	2d rose car ('52)	.25 .20
345	A68	5d orange ('52)	1.60 .20
346	A68	10d emerald ('52)	6.00 .20
347	A68	15d rose car ('52)	13.00 1.50
348	A68	20d purple	2.75 .20
349	A68	25d yel brn ('52)	8.75 .20
350	A68	30d blue	1.60 .20
351	A68	35d red brn ('52)	2.00 .20
352	A68	50d greenish bl	1.60 .20
353	A68	75d purple ('52)	2.40 .20
354	A68	100d sepia ('52)	3.75 .25
		Nos. 343-354 (12)	43.90 3.75

No. 349 exists with and without printer's inscriptions at bottom, with stamps differing slightly.

Marshal Tito
A87   A88

1952, May 25   Photo.   Perf. 11½

355 A87 15d shown   .50 .45
356 A88 28d shown   1.10 .90
357 A87 50d Tito facing left   19.00 17.50
Nos. 355-357 (3)   20.60 18.85

60th birthday of Marshal Tito

Child with Ball — A89

1952, June 1   Litho.   Perf. 12½

358 A89 15d bright rose   3.50 3.50

Issued to publicize Children's Day, June 1. For overprint see Trieste No. 60.

Girl Gymnast — A90

Split, Dalmatia — A91

1952, July 10   *Perf. 12½*
359	A90	5d shown	1.00	.35
360	A90	10d Runner	1.00	.35
361	A90	15d Swimmer	1.00	.35
362	A90	28d Boxer	1.00	.35
363	A90	50d Basketball	8.00	3.00
364	A90	100d Soccer	17.00	11.00
		Nos. 359-364 (6)	29.00	15.40

15th Olympic Games, Helsinki, 1952.
Nos. 359-364 exist imperf. Value $350.
For overprints see Trieste Nos. 51-56.

1952, Sept. 10   **Litho.**
365	A91	15d shown	1.10	1.10
366	A91	28d Naval scene	1.75	1.75
367	A91	50d St. Stefan	6.75	6.75
		Nos. 365-367 (3)	9.60	9.60

Yugoslav navy, 10th anniv.
For overprints see Trieste Nos. 57-59.

Belgrade, 16th Century A92

1952, Sept. 14   **Engr.**   *Perf. 11½*
368	A92	15d violet brn	6.00	5.00

1st Yugoslav Phil. Exhib., Sept. 14-20. Sold only at the exhibition.

Marching Workers and Congress Flag — A93

1952, Nov. 2   *Perf. 11½*
369	A93	15d red brown	1.25	1.10
370	A93	15d dark vio blue	1.25	1.10
371	A93	15d dark brown	1.25	1.10
372	A93	15d blue green	1.25	1.10
		Nos. 369-372 (4)	5.00	4.40

6th Yugoslav Communist Party Congress, Zagreb.
For overprints see Trieste Nos. 61-64.

Nikola Tesla — A94   Woman Pouring Water — A95

1953, Jan. 7   **Unwmk.**
373	A94	15d brown carmine	.65	.20
374	A94	30d chalky blue	2.00	.35

Death of Nikola Tesla, 10th anniv.
For overprints see Trieste Nos. 66-67.

1953, Mar. 24   **Litho.**   *Perf. 11½*

Designs: 30d, Hands holding two birds. 50d, Woman holding Urn.
375	A95	15d dk olive green	.90	.30
376	A95	30d chalky blue	.90	.30
377	A95	50d henna brown	8.75	2.40
		Nos. 375-377 (3)	10.55	3.00

Issued to honor the United Nations.
See Nos. RA19 and RAJ16. For overprints see Trieste Nos. 76-78.

Types of 1950-52

1953-55   **Litho.**   *Perf. 12½*

8d, Mining. 17d, Livestock raising.
378	A68	1d dull gray	.70	.20
379	A68	2d carmine	2.50	.20
380	A68	5d orange	3.50	.20
381	A68	8d blue	2.50	.20
382	A68	10d yellow green	5.50	.20
383	A68	12d lt vio brown	25.00	.20
384	A68	15d rose red	11.00	.20
384A	A68	17d vio brn ('55)	2.00	.20
		Nos. 378-384A (8)	52.70	1.60

For overprints see Trieste Nos. 68-75, 90-92.

Automobile Climbing Mt. Lovcen — A96

30d, Motorcycle & auto at Opatija. 50d, Racers leaving Belgrade. 70d, Auto near Mt. Triglav.

1953, May 10   **Photo.**   *Perf. 12½*
385	A96	15d sal & dp plum	.20	.20
386	A96	30d bl & dark blue	.30	.20
387	A96	50d ocher & choc	.60	.20
388	A96	70d lt bl grn & ol grn	15.00	3.00
		Nos. 385-388 (4)	16.10	3.60

Intl. Automobile & Motorcycle Races, 1953.

President Tito — A97   Star and Flag-encircled Globe — A98

1953, June 28   **Engr.**   **Unwmk.**
389	A97	50d deep purple	6.00	1.75

Marshal Tito's election to the presidency, Jan. 14, 1953.
For overprint see Trieste No. 83.

1953, July 25   **Engr.; Star Typo.**
390	A98	15d gray & green	2.50	2.00

38th Esperanto Cong., Zagreb, 7/25-8/1.
For overprint see Trieste No. 84.

Macedonian Revolutionary A99   Nicolas Karev A100

1953, Aug. 2   **Litho.**
391	A99	15d dark red brown	.85	.65
392	A100	30d dull green	3.00	1.75

Macedonian Insurection of 1903, 50th anniv.

Family — A101

Branko Radicevic — A102

1953, Sept. 6   **Photo.**
393	A101	15d deep green	100.00	25.00

Liberation of Istria and the Slovene coast, 10th anniv.
For overprint see Trieste No. 85.

1953, Oct. 1   **Engr.**
394	A102	15d lilac	4.25	1.50

10th death anniv. of Branko Radicevic, poet.
For overprint see Trieste No. 86.

View of Jajce — A103

Designs: 30d, First meeting place. 50d, Marshal Tito addressing Assembly.

1953, Nov. 29   *Perf. 12½x12*
395	A103	15d dark green	1.40	.70
396	A103	30d rose car	1.90	1.10
397	A103	50d dark brown	7.75	7.00
		Nos. 395-397 (3)	11.05	8.80

2nd Assembly of the Natl. Republic of Yugoslavia, 10th anniv.
For overprints see Trieste Nos. 87-89.

Wildlife A104

Lammergeier A105

1954, June 30   **Photo.**   *Perf. 11½*
398	A104	2d Ground squirrel	.35	.35
399	A104	5d Lynx	.35	.35
400	A104	10d Red deer	.35	.35
401	A104	15d Brown bear	.50	.50
402	A104	17d Chamois	.50	.50
403	A104	25d White pelican	.85	.85
404	A105	30d shown	.85	.85
405	A105	35d Black beetle	.85	.85
406	A105	50d Bush cricket	6.00	6.00
407	A105	65d Adriatic lizard	14.00	14.00
408	A105	70d Salamander	12.00	12.00
409	A105	100d Trout	21.00	21.00
		Nos. 398-409 (12)	57.60	57.60

See Nos. 497-505. For overprints see Trieste Nos. 93-104.

> **Catalogue values for unused stamps in this section, from this point to the end of the section, are for Never Hinged items.**

Ljubljana, 17th Century A106

1954, July 29   **Engr.**
410	A106	15d multicolored	13.00	13.00

2nd Yugoslav Phil. Exhib., July 29-Aug. 8. Sold for 50d, which included admission to the exhibition.

Revolutionary Flag — A107

Engr. & Typo.

1954, Oct. 3   *Perf. 12½*
411	A107	15d shown	1.60	.45
412	A107	30d Cannon	2.25	.80
413	A107	50d Revolutionary seal	5.00	1.10
414	A107	70d Karageorge	32.50	15.00
		Nos. 411-414 (4)	41.35	17.35

1st Serbian insurrection, 150th anniv.
For overprints see Trieste Nos. 105-108.

Vatroslav Lisinski — A108

30d, Andrea Kacic-Miosic. 50d, Jure Vega. 70d, Jovan Jovanovic-Zmaj. 100d, Philip Visnic.

1954, Dec. 25   **Engr.**
415	A108	15d dark green	2.75	1.00
416	A108	30d chocolate	2.75	1.60
417	A108	50d dp claret	3.75	3.00
418	A108	70d indigo	7.50	7.00
419	A108	100d purple	19.00	19.00
		Nos. 415-419 (5)	35.75	31.60

Scene from "Robinja" — A109

"A Midsummer Night's Dream" A110

1955   **Photo.**   *Perf. 12x11½, 12½*   **Glazed Paper**
420	A109	15d brown lake	1.00	.55
421	A110	30d dark blue	3.50	1.60

Festival at Dubrovnik.

Dragon Emblem of Ljubljana — A111

1955 Engr. Perf. 12½
422 A111 15d dk grn & brn 5.00 1.60

1st Intl. Exhib. of Graphic Arts, Ljubljana, July 3-Sept. 3.

Symbol of Sign Language — A112 Hops — A113

1955, Aug. 23
423 A112 15d rose lake 1.75 .45

2nd World Congress of Deaf Mutes, Zagreb, Aug. 23-27.

1955, Sept. 24 Photo. Perf. 11½

Medicinal Plants.
424 A113 5d shown .20 .20
425 A113 10d Tobacco .20 .20
426 A113 15d Poppy .20 .20
427 A113 17d Linden .20 .20
428 A113 25d Chamomile .20 .20
429 A113 30d Salvia .40 .20
430 A113 50d Dog rose 6.00 1.75
431 A113 70d Gentian 7.50 2.25
432 A113 100d Adonis 14.00 3.00
Nos. 424-432 (9) 28.90 8.20

"Peace" Statue, New York — A114

Woman and Dove — A115

1955, Oct. 24 Litho. Perf. 12½
433 A114 30d lt bl & blk 1.75 1.10

United Nations, 10th anniversary.

1955, Nov. 29 Engr.
434 A115 15d dull violet .65 .20

10th anniv. of the "New Yugoslavia."

St. Donat, Zadar — A116

Cornice, Cathedral at Sibenik A117

Yugoslav Art: 10d, Relief of a King, Split. 15d, Griffin, Studenica Monastery. 20d, Figures, Trogir Cathedral. 25d, Fresco, Sopocani Monastery. 30d, Tombstone, Radimlje. 40d, Ciborium, Kotor Cathedral. 50d, St. Martin from Tryptich, Dubrovnik. 70d, Figure, Belec Church. 100d, Rihard Jakopic, self-portrait. 200d, "Peace" Statue, New York.

1956, Mar. 24 Photo. Perf. 11½
435 A116 5d blue vio .45 .20
436 A116 10d slate grn .45 .20
437 A116 15d olive brn .45 .20
438 A116 20d brown car .45 .20
439 A116 25d black brn .45 .20
440 A116 30d dp claret .45 .20
441 A117 35d olive brn 1.00 .20
442 A117 40d red brown 1.75 .50
443 A116 50d olive brn 2.50 .70
444 A116 70d dk green 9.25 6.75
445 A116 100d dark pur 32.50 20.00
446 A116 200d deep blue 77.50 32.50
Nos. 435-446 (12) 127.20 61.85

13th Century Tower, Zagreb A118

1956, Apr. 20 Engr. Perf. 11½
Chalky Paper
447 A118 15d vio brn, bis brn & gray .60 .20
a. Miniature sheet of 4 7.50 2.50

3rd Yugoslavia Phil. Exhib. (JUFIZ III), Zagreb, May 20-27. No. 447a was sold at the exhibition, tipped into a folder, for 75 dinars. See No. C56.

Induction Motor — A119

Perf. 11½x12½
1956, July 10 Photo.
448 A119 10d shown .50 .25
449 A119 15d Transformer .60 .25
450 A119 30d Electronic controls 1.10 .50
451 A119 50d Nikola Tesla 4.00 2.00
Nos. 448-451 (4) 6.20 3.00

Birth cent. of Nikola Tesla, inventor.

Sea Horse — A120

Paper Nautilus A121

Designs: 20d, European rock lobster. 25d, "Sea Prince". 30d, Sea perch. 35d, Red mullet. 50d, Scorpion fish. 70d, Wrasse. 100d, Dory.

1956, Sept. 10 Perf. 11½
Granite Paper
Animals in Natural Colors
452 A120 10d bright grn .50 .30
453 A121 15d ultra & blk .50 .30
454 A121 20d deep blue .50 .30
455 A121 25d violet blue .70 .30
456 A121 30d brt grnsh bl .85 .30
457 A121 35d dk bl green 1.75 .30
458 A121 50d indigo 6.50 1.90
459 A121 70d slate grn 11.00 3.25
460 A121 100d dark blue 29.00 15.00
Nos. 452-460 (9) 51.30 21.95

Runner A122

Centaury — A123

Designs: 15d, Paddling kayak. 20d, Skiing. 30d, Swimming. 35d, Soccer. 50d, Water polo. 70d, Table tennis. 100d, Sharpshooting.

1956, Oct. 24 Litho. Perf. 12½
Design and Inscription in Bister
461 A122 10d dk carmine .80 .35
462 A122 15d dark blue .80 .35
463 A122 20d ultramarine 1.50 .70
464 A122 30d olive grn 1.50 .70
465 A122 35d dark brown 1.50 .70
466 A122 50d green 1.50 .70
467 A122 70d brn violet 50.00 15.00
468 A122 100d dark red 50.00 15.00
Nos. 461-468 (8) 107.60 33.50

16th Olympic Games, Melbourne, 11/22-12/8.

1957, May 25 Photo. Perf. 11½

Medicinal Plants: 15d, Belladonna. 20d, Autumn crocus. 25d, Marsh mallow. 30d, Valerian. 35d, Woolly Foxglove. 50d, Aspidium. 70d, Green Winged Orchid. 100d, Pyrethrum.

Granite Paper
Flowers in Natural Colors
469 A123 10d dk bl & grn .20 .20
470 A123 15d violet .20 .20
471 A123 20d lt ol grn & brn .20 .20
472 A123 25d dp cl & dk bl .50 .20
473 A123 30d lil rose & claret .90 .20
474 A123 35d dk gray & dl pur 1.50 .20
475 A123 50d dp grn & choc 2.50 .75
476 A123 70d pale brn & grn 4.50 1.60
477 A123 100d gray & brown 14.00 3.00
Nos. 469-477 (9) 24.50 6.55

See #538-546, 597-605, 689-694, 772-777.

Hand Holding Factory A124

1957, June 25 Engr. Perf. 12½
478 A124 15d dark car rose .35 .20
479 A124 30d violet blue 1.40 .35

Congress of Workers' Councils, Belgrade, June 25.

2nd Gymnastic Meet, Zagreb, July 10-14 — A125

Various gymnastic positions.

1957, July 1 Photo.
480 A125 10d ol grn & blk .20 .20
481 A125 15d brn red & blk .20 .20
482 A125 30d Prus bl & blk .80 .20
483 A125 50d brn & black 3.75 1.25
Nos. 480-483 (4) 4.95 1.85

Montenegro A126

Natl. Costumes: 15d, Macedonia. 30d, Croatia. 50d, Serbia. 70d, Bosnia and Herzegovina. 100d, Slovenia. 50d, 70d, 100d vert.

1957, Sept. 24 Typo. Perf. 12½
Background in Bister Brown
484 A126 10d dk brn, ultra & red .40 .25
485 A126 15d dk brn, blk & red .40 .25
486 A126 30d dk brn, grn & red .40 .25
487 A126 50d dk brn & green 1.00 .25
488 A126 70d dk brn & black 1.40 .50
489 A126 100d dk brn, grn & red 6.50 2.50
Nos. 484-489 (6) 10.10 4.00

Revolutionists A127

Simon Gregorcic — A128

Lithographed and Engraved
1957, Nov. 7 Perf. 11½x12½
490 A127 15d ocher & red .55 .40

Russian Revolution, 40th anniv.

1957, Dec. 3 Engr. Perf. 12½

Famous Yugoslavs: 30d, Anton Linhart, dramatist and historian. 50d, Oton Kucera, physicist. 70d, Stevan Mokranjac, composer. 100d, Jovan Sterija Popovic, writer

491 A128 15d sepia .45 .20
492 A128 30d indigo .60 .20
493 A128 50d reddish brn 1.25 .20
494 A128 70d dl violet 9.00 2.50
495 A128 100d olive grn 15.00 13.00
Nos. 491-495 (5) 26.30 16.10

"Young Man on Fire" — A129

Stylized Bird — A130

1958, Apr. 22　　　　　　**Photo.**
496 A129 15d deep plum　　　.55　.20

Union of Yugoslav Communists, 7th congress, Ljubljana, Apr. 22.

Types of 1954

Game birds.

1958, May 25　　　　　**Perf. 11½**
Granite Paper
Birds in Natural Colors

497	A104	10d Mallard	.30	.20
498	A104	15d Capercaillie	.30	.20
499	A104	20d Ring-necked pheasant	.30	.20
500	A104	25d Coot	.30	.20
501	A104	30d Water rail	.70	.20
502	A105	35d Great bustard	1.25	.20
503	A105	50d Rock partridge	4.50	1.25
504	A104	70d Woodcock	8.25	3.25
505	A105	100d Eurasian crane	17.50	7.50
		Nos. 497-505 (9)	33.40	13.20

1958, June 14　**Engr.**　**Perf. 12½**
506 A130 15d bluish black　　　.60　.25

Opening of Postal Museum, Belgrade.

Flag and Laurel A131

1958, July 1　　　　　　**Unwmk.**
507 A131 15d brn carmine　　　.50　.30

15th anniv. of victory over Germans at Sutjeska, Bosnia.

Onufrio Well, Dubrovnik A132

1958, Aug. 10　**Litho.**　**Perf. 12½**
508 A132 15d black & brn　　　.75　.30

Marin Drzic, dramatist, 450th birth anniv.

Sisak Steel Works — A133　　Titograd Hotel and Open-Air Theater — A134

Industrial Progress Designs: 2d, Crude oil production. 5d, Shipbuilding. 10d, Sisak steel works. 15d, Jablanica hydroelectric works. 17d, Lumber industry. 25d, Overpass, Zagreb-Ljubljana highway. 30d, Litostroy turbine factory. 35d, Lukavac coke plant. 50d, Bridge at Skopje. 70d, Railroad station, Sarajevo. 100d, Triple bridge, Ljubljana. 200d, Mestrovic station, Zagreb. 500d, Parliament, Belgrade.

1958　**Typo.**　**Perf. 12½ Horiz.**
509 A133 10d green　　　10.00　4.75
510 A133 15d orange ver　　　10.00　4.75

Engr.　　　　**Perf. 12½**

511	A133	2d olive	.20	.20
512	A133	5d brown red	.20	.20
513	A133	10d green	.40	.20
514	A133	15d orange ver	.40	.20
515	A133	17d deep claret	.40	.20
516	A133	25d slate	.40	.20
517	A133	30d blue black	.40	.20
518	A133	35d rose red	.40	.20
519	A134	40d car rose	.45	.20
520	A134	50d bright bl	.50	.20
521	A134	70d orange ver	1.25	.20
522	A134	100d green	4.75	.20
523	A134	200d red brown	4.50	.20
524	A134	500d intense bl	8.50	.30
		Nos. 511-524 (14)	22.75	2.90

Nos. 509-510 are coil stamps.
See #555-562, 627-645, 786-789, 830-840.

Ocean Exploration A135

1958, Oct. 24　　　　　　**Unwmk.**
525 A135 15d brown violet　　　.50　.25

Intl. Geophysical Year, 1957-58. See #C58.

White and Black Hands Holding Scales A136

1958, Dec. 10　　　　　**Perf. 12½**
526 A136 30d steel blue　　　1.10　.60

Universal Declaration of Human Rights, 10th anniv.

Dubrovnik A137

1959, Feb. 16　**Litho.**　**Perf. 12½**

527	A137	10d crim rose & cit	.20	.20
528	A137	10d lt grn & lt vio bl	.20	.20
529	A137	15d grnsh bl & pur	.20	.20
530	A137	15d grn & bright bl	.20	.20
531	A137	20d lt grn & grnsh bl	.20	.20
532	A137	20d ol bis & brt grn	.20	.20
533	A137	30d yel org & purple	1.40	.20
534	A137	30d lt vio bl & gray ol	1.40	.20
535	A137	70d gray & grnsh bl	4.50	2.25
		Nos. 527-535 (9)	8.50	3.85

Nos. 527, 530, 532 and 534 are inscribed in Cyrillic characters. See #650-658, 695-700.

1959, Apr. 20　**Unwmk.**　**Perf. 12½**
536 A138 20d multicolored　　　.50　.20

Yugoslav Communist Party, 40th anniv.

Red Flags — A138

Tourist attractions: #528, Bled. #529, Postojna grotto. #530, Ohrid. #531, Opatija. #532, Plitvice National Park. #533, Split. #534, Sveti Stefan. #535, Exhibition Hall, Belgrade.

Dubrovnik, 15th Century A139

1959, May 24　**Engr.**　**Perf. 11½**
537 A139 20d yel grn, dk grn & bl　　　5.00　2.50

4th Yugoslavia Phil. Exhib. (JUFIZ IV), Dubrovnik.

Type of 1957

Medicinal Plants: 10d, Lavender. 15d, Black Alder. 20d, Scopolia. 25d, Monkshood. 30d, Bilberry. 35d, Juniper. 50d, Primrose. 70d, Pomegranate. 100d, Jimson weed.

1959, May 25　　　　　　**Photo.**
Granite Paper
Flowers in Natural Colors

538	A123	10d lt bl & dk blue	.20	.20
539	A123	15d brt yel & car	.20	.20
540	A123	20d dk ol bis & mar	.20	.20
541	A123	25d ap grn & dk pur	.20	.20
542	A123	30d pink & dk bl	.20	.20
543	A123	35d bis brn & vio bl	1.25	.20
544	A123	50d brn & green	3.00	.40
545	A123	70d yel & ocher	4.00	.65
546	A123	100d lt brn & brn	7.50	2.00
		Nos. 538-546 (9)	16.75	4.25

Tug of War — A140

Sports: 15d, High jump and runners. 20d, Ring and parallel bar exercises. 35d, Women gymnasts. 40d, Sailors doing gymnastics. 55d, Field ball and basketball. 80d, Swimming. 100d, Festival emblem, vert.

1959, June 26　**Litho.**　**Perf. 12½**

547	A140	10d dk sl grn & ocher	.20	.20
548	A140	15d vio bl & sepia	.20	.20
549	A140	20d ol bis & dl lil	.20	.20
550	A140	35d deep cl & gray	.20	.20
551	A140	40d violet & gray	.25	.20
552	A140	55d sl grn & ol bis	.50	.20
553	A140	80d indigo & olive	3.25	.50
554	A140	100d pur & bister	7.00	3.50
		Nos. 547-554 (8)	11.80	5.20

Physical Culture Festival.

Types of 1958; Designs as before

Designs: 8d, Lumber industry. 15d, Overpass, Zagreb-Ljubljana highway. 20d, Jablanica hydroelectric works. 40d, Titograd Hotel. 55d, Bridge at Skopje. 80d, Railroad Station, Sarajevo.

1959　**Typo.**　**Perf. 12½ Horizontally**
555 A133 15d green　　　2.50　1.10
556 A133 20d orange ver　　　3.00　1.10

Engr.　　　　**Perf. 12½**

557	A133	8d deep claret	.40	.20
558	A133	15d green	.55	.20
559	A133	20d orange ver	.95	.20
560	A134	40d bright blue	2.25	.20
561	A134	55d carmine rose	3.50	.20
562	A134	80d orange ver	6.00	.20
		Nos. 557-562 (6)	13.65	1.20

Nos. 555-556 are coil stamps.

Fair Emblem — A141

Athletics — A142

1959, Sept. 5　**Litho.**　**Unwmk.**
563 A141 20d lt vio bl & blk　　　2.00　1.00

50th International Fair at Zagreb.

1960, Apr. 25　　　　　**Perf. 12½**

564	A142	15d shown	.40	.40
565	A142	20d Swimming	.40	.40
566	A142	30d Skiing	.40	.40
567	A142	35d Wrestling	.40	.40
568	A142	40d Bicycling	.40	.40
569	A142	55d Yachting	.40	.40
570	A142	80d Horseback riding	3.50	2.00
571	A142	100d Fencing	3.75	2.25
		Nos. 564-571 (8)	9.65	6.65

17th Olympic Games.

Hedgehog A143

1960, May 25　**Photo.**　**Perf. 12x11½**
Animals in Natural Colors

572	A143	15d shown	.40	.40
573	A143	20d Red squirrel	.40	.40
574	A143	25d Pine marten	.40	.40
575	A143	30d Hare	.40	.40
576	A143	35d Red fox	.40	.40
577	A143	40d Badger	.40	.40
578	A143	55d Wolf	.80	.80
579	A143	80d Roe deer	1.75	1.25
580	A143	100d Wild boar	2.75	2.75
		Nos. 572-580 (9)	7.70	7.20

See Nos. 663-671.

Lenin, 90th Birth Anniv. — A144

Atomic Accelerator A145

1960, June 22　**Engr.**　**Perf. 12½**
581 A144 20d dk grn & slate grn　　　.25　.20

1960, Aug. 23　　　　　**Unwmk.**
582 A145 15d shown　　　8.00　8.00
583 A145 20d Generator　　　8.00　8.00
584 A145 40d Nuclear reactor　　　8.00　8.00
　　　Nos. 582-584 (3)　　　24.00　24.00

Nuclear energy exposition, Belgrade.

Serbian National Theater, Novi Sad — A146

Ivan Cankar, Writer — A147

Designs: 20d, Woman from Croatian play. 40d, Edward Rusijan and early plane. 55d, Symbolic hand holding fruit. 80d, Atom and UN emblem.

1960, Oct. 24   Perf. 12½

585	A146	15d gray black	.65	.65
586	A146	20d brown	.65	.65
587	A146	40d dark gray blue	.65	.65
588	A146	55d dull claret	.65	.65
589	A146	80d dark green	1.00	1.00
		Nos. 585-589 (5)	3.60	3.60

Serbian Natl. Theater, Novi Sad, cent. (#585); Croatian Natl. Theater, Zagreb, cent. (#586); 1st flight in Yugoslavia, 50th anniv. (#587); 15th anniv. of the Yugoslav Republic (#588); UN, 15th anniv. (#589).

1960, Dec. 24   Engr.   Perf. 12½

Famous Yugoslavs: 20d, Silvije Strahimir Kranjcevic, poet. 40d, Paja Jovanovic, painter. 55d, Dura Jaksic, writer and painter. 80d, Mihajlo Pupin, electro-technician. 100d, Rudjer Boscovich, mathematician.

590	A147	15d dark green	.20	.20
591	A147	20d henna brown	.20	.20
592	A147	40d olive bister	.20	.20
593	A147	55d magenta	.20	.20
594	A147	80d dark blue	.30	.20
595	A147	100d Prussian bl	.60	.30
		Nos. 590-595 (6)	1.70	1.30

International Atomic Energy Commission Emblem A148

Victims' Monument, Kragujevac A149

Engr. & Litho.
1961, May 15   Perf. 12½

596	A148	25d multicolored	.50	.20

Intl. Nuclear Electronic Conf., Belgrade.

Flower Type of 1957

Medicinal plants: 10d, Yellow foxglove. 15d, Marjoram. 20d, Hyssop. 25d, Scarlet haw. 40d, Rose mallow. 50d, Soapwort. 60d, Clary. 80d, Blackthorn. 100d, Marigold.

1961, May 25   Photo.   Perf. 11½
Granite Paper
Flowers in Natural Colors

597	A123	10d lt bl & grnsh bl	.50	.50
598	A123	15d gray & chnt	.50	.50
599	A123	20d buff & green	.50	.50
600	A123	25d lt vio & vio	.50	.50
601	A123	40d lt ultra & ultra	.95	.60
602	A123	50d lt bl & blue	.95	.55
603	A123	60d beige & dk car rose	1.40	.55
604	A123	80d lt grn & green	1.60	1.10
605	A123	100d redsh brn & choc	4.75	2.50
		Nos. 597-605 (9)	11.65	7.20

1961, July 3   Perf. 12x12½

Monuments: 15d, Stevan Filipovic, Valjevo. 20d, Relief from Insurrection, Bozansko Grahovo. 60d, Victory, Nova Gradiska. 100d, Marshal Tito, Titovo Uzice.

Granite Paper
Gold Frames and Inscriptions

606	A149	15d crimson & brn	.20	.20
607	A149	20d brn & ol bis	.20	.20
608	A149	25d bl grn & gray olive	.20	.20
609	A149	60d violet	.25	.20
610	A149	100d indigo & black	.55	.40
		Nos. 606-610 (5)	1.40	1.20

Souvenir Sheet
Imperf

611	A149	500d indigo & black	100.00	100.00

Natl. Insurrection, 20th anniv.

Men of Five Races A150

National Assembly Building, Belgrade — A151

1961, Sept. 1   Litho.   Perf. 11½

613	A150	25d brown	.20	.20

Engr.

614	A151	50d blue green	.20	.20
		Nos. 613-614,C59-C60 (4)	4.65	3.10

Miniature Sheet
Imperf

615	A150	1000d claret	17.50	17.50

Conference of Non-aligned Nations, Belgrade, Sept. 1961.

St. Clement, 14th Century Wood Sculpture — A152

1961, Sept. 10   Engr.   Perf. 12½

616	A152	25d sepia & olive	2.00	.55

12th Intl. Congress for Byzantine Studies.

Serbian Women A153

Regional Costumes: 25d, Montenegro. 30d, Bosnia and Herzegovina. 50d, Macedonia. 65d, Croatia. 100d, Slovenia.

1961, Nov. 28   Litho.

617	A153	15d beige, brn & red	.20	.20
618	A153	25d beige, red brn & black	.20	.20
619	A153	30d beige, brn & dk red	.20	.20
620	A153	50d multicolored	.20	.20
621	A153	65d brn, red & yel	.60	.20
622	A153	100d multicolored	1.60	.60
		Nos. 617-622 (6)	3.00	1.60

Luka Vukalovic — A154

Hands with Flower and Rifle — A155

1961, Dec. 15   Engr.

623	A154	25d slate blue	.25	.20

Centenary of Herzegovina insurrection.

1961, Dec. 22

624	A155	25d red & vio blue	.25	.20

20th anniversary of Yugoslav army.

Miladinov Brothers A156

1961, Dec. 25   Litho.

625	A156	25d buff & claret	.25	.20

Centenary of Macedonian folksong "Koder;" Dimitri and Konstantin Miladinov, brothers who collected and published folksongs. Monument is at Struga.

Types of 1958; Designs as Before

Designs: 5d, Shipbuilding. 8d, Lumber industry. 10d, Sisak steel works. 15d, Overpass. 20d, Jablanica hydroelectric works. 25d, Cable factory, Svetozarevo. 30d, Litostroy turbine factory. 40d, Lukavac coke plant. 50d, Zenica steel works. 65d, Sevojno copper works. 100d, Crude oil production. 150d, Titograd hotel. 200d, Bridge, Skoplje. 300d, Railroad station, Sarajevo. 500d, Triple bridge, Ljubljana. 1000d, Mestrovic station, Zagreb. 2000d, Parliament, Belgrade.

1961-62   Typo.   Perf. 12½ Horiz.

627	A133	10d dark red brn	7.50	.55
628	A133	15d emerald	12.00	.30

Engr.   Perf. 12½

629	A133	5d dull orange	.20	.20
630	A133	8d gray	.20	.20
631	A133	10d dk red brn	.20	.20
632	A133	15d emerald	.20	.20
633	A133	20d violet blue	.20	.20
634	A133	25d vermilion	.20	.20
635	A133	30d red brown	.20	.20
636	A133	40d dp cl ('62)	.20	.20
637	A133	50d gray blue	.25	.20
638	A133	65d green	.20	.20
639	A133	100d yel olive	4.00	.20
640	A134	150d carmine ('62)	.90	.20
641	A134	200d slate grn ('62)	.90	.20
642	A134	300d olive ('62)	2.00	.20
643	A134	500d dull violet	2.00	.20
644	A134	1000d bister brn	4.50	.20
645	A134	2000d claret	10.00	.30
		Nos. 629-645 (17)	26.35	3.50

Nos. 627-628 are coil stamps. For surcharges see Nos. 786, 789.

Isis of Kalabsha — A157

Joy of Motherhood by Frano Krsinic — A158

Design: 50d, Ramses II, Abu Simbel.

1962, Apr. 7   Engr.   Perf. 12½

646	A157	25d grnsh blk, *cream*	.20	.20
647	A157	50d brown, *buff*	.35	.20

15th anniv. (in 1961) of UNESCO.

1962, Apr. 7

648	A158	50d black, *cream*	.30	.20

15th anniv. (in 1961) of UNICEF.

Anopheles Mosquito — A159

1962, Apr. 7   Unwmk.

649	A159	50d black, *gray*	.30	.20

WHO drive to eradicate malaria.

Scenic Type of 1959

Tourist attractions: #650, Portoroz. #651, Jajce. #652, Zadar. #653, Popova Sapka. #654, Hvar. #655, Bay of Kotor. #656, Danube, Iron Gate. #657, Rab. #658, Zagreb.

1962, Apr. 24   Litho.

650	A137	15d ol & chlky bl	.20	.20
651	A137	15d blue grn & bis	.20	.20
652	A137	25d blue & red brn	.20	.20
653	A137	25d dk bl & pale bl	.20	.20
654	A137	30d blue & brn org	.20	.20
655	A137	30d gray & chlky bl	.20	.20
656	A137	50d ol & grnsh bl	.90	.20
657	A137	50d blue & olive	.90	.20
658	A137	50d dk grn & gray bl	4.00	.80
		Nos. 650-658 (9)	7.00	2.40

#651, 653, 655-656 are inscribed in Cyrillic.

Marshal Tito, by Augustincic A160

Pole Vault — A161

Design: 50d, 200d, Sideview of bust by Antun Augustincic.

1962, May 25   Engr.   Perf. 12½

659	A160	25d dark green	.20	.20
660	A160	50d dark brown	.20	.20
661	A160	100d dark blue	.60	.35
662	A160	200d greenish blk	2.00	1.00
a.		Souv. sheet of 4, #659-662, imperf.	30.00	30.00
		Nos. 659-662 (4)	3.00	1.75

70th birthday of Pres. Tito (Josip Broz).

Animal Type of 1960

Designs: 15d, Crested newt. 20d, Fire salamander. 25d, Yellow-bellied toad. 30d, Pond frog. 50d, Pond turtle. 65d, Lizard. 100d, Emerald lizard. 150d, Leopard snake. 200d, European viper (adder).

1962, June 8   Photo.   Perf. 12x11½
Animals in Natural Colors

663	A143	15d green	.50	.50
664	A143	20d purple	.50	.50
665	A143	25d chocolate	.50	.50
666	A143	30d violet blue	.50	.50
667	A143	50d dark red	.50	.50
668	A143	65d bright grn	.50	.50
669	A143	100d black	1.10	1.10
670	A143	150d brown	3.00	3.00
671	A143	200d car rose	6.75	5.50
		Nos. 663-671 (9)	13.85	12.60

1962, July 10   Litho.   Perf. 12½

Sports: 25d, Woman discus thrower, horiz. 30d, Long distance runners. 50d, Javelin thrower, horiz. 65d, Shot put. 100d, Women runners, horiz. 150d, Hop, step and jump. 200d, High jump, horiz.

Athletes in Black

672	A161	15d blue	.35	.20
673	A161	25d magenta	.35	.20
674	A161	30d emerald	.35	.20
675	A161	50d red	.35	.20
676	A161	65d vio blue	.35	.20
677	A161	100d green	.70	.20
678	A161	150d orange	3.00	.35
679	A161	200d orange brn	8.00	.70
	Nos. 672-679 (8)		13.45	2.25

7th European Athletic Championships, Belgrade, Sept. 12-16. See No. C61.

Child at Play — A162

Litho. & Engr.
1962, Oct. 1   Perf. 12½
680	A162	25d red & black	.30	.20

Issued for Children's Week.

Gold Mask, Trebeniste, 5th Century B.C. — A163

Bathing the Infant Christ, Fresco, Decani Monastery — A164

Yugoslav Art Treasures: 25d, Horseman and bird, bronze vase (5th cent. B.C.). 50d, God Kairos, marble relief. 65d, "The Pigeons of Nerezi," fresco (12th cent.). 150d, Archangel Gabriel, icon (14th cent.).

1962, Nov. 28   Photo.
681	A163	25d Prus bl, blk & gold	.20	.20
682	A163	30d gold, saph & blk	.20	.20
683	A164	50d dk grn, brn & gold	.20	.20
684	A164	65d multicolored	.35	.20
685	A164	100d multicolored	.45	.60
686	A163	150d multicolored	1.90	1.10
	Nos. 681-686 (6)		3.30	2.50

Parched Earth and Wheat — A165

Dr. Andrija Mohorovicic and UN Emblem — A166

1963, Mar. 21   Engr.   Perf. 12½
687	A165	50d dark brn, tan	.25	.20

FAO "Freedom from Hunger" campaign.

1963, Mar. 23   Unwmk.
688	A166	50d dk blue, gray	.25	.20

UN 3rd World Meteorological Day, Mar. 23. Dr. Mohorovicic (1857-1936) was director of the Zagreb meteorological observatory.

Flower Type of 1957

Medicinal Plants: 15d, Lily of the valley. 25d, Iris. 30d, Bistort. 50d, Henbane. 65d, St. John's wort. 100d, Caraway.

1963, May 25   Photo.   Perf. 11½
Granite Paper
Flowers in Natural Colors
689	A123	15d gray grn & grn	.25	.25
690	A123	25d lt bl, ultra & pur	.25	.25
691	A123	30d gray & black	.25	.25
692	A123	50d redsh brn & red brn	.25	.25
693	A123	65d pale brn & brn	.65	.65
694	A123	100d slate & blk	3.25	2.25
	Nos. 689-694 (6)		4.90	3.90

Scenic Type of 1959

Tourist attractions: 15d, Pula. 25d, Vrnjacka Banja. 30d, Crikvenica. 50d, Korcula. 65d, Durmitor mountain. 100d, Ljubljana.

1963, June 6   Litho.   Perf. 12½
695	A137	15d multicolored	.20	.20
696	A137	25d multicolored	.20	.20
697	A137	30d multicolored	.20	.20
698	A137	50d multicolored	.20	.20
699	A137	65d multicolored	.20	.20
700	A137	100d multicolored	1.50	.40
	Nos. 695-700 (6)		2.50	1.40

Partisans on the March, by Djordje Andrejevic-Kun — A167

Sutjeska (Gorge) — A168

Design: No. 702A, As 15d, but inscribed "Vis 1944-1964." 50d, Partisans in battle.

Engr. & Litho.; Litho. (No. 702)
1963-64   Perf. 12½, 11½
701	A167	15d gray & dk sl grn	.20	.20
702	A168	25d dark slate grn	.20	.20
702A	A167	25d gray & dark car rose	.20	.20
703	A167	50d tan & purple	.20	.20
	Nos. 701-703 (4)		.80	.80

20th anniv. of the Partisan Battle of Sutjeska (Nos. 701, 702-703); 20th anniv. of the arrival of the Yugoslav General Staff on the island of Vis (No. 702A).
Issued: #702A, 7/27/64; others, 7/3/63.

Gymnast on Vaulting Horse — A169

Mother, by Ivan Mestrovic A170

1963, July 6   Litho.   Perf. 12½
704	A169	25d shown	.35	.35
705	A169	50d Parallel bars	.70	.35
706	A169	100d Rings	1.00	.40
	Nos. 704-706 (3)		2.05	1.10

5th Gymnastics Europa Prize.

1963, Sept. 28   Engr.

Sculptures by Mestrovic (1883-1962): 50d, "Reminiscences" (woman). 65d, Head of Kraljevic Marko. 100d, Indian on Horseback.

707	A170	25d brown, buff	.20	.20
708	A170	50d sl green, grnsh	.20	.20
709	A170	65d grnsh blk, grysh	.70	.30
710	A170	100d black, grayish	1.00	.60
	Nos. 707-710 (4)		2.10	1.30

Children with Toys — A171

1963, Oct. 5   Litho.
711	A171	25d multicolored	.35	.20

Issued for Children's Week.

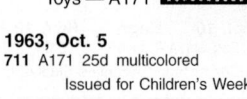

Soldier with Gun and Flag — A172

Litho. & Engr.
1963, Oct. 20   Perf. 12½
712	A172	25d ver, tan & gold	.25	.20

Yugoslavian Democratic Federation, 20th anniv.

Relief from Tombstone, Herzegovina A173

Dositej Obradovic A174

Art through the centuries: 30d, Horseback trio, Split Cathedral. 50d, King & queen on horseback, Beram Church, Istria. 65d, Archangel Michael, Dominican monastery, Dubrovnik. 100d, Man pouring water, fountain, Ljubljana. 150d, Archbishop Eufrasie, mosaic, Porec Basilica, Istria.

1963, Nov. 29   Photo.
713	A173	25d multi	.20	.20
714	A173	30d multi, horiz.	.20	.20
715	A173	50d multi, horiz.	.20	.20
716	A173	65d multi	.20	.20
717	A173	100d multi	.25	.20
718	A173	150d multi	.95	.60
	Nos. 713-718 (6)		2.00	1.60

Issued for the Day of the Republic.

1963, Dec. 10   Engr.

Famous Yugoslavians: 30d, Vuk Stefanovic Karadzic, reformer of Serbian language. 50d, Franc Miklosic, Slovenian philologist. 65d, Ljudevit Gaj, reformer of Croatian language. 100d, Peter Petrovich Nyegosh, Montenegrin prince, bishop and poet.

Variously Toned Paper
719	A174	25d black	.20	.20
720	A174	30d black	.20	.20
721	A174	50d black	.20	.20
722	A174	65d black	.60	.20
723	A174	100d black	1.00	.50
	Nos. 719-723 (5)		2.20	1.30

Vanessa Io — A175

Fireman Rescuing Child — A176

Butterflies & Moths: 30d, Vanessa antiopa. 40d, Daphnis nerii. 50d, Parnassius apollo. 150d, Saturnia pyri. 200d, Papilio machaon.

1964, May 25   Photo.   Perf. 12½
724	A175	25d multicolored	.40	.40
725	A175	30d multicolored	.40	.40
726	A175	40d multicolored	.40	.40
727	A175	50d multicolored	.40	.40
728	A175	150d multicolored	4.00	4.00
729	A175	200d multicolored	4.00	4.00
	Nos. 724-729 (6)		9.60	9.60

1964, June 14   Litho.
730	A176	25d red & black	.25	.20

Centenary of voluntary firemen.

Runner A177

1964, July 1   Unwmk.   Perf. 12½
731	A177	25d shown	.20	.20
732	A177	30d Boxing	.20	.20
733	A177	40d Rowing	.20	.20
734	A177	50d Basketball	.20	.20
735	A177	150d Soccer	3.25	1.00
736	A177	200d Water polo	3.25	1.00
	Nos. 731-736 (6)		7.30	2.80

18th Olympic Games, Tokyo, Oct. 10-25.

UN Flag over Scaffolding A178

25d, Upheaval of the earth & scaffolding.

1964, July 26   Engr.
737	A178	25d red brown	.20	.20
738	A178	50d blue	.20	.20

Earthquake at Skopje; 1st anniv.

Serbian Women — A179

Friedrich Engels — A180

Regional Costumes: 30d, Slovenia. 40d, Bosnia and Herzegovina. 50d, Croatia. 150d, Macedonia. 200d, Montenegro.

1964, Aug. 5   Litho.
Costumes Multicolored

740	A179	25d violet & brn	.30	.30
741	A179	30d slate & green	.30	.30
742	A179	40d redsh brn & blk	.30	.30
743	A179	50d blue & black	.30	.30
744	A179	150d dl grn & sepia	2.00	2.00
745	A179	200d tan, red & brn	2.00	2.00
		Nos. 740-745 (6)	5.20	5.20

Litho. & Engr.
1964, Sept. 27   Perf. 11½

746	A180	25d shown	.20	.20
747	A180	50d Karl Marx	.20	.20

1st Socialist Intl., London, Sept. 28, 1864.

Children at Play — A181

1964, Oct. 4   Litho.   Perf. 12½
748 A181 25d ver, pink & gray grn   .35   .20
Issued for Children's Week.

The Victor by Ivan Mestrovic — A182

1964, Oct. 20   Engr.   Perf. 11½
749 A182 25d gold & blk, *pnksh*   .25   .20
Liberation of Belgrade, 20th anniv.

Initial from Evangel of Hilandar — A183   Hand, "Liberty and Equality" — A184

Art through the centuries: 30d, Initial from Evangel of Miroslav (musician). 40d, Detail from Cetinje octavo, 1494 (saint with scroll). 50d, Miniature from Evangel of Trogir, 13th cent. (female saint). 150d, Miniature from Hrvoe Missal, 15th cent. (knight on horseback). 200d, Miniature from 14th cent. manuscript (symbolic fight), horiz.

Perf. 11½x12, 12x11½
1964, Nov. 29   Photo.   Unwmk.

750	A183	25d multicolored	.20	.20
751	A183	30d multicolored	.20	.20
752	A183	40d multicolored	.20	.20
753	A183	50d multicolored	.20	.20
754	A183	150d multicolored	.35	.20
755	A183	200d multicolored	.70	.40
		Nos. 750-755 (6)	1.85	1.40

Issued for Day of the Republic.

1964, Dec. 7   Perf. 12

50d, Dove over factory, "Peace and Socialism." 100d, Smokestacks, "Building Socialism."

756	A184	25d multicolored	.20	.20
757	A184	50d multicolored	.20	.20
758	A184	100d multicolored	.40	.25
		Nos. 756-758 (3)	.80	.65

Yugoslav Communist League, 8th congress.

Table Tennis Player — A185

Titograd — A186

1965, Apr. 15   Litho.   Perf. 12½
759	A185	50d shown	.20	.20
760	A185	150d Player at left	.40	.25

28th Table Tennis Championships, Ljubljana, Apr. 15-25.

1965, May 8   Engr.
761	A186	25d shown	.20	.20
762	A186	30d Skopje	.20	.20
763	A186	40d Sarajevo	.20	.20
764	A186	50d Ljubljana	.20	.20
765	A186	150d Zagreb	.30	.20
766	A186	200d Belgrade	.65	.40
		Nos. 761-766 (6)	1.75	1.40

Liberation of Yugoslavia from the Nazis, 20th anniv.

Young Pioneer — A187

ITU Emblem and Television Tower — A188

1965, May 10   Litho. & Engr.
767 A187 25d blk & tan, *buff*   .25   .20
Young Pioneer Games "20 Years of Freedom."

1965, May 17   Engr.
768 A188 50d dark blue   .25   .20
ITU, centenary.

Iron Gate, Danube — A189

Arms of Yugoslavia and Romania and Djerdap Dam — A190

50d, Iron Gate hydroelectric plant and dam.

1965, May 20   Litho.   Perf. 12½x12
769	A189	25d (30b) lt bl & grn	.25	.20
770	A189	50d (55b) lt bl & dk red	.40	.20

Miniature Sheet
Perf. 13½x13
771	A190	Sheet of 4	4.25	4.25
a.		100d multicolored	.35	.35
b.		150d multicolored	.70	.70

Nos. 769-771 were issued simultaneously by Yugoslavia and Romania to commemorate the start of the construction of the Iron Gate hydroelectric plant. Nos. 769-770 were valid for postage in both countries.

No. 771 contains one each of Nos. 771a, 771b and Romania Nos. 1747a and 1747b. Only Nos. 771a and 771b were valid in Yugoslavia. Sold for 500d.

See Romania Nos. 1745-1747.

Flower Type of 1957
Medicinal Plants: 25d, Milfoil. 30d, Rosemary. 40d, Inula. 50d, Belladonna. 150d, Mint. 200d, Foxglove.

1965, May 25   Photo.   Perf. 11½
Granite Paper
Flowers in Natural Colors
772	A123	25d deep carmine	.30	.30
773	A123	30d olive bister	.30	.30
774	A123	40d red brown	.30	.30
775	A123	50d dark blue	.30	.30
776	A123	150d violet blue	.35	.35
777	A123	200d purple	2.00	2.00
		Nos. 772-777 (6)	3.55	3.55

Intl. Cooperation Year Emblem A191

1965, June 26   Litho.   Perf. 12½
778 A191 50d dk bl & dull bl   .25   .20

Sibenik — A192

Cat — A193

1965, July 6   Unwmk.   Perf. 12½
779	A192	25d Rogaska Slatina	.25	.25
780	A192	30d shown	.25	.25
781	A192	40d Prespa Lake	.25	.25
782	A192	50d Prizren	.25	.25
783	A192	150d Scutari	.50	.50
784	A192	200d Sarajevo	.80	.80
		Nos. 779-784 (6)	2.30	2.30

1965, Oct. 3   Litho.   Perf. 12½
785 A193 30d maroon & brt yel   .45   .20
Issued for Children's Week.

Nos. 630 and 634 Surcharged in Maroon and Type of 1958
Designs: 20d, Jablanica hydroelectric works. 30d, Litostroy turbine factory.

1965   Engr.   Perf. 12½
786	A133	5d on 8d gray	.60	.20
787	A133	20d emerald	.50	.20
788	A133	30d red orange	.80	.20
789	A133	50d on 25d vermilion	.60	.20
		Nos. 786-789 (4)	2.50	.80

Branislav Nusic — A194   Marshal Tito — A195

Famous Yugoslavs: 50d, Antun Gustav Matos, poet. 60d, Ivan Mazuranic, writer. 85d, Fran Levstik, writer. 200d, Josif Pancic, physician and botanist. 500d, Dimitrije Tucovic, political writer.

1965, Nov. 28   Engr.
Variously Toned Paper
790	A194	30d dull red	.20	.20
791	A194	50d indigo	.20	.20
792	A194	60d brown	.20	.20
793	A194	85d dark blue	.20	.20
794	A194	200d dk olive grn	.20	.20
795	A194	500d deep claret	.60	.45
		Nos. 790-795 (6)	1.60	1.45

1966, Feb. 4   Litho.   Perf. 12½
796	A195	20p bluish grn	.40	.20
797	A195	30p rose pink	.55	.20

Rowing A196

30p, Long jump. 50p, Ice hockey. 3d, Hockey sticks, puck. 5d, Oars, scull.

1966, Mar. 1   Engr.
798	A196	30p dk car rose	.20	.20
799	A196	50p dk purple	.20	.20
800	A196	1d gray green	.20	.20
801	A196	3d dk red brn	1.00	1.00
802	A196	5d dark blue	1.00	1.00
		Nos. 798-802 (5)	2.60	2.60

25th Balkan Games; World ice hockey championship; 2nd rowing championships.

"T" from 15th Century Psalter — A197   Radio Amateurs' Emblem — A198

Art through the Centuries (Initials from Medieval Manuscripts): 50p, Cyrillic "V," Divosh Evangel, 14th cent. 60p, "R," Gregorius I, Libri moralium, 12th cent. 85p, Cyrillic "P," Miroslav Evangel, 12th cent. 2d, Cyrillic "B," Radomir Evangel, 13th cent. 5d, "F," Passional, 11th cent.

1966, Apr. 25   Photo.   Perf. 12

803	A197	30p multicolored	.20	.20
804	A197	50p multicolored	.20	.20
805	A197	60p multicolored	.20	.20
806	A197	85p multicolored	.20	.20
807	A197	2d multicolored	.30	.20
808	A197	5d multicolored	.65	.60
		Nos. 803-808 (6)	1.75	1.60

1966, May 23   Engr.   Perf. 12½x12

809	A198	85p dark blue	.25	.20

Union of Yugoslav Radio Amateurs, 20th anniv.; Intl. Congress of Radio Amateurs, Opatija, 5/23-28.

Stag Beetle — A199

Serbia No. 2, 1866 — A200

Beetles: 50p, Floral beetle. 60p, Oil beetle. 85p, Ladybird. 2d, Rosalia alpina. 5d, Aquatic beetle.

1966, May 25   Photo.   Perf. 12x12½

810	A199	30p gray, blk & bis	.20	.20
811	A199	50p gray, emer & blk	.20	.20
812	A199	60p bluish blk, sl grn & gray	.20	.20
813	A199	85p dl org, dp org & black	.20	.20
814	A199	2d gray, ultra & blk	.30	.20
815	A199	5d tan, brn & blk	.50	.50
		Nos. 810-815 (6)	1.60	1.50

Litho. & Engr.

1966, June 25   Perf. 12½

816	A200	30p shown	.20	.20
817	A200	50p No. 3	.20	.20
818	A200	60p No. 4	.20	.20
819	A200	85p No. 5	.20	.20
820	A200	2d No. 6	.45	.35
		Nos. 816-820 (5)	1.25	1.15

Souvenir Sheet

Imperf

821	A200	10d No. 1	2.00	2.00

Serbia's first postage stamps, cent.

Leather Shield with Farmer, Soldier and Woman — A201

Bishop Strossmayer and Franjo Racki — A202

1966, July 2   Perf. 12½

822	A201	20p pale grn, gold & red brown	.20	.20
823	A201	30p buff, gold & dp mag	.20	.20
824	A201	85p lt gray, gold & Prus bl	.20	.20
825	A201	2d lt bl, gold & vio	.25	.25
		Nos. 822-825 (4)	.85	.85

25th anniversary of National Revolution.

1966, July 15

826	A202	30p dl ol, blk & buff	.25	.20

Centenary of Academy of Arts and Sciences, founded by Bishop Josip Juraj Strossmayer with Racki as first president.

Mostar Bridge, Neretva River — A203

1966, Sept. 24   Engr.   Perf. 12½

827	A203	30p rose claret	1.75	.25

400th anniversary of Mostar Bridge.

Medieval View of Sibenik A204

1966, Sept. 24

828	A204	30p deep plum	.25	.20

900th anniversary of Sibenik.

Girl A205

Shipbuilding A206

1966, Oct. 2   Litho.

829	A205	30p ultra, org, red & blk	1.50	1.50

Issued for Children's Week.

1966   Engr.   Perf. 12½

Designs: 10p, Sisak steel works. 15p, Overpass. 20p, Jablonica hydroelectric works. 30p, Litostroy turbine factory. 40p, Lukavac coke factory. 50p, Zenica steel works. 60p, Cable factory, Svetozarevo. 65p, Sevojno copper works. 85p, Lumber industry. 1d, Crude oil production.

830	A206	5p dull orange	.35	.35
831	A206	10p brown	.35	.35
832	A206	15p vio blue	.35	.35
833	A206	20p emerald	.55	.35
834	A206	30p vermilion	2.10	.35
835	A206	40p dp claret	.35	.35
836	A206	50p gray blue	.45	.35
837	A206	60p red brown	.45	.35
838	A206	65p green	.65	.35
839	A206	85p dl purple	1.00	.35
840	A206	1d yel olive	1.50	.35
		Nos. 830-840 (11)	8.10	3.85

Issued: 5, 15p, 6/10; 10, 40, 50p, 6/8; 20, 30p, 4/28; 60, 65, 85p, 5/12; 1d, 6/18. For surcharge see No. 1322.

UNESCO Emblem — A207

Santa Claus — A208

1966, Nov. 4   Litho.

841	A207	85p violet blue	.25	.20

20th anniversary of UNESCO.

1966, Nov. 25   Litho.   Perf. 12½

Designs: 15p, Stylized winter landscape. 30p, Stylized Christmas tree.

842	A208	15p org & dk bl	.20	.20
843	A208	20p org & purple	.20	.20
844	A208	30p org & sl grn	.20	.20

1966, Dec. 23   Photo.   Perf. 12½

845	A208	15p gold & dk bl	.30	.20
846	A208	20p gold & red	.30	.20
847	A208	30p gold & green	.30	.20
		Nos. 842-847 (6)	1.50	1.20

Nos. 842-847 issued for New Year, 1967.

Wolf's Head Coin of Durad I, 1373 — A209

Medieval Coins: 50p, ½d of King Stefan, c. 1461 (arms of Bosnia). 60d, Dinar of Serbia (portrait of Durad Brankovic). 85p, Dinar of Ljubljana, c. 1250 (heraldic eagle). 2d, Dinar of Split, c. 1403-1413 (shield with arms of Duke Hrvoje Vukcic). 5d, Dinar of Emperor Stefan Dusan, c. 1346-1355 (Emperor on horseback).

1966, Nov. 28   Photo.
Coins in Silver, Gray and Black

848	A209	30p ver & blk	.20	.20
849	A209	50p ultra & blk	.20	.20
850	A209	60p magenta & blk	.20	.20
851	A209	85p violet & blk	.20	.20
852	A209	2d dk ol bis & blk	.20	.20
853	A209	5d brt grn & blk	.55	.35
		Nos. 848-853 (6)	1.55	1.35

Medicinal Plants — A210

Marshal Tito — A211

1967, May 25   Photo.   Perf. 11½
Granite Paper

854	A210	30p Arnica	.20	.20
855	A210	50p Flax	.20	.20
856	A210	85p Oleander	.20	.20
857	A210	1.20d Gentian	.20	.20
858	A210	3d Laurel	.20	.20
859	A210	5d African rue	.80	.80
		Nos. 854-859 (6)	1.80	1.80

Youth Day, May 25.

1967, May 25   Engr.   Perf. 12½
Size: 20x27½mm

860	A211	5p orange	.20	.20
861	A211	10p dk red brown	.20	.20
862	A211	15p dk vio blue	.20	.20
863	A211	20p green	.20	.20
864	A211	30p vermilion	.20	.20
865	A211	40p black	.20	.20
866	A211	50p Prussian grn	.20	.20
867	A211	60p lilac	.20	.20
868	A211	85p deep blue	.20	.20
869	A211	1d plum	.20	.20
		Nos. 860-869 (10)	2.00	2.00

75th birthday of Pres. Tito. Sheets of 15.
Nos. 860-869 were reissued in 1967 with slight differences including thinner paper and slightly darker shades.
See #924-939. For surcharge see #1414.

Coil Stamps

1968-69   Photo.   Perf. 12½ Horiz.

869A	A211	20p green	.30	.20
869B	A211	30p vermilion	.40	.20
869C	A211	50p vermilion ('69)	.30	.20
		Nos. 869A-869C (3)	1.00	.60

EXPO Emblem, Sputnik 1 and Explorer 1 — A212

ITY Emblem, St. Tripun's Church, Kotor — A213

Spacecraft: 50p, Tiros, Telstar and Molniya. 85p, Luna 9 and lunar satellite. 1.20d, Mariner 4, and Venus 3. 3d, Vostok, Gemini and Agena Rocket. 5d, Astronaut walking in space.

1967, June 26   Photo.   Perf. 11½

870	A212	30p ultra & multi	.20	.20
871	A212	50p yel & multi	.20	.20
872	A212	85p slate & multi	.20	.20
873	A212	1.20d multicolored	.20	.20
874	A212	3d vio & multi	.20	.20
875	A212	5d blue & multi	.3.75	3.75
		Nos. 870-875 (6)	3.75	3.75

EXPO '67, Montreal, Apr. 28-Oct. 27; 18th Congress of the Intl. Astronautical Federation, Belgrade.

1967, July 17   Engr.

Designs (ITY Emblem and): 50p, Municipal Building, Maribor. 85p, Cathedral, Trogir. 1.20d, Fortress gate, Nis. 3d, Drina Bridge, Visegrad. 5d, Daut-pasha's Bath, Skopje.

876	A213	30p slate bl & lt ol	.20	.20
877	A213	50p brn & dl vio	.20	.20
878	A213	85p dk bl & dp claret	.20	.20
879	A213	1.20d dp claret & brn	.20	.20
880	A213	3d brn & slate grn	.35	.20
881	A213	5d slate grn & brn	.50	.45
		Nos. 876-881 (6)	1.65	1.45

Issued for International Tourist Year, 1967.

Partridge — A214

1967, Sept. 22   Photo.   Perf. 14

882	A214	30p shown	.30	.30
883	A214	50p Pike	.30	.30
884	A214	1.20d Red deer	.50	.50
885	A214	5d Peregrine falcon	1.25	1.25
		Nos. 882-885 (4)	2.35	2.35

Intl. Fishing and Hunting Exposition and Fair, Novi Sad.

Congress Emblem with Sputnik 1 A215

Litho. & Engr.

1967, Sept. 25   Perf. 12½

886	A215	85p dk bl, lt bl & gold	.25	.20

18th Congress of the Intl. Astronautical Federation, Belgrade, Sept. 25-30.

Old Theater and Castle, Ljubljana — A216

Child's Drawing: Winter Scene — A217

1967, Sept. 29   Engr.   Perf. 12½

887	A216	30p sepia & dk grn	.25	.20

Centenary of Slovene National Theater.

1967, Oct. 2   Litho.

888	A217	30p multicolored	.50	.20

International Children's Week, Oct. 2-8.

Lenin by Mestrovic
A218

4-Leaf Clover
A219

1967, Nov. 7   Engr.   Perf. 12½

889	A218	30p dark purple	.20	.20
890	A218	85p olive gray	.25	.20

Souvenir Sheet

Imperf

891	A218	10d magenta	8.00	8.00

Russian October Revolution, 50th anniv.

1967, Nov. 15   Photo.   Perf. 14

30p, Chimney sweep. 50p, Horseshoe & flower.

Dated "1968"

892	A219	20p shown	.20	.20
893	A219	30p Chimney sweep	.20	.20
894	A219	50p Horseshoe, flower	.20	.20
		Nos. 892-894 (3)	.60	.60

New Year 1968. See Nos. 957-959.

The Young Sultana, by Vlaho
Bucovac — A220

Paintings: 85p, The Watchtower, by Dura Jaksic. 2d, Visit to the Family, by Josip Petkovsek. 3d, The Cock Fight, by Paja Jovanovic. 5d, "Spring" (woman and children), by Ivana Kobilca.

Perf. 11½x12, 12x11½

1967, Nov. 28   Engr. & Litho.

895	A220	85p multi, vert.	1.50	.35
896	A220	1d multi	1.50	.35
897	A220	2d multi	1.50	.35
898	A220	3d multi	1.50	.35
899	A220	5d multi, vert.	4.00	3.00
		Nos. 895-899 (5)	10.00	4.40

Issued for the Day of the Republic, Nov. 29. See Nos. 942-946, 995-1000.

Ski Jump — A221

Annunciation
A222

Sport: 1d, Figure skating pair. 2d, Downhill skiing. 5d, Ice hockey.

1968, Feb. 5   Engr.   Perf. 12½

900	A221	50p dk bl & dk pur	.40	.20
901	A221	1d brn & sl green	.40	.20
902	A221	2d sl grn & lake	.70	.40
903	A221	5d sl grn & dk bl	4.50	2.25
		Nos. 900-903 (4)	6.00	3.05

10th Winter Olympic Games, Grenoble, France, Feb. 6-18.

1968, Apr. 20   Photo.   Perf. 13½

Medieval Icons: 50p, Madonna, St. George's Church, Prizren. 1.50d, St. Sava and St. Simeon. 2d, Christ's descent into hell, Ohrid. 3d, Crucifixion, St. Clement's Church, Ohrid. 5d, Madonna, Church of Our Lady of the Bell Tower, Split.

906	A222	50p gold & multi	.20	.20
907	A222	1d gold & multi	.20	.20
908	A222	1.50d gold & multi	.20	.20
909	A222	2d gold & multi	.35	.25
910	A222	3d gold & multi	.50	.40
911	A222	5d gold & multi	1.10	1.00
		Nos. 906-911 (6)	2.55	2.25

European
Bullfinch — A223

800-meter Race for
Women — A224

Finches: 1d, Goldfinch. 1.50d, Chaffinch. 2d, European greenfinch. 3d, Red crossbill. 5d, Hawfinch.

1968, May 25   Photo.   Perf. 11½

Birds in Natural Colors

912	A223	50p bister	.40	.40
913	A223	1d rose lake	.40	.40
914	A223	1.50d gray blue	.40	.40
915	A223	2d deep orange	.40	.40
916	A223	3d olive green	.45	.45
917	A223	5d pale violet	5.00	2.50
		Nos. 912-917 (6)	7.05	4.55

Issued for Youth Day.

Litho. & Engr.

1968, June 28   Perf. 12½

1d, Basketball. 1.50d, Gymnast on vaulting horse. 2d, Rowing. 3d, Water polo. 5d, Wrestling.

918	A224	50p dk brn & dk red brown	.40	.40
919	A224	1d Prus bl & blk	.40	.40
920	A224	1.50d slate & dk brn	.40	.40
921	A224	2d bis & sl grn	.40	.40
922	A224	3d blk brn & ind	1.50	.40
923	A224	5d dk grn & vio blk	15.00	3.00
		Nos. 918-923 (6)	18.10	5.00

19th Olympic Games, Mexico City, 10/12-27.

Tito Type of 1967

1968-72   Engr.   Perf. 12½

Size: 20x27½mm

924	A211	20p dark blue	.20	.20
925	A211	25p lake	.20	.20
926	A211	30p green	.20	.20
927	A211	50p vermilion	.20	.20
928	A211	70p black	.30	.20
929	A211	75p slate grn	.40	.20
930	A211	80p olive	.40	.20
930A	A211	80p red org ('72)	.35	.20
931	A211	90p olive	.30	.20
932	A211	1.20d dark blue	.50	.20
932A	A211	1.20d sl grn ('72)	.40	.20
933	A211	1.25d deep blue	.45	.20
934	A211	1.50d slate grn	.40	.20

Size: 20x30½mm

935	A211	2d sepia	.60	.20
936	A211	2.50d Prussian grn	1.60	.20
937	A211	5d deep plum	1.40	.20
938	A211	10d violet blk	3.00	.35
939	A211	20d bluish black	4.25	.45
		Nos. 924-939 (18)	15.15	4.00

The shading of the background of Nos. 924-939 has been changed from the 1967 issue to intensify the contrast around the portrait.

Cannon and
Laurel
Wreath — A225

Mother Nursing
Twins, Fresco by
Jan of
Kastav — A226

1968, Aug. 2   Photo.   Perf. 12½

940	A225	50p org brn & gold	.25	.20

65th anniversary of the Ilinden uprising.

1968, Sept. 9   Litho.

941	A226	50p black & multi	.25	.20

Annexation of Istria and the Slovene Coast to Yugoslavia, 25th anniv.

Painting Type of 1967

Paintings: 1d, Lake Klansko, by Marko Pernhart. 1.50d, Bavarian Landscape, by Milan Popovic. 2d, Porta Terraferma, Zadar, by Ferdo Quiquerez. 3d, Mt. Triglav seen from Bohinj, by Anton Karinger. 5d, Studenica Monastery, by Djordje Krstic.

Engr. & Litho.

1968, Oct. 3   Perf. 14x13½

942	A220	1d gold & multi	.20	.20
943	A220	1.50d gold & multi	.20	.20
944	A220	2d gold & multi	.20	.20
945	A220	3d gold & multi	.30	.20
946	A220	5d gold & multi	1.75	.70
		Nos. 942-946 (5)	2.65	1.50

Aleksa Santic
(1868-1924),
Poet — A227

"Going for a
Walk" — A228

1968, Oct. 5   Engr.   Perf. 12½

947	A227	50p dark blue	.25	.20

1968, Oct. 6   Litho.

948	A228	50p multicolored	.25	.20

Issued for Children's Week.

Karl Marx (1818-
1883), by N.
Mitric — A229

Old Theater and
Belgrade
Castle — A230

1968, Oct. 11   Engr.

949	A229	50d dk car rose	.25	.20

1968, Nov. 22   Engr.   Perf. 12½

950	A230	50p ol brn & sl grn	.25	.20

Serbian National Theater, Belgrade, cent.

Hasan
Brkic — A231

The Family, by J.
Soldatovic
A232

Portraits: 75p, Ivan Milutinovic. 1.25d, Rade Koncar. 2d, Kuzman Josifovski. 2.50d, Tone Tomsic. 5d, Mosa Pijade.

1968, Nov. 28   Engr.   Perf. 12½

951	A231	50p violet black	.20	.20
952	A231	75p black	.20	.20
953	A231	1.25d red brown	.25	.20
a.		Souv. sheet, 2 ea #951-953	15.00	15.00
954	A231	2d bluish black	.30	.20
955	A231	2.50d slate green	.50	.25
956	A231	5d claret	1.10	.75
a.		Souv. sheet, 2 ea #954-956	15.00	15.00
		Nos. 951-956 (6)	2.55	1.80

2nd Assembly of the National Republic of Yugoslavia, 25th anniv.

Type of New Year's Issue, 1967

1968, Nov. 25   Photo.   Perf. 14

Dated "1969"

957	A219	20p Four-leaf clover	.20	.20
958	A219	30p Chimney sweep	.20	.20
959	A219	50p Horseshoe, flower	.20	.20
		Nos. 957-959 (3)	.60	.60

Issued for New Year 1969.

1968, Dec. 10   Engr.   Perf. 12½

960	A232	1.25d dark blue	.25	.20

International Human Rights Year.

ILO
Emblem — A233

Dove, Hammer
and Sickle
Emblem — A234

Litho. & Engr.

1969, Jan. 27   Perf. 12½

961	A233	1.25d red & black	.25	.20

ILO, 50th anniv.

Engr. & Photo.

1969, Mar. 11   Perf. 12½

75p, Graffiti "TITO" & 5-pointed star. 1.25d, 5-pointed crystal. 10d, Marshal Tito in 1943.

962	A234	50p black & red	.20	.20
963	A234	75p ol bis & blk	.20	.20
964	A234	1.25d red & black	.25	.20
		Nos. 962-964 (3)	.65	.60

Souvenir Sheet

964A		Sheet of 9	9.00	9.00
b.		A234 10d brown, engr.	5.00	5.00

Communist Federation of Yugoslavia, 50th anniv.; 9th party congress.
#964A contains 4 #962, 2 each #963-964, 964b.

St. Nikita, from Manasija Monastery
A235

Frescoes from Monasteries: 75p, Apostles, Zakopani. 1.25d, Crucifixion, Studenica. 2d, Wedding at Cana, Kalenic. 3d, Angel at the Grave, Mileseva. 5d, Pietá, Nerezi.

1969, Apr. 7   Photo.   Perf. 13½
965	A235	50p gold & multi	.20	.20
966	A235	75p gold & multi	.20	.20
967	A235	1.25d gold & multi	.20	.20
968	A235	2d gold & multi	.20	.20
969	A235	3d gold & multi	.45	.45
970	A235	5d gold & multi	2.00	.90
		Nos. 965-970 (6)	3.25	2.15

Roman Memorial and View of Ptuj
A236

1969, Apr. 23   Engr.   Perf. 11½
971	A236	50p violet brown	.25	.20

1900th anniv. of Ptuj, the Roman Petovio. Issued in sheets of 9 (3x3).

Vasil Glavinov — A237   Thin-leafed Peony — A238

1969, May 8   Perf. 12x12½
972	A237	50p ocher & rose lilac	.25	.20

Vasil Glavinov, Macedonian socialist, birth cent.. Issued in sheets of 9 (3x3).

1969, May 25   Photo.   Perf. 11½

Medicinal Plants: 75p, Coltsfoot. 1.25d, Primrose. 2d, Hellebore. 2.50d, Violets. 5d, Anemones.

Flowers in Natural Colors
973	A238	50p yellow brn	.20	.20
974	A238	75p dull purple	.20	.20
975	A238	1.25d blue	.20	.20
976	A238	2d brown	.20	.20
977	A238	2.50d plum	.25	.20
978	A238	5d green	2.25	2.25
		Nos. 973-978 (6)	3.30	3.25

See Nos. 1056-1061, 1140-1145.

Eber, by Vasa Ivankovic — A239

Paintings of Sailing Ships: 1.25d, Tare, by Franasovic. 1.50d, Brig Sela, by Vasa Ivankovic. 2.50d, Dubrovnik galleon, 16th century. 3.25d, Madre Mimbelli, by Antoine Roux. 5d, The Virgin Saving Seamen from Disaster, 16th century ikon.

1969, July 10   Photo.   Perf. 11½
979	A239	50p gold & multi	.20	.20
980	A239	1.25d gold & multi	.20	.20
981	A239	1.50d gold & multi	.20	.20
982	A239	2.50d gold & multi	.35	.25
983	A239	3.25d gold & multi	.65	.45
984	A239	5d gold & multi	1.40	1.00
		Nos. 979-984 (6)	3.00	2.30

Dubrovnik Summer Festival, 20th anniv.

11th World Games for the Deaf, Belgrade, Aug. 9-16 — A240

1969, Aug. 9   Engr.   Perf. 12½
985	A240	1.25d dp claret & dl vio	.40	.20

Lipice Horse
A241

Horses: 75p, Bosnian mountain horse. 3.25d, Ljutomer trotter. 5d, Half-breed.

1969, Sept. 26   Photo.   Perf. 11½
986	A241	75p multicolored	.20	.20
987	A241	1.25d olive & multi	.20	.20
988	A241	3.25d brn & multi	.25	.20
989	A241	5d multicolored	1.60	.80
		Nos. 986-989 (4)	2.25	1.40

Zagreb Veterinary College, 50th anniv.

Children and Birds, by Tanja Vucanik, 13 years
A242

1969, Oct. 5   Litho.   Perf. 12½
990	A242	50p org, blk & gray	.25	.20

Issued for Children's Week.

Arms of Belgrade — A243

Josip Smodlaka
A244

Arms: #992, Skopje (bridge & mountain). #993, Titograd (bridge & fortifications).

1969   Litho.   Perf. 12½
991	A243	50p gold & multi	.25	.20
992	A243	50p gold & multi	.25	.20
993	A243	50p gold & multi	.25	.20
		Nos. 991-993 (3)	.75	.60

Liberation of capitals of the Federated Republics, 25th anniv. See Nos. 1017-1020.

1969, Nov. 9   Engr.
994	A244	50p dark blue	.25	.20

Smodlaka (1869-1956), leader in Yugoslavia's fight for independence.

Painting Type of 1967

Paintings of Nudes: 50p, The Little Gypsy with the Rose, by Nikola Martinoski. 1.25d, Girl on a Red Chair, by Sava Sumanovic. 1.50d, Woman Combing her Hair, by Marin Tartaglia. 2.50d, Olympia, by Miroslav Kraljevic. 3.25d, The Bather, by Jovan Bijelic. 5d, Woman on a Couch, by Matej Sternen.

1969, Nov. 29   Photo. & Engr.   Perf. 13½
995	A220	50p multi, vert.	.20	.20
996	A220	1.25d multi, vert.	.35	.20
997	A220	1.25d multi, vert.	.45	.20
998	A220	2.50d multi	.55	.50
999	A220	3.25d multi, vert.	1.10	.90
1000	A220	5d multi	2.00	2.00
		Nos. 995-1000 (6)	4.65	4.00

University of Ljubljana, 50th Anniv.
A245

1969, Dec. 9   Engr.   Perf. 11½
1001	A245	50p slate grn	.25	.20

Seal of Zagreb University
A246

Jovan Cvijic, Geographer
A247

1969, Dec. 17   Photo. & Engr.   Perf. 12½
1002	A246	50p gold, bl & brn	.25	.20

University of Zagreb, 300th anniv.

Common Design Types pictured following the introduction.

Europa Issue, 1969
Common Design Type

1969, Dec. 20   Photo.   Perf. 11½
1003	CD12	1.25d grnsh gray, buff & brn	2.00	2.00
1004	CD12	3.25d rose lil, gray & dk bl	6.75	6.75

Yugoslavia's admission to CEPT.

1970, Feb. 16   Engr.   Perf. 12½

Famous Yugoslavs: 1.25d, Dr. Andrija Stampar, hygienist. 1.50d, Joakim Krcovski, author. 2.50d, Marko Miljanov, Montenegrin patriot-hero. 3.25d, Vaca Pelagic, socialist. 5d, Oton Zupancic, Slovenian poet.

1005	A247	50p reddish brn	.20	.20
1006	A247	1.25d brnsh black	.20	.20
1007	A247	1.50d lilac	.20	.20
1008	A247	2.50d slate grn	.25	.20
1009	A247	3.25d reddish brn	.25	.20
1010	A247	5d blue vio	.50	.40
		Nos. 1005-1010 (6)	1.60	1.40

Punishment of Dirce, Pulj — A248

Mosaics from the 1st-4th Centuries: 1.25d, Cerberus, Bitola, horiz. 1.50d, Angel of the Annunciation, Porec. 2.50d, Hunters, Gamzigard. 3.25d, Bull and cherry tree, horiz. 5d, Virgin and Child enthroned, Porec.

1970, Mar. 16   Photo.   Perf. 13½
1011	A248	50p gold & multi	.20	.20
1012	A248	1.25d gold & multi	.20	.20
1013	A248	1.50d gold & multi	.20	.20
1014	A248	2.50d gold & multi	.30	.25
1015	A248	3.25d gold & multi	.55	.35
1016	A248	5d gold & multi	1.00	1.00
		Nos. 1011-1016 (6)	2.45	2.20

Arms Type of 1969

#1017, Sarajevo (arcade). #1018, Zagreb (castle). #1019, Ljubljana (dragon and tower). #1020a, Yugoslavia (embossed coat of arms.)

1970   Litho.   Perf. 12½
1017	A243	50p gold & multi	.25	.20
1018	A243	50p gold & multi	.25	.20
1019	A243	50p gold & multi	.25	.20
		Nos. 1017-1019 (3)	.75	.60

Souvenir Sheet
1020		Sheet of 7	15.00 15.00
a.		A243 12d gold & black	12.50 12.50

Liberation of Yugoslavia, 25th anniv. No. 1020 contains Nos. 991-993, 1017-1019, 1020a + 2 labels.
Issued: #1017, Apr. 6; #1018, May 8; #1019, May 9; #1020, May 15.

Lenin (1870-1924), by S. Stojanovic
A249

Basketball
A250

Design: 1.25d, Lenin sculpture facing left.

1970, Apr. 22   Engr.
1021	A249	50p rose lilac	.20	.20
1022	A249	1.25d blue gray	.20	.20

1970, Apr. 25
1023	A250	1.25d plum	.25	.20

6th World Basketball Championships, Ljubljana, May 10-23.

Europa Issue, 1970
Common Design Type

1970, May 4   Photo.   Perf. 11½
Size: 32½x23mm
1024	CD13	1.25d lt bl, dk bl & lt grnsh bl	.20	.20
1025	CD13	3.25d rose lil, plum & gray	.55	.55

Istrian Shorthaired Hound
A251

Yugoslav Breeds of Dogs: 1.25d, Yugoslav tricolor hound. 1.50d, Istrian hard-haired hound. 2.50d, Balkan hound. 3.25d, Dalmatian. 5d, Shara mountain dog.

1970, May 25   Photo.   Perf. 11½
Granite Paper
1026	A251	50p tan & multi	.20	.20
1027	A251	1.25d olive & multi	.20	.20
1028	A251	1.50d violet & multi	.20	.20
1029	A251	2.50d slate & multi	.25	.20
1030	A251	3.25d multi	.45	.20
1031	A251	5d multi	2.00	2.00
		Nos. 1026-1031 (6)	3.30	3.00

Telegraph Circuit — A252

Stylized Gymnast — A254

Bird — A253

1970, June 20   Litho.   Perf. 12½
1032 A252 50p henna brn, gold & blk .25 .20
Telegraph service in Montenegro, cent.

1970, Oct. 5
1033 A253 50p multicolored .25 .20
Issued for Children's Week, Oct. 5-11.

1970, Oct. 22   Engr.
1034 A254 1.25d car & slate .25 .20
17th World Gymnastics Championships, Ljubljana, Oct. 22-27.

UN Emblem and Hand Holding Dove, by Makoto A255

Litho. & Engr.
1970, Oct. 24   Perf. 11½
1035 A255 1.25d dk brn, blk & gold .25 .20
25th anniversary of the United Nations.

Ascension, by Teodor D. Kracum A256

Baroque Paintings: 75p, Abraham's Sacrifice, by Federiko Benkovic. 1.25d, Holy Family, by Francisek Jelovsek. 2.50d, Jacob's Ladder, by Hristofor Zefarovic. 3.25d, Baptism of Christ, by unknown Serbian painter. 5.75d, The Coronation of Mary, by Tripo Kokolja.

Engr. & Photo.
1970, Nov. 28   Perf. 13½x14
1036 A256 50p gold & multi .20 .20
1037 A256 75p gold & multi .20 .20
1038 A256 1.25d gold & multi .20 .20
1039 A256 2.50d gold & multi .20 .20
1040 A256 3.25d gold & multi .45 .20
1041 A256 5.75d gold & multi .75 .70
  Nos. 1036-1041 (6) 2.00 1.70

Alpine Rhododendron — A257

European Nature Protection Year emblem and: 3.25d, Bearded vulture.

1970, Dec. 14   Photo.   Perf. 11½
1042 A257 1.25d multi 3.00 3.00
1043 A257 3.25d multi 10.00 10.00
  Sheets of 9.

Frano Supilo — A258

British, French, Canadian, Italian Satellites A259

Litho. & Engr.
1971, Jan. 25   Perf. 12½
1044 A258 50p black & buff .25 .20
Supilo (1870-1917), Croat leader for independence from Austria-Hungary. Sheets of 9.

1971, Feb. 8   Photo.   Perf. 13½
75p, Satellite. 1.25d, Automated moon exploration. 2.50d, Various spacecraft. 3.25d, 1st experimental space station. 5.75d, Astronauts on moon.
1045 A259 50p multi .20 .20
1046 A259 75p multi .20 .20
1047 A259 1.25d multi .30 .20
1048 A259 2.50d multi, horiz. .70 .45
1049 A259 3.25d multi, horiz. .95 .85
1050 A259 5.75d multi, horiz. 2.25 2.00
  Nos. 1045-1050 (6) 4.60 3.90
"Space in the service of science." Sheets of 9.

Proclamation of the Commune, Town Hall, Paris — A260

Litho. & Engr.
1971, Mar. 18   Perf. 11½
1051 A260 1.25d bis brn & gray brn .25 .20
Centenary of the Paris Commune.

Europa Issue, 1971
Common Design Type
1971, May 4   Photo.   Perf. 11½
Size: 33x23mm
1052 CD14 1.50d Prus bl, pale grn & dk bl .20 .20
1053 CD14 4d mag, pink & dk mag .50 .50

Circles — A261

Prince Lazar, Fresco, Lazarica Church — A262

1971, May 5   Perf. 13½
1054 A261 50p shown .50 .20
1055 A261 1.25d 20 circles 1.40 .70
2nd Congress of Managers of Autonomous States.

Flower Type of 1969
Medicinal Plants: 50p, Common mallow. 1.50d, Common buckthorn. 2d, Water lily. 2.50d, Poppy. 4d, Wild chicory. 6d, Physalis.

1971, May 25   Photo.   Perf. 11½
Flowers in Natural Colors
1056 A238 50p lt ultra .25 .25
1057 A238 1.50d olive bis .25 .25
1058 A238 2d dull blue .25 .25
1059 A238 2.50d dark car .30 .25
1060 A238 4d dp bister .55 .55
1061 A238 6d org brown 3.25 3.25
  Nos. 1056-1061 (6) 4.85 4.80

1971, June 28   Photo.   Perf. 13½
1062 A262 50p gray & multi .25 .20
600th anniversary of founding of Krusevac by Prince Lazar Hrebeljanovic (1329-1389).

View of Krk — A263

Views: 5p, Krusevac. 10p, Castle & church, Gradacac. 20p, Church & bridge, Bohinj. 35p, Shore & mountains, Omis. 40p, Peje. 50p, Memorial column, Krusevac. 60p, Logar Valley. 75p, Bridge & church, Bohinj. 80p, Church, Piran. 1d, Street, Bitolj. 1.20d, Minaret, Pocitelj. 1.25d, 1.50d, Gate tower, Hercegnovi. 2d, Cathedral & City Hall Square, Novi Sad. 2.50d, Crna River.

1971-73   Engr.   Perf. 13
1063 A263 5p orange ('73) .20 .20
1064 A263 10p brown ('72) .20 .20
1065 A263 20p vio blk ('73) .20 .20
1066 A263 30p ol gray ('72) .20 .20
 a.   30p green 1.00 .20
1067 A263 35p brn car ('73) .20 .20
1068 A263 40p black ('72) .20 .20
1069 A263 50p vermilion 1.50 .20
1070 A263 50p green ('72) .20 .20
1071 A263 60p purple ('72) .20 .20
1072 A263 75p slate green .20 .20
1073 A263 80p rose red ('72) 1.50 .20
1073A A263 1d violet brn 1.50 .45
1073B A263 1.20d sl grn ('72) 2.00 .20
1073C A263 1.25d deep blue 1.10 .20
1073D A263 1.50d bluish blk ('73) .25 .20
1073E A263 2d blue ('72) 1.00 .20
1073F A263 2.50d dl pur ('73) 1.00 .20
  Nos. 1063-1073F (17) 11.65 3.65
Issued with and without fluorescent bars.

See type A323. See Nos. 1482-1486, 1599-1600, 1602-1603, 1717. For surcharges see Nos. 1413, 1711-1712, 1765-1766, 1769.

Emperor Constantine, 4th Century — A264

UNICEF Emblem, Children in Balloon — A265

Tourist Issue
Antique Bronzes excavated in Yugoslavia: 1.50d, Boy with fish. 2d, Hercules, replica after Lysippus. 2.50d, Satyr. 4d, Head of Aphrodite. 6d, Citizen of Emona, 1st century tomb.

1971, Sept. 20   Photo.   Perf. 13½
1074 A264 50p rose & multi .20 .20
1075 A264 1.50d multicolored .20 .20
1076 A264 2d multicolored .20 .20
1077 A264 2.50d lem & multi .25 .20
1078 A264 4d ocher & multi .40 .25
1079 A264 6d multicolored .75 .60
  Nos. 1074-1079 (6) 2.00 1.65
  Sheets of 9.

1971, Oct. 4   Litho.   Perf. 13x13½
1080 A265 50p multicolored .25 .20
Children's Week, Oct. 3-10.

Woman in Serbian Costume, by Katarina Ivanovic A266

Portraits, 19th Century: 1.50d, The Merchant Ivanisevic, by Anastasije Bocaric. 2d, Ana Kresic, by Vjekoslav Karas. 2.50d, Pavle Jagodic, by Konstantin Danil. 4r, Luiza Pesjakova, by Mihael Stroj. 6d, Old Man and view of Ljubljana, by Matevz Langus.

Engraved and Photogravure
1971, Nov. 29   Perf. 13½x14
1081 A266 50p gold & multi .20 .20
1082 A266 1.50d gold & multi .20 .20
1083 A266 2d gold & multi .20 .20
1084 A266 2.50d gold & multi .25 .20
1085 A266 4d gold & multi .40 .30
1086 A266 6d gold & multi .90 .80
  Nos. 1081-1086 (6) 2.15 1.90
  See Nos. 1120-1125.

Letter with Postal Code, Map of Yugoslavia — A267

Damjan Gruev
(1871-1906),
Macedonian
Revolutionist
A268

1971, Dec. 15   Photo.   Perf. 13½x14
1087 A267 50p ultra & multi   .25 .20
Introduction of postal code system.

1971, Dec. 22   Engr.   Perf. 12½
1088 A268 50p dark blue   .25 .20

11th Winter
Olympic
Games,
Sapporo,
Japan, Feb.
3-13
A269

Engr. & Typo.
1972, Feb. 3   Perf. 11½
1089 A269 1.25d Speed skating   .80 .50
1090 A269 6d   Slalom   3.25 2.10
Sheets of 9.

First Page of
Statute of
Dubrovnik
A270

Lithographed and Engraved
1972, Mar. 15   Perf. 13½
1091 A270 1.25d gold & multi   .25 .20
700th anniversary of the Statute of Dubrovnik, a legal code given by Prince Marko Justiniani.

Ski Jump Track,
Planica — A271

1972, Mar. 21   Perf. 11½
1092 A271 1.25d blk, lt bl & grn   .25 .20
World Ski Jump Championships, Planica, Mar. 22-26.

Water Polo and
Olympic
Rings — A272

1972, Apr. 17   Litho.   Perf. 12½x12
1093 A272 50p   shown   .20 .20
1094 A272 1.25d Basketball   .20 .20
1095 A272 2.50d Butterfly stroke   .20 .20
1096 A272 3.25d Boxing   .30 .20
1097 A272 5d   Running   .50 .25
1098 A272 6.50d Yachting   1.00 .65
        Nos. 1093-1098 (6)   2.40 1.70
20th Olympic Games, Munich, Aug. 26-Sept. 10. Sheets of 9.

Europa Issue 1972
Common Design Type
1972, May 4   Photo.   Perf. 11½
1100 CD15 1.50d bl, grn & yel   .60 .60
1101 CD15 5d   brt rose, mag
            & org   .90 .80

Wall   Marshal Tito, by
Creeper — A275   Bozidar
                Jakac — A276

Birds: 1.25d, Little bustard. 2.50d, Red-billed chough. 3.25d, Spoonbill. 5d, Eagle owl. 6.50d, Rock ptarmigan.

1972, May 8
Birds in Natural Colors
1102 A275 50p   gray violet   .25 .25
1103 A275 1.25d ocher   .25 .25
1104 A275 2.50d gray olive   .25 .25
1105 A275 3.25d light plum   .35 .35
1106 A275 5d   red brown   .65 .65
1107 A275 6.50d violet   2.25 2.25
        Nos. 1102-1107 (6)   4.00 4.00
Nature protection.

1972, May 25   Litho.   Perf. 12½
1108 A276 50p   cream & dk brn   .20 .20
1109 A276 1.25d gray & indigo   .50 .25

Souvenir Sheet
Imperf
1110 A276 10d gray & blk brn   2.75 2.75
80th birthday of Pres. Tito. Sheets of 9. No. 1110 printed in blocks of 4.

First
Locomotive
Built in
Serbia,
1882 — A277

5d, Modern Yugoslavian electric locomotive.

1972, June 12   Photo.   Perf. 11½
1111 A277 1.50d multicolored   .20 .20
1112 A277 5d   multicolored   .80 .30
Intl. Railroad Union, 50th anniv.

Glider
A278

1972, July 8   Photo.   Perf. 12½
1113 A278 2d bl gray, gold & blk   .25 .20
13th World Gliding Championships, Vrsac Airport, July 9-23. Sheets of 9.

Pawn on
Chessboard — A279

6d, Chessboard, emblems of King and Queen.

1972, Sept. 18   Perf. 11½
1114 A279 1.50d multi   .20 .20
1115 A279 6d   multi   1.25 .70
20th Men's and 5th Women's Chess Olympiad, Skopje, Sept.-Oct. Sheets of 9.

Boy on Rocking
Horse — A280

Goce
Delchev — A281

1972, Oct. 2   Litho.   Perf. 12½
1116 A280 80p org & multi   .25 .20
Children's Week, Oct. 2-8.

1972, Oct. 16   Perf. 13
1117 A281 80p yel grn & blk   .25 .20
Delchev (1872-1903), Macedonian freedom fighter.

Grga Martic,
by Ivan
Mestrovic
A282

1972, Nov. 3   Perf. 12½
1118 A282 80p red, yel grn & blk   .25 .20
Brother Grga Martic (1822-1905), Franciscan administrator, educator and poet.

Serbian
National
Library,
Belgrade
A283

1972, Nov. 25   Engr.   Perf. 11½x12
1119 A283 50p chocolate   .25 .20
140th anniversary of the Serbian National Library and opening of new building.

Painting Type of 1971
Still-Life Paintings: 50p, by Milos Tenkovic, horiz. 1.25d, by Jozef Pekovsek. 2.50d, by Katarina Jovanovic, horiz. 3.25d, by Konstantin Danil, horiz. 5d, by Nikola Masic. 6.50d, by Celestin Medovic, horiz.

Perf. 14x13½, 13½x14
1972, Nov. 28   Engr. & Photo.
1120 A266 50p   gold & multi   .20 .20
1121 A266 1.25d gold & multi   .20 .20
1122 A266 2.50d gold & multi   .20 .20
1123 A266 3.25d gold & multi   .30 .20
1124 A266 5d   gold & multi   .40 .30
1125 A266 6.50d gold & multi   .70 .50
        Nos. 1120-1125 (6)   2.00 1.60

Battle of Stubica, by Krsto
Hegedusic — A284

6d, Battle of Krsko, by Gojmir Anton Kos.

1973, Jan. 29   Photo.   Perf. 11½
1126 A284 2d gold & multi   .30 .20
1127 A284 6d gold & multi   1.25 .70
Croatian-Slovenian Rebellion, 400th anniv. (2d); Beginning of the peasant rebellions in Slovenia, 500th anniv. (6d). Sheets of 9.

Radoje
Domanovic
(1873-1908),
Serbian
Writer — A285

1973, Feb. 3   Litho.   Perf. 12½
1128 A285 80p tan & brn   .40 .20
Sheets of 9.

Skofja Loka
A286

1973, Feb. 15   Perf. 11½
1129 A286 80p brown & buff   .30 .20
Millennium of the founding of Skofja Loka. Sheets of 9.

Novi Sad, by Peter
Demetrovic — A287

Old Engravings: 1.25d, Zagreb, by Josef Szeman. 2.50d, Kotor, by Pierre Mortier. 3.25d, Belgrade, by Mancini. 5d, Split, by Louis-Francois Cassas. 6.50d, Kranj, by Matthaus Merian.

Engraved and Photogravure
1973, Mar. 15   Perf. 13½
1130 A287 50p   gold, buff & blk   .20 .20
1131 A287 1.25d gold, gray &
            black   .20 .20
1132 A287 2.50d gold & blk   .20 .20
1133 A287 3.25d gold & blk   .20 .20
1134 A287 5d   gold, buff & blk   .35 .30
1135 A287 6.50d gold & blk   .50 .45
        Nos. 1130-1135 (6)   1.65 1.55

Championship
Poster
A288

1973, Apr. 5   Litho.   Perf. 13½x13
1136 A288 2d multicolored   .35 .20
32nd Intl. Table Tennis Championships, Sarajevo, Apr. 5-15. Sheets of 9.

Europa Issue, 1973
Common Design Type
1973, Apr. 30   Photo.   Perf. 11½
Size: 32½x23mm
1138 CD16 2d dk bl, lil & lt
            grn   .35 .30
1139 CD16 5.50d pur, cit & sal
            pink   1.40 1.25
Sheets of 9.

Flower Type of 1969
Medicinal Plants: 80p, Birthwort. 2d, Globe thistles. 3d, Olive branch. 4d, Corydalis. 5d, Mistletoe. 6d, Comfrey.

1973, May 25   **Photo.**   *Perf. 11½*
Flowers in Natural Colors

1140	A238	80p orange & grn	.20	.20
1141	A238	2d dl bl & blue	.20	.20
1142	A238	3d olive & blk	.25	.25
1143	A238	4d yel grn & grn	.40	.40
1144	A238	5d org & sepia	.60	.60
1145	A238	6d lilac & grn	1.75	1.75
		Nos. 1140-1145 (6)	3.40	3.40

Anton Jansa (1734-1773), Teacher, Apiculturist and Bee — A291

1973, Aug. 25   **Engr.**   *Perf. 12½*

1147	A291	80p black	.40	.20

Sheets of 9.

Championship Badge A292

1973, Sept. 1   **Litho.**   *Perf. 13½x13*

1148	A292	2d multicolored	.30	.20

World water sport championships (swimming, water polo, water jumps, figure swimming), Belgrade, Sept. 1-9. Sheets of 9.

"Greeting the Sun," by Ivan Vucovic A293

Post Horn — A294

1973, Oct. 1   *Perf. 12½*

1149	A293	80p multicolored	.75	.30

Children's Week, Oct. 1-7. Sheets of 9.

Coil Stamps

1973-77   **Photo.**   *Perf. 14½x14*

1150	A294	30p brown	.20	.20
1151	A294	50p gray blue	.20	.20
1152	A294	80p rose red ('74)	.20	.20
1153	A294	1d yel grn ('77)	.20	.20
1154	A294	1.20d pink ('74)	.30	.20
1155	A294	1.50d rose ('77)	.20	.20
		Nos. 1150-1155 (6)	1.30	1.20

Juraj Dalmatinac, Sculptor, Architect, 500th Anniv. of Death — A295

1973, Oct. 8   **Litho.**   *Perf. 12½*

1158	A295	80p grnsh gray & ol blk	.25	.20

Sheets of 9.

Nadezda Petrovic (1873-1915), Self-Portrait — A296

Lithographed and Engraved
1973, Oct. 12   *Perf. 11½*

1159	A296	2d gold & multi	.30	.20

Sheets of 9.

Interior, by Marko Celebonovic — A297

Paintings of Interiors by Yugoslav artists: 2d, St. Duja, by Emanuel Vidovic. 3d, Room with Slovak Woman, by Marino Tartaglia. 4d, Painter with Easel, by Miljenko Stancic. 5d, Studio, by Milan Konjovic. 6d, Tavern in Stara Loka, by France Slana.

1973, Oct. 20   **Photo.**   *Perf. 13½*

1160	A297	80p gold & multi	.20	.20
1161	A297	2d gold & multi	.20	.20
1162	A297	3d gold & multi	.20	.20
1163	A297	4d gold & multi	.20	.20
1164	A297	5d gold & multi	.35	.25
1165	A297	6d gold & multi	.45	.40
		Nos. 1160-1165 (6)	1.60	1.45

Sheets of 9.

Dragojlo Dudic — A298

Lithographed and Engraved
1973, Nov. 29   *Perf. 12½*
Gray and Indigo

1166	A298	80p shown	.20	.20
1167	A298	80p Strahil Pindzur	.20	.20
1168	A298	80p Boris Kidric	.20	.20
1169	A298	80p Radoje Dakic	.20	.20

Gray and Plum

1170	A298	2d Josip Mazar-Sosa	.25	.25
1171	A298	2d Zarko Zrenjanin	.25	.25
1172	A298	2d Emin Duraku	.25	.25
1173	A298	2d Ivan-Lola Ribar	.25	.25
a.		Sheet of 8, #1166-1173	1.50	1.50

Republic Day, Nov. 29, honoring national heroes who perished during WWII.

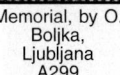

Memorial, by O. Boljka, Ljubljana A299   Winged Globe, by D. Dzamonja, at Podgaric A300

Sculptures: 4.50d, Tower by D. Dzamonja, at Kozara. 5d, Memorial, by B. Grabulovski, at Belcista. 10d, Abstract, by M. Zivkovic, at Sutjeska. 50d, Stone "V," by Zivkovic, at Kragujevac.

1974   **Engr.**   *Perf. 12½*

1174	A299	3d slate grn	1.25	.20
1175	A299	4.50d brn lake	2.00	.20
1176	A299	5d dark vio	2.00	.20
b.		Perf. 13½	6.00	.35
1177	A300	10d slate grn	2.50	.40
1178	A300	20d dull pur	3.25	.50
1179	A300	50d indigo	6.50	1.50
		Nos. 1174-1179 (6)	17.50	3.00

1978-82   **Litho.**

1176a	A299	5d	2.25	.20
1177a	A300	10d ('81)	2.25	.50
1178a	A300	20d ('81)	3.25	.50
1179a	A300	50d ('82)	4.00	1.00
		Nos. 1176a-1179a (4)	11.75	2.20

Metric Measure A301

1974, Jan. 10   **Litho.**   *Perf. 13*

1180	A301	80p plum & multi	.25	.20

Centenary of introduction of metric system.

European Ice Skating Championships, Jan. 29-Feb. 2, Zagreb — A302

1974, Jan. 29

1181	A302	2d multicolored	.65	.25

Diligence, 1874 A303

Litho. & Engr.
1974, Feb. 25   *Perf. 11½*

1182	A303	80p shown	.20	.20
1183	A303	2d New UPU headquarters	.20	.20
1184	A303	8d Jet plane	.75	.50
		Nos. 1182-1184 (3)	1.15	.90

Centenary of the Universal Postal Union.

Montenegro No. 1 — A304

Litho. & Engr.
1974, Mar. 11   *Perf. 13*

1185	A304	80p shown	.20	.20
1186	A304	6d Montenegro No. 7	.40	.20

Centenary of first Montenegrin postage stamps.

Marshal Tito — A305   Lenin, by Nandor Glid — A306

1974   **Litho.**   *Perf. 13*

1193	A305	50p green	.20	.20
a.		Perf. 13x12½	.60	.20
1196	A305	80p vermilion	.20	.20
1198	A305	1.20d slate green	.25	.20
1201	A305	2d gray blue	.25	.20
a.		Perf. 13x12½	.50	.20
		Nos. 1193-1201 (4)	.90	.80

Issued with and without fluorescence.
For surcharge see No. 1415.

1974, Apr. 20   **Litho.**   *Perf. 13*

1204	A306	2d blk & silver	.25	.20

50th death anniv. of Lenin.

Lepenski Vir Statue, c. 4950 B.C. — A307

Europa: 6d, Widow & Child, by Ivan Mestrovic.

1974, Apr. 29   **Photo.**   *Perf. 11½*

1205	A307	2d multicolored	.40	.40
1206	A307	6d multicolored	1.60	1.60

Great Tit — A308   Congress Poster — A309

1974, May 25   **Photo.**   *Perf. 11½*

1207	A308	80p shown	.20	.20
1208	A308	2d Rose	.55	.20
1209	A308	6d Cabbage butterfly	1.40	1.10
		Nos. 1207-1209 (3)	2.15	1.50

Youth Day. Issued in sheets of 9.

1974, May 27   **Litho.**   *Perf. 11½*

1210	A309	80p gold & multi	.20	.20
1211	A309	2d silver & multi	.20	.20
1212	A309	6d ocher & multi	.40	.40
		Nos. 1210-1212 (3)	.80	.80

10th Congress of Yugoslav League of Communists, Belgrade, May 27-30.

Radar Ground Station, Ivanjica — A311

Games Emblem and Soccer Cup — A312

1974, June 7   Engr.   Perf. 13
1214 A311 80p shown   .20 .20
1215 A311 6d Intelsat IV   1.10 .50
Opening of first satellite ground station in Yugoslavia at Ivanjica. Sheets of 9.

1974, June 13   Litho.   Perf. 13
1216 A312 4.50d vio bl & multi   1.25 .90
World Cup Soccer Championship, Munich, June 13-July 7. Sheets of 9.

Klek Mountain, Edelweiss, Mountaineers' Emblem — A313

1974, June 15
1217 A313 2d grn & multi   .25 .20
Mountaineering in Yugoslavia, cent. Sheets of 9.

Children's Dance, by Jano Knjazovic — A314

Paintings: 2d, "Crucified Rooster," by Ivan Generalic, vert. 5d, Laundresses, by Ivan Lackovic, vert. 8d, Dance, by Janko Brasic.

1974, Sept. 9   Photo.   Perf. 11½
1218 A314 80p multi   .20 .20
1219 A314 2d multi   .20 .20
1220 A314 5d multi   .60 .45
1221 A314 8d multi   1.90 .75
   Nos. 1218-1221 (4)   2.90 1.60
Yugoslav primitive art.

Cock and Flower, by Kaca Milinojsin A315

Designs (Children's Paintings): 3.20d, Girl and Boy, by Ewa Medrzecka, vert. 5d, Cat and Kitten, by Jelena Anastasijevic.

1974, Oct. 7   Litho.   Perf. 13
1222 A315 1.20d multi   .20 .20
1223 A315 3.20d multi   .20 .20
1224 A315 5d multi   .70 .20
   Nos. 1222-1224 (3)   1.10 .60
Children's Week, Oct. 1-7, and Joy of Europe meeting in Belgrade. Sheets of 9.

Library and Primoz Trubar Statue A316

1974, Oct. 21   Engr.   Perf. 13
1225 A316 1.20d black   .25 .20
Natl. University Library, Ljubljana, 200th anniv.

White Peonies, by Petar Dobrovic A317

Paintings of Flowers by Yugoslav artists: 2d, Carnations, by Vilko Gecan. 3d, Flowers, still-life, by Milan Konjovic. 4d, White Vase, by Sava Sumanovic. 5d, Larkspur, by Stane Kregar. 8d, Roses, by Petar Lubarda.

1974, Nov. 28   Photo.   Perf. 11½
1226 A317 80p gold & multi   .20 .20
1227 A317 2d gold & multi   .20 .20
1228 A317 3d gold & multi   .20 .20
1229 A317 4d gold & multi   .30 .20
1230 A317 5d gold & multi   .45 .20
1231 A317 8d gold & multi   .85 .35
   Nos. 1226-1231 (6)   2.20 1.35
Sheets of 9.

Title Page and View of Belgrade A318

1975, Jan. 8   Litho.   Perf. 13
1232 A318 1.20d citron   .25 .20
   a.   Perf. 12½   30.00 30.00
Sesquicentennial of the first publication of Matica Srpska, literary journal.

Map of Europe and Dove — A319

Svetozar Markovic, by Stevan Bodnarov A321

Gold-plated Bronze Earring A320

1975, Jan. 30   Perf. 12x11½
1233 A319 3.20d bl & multi   .55 .25
1234 A319 8d multi   1.75 .90
Interparliamentary Union for European Cooperation and Security, 2nd Conference, Belgrade, Jan. 31-Feb. 6.

1975, Feb. 25   Photo.   Perf. 14x13
Antique jewelry in Yugoslav museums: 2.10d, Silver bracelet, 18th cent. 3.20d, Silver gilt belt buckle, 18th cent. 5d, Silver ring with Nike cameo, 14th cent. 6d, Silver necklace, 17th cent. 8d, Bronze gilt bracelet, 14th cent.

1235 A320 1.20d multi   .20 .20
1236 A320 2.10d multi   .20 .20
1237 A320 3.20d multi   .20 .20
1238 A320 5d multi   .35 .25

1239 A320 6d multi   .65 .40
1240 A320 8d multi   .80 .75
   Nos. 1235-1240 (6)   2.40 2.00

1975, Feb. 26   Engr.   Perf. 13
1241 A321 1.20d blue blk   .50 .20
Markovic (1846-1875), writer and poet.

Fettered Woman, by Frano Krsinic A322

Street, Ohrid — A323

1975, Mar. 8   Photo.   Perf. 14½x14
1242 A322 3.20d gold & sepia   .30 .20
International Women's Year.

1975-77   Litho.   Perf. 13
Views: 25p, Budva. 75p, City Hall, Rijeka (Fiume). Nos. 1245, 1246, Street, Ohrid. 1.50d, Church, Bihac. 2.10d, Street and fountain, Hvar. 3.20d, Skofja Loka. 3.40d, Main Square, Vranje. 4.90d, Mosque, Perast.

No Inscription at Bottom
1243 A323 25p carmine ('76)   .40 .20
1244 A323 75p purple ('76)   .40 .20
1245 A323 1d dull purple   .50 .20
1246 A323 1d dl grn ('76)   .40 .20
   a.   Perf. 13x12½   .40 .20
1247 A323 1.50d rose red ('76)   1.00 .20
   a.   Perf. 13x12½   20.00 20.00
1248 A323 2.10d gray green   .60 .20
1249 A323 3.20d dull blue   .80 .20
1250 A323 3.40d gray grn ('77)   .70 .20
   a.   Perf. 13x12½   1.25 .25
1251 A323 4.90d dl bl ('76)   1.25 .20
   Nos. 1243-1251 (9)   6.05 1.80

See Nos. 1487-1491, 1598, 1601, 1603A, 1713, 1718-1719. For surcharges see Nos. 1382-1383, 1481, 1502, 1545, 1550, 1594-1597A, 1764, 1767-1768, 1770-1771, 1964, 1973.

Europa Issue 1975

Still Life with Eggs, by Mosa Pijade A325

Painting: 8d, Three Graces, by Ivan Radovic.

1975, Apr. 28
1252 A325 3.20d gold & multi   .20 .20
1253 A325 8d gold & multi   .60 .60

Srem Front Fighters' Monument, by Dusan Dzamonja A326

1975, May 9   Litho.   Perf. 13½
1254 A326 3.20d red & multi   .30 .20
Victory over Fascism in WWII; liberation of Yugoslavia, 30th anniv.

Garland Flower — A327   Kayak — A328

1975, May 24   Photo.   Perf. 14x14½
1255 A327 1.20d shown   .20 .20
1256 A327 2.10d Garden balsam   .20 .20
1257 A327 3.20d Rose mallow   .20 .20
1258 A327 5d Geranium   .40 .25
1259 A327 6d Crocus   .55 .30
1260 A327 8d Oleander   .85 .60
   Nos. 1255-1260 (6)   2.40 1.75
Youth Day.

1975, June 20   Litho.   Perf. 13½
1261 A328 3.20d grnsh bl & multi   .25 .20
9th World Championship of Wild Water Racing, Radika River, June 24-25, and 14th World Championship of Canoe-Slalom, Treska River, June 28-29.

Ambush, Herzegovinian Insurgents, by Ferdo Quiquerez — A329

1975, July 9   Photo.   Perf. 13½x14½
1262 A329 1.20d gold & multi   .25 .20
Bosnian & Herzegovinian Uprising, cent.

Stjepan Mitrov Ljubisa (1824-1878) A330

Yugoslav writers: 2.10d, Ivan Prijatelj (1875-1937). 3.20d, Jakov Ignjatovic (1824-1889). 5d, Dragojla Jarnevic (1824-1889). 6d, Svetozar Corovic (1875-1919). 8d, Ivana Brlic-Mazuranic (1874-1938).

1975, Sept. 16   Litho.   Perf. 13
1263 A330 1.20d brick red & blk   .20 .20
1264 A330 2.10d dl grn & blk   .20 .20
1265 A330 3.20d ol bis & blk   .20 .20
1266 A330 5d brn org & blk   .35 .20
1267 A330 6d yel grn & blk   .40 .20
1268 A330 8d Prus bl & blk   .50 .20
   Nos. 1263-1268 (6)   1.85 1.30

"Joy of Europe" Children's Meeting, Oct. 2-7, Belgrade A331

Children's drawings.

1975, Oct. 1   Litho.   Perf. 13½
1269 A331 3.20d Young Lion   .35 .20
1270 A331 6d Baby Carriage   1.60 .65

Peace Dove A332

1975, Oct. 10
1271	A332	3.20d multi	.20 .20
1272	A332	8d multi	.75 .45

European Security and Cooperation Conference, Helsinki, July 30-Aug. 1.

Red Cross, "100", Map of Yugoslavia
A333

8d, Red Cross, people seeking help.

1975, Nov. 1   Litho.   Perf. 13½x13
1273	A333	1.20d red & multi	.20 .20
1274	A333	8d red & multi	.45 .30

Centenary of Red Cross in Yugoslavia.

Soup Kitchen, by Dorde Andrejevic-Kun
A334

Social paintings by 20th century Yugoslav artists: 2.10d, People at the Door, by Vinko Grdan. 3.20d, Drunks in Coach, by Marijan Detoni, horiz. 5d, Workers' Lunch, by Tone Kralj, horiz. 6d, Water Wheel, by Lazar Licenoski. 8d, The Hanging, by Krsto Hegedusic.

Perf. 14½x13½, 13½x14½
1975, Nov. 28   Photo.
1275	A334	1.20d gold & multi	.20 .20
1276	A334	2.10d gold & multi	.20 .20
1277	A334	3.20d gold & multi	.20 .20
1278	A334	5d gold & multi	.20 .20
1279	A334	6d gold & multi	.30 .25
1280	A334	8d gold & multi	.55 .55
	Nos. 1275-1280 (6)		1.65 1.60

Sheets of 9.

Diocletian's Palace, 304 A.D. — A335

3.20d, House of Ohrid, 19th cent., vert. 8d, Gracanica Monastery, Kosovo, 1321.

1975, Dec. 10   Engr.   Perf. 13½
1281	A335	1.20d dark brown	.20 .20
1282	A335	3.20d bluish black	.30 .20
1283	A335	8d dk vio brown	.80 .35
	Nos. 1281-1283 (3)		1.30 .75

European Architectural Heritage Year 1975. Sheets of 9.

12th Winter Olympic Games, Feb. 4-15, Innsbruck, Austria
A336

1976, Feb. 4   Engr.   Perf. 13½
1284	A336	3.20d Ski jump	.20 .20
1285	A336	8d Pair figure skating	.70 .40

Red Flag — A337

1976, Feb. 14   Litho.
1286	A337	1.20d red & multi	.25 .20

"Red Flag" workers demonstration, Kragujevac, Feb. 15, 1876.

Svetozar Miletic (1826-1901), Lawyer, Founder of United Serbian Youth — A338

1976, Feb. 23   Perf. 13½x13
1287	A338	1.20d grnsh gray & dl grn	.25 .20

Borislav "Bora" Stankovic, (1876-1927), Writer
A339

1976, Mar. 31   Litho.   Perf. 13½x13
1288	A339	1.20d lem, ol & mar	.25 .20

Sheets of 9.

Europa Issue 1976

King Matthias, by Jakob Pogorelec, 1931 — A340

1976, Apr. 26   Photo.   Perf. 11½
1289	A340	3.20d shown	.25 .25
1290	A340	8d Bowl, 14th cent	.35 .35

Ivan Cankar (1876-1918), Slovenian Writer
A341

1976, May 8   Litho.   Perf. 13½x13
1291	A341	1.20d orange & plum	.25 .20

Train on Viaduct in Bosnia
A342

Design: 8d, Train on viaduct in Montenegro.

1976, May 15   Engr.   Perf. 13½
1292	A342	3.20d deep magenta	.20 .20
1293	A342	8d deep blue	.55 .25

Inauguration of the Belgrade-Bar railroad.

Hawker Dragonfly
A343

Fresh-water Fauna: 2.10d, Winkle. 3.20d, Rudd. 5d, Green frog. 6d, Ferruginous duck. 8d, Muskrat.

1976, May 25   Litho.
1294	A343	1.20d yel & multi	.30 .30
1295	A343	2.10d bl & multi	.30 .30
1296	A343	3.20d vio & multi	.30 .30
1297	A343	5d multicolored	.80 .80
1298	A343	6d multicolored	.80 .80
1299	A343	8d multicolored	2.40 2.40
	Nos. 1294-1299 (6)		4.90 4.90

Youth Day.

Vladimir Nazor, Croatian Writer, Birth Cent. — A344

1976, May 29   Perf. 13
1300	A344	1.20d pale lil & dl bl	.25 .20

Battle of Vucji Dol, 1876
A345

1976, June 16   Litho.   Perf. 13
1301	A345	1.20d gold, brn & buff	.25 .20

Liberation of Montenegro from Turkey, cent.

Serbian Pitcher
A346

Water Pitchers: 2.10d, Slovenia. 3.20d, Bosnia-Herzegovina. 5d, Vojvodina 6d, Macedonia. 8d, Kosovo.

1976, June 22   Photo.   Perf. 14x13
1302	A346	1.20d dk car & multi	.20 .20
1303	A346	2.10d olive & multi	.20 .20
1304	A346	3.20d red & multi	.20 .20
1305	A346	5d brown & multi	.30 .20
1306	A346	6d dk grn & multi	.40 .30
1307	A346	8d dk bl & multi	.85 .35
	Nos. 1302-1307 (6)		2.15 1.45

Tesla Monument, Belgrade, and Niagara Falls — A347

1976, July 10   Engr.   Perf. 13
1308	A347	5d slate grn & indigo	.50 .20

Nikola Tesla (1856-1943), electrical engineer and inventor. Sheets of 9.

21st Olympic Games, July 17-Aug. 1, Montreal, Canada, A348

1976, July 17
1309	A348	1.20d Long jump	.20 .20
1310	A348	3.20d Team handball	.20 .20
1311	A348	5d Target shooting	.25 .20
1312	A348	8d Single scull rowing	.75 .40
	Nos. 1309-1312 (4)		1.40 1.00

Sheets of 9.

World Map and Peace Dove
A349

1976, Aug. 16   Litho.   Perf. 13
1313	A349	4.90d multi	.30 .20

5th Summit Conference of Non-Aligned Countries, Colombo, Sri Lanka, Aug. 9-19. Sheets of 9.

Children's Train — A350

Children's drawings: 4.90d, Navy Day (submarine).

1976, Oct. 2   Litho.   Perf. 13
1314	A350	4.90d multi	.35 .20
1315	A350	8d multi	.90 .35

"Joy of Europe" Children's Meeting, Belgrade, Oct. 2-7.

Herzegovinian Fugitives, by Uros Predic — A351

Historical paintings by 19th-20th century Yugoslav painters: 1.20d, Battle of the Montenegrins, by Djura Jaksic, vert. 2.10d, Nikola S. Zrinjski at Siget, by Oton Ivekovic, vert. 5d, Uprising at Razlovci, by Borko Lazeski. 6d, Enthroning of Slovenian Duke at Gospovetsko Field, by Anton Gojmir Kos. 8d, Break-through at Solun Front, by Veljko Stanojevic.

Perf. 13½x12½, 12½x13½
1976, Nov. 29   Photo.
1316	A351	1.20d gold & multi	.20 .20
1317	A351	2.10d gold & multi	.20 .20
1318	A351	3.20d gold & multi	.20 .20
1319	A351	5d gold & multi	.25 .25
1320	A351	6d gold & multi	.45 .35
1321	A351	8d gold & multi	.55 .50
	Nos. 1316-1321 (6)		1.85 1.70

Sheets of 9.

No. 839 Surcharged with New Value and 3 Bars in Rose

1976, Dec. 8   Engr.   Perf. 12½
1322	A206	1d on 85p dl pur	.25 .20

Mateja Nenadovic
A352

Rajko Zinzifov — A353

1977, Feb. 4   Photo.
1323 A352 4.90d multicolored   .30 .20
Prota Mateja Nenadovic (1777-1854), Serbian Duke, archbishop and writer.

1977, Feb. 10   Litho.   Perf. 13x13½
1324 A353 1.50d brn & sepia   .25 .20
Rajko Zinzifov (1839-1877), writer.

Phlox — A354

Alojz Kraigher — A356

Croatian Music Institute, Zagreb, 150th Anniv. A355

Flowers: 3.40d, Lily. 4.90d, Bleeding heart. 6d, Zinnia. 8d, Spreading marigold. 10d, Horseshoe geranium.

1977, Mar. 8   Perf. 13½x13
1325 A354 1.50d multi   .20 .20
1326 A354 3.40d multi   .25 .20
1327 A354 4.90d multi   .30 .20
1328 A354   6d multi   .35 .20
1329 A354   8d multi   .55 .20
1330 A354   10d multi   .90 .55
        Nos. 1325-1330 (6)   2.55 1.55

1977, Apr. 4   Engr.   Perf. 13
1331 A355 4.90d bl & sepia   .30 .20

1977, Apr. 11   Litho.   Perf. 13½
1332 A356 1.50d lemon & brn   .30 .20
Kraigher (1877-1959), Slovenian writer.

Boka Kotorska, by Milo Milunovic A357

10d, Zagorje in November, by Ljubo Babie.

1977, May 4   Photo.   Perf. 11½
1333 A357 4.90d gold & multi   .20 .20
1334 A357   10d gold & multi   .55 .55
Europa. Issued in sheets of 9.

Marshal Tito, by Omer Mujadzic A358

Mountain Range and Gentian — A359

1977, May 25   Perf. 11½x12
1335 A358 1.50d gold & multi   .20 .20
1336 A358 4.90d gold & multi   .30 .25
1337 A358   8d gold & multi   .60 .40
        Nos. 1335-1337 (3)   1.10 .85
85th birthday of Pres. Tito. Sheets of 9.

1977, June 6   Litho.   Perf. 13x13½
Design: 10d, Plitvice Lakes Falls, trees, robin and environmental protection emblem.
1338 A359 4.90d multicolored   .30 .20
1339 A359   10d multicolored   .70 .50
World Environment Day.

Petar Kocic (1877-1916), Writer A360

1977, June 15   Perf. 13½
1340 A360 1.50d pale grn & brn   .30 .20

Map of Europe and Peace Dove A361

1977, June 15   Litho.   Perf. 13½
1341 A361 1.50d multi   .20 .20
1342 A361   10d multi   2.25 2.25
Security and Cooperation Conference, Belgrade, June 15.

Child on Float — A362

Children's drawings: 10d, Fruit picking.

1977, Oct. 3   Litho.   Perf. 13½
1343 A362 4.90d multi   .35 .20
1344 A362   10d multi   .90 .40
"Joy of Europe" Children's Meeting.

Sava Congress Center, Belgrade A363

1977, Oct. 4   Litho.   Perf. 13½
1345 A363 4.90d bl & multi   .25 .25
1346 A363   10d car & multi   2.50 2.50
European Security and Cooperation Conference, Belgrade.

Exhibition Emblem — A364

1977, Oct. 20   Litho.   Perf. 13½
1347 A364 4.90d gold & multi   .30 .20
Balkanfila 1977, 6th Intl. Phil. Exhib. of Balkan Countries, Belgrade, Oct. 24-30.

Double Flute and Shepherd A365

Landscape and Musician: 3.40d, 4.90d, 6d, Various string instruments. 8d, Bagpipes. 10d, Panpipes.

1977, Oct. 25   Engr.   Perf. 13½
1348 A365 1.50d och & red brn   .20 .20
1349 A365 3.40d green & brn   .20 .20
1350 A365 4.90d dk brn & yel   .20 .20
1351 A365   6d bl & red brn   .40 .20
1352 A365   8d brick red & sep   .60 .20
1353 A365   10d sl grn & bis   .90 .25
        Nos. 1348-1353 (6)   2.55 1.25
Musical instruments from Belgrade Ethnographical Museum.

Ivan Vavpotic, Self-portrait A366

Self-portraits of Yugoslav artists: 3.40d, Mihailo Vukotic. 4.90d, Kosta Hakman. 6d, Miroslav Kraljevic. 8d, Nikola Martinovski. 10d, Milena Pavlovic-Barili.

**   Perf. 13½x12½**
1977, Nov. 26   Photo.
1354 A366 1.50d gold & multi   .20 .20
1355 A366 3.40d gold & multi   .20 .20
1356 A366 4.90d gold & multi   .20 .20
1357 A366   6d gold & multi   .30 .20
1358 A366   8d gold & multi   .45 .20
1359 A366   10d gold & multi   .65 .65
        Nos. 1354-1359 (6)   2.00 1.65

Festival of Testaccio, by Klovic — A367

Julija Klovic, by El Greco — A368

1978, Jan. 14   Photo.   Perf. 13½
1360 A367 4.90d multicolored   .20 .20
1361 A368   10d multicolored   .35 .30
Julija Klovic (1498-1578), Croat miniaturist.

Stampless Cover, Banaviste to Kubin, 1869 — A369

Designs: 3.40d, Mailbox. 4.90d, Ericsson telephone, 1900. 10d, Morse telegraph, 1844.

1978, Jan. 28   Perf. 13x14
1362 A369 1.50d multicolored   .20 .20
1363 A369 3.40d multicolored   .20 .20
1364 A369 4.90d multicolored   .25 .20
1365 A369   10d multicolored   .50 .40
        Nos. 1362-1365 (4)   1.15 1.00
Post Office Museum, Belgrade.

Battle of Pirot A370

1978, Feb. 20   Litho.   Perf. 13½
1366 A370 1.50d gold, blk & sl grn 1.75 1.75
Centenary of Serbo-Turkish War.

Airplanes A371

1978, Apr. 24   Litho.   Perf. 13½
1367 A371 1.50d S-49A, 1949   .20 .20
1368 A371 3.40d Galeb, 1961   .25 .20
1369 A371 4.90d Utva-75, 1976   .35 .20
1370 A371   10d Orao, 1974   .95 .40
        Nos. 1367-1370 (4)   1.75 1.00
Aeronautical Day.

Europa Issue

View of Golubac A372

1978, May 3   Photo.   Perf. 11½
1371 A372 4.90d shown   .20 .20
1372 A372   10d St. Naum Monastery, Ohrid   .80 .80

Boxing Glove A373

Honeybee A374

1978, May 5   Litho.   Perf. 13½
1373 A373 4.90d multicolored   .35 .20
Amateur Boxing Championships.

1978, May 25   Photo.   Perf. 11½

Bees of Yugoslavia: 3.40d, Halictus scabiosae. 4.90d, Blue carpenter bee. 10d, Large earth bumblebee.

1374	A374	1.50d multi	.20	.20
1375	A374	3.40d multi	.25	.20
1376	A374	4.90d multi	.40	.25
1377	A374	10d multi	.95	.70
	Nos. 1374-1377 (4)		1.80	1.35

Filip Filipovic (1878-1938), Radovan Radovic (1878-1906), Revolutionaries — A375

1978, June 19   Litho.   Perf. 13½

1378	A375	1.50d dk pur & dl ol	.25	.20

Marshal Tito — A376

Congress Emblem — A377

1978, June 20

1379	A376	2d red & multi	.20	.20
1380	A377	4.90d red & multi	.45	.20

Souvenir Sheet
Imperf

1381	A376	15d red & multi	3.75	2.60

11th Congress of Yugoslav League of Communists, Belgrade, June 20-23.

Nos. 1246, 1248 Surcharged with New Value and Two Bars in Brown

1978   Litho.   Perf. 13

1382	A323	2d on 1d	2.00	.20
1383	A323	3.40d on 2.10d	.40	.20

Issue dates: #1382, July 17; #1383, Aug. 1.

Conference Emblem over Belgrade — A378

Championship Emblem — A379

1978, July 25   Photo.   Perf. 13½

1384	A378	4.90d bl & lt blue	.30	.20

Conference of Foreign Ministers of Nonaligned Countries, Belgrade, July 25-29.

1978, Aug. 10   Litho.   Perf. 13½x13

1385	A379	4.90d multicolored	.30	.20

14th Kayak and Canoe Still Water Championships, Lake Sava, Aug. 10-14.

Mt. Triglav, North Rock — A380

Black Lake, Mt. Durmitor A381

1978, Aug. 26   Photo.   Perf. 14

1386	A380	2d multicolored	.25	.20

Bicentenary of first ascent of Mt. Triglav by Slovenian climbers.

1978, Sept. 20

1387	A381	4.90d shown	.25	.20
1388	A381	10d Tara River	.55	.30

Protection of the environment.

Night Sky A382

1978, Sept. 30   Litho.   Perf. 13x12½

1389	A382	4.90d bl blk, blk & gold	.30	.20

29th Congress of International Astronautical Federation, Dubrovnik, Oct. 1-8.

People in Forest A383

Children's drawings: 10d, Family around pond.

1978, Oct. 2   Perf. 13½x13

1390	A383	4.90d multi	.35	.20
1391	A383	10d multi	.80	.45

"Joy of Europe" Children's Meeting.

Seal on Insurrection Declaration A384

1978, Oct. 5   Perf. 13½

1392	A384	2d gold, brn & blk	.25	.20

Centenary of Kresna uprising.

Teachers' Training Institute, Sombor, Bicent. A385

1978, Oct. 16

1393	A385	2d multicolored	.25	.20

Croatian Red Cross, Cent. A386

1978, Oct. 21

1394	A386	2d lt bl, blk & red	.25	.20

Metallic Sculpture XXII, by Dusan Dzamonja A387

Modern Sculptures: 3.40d, Circulation in Space I, by Vojin Bakic, vert. 4.90d, Tectonic Octopode, by Olga Jevric, vert. 10d, Tree of Life, by Drago Trsar.

Perf. 13½x13, 13x13½

1978, Nov. 4   Litho.

1395	A387	2d multicolored	.20	.20
1396	A387	3.40d multicolored	.20	.20
1397	A387	4.90d multicolored	.25	.20
1398	A387	10d multicolored	.65	.40
	Nos. 1395-1398 (4)		1.30	1.00

Crossing of Neretva Pass, by Ismet Mujezinovic A388

1978, Nov. 10   Litho.   Perf. 13

1399	A388	2d multicolored	.25	.20

35th anniversary of Battle of Neretva.

Workers Leaving Factory, by Marijan Detoni — A389

Larch Cone — A390

Engravings: 3.40d, Workers, by Maksim Sedej. 4.90d, Lumberjacks, by Daniel Ozmo. 6d, Meal Break, by Pivo Karamatijevic. 10d, Hanged Man and Raped Woman, by Djordje Andrejevic Kun.

1978, Nov. 28   Photo.   Perf. 14x13½

1400	A389	2d gold, blk & buff	.20	.20
1401	A389	3.40d gold & black	.20	.20
1402	A389	4.90d gold, yel & blk	.30	.20
1403	A389	6d gold, buff & blk	.40	.25
1404	A389	10d gold, cr & blk	.70	.50
	Nos. 1400-1404 (5)		1.80	1.35

Republic day.

1978, Dec. 11   Photo.   Perf. 13x12½

1405	A390	1.50d shown	.20	.20
1406	A390	1.50d Red squirrel	.20	.20
1407	A390	2d Sycamore leaves	.25	.20
1408	A390	2d Red deer	.25	.20
a.	Bklt. pane of 8		1.25	
1409	A390	3.40d Alder leaves	.35	.20
1410	A390	3.40d Partridge	.35	.20
1411	A390	4.90d Oak leaves	.45	.20
1412	A390	4.90d Grouse	.45	.20
a.	Bklt. pane of 8		3.25	
	Nos. 1405-1412 (8)		2.50	1.60

New Year 1979. Nos. 1405-1412 printed se-tenant in sheets of 25.

No. 1408a contains 4 each of Nos. 1407-1408; No. 1412a 2 each of Nos. 1409-1412, with background colors changed.

Nos. 1064, 868, 1198 Surcharged with New Value and Bars

1978   Engr.; Litho.   Perf. 12½, 13½

1413	A263	35p on 10p brown	.60	.30
1414	A211	60p on 85p dp bl	.60	.30
1415	A305	80p on 1.20d sl grn	.60	.30
	Nos. 1413-1415 (3)		1.80	.90

First Masthead of Politika A391

1979, Jan. 25   Litho.   Perf. 13½

1416	A391	2d gold & black	.25	.20

Politika daily newspaper, 75th anniv.

Red Flags and Emblem A392

Child and IYC Emblem A393

1979, Feb. 15

1417	A392	2d red & gold	.25	.20

11th Meeting of Self-managers, Kragujevac, Feb. 15-16.

1979, Mar. 1   Photo.   Perf. 11½x12

1418	A393	4.90d gold vio & bl	.45	.30

International Year of the Child.

Sabre, Mace, Koran Pouch A394

Old Weapons: 3.40d, Pistol and ramrod, Montenegro. 4.90d, Short carbine and powder horn, Slovenia and Croatia. 10d, Oriental rifle and cartridge pouch.

1979, Mar. 26   Photo.   Perf. 14

1419	A394	2d multicolored	.20	.20
1420	A394	3.40d multicolored	.20	.20
1421	A394	4.90d multicolored	.20	.20
1422	A394	10d multicolored	.50	.50
	Nos. 1419-1422 (4)		1.10	1.10

5-Pointed Star, Hammer and Sickle — A395

1979, Apr. 20   Photo.   Perf. 13½
1423 A395   2d multicolored   .20 .20
1424 A395   4.90d multicolored   .35 .20
Communist and Communist Youth Leagues, 60th anniversary.

Cyril and Methodius University and Emblem A396

1979, Apr. 24   Litho.
1425 A396 2d multicolored   .25 .20
Sts. Cyril and Methodius University, Skopje, 30th anniv.

19th Century Belgrade, by C. Goebel A397

Europa: 10d, Postilion and Ljubljana, 17th century, by Jan van der Heyden.

1979, Apr. 30   Photo.   Perf. 11½
1426 A397 4.90d multicolored   .20 .20
1427 A397 10d multicolored   .55 .55

Blue Sow Thistles A398   Milutin Milankovic, by Paja Jovanovic A399

Flowers: 3.40d, Anemones. 4.90d, Astragalus. 10d, Alpine trifolium.

1979, May 25   Photo.   Perf. 13½
1428 A398   2d multicolored   .20 .20
1429 A398   3.40d multicolored   .20 .20
1430 A398   4.90d multicolored   .30 .30
1431 A398   10d multicolored   .70 .70
      Nos. 1428-1431 (4)   1.40 1.40

1979, May 28
1432 A399 4.90d multi   .35 .20
Milutin Milankovic (1879-1958), scientist.

Kosta Abrasevic (1879-1898), Poet — A400

1979, May 29   Litho.   Perf. 13½x13
1433 A400 2d org, blk & gray   .25 .20

Eight-Oared Shell A401

1979, Aug. 28   Litho.   Perf. 13
1434 A401 4.90d multicolored   .40 .25
9th World Rowing Championship, Lake Bled.

8th Mediterranean Games, Sept. 15-29, Split — A402

1979, Sept. 10
1435 A402   2d Games Emblem   .20 .20
1436 A402   4.90d Mascot   .30 .20
1437 A402   10d Map, Flags   .60 .30
      Nos. 1435-1437 (3)   1.10 .70

Seal, 15th Century A403

1979, Sept. 14   Perf. 12½
1438 A403 2d multicolored   .25 .20
Zagreb Postal Service, 450th anniversary.

Lake Palic — A404

Environment Protection: 10d, Lakefront, Prokletije Mountains.

1979, Sept. 20 Photo. Perf. 14x13½
1439 A404 4.90d multicolored   .35 .20
1440 A404 10d multicolored   .65 .40

Bank and Fund Emblems A405

Engr. & Photo.
1979, Oct. 1   Perf. 13½
1441 A405 4.90d multicolored   .40 .20
1442 A405 10d multicolored   .80 .40
Meeting of the World Bank and International Monetary Fund, Belgrade, Oct. 2-5.

"Joy of Europe" A406

Children's drawings.

1979, Oct. 2   Litho.
1443 A406 4.90d shown   .40 .20
1444 A406 10d Child in yard   .85 .45

Mihailo Pupin (1854-1935), Physicist, Inventor — A407

1979, Oct. 9   Perf. 13x13½
1445 A407 4.90d multicolored   .40 .20

Marko Cepenkov A408

Radovan Portal, Trogir Cathedral A410

Pristina University, 10th Anniversary A409

1979, Nov. 15   Litho.   Perf. 13½
1446 A408 2d multicolored   .25 .20
Cepenkov (1829-1920), Macedonian folklorist.

1979, Nov. 17
1447 A409 2d multicolored   .25 .20

1979, Nov. 28   Photo.
Romanesque Sculptures: 3.40d, Choir stall, Cathedral of Split. 4.90d, Triforium, Church of the Resurrection, Decani. 6d, Buvina Portal, Cathedral of Split. 10d, Western portal, Church of Our Lady, Studenica.
1448 A410   2d multi   .20 .20
1449 A410   3.40d multi   .25 .20
1450 A410   4.90d multi   .30 .20
1451 A410   6d multi   .35 .20
1452 A410   10d multi   .70 .30
      Nos. 1448-1452 (5)   1.80 1.10

Sarajevo University, 30th Anniversary A411

1979, Dec. 1   Litho.
1453 A411 2d multicolored   .25 .20

Duro Dakovic and Nikola Hecimovic, Communist Revolutionaries, 50th Death Annivs. — A412

1979, Dec. 10
1454 A412 2d multicolored   .25 .20

Sidewheeler Deligrad, 1862-1914 — A413

1979, Dec. 14
1455 A413 4.90d shown   .60 .60
1456 A413 10d Sidewheeler
            Serbia, 1917-
            72   1.25 1.25
Danube Conference.

Milton Manaki and Camera A414

Edward Kardelj, by Zdenko Kalin — A415

1980, Jan. 21   Litho.   Perf. 13½
1457 A414 2d deep bister & plum   .25 .20
Manaki (1880-1964), photographer and documentary film maker.

1980, Jan. 26
1458 A415 2d multicolored   .25 .20
Kardelj (1910-1979), labor movement leader.

No. 1458 Overprinted in Red

1980, Jan. 26
1459 A415 2d multicolored   .25 .20
Ploce renamed Kardeljevo.

13th Winter Olympic Games, Feb. 12-24, Lake Placid, NY — A416

1980, Feb. 13
1460 A416 4.90d Speed skating   .35 .35
1461 A416 10d Cross-country
            skiing   1.40 1.40

University of Belgrade, 75th Anniversary A417

1980, Feb. 27
1462 A417 2d multicolored   .25 .20

22nd Summer Olympic Games, July 19-Aug. 3, Moscow A418

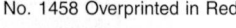

1980, Apr. 21
1463	A418	2d Fencing	.20	.20
1464	A418	3.40d Bicycling	.25	.25
1465	A418	4.90d Field hockey	.35	.35
1466	A418	10d Archery	.75	.75
		Nos. 1463-1466 (4)	1.55	1.55

Marshal Tito,
by Antun
Augustincic
A419

Europa: 13d, Tito, by Djordje Prudnikov.

1980, Apr. 28   Photo.   Perf. 11½
Granite Paper
1467	A419	4.90d multi	.25	.25
1468	A419	13d multi	1.75	1.75

Marshal Tito,
by Bozidar
Jakac — A420

1980, May 4   Litho.   Perf. 13½
1469	A420	2.50d purplish blk	.25	.20
a.		Perf. 10½	.40	.35
1470	A420	4.90d gray black	1.25	1.25

Marshal Tito (1892-1980) memorial. Issued in sheets of 8 plus label.

Sava Kovacevic (1905-1943),
Revolutionary — A421

1980, May 11   Litho.   Perf. 13½
1471	A421	2.50d multicolored	.25	.20

Wood
Baton and
Letter
A422

1980, May 14
1472	A422	2d multicolored	.25	.20

1st Tito Youth Relay Race, 35th anniv.

Flying
Gunard — A423

Emperor Trajan
Decius Coin, 3rd
Cent. — A424

1980, May 24   Photo.   Perf. 12
1473	A423	2d shown	.20	.20
1474	A423	3.40d Loggerhead turtle	.40	.20
1475	A423	4.90d Sea swallow	.35	.25
1476	A423	10d Dolphin	1.25	1.10
		Nos. 1473-1476 (4)	2.20	1.75

1980, June 10

3rd Century Roman Coins (Illyrian Emperors): 3.40d, Aurelianus. 4.90d, Probus. 10d, Diocletianus.
1477	A424	2d multicolored	.20	.20
1478	A424	3.40d multicolored	.25	.20
1479	A424	4.90d multicolored	.30	.20
1480	A424	10d multicolored	.60	.40
		Nos. 1477-1480 (4)	1.35	1.00

No. 1247 Surcharged with New Value
and Bars

1980, June 17   Litho.   Perf. 13½
1481	A323	2.50d on 1.50d	.40	.20

Types of 1971-77

Views: 5p, Krusevac. 10p, Gradacac. 20p, Church and bridge, Bohinj. 30p, Krk. 35p, Omis. 40p, Pec. 60p, Logar Valley. 2.50d, Kragujevac. 3.50d, Vrsac. 5.60d, Travnik. 8d, Dubrovnik.

Perf. 13½, 13¼x12½ (#1487), 13¼
(#1486A)

1980-81
1482	A263	5p deep orange	.35	.20
1483	A263	10p brown	.40	.20
1483A	A263	20p purple ('78)	.35	.20
1484	A263	30p olive gray	.35	.20
1485	A263	35p brown red	.35	.20
1486	A263	40p gray	.35	.20
1486A	A263	60p purple	.35	.20
1487	A323	2.50d rose red	.35	.20
1488	A323	3.50d bl gray ('81)	.35	.20
1489	A323	3.50d red org ('81)	.50	.20
1490	A323	5.60d gray grn ('81)	.65	.20
1491	A323	8d gray ('81)	.85	.20
		Nos. 1482-1491 (12)	5.20	2.40

No. 1483A has all three numerals in denomination the same size. On No. 1065 "20" is taller than first "0."

Perf. 13¼x12½
1482a	A263	5p	.45	.20
1483b	A263	10p	.50	.20
1483Ac	A263	20p	.45	.20
1484a	A263	30p	.45	.20
1485a	A263	35p	.45	.20
1486b	A263	40p	.45	.20
1486Ac	A263	60p	.45	.20
1487a	A323	2.50d	.45	.20
1488a	A323	2.50d	.45	.20
1489a	A323	3.50d	.60	.20
1490a	A323	5.60d	.75	.20
1491a	A323	8d	1.00	.20

400th Anniversary of Lipica Stud
Farm — A425

1980, June 25
1493	A425	2.50d black	.25	.20

A426

1980, June 27   Perf. 13½
1494	A426	2.50d magenta & red	.25	.20

Tito, Basic Law of Self-management, 30th anniv.

A427

1980, June 28   Perf. 13
1495	A427	2.50d light green	.25	.20

University of Novi Sad, 20th anniv.

Mljet National
Park — A428

Minerals — A429

1980, Sept. 5   Photo.   Perf. 14
1496	A428	4.90d shown	.25	.20
1497	A428	13d Galicica Natl. Park	.65	.40

European Nature Protection Year.

1980, Sept. 10   Litho.   Perf. 13½
1498	A429	2.50d Pyrrhotine	.20	.20
1499	A429	3.40d Dolomite	.20	.20
1500	A429	4.90d Sphalerite	.30	.20
1501	A429	13d Wulfenite	.65	.40
		Nos. 1498-1501 (4)	1.35	1.00

No. 1244 Surcharged with New Value
and Bars

1980, Oct. 15   Litho.   Perf. 13
1502	A323	5d on 75p purple	1.00	.20

View of
Kotor,
UNESCO
Emblem
A430

1980, Sept. 23   Perf. 13½
1503	A430	4.90d multicolored	.30	.20

21st UNESCO General Conf., Belgrade,

Children in
Garden
A431

Joy of Europe Children's Festival: 13d, 3 faces.

1980, Oct. 2   Perf. 13½x13
1504	A431	4.90d multi	.35	.25
1505	A431	13d multi	.90	.50

Dove over
Madrid
Meeting
Hall — A432

Lithographed and Engraved
1980, Nov. 11   Perf. 13½
1506	A432	4.90d dk grn & bl grn	.25	.25
1507	A432	13d dk brn & yel brown	.70	.70

European Security Conference, Madrid.

Federal Flag
of Yugoslavia
A433

Republic Day: Socialist Republic flags. Nos. 1508-1515 se-tenant. No. 1511 has Latin letters.

1980, Nov. 28   Litho.   Perf. 12½
1508	A433	2.50d Bosnia & Herzegovina	.20	.20
1509	A433	2.50d Croatia	.20	.20
1510	A433	2.50d shown	.20	.20
1511	A433	2.50d Yugoslavia	.20	.20
1512	A433	2.50d Macedonia	.20	.20
1513	A433	2.50d Montenegro	.20	.20
1514	A433	2.50d Serbia	.20	.20
1515	A433	2.50d Slovenia	.20	.20
		Nos. 1508-1515 (8)	1.60	1.60

Woman with Straw Hat — A434

Paintings: 3.40d, Atelier No. 1, by Gabriel Stupica. 4.90d, To the Glory of the Sutjeska Fighters, by Ismet Mujezinovic. 8d, Serenity, by Marino Tartaglia. 13d, Complaint, by Milos Vuskovic.

1980, Dec. 16   Perf. 13½
1516	A434	2.50d multi	.20	.20
1517	A434	3.40d multi	.20	.20
1518	A434	4.90d multi	.25	.20
1519	A434	8d multi, vert.	.35	.30
1520	A434	13d multi, vert.	.70	.55
		Nos. 1516-1520 (5)	1.70	1.45

Ivan Ribar (1881-
1968),
Politician — A435

1981, Jan. 21   Litho.   Perf. 13½
1521	A435	2.50d rose red & blk	.25	.20

Cementusa
Hand
Bomb
A436

Partisan Weapons: 5.60d, Rifle. 8d, 52-mm Cannon. 13d, Man-powered tank.

1981, Feb. 16
1522	A436	3.50d brick red & blk	.20	.20
1523	A436	5.60d grn & blk	.25	.20
1524	A436	8d bis brn & blk	.35	.20
1525	A436	13d rose vio & blk	.55	.30
		Nos. 1522-1525 (4)	1.35	.90

Monastery of
the Virgin,
Eleousa,
900th
Anniversary
A437

1981, Mar. 3
1526	A437	3.50d multicolored	.30	.20

36th World Table Tennis
Championship, Novi Sad, Apr. 14-
26 — A438

1981, Apr. 14   Litho.   Perf. 13½
1527	A438	8d multicolored	.40	.25

Europa Issue

Wedding in Herzegovina, by Nikola Arsenovic A439

Paintings by Nikola Arsenovic (1823-85): 13d, Witnesses at a Wedding.

1981, May 5   Photo.   Perf. 12
Granite Paper
1528 A439 8d multicolored   .25 .20
1529 A439 13d multicolored   .50 .35

Dimitrije Tucovic and Slavija Square, Belgrade A440

1981, May 13   Litho.   Perf. 13½
1530 A440 3.50d bl vio & red   .30 .20
Tucovic (1881-1914), Socialist leader.

Marshal Tito, by Milivoje Unkovic — A441

1981, May 25   Photo.   Perf. 11½x12
Granite Paper
1531 A441 3.50d gold & dk brn   .40 .40
Marshal Tito's 89th birth anniversary.

Sunflower A442

3rd Autonomous Enterprises Cong. A443

1981, May 28   Photo.   Perf. 11½
Granite Paper
1532 A442 3.05d shown   .20 .20
1533 A442 5.60d Hops   .20 .20
1534 A442 8d Corn   .30 .25
1535 A442 13d Wheat   .55 .35
      Nos. 1532-1535 (4)   1.25 1.00

1981, June 16   Litho.   Perf. 13½
1536 A443 3.50d multicolored   .25 .20

Djordje Petrov (1864-1921), Macedonian Revolutionary A444

1981, June 22
1537 A444 3.50d bister & black   .25 .20

National Insurrection, 40th Anniv. A445

1981, July 4   Perf. 12½
1538 A445 3.50d red org & tan   .20 .20
1539 A445 8d red org & tan   .35 .20
Souvenir Sheet
Imperf
1540 A445 30d Lenin monument   1.60 1.60

800th Anniv. of Varazdin A446

1981, Aug. 20   Litho.   Perf. 13½
1541 A446 3.50d multicolored   .25 .20

Parliament Building, Belgrade — A447

1981, Sept. 1
1542 A447 8d red & blue   .35 .30
Belgrade Conference of Non-Aligned Countries, 20th anniv.

Serbian Printing Office, 150th Anniv. A448

1981, Sept. 15
1543 A448 3.50d pale rose & dk bl .25 .20

Fran Levstik (1831-1887), Writer A449

1981, Sept. 28   Perf. 12x11½
1544 A449 3.50d dl red & gray   .25 .20

No. 1251 Surcharged with New Value and Bars
1981, Oct.   Perf. 13
1545 A323 5d on 4.90d dl bl   .75 .20
  a.   Perf. 13x12½   1.25 .40

Joy of Europe Children's Festival A450

1981, Oct. 2
1546 A450 8d Barnyard   .30 .30
1547 A450 13d Skiers   .60 .40

125th Anniv. of European Danube Commission — A451

1981, Oct. 28   Litho.   Perf. 13½
1548 A451 8d Tugboat Karlovac   .30 .30
1549 A451 13d Train hauling boat, Sip Canal .70 .70
Nos. 1548-1549 exist imperf. Value, set $75.

No. 1250a Surcharged with New Value and Bars
1981, Oct. 9   Litho.   Perf. 13x12½
1550 A323 3.50d on 3.40d gray grn 1.75 .30
  a.   on #1250   .40 .20

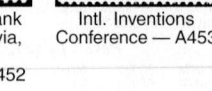

Savings Bank of Yugoslavia, 60th Anniv. — A452

Intl. Inventions Conference — A453

1981, Oct. 31   Perf. 11½x12
1551 A452 3.50d multicolored   .25 .20

1981, Nov. 4   Perf. 13½
1552 A453 8d red & gold   .30 .30

Nature Protection — A454

1981, Nov. 14
1553 A454 8d Plant, Ruguvo Ravine .35 .35
1554 A454 13d Lynx, Prokletjie Mountains .75 .75

August Senoa (1838-1881), Writer — A455

1981, Dec. 12   Perf. 11½x12
1555 A455 3.50d dl gray vio & gldn brn .40 .20

Still Life with a Fish, by Jovan Bijelic (1886-1964) — A456

Paintings of Animals: 5.60d, Raven, by Milo Milunovic (1897-1967). 8d, Bird on Blue Background, by Marko Celebonovic (b. 1902). 10d, Horses, by Peter Lubarda (1907-1974). 13d, Sheep, by Nikola Masic (1852-1902).

1981, Dec. 29   Photo.   Perf. 13½
1556 A456 3.50d multi   .20 .20
1557 A456 5.60d multi   .20 .20
1558 A456 8d multi   .25 .25
1559 A456 10d multi   .35 .35
1560 A456 13d multi   .55 .55
      Nos. 1556-1560 (5)   1.55 1.55

40th Anniv. of Foca Regulations A457

1982, Jan. 14   Litho.   Perf. 13½
1561 A457 3.50d Mosa Pijade   .25 .20

60th Anniv. of Communist Newspaper Borba A458

1982, Feb. 19   Litho.
1562 A458 3.50d red & blk   .25 .20

500th Anniv. of City of Cetinje — A459

1982, Mar. 10
1563 A459 3.50d dull red brn   .25 .20

Capt. Ivo Visin (1806-1868), Boka Kotorska's Map — A460

1982, May 5   Photo.   Perf. 11½
1564 A460 8d shown   .25 .25
1565 A460 15d Ship Splendido   .40 .40
Europa, 1st Yugoslavian circumnavigation, 1852-1859.

Male House Sparrow A461

1982, May 24   Litho.   Perf. 13½
1566 A461 3.50d shown   .20 .20
1567 A461 5.60d Female house sparrow .25 .25
1568 A461 8d Male field sparrow .40 .40
1569 A461 15d Female field sparrow 1.00 1.00
      Nos. 1566-1569 (4)   1.85 1.85
      See Nos. 1687-1690.

90th Birth Anniv. of Marshal Tito — A462

1982, May 25   Photo.   Perf. 11½x12
Granite Paper
1570 A462 3.50d multicolored   .25 .20

1982 World Cup — A463

Designs: Soccer ball in various positions.

1982, June 12   Perf. 11½
Granite Paper
1571   Sheet of 4   1.50 1.50
  a. A463 3.50d multicolored   .25 .25
  b. A463 5.60d multicolored   .25 .25
  c. A463 8d multicolored   .35 .35
  d. A463 15d multicolored   .65 .65

12th Congress of Yugoslavian Communists' League, Belgrade, June 26-29 A464

1982 June 26   Litho.   Perf. 13½
1572 A464 3.50d orange & red   .20 .20
1573 A464 8d gray & red   .25 .25
Souvenir Sheet
Perf. 12½
1574   Sheet of 2   1.25 1.25
  a. A464 10d like 3.50d   .40 .40
  b. A464 20d like 8d   .80 .80

Dura Jaksic (1832-1878), Writer, Painter A465

1982, July 27   Litho.   Perf. 14
1575 A465 3.50d Self-portrait   .25 .20

1982 World Championships Held in Yugoslavia — A466

1982, July 30   Perf. 13½
1576 A466 8d Gymnastics   .30 .30
1577 A466 6.10d Kayak   .30 .30
1578 A466 8d Weightlifting   .30 .30
  Nos. 1576-1578 (3)   .90 .90

Ivan Zajc (1832-1914), Composer and Conductor A467

1982, Aug. 3
1579 A467 4d brown   .25 .20

Breguet XIX and Potez XXV A468

1982, Sept. 1   Litho.   Perf. 13½
1580 A468 4d shown   .20 .20
1581 A468 6.10d Super Galeb G-4   .20 .20
1582 A468 8.80d Armed boat   .35 .35
1583 A468 15d Rocket gun boat   .50 .50
  Nos. 1580-1583 (4)   1.25 1.25

40th anniv. of Air Force/Anti-aircraft Defense and Navy.

Spruce Branch, Tara Natl. Park A469

1982, Sept. 3
1584 A469 8.80d shown   .40 .40
1585 A469 15d Mediterranean monk seal, Kornati   .60 .60

14th Joy of Europe Children's Festival — A470

1982, Oct. 2
1586 A470 8.80d Traffic   .35 .35
1587 A470 15d In the Bath   .55 .55

Small Onofrio's Fountain, 15th Cent. A471

1982, Oct. 23
1588 A471 8.80d multi   .25 .25

16th Universal Federation of Travel Agents' Assoc. Cong., Dubrovnik, Oct. 24-30.

600th Anniv. of Hercegnovi A472

1982, Oct. 28
1589 A472 4d multicolored   .50 .50

14th Winter Olympic Games, Sarajevo, Feb. 8-19, 1984 — A473

1982, Nov. 20   Perf. 12½
1590 A473 4d Bridge, Miljacka River   .20 .20
1591 A473 6.10d Minaret, Mosque   .20 .20
1592 A473 8.80d Evangelical Church   .50 .50
1593 A473 15d Street   1.40 1.40
  Nos. 1590-1593 (4)   2.30 2.30

Nos. 1488a and 1489a Surcharged In Red, Blue, Black or Red Violet with Two Bars or Shield

1982-83   Litho.   Perf. 13x12½
1594 A323 30p on 2.50d (R)   .50 .20
1595 A323 50p on 2.50d (Bl)   .50 .20
1596 A323 60p on 2.50d ('83) .50 .20
1597 A323 1d on 3.50d   .50 .20
1597A A323 2d on 2.50d (RV)   .50 .20
  Nos. 1594-1597A (5)   2.50 1.00

Perf. 13
1594a A323 30p on #1488   1.00 .20
1595a A323 50p on #1488   1.00 .20
1596a A323 60p on #1488   1.00 .20
1597b A323 1d on #1489   1.00 .20

Types of 1971-77
Designs: 3d, Skofja Loka. 4d, Pocitelj. 5d, Osijek. 6.10d, like 2.10d. 8.80d, Hercegnovi. 10d, Sarajevo. 16.50d, Ohrid.

1982-83   Litho.   Perf. 13x12½
1598 A323 3d gray bl   .40 .20
1599 A263 4d red org   .40 .20
1600 A263 5d grnsh bl ('83)   .40 .20
1601 A323 6.10d olive grn   .60 .20
1602 A263 8.80d multi   1.00 .20
Perf. 13½
1603 A263 10d red lil ('83)   1.00 .20
1603A A323 16.50d dl bl ('83) 1.75 .25
  Nos. 1598-1603A (7)   5.55 1.45

Type styles of Nos. 1600, 1603-1603A differ somewhat from illustrations.

Perf. 13
1598a A323 3d   .50 .20
1599a A323 4d   .50 .20
1600a A323 5d   .50 .20
1601a A323 6.10d   .80 .20
1602a A323 8.80d   .90 .20
1603b A323 10d   1.10 .20
1603c A323 16.50d   1.25 .30

40th Anniv. of Anti-Fascist Council A474

1982, Nov. 26   Perf. 13½
1604 A474 4d Bihac, 1942   .25 .20

The Manuscript, by Janez Bernik (b. 1933) — A475

4d, Prophet on Golden Background, by Joze Ciuha (b. 1924). 6.10d, Journey to the West, by Andrej Jemec (b. 1934). 8.80d, Black Comb with Red Band, by Riko Debenjak (b. 1908). 15d, The Vitrine, by Adriana Maraz (b. 1931).

1982, Nov. 27
1605 A475 4d multi, vert.   .20 .20
1606 A475 6.10d multi, vert. .20 .20
1607 A475 8.80d multi, vert. .25 .20
1608 A475 10d multi   .25 .20
1609 A475 15d multi   .55 .45
  Nos. 1605-1609 (5)   1.45 1.25

Uros Predic (1857-1953), Painter — A476   Union of Pioneers, 40th Anniv. — A477

1982, Dec. 7
1610 A476 4d multicolored   .25 .20

1982, Dec. 27   Perf. 12
1611 A477 4d multicolored   .25 .20

Articles from Museum of Applied Art, Belgrade A478

Designs: 4d, Lead pitcher, Gnjilane, 16th cent. 6.10d, Silver-plated jug, Macedonia, 18th cent. 8.80d, Goblet, 16th cent., Dalmatia. 15d, Mortar, 15th cent., Kotor.

1983, Feb. 19
1612 A478 4d multicolored   .20 .20
1613 A478 6.10d multicolored .20 .20
1614 A478 8.80d multicolored .20 .20
1615 A478 15d multicolored   .40 .30
  Nos. 1612-1615 (4)   1.00 .90

Mount Jalovec — A479   Serbian Telephone Service Centenary — A480

1983, Feb. 26
1616 A479 4d blue & lt bl   .25 .20

Slovenian Mountaineering Soc., 90th anniv.

1983, Mar. 15
1617 A480 3d Ericsson phone   .25 .20

25th Anniv. of Intl. Org. for Maritime Navigation (OMI) — A481

1983, Mar. 17   Perf. 13½x14
1618 A481 8.80d multi   .30 .30

Edible Mushrooms A482

1983, Mar. 21   Perf. 14
1619 A482 4d Agaricus campestris   .30 .30
1620 A482 6.10d Morchella vulgaris   .30 .30
1621 A482 8.80d Boletus edulis   .30 .30
1622 A482 15d Cantharellus cibarius   .80 .80
  Nos. 1619-1622 (4)   1.70 1.70

Rijeka Railway, 110th Anniv. — A483

Boro and Ramiz Monument, Landovica A484

1983, Apr. 5
1623 A483 4d Steam engine series
401 .25 .25
1624 A483 23.70d on 8.80d Thyris-
tor locomotive
442 .50 .50

No. 1624 not issued without surcharge.

1983, Apr. 10
1625 A484 4d multi .25 .20

Boro Vukmirovic and Ramiz Sadiku, revolutionary martyrs, 40th death anniv.

Ivo Andric
(1892-1975),
Poet, 1961
Nobel Prize
Winner
A485

1983, May 5   Photo.   Perf. 11½
Granite Paper
1626 A485 8.80d Medal, Travnik
Chronicle text .20 .20
1627 A485 20d Portrait, Bridge,
Drina River .40 .35

Europa.

50th Intl.
Agricultural
Fair, Novi
Sad — A486

1983, May 13   Litho.   Perf. 14
1628 A486 4d Combine harvester .25 .20

40th Anniv. of
Battle of
Sutjeska
A487

1983, May 14   Perf. 12½
1629 A487 3d Assault, by Pivo
Karamatijevic .25 .20

A488

A489

1983, May 25   Perf. 13½
1630 A488 4d Tito, Parliament .25 .20
a. Perf. 12½ 1.00 1.00

30th anniv. of election of Pres. Tito.

1983, May 27
1631 A489 4d First mail and passenger car .20 .20
1632 A489 16.50d Mountain road,
Kotor .40 .20

80th anniv. of automobile service in
Montenegro.

A490

A491

1983, June 5   Perf. 14
1633 A490 23.70d multi .70 .35

UN Conference on Trade and Development,
6th session, Belgrade, June 6-30.

1983, June 7   Perf. 12½
1634 A491 4d Engraving by
Valvasor .25 .20

Town of Pazin millenium.

Triumphal
Arch,
Titograd
A492

1983, June 9   Perf. 12½
1635 A492 100d Memorial to S.
Filipovic,
Valjevo, vert. 4.00 .50
a. Perf. 13x13½ 3.75 .50
1636 A492 200d shown 4.50 .90
a. Perf. 13½x13 5.00 .90

Skopje
Earthquake,
20th
Anniv. — A493

1983, July 26   Litho.   Perf. 12½
1637 A493 23.70d deep magenta .55 .25
a. Perf. 13½ .75 .45

For surcharge, see No. 1715.

Sculpture by   Joy of Europe
Ivan Mestrovic   A496
A494

European Nature Protection — A495

1983, Aug. 15
1638 A494 6d multicolored .25 .20

1983, Sept. 10   Litho.   Perf. 13
16.50d, Gentian, Kopaonik National Park.
23.70d, Chamois, Perucica Gorge.

1639 A495 16.50d multi .40 .25
1640 A495 23.70d multi .80 .35

See Nos. 1685-1686.

1983, Oct. 3   Litho.   Perf. 13½
Children's Paintings: 16.50d, Bride and
Bridegroom by Verna Paunkonik. 23.70d,
Andres and his Mother by Marta Lopez-Ibor.

1641 A496 16.50d multi .35 .20
1642 A496 23.70d multi .45 .25

A497   A498

1983, Oct. 17   Litho.   Perf. 12½
1643 A497 5d multicolored .25 .20

Kragujevac High School sesquicentenary.

1983, Oct. 17   Litho.   Perf. 13½
1644 A498 5d multicolored .25 .20

Timok Uprising centenary.

14th Winter
Olympic
Games,
Sarajevo,
Feb. 8-19,
1984
A499

1983, Nov. 25   Engr.   Perf. 13½
1645 A499 4d Ski jump .20 .20
1646 A499 4d Slalom .20 .20
1647 A499 16.50d Bobsledding .60 .30
1648 A499 16.50d Downhill skiing .60 .30
1649 A499 23.70d Speed skating .90 .45
1650 A499 23.70d Hockey .90 .45
Nos. 1645-1650 (6) 3.40 1.90

Souvenir Sheet
Imperf
1651 A499 50d Emblem 1.75 .70

Jovan
Jovanovic
Zmaj (1833-
1904), Poet,
Neven
Masthead
A500

1983, Nov. 24   Litho.   Perf. 12½
1652 A500 5d multicolored .25 .20

Peasant
Wedding, by
Pieter
Brueghel
A501

Paintings: No. 1654, Susanna with the Old
Men, by the 'Master of the Prodigal Son.' No.
1655, Allegory of Wisdom and Strength, by
Paolo Veronese (1528-1588). No. 1656, Virgin Mary from Salamanca, by Robert Campin
(1375-1444). No. 1657, St. Ann with Madonna
and Jesus, by Albrecht Dürer (1471-1528).

1983, Nov. 26   Perf. 14
1653 A501 4d multi .20 .20
1654 A501 16.50d multi .40 .20
1655 A501 16.50d multi .40 .20
1656 A501 23.70d multi .50 .25
1657 A501 23.70d multi .50 .25
Nos. 1653-1657 (5) 2.00 1.10

View of   Koco Racin
Jajce — A502   (1908-1943),
Writer — A504

World Communications Year — A503

1983, Nov. 28   Perf. 13x12½
1658 A502 5d multicolored .25 .20

Souvenir Sheet
Imperf
1659 A502 30d Tito 1.25 .60

40th anniv. of Second Session of the
Antifascist Council of the Natl. Liberation of
Yugoslavia, Jajce, Nov. 29-30.

1983, Dec. 10   Perf. 13½
1660 A503 23.70d multi .50 .25

1983, Dec. 22
1661 A504 5d multicolored .25 .20

Politika Front
Page, Oct.
28,
1944 — A505

1984, Jan. 25   Litho.   Perf. 12½
1662 A505 5d red & black .25 .20

80th anniv. of Politika newspaper and 40th
anniv. in Yugoslavia.

Veljko Petrovic
(1884-1967),
Poet — A506

1984, Feb. 4   Litho.   Perf. 13½
1663 A506 5d multicolored .25 .20

1984
Winter
Olympics
A507

1984, Feb. 8
1664 A507 4d Biathlon .20 .20
1665 A507 4d Giant slalom .20 .20
1666 A507 5d Bobsledding .20 .20
1667 A507 5d Slalom .20 .20
1668 A507 16.50d Speed skating .45 .20
1669 A507 16.50d Hockey .45 .20
1670 A507 23.70d Ski jumping .65 .30
1671 A507 23.70d Downhill skiing .65 .30
Nos. 1664-1671 (8) 3.00 1.80

Souvenir Sheets
Imperf
1672 A507 50d Flame, rings 2.00 1.00
1673 A507 100d Flame, map 4.00 2.00

Natl. Heroines
A508

Designs: a, Marija Bursac (1902-43). b,
Jelena Cetkovic (1916-43). c, Nada Dimic
(1923-42). d, Elpida Karamandi (1920-42). e,
Toncka Cec Olga (1896-1943). f, Spasenija
Babovic Cana (1907-77). g, Jovanka
Radivojevic Kica (1922-43). h, Sonja
Marinkovic (1916-41).

1984, Mar. 8   Litho.   Perf. 14
1674   Sheet of 8 + label 3.50 2.50
a.-h. A508 5d any single .20 .20

Slovenia Monetary Institute, 40th Anniv. A509

1984, Mar. 12   **Perf. 12½**
1675 A509 5d Bond, note   .25 .20

Railroad Service in Serbia (Belgrade-Nis) Centenary — A510

1984, Apr. 9   **Perf. 13**
1676 A510 5d Train, Central Belgrade Station   .25 .20

Jure Franko, Giant Slalom Silver Medalist, 1984 — A511

1984, Apr. 28
1677 A511 23.70d multi   .60 .35
Yugoslavia's first Winter Olympic medalist.

Europa (1959-84) A512

1984, Apr. 30   **Perf. 13½**
1678 A512 23.70d multi   .30 .25
1679 A512 50d multi   .80 .50

1984 Summer Olympics, Los Angeles A513

1984, May 14
1680 A513   5d Basketball   .20 .20
1681 A513 16.50d Diving   .35 .20
1682 A513 23.70d Equestrian   .45 .20
1683 A513   50d Running   1.10 .50
    Nos. 1680-1683 (4)   2.10 1.10

Marshal Tito — A514

1984, May 25   **Perf. 13**
1684 A514 5d brown red   .25 .20

Nature Type of 1983

Designs: 26d, Centaurea gloriosa (flower), Biokovo Mountain Park. 40d, Anophthalmus (insect), Pekel Cave, Savinja Valley.

1984, June 11   **Litho.**   **Perf. 13½**
1685 A495 26d multicolored   .50 .25
1686 A495 40d multicolored   .80 .40

Bird Type of 1982

1984, June 28
1687 A461   4d Great black-backed gull   .40 .30
1688 A461   5d Black-headed gull   .40 .30
1689 A461 16.50d Herring gull   .40 .30
1690 A461   40d Common tern   2.00 1.10
    Nos. 1687-1690 (4)   3.20 2.00

19th Cent. Cradles A515

1984, Sept. 1   **Litho.**   **Perf. 12½**
1691 A515   4d Bosnia & Herzegovina   .20 .20
1692 A515   5d Montenegro   .20 .20
1693 A515 26d Macedonia   .50 .50
1694 A515 40d Serbia   .80 .80
    Nos. 1691-1694 (4)   1.70 1.70

Olive Tree, Mirovica A516

1984, Sept. 1
1695 A516 5d multi   .25 .20

Joy of Europe — A517

Map, Concentric Waves — A519

City of Virovitica, 750th Anniv. A518

Children's Drawings.

1984, Oct. 2   **Litho.**   **Perf. 14**
1696 A517 26d Traditional costumes   .40 .40
1697 A517 40d Girl with doll carriage   1.10 1.10

1984, Oct. 4   **Perf. 13½**
1698 A518 5d Engraving, 17th cent.   .25 .20

1984, Oct. 10
1699 A519 6d Prus bl & brt grn   .25 .20
Radio and telegraph service in Montenegro, 80th anniv.

Veterans Conference A520

1984, Oct. 18
1700 A520 26d multicolored   1.25 1.25
1701 A520 40d multicolored   1.75 1.75
Conf. of Veterans on Security, Disarmament & Cooperation in Europe, Belgrade, 10/18-20.

Liberation of Belgrade, 40th Anniv. — A521

Miloje Milojevic (1884-1946), Composer A522

1984, Oct. 20
1702 A521 6d "40," arms   .25 .20

1984, Oct. 27
1703 A522 6d Portrait, score   .25 .20

Medals Events, 1984 Summer Olympics A522a

Designs: a, Wrestling. b, Running. c, Field hockey. d, Shot put. e, Soccer. f, Basketball. g, Netball. h, Rowing.

1984, Nov. 14   **Litho.**   **Perf. 13½**
1704   Sheet of 8   5.00 4.75
 a.-h.   A522a 26d any single   .30 .25

The Tahitians, by Gauguin — A523

Paintings by Foreign Artists in Yugoslav Museums: 6d, Portrait of Madame Tatichek, by Ferdinand Waldmuller (1793-1865). No. 1706, The Bathers, by Renoir (1841-1919). No. 1707, At the Window, by Henri Matisse (1869-1954). 40d, Ballerinas, by Edgar Degas (1834-1917).

Perf. 13½x14, 14x13½
1984, Nov. 15
1705 A523   6d multi, vert.   .20 .20
1706 A523 26d multi, vert.   .35 .30
1707 A523 26d multi, vert.   .35 .20
1708 A523 38d multi   .50 .30
1709 A523 40d multi   .60 .30
    Nos. 1705-1709 (5)   2.00 1.30

Nova Macedonia Newspaper, 40th Anniv. A523a

1984, Nov. 29   **Perf. 13½**
1710 A523a 6d 1st & recent editions   .25 .20

Nos. 1602, 1599 and 1637 Surcharged with Three Bars in Red Brown or Black, Types of 1975 and

Exhibition Center, Zagreb A524

Bird, Jet, Landscape A525

Designs: 6d, Kikinda. 26d, Korcula. 38d, Maribor. 70d, Trumpeter monument, riverside buildings in Zagreb. 1000d, bird, tail of jet on airfield.

Perf. 13½x12½, 13 (#1713, 1717), 12½ (#1715)
1984-86   **Litho.**
1711 A263   2d on 8.80d   1.50 .20
 a.   on #1602a   .50 .20
1712 A263   6d on 4d (RBr)   .30 .20
 a.   on #1599a   1.00 .20
1713 A323   6d lt red brn   .30 .20
      Perf. 13x12½   .50 .20
1715 A493 20d on 23.70d   .30 .20
1717 A263 26d dp ultra   .50 .20
      Perf. 13x12½   .75 .20
1718 A323 38d dp lil rose   1.50 .20
 a.   Perf. 13   .50 .20
1719 A323 70d brt ultra ('85)   1.50 .40
 b.   Perf. 13   .50 .30
       Perf. 14
1719A A524 100d brt org yel & vio   .65 .35
       Perf. 12½
1720 A525 500d redsh brn & multi ('85)   5.00 3.50
1721 A525 1000d org brn & multi ('85)   7.50 5.25
 a.   Perf. 13½
    Nos. 1711-1721 (10)   19.05 10.70
Type styles for Nos. 1717-1718 differ somewhat from illustration.
For surcharge, see No. 1973.

Museum Exhibits - Fossils A526

1985, Feb. 4   **Litho.**   **Perf. 12½**
1722 A526   5d Aturia aturi   .20 .20
1723 A526   6d Pachyophis woodwardi   .20 .20
1724 A526 33d Chaetodon hoeferi   .40 .40
1725 A526 60d Homo sapiens neanderthalensis   .90 .90
    Nos. 1722-1725 (4)   1.70 1.70

40th Anniv., Monument Protection A527

1985, Feb. 20   **Litho.**   **Perf. 12½**
1726 A527 6d Hopovo church   .40 .20

Ski Jumping at
Planica, 50th
Anniv.
A528

European Nature
Conservation
A529

1985, Mar. 15   Litho.   Perf. 13½
1727 A528 6d Three herons in
flight   1.50   .60

1985, Mar. 30   Perf. 14
1728 A529 42d Pandion haliaetus   1.50 1.00
1729 A529 60d Upupa epops   3.00 1.50
Audubon birth bicentenary, European Information Center for Nature Protection.

A530

A531

Fresco of St. Methodius, St. Naum Monastery, Ohrid.

1985, Apr. 6   Litho.   Perf. 11½x12
1730 A530 10d multicolored   1.75 1.25
St. Methodius (d. 885), archbishop of Pannonia and Moravia.

1985, Apr. 16   Litho.   Perf. 12½
1731 A531 6d Clasped hands   .25 .20
Osimo Agreements, 10th anniv. Yugoslavia-Italy political and economic cooperation.

Josip
Slavenski
(1896-1955),
Composer
A532

Europa: 60d, Portrait, block flute, darabukka. 80d, Balkanophonia score, signature.

1985, Apr. 29   Perf. 14
1732 A532 60d multi   .70 .70
1733 A532 80d multi   .70 .70

Joachim
Vujic, by
Dimitrije
Avramovic
(1815-1855)
A533

1985, May 8   Perf. 12x11½
1734 A533 10d multi   .25 .20
Joachim Vujic Theater, Kragujevac, 150th anniv.

Liberation from German Occupation
Forces, 40th Anniv. — A534

1985, May 9   Perf. 13½
1735 A534 10d shown   .40 .20
1736 A534 10d Order of Natl.
Liberation   .40 .20

Franjo Kluz
(1912-1944), Rudi
Cajavec (1911-
1942), Breguet-19
Fighter — A535

1985, May 21   Perf. 13x12½
1737 A535 10d multi   .75 .35
Air Force Day.

Pres. Tito (1892-
1980)
A536

Cres-Losinj
Municipal
Tourism Bureau,
Cent. — A537

1985, May 25   Perf. 13½
1738 A536 10d Portrait   .50 .25

1985, June 12
1739 A537 10d Map, town arms,
villa   .40 .20

UN 40th
Anniv. — A538

Rowing — A539

1985, June 26   Litho.   Perf. 12½
1740 A538 70d Emblem, rainbow   .55 .25

1985, June 29   Litho.   Perf. 13½
1741 A539 70d multicolored   .65 .30

Souvenir Sheet
1742 A539 100d Course map,
arms   1.75 .85
Intl. European-Danube Rowing Regatta, 30th anniv.

Nautical
Tourism — A540

1985, July 1   Litho.
1743 A540 8d Sailboat   .50 .30
1744 A540 10d Windsurfing   .50 .30
1745 A540 50d Sailboat, diff.   .50 .30
1746 A540 70d Sailboat, diff.   1.75 1.00
Nos. 1743-1746 (4)   3.25 1.90

F1B Class
Motorized
Model Plane
A541

1985, Aug. 10   Litho.   Perf. 12½x13
1747 A541 70d multicolored   .75 .65
Free Flight World Championships, Livno, Aug. 12-18.

Algae — A542

1985, Sept. 20   Perf. 14
1748 A542 8d Corallina officinalis   .20 .20
1749 A542 10d Desmarestia
viridis   .20 .20
1750 A542 50d Fucus
vesiculosus   .30 .30
1751 A542 70d Padina pavonia   1.75 1.75
Nos. 1748-1751 (4)   2.45 2.45

Intl. Federation of Stomatologists, 73rd
Congress, Belgrade, Sept. 21-
28 — A543

1985, Sept. 21   Perf. 12x11½
1752 A543 70d multicolored   .60 .35

Children's
Drawings
A544

Designs: 50d, Children in a Horse-drawn
Cart, by Branka Lukic, age 14, Yugoslavia.
70d, Children in Field, by Suzanne Straathof,
age 9, Netherlands.

1985, Oct. 2   Perf. 14
1753 A544 50d multicolored   .50 .25
1754 A544 70d multicolored   1.50 1.25

Croatian
Natl.
Theater,
Zagreb,
125th Anniv.
A545

1985, Nov. 23   Perf. 12½
1755 A545 10d Facade detail   .40 .25

Miladin Popovic
A546

Natl. Coat of Arms
A547

1985, Nov. 26   Perf. 11½x12
1756 A546 10d Portrait   .25 .20
Popovic (1910-1945), revolutionary.

1985, Nov. 28   Perf. 13½
1757 A547 10d multicolored   .25 .20

Souvenir Sheet
Imperf
1758 A547 100d multicolored   1.25 1.00
Socialist Federal Republic of Yugoslavia, 40th anniv. No. 1758 contains one stamp 18x27mm.

Royal Procession, by Iromie
Wijewardena, Sri Lanka — A548

Paintings from the Art Gallery of Non-aligned Countries, Titograd: 10d, Return from Hunting, by Mama Cangare, Mali. No. 1761, Drum of Coca, by Agnes Ovando Sanz De Franck, Bolivia. No. 1762, The Cock, by Mariano Rodriguez, Cuba. 70d, Three Women, by Quamrul Hassan, Bangladesh.

1985, Dec. 2   Perf. 14
1759 A548 8d multicolored   .20 .20
1760 A548 10d multicolored   .20 .20
1761 A548 50d multicolored   .30 .20
1762 A548 50d multicolored   .30 .20
1763 A548 70d multicolored   1.75 1.50
Nos. 1759-1763 (5)   2.75 2.30

Nos. 1243, 1482, 1485a, 1490, 1491,
1713a, 1717a, 1603A and 1718
Surcharged in Light Red Brown,
Brown or Dark Brown

1985-86   Litho.   Perf. 13½, 13½x12½
1764 A323 1d on 25p (B)   1.00 .20
1765 A263 2d on 5p (DB)   .65 .20
   a.   on #1482a   .65 .20
1766 A263 3d on 35p (DB)   .50 .20
   a.   on #1485a   .50 .20
1767 A323 4d on 5.60d (B)   .40 .20
   b.   on #1490   1.50 .50
1767A A323 5d on 8d (B)   .30 .20
   c.   on #1491a   .75 .30
1768 A323 8d on 6d   .45 .20
   a.   on #1713   .45 .20
1769 A263 20d on 26d   .35 .20
   a.   on #1717   9.50 4.00
1770 A323 50d on 16.50d (B)   1.25 .40
   a.   on #1603c   1.25 .40
1771 A323 70d on 38d   1.75 .50
Nos. 1764-1771 (9)   6.65 2.30
Issued: #1767A, 3/17/86; others, 12/85.

Natl.
Automobile
Assoc., 40th
Anniv.
A549

1986, Feb. 25   Perf. 12½
1772 A549 10d Car   .30 .20
1773 A549 70d Helicopter   1.10 1.00

Tara River,
Montenegro
A550

1986, Mar. 3 **Perf. 14**
1774 A550 100d Canyon .55 .40
1775 A550 150d Bridge .95 .60
European nature protection. Sheets of 9.

Studenica
Monastery, 800th
Anniv. — A551

1986, Mar. 15 **Perf. 13½**
1776 A551 10d Chapel of Our Lady .75 .50

A552

Various soccer plays.

1986, Apr. 5 **Litho.** **Perf. 14**
1777 A552 70d multi .90 .45
1778 A552 150d multi 1.10 .55
1986 World Cup Soccer Championships,
Mexico.

Arrival of St.
Clement in
Ohrid, 1100th
Anniv.
A553

1986, Apr. 12 **Perf. 12½**
1779 A553 10d Township model 2.00 1.50

Europa Issue

Brain,
Mushroom
Cloud — A554

1986, Apr. 28 **Perf. 14**
1780 A554 100d shown .50 .35
1781 A554 200d Injured deer .90 .70

European Men's
Senior Judo
Championships,
Belgrade, May 8-
11 — A555

1986, May 7 **Perf. 12½**
1782 A555 70d multi .70 .50

Natl. Costumes A556   Yachts, Moscenika Draga Bay A557

a, Slovenia. b, Vojvodina. c, Croatia. d, Macedonia. e, Serbia. f, Montenegro. g, Kosovo. h, Bosnia & Herzegovina.

1986, May 22 **Litho.** **Perf. 12x13**
Booklet Stamps
1783 Bklt. pane of 8 4.25
a.-h. A556 50d any single .40 .30

1986, May 23 **Perf. 14**
1784 A557 50d multi .30 .20
1785 A557 80d multi, diff. .50 .30

Souvenir Sheet
Imperf
1786 A557 100d multi 3.00 2.50
European Sailing Championships, Croatia,
May 29-June 7, Flying Dutchman Class. No.
1786 contains one stamp 22x28mm.

Marshal
Tito — A557a

1986, May 24 **Perf. 13x12½**
1787 A557a 10d multicolored .25 .20

Moths and
Butterflies
A558

1986, May 26 **Perf. 14**
1788 A558 10d Eudia pavonia .45 .45
1789 A558 20d Inachis io .45 .45
1790 A558 50d Parnassius
apollo .45 .45
1791 A558 100d Apatura iris 1.25 1.25
Nos. 1788-1791 (4) 2.60 2.60

Ancient
Manuscripts
A558a

Designs: 10d, Evangelical, 18th cent. 20d,
Leontijevo Evangelical, 16th cent. 50d, Astrological, Mesopotamia, 15th cent. 100d,
Hebrew Haggadah, Spain, 14th cent.

1986, June 12 **Litho.** **Perf. 14**
1792 A558a 10d multicolored .20 .20
1793 A558a 20d multicolored .20 .20
1794 A558a 50d multicolored .50 .50
1795 A558a 100d multicolored 1.00 1.00
Nos. 1792-1795 (4) 1.90 1.90

A559

A560

Designs: 20d, Postman on motorcycle. 30d,
Postman, resident. 40d, Forklift, mail pallets.
50d, Mail train. 60d, Man posting letters in
mailbox. 93d, Open envelope and greetings
telegram form. 100d, Postman, mail van. No.
1803, Computer operator facing right. No.
1804, 140d, Computer operator facing left.
120d, Woman sending love letter. 200d,
Freighter in high seas. 500d, Postal employee
sorting mail. 1000d, Woman at telephone station. 2000d, Aircraft, hemispheres on world
map. 30d, 60d, 93d, 106d, 120d, 140d, 500d,
1000d vert.

**Perf. 13½, 12½x13½ (20d, 40d, 50d),
14 (100d)**
1986-88 **Litho.**
1796 A559 20d brt pink .20 .20
a. Perf. 13 .20 .20
1797 A559 30d lt brn vio .20 .20
a. Perf. 13x12½ .30 .20
1798 A559 40d brt red .25 .20
a. Perf. 13 .25 .20
1799 A559 50d violet .30 .20
a. Perf. 13 .50 .20
1800 A559 60d lt sage grn .25 .20
1801 A559 93d ultra .25 .20
1802 A559 100d dl magenta .65 .30
1803 A559 106d rose red .30 .20
1804 A559 106d brn org .20 .20
1805 A559 120d dull blue
grn .20 .20
1806 A559 140d dull rose .20 .20
1807 A559 200d greenish bl 1.25 .60
a. Perf. 12½ 2.50 2.00
b. Perf. 12½x13½ 7.50 2.50
1808 A559 500d deep blue
& beige .75 .35
1809 A559 500d chalky blue
& yel .60 .25
1810 A559 1000d vio & blue
grn 1.10 .60
b. Perf. 12½ .80 .35
1810A A560 2000d brt blue,
red & brt
vio 2.25 1.10
Nos. 1796-1810A (16) 8.95 5.20
Size of No. 1802: 19½x18mm.
Issued: 20d, 3/17; 50d, 200d, 6/4; 40d,
7/17; 100d, 6/12; 30d, 7/26; 60d, 6/5/87;
#1803, 12/10/87; 93d, 12/16/87; #1804,
1/22/88; #1808, 4/29/88; 1000d, 7/21/88; 20d,
140d, 2000d, #1809, 9/5/88.
See Nos. 1935-1945, 2004-2007, 2013-
2015, 2021. For surcharges see Nos. 1877,
1912-1913, 1947-1948, 1972, 1974-1975,
2017, 2019, 2048-2051, 2053.

13th
Communist
Federations
Congress
(SKJ)
A561

1986, June 25 **Perf. 12½**
1811 A561 10d shown .25 .20
1812 A561 20d Star .25 .20

Souvenir Sheet
Imperf
1813 A561 100d Tito 1.00 .50

Trubar,
Abecedarian
Manuscript
Title Page
A562

1986, June 28 **Litho.** **Perf. 12½x13**
1814 A562 20d multi .70 .50
Primoz Trubar (1508-1568), Slovenian philologist and religious reformer.

Serbian Natl.
Theater, Novi
Sad, 125th
Anniv. — A563

1986, July 28 **Perf. 14**
1815 A563 40d Thalia .25 .20

Rugovo Dance,
Kosovo
Province — A564

1987 Universiade
Games, Zagreb,
July 8-19 — A565

1986, Sept. 10
1816 A564 40d multi .25 .20

1986, Sept. 22 **Perf. 13½**
1817 A565 30d Volleyball .40 .20
1818 A565 40d Canoeing .40 .20
1819 A565 100d Gymnastics .70 .30
1820 A565 150d Fencing 1.00 .45
Nos. 1817-1820 (4) 2.50 1.15

18th Joy of Europe
Youth Conference
A566

Children's drawings: 100d, Dove, by Tanja
Faletic, 14. 150d, Buildings, by Johanna
Kraus, 12, DDR.

1986, Oct. 2 **Perf. 14**
1821 A566 100d multicolored .75 .35
1822 A566 150d multicolored 1.10 .50

Rotary Switching Apparatus, Village of
Bled — A567

1986, Oct. 4 **Perf. 13½**
1823 A567 40d multicolored .25 .20
Telephone exchanges connected with automatic switching equipment, 50th anniv.

INTERPOL 55th
General
Assembly,
Belgrade, Oct. 6-
13 — A568

Intl. Brigades, 50th Anniv. — A569

1986, Oct. 6   *Perf. 14*
1824 A568 150d multicolored   .65 .30

1986, Oct. 21   *Perf. 13½*
1825 A569 40d multicolored   .25 .20

Intl. Peace Year — A570

1986, Nov. 20
1826 A570 150d multicolored   .65 .30

Serbian Academy of the Arts and Sciences, Cent. A571

1986, Nov. 1   **Photo.**   *Perf. 13½*
1827 A571 40d multicolored   .25 .20

Paintings by Foreign Artists in the Museum of Contemporary Art, Skopje — A572

No. 1828, Still Life, by Frantisek Muzika, Czechoslovakia. #1829, Disturance, by Rafael Canogar, England. #1830, Iol, by Victor Vasarely, France. #1831, Portrait, by Bernard Buffet, France. #1832, Woman's Head, by Pablo Picasso, Spain.

1986, Dec. 10   **Litho.**   *Perf. 14*
1828 A572 30d multi   .20 .20
1829 A572 40d multi   .20 .20
1830 A572 100d multi, vert.   .55 .25
1831 A572 100d multi, vert.   .55 .25
1832 A572 150d multi, vert.   .75 .40
   Nos. 1828-1832 (5)   2.25 1.30

Wildlife Conservation A573

30d, Lutra lutra. 40d, Ovis musimon. 100d, Cervus elaphus. 150d, Ursus arctos.

1987, Jan. 22   **Litho.**   *Perf. 13½x14*
1833   Strip of 4 + label   5.00 2.75
   a. A573 30d multi   .75 .50
   b. A573 40d multi   .75 .50
   c. A573 100d multi   .75 .50
   d. A573 150d multi   .75 .50
   Label pictures nature reserve.

Rudjer Boscovich (1711-1787), Scientist, and Solar Eclipse over Brera Observatory, Italy — A574

1987, Feb. 13   *Perf. 14*
1834 A574 150d multicolored   1.00 .50

European Nature Protection — A575

1987 World Alpine Skiing Championships, Crans Montana — A576

1987, Mar. 9
1835 A575 150d shown   1.25 .60
1836 A575 400d Triglav glacial lake   2.00 1.00

1987, Mar. 20   **Litho.**   *Perf. 14*
1837 A576 200d multicolored   .75 .40
   No. 1837 printed in sheets of 8 plus center label.

Natl. Civil Aviation, 60th Anniv. A577

1987, Mar. 20   *Perf. 14*
1838 A577 150d POTEZ-29   1.00 .50
1839 A577 400d DC-10   1.75 .85
   Each printed in sheets of 8 plus center label.

Kole Nedelkovski (1912-1941), Poet, Revolutionary A578

1987, Apr. 2   *Perf. 13½*
1840 A578 40d multicolored   .25 .20

Liberation of Montenegro from Turkey, 125th Anniv. A579

1987, Apr. 16   *Perf. 13½*
1841 A579 40d Battle flags, folk guitar   .25 .20

Slovenian Communist Party, Cebine, 50th Anniv. — A580

1987, Apr. 18   *Perf. 14*
1842 A580 40d multicolored   .25 .20

Europa Issue

Tito Bridge, Krk — A581

1987, Apr. 30   **Litho.**   *Perf. 14*
1843 A581 200d shown   .70 .45
1844 A581 400d Bridges over canal   1.00 .75

Fruit Trees — A582

Tito, 1930, by Mosa Pijade — A583

1987, May 15   **Litho.**   *Perf. 14*
1845 A582 60d Almond   .20 .20
1846 A582 150d Pear   .70 .35
1847 A582 200d Apple   1.00 .50
1848 A582 400d Plum   1.50 .80
   Nos. 1845-1848 (4)   3.40 1.85

1987, May 25
1849 A583 60d multi   .35 .20
   50th anniv. of Tito's assumption of Yugoslavian communist party leadership.

Vuk Stefanovik Karadzic (1787-1864), Linguist and Historian — A584

60d, Bust by Petar Ubavkic, his Trsic residence & Vienna. 200d, Portrait by Uros Knezevic, & alphabet from Karadzic's Serbian Dictionary, 1818.

1987, June 10
1850 A584 60d multi   .20 .20
1851 A584 200d multi   .50 .25

Zrenjanin Postal Service, 250th Anniv. A585

1987, June 22   *Perf. 13½*
1852 A585 60d multi   .25 .20

UNIVERSIADE '87, Zagreb, July 8-19 — A586

1987, July 8   **Litho.**   *Perf. 13½*
1853 A586 60d Hurdling   .30 .20
1854 A586 150d Basketball   .50 .25
1855 A586 200d Balance beam   .70 .35
1856 A586 400d Swimming   1.50 .75
   Nos. 1853-1856 (4)   3.00 1.55
   Each printed in sheets of eight plus label.

Fire Fighting A587

Monument, Anindol Park, Samobor — A588

1987, July 20   *Perf. 14*
1857 A587 60d Canadair CL-215 spraying forest   .20 .20
1858 A587 200d Fire boat   .45 .25
   Each printed in sheets of eight plus label.

1987, Aug. 1   *Perf. 13½*
1859 A588 60d multi   .25 .20
   Communist Party of Croatia, 50th anniv.

Sabac High School, 150th Anniv. A589

1987, Sept. 10   **Litho.**   *Perf. 13½*
1860 A589 80d multi   .25 .20

Exhibition Emblem, Balkan Peninsula, Flowers A590

Clock Tower, Petrovaradin Fortress and Novi Sad — A591

1987, Sept. 19   *Perf. 14*
1861 A590 250d multi   .50 .25

Souvenir Sheet
Imperf

1862 A591 400d multi   1.50 1.50

BALKANFILA XI, Novi Sad, Sept. 19-26.

19th Joy of Europe
Conference
A592

Bridges
A593

Children's drawings: 250d, Girls in forest, by
Bedic Aranka, Juguoslavia. 400d, Scarecrow,
by Schaffer Ingeborg, Austria.

1987, Oct. 2   **Litho.**   *Perf. 14*
1863 A592 250d multi   .90 .45
1864 A592 400d multi   1.10 .55

Printed in sheets of nine.

1987, Oct. 15
1865 A593 80d Arslanagica,
    Trebinje, 16th
    cent.   .30 .20
1866 A593 250d Terzija, Djakovica,
    15th cent.   .80 .40

Ship, Dunav-
Tisa Channel
A594

1987, Oct. 20   *Perf. 13½*
1867 A594 80d multi   .25 .20

City of Titov Vrbas, 600th anniv.

Astronomical and Meteorological
Observatory, Belgrade, Cent. — A595

1987, Nov. 21   *Perf. 14*
1868 A595 80d multi   .25 .20

St. Luke the
Evangelist, by
Raphael
A596

Paintings by foreign artists in national museums: 200d, Infanta Maria Theresa, by Velazquez. 250d, Nicholas Rubens, Painter's Son,
by Rubens. 400d, Louis Laure Sennegon,
Painter's Niece, by Jean-Baptiste-Camille
Corot (1796-1875).

1987, Nov. 28
1869 A596 80d shown   .20 .20
1870 A596 200d multi   .50 .30
1871 A596 250d multi   .60 .45
1872 A596 400d multi   1.10 .65
    Nos. 1869-1872 (4)   2.40 1.55

Traditional
Competitions
A597

80d, Bull fighting. 200d, Ljubicevo Horse
Games. 250d, Moresca game. 400d, Sinj iron
ring.

1987, Dec. 10
1873 A597 80d multi   .20 .20
1874 A597 200d multi   .40 .20
1875 A597 250d multi   .55 .25
1876 A597 400d multi   1.10 .60
    Nos. 1873-1876 (4)   2.25 1.25

No. 1800 Surcharged

1987, Sept. 22   *Perf. 13½*
1877 A559 80d on 60d sg grn   .25 .20

Vinodol Codex, City of Vinodolski,
Coat of Arms — A598

1988, Jan. 6   **Litho.**   *Perf. 14*
1878 A598 100d multi   .25 .20

Vinodol Codex, 700th anniv.

Intl. Women's
Golden Fox Skiing
Championships,
25th
Anniv. — A599

1988, Jan. 30
1879 A599 350d Slalom, emblem,
    Mirobor City   .85 .40

Printed in sheets of eight plus center label.

World Wildlife
Fund — A600

Brown bears (Ursus arctos).

1988, Feb. 1
1880 A600 70d Cub   2.00 1.10
1881 A600 80d Cubs   2.00 1.10
1882 A600 200d Adult, head   2.50 1.50
1883 A600 350d Adult   5.00 1.75
    Nos. 1880-1883 (4)   11.50 5.45

1988 Winter
Olympics,
Calgary — A601

1988, Feb. 13   *Perf. 14x13½*
1884 A601 350d Slalom   .85 .40
1885 A601 1200d Ice hockey   1.75 .85

Each printed in sheets of 8 plus center label.

Souvenir Sheet

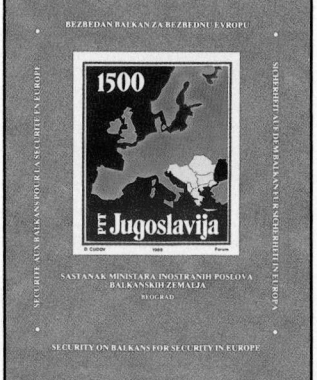

Map of Europe Highlighting Balkan
Nations — A602

1988, Feb. 24   **Litho.**   *Imperf.*
1886 A602 1500d multi   3.00 3.00

Congress of Foreign Affairs Ministers from
the Balkan Countries, Belgrade, Feb. 24-26.

1988 Summer
Olympics,
Seoul — A603

South Korean Landscape — A604

1988, Mar. 21   *Perf. 14x13½*
1887 A603 106d Basketball   .20 .20
1888 A603 450d High jump   .90 .45
1889 A603 500d Pommel horse   1.00 .50
1890 A603 1200d Boxing   2.40 1.25
    Nos. 1887-1890 (4)   4.50 2.40

Souvenir Sheet
Imperf

1891 A604 1500d multi   2.75 2.75

Nos. 1887-1890 printed in sheets of 8 plus
center label.

Europa Issue

Telecommunications — A605

1988, Apr. 30   **Litho.**   *Perf. 13½x14*
1892 A605 450d shown   .45 .30
1893 A605 1200d Transportation   1.25 .80

Sea
Shells — A606

1988, May 14
1894 A606 106d Gibbula magus   .20 .20
1895 A606 550d Pecten
    jacobaeus   .90 .45
1896 A606 600d Tonna galea   1.00 .50
1897 A606 1000d Argonauta ar-
    go   1.50 .75
    Nos. 1894-1897 (4)   3.60 1.90

Trial of Tito
and Five
Comrades,
60th
Anniv. — A607

1988, May 25
1898 A607 106d black & brn   .25 .20

Palace of
Princess
Ljubica of
Serbia, 1st
University
Building
A608

1988, June 14   **Litho.**   *Perf. 13½*
1899 A608 106d multi   .25 .20

Belgrade University, 150th anniv.

Flowers — A609

Esperanto,
Cent. — A610

1988, July 2   *Perf. 14*
1900 A609 600d Phelypaea
    boissieri   .75 .35
1901 A609 1000d Campanula
    formanekiana   1.25 .60

Council of Europe.

1988, July 14   *Perf. 13½*
1902 A610 600d dull vio & ol grn   .80 .40

Printed in sheets of 8 plus center label.

Cargo Ships — A611

Map of the Danube Basin — A612

1988, Aug. 18   **Litho.**   **Perf. 14**
1903 A611 1000d multi   .80   .40
          Souvenir Sheet
              Imperf
1904 A612 2000d multi   2.75 2.75
    Danube Conference, 40th anniv.

13th European Junior Basketball Championships, Aug. 21-28 — A613

1988, Aug. 20   **Perf. 14**
1905 A613 600d multi   .60   .30

1st Horse Race in Belgrade, 125th Anniv. — A614

1988, Aug. 27
1906 A614 140d Thoroughbred
                    racing   .30   .20
1907 A614 600d Steeplechase   .70   .35
1908 A614 1000d Harness racing   1.00   .50
       Nos. 1906-1908 (3)   2.00 1.05

Museum of Bosnia and Herzegovina, Sarajevo, Cent. A615

1988, Sept. 10   **Perf. 13½**
1909 A615 140d Museum, Bosnian
                   bellflower   .25   .20

Anti-Cancer and AIDS Campaigns A616

1988, Sept. 24   **Perf. 14**
1910 A616 140d Arm, lobster
                    claw   .30   .20
1911 A616 1000d Blood, scream   1.25   .60

    Nos. 1801 and 1804 Surcharged
1988, July   **Litho.**   **Perf. 13½**
1912 A559 120d on 93d ultra   .30   .20
1913 A559 140d on 106d brn org   .30   .20

Joy of Europe Youth Conference A617

Portraits of girls by: 1000d, P. Ranosovic. 1100d, Renoir.

1988, Oct. 1   **Litho.**   **Perf. 14**
1914 A617 1000d multi   .90   .45
1915 A617 1100d multi   1.00   .50
         See Nos. 1987-1988.

Slovenski Academy, 50th Anniv. — A618

1988, Oct. 13   **Litho.**   **Perf. 14**
1916 A618 200d multi   .25   .20

Museum Exhibits and Places of Origin A618a

200d, Wood bassinet, traditional wedding (Galicka). #1918, Embroidery, man and woman wearing folk costumes of Vojvodina. #1919, Scimitar, flintlock, man & woman wearing folk costumes of Kotor (Bokelji). 1100d, Masks (Kurenti).

1988, Oct. 18
1917 A618a 200d multi, vert.   .20   .20
1918 A618a 1000d shown   .75   .40
1919 A618a 1000d multi, vert.   .75   .40
1920 A618a 1100d multi   .85   .45
       Nos. 1917-1920 (4)   2.55 1.45

Woman with Lyre, 4th Cent. B.C. — A618b

Grecian terra cotta figurines: #1922, Eros & Psyche, 2nd cent. BC. #1923, Seated woman, 3rd cent. BC. 1100d, Woman by Stele, 3rd cent. BC.

1988, Oct. 28
1921 A618b 200d multi   .20   .20
1922 A618b 1000d multi   .75   .35
1923 A618b 1000d multi   .75   .35
1924 A618b 1100d multi   .75   .35
       Nos. 1921-1924 (4)   2.45 1.25

Peter II (1813-1851), Prince Bishop and Poet — A618c

Portraits and: 200d, Cetinje Monastery and frontispiece of his principal work. 1000d, Njegos Mausoleum.

1988, Nov. 1
1925 A618c 200d multi   .20   .20
1926 A618c 1000d multi   .80   .40

Postal Service Types of 1986 and

Telephone Receiver and Telephone Card — A619

Bird, Posthorn, Simulated Stamp — A620

Propeller Plane, Two Arrows and Map — A621

Designs: 170d, 300d, Flower, envelope, mailbox and simulated stamp. 220d, PTT emblem on simulated stamp, mail coach. 800d, Postman on motorcycle. No. 1941, Postman, resident. No. 1942, Mail train. No. 1943, Envelopes, satellite dish. No. 1944, Earth, telecommunications satellite. 100,000d, Bird, open envelope, flower. 170d, 220d, 300d, 2000d, 5000d, No. 1941 vert.

1988-89   **Litho.**   **Perf. 13¼**
1935 A559   170d dl grn   .40   .20
1936 A559   220d brn org   .40   .20
1937 A559   300d ver   .40   .20
1938 A559   800d brt ultra   .40   .20
1939 A619   2000d multi   .40   .20
1940 A620   5000d dk red &
                     ultra   1.40   .65
1941 A559 10,000d org & brt
                     lil   1.25   .50
1942 A559 20,000d lt ol grn &
                     lt red brn 1.25   .50
            Perf. 13½
1943 A560 10,000d multi   2.50 1.60
1944 A560 20,000d multi   1.75 1.25
1944A A621 50,000d org & dl
                     bl   2.00   .90
1945 A560 100,000d org & dl
                     grn   1.75 1.25
     Nos. 1935-1945 (12)   13.90 7.65
            Perf. 12½
1937a A559   300d   .40   .20
1938a A559   800d   .75   .30
1939a A619   2000d   .75   .30
1940a A620   5000d   1.50   .75
1941a A559 10,000d   1.50   .75
     Nos. 1937a-1941a (5)   4.90 2.30

Issued: 1988 — 170d, 11/17; 220d, 12/6; 1989 — 300d, 5/11; 800d, 2000d, 7/20; 5000d, 1/20; #1941, 11/28; #1942, 12/8; #1943, 3/20; #1944, 7/19; 50,000d, 11/8; 100,000d, 12/4.
    See Nos. 2008-2009, 2017, 2052. For surcharges see Nos. 1972, 1974, 2048.

Yugoslavia, 70th Anniv. — A622

1988, Dec. 1   **Litho.**   **Perf. 14**
1946 A622 200d Krsmanovic Hall,
                  Belgrade   .25   .20

    Nos. 1805-1806 Surcharged
1988   **Litho.**   **Perf. 13½**
1947 A559 170d on 120d   .50   .25
1948 A559 220d on 140d   .50   .25
   Issued: #1947, Dec. 21; #1948, Dec. 15.

              Miniature Sheet

Victory of Yugoslavian Athletes at the 1988 Summer Olympics, Seoul — A623

Medals and events: a, Women's air pistol. b, Team handball. c, Table tennis. d, Wrestling. e, Double sculls. f, Basketball. g, Water polo. h, Boxing.

1988, Dec. 31   **Litho.**   **Perf. 14**
1949   Sheet of 8 + label   3.00 3.00
a.-h. A623 500d any single   .30   .20

Ivan Gundulic (1589-1638), Poet — A624

1989, Jan. 7   **Perf. 13½**
1950 A624 220d multi   .40   .20

World Wildlife Fund — A625

Ducks.

1989, Feb. 23   **Litho.**   **Perf. 14**
1951   Strip of 4 + label   14.00 8.00
  a. A625 300d Anas platyrhynchos 1.25   .50
  b. A625 2100d Anas crecca   3.50 1.75
  c. A625 2200d Anas acuta   3.50 1.75
  d. A625 2200d Anas clypeata   3.50 1.75

Printed in sheets of 20+5 labels. Label pictures WWF emblem.

Publication of The Glory of the Duchy of Kranjska, by Johann Valvasor (1641-1693), 300th Anniv. A626

1989, Mar. 10   **Perf. 13½**
1952 A626 300d Portrait   .25   .20

Flowering Plants — A627

1989, Mar. 20   **Perf. 14**
1953 A627 300d Bulbocodium
                   vernum   .20   .20
1954 A627 2100d Nymphaea al-
                   ba   1.10   .55
1955 A627 2200d Fritillaria
                   degeniana,
                   vert.   1.25   .60
1956 A627 3000d Orchis simia,
                   vert.   1.75   .85
     Nos. 1953-1956 (4)   4.30 2.20

6th World Air-Gun Championships, Sarajevo, Apr. 27-30 — A628

1989, Apr. 26
1957 A628 3000d multi .80 .40

Europa 1989 — A629

1989, Apr. 29
1958 A629 3000d shown .75 .60
1959 A629 6000d Marbles 1.75 1.25

15th European Trophy for Natl. Athletic Club Champions, Belgrade, June 3-4 — A630

1989, June 1   Litho.   Perf. 13½
1960 A630 4000d Pole vault .50 .25

Printed in sheets of 8+label picturing flags of participating nations.

Yugoslavia Motorcycle Grand Prix, Rijeka, June 9-11 — A631

Various race scenes.

1989, June 9   Perf. 14
1961 A631 500d multi .20 .20
1962 A631 4000d multi .60 .30

Souvenir Sheet
Perf. 14x13½
1963 A631 6000d multi 1.75 .85

No. 1963 contains one 54x35 stamp.

No. 1246 Surcharged
1989, Apr. 6   Litho.   Perf. 13
1964 A323 100d on 1d dull grn .50 .25
a.   Perf. 13x12½ .80 .40

Tito — A632

1989, May 25   Perf. 13½x14
1965 A632 300d multi .25 .20

Early Adriatic Ships A633

a, Ancient Greek galley. b, Roman galley. c, Crusade galleon, 13th cent. d, Nava of Dubrovnik, 16th cent. e, French ship, 17th cent. f, Vessels, 18th cent. 3000d, View of Dubrovnik seaport, called Ragusa in Italian, from a 17th cent. engraving.

1989, June 10   Perf. 13½
1966   Block of 6 2.00 1.00
a.-f. A633 1000d any single .30 .20
Souvenir Sheet
1967 A633 3000d multi .75 .35

No. 1967 contains one 75x32mm stamp. Nos. 1966-1967 printed se-tenant and sold folded in booklet cover.

26th European Basketball Championships — A634

Map of Europe, basketball and flags of: No. 1968, France, Yugoslavia, Greece, Bulgaria. No. 1969, Netherlands, Italy, Russia, Spain.

1989, June 20   Litho.   Perf. 13½x14
1968 A634 2000d multi .25 .20
1969 A634 2000d multi .25 .20

Nos. 1968-1969 exist with setenant label.

Defeat of the Serbians at the Battle of Kosovo, 1389 — A635

1989, June 28
1970 A635 500d multi .25 .20

Danilovgrad Library, Cent. A636

1989, July 15   Litho.   Perf. 13½
1971 A636 500d multi .25 .20

Nos. 1797, 1719, 1935, 1936 Surcharged

1989
1972 A559 400d on 30d lt brn vio .50 .20
1973 A323 700d on 70d brt ultra .50 .20
1974 A559 700d on 170d dull green .50 .20
1975 A559 700d on 220d brn org .50 .20
Nos. 1972-1975 (4) 2.00 .80

Issued: #1975, 7/19; #1974, 8/10; #1972, 8/23; #1973, 12/13.

Kulin Ban Charter, 800th Anniv. A638

1989, Aug. 29   Litho.   Perf. 14
1976 A638 500d multi .25 .20

World Rowing Championships A639

1989, Sept. 2   Perf. 13½
1977 A639 10,000d multi .75 .35

Interparliamentary Union, Cent. — A640

Architecture: No. 1978, Parliament, London (emblem at R). No. 1979, Notre Dame Cathedral (emblem at L).

1989, Sept. 4   Perf. 13½x14
1978 A640 10,000d multi .65 .30
1979 A640 10,000d multi .65 .30

A641

View of Belgrade and Maps BEOGRAD '89 — A642

Architecture & antiquities of exhibition host cities: #1980, Belgrade '61, Cairo '64. #1981, Lusaka '70, Algiers '73. #1982, Colombo '76, Havana '79. #1983, New Delhi '83, Harare '76.

1989, Sept. 4
1980 A641 10,000d multi .65 .30
1981 A641 10,000d multi .65 .30
1982 A641 10,000d multi .65 .30
1983 A641 10,000d multi .65 .30
Nos. 1980-1983 (4) 2.60 1.20
Souvenir Sheet
Perf. 14
1984 A642 20,000d multi 1.75 1.75

European Nature Protection A643

8000d, Paeonia officinalis, Brezovica-Jazinac Lake. 10,000d, Paeonia corallina, Mirusa Canyon.

1989, Sept. 11   Perf. 14
1985 A643 8000d multi .45 .20
1986 A643 10,000d multi .55 .25

Joy of Europe Type of 1988

Portraits of children: No. 1987, Child with Lamb, by Jovan Popovic. No. 1988, Girl Feeding Dog, by Albert Cuyp (1620-1691).

1989, Oct. 2   Litho.   Perf. 14
1987 A617 10,000d multi .80 .40
1988 A617 10,000d multi .80 .40

Karpos Uprising, 300th Anniv. — A644

1989, Oct. 20   Litho.   Perf. 13½
1989 A644 1200d ver & dark brn .25 .20

No. 1833c, Cancellation, Quill Pen, Wax Seals and Seal Device on Parchment A645

1989, Oct. 31   Perf. 14
1990 A645 1200d multicolored .25 .20

Stamp Day.

Museum Exhibits A646

1989, Nov. 2
1991 A646 1200d Pack-saddle maker .20 .20
1992 A646 14,000d Cooper .60 .30
1993 A646 15,000d Winegrower .65 .35
1994 A646 30,000d Weaver 1.40 .70
Nos. 1991-1994 (4) 2.85 1.55

Religious Paintings — A647

2100d, Apostle Matthew, vert. 21,000d, St. Barbara, vert. 30,000d, The Fourth Day of Creation. 50,000d, The Fifth Day of Creation.

1989, Nov. 28   Litho.   Perf. 14
1997 A647 2100d multicolored .20 .20
1998 A647 21,000d multicolored .65 .30
1999 A647 30,000d multicolored .90 .45
2000 A647 50,000d multicolored 1.50 .75
Nos. 1997-2000 (4) 3.25 1.70

A648

League of Communists 14th
Congress — A649

1990, Jan. 20 Litho. Perf. 13½x14
2001 A648 10,000d Star .30 .20
2002 A648 50,000d Computer .75 .35

Souvenir Sheet
Imperf
2003 A649 100,000d Star, diff. 1.60 1.60

Postal Service Types of 1986-88

10p, Man posting letters in mailbox. 20p, Postal employee sorting mail. 30p, Postman, resident. 40p, Woman at telephone station. 1d, Mail train. 2d, Ship & envelope. 3d, Flower, mailbox, envelope & simulated stamp. 5d, Airplane, letters, map of Europe. 10d, Bird, open envelope, flower. 20d, Woman at telephone station.
Designs for other values as before.
10p, 20p, 30p, 3d, 5d vert.

1990 Perf. 12½
2004 A559 10p br yel grn & vio .50 .20
2005 A559 20p red vio & org .50 .20
2006 A559 30p org & yel grn .50 .20
2007 A559 40p blue grn & red
  vio .50 .20
2008 A620 50p pur & blue grn .50 .20
2009 A619 60p red org & brt
  vio .50 .20
2013 A559 1d rose lil & greenish bl .50 .20
2014 A559 2d red lil & blue .50 .20
2015 A559 3d org & dl blue .60 .30
2017 A619 5d ultra & grnsh
  blue 1.25 .60
2019 A559 10d red org & vio bl 2.25 1.75
  Nos. 2004-2019 (11) 8.10 4.25

Issued: 10p, 20p, 2/9; 30p, 40p, 1/24; 50p, 1/29; 60p, 2/6; 2d, 2/14; 3d, 2/22; 5d, 1/31; 1d, 5/24; 10d, 6/12.
For surcharges see Nos. 2049-2053, 2168//2174.

1990-92 Perf. 13¼
2004a A559 10p br yel grn & vio .70 .30
2005a A559 20p red vio & org .70 .30
2006a A559 30p org & yel grn .70 .30
2007a A559 40p blue grn & red
  vio .70 .30
2008a A620 50p pur & blue grn .70 .30
2009a A619 60p red org & brt
  vio .70 .30
2013a A559 1d rose lil & greenish bl 2.75 2.50
2014a A559 2d red lil & blue .70 .30
2015a A559 3d org & dl blue> 2.50 2.25
2017a A619 5d ultra & grnsh
  blue 1.25 1.00
2019a A559 10d red org & vio bl 8.00 8.00
2021 A559 20d car rose &
  org .40 .20
  Nos. 2004a-2021 (12) 19.80 16.05

Issued: 30p, 40p, 1/24; 50p, 1/29; 5d, 1/31; 60p, 2/6; 10p, 20p, 2/9; 2d, 2/14; 3d, 2/22; 10d, 6/12; 1d, 7/2; 20d, 1/27/92.
For surcharges see Nos. 2049a-2053a, 2170//2176.

Anti-smoking
Campaign
A650

1990, Jan. 31 Litho. Perf. 13½x13
2034 A650 10d gry & yel brn 1.75 .85

Protected
Fish — A651

1990, Feb. 15 Perf. 13½
2035 Strip of 4 + label 7.00 3.75
  a. A651 1d *Esox lucius* .40 .20
  b. A651 5d *Silurus glanis* 1.10 .55
  c. A651 10d *Lota lota* 2.00 1.00
  d. A651 15d *Perca fluviatilis* 3.50 1.75

Zabljak Fortress, Illuminated
Manuscript, Coat of Arms — A652

1990, Mar. 9 Perf. 14x13½
2036 A652 50p multicolored .80 .40

Enthronement of Djuradj Crnojevic, 500th anniv.

ITU,
125th
Anniv.
A653

1990, Mar. 23
2037 A653 6.50d Telegrapher,
  computer 1.10 .55

1990 World Cup
Soccer
Championships,
Italy — A654

1990, Apr. 16
2038 A654 6.50d shown 1.75 .85
2039 A654 10d multi, diff. 2.00 1.00

Europa
1990 — A655

Post offices: 6.50d, PTT Central, Skopje. 10d, Telecommunications Central, Belgrade.

1990, Apr. 23 Perf. 13½x14
2040 A655 6.50d multicolored 1.25 .55
2041 A655 10d multicolored 2.00 .80

A656

A657

1990, Apr. 30 Litho. Perf. 13½
2042 A656 6.50d multicolored 1.25 .60

Labor Day, cent.

No. 2043 exists with setenant label.

1990, May 5 Perf. 14x13½
Eurovision Song Contest: 10d, Conductor, musical score.
2043 A657 6.50d multicolored 1.25 .60
2044 A657 10d multicolored 1.75 .90

Tennis — A658

1990, May 15 Litho. Perf. 14
2045 A658 6.50d multicolored 1.40 .70
2046 A658 10d multicolored 2.10 1.00

Tito — A659

1990, May 25 Perf. 13½x14
2047 A659 50p multicolored .40 .20

Nos. 1938, 2004-2009a Surcharged

No. 2048 No. 2049

1990-91 Litho. Perf. 12½
2048 A559 50p on 800d (#1938a) .20 .20
  a. Perf 13¼ (#1938) .20 .20
2049 A559 50p on 20p (#2005) .20 .20
  a. Perf 13¼ (#2005a) ('91) 2.75 2.75
2050 A559 1d on 30p (#2006) .20 .20
  a. Perf 13¼ (#2006a) 3.25 3.25
2051 A559 2d on 40p (#2007), I .90 .90
  a. Type II, perf. 13¼ (#2007a) 1.25 .90
  b. Type I, perf. 13¼ (#2007a) 2.00 2.00
2052 A619 5d on 60p (#2009) .40 .20
  a. Type II, perf. 13¼ (#2009a) 2.75 1.75
2053 A559 10d on 10p (#2004) .40 .20
  a. Perf 13¼ (#2004a) 1.00 .45
  Nos. 2048-2053 (6) 2.30 1.90

Type II surcharge has 3 instead of 2 bars obliterating old value, new denomination is at bottom of stamp.
Issued: #2048, 2048a, 5/24; #2050, 8/7; #2049, 2049a, 9/18; #2051-2051b, 10/2; #2050a, 1/4/91; #2053, 2053a, 12/12/91; #2052, 2052a, 12/17/91.

Public
Postal
Service
in
Serbia,
150th
Anniv.
A660

1990, May 25
2056 A660 50p multicolored 1.50 .75

Pigeons
A661

1990, June 8 Perf. 13½
2057 A661 50p multicolored .50 .25
2058 A661 6.50d multicolored 1.25 .60
2059 A661 6.50d multi, vert. 1.25 .60
2060 A661 10d multi, vert. 3.00 1.50
  Nos. 2057-2060 (4) 6.00 2.95

Mercury Mine
at Idrija, 500th
Anniv. — A662

Designs: 6.50d, Miners at work, ca. 1490.

1990, June 22 Perf. 13½x14
2061 A662 50p multicolored .20 .20
2062 A662 6.50d multicolored 1.10 .55

Newspaper
"Vjesnik," 50th
Anniv. — A663

1990, June 23 Perf. 13½
2063 A663 60p multicolored .60 .30

Serbian Migration, 300th
Anniv. — A664

1990, Sept. 20 Perf. 14
2064 A664 1d shown .20 .20
2065 A664 6.50d Caravan 1.25 .60

European Track & Field
Championships, Split — A665

1990, Aug. 27 Perf. 13½
2067 A665 1d Start of race .80 .40

2068 A665 6.50d Runners' feet 1.10 .55
2069 A665 10d Runners 2.75 1.40

Souvenir Sheet

No. 2069 contains one 54x35mm stamp. A 50p exists but no information on its postal category is available.

Joy of Europe
A666

Paintings: 6.50d, Children by I. Kobilca. 10d, William III of Orange as a Child by A. Hanneman, vert.

1990, Oct. 2 **Litho.** **Perf. 14**
2070 A666 6.50d multicolored 1.40 .70
2071 A666 10d multicolored 1.75 .80

Souvenir Sheets

29th Chess Olympics, Novi Sad — A667

1990, Oct. 2 **Perf. 11½**
Granite Paper
2072 Sheet of 4 8.00 8.00
  a. A667 1d shown .25 .25
  b. A667 5d Rook, bishop, knight 1.75 1.75
  c. A667 6.50d King, bishop, knght, pawn 2.25 2.25
  d. A667 10d Chess pieces 3.75 3.75

Imperf
2073 Sheet of 4 8.00 8.00
  a. A667 1d like No. 2072a .25 .25
  b. A667 5d like No. 2072b 1.75 1.75
  c. A667 6.50d like No. 2072c 2.25 2.25
  d. A667 10d like No. 2072d 3.75 3.75

No. 2073 has blue margin inscriptions. Emblems on Nos. 2072a-2072d are in silver, those on Nos. 2073a-2073d are in gold.

Stamp Day A668

1990, Oct. 2 **Perf. 14**
2074 A668 2d multicolored .80 .70

150th anniv. of the Penny Black.

Environmental Protection A669

1990, Nov. 16 **Litho.** **Perf. 14**
2075 A669 6.50d Vransko Lake 1.50 1.50
2076 A669 10d Gyps fulvus 2.00 2.00

Frescoes — A670

Designs: 2d, King Milutin, Monastery of Our Lady, Ljeviska. 5d, Saint Sava, Mileseva Monastery. 6.50d, Saint Elias, Moraca Monastery. 10d, Jesus Christ, Sopocani Monastery.

1990, Nov. 28
2077 A670 2d multicolored .40 .40
2078 A670 5d multicolored .95 .95
2079 A670 6.50d multicolored 1.25 1.25
2080 A670 10d multicolored 1.90 1.90
  Nos. 2077-2080 (4) 4.50 4.50

Dr. Bozo Milanovic (1890-1980), Religious and Political Leader A671

1990, Dec. 20 **Litho.** **Perf. 13½**
2081 A671 2d multicolored .35 .35

Religious Carvings A672

Designs: 2d, Christ in the temple. 5d, Nativity scene. 6.50d, Flight from Egypt, horiz. 10d, Entry into Jerusalem, horiz.

1990, Dec. 24 **Perf. 13½x14, 14x13½**
2082 A672 2d gld, brn, & blk .35 .35
2083 A672 5d gld, brn, & blk .90 .90
2084 A672 6.50d gld, brn, & blk 1.10 1.10
2085 A672 10d gld, brn, & blk 1.90 1.90
  Nos. 2082-2085 (4) 4.25 4.25

Protected Birds — A673

1991, Jan. 31 **Litho.** **Perf. 14x13½**
2086 Strip of 4 + label 4.50 4.50
  a. A673 2d Vanellus vanellus .35 .35
  b. A673 5d Lanius senator .95 .95
  c. A673 6.50d Grus grus 1.25 1.25
  d. A673 10d Mergus merganser 1.90 1.90

1991, Feb. 20
2087 A674 2d Crocus kosaninii .30 .30
2088 A674 6d Crocus scardicus .90 .90
2089 A674 7.50d Crocus rujanesis 1.10 1.10
2090 A674 15d Crocus adamii 2.40 2.40
  Nos. 2087-2090 (4) 4.70 4.70

Bishop Josip J. Strossmayer (1815-1905), Founder of Academy of Arts and Sciences A675

1991, Mar. 4 **Litho.** **Perf. 13½x14**
2091 A675 2d multicolored .80 .80

Academy of Arts and Sciences, 125th Anniv.

Wolfgang Amadeus Mozart, Composer A676

1991, Mar. 20 **Perf. 14**
2092 A676 7.50d multicolored 1.00 1.00

Otto Lilienthal's First Glider Flight, Cent. — A677

Designs: 7.50d, Edvard Rusjan (1886-1911), pilot, aircraft designer. 15d, Otto Lilienthal (1848-1896), aviation pioneer.

1991, Apr. 1
2093 A677 7.50d multicolored 1.25 1.25
2094 A677 15d multicolored 1.50 1.50

Printed in sheets of 8 plus label.

Lhotse I, Himalayas, South Face First Climbed by Tomo Cesen, 1990 — A678

1991, Apr. 24 **Perf. 14x13½**
2095 A678 7.50d multicolored .75 .75

Europa A679

Designs: 7.50d, Telecommunications satellite. 15d, Satellite, antenna, telephone.

1991, May 6 **Perf. 14**
2096 A679 7.50d multicolored 1.00 .60
2097 A679 15d multicolored 2.00 1.25

Franciscan Monastery, Trsat, 700th Anniv. — A680

1991, May 10 **Litho.** **Perf. 13½x14**
2098 A680 3.50d multicolored .65 .65

Governments of Danube River Region Conf., Belgrade — A681

15d, Danube River shipping. 20d, Course of Danube, landmarks, regional animals.

1991, May 15 **Perf. 13½**
2099 A681 7.50d multicolored 1.00 1.00
2100 A681 15d multicolored 1.50 1.50

Souvenir Sheet

2101 A681 20d multicolored 6.75 6.75

No. 2101 contains one 55x35mm stamp.

Opening of Karavanke Tunnel — A682

Designs: 4.50d, Passage Over Karavanke by J. Valvasor, 17th century. 11d, Entrance to new Karavanke Tunnel.

1991, June 1 **Perf. 14x13½**
2102 A682 4.50d multicolored .35 .35
2103 A682 11d multicolored .90 .90

Basketball, Cent. — A683

1991, June 15 **Perf. 13½x14**
2104 A683 11d shown 1.10 1.10
2105 A683 15d Nets, "100" 1.60 1.60

Yugoslavian Insurrection, 50th Anniv. — A684

Tin Ujevic (1891-1955), Writer — A685

Designs: 4.50d, Partisan Memorial Medal, 1941. 11d, Medal for Courage.

1991, July 4 **Litho.** **Perf. 14**
2106 A684 4.50d multicolored .35 .35
2107 A684 11d multicolored .90 .90

Yugoslav Natl. Army, 50th Anniv.

1991, July 5 **Perf. 13½**
2108 A685 4.50d multicolored .60 .60

Jacobus Gallus (1550-1591), Composer A686

1991, July 18
2109 A686 11d multicolored .80 .80

Lighthouses of Adriatic and Danube — A687

Designs: a, Savudrija, 1818. b, Sveti Ivan na pucini, 1853. c, Porer, 1833. d, Stoncica, 1865. e, Olipa, c. 1842. f, Glavat, 1884. g, Veli rat, 1849. h, Vir, 1881. i, Tajerske sestrice, 1876. j, Razanj, 1875. k, Derdap-Danube. l, Tamis-Danube.

1991, July 25   Litho.   Perf. 13½
2110 A687 10d Bklt. pane of
12, #a.-l.   15.00 15.00

Sremski Karlovci High School,
Bicent. — A688

1991, Sept. 12   Litho.   Perf. 14
2111 A688 4.50d multicolored   .45 .45

European
Nature
Protection
A689

1991, Sept. 24   Perf. 13½x14
2112 A689 11d Palingenia longi-
cauda   1.10 1.10
2113 A689 15d Phalacrocorax
pygmaeus   1.40 1.40

A690

A691

1991, Sept. 28   Perf. 14
2114 A690 4.50d multicolored   .45 .45
Town of Subotica, 600th anniv.

1991, Oct. 2
Paintings: 15d, Little Dubravka, by Jovan
Bijelic (1886-1964). 30d, Little Girl with a Cat
by Mary Cassatt (1845-1926).
2115 A691 15d multicolored   1.10 1.10
2116 A691 30d multicolored   2.25 2.25
Joy of Europe.

33rd Intl.
Apicultural
Congress,
APIMONDIA
'91 — A692

1991, Sept. 28   Litho.   Perf. 13½x14
2117 A692 11d multicolored   .85 .85

Stamp Day, Monument to Prince
Michael Obrenovich,
Serbia #1 — A693

1991, Oct. 31   Perf. 14
2118 A693 4.50d multicolored   .50 .50
First Serbia Postage Stamps, 125th Anniv.

Museum
Exhibits
A694

Flags and medals: 20d, Vucjido battle flag,
medal for courage. 30d, Grahovac battle flag
and medal. 40d, Montenegrin state flag, medal
for bravery. 50d, Montenegrin court flag,
medal of Petrovich Nyegosh Dynasty.

1991, Nov. 28   Perf. 13½x14
2119 A694 20d multicolored   .50 .50
2120 A694 30d multicolored   .75 .75
2121 A694 40d multicolored   1.00 1.00
2122 A694 50d multicolored   1.25 1.25
    Nos. 2119-2122 (4)   3.50 3.50

Illustrations
from Ancient
Manuscripts
A695

Designs: 20d, Angel carrying Sun around
Earth, 17th cent. 30d, Celnica Gospel, menol-
ogy for April, 14th cent. 40d, Angel from the
Annunciation, 13th cent. 50d, Mary Magdalene, 12th cent.

1991, Dec. 12
2123 A695 20d multicolored   .50 .50
2124 A695 30d multicolored   .75 .75
2125 A695 40d multicolored   1.00 1.00
2126 A695 50d multicolored   1.25 1.25
    Nos. 2123-2126 (4)   3.50 3.50

Gotse Deltchev
(1872-1903),
Macedonian
Revolutionary
A696

1992, Jan. 29   Litho.   Perf. 13½
2127 A696 5d multicolored   1.40 .70

Red Star,
European and
World Soccer
Champions
A697

1992, Jan. 29   Litho.   Perf. 14x13½
2128 A697 17d multicolored   4.00 2.00

A698   A699

1992, Feb. 8   Perf. 14x13½
2129 A698 80d Ski jumping   1.25 .60
2130 A698 100d Freestyle skiing 1.60 .80
1992 Winter Olympics, Albertville.

1992, Mar. 10   Litho.   Perf. 14
Protected Animals: a, 50d, Lepus
europaeus. b, 60d, Pteromys volans. c, 80d,
Dryomys nitedula. d, 100d, Cricetus cricetus.
2131 A699 Strip of 4, #a.-d. +
label   5.00 2.50

Madonna and
Child, 14th
century,
Pec — A700

1992, Mar. 14   Perf. 13½x14
2132 A700 80d multicolored   1.25 .60
Promotion of Breastfeeding.

Ski Association of Montenegro — A701

1992, Mar. 25   Perf. 14x13½
2133 A701 8d multicolored   2.50 1.25
Skiing in Montenegro, cent.

1860 Fountain,   A702a
Belgrade —
A702

A702b   A702c

A702d   A702e

A702f   A702g

A702h   A702i

A702j

5d, Griffins, 14th cent. #2136, #2139, Fisherman Fountain, Belgrade. #2138, like #2137.
300d, Kalemegdan Fountain, Belgrade. 500d,
Fountain, Sremski Karlovci. #2142, Symbols
of Miroslav-Evangelium, 12th cent. 3000d,
Fountain, Studenica. 5000d, Fountain,
Oplenzu. 10,000d, 500,000d, Health spa,
Vrnjacka Banja. 50,000d, Envelopes over map
of Europe. #2147, Airplane. #2148, Health
spa, Bukovacka Banja.

1992-93   Litho.   Perf. 13½
2135 A702a   5d brn & olive   1.00 .20
2136 A702   50d dk bl & lt bl .75 .25
2137 A702   50d violet   .75 .20
2138 A702   100d lil rose &
              pink   1.00 .20
2139 A702   100d dk grn & lt
              grn   .60 .20
2140 A702b   300d brn & red
              brn   1.50 .20
2141 A702c   500d dk ol & pale
              org   2.00 .20
2142 A702d   (A) red,
              18x22mm   1.50 .25
  a.   Perf. 12½   4.00 4.00
2143 A702e   3000d red brn   2.00 .20
  a.   Perf. 12½   4.00 4.00
2144 A702f   5000d vio &
              yel brn   1.25 .20
2145 A702g   10,000d vio bl &
              grn bl   1.00 .20
2146 A702h   50,000d gray &
              gray bl   3.00 .20
  a.   Perf. 12½   3.00 3.00
2147 A702i   100,000d red & bl 2.00 .25
  a.   Perf. 12½   2.00 2.00
2148 A702j   100,000d brn red
              & brn   1.50 .20
2149 A702g   500,000d bl & vio 1.75 .25
    Nos. 2135-2149 (15)   21.60 3.20

Issued: #2137, 4/1/92; #2139, 5/6/92; 5d,
11/24/92; #2136, 12/15/92; #2138, 12/22/92;
300d, 12/3/92; 500d, 1/14/93; #2142, 4/5/93;
#2142a, 1993; #2143, 4/23/93; 5000d,
3/18/93; 10,000d, 11/9/93; 50,000d, 6/10/93;
100,000d, 6/28/93; 100,000d, 12/6/93;
500,000d, 8/10/93.

No. 2142 was valued at 3000d on day of
issue.

See No. 2386. For surcharges see Nos.
2220A-2220I, 2253-2254.

Sinking of the
Titanic, 80th
Anniv. — A703

1992, Apr. 14   Perf. 14
2152 A703 150d multicolored   1.50 .90

Expo
'92,
Seville
A704

1992, Apr. 20
2153 A704 150d multicolored   1.25 .80

Discovery of
America,
500th
Anniv. — A705

1992, May 5   Litho.   Perf. 13½x14
2154 A705 300d Columbus,
                 ship   2.00 1.25
2155 A705 500d Columbus'
                 fleet   3.25 2.10

Souvenir Sheet
Perf. 14x13½
2156 A705 1200d Ships in port 10.00 10.00
Europa. No. 2156 contains one 54x34mm
stamp.

1992 Summer
Olympics,
Barcelona — A706

1992, May 20   Perf. 14x13½
2157 A706 500d Pistol shoot-
                 ing   1.25   .60
2158 A706 500d Water polo   1.25   .60
2159 A706 500d Tennis   1.25   .60
2160 A706 500d Handball   1.25   .60
     Nos. 2157-2160 (4)   5.00 2.40

European Soccer
Championships — A707

Various soccer plays.

1992, June 1   Perf. 13½
2161 A707 1000d shown   2.25 1.10
2162 A707 1000d multicolored   2.25 1.10

Domestic
Cats — A708

Designs: No. 2163, Red Persian. No. 2164,
White Persian. No. 2165, Yellow tabby. No.
2166, British blue short-hair.

1992, June 25   Litho.   Perf. 13½x14
Background Color
Cyrillic Letters
2163 A708 1000d blue   1.90 1.25
2164 A708 1000d purple   1.90 1.25
Latin Letters
2165 A708 1000d dark purple   1.90 1.25
2166 A708 1000d brown   1.90 1.25
     Nos. 2163-2166 (4)   7.60 5.00

Steam
Locomotives
A709

Designs: a, JDZ 162. b, JDZ 151. c, JDZ 73.
d, JDZ 83. e, JDZ 16. f, Prince Nicholas'
coach.

1992, July 3   Litho.   Perf. 14
2167 A709 1000d Booklet
                 pane of 6,
                 #a.-f.   15.00 12.50

Nos. 2005-2006,
2007a, 2008, 2013a,
2014a, 2015a, 2017a
Surcharged

1992   Perfs., Etc. as Before
2168 A559   2d on 30p #2006   .40   .20
2169 A559   5d on 20p #2005   .40   .20
2170 A559   5d on 40p #2007a   .40   .20
2171 A620 10d on 50p #2008   .40   .20
2172 A621 10d on 5d #2017a   .40   .20
2173 A559 20d on 1d #2013a   .80   .25
2174 A621 20d on 5d like
                 #2017,yel, bl &
                 grn bl   .80   .25
2175 A559 20d on 2d #2014a   2.00   .70
2176 A559 100d on 3d #2015a   4.25 1.40
     Nos. 2168-2176 (9)   9.85 3.60

Issued: #2168, 2170, 10/26; #2169, 9/12;
#2171, 9/17; #2172, 10/29; #2173, 2175-2176,
8/6; #2174, 11/9.

World Chess
Champions
A710

1992, Sept. 14   Litho.   Perf. 14
2177 A710 500d Bobby Fischer   2.25 1.40
2178 A710 500d Boris Spassky   2.25 1.40

Telephone
Service in
Vojvodina,
Cent.
A711

1892 Telephone, buildings of Novi Sad,
Subotica and Zrenjanin.

1992, Oct. 1   Perf. 13½
2179 A711 10d multicolored   1.75 1.25

Stamp
Day
A712

Design: Montenegro #7, musician.

1992, Oct. 2
2180 A712 50d multicolored   1.50 1.00

European
Art — A713

Protection of
Nature — A714

Europa: No. 2181, Ballet Dancer, by Edgar
Degas (1834-1917). No. 2182, Painting of
young man, by V. Knezevic.

1992, Oct. 2
2181 A713 500d multicolored   1.90 1.25
2182 A713 500d multicolored   1.90 1.25

1992, Nov. 14   Perf. 13½
2183 A714 500d Tetrao urogallus 4.00 2.50
2184 A714 500d Pelecanus
                 onocrotalus   4.00 2.50

Serbian
Writers
Assoc.,
Cent. — A715

1992, Nov. 20   Perf. 14
2185 A715 100d multicolored   1.00 .70

Traditional Architecture — A716

Designs: No. 2186, Ancient hut, Zlatibor
region. No. 2187, Round house, Morava
region. No. 2188, House, on stone cliff,
Metohija region. No. 2189, Large estate
house, Vojvodina region.

1992, Dec. 12
2186 A716 500d multicolored   1.25 .75
2187 A716 500d multicolored   1.25 .75
2188 A716 500d multicolored   1.25 .75
2189 A716 500d multicolored   1.25 .75
     Nos. 2186-2189 (4)   5.00 3.00

Icons, Mosaics — A717

#2190, St. Petka, St. Petka Church, Bel-
grade. #2191, St. Vasilije-Ostronoski, St.
Vasilije-Ostronoski Church, Montenegro.
#2192, Mosaic of Simeon Nemanja with model
of Blessed Virgin Church, Studenica. #2193,
Mosaic of St. Lazar with model of Ravanica
Monastery.

1992, Dec. 15
2190 A717 500d multi   1.40 1.00
2191 A717 500d multi   1.40 1.00
2192 A717 500d multi, vert.   1.40 1.00
2193 A717 500d multi, vert.   1.40 1.00
     Nos. 2190-2193 (4)   5.60 4.00

Aviation in
Yugoslavia,
80th
Anniv. — A718

1992, Dec. 24
2194 A718 500d Bleriot XI   1.75 1.10

Diocletian's
Reformation of
the Roman
Empire, 1700th
Anniv. — A719

Design: Detail of Roman fresco.

1993, Jan. 28   Litho.   Perf. 13½
2195 A719 1500d multicolored   1.60 1.00

State
Museum,
Cetinje,
Cent. — A720

1993, Feb. 12   Perf. 14
2196 A720 2500d multicolored   1.60 1.00

Marine
Life — A721

Designs: a, Acipenser sturio. b, Scorpaena
scrofa. c, Xiphias gladius. d, Tursiops
truncatus.

1993, Mar. 20   Perf. 13½
2197 A721 10,000d Strip of 4,
                 #a.-d. +
                 label   10.00 10.00

Serbian
Money — A722

#2198, Ancient document, 10 para coins.
#2199, 5 dinar banknotes, 5 dinar coins.

1993, Mar. 30
2198 A722 10,000d multicolored 1.75 1.10
2199 A722 10,000d multicolored 1.75 1.10

Restablishment of Serbian monetary system, 125th anniv. (No. 2198). Restoring dinars
as Serbian currency, 120th anniv. (No. 2199).

Famous
People
A723

Designs: No. 2200, Milos Crnjanski (1893-
1977), writer, journalist. No. 2201, Nicola
Tesla (1856-1943), physicist. No. 2202,
Mihailo Petrovic (1868-1943), mathematician.
No. 2203, Aleksa Santic (1868-1924), poet.

1993, Apr. 1
2200 A723 40,000d multicolored 1.60 1.10
2201 A723 40,000d multicolored 1.60 1.10
2202 A723 40,000d multicolored 1.60 1.10
2203 A723 40,000d multicolored 1.60 1.10
     Nos. 2200-2203 (4)   6.40 4.40

Joy of
Europe — A724

Contemporary
Art — A725

Children's paintings: No. 2204, Girl holding
flowers, children, dove, by M. Markovski. No.
2205, Angels, birds, by J. Rugovac.

1993, Apr. 5
2204 A724 50,000d multicolored 1.75 1.10
2205 A724 50,000d multicolored 1.75 1.10

1993, May 5
Europa: No. 2206, Nude with a Mirror, by M.
Milunovic. No. 2207, Composition, by M.P.
Barili.

2206 A725 95,000d multicolored 3.00 2.50
2207 A725 95,000d multicolored 3.00 2.50

A726

A727

A728

A729

A730

Ancient Fortresses: No. 2208, Sutorina,
Montenegro. No. 2209, Kalemegdan, Belgrade. No. 2210, Medun, Montenegro. No.
2211, Petrovaradin, near Novi Sad. No. 2212,
Bar, Montenegro. No. 2213, Golubac.

1993, July 9
Booklet Stamps
2208 A726 900,000d multi 2.00 1.25
2209 A727 900,000d multi 2.00 1.25
2210 A728 900,000d multi 2.00 1.25
2211 A729 900,000d multi 2.00 1.25
2212 A730 900,000d multi 2.00 1.25
2213 A730 900,000d multi 2.00 1.25
　a. Booklet pane, #2208-2213 12.00
　　Complete booklet, #2213a 12.00

Flowers
A731

Colors of various flowers in vases: No.
2214, Yellow, white. No. 2215, Orange, red.
No. 2216, Purple, pink, white. No. 2217,
Mixed.

1993, July 10 **Perf. 14**
2214 A731 1,000,000d multi 1.75 1.10
2215 A731 1,000,000d multi 1.75 1.10
2216 A731 1,000,000d multi 1.75 1.10
2217 A731 1,000,000d multi 1.75 1.10
　Nos. 2214-2217 (4) 7.00 4.40

Electrification
of Serbia,
Cent.
A732

1993, July 28 **Perf. 13½**
2218 A732 2,500,000d multi 1.25 .80

Protection of
Nature
A733

Designs: No. 2219, Garrulus glandarius.
No. 2220, Oriolus oriolus.

1993, Sept. 30
2219 A733 300,000,000d multi 3.50 2.25
2220 A733 300,000,000d multi 3.50 2.25

Nos. 2147a, 2135, 2144, 2136 and
2140 Surcharged

No. 2143 Surcharged

1993 **Perfs., Etc. as Before**
2220A A702i 10d on 100,000d .35 .20
2220C A702a 50d on 5d .35 .20
2220D A702f 100d on 5000d .35 .20
2220E A702 500d on 50d .35 .20
2220F A702e 1000d on 3000d .35 .20
2220H A702b 10,000d on 300d 1.10 .40
2220I A702a 50,000d on 5d 5.25 2.00
　Nos. 2220A-2220I (7) 8.10 3.40

Issued: 50,000d, 11/9/93; others, 10/18/93.
Size and location of surcharge varies.

A734

Cooperation on the Danube
River — A735

Designs: No. 2221, Ships on river. No.
2222, Ship going down river. 20,000d, Map
showing location of Danube River.
Illustration reduced (A735).

1993, Oct. 20 **Perf. 14**
2221 A734 15,000d multicolored 2.00 1.40
2222 A734 15,000d multicolored 2.00 1.40

Souvenir Sheet
2223 A735 20,000d multicolored 5.00 3.50

Post Office in
Jagodina,
150th Anniv.
A736

1993, Oct. 30 **Perf. 13½**
2224 A736 12,000d multicolored 1.50 1.00

Stamp Day.

Joy of
Europe — A737

Icons in
Monasteries
A738

Paintings: No. 2225, Boy with Cat, by Sava
Sumanovic (1896-1942). No. 2226, Circus
Rider, by Georges Rouault (1871-1958).

1993, Nov. 26
2225 A737 2,000,000d multi 2.00 1.25
2226 A737 2,000,000d multi 2.00 1.25

1993, Dec. 15
Designs: No. 2227, The Annunciation,
Mileseva. No. 2228, Nativity, Studenica. No.
2229, Madonna and Child, Bogorodica
Ljeviska. No. 2230, Flight into Egypt, Oplenac.

2227 A738 400,000,000d multi 1.60 1.00
2228 A738 400,000,000d multi 1.60 1.00
2229 A738 400,000,000d multi 1.60 1.00
2230 A738 400,000,000d multi 1.60 1.00
　Nos. 2227-2230 (4) 6.40 4.00

Traditional
Houses — A739

Publication of
Oktoechos, 500th
Anniv. — A740

#2231, A-frame huts, Savardak, horiz.
#2232, Watchtower. #2233, Stone house on
edge of river. #2234, Crmnicka house, Bar,
horiz.

1993, Dec. 31
2231 A739 50d multicolored 1.60 1.00
2232 A739 50d multicolored 1.60 1.00
2233 A739 50d multicolored 1.60 1.00
2234 A739 50d multicolored 1.60 1.00
　Nos. 2231-2234 (4) 6.40 4.00

1994, Jan. 17 **Litho.** **Perf. 13½**
2235 A740 1000d Text .90 .60
2236 A740 1000d Liturgists .90 .60

Raptors
A741

Designs: a, Neophron percnopterus. b,
Falco cherrug. c, Buteo rufinus. d, Falco
naumanni.

1994, Feb. 7
2237 A741 80p Strip of 4, #a.-
　　　　d. + label 17.50 17.50

Intl. Mimosa
Festival, Herceg-
Novi
A742

1994, Feb. 28
2238 A742 80p multicolored 2.50 1.60

Natl.
Museum,
Belgrade,
150th Anniv.
A743

Design: No. 2240, National Theater, Belgrade, 125th anniv., portrait of Prince Milos
Obrenovic.

1994, Mar. 19
2239 A743 80p multicolored 2.50 1.60
2240 A743 80p multicolored 2.50 1.60

1994 Winter Olympics,
Lillehammer — A744

a, Speed skater. b. Olympic rings, flame. c,
Skier.

1994, Apr. 11
2241 A744 60p Strip of 3, #a.-c. 5.00 5.00

Europa
A745

Map of flight route and: 60p, Kodron C61, automobile. 1.80d, Kodron C61 in air over Belgrade.

1994, May 5

2242	A745	60p multicolored	1.75	1.10
2243	A745	1.80d multicolored	2.75	1.60

First night flight Paris-Belgrade-Bucharest-Istanbul, piloted by Louis Guidon, 1923.

Burning of Relics of Holy Sava, 400th Anniv. A746

1994, May 10 *Perf. 14*

2244	A746	60p multicolored	2.25	1.25

1994 World Cup Soccer Championships, U.S. — A747

60p, Three players with arms raised in victory. 1d, Three players down on ground.

1994, June 10 *Perf. 13½*

2245	A747	60p multicolored	2.50	1.60
2246	A747	1d multicolored	2.50	1.60

A748

A749

1994, July 8

2247	A748	60p Basset hound	2.00	1.25
2248	A748	60p Maltese	2.00	1.25
2249	A748	60p Welsh terrier	2.00	1.25
2250	A748	1d Husky	2.00	1.25
		Nos. 2247-2250 (4)	8.00	5.00

1994, July 20

2251	A749	60p multicolored	2.00	1.25

Assembly of Eastern Orthodox Christian nations.

Protecting the Ecology of Montenegro A750

1994, July 28

2252	A750	50p Tcherna Gora Park	2.25	1.40

Nos. 2148, 2145 Surcharged

1994, July 15 *Perf. 13½*

2253	A702j	10p on 100,000d	.75	.50
2254	A702g	50p on 10,000d	2.00	1.25

A751

A752

Monasteries: 1p, Moraca, 13th cent. 5p, Gracanica, 14th cent. 10p, Ostrog. No. 2258-2259, Lazarica, 14th cent. 50p, Studenica, 12th cent. 1d, Sopocani, 13th cent.

1994 *Litho.* *Perf. 13½*

2255	A751	1p bister & purple	.20	.20
2256	A751	5p yel brn & blue	.20	.20
2257	A751	10p magenta & slate	.20	.20
2258	A751	20p lil rose & pale vio	.40	.25
2259	A751	20p pale car & gray	.40	.25
2260	A751	50p deep pur & mag	1.00	.70
2261	A751	1d blue & org brown	2.10	1.40
		Nos. 2255-2261 (7)	4.50	3.20

UNESCO (#2260-2261).
Issued: 1p, 5p, #2258, 1d, 8/15; #2259, 9/10; 10p, 50p, 11/10.
Nos. 2262-2271 are unassigned.
For surcharge, see Serbia No. 195.

1994, Sept. 10

2272	A752	50p multicolored	2.00	1.25

St. Arsenius Seminary, Sremski Karlovci, bicent.

Protection of Nature A753

Designs: 1d, Fishing pier, Reka Bojana. 1.50d, Lake, Belgrade.

1994, Sept. 20

2273	A753	1d multicolored	3.25	2.10
2274	A753	1.50d multicolored	5.00	3.00

Painting by U. Knezevic — A754

Sailing Ships in Bottles — A755

1994, Oct. 5 *Perf. 14*

2275	A754	1d multicolored	3.00	1.75

Joy of Europe.

1994, Oct. 27 *Perf. 13½*

a, Revenge, 1585. b, Grand yacht, 1678. c, Santa Maria, 15th cent. d, Nava, 15th cent. e, Mayflower, 1615. f, Carrack, 14th cent.

2276	A755	50p Bklt. pane of 6, #a.-f.	10.00	10.00
		Complete booklet, #2276	10.00	

Stamp Day — A756

Drawings on Gravestones A757

1994, Oct. 31

2277	A756	50p multicolored	4.00	2.75

1994, Nov. 25

#2278, Man holding umbrella, purse. #2279, 2 men. #2280, Cemetery, stone with man on horse, inscriptions. #2281, Fence, 2 gravestones, cross, man.

2278	A757	50p multicolored	1.60	1.10
2279	A757	50p multicolored	1.60	1.10
2280	A757	50p multicolored	1.60	1.10
2281	A757	50p multicolored	1.60	1.10
		Nos. 2278-2281 (4)	6.40	4.40

Religious Art — A758

#2282, The Annunciation, by D. Bacevic. #2283, Adoration of the Magi, by N. Neskovic. #2284, Madonna and Child, by T.N. Cesljar. #2285, St. John Baptizing Christ, by T. Kracun.

1994, Dec. 15

2282	A758	60p multicolored	1.60	1.10
2283	A758	60p multicolored	1.60	1.10
2284	A758	60p multicolored	1.60	1.10
2285	A758	60p multicolored	1.60	1.10
		Nos. 2282-2285 (4)	6.40	4.40

Natl. Symbols A759

1995, Jan. 26 *Litho.* *Perf. 13½*

2286	A759	1d Flag	1.50	1.00
2287	A759	1d Arms	1.50	1.00

Sheets of 8

World Chess Champions A760

#2288: a, Wilhelm Steinitz (1836-1900), Austria. b, Silhouettes of chessman. c, Emmanuel Lasker (1868-1941), Germany. d, Knight. e, Chessman, row of pawns at top. f, José Raúl Capablanca (1888-1942), Cuba. g, Chessman, rook at left. h, Alexander Alekhine (1892-1946), Russia.
#2289: a, Max Euwe, Netherlands. b, Board, pawn in center. c, Mikhail M. Botvinik, Soviet Union. d, Board, queen in middle. e, Board, bishop, knight. f, Vassili Smyslov, Soviet Union. g, Silhouette of knight, rook queen, chessboard. h, Mikhail N. Tal, Soviet Union.

1995

2288	A760	60p #a.-h. + label	10.00	10.00
2289	A760	60p #a.-h. + label	10.00	10.00

Issued: No. 2288, 2/28; No. 2289, 9/1.

Red Star Army Sport Club, 50th Anniv. A761

1995, Mar. 4

2290	A761	60p bl, red & bister	1.75	1.10

Protection of Nature A762

a, Salamandra salamandra. b, Triturus alpestris. c, Rana graeca. d, Pelobates syriacus balcanicus.

1995, Mar. 23

2291	A762	60p Strip of 4, #a.-d. + label	7.00	6.00

A763

A764

1995, Apr. 20

2292	A763	60p multicolored	2.00	1.10

Radnicki Soccer Club, Belgrade, 75th anniv.

1995, May 6

Europa: 60p, Eagle, mountains. 1.90d, Girl on tricycle, elderly man, woman on park bench, horiz.

2293	A764	60p multicolored	4.00	2.50
2294	A764	1.90d multicolored	4.00	2.50

A765

A766

1995, May 9
2295 A765 60p multicolored 2.00 1.25
End of World War II, 50th anniv.

1995, May 28
2296 A766 60p multicolored 2.25 1.40
Opening of Vukov-Denkmal Subway Station, Belgrade.

Draba Bertiscea A767

a, shown. b, Plants, diff. c, Flowers, mountain. d, Plants on rock, stems at right.

1995, June 12
2297 A767 60p Strip of 4, #a.-d.
+ label 8.00 8.00

European Nature Protection A768

Designs: 60p, Eremophila alpestris balcanica. 1.90d, Rhinolophus blasii.

1995, July 10
2298 A768 60p multicolored 1.10 .65
2299 A768 1.90d multicolored 3.50 2.10

Slovakian Folk Festival, by Zuzka Medvedova (1897-1985), Painter — A769

1995, Aug. 3
2300 A769 60p multicolored 1.50 1.00

Volleyball, Cent. — A770

Church of St. Luke, Kotor, 800th Anniv. — A771

1995, Sept. 10
2301 A770 90d multicolored 1.50 1.00

1995, Sept. 20
2302 A771 80p multicolored 1.50 1.00

Motion Pictures, Cent. A772

Designs: 1.10d, Newsreel showing coronation of King Peter II. 2.20d, Auguste and Louis Jean Lumière, film projector.

1995, Oct. 3
2303 A772 1.10d dk brn, lt red
brn 1.25 .80
2304 A772 2.20d dk brn, lt red
brn 2.25 1.50

Army Sports Club "Partisan," 50th Anniv. — A773

1995, Oct. 4
2305 A773 80p multi + label 1.50 1.00

UN, 50th Anniv. — A774

Stamp Day — A775

1995, Oct. 24
2306 A774 1.10d multicolored 1.50 1.00

1995, Oct. 31
2307 A775 1.10d multicolored 1.50 1.00

Joy of Europe — A776

Paintings: 1.10d, Young boy by Milos Tenkovic. 2.20d, Young girl by Pierre Bonnard.

1995, Nov. 26
2308 A776 1.10d multicolored 1.25 .80
2309 A776 2.20d multicolored 2.25 1.50
Children's Day.

Souvenir Sheet

JUFIZ VIII, Natl. Philatelic Exhibition, Budva — A777

Design: Montenegro #37, Serbia #6.

1995, Dec. 13 **Perf. 14**
2310 A777 2.50d Sheet of 1 + label 2.00 1.25

Christmas A778

Contemporary religious paintings: No. 2311, Flight into Egypt, by Z. Halupova. No. 2312, Nativity, by D. Milojevic, vert. No. 2313, Outdoor Christmas scene, by M. Rasic, vert. No. 2314, Indoor traditional Christmas scene, by J. Brasic.

1995, Dec. 26 **Perf. 13½**
2311 A778 1.10d multicolored .60 .40
2312 A778 1.10d multicolored .60 .40
2313 A778 2.20d multicolored 1.10 .75
2314 A778 2.20d multicolored 1.10 .75
Nos. 2311-2314 (4) 3.40 2.30

Airplanes A779

1995, Dec. 26
2315 A779 1.10d Saric No. 1 .60 .40
2316 A779 1.10d Douglas DC-3 .60 .40
2317 A779 2.20d Fizir FN 1.10 .75
2318 A779 2.20d Caravelle 1.10 .75
Nos. 2315-2318 (4) 3.40 2.30

Battle of Mojkovac, 80th Anniv. — A780

Design: Montenegrins on mountain.

1996, Jan. 6
2319 A780 1.10d multicolored .55 .35

Birth of Sava Sumanovic, Cent. A781

Design: 1927 Painting, "Drink Boat."

1996, Jan. 22
2320 A781 1.10d multicolored .60 .40

A782 A783

Insects: a, Pyrgomorphela serbica. b, Calosoma sycopanta. c, Formica rufa. d, Ascalaphus macaronius.

1996, Feb. 15
2321 A782 2.20d Strip of 4, #a.-
d. + label 4.75 4.75
Protection of nature.

1996, Feb. 29 **Litho.** **Perf. 12½**
Churches.
2322 A783 5d Ljeviska 2.00 1.25
2323 A783 10d Zica 4.00 2.50
2324 A783 20d Decani 8.00 5.00
Nos. 2322-2324 (3) 14.00 8.75

Chess Champions — A784

Designs: a, Tigran Petrosian, Soviet Union. b, Chess pieces, sundial, chess board. c, Boris Spassky, Soviet Union. d, Chess pieces, board, clock showing two time zones. e, Garry Kasparov, Soviet Union. f, Chess pieces, hand holding hour glass. g, Bobby Fischer, US. h, Chess pieces, six clocks. i, Anatoly Karpov, Soviet Union.

1996, Mar. 15 **Litho.** **Perf. 13½**
2325 A784 1.50d Sheet of 9, #a.-
i. 6.25 6.00

Olympic Games, Cent. A786

1.50d, Discus throwers. 2.50d, Runners.

Perf. 13½x13¼
1996, Mar. 30 **Litho.**
2326 A786 1.50d multi .75 .75
2327 A786 2.50d multi 1.25 1.25

1996 Summer Olympics, Atlanta — A787

1996, Apr. 12
2328 A787 1.50d shown 1.25 .95
2329 A787 1.50d Basketball 1.25 .95
2330 A787 1.50d Handball 1.25 .95
2331 A787 1.50d Volleyball 1.25 .95
2332 A787 1.50d Shooting 1.25 .95
2333 A787 1.50d Water polo 1.25 .95
Nos. 2328-2333 (6) 7.50 5.70

1996 Summer Olympic Games, Atlanta — A787a

1996, Apr. 12   Litho.   Perf. 13
2334 A787 5d Sheet of 1 + label   2.00 1.50

Stamp Day — A788

1996, Apr. 30   Litho.   Perf. 13½
2335 A788 1.50d Railway mail car   .80 .60

Famous Women Writers — A789

Europa: 2.50d, Isidora Sekulic (1877-1958). 5d, Desanka Maksimovic (1898-1993).

1996, May 7   Litho.   Perf. 13½
2336 A789 2.50d multicolored   2.00 1.25
2337 A789 5d multicolored   4.50 3.00

Serbian Red Cross, 120th Anniv. A790

1996, May 8
2338 A790 1.50d Dr. Vladan Djordjevic   .75 .60

Architectural Education in Yugoslavia, 150th Anniv. — A791

1996, June 1   Litho.   Perf. 13½
2339 A791 1.50d multicolored   .65 .50

Birds A792

1996, June 28
2340 A792 2.50d Platalea leucorodia   1.00 .70
2341 A792 5d Plegadis falcinellus   2.00 1.50

Prince Peter I Petrovic at Battle of Martinici, 1796 — A793

Design: 2.50d, Prince's Guard at Battle of Kruse (1796), by Valerio, vert.

1996, July 22
2342 A793 1.50d multicolored   .65 .50
2343 A793 2.50d multicolored   1.00 .75

Horse Racing, Ljubicevo A794

1996, Sept. 2   Litho.   Perf. 13½
2344 A794 1.50d shown   .70 .55
2345 A794 2.50d 3 horses racing   1.25 1.00

Fauna A795

Designs: a, 1.50d, Probosciger aterrimus. b, 2.50d, Goura scheepmakeri. c, 1.50d, Equus burchelli. d, 2.50d, Panthera tigris.

1996, Sept. 25
2346 A795 Strip of 4, #a.-d. + label   3.75 3.50

Belgrade Zoo, 60th anniv.

Children's Day — A796

1996, Oct. 2
2347 A796 1.50d multicolored   .70 .55
2348 A796 2.50d Bird   1.25 1.00

Medalists, 1996 Summer Olympic Games A797

Designs: No. 2349, Shooting, bronze. No. 2350, Shooting, gold. No. 2351, Volleyball, bronze. No. 2352, Basketball, silver.

1996, Oct. 31   Litho.   Perf. 13½
2349 A797 2.50d multicolored   1.10 1.00
2350 A797 2.50d multicolored   1.10 1.00
2351 A797 2.50d multicolored   1.10 1.00
2352 A797 2.50d multicolored   1.10 1.00
    Nos. 2349-2352 (4)   4.40 4.00

Savings Accounts, 75th Anniv. — A798

1996, Oct. 31   Litho.   Perf. 13½
2353 A798 1.50d multicolored   .65 .55

Soccer in Yugoslavia, Cent. — A799

Archaeological Finds — A800

1996, Nov. 8   Litho.   Perf. 13½
2354 A799 1.50d multicolored   .70 .60

1996, Nov. 25
Sculptures: No. 2355, God of Autumn. No. 2356, Mother with child. No. 2357, Head of woman. No. 2358, Redheaded goddess.

2355 A800 1.50d multicolored   .60 .50
2356 A800 1.50d multicolored   .60 .50
2357 A800 2.50d multicolored   1.00 .75
2358 A800 2.50d multicolored   1.00 .75
    Nos. 2355-2358 (4)   3.20 2.50

A801

A802

Christmas (Paintings): No. 2359, Annunciation. No. 2360, Mother of God with Christ. No. 2361, Birth of Christ. No. 2362, Palm Sunday.

1996, Dec. 10
2359 A801 1.50d multicolored   .60 .50
2360 A801 1.50d multicolored   .60 .50
2361 A801 2.50d multicolored   1.00 .75
2362 A801 2.50d multicolored   1.00 .75
    Nos. 2359-2362 (4)   3.20 2.50

1997, Jan. 24   Litho.   Perf. 13½
2363 A802 1.50d multicolored   .35 .25
Radomir Putnik Voivode, 150th birth anniv.

25th Intl. Film Festival, Belgrade A803

1997, Jan. 31
2364 A803 1.50d multicolored   1.00 .70

Protected Birds — A804

Designs: No. 2365, Dendrocopos major. No. 2366, Nucifraga caryocatactes. No. 2367, Parus cristatus. No. 2368, Erithacus rubecula.

1997, Feb. 21
2365 A804 1.50d multicolored   .50 .50
2366 A804 2.50d multicolored   .50 .50
2367 A804 2.50d multicolored   .70 .70
2368 A804 2.50d multicolored   .70 .70
    a.   Strip of 4, #2365-2368 + label   5.00 5.00

A805

A806

1997, Mar. 17   Litho.   Perf. 13
2369 A805 1.50d multicolored   .75 .65
St. Achilleus Church, 700th Anniv.

1997, Apr. 3   Perf. 13½
Design: Prince Peter I Petrovic (1747-1830), Bishop of Montenegro.
2370 A806 1.50d multicolored   .75 .65

A807

A808

1997, Apr. 19
2371 A807 2.50d multicolored   1.00 .80
10th Belgrade Marathon.

1997, Apr. 22   Litho.   Perf. 13½
2372 A808 2.50d multicolored   1.00 .80
Serbian Medical Assoc., 125th anniv.

Air Mail Being Loaded at Night A809

1997, May 3
2373 A809 2.50d multicolored   1.00 .80
Stamp Day.

Tennis Tournaments in
Yugoslavia — A810

Stylized designs: No. 2374, Player, large
racket overhead, Budva. No. 2375, Player with
ball flying from racket, Belgrade. No. 2376,
Player with racket out in front, Novi Sad.

1997, May 8
2374	A810	2.50d multi + label	1.00	.80
2375	A810	2.50d multi + label	1.00	.80
2376	A810	2.50d multi + label	1.00	.80
	Nos. 2374-2376 (3)		3.00	2.40

Stories and
Legends
A811

Europa: 2.50d, Shackled Bach Chelik surrounded by creatures. 6d, Bach Chelik in
chains, prince fighting with him, princess,
castle.

1997, May 30　　　　　　*Perf. 11½*
2377	A811	2.50d multicolored	1.00	.80
2378	A811	6d multicolored	3.00	2.25

Each issued in sheets of 8 + label.

Nature
Protection
A812

1997, June 5
2379	A812	2.50d Cerambyx cerdo	1.00	.80
2380	A812	6d Quercus robur	2.25	1.75

Stanislav Binicki
(1872-1947)
A813

1997, June 7　　　　　　*Perf. 13½*
2381	A813	2.50d multicolored	1.00	.80

Printing of Gorski
Vijenac, 150th
Anniv. — A814

1997, June 7
2382	A814	2.50d multicolored	1.00	.80

Flowers — A815

Designs: a, 1.50d, Pelargonium
grandiflorum. b, 2.50d, Saintpaulia ionantha.

---

c, 1.50d, Hydrangea macrophylla. d, 2.50d,
Oncidium varicosum.

1997, Sept. 10　　*Litho.*　　*Perf. 13*
2383	A815	Strip of 4, #a.-d. + label	4.25	4.25

Souvenir Sheet

JUFIZ IX, 9th Natl. Philatelic
Exhibition — A816

Design: Sculpture, by Dragomir Arambasic,
in front of art gallery. Illustration reduced.

1997, Sept. 10　　　　　　*Perf. 14*
2384	A816	5d multicolored	2.50	2.50

A817

1997, Sept. 24　　　*Perf. 13½x14*
2385	A817	2.50d multicolored	1.00	.80

Serbian Chemical Society, cent.

A818

Type of 1993
1997, Oct. 2　　　　　　*Perf. 14*
Size: 18x18mm
2386	A702d (A) like #2142		.80	.20

Exists dated "1999."

1997, Oct. 2

Joy of Europe children's art works: 2.50d,
5d, Busts of people formed from collage of
various food products.

2387	A818	2.50d multicolored	1.00	.80
2388	A818	5d multicolored	2.00	1.60

"May Assembly in Sremski Karlivoci,"
by Pavle Simic — A819

1997, Oct. 10　　*Litho.*　　*Perf. 14*
2389	A819	2.50d multicolored	1.00	.80

Matica Srpska Gallery, 150th anniv.

A820

Museum exhibits: No. 2390, Two-headed
statuette. No. 2391, Parade helmet. No. 2392,
Terra cotta statuette. No. 2393, Virgin icon.

A821

1997, Nov. 12
2390	A820	1.50d multicolored	.60	.45
2391	A820	1.50d multicolored	.60	.45
2392	A820	2.50d multicolored	1.00	.70
2393	A820	2.50d multicolored	1.00	.70
	Nos. 2390-2393 (4)		3.20	2.30

1997, Dec. 2　　　　　*Perf. 11½*

Icons (Chelandari Serbian Monastery,
Mount Athos): No. 2394, Christ. No. 2395,
Madonna and Child, 12th cent. No. 2396,
Madonna and Child, 13th cent. No. 2397, 3-
handed Madonna.

Granite Paper
2394	A821	1.50d multicolored	.60	.45
2395	A821	1.50d multicolored	.60	.45
2396	A821	2.50d multicolored	1.00	.70
2397	A821	2.50d multicolored	1.00	.70
	Nos. 2394-2397 (4)		3.20	2.30

A822

A823

1998, Jan. 20　　*Litho.*　　*Perf. 13½*
2398	A822	1.50d Savina	.55	.45
2399	A822	2.50d Donji Brceli	.95	.75

Monasteries of Montenegro.

1998, Feb. 6　　　　　　*Perf. 14*
2400	A823	2.50d Figure skater	.95	.75
2401	A823	6d Skier	2.25	1.75

1998 Winter Olympic Games, Nagano.

Horses
A824

Designs: a, 1.50d, Two running. b, 2.50d,
Arabian up close. c, 1.50d, Thoroughbred. d,
2.50d, Thoroughbred running on race track.

1998, Feb. 26　　*Litho.*　*Perf. 12x11½*
2402	A824	Strip of 4, #a.-d. + label	7.00	7.00

Intl.
Women's
Day
A825

1998, Mar. 7　　　　　　*Perf. 13½*
2403	A825	2.50d multicolored	.95	.75

Yugoslav
Airlines
Assoc., 50th
Anniv.
A826

1998, Apr. 24
2404	A826	2.50d multicolored	.95	.75

Europa — A827

Paintings: 6d, "Dressing the Bride," by Paja
Jovanovic (1859-1957). 9d, "Bishop's Congratulations," by Pero Pocek (1878-1963).

1998, May 4　　*Litho.*　　*Perf. 12*
Granite Paper
2405	A827	6d multicolored	2.50	2.25
2406	A827	9d on 2.50d, multi	2.50	2.25

No. 2406 was not issued without the silver
surcharge.

1998 World Cup
Soccer
Championships,
France — A828

1998, May 15　　*Litho.*　　*Perf. 13½*
2407	A828	6d shown	1.75	1.75
2408	A828	9d Soccer players, diff.	2.75	2.75

Souvenir Sheet

Danube Commission, 50th
Anniv. — A829

Illustration reduced.

1998, May 19　　　　　　*Perf. 14*
2409	A829	9d multicolored	3.75	3.75

Nature
Protection
A830

Designs: 6d, Heracium blecicii. 9d, Mola mola, vert.

1998, June 17   Litho.   Perf. 13¾
2410 A830 6d multi   1.50 1.50
2411 A830 9d multi   1.50 1.50

Each stamp was printed in sheets of 8 + label.

Famous People of Serbia — A831

a, Djura Jaksic (1832-78), poet, painter. b, Nadezda Petrovic (1873-1915), painter. c, Radoje Domanovic (1873-1908), writer. d, Vasilije Mokranjac (1923-1984), composer. e, Streten Stojanovic (1898-1960), sculptor. f, Milan Konjovic (1898-1993), painter. g, Desanka Maksimovic (1898-1993), poet. h, Ivan Tabakovic (1898-1977), painter.

1998, June 30   Litho.   Perf. 12
Granite Paper
Sheet of 8
2412 A831 1.50d #a.-h. + label   3.00 3.00

Souvenir Sheet

Yugoslavia, Winner of World Basketball Championships — A832

1998, Aug. 21   Perf. 13½
2413 A832 10d multicolored   6.00 6.00

Protected Animals — A833

a, 2d, Martes martes. b, 2d, Anthropoides virgo. c, 5d, Lynx lynx. d, 5d, Loxia curvirostra.

1998, Sept. 2
2414 A833 Strip of 4, #a.-d. + label   5.00 5.00

Breaking of the Thessaloniki Front, 80th Anniv. A834

Designs: No. 2415, 5d, Soldiers and cannons. No. 2416, 5d, Soldiers with machine guns, binoculars.

1998, Sept. 15   Engr.   Perf. 13½
2415-2416 A834 Set of 2   2.50 2.50

Stamp Day — A835

1998, Sept. 28
2417 A835 6d Prussian blue   1.25 1.25

Serbian Philatelic Society, 50th anniv.

Joy of Europe Children's Drawings A836

Designs: 6d, Fish. 9d, Fish, diff.

1998, Oct. 2   Litho.   Perf. 13¾
2418-2419 A836   Set of 2   3.25 3.25

Development of the Railway — A837

Trains: a, 1847. b, 1900. c, 1920. d, 1930. e, Diesel locomotive. f, 1990.

1998, Nov. 3   Litho.   Perf. 13½
2420 A837 2.50d Booklet pane of 6, #a.-f.   4.50 4.50
Complete booklet, #2420   5.00

Paintings of Sailing Ships, Maritime Museum, Kotor A838

#2421, Veracruz, 1873. #2422, Pierino, 1883. #2423, Draghetto, 1865. #2424, Group of ships.

1998, Nov. 11   Perf. 12
Granite Paper
2421 A838 2d multicolored   .40   .30
2422 A838 2d multicolored   .40   .30
2423 A838 5d multicolored   1.25   .90
2424 A838 5d multicolored   1.25   .90
          Nos. 2421-2424 (4)   3.30 2.40

Chelandari Monastery, 800th Anniv. — A839

Views of monastery: No. 2425, Looking from center of complex, two trees. No. 2426, Group of taller buildings. No. 2427, Aerial view. No. 2428, Looking across group of buildings, crosses on turrets.

1998, Dec. 9   Perf. 14
2425 A839 2d multicolored   .40   .30
2426 A839 2d multicolored   .40   .30
2427 A839 5d multicolored   1.00   .80
2428 A839 5d multicolored   1.00   .80
          Nos. 2425-2428 (4)   2.80 2.20

Third Meeting of Southeast European Postal Ministers A840

1998, Dec. 17   Litho.   Perf. 14
2429 A840 5d multicolored   2.00 1.50

Souvenir Sheet

Yugoslavia, Silver Medalists at 1998 World Volleyball Championships — A841

Illustration reduced.

1998, Dec. 19   Perf. 13½
2430 A841 10d multicolored   40.00 40.00

Post and Telecommunications Museum, Belgrade, 75th Anniv. — A842

#2431, Postrider. #No. 2432, Antique telegraph equipment, museum building.

1998, Dec. 21   Engr.
2431 A842 5d olive brown & slate 1.00   .80
2432 A842 5d red & brown   1.00   .80

Serbian Monasteries A843

1999, Jan. 14   Litho.   Perf. 13¾
2433 A843 2d Visoki Decani   .40   .30
2434 A843 5d Grachanica   1.00   .80

Farm Animals A844

Designs: a, 2d, Pigs. b, 6d, Goat. c, 2d, Oxen. d, 6d, Long-horn sheep.

1999, Feb. 5   Litho.   Perf. 13½
2435 A844 Strip of 4, #a.-d. + label   4.25 4.25

A845

A846

1999, Feb. 24   Litho.   Perf. 13¼
2436 A845 6d Scouting   1.60 1.40

1999, Mar.
2437 A846 6d brown & buff   1.40 1.25

Yugoslav Bar Association, 70th anniv.

Target
A847   A848

1999   Perf. 12¼x12½
2438 A847 (A) black   .50   .30
2439 A848 (A) black & red   .50   .30

Nos. 2438-2439 sold for 2.04d when issued.

World Table Tennis Championships, Belgrade — A849

1999, Apr.   Perf. 13¼
Player colors
2440 A849 6d blue & red   1.75 1.50
2441 A849 6d green & red   1.75 1.50

A850

A851

Europa, National Parks and Reserves: 6d, Falcon, trees, mountains, Kopaonik Natl. Park. 15d, Flowers, mountains, Lovcen Natl. Park.

1999, May 5　　Photo.　　Perf. 11¾
Granite Paper
2442　A850　6d multicolored　　3.00　2.00
2443　A850　15d multicolored　　5.00　3.50
Each printed in shhets of 8 + 1 central label.

1999, May　　　　　Perf. 11¾x12
Nature protection.
2444　A851　6d Shovel, spider
　　　　web　　　　　2.00　1.75
2445　A851　15d Thumb squeezing
　　　　earth　　　　2.75　2.00

Mushrooms
A852

Designs: a, Amanita virosa. b, Amanita pantherina. c, Hypholoma fasciculare. d, Ramaria pallida.

1999, June 18　Litho.　Perf. 11¾x12
Granite Paper
2446　A852　6d Strip of 4, #a.-d., +
　　　　central label　　8.00　8.00
Central labels differ on sheet.

Famous Montenegrins — A853

Designs: a, Stjepan Mitrov Ljubisa (1824-78). b, Marko Milanov (1833-1901). c, Pero Pocek (1878-1963). d, Risto Stijovic (1894-1974). e, Milo Milunovic (1897-1967). f, Petar Lubarda (1907-74). g, Vuko Radovic (1911-96). h, Mihailo Lalic (1914-92).

1999, June 30　　　　Perf. 13¼
2447　A853　2d Sheet of 8, #a.-h.,
　　　　+ central label　2.75　2.50

UPU, 125th
Anniv.
A854

1999, Sept. 15　　　Perf. 13¼
2448　A854　6d shown　　1.00　.80
2449　A854　12d Envelopes cir-
　　　　cling globe　　2.00　1.60

Joy of Europe
Children's
Drawings
A855

1999, Oct. 1　　　　Perf. 13¾
2450　A855　6d Lion　　1.10　.90
2451　A855　15d Family, vert.　2.75　2.00

Frédéric Chopin
(1810-49),
Composer
A856

1999, Oct. 15　　　　Perf. 13¼
2452　A856　10d multi　　2.25　2.00

No. 2438,
Mastheads of
"Filatelista"
A857

1999, Oct. 18
2453　A857　10d multi　　1.75　1.40
Stamp Day.

A858

Bridges
Destroyed by
NATO Air
Strikes
A859

Bridges: #2454, Varadinski. #2455, Ostruznica. #2456, Murino. #2457, Grdelica. #2458, Bistrica. #2459, Zezeljev.

1999, Oct. 29　　　　Perf. 13¾
2454　A858　2d shown　　.30　.25
2455　A859　2d shown　　.30　.25
2456　A859　2d multi　　.30　.25
2457　A859　6d multi　　1.00　.75
2458　A859　6d multi　　1.00　.75
2459　A859　6d multi　　1.00　.75
　　Nos. 2454-2459 (6)　3.90　3.00

Millennium
A860

a, 6d, Roman altars, statue of Jupiter. b, 6d, Sculpture of Emperor Trajan and army leaders, mosaic, lamp, lead mirror. c, 6d, Mosaic of Dionysius, arch. d, 6d, Hagia Sophia, mosaic of Madonna and Child, Emperor Constantine. e, 6d, Large cross, candle, fibula, pot. f, 6d, Church, boats, manuscript. g, 15d, Nativity and crucifixion of Christ, boats, farmers.

1999, Nov. 19
2460　A860　Booklet pane of 7,
　　　　#a.-g., + 2 labels　9.00　8.00
　　Complete booklet, #2460　9.00
　　Size of #2460g: 105x55mm.

A861

Bomb Damage
A862

#2461, Bolnice. #2462, Telecommunications complex. #2463, Refinery. #2464, Bolnice, diff. #2465, Telecommunications complex, diff. #2466, Television complex.

1999, Nov. 27　　Litho.　Perf. 13¾
2461　A861　2d shown　　.30　.25
2462　A862　2d shown　　.30　.25
2463　A862　2d multi　　.30　.25
2464　A862　6d multi　　1.00　.75
2465　A862　6d multi　　1.00　.75
2466　A862　6d multi　　1.00　.75
　　Nos. 2461-2466 (6)　3.90　3.00

A863

Frescoes of Poganovo Monastery,
500th Anniv. — A864

Design A863 has Latin letters, A864 has Cyrillic letters.

1999, Dec. 23
2467　A863　6d shown　　　.75　.75
2468　A864　6d shown　　　.75　.75
2469　A863　6d Fresco, diff.　.75　.75
2470　A864　6d Fresco, diff.　.75　.75
　　Nos. 2467-2470 (4)　3.00　3.00

A865

Gold
Prospectors in
Pec
River — A866

Design A865 has Latin letters, A866 has Cyrillic letters.

1999, Dec. 30
2471　A865　6d shown　　　.75　.75
2472　A866　6d shown　　　.75　.75
2473　A865　6d Prospectors, diff.　.75　.75
2474　A866　6d Prospectors, diff.　.75　.75
　　Nos. 2471-2474 (4)　3.00　3.00

Krusedol
Monastery
A867

2000, Jan. 13　　　　Perf. 13¼
2475　A867　10d shown　　1.75　1.40
2476　A867　10d Rakovac Monas-
　　　　tery　　　　1.75　1.40

Yugoslavian
Archives,
50th Anniv.
A868

2000, Jan. 21
2477　A868　10d multi　　22.50　22.50

Butterflies — A869

No. 2478: a, Nymphalis antiopa. b, Parnalius polyxena. c, Limenitis populi. d, Melanargia galathea.

2000, Feb. 25　　Litho.　Perf. 13¾
2478　　Horiz. strip of 4 + cen-
　　　　tral label　　10.00　10.00
　　a.-d.　A869　10d Any single　2.25　2.25

Worldwide
Fund for
Nature
A870

Perdix perdix: a, Pair in snow. b, Pair facing right. c, Bird on nest. d, Pair, one facing left.

2000, Mar. 14　Litho.　Perf. 12x11¾
2479　A870　10d Strip of 4, #a.-
　　　　d., + central
　　　　label　　10.00　10.00

Damage
from NATO
Airstrikes
A871

Various destroyed buildings. Colors: 10d, Blue. 20d, Brown.

2000, Mar. 24　Engr.　Perf. 13¼
2480-2481　A871　Set of 2　5.00　4.00

Souvenir Sheet

JUFIZ X Philatelic Exhibition,
Belgrade — A872

Illustration reduced.

2000, May 2　　　　　Litho.
2482　A872　15d multi　　47.50　47.50

Nature Protection A873

Designs: No. 2483, 30d, Feeding chicks by hand. No. 2484, 30d, Map of Europe in tree's leaves, vert.

Perf. 12x11¾, 11¾x12

2000, May 4   Litho.
2483-2484 A873   Set of 2   6.00 5.00

Europa — A874

"2000" and: No. 2485, 30d, Astronaut on moon. No. 2486, 30d, Star and mountains.

2000, May 9   **Perf. 11¾x12**
2485-2486 A874   Set of 2   9.00 7.50

European Soccer Championships A875

Inscriptions in: No. 2487, 30d, Cyrillic letters. No. 2488, 30d, Latin letters.

2000, May 20   Litho.   **Perf. 13¾**
2487-2488 A875   Set of 2   9.00 7.50

Postal Services in Serbia, 160th Anniv. — A876

2000, June 7   Litho.   **Perf. 13¾**
2489 A876 10d multi   1.60 1.25

2000 Summer Olympics, Sydney — A877

Map of Australia and: 6d, Kangaroo. 12d, Emu. 24d, Koala and soccer ball. 30d, Parrot.

2000, June 28
2490-2493 A877   Set of 4   7.00 5.25

Stamp Day — A878

2000, Sept. 26   **Perf. 13¼**
2494 A878 10d multi   3.50 2.75

"Joy of Europe" A879

Children's art: 30d, Cows. 40d, Cranes, vert.

2000, Oct. 2
2495-2496 A879   Set of 2   8.00 6.00

World Teachers' Day — A880

2000, Oct. 5
2497 A880 10d multi   10.00 9.00

13th Apiarists Congress A881

2000, Oct. 6
2498 A881 10d multi   3.00 2.25

Medals Won at 2000 Summer Olympics A882

Designs: No. 2499, 20d, Water polo (bronze). No. 2500, 20d, Shooting (silver). 30d, Volleyball, vert.

2000, Oct. 23   **Perf. 13¾**
2499-2500 A882   Set of 2   3.50 2.50
Souvenir Sheet
2501 A882 30d multi   15.00 15.00

No. 2501 contains one 35x46mm stamp.

Millennium A883

No. 2502: a, Ships. b, Papermaking. c, Galileo and telescopes. d, Steam locomotive and steamship. e, Nikola Tesla, invention of the telephone. f, Astronaut, outer space settlement. g, Ships, airplanes, balloons, horses.

2000, Nov. 2   Litho.   **Perf. 13¾**
2502   Booklet pane of 7 + 2
     labels   6.00   —
  a.-f.   A883 12d Any single   .60 .60
  g.   A883 40d multi   2.00 2.00
       Booklet, #2502   6.00

Size of No. 2502g: 105x55mm.

Nativity Fresco, Pec — A884

2000, Nov. 7   Litho.   **Perf. 13¾**
2503 A884 A multi   2.50 .40

No. 2503 sold for 3.56d on day of issue.

Serb Clothing From the 1900s — A885

Designs: 6d, Vest, Jagodina. 12d, Dresses, Metochija. 24d, Blouse, Pec. 30d, Vest, Kupres.

2000, Dec. 7
2504-2507 A885   Set of 4   6.00 4.50

Montenegrin Religious Art — A886

Designs: 6d, Madonna and Child, 1573-74. 12d, Nativity, 1666-67. 24d, St. Luke, 1672-73. 30d, Madonna and Child, 1642.

2000, Dec. 19
2508-2511 A886   Set of 4   6.00 4.50

A887

A887a

2000, Dec. 29   Litho.   **Perf. 13¾**
2512 A887   6d multi   .50 .35
2513 A887a 12d multi   .50 .35

Resumption of Yugoslavia's membership in Organization for Security and Cooperation in Europe (#2512), and United Nations (#2513).

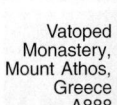

Vatoped Monastery, Mount Athos, Greece A888

Esfigmen Monastery, Mount Athos, Greece A889

2001, Jan. 26   Litho.   **Perf. 13¼**
2514 A888 10d multi   .50 .50
2515 A889 27d multi   1.50 1.50

Matica Srpska, 175th Anniv. — A890

2001, Feb. 16   **Perf. 13¾**
2516 A890 15d multi   .60 .60

Animals — A891

No. 2517: a, Felis leo. b, Ursus maritimus. c, Macaca fuscata. d, Spheniscus humboldti.

2001, Feb. 23
2517   Horiz. strip of 4 + central label   6.00 6.00
  a.   A891 6d multi   .50 .50
  b.   A891 12d multi   .90 .90
  c.   A891 24d multi   2.00 2.00
  d.   A891 30d multi   2.50 2.50

Women's World Chess Champions — A892

No. 2518: a, Vera Menchik (1927-44). b, Lyudmila Rudenko (1950-53). c, Yelisavyeta Bykova (1953-56, 1958-62). d, Olga Rubtsova (1956-58). e, Nona Gaprindashvili (1962-78). f, Maia Chiburdanidze (1978-91). g, Zsuzsa Polgar (1996-99). h, Xie Jun (1991-96, 1999-2000).

2001, Mar. 8   **Perf. 13¼**
2518 A892 10d Sheet of 8, #a-h, + label   3.00 3.00

Famous Men — A893

Designs: 50d, Stevan Mokranjac (1856-1914), composer. 100d, Nikola Tesla (1856-1943), inventor.

2001, Mar. 19   **Perf. 13¾**
2519-2520 A893   Set of 2   6.50 6.50

Flowers A894

No. 2521: a, Hibiscus syriacus. b, Nerium oleander. c, Lapageria rosea. d, Sorbus aucuparia.

2001, Apr. 13   **Perf. 12x11¾**
2521   Horiz. strip of 4 + cen-
       tral label   4.50 4.50
    a.   A894 6d multi   .40   .40
    b.   A894 12d multi   .85   .85
    c.   A894 24d multi   1.50 1.50
    d.   A894 30d multi   1.25 1.25

Europa — A895

Designs: 30d, Vratna River. 45d, Jerme Canyon.

2001, May 4   **Perf. 11¾x12**
2522-2523 A895   Set of 2   4.00 4.00

Serbian Mountaineering Association, Cent. — A896

2001, June 8   **Perf. 13¼**
2524 A896 15d multi   .70 .70

Nature Protection A897

Designs: 30d, Bird on branch, Lake Ludasko. 45d, Stork flying above Begej River.

2001, June 22   **Perf. 12x11¾**
2525-2526 A897   Set of 2   2.75 2.75

14th Cent. Book Illumination A898

2001, July 2   **Perf. 13¼**
2527 A898 E multi   1.50 1.50
    Sold for 28.70d on day of issue.

Souvenir Sheet

Yugoslavian Victory in European Water Polo Championships — A899

2001, July 5   **Perf. 13¾**
2528 A899 30d multi   4.25 4.25

Souvenir Sheet

Serbiafila XII Stamp Exhibition — A900

2001, Sept. 8
2529 A900 30d multi   1.60 1.60

Solar Energy — A901

2001, Sept. 19   **Perf. 13¼**
2530 A901 15d multi   1.25 1.25

Danube Commission A902

Designs: 30d, Ships, hands raising bridge. 45d, Ship, hand, clock.

2001, Sept. 20   **Perf. 13¾**
2531-2532 A902   Set of 2   3.00 3.00

Joy of Europe — A903

Paintings: 30d, Child, by Marko Chelebonovic. 45d, Girl Under a Fruit Tree, by Beta Vukanovic.

2001, Oct. 2   **Perf. 13¼**
2533-2534 A903   Set of 2   3.00 3.00

Yugoslavian Victories in European Sports Championships A904

Designs: No. 2535, 30d, Men's basketball. No. 2536, 30d, Men's volleyball.

2001, Oct. 1
2535-2536 A904   Set of 2   35.00 35.00

Intl. Federation of Philately (FIP), 75th Anniv. A905

2001, Oct. 24
2537 A905 15d multi   1.00 1.00

    Stamp Day.

Minerals A906

2001, Nov. 2   **Perf. 13¾**
2538   Horiz. strip of 4 + cen-
       tral label   3.50 3.50
    a.   A906 7d Antimonite   .25   .25
    b.   A906 14d Calcite   .60   .60
    c.   A906 26.20d Quartz   1.25 1.25
    d.   A906 28.70d Calcite and galenite   1.40 1.40

Pljevlja Gymnasium, Cent. — A907

2001, Nov. 18   **Perf. 13¼**
2539 A907 15d multi   1.25 1.25

Public Telephone Booths in Serbia, Cent. — A908

2001, Nov. 20
2540 A908 15d multi   .80 .80

Christmas A910

Paintings of the Birth of Jesus Christ: 7d, 14d, 26.20d, 28.70d.

2001, Dec. 1   **Perf. 13¾**
2541-2544 A910   Set of 4   3.00 3.00

Junior World Ice Hockey Championships, Belgrade — A911

2002, Jan. 5   **Perf. 13¼**
2545 A911 14d multi   1.00 1.00

2002 Winter Olympics, Salt Lake City — A912

Designs: 28.70d, Skier. 50d, Four-man bobsled, vert.

2002, Jan. 25   **Perf. 13¼**
2546-2547 A912   Set of 2   10.00 10.00

Jovan Karamata (1902-67), Mathematician A913

2002, Feb. 1
2548 A913 14d multi   1.00 1.00

Birds — A914

No. 2549: a, Saxicola torquata. b, Saxicola rubetra. c, Parus caeruleus. d, Turdus philomelos.

2002, Feb. 22
2549   Horiz. strip of 4 + cen-
       tral label   4.50 4.50
    a.   A914 7d multi   .35   .35
    b.   A914 14d multi   .80   .80
    c.   A914 26.20d multi   1.60 1.60
    d.   A914 28.70d multi   1.75 1.75

Easter — A915

Designs: 7d, Crucifixion, fresco from Studenica Monastery, 1208. 14d, King Milutin's Veil, 1300. 26.20d, Christ's Descent to Hell, silverwork, 1540. 28.70d, Easter egg, Pec Patriarchy, 1980.

2002, Mar. 7   **Perf. 13¾**
2550-2553 A915   Set of 4   3.00 3.00

Bunjevac Women's Clothing — A916

Woman with: 7d, White blouse. 28.70d, Kerchief.

2002, Mar. 29   **Perf. 13¼**
2554-2555 A916   Set of 2   2.00 2.00

Zarko Tomic-Sremac (b. 1900), World War II Hero — A917

2002, Apr. 15
2556 A917 14d multi   1.00 1.00

Danube Fish — A918

No. 2557: a, Rutilus rutilus. b, Acipenser ruthenus. c, Huso huso. d, Stizostedion lucioperca.

2002, Apr. 25 Litho. Perf. 13¼
2557   Horiz. strip of 4 + cen-
       tral label   4.50 4.50
  a.   A918 7d multi   .35   .35
  b.   A918 14d multi   .80   .80
  c.   A918 26.20d multi   1.60 1.60
  d.   A918 28.70d multi   1.75 1.75

Europa
A919

Designs: 28.70d, Trapeze artists. 50d, Tiger trainer.

2002, May 3 Perf. 13¾
2558-2559 A919 Set of 2   5.00 5.00

Europa Type of 2002
Souvenir Sheet

Design: 45d, Trained horse act.

2002, May 3 Litho. Perf. 13¾
2560 A919 45d multi   40.00 40.00

No. 2560 contains one 46x35mm stamp.

Civil Aviation
in
Yugoslavia,
75th Anniv.
A920

Designs: 7d, Potez-29. 28.70d, Boeing 737-300.

Perf. 13¼ Syncopated
2002, June 17 Litho.
2561-2562 A920 Set of 2   4.00 4.00

Types of 1993 and 2001
2002, July 25 Litho. Perf. 12½
Size: 19x21mm (#2563)
2563 A702d A blue   1.50 1.50

Perf. 13¼
"E" in Green
2564 A898 E multi   3.00 3.00

Nos. 2563-2564 were intended for use in Montenegro and were sold there for 13c and 52c in euro currency respectively. The stamps were valid for use in the Serbian section of Yugoslavia.

European
Nature
Protection
A921

Designs: 28.70d, Tara National Park. 50d, Golija Nature Park.

Perf. 13¼ Syncopated
2002, June 28 Litho.
2565-2566 A921 Set of 2   5.00 5.00

Mills — A922

Designs: 7d, Windmill, Melenci. 28.70d, Water mill, Lyuberada.

2002, Sept. 14
2567-2568 A922 Set of 2   3.00 3.00

Liberation of
Niskic, 125th
Anniv. — A923

2002, Sept. 18 Perf. 13¾
2569 A923 14d multi   2.00 2.00

Souvenir Sheet

Victory in 2002 World Basketball
Championships — A924

2002, Sept. 20
2570 A924 30d multi   6.00 6.00

Souvenir Sheet

JUFIZ XI Philatelic Exhibition — A925

2002, Sept. 23
2571 A925 30d multi   3.00 3.00

Joy of
Europe — A926

Children's art: 28.70d, Boat. 50d, Bird.

2002, Oct. 2
2572-2573 A926 Set of 2   4.50 4.50

Moraca
Monastery,
750th
Anniv. — A927

2002, Oct. 10
2574 A927 16d multi   2.00 2.00

Types of Nos. 2255 and 2256
Surcharged in Black or Violet

2002 Perfs, etc., as Before
2575 A751 50p on 5p #2256
             multi   1.00 1.00
2576 A702g 10d on 10,000d
             #2145   2.00 2.00
2577 A751 12d on 1p #2255
             multi (V)   2.00 2.00
      Nos. 2575-2577 (3)   5.00 5.00

Issued: No. 2575, 10/17; No. 2576, 11/28; No. 2577, 12/19.
For stamp like No. 2577, but with black surcharge, see Serbia and Montenegro No. 260.

Intl. Federation
of Stamp
Dealers
Associations,
50th
Anniv. — A928

2002, Oct. 24 Litho. Perf. 13¾
2578 A928 16d multi   1.25 1.25

Serbian Folk
Costumes — A929

Paintings of costumes by Olga Benson in Ethnographic Institute of Serbian Academy of Sciences and Arts: a, Man, Kusadak. b, Woman with red headdress, Belgrade. c, Man, Novo Selo. d, Woman in profile, Belgrade.

2002, Nov. 8 Perf. 13¾
2579   Horiz. strip of 4, + cen-
       tral label   5.00 5.00
  a.   A929 16d multi   .85   .85
  b.   A929 24d multi   1.25 1.25
  c.   A929 26.20d multi   1.40 1.40
  d.   A929 28.70d multi   1.50 1.50

Christmas
A930

Religious art: 12d, Nativity, Stavronikita Monastery, Mount Athos, Greece, 1546. 16d, Nativity, Chilandari Monastery, Mount Athos, Greece, c. 1618. 26.20d, Nativity, Tretyakov Gallery, Moscow, 15th cent. 28.70d, Adoration of the Magi, by Sandro Botticelli.

2002, Dec. 2
2580-2583 A930 Set of 4   4.50 4.50

Abandoned
Dogs — A931

Various dogs.

2003, Jan. 31 Perf. 13¾
2584   Horiz. strip of 4, + cen-
       tral label   4.00 4.00
  a.   A931 16d multi   .70   .70
  b.   A931 24d multi   .95   .95
  c.   A931 26.20d multi   1.10 1.10
  d.   A931 28.70d multi   1.25 1.25

Yugoslavia became Serbia & Montenegro on Feb. 4, 2003. See Serbia & Montenegro for subsequent issues.

SEMI-POSTAL STAMPS

Giving Succor
to Wounded
SP1

Wounded
Soldier
SP2

Symbolical of
National
Unity — SP3

1921, Jan. 30 Unwmk. Engr. Perf. 12
B1 SP1 10p carmine   .20   .20
B2 SP2 15p violet brown   .20   .20
B3 SP3 25p light blue   .20   .20
     Nos. B1-B3 (3)   .60   .60

Nos. B1-B3 were sold at double face value, the excess being for the benefit of invalid soldiers.
For surcharges see Nos. 15-21.

This overprint was applied to 500,000 copies of No. B1 in 1923 and they were given to the Society for Wounded Invalids (Uprava Ratnih Invalida) which sold them for 2d apiece. These over-printed stamps had no franking power, but some were used through ignorance.

Regular Issue of
1926-27 Surcharged
in Dark Red

1926, Nov. 1 Perf. 13
B5   A6 25p + 25p green   .20   .20
B6   A6 50p + 50p olive brn   .20   .20
B7   A6 1d + 50p scarlet   .20   .20
B8   A6 2d + 50p black   .60   .20
B9   A6 3d + 50p slate blue   .50   .20
B10 A6 4d + 50p red org   1.40   .20
B11 A6 5d + 50p brt vio   .75   .20
B12 A6 8d + 50p black brn   1.90   .60
B13 A6 10d + 1d olive brn   1.75   .60
B14 A6 15d + 1d brown   6.00 1.00
B15 A6 20d + 1d dark vio   8.00   .75
B16 A6 30d + 1d orange   19.00 3.00
  a.   Double surcharge
     Nos. B5-B16 (12)   40.50 7.35

The surtax on these stamps was intended for a fund for relief of sufferers from floods.
For overprints see Nos. 99-101.

Cathedral at
Duvno
SP4

King Tomislav
SP6

Kings Tomislav and Alexander SP5

Perf. 12½, 11½x12

1929, Nov. 1 **Typo.**
B17 SP4 50p (+ 50p) olive green .20 .20
B18 SP5 1d (+ 50p) red .60 .20
B19 SP6 3d (+ 1d) blue 1.60 1.10
Nos. B17-B19 (3) 2.40 1.50

Millenary of the Croatian kingdom. The surtax was used to create a War Memorial Cemetery in France and to erect a monument to Serbian soldiers who died there.

View of Dobropolje SP7

War Memorial — SP8

View of Kajmaktchalan SP9

1931, Apr. 1 **Perf. 12½, 11½**
B20 SP7 50p + 50p blue grn .20 .20
B21 SP8 1d + 1d scarlet .20 .20
B22 SP9 3d + 3d deep blue .20 .20
Nos. B20-B22 (3) .60 .60

The surtax was added to a fund for a War Memorial to Serbian soldiers who died in France during World War I.

SP10 SP12

SP11

Black Overprint

1931, Nov. 1 **Perf. 12½, 11½x12**
B23 SP10 50p (+ 50p) olive grn .20 .20
B24 SP11 1d (+ 50p) red .20 .20
B25 SP12 3d (+ 1d) blue .30 .30
Nos. B23-B25 (3) .70 .70

Surtax for War Memorial fund.

Rower on Danube at Smederevo SP13

Bled Lake SP14

Danube near Belgrade SP15

View of Split Harbor SP16

Zagreb Cathedral — SP17

Prince Peter — SP18

1932, Sept. 2 **Litho.** **Perf. 11½**
B26 SP13 75p + 50p dl grn & lt blue .50 1.00
B27 SP14 1d + ½d scar & lt blue .50 1.10
B28 SP15 1½d + ½d rose & green .80 1.25
B29 SP16 3d + 1d bl & lt bl 1.60 2.25
B30 SP17 4d + 1d red org & lt blue 6.50 14.00
B31 SP18 5d + 1d dl vio & lilac 6.50 10.00
Nos. B26-B31 (6) 16.40 29.60

European Rowing Championship Races, Belgrade.

King Alexander SP19

Prince Peter SP20

1933, May 25 **Typo.** **Perf. 12½**
B32 SP19 50p + 25p black 4.00 8.00
B33 SP19 75p + 25p yel grn 4.00 8.00
B34 SP19 1.50d + 50p rose 4.00 8.00
B35 SP19 3d + 1d bl vio 4.00 8.00
B36 SP19 4p + 1d dk grn 4.00 8.00
B37 SP19 5d + 1d orange 4.00 8.00
Nos. B32-B37 (6) 24.00 48.00

11th Intl. Congress of P.E.N. (Poets, Editors and Novelists) Clubs, Dubrovnik, May 25-27.
The labels at the foot of the stamps are printed in either Cyrillic or Latin letters and each bears the amount of a premium for the benefit of the local P.E.N. Club at Dubrovnik.

1933, June 28
B38 SP20 75p + 25p slate grn .20 .25
B39 SP20 1½d + ½d deep red .20 .25

60th anniv. meeting of the National Sokols (Sports Associations) at Ljubljana, July 1.

Eagle Soaring over City — SP22

Athlete and Eagle — SP23

1934, June 1 **Perf. 12½**
B40 SP22 75p + 25p green 4.00 7.00
B41 SP22 1.50d + 50p car 6.00 8.00
B42 SP22 1.75d + 25p brown 10.00 8.00
Nos. B40-B42 (3) 20.00 23.00

20th anniversary of Sokols of Sarajevo.

1934, June 1
B43 SP23 75p + 25p Prus grn 2.00 2.75
B44 SP23 1.50d + 50p car 2.00 4.00
B45 SP23 1.75d + 25p choc 6.00 10.00
Nos. B43-B45 (3) 10.00 16.75

60th anniversary of Sokols of Zagreb.

Mother and Children SP24 SP25

Perf. 12½x11½

1935, Dec. 25 **Photo.**
B46 SP24 1.50d + 1d dk brn & brown 1.25 1.00
a. Perf. 11½ 12.00 12.00
B47 SP25 3.50d + 1.50d bright ultra & bl 2.00 2.50

The surtax was for "Winter Help."

Queen Mother Marie SP26

Prince Regent Paul SP27

1936, May 3 **Litho.**
B48 SP26 75p + 25p grnsh bl .40 .40
B49 SP26 1.50d + 50p rose pink .45 .45
B50 SP26 1.75d + 75p brown 1.25 1.00
B51 SP26 3.50d + 1d brt bl 1.60 2.25
Nos. B48-B51 (4) 3.70 4.10

1936, Sept. 20 **Typo.**
B52 SP27 75p + 50p turq grn & red .20 .50
B53 SP27 1.50d + 50p cer & red .20 .50

Surtax for the Red Cross.

Princes Tomislav and Andrej SP28 SP29

Perf. 11½x12½, 12½x11½

1937, May 1
B54 SP28 25p + 25p red brn .20 .25
B55 SP28 75p + 75p emerald .20 .35
B56 SP29 1.50d + 1d org red .30 .50
B57 SP29 2d + 1d magenta .60 1.00
Nos. B54-B57 (4) 1.30 2.15

Souvenir Sheet

National Costumes — SP30

1937, Sept. 12 **Perf. 14**
B57A SP30 Sheet of 4 4.75 8.00
b. 1d blue green 1.00 1.75
c. 1.50d bright violet 1.00 1.75
d. 2d rose red 1.00 1.75
e. 4d dark blue 1.00 1.75

1st Yugoslavian Phil. Exhib., Belgrade. Sold only at the exhibition post office at 15d each.

SP31 SP32

Perf. 11½x12½, 12½x11½

1938, May 1 **Photo.**
B58 SP31 50p + 50p dark brn .25 .30
B59 SP32 1d + 1d dk green .30 .35
B60 SP31 1.50d + 1.50d scar .35 .40
B61 SP32 2d + 2d magenta 1.25 .70
Nos. B58-B61 (4) 2.15 1.75

Surtax for the benefit of Child Welfare. For overprints see Nos. B75-B78.

Bridge and Anti-aircraft Lights — SP33

1938, May 28 **Perf. 11½x12½**
B62 SP33 1d + 50p dk grn .40 .50
B63 SP33 1.50d + 1d scarlet .60 .70
a. Perf. 11½ 17.50 17.50
B64 SP33 2d + 1d rose vio 1.25 1.50
a. Perf. 11½ 16.00 16.00
B65 SP33 3d + 1.50d dp bl 2.00 2.50
Nos. B62-B65 (4) 4.25 5.20

Intl. Aeronautical Exhib., Belgrade.

Cliff at Demir-Kapiya — SP34

Modern Hospital SP35

Runner Carrying Torch — SP36

Alexander I — SP37

Perf. 11½x12½, 12½x11½
1938, Aug. 1
B66 SP34   1d + 1d slate grn & dp grn   .45 .55
B67 SP35   1.50d + 1.50d scar   .70 .75
B68 SP36   2d + 2d claret & dp rose   1.60 2.25
B69 SP37   3d + 3d dp bl   1.60 2.25
    Nos. B66-B69 (4)   4.35 5.80

The surtax was to raise funds to build a hospital for railway employees.

Runner SP38

Shot-Putter SP41

Hurdlers SP39

Pole Vaulter SP40

1938, Sept. 11
B70 SP38   50p + 50p org brn   1.25 1.25
B71 SP39   1d + 1d sl grn & dp grn   1.25 1.25
B72 SP40   1.50d + 1.50d rose & dk mag   1.25 1.25
B73 SP41   2d + 2d dk blue   2.50 2.50
    Nos. B70-B73 (4)   6.25 6.25

Ninth Balkan Games.

Stamps of 1938 Overprinted in Black

a

b

1938, Oct. 1
B75 SP31(a)   50p + 50p dk brn   .50 .50
B76 SP32(b)   1d + 1d dk grn   .50 .50
B77 SP31(a)   1.50d + 1.50d scar   .60 .60
B78 SP32(b)   2d + 2d mag   1.25 1.25
    Nos. B75-B78 (4)   2.85 2.85

Surtax for the benefit of Child Welfare.

Postriders SP43

1d+1d, Rural mail delivery. 1.50d+1.50d, Mail train. 2d+2d, Mail bus. 4d+4d, Mail plane.

1939, Mar. 15   **Photo.**   **Perf. 11½**
B79 SP43   50p + 50p buff, bis & brown   .40 .50
B80 SP43   1d + 1d sl grn & dp green   .55 .75
B81 SP43   1.50d + 1.50d red, cop red & brn car   1.50 1.75
B82 SP43   2d + 2d dp plum & rose lilac   1.50 2.50
B83 SP43   4d + 4d ind & sl bl   2.00 3.00
    Nos. B79-B83 (5)   5.95 8.50

Centenary of the present postal system in Yugoslavia. The surtax was used for the Railway Benevolent Association.

The Cyrillic and Latin inscriptions are transposed on Nos. B82 and B83.

Child Eating SP48

Children at Seashore — SP49

Children in Crib — SP51

Boy Planing Board SP50

1939, May 1   **Perf. 12½**
B84 SP48   1d + 1d blk & dp bl green   1.25 1.40
B85 SP49   1.50d + 1.50d org brn & sal   2.00 2.75
   a.   Perf. 11½   80.00 140.00
B86 SP50   2d + 2d mar & vio rose   1.40 2.50
B87 SP51   4d + 4d ind & royal blue   1.40 2.50
    Nos. B84-B87 (4)   6.05 9.15

The surtax was for the benefit of Child Welfare.

Czar Lazar of Serbia — SP52

Milosh Obilich — SP53

1939, June 28   **Perf. 11½**
B88 SP52   1d + 1d sl grn & bl grn   1.60 1.40
B89 SP53   1.50d + 1.50d mar & brt car   1.60 1.40

Battle of Kosovo, 550th anniversary.

Training Ship "Jadran" SP54

Designs: 1d+50p, Steamship "King Alexander." 1.50d+1d, Freighter "Triglan." 2d+1.50d, Cruiser "Dubrovnik."

1939, Sept. 6   **Engr.**
B90 SP54   50p + 50p brn org   .60 .70
B91 SP54   1d + 50p dull grn   .80 .95
B92 SP54   1.50d + 1d dp rose   1.25 1.50
B93 SP54   2d + 1.50d dark bl   2.00 3.50
    Nos. B90-B93 (4)   4.65 6.65

Yugoslav Navy and Merchant Marine. The surtax aided a Marine Museum.

Motorcycle and Sidecar — SP58

Motorcycle SP60

Racing Car SP59

Racing Car SP61

1939, Sept. 3   **Photo.**
B94 SP58   50p + 50p multi   .55 .60
B95 SP59   1d + 1d multi   1.00 1.40
B96 SP60   1.50d + 1.50d multi   1.40 2.00
B97 SP61   2d + 2d multi   2.50 3.50
    Nos. B94-B97 (4)   5.45 7.50

Automobile and Motorcycle Races, Belgrade. The surtax was for the Race Organization and the State Treasury.

Unknown Soldier Memorial SP62

1939, Oct. 9   **Perf. 12½**
B98 SP62   1d + 50p sl grn & green   1.00 1.40
B99 SP62   1.50d + 1d red & rose red   1.00 1.40

B100 SP62   2d + 1.50d dp cl & vio rose   1.25 2.00
B101 SP62   3d + 2d dp bl & bl   2.50 3.50
    Nos. B98-B101 (4)   5.75 8.30

Assassination of King Alexander, 5th anniv. The surtax was used to aid World War I invalids.

Postman Delivering Mail — SP64

Postman Emptying Mail Box — SP65

Parcel Post Delivery Wagon SP66

Parcel Post SP67

Repairing Telephone Wires — SP68

1940, Jan. 1
B102 SP64   50p + 50p brn & deep org   .60 .90
B103 SP65   1d + 1d sl grn & blue grn   .60 .90
B104 SP66   1.50d + 1.50d red brn & scar   1.00 2.00
B105 SP67   2d + 2d dl vio & red lilac   1.25 2.00
B106 SP68   4d + 4d sl bl & bl   4.00 5.25
    Nos. B102-B106 (5)   7.45 11.05

The surtax was used for the employees of the Postal System in Belgrade.

Croats' Arrival at Adriatic in 640 SP69

King Tomislav — SP70

Death of Matija
Gubec — SP71

Anton and
Stjepan
Radic
SP72

Map of
Yugoslavia
SP73

1940, Mar. 1   Typo.   Perf. 11½

B107	SP69	50p + 50p brn org	.30	.50
B108	SP70	1d + 1d green	.30	.50
B109	SP71	1.50d + 1.50d brt red	.50	.50
B110	SP72	2d + 2d dk cerise	1.25	2.00
B111	SP73	4d + 2d dark blue	1.50	2.25
	Nos. B107-B111 (5)		3.85	5.75

The surtax was used for the benefit of postal
employees in Zagreb.

Children
Playing in
Snow
SP74

Children at
Seashore — SP75

1940, May 1 Photo.   Perf. 11½, 12½

B112	SP74	50p + 50p brn org & org yellow	.25	.30
B113	SP75	1d + 1d sl grn & dk green	.30	.40
B114	SP74	1.50d + 1.50d brn red & scarlet	.60	.70
B115	SP75	2d + 2d mar & vio rose	1.00	1.40
	Nos. B112-B115 (4)		2.15	2.80

The surtax was for Child Welfare.

Nos. C11-C14
Surcharged in
Carmine

Perf. 11½x12½, 12½x11½

1940, Dec. 23

B116	AP6	50p + 50p on 5d	.30	.30
B117	AP7	1d + 1d on 10d	.30	.30
B118	AP8	1.50d + 1.50d on 20d	.80	1.10
B119	AP9	2d + 2d on 30d	.90	1.25
	Nos. B116-B119 (4)		2.30	2.95

The surtax was used to fight tuberculosis.
For surcharges see Nos. NB1-NB4.

St. Peter's Cemetery,
Ljubljana — SP76

Croatian, Serbian
and Slovenian
SP77

Chapel at
Kajmaktchalan
SP78

Memorial
at Brezje
SP79

1941, Jan. 1   Perf. 12½

B120	SP76	50p + 50p gray grn & yel green	.30	.35
B121	SP77	1d + 1d brn car & dl rose	.30	.35
B122	SP78	1.50d + 1.50d myr grn & bl green	.60	1.00
B123	SP79	2d + 2d gray bl & pale lilac	1.00	1.75
	Nos. B120-B123 (4)		2.20	3.45

Surtax for the Ljubljana War Veterans Assoc.

Kamenita Gate,
Zagreb — SP80

13th Century
Cathedral,
Zagreb — SP81

1941, Mar. 16   Engr.   Perf. 11½

B124	SP80	1.50d + 1.50d choc	.60	1.00
B125	SP81	4d + 3d blue blk	.60	1.00

2nd Philatelic Exhibition of Croatia, at
Zagreb, Mar. 16-27.
Nos. B124-B125 exist perf. 9½ on right side.
Value, each $25.

1941, Apr.

B126	SP80	1.50d + 1.50d bl black	10.00	15.00
B127	SP81	4d + 3d choc	10.00	15.00

Regional philatelic exhibition at Slavonski
Brod. Nos. B126-B127 with gold overprint,
"Nezavisna Drzava Hrvatska," are Croatia
Nos. B1-B2.
Nos. B126-B127 exist perf. 9½ on right side.
Value, each $55 unused, $70 used.

Issues for Federal Republic

Carrying
Wounded
Soldier — SP82

Child — SP83

1945, Sept. 15   Typo.   Perf. 11½

B131	SP82	1d + 4d deep ultra	.70	.70
B132	SP83	2d + 6d scarlet	.70	.70

The surtax was for the Red Cross.

Russia,
Yugoslavia
Flags
SP84

1945, Oct. 20   Photo.   Unwmk.

B133	SP84	2d + 5d multi	.80	.80

Liberation of Belgrade, 1st anniv.

Communications
Symbols — SP85

1946, May 10   Perf. 12½

B134	SP85	1.50d + 1d emer	2.75	2.50
B135	SP85	2.50d + 1.50d car rose	2.75	2.50
B136	SP85	5d + 2d gray bl	2.75	2.50
B137	SP85	8d + 3.50d dl brn	2.75	2.50
	Nos. B134-B137 (4)		11.00	10.00

1st PTT Congress since liberation, May 10.

Flag and Young
Laborers
SP86

Handstand on
Horizontal Bar
SP87

**1946, Aug. 1   Litho.
Flag in Red or Carmine and Deep or
Dark Blue**

B138	SP86	50p + 50p brn & buff	2.25	1.40
B139	SP86	1.50d + 1d dk grn & lt green	2.25	1.40
B140	SP86	2.50d + 2d rose vio & rose lilac	2.25	1.40
B141	SP86	5d + 3d gray bl & blue	2.25	1.40
	Nos. B138-B141 (4)		9.00	5.60

The surtax aided railroad reconstruction
carried out by Yugoslav youths.

1947, Sept. 5   Perf. 11½

B142	SP87	1.50d + 50p dark grn	2.00	2.00
B143	SP87	2.50d + 50p carmine	2.00	2.00
B144	SP87	4d + 50p brt blue	2.00	2.00
	Nos. B142-B144 (3)		6.00	6.00

1947 Balkan Games, Sept. 5-7, Ljubljana.

Young
Railway
Laborers
SP88

1947, Sept. 25   Typo.   Perf. 11½x12

B145	SP88	1d + 50p orange	.50	.50
B146	SP88	1.50d + 1d yel green	.50	.50
B147	SP88	2.50d + 1.50d car lake		.50
B148	SP88	5d + 2d deep blue	.50	.50
	Nos. B145-B148 (4)		2.00	2.00

The surtax was for youth brigades employed
in the construction of the Samac-Sarajevo
railway.

Symbolizing
Protection of
"B.C.G."
Vaccine
SP89

Dying Serpent
SP91

"Illness" and
"Recovery"
SP90

1948, Apr. 1   Litho.   Perf. 12½

B149	SP89	1.50d + 1d sl blk & red	.40	.40
B150	SP90	2.50d + 2d grnsh gray, ol blk & red	.40	.40
B151	SP91	5d + 3d dk bl & car	.40	.40
	Nos. B149-B151 (3)		1.20	1.20

Fight against tuberculosis. The surtax was
for the Yugoslav Red Cross.

Juro
Danicic
SP92

1948, July 28   Perf. 11

B152	SP92	1.50d + 50p blk green	.40	.40
B153	SP92	2.50d + 1d dark red	.40	.40
B154	SP92	4d + 2d dark blue	.40	.40
	Nos. B152-B154 (3)		1.20	1.20

Yugoslav Academy of Arts and Sciences,
Zagreb, 80th anniv. The surtax was for the
Academy.

Shot Put — SP93

Portraits: 2.50d+1d, Franjo Racki. 4d+2d,
Josip J. Strossmayer.

1948, Sept. 10   Perf. 12½

B155	SP93	2d + 1d shown	.40	.40
B156	SP93	3d + 1d Hurdles	.40	.40
B157	SP93	5d + 2d Pole vault	1.00	1.00
	Nos. B155-B157 (3)		1.80	1.80

Balkan and Central Europe Games, 1948.
On sale 4 days.

AIR POST STAMPS

Dubrovnik
AP1

Lake Bled
AP2

Falls of
Jaice — AP3

Church at
Oplenac — AP4

Bridge at
Mostar — AP5

Perf. 12½

1934, June 15   Typo.   Unwmk.

C1	AP1	50p violet brown	.20	.20
C2	AP2	1d green	.20	.20
C3	AP3	2d rose red	.45	.20
C4	AP4	3d ultramarine	.90	.35
C5	AP5	10d vermilion	2.00	1.75
		Nos. C1-C5 (5)	3.75	2.70

King Alexander Memorial Issue

1935, Jan. 1

Border in Black

C6	AP4	3d ultramarine	2.50	2.25

St. Naum
Convent — AP6

Sarajevo
AP8

Port of Rab — AP7

Ljubljana
AP9

Perf. 12½, 11½x12½, 12½x11½

1937, Sept. 12   Photo.

C7	AP6	50p brown	.20	.20
C8	AP7	1d yellow grn	.20	.20
C9	AP8	2d blue gray	.20	.20
C10	AP9	2.50d rose red	.20	.20
C11	AP6	5d brn violet	.20	.20
C12	AP7	10d brown lake	.50	.20
C13	AP8	20d dark green	.70	.70
C14	AP9	30d ultramarine	1.00	1.00
		Nos. C7-C14 (8)	3.20	2.90

For surcharges see Nos. B116-B119, NB1-NB4, NC1-NC8.

Cathedral
of Zagreb
AP10

Bridge at
Belgrade
AP11

1940, Aug. 15   Litho.   Perf. 12½

C15	AP10	40d Prus grn & pale green	2.50	1.75
C16	AP11	50d slate bl & gray bl	3.50	3.00

For overprints see Nos. NC9-NC10.

Issues for Federal Republic

Plane over
Terrace of
Kalimegdan,
Belgrade
AP12

Plane over
Dubrovnik
AP13

1947, Apr. 21   Typo.   Perf. 11½

Cyrillic Inscription at Top

C17	AP12	50p ol gray & brn vio	.20	.20
C18	AP13	1d mag & ol gray	.20	.20
C19	AP12	2d blue & black	.20	.20
C20	AP13	5d green & gray	.30	.20
C21	AP12	10d olive bis & choc	.35	.20
C22	AP13	20d ultra & olive	.75	.35

Roman Inscription at Top

C23	AP12	50p ol gray & brn vio	.20	.20
C24	AP13	1d mag & ol gray	.20	.20
C25	AP12	2d blue & black	.20	.20
C26	AP13	5d green & gray	.30	.20
C27	AP12	10d olive bis & choc	.35	.20
C28	AP13	20d ultra & olive	.75	.35
		Nos. C17-C28 (12)	4.00	2.70

Sheets of each denomination contain alternately stamps with Cyrillic or Roman inscription at top. Value, 6 se-tenant pairs, $40.

Laurent
Kosir and
Birthplace
AP14

1948, Aug. 27   Engr.

C29	AP14	15d red violet	1.00	.80

Kosir, recognized by Yugoslavia as inventor of the postage stamp, 80th death anniv. Issued in sheets of 25 stamps and 25 labels.

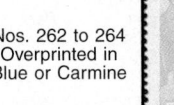

Nos. 262 to 264
Overprinted in
Blue or Carmine

1949, Aug. 25   Unwmk.   Perf. 12½

C30	A55	3d carmine rose	2.25	5.00
C31	A56	5d dull blue (C)	2.25	5.00
C32	A57	12d red brown	2.25	5.00
		Nos. C30-C32 (3)	6.75	15.00

Liberation of Macedonia, 5th anniv.
It is reported that No. C32 was not sold to the public at the post office.

Souvenir Sheet

Electric
Train
AP15

Perf. 11½x12½

1949, Dec. 15   Photo.

C33	AP15	10d lilac rose	40.00	20.00
a.		Imperf.	40.00	20.00

Centenary of Yugoslav railroads.
For overprint see Trieste No. C17.

Iron Gate,
Derdap
AP16

Belgrade
AP17

Designs: 2d, Cascades, Plitvice. 3d, Carolina. 6d, Roman bridge, Mostar. 10d, Ohrid. 20d, Gulf of Kotor. 30d, Dubrovnik. 50d, Bled.

Perf. 12½

1951, June 16   Unwmk.   Engr.

C34	AP16	1d deep org	.20	.20
C35	AP16	2d dk green	.20	.20
C36	AP16	3d dark red	.20	.20
C37	AP16	6d ultra	3.00	3.50
C38	AP16	10d dark brn	.25	.20
C39	AP16	20d grnsh blk	.40	.20
C40	AP16	30d dp claret	1.00	.20
C41	AP16	50d dk purple	1.40	.20
C42	AP17	100d dk gray bl	27.50	7.75
		Nos. C34-C42 (9)	34.15	12.65

Souvenir Sheet

Imperf

C43	AP17	100d red brn	65.00	65.00

See Nos. C50-C53. For overprints see Nos. C44, C49, Trieste C22-C32.

Roman Bridge Type of 1951
Overprinted "ZEFIZ 1951" in Carmine

1951, June 16   Perf. 12½

C44	AP16	6d dark green	2.00	1.75

Nos. C43-C44 were issued for Zagreb Philatelic Exhibition, June 16-26.

View on Mt.
Kapaonik
AP18

Plane and
Parachutists
AP19

Perf. 12½

1951, July   Unwmk.   Photo.

C45	AP18	3d shown	1.00	.70
C46	AP18	5d Mt. Triglav	1.00	.70
C47	AP18	20d Mt. Kalnik	32.50	27.50
		Nos. C45-C47 (3)	34.50	28.90

Intl. Union of Mountaineers, 12th Assembly, Bled, July 13-18.

1951, Aug. 16   Engr.

C48	AP19	6d carmine	2.25	1.10

Type of
1951
Overprinted
in Carmine

C49	AP16	50d blue	32.50	25.00

First World Parachute Championship, Bled, Aug. 16-20.

> **Catalogue values for unused stamps in this section, from this point to the end of the section, are for Never Hinged items.**

Types of 1951

Designs: 5d, Cascades, Plitvice. 100d, Carniola. 200d, Roman bridge, Mostar.

1951-52

C50	AP16	5d yel brn ('52)	.40	.20
C51	AP16	100d green	1.75	.20
C52	AP16	200d deep car ('52)	2.50	.30
C53	AP17	500d blue vio ('52)	10.00	.65
		Nos. C50-C53 (4)	14.65	1.35

Marshal Tito,
Tank, Factory
and Planes
AP20

1951, Dec. 22   Unwmk.

C54	AP20	150d deep blue	15.00	12.50

Army Day, Dec. 22; 10th anniv. of the formation of the 1st military unit of "New" Yugoslavia.

Star and Flag-
encircled
Globe — AP21

1953, July 30   Engr.

C55	AP21	300d bl & grn	250.00	250.00

38th Esperanto Congress, Zagreb, 7/25-8/1.
For overprint see Trieste No. C21.

13th
Century
Tower,
Zagreb
AP22

1956, May 20   Perf. 11½

Chalky Paper

C56	AP22	30d gray, vio bl & org red	2.50	1.25

Yugoslav Intl. Phil. Exhib., JUFIZ III, Zagreb, May 20-27.

Workers and
Cogwheel — AP23

Moon and Earth
with
Satellites — AP24

1956, June 15　　　　　**Photo.**
Glossy Paper
C57　AP23　30d car rose & blk　1.60　1.60

10th anniversary of technical education.

1958, Oct. 24　**Engr.**　**Perf. 12½**
C58　AP24　300d dark blue　10.00　3.50

Intl. Geophysical Year, 1957-58.

Types of Regular Issue, 1961

1961, Sept. 1　　　　　**Perf. 11½**
C59　A150　250d dark purple　1.25　.70
C60　A151　500d violet blue　3.00　2.00

Type of Athletic Regular Issue, 1962
Souvenir Sheet

Design: Army Stadium, Belgrade.

1962, Sept. 12　**Litho.**　**Imperf.**
C61　A161　600d vio & blk　5.00　3.75

7th European Athletic Championships, Belgrade, Sept. 12-16.

REGISTERED LETTER STAMP

Catalogue values for unused
stamps in this section are for
Never Hinged items.

RL1

1993, June 28　**Litho.**　**Perf. 12½**
F1　RL1　(R) ultra　6.00　.50

No. F1 was valued at 11,000d on day of issue.
For surcharge, see Serbia No. 194.

Type of 1993
2002, July 25　**Litho.**　**Perf. 12½**
F2　RL1　R red　2.00　1.50

No. F2 was intended for use in Montenegro and was sold there for 39c in euro currency. The stamp was valid for use in the Serbian section of Yugoslavia.

POSTAGE DUE STAMPS

King
Alexander — D1

1921　**Typo.**　**Unwmk.**　**Perf. 11½**
Red or Black Surcharge
J1　D1　10p on 5p green (R)　.20　.20
J2　D1　30p on 5p green (Bk)　.20　.20

D2

D3

1921-22　**Typo.**　**Perf. 11½, Rough**
J3　D2　10p rose　.20　.20
J4　D2　30p yellow green　.20　.20
J5　D2　50p violet　.30　.20
J6　D2　1d brown　.35　.20
J7　D2　2d blue　.35　.20
J8　D3　5d orange　7.50　.40
J9　D3　10d violet brown　9.25　.45
　　a.　Cliche of 10p in sheet of
　　　　10d　　　75.00　100.00
J10　D3　25d pink　35.00　2.00
J11　D3　50d green　30.00　1.60
　　　Nos. J3-J11 (9)　83.15　5.45

1924　**Perf. 9, 10½, 11½, Clean-cut**
J12　D3　10p rose red　.20　.20
J13　D3　30p yellow green　.45　.35
J14　D3　50p violet　.20　.20
J15　D3　1d brown　.35　.20
J16　D3　2d deep blue　.55　.20
J17　D3　5d orange　9.25　.20
J18　D3　10d violet brown　21.00　.20
J19　D3　25d pink　42.50　1.00
J20　D3　50d green　57.50　.85
　　　Nos. J12-J20 (9)　132.00　3.40

Nos. J19-J20 do not exist perf 9. Nos. J18-J20 do not exist perf 11½.

Nos. J19-J20 Surcharged

1928
J21　D3　10d on 25d pink　3.25　.25
J22　D3　10d on 50d green　3.25　.25
　　a.　Inverted surcharge　30.00　18.00

A second type of "1" in surcharge has flag projecting horizontally. Value, each $15 unused, $3 used.

Coat of　　　　Numeral of
Arms — D4　　　Value — D5

1931　**Typo.**　**Perf. 12½**
With Imprint at Foot
J23　D4　50p violet　1.40　.20
J24　D4　1d deep magenta　3.00　.20
J25　D4　2d deep blue　8.00　.20
J26　D4　5d orange　2.00　.20
J27　D4　10d chocolate　10.00　1.25
　　　Nos. J23-J27 (5)　24.40　2.05

For overprints see Nos. NJ1-NJ13, Croatia 26-29, J1-J5.

1932
Without Imprint at Foot
J28　D4　50p violet　.20　.20
J29　D4　1d deep magenta　.20　.20
J30　D4　2d deep blue　.20　.20
J31　D4　5d orange　.20　.20
J32　D4　10d chocolate　1.00　1.00
　　　Nos. J28-J32 (5)　1.20　1.00

1933　　　　**Perf. 9, 10½, 11½**
Overprint in Green, Blue or Maroon
J33　D5　50p vio (G)　.20　.20
J34　D5　1d brown (Bl)　.20　.20
　　a.　Perf. 10½　4.00　1.25
J35　D5　2d blue (M)　.50　.20
　　a.　Perf. 10½　2.00　1.00
J36　D5　5d orange (Bl)　2.75　.20
J37　D5　10d violet brn (Bl)　8.00　1.00
　　　Nos. J33-J37 (5)　11.65　1.80

Issues for Federal Republic

Redrawn Type OD5,
German Occupation
of Serbia,
Overprinted in Black

1945　　　**Unwmk.**　　**Perf. 12½**
J37A　OD5　10d red　.60　.50
J37B　OD5　20d ultramarine　.60　.50

In the redrawn design the eagle is replaced by a colorless tablet.

Coat of　　　　Torches and
Arms — D6　　　Star — D7

1945　　**Litho.**　　**Perf. 12½**
Numerals in Black
J38　D6　2d brown violet　.20　.25
J39　D6　3d violet　.20　.25
J40　D6　5d green　.20　.25
J41　D6　7d orange brown　.20　.25
J42　D6　10d rose lilac　.20　.25
J43　D6　20d blue　.20　.25
J44　D6　30d light bl grn　.40　.35
J45　D6　40d rose red　.40　.35

Numerals in Color of Stamp
J46　D6　1d blue green　.20　.20
J47　D6　1.50d blue　.20　.20
J48　D6　2d vermilion　.40　.20
J49　D6　3d violet brown　.40　.20
J50　D6　4d rose violet　.60　.20
　　　Nos. J38-J50 (13)　3.80　3.20

For overprints see Nos. J64-J66.

1946-47　　**Typo.**　　**Unwmk.**
J51　D7　50p dp orange ('47)　.20　.20
J52　D7　1d orange　.20　.20
J53　D7　2d dark blue　.20　.20
J54　D7　3d yellow green　.20　.20
J55　D7　5d bright purple　.20　.20
J56　D7　7d crimson　.80　.20
J57　D7　10d brt pink ('47)　.80　.20
J58　D7　20d rose lake ('47)　2.00　.50
　　　Nos. J51-J58 (8)　4.60　1.90

See Nos. J67-J79. For overprints see Trieste Nos. J1-J5, J11-J18.

Nos. J47, J49 and
J50 Overprinted in
Black

1950　　　　　　　**Litho.**
J64　D6　1.50d blue　.20　.20
J65　D6　3d violet brown　.20　.20
J66　D6　4d rose violet　.20　.20
　　　Nos. J64-J66 (3)　.60　.60

Catalogue values for unused
stamps in this section, from this
point to the end of the section, are
for Never Hinged items.

Type of 1946-47
1951-52　　**Typo.**　　**Perf. 12½**
J67　D7　1d brown ('52)　.40　.20
J68　D7　2d emerald　.40　.20
J69　D7　5d blue　.55　.20
J70　D7　10d scarlet　1.75　.20
J71　D7　20d purple　2.00　.20
J72　D7　30d org yel ('52)　4.00　.20
J73　D7　50d ultramarine　16.00　.40
J74　D7　100d dp plum ('52)　50.00　2.00
　　　Nos. J67-J74 (8)　75.10　3.60

For overprints see Istria Nos. J20-J24, Trieste J11-J18.

1962　　　　**Litho.**　　**Perf. 12½**
J75　D7　10d red orange　3.25　.20
J76　D7　20d purple　3.25　.20
J77　D7　30d orange　6.75　.20

J78　D7　50d ultramarine　25.00　.80
J79　D7　100d rose lake　15.00　1.00
　　　Nos. J75-J79 (5)　53.25　2.40

OFFICIAL STAMPS

Issues for Federal Republic

Arms of the
Federated
People's
Republic — O1

Perf. 12½
1946, Nov. 1　**Unwmk.**　**Typo.**
O1　O1　50p orange　.20　.20
O2　O1　1d blue green　.20　.20
O3　O1　1.50d olive green　.20　.20
O4　O1　2.50d red　.20　.20
O5　O1　4d yellow brown　.40　.20
O6　O1　5d deep blue　.60　.20
O7　O1　8d chocolate　1.25　.20
O8　O1　12d violet　1.40　.25
　　　Nos. O1-O8 (8)　4.45　1.65

For surcharges see Nos. 272A-272B, Istria 43, 45, 47, 49, 51.

POSTAL TAX STAMPS

Catalogue values for unused
stamps in this section are for
Never Hinged items.

The tax was for the Red Cross or The Olympic Fund unless otherwise noted.

Red Cross　　　　Dr. Vladen
Emblem　　　　Djordjevic
PT1　　　　　　　PT2

Unwmk.
1933, Sept. 17　**Litho.**　**Perf. 13**
RA1　PT1　50p dark blue & red　1.10　.25

Obligatory on inland letters during Red Cross Week, Sept. 17-23.
See No. RAJ1.

1936, Sept. 20　**Typo.**　**Perf. 12**
RA2　PT2　50p brn blk & red　.75　.25

Obligatory on inland letters during Red Cross Week, Sept. 20-26.

Aiding the
Wounded
PT3

1938, Sept. 18　**Litho.**　**Perf. 12½**
RA3　PT3　50p dk bl, red, yel &
　　　　　grn　.75　.25

1940, Sept. 15　　　　　**Redrawn**
RA4　PT3　50p slate blue & red　1.10　.25

The inscription at the upper right of this stamp and the numerals of value are in smaller characters.
Obligatory on all letters during the second week of September.

Issues for Federal Republic

Ruined Dwellings — PT4

Red Cross Nurse — PT5

1947, Jan. 1   Litho.   Perf. 12½
RA5 PT4 50p brn & scarlet   .50 .20
See No. RAJ2. For overprints see Trieste Nos. RA1, RAJ1.

1948, Oct. 1
RA6 PT5 50p dk vio bl & red   .50 .20
See No. RAJ3.

Nurse and Child — PT6

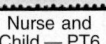
Nurse Holding Book — PT7

1949, Nov. 5
RA7 PT6 50p red & brown   .50 .20
See No. RAJ4. For overprints see Trieste Nos. RA2, RAJ2.

1950, Oct. 1
RA8 PT7 50p dark green & red   .50 .20
Obligatory Oct. 1-8, 1950.
See No. RAJ6.

Hands Raising Red Cross Flag — PT8

Nurse — PT9

1951, Oct. 7
RA9 PT8 50p vio bl & red   .50 .20
Obligatory Oct. 7-14.
For overprints see Trieste Nos. RA3, RAJ3.

1952, Oct. 5   Photo.   Perf. 12½
RA10 PT9 50p gray & carmine   .50 .20
For overprint see Trieste No. RA4.

Child Receiving Blood Transfusion PT10

Youths Carrying Flags PT11

1953, Oct. 25   Litho.
RA11 PT10 2d red vio & red   .50 .20
See No. RAJ8. For overprints see Trieste Nos. RA5, RAJ5.

1954, Nov. 1
RA12 PT11 2d gray grn & red   .50 .20
See Nos. RAJ9.

Infant — PT11a

1954, Oct. 4
RA12A PT11a 2d brn & salmon   1.75 .80
The tax was for Children's Week.

Girl PT12

Nurse Opening Window PT13

1955, Oct. 2   Unwmk.   Perf. 12½
RA13 PT12 2d dull red   .50 .20
The tax was for child welfare.
See No. RAJ10.

1955, Oct. 31
RA14 PT13 2d vio blk & red   .50 .20
See No. RAJ11.

Ruins in the Snow — PT14

Children and Goose — PT15

1956, May 6   Perf. 12½
RA15 PT14 2d sepia & red   .50 .20
See No. RAJ12.

1956, Sept. 30
RA16 PT15 2d gray green   .50 .20
The tax was for child welfare.
See No. RAJ13.

Plane over Temporary Shelter — PT16

1957, May 5   Litho.
RA17 PT16 2d lt bl, blk & car   .50 .20
See No. RAJ14.

Girl and Boy Pioneers PT17

1957, Sept. 30   Unwmk.   Perf. 12½
RA18 PT17 2d rose & gray   .50 .20
Children's Week. Obligatory Oct. 2-6.
See No. RAJ15.

Redrawn Type of Regular Issue, 1953
1958, May 4   Perf. 12½x12
RA19 A95 2d multicolored   .50 .20
On No. RA19 the UN emblem has been left out, Cyrillic inscriptions at left added, country name in Latin letters.

Playing Children — PT18

Helping Hand and Family — PT19

1958, Oct. 5   Litho.   Perf. 12½
RA20 PT18 2d brt yel & black   .50 .20
Children's Week, Oct. 5-11.

1959, May 3
RA21 PT19 2d blue vio & red   .50 .20
Red Cross centenary. Obligatory May 3-9.
See No. RAJ18.

Blackboard, Flower and Fish — PT20

"Reconstruction" PT21

1959, Oct. 5   Unwmk.
RA22 PT20 2d ocher & Prus grn   .50 .20
Children's Week. Obligatory on domestic mail, Oct. 5-11.
See No. RAJ19.

1960, May 8   Perf. 12½
RA23 PT21 2d slate & red   .50 .20
Obligatory May 8-14. See No. RAJ20.

Girl and Toys — PT22

Blood Donor Symbolism PT23

1960, Oct. 2   Litho.   Perf. 12½
RA24 PT22 2d red   .50 .20
Issued for Children's Week. Obligatory on domestic mail Oct. 2-8.

See No. RAJ21.

1961, May 7
RA25 PT23 2d multicolored   .50 .20
Obligatory May 7-13. Exists imperf. Value $14.
See No. RAJ22.

Bird Holding Flower PT24

1961, Oct. 1
RA26 PT24 2d orange & violet   .50 .20
Children's Week. Obligatory on domestic mail, Oct. 1-7.
See No. RAJ23.

Bandages and Symbols of Home, Industry, Weather, Transportation, Fire and Flood — PT25

1962, Apr. 30   Perf. 12½
RA27 PT25 5d red brn, gray & red   .50 .20
Obligatory on domestic mail May 6-12.
See No. RAJ24.

Centenary Emblem — PT26

Parachute Drop of Supplies, Yugoslav Flag — PT27

1963, May 5   Unwmk.   Perf. 12½
RA28 PT26 5d dl yel, red & gray   .50 .20
Intl. Red Cross, centenary. Obligatory on all domestic mail during Red Cross Week, May 5-11.
See No. RAJ25.

1964, Apr. 27   Litho.
RA29 PT27 5d blue, rose & dk bl   .50 .20
Obligatory on domestic mail, May 3-9.

Children in Circle — PT28

1965, May 2   Litho.   Perf. 12½
RA30 PT28 5d tan & red   .50 .20
Obligatory on domestic mail, May 2-8.

Arrows
PT29

1966, Apr. 28   Litho.   Perf. 12½
RA31 PT29 5p gray & multi   .50   .20
Obligatory on domestic mail, May 1-7.

Crosses and
Flower
PT30

1967, Apr. 28   Litho.   Perf. 12½
RA32 PT30 5p vio, red & yel grn   .50   .20

Honeycomb and
Red
Cross — PT31

1968, Apr. 30   Litho.   Perf. 12
RA33 PT31 5p multicolored   .50   .20
Obligatory on all domestic mail May 5-11.

Aztec Calendar
Stone and
Olympic
Rings — PT32

1968, Oct. 12   Perf. 12½
RA34 PT32 10p black & multi   .50   .20

Red Cross,
Hands and
Globe — PT33

Globe, Olympic
Torch and
Rings — PT34

1969, May 18   Litho.   Perf. 12
RA35 PT33 20p red org, dl red &
          blk   .50   .20

1969, Nov. 24   Litho.   Perf. 11
RA36 PT34 10p gold & multi   .50   .20
Yugoslav Olympic Committee, 50th anniv.

Symbolic
Flower and
People
PT35

1970, Apr. 27   Litho.   Perf. 13
RA37 PT35 20p vio bl, org & red   .50   .20

Olympic
Flag — PT36

Red Cross
Encircling
Globe
PT37

Olympic Rings
and Disk — PT38

1970, June 10   Litho.   Perf. 13x13½
RA38 PT36 10p multicolored   .50   .20

1971, Apr. 26   Litho.   Perf. 12½
RA39 PT37 20p blue, yel & red   .50   .20

1971, June 15   Litho.   Perf. 12½
RA40 PT38 10p blue & black   .50   .20

Red Cross
and
Hemispheres
PT39

1972, Apr. 27   Perf. 13½x13
RA41 PT39 20p red & multi   .50   .20

Olympic Rings,
TV Tower, Munich
and Sapporo
Emblems — PT40

1972, May   Perf. 13x13½
RA42 PT40 10p ultra & multi   .50   .20

Red Cross,
Crescent and Lion
Emblems — PT41

Globe and
Olympic
Rings — PT42

1973, Apr. 24   Litho.   Perf. 13x13½
RA43 PT41 20p blue & multi   .50   .20

1973, June 1   Litho.   Perf. 13x13½
RA44 PT42 10p multicolored   .50   .20

Drop of
Blood, Red
Cross
Emblems
PT43

1974, Apr. 25   Litho.   Perf. 13
RA45 PT43 20p red & multi   .50   .20

Olympic
Rings
PT44

1974, June 1   Litho.   Perf. 13
RA46 PT44 10p blue & multi   .50   .20

Red Cross,
Hands
PT45

1975, Apr. 23   Photo.   Perf. 11½
RA47 PT45 20p blue, car & blk   .50   .20

Olympic
Rings — PT46

1975, June 2   Litho.   Perf. 13½
RA48 PT46 10p multicolored   .50   .20

Ruin and
Clock — PT47

1975, July 26   Litho.   Perf. 13x13½
RA49 PT47 30p blk & dk bl   .75   .20
Solidarity Week, July 26-Aug. 1. See Nos.
RA61-RA62.

Red
Crescent,
Red Cross,
Red
Lion — PT48

1976, May 8   Photo.   Perf. 12½x13
RA50 PT48 20p multicolored   1.00   .50

1984 Olympics
PT49

1976, July 26   Litho.   Perf. 13½
RA51 PT49 10p intense blue   .60   .20

Fight
Tuberculosis, Red
Cross — PT50

1977, Sept. 14   Photo.
RA52 PT50 50p multicolored   7.00 7.00
RA53 PT50 1d multicolored   .80   .80

1984
Olympics
PT51

1977, Dec. 17   Perf. 13½x13
RA54 PT51 10p multicolored   .50   .20

Postal Tax Stamps for use in a particular republic or republics fall beyond the
scope of this catalogue and are not
listed. These stamps, issued since
1977, were not intended for nationwide
use. Some of these issues have
designs which are similar to stamps
used nationwide, most notably those
using variations of the Ruin and Clock
(PT47) design. Most others show the
Red Cross or the Tuberculosis Cross.

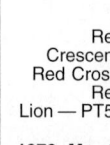

Red
Crescent,
Red Cross,
Red
Lion — PT52

1978, May 7   Litho.   Perf. 13½
RA55 PT52 20p on 1d bl & red   1.00   .35
RA56 PT52 1d blue & red   .60   .20

1984
Olympics
PT53

1978, Sept.
RA57 PT53 30p multicolored   1.00   .25

8th
Mediterranean
Games, Split,
Sept. 15-
29 — PT54

1979, Mar. 1   Photo.   Perf. 13½x13
RA58 PT54 1d violet   .50   .25
RA59 PT54 1d greenish blue   .50   .25

Red Cross Week PT55

1979, May 6   *Perf. 13½*
RA60 PT55 1d multicolored   .50 .25

Ruin and Clock Type of 1975 Inscribed "1.-7.VI"

1979, June 1
RA61 PT47 30p blk & intense bl   .60 .20

Solidarity Week.

Ruin and Clock Type of 1975 Inscribed "1.-7.VI"

1980, June 1   **Litho.**   *Perf. 13x13½*
RA62 PT47 1d black & blue   .50 .25

Solidarity Week, June 1-7.

Olympic Week — PT57

1979, Oct. 15   **Photo.**   *Perf. 14*
RA63 PT57 30p blue & red   .50 .25

Sculpture, Red Cross — PT58

Olympic Week — PT59

1980, May 4   **Litho.**   *Perf. 13½*
RA64 PT58 1d multicolored   .60 .30

1980, Oct. 20   *Perf. 14*
RA65 PT59 50p multicolored   .50 .25

SPENS '81, Novi Sad — PT60

1980, Dec. 20   *Perf. 13½*
RA66 PT60 1d multicolored   .50 .20

Red Cross — PT61

Fight Tuberculosis, Red Cross — PT62

1981, May 4   **Photo.**
RA67 PT61 1d multicolored   .50 .20

1981, Sept. 14
RA68 PT62 1d multicolored   .50 .20

Handshake PT63

Robert Koch PT64

Fight Tuberculosis, Red Cross — PT65

1982, May   **Litho.**   *Perf. 13*
RA69 PT63 1d black & red   .50 .20

1983, Sept. 18   **Litho.**   *Perf. 13*
RA70 PT64 1d multicolored   .50 .20

For surcharge see No. RA76.

1983, Sept. 14   **Litho.**   *Perf. 13½*
RA71 PT65 1d bluish grn, blk & red   .50 .20
RA72 PT65 2d bluish grn, blk & red   .50 .20

1984 Winter Olympics, Sarajevo PT66

1983, Oct. 20   **Litho.**   *Perf. 12½*
RA73 PT66 2d greenish blue   .50 .20

PLANICA 50 — PT67

1985, Apr. 1   **Photo.**   *Perf. 14*
RA74 PT67 2d brt ultra & blue   .50 .20

Ruin, Clock and Red Cross — PT68

1987, June 1   **Litho.**   *Perf. 10*
RA75 PT68 30d multicolored   .50 .20

Solidarity Week, June 1-7.

No. RA70 Surcharged in Silver

1988, Sept. 14   **Litho.**   *Perf. 13*
RA76 PT64 12d on 1d multi   .50 .20

Intl. Red Cross, 125th Anniv. — PT69

1989, May 8   **Litho.**   *Perf. 12x11*
Without Gum
RA77 PT69 20d bl, sil & red   .50 .20
RA78 PT69 80d bl, sil & red   .50 .20
RA79 PT69 150d bl, sil & red   .50 .20
RA80 PT69 160d bl, sil & red   .50 .20
Nos. RA77-RA80 (4)   2.00 .80

Souvenir folders with perf. or imperf. miniature sheets of 4 sold for 3200d.

Ruin, Clock and Red Cross — PT70   Building, Clock and Red Cross — PT71

1989, June 1   *Perf. 10*
Without Gum
RA81 PT70 250d red & silver   .50 .20
Roulette 10
RA82 PT71 400d brt bl gray & red   .50 .20

Souvenir folders with perf. or imperf. miniature sheets containing one 45x65mm stamp like RA81 sold for 3200d.

Fight TB, Red Cross — PT72   Red Cross — PT73

1989, Sept. 14   **Rough Perf. 10½**
Without Gum
RA83 PT72 20d black & red   .50 .20
RA84 PT72 200d black & red   .50 .20
RA85 PT72 250d black & red   .50 .20
RA86 PT72 400d black & red   .50 .20
RA87 PT72 650d black & red   .50 .20
Nos. RA83-RA87 (5)   2.50 1.00

1990, May 8   *Perf. 13½*
Without Gum
RA88 PT73 10p green & red   .50 .20
RA89 PT73 20p green & red   .50 .20
RA90 PT73 30p green & red   .50 .20
Nos. RA88-RA90 (3)   1.50 .60

Flowers — PT74

Macedonian Red Cross, 45th Anniv. — PT75

1990, May 8   *Perf. 10*
Without Gum
RA91 PT74 20p shown   .50 .20
RA92 PT74 20p multi, diff.   .50 .20
RA93 PT75 20p multicolored   .50 .20
   a.   Block of 3 + label, #RA91-RA93   .75 .75

Souvenir folders with perf. or imperf. miniature sheets of 3 + label sold for 4d.

PT76   PT77

1990, Sept. 14   **Litho.**   *Perf. 10*
Without Gum
RA94 PT76 20p blue, org & red   .50 .20
RA95 PT76 25p blue, yel & red   .50 .20
RA96 PT76 50p blue, yel & red   .70 .20
Nos. RA94-RA96 (3)   1.70 .60

Fight tuberculosis, Red Cross.

1991, Sept. 14   **Litho.**   *Perf. 12½*
Without Gum
RA97 PT77 1.20d dk bl, yel & red   .70 .35
RA98 PT77 2.50d multicolored   1.00 .40

Required on mail 9/14-21/91.

PT78   PT79

1994, May 8   **Litho.**   *Perf. 13½*
RA99 PT78 10p multicolored   .50 .50

No. RA99 was required on mail 5/8-15/94.

1994, Sept. 14   **Litho.**   *Perf. 13x13½*
RA100 PT79 10p multicolored   .50 .50

No. RA100 was required on mail 9/14-21/94.

PT80

PT81

1995, May 8   Litho.   Perf. 13½x13
RA101 PT80 10p multicolored   .50 .50

No. RA101 was required on mail 5/8-15/95.

1995, Sept. 9   Litho.   Perf. 13½x13
RA102 PT81 10p Wilhelm Rönt-
        gen   .50 .50

Fight Tuberculosis. No. RA102 was required
on mail 9/9-14/95.

PT82

PT83

1996, May 8   Litho.   Perf. 12x12½
RA103 PT82 15p multicolored   .50 .50

No. RA103 was required on mail 5/8-15/96.

1996, Sept.   Litho.   Perf. 12x12½
RA104 PT83 20p multicolored   .50 .50

PT84

1997, May 8   Litho.   Perf. 13
RA105 PT84 20p multicolored   .50 .50

No. RA105 was required on mail 5/8-15/97.

Milutin Rankovic
(1880-1967),
Artist — PT85

1997, Sept. 14   Litho.   Perf. 14
RA106 PT85 20p multicolored   .50 .50

Fight Tuberculosis. No. RA106 was required
on mail 9/14-21/97.

PT86

1998, May 8   Litho.   Perf. 13¾
RA107 PT86 20p multicolored   .50 .50

No. RA107 was required on mail 5/8-15/98.

Red Cross — PT87

1999, May 8   Litho.   Perf. 13¾
RA108 PT87 1d multi   .50 .50

No. RA108 was required on mail 5/8-5/15/99.

Red Cross — PT88

1999, Sept. 14
RA109 PT88 1d multi   .50 .50

No. RA109 was required on mail 9/14-
9/21/99.

POSTAL TAX DUE STAMPS

Catalogue values for unused stamps in this section are for Never Hinged items.

The tax of Nos. RAJ1-RAJ9, RAJ11-
RAJ12, RAJ14 and RAJ18 was for the
Red Cross.

Inscribed "PORTO."

Type of Postal Tax Stamp, 1933
1933   Unwmk.   Litho.   Perf. 13
RAJ1 PT1 50p dull grn & red   1.75 .20

Type of Postal Tax Stamp, 1947
1947   Perf. 12½
RAJ2 PT4 50p blue grn & scar   1.10 .25
For surcharge see Trieste No. RAJ1.

Type of Postal Tax Stamp, 1948
1948
RAJ3 PT5 50p dark grn & red   1.10 .20

Type of Postal Tax Stamp, 1949
1949
RAJ4 PT6 50p red & violet   1.50 .25
For overprint see Trieste No. RAJ2.

Cross and Map
of Yugoslavia
PTD2

Red Cross
PTD3

1950   Unwmk.   Perf. 12½
RAJ5 PTD2 50p red brown & red 1.00 .20

Type of Postal Tax Stamp, 1951
1951
RAJ6 PT8 50p emerald & red   1.10 .20
For overprint see Trieste No. RAJ3.

1952   Unwmk.   Photo.   Perf. 12½
RAJ7 PTD3 50p gray & car   1.10 .20
For overprint see Trieste No. RAJ4.

Types of Postal Tax Stamps, 1953-57
1953-57   Litho.
RAJ8 PT10 2d yel brown & red 1.25 .25
RAJ9 PT11 2d lilac & red ('54) 1.25 .25
RAJ10 PT12 2d yel grn ('55) 1.10 .25
RAJ11 PT13 2d dk vio brn & red
        ('55) 1.40 .25
RAJ12 PT14 2d blue grn & red
        ('56) .75 .25
RAJ13 PT15 2d violet brn ('56) 1.10 .25
RAJ14 PT16 2d gray, blk & car
        ('57) 1.00 .25
RAJ15 PT17 2d lt bl, bis & grn
        ('57) .90 .25
    Nos. RAJ8-RAJ15 (8) 8.75 2.00
For overprints see Trieste Nos. RAJ5-RAJ5.

Redrawn Type of Regular Issue, 1953
1958   Perf. 12½x12
RAJ16 A95 2d multicolored   .75 .20

Child With
Toy — PTD4

1958   Litho.   Perf. 12½
RAJ17 PTD4 2d lt ultra & blk .70 .25
Issued for Children's Week, Oct. 5-11.

Type of Postal Tax Stamp, 1959
1959
RAJ18 PT19 2d yel org & red .70 .25

Type of Postal Tax Stamp, 1959
Design: Tree, cock and wheat.
1959
RAJ19 PT20 2d ocher & mar .85 .25

Type of Postal Tax Stamp, 1960
1960
RAJ20 PT21 2d vio brn & red 1.00 .25

Type of Postal Tax Stamp, 1960
Design: Boy, tools and ball.
1960
RAJ21 PT22 2d Prussian blue .90 .25

Type of Postal Tax Stamp, 1961
1961, May 7
RAJ22 PT23 2d multicolored 1.10 .25

Type of Postal Tax Stamp, 1961
1961, Oct. 1
RAJ23 PT24 2d apple grn & brn .60 .25

Type of Postal Tax Stamp, 1962
1962, Apr. 30
RAJ24 PT25 5d brn red, bl & red .50 .25

Type of Postal Tax Stamp, 1963
1963, May 5
RAJ25 PT26 5d red org, red &
        gray .60 .25

OFFICES ABROAD

King Peter II — A1

1943   Unwmk.   Typo.   Perf. 12½
1K1 A1 2d dark blue .30 4.00
1K2 A1 3d slate .30 4.00
1K3 A1 5d carmine .30 4.00
1K4 A1 10d black .30 4.00
    Nos. 1K1-1K4 (4) 1.20 16.00
For surcharges see Nos. 1KB1-1KB4.

V. Vodnik — A2   Peter
                        Nyegosh — A3

3d, Ljudovit Gaj. 4d, Vuk Stefanovic
Karadzic. 5d, Bishop Joseph Strossmayer.
10d, Karageorge.

1943, Dec. 1   Engr.   Perf. 12½x13
1K5 A2 1d red org & black .40 8.25
1K6 A3 2d yel green & blk .65 8.50
1K7 A2 3d dp ultra & blk .65 8.75
1K8 A2 4d dk pur & brn blk 1.25 9.25
1K9 A2 5d brn vio & brn blk 1.25 9.75
1K10 A3 10d brn & brown blk 4.00 10.00
    Nos. 1K5-1K10 (6) 8.20 54.50

**Souvenir Sheet
Perf. 13½
Center in Black**
1K11   Sheet of 6, #1K5-1K10   6.75

25th anniv. of the Union of Liberated Yugoslavia. Valid on ships of the Yugoslav Navy
and Mercantile Marine.
    Nos. 1K5-1K10 overprinted diagonally
"1945" in London were not issued. In 1950,
they were sold by the Yugoslav Government
without postal validity. Later they appeared
with the additional overprint of the outline of a
plane at upper left in carmine or black.

OFFICES ABROAD SEMI-POSTAL STAMPS

Nos. 1K1-1K4
Surcharged in
Orange or Black

1943   Unwmk.   Perf. 12½
1KB1 A1 2d + 12.50d dk bl 1.50 8.25
1KB2 A1 3d + 12.50d slate 1.50 8.25
1KB3 A1 5d + 12.50d car (Bk) 1.50 8.25
1KB4 A1 10d + 12.50d black 1.50 8.25
    Nos. 1KB1-1KB4 (4) 6.00 33.00

The surtax was for the Red Cross.

LJUBLJANA
(Lubiana, Laibach)
Italian Occupation

Under Italian occupation in 1941, the
western half of Slovenia was known as
the Province of Ljubljana (Lubiana to
the Italians, Laibach to the Germans)
and a quisling administration was set up
under the profascist General Rupnik.

100 Centesimi = 1 Lira

Yugoslavia Nos. 127,
128, 142-154
Overprinted in Black

1941   Unwmk.   Perf. 12½, 13x12½
N1 A16 25p black .75 1.00
N2 A16 50p orange .75 1.00
N3 A16 1d yellow grn .75 1.00
N4 A16 1.50d red .75 1.00
N5 A16 2d dp magenta .75 1.00
N6 A16 3d dl red brn .75 1.00
N7 A16 4d ultra .75 1.00
N8 A16 5d dark blue .75 1.00
N9 A16 5.50d dk vio brn .75 1.00
N10 A16 6d slate blue 1.00 1.50
N11 A16 8d sepia 1.00 1.50
N12 A10 10d bright vio 1.00 1.50
N13 A16 12d brt violet 2.00 2.50
N14 A10 15d brown 150.00 175.00
N15 A16 16d dl violet 2.00 2.50
N16 A16 20d blue 5.00 6.50
N17 A16 30d brt pink 35.00 40.00
    Nos. N1-N17 (17) 203.75 240.00

Yugoslavia Nos. 127,
142-154 Overprinted
in Black

N18 A16 25p black .60 .50
N19 A16 50p orange .60 .50
N20 A16 1d yellow grn .60 .50
N21 A16 1.50d red .60 .50
N22 A16 2d dp magenta .60 .50
N23 A16 3d dl red brn .60 .50
N24 A16 4d ultra .60 .50
N25 A16 5d dark blue .60 .50
N26 A16 5.50d dk vio brn .60 .50
N27 A16 6d slate blue .60 .50
N28 A16 8d sepia .60 .50
N29 A10 10d brt violet 1.40 1.25

N30	A16	12d bright vio	.60	.50
N31	A16	16d dl violet	1.40	1.25
N32	A16	20d blue	5.00	4.50
N33	A16	30d brt pink	50.00	35.00

Yugoslavia Nos. 145,
148 Surcharged in
Black

N34	A16	50p on 1.50d red	.50	.60
N35	A16	1d on 4d ultra	.50	.60
		Nos. N18-N35 (18)	66.00	49.20

German Occupation

Stamps of Italy, 1929-42, Overprinted
or Surcharged in Blue, Carmine, Black
or Green

a

b

c

1944　　Wmk. 140　　Perf. 14

N36	A90(a)	5c ol brown	.25	1.75
N37	A92(b)	10c dark brn	.25	1.75
N38	A93(a)	15c ol brown	.25	1.75
N39	A91(a)	20c rose red	.25	1.75
N40	A95(a)	25c dp grn (C)	.25	1.75
N41	A95(a)	30c ol brown	.25	1.75
N42	A93(a)	35c dp bl (C)	.40	1.75
N43	A95(a)	50c purple (C)	.40	2.75
N44	A94(a)	75c rose red	.40	4.00
N45	A91(a)	1 l deep vio	.40	4.00
N46	A94(a)	1.25 l dp bl (C)	.40	2.00
N47	A95(a)	1.75 l red org	6.00	21.00
N48	A93(a)	2 l car lake	.40	4.00
N49	A90(c)	2.55 l on 5c ol brn (Bk)	2.00	10.00
N50	A94(a)	5 l on 25c dp grn	2.00	17.50
N51	A93(b)	10 l purple	8.75	50.00
N52	A91(a)	20 l on 20c rose red (G)	7.00	55.00
N53	A93(b)	25 l on 2 l car lake (G)	8.00	100.00
N54	A92(a)	50 l on 1.75 l red org (C)	40.00	350.00
		Nos. N36-N54 (19)	77.65	632.50

Krizna Jama — A1

Cerknica
Lake — A2

Designs: 20c, Railroad Bridge, Borovnica.
25c, Landscape near Ljubljana. 50c, Church,
Ribnica. 75c, View, Ljubljana. 1 l, Old Castle,
Ljubljana. 1.25 l, Kocevje (Gottschee). 1.50 l,
Borovnica Falls. 2 l, Castle, Konstanjevnica.
2.50 l, Castle, Turjak. 3 l, Castle, Zuzemperk.
5 l, View of Krk. 10 l, View of Otolac. 20 l,
Farm, Carniola. 30 l, Castle and church,
Tabor.

Perf. 10½x11½, 11½x10½

1945		Photo.	Unwmk.	
N55	A1	5c black	.40	3.50
N56	A2	10c red orange	.40	3.50
N57	A2	20c brn carmine	.40	3.50
N58	A2	25c dk sl green	.40	3.50
N59	A1	50c deep violet	.40	3.50
N60	A2	75c vermilion	.40	3.50
N61	A2	1 l dark ol grn	.40	3.50

N62	A1	1.25 l dark blue	.40	7.00
N63	A1	1.50 l olive black	.40	7.00
N64	A2	2 l ultramarine	.60	8.50
N65	A2	2.50 l brown	.60	8.50
N66	A1	3 l brt red vio	1.50	14.00
N67	A2	5 l dk red brn	1.60	14.00
N68	A2	10 l slate green	3.25	62.50
N69	A2	20 l sapphire	16.00	175.00
N70	A1	30 l rose pink	90.00	775.00
		Nos. N55-N70 (16)	117.15	1,096.

SEMI-POSTAL STAMPS

Italian Occupation

Yugoslavia Nos. B116-B119 with
Additional Overprint in Black

Perf. 11½x12½, 12½x11½

1941			Unwmk.	
NB1	AP6	50p + 50p on 5d	15.00	20.00
NB2	AP7	1d + 1d on 10d	15.00	20.00
NB3	AP8	1.50d + 1.50d on 20d	15.00	20.00
NB4	AP9	2d + 2d on 30d	15.00	20.00
		Nos. NB1-NB4 (4)	60.00	80.00

German Occupation

Italy Nos. E14 and E15 Surcharged in
Red:

1944			Wmk. 140	
NB5	SD4	1.25 l + 50 l green	27.50	450.00
NB6	SD4	2.50 l + 50 l dp org	27.50	450.00

The surtax aided the Red Cross.

Same, Surcharged in Blue or Green:

NB7	SD4	1.25 l + 50 l grn (B)	27.50	450.00
NB8	SD4	2.50 l + 50 l dp org	27.50	450.00
		Nos. NB5-NB8 (4)	110.00	1,800.

The surtax aided the Homeless Relief Fund.
The German and Slovenian inscriptions in
the surcharges are transposed on Nos. NB6
and NB8.

Italy Nos. C12-C14, C16-C18
Surcharged "DEN WAISEN,"
"SIROTAM," Heraldic Eagle and Surtax
in Blue or Red

1944			Wmk. 140	
NB9	AP4	25c + 10 l dk grn	10.00	350.00
NB10	AP3	50c + 10 l ol brn	10.00	350.00
NB11	AP5	75c + 20 l org brn	10.00	350.00
NB12	AP5	1 l + 20 l purple	10.00	350.00
NB13	AP6	2 l + 20 l dp bl (R)	10.00	350.00
NB14	AP3	10 l + 20 l dp car (C)	10.00	350.00
		Nos. NB9-NB14 (6)	60.00	2,100.

The surcharge aided orphans.

Same, Surcharged "WINTERHILFE,"
"ZIMSKA POMOC," Heraldic Eagle
and Surtax in Blue or Red

NB15	AP4	25c + 10 l dk grn	10.00	350.00
NB16	AP3	50c + 10 l ol brn	10.00	350.00
NB17	AP5	75c + 20 l org brn	10.00	350.00
NB18	AP5	1 l + 20 l purple	10.00	350.00
NB19	AP6	2 l + 20 l dp bl (R)	10.00	350.00
NB20	AP3	5 l + 20 l dk grn	10.00	350.00
		Nos. NB15-NB20 (6)	60.00	2,100.

The surcharge was for winter relief.

AIR POST STAMPS

Italian Occupation

Yugoslavia Nos. C7-C16 Ovptd. like
Nos. NB1-NB4

Perf. 12½, 12½x11½, 11½x12½

1941			Unwmk.	
NC1	AP6	50p brown	1.40	2.00
NC2	AP7	1d yel grn	1.40	2.00
NC3	AP8	2d bl gray	1.60	2.00
NC4	AP9	2.50d rose red	1.60	2.00
NC5	AP7	5d brn vio	4.00	5.25
NC6	AP7	10d brn lake	4.00	5.25
NC7	AP8	20d dark grn	16.00	17.50
NC8	AP9	30d ultra	40.00	30.00
NC9	AP10	40d Prus grn & pale grn	125.00	90.00
NC10	AP11	50d sl bl & gray bl	95.00	75.00
a.		Inverted overprint	250.00	
		Nos. NC1-NC10 (10)	290.00	231.00

German Occupation

Italy Nos. C12-C14, C16-C19
Overprinted Types "a" and "b" in
Carmine, Green or Blue

1944			Wmk. 140	Perf. 14
NC11	AP4(a)	25c dk grn (C)	4.75	35.00
NC12	AP3(b)	50c ol brn (C)	8.00	110.00
NC13	AP5(a)	75c org brn (G)	4.75	35.00
NC14	AP5(b)	1 l pur (C)	10.00	110.00
NC15	AP6(a)	2 l dp bl (Bl)	4.75	77.50
NC16	AP3(b)	5 l dk grn (C)	4.75	110.00
NC17	AP3(a)	10 l dp car (G)	4.00	77.50
		Nos. NC11-NC17 (7)	41.00	555.00

AIR POST SPECIAL DELIVERY STAMP

German Occupation

Italy #CE3 Ovptd. Type "b" in Blue

1944			Wmk. 140	Perf. 14
NCE1	APSD2	2 l gray blk	10.00	77.50

SPECIAL DELIVERY STAMP

German Occupation

Italy #E14 Ovptd. Type "b" in Green

1944			Wmk. 140	Perf. 14
NE1	SD4	1.25 l green	6.00	21.00

POSTAGE DUE STAMPS

Italian Occupation

Yugoslavia Nos. J28-J32 Overprinted
in Black Like Nos. N1-N17

1941			Unwmk.	Perf. 12½
NJ1	D4	50p violet	.40	.70
NJ2	D4	1d rose	.40	.70
NJ3	D4	2d deep blue	.40	.70
NJ4	D4	5d orange	7.25	8.00
NJ5	D4	10d chocolate	7.25	8.00
		Nos. NJ1-NJ5 (5)	15.70	18.10

Same Overprinted in
Black

NJ6	D4	50p violet	.40	.50
NJ7	D4	1d rose	.40	.50
NJ8	D4	2d deep blue	.80	.80
NJ9	D4	5d orange	30.00	35.00
NJ10	D4	10d chocolate	10.00	15.00
		Nos. NJ6-NJ10 (5)	41.60	51.80

Same Overprinted in
Black

NJ11	D4	50p violet	.80	.70
NJ12	D4	1d rose	1.25	1.00
NJ13	D4	2d deep blue	24.00	30.00
		Nos. NJ11-NJ13 (3)	26.05	31.70

German Occupation

Postage Due Stamps of Italy, 1934,
Overprinted or Surcharged in Various
Colors

d

e

f

g

1944			Wmk. 140	Perf. 14
NJ14	D6(d)	5c brown (Br)	2.00	62.50
NJ15	D6(e)	10c blue (Bl)	2.00	62.50
NJ16	D6(e)	20c rose red (R)	.40	1.40
NJ17	D6(e)	25c green (G)	.60	1.40
NJ18	D6(f)	30c on 50c vio (Bk)	.60	1.40
NJ19	D6(g)	40c on 5c brn (Bl)	.60	1.40
NJ20	D6(d)	50c violet (V)	.40	1.40
NJ21	D7(e)	1 l red orange (R)	2.00	70.00
NJ22	D7(d)	2 l green (Bl)	2.00	70.00
		Nos. NJ14-NJ22 (9)	10.60	272.00

Fiume-Kupa Zone
Italian Occupation

Four issues of 1941-42 consist of
overprints on Yugoslav stamps of 1939-
41: (a.) 14 stamps overprinted "ZONA
OCCUPATO FIUMANO KUPA" and
"ZOFK ZOFK ZOFK." (b.) 3 stamps
overprinted as illustrated. (c.) 1 stamp
surcharged "MEMENTO AVDERE
SEMPER." "L1," etc. (d.) 3 stamps
overprinted in arch: "Pro Maternite e
Infanzia."

ISSUES FOR ISTRIA AND
THE SLOVENE COAST
(ZONE B)

Grapes — A1

Olive
Branch — A2

Sailboat, Pola — A3

Designs: 50c, Donkey. Nos. 25-26, Ruined home. 2 l, Duino Castle. 5 l, Birthplace of Vladimir Gortan. 10 l, Plowing. Nos. 33-34, Tuna. 30 l, Viaduct at Solkan, Soca River.

Perf. 11½, 12, 10½x11½

1945-46 *Photo.*

23	A1	25c dark green	.85	1.00
24	A1	50c red brown	.20	.20
25	A1	1 l green	.20	.20
26	A1	1 l red	.20	.20
27	A2	1.50 l olive brown	.20	.20
28	A2	2 l dk Prus grn	.20	.20
29	A3	4 l red	.20	.20
30	A3	4 l bright blue	.30	.40
31	A3	5 l gray black	.20	.20
32	A3	10 l brown	.20	.20
33	A3	20 l blue	1.60	.85
34	A3	20 l dark violet	4.50	4.00
35	A3	30 l magenta	1.25	.60
		Nos. 23-35 (13)	10.10	8.45

The first (Ljubljana) printing is perf. 10½x11½ and consists of Nos. 23-24, 26-28, 30-32, 34-35. The second (Zagreb) printing is perf. 12 and consists of Nos. 23-25, 27-29, 31-33, 35. The third (Belgrade) printing is perf. 11½ and consists of Nos. 25, 28, 40-41.
See Nos. 40-41. For surcharges see Nos. 36-37, J1-J19.

Nos. 33 and 35 Surcharged with New Values and Bars in Black

1946 **Unwmk.** *Perf. 11½*

36	A3	1 l on 20 l blue	.70	1.00
37	A3	2 l on 30 l magenta	.65	1.00

Types of 1945

Design: 3 l, Duino Castle

1946, Nov. 30

40	A2	3 l crimson	1.50	1.50
41	A3	6 l ultra	3.25	3.25

Types of Yugoslavia and of Official Stamps of 1946 Surcharged in Black

On A26

On O1

1947 **Unwmk.** *Perf. 12½*

42	A26	1 l on 9d lilac rose	.20	.35
43	O1	1.50 l on 50p blue	.20	.35
44	A26	2 l on 9d lilac rose	.20	.35
45	O1	3 l on 50p blue	.20	.35
46	A26	5 l on 9d lilac rose	.20	.35
47	O1	6 l on 50p blue	.20	.35
48	A26	10 l on 9d lilac rose	.20	.35
49	O1	15 l on 50p blue	.20	.50
50	A26	20 l on 9d lilac rose	.20	.75
51	O1	50 l on 50p blue	.20	.75
		Nos. 42-51 (10)	2.00	4.45

POSTAGE DUE STAMPS

Nos. 23, 24 34 and 35 Surcharged in Black

1945 **Unwmk.** *Perf. 10½x11½*

J1	A3	50c on 20 l dk vio	.50	1.25
J2	A1	1 l on 25c dk grn	6.00	3.50
J3	A3	2 l on 30 l magenta	.90	2.00
J4	A1	4 l on 50c red brn	.70	.55
J5	A1	8 l on 50c red brn	.70	.55

J6	A1	10 l on 50c red brn	4.00	1.75
J7	A1	20 l on 50c red brn	4.50	3.00
		Nos. J1-J7 (7)	17.30	12.60

Nos. 25 and 35 Surcharged in Black

1945 *Perf. 12*

J8	A1	1 l on 1 l green	.25	.35
J9	A1	2 l on 1 l green	.25	.35
J10	A1	4 l on 1 l green	.30	.35
J11	A3	10 l on 30 l magenta	2.50	1.75
J12	A3	20 l on 30 l magenta	4.00	3.75
J13	A3	30 l on 30 l magenta	4.00	3.75
		Nos. J8-J13 (6)	11.30	10.30

The surcharges are arranged to fit the designs of the stamps.

No. 23 Surcharged in Black

1946

J14	A1	1 l on 25c dark green	.60	.70
J15	A1	2 l on 25c dark green	.85	1.00
J16	A1	4 l on 25c dark green	1.00	1.10

No. 33 Surcharged in Black

J17	A3	10 l on 20 l blue	3.00	1.50
J18	A3	20 l on 20 l blue	5.50	4.00
J19	A3	30 l on 20 l blue	6.75	5.00
		Nos. J14-J19 (6)	17.70	13.30

Type of Yugoslavia Postage Due Stamps, 1946, Surcharged in Black

1947

J20	D7	1 l on 1d brt blue grn	.20	.40
J21	D7	2 l on 1d brt blue grn	.20	.40
J22	D7	6 l on 1d brt blue grn	.20	.40
J23	D7	10 l on 1d brt blue grn	.20	.40
J24	D7	30 l on 1d brt blue grn	.30	.55
		Nos. J20-J24 (5)	1.10	2.15

TRIESTE, ZONE A
See listing under Italy, Vol. 3.

TRIESTE

A free territory (1947-1954) on the Adriatic Sea between Italy and Yugoslavia. In 1954 the territory was divided, Italy acquiring the northern section and seaport, Yugoslavia the southern section (Zone B).

Catalogue values for all unused stamps in this country are for Never Hinged items.

ZONE B

Issued by the Yugoslav Military Government

100 Centesimi = 1 Lira
100 Paras = 1 Dinar (1949)

See Istria and the Slovene Coast (Zone B) for preceding issues of 1945-47.

Stylized Gymnast and Arms of Trieste — A1

1948 Unwmk. Litho. Perf. 10½x11
Inscriptions in:

1	A1	100 l Italian	4.00	1.75
2	A1	100 l Croatian	4.00	1.75
3	A1	100 l Slovene	4.00	1.75
a.		Strip of 3, #1-3	35.00	40.00
		Nos. 1-3 (3)	12.00	5.25

May Day.

Clasped Hands, Hammer and Sickle — A2

1949 *Photo.* *Perf. 11½x12½*

4	A2	10 l grnsh blk & ol grn	.80	.80

Labor Day, May 1, 1949.
"V.U.J.A. S.T.T." are the initials of "Vojna Uprava Jugoslovenske Armije, Slobodna Teritorija Trsta" (Military Administration Yugoslav Army, Free Territory of Trieste).

Stamps of Yugoslavia, 1945-47 Overprinted in Carmine or Ultramarine

1949, Aug. 15 *Perf. 12½*

5	A22	50p ol gray	.40	.30
6	A22	1d bl grn	.40	.30
7	A24	2d scar (U)	.40	.30
8	A25	3d dl red (U)	.40	.30
9	A24	4d dk bl	.80	.30
10	A25	5d dk bl	.80	.30
11	A26	9d rose vio (U)	5.50	.80
12	A23	12d ultra	5.50	3.50
13	A23	16d blue	8.00	4.25
14	A23	20d org ver (U)	16.00	5.50
		Nos. 5-14 (10)	38.20	15.85

The letters of the overprint are set closer and in one line on Nos. 7 and 9.

Yugoslavia Nos. 266 and 267 Overprinted in Carmine

Burelage in Color of Stamp

1949

15	A58	5d blue	8.00	7.00
16	A58	12d brown	8.00	7.00

75th anniv. of the UPU.

Yugoslavia, Nos. 269 to 272, Overprinted in Carmine

1950

17	A60	2d bl grn	3.00	.70
18	A60	3d car rose	3.00	.70
19	A60	5d blue	3.00	2.00
20	A60	10d dp org	14.00	7.00
		Nos. 17-20 (4)	23.00	10.40

Workers Carrying Tools and Flag — A3

Peasant on Ass — A4

1950, May 1 *Photo.*

21	A3	3d violet	.50	.40
22	A3	10d carmine	1.00	.60

Labor Day, May 1, 1950.

1950 **Unwmk.** *Perf. 12½*

Designs: 1d, Cockerel. 2d, Goose. 3d, Bees and honeycomb. 5d, Oxen. 10d, Turkey. 15d, Goats. 20d, Silkworms.

23	A4	50p dk gray	.40	.30
24	A4	1d brn car	.40	.30
25	A4	2d dp bl	.40	.30
26	A4	3d org brn	.40	.30
27	A4	5d aqua	3.00	.30
28	A4	10d brown	3.00	.30
29	A4	15d violet	20.00	7.00
30	A4	20d dk grn	8.00	3.50
		Nos. 23-30 (8)	35.60	12.30

1951

31	A4	1d orange brown	1.25	.35
32	A4	3d rose brown	1.60	.35

Worker A5

1951, May 1

33	A5	3d dark red	.80	.40
34	A5	10d brown olive	1.25	.70

Labor Day.

Pietro Paolo Vergerio — A7

Bicycle Race — A8

1951, Oct. 21 *Litho.*

37	A7	5d blue	1.00	1.00
38	A7	10d claret	1.00	1.00
39	A7	20d sepia	1.00	1.00
		Nos. 37-39 (3)	3.00	3.00

Types of Yugoslavia, 1951, Overprinted "STT VUJA"

1951, Nov.

40	A81	10d brn org (V)	1.00	.70
41	A81	12d grnsh blk (C)	1.00	.70

1952 *Photo.*

42	A8	5d shown	.40	.30
43	A8	10d Soccer	.40	.30
44	A8	15d Rowing	.40	.30
45	A8	28d Sailing	1.60	1.00
46	A8	50d Volleyball	3.25	2.00
47	A8	100d Diving	10.00	3.50
		Nos. 42-47 (6)	16.05	7.40

Marshal Tito
A9   A10

1952, May 25   *Perf. 11½*
48 A9   15d dk brn   2.50   1.00
49 A10 28d red brn   2.50   2.00
50 A9   50d dk gray grn   4.50   2.00
     Nos. 48-50 (3)   9.50   5.00

60th birthday of Marshal Tito.

Types of Yugoslavia 1952 Overprinted
in Carmine "STT VUJNA"

1952, July 26   *Perf. 12½*
51 A90 5d dk brn & sal, cr   1.60   .40
52 A90 10d dk grn & grn   1.60   .40
53 A90 15d dk brn & bl, lil 1.60   .40
54 A90 28d dk brn & buff, cr 1.75   1.40
55 A90 50d dk brn & buff,
          yel   14.00 8.50
56 A90 100d ind & lil, pink 32.50 24.00
     Nos. 51-56 (6)   53.05 35.10

15th Olympic Games, Helsinki, 1952. Nos.
52, 54, 56 inscribed in Cyrillic characters.
The added "N" in "VUJNA" stands for
"Narodna" (Peoples'). See note after No. 4.
Nos. 51-56 exist imperf. Value of set, $750.

Yugoslavia Nos. 365 to 367
Overprinted in Carmine "STT VUJNA"

1952, Sept. 13
57 A91 15d deep claret   2.00   2.00
58 A91 28d dark brown   2.50   2.50
59 A91 50d gray   3.50   3.50
     Nos. 57-59 (3)   8.00   8.00

Formation of the Yugoslav navy, 10th anniv.

Yugoslavia No. 358 Overprinted "STT
VUJA" in Blue

1952, June 22
60 A89 15d bright rose   1.60   .75

Children's Week.

Yugoslavia Nos. 369-372 Overprinted
"VUJNA STT" in Blue or Carmine

1952, Nov. 4
61 A93 15d red brn (Bl)   .95   .65
62 A93 15d dk vio bl   .95   .65
63 A93 15d dk brn   .95   .65
64 A93 15d bl grn   .95   .65
     Nos. 61-64 (4)   3.80   2.60

Issued to publicize the 6th Yugoslavia Communist Party Congress, Zagreb, 1952.

Anchovies and Starfish — A11

1952 Unwmk. Photo. *Perf. 11x11½*
65   A11 15d red brown   3.50   3.50
  a.   Souvenir sheet, imperf. 40.00 40.00

Capodistria Phil. Exhib., Nov. 29-Dec. 7.
No. 65a was a 50d dark blue green
stamp. Sold for 85d.

Stamps or Types of Yugoslavia
Overprinted "STT VUJNA" in Various
Colors

1953, Feb. 3   *Perf. 12½*
66   A94 15d brn carmine (Bl) .40   .40
67   A94 30d chalky blue (R) 1.50   1.50

10th anniv. of the death of Nikola Tesla.

1953
68   A68 1d gray   7.50   6.00
69   A68 2d car (V)   .45   .50
70   A68 3d rose red (R)   .45   .50
71   A68 5d orange   .45   .50
72   A68 10d emerald (G)   .45   .50
73   A68 15d rose red (V)   .90   1.10

74   A68 30d blue (Bl)   4.00   2.00
75   A68 50d grnsh bl (Bl)   8.00   4.00
     Nos. 68-75 (8)   22.20 15.10

Nos. 69, 71 and 73 are lithographed.
See Nos. 90-92.

1953, Apr. 21   *Perf. 11½*
76   A95 15d dk ol grn (O)   .35   .40
77   A95 30d chalky blue (O) .35   .40
78   A95 50d henna brown   1.10   1.10
     Nos. 76-78 (3)   1.80   1.90

Issued in honor of the United Nations.

Automobile
Climbing Mt.
Lovcen — A12

Various automobiles and motorcycles.

1953, June 2   *Perf. 12½*
79   A12 15d ocher & choc   .35   .20
80   A12 30d lt bl grn & ol grn .35 .40
81   A12 50d salmon & dp plum .35   .40
82   A12 70d bl & dk bl   2.75   1.75
     Nos. 79-82 (4)   3.80   2.75

Intl. Automobile and Motorcycle Races, 1953.

Stamps or Types of Yugoslavia
Overprinted "STT VUJNA" in Various
Colors

1953, July 8   Engr.
83   A97 50d grnsh gray (C)   3.00   3.00

Tito's election to the presidency, 1/14/53.

1953, July 31
84   A98 15d gray & grn (C)   3.00   3.00

38th Esperanto Cong., Zagreb, July 25-Aug.
1, 1953. See No. C21.

1953, Sept. 5
85   A101 15d blue (C)   4.00   4.00

Liberation of Istria & the Slovene coast, 10th
anniv.

1953, Oct. 3
86   A102 15d gray   2.00   1.50

Cent. of the death of Branko Radicevic, poet.

1953, Nov. 29   *Perf. 12½x12*
87   A103 15d gray vio (V)   1.10   .70
88   A103 30d claret (Br)   1.10   .70
89   A103 50d dl bl grn (Dk Bl) 1.10 .70
     Nos. 87-89 (3)   3.30   2.10

10th anniv. of the 1st republican legislative
assembly of Yugoslavia.

1954, Mar. 5   *Perf. 12½*
90   A68 5d org (V)   1.00   .40
91   A68 10d yel grn (C)   .80   .30
92   A68 15d rose red (G)   1.00   .40
     Nos. 90-92 (3)   2.80   1.10

Overprinted in Carmine

1954   **Photo.**   *Perf. 11½*
93   A104 2d red brn, sl & cr .75   .40
94   A104 5d gray & dk yel
            brn   .75   .40
95   A104 10d ol grn & dk org
            brn   .75   .40
96   A104 15d dp bl grn & dk
            org brn   .75   .40
97   A104 17d gray brn, dk
            brn & cr   .75   .40
98   A104 25d bis, gray bl &
            org yel   .75   .40
99   A105 30d lil & dk brn   .75   .40
100 A105 35d rose vio & bl
            blk   .75   .60
101 A105 50d yel grn & vio
            brn   1.50 1.00
102 A105 65d org brn & gray
            blk   4.50 2.50
103 A105 70d bl & org brn   10.00 5.00
104 A105 100d brt bl & blk brn 30.00 20.00
     Nos. 93-104 (12)   52.00 31.90

Overprinted in Various Colors

1954, Oct. 8   *Perf. 12½*
105 A107 15d mar, red, ocher &
            dk bl (Bk)   .80   .55
106 A107 30d dk bl, grn, sal buff
            & choc (G)   .80   .55
107 A107 50d brn, bis & red (G) .80 .55

108 A107 70d dk grn, gray grn &
            choc (R)   1.60   1.00
     Nos. 105-108 (4)   4.00   2.65

150th anniv. of the 1st Serbian insurrection.

AIR POST STAMPS

AP1

                 Perf. 12½x11½
1948, Oct. 17   Photo.   Unwmk.
C1   AP1 25 l gray   .80   .80
C2   AP1 50 l orange   .80   .80

Economic Exhib. at Capodistria, Oct. 17-24.

Fishermen — AP2   Farmer and
                         Pack
                         Mule — AP3

Mew over
Chimneys
AP4

1949, June 1   *Perf. 11½*
C3   AP2 1 l grnsh bl   .40   .30
C4   AP3 2 l red brn   .40   .30
C5   AP2 5 l blue   .40   .30
C6   AP3 10 l purple   2.00   1.50
C7   AP3 25 l brown   5.50   3.50
C8   AP3 50 l ol grn   5.50   3.50
C9   AP4 100 l dk vio brn   10.00 5.50
     Nos. C3-C9 (7)   24.20 14.90

Italian inscriptions on Nos. C5 and C6, Croatian on No. C7, Slavonic on No. C8.
Nos. C3-C4 exist imperf. Value, each $150.

Nos. C3-C9 Surcharged "DIN," or New
Value and "DIN" in Various Colors

1949, Nov. 5
C10 AP2 1d on 1 l (Bk)   .40   .30
C11 AP3 2d on 2 l (S)   .40   .30
C12 AP2 5d on 5 l (Bl)   .40   .30
C13 AP3 10d on 10 l (V)   .45   .40
C14 AP2 15d on 25 l (Br)   15.00 8.00
C15 AP3 20d on 50 l (Gr)   4.75   2.50
C16 AP4 30d on 100 l (Bk)   4.75   2.50
     Nos. C10-C16 (7)   26.15 14.30

On Nos. C14 and C15 the original value is
obliterated by a framed block, on No. C16 by
four parallel lines.

Yugoslavia No. C33 Overprinted in
Carmine and Lilac Rose Network

C17ovpt

Souvenir Sheet
1950   *Perf. 11½x12½*
C17 AP15 10d lilac rose   150.00 125.00
  a.   Imperf.   150.00 125.00

Main Square,   Lighthouse,
Capodistria — AP5   Pirano — AP6

Design: 25d, Hotel, Portorose.

1952   Unwmk.   Photo.   *Perf. 12½*
C18 AP5 5d brown   10.00 10.00
C19 AP6 15d brt bl   7.50   7.50
C20 AP5 25d green   7.50   7.50
     Nos. C18-C20 (3)   25.00 25.00

75th anniv. (in 1949) of the UPU.

Type of Yugoslavia, 1953 Overprinted
"STT VUJNA" in Carmine

1953, July 31
C21 AP21 300d vio & grn   250.00 250.00

38th Esperanto Cong., Zagreb, 7/25-8/1.
Sheets of 12 (12,000 stamps) and sheets of
8 (3,000 stamps in light violet and green).
  A private red overprint was applied margin-
ally to 250 sheets of 8: "Esperantski Kongres
— 38 — a Universala Kongreso de Esperanto
— Congresso del Esperanto."

Air Post Stamps of Yugoslavia
in New Colors Overprinted "STT
VUJNA" in Various Colors

1954   Engr.
C22 AP16 1d dp pur gray   .80   .35
C23 AP16 2d brt grn (G)   .80   .35
C24 AP16 3d red brn (Br)   .80   .35
C25 AP16 5d chocolate   .80   .35
C26 AP16 10d bl grn   .80   .35
C27 AP16 20d brn (Br)   .80   .35
C28 AP16 30d blue   .80   .35
C29 AP16 50d olive blk   .80   .60
C30 AP16 100d scar (R)   2.50   1.60
C31 AP16 200d dk bl vio (Bl) 4.75   3.00
             Perf. 11x11½
C32 AP17 500d orange (Br)   27.50 17.50
     Nos. C22-C32 (11)   41.15 25.15

POSTAGE DUE STAMPS

Yugoslavia Nos. J51 to J55
Overprinted "S T T VUJA" in Two
Lines in Ultramarine or Carmine

1949   Unwmk.   *Perf. 12½*
J1   D7 50p dp org   .80   .40
J2   D7 1d orange   .80   .40
J3   D7 2d dk bl (C)   .80   .40
J4   D7 3d grn (C)   1.50   .40
J5   D7 5d brt pur (C)   4.00   1.50
     Nos. J1-J5 (5)   7.90   3.10

Croakers   Anchovies
D1   D2

1950   Photo.
J6   D1 50p brn org   3.00   .70
J7   D1 1d dp ol grn   3.00   1.40
J8   D2 2d dk grnsh bl   3.00   1.40
J9   D2 3d dk vio bl   3.00   1.40
J10 D2 5d plum   15.00 5.50
     Nos. J6-J10 (5)   27.00 9.90

Yugoslavia Nos. J67-J74 Overprinted
"STT VUJNA" in Blue or Carmine

1952
J11 D7 1d brown (Bl)   .40   .30
J12 D7 2d emerald (C)   .40   .30
J13 D7 5d blue   .40   .30
J14 D7 10d scar (Bl)   .40   .30
J15 D7 20d purple   .40   .30
J16 D7 30d org yel (Bl)   .40   .30

J17	D7	50d ultra	.40 .30
J18	D7	100d dp plum (Bl)	10.00 7.00
		Nos. J11-J18 (8)	12.80 9.10

POSTAL TAX STAMPS

Yugoslavia No.
RA5 Surcharged
in Blue

1948   Unwmk.   Perf. 12½
RA1 PT4 2 l on 50p brn & scar   30.00 *30.00*
   Obligatory on all mail from May 22-30.

Yugoslavia No. RA7 Overprinted
"VUJA STT" in Black

1950, July 3
RA2 PT6 50p red & brn   1.50   1.00

Yugoslavia No. RA9 Overprinted "STT
VUJA" in Black

1951
RA3 PT8 50p vio bl & red   17.50 12.00

Yugoslavia No. RA10 Overprinted
"STT VUJNA" in Carmine

1952
RA4 PT9 50p gray & carmine   1.00   .60

Type of Yugoslavia, 1953, Overprinted
"STT VUJNA" in Blue

1953
RA5 PT10 2d org brn & red   1.00   .60

   The tax of Nos. RA1-RA5 was for the Red
Cross.

POSTAL TAX DUE STAMPS

Yugoslavia No. RAJ2 Surcharged Like
No. RA1 in Scarlet

1948   Unwmk.   Perf. 12½
RAJ1 PT4 2 l on 50p bl grn
     & scar   225.00 225.00

Yugoslavia No. RAJ4 Overprinted
"VUJA STT" in Black

1950, July 3
RAJ2 PT6 50p red & vio   1.50 1.00

Yugoslavia No. RAJ6 Overprinted
"STT VUJA" in Black

1951
RAJ3 PT8 50p emer & red   200.00 200.00

Yugoslavia No. RAJ7 Overprinted
"STT VUJNA" in Carmine

1952
RAJ4 PTD3 50p gray & car   1.00 .60

Type of Yugoslavia, 1953, Overprinted
"STT VUJNA" in Blue

1953
RAJ5 PT10 2d lilac rose & red   1.00 .60

ZAIRE

zä-'ir

(Congo Democratic Republic)

LOCATION — Central Africa
GOVT. — Republic
AREA — 905,365 sq. mi.
POP. — 50,481,305 (1999 est.)
CAPITAL — Kinshasa

   Congo Democratic Republic changed
its name to Republic of the Zaire in
November 1971. Issues before that

---

date are listed in Vol. 2 under Congo
Democratic Republic.

    100 Sengi = 1 Li-Kuta
    100 Ma-Kuta = 1 Zaire
    100 Centimes = 1 Franc (July 1998)

> **Catalogue values for all unused
> stamps in this country are for
> Never Hinged items.**

UNICEF Emblem,
Child
Care — A143

   UNICEF Emblem and: 14k, Map of Africa
showing Zaire. 17k, Boy in African village.

Perf. 14x13½
1971, Dec. 18   Unwmk.

750	A143	4k gold & multi	.50 .20
751	A143	14k lt bl, gold, red & grn	1.25 .65
752	A143	17k gold & multi	2.00 .60
		Nos. 750-752 (3)	3.75 1.45

   25th anniv. of UNICEF. For surcharge see
No. 1327.

Pres.
Mobutu,
MPR
Emblem
A144

1972   Photo.   Perf. 11½

753	A144	4k multi	3.25 2.50
754	A144	14k multi	3.25 2.50
755	A144	22k multi	3.25 2.50
		Nos. 753-755 (3)	9.75 7.50

   5th anniv. of the People's Revolutionary
Movement (MPR). For surcharge see #1308.

Zaire
Arms — A145   Pres. Joseph D.
Mobutu — A146

1972   Litho.   Perf. 14

756	A145	10s red org & blk	.20 .20
757	A145	40s brt bl & multi	.20 .20
758	A145	50s citron & multi	.20 .20

Perf. 13

759	A146	1k sky bl & multi	.20 .20
760	A146	2k org & multi	.20 .20
761	A146	3k multi	.20 .20
762	A146	4k emer & multi	.20 .20
763	A146	5k multi	.20 .20
764	A146	6k multi	.20 .20
765	A146	8k cit & multi	.45 .20
766	A146	9k multi	.55 .20
767	A146	10k lt lil & multi	.55 .20
768	A146	14k multi	.70 .35
769	A146	17k multi	.80 .45
770	A146	20k yel & multi	1.00 .50
771	A146	50k multi	2.40 1.00
772	A146	100k fawn & multi	4.00 2.25
		Nos. 756-772 (17)	12.25 6.95

   For surcharges and overprints see Nos.
860, 1328, O1-O11.

     Same, Denominations in Zaires
1973, Feb. 21

773	A146	0.01z sky bl & multi	.20 .20
774	A146	0.02z org & multi	.20 .20
775	A146	0.03z multi	.20 .20
776	A146	0.04z multi	.20 .20
777	A146	0.10z multi	.25 .20
778	A146	0.14z multi	.35 .30
		Nos. 773-778 (6)	1.40 1.30

Inga Dam
A147

1973, Jan. 25   Litho.   Perf. 13½

790	A147	0.04z multi	.25 .25
791	A147	0.14z pink & multi	.35 .30
792	A147	0.18z yel & multi	.60 .50
		Nos. 790-792 (3)	1.20 1.05

   Completion of first section of Inga Dam Nov.
24, 1972.

World
Map
A148

1973, June 23   Photo.   Perf. 12½x12

793	A148	0.04z lil & multi	.20 .20
794	A148	0.07z multi	.30 .20
795	A148	0.18z multi	.75 .35
		Nos. 793-795 (3)	1.25 .75

   3rd Intl. Fair at Kinshasa, June 23-July 8.
   The dark brown ink of the inscription was
applied by a thermographic process and
varnished, producing a shiny, raised effect.

Hand and
INTERPOL
Emblem — A149

1973, Sept. 28   Litho.   Perf. 12½

796	A149	0.06z multi	.40 .20
797	A149	0.14z multi	.85 .40

   50th anniversary of International Criminal
Police Organization.

Leopard
with Soccer
Ball on
Globe
A150

1974, July 17   Photo.   Perf. 11½x12

798	A150	1k multi	.20 .20
799	A150	2k multi	.25 .20
800	A150	3k multi	.75 .35
801	A150	4k multi	.85 .45
802	A150	5k multi	1.00 .55
803	A150	14k multi	2.75 1.10
a.		Souvenir sheet, 1 #803	36.00 —
		Nos. 798-803 (6)	5.80 2.85

   World Cup Soccer Championship, Munich,
June 13-July 7.

Foreman-Ali
Fight — A151

1974, Nov. 9   Litho.   Perf. 12x12½

804	A151	1k multi	.20 .20
805	A151	4k multi	.20 .20
806	A151	6k multi	.30 .25

807	A151	14k multi	.60 .45
808	A151	20k multi	.90 .85
		Nos. 804-808 (5)	2.20 1.95

   World Heavyweight Boxing Championship
match between George Foreman and Muhammad Ali, Kinshasa, Oct. 30 (postponed from
Sept. 25).

Same, Type of
1974,
Denominations
in Zaires and
Inscribed in
Various Colors

1975, Aug.   Litho.   Perf. 12x12½

809	A151	0.01z multi (R)	.20 .20
810	A151	0.04z multi (Br)	.20 .20
811	A151	0.06z multi (Bk)	.25 .25
812	A151	0.14z multi (G)	.55 .45
813	A151	0.20z multi (Bk)	.90 .85
		Nos. 809-813 (5)	2.10 1.95

Judge,
Lawyers,
IWY
Emblem
A152

1975, Dec.   Photo.   Perf. 11½

814	A152	1k dull blk & multi	.25 .20
815	A152	2k dp rose & multi	.25 .20
816	A152	4k dull grn & multi	.75 .35
817	A152	14k violet & multi	1.50 .60
		Nos. 814-817 (4)	2.75 1.35

   International Women's Year 1975.

Waterfall — A153

Okapis
A154

1975   Photo.   Perf. 11½

818	A153	1k multicolored	.20 .20
819	A153	2k lt blue & multi	.30 .20
820	A153	3k multicolored	.45 .25
821	A153	4k salmon & multi	1.00 .55
822	A153	5k green & multi	1.00 .55
		Nos. 818-822 (5)	2.95 1.75

   12th General Assembly of the Intl. Union for
Nature Preservation (U.I.C.N.), Kinshasa,
Sept. 1975.

1975

823	A154	1k blue & multi	.50 .20
824	A154	2k yellow grn & multi	.75 .20
825	A154	3k brown red & multi	1.25 .25
826	A154	4k green & multi	2.00 .40
827	A154	5k yellow & multi	2.75 .50
		Nos. 823-827 (5)	7.25 1.55

   Virunga National Park, 50th anniversary.

Siderma
Maluku
Industry
A155

   Designs: 1k, Sozacom apartment building,
vert. 3k, Matadi flour mill, vert. 4k, Women

parachutists. 8k, Pres. Mobutu visiting Chairman Mao, vert. 10k, Soldiers working along the Salongo. 14k, Pres. Mobutu addressing UN Gen. Assembly, Oct. 1974. 15k, Celebrating crowd.

1975

828	A155	1k ocher & multi	.30	.20
829	A155	2k yel grn & multi	.30	.20
830	A155	3k multi	.60	.20
831	A155	4k multi	.85	.20
832	A155	8k dk brn & multi	1.25	.30
833	A155	10k sep & multi	1.90	.40
834	A155	14k bl & multi	3.75	.60
835	A155	15k org & multi	5.25	.85
		Nos. 828-835 (8)	14.20	2.95

10th anniversary of new government.

Tshokwe   Map of Zaire, UPU
Mask — A156   Emblem — A157

Designs: 2k, 4k, Seated woman, Pende. 7k, like 5k. 10k, 14k, Antelope mask, Suku. 15k, 18k, Kneeling woman, Kongo. 20k, 25k, Kuba mask.

1977, Jan. 8   Photo.   Perf. 11½

836	A156	2k multi	.20	.20
837	A156	4k multi	.20	.20
838	A156	5k gray & multi	.20	.20
839	A156	7k multi	.20	.20
840	A156	10k multi	.25	.20
841	A156	14k multi	.35	.20
842	A156	15k multi	.40	.20
843	A156	18k multi	.50	.25
844	A156	20k multi	1.00	.35
845	A156	25k vio & multi	1.10	.45
		Nos. 836-845 (10)	4.40	2.45

Wood carving and masks of Zaire.

1977, Apr.   Litho.   Perf. 13½

846	A157	1k org & multi	.25	.20
847	A157	4k dk bl & multi	.75	.20
848	A157	7k ol grn & multi	1.10	.25
849	A157	50k brn & multi	5.25	3.25
		Nos. 846-849 (4)	7.35	3.90

Cent. of UPU (in 1974).

Congo Stamps of 1968-1971
Surcharged with New Value, Bars and
"RÉPUBLIQUE DU ZAIRE"

1977

850	A126	1k on 10s (#642)	.70	.70
851	A122	2k on 9.6k (#618)	.70	.70
852	A140	10k on 10s (#735)	.85	.70
853	A134	25k on 10s (#703)	2.25	1.60
854	A127	40k on 9.6k (#652)	3.75	2.40
855	A135	48k on 10s (#713)	5.00	3.00
		Nos. 850-855 (6)	13.25	9.10

Congo Nos. 644, 643, 635, 746
Surcharged with New Value, Bars and
"REPUBLIQUE DU ZAIRE" in Black or
Carmine, Zaire No. 757 Surcharged

1977

856	A126	5k on 30s	.70	.70
857	A126	10k on 15s (C)	.70	.70
858	A124	20k on 9.60k	1.75	.90
859	A141	30k on 12k	3.25	1.25
860	A145	100k on 40s (C)	9.50	5.25
		Nos. 856-860 (5)	15.90	8.60
		Nos. 850-860 (11)	29.15	17.70

Souvenir Sheet

Adoration of the Kings, by
Rubens — A158

1977, Dec. 19   Photo.   Perf. 13½
861 A158 5z multi   160.00 125.00

Christmas 1977.

Pantodon
Buchholzi
A159

Soccer Game,
Argentina-France
A160

Fish: 70s, Aphyosemion striatum. 55, Ctenopoma fasciolatum. 8k, Malapterurus electricus. 10k, Hemichromis bimaculatus. 30k, Marcusenius isidori. 40k, Synodontis nigriventris. 48k, Julidochromis ornatus. 100k, Nothobranchius brieni. 250k, Micralestes interruptus.

1978, Jan. 23   Litho.   Perf. 14

862	A159	30s multi	.20	.20
863	A159	70s multi	.20	.20
864	A159	5k multi	.25	.20
865	A159	8k multi	.40	.30
866	A159	10k multi	.70	.70
867	A159	30k multi	1.25	.90
868	A159	40k multi	1.75	1.00
869	A159	48k multi	2.25	1.25
870	A159	100k multi	7.00	2.75
		Nos. 862-870 (9)	14.00	7.50

Souvenir Sheet
Perf. 13½

871 A159 250k multi   10.00 10.00

No. 871 contains one 46x35mm stamp. For surcharges see Nos. 1294, 1311.

1978, Aug. 7   Litho.   Perf. 12½

Various Soccer Games and Jules Rimet Cup: 3k, Austria-Brazil. 7k, Scotland-Iran. 9k, Netherlands-Peru. 10k, Hungary-Italy. 20k, Fed. Rep. of Germany-Mexico. 50k, Tunisia-Poland. 100k, Spain-Sweden. 500k, Rimet Cup, Games' emblem and cartoon of soccer player, horiz.

872	A160	1k multi	.20	.20
873	A160	3k multi	.20	.20
874	A160	7k multi	.20	.20
875	A160	9k multi	.20	.20
876	A160	10k multi	.20	.20
877	A160	20k multi	.30	.20
878	A160	50k multi	.85	.50
879	A160	100k multi	1.65	1.00
		Nos. 872-879 (8)	3.80	2.70

Souvenir Sheets

880	A160	500k blue & multi	17.50	17.50
881	A160	500k red & multi	17.50	17.50

11th World Cup Soccer Championship, Argentina, June 1-25. Nos. 880-881 contain one stamp each (47x36mm). Stamp of No. 880 has blue frameline. Stamp of No. 881 has red frame line.

For surcharge see No. 1259.

Mama
Mobutu — A161

Pres. Joseph D.
Mobutu — A162

1978, Oct. 23   Photo.   Perf. 12
882 A161 8k multi   .20 .20

Mama Mobutu (1941-77), wife of Pres. Mobutu.

Frame Color

1978   Photo.   Perf. 12
Granite Paper

883	A162	2k blue	.20	.20
884	A162	5k bister	.20	.20
885	A162	6k Prussian blue	.20	.20
886	A162	8k red brown	.20	.20
887	A162	10k emerald	.20	.20
888	A162	25k red	.20	.20
889	A162	48k purple	.50	.30
890	A162	1z green	.95	.70
		Nos. 883-890 (8)	2.65	2.20

See Nos. 1053, 1055-1056. For surcharges see Nos. 1313, 1333-1336.

Souvenir Sheet

Elizabeth II in Westminster
Abbey — A163

1978, Dec. 11   Photo.   Perf. 13½
891 A163 5z multi   10.50 10.50

Coronation of Queen Elizabeth II, 25th anniv.

Souvenir Sheet

Albrecht Dürer, Self-portrait — A164

1978, Dec. 18   Perf. 13
892 A164 5z multi   10.50 10.50

Albrecht Dürer (1471-1528), German painter and engraver.

Leonardo da Vinci and his
Drawings — A165

History of Aviation: 70s, Planes of Wright Brothers, 1905, and Santos Dumont, 1906. 1k, Bleriot XI, 1909, and Farman F-60, 1909. 5k, Junkers G-38, 1929, and Spirit of St. Louis, 1927. 8k, Sikorsky S-42B, 1934 and Macchi-Castoldi MC-72, 1934. 10k, Boeing 707, 1960, and Fokker F-VII, 1935. 50k, Apollo XI, 1969, and Concorde, 1976. 75k, Helicopter and Douglas DC-10, 1971. 5z, Giffard's balloon, 1852, and Hindenburg LZ 129, 1936.

1978, Dec. 28   Litho.   Perf. 13

893	A165	30s multi	.20	.20
894	A165	70s multi	.20	.20
895	A165	1k multi	.20	.20
896	A165	5k multi	.25	.20
897	A165	8k multi	.25	.20
898	A165	10k multi	.55	.20
899	A165	50k multi	2.40	1.00
900	A165	75k multi	3.25	1.25
		Nos. 893-900 (8)	7.30	3.45

Souvenir Sheet
Perf. 11½

901 A165 5z multi   12.00 12.00

For overprint and surcharges see Nos. 993, 1173-1181, 1291, 1295.

Pres. Mobutu, Map of Zaire, N'tombe
Dancer — A166

Pres. Mobutu & Map: 3k, Bird. 4k, Elephant. 10k, Diamond and cotton boll. 14k, Hand holding torch. 17k, Leopard's head and Victoria Regia lily. 25k, Finzia waterfall. 50k, Wagenia fishermen.

1979, Feb.   Litho.   Perf. 14x13½

902	A166	1k multicolored	.20	.20
903	A166	3k multicolored	.20	.20
904	A166	4k multicolored	.20	.20
905	A166	10k multicolored	.20	.20
a.		Souvenir sheet of 4, #902-905	10.00	—
906	A166	14k multicolored	.20	.20
907	A166	17k multicolored	.30	.20
908	A166	25k multicolored	.45	.30
909	A166	50k multicolored	.90	.65
a.		Souvenir sheet of 4, #906-909	10.00	—
		Nos. 902-909 (8)	2.65	2.15

Zaire (Congo) River expedition.

Phylloporus
Ampliporus
A167

Mushrooms: 5k, Engleromyces goetzei. 8k, Scutellinia virungae. 10k, Pycnoporus sanguineus. 30k, Cantharellus miniatescens. 40k, Lactarius phlebonemus. 48k, Phallus indusiatus. 100k, Ramaria moelleriana.

1979, Mar.   Photo.   Perf. 13½x13
910	A167	30s multicolored	.25	.20
911	A167	5k multicolored	.30	.25
912	A167	8k multicolored	.45	.30
913	A167	10k multicolored	.60	.40
914	A167	30k multicolored	1.25	.90
915	A167	40k multicolored	1.50	1.00
916	A167	48k multicolored	3.00	1.40
917	A167	100k multicolored	4.25	2.50
		Nos. 910-917 (8)	11.60	6.95

For surcharges see Nos. 1296, 1298, 1312, 1361-1362, 1365-1366, 1368-1369, 1372, 1375.

Souvenir Sheets

Pope John XXIII (1881-1963)
A168

Popes: No. 919, Paul VI (1897-1978). No. 920, John Paul I (1912-78).

1979, June 25   Litho.   Perf. 11½
918	A168	250k multi	3.50	3.50
919	A168	250k multi	3.50	3.50
920	A168	250k multi	3.50	3.50
		Nos. 918-920 (3)	10.50	10.50

Boy Beating
Drum — A169

IYC Emblem on Map of Zaire and: 10k, 20k, Girl, diff. 50k, Boy. 100k, Boys. 300k, Mother and child. 10z, Mother and children, horiz.

1979, July 23   Litho.   Perf. 12½
921	A169	5k multi	.20	.20
922	A169	10k multi	.20	.20
923	A169	20k multi	.25	.20
924	A169	50k multi	.60	.35
925	A169	100k multi	1.25	.70
926	A169	300k multi	3.50	1.65
		Nos. 921-926 (6)	6.00	3.30

Souvenir Sheet
927	A169	10z multi	12.00	9.25

International Year of the Child.
For surcharges see Nos. 997, 999, 1299, 1306.

Globe and
Drummer
A170

1979, July 23
928	A170	1k multi	.20	.20
929	A170	9k multi	.20	.20
930	A170	90k multi	.60	.40
931	A170	100k multi	.65	.45
		Nos. 928-931 (4)	1.65	1.25

Souvenir Sheet
932	A170	500k multi	4.75	2.75

6th International Fair, Kinshasa. No. 932 contains one 52x31mm stamp.
For overprint & surcharge see #996, 1320.

Globe and
School
Desk — A171

1979, Dec. 24   Litho.   Perf. 13
933	A171	10k multi	.25	.20

Intl. Bureau of Education, Geneva, 50th anniv.

Adoration of the Kings, by
Memling — A172

1979, Dec. 24   Imperf.
934	A172	5z multi	5.00	2.50

Christmas 1979.

"Puffing
Billy,"
1814, Gt.
Britain
A173

1980, Jan. 14   Litho.   Perf. 13½x13
935	A173	50s shown	.20	.20
936	A173	1.50k Buddicom No. 33, 1843, France	.20	.20
937	A173	5k "Elephant," 1835, Belgium	.20	.20
938	A173	8k No. 601, 1906, Zaire	.20	.20
939	A173	50k "Slieve Gullion 440," Ireland	.50	.20
940	A173	75k "Black Elephant," Germany	.75	.50
941	A173	2z Type 1-15, Zaire	1.50	1.25
942	A173	5z "Golden State," US	4.00	4.00
		Nos. 935-942 (8)	7.55	6.75

Souvenir Sheet
943	A173	10z Type E.D.75, Zaire	11.00	11.00

For overprints and surcharges see Nos. 991-992, 994, 1325.

Hill,
Belgian
Congo
No. 257
A174

1980, Jan. 28   Perf. 13½x14
944	A174	2k No. 5	.20	.20
945	A174	4k No. 13	.20	.20
946	A174	10k No. 24	.20	.20
947	A174	20k No. 38	.20	.20
948	A174	40k No. 111	.35	.20
949	A174	150k No. B29	1.00	.70
950	A174	200k No. 198	1.25	.85
951	A174	250k shown	1.60	1.00
		Nos. 944-951 (8)	5.00	3.55

Souvenir Sheet
952	A174	10z No. 198	8.50	8.50

Sir Rowland Hill (1795-1879), originator of penny postage.
For overprint and surcharge see Nos. 998, 1329.

Albert Einstein
(1879-1955),
Theoretical
Physicist
A175

1980, Feb. 18   Perf. 13
953	A175	40s multi	.20	.20
954	A175	2k multi	.20	.20
955	A175	4k multi	.20	.20
956	A175	15k multi	.20	.20
957	A175	50k multi	.40	.25
958	A175	300k multi	1.50	.75
		Nos. 953-958 (6)	2.70	1.80

Souvenir Sheet
959	A175	5z multi, diff.	4.50	2.50

For surcharges see Nos. 1285, 1290, 1304.

Salvation Army Brass Players — A176

50s, Booth Memorial Hospital, NYC. 4.50k, Commissioner George Railton sailing for US mission. 10k, Mobile dispensary, Masina. 20k, Gen. Evangeline Booth, officer holding infant, vert. 75k, Outdoor well-baby clinic. 1.50z, Disaster relief. 2z, Parade, vert. 10z, Gen. & Mrs. Arnold Brown.

1980, Mar. 3   Perf. 11
960	A176	50s multi	.20	.20
961	A176	4.50k multi	.20	.20
962	A176	10k multi	.20	.20
963	A176	20k multi	.20	.20
964	A176	40k multi	.35	.20
965	A176	75k multi	.55	.25
966	A176	1.50z multi	1.10	.55
967	A176	2z multi	1.60	.80
		Nos. 960-967 (8)	4.40	2.60

Souvenir Sheet
968	A176	10z multi	7.50	5.00

Salvation Army cent. in US. No. 968 contains one 53x38mm stamp and 2 labels.

Souvenir Sheets

Pope John Paul II — A177

1980, May 2   Litho.   Perf. 11½
969	A177	10z multi	14.00	14.00

Visit of Pope John Paul II to Zaire, May.

Baia Castle, by Antonio Pitloo — A178

1980, May 5
970	A178	10z multi	5.50	5.50

20th International Philatelic Exhibition, Europa '80, Naples, Apr. 26-May 4.

A179

Perf. 12½x13, 13x12½
1980, May 24   Litho.
971	A179	50k Woman, line-drawing	.25	.20
972	A179	100k Plutiarch	.50	.40
973	A179	500k Kneeling man, sculpture, vert.	1.75	1.75
a.		Souvenir sheet of 3	3.50	2.50
		Nos. 971-973 (3)	3.25	2.35

Rotary Intl., 75th anniv. No. 973a contains 3 stamps similar to Nos. 971-973, size: 55x35, 35x55mm. Exists imperf.
For surcharge see No. 1313.

Tropical Fish — A180

1980, Oct. 20   Litho.   Perf. 14x13½
974	A180	1k Chaetodon collaris	.20	.20
975	A180	5k Zebrasoma veliferum	.20	.20
976	A180	10k Euxiphipops xanthometapon	.20	.20
977	A180	20k Pomacanthus annularis	.20	.20
978	A180	50k Centropyge oriculus	.45	.40

979	A180	150k	Oxymona-canthus longirostris	1.00	.50
980	A180	200k	Balistoides niger	1.40	.60
981	A180	250k	Rhinecanthus aculeatus	1.75	.90
		Nos. 974-981 (8)		5.40	3.20

Souvenir Sheet

981A	A180	5z	Baliste ondule	4.50	4.50

For surcharge see No. 1307.

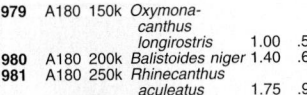

Exhibition Emblem, Congo
#365 — A181

1980, Dec. 6   Litho.   Perf. 13

982		Block of 4	2.00	1.60
a.	A181	1z, UR shown	.45	.35
b.	A181	1z, UL Belgium #511	.45	.35
c.	A181	1z, UL like #982b	.45	.35
d.	A181	1z, UL like #982a	.45	.35
983		Block of 4	4.00	2.50
a.	A181	2z, UR Congo #432	.95	.60
b.	A181	2z, UL Belgium # B835	.95	.60
c.	A181	2z, UL like #983b	.95	.60
d.	A181	2z, UL like #983a	.95	.60
984		Block of 4	5.75	4.00
a.	A181	3z, UR Zaire #755	1.40	.90
b.	A181	3z, UL Belgium # B878	1.40	.90
c.	A181	3z, UL like #984b	1.40	.90
d.	A181	3z, UL like #984a	1.40	.90
985		Block of 4	8.00	5.00
a.	A181	4z, UR Congo #572	1.75	1.10
b.	A181	4z, UL Belgium # B996	1.75	1.10
c.	A181	4z, UL like #985b	1.75	1.10
d.	A181	4z, UL like #985a	1.75	1.10
		Nos. 982-985 (4)	19.75	13.10

PHIBELZA, Belgium-Zaire Phil. Exhib.
#982-985 can be collected as strips of 4.
For surcharge see No. 1342.

Map of Africa, King Leopold I A182

Belgian independence sesquicentennial: 75k, Stanley expedition, Leopold II. 100k, Colonial troops, Albert I. 270k, 145k, protected animals, Leopold III. Visit of King Baudouin and Queen Fabiola.

1980, Dec. 13   Photo.   Perf. 14

986	A182	10k multi	.25	.20
987	A182	75k multi	.90	.40
988	A182	100k multi	1.40	.55
989	A182	145k multi	2.00	.70
990	A182	270k multi	3.50	1.25
		Nos. 986-990 (5)	8.05	3.10

For surcharges see Nos. 1326, 1331, 1345, 1357, 1408-1412, 1426.

Nos. 935, 936, 898, 939, 900, 931, 925, 951, Overprinted in Red, Silver or Black: 20e Anniversaire-Independence / 1960-1980

1980, Dec. 13   Litho.

991	A173	50s multi	.20	.20
992	A173	1.50z multi	.20	.20
993	A165	10k multi	.20	.20
994	A173	50k multi	.55	.20
995	A165	75k multi	.70	.20
996	A170	100k multi (S)	1.00	.65
997	A169	1z on 5z on 100k multi (B)	1.25	.65
998	A174	250k multi	2.50	1.40
999	A169	5z on 100k multi (B)	5.00	2.75
		Nos. 991-999 (9)	11.60	6.45

20th anniversary of independence. For surcharges see Nos. 1300, 1316.

Nativity A183

1980, Dec. 24   Perf. 13

1000	A183	10k	Shepherds and angels	.25	.20
1001	A183	75k	Flight into Egypt	.75	.40
1002	A183	80k	Three kings	.75	.40
1003	A183	145k	multi	1.40	.60
		Nos. 1000-1003 (4)		3.15	1.60

Souvenir Sheet

1004	A183	10z	Church, nativity	5.50	5.50

Christmas 1980. No. 1004 contains one 49x33mm stamp. Exists imperf. For surcharges see Nos. 1301, 1317-1318.

Postal Clerk Sorting Mail, by Norman Rockwell A184

Designs: Saturday Evening Post covers by Norman Rockwell.

1981, Apr. 27   Litho.   Perf. 14

1005	A184	10k multi	.20	.20
1006	A184	20k multi	.20	.20
1007	A184	50k multi	.30	.20
1008	A184	80k multi	.50	.30
1009	A184	100k multi	.55	.35
1010	A184	125k multi	.65	.40
1011	A184	175k multi	.95	.55
1012	A184	200k multi	1.10	.60
		Nos. 1005-1012 (8)	4.45	2.80

For surcharges see Nos. 1262, 1265, 1269, 1275, 1281, 1354.

First Anniv. of Visit of Pope John Paul II A185

Scenes of Pope's visit. 50k, 500k, vert.

1981, May 2   Perf. 13

1013	A185	5k multi	.20	.20
1014	A185	10k multi	.20	.20
1015	A185	50k multi	.30	.25
1016	A185	100k multi	.75	.45
1017	A185	500k multi	4.25	2.25
1018	A185	800k multi	6.00	3.75
		Nos. 1013-1018 (6)	11.70	7.10

For surcharges see #1190-1194, 1292, 1302, 1343.

Soccer Players — A186

Designs: Soccer scenes.

1981, July 6   Litho.   Perf. 12½

1019	A186	2k multi	.20	.20
1020	A186	10k multi	.20	.20
1021	A186	25k multi	.20	.20
1022	A186	90k multi	.45	.25
1023	A186	2z multi	.90	.60
1024	A186	3z multi	1.40	.90
1025	A186	6z multi	2.50	1.60
1026	A186	8z multi	4.00	3.00
		Nos. 1019-1026 (8)	9.85	6.95

Souvenir Sheet

1027		Sheet of 2	4.75	4.75
a.		A186 5z like #1019	2.25	2.25
b.		A186 5z like #1025	2.25	2.25

ESPANA '82 World Cup Soccer Championship. For surcharges see Nos. 1287, 1303, 1309, 1321.

Intl. Year of the Disabled — A187

1981, Nov. 2   Litho.   Perf. 14x14½

1028	A187	2k	Archer	.20	.20
1029	A187	5k	Ear, sound waves	.20	.20
1030	A187	10k	Amputee	.20	.20
1031	A187	18k	Cane braille, sunglasses	.20	.20
1032	A187	50k	Boy with leg braces	.20	.20
1033	A187	150k	Sign language	.40	.25
1034	A187	500k	Hands	1.10	.95
1035	A187	800k	Dove	2.00	1.75
		Nos. 1028-1035 (8)		4.50	3.95

For surcharges see Nos. 1288, 1293, 1305, 1314.

Souvenir Sheet

Birth Sesqui. of Heinrich von Stephan, UPU Founder — A188

Photogravure and Engraved
1981, Dec. 21   Perf. 11½x12

1036	A188	15z purple	5.75	5.75

Christmas 1981 — A189

1981, Dec. 21   Litho.   Perf. 14

Designs: 25k, 1z, 1.50z, 3z, 5z, Various children. 10z, Holy Family, horiz.

1037	A189	25k multi	.20	.20
1038	A189	1z multi	.45	.20
1039	A189	1.50z multi	.55	.25
1040	A189	3z multi	1.10	.55
1041	A189	5z multi	1.90	1.00
		Nos. 1037-1041 (5)	4.20	2.20

Souvenir Sheet

1042	A189	10z multi	4.25	4.25

13th World Telecommunications Day (1981) — A190

Designs: Symbols of communications and health care delivery.

1982, Feb. 8   Litho.   Perf. 13

1043	A190	1k multi	.20	.20
1044	A190	25k multi	.20	.20
1045	A190	90k multi	.25	.20
1046	A190	1z multi	.25	.20
1047	A190	1.70z multi	.50	.40
1048	A190	3z multi	.95	.70
1049	A190	4.50z multi	1.40	.95
1050	A190	5z multi	1.60	1.10
		Nos. 1043-1050 (8)	5.35	3.95

For surcharges see Nos. 1270, 1282.

Pres. Mobutu Type of 1978
Frame Color

1982   Photo.   Perf. 12
Granite Paper

1053	A162	50k purple	.20	.20
1055	A162	2z bister	.35	.20
1056	A162	5z Prussian blue	1.90	1.10
		Nos. 1053-1056 (3)	2.45	1.50

20th Anniv. of African Postal Union (1981) — A191

1982, Mar. 8   Litho.   Perf. 13

1057	A191	1z yel grn & gold	.35	.20

For surcharges see Nos. 1348, 1352.

1982 World Cup A192

Designs: Flags and players of finalists.

1982

1058	A192	2k multi	.20	.20
1059	A192	8k multi	.20	.20
1060	A192	50k multi	.20	.20
1061	A192	90k multi	.20	.20
1062	A192	90k multi	.30	.25
1063	A192	1z multi	.45	.30
1064	A192	1.45z multi	.55	.45
1065	A192	1.70z multi	.75	.55
1066	A192	3z multi	1.00	.90
1067	A192	3.50z multi	1.40	1.10
1068	A192	5z multi	2.25	1.60
1069	A192	6z multi	2.50	1.90
		Nos. 1058-1069 (12)	10.00	7.85

Souvenir Sheet

1070	A192	10z multi	5.75	5.75

Issued: #1058-1069, July 6; #1070, Sept. 21. For surcharges see #1289, 1315, 1322, 1344, 1435 and footnote after #1336.

9th Conference of Heads of State of Africa and France, Kinshasa, Oct. — A193

1982, Oct. 8   Litho.   Perf. 13

1071	A193	75k multi	.20	.20
1072	A193	90k multi	.20	.20
1073	A193	1z multi	.20	.20
1074	A193	1.50z multi	.20	.20
1075	A193	3z multi	.50	.40
1076	A193	5z multi	.75	.60
1077	A193	8z multi	1.25	1.00
		Nos. 1071-1077 (7)	3.30	2.80

For surcharges see Nos. 1268, 1271, 1280, 1283, 1347, 1351.

Animals from Virunga Natl.
Park — A194

1982, Nov. 5
1078	A194	1z Lions	.25	.20
1079	A194	1.70z Buffalo	.90	.60
1080	A194	3.50z Elephants	2.10	1.40
1081	A194	6.50z Antelope	3.50	2.25
1082	A194	8z Hippopota-mus	5.00	3.25
1083	A194	10z Monkeys	5.75	3.75
1084	A194	10z Leopard	5.75	3.75
a.		Pair, #1083-1084 + label	12.00	12.00
		Nos. 1078-1084 (7)	23.25	15.20

#1084a has continuous design.
For surcharge see No. 1430.

Scouting
Year — A195

1982, Nov. 29   Photo.   Perf. 11½
Granite Paper
1085	A195	90k Camp	.30	.25
1086	A195	1.70z Campfire	.75	.55
1087	A195	3z Scout	1.25	.90
1088	A195	5z First aid	2.75	1.60
1089	A195	8z Flag signals	5.00	3.00
		Nos. 1085-1089 (5)	10.05	6.30

Souvenir Sheet
1090	A195	10z Baden-Powell	8.50	8.50

For surcharges see Nos. 1207-1214.

Local
Birds — A196

1982, Dec. 6   Litho.   Perf. 13
1091	A196	25k Quelea quelea	.20	.20
1092	A196	50k Ceyx picta	.20	.20
1093	A196	90k Tauraco persa	.50	.20
1094	A196	1.50z Charadrius tricollaris	.55	.35
1095	A196	1.70z Cursorius tem-minckii	.60	.35
1096	A196	2z Campethera bennettii	.80	.50
1097	A196	3z Podiceps ruficollis	1.10	.65
1098	A196	3.50z Kaupifalco monogram-micus	1.25	.70
1099	A196	5z Limnocorax flavirostris	1.90	1.00
1100	A196	8z White-headed vulture	3.00	1.75
		Nos. 1091-1100 (10)	10.10	5.90

All except 3.50z, 8z horiz.
For surcharges see Nos. 1263, 1266, 1272,
1276, 1278, 1284, 1425, 1432, 1438, 1440.

Souvenir Sheet

Christmas — A197

1982, Dec. 20   Photo.   Perf. 13½
1101	A197	15z Adoration of the Magi, by van der Goes	5.75	5.75

Quartz
A198

1983, Feb. 13   Photo.   Perf. 11½
Granite Paper
1102	A198	2k Malachite, vert.	.20	.20
1103	A198	45k shown	.25	.20
1104	A198	75k Gold	.45	.20
1105	A198	1z Uraninite	.70	.20
1106	A198	1.50z Bournonite, vert.	1.00	.55
1107	A198	3z Cassiterite	2.00	1.00
1108	A198	6z Dioptase, vert.	4.00	2.00
1109	A198	8z Cuprite, vert.	5.00	2.75
		Nos. 1102-1109 (8)	13.60	7.10

Souvenir Sheet
1110	A198	10z Diamonds	7.50	7.50

For surcharges see Nos. 1324, 1330, 1332,
1346.

TB Bacillus Centenary — A199

1983, Feb. 21   Litho.   Perf. 13
1111	A199	80k multi	.25	.20
1112	A199	1.20z multi	.40	.20
1113	A199	3.60z multi	1.25	.60
1114	A199	9.60z multi	3.50	1.75
		Nos. 1111-1114 (4)	5.40	2.75

For surcharges see Nos. 1319, 1356, 1358,
1360, 1433, 1436, 1441.

Kinshasa Monuments — A200

1983, Apr. 25
1115	A200	50k Zaire Diplo-mat, vert.	.20	.20
1116	A200	1z Echo of Zaire	.20	.20
1117	A200	1.50z Messengers, vert.	.30	.20
1118	A200	3z Shield of Revolution, vert.	.60	.30
1119	A200	5z Weeping Wo-man	.95	.50
1120	A200	10z Militant, vert.	2.10	.95
		Nos. 1115-1120 (6)	4.35	2.35

For surcharges see Nos. 1267, 1279, 1349-
1350.

ITU Plenipotentiaries Conference,
Nairobi, Sept. 1982 — A201

Various satellites, dish antennae and maps.

1983, June 13   Litho.   Perf. 13
1121	A201	2k multi	.20	.20
1122	A201	4k multi	.20	.20
1123	A201	25k multi	.20	.20
1124	A201	1.20z multi	.40	.20
1125	A201	2.05z multi	.65	.35
1126	A201	3.60z multi	1.25	.60
1127	A201	6z multi	2.00	1.00
1128	A201	8z multi	2.50	1.40
		Nos. 1121-1128 (8)	7.40	4.15

For surcharges see Nos. 1260-1261, 1264,
1273-1274, 1277, 1355, 1359, 1429, 1434,
1437, 1439, 1442.

Christmas
1983 — A202

Raphael Paintings; No. 1129: a, Virgin and
Child. b, Holy Family. c, Esterhazy Madonna.
d, Sistine Madonna. No. 1130: a, La Belle
Jardiniere. b, Virgin of Alba. c, Holy Family,
diff. d, Virgin and Child, diff.

1983, Dec. 26   Photo.   Perf. 13½x13
1129		Sheet of 4	3.50	3.50
a.-d.	A202	10z, any single	.85	.85
1130		Sheet of 4	5.25	5.25
a.-d.	A202	15z, any single	1.25	1.25

Garamba Park — A203

1984, Apr. 2   Litho.   Perf. 13
1131	A203	10k Darby's Eland	.20	.20
1132	A203	15k Eagles	.20	.20
1133	A203	3z Servals	.20	.20
1134	A203	10z White rhi-noceros	1.25	1.25
1135	A203	15z Lions	1.75	1.75
1136	A203	37.50z Warthogs	4.25	4.25
1137	A203	40z Koris bus-tards	4.75	4.75
1138	A203	40z Crowned cranes	4.75	4.75
a.		Pair, #1137-1138 + label	9.50	9.50
		Nos. 1131-1138 (8)	17.35	17.35

Nos. 1137-1138 are narrower, 49x34mm,
with continuous design.
For surcharge see No. 1428.

Hypericum
Revolutum
A205

Local flowers: 15k, Borreria dibrachiata. 3z,
Disa erubescens. 8.50z, Scaevola plumieri.
10z, Clerodendron thompsonii. 15z,
Thumbergia erecta. 37.50z, Impatiens
niamniamensis. 100z, Canarina eminii.

1984, May 28   Photo.   Perf. 14x13½
1146	A205	10k multi	.20	.20
1147	A205	15k multi	.20	.20
1148	A205	3z multi	.20	.20
1149	A205	8.50z multi	.80	.80
1150	A205	10z multi	.90	.90
1151	A205	15z multi	1.25	1.25
1152	A205	37.50z multi	3.25	3.25
1153	A205	100z multi	9.00	9.00
		Nos. 1146-1153 (8)	15.80	15.80

1984 Summer
Olympics
A206

Manned Flight
Bicent. — A207

1984, June 5   Litho.   Perf. 13
1154	A206	2z Basketball	.20	.20
1155	A206	3z Equestrian	.25	.25
1156	A206	10z Running	.75	.75
1157	A206	15z Long jump	1.10	1.10
1158	A206	20z Soccer	1.75	1.75
		Nos. 1154-1158 (5)	4.05	4.05

Souvenir Sheet
Perf. 11½
1159	A206	50z Kayak	4.25	4.25

No. 1159 contains one 31x49mm stamp.
For surcharge see No. 1427.

1984, June 28   Litho.   Perf. 14
10k, Montgolfiere, 1783. 15k, Charles &
Robert, 1783. 3z, Gustave, 1783. 5z, Santos-
Dumont III, 1899. 10z, Stratospheric balloon,
1934. 15z, Zeppelin LZ-129, 1936. 37.50z,
Double Eagle II, 1978. 80z, Hot air balloons.
1160	A207	10k multi	.20	.20
1161	A207	15k multi	.20	.20
1162	A207	3z multi	.20	.20
1163	A207	5z multi	.40	.40
1164	A207	10z multi	.75	.75
1165	A207	15z multi	1.10	1.10
1166	A207	37.50z multi	2.75	2.75
1167	A207	80z multi	6.00	6.00
		Nos. 1160-1167 (8)	11.60	11.60

For surcharges see Nos. 1413-1420.

World Communications Year — A204

Designs: 10k, Computer operator, Congo
River ferry. 15k, Communications satellite.
8.50z, Engineer, Congo River Bridge. 10z,
Satellite, ground receiving station. 15z, TV
camerawoman filming crowed crane. 37.50z,
Satellite, dish antennas. 80z, Switchboard
operator, bus.

1984, May 14   Litho.   Perf. 13x12½
1139	A204	10k multi	.20	.20
1140	A204	15k multi	.20	.20
1141	A204	8.50z multi	.65	.65
1142	A204	10z multi	.70	.70
1143	A204	15z multi	1.10	1.10
1144	A204	37.50z multi	2.75	2.75
1145	A204	80z multi	5.75	5.75
		Nos. 1139-1145 (7)	11.35	11.35

Okapi — A208

1984, Oct. 15   Litho.   Perf. 13
1168	A208	2z	Grazing	1.25	.60
1169	A208	3z	Resting	1.75	.60
1170	A208	8z	Mother and young	2.75	2.00
1171	A208	10z	In water	4.50	3.50
		Nos. 1168-1171 (4)	10.25	6.70

Souvenir Sheet
Perf. 11½
1172	A208	50z	like 10z	5.25	5.25

World Wildlife Fund. No. 1172 contains one 36x51mm stamp, margin continues the design of the 10z without emblem.

Nos. 893-900 Surcharged in Silver Over Black Bar and With One of Three Different Sabena Airlines Emblems and "1925 1985" in Silver
1985, Feb. 19   Perf. 13
1173	A165	2.50z on 30s #893	.20	.20
1174	A165	5z on 5k #896	.40	.40
1175	A165	6z on 70s #894	.40	.40
1176	A165	7.50z on 1k #895	.60	.60
1177	A165	8.50z on 10k #898	.60	.60
1178	A165	10z on 8k #897	.75	.75
1179	A165	12.50z on 75k #900	.95	.95
1180	A165	30z on 50k #899	2.25	2.25
		Nos. 1173-1180 (8)	6.15	6.15

No. 901 Surcharged in Silver Over Black Bar and With Silver Text "60e ANNIVERSAIRE/1re LIASON AERIENNE/BRUXELLES-KINSHASAL/PAR EDMOND THIEFFRY"
Souvenir Sheet
1985, Feb. 19   Perf. 11½
1181	A165	50z on 5z #901	60.00 60.00

OLYMPHILEX '85, Lausanne — A209

1985, Apr. 19   Perf. 13
1182	A209	1z	Swimming	.20	.20
1183	A209	2z	Soccer, vert.	.20	.20
1184	A209	3z	Boxing	.20	.20
1185	A209	4z	Basketball, vert.	.25	.25
1186	A209	5z	Equestrian	.40	.40
1187	A209	10z	Volleyball, vert.	.75	.75
1188	A209	15z	Running	1.25	1.25
1189	A209	30z	Cycling, vert.	2.50	2.50
		Nos. 1182-1189 (8)	5.75	5.75

Nos. 1013-1018, 969 Ovptd. and Surcharged with 1 or 2 Gold Bars and "AOUT 1985" in Gold or Black
1985, Aug. 15   Perf. 13, 11½
1190	A185	2z on 5k	.25	.25
1191	A185	3z on 10k	.30	.30
1192	A185	5z on 50k	.45	.45
1192A	A185	10z on 100k	1.00	1.00
1192B	A185	15z on 500k	1.40	1.40
1193	A185	40z on 800k	4.25	4.25
		Nos. 1190-1193 (6)	7.65	7.65

Souvenir Sheet
1194	A177	50z on 10z (B)	11.00 11.00

Second visit of Pope John Paul II.

Audubon Birth Bicent. — A210

Illustrations of North American bird species by John Audubon.

1985, Oct. 1   Perf. 13
1195	A210	5z	Great egret	.60	.40
1196	A210	10z	Yellow-beaked duck	1.25	.75
1197	A210	15z	Small heron	2.00	1.25
1198	A210	25z	White-fronted duck	3.50	2.25
		Nos. 1195-1198 (4)	7.35	4.65

For surcharges see Nos. 1421-1424.

Natl. Independence, 25th Anniv. — A211

1985, Oct. 23   Photo.   Perf. 12
Granite Paper
1200	A211	5z multi	.25	.25
1201	A211	10z multi	.45	.45
1202	A211	15z multi	.70	.70
1203	A211	20z multi	1.10	1.10
		Nos. 1200-1203 (4)	2.50	2.50

Souvenir Sheet
Perf. 11½
1204	A211	50z multi	2.25 2.25

UN, 40th Anniv. A212

1985, Nov. 26
1205	A212	10z	Flags, vert.	.50	.50
1206	A212	50z	Emblem, UN building	2.50	2.50

Nos. 1087-1088, 1085-1086, 1089-1090 Surcharged

1985, Dec. 2   Perf. 11½
Granite Paper
1207	A195	3z on 3z multi	.40	.40
1208	A195	5z on 5z multi	.55	.55
1209	A195	7z on 90k multi	.70	.70
1210	A195	10z on 90k multi	1.00	1.00
1211	A195	15z on 1.70z multi	1.60	1.60
1212	A195	20z on 8z multi	2.25	2.25
1213	A195	50z on 90k multi	5.75	5.75
		Nos. 1207-1213 (7)	12.25	12.25

Souvenir Sheet
1214	A195	50z on 10z multi	9.00 9.00

Intl. Youth Year.

Souvenir Sheet

Virgin and Child, by Titian — A213

Photogravure and Engraved
1985, Dec. 23   Perf. 13½
1215	A213	100z brown	5.25 5.25

Christmas 1985.

Natl. Transit Authority, 50th Anniv. — A214

1985, Dec. 31   Perf. 13
1216	A214	7z	Kokolo mail ship	.25	.25
1217	A214	10z	Steam locomotive	.40	.40
1218	A214	15z	Luebo ferry	.60	.60
1219	A214	50z	Stanley locomotive	2.00	2.00
		Nos. 1216-1219 (4)	3.25	3.25

Postage Stamp, Cent. A215

Stamps on stamps: 7z, Belgian Congo No. 30. 15z, Belgian Congo No. B28. 20z, Belgian Congo No. 226. 25z, Zaire No. 1059. 40z, Zaire No. 1152. 50z, Zaire No. 883 and Belgium No. 1094.

1986, Feb. 23   Perf. 13
1220	A215	7z multi	.50	.50
1221	A215	15z multi	1.00	1.00
1222	A215	20z multi	1.40	1.40
1223	A215	25z multi	1.60	1.60
1224	A215	40z multi	2.75	2.75
		Nos. 1220-1224 (5)	7.25	7.25

Souvenir Sheet
Perf. 11½
1225	A215	50z multi	2.50 2.50

No. 1225 contains one 50x35mm stamp.

Beatification of Sister Anuarite Nengapeta, Aug. 15, 1985 — A216

1986, Feb. 21   Litho.   Perf. 13
1226	A216	10z	Pope John Paul II	.60	.45
1227	A216	15z	Sr. Anuarite	.85	.60
1228	A216	25z	Both portraits	1.25	1.00
		Nos. 1226-1228 (3)	2.70	2.05

Souvenir Sheet
Imperf
1229	A216	100z	Both portraits, triangular	4.00 4.00

Nos. 1226-1227 vert. No. 1229 contains one quadrilateral stamp, size: 30x36x60mm.
For surcharges see Nos. 1370-1371, 1373, 1376-1377.

Congo Stamp Cent. — A217

1986, Feb. 22   Litho.   Perf. 13
1230	A217	25z Belgian Congo No. 3	1.00 1.00

Imperfs exist. Value $5.
See Belgium No. 1236.

Indigenous Reptiles — A218

1987, Feb. 11   Litho.   Perf. 13
1231	A218	2z	Dasypeltis scaber	.20	.20
1232	A218	5z	Agama agama	.20	.20
1233	A218	10z	Python regius	.30	.30
1234	A218	15z	Chamaeleo dilepis	.60	.60
1235	A218	25z	Dendroaspis jamesoni	.85	.85
1236	A218	50z	Naja nigricolis	1.60	1.60
		Nos. 1231-1236 (6)	3.75	3.75

Christmas 1987 — A219

Paintings (details) by Fra Angelico: 50z, Virgin and Child, center panel of the Triptych of Cortona, 1435. 100z, The Nativity. 120z, Virgin and Child with Angels and Four Saints, Fiesole Retable. 180z, Virgin and Child with Six Saints, Annalena Retable.

1987, Dec. 24   Litho.   Perf. 13
1237	A219	50z multi	.75	.75
1238	A219	100z multi	1.50	1.50
1239	A219	120z multi	1.90	1.90
1240	A219	180z multi	2.80	2.80
		Nos. 1237-1240 (4)	6.95	6.95

French Revolution, Bicent. — A220

Designs: 50z, Declaration of the Rights of Man and Citizen. 100z, Abstract art. 120z, Globe showing Africa, South America.

1989   **Litho.**   *Perf. 13½x14½*
1241 A220 40z multicolored .45 .45
1242 A220 50z multicolored .55 .55
1243 A220 100z multicolored 1.10 1.10
1244 A220 120z multicolored 1.40 1.40
   Nos. 1241-1244 (4) 3.50 3.50

REGIDESCO, 50th Anniv. — A221

1989
1245 A221 40z Administration
     bldg. .40 .40
1246 A221 50z Modern factory .50 .50
1247 A221 75z Water works .75 .75
1248 A221 120z Woman drawing
     water 1.25 1.25
   Nos. 1245-1248 (4) 2.90 2.90

Fight Against AIDS — A222

Designs: 40z, Bowman firing arrow through SIDA. 80z, "SIDA" on Leopard. 150z, World map with AIDS symbols.

1989
1249 A222 30z multicolored .90 .90
1250 A222 40z multicolored 1.25 1.25
1251 A222 80z multicolored 2.50 2.50
   Nos. 1249-1251 (3) 4.65 4.65

Souvenir Sheet
Perf. 14
1252 A222 150z multicolored 4.50 4.50

Tourist Attractions — A223

1990   **Litho.**   *Perf. 13½x14½*
1253 A223 40z Waterfalls of Ve-
     nus .55 .55
1254 A223 60z Rural village .85 .85
1255 A223 100z Kivu Lake 1.40 1.40
1256 A223 120z Niyara Gongo
     Volcano 1.75 1.75
   Nos. 1253-1256 (4) 4.55 4.55

Souvenir Sheet
Perf. 14½
1257 A223 300z Kisantu Botani-
     cal Gardens,
     vert. 4.25 4.25

Souvenir Sheet

Christmas — A224

Illustration reduced.

1990   **Litho.**   *Perf. 14*
1258 A224 500z multicolored 3.50 3.50

Various 1971-1983
Stamps Surcharged
in Gold

1990   *Perfs., Etc. as Before*
1259 A160 20z on 20k
     #877 .40 .40
1260 A201 40z on 2k
     #1121 .40 .40
1261 A201 40z on 4k
     #1122 .40 .40
1262 A184 40z on 10k
     #1005 .40 .40
1263 A196 40z on 25k
     #1091 .40 .40
1264 A201 40z on 25k
     #1123 .40 .40
1265 A184 40z on 50k
     #1007 .40 .40
1266 A196 40z on 50k
     #1092 .40 .40
1267 A200 40z on 50k
     #1115 .40 .40
1268 A193 40z on 75k
     #1071 .40 .40
1269 A184 40z on 80k
     #1008 .40 .40
1270 A190 40z on 90k
     #1045 .40 .40
1271 A193 40z on 90k
     #1072 .40 .40
1272 A196 40z on 90k
     #1093 .40 .40
1273 A201 80z on 2k
     #1121 1.00 1.00
1274 A201 80z on 4k
     #1122 1.00 1.00
1275 A184 80z on 10k
     #1005 1.00 1.00
1276 A196 80z on 25k
     #1091 1.00 1.00
1277 A201 80z on 25k
     #1123 1.00 1.00
1278 A196 80z on 50k
     #1092 1.00 1.00
1279 A200 80z on 50k
     #1115 1.00 1.00
1280 A193 80z on 75k
     #1071 1.00 1.00
1281 A184 80z on 80k
     #1008 1.00 1.00
1282 A190 80z on 90k
     #1045 1.00 1.00
1283 A193 80z on 90k
     #1072 1.00 1.00
1284 A196 80z on 90k
     #1093 1.00 1.00
1285 A175 100z on 40s
     #953 1.40 1.40
1287 A186 100z on 2k
     #1019 1.40 1.40
1288 A187 100z on 2k
     #1028 1.40 1.40
1289 A192 100z on 2k
     #1058 1.40 1.40
1290 A175 100z on 4k #955 1.40 1.40
1291 A165 100z on 5k #896 1.40 1.40
1292 A185 100z on 5k
     #1013 1.40 1.40
1293 A187 100z on 5k
     #1029 1.40 1.40
1294 A159 100z on 8k #865 1.40 1.40
1295 A165 100z on 8k #897 1.40 1.40
1296 A167 100z on 8k #912 1.40 1.40
1298 A167 100z on 10k
     #913 1.40 1.40
1299 A169 100z on 10k
     #922 1.40 1.40
1300 A165 100z on 10k
     #993 1.40 1.40
1301 A183 100z on 10k
     #1000 1.40 1.40
1302 A185 100z on 10k
     #1014 1.40 1.40
1303 A186 100z on 10k
     #1020 1.40 1.40
1304 A175 100z on 15k
     #956 1.40 1.40
1305 A187 100z on 18k
     #1031 1.40 1.40
1306 A169 100z on 20k
     #923 1.40 1.40
1307 A180 100z on 20k
     #977 1.40 1.40
1308 A144 100z on 22k
     #755 1.40 1.40
1309 A186 100z on 25k
     #1021 1.40 1.40
1311 A159 100z on 48k
     #869 1.40 1.40
1312 A167 100z on 48k
     #916 1.40 1.40

1313 A179 100z on 50k
     #971 1.40 1.40
1314 A187 100z on 50k
     #1032 1.40 1.40
1315 A192 100z on 50k
     #1061 1.40 1.40
1316 A165 100z on 75k
     #995 1.40 1.40
1317 A183 100z on 75k
     #1001 1.40 1.40
1318 A183 100z on 80k
     #1002 1.40 1.40
1319 A199 100z on 80k
     #1111 1.40 1.40
1320 A170 100z on 90k
     #930 1.40 1.40
1321 A186 100z on 90k
     #1022 1.40 1.40
1322 A192 100z on 90k
     #1062 1.40 1.40
1324 A198 300z on 2k
     #1102 4.25 4.25
1325 A173 300z on 8k #938 4.25 4.25
1326 A182 300z on 10k
     #986 4.25 4.25
1327 A143 300z on 14k
     #751 4.25 4.25
1328 A146 300z on 17k
     #769 4.25 4.25
1329 A174 300z on 20k
     #947 4.25 4.25
1330 A198 300z on 45k
     #1103 4.25 4.25
1331 A198 300z on 75k
     #987 4.25 4.25
1332 A198 300z on 75k
     #1104 4.25 4.25
1333 A162 500z on 8k #886 7.50 7.50
1334 A162 500z on 10k
     #887 7.50 7.50
1335 A162 500z on 25k
     #888 7.50 7.50
1336 A162 500z on 48k
     #889 7.50 7.50
   Nos. 1259-1336 (74) 134.85 134.85

Size and location of surcharge varies. Some surcharges show "z" before numeral.
100z on #1060 was surcharged in error.
Numbers have been reserved for additional values in this set.

Various 1980-1983 Stamps
Surcharged

1991   *Perfs., Etc., as Before*
1342 A181 1000z on 1z
     #982a-
     982d 1.40 1.40
1343 A185 1000z on 100k
     #1016 .35 .35
1344 A192 1000z on 1z
     #1063 .35 .35
1345 A182 2000z on 100k
     #988 .70 .70
1346 A198 2000z on 1z
     #1105 .70 .70
1347 A193 2500z on 1z
     #1073 1.00 1.00
1348 A191 3000z on 1z
     #1057 1.40 1.40
1349 A200 4000z on 1z
     #1116 2.00 2.00
1350 A200 5000z on 1z
     #1116 2.90 2.90
1351 A193 10,000z on 1z
     #1073 3.75 3.75
1352 A191 15,000z on 1z
     #1057 5.75 5.75
   Nos. 1342-1352 (11) 20.30 20.30

Size and location of surcharge varies.

The editors have received from a collector mint stamps bearing the surcharges shown below. There is conflicting data as to the validity of these surcharges, and anyone with information on them is asked to contact the new issues editor.

12 - 6 - 92
6° ANNIVERSAIRE DE
OFFICE NATIONAL
DU TOUR.SME

■ 1.000 000 Z

12 - 3 - 92
INAUGURATION
STATION POMPAGE

600.000 Z.

Du 8 au 15 - 6 - 92
2° Conférence Addis - Abeba
Virus VIH 1 - et VIH 2
EN AFRIQUE

10.000.000 Z ■

■ 5.000.000 Z

**Conference
Nationale
Souveraine
3 mars - 4 decembre
1991 - 1992**

Nos. 989, 1010, 1112, 1124
Surcharged

1992, Aug. 18   *Perfs., Etc. as Before*
1354 A184 50th z on 125k
     #1010 .30 .30
1355 A201 100th z on 1.20z
     #1124 .40 .40
1356 A199 150th z on 1.20z
     #1112 .70 .70
1357 A182 200th z on 145k
     #989 1.00 1.00
1358 A199 250th z on 1.20z
     #1112 1.25 1.25
1359 A201 300th z on 1.20z
     #1124 1.50 1.50
1360 A199 500th z on 1.20z
     #1112 2.50 2.50
   Nos. 1354-1360 (7) 7.65 7.65

Size and location of surcharge varies. Numbers have been reserved for additional values in this set.

#1361-1366

#1368-1374

1993, Oct. 29   **Photo.**   *Perf. 13½x13*
1361 A167 500th z on 30s
     #910 .55 .55
1362 A167 500th z on 5k
     #911 .55 .55
1365 A167 750th z on 8k
     #912 .80 .80
1366 A167 750th z on 10k
     #913 .80 .80
1368 A167 1 mil z on 30k
     #914 1.10 1.10
1369 A167 1 mil z on 40k
     #915 1.10 1.10
1370 A167 5 mil z on 48k
     #916 5.25 5.25
1371 A167 10 mil z on 100k
     #917 10.50 10.50
   Nos. 1361-1371 (8) 20.65 20.65

Nos. 1226-1229 Surcharged in Black
or Red (#1374)

1993, Oct. 29   Litho.   Perf. 13
1373 A216   3 mil z on 10z
                  #1226   2.75 2.75
1374 A216   3 mil z on 10z
                  #1226
1375 A216   5 mil z on 15z
                  #1227   4.50 4.50
1376 A216 10 mil z on 25z
                  #1228   8.75 8.75

Souvenir Sheet
1377 A216 10 mil z on 100z
                  #1229   8.50 8.50

Size and location of surcharge varies.

Natl.
Game
Parks,
50th
Anniv.
A225

1993   Litho.   Perf. 13
1403 A225   30k Cape eland   .25   .25
1404 A225   50k Elephants   .25   .25
1405 A225 1.50z Giant eland   .70   .70
1406 A225 3.50z White rhinocer-
                  os   1.75 1.75
1407 A225   5z Bongo   2.40 2.40
       Nos. 1403-1407 (5)   5.35 5.35

For surcharge see No. 1431.

Nos. 986-900 Surcharged

1994, Apr. 23   Photo.   Perf. 14
1408 A182   30k on 10k   .45   .45
1409 A182   50k on 75k   .90   .90
1410 A182 1.50z on 100k   2.25 2.25
1411 A182 3.50z on 145k   4.50 4.50
1412 A182   5z on 270k   7.25 7.25
       Nos. 1408-1412 (5)   15.35 15.35

Nos. 1160-1167 Surcharged

1994, Apr. 23   Litho.   Perf. 14
1413 A207   30k on 10k   .40   .40
1414 A207   50k on 15k   .55   .55
1415 A207 1.50z on 3z   1.60 1.60
1416 A207 2.50z on 5z   2.50 2.50
1417 A207 3.50z on 10z   3.75 3.75
1418 A207   5z on 15z   5.25 5.25
1419 A207 7.50z on 37.50z   8.50 8.50
1420 A207   10z on 80z   10.50 10.50
       Nos. 1413-1420 (8)   33.05 33.05

Nos. 1195-1198 Surcharged

1994, Apr. 23   Litho.   Perf. 13
1421 A210   50k on 5z   1.00 1.00
1422 A210 1.50z on 10z   2.75 2.75
1423 A210 3.50z on 15z   5.25 5.25
1424 A210   5z on 25z   10.50 10.50
       Nos. 1421-1424 (4)   19.50 19.50

Nos. 990, 1079, 1094, 1097, 1113,
1125-1126, 1133, 1155, & 1404
Surcharged in Gold

1994, Aug. 31   Perfs., Etc. as Before
1425 A196   20z on 3z #1097   .20   .20
1426 A182   40z on 270k #990   .25   .25
1427 A203   50z on 3z #1133   .40   .40
1428 A206   75z on 3z #1155   .40   .40
1429 A201 100z on 2.05z
                  #1125   .55   .55
1430 A194 150z on 1.70z
                  #1079   .90   .90
1431 A225 200z on 50k #1404   1.00 1.00
1432 A196 250z on 1.50z
                  #1094   1.25 1.25
1433 A199 300z on 3.60z
                  #1113   1.40 1.40
1434 A201 500z on 3.60z
                  #1126   2.25 2.25
       Nos. 1425-1434 (10)   8.60 8.60

Size and location of surcharge varies.

Nos. 1067, 1094, 1113, 1125-1126
Surcharged in Gold

100NZ

1000 NZ

1996   Perfs., Etc. as Before
1435 A192 100z on 3.50z
                  #1067   .25   .25
1436 A199 500z on 3.60z
                  #1113   .25   .25
1437 A201 1000z on 2.05z
                  #1125   .25   .25
1438 A196 2500z on 1.50z
                  #1094   .90   .90
1439 A201 5000z on 3.60z
                  #1125   1.60 1.60
1440 A196 6000z on 1.50z
                  #1094   2.10 2.10
1441 A199 15,000z on 3.60z
                  #1113   5.00 5.00
1442 A201 25,000z on 3.60z
                  #1126   8.50 8.50
       Nos. 1435-1442 (8)   18.85 18.85

1996
Summer
Olympic
Games,
Atlanta
A226

1996, July 29   Litho.   Perf. 11½
1444 A226   1000z Equestrian   .20   .20
1445 A226 12,500z Boxing   .80   .80
1446 A226 25,000z Table tennis 2.00 2.00
1447 A226 35,000z Basketball,
                  vert.   2.75 2.75
1448 A226 50,000z Tennis   3.25 3.25
       Nos. 1444-1448 (5)   9.00 9.00

Insects &
Spiders
A227

No. 1449: a, Lasius niger. b, Caloptery-
gides. c, Peucetia. d, Sphecides.

1996   Litho.   Perf. 13½
1449 A227 15,000z Sheet of 4,
                  #a.-d.   9.00 9.00

Minerals
A228

No. 1450: a, Uraninite. b, Malachite. c,
Ruby. d, Diamond.
No. 1452, Uranotile, cuprosklodowskite,
horiz.

1996
1450 A228 40,000z Sheet of
                  4, #a.-d.   25.00 25.00

Souvenir Sheet
1452 A228 105,000z multi   11.00 11.00

A number has been reserved for an additional sheet with this set.

Raptors
A229

No. 1453: a, Congo eagle. b, Crowned
eagle. c, Melierax metabates. d, Urotriorchis
macrourus.

1996
1453 A229 50,000z Sheet of 4,
                  #a.-d.   23.00 23.00

Butterflies
A230

No. 1454: a, Cymothoe sangaris. b, Colotis
zoe. c, Physcaeneura leda. d, Charaxes
candiope.

1996

Sheet of 4
1454 A230 70,000z #a.-d.   27.50 27.50

The validity of Nos. 1455-1481 and
other stamps from the same time period
has been questioned. The editors are
attempting to find out more about these
stamps.

1998 World Cup Soccer
Championships, France — A231

Numbers on players: No. 1455, #12. No.
1456, none. No. 1457, #7. No. 1458, #3.
No. 1459: a, British player. b, Brazilian
player.
No. 1460: a-d, Like #1455-1458, but with
part of World Cup Trophy behind each player.

1996
1455-1458 A231 35,000z Set of 4 9.00 9.00

Souvenir Sheets
1459 A231 10,500z Sheet of 2,
                  #a.-b.   1.25 1.25
1460 A231 35,000z Sheet of 4,
                  #a.-d.   9.00 9.00

No. 1459 contains 2 42x39mm stamps.
See Nos. 1467-1476.

World
Wildlife
Fund —
A231a

No. 1466 — Pan paniscus: a, With young. b,
Two in trees. c, Holding vines. d, Head.

1997
1466 A231a 20,000z Block of 4,
                  #a.-d.   6.50 6.50

1998 World Cup Soccer
Championships Type of 1996

African soccer players: No. 1467, 20,000z,
Soccer ball at his right. No. 1468, 20,000z,
Ball at head. No. 1469, 20,000z, Yellow uni-
form. No. 1470, 20,000z, Ball on knee.
German soccer players, soccer ball on
stamp at: No. 1471, 50,000z, UR. No. 1472,
50,000z, LL. No. 1473, 50,000z, LR. No. 1474,
50,000z, UL.
Nos. 1475a-1475d, 1476a-1476d are like
Nos. 1467-1474 but with part of World Cup
Trophy behind each player.

1996   Litho.   Perf. 13½
1467-1470 A231 Set of 4   5.00 5.00
1471-1474 A231 Set of 4   12.25 12.25

Souvenir Sheets
1475 A231 20,000z Sheet of 4,
                  #a.-d.   5.00 5.00
1476 A231 50,000z Sheet of 4,
                  #a.-d.   12.25 12.25

Boy
Scouts
and Lions
Intl. Clubs
A232

No. 1477 — Diceros bicornis: a, Walking
forward. b, Walking left, left leg up. c, Facing
left. d, Holding head up.
No. 1478 — Panthera leo: a, Cubs. b, Adult
male. c, Adult male facing forward, mouth
open. d, Adult female on fallen tree.
No. 1479 — Loxodonta africana: a, Walking
right, trunk in air. b, Reaching up to tree limb
with trunk. c, Walking right, trunk down. d,
Mother with calf.
105,000z, Hippopotamus amphibius.

1997   Litho.   Perf. 13x13½
1477 A232 40,000z Sheet of
                  4, #a.-d.   9.50 9.50
1478 A232 50,000z Sheet of
                  4, #a.-d.   11.75 11.75

1479 A232   70,000z   Sheet of
                     4, #a.-d.   19.00 19.00
Souvenir Sheet
1480 A232   105,000z multi   6.25   6.25
Boy Scouts (#1477, 1479-1480). Lions Intl.
Clubs (#1478).

Jacqueline
Kennedy
Onassis
(1929-94)
A233

Various portraits.

1997   Litho.   Perf. 13½
1481 A233   15,000z Sheet of 9,
                     #a.-i.   11.00 11.00
No. 1481 also exists imperf.

Stamps from this country are now
being released under the previous
name, "Republique Democratique du
Congo," or Congo Democratic Republic, despite the resumption of civil war.
We will continue to list these stamps
under the country's name of Zaire until
the situation is resolved.

Diana, Princess of   Mother Teresa
Wales (1961-   (1910-97) — A235
97) — A234

No. 1482: a, Wearing tiara. b, In white
jacket. c, In white hat. d, In polka dotted dress.
e, Scarf around neck. f, Low cut evening
dress.
No. 1483: a, Wearing tiara. b, Hand under
chin. c, Leaning chin on both hands. d, One-
shoulder-covered outfit.
No. 1484: a, Red & black dress. b, White
jacket, pearls. c, Profile view. d, Wearing tiara.
No. 1485, 400,000z, In black evening dress.
No. 1486, 400,000z, Holding flowers.

1998, Aug. 6   Litho.   Perf. 14
1482 A234   50,000z Sheet of
                     6, #a.-f.   9.50   5.50
1483 A234   100,000z Sheet of
                     4, #a.-d.   12.50   7.50
1484 A234   125,000z Sheet of
                     4, #a.-d.   17.00 10.50
Souvenir Sheets
1485-1486 A234   Set of 2   35.00 17.50

1998, Aug. 6
1487 A235   50,000z shown   1.50   1.00
Souvenir Sheet
1488 A235   325,000z Portrait,
                     diff.   7.50   5.00
No. 1487 was issued in sheets of 6.

100 Centimes = 1 Franc (1998)

Native Dwelling — A236

Arms — A237

Inauguration of
Pres. Laurent
Kabila — A238

Designs: 1.25fr, Troops and civilians in Kinshasa. 3fr, Flag, crowd, Pres. Kabila breaking
chain with sword, horiz.
2.50fr, Gun, arrow, handshake, tractor.
3.50fr, Pres. Kabila.

1999, May 12   Litho.   Perf. 14
1489 A236   25c multi   .25   .25
1490 A237   50c multi   .55   .55
1491 A238   75c multi   .80   .80
1492 A238   1.25fr multi   1.40   1.40
1493 A238   3fr multi   3.25   3.25
          Nos. 1489-1493 (5)   6.25   6.25
Souvenir Sheets
1494 A238   2.50fr multi   2.60   2.60
1495 A238   3.50fr multi   3.75   3.75
Conquest of Kinshasa by troops of Laurent
Kabila, 2nd anniv.

Chinese Zodiac Animals — A239

No. 1496: a, Rat. b, Ox. c, Tiger. d, Rabbit.
e, Dragon. f, Snake. g, Horse. h, Ram. i, Monkey. j, Cock. k, Dog. l, Boar.

1999, Aug. 20   Perf. 13¼x13½
1496 A239   78c Sheet of 12,
                     #a-l   20.00 20.00

A240

A241

No. 1497 — Sheet with text starting with
"The historical novel. . .": a, 1.45fr, Men fight-
ing. b, 1.50fr, Man uprooting tree. c, 1.60fr,
Man with sword in snowstorm. d, 1.70fr, Man
with sword, other men at bridge. e, 1.80fr,
Three men at table.
No. 1498 — Sheet with text starting with
"The main theme. . .": a, 1.45fr, Men and baskets. b, 1.50fr, Man threatening another man
with sword. c, 1.60fr, Man attacking tiger. d,
1.70fr, People watching men in martial arts
battle. e, 1.80fr, Battling horsemen.
No. 1499 — Sheet with text starting with
"The common people. . .": a, 1.45fr, Men fighting in boat. b, 1.50fr, Man with sword fighting
man with hatchets. c, 1.60fr, Men near fortified wall. d, 1.70fr, Men fighting on cobble-
stone street. e, 1.80fr, Archer on horseback at
doorway.
No. 1500 — Sheet with text starting with
"Today, it is thought. . .": a, 1.45fr, Man seated
and other man standing near table. b, 1.50fr,
Man setting fire to building. c, 1.60fr, Man in
room. d, 1.70fr, Man lifting another man in a
battle. e, 1.80fr, Man holding torn scroll.

1999, Aug. 20   Perf. 13¼
Sheets of 5, #a-e
1497-1500 A240   Set of 4   42.50 42.50
Souvenir Sheets
Perf. 13¼x13½
1501 A241   10fr multi   12.50 12.50
1502 A242   10fr multi   12.50 12.50
1503 A243   10fr multi   12.50 12.50
1504 A244   10fr multi   12.50 12.50

A245

A246

A242

A243

Outlaws of the Marsh — A244

African Flora and Fauna — A247

Designs: 1fr, Telophorus quadricolor. 1.50fr,
Panthera pardus. No. 1507, 2fr, Colotis
protomedia. No. 1508, 2fr, Kobus vardoni. No.
1509, 3fr, Canarina abyssinica. No. 1510, 3fr,
Smutsia temminckii.
7.80fr, Lion.
No. 1512: a, Okapi. b, Bird, rainbow, waterfalls. c, Giraffe, rainbow, waterfalls. d, Giraffe,
waterfall mist. e, Mandrill. f, Chimpanzee. g,
Leopard. h, Butterflies. i, Hippopotamus. j, Bird
in water. k, Flowers. l, Antelope.
No. 1513: a, Sun. b, Pieris citrina. c, Merops
apiaster. d, Lanius collurio. e, Ploceus cucullatus. f, Charaxes pelias. g, Charaxes eupale.
h, Giraffa camelopardalis. i, Galago moholi. j,
Strelitzia reginae. k, Gazella thomsoni. l,
Upupa epops.
No. 1514, 10fr, Taurotragus oryx. No. 1515,
10fr, Hippopotamus amphibus.
No. 1516, 10fr, Warthog.

**Perf. 14, 14¼x14¾ (#1511), 14¼x14
(#1516)**

2000, Feb. 28
1505-1510 A245   Set of 6   8.50   8.50
1511 A246   7.80fr multi   5.00   5.00
1512 A247   1fr Sheet of 12,
                     #a-l   8.50   8.50
1513 A245   1.50fr Sheet of 12,
                     #a-l   15.00 15.00
Souvenir Sheets
1514-1515 A245   Set of 2   14.00 14.00
1516 A247   10fr multi   7.00   7.00
No. 1516 contains one 42x57mm.

Millennium
A249

Wild Felines and Canines — A248

No. 1517, 1.50fr: a, Felis bengalensis. b,
Felis aurata. c, Felis caracal. d, Felis conoclor.
e, Felis nigripes. f, Panthera leo. g, Neofelis
nebulosa. h, Felis wiedii. i, Acinonyx jubatus. j,
Felis pardina. k, Felis yagouaroundi. l, Felis
serval.
No. 1518, 2fr: a, Canis mesomelas. b, Otocyon megalotis. c, Speothos venaticus. d,
Canis latrans. e, Cuon alpinus. f, Fennecus
zerda. g, Urocyon cinereoargenteus. h, Canis
lupus. i, Vulpes macrotis. j, Chrysocyon
brachyurus. k, Nyctereutes procyonoides. l,
Vulpes vulpes.
No. 1519, 10fr, Panthera pardus. No. 1520,
10fr, Alopex lagopus.

2000, Feb. 28   Perf. 14
Sheets of 12, #a-l
1517-1518 A248   Set of 2   27.50 27.50
Souvenir Sheets
1519-1520 A248   Set of 2   11.50 11.50

2000, June 10
1521   Horiz. strip of 3   16.00 16.00
a. A249   4.50fr multi   2.25   2.25
b. A249   9fr multi   4.50   4.50
c. A249   15fr multi   8.00   8.00
Printed in sheets containing two strips.

A250 A251

Birds
A252

Designs: No. 1522, 3fr, Alopochen aegyptiacus. No. 1523, 3fr, Ardeola ibis. No. 1524, 4.50fr, Oena capensis. No. 1525, 4.50fr, Lybius torquatus. No. 1526, 9fr, Falco tinnunculus. No. 1527, 9fr, Corythaelo cristata.
No. 1528, 4.50fr, Psephotus chrysopterygius chrysopterygius. 8fr, Amazona aestiva. No. 1530, 8.50fr, Are nobilis cumanensis. No. 1531, 9fr, Agapornis roseicollis. No. 1532, 8.50fr, Lophornis ornata. No. 1533, 9fr, Polytrus guauvunibi.
No. 1534, 9fr: a, Euplectes orix. b, Euplectes ardens. c, Oriolus auratus. d, Plocens cucullatus. e, Amandava subflava. f, Nectarina senegalensis.
No. 1535, 9fr: a, Halcyon malimbicus. b, Tachymarptis melba. c, Haliaeetus vocifer. d, Ardea purpurea. e, Balaeniceps rex. f, Balearica regulorum.
No. 1536: a, Ertoxeres aquila. b, Aglaiolepus kinde. c, Archilochus calobris. d, Trochlus polytaus. e, Chaliostigna herrani. f, Ensifera. g, Chrysolampus mosquitus. h, Phorethornus syrmatophorus. i, Calypre hetervare.
No. 1537, 5fr: a, Eos squamata squamata. b, Aratinga guarouba. c, Aratinga aurea. d, Psuedeos fuscata. e, Agapornis fischeri. f, Aratinga nana nana. g, Aratinga mitrata. h, Trichoglossus haematodus rubitorquis. i, Cacatua galerita galerita.
No. 1538, 5fr: a, Ara macao. b, Neophema elegans. c, Loriculus vernalis. d, Aratinga solstitialis. e, Pionites melancephala. f, Bolborhynchus lineola. g, Ara severa. h, Psephotus chrysopterygius dissimilis. i, Ara militaris.
No. 1539, 15fr, Actophilornis africanus, horiz. No. 1540, 20fr, Ceryle rudis, horiz.
No. 1541, 15fr, Opopsitta diophthalma. No. 1542, 15fr, Ara ararrauna, horiz.
No. 1543, 15fr, Coeligena torgoata. No. 1544, 20fr, Campylopterus hemileicurus.

2000, Aug. 16 **Perf. 14**
1522-1527	A250	Set of 6	15.00	15.00
1528-1531	A251	Set of 4	13.50	13.50
1532-1533	A252	Set of 2	7.75	7.75

Sheets of 6, #a-f
1534-1535	A250	Set of 2	47.50	47.50
1536	A252	4.50fr Sheet of 9, #a-i		18.00 18.00

Sheets of 9, #a-i
1537-1538	A251	Set of 2	40.00	40.00

Souvenir Sheets
1539-1540	A250	Set of 2	16.00	16.00
1541-1542	A251	Set of 2	13.50	13.50
1543-1544	A252	Set of 2	16.00	16.00

Surcharges on
Unissued
Stamps
A253

Designs: 10fr on 70,000z, Colotis zoe. 15fr on 25,000z, Bulbophyllum falcatum. 25fr on 20,000z, Scutellosaurus. 35fr on 15,000z, Sphecides. 45fr on 100,000z, Diamond. 50fr on 35,000z, Termitomyces aurantiacus. 70fr on 50,000z, Melierax metabates. 100fr on 40,000z, Malachite. 150fr on 25,000z, Panda.

2000 **Litho.** **Perf. 13¼**
1545	A253	10fr on 70,000z multi	—	—
1546	A253	15fr on 25,000z multi	—	—
1547	A253	25fr on 20,000z multi	—	—
1548	A253	35fr on 15,000z multi	—	—
1549	A253	45fr on 100,000z multi	—	—
1550	A253	50fr on 35,000z multi	—	—
1551	A253	70fr on 50,000z multi	—	—
1552	A253	100fr on 40,000z multi	—	—
1553	A253	150fr on 25,000z multi	—	—

Location of surcharges varies. All surcharged stamps have white margins.

A254

Trains — A255

Designs: 1fr, Missouri-Kansas-Texas Line locomotive. 2fr, Spremberg steam locomotive. No. 1556, 3fr, King Class, Great Western Railway. No. 1557, 3fr, Crocodile locomotive. 5fr, Inner-city trains, Great Britain. 6fr, Big Boy, Union Pacific.
No. 1560, 4.50fr: a, Class SU, 2-6-2, Russia. b, Prussian locomotive. c, Zimbabwe locomotive. d, Hunslet 2-8-2, Peru. e, London, Midland & Scottish Railway locomotive. f, London Northeastern Railway locomotive.
No. 1561, 8fr: a, Denver & Rio Grande Western Railroad locomotive. b, Mikado 2-8-2, Louisville & Nashville. c, Mogul, Rio Grande. d, New York Central Railway locomotive. e, Sumpter Valley Railway steam locomotive. f, Three-truck Shay No. 7.
No. 1562, 9.50fr: a, Compagnie du Nord locomotive, France. b, Union Pacific locomotive. c, Great Northern Railway locomotive. d, Liverpool & Manchester Railway locomotive. e, Patentee 2-2-2, London & Birmingham. f, Puffing Billy.
No. 1563, 10fr: a, Chicago, Rock Island & Pacific Railway locomotive. b, Powhattan Arrow, Norfolk & Western. c, Class S-1, New York Central Hudson River Railway. d, Reading Railroad locomotive. e, Great Bear, Great Western Railway. f, Bi-polar, Chicago, Milwaukee, St. Paul & Pacific Railway.
No. 1564, 5fr: a, Beyer-Garratt 50 4-8-2+2-8-4 locomotive. b, Locomotive Express 4-6-2. c, 780CV electric locomotive. d, Electric locomotive on curve. e, Class 2-10-0 Locomotive 56001. f, Electric locomotive on straight track. g, Class 2-8-4 Locomotive 284. h, Class G 6/6 electric locomotive.
No. 1565, 8.50fr: a, Class B-B electric locomotive AE4/4. b, Class EX, Paris-Lyon-Mediterranean. c, Big Boy. d, Tourist car. e, Class 4-8-4 GS-4. f, Class 46 electric locomotive. g, Class-4-6-0 County. h, Class DA Diesel-electric locomotive.
No. 1566, 15fr, New York Central & Hudson River Railway locomotive. No. 1567, 20fr, Mohawk & Hudson Railroad locomotive. No. 1568, 20fr, Broadway Limited, Pennsylvania Railroad. No. 1569, 20fr, Trans-Europe Express.
No. 1570, 20fr, Deltic electric locomotive, Great Britain. No. 1571, 20fr, Diesel-electric locomotive, Canada Pacific.

2001, Jan. 15 **Litho.** **Perf. 14**
1554-1559	A254	Set of 6	7.50	7.50

Sheets of 6, #a-f
1560-1563	A254	Set of 4	45.00	45.00

Sheets of 8, #a-h
1564-1565	A255	Set of 2	30.00	30.00

Souvenir Sheets
1566-1569	A254	Set of 4	17.00	17.00
1570-1571	A255	Set of 2	10.00	10.00

Ships
A256

Designs: 2.50fr, Clipper. 5fr, Arab bum. 20fr, Flemish galley. 21.70fr, Trabaccolo, vert. 30fr, Dutch galliot. 45.80fr, Japanese coaster.
No. 1578, 10fr: a, Trireme. b, Roman caudicaria. c, 13th cent. warship. d, Byzantine galley. e, Lateneer. f, 14th century cog. g, Arab dhow. h, Hanseatic cog. i, Portuguese galley.
No. 1579, 10fr: a, Egyptian sailing ship. b, Egyptian rowing craft. c, Egyptian seagoing ship. d, Greek galley. e, Etruscan merchantman f, Etruscan fishing skiff. g, Greek merchantman. h, Minoan passenger ship. i, Roman harbor boat.
No. 1580, 10fr: a, Flemish galleon. b, English galleon. c, Carrack. d, Chinese war galley. e, Venetian galley. f, Polacre. g, Hemmena. h, Venetian bragozzo. i, Schooner.
No. 1581, 25fr, Viking drakkar. No. 1582, 25fr, Portuguese caravel, vert. No. 1583, 25fr, HMS Endeavour, vert.

2001, June 22 **Perf. 14**
1572-1577	A256	Set of 6	14.00	14.00

Sheets of 9, #a-i
1578-1580	A256	Set of 3	30.00	30.00

Souvenir Sheets
Perf. 13¾
1581-1583	A256	Set of 3	16.00	16.00

No. 1581 contains one 50x38mm stamp; Nos. 1582-1583 each contain one 38x50mm stamp.

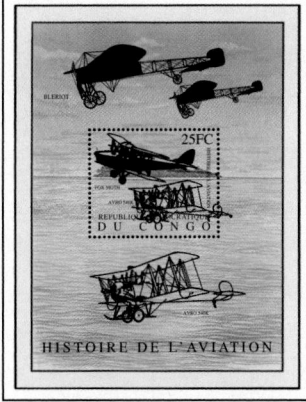

History of Aviation — A257

No. 1584: a, Montgolfier balloon (36x61mm). b, Boxkite and Tiger Moth airplanes (36x61mm). c, Gladiator. d, Eurofighter. e, Mosquito. f, Chipmunk.
No. 1585: a, Blackburn and Spartan Arrow airplanes (36x61mm). b, Tiger Moth. c, Lightning. d, Vulcan B2. e, Tornado.
No. 1586, 25fr, Fox Moth and Avro 540K airplanes. No. 1587, 25fr, Avro 504K and Fox Moth airplanes.

2001, June 22 **Perf. 14¼**
1584	A257	10fr Sheet of 6, #a-f	7.00	7.00
1585	A257	10fr Sheet of 6, #1584a, 1585a-1585e	7.00	7.00

Souvenir Sheets
Perf. 14¼x14½
1586-1587	A257	Set of 2	11.00	11.00

First Zeppelin Flight, Cent. — A258

No. 1588: a, LZ-6. b, LZ-7. c, US Navy airship Akron. c, Lindstrand HS-110 Pittsburgh Tribune-Review airship.

No. 1589, 100fr, LZ-130 Graf Zeppelin II. No. 1590, 100fr, LZ-1.

2001, June 22 **Perf. 14**
1588	A258	60fr Sheet of 4, #a-d	18.00	18.00

Souvenir Sheets
1589-1590	A258	Set of 2	15.00	15.00

Butterflies — A259

Designs: 5fr, Striped policeman. 21.70fr, Brown-veined white. 45fr, Common dotted border. 45.80fr, Cabbage. 50fr, African migrant. 51.80fr, Mocker swallowtail.
No. 1597, 6fr, horiz.: a, Common grass blue. b, Golden tiger. c, Palla. d, Blue diadem. e, African giant swallowtail. f, African leaf. g, Gold-banded forester. h, Small harvester.
No. 1598, 6fr, horiz.: a, Guinea fowl. b, Forest queen. c, Sweet potato acraea. d, Wanderer. e, Evening brown. f, African ringlet. g, Plain tiger. h, Monarch.
No. 1599, 8fr, horiz.: a, Broad-bordered grass yellow. b, Crimson tip. c, Orange-banded protea. d, Azure hairstreak. e, Marshall's false monarch. f, Blue swallowtail. g, Figtree blue. h, Grass jewel.
No. 1600, 25fr, Long-tailed blue, horiz. No. 1601, 25fr, Chief, horiz. No. 1602, 25fr, Large spotted acraea, horiz.

2001, June 22
1591-1596	A259	Set of 6	16.00	16.00

Sheets of 8, #a-h
1597-1599	A259	Set of 3	37.50	37.50

Souvenir Sheets
1600-1602	A259	Set of 3	16.00	16.00

Flowers and
Insects — A260

Designs: 20fr, Aconite, Brazilian frog-hopper. 21.70fr, Larkspur, Mexican cicada. 25fr, Blue orchid, dragonfly. 45.80fr, Spotted blossom orchid, buck moth.
No. 1607, 10fr, horiz.: a, Rein orchids, tiger moth. b, Ivy, Siamese wasp. c, Pink lady's slipper, goat weed emperor. d, Gletscherpetersbart, velvet ant. e, Licorice, viceroy butterfly. f, Grass pink, aphid. g, Ranunculus, spider wasp. h, Clamshell orchid, tropical bee. i, Bog orchids, mayfly.
No. 1608, 10fr, horiz.: a, Common lantana, red-spotted purple butterfly. b, Deep purple lilac, zebra swallowtail. c, Mt. Fujiyama, ruddy copper butterfly. d, Pinafore pink, red admiral butterfly. e, Argemone mexicana, purple hairstreak butterfly. f, Soapwort, sulphur butterfly. g, Lungwort, Buckeye butterfly. h, Wild thyme, pipevine swallowtail. i, Loeselia mexicana, banded purple butterfly.
No. 1609, 10fr, horiz.: a, Cymbidium Stanley Fouraker Highlander, scarlet tiger moth. b, Cymbidium Sparkle "Ruby Lips," Sumatran carpenter bee. c, Dendrobium Sussex, ant lion. d, Cymbidium Vieux Rose Loch Lomond, nachahmend butterfly. e, Cymbidium, cicada-killer wasp. f, Dendrobium Mousmee, spechosoma wasp. g, Arachnis flos-aeris, green lacewing. h, Paphiopedilum, seven-spot ladybug. i, Eulophia quartiniana, damselfly.
No. 1610, 25fr, Jolly Jocker pansy, monarch butterfly, horiz. No. 1611, 25fr, Pink peony, wasp (inscribed erroneously like No. 1610), horiz. No. 1612, 25fr, Plumbago capensis, honey bee, horiz.

2001, June 22 **Perf. 14**
1603-1606	A260	Set of 4	11.50	11.50

Sheets of 9, #a-i
Perf. 14¼x14½
1607-1609   A260   Set of 3   30.00 30.00
Souvenir Sheets
1610-1612   A260   Set of 3   16.00 16.00

Nos. 1607-1609 each contain nine 37x30mm stamps; Nos. 1610-1612 each contain one 50x37mm stamp.

Tintin in Africa — A261

Designs: 190fr, Tintin with hand above eyes. 461fr, Tintin in car with dog and native.

2001, Dec. 31   **Photo.**   **Perf. 11½**
1613   A261   190fr multi   1.75   1.75
Souvenir Sheet
1614   A261   461fr multi   5.00   5.00

No. 1614 contains one 48x38mm stamp. Imperfs exist. Value: 1613, $15; 1614, $30. See Belgium Nos. 1875-1876.

Native Handicrafts A262

Designs: 10fr, Tabwa buffalo mask. 50fr, Kongo bedpost. 60fr, Loi drum. 150fr, Kuba royal statue, vert. 200fr, Tshokwe mask, vert. 300fr, Luba mask, vert.

2002, Mar. 7   **Litho.**   **Perf. 11½**
1615-1620   A262   Set of 6   9.00   9.00

Lions A263

Designs: 50fr, Lioness and cub. 75fr, Lion and dead animal. 150fr, Lioness and cubs at water's edge. 250fr, Lion and lioness. 300fr, Lion leaping in water.

2002, Mar. 7   **Litho.**   **Perf. 11½**
1621-1625   A263   Set of 5   9.00   9.00

Minerals A265

Designs: 190fr, Beryl, vert. 340fr, Willemite mimetite. 410fr, Quartz chlorite. 445fr, Allophane copper. 455fr, Rhodochrosite, vert. 480fr, Zircon.

Perf. 11½x11¼
2002, Aug. 30   **Litho.**
1631	A265	190fr multi	1.50	1.50
1632	A265	340fr multi	2.75	2.75
1633	A265	410fr multi	3.25	3.25
1634	A265	445fr multi	3.50	3.50
1635	A265	455fr multi	3.50	3.50
1636	A265	480fr multi	3.75	3.75

An additional stamp was issued in the set. The editors would like to examine it.

OFFICIAL STAMPS

Nos. 756-772 Overprinted

1975   **Litho.**   **Perf. 14**
O1	A145	10s red org & blk	.20	.20
O2	A145	40s multi	.20	.20
O3	A145	50s multi	.20	.20

                Perf. 13
O4	A146	1k multi	.20	.20
O5	A146	2k multi	.20	.20
O6	A146	3k multi	.20	.20
O7	A146	4k multi	.30	.20
O8	A146	5k multi	.30	.20
O9	A146	6k multi	.45	.20
O10	A146	8k multi	.60	.20
O11	A146	9k multi	.60	.25
O12	A146	10k multi	.70	.25
O13	A146	14k multi	1.00	.40
O14	A146	17k multi	1.10	.45
O15	A146	20k multi	1.10	.45
O16	A146	50k multi	3.00	1.40
O17	A146	100k multi	10.00	3.50
	Nos. O1-O17 (17)		20.35	8.70

"SP" are the initials of "Service Public."

ZAMBEZIA

zam-'bē-zē-ə

LOCATION — A former district of the Mozambique Province in Portuguese East Africa
GOVT. — Part of the Portuguese East Africa Colony

The districts of Quelimane and Tete were created from Zambezia. Eventually stamps of Mozambique came into use. See Quelimane and Tete.

1000 Reis = 1 Milreis

King Carlos
A1   A2

Perf. 11½, 12½, 13½

			1894 Typo.	Unwmk.	
1	A1	5r	yellow	.25	.25
2	A1	10r	red violet	.75	.45
3	A1	15r	chocolate	1.00	.65
a.		Perf. 12½		27.50	19.00
4	A1	20r	lavender	1.00	.65
5	A1	25r	blue green	2.00	1.25
a.		Perf. 11½			
6	A1	50r	lt blue	2.00	1.25
7	A1	75r	carmine	4.50	3.25
a.		Perf. 11½		50.00	35.00
8	A1	80r	yellow grn	5.00	2.50
9	A1	100r	brown, buff	4.00	1.75
10	A1	150r	car, rose	7.00	3.00
11	A1	200r	dk blue, bl	8.00	3.00
a.		Perf. 11½		200.00	150.00
b.		Perf. 13½		32.50	24.00
12	A1	300r	dk bl, salmon	10.00	4.50
a.		Perf. 11½		25.00	20.00
		Nos. 1-12 (12)		45.50	22.50

For surcharges and overprints see Nos. 36-47, 73-74, 77-81, 84-88.

		1898-1903	Perf. 11½

Name and Value in Black or Red (500r)

13	A2	2½r	gray	.45	.45
14	A2	5r	orange	.45	.45
15	A2	10r	lt green	.75	.50
16	A2	15r	brown	1.25	1.00
17	A2	15r	gray grn ('03)	1.60	1.40
18	A2	20r	gray violet	1.25	1.00
19	A2	25r	sea green	1.25	1.00
20	A2	25r	carmine ('03)	1.00	.85
21	A2	50r	blue	1.25	1.10
22	A2	50r	brown ('03)	2.75	2.25
23	A2	65r	dull bl ('03)	8.00	5.50
24	A2	75r	rose	10.00	5.25
25	A2	75r	lilac ('03)	3.25	2.75
26	A2	80r	violet	5.00	3.00
27	A2	100r	dk bl, bl	2.00	2.00
28	A2	115r	org brn, pink ('03)	10.00	7.25
29	A2	130r	brn, straw ('03)	10.00	7.25
30	A2	150r	brn, buff	6.00	3.50
31	A2	200r	red vio, pnksh	6.00	3.50
32	A2	300r	dk bl, rose	8.00	3.50
33	A2	400r	dull bl, straw ('03)	10.00	8.50
34	A2	500r	blk, bl ('01)	12.00	6.75
35	A2	700r	vio, yelsh ('01)	15.00	8.75
		Nos. 13-35 (23)		117.25	77.50

For surcharges and overprints see Nos. 49-68, 72, 82-83, 93-107.

Stamps of 1894 Surcharged

		1902		Perf. 11½, 12½
36	A1	65r on 10r red vio	9.00	7.00
37	A1	65r on 15r choc	9.00	7.00
38	A1	65r on 20r lav	9.00	7.00
39	A1	65r on 300r bl, sal	9.00	7.00
40	A1	115r on 5r yel	9.00	7.00
41	A1	115r on 25r bl grn	9.00	7.00
42	A1	115r on 80r yel grn	9.00	7.00
43	A1	130r on 75r car	7.00	7.00
44	A1	130r on 150r car, rose	5.25	5.25
45	A1	400r on 50r lt bl	2.00	3.25
46	A1	400r on 100r brn, buff	2.00	3.50
47	A1	400r on 200r bl, bl	2.00	3.50

Same Surcharge on No. P1

48	N1	130r on 2½r brn	9.00	7.00
		Nos. 36-48 (13)	90.25	78.50

Stamps of 1898 Overprinted

		1902		Perf. 11½
49	A2	15r brown	2.00	1.40
50	A2	25r sea green	2.00	1.40
51	A2	50r blue	2.00	1.40
52	A2	75r rose	6.00	3.75
		Nos. 49-52 (4)	12.00	7.95

No. 23 Surcharged in Black

		1905		
53	A2	50r on 65r dull blue	5.75	4.00

Stamps of 1898-1903 Overprinted in Carmine or Green

		1911		
54	A2	2½r gray	.35	.20
55	A2	5r orange	.35	.20
56	A2	10r light green	.40	.25
a.		Inverted overprint	15.00	12.50
57	A2	15r gray green	.40	.25
58	A2	20r gray violet	.50	.30
59	A2	25r carmine (G)	1.50	.50
60	A2	50r brown	.40	.35
61	A2	75r lilac	1.25	.90
62	A2	100r dk bl, bl	1.25	.90
63	A2	115r org brn, pink	1.25	.90
64	A2	130r brown, straw	1.25	.90
65	A2	200r red vio, pnksh	1.25	.90
66	A2	400r dull bl, straw	2.10	1.10
67	A2	500r blk & red, bl	2.10	1.10
68	A2	700r violet, yelsh	2.25	1.50
		Nos. 54-68 (15)	16.60	10.25

Stamps of 1902-05 Overprinted in Carmine or Green

		1914		
			Without Gum	
72	A2	50r on 65r dl bl	4,000.	1,200.
73	A1	115r on 5r yellow	1.25	1.50
74	A1	115r on 25r bl grn	1.25	1.50
75	A1	115r on 80r yel grn	1.25	1.50
76	N1	130r on 2½r brn (G)	1.25	1.50
a.		Carmine overprint	22.50	22.50
77	A1	130r on 75r car	1.75	1.50
a.		Perf. 12½	5.50	7.00
78	A1	130r on 150r car, rose	1.75	1.50
79	A1	400r on 50r lt bl	2.50	3.00
a.		Perf. 12½	11.00	11.00
80	A1	400r on 100r brn, buff	2.50	2.50
81	A1	400r on 200r bl, bl	2.50	2.50
		On Nos. 51-52		
82	A2	50r blue	1.50	1.50
83	A2	75r rose	1.50	1.50
		Nos. 73-83 (11)	19.00	20.00

Preceding Issues Overprinted in Carmine

		1915		
		On Surcharged Issue of 1902		
84	A1	115r on 5r yellow	.85	.45
85	A1	115r on 25r bl grn	.85	.45
86	A1	115r on 80r lt grn	.85	.45
87	A1	130r on 75r carmine	.85	.45
a.		Perf. 12½	4.50	2.25
88	A1	130r on 150r car, rose	.85	.45
92	N1	130r on 2½r (down)	.85	.45
		On Nos. 51, 53		
93	A2	50r blue	.85	.50
a.		"Republica" inverted	15.00	15.00
94	A2	50r on 65r dull bl	3.50	4.50
		Nos. 84-94 (8)	9.45	7.70

Stamps of 1898-1903 Overprinted Locally in Carmine

		1917		
			Without Gum	
95	A2	2½r gray	1.50	3.00
96	A2	5r orange	7.00	6.50
97	A2	10r light green	7.00	6.00
98	A2	15r gray green	6.50	6.50
99	A2	20r gray violet	7.25	6.50
100	A2	25r sea green	13.50	15.00
101	A2	100r blue, blue	4.00	2.75
102	A2	115r org brn, pink	4.00	2.75
103	A2	130r brown, straw	4.00	2.75
104	A2	200r red vio, pnksh	4.00	2.75
105	A2	400r dull bl, straw	4.50	3.50
106	A2	500r blk & red, bl	5.50	3.75
107	A2	700r vio, yelsh	9.00	5.25
		Nos. 95-107 (13)	77.75	67.00

NEWSPAPER STAMP

N1

		1894 Unwmk. Typo.	Perf. 12½
P1	N1	2½r brown	.60	.35

For overprints and surcharges see Nos. 76, 92.

ZAMBIA

'zam-bē-ə

LOCATION — Southern Africa
GOVT. — Republic
AREA — 290,586 sq. mi.
POP. — 9,663,535 (1999 est.)
CAPITAL — Lusaka

The former British protectorate of Northern Rhodesia became an independent republic Oct. 24, 1964, taking the name Zambia. See Northern Rhodesia; see Rhodesia and Nyasaland.

12 Pence = 1 Shilling
20 Shillings = 1 Pound
100 Ngwee = 1 Kwacha (1968)

> **Catalogue values for all unused stamps in this country are for Never Hinged items.**

Pres. Kenneth D. Kaunda, Victoria Falls — A1

College of Further Education, Lusaka — A2

Perf. 14½x14, 14x14½

		1964, Oct. 24 Photo.	Unwmk.
1	A1	3p shown	.20	.20
2	A2	6p shown	.30	.20
3	A1	1sh3p Barotse dancer	.50	.30
		Nos. 1-3 (3)	1.00	.70

Zambia's independence, Oct. 24, 1964.

Farmer and Silo A3   X-Ray Technician A4

Designs: 2p, Chinyau dancer. 3p, Woman picking cotton. 4p, Angoni bull. 6p, Communications by drum and teletype. 9p, Redwood blossoms and factory. 1sh, Night fishing on Lake Tanganyika. 1sh3p, Woman tobacco worker. 2sh, Tonga basket maker and child. 2sh6p, Elephants in Luangwa Valley Game Reserve. 5sh, Child and school. 10sh, Copper mining. £1, Makishi dancer.

		1964, Oct. 24 Photo.	Perf. 14½
		Size: 23x19mm, 19x23mm	
4	A3	½p emerald, blk & red	.20	.25
5	A4	1p ultra, blk & brn	.20	.20
6	A4	2p orange, blk & red	.20	.20
7	A4	3p red & black	.20	.20
8	A3	4p orange & black	.20	.20
		Perf. 13½x14½, 14½x13½	
		Size: 32x23mm, 23x32mm	
9	A3	6p Prus grn, brn & org	.20	.20
10	A3	9p ultra, brn & dk car rose	.20	.20
11	A3	1sh blue, bis & blk	.20	.20
12	A4	1sh3p dk bl, ver, blk & yel	.30	.20
13	A4	2sh org, blk, brn & ultra	.35	.20
14	A3	2sh6p org yel & blk	.85	.45
15	A3	5sh emerald, blk & yel	1.40	.65
16	A3	10sh orange & blk	4.00	4.00
17	A4	£1 red, blk, brn & yel	3.00	4.00
		Nos. 4-17 (14)	11.50	11.15

ITU Emblem, Old and New Communication Equipment — A5

		1965, July 26 Photo.	Perf. 14
18	A5	6p brt lilac & gold	.20	.20
19	A5	2sh6p gray & gold	1.25	1.50

Cent. of the ITU.

ICY Emblem A6

		1965, July 26	Perf. 14
20	A6	3p grnsh blue & gold	.20	.20
21	A6	1sh3p ultra & gold	.80	.65

International Cooperation Year, 1965.

Pres. Kaunda and State House, Lusaka — A7

Clematopsis — A8

Designs: 6p, Fireworks over Independence Stadium. 2sh6p, Tithonia diversifolia.

Perf. 13½x14½

1965, Oct. 18   Unwmk.
| 22 | A7 | 3p multicolored | .20 | .20 |
| 23 | A7 | 6p ind, yel & brt pink | .20 | .20 |

Perf. 14
24	A8	1sh3p pink, yel & brn	.20	.20
25	A8	2sh6p brt grn, dp org & brn	.40	.40
		Nos. 22-25 (4)	1.00	1.00

1st anniv. of independence, Oct. 24.

Inauguration of WHO Headquarters, Geneva — A9

1966, May 18   Perf. 14
| 26 | A9 | 3p rose brn, brt bl & gold | .20 | .20 |
| 27 | A9 | 1sh3p vio bl, brt bl & gold | 1.25 | 1.00 |

University of Zambia — A10

1966, July 12   Photo.   **Perf. 14**
| 28 | A10 | 3p brt green & gold | .20 | .20 |
| 29 | A10 | 1sh3p brt purple & gold | .40 | .20 |

University of Zambia opening, Mar. 17.

National Assembly Building — A11

1967, May 2   Unwmk.   **Perf. 14**
| 30 | A11 | 3p slate & bronze | .20 | .20 |
| 31 | A11 | 6p yellow grn & bronze | .40 | .20 |

Completion of National Assembly Building.

Lusaka Airport — A12

1967, Oct. 2   Photo.   **Perf. 13½x14½**
| 32 | A12 | 6p vio blue & bronze | .20 | .20 |
| 33 | A12 | 2sh6p brown & bronze | .90 | .90 |

Opening of Lusaka International Airport.

Symbols of Agriculture A13

Radio, Telephone and Television — A14

Designs: 4p, Emblem of Zambia Youth Service. 1sh, Map showing locations of Zambia coalfields. 8n, Vimbuza dancer. 1sh6p, Map showing Zambia-Tanzania Road.

Perf. 14½x13½, 13½x14½

1967, Oct. 23
34	A14	4p gray, red & gold	.20	.20
35	A13	6p lt vio bl, gold & blk	.20	.20
36	A14	9p dull blue, sil & blk	.35	.35
37	A14	1sh gold, red, blk & vio bl	.65	.20
38	A13	1sh6p bl grn, ultra, gold & blk	1.00	1.25
		Nos. 34-38 (5)	2.40	2.20

Issued to publicize National Development.

Lusaka Cathedral — A15   Baobab Tree — A16

Designs: 3n, Zambia Airways plane. 5n, National Museum, Livingstone. 8n, Vimbuza dancer. 10n, Woman tobacco picker. 15n, Nudaurelia zambesina butterfly. 20n, Crowned cranes. 25n, Angoni warrior. 50n, Chokwe dancer. 1k, Railroad bridge, Kafue River. 2k, Eland.

Perf. 13½x14½, 14½x13½

1968, Jan. 16   Photo.
Size: 26x22mm, 22x26mm
39	A15	1n bronze & multi	.20	.20
a.		Booklet pane of 6	.20	
b.		Booklet pane of 4	.20	
40	A16	2n bronze & multi	.20	.20
41	A16	3n bronze & multi	.20	.20
a.		Booklet pane of 6	.60	
b.		Booklet pane of 4	.40	
42	A16	5n sepia & bronze	.20	.20
43	A16	8n bronze & multi	.20	.20
44	A16	10n bronze & multi	.25	.20

Size: 32x26mm, 26x32mm
45	A15	15n bronze & multi	3.00	.20
46	A16	20n bronze & multi	5.00	.20
47	A16	25n bronze & multi	.55	.20
48	A16	50n bronze, org & blk	.50	.25
49	A15	1k dk blue & brnz	5.00	.30
50	A15	2k copper & blk	3.50	1.25
		Nos. 39-50 (12)	18.80	3.60

Used values of Nos. 48-50 are for canceled-to-order stamps. Postally used examples sell for more.

Map of Zambia, Arrow Pointing to Ndola — A17

Perf. 14½x14

1968, June 29   Photo.   Unwmk.
| 51 | A17 | 15n brt green & gold | .40 | .40 |

Zambia Trade Fair at Ndola.

Children and Human Rights Flame — A18

WHO Emblem A19

Children A20

Photogravure; Gold Impressed
Perf. 14½x14

1968, Oct. 23
52	A18	3n ultra, dk bl & gold	.40	.40
53	A19	10n brt violet & gold	.40	.40
54	A20	25n brt blue, blk & gold	.50	.50
		Nos. 52-54 (3)	1.30	1.30

Intl. Human Rights Year; 20th anniv. of WHO; 21st anniv. of UNICEF (25n).

Copper Miner — A21

Map of Africa with Zambia — A22

Design: 25n, Worker poling furnace, horiz.

Perf. 14½x13½

1969, June 18   Photo.
| 55 | A21 | 3n dp violet & copper | .30 | .20 |
| 56 | A21 | 25n yellow, blk & copper | 1.50 | 1.10 |

50th anniv. of the ILO.

Perf. 13½x14, 14x13½

1969, Oct. 23   Photo.

10n, Waterbucks, Kafue National Park, horiz. 15n, Golden perch, Kasaba Bay, horiz. 25n, Carmine bee-eater, Luangwa Valley.
57	A22	5n ultra, yel & copper	.20	.20
58	A22	10n copper & multi	.35	.20
59	A22	15n copper & multi	.70	.40
60	A22	25n copper & multi	1.75	1.25
		Nos. 57-60 (4)	3.00	2.05

International Year of African Tourism.

Nimbus III Weather Satellite — A23

1970, Mar. 23   Litho.   **Perf. 13x11**
| 61 | A23 | 15n multicolored | .50 | .50 |

Issued for World Meteorological Day.

"Clean Water" — A24

Designs: 15n, "Nutrition" (infant on scale). 25n, Children's immunization and Edward Jenner, M.D.

1970, July 4   Litho.   **Perf. 13x12½**
62	A24	3n multicolored	.20	.20
63	A24	15n multicolored	.80	.80
64	A24	25n multicolored	1.40	1.40
		Nos. 62-64 (3)	2.40	2.40

Issued to publicize preventive medicine and the "Under Five" children's clinics.

Mural by Gabriel Ellison A25

1970, Sept. 8   Litho.   **Perf. 14x14½**
| 65 | A25 | 15n multicolored | .50 | .50 |

Opening of the Conf. of Non-Aligned Nations in Mulungushi Hall (decorated with murals by Mrs. Ellison) in Zambia.

Ceremonial Axe — A26

Traditional Crafts: 5n, Clay pipe bowl with antelope head. 15n, Makishi mask, vert. 25n, The Kuomboka Ceremony (dancers and ceremonial boat).

1970, Nov. 30   Litho.   **Perf. 14x14½**
Size: 34x25mm
| 66 | A26 | 3n dp lil rose & multi | .20 | .20 |
| 67 | A26 | 5n dp org, blk & sepia | .20 | .20 |

Perf. 13x13½
Size: 30x45½mm
| 68 | A26 | 15n dp lil rose & multi | .55 | .55 |

Perf. 12½
Size: 71½x23½mm
69	A26	25n violet, blue & multi	.85	.85
a.		Souvenir sheet of 4, #66-69	11.50	11.50
		Nos. 66-69 (4)	1.80	1.80

Dag Hammarskjold and UN General Assembly — A27

Hammarskjold and: 10n, Downed plane. 15n, Dove with olive branch. 25n, Plaque and flowers.

1971, Sept. 18   Perf. 13½
70	A27	4n brown & multi	.20	.20
71	A27	10n yellow grn & multi	.20	.20
72	A27	15n blue & multi	.50	.50
73	A27	25n plum & multi	.75	.75
		Nos. 70-73 (4)	1.65	1.65

10th anniv. of the death of Dag Hammarskjold, (1905-61) Secretary-General of the UN, near Ndola, Zambia.

Red-Breasted Bream — A28

1971, Dec. 10

74	A28	4n shown	.20	.20
75	A28	10n Green-headed bream	.75	.60
76	A28	15n Tiger fish	1.75	.85
		Nos. 74-76 (3)	2.70	1.65

Christmas.

Cheetah — A29

Soil Conservation A30

1972, Mar. 15   *Perf. 13½x14*

77	A29	4n shown	.30	.20
78	A29	10n Lechue	.70	.55

Perf. 14x13½

79	A30	15n Cape porcupine	1.10	.85
80	A30	25n Elephant	2.75	1.40
		Nos. 77-80 (4)	4.85	3.00

Conservation Year.

1972, June 30   Litho.   *Perf. 14x13½*
Size: 18½x45mm

81	A30	4n shown	.25	.25
82	A30	10n Forest conservation	.75	.75

Perf. 13½x14

83	A29	15n Water conservation (river view)	1.10	1.10
84	A29	25n Woman in corn field	1.90	1.90
		Nos. 81-84 (4)	4.00	4.00

Souvenir Sheet

85		Sheet of 4	10.00	12.50
a.	A30	10n Giraffe and zebra	1.40	1.75
b.	A30	10n Rhinoceros	1.40	1.75
c.	A30	10n Hippopotamus and deer	1.40	1.75
d.	A30	10n Lion	1.40	1.75

Conservation Year. Stamp size: 27x50mm.

1972, Sept. 22   *Perf. 13½x14*

Designs: All horizontal.

Size: 48x35mm

86	A30	4n Zambian flowers	1.10	.60
87	A30	10n Citrus swallowtails and roses	1.90	1.60
88	A30	15n Bee	3.50	2.40
89	A30	25n Locusts in corn field	5.50	3.50
		Nos. 86-89 (4)	12.00	8.10

Conservation Year.

Mary and Joseph Going to Bethlehem — A31

1972, Dec. 1   Litho.   *Perf. 14*

90	A31	4n shown	.20	.20
91	A31	9n Holy Family	.25	.25
92	A31	15n Adoration of the shepherds	.40	.40
93	A31	25n Kings following the star	.75	.75
		Nos. 90-93 (4)	1.60	1.60

Christmas.

Broken Hill Man A32

Designs: 4n, Oudenodon and rubidgea (artist's conception; vert.). 10n, Zambiasaurus. 15n, Skull of Luangwa Drysdalli. 25n, Glossoptoris (seed).

Perf. 14x13½, 14

1973, Feb. 1   Litho.
Size: 29x45mm

94	A32	4n org ver & multi	.75	.35

Size: 37½x21mm

95	A32	9n org ver & multi	1.10	.75
96	A32	10n apple grn & multi	1.25	.95
97	A32	15n lilac & multi	1.75	1.25
98	A32	25n orange brn & multi	3.25	3.25
		Nos. 94-98 (5)	8.10	6.55

Fossils from Luangwa area (except 9n), over 200 million years old.

Meeting of Stanley and Livingstone at Ujiji — A33

4n, Livingstone, the missionary. 9n, Livingstone at Victoria Falls. 10n, Livingstone stopping slave traders. 15n, Livingstone, the physician. 25n, Portrait & tree in Chitumbu, marking burial place of heart.

1973, May 1   *Perf. 13x13½*

99	A33	3n multicolored	.20	.20
100	A33	4n multicolored	.30	.30
101	A33	9n multicolored	.60	.60
102	A33	10n multicolored	.75	.75
103	A33	15n multicolored	1.10	1.10
104	A33	25n multicolored	1.75	1.75
		Nos. 99-104 (6)	4.70	4.70

Dr. David Livingstone (1813-73), medical missionary and explorer.

Parliamentary Mace — A34

1973, Sept. 24   Litho.   *Perf. 13½x14*

105	A34	9n tan & multi	.70	.70
106	A34	15n gray & multi	1.40	1.40
107	A34	25n brt green & multi	1.90	1.90
		Nos. 105-107 (3)	4.00	4.00

Third Commonwealth Conference of Speakers and Presiding Officers, Lusaka.

Vaccination — A35

WHO Emblem and: 4n, Mother washing infant, vert. 9n, Nurse weighing infant, vert. 15n, Child eating cereal and fruit.

1973, Oct. 16   Litho.   *Perf. 14*

108	A35	4n blue & multi	65.00	27.50
109	A35	9n orange & multi	.30	.30
110	A35	10n brt grn & multi	.40	.40
111	A35	15n violet & multi	.50	.50
		Nos. 108-111 (4)	66.20	28.70

WHO, 25th anniv.

A36

A37

Birth of the Second Republic: 4n, UNIP flag. 9n, United National Independence Party Headquarters, Lusaka. 10n, Army band. 15n, Women dancing and singing. 25n, President's parliamentary chair.

1973, Dec. 13   Litho.   *Perf. 14x13½*

112	A36	4n multicolored	17.50	7.50
113	A36	9n multicolored	.25	.25
114	A36	10n multicolored	.30	.30
115	A36	15n multicolored	.45	.45
116	A37	25n multicolored	.75	.75
		Nos. 112-116 (5)	19.25	9.25

Pres. Kaunda and his Home During Struggle for Independence — A38

4n, Pres. Kaunda at Mulungushi. 15n, Pres. Kaunda holding torch of freedom.

1974, Apr. 28   Litho.   *Perf. 14½x14*

117	A38	4n multi, vert.	.70	.70
118	A38	9n multi	.90	.90
119	A38	15n multi	1.40	1.40
		Nos. 117-119 (3)	3.00	3.00

50th birthday of Pres. Kenneth Kaunda.

Nakambla Sugar Estate — A39

Designs: 4n, Local market. 9n, Kapiri glass factory. 10n, Kafue hydroelectric plant. 15n, Kafue Bridge. 25n, Conference of Non-aligned Nations, Lusaka, 1970.

1974, Oct. 24   Litho.   *Perf. 13½x14*

120	A39	3n multicolored	.20	.20
121	A39	4n multicolored	.20	.20
122	A39	9n multicolored	.40	.40
123	A39	10n multicolored	.50	.50
124	A39	15n multicolored	.70	.70
125	A39	25n multicolored	1.10	1.10
		Nos. 120-125 (6)	3.10	3.10

Souvenir Sheet

126		Sheet of 4	8.00	10.00
a.	A39	15n Academic education	1.50	1.90
b.	A39	15n Teacher Training College	1.50	1.90
c.	A39	15n Technical education	1.50	1.90
d.	A39	15n University of Zambia	1.50	1.90

10th anniversary of indepdence.

Mobile Post Office — A40

UPU Emblem and: 9n, Rural mail service by Zambia Airways. 10n, Modern Post Office, Chipata. 15n, Ndola Postal Training Center.

1974, Nov. 15

127	A40	4n multicolored	.20	.20
128	A40	9n multicolored	.25	.20
129	A40	10n multicolored	.30	.20
130	A40	15n multicolored	.45	.30
		Nos. 127-130 (4)	1.20	.90

Centenary of Universal Postal Union.

Radar by Day A41

1974, Dec. 16

131	A41	4n shown	.25	.20
132	A41	9n Radar by night	.50	.40
133	A41	15n Radar at dawn	1.00	.70
134	A41	25n Radar station	1.75	1.25
		Nos. 131-134 (4)	3.50	2.55

Inauguration of Mwembeshi Earth Station, Oct. 21, 1974.

Rhinoceros and Calf — A42

Peanut Harvest — A43

1975, Jan. 3   Litho.   *Perf. 13½x14*

135	A42	1n shown	.55	.55
136	A42	2n Guinea fowl	.55	.55
137	A42	3n Zambian dancers	.25	.40
138	A42	4n Fish eagle	1.00	.20
139	A42	5n Bridge, Victoria Falls	1.00	1.00
140	A42	8n Sitatunga	1.00	.90
141	A42	9n Elephant, Kasaba Bay Resort	1.25	.85
142	A42	10n Giant pangolin	.25	.20

Perf. 13

143	A43	15n Zambezi River source, Monument	.35	.20
144	A43	20n shown	1.00	1.40
145	A43	25n Tobacco field	1.60	.65
146	A43	50n Flying doctor service	4.00	2.75
147	A43	1k Lady Ross's touraco	5.75	2.25
148	A43	2k Village scene	4.00	5.75
		Nos. 135-148 (14)	22.55	17.65

For surcharges see #188-191, 319.

Map of Namibia (South-West Africa) — A44

1975, Aug. 26 Litho.   Perf. 14x13½
149 A44 4n green & dk green   .20   .20
150 A44 9n dk blue & gray bl   .30   .25
151 A44 15n yellow & orange   .40   .40
152 A44 25n orange & dp orange .50   .70
        Nos. 149-152 (4)   1.40 1.55

Namibia Day.

Sprinkler Irrigation — A45

Designs: 9n, Sprinkler irrigation over rows of vegetables. 15n, Furrow irrigation.

1975, Dec. 16 Litho.   Perf. 13
153 A45 4n multicolored   .20   .20
154 A45 9p multicolored   .50   .50
155 A45 15n multicolored .80   .80
        Nos. 153-155 (3)   1.50 1.50

Intl. Commission on Irrigation and Drainage, 25th anniv.

Julbernardia Paniculata — A46

Trees of Zambia: 4n, Sycamore fig. 9n, Baikiaea plurijuga. 10n, Colophospermum. 15n, Uapaca kirkiana. 25n, Pterocarpus angolensis.

1976, Mar. 22 Litho.   Perf. 13
156 A46 3n multicolored   .35   .35
157 A46 4n multicolored   .35   .35
158 A46 9n multicolored   .55   .55
159 A46 10n multicolored .55   .55
160 A46 15n multicolored .90   .90
161 A46 25n multicolored 1.10 1.10
        Nos. 156-161 (6)   3.80 3.80

World Forestry Day, Mar. 21.

TAZARA Passenger Train — A47

9n, Train carrying copper. 10n, Clearing the bush. #164, Train carrying heavy machinery. #166b, Track laying. 20n, Reinforcing railroad track. #165, Train carrying various goods. #166d, Completed tracks.

1976, Dec. 10 Litho.   Perf. 13
162 A47 4n multicolored   .20   .20
163 A47 9n multicolored   .65   .65
164 A47 15n multicolored 1.10 1.10
165 A47 25n multicolored 1.75 1.75
        Nos. 162-165 (4)   3.70 3.70

Souvenir Sheet
Perf. 13½x14
166   Sheet of 4   4.00 4.00
a. A47 10n multicolored   .40   .30
b. A47 15n multicolored   .60   .45
c. A47 20n multicolored   .70   .50
d. A47 25n multicolored   1.00 .65

Completion of Tanzania-Zambia Railroad.

Kayowe Dance — A48

1977, Jan. 18 Litho.   Perf. 13½x14
167 A48 4n shown   .20   .20
168 A48 9n Lilombola dance   .25   .20
169 A48 15n Initiation ceremony .45   .40
170 A48 25n Munkhwele dance   .75   .50
        Nos. 167-170 (4)   1.65 1.30

2nd World Black and African Festival, Lagos, Nigeria, Jan. 15-Feb. 12.

Grimwood's Longclaw — A49

Birds of Zambia: 9n, Shelley's sunbird. 10n, Black-cheeked lovebird. 15n, Locust finch. 20n, White-chested tinkerbird. 25n, Chaplin's barbet.

1977, July 1 Litho.   Perf. 14½
171 A49 4n multicolored   .45   .45
172 A49 9n multicolored   .80   .60
173 A49 10n multicolored .95   .60
174 A49 15n multicolored 1.25 1.90
175 A49 20n multicolored 2.00 2.00
176 A49 25n multicolored 2.50 2.50
        Nos. 171-176 (6)   7.95 7.80

Children Playing with Blocks A50

Designs: 9n, Women of various races dancing in circle. 15n, Black and white girls with young bird.

1977, Oct. 20 Litho.   Perf. 14x14½
177 A50 4n multicolored   .20   .20
178 A50 9n multicolored   .20   .20
179 A50 15n multicolored .50   .50
        Nos. 177-179 (3)   .90   .90

Combat racism and racial discrimination.

"Glory to God in the Highest" A51

Christmas: 9n, Nativity. 10n, Three Kings and camel. 15n, Presentation at the Temple.

1977, Dec. 20 Litho.   Perf. 14
180 A51 4n multicolored   .20   .20
181 A51 9n multicolored   .20   .20
182 A51 10n multicolored .20   .20
183 A51 15n multicolored .30   .30
        Nos. 180-183 (4)   .90   .90

Elephant and Road Check A52

Designs: 18n, Waterbuck and Kafue River boat patrol. 28n, Warthog and helicopter surveillance of National Parks. 32n, Cheetah and armed wildlife guards in Parks and Game Management Areas.

1978, Aug. 1 Litho.   Perf. 14x14½
184 A52 8n multicolored   .35   .35
185 A52 18n multicolored .65   .65
186 A52 28n multicolored 1.10 1.10
187 A52 32n multicolored 1.40 1.40
        Nos. 184-187 (4)   3.50 3.50

Anti-poaching Campaign of Zambia Wildlife Conservation Society, Aug. 1978.

Nos. 141, 137, 145 and 143 Surcharged with New Value and 2 Bars

1979, Mar. 15   Perf. 13½x14, 13
188 A42 8n on 9n multi   .60   .20
189 A42 10n on 3n multi   .20   .20
190 A43 18n on 25n multi .20   .20
191 A43 28n on 15n multi .20   .20
        Nos. 188-191 (4)   1.20 .80

Kayowe Dance A53

Designs: 32n, Kutambala dance. 42n, Chitwansombo drummers. 58n, Lilombola dance.

1979, Aug. 1
192 A53 18n multicolored .35   .35
193 A53 32n multicolored .50   .50
194 A53 42n multicolored .50   .50
195 A53 58n multicolored .65   .65
        Nos. 192-195 (4)   2.00 2.00

Commonwealth Summit Conf., Lusaka, Aug. 1-9.

"Why the Zebra is Hornless" — A54

Children's Stories: 18n, Kalulu and the Tug of War. 42n, How the Tortoise got his Shell. 58n, Kalulu and the Lion.

1979, Sept. 21 Litho.   Perf. 14
196 A54 18n multicolored .30   .20
197 A54 32n multicolored .45   .55
198 A54 42n multicolored .55   .75
199 A54 58n multicolored .70 1.00
a. Souvenir sheet of 4, #196-199 3.00 3.00
        Nos. 196-199 (4)   2.00 2.50

International Year of the Child.

Girls of Different Races Holding Emblem A55

Anti-Apartheid Year (1978): 32n, Boys and toy car. 42n, Infants and butterfly. 58n, Children and microscope.

1979, Nov. 16 Litho.   Perf. 14½x15
200 A55 18n multicolored .25   .25
201 A55 32n multicolored .45   .45
202 A55 42n multicolored .65   .65
203 A55 58n multicolored .90   .90
        Nos. 200-203 (4)   2.25 2.25

Hill, Zambia No. 13 A56

Hill and: 32n, Mailman & bicycle. 42n, No. Rhodesia #75. 58n, Mailman & oxcart.

1979, Dec. 20 Litho.   Perf. 14½
204 A56 18n multicolored .40   .25
205 A56 32n multicolored .50   .50
206 A56 42n multicolored .50   .65
207 A56 58n multicolored .60 1.10
a. Souvenir sheet of 4, #204-207 3.00 3.50
        Nos. 204-207 (4)   2.00 2.50

Sir Rowland Hill (1795-1879), originator of penny postage.

Nos. 204-207a Overprinted "LONDON 1980"

1980, Mar 6 Litho.   Perf. 15
208 A56 18n multicolored .30   .40
209 A56 32n multicolored .40   .55
210 A56 42n multicolored .50   .70
211 A56 58n multicolored .80   .85
a. Souvenir sheet of 4   3.50 4.00
        Nos. 208-211 (4)   2.00 2.50

London 80 Intl. Stamp Exhib., May 6-14.

Anniverary Emblem on Map of Zambia — A57

1980, June 18 Litho.   Perf. 14
212 A57 8n multicolored   .20   .20
213 A57 32n multicolored .60   .60
214 A57 42n multicolored .75   .75
215 A57 58n multicolored .95   .95
a. Souvenir sheet of 4, #212-215 3.00 3.00
        Nos. 212-215 (4)   2.50 2.50

Rotary International, 75th anniversary.

Running A58

1980, July 19 Litho.   Perf. 13
216 A58 18n shown   .35   .35
217 A58 32n Boxing   .60   .60
218 A58 42n Soccer   .70   .70
219 A58 58n Swimming   1.10 1.10
a. Souvenir sheet of 4, #216-219 3.00 3.00
        Nos. 216-219 (4)   2.75 2.75

22nd Summer Olympic Games, Moscow, July 19-Aug. 3.

Zaddach's Forester — A59

1980, Sept. 22
220 A59 18n shown   .40   .40
221 A59 32n Northern highflier .65   .45
222 A59 42n Zambezi skipper .95   .95
223 A59 58n Modest blue   1.50 1.90
a. Souvenir sheet of 4, #220-223 9.00 9.00
        Nos. 220-223 (4)   3.50 3.50

Coat of Arms — A60

A61

1980, Sept. 27   Litho.   Perf. 14½
224 A60 18n multicolored .30 .25
225 A60 32n multicolored .50 .55
226 A60 42n multicolored .60 .70
227 A60 58n multicolored .85 1.25
    Nos. 224-227 (4) 2.25 2.75

26th Commonwealth Parliamentary Association Conference, Lusaka.

1980, Oct.   Litho.   Perf. 14

Nativity and St. Francis of Assisi (stained glass window), Ndola Church.

228 A61 8n multicolored .20 .20
229 A61 28n multicolored .75 1.00
230 A61 32n multicolored .75 1.00
231 A61 42n multicolored 1.25 1.40
    Nos. 228-231 (4) 2.95 3.60

Christmas and 50th anniv. of Catholic Church in Copperbelt (central Zambia).

Trichilia Emetica Seed Pods, Musikili A62

Designs: Seed Pods.

1981, Mar. 21   Litho.   Perf. 14
232 A62 8n shown .20 .20
233 A62 18n Afzelia quanzensis, Mupapa .40 .40
234 A62 28n Erythrina abyssinica, Mulunguti .45 .65
235 A62 32n Combretum collinum, Mulama .45 1.00
    Nos. 232-235 (4) 1.50 2.25

World Forestry Day.

ITU Emblem — A63
Mask Maker — A64

Designs: 18n, 32n, WHO emblem.

1981, May 15   Litho.   Perf. 14½
236 A63 8n multicolored .75 .75
237 A63 18n multicolored .95 .95
238 A63 28n multicolored 1.10 1.10
239 A63 32n multicolored 1.25 1.25
    Nos. 236-239 (4) 4.05 4.05

13th World Telecommunications Day (8n, 28n).

1981-83
240 A64 1n shown .20 .20
241 A64 2n Blacksmiths .20 .20
242 A64 5n Potter .20 .20

243 A64 8n Straw basket fishing .20 .20
244 A64 10n Roof thatching .20 .20
244A A64 12n Picking mushrooms ('83) 3.50 2.75
245 A64 18n Millet grinding .50 .20
246 A64 28n Royal Barge paddler .70 .20
247 A64 30n Makishi tight-rope dancer .70 .20
248 A64 35n Tonga-ila granary, house .75 .20
249 A64 42n Cattle herding .75 1.25
    Perf. 14
    Size: 37x25mm
250 A64 50n Traditional healer .75 .20
251 A64 75n Carrying water jugs ('83) .75 .90
252 A64 1k Grinding corn ('83) .75 .90
253 A64 2k Woman smoking pipe .75 .90
    Nos. 240-253 (15) 10.90 8.70

For surcharges see Nos. 358, 372, 499-506, 596.

Kankobele — A65
Banded Ironstone — A66

Designs: Traditional musical instruments.

1981, Sept. 30   Litho.   Perf. 14½
254 A65 8n shown .55 .20
255 A65 18n Inshingili .65 .55
256 A65 28n Ilimba .90 1.25
257 A65 32n Bango .90 1.50
    Nos. 254-257 (4) 3.00 3.50

1982, Jan. 5   Litho.   Perf. 14
258 A66 8n shown 1.25 .20
259 A66 18n Cobaltocalcite 2.50 .90
260 A66 28n Amazonite 3.25 2.50
261 A66 32n Tourmaline 3.50 3.25
262 A66 42n Uranium ore 4.00 4.50
    Nos. 258-262 (5) 14.50 11.35

1982, July 1   Litho.   Perf. 14
263 A66 8n Bornite 1.25 .30
264 A66 18n Chalcopyrite 2.75 1.40
265 A66 28n Malachite 3.50 3.75
266 A66 32n Azurite 3.50 3.75
267 A66 42n Vanadinite 4.00 4.25
    Nos. 263-267 (5) 15.00 13.45

Scouting Year A67

1982, Mar. 30   Litho.   Perf. 14
268 A67 8n Scouts, flag .40 .40
269 A67 18n Baden-Powell .80 .80
270 A67 28n Horned buffalo, patrol pennant .80 .80
271 A67 1k Eagle, conservation badge 2.50 2.50
    a. Souvenir sheet of 4, #268-271 5.50 6.25
    Nos. 268-271 (4) 4.50 4.50

Drilling Rig, 1926 A68

Steam locomotives.

1983, Jan. 26   Perf. 14x14½
272 A68 8n shown .65 .30
273 A68 18n Class B6, 1910 1.00 1.00
274 A68 28n Borsig engine, 1925 1.60 2.50
275 A68 32n 7th class, 1900 2.00 2.75
    Nos. 272-275 (4) 5.25 6.55

Commonwealth Day — A68a

1983, Mar. 10   Litho.   Perf. 14
276 A68a 12n Cotton picking .20 .20
277 A68a 18n Miners .30 .20
278 A68a 28n Ritual pot, dancers .25 .35
279 A68a 1k Victoria Falls, purple-crested lorie 3.25 4.25
    Nos. 276-279 (4) 4.00 5.00

Local Flowers — A69

1983, May 26   Litho.   Perf. 14
280 A69 12n Eulophia cucullata .20 .20
281 A69 28n Kigelia africana .60 .60
282 A69 35n Protea gaguedi .75 .75
283 A69 50n Leonotis nepotifolia 1.50 3.25
    a. Souvenir sheet of 4, #280-283, perf. 12x12½ 3.25 4.50
    Nos. 280-283 (4) 3.05 4.80

Thornicroft's Giraffes — A70

1983, July 21   Litho.   Perf. 14
284 A70 12n shown .80 .80
285 A70 28n Cookson's wildebeest 1.10 1.10
286 A70 35n Black lechwe 1.50 1.50
287 A70 1k Yellow-backed duiker 3.00 3.00
    Nos. 284-287 (4) 6.40 6.40

Tiger Fish A71

1983, Sept. 29   Litho.   Perf. 14
288 A71 12n shown .65 .20
289 A71 28n Silver Barbel 1.10 .70
290 A71 35n Spotted Squeaker 1.25 2.00
291 A71 38n Red Breasted Bream 1.40 2.00
    Nos. 288-291 (4) 4.40 4.90

For surcharge see No. 597.

Christmas — A72

1983, Dec. 12   Litho.   Perf. 14x14½
292 A72 12n Annunciation .20 .20
293 A72 28n Shepherds .35 .30
294 A72 35n Three Kings .45 .75
295 A72 38n Flight into Egypt .50 1.00
    Nos. 292-295 (4) 1.50 2.25

40th Anniv. of Intl. Civil Aviation Org. — A73

1984, Jan. 26   Litho.   Perf. 14
296 A73 12n Boeing 737, 1983 .20 .20
297 A73 28n Beaver, 1954 .55 .55
298 A73 35n Short Solent Flying Boat, 1948 .70 .70
299 A73 1k DH-66, 1931 2.00 2.00
    Nos. 296-299 (4) 3.45 3.45

60th Birthday of Pres. Kaunda A74

Perf. 14½x14, 14x14½
1984, Apr. 28   Litho.
300 A74 12n Receiving greetings .50 .50
301 A74 28n Swearing in, 1983, vert. .75 .75
302 A74 60n Planting cherry tree 1.40 1.40
303 A74 1k Opening Natl. Assembly, vert. 1.75 1.75
    Nos. 300-303 (4) 4.40 4.40

1984 Summer Olympics — A75

1984, July 18   Litho.   Perf. 14
304 A75 12n Soccer .20 .20
305 A75 28n Running .60 .60
306 A75 35n Hurdles .70 .70
307 A75 50n Boxing 1.00 1.00
    Nos. 304-307 (4) 2.50 2.50

Reptiles A76

1984, Sept. 5   Litho.   Perf. 14
308 A76 12n Gabon viper .30 .30
309 A76 28n Chameleon .65 .65
310 A76 35n Nile crocodile .80 .80
311 A76 1k Blue-headed agama 1.75 1.75
    a. Souvenir sheet of 4, #308-311 5.00 5.00
    Nos. 308-311 (4) 3.50 3.50

20th Anniv. of Independence — A77

1984, Oct. 22   Litho.   Perf. 14
312 A77 12n Pres. Kaunda, Mulungushi Rock .35 .35
313 A77 28n Freedom Statue .60 .60
314 A77 1k Produce 1.75 1.75
    Nos. 312-314 (3) 2.70 2.70

Local Mushrooms
A78

1984, Dec. 12 Litho. Perf. 14x14½
315 A78 12n Amanita flamme-
ola 1.75 1.75
316 A78 28n Amanita zambiana 2.00 2.00
317 A78 32n Termitomyces
letestui 3.00 3.00
318 A78 75n Cantharellus
miniatescens 5.25 5.25
Nos. 315-318 (4) 12.00 12.00
For surcharge see No. 600.

No. 146 Surcharged with New Value
and Two Bars
1985, Mar. 5 Litho. Perf. 13½
319 A43 5k on 50n multi 2.25 2.75

Primates
A79

1985, Apr. 25 Litho. Perf. 14
320 A79 12n Chacma baboon .75 .75
321 A79 20n Moloney's monkey 1.00 1.00
322 A79 45n Blue monkey 2.10 2.10
323 A79 1k Vervet monkey 3.25 3.25
Nos. 320-323 (4) 7.10 7.10
For surcharge see No. 604.

SADCC,
5th Anniv.
A80

1985, July 9 Litho. Perf. 14
324 A80 20n Map .95 .95
325 A80 45n Mining 2.40 2.40
326 A80 1k Mulungushi Hall 2.50 2.50
Nos. 324-326 (3) 5.85 5.85
Southern African Development Coordination
Conference.
For surcharge see No. 605.

Queen
Mother,
85th
Birthday
— A81

25n, Portrait in blue, age 80. 45n, Queen
Consort at Clarence House, 1963. 55n, With
Elizabeth II and Princess Margaret. 5k, With
royal family, christening of Prince Henry, 1984.

1985, Aug. 2
327 A81 25n multi, vert. .20 .20
328 A81 45n multi, vert. .20 .20
329 A81 55n multi .20 .20
330 A81 5k multi 1.90 1.90
Nos. 327-330 (4) 2.50 2.50
For surcharges see Nos. 401, 406, 410,
414, 595, 606, 611.

National Anniversaries — A81a

#330A, Pres. Kenneth Kaunda, Mulungushi
Rock. #330B, Kaunda, agricultural products.
#330C, Freedom statue, flags.

Die Cut Perf. 10
1985, Oct. 23 Embossed
330A-
330C A81a 5k gold
25.00 25.00
United National Independence Party, 26th
anniv. (No. 330A); Independence, 20th anniv.
(Nos. 330B-330C).

Postal and Telecommunications Corp.,
10th Anniv. — A82

1985, Dec. 12 Perf. 13½x13
331 A82 20n Lusaka P.O., 1958 .65 .65
332 A82 45n Livingstone P.O.,
1950 .95 .95
333 A82 55n Kalomo P.O., 1902 1.10 1.10
334 A82 5k Transcontinental
Telegraph, 1900 3.50 3.50
Nos. 331-334 (4) 6.20 6.20
For surcharges see Nos. 590-593.

UN, 40th
Anniv. — A83

1985, Dec. 19 Perf. 14
335 A83 20n Boy in cornfield .45 .45
336 A83 45n Emblem .80 .80
337 A83 1k Pres. Kaunda, 1970 1.50 1.50
338 A83 2k Charter signing,
1945 2.25 2.25
Nos. 335-338 (4) 5.00 5.00
For surcharges see #594, 607.

Beetles
A84

1986, Mar. 20
339 A84 35n Mylabris tricolor .20 .20
340 A84 1k Phasgonocnema
melanianthe .55 .55
341 A84 1.70k Amaurodes pas-
serinii .95 .95
342 A84 5k Ranzania petersiana 3.00 3.00
Nos. 339-342 (4) 4.70 4.70
For surcharges see #609, 612.

Common Design Types
pictured following the introduction.

Queen Elizabeth II 60th Birthday
Common Design Type
Designs: 35n, At the Flower Ball, Savoy
Hotel, London, 1951. 1.25k, With Prince
Andrew at Lusaka Airport, Commonwealth
Conf., 1979. 1.70k, With Dr. Kaunda observ-
ing natl. anthem. 1.95k, Wearing Queen Mary
tiara, state visit to Luxembourg, 1976. 5k, Vis-
iting Crown Agents' offices, 1983.

1986, Apr. 21 Wmk. 384 Perf. 14
343 CD337 35n scar, blk & sil .30 .30
344 CD337 1.25k ultra & multi .40 .40
345 CD337 1.70k grn, blk & sil .45 .45
346 CD337 1.95k vio & multi .45 .45
347 CD337 5k rose vio & multi .65 .65
Nos. 343-347 (5) 2.25 2.25
For surcharges see Nos. 402, 405, 407,
411, 415.

Royal Wedding Issue, 1986
Common Design Type
Designs: 1.70k, Sarah Ferguson kissing
Prince Andrew. 5k, Andrew in informal dress.

1986, July 23 Litho. Perf. 14
348 CD338 1.70k multicolored .40 .40
349 CD338 5k multicolored 1.00 1.00

1986 World Cup
Soccer
Championships,
Mexico — A85

Various soccer plays.

1986, June 27 Litho. Perf. 14½
350 A85 35n multicolored 1.00 1.00
351 A85 1.25k multicolored 2.25 2.25
352 A85 1.70k multicolored 2.50 2.50
353 A85 5k multicolored 3.75 3.75
Nos. 350-353 (4) 9.50 9.50
For surcharges see Nos. 403, 408, 412, 416.

Halley's
Comet
A86

Designs: 1.25k, Edmond Halley (1656-
1742), by Henry Pegram. 1.70k, Giotto space
probe approaching comet. 2k, Youth, astronomer. 5k, Halley's map of the southern
constellations.

1986, July 4
354 A86 1.25k multicolored 1.00 1.00
355 A86 1.70k multicolored 1.25 1.25
356 A86 2k multicolored 1.75 1.75
357 A86 5k multicolored 3.75 3.75
Nos. 354-357 (4) 7.75 7.75
For surcharges see Nos. 404, 409, 413, 417.

#244A Surchd. in Light Red Brown
1986, July Perf. 14½
358 A64 20n on 12n multi 10.00 .50

Christmas
A87

Children's drawings.

1986, Dec. 15 Litho. Perf. 14
359 A87 35n Nativity .40 .40
360 A87 1.25k Magi 1.50 1.50
361 A87 1.60k Nativity 1.75 1.75
362 A87 5k Angel, house, tree 3.50 3.50
Nos. 359-362 (4) 7.15 7.15
For surcharges see #602, 608.

Tazara
Railroad,
10th
Anniv.
A88

Locomotive traveling various railway lines.

1986, Dec. 22
363 A88 35n Overpass,
Kasama .35 .35
364 A88 1.25k Tunnel 21 vicinity .55 .55
365 A88 1.70k Tunnels 6-7 .70 .70
366 A88 5k Mpika Station
grade separation 1.40 1.40
Nos. 363-366 (4) 3.00 3.00

University
of Zambia
A89

Designs: 35n, Pres. Kaunda shaking council
member's hand. 1.25k, University crest, vert.
1.60k, University statue. 5k, Kaunda laying
university building cornerstone, vert.

1987, Jan. 27 Litho. Perf. 14
367 A89 35n multicolored .45 .45
368 A89 1.25k multicolored .95 .95
369 A89 1.60k multicolored 1.10 1.10
370 A89 5k multicolored 3.75 3.75
Nos. 367-370 (4) 6.25 6.25

No. 137 Surcharged in Blue
1987 Perf. 14½
372 A64 25n on 8n multi .65 .45

Municipal
Arms — A90

Birds — A91

1987, Mar. 26 Perf. 14
373 A90 35n Kitwe .20 .20
374 A90 1k Ndola .35 .35
375 A90 1.70k Lusaka .45 .45
376 A90 20k Livingstone 3.25 3.25
Nos. 373-376 (4) 4.25 4.25
For surcharge see No. 603.

1987-88 Perf. 11x13
Size: 20x25½mm
377 A91 25n Long-toed fluff tail 3.00 3.00
378 A91 30n Miombo pied bar-
bet .20 .20
379 A91 35n Black-and-rufous
swallow 3.00 3.00
Size: 25x38½mm
Perf. 14
380 A91 50n Slaty egret .20 .20
381 A91 1k Bradfield's hornbill 3.00 3.00
382 A91 1.25k Margaret's batis 3.00 3.00
383 A91 1.60k Red-and-blue sunbird 3.00 3.00
384 A91 1.70k Boehm's bee-eater 3.25 3.25
385 A91 1.95k Gorgeous bush
shrike 3.25 3.25
386 A91 2k Shoebill .40 .40
387 A91 5k Taita falcon 3.75 3.75

Surcharged

Size: 20x25½mm
Perf. 11x13
388 A91 20n on 1n Yellow
swamp warbler .30 .30
389 A91 75n on 2n Olive-
flanked robin .30 .30
390 A91 1.65k on 30n #378 .30 .30
Size: 25x38½mm
Perf. 14
391 A91 10k on 50n #380 1.90 1.90
392 A91 20k on 2k #386 2.40 2.40
Nos. 377-392 (16) 31.25 31.25
Issued: #377, 379, 381-385, 387, 9/14/87;
#391-392, 3/10/88; others 10/8/87.
Nos. 388-389 not issued without overprint.
See Nos. 433-435, 527-547. For surcharges
see Nos. 490, 492-498.

Look-out Tree, Livingstone — A92

1987, June 30 *Perf. 14*
393 A92 35n shown .35 .35
394 A92 1.25k Rafting, Zambezi
River .40 .40
395 A92 1.70k Walking safari,
Luangwa Valley 1.75 1.75
396 A92 10k White pelicans 6.75 6.75
Nos. 393-396 (4) 9.25 9.25

Zambia Airways, 20th Anniv. A93

1987, Sept. 21
397 A93 35n De Havilland
Beaver .75 .75
398 A93 1.70k DC-10 1.75 1.75
399 A93 5k DC-3 4.00 4.00
400 A93 10k Boeing 707 6.00 6.00
Nos. 397-400 (4) 12.50 12.50

Issues of 1985-86 Surcharged in Gold or Black

1987, Sept. 14 *Perfs. as Before*
401 A81 3k on 25n #327
(G) 1.00 1.00
402 CD337 3k on 35n #343 .80 .80
403 A85 3k on 35n #350 1.00 1.00
404 A86 3k on 1.25k #354
1.75 1.75
405 CD337 4k on 1.25k #344 .95 .95
406 A81 6k on 45n #328 1.75 1.75
407 CD337 6k on 1.70k #345 1.40 1.40
408 A85 6k on 1.25k #351 1.75 1.75
409 A86 6k on 1.70k #355
2.75 2.75
410 A81 10k on 55n #329 2.50 2.50
411 CD337 10k on 1.95k #346 2.40 2.40
412 A85 10k on 1.70k #352 2.50 2.50
413 A86 10k on 2k #356
4.75 4.75
414 A81 20k on 5k #330
(G) 5.00 5.00
415 CD337 20k on 5k #347 5.00 5.00
416 A85 20k on 5k #353 5.00 5.00
417 A86 20k on 5k #357
(G) 8.75 8.75
Nos. 401-417 (17) 49.05 49.05

World Food Day — A94

Cattle.

1987, Oct. 1 *Perf. 14½x15*
418 A94 35n Friesian-Holstein .20 .20
419 A94 1.25k Simmental .50 .50
420 A94 1.70k Sussex .50 .50
421 A94 20k Brahma 2.50 2.50
Nos. 418-421 (4) 3.70 3.70

Traditional Heritage — A95

Zambian people.

1987, Oct. 20 *Perf. 13x12½*
422 A95 35n Mpoloto Ne
Mikobango .25 .25
423 A95 1.25k Zintaka .40 .40
424 A95 1.70k Mufuluhi .60 .60
425 A95 10k Ntebwe 1.75 1.75

426 A95 20k Kubangwa Aa
Mbulunga 3.00 3.00
Nos. 422-426 (5) 6.00 6.00

World Wildlife Fund — A96

Wild Cats — A97

1987, Dec. 21 *Litho.* *Perf. 14*
427 A96 50n Black lechwe
drinking water 1.50 1.50
428 A96 2k Adults and
young, horiz. 2.75 2.75
429 A96 2.50k Running, horiz. 2.75 2.75
430 A96 10k Male, diff. 6.00 6.00
Nos. 427-430 (4) 13.00 13.00

Souvenir Sheets
431 A97 20k Cheetah 7.50 7.50
432 A97 20k Caracal 7.50 7.50

Bird Type of 1987

1987 *Litho.* *Perf. 11x13*
433 A91 5n Black-tailed cisticola .20 .20
434 A91 10n White-winged star-
ling .20 .20
435 A91 40n Wattled crane .20 .20
Nos. 433-435 (3) .60 .60

For surcharge see No. 491.

Intl. Fund for Agricultural Development (IFAD), 10th Anniv. — A98

1988, Apr. 2 *Perf. 14*
436 A98 50n Cassava crop .20 .20
437 A98 2.50k Net fishing .65 .65
438 A98 2.85k Cattle breeding .75 .75
439 A98 10k Coffee picking 2.50 2.50
Nos. 436-439 (4) 4.10 4.10

A99

A100

1988, Sept. 12 *Litho.* *Perf. 12½*
440 A99 50n Breast-feeding .20 .20
441 A99 2k Growth monitoring .55 .55
442 A99 2.85k Immunization .75 .75
443 A99 10k Oral rehydration 2.50 2.50
Nos. 440-443 (4) 4.00 4.00

UN child survival campaign.

1988, Oct. 10 *Litho.* *Perf. 12½x13*
444 A100 50n Asbestos cement .20 .20
445 A100 2.35k Textiles .60 .60
446 A100 2.50k Tea .70 .70
447 A100 10k Poultry 2.50 2.50
Nos. 444-447 (4) 4.00 4.00

Preferential Trade Area Fair.

Intl. Red Cross and Red Crescent Organizations, 125th Anniv. — A101

1988, Oct. 20 *Perf. 14*
448 A101 50n Famine relief .20 .20
449 A101 2.50k Giving first aid .70 .70
450 A101 2.85k Teaching first aid .85 .85
451 A101 10k Jean-Henri Du-
nant 3.25 3.25
Nos. 448-451 (4) 5.00 5.00

Endangered Species — A102

1988, Dec. 5 *Litho.* *Perf. 14*
452 A102 50n Aardvark .30 .20
453 A102 2k Pangolin .65 .65
454 A102 2.85k Wild dog .85 .85
455 A102 20k Black rhinoceros 7.75 7.75
Nos. 452-455 (4) 9.55 9.45

1988 Summer Olympics, Seoul A103

1988, Dec. 30 *Litho.* *Perf. 14*
456 A103 50n Boxing .20 .20
457 A103 2k Running .50 .50
458 A103 2.50k Hurdling .65 .65
459 A103 20k Soccer 5.25 5.25
Nos. 456-459 (4) 6.60 6.60

Souvenir Sheets
460 A103 30k Tennis 6.50 6.50
461 A103 30k Martial arts 6.50 6.50

Frogs and Toads A104

1989, Jan. 25 *Litho.* *Perf. 12½*
462 A104 50n Red toad .20 .20
463 A104 2.50k Puddle frog .75 .75
464 A104 2.85k Marbled reed
frog .90 .90
465 A104 10k Young reed frogs 3.00 3.00
Nos. 462-465 (4) 4.85 4.85

Bats A105

1989, Mar. 22 *Litho.* *Perf. 12½x13*
466 A105 50n Common slit-
faced .20 .20
467 A105 2.50k Little free-tailed .75 .75
468 A105 2.85k Hildebrandt's
horseshoe .90 .90
469 A105 10k Peters' epauletted fruit 3.00 3.00
Nos. 466-469 (4) 4.85 4.85

A106 A107

1989, May 2 *Litho.* *Perf. 12½*
470 A106 50n Map of
Zambia 1.00 .20
471 A106 6.85k Peace dove 4.00 4.00
472 A106 7.85k Papal arms 4.50 4.50
473 A106 10k Victoria Falls 6.50 6.50
Nos. 470-473 (4) 16.00 15.20

State visit of Pope John Paul II, May 2-4.
For surcharges see #614, 616.

1989, July 26 *Litho.* *Perf. 14½x15*
Edible wild fruits.
474 A107 50n Parinari curatel-
lifolia .20 .20
475 A107 6.50k Uapaca kirkiana 1.75 2.25
476 A107 6.85k Ficus capensis 1.75 2.25
477 A107 10k Borassus aethi-
opum 3.25 3.75
Nos. 474-477 (4) 6.95 8.45

For surcharges see #613, 615.

Grasshoppers — A108

1989, Nov. 8 *Litho.* *Perf. 14x13½*
478 A108 70n Phamphagid .20 .20
479 A108 10.40k Pyrgomorphid 2.25 2.40
480 A108 12.50k Brown katydid 2.75 3.00
481 A108 15k Bush locust 3.50 4.25
Nos. 478-481 (4) 8.70 9.85

No. 480 misspelled "Catydid."

Christmas — A109

Flowers.

1989, Dec. 6 *Litho.* *Perf. 14½*
482 A109 70n Fireball .20 .20
483 A109 10.40k Flame lily 1.40 1.60
484 A109 12.50k Foxglove lily 2.00 2.25
485 A109 20k Vlei lily 3.25 4.00
Nos. 482-485 (4) 6.85 8.05

Stamp World London '90 A110

Designs: 1.20k, Lusaka Main P.O., van, mailman, bicycle. 19.50k, Zambia #220. 20.50k, Rhodesia and Nyasaland #164A, Northern Rhodesia #1. 50k, Great Britain #1, Maltese Cross cancel in red.

Unwmk.
1990, May 2   Litho.   Perf. 14
486 A110 1.20k multicolored   .20   .20
487 A110 19.50k multicolored 3.00 3.00
488 A110 20.50k multicolored 3.00 3.00
489 A110 50k multicolored   6.00 7.00
Nos. 486-489 (4)   12.20 13.20

Nos. 379, 381-387, 433 Surcharged

1989, July 1   Perf. 11x13
490 A91 70n on 35n #379 1.00 .20
491 A91 3k on 5n #433   1.25 .40

Size: 25x38½mm
Perf. 14
492 A91 8k on 1.25k #382   1.50 1.00
493 A91 9.90k on 1.70k #384 1.75 1.75
494 A91 10.40k on 1.60k #383 1.75 1.75
495 A91 12.50k on 1k #381 2.00 2.00
496 A91 15k on 1.95k #385 2.00 2.00
497 A91 20k on 2k #386   3.00 3.00
498 A91 20.35k on 5k #387 3.00 3.00
Nos. 490-498 (9)   17.25 15.10

Nos. 242, 244-245, 247-248 251, 253 Surcharged in Black, Orange Brown, Red Brown, or Violet

a

b

c

1989   Perf. 14½
Size: 22x26mm
499 A64(a) 1.20k on 35n #248 (OB) .25 .25
500 A64(b) 3.75k on 5n #242 .40 .40
501 A64(b) 8.11k on 10n #244 1.00 1.00
502 A64(b) 9k on 30n #247 1.00 1.00
Size: 37x25mm
Perf. 14
503 A64(b) 10k on 75n #251 1.00 1.00
504 A64(c) 18.50k on 2k #253 2.00 2.00
Size: 22x26mm
Perf. 14½
505 A64(a) 19.50k on 12n #244A (RB) 4.00 4.00
506 A64(a) 20.50k on 18n #245 (V) 2.00 1.75
Nos. 499-506 (8) 11.65 11.40
Issued: #500-504, 7/1; others, 11/1.

World Cup Soccer Championships, Italy — A111

Soccer players in various positions.

1990, July 7   Litho.   Perf. 14
507 A111 1.20k multicolored   .20 .20
508 A111 18.50k multicolored 2.25 2.50
509 A111 19.50k multicolored 2.25 2.50
510 A111 20.50k multicolored 2.25 2.50
Nos. 507-510 (4)   6.95 7.70
Souvenir Sheet
510A A111 50k multicolored 11.00 12.00

Southern African Development Co-ordination Conf. (SADCC), 10th Anniv. — A112

Map of SADCC members and: 1.20k, Truck. 19.50k, Telecommunications. 20.50k, Regional cooperation. 50k, Coal transport by cable car.

1990, July 23   Perf. 12½
511 A112 1.20k multicolored .30 .20
512 A112 19.50k multicolored 2.25 2.25
513 A112 20.50k multicolored 2.25 2.25
514 A112 50k multicolored   7.50 7.50
Nos. 511-514 (4)   12.30 12.20

Independence, 26th Anniv. — A113

1990, Oct. 23   Litho.   Perf. 14
515 A113 1.20k Agriculture .20 .20
516 A113 19.50k Shoe factory 1.25 1.25
517 A113 20.50k Satellite communications 1.40 1.40
518 A113 50k Mother and child statue 3.00 3.00
Nos. 515-518 (4) 5.85 5.85

Small Carnivores — A114

1990, Nov. 12
519 A114 1.20k Genet .20 .20
520 A114 18.50k Civet 2.75 2.75
521 A114 19.50k Serval 3.00 3.00
522 A114 20.50k African wild cat 3.25 3.25
Nos. 519-522 (4) 9.20 9.20

Intl. Literacy Year — A115
Soy Beans — A116

Children's stories.

1991, Jan. 11   Litho.   Perf. 14
523 A115 1.20k Bird and the Snake .20 .20
524 A115 18.50k Hare and the Leopard 2.00 2.00
525 A115 19.50k Mouse and Lion 2.75 2.75
526 A115 20.50k Hare and the Hippo 3.00 3.00
Nos. 523-526 (4) 7.95 7.95

Bird Type of 1987
1990-91   Litho.   Perf. 11x13
527 A91 10n Livingstone's flycatcher .80 .45
528 A91 15n Bar-winged weaver .80 .45
529 A91 30n Purple-throated cuckoo shrike 1.25 .45
530 A91 50n Red-billed helmet shrike 1.25 .50
531 A91 50n like #527 1.25 .60
532 A91 1k like #528 1.50 .20
533 A91 1.20k Western bronze-naped pigeon 1.50 .20
534 A91 2k like #529 1.50 .65
535 A91 3k like #530 1.50 .65
536 A91 5k like #533 1.75 .65
Size: 25x38½mm
Perf. 14
537 A91 15k Corn crake 1.25 .60
538 A91 20k Dickinson's grey kestrel 2.50 1.75
539 A91 20.50k like #538 1.25 .85
540 A91 50k Denham's bustard 2.00 2.00
Nos. 527-540 (14) 20.10 10.00
Issued: #533, 1k, 2k, 3k, 5k, 20k, 5/7/91; others, 10/30.

1991, June 28   Litho.   Perf. 13½
548 A116 1k Woman cooking .20 .20
549 A116 2k Soy bean seed .20 .20
550 A116 5k Woman feeding child .35 .20
551 A116 20k Malnourished, healthy children 2.00 2.00
552 A116 50k Pres. Kaunda, child 3.75 3.75
Nos. 548-552 (5) 6.50 6.35
United Church of Zambia / Rotary Foundation Project.

St. Ignatius of Loyola (1491-1556), Founder of Jesuit Order — A117

1k, Chilubula Church near Kasama. 2k, Chikuni Church near Monze. 20k, Bishop Joseph Du Pont.

1991, July 18   Litho.   Perf. 13½
553 A117 1k multicolored   .20 .20
554 A117 2k multicolored   .20 .20
555 A117 20k multicolored 2.75 2.75
556 A117 50k shown   5.00 5.00
Nos. 553-556 (4) 8.15 8.15

Flowering Trees A118

1991, Nov. 29   Litho.   Perf. 13½
557 A118 1k Baobab .20 .20
558 A118 2k Dichrostachys cinerea .35 .20
559 A118 10k Sterospermum kunthianum 2.00 1.50
560 A118 30k Azanza garckeana 3.75 3.75
Nos. 557-560 (4) 6.30 5.65

Queen Elizabeth II's Accession to the Throne, 40th Anniv.
Common Design Type
Perf. 14x13½
1992, Feb. 2   Litho.   Wmk. 373
561 CD349 4k multicolored   .20 .20
562 CD349 32k multicolored 1.25 1.25
563 CD349 35k multicolored 1.40 1.40
564 CD349 38k multicolored 1.50 1.50
565 CD349 50k multicolored 2.00 2.00
Nos. 561-565 (5) 6.35 6.35
For surcharges see Nos. 690-692.

Orchids — A119

Masks — A120

Perf. 13x13½
1992, Feb. 28   Unwmk.
566 A119 1k Disa hamatopetala .55 .20
567 A119 2k Eulophia paivaeana .55 .20
568 A119 5k Eulophia quartiniana .90 .45
569 A119 20k Aerangis verdickii 4.00 4.00
Nos. 566-569 (4) 6.00 4.85

1992, Mar. 10
570 A120 1k Kasinja .20 .20
571 A120 2k Chizaluke .20 .20
572 A120 10k Mwanapweu .90 .75
573 A120 30k Maliya 2.50 3.00
Nos. 570-573 (4) 3.80 4.15

Antelopes A121

1992, Sept. 14   Litho.   Perf. 14
574 A121 4k Bushbuck .20 .20
575 A121 40k Eland 1.50 .95
576 A121 45k Roan antelope 1.50 .95
577 A121 100k Sable antelope 3.00 4.00
Nos. 574-577 (4) 6.20 6.10

Airmail Services, 75th Anniv. A122

1992, Nov. 24   Litho.   Perf. 14
578 A122 4k DH66 Hercules .45 .35
579 A122 40k VC10 2.50 1.00
580 A122 45k C Class flying boat 2.50 1.00
581 A122 100k DC10 4.50 5.50
Nos. 578-581 (4) 9.95 7.85

1992 Summer Olympics, Barcelona — A123

1992, Dec. 28
582 A123 10k 400-meter hurdles .20 .20
583 A123 40k Boxing .85 .55
584 A123 80k Judo 1.75 1.75
585 A123 100k Cycling 4.25 4.25
Nos. 582-585 (4) 7.05 6.75

Christmas — A124

1992, Dec. 23   Litho.   *Perf. 14*
586	A124	10k Wise men	.20	.20
587	A124	80k Nativity scene	2.00	2.00
588	A124	90k Angels singing	2.25	2.25
589	A124	100k Angel, shepherds	2.25	2.25
a.		Souvenir sheet of 4, #586-589	10.00	10.00
		Nos. 586-589 (4)	6.70	6.70

For surcharges see Nos. 658-659.

K2

Nos. 331-334 Surcharged

═══

1991, Mar. 4   Litho.   *Perf. 13½x13*
590	A82	2k on 20n #331	35.00	5.75
591	A82	2k on 45n #332	.75	5.75
592	A82	2k on 55n #333	—	5.75
593	A82	2k on 5k #334	17.50	5.75

Stamps of 1981-89
Surcharged in
Black or Gold

Perfs. as Before

1991, July 5   Litho.
594	A83	2k on 20n #335	10.00	6.00
595	A81	2k on 25n #327		
		(G)	10.00	6.00
596	A64	2k on 28n #246	—	
597	A71	2k on 28n #289	—	
600	A78	2k on 32n #317	30.00	8.00
601	CD337	2k on 35n #343	—	20.00
602	A87	2k on 35n #359	75.00	6.00
603	A90	2k on 35n #373	45.00	6.00
604	A79	2k on 45n #322	45.00	6.00
605	A80	2k on 45n #325	60.00	6.00
606	A81	2k on 45n #328	90.00	6.00
607	A83	2k on 45n #336	47.50	6.00
608	A87	2k on 1.60k #361	80.00	6.00
609	A84	2k on 1.70k #341	47.50	6.00
611	A81	2k on 5k #330	17.50	6.00
612	A84	2k on 5k #342	17.50	6.00
613	A107	2k on 6.50k #475	47.50	6.00
614	A106	2k on 6.85k #471	62.50	6.00
615	A107	2k on 6.85k #476	17.50	6.00
616	A106	2k on 7.85k #472	90.00	6.00

Numbers have been reserved for additional surcharges in this set.

Waterfalls
A125

1993, Sept. 30   Litho.   *Perf. 13½*
617	A125	50k Nkundalila	.20	.20
618	A125	200k Chishimba	1.25	1.25
619	A125	250k Chipoma	1.50	1.50
620	A125	300k Lumangwe	2.10	2.10
		Nos. 617-620 (4)	5.05	5.05

Healthy
Hearts — A126

1993, Oct. 20   Litho.   *Perf. 14½*
| 621 | A126 | O Runner | 1.25 | 1.25 |
| 622 | A126 | P Heart | 1.25 | 1.25 |

No. 621 sold for 50k and No. 622 sold for 80k on date of issue.

Sunbirds
A127

Designs: 20k, Bronze. 50k, Violet-backed. No. 625, Marico. No. 626, Eastern double-collared. 100k, Scarlet-chested. 150k, Bannerman's blue-headed. 200k, Oustalet's. 250k, Red and blue. 300k, Olive. 350k, Greenheaded. 400k, Scarlet tufted malachite. 500k, Yellow-bellied. 800k, Copper. 1000k, Orange-tufted. 1500k, Black. 2000k, Green-throated.

1993, May 30   Litho.   *Perf. 13*
623	A127	20k multicolored	.20	.20
624	A127	50k multicolored	.20	.20
625	A127	O multicolored	.20	.20
626	A127	P multicolored	.30	.30
627	A127	100k multicolored	.35	.35
628	A127	150k multicolored	.55	.55
629	A127	200k multicolored	.65	.65
630	A127	250k multicolored	.80	.80
631	A127	300k multicolored	1.00	1.00
632	A127	350k multicolored	1.25	1.25
633	A127	400k multicolored	1.40	1.40
634	A127	500k multicolored	1.60	1.60
635	A127	800k multicolored	2.75	2.75
636	A127	1000k multicolored	3.50	3.50
637	A127	1500k multicolored	5.25	5.25
638	A127	2000k multicolored	7.00	7.00
		Nos. 623-638 (16)	27.00	27.00

Nos. 625 sold for 50k and 626 sold for 80k on date of issue.
For surcharge, see No. 997.

Snakes — A128

1994, Sept. 28   Litho.   *Perf. 14*
639	A128	50k Tiger snake	.20	.20
640	A128	200k Egyptian cobra	1.75	1.75
641	A128	300k African python	2.75	2.75
642	A128	500k Green mamba	4.50	4.50
		Nos. 639-642 (4)	9.20	9.20

For surcharge, see No. 996.

ILO, 75th
Anniv.
A129

1995, Apr. 3   Litho.   *Perf. 14*
| 643 | A129 | 100k Road rehabilitation | .60 | .60 |
| 644 | A129 | 450k Block making | 2.75 | 2.75 |

For surcharge see No. 781A.

Christmas Angels — A130

1995, Aug. 29   *Perf. 14½x14*
645	A130	100k shown	.40	.40
646	A130	300k With animals	1.10	1.10
647	A130	450k Blowing horn, birds	1.75	1.75
648	A130	500k Playing drum	1.90	1.90
		Nos. 645-648 (4)	5.15	5.15

UN, 50th
Anniv.
A131

1995, Dec. 30   Litho.   *Perf. 11½*
Granite Paper
| 649 | A131 | 700k multicolored | 2.25 | 2.25 |

Natl. Monuments
A132

Designs: 100k, David Livingstone. 300k, Mbereshi Mission. 450k, Von Lettow-Vorbeck. 500k, Niamkolo Church.

1996, Feb. 21   Litho.   *Perf. 14*
650	A132	100k multicolored	.40	.20
651	A132	300k multicolored	1.25	1.25
652	A132	450k multicolored	1.60	1.60
653	A132	500k multicolored	1.90	1.90
		Nos. 650-653 (4)	5.15	4.95

World
Wildlife
Fund
A133

Designs: 200k, Saddle-billed stork. 300k, Black-cheeked lovebird. 500k, Two black-cheeked lovebirds. 900k, Saddle-billed stork with young.

1996, Nov. 27   Litho.   *Perf. 14x14½*
654	A133	200k multicolored	.75	.75
655	A133	300k multicolored	1.00	1.00
656	A133	500k multicolored	1.50	1.50
657	A133	900k multicolored	2.50	2.50
		Nos. 654-657 (4)	5.75	5.75

Nos. 587-588 Surcharged

1996   Litho.   *Perf. 14*
| 658 | A124 | (O) on 90k #588 | 1.75 | 1.75 |
| 659 | A124 | 900k on 80k #587 | 3.00 | 3.00 |

No. 658 was valued at 500k on day of issue.
Size and location of surcharge varies.

New Year 1997 (Year of the
Ox) — A134

Disney characters posing for portrait in Chinese scene, vert.: #660: a, Clarabelle seated. b, Holding scroll. c, Playing musical instrument. d, On bicycle. e, Minnie, Mickey, Clarabelle. f, Holding mirror.
No. 661: a, 250k, Faces of Minnie, Mickey, Clarabelle Cow. b, 400k, Clarabelle seated. c, 500k, Clarabelle standing. d, 600k, Mickey, Clarabelle, Minnie dressed in Chinese outfits. e, 750k, Minnie, Clarabelle, Mickey dancing. f, 1000k, Clarabelle with parasol.

1997, Jan. 28   Litho.   *Perf. 14x13½*
| 660 | A134 | 500k Sheet of 6, #a.-f. | 5.00 | 5.00 |
| 661 | A134 | Sheet of 6, #a.-f. | 6.00 | 6.00 |

No. 660 contains six 35x61mm stamps.

Endangered Species — A135

Species of the world, each 500k: No. 662: a, Spider monkey. b, Manatee. c, Jaguar. d, Puerto Rican parrot. d, Green sea turtle. e, Harpy eagle.
Species of Africa, each 1000k: No. 663a, Black rhinoceros. b, Leopard. c, Chimpanzee. d, Zebra (Grants). e, Mountain gorilla. f, African elephant.
Each, 3000k: No. 664, Lion (African). No. 665, Margay cat.

1997, Feb. 12   *Perf. 14*
| 662 | A135 | Sheet of 6, #a.-f. | 5.00 | 5.00 |
| 663 | A135 | Sheet of 6, #a.-f. | 10.00 | 10.00 |

Souvenir Sheets
| 664-665 | A135 | Set of 2 | 10.00 | 10.00 |

Deng Xiaoping (1904-97) — A136

Various portraits of Deng Xiaoping and: 800k, Flags, map of Hong Kong. 1000k, Flag, Hong Kong harbor. 2000k, Hong Kong at night, countdown clock. 2500k, World map with China highlighted.

1997, May 26   Litho.   *Perf. 14*
| 666 | A136 | 800k multicolored | 1.40 | 1.40 |
| 667 | A136 | 1000k multicolored | 1.75 | 1.75 |

Souvenir Sheets
| 668 | A136 | 2000k multicolored | 3.25 | 3.25 |
| 669 | A136 | 2500k multicolored | 4.25 | 4.25 |

Nos. 666-667 were issued in sheets of 3 each. No. 669 contains one 72x47mm stamp.

Trains — A137   A138

Locomotives: 200k, Suburban tank, Eastern Railway, France. 300k, Streamlined express, Belgian Natl. Railways. 500k, "Mountain" type express, Union Pacific Railraod. 900k, 2-8-2 "Mikado," Kenya & Uganda Railway. 1000k, 4-6-0 "Royal Scot," LM & S Railway. 1500k, 4-6-0 "Lord Nelson" type, Southern Railway.

No. 676, each 500k: a, Express, German State Railways. b, Express, "Duke of Abercorn," NCC (LMSR), Ireland. c, Heavy freight tank, Netherlands Railways. d, Express, Austrian Federal Railways. e, "Governor" class, Gold Coast Railways. f, 4-8-4 Express, Canadian Natl. Railways.

Each 3000k: No. 677, Diesel-electric passenger, Royal Siamese State Railways. No. 678, "Pacific" type, South African Railways.

1997, June 2
| 670-675 | A137 | Set of 6 | 7.25 | 7.25 |
| 676 | A137 | Sheet of 6, #a.-f. | 5.00 | 5.00 |

Souvenir Sheets
| 677-678 | A137 | Set of 2 | 10.00 | 10.00 |

1997, Aug. 8   Litho.   Perf. 14

Butterflies and Moths: 300k, No. 683a, Gaudy commodore. 500k, No. 683b, African moon moth. 700k, No. 683c, Emperor moth. No. 682, 900k, Emperor swallowtail.

| 679-682 | A138 | Set of 4 | 5.00 | 5.00 |
| 683 | A138 | 900k Sheet of 4, #a.-c., #682 | 7.00 | 7.00 |

Queen Elizabeth II and Prince Philip,
50th Wedding Anniv.
A139

No. 684, each 500k: a, Queen Elizabeth II. b, Royal arms. c, Queen wearing crown, Prince in uniform. d, Queen, Prince riding in open carriage. e, Buckingham Palace. f, Prince waving.
3200k, Queen, Prince waving from balcony.

1997, Aug. 26   Litho.   Perf. 14
| 684 | A139 | Sheet of 6, #a.-f. | 7.00 | 7.00 |

Souvenir Sheet
| 685 | A139 | 3200k multicolored | 8.00 | 8.00 |

Paul P. Harris (1868-1947), Founder
of Rotary, Intl. — A140

1000k, First Rotarians, Silvester Schiele, Harris, Hiram Shorey, Gus Loehr, portrait of Harris.
3200k, Zambian interactors with retirees.

1997, Aug. 27
| 686 | A140 | 1000k multicolored | 1.50 | 1.50 |

Souvenir Sheet
| 687 | A140 | 3200k multicolored | 5.00 | 5.00 |

Heinrich von Stephan (1831-97), Founder of UPU A141

Each 1000k, Portrait of Von Stephan and: #688a, World Postal Congress, Berne, 1874. #688b, UPU emblem. #688c, Savannah, paddle steamer, 1819.
3200k, Von Stephan, Prussian postilion, 1715.

1997, Aug. 28
| 688 | A141 | Sheet of 3, #a.-c. | 4.50 | 4.50 |

Souvenir Sheet
| 689 | A141 | 3200k multicolored | 5.00 | 5.00 |

Nos. 562-564 Surcharged

1997, Sept. 19   Litho.   Perf. 14x13½
690	CD349	500k on 35k	.75	.75
691	CD349	(0) on 32k	.90	.90
692	CD349	900k on 38k	1.25	1.25
		Nos. 690-692 (3)	2.90	2.90

No. 691 was valued at 600k on day of issue.

Owls — A142

300k, #697b, Verreaux's eagle owl. 500k, #697c, Pel's fishing owl. 700k, #697a, Barn owl. #696, Spotted eagle owl.

1997, Dec. 18   Litho.   Perf. 14
693	A142	300k multicolored	.80	.80
694	A142	500k multicolored	1.40	1.40
695	A142	700k multicolored	2.00	2.00
696	A142	900k multicolored	2.40	2.40
		Nos. 693-696 (4)	6.60	6.60

Sheet of 4
| 697 | A142 | 900k #a.-c., #696 | 10.00 | 10.00 |

Christmas
A143

Entire paintings or details, sculpture: No. 698, 50k, Winged Victory of Samothrace. No. 699, 50k, Ognissanti Madonna, by Giotto. No. 700, 100k, Angel, by Antonio Pollaiuolo. No. 701, 100k, Angel of the Annunciation, by Jacopo da Pontormo. No. 702, 500k, No. 703, 1000k, The Virgin and Child Enthroned Among Angels and Saints, by Benozzo Gozzoli.
Each 3200k: No. 704, All of the Rebel Angels, detail, by Rubens. No. 705, The Resurrection of the Dead, by Joseph Christian.

1997, Dec. 18   Litho.   Perf. 14
| 698-703 | A143 | Set of 6 | 2.75 | 2.75 |

Souvenir Sheets
| 704-705 | A143 | Set of 2 | 10.00 | 10.00 |

No. 704 incorrectly inscribed "The Virgin and Child Enthroned Among Angels and Saints, by Bonozzo Gozzoli."

Diana, Princess of
Wales (1961-
97) — A144

Various portraits with color of sheet margin: No. 706, Pale green. No. 707, Pale yellow.
Each 2500k: No. 708, Touching hand of blind man (in sheet margin). No. 709, With Barbara Bush (in sheet margin).

1997
| 706 | A144 | 500k Sheet of 6, #a.-f. | 4.50 | 4.50 |
| 707 | A144 | 700k Sheet of 6, #a.-f. | 6.50 | 6.50 |

Souvenir Sheets
| 708-709 | A144 | Set of 2 | 8.00 | 8.00 |

PAPU (Pan African Postal Union), 18th Anniv. A145

Designs: 500k, Kobus leche kafuensis. (O), Dove carrying letter over map. 900k, Emblem of dove carrying letter.

1998   Perf. 14½
710	A145	500k multicolored	.75	.75
711	A145	(O) multicolored	.95	.95
712	A145	900k multicolored	1.25	1.25
		Nos. 710-712 (3)	2.95	2.95

No. 711 was valued at 600k on day of issue.

Mahatma Gandhi (1869-1948) — A146

Portraits of Gandhi: 250k, As law student in London, 1888. 500k, With Nehru, 1946. No. 715, (O), In front of Red Fort, New Dehli. 900k, At prayer.
2000k, Gandhi at 2nd Round Table Conference, London, 1931.

1998, Jan. 30   Litho.   Perf. 13½
| 713-716 | A146 | Set of 4 | 6.50 | 6.50 |

Souvenir Sheet
| 717 | A146 | 2000k multicolored | 6.00 | 6.00 |

No. 715 was valued at 600k on day of issue. Nos. 713, 715-717 are vert.

Flowers — A147

Designs: No. 718, Lantana camara. No. 719, Clusia rosea. No. 720, Nymphaea hybrids. No. 721, Portulaca grandiflora.
No. 722: a, Hibiscus rosa-sinensis. b, Plumeria. c, Erythrina variegata. d, Bauhinia blakeana. e, Carissa grandiflora. f, Cordia sebestena. g, Couroupita guianensis. h, Eustoma grandiflorum. i, Passiflora.
3200k, Strelitzia reginae, horiz.

1998, Feb. 27   Litho.   Perf. 14
| 718-721 | A147 | 500k Set of 4 | 3.25 | 3.25 |
| 722 | A147 | 500k Sheet of 9, #a.-i. | 7.50 | 7.50 |

Souvenir Sheet
| 723 | A147 | 3200k multicolored | 5.25 | 5.25 |

New Year 1998 (Year of the Tiger) A148

Chinese symbols and stylized tigers, each 700k: No. 724: a, Looking right. b, Looking left. c, Facing forward, denomination UL. d, Facing forward, denomination UR.
1500k, Tiger, symbols on both sides.

1998   Litho.   Perf. 14
| 724 | A148 | Sheet of 4, #a.-d. | 4.00 | 4.00 |

Souvenir Sheet
| 725 | A148 | 1500k multicolored | 2.10 | 2.10 |

Sites of
India
A149

Designs: a, Taj Mahal, Agra. b, Gateway to India, Calcutta. c, Great Imambara Mosque, Lucknow.

1998
| 726 | A149 | 900k Sheet of 3, #a.-c. | 3.75 | 3.75 |

Art of India A150

No. 727, each 700k: a, Ragmala, School of Mewar, 17th cent. b, Babur Nama, Mogul School, 16th cent. c, Hamza Nama, Mogul School, 16th cent. d, Meghamallar, School of Mewar, 16th cent.
2500k, Hindola Raga, School of Deccan, 17th-18th cent.

1998
| 727 | A150 | Sheet of 4, #a.-d. | 4.00 | 4.00 |

Souvenir Sheet
| 728 | A150 | 2500k multicolored | 3.50 | 3.50 |

1998 World Cup Soccer
Championships, France — A151

No. 729, each 450k: a, Albert, Belgium. b, Bebeto, Brazil. c, Beckenbauer, W. Germany. d, Littbarski, W. Germany. e, Juninho, Brazil. f, Lineker, England. g, Lato, Poland. h, McCoist, Scotland.
No. 730, each 500k: a, Maier, W. Germany, 1974. b, Bellini, Brazil, 1958. c, Kempes, Argentina, 1978. d, Nazassi, Uruguay, 1930. e, Pele, Brazil, 1970. f, Beckenbauer, W. Germany, 1974. g, Combi, Italy, 1934. h, Zoff, Italy, 1982.
No. 731, each 500k: a, Keane, Rep. of Ireland. b, Seaman, England. c, Like #729b. d, Futre, Portugal. e, Ravanelli, Italy. f, Weah, Liberia. g, Bergkamp, Holland. h, Raducioiu, Romania.
Each 3200k: No. 732, Juninho, Brazil. No. 733, Romario, Brazil, horiz. No. 734, McCoist, Scotland, horiz.

1998, Apr. 17   Perf. 13½x14, 14x13½
Sheets of 8, #a-h, + Label
| 729 | A151 | multi | 5.25 | 5.25 |
| 730-731 | A151 | Set of 2 | 11.50 | 11.50 |

Souvenir Sheets
| 732-734 | A151 | Set of 3 | 13.50 | 13.50 |

Parrots — A152

No. 735, each 500k: a, Rainbow lorikeet. b, Budgerigar, blossom-headed parakeet. c, Blue-yellow macaw. d, Blue-crowned parrot. e, Golden conure. f, Sulphur-crested cockatoo.

No. 736, each 1000k: a, Ara ararauna. b, Ara chloropterd. c, Pale-headed rosellas. d, Northern rosella. e, Gang-gang cockatoo. f, Palm cockatoo.

Each 3200k: No. 737, Mulga parakeet. No. 738, Major Mitchell cockatoo, horiz.

1998, June 1   Litho.   Perf. 14
735 A152 Sheet of 6, #a.-f.   4.25 4.25
736 A152 Sheet of 6, #a.-f.   8.50 8.50
Souvenir Sheets
737-738 A152 Set of 2   9.50 9.50

Mushrooms — A153

No. 739, 250k, Red-tufted wood tricholoma. No. 740, 250k, Chlorophyllum molybdites. No. 741, 450k, Stuntz's psilocybe. No. 742, 450k, Lepista sordida. No. 743, 500k, Lepiota. No. 744, 500k, Rosy gomphidius. No. 745, 900k, Cantharellus cybrina. No. 746, 900k, Olive-capped boletus. No. 747, 1000k, Showy volvaria. No. 748, 1000k, Sooty brown waxy cap.

No. 749, each 900k: a, Leller's boletus. b, Short-stemmed russula. c, Anise-scented clitocybe. d, Dung roundhead. e, Oak-loving collybia. f, Wine-red stropharia.

No. 750, each 900k: a, Flat-topped mushroom. b, Alice Eastwood's boletus. c, Pitted milky cap. d, Short-stemmed slippery jask. e, Rose-red russula. f, Zeller's tricholoma.

Each 3200k: No. 751, Honey mushroom. No. 752, Velvet-stemmed flammulina.

1998, July 1
739-748 A153 Set of 10   8.00 8.00
Sheets of 6
749-750 A153 Set of 2   15.50 15.50
Souvenir Sheets
751-752 A153 Set of 2   9.00 9.00

Nos. 749-752 are continuous designs.

Traditional Stories — A154

No. 755, each 2000k: a, like #753. b, like #754.

1998, Dec. 2   Litho.   Perf. 14
753 A154 300k Luchela nganga   .45 .45
754 A154 500k Kasuli   .70 .70
Souvenir Sheet
755 A154 Sheet of 2, #a.-b.   4.25 4.25
Christmas.

Orchids A155

Designs, vert: No. 756, 100k, Paphiopedilum callosum. No. 757, 100k, Phaius tankervilleae. No. 758, 500k, Paphiopedilum fairrieanum. No. 759, 500k, Barkeria lindleyana. No. 760, 1000k, Laelia flava. No. 761, 1000k, Masdervallia unifloria, masdervallia angulifera.

No. 762, each 900k: a, Acacallis cyanea. b, Miltoniopsis phalaenopsis. c, Dendrobium bellatulum. d, Polystachya campyloglossa. e, Pleione bulbocodioides. f, Rhynchostylis gigantea. g, Cattleya lawrenceana. h, Sobrolaelia. i, Laelia tenebrosa.

No. 763, each 900k: a, Acacallis cyanea, diff. b, Epidendrum gastropodium. c, Laelia rubescens. d, Paphiopedilum dayanum. e, Laelia lobata. f, Dendrobium crepidatum. g, Cattleya nobilior. h, Dendrobium johnsoniae. i, Trichopilia fragrans.

Each 4000k: No. 764, Cattleya maxima, vert. No. 765, Cattleya violacea.

1998, Dec. 23
756-761 A155 Set of 6   3.50 3.50
Sheets of 9
762-763 A155 Set of 2   17.50 17.50
Souvenir Sheets
764-765 A155 Set of 2   9.00 9.00

Classic Cars A156

Designs: 300k, Ferrari Daytona 365 GTB/4. 500k, Austin Healey Sprite. 900k, Gordon Keeble. 1000k, Alvis TD.

No. 770: a, Mercedes-Benz 300Sl. b, Chevrolet Corvair. c, AC Cobra 427. d, Aston Martin DB5. e, BMW 2002 Turbo. f, Cadillac Eldorado Brougham.

No. 771: a, Mercedes-Benz 280SE 3.5. b, Aston Martin DB2. c, Volkswagen Beetle. d, Lancia Aurelia B20 GT. e, Lamborghini 350 GT. f, Cisitalia 202 Coupe.

No. 771G: h, 1995 Ferrari 750 Pinnafarina. i, 1997 Federrari 312T2/77. j, 1983 Ferrari 208 Turbo. k, 1962 Ferrari Dino 268 SP. l, 1994 Ferrari F355 Berlinetta. m, Ferrari 250 GTE Coupe 2+2 California.

Each 4000k: No. 772, Citroen Light 15. No. 773, Austin Healey MKII 3000.

1998, Dec. 23
766-769 A156 Set of 4   3.00 3.00
Sheets of 6, #a-f
770-771G A156 900k Set of 3   17.50 17.50
Souvenir Sheets
772-773 A156 Set of 2   9.00 9.00

New Year 1999 (Year of the Rabbit) A157

Various rabbits, denomination at — #774 (each 700k): a, LL. b, LR. c, LL (scratching). d, LR (nose near ground).
2000k, Rabbit, vert.

1999, Jan. 4
774 A157 Sheet of 4, #a.-d.   3.00 3.00
Souvenir Sheet
775 A157 2000k multicolored   2.25 2.25

Trains A158

Locomotives: No. 776, (0), U20C Diesel electric, 1967. No. 777, 800k, 7th Class No. 70, 1900. No. 778, 800k, 15A Class Beyer-Garrat No. 401, 1950. No. 779, 900k, HP diesel electric, 1966. No. 780, 900k, 20th Class No. 708, 1954.

4000k, 7th Class No. 955, 1892.

1999, Feb. 1   Litho.   Perf. 14½
776-780 A158 Set of 5   4.50 4.50
Souvenir Sheet
781 A158 4000k multicolored   4.50 4.50
No. 776 was valued at 600k on day of issue.

No. 643 Surcharged

Methods and Perfs as Before
1999, June 1
781A A129 500k on 100k multi

Queen Mother (b. 1900) — A159

No. 782: a, With Princess Elizabeth, 1936. b, Lady of the Garter. c, With Prince Andrew, 1960. d, At Ascot.
5000k, Wedding photograph, 1923.

1999, Sept. 1   Perf. 14
782 A159 2000k Sheet of 4, #a.-d., + label   7.50 7.50
Souvenir Sheet
Perf. 13¾
783 A159 5000k multicolored   4.75 4.75
No. 783 contains one 38x51mm stamp.

Dinosaurs A160

Designs: 50k, Dimetrodon. 100k, Deinonychus. 500k, Protoceratops. 900k, Heterodontosaurus. 1000k, Oviraptor. 1800k, Psittacosaurus.

No. 790, each 900k: a, Stegosaurus. b, Triceratops. c, Brontosaurus. d, Gallimimus. e, Saurolophus. f, Lambeosaurus. g, Centrosaurus. h, Edmontonia. i, Parasaurolophus.

No. 791, each 900k: a, Ceratosaurus. b, Daspletosaurus. c, Baryonyx. d, Ornitholestes. e, Troodon. f, Coelophysis. g, Tyrannosaurus. h, Allosaurus. i, Compsognathus.

Each 4000k: No. 792, Saltasaurus, vert. No. 793, Stygimoloch, vert.

1999, Sept. 27   Litho.   Perf. 14
784-789 A160 Set of 6   3.75 3.75
Sheets of 9
790-791 A160 Set of 2   13.50 13.50
Souvenir Sheets
792-793 A160 Set of 2   7.00 7.00

Johann Wolfgang von Goethe (1749-1832), German Poet — A161

No. 794, each 2000k: a, A drinking party in Amerbach's cellar. b, Goethe and Friedrich von Schiller. c, Faust falls in love with Margaret.
5000k, Angel.

1999, Oct. 4   Litho.   Perf. 14
794 A161 Sheet of 3, #a.-c.   4.25 4.25
Souvenir Sheet
795 A161 5000k org brn & brn   3.75 3.75

A162

A163

Cats: 50k, White Devon Rex. 100k, Red Persian. 500k, Chartreux. 900k, Brown tabby Maine Coon.

No. 800, each 1000k, horiz.: a, Tortie point Himalayan. b, Blue mackerel tabby Scottish Fold. c, Chocolate lynx point Balinese. d, Havana Brown. e, Seal point Ragdoll. f, Silver shaded Persian.

No. 801, each 1000k, horiz.: a, Red spotted tabby Exotic Shorthair. b, Blue tortie smoke Persian. c, Brown classic tabby longhaired Scottish Fold. d, Spotted tabby American Bobtail. e, Silver spotted tabby Ocicat. f, Blue British Shorthair.

Each 4000k: No. 802, Silver tabby longhair Persian, horiz. No. 803, Tabby point Siamese.

1999, Oct. 18
796-799 A162 Set of 4   1.10 1.10
Sheets of 6, #a.-f.
800-801 A162 Set of 2   8.50 8.50
Souvenir Sheets
802-803 A162 Set of 2   6.00 6.00

1999, Oct. 18
Dogs: 100k, Welsh corgi. 500k, Shetland sheepdog. 900k, Italian greyhound. 1000k, Tibetan spaniel.

No. 808, each 1000k, horiz.: a, Dalmatian. b, Shetland sheepdogs. c, Bearded collie. d, Eskimo. e, Basenji. f, Saluki.

No. 809, each 1000k, horiz.: a, Norwegian elkhound. b, Flat-coated retriever. c, St. Bernard. d, Basset hound, Pembroke Welsh corgi. e, Pembroke Welsh corgi, Pointer. f, Petit Basset Griffon Vendeen.

Each 4000k: No. 810, Whippet. No. 811, Rottweiler.

804-807 A163 Set of 4   1.75 1.75
Sheets of 6, #a.-f.
808-809 A163 Set of 2   8.50 8.50
Souvenir Sheets
810-811 A163 Set of 2   6.00 6.00

11th Intl. Conference on AIDS in Africa, Lusaka — A164

Designs: 500k, Emblem, waterfalls. 900k, Emblem, close-up view of waterfalls.

1999, Oct. 20
812-813 A164 Set of 2   2.00 2.00

Paintings by Zhang Daqian (1899-1983) A165

No. 814, each 500k: a, Water Lily in the Rain. b, Chinghai Tribal Girl and a Black Hound. c, Taking a Nap. d, Monkey and Old Tree. e, Bird and Tree of Chin-Chang Mountain. f, Watching Waterfalls. g, On the Way to

Switzerland and Austria. h, A Boat Brings the Wine. i, Brown Landscape. j, Nice Autumn.
No. 815: a, 1000k, White Water Lily, horiz. b, 2000k, Cloudy Waterfalls and Summer Mountain, horiz.

1999, Oct. 21   **Perf. 13**
814 A165 Sheet of 10, #a.-j.   3.75   3.75
815 A165 Sheet of 2, #a.-b.   2.10   2.10

China 1999 World Philatelic Exhibition, 22nd UPU Congress, Beijing. #815 contains two 52x39mm stamps.

A166

Flora & Fauna
A167

Designs: 50k, Leatherback turtle. 100k, American kestrel. No. 818, 500k, Great blue heron. 900k, Mesene phareus. 1000k, Laeliocattleya. 1800k, Papilio cresphontes.
Each 500k: No. 822, Cairn's birdwing. No. 823, Pintail. No. 824, Rose. No. 825, Gray tree frog.
No. 826, each 700k: a, White-tailed tropicbird. b, Sooty tern. c, Laughing gull. d, Black skimmer. e, Brown pelican. f, Bottle-nosed dolphin. g, Common dolphin. h, Man in sailboat. i, Blue tang. j, Southern stingray. k, Hammerhead shark. l, Mako shark.
No. 827, each 700k: a, Heliconia. b, Purplethroated Carib. c, St. Vincent parrot. d, Bananaquit. e, prepona meander. f, Unidentified butterfly. g, Hawksbill turtle. h, Blacknecked stilt. i, Banded butterflyfish. j, Porkfish. k, Seahorse. l, Chain moray eel.
No. 828: a, Baltimore oriole. b, Chipmunk. c, Blue jay. d, Monarch butterfly. e, Gray heron. f, Mallard. g, Canadian otter. h, American lotus. i, Fowler's toad. j, Bluegill sunfish. k, Rainbow trout. l, Terrapin.
Each 4000k: No. 829, Amazona guildingii. No. 830, Bottle-nosed dolphin, diff. No. 831, Fuchsia. No. 832, Red-banded pereute.

1999, Oct. 27
816-821 A166   Set of 6   3.25   3.25
822-825 A167   Set of 4   1.40   1.40
     Sheets of 12, #a.-l.
826-827 A166   Set of 2   12.00   12.00
828 A167   700k multi   6.00   6.00
     Souvenir Sheets
829-830 A167   Set of 2   6.00   6.00
831-832 A167   Set of 2   6.00   6.00

IBRA '99 — A168

Trains: 1000k, Crampton. 3200k, Post standard 2-8-4 tank locomotive.
Illustration reduced.

1999   **Perf. 14x14¾**
833-834 A168   Set of 2   3.00   3.00

     Souvenir Sheets

PhilexFrance '99 — A169

Each 5000k: #835, Paris-Orleans Railway 4-4-0. #836, paris, Lyon & Mediterranean Railway 2-4-2.

1999   **Perf. 14¼**
835-836 A169   Set of 2   7.50   7.50

Wedding of Prince Edward and Sophie Rhys-Jones
A170

No. 837: a, 500k, Sophie. b, 900k, Couple. c, 100k, Edward.
3000k, Couple kissing.

1999   **Perf. 14**
837 A170   Sheet of 3, #a.-c.   1.75   1.75
     Souvenir Sheet
838 A170   3000k multi   2.10   2.10

Birds — A171

Designs: 50k, Blacksmith plover. 100k, Sacred ibis. 200k, Purple gallinule. 250k, Purple heron. 300k, Glossy ibis. 400k, Marabou stork. 450k, African spoonbill. 500k, African finfoot. O, No. 847, Knot-billed duck. 600k, Darter. 700k, African skimmer. 800k, Spurwinged goose. 900k, Hammerkop. 1000k, White pelican. 1500k, Black-winged stilt. 2000k, Black-crowned night heron.

1999, Dec. 20   Litho.   Perf. 14½x15
839-854 A171   Set of 16   7.00   7.00

No. 847 sold for 500k on day of issue.
Design size of No. 847 is 30½mm wide. See Nos. 927-930.

Flowers
A172

Various flowers making up a photomosaic of Princess Diana, each 1000k.

1999, Dec. 31   **Perf. 13¾**
855 A172   Sheet of 8, #a.-h.   6.25   6.25

Millennium
A173

Highlights of 1950-2000: a, Venice Biennale shows Jackson Pollock and Abstract Expressionism. b, James Watson and Francis Crick piece together the structure of DNA. c, Edmund Hillary reaches the summit of Mount Everest. d, Jonas Salk's polio vaccine. e, Ghana achieves independence. f, Yuri Gagarin becomes 1st man in space. g, Rachel Carson and the beginning of the environmental movement. h, Indira Gandhi becomes Prime Minister of India. i, 1st successful heart transplant. j, Apollo 11 lands on moon. k, Microprocessor developed. l, Richard Nixon visits People's Republic of China. m, Qin Shi Huang Mausoleum discovered. n, Stephen Hawking proposes new ideas about the universe and black holes. o, Margaret Thatcher elected 1st female Prime Minister of Great Britain. p, Mikhail Gorbachev becomes leader of Soviet Union. q, Fall of the Berlin Wall. r, Nelson Mandela elected Pres. of South Africa.

2000, Feb. 7   **Perf. 12¾x12½**
856 A173 500k Sheet of 18, #a.-   r., + label   6.25   6.25

Butterflies
A174

400k, Papilio antimachus. 450k, Amauris niavius. 500k, Charaxes smaragdalis. 800k, Charaxes zelica. 900k, Cymothoe confusa. 1000k, #862, Labobunea ansorgei.
No. 863, each 1000k: a, Palla ussheri. b, Euphaedra aureola. c, Graphium cyrnus nuscyrus. d, Salamis cacta. e, Salamis parhassus. f, Charaxes pelias.
No. 864, each 1000k: a, Large Spotted Acraea. b, Palla (orange wings). c, Palla (blue wings). d, Gold-banded Forester (white wings). e, Figtree blue. f, Gold-banded Forester (pink wings).
No. 865, each 1500k: a, Colotis ione. b, Charaxes acraeoides. c, Euphaedra edwardsi. d, Colotis phisadia. e, Charaxes lydiae. f, Euphaedra eupaulus.
No. 866, each 1500k: a, Papilio zalmoxis. b, Amauris niavius. c, Salamis cytora. d, Salamis temora. e, Charaxes eupale. f, Cymothoe hypatha.
Each 5000k: No. 867, Euphaedra ceres. No. 868, Cymothoe fumana. No. 869, Euphaedra spatiosa. No. 870, Euryphene gambiae.

2000, Feb. 8   **Perf. 14**
857-862 A174   Set of 6   2.75   2.75
     Sheets of 6, #a.-f.
863-864 A174   Set of 2   8.50   8.50
865-866 A174   Set of 2   12.50   12.50
     Souvenir Sheets
867-870 A174   Set of 4   14.00   14.00

No. 650 Surcharged

Method and Perf. as Before
2000, Apr. 11
870A A132 700k on 100k multi

Orchids — A175

Illustration reduced.
No. 871, each 1500k: a, Paphiopedilum sioux. b, Phalaenopsis amabilis hybrid. c, Thelymitza ixioides. d, Phalaenopsis schilleriana.
No. 872, each 1500k: a, Miltoniopsis pansy orchid. b, Paphiopedilum venustum. c, Odontoglossum grande. d, Vanda sanderiana alba. e, Phalaenopsis violacea. f, Pleione alishan.
No. 873, each 1500k: a, Cyrtorchis arcuata. b, Cymbioiella rhodochila. c, Unidentified orchid. d, Eulophia quartiana. e, Augraecum montanum. f, Polystacha vulcanica.
No. 874, each 1500k, vert.: a, Catasetum splendens. b, Miltonia spectabilis. c, Stenia pallida. d, Cozacias spatulata. e, Eriopsis sceptzum. f, Paphinia cristata.
Each 6000k: No. 875, Cattleya hybrid. No. 876, Brachycorythis kalbreyeri.

2000, May 16   Litho.   Perf. 14
871 A175   Sheet of 4, #a.-d.   4.00   4.00
     Sheets of 6, #a.-f.
872-874 A175   Set of 3   18.00   18.00
     Souvenir Sheets
875-876 A175   Set of 2   8.00   8.00

The Stamp Show 2000, London.

Popes — A176

No. 877: a, Liberius, 352-66. b, Linus, 67-76. c, Lucius I, 253-54. d, Marcellinus, 296-304. e, Mark, 336. f, Pius I, 140-155.
No. 878: a, Simplicius, 468-83. b, Siricius, 384-99. c, Stephen I, 254-57. d, Urban I, 222-30. e, Zephyrinus, 199-217. f, Zosimus, 417-18.
No. 879, Silverius, 536-37. No. 880, Vigilius, 537-55.
Illustration reduced.

2000, July 7   Litho.   Perf. 13¾
     Sheets of 6, #a-f
877-878 A176   1500k Set of 2   11.00   11.00
     Souvenir Sheets
879-880 A176   5000k Set of 2   6.00   6.00

Birds — A177

400k, Great Indian hornbill. 500k, Cockatiel. 600k, Amazonian umbrellabird. 1000k, Unidentified bird. 2000k, Rainbow lorikeet.

No. 886: a, Green aracari. b, Eclectus parrot. c, Crimson topaz. d, King bird of paradise. e, keel-billed toucan. f, Australian king parrot. g, Sailboat. h, Hyacinth macaw.

No. 887: a, Resplendent quetzal. b, Carmine bee-eater. c, Wattled false sunbird. d, Palm trees. e, Sulphur-crested cockatoo. f, Great blue turaco. g, Crimson rosella. h, Malabar pied hornbill.

No. 888: a, Yellow-crowned amazon. b, Green turaco. c, Butterfly and palm trees. d, Plate-billed mountain toucan. e, Scarlet macaw. f, Blue and yellow macaw. g, Guianan cock of the rock. h, Palm cockatoo.

No. 889, Red-crested pochard. No. 890, Toco toucan, horiz. No. 891, Blue and yellow macaw, horiz.

2000, Sept. 8   *Perf. 14*
881-885   A177   Set of 5   2.75   2.75
Sheets of 8, #a-h
886-888   A177   1500k Set of 3   21.00   21.00
Souvenir Sheets
889-891   A177   5000k Set of 3   9.00   9.00

Birds — A178

Designs: 700k, Red-backed shrike. 800k, Golden pipet. No. 894, 1200k, Orange-breasted sunbird. No. 895, 1400k, Eurasian goldfinch. 1500k, Red-crested turaco. 3000k, Carmine bee-eater.

No. 898, 1000k: a, Gouldian finch. b, Parrot finch. c, Purple grenadier. d, Red bishop. e, Red-crested cardinal. f, Spectacled monarch. g, Crimson chat. h, Necklaced laughing thrush. i, Chestnut-backed jewel babbler.

No. 899, 1200k: a, Lovely cotinga. b, Andean cock-of-the-rock. c, Orange-bellied leafbird. d, Pin-tailed manakin. e, Pin-tailed broadbill. f, Rufous motmot. g, American goldfinch. h, Double-barred finch. i, Golden-breasted starling.

No. 900, 1400k: a, Campo oriole. b, Hooded warbler. c, Purple honeycreeper. d, Blue-faced honeyeater. e, Scarlet tanager. f, Green-headed tanager. g, Blue-breasted fairy wren. h, Banded pitta. i, Wire-tailed manakin.

No. 901, 5000k, Pin-tailed sandgrouse. No. 902, 5000k, Black bustard.

2000, Sept. 8   Litho.   *Perf. 14*
892-897   A178   Set of 6   4.75   4.75
Sheets of 9, #a-i
898-900   A178   Set of 3   18.00   18.00
Souvenir Sheets
901-902   A178   Set of 2   5.75   5.75

African Creation Legends A179

Designs: Nos, 903, 906a, 600k, Creation in Clay. Nos. 904, 906b, 1000k, The Chameleon and the Lizard. Nos. 905, 906c, 1400k, Why the Stones Do Not Die.

Perf. 14¼x14½
2000, Nov. 10   Litho.
903-905   A179   Set of 3   1.40   1.40
With Brown Frame
906   A179   Horiz. strip of 3, #a-c   1.40   1.40
Souvenir Sheet
No Frame Around Stamp
907   A179   3500k The Rooster in the Sky   1.60   1.60

No. 906 issued in sheets of 9 stamps.

Common Market for Eastern and Southern Africa A180

Designs: 600k, Map of member nations. 700k, Truck crossing border. 1000k, Exchange of money and sale of goods at border.

2000
908-910   A180   Set of 3   1.10   1.10

Nos. 713-714 Surcharged

2000   **Method and Perf. as Before**
911   A146   1200k on 250k multi
912   A146   1500k on 500k multi

UN High Commissioner for Refugees, 50th Anniv. — A181

Designs: 700k, Children receiving food. 1500k, Woman carrying child.

Perf. 13¾x14¼
2001, Mar. 13   Litho.
915-916   A181   Set of 2   1.40   1.40

A182

Animals — A183

Designs: 500k, African buffalo. 1000k, Cheetah, vert. No. 919, 2000k, Female elephant. 3200k, Ruffed lemur, vert.

No. 921, 2000k: a, Crimson-breasted shrike. b, Common bee-eater. c, Blue monkey. d, Chimpanzee. e, Bush baby. f, Genet.

No. 922, 2000k, horiz.: a, Defassa waterbuck. b, Crowned crane. c, Red hartebeest. d, Pygmy hippopotamus. e, White rhinoceros. f, Giant forest hog.

No. 923, 2000k, horiz.: a, Cheetah. b, Three adult, one young impala. c, Four adult impalas. d, Warthog. e, Two lions. f, Four lions.

No. 924, 6000k, Bull elephant. No. 925, 6000k, Black rhinoceros. No. 926, 6000k, Zebras, vert.

Perf. 13¼x13½, 13½x13¼
2001, Mar. 30
917-920   A182   Set of 4   4.00   4.00
Sheets of 6, #a-f
921-923   A183   Set of 3   22.50   22.50
Souvenir Sheets
924-926   A182   Set of 3   11.00   11.00

Bird Type of 1999

Designs: No. 927, O, Knob-billed duck. No. 928, A, Blacksmith plover. No. 929, B, Sacred ibis. No. 930, C, Purple gallinule.

Perf. 14½x14¾
2001, Mar. 19   Litho.
927-930   A171   Set of 4   3.00   3.00

Nos. 927-930 each sold for 700k, 1200k, 1400k, and 1500k respectively on day of issue. No. 927 is dated "2000" and has a design width of 31½mm. No. 847 has no date and has a design width of 30½mm.

Total Solar Eclipse, June 21 — A184

Eclipse and: 1000k, Woman. 1500k, Bird. 1700k, Lizard. 1800k, Elephant and man. 2200k, Man.

2001, June 1   Litho.   *Perf. 13¾*
931-935   A184   Set of 5   4.50   4.50

Phila Nippon '01, Japan — A185

Designs: No. 936, 500k, Senya Nakamura as Toknatsu, by Kiyomasu Torii I. No. 937, 500k, Kantaro Sanjo II and Monosuke Ichikawa I, by Okumura Masanobu, 1720. No. 938, 1000k, Kantaro Sanjo and Monosuke Ichikawa, by Masanobu, c. 1730. No. 939, 1000k, Standing Figure of a Woman, by Kiyomasu Torii I. 1500k, Ono no Komachi, by Masanobu. 1800k, Dog Bringing a Love Letter, by Shigenaga.

No. 942, 3200k: a, Matsue Nakamura as a Cat Woman, by Shunsho. b, Kantaro Sanjo With Branch of Bamboo, by Kiyomasu Torii I. c, Kinsaku Yamashika I as Peddler, by Kiyomasu Torii I. d, Portrait of an Actor, by Shunsho.

No. 943, 3200k: a, Kumetaro Nakamura I, by Shunsho. b, Actor in Female Role, by Kiyomasu Torii I. c, Kikunojo Segawa Leaning on Sugoroku Board, by Kiyomasu Torii I. d, Gennosuke Ichikawa as a Wakashu, by Kiyomasu Torii I.

No. 944, 6000k, Akashi of the Tamaya, by Ryukoku Hishikawa. No. 945, 6000k, Events of Year in the Floating World, by Moroshige, horiz.

2001, July 4   *Perf. 14*
936-941   A185   Set of 6   3.50   3.50
Sheets of 4, #a-d
942-943   A185   Set of 2   14.00   14.00
Souvenir Sheets
944-945   A185   Set of 2   6.50   6.50

SOS Children's Village A186

2001, July 30
946   A186   2500k multi   1.40   1.40

Royal Navy Submarines, Cent. — A187

No. 947, horiz.: a, HMS Tabard. b, HMS Opossum. c, HMS Unicorn. d, HMS Churchill. e, HMS Victorious. f, HMS Triumph.

6000k, Lieutenant Commander Malcolm David Wanklyn.

2001, July 30
947   A187   2000k Sheet of 6, #a-f   6.75   6.75
Souvenir Sheet
948   A187   6000k multi   3.50   3.50

Giuseppe Verdi (1813-1901), Opera Composer — A188

No. 949 — Actors in Falstaff : a, Benjamin Luxon (without hat). b, Luxon (with hat). c, Paul Plishka. d, Anne Collin.
8000k, Falstaff.

2001, July 30
949 A188 4000k Sheet of 4, #a-d 9.00 9.00
Souvenir Sheet
950 A188 8000k multi   4.50 4.50

Monet Paintings — A189

No. 951, horiz.: a, The Promenade at Argenteuil. b, View of the Argenteuil Plain from the Sannois Hills. c, The Seine at Argenteuil. d, The Basin at Argenteuil.
6000k, Rouen Cathedral Portal, Overcast Weather.

2001, July 30   Perf. 13¾
951 A189 1500k Sheet of 4, #a-d 6.00 6.00
Souvenir Sheet
952 A189 6000k multi   6.00 6.00

Mao Zedong (1893-1976) — A190

No. 953 — Mao in: a, 1918. b, 1945. c, 1937.
4000k, Portrait.

2001, July 30
953 A190 3200k Sheet of 3, #a-c 7.00 7.00
Souvenir Sheet
954 A190 4000k multi   3.25 3.25

Queen Victoria (1819-1901) — A191

No. 955: a, As child. b, Wearing black dress. c, With child. d, With Prince Albert. e, Wearing crown and red sash. f, Wearing red dress.
7000k, Portrait.

2001, July 30   Perf. 14
955 A191 2000k Sheet of 6, #a-f 7.25 7.25
Souvenir Sheet
956 A191 7000k multi   4.75 4.75

Queen Elizabeth II, 75th Birthday — A192

No. 957: a, As infant. b, As child. c, As child, in garden. d, Wearing hat.
8000k, Wearing green and black hat.

2001, July 30
957 A192 4000k Sheet of 4, #a-d 9.00 9.00
Souvenir Sheet
958 A192 8000k multi   6.00 6.00
No. 957 contains four 28x42mm stamps.

First Zeppelin Flight, Cent. — A193

No. 959: a, LZ-1. b, Parseval PL25. c, LZ-3. d, Baldwin. e, LZ-129. f, Norge Nobile N1.
No. 960, 700k, Graf Zeppelin, vert.

2001, July 30
959 A193 2000k Sheet of 6, #a-f 6.75 6.75
Souvenir Sheet
960 A173 700k multi   .40 .40
No. 960 contains one 38x51mm stamp.

Pres. F. J. T. Chiluba — A194

Chiluba: 1000k, Recieving Master's degree. 1500k, Signing forms. 1700k, With arm raised, horiz.
6000k, Receiving Master's degree, diff.

2001   Litho.   Perf. 14
961-963 A194 Set of 3   2.25 2.25
Souvenir Sheet
964 A194 6000k multi   3.00 3.00

Nobel Prizes, Cent. (in 2001) — A195

No. 965, 2000k — Peace laureates: a, Norman E. Borlaug, 1970. b, Lester B. Pearson, 1957. c, Intl. Red Cross, 1944. d, Anwar Sadat, 1978. e, Georges Pire, 1958. f, Linus Pauling, 1962.
No. 966, 2000k — Literature laureates: a, Isaac Bashevis Singer, 1978. b, Gao Xingjian, 2000. c, Claude Simon, 1985. d, Naguib Mahfouz, 1988. e, Camilo Jose Cela, 1989. f, Czeslaw Milosz, 1980.
No. 967, 2000k — Literature laureates: a, Seamus Heaney, 1995. b, Toni Morrison, 1993. c, Günter Grass, 1999. d, Wislawa Szymborska, 1996. e, Dario Fo, 1997. f, José Saramago, 1998.
No. 968, 6000k, George C. Marshall, Peace, 1953. No. 969, 6000k, Gerard Debreu, Economics, 1983. No. 970, 6000k, Robert W. Fogel, Economics, 1993.

2002, Feb. 11   Litho.   Perf. 14
Sheets of 6, #a-f
965-967 A195 Set of 3   16.00 16.00
Souvenir Sheets
968-970 A195 Set of 3   8.25 8.25
Souvenir Sheet

New Year 2002 (Year of the Horse) — A196

2002, Feb. 18   Perf. 13¼
971 A196 5000k multi   2.40 2.40

2002 World Cup Soccer Championships, Japan and Korea — A197

No. 972, 2000k: a, Poster from 1954 World Cup, Switzerland. b, Stanly Matthews and English flag. c, Scottish player and flag. d, Belgian player and flag. e, Player and Daejon World Cup Stadium, Korea, horiz.
No. 973, 2000k: a, Ferenc Puskas and Hungarian flag. b, Poster from 1962 World Cup, Chile. c, Spanish player and flag. d, English player and flag. e, Player and Jeonju World Cup Stadium, Korea, horiz.
No. 974, 8000k, Bryan Robson's goal against France, 1982. No. 975, 8000k, Salenko's fifth goal against Cameroon, 1994, horiz.

2002, Feb. 26   Perf. 14
Sheets of 5, #a-e
972-973 A197 Set of 2   8.75 8.75
Souvenir Sheets
974-975 A197 Set of 2   7.00 7.00
Size of Nos. 972a-972d, 973a-973d: 28x42mm.

United We Stand — A198

2002, Feb.   Perf. 13½x13¼
976 A198 3200k multi   1.40 1.40
Issued in sheets of 4.

Reign of Queen Elizabeth, 50th Anniv. — A199

No. 977: a, Wearing blue and white hat. b, Without hat. c, Wearing scarf. d, Wearing tiara.
7500k, With Prince Philip.

2002, July 15   Litho.   Perf. 14¼
977 A199 3200k Sheet of 4, #a-d   5.75 5.75
Souvenir Sheet
978 A199 7500k multi   3.50 3.50

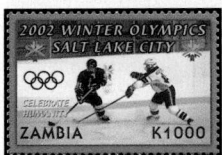
2002 Winter Olympics, Salt Lake City A200

Designs: 1000k, Ice hockey. 3200k, Cross-country skiing.

2002, July 30   Perf. 13¼x13¾
979-980 A200   Set of 2   1.90 1.90

20th World Scout Jamboree, Thailand — A201

No. 981, horiz.: a, Troop hiking. b, Knot tying. c, Archery. d, Fire making.
8000k, Camping.

2002, July 30   Perf. 14
981 A201 3200k Sheet of 4, #a-d   5.75 5.75
Souvenir Sheet
982 A201 8000k multi   3.50 3.50

Intl. Year of Mountains — A202

No. 983: a, Mt. Whitney, US. b, Mt. Aconcagua, Argentina and Chile. c, Mt. Mönch, Switzerland. d, Mt. Ararat, Turkey.
9000k, Mt. Everest, Nepal and China.

2002, July 30
983 A202 1500k Sheet of 4, #a-d 2.75 2.75
Souvenir Sheet
984 A202 9000k multi   4.00 4.00

Birds — A203

Designs: 700k, Bee-eater. 1200k, Blue-cheeked bee-eater. 1400k, Boehn's bee-eater. 1500k, Little bee-eater.

2002, Aug. 12
985-988 A203   Set of 4   2.10 2.10

Flowers, Butterflies and Mushrooms — A204

No. 989, 2500k — Flowers: a, Camel's foot. b, Christmas bells. c, Impala lily. d, Everlasting. e, Anomatheca grandiflora. f, Soldier lily.
No. 990, 2500k — Butterflies: a, False monarch. b, Golden piper. c, Blue pansy. d, Christmas tree acraea. e, Grass yellow. f, Gold-spotted sylph.
No. 991, 2500k — Mushrooms: a, Copper trumpet. b, King bolete. c, Death cap. d, Fly agaric. e, Chanterelle. f, Deadly fiber cap.
No. 992, 8000k, Arum lily. No. 993, 8000k, African monarch butterfly. No. 994, 8000k, Stump brittle-head mushrooms.

2002, Sept. 9   Litho.
Sheets of 6, #a-f
989-991 A204   Set of 3   20.00 20.00
Souvenir Sheets
992-994 A204   Set of 3   11.00 11.00

Nos. 624, 629, 645 Surcharged

Methods & Perfs as Before
2002, July 1
996 A128   250k on 50k #639   — —
997 A128   300k on 50k #624   — —
998 A130   1000k on 100k #645   — —

Numbers have been reserved for three additional surcharges. The editors would like to examine any examples.

Coronation of Queen Elizabeth II, 50th Anniv. — A205

No. 999: a, Wearing crown and pearl necklace. b, Wearing tiara and jeweled necklace. c, Wearing pink and black hat.
10,000k, Wearing flowered dress and hat.

2003, May 19   Litho.   Perf. 14
999 A205 5000k Sheet of 3, #a-c   6.25 6.25
Souvenir Sheet
1000 A205 10,000k multi   4.25 4.25

Prince William, 21st Birthday — A206

No. 1001: a, Wearing bow tie. b, Wearing blue shirt and tie. c, Wearing yellow and black sports shirt.
10,000k, Wearing sweater.

2003, May 19
1001 A206   5000k Sheet of 3, #a-c   6.25 6.25
Souvenir Sheet
1002 A206 10,000k multi   4.25 4.25

Nos. 654-657 Surcharged

Nos. 639-642 Surcharged

Nos. 617-620 Surcharged

Nos. 650-653 Surcharged

Nos. 710-712 Surcharged

Methods & Perfs. as Before
2003, June 26

1003 A133 1000k on 200k #654	25.00	25.00
1004 A133 1000k on 300k #655	25.00	25.00
1005 A133 1000k on 500k #656	25.00	25.00
1006 A133 1000k on 900k #657	25.00	25.00
1007 A128 1700k on 50k #639	1.00	1.00
1008 A128 1700k on 200k #640	1.00	1.00
1009 A128 1700k on 300k #641	1.00	1.00
1010 A128 1700k on 500k #642	1.00	1.00
1011 A125 1800k on 50k #617	1.10	1.10
1012 A125 1800k on 200k #618	1.10	1.10
1013 A125 1800k on 250k #619	1.10	1.10
1014 A125 1800k on 300k #620	1.10	1.10
1015 A132 2200k on 100k #650	1.25	1.25
1016 A132 2200k on 300k #651	1.25	1.25
1017 A132 2200k on 450k #652	1.25	1.25
1018 A132 2200k on 500k #653	1.25	1.25
1019 A145 2500k on 500k #710	1.50	1.50
1020 A145 2500k on (O) #711	1.50	1.50
1021 A145 2500k on 900k #712	1.50	1.50
Nos. 1003-1021 (19)	117.90	117.90

Location of surcharges vary on Nos. 1019-1021.

Miniature Sheet

New Year 2003 (Year of the Ram) — A207

No. 1022 — Background colors: a, Green. b, Blue violet. c, Maroon. d, Purple.

2003, July 30   Litho.   Perf. 13¼
1022 A207 3200k Sheet of 4, #a-d   5.50 5.50

Intl. Year of Fresh Water — A208

No. 1023: a, Cabora Bassa Dam. b, Lake Kariba. c, Mana Pools National Park.
10,000k, Victoria Falls.

2003, July 30   Perf. 13½x13¼
1023 A208 5000k Sheet of 3, #a-c   6.50 6.50
Souvenir Sheet
1024 A208 10,000k multi   4.25 4.25

Powered Flight, Cent. — A209

No. 1025: a, Avro 547A. b, Avro 504O with floats. c, Avro 584 Avrocet. d, Avro 504M. 10,000k, Avro 621 Tutor Replica.

2003, July 30   **Perf. 14**
1025 A209 4000k Sheet of 4, #a-d   6.75 6.75

Souvenir Sheet
1026 A209 9000k multi   4.00 4.00

Bird Type of 2002

Designs: 1000k, White-fronted bee-eaters. 1200k, Little bee-eaters. 1500k, Blue-cheeked bee-eater. 1800k, Boehn's bee-eater.

2003, Dec. 26   **Perf. 13¼**
Size: 25x20mm
1027-1030 A203   Set of 4   2.50 2.50

Rotary International in Zambia, 50th Anniv. — A210

Design: 1000k, Rotary emblem and hands.

2003, Nov. 21   **Litho.**   **Perf. 13**
1031 A210 1000k multi   — —

Rotary Type of 2003

Design: 1200k, Rotary emblem.

2003, Nov. 21   **Litho.**   **Perf. 13**
1032 A210 1200k multi   — —

Miniature Sheet

Birds — A211

No. 1033: a, 500k, African fish eagles, national bird of Zimbabwe. b, 750k, Cattle egrets, national bird of Botswana. c, 1000k, African fish eagles, national bird of Zambia. d, 1100k, Peregrine falcons, national bird of Angola. e, 1500k, Bar-tailed trogons. f, 1700k, African fish eagles, national bird of Namibia. g, 1800k, Purple-crested louries, national bird of Swaziland. h, 2200k, Blue cranes, national bird of South Africa.

2004, Oct. 11   **Litho.**   **Perf. 14**
1033 A211   Sheet of 8, #a-h   4.50 4.50

See Angola No. , Botswana Nos. 792-793, Malawi No. , Namibia No. 1052, South Africa No. 1342, Swaziland Nos. 727-735, and Zimbabwe No. 975.

Independence, 40th Anniv. — A212

Design: 3300k, Ukishi dancer.

2004, Oct. 23   **Litho.**   **Perf. 13x13¼**
1037 A212 3300k multi

Three additional stamps were issued in this set. The editors would like to examine any examples.

No. 649 Surcharged

Methods and Perfs As Before
2004, Dec. 28
Granite Paper
1038 A131 1000k on 700k #649   1.50 1.50

Mammals A213

Designs: No. 1039, 2250k, Acionyx jubatus. No. 1040, 2250k, Phacochoerus aethiopicus. No. 1041, 2250k, Giraffa camelopardalis. 2700k, Syncerus caffer.
No. 1043, vert.: a, Panthera pardus. b, Pan troglodytes. c, Lycaon pictus. d, Equus burchelli.
10,000k, Diceros bicornis, vert.

2005, June 27   **Litho.**   **Perf. 14**
1039-1042 A213   Set of 4   4.25 4.25
1043 A213   3300k Sheet of 4, #a-d   5.75 5.75

Souvenir Sheet
1044 A213 10,000k multi   4.50 4.50

Insects — A214

Designs: 1500k, Fornasinius russus. No. 1046, 2250k, Goliathus giganteus. No. 1047, 2250k, Macrorhina. 2700k, Chelorrhina polyphemus.
No. 1048: a, Sternotomis virescens. b, Cicindela regalis. c, Goliathus meleagris. d, Mecosasms explanta.
10,000k, Meloid.

2005, June 27
1045-1048 A214   Set of 4   3.75 3.75
1049 A214   3300k Sheet of 4, #a-d   5.75 5.75

Souvenir Sheet
1050 A214 10,000k multi   4.50 4.50

Butterflies — A215

Designs: No. 1051, 2250k, Ropalo ceres. No. 1052, 2250k, Morpho portis nymphalidae. No. 1053, 2250k, Phyllocnistis citrella. 2700k, H. misippus.
No. 1055: a, Colotis evippe. b, Papilio lormieri. c, Papilio dardanus. d, Papilio zalmoxis.
10,000k, Epiphora albida druce.

2005, June 27
1051-1054 A215   Set of 4   4.25 4.25

1055 A215   3300k Sheet of 4, #a-d   5.75 5.75

Souvenir Sheet
1056 A215 10,000k multi   4.50 4.50

Orchids — A216

Designs: No. 1057, 1500k, Disa draconis. No. 1058, 1500k, Disa uniflora. No. 1059, 1500k, Disa uniflora orange. 2700k, Phalaenopsis penetrate.
No. 1061: a, Ansellia africana (yellow flower). b, Ansellia africana (spotted flower). c, Cattleya lueddemanniana. d, Laelia tenebrosa.
10,000k, Cymbidium.

2005, June 27
1057-1060 A216   Set of 4   3.25 3.25
1061 A216   3300k Sheet of 4, #a-d   5.75 5.75

Souvenir Sheet
1062 A216 10,000k multi   4.50 4.50

Jesuits in Zambia, Cent. A217

Designs: 1500k, Bishop Paul Lungu, Map of Zambia. 2550k, Father Torrend, Kasisi Church. 2700k, Father Moreau, Chikuni Church. 3300k, St. Ignatius of Loyola.

2005, June 25   **Litho.**   **Perf. 13¼x13**
1063-1066 A217   Set of 4   4.50 4.50
1066a   Souvenir sheet, #1063-1066   4.50 4.50

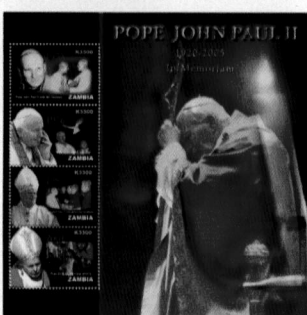

Pope John Paul II (1920-2005) and Pres. Jimmy Carter — A219

Pope John Paul II — A220

No. 1070: a, With Sri Chinmoy. b, With boy and dove. c, With Schneider brothers. d, Visiting Ukraine.

2005, Aug. 22   **Litho.**   **Perf. 12¾**
1069 A219 7000k multi   3.00 3.00
1070 A220 3300k Sheet of 4, #a-d   5.75 5.75

No. 1069 was printed in sheets of 4.

Railroads, 200th Anniv. — A222

A221

No. 1071: a, Chinese Class KF 4-8-4. b, Indian Class WP 4-6-2. c, Irish 800 Class 4-6-0. d, French 241A Class 4-8-2.
No. 1072, 1700k: a, British Rail Class 4MT 2-6-4T. b, South African Railways Class 12A. c, Cuban sugar plantation locomotive. d, LNER A4 Pacific facing right. e, LNER A4 Pacific facing left. f, GWR City of Truro 4-4-0. g, British Rail HST Intercity 125. h, Eurostar. i, LNER A3 Flying Scotsman.
No. 1073, 1700k: a, Southern Railway King Arthur Class 4-6-0. b, Berkshire at Kailman's Bridge. c, Indian Railways WT Class 2-84 Suburban Tank steam locomotive. d, Ladders on shell of railway car being built. e, Worker on knees inside railway car. f, Yellow staircase next to railway car. g, Workers looking at undercarriage of raised railway car. h, Railway car between blue machinery. i, Model of steam locomotive.
No. 1074, 1700k: a, Great Western Hall Class 4-6-0. b, Argentinian 15B Class 4-8-0. c, Mallet Meter Gauge steam locomotive. d, Worker cutting track. e, Worker and pulley. f, Workers in cherrypicker. g, Workers on tracks and in cherrypickers. h, Workers pouring cement. i, Track workers.
No. 1075, Finnish Class HV2 4-6-0.
No. 1076, 8000k, Orient Express. No. 1077, 8000k, Edinburgh to London train. No. 1078, 800k, Bernina Express.

2005, Aug. 22
1071 A221 4200k Sheet of 4, #a-d   7.50 7.50
Sheets of 9, #a-i
1072-1074 A222   Set of 3   20.00 20.00
Souvenir Sheets
1075 A221 8000k multi   3.50 3.50
1076-1078 A222   Set of 3   10.50 10.50

David Livingstone at Victoria Falls, 150th Anniv. A223

Designs: 1500k, Livingstone, Victoria Falls. 2700k, Statue of Livingstone, railroad bridge.

2006, Jan. 20   **Litho.**   **Perf. 13x13¼**
1079-1080 A223   Set of 2   2.60 2.60

Queen Elizabeth II, 80th Birthday — A225

No. 1085 — Queen: a, Wearing crown. b, Wearing necklace. c, Wearing necklace and jacket. d, With Princess Anne.
6500k, Wearing green hat.

2006, Aug. 8   Litho.   Perf. 13¼
1085 A225 3200k Sheet of 4, #a-d   6.50 6.50

Souvenir Sheet
1086 A225 6500k multi   3.25 3.25

Scouting, Cent. (in 2007) — A226

No. 1087, vert. — Scouting emblem, doves, Lord Robert Baden-Powell and background colors of: a, Pink and lilac. b, Yellow and orange. c, Blue and light blue. d, Light green and green.
6500k, Purple and red.

2006, Aug. 8
1087 A226 3200k Sheet of 4, #a-d   6.50 6.50

Souvenir Sheet
1088 A226 6500k multi   3.25 3.25

Nos. 623, 987 and 1028 Surcharged

Methods and Perfs As Before

2007
1089 A203 1500k on 1200k #1028   .70 .70
1090 A127 1850k on 20k #623   .95 .95
1091 A203 3300k on 1400k #987   1.60 1.60
Nos. 1089-1091 (3)   3.25 3.25

Issued: Nos. 1089, 1091, 3/19; No. 1090, 5/30.

Miniature Sheet

Tazara Railway, 30th Anniv. (in 2006) — A227

No. 1092: a, Map of Tanzania and Zambia, waterfall, mountain, people waving, and men signing agreement. b, Men and train, elephant and antelope. c, Dar es Salaam Station, sign and wreaths with Chinese inscriptions. d, New Kapiri Mposhi Station, people near train. e, Train, bridge and tunnel, zebra and giraffe. f, Train on bridge, lion and lioness.

2007, May 28   Litho.   Perf. 12
1092 A227 1500k Sheet of 6, #a-f   4.75 4.75

Mammals
A228

Designs: 1500k, Bat-eared fox. 2250k, Spotted hyena. 2700k, Aardwolf. 3300k, Side-striped jackal.

2007, June 29   Perf. 13¼x13
1093-1096 A228 Set of 4   5.25 5.25
1096a   Souvenir sheet, #1093-1096   5.25 5.25

POSTAGE DUE STAMPS

Type of Northern Rhodesia
Perf. 12½

				Unwmk.
1964, Oct. 24		**Litho.**		
J1	D1	1p orange	.20	.20
J2	D1	2p dark blue	.20	.20
J3	D1	3p rose claret	.25	.25
J4	D1	4p violet blue	.35	.35
J5	D1	6p purple	.50	.50
J6	D1	1sh emerald	1.50	1.50
		Nos. J1-J6 (6)	3.00	3.00

ZANZIBAR

'zan-zə-ˌbär

LOCATION — Group of islands about twenty miles off the coast of Tanganyika in East Africa
GOVT. — Republic
AREA — 1,044 sq. mi. (approx.)
POP. — 354,360 (est. 1967)
CAPITAL — Zanzibar

Before 1895, unoverprinted stamps of India were used in Zanzibar.

Zanzibar was a British protectorate until Dec. 10, 1963, when it became independent. After a revolt in January, 1964, a republic was established. Zanzibar joined Tanganyika Apr. 26, 1964, to form the United Republic of Tanganyika and Zanzibar (later renamed Tanzania). See Tanzania.

12 Pies = 1 Anna
16 Annas = 1 Rupee
100 Cents = 1 Rupee (1908)
100 Cents = 1 Shilling (1935)

Catalogue values for unused stamps in this country are for Never Hinged items, beginning with Scott 201 in the regular postage section and Scott J18 in the postage due section.

Watermarks

Wmk. 47 —
Multiple Rosette

Wmk. 71 —
Rosette

Stamps of British India Overprinted

On Stamps of 1882-95

1895		**Wmk. Star (39)**		**Perf. 14**	
		Blue Overprint			
1	A17	½a green		17,500.	5,250.
2	A19	1a violet brown		2,750.	600.
a.		"Zanzibar"			25,000.

1895-96

Black Overprint
3	A17	½a green		4.75	4.00
a.		"Zanzibar"		1,350.	725.00
b.		"Zanzibar"		1,350.	
c.		"Zapzibar"			1,800.

4	A19	1a violet brn		4.50	4.00
a.		"Zanzibar"		—	3,250.
b.		"Zanzibar"		1,750.	2,000.
5	A20	1a6p bister brn		5.25	3.75
a.		"Zanzibar"		3,750.	1,100.
b.		"Zanzibar"		1,750.	
c.		"Zanzibar"		1,600.	1,750.
d.		"Zapzibar"			
6	A21	2a ultra		6.25	5.75
a.		"Zanzibar"		5,250.	2,400.
b.		"Zanzibar"		5,250.	2,400.
c.		"Zapzibar"			
7	A28	2a6p green		9.00	5.50
a.		"Zanzibar"		4,500.	1,800.
b.		"Zanzibar"		700.00	1,250.
c.		"Zanzibar"			
d.		"Zanzibar"			1,250.
8	A22	3a orange		12.50	11.50
a.		"Zanzibar"		850.00	1,600.
b.		"Zanzibar"		5,000.	5,250.
9	A23	4a olive grn		15.00	17.50
a.		"Zanzibar"		8,750.	4,250.
10	A25	8a red vio		20.00	24.00
a.		"Zanzibar"		8,250.	7,000.
11	A26	12a vio, red		18.00	11.50
a.		"Zanzibar"		8,250.	4,250.
12	A27	1r gray		87.50	80.00
a.		"Zanzibar"		7,750.	4,750.
13	A29	1r car rose & grn		22.50	30.00
a.		Vertical overprint		475.00	
14	A30	2r brn & rose		87.50	92.50
a.		"Zanzibar"		22,000.	4,750.
b.		Inverted "r"		4,250.	4,250.
c.		Pair, one without overprint			
15	A30	3r grn & brn		62.50	72.50
a.		"Zanzibar"		22,000.	
b.		Inverted "r"		4,500.	4,750.
16	A30	5r vio & blue		75.00	92.50
a.		"Zanzibar"		22,000.	
b.		Inverted "r"		3,750.	5,250.
c.		Dbl. ovpt., one invtd.		950.00	

On Stamp of 1873-76
Wmk. Elephant's Head (38)
17	A14	6a bister		21.00	12.50
a.		"Zanzibar"		8,750.	4,000.
b.		"Zanzibarr"		5,250.	4,250.
c.		"Zanibar"		725.00	1,400.
d.		"Zapzibar"			
e.		Double overprint		160.00	
		Nos. 3-17 (15)		451.25	467.50

Nos. 4-6 Surcharged:

a   b

c   d

e   f

1896   Wmk. Star (39)
Black Surcharge
18	(a) 2½a on 1a		175.00	110.00
19	(b) 2½a on 1a		450.00	350.00
20	(c) 2½a on 1a		180.00	125.00

Red Surcharge
21	(a) 2½a on 1a		260.00	675.00
22	(b) 2½a on 1a		500.00	1,000.
23	(c) 2½a on 1a		275.00	675.00
24	(a) 2½a on 1a6p		60.00	50.00
a.	"Zanzibar"		1,600.	1,800.
b.	"Zanzibar"		4,250.	2,250.
24C	(b) 2½a on 1a6p		210.00	500.00
25	(c) 2½a on 1a6p		130.00	275.00
26	(d) 2½a on 1a6p		150.00	125.00
27	(e) 2½a on 1a6p		425.00	400.00
27A	(f) 2½a on 1a6p		13,500.	9,000.
28	(a) 2½a on 2a		110.00	275.00
28A	(b) 2½a on 2a		225.00	525.00
29	(c) 2½a on 2a		125.00	350.00
30	(d) 2½a on 2a		65.00	35.00
31	(e) 2½a on 2a		200.00	125.00
31A	(f) 2½a on 2a		5,000.	2,250.

Certain type varieties are found in the word "Zanzibar" on Nos. 1 to 31A viz: Inverted "q" for "b," broken "p" for "n," "i" without dot, small second "z" and tall second "z." These varieties are found on all values from ½a to 1r inclusive and the tall "z" is also found on the 2r, 3r and 5r.

Stamps of British East Africa, 1896, Overprinted in Black or Red

1896   Wmk. Crown and C A (2)
32	A8	½a yellow grn	35.00	20.00
33	A8	1a carmine	32.50	18.00
34	A8	2½a dk blue (R)	85.00	50.00
35	A8	4½a orange	50.00	57.50
36	A8	5a dark ocher	57.50	37.50
37	A8	7½a lilac	45.00	57.50
		Nos. 32-37 (6)	305.00	240.50

A2

Sultan Seyyid
Hamed-bin-Thwain
A3

1896, Sept. 20   Engr.   Wmk. 71
38	A2	½a yel grn & red	4.50	2.00
39	A2	1a indigo & red	3.00	1.75
40	A2	2a red brn & red	3.25	.85
41	A2	2½a ultra & red	16.00	1.60
42	A2	3a slate & red	14.00	7.50
43	A2	4a dk green & red	9.50	4.00
44	A2	4½a orange & red	7.00	6.75
45	A2	5a bister & red	6.50	3.00
a.		Half used as 2½a on cover		3,750.
46	A3	7½a lilac & red	4.75	4.00
47	A3	8a ol gray & red	13.50	9.00
48	A3	1r ultra & red	22.50	12.00
49	A3	2r green & red	30.00	13.00
50	A3	3r violet & red	36.00	13.00
51	A3	4r lake & red	27.50	20.00
52	A3	5r blk brn & red	38.00	20.00
		Nos. 38-52 (15)	236.00	118.45

No. 43 Surcharged in Red

1897
53	A2 (a) 2½a on 4a		67.50	45.00
54	A2 (b) 2½a on 4a		225.00	200.00
55	A2 (c) 2½a on 4a		85.00	57.50
	Nos. 53-55 (3)		377.50	302.50

1898   Engr.   Wmk. 47
56	A2	½a yel grn & red	1.75	.45
57	A2	1a indigo & red	3.50	.75
58	A2	2a red brn & red	6.00	2.25
58A	A2	2½a ultra & red	4.25	.45
59	A2	3a slate & red	7.00	.75
60	A2	4a dk grn & red	4.25	1.25
60A	A2	4½a orange & red	11.00	1.25
61	A2	5a bister & red	20.00	2.25
61A	A2	7½a lilac & red	14.50	3.50
61B	A2	8a ol gray & red	17.50	3.25
		Nos. 56-61B (10)	89.75	16.15

Sultan Seyyid Hamoud-bin-Mahommed-bin-Said
A4   A5

1899-1901
62	A4	½a yel grn & red	2.25	.65
63	A4	1a indigo & red	5.00	.25
64	A4	1a car & red ('01)	2.25	.25
65	A4	2a red brn & red	2.50	.55
66	A4	2½a ultra & red	2.50	.65
67	A4	3a slate & red	3.50	2.50
68	A4	4a dk green & red	3.75	1.60
69	A4	4½a orange & red	15.00	4.00
70	A4	4½a ind & red ('01)	17.00	13.50
71	A4	5a bister & red	3.50	1.40
72	A4	7½a lilac & red	3.75	4.25
73	A4	8a ol gray & red	3.75	5.00

Wmk. 71
74	A5	1r ultra & red	21.00	17.50
75	A5	2r green & red	21.00	21.00
76	A5	3r violet & red	45.00	52.50

77	A5	4r lilac rose & red	75.00	77.50
78	A5	5r gray brown & red	85.00	87.50

Nos. 62-78 (17)   311.75 290.60

For surcharges see Nos. 94-98.

Monogram of Sultan Ali bin
Hamoud
A6   A7

1904, June 8   Typo.   Wmk. 47

79	A6	½a emerald	2.25	1.00
80	A6	1a rose red	2.25	.20
81	A6	2a bister brown	2.75	.50
82	A6	2½a ultra	3.50	.40
83	A6	3a gray	3.00	2.50
84	A6	4a blue green	2.75	1.75
85	A6	4½a black	3.75	2.75
86	A6	5a ocher	4.50	1.40
87	A6	7½a violet	5.25	8.00
88	A6	8a olive green	4.75	3.00
89	A7	1r ultra & red	25.00	16.00
90	A7	2r green & red	30.00	42.50
91	A7	3r violet & red	50.00	85.00
92	A7	4r magenta & red	75.00	120.00
93	A7	5r olive & red	75.00	132.50

Nos. 79-93 (15)   289.75 417.50

Nos. 69-70, 72-73 Surcharged in Black
or Lake:

g   h

i

1904

94	A4 (g)	1a on 4½a	5.00	6.00
95	A4 (g)	1a on 4½a (L)	5.75	24.00
96	A4 (h)	2a on 4a (L)	19.00	24.00
97	A4 (i)	2½a on 7½a	17.50	25.00
a.		"Hlaf"	15,000.	
98	A4 (i)	2½a on 8a	22.50	37.50
a.		"Hlaf"	13,500.	9,750.

Nos. 94-98 (5)   69.75 116.50

Sultan Ali bin Hamoud
A8   A9

A10

Palace of the
Sultan — A11

1908-09   Engr.   Wmk. 47

99	A8	1c gray ('09)	2.75	.35
100	A8	3c yellow grn	8.50	.20
101	A8	6c carmine	11.00	.20
102	A8	10c org brn ('09)	4.75	2.25
103	A8	12c violet	17.00	3.50

104	A9	15c ultra	15.50	.45
105	A9	25c brown	5.50	1.10
106	A9	50c dp green	8.50	5.75
107	A9	75c slate ('09)	15.00	17.50
108	A10	1r yellow green	30.00	14.00
109	A10	2r violet	21.00	18.00
110	A10	3r yellow brown	27.50	57.50
111	A10	4r red	75.00	100.00
112	A10	5r blue	65.00	90.00
113	A11	10r brn & dk grn	175.00	300.00
114	A11	20r yel grn & blk	400.00	575.00
115	A11	30r dk brn & blk	425.00	725.00
116	A11	40r org brn & blk	575.00	
117	A11	50r lilac & blk	525.00	
118	A11	100r blue & blk	750.00	
119	A11	200r black & brn	1,200.	

Nos. 99-112 (14)   307.00 310.80

It is probable that Nos. 118 and 119 were
used only for fiscal purposes.

Sultan   Dhow — A13
Khalifa bin
Harub — A12

Dhow — A14

1913   Perf. 14

120	A12	1c gray	.50	.20
121	A12	3c yellow grn	.70	.50
122	A12	6c carmine	1.75	.20
123	A12	10c brown	1.25	2.75
124	A12	12c violet	1.40	.35
125	A12	15c ultra	1.75	.40
126	A12	25c black brn	1.40	1.75
127	A12	50c dk green	2.75	5.00
128	A12	75c dk gray	2.75	4.00
129	A13	1r yellow grn	11.00	12.00
130	A13	2r dk violet	12.50	30.00
131	A13	3r orange	16.00	47.50
132	A13	4r red	30.00	80.00
133	A13	5r blue	42.50	50.00
134	A14	10r brown & grn	160.00	275.00
135	A14	20r yel grn & blk	210.00	450.00
136	A14	30r dk brn & blk	225.00	525.00
137	A14	40r orange & blk	425.00	725.00
138	A14	50r dull vio & blk	400.00	775.00
139	A14	100r blue & blk	500.00	
140	A14	200r black & brn	1,000.	

Nos. 120-134 (15)   286.25 509.65

1914-22   Wmk. 3

141	A12	1c gray	.90	.30
142	A12	3c yellow grn	1.40	.20
143	A12	6c carmine	.95	.20
144	A12	8c vio, yel ('22)	.85	4.00
145	A12	10c dk grn, yel ('22)	.85	.40
146	A12	15c ultra	1.25	5.75
148	A12	50c dark green	5.00	4.75
149	A12	75c deep gray	3.50	26.00
150	A13	1r yellow grn	4.50	4.00
151	A13	2r dark violet	7.00	10.00
152	A13	3r brown org	20.00	37.50
153	A13	4r red	19.00	95.00
154	A13	5r blue	19.00	72.50
155	A14	10r brown & grn	150.00	500.00

Nos. 141-155 (14)   234.20 760.60

1921-29   Wmk. 4

156	A12	1c gray	.20	8.00
157	A12	3c yellow grn	1.25	4.00
158	A12	3c orange ('22)	.35	.20
159	A12	4c green ('22)	.55	1.10
160	A12	6c carmine	.35	.55
161	A12	6c vio, bl ('22)	.45	.20
162	A12	10c lt brown	.80	11.00
163	A12	12c violet	.50	.35
164	A12	12c carmine ('22)	.50	.50
165	A12	15c ultra	.80	10.50
166	A12	20c dk blue ('22)	1.25	.40
167	A12	25c black brn	.90	14.00
168	A12	50c blue green	1.75	4.75
169	A12	75c dark gray	3.25	57.50
170	A13	1r yellow grn	6.00	4.00
171	A13	2r dk violet	4.50	9.50
172	A13	3r ocher	5.50	8.50
173	A13	4r red	17.50	40.00
174	A13	5r blue	24.00	72.50
175	A14	10r brown & grn	140.00	350.00

176	A14	20r green & blk	275.00	525.00
177	A14	30r dk brn & blk ('29)	225.00	625.00

Nos. 156-175 (20)   210.40 597.55

Sultan Khalifa bin
Harub ("CENTS" with
Serifs) — A15

1926-27

184	A15	1c brown	.65	.20
185	A15	3c yellow org	.20	.20
186	A15	4c deep green	.25	.35
187	A15	6c dark violet	.35	.20
188	A15	8c slate	1.10	5.50
189	A15	10c olive green	1.10	.45
190	A15	12c deep red	2.00	.20
191	A15	20c ultra	.65	.40
192	A15	25c violet, yel	5.25	3.00
193	A15	50c claret	2.25	.50
194	A15	75c olive brown	28.00	28.00

Nos. 184-194 (11)   41.80 39.00

> Catalogue values for unused
> stamps in this section, from this
> point to the end of the section, are
> for Never Hinged items.

"CENTS"   Dhow — A17
without
Serifs — A16

Dhow — A18

1936   Perf. 14

201	A16	5c deep green	.20	.20
202	A16	10c black	.20	.20
203	A16	15c carmine	.30	.20
204	A16	20c brown org	.20	.20
205	A16	25c violet, yel	.20	.20
206	A16	30c ultra	.25	.20
207	A16	40c black brown	.25	.20
208	A16	50c claret	.50	.20
209	A17	1sh yellow grn	.75	.20
210	A17	2sh dark violet	1.50	2.50
211	A17	5sh red	22.50	8.00
212	A17	7.50sh blue	32.50	32.50
213	A18	10sh brn & grn	37.50	27.50

Nos. 201-213 (13)   96.85 72.30

For overprints see Nos. 222-223.

A19

A20

1936, Dec. 9

214	A19	10c olive grn & blk	3.25	.35
215	A19	20c red violet & blk	5.75	1.25
216	A19	30c deep ultra & blk	14.50	.85
217	A19	50c red orange & blk	15.50	5.50

Nos. 214-217 (4)   39.00 7.95

Reign of Sultan Khalifa bin Harub, 25th
anniv.

Perf. 14
1944, Nov. 20   Engr.   Wmk. 4

Dhow & Map Showing Zanzibar & Muscat.

218	A20	10c violet blue	.90	3.25
219	A20	20c brown orange	.95	3.50
220	A20	50c Prus green	1.10	.40
221	A20	1sh dull purple	1.10	.75

Nos. 218-221 (4)   4.05 7.90

200th anniv. of the Al Busaid Dynasty.

Nos. 202 and 206
Overprinted in Red

1946, Nov. 11

222	A16	10c black	.25	.25
223	A16	30c ultra	.40	.40

Victory of the Allied Nations in WW II.

Common Design Types
pictured following the introduction.

Silver Wedding Issue
Common Design Types
1949, Jan. 10   Photo.   Perf. 14x14½

224	CD304	20c orange	.60	.60

Engraved; Name Typographed
Perf. 11½x11

225	CD305	10sh light brown	28.50	36.50

UPU Issue
Common Design Types
Engr.; Name Typo. on 30c, 50c
Perf. 13½, 11x11½
1949, Oct. 10   Wmk. 4

226	CD306	20c red orange	.45	3.00
227	CD307	30c indigo	3.00	1.50
228	CD308	50c red lilac	1.40	3.00
229	CD309	1sh blue green	1.40	4.25

Nos. 226-229 (4)   6.25 11.75

Sultan Khalifa bin
Harub — A21

Seyyid
Khalifa
Schools
A22

Perf. 12x12½, 13x12½
1952, Aug. 26   Engr.

230	A21	5c black	.20	.20
231	A21	10c red orange	.20	.20
232	A21	15c green	.75	2.50
233	A21	20c carmine	.55	.20
234	A21	25c plum	1.10	.20
235	A21	30c blue green	1.10	.20
236	A21	35c ultra	.75	5.00
237	A21	40c chocolate	.75	2.00
238	A21	50c purple	3.25	.20
239	A22	1sh choc & bl grn	.75	.20
240	A22	2sh claret & ultra	3.00	3.75
241	A22	5sh carmine & blk	3.00	5.00
242	A22	7.50sh emer & gray	24.00	27.50
243	A22	10sh gray blk & rose red	14.00	15.00

Nos. 230-243 (14)   53.40 62.15

Sultan Khalifa bin Harub — A23

1954, Aug. 26   **Perf. 12½x12**
244	A23	15c green	.20	.20
245	A23	20c scarlet	.20	.20
246	A23	30c ultra	.20	.20
247	A23	50c purple	.30	.30
248	A23	1.25sh brown orange	.75	.75
		Nos. 244-248 (5)	1.65	1.65

The frames differ on Nos. 245 and 247. Sultan Khalifa bin Harub, 75th birth anniv.

Cloves — A24

Sultan's Barge — A26

Dhows A25

Malindi Minaret Mosque — A27   Kibweni Palace — A28

Sultan Khalifa bin Harub and: 25c, 35c, and 50c Map showing location of Zanzibar. 1sh, 2sh, Dimbani Mosque.

Perf. 11½ (A24), 11x11½ (A25), 14x13½ (A26), 13½x14 (A27), 13x13½ (A28)

1957, Aug. 26   **Engr.**   **Wmk. 314**
249	A24	5c dull grn & org	.20	.20
250	A24	10c rose car & brt grn	.20	.20
251	A25	15c dk brn & grn	.20	3.25
252	A26	20c ultra	.20	.20
253	A26	25c blk & brn org	.20	1.50
254	A25	30c int blk & rose car	.20	1.50
255	A26	35c brt grn & ind	.20	.20
256	A27	40c int blk & redsh brn	.20	.20
257	A26	50c dull grn & bl	.30	.30
258	A27	1sh int blk & brt car	.30	.30
259	A25	1.25sh rose car & dk grn	5.00	.45
260	A27	2sh dull grn & org	5.00	3.50
261	A28	5sh ultra	7.00	3.00
262	A28	7.50sh green	12.00	5.50
263	A28	10sh rose carmine	13.00	8.50
		Nos. 249-263 (15)	44.20	28.80

Sultan Seyyid Abdulla bin Khalifa — A29

Designs as before with portrait of Sultan Seyyid Abdulla bin Khalifa.

Perf. 11½ (A29), 11x11½ (A25), 14x13½ (A26), 13½x14 (A27)

1961, Oct. 17   **Engr.**   **Wmk. 314**
264	A29	5c dull grn & org	.20	.90
265	A29	10c rose car & brt grn	.20	.20
266	A25	15c dk brn & grn	.90	4.00
267	A26	20c ultra	.40	.45
268	A26	25c blk & brn org	.80	1.10
269	A25	30c int blk & rose car	3.75	2.50
270	A26	35c brt grn & indigo	3.25	5.00
271	A27	40c int blk & redsh brn	.40	.20
272	A26	50c dull grn & bl	2.00	.20
273	A27	1sh int blk & brt car	.50	1.75
274	A25	1.25sh rose car & dk grn	3.75	5.50
275	A27	2sh dull grn & org	1.00	4.00

Perf. 13x13½
276	A28	5sh ultra	5.50	10.00
277	A28	7.50sh green	5.00	19.00
278	A28	10sh rose carmine	5.00	11.00
279	A28	20sh dk brown	24.00	40.00
		Nos. 264-279 (16)	56.65	105.80

For overprints see Nos. 285-300.

Freedom from Hunger Issue
Common Design Type with Portrait of Sultan Seyyid Abdulla bin Khalifa

1963, June 4   **Photo.**   **Perf. 14x14½**
280	CD314	1.30sh sepia	1.40	.80

Independent State

Sultan Seyyid Jamshid bin Abdulla and Zanzibar Clove — A30

Designs: 50c, "To Prosperity," arch and sun. 1.30sh, "Religious Tolerance," composite view of churches and mosques, horiz. 2.50sh, "Towards the Light," Mangapwani Cave.

Perf. 12½

1963, Dec. 10   **Photo.**   **Unwmk.**
281	A30	30c multicolored	.20	.20
282	A30	50c multicolored	.30	.30
283	A30	1.30sh multicolored	.40	2.00
284	A30	2.50sh multicolored	.50	2.00
		Nos. 281-284 (4)	1.40	4.50

Zanzibar's independence, Dec. 10, 1963.
For overprints see Nos. 301-304.

Republic

Nos. 264-279 Overprinted

1964, Feb. 28   **As Before**
285	A29	5c dull grn & org	.20	.20
286	A29	10c rose car & brt grn	.20	.20
287	A25	15c dk brn & grn	.20	.20
288	A26	20c ultra	.20	.20
289	A26	25c blk & brn org	.20	.20
290	A25	30c int blk & rose car	.20	.20
291	A26	35c brt grn & ind	.20	.20
292	A27	40c int blk & redsh brn	.20	.20
293	A26	50c dull grn & blue	.20	.20
294	A27	1sh int blk & brt car	.30	.30
295	A25	1.25sh rose car & dk grn	2.25	.20
296	A27	2sh dull grn & org	1.50	.35
297	A28	5sh ultra	2.00	.50
298	A28	7.50sh green	3.50	7.00
299	A28	10sh rose carmine	3.50	7.00
300	A28	20sh dark brown	4.75	9.50
		Nos. 285-300 (16)	19.60	26.55

The overprint was applied in England. It is in 2 lines on 40c and 1sh to 20sh. "Jamhuri" means "republic."

Overprint Handstamped

285a	A29	5c	1.00	.50
286a	A29	10c	1.00	.25
287a	A25	15c	1.00	2.00
288a	A26	20c	1.00	.25
289a	A26	25c	1.00	.25
290a	A25	30c	1.00	.50
291a	A26	35c	1.00	1.00
292a	A27	40c	1.00	1.00
293a	A26	50c	1.00	.25
294a	A27	1sh	1.00	.60
295a	A25	1.25sh	1.00	.60
296a	A27	2sh	3.00	1.50
297a	A28	5sh	4.00	3.50
298a	A28	7.50sh	8.00	6.50
299a	A28	10sh	10.00	7.00
300a	A28	20sh	15.00	10.00
		Nos. 285a-300a (16)	51.00	35.70

This overprint was applied locally. It has one line of serifed letters. These are found diagonal, vertical, horizontal, double and inverted. See Nos. 301a-304b. Other stamps with this overprint, including postage dues, were unofficial.

Nos. 281-284 Overprinted

1964, Feb. 28   **As Before**
301	A30	30c multi	.25	.25
302	A30	50c multi	.30	.30
303	A30	1.30sh multi	.50	.50
304	A30	2.50sh multi	.80	.85
a.		Green omitted	125.00	
		Nos. 301-304 (4)	1.85	1.90

One-line overprint on 1.30sh.

Overprint Handstamped

301a	A30	30c	.30	.30
302a	A30	50c	.35	.35
303a	A30	1.30sh	.60	.60
304b	A30	2.50sh	1.50	1.50
		Nos. 301a-304b (4)	2.75	2.75

See note after No. 300a.

Moorish Arch, Ax, Sword and Spear — A31

Designs: 10c, 20c, Arch and arrow piercing chain. 25c, 40c, Man with rifle. 30c, 50c, Man breaking chain. 1sh, Man, flag and sun. 1.30sh, Hands breaking chain and cloves, horiz. 2sh, Hands waving flag, horiz. 5sh, Map of Zanzibar and Pemba and flag, horiz. 10sh, Flag and map of Zanzibar and Pemba. 20sh, Flag of Zanzibar, horiz

Perf. 13x13½, 13½x13

1964, June 21   **Litho.**   **Unwmk.**
305	A31	5c multicolored	.40	.20
306	A31	10c multicolored	.40	.20
307	A31	15c multicolored	.40	.20
308	A31	20c multicolored	.40	.20
309	A31	25c multicolored	.40	.20
310	A31	30c multicolored	.40	.20
311	A31	40c multicolored	.40	.20
312	A31	50c multicolored	.40	.20
313	A31	1sh multicolored	.50	.25
314	A31	1.30sh multicolored	.30	1.25
315	A31	2sh multicolored	.50	.50
316	A31	5sh multicolored	1.25	3.75
317	A31	10sh multicolored	4.00	5.00
318	A31	20sh multicolored	5.75	22.50
		Nos. 305-318 (14)	15.50	34.85

Soldier and Maps of Zanzibar and Pemba A32

Reconstruction A33

Perf. 13½x13, 13x13½

1965, Jan. 12   **Unwmk.**
319	A32	20c green & yel grn	.20	.20
320	A33	30c dk brn & ocher	.20	.20
321	A32	1.30sh vio blue & blue	.25	.20
322	A33	2.50sh purple & rose	.75	.50
		Nos. 319-322 (4)	1.40	1.10

First anniversary of the revolution.

Zanzibar and Tanzania

Rice Planting A34

Design: 30c, 1.30sh, Hands holding rice.

Perf. 13x12½

1965, Oct. 17   **Litho.**   **Unwmk.**
323	A34	20c blue & blk brn	.20	1.00
324	A34	30c brt pink & blk brn	.25	1.00
325	A34	1.30sh org & blk brn	.35	2.25
326	A34	2.50sh emer & blk brn	.55	4.00
		Nos. 323-326 (4)	1.35	8.25

Issued to publicize agricultural development.

Symbols of Trade, Agriculture, Industry and Education A35

Pres. Abeid Amani Karume and Vice-Pres. Abdulla Kassim Hanga A36

Designs: 50c, 2.50sh, Soldier and sunburst.

1966, Jan. 12   **Litho.**   **Perf. 12½x13**
327	A35	20c ultra, red & gray	.20	.20
328	A35	50c black & yel	.25	.20
329	A35	1.30sh multicolored	.30	.35
330	A35	2.50sh black & org	.60	1.00
		Nos. 327-330 (4)	1.35	1.75

2nd anniv. of the revolution of Jan. 12, 1964.

1966, Apr. 26   **Photo.**   **Perf. 13½x13**

Design: 50c, 1.30sh, Flag, laurel and hands holding Flame of the Union (inscribed: Jamhuri Tanzania Zanzibar).
331	A36	30c multicolored	.20	.20
332	A36	50c multicolored	.20	.20
333	A36	1.30sh multicolored	.35	.30
334	A36	2.50sh multicolored	.60	1.25
		Nos. 331-334 (4)	1.35	1.95

Union of Tanganyika and Zanzibar, 2nd anniv.

Logging
A37

10c, 1sh, Clove trees & man. 15c, 40c, Cabinetmaker. 20c, 5sh, Lumumba College & book. 25c, 1.30sh, Farmer & tractor. 30c, 2sh, Volunteer farm workers. 50c, 10sh, Street scene, vert.

Perf. 13x12½, 12½x13

1966, June 5			Litho.	
335	A37	5c lemon & vio brn	.70	.60
336	A37	10c brt grn & vio brn	.70	1.00
337	A37	15c vio brn & bl	.70	1.00
338	A37	20c vio bl & org	.70	.20
339	A37	25c vio brn & yel	.70	.20
340	A37	30c vio brn & dl yel	.80	.20
341	A37	40c vio brn & rose	.90	.20
342	A37	50c green & yel	.90	.20
343	A37	1sh ultra & vio brn	.90	.25
344	A37	1.30sh lt bl grn & vio brn	1.00	3.25
345	A37	2sh brt grn & vio brn	1.00	.60
346	A37	5sh ver & gray	1.50	6.00
347	A37	10sh red brn & yel	2.50	22.50
348	A37	20sh brt pink & vio brn	5.00	32.50
		Nos. 335-348 (14)	18.00	68.70

Symbols of Education — A38

1966, Sept. 25			Perf. 13½x13	
349	A38	50c blue, blk & org	.20	1.00
350	A38	1.30sh blue, blk & yel grn	.30	1.75
351	A38	2.50sh blue, blk & pink	.80	4.00
		Nos. 349-351 (3)	1.30	6.75

Introduction of free education.

People and Flag
A39

Design: 50c, 1.30sh, Vice-President Abdulla Kassim Hanga, flag and crowd, vert.

Perf. 14x14½, 14½x14

1967, Feb. 5			Litho.	Unwmk.
352	A39	30c multicolored	.20	1.00
353	A39	50c multicolored	.20	1.00
354	A39	1.30sh multicolored	.25	1.25
355	A39	2.50sh multicolored	.40	3.00
		Nos. 352-355 (4)	1.05	6.25

10th anniversary of Afro-Shirazi Party.

Volunteer Workers
A40

Perf. 12½x12

1967, Aug. 20			Photo.	Unwmk.
356	A40	1.30sh multicolored	.30	2.50
357	A40	2.50sh multicolored	.55	6.50

Volunteer (Young) Workers Brigade.
All Zanzibar stamps were withdrawn July 1, 1968, and replaced with current Kenya, Uganda and Tanzania stamps.

POSTAGE DUE STAMPS

D1

1931		Rouletted 10 Typeset Thin Paper Without Gum	Unwmk.	
J1	D1	1c blk, *orange*	12.50	150.00
J2	D1	2c blk, *orange*	5.50	75.00
J3	D1	3c blk, *orange*	5.75	52.50
J3A	D1	6c blk, *orange*		8,000.
J4	D1	9c blk, *orange*	3.25	27.50
J4A	D1	12c blk, *orange*	11,000.	10,000.
J4B	D1	12c blk, *green*	1,600.	675.00
J5	D1	15c blk, *orange*	3.25	30.00
J6	D1	18c blk, *orange*	22.50	85.00
a.		18c black, *salmon*	5.00	50.00
J7	D1	20c blk, *orange*	4.50	75.00
J8	D1	21c blk, *orange*	4.00	45.00
J8A	D1	25c blk, *orange*	14,000.	13,000.
J8B	D1	25c blk, *magenta*	3,250.	1,500.
J9	D1	31c blk, *orange*	11.00	100.00
J10	D1	50c blk, *orange*	24.00	240.00
J11	D1	75c blk, *orange*	72.50	550.00

The variety "cent.s" occurs once on each sheet of Nos. J3 to J11 inclusive.

D2

D3

1931-33		Rouletted 5 Thick Paper		
J12	D2	2c blk, *salmon*	17.50	32.50
J13	D2	3c blk, *rose*	4.00	60.00
J14	D2	6c blk, *yellow*	4.00	40.00
J15	D2	12c blk, *blue*	5.00	32.50
J16	D2	25c blk, *pink*	11.00	95.00
J17	D2	25c blk, *dull violet*	19.00	70.00
		Nos. J12-J17 (6)	60.50	330.00

> Catalogue values for unused stamps in this section, from this point to the end of the section, are for Never Hinged items.

1936		Typo. Wmk. 4	Perf. 14	
J18	D3	5c violet	6.25	11.00
J19	D3	10c carmine	5.50	3.25
J20	D3	20c green	2.50	5.25
J21	D3	30c brown	12.50	22.50
J22	D3	40c ultra	10.00	30.00
J23	D3	1sh gray	12.50	37.50
		Nos. J18-J23 (6)	49.25	109.50

Chalky paper was introduced in 1956 for the 5c, 30c, 40c, 1sh, and in 1962 for the 10c, 20c. Value for set of 6, unused $3.25, used $110.
See note after No. 300a.

ZIMBABWE

zim-'bä-bwē

LOCATION — Southeastern Africa, bordered by Zambia, Mozambique, South Africa, and Botswana
GOVT. — Republic
AREA — 150,872 sq. mi.
POP. — 11,163,160 (1999 est.)
CAPITAL — Harare

Formerly Rhodesia, the Republic of Zimbabwe was established April 18, 1980.

100 Cents = 1 Dollar

> Catalogue values for all unused stamps in this country are for Never Hinged items.

Morganite
A69

Black Rhinoceros
A70

Odzani Falls — A71

Perf. 14½, 14½x14 (A70)

1980			Litho.	
414	A69	1c shown	.20	.35
415	A69	3c Amethyst	.40	.35
416	A69	4c Garnet	.40	.20
417	A69	5c Citrine	.40	.20
418	A69	7c Blue topaz	.40	.20
419	A70	9c shown	.20	.20
420	A70	11c Lion	.20	.20
421	A70	13c Warthog	.20	.20
422	A70	15c Giraffe	.20	.20
423	A70	17c Zebra	.20	.20
424	A71	21c shown	.20	.20
425	A71	25c Goba Falls	.35	.35
426	A71	30c Inyangombe Falls	.40	.55
426A	A71	40c Bundi Falls	7.75	5.25
427	A71	$1 Bridal Veil Falls	.55	2.25
428	A71	$2 Victoria Falls	.95	4.00
		Nos. 414-428 (16)	13.00	14.90

Rotary International, 75th Anniversary — A72

1980, June 18			Perf. 14½	
429	A72	4c multicolored	.20	.20
430	A72	13c multicolored	.20	.30
431	A72	21c multicolored	.25	.50
432	A72	25c multicolored	.35	.75
a.		Souvenir sheet of 4, #429-432	1.40	1.40
		Nos. 429-432 (4)	1.00	1.75

Olympic Rings
A73

1980, July 19				
433	A73	17c multicolored	.30	.35

22nd Summer Olympic Games, Moscow, July 19-Aug. 3.

Gatooma Post Office, 1912
A74

Post Offices: 7c, Salisbury, 1912. 9c, Umtali, 1901. 17c, Bulawayo, 1895.

1980			Litho.	Perf. 14½
434	A74	5c multicolored	.20	.20
435	A74	7c multicolored	.20	.20
436	A74	9c multicolored	.20	.20
437	A74	17c multicolored	.25	.25
a.		Souvenir sheet of 4, #434-437	1.00	1.00
		Nos. 434-437 (4)	.85	.85

Post Office Savings Bank, 75th anniv.

Intl. Year of the Disabled — A75   Natl. Tree Day — A76

Designs: Various disabilities. Nos. 438-441 form a continuous design.

1981, Sept. 23			Litho.	Perf. 14½
438	A75	5c multicolored	.20	.20
439	A75	7c multicolored	.20	.20
440	A75	11c multicolored	.20	.20
441	A75	17c multicolored	.50	.50
		Nos. 438-441 (4)	1.10	1.10

1981, Dec. 4				
442	A76	5c Msasa	.20	.20
443	A76	7c Mopane	.20	.20
444	A76	21c Flat-crowned acacia	.70	.70
445	A76	30c Pod mahogany	.90	.90
		Nos. 442-445 (4)	2.00	2.00

Rock Paintings
A77

Designs: 9c, Khoisan figures, Gwamgwadza Cave. 11c, Kudus, human figures, Epworth Mission. 17c, Diana's Vow, Rusape. 21c, Giraffes, Gwamgwadza Cave. 25c, Warthog, Mucheka Cave. 30c, Hunters, Shinzwini Shelter.

1982, Mar. 17			Litho.	Perf. 14½
446	A77	9c multicolored	.75	.75
447	A77	11c multicolored	.90	.90
448	A77	17c multicolored	1.25	1.25
449	A77	21c multicolored	1.75	1.75
450	A77	25c multicolored	1.75	1.75
451	A77	30c multicolored	2.75	2.75
		Nos. 446-451 (6)	9.15	9.15

Scouting Year — A78

1982, July 21				
452	A78	9c Emblem	.35	.35
453	A78	11c Campfire	.40	.40
454	A78	21c Map reading	.75	.75
455	A78	30c Baden Powell	1.00	1.00
		Nos. 452-455 (4)	2.50	2.50

TB Bacillus Centenary
A79

1982, Nov. 17			Perf. 14½	
456	A79	11c Koch	1.00	1.25
457	A79	30c Scientist examining slide	2.00	2.25

Commonwealth Day — A80

Sculptures: 9c, Wing Woman, by Henry Mudzengerere, vert. 11c, Telling Secrets, by Joseph Ndandarika. 30c, Hornbill Man, by John Takawira. $1, The Chief, by Nicholas Mukomberanwa, vert.

1983, Mar. 14   **Perf. 14½**
458	A80	9c multicolored	.20	.20
459	A80	11c multicolored	.20	.20
460	A80	30c multicolored	.30	.35
461	A80	$1 multicolored	.80	1.50
		Nos. 458-461 (4)	1.50	2.25

World Plowing Contest, May — A81

No. 463, mechanized plowing.

1983, May 13   **Litho.**   **Perf. 14½**
462	A81	Pair	.70	.70
a.-b.		21c, any single	.35	.35
463	A81	Pair	.90	.90
a.-b.		30c, any single	.45	.45

World Communications Year — A82

Means of communication and transportation. Nos. 464-467 vert.

1983, Oct. 12   **Litho.**   **Perf. 14½**
464	A82	9c Mailman	.20	.20
465	A82	11c Signaling airplane	.30	.30
466	A82	15c Telephone operators	.45	.45
467	A82	17c Reading newspapers	.60	.60
468	A82	21c Truck on highway	.70	.70
469	A82	30c Train	1.00	1.00
		Nos. 464-469 (6)	3.25	3.25

Zimbabwe Intl. Trade Fair, Bulawayo, May 5-13 — A83

1984, Apr. 11   **Litho.**   **Perf. 14½**
470	A83	9c shown	.20	.20
471	A83	11c Globe	.20	.20
472	A83	30c Emblem	.80	.80
		Nos. 470-472 (3)	1.20	1.20

1984 Summer Olympics A84

Children's Drawings.

1984, July 18   **Litho.**   **Perf. 14½**
473	A84	11c Bicycling	.30	.20
474	A84	21c Swimming	.65	.65
475	A84	30c Running	1.00	1.00
476	A84	40c Hurdles	1.40	2.25
		Nos. 473-476 (4)	3.35	4.10

Heroes' Day A85

1984, Aug. 8   **Litho.**   **Perf. 14½**
477	A85	9c Heroes	.20	.20
478	A85	11c Monument, vert.	.25	.25
479	A85	17c Statue, vert.	.45	.45
480	A85	30c Bas-relief	.75	.75
		Nos. 477-480 (4)	1.65	1.65

Fish Eagle — A86

1984, Oct. 10   **Litho.**   **Perf. 14½**
481	A86	9c shown	.75	.75
482	A86	11c Long crested eagle	.80	.80
483	A86	13c Bateleur	.90	.90
484	A86	17c Black eagle	1.25	1.25
485	A86	21c Martial eagle	1.50	1.50
486	A86	30c African hawk eagle	2.10	2.10
		Nos. 481-486 (6)	7.30	7.30

Superheat Engine No. 86, Mashonaland Railways, 1918 — A87

Steam locomotives: 11c, Engine No. 190, North British Locomotive Co., 1926. 17c, Engine No. 424, Beyer Peacock & Co., 1950. Engine No. 726, Beyer Peacock & Co., 1957.

1985, May 15   **Litho.**
487	A87	9c multicolored	1.00	1.00
488	A87	11c multicolored	1.40	1.40
489	A87	17c multicolored	2.10	2.10
490	A87	30c multicolored	3.75	3.75
		Nos. 487-490 (4)	8.25	8.25

INTELSAT V A88

57c, Mazowe Earth Satellite Station.

Perf. 14½x14, 14½
1985, July 8   **Litho.**
491	A88	26c multicolored	2.10	2.40

Size: 62x23mm
492	A88	57c multicolored	4.25	4.75

Zimbabwe Bird and Tobacco — A89

Agriculture and industry.

Perf. 14¾x14½
1985, Aug. 21   **Litho.**
493	A89	1c shown	.20	.20
a.		Perf 14¼x13¾	—	—
494	A89	3c Corn	.20	.20
495	A89	4c Cotton	.20	.20
a.		Perf 14¼x13¾	—	—
496	A89	5c Tea	.45	.20
497	A89	10c Cattle	.45	.20
a.		Perf 14¼x13¾	—	—
498	A89	11c Birchenough Bridge	1.10	.20
499	A89	12c Stamp mill	1.75	.20
500	A89	13c Gold production	3.25	.20
501	A89	15c Coal mining	2.50	.20
a.		Perf 14¼x13¾	—	—
502	A89	17c Amethyst mining	3.25	.45
503	A89	18c Electric train	3.25	.45
504	A89	20c Kariba Dam	2.25	.20
a.		Perf 14¼x13¾	—	—
505	A89	23c Elephants	3.50	.45
506	A89	25c Zambezi River sunset	.90	.45
507	A89	26c Baobab tree	.90	.30
508	A89	30c Great Zimbabwe ruins	1.10	.45
509	A89	35c Folk dancing	.90	.45
510	A89	45c Crushing corn	1.10	.60
511	A89	57c Wood carving	1.10	1.00
512	A89	$1 Mbira drum	1.75	1.25
513	A89	$2 Mule-drawn scotch cart	3.00	4.00
514	A89	$5 Natl. coat of arms	5.50	7.00
		Nos. 493-514 (22)	38.60	18.85

Natl. Archives, 50th Anniv. A90

Designs: 12c, Gatsi Rusere (c. 1589-1623), ruler of Mashonaland and Zambezi area; mutapa, 17th cent. 18c, Lobengula, ruler of Ndebele State (1870-94), sketch by E. A. Maund, 1889; 1888 Moffat Treaty and elephant seal. 26c, Archives exhibition hall. 35c, Archives building.

1985, Sept. 18   **Perf. 14½**
515	A90	12c multicolored	.20	.20
516	A90	18c multicolored	.30	.30
517	A90	26c multicolored	.45	.45
518	A90	35c multicolored	.65	.65
		Nos. 515-518 (4)	1.60	1.60

UN Decade for Women A91

1985, Nov. 13
519	A91	10c Computer operator	.70	.70
520	A91	17c Nurse, child	1.00	1.00
521	A91	26c Engineer	1.75	1.75
		Nos. 519-521 (3)	3.45	3.45

Harare Conference Center — A92

1986, Jan. 29   **Litho.**   **Perf. 14½**
523	A92	26c Facade	.90	.90
524	A92	35c Interior	1.60	1.60

Southern African Development Coordination Conference — A93

1986, Apr. 1   **Perf. 14½**
525	A93	12c Grain elevators	.50	.50
526	A93	18c Rhinoceros	2.75	2.75
527	A93	26c Map, jet	2.75	2.75
528	A93	35c Map, flags	3.00	3.00
		Nos. 525-528 (4)	9.00	9.00

Moths — A94

1986, June 18   **Litho.**   **Perf. 14½x14**
529	A94	12c Jackson's emperor	1.60	1.60
530	A94	18c Oleander hawk	2.10	2.10
531	A94	26c Zaddach's emperor	2.75	2.75
532	A94	35c Southern marbled emperor	3.25	3.25
		Nos. 529-532 (4)	9.70	9.70

8th Non-aligned Summit Conference A95

1986, Aug. 28   **Litho.**   **Perf. 14½x14**
533	A95	26c Victoria Falls	3.25	3.25

Size: 66x26mm
Perf. 14½
534	A95	$1 Great Zimbabwe Enclosure	7.50	7.50

Motoring Cent. A96

1986, Oct. 8   **Perf. 14½**
535	A96	10c Sopwith, 1921	.75	.75
536	A96	12c Gladiator, 1902	.75	.75
537	A96	17c Douglas, 1920	1.10	1.10
538	A96	26c Ford Model-A, 1930	1.75	1.75
539	A96	35c Schacht, 1909	2.25	2.25
540	A96	40c Benz Velocipede, 1886	2.25	2.25
		Nos. 535-540 (6)	8.85	8.85

A97

A98

UN Child Survival Campaign: a, Growth monitoring. b, Breast-feeding. c, Oral rehydration. d, Immunization.

1987, Feb. 11   **Litho.**   **Perf. 14x14½**
541		Block of 4	9.00	9.00
a.-d.	A97	12c any single	2.00	2.00

1987, Apr. 15   **Perf. 14½**

Indigenous owls.

542	A98	12c Barred	2.75	2.75
543	A98	18c Pearl-spotted	3.50	3.50
544	A98	26c White-faced	4.00	4.00
545	A98	35c Scops	6.25	6.25
		Nos. 542-545 (4)	16.50	16.50

Natl. Girl Guides Movement, 75th Anniv. — A99

1987, June 24
546	A99	15c	Commitment	.80	.80
547	A99	23c	Adventure	1.00	1.00
548	A99	35c	Service	1.25	1.25
549	A99	$1	Intl. friendship	2.75	2.75
			Nos. 546-549 (4)	5.80	5.80

Duikers and Population Maps — A100

1987, Oct. 7   Perf. 14½x14
550	A100	15c	Common gray	1.10	1.10
551	A100	23c	Zebra	1.25	1.25
552	A100	25c	Yellow-backed	1.25	1.25
553	A100	30c	Blue	1.50	1.50
554	A100	35c	Jentink's	1.50	1.50
555	A100	38c	Red	1.50	1.50
			Nos. 550-555 (6)	8.10	8.10

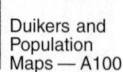

Insects A101

1988, Jan. 12   Litho.   Perf. 14½
556	A101	15c	Praying mantis	1.00	.20
557	A101	23c	Scarab beetle	1.40	.50
558	A101	35c	Short-horned grasshopper	1.90	1.50
559	A101	45c	Giant shield bug	2.25	3.75
			Nos. 556-559 (4)	6.55	5.95

Natl. Gallery of Art, 30th Anniv. — A102

Aloes and Succulents A103

Sculpture and paintings: 15c, Cockerel, by Arthur Azevedo. 23c, Changeling, by Bernard Matemera. 30c, Spirit Python, by Henry Munyaradzi. 35c, Spirit Bird Carrying People, by Thomas Mukarobgwa, horiz. 38c, The Song of the Shepherd Boy, by George Nene, horiz. 45c, War Victim, by Joseph Muzondo, horiz.

Perf. 14x14½, 14½x14
1988, Apr. 14   Litho.
560	A102	15c	multicolored	.30	.30
561	A102	23c	multicolored	.45	.45
562	A102	30c	multicolored	.60	.60
563	A102	35c	multicolored	.80	.80
564	A102	38c	multicolored	.80	.80
565	A102	45c	multicolored	.95	.95
			Nos. 560-565 (6)	3.90	3.90

1988, July 14   Perf. 14½
566	A103	15c	Aloe cameronii bondana	.40	.40
567	A103	23c	Orbeopsis caudata	.75	.75
568	A103	25c	Euphorbia wildii	.75	.75
569	A103	30c	Euphorbia fortissima	.85	.85
570	A103	35c	Aloe aculeata	.85	.85
571	A103	38c	Huernia zebrina	1.10	1.10
			Nos. 566-571 (6)	4.70	4.70

A104

1988, Oct. 6   Litho.   Perf. 14½x14
572	A104	15c	White-faced duck	1.10	.20
573	A104	23c	Pygmy goose	1.25	.45
574	A104	30c	Hottentot teal	1.40	1.40
575	A104	35c	Knob-billed duck	1.60	1.60
576	A104	38c	White-backed duck	1.75	1.75
577	A104	45c	Maccoa	2.40	3.25
			Nos. 572-577 (6)	9.50	8.65

Geckos A105

1989, Jan. 10   Litho.   Perf. 14½
578	A105	15c	O'Shaughnessy's banded	1.25	1.25
579	A105	23c	Tiger rock	1.40	1.40
580	A105	35c	Tasman's	2.25	2.25
581	A105	45c	Bibron's	2.50	2.50
			Nos. 578-581 (4)	7.40	7.40

Wildflowers A106

1989, Apr. 12   Litho.   Perf. 14½
582	A106	15c	Spotted-leaved arum-lily	.60	.60
583	A106	23c	Grassland vlei-lily	.75	.75
584	A106	30c	Manica protea	.75	.75
585	A106	35c	Flame lily	.90	.90
586	A106	38c	Poppy hibiscus	1.00	1.00
587	A106	45c	Blue sesbania	1.10	1.10
			Nos. 582-587 (6)	5.10	5.10

Fish A107

1989, July 12   Litho.   Perf. 14½
588	A107	15c	Red-breasted bream	.90	.20
589	A107	23c	Chessa	1.10	.20
590	A107	30c	Eastern bottle-nose	1.25	1.00
591	A107	35c	Vundu	1.25	1.00
592	A107	38c	Largemouth black bass	1.50	1.50
593	A107	45c	Tiger fish	2.00	2.40
			Nos. 588-593 (6)	8.00	6.30

See Nos. 696-701.

Endangered Species A108

1989   Litho.   Perf. 14½x14
594	A108	15c	Black rhinoceros	1.90	1.90
595	A108	23c	Cheetah	2.25	2.25
596	A108	30c	Wild dog	2.40	2.40
597	A108	35c	Pangolin	2.40	2.40
598	A108	38c	Brown hyena	2.50	2.50
599	A108	45c	Roan antelope	2.75	2.75
			Nos. 594-599 (6)	14.20	14.20

Achievements, 1980-1990 A109

1990, Apr. 17   Litho.   Perf. 14½x14
600	A109	15c	Unity accord	.65	.20
601	A109	23c	Conference center	.75	.20
602	A109	30c	Education	.85	.85
603	A109	35c	Satellite dish	1.00	1.00
604	A109	38c	Sports stadium	1.00	1.00
605	A109	45c	Agriculture	1.60	2.75
			Nos. 600-605 (6)	5.85	6.00

City of Harare, Cent. A110

1990, July 11   Litho.   Perf. 14½
606	A110	15c	Runhare house, 1986	.60	.60
607	A110	23c	Market hall, 1894	.85	.85
608	A110	30c	Charter house, 1959	.90	.90
609	A110	35c	Supreme Court, 1927	1.00	1.00
610	A110	38c	Standard Chartered Bank, 1911	1.00	1.00
611	A110	45c	Town house, 1933	1.50	1.50
			Nos. 606-611 (6)	5.85	5.85

36th Commonwealth Parliamentary Conf. — A111

1990, Sept. 17
612	A111	35c	Speaker's mace	.75	.75
613	A111	$1	Speaker's chair	2.25	2.25

Animals — A112

Hand Crafts — A113

Transportation — A114

Perf. 14, 14¾x14½ (#615, 617, 619), 14½x14 (#620-625), 14¼ (#626)
1990, Jan. 2   Litho.
614	A112	1c	Tiger fish	.20	.20
a.			Perf 14¾x14½	—	—
615	A112	2c	Helmeted guineafowl	.95	.95
616	A112	3c	Scrub hare	.20	.20
a.			Perf 14¾x14½	—	—
617	A112	4c	Pangolin	.20	.20
a.			Perf 14x13½	—	—
618	A112	5c	Greater kudu	.85	.85
619	A112	9c	Black rhinoceros	2.40	2.40
a.			Perf 14	—	—
620	A113	15c	Head rest	.20	.20
621	A113	20c	Hand axe	.20	.20

622	A113	23c	Gourd, water pot	.20	.20
623	A113	25c	Snuff box	.20	.20
624	A113	26c	Winnowing basket	.65	.65
625	A113	30c	Grinding stone	.65	.65
626	A114	33c	Riding bicycles	1.50	1.50
627	A114	35c	Buses	2.40	2.40
628	A114	38c	Train	2.40	2.40
629	A114	45c	Motorcycle, trailer	2.40	2.40
630	A114	$1	Jet	4.00	4.00
631	A114	$2	Tractor-trailer truck	4.00	4.00
			Nos. 614-631 (18)	23.60	23.60

Animals A115

A116

1991, Jan. 15   Litho.   Perf. 14½x14
632	A115	15c	Small-spotted genet	1.40	1.40
633	A115	23c	Red squirrel	1.50	1.50
634	A115	35c	Night ape	2.10	2.10
635	A115	45c	Bat-eared fox	3.00	3.00
			Nos. 632-635 (4)	8.00	8.00

1991, Apr. 16   Litho.   Perf. 14½

Traditional musical instruments.
636	A116	15c	Hosho	.80	.20
637	A116	23c	Mbira	.85	.20
638	A116	30c	Ngororombe	.95	.95
639	A116	35c	Chipendani	1.25	1.25
640	A116	38c	Marimba	1.25	1.25
641	A116	45c	Ngoma	1.40	1.90
			Nos. 636-641 (6)	6.50	5.75

Wild Fruits — A117

A118

1991, July 17   Litho.   Perf. 14x14½
642	A117	20c	Snot-apple	.75	.75
643	A117	39c	Marula	.90	.90
644	A117	51c	Mobola plum	1.00	1.00
645	A117	60c	Water berry	1.10	1.10
646	A117	65c	Northern dwaba berry	1.25	1.25
647	A117	77c	Mahobohobo	1.50	1.50
			Nos. 642-647 (6)	6.50	6.50

See Nos. 870-875.

1991, Oct. 16   Litho.   Perf. 14½
648	A118	20c	Bridal Veil Falls	1.50	1.50
649	A118	39c	Conference Emblem	1.50	1.50
650	A118	51c	Chinhoyi Caves	2.00	2.00
651	A118	60c	Kariba Dam Wall	2.25	2.25
652	A118	65c	Victoria Falls	2.50	2.50

653 A118 77c Balancing
         Rocks   2.50 2.50
Nos. 648-653 (6)   12.25 12.25
Commonwealth Heads of Government
meeting, Harare.

Wild Cats
A119

1992, Jan. 8   Litho.   *Perf. 14½*
654 A119 20c Lion   1.25 .20
655 A119 39c Leopard   2.00 .90
656 A119 60c Cheetah   3.00 3.00
657 A119 77c Serval   4.00 3.75
Nos. 654-657 (4)   10.25 7.85

Mushrooms
A120

Birds — A121

Designs: 20c, Amanita zambiana. 39c,
Boletus edulis. 51c, Termitomyces. 60c,
Cantharellus densifolius. 65c, Cantharellus
longisporus. 77c, Cantharellus cibarius.

1992, Apr. 8   Litho.   *Perf. 14x14½*
658 A120 20c multicolored   1.25 1.25
659 A120 39c multicolored   1.50 1.50
660 A120 51c multicolored   1.60 1.60
661 A120 60c multicolored   1.75 1.75
662 A120 65c multicolored   2.10 2.10
663 A120 77c multicolored   2.75 2.75
Nos. 658-663 (6)   10.95 10.95

1992, July 17   Litho.   *Perf. 14½*
664 A121 25c Blackeyed bul-
        bul   1.50 1.50
665 A121 59c Fiscal shrike   2.00 2.00
666 A121 77c Forktailed
        drongo   2.25 2.25
667 A121 90c Cardinal
        woodpecker   2.50 2.50
668 A121 98c Yellowbilled
        hornbill   2.50 2.50
669 A121 $1.16 Crested fran-
        colin   2.75 2.75
Nos. 664-669 (6)   13.50 13.50

Butterflies
A122

1992, Oct. 15   Litho.   *Perf. 14½x14*
670 A122 25c Foxy charaxes   1.40 1.40
671 A122 59c Orange & lem-
        on   2.50 2.50
672 A122 77c Emperor swal-
        lowtail   3.00 3.00
673 A122 90c Blue pansy   3.50 3.50
674 A122 98c African mon-
        arch   3.75 3.75
675 A122 $1.16 Gaudy com-
        modore   4.25 4.25
Nos. 670-675 (6)   18.40 18.40

Minerals
A123

Owls — A124

1993, Jan. 12   Litho.   *Perf. 14½x14*
676 A123 25c Autunite   2.10 2.10
677 A123 59c Chromite   3.00 3.00
678 A123 77c Azurite   2.75 2.75
679 A123 90c Coal   4.25 4.25
680 A123 98c Gold   4.50 4.50
681 A123 $1.16 Emerald   5.75 5.75
Nos. 676-681 (6)   22.35 22.35

1993, Apr. 6   Litho.   *Perf. 14½*
682 A124 25c Wood owl   3.50 3.50
683 A124 59c Pels fishing
        owl   4.50 4.50
684 A124 90c Spotted eagle
        owl   6.50 6.50
685 A124 $1.16 Giant eagle
        owl   8.50 8.50
Nos. 682-685 (4)   23.00 23.00

Household
Pottery
A125

Orchids — A126

1993, July 13   Litho.   *Perf. 14½x14*
686 A125 25c Hadyana   1.00 1.00
687 A125 59c Chirongo   1.25 1.25
688 A125 77c Mbiya   1.50 1.50
689 A125 90c Pfuko   1.75 1.75
690 A125 98c Tsaya   2.00 2.00
691 A125 $1.16 Gate   2.40 2.40
Nos. 686-691 (6)   9.90 9.90

1993, Oct. 12   Litho.   *Perf. 14½*
692 A126 35c Polystachya
        dendrobiflora   1.10 1.10
693 A126 $1 Diaphananthe
        subsimplex   2.25 2.25
694 A126 $1.50 Ansellia gi-
        gantea   3.50 3.50
695 A126 $1.95 Vanilla poly-
        epis   4.50 4.50
Nos. 692-695 (4)   11.35 11.35

Fish Type of 1989

1994, Jan. 20   Litho.   *Perf. 14½*
696 A107 35c Hunyani salmon   .50 .50
697 A107 $1 Barbel   1.00 1.00
698 A107 $1.30 Rainbow trout   1.25 1.25
699 A107 $1.50 Mottled eel   1.50 1.50
700 A107 $1.65 Mirror carp   1.75 1.75
701 A107 $1.95 Robustus bream   2.00 2.00
Nos. 696-701 (6)   8.00 8.00

City of
Bulawayo,
Cent.
A127

1994, Apr. 5   Litho.   *Perf. 14½*
702 A127 35c City Hall   .55 .55
703 A127 80c Cresta Churchill
        Hotel   .55 .55
704 A127 $1.15 High Court   .85 .85
705 A127 $1.75 Douslin House   1.10 1.10
706 A127 $1.95 Goldfields Build-
        ing   1.40 1.40
707 A127 $2.30 Parkade Centre   1.50 1.50
Nos. 702-707 (6)   5.95 5.95

Export
Flowers — A128

Christmas — A129

1994, July 12   Litho.   *Perf. 14½*
708 A128 35c Strelitzia   .75 .75
709 A128 80c Protea   .75 .75
710 A128 $1.15 Phlox   1.25 1.25
711 A128 $1.75 Chrysanthemum   1.75 1.75
712 A128 $1.95 Lillum   1.90 1.90
713 A128 $2.30 Rose   2.25 2.25
Nos. 708-713 (6)   8.65 8.65

1994, Oct. 11   Litho.   *Perf. 14½*
Designs: 35c, Archangel Gabriel, Virgin
Mary. 80c, Mary, Joseph on way to Bethlehem. $1.15, Nativity scene. $1.75, Angel
pointing way to shepherds. $1.95, Magi follow-
ing star. $2.30, Madonna and child.

714 A129 35c multicolored   .95 .95
715 A129 80c multicolored   .95 .95
716 A129 $1.15 multicolored   1.40 1.40
717 A129 $1.75 multicolored   1.75 1.75
718 A129 $1.95 multicolored   2.40 2.40
719 A129 $2.30 multicolored   2.50 2.50
Nos. 714-719 (6)   9.95 9.95

A130

1995-96   Litho.   *Perf. 14*
720 A130 1c Corn   .40 .40
721 A130 2c Sugar cane   .40 .40
722 A130 3c Sunflowers   .40 .40
723 A130 4c Sorghum   .40 .40
724 A130 5c Mine workers   .40 .40
725 A130 10c Underground
        mining   .40 .40
726 A130 20c Coal mining   .40 .40
727 A130 30c Chrome
        smelting   .40 .40
728 A130 40c Opencast
        mining   .40 .40
728A A130 45c Underground
        drilling   .40 .40
729 A130 50c Gold smelting   .40 .40
730 A130 70c Boggie Clock
        Tower   .40 .40
731 A130 80c Masvingo
        Watchtower   .40 .40
732 A130 $1 Hanging tree   .50 .50
733 A130 $2 Cecil House   .95 .95
734 A130 $5 The To-
        poscope   2.40 2.40
735 A130 $10 Paper House   4.75 4.75
Nos. 720-735 (17)   13.80 13.80
Issued: 45c, 6/3/96; others, 1/17/95.

Insects
A131

1995, Apr. 4   Litho.   *Perf. 14½*
736 A131 35c Spider-hunting
        wasp   1.40 1.40
737 A131 $1.15 Emperor drag-
        onfly   2.10 2.10
738 A131 $1.75 Foxy charaxes   2.75 2.75
739 A131 $2.30 Antlion   3.75 3.75
Nos. 736-739 (4)   10.00 10.00

6th All Africa
Games,
Harare — A132

1995, July 11   Litho.   *Perf. 14x14½*
740 A132 35c Soccer   1.00 1.00
741 A132 80c Track   1.00 1.00
742 A132 $1.15 Boxing   1.50 1.50
743 A132 $1.75 Swimming   2.00 2.00
744 A132 $1.95 Field hockey   2.25 2.25
745 A132 $2.30 Volleyball   2.75 2.75
Nos. 740-745 (6)   10.50 10.50

UN, 50th
Anniv. — A133

1995, Oct. 17   Litho.   *Perf. 14½*
746 A133 35c Health   .40 .40
747 A133 $1.15 Environment   .65 .65
748 A133 $1.75 Food distribution   .80 .80
749 A133 $2.30 Education   1.10 1.10
Nos. 746-749 (4)   2.95 2.95

Flowering
Trees — A134

1996, Jan. 24   Litho.   *Perf. 14½*
750 A134 45c Fernandoa   .40 .40
751 A134 $1 Round leaf
        mukwa   .40 .40
752 A134 $1.50 Luckybean tree   .80 .80
753 A134 $2.20 Winter cassia   1.25 1.25
754 A134 $2.50 Sausage tree   1.40 1.40
755 A134 $3 Sweet thorn   1.75 1.75
Nos. 750-755 (6)   6.00 6.00

Dams of
Zimbabwe
A135

1996, Apr. 9   Litho.   *Perf. 14½*
756 A135 45c Mazvikadei   .45 .45
757 A135 $1.50 Mutirikwi   .80 .80
758 A135 $2.20 Ncema   1.25 1.25
759 A135 $3 Odzani   1.50 1.50
Nos. 756-759 (4)   4.00 4.00

Scenic
Views
A136

Designs: 45c, Matusadonha Natl. Park.
$1.50, Juliasdale Rocky Outcrops. $2.20,
Honde Valley. $3, Finger Rocks, Morgenster
Mission.

1996, July 18   Litho.   *Perf. 14½*
760 A136 45c multicolored   .45 .45
761 A136 $1.50 multicolored   .65 .65
762 A136 $2.20 multicolored   1.00 1.00
763 A136 $3 multicolored   1.40 1.40
Nos. 760-763 (4)   3.50 3.50

Wood
Carvings
A137

1996, Oct. 15   Litho.   Perf. 14½
764	A137	45c Frog	.35	.35
765	A137	$1.50 Tortoise	.50	.50
766	A137	$1.70 Kudu	.60	.60
767	A137	$2.20 Chimpanzee	.75	.75
768	A137	$2.50 Porcupine	.90	.90
769	A137	$3 Rhinoceros	1.00	1.00
		Nos. 764-769 (6)	4.10	4.10

Cattle
A138

1997, Jan. 7   Litho.   Perf. 14½
770	A138	45c Mashona cow	.70	.70
771	A138	$1.50 Tuli cow	1.10	1.10
772	A138	$2.20 Nkoni bull	1.40	1.40
773	A138	$3 Brahman bull	2.00	2.00
		Nos. 770-773 (4)	5.20	5.20

Convention on Intl. Trade in
Endangered Species of Flora and
Fauna (CITES) — A139

1997, Apr. 15   Litho.   Perf. 14½
774	A139	45c Cycad	.60	.60
775	A139	$1.50 Peregrine falcon	.75	.75
776	A139	$1.70 Pangolin	.90	.90
777	A139	$2.20 Black rhinoceros	1.25	1.25
778	A139	$2.50 Elephant	1.40	1.40
779	A139	$3 Python	1.75	1.75
		Nos. 774-779 (6)	6.65	6.65

Aspects of
Rural Life
A140

1997, July 22   Litho.   Perf. 14½
780	A140	65c Carving	.20	.20
781	A140	$1 Winnowing	.20	.20
782	A140	$2.40 Dancing	.70	.70
783	A140	$2.50 Plowing	.80	.80
784	A140	$3.10 Stamping	1.00	1.00
785	A140	$4.20 Fetching water	1.50	1.50
		Nos. 780-785 (6)	4.40	4.40

Zimbabwe
Railway,
Cent.
A141

1997, Oct. 28   Litho.   Perf. 14½
786	A141	65c Passenger coach	.40	.40
787	A141	$1 12th Class, No. 257	.40	.40
788	A141	$2.40 16A Class, No. 605	.85	.85
789	A141	$2.50 El 1, No. 4107	.85	.85
790	A141	$3.10 Jack Tar	1.10	1.10
791	A141	$4.20 DE 2, No. 1211	1.40	1.40
		Nos. 786-791 (6)	5.00	5.00

Wildlife
A142

1998, Jan. 20   Litho.   Perf. 14½
792	A142	65c Aardwolf	.55	.55
793	A142	$2.40 Large gray mongoose	.70	.70
794	A142	$3.10 Clawless otter	1.00	1.00
795	A142	$4.20 Antbear (Aardvark)	1.25	1.25
		Nos. 792-795 (4)	3.50	3.50

Apiculture
A143

Designs: $1.20, Honeybee on flower. $4.10,
Queen, worker, drone. $4.70, Queen, retinue.
$5.60, Rural beekeeper. $7.40, Commercial
beekeepers. $9.90, Products of the hive.

1998, Apr. 14   Litho.   Perf. 14
796	A143	$1.20 multicolored	.35	.35
797	A143	$4.10 multicolored	.90	.90
798	A143	$4.70 multicolored	1.00	1.00
799	A143	$5.60 multicolored	1.25	1.25
800	A143	$7.40 multicolored	1.50	1.50
801	A143	$9.90 multicolored	2.00	2.00
		Nos. 796-801 (6)	7.00	7.00

Fossils
A144

1998, July 21   Litho.   Perf. 14½
802	A144	$1.20 Fossil fish	1.10	.45
803	A144	$5.60 Allosaurus footprints	1.60	.95
804	A144	$7.40 Massospondylus	1.90	1.60
805	A144	$9.90 Fossil wood	2.40	2.40
		Nos. 802-805 (4)	7.00	5.40

Birds — A145

Designs: $1.20, Yellow-bellied sunbird.
$4.10, Lesser blue-eared starling. $4.70,
Greyhooded kingfisher. $5.60, Mombo gray tit.
$7.40, Chirinda apalis. $9.90, Swynnerton's
robin.

1998, Oct. 20   Litho.   Perf. 14
806	A145	$1.20 multicolored	.85	.85
807	A145	$4.10 multicolored	1.00	1.00
808	A145	$4.70 multicolored	1.25	1.25
809	A145	$5.60 multicolored	1.50	1.50
810	A145	$7.40 multicolored	1.75	1.75
811	A145	$9.90 multicolored	2.25	2.25
		Nos. 806-811 (6)	8.60	8.60

UPU, 125th
Anniv. — A146

$1.20, Counter services at Post Office and
Philatelic Bureau. $5.60, Postman delivering
mail on bicycle. $7.40, 19th cent. runner,
EMS, PTC delivery today. $9.90, Harare Central Sorting Office.

1999, Jan. 19   Litho.   Perf. 14
812	A146	$1.20 multicolored	.70	.70
813	A146	$5.60 multicolored	.95	.95
814	A146	$7.40 multicolored	1.25	1.25
815	A146	$9.90 multicolored	1.60	1.60
		Nos. 812-815 (4)	4.50	4.50

A147

A148

Wild cats of Zimbabwe.

1999, Mar. 16   Litho.   Perf. 14
816	A147	$1.20 Serval	.65	.65
817	A147	$5.60 Cheetah	1.00	1.00
818	A147	$7.40 Caracal	1.40	1.40
819	A147	$9.90 Leopard	1.90	1.90
		Nos. 816-819 (4)	4.95	4.95

1999, June 8   Litho.   Perf. 14¼
Owls.
820	A148	$1.20 Cape eagle owl	1.50	1.50
821	A148	$5.60 Grass owl	2.40	2.40
822	A148	$7.40 Barn owl	3.00	3.00
823	A148	$9.90 Marsh owl	3.75	3.75
		Nos. 820-823 (4)	10.65	10.65

Tourist
Activities
A149

1999, Aug. 10   Litho.   Perf. 14¼x14
824	A149	$2 Canoeing	.45	.45
825	A149	$6.70 Rock climbing	.80	.80
826	A149	$7.70 Microlighting	.90	.90
827	A149	$9.10 White water rafting	1.10	1.10
828	A149	$12 Scenic view	1.50	1.50
829	A149	$16 Viewing game	2.10	2.10
		Nos. 824-829 (6)	6.85	6.85

A150   A151

Christmas: $2, Christmas time — Family
time. $6.70, Christmas tree in Africa. $7.70,
Joy to you this Christmas. $9.10, Christmas
time — Flame lily time. $12, Glory to God &
Peace on Earth. $16, The House of
Christmas.

1999, Oct. 12   Litho.   Perf. 14x14¼
830	A150	$2 multi	.35	.35
831	A150	$6.70 multi	.65	.65
832	A150	$7.70 multi	.70	.45
833	A150	$9.10 multi	.95	.95
834	A150	$12 multi	1.25	1.25
835	A150	$16 multi	1.60	1.60
		Nos. 830-835 (6)	5.50	5.25

2000, Jan. 25   Litho.   Perf. 14¾
Designs: 1c, Nyala. 10c, Construction. 30c,
Timber. 50c, Tobacco auction floors. 70c,
Harare Central Sorting Office. 80c, New international airport, Harare. $1, Westgate Shopping Complex. $2, Nile crocodile. $3, Pungwe

water project. $4, Zebra. $5, Mining. $7,
National University of Science and Technology. $10, Ostrich. $15, Cape parrot. $20,
Leather products. $30, Lilac-breasted roller.
$50, Victoria Falls. $100, Tokwe Mukorsi Dam.
836	A151	1c multi	.20	.20
837	A151	10c multi	.20	.20
838	A151	30c multi	.20	.20
839	A151	50c multi	.20	.20
840	A151	70c multi	.20	.20
841	A151	80c multi	.20	.20
842	A151	$1 multi	.20	.20
843	A151	$2 multi	.20	.20
844	A151	$3 multi	.20	.20
845	A151	$4 multi	.20	.20
846	A151	$5 multi	.30	.30
847	A151	$7 multi	.40	.40
848	A151	$10 multi	.65	.65
849	A151	$15 multi	1.10	1.10
850	A151	$20 multi	1.25	1.25
851	A151	$30 multi	1.90	1.90
852	A151	$50 multi	3.00	3.00
853	A151	$100 multi	6.25	6.25
		Nos. 836-853 (18)	16.85	16.85

Sports — A152

2000, Apr. 25   Litho.   Perf. 14
854	A152	$2 Basketball	.40	.40
855	A152	$6.70 Lawn tennis	.65	.65
856	A152	$7.70 Netball	.85	.85
857	A152	$9.10 Weight lifting	.95	.95
858	A152	$12 Taekwondo	1.25	1.25
859	A152	$16 Diving	1.75	1.75
		Nos. 854-859 (6)	5.85	5.85

Dr. Joshua
Nkomo (1917-
99), Vice-
President
A153

Designs: $2, $12, Wearing suit. $9.10, $16,
Wearing headdress.

2000, June 27   Litho.   Perf. 14x14¼
Background Color
860	A153	$2 blue	.55	.55
861	A153	$9.10 green	1.40	1.40
862	A153	$12 red	1.75	1.75
863	A153	$16 orange	2.25	2.25
		Nos. 860-863 (4)	5.95	5.95

Organizations
Combatting
Disease
A154

Designs: $2, Ministry of Health. $6.70,
Rehabilitation and Prevention of Tuberculosis
(RAPT). $7.70, New Start centers. $9.10, Riders for Health. $12, Natl. Aids Coordination
Program (NACP). $16, Rotary Intl.

2000, July 18   Litho.   Perf. 14¼x14
864	A154	$2 multi	.45	.45
865	A154	$6.70 multi	.75	.75
866	A154	$7.70 multi	.95	.95
867	A154	$9.10 multi	1.25	1.25
868	A154	$12 multi	1.50	1.50
869	A154	$16 multi	2.10	2.10
		Nos. 864-869 (6)	7.00	7.00

Wild Fruits Type of 1991
$2, Masawu. $6.70, Spiny monkey orange.
$7.70, Bird plum. $9.10, Shakama plum. $12,
Wild medlar. $16, Wild custard apple.

2000, Oct. 24   Litho.   Perf. 14x14½
870-875	A117	Set of 6	4.50	4.50

Aviation
A155

Designs: $8, Boeing 737-200. $12, BAe Hawk MK 60. $14, Hawker Hunter FGA-9. $16, Cessna/Reims F-337. $21, Aerospatiale Alouette III helicopter. $28, Boeing 767-200ER.

2001, Jan. 31   Litho.   Perf. 14¼
876-881 A155   Set of 6   6.50 6.50

Total Solar Eclipse, June 21, 2001 — A156

Designs: $8, Solar prominences. $21, Eclipse path over Africa. $28, Eclipse phases (62x24mm).

Perf. 14¼x14, 14½ ($28)
2001, Apr. 24   Litho.
882-884 A156   Set of 3   4.50 4.50

Folklore — A157

Designs: $8, The Hare Who Rode Horseback. $12, The Hippo Who Lost His Hair. $13, The Lion Who Was Saved by a Mouse. $16, The Bush Fowl Who Wakes the Sun. $21, The Chameleon Who Came Too Late. $28, The Tortoise Who Collected Wisdom.

2001, July 24   Litho.   Perf. 14x14¼
885-890 A157   Set of 6   6.00 6.00
  a. Souvenir sheet, #885-890   8.00 8.00

Heroes' Acre — A158

Designs: $8, Main entrance gate. $16, Statue of the Unknown Soldier. $21, General view. $28, Aerial view.

2001, Aug. 7   Litho.   Perf. 14¼x14
891-894 A158   Set of 4   5.00 5.00

Year of Dialogue Among Civilizations A159

Winning stamp design entry in: $8, National competition (Three Faces, by Nation Mandla Mguni). $21, International competition.

2001, Oct. 16   Litho.   Perf. 14¼
895-896 A159   Set of 2   4.00 4.00

Butterflies
A160

Designs: $12, Large blue charaxes. $20, Painted lady. $25, Yellow pansy. $30, Gold-banded forester. $35, Sapphire. $45, Clear-spotted acrea.

2001, Dec. 6   Litho.   Perf. 14¼x14
897-902 A160   Set of 6   12.00 12.00
  902a   Souvenir sheet, #897-902   12.00 12.00

Craftsmanship
A161

Designs: $12, Knitting and crocheting. $20, Art and design. $25, Basket making. $30, Pottery. $35, Wood carving. $45, Sculpture.

2002, Jan. 22
903-908 A161   Set of 6   12.00 12.00

Gemstones
A162

Designs: $12, Agate. $25, Aquamarine. $35, Diamond. $45, Emerald.

2002, Apr. 23   Litho.   Perf. 14¼x14
909-912 A162   Set of 4   12.00 12.00

Childline
A163

Children's art: $12, Children embracing. $25, Girl on phone. $35, Teddy bear. $45, Arm with phone receiver.

2002, June 4   Litho.   Perf. 14¼x14
913-916 A163   Set of 4   8.00 8.00

First Lady Sally Mugabe (1931-92) — A164

Various portraits: $20, $50, $70, $90.

2002, Aug. 6   Perf. 14x14¼
917-920 A164   Set of 4   14.50 14.50

Children's Stamp Design Contest Winners A165

Designs: $20, Mail runner and bicycle at post office, by Agreement Ngwenya. $70, Mail runner and airplane, by Kudzai Chikomo.

2002, Oct. 8   Litho.   Perf. 14¼
921-922 A165   Set of 2   6.00 6.00

Wild Flowers
A166

Designs: $20, Dissotis princeps. $35, Leonotis nepetifolia. $40, Hibiscus vitifolius. $50, Boophane disticha. $70, Pycnostachys urticifolia. $90, Gloriosa superba.

2002, Oct. 22   Perf. 14¼x14
923-928 A166   Set of 6   18.00 18.00
  928a   Souvenir sheet, #923-928   19.00 19.00

History Society of Zimbabwe, 50th Anniv. — A167

Map of Zimbabwe and: $30, Society emblem. $80, Hourglass, books, diploma. $110, People listening to speaker. $140, Old building.

2003, Jan. 28   Litho.   Perf. 14x14¼
929-932 A167   Set of 4   10.00 10.00

Harare Intl. Festival of the Arts — A168

Designs: $30, Festival emblem. $80, Emblem and flower. $110, Eye and flowers. $140, Emblem and flowers.

2003, Apr. 22   Litho.   Perf. 14x14¼
933-936 A168   Set of 4   5.00 5.00

Type of 2000

Designs: ($100), Bateleur eagle. $500, Goliath heron. $1000, White rhinoceros. $5000, Cheetah.

2003, June 24   Litho.   Perf. 14¾
937 A151 ($100) multi   .25 .25
938 A151 $500 multi   1.25 1.25
939 A151 $1000 multi   2.50 2.50
940 A151 $5000 multi   12.50 12.50
  Nos. 937-940 (4)   16.50 16.50

Spiders
A169

Designs: $150, Baboon spider. $200, Rain spider. $600, Black widow spider. $900, Wolf spider. $1250, Violin spider. $1600, Wall spider.

2003, July 30   Perf. 14¼
941-946 A169   Set of 6   11.50 11.50
  946a   Souvenir sheet, #941-946   11.50 11.50

Women Empowerment A170

Woman in cap and gown with: $300, Globe, hoe and briefcase. $2100, Traditional woman.

2003, Oct. 14   Litho.   Perf. 14¼
947-948 A170   Set of 2   6.00 6.00

Endangered Medicinal Herbs — A171

Designs: $200, Wild verbena. $500, Pimpernel. $1000, African arrowroot. $3000, Bird pepper. $4200, Wild garlic. $5400, Cleome.

2003, Oct. 28   Perf. 14x14¼
949-954 A171   Set of 6   24.50 24.50
  a. Miniature sheet, #949-954   24.50 24.50

Environmental Awareness A172

Designs: $500, Environment Africa. $3000, Sondela. $4200, Water Africa. $5400, Tree Africa.

2004, Feb. 17   Litho.   Perf. 14x14¼
955-958 A172   Set of 4   22.50 22.50

Medals — A173

Designs: $1500, Zimbabwe Independence Medal. $9000, Bronze Cross of Zimbabwe. $13,000, Silver Cross of Zimbabwe. $16,500, Gold Cross of Zimbabwe.

2004, Apr. 6   Litho.   Perf. 14¼
959-962 A173   Set of 4   65.00 65.00

Aloes — A174

Designs: $1500, Aloe ballii. $3,000, Aloe rhodesiana. $9000, Aloe greatheadii. $10,000, Aloe ortholopha. $13,000, Aloe inyangensis. $16,500, Aloe arborescens.

2004, July 20   Litho.   Perf. 14x14¼
963-968 A174   Set of 6   30.00 30.00
  968a   Miniature sheet, #963-968   30.00 30.00

Co-Vice President Simon Vengai Muzenda (1922-2003) A175

Background colors: $2300, Red. $12,000, Yellow. $17,000, Green. $22,000, Gray.

2004, Sept. 20   Litho.   Perf. 14x14¼
969-972 A175   Set of 4   40.00 40.00

Conservation
A176

Winning art in conservation stamp design contest: $4600, Butterfly, by Kingston Chigidhani. $33,500, Hands and wildlife, by Kudzai Chikomo.

2004, Oct. 26   Litho.   Perf. 14¼x14
973-974 A176   Set of 2   14.00 14.00

Miniature Sheet

Birds — A177

No. 975: a, $500, African fish eagles, national bird of Zambia. b, $1000, Purple-crested louries, national bird of Swaziland. c, $2300, African fish eagles, national bird of Zimbabwe. d, $3000, Blue cranes, national bird of South Africa. e, $5000, Cattle egrets, national bird of Botswana. f, $9000, Peregrine falcons, national bird of Angola. g, $12,000, Bar-tailed trogons. h, $17,000, African fish eagles, national bird of Namibia.

2004, Oct. 11   Litho.   Perf. 14
975 A177   Sheet of 8, #a-h   70.00 70.00

See Angola No. , Botswana Nos. 792-793, Malawi No. , Namibia No. 1052, South Africa No. 1342, Swaziland Nos. 727-735, and Zambia No. 1033.

Birds — A178

Designs: $500, Black-collared barbet. $5000, Gray-headed bush shrike. Z, Red-headed weaver. $10,000, Golden-breasted bunting. $20,000, Cut-throat finch. A, Cabanis's bunting. E, Miombo double-collared sunbird. R, Crested barbet. $50,000, Heuglin's robin. $100,000, Giant kingfisher.

2005, Feb. 8   Litho.   Perf. 14¾x14½
976 A178 $500 multi   .20   .20
977 A178 $5000 multi   1.75   1.75
978 A178 Z multi   2.25   2.25
979 A178 $10,000 multi 3.50   3.50
980 A178 $20,000 multi 6.75   6.75
981 A178 A multi   10.00 10.00
982 A178 E multi   13.00 13.00
983 A178 R multi   16.50 16.50
984 A178 $50,000 multi 16.50 16.50
985 A178 $100,000 multi 32.50 32.50
        Nos. 976-985 (10) 102.95 102.95

On day of issue No. 978 sold for $6900, No. 981 sold for $30,000, No. 982 sold for $40,000, and No. 983 sold for $50,000.

Clouds
A179

Designs: $6,900, Cirrus. $13,800, Nimbostratus. $30,000, Altocumulus. $40,000, Cumulonimbus.

2005, Apr. 26   Perf. 14¼
986-989 A179   Set of 4   17.50 17.50

Snakes — A180

Designs: $6900, Banded Egyptian cobra. $13,800, Puff adder. $20,000, Boomslang. $25,000, Mozambique spitting cobra. $30,000, Gaboon viper. $40,000, Black mamba.

2005, July 12   Litho.   Perf. 14¼x14
990-995 A180   Set of 6   16.00 16.00
995a   Miniature sheet, #990-995 16.00 16.00

Governmental
Officials — A181

Designs: $6900, Josiah Tongogara (1940-79), Chief of Defense. $13,800, Herbert Chitepo (1923-75), Director of Public Prosecutions. $30,000, Bernard Chidzero (1927-2002), Minister of Economic Planning. $50,000, Moven Mahachi (1948-2001), Minister of various departments.

2005, Aug. 4   Litho.   Perf. 14x14¼
996-999 A181   Set of 4   16.00 16.00

UNESCO
World
Heritage
Sites
A182

Designs: Z, Soapstone Zimbabwe bird, Great Zimbabwe National Park. $15,500, Wall, Khami Ruins. $52,000, Elephant, Mana Pools National Park. $62,000, Victoria Falls.

2005, Oct. 6   Litho.   Perf. 14¼
1000-1003 A182   Set of 4   30.00 30.00
1003a   Souvenir sheet, #1000-1003   11.00 11.00

No. 1000 sold for $10,250 on day of issue.

World AIDS
Day — A183

Designs: $18,000, Cooking pot, field tender, care for the ill. $80,000, Children teaching AIDS prevention.

2005, Dec. 1   Litho.   Perf. 14¼x14
1004-1005 A183   Set of 2   15.00 15.00

Food — A184

Designs: $25,000, Mushrooms. $35,000, Rapoko, corn and sorghum. $50,000, Pumpkin, watermelon, spiny cucumber. $150,000, Wild fruits. $250,000, Herbs. $300,000, Sweet potato, cassava, peanuts.

2006, Jan. 17   Litho.   Perf. 14x14¼
1006-1011 A184   Set of 6   16.50 16.50
1011a   Miniature sheet, #1006-1011   16.50 16.50

Pope John Paul
II (1920-2005)
A185

Pope: $25,000, Wearing crucifix. $250,000, Holding crucifix.

2006, Feb. 9
1012-1013 A185   Set of 2   15.00 15.00
1013a   Souvenir sheet, #1012-1013   15.00 15.00

Water
Conservation
A186

Designs: $30,000, Faucet and pail. $225,000, Flood irrigation system. $375,000, Lions at waterhole. $450,000, Kariba Dam.

2006, Apr. 25   Litho.   Perf. 14x14¼
1014-1017 A186   Set of 4   21.00 21.00

National
Heroes — A187

Flag and: $60,000, Leopold T. Takawira (1916-70), first vice-president of Zimbabwe African National Union. $350,000, Simon C. Mazorodze (1933-81), health minister. $500,000, Herbert M. Ushewokunze (1933-95), government minister. $650,000, Tichafa S. Parirenyatwa (1927-62), deputy president of Zimbabwe African People's Union.

2006, July 25   Litho.   Perf. 14x14¼
1018-1021 A187   Set of 4   30.00 30.00

Huts — A188

Designs: $100, One hut. $800, Three huts.

2006, Oct. 24   Litho.   Perf. 14¼x14
1022-1023 A188   Set of 2   12.00 12.00
1023a   Souvenir sheet, #1022-1023   7.25   7.25

Bridges
A189

Designs: Z, Mpudzi River Bridge. $450, Victoria Falls Bridge. $600, Limpopo River Bridge. $750, Otto Beit Bridge. $800, Kariba Barrage Bridge. $1000, Birchenough Bridge.

2006, Oct. 24
1024-1029 A189   Set of 6   22.50 22.50
1029a   Souvenir sheet, #1024-1029   30.00 30.00

No. 1024 sold for $100 on day of issue.

Trees — A190

Designs: $150, Ziziphuus mauritania. $600, Schlerochra birrea. $750, Jatropha carcus. $1000, Uaparca kirkiana.

2006, Dec. 1   Litho.   Perf. 14x14¼
1030-1033 A190   Set of 4   21.00 21.00
1033a   Souvenir sheet, #1030-1033   20.00 20.00

Birds — A191

Designs: $50, Hoopoe. $100, Cattle egret. $500, Malachite kingfisher. $1000, Little bee-eater. $2000, Purple-crested lorie. $5000, Purple gallinule. $10,000, African jacana. $20,000, Ground hornbill. $50,000, Gorgeous bush shrike. $100,000, Secretary bird.

**   Perf. 14¾x14½**
2007, Feb. 20   Litho.
1034 A191 $50 multi   .20   .20
1035 A191 $100 multi   .20   .20
1036 A191 $500 multi   .20   .20
1037 A191 $1000 multi   .35   .35
1038 A191 $2000 multi   .65   .65
1039 A191 $5000 multi   1.75   1.75
1040 A191 $10,000 multi   3.25   3.25
1041 A191 $20,000 multi   6.75   6.75
1042 A191 $50,000 multi 17.00 17.00
1043 A191 $100,000 multi 35.00 35.00
    a.   Souvenir sheet, #1034-1043 67.50 67.50
        Nos. 1034-1043 (10) 65.35 65.35

Scouting,
Cent. — A192

Scouting emblem and: $400, Great Zimbabwe Ruins. $1500, Map of Zimbabwe. $2000, Centenary emblem. $2500, Map of Africa.

2007, Feb. 20   Perf. 14x14¼
1044-1047 A192   Set of 4   15.00 15.00

Women
A193

Designs: $7500, Mbuya Nehanda (?-1898), colonial resistance organizer. $29,000, Queen Lozikeyi (c. 1855-1919). $35,000, Mother Patrick (1863-1900), educator. $45,000, Amai Sally Mugabe (1932-92), First Lady.

2007, July 10   Perf. 14¼
1048-1051 A193   Set of 4   7.75   7.75

POSTAGE DUE STAMPS

D1   D2

1981   **Litho.**   **Perf. 14½**

J20	D1	1c emerald	.40	1.10
J21	D1	2c ultramarine	.40	1.10
J22	D1	5c lilac	.50	1.40
J23	D1	6c yellow	.65	2.00
J24	D1	10c red	1.40	4.25
		Nos. J20-J24 (5)	3.35	9.85

For surcharge see No. J30.

1985, Aug. 21   **Litho.**   **Perf. 14½**

J25	D2	1c pale orange	.40	.75
J26	D2	2c lilac rose	.40	.75
J27	D2	6c light green	.40	.75
J28	D2	10c tan	.40	.75
J29	D2	13c bright blue	.40	.75
		Nos. J25-J29 (5)	2.00	3.75

No. J24
Surcharged

1990, Jan. 2   **Litho.**   **Perf. 14½**

J30	D1	25c on 10c #J24	11.00	11.00

D3   D4

1995, Jan. 17   **Litho.**   **Perf. 14½**

J31	D3	1c yellow	.35	.35
J32	D3	2c yellow orange	.35	.35
J33	D3	5c rose lilac	.35	.35
J34	D3	10c pale blue	.35	.35
J35	D3	25c violet	.35	.35
J36	D3	40c green	.35	.35
J37	D3	60c orange	.35	.35
J38	D3	$1 brown	.55	.55
		Nos. J31-J38 (8)	3.00	3.00

2000, Jan. 25   **Litho.**   **Perf. 14½**

Bird sculpture.

J39	D4	1c blk, lt grn & grn	.20	.20
J40	D4	10c blk, lt blue & blue	.20	.20
J41	D4	50c blk, lt brn & brn	.20	.20
J42	D4	$1 blk, pink & red	.20	.20
J43	D4	$2 blk, lt yel & yel	.20	.20
J44	D4	$5 blk, lil & red vio	.25	.25
J45	D4	$10 blk, lt ver & ver	.55	.55
		Nos. J39-J45 (7)	1.80	1.80

ZULULAND

'zü-ₐlü-ₗland

LOCATION — Northeastern part of Natal, South Africa
GOVT. — British Colony, 1887-1897
AREA — 10,427 sq. mi.
POP. — 230,000 (estimated 1900)
CAPITAL — Eshowe

12 Pence = 1 Shilling
20 Shillings = 1 Pound

Stamps of Great Britain
Overprinted

1888-93   **Wmk. 30**   **Perf. 14**

1	A54	½p vermilion	5.00	3.00
2	A40	1p violet	31.00	4.50
3	A56	2p green & red	19.50	32.50
4	A57	2½p vio, bl ('91)	27.50	22.50
5	A58	3p violet, yel	29.00	25.00
6	A59	4p green & brn	50.00	65.00
7	A61	5p lil & bl ('93)	100.00	150.00
8	A62	6p vio, rose	16.00	20.00
9	A63	9p blue & lil ('92)	110.00	115.00
10	A65	1sh green ('92)	125.00	150.00

Wmk. 31

11	A51	5sh rose ('92)	600.00	700.00
		Nos. 1-10 (10)	513.00	587.50

Natal No. 66
Overprinted

1888-94   **Wmk. 2**

12	A14	½p green, no period	28.50	46.00
a.		Period after "Zululand"	62.50	92.50
b.		As "a," double overprint	3,000.	1,750.
c.		As "a," invtd. overprint	1,400.	
d.		As "a," pair, one without ovpt.	8,500.	
e.		As No. 12, double overprint	1,600.	1,750.

Natal No. 71 Ovptd. Like Nos. 1-11

13	A11	6p violet ('94)	70.00	62.50

A1   A2

1891

14	A1	1p lilac	3.50	3.50

By proclamation of the Governor of Zululand, dated June 27th, 1891, No. 14 was declared to be a postage stamp.

1894-96   **Typo.**

15	A2	½p lilac & grn	4.00	5.50
16	A2	1p lilac & rose	5.75	3.00
17	A2	2½p lilac & blue	16.00	9.75
18	A2	3p lilac & brn	9.25	4.00
19	A2	6p lilac & blk	22.50	25.00
20	A2	1sh green	45.00	45.00
21	A2	2sh6p grn & blk ('96)	85.00	100.00
22	A2	4sh grn & car rose	125.00	175.00
23	A2	£1 violet, red	600.00	625.00
24	A2	£5 vio & blk, red	5,750.	1,750.
		Nos. 15-23 (9)	912.50	992.25

Numerals of #19-24 are in color on plain tablet.

Purple or violet cancellations are not necessarily revenue cancels. 14 of the 17 post offices and agencies used violet as well as black postal cancellations.

Zululand was annexed to Natal in Dec. 1897 and separate stamps were discontinued June 30, 1898.

Vol. 6 Number Additions, Deletions & Changes

Number in 2008 Catalogue	Number in 2009 Catalogue
Solomon Islands	
new	884A
Somali Coast	
32b	deleted
new	32b
new	32c
new	32d
new	54a
new	58a
new	208b
new	240a
new	240b
new	241a
new	241b
new	243a
new	244b
new	245a
new	245b
new	247a
new	248b
Sudan	
new	1596
new	O73b
Tokelau	
new	272a
Trinidad & Tobago	
new	MR13b
Vietnam	
new	389a
Western Ukraine	
new	97a
Yugoslavia	
new	2146a

National Album Series

The National series offers a panoramic view of our country's heritage through postage stamps. It is the most complete and comprehensive U.S. album series you can buy. There are spaces for every major U.S. stamp listed in the Scott Catalogue, including Special Printings, Newspaper stamps and much more.

- Pages printed on one side.

- All spaces identified by Scott numbers.

- All major variety of stamps are either illustrated or described.

- Chemically neutral paper protects stamps.

- Sold as page units only. Binders, slipcases and labels sold separately.

Item			Retail
100NTL1	1845-1934	108 pgs	$39.95
100NTL2	1935-1976	108 pgs	$39.95
100NTL3	1977-1993	114 pgs	$39.95
100NTL4	1994-1999	100 pgs	$39.95
100NTL5	2000-2004	108 pgs	$39.95

Supplemented in March.

U.S. National Kit

The most complete and comprehensive U.S. stamp album is now available in a money-saving complete kit package! This kit contains all five National album parts, 4 large National Series 3-ring binders, slipcases, protector sheets and National album labels, pre-cut value pack of black ScottMounts and the *U.S. Specialized Catalogue*.

Item	Retail
NATLKIT	$519.99

What ever your collecting specialty Scott Publishing has an album for you. For more information on the entire line of Scott albums and products visit your local stamp dealer or online at:

www.amosadvantage.com

SCOTT.

1-800-572-6885
P.O. BOX 828
Sidney OH 45365
www.amosadvantage.com

AMOS
PUBLISHING

Illustrated Identifier

This section pictures stamps or parts of stamp designs that will help identify postage stamps that do not have English words on them.

Many of the symbols that identify stamps of countries are shown here as well as typical examples of their stamps.

See the Index and Identifier on the previous pages for stamps with inscriptions such as "sen," "posta," "Baja Porto," "Helvetia," "K.S.A.," etc.

Linn's Stamp Identifier is now available. The 144 pages include more 2,000 inscriptions and over 500 large stamp illustrations. Available from Linn's Stamp News, P.O. Box 29, Sidney, OH 45365-0029.

1. HEADS, PICTURES AND NUMERALS

GREAT BRITAIN

Great Britain stamps never show the country name, but, except for postage dues, show a picture of the reigning monarch.

Victoria

Edward VII   George V   Edward VIII

George VI

Elizabeth II

Some George VI and Elizabeth II stamps are surcharged in annas, new paisa or rupees. These are listed under Oman.

Silhouette (sometimes facing right, generally at the top of stamp)

The silhouette indicates this is a British stamp. It is not a U.S. stamp.

VICTORIA

Queen Victoria

INDIA

Other stamps of India show this portrait of Queen Victoria and the words "Service" and "Annas."

AUSTRIA

YUGOSLAVIA

(Also BOSNIA & HERZEGOVINA if imperf.)

BOSNIA & HERZEGOVINA

Denominations also appear in top corners instead of bottom corners.

HUNGARY

Another stamp has posthorn facing left

BRAZIL

AUSTRALIA

Kangaroo and Emu

GERMANY

Mecklenburg-Vorpommern

SWITZERLAND

PALAU

2. ORIENTAL INSCRIPTIONS

CHINA

Any stamp with this one character is from China (Imperial, Republic or People's Republic). This character appears in a four-character over-print on stamps of Manchukuo. These stamps are local provisionals, which are unlisted. Other overprinted Manchukuo stamps show this character, but have more than four characters in the overprints. These are listed in People's Republic of China.

Some Chinese stamps show the Sun.

Most stamps of Republic of China show this series of characters.

Stamps with the China character and this character are from People's Republic of China.

Calligraphic form of People's Republic of China

(一)	(二)	(三)	(四)	(五)	(六)
1	2	3	4	5	6
(七)	(八)	(九)	(十)	(一十)	(二十)
7	8	9	10	11	12

Chinese stamps
without China character

REPUBLIC OF CHINA

PEOPLE'S REPUBLIC OF CHINA

Mao Tse-tung

MANCHUKUO

Temple   Emperor Pu-Yi

The first 3 characters are common to
many Manchukuo stamps.

The last 3 characters are common
to other Manchukuo stamps.

Orchid Crest

Manchukuo
stamp with-
out these
elements

JAPAN

Chrysanthemum Crest   Country Name

Japanese stamps without these elements

The number of characters in the center and the
design of dragons on the sides will vary.

RYUKYU ISLANDS

Country Name

PHILIPPINES
(Japanese Occupation)

Country Name

NORTH BORNEO
(Japanese Occupation)

Indicates Japanese   Country
Occupation   Name

MALAYA
(Japanese Occupation)

Indicates Japanese Occupation   Country Name

BURMA
Union of Myanmar

Union of Myanmar
(Japanese Occupation)

Indicates Japanese Occupation   Country Name

Other Burma Japanese Occupation stamps without these elements

Burmese Script

KOREA

These two characters, in any order, are common to stamps from the Republic of Korea (South Korea) or of the People's Democratic Republic of Korea (North Korea).

This series of four characters can be found on the stamps of both Koreas. Most stamps of the Democratic People's Republic of Korea (North Korea) have just this inscription.

Indicates Republic of Korea (South Korea)

South Korean postage stamps issed after 1952 do not show currency expressed in Latin letters. Stamps wiith "HW," "HWAN," "WON," "WN," "W" or "W" with two lines through it, if not illustrated in listings of stamps before this date, are revenues. North Korean postage stamps do not have currency expressed in Latin letters.

Yin Yang appears on some stamps.

REPUBLIC OF KOREA

THAILAND

Country Name

King Chulalongkorn

King Prajadhipok and Chao P'ya Chakri

3. CENTRAL AND EASTERN ASIAN INSCRIPTIONS

INDIA - FEUDATORY STATES

Alwar **Bhor**

Bundi

Similar stamps come with different designs in corners and differently drawn daggers (at center of circle).

Dhar **Faridkot**

Hyderabad

Similar stamps exist with straight line frame around stamp, and also with different central design which is inscribed "Postage" or "Post & Receipt."

Indore **Jhalawar**

A similar stamp has the central figure in an oval.

Nandgaon

Nowanuggur

Poonch

Similar stamps exist
in various sizes

Rajpeepla   Soruth

BANGLADESH

Country Name

NEPAL

Similar stamps are smaller, have squares in
upper corners and have five or nine
characters in central bottom panel.

TANNU TUVA   ISRAEL

GEORGIA

This inscription is found on
other pictorial stamps.

Country Name

ARMENIA

The four characters are found somewhere
on pictorial stamps. On some stamps only
the middle two are found.

4. AFRICAN INSCRIPTIONS

ETHIOPIA

5. ARABIC INSCRIPTIONS

١ ٢ ٣ ٤ ٥
1   2   3   4   5

٦ ٧ ٨ ٩ ٠
6   7   8   9   0

AFGHANISTAN

Many early Afghanistan stamps show Tiger's head, many of these have ornaments protruding from outer ring, others show inscriptions in black.

Arabic Script

Mosque Gate & Crossed Cannons
The four characters are found somewhere on pictorial stamps. On some stamps only the middle two are found.

BAHRAIN

EGYPT

Postage

INDIA - FEUDATORY STATES

Jammu & Kashmir

Text and thickness of
ovals vary. Some stamps
have flower devices
in corners.

India-Hyderabad

IRAN

Country Name

Royal Crown

Lion with Sword

Symbol

IRAQ

JORDAN

LEBANON

Similar types have
denominations at top and
slightly different design.

LIBYA

Country Name in various styles

Other Libya stamps show Eagle and Shield (head
facing either direction) or Red, White and Black
Shield (with or without eagle in center).

Without Country Name

SAUDI ARABIA

Tughra (Central design)

Palm Tree and Swords

SYRIA

THRACE   YEMEN

PAKISTAN

PAKISTAN - BAHAWALPUR

Country Name in top panel, star and crescent

TURKEY

Star & Crescent is a device found on many Turkish stamps, but is also found on stamps from other Arabic areas (see Pakistan-Bahawalpur)

Tughra (similar tughras can be found on stamps of Turkey in Asia, Afghanistan and Saudi Arabia)

Mohammed V

Mustafa Kemal

Plane, Star and Crescent

TURKEY IN ASIA

Other Turkey in Asia pictorials show star & crescent.
Other stamps show tughra shown under Turkey.

6. GREEK INSCRIPTIONS

GREECE

Country Name in various styles
(Some Crete stamps overprinted with the Greece country name are listed in Crete.)

Lepta

  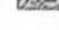
Drachma   Drachmas   Lepton

Abbreviated Country Name

Other forms of Country Name

No country name

CRETE

Country Name

These words are on other stamps

Grosion

Crete stamps with a surcharge that have the year "1922" are listed under Greece.

EPIRUS   IONIAN IS.

Country Name

---

7. CYRILLIC INSCRIPTIONS

RUSSIA

Postage Stamp

Imperial Eagle

Postage in various styles

Abbreviation   Abbreviation   Russian
for Kopeck   for Ruble

Abbreviation for Russian Soviet
Federated Socialist Republic
RSFSR stamps were overprinted (see below)

Abbreviation for Union of Soviet
Socialist Republics

This item is footnoted in Latvia

RUSSIA - Army of the North

"OKCA"

RUSSIA - Wenden

RUSSIAN OFFICES IN THE TURKISH EMPIRE

These letters appear on other stamps of the Russian offices.

The unoverprinted version of this stamp and a similar stamp were overprinted by various countries (see below).

ARMENIA

BELARUS

FAR EASTERN REPUBLIC

Country Name

SOUTH RUSSIA

Country Name

FINLAND

Circles and Dots on stamps similar to Imperial Russia issues

BATUM

Forms of Country Name

TRANSCAUCASIAN FEDERATED REPUBLICS

 Abbreviation for Country Name

KAZAKHSTAN

Country Name

KYRGYZSTAN

  Country Name

ROMANIA

TADJIKISTAN

Country Name & Abbreviation

UKRAINE

Country Name in various forms

The trident appears on many stamps, usually as an overprint.

Abbreviation for Ukrainian Soviet Socialist Republic

WESTERN UKRAINE

Abbreviation for Country Name

AZERBAIJAN

Country Name

A.C.C.P.

Abbreviation for Azerbaijan
Soviet Socialist Republic

MONTENEGRO

ЦРНЕЦОРЕ

ЦРНА ГОРА

Country Name in various forms

ПРГОРЕ

Abbreviation
for country
name

No country name
(A similar Montenegro
stamp without country
name has same vignette.)

SERBIA

СРПСКА   С Р Б И Ј А

Country Name in various forms

СРП.   К. С.

Abbreviation for country name

No country name

SERBIA & MONTENEGRO

YUGOSLAVIA

ЈУГОСЛАВИЈА

Showing country name

No Country Name

MACEDONIA

МАКЕДОНИЈА

Country Name

МАКЕДОНСКИ

Different form of Country Name

BOSNIA & HERZEGOVINA
(Serb Administration)

РЕПУБЛИКА СРПСКА

Country Name

РЕПУБЛИКЕ СРПСКЕ

Different form of Country Name

No Country Name

BULGARIA

Country Name   Postage

Stotinka

Stotinki (plural)   Abbreviation for
                      Stotinki

Country Name in various forms and styles

No country name

Abbreviation for
Lev, leva

MONGOLIA

Country name in   Tugrik in Cyrillic
one word

Country name in   Mung in Cyrillic
two words

Mung
in Mongolian

Tugrik
in Mongolian

Arms

No Country Name

scott**mounts**

For stamp presentation unequaled in beauty and clarity, insist on ScottMounts. Made of 100% inert polystyrol foil, ScottMounts protect your stamps from the harmful effects of dust and moisture. Available in your choice of clear or black backs, ScottMounts are center-split across the back for easy insertion of stamps and feature crystal clear mount faces. Double layers of gum assure stay-put bonding on the album page. Discover the quality and value ScottMounts have to offer. ScottMounts are available from your favorite stamp dealer or direct from:

SCOTT.

Scott Publishing Co.
1-800-572-6885
P.O. Box 828 Sidney OH 45365-0828
www.amosadvantage.com

Discover the quality and value ScottMounts have to offer. For a complete list of ScottMount sizes call or write Scott Publishing Co.

AMOS PUBLISHING

Publishers of:
Coin World, Linn's Stamp News and Scott Publishing Co.

INDEX AND IDENTIFIER

All page numbers shown are those in this Volume 6.

Postage stamps that do not have English words on them are shown in the Identifier which begins on page 1194.

Pronunciation Symbols

ə .... banana, collide, abut

ˈə, ˌə .... humdrum, abut

ə .... immediately preceding \l\, \n\, \m\, \ŋ\, as in battle, mitten, eaten, and sometimes open \ˈō-pᵊm\, lock and key \-ᵊŋ-\; immediately following \l\, \m\, \r\, as often in French table, prisme, titre

ər .... further, merger, bird

ˈər-
ˈə-r } .... as in two different pronunciations of hurry \ˈhər-ē, ˈhə-rē\

a .... mat, map, mad, gag, snap, patch

ā .... day, fade, date, aorta, drape, cape

ä .... bother, cot, and, with most American speakers, father, cart

ȧ .... father as pronunced by speakers who do not rhyme it with bother; French patte

au̇ .... now, loud, out

b .... baby, rib

ch .... chin, nature \ˈnā-chər\

d .... did, adder

e .... bet, bed, peck

ˈē, ˌē .... beat, nosebleed, evenly, easy

ē .... easy, mealy

f .... fifty, cuff

g .... go, big, gift

h .... hat, ahead

hw .... whale as pronounced by those who do not have the same pronunciation for both whale and wail

i .... tip, banish, active

ī .... site, side, buy, tripe

j .... job, gem, edge, join, judge

k .... kin, cook, ache

k̲ .... German ich, Buch; one pronunciation of loch

l .... lily, pool

m .... murmur, dim, nymph

n .... no, own

ⁿ .... indicates that a preceding vowel or diphthong is pronounced with the nasal passages open, as in French un bon vin blanc \œⁿ -bōⁿ -vaⁿ -bläⁿ\

ŋ .... sing \ˈsiŋ\, singer \ˈsiŋ-ər\, finger \ˈfiŋ-gər\, ink \ˈiŋk\

ō .... bone, know, beau

ȯ .... saw, all, gnaw, caught

œ .... French boeuf, German Hölle

œ̄ .... French feu, German Höhle

ȯi .... coin, destroy

p .... pepper, lip

r .... red, car, rarity

s .... source, less

sh .... as in shy, mission, machine, special (actually, this is a single sound, not two); with a hyphen between, two sounds as in grasshopper \ˈgras-ˌhä-pər\

t .... tie, attack, late, later, latter

th .... as in thin, ether (actually, this is a single sound, not two); with a hyphen between, two sounds as in knighthood \ˈnīt-ˌhu̇d\

t̲h̲ .... then, either, this (actually, this is a single sound, not two)

ü .... rule, youth, union \ˈyün-yən\, few \ˈfyü\

u̇ .... pull, wood, book, curable \ˈkyu̇r-ə-bəl\, fury \ˈfyu̇r-ē\

ᵫ .... German füllen, hübsch

ᵫ̄ .... French rue, German fühlen

v .... vivid, give

w .... we, away

y .... yard, young, cue \ˈkyü\, mute \ˈmyüt\, union \ˈyün-yən\

ʸ .... indicates that during the articulation of the sound represented by the preceding character the front of the tongue has substantially the position it has for the articulation of the first sound of yard, as in French digne \dēnʸ\

z .... zone, raise

zh .... as in vision, azure \ˈa-zhər\ (actually, this is a single sound, not two); with a hyphen between, two sounds as in hogshead \ˈhȯgz-ˌhed, ˈhägz-\

\ .... slant line used in pairs to mark the beginning and end of a transcription: \ˈpen\

ˈ .... mark preceding a syllable with primary (strongest) stress: \ˈpen-mən-ˌship\

ˌ .... mark preceding a syllable with secondary (medium) stress: \ˈpen-mən-ˌship\

- .... mark of syllable division

( ) .... indicate that what is symbolized between is present in some utterances but not in others: factory \ˈfak-t(ə-)rē\

÷ .... indicates that many regard as unacceptable the pronunciation variant immediately following: cupola \ˈkyü-pə-lə, ÷-ˌlō\

The system of pronunciation is used by permission from Merriam-Webster's Collegiate® Dictionary, Tenth Edition ©1993 by Merrian-Webster Inc., publisher of the Merriam-Webster® dictionaries.

MINKUS
Album Series

The Minkus album line is now available through Amos Hobby Publishing. The supplement schedule is listed below. Pages are punched to fit 2 or 3-ring binders. Sold as page units only. Binders, slipcases and labels sold separately. For more information album contents visit our web site at www.amosadvantage.com.

FEBRUARY
Global Part 1
Global Part 2
All American Regular & Commemoratives

MARCH
All American Part 3 United Nations
U.N Singles
U.N. Imprint Blocks
U.N. Postal Stationery

APRIL
All American Part 2 Postal Stationery
All American Part 4 Booklet Panes
All American Part 5 Sheetlets
All American Part 7 Postal Cards
U.S. Commemoratives
U.S. Plate Blocks
U.S. Regular Issues
U.S. Booklet Panes
U.S. Postal Stationery
U.S. Sheetlets

MAY
Albania
Austria
Bulgaria
Canada
Croatia
France
French Andorra
Germany
Gibraltar
Great Britain, Ireland
Guernsey, Jersey, Isle Of Man
Hong Kong
Ireland
Monaco
Romania
Serbia & Montenegro
Singapore
Slovenia

JUNE
Denmark
Egypt
Finland
Greece
Israel Singles
Israel Plate Blocks
Israel Tab Singles
Korea
Liechtenstein
Norway
Sweden
Switzerland

JULY
Bangladesh
India
Italy
Japan
Pakistan
People's Republic of China
Portugal/Azores/Maderia
San Marino
Spain
Sri Lanka
Thailand
Vatican City

AUGUST
Armenia
Azerbaijan
Belarus
Belgium
Czech Republic & Slovakia
Georgia
Hungary
Kazakhstan
Kyrgyzstan
Latvia, Lithuania, Estonia
Luxembourg
Moldova
Netherlands
Poland
Russia
Tajikistan
Turkmenistan
Ukraine
Uzbekistan

SEPTEMBER
Argentina
Australia
Brazil
Chile
Colombia
Dominican Republic
Haiti
Mexico
New Zealand
Venezuela

DECEMBER
All American Part 6 Plate No. Coils
U.S. Plate No. Coils

INDEX TO ADVERTISERS
2009 VOLUME 6

2009
VOLUME 6
DEALER DIRECTORY
YELLOW PAGE LISTINGS

This section of your Scott Catalogue contains advertisements to help you conveniently find what you need, when you need it...!

Accessories

BROOKLYN GALLERY COIN & STAMP, INC.
8725 4th Ave.
Brooklyn, NY 11209
PH: 718-745-5701
FAX: 718-745-2775
info@brooklyngallery.com
www.brooklyngallery.com

Appraisals

COLONIAL STAMP COMPANY
5757 Wilshire Blvd. PH #8
Los Angeles, CA 90036
PH: 323-933-9435
FAX: 323-939-9930
Toll Free in North America
PH: 877-272-6693
FAX: 877-272-6694
info@colonialstampcompany.com
www.colonialstampcompany.com

PHILIP WEISS AUCTIONS
1 Neil Court
Oceanside, NY 11572
PH: 516-594-0731
FAX: 516-594-9414

Asia

MICHAEL ROGERS, INC.
415 South Orlando Ave
Winter Park, FL 32789-3683
PH: 407-644-2290
PH: 800-843-3751
FAX: 407-645-4434
Stamps@michaelrogersinc.com
www.michaelrogersinc.com

Asia

THE STAMP ACT
PO Box 1136
Belmont, CA 94002
PH: 650-703-2342
PH: 650-592-3315
FAX: 650-508-8104
thestampact@sbcglobal.net
www.thestampact.com

Auctions

COLONIAL STAMP COMPANY
5757 Wilshire Blvd. PH #8
Los Angeles, CA 90036
PH: 323-933-9435
FAX: 323-939-9930
Toll Free in North America
PH: 877-272-6693
FAX: 877-272-6694
info@colonialstampcompany.com
www.colonialstampcompany.com

DANIEL F. KELLEHER CO., INC.
20 Walnut St.
Suite 213
Wellesley, MA 02481
PH: 781-235-0990
FAX: 781-235-0945

JACQUES C. SCHIFF, JR., INC.
195 Main St.
Ridgefield Park, NJ 07660
PH: 201-641-5566
FAX: 201-641-5705

Auctions

MICHAEL ROGERS, INC.
415 South Orlando Ave
Winter Park, FL 32789-3683
PH: 407-644-2290
PH: 800-843-3751
FAX: 407-645-4434
Stamps@michaelrogersinc.com
www.michaelrogersinc.com

MODLOW-ARVAI STAMPS & COLLECTIBLES
504 E. 118th St. Apt #2
New York, NY 10035
PH: 917-868-4850
FAX: 888-655-1655
Mastamps@aol.com
Visit our Free Auction site:
http://www.modlow-arvai.com

PHILIP WEISS AUCTIONS
1 Neil Court
Oceanside, NY 11572
PH: 516-594-0731
FAX: 516-594-9414

R. MARESCH & SON LTD.
5th Floor - 6075 Yonge St.
Toronto, ON M2M 3W2
CANADA
PH: 416-363-7777
FAX: 416-363-6511
www.maresch.com

THE STAMP CENTER DUTCH COUNTRY AUCTIONS
4115 Concord Pike
Wilmington, DE 19803
PH: 302-478-8740
FAX: 302-478-8779
auctions@thestampcenter.com
www.thestampcenter.com

Auctions - Public

ALAN BLAIR STAMPS/ AUCTIONS
5405 Lakeside Ave.
Suite 1
Richmond, VA 23228
PH: 800-689-5602
FAX: 804-262-9307
alanblair@verizon.net
www.alanblairstamps.com

British Commonwealth

ARON R. HALBERSTAM PHILATELISTS, LTD.
PO Box 150168
Van Brunt Station
Brooklyn, NY 11215-0168
PH: 718-788-3978
FAX: 718-965-3099
arh@arhstamps.com
www.arhstamps.com

WWW.WORLDSTAMPS.COM
242 West Saddle River Road
Suite C
Upper Saddle River, NJ 07458
PH: 201-236-8122
FAX: 201-236-8133
by mail:
Frank Geiger Philatelists
info@WorldStamps.com
www.WorldStamps.com

Auctions

British Commonwealth

Central America

GUY SHAW
PO Box 27138
San Diego, CA 92198
PH/FAX: 858-485-8269
guyshaw@guyshaw.com
www.guyshaw.com

China

MICHAEL ROGERS, INC.
415 South Orlando Ave
Winter Park, FL 32789-3683
PH: 407-644-2290
PH: 800-843-3751
FAX: 407-645-4434
Stamps@michaelrogersinc.com
www.michaelrogersinc.com

Cuba

R.D.C. STAMPS
R. del Campo
Museo Historico Cubano
3131 Coral Way
Miami, FL 33145
PH: 305-815-0577
PH: 305-567-3131
FAX: 305-567-1416
rdcstamps@aol.com

Ducks

MICHAEL JAFFE
PO Box 61484
Vancouver, WA 98666
PH: 360-695-6161
PH: 800-782-6770
FAX: 360-695-1616
mjaffe@brookmanstamps.com
www.brookmanstamps.com

Europe

WWW.WORLDSTAMPS.COM
242 West Saddle River Road
Suite C
Upper Saddle River, NJ 07458
PH: 201-236-8122
FAX: 201-236-8133
by mail:
Frank Geiger Philatelists
info@WorldStamps.com
www.WorldStamps.com

German Colonies

COLONIAL STAMP COMPANY
View our on-line price list
at our website!
5757 Wilshire Blvd. PH #8
Los Angeles, CA 90036
PH: 323-933-9435
FAX: 323-939-9930
Toll Free in North America
PH: 877-272-6693
FAX: 877-272-6694
info@colonialstampcompany.com
www.colonialstampcompany.com

Germany

**HENRY GITNER
PHILATELISTS, INC.**
PO Box 3077-S
Middletown, NY 10940
PH: 845-343-5151
PH: 800-947-8267
FAX: 845-343-0068
hgitner@hgitner.com
www.hgitner.com

Insurance

**COLLECTIBLES INSURANCE
SERVICES, LLC.**
11350 McCormick Rd., Ste. 700
Hunt Valley, MD 21031
PH: 888-837-9537
www.collectinsure.com

Japan

MICHAEL ROGERS, INC.
415 South Orlando Ave
Winter Park, FL 32789-3683
PH: 407-644-2290
PH: 800-843-3751
FAX: 407-645-4434
Stamps@michaelrogersinc.com
www.michaelrogersinc.com

Korea

MICHAEL ROGERS, INC.
415 South Orlando Ave
Winter Park, FL 32789-3683
PH: 407-644-2290
PH: 800-843-3751
FAX: 407-645-4434
Stamps@michaelrogersinc.com
www.michaelrogersinc.com

Latin America

GUY SHAW
PO Box 27138
San Diego, CA 92198
PH/FAX: 858-485-8269
guyshaw@guyshaw.com
www.guyshaw.com

Manchukuo

MICHAEL ROGERS, INC.
415 South Orlando Ave
Winter Park, FL 32789-3683
PH: 407-644-2290
PH: 800-843-3751
FAX: 407-645-4434
Stamps@michaelrogersinc.com
www.michaelrogersinc.com

British Commonwealth